# 2024
# STANDARD POSTAGE
# STAMP CATALOGUE

## ONE HUNDRED AND EIGHTIETH EDITION IN SIX VOLUMES

## Volume 4A

### J-L

| | |
|---|---|
| EDITOR-IN-CHIEF | Jay Bigalke |
| EDITOR-AT-LARGE | Donna Houseman |
| CONTRIBUTING EDITOR | Charles Snee |
| EDITOR EMERITUS | James E. Kloetzel |
| SENIOR EDITOR /NEW ISSUES AND VALUING | Martin J. Frankevicz |
| ADMINISTRATIVE ASSISTANT/CATALOGUE LAYOUT | Eric Wiessinger |
| SENIOR GRAPHIC DESIGNER | Cinda McAlexander |
| SALES DIRECTOR | David Pistello |
| SALES DIRECTOR | Eric Roth |
| SALES DIRECTOR | Brenda Wyen |
| SALES REPRESENTATIVE | Julie Dahlstrom |

### Released July 2023

Includes New Stamp Listings through the May 2023 *Scott Stamp Monthly* Catalogue Update

Copyright© 2023 by

# AMOS MEDIA

1660 Campbell Road, Suite A, Sidney, OH 45365
Publishers of *Linn's Stamp News*, *Scott Stamp Monthly*, *Coin World* and *Coin World Monthly*.

# Table of contents

See the following volumes for other country listings:
Volume 1A: United States, United Nations, Abu Dhabi-Australia; Volume 1B: Austria-B
Volume 2A: C-Cur; Volume 2B: Cyp-F
Volume 3B: H-I
Volume 4B: M
Volume 5A: N-Phil; Volume 5B: Pit-Sam
Volume 6A: San-Tete; Volume 6B: Thai-Z

---

### Scott Catalogue Mission Statement
The Scott Catalogue Team exists to serve the recreational,
educational and commercial hobby needs of stamp collectors and dealers.
We strive to set the industry standard for philatelic information and products by developing and
providing goods that help collectors identify, value, organize and present their collections.
Quality customer service is, and will continue to be, our highest priority.
We aspire toward achieving total customer satisfaction.

---

# Acknowledgments

Our appreciation and gratitude go to the following individuals who have assisted us in preparing information included in this year's Scott catalogues. Some helpers prefer anonymity. These individuals have generously shared their stamp knowledge with others through the medium of the Scott catalogue.

Those who follow provided information that is in addition to the hundreds of dealer price lists and advertisements and scores of auction catalogues and realizations that were used in producing the catalogue values. It is from those noted here that we have been able to obtain information on items not normally seen in published lists and advertisements. Support from these people goes beyond data leading to catalogue values, for they also are key to editorial changes.

> A special acknowledgment to Liane and Sergio Sismondo of The Classic Collector for their assistance and knowledge sharing that have aided in the preparation of this year's Standard and Classic Specialized Catalogues.

Clifford J. Alexander
    (Carriers and Locals Society)
Roland Austin
Michael & Cecilia Ball (A To Z Stamps)
Jim Bardo (Bardo Stamps)
Brian M. Bleckwenn
    (The Philatelic Foundation)
Les Bootman
Roger S. Brody
Tom Brougham
    (Canal Zone Study Group)
Paul and Josh Buchsbayew
    (Cherrystone Auctions, Inc.)
Timothy Bryan Burgess
Tina and John Carlson (JET Stamps)
Jay T. Carrigan
Carlson Chambliss
Bob Coale
Tony L. Crumbley
    (Carolina Coin and Stamp, Inc.)
Christopher Dahle
Charles Deaton
Bob and Rita Dumaine
    (Sam Houston Duck Co.)
Charles Epting (H.R. Harmer)
Mike Farrell
David Feldman International Auctioneers
Robert A. Fisher
Jeffrey M. Forster
Robert S. Freeman

Henry L. Gitner
    (Henry Gitner Philatelists, Inc.)
Stan Goldfarb
Marc E. Gonzales
Daniel E. Grau
Bruce Hecht (Bruce L. Hecht Co.)
Eric Jackson
Michael Jaffe (Michael Jaffe Stamps, Inc.)
William A. (Bill) Jones
Allan Katz (Ventura Stamp Co.)
Patricia A. Kaufmann
    (Civil War Philatelic Society)
Jon Kawaguchi
    (Ryukyu Philatelic Specialist Society)
Han Ki Kim
Ingert Kuzych
Ulf Lindahl (Ethiopian Philatelic Society)
Ignacio Llach (Filatelia Llach, S.L.)
William K. McDaniel
Pat McElroy
Brian Metz
Mark S. Miller (India Study Circle)
Gary Morris (Pacific Midwest Co.)
Peter Mosiondz Jr.
Bruce M. Moyer
    (Moyer Stamps & Collectables)
Scott Murphy
    (Professional Stamp Experts)
Dr. Tiong Tak Ngo
Nik and Lisa Oquist

Don Peterson
    (International Philippine Philatelic
    Society)
Todor Drumev Popov
Dr. Charles Posner
Peter W. W. Powell
Ed Reiser (Century Stamp Co.)
Ghassan D. Riachi
Robert G. Rufe
Theodosios D. Sampson Ph.D.
Dennis W. Schmidt
Joyce and Chuck Schmidt
Guy Shaw
    (Mexico-Elmhurst Philatelic Society
    International)
J. Randall Shoemaker
    (Philatelic Stamp Authentication and
    Grading, Inc.)
Sergio and Liane Sismondo
    (The Classic Collector)
Jay Smith
Telah Smith
Mark Stelmacovich
Scott R. Trepel
    (Robert A. Siegel Auction Galleries)
Dan Undersander
Steven Unkrich
Herbert R. Volin
Val Zabijaka (Zabijaka Auctions)

# What's new for 2024 Scott Standard Volume 4

Another catalog season is upon us as we continue the journey of the 155-year history of the Scott catalogs. The 2024 volumes are the 180th edition of the Scott *Standard Postage Stamp Catalogue*.

Volume 4A includes listings for countries of the world Jamaica through Luxembourg. Listings for countries of the world Macao through Mozambique can be found in Vol. 4B.

Because Vol. 4B is a continuation of the first part of the Vol. 4 catalog, the introduction pages are not repeated in each volume.

This year's Vol. 4A cover features an 84-yen stamp (Scott 4402i) from Japan's 2020 pane of 10 Summer Greetings stamps (4402).

The Malaysia 2015 70-sen Pulau Tenggol, Trengganu stamp (Scott 1571a) from a pair of Islands stamps (1571) is shown on the Vol. 3B cover. The 2015 Islands issue (1571-1573) consists of two pairs of stamps and a souvenir sheet of one.

For the 2024 Scott catalog season, we continue a review of the Portuguese areas, which for Vol. 4 includes Lourenco Marques, Macao, Mozambique and Mozambique Company.

One important note for Macao needs to be emphasized. The values for unused stamps of all periods are for well-centered examples with original gum showing no traces of toning or disturbance. Any deviations would result in a substantial value decrease. For stamps issued without gum, the same condition standards still apply, except for the part about gum condition.

Approximately 2,900 value changes, mostly increases and very few decreases, were made for Macao. In the classic period, one example of an increase was for the 1892 30-real-on-200r surcharged stamp (Scott 45), which moved from $60 and $30 in unused and used condition to $120 and $55, respectively.

For a modern Macao issue, the 2013 block of six and souvenir sheet of the Chinese Calligraphy and Painting issue (Scott 1402-1403) increased from $5 and $7 in unused and used condition, respectively, to $11 and $25.

For both Mozambique and Mozambique Company, numerous value changes were made.

Mozambique had approximately 1,400 value changes with only a handful of decreases. Mozambique Company had more than 700 value changes, also with only a small number of decreases.

For Mozambique, the set of 13 1877-85 Portuguese Crown stamps (Scott 1-14) moved from $882.45 unused to $1,655.15. A large part of the jump was the 20r rose stamp (5) which increased substantially in value in unused condition. The value is now italicized to reflect an item that does not trade frequently.

For Mozambique Company, the set of 10 1919 Company Arms postage due stamps (Scott J31-J40) moved from $8.05 unused and used to $10.30 both ways.

Lourenco Marques was also reviewed, and almost every value changed. Most values increased slightly compared to values for the other countries already mentioned. For example, the 1899 50-real-on-75r rose stamp (Scott 57) increased from $6 and $2.50 in unused and used condition to $7.75 and $4.50, respectively.

Mexico was also extensively reviewed, and more than 4,000 value changes were recorded. Many of the changes were increases. One example was the first special delivery stamp, the 1919 20-centavo Motorcycle Postman (Scott E1), which advanced from $70 unused to $110.

Other reviewed countries include Japan, Jordan, Kuwait, Lebanon and Libya.

Many other countries received less extensive reviews that are not noted in this letter. We encourage you to pay special attention to the Number Additions, Deletions and Changes listing in this volume. We also suggest reading the catalog introduction, which includes an abundance of useful information.

A digital subscription is also available for the Scott catalogs, and information about the subscription can be found online at www.amosadvantage.com.

Approximately 1,000 images of stamps not pictured in the Vol. 4 print edition were added to this year's Vol. 4 digital catalog.

Best wishes in your collecting pursuits!

Jay Bigalke, Scott catalog editor-in-chief

# Addresses, telephone numbers, web sites, email addresses of general and specialized philatelic societies

Collectors can contact the following groups for information about the philately of the areas within the scope of these societies, or inquire about membership in these groups. Aside from the general societies, we limit this list to groups that specialize in particular fields of philately, particular areas covered by the Scott *Standard Postage Stamp Catalogue*, and topical groups. Many more specialized philatelic society exist than those listed below. These addresses are updated yearly, and they are, to the best of our knowledge, correct and current. Groups should inform the editors of address changes whenever they occur. The editors also want to hear from other such specialized groups not listed.

Unless otherwise noted all website addresses begin with http://

## General Societies

**American Philatelic Society,** 100 Match Factory Place, Bellefonte, PA 16823-1367; (814) 933-3803; https://stamps.org; apsinfo@stamps.org

**International Society of Worldwide Stamp Collectors,** Joanne Murphy, M.D., P.O. Box 19006, Sacramento, CA 95819; www.iswsc.org; executivedirector@iswsc.org

**Royal Philatelic Society of Canada,** P.O. Box 69080, St. Clair Post Office, Toronto, ON M4T 3A1 Canada; (888) 285-4143; www.rpsc.org; info@rpsc.org

**Royal Philatelic Society London,** 15 Abchurch Lane, London EX4N 7BW, United Kingdom; +44 (0) 20 7486 1044; www.rpsl.org.uk; secretary@rpsl.org.uk

## Libraries, Museums, and Research Groups

**American Philatelic Research Library,** 100 Match Factory Place, Bellefonte, PA 16823; (814) 933-3803; www.stamplibrary.org; library@stamps.org.

**V. G. Greene Philatelic Research Foundation,** P.O. Box 69100, St. Clair Post Office, Toronto, ON M4T 3A1, Canada; (416) 921-2073; info@greenefoundation.ca

### Aero/Astro Philately

**American Air Mail Society,** Stephen Reinhard, P.O. Box 110, Mineola, NY 11501; www.americanairmailsociety.org; sreinhard1@optonline.net

## Postal History

**Auxiliary Markings Club,** Jerry Johnson, 6621 W. Victoria Ave., Kennewick, WA 99336; www.postal-markings.org; membership-2010@postal-markings.org

**Postage Due Mail Study Group,** Bob Medland, Camway Cottage, Nanny Hurn's Lane, Cameley, Bristol BS39 5AJ, United Kingdom; 01761 45959; www.postageduemail.org.uk; secretary.pdmsg@gmail.com

**Postal History Society,** Yamil Kouri, 405 Waltham St. #347, Lexington, MA 02421; www.postalhistorysociety.org; yhkouri@massmed.org

**Post Mark Collectors Club,** Bob Milligan, 7014 Woodland Oaks Drive, Magnolia, TX 77354; (281) 259-2735; www.postmarks.org; bob.milligan0@gmail.com

**U.S. Cancellation Club,** Roger Curran, 18 Tressler Blvd., Lewisburg, PA 17837; rdcnrc@ptd.net

## Revenues and Cinderellas

**American Revenue Association,** Lyman Hensley, 473 E. Elm St., Sycamore, IL 60178-1934; www.revenuer.org; ilrno2@netzero.net

**Christmas Seal and Charity Stamp Society,** John Denune Jr., 234 E. Broadway, Granville, OH 43023; (740) 814-6031; www.seal-society.org

**National Duck Stamp Collectors Society,** Anthony J. Monico, P.O. Box 43, Harleysville, PA 19438-0043; www.ndscs.org; ndscs@ndscs.org

**State Revenue Society,** Kent Gray, P.O. Box 67842, Albuquerque, NM 87193; www.staterevenue.org; srssecretary@comcast.net

## Thematic Philately

**Americana Unit,** Dennis Dengel, 17 Peckham Road, Poughkeepsie, NY 12603-2018; www.americanaunit.org; ddengel@americanaunit.org

**American Topical Association,** Jennifer Miller, P.O. Box 2143, Greer, SC 29652-2143; (618) 985-5100; americantopical.org; ata@americantopical.org

**Astronomy Study Unit,** Leonard Zehr, 1411 Chateau Ave., Windsor, ON N8P 1M2, Canada; (416) 833-9317; www.astronomystudyunit.net; lenzehr@gmail.com

**Bicycle Stamps Club,** Corey Hjalseth, 1102 Broadway, Suite 200, Tacoma, WA 98402; (253) 318-6222; www.bicyclestampsclub.org; coreyh@evergreenhomeloans.com

**Biology Unit,** Chris Dahle, 1401 Linmar Drive NE, Cedar Rapids, IA 52402-3724; www.biophilately.org; chris-dahle@biophilately.org

**Bird Stamp Society,** Mr. S. A. H. (Tony) Statham, Ashlyns Lodge, Chesham Road, Berkhamsted, Herts HP4 2ST United Kingdom; www.bird-stamps.org/bss; tony.statham@sky.com

**Captain Cook Society,** Jerry Yucht, 8427 Leale Ave., Stockton, CA 95212, www.captaincooksociety.com; us@captaincooksociety.com

**The CartoPhilatelic Society,** Marybeth Sulkowski, 2885 Sanford Ave., SW, #32361, Grandville, MI 49418-1342; www.mapsonstamps.org; secretary@mapsonstamps.org

**Casey Jones Railroad Unit,** Jeff Lough, 2612 Redbud Land, Apt. C, Lawrence, KS 66046; www.uqp.de/cjr; jeffydplaugh@gmail.com

**Cats on Stamps Study Unit,** Robert D. Jarvis, 2731 Teton Lane, Fairfield, CA 94533; www.catstamps.info; catmews1@yahoo.com

**Chemistry and Physics on Stamps Study Unit,** Dr. Roland Hirsch, 13830 Metcalf Ave., Apt. 15218, Overland Park, KS 66223-8017; (301) 792-6296; www.cpossu.org; rfhirsch@cpossu.org

**Chess on Stamps Study Unit,** Barry Keith, 511 First St. N., Apt. 106; Charlottesville, VA 22902; www.chessonstamps.org; keithfam@embarqmail.com

**Cricket Philatelic Society,** A. Melville-Brown, 11 Weppons, Ravens Road, Shorham-by-Sea, West Sussex BN43 5AW, United Kingdom; www.cricketstamp.net; mel.cricket.100@googlemail.com

**Earth's Physical Features Study Group,** Fred Klein, 515 Magdalena Ave., Los Altos, CA 94024; http://epfsu.jeffhayward.com; epfsu@jeffhayward.com

**Ebony Society of Philatelic Events and Reflections (ESPER),** Don Neal, P.O. Box 5245, Somerset, NJ 08875-5245; www.esperstamps.org; esperdon@verizon.net

**Europa Study Unit,** Tonny E. Van Loij, 3002 S. Xanthia St.; Denver, CO 80231-4237; (303) 752-0189; www.europastudyunit.org; tvanloij@gmail.com

**Fire Service in Philately,** John Zaranek, 81 Hillpine Road, Cheektowaga, NY 14227-2259; (716) 668-3352; jczaranek@roadrunner.com

**Gastronomy on Stamps Study Unit,** David Wolfersburger, 5062 NW 35th Lane Road, Ocala, FL 34482; (314) 494-3795; www.gastronomystamps.org

**Gay and Lesbian History on Stamps Club,** Joe Petronie, P.O. Box 190842, Dallas, TX 75219-0842; www.glhsonline.org; glhsc@aol.com

**Gems, Minerals and Jewelry Study Unit,** Fred Haynes, 10 Country Club Drive, Rochester, NY 14618-3720; fredmhaynes55@gmail.com

**Graphics Philately Association,** Larry Rosenblum. 1030 E. El Camino Real, PMB 107, Sunnyvale, CA 94087-3759; www.graphics-stamps.org; larry@graphics-stamps.org

**Journalists, Authors and Poets on Stamps,** Christopher D. Cook, 7222 Hollywood Road, Berrien Springs, MI 49103; cdcook2@gmail.com

**Lighthouse Stamp Society,** www.lighthousestampsociety.org

**Lions International Stamp Club,** David McKirdy, s-Gravenwetering 248, 3062 SJ Rotterdam, Netherlands; 31(0) 10 212 0313; www.lisc.nl; davidmckirdy@aol.com

**Masonic Study Unit,** Gene Fricks, 25 Murray Way, Blackwood, NJ 08012-4400; genefricks@comcast.net

**Medical Subjects Unit,** Dr. Frederick C. Skvara, P.O. Box 6228, Bridgewater, NJ 08807; fcskvara@optonline.net

**Napoleonic Age Philatelists,** Ken Berry, 4117 NW 146th St., Oklahoma City, OK 73134-1746; (405) 748-8646; www.nap-stamps.org; krb4117@att.net

**Old World Archaeological Study Unit,** Caroline Scannell, 14 Dawn Drive, Smithtown, NY 11787-176; www.owasu.org; editor@owasu.org

**Petroleum Philatelic Society International,** Feitze Papa, 922 Meander Drive, Walnut Creek, CA 94598-4239; www.ppsi.org.uk; oildad@astound.net

**Rotary on Stamps Fellowship,** Gerald L. Fitzsimmons, 105 Calle Ricardo, Victoria, TX 77904; www.rotaryonstamps. org; glfitz@suddenlink.net

**Scouts on Stamps Society International,** Woodrow (Woody) Brooks, 498 Baldwin Road, Akron, OH 44312; (330) 612-1294; www.sossi.org; secretary@sossi.org

**Ships on Stamps Unit,** Erik Th. Matzinger, Voorste Havervelden 30, 4822 AL Breda, Netherlands; www. shipsonstamps.org; erikships@gmail.com

**Space Topic Study Unit,** David Blog, P.O. Box 174, Bergenfield, NJ 07621; www.space-unit.com; davidblognj@ gmail.com

**Stamps on Stamps Collectors Club,** Michael Merritt, 73 Mountainside Road, Mendham, NJ 07945; www. stampsonstamps.org; michael@mischu.me

**Windmill Study Unit,** Walter J. Hallien, 607 N. Porter St., Watkins Glenn, NY 14891-1345; (607) 229-3541; www. windmillworld.com

**Wine On Stamps Study Unit,** David Wolfersburger, 5062 NW 35th Lane Road, Ocala, FL 34482; (314) 494-3795; www.wine-on-stamps.org;

## United States

**American Air Mail Society,** Stephen Reinhard, P.O. Box 110, Mineola, NY 11501; www.americanairmailsociety. org; sreinhard1@optonline.net

**American First Day Cover Society,** P.O. Box 246, Colonial Beach VA 22443-0246; (520) 321-0880; www.afdcs.org; afdcs@afdcs.org

**Auxiliary Markings Club,** Jerry Johnson, 6621 W. Victoria Ave., Kennewick, WA 99336; www.postal-markings.org; membership-2010@ postal-markings.org

**American Plate Number Single Society,** Rick Burdsall, APNSS Secretary, P.O. BOX 1023, Palatine, IL 60078-1023; www.apnss.org; apnss.sec@gmail.com

**American Revenue Association,** Lyman Hensley, 473 E. Elm St., Sycamore, IL 60178-1934; www. revenuer.org; ilrno2@netzero.net

**American Society for Philatelic Pages and Panels,** Ron Walenciak, P.O. Box 1042, Washington Township, NJ 07676; www.asppp.org; ron.walenciak@asppp. org

**Canal Zone Study Group,** Mike Drabik, P.O. Box 281, Bolton, MA 01740, www.canalzonestudygroup.com; czsgsecretary@gmail.com

**Carriers and Locals Society,** John Bowman, 14409 Pentridge Drive, Corpus Christi, TX 78410; (361) 933-0757; www.pennypost.org; jbowman@stx. rr.com

**Christmas Seal & Charity Stamp Society,** John Denune Jr., 234 E. Broadway, Granville, OH 43023; (740) 814-6031; www.seal-society.org; john@ christmasseals.net

**Civil War Philatelic Society,** Patricia A. Kaufmann, 10194 N. Old State Road, Lincoln, DE 19960-3644; (302) 422-2656; www.civilwarphilatelicsociety.org; trishkauf@comcast.net

**Error, Freaks, and Oddities Collectors Club,** Scott Shaulis, P.O. Box 549, Murrysville, PA 15668-0549; (724) 733-4134; www.efocc.org; scott@ shaulisstamps.com

**National Duck Stamp Collectors Society,** Anthony J. Monico, P.O. Box 43, Harleysville, PA 19438-0043; www. ndscs.org; ndscs@ndscs.org

**Plate Number Coil Collectors Club (PNC3),** Gene Trinks, 16415 W. Desert Wren Court, Surprise, AZ 85374; (623) 322-4619; www.pnc3.org; gctrinks@ cox.net

**Post Mark Collectors Club,** Bob Milligan, 7014 Woodland Oaks Drive, Magnolia, TX 77354; (281) 259-2735; www.postmarks.org; bob.milligan0@ gmail.com

**Souvenir Card Collectors Society,** William V. Kriebel, www.souvenircards. org; kriebewv@drexel.edu

**United Postal Stationery Society,** Dave Kandziolka, 404 Sundown Drive, Knoxville, TN 37934; www.upss.org; membership@upss.org

**U.S. Cancellation Club,** Roger Curran, 18 Tressler Blvd., Lewisburg, PA 17837; rdcnrc@ptd.net

**U.S. Philatelic Classics Society,** Rob Lund, 2913 Fulton St., Everett, WA 98201-3733; www.uspcs.org; membershipchairman@uspcs.org

**US Possessions Philatelic Society,** Daniel F. Ring, P.O. Box 113, Woodstock, IL 60098; http://uspps.tripod.com; danielfring@hotmail.com

**United States Stamp Society,** Rod Juell, P.O. Box 3508, Joliet, IL 60434-3508; www.usstamps.org; execsecretary@usstamps.org

## Africa

**Bechuanalands and Botswana Society,** Otto Peetoom, Roos, East Yorkshire HU12 0LD, United Kingdom; 44(0)1964 670239; www. bechuanalandphilately.com; info@ bechuanalandphilately.com

**Egypt Study Circle,** Mike Murphy, 11 Waterbank Road, Bellingham, London SE6 3DJ United Kingdom; (44) 0203 6737051; www.egyptstudycircle.org.uk; secretary@egyptstudycircle.org.uk

**Ethiopian Philatelic Society,** Ulf Lindahl, 21 Westview Place, Riverside, CT 06878; (203) 722-0769; https:// ethiopianphilatelicsociety.weebly.com; ulindahl@optonline.net

**Liberian Philatelic Society,** P.O. Box 1570, Parker, CO 80134; www. liberiastamps.org; liberiastamps@ comcast.net

**Orange Free State Study Circle,** J. R. Stroud, RDPSA, 24 Hooper Close, Burnham-on-sea, Somerset TA8 1JQ United Kingdom; 44 1278 782235; www.orangefreestatephilately.org.uk; richard@richardstroud.plus.com

**Philatelic Society for Greater Southern Africa,** David McNamee, 15 Woodland Drive, Alamo, CA 94507; www.psgsa.org; alan.hanks@sympatico. ca

**Rhodesian Study Circle,** William R. Wallace, P.O. Box 16381, San Francisco, CA 94116; (415) 564-6069; www.rhodesianstudycircle.org.uk; bwall8rscr@earthlink.net

**Society for Moroccan and Tunisian Philately,** S.P.L.M., 206, Bld Pereire, 75017 Paris, France; http://splm-philatelie.org; splm206@aol.com

**South Sudan Philatelic Society,** William Barclay, 1370 Spring Hill Road, South Londonderry, VT 05155; barclayphilatelics@gmail.com

**Sudan Study Group,** Andy Neal, Bank House, Coedway, Shrewsbury SY5 9AR United Kingdom; www.sudanstamps.org; andywneal@gmail.com

**Transvaal Study Circle,** c/o 9 Meadow Road, Gravesend, Kent DA11 7LR United Kingdom; www.transvaalstamps.org.uk; transvaalstudycircle@aol.co.uk

**West Africa Study Circle,** Martin Bratzel, 1233 Virginia Ave., Windsor, ON N8S 2Z1 Canada; www.wasc.org.uk; marty_bratzel@yahoo.ca

## Asia

**Aden & Somaliland Study Group,** Malcom Lacey, 108 Dalestorth Road, Sutton-in-Ashfield, Nottinghamshire NG17 3AA, United Kingdom; www.stampdomain.com/aden; neil53williams@yahoo.co.uk

**Burma (Myanmar) Philatelic Study Circle,** Michael Whittaker, 1, Ecton Leys, Hillside, Rugby, Warwickshire CV22 5SL United Kingdom; https:// burmamyanmarphilately.wordpress.com/ burma-myanmar-philatelic-study-circle; manningham8@mypostoffice.co.uk

**Ceylon Study Circle,** Rodney W. P. Frost, 42 Lonsdale Road, Cannington, Bridgwater, Somerset TA5 2JS United Kingdom; 01278 652592; www. ceylonsc.org; rodney.frost@tiscali.co.uk

**China Stamp Society,** H. James Maxwell, 1050 W. Blue Ridge Blvd., Kansas City, MO 64145-1216; www. chinastampsociety.org; president@ chinastampsociety.org

**Hong Kong Philatelic Society,** John Tang, G.P.O. Box 446, Hong Kong; www. hkpsociety.com; hkpsociety@outlook.com

**Hong Kong Study Circle,** Robert Newton, www.hongkongstudycircle.com/ index.html; newtons100@gmail.com

**India Study Circle,** John Warren, P.O. Box 7326, Washington, DC 20044; (202) 488-7443; https://indiastudycircle.org; jw-kbw@earthlink.net

**International Philippine Philatelic Society,** James R. Larot, Jr., 4990 Bayleaf Court, Martinez, CA 94553; (925) 260-5425; www.theipps.info; jlarot@ccwater.com

**International Society for Japanese Philately,** P.O. Box 1283, Haddonfield NJ 08033; www.isjp.org; secretary@ isjp.org

**Iran Philatelic Study Circle,** Nigel Gooch, Marchwood, 56, Wickham Ave., Bexhill-on-Sea, East Sussex TN39 3ER United Kingdom; www.iranphilately.org; nigelmgooch@gmail.com

**Korea Stamp Society,** Peter Corson, 1109 Gunnison Place, Raleigh, NC 27609; (919) 787-7611; koreastampsociety.org; pbcorson@aol. com

**Nepal & Tibet Philatelic Study Circle,** Colin Hepper, 12 Charnwood Close, Peterborough, Cambs PE2 9BZ United Kingdom; http://fuchs-online.com/ntpsc; ntpsc@fuchs-online.com

**Pakistan Philatelic Study Circle,** Jeff Siddiqui, P.O. Box 7002, Lynnwood, WA 98046; jeffsiddiqui@msn.com

**Society of Indo-China Philatelists,** Ron Bentley, 2600 N. 24th St., Arlington, VA 22207; (703) 524-1652; www.sicp-online.org; ron.bentley@verizon.net

**Society of Israel Philatelists, Inc.,** Sarah Berezenko, 100 Match Factory Place, Bellefonte, PA 16823-1367; (814) 933-3803 ext. 212; www.israelstamps.com; israelstamps@gmail.com

## Australasia and Oceania

**Australian States Study Circle of the Royal Sydney Philatelic Club,** Ben Palmer, G.P.O. 1751, Sydney, NSW 2001 Australia; http://club.philas.org.au/states

**Fellowship of Samoa Specialists,** Trevor Shimell, 18 Aspen Drive, Newton Abbot, Devon TQ12 4TN United Kingdom; www.samoaexpress.org; trevor.shimell@gmail.com

**Malaya Study Group,** Michael Waugh, 151 Roker Lane, Pudsey, Leeds LS28 9ND United Kingdom; http://malayastudygroup.com; mawpud43@gmail.com

**New Zealand Society of Great Britain,** Michael Wilkinson, 121 London Road, Sevenoaks, Kent TN13 1BH United Kingdom; 01732 456997; www.nzsgb.org.uk; mwilkin799@aol.com

**Pacific Islands Study Circle,** John Ray, 24 Woodvale Ave., London SE25 4AE United Kingdom; www.pisc.org.uk; secretary@pisc.org.uk

**Papuan Philatelic Society,** Steven Zirinsky, P.O. Box 49, Ansonia Station, New York, NY 10023; (718) 706-0616; www.papuanphilatelicsociety.com; szirinsky@cs.com

**Pitcairn Islands Study Group,** Dr. Everett L. Parker, 207 Corinth Road, Hudson, ME 04449-3057; (207) 573-1686; www.pisg.net; eparker@hughes.net

**Ryukyu Philatelic Specialist Society,** Laura Edmonds, P.O. Box 240177, Charlotte, NC 28224-0177; (336) 509-3739; www.ryukyustamps.org; secretary@ryukyustamps.org

**Society of Australasian Specialists / Oceania,** Steve Zirinsky, P.O. Box 230049, New York, NY 10023-0049; www.sasoceania.org; president@sosoceania.org

**Sarawak Specialists' Society,** Stephen Schumann, 2417 Caballo Drive, Hayward, CA 94545; (510) 785-4794; www.britborneostamps.org.uk; vpnam@s-s-s.org.uk

**Western Australia Study Group,** Brian Pope, P.O. Box 423, Claremont, WA 6910 Australia; (61) 419 843 943; www.wastudygroup.com; wastudygroup@hotmail.com

## Europe

**American Helvetia Philatelic Society,** Richard T. Hall, P.O. Box 15053, Asheville, NC 28813-0053; www.swiss-stamps.org; secretary2@swiss-stamps.org

**American Society for Netherlands Philately,** Hans Kremer, 50 Rockport Court, Danville, CA 94526; (925) 820-5841; www.asnp1975.com; hkremer@usa.net

**Andorran Philatelic Study Circle,** David Hope, 17 Hawthorn Drive, Stalybridge, Cheshire SK15 1UE United Kingdom; www.andorranpsc.org.uk; andorranpsc@btinternet.com

**Austria Philatelic Society,** Ralph Schneider, P.O. Box 978, Iowa Park, TX 76376; (940) 213-5004; www.austriaphilatelicsociety.com; rschneiderstamps@gmail.com

**Channel Islands Specialists Society,** Richard Flemming, Burbage, 64 Falconers Green, Hinckley, Leicestershire, LE102SX, United Kingdom; www.ciss.uk; secretary@ciss.uk

**Cyprus Study Circle,** Rob Wheeler, 47 Drayton Ave., London W13 0LE United Kingdom; www.cyprusstudycircle.org; robwheeler47@aol.com

**Danish West Indies Study Unit of Scandinavian Collectors Club,** Arnold Sorensen, 7666 Edgedale Drive, Newburgh, IN 47630; (812) 480-6532; www.scc-online.org; valbydwi@hotmail.com

**Eire Philatelic Association,** John B. Sharkey, 1559 Grouse Lane, Mountainside, NJ 07092-1340; www.eirephilatelicassoc.org; jsharkeyepa@me.com

**Faroe Islands Study Circle,** Norman Hudson, 40 Queen's Road, Vicar's Cross, Chester CH3 5HB United Kingdom; www.faroeislandssc.org; jntropics@hotmail.com

**France & Colonies Philatelic Society,** Edward Grabowski, 111 Prospect St., 4C, Westfield, NJ 07090; (908) 233-9318; www.franceandcolsps.org; edjjg@alum.mit.edu

**Germany Philatelic Society,** P.O. Box 6547, Chesterfield, MO 63006-6547; www.germanyphilatelicusa.org; info@germanyphilatelicsocietyusa.org

**Gibraltar Study Circle,** Susan Dare, 22, Byways Park, Strode Road, Clevedon, North Somerset BS21 6UR United Kingdom; www.gibraltarstudycircle.wordpress.com; smldare@yahoo.co.uk

**International Society for Portuguese Philately,** Clyde Homen, 1491 Bonnie View Road, Hollister, CA 95023-5117; www.portugalstamps.com; ispp1962@sbcglobal.net

**Italy and Colonies Study Circle,** Richard Harlow, 7 Duncombe House, 8 Manor Road, Teddington, Middlesex TW118BE United Kingdom; 44 208 977 8737; www.icsc-uk.com; richardharlow@outlook.com

**Liechtenstudy USA,** Paul Tremaine, 410 SW Ninth St., Dundee, OR 97115-9731; (503) 538-4500; www.liechtenstudy.org; tremaine@liechtenstudy.org

**Lithuania Philatelic Society,** Audrius Brazdeikis, 9915 Murray Landing, Missouri City, TX 77459; (281) 450-6224; www.lithuanianphilately.com/lps; audrius@lithuanianphilately.com

**Luxembourg Collectors Club,** Gary B. Little, 7319 Beau Road, Sechelt, BC V0N 3A8 Canada; (604) 885-7241; http://lcc.luxcentral.com; gary@luxcentral.com

**Plebiscite-Memel-Saar Study Group of the German Philatelic Society,** Clayton Wallace, 100 Lark Court, Alamo, CA 94507; claytonwallace@comcast.net

**Polonus Polish Philatelic Society,** Daniel Lubelski, P.O. Box 2212, Benicia, CA 94510; (419) 410-9115; www.polonus.org; info@polonus.org

**Rossica Society of Russian Philately,** Alexander Kolchinsky, 1506 Country Lake Drive, Champaign, IL 61821-6428; www.rossica.org; alexander.kolchinsky@rossica.org

**Scandinavian Collectors Club,** Alan Warren, Scandinavian Collectors Club, P.O. Box 39, Exton PA 19341-0039; (612) 810-8640; www.scc-online.org; alanwar@att.net

**Society for Czechoslovak Philately,** Tom Cossaboom, P.O. Box 4124, Prescott, AZ 86302; (928) 771-9097; www.csphilately.org; klfck1@aol.com

**Society for Hungarian Philately,** Alan Bauer, P.O. Box 4028, Vineyard Haven, MA 02568; (617) 645-4045; www.hungarianphilately.org; alan@hungarianstamps.com

**Spanish Study Circle,** Edith Knight, www.spaincircle.wixsite.com/spainstudycircle; spaincircle@gmail.com

**Ukrainian Philatelic & Numismatic Society,** Martin B. Tatuch, 5117 8th Road N., Arlington, VA 22205-1201; www.upns.org; treasurer@upns.org

**Vatican Philatelic Society,** Dennis Brady, 4897 Ledyard Drive, Manlius NY 13104-1514; www.vaticanphilately.org; dbrady7534@gmail.com

**Yugoslavia Study Group,** Michael Chant, 1514 N. Third Ave., Wausau, WI 54401; 208-748-9919; www.yugosg.org; membership@yugosg.org

## Interregional Societies

**American Society of Polar Philatelists,** Alan Warren, P.O. Box 39, Exton, PA 19341-0039; (610) 321-0740; www.polarphilatelists.org; alanwar@att.net

**First Issues Collector's Club,** Kurt Streepy, 3128 E. Mattatha Drive, Bloomington, IN 47401; www.firstissues.org; secretary@firstissues.org

**Former French Colonies Specialist Society,** Col.fra, BP 628, 75367 Paris, France; www.colfra.org; postmaster@colfra.org

**France & Colonies Philatelic Society,** Edward Grabowski, 111 Prospect St., 4C, Westfield, NJ 07090; (908) 233-9318, www.franceandcolsps.org; edjjg@alum.mit.edu

**Joint Stamp Issues Society,** Richard Zimmermann, 29A, Rue Des Eviats, 67220 Lalaye, France; www.philarz.net; richard.zimmermann@club-internet.fr

**The King George VI Collectors Society,** Brian Livingstone, 21 York Mansions, Prince of Wales Drive, London SW11 4DL United Kingdom; www.kg6.info; livingstone484@btinternet.com

**International Society of Reply Coupon Collectors,** Peter Robin, P.O. Box 353, Bala Cynwyd, PA 19004; peterrobin@verizon.net

**Italy and Colonies Study Circle,** Richard Harlow, 7 Duncombe House, 8 Manor Road, Teddington, Middlesex TW118BE United Kingdom; 44 208 977 8737; www.icsc-uk.com; richardharlow@outlook.com

**St. Helena, Ascension & Tristan Da Cunha Philatelic Society,** Dr. Everett L. Parker, 207 Corinth Road, Hudson, ME 04449-3057; (207) 573-1686; www.shatps.org; eparker@hughes.net

**United Nations Philatelists,** Blanton Clement, Jr., P.O. Box 146, Morrisville, PA 19067-0146; www.unpi.com; bclemjunior@gmail.com

## Latin America

**Asociación Filatélica de Panamá,** Edward D. Vianna B. ASOFILPA, 0819-03400, El Dorado, Panama; http://asociacionfilatelicadepanama.blogspot.com; asofilpa@gmail.com

**Asociacion Mexicana de Filatelia (AMEXFIL),** Alejandro Grossmann, Jose Maria Rico, 129, Col. Del Valle, 3100 Mexico City, DF Mexico; www.amexfil.mx; amexfil@gmail.com

**Associated Collectors of El Salvador,** Pierre Cahen, Vipsal 1342, P.O. Box 02-5364, Miami FL 33102; www.elsalvadorphilately.org; sfes-aces@elsalvadorphilately.org

**Association Filatelic de Costa Rica,** Giana Wayman (McCarty), #SJO 4935, P.O. Box 025723, Miami, FL 33102-5723; 011-506-2-228-1947; scotland@racsa.co.cr

**Brazil Philatelic Association,** William V. Kriebel, www.brazilphilatelic.org, info@brazilphilatelic.org

**Canal Zone Study Group,** Mike Drabik, P.O. Box 281, Bolton, MA 01740; www.canalzonestudygroup.com; czsgsecretary@gmail.com

**Colombia-Panama Philatelic Study Group,** Allan Harris, 26997 Hemmingway Ct, Hayward CA 94542-2349; www.copaphil.org; copaphilusa@aol.com

**Falkland Islands Philatelic Study Groups,** Morva White, 42 Colton Road, Shrivenham, Swindon SN6 8AZ United Kingdom; 44(0) 1793 783245; www.fipsg.org.uk; morawhite@supanet.com

**Federacion Filatélica de la Republica de Honduras,** Mauricio Mejia, Apartado Postal 1465, Tegucigalpa, D.C. Honduras; 504 3399-7227; www.facebook.com/filateliadehonduras; ffrh@hotmail.com

**International Cuban Philatelic Society (ICPS),** Ernesto Cuesta, P.O. Box 34434, Bethesda, MD 20827; (301) 564-3099; www.cubafil.org; ecuesta@philat.com

**International Society of Guatemala Collectors,** Jaime Marckwordt, 449 St. Francis Blvd., Daly City, CA 94015-2136; (415) 997-0295; www.guatemalastamps.com; president@guatamalastamps.com

**Mexico-Elmhurst Philatelic Society International,** Eric Stovner, P.O. Box 10097, Santa Ana, CA 92711-0097; www.mepsi.org; treasurer@mepsi.org

**Nicaragua Study Group,** Erick Rodriguez, 11817 S. W. 11th St., Miami, FL 33184-2501; nsgsec@yahoo.com

## North America (excluding United States)

**British Caribbean Philatelic Study Group,** Bob Stewart, 7 West Dune Lane, Long Beach Township, NJ 08008; (941) 379-4108; www.bcpsg.com; bcpsg@comcast.net

**British North America Philatelic Society,** Andy Ellwood, 10 Doris Ave., Gloucester, ON K1T 3W8 Canada; www.bnaps.org; secretary@bnaps.org

**British West Indies Study Circle,** Steve Jarvis, 5 Redbridge Drive, Andover, Hants SP10 2LF United Kingdom; 01264 358065; www.bwisc.org; info@bwisc.org

**Bermuda Collectors Society,** John Pare, 405 Perimeter St., Mount Horeb, WI 53572; (608) 852-7358; www.bermudacollectorssociety.com; pare16@mhtc.net

**Haiti Philatelic Society,** Ubaldo Del Toro, 5709 Marble Archway, Alexandria, VA 22315; www.haitiphilately.org; u007ubi@aol.com

**Hawaiian Philatelic Society,** Gannon Sugimura, P.O. Box 10115, Honolulu, HI 96816-0115, www.hpshawaii.com; hiphilsoc@gmail.com

## Stamp Dealer Associations

**American Stamp Dealers Association, Inc.,** P.O. Box 513, Centre Hall PA 16828; (800) 369-8207; www.americanstampdealer.com; asda@americanstampdealer.com

**National Stamp Dealers Association,** Sheldon Ruckens, President, 3643 Private Road 18, Pinckneyville, IL 62274-3426; (618) 357-5497; www.nsdainc.org; nsda@nsdainc.org

## Youth Philately

**Young Stamp Collectors of America,** 100 Match Factory Place, Bellefonte, PA 16823; (814) 933-3803; https://stamps.org/learn/youth-in-philately; ysca@stamps.org

# Expertizing services

The following organizations will, for a fee, provide expert opinions about stamps submitted to them. Collectors should contact these organizations to find out about their fees and requirements before submitting philatelic material to them. The listing of these groups here is not intended as an endorsement by Amos Media Co.

## General Expertizing Services

**American Philatelic Expertizing Service (a service of the American Philatelic Society)**
100 Match Factory Place
Bellefonte PA 16823-1367
(814) 237-3803
www.stamps.org/stamp-authentication
apex@stamps.org
Areas of Expertise: Worldwide

**BPA Expertising, Ltd.**
P.O. Box 1141
Guildford, Surrey, GU5 0WR
United Kingdom
www.bpaexpertising.com
sec@bpaexpertising.org
Areas of Expertise: British Commonwealth, Great Britain, Classics of Europe, South America and the Far East

**Philatelic Foundation**
353 Lexington Avenue, Suite 804
New York NY 10016
(212) 221-6555
www.philatelicfoundation.org
philatelicfoundation@verizon.net
Areas of Expertise: U.S. & Worldwide

**Philatelic Stamp Authentication and Grading, Inc.**
P.O. Box 41-0880
Melbourne FL 32941-0880
(305) 345-9864
www.psaginc.com
info@psaginc.com
Areas of Expertise: U.S., Canal Zone, Hawaii, Philippines, Canada & Provinces

**Professional Stamp Experts**
P.O. Box 539309
Henderson NV 89053-9309
(702) 776-6522
www.gradingmatters.com
www.psestamp.com
info@gradingmatters.com
Areas of Expertise: Stamps and Covers of U.S., U.S. Possessions, British Commonwealth

**Royal Philatelic Society London Expert Committee**
15 Abchurch Lane
London, EX4N 7BW
United Kingdom
www.rpsl.limited/experts.aspx
experts@rpsl.limited
Areas of Expertise: Worldwide

## Expertizing Services Covering Specific Fields or Countries

**China Stamp Society Expertizing Service**
1050 W. Blue Ridge Blvd.
Kansas City MO 64145
(816) 942-6300
hjmesq@aol.com
Areas of Expertise: China

**Civil War Philatelic Society Authentication Service**
C/O Stefan T. Jaronski
P.O. Box 232
Sidney, MT 59270-0232
www.civilwarphilatelicsociety.org/authentication/
authentication@civilwarphilatelicsociety.org
Areas of Expertise: Confederate stamps and postal history

**Errors, Freaks and Oddities Collectors Club Expertizing Service**
138 East Lakemont Drive
Kingsland GA 31548
(912) 729-1573
Areas of Expertise: U.S. errors, freaks and oddities

**Hawaiian Philatelic Society Expertizing Service**
P.O. Box 10115
Honolulu HI 96816-0115
www.stampshows.com/hps.html
hiphilsoc@gmail.com
Areas of Expertise: Hawaii

**Hong Kong Stamp Society Expertizing Service**
P.O. Box 206
Glenside PA 19038
Areas of Expertise: Hong Kong

**International Association of Philatelic Experts United States Associate members:**
Paul Buchsbayew
300 Frank W. Burr Blvd. - Second Floor
Box 35
Teaneck, NJ 07666.
(212) 977-7734
Areas of Expertise: Russia, Soviet Union

William T. Crowe
P.O. Box 2090
Danbury CT 06813-2090
wtcrowe@aol.com
Areas of Expertise: United States

**International Society for Japanese Philately Expertizing Committee**
132 North Pine Terrace
Staten Island NY 10312-4052
(718) 227-5229
Areas of Expertise: Japan and related areas, except WWII Japanese Occupation issues

**International Society for Portuguese Philately Expertizing Service**
P.O. Box 43146
Philadelphia PA 19129-3146
(215) 843-2106
s.s.washburne@worldnet.att.net
Areas of Expertise: Portugal and Colonies

**Mexico-Elmhurst Philatelic Society International Expert Committee**
Expert Committee Administrator
Marc E. Gonzales
P.O. Box 29040
Denver CO 80229-0040
www.mepsi.org/expert_committeee.htm
expertizations@mepsi.org
Areas of Expertise: Mexico

**Ukrainian Philatelic & Numismatic Society Expertizing Service**
30552 Dell Lane
Warren MI 48092-1862
Areas of Expertise: Ukraine, Western Ukraine

**V. G. Greene Philatelic Research Foundation**
P.O. Box 69100
St. Clair Post Office
Toronto, ON M4T 3A1
Canada
(416) 921-2073
www.greenefoundation.ca
info@greenefoundation.ca
Areas of Expertise: British North America

# Information on catalogue values, grade and condition

## Catalogue value

The Scott Catalogue value is a retail value; that is, an amount you could expect to pay for a stamp in the grade of Very Fine with no faults. Any exceptions to the grade valued will be noted in the text. The general introduction on the following pages and the individual section introductions further explain the type of material that is valued. The value listed for any given stamp is a reference that reflects recent actual dealer selling prices for that item.

Dealer retail price lists, public auction results, published prices in advertising and individual solicitation of retail prices from dealers, collectors and specialty organizations have been used in establishing the values found in this catalogue. Amos Media Co. values stamps, but Amos Media is not a company engaged in the business of buying and selling stamps as a dealer.

Use this catalogue as a guide for buying and selling. The actual price you pay for a stamp may be higher or lower than the catalogue value because of many different factors, including the amount of personal service a dealer offers, or increased or decreased interest in the country or topic represented by a stamp or set. An item may occasionally be offered at a lower price as a "loss leader," or as part of a special sale. You also may obtain an item inexpensively at public auction because of little interest at that time or as part of a large lot.

Stamps that are of a lesser grade than Very Fine, or those with condition problems, generally trade at lower prices than those given in this catalogue. Stamps of exceptional quality in both grade and condition often command higher prices than those listed.

Values for pre-1900 unused issues are for stamps with approximately half or more of their original gum. Stamps with most or all of their original gum may be expected to sell for more, and stamps with less than half of their original gum may be expected to sell for somewhat less than the values listed. On rarer stamps, it may be expected that the original gum will be somewhat more disturbed than it will be on more common issues. Post-1900 unused issues are assumed to have full original gum. From breakpoints in most countries' listings, stamps are valued as never hinged, due to the wide availability of stamps in that condition. These notations are prominently placed in the listings and in the country information preceding the listings. Some countries also feature listings with dual values for hinged and never-hinged stamps.

## Grade

A stamp's grade and condition are crucial to its value. The accompanying illustrations show examples of Very Fine stamps from different time periods, along with examples of stamps in Fine to Very Fine and Extremely Fine grades as points of reference. When a stamp seller offers a stamp in any grade from fine to superb without further qualifying statements, that stamp should not only have the centering grade as defined, but it also should be free of faults or other condition problems.

**FINE** stamps (illustrations not shown) have designs that are quite off center, with the perforations on one or two sides very close to the design but not quite touching it. There is white space between the perforations and the design that is minimal but evident to the unaided eye. Imperforate stamps may have small margins, and earlier issues may show the design just touching one edge of the stamp design. Very early perforated issues normally will have the perforations slightly cutting into the design. Used stamps may have heavier than usual cancellations.

**FINE-VERY FINE** stamps will be somewhat off center on one side, or slightly off center on two sides. Imperforate stamps will have two margins of at least normal size, and the design will not touch any edge. For perforated stamps, the perfs are well clear of the design, but are still noticeably off center. *However, early issues of a country may be printed in such a way that the design naturally is very close to the edges. In these cases, the perforations may cut into the design very slightly.* Used stamps will not have a cancellation that detracts from the design.

**VERY FINE** stamps will be just slightly off center on one or two sides, but the design will be well clear of the edge. The stamp will present a nice, balanced appearance. Imperforate stamps will be well centered within normal-sized margins. *However, early issues of*

*many countries may be printed in such a way that the perforations may touch the design on one or more sides. Where this is the case, a boxed note will be found defining the centering and margins of the stamps being valued.* Used stamps will have light or otherwise neat cancellations. This is the grade used to establish Scott Catalogue values.

**EXTREMELY FINE** stamps are close to being perfectly centered. Imperforate stamps will have even margins that are slightly larger than normal. Even the earliest perforated issues will have perforations clear of the design on all sides.

**Amos Media Co. recognizes that there is no formally enforced grading scheme for postage stamps, and that the final price you pay or obtain for a stamp will be determined by individual agreement at the time of transaction.**

## Condition

*Grade addresses* only centering and (for used stamps) cancellation. *Condition* refers to factors other than grade that affect a stamp's desirability.

Factors that can increase the value of a stamp include exceptionally wide margins, particularly fresh color, the presence of selvage, and plate or die varieties. Unusual cancels on used stamps (particularly those of the 19th century) can greatly enhance their value as well.

Factors other than faults that decrease the value of a stamp include loss of original gum, regumming, a hinge remnant or foreign object adhering to the gum, natural inclusions, straight edges, and markings or notations applied by collectors or dealers.

Faults include missing pieces, tears, pin or other holes, surface scuffs, thin spots, creases, toning, short or pulled perforations, clipped perforations, oxidation or other forms of color changelings, soiling, stains, and such man-made changes as reperforations or the chemical removal or lightening of a cancellation.

## Grading illustrations

On the following two pages are illustrations of various stamps from countries appearing in this volume. These stamps are arranged by country, and they represent early or important issues that are often found in widely different grades in the marketplace. The editors believe the illustrations will prove useful in showing the margin size and centering that will be seen on the various issues.

In addition to the matters of margin size and centering, collectors are reminded that the very fine stamps valued in the Scott catalogues also will possess fresh color and intact perforations, and they will be free from defects.

Examples shown are computer-manipulated images made from single digitized master illustrations.

## Stamp illustrations used in the catalogue

It is important to note that the stamp images used for identification purposes in this catalogue may not be indicative of the grade of stamp being valued. Refer to the written discussion of grades on this page and to the grading illustrations on the following two pages for grading information.

**Fine-Very Fine** →

**SCOTT
CATALOGUES
VALUE
STAMPS IN
THIS GRADE**

**Very Fine** →

**Extremely Fine** →

**Fine-Very Fine** →

**SCOTT
CATALOGUES
VALUE
STAMPS IN
THIS GRADE**

**Very Fine** →

**Extremely Fine** →

**Fine-Very Fine** →

**SCOTT CATALOGUES VALUE STAMPS IN THIS GRADE**

**Very Fine** →

**Extremely Fine** →

**Fine-Very Fine** →

**SCOTT CATALOGUES VALUE STAMPS IN THIS GRADE**

**Very Fine** →

**Extremely Fine** →

# Gum Conditions

For purposes of helping to determine the gum condition and value of an unused stamp, Scott presents the following chart which details different gum conditions and indicates how the conditions correlate with the Scott values for unused stamps. Used together, the Illustrated Grading Chart on the previous pages and this Illustrated Gum Chart should allow catalogue users to better understand the grade and gum condition of stamps valued in the Scott catalogues.

**Never Hinged (NH; ★★):** A never-hinged stamp will have full original gum that will have no hinge mark or disturbance. The presence of an expertizer's mark does not disqualify a stamp from this designation.

**Original Gum (OG; ★):** Pre-1900 stamps should have approximately half or more of their original gum. On rarer stamps, it may be expected that the original gum will be somewhat more disturbed than it will be on more common issues. Post-1900 stamps should have full original gum. Original gum will show some disturbance caused by a previous hinge(s) which may be present or entirely removed. The actual value of a post-1900 stamp will be affected by the degree of hinging of the full original gum.

**Disturbed Original Gum:** Gum showing noticeable effects of humidity, climate or hinging over more than half of the gum. The significance of gum disturbance in valuing a stamp in any of the Original Gum categories depends on the degree of disturbance, the rarity and normal gum condition of the issue and other variables affecting quality.

**Regummed (RG; (★))**: A regummed stamp is a stamp without gum that has had some type of gum privately applied at a time after it was issued. This normally is done to deceive collectors and/or dealers into thinking that the stamp has original gum and therefore has a higher value. A regummed stamp is considered the same as a stamp with none of its original gum for purposes of grading.

| Gum Categories: | MINT N.H. | ORIGINAL GUM (O.G.) | | | | NO GUM |
|---|---|---|---|---|---|---|
| | Mint **Never Hinged** *Free from any disturbance* | **Lightly Hinged** *Faint impression of a removed hinge over a small area* | **Hinge Mark or Remnant** *Prominent hinged spot with part or all of the hinge remaining* | **Large part o.g.** *Approximately half or more of the gum intact* | **Small part o.g.** *Approximately less than half of the gum intact* | **No gum** *Only if issued with gum* |
| **Commonly Used Symbol:** | ★ ★ | ★ | ★ | ★ | ★ | (★) |
| Pre-1900 Issues (Pre-1881 for U.S.) | *Very fine pre-1900 stamps in these categories trade at a premium over Scott value* | | | Scott Value for "Unused" | | Scott "No Gum" listings for selected unused classic stamps |
| From 1900 to breakpoints for listings of never-hinged stamps | Scott "Never Hinged" listings for selected unused stamps | Scott Value for "Unused" (Actual value will be affected by the degree of hinging of the full o.g.) | | | | |
| *From breakpoints noted for many countries* | Scott Value for "Unused" | | | | | |

# Catalogue listing policy

It is the intent of Amos Media Co. to list all postage stamps of the world in the Scott *Standard Postage Stamp Catalogue*. The only strict criteria for listing is that stamps be decreed legal for postage by the issuing country and that the issuing country actually have an operating postal system. Whether the primary intent of issuing a given stamp or set was for sale to postal patrons or to stamp collectors is not part of our listing criteria. Scott's role is to provide basic comprehensive postage stamp information. It is up to each stamp collector to choose which items to include in a collection.

It is Scott's objective to seek reasons why a stamp should be listed, rather than why it should not. Nevertheless, there are certain types of items that will not be listed. These include the following:

1. Unissued items that are not officially distributed or released by the issuing postal authority. If such items are officially issued at a later date by the country, they will be listed. Unissued items consist of those that have been printed and then held from sale for reasons such as change in government, errors found on stamps or something deemed objectionable about a stamp subject or design.

2. Stamps "issued" by non-existent postal entities or fantasy countries, such as Nagaland, Occusi-Ambeno, Staffa, Sedang, Torres Straits and others. Also, stamps "issued" in the names of legitimate, stamp-issuing countries that are not authorized by those countries.

3. Semi-official or unofficial items not required for postage. Examples include items issued by private agencies for their own express services. When such items are required for delivery, or are valid as prepayment of postage, they are listed.

4. Local stamps issued for local use only. Postage stamps issued by governments specifically for "domestic" use, such as Haiti Scott 219-228, or the United States nondenominated stamps, are not considered to be locals, since they are valid for postage throughout the country of origin.

5. Items not valid for postal use. For example, a few countries have issued souvenir sheets that are not valid for postage. This area also includes a number of worldwide charity labels (some denominated) that do not pay postage.

6. Egregiously exploitative issues such as stamps sold for far more than face value, stamps purposefully issued in artificially small quantities or only against advance orders, stamps awarded only to a selected audience such as a philatelic bureau's standing order customers, or stamps sold only in conjunction with other products. All of these kinds of items are usually controlled issues and/or are intended for speculation. These items normally will be included in a footnote.

7. Items distributed by the issuing government only to a limited group, club, philatelic exhibition or a single stamp dealer or other private company. These items normally will be included in a footnote.

8. Stamps not available to collectors. These generally are rare items, all of which are held by public institutions such as museums. The existence of such items often will be cited in footnotes.

The fact that a stamp has been used successfully as postage, even on international mail, is not in itself sufficient proof that it was legitimately issued. Numerous examples of so-called stamps from non-existent countries are known to have been used to post letters that have successfully passed through the international mail system.

There are certain items that are subject to interpretation. When a stamp falls outside our specifications, it may be listed along with a cautionary footnote.

A number of factors are considered in our approach to analyzing how a stamp is listed. The following list of factors is presented to share with you, the catalogue user, the complexity of the listing process.

**Additional printings** — "Additional printings" of a previously issued stamp may range from an item that is totally different to cases where it is impossible to differentiate from the original. At least a minor number (a small-letter suffix) is assigned if there is a distinct change in stamp shade, noticeably redrawn design, or a significantly different perforation measurement. A major number (numeral or numeral and capital-letter combination) is assigned if the editors feel the "additional printing" is sufficiently different from the original that it constitutes a different issue.

**Commemoratives** — Where practical, commemoratives with the same theme are placed in a set. For example, the U.S. Civil War Centennial set of 1961-65 and the Constitution Bicentennial series of 1989-90 appear as sets. Countries such as Japan and Korea issue such material on a regular basis, with an announced, or at least predictable, number of stamps known in advance. Occasionally, however, stamp sets that were released over a period of years have been separated. Appropriately placed footnotes will guide you to each set's continuation.

**Definitive sets** — Blocks of numbers generally have been reserved for definitive sets, based on previous experience with any given country. If a few more stamps were issued in a set than originally expected, they often have been inserted into the original set with a capital-letter suffix, such as U.S. Scott 1059A. If it appears that many more stamps than the originally allotted block will be released before the set is completed, a new block of numbers will be reserved, with the original one being closed off. In some cases, such as the U.S. Transportation and Great Americans series, several blocks of numbers exist. Appropriately placed footnotes will guide you to each set's continuation.

**New country** — Membership in the Universal Postal Union is not a consideration for listing status or order of placement within the catalogue. The index will tell you in what volume or page number the listings begin.

**"No release date" items** — The amount of information available for any given stamp issue varies greatly from country to country and even from time to time. Extremely comprehensive information about new stamps is available from some countries well before the stamps are released. By contrast some countries do not provide information about stamps or release dates. Most countries, however, fall between these extremes. A country may provide denominations or subjects of stamps from upcoming issues that are not issued as planned. Sometimes, philatelic agencies, those private firms hired to represent countries, add these later-issued items to sets well after the formal release date. This time period can range from weeks to years. If these items were officially released by the country, they will be added to the appropriate spot in the set. In many cases, the specific release date of a stamp or set of stamps may never be known.

**Overprints** — The color of an overprint is always noted if it is other than black. Where more than one color of ink has been used on overprints of a single set, the color used is noted. Early overprint and surcharge illustrations were altered to prevent their use by forgers.

**Personalized Stamps** — Since 1999, the special service of personalizing stamp vignettes, or labels attached to stamps, has been offered to customers by postal administrations of many countries. Sheets of these stamps are sold, singly or in quantity, only through special orders made by mail, in person, or through a sale on a computer website with the postal administrations or their agents for which an extra fee is charged, though some countries offer to collectors at face value personalized stamps having generic images in the vignettes or on the attached labels. It is impossible for any catalogue to know what images have been chosen by customers. Images can be 1) owned or created by the customer, 2) a generic image, or 3) an image pulled from a library of stock images on the stamp creation website. It is also impossible to know the quantity printed for any stamp having a particular image. So from a valuing standpoint, any image is equivalent to any other image for any personalized stamp having the same catalogue number. Illustrations of personalized stamps in the catalogue are not always those of stamps having generic images.

Personalized items are listed with some exceptions. These include:

1. Stamps or sheets that have attached labels that the customer cannot personalize, but which are nonetheless marketed as "personalized," and are sold for far more than the franking value.

2. Stamps or sheets that can be personalized by the customer, but where a portion of the print run must be ceded to the issuing country for sale to other customers.

3. Stamps or sheets that are created exclusively for a particular commercial client, or clients, including stamps that differ from any similar stamp that has been made available to the public.

4. Stamps or sheets that are deliberately conceived by the issuing authority that have been, or are likely to be, created with an excessive number of different face values, sizes, or other features that are changeable.

5. Stamps or sheets that are created by postal administrations using the same system of stamp personalization that has been put in place for use by the public that are printed in limited quantities and sold above face value.

6. Stamps or sheets that are created by licensees not directly affiliated or controlled by a postal administration.

Excluded items may or may not be footnoted.

**Se-tenants** — Connected stamps of differing features (se-tenants) will be listed in the format most commonly collected. This includes pairs, blocks or larger multiples. Se-tenant units are not always symmetrical. An example is Australia Scott 508, which is a block of seven stamps. If the stamps are primarily collected as a unit, the major number may be assigned to the multiple, with minors going to each component stamp. In cases where continuous-design or other unit se-tenants will receive significant postal use, each stamp is given a major Scott number listing. This includes issues from the United States, Canada, Germany and Great Britain, for example.

# Understanding the listings

On the opposite page is an enlarged "typical" listing from this catalogue. Below are detailed explanations of each of the highlighted parts of the listing.

**1 Scott number** — Scott catalogue numbers are used to identify specific items when buying, selling or trading stamps. Each listed postage stamp from every country has a unique Scott catalogue number. Therefore, Germany Scott 99, for example, can only refer to a single stamp. Although the Scott catalogue usually lists stamps in chronological order by date of issue, there are exceptions. When a country has issued a set of stamps over a period of time, those stamps within the set are kept together without regard to date of issue. This follows the normal collecting approach of keeping stamps in their natural sets.

When a country issues a set of stamps over a period of time, a group of consecutive catalogue numbers is reserved for the stamps in that set, as issued. If that group of numbers proves to be too few, capital-letter suffixes, such as "A" or "B," may be added to existing numbers to create enough catalogue numbers to cover all items in the set. A capital-letter suffix indicates a major Scott catalogue number listing. Scott generally uses a suffix letter only once. Therefore, a catalogue number listing with a capital-letter suffix will seldom be found with the same letter (lower case) used as a minor-letter listing. If there is a Scott 16A in a set, for example, there will seldom be a Scott 16a. However, a minor-letter "a" listing may be added to a major number containing an "A" suffix (Scott 16Aa, for example).

Suffix letters are cumulative. A minor "b" variety of Scott 16A would be Scott 16Ab, not Scott 16b.

There are times when a reserved block of Scott catalogue numbers is too large for a set, leaving some numbers unused. Such gaps in the numbering sequence also occur when the catalogue editors move an item's listing elsewhere or have removed it entirely from the catalogue. Scott does not attempt to account for every possible number, but rather attempts to assure that each stamp is assigned its own number.

Scott numbers designating regular postage normally are only numerals. Scott numbers for other types of stamps, such as air post, semi-postal, postal tax, postage due, occupation and others have a prefix consisting of one or more capital letters or a combination of numerals and capital letters.

**2 Illustration number** — Illustration or design-type numbers are used to identify each catalogue illustration. For most sets, the lowest face-value stamp is shown. It then serves as an example of the basic design approach for other stamps not illustrated. Where more than one stamp use the same illustration number, but have differences in design, the design paragraph or the description line clearly indicates the design on each stamp not illustrated. Where there are both vertical and horizontal designs in a set, a single illustration may be used, with the exceptions noted in the design paragraph or description line. When an illustration is followed by a lower-case letter in parentheses, such as "A2(b)," the trailing letter indicates which overprint or surcharge illustration applies.

Illustrations normally are 70 percent of the original size of the stamp. Oversized stamps, blocks and souvenir sheets are reduced even more. Overprints and surcharges are shown at 100 percent of their original size if shown alone, but are 70 percent of original size if shown on stamps. In some cases, the illustration will be placed above the set, between listings or omitted completely. Overprint and surcharge illustrations are not placed in this catalogue for purposes of expertizing stamps.

**3 Paper color** — The color of a stamp's paper is noted in italic type when the paper used is not white.

**4 Listing styles** — There are two principal types of catalogue listings: major and minor.

Major listings are in a larger type style than minor listings. The catalogue number is a numeral that can be found with or without a capital-letter suffix, and with or without a prefix.

Minor listings are in a smaller type style and have a small-letter suffix or (if the listing immediately follows that of the major number) may show only the letter. These listings identify a variety of the major item. Examples include perforation and shade differences, multiples (some souvenir sheets, booklet panes and se-tenant combinations), and singles of multiples.

Examples of major number listings include 16, 28A, B97, C13A, 10N5, and 10N6A. Examples of minor numbers are 16a and C13Ab.

**5 Basic information about a stamp or set** — Introducing each stamp issue is a small section (usually a line listing) of basic information about a stamp or set. This section normally includes the date of issue, method of printing, perforation, watermark and, sometimes, some additional information of note. *Printing method, perforation and watermark apply to the following sets until a change is noted.* Stamps created by overprinting or surcharging previous issues are assumed to have the same perforation, watermark, printing method and other production characteristics as the original. Dates of issue are as precise as Scott is able to confirm and often reflect the dates on first-day covers, rather than the actual date of release.

**6 Denomination** — This normally refers to the face value of the stamp; that is, the cost of the unused stamp at the post office at the time of issue. When a denomination is shown in parentheses, it does not appear on the stamp. This includes the nondenominated stamps of the United States, Brazil and Great Britain, for example.

**7 Color or other description** — This area provides information to solidify identification of a stamp. In many recent cases, a description of the stamp design appears in this space, rather than a listing of colors.

**8 Year of issue** — In stamp sets that have been released in a period that spans more than a year, the number shown in parentheses is the year that stamp first appeared. Stamps without a date appeared during the first year of the issue. Dates are not always given for minor varieties.

**9 Value unused and Value used** — The Scott catalogue values are based on stamps that are in a grade of Very Fine unless stated otherwise. Unused values refer to items that have not seen postal, revenue or any other duty for which they were intended. Pre-1900 unused stamps that were issued with gum must have at least most of their original gum. Later issues are assumed to have full original gum. From breakpoints specified in most countries' listings, stamps are valued as never hinged. Stamps issued without gum are noted. Modern issues with PVA or other synthetic adhesives may appear ungummed. Unused self-adhesive stamps are valued as appearing undisturbed on their original backing paper. Values for used self-adhesive stamps are for examples either on piece or off piece. For a more detailed explanation of these values, please see the "Catalogue Value," "Condition" and "Understanding Valuing Notations" sections elsewhere in this introduction.

In some cases, where used stamps are more valuable than unused stamps, the value is for an example with a contemporaneous cancel, rather than a modern cancel or a smudge or other unclear marking. For those stamps that were released for postal and fiscal purposes, the used value represents a postally used stamp. Stamps with revenue cancels generally sell for less.

Stamps separated from a complete se-tenant multiple usually will be worth less than a pro-rated portion of the se-tenant multiple, and stamps lacking the attached labels that are noted in the listings will be worth less than the values shown.

**10 Changes in basic set information** — Bold type is used to show any changes in the basic data given for a set of stamps. These basic data categories include perforation gauge measurement, paper type, printing method and watermark.

**11 Total value of a set** — The total value of sets of three or more stamps issued after 1900 are shown. The set line also notes the range of Scott numbers and total number of stamps included in the grouping. The actual value of a set consisting predominantly of stamps having the minimum value of 25 cents may be less than the total value shown. Similarly, the actual value or catalogue value of se-tenant pairs or of blocks consisting of stamps having the minimum value of 25 cents may be less than the catalogue values of the component parts.

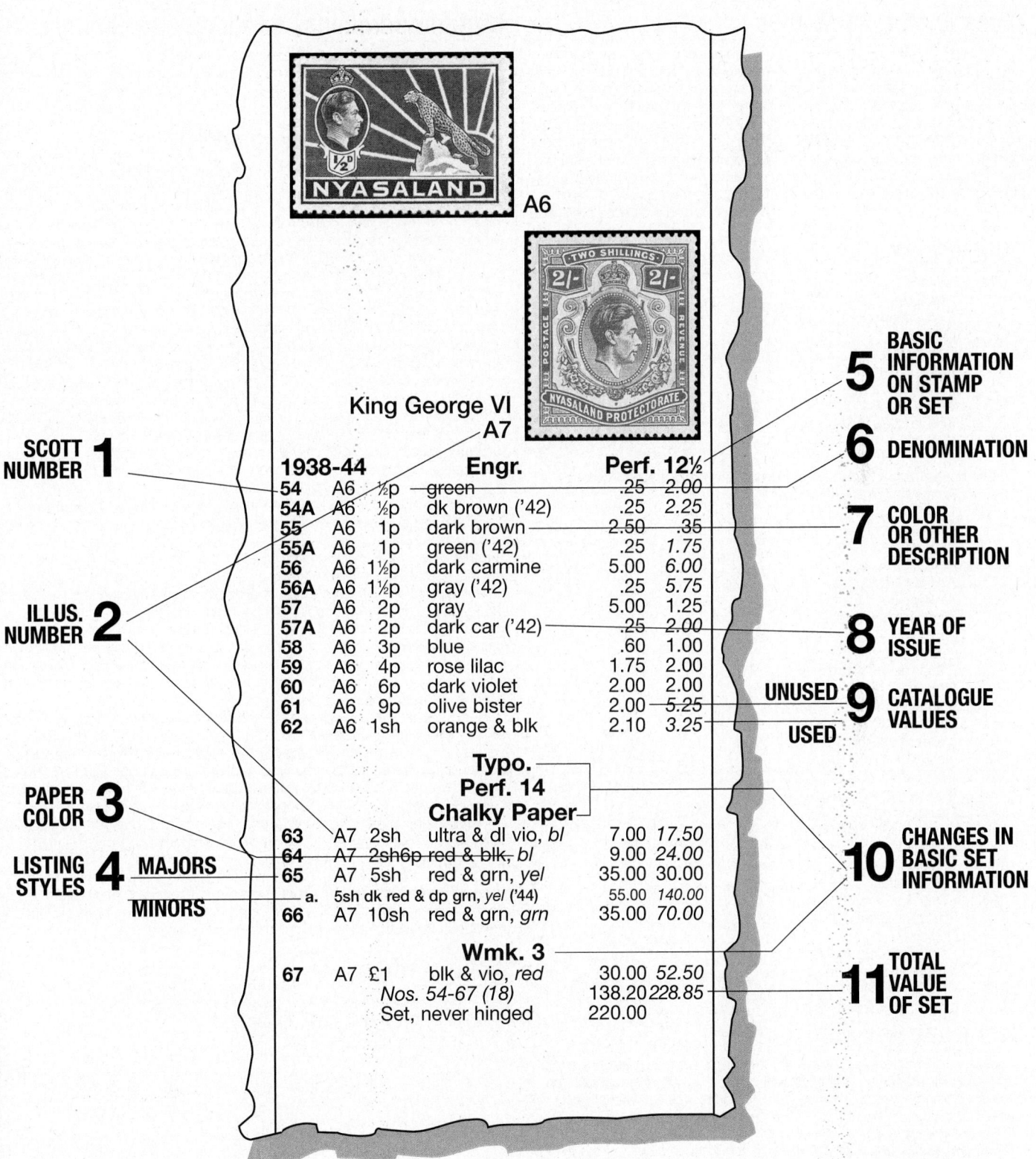

King George VI
A7

| | | | | | UNUSED | USED |
|---|---|---|---|---|---|---|
| **1938-44** | | | **Engr.** | | **Perf. 12½** | |
| 54 | A6 | ½p | green | | .25 | 2.00 |
| **54A** | A6 | ½p | dk brown ('42) | | .25 | 2.25 |
| **55** | A6 | 1p | dark brown | | 2.50 | .35 |
| **55A** | A6 | 1p | green ('42) | | .25 | 1.75 |
| 56 | A6 | 1½p | dark carmine | | 5.00 | 6.00 |
| **56A** | A6 | 1½p | gray ('42) | | .25 | 5.75 |
| 57 | A6 | 2p | gray | | 5.00 | 1.25 |
| **57A** | A6 | 2p | dark car ('42) | | .25 | 2.00 |
| 58 | A6 | 3p | blue | | .60 | 1.00 |
| 59 | A6 | 4p | rose lilac | | 1.75 | 2.00 |
| 60 | A6 | 6p | dark violet | | 2.00 | 2.00 |
| 61 | A6 | 9p | olive bister | | 2.00 | 5.25 |
| 62 | A6 | 1sh | orange & blk | | 2.10 | 3.25 |

**Typo.**
**Perf. 14**
**Chalky Paper**

| | | | | | | |
|---|---|---|---|---|---|---|
| 63 | A7 | 2sh | ultra & dl vio, *bl* | | 7.00 | *17.50* |
| 64 | A7 | 2sh6p | red & blk, *bl* | | 9.00 | *24.00* |
| 65 | A7 | 5sh | red & grn, *yel* | | 35.00 | 30.00 |
| a. | | 5sh dk red & dp grn, *yel* ('44) | | | 55.00 | *140.00* |
| 66 | A7 | 10sh | red & grn, *grn* | | 35.00 | *70.00* |

**Wmk. 3**

| | | | | | | |
|---|---|---|---|---|---|---|
| 67 | A7 | £1 | blk & vio, *red* | | 30.00 | *52.50* |
| | | *Nos. 54-67 (18)* | | | 138.20 | *228.85* |
| | | Set, never hinged | | | 220.00 | |

Legend (left and right annotations):

1 SCOTT NUMBER
2 ILLUS. NUMBER
3 PAPER COLOR
4 LISTING STYLES — MAJORS / MINORS
5 BASIC INFORMATION ON STAMP OR SET
6 DENOMINATION
7 COLOR OR OTHER DESCRIPTION
8 YEAR OF ISSUE
9 CATALOGUE VALUES
10 CHANGES IN BASIC SET INFORMATION
11 TOTAL VALUE OF SET

# Special notices

## Classification of stamps

The Scott Standard Postage Stamp Catalogue lists stamps by country of issue. The next level of organization is a listing by section on the basis of the function of the stamps. The principal sections cover regular postage, semi-postal, air post, special delivery, registration, postage due and other categories. Except for regular postage, catalogue numbers for all sections include a prefix letter (or number-letter combination) denoting the class to which a given stamp belongs. When some countries issue sets containing stamps from more than one category, the catalogue will at times list all of the stamps in one category (such as air post stamps listed as part of a postage set).

The following is a listing of the most commonly used catalogue prefixes.

Prefix.......Category
C..........Air Post
M.........Military
P..........Newspaper
N..........Occupation - Regular Issues
O..........Official
Q..........Parcel Post
J ..........Postage Due
RA .......Postal Tax
B..........Semi-Postal
E..........Special Delivery
MR.......War Tax

Other prefixes used by more than one country include the following:
H..........Acknowledgment of Receipt
I ...........Late Fee
CO.......Air Post Official
CQ.......Air Post Parcel Post
RAC.....Air Post Postal Tax
CF........Air Post Registration
CB .......Air Post Semi-Postal
CBO ....Air Post Semi-Postal Official
CE .......Air Post Special Delivery
EY........Authorized Delivery
S..........Franchise
G..........Insured Letter
GY .......Marine Insurance
MC.......Military Air Post
MQ ......Military Parcel Post
NC .......Occupation - Air Post
NO.......Occupation - Official
NJ........Occupation - Postage Due
NRA.....Occupation - Postal Tax
NB .......Occupation - Semi-Postal
NE .......Occupation - Special Delivery
QY .......Parcel Post Authorized Delivery
AR .......Postal-fiscal
RAJ......Postal Tax Due
RAB .....Postal Tax Semi-Postal
F ..........Registration
EB........Semi-Postal Special Delivery
EO .......Special Delivery Official
QE .......Special Handling

## New issue listings

Updates to this catalogue appear each month in the *Linn's Stamp News* monthly magazine. Included in this update are additions to the listings of countries found in the Scott *Standard Postage Stamp Catalogue* and the *Specialized Catalogue of United States Stamps and Covers,* as well as corrections and updates to current editions of this catalogue.

From time to time there will be changes in the final listings of stamps from the *Linn's Stamp News* magazine to the next edition of the catalogue. This occurs as more information about certain stamps or sets becomes available.

The catalogue update section of the *Linn's Stamp News* magazine is the most timely presentation of this material available. Annual subscriptions to *Linn's Stamp News* are available from Linn's Stamp News, Box 4129, Sidney, OH 45365-4129.

## Number additions, deletions and changes

A listing of catalogue number additions, deletions and changes from the previous edition of the catalogue appears in each volume. See Catalogue Number Additions, Deletions & Changes in the table of contents for the location of this list.

## Understanding valuing notations

The *minimum catalogue value* of an individual stamp or set is 25 cents. This represents a portion of the cost incurred by a dealer when he prepares an individual stamp for resale. As a point of philatelic-economic fact, the lower the value shown for an item in this catalogue, the greater the percentage of that value is attributed to dealer mark up and profit margin. In many cases, such as the 25-cent minimum value, that price does not cover the labor or other costs involved with stocking it as an individual stamp. The sum of minimum values in a set does not properly represent the value of a complete set primarily composed of a number of minimum-value stamps, nor does the sum represent the actual value of a packet made up of minimum-value stamps. Thus a packet of 1,000 different common stamps — each of which has a catalogue value of 25 cents — normally sells for considerably less than $250!

The *absence of a retail value* for a stamp does not necessarily suggest that a stamp is scarce or rare. A dash in the value column means that the stamp is known in a stated form or variety, but information is either lacking or insufficient for purposes of establishing a usable catalogue value.

Stamp values in *italics* generally refer to items that are difficult to value accurately. For expensive items, such as those priced at $1,000 or higher, a value in italics indicates that the affected item trades very seldom. For inexpensive items, a value in italics represents a warning. One example is a "blocked" issue where the issuing postal administration may have controlled one stamp in a set in an attempt to make the whole set more valuable. Another example is an item that sold at an extreme multiple of face value in the marketplace at the time of its issue.

One type of warning to collectors that appears in the catalogue is illustrated by a stamp that is valued considerably higher in used condition than it is as unused. In this case, collectors are cautioned to be certain the used version has a genuine and contemporaneous cancellation. The type of cancellation on a stamp can be an important factor in determining its sale price. Catalogue values do not apply to fiscal, telegraph or non-contemporaneous postal cancels, unless otherwise noted.

Some countries have released back issues of stamps in canceled-to-order form, sometimes covering as much as a 10-year period. The Scott Catalogue values for used stamps reflect canceled-to-order material when such stamps are found to predominate in the marketplace for the issue involved. Notes frequently appear in the stamp listings to specify which items are valued as canceled-to-order, or if there is a premium for postally used examples.

Many countries sell canceled-to-order stamps at a marked reduction of face value. Countries that sell or have sold canceled-to-order stamps at *full* face value include United Nations, Australia, Netherlands, France and Switzerland. It may be almost impossible to identify such stamps if the gum has been removed, because official government canceling devices are used. Postally used examples of these items on cover, however, are usually worth more than the canceled-to-order stamps with original gum.

## Abbreviations

Scott uses a consistent set of abbreviations throughout this catalogue to conserve space, while still providing necessary information.

## Color Abbreviations

| | | | |
|---|---|---|---|
| amb...........amber | crim.........crimson | ol.................olive | LL................Lower left |
| anil............aniline | cr...............cream | olvn..........olivine | LR ...............Lower right |
| ap...............apple | dk................dark | org ..........orange | mm .............Millimeter |
| aqua..aquamarine | dl...................dull | pck.........peacock | Ms...............Manuscript |
| az...............azure | dp..............deep | pnksh    pinkish | Natl. .............National |
| bis............bister | db...............drab | Prus .......Prussian | No. ...............Number |
| bl.................blue | emer.......emerald | pur ...........purple | NY................New York |
| bld...........blood | gldn..........golden | redsh........reddish | NYC.............New York City |
| blk............black | grysh.......grayish | res............reseda | Ovpt............Overprint |
| bril...........brilliant | grn...........green | ros.............rosine | Ovptd..........Overprinted |
| brn ............brown | grnsh......greenish | ryl.............royal | P .................Plate number |
| brnsh ....brownish | hel.......heliotrope | sal ..........salmon | Perf. ............Perforated, perforation |
| brnz........bronze | hn..............henna | saph......sapphire | Phil..............Philatelic |
| brt ............bright | ind..............indigo | scar..........scarlet | Photo. ..........Photogravure |
| brnt ...........burnt | int..............intense | sep...........sepia | PO................Post office |
| car............carmine | lav .........lavender | sien ..........sienna | Pr. ...............Pair |
| cer...........cerise | lem............lemon | sil ...............silver | P.R. .............Puerto Rico |
| chlky ........chalky | lil ..................lilac | sl ...............slate | Prec. ...........Precancel, precanceled |
| cham......chamois | lt..................light | stl..............steel | Pres. ...........President |
| chnt.........chestnut | mag.......magenta | turq ......turquoise | PTT ............Post, Telephone and Telegraph |
| choc.....chocolate | man...........manila | ultra... ultramarine | R .................Right |
| chr...........chrome | mar .........maroon | Ven.........Venetian | Rio ..............Rio de Janeiro |
| cit..............citron | mv.............mauve | ver.........vermilion | Sgt. .............Sergeant |
| cl.................claret | multi..multicolored | vio ..............violet | Soc. ............Society |
| cob............cobalt | mlky ...........milky | yel ............yellow | Souv.............Souvenir |
| cop..........copper | myr.............myrtle | yelsh .....yellowish | SSR.............Soviet Socialist Republic, see ASSR |

St. ...............Saint, street
Surch. ..........Surcharge
Typo. ............Typographed
UL................Upper left
Unwmkd. ......Unwatermarked
UPU .............Universal Postal Union
UR................Upper Right
US................United States
USPOD ........United States Post Office Department
USSR...........Union of Soviet Socialist Republics
Vert. ............Vertical
VP ................Vice president
Wmk. ...........Watermark
Wmkd. .........Watermarked
WWI ............World War I
WWII ...........World War II

When no color is given for an overprint or surcharge, black is the color used. Abbreviations for colors used for overprints and surcharges include: "(B)" or "(Blk)," black; "(Bl)," blue; "(R)," red; and "(G)," green.

Additional abbreviations in this catalogue are shown below:

Adm. ............Administration
AFL .............American Federation of Labor
Anniv. ..........Anniversary
APS.............American Philatelic Society
Assoc...........Association
ASSR. ..........Autonomous Soviet Socialist Republic
b...................Born
BEP.............Bureau of Engraving and Printing
Bicent. .........Bicentennial
Bklt. .............Booklet
Brit. .............British
btwn.............Between
Bur. .............Bureau
c. or ca. ........Circa
Cat. .............Catalogue
Cent.............Centennial, century, centenary
CIO .............Congress of Industrial Organizations
Conf.............Conference
Cong. ...........Congress
Cpl. .............Corporal
CTO .............Canceled to order
d...................Died
Dbl. .............Double
EDU .............Earliest documented use
Engr.............Engraved
Exhib............Exhibition
Expo. ...........Exposition
Fed..............Federation
GB ..............Great Britain
Gen. ............General
GPO.............General post office
Horiz. ...........Horizontal
Imperf. .........Imperforate
Impt. ............Imprint
Intl...............International
Invtd.............Inverted
L...................Left
Lieut., lt........Lieutenant
Litho.............Lithographed

## Examination

Amos Media Co. will not comment upon the genuineness, grade or condition of stamps, because of the time and responsibility involved. Rather, there are several expertizing groups that undertake this work for both collectors and dealers. Neither will Amos Media Co. appraise or identify philatelic material. The company cannot take responsibility for unsolicited stamps or covers sent by individuals.

All letters, emails, etc. are read attentively, but they are not always answered because of time considerations.

## How to order from your dealer

When ordering stamps from a dealer, it is not necessary to write the full description of a stamp as listed in this catalogue. All you need is the name of the country, the Scott catalogue number and whether the desired item is unused or used. For example, "Japan Scott 422 unused" is sufficient to identify the unused stamp of Japan listed as "422 A206 5y brown."

# Basic stamp information

A stamp collector's knowledge of the combined elements that make a given stamp issue unique determines his or her ability to identify stamps. These elements include paper, watermark, method of separation, printing, design and gum. On the following pages each of these important areas is briefly described.

## Paper

Paper is an organic material composed of a compacted weave of cellulose fibers and generally formed into sheets. Paper used to print stamps may be manufactured in sheets, or it may have been part of a large roll (called a web) before being cut to size. The fibers most often used to create paper on which stamps are printed include bark, wood, straw and certain grasses. In many cases, linen or cotton rags have been added for greater strength and durability. Grinding, bleaching, cooking and rinsing these raw fibers reduces them to a slushy pulp, referred to by paper makers as "stuff." Sizing and, sometimes, coloring matter is added to the pulp to make different types of finished paper.

After the stuff is prepared, it is poured onto sieve-like frames that allow the water to run off, while retaining the matted pulp. As fibers fall onto the screen and are held by gravity, they form a natural weave that will later hold the paper together. If the screen has metal bits that are formed into letters or images attached, it leaves slightly thinned areas on the paper. These are called watermarks.

When the stuff is almost dry, it is passed under pressure through smooth or engraved rollers — dandy rolls — or placed between cloth in a press to be flattened and dried.

| Wove | Laid | Granite |
| Quadrille | Oblong Quadrille | Laid Batonne |

Stamp paper falls broadly into two types: wove and laid. The nature of the surface of the frame onto which the pulp is first deposited causes the differences in appearance between the two. If the surface is smooth and even, the paper will be of fairly uniform texture throughout. This is known as wove paper. Early papermaking machines poured the pulp onto a continuously circulating web of felt, but modern machines feed the pulp onto a cloth-like screen made of closely interwoven fine wires. This paper, when held to a light, will show little dots or points very close together. The proper name for this is "wire wove," but the type is still considered wove. Any U.S. or British stamp printed after 1880 will serve as an example of wire wove paper.

Closely spaced parallel wires, with cross wires at wider intervals, make up the frames used for what is known as laid paper. A greater thickness of the pulp will settle between the wires. The paper, when held to a light, will show alternate light and dark lines. The spacing and the thickness of the lines may vary, but on any one sheet of paper they are all alike. See Russia Scott 31-38 for examples of laid paper.

**Batonne,** from the French word meaning "a staff," is a term used if the lines in the paper are spaced quite far apart, like the printed ruling on a writing tablet. Batonne paper may be either wove or laid. If laid, fine laid lines can be seen between the batons.

**Quadrille** is the term used when the lines in the paper form little squares. Oblong quadrille is the term used when rectangles, rather than squares, are formed. Grid patterns vary from distinct to extremely faint. See Mexico-Guadalajara Scott 35-37 for examples of oblong quadrille paper.

Paper also is classified as thick or thin, hard or soft, and by color. Such colors may include yellowish, greenish, bluish and reddish.

Brief explanations of other types of paper used for printing stamps, as well as examples, follow.

**Colored** — Colored paper is created by the addition of dye in the paper-making process. Such colors may include shades of yellow, green, blue and red. Surface-colored papers, most commonly used for British colonial issues in 1913-14, are created when coloring is added only to the surface during the finishing process. Stamps printed on surface-colored paper have white or uncolored backs, while true colored papers are colored through. See Jamaica Scott 71-73.

**Pelure** — Pelure paper is a very thin, hard and often brittle paper that is sometimes bluish or grayish in appearance. See Serbia Scott 169-170.

**Native** — This is a term applied to handmade papers used to produce some of the early stamps of the Indian states. Stamps printed on native paper may be expected to display various natural inclusions that are normal and do not negatively affect value. Japanese paper, originally made of mulberry fibers and rice flour, is part of this group. See Japan Scott 1-18.

**Manila** — This type of paper is often used to make stamped envelopes and wrappers. It is a coarse-textured stock, usually smooth on one side and rough on the other. A variety of colors of manila paper exist, but the most common range is yellowish-brown.

**Silk** — Introduced by the British in 1847 as a safeguard against counterfeiting, silk paper contains bits of colored silk thread scattered throughout. The density of these fibers varies greatly and can include as few as one fiber per stamp or hundreds. U.S. revenue Scott R152 is a good example of an easy-to-identify silk paper stamp.

Silk-thread paper has uninterrupted threads of colored silk arranged so that one or more threads run through the stamp or postal stationery. See Great Britain Scott 5-6 and Switzerland Scott 14-19.

**Granite** — Filled with minute cloth or colored paper fibers of various colors and lengths, granite paper should not be confused with either type of silk paper. Austria Scott 172-175 and a number of Swiss stamps are examples of granite paper.

**Chalky** — A chalk-like substance coats the surface of chalky paper to discourage the cleaning and reuse of canceled stamps, as well as to provide a smoother, more acceptable printing surface. Because the designs of stamps printed on chalky paper are imprinted on what is often a water-soluble coating, any attempt to remove a cancellation will destroy the stamp. Do not soak these stamps in any fluid. To remove a stamp printed on chalky paper from an envelope, wet the paper from underneath the stamp until the gum dissolves enough to release the stamp from the paper. See St. Kitts-Nevis Scott 89-90 for examples of stamps printed on this type of chalky paper.

**India** — Another name for this paper, originally introduced from China about 1750, is "China Paper." It is a thin, opaque paper often used for plate and die proofs by many countries.

**Double** — In philately, the term double paper has two distinct meanings. The first is a two-ply paper, usually a combination of a thick and a thin sheet, joined during manufacture. This type was used experimentally as a means to discourage the reuse of stamps.

The design is printed on the thin paper. Any attempt to remove a cancellation would destroy the design. U.S. Scott 158 and other Banknote-era stamps exist on this form of double paper.

The second type of double paper occurs on a rotary press, when the end of one paper roll, or web, is affixed to the next roll to save time feeding the paper through the press. Stamp designs are printed over the joined paper and, if overlooked by inspectors, may get into post office stocks.

**Goldbeater's Skin** — This type of paper was used for the 1866 issue of Prussia, and was a tough, translucent paper. The design was printed in reverse on the back of the stamp, and the gum applied over the printing. It is impossible to remove stamps printed on this type of paper from the paper to which they are affixed without destroying the design.

**Ribbed** — Ribbed paper has an uneven, corrugated surface made by passing the paper through ridged rollers. This type exists on some copies of U.S. Scott 156-165.

Various other substances, or substrates, have been used for stamp manufacture, including wood, aluminum, copper, silver and gold foil, plastic, and silk and cotton fabrics.

# Watermarks

Watermarks are an integral part of some papers. They are formed in the process of paper manufacture. Watermarks consist of small designs, formed of wire or cut from metal and soldered to the surface of the mold or, sometimes, on the dandy roll. The designs may be in the form of crowns, stars, anchors, letters or other characters or symbols. These pieces of metal — known in the paper-making industry as "bits" — impress a design into the paper. The design sometimes may be seen by holding the stamp to the light. Some are more easily seen with a watermark detector. This important tool is a small black tray into which a stamp is placed face down and dampened with a fast-evaporating watermark detection fluid that brings up the watermark image in the form of dark lines against a lighter background. These dark lines are the thinner areas of the paper known as the watermark. Some watermarks are extremely difficult to locate, due to either a faint impression, watermark location or the color of the stamp. There also are electric watermark detectors that come with plastic filter disks of various colors. The disks neutralize the color of the stamp, permitting the watermark to be seen more easily.

**Multiple watermarks of Crown Agents and Burma**

**Watermarks of Uruguay, Vatican City and Jamaica**

**WARNING: Some inks used in the photogravure process dissolve in watermark fluids (Please see the section on Soluble Printing Inks).** Also, see "chalky paper."

Watermarks may be found normal, reversed, inverted, reversed and inverted, sideways or diagonal, as seen from the back of the stamp. The relationship of watermark to stamp design depends on the position of the printing plates or how paper is fed through the press. On machine-made paper, watermarks normally are read from right to left. The design is repeated closely throughout the sheet in a "multiple-watermark design." In a "sheet watermark," the design appears only once on the sheet, but extends over many stamps. Individual stamps may carry only a small fraction or none of the watermark.

"Marginal watermarks" occur in the margins of sheets or panes of stamps. They occur on the outside border of paper (ostensibly outside the area where stamps are to be printed). A large row of letters may spell the name of the country or the manufacturer of the paper, or a border of lines may appear. Careless press feeding may cause parts of these letters and/or lines to show on stamps of the outer row of a pane.

# Soluble printing inks

**WARNING:** Most stamp colors are permanent; that is, they are not seriously affected by short-term exposure to light or water. Many colors, especially of modern inks, fade from excessive exposure to light. There are stamps printed with inks that dissolve easily in water or in fluids used to detect watermarks. Use of these inks was intentional to prevent the removal of cancellations. Water affects all aniline inks, those on so-called safety paper and some photogravure printings - all such inks are known as fugitive colors. Removal from paper of such stamps requires care and alternatives to traditional soaking.

# Separation

"Separation" is the general term used to describe methods used to separate stamps. The three standard forms currently in use are perforating, rouletting and die-cutting. These methods are done during the stamp production process, after printing. Sometimes these methods are done on-press or sometimes as a separate step. The earliest issues, such as the 1840 Penny Black of Great Britain (Scott 1), did not have any means provided for separation. It was expected the stamps would be cut apart with scissors or folded and torn. These are examples of imperforate stamps. Many stamps were first issued in imperforate formats and were later issued with perforations. Therefore, care must be observed in buying single imperforate stamps to be certain they were issued imperforate and are not perforated copies that have been altered by having the perforations trimmed away. Stamps issued imperforate usually are valued as singles. However, imperforate varieties of normally perforated stamps should be collected in pairs or larger pieces as indisputable evidence of their imperforate character.

## PERFORATION

The chief style of separation of stamps, and the one that is in almost universal use today, is perforating. By this process, paper between the stamps is cut away in a line of holes, usually round, leaving little bridges of paper between the stamps to hold them together. Some types of perforation, such as hyphen-hole perfs, can be confused with roulettes, but a close visual inspection reveals that paper has been removed. The little perforation bridges, which project from the stamp when it is torn from the pane, are called the teeth of the perforation.

As the size of the perforation is sometimes the only way to differentiate between two otherwise identical stamps, it is necessary to be able to accurately measure and describe them. This is done with a perforation gauge, usually a ruler-like device that has dots or graduated lines to show how many perforations may be counted in the space of two centimeters. Two centimeters is the space universally adopted in which to measure perforations.

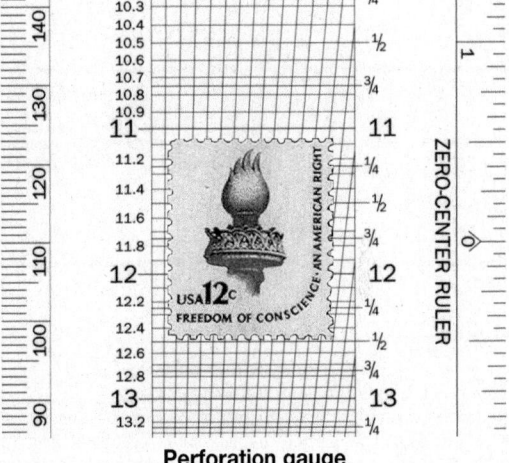

**Perforation gauge**

To measure a stamp, run it along the gauge until the dots on it fit exactly into the perforations of the stamp. If you are using a graduated-line perforation gauge, simply slide the stamp along the surface until the lines on the gauge perfectly project from the center of the bridges or holes. The number to the side of the line of dots or lines that fit the stamp's perforation is the measurement. For example, an "11" means that 11 perforations fit between two centimeters. The description of the stamp therefore is "perf. 11." If the gauge of the perforations on the top and bottom of a stamp differs from that on the sides, the result is what is known as compound perforations. In measuring compound perforations, the gauge at top and bottom is always given first, then the sides. Thus, a stamp that measures 11 at top and bottom and 10½ at the sides is "perf. 11 x 10½." See U.S. Scott 632-642 for examples of compound perforations.

Stamps also are known with perforations different on three or all four sides. Descriptions of such items are clockwise, beginning with the top of the stamp.

A perforation with small holes and teeth close together is a "fine perforation." One with large holes and teeth far apart is a "coarse perforation." Holes that are jagged, rather than clean-cut, are "rough perforations." *Blind perforations* are the slight impressions left by the perforating pins if they fail to puncture the paper. Multiples of stamps showing blind perforations may command a slight premium over normally perforated stamps.

The term *syncopated perfs* describes intentional irregularities in the perforations. The earliest form was used by the Netherlands from 1925-33, where holes were omitted to create distinctive patterns. Beginning in 1992, Great Britain has used an oval perforation to help prevent counterfeiting. Several other countries have started using the oval perfs or other syncopated perf patterns.

A new type of perforation, still primarily used for postal stationery, is known as microperfs. Microperfs are tiny perforations (in some cases hundreds of holes per two centimeters) that allows items to be intentionally separated very easily, while not accidentally breaking apart as easily as standard perforations. These are not currently measured or differentiated by size, as are standard perforations.

perce en arc      perce en lignes

perce en points      oblique roulette

perce en scie      perce serpentin

## ROULETTING

In rouletting, the stamp paper is cut partly or wholly through, with no paper removed. In perforating, some paper is removed. Rouletting derives its name from the French roulette, a spur-like wheel. As the wheel is rolled over the paper, each point makes a small cut. The number of cuts made in a two-centimeter space determines the gauge of the roulette, just as the number of perforations in two centimeters determines the gauge of the perforation.

The shape and arrangement of the teeth on the wheels varies. Various roulette types generally carry French names:

*Perce en lignes* — rouletted in lines. The paper receives short, straight cuts in lines. This is the most common type of rouletting. See Mexico Scott 500.

*Perce en points* — pin-rouletted or pin-perfed. This differs from a small perforation because no paper is removed, although round, equidistant holes are pricked through the paper. See Mexico Scott 242-256.

*Perce en arc and perce en scie* — pierced in an arc or saw-toothed designs, forming half circles or small triangles. See Hanover (German States) Scott 25-29.

*Perce en serpentin* — serpentine roulettes. The cuts form a serpentine or wavy line. See Brunswick (German States) Scott 13-18.

Once again, no paper is removed by these processes, leaving the stamps easily separated, but closely attached.

## DIE-CUTTING

The third major form of stamp separation is die-cutting. This is a method where a die in the pattern of separation is created that later cuts the stamp paper in a stroke motion. Although some standard stamps bear die-cut perforations, this process is primarily used for self-adhesive postage stamps. Die-cutting can appear in straight lines, such as U.S. Scott 2522, shapes, such as U.S. Scott 1551, or imitating the appearance of perforations, such as New Zealand Scott 935A and 935B.

# Printing processes

### ENGRAVING (Intaglio, Line-engraving, Etching)

**Master die** — The initial operation in the process of line engraving is making the master die. The die is a small, flat block of softened steel upon which the stamp design is recess engraved in reverse.

Photographic reduction of the original art is made to the appropriate size. It then serves as a tracing guide for the initial outline of the design. The engraver lightly traces the design on the steel with his graver, then slowly works the design until it is completed. At various points during the engraving process, the engraver hand-inks the die and makes an impression to check his progress. These are known as progressive die proofs. After completion of the engraving, the die is hardened to withstand the stress and pressures of later transfer operations.

**Transfer roll**

**Transfer roll** — Next is production of the transfer roll that, as the name implies, is the medium used to transfer the subject from the master die to the printing plate. A blank roll of soft steel, mounted on a mandrel, is placed under the bearers of the transfer press to allow it to roll freely on its axis. The hardened die is placed on the bed of the press and the face of the transfer roll is applied to the die, under pressure. The bed or the roll is then rocked back and forth under increasing pressure, until the soft steel of the roll is forced into every engraved line of the die. The resulting impression on the roll is known as a "relief" or a "relief transfer." The engraved image is now positive in appearance and stands out from the steel. After the required number of reliefs are "rocked in," the soft steel transfer roll is hardened.

Different flaws may occur during the relief process. A defective relief may occur during the rocking in process because of a minute piece of foreign material lodging on the die, or some other cause. Imperfections in the steel of the transfer roll may result in a breaking away of parts of the design. This is known as a relief break, which will show up on finished stamps as small, unprinted areas. If a damaged relief remains in use, it will transfer a repeating defect to the plate. Deliberate alterations of reliefs sometimes occur. "Altered reliefs" designate these changed conditions.

**Plate** — The final step in pre-printing production is the making of the printing plate. A flat piece of soft steel replaces the die on the bed of the transfer press. One of the reliefs on the transfer roll is positioned over this soft steel. Position, or layout, dots determine the correct position on the plate. The dots have been lightly marked on the plate in advance. After the correct position of the relief is determined, the design is rocked in by following the same method used in making the transfer roll. The difference is that this time the image is being transferred from the transfer roll, rather than to it. Once the design is entered on the plate, it appears in reverse and is recessed. There are as many transfers entered on the plate as there are subjects printed on the sheet of stamps. It is during this process that double and shifted transfers occur, as well as re-entries. These are the result of improperly entered images that have not been properly burnished out prior to rocking in a new image.

Modern siderography processes, such as those used by the U.S. Bureau of Engraving and Printing, involve an automated form of rocking designs in on preformed cylindrical printing sleeves. The same process also allows for easier removal and re-entry of worn images right on the sleeve.

**Transferring the design to the plate**

Following the entering of the required transfers on the plate, the position dots, layout dots and lines, scratches and other markings generally are burnished out. Added at this time by the siderographer are any required guide lines, plate numbers or other marginal markings. The plate is then hand-inked and a proof impression is taken. This is known as a plate proof. If the impression is approved, the plate is machined for fitting onto the press, is hardened and sent to the plate vault ready for use.

On press, the plate is inked and the surface is automatically wiped clean, leaving ink only in the recessed lines. Paper is then forced under pressure into the engraved recessed lines, thereby receiving the ink. Thus, the ink lines on engraved stamps are slightly raised, and slight depressions (debossing) occur on the back of the stamp. Prior to the advent of modern high-speed presses and more advanced ink formulations, paper had to be dampened before receiving the ink. This sometimes led to uneven shrinkage by the time the stamps were perforated, resulting in improperly perforated stamps, or misperfs. Newer presses use drier paper, thus both *wet and dry printings* exist on some stamps.

**Rotary Press** — Until 1914, only flat plates were used to print engraved stamps. Rotary press printing was introduced in 1914, and slowly spread. Some countries still use flat-plate printing.

After approval of the plate proof, older rotary press plates require additional machining. They are curved to fit the press cylinder. "Gripper slots" are cut into the back of each plate to receive the "grippers," which hold the plate securely on the press. The plate is then hardened. Stamps printed from these bent rotary press plates are longer or wider than the same stamps printed from flat-plate presses. The stretching of the plate during the curving process is what causes this distortion.

**Re-entry** — To execute a re-entry on a flat plate, the transfer roll is re-applied to the plate, often at some time after its first use on the press. Worn-out designs can be resharpened by carefully burnishing out the original image and re-entering it from the transfer roll. If the original impression has not been sufficiently removed and the transfer roll is not precisely in line with the remaining impression, the resulting double transfer will make the re-entry obvious. If the registration is true, a re-entry may be difficult or impossible to distinguish. Sometimes a stamp printed from a successful re-entry is identified by having a much sharper and clearer impression than its neighbors. With the advent of rotary presses, post-press re-entries were not possible. After a plate was curved for the rotary press, it was impossible to make a re-entry. This is because the plate had already been bent once (with the design distorted).

However, with the introduction of the previously mentioned modern-style siderography machines, entries are made to the preformed cylindrical printing sleeve. Such sleeves are dechromed and softened. This allows individual images to be burnished out and re-entered on the curved sleeve. The sleeve is then rechromed, resulting in longer press life.

**Double Transfer** — This is a description of the condition of a transfer on a plate that shows evidence of a duplication of all, or a portion of the design. It usually is the result of the changing of the registration between the transfer roll and the plate during the rocking in of the original entry. Double transfers also occur when only a portion of the design has been rocked in and improper positioning is noted. If the worker elected not to burnish out the partial or completed design, a strong double transfer will occur for part or all of the design.

It sometimes is necessary to remove the original transfer from a plate and repeat the process a second time. If the finished re-worked image shows traces of the original impression, attributable to incomplete burnishing, the result is a partial double transfer.

With the modern automatic machines mentioned previously, double transfers are all but impossible to create. Those partially doubled images on stamps printed from such sleeves are more than likely re-entries, rather than true double transfers.

**Re-engraved** — Alterations to a stamp design are sometimes necessary after some stamps have been printed. In some cases, either the original die or the actual printing plate may have its "temper" drawn (softened), and the design will be re-cut. The resulting impressions from such a re-engraved die or plate may differ slightly from the original issue, and are known as "re-engraved." If the alteration was made to the master die, all future printings will be consistently different from the original. If alterations were made to the printing plate, each altered stamp on the plate will be slightly different from each other, allowing specialists to reconstruct a complete printing plate.

**Dropped Transfers** — If an impression from the transfer roll has not been properly placed, a dropped transfer may occur. The final stamp image will appear obviously out of line with its neighbors.

**Short Transfer** — Sometimes a transfer roll is not rocked its entire length when entering a transfer onto a plate. As a result, the finished transfer on the plate fails to show the complete design, and the finished stamp will have an incomplete design printed. This is known as a "short transfer." U.S. Scott No. 8 is a good example of a short transfer.

## TYPOGRAPHY (Letterpress, Surface Printing, Flexography, Dry Offset, High Etch)

Although the word "Typography" is obsolete as a term describing a printing method, it was the accepted term throughout the first century of postage stamps. Therefore, appropriate Scott listings in this catalogue refer to typographed stamps. The current term for this form of printing, however, is "letterpress."

As it relates to the production of postage stamps, letterpress printing is the reverse of engraving. Rather than having recessed areas trap the ink and deposit it on paper, only the raised areas of the design are inked. This is comparable to the type of printing seen by inking and using an ordinary rubber stamp. Letterpress includes all printing where the design is above the surface area, whether it is wood, metal or, in some instances, hardened rubber or polymer plastic.

For most letterpress-printed stamps, the engraved master is made in much the same manner as for engraved stamps. In this instance, however, an additional step is needed. The design is transferred to another surface before being transferred to the transfer roll. In this way, the transfer roll has a recessed stamp design, rather than one done in relief. This makes the printing areas on the final plate raised, or relief areas.

For less-detailed stamps of the 19th century, the area on the die not used as a printing surface was cut away, leaving the surface area raised. The original die was then reproduced by stereotyping or electrotyping. The resulting electrotypes were assembled in the required number and format of the desired sheet of stamps. The plate used in printing the stamps was an electroplate of these assembled electrotypes.

Once the final letterpress plates are created, ink is applied to the raised surface and the pressure of the press transfers the ink impression to the paper. In contrast to engraving, the fine lines of letterpress are impressed on the surface of the stamp, leaving a debossed surface. When viewed from the back (as on a typewritten page), the corresponding line work on the stamp will be raised slightly (embossed) above the surface.

## PHOTOGRAVURE (Gravure, Rotogravure, Heliogravure)

In this process, the basic principles of photography are applied to a chemically sensitized metal plate, rather than photographic paper. The design is transferred photographically to the plate through a halftone, or dot-matrix screen, breaking the reproduction into tiny dots. The plate is treated chemically and the dots form depressions, called cells, of varying depths and diameters, depending on the degrees of shade in the design. Then, like engraving, ink is applied to the plate and the surface is wiped clean. This leaves ink in the tiny cells that is lifted out and deposited on the paper when it is pressed against the plate.

Gravure is most often used for multicolored stamps, generally using the three primary colors (red, yellow and blue) and black. By varying the dot matrix pattern and density of these colors, virtually any color can be reproduced. A typical full-color gravure stamp will be created from four printing cylinders (one for each color). The original multicolored image will have been photographically separated into its component colors.

Modern gravure printing may use computer-generated dot-matrix screens, and modern plates may be of various types including metal-coated plastic. The catalogue designation of Photogravure (or "Photo") covers any of these older and more modern gravure methods of printing.

For examples of the first photogravure stamps printed (1914), see Bavaria Scott 94-114.

## LITHOGRAPHY (Offset Lithography, Stone Lithography, Dilitho, Planography, Collotype)

The principle that oil and water do not mix is the basis for lithography. The stamp design is drawn by hand or transferred from engraving to the surface of a lithographic stone or metal plate in a greasy (oily) substance. This oily substance holds the ink, which will later be transferred to the paper. The stone (or plate) is wet with an acid fluid, causing it to repel the printing ink in all areas not covered by the greasy substance.

Transfer paper is used to transfer the design from the original stone or plate. A series of duplicate transfers are grouped and, in turn, transferred to the final printing plate.

**Photolithography** — The application of photographic processes to lithography. This process allows greater flexibility of design, related to use of halftone screens combined with line work. Unlike photogravure or engraving, this process can allow large, solid areas to be printed.

**Offset** — A refinement of the lithographic process. A rubber-covered blanket cylinder takes the impression from the inked lithographic plate. From the "blanket" the impression is offset or transferred to the paper. Greater flexibility and speed are the principal reasons offset printing has largely displaced lithography. The term "lithography" covers both processes, and results are almost identical.

### EMBOSSED (Relief) Printing

Embossing, not considered one of the four main printing types, is a method in which the design first is sunk into the metal of the die. Printing is done against a yielding platen, such as leather or linoleum. The platen is forced into the depression of the die, thus forming the design on the paper in relief. This process is often used for metallic inks.

Embossing may be done without color (see Sardinia Scott 4-6); with color printed around the embossed area (see Great Britain Scott 5 and most U.S. envelopes); and with color in exact registration with the embossed subject (see Canada Scott 656-657).

### HOLOGRAMS

For objects to appear as holograms on stamps, a model exactly the same size as it is to appear on the hologram must be created. Rather than using photographic film to capture the image, holography records an image on a photoresist material. In processing, chemicals eat away at certain exposed areas, leaving a pattern of constructive and destructive interference. When the photoresist is developed, the result is a pattern of uneven ridges that acts as a mold. This mold is then coated with metal, and the resulting form is used to press copies in much the same way phonograph records are produced.

A typical reflective hologram used for stamps consists of a reproduction of the uneven patterns on a plastic film that is applied to a reflective background, usually a silver or gold foil. Light is reflected off the background through the film, making the pattern present on the film visible. Because of the uneven pattern of the film, the viewer will perceive the objects in their proper three-dimensional relationships with appropriate brightness. The first hologram on a stamp was produced by Austria in 1988 (Scott 1441).

### FOIL APPLICATION

A modern technique of applying color to stamps involves the application of metallic foil to the stamp paper. A pattern of foil is applied to the stamp paper by use of a stamping die. The foil usually is flat, but it may be textured. Canada Scott 1735 has three different foil applications in pearl, bronze and gold. The gold foil was textured using a chemical-etch copper embossing die. The printing of this stamp also involved two-color offset lithography plus embossing.

### THERMOGRAPHY

In the 1990s stamps began to be enhanced with thermographic printing. In this process, a powdered polymer is applied over a sheet that has just been printed. The powder adheres to ink that lacks drying or hardening agents and does not adhere to areas where the ink has these agents. The excess powder is removed and the sheet is briefly heated to melt the powder. The melted powder solidifies after cooling, producing a raised, shiny effect on the stamps. See Scott New Caledonia C239-C240.

### COMBINATION PRINTINGS

Sometimes two or even three printing methods are combined in producing stamps. In these cases, such as Austria Scott 933 or Canada 1735 (described in the preceding paragraph), the multiple-printing technique can be determined by studying the individual characteristics of each printing type. A few stamps, such as Singapore Scott 684-684A, combine as many as three of the four major printing types (lithography, engraving and typography). When this is done it often indicates the incorporation of security devices against counterfeiting.

### INK COLORS

Inks or colored papers used in stamp printing often are of mineral origin, although there are numerous examples of organic-based pigments. As a general rule, organic-based pigments are far more subject to varieties and change than those of mineral-based origin.

The appearance of any given color on a stamp may be affected by many aspects, including printing variations, light, color of paper, aging and chemical alterations.

Numerous printing variations may be observed. Heavier pressure or inking will cause a more intense color, while slight interruptions in the ink feed or lighter impressions will cause a lighter appearance. Stamps printed in the same color by water-based and solvent-based inks can differ significantly in appearance. This affects several stamps in the U.S. Prominent Americans series. Hand-mixed ink formulas (primarily from the 19th century) produced under different conditions (humidity and temperature) account for notable color variations in early printings of the same stamp (see U.S. Scott 248-250, 279B, for example). Different sources of pigment can also result in significant differences in color.

Light exposure and aging are closely related in the way they affect stamp color. Both eventually break down the ink and fade colors, so that a carefully kept stamp may differ significantly in color from an identical copy that has been exposed to light. If stamps are exposed to light either intentionally or accidentally, their colors can be faded or completely changed in some cases.

Papers of different quality and consistency used for the same stamp printing may affect color appearance. Most pelure papers, for example, show a richer color when compared with wove or laid papers. See Russia Scott 181a, for an example of this effect.

The very nature of the printing processes can cause a variety of differences in shades or hues of the same stamp. Some of these shades are scarcer than others, and are of particular interest to the advanced collector.

# Luminescence

All forms of tagged stamps fall under the general category of luminescence. Within this broad category is fluorescence, dealing with forms of tagging visible under longwave ultraviolet light, and phosphorescence, which deals with tagging visible only under shortwave light. Phosphorescence leaves an afterglow and fluorescence does not. These treated stamps show up in a range of different colors when exposed to UV light. The differing wavelengths of the light activates the tagging material, making it glow in various colors that usually serve different mail processing purposes.

Intentional tagging is a post-World War II phenomenon, brought about by the increased literacy rate and rapidly growing mail volume. It was one of several answers to the problem of the need for more automated mail processes. Early tagged stamps served the purpose of triggering machines to separate different types of mail. A natural outgrowth was to also use the signal to trigger machines that faced all envelopes the same way and canceled them.

Tagged stamps come in many different forms. Some tagged stamps have luminescent shapes or images imprinted on them as a form of security device. Others have blocks (United States), stripes, frames (South Africa and Canada), overall coatings (United States), bars (Great Britain and Canada) and many other types. Some types of tagging are even mixed in with the pigmented printing ink (Australia Scott 366, Netherlands Scott 478 and U.S. Scott 1359 and 2443).

The means of applying taggant to stamps differs as much as the intended purposes for the stamps. The most common form of tagging is a coating applied to the surface of the printed stamp. Since the taggant ink is frequently invisible except under UV light, it does not interfere with the appearance of the stamp. Another common application is the use of phosphored papers. In this case the paper itself either has a coating of taggant applied before the stamp is printed, has taggant applied during the papermaking process (incorporating it into the fibers), or has the taggant mixed into the coating of the paper. The latter method, among others, is currently in use in the United States.

Many countries now use tagging in various forms to either expedite mail handling or to serve as a printing security device against counterfeiting. Following the introduction of tagged stamps for public use in 1959 by Great Britain, other countries have steadily joined the parade. Among those are Germany (1961); Canada and Denmark (1962); United States, Australia, France and Switzerland (1963); Belgium and Japan (1966); Sweden and Norway (1967); Italy (1968); and Russia (1969). Since then, many other countries have begun using forms of tagging, including Brazil, China, Czechoslovakia, Hong Kong, Guatemala, Indonesia, Israel, Lithuania, Luxembourg, Netherlands, Penrhyn Islands, Portugal, St. Vincent, Singapore, South Africa, Spain and Sweden to name a few.

In some cases, including United States, Canada, Great Britain and Switzerland, stamps were released both with and without tagging. Many of these were released during each country's experimental period. Tagged and untagged versions are listed for the aforementioned countries and are noted in some other countries' listings. For at least a few stamps, the experimentally tagged version is worth far more than its untagged counterpart, such as the 1963 experimental tagged version of France Scott 1024.

In some cases, luminescent varieties of stamps were inadvertently created. Several Russian stamps, for example, sport highly fluorescent ink that was not intended as a form of tagging. Older stamps, such as early U.S. postage dues, can be positively identified by the use of UV light, since the organic ink used has become slightly fluorescent over time. Other stamps, such as Austria Scott 70a-82a (varnish bars) and Obock Scott 46-64 (printed quadrille lines), have become fluorescent over time.

Various fluorescent substances have been added to paper to make it appear brighter. These optical brightners, as they are known, greatly affect the appearance of the stamp under UV light. The brightest of these is known as Hi-Brite paper. These paper varieties are beyond the scope of the Scott Catalogue.

Shortwave UV light also is used extensively in expertizing, since each form of paper has its own fluorescent characteristics that are impossible to perfectly match. It is therefore a simple matter to detect filled thins, added perforation teeth and other alterations that involve the addition of paper. UV light also is used to examine stamps that have had cancels chemically removed and for other purposes as well.

## Gum

The Illustrated Gum Chart in the first part of this introduction shows and defines various types of gum condition. Because gum condition has an important impact on the value of unused stamps, we recommend studying this chart and the accompanying text carefully.

The gum on the back of a stamp may be shiny, dull, smooth, rough, dark, white, colored or tinted. Most stamp gumming adhesives use gum arabic or dextrine as a base. Certain polymers such as polyvinyl alcohol (PVA) have been used extensively since World War II.

The *Scott Standard Postage Stamp Catalogue* does not list items by types of gum. The *Scott Specialized Catalogue of United States Stamps and Covers* does differentiate among some types of gum for certain issues.

Reprints of stamps may have gum differing from the original issues. In addition, some countries have used different gum formulas for different seasons. These adhesives have different properties that may become more apparent over time.

Many stamps have been issued without gum, and the catalogue will note this fact. See, for example, United States Scott 40-47. Sometimes, gum may have been removed to preserve the stamp. Germany Scott B68, for example, has a highly acidic gum that eventually destroys the stamps. This item is valued in the catalogue with gum removed.

## Reprints and reissues

These are impressions of stamps (usually obsolete) made from the original plates or stones. If they are valid for postage and reproduce obsolete issues (such as U.S. Scott 102-111), the stamps are reissues. If they are from current issues, they are designated as *second, third,*

etc., *printing*. If designated for a particular purpose, they are called *special printings*.

When special printings are not valid for postage, but are made from original dies and plates by authorized persons, they are *official reprints*. *Private reprints* are made from the original plates and dies by private hands. An example of a private reprint is that of the 1871-1932 reprints made from the original die of the 1845 New Haven, Conn., postmaster's provisional. *Official reproductions* or imitations are made from new dies and plates by government authorization. Scott will list those reissues that are valid for postage if they differ significantly from the original printing.

The U.S. government made special printings of its first postage stamps in 1875. Produced were official imitations of the first two stamps (listed as Scott 3-4), reprints of the demonetized pre-1861 issues (Scott 40-47) and reissues of the 1861 stamps, the 1869 stamps and the then-current 1875 denominations. Even though the official imitations and the reprints were not valid for postage, Scott lists all of these U.S. special printings.

Most reprints or reissues differ slightly from the original stamp in some characteristic, such as gum, paper, perforation, color or watermark. Sometimes the details are followed so meticulously that only a student of that specific stamp is able to distinguish the reprint or reissue from the original.

## Remainders and canceled to order

Some countries sell their stock of old stamps when a new issue replaces them. To avoid postal use, the remainders usually are canceled with a punch hole, a heavy line or bar, or a more-or-less regular-looking cancellation. The most famous merchant of remainders was Nicholas F. Seebeck. In the 1880s and 1890s, he arranged printing contracts between the Hamilton Bank Note Co., of which he was a director, and several Central and South American countries. The contracts provided that the plates and all remainders of the yearly issues became the property of Hamilton. Seebeck saw to it that ample stock remained. The "Seebecks," both remainders and reprints, were standard packet fillers for decades.

Some countries also issue stamps *canceled-to-order (CTO)*, either in sheets with original gum or stuck onto pieces of paper or envelopes and canceled. Such CTO items generally are worth less than postally used stamps. In cases where the CTO material is far more prevalent in the marketplace than postally used examples, the catalogue value relates to the CTO examples, with postally used examples noted as premium items. Most CTOs can be detected by the presence of gum. However, as the CTO practice goes back at least to 1885, the gum inevitably has been soaked off some stamps so they could pass as postally used. The normally applied postmarks usually differ slightly from standard postmarks, and specialists are able to tell the difference. When applied individually to envelopes by philatelically minded persons, CTO material is known as *favor canceled* and generally sells at large discounts.

## Cinderellas and facsimiles

*Cinderella* is a catch-all term used by stamp collectors to describe phantoms, fantasies, bogus items, municipal issues, exhibition seals, local revenues, transportation stamps, labels, poster stamps and many other types of items. Some cinderella collectors include in their collections local postage issues, telegraph stamps, essays and proofs, forgeries and counterfeits.

A *fantasy* is an adhesive created for a nonexistent stamp-issuing authority. Fantasy items range from imaginary countries (Occusi-Ambeno, Kingdom of Sedang, Principality of Trinidad or Torres Straits), to non-existent locals (Winans City Post), or nonexistent transportation lines (McRobish & Co.'s Acapulco-San Francisco Line).

On the other hand, if the entity exists and could have issued stamps (but did not) or was known to have issued other stamps, the items are considered bogus stamps. These would include the Mormon postage stamps of Utah, S. Allan Taylor's Guatemala and Paraguay inventions, the propaganda issues for the South Moluccas and the adhesives of the Page & Keyes local post of Boston.

*Phantoms* is another term for both fantasy and bogus issues.

*Facsimiles* are copies or imitations made to represent original stamps, but which do not pretend to be originals. A catalogue illustration is such a facsimile. Illustrations from the Moens catalogue of the last century were occasionally colored and passed off as stamps. Since the beginning of stamp collecting, facsimiles have been made for collectors as space fillers or for reference. They often carry the word "facsimile," "falsch" (German), "sanko" or "mozo" (Japanese), or "faux" (French) overprinted on the face or stamped on the back. Unfortunately, over the years a number of these items have had fake cancels applied over the facsimile notation and have been passed off as genuine.

# Forgeries and counterfeits

Forgeries and counterfeits have been with philately virtually from the beginning of stamp production. Over time, the terminology for the two has been used interchangeably. Although both forgeries and counterfeits are reproductions of stamps, the purposes behind their creation differ considerably.

Among specialists there is an increasing movement to more specifically define such items. Although there is no universally accepted terminology, we feel the following definitions most closely mirror the items and their purposes as they are currently defined.

Forgeries (also often referred to as Counterfeits) are reproductions of genuine stamps that have been created to defraud collectors. Such spurious items first appeared on the market around 1860, and most old-time collections contain one or more. Many are crude and easily spotted, but some can deceive experts.

An important supplier of these early philatelic forgeries was the Hamburg printer Gebruder Spiro. Many others with reputations in this craft included S. Allan Taylor, George Hussey, James Chute, George Forune, Benjamin & Sarpy, Julius Goldner, E. Oneglia and L.H. Mercier. Among the noted 20th-century forgers were Francois Fournier, Jean Sperati and the prolific Raoul DeThuin.

Forgeries may be complete replications, or they may be genuine stamps altered to resemble a scarcer (and more valuable) type. Most forgeries, particularly those of rare stamps, are worth only a small fraction of the value of a genuine example, but a few types, created by some of the most notable forgers, such as Sperati, can be worth as much or more than the genuine. Fraudulently produced copies are known of most classic rarities and many medium-priced stamps.

In addition to rare stamps, large numbers of common 19th- and early 20th-century stamps were forged to supply stamps to the early packet trade. Many can still be easily found. Few new philatelic forgeries have appeared in recent decades. Successful imitation of well-engraved work is virtually impossible. It has proven far easier to produce a fake by altering a genuine stamp than to duplicate a stamp completely.

Counterfeit (also often referred to as Postal Counterfeit or Postal Forgery) is the term generally applied to reproductions of stamps that have been created to defraud the government of revenue. Such items usually are created at the time a stamp is current and, in some cases, are hard to detect. Because most counterfeits are seized when the perpetrator is captured, postal counterfeits, particularly used on cover, are usually worth much more than a genuine example to specialists. The first postal counterfeit was of Spain's 4-cuarto carmine of 1854 (the real one is Scott 25). Apparently, the counterfeiters were not satisfied with their first version, which is now very scarce, and they soon created an engraved counterfeit, which is common. Postal counterfeits quickly followed in Austria, Naples, Sardinia and the Roman States. They have since been created in many other countries as well, including the United States.

An infamous counterfeit to defraud the government is the 1-shilling Great Britain "Stock Exchange" forgery of 1872, used on telegraph forms at the exchange that year. The stamp escaped detection until a stamp dealer noticed it in 1898.

# Fakes

*Fakes* are genuine stamps altered in some way to make them more desirable. One student of this part of stamp collecting has estimated that by the 1950s more than 30,000 varieties of fakes were known. That number has grown greatly since then. The widespread existence of fakes makes it important for stamp collectors to study their philatelic holdings and use relevant literature. Likewise, collectors should buy from reputable dealers who guarantee their stamps and make full and prompt refunds should a purchased item be declared faked or altered by some mutually agreed-upon authority. Because fakes always have some genuine characteristics, it is not always possible to obtain unanimous agreement among experts regarding specific items. These students may change their opinions as philatelic knowledge increases. More than 80 percent of all fakes on the philatelic market today are regummed, reperforated (or perforated for the first time), or bear forged overprints, surcharges or cancellations.

Stamps can be chemically treated to alter or eliminate colors. For example, a pale rose stamp can be re-colored to resemble a blue shade of high market value. In other cases, treated stamps can be made to resemble missing color varieties. Designs may be changed by painting, or a stroke or a dot added or bleached out to turn an ordinary variety into a seemingly scarcer stamp. Part of a stamp can be bleached and reprinted in a different version, achieving an inverted center or frame. Margins can be added or repairs done so deceptively that the stamps move from the "repaired" into the "fake" category.

Fakers have not left the backs of the stamps untouched either. They may create false watermarks, add fake grills or press out genuine grills.

A thin India paper proof may be glued onto a thicker backing to create the appearance an issued stamp, or a proof printed on cardboard may be shaved down and perforated to resemble a stamp. Silk threads are impressed into paper and stamps have been split so that a rare paper variety is added to an otherwise inexpensive stamp. The most common treatment to the back of a stamp, however, is regumming.

Some in the business of faking stamps have openly advertised fool-proof application of "original gum" to stamps that lack it, although most publications now ban such ads from their pages. It is believed that very few early stamps have survived without being hinged. The large number of never-hinged examples of such earlier material offered for sale thus suggests the widespread extent of regumming activity. Regumming also may be used to hide repairs or thin spots. Dipping the stamp into watermark fluid, or examining it under longwave ultraviolet light often will reveal these flaws.

Fakers also tamper with separations. Ingenious ways to add margins are known. Perforated wide-margin stamps may be falsely represented as imperforate when trimmed. Reperforating is commonly done to create scarce coil or perforation varieties, and to eliminate the naturally occurring straight-edge stamps found in sheet margin positions of many earlier issues. Custom has made straight-edged stamps less desirable. Fakers have obliged by perforating straight-edged stamps so that many are now uncommon, if not rare.

Another fertile field for the faker is that of overprints, surcharges and cancellations. The forging of rare surcharges or overprints began in the 1880s or 1890s. These forgeries are sometimes difficult to detect, but experts have identified almost all. Occasionally, overprints or cancellations are removed to create non-overprinted stamps or seemingly unused items. This is most commonly done by removing a manuscript cancel to make a stamp resemble an unused example. "SPECIMEN" overprints may be removed by scraping and repainting to create non-overprinted varieties. Fakers use inexpensive revenues or pen-canceled stamps to generate unused stamps for further faking by adding other markings. The quartz lamp or UV lamp and a high-powered magnifying glass help to easily detect removed cancellations.

The bigger problem, however, is the addition of overprints, surcharges or cancellations — many with such precision that they are very difficult to ascertain. Plating of the stamps or the overprint can be an important method of detection.

Fake postmarks may range from many spurious fancy cancellations to a host of markings applied to transatlantic covers, to adding normally appearing postmarks to definitives of some countries with stamps that are valued far higher used than unused. With the increased popularity of cover collecting, and the widespread interest in postal history, a fertile new field for fakers has come about. Some have tried to create entire covers. Others specialize in adding stamps, tied by fake cancellations, to genuine stampless covers, or replacing less expensive or damaged stamps with more valuable ones. Detailed study of postal rates in effect at the time a cover in question was mailed, including the analysis of each handstamp used during the period, ink analysis and similar techniques, usually will unmask the fraud.

# Restoration and repairs

Scott bases its catalogue values on stamps that are free of defects and otherwise meet the standards set forth earlier in this introduction. Most stamp collectors desire to have the finest copy of an item possible. Even within given grading categories there are variances. This leads to a controversial practice that is not defined in any universal manner: stamp *restoration*.

There are broad differences of opinion about what is permissible when it comes to restoration. Carefully applying a soft eraser to a stamp or cover to remove light soiling is one form of restoration, as is washing a stamp in mild soap and water to clean it. These are fairly accepted forms of restoration. More severe forms of restoration include pressing out creases or removing stains caused by tape. To what degree each of these is acceptable is dependent upon the individual situation. Further along the spectrum is the freshening of a stamp's color by removing oxide build-up or the effects of wax paper left next to stamps shipped to the tropics.

At some point in this spectrum the concept of *repair* replaces that of restoration. Repairs include filling thin spots, mending tears by reweaving or adding a missing perforation tooth. Regumming stamps may have been acceptable as a restoration or repair technique many decades ago, but today it is considered a form of fakery.

Restored stamps may or may not sell at a discount, and it is possible that the value of individual restored items may be enhanced over that of their pre-restoration state. Specific situations dictate the resultant value of such an item. Repaired stamps sell at substantial discounts from the value of sound stamps.

# Terminology

**Booklets** — Many countries have issued stamps in small booklets for the convenience of users. This idea continues to become increasingly popular in many countries. Booklets have been issued in many sizes and forms, often with advertising on the covers, the panes of stamps or on the interleaving.

The panes used in booklets may be printed from special plates or made from regular sheets. All panes from booklets issued by the United States and many from those of other countries contain stamps that are straight edged on the sides, but perforated between. Others are distinguished by orientation of watermark or other identifying features. Any stamp-like unit in the pane, either printed or blank, that is not a postage stamp, is considered to be a *label* in the catalogue listings.

Scott lists and values booklet panes. Modern complete booklets also are listed and valued. Individual booklet panes are listed only when they are not fashioned from existing sheet stamps and, therefore, are identifiable from their sheet stamp counterparts.

Panes usually do not have a used value assigned to them because there is little market activity for used booklet panes, even though many exist used and there is some demand for them.

**Cancellations** — The marks or obliterations put on stamps by postal authorities to show that they have performed service and to prevent their reuse are known as cancellations. If the marking is made with a pen, it is considered a "pen cancel." When the location of the post office appears in the marking, it is a "town cancellation." A "postmark" is technically any postal marking, but in practice the term generally is applied to a town cancellation with a date. When calling attention to a cause or celebration, the marking is known as a "slogan cancellation." Many other types and styles of cancellations exist, such as duplex, numerals, targets, fancy and others. See also "precancels," below.

**Coil Stamps** — These are stamps that are issued in rolls for use in dispensers, affixing and vending machines. Those coils of the United States, Canada, Sweden and some other countries are perforated horizontally or vertically only, with the outer edges imperforate. Coil stamps of some countries, such as Great Britain and Germany, are perforated on all four sides and may in some cases be distinguished from their sheet stamp counterparts by watermarks, counting numbers on the reverse or other means.

**Covers** — Entire envelopes, with or without adhesive postage stamps, that have passed through the mail and bear postal or other markings of philatelic interest are known as covers. Before the introduction of envelopes in about 1840, people folded letters and wrote the address on the outside. Some people covered their letters with an extra sheet of paper on the outside for the address, producing the term "cover." Used airletter sheets, stamped envelopes and other items of postal stationery also are considered covers.

**Errors** — Stamps that have some major, consistent, unintentional deviation from the normal are considered errors. Errors include, but are not limited to, missing or wrong colors, wrong paper, wrong watermarks, inverted centers or frames on multicolor printing, inverted or missing surcharges or overprints, double impressions, missing perforations, unintentionally omitted tagging and others. Factually wrong or misspelled information, if it appears on all examples of a stamp, are not considered errors in the true sense of the word. They are errors of design. Inconsistent or randomly appearing items, such as misperfs or color shifts, are classified as freaks.

**Color-Omitted Errors** — This term refers to stamps where a missing color is caused by the complete failure of the printing plate to deliver ink to the stamp paper or any other paper. Generally, this is caused by the printing plate not being engaged on the press or the ink station running dry of ink during printing.

**Color-Missing Errors** — This term refers to stamps where a color or colors were printed somewhere but do not appear on the finished stamp. There are four different classes of color-missing errors, and the catalog indicates with a two-letter code appended to each such listing what caused the color to be missing. These codes are used only for the United States' color-missing error listings.

**FO** = A *foldover* of the stamp sheet during printing may block ink from appearing on the face of a stamp. Instead, the color will appear on the back of the foldover (where it might fall on the back of the selvage or perhaps a bit on the back of the stamp or on the back of another stamp. FO also will be used in the case of foldunders, where the paper may fold underneath the other stamp paper and the color will print on the platen.

**EP** = When the extraneous paper is removed, an unprinted area of stamp paper remains and may show a color or colors to be totally missing on the finished stamp.

**CM** = A misregistration of the printing plates during printing will result in a *color misregistration*, and such a misregistraion may result in a color not appearing on the finished stamp.

**PS** = A *perforation shift* after printing may remove a color from the finished stamp. Normally, this will occur on a row of stamps at the edge of the stamp pane.

**Measurements** – When measurements are given in the Scott catalogues for stamp size, grill size or any other reason, the first measurement given is always for the top and bottom dimension, while the second measurement will be for the sides (just as perforation gauges are measured). Thus, a stamp size of 15mm x 21mm will indicate a vertically oriented stamp 15mm wide at top and bottom, and 21mm tall at the sides. The same principle holds for measuring or counting items such as U.S. grills. A grill count of 22x18 points (B grill) indicates that there are 22 grill points across by 18 grill points down.

**Overprints and Surcharges** — Overprinting involves applying wording or design elements over an already existing stamp. Overprints can be used to alter the place of use (such as "Canal Zone" on U.S. stamps), to adapt them for a special purpose ("Porto" on Denmark's 1913-20 regular issues for use as postage due stamps, Scott J1-J7) or to commemorate a special occasion (United States Scott 647-648).

A *surcharge* is a form of overprint that changes or restates the face value of a stamp or piece of postal stationery.

Surcharges and overprints may be handstamped, typeset or, occasionally, lithographed or engraved. A few hand-written overprints and surcharges are known.

**Personalized Stamps** — In 1999, Australia issued stamps with se-tenant labels that could be personalized with pictures of the customer's choice. Other countries quickly followed suit, with some offering to print the selected picture on the stamp itself within a frame that was used exclusively for personalized issues. As the picture used on these stamps or labels vary, listings for such stamps are for any picture within the common frame (or any picture on a se-tenant label), be it a "generic" image or one produced especially for a customer, almost invariably at a premium price.

**Precancels** — Stamps that are canceled before they are placed in the mail are known as precancels. Precanceling usually is done to expedite the handling of large mailings and generally allow the affected mail pieces to skip certain phases of mail handling.

In the United States, precancellations generally identified the point of origin; that is, the city and state. This information appeared across the face of the stamp, usually centered between parallel lines. More recently, bureau precancels retained the parallel lines, but the city and state designations were dropped. Recent coils have a service inscription that is present on the original printing plate. These show the mail service paid for by the stamp. Since these stamps are not intended to receive further cancellations when used as intended, they are considered precancels. Such items often do not have parallel lines as part of the precancellation.

In France, the abbreviation *Affranchts* in a semicircle together with the word *Postes* is the general form of precancel in use. Belgian precancellations usually appear in a box in which the name of the city appears. Netherlands precancels have the name of the city enclosed between concentric circles, sometimes called a "lifesaver." Precancellations of other countries usually follow these patterns, but may be any arrangement of bars, boxes and city names.

Precancels are listed in the Scott catalogues only if the precancel changes the denomination (Belgium Scott 477-478); if the precanceled stamp is different from the non-precanceled version (such as untagged U.S. precancels); or if the stamp exists only precanceled (France Scott 1096-1099, U.S. Scott 2265).

**Proofs and Essays** — Proofs are impressions taken from an approved die, plate or stone in which the design and color are the same as the stamp issued to the public. Trial color proofs are impressions taken from approved dies, plates or stones in colors that vary from the final version. An essay is the impression of a design that differs in some way from the issued stamp. "Progressive die proofs" generally are considered to be essays.

**Provisionals** — These are stamps that are issued on short notice and intended for temporary use pending the arrival of regular issues. They usually are issued to meet such contingencies as changes in government or currency, shortage of necessary postage values or military occupation.

During the 1840s, postmasters in certain American cities issued stamps that were valid only at specific post offices. In 1861, postmasters of the Confederate States also issued stamps with limited validity. Both of these examples are known as "postmaster's provisionals."

**Se-tenant** — This term refers to an unsevered pair, strip or block of stamps that differ in design, denomination or overprint.

Unless the se-tenant item has a continuous design (see U.S. Scott 1451a, 1694a) the stamps do not have to be in the same order as shown in the catalogue (see U.S. Scott 2158a).

**Specimens** — The Universal Postal Union required member nations to send samples of all stamps they released into service to the International Bureau in Switzerland. Member nations of the UPU received these specimens as samples of what stamps were valid for postage. Many are overprinted, handstamped or initial-perforated "Specimen," "Canceled" or "Muestra." Some are marked with bars across the denominations (China-Taiwan), punched holes (Czechoslovakia) or back inscriptions (Mongolia).

Stamps distributed to government officials or for publicity purposes, and stamps submitted by private security printers for official approval, also may receive such defacements.

The previously described defacement markings prevent postal use, and all such items generally are known as "specimens."

**Tete-Beche** — This term describes a pair of stamps in which one is upside down in relation to the other. Some of these are the result of intentional sheet arrangements, such as Morocco Scott B10-B11. Others occurred when one or more electrotypes accidentally were placed upside down on the plate, such as Colombia Scott 57a. Separation of the tete-beche stamps, of course, destroys the tete beche variety.

# Carson Products

## MicroMini 20x LED Microscope
Item No. MSMM-2800

**$9.99** *AA\* price*

$14.00 Retail

## Pop-Up Keychain Magnifier
Item No. MGGN-70

**$6.99** *AA\* price*

$10.00 Retail

## Bar Ruler Magnifier 1.5x
Item No. MGMR-65

**$9.99** *AA\* price*

$13.00 Retail

## ZPix Digital Microscope
Item No. MCPIX

**$99.99** *AA\* price*

$129.99 Retail

## MicroFlip Phone Scope
Item No. MCFLIP

**ON SALE**

**$21.99** *AA\* price*

$27.99 Retail

**SAVE 33%**

## zOrb Digital Microscope
Item No. MCZORB2

**$50.99** *AA\* price*

$74.99 Retail

## MicroPen Pocket Microscope
Item No. MCPEN

**$12.99** *AA\* price*

$14.99 Retail

## SmartPhone Microscope
Item No. MCSCOPE

**$119.99** *AA\* price*

$164.99 Retail

**SAVE $45**

**FREE SHIPPING!** on orders $75 or more

# AmosAdvantage.com | 1-800-572-6885

# Pronunciation Symbols

ə .... banana, collide, abut

ˈə, ˌə .... humdrum, abut

ə .... immediately preceding \l\, \n\, \m\, \ŋ\, as in battle, mitten, eaten, and sometimes open \ˈō-pᵊm\, lock and key \-ᵊŋ-\; immediately following \l\, \m\, \r\, as often in French table, prisme, titre

ər .... further, merger, bird

ˈər-
ˈə-r }  .... as in two different pronunciations of hurry \ˈhər-ē, ˈhə-rē\

a .... mat, map, mad, gag, snap, patch

ā .... day, fade, date, aorta, drape, cape

ä .... bother, cot, and, with most American speakers, father, cart

ȧ .... father as pronunced by speakers who do not rhyme it with bother; French patte

au̇ .... now, loud, out

b .... baby, rib

ch .... chin, nature \ˈnā-chər\

d .... did, adder

e .... bet, bed, peck

ˈē, ˌē .... beat, nosebleed, evenly, easy

ē .... easy, mealy

f .... fifty, cuff

g .... go, big, gift

h .... hat, ahead

hw .... whale as pronounced by those who do not have the same pronunciation for both whale and wail

i .... tip, banish, active

ī .... site, side, buy, tripe

j .... job, gem, edge, join, judge

k .... kin, cook, ache

k̲ .... German ich, Buch; one pronunciation of loch

l .... lily, pool

m .... murmur, dim, nymph

n .... no, own

ⁿ .... indicates that a preceding vowel or diphthong is pronounced with the nasal passages open, as in French un bon vin blanc \œ̃ⁿ -bōⁿ -vaⁿ -bläⁿ\

ŋ .... sing \ˈsiŋ\, singer \ˈsiŋ-ər\, finger \ˈfiŋ-gər\, ink \ˈiŋk \

ō .... bone, know, beau

ȯ .... saw, all, gnaw, caught

œ .... French boeuf, German Hölle

ō̅e .... French feu, German Höhle

ȯi .... coin, destroy

p .... pepper, lip

r .... red, car, rarity

s .... source, less

sh .... as in shy, mission, machine, special (actually, this is a single sound, not two); with a hyphen between, two sounds as in grasshopper \ˈgras-ˌhä-pər\

t .... tie, attack, late, later, latter

th .... as in thin, ether (actually, this is a single sound, not two); with a hyphen between, two sounds as in knighthood \ˈnīt-ˌhu̇d\

th̲ .... then, either, this (actually, this is a single sound, not two)

ü .... rule, youth, union \ˈyün-yən\, few \ˈfyü\

u̇ .... pull, wood, book, curable \ˈkyu̇r-ə-bəl\, fury \ˈfyu̇r-ē\

ue .... German füllen, hübsch

u̅e .... French rue, German fühlen

v .... vivid, give

w .... we, away

y .... yard, young, cue \ˈkyü\, mute \ˈmyüt\, union \ˈyün-yən\

ʸ .... indicates that during the articulation of the sound represented by the preceding character the front of the tongue has substantially the position it has for the articulation of the first sound of yard, as in French digne \dēnʸ\

z .... zone, raise

zh .... as in vision, azure \ˈa-zhər\ (actually, this is a single sound, not two); with a hyphen between, two sounds as in hogshead \ˈhȯgz-ˌhed, ˈhägz-\

\ .... slant line used in pairs to mark the beginning and end of a transcription: \ˈpen\

ˈ .... mark preceding a syllable with primary (strongest) stress: \ˈpen-mən-ˌship\

ˌ .... mark preceding a syllable with secondary (medium) stress: \ˈpen-mən-ˌship\

- .... mark of syllable division

( ) .... indicate that what is symbolized between is present in some utterances but not in others: factory \ˈfak-t(ə-)rē\

÷ .... indicates that many regard as unacceptable the pronunciation variant immediately following: cupola \ˈkyü-pə-lə, ÷-ˌlō\

# Currency conversion

| Country | Dollar | Pound | S Franc | Yen | HK $ | Euro | Cdn $ | Aus $ |
|---|---|---|---|---|---|---|---|---|
| Australia | 1.4750 | 1.7808 | 1.5770 | 0.0109 | 0.1879 | 1.5767 | 1.0848 | — |
| Canada | 1.3597 | 1.6416 | 1.4538 | 0.0100 | 0.1732 | 1.4534 | — | 0.9218 |
| European Union | 0.9355 | 1.1294 | 1.0002 | 0.0069 | 0.1192 | — | 0.6880 | 0.6342 |
| Hong Kong | 7.8496 | 9.4770 | 8.3962 | 0.0579 | — | 8.3908 | 5.7730 | 5.3218 |
| Japan | 135.59 | 163.70 | 144.97 | — | 17.273 | 144.94 | 99.721 | 91.925 |
| Switzerland | 0.9353 | 1.1292 | — | 0.0069 | 0.1192 | 0.9998 | 0.6879 | 0.6341 |
| United Kingdom | 0.8283 | — | 0.8856 | 0.0061 | 0.1055 | 0.8854 | 0.6092 | 0.5616 |
| United States | — | 1.2073 | 1.0692 | 0.0074 | 0.1274 | 1.0689 | 0.7355 | 0.6780 |

| Country | Currency | U.S. $ Equiv. |
|---|---|---|
| Jamaica | dollar | .0065 |
| Japan | yen | .0074 |
| Jordan | dinar | 1.4104 |
| Kazakhstan | tenge | .0023 |
| Kenya | shilling | .0079 |
| Kiribati | Australian dollar | .6780 |
| Korea (South) | won | .0008 |
| Korea (North) | won | .0011 |
| Kosovo | euro | 1.0689 |
| Kuwait | dinar | 3.2595 |
| Kyrgyzstan | som | .0114 |
| Laos | kip | .0001 |
| Latvia | euro | 1.0689 |
| Lebanon | pound | .0001 |
| Lesotho | maloti | .0551 |
| Liberia | dollar | .0063 |
| Libya | dinar | .2067 |
| Liechtenstein | Swiss franc | 1.0692 |
| Lithuania | euro | 1.0689 |
| Luxembourg | euro | 1.0689 |
| Macao | pataca | .1237 |
| Macedonia | denar | .0173 |
| Malagasy Republic | ariary | .0002 |
| Malawi | kwacha | .0010 |
| Malaysia | ringgit (dollar) | .2236 |
| Maldive Islands | rafiyaa | .0649 |
| Mali | Community of French Africa (CFA) franc | .0016 |
| Malta | euro | 1.0689 |
| Marshall Islands | U.S. dollar | 1.000 |
| Mauritania | ouguiya | .0275 |
| Mauritius | rupee | .0216 |
| Mexico | peso | .0548 |
| Micronesia | U.S. dollar | 1.000 |
| Moldova | leu | .0529 |
| Monaco | euro | 1.0689 |
| Mongolia | tugrik | .0003 |
| Montenegro | euro | 1.0689 |
| Montserrat | East Caribbean dollar | .3704 |
| Morocco | dirham | .0966 |
| Mozambique | metical | .0156 |

*Source: xe.com  Mar. 1, 2023. Figures reflect values as of Mar. 1, 2023.*

# COMMON DESIGN TYPES

Pictured in this section are issues where one illustration has been used for a number of countries in the Catalogue. Not included in this section are overprinted stamps or those issues which are illustrated in each country. Because the location of Never Hinged breakpoints varies from country to country, some of the values in the listings below will be for unused stamps that were previously hinged.

## EUROPA
### Europa, 1956

The design symbolizing the cooperation among the six countries comprising the Coal and Steel Community is illustrated in each country.

Belgium.................................496-497
France..................................805-806
Germany...............................748-749
Italy.....................................715-716
Luxembourg...........................318-320
Netherlands...........................368-369

| | | |
|---|---|---|
| Nos. 496-497 (2) | 9.00 | .50 |
| Nos. 805-806 (2) | 5.25 | 1.00 |
| Nos. 748-749 (2) | 7.40 | 1.10 |
| Nos. 715-716 (2) | 9.25 | 1.25 |
| Nos. 318-320 (3) | 65.50 | 42.00 |
| Nos. 368-369 (2) | 25.75 | 1.50 |
| Set total (13) Stamps | 122.15 | 47.35 |

### Europa, 1958

"E" and Dove — CD1

European Postal Union at the service of European integration.

**1958, Sept. 13**

Belgium....................................527-528
France..................................889-890
Germany...............................790-791
Italy.....................................750-751
Luxembourg...........................341-343
Netherlands...........................375-376
Saar.....................................317-318

| | | |
|---|---|---|
| Nos. 527-528 (2) | 3.75 | .60 |
| Nos. 889-890 (2) | 1.65 | .55 |
| Nos. 790-791 (2) | 2.95 | .60 |
| Nos. 750-751 (2) | 1.05 | .60 |
| Nos. 341-343 (3) | 1.35 | .90 |
| Nos. 375-376 (2) | 1.25 | .75 |
| Nos. 317-318 (2) | 1.05 | 2.30 |
| Set total (15) Stamps | 13.05 | 6.30 |

### Europa, 1959

6-Link Enless Chain — CD2

**1959, Sept. 19**

Belgium....................................536-537
France..................................929-930
Germany...............................805-806
Italy.....................................791-792
Luxembourg...........................354-355
Netherlands...........................379-380

| | | |
|---|---|---|
| Nos. 536-537 (2) | 1.55 | .60 |
| Nos. 929-930 (2) | 1.40 | .80 |
| Nos. 805-806 (2) | 1.35 | .60 |
| Nos. 791-792 (2) | .80 | .50 |
| Nos. 354-355 (2) | 2.65 | 1.00 |
| Nos. 379-380 (2) | 2.10 | 1.85 |
| Set total (12) Stamps | 9.85 | 5.35 |

### Europa, 1960

19-Spoke Wheel CD3

First anniverary of the establishment of C.E.P.T. (Conference Europeenne des Administrations des Postes et des Telecommunications.) The spokes symbolize the 19 founding members of the Conference.

**1960, Sept.**

Belgium....................................553-554
Denmark................................379
Finland..................................376-377
France..................................970-971
Germany...............................818-820
Great Britain..........................377-378
Greece..................................688
Iceland..................................327-328
Ireland..................................175-176
Italy.....................................809-810
Luxembourg...........................374-375
Netherlands...........................385-386
Norway..................................387
Portugal................................866-867
Spain....................................941-942
Sweden.................................562-563
Switzerland............................400-401
Turkey ..................................1493-1494

| | | |
|---|---|---|
| Nos. 553-554 (2) | 1.25 | .55 |
| No. 379 (1) | .55 | .50 |
| Nos. 376-377 (2) | 1.80 | 1.40 |
| Nos. 970-971 (2) | .50 | .50 |
| Nos. 818-820 (3) | 1.90 | 1.35 |
| Nos. 377-378 (2) | 7.00 | 2.75 |
| No. 688 (1) | 4.25 | 1.75 |
| Nos. 327-328 (2) | 1.30 | 1.85 |
| Nos. 175-176 (2) | 47.50 | 27.50 |
| Nos. 809-810 (2) | .50 | .50 |
| Nos. 374-375 (2) | 1.00 | .80 |
| Nos. 385-386 (2) | 2.00 | 2.00 |
| No. 387 (1) | 1.00 | .80 |
| Nos. 866-867 (2) | 3.00 | 1.75 |
| Nos. 941-942 (2) | 1.50 | .75 |
| Nos. 562-563 (2) | 1.05 | .55 |
| Nos. 400-401 (2) | 1.75 | .75 |
| Nos. 1493-1494 (2) | 2.10 | 1.35 |
| Set total (34) Stamps | 79.95 | 47.40 |

### Europa, 1961

19 Doves Flying as One — CD4

The 19 doves represent the 19 members of the Conference of European Postal and Telecommunications Administrations C.E.P.T.

**1961-62**

Belgium....................................572-573
Cyprus...................................201-203
France..................................1005-1006
Germany...............................844-845
Great Britain..........................382-384
Greece..................................718-719
Iceland..................................340-341
Italy.....................................845-846
Luxembourg...........................382-383
Netherlands...........................387-388
Spain ...................................1010-1011
Switzerland............................410-411
Turkey ..................................1518-1520

| | | |
|---|---|---|
| Nos. 572-573 (2) | .75 | .50 |
| Nos. 201-203 (3) | 2.10 | 1.20 |
| Nos. 1005-1006 (2) | .50 | .50 |
| Nos. 844-845 (2) | .60 | .75 |
| Nos. 382-384 (3) | .75 | .75 |
| Nos. 718-719 (2) | .80 | .50 |
| Nos. 340-341 (2) | 1.10 | 1.60 |
| Nos. 845-846 (2) | .50 | .50 |
| Nos. 382-383 (2) | .55 | .55 |
| Nos. 387-388 (2) | .50 | .50 |
| Nos. 1010-1011 (2) | .60 | .50 |
| Nos. 410-411 (2) | 1.90 | .60 |
| Nos. 1518-1520 (3) | 1.55 | .90 |
| Set total (29) Stamps | 12.20 | 9.35 |

### Europa, 1962

Young Tree with 19 Leaves CD5

The 19 leaves represent the 19 original members of C.E.P.T.

**1962-63**

Belgium....................................582-583
Cyprus...................................219-221
France..................................1045-1046
Germany...............................852-853
Greece..................................739-740
Iceland..................................348-349
Ireland..................................184-185
Italy.....................................860-861
Luxembourg...........................386-387
Netherlands...........................394-395
Norway..................................414-415
Switzerland............................416-417
Turkey ..................................1553-1555

| | | |
|---|---|---|
| Nos. 582-583 (2) | .65 | .65 |
| Nos. 219-221 (3) | 76.25 | 6.75 |
| Nos. 1045-1046 (2) | .60 | .50 |
| Nos. 852-853 (2) | .65 | .75 |
| Nos. 739-740 (2) | 2.00 | 1.15 |
| Nos. 348-349 (2) | .85 | .85 |
| Nos. 184-185 (2) | 2.00 | .50 |
| Nos. 860-861 (2) | 1.00 | .55 |
| Nos. 386-387 (2) | .75 | .55 |
| Nos. 394-395 (2) | 1.35 | .90 |
| Nos. 414-415 (2) | 1.75 | 1.70 |
| Nos. 416-417 (2) | 1.65 | 1.00 |
| Nos. 1553-1555 (3) | 2.05 | 1.10 |
| Set total (28) Stamps | 91.55 | 16.95 |

### Europa, 1963

Stylized Links, Symbolizing Unity — CD6

**1963, Sept.**

Belgium....................................598-599
Cyprus...................................229-231
Finland..................................419
France..................................1074-1075
Germany...............................867-868
Greece..................................768-769
Iceland..................................357-358
Ireland..................................188-189
Italy.....................................880-881
Luxembourg...........................403-404
Netherlands...........................416-417
Norway..................................441-442
Switzerland............................429
Turkey ..................................1602-1603

| | | |
|---|---|---|
| Nos. 598-599 (2) | 1.60 | .55 |
| Nos. 229-231 (3) | 64.00 | 9.40 |
| No. 419 (1) | 1.25 | .55 |
| Nos. 1074-1075 (2) | .60 | .50 |
| Nos. 867-868 (2) | .50 | .55 |
| Nos. 768-769 (2) | 4.65 | 1.65 |
| Nos. 357-358 (2) | 1.20 | 1.20 |
| Nos. 188-189 (2) | 4.75 | 3.25 |
| Nos. 880-881 (2) | .50 | .50 |
| Nos. 403-404 (2) | .75 | .55 |
| Nos. 416-417 (2) | 1.30 | 1.00 |
| Nos. 441-442 (2) | 2.60 | 2.40 |
| No. 429 (1) | .90 | .60 |
| Nos. 1602-1603 (2) | 1.20 | .50 |
| Set total (27) Stamps | 85.80 | 23.20 |

### Europa, 1964

Symbolic Daisy — CD7

5th anniversary of the establishment of C.E.P.T. The 22 petals of the flower symbolize the 22 members of the Conference.

### 1964, Sept.

Austria .................................738
Belgium.................................614-615
Cyprus .................................244-246
France .................................1109-1110
Germany...............................897-898
Greece .................................801-802
Iceland .................................367-368
Ireland .................................196-197
Italy .....................................894-895
Luxembourg...........................411-412
Monaco.................................590-591
Netherlands ..........................428-429
Norway .................................458
Portugal ...............................931-933
Spain ...................................1262-1263
Switzerland ...........................438-439
Turkey .................................1628-1629

| | | |
|---|---|---|
| No. 738 (1) | 1.10 | .25 |
| Nos. 614-615 (2) | 1.40 | .60 |
| Nos. 244-246 (3) | 32.25 | 5.10 |
| Nos. 1109-1110 (2) | .50 | .50 |
| Nos. 897-898 (2) | .50 | .50 |
| Nos. 801-802 (2) | 4.15 | 1.55 |
| Nos. 367-368 (2) | 1.40 | 1.15 |
| Nos. 196-197 (2) | 17.00 | 4.25 |
| Nos. 894-895 (2) | .50 | .50 |
| Nos. 411-412 (2) | .75 | .55 |
| Nos. 590-591 (2) | 2.50 | .70 |
| Nos. 428-429 (2) | .75 | .60 |
| No. 458 (1) | 3.50 | 3.50 |
| Nos. 931-933 (3) | 10.00 | 2.00 |
| Nos. 1262-1263 (2) | 1.15 | .80 |
| Nos. 438-439 (2) | 1.65 | .50 |
| Nos. 1628-1629 (2) | 2.00 | .80 |
| Set total (34) Stamps | 81.10 | 23.85 |

### Europa, 1965

Leaves and "Fruit" CD8

### 1965

Belgium.................................636-637
Cyprus .................................262-264
Finland .................................437
France .................................1131-1132
Germany...............................934-935
Greece .................................833-834
Iceland .................................375-376
Ireland .................................204-205
Italy .....................................915-916
Luxembourg...........................432-433
Monaco.................................616-617
Netherlands ..........................438-439
Norway .................................475-476
Portugal ...............................958-960
Switzerland ...........................469
Turkey .................................1665-1666

| | | |
|---|---|---|
| Nos. 636-637 (2) | .50 | .50 |
| Nos. 262-264 (3) | 25.35 | 6.00 |
| No. 437 (1) | 1.25 | .55 |
| Nos. 1131-1132 (2) | .70 | .55 |
| Nos. 934-935 (2) | .50 | .50 |
| Nos. 833-834 (2) | 2.25 | 1.15 |
| Nos. 375-376 (2) | 2.50 | 1.75 |
| Nos. 204-205 (2) | 16.00 | 3.35 |
| Nos. 915-916 (2) | .50 | .50 |
| Nos. 432-433 (2) | .75 | .55 |
| Nos. 616-617 (2) | 3.25 | 1.65 |
| Nos. 438-439 (2) | .55 | .50 |
| Nos. 475-476 (2) | 2.40 | 1.90 |
| Nos. 958-960 (3) | 10.00 | 2.75 |
| No. 469 (1) | 1.15 | .50 |
| Nos. 1665-1666 (2) | 2.00 | 1.25 |
| Set total (32) Stamps | 69.65 | 23.95 |

### Europa, 1966

Symbolic Sailboat — CD9

### 1966, Sept.

Andorra, French .....................172
Belgium.................................675-676
Cyprus .................................275-277
France .................................1163-1164
Germany...............................963-964

Greece.................................862-863
Iceland................................384-385
Ireland................................216-217
Italy....................................942-943
Liechtenstein .............................415
Luxembourg.......................440-441
Monaco...............................639-640
Netherlands........................441-442
Norway...............................496-497
Portugal..............................980-982
Switzerland.........................477-478
Turkey.............................1718-1719

| | | |
|---|---:|---:|
| No. 172 (1) | 3.00 | 3.00 |
| Nos. 675-676 (2) | .80 | .50 |
| Nos. 275-277 (3) | 4.75 | 2.75 |
| Nos. 1163-1164 (2) | .55 | .50 |
| Nos. 963-964 (2) | .50 | .55 |
| Nos. 862-863 (2) | 2.10 | 1.05 |
| Nos. 384-385 (2) | 4.50 | 3.50 |
| Nos. 216-217 (2) | 6.75 | 2.00 |
| Nos. 942-943 (2) | .50 | .50 |
| No. 415 (1) | .40 | .35 |
| Nos. 440-441 (2) | .70 | .55 |
| Nos. 639-640 (2) | 2.00 | .65 |
| Nos. 441-442 (2) | .85 | .50 |
| Nos. 496-497 (2) | 2.35 | 2.15 |
| Nos. 980-982 (3) | 9.75 | 2.25 |
| Nos. 477-478 (2) | 1.40 | .60 |
| Nos. 1718-1719 (2) | 3.35 | 1.75 |
| Set total (34) Stamps | 44.25 | 23.15 |

### Europa, 1967

Cogwheels
CD10

### 1967

Andorra, French ......................174-175
Belgium...............................688-689
Cyprus................................297-299
France..............................1178-1179
Germany..............................969-970
Greece................................891-892
Iceland................................389-390
Ireland................................232-233
Italy....................................951-952
Liechtenstein .............................420
Luxembourg.......................449-450
Monaco...............................669-670
Netherlands........................444-447
Norway...............................504-505
Portugal..............................994-996
Spain...............................1465-1466
Switzerland...............................482
Turkey............................B120-B121

| | | |
|---|---:|---:|
| Nos. 174-175 (2) | 10.75 | 6.25 |
| Nos. 688-689 (2) | 1.05 | .55 |
| Nos. 297-299 (3) | 4.25 | 2.50 |
| Nos. 1178-1179 (2) | .55 | .50 |
| Nos. 969-970 (2) | .55 | .55 |
| Nos. 891-892 (2) | 3.05 | .85 |
| Nos. 389-390 (2) | 3.00 | 2.00 |
| Nos. 232-233 (2) | 5.90 | 2.30 |
| Nos. 951-952 (2) | .60 | .50 |
| No. 420 (1) | .45 | .40 |
| Nos. 449-450 (2) | 1.00 | .70 |
| Nos. 669-670 (2) | 2.75 | .70 |
| Nos. 444-447 (4) | 2.70 | 2.05 |
| Nos. 504-505 (2) | 1.00 | 1.80 |
| Nos. 994-996 (3) | 9.50 | 1.85 |
| Nos. 1465-1466 (2) | .50 | .50 |
| No. 482 (1) | .60 | .30 |
| Nos. B120-B121 (2) | 2.50 | 2.00 |
| Set total (38) Stamps | 51.70 | 26.30 |

### Europa, 1968

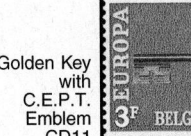

Golden Key with C.E.P.T. Emblem
CD11

### 1968

Andorra, French ......................182-183
Belgium...............................705-706
Cyprus................................314-316
France..............................1209-1210
Germany..............................983-984
Greece................................916-917
Iceland................................395-396
Ireland................................242-243
Italy....................................979-980

Liechtenstein .............................442
Luxembourg.......................466-467
Monaco...............................689-691
Netherlands........................452-453
Portugal............................1019-1021
San Marino................................687
Spain.......................................1526
Switzerland...............................488
Turkey.............................1775-1776

| | | |
|---|---:|---:|
| Nos. 182-183 (2) | 16.50 | 10.00 |
| Nos. 705-706 (2) | 1.25 | .50 |
| Nos. 314-316 (3) | 2.90 | 2.50 |
| Nos. 1209-1210 (2) | .85 | .55 |
| Nos. 983-984 (2) | .50 | .55 |
| Nos. 916-917 (2) | 3.10 | 1.45 |
| Nos. 395-396 (2) | 3.00 | 2.20 |
| Nos. 242-243 (2) | 3.30 | 2.25 |
| Nos. 979-980 (2) | .50 | .50 |
| No. 442 (1) | .45 | .40 |
| Nos. 466-467 (2) | .80 | .70 |
| Nos. 689-691 (3) | 5.40 | .95 |
| Nos. 452-453 (2) | 1.05 | .70 |
| Nos. 1019-1021 (3) | 9.75 | 2.10 |
| No. 687 (1) | .55 | .35 |
| No. 1526 (1) | .25 | .25 |
| No. 488 (1) | .40 | .25 |
| Nos. 1775-1776 (2) | 2.50 | 1.25 |
| Set total (35) Stamps | 53.05 | 27.45 |

### Europa, 1969

"EUROPA" and "CEPT"
CD12

Tenth anniversary of C.E.P.T.

### 1969

Andorra, French ......................188-189
Austria....................................837
Belgium...............................718-719
Cyprus................................326-328
Denmark...................................458
Finland.....................................483
France..............................1245-1246
Germany..............................996-997
Great Britain.............................585
Greece................................947-948
Iceland................................406-407
Ireland................................270-271
Italy.................................1000-1001
Liechtenstein .............................453
Luxembourg.......................475-476
Monaco...............................722-724
Netherlands........................475-476
Norway...............................533-534
Portugal............................1038-1040
San Marino........................701-702
Spain.......................................1567
Sweden..............................814-816
Switzerland........................500-501
Turkey..............................1799-1800
Vatican...............................470-472
Yugoslavia.......................1003-1004

| | | |
|---|---:|---:|
| Nos. 188-189 (2) | 18.50 | 12.00 |
| No. 837 (1) | .55 | .25 |
| Nos. 718-719 (2) | .75 | .50 |
| Nos. 326-328 (3) | 3.00 | 2.25 |
| No. 458 (1) | .75 | .75 |
| No. 483 (1) | 2.50 | .60 |
| Nos. 1245-1246 (2) | .55 | .50 |
| Nos. 996-997 (2) | .70 | .50 |
| No. 585 (1) | .25 | .25 |
| Nos. 947-948 (2) | 4.00 | 1.25 |
| Nos. 406-407 (2) | 4.20 | 2.40 |
| Nos. 270-271 (2) | 3.50 | 2.00 |
| Nos. 1000-1001 (2) | .50 | .50 |
| No. 453 (1) | .45 | .45 |
| Nos. 475-476 (2) | .95 | .50 |
| Nos. 722-724 (3) | 10.50 | 2.00 |
| Nos. 475-476 (2) | 1.35 | 1.00 |
| Nos. 533-534 (2) | 2.20 | 1.95 |
| Nos. 1038-1040 (3) | 17.75 | 2.40 |
| Nos. 701-702 (2) | .90 | .90 |
| No. 1567 (1) | .25 | .25 |
| Nos. 814-816 (3) | 4.00 | 2.85 |
| Nos. 500-501 (2) | 1.85 | 1.00 |
| Nos. 1799-1800 (2) | 2.50 | 1.65 |
| Nos. 470-472 (3) | .75 | .75 |
| Nos. 1003-1004 (2) | 4.00 | 4.00 |
| Set total (51) Stamps | 87.20 | 43.45 |

### Europa, 1970

Interwoven Threads
CD13

### 1970

Andorra, French ......................196-197
Belgium...............................741-742
Cyprus................................340-342
France..............................1271-1272
Germany..........................1018-1019
Greece.............................985, 987
Iceland................................420-421
Ireland................................279-281
Italy.................................1013-1014
Liechtenstein .............................470
Luxembourg.......................489-490
Monaco...............................768-770
Netherlands........................483-484
Portugal............................1060-1062
San Marino........................729-730
Spain.......................................1607
Switzerland........................515-516
Turkey..............................1848-1849
Yugoslavia.......................1024-1025

| | | |
|---|---:|---:|
| Nos. 196-197 (2) | 20.00 | 8.50 |
| Nos. 741-742 (2) | 1.10 | .55 |
| Nos. 340-342 (3) | 2.70 | 2.75 |
| Nos. 1271-1272 (2) | .65 | .50 |
| Nos. 1018-1019 (2) | .60 | .50 |
| Nos. 985,987 (2) | 6.35 | 1.60 |
| Nos. 420-421 (2) | 6.00 | 4.00 |
| Nos. 279-281 (3) | 7.50 | 2.50 |
| Nos. 1013-1014 (2) | .50 | .50 |
| No. 470 (1) | .45 | .45 |
| Nos. 489-490 (2) | .80 | .55 |
| Nos. 768-770 (3) | 6.35 | 2.10 |
| Nos. 483-484 (2) | 1.30 | 1.15 |
| Nos. 1060-1062 (3) | 9.75 | 2.35 |
| Nos. 729-730 (2) | .90 | .55 |
| No. 1607 (1) | .25 | .25 |
| Nos. 515-516 (2) | 1.85 | .70 |
| Nos. 1848-1849 (2) | 2.50 | 1.50 |
| Nos. 1024-1025 (2) | .80 | .80 |
| Set total (40) Stamps | 70.35 | 31.80 |

### Europa, 1971

"Fraternity, Cooperation, Common Effort"
CD14

### 1971

Andorra, French ......................205-206
Belgium...............................803-804
Cyprus................................365-367
Finland.....................................504
France.....................................1304
Germany..........................1064-1065
Greece.............................1029-1030
Iceland................................429-430
Ireland................................305-306
Italy.................................1038-1039
Liechtenstein .............................485
Luxembourg.......................500-501
Malta.................................425-427
Monaco...............................797-799
Netherlands........................488-489
Portugal............................1094-1096
San Marino........................749-750
Spain.............................1675-1676
Switzerland........................531-532
Turkey..............................1876-1877
Yugoslavia.......................1052-1053

| | | |
|---|---:|---:|
| Nos. 205-206 (2) | 20.00 | 7.75 |
| Nos. 803-804 (2) | 1.30 | .55 |
| Nos. 365-367 (3) | 2.60 | 3.25 |
| No. 504 (1) | 2.50 | .50 |
| No. 1304 (1) | .45 | .40 |
| Nos. 1064-1065 (2) | .60 | .50 |
| Nos. 1029-1030 (2) | 4.00 | 1.80 |
| Nos. 429-430 (2) | 5.00 | 3.75 |
| Nos. 305-306 (2) | 4.50 | 1.50 |
| Nos. 1038-1039 (2) | .65 | .50 |
| No. 485 (1) | .45 | .45 |
| Nos. 500-501 (2) | 1.00 | .65 |
| Nos. 425-427 (3) | .80 | .80 |
| Nos. 797-799 (3) | 15.00 | 2.80 |
| Nos. 488-489 (2) | 1.20 | .95 |
| Nos. 1094-1096 (3) | 9.75 | 1.75 |
| Nos. 749-750 (2) | .65 | .55 |
| Nos. 1675-1676 (2) | .75 | .55 |
| Nos. 531-532 (2) | 1.85 | .65 |
| Nos. 1876-1877 (2) | 2.50 | 1.25 |
| Nos. 1052-1053 (2) | .50 | .50 |
| Set total (43) Stamps | 76.05 | 31.40 |

### Europa, 1972

Sparkles, Symbolic of Communications
CD15

### 1972

Andorra, French ......................210-211
Andorra, Spanish .........................62
Belgium...............................825-826
Cyprus................................380-382
Finland................................512-513
France.....................................1341
Germany..........................1089-1090
Greece.............................1049-1050
Iceland................................439-440
Ireland................................316-317
Italy.................................1065-1066
Liechtenstein .............................504
Luxembourg.......................512-513
Malta.................................450-453
Monaco...............................831-832
Netherlands........................494-495
Portugal............................1141-1143
San Marino........................771-772
Spain.......................................1718
Switzerland........................544-545
Turkey..............................1907-1908
Yugoslavia.......................1100-1101

| | | |
|---|---:|---:|
| Nos. 210-211 (2) | 21.00 | 7.00 |
| No. 62 (1) | 60.00 | 60.00 |
| Nos. 825-826 (2) | .95 | .55 |
| Nos. 380-382 (3) | 5.95 | 4.25 |
| Nos. 512-513 (2) | 4.00 | 1.00 |
| No. 1341 (1) | .50 | .35 |
| Nos. 1089-1090 (2) | 1.10 | .50 |
| Nos. 1049-1050 (2) | 2.00 | 1.55 |
| Nos. 439-440 (2) | 2.90 | 2.65 |
| Nos. 316-317 (2) | 13.00 | 4.50 |
| Nos. 1065-1066 (2) | .55 | .50 |
| No. 504 (1) | .45 | .45 |
| Nos. 512-513 (2) | .95 | .65 |
| Nos. 450-453 (4) | 1.05 | 1.40 |
| Nos. 831-832 (2) | 5.00 | 1.40 |
| Nos. 494-495 (2) | 1.20 | .90 |
| Nos. 1141-1143 (3) | 9.75 | 1.50 |
| Nos. 771-772 (2) | .70 | .50 |
| No. 1718 (1) | .50 | .40 |
| Nos. 544-545 (2) | 1.65 | .60 |
| Nos. 1907-1908 (2) | 4.00 | 2.00 |
| Nos. 1100-1101 (2) | 1.20 | 1.20 |
| Set total (44) Stamps | 138.40 | 93.85 |

### Europa, 1973

Post Horn and Arrows
CD16

### 1973

Andorra, French ......................219-220
Andorra, Spanish ..........................76
Belgium...............................839-840
Cyprus................................396-398
Finland.....................................526
France.....................................1367
Germany..........................1114-1115
Greece.............................1090-1092
Iceland................................447-448
Ireland................................329-330
Italy.................................1108-1109
Liechtenstein ........................528-529
Luxembourg.......................523-524
Malta.................................469-471
Monaco...............................866-867
Netherlands........................504-505
Norway...............................604-605
Portugal............................1170-1172
San Marino........................802-803
Spain.......................................1753
Switzerland........................580-581
Turkey..............................1935-1936
Yugoslavia.......................1138-1139

| | | |
|---|---:|---:|
| Nos. 219-220 (2) | 20.00 | 11.00 |
| No. 76 (1) | 1.25 | .85 |
| Nos. 839-840 (2) | 1.00 | .65 |
| Nos. 396-398 (3) | 4.25 | 3.85 |
| No. 526 (1) | 1.25 | .55 |
| No. 1367 (1) | 1.25 | .75 |
| Nos. 1114-1115 (2) | .85 | .50 |
| Nos. 1090-1092 (3) | 2.10 | 1.40 |
| Nos. 447-448 (2) | 6.65 | 3.35 |

| | | |
|---|---|---|
| *Nos. 329-330 (2)* | 5.25 | 2.00 |
| *Nos. 1108-1109 (2)* | .50 | .50 |
| *Nos. 528-529 (2)* | .60 | .60 |
| *Nos. 523-524 (2)* | .90 | .75 |
| *Nos. 469-471 (3)* | .90 | 1.20 |
| *Nos. 866-867 (2)* | 15.00 | 2.40 |
| *Nos. 504-505 (2)* | 1.20 | .95 |
| *Nos. 604-605 (2)* | 4.00 | 1.80 |
| *Nos. 1170-1172 (3)* | 13.00 | 2.15 |
| *Nos. 802-803 (2)* | 1.00 | .60 |
| *No. 1753 (1)* | .35 | .25 |
| *Nos. 580-581 (2)* | 1.55 | .60 |
| *Nos. 1935-1936 (2)* | 4.15 | 2.25 |
| *Nos. 1138-1139 (2)* | 1.15 | 1.10 |
| *Set total (46) Stamps* | 88.15 | 40.05 |

### Europa, 2000

CD17

## 2000

Albania...................................2621-2622
Andorra, French ............................522
Andorra, Spanish .........................262
Armenia...............................610-611
Austria .........................................1814
Azerbaijan.............................698-699
Belarus.........................................350
Belgium.......................................1818
Bosnia & Herzegovina (Moslem) ....358
Bosnia & Herzegovina (Serb) ........111-112
Croatia....................................428-429
Cyprus..........................................959
Czech Republic ...........................3120
Denmark......................................1189
Estonia.........................................394
Faroe Islands................................376
Finland........................................1129
Aland Islands................................166
France.........................................2771
Georgia...................................228-229
Germany.................................2086-2087
Gibraltar..................................837-840
Great Britain (Jersey)............935-936
Great Britain (Isle of Man)...........883
Greece........................................1959
Greenland.....................................363
Hungary..................................3699-3700
Iceland.........................................910
Ireland.....................................1230-1231
Italy.............................................2349
Latvia...........................................504
Liechtenstein..............................1178
Lithuania......................................668
Luxembourg................................1035
Macedonia....................................187
Malta......................................1011-1012
Moldova.......................................355
Monaco...................................2161-2162
Poland.........................................3519
Portugal.......................................2358
Portugal (Azores) .........................455
Portugal (Madeira)........................208
Romania......................................4370
Russia.........................................6589
San Marino..................................1480
Slovakia.......................................355
Slovenia.......................................424
Spain...........................................3036
Sweden........................................2394
Switzerland..................................1074
Turkey .........................................2762
Turkish Rep. of Northern Cyprus....500
Ukraine.........................................379
Vatican City .................................1152

| | | |
|---|---|---|
| *Nos. 2621-2622 (2)* | 9.50 | 9.50 |
| *No. 522 (1)* | 2.00 | 1.00 |
| *No. 262 (1)* | 1.75 | .80 |
| *Nos. 610-611 (2)* | 4.75 | 4.75 |
| *No. 1814 (1)* | 1.25 | 1.25 |
| *Nos. 698-699 (2)* | 6.00 | 6.00 |
| *No. 350 (1)* | 1.75 | 1.75 |
| *No. 1818 (1)* | 1.40 | .60 |
| *No. 358 (1)* | 4.75 | 4.75 |
| *Nos. 111-112 (2)* | 110.00 | 110.00 |
| *Nos. 428-429 (2)* | 6.25 | 6.25 |
| *No. 959 (1)* | 2.10 | 1.40 |
| *No. 3120 (1)* | 1.20 | .40 |
| *No. 1189 (1)* | 3.50 | 2.25 |
| *No. 394 (1)* | 1.25 | 1.25 |
| *No. 376 (1)* | 2.40 | 2.40 |
| *No. 1129 (1)* | 2.00 | .40 |
| *No. 166 (1)* | 1.10 | 1.20 |
| *No. 2771 (1)* | 1.25 | .40 |
| *Nos. 228-229 (2)* | 9.00 | 9.00 |
| *Nos. 2086-2087 (2)* | 4.35 | 2.10 |
| *Nos. 837-840 (4)* | 5.50 | 5.30 |

| | | |
|---|---|---|
| *Nos. 935-936 (2)* | 2.40 | 2.40 |
| *No. 883 (1)* | 1.75 | 1.75 |
| *No. 363 (1)* | 1.90 | 1.90 |
| *Nos. 3699-3700 (2)* | 6.50 | 2.50 |
| *No. 910 (1)* | 1.60 | 1.60 |
| *Nos. 1230-1231 (2)* | 4.35 | 4.35 |
| *No. 2349 (1)* | 1.50 | .40 |
| *No. 504 (1)* | 5.00 | 2.40 |
| *No. 1178 (1)* | 2.25 | 1.75 |
| *No. 668 (1)* | 1.50 | 1.50 |
| *No. 1035 (1)* | 1.40 | .85 |
| *No. 187 (1)* | 3.00 | 3.00 |
| *Nos. 1011-1012 (2)* | 4.35 | 4.35 |
| *No. 355 (1)* | 3.50 | 3.50 |
| *Nos. 2161-2162 (2)* | 2.80 | 1.40 |
| *No. 3519 (1)* | 1.25 | .75 |
| *No. 2358 (1)* | 1.25 | .65 |
| *No. 455 (1)* | 1.25 | .50 |
| *No. 208 (1)* | 1.25 | .50 |
| *No. 4370 (1)* | 2.50 | 1.25 |
| *No. 6589 (1)* | 4.00 | .85 |
| *No. 1480 (1)* | 1.00 | 1.00 |
| *No. 355 (1)* | 1.60 | .80 |
| *No. 424 (1)* | 3.25 | 3.25 |
| *No. 3036 (1)* | 1.00 | .40 |
| *No. 2394 (1)* | 3.00 | 1.50 |
| *No. 1074 (1)* | 2.10 | 1.05 |
| *No. 2762 (1)* | 2.75 | 2.50 |
| *No. 500 (1)* | 2.50 | 2.50 |
| *No. 379 (1)* | 4.50 | 3.00 |
| *No. 1152 (1)* | 1.75 | 1.75 |
| *Set total (68) Stamps* | 261.80 | 228.35 |

The Gibraltar stamps are similar to the stamp illustrated, but none have the design shown above. All other sets listed above include at least one stamp with the design shown, but some include stamps with entirely different designs. Bulgaria Nos. 4131-4132, Guernsey Nos. 802-803 and Yugoslavia Nos. 2485-2486 are Europa stamps with completely different designs.

### PORTUGAL & COLONIES
### Vasco da Gama

Fleet Departing CD20

Fleet Arriving at Calicut — CD21

Embarking at Rastello CD22 | Muse of History CD23

San Gabriel, da Gama and Camoens CD24 | Archangel Gabriel, the Patron Saint CD25

Flagship San Gabriel — CD26

Vasco da Gama — CD27

Fourth centenary of Vasco da Gama's discovery of the route to India.

## 1898

Azores .......................................93-100
Macao..........................................67-74
Madeira.......................................37-44
Portugal ..................................147-154
Port. Africa ......................................1-8
Port. Congo ...............................75-98
Port. India.............................189-196
St. Thomas & Prince Islands ...170-193
Timor........................................45-52

| | | |
|---|---|---|
| *Nos. 93-100 (8)* | 113.50 | 73.50 |
| *Nos. 67-74 (8)* | 250.25 | 170.25 |
| *Nos. 37-44 (8)* | 60.55 | 37.25 |
| *Nos. 147-154 (8)* | 155.00 | 50.25 |
| *Nos. 1-8 (8)* | 44.00 | 29.25 |
| *Nos. 75-98 (24)* | 78.50 | 64.65 |
| *Nos. 189-196 (8)* | 25.25 | 15.50 |
| *Nos. 170-193 (24)* | 56.30 | 43.00 |
| *Nos. 45-52 (8)* | 33.50 | 23.25 |
| *Set total (104) Stamps* | 816.85 | 506.90 |

### Pombal
### POSTAL TAX
### POSTAL TAX DUES

Marquis de Pombal — CD28 | Planning Reconstruction of Lisbon, 1755 — CD29

Pombal Monument, Lisbon — CD30

Sebastiao Jose de Carvalho e Mello, Marquis de Pombal (1699-1782), statesman, rebuilt Lisbon after earthquake of 1755. Tax was for the erection of Pombal monument. Obligatory on all mail on certain days throughout the year. Postal Tax Dues are inscribed "Multa."

## 1925

Angola ............. RA1-RA3, RAJ1-RAJ3
Azores ........... RA9-RA11, RAJ2-RAJ4
Cape Verde ...... RA1-RA3, RAJ1-RAJ3
Macao.............. RA1-RA3, RAJ1-RAJ3
Madeira............ RA1-RA3, RAJ1-RAJ3
Mozambique..... RA1-RA3, RAJ1-RAJ3
Nyassa ............. RA1-RA3, RAJ1-RAJ3
Portugal ........ RA11-RA13, RAJ2-RAJ4
Port. Guinea ..... RA1-RA3, RAJ1-RAJ3
Port. India......... RA1-RA3, RAJ1-RAJ3
St. Thomas & Prince
Islands ........... RA1-RA3, RAJ1-RAJ3
Timor ............... RA1-RA3, RAJ1-RAJ3

| | | |
|---|---|---|
| *Nos. RA1-RA3,RAJ1-RAJ3 (6)* | 6.60 | 6.60 |
| *Nos. RA9-RA11,RAJ2-RAJ4 (6)* | 6.60 | 6.60 |
| *Nos. RA1-RA3,RAJ1-RAJ3 (6)* | 7.80 | 7.65 |
| *Nos. RA1-RA3,RAJ1-RAJ3 (6)* | 36.50 | 17.25 |
| *Nos. RA1-RA3,RAJ1-RAJ3 (6)* | 7.95 | 14.70 |
| *Nos. RA1-RA3,RAJ1-RAJ3 (6)* | 3.75 | 3.60 |
| *Nos. RA1-RA3,RAJ1-RAJ3 (6)* | 85.50 | 76.50 |
| *Nos. RA11-RA13,RAJ2-RAJ4 (6)* | 5.95 | 5.20 |
| *Nos. RA1-RA3,RAJ1-RAJ3 (6)* | 5.10 | 4.65 |
| *Nos. RA1-RA3,RAJ1-RAJ3 (6)* | 3.45 | 3.45 |
| *Nos. RA1-RA3,RAJ1-RAJ3 (6)* | 4.50 | 4.50 |
| *Nos. RA1-RA3,RAJ1-RAJ3 (6)* | 3.90 | 3.45 |
| *Set total (72) Stamps* | 177.60 | 154.15 |

Vasco da Gama CD34 | Mousinho de Albuquerque CD35

Dam CD36 | Prince Henry the Navigator CD37

Affonso de Albuquerque CD38 | Plane over Globe CD39

## 1938-39

Angola ........................274-291, C1-C9
Cape Verde ................234-251, C1-C9
Macao.....................289-305, C7-C15
Mozambique...............270-287, C1-C9
Port. Guinea ...............233-250. C1-C9
Port. India..................439-453, C1-C8
St. Thomas & Prince
Islands ... 302-319, 323-340, C1-C18
Timor ........................223-239, C1-C9

| | | |
|---|---|---|
| *Nos. 274-291,C1-C9 (27)* | 129.40 | 22.85 |
| *Nos. 234-251,C1-C9 (27)* | 122.40 | 38.30 |
| *Nos. 289-305,C7-C15 (26)* | 889.60 | 338.55 |
| *Nos. 270-287,C1-C9 (27)* | 95.71 | 15.95 |
| *Nos. 233-250,C1-C9 (27)* | 130.20 | 49.15 |
| *Nos. 439-453,C1-C8 (23)* | 82.75 | 30.95 |
| *Nos. 302-319,323-340,C1-C18 (54)* | 467.70 | 244.80 |
| *Nos. 223-239,C1-C9 (26)* | 213.85 | 104.90 |
| *Set total (237) Stamps* | 2,132. | 845.45 |

### Lady of Fatima

Our Lady of the Rosary, Fatima, Portugal — CD40

## 1948-49

Angola ..........................................315-318
Cape Verde ......................................266
Macao................................................336
Mozambique.................................325-328
Port. Guinea ......................................271
Port. India..........................................480
St. Thomas & Prince Islands .........351
Timor ................................................254

| | | |
|---|---|---|
| *Nos. 315-318 (4)* | 68.00 | 17.25 |
| *No. 266 (1)* | 8.50 | 9.00 |
| *No. 336 (1)* | 90.00 | 30.00 |
| *Nos. 325-328 (4)* | 73.25 | 27.50 |
| *No. 271 (1)* | 6.50 | 3.50 |
| *No. 480 (1)* | 4.50 | 3.00 |
| *No. 351 (1)* | 8.50 | 7.00 |
| *No. 254 (1)* | 6.00 | 12.50 |
| *Set total (14) Stamps* | 265.25 | 109.75 |

A souvenir sheet of 9 stamps was issued in 1951 to mark the extension of the 1950 Holy Year. The sheet contains: Angola No. 316, Cape Verde No. 266, Macao No. 336, Mozambique No. 325, Portuguese Guinea No. 271, Portuguese India Nos. 480, 485, St. Thomas & Prince Islands No. 351, Timor No. 254. The sheet also contains a portrait of Pope Pius XII and is inscribed "Encerramento do

Ano Santo, Fatima 1951." It was sold for 11 escudos.

## Holy Year

Church Bells and Dove
CD41

Angel Holding Candelabra
CD42

Holy Year, 1950.

### 1950-51

| | | |
|---|---|---|
| Angola | | 331-332 |
| Cape Verde | | 268-269 |
| Macao | | 339-340 |
| Mozambique | | 330-331 |
| Port. Guinea | | 273-274 |
| Port. India | | 490-491, 496-503 |
| St. Thomas & Prince Islands | | 353-354 |
| Timor | | 258-259 |

| | | |
|---|---|---|
| Nos. 331-332 (2) | 7.60 | 1.35 |
| Nos. 268-269 (2) | 7.35 | 4.75 |
| Nos. 339-340 (2) | 110.00 | 34.00 |
| Nos. 330-331 (2) | 3.00 | 1.60 |
| Nos. 273-274 (2) | 11.25 | 3.50 |
| Nos. 490-491,496-503 (10) | 10.40 | 4.95 |
| Nos. 353-354 (2) | 7.75 | 4.90 |
| Nos. 258-259 (2) | 8.75 | 5.00 |
| Set total (24) Stamps | 166.10 | 60.05 |

A souvenir sheet of 8 stamps was issued in 1951 to mark the extension of the Holy Year. The sheet contains: Angola No. 331, Cape Verde No. 269, Macao No. 340, Mozambique No. 331, Portuguese Guinea No. 275, Portuguese India No. 490, St. Thomas & Prince Islands No. 354, Timor No. 258, some with colors changed. The sheet contains doves and is inscribed 'Encerramento do Ano Santo, Fatima 1951.' It was sold for 17 escudos.

## Holy Year Conclusion

Our Lady of Fatima — CD43

Conclusion of Holy Year. Sheets contain alternate vertical rows of stamps and labels bearing quotation from Pope Pius XII, different for each colony.

### 1951

| | | |
|---|---|---|
| Angola | | 357 |
| Cape Verde | | 270 |
| Macao | | 352 |
| Mozambique | | 356 |
| Port. Guinea | | 275 |
| Port. India | | 506 |
| St. Thomas & Prince Islands | | 355 |
| Timor | | 270 |

| | | |
|---|---|---|
| No. 357 (1) | 5.25 | 1.50 |
| No. 270 (1) | 1.75 | 1.25 |
| No. 352 (1) | 110.00 | 23.00 |
| No. 356 (1) | 3.25 | 1.75 |
| No. 275 (1) | 1.75 | .90 |
| No. 506 (1) | 2.50 | 1.00 |
| No. 355 (1) | 3.00 | 2.00 |
| No. 270 (1) | 3.75 | 2.75 |
| Set total (8) Stamps | 131.25 | 34.15 |

## Medical Congress

CD44

First National Congress of Tropical Medicine, Lisbon, 1952. Each stamp has a different design.

### 1952

| | | |
|---|---|---|
| Angola | | 358 |
| Cape Verde | | 287 |
| Macao | | 364 |

| | | |
|---|---|---|
| Mozambique | | 359 |
| Port. Guinea | | 276 |
| Port. India | | 516 |
| St. Thomas & Prince Islands | | 356 |
| Timor | | 271 |

| | | |
|---|---|---|
| No. 358 (1) | 1.50 | .50 |
| No. 287 (1) | .95 | .75 |
| No. 364 (1) | 20.00 | 7.00 |
| No. 359 (1) | 1.90 | .90 |
| No. 276 (1) | 1.00 | .45 |
| No. 516 (1) | 5.50 | 2.00 |
| No. 356 (1) | .35 | .30 |
| No. 271 (1) | 2.00 | 1.60 |
| Set total (8) Stamps | 33.20 | 13.50 |

## Postage Due Stamps

CD45

### 1952

| | | |
|---|---|---|
| Angola | | J37-J42 |
| Cape Verde | | J31-J36 |
| Macao | | J53-J58 |
| Mozambique | | J51-J56 |
| Port. Guinea | | J40-J45 |
| Port. India | | J47-J52 |
| St. Thomas & Prince Islands | | J52-J57 |
| Timor | | J31-J36 |

| | | |
|---|---|---|
| Nos. J37-J42 (6) | 4.30 | 2.55 |
| Nos. J31-J36 (6) | 2.80 | 2.30 |
| Nos. J53-J58 (6) | 27.80 | 12.05 |
| Nos. J51-J56 (6) | 2.40 | 1.95 |
| Nos. J40-J45 (6) | 2.55 | 2.55 |
| Nos. J47-J52 (6) | 6.10 | 6.10 |
| Nos. J52-J57 (6) | 3.85 | 3.85 |
| Nos. J31-J36 (6) | 4.00 | 2.35 |
| Set total (48) Stamps | 53.80 | 33.70 |

## Sao Paulo

Father Manuel da Nobrega and View of Sao Paulo — CD46

Founding of Sao Paulo, Brazil, 400th anniv.

### 1954

| | | |
|---|---|---|
| Angola | | 385 |
| Cape Verde | | 297 |
| Macao | | 382 |
| Mozambique | | 395 |
| Port. Guinea | | 291 |
| Port. India | | 530 |
| St. Thomas & Prince Islands | | 369 |
| Timor | | 279 |

| | | |
|---|---|---|
| No. 385 (1) | .80 | .50 |
| No. 297 (1) | .95 | .80 |
| No. 382 (1) | 30.00 | 6.00 |
| No. 395 (1) | .75 | .30 |
| No. 291 (1) | .35 | .25 |
| No. 530 (1) | .80 | .40 |
| No. 369 (1) | .70 | .50 |
| No. 279 (1) | 2.00 | 1.40 |
| Set total (8) Stamps | 36.35 | 10.15 |

## Tropical Medicine Congress

CD47

Sixth International Congress for Tropical Medicine and Malaria, Lisbon, Sept. 1958. Each stamp shows a different plant.

### 1958

| | | |
|---|---|---|
| Angola | | 409 |
| Cape Verde | | 303 |
| Macao | | 392 |
| Mozambique | | 404 |
| Port. Guinea | | 295 |
| Port. India | | 569 |
| St. Thomas & Prince Islands | | 371 |

| | | |
|---|---|---|
| Timor | | 289 |

| | | |
|---|---|---|
| No. 409 (1) | 3.50 | 1.10 |
| No. 303 (1) | 6.75 | 3.25 |
| No. 392 (1) | 13.00 | 6.00 |
| No. 404 (1) | 3.50 | 1.50 |
| No. 295 (1) | 3.00 | 1.10 |
| No. 569 (1) | 1.75 | .75 |
| No. 371 (1) | 2.75 | 2.00 |
| No. 289 (1) | 5.50 | 4.25 |
| Set total (8) Stamps | 39.75 | 19.95 |

## Sports

CD48

Each stamp shows a different sport.

### 1962

| | | |
|---|---|---|
| Angola | | 433-438 |
| Cape Verde | | 320-325 |
| Macao | | 394-399 |
| Mozambique | | 424-429 |
| Port. Guinea | | 299-304 |
| St. Thomas & Prince Islands | | 374-379 |
| Timor | | 313-318 |

| | | |
|---|---|---|
| Nos. 433-438 (6) | 5.50 | 3.20 |
| Nos. 320-325 (6) | 16.05 | 7.40 |
| Nos. 394-399 (6) | 129.85 | 28.95 |
| Nos. 424-429 (6) | 6.55 | 2.45 |
| Nos. 299-304 (6) | 6.00 | 3.00 |
| Nos. 374-379 (6) | 6.75 | 3.20 |
| Nos. 313-318 (6) | 11.65 | 5.90 |
| Set total (42) Stamps | 182.35 | 54.10 |

## Anti-Malaria

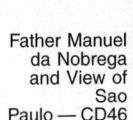

Anopheles Funestus and Malaria Eradication Symbol — CD49

World Health Organization drive to eradicate malaria.

### 1962

| | | |
|---|---|---|
| Angola | | 439 |
| Cape Verde | | 326 |
| Macao | | 400 |
| Mozambique | | 430 |
| Port. Guinea | | 305 |
| St. Thomas & Prince Islands | | 380 |
| Timor | | 319 |

| | | |
|---|---|---|
| No. 439 (1) | 1.75 | .90 |
| No. 326 (1) | 1.90 | 1.60 |
| No. 400 (1) | 12.00 | 4.00 |
| No. 430 (1) | 2.00 | .50 |
| No. 305 (1) | 1.25 | .45 |
| No. 380 (1) | 2.25 | 1.25 |
| No. 319 (1) | 2.25 | 1.40 |
| Set total (7) Stamps | 23.40 | 10.10 |

## Airline Anniversary

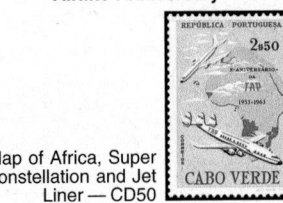

Map of Africa, Super Constellation and Jet Liner — CD50

Tenth anniversary of Transportes Aereos Portugueses (TAP).

### 1963

| | | |
|---|---|---|
| Angola | | 490 |
| Cape Verde | | 327 |
| Mozambique | | 434 |
| Port. Guinea | | 318 |
| St. Thomas & Prince Islands | | 381 |

| | | |
|---|---|---|
| No. 490 (1) | 1.00 | .35 |
| No. 327 (1) | 1.50 | 1.10 |
| No. 434 (1) | .55 | .25 |

| | | |
|---|---|---|
| No. 318 (1) | .65 | .35 |
| No. 381 (1) | .80 | .50 |
| Set total (5) Stamps | 4.50 | 2.55 |

## National Overseas Bank

Antonio Teixeira de Sousa — CD51

Centenary of the National Overseas Bank of Portugal.

### 1964, May 16

| | | |
|---|---|---|
| Angola | | 509 |
| Cape Verde | | 328 |
| Port. Guinea | | 319 |
| St. Thomas & Prince Islands | | 382 |
| Timor | | 320 |

| | | |
|---|---|---|
| No. 509 (1) | .90 | .30 |
| No. 328 (1) | 1.50 | 1.30 |
| No. 319 (1) | .65 | .40 |
| No. 382 (1) | .70 | .50 |
| No. 320 (1) | 1.50 | 1.30 |
| Set total (5) Stamps | 5.25 | 3.80 |

## ITU

ITU Emblem and the Archangel Gabriel — CD52

International Communications Union, Cent.

### 1965, May 17

| | | |
|---|---|---|
| Angola | | 511 |
| Cape Verde | | 329 |
| Macao | | 402 |
| Mozambique | | 464 |
| Port. Guinea | | 320 |
| St. Thomas & Prince Islands | | 383 |
| Timor | | 321 |

| | | |
|---|---|---|
| No. 511 (1) | 1.25 | .65 |
| No. 329 (1) | 2.90 | 2.25 |
| No. 402 (1) | 9.00 | 3.00 |
| No. 464 (1) | .65 | .25 |
| No. 320 (1) | 1.90 | .75 |
| No. 383 (1) | 2.00 | 1.00 |
| No. 321 (1) | 2.20 | 1.40 |
| Set total (7) Stamps | 19.90 | 9.30 |

## National Revolution

CD53

40th anniv. of the National Revolution. Different buildings on each stamp.

### 1966, May 28

| | | |
|---|---|---|
| Angola | | 525 |
| Cape Verde | | 338 |
| Macao | | 403 |
| Mozambique | | 465 |
| Port. Guinea | | 329 |
| St. Thomas & Prince Islands | | 392 |
| Timor | | 322 |

| | | |
|---|---|---|
| No. 525 (1) | .50 | .25 |
| No. 338 (1) | .85 | .75 |
| No. 403 (1) | 9.00 | 3.75 |
| No. 465 (1) | .65 | .30 |
| No. 329 (1) | .55 | .35 |
| No. 392 (1) | .80 | .50 |
| No. 322 (1) | 2.40 | 1.40 |
| Set total (7) Stamps | 14.75 | 7.30 |

## Navy Club

CD54

Centenary of Portugal's Navy Club. Each stamp has a different design.

**1967, Jan. 31**

| | | |
|---|---|---|
| Angola | | 527-528 |
| Cape Verde | | 339-340 |
| Macao | | 412-413 |
| Mozambique | | 478-479 |
| Port. Guinea | | 330-331 |
| St. Thomas & Prince Islands | | 393-394 |
| Timor | | 323-324 |

| | | |
|---|---|---|
| Nos. 527-528 (2) | 1.75 | .75 |
| Nos. 339-340 (2) | 2.70 | 2.30 |
| Nos. 412-413 (2) | 18.00 | 4.70 |
| Nos. 478-479 (2) | 1.75 | .65 |
| Nos. 330-331 (2) | 1.20 | .90 |
| Nos. 393-394 (2) | 3.30 | 1.30 |
| Nos. 323-324 (2) | 4.25 | 2.40 |
| Set total (14) Stamps | 32.95 | 13.00 |

### Admiral Coutinho

CD55

Centenary of the birth of Admiral Carlos Viegas Gago Coutinho (1869-1959), explorer and aviation pioneer. Each stamp has a different design.

**1969, Feb. 17**

| | | |
|---|---|---|
| Angola | | 547 |
| Cape Verde | | 355 |
| Macao | | 417 |
| Mozambique | | 484 |
| Port. Guinea | | 335 |
| St. Thomas & Prince Islands | | 397 |
| Timor | | 335 |

| | | |
|---|---|---|
| No. 547 (1) | .85 | .35 |
| No. 355 (1) | .60 | .25 |
| No. 417 (1) | 7.50 | 2.25 |
| No. 484 (1) | .30 | .25 |
| No. 335 (1) | .35 | .25 |
| No. 397 (1) | .60 | .35 |
| No. 335 (1) | 2.50 | 1.40 |
| Set total (7) Stamps | 12.70 | 5.10 |

### Administration Reform

Luiz Augusto Rebello da Silva — CD56

Centenary of the administration reforms of the overseas territories.

**1969, Sept. 25**

| | | |
|---|---|---|
| Angola | | 549 |
| Cape Verde | | 357 |
| Macao | | 419 |
| Mozambique | | 491 |
| Port. Guinea | | 337 |
| St. Thomas & Prince Islands | | 399 |
| Timor | | 338 |

| | | |
|---|---|---|
| No. 549 (1) | .35 | .25 |
| No. 357 (1) | .65 | .40 |
| No. 419 (1) | 12.50 | 2.00 |
| No. 491 (1) | .30 | .25 |
| No. 337 (1) | .25 | .25 |
| No. 399 (1) | .45 | .45 |
| No. 338 (1) | 1.40 | .70 |
| Set total (7) Stamps | 15.90 | 4.30 |

### Marshal Carmona

CD57

Birth centenary of Marshal Antonio Oscar Carmona de Fragoso (1869-1951), President of Portugal. Each stamp has a different design.

**1970, Nov. 15**

| | | |
|---|---|---|
| Angola | | 563 |
| Cape Verde | | 359 |
| Macao | | 422 |
| Mozambique | | 493 |
| Port. Guinea | | 340 |
| St. Thomas & Prince Islands | | 403 |
| Timor | | 341 |

| | | |
|---|---|---|
| No. 563 (1) | .45 | .25 |
| No. 359 (1) | .70 | .50 |
| No. 422 (1) | 5.00 | 1.75 |
| No. 493 (1) | .40 | .25 |
| No. 340 (1) | .35 | .25 |
| No. 403 (1) | .75 | .40 |
| No. 341 (1) | 1.00 | .50 |
| Set total (7) Stamps | 8.65 | 3.90 |

### Olympic Games

CD59

20th Olympic Games, Munich, Aug. 26-Sept. 11. Each stamp shows a different sport.

**1972, June 20**

| | | |
|---|---|---|
| Angola | | 569 |
| Cape Verde | | 361 |
| Macao | | 426 |
| Mozambique | | 504 |
| Port. Guinea | | 342 |
| St. Thomas & Prince Islands | | 408 |
| Timor | | 343 |

| | | |
|---|---|---|
| No. 569 (1) | .65 | .25 |
| No. 361 (1) | .85 | .40 |
| No. 426 (1) | 2.50 | 1.50 |
| No. 504 (1) | .30 | .25 |
| No. 342 (1) | .45 | .25 |
| No. 408 (1) | .45 | .25 |
| No. 343 (1) | 1.60 | .80 |
| Set total (7) Stamps | 6.80 | 3.70 |

### Lisbon-Rio de Janeiro Flight

CD60

50th anniversary of the Lisbon to Rio de Janeiro flight by Arturo de Sacadura and Coutinho, March 30-June 5, 1922. Each stamp shows a different stage of the flight.

**1972, Sept. 20**

| | | |
|---|---|---|
| Angola | | 570 |
| Cape Verde | | 362 |
| Macao | | 427 |
| Mozambique | | 505 |
| Port. Guinea | | 343 |
| St. Thomas & Prince Islands | | 409 |
| Timor | | 344 |

| | | |
|---|---|---|
| No. 570 (1) | .35 | .25 |
| No. 362 (1) | .85 | .40 |
| No. 427 (1) | 40.00 | 12.00 |
| No. 505 (1) | .30 | .25 |
| No. 343 (1) | .25 | .25 |
| No. 409 (1) | .50 | .25 |
| No. 344 (1) | 1.25 | .90 |
| Set total (7) Stamps | 43.50 | 14.30 |

### WMO Centenary

WMO Emblem — CD61

Centenary of international meterological cooperation.

**1973, Dec. 15**

| | | |
|---|---|---|
| Angola | | 571 |
| Cape Verde | | 363 |
| Macao | | 429 |
| Mozambique | | 509 |
| Port. Guinea | | 344 |
| St. Thomas & Prince Islands | | 410 |
| Timor | | 345 |

| | | |
|---|---|---|
| No. 571 (1) | .45 | .25 |
| No. 363 (1) | .85 | .40 |
| No. 429 (1) | 15.00 | 2.50 |
| No. 509 (1) | .40 | .25 |
| No. 344 (1) | .45 | .35 |
| No. 410 (1) | .60 | .50 |
| No. 345 (1) | 3.75 | 2.75 |
| Set total (7) Stamps | 21.50 | 7.00 |

### FRENCH COMMUNITY

Upper Volta can be found under
Burkina Faso in Vol. 1
Madagascar can be found under
Malagasy in Vol. 3

### Colonial Exposition

People of French Empire
CD70

Women's Heads
CD71

France Showing Way to Civilization
CD72

"Colonial Commerce"
CD73

International Colonial Exposition, Paris.

**1931**

| | | |
|---|---|---|
| Cameroun | | 213-216 |
| Chad | | 60-63 |
| Dahomey | | 97-100 |
| Fr. Guiana | | 152-155 |
| Fr. Guinea | | 116-119 |
| Fr. India | | 100-103 |
| Fr. Polynesia | | 76-79 |
| Fr. Sudan | | 102-105 |
| Gabon | | 120-123 |
| Guadeloupe | | 138-141 |
| Indo-China | | 140-142 |
| Ivory Coast | | 92-95 |
| Madagascar | | 169-172 |
| Martinique | | 129-132 |
| Mauritania | | 65-68 |
| Middle Congo | | 61-64 |
| New Caledonia | | 176-179 |
| Niger | | 73-76 |
| Reunion | | 122-125 |
| St. Pierre & Miquelon | | 132-135 |
| Senegal | | 138-141 |
| Somali Coast | | 135-138 |
| Togo | | 254-257 |
| Ubangi-Shari | | 82-85 |
| Upper Volta | | 66-69 |
| Wallis & Futuna Isls. | | 85-88 |

| | | |
|---|---|---|
| Nos. 213-216 (4) | 23.00 | 18.25 |
| Nos. 60-63 (4) | 22.00 | 22.00 |
| Nos. 97-100 (4) | 26.00 | 26.00 |
| Nos. 152-155 (4) | 22.00 | 22.00 |
| Nos. 116-119 (4) | 19.75 | 19.75 |
| Nos. 100-103 (4) | 18.00 | 18.00 |
| Nos. 76-79 (4) | 30.00 | 30.00 |
| Nos. 102-105 (4) | 19.00 | 19.00 |
| Nos. 120-123 (4) | 17.50 | 17.50 |
| Nos. 138-141 (4) | 19.00 | 19.00 |
| Nos. 140-142 (3) | 12.00 | 11.50 |
| Nos. 92-95 (4) | 22.50 | 22.50 |
| Nos. 169-172 (4) | 9.25 | 6.50 |
| Nos. 129-132 (4) | 21.00 | 21.00 |
| Nos. 65-68 (4) | 22.00 | 22.00 |
| Nos. 61-64 (4) | 20.00 | 18.50 |
| Nos. 176-179 (4) | 24.00 | 24.00 |
| Nos. 73-76 (4) | 20.50 | 20.50 |
| Nos. 122-125 (4) | 22.00 | 22.00 |
| Nos. 132-135 (4) | 24.00 | 24.00 |
| Nos. 138-141 (4) | 20.00 | 20.00 |
| Nos. 135-138 (4) | 22.00 | 22.00 |
| Nos. 254-257 (4) | 22.00 | 22.00 |

| | | |
|---|---|---|
| Nos. 82-85 (4) | 21.00 | 21.00 |
| Nos. 66-69 (4) | 19.00 | 19.00 |
| Nos. 85-88 (4) | 31.00 | 35.00 |
| Set total (103) Stamps | 548.50 | 543.00 |

### Paris International Exposition
### Colonial Arts Exposition

"Colonial Resources"
CD74       CD77

Overseas Commerce
CD75

Exposition Building and Women
CD76

"France and the Empire"
CD78

Cultural Treasures of the Colonies
CD79

Souvenir sheets contain one imperf. stamp.

**1937**

| | | |
|---|---|---|
| Cameroun | | 217-222A |
| Dahomey | | 101-107 |
| Fr. Equatorial Africa | | 27-32, 73 |
| Fr. Guiana | | 162-168 |
| Fr. Guinea | | 120-126 |
| Fr. India | | 104-110 |
| Fr. Polynesia | | 117-123 |
| Fr. Sudan | | 106-112 |
| Guadeloupe | | 148-154 |
| Indo-China | | 193-199 |
| Inini | | 41 |
| Ivory Coast | | 152-158 |
| Kwangchowan | | 132 |
| Madagascar | | 191-197 |
| Martinique | | 179-185 |
| Mauritania | | 69-75 |
| New Caledonia | | 208-214 |
| Niger | | 77-83 |
| Reunion | | 167-173 |
| St. Pierre & Miquelon | | 165-171 |
| Senegal | | 172-178 |
| Somali Coast | | 139-145 |
| Togo | | 258-264 |
| Wallis & Futuna Isls. | | 89 |

| | | |
|---|---|---|
| Nos. 217-222A (7) | 18.80 | 20.30 |
| Nos. 101-107 (7) | 23.60 | 27.60 |
| Nos. 27-32, 73 (7) | 28.10 | 32.10 |
| Nos. 162-168 (7) | 22.50 | 24.50 |
| Nos. 120-126 (7) | 24.00 | 28.00 |
| Nos. 104-110 (7) | 21.15 | 36.50 |
| Nos. 117-123 (7) | 58.50 | 75.00 |
| Nos. 106-112 (7) | 23.60 | 27.60 |
| Nos. 148-154 (7) | 19.55 | 21.05 |
| Nos. 193-199 (7) | 17.70 | 19.70 |
| No. 41 (1) | 21.00 | 27.50 |
| Nos. 152-158 (7) | 22.20 | 26.20 |
| No. 132 (1) | 9.25 | 11.00 |
| Nos. 191-197 (7) | 19.25 | 21.75 |
| Nos. 179-185 (7) | 19.95 | 21.70 |
| Nos. 69-75 (7) | 20.50 | 24.50 |
| Nos. 208-214 (7) | 39.00 | 50.50 |
| Nos. 73-83 (11) | 40.60 | 45.10 |
| Nos. 167-173 (7) | 21.70 | 23.05 |
| Nos. 165-171 (7) | 49.60 | 64.00 |
| Nos. 172-178 (7) | 21.00 | 23.80 |
| Nos. 139-145 (7) | 25.60 | 32.60 |
| Nos. 258-264 (7) | 20.40 | 20.40 |
| No. 89 (1) | 19.00 | 37.50 |
| Set total (154) Stamps | 606.55 | 742.10 |

## Curie

Pierre and Marie Curie
CD80

40th anniversary of the discovery of radium. The surtax was for the benefit of the Intl. Union for the Control of Cancer.

### 1938

| | |
|---|---|
| Cameroun | B1 |
| Cuba | B1-B2 |
| Dahomey | B2 |
| France | B76 |
| Fr. Equatorial Africa | B1 |
| Fr. Guiana | B3 |
| Fr. Guinea | B2 |
| Fr. India | B6 |
| Fr. Polynesia | B5 |
| Fr. Sudan | B1 |
| Guadeloupe | B3 |
| Indo-China | B14 |
| Ivory Coast | B2 |
| Madagascar | B2 |
| Martinique | B2 |
| Mauritania | B3 |
| New Caledonia | B4 |
| Niger | B1 |
| Reunion | B4 |
| St. Pierre & Miquelon | B3 |
| Senegal | B3 |
| Somali Coast | B2 |
| Togo | B1 |

| | | |
|---|---|---|
| No. B1 (1) | 10.00 | 10.00 |
| Nos. B1-B2 (2) | 12.00 | 3.35 |
| No. B2 (1) | 9.50 | 9.50 |
| No. B76 (1) | 21.00 | 12.50 |
| No. B1 (1) | 24.00 | 24.00 |
| No. B3 (1) | 13.50 | 13.50 |
| No. B2 (1) | 8.75 | 8.75 |
| No. B6 (1) | 10.00 | 10.00 |
| No. B5 (1) | 20.00 | 20.00 |
| No. B1 (1) | 12.50 | 12.50 |
| No. B3 (1) | 11.00 | 10.50 |
| No. B14 (1) | 12.00 | 12.00 |
| No. B2 (1) | 11.00 | 7.50 |
| No. B2 (1) | 11.00 | 11.00 |
| No. B2 (1) | 13.00 | 13.00 |
| No. B3 (1) | 7.75 | 7.75 |
| No. B4 (1) | 16.50 | 17.50 |
| No. B1 (1) | 16.50 | 16.50 |
| No. B4 (1) | 14.00 | 14.00 |
| No. B3 (1) | 21.00 | 22.50 |
| No. B3 (1) | 10.50 | 10.50 |
| No. B2 (1) | 7.75 | 7.75 |
| No. B1 (1) | 20.00 | 20.00 |
| Set total (24) Stamps | 313.25 | 294.60 |

## Caillie

Rene Caillie and Map of Northwestern Africa — CD81

Death centenary of Rene Caillie (1799-1838), French explorer. All three denominations exist with colony name omitted.

### 1939

| | |
|---|---|
| Dahomey | 108-110 |
| Fr. Guinea | 161-163 |
| Fr. Sudan | 113-115 |
| Ivory Coast | 160-162 |
| Mauritania | 109-111 |
| Niger | 84-86 |
| Senegal | 188-190 |
| Togo | 265-267 |

| | | |
|---|---|---|
| Nos. 108-110 (3) | 1.20 | 3.60 |
| Nos. 161-163 (3) | 1.20 | 3.20 |
| Nos. 113-115 (3) | 1.20 | 3.20 |
| Nos. 160-162 (3) | 1.05 | 2.55 |
| Nos. 109-111 (3) | 1.05 | 3.80 |
| Nos. 84-86 (3) | 2.35 | 2.35 |
| Nos. 188-190 (3) | 1.05 | 2.90 |
| Nos. 265-267 (3) | 1.05 | 3.30 |
| Set total (24) Stamps | 10.15 | 24.90 |

## New York World's Fair

Natives and New York Skyline CD82

### 1939

| | |
|---|---|
| Cameroun | 223-224 |
| Dahomey | 111-112 |
| Fr. Equatorial Africa | 78-79 |
| Fr. Guiana | 169-170 |
| Fr. Guinea | 164-165 |
| Fr. India | 111-112 |
| Fr. Polynesia | 124-125 |
| Fr. Sudan | 116-117 |
| Guadeloupe | 155-156 |
| Indo-China | 203-204 |
| Inini | 42-43 |
| Ivory Coast | 163-164 |
| Kwangchowan | 133-134 |
| Madagascar | 209-210 |
| Martinique | 186-187 |
| Mauritania | 112-113 |
| New Caledonia | 215-216 |
| Niger | 87-88 |
| Reunion | 174-175 |
| St. Pierre & Miquelon | 205-206 |
| Senegal | 191-192 |
| Somali Coast | 179-180 |
| Togo | 268-269 |
| Wallis & Futuna Isls. | 90-91 |

| | | |
|---|---|---|
| Nos. 223-224 (2) | 2.80 | 2.40 |
| Nos. 111-112 (2) | 1.60 | 3.20 |
| Nos. 78-79 (2) | 1.60 | 3.20 |
| Nos. 169-170 (2) | 2.60 | 2.60 |
| Nos. 164-165 (2) | 1.60 | 3.20 |
| Nos. 111-112 (2) | 3.00 | 8.00 |
| Nos. 124-125 (2) | 4.80 | 4.80 |
| Nos. 116-117 (2) | 1.60 | 3.20 |
| Nos. 155-156 (2) | 2.50 | 2.50 |
| Nos. 203-204 (2) | 2.05 | 2.05 |
| Nos. 42-43 (2) | 7.50 | 9.00 |
| Nos. 163-164 (2) | 1.50 | 3.00 |
| Nos. 133-134 (2) | 2.50 | 2.50 |
| Nos. 209-210 (2) | 1.50 | 2.50 |
| Nos. 186-187 (2) | 2.35 | 2.35 |
| Nos. 112-113 (2) | 1.40 | 2.80 |
| Nos. 215-216 (2) | 3.35 | 3.35 |
| Nos. 87-88 (2) | 1.60 | 2.80 |
| Nos. 174-175 (2) | 2.80 | 2.80 |
| Nos. 205-206 (2) | 4.80 | 6.00 |
| Nos. 191-192 (2) | 1.40 | 2.80 |
| Nos. 179-180 (2) | 1.40 | 2.80 |
| Nos. 268-269 (2) | 1.40 | 2.80 |
| Nos. 90-91 (2) | 5.00 | 6.00 |
| Set total (48) Stamps | 62.65 | 86.65 |

## French Revolution

Storming of the Bastille CD83

French Revolution, 150th anniv. The surtax was for the defense of the colonies.

### 1939

| | |
|---|---|
| Cameroun | B2-B6 |
| Dahomey | B3-B7 |
| Fr. Equatorial Africa | B4-B8, CB1 |
| Fr. Guiana | B4-B8, CB1 |
| Fr. Guinea | B3-B7 |
| Fr. India | B7-B11 |
| Fr. Polynesia | B6-B10, CB1 |
| Fr. Sudan | B2-B6 |
| Guadeloupe | B4-B8 |
| Indo-China | B15-B19, CB1 |
| Inini | B1-B5 |
| Ivory Coast | B3-B7 |
| Kwangchowan | B1-B5 |
| Madagascar | B3-B7, CB1 |
| Martinique | B3-B7 |
| Mauritania | B4-B8 |
| New Caledonia | B5-B9, CB1 |
| Niger | B2-B6 |
| Reunion | B5-B9, CB1 |
| St. Pierre & Miquelon | B4-B8 |
| Senegal | B4-B8, CB1 |
| Somali Coast | B3-B7 |
| Togo | B2-B6 |
| Wallis & Futuna Isls. | B1-B5 |

| | | |
|---|---|---|
| Nos. B2-B6 (5) | 60.00 | 60.00 |
| Nos. B3-B7 (5) | 47.50 | 47.50 |
| Nos. B4-B8, CB1 (6) | 120.00 | 120.00 |
| Nos. B4-B8, CB1 (6) | 79.50 | 79.50 |
| Nos. B3-B7 (5) | 47.50 | 47.50 |
| Nos. B7-B11 (5) | 28.75 | 32.50 |
| Nos. B6-B10, CB1 (6) | 122.50 | 122.50 |
| Nos. B2-B6 (5) | 50.00 | 50.00 |
| Nos. B4-B8 (5) | 50.00 | 50.00 |
| Nos. B15-B19, CB1 (6) | 85.00 | 85.00 |
| Nos. B1-B5 (5) | 80.00 | 100.00 |
| Nos. B3-B7 (5) | 43.75 | 43.75 |
| Nos. B1-B5 (5) | 46.25 | 46.25 |
| Nos. B3-B7, CB1 (6) | 65.50 | 65.50 |
| Nos. B3-B7 (5) | 52.50 | 52.50 |
| Nos. B4-B8 (5) | 42.50 | 42.50 |
| Nos. B5-B9, CB1 (6) | 101.50 | 101.50 |
| Nos. B2-B6 (5) | 60.00 | 60.00 |
| Nos. B5-B9, CB1 (6) | 87.50 | 87.50 |
| Nos. B4-B8 (5) | 67.50 | 72.50 |
| Nos. B4-B8, CB1 (6) | 56.50 | 56.50 |
| Nos. B3-B7 (5) | 45.00 | 45.00 |
| Nos. B2-B6 (5) | 42.50 | 42.50 |
| Nos. B1-B5 (5) | 80.00 | 110.00 |
| Set total (128) Stamps | 1,562. | 1,621. |

Plane over Coastal Area CD85

All five denominations exist with colony name omitted.

### 1940

| | |
|---|---|
| Dahomey | C1-C5 |
| Fr. Guinea | C1-C5 |
| Fr. Guinea | C1-C5 |
| Ivory Coast | C1-C5 |
| Mauritania | C1-C5 |
| Niger | C1-C5 |
| Senegal | C12-C16 |
| Togo | C1-C5 |

| | | |
|---|---|---|
| Nos. C1-C5 (5) | 4.00 | 4.00 |
| Nos. C1-C5 (5) | 4.00 | 4.00 |
| Nos. C1-C5 (5) | 4.00 | 4.00 |
| Nos. C1-C5 (5) | 3.80 | 3.80 |
| Nos. C1-C5 (5) | 3.50 | 3.50 |
| Nos. C1-C5 (5) | 3.50 | 3.50 |
| Nos. C12-C16 (5) | 3.50 | 3.50 |
| Nos. C1-C5 (5) | 3.15 | 3.15 |
| Set total (40) Stamps | 29.45 | 29.45 |

## Defense of the Empire

Colonial Infantryman — CD86

### 1941

| | |
|---|---|
| Cameroun | B13B |
| Dahomey | B13 |
| Fr. Equatorial Africa | B8B |
| Fr. Guiana | B10 |
| Fr. Guinea | B13 |
| Fr. India | B13 |
| Fr. Polynesia | B12 |
| Fr. Sudan | B12 |
| Guadeloupe | B10 |
| Indo-China | B19B |
| Inini | B7 |
| Ivory Coast | B13 |
| Kwangchowan | B7 |
| Madagascar | B9 |
| Martinique | B9 |
| Mauritania | B14 |
| New Caledonia | B11 |
| Niger | B12 |
| Reunion | B11 |
| St. Pierre & Miquelon | B8B |
| Senegal | B14 |
| Somali Coast | B9 |
| Togo | B10B |
| Wallis & Futuna Isls. | B7 |

| | |
|---|---|
| No. B13B (1) | 1.60 |
| No. B13 (1) | 1.20 |
| No. B8B (1) | 3.50 |
| No. B10 (1) | 1.40 |
| No. B13 (1) | 1.40 |
| No. B13 (1) | 1.25 |
| No. B12 (1) | 3.50 |
| No. B12 (1) | 1.40 |
| No. B10 (1) | 1.00 |
| No. B19B (1) | 3.00 |
| No. B7 (1) | 1.75 |
| No. B13 (1) | 1.25 |
| No. B7 (1) | .85 |
| No. B9 (1) | 1.50 |
| No. B9 (1) | 1.40 |
| No. B14 (1) | .95 |
| No. B12 (1) | 1.40 |
| No. B11 (1) | 1.60 |
| No. B8B (1) | 4.50 |
| No. B14 (1) | 1.25 |
| No. B9 (1) | 1.60 |
| No. B10B (1) | 1.10 |
| No. B7 (1) | 1.75 |
| Set total (23) Stamps | 40.15 |

Each of the CD86 stamps listed above is part of a set of three stamps. The designs of the other two stamps in the set vary from country to country. Only the values of the Common Design stamps are listed here.

## Colonial Education Fund

CD86a

### 1942

| | |
|---|---|
| Cameroun | CB3 |
| Dahomey | CB4 |
| Fr. Equatorial Africa | CB5 |
| Fr. Guiana | CB4 |
| Fr. Guinea | CB4 |
| Fr. India | CB3 |
| Fr. Polynesia | CB4 |
| Fr. Sudan | CB4 |
| Guadeloupe | CB3 |
| Indo-China | CB5 |
| Inini | CB3 |
| Ivory Coast | CB4 |
| Kwangchowan | CB5 |
| Malagasy | CB5 |
| Martinique | CB3 |
| Mauritania | CB4 |
| New Caledonia | CB4 |
| Niger | CB4 |
| Reunion | CB4 |
| St. Pierre & Miquelon | CB3 |
| Senegal | CB5 |
| Somali Coast | CB3 |
| Togo | CB3 |
| Wallis & Futuna | CB3 |

| | | |
|---|---|---|
| No. CB3 (1) | 1.10 | |
| No. CB4 (1) | .80 | 5.50 |
| No. CB5 (1) | .80 | |
| No. CB4 (1) | 1.10 | |
| No. CB4 (1) | .40 | 5.50 |
| No. CB3 (1) | .90 | |
| No. CB4 (1) | 2.00 | |
| No. CB4 (1) | .40 | 5.50 |
| No. CB3 (1) | 1.10 | |
| No. CB5 (1) | 2.00 | |
| No. CB3 (1) | 1.25 | |
| No. CB4 (1) | 1.00 | 5.50 |
| No. CB4 (1) | 1.00 | |
| No. CB5 (1) | .65 | |
| No. CB3 (1) | 1.00 | |
| No. CB4 (1) | .80 | |
| No. CB4 (1) | 2.25 | |
| No. CB4 (1) | .35 | |
| No. CB4 (1) | .90 | |
| No. CB3 (1) | 7.00 | |
| No. CB5 (1) | .80 | 6.50 |
| No. CB3 (1) | .70 | |
| No. CB3 (1) | .35 | |
| No. CB3 (1) | 2.00 | |
| Set total (24) Stamps | 30.65 | 28.50 |

Cross of Lorraine & Four-motor Plane CD87

### 1941-5

| | |
|---|---|
| Cameroun | C1-C7 |
| Fr. Equatorial Africa | C17-C23 |
| Fr. Guiana | C9-C10 |
| Fr. India | C1-C6 |
| Fr. Polynesia | C3-C9 |
| Fr. West Africa | C1-C3 |
| Guadeloupe | C1-C2 |
| Madagascar | C37-C43 |

| | | |
|---|---|---|
| Martinique | C1-C2 | |
| New Caledonia | C7-C13 | |
| Reunion | C18-C24 | |
| St. Pierre & Miquelon | C1-C7 | |
| Somali Coast | C1-C7 | |

| | | |
|---|---|---|
| Nos. C1-C7 (7) | 6.30 | 6.30 |
| Nos. C17-C23 (7) | 10.40 | 6.35 |
| Nos. C9-C10 (2) | 3.80 | 3.10 |
| Nos. C1-C6 (6) | 9.30 | 15.00 |
| Nos. C3-C9 (7) | 13.75 | 10.00 |
| Nos. C1-C3 (3) | 9.50 | 3.90 |
| Nos. C1-C2 (2) | 3.75 | 2.50 |
| Nos. C37-C43 (7) | 5.60 | 3.80 |
| Nos. C1-C2 (2) | 3.00 | 1.60 |
| Nos. C7-C13 (7) | 8.85 | 7.30 |
| Nos. C18-C24 (7) | 7.05 | 5.00 |
| Nos. C1-C7 (7) | 11.60 | 9.40 |
| Nos. C1-C7 (7) | 13.95 | 11.10 |
| Set total (71) Stamps | 106.85 | 85.35 |

Somali Coast stamps are inscribed "Djibouti".

Transport Plane CD88

Caravan and Plane CD89

## 1942

| | |
|---|---|
| Dahomey | C6-C13 |
| Fr. Guinea | C6-C13 |
| Fr. Sudan | C6-C13 |
| Ivory Coast | C6-C13 |
| Mauritania | C6-C13 |
| Niger | C6-C13 |
| Senegal | C17-C25 |
| Togo | C6-C13 |

| | |
|---|---|
| Nos. C6-C13 (8) | 7.15 |
| Nos. C6-C13 (8) | 5.75 |
| Nos. C6-C13 (8) | 8.00 |
| Nos. C6-C13 (8) | 11.15 |
| Nos. C6-C13 (8) | 9.75 |
| Nos. C6-C13 (8) | 6.20 |
| Nos. C17-C25 (9) | 9.45 |
| Nos. C6-C13 (8) | 6.75 |
| Set total (65) Stamps | 64.20 |

### Red Cross

Marianne CD90

The surtax was for the French Red Cross and national relief.

## 1944

| | |
|---|---|
| Cameroun | B28 |
| Fr. Equatorial Africa | B38 |
| Fr. Guiana | B12 |
| Fr. India | B14 |
| Fr. Polynesia | B13 |
| Fr. West Africa | B1 |
| Guadeloupe | B12 |
| Madagascar | B15 |
| Martinique | B11 |
| New Caledonia | B13 |
| Reunion | B15 |
| St. Pierre & Miquelon | B13 |
| Somali Coast | B13 |
| Wallis & Futuna Isls. | B9 |

| | | |
|---|---|---|
| No. B28 (1) | 2.00 | 1.60 |
| No. B38 (1) | 1.60 | 1.20 |
| No. B12 (1) | 1.75 | 1.25 |
| No. B14 (1) | 1.50 | 1.25 |
| No. B13 (1) | 2.00 | 1.60 |
| No. B1 (1) | 6.50 | 4.75 |
| No. B12 (1) | 1.40 | 1.00 |
| No. B15 (1) | .90 | .90 |
| No. B11 (1) | 1.20 | 1.20 |
| No. B13 (1) | 1.50 | 1.50 |
| No. B15 (1) | 1.60 | 1.10 |
| No. B13 (1) | 2.60 | 2.60 |
| No. B13 (1) | 1.75 | 2.00 |
| No. B9 (1) | 3.00 | 3.00 |
| Set total (14) Stamps | 29.30 | 24.95 |

### Eboue

CD91

Felix Eboue, first French colonial administrator to proclaim resistance to Germany after French surrender in World War II.

## 1945

| | |
|---|---|
| Cameroun | 296-297 |
| Fr. Equatorial Africa | 156-157 |
| Fr. Guiana | 171-172 |
| Fr. India | 210-211 |
| Fr. Polynesia | 150-151 |
| Fr. West Africa | 15-16 |
| Guadeloupe | 187-188 |
| Madagascar | 259-260 |
| Martinique | 196-197 |
| New Caledonia | 274-275 |
| Reunion | 238-239 |
| St. Pierre & Miquelon | 322-323 |
| Somali Coast | 238-239 |

| | | |
|---|---|---|
| Nos. 296-297 (2) | 2.40 | 1.95 |
| Nos. 156-157 (2) | 2.55 | 2.00 |
| Nos. 171-172 (2) | 2.45 | 2.00 |
| Nos. 210-211 (2) | 2.20 | 1.95 |
| Nos. 150-151 (2) | 3.60 | 2.85 |
| Nos. 15-16 (2) | 2.40 | 2.40 |
| Nos. 187-188 (2) | 2.05 | 1.60 |
| Nos. 259-260 (2) | 2.00 | 1.45 |
| Nos. 196-197 (2) | 2.05 | 1.55 |
| Nos. 274-275 (2) | 3.40 | 3.00 |
| Nos. 238-239 (2) | 2.40 | 2.00 |
| Nos. 322-323 (2) | 4.40 | 3.45 |
| Nos. 238-239 (2) | 2.45 | 2.10 |
| Set total (26) Stamps | 34.35 | 28.30 |

### Victory

Victory — CD92

European victory of the Allied Nations in World War II.

## 1946, May 8

| | |
|---|---|
| Cameroun | C8 |
| Fr. Equatorial Africa | C24 |
| Fr. Guiana | C11 |
| Fr. India | C7 |
| Fr. Polynesia | C10 |
| Fr. West Africa | C4 |
| Guadeloupe | C3 |
| Indo-China | C19 |
| Madagascar | C44 |
| Martinique | C3 |
| New Caledonia | C14 |
| Reunion | C25 |
| St. Pierre & Miquelon | C8 |
| Somali Coast | C8 |
| Wallis & Futuna Isls. | C1 |

| | | |
|---|---|---|
| No. C8 (1) | 1.60 | 1.20 |
| No. C24 (1) | 1.60 | 1.25 |
| No. C11 (1) | 1.75 | 1.25 |
| No. C7 (1) | 1.00 | 4.00 |
| No. C10 (1) | 2.75 | 2.00 |
| No. C4 (1) | 1.60 | 1.20 |
| No. C3 (1) | 1.25 | 1.00 |
| No. C19 (1) | 1.00 | .55 |
| No. C44 (1) | 1.00 | .35 |
| No. C3 (1) | 1.30 | 1.00 |
| No. C14 (1) | 1.50 | 1.25 |
| No. C25 (1) | 1.10 | .90 |
| No. C8 (1) | 2.10 | 2.10 |
| No. C8 (1) | 1.75 | 1.40 |
| No. C1 (1) | 2.25 | 1.90 |
| Set total (15) Stamps | 23.55 | 21.35 |

### Chad to Rhine

Leclerc's Departure from Chad — CD93

Battle at Cufra Oasis — CD94

Tanks in Action, Mareth — CD95

Normandy Invasion — CD96

Entering Paris — CD97

Liberation of Strasbourg — CD98

"Chad to the Rhine" march, 1942-44, by Gen. Jacques Leclerc's column, later French 2nd Armored Division.

## 1946, June 6

| | |
|---|---|
| Cameroun | C9-C14 |
| Fr. Equatorial Africa | C25-C30 |
| Fr. Guiana | C12-C17 |
| Fr. India | C8-C13 |
| Fr. Polynesia | C11-C16 |
| Fr. West Africa | C5-C10 |
| Guadeloupe | C4-C9 |
| Indo-China | C20-C25 |
| Madagascar | C45-C50 |
| Martinique | C4-C9 |
| New Caledonia | C15-C20 |
| Reunion | C26-C31 |
| St. Pierre & Miquelon | C9-C14 |
| Somali Coast | C9-C14 |
| Wallis & Futuna Isls. | C2-C7 |

| | | |
|---|---|---|
| Nos. C9-C14 (6) | 12.05 | 9.70 |
| Nos. C25-C30 (6) | 14.70 | 10.80 |
| Nos. C12-C17 (6) | 12.65 | 10.35 |
| Nos. C8-C13 (6) | 12.80 | 15.00 |
| Nos. C11-C16 (6) | 17.55 | 13.40 |
| Nos. C5-C10 (6) | 16.05 | 11.95 |
| Nos. C4-C9 (6) | 12.00 | 9.60 |
| Nos. C20-C25 (6) | 6.40 | 6.40 |
| Nos. C45-C50 (6) | 10.30 | 8.40 |
| Nos. C4-C9 (6) | 8.85 | 7.30 |
| Nos. C15-C20 (6) | 13.40 | 11.90 |
| Nos. C26-C31 (6) | 10.25 | 6.55 |
| Nos. C9-C14 (6) | 17.30 | 14.35 |

| | | |
|---|---|---|
| Nos. C9-C14 (6) | 18.10 | 12.65 |
| Nos. C2-C7 (6) | 13.75 | 10.45 |
| Set total (90) Stamps | 196.15 | 158.80 |

### UPU

French Colonials, Globe and Plane — CD99

Universal Postal Union, 75th anniv.

## 1949, July 4

| | |
|---|---|
| Cameroun | C29 |
| Fr. Equatorial Africa | C34 |
| Fr. India | C17 |
| Fr. Polynesia | C20 |
| Fr. West Africa | C15 |
| Indo-China | C26 |
| Madagascar | C55 |
| New Caledonia | C24 |
| St. Pierre & Miquelon | C18 |
| Somali Coast | C18 |
| Togo | C18 |
| Wallis & Futuna Isls. | C10 |

| | | |
|---|---|---|
| No. C29 (1) | 8.00 | 4.75 |
| No. C34 (1) | 16.00 | 12.00 |
| No. C17 (1) | 11.50 | 8.75 |
| No. C20 (1) | 20.00 | 15.00 |
| No. C15 (1) | 12.00 | 8.75 |
| No. C26 (1) | 4.75 | 4.00 |
| No. C55 (1) | 4.00 | 2.75 |
| No. C24 (1) | 7.50 | 5.00 |
| No. C18 (1) | 20.00 | 12.00 |
| No. C18 (1) | 14.00 | 10.50 |
| No. C18 (1) | 8.50 | 7.00 |
| No. C10 (1) | 11.00 | 8.25 |
| Set total (12) Stamps | 137.25 | 98.75 |

### Tropical Medicine

Doctor Treating Infant CD100

The surtax was for charitable work.

## 1950

| | |
|---|---|
| Cameroun | B29 |
| Fr. Equatorial Africa | B39 |
| Fr. India | B15 |
| Fr. Polynesia | B14 |
| Fr. West Africa | B3 |
| Madagascar | B17 |
| New Caledonia | B14 |
| St. Pierre & Miquelon | B14 |
| Somali Coast | B14 |
| Togo | B11 |

| | | |
|---|---|---|
| No. B29 (1) | 7.25 | 5.50 |
| No. B39 (1) | 7.25 | 5.50 |
| No. B15 (1) | 6.00 | 4.00 |
| No. B14 (1) | 10.50 | 8.00 |
| No. B3 (1) | 9.50 | 7.25 |
| No. B17 (1) | 5.50 | 5.50 |
| No. B14 (1) | 6.75 | 5.25 |
| No. B14 (1) | 16.00 | 15.00 |
| No. B14 (1) | 7.75 | 6.25 |
| No. B11 (1) | 5.00 | 3.50 |
| Set total (10) Stamps | 81.50 | 65.75 |

### Military Medal

Medal, Early Marine and Colonial Soldier — CD101

Centenary of the creation of the French Military Medal.

## 1952

| | |
|---|---|
| Cameroun | 322 |
| Comoro Isls. | 39 |
| Fr. Equatorial Africa | 186 |

Fr. India..........233
Fr. Polynesia..........179
Fr. West Africa..........57
Madagascar..........286
New Caledonia..........295
St. Pierre & Miquelon..........345
Somali Coast..........267
Togo..........327
Wallis & Futuna Isls. ..........149

| | | |
|---|---|---|
| No. 322 (1) | 7.25 | 3.25 |
| No. 39 (1) | 45.00 | 37.50 |
| No. 186 (1) | 8.00 | 5.50 |
| No. 233 (1) | 5.50 | 7.00 |
| No. 179 (1) | 13.50 | 10.00 |
| No. 57 (1) | 8.75 | 6.50 |
| No. 286 (1) | 3.75 | 2.50 |
| No. 295 (1) | 6.50 | 6.00 |
| No. 345 (1) | 16.00 | 15.00 |
| No. 267 (1) | 9.00 | 8.00 |
| No. 327 (1) | 5.50 | 4.75 |
| No. 149 (1) | 7.25 | 7.25 |
| Set total (12) Stamps | 136.00 | 113.25 |

### Liberation

Allied Landing, Victory Sign and Cross of Lorraine — CD102

Liberation of France, 10th anniv.

### 1954, June 6

Cameroun..........C32
Comoro Isls. ..........C4
Fr. Equatorial Africa..........C38
Fr. India..........C18
Fr. Polynesia..........C22
Fr. West Africa..........C17
Madagascar..........C57
New Caledonia..........C25
St. Pierre & Miquelon..........C19
Somali Coast..........C19
Togo..........C19
Wallis & Futuna Isls. ..........C11

| | | |
|---|---|---|
| No. C32 (1) | 7.25 | 4.75 |
| No. C4 (1) | 32.50 | 19.00 |
| No. C38 (1) | 12.00 | 8.00 |
| No. C18 (1) | 11.00 | 8.00 |
| No. C22 (1) | 10.00 | 8.00 |
| No. C17 (1) | 12.00 | 5.50 |
| No. C57 (1) | 3.25 | 2.00 |
| No. C25 (1) | 7.50 | 5.00 |
| No. C19 (1) | 19.00 | 12.00 |
| No. C19 (1) | 10.50 | 8.50 |
| No. C19 (1) | 7.00 | 5.50 |
| No. C11 (1) | 11.00 | 8.25 |
| Set total (12) Stamps | 143.00 | 94.50 |

### FIDES

Plowmen CD103

Efforts of FIDES, the Economic and Social Development Fund for Overseas Possessions (Fonds d' Investissement pour le Developpement Economique et Social). Each stamp has a different design.

### 1956

Cameroun..........326-329
Comoro Isls. ..........43
Fr. Equatorial Africa..........189-192
Fr. Polynesia..........181
Fr. West Africa..........65-72
Madagascar..........292-295
New Caledonia..........303
St. Pierre & Miquelon..........350
Somali Coast..........268-269
Togo..........331

| | | |
|---|---|---|
| Nos. 326-329 (4) | 6.90 | 3.20 |
| No. 43 (1) | 2.25 | 1.60 |
| Nos. 189-192 (4) | 3.20 | 1.65 |
| No. 181 (1) | 4.00 | 2.00 |
| Nos. 65-72 (8) | 16.00 | 6.35 |
| Nos. 292-295 (4) | 2.25 | 1.20 |
| No. 303 (1) | 1.90 | 1.10 |
| No. 350 (1) | 6.00 | 4.00 |

| | | |
|---|---|---|
| Nos. 268-269 (2) | 5.35 | 3.15 |
| No. 331 (1) | 4.25 | 2.10 |
| Set total (27) Stamps | 52.10 | 26.35 |

### Flower

CD104

Each stamp shows a different flower.

### 1958-9

Cameroun..........333
Comoro Isls. ..........45
Fr. Equatorial Africa..........200-201
Fr. Polynesia..........192
Fr. So. & Antarctic Terr. ..........11
Fr. West Africa..........79-83
Madagascar..........301-302
New Caledonia..........304-305
St. Pierre & Miquelon..........357
Somali Coast..........270
Togo..........348-349
Wallis & Futuna Isls. ..........152

| | | |
|---|---|---|
| No. 333 (1) | 1.60 | .80 |
| No. 45 (1) | 5.25 | 4.25 |
| Nos. 200-201 (2) | 3.60 | 1.60 |
| No. 192 (1) | 6.50 | 4.00 |
| No. 11 (1) | 8.75 | 7.50 |
| Nos. 79-83 (5) | 10.45 | 5.60 |
| Nos. 301-302 (2) | 1.60 | .60 |
| Nos. 304-305 (2) | 8.00 | 3.00 |
| No. 357 (1) | 4.50 | 2.25 |
| No. 270 (1) | 4.25 | 1.40 |
| Nos. 348-349 (2) | 1.10 | .50 |
| No. 152 (1) | 3.25 | 3.25 |
| Set total (20) Stamps | 58.85 | 34.75 |

### Human Rights

Sun, Dove and U.N. Emblem CD105

10th anniversary of the signing of the Universal Declaration of Human Rights.

### 1958

Comoro Isls. ..........44
Fr. Equatorial Africa..........202
Fr. Polynesia..........191
Fr. West Africa..........85
Madagascar..........300
New Caledonia..........306
St. Pierre & Miquelon..........356
Somali Coast..........274
Wallis & Futuna Isls. ..........153

| | | |
|---|---|---|
| No. 44 (1) | 9.00 | 9.00 |
| No. 202 (1) | 2.40 | 1.25 |
| No. 191 (1) | 13.00 | 8.75 |
| No. 85 (1) | 2.40 | 2.00 |
| No. 300 (1) | .80 | .40 |
| No. 306 (1) | 2.00 | 1.50 |
| No. 356 (1) | 3.50 | 2.50 |
| No. 274 (1) | 3.50 | 2.10 |
| No. 153 (1) | 4.50 | 4.50 |
| Set total (9) Stamps | 41.10 | 32.00 |

### C.C.T.A.

CD106

Commission for Technical Cooperation in Africa south of the Sahara, 10th anniv.

### 1960

Cameroun..........339
Cent. Africa..........3
Chad..........66
Congo, P.R..........90
Dahomey..........138
Gabon..........150
Ivory Coast..........180
Madagascar..........317

Mali..........9
Mauritania..........117
Niger..........104
Upper Volta..........89

| | | |
|---|---|---|
| No. 339 (1) | 1.60 | .75 |
| No. 3 (1) | 1.60 | .75 |
| No. 66 (1) | 1.75 | .50 |
| No. 90 (1) | 1.00 | 1.00 |
| No. 138 (1) | .50 | .25 |
| No. 150 (1) | 1.25 | 1.10 |
| No. 180 (1) | 1.10 | .50 |
| No. 317 (1) | .60 | .30 |
| No. 9 (1) | 1.20 | .50 |
| No. 117 (1) | .75 | .40 |
| No. 104 (1) | .85 | .45 |
| No. 89 (1) | .65 | .40 |
| Set total (12) Stamps | 12.85 | 6.90 |

### Air Afrique, 1961

Modern and Ancient Africa, Map and Planes — CD107

Founding of Air Afrique (African Airlines).

### 1961-62

Cameroun..........C37
Cent. Africa..........C5
Chad..........C7
Congo, P.R..........C5
Dahomey..........C17
Gabon..........C5
Ivory Coast..........C18
Mauritania..........C17
Niger..........C22
Senegal..........C31
Upper Volta..........C4

| | | |
|---|---|---|
| No. C37 (1) | 1.00 | .50 |
| No. C5 (1) | 1.00 | .65 |
| No. C7 (1) | 1.00 | .25 |
| No. C5 (1) | 1.75 | .90 |
| No. C17 (1) | .80 | .40 |
| No. C5 (1) | 11.00 | 6.00 |
| No. C18 (1) | 2.00 | 1.25 |
| No. C17 (1) | 2.40 | 1.25 |
| No. C22 (1) | 1.75 | .90 |
| No. C31 (1) | .80 | .30 |
| No. C4 (1) | 3.50 | 1.75 |
| Set total (11) Stamps | 27.00 | 14.15 |

### Anti-Malaria

CD108

World Health Organization drive to eradicate malaria.

### 1962, Apr. 7

Cameroun..........B36
Cent. Africa..........B1
Chad..........B1
Comoro Isls. ..........B1
Congo, P.R..........B3
Dahomey..........B15
Gabon..........B4
Ivory Coast..........B15
Madagascar..........B19
Mali..........B1
Mauritania..........B16
Niger..........B14
Senegal..........B16
Somali Coast..........B15
Upper Volta..........B1

| | | |
|---|---|---|
| No. B36 (1) | 1.00 | .45 |
| No. B1 (1) | 1.40 | 1.40 |
| No. B1 (1) | 1.00 | .50 |
| No. B1 (1) | 3.50 | 3.50 |
| No. B3 (1) | 1.40 | 1.00 |
| No. B15 (1) | .75 | .75 |
| No. B4 (1) | 1.00 | 1.00 |
| No. B15 (1) | 1.25 | 1.25 |
| No. B19 (1) | .75 | .50 |
| No. B1 (1) | 1.25 | .60 |
| No. B16 (1) | .50 | .50 |
| No. B14 (1) | .75 | .75 |

| | | |
|---|---|---|
| No. B16 (1) | 1.10 | .65 |
| No. B15 (1) | 7.00 | 7.00 |
| No. B1 (1) | .75 | .70 |
| Set total (15) Stamps | 23.40 | 20.55 |

### Abidjan Games

CD109

Abidjan Games, Ivory Coast, Dec. 24-31, 1961. Each stamp shows a different sport.

### 1962

Cent. Africa..........19-20, C6
Chad..........83-84, C8
Congo, P.R..........103-104, C7
Gabon..........163-164, C6
Niger..........109-111
Upper Volta..........103-105

| | | |
|---|---|---|
| Nos. 19-20,C6 (3) | 4.15 | 2.85 |
| Nos. 83-84,C8 (3) | 5.80 | 1.55 |
| Nos. 103-104,C7 (3) | 3.85 | 1.80 |
| Nos. 163-164,C6 (3) | 5.00 | 3.00 |
| Nos. 109-111 (3) | 2.60 | 1.25 |
| Nos. 103-105 (3) | 2.80 | 1.75 |
| Set total (18) Stamps | 24.20 | 12.20 |

### African and Malagasy Union

Flag of Union CD110

First anniversary of the Union.

### 1962, Sept. 8

Cameroun..........373
Cent. Africa..........21
Chad..........85
Congo, P.R..........105
Dahomey..........155
Gabon..........165
Ivory Coast..........198
Madagascar..........332
Mauritania..........170
Niger..........112
Senegal..........211
Upper Volta..........106

| | | |
|---|---|---|
| No. 373 (1) | 2.00 | .75 |
| No. 21 (1) | 1.25 | .75 |
| No. 85 (1) | 1.25 | .25 |
| No. 105 (1) | 1.50 | .50 |
| No. 155 (1) | 1.25 | .90 |
| No. 165 (1) | 1.60 | 1.25 |
| No. 198 (1) | 2.10 | .75 |
| No. 332 (1) | .80 | .80 |
| No. 170 (1) | .75 | .50 |
| No. 112 (1) | .80 | .50 |
| No. 211 (1) | .80 | .50 |
| No. 106 (1) | 1.10 | .75 |
| Set total (12) Stamps | 15.20 | 8.20 |

### Telstar

Telstar and Globe Showing Andover and Pleumeur-Bodou — CD111

First television connection of the United States and Europe through the Telstar satellite, July 11-12, 1962.

### 1962-63

Andorra, French ..........154
Comoro Isls. ..........C7
Fr. Polynesia..........C29
Fr. So. & Antarctic Terr. ..........C5
New Caledonia..........C33
St. Pierre & Miquelon..........C26
Somali Coast..........C31
Wallis & Futuna Isls. ..........C17

| | | |
|---|---|---|
| No. 154 (1) | 2.00 | 1.60 |
| No. C7 (1) | 4.50 | 2.75 |
| No. C29 (1) | 11.50 | 8.00 |

| | | |
|---|---|---|
| No. C5 (1) | 29.00 | 21.00 |
| No. C33 (1) | 25.00 | 18.50 |
| No. C26 (1) | 7.25 | 4.50 |
| No. C31 (1) | 1.00 | 1.00 |
| No. C17 (1) | 3.75 | 3.75 |
| Set total (8) Stamps | 84.00 | 61.10 |

### Freedom From Hunger

World Map and Wheat Emblem CD112

U.N. Food and Agriculture Organization's "Freedom from Hunger" campaign.

### 1963, Mar. 21

| | |
|---|---|
| Cameroun | B37-B38 |
| Cent. Africa | B2 |
| Chad | B2 |
| Congo, P.R. | B4 |
| Dahomey | B16 |
| Gabon | B5 |
| Ivory Coast | B16 |
| Madagascar | B21 |
| Mauritania | B17 |
| Niger | B15 |
| Senegal | B17 |
| Upper Volta | B2 |

| | | |
|---|---|---|
| Nos. B37-B38 (2) | 2.25 | .75 |
| No. B2 (1) | 1.25 | 1.25 |
| No. B2 (1) | 1.10 | .50 |
| No. B4 (1) | 1.40 | 1.00 |
| No. B16 (1) | .80 | .80 |
| No. B5 (1) | 1.00 | 1.00 |
| No. B16 (1) | 1.50 | 1.50 |
| No. B21 (1) | .60 | .45 |
| No. B17 (1) | .60 | .60 |
| No. B15 (1) | .75 | .75 |
| No. B17 (1) | .80 | .50 |
| No. B2 (1) | .75 | .70 |
| Set total (13) Stamps | 12.80 | 9.80 |

### Red Cross Centenary

CD113

Centenary of the International Red Cross.

### 1963, Sept. 2

| | |
|---|---|
| Comoro Isls. | 55 |
| Fr. Polynesia | 205 |
| New Caledonia | 328 |
| St. Pierre & Miquelon | 367 |
| Somali Coast | 297 |
| Wallis & Futuna Isls. | 165 |

| | | |
|---|---|---|
| No. 55 (1) | 7.50 | 6.00 |
| No. 205 (1) | 15.00 | 12.00 |
| No. 328 (1) | 8.00 | 6.75 |
| No. 367 (1) | 12.00 | 5.50 |
| No. 297 (1) | 6.25 | 6.25 |
| No. 165 (1) | 4.00 | 4.00 |
| Set total (6) Stamps | 52.75 | 40.50 |

### African Postal Union, 1963

UAMPT Emblem, Radio Masts, Plane and Mail CD114

Establishment of the African and Malagasy Posts and Telecommunications Union.

### 1963, Sept. 8

| | |
|---|---|
| Cameroun | C47 |
| Cent. Africa | C10 |
| Chad | C9 |
| Congo, P.R. | C13 |

| | |
|---|---|
| Dahomey | C19 |
| Gabon | C13 |
| Ivory Coast | C25 |
| Madagascar | C75 |
| Mauritania | C22 |
| Niger | C27 |
| Rwanda | 36 |
| Senegal | C32 |
| Upper Volta | C9 |

| | | |
|---|---|---|
| No. C47 (1) | 2.25 | 1.00 |
| No. C10 (1) | 1.90 | .90 |
| No. C9 (1) | 1.80 | .60 |
| No. C13 (1) | 1.40 | .75 |
| No. C19 (1) | .75 | .25 |
| No. C13 (1) | 1.90 | .90 |
| No. C25 (1) | 2.50 | 1.50 |
| No. C75 (1) | 1.25 | .80 |
| No. C22 (1) | 1.50 | .60 |
| No. C27 (1) | 1.25 | .60 |
| No. 36 (1) | 1.10 | .75 |
| No. C32 (1) | 1.75 | .50 |
| No. C9 (1) | 1.50 | .75 |
| Set total (13) Stamps | 20.85 | 9.80 |

### Air Afrique, 1963

Symbols of Flight — CD115

First anniversary of Air Afrique and inauguration of DC-8 service.

### 1963, Nov. 19

| | |
|---|---|
| Cameroun | C48 |
| Chad | C10 |
| Congo, P.R. | C14 |
| Gabon | C18 |
| Ivory Coast | C26 |
| Mauritania | C26 |
| Niger | C35 |
| Senegal | C33 |

| | | |
|---|---|---|
| No. C48 (1) | 1.25 | .40 |
| No. C10 (1) | 1.80 | .60 |
| No. C14 (1) | 1.60 | .60 |
| No. C18 (1) | 1.25 | .65 |
| No. C26 (1) | 1.00 | .50 |
| No. C26 (1) | .70 | .25 |
| No. C35 (1) | 1.00 | .55 |
| No. C33 (1) | 2.00 | .65 |
| Set total (8) Stamps | 10.60 | 4.20 |

### Europafrica

Europe and Africa Linked — CD116

Signing of an economic agreement between the European Economic Community and the African and Malagasy Union, Yaounde, Cameroun, July 20, 1963.

### 1963-64

| | |
|---|---|
| Cameroun | 402 |
| Cent. Africa | C12 |
| Chad | C11 |
| Congo, P.R. | C16 |
| Gabon | C19 |
| Ivory Coast | 217 |
| Niger | C43 |
| Upper Volta | C11 |

| | | |
|---|---|---|
| No. 402 (1) | 2.25 | .60 |
| No. C12 (1) | 2.50 | 1.75 |
| No. C11 (1) | 1.60 | .50 |
| No. C16 (1) | 1.60 | 1.00 |
| No. C19 (1) | 1.25 | .75 |
| No. 217 (1) | 1.10 | .50 |
| No. C43 (1) | .85 | .50 |
| No. C11 (1) | 1.50 | .80 |
| Set total (8) Stamps | 12.65 | 6.25 |

### Human Rights

Scales of Justice and Globe CD117

15th anniversary of the Universal Declaration of Human Rights.

### 1963, Dec. 10

| | |
|---|---|
| Comoro Isls. | 56 |
| Fr. Polynesia | 206 |
| New Caledonia | 329 |
| St. Pierre & Miquelon | 368 |
| Somali Coast | 300 |
| Wallis & Futuna Isls. | 166 |

| | | |
|---|---|---|
| No. 56 (1) | 7.50 | 6.00 |
| No. 205 (1) | 15.00 | 12.00 |
| No. 329 (1) | 7.00 | 6.00 |
| No. 368 (1) | 7.00 | 3.50 |
| No. 300 (1) | 8.50 | 8.50 |
| No. 166 (1) | 7.00 | 7.00 |
| Set total (6) Stamps | 52.00 | 43.00 |

### PHILATEC

Stamp Album, Champs Elysees Palace and Horses of Marly CD118

Intl. Philatelic and Postal Techniques Exhibition, Paris, June 5-21, 1964.

### 1963-64

| | |
|---|---|
| Comoro Isls. | 60 |
| France | 1078 |
| Fr. Polynesia | 207 |
| New Caledonia | 341 |
| St. Pierre & Miquelon | 369 |
| Somali Coast | 301 |
| Wallis & Futuna Isls. | 167 |

| | | |
|---|---|---|
| No. 60 (1) | 4.00 | 3.50 |
| No. 1078 (1) | .25 | .25 |
| No. 206 (1) | 15.00 | 10.00 |
| No. 341 (1) | 6.50 | 6.50 |
| No. 369 (1) | 11.00 | 8.00 |
| No. 301 (1) | 7.75 | 7.75 |
| No. 167 (1) | 3.00 | 3.00 |
| Set total (7) Stamps | 47.50 | 39.00 |

### Cooperation

CD119

Cooperation between France and the French-speaking countries of Africa and Madagascar.

### 1964

| | |
|---|---|
| Cameroun | 409-410 |
| Cent. Africa | 39 |
| Chad | 103 |
| Congo, P.R. | 121 |
| Dahomey | 193 |
| France | 1111 |
| Gabon | 175 |
| Ivory Coast | 221 |
| Madagascar | 360 |
| Mauritania | 181 |
| Niger | 143 |
| Senegal | 236 |
| Togo | 495 |

| | | |
|---|---|---|
| Nos. 409-410 (2) | 2.50 | .50 |
| No. 39 (1) | .90 | .50 |
| No. 103 (1) | 1.00 | .25 |
| No. 121 (1) | .90 | .35 |
| No. 193 (1) | .80 | .35 |
| No. 1111 (1) | .25 | .25 |
| No. 175 (1) | .90 | .60 |
| No. 221 (1) | 1.10 | .35 |

| | | |
|---|---|---|
| No. 360 (1) | .60 | .25 |
| No. 181 (1) | .60 | .35 |
| No. 143 (1) | .80 | .40 |
| No. 236 (1) | 1.60 | .85 |
| No. 495 (1) | .70 | .25 |
| Set total (14) Stamps | 12.65 | 5.25 |

### ITU

Telegraph, Syncom Satellite and ITU Emblem CD120

Intl. Telecommunication Union, Cent.

### 1965, May 17

| | |
|---|---|
| Comoro Isls. | C14 |
| Fr. Polynesia | C33 |
| Fr. So. & Antarctic Terr. | C8 |
| New Caledonia | C40 |
| New Hebrides | 124-125 |
| St. Pierre & Miquelon | C29 |
| Somali Coast | C36 |
| Wallis & Futuna Isls. | C20 |

| | | |
|---|---|---|
| No. C14 (1) | 18.00 | 9.00 |
| No. C33 (1) | 80.00 | 52.50 |
| No. C8 (1) | 200.00 | 160.00 |
| No. C40 (1) | 10.00 | 8.00 |
| Nos. 124-125 (2) | 32.25 | 27.25 |
| No. C29 (1) | 24.00 | 11.50 |
| No. C36 (1) | 15.00 | 9.00 |
| No. C20 (1) | 16.00 | 16.00 |
| Set total (9) Stamps | 395.25 | 293.25 |

### French Satellite A-1

Diamant Rocket and Launching Installation — CD121

Launching of France's first satellite, Nov. 26, 1965.

### 1965-66

| | |
|---|---|
| Comoro Isls. | C16a |
| France | 1138a |
| Reunion | 359a |
| Fr. Polynesia | C41a |
| Fr. So. & Antarctic Terr. | C10a |
| New Caledonia | C45a |
| St. Pierre & Miquelon | C31a |
| Somali Coast | C40a |
| Wallis & Futuna Isls. | C23a |

| | | |
|---|---|---|
| No. C16a (1) | 9.00 | 9.00 |
| No. 1138a (1) | .65 | .65 |
| No. 359a (1) | 3.50 | 3.00 |
| No. C41a (1) | 14.00 | 14.00 |
| No. C10a (1) | 29.00 | 24.00 |
| No. C45a (1) | 7.00 | 7.00 |
| No. C31a (1) | 14.50 | 14.50 |
| No. C40a (1) | 7.00 | 7.00 |
| No. C23a (1) | 8.50 | 8.50 |
| Set total (9) Stamps | 93.15 | 87.65 |

### French Satellite D-1

D-1 Satellite in Orbit — CD122

Launching of the D-1 satellite at Hammaguir, Algeria, Feb. 17, 1966.

### 1966

| | |
|---|---|
| Comoro Isls. | C17 |
| France | 1148 |

Fr. Polynesia......................................C42
Fr. So. & Antarctic Terr. ................C11
New Caledonia..................................C46
St. Pierre & Miquelon.....................C32
Somali Coast.....................................C49
Wallis & Futuna Isls.......................C24

| | | |
|---|---|---|
| No. C17 (1) | 4.00 | 4.00 |
| No. 1148 (1) | .25 | .25 |
| No. C42 (1) | 7.00 | 4.75 |
| No. C11 (1) | 57.50 | 40.00 |
| No. C46 (1) | 2.25 | 2.00 |
| No. C32 (1) | 9.00 | 6.00 |
| No. C49 (1) | 4.25 | 2.75 |
| No. C24 (1) | 3.50 | 3.50 |
| Set total (8) Stamps | 87.75 | 63.25 |

## Air Afrique, 1966

Planes and Air Afrique
Emblem — CD123

Introduction of DC-8F planes by Air Afrique.

### 1966

Cameroun..............................................C79
Cent. Africa ........................................C35
Chad......................................................C26
Congo, P.R...........................................C42
Dahomey ..............................................C42
Gabon...................................................C47
Ivory Coast ..........................................C32
Mauritania............................................C57
Niger.....................................................C63
Senegal .................................................C47
Togo......................................................C54
Upper Volta..........................................C31

| | | |
|---|---|---|
| No. C79 (1) | .80 | .25 |
| No. C35 (1) | 1.00 | .50 |
| No. C26 (1) | .85 | .25 |
| No. C42 (1) | 1.00 | .25 |
| No. C42 (1) | .75 | .25 |
| No. C47 (1) | .90 | .35 |
| No. C32 (1) | 1.00 | .60 |
| No. C57 (1) | .60 | .30 |
| No. C63 (1) | .70 | .35 |
| No. C47 (1) | .80 | .30 |
| No. C54 (1) | .80 | .25 |
| No. C31 (1) | .75 | .50 |
| Set total (12) Stamps | 9.95 | 4.15 |

## African Postal Union, 1967

Telecommunications Symbols and Map
of Africa — CD124

Fifth anniversary of the establishment of the
African and Malagasy Union of Posts and
Telecommunications, UAMPT.

### 1967

Cameroun..............................................C90
Cent. Africa ........................................C46
Chad......................................................C37
Congo, P.R...........................................C57
Dahomey ..............................................C61
Gabon...................................................C58
Ivory Coast ..........................................C34
Madagascar..........................................C85
Mauritania............................................C65
Niger.....................................................C75
Rwanda .............................................C1-C3
Senegal .................................................C60
Togo......................................................C81
Upper Volta..........................................C50

| | | |
|---|---|---|
| No. C90 (1) | 2.40 | .65 |
| No. C46 (1) | 2.25 | .85 |
| No. C37 (1) | 2.00 | .60 |
| No. C57 (1) | 1.60 | .60 |
| No. C61 (1) | 1.75 | .95 |
| No. C58 (1) | 2.00 | .85 |
| No. C34 (1) | 3.50 | 1.50 |
| No. C85 (1) | 1.25 | .60 |
| No. C65 (1) | 1.25 | .60 |
| No. C75 (1) | 1.40 | .60 |

| | | |
|---|---|---|
| Nos. C1-C3 (3) | 2.05 | 1.25 |
| No. C60 (1) | 1.75 | .50 |
| No. C81 (1) | 1.90 | .30 |
| No. C50 (1) | 1.80 | .70 |
| Set total (16) Stamps | 26.90 | 10.55 |

## Monetary Union

Gold Token of the
Ashantis, 17-18th
Centuries — CD125

West African Monetary Union, 5th anniv.

### 1967, Nov. 4

Dahomey ...............................................244
Ivory Coast ..........................................259
Mauritania............................................238
Niger.....................................................204
Senegal .................................................294
Togo......................................................623
Upper Volta..........................................181

| | | |
|---|---|---|
| No. 244 (1) | .65 | .65 |
| No. 259 (1) | .85 | .40 |
| No. 238 (1) | .45 | .25 |
| No. 204 (1) | .55 | .25 |
| No. 294 (1) | .60 | .25 |
| No. 623 (1) | .60 | .25 |
| No. 181 (1) | .65 | .35 |
| Set total (7) Stamps | 4.35 | 2.40 |

## WHO Anniversary

Sun,
Flowers
and WHO
Emblem
CD126

World Health Organization, 20th anniv.

### 1968, May 4

Afars & Issas ......................................317
Comoro Isls. .........................................73
Fr. Polynesia.............................241-242
Fr. So. & Antarctic Terr. .................31
New Caledonia..................................367
St. Pierre & Miquelon.....................377
Wallis & Futuna Isls.......................169

| | | |
|---|---|---|
| No. 317 (1) | 3.00 | 3.00 |
| No. 73 (1) | 2.40 | 1.75 |
| Nos. 241-242 (2) | 22.00 | 12.75 |
| No. 31 (1) | 62.50 | 47.50 |
| No. 367 (1) | 4.00 | 2.25 |
| No. 377 (1) | 12.00 | 9.00 |
| No. 169 (1) | 5.75 | 5.75 |
| Set total (8) Stamps | 111.65 | 82.00 |

## Human Rights Year

Human Rights
Flame — CD127

### 1968, Aug. 10

Afars & Issas .............................322-323
Comoro Isls. .........................................76
Fr. Polynesia.............................243-244
Fr. So. & Antarctic Terr. .................32
New Caledonia..................................369
St. Pierre & Miquelon.....................382
Wallis & Futuna Isls.......................170

| | | |
|---|---|---|
| Nos. 322-323 (2) | 6.75 | 4.00 |
| No. 76 (1) | 3.25 | 3.25 |
| Nos. 243-244 (2) | 24.00 | 14.00 |
| No. 32 (1) | 55.00 | 47.50 |
| No. 369 (1) | 2.75 | 1.50 |
| No. 382 (1) | 8.00 | 5.50 |
| No. 170 (1) | 3.25 | 3.25 |
| Set total (9) Stamps | 103.00 | 79.00 |

## 2nd PHILEXAFRIQUE

CD128

Opening of PHILEXAFRIQUE, Abidjan, Feb.
14. Each stamp shows a local scene and
stamp.

### 1969, Feb. 14

Cameroun............................................C118
Cent. Africa ......................................C65
Chad....................................................C48
Congo, P.R.........................................C77
Dahomey ............................................C94
Gabon.................................................C82
Ivory Coast .............................C38-C40
Madagascar........................................C92
Mali.....................................................C65
Mauritania..........................................C80
Niger...................................................C104
Senegal ...............................................C68
Togo....................................................C104
Upper Volta........................................C62

| | | |
|---|---|---|
| No. C118 (1) | 3.25 | 1.25 |
| No. C65 (1) | 1.75 | 1.75 |
| No. C48 (1) | 2.40 | 1.00 |
| No. C77 (1) | 2.00 | 1.75 |
| No. C94 (1) | 2.25 | 2.25 |
| No. C82 (1) | 2.00 | 2.00 |
| Nos. C38-C40 (3) | 14.50 | 14.50 |
| No. C92 (1) | 1.75 | .85 |
| No. C65 (1) | 1.75 | 1.00 |
| No. C80 (1) | 1.90 | .75 |
| No. C104 (1) | 3.00 | 1.90 |
| No. C68 (1) | 2.00 | 1.40 |
| No. C104 (1) | 2.25 | .45 |
| No. C62 (1) | 4.00 | 3.25 |
| Set total (16) Stamps | 44.80 | 34.10 |

## Concorde

Concorde in
Flight
CD129

First flight of the prototype Concorde supersonic plane at Toulouse, Mar. 1, 1969.

### 1969

Afars & Issas .....................................C56
Comoro Isls. ......................................C29
France .................................................C42
Fr. Polynesia.....................................C50
Fr. So. & Antarctic Terr. ...............C18
New Caledonia..................................C63
St. Pierre & Miquelon...................C40
Wallis & Futuna Isls.....................C30

| | | |
|---|---|---|
| No. C56 (1) | 26.00 | 16.00 |
| No. C29 (1) | 18.00 | 12.00 |
| No. C42 (1) | .75 | .35 |
| No. C50 (1) | 55.00 | 35.00 |
| No. C18 (1) | 55.00 | 37.50 |
| No. C63 (1) | 27.50 | 20.00 |
| No. C40 (1) | 32.50 | 11.00 |
| No. C30 (1) | 15.00 | 10.00 |
| Set total (8) Stamps | 229.75 | 141.85 |

## Development Bank

Bank
Emblem — CD130

African Development Bank, fifth anniv.

### 1969

Cameroun..............................................499
Chad......................................................217
Congo, P.R................................181-182

Ivory Coast .........................................281
Mali............................................127-128
Mauritania............................................267
Niger.....................................................220
Senegal ......................................317-318
Upper Volta..........................................201

| | | |
|---|---|---|
| No. 499 (1) | .80 | .25 |
| No. 217 (1) | .90 | .25 |
| Nos. 181-182 (2) | 1.00 | .50 |
| No. 281 (1) | .70 | .40 |
| Nos. 127-128 (2) | 1.00 | .50 |
| No. 267 (1) | .60 | .25 |
| No. 220 (1) | .70 | .30 |
| Nos. 317-318 (2) | 1.55 | .50 |
| No. 201 (1) | .65 | .30 |
| Set total (12) Stamps | 7.90 | 3.25 |

## ILO

ILO Headquarters, Geneva, and
Emblem — CD131

Intl. Labor Organization, 50th anniv.

### 1969-70

Afars & Issas ......................................337
Comoro Isls. .........................................83
Fr. Polynesia.............................251-252
Fr. So. & Antarctic Terr. .................35
New Caledonia..................................379
St. Pierre & Miquelon.....................396
Wallis & Futuna Isls.......................172

| | | |
|---|---|---|
| No. 337 (1) | 2.75 | 2.00 |
| No. 83 (1) | 1.25 | .75 |
| Nos. 251-252 (2) | 24.00 | 12.50 |
| No. 35 (1) | 15.00 | 10.00 |
| No. 379 (1) | 2.25 | 1.10 |
| No. 396 (1) | 10.00 | 5.50 |
| No. 172 (1) | 2.75 | 2.75 |
| Set total (8) Stamps | 58.00 | 34.60 |

## ASECNA

Map of
Africa,
Plane and
Airport
CD132

10th anniversary of the Agency for the
Security of Aerial Navigation in Africa and
Madagascar (ASECNA, Agence pour la
Securite de la Navigation Aerienne en Afrique
et a Madagascar).

### 1969-70

Cameroun..............................................500
Cent. Africa ......................................119
Chad......................................................222
Congo, P.R...........................................197
Dahomey ..............................................269
Gabon...................................................260
Ivory Coast ..........................................287
Mali......................................................130
Niger.....................................................221
Senegal .................................................321
Upper Volta..........................................204

| | | |
|---|---|---|
| No. 500 (1) | 2.00 | .60 |
| No. 119 (1) | 2.00 | .80 |
| No. 222 (1) | 1.00 | .25 |
| No. 197 (1) | 2.00 | .40 |
| No. 269 (1) | .90 | .55 |
| No. 260 (1) | 1.75 | .75 |
| No. 287 (1) | .90 | .40 |
| No. 130 (1) | .90 | .40 |
| No. 221 (1) | 1.40 | .70 |
| No. 321 (1) | 1.60 | .50 |
| No. 204 (1) | 1.75 | 1.00 |
| Set total (11) Stamps | 16.20 | 6.35 |

## U.P.U. Headquarters

CD133

New Universal Postal Union headquarters,
Bern, Switzerland.

## 1970

| | |
|---|---|
| Afars & Issas | 342 |
| Algeria | 443 |
| Cameroun | 503-504 |
| Cent. Africa | 125 |
| Chad | 225 |
| Comoro Isls. | 84 |
| Congo, P.R. | 216 |
| Fr. Polynesia | 261-262 |
| Fr. So. & Antarctic Terr. | 36 |
| Gabon | 258 |
| Ivory Coast | 295 |
| Madagascar | 444 |
| Mali | 134-135 |
| Mauritania | 283 |
| New Caledonia | 382 |
| Niger | 231-232 |
| St. Pierre & Miquelon | 397-398 |
| Senegal | 328-329 |
| Tunisia | 535 |
| Wallis & Futuna Isls. | 173 |

| | | |
|---|---|---|
| No. 342 (1) | 2.50 | 1.40 |
| No. 443 (1) | 1.10 | .40 |
| Nos. 503-504 (2) | 2.60 | .55 |
| No. 125 (1) | 1.75 | .70 |
| No. 225 (1) | 1.20 | .25 |
| No. 84 (1) | 5.50 | 2.00 |
| No. 216 (1) | 1.00 | .25 |
| Nos. 261-262 (2) | 20.00 | 10.00 |
| No. 36 (1) | 40.00 | 27.50 |
| No. 258 (1) | .90 | .55 |
| No. 295 (1) | 1.10 | .25 |
| No. 444 (1) | .55 | .25 |
| Nos. 134-135 (2) | 1.05 | .50 |
| No. 283 (1) | .60 | .30 |
| No. 382 (1) | 3.00 | 1.50 |
| Nos. 231-232 (2) | 1.50 | .60 |
| Nos. 397-398 (2) | 34.00 | 16.25 |
| Nos. 328-329 (2) | 1.55 | .55 |
| No. 535 (1) | .60 | .25 |
| No. 173 (1) | 3.25 | 3.25 |
| Set total (26) Stamps | 123.75 | 67.55 |

### De Gaulle

CD134

First anniversary of the death of Charles de Gaulle, (1890-1970), President of France.

## 1971-72

| | |
|---|---|
| Afars & Issas | 356-357 |
| Comoro Isls. | 104-105 |
| France | 1325a |
| Fr. Polynesia | 270-271 |
| Fr. So. & Antarctic Terr. | 52-53 |
| New Caledonia | 393-394 |
| Reunion | 380a |
| St. Pierre & Miquelon | 417-418 |
| Wallis & Futuna Isls. | 177-178 |

| | | |
|---|---|---|
| Nos. 356-357 (2) | 12.50 | 7.50 |
| Nos. 104-105 (2) | 9.00 | 5.75 |
| No. 1325a (1) | 3.00 | 2.50 |
| Nos. 270-271 (2) | 51.50 | 29.50 |
| Nos. 52-53 (2) | 40.00 | 29.50 |
| Nos. 393-394 (2) | 23.00 | 11.75 |
| No. 380a (1) | 9.25 | 8.00 |
| Nos. 417-418 (2) | 56.50 | 31.00 |
| Nos. 177-178 (2) | 20.00 | 16.25 |
| Set total (16) Stamps | 224.75 | 141.75 |

### African Postal Union, 1971

UAMPT Building, Brazzaville, Congo — CD135

10th anniversary of the establishment of the African and Malagasy Posts and Telecommunications Union, UAMPT. Each stamp has a different native design.

## 1971, Nov. 13

| | |
|---|---|
| Cameroun | C177 |
| Cent. Africa | C89 |
| Chad | C94 |

| | |
|---|---|
| Congo, P.R. | C136 |
| Dahomey | C146 |
| Gabon | C120 |
| Ivory Coast | C47 |
| Mauritania | C113 |
| Niger | C164 |
| Rwanda | C8 |
| Senegal | C105 |
| Togo | C166 |
| Upper Volta | C97 |

| | | |
|---|---|---|
| No. C177 (1) | 2.00 | .50 |
| No. C89 (1) | 2.25 | .85 |
| No. C94 (1) | 1.50 | .50 |
| No. C136 (1) | 1.60 | .75 |
| No. C146 (1) | 1.75 | .80 |
| No. C120 (1) | 1.75 | .70 |
| No. C47 (1) | 2.00 | 1.00 |
| No. C113 (1) | 1.10 | .65 |
| No. C164 (1) | 1.25 | .50 |
| No. C8 (1) | 2.75 | 2.50 |
| No. C105 (1) | 1.60 | .50 |
| No. C166 (1) | 1.25 | .40 |
| No. C97 (1) | 1.50 | .70 |
| Set total (13) Stamps | 22.30 | 10.45 |

### West African Monetary Union

African Couple, City, Village and Commemorative Coin — CD136

West African Monetary Union, 10th anniv.

## 1972, Nov. 2

| | |
|---|---|
| Dahomey | 300 |
| Ivory Coast | 331 |
| Mauritania | 299 |
| Niger | 258 |
| Senegal | 374 |
| Togo | 825 |
| Upper Volta | 280 |

| | | |
|---|---|---|
| No. 300 (1) | .65 | .25 |
| No. 331 (1) | 1.00 | .50 |
| No. 299 (1) | .75 | .25 |
| No. 258 (1) | .65 | .30 |
| No. 374 (1) | .50 | .30 |
| No. 825 (1) | .60 | .25 |
| No. 280 (1) | .60 | .25 |
| Set total (7) Stamps | 4.75 | 2.10 |

### African Postal Union, 1973

Telecommunications Symbols and Map of Africa — CD137

11th anniversary of the African and Malagasy Posts and Telecommunications Union (UAMPT).

## 1973, Sept. 12

| | |
|---|---|
| Cameroun | 574 |
| Cent. Africa | 194 |
| Chad | 294 |
| Congo, P.R. | 289 |
| Dahomey | 311 |
| Gabon | 320 |
| Ivory Coast | 361 |
| Madagascar | 500 |
| Mauritania | 304 |
| Niger | 287 |
| Rwanda | 540 |
| Senegal | 393 |
| Togo | 849 |
| Upper Volta | 297 |

| | | |
|---|---|---|
| No. 574 (1) | 1.75 | .40 |
| No. 194 (1) | 1.25 | .75 |
| No. 294 (1) | 1.75 | .40 |
| No. 289 (1) | 1.60 | .50 |
| No. 311 (1) | 1.25 | .55 |
| No. 320 (1) | 1.40 | .75 |
| No. 361 (1) | 2.50 | 1.00 |
| No. 500 (1) | 1.10 | .35 |
| No. 304 (1) | 1.10 | .40 |
| No. 287 (1) | .90 | .60 |
| No. 540 (1) | 3.00 | 2.00 |
| No. 393 (1) | 1.60 | .50 |

| | | |
|---|---|---|
| No. 849 (1) | 1.00 | .35 |
| No. 297 (1) | 1.25 | .70 |
| Set total (14) Stamps | 21.45 | 9.25 |

### Philexafrique II — Essen

CD138

CD139

Designs: Indigenous fauna, local and German stamps. Types CD138-CD139 printed horizontally and vertically se-tenant in sheets of 10 (2x5). Label between horizontal pairs alternately commemorates Philexafrique II, Libreville, Gabon, June 1978, and 2nd International Stamp Fair, Essen, Germany, Nov. 1-5.

## 1978-1979

| | |
|---|---|
| Benin | C286a |
| Central Africa | C201a |
| Chad | C239a |
| Congo Republic | C246a |
| Djibouti | C122a |
| Gabon | C216a |
| Ivory Coast | C65a |
| Mali | C357a |
| Mauritania | C186a |
| Niger | C292a |
| Rwanda | C13a |
| Senegal | C147a |
| Togo | C364a |

| | | |
|---|---|---|
| No. C286a (1) | 9.00 | 8.50 |
| No. C201a (1) | 7.50 | 7.50 |
| No. C239a (1) | 7.50 | 4.00 |
| No. C246a (1) | 7.00 | 7.00 |
| No. C122a (1) | 6.50 | 6.50 |
| No. C216a (1) | 6.50 | 4.00 |
| No. C65a (1) | 9.00 | 9.00 |
| No. C357a (1) | 5.00 | 3.00 |
| No. C186a (1) | 5.50 | 3.00 |
| No. C292a (1) | 6.00 | 6.00 |
| No. C13a (1) | 4.00 | 4.00 |
| No. C147a (1) | 10.00 | 4.00 |
| No. C364a (1) | 3.00 | 1.50 |
| Set total (13) Stamps | 86.50 | 70.00 |

### BRITISH COMMONWEALTH OF NATIONS

The listings follow established trade practices when these issues are offered as units by dealers. The Peace issue, for example, includes only one stamp from the Indian state of Hyderabad. The U.P.U. issue includes the Egypt set. Pairs are included for those varieties issued with bilingual designs se-tenant.

### Silver Jubilee

Windsor Castle and King George V
CD301

Reign of King George V, 25th anniv.

## 1935

| | |
|---|---|
| Antigua | 77-80 |
| Ascension | 33-36 |
| Bahamas | 92-95 |
| Barbados | 186-189 |
| Basutoland | 11-14 |

| | |
|---|---|
| Bechuanaland Protectorate | 117-120 |
| Bermuda | 100-103 |
| British Guiana | 223-226 |
| British Honduras | 108-111 |
| Cayman Islands | 81-84 |
| Ceylon | 260-263 |
| Cyprus | 136-139 |
| Dominica | 90-93 |
| Falkland Islands | 77-80 |
| Fiji | 110-113 |
| Gambia | 125-128 |
| Gibraltar | 100-103 |
| Gilbert & Ellice Islands | 33-36 |
| Gold Coast | 108-111 |
| Grenada | 124-127 |
| Hong Kong | 147-150 |
| Jamaica | 109-112 |
| Kenya, Uganda, Tanzania | 42-45 |
| Leeward Islands | 96-99 |
| Malta | 184-187 |
| Mauritius | 204-207 |
| Montserrat | 85-88 |
| Newfoundland | 226-229 |
| Nigeria | 34-37 |
| Northern Rhodesia | 18-21 |
| Nyasaland Protectorate | 47-50 |
| St. Helena | 111-114 |
| St. Kitts-Nevis | 72-75 |
| St. Lucia | 91-94 |
| St. Vincent | 134-137 |
| Seychelles | 118-121 |
| Sierra Leone | 166-169 |
| Solomon Islands | 60-63 |
| Somaliland Protectorate | 77-80 |
| Straits Settlements | 213-216 |
| Swaziland | 20-23 |
| Trinidad & Tobago | 43-46 |
| Turks & Caicos Islands | 71-74 |
| Virgin Islands | 69-72 |

The following have different designs but are included in the omnibus set:

| | |
|---|---|
| Great Britain | 226-229 |
| Offices in Morocco (Sp. Curr.) | 67-70 |
| Offices in Morocco (Br. Curr.) | 226-229 |
| Offices in Morocco (Fr. Curr.) | 422-425 |
| Offices in Morocco (Tangier) | 508-510 |
| Australia | 152-154 |
| Canada | 211-216 |
| Cook Islands | 98-100 |
| India | 142-148 |
| Nauru | 31-34 |
| New Guinea | 46-47 |
| New Zealand | 199-201 |
| Niue | 67-69 |
| Papua | 114-117 |
| Samoa | 163-165 |
| South Africa | 68-71 |
| Southern Rhodesia | 33-36 |
| South-West Africa | 121-124 |

| | | |
|---|---|---|
| Nos. 77-80 (4) | 20.25 | 23.25 |
| Nos. 33-36 (4) | 58.50 | 127.50 |
| Nos. 92-95 (4) | 25.00 | 46.00 |
| Nos. 186-189 (4) | 30.00 | 50.30 |
| Nos. 11-14 (4) | 11.60 | 21.25 |
| Nos. 117-120 (4) | 15.75 | 36.00 |
| Nos. 100-103 (4) | 16.80 | 58.50 |
| Nos. 223-226 (4) | 22.35 | 35.50 |
| Nos. 108-111 (4) | 15.25 | 16.35 |
| Nos. 81-84 (4) | 21.60 | 24.50 |
| Nos. 260-263 (4) | 10.40 | 21.60 |
| Nos. 136-139 (4) | 39.75 | 34.40 |
| Nos. 90-93 (4) | 18.85 | 19.85 |
| Nos. 77-80 (4) | 55.00 | 14.75 |
| Nos. 110-113 (4) | 20.25 | 34.00 |
| Nos. 125-128 (4) | 13.05 | 25.25 |
| Nos. 100-103 (4) | 28.75 | 42.75 |
| Nos. 33-36 (4) | 36.80 | 67.00 |
| Nos. 108-111 (4) | 25.75 | 78.10 |
| Nos. 124-127 (4) | 16.70 | 40.60 |
| Nos. 147-150 (4) | 73.75 | 20.75 |
| Nos. 109-112 (4) | 24.20 | 50.50 |
| Nos. 42-45 (4) | 10.25 | 11.75 |
| Nos. 96-99 (4) | 35.75 | 49.60 |
| Nos. 184-187 (4) | 22.00 | 33.70 |
| Nos. 204-207 (4) | 44.60 | 58.25 |
| Nos. 85-88 (4) | 10.25 | 30.25 |
| Nos. 226-229 (4) | 17.50 | 12.05 |
| Nos. 34-37 (4) | 17.50 | 73.00 |
| Nos. 18-21 (4) | 17.00 | 15.00 |
| Nos. 47-50 (4) | 43.50 | 82.50 |
| Nos. 111-114 (4) | 31.15 | 36.50 |
| Nos. 72-75 (4) | 11.80 | 18.65 |
| Nos. 91-94 (4) | 16.00 | 20.80 |
| Nos. 134-137 (4) | 9.45 | 21.25 |
| Nos. 118-121 (4) | 15.75 | 40.00 |
| Nos. 166-169 (4) | 23.60 | 50.35 |
| Nos. 60-63 (4) | 29.00 | 38.00 |
| Nos. 77-80 (4) | 17.00 | 48.25 |
| Nos. 213-216 (4) | 15.00 | 25.10 |
| Nos. 20-23 (4) | 6.80 | 18.25 |
| Nos. 43-46 (4) | 18.60 | 37.50 |
| Nos. 71-74 (4) | 9.90 | 14.50 |
| Nos. 69-72 (4) | 25.00 | 55.25 |
| Nos. 226-229 (4) | 5.15 | 9.90 |

| | | |
|---|---|---|
| Nos. 67-70 (4) | 13.60 | 30.70 |
| Nos. 226-229 (4) | 16.30 | 56.00 |
| Nos. 422-425 (4) | 9.35 | 3.95 |
| Nos. 508-510 (3) | 26.00 | 33.50 |
| Nos. 152-154 (3) | 49.50 | 45.35 |
| Nos. 211-216 (6) | 23.85 | 13.35 |
| Nos. 98-100 (3) | 9.65 | 12.00 |
| Nos. 142-148 (7) | 28.85 | 14.00 |
| Nos. 31-34 (4) | 12.35 | 13.15 |
| Nos. 46-47 (2) | 4.35 | 1.70 |
| Nos. 199-201 (3) | 23.00 | 28.50 |
| Nos. 67-69 (3) | 19.25 | 31.00 |
| Nos. 114-117 (4) | 9.20 | 17.50 |
| Nos. 163-165 (3) | 4.40 | 6.50 |
| Nos. 68-71 (4) | 57.50 | 153.00 |
| Nos. 33-36 (4) | 27.75 | 45.25 |
| Nos. 121-124 (4) | 13.00 | 36.10 |
| Set total (245) Stamps | 1,401. | 2,231. |

### Coronation

Queen Elizabeth and King George VI CD302

**1937**

| | |
|---|---|
| Aden | 13-15 |
| Antigua | 81-83 |
| Ascension | 37-39 |
| Bahamas | 97-99 |
| Barbados | 190-192 |
| Basutoland | 15-17 |
| Bechuanaland Protectorate | 121-123 |
| Bermuda | 115-117 |
| British Guiana | 227-229 |
| British Honduras | 112-114 |
| Cayman Islands | 97-99 |
| Ceylon | 275-277 |
| Cyprus | 140-142 |
| Dominica | 94-96 |
| Falkland Islands | 81-83 |
| Fiji | 114-116 |
| Gambia | 129-131 |
| Gibraltar | 104-106 |
| Gilbert & Ellice Islands | 37-39 |
| Gold Coast | 112-114 |
| Grenada | 128-130 |
| Hong Kong | 151-153 |
| Jamaica | 113-115 |
| Kenya, Uganda, Tanzania | 60-62 |
| Leeward Islands | 100-102 |
| Malta | 188-190 |
| Mauritius | 208-210 |
| Montserrat | 89-91 |
| Newfoundland | 230-232 |
| Nigeria | 50-52 |
| Northern Rhodesia | 22-24 |
| Nyasaland Protectorate | 51-53 |
| St. Helena | 115-117 |
| St. Kitts-Nevis | 76-78 |
| St. Lucia | 107-109 |
| St. Vincent | 138-140 |
| Seychelles | 122-124 |
| Sierra Leone | 170-172 |
| Solomon Islands | 64-66 |
| Somaliland Protectorate | 81-83 |
| Straits Settlements | 235-237 |
| Swaziland | 24-26 |
| Trinidad & Tobago | 47-49 |
| Turks & Caicos Islands | 75-77 |
| Virgin Islands | 73-75 |

The following have different designs but are included in the omnibus set:

| | |
|---|---|
| Great Britain | 234 |
| Offices in Morocco (Sp. Curr.) | 82 |
| Offices in Morocco (Fr. Curr.) | 439 |
| Offices in Morocco (Tangier) | 514 |
| Canada | 237 |
| Cook Islands | 109-111 |
| Nauru | 35-38 |
| Newfoundland | 233-243 |
| New Guinea | 48-51 |
| New Zealand | 223-225 |
| Niue | 70-72 |
| Papua | 118-121 |
| South Africa | 74-78 |
| Southern Rhodesia | 38-41 |
| South-West Africa | 125-132 |

| | | |
|---|---|---|
| Nos. 13-15 (3) | 2.70 | 5.65 |
| Nos. 81-83 (3) | 1.85 | 8.00 |
| Nos. 37-39 (3) | 2.75 | 2.75 |
| Nos. 97-99 (3) | 1.05 | 3.05 |
| Nos. 190-192 (3) | 1.10 | 1.95 |
| Nos. 15-17 (3) | 1.15 | 3.00 |
| Nos. 121-123 (3) | .95 | 3.35 |
| Nos. 115-117 (3) | 1.25 | 5.00 |
| Nos. 227-229 (3) | 1.45 | 3.05 |
| Nos. 112-114 (3) | 1.20 | 2.40 |
| Nos. 97-99 (3) | 1.10 | 2.70 |
| Nos. 275-277 (3) | 8.25 | 10.35 |

| | | |
|---|---|---|
| Nos. 140-142 (3) | 3.75 | 6.50 |
| Nos. 94-96 (3) | .85 | 2.40 |
| Nos. 81-83 (3) | 2.90 | 2.30 |
| Nos. 114-116 (3) | 1.35 | 5.75 |
| Nos. 129-131 (3) | .95 | 3.95 |
| Nos. 104-106 (3) | 2.25 | 6.45 |
| Nos. 37-39 (3) | .85 | 2.15 |
| Nos. 112-114 (3) | 3.10 | 10.00 |
| Nos. 128-130 (3) | 1.00 | .85 |
| Nos. 151-153 (3) | 17.00 | 17.75 |
| Nos. 113-115 (3) | 1.25 | 1.25 |
| Nos. 60-62 (3) | 1.25 | 2.35 |
| Nos. 100-102 (3) | 1.55 | 4.00 |
| Nos. 188-190 (3) | 1.25 | 1.60 |
| Nos. 208-210 (3) | 1.75 | 3.50 |
| Nos. 89-91 (3) | 1.00 | 3.35 |
| Nos. 230-232 (3) | 7.00 | 2.80 |
| Nos. 50-52 (3) | 3.25 | 8.50 |
| Nos. 22-24 (3) | .95 | 2.25 |
| Nos. 51-53 (3) | 1.05 | 1.30 |
| Nos. 115-117 (3) | 1.45 | 2.05 |
| Nos. 76-78 (3) | .95 | 2.15 |
| Nos. 107-109 (3) | 1.05 | 2.05 |
| Nos. 138-140 (3) | .80 | 4.75 |
| Nos. 122-124 (3) | 1.20 | 1.90 |
| Nos. 170-172 (3) | 1.95 | 5.65 |
| Nos. 64-66 (3) | .90 | 2.00 |
| Nos. 81-83 (3) | 1.10 | 3.50 |
| Nos. 235-237 (3) | 3.25 | 1.60 |
| Nos. 24-26 (3) | .75 | 2.70 |
| Nos. 47-49 (3) | 1.10 | 3.20 |
| Nos. 75-77 (3) | 1.25 | .95 |
| Nos. 73-75 (3) | 2.20 | 6.90 |

| | | |
|---|---|---|
| No. 234 (1) | .30 | .25 |
| No. 82 (1) | .80 | .60 |
| No. 439 (1) | .50 | .25 |
| No. 514 (1) | 1.25 | .50 |
| No. 237 (1) | .35 | .25 |
| Nos. 109-111 (3) | .85 | .40 |
| Nos. 35-38 (4) | 1.25 | 5.50 |
| Nos. 233-243 (11) | 41.90 | 30.40 |
| Nos. 48-51 (4) | 1.40 | 7.90 |
| Nos. 223-225 (3) | 1.75 | 2.25 |
| Nos. 70-72 (3) | .90 | 2.05 |
| Nos. 118-121 (4) | 1.60 | 5.25 |
| Nos. 74-78 (5) | 7.60 | 9.35 |
| Nos. 38-41 (4) | 3.55 | 15.50 |
| Nos. 125-132 (8) | 5.00 | 8.40 |
| Set total (189) Stamps | 166.05 | 268.90 |

### Peace

King George VI and Parliament Buildings, London CD303

Return to peace at the close of World War II.

**1945-46**

| | |
|---|---|
| Aden | 28-29 |
| Antigua | 96-97 |
| Ascension | 50-51 |
| Bahamas | 130-131 |
| Barbados | 207-208 |
| Bermuda | 131-132 |
| British Guiana | 242-243 |
| British Honduras | 127-128 |
| Cayman Islands | 112-113 |
| Ceylon | 293-294 |
| Cyprus | 156-157 |
| Dominica | 112-113 |
| Falkland Islands | 97-98 |
| Falkland Islands Dep. | 1L9-1L10 |
| Fiji | 137-138 |
| Gambia | 144-145 |
| Gibraltar | 119-120 |
| Gilbert & Ellice Islands | 52-53 |
| Gold Coast | 128-129 |
| Grenada | 143-144 |
| Jamaica | 136-137 |
| Kenya, Uganda, Tanzania | 90-91 |
| Leeward Islands | 116-117 |
| Malta | 206-207 |
| Mauritius | 223-224 |
| Montserrat | 104-105 |
| Nigeria | 71-72 |
| Northern Rhodesia | 46-47 |
| Nyasaland Protectorate | 82-83 |
| Pitcairn Islands | 9-10 |
| St. Helena | 128-129 |
| St. Kitts-Nevis | 91-92 |
| St. Lucia | 127-128 |
| St. Vincent | 152-153 |
| Seychelles | 149-150 |
| Sierra Leone | 186-187 |
| Solomon Islands | 80-81 |
| Somaliland Protectorate | 108-109 |
| Trinidad & Tobago | 62-63 |
| Turks & Caicos Islands | 90-91 |
| Virgin Islands | 88-89 |

The following have different designs but are included in the omnibus set:

| | |
|---|---|
| Great Britain | 264-265 |

| | |
|---|---|
| Offices in Morocco (Tangier) | 523-524 |
| Aden | |
| Kathiri State of Seiyun | 12-13 |
| Qu'aiti State of Shihr and Mukalla | |
| | 12-13 |
| Australia | 200-202 |
| Basutoland | 29-31 |
| Bechuanaland Protectorate | 137-139 |
| Burma | 66-69 |
| Cook Islands | 127-130 |
| Hong Kong | 174-175 |
| India | 195-198 |
| Hyderabad | 51-53 |
| New Zealand | 247-257 |
| Niue | 90-93 |
| Pakistan-Bahawalpur | O16 |
| Samoa | 191-194 |
| South Africa | 100-102 |
| Southern Rhodesia | 67-70 |
| South-West Africa | 153-155 |
| Swaziland | 38-40 |
| Zanzibar | 222-223 |

| | | |
|---|---|---|
| Nos. 28-29 (2) | .95 | 2.50 |
| Nos. 96-97 (2) | .50 | .80 |
| Nos. 50-51 (2) | .80 | 2.00 |
| Nos. 130-131 (2) | .50 | 1.40 |
| Nos. 207-208 (2) | .50 | 1.10 |
| Nos. 131-132 (2) | .55 | .55 |
| Nos. 242-243 (2) | 1.05 | 1.40 |
| Nos. 127-128 (2) | .50 | .50 |
| Nos. 112-113 (2) | .80 | .80 |
| Nos. 293-294 (2) | .60 | 2.10 |
| Nos. 156-157 (2) | .90 | .70 |
| Nos. 112-113 (2) | .50 | .50 |
| Nos. 97-98 (2) | .90 | 1.35 |
| Nos. 1L9-1L10 (2) | 1.30 | 1.00 |
| Nos. 137-138 (2) | .75 | 1.75 |
| Nos. 144-145 (2) | .60 | .95 |
| Nos. 119-120 (2) | .75 | 1.00 |
| Nos. 52-53 (2) | .50 | 1.10 |
| Nos. 128-129 (2) | 1.85 | 3.75 |
| Nos. 143-144 (2) | .50 | .95 |
| Nos. 136-137 (2) | 2.00 | 13.50 |
| Nos. 90-91 (2) | .65 | .85 |
| Nos. 116-117 (2) | .50 | 1.50 |
| Nos. 206-207 (2) | .65 | 2.00 |
| Nos. 223-224 (2) | .50 | 1.05 |
| Nos. 104-105 (2) | .50 | .50 |
| Nos. 71-72 (2) | .70 | 2.75 |
| Nos. 46-47 (2) | 1.25 | 2.00 |
| Nos. 82-83 (2) | .55 | .60 |
| Nos. 9-10 (2) | 1.40 | .60 |
| Nos. 128-129 (2) | .65 | .70 |
| Nos. 91-92 (2) | .50 | .50 |
| Nos. 127-128 (2) | .50 | .60 |
| Nos. 152-153 (2) | .50 | .50 |
| Nos. 149-150 (2) | .55 | .50 |
| Nos. 186-187 (2) | .50 | .50 |
| Nos. 80-81 (2) | .50 | 1.50 |
| Nos. 108-109 (2) | .70 | .50 |
| Nos. 62-63 (2) | .75 | 1.85 |
| Nos. 90-91 (2) | .50 | .50 |
| Nos. 88-89 (2) | .50 | .50 |

| | | |
|---|---|---|
| Nos. 264-265 (2) | .50 | .50 |
| Nos. 523-524 (2) | 2.00 | 2.55 |
| Nos. 12-13 (2) | .50 | .90 |
| Nos. 12-13 (2) | .50 | 1.25 |
| Nos. 200-202 (3) | 1.60 | 1.25 |
| Nos. 29-31 (3) | 2.10 | 2.60 |
| Nos. 137-139 (3) | 2.05 | 4.75 |
| Nos. 66-69 (4) | 1.50 | 1.25 |
| Nos. 127-130 (4) | 2.00 | 1.85 |
| Nos. 174-175 (2) | 6.75 | 2.75 |
| Nos. 195-198 (4) | 5.60 | 5.50 |
| Nos. 51-53 (3) | 1.50 | 1.70 |
| Nos. 247-257 (11) | 3.35 | 3.65 |
| Nos. 90-93 (4) | 1.70 | 2.20 |
| No. O16 (1) | 15.00 | 10.00 |
| Nos. 191-194 (4) | 2.05 | 1.00 |
| Nos. 100-102 (3) | 1.00 | 3.25 |
| Nos. 67-70 (4) | 1.40 | 1.75 |
| Nos. 153-155 (3) | 1.85 | 3.25 |
| Nos. 38-40 (3) | 2.40 | 5.50 |
| Nos. 222-223 (2) | .65 | 1.00 |
| Set total (151) Stamps | 86.15 | 118.15 |

### Silver Wedding

King George VI and Queen Elizabeth

CD304      CD305

**1948-49**

| | |
|---|---|
| Aden | 30-31 |
| Kathiri State of Seiyun | 14-15 |
| Qu'aiti State of Shihr and Mukalla | |
| | 14-15 |

| | |
|---|---|
| Antigua | 98-99 |
| Ascension | 52-53 |
| Bahamas | 148-149 |
| Barbados | 210-211 |
| Basutoland | 39-40 |
| Bechuanaland Protectorate | 147-148 |
| Bermuda | 133-134 |
| British Guiana | 244-245 |
| British Honduras | 129-130 |
| Cayman Islands | 116-117 |
| Cyprus | 158-159 |
| Dominica | 114-115 |
| Falkland Islands | 99-100 |
| Falkland Islands Dep. | 1L11-1L12 |
| Fiji | 139-140 |
| Gambia | 146-147 |
| Gibraltar | 121-122 |
| Gilbert & Ellice Islands | 54-55 |
| Gold Coast | 142-143 |
| Grenada | 145-146 |
| Hong Kong | 178-179 |
| Jamaica | 138-139 |
| Kenya, Uganda, Tanzania | 92-93 |
| Leeward Islands | 118-119 |
| Malaya | |
| Johore | 128-129 |
| Kedah | 55-56 |
| Kelantan | 44-45 |
| Malacca | 1-2 |
| Negri Sembilan | 36-37 |
| Pahang | 44-45 |
| Penang | 1-2 |
| Perak | 99-100 |
| Perlis | 1-2 |
| Selangor | 74-75 |
| Trengganu | 47-48 |
| Malta | 223-224 |
| Mauritius | 229-230 |
| Montserrat | 106-107 |
| Nigeria | 73-74 |
| North Borneo | 238-239 |
| Northern Rhodesia | 48-49 |
| Nyasaland Protectorate | 85-86 |
| Pitcairn Islands | 11-12 |
| St. Helena | 130-131 |
| St. Kitts-Nevis | 93-94 |
| St. Lucia | 129-130 |
| St. Vincent | 154-155 |
| Sarawak | 174-175 |
| Seychelles | 151-152 |
| Sierra Leone | 188-189 |
| Singapore | 21-22 |
| Solomon Islands | 82-83 |
| Somaliland Protectorate | 110-111 |
| Swaziland | 48-49 |
| Trinidad & Tobago | 64-65 |
| Turks & Caicos Islands | 92-93 |
| Virgin Islands | 90-91 |
| Zanzibar | 224-225 |

The following have different designs but are included in the omnibus set:

| | |
|---|---|
| Great Britain | 267-268 |
| Offices in Morocco (Sp. Curr.) | 93-94 |
| Offices in Morocco (Tangier) | 525-526 |
| Bahrain | 62-63 |
| Kuwait | 82-83 |
| Oman | 25-26 |
| South Africa | 106 |
| South-West Africa | 159 |

| | | |
|---|---|---|
| Nos. 30-31 (2) | 40.40 | 56.50 |
| Nos. 14-15 (2) | 17.85 | 16.00 |
| Nos. 14-15 (2) | 18.55 | 12.50 |
| Nos. 98-99 (2) | 13.55 | 15.75 |
| Nos. 52-53 (2) | 55.55 | 50.45 |
| Nos. 148-149 (2) | 45.25 | 40.30 |
| Nos. 210-211 (2) | 18.35 | 13.55 |
| Nos. 39-40 (2) | 52.80 | 55.25 |
| Nos. 147-148 (2) | 42.85 | 47.75 |
| Nos. 133-134 (2) | 47.75 | 55.25 |
| Nos. 244-245 (2) | 24.25 | 28.45 |
| Nos. 129-130 (2) | 25.25 | 53.20 |
| Nos. 116-117 (2) | 25.25 | 33.50 |
| Nos. 158-159 (2) | 58.50 | 78.05 |
| Nos. 114-115 (2) | 25.25 | 32.75 |
| Nos. 99-100 (2) | 112.10 | 76.10 |
| Nos. 1L11-1L12 (2) | 4.25 | 6.00 |
| Nos. 139-140 (2) | 18.20 | 11.50 |
| Nos. 146-147 (2) | 21.30 | 21.25 |
| Nos. 121-122 (2) | 61.00 | 78.00 |
| Nos. 54-55 (2) | 14.25 | 26.25 |
| Nos. 142-143 (2) | 35.25 | 48.20 |
| Nos. 145-146 (2) | 21.75 | 21.75 |
| Nos. 178-179 (2) | 329.00 | 106.75 |
| Nos. 138-139 (2) | 30.35 | 75.25 |
| Nos. 92-93 (2) | 51.00 | 68.00 |
| Nos. 118-119 (2) | 7.00 | 8.25 |
| Nos. 128-129 (2) | 29.25 | 53.25 |
| Nos. 55-56 (2) | 35.25 | 50.25 |
| Nos. 44-45 (2) | 35.75 | 62.75 |
| Nos. 1-2 (2) | 35.40 | 49.75 |
| Nos. 36-37 (2) | 28.10 | 38.20 |
| Nos. 44-45 (2) | 28.00 | 38.05 |
| Nos. 1-2 (2) | 40.50 | 37.80 |

| | | |
|---|---|---|
| *Nos. 99-100 (2)* | 27.80 | *37.75* |
| *Nos. 1-2 (2)* | 33.50 | *58.00* |
| *Nos. 74-75 (2)* | 30.25 | *25.30* |
| *Nos. 47-48 (2)* | 32.75 | *61.75* |
| *Nos. 223-224 (2)* | 40.55 | *45.25* |
| *Nos. 229-230 (2)* | 19.25 | *45.25* |
| *Nos. 106-107 (2)* | 8.75 | *17.25* |
| *Nos. 73-74 (2)* | 17.85 | *22.80* |
| *Nos. 238-239 (2)* | 35.30 | *45.75* |
| *Nos. 48-49 (2)* | 100.30 | *90.25* |
| *Nos. 85-86 (2)* | 18.25 | *35.25* |
| *Nos. 11-12 (2)* | 44.50 | *54.00* |
| *Nos. 130-131 (2)* | 32.80 | *42.80* |
| *Nos. 93-94 (2)* | 13.25 | *10.50* |
| *Nos. 129-130 (2)* | 22.25 | *40.25* |
| *Nos. 154-155 (2)* | 27.75 | *30.25* |
| *Nos. 174-175 (2)* | 52.80 | *67.80* |
| *Nos. 151-152 (2)* | 16.25 | *48.25* |
| *Nos. 188-189 (2)* | 25.25 | *29.75* |
| *Nos. 21-22 (2)* | 116.00 | *45.40* |
| *Nos. 82-83 (2)* | 13.40 | *13.40* |
| *Nos. 110-111 (2)* | 8.40 | *8.75* |
| *Nos. 48-49 (2)* | 40.30 | *47.75* |
| *Nos. 64-65 (2)* | 31.80 | *50.25* |
| *Nos. 92-93 (2)* | 16.25 | *22.75* |
| *Nos. 90-91 (2)* | 16.25 | *22.25* |
| *Nos. 224-225 (2)* | 29.60 | *38.00* |
| | | |
| *Nos. 267-268 (2)* | 30.40 | *25.75* |
| *Nos. 93-94 (2)* | 17.10 | *25.75* |
| *Nos. 525-526 (2)* | 22.90 | *32.75* |
| *Nos. 62-63 (2)* | 38.50 | *57.75* |
| *Nos. 82-83 (2)* | 69.50 | *45.50* |
| *Nos. 25-26 (2)* | 41.00 | *42.50* |
| *No. 106 (1)* | .80 | *1.00* |
| *No. 159 (1)* | 1.10 | *.35* |
| *Set total (136) Stamps* | 2,542. | *2,754.* |

## U.P.U.

Mercury and Symbols of Communications — CD306

Plane, Ship and Hemispheres — CD307

Mercury Scattering Letters over Globe CD308

U.P.U. Monument, Bern CD309

Universal Postal Union, 75th anniversary.

### 1949

| | |
|---|---|
| Aden | 32-35 |
|   Kathiri State of Seiyun | 16-19 |
|   Qu'aiti State of Shihr and Mukalla | 16-19 |
| Antigua | 100-103 |
| Ascension | 57-60 |
| Bahamas | 150-153 |
| Barbados | 212-215 |
| Basutoland | 41-44 |
| Bechuanaland Protectorate | 149-152 |
| Bermuda | 138-141 |
| British Guiana | 246-249 |
| British Honduras | 137-140 |
| Brunei | 79-82 |
| Cayman Islands | 118-121 |
| Cyprus | 160-163 |
| Dominica | 116-119 |
| Falkland Islands | 103-106 |
| Falkland Islands Dep. | 1L14-1L17 |
| Fiji | 141-144 |
| Gambia | 148-151 |
| Gibraltar | 123-126 |

| | |
|---|---|
| Gilbert & Ellice Islands | 56-59 |
| Gold Coast | 144-147 |
| Grenada | 147-150 |
| Hong Kong | 180-183 |
| Jamaica | 142-145 |
| Kenya, Uganda, Tanzania | 94-97 |
| Leeward Islands | 126-129 |
| Malaya | |
|   Johore | 151-154 |
|   Kedah | 57-60 |
|   Kelantan | 46-49 |
|   Malacca | 18-21 |
|   Negri Sembilan | 59-62 |
|   Pahang | 46-49 |
|   Penang | 23-26 |
|   Perak | 101-104 |
|   Perlis | 3-6 |
|   Selangor | 76-79 |
|   Trengganu | 49-52 |
| Malta | 225-228 |
| Mauritius | 231-234 |
| Montserrat | 108-111 |
| New Hebrides, British | 62-65 |
| New Hebrides, French | 79-82 |
| Nigeria | 75-78 |
| North Borneo | 240-243 |
| Northern Rhodesia | 50-53 |
| Nyasaland Protectorate | 87-90 |
| Pitcairn Islands | 13-16 |
| St. Helena | 132-135 |
| St. Kitts-Nevis | 95-98 |
| St. Lucia | 131-134 |
| St. Vincent | 170-173 |
| Sarawak | 176-179 |
| Seychelles | 153-156 |
| Sierra Leone | 190-193 |
| Singapore | 23-26 |
| Solomon Islands | 84-87 |
| Somaliland Protectorate | 112-115 |
| Southern Rhodesia | 71-72 |
| Swaziland | 50-53 |
| Tonga | 87-90 |
| Trinidad & Tobago | 66-69 |
| Turks & Caicos Islands | 101-104 |
| Virgin Islands | 92-95 |
| Zanzibar | 226-229 |

The following have different designs but are included in the omnibus set:

| | |
|---|---|
| Great Britain | 276-279 |
| Offices in Morocco (Tangier) | 546-549 |
| Australia | 223 |
| Bahrain | 68-71 |
| Burma | 116-121 |
| Ceylon | 304-306 |
| Egypt | 281-283 |
| India | 223-226 |
| Kuwait | 89-92 |
| Oman | 31-34 |
| Pakistan-Bahawalpur | 26-29, O25-O28 |
| South Africa | 109-111 |
| South-West Africa | 160-162 |

| | | |
|---|---|---|
| *Nos. 32-35 (4)* | 5.85 | *8.45* |
| *Nos. 16-19 (4)* | 2.75 | *16.00* |
| *Nos. 16-19 (4)* | 2.60 | *8.00* |
| *Nos. 100-103 (4)* | 3.60 | *7.70* |
| *Nos. 57-60 (4)* | 11.10 | *9.00* |
| *Nos. 150-153 (4)* | 5.35 | *9.30* |
| *Nos. 212-215 (4)* | 4.40 | *14.85* |
| *Nos. 41-44 (4)* | 4.75 | *10.00* |
| *Nos. 149-152 (4)* | 3.35 | *7.25* |
| *Nos. 138-141 (4)* | 4.75 | *6.15* |
| *Nos. 246-249 (4)* | 2.75 | *4.20* |
| *Nos. 137-140 (4)* | 3.30 | *6.35* |
| *Nos. 79-82 (4)* | 9.50 | *8.45* |
| *Nos. 118-121 (4)* | 3.60 | *7.25* |
| *Nos. 160-163 (4)* | 4.60 | *10.70* |
| *Nos. 116-119 (4)* | 2.30 | *5.65* |
| *Nos. 103-106 (4)* | 14.00 | *17.10* |
| *Nos. 1L14-1L17 (4)* | 14.60 | *14.50* |
| *Nos. 141-144 (4)* | 3.35 | *15.75* |
| *Nos. 148-151 (4)* | 2.75 | *7.10* |
| *Nos. 123-126 (4)* | 5.90 | *8.75* |
| *Nos. 56-59 (4)* | 4.30 | *13.00* |
| *Nos. 144-147 (4)* | 2.55 | *10.35* |
| *Nos. 147-150 (4)* | 2.15 | *3.55* |
| *Nos. 180-183 (4)* | 66.75 | *19.95* |
| *Nos. 142-145 (4)* | 2.50 | *2.45* |
| *Nos. 94-97 (4)* | 2.90 | *4.00* |
| *Nos. 126-129 (4)* | 3.05 | *9.60* |
| *Nos. 151-154 (4)* | 4.70 | *8.90* |
| *Nos. 57-60 (4)* | 4.80 | *12.00* |
| *Nos. 46-49 (4)* | 4.25 | *12.65* |
| *Nos. 18-21 (4)* | 4.25 | *17.30* |
| *Nos. 59-62 (4)* | 3.50 | *10.75* |
| *Nos. 46-49 (4)* | 3.00 | *7.25* |
| *Nos. 23-26 (4)* | 5.10 | *11.75* |
| *Nos. 101-104 (4)* | 3.65 | *10.75* |
| *Nos. 3-6 (4)* | 3.95 | *14.25* |
| *Nos. 76-79 (4)* | 4.90 | *12.30* |
| *Nos. 49-52 (4)* | 5.55 | *12.25* |
| *Nos. 225-228 (4)* | 4.50 | *4.85* |
| *Nos. 231-234 (4)* | 3.70 | *7.05* |
| *Nos. 108-111 (4)* | 3.30 | *4.35* |
| *Nos. 62-65 (4)* | 1.60 | *4.25* |
| *Nos. 79-82 (4)* | 15.40 | *22.00* |

| | | |
|---|---|---|
| *Nos. 75-78 (4)* | 2.80 | *9.25* |
| *Nos. 240-243 (4)* | 7.15 | *6.50* |
| *Nos. 50-53 (4)* | 5.00 | *6.50* |
| *Nos. 87-90 (4)* | 4.55 | *6.60* |
| *Nos. 13-16 (4)* | 15.05 | *14.25* |
| *Nos. 132-135 (4)* | 4.85 | *7.10* |
| *Nos. 95-98 (4)* | 4.35 | *5.55* |
| *Nos. 131-134 (4)* | 2.55 | *3.85* |
| *Nos. 170-173 (4)* | 2.20 | *5.05* |
| *Nos. 176-179 (4)* | 13.40 | *13.35* |
| *Nos. 153-156 (4)* | 3.00 | *5.15* |
| *Nos. 190-193 (4)* | 2.90 | *9.15* |
| *Nos. 23-26 (4)* | 19.00 | *13.70* |
| *Nos. 84-87 (4)* | 4.05 | *4.90* |
| *Nos. 112-115 (4)* | 3.95 | *9.95* |
| *Nos. 71-72 (4)* | 1.95 | *2.25* |
| *Nos. 50-53 (4)* | 2.80 | *4.65* |
| *Nos. 87-90 (4)* | 3.00 | *5.25* |
| *Nos. 66-69 (4)* | 3.55 | *6.80* |
| *Nos. 101-104 (4)* | 3.05 | *8.90* |
| *Nos. 92-95 (4)* | 2.60 | *5.90* |
| *Nos. 226-229 (4)* | 4.95 | *13.50* |
| | | |
| *Nos. 276-279 (4)* | 1.35 | *1.00* |
| *Nos. 546-549 (4)* | 2.60 | *16.00* |
| *No. 223 (1)* | .40 | *.40* |
| *Nos. 68-71 (4)* | 4.75 | *16.50* |
| *Nos. 116-121 (6)* | 7.30 | *5.35* |
| *Nos. 304-306 (3)* | 3.35 | *4.25* |
| *Nos. 281-283 (3)* | 5.75 | *2.70* |
| *Nos. 223-226 (4)* | 27.25 | *10.50* |
| *Nos. 89-92 (4)* | 6.10 | *10.25* |
| *Nos. 31-34 (4)* | 8.00 | *17.50* |
| *Nos. 26-29, O25-O28 (8)* | 2.40 | *44.00* |
| *Nos. 109-111 (3)* | 2.00 | *2.70* |
| *Nos. 160-162 (3)* | 3.00 | *5.50* |
| *Set total (313) Stamps* | 466.45 | *742.80* |

## University

Arms of University College CD310

Alice, Princess of Athlone CD311

1948 opening of University College of the West Indies at Jamaica.

### 1951

| | |
|---|---|
| Antigua | 104-105 |
| Barbados | 228-229 |
| British Guiana | 250-251 |
| British Honduras | 141-142 |
| Dominica | 120-121 |
| Grenada | 164-165 |
| Jamaica | 146-147 |
| Leeward Islands | 130-131 |
| Montserrat | 112-113 |
| St. Kitts-Nevis | 105-106 |
| St. Lucia | 149-150 |
| St. Vincent | 174-175 |
| Trinidad & Tobago | 70-71 |
| Virgin Islands | 96-97 |

| | | |
|---|---|---|
| *Nos. 104-105 (2)* | 1.35 | *3.75* |
| *Nos. 228-229 (2)* | 1.75 | *2.65* |
| *Nos. 250-251 (2)* | 1.10 | *1.25* |
| *Nos. 141-142 (2)* | 1.40 | *2.20* |
| *Nos. 120-121 (2)* | 1.40 | *1.75* |
| *Nos. 164-165 (2)* | 1.20 | *1.60* |
| *Nos. 146-147 (2)* | 1.05 | *.70* |
| *Nos. 130-131 (2)* | 1.35 | *4.00* |
| *Nos. 112-113 (2)* | .85 | *2.00* |
| *Nos. 105-106 (2)* | 1.40 | *2.25* |
| *Nos. 149-150 (2)* | 1.40 | *1.50* |
| *Nos. 174-175 (2)* | 1.00 | *2.15* |
| *Nos. 70-71 (2)* | 1.00 | *4.20* |
| *Nos. 96-97 (2)* | 1.50 | *3.75* |
| *Set total (28) Stamps* | 17.75 | *33.75* |

## Coronation

Queen Elizabeth II — CD312

### 1953

| | |
|---|---|
| Aden | 47 |
|   Kathiri State of Seiyun | 28 |

| | |
|---|---|
|   Qu'aiti State of Shihr and Mukalla | 28 |
| Antigua | 106 |
| Ascension | 61 |
| Bahamas | 157 |
| Barbados | 234 |
| Basutoland | 45 |
| Bechuanaland Protectorate | 153 |
| Bermuda | 142 |
| British Guiana | 252 |
| British Honduras | 143 |
| Cayman Islands | 150 |
| Cyprus | 167 |
| Dominica | 141 |
| Falkland Islands | 121 |
| Falkland Islands Dependencies | 1L18 |
| Fiji | 145 |
| Gambia | 152 |
| Gibraltar | 131 |
| Gilbert & Ellice Islands | 60 |
| Gold Coast | 160 |
| Grenada | 170 |
| Hong Kong | 184 |
| Jamaica | 153 |
| Kenya, Uganda, Tanzania | 101 |
| Leeward Islands | 132 |
| Malaya | |
|   Johore | 155 |
|   Kedah | 82 |
|   Kelantan | 71 |
|   Malacca | 27 |
|   Negri Sembilan | 63 |
|   Pahang | 71 |
|   Penang | 27 |
|   Perak | 126 |
|   Perlis | 28 |
|   Selangor | 101 |
|   Trengganu | 74 |
| Malta | 241 |
| Mauritius | 250 |
| Montserrat | 127 |
| New Hebrides, British | 77 |
| Nigeria | 79 |
| North Borneo | 260 |
| Northern Rhodesia | 60 |
| Nyasaland Protectorate | 96 |
| Pitcairn Islands | 19 |
| St. Helena | 139 |
| St. Kitts-Nevis | 119 |
| St. Lucia | 156 |
| St. Vincent | 185 |
| Sarawak | 196 |
| Seychelles | 172 |
| Sierra Leone | 194 |
| Singapore | 27 |
| Solomon Islands | 88 |
| Somaliland Protectorate | 127 |
| Swaziland | 54 |
| Trinidad & Tobago | 84 |
| Tristan da Cunha | 13 |
| Turks & Caicos Islands | 118 |
| Virgin Islands | 114 |

The following have different designs but are included in the omnibus set:

| | |
|---|---|
| Great Britain | 313-316 |
| Offices in Morocco (Tangier) | 579-582 |
| Australia | 259-261 |
| Bahrain | 92-95 |
| Canada | 330 |
| Ceylon | 317 |
| Cook Islands | 145-146 |
| Kuwait | 113-116 |
| New Zealand | 280-284 |
| Niue | 104-105 |
| Oman | 52-55 |
| Samoa | 214-215 |
| South Africa | 192 |
| Southern Rhodesia | 80 |
| South-West Africa | 244-248 |
| Tokelau Islands | 4 |

| | | |
|---|---|---|
| *No. 47 (1)* | 1.25 | *1.25* |
| *No. 28 (1)* | .75 | *1.50* |
| *No. 28 (1)* | 1.10 | *.60* |
| *No. 106 (1)* | .40 | *.75* |
| *No. 61 (1)* | 1.25 | *2.75* |
| *No. 157 (1)* | 1.40 | *.75* |
| *No. 234 (1)* | 1.00 | *.25* |
| *No. 45 (1)* | .50 | *.60* |
| *No. 153 (1)* | .50 | *.35* |
| *No. 142 (1)* | .85 | *.50* |
| *No. 252 (1)* | .45 | *.25* |
| *No. 143 (1)* | .60 | *.40* |
| *No. 150 (1)* | .40 | *1.75* |
| *No. 167 (1)* | 1.60 | *.75* |
| *No. 141 (1)* | .40 | *.40* |
| *No. 121 (1)* | .90 | *1.50* |
| *No. 1L18 (1)* | 1.80 | *1.40* |
| *No. 145 (1)* | 1.00 | *.60* |
| *No. 152 (1)* | .50 | *.50* |
| *No. 131 (1)* | .50 | *.50* |
| *No. 60 (1)* | .65 | *2.25* |
| *No. 160 (1)* | 1.00 | *.25* |

| | | |
|---|---|---|
| No. 170 (1) | .30 | .25 |
| No. 184 (1) | 3.00 | .30 |
| No. 153 (1) | .70 | .25 |
| No. 101 (1) | .40 | .25 |
| No. 132 (1) | 1.00 | 2.25 |
| No. 155 (1) | 1.40 | .30 |
| No. 82 (1) | 2.25 | .60 |
| No. 71 (1) | 1.60 | 1.60 |
| No. 27 (1) | 1.10 | 1.50 |
| No. 63 (1) | 1.40 | .65 |
| No. 71 (1) | 2.25 | .25 |
| No. 27 (1) | 1.75 | .30 |
| No. 126 (1) | 1.60 | .25 |
| No. 28 (1) | 1.75 | 4.00 |
| No. 101 (1) | 1.75 | .25 |
| No. 74 (1) | 1.50 | 1.00 |
| No. 241 (1) | .50 | .25 |
| No. 250 (1) | 1.10 | .25 |
| No. 127 (1) | .60 | .45 |
| No. 77 (1) | .75 | .60 |
| No. 79 (1) | .40 | .25 |
| No. 260 (1) | 1.75 | 1.00 |
| No. 60 (1) | .70 | .25 |
| No. 96 (1) | .75 | .75 |
| No. 19 (1) | 2.00 | 3.50 |
| No. 139 (1) | 1.25 | 1.25 |
| No. 119 (1) | .35 | .25 |
| No. 156 (1) | .70 | .35 |
| No. 185 (1) | .50 | .30 |
| No. 196 (1) | 1.75 | 1.75 |
| No. 172 (1) | .80 | .80 |
| No. 194 (1) | .40 | .40 |
| No. 27 (1) | 2.50 | .40 |
| No. 88 (1) | 1.00 | 1.00 |
| No. 127 (1) | .40 | .25 |
| No. 54 (1) | .30 | .25 |
| No. 84 (1) | .30 | .25 |
| No. 13 (1) | 1.00 | 1.75 |
| No. 118 (1) | .40 | 1.10 |
| No. 114 (1) | .40 | 1.00 |
| Nos. 313-316 (4) | 11.40 | 4.05 |
| Nos. 579-582 (4) | 10.90 | 5.30 |
| Nos. 259-261 (3) | 3.60 | 2.75 |
| Nos. 92-95 (4) | 15.25 | 12.75 |
| No. 330 (1) | .30 | .25 |
| No. 317 (1) | 1.40 | .25 |
| Nos. 145-146 (2) | 2.65 | 2.65 |
| Nos. 113-116 (4) | 16.00 | 8.50 |
| Nos. 280-284 (5) | 3.30 | 4.55 |
| Nos. 104-105 (2) | 2.25 | 1.50 |
| No. 52-55 (4) | 14.25 | 6.50 |
| Nos. 214-215 (2) | 2.50 | .80 |
| No. 192 (1) | .45 | .30 |
| No. 80 (1) | 7.25 | 7.25 |
| Nos. 244-248 (5) | 3.00 | 2.35 |
| No. 4 (1) | 2.75 | 2.75 |
| Set total (106) Stamps | 160.40 | 114.75 |

Separate designs for each country for the visit of Queen Elizabeth II and the Duke of Edinburgh.

### Royal Visit 1953

**1953**

| | | |
|---|---|---|
| Aden | | .62 |
| Australia | | 267-269 |
| Bermuda | | 163 |
| Ceylon | | 318 |
| Fiji | | 146 |
| Gibraltar | | 146 |
| Jamaica | | 154 |
| Kenya, Uganda, Tanzania | | 102 |
| Malta | | 242 |
| New Zealand | | 286-287 |

| | | |
|---|---|---|
| No. 62 (1) | .65 | 4.00 |
| Nos. 267-269 (3) | 2.75 | 2.05 |
| No. 163 (1) | .50 | .25 |
| No. 318 (1) | 1.00 | .25 |
| No. 146 (1) | .65 | .35 |
| No. 146 (1) | .50 | .30 |
| No. 154 (1) | .50 | .25 |
| No. 102 (1) | .50 | .25 |
| No. 242 (1) | .35 | .25 |
| Nos. 286-287 (2) | .50 | .50 |
| Set total (13) Stamps | 7.90 | 8.45 |

### West Indies Federation

Map of the Caribbean CD313

Federation of the West Indies, April 22, 1958.

**1958**

| | | |
|---|---|---|
| Antigua | | 122-124 |
| Barbados | | 248-250 |
| Dominica | | 161-163 |
| Grenada | | 184-186 |
| Jamaica | | 175-177 |
| Montserrat | | 143-145 |
| St. Kitts-Nevis | | 136-138 |
| St. Lucia | | 170-172 |

| | | |
|---|---|---|
| St. Vincent | | 198-200 |
| Trinidad & Tobago | | 86-88 |

| | | |
|---|---|---|
| Nos. 122-124 (3) | 5.80 | 3.80 |
| Nos. 248-250 (3) | 1.60 | 2.90 |
| Nos. 161-163 (3) | 1.95 | 1.85 |
| Nos. 184-186 (3) | 1.50 | 1.20 |
| Nos. 175-177 (3) | 2.65 | 3.45 |
| Nos. 143-145 (3) | 2.35 | 1.35 |
| Nos. 136-138 (3) | 3.00 | 3.10 |
| Nos. 170-172 (3) | 2.05 | 2.80 |
| Nos. 198-200 (3) | 1.50 | 1.75 |
| Nos. 86-88 (3) | 2.40 | 2.35 |
| Set total (30) Stamps | 24.80 | 24.55 |

### Freedom from Hunger

Protein Food CD314

U.N. Food and Agricultural Organization's "Freedom from Hunger" campaign.

**1963**

| | |
|---|---|
| Aden | .65 |
| Antigua | 133 |
| Ascension | .89 |
| Bahamas | 180 |
| Basutoland | .83 |
| Bechuanaland Protectorate | 194 |
| Bermuda | 192 |
| British Guiana | 271 |
| British Honduras | 179 |
| Brunei | 100 |
| Cayman Islands | 168 |
| Dominica | 181 |
| Falkland Islands | 146 |
| Fiji | 198 |
| Gambia | 172 |
| Gibraltar | 161 |
| Gilbert & Ellice Islands | .76 |
| Grenada | 190 |
| Hong Kong | 218 |
| Malta | 291 |
| Mauritius | 270 |
| Montserrat | 150 |
| New Hebrides, British | .93 |
| North Borneo | 296 |
| Pitcairn Islands | .35 |
| St. Helena | 173 |
| St. Lucia | 179 |
| St. Vincent | 201 |
| Sarawak | 212 |
| Seychelles | 213 |
| Solomon Islands | 109 |
| Swaziland | 108 |
| Tonga | 127 |
| Tristan da Cunha | .68 |
| Turks & Caicos Islands | 138 |
| Virgin Islands | 140 |
| Zanzibar | 280 |

| | | |
|---|---|---|
| No. 65 (1) | 1.50 | 1.75 |
| No. 133 (1) | .35 | .35 |
| No. 89 (1) | 1.00 | .50 |
| No. 180 (1) | .65 | .65 |
| No. 83 (1) | .50 | .25 |
| No. 194 (1) | .50 | .50 |
| No. 192 (1) | 1.00 | .50 |
| No. 271 (1) | .45 | .25 |
| No. 179 (1) | .60 | .25 |
| No. 100 (1) | 3.25 | 2.25 |
| No. 168 (1) | .55 | .30 |
| No. 181 (1) | .30 | .30 |
| No. 146 (1) | 10.50 | 2.50 |
| No. 198 (1) | 3.50 | 2.25 |
| No. 172 (1) | .50 | .25 |
| No. 161 (1) | 4.00 | 2.25 |
| No. 76 (1) | 1.40 | .40 |
| No. 190 (1) | .50 | .25 |
| No. 218 (1) | 37.50 | 5.00 |
| No. 291 (1) | 2.00 | 2.00 |
| No. 270 (1) | .45 | .25 |
| No. 150 (1) | .55 | .35 |
| No. 93 (1) | .60 | .25 |
| No. 296 (1) | 1.90 | .75 |
| No. 35 (1) | 3.50 | 1.50 |
| No. 173 (1) | 2.25 | 1.10 |
| No. 179 (1) | .40 | .40 |
| No. 201 (1) | .90 | .50 |
| No. 212 (1) | 1.60 | 1.00 |
| No. 213 (1) | .85 | .35 |
| No. 109 (1) | 3.00 | .85 |
| No. 108 (1) | .50 | .50 |
| No. 127 (1) | .60 | .35 |
| No. 68 (1) | .75 | .35 |
| No. 138 (1) | .30 | .25 |
| No. 140 (1) | .50 | .50 |
| No. 280 (1) | 1.50 | .30 |
| Set total (37) Stamps | 90.50 | 32.80 |

### Red Cross Centenary

Red Cross and Elizabeth II CD315

**1963**

| | |
|---|---|
| Antigua | 134-135 |
| Ascension | 90-91 |
| Bahamas | 183-184 |
| Basutoland | 84-85 |
| Bechuanaland Protectorate | 195-196 |
| Bermuda | 193-194 |
| British Guiana | 272-273 |
| British Honduras | 180-181 |
| Cayman Islands | 169-170 |
| Dominica | 182-183 |
| Falkland Islands | 147-148 |
| Fiji | 203-204 |
| Gambia | 173-174 |
| Gibraltar | 162-163 |
| Gilbert & Ellice Islands | 77-78 |
| Grenada | 191-192 |
| Hong Kong | 219-220 |
| Jamaica | 203-204 |
| Malta | 292-293 |
| Mauritius | 271-272 |
| Montserrat | 151-152 |
| New Hebrides, British | 94-95 |
| Pitcairn Islands | 36-37 |
| St. Helena | 174-175 |
| St. Kitts-Nevis | 143-144 |
| St. Lucia | 180-181 |
| St. Vincent | 202-203 |
| Seychelles | 214-215 |
| Solomon Islands | 110-111 |
| South Arabia | 1-2 |
| Swaziland | 109-110 |
| Tonga | 134-135 |
| Tristan da Cunha | 69-70 |
| Turks & Caicos Islands | 139-140 |
| Virgin Islands | 141-142 |

| | | |
|---|---|---|
| Nos. 134-135 (2) | 1.00 | 2.00 |
| Nos. 90-91 (2) | 6.75 | 3.35 |
| Nos. 183-184 (2) | 2.30 | 2.80 |
| Nos. 84-85 (2) | 1.20 | .90 |
| Nos. 195-196 (2) | .95 | .85 |
| Nos. 193-194 (2) | 3.00 | 2.80 |
| Nos. 272-273 (2) | .85 | .60 |
| Nos. 180-181 (2) | 1.00 | 2.50 |
| Nos. 169-170 (2) | 1.10 | 3.00 |
| Nos. 182-183 (2) | .70 | 1.05 |
| Nos. 147-148 (2) | 18.00 | 5.50 |
| Nos. 203-204 (2) | 3.25 | 2.80 |
| Nos. 173-174 (2) | .80 | 1.00 |
| Nos. 162-163 (2) | 6.25 | 5.40 |
| Nos. 77-78 (2) | 2.00 | 3.50 |
| Nos. 191-192 (2) | .80 | .50 |
| Nos. 219-220 (2) | 18.75 | 7.35 |
| Nos. 203-204 (2) | .75 | 1.65 |
| Nos. 292-293 (2) | 2.50 | 4.75 |
| Nos. 271-272 (2) | .85 | .50 |
| Nos. 151-152 (2) | 1.00 | .75 |
| Nos. 94-95 (2) | 1.00 | .50 |
| Nos. 36-37 (2) | 2.50 | 4.00 |
| Nos. 174-175 (2) | 1.70 | 2.30 |
| Nos. 143-144 (2) | .90 | .90 |
| Nos. 180-181 (2) | 1.25 | 1.25 |
| Nos. 202-203 (2) | .90 | .90 |
| Nos. 214-215 (2) | 1.00 | 1.50 |
| Nos. 110-111 (2) | 1.25 | 1.15 |
| Nos. 1-2 (2) | 1.25 | 1.25 |
| Nos. 109-110 (2) | 1.10 | 1.10 |
| Nos. 134-135 (2) | 1.00 | 1.25 |
| Nos. 69-70 (2) | 1.15 | .80 |
| Nos. 139-140 (2) | .55 | 1.00 |
| Nos. 141-142 (2) | .80 | 1.25 |
| Set total (70) Stamps | 90.15 | 72.70 |

### Shakespeare

Shakespeare Memorial Theatre, Stratford-on-Avon — CD316

400th anniversary of the birth of William Shakespeare.

**1964**

| | |
|---|---|
| Antigua | 151 |
| Bahamas | 201 |
| Bechuanaland Protectorate | 197 |
| Cayman Islands | 171 |

| | |
|---|---|
| Dominica | 184 |
| Falkland Islands | 149 |
| Gambia | 192 |
| Gibraltar | 164 |
| Montserrat | 153 |
| St. Lucia | 196 |
| Turks & Caicos Islands | 141 |
| Virgin Islands | 143 |

| | | |
|---|---|---|
| No. 151 (1) | .35 | .25 |
| No. 201 (1) | .60 | .35 |
| No. 197 (1) | .35 | .35 |
| No. 171 (1) | .35 | .30 |
| No. 184 (1) | .35 | .35 |
| No. 149 (1) | 1.60 | .50 |
| No. 192 (1) | .35 | .25 |
| No. 164 (1) | .65 | .55 |
| No. 153 (1) | .35 | .25 |
| No. 196 (1) | .45 | .25 |
| No. 141 (1) | .30 | .25 |
| No. 143 (1) | .45 | .45 |
| Set total (12) Stamps | 6.15 | 4.10 |

### ITU

ITU Emblem CD317

Intl. Telecommunication Union, cent.

**1965**

| | |
|---|---|
| Antigua | 153-154 |
| Ascension | 92-93 |
| Bahamas | 219-220 |
| Barbados | 265-266 |
| Basutoland | 101-102 |
| Bechuanaland Protectorate | 202-203 |
| Bermuda | 196-197 |
| British Guiana | 293-294 |
| British Honduras | 187-188 |
| Brunei | 116-117 |
| Cayman Islands | 172-173 |
| Dominica | 185-186 |
| Falkland Islands | 154-155 |
| Fiji | 211-212 |
| Gibraltar | 167-168 |
| Gilbert & Ellice Islands | 87-88 |
| Grenada | 205-206 |
| Hong Kong | 221-222 |
| Mauritius | 291-292 |
| Montserrat | 157-158 |
| New Hebrides, British | 108-109 |
| Pitcairn Islands | 52-53 |
| St. Helena | 180-181 |
| St. Kitts-Nevis | 163-164 |
| St. Lucia | 197-198 |
| St. Vincent | 224-225 |
| Seychelles | 218-219 |
| Solomon Islands | 126-127 |
| Swaziland | 115-116 |
| Tristan da Cunha | 85-86 |
| Turks & Caicos Islands | 142-143 |
| Virgin Islands | 159-160 |

| | | |
|---|---|---|
| Nos. 153-154 (2) | 1.45 | 1.35 |
| Nos. 92-93 (2) | 1.90 | 1.30 |
| Nos. 219-220 (2) | 1.35 | 1.50 |
| Nos. 265-266 (2) | 1.50 | 1.25 |
| Nos. 101-102 (2) | .85 | .65 |
| Nos. 202-203 (2) | 1.10 | .75 |
| Nos. 196-197 (2) | 2.15 | 2.25 |
| Nos. 293-294 (2) | .50 | .50 |
| Nos. 187-188 (2) | .75 | .75 |
| Nos. 116-117 (2) | 1.75 | 1.75 |
| Nos. 172-173 (2) | 1.00 | .85 |
| Nos. 185-186 (2) | .55 | .55 |
| Nos. 154-155 (2) | 6.75 | 3.15 |
| Nos. 211-212 (2) | 2.00 | 1.05 |
| Nos. 167-168 (2) | 9.00 | 5.95 |
| Nos. 87-88 (2) | .85 | .60 |
| Nos. 205-206 (2) | .50 | .50 |
| Nos. 221-222 (2) | 10.50 | 4.75 |
| Nos. 291-292 (2) | 1.10 | .50 |
| Nos. 157-158 (2) | 1.05 | 1.15 |
| Nos. 108-109 (2) | .65 | .50 |
| Nos. 52-53 (2) | 1.65 | 1.90 |
| Nos. 180-181 (2) | .80 | .60 |
| Nos. 163-164 (2) | .60 | .60 |
| Nos. 197-198 (2) | 1.25 | 1.25 |
| Nos. 224-225 (2) | .80 | .90 |
| Nos. 218-219 (2) | .75 | .60 |
| Nos. 126-127 (2) | .70 | .55 |
| Nos. 115-116 (2) | .70 | .70 |
| Nos. 85-86 (2) | 1.00 | .65 |
| Nos. 142-143 (2) | .50 | .50 |
| Nos. 159-160 (2) | .85 | .85 |
| Set total (64) Stamps | 56.85 | 40.70 |

## Intl. Cooperation Year

ICY Emblem CD318

### 1965

| | | |
|---|---|---|
| Antigua | 155-156 | |
| Ascension | 94-95 | |
| Bahamas | 222-223 | |
| Basutoland | 103-104 | |
| Bechuanaland Protectorate | 204-205 | |
| Bermuda | 199-200 | |
| British Guiana | 295-296 | |
| British Honduras | 189-190 | |
| Brunei | 118-119 | |
| Cayman Islands | 174-175 | |
| Dominica | 187-188 | |
| Falkland Islands | 156-157 | |
| Fiji | 213-214 | |
| Gibraltar | 169-170 | |
| Gilbert & Ellice Islands | 104-105 | |
| Grenada | 207-208 | |
| Hong Kong | 223-224 | |
| Mauritius | 293-294 | |
| Montserrat | 176-177 | |
| New Hebrides, British | 110-111 | |
| New Hebrides, French | 126-127 | |
| Pitcairn Islands | 54-55 | |
| St. Helena | 182-183 | |
| St. Kitts-Nevis | 165-166 | |
| St. Lucia | 199-200 | |
| Seychelles | 220-221 | |
| Solomon Islands | 143-144 | |
| South Arabia | 17-18 | |
| Swaziland | 117-118 | |
| Tristan da Cunha | 87-88 | |
| Turks & Caicos Islands | 144-145 | |
| Virgin Islands | 161-162 | |

| | | |
|---|---|---|
| Nos. 155-156 (2) | .55 | .50 |
| Nos. 94-95 (2) | 1.30 | 1.40 |
| Nos. 222-223 (2) | .65 | 1.90 |
| Nos. 103-104 (2) | .75 | .85 |
| Nos. 204-205 (2) | .85 | 1.00 |
| Nos. 199-200 (2) | 2.05 | 1.25 |
| Nos. 295-296 (2) | .55 | .50 |
| Nos. 189-190 (2) | .60 | .55 |
| Nos. 118-119 (2) | .85 | .85 |
| Nos. 174-175 (2) | 1.00 | .75 |
| Nos. 187-188 (2) | .55 | .55 |
| Nos. 156-157 (2) | 6.00 | 1.65 |
| Nos. 213-214 (2) | 1.95 | 1.25 |
| Nos. 169-170 (2) | 1.25 | 2.75 |
| Nos. 104-105 (2) | .85 | .60 |
| Nos. 207-208 (2) | .50 | .50 |
| Nos. 223-224 (2) | 11.00 | 3.50 |
| Nos. 293-294 (2) | .65 | .50 |
| Nos. 176-177 (2) | .80 | .65 |
| Nos. 110-111 (2) | .50 | .50 |
| Nos. 126-127 (2) | 12.00 | 12.00 |
| Nos. 54-55 (2) | 1.60 | 1.85 |
| Nos. 182-183 (2) | .95 | .50 |
| Nos. 165-166 (2) | .80 | .60 |
| Nos. 199-200 (2) | .55 | .55 |
| Nos. 220-221 (2) | .80 | .60 |
| Nos. 143-144 (2) | .70 | .60 |
| Nos. 17-18 (2) | 1.20 | .50 |
| Nos. 117-118 (2) | .75 | .75 |
| Nos. 87-88 (2) | 1.05 | .65 |
| Nos. 144-145 (2) | .50 | .50 |
| Nos. 161-162 (2) | .65 | .50 |
| Set total (64) Stamps | 54.75 | 41.60 |

## Churchill Memorial

Winston Churchill and St. Paul's, London, During Air Attack CD319

### 1966

| | | |
|---|---|---|
| Antigua | 157-160 | |
| Ascension | 96-99 | |
| Bahamas | 224-227 | |
| Barbados | 281-284 | |
| Basutoland | 105-108 | |
| Bechuanaland Protectorate | 206-209 | |
| Bermuda | 201-204 | |
| British Antarctic Territory | 16-19 | |
| British Honduras | 191-194 | |
| Brunei | 120-123 | |
| Cayman Islands | 176-179 | |
| Dominica | 189-192 | |
| Falkland Islands | 158-161 | |
| Fiji | 215-218 | |

| | | |
|---|---|---|
| Gibraltar | 171-174 | |
| Gilbert & Ellice Islands | 106-109 | |
| Grenada | 209-212 | |
| Hong Kong | 225-228 | |
| Mauritius | 295-298 | |
| Montserrat | 178-181 | |
| New Hebrides, British | 112-115 | |
| New Hebrides, French | 128-131 | |
| Pitcairn Islands | 56-59 | |
| St. Helena | 184-187 | |
| St. Kitts-Nevis | 167-170 | |
| St. Lucia | 201-204 | |
| St. Vincent | 241-244 | |
| Seychelles | 222-225 | |
| Solomon Islands | 145-148 | |
| South Arabia | 19-22 | |
| Swaziland | 119-122 | |
| Tristan da Cunha | 89-92 | |
| Turks & Caicos Islands | 146-149 | |
| Virgin Islands | 163-166 | |

| | | |
|---|---|---|
| Nos. 157-160 (4) | 3.05 | 3.05 |
| Nos. 96-99 (4) | 10.00 | 6.40 |
| Nos. 224-227 (4) | 2.30 | 3.20 |
| Nos. 281-284 (4) | 3.00 | 4.95 |
| Nos. 105-108 (4) | 2.80 | 3.25 |
| Nos. 206-209 (4) | 2.50 | 2.50 |
| Nos. 201-204 (4) | 4.00 | 4.75 |
| Nos. 16-19 (4) | 41.20 | 18.00 |
| Nos. 191-194 (4) | 2.45 | 1.30 |
| Nos. 120-123 (4) | 7.65 | 6.55 |
| Nos. 176-179 (4) | 3.10 | 3.65 |
| Nos. 189-192 (4) | 1.15 | 1.15 |
| Nos. 158-161 (4) | 12.75 | 9.55 |
| Nos. 215-218 (4) | 4.40 | 3.00 |
| Nos. 171-174 (4) | 3.05 | 5.30 |
| Nos. 106-109 (4) | 1.50 | 1.30 |
| Nos. 209-212 (4) | 1.10 | 1.10 |
| Nos. 225-228 (4) | 52.50 | 11.40 |
| Nos. 295-298 (4) | 3.70 | 3.75 |
| Nos. 178-181 (4) | 1.60 | 1.55 |
| Nos. 112-115 (4) | 2.30 | 1.00 |
| Nos. 128-131 (4) | 8.35 | 8.35 |
| Nos. 56-59 (4) | 4.45 | 6.10 |
| Nos. 184-187 (4) | 1.85 | 1.95 |
| Nos. 167-170 (4) | 1.50 | 1.70 |
| Nos. 201-204 (4) | 1.50 | 1.50 |
| Nos. 241-244 (4) | 1.50 | 1.75 |
| Nos. 222-225 (4) | 3.20 | 4.35 |
| Nos. 145-148 (4) | 1.50 | 1.60 |
| Nos. 19-22 (4) | 2.95 | 2.20 |
| Nos. 119-122 (4) | 1.70 | 2.55 |
| Nos. 89-92 (4) | 5.95 | 2.70 |
| Nos. 146-149 (4) | 1.60 | 1.75 |
| Nos. 163-166 (4) | 1.90 | 1.90 |
| Set total (136) Stamps | 204.05 | 135.10 |

## Royal Visit, 1966

Queen Elizabeth II and Prince Philip CD320

Caribbean visit, Feb. 4 - Mar. 6, 1966.

### 1966

| | | |
|---|---|---|
| Antigua | 161-162 | |
| Bahamas | 228-229 | |
| Barbados | 285-286 | |
| British Guiana | 299-300 | |
| Cayman Islands | 180-181 | |
| Dominica | 193-194 | |
| Grenada | 213-214 | |
| Montserrat | 182-183 | |
| St. Kitts-Nevis | 171-172 | |
| St. Lucia | 205-206 | |
| St. Vincent | 245-246 | |
| Turks & Caicos Islands | 150-151 | |
| Virgin Islands | 167-168 | |

| | | |
|---|---|---|
| Nos. 161-162 (2) | 3.50 | 2.60 |
| Nos. 228-229 (2) | 3.05 | 3.05 |
| Nos. 285-286 (2) | 3.00 | 2.00 |
| Nos. 299-300 (2) | 2.35 | .85 |
| Nos. 180-181 (2) | 3.45 | 1.80 |
| Nos. 193-194 (2) | 3.00 | .60 |
| Nos. 213-214 (2) | .80 | .50 |
| Nos. 182-183 (2) | 2.00 | 1.00 |
| Nos. 171-172 (2) | .90 | .75 |
| Nos. 205-206 (2) | 1.50 | 1.35 |
| Nos. 245-246 (2) | 2.75 | 1.35 |
| Nos. 150-151 (2) | 1.00 | 1.00 |
| Nos. 167-168 (2) | 1.75 | 1.75 |
| Set total (26) Stamps | 29.05 | 18.10 |

## World Cup Soccer

Soccer Player and Jules Rimet Cup CD321

World Cup Soccer Championship, Wembley, England, July 11-30.

### 1966

| | | |
|---|---|---|
| Antigua | 163-164 | |
| Ascension | 100-101 | |
| Bahamas | 245-246 | |
| Bermuda | 205-206 | |
| Brunei | 124-125 | |
| Cayman Islands | 182-183 | |
| Dominica | 195-196 | |
| Fiji | 219-220 | |
| Gibraltar | 175-176 | |
| Gilbert & Ellice Islands | 125-126 | |
| Grenada | 230-231 | |
| New Hebrides, British | 116-117 | |
| New Hebrides, French | 132-133 | |
| Pitcairn Islands | 60-61 | |
| St. Helena | 188-189 | |
| St. Kitts-Nevis | 173-174 | |
| St. Lucia | 207-208 | |
| Seychelles | 226-227 | |
| Solomon Islands | 167-168 | |
| South Arabia | 23-24 | |
| Tristan da Cunha | 93-94 | |

| | | |
|---|---|---|
| Nos. 163-164 (2) | .80 | .85 |
| Nos. 100-101 (2) | 2.50 | 2.00 |
| Nos. 245-246 (2) | .65 | .65 |
| Nos. 205-206 (2) | 1.75 | 1.75 |
| Nos. 124-125 (2) | 1.30 | 1.25 |
| Nos. 182-183 (2) | .75 | .65 |
| Nos. 195-196 (2) | 1.20 | .75 |
| Nos. 219-220 (2) | 1.70 | .60 |
| Nos. 175-176 (2) | 1.85 | 1.75 |
| Nos. 125-126 (2) | .70 | .60 |
| Nos. 230-231 (2) | .65 | .95 |
| Nos. 116-117 (2) | 1.00 | 1.00 |
| Nos. 132-133 (2) | 7.00 | 7.00 |
| Nos. 60-61 (2) | 2.00 | 2.00 |
| Nos. 188-189 (2) | 1.25 | .60 |
| Nos. 173-174 (2) | .85 | .80 |
| Nos. 207-208 (2) | 1.15 | .90 |
| Nos. 226-227 (2) | .85 | .75 |
| Nos. 167-168 (2) | 1.10 | 1.10 |
| Nos. 23-24 (2) | 1.90 | .55 |
| Nos. 93-94 (2) | 1.25 | .80 |
| Set total (42) Stamps | 32.20 | 27.30 |

## WHO Headquarters

World Health Organization Headquarters, Geneva — CD322

### 1966

| | | |
|---|---|---|
| Antigua | 165-166 | |
| Ascension | 102-103 | |
| Bahamas | 247-248 | |
| Brunei | 126-127 | |
| Cayman Islands | 184-185 | |
| Dominica | 197-198 | |
| Fiji | 224-225 | |
| Gibraltar | 180-181 | |
| Gilbert & Ellice Islands | 127-128 | |
| Grenada | 232-233 | |
| Hong Kong | 229-230 | |
| Montserrat | 184-185 | |
| New Hebrides, British | 118-119 | |
| New Hebrides, French | 134-135 | |
| Pitcairn Islands | 62-63 | |
| St. Helena | 190-191 | |
| St. Kitts-Nevis | 177-178 | |
| St. Lucia | 209-210 | |
| St. Vincent | 247-248 | |
| Seychelles | 228-229 | |
| Solomon Islands | 169-170 | |
| South Arabia | 25-26 | |
| Tristan da Cunha | 99-100 | |

| | | |
|---|---|---|
| Nos. 165-166 (2) | 1.15 | .55 |
| Nos. 102-103 (2) | 6.60 | 3.35 |
| Nos. 247-248 (2) | .80 | .80 |
| Nos. 126-127 (2) | 1.35 | 1.35 |
| Nos. 184-185 (2) | 2.25 | 1.20 |
| Nos. 197-198 (2) | .75 | .75 |
| Nos. 224-225 (2) | 4.70 | 3.30 |
| Nos. 180-181 (2) | 6.50 | 4.50 |
| Nos. 127-128 (2) | .80 | .70 |
| Nos. 232-233 (2) | .80 | .50 |
| Nos. 229-230 (2) | 11.25 | 2.30 |
| Nos. 184-185 (2) | 1.00 | 1.00 |
| Nos. 118-119 (2) | .75 | .50 |
| Nos. 134-135 (2) | 8.50 | 8.50 |
| Nos. 62-63 (2) | 5.50 | 7.00 |
| Nos. 190-191 (2) | 3.50 | 1.50 |
| Nos. 177-178 (2) | .60 | .60 |
| Nos. 209-210 (2) | .80 | .80 |
| Nos. 247-248 (2) | 1.15 | 1.05 |
| Nos. 228-229 (2) | 1.25 | .65 |
| Nos. 169-170 (2) | .95 | .80 |

| | | |
|---|---|---|
| Nos. 25-26 (2) | 2.10 | .70 |
| Nos. 99-100 (2) | 1.90 | 1.25 |
| Set total (46) Stamps | 64.95 | 43.65 |

## UNESCO Anniversary

"Education" — CD323

"Science" (Wheat ears & flask enclosing globe). "Culture" (lyre & columns). 20th anniversary of the UNESCO.

### 1966-67

| | | |
|---|---|---|
| Antigua | 183-185 | |
| Ascension | 108-110 | |
| Bahamas | 249-251 | |
| Barbados | 287-289 | |
| Bermuda | 207-209 | |
| Brunei | 128-130 | |
| Cayman Islands | 186-188 | |
| Dominica | 199-201 | |
| Gibraltar | 183-185 | |
| Gilbert & Ellice Islands | 129-131 | |
| Grenada | 234-236 | |
| Hong Kong | 231-233 | |
| Mauritius | 299-301 | |
| Montserrat | 186-188 | |
| New Hebrides, British | 120-122 | |
| New Hebrides, French | 136-138 | |
| Pitcairn Islands | 64-66 | |
| St. Helena | 192-194 | |
| St. Kitts-Nevis | 179-181 | |
| St. Lucia | 211-213 | |
| St. Vincent | 249-251 | |
| Seychelles | 230-232 | |
| Solomon Islands | 171-173 | |
| South Arabia | 27-29 | |
| Swaziland | 123-125 | |
| Tristan da Cunha | 101-103 | |
| Turks & Caicos Islands | 155-157 | |
| Virgin Islands | 176-178 | |

| | | |
|---|---|---|
| Nos. 183-185 (3) | 1.90 | 2.50 |
| Nos. 108-110 (3) | 11.00 | 5.80 |
| Nos. 249-251 (3) | 2.35 | 2.35 |
| Nos. 287-289 (3) | 2.35 | 2.15 |
| Nos. 207-209 (3) | 3.80 | 3.90 |
| Nos. 128-130 (3) | 4.65 | 5.40 |
| Nos. 186-188 (3) | 2.50 | 1.50 |
| Nos. 199-201 (3) | 1.60 | .75 |
| Nos. 183-185 (3) | 6.50 | 3.25 |
| Nos. 129-131 (3) | 2.50 | 2.45 |
| Nos. 234-236 (3) | 1.10 | 1.20 |
| Nos. 231-233 (3) | 49.50 | 24.00 |
| Nos. 299-301 (3) | 2.10 | 1.50 |
| Nos. 186-188 (3) | 2.40 | 2.40 |
| Nos. 120-122 (3) | 1.90 | 1.90 |
| Nos. 136-138 (3) | 7.75 | 7.75 |
| Nos. 64-66 (3) | 4.05 | 4.00 |
| Nos. 192-194 (3) | 5.25 | 3.65 |
| Nos. 179-181 (3) | .90 | .90 |
| Nos. 211-213 (3) | 1.15 | 1.15 |
| Nos. 249-251 (3) | 2.30 | 1.35 |
| Nos. 230-232 (3) | 2.40 | 2.40 |
| Nos. 171-173 (3) | 2.00 | 1.50 |
| Nos. 27-29 (3) | 5.50 | 5.50 |
| Nos. 123-125 (3) | 1.40 | 1.40 |
| Nos. 101-103 (3) | 2.00 | 1.40 |
| Nos. 155-157 (3) | 1.15 | 1.20 |
| Nos. 176-178 (3) | 1.40 | 1.30 |
| Set total (84) Stamps | 133.40 | 94.55 |

## Silver Wedding, 1972

Queen Elizabeth II and Prince Philip — CD324

Designs: borders differ for each country.

### 1972

| | | |
|---|---|---|
| Anguilla | 161-162 | |
| Antigua | 295-296 | |
| Ascension | 164-165 | |
| Bahamas | 344-345 | |
| Bermuda | 296-297 | |
| British Antarctic Territory | 43-44 | |
| British Honduras | 306-307 | |
| British Indian Ocean Territory | 48-49 | |

| | |
|---|---|
| Brunei | 186-187 |
| Cayman Islands | 304-305 |
| Dominica | 352-353 |
| Falkland Islands | 223-224 |
| Fiji | 328-329 |
| Gibraltar | 292-293 |
| Gilbert & Ellice Islands | 206-207 |
| Grenada | 466-467 |
| Hong Kong | 271-272 |
| Montserrat | 286-287 |
| New Hebrides, British | 169-170 |
| New Hebrides, French | 188-189 |
| Pitcairn Islands | 127-128 |
| St. Helena | 271-272 |
| St. Kitts-Nevis | 257-258 |
| St. Lucia | 328-329 |
| St.Vincent | 344-345 |
| Seychelles | 309-310 |
| Solomon Islands | 248-249 |
| South Georgia | 35-36 |
| Tristan da Cunha | 178-179 |
| Turks & Caicos Islands | 257-258 |
| Virgin Islands | 241-242 |

| | | |
|---|---|---|
| Nos. 161-162 (2) | 1.10 | 1.50 |
| Nos. 295-296 (2) | .50 | .50 |
| Nos. 164-165 (2) | .70 | .70 |
| Nos. 344-345 (2) | .60 | .60 |
| Nos. 296-297 (2) | .50 | .65 |
| Nos. 43-44 (2) | 6.50 | 5.65 |
| Nos. 306-307 (2) | .80 | .80 |
| Nos. 48-49 (2) | 2.00 | 1.00 |
| Nos. 186-187 (2) | .70 | .70 |
| Nos. 304-305 (2) | .75 | .75 |
| Nos. 352-353 (2) | .65 | .65 |
| Nos. 223-224 (2) | 1.00 | 1.15 |
| Nos. 328-329 (2) | .70 | .70 |
| Nos. 292-293 (2) | .50 | .50 |
| Nos. 206-207 (2) | .50 | .50 |
| Nos. 466-467 (2) | .70 | .70 |
| Nos. 271-272 (2) | 1.70 | 1.50 |
| Nos. 286-287 (2) | .50 | .50 |
| Nos. 169-170 (2) | .50 | .50 |
| Nos. 188-189 (2) | 1.25 | 1.25 |
| Nos. 127-128 (2) | .90 | .85 |
| Nos. 271-272 (2) | .60 | 1.20 |
| Nos. 257-258 (2) | .65 | .50 |
| Nos. 328-329 (2) | .75 | .75 |
| Nos. 344-345 (2) | .55 | .55 |
| Nos. 309-310 (2) | .90 | .90 |
| Nos. 248-249 (2) | .50 | .50 |
| Nos. 35-36 (2) | 1.40 | 1.40 |
| Nos. 178-179 (2) | .70 | .70 |
| Nos. 257-258 (2) | .50 | .50 |
| Nos. 241-242 (2) | .50 | .50 |
| Set total (62) Stamps | 30.10 | 29.15 |

## Princess Anne's Wedding

Princess Anne and Mark Phillips — CD325

Wedding of Princess Anne and Mark Phillips, Nov. 14, 1973.

### 1973

| | |
|---|---|
| Anguilla | 179-180 |
| Ascension | 177-178 |
| Belize | 325-326 |
| Bermuda | 302-303 |
| British Antarctic Territory | 60-61 |
| Cayman Islands | 320-321 |
| Falkland Islands | 225-226 |
| Gibraltar | 305-306 |
| Gilbert & Ellice Islands | 216-217 |
| Hong Kong | 289-290 |
| Montserrat | 300-301 |
| Pitcairn Islands | 135-136 |
| St. Helena | 277-278 |
| St. Kitts-Nevis | 274-275 |
| St. Lucia | 349-350 |
| St. Vincent | 358-359 |
| St. Vincent Grenadines | 1-2 |
| Seychelles | 311-312 |
| Solomon Islands | 259-260 |
| South Georgia | 37-38 |
| Tristan da Cunha | 189-190 |
| Turks & Caicos Islands | 286-287 |
| Virgin Islands | 260-261 |

| | | |
|---|---|---|
| Nos. 179-180 (2) | .55 | .55 |
| Nos. 177-178 (2) | .60 | .60 |
| Nos. 325-326 (2) | 1.10 | .50 |
| Nos. 302-303 (2) | .50 | .50 |
| Nos. 60-61 (2) | 1.10 | 1.10 |
| Nos. 320-321 (2) | .50 | .50 |

| | | |
|---|---|---|
| Nos. 225-226 (2) | .70 | .60 |
| Nos. 305-306 (2) | .55 | .55 |
| Nos. 216-217 (2) | .50 | .50 |
| Nos. 289-290 (2) | 2.65 | 2.00 |
| Nos. 300-301 (2) | .55 | .55 |
| Nos. 135-136 (2) | .70 | .60 |
| Nos. 277-278 (2) | .50 | .50 |
| Nos. 274-275 (2) | .50 | .50 |
| Nos. 349-350 (2) | .50 | .50 |
| Nos. 358-359 (2) | .50 | .50 |
| Nos. 1-2 (2) | .50 | .50 |
| Nos. 311-312 (2) | .65 | .65 |
| Nos. 259-260 (2) | .70 | .70 |
| Nos. 37-38 (2) | .75 | .75 |
| Nos. 189-190 (2) | .50 | .50 |
| Nos. 286-287 (2) | .50 | .50 |
| Nos. 260-261 (2) | .50 | .50 |
| Set total (46) Stamps | 16.10 | 14.65 |

## Elizabeth II Coronation Anniv.

CD326

CD327

CD328

Designs: Royal and local beasts in heraldic form and simulated stonework. Portrait of Elizabeth II by Peter Grugeon. 25th anniversary of coronation of Queen Elizabeth II.

### 1978

| | |
|---|---|
| Ascension | 229 |
| Barbados | 474 |
| Belize | 397 |
| British Antarctic Territory | 71 |
| Cayman Islands | 404 |
| Christmas Island | 87 |
| Falkland Islands | 275 |
| Fiji | 384 |
| Gambia | 380 |
| Gilbert Islands | 312 |
| Mauritius | 464 |
| New Hebrides, British | 258 |
| New Hebrides, French | 278 |
| St. Helena | 317 |
| St. Kitts-Nevis | 354 |
| Samoa | 472 |
| Solomon Islands | 368 |
| South Georgia | 51 |
| Swaziland | 302 |
| Tristan da Cunha | 238 |
| Virgin Islands | 337 |

| | | |
|---|---|---|
| No. 229 (1) | 2.00 | 2.00 |
| No. 474 (1) | 1.35 | 1.35 |
| No. 397 (1) | 4.50 | 5.00 |
| No. 71 (1) | 6.00 | 6.00 |
| No. 404 (1) | 2.00 | 2.00 |
| No. 87 (1) | 3.50 | 4.00 |
| No. 275 (1) | 4.00 | 5.50 |
| No. 384 (1) | 1.75 | 1.75 |
| No. 380 (1) | 1.50 | 1.50 |
| No. 312 (1) | 1.25 | 1.25 |
| No. 464 (1) | 2.10 | 2.10 |
| No. 258 (1) | 1.75 | 1.75 |
| No. 278 (1) | 3.50 | 3.50 |
| No. 317 (1) | 1.75 | 1.75 |
| No. 354 (1) | 1.00 | 1.00 |
| No. 472 (1) | 2.10 | 2.10 |
| No. 368 (1) | 2.50 | 2.50 |
| No. 51 (1) | 3.00 | 3.00 |
| No. 302 (1) | 1.60 | 1.60 |
| No. 238 (1) | 1.50 | 1.50 |
| No. 337 (1) | 1.80 | 1.80 |
| Set total (21) Stamps | 50.45 | 52.95 |

## Queen Mother Elizabeth's 80th Birthday

CD330

Designs: Photographs of Queen Mother Elizabeth. Falkland Islands issued in sheets of 50; others in sheets of 9.

### 1980

| | |
|---|---|
| Ascension | 261 |
| Bermuda | 401 |
| Cayman Islands | 443 |
| Falkland Islands | 305 |
| Gambia | 412 |
| Gibraltar | 393 |
| Hong Kong | 364 |
| Pitcairn Islands | 193 |
| St. Helena | 341 |
| Samoa | 532 |
| Solomon Islands | 426 |
| Tristan da Cunha | 277 |

| | | |
|---|---|---|
| No. 261 (1) | .40 | .40 |
| No. 401 (1) | .45 | .75 |
| No. 443 (1) | .40 | .40 |
| No. 305 (1) | .40 | .40 |
| No. 412 (1) | .40 | .50 |
| No. 393 (1) | .35 | .35 |
| No. 364 (1) | 1.10 | 1.25 |
| No. 193 (1) | .60 | .60 |
| No. 341 (1) | .50 | .50 |
| No. 532 (1) | .55 | .55 |
| No. 426 (1) | .50 | .50 |
| No. 277 (1) | .45 | .45 |
| Set total (12) Stamps | 6.10 | 6.65 |

## Royal Wedding, 1981

Prince Charles and Lady Diana — CD331

CD331a

Wedding of Charles, Prince of Wales, and Lady Diana Spencer, St. Paul's Cathedral, London, July 29, 1981.

### 1981

| | |
|---|---|
| Antigua | 623-627 |
| Ascension | 294-296 |
| Barbados | 547-549 |
| Barbuda | 497-501 |
| Bermuda | 412-414 |
| Brunei | 268-270 |
| Cayman Islands | 471-473 |
| Dominica | 701-705 |
| Falkland Islands | 324-326 |
| Falkland Islands Dep | 1L59-1L61 |
| Fiji | 442-444 |
| Gambia | 426-428 |
| Ghana | 759-764 |
| Grenada | 1051-1055 |
| Grenada Grenadines | 440-443 |
| Hong Kong | 373-375 |
| Jamaica | 500-503 |
| Lesotho | 335-337 |
| Maldive Islands | 906-909 |
| Mauritius | 520-522 |
| Norfolk Island | 280-282 |
| Pitcairn Islands | 206-208 |
| St. Helena | 353-355 |
| St. Lucia | 543-549 |
| Samoa | 558-560 |
| Sierra Leone | 509-518 |
| Solomon Islands | 450-452 |
| Swaziland | 382-384 |
| Tristan da Cunha | 294-296 |
| Turks & Caicos Islands | 486-489 |
| Caicos Island | 8-11 |
| Uganda | 314-317 |
| Vanuatu | 308-310 |
| Virgin Islands | 406-408 |

| | | |
|---|---|---|
| Nos. 623-627 (5) | 6.55 | 2.55 |
| Nos. 294-296 (3) | 1.00 | 1.00 |

| | | |
|---|---|---|
| Nos. 547-549 (3) | .90 | .90 |
| Nos. 497-501 (5) | 10.95 | 10.95 |
| Nos. 412-414 (3) | 2.00 | 2.00 |
| Nos. 268-270 (3) | 2.15 | 4.50 |
| Nos. 471-473 (3) | 1.20 | 1.30 |
| Nos. 701-705 (5) | 8.35 | 2.35 |
| Nos. 324-326 (3) | 1.65 | 1.70 |
| Nos. 1L59-1L61 (3) | 1.45 | 1.45 |
| Nos. 442-444 (3) | 1.35 | 1.35 |
| Nos. 426-428 (3) | .90 | .80 |
| Nos. 759-764 (9) | 6.20 | 6.20 |
| Nos. 1051-1055 (5) | 9.85 | 1.85 |
| Nos. 440-443 (4) | 2.35 | 2.35 |
| Nos. 373-375 (3) | 3.10 | 2.85 |
| Nos. 500-503 (4) | 1.45 | 1.35 |
| Nos. 335-337 (3) | .90 | .90 |
| Nos. 906-909 (4) | 1.55 | 1.55 |
| Nos. 520-522 (3) | 2.15 | 2.15 |
| Nos. 280-282 (3) | 1.75 | 1.75 |
| Nos. 206-208 (3) | 1.20 | 1.10 |
| Nos. 353-355 (3) | .85 | .85 |
| Nos. 543-549 (5) | 7.00 | 7.00 |
| Nos. 558-560 (3) | .85 | .85 |
| Nos. 509-518 (10) | 15.50 | 15.50 |
| Nos. 450-452 (3) | 1.25 | 1.25 |
| Nos. 382-384 (3) | 1.30 | 1.25 |
| Nos. 294-296 (3) | .90 | .90 |
| Nos. 486-489 (4) | 2.20 | 2.20 |
| Nos. 8-11 (4) | 5.00 | 5.00 |
| Nos. 314-317 (4) | 3.10 | 3.00 |
| Nos. 308-310 (3) | 1.15 | 1.15 |
| Nos. 406-408 (3) | 1.10 | 1.10 |
| Set total (131) Stamps | 109.15 | 92.95 |

## Princess Diana

CD332

CD333

Designs: Photographs and portrait of Princess Diana, wedding or honeymoon photographs, royal residences, arms of issuing country. Portrait photograph by Clive Friend. Souvenir sheet margins show family tree, various people related to the princess. 21st birthday of Princess Diana of Wales, July 1.

### 1982

| | |
|---|---|
| Antigua | 663-666 |
| Ascension | 313-316 |
| Bahamas | 510-513 |
| Barbados | 585-588 |
| Barbuda | 544-547 |
| British Antarctic Territory | 92-95 |
| Cayman Islands | 486-489 |
| Dominica | 773-776 |
| Falkland Islands | 348-351 |
| Falkland Islands Dep | 1L72-1L75 |
| Fiji | 470-473 |
| Gambia | 447-450 |
| Grenada | 1101A-1105 |
| Grenada Grenadines | 485-491 |
| Lesotho | 372-375 |
| Maldive Islands | 952-955 |
| Mauritius | 548-551 |
| Pitcairn Islands | 213-216 |
| St. Helena | 372-375 |
| St. Lucia | 591-594 |
| Sierra Leone | 531-534 |
| Solomon Islands | 471-474 |
| Swaziland | 406-409 |
| Tristan da Cunha | 310-313 |
| Turks and Caicos Islands | 531-534 |
| Virgin Islands | 430-433 |

| | | |
|---|---|---|
| Nos. 663-666 (4) | 8.25 | 7.35 |
| Nos. 313-316 (4) | 3.50 | 3.50 |
| Nos. 510-513 (4) | 6.00 | 3.85 |
| Nos. 585-588 (4) | 3.40 | 3.25 |
| Nos. 544-547 (4) | 9.75 | 7.70 |
| Nos. 92-95 (4) | 4.25 | 3.45 |
| Nos. 486-489 (4) | 4.75 | 2.70 |
| Nos. 773-776 (4) | 7.05 | 7.05 |
| Nos. 348-351 (4) | 2.95 | 2.95 |
| Nos. 1L72-1L75 (4) | 2.50 | 2.60 |
| Nos. 470-473 (4) | 3.25 | 2.95 |
| Nos. 447-450 (4) | 2.90 | 2.85 |
| Nos. 1101A-1105 (7) | 16.05 | 15.55 |

| | | |
|---|---|---|
| Nos. 485-491 (7) | 17.65 | 17.65 |
| Nos. 372-375 (4) | 4.00 | 4.00 |
| Nos. 952-955 (4) | 5.50 | 3.90 |
| Nos. 548-551 (4) | 5.00 | 5.00 |
| Nos. 213-216 (4) | 1.90 | 1.85 |
| Nos. 372-375 (4) | 2.00 | 2.00 |
| Nos. 591-594 (4) | 8.70 | 8.70 |
| Nos. 531-534 (4) | 7.20 | 7.20 |
| Nos. 471-474 (4) | 2.90 | 2.90 |
| Nos. 406-409 (4) | 3.85 | 2.25 |
| Nos. 310-313 (4) | 3.65 | 1.45 |
| Nos. 486-489 (4) | 2.20 | 2.20 |
| Nos. 430-433 (4) | 3.00 | 3.00 |
| Set total (110) Stamps | 142.15 | 127.85 |

### 250th anniv. of first edition of Lloyd's List (shipping news publication) & of Lloyd's marine insurance.

CD335

Designs: First page of early edition of the list; historical ships, modern transportation or harbor scenes.

### 1984

| | |
|---|---|
| Ascension | 351-354 |
| Bahamas | 555-558 |
| Barbados | 627-630 |
| Cayes of Belize | 10-13 |
| Cayman Islands | 522-526 |
| Falkland Islands | 404-407 |
| Fiji | 509-512 |
| Gambia | 519-522 |
| Mauritius | 587-590 |
| Nauru | 280-283 |
| St. Helena | 412-415 |
| Samoa | 624-627 |
| Seychelles | 538-541 |
| Solomon Islands | 521-524 |
| Vanuatu | 368-371 |
| Virgin Islands | 466-469 |

| | | |
|---|---|---|
| Nos. 351-354 (4) | 2.90 | 2.55 |
| Nos. 555-558 (4) | 4.15 | 2.95 |
| Nos. 627-630 (4) | 6.10 | 5.15 |
| Nos. 10-13 (4) | 4.85 | 4.85 |
| Nos. 522-526 (5) | 9.30 | 8.45 |
| Nos. 404-407 (4) | 3.50 | 3.65 |
| Nos. 509-512 (4) | 5.30 | 4.90 |
| Nos. 519-522 (4) | 4.20 | 4.30 |
| Nos. 587-590 (4) | 9.40 | 9.40 |
| Nos. 280-283 (4) | 2.40 | 2.35 |
| Nos. 412-415 (4) | 2.40 | 2.40 |
| Nos. 624-627 (4) | 2.55 | 2.35 |
| Nos. 538-541 (4) | 5.00 | 5.00 |
| Nos. 521-524 (4) | 4.65 | 3.95 |
| Nos. 368-371 (4) | 1.85 | 1.85 |
| Nos. 466-469 (4) | 4.25 | 4.25 |
| Set total (65) Stamps | 72.80 | 68.35 |

### Queen Mother 85th Birthday

CD336

Designs: Photographs tracing the life of the Queen Mother, Elizabeth. The high value in each set pictures the same photograph taken of the Queen Mother holding the infant Prince Henry.

### 1985

| | |
|---|---|
| Ascension | 372-376 |
| Bahamas | 580-584 |
| Barbados | 660-664 |
| Bermuda | 469-473 |
| Falkland Islands | 420-424 |
| Falkland Islands Dep. | 1L92-1L96 |
| Fiji | 531-535 |
| Hong Kong | 447-450 |
| Jamaica | 599-603 |
| Mauritius | 604-608 |
| Norfolk Island | 364-368 |
| Pitcairn Islands | 253-257 |
| St. Helena | 428-432 |
| Samoa | 649-653 |

---

| | |
|---|---|
| Seychelles | 567-571 |
| Zil Elwannyen Sesel | 101-105 |
| Solomon Islands | 543-547 |
| Swaziland | 476-480 |
| Tristan da Cunha | 372-376 |
| Vanuatu | 392-396 |

| | | |
|---|---|---|
| Nos. 372-376 (5) | 4.65 | 4.65 |
| Nos. 580-584 (5) | 7.70 | 6.45 |
| Nos. 660-664 (5) | 8.00 | 6.70 |
| Nos. 469-473 (5) | 9.40 | 9.40 |
| Nos. 420-424 (5) | 7.35 | 6.65 |
| Nos. 1L92-1L96 (5) | 8.00 | 8.00 |
| Nos. 531-535 (5) | 6.15 | 6.15 |
| Nos. 447-450 (4) | 9.50 | 8.50 |
| Nos. 599-603 (5) | 6.15 | 7.00 |
| Nos. 604-608 (5) | 11.30 | 11.30 |
| Nos. 364-368 (5) | 5.00 | 5.00 |
| Nos. 253-257 (5) | 5.30 | 5.95 |
| Nos. 428-432 (5) | 5.25 | 5.25 |
| Nos. 649-653 (5) | 8.40 | 7.55 |
| Nos. 567-571 (5) | 8.70 | 8.70 |
| Nos. 101-105 (5) | 6.60 | 6.60 |
| Nos. 543-547 (5) | 3.95 | 3.95 |
| Nos. 476-480 (5) | 7.75 | 7.25 |
| Nos. 372-376 (5) | 5.40 | 5.40 |
| Nos. 392-396 (5) | 5.25 | 5.25 |
| Set total (99) Stamps | 139.80 | 135.70 |

### Queen Elizabeth II, 60th Birthday

CD337

### 1986, April 21

| | |
|---|---|
| Ascension | 389-393 |
| Bahamas | 592-596 |
| Barbados | 675-679 |
| Bermuda | 499-503 |
| Cayman Islands | 555-559 |
| Falkland Islands | 441-445 |
| Fiji | 544-548 |
| Hong Kong | 465-469 |
| Jamaica | 620-624 |
| Kiribati | 470-474 |
| Mauritius | 629-633 |
| Papua New Guinea | 640-644 |
| Pitcairn Islands | 270-274 |
| St. Helena | 451-455 |
| Samoa | 670-674 |
| Seychelles | 592-596 |
| Zil Elwannyen Sesel | 114-118 |
| Solomon Islands | 562-566 |
| South Georgia | 101-105 |
| Swaziland | 490-494 |
| Tristan da Cunha | 388-392 |
| Vanuatu | 414-418 |
| Zambia | 343-347 |

| | | |
|---|---|---|
| Nos. 389-393 (5) | 2.80 | 3.30 |
| Nos. 592-596 (5) | 2.75 | 3.70 |
| Nos. 675-679 (5) | 3.25 | 3.10 |
| Nos. 499-503 (5) | 4.65 | 5.15 |
| Nos. 555-559 (5) | 4.55 | 5.60 |
| Nos. 441-445 (5) | 3.95 | 4.95 |
| Nos. 544-548 (5) | 3.00 | 3.00 |
| Nos. 465-469 (5) | 8.75 | 6.75 |
| Nos. 620-624 (5) | 2.75 | 2.70 |
| Nos. 470-474 (5) | 2.25 | 2.10 |
| Nos. 629-633 (5) | 3.50 | 3.50 |
| Nos. 640-644 (5) | 4.10 | 4.10 |
| Nos. 270-274 (5) | 2.80 | 2.70 |
| Nos. 451-455 (5) | 2.50 | 3.05 |
| Nos. 670-674 (5) | 2.55 | 2.55 |
| Nos. 592-596 (5) | 2.70 | 2.70 |
| Nos. 114-118 (5) | 2.15 | 2.15 |
| Nos. 562-566 (5) | 2.90 | 2.90 |
| Nos. 101-105 (5) | 3.30 | 3.65 |
| Nos. 490-494 (5) | 2.15 | 2.15 |
| Nos. 388-392 (5) | 3.00 | 3.00 |
| Nos. 414-418 (5) | 3.10 | 3.10 |
| Nos. 343-347 (5) | 1.65 | 1.60 |
| Set total (115) Stamps | 75.10 | 77.50 |

### Royal Wedding

Marriage of Prince Andrew and Sarah Ferguson
CD338

### 1986, July 23

| | |
|---|---|
| Ascension | 399-400 |
| Bahamas | 602-603 |
| Barbados | 687-688 |

---

| | |
|---|---|
| Cayman Islands | 560-561 |
| Jamaica | 629-630 |
| Pitcairn Islands | 275-276 |
| St. Helena | 460-461 |
| St. Kitts | 181-182 |
| Seychelles | 602-603 |
| Zil Elwannyen Sesel | 119-120 |
| Solomon Islands | 567-568 |
| Tristan da Cunha | 397-398 |
| Zambia | 348-349 |

| | | |
|---|---|---|
| Nos. 399-400 (2) | 1.60 | 1.60 |
| Nos. 602-603 (2) | 2.75 | 2.75 |
| Nos. 687-688 (2) | 2.00 | 1.25 |
| Nos. 560-561 (2) | 1.70 | 2.35 |
| Nos. 629-630 (2) | 1.35 | 1.35 |
| Nos. 275-276 (2) | 2.40 | 2.40 |
| Nos. 460-461 (2) | 1.05 | 1.05 |
| Nos. 181-182 (2) | 1.50 | 2.25 |
| Nos. 602-603 (2) | 2.50 | 2.50 |
| Nos. 119-120 (2) | 2.30 | 2.30 |
| Nos. 567-568 (2) | 1.00 | 1.00 |
| Nos. 397-398 (2) | 1.40 | 1.40 |
| Nos. 348-349 (2) | 1.10 | 1.30 |
| Set total (26) Stamps | 22.65 | 23.50 |

### Queen Elizabeth II, 60th Birthday

Queen Elizabeth II & Prince Philip, 1947 Wedding Portrait — CD339

Designs: Photographs tracing the life of Queen Elizabeth II.

### 1986

| | |
|---|---|
| Anguilla | 674-677 |
| Antigua | 925-928 |
| Barbuda | 783-786 |
| Dominica | 950-953 |
| Gambia | 611-614 |
| Grenada | 1371-1374 |
| Grenada Grenadines | 749-752 |
| Lesotho | 531-534 |
| Maldive Islands | 1172-1175 |
| Sierra Leone | 760-763 |
| Uganda | 495-498 |

| | | |
|---|---|---|
| Nos. 674-677 (4) | 8.00 | 8.00 |
| Nos. 925-928 (4) | 5.50 | 6.20 |
| Nos. 783-786 (4) | 23.15 | 23.15 |
| Nos. 950-953 (4) | 7.25 | 7.25 |
| Nos. 611-614 (4) | 8.25 | 7.90 |
| Nos. 1371-1374 (4) | 6.80 | 6.80 |
| Nos. 749-752 (4) | 6.75 | 6.75 |
| Nos. 531-534 (4) | 5.25 | 5.25 |
| Nos. 1172-1175 (4) | 6.25 | 6.25 |
| Nos. 760-763 (4) | 5.25 | 5.25 |
| Nos. 495-498 (4) | 8.50 | 8.50 |
| Set total (44) Stamps | 90.95 | 91.30 |

### Royal Wedding, 1986

CD340

Designs: Photographs of Prince Andrew and Sarah Ferguson during courtship, engagement and marriage.

### 1986

| | |
|---|---|
| Antigua | 939-942 |
| Barbuda | 809-812 |
| Dominica | 970-973 |
| Gambia | 635-638 |
| Grenada | 1385-1388 |
| Grenada Grenadines | 758-761 |
| Lesotho | 545-548 |
| Maldive Islands | 1181-1184 |
| Sierra Leone | 769-772 |
| Uganda | 510-513 |

| | | |
|---|---|---|
| Nos. 939-942 (4) | 7.00 | 8.75 |
| Nos. 809-812 (4) | 14.55 | 14.55 |
| Nos. 970-973 (4) | 7.25 | 7.25 |
| Nos. 635-638 (4) | 7.80 | 7.80 |
| Nos. 1385-1388 (4) | 8.30 | 8.30 |
| Nos. 758-761 (4) | 9.00 | 9.00 |

---

| | | |
|---|---|---|
| Nos. 545-548 (4) | 7.45 | 7.45 |
| Nos. 1181-1184 (4) | 8.45 | 8.45 |
| Nos. 769-772 (4) | 5.35 | 5.35 |
| Nos. 510-513 (4) | 9.25 | 10.00 |
| Set total (40) Stamps | 84.40 | 86.90 |

### Lloyds of London, 300th Anniv.

CD341

Designs: 17th century aspects of Lloyds, representations of each country's individual connections with Lloyds and publicized disasters insured by the organization.

### 1986

| | |
|---|---|
| Ascension | 454-457 |
| Bahamas | 655-658 |
| Barbados | 731-734 |
| Bermuda | 541-544 |
| Falkland Islands | 481-484 |
| Liberia | 1101-1104 |
| Malawi | 534-537 |
| Nevis | 571-574 |
| St. Helena | 501-504 |
| St. Lucia | 923-926 |
| Seychelles | 649-652 |
| Zil Elwannyen Sesel | 146-149 |
| Solomon Islands | 627-630 |
| South Georgia | 131-134 |
| Trinidad & Tobago | 484-487 |
| Tristan da Cunha | 439-442 |
| Vanuatu | 485-488 |

| | | |
|---|---|---|
| Nos. 454-457 (4) | 5.00 | 5.00 |
| Nos. 655-658 (4) | 8.90 | 4.95 |
| Nos. 731-734 (4) | 12.50 | 8.35 |
| Nos. 541-544 (4) | 8.00 | 6.60 |
| Nos. 481-484 (4) | 5.45 | 3.85 |
| Nos. 1101-1104 (4) | 4.25 | 4.25 |
| Nos. 534-537 (4) | 11.00 | 7.85 |
| Nos. 571-574 (4) | 8.35 | 8.35 |
| Nos. 501-504 (4) | 8.70 | 7.15 |
| Nos. 923-926 (4) | 8.80 | 8.80 |
| Nos. 649-652 (4) | 12.85 | 12.85 |
| Nos. 146-149 (4) | 11.25 | 11.25 |
| Nos. 627-630 (4) | 7.00 | 4.45 |
| Nos. 131-134 (4) | 6.30 | 3.70 |
| Nos. 484-487 (4) | 10.25 | 6.35 |
| Nos. 439-442 (4) | 7.60 | 7.60 |
| Nos. 485-488 (4) | 4.85 | 4.85 |
| Set total (68) Stamps | 141.05 | 116.20 |

### Moon Landing, 20th Anniv.

CD342

Designs: Equipment, crew photographs, spacecraft, official emblems and report profiles created for the Apollo Missions. Two stamps in each set are square in format rather than like the stamp shown; see individual country listings for more information.

### 1989

| | |
|---|---|
| Ascension | 468-472 |
| Bahamas | 674-678 |
| Belize | 916-920 |
| Kiribati | 517-521 |
| Liberia | 1125-1129 |
| Nevis | 586-590 |
| St. Kitts | 248-252 |
| Samoa | 760-764 |
| Seychelles | 676-680 |
| Zil Elwannyen Sesel | 154-158 |
| Solomon Islands | 643-647 |
| Vanuatu | 507-511 |

| | | |
|---|---|---|
| Nos. 468-472 (5) | 9.40 | 8.60 |
| Nos. 674-678 (5) | 23.00 | 19.70 |
| Nos. 916-920 (5) | 29.25 | 21.60 |
| Nos. 517-521 (5) | 12.50 | 12.50 |
| Nos. 1125-1129 (5) | 8.50 | 8.50 |
| Nos. 586-590 (5) | 7.50 | 7.50 |

| | | |
|---|---|---|
| Nos. 248-252 (5) | 8.00 | 8.25 |
| Nos. 760-764 (5) | 9.85 | 9.30 |
| Nos. 676-680 (5) | 16.05 | 16.05 |
| Nos. 154-158 (5) | 26.85 | 26.85 |
| Nos. 643-647 (5) | 9.00 | 6.75 |
| Nos. 507-511 (5) | 8.60 | 8.60 |
| Set total (60) Stamps | 168.50 | 154.20 |

### Queen Mother, 90th Birthday

CD343          CD344

Designs: Portraits of Queen Elizabeth, the Queen Mother. See individual country listings for more information.

**1990**

| | |
|---|---|
| Ascension | 491-492 |
| Bahamas | 698-699 |
| Barbados | 782-783 |
| British Antarctic Territory | 170-171 |
| British Indian Ocean Territory | 106-107 |
| Cayman Islands | 622-623 |
| Falkland Islands | 524-525 |
| Kenya | 527-528 |
| Kiribati | 555-556 |
| Liberia | 1145-1146 |
| Pitcairn Islands | 336-337 |
| St. Helena | 532-533 |
| St. Lucia | 969-970 |
| Seychelles | 710-711 |
| Zil Elwannyen Sesel | 171-172 |
| Solomon Islands | 671-672 |
| South Georgia | 143-144 |
| Swaziland | 565-566 |
| Tristan da Cunha | 480-481 |

| | | |
|---|---|---|
| Nos. 491-492 (2) | 4.75 | 4.75 |
| Nos. 698-699 (2) | 5.25 | 5.25 |
| Nos. 782-783 (2) | 4.00 | 3.70 |
| Nos. 170-171 (2) | 6.00 | 6.00 |
| Nos. 106-107 (2) | 18.00 | 18.50 |
| Nos. 622-623 (2) | 4.00 | 5.50 |
| Nos. 524-525 (2) | 4.75 | 4.75 |
| Nos. 527-528 (2) | 6.05 | 6.05 |
| Nos. 555-556 (2) | 4.75 | 4.75 |
| Nos. 1145-1146 (2) | 3.25 | 3.25 |
| Nos. 336-337 (2) | 4.25 | 4.25 |
| Nos. 532-533 (2) | 5.25 | 5.25 |
| Nos. 969-970 (2) | 4.60 | 4.60 |
| Nos. 710-711 (2) | 6.60 | 6.60 |
| Nos. 171-172 (2) | 8.25 | 8.25 |
| Nos. 671-672 (2) | 5.00 | 5.30 |
| Nos. 143-144 (2) | 5.50 | 6.50 |
| Nos. 565-566 (2) | 4.10 | 4.10 |
| Nos. 480-481 (2) | 5.60 | 5.60 |
| Set total (38) Stamps | 109.95 | 112.95 |

### Queen Elizabeth II, 65th Birthday, and Prince Philip, 70th Birthday

CD345

CD346

Designs: Portraits of Queen Elizabeth II and Prince Philip differ for each country. Printed in sheets of 10 + 5 labels (3 different) between. Stamps alternate, producing 5 different triptychs.

**1991**

| | |
|---|---|
| Ascension | 506a |
| Bahamas | 731a |

| | |
|---|---|
| Belize | 970a |
| Bermuda | 618a |
| Kiribati | 572a |
| Mauritius | 734a |
| Pitcairn Islands | 349a |
| St. Helena | 555a |
| St. Kitts | 319a |
| Samoa | 791a |
| Seychelles | 724a |
| Zil Elwannyen Sesel | 178a |
| Solomon Islands | 689a |
| South Georgia | 150a |
| Swaziland | 587a |
| Vanuatu | 541a |

| | | |
|---|---|---|
| No. 506a (1) | 3.50 | 3.75 |
| No. 731a (1) | 4.00 | 4.00 |
| No. 970a (1) | 4.25 | 4.25 |
| No. 618a (1) | 3.50 | 4.00 |
| No. 572a (1) | 4.00 | 4.00 |
| No. 734a (1) | 4.00 | 4.00 |
| No. 349a (1) | 3.25 | 3.25 |
| No. 555a (1) | 2.75 | 2.75 |
| No. 319a (1) | 3.00 | 3.00 |
| No. 791a (1) | 3.75 | 3.75 |
| No. 724a (1) | 5.00 | 5.00 |
| No. 178a (1) | 6.25 | 6.25 |
| No. 689a (1) | 3.75 | 3.75 |
| No. 150a (1) | 4.75 | 7.00 |
| No. 587a (1) | 4.00 | 4.00 |
| No. 541a (1) | 2.50 | 2.50 |
| Set total (16) Stamps | 62.25 | 65.25 |

### Royal Family Birthday, Anniversary

CD347

Queen Elizabeth II, 65th birthday, Charles and Diana, 10th wedding anniversary: Various photographs of Queen Elizabeth II, Prince Philip, Prince Charles, Princess Diana and their sons William and Henry.

**1991**

| | |
|---|---|
| Antigua | 1446-1455 |
| Barbuda | 1229-1238 |
| Dominica | 1328-1337 |
| Gambia | 1080-1089 |
| Grenada | 2006-2015 |
| Grenada Grenadines | 1331-1340 |
| Guyana | 2440-2451 |
| Lesotho | 871-875 |
| Maldive Islands | 1533-1542 |
| Nevis | 666-675 |
| St. Vincent | 1485-1494 |
| St. Vincent Grenadines | 769-778 |
| Sierra Leone | 1387-1396 |
| Turks & Caicos Islands | 913-922 |
| Uganda | 918-927 |

| | | |
|---|---|---|
| Nos. 1446-1455 (10) | 21.70 | 20.05 |
| Nos. 1229-1238 (10) | 125.00 | 119.50 |
| Nos. 1328-1337 (10) | 30.20 | 30.20 |
| Nos. 1080-1089 (10) | 24.65 | 24.40 |
| Nos. 2006-2015 (10) | 25.45 | 22.10 |
| Nos. 1331-1340 (10) | 23.85 | 23.35 |
| Nos. 2440-2451 (12) | 21.40 | 21.15 |
| Nos. 871-875 (10) | 13.55 | 13.55 |
| Nos. 1533-1542 (10) | 28.10 | 28.10 |
| Nos. 666-675 (10) | 23.65 | 23.65 |
| Nos. 1485-1494 (10) | 26.75 | 25.90 |
| Nos. 769-778 (10) | 25.40 | 25.40 |
| Nos. 1387-1396 (10) | 26.35 | 26.35 |
| Nos. 913-922 (10) | 27.50 | 25.30 |
| Nos. 918-927 (10) | 17.65 | 17.65 |
| Set total (147) Stamps | 461.20 | 446.65 |

### Queen Elizabeth II's Accession to the Throne, 40th Anniv.

CD348

Various photographs of Queen Elizabeth II with local Scenes.

**1992**

| | |
|---|---|
| Antigua | 1513-1518 |
| Barbuda | 1306-1311 |
| Dominica | 1414-1419 |
| Gambia | 1172-1177 |
| Grenada | 2047-2052 |
| Grenada Grenadines | 1368-1373 |
| Lesotho | 881-885 |

| | |
|---|---|
| Maldive Islands | 1637-1642 |
| Nevis | 702-707 |
| St. Vincent | 1582-1587 |
| St. Vincent Grenadines | 829-834 |
| Sierra Leone | 1482-1487 |
| Turks and Caicos Islands | 978-987 |
| Uganda | 990-995 |
| Virgin Islands | 742-746 |

| | | |
|---|---|---|
| Nos. 1513-1518 (6) | 15.00 | 15.10 |
| Nos. 1306-1311 (6) | 125.25 | 83.65 |
| Nos. 1414-1419 (6) | 12.50 | 12.50 |
| Nos. 1172-1177 (6) | 15.00 | 14.85 |
| Nos. 2047-2052 (6) | 15.95 | 15.95 |
| Nos. 1368-1373 (6) | 17.00 | 15.35 |
| Nos. 881-885 (5) | 11.90 | 11.90 |
| Nos. 1637-1642 (6) | 17.55 | 17.55 |
| Nos. 702-707 (6) | 13.55 | 13.55 |
| Nos. 1582-1587 (6) | 14.40 | 14.40 |
| Nos. 829-834 (6) | 19.65 | 19.65 |
| Nos. 1482-1487 (6) | 22.50 | 22.50 |
| Nos. 913-922 (10) | 27.50 | 25.30 |
| Nos. 990-995 (6) | 19.50 | 19.50 |
| Nos. 742-746 (5) | 15.50 | 15.50 |
| Set total (92) Stamps | 362.75 | 317.25 |

CD349

**1992**

| | |
|---|---|
| Ascension | 531-535 |
| Bahamas | 744-748 |
| Bermuda | 623-627 |
| British Indian Ocean Territory | 119-123 |
| Cayman Islands | 648-652 |
| Falkland Islands | 549-553 |
| Gibraltar | 605-609 |
| Hong Kong | 619-623 |
| Kenya | 563-567 |
| Kiribati | 582-586 |
| Pitcairn Islands | 362-366 |
| St. Helena | 570-574 |
| St. Kitts | 332-336 |
| Samoa | 805-809 |
| Seychelles | 734-738 |
| Zil Elwannyen Sesel | 183-187 |
| Solomon Islands | 708-712 |
| South Georgia | 157-161 |
| Tristan da Cunha | 508-512 |
| Vanuatu | 555-559 |
| Zambia | 561-565 |

| | | |
|---|---|---|
| Nos. 531-535 (5) | 6.10 | 6.10 |
| Nos. 744-748 (5) | 6.90 | 4.70 |
| Nos. 623-627 (5) | 7.40 | 7.55 |
| Nos. 119-123 (5) | 22.75 | 19.25 |
| Nos. 648-652 (5) | 7.60 | 6.60 |
| Nos. 549-553 (5) | 5.95 | 5.90 |
| Nos. 605-609 (5) | 5.15 | 5.50 |
| Nos. 619-623 (5) | 5.10 | 5.25 |
| Nos. 563-567 (5) | 7.80 | 7.75 |
| Nos. 582-586 (5) | 3.85 | 3.85 |
| Nos. 362-366 (5) | 5.35 | 5.35 |
| Nos. 570-574 (5) | 5.70 | 5.70 |
| Nos. 332-336 (5) | 6.60 | 5.50 |
| Nos. 805-809 (5) | 7.85 | 5.90 |
| Nos. 734-738 (5) | 10.55 | 10.55 |
| Nos. 183-187 (5) | 9.40 | 9.40 |
| Nos. 708-712 (5) | 5.00 | 5.30 |
| Nos. 157-161 (5) | 5.60 | 5.90 |
| Nos. 508-512 (5) | 8.75 | 8.30 |
| Nos. 555-559 (5) | 3.10 | 3.10 |
| Nos. 561-565 (5) | 5.20 | 5.15 |
| Set total (105) Stamps | 151.70 | 142.60 |

### Royal Air Force, 75th Anniversary

CD350

**1993**

| | |
|---|---|
| Ascension | 557-561 |
| Bahamas | 771-775 |
| Barbados | 842-846 |
| Belize | 1003-1008 |
| Bermuda | 648-651 |
| British Indian Ocean Territory | 136-140 |
| Falkland Is. | 573-577 |
| Fiji | 687-691 |
| Montserrat | 830-834 |

| | |
|---|---|
| St. Kitts | 351-355 |

| | | |
|---|---|---|
| Nos. 557-561 (5) | 15.60 | 14.60 |
| Nos. 771-775 (5) | 24.65 | 21.45 |
| Nos. 842-846 (5) | 14.15 | 12.85 |
| Nos. 1003-1008 (6) | 21.15 | 16.50 |
| Nos. 648-651 (4) | 9.65 | 10.45 |
| Nos. 136-140 (5) | 16.10 | 16.10 |
| Nos. 573-577 (5) | 10.85 | 10.85 |
| Nos. 687-691 (5) | 17.75 | 17.40 |
| Nos. 830-834 (5) | 14.10 | 14.10 |
| Nos. 351-355 (5) | 22.80 | 23.55 |
| Set total (50) Stamps | 166.80 | 157.85 |

### Royal Air Force, 80th Anniv.

Design CD350 Re-inscribed

**1998**

| | |
|---|---|
| Ascension | 697-701 |
| Bahamas | 907-911 |
| British Indian Ocean Terr | 198-202 |
| Cayman Islands | 754-758 |
| Fiji | 814-818 |
| Gibraltar | 755-759 |
| Samoa | 957-961 |
| Turks & Caicos Islands | 1258-1265 |
| Tuvalu | 763-767 |
| Virgin Islands | 879-883 |

| | | |
|---|---|---|
| Nos. 697-701 (5) | 16.10 | 16.10 |
| Nos. 907-911 (5) | 13.60 | 12.65 |
| Nos. 136-140 (5) | 16.10 | 16.10 |
| Nos. 754-758 (5) | 15.25 | 15.25 |
| Nos. 814-818 (5) | 14.00 | 12.75 |
| Nos. 755-759 (5) | 9.70 | 9.70 |
| Nos. 957-961 (5) | 15.70 | 14.90 |
| Nos. 1258-1265 (2) | 27.50 | 27.50 |
| Nos. 763-767 (5) | 7.75 | 7.75 |
| Nos. 879-883 (5) | 15.00 | 15.00 |
| Set total (47) Stamps | 150.70 | 147.70 |

### End of World War II, 50th Anniv.

CD351

CD352

**1995**

| | |
|---|---|
| Ascension | 613-617 |
| Bahamas | 824-828 |
| Barbados | 891-895 |
| Belize | 1047-1050 |
| British Indian Ocean Territory | 163-167 |
| Cayman Islands | 704-708 |
| Falkland Islands | 634-638 |
| Fiji | 720-724 |
| Kiribati | 662-668 |
| Liberia | 1175-1179 |
| Mauritius | 803-805 |
| St. Helena | 646-654 |
| St. Kitts | 389-393 |
| St. Lucia | 1018-1022 |
| Samoa | 890-894 |
| Solomon Islands | 799-803 |
| South Georgia | 198-200 |
| Tristan da Cunha | 562-566 |

| | | |
|---|---|---|
| Nos. 613-617 (5) | 21.50 | 21.50 |

| | | |
|---|---|---|
| Nos. 824-828 (5) | 22.00 | 18.70 |
| Nos. 891-895 (5) | 14.20 | 11.90 |
| Nos. 1047-1050 (4) | 8.25 | 5.90 |
| Nos. 163-167 (5) | 16.25 | 16.25 |
| Nos. 704-708 (5) | 17.65 | 13.95 |
| Nos. 634-638 (5) | 18.65 | 17.15 |
| Nos. 720-724 (5) | 17.50 | 14.50 |
| Nos. 662-668 (7) | 12.55 | 12.55 |
| Nos. 1175-1179 (5) | 15.25 | 11.15 |
| Nos. 803-805 (3) | 7.50 | 7.50 |
| Nos. 646-654 (9) | 26.10 | 26.10 |
| Nos. 389-393 (5) | 16.40 | 16.40 |
| Nos. 1018-1022 (5) | 12.25 | 10.15 |
| Nos. 890-894 (5) | 15.25 | 14.50 |
| Nos. 799-803 (5) | 14.75 | 14.75 |
| Nos. 198-200 (3) | 14.50 | 15.50 |
| Nos. 562-566 (5) | 20.10 | 20.10 |
| Set total (91) Stamps | 290.65 | 268.55 |

### UN, 50th Anniv.

CD353

### 1995

| | | |
|---|---|---|
| Bahamas | | 839-842 |
| Barbados | | 901-904 |
| Belize | | 1055-1058 |
| Jamaica | | 847-851 |
| Liberia | | 1187-1190 |
| Mauritius | | 813-816 |
| Pitcairn Islands | | 436-439 |
| St. Kitts | | 398-401 |
| St. Lucia | | 1023-1026 |
| Samoa | | 900-903 |
| Tristan da Cunha | | 568-571 |
| Virgin Islands | | 807-810 |

| | | |
|---|---|---|
| Nos. 839-842 (4) | 7.15 | 6.40 |
| Nos. 901-904 (4) | 7.00 | 5.75 |
| Nos. 1055-1058 (4) | 6.80 | 4.70 |
| Nos. 847-851 (5) | 5.40 | 5.45 |
| Nos. 1187-1190 (4) | 10.90 | 10.90 |
| Nos. 813-816 (4) | 4.55 | 4.55 |
| Nos. 436-439 (4) | 8.15 | 8.15 |
| Nos. 398-401 (4) | 6.15 | 7.15 |
| Nos. 1023-1026 (4) | 7.50 | 7.25 |
| Nos. 900-903 (4) | 9.35 | 8.20 |
| Nos. 568-571 (4) | 13.50 | 13.50 |
| Nos. 807-810 (4) | 7.45 | 7.45 |
| Set total (49) Stamps | 93.90 | 89.45 |

### Queen Elizabeth, 70th Birthday

CD354

### 1996

| | | |
|---|---|---|
| Ascension | | 632-635 |
| British Antarctic Territory | | 240-243 |
| British Indian Ocean Territory | | 176-180 |
| Falkland Islands | | 653-657 |
| Pitcairn Islands | | 446-449 |
| St. Helena | | 672-676 |
| Samoa | | 912-916 |
| Tokelau | | 223-227 |
| Tristan da Cunha | | 576-579 |
| Virgin Islands | | 824-828 |

| | | |
|---|---|---|
| Nos. 632-635 (4) | 5.30 | 5.30 |
| Nos. 240-243 (4) | 9.45 | 8.15 |
| Nos. 176-180 (5) | 11.50 | 11.50 |
| Nos. 653-657 (5) | 13.50 | 11.20 |
| Nos. 446-449 (4) | 8.60 | 8.60 |
| Nos. 672-676 (5) | 12.45 | 12.70 |
| Nos. 912-916 (5) | 10.50 | 10.50 |
| Nos. 223-227 (5) | 10.50 | 10.50 |
| Nos. 576-579 (4) | 8.35 | 8.35 |
| Nos. 824-828 (5) | 11.30 | 11.30 |
| Set total (46) Stamps | 101.50 | 98.10 |

### Diana, Princess of Wales (1961-97)

BAHAMAS 15c

CD355

### 1998

| | |
|---|---|
| Ascension | 696 |
| Bahamas | 901A-902 |
| Barbados | 950 |
| Belize | 1091 |
| Bermuda | 753 |
| Botswana | 659-663 |
| British Antarctic Territory | 258 |
| British Indian Ocean Terr. | 197 |
| Cayman Islands | 752A-753 |
| Falkland Islands | 694 |
| Fiji | 819-820 |
| Gibraltar | 754 |
| Kiribati | 719A-720 |
| Namibia | 909 |
| Niue | 706 |
| Norfolk Island | 644-645 |
| Papua New Guinea | 937 |
| Pitcairn Islands | 487 |
| St. Helena | 711 |
| St. Kitts | 437A-438 |
| Samoa | 955A-956 |
| Seycelles | 802 |
| Solomon Islands | 866-867 |
| South Georgia | 220 |
| Tokelau | 252B-253 |
| Tonga | 980 |
| Niuafo'ou | 201 |
| Tristan da Cunha | 618 |
| Tuvalu | 762 |
| Vanuatu | 718A-719 |
| Virgin Islands | 878 |

| | | |
|---|---|---|
| No. 696 (1) | 5.25 | 5.25 |
| Nos. 901A-902 (2) | 5.30 | 5.30 |
| No. 950 (1) | 6.25 | 6.25 |
| No. 1091 (1) | 10.00 | 10.00 |
| No. 753 (1) | 5.00 | 5.00 |
| Nos. 659-663 (5) | 8.25 | 8.80 |
| No. 258 (1) | 5.50 | 5.50 |
| No. 197 (1) | 5.50 | 5.50 |
| Nos. 752A-753 (3) | 7.40 | 7.40 |
| No. 694 (1) | 5.00 | 5.00 |
| Nos. 819-820 (2) | 5.25 | 5.25 |
| No. 754 (1) | 4.75 | 4.75 |
| Nos. 719A-720 (2) | 4.60 | 4.60 |
| No. 909 (1) | 1.75 | 1.75 |
| No. 706 (1) | 5.50 | 5.50 |
| Nos. 644-645 (2) | 5.60 | 5.60 |
| No. 937 (1) | 6.25 | 6.25 |
| No. 487 (1) | 4.75 | 4.75 |
| No. 711 (1) | 4.25 | 4.25 |
| Nos. 437A-438 (2) | 5.15 | 5.15 |
| Nos. 955A-956 (2) | 7.00 | 7.00 |
| No. 802 (1) | 6.25 | 6.25 |
| Nos. 866-867 (2) | 5.40 | 5.40 |
| No. 220 (1) | 4.50 | 4.50 |
| Nos. 252B-253 (2) | 6.00 | 6.00 |
| No. 980 (1) | 4.00 | 4.00 |
| No. 201 (1) | 6.50 | 6.50 |
| No. 618 (1) | 5.00 | 5.00 |
| No. 762 (1) | 3.50 | 3.50 |
| Nos. 718A-719 (2) | 8.00 | 8.00 |
| No. 878 (1) | 4.50 | 4.50 |
| Set total (46) Stamps | 171.95 | 173.00 |

### Wedding of Prince Edward and Sophie Rhys-Jones

ASCENSION ISLAND 50p

Saturday 19 June 1999

The Wedding of HRH Prince Edward & Miss Sophie Rhys-Jones

CD356

### 1999

| | |
|---|---|
| Ascension | 729-730 |
| Cayman Islands | 775-776 |
| Falkland Islands | 729-730 |
| Pitcairn Islands | 505-506 |
| St. Helena | 733-734 |
| Samoa | 971-972 |
| Tristan da Cunha | 636-637 |

| | |
|---|---|
| Virgin Islands | 908-909 |

| | | |
|---|---|---|
| Nos. 729-730 (2) | 4.50 | 4.50 |
| Nos. 775-776 (2) | 4.95 | 4.95 |
| Nos. 729-730 (2) | 14.00 | 14.00 |
| Nos. 505-506 (2) | 7.00 | 7.00 |
| Nos. 733-734 (2) | 5.00 | 5.00 |
| Nos. 971-972 (2) | 5.00 | 5.00 |
| Nos. 636-637 (2) | 7.50 | 7.50 |
| Nos. 908-909 (2) | 7.50 | 7.50 |
| Set total (16) Stamps | 55.45 | 55.45 |

### 1st Manned Moon Landing, 30th Anniv.

ASCENSION ISLAND

CD357

### 1999

| | |
|---|---|
| Ascension | 731-735 |
| Bahamas | 942-946 |
| Barbados | 967-971 |
| Bermuda | 778 |
| Cayman Islands | 777-781 |
| Fiji | 853-857 |
| Jamaica | 889-893 |
| Kirbati | 746-750 |
| Nauru | 465-469 |
| St. Kitts | 460-464 |
| Samoa | 973-977 |
| Solomon Islands | 875-879 |
| Tuvalu | 800-804 |
| Virgin Islands | 910-914 |

| | | |
|---|---|---|
| Nos. 731-735 (5) | 12.80 | 12.80 |
| Nos. 942-946 (5) | 14.10 | 14.10 |
| Nos. 967-971 (5) | 9.45 | 8.25 |
| No. 778 (1) | 9.00 | 9.00 |
| Nos. 777-781 (5) | 9.25 | 9.25 |
| Nos. 853-857 (5) | 9.25 | 8.45 |
| Nos. 889-893 (5) | 8.30 | 7.18 |
| Nos. 746-750 (5) | 8.60 | 8.60 |
| Nos. 465-469 (5) | 7.55 | 7.10 |
| Nos. 460-464 (5) | 11.35 | 11.65 |
| Nos. 973-977 (5) | 12.60 | 12.45 |
| Nos. 875-879 (5) | 7.50 | 7.50 |
| Nos. 800-804 (5) | 6.75 | 6.75 |
| Nos. 910-914 (5) | 11.75 | 11.75 |
| Set total (66) Stamps | 138.25 | 134.83 |

### Queen Mother's Century

THE QUEEN MOTHER'S CENTURY

15p ASCENSION ISLAND

CD358

### 1999

| | |
|---|---|
| Ascension | 736-740 |
| Bahamas | 951-955 |
| Cayman Islands | 782-786 |
| Falkland Islands | 734-738 |
| Fiji | 858-862 |
| Norfolk Island | 688-692 |
| St. Helena | 740-744 |
| Samoa | 978-982 |
| Solomon Islands | 880-884 |
| South Georgia | 231-235 |
| Tristan da Cunha | 638-642 |
| Tuvalu | 805-809 |

| | | |
|---|---|---|
| Nos. 736-740 (5) | 15.50 | 15.50 |
| Nos. 951-955 (5) | 13.75 | 12.65 |
| Nos. 782-786 (5) | 8.35 | 8.35 |
| Nos. 734-738 (5) | 30.00 | 28.25 |
| Nos. 858-862 (5) | 12.80 | 13.25 |
| Nos. 688-692 (5) | 9.50 | 9.50 |
| Nos. 740-744 (5) | 16.15 | 16.15 |
| Nos. 978-982 (5) | 12.50 | 12.10 |
| Nos. 880-884 (5) | 7.50 | 7.00 |
| Nos. 231-235 (5) | 29.75 | 30.00 |
| Nos. 638-642 (5) | 18.00 | 18.00 |
| Nos. 805-809 (5) | 7.00 | 7.00 |
| Set total (60) Stamps | 180.80 | 177.75 |

### Prince William, 18th Birthday

EIIR 15p Ascension Island

CD359

### 2000

| | |
|---|---|
| Ascension | 755-759 |
| Cayman Islands | 797-801 |
| Falkland Islands | 762-766 |
| Fiji | 889-893 |
| South Georgia | 257-261 |
| Tristan da Cunha | 664-668 |
| Virgin Islands | 925-929 |

| | | |
|---|---|---|
| Nos. 755-759 (5) | 15.50 | 15.50 |
| Nos. 797-801 (5) | 11.15 | 10.90 |
| Nos. 762-766 (5) | 24.60 | 22.60 |
| Nos. 889-893 (5) | 12.90 | 12.90 |
| Nos. 257-261 (5) | 29.00 | 28.75 |
| Nos. 664-668 (5) | 21.50 | 21.50 |
| Nos. 925-929 (5) | 14.50 | 14.50 |
| Set total (35) Stamps | 129.15 | 126.55 |

### Reign of Queen Elizabeth II, 50th Anniv.

Ascension Island

CD360

### 2002

| | |
|---|---|
| Ascension | 790-794 |
| Bahamas | 1033-1037 |
| Barbados | 1019-1023 |
| Belize | 1152-1156 |
| Bermuda | 822-826 |
| British Antarctic Territory | 307-311 |
| British Indian Ocean Territory | 239-243 |
| Cayman Islands | 844-848 |
| Falkland Islands | 804-808 |
| Gibraltar | 896-900 |
| Jamaica | 952-956 |
| Nauru | 491-495 |
| Norfolk Island | 758-762 |
| Papua New Guinea | 1019-1023 |
| Pitcairn Islands | 552 |
| St. Helena | 788-792 |
| St. Lucia | 1146-1150 |
| Solomon Islands | 931-935 |
| South Georgia | 274-278 |
| Swaziland | 706-710 |
| Tokelau | 302-306 |
| Tonga | 1059 |
| Niuafo'ou | 239 |
| Tristan da Cunha | 706-710 |
| Virgin Islands | 967-971 |

| | | |
|---|---|---|
| Nos. 790-794 (5) | 14.10 | 14.10 |
| Nos. 1033-1037 (5) | 15.25 | 15.25 |
| Nos. 1019-1023 (5) | 12.90 | 12.90 |
| Nos. 1152-1156 (5) | 17.10 | 15.10 |
| Nos. 822-826 (5) | 18.00 | 18.00 |
| Nos. 307-311 (5) | 23.00 | 23.00 |
| Nos. 239-243 (5) | 19.40 | 19.40 |
| Nos. 844-848 (5) | 13.25 | 13.25 |
| Nos. 804-808 (5) | 23.00 | 22.00 |
| Nos. 896-900 (5) | 6.65 | 6.65 |
| Nos. 952-956 (5) | 16.65 | 16.65 |
| Nos. 491-495 (5) | 17.75 | 17.75 |
| Nos. 758-762 (5) | 15.90 | 15.90 |
| Nos. 1019-1023 (5) | 14.50 | 14.50 |
| No. 552 (1) | 8.50 | 8.50 |
| Nos. 788-792 (5) | 19.75 | 19.75 |
| Nos. 1146-1150 (5) | 12.25 | 12.25 |
| Nos. 931-935 (5) | 12.40 | 12.40 |
| Nos. 274-278 (5) | 28.00 | 28.50 |
| Nos. 706-710 (5) | 12.50 | 12.50 |
| Nos. 302-306 (5) | 14.50 | 14.50 |
| No. 1059 (1) | 8.00 | 8.00 |
| No. 239 (1) | 8.75 | 8.75 |
| Nos. 706-710 (5) | 18.50 | 18.50 |
| Nos. 967-971 (5) | 16.50 | 16.50 |
| Set total (113) Stamps | 387.10 | 384.60 |

## Queen Mother Elizabeth (1900-2002)

CD361

**2002**

| | | |
|---|---:|---:|
| Ascension | | 799-801 |
| Bahamas | | 1044-1046 |
| Bermuda | | 834-836 |
| British Antarctic Territory | | 312-314 |
| British Indian Ocean Territory | | 245-247 |
| Cayman Islands | | 857-861 |
| Falkland Islands | | 812-816 |
| Nauru | | 499-501 |
| Pitcairn Islands | | 561-565 |
| St. Helena | | 808-812 |
| St. Lucia | | 1155-1159 |
| Seychelles | | 830 |
| Solomon Islands | | 945-947 |
| South Georgia | | 281-285 |
| Tokelau | | 312-314 |
| Tristan da Cunha | | 715-717 |
| Virgin Islands | | 979-983 |

| | | |
|---|---:|---:|
| Nos. 799-801 (3) | 8.85 | 8.85 |
| Nos. 1044-1046 (3) | 9.10 | 9.10 |
| Nos. 834-836 (3) | 12.25 | 12.25 |
| Nos. 312-314 (3) | 18.75 | 18.75 |
| Nos. 245-247 (3) | 17.35 | 17.35 |
| Nos. 857-861 (5) | 15.00 | 15.00 |
| Nos. 812-816 (5) | 28.50 | 28.50 |
| Nos. 499-501 (3) | 14.00 | 14.00 |
| Nos. 561-565 (5) | 15.25 | 15.25 |
| Nos. 808-812 (5) | 12.00 | 12.00 |
| Nos. 1155-1159 (5) | 12.00 | 12.00 |
| No. 830 (1) | 6.50 | 6.50 |
| Nos. 945-947 (3) | 9.25 | 9.25 |
| Nos. 281-285 (5) | 19.50 | 19.50 |
| Nos. 312-314 (3) | 11.85 | 11.85 |
| Nos. 715-717 (3) | 16.25 | 16.25 |
| Nos. 979-983 (5) | 23.50 | 23.50 |
| Set total (63) Stamps | 249.90 | 249.90 |

## Head of Queen Elizabeth II

CD362

**2003**

| | | |
|---|---:|---:|
| Ascension | | 822 |
| Bermuda | | 865 |
| British Antarctic Territory | | 322 |
| British Indian Ocean Territory | | 261 |
| Cayman Islands | | 878 |
| Falkland Islands | | 828 |
| St. Helena | | 820 |
| South Georgia | | 294 |
| Tristan da Cunha | | 731 |
| Virgin Islands | | 1003 |

| | | |
|---|---:|---:|
| No. 822 (1) | 12.50 | 12.50 |
| No. 865 (1) | 50.00 | 50.00 |
| No. 322 (1) | 9.50 | 9.50 |
| No. 261 (1) | 11.00 | 11.00 |
| No. 878 (1) | 14.00 | 14.00 |
| No. 828 (1) | 9.00 | 9.00 |
| No. 820 (1) | 9.00 | 9.00 |
| No. 294 (1) | 8.50 | 8.50 |
| No. 731 (1) | 10.00 | 10.00 |
| No. 1003 (1) | 10.00 | 10.00 |
| Set total (10) Stamps | 143.50 | 143.50 |

## Coronation of Queen Elizabeth II, 50th Anniv.

CD363

**2003**

| | | |
|---|---:|---:|
| Ascension | | 823-825 |

| | | |
|---|---:|---:|
| Bahamas | | 1073-1075 |
| Bermuda | | 866-868 |
| British Antarctic Territory | | 323-325 |
| British Indian Ocean Territory | | 262-264 |
| Cayman Islands | | 879-881 |
| Jamaica | | 970-972 |
| Kiribati | | 825-827 |
| Pitcairn Islands | | 577-581 |
| St. Helena | | 821-823 |
| St. Lucia | | 1171-1173 |
| Tokelau | | 320-322 |
| Tristan da Cunha | | 732-734 |
| Virgin Islands | | 1004-1006 |

| | | |
|---|---:|---:|
| Nos. 823-825 (3) | 12.50 | 12.50 |
| Nos. 1073-1075 (3) | 13.00 | 13.00 |
| Nos. 866-868 (2) | 14.25 | 14.25 |
| Nos. 323-325 (3) | 23.00 | 23.00 |
| Nos. 262-264 (3) | 28.00 | 28.00 |
| Nos. 879-881 (3) | 19.25 | 19.25 |
| Nos. 970-972 (3) | 10.00 | 10.00 |
| Nos. 825-827 (3) | 13.00 | 13.00 |
| Nos. 577-581 (5) | 14.40 | 14.40 |
| Nos. 821-823 (3) | 7.25 | 7.25 |
| Nos. 1171-1173 (3) | 8.75 | 8.75 |
| Nos. 320-322 (3) | 17.25 | 17.25 |
| Nos. 732-734 (3) | 16.75 | 16.75 |
| Nos. 1004-1006 (3) | 25.00 | 25.00 |
| Set total (43) Stamps | 222.40 | 222.40 |

## Prince William, 21st Birthday

CD364

**2003**

| | | |
|---|---:|---:|
| Ascension | | 826 |
| British Indian Ocean Territory | | 265 |
| Cayman Islands | | 882-884 |
| Falkland Islands | | 829 |
| South Georgia | | 295 |
| Tokelau | | 323 |
| Tristan da Cunha | | 735 |
| Virgin Islands | | 1007-1009 |

| | | |
|---|---:|---:|
| No. 826 (1) | 7.25 | 7.25 |
| No. 265 (1) | 8.00 | 8.00 |
| Nos. 882-884 (3) | 6.95 | 6.95 |
| No. 829 (1) | 13.50 | 13.50 |
| No. 295 (1) | 8.50 | 8.50 |
| No. 323 (1) | 7.25 | 7.25 |
| No. 735 (1) | 6.00 | 6.00 |
| Nos. 1007-1009 (3) | 10.00 | 10.00 |
| Set total (12) Stamps | 67.45 | 67.45 |

# British Commonwealth of Nations

## Dominions, Colonies, Territories, Offices and Independent Members

Comprising stamps of the British Commonwealth and associated nations.

A strict observance of technicalities would bar some or all of the stamps listed under Burma, Ireland, Kuwait, Nepal, New Republic, Orange Free State, Samoa, South Africa, South-West Africa, Stellaland, Sudan, Swaziland, the two Transvaal Republics and others but these are included for the convenience of collectors.

## 1. Great Britain

Great Britain: Including England, Scotland, Wales and Northern Ireland.

## 2. The Dominions, Present and Past

### AUSTRALIA

The Commonwealth of Australia was proclaimed on Jan. 1, 1901. It consists of six former colonies as follows:

| | |
|---|---|
| New South Wales | Victoria |
| Queensland | Tasmania |
| South Australia | Western Australia |

The following islands and territories are, or have been, administered by Australia: Australian Antarctic Territory, Christmas Island, Cocos (Keeling) Islands, Nauru, New Guinea, Norfolk Island, Papua.

### CANADA

The Dominion of Canada was created by the British North America Act in 1867. The following provinces were former separate colonies and issued postage stamps:

| | |
|---|---|
| British Columbia and Vancouver Island | Newfoundland |
| New Brunswick | Nova Scotia |
| | Prince Edward Island |

### FIJI

The colony of Fiji became an independent nation with dominion status on Oct. 10, 1970.

### GHANA

This state came into existence March 6, 1957, with dominion status. It consists of the former colony of the Gold Coast and the Trusteeship Territory of Togoland. Ghana became a republic July 1, 1960.

### INDIA

The Republic of India was inaugurated on Jan. 26, 1950. It succeeded the Dominion of India which was proclaimed Aug. 15, 1947, when the former Empire of India was divided into Pakistan and the Union of India. The Republic is composed of about 40 predominantly Hindu states of three classes: governor's provinces, chief commissioner's provinces and princely states. India also has various territories, such as the Andaman and Nicobar Islands.

The old Empire of India was a federation of British India and the native states. The more important princely states were autonomous. Of the more than 700 Indian states, these 43 are familiar names to philatelists because of their postage stamps.

### CONVENTION STATES

| | |
|---|---|
| Chamba | Jhind |
| Faridkot | Nabha |
| Gwalior | Patiala |

### FEUDATORY STATES

| | |
|---|---|
| Alwar | Jammu and Kashmir |
| Bahawalpur | Jasdan |
| Bamra | Jhalawar |
| Barwani | Jhind (1875-76) |
| Bhopal | Kashmir |
| Bhor | Kishangarh |
| Bijawar | Kotah |
| Bundi | Las Bela |
| Bussahir | Morvi |
| Charkhari | Nandgaon |
| Cochin | Nowanuggur |
| Dhar | Orchha |
| Dungarpur | Poonch |
| Duttia | Rajasthan |
| Faridkot (1879-85) | Rajpeepla |
| Hyderabad | Sirmur |
| Idar | Soruth |
| Indore | Tonk |
| Jaipur | Travancore |
| Jammu | Wadhwan |

### NEW ZEALAND

Became a dominion on Sept. 26, 1907. The following islands and territories are, or have been, administered by New Zealand:

| | |
|---|---|
| Aitutaki | Ross Dependency |
| Cook Islands (Rarotonga) | Samoa (Western Samoa) |
| Niue | Tokelau Islands |
| Penrhyn | |

### PAKISTAN

The Republic of Pakistan was proclaimed March 23, 1956. It succeeded the Dominion which was proclaimed Aug. 15, 1947. It is made up of all or part of several Moslem provinces and various districts of the former Empire of India, including Bahawalpur and Las Bela. Pakistan withdrew from the Commonwealth in 1972.

### SOUTH AFRICA

Under the terms of the South African Act (1909) the self-governing colonies of Cape of Good Hope, Natal, Orange River Colony and Transvaal united on May 31, 1910, to form the Union of South Africa. It became an independent republic May 3, 1961.

Under the terms of the Treaty of Versailles, South-West Africa, formerly German South-West Africa, was mandated to the Union of South Africa.

### SRI LANKA (CEYLON)

The Dominion of Ceylon was proclaimed Feb. 4, 1948. The island had been a Crown Colony from 1802 until then. On May 22, 1972, Ceylon became the Republic of Sri Lanka.

## 3. Colonies, Past and Present; Controlled Territory and Independent Members of the Commonwealth

| | |
|---|---|
| Abu Dhabi | Barbuda |
| Aden | Basutoland |
| Aitutaki | Batum |
| Alderney | Bechuanaland |
| Anguilla | Bechuanaland Prot. |
| Antigua | Belize |
| Ascension | Bermuda |
| Australia | Botswana |
| Bahamas | British Antarctic Territory |
| Bahrain | British Central Africa |
| Bangladesh | British Columbia and Vancouver Island |
| Barbados | |

British East Africa
British Guiana
British Honduras
British Indian Ocean Territory
British New Guinea
British Solomon Islands
British Somaliland
Brunei
Burma
Bushire
Cameroons
Canada
Cape of Good Hope
Cayman Islands
Christmas Island
Cocos (Keeling) Islands
Cook Islands
Crete,
  British Administration
Cyprus
Dominica
East Africa & Uganda
  Protectorates
Egypt
Falkland Islands
Fiji
Gambia
German East Africa
Ghana
Gibraltar
Gilbert Islands
Gilbert & Ellice Islands
Gold Coast
Grenada
Griqualand West
Guernsey
Guyana
Heligoland
Hong Kong
Indian Native States
  (see India)
Ionian Islands
Jamaica
Jersey

Jordan
Kenya
Kenya, Uganda & Tanzania
Kiribati
Kuwait
Labuan
Lagos
Leeward Islands
Lesotho
Madagascar
Malawi
Malaya
  Federated Malay States
  Johore
  Kedah
  Kelantan
  Malacca
  Negri Sembilan
  Pahang
  Penang
  Perak
  Perlis
  Selangor
  Singapore
  Sungei Ujong
  Trengganu
Malaysia
Maldive Islands
Malta
Man, Isle of
Mauritius
Mesopotamia
Montserrat
Mozambique
Muscat
Namibia
Natal
Nauru
Nevis
New Britain
New Brunswick
Newfoundland
New Guinea
New Hebrides

New Republic
New South Wales
New Zealand
Niger Coast Protectorate
Nigeria
Niue
Norfolk Island
North Borneo
Northern Nigeria
Northern Rhodesia
North West Pacific Islands
Nova Scotia
Nyasaland Protectorate
Oman
Orange River Colony
Pakistan
Palestine
Papua New Guinea
Penrhyn Island
Pitcairn Islands
Prince Edward Island
Qatar
Queensland
Rhodesia
Rhodesia & Nyasaland
Ross Dependency
Rwanda
Sabah
St. Christopher
St. Helena
St. Kitts
St. Kitts-Nevis-Anguilla
St. Lucia
St. Vincent
Samoa
Sarawak
Seychelles
Sierra Leone
Singapore
Solomon Islands
Somaliland Protectorate
South Africa
South Arabia
South Australia

South Georgia
Southern Nigeria
Southern Rhodesia
South-West Africa
Sri Lanka
Stellaland
Straits Settlements
Sudan
Swaziland
Tanganyika
Tanzania
Tasmania
Tobago
Togo
Tokelau Islands
Tonga
Transvaal
Trinidad
Trinidad and Tobago
Tristan da Cunha
Trucial States
Turks and Caicos
Turks Islands
Tuvalu
Uganda
United Arab Emirates
Vanuatu
Victoria
Virgin Islands
Western Australia
Zambia
Zanzibar
Zimbabwe
Zululand

**POST OFFICES IN
FOREIGN COUNTRIES**
Africa
  East Africa Forces
  Middle East Forces
Bangkok
China
Morocco
Turkish Empire

# Colonies, former colonies, offices, territories controlled by parent states

## Belgium
Belgian Congo
Ruanda-Urundi

## Denmark
Danish West Indies
Faroe Islands
Greenland
Iceland

## Finland
Aland Islands

## France

### COLONIES PAST AND PRESENT, CONTROLLED TERRITORIES
Afars & Issas, Territory of
Alaouites
Alexandretta
Algeria
Alsace & Lorraine
Anjouan
Annam & Tonkin
Benin
Cambodia (Khmer)
Cameroun
Castellorizo
Chad
Cilicia
Cochin China
Comoro Islands
Dahomey
Diego Suarez
Djibouti (Somali Coast)
Fezzan
French Congo
French Equatorial Africa
French Guiana
French Guinea
French India
French Morocco
French Polynesia (Oceania)
French Southern & Antarctic Territories
French Sudan
French West Africa
Gabon
Germany
Ghadames
Grand Comoro
Guadeloupe
Indo-China
Inini
Ivory Coast
Laos
Latakia
Lebanon
Madagascar
Martinique
Mauritania
Mayotte
Memel
Middle Congo
Moheli
New Caledonia
New Hebrides
Niger Territory
Nossi-Be
Obock
Reunion
Rouad, Ile
Ste.-Marie de Madagascar
St. Pierre & Miquelon
Senegal
Senegambia & Niger
Somali Coast
Syria
Tahiti
Togo
Tunisia
Ubangi-Shari
Upper Senegal & Niger
Upper Volta
Viet Nam
Wallis & Futuna Islands

### POST OFFICES IN FOREIGN COUNTRIES
China
Crete
Egypt
Turkish Empire
Zanzibar

## Germany

### EARLY STATES
Baden
Bavaria
Bergedorf
Bremen
Brunswick
Hamburg
Hanover
Lubeck
Mecklenburg-Schwerin
Mecklenburg-Strelitz
Oldenburg
Prussia
Saxony
Schleswig-Holstein
Wurttemberg

### FORMER COLONIES
Cameroun (Kamerun)
Caroline Islands
German East Africa
German New Guinea
German South-West Africa
Kiauchau
Mariana Islands
Marshall Islands
Samoa
Togo

## Italy

### EARLY STATES
Modena
Parma
Romagna
Roman States
Sardinia
Tuscany
Two Sicilies
  Naples
  Neapolitan Provinces
  Sicily

### FORMER COLONIES, CONTROLLED TERRITORIES, OCCUPATION AREAS
Aegean Islands
  Calimno (Calino)
  Caso
  Cos (Coo)
  Karki (Carchi)
  Leros (Lero)
  Lipso
  Nisiros (Nisiro)
  Patmos (Patmo)
  Piscopi
  Rodi (Rhodes)
  Scarpanto
  Simi
  Stampalia
Castellorizo
Corfu
Cyrenaica
Eritrea
Ethiopia (Abyssinia)
Fiume
Ionian Islands
  Cephalonia
  Ithaca
  Paxos
Italian East Africa
Libya
Oltre Giuba
Saseno
Somalia (Italian Somaliland)
Tripolitania

### POST OFFICES IN FOREIGN COUNTRIES
"ESTERO"*
Austria
China
  Peking
  Tientsin
Crete
Tripoli
Turkish Empire
  Constantinople
  Durazzo
  Janina
Jerusalem
Salonika
Scutari
Smyrna
Valona
*Stamps overprinted "ESTERO" were used in various parts of the world.

## Netherlands
Aruba
Caribbean Netherlands
Curacao
Netherlands Antilles (Curacao)
Netherlands Indies
Netherlands New Guinea
St. Martin
Surinam (Dutch Guiana)

## Portugal

### COLONIES PAST AND PRESENT, CONTROLLED TERRITORIES
Angola
Angra
Azores
Cape Verde
Funchal
Horta
Inhambane
Kionga
Lourenco Marques
Macao
Madeira
Mozambique
Mozambique Co.
Nyassa
Ponta Delgada
Portuguese Africa
Portuguese Congo
Portuguese Guinea
Portuguese India
Quelimane
St. Thomas & Prince Islands
Tete
Timor
Zambezia

## Russia

### ALLIED TERRITORIES AND REPUBLICS, OCCUPATION AREAS
Armenia
Aunus (Olonets)
Azerbaijan
Batum
Estonia
Far Eastern Republic
Georgia
Karelia
Latvia
Lithuania
North Ingermanland
Ostland
Russian Turkestan
Siberia
South Russia
Tannu Tuva
Transcaucasian Fed. Republics
Ukraine
Wenden (Livonia)
Western Ukraine

## Spain

### COLONIES PAST AND PRESENT, CONTROLLED TERRITORIES
Aguera, La
Cape Juby
Cuba
Elobey, Annobon & Corisco
Fernando Po
Ifni
Mariana Islands
Philippines
Puerto Rico
Rio de Oro
Rio Muni
Spanish Guinea
Spanish Morocco
Spanish Sahara
Spanish West Africa

### POST OFFICES IN FOREIGN COUNTRIES
Morocco
Tangier
Tetuan

# Dies of British colonial stamps

**DIE A:**

1. The lines in the groundwork vary in thickness and are not uniformly straight.

2. The seventh and eighth lines from the top, in the groundwork, converge where they meet the head.

3. There is a small dash in the upper part of the second jewel in the band of the crown.

4. The vertical color line in front of the throat stops at the sixth line of shading on the neck.

**DIE B:**

1. The lines in the groundwork are all thin and straight.

2. All the lines of the background are parallel.

3. There is no dash in the upper part of the second jewel in the band of the crown.

4. The vertical color line in front of the throat stops at the eighth line of shading on the neck.

**DIE I:**

1. The base of the crown is well below the level of the inner white line around the vignette.

2. The labels inscribed "POSTAGE" and "REVENUE" are cut square at the top.

3. There is a white "bud" on the outer side of the main stem of the curved ornaments in each lower corner.

4. The second (thick) line below the country name has the ends next to the crown cut diagonally.

**DIE II:**

1. The base of the crown is aligned with the underside of the white line around the vignette.

2. The labels curve inward at the top inner corners.

3. The "bud" has been removed from the outer curve of the ornaments in each corner.

4. The second line below the country name has the ends next to the crown cut vertically.

|     DIE Ia.     |     DIE Ib.      |
|-----------------|------------------|
| 1 as die II.    | 1 and 3 as die II. |
| 2 and 3 as die I. | 2 as die I.      |

**Wmk. 1**
**Crown and C C**

**Wmk. 2**
**Crown and C A**

**Wmk. 3**
**Multiple Crown**
**and C A**

**Wmk. 4**
**Multiple Crown**
**and Script C A**

**Wmk. 4a**

**Wmk. 46**

**Wmk. 314**
**St. Edward's Crown**
**and C A Multiple**

**Wmk. 373**    **Wmk. 384**

# British Colonial and Crown Agents watermarks

Watermarks 1 to 4, 314, 373, 384 and 406, common to many British territories, are illustrated here to avoid duplication.

The letters "CC" of Wmk. 1 identify the paper as having been made for the use of the Crown Colonies, while the letters "CA" of the others stand for "Crown Agents." Both Wmks. 1 and 2 were used on stamps printed by De La Rue & Co.

Wmk. 3 was adopted in 1904; Wmk. 4 in 1921; Wmk. 46 in 1879; Wmk. 314 in 1957; Wmk. 373 in 1974; Wmk. 384 in 1985; Wmk 406 in 2008.

In Wmk. 4a, a non-matching crown of the general St. Edwards type (bulging on both sides at top) was substituted for one of the Wmk. 4 crowns which fell off the dandy roll. The non-matching crown occurs in 1950-52 printings in a horizontal row of crowns on certain regular stamps of Johore and Seychelles, and on various postage due stamps of Barbados, Basutoland, British Guiana, Gold Coast, Grenada, Northern Rhodesia, St. Lucia, Swaziland and Trinidad and Tobago. A variation of Wmk. 4a, with the non-matching crown in a horizontal row of crown-CA-crown, occurs on regular stamps of Bahamas, St. Kitts-Nevis and Singapore.

Wmk. 314 was intentionally used sideways, starting in 1966. When a stamp was issued with Wmk. 314 both upright and sideways, the sideways varieties usually are listed also — with minor numbers. In many of the later issues, Wmk. 314 is slightly visible.

Wmk. 373 is usually only faintly visible.

**Wmk. 406**

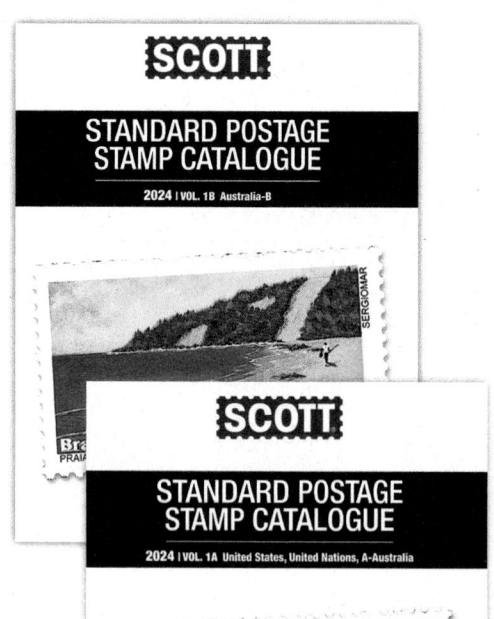

# JAMAICA

jə-'mā-kə

LOCATION — Caribbean Sea, about 90 miles south of Cuba
GOVT. — Independent state in the British Commonwealth
AREA — 4,411 sq. mi.
POP. — 2,652,443 (1999 est.)
CAPITAL — Kingston

Jamaica became an independent state in the British Commonwealth in August 1962. As a colony, it administered two dependencies: Cayman Islands and Turks and Caicos Islands.

12 Pence = 1 Shilling
20 Shillings = 1 Pound
100 Cents = 1 Dollar (1969)

Catalogue values for unused stamps in this country are for Never Hinged items, beginning with Scott 129 in the regular postage section and Scott B4 in the semi-postal section.

## Watermarks

Wmk. 45 — Pineapple

Wmk. 352 — J and Pineapple, Multiple

Values for unused stamps are for examples with original gum as defined in the catalogue introduction. Very fine examples of Nos. 1-12 will have perforations touching the design on at least one side due to the narrow spacing of the stamps on the plates. Stamps with perfs clear on all four sides are scarce and will command higher prices.

Queen Victoria
A1      A2

A3

A4

A5

A6

### 1860-63   Typo.   Wmk. 45   Perf. 14

| | | | |
|---|---|---|---|
| 1 | A1 | 1p blue | 75.00 16.00 |
| a. | Diagonal half used as ½p on cover | | 650.00 |
| b. | 1p deep blue | | 145.00 37.50 |
| c. | 1p pale blue | | 77.50 20.00 |
| d. | 1p pale greenish blue | | 115.00 21.00 |
| 2 | A2 | 2p rose | 225.00 60.00 |
| a. | 2p deep rose | | 170.00 60.00 |
| 3 | A3 | 3p green ('63) | 170.00 32.50 |
| 4 | A4 | 4p brown org | 275.00 62.50 |
| a. | 4p orange | | 225.00 50.00 |
| 5 | A5 | 6p lilac | 240.00 25.00 |
| a. | 6p deep lilac | | 1,000. 60.00 |
| b. | 6p gray lilac | | 300.00 40.00 |
| 6 | A6 | 1sh brown | 230.00 30.00 |
| a. | 1sh lilac brown | | 750.00 25.00 |
| b. | 1sh yellow brown | | 525.00 27.50 |

All except No. 3 exist imperforate.

### 1870-73   Wmk. 1

| | | | |
|---|---|---|---|
| 7 | A1 | 1p blue | 100.00 .90 |
| 8 | A2 | 2p rose | 100.00 .85 |
| a. | 2p brownish rose | | 110.00 1.10 |
| 9 | A3 | 3p green | 160.00 11.50 |
| 10 | A4 | 4p brown org ('72) | 350.00 13.50 |
| a. | 4p red orange | | 425.00 6.50 |
| 11 | A5 | 6p lilac ('71) | 100.00 6.00 |
| 12 | A6 | 1sh brown ('73) | 27.50 9.50 |
| | | Nos. 7-12 (6) | 837.50 42.25 |

The 1p and 4p exist imperf.
See Nos. 17-23, 28, 40, 43, 47-53.

A7

### 1872, Oct. 29

| | | | |
|---|---|---|---|
| 13 | A7 | ½p claret | 24.50 4.00 |
| a. | ½p deep claret | | 30.00 6.00 |

Exists imperf. See No. 16.

A8

A9

### 1875, Aug. 27   Perf. 12½

| | | | |
|---|---|---|---|
| 14 | A8 | 2sh red brown | 50.00 40.00 |
| 15 | A9 | 5sh violet | 125.00 175.00 |

Exist imperf.
See Nos. 29-30, 44, 54.

### 1883-90   Wmk. 2   Perf. 14

| | | | |
|---|---|---|---|
| 16 | A7 | ½p blue green ('85) | 12.00 1.50 |
| a. | ½p gray green | | 3.75 .25 |
| 17 | A1 | 1p blue ('84) | 325.00 8.50 |
| 18 | A1 | 1p carmine ('86) | 72.50 1.10 |
| a. | 1p rose ('85) | | 82.50 2.25 |
| 19 | A2 | 2p rose ('84) | 230.00 5.75 |
| 20 | A2 | 2p slate ('86) | 110.00 .70 |
| a. | 2p gray ('85) | | 160.00 9.00 |
| 21 | A3 | 3p ol green | 2.75 3.00 |
| 22 | A4 | 4p red brown | 2.25 .40 |
| a. | 4p orange brown | | 450.00 25.00 |
| 23 | A5 | 6p orange yel ('90) | 5.00 4.00 |
| a. | 6p yellow | | 40.00 8.50 |
| | | Nos. 16-23 (8) | 759.50 24.95 |

Nos. 18 and 20 exist imperf. Perf. 12 stamps are considered to be proofs.
For surcharge, see No. 27.

A10

### 1889-91

| | | | |
|---|---|---|---|
| 24 | A10 | 1p lilac & red vio | 14.00 .25 |
| 25 | A10 | 2p deep green | 26.00 9.00 |
| a. | 2p green | | 42.50 7.50 |
| 26 | A10 | 2½p lilac & ultra ('91) | 11.00 .75 |
| | | Nos. 24-26 (3) | 51.00 10.00 |

No. 22 Surcharged in Black

TWO PENCE HALF-PENNY

### 1890, June

| | | | |
|---|---|---|---|
| 27 | A4 | 2½p on 4p red brn | 40.00 17.50 |
| b. | Double surcharge | | 330.00 250.00 |
| d. | "PFNNY" | | 100.00 70.00 |
| f. | As "d," double surcharge | | — |

Three settings of surcharge.

### 1897

| | | | |
|---|---|---|---|
| 28 | A6 | 1sh brown | 11.00 6.50 |
| 29 | A8 | 2sh red brown | 35.00 40.00 |
| 30 | A9 | 5sh violet | 70.00 100.00 |
| | | Nos. 28-30 (3) | 116.00 146.50 |

The 2sh exists imperf.

Llandovery Falls — A12

### 1900, May 1   Engr.   Wmk. 1

| | | | |
|---|---|---|---|
| 31 | A12 | 1p red | 15.00 .25 |

### 1901, Sept. 25

| | | | |
|---|---|---|---|
| 32 | A12 | 1p red & black | 14.00 .25 |
| a. | Pair, imperf. horiz. | | 25,000. |
| b. | Bluish paper | | 115.00 110.00 |

Arms of Jamaica — A13

### 1903-04   Typo.   Wmk. 2

| | | | |
|---|---|---|---|
| 33 | A13 | ½p gray & dull grn | 2.60 .40 |
| b. | "SERv ET" for "SERVIET" | | 45.00 50.00 |
| 34 | A13 | 1p gray & car ('04) | 4.75 .25 |
| b. | "SERv ET" for "SERVIET" | | 35.00 40.00 |
| 35 | A13 | 2½p gray & ultra | 9.50 .45 |
| a. | "SERv ET" for "SERVIET" | | 65.00 75.00 |
| 36 | A13 | 5p gray & yel ('04) | 20.00 26.00 |
| a. | "SERv ET" for "SERVIET" | | 875.00 1,100. |
| | | Nos. 33-36 (4) | 36.85 27.10 |

### 1905-11   Chalky Paper   Wmk. 3

| | | | |
|---|---|---|---|
| 37 | A13 | ½p gray & dull grn | 3.00 .25 |
| b. | "SERv ET" for "SERVIET" | | 27.50 42.50 |
| 38 | A13 | 1p gray & car | 20.00 2.00 |
| 39 | A13 | 2½p gray & ultra ('07) | 7.50 9.25 |
| 39A | A3 | 3p vio, yel ('10) | 2.25 1.50 |
| 40 | A4 | 4p blk, yel ('10) | 20.00 60.00 |
| 41 | A13 | 5p gray & org yel ('07) | 67.50 82.50 |
| a. | "SERv ET" for "SERVIET" | | 1,425. 1,600. |
| 42 | A13 | 6p red vio & vio ('11) | 16.00 24.00 |
| 42A | A5 | 6p purple ('10) | 11.50 37.50 |
| 43 | A6 | 1sh blk, grn ('10) | 15.00 10.00 |
| a. | "$" for "S" in "SHILLING" | | 1,100. 1,400. |
| 44 | A8 | 2sh vio, blue ('10) | 17.00 8.50 |
| 45 | A13 | 5sh gray & vio | 57.50 65.00 |
| | | Nos. 37-45 (11) | 237.25 300.50 |

### 1905-11   Ordinary Paper

| | | | |
|---|---|---|---|
| 46a | A3 | 2½p deep ultra | 2.75 1.90 |
| 47 | A3 | 3p sage grn ('07) | 8.00 3.50 |
| a. | 3p olive green ('05) | | 13.00 4.75 |
| 48 | A3 | 3p pale pur, yel ('10) | 12.00 3.75 |
| 49 | A4 | 4p red brn ('08) | 77.50 82.50 |
| 50 | A4 | 4p red, yel ('11) | 1.75 4.00 |
| 51 | A5 | 6p dull vio ('09) | 35.00 62.50 |
| 52 | A5 | 6p org yel ('09) | 45.00 70.00 |
| a. | 6p orange ('06) | | 18.00 27.50 |
| 53 | A6 | 1sh brown ('06) | 27.50 52.50 |
| a. | 1sh deep brown | | 42.50 62.50 |
| 54 | A8 | 2sh red brn ('08) | 140.00 175.00 |
| | | Nos. 46-54 (8) | 346.75 453.75 |

A14

A15

### 1906

| | | | |
|---|---|---|---|
| 58 | A14 | ½p green | 4.00 .25 |
| a. | Booklet pane of 6 | | — |
| 59 | A15 | 1p carmine | 1.60 .25 |
| a. | Booklet pane of 6 | | — |

For overprints see Nos. MR1, MR4, MR7, MR10.

Edward VII — A16

### 1911, Feb. 3

| | | | |
|---|---|---|---|
| 60 | A16 | 2p gray | 10.00 15.00 |

George V — A17

### 1912-20

| | | | |
|---|---|---|---|
| 61 | A17 | 1p scarlet ('16) | 10.00 .80 |
| a. | 1p carmine ('12) | | 1.75 .25 |
| b. | Booklet pane of 6 | | — |
| 62 | A17 | 1½p brn org ('16) | 2.25 .70 |
| a. | 1½p yellow orange | | 18.50 1.50 |
| 63 | A17 | 2p gray | 2.50 2.00 |
| 64 | A17 | 2½p dp br blue | .90 1.25 |
| a. | 2½p ultra ('13) | | 2.00 .25 |

### Chalky Paper

| | | | |
|---|---|---|---|
| 65 | A17 | 3p violet, yel | .60 .50 |
| 66 | A17 | 4p scar & blk, yel ('13) | .60 3.00 |
| 67 | A17 | 6p red vio & dl vio | 1.90 1.60 |
| 68 | A17 | 1sh black, green | 2.60 2.25 |
| a. | 1sh blk, bl grn, olive back ('20) | | 5.50 12.50 |
| 69 | A17 | 2sh ultra & vio, blue ('19) | 27.50 45.00 |
| 70 | A17 | 5sh scar & grn, yel ('19) | 82.50 105.00 |

### Surface-colored Paper

| | | | |
|---|---|---|---|
| 71 | A17 | 3p violet, yel ('13) | .60 .45 |
| 72 | A17 | 4p scar & blk, yel ('14) | .85 3.50 |
| 73 | A17 | 6p red vio, grn ('15) | 7.50 5.00 |
| | | Nos. 61-73 (13) | 140.30 171.05 |

See Nos. 101-102. For overprints see Nos. MR2-MR3, MR5-MR6, MR8-MR9, MR11.

Exhibition Buildings of 1891 A18

Arawak Woman Preparing Cassava A19

World War I Contingent Embarking for Overseas Duty A20

King's House, Spanish Town A21

Return of Overseas Contingent, 1919 A22

Columbus Landing in Jamaica A23

Cathedral in Spanish Town A24

Statue of Queen Victoria A26

Memorial to Admiral Rodney A27

Monument to Sir Charles Metcalfe A28

Woodland Scene — A29

King George V — A30

### 1919-21   Typo.   Wmk. 3   Perf. 14
### Chalky Paper

| | | | |
|---|---|---|---|
| 75 | A18 | ½p ol grn & dk grn ('20) | 1.10 1.10 |

| | | | | |
|---|---|---|---|---|
| 76 | A19 | 1p org & car ('21) | 2.00 | 2.00 |

**Engr.**
**Ordinary Paper**

| | | | | |
|---|---|---|---|---|
| 77 | A20 | 1½p green | .45 | 1.10 |
| 78 | A21 | 2p grn & bl ('21) | 1.25 | 4.50 |
| 79 | A22 | 2½p blue blk & blue | 3.00 | 2.00 |
| a. | | 2½p blue & dark blue ('21) | 15.00 | 3.50 |
| b. | | "C" of "CA" missing from watermark | 350.00 | 300.00 |
| c. | | "A" of "CA" missing from watermark | 350.00 | |
| 80 | A23 | 3p blue & grn ('21) | 7.50 | 2.75 |
| 81 | A24 | 4p grn & dk brn ('21) | 4.00 | 10.00 |
| 83 | A26 | 1sh brt org & org ('20) | 5.00 | 5.75 |
| a. | | Frame inverted | 40,000. | 25,000. |
| | | As "a," revenue cancel | | 2,500. |
| b. | | "C" of "CA" missing from watermark | 1,100. | |
| c. | | "A" of "CA" missing from watermark | 1,800. | 1,000. |
| 84 | A27 | 2sh brn & bl ('20) | 12.50 | 37.50 |
| b. | | "C" of "CA" missing from watermark | 800.00 | |
| 85 | A28 | 3sh org & vio ('20) | 27.50 | 135.00 |
| a. | | "C" of "CA" missing from watermark | 1,200. | |
| 86 | A29 | 5sh ocher & blue ('21) | 60.00 | 100.00 |
| 87 | A30 | 10sh dk myr grn ('20) | 85.00 | 160.00 |
| | | Nos. 75-87 (12) | 209.30 | 461.70 |

See note after No. 100. Watermark varieties exist and sell for much higher values.

A 6p stamp depicting the abolition of slavery was sent to the Colony but was not issued. "Specimen" examples exist with wmk. 3 or 4. Value $875 each.

Without "Specimen," values: wmk. 3, $60,000; wmk. 4, $40,000.

Port Royal in 1853 — A31

**1921-23  Typo.  Wmk. 4  Perf. 14**
**Chalky Paper**

| | | | | |
|---|---|---|---|---|
| 88 | A18 | ½p ol grn & dk grn ('22) | .60 | .60 |
| a. | | Booklet pane of 4 | 150.00 | |
| 89 | A19 | 1p org & car ('22) | 2.00 | .25 |
| a. | | Booklet pane of 6 | 225.00 | |

**Engr.**
**Ordinary Paper**

| | | | | |
|---|---|---|---|---|
| 90 | A20 | 1½p green | 4.00 | .55 |
| 91 | A21 | 2p grn & blue | 8.50 | .90 |
| 92 | A22 | 2½p bl & dk bl | 6.50 | 2.00 |
| 93 | A23 | 3p bl & grn ('22) | 7.00 | .80 |
| 94 | A24 | 4p grn & dk brn | 1.50 | .40 |
| 95 | A31 | 6p bl & blk ('22) | 17.00 | 1.75 |
| 96 | A26 | 1sh brn org & dl org | 2.50 | .90 |
| 97 | A27 | 2sh brn & bl ('22) | 3.75 | 1.00 |
| 98 | A28 | 3sh org & violet | 20.00 | 11.00 |
| 99 | A29 | 5sh ocher & bl ('23) | 35.00 | 29.00 |
| a. | | 5sh orange & blue | 82.50 | 82.50 |
| 100 | A30 | 10sh dk myr grn ('22) | 60.00 | 60.00 |
| | | Nos. 88-100 (13) | 168.35 | 129.15 |
| | | Set, never hinged | 380.00 | |

No. 89 differs from No. 76 in having the words "Postage and Revenue" at the bottom.
On No. 79 the horizontal bar of the flag at the left has a broad white line below the colored line. On No. 92 this has been corrected and the broad white line placed above the colored line.
Watermark is sideways on Nos. 76-77, 87, 89-90. Watermark varieties other than these and normal are scarce and sell for much higher values.

**Type of 1912-19 Issue**

**1921-27  Typo.  Wmk. 4**

| | | | | |
|---|---|---|---|---|
| 101 | A17 | ½p green ('27) | 4.00 | .25 |
| a. | | Booklet pane of 6 | | |
| 102 | A17 | 6p red vio & dl vio | 18.50 | 4.50 |

No. 102 is on chalky paper.

A32

---

Type I

Type II

Type II — Cross shading beneath "Jamaica."

**1929-32  Engr.  Perf. 13½x14, 14**

| | | | | |
|---|---|---|---|---|
| 103 | A32 | 1p red, type I | 16.50 | .25 |
| a. | | 1p red, type II ('32) | 16.50 | .25 |
| b. | | Booklet pane of 6, type II | | |
| 104 | A32 | 1½p brown | 10.00 | .25 |
| 105 | A32 | 9p violet brown | 10.00 | 1.25 |
| | | Nos. 103-105 (3) | 36.50 | 1.75 |
| | | Set, never hinged | 42.50 | |

The frames on Nos. 103 to 105 differ.

Coco Palms at Columbus Cove A33

Scene near Castleton, St. Andrew A34

Priestman's River, Portland Parish — A35

**1932  Perf. 12½**

| | | | | |
|---|---|---|---|---|
| 106 | A33 | 2p grn & gray blk | 40.00 | 4.50 |
| a. | | Vertical pair, imperf. between | 22,500. | |
| 107 | A34 | 2½p ultra & sl bl | 6.75 | 2.00 |
| a. | | Vertical pair, imperf. between | 25,000. | 25,000. |
| 108 | A35 | 6p red vio & gray blk | 37.50 | 6.00 |
| | | Nos. 106-108 (3) | 84.25 | 12.50 |
| | | Set, never hinged | 125.00 | |

Common Design Types pictured following the introduction.

**Silver Jubilee Issue**
Common Design Type

**1935, May 6  Perf. 11x12**

| | | | | |
|---|---|---|---|---|
| 109 | CD301 | 1p car & blue | .45 | .25 |
| a. | | Booklet pane of 6 | 175.00 | |
| 110 | CD301 | 1½p black & ultra | .75 | 1.75 |
| 111 | CD301 | 6p indigo & grn | 14.00 | 22.50 |
| 112 | CD301 | 1sh brn vio & ind | 9.00 | 26.00 |
| | | Nos. 109-112 (4) | 24.20 | 50.50 |
| | | Set, never hinged | 35.00 | |

**Coronation Issue**
Common Design Type

**1937, May 12  Perf. 13½x14**

| | | | | |
|---|---|---|---|---|
| 113 | CD302 | 1p carmine | .25 | .25 |
| 114 | CD302 | 1½p gray black | .40 | .30 |
| 115 | CD302 | 2½p bright ultra | .60 | .70 |
| | | Nos. 113-115 (3) | 1.25 | 1.25 |
| | | Set, never hinged | 2.00 | |

King George VI — A36

Coco Palms at Columbus Cove — A37

Scene near Castleton, St. Andrew A38

Bananas A39

---

Citrus Grove — A40

Priestman's River, Portland Parish — A41

Kingston Harbor — A42

Sugar Industry — A43

Bamboo Walk — A44

Woodland Scene — A45

King George VI — A46

**1938-51  Perf. 13½x14**

| | | | | |
|---|---|---|---|---|
| 116 | A36 | ½p dk blue grn | 1.25 | .25 |
| a. | | Booklet pane of 6 | 8.00 | |
| b. | | Wmkd. sideways | — | 9,000. |
| 117 | A36 | 1p carmine | .85 | .25 |
| a. | | Booklet pane of 6 | 12.00 | |
| 118 | A36 | 1½p brown | .85 | .25 |

**Perf. 12½, 13x13½, 13½x13, 12½x13**

| | | | | |
|---|---|---|---|---|
| 119 | A37 | 2p grn & gray blk, perf. 12½ | .85 | .85 |
| a. | | Perf. 13x13½ ('39) | 1.90 | .50 |
| b. | | Perf. 12½x13 ('51) | .85 | .25 |
| 120 | A38 | 2½p ultra & sl bl | 5.75 | 2.75 |
| 121 | A39 | 3p grn & lt ultra | .75 | 1.50 |
| 122 | A40 | 4p grn & yel brn | .60 | .25 |
| 123 | A41 | 6p red vio & gray blk, perf. 13½x13 ('50) | 2.00 | .25 |
| a. | | Perf. 12½ | 5.75 | .30 |
| b. | | As "a," double impression of gray blk | — | |
| 124 | A42 | 9p rose lake | .60 | .50 |
| 125 | A43 | 1sh dk brn & brt grn | 10.00 | .25 |
| 126 | A44 | 2sh brn & brt bl | 21.00 | 1.00 |

**Perf. 13, 14**

| | | | | |
|---|---|---|---|---|
| 127 | A45 | 5sh ocher & bl, perf. 13 ('50) | 7.25 | 3.75 |
| a. | | Bluish paper, perf. 13 ('49) | 7.25 | 3.00 |
| b. | | Perf. 14 | 12.00 | 3.25 |
| 128 | A46 | 10sh dk myr grn, perf. 14 | 6.75 | 11.50 |
| a. | | Perf. 13x13½ ('50) | 11.00 | 7.50 |
| | | Nos. 116-128 (13) | 58.50 | 23.35 |
| | | Set, never hinged | 125.00 | |

See Nos. 140, 148, 149, 152.

Catalogue values for unused stamps in this section, from this point to the end of the section, are for Never Hinged items.

Courthouse, Falmouth A47

Kings Charles II and George VI A48

---

House of Assembly, 1762-1869 A50

Institute of Jamaica A49

Allegory of Labor and Learning A51

Constitution and Flag of Jamaica A52

**Perf. 12½**

**1945, Aug. 20  Engr.  Wmk. 4**

| | | | | |
|---|---|---|---|---|
| 129 | A47 | 1½p brown | .30 | .30 |
| a. | | Booklet pane of 4 | 37.50 | |
| b. | | Perf. 12½x13½ ('46) | 18.00 | 1.75 |
| 130 | A48 | 2p dp grn, perf. 12½x13½ | .40 | .50 |
| a. | | Perf. 12½ | 18.00 | 2.25 |
| 131 | A49 | 3p bright ultra | .25 | .50 |
| a. | | Perf. 13 ('46) | 4.00 | 2.50 |
| 132 | A50 | 4½p slate black | 1.50 | .45 |
| a. | | Perf. 13 ('46) | 6.50 | 6.50 |
| 133 | A51 | 2sh chocolate | 2.25 | .50 |
| 134 | A52 | 5sh deep blue | 4.50 | 2.00 |
| 135 | A49 | 10sh green | 3.50 | 2.00 |
| | | Nos. 129-135 (7) | 12.70 | 6.25 |

Granting of a new Constitution in 1944.

**Peace Issue**
Common Design Type

**1946, Oct. 14  Wmk. 4  Perf. 13½**

| | | | | |
|---|---|---|---|---|
| 136 | CD303 | 1½p black brown | 1.00 | 4.50 |
| a. | | Perf. 13½x14 | 3.00 | .25 |

**Perf. 13½x14**

| | | | | |
|---|---|---|---|---|
| 137 | CD303 | 3p deep blue | 1.00 | 9.00 |
| a. | | Perf. 13½ | 10.00 | 4.00 |

**Silver Wedding Issue**
Common Design Types

**1948, Dec. 1  Photo.  Perf. 14x14½**

| | | | | |
|---|---|---|---|---|
| 138 | CD304 | 1½p red brown | .35 | .25 |

**Engr.; Name Typo.**
**Perf. 11½x11**

| | | | | |
|---|---|---|---|---|
| 139 | CD305 | £1 red | 30.00 | 75.00 |

**Type of 1938 and**

Tobacco Industry — A53

**1949, Aug. 15  Engr.  Perf. 12½**

| | | | | |
|---|---|---|---|---|
| 140 | A39 | 3p ultra & slate blue | 4.50 | 1.25 |
| 141 | A53 | £1 violet & dk brn | 60.00 | 40.00 |

In 1956, a stamp matching the design of No. 141, but with Queen Elizabeth II, was prepared but not issued.

**UPU Issue**
Common Design Types

**Perf. 13½, 11x11½**

**1949, Oct. 10  Wmk. 4**

| | | | | |
|---|---|---|---|---|
| 142 | CD306 | 1½p red brown | .25 | .25 |
| a. | | "A" of "CA" missing from watermark | 700.00 | |
| 143 | CD307 | 2p dark green | 1.25 | 1.00 |
| 144 | CD308 | 3p indigo | .50 | .50 |
| 145 | CD309 | 6p rose violet | .50 | .70 |
| | | Nos. 142-145 (4) | 2.50 | 2.45 |

**University Issue**
Common Design Types

**1951, Feb. 16  Perf. 14x14½**

| | | | | |
|---|---|---|---|---|
| 146 | CD310 | 2p brown & gray blk | .35 | .40 |
| 147 | CD311 | 6p rose lil & gray blk | .70 | .30 |

**George VI Type of 1938**

**1951, Oct. 25  Perf. 13½x14**

| | | | | |
|---|---|---|---|---|
| 148 | A36 | ½p orange | 3.25 | .30 |
| a. | | Booklet pane of 6 | 23.00 | |
| 149 | A36 | 1p blue green | 4.75 | .25 |
| a. | | Booklet pane of 6 | 34.00 | |

Boy Scout Emblem with Map — A54

Map and Emblem — A55

**Perf. 13½x13, 13x13½**
**1952, Mar. 5    Typo.    Wmk. 4**
150 A54 2p blk, yel grn & blue    .30    .25
151 A55 6p blk, yel grn & dk red    .70    .70

1st Caribbean Boy Scout Jamboree, 1952.

**Banana Type of 1938**
**1952, July 1    Engr.    Perf. 12½**
152 A39 3p rose red & green    6.00    .30

**Coronation Issue**
**Common Design Type**
**1953, June 2    Perf. 13½x13**
153 CD312 2p dk green & black    .70    .25

Type of 1938 with Portrait of Queen Elizabeth II

Inscription: "ROYAL VISIT 1953"
**1953, Nov. 25    Perf. 13**
154 A37 2p green & gray black    .50    .25

Visit of Queen Elizabeth II and the Duke of Edinburgh, 1953.

Warship off Port Royal — A56

Designs: 2½p, Old Montego Bay. 3p, Old Kingston. 6p, Proclaiming abolition of slavery.

**1955, May 10    Engr.    Perf. 12x12½**
**Center in Black**
155 A56 2p olive green    .50    .25
156 A56 2½p light ultra    .25    .30
157 A56 3p deep plum    .25    .30
158 A56 6p rose red    .25    .25
   Nos. 155-158 (4)    1.25    1.10

300th anniv. of Jamaica's establishment as a British territory.

Palm Trees — A57

Blue Mountain Peak — A58

Arms of Jamaica A59

Arms of Jamaica A60

1p, Sugar cane. 2p, Pineapple. 2½p, Bananas. 3p, Mahoe flower. 4p, Breadfruit. 5p, Ackee fruit. 6p, Streamer (hummingbird). 1sh, Royal Botanic Gardens, Hope. 1sh6p, Rafting on the Rio Grande. 2sh, Port Charles.

**1956    Wmk. 4    Perf. 12½**
159 A57 ½p org ver & blk    .25    .25
   a.    Booklet pane of 6    .30
160 A57 1p emer & blk    .25    .25
   a.    Booklet pane of 6    .50
161 A57 2p rose red & blk    .25    .25
   a.    Booklet pane of 6    .85
162 A57 2½p lt ultra & black    1.00    .50
   a.    Booklet pane of 6    6.00
163 A57 3p brn & grn    .25    .25
164 A57 4p dk blue & ol grn    .50    .25
165 A57 5p ol green & car    1.00    2.00

166 A57 6p car & blk    3.25    .25
**Perf. 13½**
167 A58 8p red org & brt ultra    1.75    .25
168 A58 1sh blue & yel grn    1.75    .25
169 A58 1sh6p dp cl & ultra    1.00    .25
170 A58 2sh ol grn & ultra    13.50    2.50
**Perf. 11½**
171 A59 3sh blue & black    2.75    3.25
172 A59 5sh carmine & blk    4.00    6.00
173 A60 10sh blue grn & blk    27.50    14.00
174 A60 £1 purple & blk    27.50    14.00
   Nos. 159-174 (16)    86.50    44.50

For overprints see Nos. 185-196. For types overprinted see Nos. 208-216.

**West Indies Federation**
**Common Design Type**
**Perf. 11½x11**
**1958, Apr. 22    Engr.    Wmk. 314**
175 CD313 2p green    .70    .25
176 CD313 5p blue    .95    2.75
177 CD313 6p carmine rose    1.00    .45
   Nos. 175-177 (3)    2.65    3.45

Britannia Plane over 1860 Packet Boat — A61

1sh Stamps of 1860 and 1956 — A62

6p, Victorian post cart and mail truck.

**1960, Jan. 4    Perf. 13x13½**
178 A61 2p lilac & blue    .50    .25
179 A61 6p ol grn & car rose    .50    .45
**Perf. 13**
180 A62 1sh blue, yel grn & brn    .60    .50
   Nos. 178-180 (3)    1.60    1.20

Centenary of Jamaican postal service.

**Independent State**

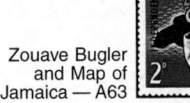

Zouave Bugler and Map of Jamaica — A63

1sh6p, Gordon House (Legislature) & hands of three races holding banner. 5sh, Map & symbols of agriculture & industry.

**1962, Aug. 8    Photo.    Perf. 13**
181 A63 2p multicolored    1.40    .25
182 A63 4p multicolored    1.00    .25
   a.    Yellow omitted
183 A63 1sh6p red, black & brn    3.00    .80
184 A63 5sh multicolored    4.25    5.50
   Nos. 181-184 (4)    9.65    6.80

**Issue of 1956 Overprinted**

a    b

**Perf. 12½**
**1962, Aug. 8    Wmk. 4    Engr.**
185 A57(a) ½p org ver & blk    .25    .80
186 A57(a) 1p emer & blk    .25    .25
187 A57(a) 2½p lt ultra & blk    .25    .80
188 A57(b) 3p brn & grn    .25    .25
189 A57(b) 5p ol grn & car    .25    .55
190 A57(b) 6p car & black    2.25    .25
**Perf. 13½**
191 A58(b) 8p red org & brt ultra    .25    .25
192 A58(b) 1sh bl & yel grn    .30    .25
193 A58(b) 2sh ol green & ultra    1.00    1.25
**Perf. 11½**
194 A59(a) 3sh blue & blk    1.00    1.50
195 A60(a) 10sh bl grn & blk    3.75    3.50
196 A60(a) £1 pur & blk    4.00    4.25
   Nos. 185-196 (12)    13.80    13.90

Nos. 181-196 issued to commemorate Jamaica's independence.
"Independence" measures 17½x1½mm on Nos. 185-187; 18x1mm on Nos. 194-196.
See Nos. 208-216.

Weight Lifting, Soccer, Boxing and Cycling — A64

Designs: 6p, Various water sports. 8p, Running and jumping. 2sh, Arms and runner.

**Perf. 14½x14**
**1962, Aug. 11    Photo.    Wmk. 314**
197 A64 1p car & dk brown    .25    .25
198 A64 6p blue & brown    .25    .25
199 A64 8p olive & dk brown    .25    .25
200 A64 2sh multicolored    .30    .70
   Nos. 197-200 (4)    1.05    1.45

IX Central American and Caribbean Games, Kingston, Aug. 11-25.
A souvenir sheet containing one each of Nos. 197-200, imperf., was sold exclusively by National Sports, Ltd., at 5sh (face 3sh3p). The Jamaican Post Office sold the entire issue of this sheet to National Sports at face value, plus the printing cost. The stamps are postally valid. The sheet has marginal inscriptions and simulated perforations in ultramarine. Value $14.

**Freedom from Hunger Issue**

Man Planting Mango Tree and Produce — A65

**Perf. 12½**
**1963, June 4    Unwmk.    Litho.**
201 A65 1p blue & multi    .25    .25
202 A65 8p rose & multi    .80    .60

See note after CD314, Common Design section.

**Red Cross Centenary Issue**
**Common Design Type**
**1963, Sept. 2    Wmk. 314    Perf. 13**
203 CD315 2p black & red    .25    .25
204 CD315 1sh6p ultra & red    .50    1.40

Carole Joan Crawford — A66

**Unwmk.**
**1964, Feb. 14    Photo.    Perf. 13**
205 A66 3p multicolored    .25    .25
206 A66 1sh olive & multi    .30    .25
207 A66 1sh6p multicolored    .40    .40
   a.    Souvenir sheet of 3    1.50    1.50
   Nos. 205-207 (3)    .95    .90

Carole Joan Crawford, Miss World, 1963.
No. 207a contains one each of Nos. 205-207 with simulated perforations. Issued May 25. Sold for 4sh.

**Types of 1956 Overprinted like 1962 Independence Issue**
**Wmk. 314**
**1963-64    Engr.    Perf. 12½**
208 A57(a) ½p org ver & blk    .25    .25
209 A57(a) 1p emer & blk    .25    1.25
   ('64)
210 A57(a) 2½p lt ultra & blk    .25    2.00
   ('64)
211 A57(b) 3p brn & grn    .25    .25
212 A57(b) 5p ol grn & car    .40    2.00
   ('64)
**Perf. 13½**
213 A58(b) 8p red org & brt ultra ('64)    .30    .75
214 A58(b) 1sh bl & yel grn    .35    .75
215 A58(b) 2sh ol grn & ultra ('64)    .60    6.00
**Perf. 11½**
216 A59(a) 3sh bl & blk ('64)    2.75    4.50
   Nos. 208-216 (9)    5.40    17.75

Overprint is at bottom on Nos. 214-215, at top on Nos. 192-193.

Lignum Vitae, National Flower, and Map — A67

1½p, Ackee, national fruit, and map. 2p, Blue Mahoe, national tree, and map, vert. 2½p, Land shells (snails). 3p, Flag over map. 4p, Murex antillarum, sea shell. 6p, Papilio homerus. 8p, Doctor bird (Trochilus polytmus). 9p, Gypsum industry. 1sh, Stadium and statue of runner. 1sh6p, Palisadoes International Airport. 2sh, Bauxite mining. 3sh, Blue marlin and boat. 5sh, Port Royal exploration of sunken city, map, ship and artifacts. 10sh, Coat of arms, vert. £1, Flag and Queen Elizabeth II.

**Perf. 14½, 14x14½**
**1964, May 4    Photo.    Wmk. 352**
**Size: 26x22mm, 22x26mm**
217 A67 1p bis, vio bl & grn    .25    .25
   a.    Booklet pane of 6    .40
218 A67 1½p multicolored    .25    .25
219 A67 2p multicolored    .25    .25
   a.    Booklet pane of 6    .90
220 A67 2½p multicolored    .90    .50
221 A67 3p emer, yel & black    .25    .25
   a.    Booklet pane of 6    3.00
222 A67 4p violet & buff    .50    .25
223 A67 6p multicolored    1.90    .25
   a.    Ultramarine omitted    95.00
   b.    Denomination omitted    2,200.
224 A67 8p multicolored    2.00    1.25
   a.    Red omitted    200.00
**Perf. 14½x14, 13½x14½, 14x14½**
**Size: 32x26mm, 26x32mm**
225 A67 9p blue & yel    1.25    .25
226 A67 1sh yel brn & blk    3.00    .25
   a.    Yellow brown omitted    3,000.    3,000.
   b.    Black omitted    2,200.
   c.    Denomination (only) omitted    1,600.
227 A67 1sh6p sl, buff & bl    3.00    .25
228 A67 2sh bl, brn red & black    2.25    .25
229 A67 3sh grn, saph & dk bl, perf. 14½x14    .35    .60
   a.    Perf. 14x14½    1.00    1.00
230 A67 5sh bl, blk & bis    1.00    1.00
231 A67 10sh multicolored    1.25    1.10
   a.    Blue ("Jamaica" etc.) omitted    450.00
232 A67 £1 multicolored    2.75    1.00
   Nos. 217-232 (16)    18.40    7.95

See Nos. 306-318. For overprints & surcharges see Nos. 248-251, 279-291, 305.

Scout Hat, Globe, Neckerchief — A68

Scout Emblem, American Crocodile — A69

Design: 3p, Scout belt buckle.

**Perf. 14½x14, 14**
**1964, Aug. 27    Wmk. 352**
233 A68 3p pink, black & red    .25    .25
234 A68 8p ultra, black & olive    .25    .25
235 A69 1sh6p ultra & gold    .25    .45
   Nos. 233-235 (3)    .75    .95

6th Inter-American Scout Conference, Kingston, Aug. 25-29.

Gordon House, Kingston, and Commonwealth Parliamentary Association Emblem — A70

6p, Headquarters House, Kingston. 1sh6p, House of Assembly, Spanish Town.

**1964, Nov. 16    Photo.    Perf. 14½x14**
236 A70 3p yel green & blk    .25    .25
237 A70 6p red & black    .30    .25
238 A70 1sh6p ultra & black    .40    .25
   Nos. 236-238 (3)    .95    .75

10th Commonwealth Parliamentary Conf.

4

Eleanor Roosevelt — A71

**1964, Dec. 10**     **Wmk. 352**
239 A71 1sh lt green, blk & red   .25 .25

Eleanor Roosevelt (1884-1962) on the 16th anniv. of the Universal Declaration of Human Rights.

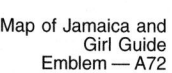

Map of Jamaica and Girl Guide Emblem — A72

Girl Guide Emblems A73

*Perf. 14x14½, 14*
**1965, May 17**   **Photo.**   **Wmk. 352**
240 A72 3p lt blue, yel & yel grn   .25 .25
241 A73 1sh lt yel grn, blk & bis   .25 .30

50th anniv. of the Girl Guides of Jamaica.

Salvation Army Cap — A74

1sh6p, Flag bearer, drummer, globe, vert.

*Perf. 14x14½, 14½x14*
**1965, Aug. 23**   **Photo.**   **Wmk. 352**
242 A74 3p dp blue, yel, mar & blk   .25 .25
243 A74 1sh6p emerald & multi   .50 .40

Centenary of the Salvation Army.

Paul Bogle, William Gordon and Morant Bay Court House — A75

**1965, Dec. 29**   **Unwmk.**   *Perf. 14x13*
244 A75 3p vio blue, blk & brn   .25 .25
245 A75 1sh6p yel grn, blk & brn   .25 .25
246 A75 3sh pink & brown   .30 .80
    *Nos. 244-246 (3)*   .80 1.30

Cent. of the Morant Bay rebellion against governor John Eyre.

ITU Emblem, Telstar, Telegraph Key and Man Blowing Horn — A76

*Perf. 14x14½*
**1965, Dec. 29**   **Photo.**   **Wmk. 352**
247 A76 1sh gray, black & red   .50 .25

Cent. of the ITU.

Nos. 221, 223, 226-227 Overprinted

*Perf. 14½, 14½x14*
**1966, Mar. 3**   **Photo.**   **Wmk. 352**
**Size: 26x22mm**
248 A67 3p emer, yel & black   .30 .25
249 A67 6p multicolored   2.00 .40

**Size: 32x26mm**
250 A67 1sh yel brown & blk   .65 .25
251 A67 1sh6p slate, buff & blue   3.25 2.50
    *Nos. 248-251 (4)*   6.20 3.40

See note after Antigua No. 162.

Winston Churchill — A77

**1966, Apr. 18**   *Perf. 14, 14x14½*
252 A77 6p olive green & gray   .55 .35
253 A77 1sh violet & sepia   .80 .95

Sir Winston Leonard Spencer Churchill (1874-1965), statesman and WWII leader.

Runner, Flags of Jamaica, Great Britain and Games' Emblem — A78

Designs: 6p, Bicyclists and waterfall. 1sh, Stadium. 3sh, Games' Emblem.

*Perf. 14½x14*
**1966, Aug. 4**   **Photo.**   **Wmk. 352**
254 A78 3p multicolored   .25 .25
255 A78 6p multicolored   .35 .25
256 A78 1sh multicolored   .25 .25
257 A78 3sh gold & dk vio blue   .35 .40
   a. Souvenir sheet of 4   5.00 5.00
    *Nos. 254-257 (4)*   1.20 1.15

8th British Empire and Commonwealth Games, Aug. 4-13, 1966.
No. 257a contains 4 imperf. stamps with simulated perforations similar to Nos. 254-257. Issued Aug. 25, 1966.

Bolivar Statue, Kingston, Flags of Jamaica and Venezuela — A79

**1966, Dec. 5**   *Perf. 14x14½*
258 A79 8p multicolored   .35 .25

150th anniv. of the "Bolivar Letter," written by Simon Bolivar, while in exile in Jamaica.

Jamaican Pavilion — A80

**1967, Apr. 28**   *Perf. 14½x14*
259 A80 6p multicolored   .25 .25
260 A80 1sh multicolored   .25 .25

EXPO '67 Intl. Exhibition, Montreal, Apr. 28-Oct. 27.

Donald Burns Sangster — A81

*Perf. 13x13½*
**1967, Aug. 28**   **Unwmk.**
261 A81 3p multicolored   .25 .25
262 A81 1sh6p multicolored   .25 .25

Sir Donald Burns Sangster (1911-1967), Prime Minister.

Traffic Police and Post Office — A82

Designs: 1sh, Officers representing various branches of police force in front of Police Headquarters. 1sh6p, Constable, 1867, Old House of Assembly, and 1967 constable with New House of Assembly.

*Perf. 13½x14*
**1967, Nov. 28**   **Photo.**   **Wmk. 352**
**Size: 42x25mm**
263 A82 3p red brown & multi   .40 .25
**Size: 56½x20½mm**
*Perf. 13½x14½*
264 A82 1sh yellow & multi   .40 .25
**Size: 42x25mm**
*Perf. 13½x14*
265 A82 1sh6p gray & multi   .70 .75
    *Nos. 263-265 (3)*   1.50 1.25

Centenary of the Constabulary Force.

A Human Rights set of three (3p, 1sh, 3sh) was prepared and announced for release on Jan. 2, 1968. The Crown Agents distributed sample sets, but the stamps were not issued. On Dec. 3, Nos. 271-273 were issued instead. Designs of the unissued set show bowls of food, an abacus and praying hands. Value, $175.

Wicketkeeper, Emblem of West Indies Cricket Team — A82a

Designs: No. 266, Wicketkeeper and emblem of West Indies Cricket Team. No. 267, Batsman and emblem of Marylebone Cricket Club. No. 268, Bowler and emblem of West Indies Cricket Team.

**1968, Feb. 8**   **Photo.**   *Perf. 14*
266 A82a 6p multicolored   .35 .35
267 A82a 6p multicolored   .35 .35
268 A82a 6p multicolored   .35 .35
   a. Horiz. strip of 3, #266-268   1.75 1.75
    *Nos. 266-268 (3)*   1.05 1.05

Visit of the Marylebone Cricket Club to the West Indies, Jan.-Feb. 1968. Miniature sheet of 3 of No 268a. Value, $5.75.

Sir Alexander and Lady Bustamante A83

**1968, May 23**   *Perf. 14½*
269 A83 3p brt rose & black   .25 .25
270 A83 1sh olive green & black   .25 .25

Labor Day, May 23, 1968.

Human Rights Flame and Map of Jamaica — A84

Designs: 1sh, Hands shielding Human Rights flame, vert. 3sh, Man kneeling on Map of Jamaica, and Human Rights flame.

**1968, Dec. 3**   **Wmk. 352**   *Perf. 14½*
271 A84 3p multicolored   .25 .25
   a. Gold (flame) omitted   150.00
272 A84 1sh multicolored   .25 .25
273 A84 3sh multicolored   .40 .80
   a. Gold (flame) omitted   175.00
    *Nos. 271-273 (3)*   .90 1.30

International Human Rights Year.

ILO Emblem — A85

Designs: 1sh, Officers...

**Unwmk.**
**1969, May 23**   **Litho.**   *Perf. 14*
274 A85 6p black & orange yel   .25 .25
275 A85 3sh black & brt green   .30 .30

50th anniv. of the ILO.

WHO Emblem, Children and Nurse — A86

Designs: 1sh, Malaria eradication, horiz. 3sh, Student nurses.

**1969, May 30**   **Photo.**   *Perf. 14*
276 A86 6p org, black & brown   .25 .25
277 A86 1sh blue grn, blk & brn   .25 .25
278 A86 3sh ultra, black & brn   .25 .80
    *Nos. 276-278 (3)*   .75 1.30

WHO, 20th anniv.

Nos. 217-219, 221-223, 225-232 Surcharged

**1969, Sept. 8**   **Wmk. 352**   *Perf. 14½*
**Size: 26x22mm, 22x26mm**
279 A67 1c on 1p multi   .25 .25
280 A67 2c on 2p multi   .25 .25
281 A67 3c on 3p multi   .25 .25
282 A67 4c on 4p multi   1.00 .25
283 A67 5c on 6p multi   1.00 .25
   a. Blue (wing dots) omitted   100.00
*Perf. 14½x14, 13½x14½, 14x14½*
**Size: 32x26mm, 26x32mm**
284 A67 8c on 9p multi   .25 .25
285 A67 10c on 1sh multi   .25 .25
286 A67 15c on 1sh6p multi   .40 .50
287 A67 20c on 2sh multi   1.10 .90
288 A67 30c on 3sh multi   2.00 1.50
289 A67 50c on 5sh multi   1.00 2.00
290 A67 $1 on 10sh multi   1.00 4.00
291 A67 $2 on £1 multi   2.00 5.00
    *Nos. 279-291 (13)*   10.75 15.65

Introduction of decimal currency.
The old denomination is obliterated by groups of small rectangles on the 1c and 3c, and with a square on the 2c, 4c and 8c; old denominations not obliterated on others.

Madonna and Child with St. John, by Raphael — A87

Christmas (Paintings): 2c, The Adoration of the Kings, by Vincenzo Foppa. 8c, The Adoration of the Kings, by Dosso Dossi.

**1969, Oct. 25**   **Litho.**   *Perf. 13*
292 A87 2c vermilion & multi   .25 .35
293 A87 5c multicolored   .25 .35
294 A87 8c orange & multi   .25 .35
    *Nos. 292-294 (3)*   .75 1.05

First Jamaica Penny — A88

Design: 3c, First Jamaica halfpenny.

**1969, Oct. 27**   *Perf. 12x12½*
295 A88 3c brt pink, blk & silver   .25 .25
296 A88 15c emerald, blk & silver   .25 .25

Centenary of the first Jamaican coinage.

George William
Gordon — A89

Portraits: 3c, Sir Alexander Bustamante (1884-1977). 5c, Norman W. Manley (1893-1969). 10c, Marcus M. Garvey (1887-1940). 15c, Paul Bogle (1820-1865).

**Perf. 12x12½**

| | | | Unwmk. | |
|---|---|---|---|---|
| **1970, Mar. 11** | | **Photo.** | | |
| 297 | A89 | 1c lt violet & multi | .25 | .25 |
| 298 | A89 | 3c lt blue & multi | .25 | .25 |
| 299 | A89 | 5c lt gray & multi | .25 | .25 |
| 300 | A89 | 10c pale rose & multi | .25 | .25 |
| 301 | A89 | 15c pale green & multi | .25 | .25 |
| | | Nos. 297-301 (5) | 1.25 | 1.25 |

National heroes connected with Jamaica's independence.

Crucifixion, by
Antonello da
Messina — A90

Easter: 3c, Christ Appearing to St. Peter, by Annibale Carracci. 20c, Easter lily.

**1970, Mar. 23**
| | | | | |
|---|---|---|---|---|
| 302 | A90 | 3c pink & multi | .25 | .25 |
| 303 | A90 | 10c gray green & multi | .25 | .25 |
| 304 | A90 | 20c gray & multi | .25 | .55 |
| | | Nos. 302-304 (3) | .75 | 1.05 |

No. 219 Surcharged

**1970, July 16  Wmk. 352  Perf. 14½**
| | | | | |
|---|---|---|---|---|
| 305 | A67 | 2c on 2p multicolored | .30 | .25 |

**Type of Regular Issue, 1964**
Values in Cents and Dollars

Designs: 1c, Lignum vitae and map. 2c, Blue mahoe and map, vert. 3c, Flag over map. 4c, Murex antillarum, sea shell. 5c, Papilio homerus. 8c, Gypsum industry. 10c, Stadium and statue of runner. 15c, Palisadoes International Airport. 20c, Bauxite mining. 30c, Blue marlin and boat. 50c, Port Royal exploration of sunken city, map, ship and artifacts. $1, Coat of arms, vert. $2, Flag and Queen Elizabeth II.

**1970  Wmk. 352  Photo.  Perf. 14½**
**Size: 26x22mm, 22x26mm**
| | | | | |
|---|---|---|---|---|
| 306 | A67 | 1c bister & multi | .65 | 1.00 |
| 307 | A67 | 2c gray grn & multi | .30 | .25 |
| 308 | A67 | 3c emer, yel & black | .50 | .80 |
| 309 | A67 | 4c violet & buff | 2.25 | .30 |
| 310 | A67 | 5c green & multi | 2.25 | .50 |

**Perf. 14½x14, 13½x14½, 14x14½**
**Size: 32x26mm, 26x32mm**
| | | | | |
|---|---|---|---|---|
| 311 | A67 | 8c blue & yellow | 1.50 | .25 |
| 312 | A67 | 10c yel brn & black | .50 | .25 |
| 313 | A67 | 15c multicolored | 2.00 | 1.50 |
| 314 | A67 | 20c multicolored | 1.00 | 1.50 |
| 315 | A67 | 30c multicolored | 3.00 | 4.50 |
| 316 | A67 | 50c multicolored | 1.25 | 3.50 |
| 317 | A67 | $1 multicolored | 1.00 | 5.00 |
| 318 | A67 | $2 multicolored | 1.50 | 4.00 |
| | | Nos. 306-318 (13) | 17.70 | 23.35 |

Issued: Nos. 306-312, 9/7; Nos. 313-318, 11/2.

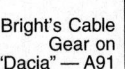

Bright's Cable
Gear on
"Dacia" — A91

Designs: 3c, Telegraph cable ship "Dacia." 50c, Double current Morse key, 1870, and map of Jamaica.

**1970, Oct. 12  Litho.  Perf. 14½**
| | | | | |
|---|---|---|---|---|
| 319 | A91 | 3c red orange & multi | .25 | .25 |
| 320 | A91 | 10c blue green & multi | .25 | .25 |
| 321 | A91 | 15c emerald & multi | .75 | .75 |
| | | Nos. 319-321 (3) | 1.25 | 1.25 |

Centenary of telegraph service.

Bananas, Citrus Fruit,
Sugar Cane and
Tobacco — A92

**1970, Nov. 2  Wmk. 352  Perf. 14**
| | | | | |
|---|---|---|---|---|
| 322 | A92 | 2c brown & multi | .25 | .30 |
| 323 | A92 | 10c black & multi | .35 | .25 |

Jamaica Agricultural Society, 75th anniv.

"The Projector,"
1845 — A93

Locomotives: 15c, Engine 54, 1944. 50c, Engine 102, 1967.

**1970, Nov. 21  Litho.  Perf. 13½**
| | | | | |
|---|---|---|---|---|
| 324 | A93 | 3c green & multi | .25 | .25 |
| 325 | A93 | 15c org brown & multi | .80 | .80 |
| 326 | A93 | 50c multicolored | 2.00 | 2.00 |
| | | Nos. 324-326 (3) | 3.05 | 3.05 |

125th anniv. of the Jamaican railroad.

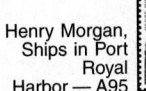

Kingston
Cathedral — A94

30c, Arms of Jamaica Bishopric. 10c, 20c, like 3c.

**1971, Feb. 22  Perf. 14½**
| | | | | |
|---|---|---|---|---|
| 327 | A94 | 3c lt green & multi | .25 | .25 |
| 328 | A94 | 10c dull orange & multi | .25 | .25 |
| 329 | A94 | 20c ultra & multi | .30 | .30 |
| 330 | A94 | 30c gray & multi | .30 | .60 |
| | | Nos. 327-330 (4) | 1.10 | 1.40 |

Centenary of the disestablishment of the Church of England.

Henry Morgan,
Ships in Port
Royal
Harbor — A95

Designs: 15c, Mary Read, Anne Bonny and pamphlet on their trial. 30c, 18th century merchantman surrendering to pirate schooner.

**1971, May 10  Litho.  Wmk. 352**
| | | | | |
|---|---|---|---|---|
| 331 | A95 | 3c red brown & multi | 1.00 | .25 |
| 332 | A95 | 15c gray & multi | 1.25 | .35 |
| 333 | A95 | 30c lilac & multi | 1.60 | 1.25 |
| | | Nos. 331-333 (3) | 3.85 | 1.85 |

Pirates and buccaneers.

Dummer
Packet Letter,
1705 — A96

Designs: 5c, Stampless cover, 1793. 8c, Post office, Kingston, 1820. 10c, Modern date cancellation on No. 312. 20c, Cover with stamps of Great Britain and Jamaica cancellations, 1859. 50c, Jamaica No. 83a, vert.

**1971, Oct. 30  Perf. 13½**
| | | | | |
|---|---|---|---|---|
| 334 | A96 | 3c dk carmine & black | .25 | .25 |
| 335 | A96 | 5c lt ol grn & black | .25 | .25 |
| 336 | A96 | 8c purple & black | .25 | .25 |
| 337 | A96 | 10c slate, black & brn | .25 | .25 |

| | | | | |
|---|---|---|---|---|
| 338 | A96 | 20c multicolored | .30 | .30 |
| 339 | A96 | 50c dk gray, blk & org | .50 | .60 |
| | | Nos. 334-339 (6) | 1.80 | 1.90 |

Tercentenary of Jamaica Post Office.

Earth Station and
Satellite — A97

**1972, Feb. 17  Perf. 14x13½**
| | | | | |
|---|---|---|---|---|
| 340 | A97 | 3c red & multi | .25 | .25 |
| 341 | A97 | 15c gray & multi | .30 | .25 |
| 342 | A97 | 50c multicolored | .65 | 1.00 |
| | | Nos. 340-342 (3) | 1.20 | 1.50 |

Jamaica's earth satellite station.

Bauxite
Industry
A98

National Stadium
A99

1c, Pimento, vert. 2c, Red ginger, vert. 4c, Kingston harbor. 5c, Oil refinery. 6c, Senate Building, Univ. of the West Indies. 9c, Devon House, Hope Road. 10c, Stewardess and Air Jamaica plane. 15c, Old Iron Bridge, vert. 20c, College of Arts, Science & Technology. 30c, Dunn's River Falls, vert. 50c, River raft. $1, Jamaica House. $2, Kings House. $5, Map and arms of Jamaica ('79).

**Perf. 14½x14, 14x14½**
**1972-79  Litho.  Wmk. 352**
| | | | | |
|---|---|---|---|---|
| 343 | A98 | 1c multicolored | .25 | .25 |
| 344 | A98 | 2c multicolored | .25 | .25 |
| 345 | A98 | 3c shown | .25 | .25 |
| 346 | A98 | 4c multicolored | .25 | .25 |
| 347 | A98 | 5c multicolored | .25 | .25 |
| 348 | A98 | 6c multicolored | .25 | .25 |

**Perf. 13½**
| | | | | |
|---|---|---|---|---|
| 349 | A99 | 8c shown | .25 | .25 |
| 350 | A99 | 9c multicolored | .25 | .25 |
| 351 | A99 | 10c multicolored | .25 | .25 |
| 352 | A99 | 15c multicolored | 1.25 | .25 |
| 353 | A99 | 20c multicolored | .30 | .25 |
| 354 | A99 | 30c multicolored | .55 | .25 |
| 355 | A99 | 50c multicolored | 1.10 | .35 |
| 356 | A99 | $1 multicolored | .60 | 1.00 |
| 357 | A99 | $2 multicolored | .80 | 1.25 |

**Perf. 14½x14**
**Size: 37x26½mm**
| | | | | |
|---|---|---|---|---|
| 358 | A99 | $5 multicolored | 1.50 | 1.75 |
| | | Nos. 343-358 (16) | 8.35 | 7.35 |

For overprints see Nos. 360-362, 451.

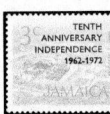

Nos. 345, 351, 355
Overprinted

**1972, Aug. 8  Perf. 14½x14, 13½**
| | | | | |
|---|---|---|---|---|
| 360 | A98 | 3c multicolored | .30 | .30 |
| 361 | A99 | 10c multicolored | .30 | .25 |
| 362 | A99 | 50c multicolored | .55 | 1.40 |
| | | Nos. 360-362 (3) | 1.15 | 1.95 |

Arms of
Kingston
A100

Design: 5c, 30c, Arms of Kingston, vert.

**1972, Dec. 4  Perf. 13½x14, 14x13½**
| | | | | |
|---|---|---|---|---|
| 363 | A100 | 5c pink & multi | .25 | .25 |
| 364 | A100 | 30c lemon & multi | .30 | .25 |
| 365 | A100 | 50c lt blue & multi | .50 | 1.50 |
| | | Nos. 363-365 (3) | 1.05 | 2.00 |

Centenary of Kingston as capital.

Mongoose and
Map of
Jamaica — A101

40c, Mongoose & rat. 60c, Mongoose & chicken.

**Perf. 14x14½**
**1973, Apr. 9  Litho.  Wmk. 352**
| | | | | |
|---|---|---|---|---|
| 366 | A101 | 8c yel green & blk | .25 | .25 |
| 367 | A101 | 40c blue & black | .35 | .35 |
| 368 | A101 | 60c salmon & black | .65 | 1.00 |
| a. | | Souvenir sheet of 3, #366-368 | 1.75 | 1.75 |
| | | Nos. 366-368 (3) | 1.25 | 1.60 |

Centenary of the introduction of the mongoose to Jamaica.

Euphorbia
Punicea — A102

Flowers: 6c, Hylocereus triangularis. 9c, Columnea argentea. 15c, Portlandia grandiflora. 30c, Samyda pubescens. 50c, Cordia sebestena.

**1973, July 9  Perf. 14**
| | | | | |
|---|---|---|---|---|
| 369 | A102 | 1c dp green & multi | .25 | .25 |
| 370 | A102 | 6c vio blue & multi | .25 | .25 |
| 371 | A102 | 9c orange & multi | .25 | .25 |
| 372 | A102 | 15c brown & multi | .25 | .25 |
| 373 | A102 | 30c olive & multi | .50 | .50 |
| 374 | A102 | 50c multicolored | .75 | 1.10 |
| | | Nos. 369-374 (6) | 2.25 | 2.60 |

Broughtonia
Sanguinea
A103

Orchids: 10c, Arpophyllum jamaicense, vert. 20c, Oncidium pulchellum, vert. $1, Brassia maculata.

**1973, Oct. 8  Perf. 14x13½, 13½x14**
| | | | | |
|---|---|---|---|---|
| 375 | A103 | 5c multicolored | .45 | .25 |
| 376 | A103 | 10c multicolored | .60 | .25 |
| 377 | A103 | 20c slate & multi | 1.25 | .30 |
| 378 | A103 | $1 ultra & multi | 3.00 | 3.25 |
| a. | | Souv. sheet of 4, #375-378, perf 12 | 5.00 | 5.00 |
| | | Nos. 375-378 (4) | 5.30 | 4.05 |

Mailboat "Mary"
(1808-1815)
A104

Mailboats: 10c, "Queensbury" (1814-27). 15c, "Sheldrake" (1829-34). 50c, "Thames" (1842).

**Perf. 13½ (5c, 50c), 14½ (10c, 15c)**
**1974, Apr. 8  Wmk. 352**
| | | | | |
|---|---|---|---|---|
| 379 | A104 | 5c shown | .80 | .25 |
| a. | | Perf. 14½ | 1.75 | 2.50 |
| 380 | A104 | 10c multicolored | .80 | .25 |
| 381 | A104 | 15c multicolored | 1.10 | .50 |
| 382 | A104 | 50c multicolored | 2.00 | 2.00 |
| a. | | Souv. sheet of 4, #379-382, perf 13½ | 5.00 | 5.00 |
| | | Nos. 379-382 (4) | 4.70 | 3.00 |

Jamaican
Dancers — A105

Designs: Dancers.

**1974, Aug. 1  Litho.  Perf. 13½**
| | | | | |
|---|---|---|---|---|
| 383 | A105 | 5c green & multi | .25 | .25 |
| 384 | A105 | 10c black & multi | .25 | .25 |
| 385 | A105 | 30c brown & multi | .30 | .30 |

| 386 | A105 | 50c lilac & multi | .45 | .45 |
| a. | | Souvenir sheet of 4, #383-386 | 2.00 | 2.00 |
| | | Nos. 383-386 (4) | 1.25 | 1.25 |

National Dance Theatre.

Globe, Letter, UPU Emblem — A106

**1974, Oct. 9**     **Perf. 14**

| 387 | A106 | 5c plum & multi | .25 | .25 |
| 388 | A106 | 9c olive & multi | .25 | .25 |
| 389 | A106 | 50c multicolored | .30 | .30 |
| | | Nos. 387-389 (3) | .80 | .80 |

Centenary of Universal Postal Union.

Senate Building and Sir Hugh Wooding — A107

10c, 50c, Chapel & Princess Alice. 30c, like 5c.

**1975, Jan. 13**     **Wmk. 352**

| 390 | A107 | 5c yellow & multi | .25 | .25 |
| 391 | A107 | 10c salmon & multi | .25 | .25 |
| 392 | A107 | 30c dull orange & multi | .25 | .25 |
| 393 | A107 | 50c multicolored | .30 | .30 |
| | | Nos. 390-393 (4) | 1.05 | 1.05 |

University College of the West Indies, 25th anniversary.

Commonwealth Symbol — A108

Commonwealth Symbol and: 10c, Arms of Jamaica. 30c, Dove of peace. 50c, Jamaican flag.

**1975, Apr. 29**     **Litho.**     **Perf. 13½**

| 394 | A108 | 5c buff & multi | .25 | .25 |
| 395 | A108 | 10c rose & multi | .25 | .25 |
| 396 | A108 | 30c violet blue & multi | .25 | .25 |
| 397 | A108 | 50c multicolored | .25 | .25 |
| | | Nos. 394-397 (4) | 1.00 | 1.00 |

Commonwealth Heads of Government Conference, Jamaica, Apr.-May.

Graphium Marcellinus — A109

Butterflies: 20c, Papilio thoas melonius. 25c, Papilio thersites. 30c, Papilio homerus.

**1975, Aug. 25**     **Litho.**     **Perf. 14**

| 398 | A109 | 10c lt green & multi | 1.00 | .25 |
| 399 | A109 | 20c lt green & multi | 1.40 | .70 |
| 400 | A109 | 25c lt green & multi | 1.50 | 1.75 |
| 401 | A109 | 30c lt green & multi | 2.00 | 2.25 |
| a. | | Souvenir sheet of 4, #398-401 | 8.00 | 8.00 |
| | | Nos. 398-401 (4) | 5.90 | 4.95 |

See Nos. 423-426, 435-438.

Koo Koo, "Actor-boy" — A110

Christmas: 10c, Red "set-girls." 20c, French "set-girls." 50c, Jawbone or "House John Canoe." Festival dancers drawn by I. M. Belisario in Kingston, 1837.

**1975, Nov. 3**     **Litho.**     **Wmk. 352**

| 402 | A110 | 8c multicolored | .25 | .25 |
| 403 | A110 | 10c olive & multi | .25 | .25 |
| 404 | A110 | 20c ultra & multi | .40 | .40 |
| 405 | A110 | 50c multicolored | .80 | .80 |
| a. | | Souvenir sheet of 4, #402-405, perf. 13½ | 2.25 | 2.25 |
| | | Nos. 402-405 (4) | 1.70 | 1.70 |

See Nos. 416-418.

Map of Jamaica, by Benedetto Bordone, 1528 — A111

Maps of Jamaica by: 20c, Tommaso Porcacchi, 1576. 30c, Theodor DeBry, 1594. 50c, Barent Langenes, 1598.

**1976, Mar. 12**     **Perf. 13½x14**

| 406 | A111 | 10c brown, buff & red | .30 | .25 |
| 407 | A111 | 20c bister & multi | .45 | .25 |
| 408 | A111 | 30c lt blue & multi | .75 | .75 |
| 409 | A111 | 50c multicolored | 1.00 | 1.25 |
| | | Nos. 406-409 (4) | 2.50 | 2.50 |

See Nos. 419-422.

Olympic Rings — A112

**1976, June 14**     **Litho.**     **Perf. 13½x14**

| 410 | A112 | 10c black & multi | .25 | .25 |
| 411 | A112 | 20c blue & multi | .30 | .25 |
| 412 | A112 | 25c red & multi | .30 | .25 |
| 413 | A112 | 50c green & multi | .45 | 1.00 |
| | | Nos. 410-413 (4) | 1.30 | 1.75 |

21st Olympic Games, Montreal, Canada, July 17-Aug. 1.

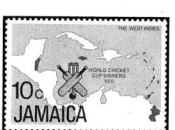

Map of West Indies, Bats, Wicket and Ball — A112a

Prudential Cup — A112b

**1976, Aug. 9**     **Unwmk.**     **Perf. 14**

| 414 | A112a | 10c lt blue & multi | .35 | .30 |
| 415 | A112b | 25c lilac rose & blk | .65 | 1.10 |

World Cricket Cup, won by West Indies Team, 1975.

### Christmas Type of 1975

Belisario Prints, 1837: 10c, Queen of the "set-girls." 20c, Band of Jawbone John Canoe. 50c, Koo Koo, "actor-boy."

**1976, Nov. 8**     **Wmk. 352**     **Perf. 13½**

| 416 | A110 | 10c brick red & multi | .25 | .25 |
| 417 | A110 | 20c bister & multi | .25 | .25 |
| 418 | A110 | 50c tan & multi | .40 | .60 |
| a. | | Souv. sheet of 3, #416-418, perf. 14 | 1.25 | 1.25 |
| | | Nos. 416-418 (3) | .90 | 1.10 |

Christmas.

### Map Type of 1976

Maps of Jamaica by: 9c, Edmund Hickeringill, 1661. 10c, John Ogilby, 1671. 25c, House of Visscher, 1680. 40c, John Thornton, 1689.

**1977, Feb. 28**     **Litho.**     **Perf. 13**

| 419 | A111 | 9c lt blue & multi | .30 | .40 |
| 420 | A111 | 10c buff & multi | .40 | .25 |
| 421 | A111 | 25c multicolored | .70 | .55 |
| 422 | A111 | 40c multicolored | .85 | 1.40 |
| | | Nos. 419-422 (4) | 2.25 | 2.60 |

### Butterfly Type of 1975

10c, Eurema elathea. 20c, Dynamine egaea. 25c, Atlantea pantoni. 40c, Hypolimnas misippus.

**1977, May 9**     **Wmk. 352**     **Perf. 13½**

| 423 | A109 | 10c black & multi | .40 | .25 |
| 424 | A109 | 20c black & multi | .80 | .50 |
| 425 | A109 | 25c black & multi | 1.25 | 1.25 |

| 426 | A109 | 40c black & multi | 2.25 | 3.50 |
| a. | | Souv. sheet of 4, #423-426, perf. 14½ | 7.00 | 7.00 |
| | | Nos. 423-426 (4) | 4.70 | 5.50 |

Scout Emblem, Doctor Bird, Outline of Jamaica — A113

**1977, Aug. 5**     **Litho.**     **Perf. 14**

| 427 | A113 | 10c multicolored | .65 | .25 |
| 428 | A113 | 20c multicolored | .90 | .25 |
| 429 | A113 | 25c multicolored | 1.00 | .35 |
| 430 | A113 | 50c multicolored | 1.50 | 1.50 |
| | | Nos. 427-430 (4) | 4.05 | 2.35 |

6th Caribbean Jamboree, Hope Gardens, Kingston, Aug. 3-17.

Trumpeter A114

10c, 2 clarinetists and oboist. 20c, kettle drummer and oboist, vert. 25c, Cellist and trumpeter, vert.

**1977, Dec. 19**     **Litho.**     **Perf. 14**

| 431 | A114 | 9c multicolored | .25 | .25 |
| 432 | A114 | 10c multicolored | .25 | .25 |
| 433 | A114 | 20c multicolored | .40 | .30 |
| 434 | A114 | 25c multicolored | .50 | .60 |
| a. | | Souvenir sheet of 4, #431-434 | 3.00 | 3.00 |
| | | Nos. 431-434 (4) | 1.40 | 1.40 |

Jamaica Military Band, 50th anniversary.

### Butterfly Type of 1975

Butterflies: 10c, Callophrys crethona. 20c, Siproeta stelenes. 25c, Urbanus proteus. 50c, Anaea troglodyta.

**1978, Apr. 17**     **Litho.**     **Perf. 14½**

| 435 | A109 | 10c black & multi | .55 | .25 |
| 436 | A109 | 20c black & multi | 1.00 | .25 |
| 437 | A109 | 25c black & multi | 1.25 | .60 |
| 438 | A109 | 50c black & multi | 2.25 | 2.75 |
| a. | | Souvenir sheet of 4, #435-438 | 5.75 | 5.75 |
| | | Nos. 435-438 (4) | 5.05 | 3.85 |

Half Figure with Canopy — A115

Arawak Artifacts, found 1792: 20c, Standing figure. 50c, Birdman.

**1978, July 10**     **Litho.**     **Perf. 13½x13**

| 439 | A115 | 10c multicolored | .25 | .25 |
| 440 | A115 | 20c multicolored | .25 | .25 |
| 441 | A115 | 50c multicolored | .35 | .35 |
| a. | | Souv. sheet of 3, #439-441, perf. 14 | 1.00 | 1.00 |
| | | Nos. 439-441 (3) | .85 | .85 |

Norman Manley Statue — A116

Designs: 20c, Alexander Bustamante statue. 25c, Kingston coat of arms. 40c, Gordon House Chamber, House of Representatives.

**1978, Sept. 25**     **Litho.**     **Wmk. 352**

| 442 | A116 | 10c multicolored | .25 | .25 |
| 443 | A116 | 20c multicolored | .25 | .25 |
| 444 | A116 | 25c multicolored | .25 | .25 |
| 445 | A116 | 40c multicolored | .30 | .35 |
| | | Nos. 442-445 (4) | 1.05 | 1.10 |

24th Commonwealth Parliamentary Conf.

Salvation Army Band — A117

Designs: 20c, Trumpeter. 25c, "S" and Cross entwined on pole of Army flag. 50c, William Booth and Salvation Army shield.

**1978, Dec. 4**     **Perf. 14**

| 446 | A117 | 10c multicolored | .30 | .25 |
| 447 | A117 | 20c multicolored | .35 | .25 |
| 448 | A117 | 25c multicolored | .35 | .30 |
| 449 | A117 | 50c multicolored | .50 | .75 |
| | | Nos. 446-449 (4) | 1.50 | 1.55 |

Christmas; Salvation Army centenary.

"Negro Aroused," by Edna Manley — A118

**1978, Dec. 11**     **Perf. 13**

| 450 | A118 | 10c multicolored | .35 | .25 |

International Anti-Apartheid Year.

No. 351 Overprinted

**1979, Apr. 2**     **Litho.**     **Perf. 13½**

| 451 | A99 | 10c multicolored | .45 | .45 |

Arawak Grinding Stone, c. 400 B.C. — A119

Arawak Artifacts (all A.D.): 10c, Stone implements, c. 500, horiz. 20c, Cooking pot, c. 300, horiz. 25c, Serving boat, c. 300, horiz. 50c, Storage jar fragment, c. 300.

**1979, Apr. 23**     **Perf. 14**

| 452 | A119 | 5c multicolored | .25 | .25 |
| 453 | A119 | 10c multicolored | .25 | .25 |
| 454 | A119 | 20c multicolored | .25 | .25 |
| 455 | A119 | 25c multicolored | .25 | .25 |
| 456 | A119 | 50c multicolored | .25 | .25 |
| | | Nos. 452-456 (5) | 1.25 | 1.25 |

Jamaica No. 183, Hill Statue — A120

Hill Statue and Stamps of Jamaica: 20c, No. 83a. 25c, No. 5. 50c, No. 271.

**1979, Aug. 13**     **Litho.**     **Perf. 14**

| 457 | A120 | 10c multicolored | .25 | .25 |
| 458 | A120 | 20c multicolored | .25 | .25 |
| a. | | Souvenir sheet of 1 | .55 | .55 |
| 459 | A120 | 25c multicolored | .25 | .25 |
| 460 | A120 | 50c multicolored | .25 | .50 |
| | | Nos. 457-460 (4) | 1.00 | 1.25 |

Sir Rowland Hill (1795-1879), originator of penny postage.

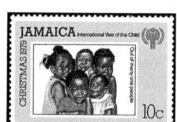

Children, IYC Emblem — A121

International Year of the Child: 20c, Doll, vert. 25c, "The Family." 25c, "House on the Hill." 25c, 50c are children's drawings.

## 1979, Oct. 1
| | | | | |
|---|---|---|---|---|
| 461 | A121 | 10c multicolored | .25 | .25 |
| 462 | A121 | 20c multicolored | .25 | .25 |
| 463 | A121 | 25c multicolored | .25 | .25 |
| 464 | A121 | 50c multicolored | .25 | .25 |
| | | Nos. 461-464 (4) | 1.00 | 1.00 |

Tennis, Montego Bay — A122

Jamaican Tody — A123

Designs: 2c, Golfing, Tryall Hanover. 4c, Horseback riding, Negril Beach. 5c, Old Waterwheel, Tryall Hanover. 6c, Fern Gully, Ocho Rios. 7c, Dunn's River Falls, Ocho Rios. 10c, Doctorbird. 12c, Yellow-billed parrot. 15c, Hummingbird. 35c, White-chinned thrush. 50c, Jamaican woodpecker. 65c, Rafting Martha Brae Trelawny. 75c, Blue marlin fishing, Port Antonio. $1, Scuba diving, Ocho Rios. $2, Sail boats, Montego Bay.

### Wmk. 352
**1979-80  Litho.  Perf. 13½**
| | | | | |
|---|---|---|---|---|
| 465 | A122 | 1c multicolored | .70 | .90 |
| 466 | A122 | 2c multicolored | 2.00 | 2.50 |
| 467 | A122 | 4c multicolored | 1.00 | 2.00 |
| 468 | A122 | 5c multicolored | 1.25 | .30 |
| 469 | A122 | 6c multicolored | 1.25 | 2.25 |
| 470 | A122 | 7c multicolored | .50 | .30 |
| 472 | A123 | 8c multicolored | 1.00 | 1.00 |
| 473 | A123 | 10c multicolored | 1.00 | .25 |
| 474 | A123 | 12c multicolored | 1.00 | 1.50 |
| 475 | A123 | 15c multicolored | 1.00 | .30 |
| 476 | A123 | 35c multicolored | 1.50 | .35 |
| 477 | A123 | 50c multicolored | 2.00 | .35 |
| 478 | A123 | 65c multicolored | 2.00 | 2.50 |
| 479 | A122 | 75c multicolored | 2.25 | 2.25 |
| 480 | A122 | $1 multicolored | 2.25 | 2.25 |
| 481 | A122 | $2 multicolored | 2.25 | 1.00 |
| | | Nos. 465-481 (16) | 22.95 | 20.00 |

Issued: Nos. 465-470, 11/26/79; Nos. 472-481, 5/80.
For surcharges see Nos. 581-582, 665-666.

Institute of Jamaica Centenary A124

15c, Institute building, 1980. 35c, "The Ascension" on microfilm reader, vert. 50c, Hawksbill and green turtles. 75c, Jamaican owl, vert.

**1980, Feb. 25  Litho.  Perf. 13½**
| | | | | |
|---|---|---|---|---|
| 484 | A124 | 5c shown | .25 | .25 |
| 485 | A124 | 15c multicolored | .25 | .25 |
| 486 | A124 | 35c multicolored | .25 | .25 |
| 487 | A124 | 50c multicolored | .30 | .30 |
| 488 | A124 | 75c multicolored | 1.50 | 1.50 |
| | | Nos. 484-488 (5) | 2.55 | 2.55 |

Don Quarrie, 1976 Gold Medalist, 200-Meter Race, Moscow '80 Emblem — A125

1952 4x400-meter Relay Team: a, Arthur Wint. b, Leslie Laing. c, Herbert McKenley. d, George Rhoden.

**1980, July 21  Litho.  Perf. 13**
| | | | | |
|---|---|---|---|---|
| 489 | A125 | 15c shown | .40 | .25 |
| 490 | | Strip of 4 | 2.00 | 2.00 |
| a.-d. | | A125 35c any single | .45 | .45 |

22nd Summer Olympic Games, Moscow, July 19-Aug. 3.

Parish Church, Kingston — A126

20c, Coke Memorial. 25c, Church of the Redeemer. $5, Holy Trinity Cathedral.

## 1980, Nov. 24  Litho.  Perf. 14
| | | | | |
|---|---|---|---|---|
| 491 | A126 | 15c shown | .25 | .25 |
| 492 | A126 | 20c multicolored | .25 | .25 |
| 493 | A126 | 25c multicolored | .25 | .25 |
| 494 | A126 | $5 multicolored | 1.00 | 1.00 |
| a. | | Souvenir sheet of 4, #491-494 | 2.00 | 2.00 |
| | | Nos. 491-494 (4) | 1.75 | 1.75 |

Christmas.

Tube Sponge — A127

20c, Blood cup sponge, vert. 60c, Black coral, vert. 75c, Tire reef.

**1981, Feb. 27  Wmk. 352  Perf. 14**
| | | | | |
|---|---|---|---|---|
| 495 | A127 | 20c multicolored | .25 | .25 |
| 496 | A127 | 45c shown | .35 | .35 |
| 497 | A127 | 60c multicolored | .45 | .45 |
| 498 | A127 | 75c multicolored | .55 | .55 |
| | | Nos. 495-498 (4) | 1.60 | 1.60 |

See Nos. 523-527.

Indian Coney — A128

Designs: b, Facing left. c, Eating. d, Family.

**1981, May 25  Wmk. 352  Perf. 14**
| | | | | |
|---|---|---|---|---|
| 499 | | Strip of 4 | 1.25 | 1.25 |
| a.-d. | | A128 20c any single | .25 | .25 |

### Royal Wedding Issue
**Common Design Type**

20c, White orchid. 45c, Royal coach. 60c, Couple. $5, St. James' Palace.

**1981, July 29  Litho.  Perf. 15**
| | | | | |
|---|---|---|---|---|
| 500 | CD331 | 20c multicolored | .25 | .25 |
| 501 | CD331 | 45c multicolored | .25 | .25 |
| 502 | CD331 | 60c multicolored | .25 | .25 |

**Perf. 13½**
| | | | | |
|---|---|---|---|---|
| 503 | CD331 | $5 multicolored | .70 | .60 |
| a. | | Souvenir sheet of 1 | .90 | .90 |
| b. | | Bklt. pane of 4, perf 14x14½ | 1.60 | |
| | | Nos. 500-503 (4) | 1.45 | 1.35 |

Also issued in sheets of 5 + label, perf. 13½.

Intl. Year of the Disabled — A129

20c, Blind weaver. 45c, Artist. 60c, Learning sign language. $1.50, Basketball players.

**1981, Sept. 14  Wmk. 352  Perf. 13½**
| | | | | |
|---|---|---|---|---|
| 504 | A129 | 20c multicolored | .25 | .25 |
| 505 | A129 | 45c multicolored | .35 | .35 |
| 506 | A129 | 60c multicolored | .45 | .45 |
| 507 | A129 | $1.50 multicolored | 1.75 | 1.75 |
| | | Nos. 504-507 (4) | 2.80 | 2.80 |

World Food Day — A130

**Perf. 13x13½, 13½x13**
**1981, Oct. 16  Wmk. 352**
| | | | | |
|---|---|---|---|---|
| 508 | A130 | 20c No. 218 | .40 | .25 |
| 509 | A130 | 45c No. 76, vert. | .70 | .40 |
| 510 | A130 | $2 No. 121 | 1.75 | 1.25 |
| 511 | A130 | $4 No. 125 | 2.75 | 2.25 |
| | | Nos. 508-511 (4) | 5.60 | 4.15 |

Bob Marley (1945-1981), Reggae Musician — A131

Portraits of Bob Marley and song titles.

## 1981, Oct. 20  Wmk. 373  Perf. 14½
| | | | | |
|---|---|---|---|---|
| 512 | A131 | 1c multicolored | .60 | .90 |
| 513 | A131 | 2c multicolored | .60 | .90 |
| 514 | A131 | 3c multicolored | .60 | .90 |
| 515 | A131 | 15c multicolored | 2.50 | .30 |
| 516 | A131 | 20c multicolored | 2.50 | .30 |
| 517 | A131 | 60c multicolored | 3.50 | 2.50 |
| 518 | A131 | $3 multicolored | 5.25 | 9.50 |
| | | Nos. 512-518 (7) | 15.55 | 15.30 |

### Souvenir Sheet
| | | | | |
|---|---|---|---|---|
| 519 | A131 | $5.25 multicolored | 6.75 | 6.75 |

Christmas A132

10c, Webb Memorial Baptist Church. 45c, Church of God. $5, Bryce United Church.

**1981, Dec. 11  Wmk. 352  Perf. 14**
| | | | | |
|---|---|---|---|---|
| 520 | A132 | 10c multicolored | .30 | .25 |
| 521 | A132 | 45c multicolored | .50 | .25 |
| 522 | A132 | $5 multicolored | 1.40 | 2.00 |
| a. | | Souvenir sheet of 3, #520-522, perf. 12½x12 | 3.50 | 3.50 |
| | | Nos. 520-522 (3) | 2.20 | 2.50 |

See Nos. 547-549.

### Marine Life Type of 1981
20c, Gorgonian coral, vert. 45c, Hard sponge. 60c, Sea cow. 75c, Plume worm. $3, Coral-banded shrimp.

**1982, Feb. 22  Litho.  Perf. 14**
| | | | | |
|---|---|---|---|---|
| 523 | A127 | 20c multicolored | .50 | .25 |
| 524 | A127 | 45c multicolored | .70 | .25 |
| 525 | A127 | 60c multicolored | .80 | .40 |
| 526 | A127 | 75c multicolored | .90 | .50 |
| 527 | A127 | $3 multicolored | 2.25 | 1.50 |
| | | Nos. 523-527 (5) | 5.15 | 2.90 |

Scouting Year — A133

20c, 45c, 60c, Various scouts. $2, Baden-Powell.

**1982, July 12  Litho.  Perf. 13½**
| | | | | |
|---|---|---|---|---|
| 528 | A133 | 20c multicolored | .50 | .25 |
| 529 | A133 | 45c multicolored | .75 | .30 |
| 530 | A133 | 60c multicolored | 1.00 | .65 |
| 531 | A133 | $2 multicolored | 1.90 | 1.90 |
| a. | | Souvenir sheet of 4, #528-531 | 5.75 | 5.75 |
| | | Nos. 528-531 (4) | 4.15 | 3.10 |

Princess Diana, 21st Birthday — A134

20c, Lignum vitae. 45c, Couple in coach. 60c, Wedding portrait. 75c, Saxifraga longifolia. $2, Diana. $3, Viola gracilis major. $5, Honeymoon.

**1982, Sept. 1  Perf. 14½**
| | | | | |
|---|---|---|---|---|
| 532 | A134 | 20c multicolored | .35 | .25 |
| 533 | A134 | 45c multicolored | .55 | .35 |
| 534 | A134 | 60c multicolored | .65 | .45 |
| a. | | Booklet pane of 3, #532-534 | 1.75 | |
| 535 | A134 | 75c multicolored | 1.00 | 1.25 |
| 536 | A134 | $2 multicolored | 1.50 | 1.50 |
| 537 | A134 | $3 multicolored | 1.75 | 2.50 |
| a. | | Booklet pane of 3, #535-537 | 7.00 | |
| | | Nos. 532-537 (6) | 5.80 | 6.30 |

### Souvenir Sheet
| | | | | |
|---|---|---|---|---|
| 538 | A134 | $5 multicolored | 3.25 | 3.25 |

Nos. 535, 537 in sheets of 5.

Nos. 532-538 Overprinted

## 1982, Sept. 13
| | | | | |
|---|---|---|---|---|
| 539 | A134 | 20c multicolored | .30 | .25 |
| 540 | A134 | 45c multicolored | .35 | .35 |
| 541 | A134 | 60c multicolored | .45 | .45 |
| a. | | Booklet pane of 3, #539-541 | 1.75 | |
| 542 | A134 | 75c multicolored | .70 | 1.25 |
| 543 | A134 | $2 multicolored | 1.00 | 1.00 |
| 544 | A134 | $3 multicolored | 1.25 | 1.75 |
| a. | | Booklet pane of 3, #542-544 | 6.00 | |
| | | Nos. 539-544 (6) | 4.05 | 5.05 |

### Souvenir Sheet
| | | | | |
|---|---|---|---|---|
| 545 | A134 | $5 multicolored | 2.75 | 2.75 |

Birth of Prince William of Wales, June 21.

Lizard Cuckoo Capturing Prey — A135

Designs: b, Searching for prey. c, Calling. d, Landing. e, Flying.

**1982, Oct. 25**
| | | | | |
|---|---|---|---|---|
| 546 | | Strip of 5 | 8.00 | 8.00 |
| a.-e. | | A135 $1 any single | 1.25 | 1.25 |

### Christmas Type of 1981
20c, United Pentecostal Church. 45c, Disciples of Christ Church. 75c, Open Bible Church.

**Perf. 13x13½**
**1982, Dec. 8  Wmk. 352**
| | | | | |
|---|---|---|---|---|
| 547 | A132 | 20c multicolored | .60 | .25 |
| 548 | A132 | 45c multicolored | .75 | .25 |
| 549 | A132 | 75c multicolored | 1.60 | 2.00 |
| | | Nos. 547-549 (3) | 2.95 | 2.50 |

Visit of Queen Elizabeth II — A136

**1983, Feb. 14  Litho.  Perf. 14**
| | | | | |
|---|---|---|---|---|
| 550 | A136 | $2 Queen Elizabeth II | 3.00 | 3.25 |
| 551 | A136 | $3 Arms | 4.00 | 5.75 |

A136a

**1983, Mar. 14  Litho.  Wmk. 352**
| | | | | |
|---|---|---|---|---|
| 552 | A136a | 20c Dancers | .25 | .25 |
| 553 | A136a | 45c Bauxite mining | .35 | .35 |
| 554 | A136a | 75c Map | .50 | .50 |
| 555 | A136a | $2 Arms, citizens | 1.00 | 1.25 |
| | | Nos. 552-555 (4) | 2.10 | 2.35 |

Commonwealth Day.

25th Anniv. of Intl. Maritime Org. — A137

15c, Cargo ship. 20c, Cruise liner. 45c, Container vessel. $1, Intl. Seabed Headquarters.

**1983, Mar. 17  Litho.  Perf. 14**
| | | | | |
|---|---|---|---|---|
| 556 | A137 | 15c multi | 1.00 | .30 |
| 557 | A137 | 20c multi | 1.50 | .35 |
| 558 | A137 | 45c multi | 2.00 | .75 |
| 559 | A137 | $1 multi | 3.00 | 4.00 |
| | | Nos. 556-559 (4) | 7.50 | 5.40 |

21st Anniv. of Independence — A138

Prime Ministers Alexander Bustamante and Norman Washington Manley.

**1983, July 25     Litho.     Perf. 14**
560  A138  15c blue & multi          .25   .25
561  A138  20c lt green & multi      .25   .25
562  A138  45c yellow & multi        .30   .30
       Nos. 560-562 (3)              .80   .80

World Communications Year — A139

20c, Ship-to-shore radio. 45c, Postal services. 75c, Telephone communication. $1, TV satellite.

**1983, Oct. 18     Wmk. 352     Perf. 14**
563  A139  20c multi         .60   .25
564  A139  45c multi        1.25   .35
565  A139  75c multi        1.50  2.00
566  A139  $1 multi         1.75  2.50
       Nos. 563-566 (4)     5.10  5.10

Christmas 1983 — A140

Paintings: 15c, Racing at Caymanas, by Sidney McLaren. 20c, Seated Figures, by Karl Parboosingh. 75c, The Petitioner, by Henry Daley, vert. $2, Banana Plantation, by John Dunkley, vert.

**1983, Dec. 12     Litho.     Perf. 13½**
567  A140  15c multicolored    .25   .25
568  A140  20c multicolored    .25   .25
569  A140  75c multicolored    .40   .50
570  A140  $2 multicolored    1.25  2.00
       Nos. 567-570 (4)       2.15  3.05

Alexander Bustamante (1884-1977), First Prime Minister — A141

**1984, Feb. 24     Litho.     Perf. 14**
571  20c Portrait                .85   .85
572  20c Blenheim (birthplace)   .85   .85
a.  A141 Pair, #571-572         2.00  2.00

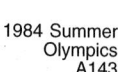
Sea Planes — A142

25c, Gypsy Moth. 55c, Consolidated Commodore. $1.50, Sikorsky S-38. $3, Sikorsky S-40.

**1984, June 11     Litho.     Perf. 14**
573  A142  25c multi          1.50   .30
574  A142  55c multi          2.00   .75
575  A142  $1.50 multi        3.00  3.50
576  A142  $3 multi           4.25  5.00
       Nos. 573-576 (4)      10.75  9.55

1984 Summer Olympics A143

25c, Bicycling. 55c, Relay race. $1.50, Running. $3, Women's running.

**1984, July 11**
577  A143  25c multi          1.75   .50
578  A143  55c multi           .75   .30
579  A143  $1.50 multi        1.60  3.25
580  A143  $3 multi           2.25  3.50
a.  Souvenir sheet of 4, #577-580  6.25  6.25
       Nos. 577-580 (4)       6.35  7.55

Nos. 469, 474 Surcharged

**1984, Aug. 7     Litho.     Perf. 13½**
581  A122  5c on 6c #469      .40   .40
582  A123  10c on 12c #474   1.25   .55

Early Steam Engines A144

25c, Enterprise, 1845. 55c, Tank Locomotive, 1880. $1.50, Kitson-Meyer Tank, 1904. $3, Superheater, 1916.

**1984, Nov. 16     Litho.     Perf. 13½**
583  A144  25c multicolored    1.40   .30
584  A144  55c multicolored    2.00   .60
585  A144  $1.50 multicolored  3.00  3.00
586  A144  $3 multicolored     3.75  5.00
       Nos. 583-586 (4)       10.15  8.90
       See Nos. 608-611.

Christmas — A145

Local sculptures: 20c, Accompong Madonna, by Namba Roy. 25c, Head, by Alvin Marriott. 55c, Moon, by Edna Manley. $1.50, All Women are Five Women, by Mallica Reynolds.

**1984, Dec. 6     Wmk. 352     Perf. 14**
587  A145  20c multicolored    .30   .25
588  A145  25c multicolored    .35   .25
589  A145  55c multicolored   1.00   .50
590  A145  $1.50 multicolored 1.90  2.25
       Nos. 587-590 (4)       3.55  3.25

Jamaican Boas — A146

25c, Head of boa. 55c, Boa over water. 70c, Boa with young. $1, Boa on branch.

**1984, Oct. 22     Litho.     Perf. 14½**
591  A146  25c multi           9.50   .60
592  A146  55c multi          10.00  1.25
593  A146  70c multi          11.50  4.25
594  A146  $1 multi           14.50  4.75
a.  Souv. sheet of 4, #591-594 11.00 11.00
       Nos. 591-594 (4)       45.50 10.85

Stamps in No. 594a do not have WWF emblem.

Brown Pelicans — A147

**1985, Apr. 15     Wmk. 352     Perf. 13**
595  A147  20c multicolored   1.00   .25
596  A147  55c multicolored   1.50   .40
597  A147  $2 multicolored    2.25  2.75
598  A147  $5 multicolored    3.00  4.75
a.  Souvenir sheet of 4, #595-598  8.00  8.00
       Nos. 595-598 (4)       7.75  8.15

Birth bicentenary of artist and naturalist John J. Audubon (1785-1851).

**Queen Mother 85th Birthday**
Common Design Type

25c, Holding photograph album, 1963. 55c, With Prince Charles, Windsor Castle, 1983.

$1.50, At Belfast University. $3, Holding Prince Henry. $5, With limousine.

**1985, June 7     Litho.     Perf. 14½x14**
599  CD336  25c multicolored    .30   .25
600  CD336  55c multicolored    .55   .25
601  CD336  $1.50 multicolored  .80  1.25
602  CD336  $3 multicolored    1.50  2.25
       Nos. 599-602 (4)        3.15  4.00

**Souvenir Sheet**
603  CD336  $5 multicolored    3.00  3.00

Maps of Americas and Jamaica, IYY and Jamboree Emblems A148

**1985, July 30     Litho.     Perf. 14**
604  A148  25c multicolored    .85   .25
605  A148  55c multicolored   1.10   .30
606  A148  70c multicolored   1.60  1.25
607  A148  $4 multicolored    3.25  5.00
       Nos. 604-607 (4)       6.80  6.80

Intl. Youth Year and 5th Pan-American Scouting Jamboree.

**Locomotives Type of 1984**
**1985, Sept. 30        Size: 39x25mm**
608  A144  25c Baldwin        1.40   .30
609  A144  55c Rogers         1.75   .50
610  A144  $1.50 Projector    2.75  2.75
611  A144  $4 Diesel          3.50  5.00
       Nos. 608-611 (4)       9.40  8.55

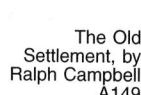
The Old Settlement, by Ralph Campbell A149

Christmas (Paintings by local artists): 55c, The Vendor, by Albert Hiue, vert. 75c, Road Menders, by Gaston Tabois. $4, Woman, Must I Not Be About My Father's Business? by Carl Abrahams, vert.

**1985, Dec. 9**
612  A149  20c multicolored   .25   .25
613  A149  25c multicolored   .25   .25
614  A149  75c multicolored   .25   .25
615  A149  $4 multicolored   1.00  1.00
       Nos. 612-615 (4)      1.75  1.75

Birds — A150

25c, Chestnut-bellied cuckoo. 55c, Jamaican becard. $1.50, White-eyed thrush. $5, Rufous-tailed flycatcher.

**1986, Feb. 10     Litho.     Perf. 14**
616  A150  25c multicolored   .55   .25
617  A150  55c multicolored   .75   .30
618  A150  $1.50 multicolored 1.00 1.00
619  A150  $5 multicolored   1.75  3.50
       Nos. 616-619 (4)      4.05  5.05

**Queen Elizabeth II 60th Birthday**
Common Design Type

Designs: 20c, With Princess Margaret, 1939. 25c, Leaving Liverpool Street Station for Sandringham with Princes Charles and Andrew, 1962. 70c, Visiting the Montego Bay war memorial, Jamaica, 1983. $3, State visit to Luxembourg, 1976. $5, Visiting Crown Agents' offices, 1983.

**1986, Apr. 21                 Perf. 14½**
620  CD337  20c scar, blk & sil    .35   .25
621  CD337  25c ultra & multi      .35   .25
622  CD337  70c green & multi      .40   .30
623  CD337  $3 violet & multi      .65   .65
624  CD337  $5 rose vio & multi   1.00  1.25
       Nos. 620-624 (5)           2.75  2.70

A151

AMERIPEX '86: 25c, Bustamante Childrens Hospital. 55c, Vacation cities. $3, Norman Manley Law School. $5, Exports.

**1986, May 19**
625  A151  25c multicolored     .60   .25
626  A151  55c multicolored    1.75   .40
627  A151  $3 multicolored     1.10  2.00
628  A151  $5 multicolored     5.75  5.75
a.  Souvenir sheet of 4, #625-628   9.75  9.75
       Nos. 625-628 (4)        9.20  8.40

**Royal Wedding Issue, 1986**
Common Design Type

Designs: 20c, At the races. $5, Andrew addressing the press.

**Perf. 14½x14**
**1986, July 23     Wmk. 352**
629  CD338  20c multicolored   .25   .25
630  CD338  $5 multicolored   1.10  1.10

Boxing Champions — A152

Champions: 45c, Richard "Shrimpy" Clarke, 1986 Commonwealth flyweight. 70c, Michael McCallum, 1984 WBA junior middleweight. $2, Trevor Berbick, 1986 WBC heavyweight. $4, Clarke, McCallum and Berbick.

**1986, Oct. 27     Litho.     Perf. 14**
631  A152  45c multicolored    .25   .25
632  A152  70c multicolored    .35   .30
633  A152  $2 multicolored     .75  1.00
634  A152  $4 multicolored    1.60  2.00
       Nos. 631-634 (4)       2.95  3.55

Flowers — A153

20c, Heliconia wagneriana, vert. 25c, Heliconia psittacorum. 55c, Heliconia rostrata, vert. $5, Strelitzia reginae.

**1986, Dec. 1                 Perf. 14**
635  A153  20c multicolored    .25   .25
636  A153  25c multicolored    .25   .25
637  A153  55c multicolored    .25   .25
638  A153  $5 multicolored    1.60  3.00
       Nos. 635-638 (4)       2.35  3.75

Christmas. See Nos. 675-678, 706-709.

Shells — A154

**1987, Feb. 23     Litho.     Perf. 15**
639  A154  35c Crown cone          .55   .25
640  A154  75c Measled cowrie      .75   .55
641  A154  $1 Trumpet triton       .85   .85
642  A154  $5 Rooster-tail conch  1.25  2.50
       Nos. 639-642 (4)           3.40  4.15

Prime Ministers A155

Natl. Coat of Arms A156

Designs: 1c-9c, 55c, Norman Washington Manley. 10c-50c, 60c-90c, Sir Alexander Bustamante.

**1987-94                     Perf. 12½x13**

## No inscription below design unless noted

| | | | | |
|---|---|---|---|---|
| 643 | A155 | 1c dull red | .25 | .85 |
| 644 | A155 | 2c rose pink | .25 | .85 |
| 645 | A155 | 3c light olive | .25 | .85 |
| 646 | A155 | 4c dull green | .25 | .85 |
| 647 | A155 | 5c slate blue | .45 | .75 |
| a. | | Inscribed "1988" | .60 | .75 |
| 648 | A155 | 6c ultramarine | .30 | .75 |
| 649 | A155 | 7c dull magenta | .60 | .75 |
| 650 | A155 | 8c red lilac | .30 | .25 |
| 651 | A155 | 9c brown olive | .70 | .25 |
| 652 | A155 | 10c deep rose | 2.00 | .75 |
| a. | | Inscribed "1993" | 1.25 | .75 |
| b. | | Inscribed "1994" | 2.75 | .75 |
| 653 | A155 | 20c bright org | .40 | .40 |
| a. | | Inscribed "1988" | .50 | .25 |
| b. | | Inscribed "1989" | .50 | .25 |
| c. | | Inscribed "1992" | .55 | .25 |
| d. | | Inscribed "1993" | .55 | .25 |
| e. | | Inscribed "1994" | .40 | .40 |
| 654 | A155 | 30c emerald | .50 | .25 |
| a. | | Inscribed "1994" | 1.25 | 1.75 |
| 655 | A155 | 40c lt blue green | 1.00 | 1.25 |
| a. | | Inscribed "1991" | 1.25 | .85 |
| b. | | Inscribed "1992" | 1.00 | 1.25 |
| c. | | Inscribed "1994" | .85 | .85 |
| 656 | A155 | 50c gray olive | 1.00 | .85 |
| a. | | Inscribed "1991" | 2.00 | 1.00 |
| b. | | Inscribed "1992" | .85 | 1.00 |
| c. | | Inscribed "1993" | .85 | .85 |
| d. | | Inscribed "1994" | .85 | .85 |
| 656A | A155 | 55c ol brn, inscr. "1994" | 1.50 | 1.50 |
| 657 | A155 | 60c light ultra | .40 | .35 |
| 658 | A155 | 70c pale violet | .40 | .30 |
| 659 | A155 | 80c violet | .55 | .45 |
| 660 | A155 | 90c light brown | 1.25 | 1.50 |
| a. | | Inscribed "1992" | 2.75 | 1.00 |
| b. | | Inscribed "1993" | 1.25 | 1.50 |
| 661 | A156 | $1 dull brn & buff | .55 | .40 |
| a. | | Inscribed "1991" | .65 | .50 |
| b. | | Inscribed "1992" | .75 | .50 |
| c. | | Inscribed "1993" | .75 | .50 |
| d. | | Inscribed "1997" | .50 | .40 |
| 661A | A156 | $1.10 dl brn & buff, inscr. "1994" | 1.00 | 1.00 |
| 662 | A156 | $2 orange | .85 | .95 |
| a. | | Inscribed "1997" | 1.50 | 1.25 |
| 663 | A156 | $5 gray ol & grnsh buff | .95 | 1.25 |
| a. | | Inscribed "1997" | 1.50 | 1.50 |
| 664 | A156 | $10 royal bl & pale bl | .90 | 1.75 |

**Perf. 13x13½**

| | | | | |
|---|---|---|---|---|
| 664A | A156 | $25 vio & pale vio, inscr. "1991" | 3.00 | 2.00 |
| 664B | A156 | $50 lil & pale lil, inscr. "1991" | 5.75 | 3.25 |
| | | Nos. 643-664B (26) | 25.35 | 24.35 |

Issued: $25, $50 (dated "1991"), 10/9/91; 55c, $1.10 (dated "1994"), 10/10/94; others (undated), 5/18/87.

Reprints issued: No. 647a, 653a, 6/6/88; 653b, 1989; 645a, 656a, 2/12/91; 661a, 6/6/91; 661b, 1992; 653c, 655b, 656b, 660a, 5/92; 653d, 656c, 660b, 661c, 1993; 652a, 11/93; 654d, 655c, 656c, 1994; 652b, 654a, 10/10/94; 661d, 662a, 663a, 4/30/97.

Nos. 477-478
Surcharged

### 1986, Nov. 3　Perf. 13½
| | | | | |
|---|---|---|---|---|
| 665 | A123 | 5c on 50c multi | 3.25 | 3.25 |
| 666 | A122 | 10c on 65c multi | 1.75 | 1.75 |

A157

### Wmk. 352
### 1987, July 27　Litho.　Perf. 14
| | | | | |
|---|---|---|---|---|
| 667 | A157 | 55c Flag, sunset | 1.60 | .60 |
| 668 | A157 | 70c Flag, horiz. | 1.60 | 2.25 |

Natl. Independence, 25th anniv.

A158

### 1987, Aug. 17
| | | | | |
|---|---|---|---|---|
| 669 | | 25c Portrait | 1.25 | 1.25 |
| 670 | | 25c Statue | 1.25 | 1.25 |
| a. | | A158 Pair, #669-670 | 3.75 | 3.75 |

Marcus Mosiah Garvey (1887-1940), natl. hero. No. 670a has a continuous design.

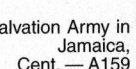

Salvation Army in
Jamaica,
Cent. — A159

Designs: 25c, School for the Blind. 55c, Col. Mary Booth, Bramwell-Booth Memorial Hall. $3, "War Chariot," 1929. $5, Arrival of col. Abram Davey on the S.S. Alene, 1887.

### 1987, Oct. 8　Perf. 13
| | | | | |
|---|---|---|---|---|
| 671 | A159 | 25c multicolored | 1.50 | .35 |
| 672 | A159 | 55c multicolored | 1.50 | .35 |
| 673 | A159 | $3 multicolored | 3.50 | 3.50 |
| 674 | A159 | $5 multicolored | 5.25 | 7.50 |
| a. | | Souvenir sheet of 4, #671-674 | 17.50 | 17.50 |
| | | Nos. 671-674 (4) | 11.75 | 11.70 |

### Flower Type of 1986

20c, Hibiscus hybrid. 25c, Hibiscus elatus. $4, Hibiscus cannabinus. $5, Hibiscus rosa sinensis.

### 1987, Nov. 30　Litho.　Perf. 14½
| | | | | |
|---|---|---|---|---|
| 675 | A153 | 20c multicolored | .25 | .25 |
| 676 | A153 | 25c multicolored | .25 | .25 |
| 677 | A153 | $4 multicolored | 2.75 | 2.50 |
| 678 | A153 | $5 multicolored | 3.00 | 3.00 |
| | | Nos. 675-678 (4) | 6.25 | 6.00 |

Christmas. Nos. 675-678 vert.

Birds
A160

Designs: No. 679, Chestnut-bellied cuckoo, black-billed parrot, Jamaican euphonia. No. 680, Jamaican white-eyed vireo, rufous-throated solitaire, yellow-crowned elaenia. No. 681, Snowy plover, little blue heron, great white heron. No. 682, Common stilt, snowy egret, black-crowned night heron.

### 1988, Jan. 22　Litho.　Perf. 14
| | | | | |
|---|---|---|---|---|
| 679 | | 45c multicolored | 1.50 | 1.50 |
| 680 | | 45c multicolored | 1.50 | 1.50 |
| a. | | A160 Pair, #679-680 | 4.75 | 4.75 |
| 681 | | $5 multicolored | 4.00 | 4.00 |
| 682 | | $5 multicolored | 4.00 | 4.00 |
| a. | | A160 Pair, #681-682 | 11.00 | 11.50 |
| | | Nos. 679-682 (4) | 11.00 | 11.00 |

Nos. 680a, 682a have continuous designs.

Marine Mammals
A161

20c, Blue whales. 25c, Gervais's whales. 55c, Killer whales. $5, Common dolphins.

### 1988, Apr. 14　Litho.　Perf. 14
| | | | | |
|---|---|---|---|---|
| 683 | A161 | 20c multicolored | 1.50 | .75 |
| 684 | A161 | 25c multicolored | 2.00 | .75 |
| 685 | A161 | 55c multicolored | 3.50 | .85 |
| 686 | A161 | $5 multicolored | 6.00 | 7.00 |
| | | Nos. 683-686 (4) | 13.00 | 9.35 |

Cricket — A162

Bat, wicket posts, ball, 18th cent. belt buckle and batsmen: 25c, Jackie Hendriks. 55c, George Headley. $2, Michael Holding. $3, R.K. Nunes. $4, Allan Rae.

### 1988, June 6　Litho.　Perf. 14
| | | | | |
|---|---|---|---|---|
| 687 | A162 | 25c multicolored | 1.60 | .45 |
| 688 | A162 | 55c multicolored | 1.75 | .45 |
| 689 | A162 | $2 multicolored | 3.00 | 3.00 |
| 690 | A162 | $3 multicolored | 3.25 | 3.25 |
| 691 | A162 | $4 multicolored | 4.50 | 4.50 |
| | | Nos. 687-691 (5) | 14.10 | 11.65 |

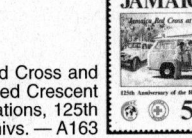

Intl. Red Cross and
Red Crescent
Organizations, 125th
Annivs. — A163

Anniversary emblem, Jamaica Red Cross emblem and: 25c, Ambulances. $5, Jean-Henri Dunant, 1828-1910, treating the wounded after the Battle of Solferino, 1859.

### 1988, Aug. 8　Litho.　Perf. 14½
| | | | | |
|---|---|---|---|---|
| 692 | A163 | 55c multicolored | .75 | .30 |
| 693 | A163 | $5 multicolored | 2.75 | 2.75 |

1988 Summer
Olympics,
Seoul — A164

### 1988, Aug. 24　Wmk. 352　Perf. 14
| | | | | |
|---|---|---|---|---|
| 694 | A164 | 25c Boxing | .45 | .25 |
| 695 | A164 | 45c Cycling | 2.00 | .65 |
| 696 | A164 | $4 Women's running | 2.50 | 2.50 |
| 697 | A164 | $5 Hurdling | 2.75 | 2.75 |
| a. | | Souvenir sheet of 4, #694-697 | 7.50 | 7.50 |
| | | Nos. 694-697 (4) | 7.70 | 6.15 |

No. 697a sold for $9.90. For surcharges see Nos. B4-B7.

Natl. Olympic
Bobsled
Team — A165

No. 698, Team members. No. 699, Two-man bobsled. No. 700, Team members, diff. No. 701, Four-man bobsled.

### 1988, Nov. 4　Litho.　Perf. 14
| | | | | |
|---|---|---|---|---|
| 698 | A165 | 25c multi | .50 | .50 |
| 699 | A165 | 25c multi | .50 | .50 |
| a. | | Pair, #698-699 | 2.50 | 3.00 |
| 700 | A165 | $5 multi | 2.00 | 2.00 |
| 701 | A165 | $5 multi | 2.00 | 2.00 |
| a. | | Pair, #700-701 | 6.00 | 7.50 |
| | | Nos. 698-701 (4) | 5.00 | 5.00 |

Nos. 699a, 701a have continuous designs.

Labor Year — A166

25c, Medicine, fire fighting. 55c, Handicrafts. $3, Garment industry. $5, Fishing.

### Perf. 14½x14
### 1988, Nov. 24　Wmk. 352
| | | | | |
|---|---|---|---|---|
| 702 | A166 | 25c multicolored | 1.25 | .45 |
| 703 | A166 | 55c multicolored | .55 | .45 |
| 704 | A166 | $3 multicolored | 1.50 | 1.25 |
| 705 | A166 | $5 multicolored | 1.75 | 1.75 |
| | | Nos. 702-705 (4) | 5.05 | 3.90 |

### Flower Type of 1986

25c, Euphorbia pulcherrima, vert. 55c, Spathodea campanulata. $3, Hylocereus triangularis, vert. $4, Broughtonia sanguinea.

### 1988, Dec. 15
| | | | | |
|---|---|---|---|---|
| 706 | A153 | 25c multicolored | .65 | .25 |
| 707 | A153 | 55c multicolored | .80 | .25 |
| 708 | A153 | $3 multicolored | 1.75 | 1.75 |
| 709 | A153 | $4 multicolored | 2.25 | 2.25 |
| | | Nos. 706-709 (4) | 5.45 | 4.50 |

Christmas.

Methodist
Church in
Jamaica,
Bicent. — A167

25c, Old York Castle School. 45c, Parade Chapel, Kingston, Rev. Thomas Coke. $5, Fr. Hugh Sherlock, St. John's Church.

### 1989, Jan. 19　Perf. 13½
| | | | | |
|---|---|---|---|---|
| 710 | A167 | 25c multicolored | .30 | .25 |
| 711 | A167 | 45c multicolored | .35 | .25 |
| 712 | A167 | $5 multicolored | 2.50 | 2.50 |
| | | Nos. 710-712 (3) | 3.15 | 3.00 |

Indigenous
Moths — A168

25c, Syntomidopsis variegata. 55c, Himantoides undata-perkinsi. $3, Hypercompe nigriplaga. $5, Sthenognatha toddi.

### Wmk. 352
### 1989, Aug. 30　Litho.　Perf. 14
| | | | | |
|---|---|---|---|---|
| 713 | A168 | 25c multicolored | .75 | .25 |
| 714 | A168 | 55c multicolored | 1.25 | .30 |
| 715 | A168 | $3 multicolored | 2.00 | 2.00 |
| 716 | A168 | $5 multicolored | 3.50 | 3.50 |
| | | Nos. 713-716 (4) | 7.50 | 6.05 |

See Nos. 725-728, 752-755. For surcharges & overprints see Nos. 729-732, 756-759.

A169

Discovery of America, 500th Anniv. (in 1992): 25c, Arawak spear fisherman. 70c, Smoking tobacco. $5, Ferdinand and Isabella inspecting caravels. $10, Columbus studying chart.

### 1989, Dec. 22　Perf. 13½
| | | | | |
|---|---|---|---|---|
| 717 | A169 | 25c multicolored | .25 | .25 |
| 718 | A169 | 70c multicolored | .50 | .30 |
| 719 | A169 | $5 multicolored | 2.00 | 2.00 |
| 720 | A169 | $10 multicolored | 5.75 | 5.75 |
| a. | | Souvenir sheet of 4, #717-720, perf. 12½ | 17.50 | 17.50 |
| | | Nos. 717-720 (4) | 8.50 | 8.30 |

No. 720a exists imperf. Value $25.

A171

### Wmk. 352
### 1990, June 28　Litho.　Perf. 14
| | | | | |
|---|---|---|---|---|
| 721 | A171 | 45c multicolored | 1.25 | .30 |
| 722 | A171 | 55c multi, diff. | 1.25 | .30 |
| 723 | A171 | $5 multi, diff. | 5.50 | 7.00 |
| | | Nos. 721-723 (3) | 8.00 | 7.60 |

Girl Guides of Jamaica, 75th anniv.

### Indigenous Moths Type of 1989

25c, Eunomia rubripunctata. 55c, Perigonia jamaicensis. $4, Uraga haemorrhoa. $5, Empyreuma pugione.

### Wmk. 352
### 1990, Sept. 12　Litho.　Perf. 14
| | | | | |
|---|---|---|---|---|
| 725 | A168 | 25c multicolored | 1.00 | .30 |
| 726 | A168 | 55c multicolored | 1.60 | .30 |
| 727 | A168 | $4 multicolored | 2.75 | 3.00 |
| 728 | A168 | $5 multicolored | 3.00 | 3.00 |
| | | Nos. 725-728 (4) | 8.35 | 6.60 |

Nos. 725-728 Ovptd.
in Black

**1990, Sept. 12**

| | | | | |
|---|---|---|---|---|
| 729 | A168 | 25c No. 725 | .80 | .35 |
| 730 | A168 | 55c No. 726 | 1.25 | .35 |
| 731 | A168 | $4 No. 727 | 2.75 | 2.75 |
| 732 | A168 | $5 No. 728 | 3.25 | 3.25 |
| | | Nos. 729-732 (4) | 8.05 | 6.70 |

Expo '90, International Garden and Greenery Exposition, Osaka, Japan.

Intl. Literacy Year — A172

Design: $5, Mathematics class.

**Wmk. 352**

**1990, Oct. 10    Litho.    Perf. 14**

| | | | | |
|---|---|---|---|---|
| 733 | A172 | 55c multi | .75 | .30 |
| 734 | A172 | $5 multi | 5.00 | 6.00 |

Christmas A173

Children's art — 20c, To the market. 25c, Untitled (houses). 55c, Jack and Jill. 70c, Untitled (market). $1.50, Lonely (beach). $5, Market woman, vert.

**Perf. 13½x14**

**1990, Dec. 7    Litho.    Wmk. 352**

| | | | | |
|---|---|---|---|---|
| 735 | A173 | 20c multicolored | .50 | .25 |
| 736 | A173 | 25c multicolored | .60 | .25 |
| 737 | A173 | 55c multicolored | .70 | .25 |
| 738 | A173 | 70c multicolored | 1.00 | .40 |
| 739 | A173 | $1.50 multicolored | 1.75 | 1.75 |
| 740 | A173 | $5 multicolored | 2.25 | 4.25 |
| | | Nos. 735-740 (6) | 6.80 | 7.15 |

See Nos. 760-763.

Discovery of America, 500th Anniv. (in 1992) — A174

Maps of Columbus' voyages.

**1990, Dec. 19        Perf. 14**

| | | | | |
|---|---|---|---|---|
| 741 | A174 | 25c First, 1492 | 1.00 | .40 |
| 742 | A174 | 45c Second, 1493 | 1.25 | .40 |
| 743 | A174 | $5 Third, 1498 | 3.75 | 3.75 |
| 744 | A174 | $10 Fourth, 1502 | 6.50 | 8.00 |
| | | Nos. 741-744 (4) | 12.50 | 12.55 |

**Souvenir Sheet**

| | | | | |
|---|---|---|---|---|
| 745 | | Sheet of 4 | 13.00 | 13.00 |
| a. | A174 | 25c Cuba, Jamaica | 1.00 | 1.00 |
| b. | A174 | 45c Hispaniola, Puerto Rico | 1.10 | 1.10 |
| c. | A174 | $5 Central America | 3.00 | 3.00 |
| d. | A174 | $10 Venezuela | 5.00 | 5.00 |

Souvenir sheet also exists imperf. Value, $20.
See Nos. 764-767.

Natl. Meteorological Service — A175

**1991, May 20    Litho.    Wmk. 352**

| | | | | |
|---|---|---|---|---|
| 746 | A175 | 50c multicolored | .55 | .25 |
| 747 | A175 | $10 multicolored | 6.00 | 6.00 |

11th World Meteorological Congress.

Intl. Council of Nurses Council of Natl. Representatives, Jamaica — A176

50c, Mary Seacole. $1.10, Mary Seacole House. $8, Hospital at Scutari.

**Wmk. 352**

**1991, June 24    Litho.    Perf. 13½**

| | | | | |
|---|---|---|---|---|
| 748 | A176 | 50c multicolored | 1.00 | .35 |

| | | | | |
|---|---|---|---|---|
| 749 | A176 | $1.10 multicolored | 1.75 | 1.75 |

**Souvenir Sheet**

| | | | | |
|---|---|---|---|---|
| 750 | A176 | $8 multicolored | 4.00 | 4.00 |

Cyclura Collei (Jamaican Iguana) — A177

Designs: a, Head pointed to UR. b, Facing right. c, Climbing rock. d, Facing left. e, Head pointed to UL.

**Wmk. 352**

**1991, July 29    Litho.    Perf. 13**

| | | | | |
|---|---|---|---|---|
| 751 | A177 | $1.10 Strip of 5, #a.-e. | 4.50 | 4.50 |

Natural History Soc. of Jamaica, 50th anniv.

**Moths Type of 1989**

50c, Urania sloanus. $1.10, Phoenicoprocta jamaicensis. $1.40, Horama grotei. $8, Amplypterus gannascus.

**1991, Aug. 12        Perf. 14**

| | | | | |
|---|---|---|---|---|
| 752 | A168 | 50c multicolored | 1.00 | .25 |
| 753 | A168 | $1.10 multicolored | 1.10 | .50 |
| 754 | A168 | $1.40 multicolored | 1.25 | 1.00 |
| 755 | A168 | $8 multicolored | 3.25 | 3.25 |
| | | Nos. 752-755 (4) | 6.60 | 5.00 |

Nos. 752-755 Overprinted

**1991, Sept. 23**

| | | | | |
|---|---|---|---|---|
| 756 | A168 | 50c on No. 752 | 1.00 | .25 |
| 757 | A168 | $1.10 on No. 753 | 1.25 | .65 |
| 758 | A168 | $1.40 on No. 754 | 1.50 | 1.10 |
| 759 | A168 | $8 on No. 755 | 4.50 | 6.50 |
| | | Nos. 756-759 (4) | 8.25 | 8.50 |

**Children's Christmas Art Type**

Children's drawings.

**1991, Nov. 27        Perf. 14x15**

| | | | | |
|---|---|---|---|---|
| 760 | A173 | 50c Doctor bird | .70 | .25 |
| 761 | A173 | $1.10 Road scene | 1.00 | .30 |
| 762 | A173 | $5 House, people | 3.00 | 3.00 |
| 763 | A173 | $10 Cows grazing | 6.00 | 8.00 |
| | | Nos. 760-763 (4) | 10.70 | 11.55 |

Christmas.

**Discovery of America Type of 1990**

Designs: 50c, Explorers did not land at Santa Gloria because of hostile Indians. $1.10, Fierce dog used to subdue the Indians. $1.40, Indians brought gifts of fruit. $25, Columbus describes Jamaica with crumpled paper.

**1991, Dec. 16        Perf. 13½x14**

| | | | | |
|---|---|---|---|---|
| 764 | A174 | 50c multicolored | .65 | .25 |
| 765 | A174 | $1.10 multicolored | .85 | .30 |
| 766 | A174 | $1.40 multicolored | .95 | .30 |
| 767 | A174 | $25 multicolored | 6.25 | 8.00 |
| a. | | Souvenir sheet of 4, #764-767 | 9.00 | 9.00 |
| | | Nos. 764-767 (4) | 8.70 | 8.85 |

Souvenir sheet also exists imperf. Same value as perf.

First Provincial Grand Master of English Freemasonry in Jamaica, 250th Anniv. — A178

Masonic symbols: 50c, Square and compass. $1.10, Stained glass window. $1.40, Square and compass on Bible. $25, Seeing eye.

**1992, May 1        Perf. 13½**

| | | | | |
|---|---|---|---|---|
| 768 | A178 | 50c multicolored | .85 | .30 |
| 769 | A178 | $1.10 multicolored | 1.00 | .40 |
| 770 | A178 | $1.40 multicolored | 1.25 | .45 |

| | | | | |
|---|---|---|---|---|
| 771 | A178 | $25 multicolored | 10.00 | 10.00 |
| a. | | Souvenir sheet of 4, #768-771 | 18.00 | 18.00 |
| | | Nos. 768-771 (4) | 13.10 | 11.15 |

Destruction of Port Royal by Earthquake, 300th Anniv. — A179

Scenes of destruction: 50c, Ship in harbor. $1.10, Homes, church. $1.40, Homes toppling. $5, Port Royal from contemporary broadsheet. $25, Fissure in street.

**1992, June 7        Perf. 14x13½**

| | | | | |
|---|---|---|---|---|
| 772 | A179 | 50c multicolored | .50 | .40 |
| 773 | A179 | $1.10 multicolored | .60 | .45 |
| 774 | A179 | $1.40 multicolored | .75 | .50 |
| 775 | A179 | $25 multicolored | 7.75 | 8.75 |
| | | Nos. 772-775 (4) | 9.60 | 10.10 |

**Souvenir Sheet**

**Perf. 13x12**

| | | | | |
|---|---|---|---|---|
| 776 | A179 | $5 multicolored | 5.75 | 5.75 |

No. 776 inscribed on reverse.

Independence, 30th Anniv. — A180

**1992, Aug. 6        Perf. 13½**

| | | | | |
|---|---|---|---|---|
| 777 | A180 | 50c black & multi | .25 | .25 |
| 778 | A180 | $1.10 green & multi | .35 | .35 |
| 779 | A180 | $25 yellow & multi | 3.00 | 3.00 |
| | | Nos. 777-779 (3) | 3.60 | 3.60 |

Credit Union Movement in Jamaica, 50th Anniv. A181

50c, Emblem. $1.40, Emblem, O'Hare Hall.

**1992, Aug. 24        Perf. 14x15**

| | | | | |
|---|---|---|---|---|
| 780 | A181 | 50c multi | 1.00 | .50 |
| 781 | A181 | $1.40 multi | 2.00 | 1.75 |

Pottery — A182

Designs: 50c, "Rainbow" vase, by Cecil Baugh O.D. $1.10, "Yabba Pot," by Louisa Jones (MaLou) O.D. $1.40, "Sculptured Vase," by Gene Pearson. $25, "Lidded Form," by Norma Rodney Harrack.

**1993, Apr. 26        Perf. 13½**

| | | | | |
|---|---|---|---|---|
| 782 | A182 | 50c multicolored | .25 | .25 |
| 783 | A182 | $1.10 multicolored | .35 | .25 |
| 784 | A182 | $1.40 multicolored | .40 | .25 |
| 785 | A182 | $25 multicolored | 3.75 | 3.75 |
| | | Nos. 782-785 (4) | 4.75 | 4.50 |

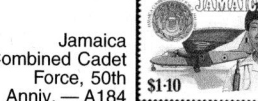

Girls' Brigade, Cent. — A183

50c, Parade. $1.10, Brigade members.

**1993, Aug. 9        Perf. 14x13½**

| | | | | |
|---|---|---|---|---|
| 786 | A183 | 50c multicolored | 1.00 | .50 |
| 787 | A183 | $1.10 multicolored | 1.25 | 1.25 |

Jamaica Combined Cadet Force, 50th Anniv. — A184

Designs: 50c, Tank, cadet, vert. $1.10, Airplane, female cadet, vert. $1.40, Ships, female cadet, vert. $3, Cap badge, cadet.

**1993, Nov. 8        Perf. 14**

| | | | | |
|---|---|---|---|---|
| 788 | A184 | 50c multicolored | .35 | .25 |
| 789 | A184 | $1.10 multicolored | .45 | .40 |
| 790 | A184 | $1.40 multicolored | .55 | .40 |
| 791 | A184 | $3 multicolored | 1.10 | 1.25 |
| | | Nos. 788-791 (4) | 2.45 | 2.30 |

Golf Courses — A185

50c, $1.10, Constant Spring. $1.40, $2, Half Moon. $3, $10, Jamaica Jamaica. $25, Tryall, vert.

**1993-94    Litho.    Wmk. 352    Perf. 14**

| | | | | |
|---|---|---|---|---|
| 792 | A185 | 50c yellow & multi | .40 | .25 |
| 793 | A185 | $1.10 blue & multi | .45 | .25 |
| 794 | A185 | $1.40 brn org & multi | .60 | .25 |
| 795 | A185 | $2 lilac & multi | .90 | .90 |
| 796 | A185 | $3 dark blue & multi | 1.00 | 1.00 |
| 797 | A185 | $10 tan & multi | 2.00 | 2.00 |
| | | Nos. 792-797 (6) | 5.35 | 4.65 |

**Souvenir Sheets**

| | | | | |
|---|---|---|---|---|
| 798 | A185 | $25 green & multi | 5.50 | 5.50 |
| 799 | A185 | $25 #798 inscribed with Hong Kong '94 emblem | 5.50 | 5.50 |

Issued: Nos. 792-797, 12/21/93; No. 798, 12/16/93; No. 799, 2/18/94.

A186

**1994, Jan. 12        Perf. 14x15**

| | | | | |
|---|---|---|---|---|
| 800 | | $25 Portrait | 2.50 | 2.50 |
| 801 | | $50 Portrait, diff. | 3.00 | 3.00 |
| a. | | A186 Pair, #800-801 | 8.25 | 10.00 |

Norman Washington Manley, birth cent.

A187

Royal Visit: $1.10, Jamaican, United Kingdom flags. $1.40, Royal yacht Britannia. $25, Queen Elizabeth II. $50, Prince Philip, Queen.

**1994, Mar. 1        Perf. 14**

| | | | | |
|---|---|---|---|---|
| 802 | A187 | $1.10 multicolored | .75 | .25 |
| 803 | A187 | $1.40 multicolored | 1.60 | .40 |
| 804 | A187 | $25 multicolored | 3.25 | 3.25 |
| 805 | A187 | $50 multicolored | 5.25 | 6.50 |
| | | Nos. 802-805 (4) | 10.85 | 10.40 |

Air Jamaica, 25th Anniv. A188

**Wmk. 352**

**1994, Apr. 26    Litho.    Perf. 14**

| | | | | |
|---|---|---|---|---|
| 806 | A188 | 50c Douglas DC9 | .30 | .25 |
| 807 | A188 | $1.10 Douglas DC8 | .35 | .25 |
| 808 | A188 | $5 Boeing 727 | .75 | .75 |
| 809 | A188 | $50 Airbus A300 | 3.75 | 3.75 |
| | | Nos. 806-809 (4) | 5.15 | 5.00 |

Giant Swallowtail — A189

Various views of the butterfly.

**Perf. 14x13½**
**1994, Aug. 18    Litho.    Wmk. 352**
| | | | | |
|---|---|---|---|---|
| 810 | A189 | 50c multicolored | .50 | .30 |
| 811 | A189 | $1.10 multicolored | .50 | .30 |
| 812 | A189 | $10 multicolored | 2.00 | 2.00 |
| 813 | A189 | $25 multicolored | 3.75 | 3.75 |
| | | Nos. 810-813 (4) | 6.75 | 6.35 |

**Souvenir Sheet**
| 814 | 189 | $50 multicolored | 9.50 | 9.50 |
|---|---|---|---|---|

A190

Tourism — A191

Designs: 50c, Royal Botanical Gardens, by Sidney McClaren. $1.10, Blue Mountains, coffee beans, leaves. $5, Woman in hammock, waterfalls.
Tourist poster: No. 818a, Flowers, birds (c). b, Diver (d). c, Vegetation, coastline (a, d). d, Guide, tourists on raft.

**Wmk. 352**
**1994, Sept. 7    Perf. 14**
| 815 | A190 | 50c multicolored | .40 | .25 |
|---|---|---|---|---|
| 816 | A190 | $1.10 multicolored | .65 | .30 |
| 817 | A190 | $5 multicolored | 3.00 | 3.00 |
| | | Nos. 815-817 (3) | 4.05 | 3.55 |

**Souvenir Sheet**
| 818 | A191 | $25 Sheet of 4, #a.-d. | 6.50 | 6.50 |
|---|---|---|---|---|

Caribbean Tourism Conf. (No. 818).

Red Poll Cattle — A192

**1994, Nov. 16    Perf. 14x13½**
| 819 | A192 | 50c Calf | .25 | .25 |
|---|---|---|---|---|
| 820 | A192 | $1.10 Heifer | .25 | .25 |
| 821 | A192 | $25 Cow | 1.50 | 1.50 |
| 822 | A192 | $50 Bull | 3.75 | 3.75 |
| | | Nos. 819-822 (4) | 5.75 | 5.75 |

Christmas A193

Paintings by Children: 50c, Clean-up crew. 90c, Hospital Room. $1.10, House. $50, Meadow.

**1994, Dec. 1    Perf. 14x14½**
| 823 | A193 | 50c multicolored | .25 | .25 |
|---|---|---|---|---|
| 824 | A193 | 90c multicolored | .25 | .25 |
| 825 | A193 | $1.10 multicolored | 1.00 | .25 |
| 826 | A193 | $50 multicolored | 2.00 | 3.75 |
| | | Nos. 823-826 (4) | 3.50 | 4.50 |

Birds — A194

50c, Ring-tailed pigeon. 90c, Yellow-billed parrot. $1.10, Black-billed parrot. No. 830, Brown owl.
No. 831, Streamertail.

**Wmk. 384**
**1995, Apr. 24    Litho.    Perf. 14**
| 827 | A194 | 50c multicolored | .70 | .35 |
|---|---|---|---|---|
| 828 | A194 | 90c multicolored | .80 | .35 |
| 829 | A194 | $1.10 multicolored | .80 | .35 |
| 830 | A194 | $50 multicolored | 5.50 | 7.00 |
| | | Nos. 827-830 (4) | 7.80 | 8.05 |

**Souvenir Sheet**
| 831 | A194 | $50 multicolored | 7.50 | 7.50 |
|---|---|---|---|---|
| a. | | Ovptd. in sheet margin | 6.00 | 6.00 |

No. 831 is a continuous design.
No. 831a ovptd. with Singapore '95 emblem. Issued: 9/1/95.

Caribbean Development Bank, 25th Anniv. — A195

Anniversary emblem and: 50c, $1, Jamaican flag, graph, vert. $1.10, Industries, agriculture. $50, Bank notes, coins.

**Wmk. 352**
**1995, May 11    Litho.    Perf. 13½**
| 832 | A195 | 50c green & multi | .25 | .25 |
|---|---|---|---|---|
| 833 | A195 | $1 black & multi | .25 | .25 |
| 834 | A195 | $1.10 multicolored | .25 | .25 |
| 835 | A195 | $50 multicolored | 3.50 | 4.00 |
| | | Nos. 832-835 (4) | 4.25 | 4.75 |

Bob Marley (1945-81), Reggae Musician — A196

Marley performing songs: 50c, Songs of Freedom, by Adrian Boot. $1.10, Fire, by Neville Garrick. $1.40, Time Will Tell, by Peter Murphy. $3, Natural Mystic, by Boot. $10, Live at Lyceum, by Boot.
$100, Legend, by Boot.

**Wmk. 352**
**1995, July 31    Litho.    Perf. 14**
| 836 | A196 | 50c multicolored | .35 | .25 |
|---|---|---|---|---|
| 837 | A196 | $1.10 multicolored | .55 | .25 |
| 838 | A196 | $1.40 multicolored | .60 | .35 |
| 839 | A196 | $3 multicolored | .90 | .90 |
| 840 | A196 | $10 multicolored | 1.75 | 1.75 |
| | | Nos. 836-840 (5) | 4.15 | 3.50 |

**Souvenir Sheet**
| 841 | A196 | $100 multicolored | 7.50 | 7.50 |
|---|---|---|---|---|

**Souvenir Sheet**

Queen Mother, 95th Birthday A197

**1995, Aug. 4    Perf. 14x13½**
| 842 | A197 | $75 multicolored | 5.25 | 5.25 |
|---|---|---|---|---|

Order of the Caribbean Community A198

Designs: 50c, Michael Manley, former prime minister, Jamaica. $1.10, Sir Alister McIntyre, Vice Chancellor, UWI, Jamaica. $1.40, P. Telford Georges, former Chief Justice, Bahamas. $50, Dame Nita Barrow, Governor General, Barbados.

**1995, Aug. 23    Perf. 14x14½**
| 843 | A198 | 50c multicolored | .25 | .25 |
|---|---|---|---|---|
| 844 | A198 | $1.10 multicolored | .25 | .25 |
| 845 | A198 | $1.40 multicolored | .30 | .25 |
| 846 | A198 | $50 multicolored | 3.25 | 5.00 |
| | | Nos. 843-846 (4) | 4.05 | 5.75 |

**UN, 50th Anniv.**
**Common Design Type**

Designs: 50c, Signals Land Rover. $1.10, Antonov AN-32. $3, Bedford Articulated Tanker. $5, Fairchild DC-119 Flying Boxcar. $50, Observation vehicles.

**Wmk. 352**
**1995, Oct. 24    Litho.    Perf. 14**
| 847 | CD353 | 50c multicolored | .30 | .25 |
|---|---|---|---|---|
| 848 | CD353 | $1.10 multicolored | .50 | .25 |
| 849 | CD353 | $3 multicolored | .70 | .70 |
| 850 | CD353 | $5 multicolored | .90 | 1.25 |
| | | Nos. 847-850 (4) | 2.40 | 2.45 |

**Souvenir Sheet**
| 851 | CD353 | $50 multicolored | 3.00 | 3.00 |
|---|---|---|---|---|

No. 851 has continuous design.

Arrival of East Indians in Jamaica, 150th Anniv. — A199

$2.50, Coming ashore. $10, Musicians, dancers.

**Wmk. 352**
**1996, May 22    Litho.    Perf. 14**
| 852 | A199 | $2.50 multicolored | .25 | .25 |
|---|---|---|---|---|
| 853 | A199 | $10 multicolored | .75 | .75 |

UNICEF, 50th Anniv. — A200

**1996, Sept. 2    Perf. 14½x14**
| 854 | A200 | $2.50 multicolored | .60 | .60 |
|---|---|---|---|---|
| 855 | A200 | $8 multicolored | 1.10 | 1.10 |
| 856 | A200 | $10 multicolored | 1.50 | 1.50 |
| | | Nos. 854-856 (3) | 3.20 | 3.20 |

Jamaican Hutia (Indian Coney) — A201

$2.50, Two in den. $10, One on ledge. $12.50, Mother, young. $25, One up close.

**1996, Sept. 23    Perf. 13½x14**
| 857 | A201 | $2.50 multicolored | .30 | .25 |
|---|---|---|---|---|
| 858 | A201 | $10 multicolored | .65 | .25 |
| 859 | A201 | $12.50 multicolored | .80 | .80 |
| 860 | A201 | $25 multicolored | 1.40 | 2.50 |
| | | Nos. 857-860 (4) | 3.15 | 3.80 |

World Wildlife Fund.

Kingston Parish Church of St. Thomas the Apostle, 300th Anniv. — A202

$2, High altar. $8, Exterior view. $12.50, Carving, "The Angel," by Edna Manley, vert. $60, Exterior view at sunset.

**Unwmk.**
**1997, Feb. 7    Litho.    Perf. 14**
| 861 | A202 | $2 multicolored | .40 | .25 |
|---|---|---|---|---|
| 862 | A202 | $8 multicolored | 1.00 | 1.00 |
| 863 | A202 | $12.50 multicolored | 1.50 | 1.50 |
| | | Nos. 861-863 (3) | 2.90 | 2.75 |

**Souvenir Sheet**
| 864 | A202 | $60 multicolored | 3.50 | 3.50 |
|---|---|---|---|---|

No. 864 contains one 42x56mm stamp.

Chernobyl's Children A203

**Perf. 13½x14**
**1997, Apr. 7    Litho.    Unwmk.**
| 865 | A203 | $55 multicolored | 4.00 | 4.00 |
|---|---|---|---|---|

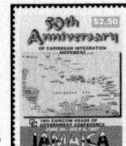

Caribbean Integration, 50th Anniv. — A203a

$2.50, Map of Caribbean. $8, $10, View of coastline.

**Wmk. 352**
**1997, June 30    Litho.    Perf. 14**
| 865A | A203a | $2.50 multi | 8.00 | 7.00 |
|---|---|---|---|---|
| 865B | A203a | $8 multi | 9.00 | 3.25 |
| 865C | A203a | $10 multi | 10.00 | 3.25 |
| | | Nos. 865A-865C (3) | 27.00 | 13.50 |

Orchids — A204

$1, Coelia triptera. $2, Oncidium pulchellum. $2.50, Oncidium triquetrum. $3, Broughtonia negrilensis. $5, Encyclia frangrans.

**Wmk. 352**
**1997, Oct. 6    Litho.    Perf. 14**
| 866 | A204 | $1 multi, vert. | .30 | .25 |
|---|---|---|---|---|
| 867 | A204 | $2 multi | .35 | .25 |
| 868 | A204 | $2.50 multi, vert. | .40 | .25 |
| 869 | A204 | $3 multi, vert. | .45 | .25 |
| 870 | A204 | $5 multi | .50 | .35 |
| | | Nos. 866-870 (5) | 2.00 | 1.35 |

See Nos. 873-877.

Diana, Princess of Wales (1961-97) — A205

**Unwmk.**
**1998, Feb. 24    Litho.    Perf. 14**
| 871 | A205 | $20 Portrait | 1.25 | 1.25 |
|---|---|---|---|---|

**Souvenir Sheet**
| 872 | A205 | $80 With Mother Teresa | 6.00 | 6.00 |
|---|---|---|---|---|

No. 871 was issued in sheets of 6. No. 872 contains one 42x56mm stamp.

**Orchid Type of 1997**

Designs: $4.50, Oncidium gauntlettii. $8, Broughtonia sanguinea. $12, Phaius tankervilleae, vert. $25, Cochleanthes flabelliformis. $50, Broughtonia sanguinea (3 varieties).

**Wmk. 352**
**1997, Dec. 1    Litho.    Perf. 14**
| 873 | A204 | $4.50 multicolored | .60 | .60 |
|---|---|---|---|---|
| 874 | A204 | $8 multicolored | .85 | .85 |
| 875 | A204 | $12 multicolored | 1.00 | 1.00 |
| 876 | A204 | $25 multicolored | 2.00 | 2.00 |
| a. | | Inscribed "1999" | 2.00 | 2.00 |
| 877 | A204 | $50 multicolored | 2.00 | 2.00 |
| | | Nos. 873-877 (5) | 6.45 | 6.45 |

CARICOM, 25th Anniv. — A206

**Perf. 13½**
**1998, Sept. 17    Litho.    Unwmk.**
| 878 | A206 | $30 multicolored | 3.00 | 3.00 |
|---|---|---|---|---|

University of the West Indies, Mona, 50th Anniv. — A207

$8, Chapel. $10, Philip Sherlock Centre for the Creative Arts. $50, University arms.

**1998, July 31    Wmk. 352**
| 879 | A207 | $8 multi | .50 | .50 |
|---|---|---|---|---|
| 880 | A207 | $10 multi | .50 | .50 |
| 881 | A207 | $50 multi, vert. | 2.25 | 2.25 |
| | | Nos. 879-881 (3) | 3.25 | 3.25 |

1998 World Cup Soccer
Championships, France, Jamaica's
Debut in Tournament
A208

**Wmk. 373**

| | | | | |
|---|---|---|---|---|
| **1998, Sept. 28** | | **Litho.** | ***Perf. 13½*** | |
| 882 | A208 | $10 Player, vert. | .50 | .35 |
| 883 | A208 | $25 Team picture | 1.40 | 1.25 |
| 884 | A208 | $100 Team picture, diff. | 4.50 | *5.50* |
| | | *Nos. 882-884 (3)* | 6.40 | 7.10 |

Intl. Year of the
Ocean — A209

Designs: $10, Underwater scene. $30, Fishermen, Negril. $50, Long spiny black urchin. $100, Design elements from Nos. 885-887, vert.

**Wmk. 352**

| | | | | |
|---|---|---|---|---|
| **1998, Dec. 23** | | **Litho.** | ***Perf. 14*** | |
| 885 | A209 | $10 multicolored | 1.50 | .40 |
| 886 | A209 | $30 multicolored | 2.75 | 1.50 |
| 887 | A209 | $50 multicolored | 4.00 | 4.00 |
| | | **Size: 28x42mm** | | |
| 888 | A209 | $100 multicolored | 7.50 | *10.00* |
| | | *Nos. 885-888 (4)* | 15.75 | 15.90 |

Christmas.

**1st Manned Moon Landing, 30th
Anniv.**

Common Design Type

Designs: $7, Michael Collins. $10, Service module reverses to dock with lunar module. $25, Aldrin walks on lunar surface. $30, Command module back in earth orbit.
$100, Looking at earth from moon.

***Perf. 14x13¾***

| | | | | |
|---|---|---|---|---|
| **1999, July 20** | | **Litho.** | **Wmk. 352** | |
| 889 | CD357 | $7 multicolored | .50 | .50 |
| 890 | CD357 | $10 multicolored | .65 | .65 |
| 891 | CD357 | $25 multicolored | 1.25 | 1.25 |
| 892 | CD357 | $30 multicolored | 1.40 | 1.40 |
| | | *Nos. 889-892 (4)* | 3.80 | 2.68 |

**Souvenir Sheet**

***Perf. 14***

| | | | | |
|---|---|---|---|---|
| 893 | CD357 | $100 multicolored | 4.50 | 4.50 |

No. 893 contains one 40mm circular stamp.

Athletes — A210

Designs: $5, Polo player Lesley Ann Masterton Fong-Yee. $10, Men's cricketers Collie Smith, Lawrence Rowe and Alfred Valentine. $20, Women's cricketer Vivalyn Latty-Scott, vert. $25, Soccer player Lindy Delapenha, vert. $30, Netball player Joy Grant-Charles, vert. $50, Boxers Percy Hayles, Gerald Gray and Bunny Grant.
$100, Delapenha and Grant-Charles.

***Perf. 13¼x13¾, 13¾x13¼***

| | | | | |
|---|---|---|---|---|
| **1999, Aug. 3** | | **Litho.** | **Wmk. 352** | |
| 894 | A210 | $5 multicolored | .75 | .45 |
| 895 | A210 | $10 multicolored | 1.00 | .55 |
| 896 | A210 | $20 multicolored | 1.25 | 1.25 |
| 897 | A210 | $25 multicolored | 1.50 | 1.50 |
| 898 | A210 | $30 multicolored | 1.60 | 1.60 |
| 899 | A210 | $50 multicolored | 1.75 | *2.50* |
| | | *Nos. 894-899 (6)* | 7.85 | 7.85 |

**Souvenir Sheet**

| | | | | |
|---|---|---|---|---|
| 900 | A210 | $100 multicolored | 6.50 | 6.50 |

No. 900 contains one 52x38mm stamp.

UPU, 125th
Anniv. — A211

Designs: $7, Mail ship "Spey." $10, Mail ship "Jamaica Planter." $25, Lockheed Constellation. $30, Airbus A-310.

**Wmk. 352**

| | | | | |
|---|---|---|---|---|
| **1999, Oct. 8** | | **Litho.** | ***Perf. 14*** | |
| 901 | A211 | $7 multicolored | 1.00 | .40 |
| 902 | A211 | $10 multicolored | 1.25 | .50 |
| 903 | A211 | $25 multicolored | 2.00 | 2.00 |
| 904 | A211 | $30 multicolored | 2.25 | *2.75* |
| | | *Nos. 901-904 (4)* | 6.50 | 5.65 |

Air Jamaica,
30th
Anniv. — A212

**Wmk. 352**

| | | | | |
|---|---|---|---|---|
| **1999, Nov. 1** | | **Litho.** | ***Perf. 14*** | |
| 905 | A212 | $10 A-310 | .75 | .50 |
| 906 | A212 | $25 A-320 | 1.25 | 1.25 |
| 907 | A212 | $30 A-340 | 1.75 | *2.25* |
| | | *Nos. 905-907 (3)* | 3.75 | 4.00 |

Dogs — A213

| | | | | |
|---|---|---|---|---|
| **1999, Nov. 25** | | | ***Perf. 14¼*** | |
| 908 | A213 | $7 Shih tzu | 1.25 | .75 |
| 909 | A213 | $10 German shepherd | 1.75 | .75 |
| 910 | A213 | $30 Doberman pin-<br>scher | 3.00 | *3.25* |
| | | *Nos. 908-910 (3)* | 6.00 | 4.75 |

Parks — A214

Designs: $7, Nelson Mandela Park. $10, St. William Grant Park. $25, Seaview Park. $30, Holruth Park.

| | | | | |
|---|---|---|---|---|
| **1999, Dec. 15** | | | ***Perf. 14*** | |
| 911 | A214 | $7 multi | .40 | .35 |
| 912 | A214 | $10 multi | .50 | .40 |
| 913 | A214 | $25 multi | 1.10 | 1.00 |
| 914 | A214 | $30 multi | 1.40 | 1.40 |
| | | *Nos. 911-914 (4)* | 3.40 | 3.15 |

Edna Manley
(1900-87),
Sculptor — A215

Designs: $10, The Prophet, 1935. $25, Horse of the Morning, 1943. $30, The Angel, 1970. $100, Portrait of Manley.

| | | | | |
|---|---|---|---|---|
| **2000, Mar. 1** | | **Litho.** | ***Perf. 13¾*** | |
| 915 | A215 | $10 multi | .65 | .65 |
| 916 | A215 | $25 multi | 1.50 | 1.50 |
| 917 | A215 | $30 multi | 1.75 | 1.75 |
| 918 | A215 | $100 multi | 5.00 | 5.00 |
| *a.* | | Souvenir sheet, #915-918 | 9.00 | 9.00 |
| | | *Nos. 915-918 (4)* | 8.90 | 8.90 |

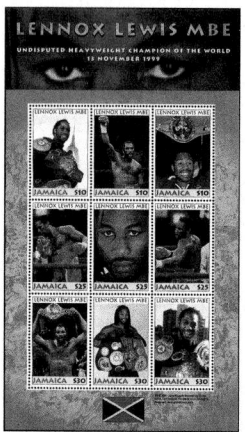

Lennox Lewis, Heavyweight Boxing
Champion of the World — A216

a, $10, With belt & Empire State Building. b, $10, Holding up arm. c, $10, Holding up belt. d, $25, In ring with opponent. e, $25, Closeup. f, $25, In ring with referee. g, $30, Holding up belt, diff. h, $30, Holding 4 belts. i, $30, Holding belts in front of buildings.

**Wmk. 352**

| | | | | |
|---|---|---|---|---|
| **2000, Mar. 24** | | **Litho.** | ***Perf. 14*** | |
| 919 | A216 | Sheet of 9, #a.-i. | 9.00 | 9.00 |

Ferrari
Automobiles
A217

**Unwmk.**

| | | | | |
|---|---|---|---|---|
| **2000, May 26** | | **Litho.** | ***Perf. 14*** | |
| 920 | A217 | $10 1947 125S | .75 | .75 |
| 921 | A217 | $10 1950 375F1 | .75 | .75 |
| 922 | A217 | $10 1966 312F1 | .75 | .75 |
| 923 | A217 | $25 1965 Dino 166P | 1.50 | 1.50 |
| 924 | A217 | $25 1971 312P | 1.50 | 1.50 |
| 925 | A217 | $25 1990 F190 | 1.50 | 1.50 |
| | | *Nos. 920-925 (6)* | 6.75 | 6.75 |

Queen Mother, 100th
Birthday — A218

Various photos.

| | | | | |
|---|---|---|---|---|
| **2000, Aug. 4** | | | **Wmk. 352** | |
| 926 | A218 | $10 multi | .60 | .60 |
| 927 | A218 | $25 multi | 1.00 | 1.00 |
| 928 | A218 | $30 multi | 1.50 | 1.50 |
| 929 | A218 | $50 multi | 3.25 | 3.25 |
| | | *Nos. 926-929 (4)* | 6.35 | 6.35 |

2000 Summer
Olympics,
Sydney — A219

Jamaican flag and various views of sculpture, "The Runner," by Alvin Marriott. Denominations, $10, $25, $30, vert., $50, vert.

**Wmk. 352**

| | | | | |
|---|---|---|---|---|
| **2000, Sept. 1** | | **Litho.** | ***Perf. 14*** | |
| 930-933 | A219 | Set of 4 | 6.75 | 6.75 |

Trees — A220

Designs: $10, Bull thatch palm. $25, Blue mahoe. $30, Silk cotton. $50, Yellow pout.

$100, Lignum vitae, horiz.

| | | | | |
|---|---|---|---|---|
| **2000, Oct. 6** | | | | |
| 934-937 | A220 | Set of 4 | 7.75 | 7.75 |
| | | **Souvenir Sheet** | | |
| 938 | A220 | $100 multi | 8.00 | 8.00 |

Christmas
A221

Designs: $10, Madonna and Child, by Osmond Watson, vert. $20, Boy in the Temple, by Carl Abrahams. $25, Ascension, by Abrahams, vert. $30, Jah Lives, by Watson.

**Wmk. 352**

| | | | | |
|---|---|---|---|---|
| **2000, Dec. 6** | | **Litho.** | ***Perf. 13¾*** | |
| 939-942 | A221 | Set of 4 | 4.25 | 4.25 |

Commonwealth Day,
25th Anniv. — A222

**Wmk. 352**

| | | | | |
|---|---|---|---|---|
| **2001, Mar. 12** | | **Litho.** | ***Perf. 12½*** | |
| 943 | A222 | $30 multi | 2.00 | 2.00 |

Father Andrew
Duffus Mowatt,
Founder of Jamaica
Burial Scheme
Society — A223

**Wmk. 352**

| | | | | |
|---|---|---|---|---|
| **2001, Oct. 12** | | **Litho.** | ***Perf. 13¼*** | |
| 944 | A223 | $15 multi | 1.50 | 1.50 |

Lithographs of Daguerrotypes by
Adolphe Duperly (1801-64) — A224

Designs: $15, The Market, Falmouth. $40, Ferry Inn, Spanish Town Road. $45, Coke Chapel. $60, King Street, Kingston.

| | | | | |
|---|---|---|---|---|
| **2001, Nov. 14** | | | ***Perf. 13*** | |
| 945-948 | A224 | Set of 4 | 9.25 | 9.25 |
| *a.* | | Souvenir sheet, #945-948 | 8.75 | 8.75 |

Christmas — A225

Poinsettias with background colors of: $15, Light blue. $30, Pink. $40, Pale orange.

| | | | | |
|---|---|---|---|---|
| **2001, Dec. 10** | | | ***Perf. 13¼*** | |
| 949-951 | A225 | Set of 3 | 6.00 | 6.00 |

**Reign Of Queen Elizabeth II, 50th
Anniv. Issue**

Common Design Type

Designs: Nos. 952, 956a, $15, Princess Elizabeth. Nos. 953, 953b, $40, Wearing striped dress. Nos. 954, 956c, $45, In 1953. Nos. 955, 956d, $60, In 1995. No. 956e, $30, 1955 portrait by Annigoni (38x50mm).

**Perf. 14¼x14½, 13¾ (#956e)**

**2002, Feb. 6     Litho.     Wmk. 373**

**With Gold Frames**

| | | | | |
|---|---|---|---|---|
| 952 | CD360 | $15 multicolored | .65 | .65 |
| 953 | CD360 | $40 multicolored | 2.00 | 2.00 |
| 954 | CD360 | $45 multicolored | 2.25 | 2.25 |
| 955 | CD360 | $60 multicolored | 3.25 | 3.25 |
| | | Nos. 952-955 (4) | 8.15 | 8.15 |

**Souvenir Sheet**

**Without Gold Frames**

| | | | | |
|---|---|---|---|---|
| 956 | CD360 | Sheet of 5, #a-e | 8.50 | 8.50 |

Visit of Queen Elizabeth II and Prince Philip, Feb. 18-20 — A226

Designs: $15, Queen and Prince in 1983, flag of the Royal Standard. $45, Queen in 1983, Jamaican arms.

**Perf. 13¼x13¾**

**2002, Feb. 18     Litho.     Wmk. 352**

| | | | | |
|---|---|---|---|---|
| 957-958 | A226 | Set of 2 | 5.75 | 5.75 |

Sir Philip Sherlock (1902-2000), Educator — A227

**2002, Mar. 11     Perf. 13¾**

| | | | | |
|---|---|---|---|---|
| 959 | A227 | $40 multi | 2.00 | 2.00 |

Pan-American Health Organization, Cent. — A228

**Wmk. 352**

**2002, Dec. 2     Litho.     Perf. 13¾**

| | | | | |
|---|---|---|---|---|
| 960 | A228 | $40 multi | 2.25 | 2.25 |

Christmas A229

Art: $15, Masquerade, by Osmond Watson, vert. $40, John Canoe in Guanaboa Vale, by Gaston Tabois. $45, Mother and Child, sculpture, by Kapo, vert. $60, Hills of Papine, sculpture by Edna Manley.

**2002, Dec. 6**

| | | | | |
|---|---|---|---|---|
| 961-964 | A229 | Set of 4 | 6.75 | 6.75 |

Natl. Dance Theater Company, 40th Anniv. — A230

**2002, Dec. 27     Perf. 14**

| | | | | |
|---|---|---|---|---|
| 965 | A230 | $15 multi | 1.75 | 1.75 |

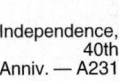

Independence, 40th Anniv. — A231

Flag and: $15, Natl. Dance Theater Company performers. $40, Sir Alexander Bustamante, Michael Manley. $60, Factory workers.

**2002, Dec. 27**

| | | | | |
|---|---|---|---|---|
| 966-968 | A231 | Set of 3 | 7.25 | 7.25 |

Kingston, Bicent. — A232

Historical views of Kingston and panel colors of: a, Brown. b, Olive green. c, Indigo.

**2002, Dec. 31     Perf. 13¾**

| | | | | |
|---|---|---|---|---|
| 969 | A232 | Horiz. strip of 3 | 3.75 | 3.75 |
| a.-c. | | $15 Any single | 1.00 | 1.00 |

**Coronation of Queen Elizabeth II, 50th Anniv.**

**Common Design Type**

Designs: Nos. 970, $15, 972b, $100, Queen in chair awaiting crown. Nos. 971, $45, 972a, $50, Queen and Prince Philip in carriage.

**Perf. 14¼x14½**

**2003, June 2     Litho.     Wmk. 352**

**Vignettes Framed, Red Background**

| | | | | |
|---|---|---|---|---|
| 970 | CD363 | $15 multicolored | 1.00 | 1.00 |
| 971 | CD363 | $45 multicolored | 3.00 | 3.00 |

**Souvenir Sheet**

**Vignettes Without Frame, Purple Panel**

| | | | | |
|---|---|---|---|---|
| 972 | CD363 | Sheet of 2, #a-b | 6.00 | 6.00 |

Caribbean Community (CARICOM), 30th Anniv. — A233

**Wmk. 352**

**2003, July 4     Litho.     Perf. 14**

| | | | | |
|---|---|---|---|---|
| 973 | A233 | $40 multi | 3.25 | 3.25 |

Bird Life International A234

Designs: $15, Jamaican stripe-headed tanager, vert. $40, Crested quail dove. $45, Jamaican tody. $60, Blue Mountain vireo.
No. 978 — Jamaican blackbird: a, With beak open (35x30mm). b, Chicks in nest (35x30mm). c, In palm fronds, vert. (30x35mm). d, With beak open, vert. (30x35mm) e, With insect in beak (35x30mm).

**2003, Sept. 19     Perf. 14**

| | | | | |
|---|---|---|---|---|
| 974-977 | A234 | Set of 4 | 8.50 | 8.50 |

**Souvenir Sheet**

**Perf. 14¼x14½, 14½x14¼**

| | | | | |
|---|---|---|---|---|
| 978 | A234 | $30 Sheet of 5, #a-e | 9.00 | 9.00 |

Maritime Heritage — A235

No. 979: a, Map, sailing ships. b, Sailing ships, ship with passengers. c, The Sugar Refiner and barges.

**2003, Sept. 25     Perf. 14x14¾**

| | | | | |
|---|---|---|---|---|
| 979 | A235 | Horiz. strip of 3 | 8.00 | 8.00 |
| a.-c. | | $40 Any single | 2.00 | 2.00 |

Christmas A236

Flowers and: $15, Adoration of the Magi. $30, Christ child. $60, Holy Family.

**2003, Dec.     Perf. 13¼**

| | | | | |
|---|---|---|---|---|
| 980-982 | A236 | Set of 3 | 6.00 | 6.00 |

Haitian Revolution, Bicent. — A237

**Wmk. 352**

**2004, Jan. 30     Litho.     Perf. 13½**

| | | | | |
|---|---|---|---|---|
| 983 | A237 | $40 multi | 2.75 | 2.75 |

Caribbean Bird Festival — A238

No. 984: a, Yellow-billed amazon. b, Jamaican oriole. c, Orangequit. d, Yellow-shouldered grassquit. e, Jamaican woodpecker. f, Red-billed streamertail. g, Jamaican mango. h, White-eyed thrush. i, Jamaican lizard cuckoo. j, Arrow-headed warbler.

**Wmk. 352**

**2004, May 17     Litho.     Perf. 13¾**

| | | | | |
|---|---|---|---|---|
| 984 | | Block of 10 | 10.00 | 10.00 |
| a.-j. | | A238 $10 Any single | .80 | .60 |

**Miniature Sheet**

World Environment Day — A239

No. 985: a, $10, Water lilies. b, $10, Hawksbill turtle. c, $10, Tube sponge. d, $10, Boater on Parattee Pond. e, $40, Vase sponge, star coral. f, $40, Sea fan, black and white crinoid. g, $40, Glassy sweepers. h, $40, Giant sea anemone.

**Unwmk.**

**2004, June 4     Litho.     Perf. 14**

| | | | | |
|---|---|---|---|---|
| 985 | A239 | Sheet of 8, #a-h | 9.50 | 9.50 |

2004 Summer Olympics, Athens — A240

Jamaican athletes: $30, Women's hurdles. $60, Running. $70, Swimming. $90, Rifle shooting, women's badminton.

**Wmk. 352**

**2004, Aug. 10     Litho.     Perf. 14**

| | | | | |
|---|---|---|---|---|
| 986-989 | A240 | Set of 4 | 9.50 | 9.50 |

FIFA (Fédération Internationale de Football Association), Cent. — A241

FIFA emblem and various soccer players: $10, $30, $45, $50.

**Wmk. 352**

**2004, Oct. 13     Litho.     Perf. 14**

| | | | | |
|---|---|---|---|---|
| 990-993 | A241 | Set of 4 | 6.75 | 6.75 |

Jamaica Hotels Law, Cent. — A242

Designs: No. 994, Ralph Lauren, Doctors Cave Beach, Montego Bay.
No. 995 — Ambassador John Pringle, Round Hill Hotel and: a, Pink panel. b, Lilac panel.
No. 996 — Tower Isle Hotel and: a, Abe Issa, yellow green panels. b, John Issa, green panels. c, Abe Issa, red panels. d, John Issa, yellow green panels. e, Abe Issa, green panels. f, John Issa, red panels.

**2004     Unwmk.     Perf. 13¼x13½**

| | | | | |
|---|---|---|---|---|
| 994 | A242 | $40 multi | 6.00 | 6.00 |
| 995 | A242 | $40 Pair, #a-b | 8.00 | 8.00 |
| 996 | A242 | $40 Sheet of 6, #a-f | 10.00 | 10.00 |
| | | Nos. 994-996 (3) | 24.00 | 24.00 |

Issued: No. 994, 11/19; Nos. 995-996, 11/12. No. 994 printed in sheets of six; No. 995 printed in sheets containing three pairs. Value, set of three sheets $45.

Christmas — A243

White sorrel stalks: $10, $20, $50, $60. $50 and $60 are horiz.

**Wmk. 352**

**2004, Nov. 22     Litho.     Perf. 14¼**

| | | | | |
|---|---|---|---|---|
| 997-1000 | A243 | Set of 4 | 7.50 | 7.50 |

Founding of Moravian Church in Jamaica, 250th Anniv. — A244

Designs: 90c, Mary Morris Knibb, Mizpah Moravian Church. $10, Rev. W. O'Meally, Mizpah Moravian Church. $50, Bishop S. U. Hastings, Redeemer Moravian Church.

**2004, Dec. 14**

| | | | | |
|---|---|---|---|---|
| 1001-1003 | A244 | Set of 3 | 4.00 | 4.00 |

Buildings — A245

Designs: 90c, Rose Hall Great House, St. James. $5, Holy Trinity Cathedral. $30, National Commercial Bank, New Kingston. $60, Court House, Falmouth.

**2005, Jan. 13     Wmk. 352     Perf. 13¼**

| | | | | |
|---|---|---|---|---|
| 1004 | A245 | 90c multi | .25 | .25 |
| 1004A | A245 | $5 multi | .30 | .25 |
| 1005 | A245 | $30 multi | 1.50 | 1.10 |
| a. | | Dated 2006 at bottom | 2.00 | 1.50 |
| b. | | Dated 2008 at bottom | 1.00 | .75 |
| 1006 | A245 | $60 multi | 3.00 | 2.75 |
| a. | | Dated 2008 at bottom | 2.00 | 1.50 |
| | | Nos. 1004-1006 (4) | 5.05 | 4.35 |

**Self-Adhesive**

**Serpentine Die Cut 12¼x12½**

**Unwmk.**

| | | | | |
|---|---|---|---|---|
| 1008 | A245 | $5 multi | .40 | .25 |
| 1008A | A245 | $30 multi | 1.50 | 1.50 |
| b. | | Booklet pane of 10 | 15.00 | |
| | | Complete booklet, #1008Ab | 15.00 | |
| c. | | Dated 2006 at right | 2.00 | 2.00 |
| 1009 | A245 | $60 multi | 3.50 | 3.50 |

See Nos. 1038-1053.

Chinese in Jamaica, 150th Anniv. — A246

Flags of People's Republic of China and Jamaica and: $30, Food and fruits from China and Jamaica. $60, Chinatown. $90, Chinese Benevolent Association Building.

**2005, Feb. 5     Wmk. 352     Perf. 14¼**

| | | | | |
|---|---|---|---|---|
| 1010-1012 | A246 | Set of 3 | 9.00 | 9.00 |

European Philatelic Cooperation, 50th Anniv. (in 2006) — A247

Designs: $60, Green square. $70, Yellow diamond. $100 Blue square.

**Perf. 13½**

**2005, June 1     Litho.     Unwmk.**

| | | | | |
|---|---|---|---|---|
| 1013-1015 | A247 | Set of 3 | 8.00 | 8.00 |
| 1015a | | Souvenir sheet, #1013-1015 | 8.00 | 8.00 |

Europa stamps, 50th anniv. (in 2006).

Battle of
Trafalgar,
Bicent.
A248

Designs: $20, Gun captain holding powder
cartridge. $30, Admiral Horatio Nelson, vert.
$50, British 12-pounder cannon. $60, HMS
Africa, vert. $70, HMS Leviathan being
attacked by the Intrepide, vert. $90, HMS
Victory.
$200, HMS Africa at Port Royal, Jamaica.

**Wmk. 352, Unwmkd. ($90)**
**2005, June 23    Litho.    Perf. 13¼**
1016-1021 A248    Set of 6        12.00 12.00
**Souvenir Sheet**
**Perf. 13½**
1022 A248 $200 multi              10.00 10.00

No. 1021 has particles of wood from the
HMS Victory embedded in areas covered by a
thermographic process that produces a raised,
shiny effect. No. 1022 contains one 44x44mm
stamp.

Rotary International,
Cent. — A249

**2005, June 30  Wmk. 352  Perf. 13¾**
1023 A249 $30 multi                2.00 2.00

Pope John Paul II
(1920-2005) — A250

**Unwmk.**
**2005, Aug. 18    Litho.    Perf. 14**
1024 A250 $30 multi                1.75 1.75

Battle of Trafalgar,
Bicent. — A251

Designs: $50, HMS Victory. $90, Ships in
battle, horiz. $100, Admiral Horatio Nelson.

**Perf. 13¼**
**2005, Oct. 18    Litho.    Unwmk.**
1025-1027 A251    Set of 3        12.50 12.50

Mary Seacole
(1805-81),
Nurse — A252

Seacole and: $30, Herbal remedies and
medicines. $50, Seacole Hall, University of the
West Indies. $60, Crimean War soldiers. $70,
Medals.

**Wmk. 352**
**2005, Nov. 21    Litho.    Perf. 13½**
1028-1031 A252    Set of 4         7.50 7.50

---

World AIDS
Day — A253

**2005, Dec. 1              Perf. 14¾x14**
1032 A253 $30 multi                1.50 1.50

Christmas — A254

Star of Bethlehem and poinsettia with various frame designs: $20, $30, $50, $80.

**2005, Dec. 1**
1033-1036 A254    Set of 4         6.75 6.75

Jessie Ripoll (Sister
Mary Peter Claver),
Founder of Alpha
Schools — A255

**2005, Dec. 12              Perf. 13½**
1037 A255 $30 multi                1.25 1.25
Alpha Schools, 125th anniv.

**Buildings Type of 2005**
Designs: $10, Court House, Morant Bay.
$15, Spanish Town Square, St. Catherine.
$20, Mico College. $25, Simms Building,
Jamaica College. $50, Devon House, St.
Andrew. $70, Ward Theater, Kingston. $90,
Vale Royal, St. Andrew. $100, Falmouth Post
Office.

**Perf. 14x13¼**
**2006, May 12    Litho.    Wmk. 352**
**No date inscription below design**
1038 A245 $10 multi           .70      .40
  a.    Inscribed "2008"      .35      .35
1039 A245 $15 multi           .60      .50
1040 A245 $20 multi          1.25     1.00
  a.    Inscribed "2008"      .70      .65
1041 A245 $25 multi           .90      .80
1042 A245 $50 multi          2.75     1.75
  a.    Inscribed "2008"     1.75     1.00
1043 A245 $70 multi          3.25     3.25
  a.    Inscribed "2008"     2.25     1.75
1044 A245 $90 multi          4.50     4.50
  a.    Inscribed "2008"     2.75     2.25
1045 A245 $100 multi         3.25     3.25
    Nos. 1038-1045 (8)      17.20    15.45
**Self-Adhesive**
**Unwmk.**
**Serpentine Die Cut 13¼x14**
1046 A245 $10 multi           .40      .40
1047 A245 $15 multi           .65      .65
1048 A245 $20 multi           .75      .75
1049 A245 $25 multi           .90      .90
1050 A245 $50 multi          2.00     2.00
1051 A245 $70 multi          2.50     2.50
1052 A245 $90 multi          3.00     3.00
1053 A245 $100 multi         3.25     3.25
    Nos. 1046-1053 (8)      13.45    13.45

Worldwide Fund for
Nature
(WWF) — A256

Black-billed Amazon parrot: $5, Chicks. $10,
Head of adult bird. $30, Bird on branch. $50,
Two birds.

**Perf. 13¼x13½**
**2006, Nov. 30    Litho.    Wmk. 352**
1054-1057 A256    Set of 4        7.00  7.00
1057a    Sheet, 4 each #1054-
            1057                 28.00 28.00

---

Christmas
A257

Flowers: $20, Cup and saucer. $30, Lignum
vitae. $50, Neocogniauxia monophylla. vert.
$60, Ghost orchid, vert.

**Perf. 13¼x13¾, 13¾x13¼**
**2006, Nov. 30**
1058-1061 A257    Set of 4         7.00 7.00

2007 ICC Cricket
World Cup, West
Indies — A258

Designs: No. 1062, $30, Courtney Walsh.
No. 1063, $30, Collie Smith. $40, New Sabrina
Park, horiz. $50, Like #1062. $60, Trelawney
Multi-purpose Sports Complex, horiz.
$200, ICC Cricket World Cup.

**Wmk. 352**
**2007, Feb. 28    Litho.    Perf. 14**
1062-1066 A258    Set of 5       11.00 11.00
**Souvenir Sheet**
1067 A258 $200 multi             10.00 10.00

British Abolition of the
Slave Trade,
Bicent. — A259

**Wmk. 352**
**2007, June 7    Litho.    Perf. 14**
1068 A259 $30 multi                1.50 1.50

Scouting,
Cent. — A260

Designs: $5, Boy scout, Jamaican flag,
Scout salute. $10, Scouts, compass. $30,
Scouts, lashed poles. $70, Scouts handling
Jamaican flag, Scout making craft.
No. 1073, vert.: a, $50, Scouts on parade. b,
$100, Lord Robert Baden-Powell blowing kudu
horn.

**2007, July 9              Perf. 13¾**
1069-1072 A260    Set of 4         5.00 5.00
**Souvenir Sheet**
1073 A260    Sheet of 2, #a-b     8.00 8.00

Christmas — A261

Flowers: $20, Tolumnia triquetra. $30,
Broughtonia negrilensis, horiz. $50, Brought-
onia sanguinea, horiz. $60, Spathelia
sorbifolia.

**Wmk. 352**
**2007, Nov. 9    Litho.    Perf. 14**
1074-1077 A261    Set of 4         7.00 7.00

2008 Summer
Olympics,
Beijing — A262

---

Designs: $20, Fish, Asafa Powell. $60, Lanterns, Veronica Campbell-Brown.
No. 1079: a, Bamboo, Aleen Bailey, Veronica Campbell-Brown. b, Sherone Simpson,
Tayna Lawrence, dragon.

**Wmk. 352**
**2008, Apr. 30    Litho.    Perf. 13¼**
1078 A262 $20 multi                1.00 1.00
1079 A262 $30 Horiz. pair, #a-b    3.00 3.00
1080 A262 $60 multi                3.00 3.00
    Nos. 1078-1080 (3)             7.00 7.00

University of
Technology, 50th
Anniv. — A263

**2008, May 26    Litho.    Perf. 14**
1081 A263 $30 multi                2.00 2.00
  a.    Souvenir sheet of 1        2.10 2.10

Associated Board of
the Royal Schools of
Music in Jamaica,
Cent. — A264

Map of Jamaica and: $30, Piano keyboard.
$70, Violin.

**Wmk. 352**
**2008, Oct. 30    Litho.    Perf. 14**
1082-1083 A264    Set of 2         5.00 5.00

Christmas — A265

Various ferns: $20, $30, $50, $60.

**Wmk. 352**
**2008, Nov. 21    Litho.    Perf. 13¾**
1084-1087 A265    Set of 4         7.00 7.00

George Headley (1909-
83), Cricket
Player — A266

Designs: $10, Head of Headley. $30,
Headley in front of wickets. $200, Statue of
Headley.
$250, Statue of Headley, Sabina Park,
Kingston.

**Wmk. 352**
**2009, Sept. 25    Litho.    Perf. 14**
1088-1090 A266    Set of 3         8.00 8.00
**Souvenir Sheet**
**Perf. 14¼x14**
1091 A266 $250 multi               8.50 8.50

No. 1091 contains one 43x57mm stamp.

Christmas — A267

Paintings by Juanita Isabel Ramos: $20,
Guardian Angel. $30, Madonna and Child.
$50, Madonna and Flowers, horiz.

**Wmk. 352**
**2009, Nov. 20    Litho.    Perf. 13½**
1092-1094 A267    Set of 3         3.50 3.50

Christmas — A268

Musical groups: $40, NDTC Singers. $60, Kingston College Chapel Choir. $120, The University Singers. $160, The Jamaican Folk Singers.

**Wmk. 352**
**2010, Dec. 13** **Litho.** *Perf. 13¾*
1095-1098 A268 Set of 4    11.00 11.00

**Souvenir Sheet**

Wedding of Prince William and Catherine Middleton — A269

**2011, Apr. 29** *Perf. 14¾x14¼*
1099 A269 $400 multi    11.00 11.00

Lighthouses A270

Designs: $20, Negril Lighthouse. $50, Morant Point Lighthouse. $60, Lover's Leap Lighthouse, vert. $200, Galina Lighthouse, vert.

**2011, July 4** *Perf. 14*
| | | | |
|---|---|---|---|
| 1100 A270 $20 multi | | .50 | .50 |
| a. | Dated "2012" | .50 | .50 |
| b. | Dated "2013" | .40 | .40 |
| c. | Dated "2015" | .35 | .35 |
| 1101 A270 $50 multi | | 1.25 | 1.25 |
| a. | Dated "2012" | 1.25 | 1.25 |
| b. | Dated "2013" | 1.00 | 1.00 |
| c. | Dated "2015" | .85 | .85 |
| 1102 A270 $60 multi | | 1.40 | 1.40 |
| a. | Dated "2012" | 1.40 | 1.40 |
| b. | Dated "2013" | 1.25 | 1.25 |
| c. | Dated "2015" | 1.00 | 1.00 |
| d. | Perf. 13½x13¼, dated "2018" | .95 | .95 |
| 1103 A270 $200 multi | | 4.75 | 4.75 |
| a. | Dated "2012" | 4.75 | 4.75 |
| b. | Dated "2013" | 4.00 | 4.00 |
| c. | Dated "2015" | 3.25 | 3.25 |
| *Nos. 1100-1103 (4)* | | 7.90 | 7.90 |

Issued: Nos. 1100a, 1101a, 1102a, 1103a, 3/23/12. Nos. 1100b, 1101b, 1102b, 1103b, 6/13/13. Nos. 1100c, 1101c, 112c, 1103c, 3/14/16.
See Nos. 1122-1125.

Independence, 50th Anniv. — A271

Designs: $60, Fiftieth anniversary emblem. $120, Coat of arms, vert.

*Perf. 14x14¾, 14¾x14*
**2012, Aug. 31**
1104-1105 A271 Set of 2    4.25 4.25

Medalists at 2008 Summer Olympics — A272

Designs: No. 1106, $60, Usain Bolt, Men's 100-meter and 200-meter gold medalist (orange panel). No. 1107, $60, Melaine Walker, Women's 400-meter hurdles gold medalist (red panel). No. 1108, $60, Veronica Campbell-Brown, women's 200-meter gold medalist (blue panel). No. 1109, $60, Men's 4x100-meter relay team (Bolt, Michael Frater, Nesta Carter, Asafa Powell) (green panel). No.

1110, $60, Shelly-Ann Fraser, gold medalist, Sherone Simpson and Kerron Stewart, silver medalists in women's 100-meter (black panel).

**2013, May 3** *Perf. 13¼*
1106-1110 A272 Set of 5    6.25 6.25

Christmas — A273

Bells and: $20, Night-blooming cereus. $60, Coffee berries and flowers. $120, Century palm. $160, Cactus flower.

**Wmk. 352**
**2013, Dec. 6** **Litho.** *Perf. 13¼*
1111-1114 A273 Set of 4    7.50 7.50

St. Andrew Parish Church, 350th Anniv. A274

Various views of church's exterior: $20, $60, $120. $200, Stained-glass windows, vert.

*Perf. 14¼x14¾*
**2014, Dec. 11** **Litho.**
1115-1117 A274 Set of 3    3.50 3.50
**Souvenir Sheet**
*Perf. 14¾x14¼*
1118 A274 $200 multi    3.50 3.50

2016 Summer Olympics, Rio de Janeiro — A275

No. 1119: a, Shelly-Ann Fraser-Price with medal. b, Usain Bolt with medal. $120, Fraser-Price and Bolt in track uniforms. $300, Fraser-Price and Bolt with medal ribbons around necks.

**Wmk. 352**
**2016, July 3** **Litho.** *Perf. 14*
| | | | |
|---|---|---|---|
| 1119 | Horiz. pair | 1.90 | 1.90 |
| a.-b. | A275 $60 Either single | .95 | .95 |
| c. | Souvenir sheet of 2, #1119a-1119b | 1.90 | 1.90 |
| 1120 | A275 $120 multi | 1.90 | 1.90 |
| 1121 | A275 $300 multi | 4.75 | 4.75 |
| *Nos. 1119-1121 (3)* | | 8.55 | 8.55 |

**Lighthouses Type of 2011**

Designs: $40, Folly Lighthouse, vert. $140, Rosehall Lighthouse. $180, Plumb Point Lighthouse, vert. $300, Portland Point Lighthouse.

**2016** **Litho.** **Wmk. 352** *Perf. 14*
| | | | |
|---|---|---|---|
| 1122 A270 $40 multi | | .65 | .65 |
| 1123 A270 $140 multi | | 2.25 | 2.25 |
| 1124 A270 $180 multi | | 2.75 | 2.75 |
| 1125 A270 $300 multi | | 4.75 | 4.75 |
| *Nos. 1122-1125 (4)* | | 10.40 | 10.40 |

Dated 2015.

Butterflies — A276

No. 1126: a, Giant swallowtail. b, Monarch.

*Perf. 13¼*
**2016, Oct. 28** **Litho.** **Unwmk.**
1126 A276 $60 Horiz. pair, #a-b    1.90 1.90
See Mexico Nos. 3029-3030.

Jamaica Civil Service Association, Cent. — A277

Denominations: $60, $120, $140, $180, $200.

*Perf. 13¼x13½*
**2019, May 6** **Litho.** **Unwmk.**
1127-1131 A277 Set of 5    10.50 10.50

Louise "Miss Lou" Bennett-Coverley (1919-2006), Poet — A278

Various photographs of Bennett-Coverley: $20, $50, $60, $500.

*Perf. 13¼x13½*
**2020, Sept. 7** **Litho.** **Unwmk.**
| | | | |
|---|---|---|---|
| 1132-1135 A278 Set of 4 | | 9.00 | 9.00 |
| *1135a* | Souvenir sheet of 4, #1132-1135 | 9.00 | 9.00 |

Jamaica Post Office, 350th Anniv. A279

No. 1136: a, Cross Road Post Office, 1920. b, Central Sorting Office Headquarters, Kingston, 2020. c, Mobile Post and mail delivery vans. d, Postmen at General Post Office, Kingston. e, Gordon Town Post Office, 2020. f, Ocho Rios Post Office, 2019. g, Royal mail van delivery. h, Spanish Town Post Office, 2020. i, Postmen on motorbikes. j, Mail dispatch, Constant Spring Post Office, 1930s. k, Mail sorting. l, Port Royal Post Office, 2020. m, Airmail arrival in Jamaica. n, Stonehenge Post Office. o, Mobile Post van. p, Falmouth Post Office, 1815. q, Mail delivery at the Mona Housing Estate, Kingston, 1961. r, Black River Post Office, 2020.
$350, 350th anniv. emblem.

**Wmk. 352**
**2021, Oct. 29** **Litho.** *Perf. 14*
| | | | |
|---|---|---|---|
| 1136 A279 | Sheet of 18 | 65.00 | 65.00 |
| a.-c. | $60 Any single | .75 | .75 |
| d.-f. | $100 Any single | 1.30 | 1.30 |
| g.-i. | $120 Any single | 1.60 | 1.60 |
| j.-l. | $180 Any single | 2.40 | 2.40 |
| m.-o. | $200 Any single | 2.60 | 2.60 |
| p.-r. | $1000 Any single | 13.00 | 13.00 |
| s. | Souvenir sheet of 6, #1136d, 1136g, 1136i, 1136j, 1136m, 1136o | 12.50 | 12.50 |

**Souvenir Sheet**

1137 A279 $350 multi    4.50 4.50

No. 1137 contains one 50x30mm stamp in the shape of a parallelogram.

Independence, 60th Anniv. — A280

Panel color: $60, Bister. $120, Green.

*Perf. 13¼x13½*
**2022, July 21** **Litho.** **Wmk. 352**
1138-1139 A280 Set of 2    2.40 2.40

---

**SEMI-POSTAL STAMPS**

Native Girl — SP1

Native Boy — SP2

Native Boy and Girl — SP3

**1923, Nov. 1** **Engr.** *Perf. 12*
| | | | | | |
|---|---|---|---|---|---|
| B1 | SP1 | ½p green & black | | 1.25 | 6.00 |
| B2 | SP2 | 1p car & black | | 4.00 | 13.50 |
| B3 | SP3 | 2½p blue & black | | 22.50 | 22.00 |
| *Nos. B1-B3 (3)* | | | | 27.75 | 41.50 |

Each stamp was sold for ½p over face value. The surtax benefited the Child Saving League of Jamaica.

> **Catalogue values for unused stamps in this section, from this point to the end of the section, are for Never Hinged items.**

**Nos. 694-697 Surcharged in Black**

**Wmk. 352**
**1988, Nov. 11** **Litho.** *Perf. 14*
| | | | | |
|---|---|---|---|---|
| B4 | A164 | 25c +25c multi | .30 | .25 |
| B5 | A164 | 45c +45c multi | .40 | .25 |
| B6 | A164 | $4 +$4 multi | 2.25 | 3.00 |
| B7 | A164 | $5 +$5 multi | 2.50 | 3.00 |
| *Nos. B4-B7 (4)* | | | 5.45 | 6.50 |

**Red Surcharge**
| | | | | |
|---|---|---|---|---|
| B4a | A164 | 25c + 25c | .30 | .25 |
| B5a | A164 | 45c + 45c | .40 | .25 |
| B6a | A164 | $4 + $4 | 2.25 | 3.00 |
| B7a | A164 | $5 + $5 | 2.50 | 3.00 |
| *Nos. B4a-B7a (4)* | | | 5.45 | 6.50 |

**WAR TAX STAMPS**

**Regular Issues of 1906-19 Overprinted**

**1916** **Wmk. 3** *Perf. 14*
| | | | | | |
|---|---|---|---|---|---|
| MR1 | A14 | ½p green | | 1.00 | .75 |
| a. | | Without period | | 20.00 | 27.50 |
| b. | | Double overprint | | 140.00 | 160.00 |
| c. | | Inverted overprint | | 130.00 | 150.00 |
| d. | | As "c," without period | | 350.00 | |
| MR2 | A17 | 3p violet, *yel* | | 4.50 | 25.00 |
| a. | | Without period | | 45.00 | 100.00 |

**Surface-colored Paper**
| | | | | | |
|---|---|---|---|---|---|
| MR3 | A17 | 3p violet, *yel* | | 37.50 | 52.50 |
| *Nos. MR1-MR3 (3)* | | | | 43.00 | 78.25 |

**Regular Issues of 1906-18 Overprinted**

| | | | | | |
|---|---|---|---|---|---|
| MR4 | A14 | ½p green | | .25 | .30 |
| a. | | Without period | | 22.50 | 57.50 |
| b. | | Pair, one without ovpt. | | 6,500. | 5,250. |
| c. | | "R" inserted by hand | | 1,800. | 1,500. |
| d. | | "WAR" only | | 125.00 | |
| MR5 | A17 | 1 ½p orange | | .75 | .35 |
| a. | | Without period | | 7.50 | 8.50 |
| b. | | "TAMP" | | 250.00 | 240.00 |
| c. | | "S" inserted by hand | | 450.00 | 450.00 |
| d. | | "R" omitted | | 3,600. | 3,100. |
| e. | | "R" inserted by hand | | 1,550. | 1,250. |
| MR6 | A17 | 3p violet, *yel* | | 10.00 | 1.50 |
| a. | | Without period | | 75.00 | 75.00 |
| b. | | "TAMP" | | 1,000. | 1,000. |
| c. | | "S" inserted by hand | | 225.00 | 225.00 |

| | | | |
|---|---|---|---|
| *d.* | Inverted overprint | 325.00 | 250.00 |
| *e.* | As "a," inverted | | |
| | *Nos. MR4-MR6 (3)* | 11.00 | 2.15 |

### Regular Issues of 1906-19 Overprinted

**1917, Mar.**

| | | | | |
|---|---|---|---|---|
| MR7 | A14 | ½p green | 3.00 | .35 |
| *a.* | | Without period | 18.50 | 30.00 |
| *b.* | | Overprinted on back instead of face | 290.00 | |
| *c.* | | Inverted overprint | 27.50 | 57.50 |
| MR8 | A17 | 1½p orange | 1.00 | .25 |
| *a.* | | Without period | 5.00 | 20.00 |
| *b.* | | Double overprint | 85.00 | 100.00 |
| *c.* | | Inverted overprint | 85.00 | 85.00 |
| *d.* | | As "a," inverted | 400.00 | |
| MR9 | A17 | 3p violet, *yel* | 3.50 | *1.75* |
| *a.* | | Without period | 30.00 | 52.50 |
| *b.* | | Vertical overprint | 425.00 | 425.00 |
| *c.* | | Inverted overprint | 160.00 | 190.00 |
| *d.* | | As "a," inverted | 450.00 | |
| *e.* | | Pair, overprint omitted on one | 5,000. | |
| | | *Nos. MR7-MR9 (3)* | 7.50 | 2.35 |

There are many minor varieties of Nos. MR1-MR9.

### Regular Issues of 1906-19 Overprinted in Red

**1919, Oct. 4**

| | | | | |
|---|---|---|---|---|
| MR10 | A14 | ½p green | 1.00 | 1.00 |
| MR11 | A17 | 3p violet, *yel* | 15.00 | 4.00 |
| *a.* | | 3p pale pur, *buff* | 8.00 | 2.00 |

---

### OFFICIAL STAMPS

### No. 16 Overprinted in Black

Type I — Word 15 to 16mm long.
Type II — Word 17 to 17½mm long.

| **1890** | | **Wmk. 2** | | **Perf. 14** |
|---|---|---|---|---|
| O1 | A7 | ½p green (II) | 18.50 | 2.50 |
| *a.* | | Type I | 47.50 | 30.00 |
| *b.* | | Inverted overprint (II) | 110.00 | 120.00 |
| *c.* | | Double overprint (II) | 110.00 | 120.00 |
| *d.* | | Dbl. ovpt., one invtd. (II) | 575.00 | 575.00 |
| *e.* | | Dbl. ovpt., one vert. (II) | 1,100. | |
| *f.* | | Double overprint (I) | 825.00 | |

Missing "O," "L" or one or both "I"s known.

### No. 16 and Type of 1889 Overprinted

**1890-91**

| | | | | |
|---|---|---|---|---|
| O2 | A7 | ½p green ('91) | 10.00 | 1.80 |
| O3 | A10 | 1p carmine rose | 8.50 | 2.00 |
| O4 | A10 | 2p slate | 32.50 | 2.00 |
| | | *Nos. O2-O4 (3)* | 51.00 | 5.80 |

---

# JAPAN

jə-'pan

LOCATION — North Pacific Ocean, east of China
GOVT. — Constitutional monarchy
AREA — 142,726 sq. mi.
POP. — 126,182,077 (1999 est.)
CAPITAL — Tokyo

1000 Mon = 10 Sen
100 Sen = 1 Yen (or En)
10 Rin = 1 Sen

**Catalogue values for unused stamps in this country are for Never Hinged items, beginning with Scott 375 in the regular postage section, Scott B8 in the semipostal section, and Scott C9 in the airpost section.**

## Watermarks

Wmk. 141 — Zigzag Lines

Wmk. 142 — Parallel Lines

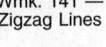

Wmk. 257 — Curved Wavy Lines

After 1945, Wmk. 257 exists also in a narrow spacing on a small number of issues.

Counterfeits of Nos. 1-71 are plentiful. Some are excellent and deceive many collectors.
Nos. 1-54A were printed from plates of 40 with individually engraved subjects. Each stamp in the sheet is slightly different.

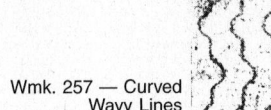

Pair of Dragons Facing Characters of Value — A1

Plate I                Plate II

48 mon:
Plate I — Solid dots in inner border.
Plate II — Tiny circles replace dots.

Plate I

Plate II

100 mon:

---

Plate I — Lowest dragon claw at upper right and at lower left point upward.
Plate II — Same two claws point downward.

Plate I                Plate II

200 mon:
Plate I — Dot in upper left corner.
Plate II — No dot. (Some Plate I copies show dot faintly; these can be mistaken for Plate II.)

Plate I                Plate II

500 mon:
Plate I — Lower right corner of Greek-type border incomplete
Plate II — Short horizontal line completes corner border pattern.

## Unwmk.
### 1871, Apr. 20    Engr.    Imperf.
### Native Laid Paper Without Gum
### Denomination in Black

| | | | | |
|---|---|---|---|---|
| 1 | A1 | 48m brown (I) | 225. | 225. |
| *a.* | | 48m red brown (I) | 375. | 375. |
| *b.* | | Wove paper (I) | 300. | 300. |
| *c.* | | 48m brown (II) | 325. | 325. |
| *d.* | | Wove paper (II) | 400. | 400. |
| 2 | A1 | 100m blue (I) | 225. | 225. |
| *a.* | | Wove paper (I) | 350. | 350. |
| *b.* | | Plate II | 550. | 550. |
| *c.* | | Wove paper (II) | 800. | 800. |
| 3 | A1 | 200m ver (I) | 350. | 325. |
| *a.* | | Wove paper (I) | 500. | 425. |
| *b.* | | Plate II | 2,500. | 2,000. |
| *c.* | | Wove paper (II) | | 4,000. |
| 4 | A1 | 500m bl grn (I) | 575. | 550. |
| *a.* | | 500m greenish blue (I) | 650. | 625. |
| *b.* | | 500m green (I) | 2,000. | 1,400. |
| *c.* | | 500m yellow green (I) | 3,500. | 1,500. |
| *d.* | | Wove paper (I) | 725. | 725. |
| *e.* | | 500m blue green (II) | 750. | 4,000. |
| *f.* | | 500m greenish blue (II) | 750. | 4,000. |
| *g.* | | Wove paper (II) | 2,750. | 5,000. |
| *h.* | | Denomination inverted (I) | | 175,000. |

### Perforations, Nos. 5-8
Perforations on Nos. 5-8 generally are rough and irregular due to the perforating equipment used and the quality of the paper. Values are for stamps with rough perfs that touch the frameline on one or more sides.

Dragons and Denomination — A1a

½ sen:
Plate I — Same as 48m Plate II. Measures not less than 19.8x19.8mm. Some subjects on this plate measure 20.3x20.2mm.
Plate II — Same as 48m Plate II. Measures not more than 19.7x19.3mm. Some subjects measure 19.3x18.7mm.

Plate I & II                Plate III

1 sen:
Plate I — Same as 100m Plate I. Narrow space between frameline and Greek-type border.
Plate II — Same as 100m Plate II. Same narrow space between frameline and border.
Plate III — Space between frameline and border is much wider. Frameline thinner. Shading on dragon heads heavier than on Plates I and II.

### Native Laid Paper
### With or Without Gum
### 1872    Perf. 9-12 & compound
### Denomination in Black

| | | | | |
|---|---|---|---|---|
| 5 | A1a | ½s brown (II) | 110.00 | 100.00 |
| *a.* | | ½s red brown (II) | 125.00 | 110.00 |
| *b.* | | ½s gray brown (II) | 125.00 | 110.00 |
| *c.* | | Wove paper (II) | 725.00 | 675.00 |
| *d.* | | ½s brown (I) | 200.00 | 200.00 |
| *e.* | | ½s red brown (I) | 200.00 | 200.00 |
| *f.* | | ½s gray brown (I) | 200.00 | 200.00 |
| *g.* | | Wove paper (I) | 275.00 | 275.00 |
| 6 | A1a | 1s blue (II) | 375.00 | 325.00 |
| *a.* | | Wove paper (II) | 675.00 | 675.00 |
| *b.* | | Plate I | 1,400. | 3,000. |
| *c.* | | Wove paper (I) | 7,000. | |
| *d.* | | Plate III | 15,000. | 2,500. |
| *e.* | | Wove paper (III) | | 7,500. |

---

| | | | | |
|---|---|---|---|---|
| 7 | A1a | 2s vermilion | 500.00 | 475.00 |
| *a.* | | Wove paper | 625.00 | 575.00 |
| 8 | A1a | 5s blue green | 800.00 | 725.00 |
| *a.* | | 5s yellow green | 850.00 | 800.00 |
| *b.* | | Wove paper | 900.00 | 900.00 |

In 1896 the government made imperforate imitations of Nos. 6-7 to include in a presentation book.

Beginning with No. 9, Japanese stamps intended for distribution outside the Postal Ministry were overprinted with three characters, as shown above, reading "Mihon" (specimen). These specimens were included in ministry announcements detailing forthcoming issues and were in presentation booklets given to government officials, foreign governments, etc.

Expect perforations on Nos. 9-71 to be rough and irregular.

Imperial Crest and Branches of Kiri Tree — A2

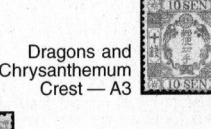

Dragons and Chrysanthemum Crest — A3

Imperial Chrysanthemum Crest — A4

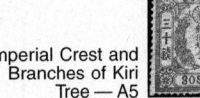

Imperial Crest and Branches of Kiri Tree — A5

### Perf. 9 to 13 and Compound
### 1872-73
### Native Wove or Laid Paper of Varying Thickness

| | | | | |
|---|---|---|---|---|
| 9 | A2 | ½s brn, *hard wove* | 25.00 | 20.00 |
| *a.* | | Upper character in left label has 2 diagonal top strokes missing | 2,100. | 1,250. |
| *b.* | | Laid paper | 80.00 | |

---

| | | | |
|---|---|---|---|
| *c.* | As "a," laid paper | 2,200. | — |
| *d.* | ½s gray brown, *soft porous native wove* | 80.00 | — |

Nos. 9, 9a are on stiff, brittle wove paper. Nos. 9b, 9c and 9d on a soft, fibrous paper. Nos. 9b, 9c and 9d probably were never put in use, though genuine used examples do exist.

| | | | | |
|---|---|---|---|---|
| 10 | A2 | 1s blue, *wove* | 50.00 | 26.00 |
| *a.* | | Laid paper | 52.50 | 29.00 |
| 11 | A2 | 2s ver, *wove* | 100.00 | 50.00 |
| 12 | A2 | 2s dull rose, *laid* | 75.00 | 35.00 |
| *a.* | | Wove paper | 100.00 | 50.00 |
| 13 | A2 | 2s yel, *laid* ('73) | 75.00 | 21.00 |
| *a.* | | Wove paper ('73) | 175.00 | 26.00 |
| 14 | A2 | 4s rose, *laid* ('73) | 67.50 | 26.00 |
| *a.* | | Wove paper ('73) | 210.00 | 32.00 |
| 15 | A3 | 10s blue grn, *wove* | 250.00 | 150.00 |
| 16 | A3 | 10s yel grn, *laid* | 400.00 | 275.00 |
| *a.* | | Wove paper ('73) | 1,150. | 500.00 |
| 17 | A4 | 20s lilac, *wove* | 600.00 | 350.00 |
| *a.* | | 20s violet, *wove* | 750.00 | 350.00 |
| *b.* | | 20s red violet, *laid* | | — |
| 18 | A5 | 30s gray, *wove* | 625.00 | 375.00 |

See Nos. 24-25, 30-31, 37-39, 51-52.

### 1874    Foreign Wove Paper

| | | | | |
|---|---|---|---|---|
| 24 | A2 | 4s rose | 650. | 300. |
| 25 | A5 | 30s gray | 30,000. | 7,500. |

A6                A7

A8

Design A6 differs from A2 by the addition of a syllabic character in a box covering crossed kiri branches above SEN. Stamps of design A6 differ for each value in border and spandrel designs.
In design A7, the syllabic character appears just below the buckle. In design A8, it appears in an oval frame at bottom center below SE of SEN. Design A3 and A4 have a syllabic character immediately below the central design, above the 'S' of 'SEN'.

## With Syllabic Characters

イ ロ ハ ニ ホ ヘ ト チ
i ro ha ni ho he to chi
1 2 3 4 5 6 7 8

リ ヌ ル ヲ ワ カ ヨ タ
ri nu ru wo wa ka yo ta
9 10 11 12 13 14 15 16

レ ソ ツ ネ ナ ラ ム
re so tsu ne na ra mu
17 18 19 20 21 22 23

### Perf. 9½ to 12½ and Compound
**1874 Native Laid or Wove Paper**

| | | | |
|---|---|---|---|
| 28 | A6 | 2s yel (Syll. 1) | 27,000. 400.00 |
| | Syllabic 16 | | 425.00 |
| 29 | A7 | 6s vio brn (Syll. 1) | 1,700. 475.00 |
| | Syllabic 2 | | 1,900. 500.00 |
| | Syllabic 3 | | 20,000. 1,100. |
| | Syllabic 4 | | 20,000. 600.00 |
| | Syllabic 5 | | 20,000. 600.00 |
| | Syllabic 6 | | 20,000. 700.00 |
| | Syllabic 7 | | 25,000. 550.00 |
| | Syllabic 8 | | 25,000. 550.00 |
| | Syllabic 9 | | 20,000. 700.00 |
| | Syllabic 10 | | 3,500. |
| | Syllabic 11 | | 3,000. |
| | Syllabic 12 | | 20,000. 1,900. |
| 30 | A4 | 20s red vio (Syll. 3) | 10,000. |
| | Syllabic 1 | | 150,000. |
| | Syllabic 2 | | 10,000. |
| 31 | A5 | 30s gray (Syll. 1) | 3,000. 3,000. |
| *a.* | Very thin laid paper | | 3,000. 3,000. |

No. 30, syll. 1, comes only with small, eliptical specimen dot (*Sumiten,* "secret mark").

### Perf. 11 to 12½ and Compound
**1874 Foreign Wove Paper**

| | | | |
|---|---|---|---|
| 32 | A6 | ½s brn (Syll. 1) | 25.00 20.00 |
| | Syllabic 2 | | 40.00 40.00 |
| 33 | A6 | 1s blue (Syll. 4) | 160.00 40.00 |
| | Syllabic 1 | | 150.00 35.00 |
| | Syllabic 2 | | 225.00 40.00 |
| | Syllabic 3 | | 200.00 40.00 |
| | Syllabic 5 | | 650.00 150.00 |
| | Syllabic 6, 9 | | 150.00 45.00 |
| | Syllabic 7 | | 350.00 50.00 |
| | Syllabic 8 | | 150.00 40.00 |
| | Syllabic 10 | | 225.00 70.00 |
| | Syllabic 11 | | 215.00 60.00 |
| | Syllabic 12 | | 250.00 65.00 |
| 34 | A6 | 2s yel (Syll. 2-4, 15, 17, 20) | 175.00 30.00 |
| | Syllabic 1 | | 400.00 35.00 |
| | Syllabic 5 | | 450.00 30.00 |
| | Syllabic 6 | | 2,000. 50.00 |
| | Syllabic 7 | | 2,000. 30.00 |
| | Syllabic 8 | | 200.00 55.00 |
| | Syllabic 9 | | 200.00 35.00 |
| | Syllabic 10 | | 2,750. 50.00 |
| | Syllabic 11 | | 200.00 30.00 |
| | Syllabic 12,22 | | 2,650. 30.00 |
| | Syllabic 13 | | 2,500. 30.00 |
| | Syllabic 14 | | 2,650. 45.00 |
| | Syllabic 16 | | 2,500. 35.00 |
| | Syllabic 18,19 | | 200.00 30.00 |
| | Syllabic 21 | | 250.00 30.00 |
| | Syllabic 23 | | 265.00 30.00 |
| 35 | A6 | 4s rose (Syll. 1) | 3,500. 475.00 |
| 36 | A7 | 6s vio brn (Syll. 16) | 175.00 65.00 |
| | Syllabic 10 | | 650.00 650.00 |
| | Syllabic 11 | | 500.00 |
| | Syllabic 13 | | 14,000. 5,000. |
| | Syllabic 14 | | 300.00 275.00 |
| | Syllabic 15 | | 25,000. 3,000. |
| | Syllabic 17 | | 225.00 80.00 |
| | Syllabic 18 | | 325.00 110.00 |
| 37 | A3 | 10s yel grn (Syll. 2) | 200.00 65.00 |
| | Syllabic 1 | | 525.00 80.00 |
| | Syllabic 3 | | 1,000. 300.00 |
| 38 | A4 | 20s violet (Syll. 5) | 425.00 90.00 |
| | Syllabic 4 | | 450.00 95.00 |
| 39 | A5 | 30s gray (Syll. 1) | 475.00 95.00 |

**1875 Perf. 9 to 13 and Compound**

| | | | |
|---|---|---|---|
| 40 | A6 | ½s gray (Syll. 2, 3) | 25.00 20.00 |
| | Syllabic 4 | | 30.00 1,000. |
| 41 | A6 | 1s brn (Syll. 15) | 35.00 22.50 |
| | Syllabic 5 | | 375.00 50.00 |
| | Syllabic 7 | | 2,250. 275.00 |
| | Syllabic 8 | | 32,500. 275.00 |
| | Syllabic 12 | | 1,300. 225.00 |
| | Syllabic 13 | | 50.00 22.50 |
| | Syllabic 14 | | 50.00 22.50 |
| | Syllabic 16-17 | | 45.00 25.00 |
| 42 | A6 | 4s grn (Syll. 1) | 130.00 29.00 |
| | Syllabic 2 | | 200.00 29.00 |
| | Syllabic 3 | | 130.00 29.00 |
| 43 | A7 | 6s org (Syll. 16,17) | 90.00 27.50 |
| | Syllabic 10 | | 175.00 55.00 |
| | Syllabic 11 | | 150.00 50.00 |
| | Syllabic 13 | | 325.00 45.00 |
| | Syllabic 14 | | 160.00 32.50 |
| | Syllabic 15 | | 162,500. |
| 44 | A8 | 6s org (Syll. 20) | 110.00 27.50 |
| | Syllabic 19 | | 125.00 27.50 |
| | Syllabic 21 | | 100.00 27.50 |
| | Syllabic 22 | | 4,250. 1,750. |

Dragons
A9

Wild Goose
A10

Wagtail — A11

Imperial Crest — A11a

Kiri Branches — A11b

Goshawk — A12

| | | | |
|---|---|---|---|
| 45 | A9 | 10s ultra (Syll. 4) | 180.00 30.00 |
| | Syllabic 5 | | 4,250. 375.00 |
| 46 | A10 | 12s rose (Syll. 1) | 375.00 160.00 |
| | Syllabic 2 | | 500.00 185.00 |
| | Syllabic 3 | | 3,500. 500.00 |
| 47 | A11 | 15s lilac (Syll. 1) | 350.00 160.00 |
| | Syllabic 2 | | 400.00 175.00 |
| | Syllabic 3 | | 350.00 190.00 |
| 48 | A11a | 20s rose (Syll. 8) | 140.00 22.50 |
| | Syllabic 9 | | |
| 49 | A11b | 30s vio (Syll. 2-4) | 175.00 70.00 |
| 50 | A12 | 45s lake (Syll. 1) | 500.00 240.00 |
| | Syllabic 2 | | 1,250. 550.00 |
| | Syllabic 3 | | 1,200. 425.00 |

Issued: No. 46, syll. 2, 1882; No. 46, syll. 3, 1883; others, 1875.

The 1s brown on laid paper, type A6, formerly listed as No. 50A, is one of several stamps of the preceding issue which exist on a laid type paper. They are difficult to identify and mainly of interest to specialists.

**1875 Without Syllabic Characters**

| | | | |
|---|---|---|---|
| 51 | A2 | 1s brown | 7,500. 675.00 |
| 52 | A2 | 4s dark gray green | 375.00 100.00 |

Branches of Kiri Tree Tied with Ribbon
A13

Imperial Crest and Kiri Branches
A14

**1875-76**

| | | | |
|---|---|---|---|
| 53 | A13 | 1s brown | 75.00 18.00 |
| 54 | A13 | 2s yellow | 110.00 18.00 |
| 54A | A14 | 5s green ('76) | 220.00 110.00 |
| | *Nos. 53-54A (3)* | | 405.00 146.00 |

### Postal Cancellations

Bota Cancel

Postal Cancel

Telegraph Cancellation

Nos. 58, 61-62, 64-65, 71-84 are found with telegraph or telephone office cancellations. These sell at considerably lower prices than postally used examples. Examples with bota cancels are valued the same as postally used examples.

A15

A16

Imperial Crest, Star and Kiri Branches
A17

Sun, Kikumon and Kiri Branches
A18

### Perf. 8 to 14 and Compound
**1876-77** Typo.

| | | | |
|---|---|---|---|
| 55 | A15 | 5r slate | 25.00 15.00 |
| 56 | A16 | 1s black | 50.00 4.75 |
| *a.* | Horiz. pair, imperf. btwn. | | |
| 57 | A16 | 2s brown ol | 90.00 4.50 |
| 58 | A16 | 4s blue grn | 50.00 4.00 |
| *a.* | 4s green | | 50.00 4.00 |
| 59 | A17 | 5s brown | 65.00 20.00 |
| 60 | A17 | 6s orange ('77) | 200.00 85.00 |
| 61 | A17 | 8s vio brn ('77) | 75.00 5.50 |
| 62 | A17 | 10s blue ('77) | 55.00 2.50 |
| 63 | A17 | 12s rose ('77) | 240.00 160.00 |
| 64 | A18 | 15s yel grn ('77) | 150.00 2.50 |
| 65 | A18 | 20s dk blue ('77) | 160.00 15.00 |
| 66 | A18 | 30s violet ('77) | 250.00 110.00 |
| *a.* | 30s red violet | | 275.00 110.00 |
| 67 | A18 | 45s carmine ('77) | 700.00 600.00 |

**1879**

| | | | |
|---|---|---|---|
| 68 | A16 | 1s maroon | 17.50 1.25 |
| 69 | A16 | 2s dk violet | 70.00 2.50 |
| 70 | A16 | 3s orange | 75.00 30.00 |
| 71 | A18 | 50s carmine | 250.00 17.50 |
| | *Nos. 68-71 (4)* | | 412.50 51.25 |

**1883**

| | | | |
|---|---|---|---|
| 72 | A16 | 1s green | 11.00 1.25 |
| 73 | A16 | 2s car rose | 16.00 .30 |
| 74 | A17 | 5s ultra | 27.50 1.10 |
| | *Nos. 72-74 (3)* | | 54.50 2.65 |

Imperial Crest and Kiri Branches
A19

Kikumon
A20

**1888-92**

| | | | |
|---|---|---|---|
| 75 | A15 | 5r gray blk ('89) | 6.00 .85 |
| 76 | A16 | 3s lilac rose ('92) | 22.50 .75 |
| 77 | A16 | 4s olive bis | 17.50 .75 |
| 78 | A17 | 8s blue lilac | 35.00 2.50 |
| 79 | A17 | 10s brown org | 25.00 .75 |
| 80 | A18 | 15s purple | 60.00 1.00 |
| 81 | A18 | 20s orange | 75.00 3.00 |
| *a.* | 20s yellow | | 75.00 3.00 |
| 82 | A19 | 25s blue green | 110.00 3.25 |
| 83 | A18 | 50s brown | 120.00 5.75 |
| 84 | A20 | 1y carmine | 160.00 6.25 |
| | *Nos. 75-84 (10)* | | 631.00 24.85 |

Stamps of types A16-A18 differ for each value, in backgrounds and ornaments.

Cranes and Imperial Crest — A21

### Perf. 11½ to 13 and Compound
**1894, Mar. 9**

| | | | |
|---|---|---|---|
| 85 | A21 | 2s carmine | 19.00 3.00 |
| 86 | A21 | 5s ultra | 30.00 14.00 |

25th wedding anniv. of Emperor Meiji (Mutsuhito) and Empress Haru.

Gen. Yoshihisa Kitashirakawa
A22 A23

Field Marshal Akihito Arisugawa
A24 A25

**1896, Aug. 1** Engr.

| | | | |
|---|---|---|---|
| 87 | A22 | 2s rose | 22.50 4.75 |
| 88 | A23 | 5s deep ultra | 45.00 4.75 |
| 89 | A24 | 2s rose | 22.50 4.75 |
| 90 | A25 | 5s deep ultra | 45.00 4.75 |
| | *Nos. 87-90 (4)* | | 135.00 19.00 |

Victory in Chinese-Japanese War (1894-95).

A26

A27

A28

A29

### Perf. 11½ to 14 and Compound
**1899-1907** Typo.

| | | | |
|---|---|---|---|
| 91 | A26 | 5r gray | 14.00 2.25 |
| 92 | A26 | ½s gray ('01) | 7.50 .25 |
| 93 | A26 | 1s lt red brn | 10.00 .30 |
| 94 | A26 | 1½s ultra ('00) | 28.00 1.75 |
| 95 | A26 | 1½s violet ('06) | 20.00 .55 |
| *a.* | Booklet pane of 6 | | 500.00 |
| 96 | A26 | 2s lt green | 20.00 .30 |
| *a.* | Booklet pane of 6 | | 130.00 |
| 97 | A26 | 3s violet brn | 20.00 .35 |
| *a.* | Double impression | | |
| 98 | A26 | 3s green ('06) | 12.00 .30 |
| *a.* | Booklet pane of 6 | | 500.00 |
| 99 | A26 | 4s rose | 14.00 2.25 |
| *a.* | 4s pink ('06) | | 37.50 4.25 |
| *b.* | As No. 99, booklet pane of 6 | | 125.00 |
| 100 | A26 | 5s orange yel | 27.50 .40 |
| 101 | A27 | 6s maroon ('07) | 50.00 5.00 |
| *a.* | Booklet pane of 6 | | 500.00 |
| 102 | A27 | 8s olive grn | 60.00 7.50 |
| 103 | A27 | 10s deep blue | 24.00 .30 |
| *a.* | Booklet pane of 6 | | 200.00 |
| 104 | A27 | 15s purple | 80.00 3.50 |
| 105 | A27 | 20s red orange | 47.50 .30 |
| 106 | A28 | 25s blue green | 80.00 1.50 |
| 107 | A28 | 50s red brown | 90.00 2.25 |
| 108 | A29 | 1y carmine | 140.00 3.25 |
| | *Nos. 91-108 (18)* | | 744.50 32.30 |

For overprints see Nos. M1, Offices in China, 1-18, Offices in Korea, 1-14.

Boxes for Rice Cakes and Marriage Certificates — A30

### Perf. 11½ to 12½ and Compound
**1900, May 10**

| | | | |
|---|---|---|---|
| 109 | A30 | 3s carmine | 30.00 1.50 |

Wedding of the Crown Prince Yoshihito and Princess Sadako.

For overprints see Offices in China No. 19, Offices in Korea No. 15.

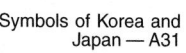

Symbols of Korea and Japan — A31

**1905, July 1**

| | | | |
|---|---|---|---|
| 110 | A31 | 3s rose red | 110.00 25.00 |

Issued to commemorate the amalgamation of the postal services of Japan and Korea. Korean stamps were withdrawn from sale June 30, 1905, but remained valid until Aug. 31. No. 110 was used in the Korea and China Offices of Japan, as well as in Japan proper.

Field-piece and Japanese Flag — A32

**1906, Apr. 29**
| | | | |
|---|---|---|---|
| 111 | A32 | 1½s blue | 40.00 6.50 |
| 112 | A32 | 3s carmine rose | 85.00 25.00 |

Triumphal military review following the Russo-Japanese War.

Empress Jingo — A33

**1908** Engr.
| | | | |
|---|---|---|---|
| 113 | A33 | 5y green | 1,200. 11.00 |
| 114 | A33 | 10y dark violet | 1,750. 15.00 |

The frame of No. 114 differs slightly from the illustration.
See Nos. 146-147.
For overprints see Offices in China Nos. 20-21, 48-49.

A34    A35

A36

**Perf. 12, 12x13, 13x13½**
**1913** Typo. Unwmk.
| | | | |
|---|---|---|---|
| 115 | A34 | ½s brown | 9.00 1.50 |
| 116 | A34 | 1s orange | 17.50 1.50 |
| 117 | A34 | 1½s lt blue | 25.00 2.50 |
| a. | | Booklet pane of 6 | 600.00 |
| 118 | A34 | 2s green | 27.50 1.50 |
| a. | | Booklet pane of 6 | 1,200. |
| 119 | A34 | 3s rose | 35.00 1.50 |
| a. | | Booklet pane of 6 | 750.00 |
| 120 | A35 | 4s red | 40.00 17.50 |
| a. | | Booklet pane of 6 | 350.00 |
| 121 | A35 | 5s violet | 47.50 3.00 |
| 122 | A35 | 10s deep blue | 120.00 2.00 |
| a. | | Booklet pane of 6 | 750.00 |
| 123 | A35 | 20s claret | 150.00 3.50 |
| 124 | A35 | 25s olive green | 140.00 6.00 |
| 125 | A36 | 1y yel grn & mar | 650.00 40.00 |
| | | Nos. 115-125 (11) | 1,262. 80.50 |

**1914-25 Wmk. 141 Granite Paper**
**Size: 19x22½mm ("Old Die")**
| | | | |
|---|---|---|---|
| 127 | A34 | ½s brown | 4.50 .25 |
| 128 | A34 | 1s orange | 5.00 .25 |
| 129 | A34 | 1½s blue | 5.50 .25 |
| a. | | Booklet pane of 6 | 100.00 |
| d. | | As "a," imperf. | |
| 130 | A34 | 2s green | 7.50 .30 |
| a. | | Booklet pane of 6 | 150.00 |
| 131 | A34 | 3s rose | 4.00 .30 |
| a. | | Booklet pane of 6 | 100.00 |
| 132 | A35 | 4s red | 25.00 2.25 |
| a. | | Booklet pane of 6 | 160.00 |
| 133 | A35 | 5s violet | 17.50 .75 |
| 134 | A35 | 6s brown ('19) | 37.50 7.00 |
| 136 | A35 | 8s gray ('19) | 32.50 17.50 |
| 137 | A35 | 10s deep blue | 22.50 .30 |
| a. | | Booklet pane of 6 | 200.00 |
| 138 | A35 | 13s olive brn ('25) | 40.00 6.00 |
| 139 | A35 | 20s claret | 120.00 2.00 |
| 140 | A35 | 25s olive grn | 22.50 2.00 |
| 141 | A36 | 30s org brn ('19) | 30.00 1.50 |
| 143 | A36 | 50s dk brown ('19) | 50.00 2.25 |
| 145 | A36 | 1y yel grn & mar | 150.00 2.50 |
| b. | | Imperf., pair | |
| 146 | A33 | 5y green | 400.00 6.00 |
| 147 | A33 | 10y violet | 600.00 11.00 |
| | | Nos. 127-147 (18) | 1,574. 62.40 |

**"New Die" Size: 18½x22mm (Flat Plate) or 18½x22½mm (Rotary)**
**1924-33**
| | | | |
|---|---|---|---|
| 127a | A34 | ½s brown | 3.75 2.25 |
| 128a | A34 | 1s orange | 3.75 2.25 |
| 129b | A34 | 1½s blue | 4.25 .30 |
| c. | | Bkt. pane of 6 ('30) | 40.00 |
| 131b | A34 | 3s rose | 3.50 .30 |
| c. | | Bkt. pane of 6 ('28) | 40.00 |
| 133a | A35 | 5s violet | 35.00 .30 |
| 135 | A35 | 7s red org ('30) | 18.00 .40 |
| 138a | A35 | 13s bister brn ('25) | 13.00 .40 |
| 140a | A35 | 25s olive green | 100.00 1.25 |
| 142 | A36 | 30s org & grn ('29) | 40.00 .60 |
| 144 | A36 | 50s yel brn & dk bl ('29) | 17.50 .90 |
| 145a | A36 | 1y yel grn & mar | 140.00 1.25 |
| | | Nos. 127a-145a (11) | 378.75 10.05 |

See Nos. 212-213, 239-241, 243, 245, 249-252, 255. For overprints see Nos. C1-C2, M2-M5, Offices in China, 22-47.

Ceremonial Cap — A37

Imperial Throne — A38

Enthronement Hall, Kyoto — A39

**Perf. 12½**
**1915, Nov. 10 Typo. Unwmk.**
| | | | |
|---|---|---|---|
| 148 | A37 | 1½s red & blk | 4.00 .80 |
| 149 | A38 | 3s orange & vio | 5.50 1.25 |

**Engr.**
**Perf. 12x12½**
| | | | |
|---|---|---|---|
| 150 | A39 | 4s carmine rose | 22.50 14.00 |
| 151 | A39 | 10s ultra | 42.50 18.00 |
| | | Nos. 148-151 (4) | 74.50 34.05 |

Enthronement of Emperor Yoshihito.

Mandarin Duck — A40

Ceremonial Cap — A41

**1916, Nov. 3 Typo. Perf. 12½**
| | | | |
|---|---|---|---|
| 152 | A40 | 1½s grn, red & yel | 4.25 1.75 |
| 153 | A40 | 3s red & yellow | 8.00 2.00 |
| 154 | A41 | 10s ultra & dk bl | 800.00 300.00 |

Nomination of the Prince Heir Apparent, later Emperor Hirohito.

A42

Dove and Olive Branch — A43

**Perf. 12, 12½, 13½x13**
**1919, July 1 Engr.**
| | | | |
|---|---|---|---|
| 155 | A42 | 1½s dark brown | 3.00 1.25 |
| 156 | A43 | 3s gray green | 3.25 2.00 |
| 157 | A42 | 4s rose | 6.00 6.50 |
| 158 | A43 | 10s dark blue | 25.00 17.50 |
| | | Nos. 155-158 (4) | 40.25 27.25 |

Restoration of peace after World War I.

Census Officer, A.D. 652 — A44

**Perf. 12½**
**1920, Sept. 25 Typo. Unwmk.**
| | | | |
|---|---|---|---|
| 159 | A44 | 1½s red violet | 7.50 5.50 |
| 160 | A44 | 3s vermilion | 9.00 6.00 |

Taking of the 1st modern census in Japan. Not available for foreign postage except to China.

Meiji Shrine, Tokyo — A45

**1920, Nov. 1 Engr.**
| | | | |
|---|---|---|---|
| 161 | A45 | 1½s dull violet | 3.75 1.75 |
| 162 | A45 | 3s rose | 3.75 1.75 |

Dedication of the Meiji Shrine. Not available for foreign postage except to China.

National and Postal Flags — A46    Ministry of Communications Building, Tokyo — A47

**Typographed (A46), Engraved (A47)**
**1921, Apr. 20 Perf. 12½, 13x13½**
| | | | |
|---|---|---|---|
| 163 | A46 | 1½s gray grn & red | 3.25 1.75 |
| 164 | A47 | 3s violet brn | 4.00 2.25 |
| 165 | A46 | 4s rose & red | 47.50 37.50 |
| 166 | A47 | 10s dark blue | 275.00 185.00 |
| | | Nos. 163-166 (4) | 329.75 226.50 |

50th anniv. of the establishment of postal service and Japanese postage stamps.

Battleships "Katori" and "Kashima" — A48

**1921, Sept. 3 Litho. Perf. 12½**
| | | | |
|---|---|---|---|
| 167 | A48 | 1½s violet | 3.25 1.75 |
| 168 | A48 | 3s olive green | 3.00 1.75 |
| 169 | A48 | 4s rose red | 35.00 20.00 |
| 170 | A48 | 10s deep blue | 47.50 27.50 |
| | | Nos. 167-170 (4) | 88.75 51.00 |

Return of Crown Prince Hirohito from his European visit.

Mount Fuji — A49

**Granite Paper**
**Size: 18½x22mm ("New Die")**
**Perf. 13x13½**
**1930-37 Typo. Wmk. 141**
| | | | |
|---|---|---|---|
| 171 | A49 | 4s green ('37) | 4.25 .80 |
| 172 | A49 | 4s orange | 12.00 .50 |
| 174 | A49 | 8s olive green | 19.00 .45 |
| 175a | A49 | 20s blue ('37) | 30.00 30.00 |
| 176 | A49 | 20s brown violet | 85.00 .50 |
| | | Nos. 171-176 (5) | 150.25 32.25 |

**1922-29**
**Size: 19x22½mm ("Old Die")**
| | | | |
|---|---|---|---|
| 171a | A49 | 4s green | 12.00 3.00 |
| 172a | A49 | 4s orange ('29) | 110.00 11.00 |
| 173 | A49 | 8s rose | 22.50 7.50 |
| 174a | A49 | 8s olive green ('29) | 275.00 90.00 |

| | | | |
|---|---|---|---|
| 175 | A49 | 20s deep blue | 35.00 1.00 |
| 176a | A49 | 20s brown vio ('29) | 110.00 2.25 |
| | | Nos. 171a-176a (6) | 564.50 114.75 |

See Nos. 242, 246, 248.

Mt. Niitaka, Taiwan — A50

**Perf. 12½**
**1923, Apr. 16 Unwmk. Engr.**
| | | | |
|---|---|---|---|
| 177 | A50 | 1½s orange | 12.50 9.50 |
| 178 | A50 | 3s dark violet | 17.50 8.50 |

1st visit of Crown Prince Hirohito to Taiwan. The stamps were sold only in Taiwan, but were valid throughout the empire.

Cherry Blossoms A51

Sun and Dragonflies A52

**Without Gum; Granite Paper**
**1923 Wmk. 142 Litho. Imperf.**
| | | | |
|---|---|---|---|
| 179 | A51 | ½s gray | 4.50 4.25 |
| 180 | A51 | 1½s lt blue | 6.75 2.00 |
| 181 | A51 | 2s red brown | 8.00 2.00 |
| 182 | A51 | 3s brt rose | 3.75 1.25 |
| 183 | A51 | 4s gray green | 40.00 32.50 |
| 184 | A51 | 5s dull violet | 17.50 2.00 |
| 185 | A51 | 8s red orange | 65.00 45.00 |
| 186 | A52 | 10s deep brown | 40.00 2.00 |
| 187 | A52 | 20s deep blue | 60.00 2.50 |
| | | Nos. 179-187 (9) | 245.50 93.50 |

Nos. 179-187 exist rouletted and with various perforations. These were made privately.

Empress Jingo — A53

**Granite Paper**
**Perf. 12, 13x13½**
**1924 Engr. Wmk. 141**
| | | | |
|---|---|---|---|
| 188 | A53 | 5y gray green | 275.00 4.00 |
| 189 | A53 | 10y dull violet | 450.00 3.25 |

See Nos. 253-254.

Cranes
A54

Phoenix
A55

*Perf. 10½ to 13½ and Compound*
**1925, May 10      Litho.      Unwmk.**
190 A54  1½s gray violet        2.25   1.75
191 A55  3s silver & brn org    7.50   3.75
a.    Vert. pair, imperf. btwn.           425.00
192 A54  8s light red          30.00  19.00
193 A55  20s sil & gray grn    67.50  57.50
     *Nos. 190-193 (4)*        107.25 82.00

25th wedding anniv. of the Emperor Yoshihito (Taisho) and Empress Sadako.

Mt. Fuji
A56

Yomei Gate,
Nikko
A57

Nagoya Castle — A58

**Granite Paper**
*Perf. 13½x13*
**1926-37      Typo.      Wmk. 141**
194 A56  2s green       3.25   .25
195 A57  6s carmine    15.00   .60
196 A58  10s dark blue 15.00   .25
197 A58  10s carmine ('37) 12.00 20.00
     *Nos. 194-197 (4)*  45.25  21.10

See Nos. 244, 247. For surcharges see People's Republic of China No. 2L5-2L6.

Baron
Hisoka
Maeshima
A59

Map of World on
Mollweide's
Projection
A60

*Perf. 12½, 13x13½*
**1927, June 20      Unwmk.**
198 A59  1½s lilac          3.75   2.00
199 A59  3s olive green     3.75   2.00
200 A60  6s carmine rose   62.50  55.00
201 A60  10s blue          80.00  55.00
     *Nos. 198-201 (4)*    150.00 114.00

50th anniv. of Japan's joining the UPU. Baron Maeshima (1835-1919) organized Japan's modern postal system and was postmaster general.

Phoenix — A61

Enthronement Hall,
Kyoto — A62

**Yellow Paper**
**1928, Nov. 10      Engr.      Perf. 12½**
202 A61  1½s deep green    1.25   .85
203 A62  3s red violet     1.25   .95
204 A61  6s carmine rose   5.50   3.25
205 A62  10s deep blue     6.00   3.75
     *Nos. 202-205 (4)*   14.00   8.80

Enthronement of Emperor Hirohito.

Great Shrines of
Ise — A63

**1929, Oct. 2                Perf. 12½**
206 A63  1½s gray violet   2.25   1.50
207 A63  3s carmine        2.75   2.10

58th rebuilding of the Ise Shrines.

Map of Japanese
Empire — A64

**1930, Sept. 25              Unwmk.**
208 A64  1½s deep violet   3.50   1.75
209 A64  3s deep red       4.00   2.50

2nd census in the Japanese Empire.

Meiji Shrine — A65

**1930, Nov. 1                Litho.**
210 A65  1½s green         2.75   2.25
211 A65  3s brown org      3.75   2.75

10th anniv. of dedication of Meiji Shrine.

**Coil Stamps**
**Wmk. Zigzag Lines (141)**
**1933      Typo.      Perf. 13 Horiz.**
212 A34  1½s light blue   22.50  22.50
213 A34  3s rose          34.00  34.00

Japanese
Red Cross
Badge
A66

Red Cross
Building,
Tokyo
A67

*Perf. 12½*
**1934, Oct. 1      Engr.      Unwmk.**
214 A66  1½s green & red   2.25   1.90
215 A67  3s dull vio & red 2.50   2.50
216 A66  6s dk car & red  13.50  10.00
217 A67  10s blue & red   16.50   8.00
     *Nos. 214-217 (4)*   34.75  22.40

15th International Red Cross Congress. Sheets of 20 with commemorative marginal inscription. One side of sheet is perf. 13.

White Tower
of Liaoyang
and Warship
"Hiei" — A68

Akasaka
Detached
Palace,
Tokyo — A69

**1935, Apr. 2**
218 A68  1½s olive green   1.75   1.50
219 A69  3s red brown      3.25   1.75
220 A68  6s carmine       11.00   8.00
221 A69  10s blue         14.50  10.00
     *Nos. 218-221 (4)*   30.50  21.25

Visit of Emperor Kang Teh of Manchukuo (Henry Pu-yi) to Tokyo, April 6, 1935. Four sheets of 20 each with commemorative marginal inscription. One side of sheet is perf. 13. Value, set of 4, $900.

Mt. Fuji — A70

**Granite Paper**

**1935      Typo.      Perf. 13x13½**
222 A70  1½s rose carmine  11.50   .75
a.    Miniature sheet of 20   700.00 500.00

Issued to pay postage on New Year's cards from Dec. 1-31, 1935. After Jan. 1, 1936, used for ordinary letter postage. No. 222 was issued in sheets of 100.

Mt. Fuji — A71

Fuji from Lake
Ashi — A72

Fuji from Lake
Kawaguchi
A73

Fuji from
Mishima — A74

**Granite Paper**
**1936, July 10      Photo.      Wmk. 141**
223 A71  1½s red brown    3.75   3.50
224 A72  3s dark green    4.75   4.25
225 A73  6s carmine rose 12.50  11.00
226 A74  10s dark blue   13.50  13.00
     *Nos. 223-226 (4)*  34.50  31.75

Fuji-Hakone National Park.

Dove, Map of
Manchuria
and
Kwantung
A75

Shinto Shrine,
Port Arthur
A76

Headquarters of
Kwantung
Government — A77

**Granite Paper**
**1936, Sept. 1      Litho.      Perf. 12½**
227 A75  1½s gray violet  17.50  17.50
228 A76  3s red brown     21.00  20.00
229 A77  10s dull green  190.00 160.00
     *Nos. 227-229 (3)*  228.50 197.50

30th anniv. of Japanese administration of Kwantung Leased Territory and the South Manchuria Railway Zone.

Imperial Diet
Building — A78

Grand
Staircase — A79

**1936, Nov. 7      Engr.      Perf. 13**
230 A78  1½s green        2.25   2.00
231 A79  3s brown vio     2.75   2.25
232 A79  6s carmine       7.50   6.50
233 A78  10s blue        14.00  10.00
     *Nos. 230-233 (4)*  26.50  20.75

Opening of the new Diet Building, Tokyo.

"Wedded Rocks,"
Futamigaura — A80

**1936, Dec. 10              Photo.**
234 A80  1½s rose carmine  4.00   .40

Issued to pay postage on New Year's greeting cards.

**Types of 1913-26**
*Perf. 13½x13, 13x13½*
**1937      Typo.      Wmk. 257**
239 A34  ½s brown          3.75   2.75
240 A34  1s orange yel     7.00   4.50
241 A34  3s rose           3.25    .55
242 A49  4s green          8.00    .40
243 A35  5s violet        11.00    .40
244 A57  6s crimson       14.50   2.75
245 A35  7s red org       12.50    .40
246 A49  8s olive bister  18.50   2.00
247 A58  10s carmine      12.50    .40
248 A49  20s blue         20.00    .60
249 A35  25s olive grn    80.00   3.75
250 A36  30s org & grn    50.00   1.00
251 A36  50s brn org & dk bl 250.00 2.75
252 A36  1y yel grn & mar 140.00  1.50
     *Nos. 239-252 (14)*  631.00 23.75

**Engr.**
253 A53  5y gray green   400.00 12.50
254 A53  10y dull violet 550.00 10.00

For overprint see People's Republic of China No. 2L6.

**Coil Stamps**
**1938      Typo.      Perf. 13 Horiz.**
255 A34  3s rose           7.50   7.50

New Year's
Decoration — A81

**1937, Dec. 15      Photo.      Perf. 13**
256 A81  2s scarlet        7.00    .50

Issued to pay postage on New Year's cards, later for ordinary use.

Trading
Ship
A82

Harvesting
A83

Gen.
Maresuke
Nogi
A84

Power
Plant
A85

Admiral
Heihachiro
Togo
A86

Mount
Hodaka
A87

Garambi
Lighthouse,
Taiwan
A88

Diamond
Mountains,
Korea
A89

Meiji
Shrine,
Tokyo
A90

Yomei
Gate,
Nikko
A91

Plane and
Map of
Japan
A92

Kasuga
Shrine,
Nara
A93

Mount Fuji
and
Cherry
Blossoms
A94

Horyu
Temple,
Nara
A95

Miyajima
Torii,
Itsukushima
Shrine
A96

Golden
Pavilion,
Kyoto
A97

Great
Buddha,
Kamakura
A98

Kamatari
Fujiwara
A99

Plum Blossoms — A100

## Typographed or Engraved
**1937-45    Wmk. 257    Perf. 13**

| | | | | |
|---|---|---|---|---|
| 257 | A82 | ½s purple | 1.25 | .75 |
| 258 | A83 | 1s fawn | 3.50 | .65 |
| 259 | A84 | 2s crimson | 1.00 | .25 |
| a. | | Booklet pane of 20 | 75.00 | |
| b. | | 2s pink, perf. 12 ('45) | 17.50 | 12.00 |
| c. | | 2s vermilion ('44) | 6.50 | 5.00 |
| 260 | A85 | 3s green ('39) | 1.00 | .30 |
| 261 | A86 | 4s dark green ('39) | 1.75 | .25 |
| a. | | Booklet pane of 20 | 22.50 | |
| 262 | A87 | 5s dark ultra ('39) | 2.25 | .25 |
| 263 | A88 | 6s orange ('39) | 4.75 | 2.00 |
| 264 | A89 | 7s deep green ('39) | 1.25 | .50 |
| 265 | A90 | 8s dk pur & pale vio ('39) | 1.50 | .65 |
| 266 | A91 | 10s lake ('38) | 7.00 | .35 |
| 267 | A92 | 12s indigo ('39) | 1.25 | 1.00 |
| 268 | A93 | 14s rose lake & pale rose ('38) | 1.40 | .50 |
| 269 | A94 | 20s ultra ('40) | 1.75 | .25 |
| 270 | A95 | 25s dk brn & pale brn ('39) | 1.25 | .35 |
| 271 | A96 | 30s pck blue ('39) | 3.25 | .30 |
| a. | | Imperf., pair | 900.00 | |
| 272 | A97 | 50s ol & pale ol ('39) | 1.75 | .30 |
| a. | | Pale olive (forest) omitted | 750.00 | 600.00 |
| 273 | A98 | 1y brn & pale brn ('39) | 6.50 | 1.00 |
| 274 | A99 | 5y dp gray grn ('39) | 35.00 | 3.25 |
| 275 | A100 | 10y dk brn vio ('39) | 32.50 | 2.00 |
| | | Nos. 257-275 (19) | 109.90 | 14.90 |

Nos. 257-261, 265, 268, 270, 272-273 are typographed; the others are engraved.

## Coil Stamps
**1938-39    Typo.    Perf. 13 Horiz.**

| | | | | |
|---|---|---|---|---|
| 276 | A82 | ½s purple ('39) | 7.00 | 7.00 |
| 277 | A84 | 2s crimson | 7.25 | 7.25 |
| 278 | A86 | 4s dark green | 7.75 | 7.75 |
| 279 | A93 | 14s rose lake & pale rose | 150.00 | 125.00 |
| | | Nos. 276-279 (4) | 172.00 | 147.00 |

See Nos. 329, 331, 333, 341, 351, 360 and 361. For surcharges see Nos. B4-B5, Burma 2N4-2N27, China-Taiwan, 8-9, People's Republic of China 2L3, 2L7, 2L9-2L10, 2L39, Korea 55-56. For overprints see Ryukyu Islands (Scott US Specialized catalogue) Nos. 2X1-2X2, 2X4-2X7, 2X10, 2X13-2X14, 2X17, 2X20, 2X23, 2X27, 2X29, 2X33-2X34, 3X2-3X7, 3X10-3X11, 3X14, 3X17, 3X19, 3X21, 3X23, 3X26-3X30, 5X1-5X3, 5X5-5X8, 5X10.

Mount Nantai
A101

Kegon Falls
A102

Sacred Bridge, Nikko — A103

Mount Hiuchi — A104

**Unwmk.**
**1938, Dec. 25    Photo.    Perf. 13**

| | | | | |
|---|---|---|---|---|
| 280 | A101 | 2s brown orange | 1.00 | 1.00 |
| 281 | A102 | 4s olive green | 1.00 | 1.00 |
| 282 | A103 | 10s deep rose | 10.00 | 7.50 |
| 283 | A104 | 20s dark blue | 10.00 | 7.50 |
| a. | | Souvenir sheet of 4, #280-283 | 90.00 | 80.00 |
| | | Never hinged | 140.00 | |
| | | Nos. 280-283 (4) | 22.00 | 17.00 |
| | | Set, never hinged | 40.00 | |

Nikko National Park.
No. 283a sold for 50s.

Many souvenir sheets were sold in folders. Values are for sheets without folders.

Mount Daisen — A106

Yashima Plateau, Inland Sea — A107

Abuto Kwannon Temple — A108

Tomo Bay, Inland Sea — A109

**1939, Apr. 20**

| | | | | |
|---|---|---|---|---|
| 285 | A106 | 2s lt brown | 1.00 | 1.00 |
| 286 | A107 | 4s yellow grn | 3.75 | 2.75 |
| 287 | A108 | 10s dull rose | 8.75 | 8.00 |
| 288 | A109 | 20s blue | 9.00 | 9.00 |
| a. | | Souvenir sheet of 4, #285-288 | 47.50 | 40.00 |
| | | Never hinged | 65.00 | |
| | | Nos. 285-288 (4) | 22.50 | 20.75 |
| | | Set, never hinged | 37.50 | |

Daisen and Inland Sea National Parks.
No. 288a sold for 50s.

View from Kuju Village, Kyushu — A111

Mount Naka — A112

Crater of Mount Naka — A113

Volcanic Cones of Mt. Aso — A114

**1939, Aug. 15**

| | | | | |
|---|---|---|---|---|
| 290 | A111 | 2s olive brown | 1.00 | 1.00 |
| 291 | A112 | 4s yellow green | 3.75 | 3.75 |
| 292 | A113 | 10s carmine | 20.00 | 17.50 |
| 293 | A114 | 20s sapphire | 25.00 | 22.50 |
| a. | | Souvenir sheet of 4, #290-293 | 145.00 | 145.00 |
| | | Never hinged | 210.00 | |
| | | Nos. 290-293 (4) | 49.75 | 44.75 |
| | | Set, never hinged | 95.00 | |

Aso National Park. No. 293a sold for 50s.

Globe
A116

Tsunetami Sano
A117

**1939, Nov. 15    Perf. 12½**
**Cross in Carmine**

| | | | | |
|---|---|---|---|---|
| 295 | A116 | 2s brown | 1.90 | 1.75 |
| 296 | A117 | 4s yellow green | 2.25 | 2.25 |
| 297 | A116 | 10s crimson | 9.00 | 8.50 |
| 298 | A117 | 20s sapphire | 9.00 | 8.50 |
| | | Nos. 295-298 (4) | 22.15 | 21.00 |
| | | Set, never hinged | 37.50 | |

Intl. Red Cross Society founding, 75th anniv.

Sacred Golden Kite
A118

Mount Takachiho
A119

Five Ayu Fish and Sake Jar
A120

Kashiwara Shrine
A121

**1940    Engr.    Perf. 12**

| | | | | |
|---|---|---|---|---|
| 299 | A118 | 2s brown orange | 1.00 | 1.00 |
| 300 | A119 | 4s dark green | .60 | .60 |
| 301 | A120 | 10s dark carmine | 4.50 | 4.50 |
| 302 | A121 | 20s dark ultra | 1.75 | 1.75 |
| | | Nos. 299-302 (4) | 7.85 | 7.85 |
| | | Set, never hinged | 12.50 | |

2,600th anniv. of the legendary date of the founding of Japan.

Mt. Hokuchin, Hokkaido
A122

Mt. Asahi, Hokkaido
A123

Sounkyo Gorge
A124

Tokachi Mountain Range — A125

**1940, Apr. 20    Photo.    Perf. 13**

| | | | | |
|---|---|---|---|---|
| 303 | A122 | 2s brown | 1.00 | 1.00 |
| 304 | A123 | 4s yellow green | 3.00 | 3.00 |
| 305 | A124 | 10s carmine | 10.00 | 10.00 |
| 306 | A125 | 20s sapphire | 12.50 | 12.50 |
| a. | | Souvenir sheet of 4, #303-306 | 185.00 | 175.00 |
| | | Never hinged | 350.00 | |
| | | Nos. 303-306 (4) | 26.50 | 26.50 |
| | | Set, never hinged | 55.00 | |

Daisetsuzan National Park. No. 306a sold for 50s.

Mt. Karakuni, Kyushu — A127

Mt. Takachiho
A128

Torii of Kirishima Shrine — A129

Lake of the Six Kwannon
A130

**1940, Aug. 21**

| | | | | |
|---|---|---|---|---|
| 308 | A127 | 2s brown | 1.00 | 1.00 |
| 309 | A128 | 4s green | 1.25 | 1.25 |
| 310 | A129 | 10s carmine | 10.00 | 10.00 |
| 311 | A130 | 20s deep ultra | 13.00 | 13.00 |
| a. | | Souvenir sheet of 4, #308-311 | 240.00 | 225.00 |
| | | Never hinged | 360.00 | |
| | | Nos. 308-311 (4) | 25.25 | 25.25 |
| | | Set, never hinged | 55.00 | |

Kirishima National Park.
No. 311a sold for 50s.

Education Minister with Rescript on Education
A132

Characters Signifying Loyalty and Filial Piety
A133

**1940, Oct. 25    Engr.    Perf. 12½**

| | | | | |
|---|---|---|---|---|
| 313 | A132 | 2s purple | 1.00 | 1.00 |
| 314 | A133 | 4s green | 1.40 | 1.40 |
| | | Set, never hinged | 4.00 | |

50th anniv. of the imperial rescript on education, given by Emperor Meiji to clarify Japan's educational policy.

Mt. Daiton, Taiwan — A134

Central Peak of
Mt.
Niitaka — A135

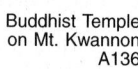

Buddhist Temple
on Mt. Kwannon
A136

View from Mt.
Niitaka — A137

**1941, Mar. 10     Photo.     Perf. 13**

| | | | | |
|---|---|---|---|---|
| 315 | A134 | 2s brown | 1.25 | 1.25 |
| 316 | A135 | 4s brt green | 2.50 | 2.50 |
| 317 | A136 | 10s rose red | 7.00 | 7.00 |
| 318 | A137 | 20s brilliant ultra | 9.00 | 9.00 |
| a. | | Souv. sheet of 4, #315-318 | 125.00 | 125.00 |
| | | Never hinged | 175.00 | |
| | | Nos. 315-318 (4) | 19.75 | 19.75 |
| | | Set, never hinged | 47.50 | |

Daiton and Niitaka-Arisan National Parks.
No. 318a sold with No. 323a in same folder
for 90s.

Seisui
Precipice,
East Taiwan
Coast
A139

Taroko
Gorge
A141

Mt. Tsugitaka
A140

Upper River
Takkiri
District — A142

**1941, Mar. 10**

| | | | | |
|---|---|---|---|---|
| 320 | A139 | 2s brown | 1.25 | 1.25 |
| 321 | A140 | 4s lt green | 2.50 | 2.50 |
| 322 | A141 | 10s rose red | 7.00 | 7.00 |
| 323 | A142 | 20s brt ultra | 9.00 | 9.00 |
| a. | | Souv. sheet of 4, #320-323 | 125.00 | 125.00 |
| | | Never hinged | 175.00 | |
| | | Nos. 320-323 (4) | 19.75 | 19.75 |
| | | Set, never hinged | 42.50 | |

Tsugitaka-Taroko National Park.
See note after No. 318.

War
Factory
Girl
A144

Building of
Wooden
Ship
A145

Hyuga
Monument
and Mt.
Fuji
A146

War
Worker
and
Planes
A147

Palms and
Map of
"Greater
East Asia"
A148

Aviator
Saluting
and
Japanese
Flag
A150

Mt. Fuji
and
Cherry
Blossoms
A152

Garambi Lighthouse,
Taiwan — A154

### Typographed; Engraved

**1942-45     Wmk. 257     Perf. 13**

| | | | | |
|---|---|---|---|---|
| 325 | A144 | 1s org brn ('43) | .50 | .40 |
| 328 | A145 | 2s green | .70 | .70 |
| 329 | A84 | 3s brown ('44) | 1.50 | .70 |
| 330 | A146 | 4s emerald | .45 | .30 |
| 331 | A86 | 5s brown lake | .50 | .40 |
| 332 | A147 | 6s lt ultra ('44) | .75 | .60 |
| a. | | Imperf., pair | | |
| 333 | A86 | 7s org ver ('44) | .50 | .40 |
| 334 | A148 | 10s crim & dl rose | 1.00 | .25 |
| a. | | Dull rose (map) omitted | 475.00 | 475.00 |
| 335 | A149 | 10s lt gray ('45) | 5.25 | 5.25 |
| 336 | A150 | 15s dull blue | 3.50 | 2.00 |
| 337 | A151 | 17s gray vio ('43) | 1.00 | .60 |
| 338 | A152 | 20s blue ('44) | 1.10 | .30 |
| 339 | A151 | 27s rose brn ('45) | 1.00 | 1.00 |
| 340 | A153 | 30s bluish grn ('44) | 3.25 | 2.00 |
| 341 | A88 | 40s dull violet | 2.00 | .30 |
| 342 | A154 | 40s dk violet ('44) | 2.75 | 2.50 |
| | | Nos. 325,328-342 (16) | 25.75 | 17.70 |

Nos. 325-335, 337-340 and 342 are typo.
Nos. 336 and 341 are engr.
Nos. 329, 331, 333-334, 342 issued with
and without gum. No. 335 issued only without
gum. These are valued without gum.
Nos. 328, 342 exist with watermark sideways. No. 328 exists printed on gummed side.
Most stamps of the above series exist in
numerous shades.
For overprints and surcharges see North
Borneo Nos. N34, N37, N41-N42, People's
Republic of China 2L4, 2L8, Korea 57-60,
Ryukyu Islands (US Specialized) Nos. 2X3,
2X9, 2X12, 2X15-2X16, 2X18-2X19, 2X21-
2X22, 2X24-2X26, 2X28, 3X1, 3X8-3X9,
3X12-3X13, 3X15-3X16, 3X18, 3X20, 3X25,
3X31, 4X1-4X2, 5X4.

Kenkoku Shrine,
Hsinking — A155

Boys of
Japan and
Manchukuo
A156

Orchid Crest
of
Manchukuo
A157

"Enemy
Country
Surrender"
A149

Torii of
Yasukuni
Shrine
A151

Torii of
Miyajima
A153

**1942     Unwmk.     Engr.     Perf. 12**

| | | | | |
|---|---|---|---|---|
| 343 | A155 | 2s brown | .85 | .85 |
| 344 | A156 | 5s olive | 1.00 | 1.00 |
| 345 | A155 | 10s red | 1.75 | 1.75 |
| 346 | A157 | 20s dark blue | 3.25 | 5.00 |
| | | Nos. 343-346 (4) | 6.85 | 8.60 |
| | | Set, never hinged | 11.50 | |

The 2s and 10s were issued Mar. 1 for the
10th anniv. of the creation of Manchukuo; 5s
and 20s on Sept. 15 for the 10th anniv. of
Japanese diplomatic recognition of
Manchukuo.

C-59
Locomotive — A158

**1942, Oct. 14     Photo.**

| | | | | |
|---|---|---|---|---|
| 347 | A158 | 5s Prus green | 4.00 | 6.00 |
| | | Never hinged | 9.00 | |

70th anniv. of Japan's 1st railway.

Yasukuni Shrine,
Tokyo — A159

**1944, June 29     Perf. 13**

| | | | | |
|---|---|---|---|---|
| 348 | A159 | 7s Prus green | .85 | .85 |
| | | Never hinged | 2.00 | |

75th anniversary of Yasukuni Shrine.

Kwantung Shrine and
Map of Kwantung
Peninsula — A160

**1944, Oct. 1**

| | | | | |
|---|---|---|---|---|
| 349 | A160 | 3s red brown | 4.00 | 10.00 |
| 350 | A160 | 5s gray violet | 4.50 | 10.00 |
| | | Set, never hinged | 14.00 | |

Dedication of Kwantung Shrine, Port Arthur.

Sun and
Cherry
Blossoms
A161

Sunrise at
Sea and
Plane
A162

Coal
Miners
A163

Yasukuni
Shrine
A164

### Lithographed, Typographed

**1945-47     Wmk. 257     Imperf.**
**Without Gum**

| | | | | |
|---|---|---|---|---|
| 351 | A84 | 2s rose red | .90 | .90 |
| 352 | A161 | 3s rose carmine | .50 | .50 |
| 353 | A162 | 5s green | .60 | .40 |
| a. | | 5s blue | 11.00 | 7.50 |
| 354 | A149 | 10s lt gray | 11.50 | 11.50 |
| 354A | A149 | 10s blue | 29.00 | |
| 355 | A152 | 10s red orange | .60 | .30 |
| 356 | A152 | 20s ultra ('46) | .65 | .35 |
| 357 | A153 | 30s brt blue ('46) | 2.50 | 1.25 |
| 358 | A163 | 50s dk brn ('46) | .75 | .30 |
| a. | | Souvenir sheet of 5 ('47) | 11.00 | 12.50 |
| 359 | A164 | 1y dp ol grn ('46) | 2.00 | 2.00 |
| 360 | A99 | 5y dp gray grn | 7.25 | 1.50 |
| 361 | A100 | 10y dk brown vio | 40.00 | 1.60 |
| | | Nos. 351-361 (12) | 96.25 | |
| | | Nos. 351-354,355-361 (11) | | 20.60 |

Nos. 351 and 354 are typographed. The
other stamps in this set are printed by offset
lithography.
No. 358a was issued with marginal inscriptions to commemorate the Sapporo (Hokkaido) Philatelic Exhibition, Nov., 1947.
Nos. 351 to 361 are on grayish paper, and
Nos. 355 to 361 also exist on white paper.

Most stamps of the above series exist in
numerous shades and with private perforation
or roulette.
Beware of forgeries of Nos. 352, 353, 355-
357 and 360 on unwatermarked paper.
See note after No. 404. For overprints see Ryukyu
Islands (US Specialized) Nos. 2X8, 2X11,
2X30, 3X22, 4X3, 5X9.

Baron
Hisoka
Maeshima
A165

Horyu
Temple
Pagoda
A166

"Thunderstorm
below
Fuji," by
Hokusai
A167

"First
Geese,"
Print by
Hokusai
A168

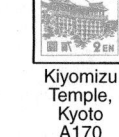

Kintai
Bridge,
Iwakuni
A169

Kiyomizu
Temple,
Kyoto
A170

Goldfish
A171

Noh Mask
A172

Plum Blossoms — A173

### Characters Read Right to Left

**1946-47     Wmk. 257     Litho.     Imperf.**
**Without Gum**

| | | | | |
|---|---|---|---|---|
| 362 | A165 | 15s dark green | .70 | .70 |
| 363 | A166 | 30s dull lilac | 1.50 | .55 |
| 364 | A167 | 1y ultra | 3.00 | .35 |
| a. | | 1y deep ultramarine | 5.00 | .35 |
| b. | | 1y light blue | 2.75 | .35 |
| 365 | A168 | 1.30y olive bister | 4.00 | 1.25 |
| 366 | A169 | 1.50y dark gray | 4.50 | 1.00 |
| 367 | A170 | 2y vermilion ('47) | 3.75 | .40 |
| a. | | Souvenir sheet of 5 ('47) | 35.00 | 55.00 |
| 368 | A171 | 5y lilac rose | 9.50 | 1.25 |
| | | Nos. 362-368 (7) | 26.95 | 5.50 |

**Engr.**

| | | | | |
|---|---|---|---|---|
| 369 | A172 | 50y bister brn | 87.50 | 2.00 |
| 370 | A173 | 100y brn car ('47) | 87.50 | 2.00 |

**Perf. 13**

| | | | | |
|---|---|---|---|---|
| 371 | A172 | 50y bis brn, with gum ('47) | 87.50 | 1.25 |
| 372 | A173 | 100y brn car, with gum ('47) | 87.50 | 1.25 |

**Litho.**
**Perf. 13x13½, 12, 12x12½**

| | | | | |
|---|---|---|---|---|
| 373 | A166 | 30s dull lilac | 4.25 | 3.50 |

**Rouletted in Colored Lines**
**Typo.     Unwmk.**
**With Gum**

| | | | | |
|---|---|---|---|---|
| 374 | A166 | 30s deep lilac | 2.50 | 2.75 |

Nos. 363, 368, 373 exist with and without
gum, valued without gum, as are Nos. 371-
372, 374.
No. 367a for the "Know Your Stamps" exhibition, Kyoto, Aug. 19-24, 1947. Size:
113x71mm
Nos. 362, 369 exist with watermark horizontal. Values, $27.50, $100, respectively.
Beware of Nos. 362-364, 364a, 364b, and 367
and 367 on unwatermarked paper.

See Nos. 384-387, 512A. For overprints see Ryukyu Islands (US Specialized) Nos. 2X32, 3X24, 4X4.

Catalogue values for unused stamps in this section, from this point to the end of the section, are for Never Hinged items.

Medieval Postman's Bell A175

Baron Hisoka Maeshima A176

Design of First Japanese Stamp A177

Communication Symbols A178

**Perf. 12½, 13½x13**

| | | | Engr. | Unwmk. |
|---|---|---|---|---|
| **1946, Dec. 12** | | | | |
| 375 | A175 | 15s orange | 5.50 | 5.00 |
| 376 | A176 | 30s deep green | 7.00 | 6.00 |
| 377 | A177 | 50s carmine | 3.50 | 3.00 |
| 378 | A178 | 1y deep blue | 3.50 | 3.00 |
| a. | | Souvenir sheet of 4, #375-378, imperf. | 200.00 | 200.00 |
| | | Hinged | 125.00 | |
| | | Nos. 375-378 (4) | 19.50 | 17.00 |

Government postal service in Japan, 75th anniv.

No. 378a measures 180-183x125-127mm and is ungummed. There were 2 printings: I — The 4 colors were printed simultaneously. Arched top inscription and other inscriptions in high relief (no more than 2,000 sheets). II — Stamps were printed in one step, sheet inscriptions and 15s orange stamp in another. Lines of top inscription and inscriptions at lower left and lower right (flanking the 1y blue stamp) are much flatter (less raised) than the lines of the green, carmine and blue stamps, almost level with paper's surface (about 49,000 sheets). 1st printing value $800.

Mother and Child, Diet Building A180

Bouquet of Japanese May Flowers A181

**Wmk. 257**

| | | | Litho. | Perf. 12½ |
|---|---|---|---|---|
| **1947, May 3** | | | | |
| | | **Without Gum** | | |
| 380 | A180 | 50s rose brown | .75 | .50 |
| 381 | A181 | 1y brt ultra | 1.25 | 1.00 |
| a. | | Souv. sheet of 2, #380-381, imperf, without gum | 14.00 | 14.00 |
| b. | | As "a," 50s stamp omitted | 800.00 | |
| c. | | As "a," 1y stamp omitted | 800.00 | |

Inauguration of the constitution of May 3, 1947.

A182

**1947, Aug. 15   Photo.   Perf. 12½**

| 382 | A182 | 1.20y brown | 3.00 | 2.25 |
|---|---|---|---|---|
| 383 | A182 | 4y brt ultra | 6.00 | 1.40 |

Reopening of foreign trade on a private basis.

The ornaments on No. 383 differ from those shown in the illustration.

---

**Types of 1946 Redrawn Characters Read Left to Right**

**1947-48   Wmk. 257   Typo.   Perf. 13**

| 384 | A166 | 30s deep lilac | 5.75 | 2.00 |
|---|---|---|---|---|
| 385 | A166 | 1.20y lt olive grn | 2.75 | .50 |
| a. | | Souvenir sheet of 15 | 225.00 | 225.00 |
| 386 | A170 | 2y vermilion | 12.50 | 1.50 |
| | | ('48) | | |
| 387 | A168 | 4y lt ultra | 8.50 | .40 |
| | | Nos. 384-387 (4) | 29.50 | 4.40 |

No. 385a was issued with marginal inscriptions to commemorate the "Know Your Stamps" Exhibition, Tokyo, May, 1947.

On No. 386, the chrysanthemum crest has been eliminated and the top inscription centered.

Plum Blossoms — A183

**1947   Typo.   Imperf.**
**Without Gum**

| 388 | A183 | 10y dk brown vio | 50.00 | 1.75 |
|---|---|---|---|---|

This stamp is similar to type A100 but with new inscription "Nippon Yubin" (Japan Post), reading from left to right. The characters for the denomination are likewise transposed.

A184

A185

Baron Hisoka Maejima A186

Whaling A187

National Art, Imperial Treasure House, Nara — A188

**1947   Typo.   Perf. 13x13½**

| 389 | A184 | 35s green | 1.25 | 1.00 |
|---|---|---|---|---|

**Litho.**

| 390 | A185 | 45s lilac rose | 1.60 | 1.40 |
|---|---|---|---|---|
| a. | | Imperf., pair | 1,500. | |
| b. | | Perf. 11x13½ | 12.00 | 10.00 |
| 391 | A186 | 1y dull brown | 6.50 | 1.00 |

**Typo.**

| 392 | A187 | 5y blue | 11.50 | .30 |
|---|---|---|---|---|
| a. | | Imperf., pair | 650.00 | |
| b. | | Perf. 11x13½ | 32.50 | 4.75 |

**Engr.**
**Perf. 13½x13**

| 393 | A188 | 10y lilac | 15.00 | .25 |
|---|---|---|---|---|
| a. | | Imperf., pair | | 3,000. |
| | | Nos. 389-393 (5) | 35.85 | 3.95 |

No. 389 was produced on both rotary and flat press. Sheets of the rotary press printing have a border. Those of the flat press printing have none.

Lily of the Valley — A188a

**1947, Sept. 13   Unwmk.   Perf. 12½**

| 394 | A188a | 2y dk Prus green | 6.00 | 3.25 |
|---|---|---|---|---|

Relief of Ex-convicts Day, Sept. 13, 1947.

**Souvenir Sheet**

A189

---

**1947   Wmk. 257   Litho.   Imperf.**
**Without Gum**

| 395 | A189 | Sheet of 5, ultra | 4.75 | 4.75 |
|---|---|---|---|---|

Stamp Hobby Week, Nov. 1-7, 1947. Sheet size: 113½x71½mm, on white or grayish paper.

For overprint, see No. 408.

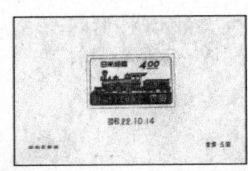

"Benkei," 1880 Locomotive — A190

**1947, Oct. 14   Unwmk.   Engr.**
**Without Gum**

| 396 | A190 | 4y deep ultra | 20.00 | 20.00 |
|---|---|---|---|---|

75th anniv. of railway service in Japan.

Hurdling A191

Diving A192

Discus Throwing A193

Volleyball A194

**1947, Oct. 25   Photo.   Perf. 12½**

| 397 | A191 | 1.20y red violet | 8.50 | 7.50 |
|---|---|---|---|---|
| 398 | A192 | 1.20y red violet | 8.50 | 7.50 |
| 399 | A193 | 1.20y red violet | 8.50 | 7.50 |
| 400 | A194 | 1.20y red violet | 8.50 | 7.50 |
| a. | | Block of 4, #397-400 | 50.00 | 50.00 |

2nd Natl. Athletic Meet, held in Kanazawa, Oct. 30-Nov. 3.

**Souvenir Sheets**

A195

**1948   Wmk. 257   Litho.   Imperf.**
**Without Gum**

| 401 | A195 | Sheet of 2, As #368, rose carmine | 17.50 | 17.50 |
|---|---|---|---|---|

**Same, Inscribed with Three instead of Two Japanese Characters at Bottom Center**

| 402 | A195 | Sheet of 2, #368 | 20.00 | 20.00 |
|---|---|---|---|---|

Philatelic exhibitions at Osaka (No. 401) and Nagoya (No. 402).

For Nos. 401-402 overprinted in green, see Nos. 407, 407b.

Stylized Tree — A196

**Perf. 12½**

**1948, Apr. 1   Unwmk.   Photo.**

| 403 | A196 | 1.20y dp yellow grn | 1.40 | 1.25 |
|---|---|---|---|---|

Forestation movement. Sheets of 30, marginal inscription.

---

**Coal Miners Type of 1946 and**

National Art Treasure, Nara — A197

**Perf. 13x13½**

**1948   Wmk. 257   Litho.**

| 404 | A163 | 50s dark brown | 1.60 | 1.25 |
|---|---|---|---|---|

**Typo.**
**Perf. 13x13½**

| 405 | A197 | 10y rose violet | 15.00 | .30 |
|---|---|---|---|---|
| a. | | Imperf., pair | | |

See No. 515A.

School Children — A198

**Perf. 12½**

**1948, May 3   Unwmk.   Photo.**

| 406 | A198 | 1.20y dark carmine | 1.40 | 1.25 |
|---|---|---|---|---|

Reorganization of Japan's educational system. Sheets of 30, marginal inscription.

**No. 402 Overprinted at Top, Bottom and Sides with Japanese Characters and Flowers in Green**

**1948, Apr. 3   Souvenir Sheets**

| 407 | A195 | Sheet of 2 | 75.00 | 40.00 |
|---|---|---|---|---|
| a. | | Overprint inverted | 150.00 | 150.00 |
| b. | | Overprint on No. 401 | 125.00 | 125.00 |

Mishima Philatelic Exhibition, Apr. 3-9.

**No. 395 Overprinted at Top and Bottom With Japanese Characters in Plum**

**1948, Apr. 18**

| 408 | A189 | Sheet of 5, ultra | 27.50 | 27.50 |
|---|---|---|---|---|

Centenary of the death of Katsushika Hokusai, painter.

Sampans on Inland Sea, Near Suma — A199

**Engr. & Litho.**

**1948, Apr. 22   Unwmk.   Imperf.**
**Without Gum**

| 409 | A199 | Sheet of 2, grn & rose car | 16.00 | 11.00 |
|---|---|---|---|---|

Communications Exhib., Tokyo, Apr. 27-May 3, 1948. Sheet contains two 2y deep carmine stamps.

Sheet exists with green border omitted.

**1948, May 20   Without Gum**

| 410 | A199 | Sheet of 2, ultra & rose car | 20.00 | 18.00 |
|---|---|---|---|---|

Aomori Newspaper and Stamp Exhibition. Border design of apples and apple blossoms.

**Type A199 With Altered Border and Inscriptions**

**1948, May 23   Without Gum**

| 411 | A199 | Sheet of 2, blue & rose car | 20.00 | 18.00 |
|---|---|---|---|---|

Fukushima Stamp Exhibition. Border design of cherries and crossed lines.

Horse Race — A200

**1948, June 6   Photo.   Perf. 12½**

| 412 | A200 | 5y brown | 3.50 | 1.75 |
|---|---|---|---|---|

25th anniv. of the enforcement of Japan's horse racing laws. Each sheet contains 30 stamps and 2 labels, with marginal inscription.

Stamps with labels are worth more than values listed.

A201

A202

**Wmk. 257**
**1948, Sept. 10    Litho.    Perf. 13**
413  A201  1.50y blue                4.00    .80
414  A202  3.80y lt brown           11.50   5.25

**Souvenir Sheet**
**Without Gum**
*Imperf*
415           Sheet of 4      35.00  35.00

Kumamoto Stamp Exhibition, Sept. 20. Souvenir sheet, issued Sept. 20, contains two each of 1.50y deep blue (A201) and 3.80y brown (A202).

Rectifying Tower — A203

**Perf. 12½**
**1948, Sept. 14    Photo.    Unwmk.**
416  A203  5y dark olive bister       4.50  2.75

Government alcohol monopoly.

Swimmer          Runner
A204             A205

Designs: No. 419, High jumper. No. 420, Baseball players. No. 421, Bicycle racers.

**1948**
417  A204  5y blue                    4.50  1.25
418  A205  5y green                  11.00  5.50
419  A205  5y green                  11.00  5.50
420  A205  5y green                  11.00  5.50
421  A205  5y green                  11.00  5.50
  a.    Block of 4, #418-421          60.00  60.00
        Nos. 417-421 (5)              48.50  23.25

3rd Natl. Athletic Meet. Swimming matches held at Yawata, Sept. 16-19, field events, Fukuoka, Oct. 29-Nov. 3.
No. 417 was issued in sheets of 50 with labels. Stamps with labels, value, $13.

"Beauty Looking Back,"
Print by
Moronobu — A206

**1948, Nov. 29                Perf. 13**
422  A206  5y brown                   25.00  40.00
  a.    Sheet of 5                    350.00 300.00
        Sheet, hinged                 250.00   —

Philatelic Week, Nov. 29-Dec. 5.
See Nos. 2418-2419.

**Souvenir Sheets**

**1948, Dec. 3   Without Gum   Imperf.**
423  A206  5y brown, sheet of 1      45.00  40.00

Kanazawa and Takaoka stamp exhibitions.

Child Playing Hane-
tsuki — A207

**1948, Dec. 13    Litho.    Perf. 13**
424  A207  2y scarlet                  6.00  5.00

Issued to pay postage on New Year's cards, later for ordinary use.

Farm
Woman
A208

Whaling
A209

Miner
A210

Tea
Picking
A211

Girl
Printer
A212

Factory
Girl with
Cotton
Bobbin
A213

Mt. Hodaka
A214

Planting
A215

Postman
A216

Blast
Furnace
A217

Locomotive
Assembly — A218

**Typographed, Engraved**
**1948-49    Wmk. 257    Perf. 13x13½**
425  A208   2y green                   3.50    .25
  a.    Overprinted with 4 charac-
        ters in frame                  1.40   1.00
  b.    As "a," overprint inverted   125.00
426  A209   3y lt grnsh bl
            ('49)                      7.50    .30
427  A210   5y olive bis             22.50   1.50
  a.    Booklet pane of 20          475.00  15.00
        Hinged                      175.00
428  A211   5y blue grn
            ('49)                    60.00   9.50
429  A212   6y red org ('49)         12.50    .25
430  A210   8y brn org ('49)         14.00    .25
  a.    Booklet pane of 20          325.00  10.00
        Hinged                      175.00
431  A213  15y blue                   4.50    .25
432  A214  16y ultra ('49)           15.00   7.00
433  A215  20y dk grn ('49)          52.50    .25
434  A216  30y violet bl ('49)       62.50    .25
435  A217 100y car lake
            ('49)                   600.00   4.50
436  A218 500y dp blue ('49)        550.00   7.00
        Nos. 425-436 (12)         1,405.   31.30
        Set, hinged                 550.00

No. 425a has a red control overprint of four characters ("Senkyo Jimu," or "Election Business") arranged vertically in a rectangular frame. Each candidate received 1,000 copies.
Nos. 432, 435-436 are engraved.
See Nos. 442, 511-512, 514-515, 518, 520, 521A-521B.

**Souvenir Sheets**

**Typo. and Litho.**
**1948, Oct. 16            Imperf.**
437  A213  15y blue, sheet of 1   50.00  45.00

Nagano Stamp Exhibition, Oct. 16.

**1948, Nov. 2              Imperf.**
438  A210   5y ol bis, sheet of 2  60.00  45.00

Shikoku Traveling Stamp Exhib., Nov. 1948.

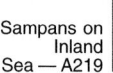
Sampans on
Inland
Sea — A219

**Perf. 13x13½**
**1949    Wmk. 257          Engr.**
439  A219  10y rose lake            30.00  20.00
440  A219  10y car rose             22.50  17.50
441  A219  10y orange ver           45.00  25.00
442  A214  16y brt blue             11.00   6.25
        Nos. 439-442 (4)           108.50  68.75
        Set, hinged                 60.00

Issued in sheets of 20 stamps with marginal inscription publicizing expositions at Takamatsu (No. 439), Okayama (No. 440) and Matsuyama (No. 441), Nagano Peace Exposition, Apr. 1-May 31, 1949 (No. 442).

Ice Skater
A221

Ski Jumper
A222

**1949    Unwmk.    Photo.    Perf. 12**
444  A221   5y violet                3.25  2.25
445  A222   5y ultra                 4.00  2.25

Winter events of the 4th Natl. Athletic Meet: skating at Suwa Jan. 27-30, skiing at Sapporo Mar. 3-6. Issued: No. 444, 1/27; No. 445, 3/3.

Steamer in Beppu
Bay — A223

**1949, Mar. 10    Engr.    Perf. 13x13½**
446  A223   2y carmine & ultra       1.50  1.25
447  A223   5y green & ultra         5.75  1.75

Scene at Fair — A224

**1949, Mar. 15    Photo.    Imperf.**
448  A224   5y brt rose              2.50  1.75
  a.    Perf. 13                     4.00   2.50
  b.    Sheet of 20, imperf.        65.00  45.00

Issued to publicize the Japan Foreign Trade Fair, Yokohama, 1949.
No. 448a was printed in sheets of 50 (10x5); No. 448 in sheets of 20 (4x5) with marginal inscriptions (No. 448b).

Stylized Trees — A225

**1949, Apr. 1    Unwmk.    Perf. 12**
449  A225   5y bright green         12.00  2.50

Issued to publicize the forestation movement.

Lion
Rock — A226

**Souvenir Sheets**

Daiho-zan (Mt.
Ohmine)
A227

Doro
Gorge — A228

Bridge Pier
Rocks — A229

**1949, Apr. 10    Photo.    Perf. 13**
450  A226   2y brown                 1.50  1.00
451  A227   5y yellow grn            5.00  1.75
452  A228  10y scarlet              22.00 14.00
453  A229  16y blue                 10.00  8.50
  a.    Souv. sheet of 4, #450-453,
        no gum                      50.00 37.50
  b.    As "a," 10y stamp omitted
        Nos. 450-453 (4)            38.50 25.25

Yoshino-Kumano National Park.
No. 453a sold for 40y.

Boy — A230

**1949, May 5              Perf. 12**
455  A230   5y rose brn & org       7.50  2.57
  a.    Orange omitted            275.00

Children's Day, May 5, 1949.

**Souvenir Sheets**
**1949, May 5              Imperf.**
456  A230   5y rose brn & org,
            sheet of 10           450.00 300.00
        Hinged                    275.00

Children's Exhib., Inuyama, Apr. 1-May 31.

Radio
Tower
and Star
A231

**1949, May 11             Perf. 13**
457  A231  20y dp blue            140.00 120.00
        Hinged                     75.00

Electrical Communication Week, May 11-18.

Symbols of
Communication — A232

**Wmk. 257**
**1949, June 1    Engr.    Perf. 12**
458  A232   8y brt ultra             4.50  2.25

Establishment of the Post Ministry and the Ministry of Electricity and Communication.

Central Meteorological Observatory, Tokyo — A233

**1949, June 1   Unwmk.   Perf. 12½**
459 A233 8y deep green          4.50  2.25
  75th anniv. of the establishment of the Central Meteorological Observatory.

Mt. Fuji in Autumn — A234

Lake Kawaguchi A235

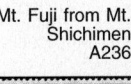

Mt. Fuji from Mt. Shichimen A236

Shinobuno Village and Mt. Fuji — A237

**1949, July 15   Photo.   Perf. 13**
460 A234  2y yellow brown     4.50  1.00
461 A235  8y yellow green     5.00  1.75
462 A236 14y carmine lake     2.50   .75
463 A237 24y blue             9.00  1.00
  a.  Souv. sheet of 4, #460-463  47.50 47.50
    Nos. 460-463 (4)          21.00  4.50
  Fuji-Hakone National Park.
  No. 463a sold for 55y.

Allegory of Peace A238

Doves over Nagasaki A239

**Perf. 13x13½, 13½x13**
**1949   Photo.   Unwmk.**
465 A238 8y yellow brown     11.00  3.00
466 A239 8y green             6.50  3.00
  Establishment of Hiroshima as the City of Eternal Peace and of Nagasaki as the International City of Culture. Issued: No. 465, 8/6; No. 466, 8/9.

Boy Scout — A240

**1949, Sept. 22   Perf. 13x13½**
467 A240 8y brown             9.00  3.00
  Natl. Boy Scout Jamboree.

Pen Nib of Newspaper Stereotype Matrix — A241

**1949, Oct. 1   Perf. 13½x13**
468 A241 8y deep blue         7.00  3.00
  Natl. Newspaper Week.

Racing Swimmer Poised for Dive A242

Javelin Thrower A243

**1949   Perf. 13½**
469 A242 8y dull blue         6.00  2.25
  **Perf. 12**
470 A243 8y shown             8.00  3.00
471 A243 8y Yacht Racing      8.00  3.00
472 A243 8y Relay Race        8.00  3.00
473 A243 8y Tennis            8.00  3.00
  a.  Block of 4, #470-473    40.00 55.00
    Nos. 469-473 (5)          38.00 14.25
  4th Natl. Athletic Meet. The swimming matches were held at Yokohama, Sept. 15-18 and the fall events at Tokyo, Oct. 30. Issued: No. 469, 9/15; Nos. 470-473, 10/30. Nos. 470-473 exist perf 12½. Values 50 percent above those of perf 12 copies. No. 469 was issued in sheets with labels. Value, stamp with label, $22.50.

Map and Envelopes Forming "75" — A244

Symbols of UPU — A245

**1949, Oct. 10   Engr.   Perf. 12, 13½**
474 A244  2y dull green       4.00  2.25
475 A245  8y maroon           5.00  2.25
  a.  Souv. sheet of 2, #474-475, imperf.  7.00  7.00
476 A244 14y carmine         13.00  9.00
477 A245 24y aqua            19.00 11.00
  a.  Imperf., pair
    Nos. 474-477 (4)          41.00 24.50
  75th anniv. of the UPU.
  No 475a was issued without gum.

Floating Zenith Telescope — A246

**1949, Oct. 30   Photo.   Perf. 12**
478 A246 8y dk blue grn       5.50  2.25
  50th anniv. of the Mizusawa Latitudinal Observatory.

"Moon and Geese," Print by Hiroshige — A247

**1949, Nov. 1   Perf. 13x13½**
479 A247 8y purple          150.00 55.00
  a.  Sheet of 5            800.00 450.00
    Sheet, hinged           240.00
  Postal Week, Nov. 1-7. See Nos. 2420-2421.

Dr. Hideyo Noguchi A248

Yukichi Fukuzawa A249

**1949-52   Unwmk.   Engr.   Perf. 12½**
480 A248  8y green            10.00  1.25
  a.  Imperf., pair
481 A249  8y deep olive ('50)  5.00  1.25
  a.  Imperf., pair
482 A250  8y dk Prus grn ('50)  5.00  1.25
483 A251  8y Prus grn ('50)    4.50  1.25
  a.  Imperf., pair
484 A252  8y dk violet ('50)  12.00  4.00
485 A253  8y vio brn ('50)     4.00  1.25
486 A254  8y dk green ('50)   11.00  3.00
487 A255  8y dp purple ('51)  11.00  3.00
488 A256  8y carmine ('51)    17.50  3.00
489 A257  8y vio brn ('51)    30.00  4.00
490 A258  8y choc ('51)       17.50  4.00
491 A259  8y dk blue ('51)    14.00  4.00
492 A260 10y dk green ('52)   16.00  5.00
493 A261 10y brn vio ('52)    12.50  2.00
494 A262 10y carmine ('52)     4.00  2.00
495 A263 10y dk grn ('52)      5.50  2.00

Soseki Natsume A250

Danjuro Ichikawa A252

Hogai Kano A254

Ichiyo Higuchi A256

Shiki Masaoka A258

Amane Nishi A260

Hisashi Kimura A262

Torahiko Terada A264

Shoyo Tsubouchi A251

Joseph Hardy Niijima A253

Kanzo Uchimura A255

Ogai Mori A257

Shunso Hishida A259

Kenjiro Ume A261

Inazo Nitobe A263

Tenshin Okakura A265

496 A264 10y choc ('52)        5.00  2.00
497 A265 10y dk blue ('52)     5.50  2.00
    Nos. 480-497 (18)        239.00 46.25
    Set, hinged              100.00

Tiger — A266

**1950, Feb. 1   Photo.   Perf. 12**
498 A266 2y dark red          11.00  3.00
  New Year, 1950. 6th prize (lottery), sheet of 5, value $225.

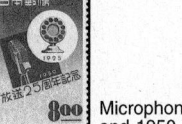

Microphones of 1925 and 1950 — A267

**1950, Mar. 21   Perf. 13**
499 A267 8y ultra             6.00  2.50
  25th anniversary of broadcasting in Japan. Sheets of 20 with marginal inscription.

Dove and Olive Twig on Letter Box — A268

**1950, Apr. 20   Perf. 12**
500 A268 8y dp yellow grn     5.00  2.50
  Day of Posts, Apr. 20.

Lake Akan and Mt. Akan — A269

Lake Kutcharo, Hokkaido A270

Mt. Akan-Fuji A271

Lake Mashu — A272

**1950, July 15   Unwmk.   Perf. 13**
501 A269  2y yellow brn       2.50  1.25
502 A270  8y dp yellow grn    3.50  1.75
503 A271 14y rose car        16.00  7.00
504 A272 24y brt blue        18.00  7.75
  a.  Souv. sheet of 4, #501-504  55.00 40.00
    Nos. 501-504 (4)          40.00 17.75
  Akan National Park.
  No. 504a sold for 55y.

Gymnast on Rings — A273

  Designs: No. 506, Pole vault. No. 507, Soccer. No. 508, Equestrian.

**1950, Oct. 28   Perf. 13½x13**
505 A273 8y rose brown       40.00 17.50
506 A273 8y rose brown       40.00 17.50
507 A273 8y rose brown       40.00 17.50

**508** A273 8y rose brown    40.00   17.50
  *a.*   Strip of 4, #505-508   175.00   *140.00*
  *b.*   Block of 4, #505-508   190.00   *150.00*
      As "b," hinged   85.00

5th National Athletic Meet. Sheets of 20 stamps in which each horizontal row contains all four designs. Value, sheet $850.

### Types of 1947-49 and

Ishiyama-dera Pagoda A274

Hisoka Maeshima A275

Long-tailed Cock of Tosa A276

Goddess Kannon A277

Himeji Castle A278

Nyoirin Kannon of Chuguji A280

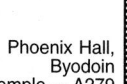
Phoenix Hall, Byodoin Temple — A279

*Perf. 13x13½, 13½x13 (14y)*

**1950-52**   Typo.   Unwmk.
**509** A274 80s carmine ('51)   2.75   2.25
  *a.*   Sheet of 1   11.00   *13.00*

Photo.
**510** A275 1y dk brn ('51)   5.00   1.00
  *a.*   Souvenir sheet of 4   22.50   17.50

Typo.
**511** A208 2y green ('51)   2.50   .25
**512** A209 3y lt grnsh bl ('51)   67.50   2.25
**512A** A168 4y lt ultra ('52)   45.00   4.00
**513** A276 5y dp grn & org brn ('51)   7.50   .25
  *a.*   Orange brown omitted   425.00
**514** A212 6y red org ('51)   9.00   .75
**515** A210 8y dk org brn ('51)   45.00   1.00
**515A** A197 10y rose vio ('51)   77.50   6.50
**516** A277 10y red brn & lil ('51)   27.50   .25

Engr.
**517** A278 14y brn & car ('51)   65.00   42.50
  *a.*   Sheet of 1   80.00   75.00

Typo.
**518** A215 20y dk green ('51)   70.00   2.50

Engr.
**519** A279 24y dp ultra   52.50   22.50
  *a.*   Sheet of 1   65.00   45.00

Typo.
**520** A216 30y vio brn ('52)   225.00   3.00

Photo.
**521** A280 50y dk brn ('51)   175.00   2.50
      Hinged   85.00
  *c.*   Sheet of 1   375.00   375.00
      Hinged   175.00

Engr.
**521A** A217 100y car lake ('52)   500.00   3.25
**521B** A218 500y dp blue ('52)   450.00   3.75
      *Nos. 509-521B (17)*   1,827.   98.50

No. 510a for the 80th anniv. of Japan's postal service. On No. 512A, characters read from left to right.
Compare designs: A274 with A314c; A275 with A314a, A447, A563a, A5174; A277 with

A332a; A278 with A373a; A279 with A385a; A280 with A314b and A565f.

Girl and Rabbit — A281

**1951, Jan. 1**   Photo.   *Perf. 12*
**522** A281 2y rose pink   8.00   1.25
New Year Greetings 1951. 9th prize (lottery), sheet of 5, value $50.
See No. 2655a.

### Scenic Spots Issue

Skiers on Mt. Zao A282   A283

**1951, Feb. 15**   *Perf. 13*
**523** A282 8y olive   15.00   2.50
**524** A283 24y blue   17.00   6.00

Tea Picking A284   Mt. Fuji Seen from Nihon Plateau A285

Nihon-daira Plateau.

**1951, Apr. 2**
**525** A284 8y olive green   12.00   2.75
**526** A285 24y bright blue   90.00   25.00

Hot Springs, Hakone A286   Lake Ashi, Hakone A287

**1951, May 25**
**527** A286 8y chestnut brown   10.00   2.50
**528** A287 24y deep blue   8.00   3.50

Senju Waterfall A288   Ninai Waterfall A289

Akame 48 Waterfalls.

**1951, June 1**
**529** A288 8y deep green   12.50   2.75
**530** A289 24y deep blue   12.50   4.00

Pavilion, Wakanoura Bay — A290   Wakanoura Bay — A291

Wakanoura & Tomogashima.

**1951, June 25**
**531** A290 8y brown   9.00   2.75
**532** A291 24y brt blue   9.00   4.00

Uji River A292   View from Uji Bridge A293

*Perf. 13x13½, 13½x13*   Engr.
**1951, Aug. 1**
**533** A292 8y brown   8.50   2.75
**534** A293 24y deep blue   8.00   3.50

 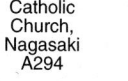
Oura Catholic Church, Nagasaki A294   Sofuku Temple A295

**1951, Sept. 15**   Photo.   *Perf. 13½*
**535** A294 8y carmine rose   11.00   2.75
**536** A295 24y dull blue   10.00   3.50

Marunuma A296   Sugenuma A297

**1951, Oct. 1**
**537** A296 8y rose violet   12.50   2.75
  *a.*   Imperf., pair
**538** A297 24y dull blue grn   7.50   4.00

Kakuenpo (peak) A298   Nagatoro Bridge A299

Shosenkyo Gorge.

**1951, Oct. 15**
**539** A298 8y brown red   11.00   2.75
**540** A299 24y dp Prus grn   12.00   4.00
      *Nos. 523-540 (18)*   275.50   81.75

Boy's Head and Seedling — A300

**1951, May 5**   *Perf. 13½*
**541** A300 8y orange brown   22.50   3.00
Issued to publicize Children's Day, May 5, 1951.

Oirase River — A301

Lake Towada — A302

View from Kankodai A303

Mt. Hakkoda from Mt. Yokodake A304

**1951, July 20**   Photo.   *Perf. 13x13½*
**542** A301 2y brown   2.50   .95
**543** A302 8y green   10.00   1.40
**544** A303 14y dark red   11.50   4.75
**545** A304 24y blue   12.00   5.50
  *a.*   Souv. sheet of 4, #542-545   45.00   45.00
      *Nos. 542-545 (4)*   36.00   12.60
Towada Natl. Park. No. 545a sold for 55y.

Chrysanthemum A305   National Flag A306

**1951, Sept. 9**   *Perf. 13½*
**546** A305 2y orange brown   2.25   1.10
**547** A306 8y slate blue & red   6.75   2.75
**548** A305 24y blue green   20.00   7.00
      *Nos. 546-548 (3)*   29.00   10.85
Signing of the peace treaty of 1951.

Putting the Shot A307   Hockey A308

**1951, Oct. 27**
**549** A307 2y orange brown   3.50   1.75
**550** A308 2y gray blue   3.50   1.75
  *a.*   Pair, #549-550   10.00   8.00
6th Natl. Athletic Meet, Hiroshima, 10/27-31.

Okina Mask — A309

**1952, Jan. 16**   Photo.   *Perf. 13½x13*
**551** A309 5y crimson rose   14.00   1.25
New Year Greetings 1952
Sheets reproducing four of these stamps with Japanese inscriptions and floral ornament at left were awarded as sixth prize in the national lottery. Value $150.

Southern Cross from Ship A310   Earth and Big Dipper A311

**1952, Feb. 19**
**552** A310 5y purple   6.00   1.25
**553** A311 10y dark green   17.50   3.00
75th anniv. of Japan's admission to the UPU.

Red Cross and Lilies
A312

Red Cross Nurse
A313

**1952, May 1**
554 A312 5y rose red & dk red 4.25 .95
555 A313 10y dk green & red 10.00 2.00
  *a.* Red cross omitted *500.00*
  *b.* Imperf., pair *75.00*

75th anniv. of the formation of the Japanese Red Cross Society.

Goldfish — A314

A314a

A314b

A314c

**1952**      *Perf. 13x13½*
556 A314 35y red orange 10.00 .25
  *a.* Imperf., pair

**Types of 1951**
**Redrawn; Zeros Omitted**
**Unwmk.**
557 A314a 1y dark brown .55 .25
558 A314b 50y org brn 5.00 .25
**Typo.**
559 A314c 4y dp cl & pale rose 1.50 .25
  *a.* Background (pale rose) omitted

Ornamental frame and background added, denomination at upper left, Japanese characters at upper right.

Japanese Serow — A315

**Photo.**
560 A315 8y brown .30 .25
  *Nos. 556-560 (5)* 17.35 1.25

Mt. Yari
A316

Kurobe Valley
A317

Mt. Shirouma
A318

Mt. Norikura — A319

**1952, July 5**    *Perf. 13½x13, 13x13½*
561 A316 5y red brn 6.00 1.00
562 A317 10y blue green 27.50 3.50
563 A318 14y bright red 7.50 7.00

---

564 A319 24y bright blue 12.50 7.00
  *a.* Souv. sheet of 4, #561-564, imperf. 100.00 75.00
  *Nos. 561-564 (4)* 53.50 18.50

Japan Alps (Chubu-Sangaku) National Park. No. 564a sold for 60y.

Yasuda Hall, Tokyo University — A320

**1952, Oct. 1**   **Engr.**    *Perf. 13*
565 A320 10y green 18.00 2.50

75th anniversary of the founding of Tokyo University.

Yomei Gate, Nikko — A321

**1952, Oct. 15**   **Photo.**   *Perf. 13x13½*
566 A321 45y blue 4.50 .25

Mountain Climber — A322

**1952, Oct. 18**    **Dated "1952"**
567 A322 5y shown 7.50 2.00
568 A322 5y Wrestlers 7.50 2.00
  *a.* Pair, #567-568 17.50 9.00

7th Nat.l Athletic Meet, Fukushima, 10/18-22.

Mt. Azuma — A323

Mt. Asahi — A324

Mt. Bandai — A325

Mt. Gatsun — A326

**Unwmk.**
**1952, Oct. 18**   **Photo.**    *Perf. 13*
569 A323 5y org brn 3.75 .60
570 A324 10y olive grn 11.50 1.50
571 A325 14y rose red 4.50 2.25
572 A326 24y Prus blue 10.00 4.00
  *a.* Souv. sheet of 4, #569-572, imperf. 80.00 60.00
  *Nos. 569-572 (4)* 29.75 8.35

Bandai-Asahi National Park. No. 572a sold for 60y.

Kirin A327

Flag of Crown Prince A328

**Engr. and Photo.**
**1952, Nov. 10**      *Perf. 13½*
573 A327 5y red org & pur 2.25 1.00
574 A327 10y red org & dk grn 2.50 1.50

---

575 A328 24y deep blue 16.00 8.00
  *a.* Souv. sheet of 3, #573-575, imperf. 80.00 90.00
  *Nos. 573-575 (3)* 20.75 10.50

Issued to commemorate the nomination of Crown Prince Akihito as Heir Apparent.

No. 575a measures 130x129mm, and has a background design of phoenix and clouds in violet brown and blue. Sold for 50y.

Sambaso Doll — A329

     *Perf. 13½x13*
**1953, Jan, 1**   **Photo.**   **Unwmk.**
576 A329 5y carmine 9.50 1.00

For postage on New Year's cards, later for ordinary use.
Sheets of 4 were awarded as 6th prize in the natl. lottery. Value $100.

First Electric Lamp in Japan — A330

**1953, Mar. 25**
577 A330 10y brown 8.00 2.25

75th anniv. of electric lighting in Japan.

"Kintai Bridge," Print by Hiroshige — A331

Kintai Bridge as Rebuilt in 1953 — A332

**1953, May 3**      *Perf. 13*
578 A331 10y chestnut 8.00 2.50
579 A332 24y blue 8.00 4.00

**Kannon Type of 1951**
**Redrawn; Zeros Omitted**

A332a

**1953-54**      **Typo.**
580 A332a 10y red brn & lil 4.00 .25
  *a.* Booklet pane 10 + 2 labels (souvenir) ('54) 150.00 140.00
  *b.* Bklt. pane 10 + 2 labels ('54) 67.50 60.00

No. 580a was issued in honor of Philatelic Week 1954. The inscriptions on the two labels are arranged in two columns of boldface characters.
On No. 580b, the left-hand label inscriptions are arranged in three columns of mixed heavy and thin characters.
See Nos. 611a-611b and 672.

Lake Shikotsu, Hokkaido A333

Mt. Yotei — A334

**1953, July 25**   **Photo.**    *Perf. 13*
581 A333 5y ultra 2.00 .55
582 A334 10y deep green 5.00 1.10
  *a.* Souv. sheet of 2, #581-582, imperf., no gum 45.00 35.00

Shikotsu-Toya National Park. No. 582a sold for 20 yen.

---

Akita Dog A335

Cormorant Fishing A336

**1953**      **Unwmk.**
583 A335 2y gray .30 .25
**Engr.**
584 A336 100y dark red 35.00 .25
  *a.* Imperf., pair *2,750.*
  See No. 1622.

Futamigaura Beach — A337

Namikiri Coast — A338

**1953, Oct. 2**      **Photo.**
585 A337 5y red 2.50 .75
586 A338 10y blue 6.00 1.50
  *a.* Souv. sheet of 2, #585-586, imperf., no gum 25.00 20.00

Ise-Shima National Park.

Phoenix — A339

Design: 10y, Japanese crane in flight.

**1953, Oct. 12**   **Engr.**   *Perf. 12½*
587 A339 5y brown carmine 3.50 1.50
**Photo.**
588 A339 10y dark blue 7.50 2.50

Nos. 587-588 were issued on the occasion of the return of Crown Prince Akihito from his visit to Europe and America. Issued in sheets of 20 with marginal inscription.

Rugby Match — A340

Judo — A341

**1953, Oct. 22**      *Perf. 13½*
589 A340 5y black 5.75 1.25
590 A341 5y blue green 5.75 1.25
  *a.* Pair, #589-590 13.50 7.50

8th Natl. Athletic Meet, Matsuyama, Oct. 22-26.

Sky and Top of Observatory — A342

**1953, Oct. 29**
591 A342 10y dk gray blue 12.00 2.50

75th anniversary of the Tokyo Astronomical Observatory.

Mt. Unzen from Golf Course — A343

Mt. Unzen from Chijiwa Beach — A344

**1953, Nov. 20** — *Perf. 13*
592 A343 5y red — 2.00 .75
593 A344 10y blue — 6.00 1.50
  a.  Souv. sheet of 2, #592-593, imperf., no gum — 25.00 20.00

Unzen National Park.

Toy Horse — A345

**1953, Dec. 25** — *Perf. 13½x13*
594 A345 5y rose — 7.50 .80

New Year Greetings 1953
Issued to pay postage on New Year's cards, later for ordinary use. A sheet reproducing four of these stamps was awarded as sixth prize in the national lottery. Value, $47.50.

Racing Skaters — A346

**1954, Jan. 16**
595 A346 10y blue — 6.00 2.00

World Speed Skating Matches for Men, Sapporo City, Jan. 16-17, 1954.

Golden Hall, Chusonji Temple — A347

**1954, Jan. 20**
596 A347 20y olive green — 1.25 .25

Thread, Pearls, Gears, Buttons and Globe — A348

**1954, Apr. 10**
597 A348 10y dark red — 6.00 2.00

International Trade Fair, Osaka, Apr. 10-23.

Little Cuckoo — A349

**1954, May 10** — *Perf. 13x13½*
598 A349 3y blue green — .30 .25
  a.  Imperf., pair — 500.00

For stamp inscribed "NIPPON," see No. 1067.

Wrestlers — A350

**1954, May 22** — *Engr.*
599 A350 10y deep green — 3.50 1.75

World Free Style Wrestling Championship Matches, Tokyo, 1954.

Mt. Asama — A351

Mt. Tanikawa A352

**1954, June 25** — *Perf. 13*
600 A351 5y dk gray brn — 2.50 .75
601 A352 10y dk blue grn — 5.00 1.50
  a.  Souvenir sheet of 2, #600-601, no gum — 25.00 20.00

Jo-Shin-etsu National Park.

Table Tennis A353    Archery A354

**1954, Aug. 22** — *Engr.* — *Perf. 12*
602 A353 5y dull brown — 4.50 1.00
603 A354 5y gray green — 4.50 1.00
  a.  Pair, #602-603 — 10.00 5.75

9th Natl. Athletic Meet, Sapporo, Aug. 22-26.

Morse Telegraph Instrument A355    ITU Monument A356

**1954, Oct. 13** — *Perf. 13x13½, 13½x13*
604 A355 5y dark purple brown — 2.00 1.00
605 A356 10y deep blue — 6.00 2.00

75th anniv. of Japanese membership in the ITU.

Daruma Doll — A357

**1954, Dec. 20 Photo.** — *Perf. 13½x13*
606 A357 5y black & red — 6.00 .75

Sheets reproducing four of these stamps with Japanese inscriptions and ornaments were awarded as fifth prize in the national lottery. Value $45.

Mountain Stream, Tama Gorge A358    Chichibu Mountains A359

**1955, Mar. 1** — *Engr.* — *Perf. 13*
607 A358 5y blue — 1.75 .75
608 A359 10y red brown — 2.25 1.00
  a.  Souv. sheet of 2, #607-608, imperf., no gum — 25.00 20.00

Chichibu-Tama National Park.

Bridge and Iris — A360

**1955, Mar. 15** — *Perf. 13x13½*
609 A360 500y brown purple — 60.00 .25

Paper Carp as Flown on Boys' Day — A361

**1955, May 16 Unwmk. Photo.** — *Perf. 13*
610 A361 10y multicolored — 6.00 2.00

15th congress of the International Chamber of Commerce, Tokyo, May 16-21, 1955.

Mandarin Ducks — A362

**1955-64**
611 A362 5y lt bl & red brn — .30 .25
  a.  Bklt. pane, 4 #611, 8 #580 ('59) — 50.00
  b.  Bklt. pane, 4 #611, 8 #725 ('63) — 35.00 17.00
  c.  Bklt. pane of 4 ('64) — 4.25 2.75
  d.  Imperf., pair — 1,400.

See Nos. 738, 881d, 914b.

Benten Cape A363    Jodo Beach A364

**1955, Sept. 30**
612 A363 5y deep green — 1.50 .60
613 A364 10y rose lake — 2.00 1.00
  a.  Souv. sheet of 2, #612-613, imperf., no gum — 25.00 20.00

Rikuchu-Kaigan National Park. No. 613a sold for 20y.

Gymnastics A365    Runners A366

**1955, Oct. 30** — *Engr.*
614 A365 5y brown lake — 1.75 .75
615 A366 5y bluish black — 1.75 .75
  a.  Pair, #614-615 — 6.50 5.00

10th National Athletic Meet, Kanagawa Prefecture.
See Nos. 639-640, 657.

"A Girl Blowing Glass Toy," by Utamaro — A367

**1955, Nov. 1** — *Photo.*
616 A367 10y multicolored — 10.00 7.50

150th anniv. of the death of Utamaro, woodcut artist, and to publicize Philatelic Week, Nov. 1955. Issued in sheets of 10.

Kokeshi Dolls — A368

**1955, Dec. 30 Unwmk.** — *Perf. 13*
617 A368 5y olive grn & red — 2.50 .35

New Year Greetings 1956
Sheets reproducing four of these stamps, were awarded as fifth prize in the New Year's lottery. Value, $35.

Table Tennis — A369

**1956, Apr. 2** — *Perf. 13x13½*
618 A369 10y red brown — 2.00 .75

Intl. Table Tennis Championship, Tokyo, 4/2-11.

Judo — A370

**1956, May 2** — *Perf. 13*
619 A370 10y green & brn pur — 2.00 .75

Issued to publicize the first World Judo Championship Meet, Tokyo, May 3, 1956.

Boy and Girl with Paper Carp — A371

**1956, May 5**
620 A371 5y lt blue & blk — 1.50 .75

Establishment of World Children's Day, 5/5/56.

Water Plants, Lake Akan A372    Big Purple Butterfly A373

**1956 Unwmk.** — *Perf. 13*
621 A372 55y lt blue, grn & blk — 12.50 .55
622 A373 75y multicolored — 8.00 .55

See Nos. 887A, 917.

**Castle Type of 1951 Redrawn; Zeros Omitted**

A373a

**1956 Engr.** — *Perf. 13½x13*
623 A373a 14y gray olive — 6.00 2.00

Osezaki Promontory A374

Kujuku Island — A375

**1956, Oct. 1** — *Photo.*
624 A374 5y red brown — 1.00 .45

**Engr. & Photo.**
625 A375 10y lt blue & indigo — 1.50 1.00
  a.  Souv. sheet of 2, #624-625, imperf., no gum — 20.00 17.50

Saikai National Park. No. 625a sold for 20y.

Palace Moat and Modern Tokyo — A376

**1956, Oct. 1** — *Engr.*
626 A376 10y dull purple — 2.50 1.00

500th anniv. of the founding of Tokyo.

Sakuma Dam — A377

**1956, Oct. 15** **Unwmk.** *Perf. 13*
627 A377 10y dark blue   2.25 1.00
Completion of Sakuma Dam.

Long Jump
A378

Basketball
A379

**1956, Oct. 28** *Perf. 13½x13*
628 A378 5y brown violet   1.00 .75
629 A379 5y steel blue   1.00 .75
a. Pair, #628-629   3.00 3.00
11th Natl. Athletic Meet, Hyogo Prefecture.
See No. 658.

Kabuki Actor Ebizo
Ichikawa by
Sharaku — A380

**1956, Nov. 1** **Photo.** *Perf. 13*
630 A380 10y multicolored   10.00 7.50
Stamp Week. Sheets of 10.

Mount
Manaslu — A381

**1956, Nov. 3**
631 A381 10y multicolored   4.00 2.00
Japanese expedition which climbed Mount
Manaslu in the Himalayas on May 9 and 11,
1956.

Electric
Locomotive and
Hiroshige's "Yui
Stage" — A382

**1956, Nov. 19** **Unwmk.** *Perf. 13*
632 A382 10y dk ol bis, blk & grn  6.00 2.00
Electrification of Tokaido Line.

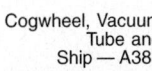

Cogwheel, Vacuum
Tube and
Ship — A383

**1956, Dec. 18** **Engr.**
633 A383 10y ultra   1.00 .75
Japanese Machinery Floating Fair.

Toy Whale — A384

**1956, Dec. 20** **Photo.**
634 A384 5y multicolored   1.50 .35
a. Imperf., pair
Sheets reproducing four of these stamps,
with inscriptions and ornaments, were
awarded as sixth prize in the national lottery.
Value $13.50.

United Nations
Emblem — A385

**Photogravure and Engraved**
**1957, Mar. 8 Unwmk.** *Perf. 13½x13*
635 A385 10y lt blue & dk car   .70 .55
Japan's admission to the UN, Dec. 18, 1956.

**Temple Type of 1950**
**Redrawn; Zeros Omitted**

A385a

**1957-59** **Engr.** *Perf. 13x13½*
636 A385a 24y violet   17.50 3.00
636A A385a 30y rose lil   45.00 .90
('59)
b. Imperf., pair   6,000. 2,000.

IGY Emblem, Penguin
and "Soya" — A386

**1957, July 1** **Photo.** *Perf. 13*
637 A386 10y blue, yel & blk   1.00 .50
International Geophysical Year.

Atomic Reactor — A387

**1957, Sept. 18** **Engr.** *Perf. 13*
638 A387 10y dark purple   .45 .25
Completion of Japan's atomic reactor at
Tokai-Mura, Ibaraki Prefecture.

**Sports Type of 1955**
No. 639, Girl on parallel bars. No. 640,
Boxers.

**1957, Oct. 26** **Unwmk.** *Perf. 13*
639 A366 5y ultra   .35 .25
640 A366 5y dark red   .35 .25
a. Pair, #639-640   1.00 .75
12th Natl. Athletic Meet, Shizuoka
Prefecture.

"Girl Bouncing Ball,"
by Suzuki
Harunobu — A388

**1957, Nov. 1** **Photo.**
641 A388 10y multicolored   1.75 1.50
1957 Stamp Week. Issued in sheets of 10.
See Nos. 646, 671, 728, 757.

Lake Okutama and
Ogochi Dam — A389

**1957, Nov. 26** **Engr.** *Perf. 13½*
642 A389 10y ultra   .40 .25
Completion of Ogochi Dam, part of the
Tokyo water supply system.

Modern and First
Japanese Blast
Furnaces — A390

**1957, Dec. 1** **Photo.** **Unwmk.**
643 A390 10y orange & dk pur   .40 .25
Centenary of Japan's iron industry.

Toy Dog (Inu-
hariko) — A391

**1957, Dec. 20** *Perf. 13½x13*
644 A391 5y multicolored   .50 .40
New Year 1958. Sheets reproducing 4 No.
644, with inscriptions and ornaments, were
awarded as 5th prize in the New Year lottery.
Value $7.50.

Shimonoseki-Moji Tunnel — A392

**1958, Mar. 9** *Perf. 13x13½*
645 A392 10y multicolored   .25 .25
Completion of the Kan-Mon Underwater
Highway connecting Honshu and Kyushu
Islands.

**Stamp Week Type of 1957**
Design: 10y, Woman with Umbrella, woodcut by Kiyonaga.

**1958, Apr. 20** **Unwmk.** *Perf. 13*
646 A388 10y multicolored   .65 .25
Stamp Week, 1958. Sheets of 10.

Statue of Ii
Naosuke and
Harbor — A393

**Unwmk.**
**1958, May 10** **Engr.** *Perf. 13*
647 A393 10y gray blue & car   .30 .25
Cent. of the opening of the ports of Yokohama, Nagasaki and Hakodate to foreign
powers.

National
Stadium — A394

3rd Asian Games, Tokyo: 10y, Torch and
emblem. 14y, Runner. 24y, Woman diver.

**1958, May 24** **Photo.**
648 A394 5y bl grn, bis & pink   .30 .25
649 A394 10y multicolored   .30 .30
650 A394 14y multicolored   .30 .25
651 A394 24y multicolored   .35 .30
Nos. 648-651 (4)   1.25 1.10

Kasato Maru,
Map and
Brazilian
Flag — A395

**1958, June 18**
652 A395 10y multicolored   .30 .25
50 years of Japanese emigration to Brazil.

Sado Island and
Local
Dancer — A396

Mt. Yahiko and
Echigo
Plain — A397

**1958, Aug. 20** **Unwmk.** *Perf. 13*
653 A396 10y multicolored   .70 .25
654 A397 10y multicolored   .55 .25
Sado-Yahiko Quasi-National Park.

Stethoscope
A398

**1958, Sept. 7** **Photo.** *Perf. 13*
655 A398 10y Prussian green   .30 .25
5th Intl. Cong. on Diseases of the Chest and
the 7th Intl. Cong. of Bronchoesophagology.

"Kyoto" (Sanjo
Bridge), Print by
Hiroshige — A399

**1958, Oct. 5**
656 A399 24y multicolored   2.50 .70
Issued for International Letter Writing Week,
Oct. 5-11. See No. 679.

**Sports Types of 1955-56**
Designs: No. 657, Weight lifter. No. 658, Girl
badminton player.

**1958, Oct. 19** **Engr.**
657 A365 5y gray blue   .30 .25
658 A379 5y claret   .30 .25
a. Pair, #657-658   1.00 2.00
13th Natl. Athletic Meet, Toyama Prefecture.

Keio University and
Yukichi
Fukuzawa — A400

**1958, Nov. 8** **Engr.** *Perf. 13½*
659 A400 10y magenta   .35 .25
Centenary of Keio University.

Globe and Playing
Children — A401

**1958, Nov. 23** **Photo.** *Perf. 13*
660 A401 10y deep green   .30 .25
9th Intl. Conf. of Social Work and the 2nd
Intl. Study Conf. on Child Welfare.

Flame: Symbol of
Human Rights — A402

**1958, Dec. 10** **Unwmk.** *Perf. 13*
661 A402 10y multicolored   .30 .25
10th anniv. of the signing of the Universal
Declaration of Human Rights.

Toy of Takamatsu (Tai-Ebisu) — A403

**1958, Dec. 20** *Perf. 13½*
662 A403 5y multicolored                .50  .30
New Year 1959. Sheets reproducing 4 No. 662, with inscriptions and ornaments, were awarded as prizes in the New Year lottery. Size: 103x89mm. Value $7.50.

Tractor and Map of Kojima Bay — A404

**1959, Feb. 1** *Perf. 12½*
663 A404 10y claret & bister brn   .30  .25
Completion of the embankment closing Kojima Bay for reclamation.

Karst Plateau A405

Akiyoshi Cave A406

**1959, Mar. 16  Photo.  Perf. 13½**
664 A405 10y green, bl & ocher   .90  .25
665 A406 10y multicolored        1.50  .25
Akiyoshidai Quasi-National Park.

Map of Southeast Asia — A407

**1959, Mar. 27**
666 A407 10y deep carmine        .30  .25
Asian Cultural Cong., Tokyo, Mar. 27-31, marking the 2,500th anniv. of the death of Buddha.

Ceremonial Fan — A408

Prince Akihito and Princess Michiko — A409

**Photogravure; Portraits Engraved**
**1959, Apr. 10**
667 A408  5y magenta & violet    .30  .25
668 A409 10y red brn & dull pur   .50  .25
   a.  Souv. sheet of 2, #667-668, im-
       perf.                        6.00 6.00
669 A408 20y org brn & brn        .85  .25
670 A409 30y yel grn & dk grn    2.50  .30
      Nos. 667-670 (4)            4.15 1.05
Wedding of Crown Prince Akihito and Princess Michiko, Apr. 10, 1959.

**Type of 1957**
Women Reading Poetry, print by Eishi Fujiwara.

**1959, May 20  Photo.  Perf. 13**
671 A388 10y multicolored        2.10  .90
Stamp Week. Issued in sheets of 10.

**Redrawn Kannon Type of 1953**
Coil Stamp
**Perf. 13 Horiz.**
**1959, Jan. 20  Typo.  Unwmk.**
672 A332a 10y red brn & lilac  18.00 20.00

---

Measuring Glass, Tape Measure and Scales — A410

**1959, June 5  Photo.  Perf. 13**
673 A410 10y lt blue & blk       .30  .25
Adoption of the metric system.

Nurses Carrying Stretcher — A411

**1959, June 24**
674 A411 10y olive grn & red     .30  .25
Centenary of the Red Cross idea.

Mt. Fuji and Lake Motosu — A412

**1959, July 21  Engr.  Perf. 13**
675 A412 10y green, bl & sepia   .50  .25
Establishment of Natural Park Day and 1st Natural Park Convention, Yumoto, Nikko, July 21, 1959.

Ao Cave Area of Yabakei A413

Hita, Mt. Hiko and Great Cormorant A414

**1959, Sept. 25  Photo.  Perf. 13**
676 A413 10y multicolored        .90  .25
677 A414 10y multicolored        .90  .25
Yaba-Hita-Hiko Quasi National Park.

Golden Dolphin, Nagoya Castle — A415

**1959, Oct. 1**
678 A415 10y brt bl, gold & blk  .50  .25
350th anniversary of Nagoya.

**Hiroshige Type of 1958**
Design: 30y, "Kuwana," the 7-ri Crossing Point, print by Hiroshige.

**1959, Oct. 4  Unwmk.**
679 A399 30y multicolored       7.50 1.50
Intl. Letter Writing Week, Oct. 4-10. See listing of No. 4448 for image of the Hiroshige print.

Japanese Crane, IATA Emblem — A416

**1959, Oct. 12  Engr.**
680 A416 10y brt grnsh blue      .35  .25
15th General Meeting of the International Air Transport Association.

---

Shoin Yoshida and PTA Symbol — A417

**1959, Oct. 27  Photo.  Perf. 13**
681 A417 10y brown               .30  .25
Centenary of the death of Shoin Yoshida, educator, and in connection with the Parent-Teachers Association convention.

Throwing the Hammer — A418

Design: No. 683, Woman Fencer.

**1959, Oct. 25  Engr.**
682 A418 5y gray blue            .35  .25
683 A418 5y olive bister         .35  .25
   a.  Pair, #682-683             1.00 1.00
14th National Athletic Meet, Tokyo.

Globes — A419

**1959, Nov. 2  Photo.**
684 A419 10y brown red           .30  .25
15th session of GATT (General Agreement on Tariffs & Trade), Tokyo, Oct. 12-Nov. 21.

Toy Mouse of Kanazawa — A420

**1959, Dec. 19  Unwmk.  Perf. 13½**
685 A420 5y gold, red, grn & blk  .60  .25
New Year 1960. Sheets reproducing 4 No. 685, with marginal inscription and ornaments, were awarded as prizes in natl. lottery. Value $7.50.

Yukio Ozaki and Clock Tower, Ozaki Memorial Hall — A421

**1960, Feb. 25  Photo.  Perf. 13½**
686 A421 10y red brn & dk brn    .30  .25
Completion of Ozaki Memorial Hall, erected in memory of Yukio Ozaki (1858-1954), statesman.

Nara Period Artwork, Shosoin Treasure House — A422

**1960, Mar. 10**
687 A422 10y olive gray          .40  .25
Transfer of the capital to Nara, 1250th anniv.

**Scenic Trio Issue**

Bay of Matsushima A423

Ama-no-hashidate (Heavenly Bridge) — A424

---

Miyajima from the Sea — A425

**1960**                              **Engr.**
688 A423 10y maroon & bl grn    1.25  .45
689 A424 10y green & lt bl      1.60  .45
690 A425 10y vio blk & bl grn   1.60  .45
      Nos. 688-690 (3)            4.45 1.35
Issued: No. 688, 3/15; No. 689, 7/15; No. 690, 11/15.

Takeshima, off Gamagori — A426

**1960, Mar. 20  Photo.  Perf. 13½**
691 A426 10y multicolored        .95  .25
Mikawa Bay Quasi-National Park.

Poetess Isé, 13th Century Painting A427

**1960, Apr. 20  Unwmk.  Perf. 13**
692 A427 10y multicolored       2.25 2.25
Stamp Week, 1960.

Kanrin Maru — A428

Design: 30y, Pres. Buchanan receiving first Japanese diplomatic mission.

**1960, May 17  Engr.**
693 A428 10y bl grn & brn        .40  .25
694 A428 30y car & indigo       1.50  .40
Cent. of the Japan-US Treaty of Amity and Commerce. Nos. 694 and 693 form pages of an open book when placed next to each other. Souvenir sheet is No. 703.

Crested Ibis (Toki) — A429

**1960, May 24  Photo.  Perf. 13½**
695 A429 10y gray, pink & red    .55  .45
12th Intl. Congress for Bird Preservation.

Radio Waves Encircling Globe — A430

**1960, June 1  Engr.**
696 A430 10y carmine rose        .30  .25
25th anniv. of the Intl. Radio Program by the Japanese Broadcasting Corporation.

Flower Garden (Gensei Kaen) — A431

**1960, June 15  Photo.**
697 A431 10y multicolored       1.00  .40
Abashiri Quasi-National Park.

Cape Ashizuri — A432

**1960, Aug. 1**                    **Unwmk.**
698  A432  10y multicolored           .65  .40
Ashizuri Quasi-National Park.

Rainbow Spanning Pacific, Cherry Blossoms and Pineapples — A433

**1960, Aug. 20**                    **Perf. 13½**
699  A433  10y multicolored           .60  .25
75th anniversary of Japanese contract emigration to Hawaii.

Henri Farman's Biplane and Jet — A434

**1960, Sept. 20**                    **Perf. 13**
700  A434  10y brn & chlky bl        .35  .25
50th anniversary of Japanese aviation.

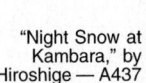

Seat Plan of Diet A435

"Red Fuji" by Hokusai and Diet Building A436

**1960, Sept. 27**
701  A435  5y indigo & org           .30  .25
702  A436  10y blue & red brn        .50  .25
49th Inter-Parliamentary Conference.

**Souvenir Sheet**
**1960, Sept. 27**                    **Engr.**
703  A428  Sheet of 2, #693-
           694                      27.50 27.50
Visit of Prince Akihito and Princess Michiko to the US.

"Night Snow at Kambara," by Hiroshige — A437

**1960, Oct. 9**                    **Photo.**
704  A437  30y multicolored        15.00  5.00
Issued for International Letter Writing Week, Oct. 9-15. See Nos. 735, 769.

Japanese Fencing (Kendo) — A438

No. 706, Girl gymnast and vaulting horse.

**1960, Oct. 23**       **Engr.**   **Perf. 13½**
705  A438  5y dull blue             .40  .30
706  A438  5y rose violet           .40  .30
a.    Pair, #705-706               1.50 1.50
15th National Athletic Meet, Kumamoto.

---

Okayama Astrophysical Observatory A439

**1960, Oct. 19**
707  A439  10y brt violet            .50  .25
Opening of the Okayama Astrophysical Observatory.

Lt. Naoshi Shirase and Map of Antarctica — A440

**1960, Nov. 29**                    **Photo.**
708  A440  10y fawn & black          .55  .25
50th anniv. of the 1st Japanese Antarctic expedition.

Little Red Calf of Aizu, Gold Calf of Iwate — A441

**1960, Dec. 20   Unwmk.   Perf. 13½**
709  A441  5y multicolored           .80  .30
New Year 1961. Sheets reproducing 4 No. 709 were awarded as prizes in the New Year lottery. Size: 102x89mm. Value $8.50.

Diet Building at Night A442

Opening of First Session A443

**1960, Dec. 24   Photo.; Engr. (10y)**
710  A442  5y gray & dk bl           .35  .25
711  A443  10y carmine               .45  .25
70th anniversary of the Japanese Diet.

Narcissus — A444

No. 713, Plum blossoms. No. 714, Camellia japonica. No. 715, Cherry blossoms. No. 716, Peony. No. 717, Iris. No. 718, Lily. No. 719, Morning glory. No. 720, Bellflower. No. 721, Gentian. No. 722, Chrysanthemum. No. 723, Camellia sasanqua.

**1961**          **Photo.**      **Perf. 13½**
712  A444  10y lilac, yel & grn     3.75  .80
713  A444  10y brown, grn & yel     1.60  .80
714  A444  10y lem, grn, pink &
           yel                      1.40  .80
715  A444  10y gray, brn, pink,
           yel & blk                1.40  .80
716  A444  10y blk, grn, pink &
           yel                      1.00  .80
717  A444  10y gray, pur, grn &
           yel                       .65  .50
718  A444  10y gray grn, yel &
           brn                       .50  .40
719  A444  10y lt bl, grn & lil      .50  .40
720  A444  10y lt yel grn, vio &
           grn                       .50  .40
721  A444  10y org, vio bl & grn     .50  .40
722  A444  10y blue, yel & grn       .50  .40
723  A444  10y sl, pink, yel & grn   .50  .40
           Nos. 712-723 (12)       12.80 6.90

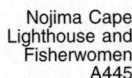

Nojima Cape Lighthouse and Fisherwomen A445

**1961, Mar. 15**
724  A445  10y multicolored          .55  .25
South Boso Quasi-National Park.

---

Cherry Blossoms — A446

**Unwmk.**
**1961, Apr. 1     Photo.     Perf. 13**
725  A446  10y lilac rose & gray     .30  .25
a.    Lilac rose omitted           300.00
b.    Imperf., pair              1,100.
c.    Booklet pane of 4             5.50 2.25
d.    Gray omitted                 200.00
           See No. 611b.

**Coil Stamp**
**1961, Apr. 25     Perf. 13 Horiz.**
726  A446  10y lil rose & gray      5.00 2.50

Hisoka Maeshima — A447

**1961, Apr. 20**                    **Perf. 13**
727  A447  10y olive & black        1.10  .25
90th anniv. of Japan's modern postal service from Tokyo to Osaka, inaugurated by Deputy Postmaster General Hisoka Maeshima.

**Type of 1957**
"Dancing Girl" from a "Screen of Dancers."

**1961, Apr. 20**                    **Perf. 13½**
728  A388  10y multicolored         1.25 1.00
Stamp Week, 1961. Sheets of 10 (5x2).

Lake Biwa — A448

**1961, Apr. 25**
729  A448  10y blk, dk bl & yel grn  .55  .25
Lake Biwa Quasi-National Park.

Rotary Emblem and People of Various Races — A449

**1961, May 29     Engr.     Perf. 13**
730  A449  10y gray & orange         .30  .25
52nd convention of Rotary Intl., Tokyo, May 29-June 1, 1961.

Faucet, Wheat, Insulator & Cogwheel — A450

**1961, July 7     Photo.     Perf. 13½**
731  A450  10y violet & aqua         .30  .25
Aichi irrigation system, Kiso river.

Sun, Earth and Meridian — A451

**1961, July 12**
732  A451  10y yellow, red & blk     .30  .25
75th anniv. of Japanese standard time.

---

Parasol Dance on Dunes of Tottori — A452

**1961, Aug. 15**
733  A452  10y multicolored          .55  .25
San'in Kaigan Quasi-National Park.

Onuma Lake and Komagatake Volcano — A453

**1961, Sept. 15**
734  A453  10y grn, red brn & bl     .60  .25
Onuma Quasi-National Park.

**Hiroshige Type of 1960**
Design: 30y, "Hakone," print by Hiroshige from the 53 Stages of the Tokaido.

**1961, Oct. 8**                    **Perf. 13**
735  A437  30y multicolored         7.50 6.00
Intl. Letter Writing Week, Oct. 8-14. See listing of No. 4448 for image of the Hiroshige print.

Gymnast on Horizontal Bar — A454

Design: No. 737, Women rowing.

**1961, Oct. 8     Engr.     Perf. 13½**
736  A454  5y blue green            .30  .25
737  A454  5y ultra                 .30  .25
a.    Pair, #736-737               1.00 1.00
16th National Athletic Meet, Akita. See Nos. 770-771, 816-817, 852-853.

**Duck Type of 1955**
Coil Stamp
**1961, Oct. 2  Photo.  Perf. 13 Horiz.**
738  A362  5y lt bl & red brn       2.50 2.00

National Diet Library and Book — A455

**1961, Nov. 1**                    **Perf. 13½**
739  A455  10y dp ultra & gold       .30  .25
Opening of the new Natl. Diet Library, Tokyo.

Paper Mâché Tiger — A456

**1961, Dec. 15**                    **Perf. 13½**
740  A456  5y multicolored           .35  .25
New Year 1962. Sheets reproducing 4 No. 740 were awarded as 5th prize in the New Year lottery. Size: 102x90, Value $9.

Mt. Fuji from Lake Ashi — A457

Minokake-Iwa at Irozaki — A458

Mt. Fuji from Mitsu Pass — A459

Mt. Fuji from Cape of Ose — A460

**1962, Jan. 16     Unwmk.     Photo.**
741  A457  5y deep green              .40   .25
742  A458  5y dark blue               .40   .25
743  A459  10y red brown             1.10   .25
744  A460  10y black                 1.10   .30
     *Nos. 741-744 (4)*              3.00  1.05
     Fuji-Hakone-Izu National Park.

Omishima — A461

**1962, Feb. 15                    Perf. 13½**
745  A461  10y ultra, red & yel       .55   .25
     Kitanagato-Kaigan Quasi-National Park.

Perotrochus
Hirasei
A462

Sacred
Bamboo
A463

Shari-den
of
Engakuji
A464

Yomei
Gate,
Nikko
A465

Noh Mask — A466

Copper
Pheasant
A466a

Wind God,
Fujin, by
Sotatsu
A467

Japanese
Crane
A468

Mythical
Winged
Woman,
Chusonji
A469

**1962-65       Unwmk.       Perf. 13**
746  A462    4y dk brn & red
                 ('63)            .30   .25
747  A463    6y gray grn & car    .30   .25
748  A464   30y violet black     5.00   .25
749  A465   40y rose red         6.00   .25
750  A466   70y yel brn & blk
                 ('65)           2.25   .25
751  A466a  80y crim & brn       1.25   .25
752  A467   90y brt blue grn    26.00   .35
753  A468  100y pink & blk ('63) 10.00   .25
754  A469  120y purple          10.00   .65
     *Nos. 746-754 (9)*          61.10  2.75
     See Nos. 888, 888A, 1076, 1079, 1257.

**Coil Stamp**
**Perf. 13 Horiz.**
755  A464  30y dull violet ('63)  4.50  3.00

Hinamatsuri, Doll
Festival — A470

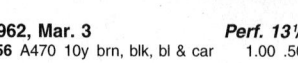

**1962, Mar. 3                     Perf. 13½**
756  A470  10y brn, blk, bl & car   1.00   .50
     The Doll Festival is celebrated Mar. 3 in
honor of young girls.

**Type of 1957**
Design: Dancer from "Flower Viewing
Party" by Naganobu Kano.

**1962, Apr. 20     Photo.     Perf. 13½**
757  A388  10y multicolored        1.00   .75
     Stamp Week, 1962. Sheets of 10.

Sakurajima Volcano
and Kagoshima
Bay — A471

**1962, Apr. 30**
758  A471  10y multicolored         .35   .25
     Kinkowan Quasi-National Park.

Mount
Kongo — A472

**1962, May 15                     Perf. 13½**
759  A472  10y gray bl, dk grn & sal  .35  .25
     Kongo-Ikoma Quasi-National Park.

Suigo Park Scene
and Iris — A473

**1962, June 1                     Perf. 13½**
760  A473  10y multicolored         .35   .25
     Suigo Quasi-National Park.

Train Emerging from
Hokuriku
Tunnel — A474

**1962, June 10                    Photo.**
761  A474  10y olive gray           .85   .40
     Opening of Hokuriku Tunnel between
Tsuruga and Imajo, Fukui Prefecture.

Star Festival (Tanabata
Matsuri) — A475

**1962, July 7     Unwmk.     Perf. 13½**
762  A475  10y multicolored         .30   .25
     The Tanabata festival is celebrated on the
evening of July 7.

Boy Scout Hat on Map
of Southeast
Asia — A476

**1962, Aug. 3**
763  A476  10y red org, blk & bis   .30   .25
     Asian Boy Scout Jamboree, Mt. Fuji, Aug. 3-
7.

Ozegahara
Swampland and
Mt.
Shibutsu — A477

Fumes on Mt.
Chausu,
Nasu — A478

Lake Chuzenji
and Mt.
Nantai — A479

Senryu-kyo
Narrows,
Shiobara — A480

**1962, Sept. 1**
764  A477  5y greenish blue     .35   .30
765  A478  5y maroon           .35   .30
766  A479  10y purple          .45   .30
767  A480  10y olive           .45   .30
     *Nos. 764-767 (4)*        1.60  1.20
     Nikko National Park.

Wakato Suspension
Bridge — A481

**Perf. 13½x13**
**1962, Sept. 26     Engr.     Unwmk.**
768  A481  10y rose red           .65   .25
     Opening of Wakato Bridge over Dokai Bay
in North Kyushu.

**Hiroshige Type of 1960**
Design: 40y, "Nihonbashi," print by
Hiroshige from the 53 Stages of the Tokaido.

**1962, Oct. 7     Photo.     Perf. 13**
769  A437  40y multicolored      5.00  4.00
     Intl. Letter Writing Week, Oct. 7-13. See list-
ing of No. 4448 for image of the Hiroshige
print.

**Sports Type of 1961**
Design: No. 770, Woman softball pitcher.
No. 771, Rifle shooting.

**1962, Oct. 21     Engr.     Perf. 13½**
770  A454  5y bluish black        .30   .25
771  A454  5y brown violet       .30   .25
  a.   Pair, #770-771             .85   .85
     17th National Athletic Meeting, Okayama.

Shichi-go-san
Festival — A482

**1962, Nov. 15     Photo.     Perf. 13½**
772  A482  10y multicolored       .30   .25
     This festival for 7 and 3-year-old girls and 5-
year-old boys is celebrated on Nov. 15.

Rabbit Bell — A483

**1962, Dec. 15**
773  A483  10y multicolored       .35   .25
     New Year 1963. Sheets reproducing 4 No.
773 were awarded as prizes in the New Year
lottery. Value $7.50.
     See No. 2655b.

Mt.
Ishizuchi — A484

**1963, Jan. 11     Unwmk.     Perf. 13½**
774  A484  10y multicolored       .35   .25
     Ishizuchi Quasi-National Park.

Setsubun, Spring
Festival, Bean Scattering
Ceremony — A485

**1963, Feb. 3                      Photo.**
775  A485  10y multicolored       .30   .25

Map of City, Birds,
Ship and
Factory — A486

**1963, Feb. 10**
776  A486  10y chocolate          .30   .25
     Consolidation of the communities of Moji,
Kokura, Wakamatsu, Yawata and Tobata into
Kita-Kyushu City.

"Frost Flowers"
on Mt.
Fugen — A487

Amakusa Island
and Mt.
Unzen — A488

**1963, Feb. 15**
777  A487  5y gray blue           .30   .25
778  A488  10y carmine rose       .35   .25
     Unzen-Amakusa National Park.

Green Pond,
Midorigaike
A489

Hakusan Range
A490

**Perf. 13½**
**1963, Mar. 1     Unwmk.     Photo.**
779  A489  5y violet brown        .30   .25
780  A490  10y dark green         .35   .25
     Hakusan National Park.

Keya-no-Oto
Rock — A491

**1963, Mar. 15**
781  A491  10y multicolored       .30   .25
     Genkai Quasi-National Park.

Wheat Emblem and
Globe — A492

**1963, Mar. 21**
782  A492  10y dark green         .30   .25
     FAO "Freedom from Hunger" campaign.

"Girl Reading
Letter," Yedo
Screen — A493

**1963, Apr. 20                    Perf. 13½**
783  A493  10y multicolored       .45   .45
     Issued to publicize Stamp Week, 1963.

World Map and Centenary Emblem — A494

**1963, May 8**
784 A494 10y multicolored .30 .25
Centenary of the International Red Cross.

Globe and Leaf with Symbolic River System — A495

**1963, May 15** **Photo.**
785 A495 10y blue .30 .25
5th Congress of the Intl. Commission on Irrigation and Drainage.

Ito-dake, Asahi Range — A496    Lake Hibara and Mt. Bandai — A497

**1963, May 25** **Unwmk.** **Perf. 13½**
786 A496 5y green .30 .25
787 A497 10y red brown .35 .25
Bandai-Asahi National Park.

Lidth's Jay — A498

No. 789, Rock ptarmigan. No. 790, Eastern turtle dove. No. 791, Japanese white stork. No. 792, Bush warbler. No. 792A, Meadow bunting.

**1963-64** **Perf. 13½**
**Design and Inscription**
788 A498 10y lt green .75 .45
789 A498 10y blue .30 .25
790 A498 10y pale yellow .30 .25
791 A498 10y grnsh blue ('64) .30 .25
792 A498 10y green ('64) .30 .25
792A A498 10y lt rose brn ('64) .30 .25
  Nos. 788-792A (6) 2.25 1.70

Intersection at Ritto, Shiga — A499

**1963, July 15** **Unwmk.** **Perf. 13½**
793 A499 10y bl grn, blk & org .30 .25
Opening of the Nagoya-Kobe expressway, linking Nagoya with Kyoto, Osaka and Kobe.

Girl Scout and Flag — A500

**1963, Aug. 1** **Photo.**
794 A500 10y multicolored .30 .25
Asian Girl Scout and Girl Guides Camp, Togakushi Heights, Nagano, Aug. 1-7.

View of Nashu — A501    Whirlpool at Naruto — A502

**1963, Aug. 20**
795 A501 5y olive bister .30 .25
796 A502 10y dark green .35 .25
Inland Sea National Park.

Lake Shikaribetsu, Hokkaido — A503    Mt. Kurodake from Sounkyo Valley — A504

**1963, Sept. 1** **Unwmk.** **Perf. 13½**
797 A503 5y deep Prus blue .30 .25
798 A504 10y rose violet .35 .25
Daisetsuzan National Park.

Parabolic Antenna for Space Communications — A505

**1963, Sept. 9** **Photo.**
799 A505 10y multicolored .30 .25
14th General Assembly of the International Scientific Radio Union, Tokyo.

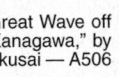

"Great Wave off Kanagawa," by Hokusai — A506

**1963, Oct. 10** **Perf. 13**
800 A506 40y gray, dk bl & yel 4.00 1.50
Issued for International Letter Writing Week, Oct. 6-12. Design from Hokusai's "36 Views of Fuji." Printed in sheets of 10 (5x2).

Diver, Pole Vaulter and Relay Runner — A507

**1963, Oct. 11** **Perf. 13½**
801 A507 10y bl, ocher, blk & red .30 .25
Tokyo Intl. (Pre-Olympic) Sports Meet, Tokyo, Oct. 11-16.

Woman Gymnast — A508

No. 803, Japanese wrestling (sumo).

**Perf. 13½**
**1963, Oct. 27** **Unwmk.** **Engr.**
802 A508 5y slate green .30 .25
803 A508 5y brown .30 .25
  a. Pair, #802-803 .60 .85
18th National Athletic Meet, Yamaguchi.

Phoenix Tree and Hachijo Island — A509

**1963, Dec. 10** **Photo.**
804 A509 10y multicolored .30 .25
Izu Islands Quasi-National Park.

Toy Dragons of Tottori and Yamanashi — A510

**1963, Dec. 16**
805 A510 5y gold, pink, aqua, ind & red .30 .25
  a. Aqua omitted
New Year 1964. Sheets containing 4 No. 805 were awarded as 5th prize in the New Year lottery. Value $4.75.

Wakasa-Fuji from Takahama — A511

**1964, Jan 25** **Perf. 13½**
806 A511 10y multicolored .30 .25
Wakasa Bay Quasi-National Park.

Agave and View from Horikiri Pass — A512

**1964, Feb. 20** **Unwmk.**
807 A512 10y multicolored .30 .25
Nichinan-Kaigan Quasi-National Park.

Uji Bridge — A513    View of Toba — A514

**1964, Mar. 15** **Photo.**
808 A513 5y sepia .30 .25
809 A514 10y red lilac .35 .25
Ise-Shima National Park.

Takayama Festival Float and Mt. Norikura — A515

No. 811, Yamaboko floats & Gion Shrine, Kyoto.

**1964** **Photo.** **Perf. 13½**
810 A515 10y lt green & multi .30 .25
811 A515 10y grnsh blue & multi .30 .25
No. 810 issued for the annual Takayama spring and autumn festivals, Takayama City, Gifu Prefecture. No. 811 for the annual Gion festival of Kyoto, July 10-30.
  Issue dates: No. 810, 4/15. No. 811, 7/15.

Yadorigi Scene from Genji Monogatari Scroll A516

**1964, Apr. 20**
814 A516 10y multicolored .35 .25
Stamp Week, 1964. Sheets of 10 (2x5).

Himeji Castle — A517

**1964, June 1** **Perf. 13½**
815 A517 10y dark brown .30 .25
Restoration of Himeji Castle.

**Sports Type of 1961**
**1964, June 6** **Perf. 13½**
816 A454 5y Handball .30 .25
817 A454 5y Woman on beam .30 .25
  a. Pair, #816-817 .65 .65
19th National Athletic Meeting, Niigata.

Cable Cross Section, Map of Pacific Ocean — A518

**1964, June 19**
818 A518 10y gray grn, dp mag & yel .30 .25
Opening of the transpacific cable.

Tokyo Expressway Crossing Nihonbashi — A519

**1964, Aug. 1** **Photo.**
819 A519 10y green, silver & blk .30 .25
Opening of the Tokyo Expressway.

Coin-like Emblems — A520

**1964, Sept. 7** **Unwmk.** **Perf. 13½**
820 A520 10y scarlet, gold & blk .30 .25
Annual general meeting of the Intl. Monetary Fund, Intl. Bank for Reconstruction and Development, Intl. Financial Corporation and the Intl. Development Assoc., Tokyo, Sept. 7-11.

Athletes, Olympic Flame and Rings A521    National Stadium, Tokyo A522

30y, Nippon Bodokan (fencing hall). 40y, Natl. Gymnasium. 50y, Komazawa Gymnasium.

**1964**
821 A521 5y multicolored .30 .25
822 A522 10y multicolored .30 .25
823 A522 30y multicolored .45 .25
824 A522 40y multicolored .55 .25
825 A522 50y multicolored .65 .25
  a. Souvenir sheet of 5, #821-825 5.00 6.00
  Nos. 821-825 (5) 2.25 1.25
18th Olympic Games, Tokyo, Oct. 10-25.
Issue dates: 5y, Sept. 9. Others, Oct. 10.

Hand with Grain, Cow and Fruit — A523

**1964, Sept. 15** **Perf. 13½**
826 A523 10y violet brn & gold .30 .25
Draining of Hachirogata Lagoon, providing new farmland for the future.

Express Train — A524

**1964, Oct. 1**
827 A524 10y blue & black .35 .25
Opening of the new Tokaido railroad line.

Mt. Fuji Seen from Tokaido, by Hokusai — A525

**1964, Oct. 4** **Perf. 13**
828 A525 40y multicolored　1.00 .50

Issued for International Letter Writing Week, Oct. 4-10. Issued in sheets of 10 (5x2). See Nos. 850, 896, 932, 971, 1016.

"Straw Snake" Mascot — A526

**1964, Dec. 15** **Photo.** **Perf. 13½**
829 A526 5y crimson, blk & yel　.30 .30

New Year 1965. Sheets containing 4 No. 829 were awarded as prizes in the New Year lottery (issued Jan. 20, 1965). Value $2.75.

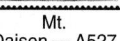

Mt. Daisen — A527

Paradise Cove, Oki Islands — A528

**1965, Jan. 20** **Unwmk.** **Perf. 13½**
830 A527 5y dark blue　.30 .25
831 A528 10y brown orange　.35 .25

Daisen-Oki National Park.

Niseko-Annupuri A529

**1965, Feb. 15** **Photo.**
832 A529 10y multicolored　.30 .25

Niseko-Shakotan-Otarukaigan Quasi-Natl. Park.

Meteorological Radar Station on Mt. Fuji — A530

**1965, Mar. 10** **Photo.** **Perf. 13½**
833 A530 10y multicolored　.30 .25

Completion of the Meteorological Radar Station on Kengamine Heights of Mt. Fuji.

Kiyotsu Gorge A531

Lake Nojiri and Mt. Myoko A532

**1965, Mar. 15**
834 A531 5y brown　.30 .25
835 A532 10y magenta　.35 .25

Jo-Shin-etsu Kogen National Park.

Communications Museum, Tokyo — A533

**1965, Mar. 25** **Unwmk.** **Perf. 13½**
836 A533 10y green　.30 .25

Philatelic Exhibition celebrating the completion of the Communications Museum.

"The Prelude" by Shoen Uemura — A534

**1965, Apr. 20** **Photo.**
837 A534 10y gray & multi　.35 .30

Issued for Stamp Week, 1965.

Playing Children, Cows and Swan — A535

**1965, May 5** **Unwmk.** **Perf. 13½**
838 A535 10y pink & multi　.30 .25

Opening of the National Garden for Children, Tokyo-Yokohama.

Stylized Tree and Sun — A536

**1965, May 9**
839 A536 10y multicolored　.30 .25

Issued to publicize the forestation movement and the forestation ceremony, Tottori Prefecture.

Globe, Old and New Communication Equipment — A537

**1965, May 17**
840 A537 10y brt blue, yel & blk　.30 .25

Cent. of the ITU.

Crater of Mt. Naka, Kyushu — A538

Five Central Peaks of Aso and Mountain Road — A539

**1965, June 15** **Photo.** **Perf. 13½**
841 A538 5y carmine rose　.30 .25
842 A539 10y deep green　.35 .25

Aso National Park.

ICY Emblem and Doves — A540

**1965, June 26** **Unwmk.**
843 A540 40y multicolored　.65 .30

Intl. Cooperation Year, 1965, and 20th anniv. of the UN.

Horse Chase, Soma — A541

Chichibu Festival Scene — A542

**1965** **Photo.** **Perf. 13x13½**
844 A541 10y multicolored　.30 .25
845 A542 10y multicolored　.30 .25

No. 844 issued to publicize the ancient Soma Nomaoi Festival, Fukushima Prefecture; No. 845, to publicize the festival dedicated to the Chichibu Myoken Shrine (built 1584).
Issue dates: No. 844, 7/16; No. 845, 12/3.

Meiji Maru, Black-tailed Gulls — A543

**1965, July 20** **Perf. 13½**
846 A543 10y grn, gray, blk & yel　.30 .25

25th Maritime Day, July 20.

Drop of Blood, Girl's Face and Bloodmobile A544

**1965, Sept. 1** **Perf. 13½**
847 A544 10y yel, grn, blk & red　.30 .25

Issued to publicize the national campaign for blood donations, Sept. 1-30.

Tokai Atomic Power Station and Structure of Alpha Uranium — A545

**1965, Sept. 21** **Photo.**
848 A545 10y multicolored　.30 .25

9th General Conf. of the Intl. Atomic Energy Agency, IAEA, Tokyo, Sept. 21-30.

People and Flag — A546

**1965, Oct. 1**
849 A546 10y multicolored　.30 .25

Tenth national census.

### Hokusai Type of 1964

Design: No. 850, "Waters at Misaka" by Hokusai (Mt. Fuji seen across Lake Kawaguchi).

**1965, Oct. 6** **Unwmk.** **Perf. 13**
850 A525 40y multicolored　1.00 .60

Issued for International Letter Writing Week, Oct. 6-12. Issued in sheets of 10 (5x2).

Emblems and Diagram of Seats in National Diet — A547

**1965, Oct. 15** **Perf. 13½**
851 A547 10y multicolored　.30 .25

75th anniv. of natl. suffrage, 40th anniv. of universal suffrage and 20th anniv. of women's suffrage.

### Sports Type of 1961

Designs: No. 852, Gymnast on vaulting horse. No. 853, Walking race.

**1965, Oct. 24** **Engr.** **Perf. 13½**
852 A454 5y red brown　.30 .25
853 A454 5y yellow green　.30 .25
　a. Pair, #852-853　.65 .65

20th National Athletic Meeting, Gifu.

Profile and Infant — A548

**1965, Oct. 30** **Photo.** **Perf. 13**
854 A548 30y car lake, yel & lt bl　.45 .25

8th Intl. Conf. of Otorhinolaryngology and the 11th Intl. Conf. of Pediatrics.

Mt. Iwo from Shari Coast, Hokkaido A549

Rausu Lake and Mt. Rausu A550

**1965, Nov. 15** **Perf. 13½**
855 A549 5y Prus green　.30 .25
856 A550 10y bright blue　.35 .25

Shiretoko National Park.

Aurora Australis, Map of Antarctica and "Fuji" — A551

**1965, Nov. 20**
857 A551 10y bl, yel & dk bl　.30 .25

Issued to publicize the Antarctic expedition, which left on the observation ship "Fuji," Nov. 20, 1965.

"Secret Horse" Straw Toy, Iwate Prefecture — A552

**1965, Dec. 10**
858 A552 5y lt blue & multi　.30 .25

Issued for New Year 1966. Sheets containing four of No. 858 were awarded as prizes in the New Year lottery (issued Jan. 20, 1966). Value $2.50.

Telephone Dial and 1890 Switchboard — A553

**1965, Dec. 16**
859 A553 10y multicolored　.30 .25

75th anniversary of telephone service in Japan.

Japanese Spiny Lobster — A554

Carp — A555

Bream — A555a

Skipjack Tuna — A555b

Three Ayu — A555c

Eel — A555d

Jack Mackerel — A555e   Chum Salmon — A555f

Yellowtail A555g   Tiger Puffer A555h

Squid — A555i   Turbo Cornutus — A555j

**1966-67 Photo. Perf. 13**
**Multicolored; Background in Colors Indicated**

| 860 | A554 | 10y green & ultra | .30 | .25 |
|---|---|---|---|---|
| 861 | A555 | 10y blue green | .30 | .25 |
| 862 | A555a | 10y dk blue | .30 | .25 |
| 863 | A555b | 10y dk ultra | .30 | .25 |
| 864 | A555c | 10y bis & dk grn | .30 | .25 |
| 865 | A555d | 15y grnsh bl & yel | .30 | .25 |
| 866 | A555e | 15y brt grn | .30 | .25 |
| 867 | A555f | 15y brt grn & bl | .30 | .25 |
| 868 | A555g | 15y lt bl grn ('67) | .30 | .25 |
| 869 | A555h | 15y brt grn ('67) | .30 | .25 |
| 870 | A555i | 15y ultra & grn ('67) | .30 | .25 |
| 871 | A555j | 15y chlky bl ('67) | .30 | .25 |
|  |  | *Nos. 860-871 (12)* | 3.60 | 3.00 |

**Famous Gardens Issue**

A556   A557

A558

10y, Kobuntei Pavilion and plum blossoms, Kairakuen Garden, Ibaraki. No. 873, Japanese cranes and Okayama Castle, Korakuen Garden, Okayama. No. 874, Kenrokuen Garden in the snow.

**1966-67 Perf. 13½**

| 872 | A556 | 10y gold, blk & grn | .30 | .25 |
|---|---|---|---|---|
| 873 | A557 | 15y blue, blk & mag | .35 | .25 |
| 874 | A558 | 15y silver, grn & dk brn | .35 | .25 |
|  |  | *Nos. 872-874 (3)* | 1.00 | .75 |

Issued: 10y, 2/25; No. 873, 11/3; No. 874, 1/25/67.

Crater Lake, Zao — A559

**1966, Mar. 15**
875 A559 10y multicolored .30 .25
Zao Quasi-National Park.

Muroto Cape A560   Senba Cliffs, Anan Coast A561

**1966, Mar. 22 Perf. 13½**
876 A560 10y multicolored .30 .25
877 A561 10y multicolored .30 .25
Muroto-Anan Coast Quasi-National Park.

AIPPI Emblem — A562

**1966, Apr. 11 Perf. 13**
878 A562 40y multicolored .75 .25
26th General Assembly of the Intl. Association for the Protection of Industrial Properties, Tokyo, Apr. 11-16.

"Butterflies" by Takeji Fujishima A563

**Photogravure and Engraved**
**1966, Apr. 20 Perf. 13½**
879 A563 10y gray & multi .30 .25
Stamp Week, 1966. Sheets of 10 (2x5). See No. 907.

Hisoka Maeshima — A563a

Goldfish — A564

Chrysanthemums   A565

Wisteria A565a

Hydrangea A565b

Golden Hall, Chusonji A565c   Yomei Gate, Nikko A565d

Nyoirin Kannon of Chuguji — A565f

Central Hall, Enryakuji Temple A566   Ancient Clay Horse (Haniwa) A567

A567a   A567b

A567c

Katsura Palace Garden — A568

A569

Bodhisattva Playing Flute (from Todaiji Lantern) — A570

Designs: 20y, Wisteria. 25y, Hydrangea. 35y, Luminescent squid. 45y, Lysichiton camtschatsense (white flowers). 500y, Deva King statue, South Gate, Todaiji.

**1966-69 Photo. Perf. 13**

| 879A | A563a | 1y olive bis ('68) | .30 | .25 |
|---|---|---|---|---|
| 880 | A564 | 7y ol & dp org | 1.50 | .25 |
| 881 | A565 | 15y bl & yel (bl "15") | .95 | .25 |
| b. |  | Bklt. pane of 2 + label ('67) | 3.25 |  |
| c. |  | Bklt. pane of 4 ('67) | 2.25 |  |
| d. |  | Bklt. pane of 4 (2 #881 + 2 #611) ('67) | 6.00 |  |
| e. |  | Imperf., pair | 400.00 |  |
| 881A | A565a | 20y vio & multi ('67) | 2.25 | 2.50 |
| 882 | A565b | 25y grn & lt ultra | .50 | .25 |
| 882A | A565c | 30y dp ultra & gold ('68) | .55 | .25 |
| 883 | A564 | 35y blue, gray & blk | 1.50 | .25 |
| 883A | A565d | 40y bl grn & brn ('68) | .60 | .25 |
| 884 | A565 | 45y blue & multi ('67) | .55 | .25 |
| 885 | A565f | 50y dk car rose | 7.50 | .25 |

**Engr.**

| 886 | A566 | 60y slate green | 1.25 | .25 |
|---|---|---|---|---|

**Photo.**

| 887 | A567 | 65y orange brown | 9.00 | .25 |
|---|---|---|---|---|
| 887A | A567a | 75y rose, blk, yel & pur | 1.10 | .25 |
| 888 | A567b | 90y gold & brn | 2.00 | .25 |
| 888A | A567c | 100y ver & blk ('68) | 1.90 | .25 |

**Engr.**

| 889 | A568 | 110y brown | 1.90 | .25 |
|---|---|---|---|---|
| 890 | A569 | 120y red | 2.50 | .25 |
| 891 | A570 | 200y Prus grn (22x33mm) | 4.00 | .25 |
| 891A | A570 | 500y dull pur ('69) | 9.50 | .25 |
|  |  | *Nos. 879A-891A (19)* | 49.35 | 7.00 |

Nos. 880-881 were also issued with fluorescent frame on July 18, 1966.
Compare type A563a with type A2682.
See Nos. 913-916, 918, 926, 1072, 1079, 1081, 1244, 1256.

UNESCO Emblem — A571

**1966, July 2 Photo. Perf. 13**
892 A571 15y multicolored .30 .25
20th anniv. of UNESCO.

Map of Pacific Ocean — A572

**1966, Aug. 22 Perf. 13**
893 A572 15y bis brn, dl bl & rose .30 .25
11th Pacific Science Congress, Tokyo, Aug. 22-Sept. 10.

Amakusa Bridges, Kyushu — A573

**1966, Sept. 24 Photo. Perf. 13**
894 A573 15y multicolored .30 .25
Completion of five bridges linking Misumi Harbor, Kyushu, with Amakusa islands.

Emblem of Post Office Life Insurance and Family — A574

**1966, Oct. 1**
895 A574 15y yellow grn & multi .30 .25
Post office life insurance service, 50th anniv.

**Hokusai Type of 1964**
50y, "Sekiya on the Sumida" (horseback riders and Mt. Fuji) from Hokusai's "36 Views of Fuji."

**1966, Oct. 6**
896 A525 50y multicolored 1.25 .70
Intl. Letter Writing Week, Oct. 6-12. Printed in sheets of 10 (5x2).

Sharpshooter — A575

Design: No. 898, Hop, skip and jump.

**1966, Oct. 23 Engr. Perf. 13½**
897 A575 7y ultra .30 .25
898 A575 7y carmine rose .30 .25
a. Pair, #897-898 .55 .55
21st Natl. Athletic Meet, Oita, Oct. 23-28.

National Theater — A576

Kabuki Scene A577

Bunraku Puppet Show — A578

**1966, Nov. 1 Perf. 13, 13½**
899 A576 15y multicolored .30 .25
900 A577 25y multicolored .45 .30
901 A578 50y multicolored .85 .45
*Nos. 899-901 (3)* 1.60 1.00
Inauguration of first National Theater in Japan. Nos. 900-901 issued in sheets of 10.

Rice Year Emblem — A579

**1966, Nov. 21 Perf. 13½**
902 A579 15y red, blk & ocher .30 .25
FAO International Rice Year.

Ittobori Carved Sheep, Nara Prefecture — A580

**1966, Dec. 10    Photo.    Perf. 13½**
903  A580  7y bl, gold, blk & pink    .30  .25
New Year 1967. Sheets containing 4 No. 903 were awarded as prizes in the New Year lottery. Value $2.

International Communications Satellite, Lani Bird 2 — A581

**1967, Jan. 27                        Perf. 13½**
904  A581  15y dk Prus bl & sepia    .30  .25
Inauguration in Japan of Intl. commercial communications service via satellite.

Around the World Air Route and Jet Plane — A582

**1967, Mar. 6    Photo.    Perf. 13½**
905  A582  15y multicolored    .30  .25
Issued to publicize the inauguration of Japan Air Lines Tokyo-London service via New York, which completes the around the world air route.

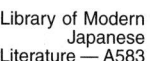

Library of Modern Japanese Literature — A583

**1967, Apr. 11**
906  A583  15y grnsh bl, lt & dk brn  .30 .25
Opening of the Library of Modern Japanese Literature, Komaba Park, Meguro-ku, Tokyo.

**Painting Type of 1966**

Design: 15y, Lakeside (seated woman), by Seiki (Kiyoteru) Kuroda.

**1967, Apr. 20**
907  A563  15y multicolored    .40  .25
Stamp Week, 1967. Sheets of 10 (2x5).

Kobe Harbor — A584

**1967, May 8    Photo.    Perf. 13x13½**
908  A584  50y multicolored    .95  .25
5th Cong. of the Intl. Association of Ports and Harbors, Tokyo, May 8-13.

Welfare Commissioner's Emblem — A585

**1967, May 12                        Perf. 13½**
909  A585  15y dk brown & gold    .30  .25
50th anniversary of the Welfare Commissioner System.

Traffic Light, Automobile and Children — A586

**1967, May 22                   Perf. 13x13½**
910  A586  15y emer, red, blk & yel  .30 .25
Issued to publicize traffic safety.

---

Kita and Kai-Koma Mountains A587

Akaishi and Hijiri Mountains A588

**1967, July 10**
911  A587  7y Prus blue    .30  .25
912  A588  15y rose lilac    .35  .25
South Japan Alps National Park.

**Types of 1966-69 Redrawn and**

A588a

Original - No. 881A

Redrawn - No. 915

On No. 915 the wisteria leaves do not touch frame at left and top. On No. 881A they do.

**1967-69        Photo.        Perf. 13**
913  A564  7y brt yel grn & dp org        .30    .25
914  A565  15y bl & yel (white "15")       .30    .25
  a.  Pane of 10 (5x2) ('68)    2.75
  b.  Bklt. panes of 4 with gutter (6 #914 + 2 #611) ('68)   7.00
  c.  Imperf., pair    500.00
  d.  Blue shading omitted
  e.  Bklt. panes of 2 & 4 with gutter ('68)   45.00  45.00
915  A565a  20y vio & multi ('69)    1.10    .25
916  A565f  50y brt carmine    .90    .25
917  A588a  55y lt bl, grn & blk ('69)    .85    .25
918  A567  65y deep orange    1.10    .25
  Nos. 913-918 (6)    4.55   1.50

Issued for use in facer-canceling machines. Issue dates: 7y, Aug. 1; 15y, 50y, July 1; 65y, July 20, 1967; 20y, Apr. 1, 1969; 55y, Sept. 1, 1969.
On No. 913 the background has been lightened and a frame line of shading added at top and right side.
No. 914a is imperf. on four sides.
The two panes of Nos. 914b and 914e are connected by a vertical creased gutter 21mm wide. The left pane of No. 914b consists of 2 No. 914 and 2 No. 611; the right pane, 4 of No. 914. The left pane of 2 of No. 914e includes a 4-line inscription.

**Coil Stamp**

**1968, Jan. 9                 Perf. 13 Horiz.**
926  A565  15y bl & yel (white "15")  .55  .30

Mitochondria and Protein Model — A589

**1967, Aug. 19    Photo.    Perf. 13**
927  A589  15y gray & multi    .30  .25
7th Intl. Biochemistry Cong., Tokyo, Aug. 19-25.

Gymnast on Horizontal Bar A590

Universiade Emblem A591

---

**1967, Aug. 26**
928  A590  15y red & multi    .30  .25
929  A591  50y yellow & multi    .95  .25
World University Games, Universiade 1967, Tokyo, Aug. 26-Sept. 4.

Paper Lantern, ITY Emblem — A592

"Sacred Mt. Fuji" by Taikan Yokoyama A593

**1967, Oct. 2    Photo.    Perf. 13**
930  A592  15y ultra & multi    .30  .25
931  A593  50y multicolored    1.25  1.00
International Tourist Year, 1967. No. 931 issued in sheets of 10.

**Hokusai Type of 1964**

50y, "Kajikazawa, Koshu" (fisherman and waves) from Hokusai's "36 Views of Fuji."

**1967, Oct. 6**
932  A525  50y multicolored    1.25  .55
Issued for International Letter Writing Week, Oct. 6-12. Sheets of 10 (5x2).

Athlete, Wild Primrose and Chichibu Mountains — A594

**1967, Oct. 22    Photo.    Perf. 13**
933  A594  15y gold & multi    .30  .25
22nd Natl. Athletic Meet, Saitama, 10/22-27.

Miroku Bosatsu, Koryuji Temple, Kyoto — A595

Kudara Kannon, Horyuji Temple, Nara — A596

Golden Hall and Pagoda, Horyuji Temple, Nara — A597

**1967, Nov. 1                        Photo.**
934  A595  15y multicolored    .30  .25
**Engr.**
935  A596  15y pale grn, blk & red  .30  .25
**Photo. & Engr.**
936  A597  50y multicolored    1.25  .75
  Nos. 934-936 (3)    1.85  1.25
National treasures of Asuka Period (6th-7th centuries). No. 936 issued in sheets of 10.

Highway and Congress Emblem — A598

**1967, Nov. 5    Photo.    Perf. 13**
937  A598  50y multicolored    .95  .25
13th World Road Cong., Tokyo, Nov. 5-11.

---

Mt. Kumotori — A599

Lake Chichibu — A600

**1967, Nov. 27**
938  A599  7y olive    .30  .25
939  A600  15y red lilac    .35  .25
Chichibu-Tama National Park

Climbing Monkey Toy (Noborizaru), Miyazaki Prefecture — A601

**1967, Dec. 11    Photo.    Perf. 13**
940  A601  7y multicolored    .30  .25
New Year 1968. Sheets containing 4 No. 940 were awarded as prizes in the New Year lottery. Value $1.75.

Mt. Sobo — A602

Takachiho Gorge — A603

**1967, Dec. 20**
941  A602  15y multicolored    .30  .25
942  A603  15y multicolored    .30  .25
Sobo Katamuki Quasi-National Park.

Girl, Boy and Sakura Maru — A604

**1968, Jan. 19    Photo.    Perf. 13**
943  A604  15y ultra, ocher & blk  .30  .25
Cent. of the Meiji Era, and 1st Japanese Youth Good Will Cruise in celebration of the centenary.

Ashura, Kofukuji Temple, Nara — A605

Gakko Bosatsu, Todaiji Temple, Nara — A606

Kichijo Ten, Yakushiji Temple, Nara — A607

**1968, Feb. 1    Engr.    Perf. 13**
944  A605  15y sepia & car    .30  .25
**Engr. & Photo.**
945  A606  15y dk brn, pale grn & org    .30  .25
**Photo.**
946  A607  50y multicolored    1.25  1.25
  Nos. 944-946 (3)    1.85  1.25
Issued to show National Treasures of the Nara Period (710-784).

Grazing Cows
and Mt.
Yatsugatake
A608

Mt. Tateshina
A609

**1968, Mar. 21    Photo.    *Perf. 13***
947  A608  15y multicolored              .30  .25
948  A609  15y multicolored              .30  .25
Yatsugatake-Chushin-Kogen  Quasi-Natl.
Park.

Young Dancer
(Maiko) in Tenjuan
Garden, by
Bakusen
Tsuchida — A610

**1968, Apr. 20    Photo.    *Perf. 13***
949  A610  15y multicolored              .30  .25
Stamp Week, 1968. Sheets of 10 (5x2).

Rishiri Isl. Seen
from Rebun
Isl. — A611

**1968, May 10    Photo.    *Perf. 13***
950  A611  15y multicolored              .30  .25
Rishiri-Rebun Quasi-National Park.

Gold Lacquer and
Mother-of-Pearl
Box — A612

"The Origin of Shigisan" Painting from
Chogo-sonshiji, Nara — A613

Bodhisattva
Samantabhadra
A614

**1968, June 1    Engr. & Photo.**
951  A612  15y lt blue & multi           .30  .25
**Photo.**
952  A613  15y tan & multi               .30  .25
953  A614  50y sepia & multi            1.75 1.50
    Nos. 951-953 (3)                    2.35 2.00
Issued to show national treasures of the
Heian Period (8-12th centuries).

Memorial Tower and
Badge of
Hokkaido — A615

**1968, June 14**
954  A615  15y grn, vio bl, bis & red  .30  .25
Centenary of development of Hokkaido.

Sunrise over Pacific
and Fan
Palms — A616

**1968, June 26    Photo.    *Perf. 13***
955  A616  15y blk, org & red org        .30  .25
Return of Bonin Islands to Japan by US.

Map of Japan Showing
Postal Codes — A617

**Two types of inscription:**
Type I (enlarged)

あなたの住所にも郵便番号を

"Postal code also on your address"

Type II (enlarged)

あて名に郵便番号を

"Don't omit postal code on the
address"

**1968, July 1**
956  A617  7y yel grn & red (I)          2.00  .25
957  A617  7y yel grn & red (II)         2.00  .25
 *a.*   Pair, #956-957                   5.00 1.50
958  A617  15y sky bl & car (I)           .60  .25
 *a.*   Bklt. panes of 4 with gutter (4
        #958 + 2 #959 + 2 #611)        80.00 80.00
959  A617  15y sky bl & car (II)          .60  .25
 *d.*   Bklt. pane #958-959             1.75 1.25
        Nos. 956-959 (4)                5.20 1.00
Introduction of the postal code system.
The double booklet pane, No. 958a, comes
in two forms, the positions of the Postal Code
types being transposed.

**Coil Stamps**
***Perf. 13 Horiz.***
959A  A617  15y sky blue & car (I)  1.50  .85
959B  A617  15y sky blue & car
                           (II)      1.50  .85
 *c.*   Pair, #959A-959B            4.00 4.00

Kiso River
A618

Inuyama Castle
A619

**1968, July 20    *Perf. 13½***
960  A618  15y multicolored              .30  .25
961  A619  15y multicolored              .30  .25
Hida-Kisogawa Quasi-National Park.

Youth Hostel
Emblem, Trees and
Sun — A620

**1968, Aug. 6    Photo.    *Perf. 13***
962  A620  15y citron & multi            .30  .25
27th Intl. Youth Hostel Cong., Tokyo, 8/6-20.

Boys Forming
Tournament
Emblem — A621

Pitcher and
Tournament
Flag — A622

**1968, Aug. 9**
963  A621  15y yel grn, yel, blk &
                            red          .30  .25
964  A622  15y blk, yellow & blk         .30  .25
 *a.*   Pair, #963-964                   .65  .60
50th All-Japan High School Baseball Championship Tournament, Koshi-en Baseball
Grounds, Aug. 9. Nos. 963-964 printed
checkerwise.

Minamoto Yoritomo,
Jingoji, Kyoto — A623

Heiji
Monogatari
Scroll
Painting
A624

Red-threaded
Armor, Kasuga
Shrine,
Nara — A625

**1968, Sept. 16    Photo.    *Perf. 13***
965  A623  15y black & multi             .35  .25
966  A624  15y tan & multi               .35  .25
**Photo. & Engr.**
967  A625  50y multicolored             1.25 1.25
    Nos. 965-967 (3)                    1.95 1.75
National treasures of Kamakura period
(1180-1192 to 1333).

Mt. Iwate, seen
from
Hachimantai
A626

Lake Towada,
seen from Mt.
Ohanabe
A627

**1968, Sept. 16    Photo.**
968  A626  7y red brown                  .30  .25
969  A627  15y green                     .35  .25
Towada-Hachimantai National Park.

Gymnast, Tojimbo Cliff
and Narcissus — A628

**1968, Oct. 1    Photo.    *Perf. 13***
970  A628  15y multicolored              .30  .25
23rd National Athletic Meet, Fukui Prefecture, Oct. 1-6.

**Hokusai Type of 1964**
Design: 50y, "Fujimihara in Owari Province"
(cooper working on a barrel) from Hokusai's
"36 Views of Fuji."

**1968, Oct. 7**
971  A525  50y multicolored             1.00 1.00
Issued for International Letter Writing Week,
Oct. 7-13. Sheets of 10 (5x2).

Centenary
Emblem, Sun
and First
Western
Style Warship
A629

Imperial Carriage
Arriving in Tokyo
(1868), by Tomote
Kobori
A630

**1968, Oct. 23**
972  A629  15y vio bl, red, gold &
                          gray           .30  .25
973  A630  15y multicolored              .30  .25
 *a.*   Imperf., pair
Meiji Centenary Festival.

Old and New
Lighthouses — A631

**1968, Nov. 1    Photo.    *Perf. 13***
974  A631  15y multicolored              .30  .25
Centenary of the first western style lighthouse in Japan.

Ryo'o Court
Dance and
State Hall,
Imperial
Palace
A632

**1968, Nov. 14**
975  A632  15y multicolored              .30  .25
Completion of the new Imperial Palace.

Mt. Takachiho
A633

Mt. Motobu, Yaku
Island
A634

**1968, Nov. 20**
976  A633  7y purple                     .30  .25
977  A634  15y orange                    .35  .25
Kirishima-Yaku National Park.

Carved Toy Cock of
Yonezawa, Yamagata
Prefecture — A635

**1968, Dec. 5    Photo.    *Perf. 13***
978  A635  7y lt blue & multi            .30  .25
New Year 1969. Sheets containing 4 No.
978 were awarded as prizes in the New Year
lottery. Value $1.75.

Human Rights Flame,
Dancing Children and
Globe — A636

**1968, Dec. 10**
979  A636  50y orange & multi            .95  .25
International Human Rights Year.

Striped Squirrel — A637

**1968, Dec. 14**
980  A637  15y emerald & blk             .30  .25
Issued to promote saving.

Kochomon Cave
and Road — A638

**1969, Jan. 27    Photo.**
981  A638  15y multicolored              .30  .25
Echizen-Kaga-Kaigan Quasi-National Park.

Silver Pavilion, Jishoji Temple, Kyoto A639

Pagoda, Anrakuji Temple, Nagano A640

Winter Landscape by Sesshu — A641

**1969, Feb. 10    Photo.    Perf. 13**
982 A639 15y multicolored        .30  .25
**Photo. & Engr.**
983 A640 15y lt green & multi     .30  .25
**Photo.**
984 A641 50y tan, blk & ver      1.25 1.00
   Nos. 982-984 (3)          1.85 1.50
Issued to show national treasures of the Muromachi Period (1333-1572).

Mt. Chokai, seen from Tobishima Island — A642

**1969, Feb. 25                 Photo.**
985 A642 15y brt blue & multi    .30  .25
Chokai Quasi-National Park.

Mt. Koya Seen from Jinnogamine A643

Mt. Gomadan and Rhododendron A644

**1969, Mar. 25    Photo.    Perf. 13**
986 A643 15y multicolored        .30  .25
987 A644 15y multicolored        .30  .25
Koya-Ryujin Quasi-National Park.

Hair (Kami), by Kokei Kobayashi — A645

**1969, Apr. 20    Photo.    Perf. 13**
988 A645 15y multicolored        .30  .25
Issued for Philatelic Week.

Mother, Son Crossing Street — A646

**1969, May 10    Photo.    Perf. 13**
989 A646 15y lt blue, red & grn   .30  .25
National traffic safety campaign.

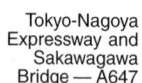

Tokyo-Nagoya Expressway and Sakawagawa Bridge — A647

**1969, May 26**
990 A647 15y multicolored        .30  .25
Completion of Tokyo-Nagoya Expressway.

Nuclear Ship Mutsu and Atom Diagram — A648

**1969, June 12**
991 A648 15y gray, blk, pink & bl  .30  .25
Issued to publicize the launching of the first Japanese nuclear ship, Mutsu.

Museum of Modern Art and Palette — A649

**1969, June 11    Photo.    Perf. 13½**
992 A649 15y lt bl, brn, yel & blk  .30  .25
Opening of the new National Museum of Modern Art, Tokyo.

Cable Ship KKD Maru and Map of Japan Sea — A650

**1969, June 25**
993 A650 15y lt bl, blk & ocher    .30  .25
Completion of the Japan sea cable between Naoetsu, Japan, and Nakhodka, Russia.

Postcards, Postal Code Symbol A651

Mailbox, Postal Code Symbol A652

**1969, July 1    Photo.    Perf. 13**
997 A651 7y yellow grn & car      .30  .25
998 A652 15y sky blue & car       .30  .25
1st anniv. of the postal code system and to promote its use.

Lions Emblem and Rose — A653

**1969, July 2**
999 A653 15y bl, blk, rose & gold  .30  .25
52nd Convention of Lions Intl., Tokyo, July 2-5.

Hotoke-ga-ura on Shimokita Peninsula, Northern Honshu — A654

**1969, July 15**
1000 A654 15y multicolored       .30  .25
Shimokita Hanto Quasi-National Park.

Himeji Castle, Hyogo Prefecture A655

"Pine Forest" (Detail), by Tohaku Hasegawa A656

"Cypresses," Attributed to Eitoku Kano A657

**1969, July 21    Photo. & Engr.**
1001 A655 15y lt blue & multi     .30  .25
**Photo.**
1002 A656 15y pale brown & blk    .30  .25
1003 A657 50y gold & multi       1.10  .60
   Nos. 1001-1003 (3)         1.70 1.10
Issued to show national treasures of the Momoyama period (1573-1614). The 50y is in sheets of 10 (2x5); Nos. 1001-1002 in sheets of 20 (5x4).

Harano-fudo Waterfall A658

Mt. Nagisan A659

**1969, Aug. 20**
1004 A658 15y multicolored       .30  .25
1005 A659 15y multicolored       .30  .25
Hyobosen-Ushiroyama-Nagisan Quasi-Natl. Park.

Mt. O-akan, Hokkaido A660

Mt. Iwo A661

**1969, Aug. 25    Photo.    Perf. 13**
1006 A660 7y bright blue         .30  .25
1007 A661 15y sepia              .30  .25
Akan National Park.

Angling, by Taiga Ikeno — A662

The Red Plum, by Korin Ogata — A663

Pheasant-shaped Incense Burner — A664

No. 1010, The White Plum, by Korin Ogata.

**1969, Sept. 25    Photo.    Perf. 13x13½**
1008 A662 15y multicolored       .30  .25

**Perf. 13**
1009 A663 15y gold & multi       .30  .25
1010 A663 15y gold & multi       .30  .25
  a.  Pair, #1009-1010          .75  .75
**Photo. & Engr.**
1011 A664 50y multicolored      1.00  .65
   Nos. 1008-1011 (4)       1.90 1.40
Natl. treasures, Edo Period (1615-1867).

Birds Circling Globe and UPU Congress Emblem — A665

Woman Reading Letter, by Utamaro — A666

Designs (UPU Congress Emblem and): 50y, Two Women Reading a Letter, by Harunobu. 60y, Man Reading a Letter (Miyako Dennai), by Sharaku.

**1969, Oct. 1    Photo.    Perf. 13**
1012 A665 15y red & multi        .30  .25
1013 A666 30y multicolored       .60  .40
1014 A666 50y multicolored      1.00  .50
1015 A666 60y multicolored      1.25  .75
   Nos. 1012-1015 (4)       3.15 1.90
16th UPU Congress, Tokyo, 10/1-11/16. 15y issued in sheets of 20, others in sheets of 10.

**Hokusai Type of 1964**
Design: 50y, "Passing through Koshu down to Mishima" from Hokusai's 36 Views of Fuji.

**1969, Oct. 7    Photo.    Perf. 13**
1016 A525 50y multicolored      1.25  .65
Issued for International Letter Writing Week Oct. 7-13. Sheets of 10 (5x2).

Rugby Player, Camellia and Oura Catholic Church — A667

**1969, Oct. 26**
1017 A667 15y lt ultra & multi    .30  .25
24th Natl. Athletic Meet, Nagasaki, 10/26-31.

Cape Kitayama A668

Goishi Coast A669

**1969, Nov. 20    Photo.    Perf. 13**
1018 A668 7y gray & dk blue      .30  .25
1019 A669 15y salmon & dk red     .30  .25
Rikuchu Coast National Park.

Worker in Hard Hat — A670

**1969, Nov. 26**
1020 A670 15y ultra, blk yel & brn  .30  .25
50th anniv. of the ILO.

Dog Amulet, Hokkeji, Nara — A671

**1969, Dec. 10**
1021 A671 7y orange & multi   .30 .25
New Year 1970. Sheets containing 4 No. 1021 were awarded as prizes in the New Year lottery. Value $1.50.

Aso Bay and Tsutsu Women with Horse — A672

**1970, Feb. 25**   **Photo.**   *Perf. 13*
1022 A672 15y multicolored   .30 .25
Iki-Tsushima Quasi-National Park.

Fireworks over EXPO '70 A673

Cherry Blossoms Around Globe A674

Irises, by Korin Ogata (1658-1716) A675

**1970, Mar. 14**   **Photo.**   *Perf. 13*
1023 A673 7y red & multi   .30 .25
1024 A674 15y gold & multi   .30 .25
1025 A675 50y gold & multi   .90 .45
  *a.*   Souv. sheet of 3, #1023-1025   1.75 1.75
  *b.*   Bklt. pane of 4 & 3 with gutter   3.00
  *Nos. 1023-1025 (3)*   1.50 .95
EXPO '70 Intl. Exposition, Senri, Osaka, Mar. 15-Sept. 13.
No. 1025b contains a pane of 4 No. 1023 and a pane with Nos. 1023-1025. A 35mm gutter separates the panes.

Woman with Hand Drum, by Saburosuke Okada — A676

**1970, Apr. 20**   **Photo.**   *Perf. 13*
1026 A676 15y multicolored   .45 .25
Issued for Stamp Week, Apr. 20-26.

Mt. Yoshino A677

Nachi Waterfall A678

**1970, Apr. 30**   **Photo.**   *Perf. 13*
1027 A677 7y gray & pink   .30 .25
1028 A678 15y pale blue & grn   .30 .25
Yoshino-Kumano National Park.

Pole Lanterns at EXPO A679

View of EXPO Within Globe A680

Grass in Autumn Wind, by Hoitsu Sakai (1761-1828) A681

**1970, June 15**   **Photo.**   *Perf. 13*
1029 A679 7y red & multi   .30 .25
1030 A680 15y blue & multi   .30 .25
1031 A681 50y silver & multi   .75 .30
  *a.*   Souv. sheet of 3, #1029-1031   2.00
  *b.*   Bklt. panes of 4 & 3 with gutter   2.50
  *Nos. 1029-1031 (3)*   1.35 .80
EXPO '70, 2nd issue.
No. 1031b contains a pane of 4 No. 1029 and a pane with Nos. 1029-1031. A 35mm gutter separates the panes.

Buildings and Postal Code Symbol — A682

**1970, July 1**   **Photo.**   *Perf. 13*
1032 A682 7y emerald & vio   .30 .25
1033 A682 15y brt blue & choc   .40 .25
Postal code system.

"Maiden at Dojo Temple" A683

Scene from "Sukeroku" A684

"The Subscription List" (Kanjincho) A685

**1970, July 10**
1034 A683 15y multicolored   .30 .25
1035 A684 15y multicolored   .30 .25
1036 A685 50y multicolored   .90 .30
  *Nos. 1034-1036 (3)*   1.50 .80
Issued to publicize the Kabuki Theater.

Girl Scout — A686

**1970, July 26**
1037 A686 15y multicolored   .30 .25
50th anniversary of Japanese Girl Scouts.

Kinoura Coast and Festival Drum — A687

Tate Mountains Seen from Himi Coast — A688

**1970, Aug. 1**
1038 A687 15y multicolored   .30 .25
1039 A688 15y multicolored   .30 .25
Noto Hanto Quasi-National Park.

Sunflower and UN Emblem — A689

**1970, Aug. 17**
1040 A689 15y lt blue & multi   .30 .25
Issued to publicize the 4th United Nations Congress on the Prevention of Crime and the Treatment of Offenders, Kyoto, Aug. 17-26.

Mt. Myogi — A690

Mt. Arafune — A691

**1970, Sept. 11**   **Photo.**   *Perf. 13*
1041 A690 15y multicolored   .30 .25
1042 A691 15y multicolored   .30 .25
Myogi-Arafune-Sakukogen Quasi-Natl. Park.

G.P.O., Tokyo, by Hiroshige III — A692

**1970, Oct. 6**
1043 A692 50y multicolored   .75 .30
Intl. Letter Writing Week, Oct. 6-12. Sheets of 10 (5x2). Design from wood block series, "Noted Places in Tokyo."

Equestrian, Mt. Iwate and Paulownia — A693

**1970, Oct. 10**   **Photo.**   *Perf. 13*
1044 A693 15y silver & multi   .30 .25
25th Natl. Athletic Meet, Morioka, 10/10-16.

Hodogaya Stage, by Hiroshige III — A694

**1970, Oct. 20**
1045 A694 15y silver & multi   .30 .25
Centenary of telegraph service in Japan.

Tree and UN Emblem — A695

50y, UN emblem and Headquarters with flags.

**1970, Oct. 24**
1046 A695 15y olive, ap grn & gold   .30 .25
1047 A695 50y multicolored   .65 .30
25th anniversary of United Nations.

Vocational Training Competition Emblem — A696

**1970, Nov. 10**   **Photo.**   *Perf. 13*
1048 A696 15y multicolored   .30 .25
The 19th International Vocational Training Competition, Chiba City, Nov. 10-19.

Diet Building and Doves — A697

**1970, Nov. 29**
1049 A697 15y multicolored   .30 .25
80th anniversary of Japanese Diet.

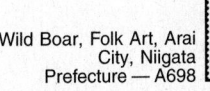

Wild Boar, Folk Art, Arai City, Niigata Prefecture — A698

**1970, Dec. 10**
1050 A698 7y multicolored   .30 .25
New Year 1971. Sheets containing 4 No. 1050 were awarded as prizes in the New Year lottery. Value $1.60.

Gen-jo-raku A699

Ko-cho A700

Tai-hei-raku A701

**1971, Apr. 1**   **Photo.**   *Perf. 13*
1051 A699 15y multicolored   .30 .25
1052 A700 15y multicolored   .30 .25
1053 A701 50y multicolored   .75 .25
  *Nos. 1051-1053 (3)*   1.35 .75
Gagaku, classical Japanese court entertainment.

Woman Voter and Parliament — A702

**1971, Apr. 10**   **Photo.**   *Perf. 13*
1054 A702 15y orange & multi   .30 .25
25th anniversary of woman suffrage.

Pines and Maple Leaves — A703

**1971, Apr. 18**
1055 A703 7y emerald & violet   .30 .25
National forestation campaign.

40 JAPAN

Woman of Tokyo, by
Kiyokata
Kaburagi — A704

**1971, Apr. 19**
1056 A704 15y gray & multi .35 .25
Philatelic Week, Apr. 19-25.

Mailman
A705

Mailbox
A706

Railroad Post
Office — A707

**1971, Apr. 20**
1057 A705 15y blk & org brn .30 .25
1058 A706 15y multicolored .30 .25
1059 A707 15y multicolored .30 .25
Nos. 1057-1059 (3) .90 .75
Centenary of Japanese postage stamps.

Titmouse — A708

**1971, May 10    Photo.    Perf. 13**
1060 A708 15y emer, blk & bis .30 .25
25th Bird Week.

Penguins — A709

**1971, June 23    Photo.    Perf. 13**
1061 A709 15y dk blue, yel & grn .30 .25
Antarctic Treaty pledging peaceful uses of
and scientific co-operation in Antarctica, 10th
anniv.

Goto
Wakamatsu
Seto Region
A710

Kujukushima ("99
Islands"), Kyushu
A711

**1971, June 26    Photo.    Perf. 13**
1062 A710 7y dark green .30 .25
1063 A711 15y deep brown .30 .25
Saikai National Park.

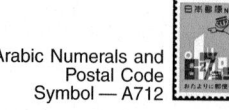

Arabic Numerals and
Postal Code
Symbol — A712

**1971, July 1**
1064 A712 7y emerald & red .30 .25
1065 A712 15y blue & carmine .30 .25
Promotion for postal code system.

## Types of 1962-67 and

Little
Cuckoo
A713

Mute
Swan
A714

Sika Deer
A715

Beetle
A716

Pine — A717

Noh Mask
A717a

Pheasant
A717b

Golden Eagle — A717c

Bronze Phoenix, Uji —
A718

Burial
Statue of
Warrior,
Ota
A718a

Buddha,
Sculpture,
685
A718b

Tentoki
Sculpture,
11th
Century
A718c

Bazara-
Taisho, c.
710-794
A718d

Goddess
Kissho — A718e

### Inscribed "NIPPON"
**Photo., Engr. (No. 1087)**

**1971-75                    Perf. 13**
1067 A713      3y emerald        .30  .25
  a.    Bklt. pane of 20 ('72)       2.00
1068 A714      5y bright blue    .30  .25
1069 A715     10y yel grn &
                 sep ('72)        .30  .25
  a.    Bklt. pane of 6 (2 #1069, 4
        #1071 with gutter btwn.)
        ('72)                        2.50
1070 A716     12y deep brown    .30  .25
1071 A717     20y grn & sep
                 ('72)           .30  .25
  a.    Pane of 10 (5x2) ('72)       4.00
1072 A565b    25y emer & lt
                 ultra ('72)     .40  .25
1074 A717a    70y dp org &
                 blk            1.00  .25
1075 A717b    80y crim & brn   1.25  .25
1076 A467     90y org & dk
                 brn           1.50  .25
1077 A717c    90y org & brn
                 ('73)         1.50  .25

1079 A569    120y dk brn & lt
                 grn ('72)     1.75  .25
1080 A718    150y lt & dk grn  2.50  .25
1081 A570    200y dp car
                 (18x22mm;
                 '72)          3.50  .25
1082 A718a   200y red brn
                 ('74)         3.50  .30
1083 A718b   300y dk blue
                 ('74)         5.50  .25
1084 A718c   400y car rose
                 ('74)         7.00  .25
1085 A718d   500y green ('74)  9.00  .35
1087 A718e  1000y multi ('75) 15.00  .75
  a.    Miniature sheet of 1   20.00 15.00
  Nos. 1067-1087 (18)         54.90  5.15
No. 1071a is imperf. on four sides.
Compare type A718a with types A1207 and
A2686. Compare types A713, A714 and
A718d with types A2683, A2684 and A2687.
See Nos. 1249-1250, 1254.

### Coil Stamp
**Perf. 13 Horiz.**
1088 A717 20y green & sep ('72)  .45 .30

Boy Scout
Bugler — A719

**1971, Aug. 2**
1090 A719 15y lt blue & multi    .30 .25
13th World Boy Scout Jamboree, Asagiri
Plain, Aug. 2-10.

Rose and
Rings — A720

**1971, Oct. 1**
1091 A720 15y ultra & multi      .30 .25
50th anniv. of Japanese Conciliation System.

Tokyo Horsedrawn
Streetcar, by
Yoshimura — A721

**1971, Oct. 6**
1092 A721 50y multicolored       .95 .30
Intl. Letter Writing Week. Sheets of 10 (5x2).

Emperor's Flag,
Chrysanthemums
and
Phoenix — A722

"Beyond the Sea,"
by Empress
Nagako — A723

**1971, Oct. 14**
1093 A722 15y gold, vio, red & bl  .30 .25
1094 A723 15y gold, vio, red & bl  .30 .25
  a.    Souv. sheet of 2, #1093-1094, im-
        perf.                        .85 .85
  b.    Pair, #1093-1094
European trip of Emperor Hirohito and
Empress Nagako, Sept. 28-Oct. 15. No. 1094a
has violet map of Asia, Africa and Europe in
background.

Tennis, Cape Shiono-
misaki, Plum
Blossoms — A724

**1971, Oct. 24    Photo.    Perf. 13**
1095 A724 15y orange & multi     .30 .25
26th National Athletic Meet, Wakayama Prefecture, Oct. 24-29.

Child's Face and
"100" — A725

**1971, Oct. 27**
1096 A725 15y pink, car & blk    .30 .25
Centenary of Japanese Family Registration
System.

Tiger, by Gaho
Hashimoto — A726

Design: No. 1098, Dragon, from "Dragon
and Tiger," by Gaho Hashimoto.

**1971, Nov. 1    Engr.    Perf. 13**
1097 A726 15y olive & multi      .30 .25
1098 A726 15y olive & multi      .30 .25
  a.    Pair, #1097-1098           .75 .65
Centenary of Government Printing Works.
Nos. 1097-1098 printed checkerwise.

Mt. Yotei from
Lake Toya
A727

Mt. Showa-
Shinzan
A728

**1971, Dec. 6**
1099 A727 7y slate grn & yel     .30 .25
1100 A728 15y pink & vio bl      .30 .25
Shikotsu-Toya National Park.

Treasure Ship — A729

**1971-72**
1101 A729 7y emerald, gold & org  .35 .30
1102 A729 10y lt blue, org & gold  .35 .30
New Year 1972. Sheets containing 3 No.
1102 were awarded as prizes in the New Year
lottery. Value $1.50.
Issued: 7y, 12/10; 10y, 1/11/72.

Downhill Skiing — A730

No. 1104, Bobsledding. 50y, Figure skating,
pairs.

**1972, Feb. 3    Photo.    Perf. 13**
**Size: 24x34mm**
1103 A730 20y ultra & multi      .30 .25
1104 A730 20y ultra & multi      .30 .25
**Size: 49x34mm**
1105 A730 50y ultra & multi      .65 .25
  a.    Souv. sheet of 3, #1103-1105  1.60 1.60
  Nos. 1103-1105 (3)            1.25 .75
11th Winter Olympic Games, Sapporo, Feb.
3-13. No. 1105a has continuous design
extending into margin.

Bunraku, Ningyo Jyoruri
Puppet Theater
A731         A732

A733

**1972, Mar. 1    Photo.    Perf. 13½**
1106 A731 20y gray & multi          .30  .25
**Perf. 12½x13**
1107 A732 20y multicolored     .30  .25
**Lithographed and Engraved**
**Perf. 13½x13**
1108 A733 50y multicolored     .75  .25
  Nos. 1106-1108 (3)     1.35  .75
  Japanese classical entertainment.

Express Train on New
Sanyo Line — A734

**1972, Mar. 15    Photo.    Perf. 13**
1109 A734 20y multicolored          .30  .25
  Centenary of first Japanese railroad.

Taishaku-
kyo Valley
A735

Hiba Mountains
Seen from Mt.
Dogo
A736

**1972, Mar. 24**
1110 A735 20y gray & multi     .30  .25
1111 A736 20y green & multi     .30  .25
  Hiba-Dogo-Taishaku Quasi-National Park.

Heart and UN
Emblem — A737

**1972, Apr. 15**
1112 A737 20y gray, red & black  .30  .25
  "Your heart is your health," World Health
Day.

"A Balloon Rising," by
Gakuryo
Nakamura — A738

**1972, Apr. 20**
1113 A738 20y violet bl & multi   .30  .25
  Philatelic Week, Apr. 20-26.

Shurei Gate,
Okinawa — A739

**1972, May 15**
1114 A739 20y ultra & multi          .30  .25
  Ratification of the Reversion Agreement
with US under which the Ryukyu Islands were
returned to Japan.

Camellia — A740

**1972, May 20**
1115 A740 20y brt grn, vio bl & yel  .30  .25
  National forestation campaign and 23rd
Arbor Day, May 21.

Mt. Kurikoma and
Kijiyama Kokeshi
Doll — A741

Naruko-kyo
Gorge and
Naruko Kokeshi
Doll — A742

**1972, June 20    Photo.    Perf. 13**
1116 A741 20y blue & multi     .30  .25
1117 A742 20y red & multi     .30  .25
  Kurikoma Quasi-National Park.

Envelope,
Postal
Code
Symbol
A743

Mailbox,
Postal
Code
Symbol
A744

**1972, July 1**
1118 A743 10y blue, blk & gray     .30  .25
1119 A744 20y emerald & org     .30  .25
  Publicity for the postal code system.

Mt.
Hodaka — A745

Mt. Tate — A746

**1972, Aug. 10    Photo.    Perf. 13**
1120 A745 10y rose & violet     .30  .25
1121 A746 20y blue & buff     .30  .25
  Chubu Sangaku National Park.

Ghost in
"Tamura"
A747

Lady Rokujo
in "Lady
Hollyhock"
A748

"Hagoromo"
(Feather
Robe)
A749

**1972, Sept. 20    Engr.**
1122 A747 20y multicolored     .30  .25
**Photo.**
1123 A748 20y multicolored     .30  .25
**Perf. 13½x13**
1124 A749 50y multicolored     .85  .25
  Nos. 1122-1124 (3)     1.45  .75
  Noh, classical public entertainment.

School Children — A750

**1972, Oct. 5    Photo.    Perf. 13**
1125 A750 20y lt ultra, vio bl & car  .30  .25
  Centenary of modern education system.

Eitai Bridge, Tokyo, by
Hiroshige III — A751

**1972, Oct. 9**
1126 A751 50y multicolored          .90  .25
  Intl. Letter Writing Week, Oct. 9-15.

Inauguration of
Railway Service,
by Hiroshige
III — A752

Locomotive, Class
C62 — A753

**1972, Oct. 14**
1127 A752 20y multicolored          .40  .25
1128 A753 20y multicolored          .40  .25
  Centenary of Japanese railroad system.

Kendo (Fencing) and
Sakurajima
Volcano — A754

**1972, Oct. 22**
1129 A754 10y yellow & multi          .30  .25
  27th National Athletic Meet, Kagoshima
Prefecture, Oct. 22-27.

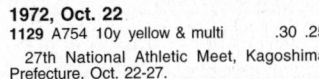

Boy Scout Shaking
Hand of Cub
Scout — A755

**1972, Nov. 4**
1130 A755 20y yellow & multi          .30  .25
  50th anniversary of the Boy Scouts of Japan.

US Ship, Yokohama
Harbor — A756

**1972, Nov. 28    Photo.    Perf. 13**
1131 A756 20y multicolored          .30  .25
  Centenary of Japanese customs. Wood
block by Hiroshige III (d. 1896).

"Clay Plate with Plum
Blossoms" — A757

**1972, Dec. 11**
1132 A757 10y blue & multi          .30  .25
  New Year 1973. Art work by Kenzan Ogata
(1663-1743). Sheets containing 3 No. 1132
were awarded as prizes in the New Year lottery. Value $1.60.

Mt.
Tsurugi — A758

Oboke
Valley — A759

**1973, Feb. 20    Photo.    Perf. 13**
1133 A758 20y multicolored          .30  .25
1134 A759 20y multicolored          .30  .25
  Mt. Tsurugi Quasi-National Park.

Mt. Takao
A760

Minoo Falls
A761

**1973, Mar. 12    Photo.    Perf. 13**
1135 A760 20y multicolored     .30  .25
1136 A761 20y multicolored     .30  .25
  Meiji Forests Quasi-National Park.

Phoenix Tree — A762

**1973, Apr. 7    Photo.    Perf. 13**
1137 A762 20y brt grn, yel & dk bl  .30  .25
  National forestation campaign.

Sumiyoshi Shrine
Visitor — A763

**1973, Apr. 20**
1138 A763 20y multicolored          .30  .25
  Philatelic Week, Apr. 20-26. Design from
painting by Ryusei Kishida (1891-1929) of his
daughter, "A Portrait of Reiko Visiting
Sumiyoshi Shrine."

Mt. Kamagatake
A764

Mt. Haguro
A765

**1973, May 25    Photo.    Perf. 13**
1139 A764 20y multicolored     .30  .25
1140 A765 20y multicolored     .30  .25
  Suzuka Quasi-National Park.

Chichijima
Beach — A766

Coral Reef on
Minami
Island — A767

**1973, June 26**
1141 A766 10y grnsh bl & Prus bl  .30  .25
1142 A767 20y lilac & dk pur     .30  .25
  Ogasawara National Park.
  5th anniversary of the return of the Bonin
(Ogasawara Islands) to Japan.

Tree, Postal Code Symbol
A768

Mailman, Postal Code Symbol
A769

**1973, July 1**    **Photo.**    *Perf. 13*
1143 A768 10y brt green & gold   .30 .25
1144 A769 20y blue, purple & car   .30 .25

Postal code system, 5th anniversary.

Sandan Gorge
A770

Mt. Shinnyu
A771

**1973, Aug. 28**    **Photo.**    *Perf. 13*
1145 A770 20y multicolored   .30 .25
1146 A771 20y multicolored   .30 .25

Nishi-Chugoku-Sanchi Quasi-National Park.

Tenryu Valley
A772

Mt. Horaiji
A773

**1973, Sept. 18**    **Photo.**    *Perf. 13*
1147 A772 20y lilac & multi   .30 .25
1148 A773 20y vio bl, lt bl & sil   .30 .25

Tenryu-Okumikawa Quasi-National Park.

Cock, by Jakuchu Ito (1716-1800) — A774

**1973, Oct. 6**
1149 A774 50y gold & multi   .90 .25

International Letter Writing Week, Oct. 7-13. Sheets of 10.

Woman Runner at Start — A775

**1973, Oct. 14**
1150 A775 10y silver & multi   .30 .25

28th National Athletic Meet, Chiba Prefecture, Oct. 14-19.

Kan Mon Bridge — A776

**1973, Nov. 14**    **Engr.**    *Perf. 13*
1151 A776 20y black, rose & yel   .30 .25

Opening of Kan Mon Bridge connecting Honshu and Kyushu.

Old Man and Dog — A777

Designs: No. 1153, Old man and wife pounding rice mortar, which yields gold. No. 1154, Old man sitting in tree and landlord admiring tree.

**1973, Nov. 20**       **Photo.**
1152 A777 20y multicolored   .30 .25
1153 A777 20y multicolored   .30 .25
1154 A777 20y multicolored   .30 .25
    Nos. 1152-1154 (3)   .90 .75

Folk tale "Hanasaka-jijii" (The Old Man Who Made Trees Bloom).

Bronze Lantern, Muromachi Period — A778

**1973, Dec. 10**
1155 A778 10y emerald, blk & org   .30 .25

New Year 1974. Sheets containing 3 No. 1155 were awarded as prizes in the New Year lottery. Value $1.75.

Nijubashi, Tokyo — A779

Imperial Palace, Tokyo — A780

**1974, Jan. 26**    **Photo.**    *Perf. 13*
1156 A779 20y gold & multi   .30 .25
1157 A780 20y gold & multi   .30 .25
   a.   Souv. sheet of 2, #1156-1157   1.10 1.10

50th anniversary of the wedding of Emperor Hirohito and Empress Nagako.

Young Wife — A781

Crane Weaving — A782

Cranes in Flight — A783

**1974, Feb. 20**    **Photo.**    *Perf. 13*
1158 A781 20y multicolored   .30 .25
1159 A782 20y multicolored   .30 .25
1160 A783 20y multicolored   .30 .25
    Nos. 1158-1160 (3)   .90 .75

Folk tale "Tsuru-nyobo" (Crane becomes wife of peasant).

Marudu Falls
A784

Marine Scene
A785

**1974, Mar. 15**
1161 A784 20y multicolored   .30 .25
1162 A785 20y multicolored   .30 .25

Iriomote National Park.

"Finger," by Ito Shinsui — A786

**1974, Apr. 20**    **Photo.**    *Perf. 13*
1163 A786 20y multicolored   .30 .25

Philatelic Week, Apr. 20-27.

Nambu Red Pine Sapling & Mt. Iwate — A787

**1974, May 18**
1164 A787 20y multicolored   .30 .25

National forestation campaign.

Supreme Court Building — A788

**1974, May 23**       **Engr.**
1165 A788 20y redsh brown   .30 .25

Completion of Supreme Court Building, Tokyo.

Midget Using Bowl as Boat — A789

Designs: No. 1167, Midget fighting demon. No. 1168, Princess and midget changed into prince with magic hammer.

**1974, June 10**    **Photo.**    *Perf. 13*
1166 A789 20y yellow & multi   .30 .25
1167 A789 20y bister & multi   .30 .25
1168 A789 20y bister & multi   .30 .25
    Nos. 1166-1168 (3)   .90 .75

Folk tale "Issun Hoschi" (The Story of the Mini-mini Boy).

"Police," by Kunimasa Baido — A790

**1974, June 17**       *Perf. 13*
1169 A790 20y multicolored   .30 .25

Centenary of the Tokyo Metropolitan Police Department.

Japanese Otter — A791

No. 1170, Mayailurus iriomotensis. No. 1172, Pentalagus furnessi. No. 1173, Pteropus pselaphon.

**Litho. and Engr.; Photo. and Engr.**
**(Nos. 1172-1173)**

**1974**
1170 A791 20y multicolored   .30 .25
1171 A791 20y multicolored   .30 .25
1172 A791 20y multicolored   .30 .25
1173 A791 20y multicolored   .30 .25
    Nos. 1170-1173 (4)   1.20 1.00

Nature conservation.
Issue dates: No. 1170, 3/25; No. 1171, 6/25; No. 1172, 8/30; No. 1173, 11/15.

Transfusion Bottle, Globe, Doves — A794

**1974, July 1**       **Photo.**
1174 A794 20y brt blue & multi   .30 .25

Intl. Red Cross Blood Donations Year.

Discovery of Kaguya Hime in Shining Bamboo — A795

Kaguya Hime as Grown-up Beauty — A796

Kaguya Hime and Escorts Returning to Moon — A797

**1974, July 29**    **Photo.**    *Perf. 13*
1175 A795 20y multicolored   .30 .25
1176 A796 20y multicolored   .30 .25
1177 A797 20y multicolored   .30 .25
    Nos. 1175-1177 (3)   .90 .75

Folk tale "Kaguya Hime" or "Tale of the Bamboo Cutter."

Rich and Poor Men with Wens — A798

Poor Man Dancing With Spirits — A798a

Design: No. 1180, Rich man with two wens, poor man without wen, spirits.

**1974, Sept. 9**    **Photo.**    *Perf. 13*
1178 A798 20y multicolored   .30 .25
1179 A798a 20y multicolored   .30 .25
1180 A798 20y multicolored   .30 .25
    Nos. 1178-1180 (3)   .90 .75

Folk tale "Kobutori Jiisan," or "The Old Man who had his Wen Taken by Spirits."

Goode's Projection and Diet — A799

"Aizen" by Ryushi Kawabata
A800

**1974, Oct. 1**    **Photo.**    *Perf. 13*
1181 A799 20y multicolored   .30 .25
1182 A800 50y multicolored   .90 .25

Interparliamentary Union, 61st Meeting, Tokyo, Nov. 2-11.

Pine and Hawk, by
Sesson — A801

**1974, Oct. 7**
1183 A801 50y sepia, blk & dk brn  .85 .25
Intl. Letter Writing Week, Oct. 6-12.

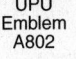

UPU
Emblem
A802

Tending Cow, Fan by
Sotatsu Tawaraya
A803

**1974, Oct. 9**
1184 A802 20y multicolored  .30 .25
1185 A803 50y multicolored  .85 .25
Centenary of Universal Postal Union.

Soccer Players and
Sailboat — A804

**1974, Oct. 20**  Photo.
1186 A804 10y multicolored  .30 .25
29th National Athletic Meet, Ibaraki Prefecture, Oct. 20-25.

Various
Mushrooms — A805

**1974, Nov. 2**
1187 A805 20y multicolored  .30 .25
9th International Congress on the Cultivation of Edible Fungi, Japan, Nov. 4-13.

Steam Locomotive
Class
D51 — A806

Class
C57 — A807

Designs: Steam locomotives.

**1974, Nov. 26**  Photo.  Perf. 13
1188 A806 20y shown  .45 .25
1189 A807 20y shown  .45 .25
 a.  Pair, #1188-1189  .95 .60

**1975, Feb. 25**
1190 A806 20y Class D52  .45 .25
1191 A807 20y Class C58  .45 .25
 a.  Pair, #1190-1191  .95 .60

Class
8620 — A808

Class
C11 — A809

**1975, Apr. 3**
1192 A808 20y shown  .30 .25
1193 A809 20y shown  .30 .25
 a.  Pair, #1192-1193  .95 .60

**1975, May 15**
1194 A806 20y Class 9600  .30 .25
1195 A807 20y Class C51  .30 .25
 a.  Pair, #1194-1195  .95 .60

**1975, June 10**  Photo. & Engr.
1196 A806 20y Class 7100  .30 .25
1197 A806 20y Class 150  .30 .25
 a.  Pair, #1196-1197  .95 .60
 Nos. 1188-1197 (10)  3.60 2.50
Japanese National Railways.

Ornamental Nail Cover,
Katsura Palace — A810

**1974, Dec. 10**
1198 A810 10y blue & multi  .30 .25
New Year 1975. Sheets containing 3 No. 1198 were awarded as prizes in the New Year Lottery. Value $1.60.

Short-tailed
Albatrosses
A811

Bonin Island
Honey-eater
A812

Temminck's
Robin — A813

Ryukyu-Yamagame
Tortoise — A814

Design: No. 1200, Japanese cranes.

**1975-76**  Photo. & Engr.  Perf. 13
1199 A811 20y multicolored  .30 .25
1200 A811 20y multicolored  .30 .25
1201 A812 20y multicolored  .30 .25
1202 A813 50y multicolored  .75 .25
1203 A814 50y multicolored  .75 .25
 Nos. 1199-1203 (5)  2.40 1.25

Nature conservation.
Issued: No. 1199, 1/16; No. 1200, 2/13; No. 1201, 8/8; No. 1202, 2/27/76; No. 1203, 3/25/76.

Taro Urashima
Releasing
Turtle — A815

Palace of the Sea
God and
Fish — A816

Smoke from
Casket Making
Taro an Old
Man — A817

**1975, Jan. 28**  Photo.  Perf. 13
1204 A815 20y multicolored  .30 .25
1205 A816 20y multicolored  .30 .25
1206 A817 20y multicolored  .30 .25
 Nos. 1204-1206 (3)  .90 .75
Folk tale "Legend of Taro Urashima."

Kan-mon-sho (Seeing
and Hearing), by Shiko
Munakata — A818

**1975, Mar. 20**  Photo.  Perf. 13
1207 A818 20y brown & multi  .30 .25
Japan Broadcasting Corp., 50th anniv.

Old Man Feeding
Mouse
A819

Man Following
Mouse
Underground
A820

Mice Entertaining
and Bringing
Gifts — A821

**1975, Apr. 15**  Photo.  Perf. 13
1208 A819 20y multicolored  .30 .25
1209 A820 20y multicolored  .30 .25
1210 A821 20y multicolored  .30 .25
 Nos. 1208-1210 (3)  .90 .75
Folk tale "Paradise for the Mice."

Matsuura
Screen
(detail),
16th
Century
A822

**1975, Apr. 21**
1211  20y denomination at LL  .30 .25
1212  20y denomination at LR  .30 .25
 a.  A822 Pair, #1211-1212  .80 .65
Philatelic Week, Apr. 21-27.

Oil Derricks, Congress
Emblem — A824

**1975, May 10**  Photo.  Perf. 13
1213 A824 20y multicolored  .30 .25
9th World Petroleum Cong., Tokyo, May 11-16.

Trees and River — A825

**1975, May 24**
1214 A825 20y green & multi  .30 .25
National forestation campaign.

IWY Emblem, Sun and
Woman — A826

**1975, June 23**
1215 A826 20y orange & multi  .30 .25
International Women's Year 1975.

Okinawan
Dancer,
EXPO 75
Emblem
A827

Birds in
Flight
(Bingata)
A828

Aquapolis
and Globe
A829

**1975, July 19**  Photo.  Perf. 13
1216 A827 20y ultra & multi  .30 .25
1217 A828 30y blue grn & multi  .50 .25
1218 A829 50y ultra & multi  .80 .25
 a.  Souv. sheet of 3, #1216-1218  1.75 1.75
 Nos. 1216-1218 (3)  1.60 .75
Oceanexpo 75, 1st Intl. Ocean Exposition, Okinawa, July 20, 1975-Jan. 18, 1976.

**Historic Ship Issue**

Kentoshi-sen 7th-
9th
Centuries — A830

Ships: No. 1220, Kenmin-sen, 7th-9th cent. No. 1221, Goshuin-sen, merchant ship, 16th-17th cent. No. 1222, Tenchi-maru, state barge, built 1630. No. 1223, Sengoku-bune (cargo ship) and fishing vessel. No. 1224, Shoheimaru, 1852, European-type sailing ship. No. 1225, Taisei-maru, four-mast bark training ship, 1903. No. 1226, Tenyomaru, first Japanese passenger liner, 1907. No. 1227, Asama-maru, passenger liner. No. 1228, Kinai-maru, transpacific freighter and Statue of Liberty. No. 1229, Container ship. No. 1230, Tanker.

**1975-76**  Engr.  Perf. 13
1219 A830 20y rose red  .30 .25
1220 A830 20y sepia  .30 .25
 a.  Pair, #1219-1220  .75 .75
1221 A830 20y lt olive  .30 .25
1222 A830 20y dark blue  .30 .25
 a.  Pair, #1221-1222  .75 .75
1223 A830 50y violet blue  .65 .25
1224 A830 50y lilac  .65 .25
 a.  Pair, #1223-1224  1.50 .75
1225 A830 50y gray  .65 .25
1226 A830 50y dark brown  .65 .25
 a.  Pair, #1225-1226  1.50 .75
1227 A830 50y olive green  .65 .25
1228 A830 50y olive brown  .65 .25
 a.  Pair, #1227-1228  1.50 .75
1229 A830 50y ultra  .65 .25
1230 A830 50y violet blue  .65 .25
 a.  Pair, #1229-1230  1.50 .75
 Nos. 1219-1230 (12)  6.40 3.00
Printed checkerwise in sheets of 20.
Issued: Nos. 1219-1220, 8/30; Nos. 1221-1222, 9/25; Nos. 1223-1224, 3/11/76; Nos. 1225-1226, 4/12/76; Nos. 1227-1228, 6/1/76; Nos. 1229-1230, 8/18/76.

Apple and Apple
Tree — A831

**1975, Sept. 17**  Photo.  Perf. 13
1231 A831 20y gray, black & red  .30 .25
Centenary of apple cultivation in Japan.

Peacock, by Korin
Ogata — A832

**1975, Oct. 6**  Photo.  Perf. 13
1232 A832 50y gold & multi  .80 .25
Intl. Letter Writing Week, Oct. 6-12.

44

JAPAN

American Flag and
Cherry
Blossoms — A833

Japanese Flag
and
Dogwood — A834

**1975, Oct. 14**
1233 A833 20y ultra & multi .30 .25
1234 A834 20y green & multi .30 .25
   a.  Souv. sheet of 2, #1233-1234 .80 .60
Visit of Emperor Hirohito and Empress
Nagako to the United States, Oct. 1-14.

Savings Box and
Coins — A835

**1975, Oct. 24**
1235 A835 20y multicolored .30 .25
Japan's Postal Savings System, centenary.

Weight Lifter — A836

**1975, Oct. 25**
1236 A836 10y multicolored .30 .25
30th National Athletic Meet, Mie Prefecture,
Oct. 26-31.

Papier-mache Dragon,
Fukushima
Prefecture — A837

**1975, Dec. 13    Photo.    Perf. 13**
1237 A837 10y multicolored .30 .25
New Year 1976. Sheets containing 3 No.
1237 were awarded as prizes in the New Year
Lottery. Value $1.60.

**Types of 1963-74 and**

Japanese
Narcissus
A841

Noh Mask,
Old Man
A843

Guardian
Dog,
Katori
Shrine
A845

Sho-
Kannon,
Yakushiji
Temple
A846

**Inscribed "NIPPON"**

Designs: 50y, Nyoirin Kannon, Chuguji Temple. 150y, Bronze
phoenix, Uji. 200y, Clay burial figure of warrior, Ota.

**1976-79    Photo.    Perf. 13**
1244 A565f 50y emerald .80 .25
   a.  Bkt. panes of 2 & 4 with gut-
       ter 5.00
1245 A841 60y multicolored 1.10 .25
1248 A843 140y lil rose & lil 2.25 .25
1249 A718 150y red org & brn 2.25 .25
1250 A718a 200y red orange 3.00 .25
1251 A845 250y blue 3.00 .25
1253 A846 350y dk violet brn 5.50 .25
   Nos. 1244-1253 (7) 17.90 1.75

**Coil Stamps**
**Perf. 13 Horiz.**
1254 A715 10y yel grn & sep
          ('79) .30 .25
1256 A565f 50y emerald .90 .25
1257 A567c 100y ver & blk ('79) 1.50 .30
   Nos. 1254-1257 (3) 2.70 .80
   See No. 1631.

Hikone
Folding
Screen
(detail),
17th
Century
A850

**1976, Apr. 20    Photo.    Perf. 13**
1258  50y denomination at LR .55 .25
1259  50y denomination at UR .55 .25
   a.  A850 Pair, #1258-1259 1.25 .75
Philatelic Week, Apr. 20-26.

Plum Blossoms, Cedars,
Mt. Tsukuba — A852

**1976, May 22**
1260 A852 50y multicolored .55 .25
National forestation campaign.

Green Tree
Frog — A853

Bitterlings — A854

Sticklebacks
A855

**1976    Photo. & Engr.    Perf. 13**
1261 A853 50y multicolored .75 .25
1262 A854 50y multicolored .75 .25
1263 A855 50y multicolored .75 .25
   Nos. 1261-1263 (3) 2.25 .75
Nature conservation.
Issued: No. 1261, 7/20; No. 1262, 8/26; No.
1263, 9/16.

Crows, by Yosa
Buson — A856

**1976, Oct. 6    Photo.    Perf. 13**
1264 A856 100y gray, blk & buff 1.25 .25
Intl. Letter Writing Week, Oct. 6-12.

Gymnasts and
Stadium — A857

**1976, Oct. 23    Photo.    Perf. 13**
1265 A857 20y multicolored .30 .25
31st National Athletic Meet, Saga Prefecture, Oct. 24-29.

Cable, Cable Ship,
Map of East China
Sea — A858

**1976, Oct. 25**
1266 A858 50y blue, blk & silver .90 .25
Opening of Sino-Japanese cable between
Shanghai and Reihoku-cho, Kumamoto
Prefecture.

Classical Court
Dance — A859

Imperial
Coach — A860

**1976, Nov. 10    Photo.    Perf. 13**
1267 A859 50y multicolored .40 .25
1268 A860 50y multicolored .40 .25
   a.  Souv. sheet of 2, #1267-1268 .90 .65
Emperor Hirohito's accession to the throne,
50th anniversary.

Kindergarten
Class — A861

**1976, Nov. 16**
1269 A861 50y multicolored .55 .25
Centenary of first kindergarten in Japan.

Healthy
Family — A862

**1976, Nov. 24**
1270 A862 50y multicolored .55 .25
Natl. Health Insurance, 50th anniv.

Bamboo Toy
Snake — A863

**1976, Dec. 1    Photo.    Perf. 13**
1271 A863 20y multicolored .30 .25
New Year 1977. Sheets containing 2 No.
1271 were awarded as prizes in the New Year
lottery. Value $1.50.

**National Treasures**

East Pagoda,
Yakushiji
Temple, c.
730 — A864

Deva King in
Armor Holding
Spear, Nara
Period — A865

**1976, Dec. 9    Photo.    Perf. 13**
1272 A864 50y multicolored .75 .25
**Engr.**
1273 A865 100y green & multi 1.50 .30

Golden
Pavilion,
Toshodai-ji
Temple, 8th
Century
A866

Praying Women,
from Heike Nokyo
Sutra, 12th
Century — A867

**Photogravure and Engraved**
**1977, Jan. 20    Perf. 13**
1274 A866 50y multicolored .75 .25
**Photo.**
1275 A867 100y multicolored 1.50 .30

Comic Picture Scroll, Attributed to
Toba Sojo Kakuyu (1053-1140)
A868

Saint on Cloud,
11th Century Wood
Carving, Byodoin
Temple — A869

**1977, Mar. 25    Photo.    Perf. 13**
1276 A868 50y multicolored .75 .25
**Engr.**
1277 A869 100y multicolored 1.50 .30

Noblemen on Way to Court, from
Picture Scroll, Heian Period
A870

Statue of Seitaka-
doji, Messenger,
Kamakura
Period — A871

**1977, June 27    Photo.    Perf. 13**
1278 A870 50y multicolored .75 .25
**Engr.**
1279 A871 100y multicolored 1.50 .30

The Recluse Han
Shan, 14th Century
Painting — A872

Tower,
Matsumoto
Castle, 16th
Century
A873

**1977, Aug. 25    Photo.    *Perf. 13***
1280  A872  50y multicolored          .75  .25
**Photogravure and Engraved**
1281  A873  100y black & multi         1.50  .30

Pine and
Flowers,
Chishakuin
Temple,
Kyoto, 1591
A874

Main Hall,
Kiyomizu
Temple,
1633
A875

**1977, Nov. 16    Photo.    *Perf. 13***
1282  A874  50y multicolored          .75  .25
**Engr.**
1283  A875  100y                      1.50  .30

Scene from
Tale of Genji,
by Sotatsu
Tawaraya
A876

Inkstone
Case, by
Koetsu
Honami
A877

**1978, Jan. 26    Photo.    *Perf. 13***
1284  A876  50y multicolored          .75  .25
**Photogravure and Engraved**
1285  A877  100y black & multi        1.50  .30

Family Enjoying Cool Evening, by
Morikage Kusumi
A878

Yomeimon,
Toshogu
Shrine, 1636
A879

**1978, Mar. 3    Photo.    *Perf. 13***
1286  A878  50y gray & multi          .75  .25
**Photogravure and Engraved**
1287  A879  100y multicolored         1.50  .30

Horseshoe Crabs
A884

Graphium
Doson
Albidum
A885

Firefly
A886

Cicada
A887

Dragonfly — A888

**1977    Photo.    *Perf. 13***
1292  A884  50y multicolored          .75  .25
**Photogravure and Engraved**
1293  A885  50y multicolored          .75  .25
1294  A886  50y multicolored          .75  .25
1295  A887  50y multicolored          .75  .25
**Photo.**
1296  A888  50y multicolored          .75  .25
     Nos. 1292-1296 (5)              3.75  1.25
Issued: No. 1292, 2/18; No. 1293, 5/18; No.
1294, 7/22; No. 1295, 8/15; No. 1296, 9/14.

Figure
Skating
A889

Figure Skating
Pair
A890

**1977, Mar. 1**
1297  A889  50y silver & multi        .55  .25
1298  A890  50y silver & multi        .55  .25
World Figure Skating Championships,
National Yoyogi Stadium, March 1-6.

Sun Shining on
Forest — A891

**1977, Apr. 16    Photo.    *Perf. 13***
1299  A891  50y green & multi         .55  .25
National forestation campaign.

Weavers
and
Dyers
(Detail
from
Folding
Screen)
A892

**1977, Apr. 20**
1300       50y denomination at LL     .55  .25
1301       50y denomination at UL     .55  .25
   a.  A892  Pair, #1300-1301         1.10  .60
Philatelic Week, Apr. 20-26.

Nurses — A894

**1977, May 30    Photo.    *Perf. 13***
1302  A894  50y multicolored          .55  .25
16th Quadrennial Congress of the Intl.
Council of Nurses, Tokyo, May 30-June 3.

Fast Breeder Reactor,
Central Part — A895

**1977, June 6**
1303  A895  50y multicolored          .55  .25
Experimental fast breeder reactor "Joyo,"
which began operating Apr. 24, 1977.

Workers
and Safety
Emblems
A896

Work on
High-rise
Buildings
A897

Cargo
Unloading
A898

Machinery
Work
A899

**1977, July 1**
1304  A896  50y multicolored          .55  .25
1305  A897  50y multicolored          .55  .25
1306  A898  50y multicolored          .55  .25
1307  A899  50y multicolored          .55  .25
   a.   Block or strip of 4, #1304-1307  3.50  1.25
National Safety Week, July 1-July 7.

Carrier Pigeons,
Mail Box, UPU
Emblem — A900

UPU Emblem,
Postal Service
Flag of Meiji Era,
world
Map — A900a

**1977, June 20    Photo.    *Perf. 13***
1308  A900   50y multicolored         .55  .25
1309  A900a  100y multicolored        1.50  .30
   a.   Souv. sheet of 2, #1308-1309  2.25  2.00
Cent. of Japan's admission to the UPU.

Surgeon in
Operating
Room — A901

**1977, Sept. 3    Photo.    *Perf. 13***
1310  A901  50y multicolored          .55  .25
27th Cong. of the Intl. Surgeon's Society on
the 75th anniv. of its founding, Kyoto, 9/3-8.

Child Using
Telephone, Map of
New Cable
Route — A902

**1977, Aug. 26**
1311  A902  50y multicolored          .55  .25
Inauguration of underwater telephone cable
linking Okinawa, Luzon and Hong Kong.

Early Speaker, Waves
and Telegraph
Key — A903

**1977, Sept. 24    Photo.    *Perf. 13***
1312  A903  50y multicolored          .55  .25
50th anniversary of amateur radio in Japan.

Bicyclist, Mt. Iwaki and
Iwaki River — A904

**1977, Oct. 1**
1313  A904  20y multicolored          .30  .25
32nd National Athletic Meet, Aomori Prefecture, Oct. 2-7.

Flowers and Ducks,
Attributed to Hasegawa
Tohaku — A905

**1977, Oct. 6**
1314  A905  100y multicolored         1.50  .30
Intl. Letter Writing Week, Oct. 6-12.

Dinosaur, Stars,
Museum — A906

**1977, Nov. 2    Photo.    *Perf. 13***
1315  A906  50y multicolored          .75  .25
Centenary of National Science Museum.

Decorated Horse, Fushimi
Toy — A907

**1977, Dec. 1    Photo.    *Perf. 13***
1316  A907  20y multicolored          .30  .25
New Year 1978. Sheets containing 2 No.
1316 were awarded as prizes in the New Year
lottery. Value $1.60.

Tokyo Subway,
1927 — A908

**1977, Dec. 6**
1317       50y shown                  .75  .25
1318       50y Subway, 1977           .75  .25
   a.  A908  Pair, #1317-1318         1.60  .60
Tokyo Subway, 50th anniversary.

Primrose
A909

Pinguicula
Ramosa
A910

Dicentra — A911

**1978 Photo. & Engr. Perf. 13**
**1319** A909 50y multicolored .75 .25
**1320** A910 50y multicolored .75 .25
**1321** A911 50y multicolored .75 .25
*Nos. 1319-1321 (3)* 2.25 .75
Nature protection.
Issued: No. 1319, 4/12; No. 1320, 6/8; No. 1321, 7/25.

Kanbun Bijinzu Folding Screen, Edo Period A912

**1978, Apr. 20 Photo. Perf. 13**
**1322** 50y inscribed at left .55 .25
**1323** 50y inscribed at right 1.40 .25
*a.* A912 Pair, #1322-1323 2.10 .65
Philatelic Week, Apr. 16-22.

Rotary Emblem, Mt. Fuji — A914

**1978, May 13 Photo. Perf. 13**
**1324** A914 50y multicolored .75 .25
69th Rotary International Convention, Tokyo, May 14-18.

Congress Emblem, by Taro Okamoto — A915

**1978, May 15**
**1325** A915 50y multicolored .55 .25
23rd International Ophthalmological Congress, Kyoto, May 14-20.

Narita International Airport, Tokyo — A916

**1978, May 20**
**1326** A916 50y multicolored .65 .25
Opening of Tokyo International Airport.

Rainbow, Japanese Cedars, Cape Ashizuri — A917

**1978, May 20**
**1327** A917 50y multicolored .55 .25
National forestation campaign.

Lion, by Sotatsu Tawaraya, Lions Emblem — A918

**1978, June 21 Photo. Perf. 13**
**1328** A918 50y multicolored .75 .25
61st Lions Intl. Convention, Tokyo, 6/21-24.

## Sumo Print Issues

Grand Champion Hidenoyama with Sword Bearer and Herald, by Kunisada I (Toyokuni III) — A919

Ekoin Drum Tower, Ryogoku, by Hiroshige — A921

### Photogravure and Engraved
**1978, July 1 Perf. 13**
**1329** 50y multicolored .55 .25
**1330** 50y multicolored .55 .25
*a.* A919 Pair, #1329-1330 1.25 .75
**Photo.**
**1331** A921 50y multicolored .55 .25
*Nos. 1329-1331 (3)* 1.65 .75

Champions Tanikaze and Onogawa in Ring-entry Ceremony, 1782, by Shunsho — A922

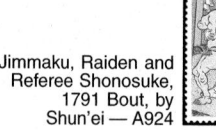

Jimmaku, Raiden and Referee Shonosuke, 1791 Bout, by Shun'ei — A924

### Photogravure and Engraved
**1978, Sept. 9 Perf. 13**
**1332** 50y multicolored .55 .25
**1333** 50y multicolored .55 .25
*a.* A922 Pair, #1332-1333 1.25 .75
**1334** A924 50y multicolored .55 .25
*Nos. 1332-1334 (3)* 1.65 .75

Referee Shonosuke and Champion Onomatsu, by Kunisada I — A925

Children's Sumo Play, by Utamaro — A927

**1978, Nov. 11 Perf. 13**
**1335** 50y multicolored .55 .25
**1336** 50y multicolored .55 .25
*a.* A925 Pair, #1335-1336 1.25 .75
**1337** A927 50y multicolored .55 .25
*Nos. 1335-1337 (3)* 1.65 .75

Wrestlers on Ryogoku Bridge, by Kunisada I — A928

Bow-receiving Ceremony at Tournament, by Kunisada II — A930

**1979, Jan. 13 Perf. 13**
**1338** 50y multicolored .55 .25
**1339** 50y multicolored .55 .25
*a.* A928 Pair, #1338-1339 1.25 .75
**1340** A930 50y multicolored .55 .25
*Nos. 1338-1340 (3)* 1.65 .75

Takekuma and Iwamigata (Hidenoyama) Wrestling, by Kuniyoshi — A931

Daidozan (Great Child Mountain) in Ring-entry Ceremony, by Sharaku — A933

**1979, Mar. 10 Perf. 13**
**1341** 50y multicolored .55 .25
**1342** 50y multicolored .55 .25
*a.* A931 Pair, #1341-1342 1.25 .75
**1343** A933 50y multicolored .55 .25
*Nos. 1341-1343 (3)* 1.65 .75

Radio Gymnastics Emblem — A934

**1978, Aug. 1 Photo. Perf. 13**
**1344** A934 50y multicolored .75 .25
Radio gymnastics program exercises, 50th anniversary.

Chamber of Commerce and Industry — A935

**1978, Aug. 28 Photo. Perf. 13**
**1345** A935 50y multicolored .55 .25
Tokyo Chamber of Commerce, centenary.

Symbolic Sculptures, Tokyo Stock Exchange — A936

**1978, Sept. 14 Engr. Perf. 13**
**1346** A936 50y lilac, grn & brn .55 .25
Centenary of the Tokyo and Osaka Stock Exchanges.

Flowering Plum with Pheasant, from Screen, Tenkyuin Temple — A937

**1978, Oct. 6 Photo. Perf. 13**
**1347** A937 100y multicolored 1.50 .30
Intl. Letter Writing Week, Oct. 6-12.

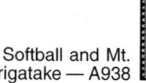

Softball and Mt. Yarigatake — A938

**1978, Oct. 14**
**1348** A938 20y multicolored .30 .25
33rd National Athletic Meet, Nagano Prefecture, Oct. 15-20.

Artificial Hip, Orthopedists' Emblem — A939

**1978, Oct. 16**
**1349** A939 50y multicolored .55 .25
14th World Cong. of Intl. Soc. of Orthopedic Surgeons (50th anniv.), Kyoto, Oct. 15-20.

Telescope and Stars — A940

**1978, Dec. 1 Photo.**
**1350** A940 50y multicolored .55 .25
Tokyo Astronomical Observatory, cent.

Sheep Bell, Nakayama Toy — A941

**1978, Dec. 4**
**1351** A941 20y multicolored .30 .25
New Year 1979. Sheets containing 2 No. 1351 were awarded as prizes in the New Year Lottery. Value $1.60.

Family, Human Rights Emblem — A942

**1978, Dec. 4**
**1352** A942 50y multicolored .55 .25
Human Rights Week, Dec. 4-10.

Hands Shielding Children — A943

**1979, Feb. 16 Photo. Perf. 13**
**1353** A943 50y multicolored .55 .25
Education of the handicapped, centenary.

Telephone Dials — A944

**1979, Mar. 14 Photo. Perf. 13**
**1354** A944 50y multicolored .55 .25
Nation-wide telephone automatization completion.

Sketch of Man, by Leonardo da Vinci — A945

**Photogravure and Engraved**
**1979, Apr. 7**          *Perf. 13*
1355 A945 50y multicolored          .55 .25
Centenary of promulgation of State Medical Act, initiating modern medicine.

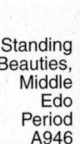

Standing Beauties, Middle Edo Period A946

**1979, Apr. 20**          **Photo.**
1356 50y multicolored          .55 .25
1357 50y multicolored          .55 .25
a. A946 Pair, #1356-1357          1.25 .65
Philatelic Week, Apr. 16-22.

Mt. Horaiji and Maple — A948

**1979, May 26**   **Photo.**   *Perf. 13*
1358 A948 50y multicolored          .55 .25
National forestation campaign.

**Modern Japanese Art Issue**

Merciful Mother Goddess, by Kano Hogai A949

Sea God's Princess, by Aoki Shigeru A950

**1979, May 30**   **Photo.**   *Perf. 13*
1359 A949 50y multicolored          .75 .25
1360 A950 50y multicolored          .75 .25

Fire Dance, by Gyoshu Hayami A951

Leaning Figure, by Tetsugoro Yorozu A952

**1979, June 25**   **Photo.**   *Perf. 13*
1361 A951 50y red & multi          .75 .25
**Photogravure and Engraved**
1362 A952 50y red & multi          .75 .25

The Black Cat, by Shunso Hishida A953

Kinyo, by Sotaro Yasui A954

**1979, Sept. 21**   **Photo.**   *Perf. 13*
1363 A953 50y multicolored          .75 .25
1364 A954 50y multicolored          .75 .25

Nude, by Kagaku Murakami — A955

Harvest, by Asai Chu — A956

**Photogravure and Engraved**
**1979, Nov. 22**          *Perf. 13*
1365 A955 50y multicolored          .75 .25
1366 A956 50y multicolored          .75 .25

Salmon, by Yuichi Takahashi A956a

Hall of the Supreme Buddha, by Kokei Kabayashi A956b

**Photogravure and Engraved**
**1980, Feb. 22**          *Perf. 13½*
1367 A956a 50y multicolored          .75 .25
**Photo.**
1368 A956b 50y multicolored          .75 .25

Quarantine Officers, Ships, Plane, Microscope — A957

**1979, July 14**          **Photo.**
1369 A957 50y multicolored          .65 .25
Centenary of Japanese Quarantine system.

Girl Mailing Letter A958

Hakata Doll with Letter-paper Roll A959

**1979, July 23**
1370 A958 20y multicolored          .30 .25
1371 A959 50y multicolored          .55 .25
Letter Writing Day.

Pitcher, Baseball with Black Lion Emblem — A960

**1979, July 27**
1372 A960 50y multicolored          .55 .25
50th National Inter-city Amateur Baseball Tournament, Tokyo, August.

Girl Floating in Space — A961

Design: No. 1374, Boy floating in space.

**1979, Aug. 1**
1373 A961 50y magenta & multi          .75 .25
1374 A961 50y blue & multi          .75 .25
a. Souv. sheet of 2, #1373-1374   1.60 1.10
International Year of the Child.

**Japanese Song Issue**

Moon over Castle, by Rentaro Taki A962

Evening Glow, by Shin Kusakawa A963

**1979, Aug. 24**          **Photo. & Engr.**
1375 A962 50y multicolored          .55 .25
1376 A963 50y multicolored          .55 .25

Maple Leaves, by Teiichi Okano A964

The Birthplace, by Teiichi Okano A965

**1979, Nov. 26**
1377 A964 50y multicolored          .55 .25
1378 A965 50y multicolored          .55 .25

Winter Landscape A966

Mt. Fuji A967

**1980, Jan. 28**          *Perf. 13*
1379 A966 50y multicolored          .55 .25
1380 A967 50y multicolored          .55 .25

Spring Brook A968

Cherry Blossoms A969

**1980, Mar. 21**
1381 A968 50y multicolored          .55 .25
1382 A969 50y multicolored          .55 .25
Nos. 1375-1382 (8)          4.40 2.00

Great Owl, by Okyo Maruyama — A970

**1979, Oct. 8**   **Photo.**   *Perf. 13*
1383 A970 100y multicolored          1.50 .30
Intl. Letter Writing Week, Oct. 8-14.

Runner — A971

**1979, Oct. 13**
1384 A971 20y multicolored          .30 .25
34th National Athletic Meet, Miyazaki, Oct. 4-19.

"ITU," Globe — A972

**1979, Oct. 13**   **Litho.**   *Perf. 13½*
1385 A972 50y multicolored          .55 .25
Admission to ITU, cent.

Woman and Fetus — A973

**1979, Nov. 12**          **Photo.**
1386 A973 50y multicolored          .55 .25
9th World Congress of Gynecology and Obstetrics, Tokyo, Oct. 25-31.

Happy Monkeys, Osaka Toy — A974

**1979, Dec. 1**   **Photo.**   *Perf. 13x13½*
1387 A974 20y multicolored          .30 .25
New Year 1980. Sheets of 2 No. 1387 were New Year Lottery prizes. Value $1.60.

Government Auditing Centenary — A975

**1980, Mar. 5**   **Photo.**   *Perf. 13½*
1388 A975 50y multicolored          .55 .25

Scenes of Outdoor Play in Spring, by Sukenobu Nishikawa — A976

**1980, Apr. 21**   **Photo.**   *Perf. 13½*
1389 50y multicolored          .55 .25
1390 50y multicolored          .55 .25
a. A976 Pair, #1389-1390          1.25 .65
Philatelic Week, Apr. 21-27. Sheets of 10.

## Japanese Song Issue

The Sea
A978

The Night of
the Hazy
Moon
A979

Memories of
Summer
A981

The Sun Flag
A980

**1980    Photo. & Engr.    Perf. 13**

| | | | |
|---|---|---|---|
| 1391 | A978 50y multicolored | .55 | .25 |
| 1392 | A979 50y multicolored | .55 | .25 |
| 1393 | A980 50y multicolored | .55 | .25 |
| 1394 | A981 50y multicolored | .55 | .25 |
| | *Nos. 1391-1394 (4)* | 2.20 | 1.00 |

Issued: Nos. 1391-1392, 4/28; Nos. 1393-1394, 6/16.

The Red
Dragonfly
A982

Song by the
Sea
A983

**1980, Sept. 18    Perf. 13**

| | | | |
|---|---|---|---|
| 1395 | A982 50y multicolored | .55 | .25 |
| 1396 | A983 50y multicolored | .55 | .25 |

Lullaby
A984

Coconut, by
Toraji Ohnaka
A985

**1981, Feb. 9    Perf. 13**

| | | | |
|---|---|---|---|
| 1397 | A984 60y multicolored | .75 | .25 |
| 1398 | A985 60y multicolored | .75 | .25 |

Spring Has
Come, by
Tatsuyuki
Takano
A986

Cherry Blossoms,
by Hagoromo
Takeshima
A987

**1981, Mar. 10    Perf. 13**

| | | | |
|---|---|---|---|
| 1399 | A986 60y multicolored | .75 | .25 |
| 1400 | A987 60y multicolored | .75 | .25 |

## Modern Japanese Art Issue

Dancers, by
Seiki Kuroda
A988

Mother and
Child, by Shoen
Uemura
A989

**1980, May 12    Photo.    Perf. 13½**

| | | | |
|---|---|---|---|
| 1401 | A988 50y multicolored | .75 | .25 |
| 1402 | A989 50y multicolored | .75 | .25 |

The Black
Fan, by Takeji
Fujishima
A990

Dear Me . . .
It's a Shower,
by Seiho
Takeuchi
A991

**1980, July 7    Photo.    Perf. 13½**

| | | | |
|---|---|---|---|
| 1403 | A990 50y multicolored | .55 | .25 |
| 1404 | A991 50y multicolored | .55 | .25 |

Woman, by
Morie Ogiwara
A992

Kurofuneya, by
Yumeji
Takehisa
A993

**1980, Oct. 27    Photo.    Perf. 13½**

| | | | |
|---|---|---|---|
| 1405 | A992 50y multicolored | .55 | .25 |
| 1406 | A993 50y multicolored | .55 | .25 |

Nippon Maru, Institute
Emblem — A994

**1980, May 17**

| | | | |
|---|---|---|---|
| 1407 | A994 50y multicolored | .75 | .25 |

Institute for Nautical Training, training ships
Nippon Maru and Kaio Maru, 50th
anniversary.

Mt. Gozaisho-dake,
Cedars, Flowers — A995

**1980, May 24    Perf. 13x13½**

| | | | |
|---|---|---|---|
| 1408 | A995 50y multicolored | .75 | .25 |

National forestation campaign.

Yayosu Fire Brigade
Review, by Hiroshige
III — A996

**1980, May 31**

| | | | |
|---|---|---|---|
| 1409 | A996 50y multicolored | .75 | .25 |

Fire fighting centenary.

A997

A997a

Letter Writing Day: 20y, Teddy Bear holding
letter. 50y, Folded and tied letter of good
wishes, horiz.

**1980, July 23    Perf. 13x13½, 13½x13**

| | | | |
|---|---|---|---|
| 1410 | A997 20y multicolored | .30 | .25 |
| 1411 | A997a 50y multicolored | .75 | .25 |

Lühdorfla
Japonica — A998

**1980, Aug. 2    Perf. 13½**

| | | | |
|---|---|---|---|
| 1412 | A998 50y multicolored | .75 | .25 |

16th Intl. Cong. of Entomology, Kyoto, Aug.
3-9.

Three-dimensional
World Map — A999

**1980, Aug. 25    Photo.**

| | | | |
|---|---|---|---|
| 1413 | A999 50y multicolored | .75 | .25 |

24th Intl. Geographic Cong. and 10th Intl.
Cartographic Conf., Tokyo, August.

Integrated
Circuit — A1000

**1980, Sept. 29**

| | | | |
|---|---|---|---|
| 1414 | A1000 50y multicolored | .75 | .25 |

Intl. Federation for Information Processing
Cong. '80, Tokyo, Oct. 6-9 and World Conf. on
Medical Informatics '80, Tokyo, 9/29-10/4.

Camellia — A1001

40y, Rape flower, cabbage butterflies. 50y,
Cherry blossoms.

**1980, Oct. 1**

| | | | |
|---|---|---|---|
| 1415 | A1001 30y shown | .30 | .25 |
| 1416 | A1001 40y multicolored | .55 | .25 |
| 1417 | A1001 50y multicolored | .75 | .25 |
| | *Nos. 1415-1417 (3)* | 1.60 | .75 |

See No. 1437.

Cranes, by Motooki
Watanabe — A1002

**1980, Oct. 6    Perf. 13**

| | | | |
|---|---|---|---|
| 1418 | A1002 100y multicolored | 1.25 | .30 |

24th Intl. Letter Writing Week, Oct. 6-12.

Archery, Mt.
Nantai — A1003

**1980, Oct. 11**

| | | | |
|---|---|---|---|
| 1419 | A1003 20y multicolored | .30 | .25 |

35th Natonal Athletic Meet, Tochigi, Oct.

Globe, Jaycee
Emblem — A1004

**1980, Nov. 8    Perf. 13**

| | | | |
|---|---|---|---|
| 1420 | A1004 50y multicolored | .65 | .25 |

35th Jaycee (Intl. Junior Chamber of Commerce) World Congress, Osaka, Nov. 9-15.

Diet Building and
Doves — A1005

**1980, Nov. 29    Perf. 13½**

| | | | |
|---|---|---|---|
| 1421 | A1005 50y multicolored | .65 | .25 |

90th anniversary of Japanese Diet.

### Type of 1980 and

Amur
Adonis
A1006

Hanging
Bell,
Byodoin
Temple
A1008

Writing
Box Cover
A1010

Heart-
shaped
Figurine
A1012

Maitreya,
Horyuji
Temple
A1014

White
Trumpet
Lily
A1007

Bronze
Buddhist
Ornament,
7th
Century
A1009

Mirror with
Figures
A1011

Silver
Crane
A1013

Ichiji
Kinrin,
Chusonji
Temple
A1015

Komokuten,
Todaiji
Temple
A1016

Enamel
Jar, by
Ninsei
Nonomura
A1018

Lady
Maya
A1017

Miroku
Bosatsu,
Koryuji
Temple
A1019

### 1980-82 Photo. Perf. 13x13½

| | | | |
|---|---|---|---|
| 1422 | A1006 | 10y multicolored | .30 .25 |
| 1423 | A1007 | 20y multicolored | .30 .25 |
| 1424 | A1008 | 60y multicolored | .65 .25 |
| a. | | Bklt. pane (#1424, 4 #1424 with gutter btwn.) ('81) | 5.00 |
| 1425 | A1009 | 70y multicolored | 1.25 .30 |
| 1426 | A1010 | 70y multicolored | 1.25 .25 |
| 1427 | A1011 | 80y multicolored | 1.50 .25 |
| 1428 | A1012 | 90y multicolored | 1.75 .25 |
| 1429 | A1013 | 100y multicolored | 1.75 .25 |
| 1430 | A1014 | 170y multicolored | 2.00 .25 |
| 1431 | A1015 | 260y multicolored | 4.00 .30 |
| 1432 | A1016 | 310y multicolored | 5.00 .30 |
| 1433 | A1017 | 410y multicolored | 7.50 .40 |
| 1434 | A1018 | 410y multicolored | 6.50 .40 |
| 1435 | A1019 | 600y multicolored | 9.00 .60 |
| | | Nos. 1422-1435 (14) | 42.75 4.50 |

### Coil Stamps
#### Perf. 13 Horiz.

| | | | |
|---|---|---|---|
| 1436 | A1006 | 10y multi ('82) | .30 .25 |
| 1437 | A1001 | 40y as #1416 | .75 .25 |
| 1438 | A1008 | 60y multi ('82) | .90 .30 |
| 1439 | A1013 | 100y multi ('82) | 1.75 .35 |
| | | Nos. 1436-1439 (4) | 3.70 1.20 |

Compare type A1013 with type A2685. See Nos. 1627-1628.

Clay Chicken, Folk
Toy — A1026

### 1980, Dec. 1 Perf. 13 Horiz.
1442 A1026 20y multicolored .30 .25
New Year 1981.
Sheets of two were New Year Lottery Prizes.
Value $1.60.

### Modern Japanese Art Issue

Snow-Covered Power Station, by
Shikanosuke Oka — A1027

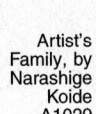

NuKada-no-Ohkimi
and Nara in Spring,
by Yukihiko
Yasuda — A1028

### 1981, Feb. 26 Perf. 13½
1443 A1027 60y multicolored .75 .25
#### Photo.
1444 A1028 60y multicolored .75 .25

Artist's
Family, by
Narashige
Koide
A1029

Bamboo Shoots, by
Heihachiro
Fukuda — A1030

### Photo. & Engr., Photo.
#### 1981, June 18 Perf. 13½
1445 A1029 60y multicolored .75 .25
1446 A1030 60y multicolored .75 .25

Portrait of
Ichiyo, by
Kiyokata
Kaburagi (1878-
1972)
A1031

Portrait of
Reiko, by
Ryusei Kishida
(1891-1929)
A1032

### Photo., Photo. and Engr.
#### 1981, Nov. 27 Engr. Perf. 13½
1447 A1031 60y multicolored .75 .25
1448 A1032 60y multicolored .75 .25

Yoritomo in
a Cave, by
Seison
Maeda
A1033

Advertisement of a Terrace, by Yuzo
Saeki — A1034

### 1982, Feb. 25 Photo. Perf. 13½
1449 A1033 60y multicolored .75 .25
1450 A1034 60y multicolored .75 .25

Emblem, Port
Island — A1035

### 1981, Mar. 20 Perf. 13
1451 A1035 60y multicolored .90 .25
Portopia '81, Kobe Port Island Exhibition,
Mar. 20-Sept. 15.

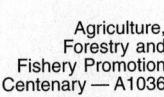

Agriculture,
Forestry and
Fishery Promotion
Centenary — A1036

### 1981, Apr. 7
1452 A1036 60y multicolored 1.00 .25

Moonflower, by Harunobu
Suzuki — A1037

### 1981, Apr. 20 Photo. Perf. 13½
1453 60y multicolored .75 .25
1454 60y multicolored .75 .25
a. A1037 Pair, #1453-1454 1.75 1.25
Philatelic Week, Apr. 21-27.

Cherry Blossoms — A1039

### 1981, May 23 Photo. Perf. 13x13½
1455 A1039 60y multicolored .90 .25

Cargo Ship and
Crane — A1040

### 1981, May 25 Perf. 13
1456 A1040 60y multicolored .90 .25
International Port and Harbor Association,
12th Convention, Nagoya, May 23-30.

Land Erosion Control
Cent. — A1041

### 1981, June 27 Perf. 13½
1457 A1041 60y multicolored .90 .25

Stylized Man and
Spinal Cord Dose
Response
Curve — A1042

### 1981, July 18 Photo. Perf. 13
1458 A1042 60y multicolored .90 .25
8th Intl. Pharmacology Cong., Tokyo, July
19-24.

Girl Writing
Letter — A1043

### 1981, July 23
1459 A1043 40y shown .65 .25
1460 A1043 60y Boy, stamp .90 .25
Letter Writing Day (23rd of each month).

Japanese Crested
Ibis — A1044

### 1981, July 27 Litho.
1461 A1044 60y multicolored 1.00 .25

Plug,
faucet
A1044a

Plugs
A1045

### 1981, Aug. 1 Photo.
1462 A1044a 40y multicolored .65 .25
1463 A1045 60y multicolored .90 .25
Energy conservation.

### Western Architecture Issue

Oura
Cathedral
A1046

Hyokei Hall, Tokyo
A1047

### Photogravure and Engraved
#### 1981, Aug. 22
1464 A1046 60y multicolored .90 .25
1465 A1047 60y multicolored .90 .25

Old Kaichi School,
Nagano — A1048

Doshisha
University Chapel,
Kyoto — A1049

### 1981, Nov. 9 Perf. 13
1466 A1048 60y multicolored .90 .25
1467 A1049 60y multicolored .90 .25

St. John's
Church, Meiji-
mura
A1050

Military Exercise
Hall (Former
Sapporo
Agricultural
School), Sapporo
A1051

### 1982, Jan. 29 Perf. 13
1468 A1050 60y multicolored .90 .25
1469 A1051 60y multicolored .90 .25

Former Kyoto
Branch of Bank of
Japan
A1052

Main
Building,
Former
Saiseikan
Hospital
A1053

### 1982, Mar. 10 Perf. 13
1470 A1052 60y multicolored .90 .25
1471 A1053 60y multicolored .90 .25

Oyama
Shrine Gate,
Kanazawa
A1054

Former Iwasaki
Family Residence,
Tokyo
A1055

### 1982, June 12 Perf. 13
1472 A1054 60y multicolored .90 .25
1473 A1055 60y multicolored .90 .25

Hokkaido
Prefectural Govt.
Building,
Sapporo — A1056

Former Residence
of Tsugumichi
Saigo — A1057

**1982, Sept. 10** — Perf. 13
1474 A1056 60y multicolored .90 .25
1475 A1057 60y multicolored .90 .25

Old Mutsuzawa School — A1058

Sakuranomiya Public Hall — A1059

**1983, Feb. 15**
1476 A1058 60y multicolored .90 .25
1477 A1059 60y multicolored .90 .25

Globe on Brain — A1060

**1981, Sept. 12** — Photo.
1478 A1060 60y multicolored .80 .25

Intl. medical conferences, Kyoto: 12th Neurology, Sept. 20-25; 10th Brainwaves and Clinical Neurophysiology, Sept. 13-17; 1981 Intl. Epilepsy Conference, Sept. 17-21.

Congress Emblem — A1061

**1981, Sept. 16**
1479 A1061 60y multicolored .90 .25

24th World PTTI (Post, Telegraph and Telephone Intl. Labor Federation) Cong., Tokyo, Sept. 16-22.

Plum Trees and Fowl, by Sanraku Kano — A1062

**1981, Oct. 6** — Photo.
1480 A1062 130y multicolored 1.75 .30

25th Intl. Letter Writing Week, Oct. 6-12.

A1063

**1981, Oct. 9** — Photo. & Engr.
1481 A1063 60y No. 1 .75 .25
1482 A1063 60y No. 2 .75 .25
1483 A1063 60y No. 3 .75 .25
1484 A1063 60y No. 4 .75 .25
a. Strip or block of 4, #1481-1484 3.50 3.50

Philatokyo '81 Intl. Stamp Exhibition, Tokyo, Oct. 9-18.

A1064

**1981, Oct. 13** — Photo.
1485 A1064 40y multicolored .75 .25

36th Natl. Athletic Meet, Oct. 13-18.

A1065

**1981, Dec. 1** — Photo. Perf. 13x13½
1486 A1065 40y multicolored .65 .30

New Year of 1982 (Year of the Dog). Sheets of 2 were lottery prizes. Value $1.60.

A1066

Ueno Zoo Centenary: a, Gorilla, flamingo. b, Penguins, lion. c, Panda, elephants. d, Zebras, giraffe.

**1982, Mar. 20** — Photo.
1487 A1066 Strip of 4 4.00 1.50
a.-d. 60y any single .90 .30

Views of the Snow on Matsuchiyama, by Kiyonaga Torii — A1067

**1982, Apr. 20** — Photo. Perf. 13½
1488 60y multicolored .90 .30
1489 60y multicolored .90 .30
a. A1067 Pair, #1488-1489 2.00 1.25

Philatelic Week.

Shisa (Lion-shaped Guard Dog) — A1069

**1982, May 15** — Photo.
1490 A1069 60y multicolored .90 .30

10th anniv. of Reversion Agreement returning Ryukyu Islands.

Natl. Forestation Campaign — A1070

**1982, May 22** — Perf. 13x13½
1491 A1070 60y multicolored .90 .25

16th Intl. Dermatology Conference Tokyo, May 23-28 — A1071

**1982, May 24** — Perf. 13
1492 A1071 60y Noh mask .90 .25

Tohoku-Shinkansen Railroad Line Opening — A1072

**1982, June 23**
1493 60y Diesel locomotive .90 .30
1494 60y Steam model 1290 .90 .30
a. A1072 Pair, #1493-1494 2.00 1.25

Letter Writing Day — A1073

**1982, July 23** — Perf. 13x13½, 13½x13
1495 A1073 40y Sea gull, letter .75 .25
1496 A1073 60y Fairy, letter, horiz. 1.00 .30

**Modern Japanese Art Issue**

Kimono Patterned with Irises, by Saburosuke Okada (1869-1939) A1074

Bodhisattva Kuan-yin on Potalaka Island, by Tessai Tomioka (1837-1924) A1075

**1982, Aug. 5** — Photo. Perf. 13½
1497 A1074 60y multicolored .90 .30
1498 A1075 60y multicolored .90 .30

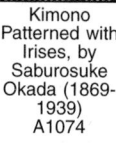

The Sarasvati, by Shiko Munakata (1903-1975) A1076

Saltimbanque, by Seiji Togo (1897-1978) A1077

**1982, Nov. 24**
1499 A1076 60y multicolored .90 .30
1500 A1077 60y multicolored .90 .30

Snowstorm, by Shinsui Ito A1078

Spiraeas and Callas with Persian Pot, by Zenzaburo Kojima A1079

**1983, Jan. 24** — Photo.
1501 A1078 60y multicolored .90 .30
1502 A1079 60y multicolored .90 .30

Innocence, by Taikan Yokoyama (1868-1958) A1080

Roen, by Koun Takamura (1852-1934) A1081

**Photo., Photo. and Engr.**
**1983, Mar. 10** — Perf. 13½
1503 A1080 60y multicolored .90 .30
1504 A1081 60y multicolored .90 .30

A1082

A1083

A1084

**1982, Aug. 23** — Perf. 13x13½
1505 A1082 60y Wreath .90 .35
1506 A1083 60y Crane .90 .35
1507 A1084 70y Tortoise 1.00 .35
Nos. 1505-1507 (3) 2.80 1.05

For use on greeting (Nos. 1506-1507) and condolence (No. 1505) cards.
See Nos. 1555-1556, 1836-1839, 2227-2230 and footnotes after Nos. 1708, 1765.

400th Anniv. of Boys' Delegation to Europe, Tensho Era — A1085

60y, 16th cent. ship, map.

**1982, Sept. 20** — Photo. Perf. 13
1508 A1085 60y multicolored 1.00 .25

10th Anniv. of Japanese-Chinese Relations Normalization A1086

Design: Hall of Prayer for Good Harvests, Temple of Heaven, Peking, by Ryuzaburo Umehara.

**1982, Sept. 29**
1509 A1086 60y multicolored .90 .30

Table Tennis — A1087

**1982, Oct. 2**
1510 A1087 40y multicolored .75 .25

37th Natl. Athletic Meet, Matsue, Oct. 3-8.

"Amusement," Doll by Goyo Hirata — A1088

**1982, Oct. 6**
1511 A1088 130y multicolored 1.75 .45

Intl. Letter Writing Week, Oct. 6-12.

Central Bank System Centenary — A1089

Design: The Bank of Japan near Eitaibashi in Snow, by Yasuji Inoue.

**Photogravure and Engraved**
**1982, Oct. 12** *Perf. 13½*
1512 A1089 60y multicolored 1.00 .25

Opening of Joetsu Shinkansen Railroad Line — A1090

**1982, Nov. 15**
1513 60y Locomotive, 1982 .90 .30
1514 60y Locomotive, 1931 .90 .30
  a. A1090 Pair, #1513-1514 2.00 1.25

New Year 1983 — A1092

40y, Kintaro on Wild Boar.

**1982, Dec. 1** *Perf. 13x13½*
1515 A1092 40y multicolored .80 .30
Sheets of 2 were lottery prizes. Value, $1.50.

Natl. Museum of History and Folklore Opening — A1093

**1983, Mar. 16 Photo.** *Perf. 13½x13*
1516 A1093 60y multicolored 1.00 .25

Women Working in the Kitchen, by Utamaro Kitagawa (1753-1806) — A1094

**1983, Apr. 20 Photo.** *Perf. 13*
1517 60y multicolored .90 .30
1518 60y multicolored .90 .30
  a. A1094 Pair, #1517-1518 2.00 1.25
Philatelic Week.

Natl. Forestation Campaign — A1096

Hakusan Mountains, black lily, forest.

**1983, May 21** *Perf. 13*
1519 A1096 60y multicolored 1.00 .25

50th Nippon Derby — A1097

**1983, May 28**
1520 A1097 60y Colt, racing horse 1.00 .25

Islands Cleanup Campaign — A1098

**1983, June 13 Photo.** *Perf. 13½*
1521 A1098 60y multicolored 1.00 .25

**Western Architecture Series**

Hohei Hall Sapporo A1099 | Old Glover House, Nagasaki A1100

**Photogravure and Engraved**
**1983, June 23** *Perf. 13*
1522 A1099 60y multicolored 1.00 .30
1523 A1100 60y multicolored 1.00 .30

Gojyuku Bank, Hirosaki — A1101 | Gakushuin Elementary School, Tokyo — A1102

**1983, Aug. 15**
1524 A1101 60y multicolored 1.00 .30
1525 A1102 60y multicolored 1.00 .30

Bank of Japan, Tokyo — A1103 | Old Hunter House, Kobe — A1104

**1984, Feb. 16**
1526 A1103 60y multicolored 1.00 .30
1527 A1104 60y multicolored 1.00 .30
  Nos. 1522-1527 (6) 6.00 1.80

Official Gazette Centenary — A1107

Design: First issue, Drawing of the Government Bulletin Board at Nihonbashi, by Hiroshige Ando III.

**1983, July 2 Photo.**
1530 A1107 60y multicolored 1.00 .25

Letter Writing Day — A1108

40y, Boy writing letter. 60y, Fairy bringing letter, horiz.

**1983, July 23 Perf. 13x13½, 13½x13**
1531 A1108 40y multicolored .70 .25
1532 A1108 60y multicolored 1.00 .30

Opening of Natl. Noh Theater, Tokyo — A1109

60y, Masked actor, theater.

**1983, Sept. 14 Photo.** *Perf. 13*
1533 A1109 60y multicolored 1.00 .25

**Endangered Birds Issue**

Rallus Okinawae A1110 | Ketupa Blakistoni A1111

**Photo. and Engr., Photo.**
**1983, Sept. 22** *Perf. 13*
1534 A1110 60y multicolored 1.00 .30
1535 A1111 60y multicolored 1.00 .30
No. 1536, Sapheopipo noguchii. No. 1537, Branta canadensis leucopareia.

**Photo., Photo. & Engr.**
**1983, Nov. 25**
1536 A1110 60y multicolored 1.00 .30
1537 A1111 60y multicolored 1.00 .30
No. 1538, Megalurus pryeri pryeri. No. 1539, Spilornis cheela perplexus.

**Photo., Photo. and Engr.**
**1984, Jan. 26**
1538 A1111 60y multicolored 1.00 .30
1539 A1110 60y multicolored 1.00 .30
No. 1540, Columba janthina nitens. No. 1541, Tringa guttifer.

**1984, Mar. 15 Photo.**
1540 A1110 60y multicolored 1.00 .30
1541 A1111 60y multicolored 1.00 .30
No. 1542, Falco peregrinus frutti. No. 1543, Dendrocopus leucutus austoni.

**1984, June 22**
1542 A1110 60y multicolored 1.00 .30

**Photo. and Engr.**
1543 A1111 60y multicolored 1.00 .30
  Nos. 1534-1543 (10) 10.00 3.00

**Souvenir Sheet**

Intl. Letter Writing Week — A1124

Chikyu Doll by Juzo Kagoshima (1898-1982).

**1983, Oct. 6 Photo.** *Perf. 13*
1548 A1124 130y multicolored 1.90 .40

38th Natl. Athletic Meet — A1125

**1983, Oct. 15** *Perf. 13*
1549 A1125 40y Naginata event .75 .25

A1126

World Communications Year — A1127

**1983, Oct. 17 Photo.** *Perf. 13*
1550 A1126 60y multicolored 1.00 .25
1551 A1127 60y multicolored 1.00 .25

Showa Memorial National Park Opening — A1128

**1983, Oct. 26 Photo.** *Perf. 13*
1552 A1128 60y multicolored 1.00 .30

A1129

**1983, Nov. 14 Photo.**
1553 A1129 60y multicolored 1.00 .25
71st World Dentistry Congress.

A1130

**1983, Nov. 14 Photo.** *Perf. 13*
1554 A1130 60y multicolored 1.00 .30
Shirase, Antarctic observation ship, maiden voyage.

**Type of 1982**
**1983, Nov. 22 Photo.** *Perf. 12½*
1555 A1082 40y Wreath .75 .25
1556 A1083 40y Crane .75 .25
For use on condolence and greeting cards.

New Year 1984 — A1131

40y, Rat riding hammer.

**1983, Dec. 1 Photo.** *Perf. 13x13½*
1557 A1131 40y multicolored .80 .30
Sheets of 2 were lottery prizes. Value, $1.90.

Emblem — A1132

**1983, Dec. 5 Photo.** *Perf. 13½*
1558 A1132 60y multicolored 1.00 .25
Universal Declaration of Human Rights, 35th anniv.

20th Grand Confectionery Fair, Tokyo, Feb. 24-Mar. 12 — A1133

60y, Confection, tea whisk.

**1984, Feb. 24**                    **Photo.**
1559  A1133  60y multicolored          1.00  .25

Natl. Bunraku
Theater Opening,
Osaka — A1134

60y, Bunraku puppet.

**1984, Apr. 6**   **Photo.**   **Perf. 13**
1560  A1134  60y multicolored          1.00  .25

A1135

Philatelic Week (Sharaku Prints): No. 1561, Hanshiro Iwai IV (facing right) Playing Shigenoi. No. 1562, Oniji Otani (facing left) Playing Edobe.

**Photogravure and Engraved**
**1984, Apr. 20**                    **Perf. 13½**
1561      60y multicolored             1.00  .30
1562      60y multicolored             1.00  .30
   a.  A1135  Pair, #1561-1562         2.25  .90

Natl. Forestation
Campaign — A1137

60y, Cedar Forest, Sakurajima.

**1984, May 19**                    **Photo.**
1563  A1137  60y multicolored          1.00  .25

Weather Forecasting
Centenary — A1138

60y, Himawari satellite, map.

**1984, June 1**                    **Perf. 13x13½**
1564  A1138  60y multicolored          1.00  .30

UNESCO Emblem,
Doves — A1139

**1984, July 16**                    **Photo.**
1565  A1139  60y multicolored          1.00  .25
UNESCO Clubs and Associations World Congress, July 16-24.

Letter Writing
Day — A1140

40y, Birds in tree. 60y, Bird holding letter, horiz.

**1984, July 23**  **Perf. 13x13½, 13½x13**
1566  A1140  40y multicolored           .75  .25
1567  A1140  60y multicolored          1.00  .30

Disaster
Relief — A1141

40y, Fire, wind. 60y, Mother, child, vert.

---

**Perf. 13x12½, 12½x13**
**1984, Aug. 23**                    **Photo.**
1568  A1141  40y multicolored           .75  .25
1569  A1141  60y multicolored          1.00  .30

**Alpine Plant Series**

Leontopodium      Lagotis Glauca
Fauriei               A1143
A1142

**Photogravure and Engraved**
**Perf. 12½x13, 13x12½**
**1984, Aug. 27**
1570  A1142  60y multicolored          1.00  .30
1571  A1143  60y multicolored          1.00  .30

Trollius          Primula
Riederianus       Cuneifolia
A1144             A1145

**1984, Sept. 21**                    **Perf. 13**
1572  A1144  60y multicolored          1.00  .30
1573  A1145  60y multicolored          1.00  .30

Rhododendron      Oxytropis
Aureum            Nigrescens Var.
A1146             Japonica
                  A1147

**1985, Jan. 25**                    **Perf. 13**
1574  A1146  60y multicolored          1.00  .30
1575  A1147  60y multicolored          1.00  .30

Draba             Dryas Octopetala
Japonica          A1149
A1148

**1985, Feb. 28**
1576  A1148  60y multicolored          1.00  .30
1577  A1149  60y multicolored          1.00  .30

Callianthemum     Gentiana
Insigne Var.      Nipponica
Miyabeanum        A1151
A1150

**1985, July 31**                    **Perf. 13**
1578  A1150  60y multicolored          1.00  .30
1579  A1151  60y multicolored          1.00  .30

---

Campanula         Viola Crassa
Chamissonis       A1153
A1152

**1985, Sept. 27**
1580  A1152  60y multicolored          1.00  .30
1581  A1153  60y multicolored          1.00  .30

Diapensia         Pedicularis
Lapponica         Apodochila
A1154             A1155

**1986, Feb. 13**                    **Perf. 13**
1582  A1154  60y multicolored          1.00  .30
1583  A1155  60y multicolored          1.00  .30

Basho's Street,
Sendai — A1156

**1984, Sept. 1**         **Photo.**    **Perf. 13**
1584  A1156  60y multicolored          1.00  .25
Intl. Microbiological Association's 6th Intl. Congress of Virology, Sendai, Sept. 1-7.

Electronic Mail — A1157

**1984, Oct. 1**                    **Photo.**
1585  A1157  500y multicolored         9.50  4.50

28th Intl. Letter Writing
Week, Oct. 6-
12 — A1158

**1984, Oct. 6**
1586  A1158  130y Wooden doll          2.00  .50

17th Intl. Internal
Medicine Congress,
Kyoto, Oct. 7-
12 — A1159

**1984, Oct. 8**
1587  A1159  60y Ginkakuji Temple  1.00  .25

39th Natl. Athletic
Meet, Nara City, Oct.
12-17 — A1160

**1984, Oct. 12**
1588  A1160  40y Field hockey          .75  .25

---

**Traditional Crafts Series**

Kutaniyaki
Plates
A1161

Nishijinori
Weavings
A1163

**1984, Nov. 2**   **Photo.**   **Perf. 12½x13**
1589      60y Birds                    1.00  .30
1590      60y Flowers                  1.00  .30
   a.  A1161  Pair, #1589-1590         2.25  .90
1591      60y Flowers                  1.00  .30
1592      60y Leaves                   1.00  .30
   a.  A1163  Pair, #1591-1592         2.25  .90

Edokimekomi Dolls — A1165

Ryukyubingata Cloth — A1167

**1985, Feb. 15**                    **Photo.**    **Perf. 13**
1593      60y Adult figures           1.00  .30
1594      60y Child and pet           1.00  .30
   a.  A1165  Pair, #1593-1594        2.25  .90
1595      60y Bird and branch         1.00  .30
1596      60y Birds                   1.00  .30
   a.  A1167  Pair, #1595-1596        2.25  .90

Ichii-ittobori Carved Birds — A1169

Imariyaki
&
Aritayaki
Ceramic
Ware
A1171

**1985, May 23**   **Photo.**   **Perf. 13**
1597      60y Bird                    1.00  .30
1598      60y Birds                   1.00  .30
   a.  A1169  Pair, #1597-1598        2.25  .90
1599      60y Bowl                    1.00  .30
1600      60y Plate                   1.00  .30
   a.  A1171  Pair, #1599-1600        2.25  .90

Kamakurabori Wood
Carvings — A1173

Ojiyachijimi Weavings — A1175

**1985, June 24**     **Photo. & Engr.**
| 1601 | 60y Bird and flower panel | 1.00 | .30 |
| 1602 | 60y Round flower panel | 1.00 | .30 |
| a. | A1173 Pair, #1601-1602 | 2.25 | .90 |

**Litho.**
| 1603 | 60y Hemp star pattern | 1.00 | .30 |
| 1604 | 60y Hemp linear pattern | 1.00 | .30 |
| a. | A1175 Pair, #1603-1604 | 2.25 | .90 |

Hakata Ningyo Clay Figures A1177

Nanbu Tekki Iron Ware A1179

**1985, Aug. 8**     **Photo.**
| 1605 | 60y Man | 1.00 | .30 |
| 1606 | 60y Woman and child | 1.00 | .30 |
| a. | A1177 Pair, #1605-1606 | 2.25 | .90 |

**Photogravure and Engraved**
| 1607 | 60y Silver kettle | 1.00 | .30 |
| 1608 | 60y Black kettle | 1.00 | .30 |
| a. | A1179 Pair, #1607-1608 | 2.25 | .90 |

Wajimanuri Lacquerware — A1181

Izumo-ishidoro Sandstone Sculptures — A1183

**Photo., Photo. & Engr. (#1611-1612)**
**1985, Nov. 15**
| 1609 | 60y Bowl on table | 1.00 | .30 |
| 1610 | 60y Bowl | 1.00 | .30 |
| a. | A1181 Pair, #1609-1610 | 2.25 | .90 |
| 1611 | 60y Columnar lantern | 1.00 | .30 |
| 1612 | 60y Lantern on four legs | 1.00 | .30 |
| a. | A1183 Pair, #1611-1612 | 2.25 | .90 |

Kyo-sensu Silk Fans A1185

Tobeyaki Porcelain A1187

**1986, Mar. 13**     **Photo.**     **Perf. 13**
| 1613 | 60y Flower bouquets | 1.00 | .30 |
| 1614 | 60y Sun and trees | 1.00 | .30 |
| a. | A1185 Pair, #1613-1614 | 2.25 | .90 |
| 1615 | 60y Jug | 1.00 | .30 |
| 1616 | 60y Jar | 1.00 | .30 |
| a. | A1187 Pair, #1615-1616 | 2.25 | .90 |
| | Nos. 1613-1616 (4) | 4.00 | 1.20 |

Japanese Professional Baseball, 50th Anniv. — A1189

**1984, Nov. 15**     **Perf. 13½**
| 1617 | 60y Pitcher | 1.00 | .30 |
| 1618 | 60y Batter | 1.00 | .30 |
| a. | A1189 Pair, #1617-1618 | 2.25 | .90 |
| 1619 | A1189 60y Matsutaro Shoriki | 1.00 | .30 |
| | Nos. 1617-1619 (3) | 3.00 | .90 |

Industrial Education Centenary — A1190

**1984, Nov. 20**     **Perf. 13x12½**
| 1620 | A1190 60y Workers, symbols | 1.00 | .25 |

New Year 1985 — A1191

40y, Sakushu Cattle Folk Toy.

**1984, Dec. 1**     **Photo.**     **Perf. 13½x13**
| 1621 | A1191 40y | | .80 | .30 |

Sheets of 2 were lottery prizes. Value, $1.90.

A1200   A1201
Akita   Ivory Shell

A1202   A1203
Hiougi-gai (Bivalve)   Rinbo Shell

A1204   A1205

A1206   A1207

A1208   A1209

**Photo., Engr. (300y)**
**1984-89**     **Perf. 13x13½**
| 1622 | A1200 2y turq blue ('89) | .30 | .25 |
| 1623 | A1201 40y multi ('88) | .70 | .25 |
| 1624 | A1202 41y multi ('89) | .70 | .25 |
| 1624B | A1202 41y Imperf., self-adhesive | .80 | .25 |
| 1625 | A1203 60y multi ('88) | 1.00 | .25 |
| a. | Bklt. pane, 5 each #1623, 1625 | 10.00 | |
| 1626 | A1204 62y multi ('89) | 1.10 | .25 |
| a. | Bklt. pane, 2 #1624, 4 #1626 | 6.00 | |
| 1626B | A1204 62y Imperf., self-adhesive | 1.10 | .25 |
| c. | Bklt. pane, 2 #1624B, 4 #1626B ('89) | 6.00 | |
| 1627 | A1205 72y dark vio, blk & org yel ('89) | 1.10 | .25 |
| 1628 | A1206 175y multi ('89) | 2.75 | .25 |
| 1629 | A1207 210y multi ('89) | 3.25 | .30 |
| 1630 | A1208 300y dk red brown | 5.00 | .35 |
| 1631 | A1209 360y dull pink & brn ('89) | 6.00 | .35 |
| | Nos. 1622-1631 (12) | 23.80 | 3.25 |

**Coil Stamps**
**Perf. 13 Horiz.**
| 1636 | A1202 41y multi ('89) | .70 | .25 |
| 1637 | A1204 62y multi ('89) | 1.10 | .25 |

No. 1622 inscribed "Nippon," unlike No. 583.
No. 1626Bc is adhered to the booklet cover, made of peelable paper, folded in half and rouletted down the center fold.
Issued: 40y, 60y, 4/1; 300y, 4/3; 2y, 72y, 4/1; 42y, Nos. 1626, 1626a, 41y, No. 1637, 3/24; 175y, 210y, 360y, 6/1; No.1626d, 7/3.

A1210   EXPO '85 — A1211

**1985, Mar. 16**     **Photo.**     **Perf. 13**
| 1640 | A1210 40y multicolored | .75 | .25 |
| 1641 | A1211 60y multicolored | 1.00 | .30 |
| a. | Souv. sheet of 2, #1640-1641 | 2.50 | 2.50 |

University of the Air — A1212

60y, University broadcast tower.

**1985, Apr. 1**     **Photo.**     **Perf. 13½**
| 1642 | A1212 60y multicolored | 1.00 | .30 |

Inauguration of adult education through broadcasting.

Nippon Telegraph & Telephone Co. — A1213

**1985, Apr. 1**
| 1643 | A1213 60y Satellite receiver | 1.00 | .25 |

Inauguration of Japan's new telecommunications system.

World Import Fair, Nagoya — A1214

60y, 16th century map of Japan.

**1985, Apr. 5**     **Photo.**     **Perf. 13**
| 1644 | A1214 60y multicolored | 1.00 | .25 |

Industrial Proprietary System Cent. — A1215

Design: Portrait of Korekiyo Takahashi, system promulgator, inscriptions in English.

**1985, Apr. 18**     **Photo.**     **Perf. 13½**
| 1645 | A1215 60y multicolored | 1.00 | .25 |

Winter in the North A1216   To the Morning Light A1217

Paintings by Yumeji Takehisa (1884-1934).

**1985, Apr. 20**     **Perf. 13**
| 1646 | A1216 60y multicolored | 1.00 | .30 |
| 1647 | A1217 60y multicolored | 1.00 | .30 |
| a. | Pair, #1646-1647 | 2.25 | .90 |

Philatelic Week. Printed in sheets of 10.

Natl. Land Forestation Project — A1218

Intl. Year of the Forest: Autumn bellflower, camphor tree, cattle and Mt. Aso.

**1985, May 10**     **Perf. 13½**
| 1648 | A1218 60y multicolored | 1.00 | .25 |

Radio Japan, 50th Anniv. A1219

Painting: Cherry Blossoms at Night, by Taikan Yokoyama.

**1985, June 1**     **Photo.**     **Perf. 13**
| 1649 | 60y multi (Left) | 1.00 | .30 |
| 1650 | 60y multi (Right) | 1.00 | .30 |
| a. | A1219 Pair, #1649-1650 | 2.25 | .90 |

Hisoka Maejima, 1st Postmaster General — A1220

60y, Portrait, former P.O. building.

**1985, June 5**     **Photo.**     **Perf. 13**
| 1651 | A1220 60y multicolored | 1.00 | .30 |

Oonaruto Bridge Opening — A1221

**1985, June 7**     **Perf. 13½**
| 1652 | A1221 60y multicolored | 1.00 | .25 |

Intl. Youth Year — A1222

60y, Emblem, silhouette.

**1985, July 20**     **Photo.**     **Perf. 13**
| 1653 | A1222 60y multicolored | 1.00 | .25 |

Owl Carrying Letter — A1223

60y, Girl, cat, bird, letter.

***Perf. 13½x13, 13x13½***
**1985, July 23**                          **Photo.**
**1654** A1223 40y shown                    .75  .25
**1655** A1223 60y multicolored            1.00  .30
Letter Writing Day (23rd of each month).

Electronic Mail — A1224

**1985, Aug. 1  Photo.  *Perf. 13x13½***
**1656** A1224 500y multicolored          9.50 2.75

Meson Theory, 50th Anniv. — A1225

60y, Portrait, nuclear particles.

**1985, Aug. 15    Photo.    *Perf. 13***
**1657** A1225 60y multicolored           1.00  .25
Dr. Hideki Yukawa was presented the Nobel Prize for Physics for the Meson Theory in 1949, which is the foundation for high-energy physics.

A1226

60y, Gymnast, horse.

**1985, Aug. 24    Photo.    *Perf. 13½***
**1658** A1226 60y multicolored           1.00  .25
Universiade 1985, Kobe.

A1227

40y, Emblem, competitor.

**1985, Sept. 13                           Photo.**
**1659** A1227 40y multicolored            .75  .25
28th Intl. Vocational Training Competition, Oct. 21-27.

Normalization of Diplomatic Relations Between Japan and the Republic of Korea, 20th Anniv. — A1228

**1985, Sept. 18**
**1660** A1228 60y Rose of Sharon         1.00  .30

Kan-Etsu Tunnel Opening — A1229

60y, Mountains, diagram, cross sections.

**1985, Oct. 2                             *Perf. 13***
**1661** A1229 60y multicolored           1.00  .25

---

Seisen Doll by Goyo Hirata (1903-1981) — A1230

**1985, Oct. 7**
**1662** A1230 130y multicolored          2.00  .50
Intl. Letter Writing Week, Oct. 6-12.

30th Intl. Apicultural Congress, Oct. 10-16, Nagoya — A1231

60y, Honeybee, strawberry plants.

**1985, Oct. 9**
**1663** A1231 60y multicolored           1.00  .25

Japanese Overseas Cooperation Volunteers, 20th Anniv. — A1232

**1985, Oct. 9                             Litho.**
**1664** A1232 60y Planting crop          1.00  .30

40th Natl. Athletic Meet, Oct. 20-25, Tottori City Sports Arena — A1233

40y, Handball player, Mt. Daisen.

**1985, Oct. 19                            Photo.**
**1665** A1233 40y multicolored            .75  .25

New Year 1986 — A1234

40y, Shinno papier-mache tiger.

**1985, Dec. 2  Photo.  *Perf. 13x13½***
**1666** A1234 40y multicolored            .80  .30
Sheets of 2 were lottery prizes. Value, $1.90.

Natl. Ministerial System of Government, Cent. — A1235

60y, Official seal, Cabinet emblem.

**1985, Dec. 20    Litho.    *Perf. 13½***
**1667** A1235 60y multicolored           1.00  .25

Building Institute, Cent. — A1236

**1986, Apr. 9      Photo.      *Perf. 13***
**1668** A1236 60y multicolored           1.00  .25

Philately Week A1237

---

Southern Hateroma (details), by Keigetsu Kikuchi.

**1986, Apr. 15**
**1669**    60y Woman standing            1.00  .30
**1670**    60y Seated woman              1.00  .30
  **a.**  A1237 Pair, #1669-1670          2.25  .90

Kyoto Imperial Palace, Phoenix — A1238

No. 1672, Imperial chrysanthemum crest & partridges.

**1986, Apr. 28**
**1671** A1238 60y multicolored           1.00  .30
**1672** A1238 60y multicolored           1.00  .30
  **a.**  Souv. sheet of 2, #1671-1672    2.40 2.40
Reign of Emperor Hirohito, 60th anniv.

6th Intl. Summit, Tokyo — A1239

**1986, May 2**
**1673** A1239 60y Mt. Fuji              1.00  .30

Shrike on Reed, Emperor Nintoku's Mausoleum — A1240

**1986, May 9                              *Perf. 13½***
**1674** A1240 60y multicolored           1.00  .30
Natl. Land Afforestation Campaign.

Japanese Pharmaceutical Regulatory Syst., Cent. — A1241

**1986, June 25    Photo.    *Perf. 13½***
**1675** A1241 60y multicolored           1.00  .30

Japanese Standard Time, Cent. — A1242

**1986, July 11    Litho.    *Perf. 13***
**1676** A1242 60y Meridian, clock        1.00  .30

Letter Writing Day — A1243

**1986, July 23  Photo.  *Perf. 13x13½***
**1677** A1243 40y Bird                    .75  .25
**1678** A1243 60y Girl, rabbit, birds    1.00  .30
  **a.**  Bklt. pane, 5 each #1677-1678   9.25
Sheets of 2 were lottery prizes. Value, *$60.*

Merchant Marine Education, 110th Anniv. — A1244

Training ship Nihonmaru & navigation training institute founders Makoto Kondo, Yataro Iwasaki.

**1986, July 26                            *Perf. 13***
**1679** A1244 60y multicolored           1.00  .30

---

CTO's exist for Nos. 1680-1681, 1684-1685, 1688-1689, 1694-1695, 1696-1697. They read "Japan" between two arcs in a corner.

### Insects

A1245

No. 1680, Parnassius eversmanni. No. 1681, Poecilocoris lewisi. No. 1682, Rasalia batesi. No. 1683, Epiophlebia superstes.

### Photogravure and Engraved
**1986, July 30                            *Perf. 13***
**1680**    60y multicolored              1.00  .35
**1681**    60y multicolored              1.00  .35
  **a.**  A1245 Pair, #1680-1681          2.25 1.00
**1682**    60y multicolored              1.00  .35
**1683**    60y multicolored              1.00  .35
  **a.**  A1245 Pair, #1682-1683          2.25 1.00

No. 1684, Dorcus hopei. No. 1685, Thermozephyrus ataxus. No. 1686, Sympetrum pedemontanum. No. 1687, Damaster blaptoides.

**1986, Sept. 26**
**1684**    60y multicolored              1.00  .35
**1685**    60y multicolored              1.00  .35
  **a.**  A1245 Pair, #1684-1685          2.25 1.00
**1686**    60y multicolored              1.00  .35
**1687**    60y multicolored              1.00  .35
  **a.**  A1245 Pair, #1686-1687          2.25 1.00

No. 1688, Elcysma westwoodii. No. 1689, Rhyothemis variegata. No. 1690, Tibicen japonicus. No. 1691, Chrysochroa holstii.

**1986, Nov. 21**
**1688**    60y multicolored              1.00  .35
**1689**    60y multicolored              1.00  .35
  **a.**  A1245 Pair, #1688-1689          2.25 1.00
**1690**    60y multicolored              1.00  .35
**1691**    60y multicolored              1.00  .35
  **a.**  A1245 Pair, #1690-1691          2.25 1.00

No. 1692, Parantica sita. No. 1693, Cheirotonus jambar. No. 1694, Lucanus maculifemoratus. No. 1695, Anotogaster sieboldii.

**1987, Jan. 23**
**1692**    60y multicolored              1.00  .35
**1693**    60y multicolored              1.00  .35
  **a.**  A1245 Pair, #1692-1693          2.25 1.00
**1694**    60y multicolored              1.00  .35
**1695**    60y multicolored              1.00  .35
  **a.**  A1245 Pair, #1694-1695          2.25 1.00

No. 1696, Ascaraphus ramburi. No. 1697, Polyphylla laticollis. No. 1698, Kallima inachus. No. 1699, Calopteryx cornelia.

**1987, Mar. 12**
**1696**    60y multicolored              1.00  .35
**1697**    60y multicolored              1.00  .35
  **a.**  A1245 Pair, #1696-1697          2.25 1.00
**1698**    60y multicolored              1.00  .35
**1699**    60y multicolored              1.00  .35
  **f.**  A1245 Pair, #1698-1699          2.25 1.00
    *Nos. 1680-1699 (20)*                20.00 7.00

### Miniature Sheet
**1699A**  Sheet of 4 (#1680,
           1692, 1699b-1699c)            5.00 5.00
  **b.**  40y Anthocaris cardamines       .75  .35
  **c.**  40y Sasakia charonda            .75  .35
  **d.**  Bklt. pane, 5 #1680, 5 #1699b   9.25
  **e.**  Bklt. pane, 5 #1692, 5 #1699c   9.25
  **g.**  A1245 Pair, #1699b, 1680        1.90
  **h.**  A1245 Pair, #1699c, 1692        1.90

Booklet panes are perf. 13x13½ on 2 or 3 sides.

Folkways in Twelve Months (Detail), by Shunsho Katsukawa — A1265

**1986, Aug. 23    Photo.    *Perf. 13***
**1700** A1265 60y multicolored           1.00  .30
52nd conference of the Intl. Federation of Library Associations, Tokyo, Aug. 24-29.

Electron Microscope — A1266

**1986, Aug. 30**
1701 A1266 60y multicolored     1.00 .30
   11th Int. Congress of Electron Microscopy, Kyoto, Aug. 31-Sept. 7.

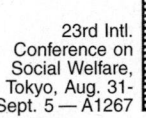

23rd Intl. Conference on Social Welfare, Tokyo, Aug. 31-Sept. 5 — A1267

**1986, Aug. 30**     **Litho.**
1702 A1267 60y multicolored     1.00 .25

Ohmorimiyage Doll, by Juzoh Kagoshima — A1268

**1986, Oct. 6**     **Photo.**
1703 A1268 130y multicolored     2.00 .60
   Intl. Letter Writing Week.

41st Natl. Athletic Meet, Oct. 12-17, Kofu — A1269

**1986, Oct. 9**
1704 A1269 40y multicolored     .75 .25

5th World Ikebana Convention A1270

   Painting: Flower in Autumn and a Girl in Rakuhoku.

**1986, Oct. 17**     **Photo.**     **Perf. 13½x13**
1705 A1270 60y multicolored     1.00 .30

A1271     Intl. Peace Year — A1272

**Lithographed, Photogravure (#1707)**
**1986, Nov. 28**
1706 A1271 40y multicolored     .75 .25
1707 A1272 60y multicolored     1.00 .30

New Year 1987 (Year of the Hare) — A1273

   Design: A Couple of Rabbits Making Rice Cake, Nagoya clay figurine.

**1986, Dec. 1**     **Photo.**     **Perf. 13x13½**
1708 A1273 40y multicolored     .80 .30
   Sheets of two containing Nos. 1506 and 1708 were lottery prizes. Value, $2.25.
   See No. 2655c.

---

Real Estate Registry System, Cent. — A1274

**1987, Jan. 30**     **Photo.**     **Perf. 13½**
1709 A1274 60y multicolored     1.00 .25

**Basho Series, Part I**

A1275

A1277

A1279

A1281

A1283

A1285

A1287

A1289

A1291

A1293

---

No. 1710, Basho. No. 1711, Basho's haiku. No. 1712, Kegon Falls. No. 1713, Haiku. No. 1714, Cuckoo. No. 1715, Horse and haiku. No. 1716, Willow Tree. No. 1717, Rice Paddy and haiku. No. 1718, Chestnut Tree in Bloom. No. 1719, Chestnut Leaves and haiku. No. 1720, Planting Rice Paddy. No. 1721, Fern Leaves and haiku. No. 1722, Sweetflags. No. 1723, Sweetflags and haiku. No. 1724, Prosperous Man, 17th Cent. No. 1725, Summer Grass and haiku. No. 1726, Safflowers in Bloom. No. 1727, Haiku. No. 1728, Yamadera (Temple). No. 1729, Forest and haiku.

**1987-89**     **Photo.**     **Perf. 13x13½**
1710   60y multicolored     1.00 .35
1711   60y multicolored     1.00 .35
   a. Sheet of 2, #1710-1711, imperf. ('89)     2.50 2.50
   b. A1275 Pair, #1710-1711     2.25 1.00
1712   60y multicolored     1.00 .35
1713   60y multicolored     1.00 .35
   a. Sheet of 2, #1712-1713, imperf. ('89)     2.50 2.50
   b. A1277 Pair, #1712-1713     2.25 1.00
1714   60y multicolored     1.00 .35
1715   60y multicolored     1.00 .35
   a. Sheet of 2, #1714-1715, imperf. ('89)     2.50 2.50
   b. A1279 Pair, #1714-1715     2.25 1.00
1716   60y multicolored     1.00 .35
1717   60y multicolored     1.00 .35
   a. Sheet of 2, #1716-1717, imperf. ('89)     2.50 2.50
   b. A1281 Pair, #1716-1717     2.25 1.00
1718   60y multicolored     1.00 .35
1719   60y multicolored     1.00 .35
   a. Sheet of 2, #1718-1719, imperf. ('89)     2.50 2.50
   b. A1283 Pair, #1718-1719     2.25 1.00
1720   60y multicolored     1.00 .35
1721   60y multicolored     1.00 .35
   a. Sheet of 2, #1720-1721, imperf. ('89)     2.50 2.50
   b. A1285 Pair, #1720-1721     2.25 1.00
1722   60y multi ('88)     1.00 .35
1723   60y multi ('88)     1.00 .35
   a. Sheet of 2, #1722-1723, imperf. ('89)     2.50 2.50
   b. A1287 Pair, #1722-1723     2.25 1.00
1724   60y multi ('88)     1.00 .35
1725   60y multi ('88)     1.00 .35
   a. Sheet of 2, #1724-1725, imperf. ('89)     2.50 2.50
   b. A1289 Pair, #1724-1725     2.25 1.00
1726   60y multi ('88)     1.00 .35
1727   60y multi ('88)     1.00 .35
   a. Sheet of 2, #1726-1727, imperf. ('89)     2.50 2.50
   b. A1291 Pair, #1726-1727     2.25 1.00
1728   60y multi ('88)     1.00 .35
1729   60y multi ('88)     1.00 .35
   a. Sheet of 2, #1728-1729, imperf. ('89)     2.50 2.50
   b. A1293 Pair, #1728-1729     2.25 1.00
   *Nos. 1710-1729 (20)*     20.00 7.00

   Issued to commemorate the 300th anniversary of a trip from Edo (now Tokyo) to northern Japan by the famous haiku poet Matsuo Munefusa "Basho" (1644-1694). His prose account of the journey, *Oku no hosomichi* (*Narrow Road to a Far Province*), contains numerous 17-syllable poems (*haiku*), which are shown on the stamps.
   In each setenant pair, a complete *haiku* by Basho is inscribed vertically at right on the left stamp and in the center of the right stamp. The same poem appears on both stamps in each pair.
   Issued: Nos. 1710-1713, 2/26; Nos. 1714-1717, 6/23; Nos. 1718-1721, 8/25; Nos. 1722-1725, 1/3; Nos. 1726-1729, 3/26.
   See Nos. 1775-1794.

12th World Orchid Congress, Tokyo
A1295     A1296

**1987, Mar. 19**     **Photo.**     **Perf. 13**
1730 A1295 60y multicolored     1.00 .30
1731 A1296 60y multicolored     1.00 .30

Railway Post Office Termination, Oct. 1, 1986 — A1297

**1987, Mar. 26**     **Litho.**     **Perf. 13½**
1732   60y Mail car     1.00 .30
1733   60y Loading mail on car     1.00 .30
   a. A1297 Pair, #1732-1733     2.25 1.00

---

Privatization of Japan Railways — A1298

   No. 1734, Locomotive No. 137, c. 1900. No. 1735, Linear induction train, 1987.

**1987, Apr. 1**     **Photo.**     **Perf. 13½**
1734 A1298 60y multicolored     1.00 .35
1735 A1298 60y multicolored     1.00 .35

Natl. Marine Biology Research, Cent. — A1299

**1987, Apr. 2**     **Perf. 13**
1736 A1299 60y Sea slugs     1.00 .25

Paintings by Hashiguchi Goyo (1880-1921) — A1300

**1987, Apr. 14**
1737   60y denomination at UR     1.00 .30
1738   60y denomination at LL     1.00 .30
   a. A1300 Pair, #1737-1738     2.25 1.00

   Philately Week.

Map of Asia and Oceania — A1302

**1987, Apr. 27**     **Photo.**     **Perf. 13½**
1739 A1302 60y multicolored     1.00 .25
   20th annual meeting of the Asian Development Bank.

Nat'l. Land Afforestation Campaign — A1303

   60y, Magpie, seashore.

**1987, May 23**
1740 A1303 60y multicolored     1.00 .25

**National Treasures Series**

A1304     A1305

   Designs: No. 1741, Yatsuhashi gold inkstone box, by Kohrin Ogata. No. 1742, Donjon of Hikone Castle, c. 1573-1592.

**1987, May 26**     **Photo.**     **Perf. 13**
1741 A1304 60y multicolored     1.00 .35

**Photo. & Engr.**
**Perf. 13½**
1742 A1305 110y multicolored     1.90 .50

Golden Turtle
Sharito
A1306

Imuyama Castle
Donjon, 1469
A1307

**1987, July 17**   **Photo.**   *Perf. 13*
1743  A1306  60y multicolored        1.00   .35
**Photo. & Engr.**
*Perf. 13½*
1744  A1307  110y multicolored       1.90   .50

Kongo
Sanmai in
Tahotoh
Temple,
Kamakura
Era — A1308

Wood Ekoh-
Dohji Statue in
the Likeness of
Kongobuji
Fudodo,
Kamakura Era,
by
Unkei — A1309

**1988, Feb. 12**   **Photo.**   *Perf. 13*
1745  A1308  60y multicolored        1.00   .35
**Photo. & Engr.**
*Perf. 13½*
1746  A1309  110y multicolored       1.90   .50

Itsukushima
Shrine, Heian
Period — A1310

Kozakura-gawa, Braided Armor Worn
by Minamoto-no-Yoshimitsu, Heian
Period War Lord, Kai
Province — A1311

**1988, June 23**   **Photo.**   *Perf. 13*
1747  A1310  60y multicolored        1.00   .35
**Photo. & Engr.**
*Perf. 13½*
1748  A1311  100y multicolored       1.75   .50

Statue of *Nakatsu-hime-no-mikoto,* a
Hachiman Goddess, Heian Period,
Yakushiji Temple — A1312

Murou-ji Temple
Pagoda, 9th
Cent. — A1313

**1988, Sept. 26**   **Photo.**   *Perf. 13*
1749  A1312  60y multicolored        1.00   .35

---

**Photo. & Engr.**
*Perf. 13½*
**1750**  A1313  100y multicolored    1.75   .50
*Nos. 1741-1750 (10)*       14.20   4.25

Letter Writing
Day — A1314

40y, Flowers, envelope. 60y, Elephant.

**1987, July 23**   **Photo.**   *Perf. 13x13½*
1751  A1314  40y multicolored        .75    .30
1752  A1314  60y multicolored       1.00    .30
*a.*   Bklt. pane, 5 ea #1751-1752   5.00  10.00

Sheets of 2, Nos. 1751-1752, were lottery
prizes. Value, $5.

Kiso Three Rivers
Flood Control,
Cent. — A1315

60y, Kiso, Nagara and Ibi Rivers.

**1987, Aug. 7**   **Photo.**   *Perf. 13½*
1753  A1315  60y multicolored        1.00   .25

Japan — Thailand
Diplomatic
Relations,
Cent. — A1316

Design: Temple of the Emerald Buddha and
cherry blossoms.

**1987, Sept. 26**           *Perf. 13*
1754  A1316  60y multicolored        1.00   .30

Intl. Letter Writing
Week — A1317

Dolls by Goyo Hirata: 130y, Gensho Kanto,
by Royojo Hori (1898-1984). 150y, Utage-no-
Hana (Fair Woman at the Party).

**1987, Oct. 6**   **Photo.**   *Perf. 13*
1755  A1317  130y multicolored       2.00   .50
1756  A1317  150y multicolored       2.25   .60

13th World Congress of
Certified Public
Accountants, Tokyo,
Oct. 11-15 — A1318

Design: Three Beauties (adaptation), by
Toyokuni Utagawa (1769-1825).

**1987, Oct. 9**           *Perf. 13*
1757  A1318  60y multicolored        1.00   .35

Modern Waterworks,
Cent. — A1319

Design: Lion's head public fountain, 1887,
Waterworks Museum, Yokohama.

**1987, Oct. 16**           **Engr.**
1758  A1319  60y multicolored        1.00   .25

---

Shurei Gate, Okinawa,
Basketball
Players — A1320

**1987, Oct. 24**           **Photo.**
1759  A1320  40y multicolored        .75   .25

42nd Natl. Athletic Meet, Okinawa.

6th World Cong. on
Smoking & Health,
Nov. 9-12,
Tokyo — A1321

**1987, Nov. 9**
1760  A1321  60y multicolored        1.00   .25

World Telecommun-
ications Conf., Nov. 15-
18, Tokyo — A1322

Design: Microwave dish antenna at Kashima
Station Radio Research Laboratory.

**1987, Nov. 13**           *Perf. 13½*
1761  A1322  60y multicolored        1.00   .25

World Conference
on Large Historic
Cities, Nov. 18-21,
Kyoto — A1323

Design: Nijo Castle guardhouse roof and
Ninomaru Hall, 17th cent.

**1987, Nov. 18**           *Perf. 13*
1762  A1323  60y multicolored        1.00   .30

Intl. Year of Shelter
for the
Homeless — A1324

Prize-winning illustrations by: 40y, Takahiro
Nahahama. 60y, Yoko Sasaki.

**1987, Nov. 25**
1763  A1324  40y multicolored        .75   .30
1764  A1324  60y multicolored        1.00   .30

New Year 1988 (Year of
the Dragon) — A1325

Design: Kurashiki papier-mache dragon,
1869, by Tajuro Omizu.

**1987, Dec. 1**           *Perf. 13x13½*
1765  A1325  40y multicolored        .80   .30

Sheets of 2, Nos. 1506, 1765, were lottery
prizes. Value, $2.40.

Seikan Tunnel
Opening — A1326

60y, ED 79 locomotive, map.

**1988, Mar. 11**   **Photo.**   *Perf. 13¼*
1766  A1326  60y multicolored        1.00   .30
*a.*   Booklet pane of 10          10.00   8.00

---

**Opening of Seto-Oohashi Bridge**

Kagawa Side
A1327        A1328

Okayama Side
A1329        A1330

**1988, Apr. 8**   **Engr.**   *Perf. 13½*
1767  A1327  60y multicolored        1.00   .35
1768  A1328  60y multicolored        1.00   .35
1769  A1329  60y multicolored        1.00   .35
1770  A1330  60y multicolored        1.00   .35
*a.*   Strip of 4, #1767-1770       4.50   2.00

Nos. 1767-1768 and 1769-1770 have continuous designs.

Philately
Week
A1331

Prints by Kotondo Torii (1900-76): No. 1771,
Long Undergarment. No. 1772, Kimono Sash.

**1988, Apr. 19**   **Photo.**   *Perf. 13*
1771       60y denomination at LR    1.00   .35
1772       60y denomination at UL    1.00   .35
*a.*   A1331 Pair, #1771-1772        2.50   1.50

Souv. sheet of 2 exists. Value $6.

Silk Road Exposition,
Apr. 24-Oct. 23,
Nara — A1333

Design: Plectrum guard playing the biwa,
detail of Raden-Shitan-no-Gogen-Biwa, a five-
panel work of gold lacquer nacre on sandalwood preserved at Shosoin.

**1988, Apr. 23**           **Photo. & Engr.**
1773  A1333  60y multicolored        1.00   .30

Natl. Afforestation
Campaign — A1334

Design: Yahsima, site of the Genji-Heike
war, and cuckoo on olive tree branch.

**1988, May 20**   **Photo.**   *Perf. 13½*
1774  A1334  60y multicolored        1.00   .25

**Basho Series, Part II**

A1335

A1337

No. 1775, Mogami River. No. 1776, Haiku and flower. No. 1777, Mt. Gassan. No. 1778, Haiku and mountain.

**1988, May 30   Photo.   Perf. 13x13½**

| | | | |
|---|---|---|---|
| 1775 | 60y multicolored | 1.00 | .35 |
| 1776 | 60y multicolored | 1.00 | .35 |
| a. | Souv. sheet of 2, #1775-1776, imperf. ('89) | 2.50 | 2.50 |
| b. | A1335 Pair, #1775-1776 | 2.25 | 1.00 |
| 1777 | 60y multicolored | 1.00 | .35 |
| 1778 | 60y multicolored | 1.00 | .35 |
| a. | Souv. sheet of 2, #1777-1778, imperf. ('89) | 2.50 | 2.50 |
| b. | A1337 Pair, #1777-1778 | 2.25 | 1.00 |

A1339

A1341

No. 1779, Mimosa in bloom. No. 1780, Verse, birds, Kisagata Inlet. No. 1781, Ocean waves. No. 1782, Verse and current.

**1988, Aug. 23**

| | | | |
|---|---|---|---|
| 1779 | 60y multicolored | 1.00 | .35 |
| 1780 | 60y multicolored | 1.00 | .35 |
| a. | Souv. sheet of 2, #1779-1780, imperf. ('89) | 2.50 | 2.50 |
| b. | A1339 Pair, #1779-1780 | 2.25 | 1.00 |
| 1781 | 60y multicolored | 1.00 | .35 |
| 1782 | 60y multicolored | 1.00 | .35 |
| a. | Souv. sheet of 2, #1781-1782, imperf. ('89) | 2.50 | 2.50 |
| b. | A1341 Pair, #1781-1782 | 2.25 | 1.00 |

A1343

A1345

No. 1783, Rice. No. 1784, Birds in flight, haiku. No. 1785, Sun glow. No. 1786, Rice, haiku.

**1988, Nov. 11**

| | | | |
|---|---|---|---|
| 1783 | 60y multicolored | 1.00 | .35 |
| 1784 | 60y multicolored | 1.00 | .35 |
| a. | Souv. sheet of 2, #1783-1784, imperf. ('89) | 2.50 | 2.50 |
| b. | A1343 Pair, #1783-1784 | 2.25 | 1.00 |
| 1785 | 60y multicolored | 1.00 | .35 |
| 1786 | 60y multicolored | 1.00 | .35 |
| a. | Souv. sheet of 2, #1785-1786, imperf. ('89) | 2.50 | 2.50 |
| b. | A1345 Pair, #1785-1786 | 2.25 | 1.00 |

A1347

A1349

No. 1787, Nata-dera Temple. No. 1788, Haiku, white grass. No. 1789, Trees. No. 1790, Haiku, moonlit forest.

**1989, Feb. 13**

| | | | |
|---|---|---|---|
| 1787 | 60y multicolored | 1.00 | .35 |
| 1788 | 60y multicolored | 1.00 | .35 |
| a. | Souv. sheet of 2, #1787-1788, imperf. | 2.50 | 2.50 |
| b. | A1347 Pair, #1787-1788 | 2.25 | 1.00 |
| 1789 | 60y multicolored | 1.00 | .35 |
| 1790 | 60y multicolored | 1.00 | .35 |
| a. | Souv. sheet of 2, #1789-1790, imperf. | 2.50 | 2.50 |
| b. | A1349 Pair, #1789-1790 | 2.25 | 1.00 |

A1351

A1353

No. 1791, Autumn on the beach. No. 1792, Haiku. No. 1793, Clams. No. 1794, Haiku.

**1989, May 12**

| | | | |
|---|---|---|---|
| 1791 | 62y multicolored | 1.00 | .35 |
| 1792 | 62y multicolored | 1.00 | .35 |
| a. | Souv. sheet of 2, #1791-1792, imperf. | 2.50 | 2.50 |
| b. | A1351 Pair, #1791-1792 | 2.25 | 1.00 |
| 1793 | 62y multicolored | 1.00 | .35 |
| 1794 | 62y multicolored | 1.00 | .35 |
| a. | Souv. sheet of 2, #1793-1794, imperf. | 2.50 | 2.50 |
| b. | A1353 Pair, #1793-1794 | 2.25 | 1.00 |

Haiku from *Oku-no-hosomichi*, "Narrow Road to a Far Province," 1694, a travel description written by Matsuo Munefusa (1644-94), a haiku poet best known by his pen-name Basho.

In each setenant pair, a complete *haiku* by Basho is inscribed vertically at right on the left stamp and in the center of the right stamp. The same poem appears on both stamps in each pair.

Issued: Nos. 1776a-1794a, Aug. 1, 1989.

Intl. Conference on Volcanoes, Kagoshima A1355

**1988, July 19   Photo.   Perf. 14**

| | | | |
|---|---|---|---|
| 1795 | A1355 60y multicolored | 1.00 | .30 |

A1356   A1357

A1358

Letter Writing Day, 10th Anniv. — A1359

Designs and contest-winning children's drawings: No. 1796, Cat and letter. No. 1797, *Crab and Letter,* by Katsuyuki Yamada. No. 1798, Fairy and letter. No. 1799, *Girl and Letter,* by Takashi Ukai.

**Photo., Litho. (Nos. 1797, 1799)**
**1988, July 23   Perf. 13x13½**

| | | | |
|---|---|---|---|
| 1796 | A1356 40y multicolored | .75 | .30 |
| 1796A | A1356 40y Imperf., self-adhesive | .75 | .30 |
| a. | Bklt. pane, 5 each #1796, 1798 | 10.00 | 10.00 |
| 1797 | A1357 40y multicolored | .75 | .30 |
| 1798 | A1358 60y multicolored | 1.00 | .30 |
| 1798B | A1358 60y Imperf., self-adhesive | 1.00 | .30 |
| c. | Bklt. pane, 3 each #1796A, 1798B | 7.50 | |
| 1799 | A1359 60y multicolored | 1.00 | .30 |
| | Nos. 1796-1799 (6) | 5.25 | 1.80 |

No. 1798c is adhered to the booklet cover, made of peelable paper, folded in half and rouletted down the center fold, with No. 1796a at left and No. 1798b at right of the roulette.

Sheets of 2 containing Nos. 1796, 1798 were lottery prizes. Value, $5.

15th World Puppetry Festival, July 27-Aug. 11 — A1360

Puppets: No. 1800, *Ohana,* string puppet from the film *Spring and Fall in the Meiji Era,* by Kinosuke Takeda (1923-1979), Japan. No. 1801, Girl, stick puppet from the Natl. Radost Puppet Theater, Brno, Czechoslovakia. No. 1802, Woman, shadow puppet from China. No. 1803, Knight, a marionette from Sicily.

**1988, July 27   Photo.   Perf. 13**

| | | | |
|---|---|---|---|
| 1800 | 60y multicolored | 1.00 | .35 |
| 1801 | 60y multicolored | 1.00 | .35 |
| 1802 | 60y multicolored | 1.00 | .35 |
| 1803 | 60y multicolored | 1.00 | .35 |
| a. | A1360 Block or strip of 4, #1800-1803 | 4.50 | 1.75 |

Japan-China Treaty, 10th Anniv. — A1364

**1988, Aug. 12   Photo.**

| | | | |
|---|---|---|---|
| 1804 | 60y Peony | 1.00 | .35 |
| 1805 | 60y Panda | 1.00 | .35 |
| a. | A1364 Pair, #1804-1805 | 2.25 | 1.00 |

18th World Poultry Congress, Nagoya, Sept. 4-9 — A1366

**1988, Sept. 3   Perf. 13½**

| | | | |
|---|---|---|---|
| 1806 | A1366 60y multicolored | 1.00 | .30 |

Rehabilitation Intl. 16th World Congress, Tokyo, Sept. 5-9 — A1367

**Photo. & Embossed**
**1988, Sept. 5   Perf. 13**

| | | | |
|---|---|---|---|
| 1807 | A1367 60y multicolored | 1.00 | .25 |

Intl. Letter-Writing Week — A1368

Prints: 80y, *Kumesaburo Iwai as Chiyo,* by Kunimasa Utagawa (1773-1810), late Edo Period. 120y, *Komazo Ichikawa III as Ganryu Sasaki,* by Toyokuni Utagawa (1769-1825).

**1988, Oct. 6   Photo.**

| | | | |
|---|---|---|---|
| 1808 | A1368 80y multicolored | 1.25 | .40 |
| 1809 | A1368 120y multicolored | 2.00 | .50 |

43rd Natl. Athletic Meet, Kyoto — A1369

Design: Gymnast on parallel bars and "Kinkakuji," Temple of the Golden Pavilion.

**1988, Oct. 14**

| | | | |
|---|---|---|---|
| 1810 | A1369 40y multicolored | .75 | .25 |

Japan-Mexico Trade Agreement, Cent. — A1370

**1988, Nov. 30   Photo.**

| | | | |
|---|---|---|---|
| 1811 | A1370 60y multicolored | 1.00 | .30 |

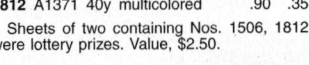

New Year 1989 (Year of the Snake) — A1371

Clay bell snake by Masanobu Ogawa.

**1988, Dec. 1**

| | | | |
|---|---|---|---|
| 1812 | A1371 40y multicolored | .90 | .35 |

Sheets of two containing Nos. 1506, 1812 were lottery prizes. Value, $2.50.

UN Declaration of Human Rights, 40th Anniv. — A1372

**1988, Dec. 5   Litho.   Perf. 13½**

| | | | |
|---|---|---|---|
| 1813 | A1372 60y multicolored | 1.00 | .25 |

**National Treasures Series**

Votive Silver Lidded Bowl Used in Todai-ji Temple Ground-Breaking Ceremony, 8th Cent. — A1373

Bronze Yakushi-nyorai Buddha, Asuka Period, 7th Cent. — A1374

**Photo., Photo & Engr. (100y)**
**1989, Jan. 20   Perf. 13, 13½ (100y)**

| | | | |
|---|---|---|---|
| 1814 | A1373 60y multicolored | 1.00 | .35 |
| 1815 | A1374 100y multicolored | 1.75 | .50 |

Kondo-Sukashibori-Kurakanagu, Bronze Saddle from Ohjin Imperial Mausoleum — A1375

Tamamushi-no-Zushi, Buddhist Altar in Lacquered Cypress from the Asuka Era — A1376

**1989, June 30**
1816 A1375 62y multicolored   1.10 .35
1817 A1376 100y multicolored   1.75 .50

Kin-in, a Gokan Era Gold Seal Given to the King of Na by Emperor Kobutei — A1377

Shinninshaba-gazokyo, a 5th Cent. European Bronze Mirror Back — A1378

**1989, Aug. 15**
1818 A1377 62y multicolored   1.10 .35
1819 A1378 100y multicolored   1.75 .50
    *Nos. 1814-1819 (6)*   8.45 2.55

Asian-Pacific Expo, Fukuoka, Mar. 17-Sept. 3 — A1383

**1989**     **Photo.**     **Perf. 13**
1822 A1383 60y multicolored   1.00 .30
1823 A1383 62y multicolored   1.75 .50
    Issue dates: 60y, Mar. 16; 62y, Apr. 18.

Yokohama Exposition (Space and Children), Yokohama City, Mar. 25 to Oct. 1 — A1384

Design: Detail of *Russian Lady Sight-seeing at the Port,* by Yoshitora, and entrance to the Yokohama City Art Museum.

**1989, Mar. 24**      **Litho.**
1824 A1384 60y multicolored   1.00 .30
1825 A1384 62y multicolored   1.75 .50

World Bonsai Convention, Omiya, Apr. 6-9 — A1385

**1989, Apr. 6**    **Photo.**    **Perf. 13**
1826 A1385 62y multicolored   1.10 .35

*Awa-odori,* by Tsunetomi Kitano (b. 1880) A1386

**1989, Apr. 18**      **Perf. 13**
1827    62y multicolored   1.10 .35
1828    62y multicolored   1.10 .35
    *a.* A1386 Pair, #1827-1828   2.25 1.00
    Philately Week. Sheets of 2 containing Nos. 1827-1828 were lottery prizes. Value, $5.

---

Holland Festival 1989 — A1388

**1989, Apr. 19**      **Perf. 13½**
1829 A1388 62y Ship   1.10 .30

Fiber-optic Cable, the 3rd Transpacific Line Relay Linking Japan and the US — A1389

62y, Station tower, map.

**1989, May 10**      **Perf. 13½x13**
1830 A1389 62y multicolored   1.10 .30

Natl. Afforestation Campaign — A1390

62y, Bayberry, lime, Mt. Tsurugi.

**1989, May 19**      **Perf. 13½**
1831 A1390 62y multicolored   1.10 .30

World Design Exposition, Nagoya, July 15-Nov. 26
A1391      A1392

**1989, July 14**
1832 A1391 41y multicolored   .80 .35
1833 A1392 62y multicolored   1.10 .35

Letter Writing Day
A1393      A1394

**1989, July 21**      **Perf. 13x13½**
1834 A1393 41y multicolored   .80 .30
1835 A1394 62y multicolored   1.10 .30
    *a.*   Bklt. pane, 5 each #1834-1835   9.50
    Sheets of 2 containing Nos. 1834-1835 were lottery prizes. Value, $3.

### Congratulations and Condolences Types of 1982

**1989, Aug. 10   Photo.   Perf. 13x13½**
1836 A1082 41y Wreath   .80 .25
1837 A1083 41y Crane   .80 .30
1838 A1083 62y Crane   1.10 .30
1839 A1084 72y Tortoise   1.30 .35
    *Nos. 1836-1839 (4)*   4.00 1.20

6th Interflora World Congress, Tokyo, Aug. 27-30 — A1395

**1989, Aug. 25**    **Photo.**    **Perf. 13½**
1840 A1395 62y multicolored   1.10 .35

### Prefecture Issues

Nos. 1841-1990 have been changed to Nos. Z1-Z150. The listings can be found in the section immediately following the postage section and preceding the semi-postal listings.

---

A1546

**1989, Sept. 14**    **Photo.**    **Perf. 13½**
1991 A1546 62y multicolored   1.10 .30
    Far East and South Pacific Games for the Disabled (FESPIC), Kobe, Sept. 15-20.

*Okuni Kabuki* Screen
A1547      A1548

**1989, Sept. 18**      **Perf. 13**
1992 A1547 62y multicolored   1.10 .35
1993 A1548 70y multicolored   1.25 .40
    EUROPALIA '89, Japan.

A1549

A1550

Scenes from the Yadorigi and Takekawa Chapters of the Tales of the Genji picture scroll, attributed to Fujiwara-no-Takeyoshi, late Heian Period (897-1185).

**1989, Oct. 6**    **Photo.**    **Perf. 13½**
1994 A1549 80y multicolored   1.40 .45
1995 A1550 120y multicolored   2.00 .55
    Intl. Letter Writing Day.

Intl. Conference on Irrigation and Drainage — A1551

**1989, Oct. 13**
1996 A1551 62y Rice   1.10 .30

100th Tenno Sho Horse Race — A1552

62y, Jockey riding Shinzan.

**1989, Oct. 27**      **Perf. 13**
1997 A1552 62y multicolored   1.10 .30

9th Hot Air Balloon World Championships, Saga — A1553

**1989, Nov. 17   Photo.   Perf. 13x13½**
1998 A1553 62y multicolored   1.10 .35

---

Copyright Control System, 50th Anniv. — A1554

**1989, Nov. 17**      **Perf. 13**
1999 A1554 62y Conductor   1.10 .30

New Year 1990 (Year of the Horse)
A1555      A1556

41y, *Yawata-Uma* festival horse. 62y, *Kazari-Uma,* Meiji Period.

**1989, Dec. 1**    **Perf. 13x13½, 13½**
2000 A1555 41y multicolored   .85 .30
2001 A1556 62y multicolored   1.25 .35
    No. 2001 was sold through Jan. 10, 1990, serving as a lottery ticket.
    Sheets of two containing Nos. 1838, 2000 were lottery prizes. Value, $2.50.

### Electric Locomotives

10,000 — A1557

#### Photo. & Engr., Photo.

**1990**      **Perf. 13**
2002 A1557 62y shown   1.10 .35
2003 A1557 62y EF58   1.10 .35
2004 A1557 62y ED40   1.10 .35
2005 A1557 62y EH10   1.10 .35
2006 A1557 62y EF53   1.10 .35
2007 A1557 62y ED70   1.10 .35
2008 A1557 62y EF55   1.10 .35
2009 A1557 62y ED61   1.10 .35
2010 A1557 62y EF57   1.10 .35
2011 A1557 62y EF30   1.10 .35
    *Nos. 2002-2011 (10)*   11.00 3.50
    Issued two stamps at a time, the first photo. & engr., the second photo.
    Issued: Nos. 2002-2003, 1/31; Nos. 2004-2005, 2/28; Nos. 2006-2007, 4/23; Nos. 2008-2009, 5/23; Nos. 2010-2011, 7/18.

Intl. Garden and Greenery Exposition, Osaka — A1558

**1990, Mar. 30**    **Photo.**    **Perf. 13**
2021 A1558 62y multicolored   1.10 .30
    See No. B45.

Philately Week — A1559

Painting: *Women Gazing at the Stars,* by Chou Ohta.

**1990, Apr. 20**    **Photo.**    **Perf. 13**
2022 A1559 62y multicolored   1.10 .30
    *a.*   Souvenir sheet of 1   1.25 1.25

A1560

62y, Azalea, Mt. Unzen.

**1990, May 18    Photo.    Perf. 13½**
2023  A1560  62y multicolored          1.10   .30
  Natl. Land Afforestation Campaign.

Flower,
Butterfly — A1561

Abstract Art —
A1561a

**1990, June 1    Photo.    Perf. 13**
2024  A1561  62y multicolored          1.10   .35
2025  A1561a 70y multicolored          1.25   .35

Japan-Turkey Relations,
Cent. — A1562

**1990, June 13**
2026  A1562  62y multicolored          1.10   .30

**Horses Series**

Horses at Stable from Umaya-zu
Byobu — A1563

Foals — A1564

Lacquered
Saddle, 16th
Cent. — A1565

Lacquered
Stirrups, 16th
Cent.
A1566

Horse by S.
Nishiyama
A1567

Kettei
A1568

"Kamo-
Kurabeuma-
Monyo-
Kosode"
A1569

**Perf. 13x13½, 13**
**1990                           Litho. & Engr.**
**Color of Horse**
2027  62y red brown      1.10   .35
2028  62y gray           1.10   .35
2029  62y beige          1.10   .35
2030  62y tan            1.10   .35
2031  62y mottled        1.10   .35
  a.   A1563 Strip of 5, #2027-2031   6.75  2.75
**Photo.**
2032  A1564  62y shown   1.10   .35
**Photo. & Engr.**
2033  A1565  62y shown   1.10   .35
2034  A1566  62y shown   1.10   .35
  a.   Pair, #2033-2034   2.75  1.00

**Photo.**
2035  A1567  62y multicolored  1.10  .35
2036  A1568  62y multicolored  1.10  .35
2037  A1569  62y multicolored  1.10  .35

Postal
Carriages
A1569a

Inkstone Case
"Sano-no-
Watashi"
A1570

"Bushu-Senju-zu"
by Hokusai
A1571

"Shudan" by
Kogetsu
Saigo — A1571a

**Photo. & Engr., Photo. (#2040, 2042)**
**1991                    Perf. 12½x13**
2038  62y one horse      1.10   .35
2039  62y two horses     1.10   .35
  a.   A1569a Pair, #2038-2039   2.75  1.00
**Perf. 13½x13**
2040  A1570  62y multicolored  1.10  .35
2041  A1571  62y multicolored  1.10  .35
2042  A1571a 62y multicolored  1.10  .35
  Nos. 2027-2042 (16)      17.60  5.60
  Issued: Nos. 2027-2032, 6/20; Nos. 2033-
2035, 7/31; Nos. 2036-2037, 9/27; Nos. 2038-
2040, 1/31. Nos. 2041-2042, 2/28.

38th Intl. Youth Hostel
Fed.
Conference — A1573

**1990, June 25    Litho.    Perf. 13**
2057  A1573  62y multicolored    1.10   .30

Letter Writing Day
A1574        A1575

**1990, July 23    Photo.    Perf. 13½**
2058  A1574  41y multicolored    .80   .35
2059  A1575  62y multicolored   1.10   .40
  a.   Souv. sheet of 1          1.25  1.25
  b.   Bklt. pane, 5 ea #2058-2059   9.50
        See No. 2117.

21st Intl. Congress
of Mathematicians
A1576

**1990, Aug. 17    Photo.    Perf. 13**
2060  A1576  62y multicolored    1.10   .30

World Cycling
Championships — A1577

**1990, Aug. 20    Litho.    Perf. 13½**
2061  A1577  62y multicolored    1.10   .30

Ogai Mori,
Educator — A1578

**1990, Aug. 27                 Photo.**
2062  A1578  62y multicolored    1.10   .30
  Intl. Assoc. for Germanic Studies (IVG), 8th
Congress.

Character "Ji" in Shape
of Rosetta
Stone — A1579

**1990, Sept. 7              Perf. 13**
2063  A1579  62y multicolored    1.10   .30
  Intl. Literacy Year.

Decade for Natural
Disaster
Reduction — A1580

**1990, Sept. 27                Photo.**
2064  A1580  62y multicolored    1.10   .30

Intl. Confederation
of Midwives, 22nd
Congress — A1581

**1990, Oct. 5                  Photo.**
2065  A1581  62y multicolored    1.10   .30

A1582

"Choju-Jinbutsu-Giga" — A1583

**Photo. & Engr.**
**1990, Oct. 5              Perf. 13½**
2066  A1582  80y multicolored    1.40   .45
2067  A1583  120y multicolored   2.00   .55
  Intl. Letter Writing Week.

"Fumizukai-zu" by
Harunobu
Suiendo — A1584

**1990, Oct. 16                 Photo.**
2068  A1584  100y multicolored   1.75   .55
  a.   Souv. sheet of 1          2.00  2.00
  No. 2068a exists with surcharge which paid
admission to PHILANIPPON '91. These were
not sold by the post office.

Court System,
Cent. — A1585

**1990, Nov. 1    Photo.    Perf. 13x13½**
2069  A1585  62y "Justice"       1.10   .35

Japanese Braille,
Cent. — A1586

**Photo & Embossed**
**1990, Nov. 1              Perf. 13½**
2070  A1586  62y multicolored    1.10   .30

Enthronement of
Akihito — A1587

  No. 2071, Chinese phoenix depicted on
Emperor's chair. No. 2072, Diamond pattern
for costume worn at banquet ceremony.

**1990, Nov. 9    Photo.    Perf. 13**
2071  A1587  62y multicolored    1.10   .35
2072  A1587  62y multicolored    1.10   .35
  a.   Souv. sheet of 2, #2071-2072  2.50  2.50

Japanese Diet,
Cent. — A1588

**1990, Nov. 29                 Litho.**
2073  A1588  62y multicolored    1.10   .35

New Year 1991 (Year of
the Sheep)
A1589        A1590

**1990, Dec. 3  Photo.  Perf. 13x13½**
2074  A1589  41y multicolored     .75   .30
**Photo. & Engr.**
**Perf. 13½**
2075  A1590  41y multicolored     .90   .35
2076  A1590  62y multi, diff.    1.40   .40
  Nos. 2074-2076 (3)            3.05  1.05
  Sheets of 2 No. 2074 were lottery prizes.
Value, $2.

Dr. Yoshio Nishina,
Physicist — A1591

**1990, Dec. 6    Photo.    Perf. 13**
2077  A1591  62y multicolored    1.10   .30
  Use of radio isotopes in Japan, 50th anniv.

Telephone Service, Cent. — A1592

**1990, Dec. 14**
2078 A1592 62y multicolored 1.10 .30

A1593

41y, Figure skating. 62y, Speed skating, horiz.

**1991, Mar. 1    Photo.    Perf. 13½**
2079 A1593 41y multi .80 .30

**Perf. 13½x13**
2080 A1593 62y multi 1.10 .30
1991 Winter Universiade.

A1594

**1991, Apr. 1    Photo.    Perf. 13**
2081 A1594 62y multicolored 1.10 .30
Postal Life Insurance System.

Philately Week
A1595    A1596

No. 2082, Beauty Looking Back by Moronobu. No. 2083, Opening Dance by Shuho Yamakawa.

**1991, Apr. 19**
2082 A1595 62y multicolored 1.10 .35
2083 A1596 62y multicolored 1.10 .35
  a.  Souv. sheet of 2, #2082-2083 2.50 2.50
  b.  Pair, #2082-2083 2.50 2.50

Postal Service, 120th anniv.
Pairs of Nos. 2082-2083 with label between are available from sheets of 20.

A1597

**1991, Apr. 19    Perf. 13½**
2084 A1597 62y multicolored 1.10 .30
Ceramic World Shigaraki '91.

A1598

**1991, May 24    Photo.    Perf. 13½**
2085 A1598 41y multicolored .80 .30
Natl. Land Afforestation Campaign.

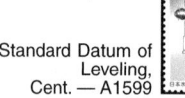

Standard Datum of Leveling, Cent. — A1599

**1991, May 30    Photo.    Perf. 13**
2086 A1599m 62y mutlicolored 1.10 .35

## Int'l Stamp Design Contest Winning Entries

Flowers
A1600

Couple in Ethnic Dress
A1601

World Peace — A1601a

Butterfly — A1601b

**1991, May 31    Photo.    Perf. 13**
2087 A1600 41y multi .80 .30
2088 A1601 62y multi 1.10 .30
2089 A1601a 70y multi 1.25 .40
2090 A1601b 100y multi 1.75 .50
  Nos. 2087-2090 (4) 4.90 1.50

Int'l. Stamp Design Contest winning entries.

## Kabuki Series

Kagamijishi
A1602

Yaegakihime
A1603

Koshiro Matsumoto VII
A1604

Danjuro Ichikawa XI
A1605

Baigyoku Nakamura III
A1606

Ganjiro Nakamura II
A1607

Kichiemon Nakamura I — A1608

Nizaemon Kataoka XIII — A1609

Enjaku Jitsukawa II
A1610

Hakuo Matsumoto I
A1611

Fuji-Musume
A1612

Kotobuki-Soganotaimen
A1613

### *Perf. 13 (62y), 13½ (100y)*
**1991-92    Photo.**
| | | | | |
|---|---|---|---|---|
| 2091 | A1602 | 62y dp bl grn & gold | 1.10 | .35 |
| 2092 | A1603 | 100y multicolored | 1.75 | .55 |
| 2093 | A1604 | 62y multicolored | 1.10 | .35 |
| 2094 | A1605 | 100y multicolored | 1.75 | .55 |
| 2095 | A1606 | 62y multicolored | 1.10 | .35 |
| 2096 | A1607 | 100y multicolored | 1.75 | .55 |
| 2097 | A1608 | 62y multicolored | 1.10 | .35 |
| 2098 | A1609 | 100y multicolored | 1.75 | .55 |
| 2099 | A1610 | 62y multicolored | 1.10 | .35 |
| 2100 | A1611 | 100y multicolored | 1.75 | .55 |
| 2101 | A1612 | 62y multicolored | 1.10 | .35 |
| 2102 | A1613 | 100y multicolored | 1.75 | .55 |
| | Nos. 2091-2102 (12) | | 17.10 | 5.40 |

Issued: Nos. 2091-2092, 6/28; Nos. 2093-2094, 9/27; Nos. 2095-2096, 11/20; Nos. 2097-2098, 2/20/92; Nos. 2099-2100, 4/10/92; Nos. 2101-2102, 6/30/92.

## Waterbird Series

Gallinago Hardwickii (Latham's Snipe) — A1614

No. 2104, Sula leucogaster. No. 2105, Larus crassirostris. No. 2106, Podiceps ruficollis. No. 2107, Lunda cirrhata. No. 2108, Grus monacha. No. 2109, Cygnus cygnus. No. 2110, Rostratula benghalensis. No. 2111, Calonectris leucomelas. No. 2112, Halcyon coromanda. No. 2113, Alcedo atthis. No. 2114, Bubulcus ibis.

**1991-93    Photo.    Perf. 13½**
| | | | | |
|---|---|---|---|---|
| 2103 | A1614 | 62y multicolored | 1.10 | .35 |
| 2104 | A1614 | 62y multicolored | 1.10 | .35 |
| 2105 | A1614 | 62y multicolored | 1.10 | .35 |
| 2106 | A1614 | 62y multicolored | 1.10 | .35 |
| 2107 | A1614 | 62y multicolored | 1.10 | .35 |
| 2108 | A1614 | 62y multicolored | 1.10 | .35 |
| 2109 | A1614 | 62y multicolored | 1.10 | .35 |
| 2110 | A1614 | 62y multicolored | 1.10 | .35 |
| 2111 | A1614 | 62y multicolored | 1.10 | .35 |
| 2112 | A1614 | 62y multicolored | 1.10 | .35 |
| 2113 | A1614 | 62y multicolored | 1.10 | .35 |
| 2114 | A1614 | 62y multicolored | 1.10 | .35 |
| | Nos. 2103-2114 (12) | | 13.20 | 4.20 |

Nos. 2103-2104 printed in blocks of 12 with gutter between in sheet of 24.
Issued: Nos. 2103-2104, 6/28; Nos. 2105-2106, 9/27; Nos. 2107-2108, 1/30/92; Nos. 2109-2110, 3/25/92; Nos. 2111-2112, 8/31/92; Nos. 2113-2114, 1/29/93.
See Nos. 2192-2195.

Intl. Conf. on Superconductivity
A1620

**1991, July 19    Litho.    Perf. 13½**
2115 A1620 62y multicolored 1.10 .30

### Type of Letter Writing Day of 1990 and

A1621

**1991, July 23    Photo.    Perf. 13x13½**
2116 A1621 41y multicolored .80 .30
2117 A1575 62y multicolored 1.10 .35
  a.  Souvenir sheet of 1 1.25 1.25
  b.  Bklt. pane, 5 each #2116-2117 9.50

Nos. 2117, 2117a have light blue frameline and inscription and violet denomination.

3rd IAAF World Track & Field Championships, Tokyo — A1622

**1991, Aug. 23    Perf. 13**
2118 A1622 41y High jump .80 .30
2119 A1622 62y Shot put 1.10 .30

Intl. Symposium on Environmental Change and Geographical Information Systems — A1623

**1991, Aug. 23**
2120 A1623 62y multicolored 1.10 .30

Intl. Letter Writing Week — A1624

Bandainagon-emaki picture scroll probably by Mitsunaga Tokiwa: 80y, Crowd of people. 120y, People, house.

**Photo. & Engr.**
**1991, Oct. 7    Perf. 13½**
2121 A1624 80y multicolored 1.40 .45
2122 A1624 120y multicolored 2.00 .55

A1625

62y, Breezy Fine Weather by Hokusai.

**1991, Oct. 8    Photo.    Perf. 13**
2123 A1625 62y multicolored 1.10 .35
Summit Conf. on Earthquake and Natural Disasters Countermeasures.

A1626

**1991, Oct. 31    Litho.    Perf. 13**
2124 A1626 62y multicolored 1.10 .35
Japanese Green Tea, 800th anniv.

A1627

Koshaku-Musume by Kunisada Utagawa.

**Photo. & Engr.**

**1991, Nov. 15**    *Perf. 13*
2125 A1627 62y multicolored  1.10 .35
  *a.*  Sheet of 2   3.50 3.50

World Stamp Exhibition, Nippon '91.

A1628

**1991, Nov. 20**    **Photo.**
2126 A1628 62y multicolored  1.10 .30

Administrative Counselors System, 30th anniv.

A1629

A1630

New Year 1992 (Year of the Monkey)
A1631     A1632

**1991, Dec. 2**   **Photo.**   *Perf. 13½*
2127 A1629 41y multicolored  .75 .30
2128 A1630 62y multicolored  1.10 .40
2129 A1631 41y +3y, multi  .90 .40
2130 A1632 62y +3y, multi  1.25 .40
  Nos. 2127-2130 (4)  4.00 1.50

Sheets of 2 No. 2127 were lottery prizes. Value, $2.10.

8th Conference on Intl. Trade in Endangered Species (CITES) — A1633

**1992, Mar. 2**   **Photo.**   *Perf. 13*
2131 A1633 62y multicolored  1.10 .30

Philately Week — A1634

Flowers on the Chair, by Hoshun Yamaguchi.

**1992, Apr. 20**
2132 A1634 62y multicolored  1.10 .30

A1635

**1992, May 15**
2133 A1635 62y multicolored  1.10 .35

Return of Ryukyu Islands to Japan, 20th anniv.

Intl. Space Year
A1636

No. 2134, Satellite at left. No. 2135, Space station upper right.

**1992, July 7**  **Photo.**  *Perf. 13*
2134  62y multicolored  1.10 .35
2135  62y multicolored  1.10 .35
  *a.*  A1636 Pair, #2134-2135  2.25 1.25

Letter Writing Day
A1638     A1639

**1992, July 23**   *Perf. 13x13½*
2136 A1638 41y multicolored  .80 .35

   *Perf. 13½*
2137 A1639 62y multicolored  1.10 .35
  *a.*  Souvenir sheet of 1  1.25 1.25
  *b.*  Bklt. pane, 5 each #2136-2137  9.50

29th Intl. Geological Congress, Kyoto — A1640

**1992, Aug. 24**  **Photo.**  *Perf. 13½x13*
2138 A1640 62y multicolored  1.10 .30

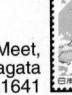

47th Natl. Athletic Meet, Yamagata Prefecture — A1641

**1992, Sept. 4**    *Perf. 13½*
2139 A1641 41y multicolored  .80 .30

Normalization of Japanese-Chinese Relations, 20th Anniv. — A1642

**Photo. & Engr.**
**1992, Sept. 29**   *Perf. 13*
2140  62y jug  1.10 .35
2141  62y long-neck jar  1.10 .35
  *a.*  A1642 Pair, #2140-2141  2.25 1.00

Intl. Letter Writing Week — A1644

Heiji picture scroll: 80y, Nobles, servants in carriages by Taikenmon gate. 120y, Fujiwara-no Nobuyori seated before samurai.

**Photo. & Engr.**
**1992, Oct. 6**    *Perf. 13½*
2142 A1644 80y multicolored  1.40 .45
2143 A1644 120y multicolored  2.00 .55

Cat and Birds — A1644a

Design: 70y, Santa Claus, snow scene, vert.

   *Perf. 13½x13, 13x13½*
**1992, Oct. 9**    **Photo.**
2144 A1644a 62y multicolored  1.10 .30
2145 A1644a 70y multicolored  1.25 .30

Winners of Third Postage Stamp Design contest.

30th Congress of Intl. Cooperative Alliance, Tokyo — A1644b

**1992, Oct. 27**   *Perf. 13x13½*
2146 A1644b 62y multicolored  1.10 .30

A1645

Cultural Pioneers: No. 2147, Takakazu Seki (1642?-1708), mathematician. No. 2148, Akiko Yosano (1878-1942), poet.

**Photo. & Engr.**
**1992, Nov. 4**    *Perf. 13*
2147 A1645 62y multicolored  1.10 .30
2148 A1645 62y multicolored  1.10 .30

See Nos. 2217-2219, 2434-2435, 2642, 2717-2718.

A1646

**1992, Nov. 9**  **Photo.**  *Perf. 13x13½*
2149 A1646 62y multicolored  1.10 .30

Certified Public Tax Accountant System, 50th anniv.

A1647       A1648

New Year 1993 (Year of the Rooster)
A1649     A1650

**1992, Nov. 16**    *Perf. 13x13½*
2150 A1647 41y multicolored  .75 .30
2151 A1648 62y multicolored  1.10 .40
  *a.*  Souvenir sheet of 2, #2150-2151  2.40 2.40

    *Perf. 13½*
2152 A1649 41y +3y multi  .90 .40
2153 A1650 62y +3y multi  1.25 .40
  Nos. 2150-2153 (4)  4.00 1.50

Surtax on Nos. 2152-2153 for lottery. No. 2151a also was a lottery prize.

Flora and Fauna — A1651

9y, Dragonfly. 15y, Swallowtail. 18y, Ladybug. 41y, Mandarin duck. No. 2158, 50y, Japanese white-eye. No. 2159, 62y, Rufous turtle dove. 72y, Varied tit. 80y, Pied kingfisher. 90y, Spotbill duck. 130y, Bullfinch. 190y, Fringed orchid. 270y, Wild pink. 350y, Adder's tongue lily. 420y, Japanese iris. 430y, Violet.

**1992-94**   **Photo.**   *Perf. 13x13½*
2154 A1651 9y multi  .30 .25
2155 A1651 15y multi  .30 .25
2156 A1651 18y multi  .40 .25
2157 A1651 41y multi  1.10 .35
2158 A1651 50y multi  1.10 .25
2159 A1651 62y multi  1.50 .25
  *a.*  Bklt. pane, 5 ea #2157, 2159  13.00
  *b.*  Booklet pane of 10  15.00
2160 A1651 72y multi  2.25 .25
2161 A1651 80y multi  1.75 .25
  *c.*  Miniature sheet, 5 #2158, 10 #2161 + 3 labels  45.00
2162 A1651 90y multi  2.00 .25
2163 A1651 130y multi  3.00 .25
2164 A1651 190y multi  4.00 .25
2165 A1651 270y multi  6.00 .25
2166 A1651 350y multi  7.00 .25
2167 A1651 420y multi  9.00 .25
2167A A1651 430y multi  9.00 .25
  Nos. 2154-2167A (15)  48.70 3.85

**Coil Stamps**
  *Perf. 13 Horiz.*
2168 A1651 50y like #2158  1.25 .25
2169 A1651 80y like #2161  2.00 .25

**Booklet Stamps**
**Self-Adhesive**
  *Die Cut*
2170 A1651 41y like #2157  1.10 .35
2171 A1651 50y like #2158  1.10 .45
2172 A1651 62y like #2159  1.50 .50
  *a.*  Bklt. pane, 2 #2170, 4 #2172  8.50
2173 A1651 80y like #2161  1.75 .70
  *a.*  Bklt. pane, 4 #2171, 4 #2173  14.00

  Issued: 41y, 62y, 72y, 11/30/92; 9y, 18y, Nos. 2158, 2161, 90y, 1/13/94; 270y, 350y, 420y, 1/24/94; 15y, 130y, 190y, 430y, 4/25/94. Nos. 2172a, 2173a are adhered to the booklet cover, made of peelable paper, folded in half and rouletted down the center fold.
  See Nos. 2475-2483, 2486-2488. Compare No. 2166 with No. 3446.

World Alpine Skiing Championships, Morioka-Shizukuishi A1657

**1993, Feb. 3**  **Photo.**  *Perf. 13*
2174 A1657 41y shown  .80 .40
2175 A1657 62y Skier, diff.  1.10 .55

**Seasonal Flowers Series**

Poppy        Cherry
A1658       Blossoms
          A1659

Lily
A1660

Thistle
A1661

Chinese
Bellflowers
A1662

Chrysanthemums
A1663

Plum
Blossom
A1664

Winter
Camellia
A1665

*Perf. 13½ (41y, 50y), 13 (62y, 80y)*

**1993-94**     **Photo.**
2176 A1658 41y multicolored   .80   .35

*Perf. 13*
2177 A1659 62y multicolored   1.10   .35
2178 A1660 41y multicolored   .80   .35

*Perf. 13*
2179 A1661 62y multicolored   1.10   .35
2180 A1662 41y multicolored   .80   .35
2181 A1663 62y multicolored   1.10   .35
2182 A1664 50y multicolored   .90   .35
2183 A1665 80y multicolored   1.40   .55
    *Nos. 2176-2183 (8)*   8.00   3.00

Issued: Nos. 2176-2177, 3/12; Nos. 2178-2179, 6/18; Nos. 2180-2181, 9/16; Nos. 2182-2183, 1/28/94.

**Waterbird Type**

**1993**     **Photo.**     *Perf. 13½*
2192 A1614 62y Grus vipio   1.10   .35
2193 A1614 62y Ansner albifrons   1.10   .35
2194 A1614 62y Anas formosa   1.10   .35
2195 A1614 62y Haliaeetus al-
    bicilla   1.10   .35
    *Nos. 2192-2195 (4)*   4.40   1.40

Issued: Nos. 2192-2193, 3/31; Nos. 2194-2195, 5/25.

Philately
Week — A1674

Painting: In the Studio, by Nampu Katayama.

**1993, Apr. 20**   **Photo.**   *Perf. 13*
2196 A1674 62y multicolored   1.10   .30

Natl. Land Afforestation
Campaign — A1675

**1993, Apr. 23**     *Perf. 13½*
2197 A1675 41y multicolored   .80   .30

---

Mandarin
Duck in the
Nest
A1676

Gardenia in
the Nest
A1677

Design: 70y, Mandarin Duck and Gardenia emblems, horiz.

**1993, June 8**     **Photo.**     *Perf. 13*
2198 A1676 62y multicolored   1.10   .35
2199 A1677 62y multicolored   1.10   .35
  *a.*    Pair, #2198-2199   2.25   1.25
2200 A1676 70y multicolored   1.25   .40
    *Nos. 2198-2200 (3)*   3.45   1.10

Royal Wedding of Crown Prince Naruhito and Masako Owada.

5th Meeting of
Signatories to
Ramsar, Iran
Convention on
Wetlands and
Waterfowl
Habitats — A1678

No. 2201, Crane with young. No. 2202, Crane's head.

**1993, June 10**    **Photo.**    *Perf. 13½*
2201 A1678 62y multicolored   1.10   .35
2202 A1678 62y multicolored   1.10   .35
  *a.*    Pair, #2201-2202   2.50   2.00

Commercial
Registration System,
Cent. — A1679

**1993, July 1**   **Photo.**   *Perf. 13x13½*
2203 A1679 62y multicolored   1.10   .30

Letter Writing Day
A1680      A1681

**1993, July 23**     *Perf. 13x13½*
2204 A1680 41y multicolored   .80   .35

*Perf. 13½x13*
2205 A1681 62y multicolored   1.10   .35
  *a.*    Souvenir sheet of 1   1.25   1.25
  *b.*    Booklet pane, 5 each #2204-
      2205   10.00

15th Intl. Botanical
Congress,
Tokyo — A1682

Designs: No. 2206, Glaucidium palmatum. No. 2207, Sciadopitys verticillata.

**1993, Aug. 23**   **Photo.**   *Perf. 13½x13*
2206    62y multicolored   1.10   .35
2207    62y multicolored   1.10   .35
  *a.*   A1682 Pair, #2206-2207   2.50   1.25

---

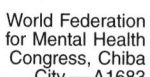

World Federation
for Mental Health
Congress, Chiba
City — A1683

**1993, Aug. 23**     *Perf. 13½x13*
2208 A1683 62y multicolored   1.10   .30

A1684

**1993, Sept. 3**    **Photo.**    *Perf. 13½*
2209    41y Swimming   .80   .30
2210    41y Karate   .80   .30
  *a.*   A1684 Pair, #2209-2210   1.75   1.00

48th natl. athletic meet, Kagawa Prefecture.

A1685

Japanese-Portuguese Relations, 450th Anniv.: No. 2211, Arrival of Portuguese, folding screen, c. 1560-1630. No. 2212, Mother-of-Pearl Host Box, Jesuit symbols and grape motif.

**1993, Sept. 22**    **Photo.**    *Perf. 13*
2211    62y multicolored   1.10   .35
2212    62y multicolored   1.10   .35
  *a.*   A1685 Pair, #2211-2212   2.50   1.25

Intl. Letter
Writing
Week — A1686

Portraits from Picture Scrolls of the Thirty-Six Immortal Poets: 80y, Ki no Tsurayuki. 120y, Kodai no Kimi.

**1993, Oct. 6**     *Perf. 13½*
2213 A1686 80y multicolored   1.40   .40
2214 A1686 120y multicolored   2.00   .50

10th World Veterans'
Track and Field
Championships,
Miyazaki
Prefecture — A1687

**1993, Oct. 7**     *Perf. 14*
2215 A1687 62y multicolored   1.10   .30

Souvenir Sheet

Wedding of Crown Prince Naruhito
and Princess Masako — A1688

**1993, Oct. 13**    **Photo.**    *Perf. 13½*
2216 A1688 62y multicolored   1.25   1.25

**Cultural Pioneers Type of 1992**

No. 2217, Kazan Watanabe (1793-1841), artist. No. 2218, Umetaro Suzuki (1874-1943), chemist. No. 2219, Toson Shimazaki (1872-1943), poet.

**1993, Nov. 4**     **Photo.**     *Perf. 13*
2217 A1645 62y multicolored   1.10   .30

---

**Photo. & Engr.**
2218 A1645 62y multicolored   1.10   .30
2219 A1645 62y multicolored   1.10   .30
    *Nos. 2217-2219 (3)*   3.30   .90

Agricultural Research
Center, Cent. — A1689

**1993, Nov. 17**     *Perf. 13½*
2220 A1689 62y multicolored   1.10   .30

A1690        A1691

New Year 1994 (Year of
the Dog)
A1692      A1693

**1993, Nov. 17**     *Perf. 13x13½*
2221 A1690 41y multicolored   .75   .30
2222 A1691 62y multicolored   1.10   .40

*Perf. 13½*
2223 A1692 41y +3y multi   .90   .40
2224 A1693 62y +3y multi   1.25   .40
    *Nos. 2221-2224 (4)*   4.00   1.50

Sheets of 2, Nos. 2221-2222, were lottery prizes. Value, $2.40.

Declaration of Human
Rights, 45th
Anniv. — A1694

Designs: 62y, Man with bird perched on head. 70y, Globe, dove, person breaking chains, peace symbol.

**1993, Dec. 10**    **Photo.**    *Perf. 13*
2225 A1694 62y multicolored   1.10   .30
2226 A1694 70y multicolored   1.25   .40

**Congratulations and Condolences
Types of 1982**

**1994, Mar. 10**   **Photo.**   *Perf. 13x13½*
2227 A1082 50y Wreath   .90   .35
2228 A1083 50y Crane   .90   .35
2229 A1083 80y Crane   1.40   .40
2230 A1084 90y Tortoise   1.60   .40
    *Nos. 2227-2230 (4)*   4.80   1.50

For use on condolence and greeting cards.

1994 World Figure
Skating
Championships,
Tokyo — A1695

No. 2231, Ice dancing. No. 2232, Women's singles. No. 2233, Men's singles, vert. No. 2234, Pairs, vert.

**1994, Mar. 17**    **Photo.**    *Perf. 13*
2231 A1695 50y multicolored   .90   .35
2232 A1695 50y multicolored   .90   .35
  *a.*    Pair, #2231-2232   2.25   1.25
2233 A1695 80y multicolored   1.40   .40
2234 A1695 80y multicolored   1.40   .40
  *a.*    Pair, #2233-2234   3.00   1.50
    *Nos. 2231-2234 (4)*   4.60   1.50

Philately
Week — A1696

**1994, Apr. 20    Photo.    Perf. 13**
2235 A1696 80y Irises                1.50  .40

Intl. Year of the
Family — A1697

Designs: No. 2236, "Love" spelled by people. No. 2237, Faces in flowers. No. 2238, Sun shining on people, homes. No. 2239, Family flying inside bird.

**1994, May 13.    Photo.    Perf. 13**
2236 A1697 50y multicolored           .90  .30
2237 A1697 50y multicolored           .90  .30
2238 A1697 80y multicolored          1.40  .35
  a.   Pair, #2236, 2238            2.50 1.25
2239 A1697 80y multicolored          1.40  .35
  a.   Pair, #2237, 2239            2.50 1.25
     Nos. 2236-2239 (4)             4.60 1.30

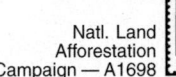

Natl. Land
Afforestation
Campaign — A1698

**1994, May 20**
2240 A1698 50y multicolored          1.00  .35

Intl. Conference on
Natural Disaster
Reduction — A1699

**1994, May 23**
2241 A1699 80y multicolored          1.50  .35
No. 2241 printed in sheets of 16 with 4 labels.

A1700

**1994, May 24**
2242 A1700 80y multicolored          1.50  .35
Prototype Fast Breeder Reactor, Monju.

Environment
Day — A1701

**1994, June 3    Photo.    Perf. 13**
2243 A1701 80y multicolored          1.50  .40

Letter Writing Day
A1702         A1703

**1994, July 22**
2244 A1702 50y multicolored          1.00  .35
2245 A1703 80y multicolored          1.50  .40
  a.   Souvenir sheet of 1          1.75 1.75
  b.   Bklt. pane, 5 each #2244-
        2245                        12.50

## Prefecture Issues
Nos. 2246-2400B have been changed to #Z151-Z307. The listings can be found in a new section immediately following the postage section and preceding the semi-postal listings.

10th Intl. Conference on
AIDS,
Yokohama — A1859

**1994, Aug. 5    Photo.    Perf. 13**
2401 A1859 80y multicolored          1.50  .35

### Postal History Series

A1860

First Japanese stamps (Baron Hisoka Maeshima and): No. 2402, #1. No. 2403, #2. No. 2404, #3. No. 2405, #4.
CTO's exist for Nos. 2402-2405. They read "Japan" between two arcs in a corner.

**Photo. & Engr.**
**1994, Aug. 10              Perf. 13**
2402 A1860 80y brown & black         1.40  .40
2403 A1860 80y blue & black          1.40  .40
2404 A1860 80y ver & black           1.40  .40
2405 A1860 80y olive grn & blk       1.40  .40
  a.   Strip of 4, #2402-2405        6.00 6.00

A1861

Early Japanese stamps (Edoardo Chiossone and): No. 2406, #55. No. 2407, Type A16. No. 2408, #63. No. 2409, #65.

**1994, Nov. 18              Perf. 13½**
2406 A1861 80y buff, slate & blk     1.40  .40
2407 A1861 80y gray & dk brown       1.40  .40
2408 A1861 80y gray lilac & rose     1.40  .40
2409 A1861 80y lt blue & dk blue     1.40  .40
  a.   Strip of 4, #2406-2409        6.00 6.00

A1862

Designs: No. 2410, #85, transporting mail by ricksha. No. 2411, #86, transporting mail by horse-drawn carriage.

**1995, Jan. 25**
2410 A1862 80y multicolored          1.40  .40
2411 A1862 80y multicolored          1.40  .40
     Nos. 2402-2411 (10)            14.00 4.00

A1863

Designs: No. 2412, #C3, First Osaka-Tokyo airmail flight. No. 2413, #C6, Workers loading freight onto airplane.

**Photo. & Engr.**
**1995, May 25              Perf. 13½**
2412 A1863 110y multicolored         2.00  .50
2413 A1863 110y multicolored         2.00  .50
Nos. 2412-2413 printed in blocks of 10 with gutter between in sheets of 20.

A1864

No. 2414, Light mail van, #436. No. 2415, Cherub commemorative mail box, #428. No. 2416, Mail box, #435. No. 2417, Van, #433.

**Photo. & Engr.**
**1995, Sept. 19              Perf. 13½**
2414 A1864 80y multicolored          1.40  .40
2415 A1864 80y multicolored          1.40  .40
2416 A1864 80y multicolored          1.40  .40
2417 A1864 80y multicolored          1.40  .40
  a.   Block of 4, #2414-2417        6.00 6.00

### Postal History Series
### Types of 1948-49 With "NIPPON"
### Inscribed at Bottom
### Size: 22x47mm
**Photo. & Engr.**
**1996, June 3              Perf. 13½**
2418 A206 80y like #422, brown       1.40  .40
2419 A206 80y like #422, multi       1.40  .40
2420 A247 80y like #479, purple      1.40  .40
2421 A247 80y like #479, multi       1.40  .40
  a.   Strip of 4, #2418-2421        6.00 6.00

Opening of Kansai Intl.
Airport — A1877

Designs: No. 2422, Airport, part of plane's vertical stabilizer. No. 2423, Aft section of airplane. No. 2424, Airport, jet.

**1994, Sept. 2    Photo.    Perf. 13**
2422 A1877 80y multicolored          1.40  .35
2423 A1877 80y multicolored          1.40  .35
  a.   Vert. pair, #2422-2423        3.00 3.00
  b.   Vert. strip of 3, #2422-2424  4.50 4.50
2424 A1877 80y multicolored          1.40  .35
     Nos. 2422-2424 (3)              4.20 1.05

A1878

**1994, Sept. 19**
2425 A1878 80y multicolored          1.50  .35
ITU Plenipotentiary Conference, Kyoto.

12th Asian Games,
Hiroshima — A1879

No. 2426, Kick volleyball. No. 2427, Steeplechase. No. 2428, Synchronized swimming

**1994, Sept. 30**
2426 A1879 50y multicolored          1.00  .30
2427 A1879 80y multicolored          1.40  .35
2428 A1879 80y multicolored          1.40  .35
  a.   Pair, #2427-2428              3.00 1.75
     Nos. 2426-2428 (3)              3.80 1.00

Intl. Letter
Writing
Week — A1880

Screen paintings of popular indoor games, Momoyama, Edo periods: 90y, Sugoroku. 110y, Japanese chess. 130y, Go.

**1994, Oct. 6    Photo.    Perf. 13x13½**
2429 A1880 90y multicolored          1.75  .45
2430 A1880 110y multicolored         2.25  .55
2431 A1880 130y multicolored         2.50  .55
     Nos. 2429-2431 (3)              6.50 1.55

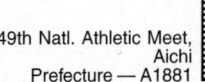

49th Natl. Athletic Meet,
Aichi
Prefecture — A1881

**1994, Oct. 28              Perf. 13½**
2432 A1881 50y multicolored          1.00  .30

A1882

**1994, Nov. 4    Photo.    Perf. 13**
2433 A1882 80y multicolored          1.50  .35
Intl. Diabetes Federation, 15th Congress, Kobe.

### Cultural Pioneers Type of 1992
Cultural pioneers: No. 2434, Michio Miyagi (1894-1956), Musician. No. 2435, Gyoshu Hayami (1894-1935), artist.

**1994, Nov. 4    Photo. & Engr.**
2434 A1645 80y multicolored          1.40  .35
2435 A1645 80y multicolored          1.40  .35

A1884

Heiankyo (Kyoto), 1200th
Anniv. — A1885

Kanpuzu, by Hideyori Kano, Momoyama period depicts autumn scene on Kiyotakigawa River: No. 2436, People seated, white birds. No. 2437, Bridge, people. No. 2438, Bridge, birds flying. No. 2439, People, Jingoji Temple, Atago-Jinja Shrine. No. 2440, People seated, tree.
No. 2441, Painting of Dry Garden (Sekitei), Ryoanji Temple, by Eizo Kato. No. 2442, Painting of artificial pond, Shugakuin Rikyu, by Kanji Kawai, horiz.

**1994, Nov. 8    Photo.    Perf. 13x13½**
2436       80y multicolored          1.40  .40
2437       80y multicolored          1.40  .40
2438       80y multicolored          1.40  .40
2439       80y multicolored          1.40  .40
2440       80y multicolored          1.40  .40
  a.   A1884 Strip of 5, #2436-2440  8.50 8.50
2441 A1885 80y multicolored          1.40  .40

**              Perf. 13½x13**
2442 A1885 80y multicolored          1.40  .40
     Nos. 2436-2442 (7)              9.80 2.80

A1886              A1887

64 JAPAN

New Year 1995 (Year of
the Boar)
A1888          A1889

**1994, Nov. 15          Perf. 13x13½**
2443  A1886  50y multicolored     1.00   .30
2444  A1887  80y multicolored     1.50   .40

**Perf. 13½**
2445  A1888  50y +3y multi        1.25   .40
2446  A1889  80y +3y multi        1.75   .40
    *Nos. 2443-2446 (4)*          5.50  1.50

Sheets of two containing Nos. 2443-2444
were lottery prizes. Value $2.75.

**World Heritage Series**

Himeji Castle
A1890          A1891

**1994, Dec. 14     Photo.     Perf. 13**
2447  A1890  80y multicolored     1.50   .40
2448  A1891  80y multicolored     1.50   .40

A1892          Horyuji
              Temple — A1893

Designs: 80y, Goddess Kannon from inner
temple wall. 110y, Temple exterior.

**1995, Feb. 22**
2449  A1892  80y multicolored     1.50   .40
2450  A1893  110y multicolored    2.25   .55

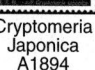

Cryptomeria          Cervus
Japonica             Nippon
A1894                Yakushimae
                     A1895

**1995, July 28**
2451  A1894  80y multicolored     1.50   .40
2452  A1895  80y multicolored     1.50   .40

Virgin Beech         Black
Forest               Woodpecker
A1896                A1897

**1995, Nov. 21**
2453  A1896  80y multicolored     1.50   .40
2454  A1897  80y multicolored     1.50   .40
    *Nos. 2447-2454 (8)*         12.75  3.35

Japan-Brazil
Friendship,
Cent. — A1898

Designs: No. 2455, Natl. emblems, flowers.
No. 2456, Soccer players.

**1995, Mar. 3     Photo.     Perf. 13½**
2455  A1898  80y multicolored     1.40   .35
2456  A1898  80y multicolored     1.40   .35

A1899

Fujiwara-Kyo Palace,
1300th Anniv. — A1900

Designs: 50y, Unebiyama, Nijozan Moun-
tains, roofing tile from palace. 80y, Portrait of a
Woman, in Asuka and Hakuho era style, by
Okada, 1925.

**1995, Mar. 28**
2457  A1899  50y multicolored     1.00   .35
2458  A1900  80y multicolored     1.50   .40

Modern Anatomical
Education — A1901

**1995, Mar. 31          Perf. 13**
2459  A1901  80y multicolored     1.50   .35

1995 Census — A1902

**1995, Apr. 12     Photo.     Perf. 13**
2460  A1902  80y multicolored     1.50   .40

A1903

**1995, Apr. 20**
2461  A1903  80y multicolored     1.50   .40

Japanese Overseas Cooperation Volunteers, 30th anniv.

A1904          A1905

A1906          A1907

A1908

**1995, Apr. 25          Perf. 13x13½**
2462  A1904  50y multicolored     1.00   .30
2463  A1905  50y multicolored     1.00   .30
2464  A1906  80y multicolored     1.50   .35
2465  A1907  80y multicolored     1.50   .35
2466  A1908  90y multicolored     1.75   .55
    *Nos. 2462-2466 (5)*          6.75  1.85

For use on condolence and greeting cards.

A1909

**1995, May 19     Photo.     Perf. 13½x13**
2467  A1909  50y multicolored     1.00   .30

Natl. land afforestation campaign.

A1910

Greetings: No. 2468, Rainbow, hearts. No.
2469, Girl holding heart-shaped balloon. No.
2470, Flower holding pencil, sign. No. 2471,
Star, sun, moon as flowers, fauna. No. 2472,
Person, dog with flowers, butterfly in hair.

**Self-Adhesive**
**1995, June 1     Die Cut Perf. 13½**
2468  A1910  80y multicolored     1.50   .40
2469  A1910  80y multicolored     1.50   .40
2470  A1910  80y multicolored     1.50   .40
2471  A1910  80y multicolored     1.50   .40
2472  A1910  80y multicolored     1.50   .40
*a.*   Miniature sheet, #2468-2472 +
       5 labels                   8.50  8.50

Letter Writing Day
A1911          A1912

**1995, July 21     Photo.     Perf. 13½**
2473  A1911  50y multicolored     1.00   .30
2474  A1912  80y multicolored     1.50   .35
*a.*   Souvenir sheet of 1        1.75  1.75
*b.*   Bklt. pane, 5 ea #2473-2474 12.50
       Complete booklet, #2474b   13.00

**Flora & Fauna Type of 1992 and**

Shikikacho-zu — A1926

Matsutaka-Zu  A1926a

10y, Scarab, dandelions. 20y, Honey bee,
flower. 30y, Hairstreak, flowers. 70y, Great tit.
110y, Plover. 120y, Shrike. 140y, Japanese
grosbeak. 160y, Jay. 390y, Dayflower.

**1995-98          Photo.          Perf. 13½**
2475  A1651  10y multi     .30   .25
2476  A1651  20y multi     .40   .25
2477  A1651  30y multi     .60   .25
2478  A1651  70y multi    1.60   .25
2479  A1651  110y multi   2.25   .25
2480  A1651  120y multi   2.50   .25
2481  A1651  140y multi   3.00   .25
2482  A1651  160y multi   3.25   .25

**Perf. 13x13½**
2483  A1651  390y multi   8.00   .25

**Perf. 13½**
2484  A1926  700y multi   21.00  1.00

**Photo. & Engr.**
2485  A1926a 1000y multi  19.00   .50
*a.*   Imperf. (3799b)    30.00  30.00

**Self-Adhesive**
**Die Cut Perf. 13x13½**
2486  A1651  50y Like
             #2158         1.10   .25
2487  A1651  80y Like
             #2161         1.75   .25

**Coil Stamp**
**Perf. 13 Horiz.**
2488  A1651  10y like #2475  .25   .25
    *Nos. 2475-2488 (14)*   65.00  4.50

Issued: 700y, 7/4/95; 390y, 1000y, 3/28/96;
70y, 110y, 7/22/97; No. 2475, 20y, 30y,
11/28/97; 120y, 140y, 2/16/98 160y, 2/23/98;
No. 2488, 9/11/98. Nos. 2486-2487, 3/25/02.
No. 2485a, 2/2/15.

Nos. 2486 and 2487 were issued in panes
of 10.

End of World War II, 50th
Anniv.
A1937          A1938

Design: No. 2491, Children holding hands
behind stained glass window, peace dove,
earth from space.

**1995, Aug. 1     Photo.     Perf. 13**
2489  A1937  50y multicolored     1.00   .30
2490  A1938  80y multicolored     1.50   .35
2491  A1938  80y multicolored     1.50   .35
    *Nos. 2489-2491 (3)*          4.00  1.00

18th Universiade,
Fukuoka — A1939

**1995, Aug. 23**
2492  A1939  80y multicolored     1.50   .35

A1940

50y, Radio controlled plane, transmitter.
80y, Radio controlled helicopter, competitor,
assistant.

**1995, Aug. 25**
2493  A1940  50y multicolored     1.00   .30
2494  A1940  80y multicolored     1.50   .35

1995 Aeromodel World Championships,
Okayama Prefecture.

World Veterinary
Congress,
Yokohama — A1941

80y, Dog, cow & horse.

**1995, Sept. 1     Photo.     Perf. 13**
2495  A1941  80y multicolored     1.50   .35

World Sports
Championships
A1942

No. 2496, 1995 World Judo Championships, Chiba Prefecture. No. 2497, 1995 World Gymnastics Championships, Sabae, Fukui Prefecture.

**1995, Sept. 28**
2496 A1942 80y multicolored    1.50  .35
2497 A1942 80y multicolored    1.50  .35

Letter Writing Week — A1943

Screen paintings: 90y, Shell-matching game. 110y, Battledore and shuttlecock. 130y, Playing cards.

**1995, Oct. 6**          *Perf. 13½*
2498 A1943 90y multicolored    1.75  .45
2499 A1943 110y multicolored   2.25  .55
2500 A1943 130y multicolored   2.50  .55
    Nos. 2498-2500 (3)         6.50 1.55

A1944

**1995, Oct. 13**       *Perf. 13x13½*
2501 A1944 50y multicolored    1.00  .30
50th Natl. athletic meet, Fukushima prefecture.

UN, UNESCO, 50th Anniv. — A1945

No. 2502, UN, hearts. No. 2503, UNESCO, children.

**1995, Oct. 24**          *Perf. 13*
2502 A1945 80y multi           1.50  .35
2503 A1945 80y multi           1.50  .35

**Cultural Pioneers Type of 1992**

No. 2504, Tadataka Ino (1745-1818), cartographer. No. 2505, Kitaro Nishida (1870-1945), philosopher.

**Photo. & Engr.**
**1995, Nov. 6**            *Perf. 13*
2504 A1645 80y multicolored    1.50  .40
2505 A1645 80y multicolored    1.50  .40

A1947               A1948

New Year 1996 (Year of the Rat)
A1949          A1950

**1995, Oct. 15  Photo.  Perf. 13x13½**
2506 A1947 50y multicolored    1.00  .30
2507 A1948 80y multicolored    1.50  .40
        **Perf. 13½**
2508 A1949 50y +3y multi       1.25  .40
2509 A1950 80y +3y multi       1.75  .40
    Nos. 2506-2509 (4)         5.50 1.50
Sheets of two containing Nos. 2506-2507 were lottery prizes. Value $2.75.

Japanese-Korean Diplomatic Relations, 30th Anniv. — A1951

**1995, Dec. 18**          *Perf. 13*
2510 A1951 80y multicolored    1.50  .35

Nos. 2511-2512 are unassigned.

A1952

**1996, Feb. 16   Photo.   Perf. 13**
2513 A1952 80y multicolored    1.50  .35
Philipp Franz von Siebold (1796-1866), naturalist.

A1953

**1996, Mar. 1**
2514 A1953 80y multicolored    1.50  .35
Labor Relations Commissions, 50th anniv.

Senior Citizens — A1954

**1996, Mar. 21**          *Perf. 13½*
2515 A1954 80y multicolored    1.50  .35
No. 2515 issued in sheets of 5.

50th Postwar Memorial Year
A1955          A1956

No. 2516, Crowd, Emperor's limosine approaching Diet. No. 2517, Prime Minister Yoshida signing Peace Treaty, San Francisco, 9/8/51. No. 2518, Women performing traditional Okinawan dance.

**1996, Apr. 1   Photo.   Perf. 13**
2516 A1955 80y multicolored    1.25  .40
2517 A1955 80y multicolored    1.25  .40
  a.   Pair, Nos. 2516-2517    3.00 2.25
2518 A1956 80y multicolored    1.50  .40
    Nos. 2516-2518 (3)         4.00 1.20
Promulgation of the the Constitution, 11/7/46 (No. 2517a). Return of Okinawa, 5/15/72 (No. 2518).

Woman Suffrage, 50th Anniv. — A1957

**1996, Apr. 10**          *Perf. 13½*
2519 A1957 80y multicolored    1.50  .35

Philately Week — A1958

**1996, Apr. 19**          *Perf. 13*
2520 A1958 80y multicolored    1.50  .40

UNICEF, 50th Anniv. — A1959

**1996, May 1   Photo.   Perf. 13**
2521 A1959 80y multicolored    1.50  .35

Child Welfare Week, 50th Anniv. — A1960

**1996, May 1**
2522 A1960 80y multicolored    1.50  .35

Bird Week, 50th Anniv. A1961

**1996, May 10**
2523   80y Birds               1.25  .40
2524   80y Field Glasses       1.25  .40
  a.   A1961 Pair, #2523-2524  3.00 1.75

Natl. Afforestation Campaign — A1963

**1996, May 17**
2525 A1963 50y multicolored    1.00  .30

50th Postwar Memorial Year
A1964          A1965

**1996, June 24   Photo.   Perf. 13**
2526 A1964 80y multicolored    1.50  .40
2527 A1965 80y multicolored    1.50  .40

River Administration System, Cent. — A1966

**1996, July 5   Photo.   Perf. 13½**
2528   80y denomination lower right   1.25  .40
2529   80y denomination lower left    1.25  .40
  a.   A1966 Pair, #2528-2529  3.25 1.75

A1968

Marine Day's Establishment — A1969

**1996, July 19**
2530 A1968 50y multicolored    1.00  .35
2531 A1969 80y multicolored    1.50  .40

Letter Writing Day
A1970          A1971

**1996, July 23**
2532 A1970 50y multicolored    1.00  .35
2533 A1971 80y multicolored    1.50  .40
  a.   Souvenir sheet of 1     1.75 1.75
  b.   Bklt. pane, 5 ea #2532-2533  12.00
       Complete booklet        13.00

**Cultural Pioneers Type of 1992**

No. 2534, Kenji Miyazaw (1896-1933). No. 2535, Hokiichi Hanawa (1746-1821).

**Photo. & Engr.**
**1996, Aug. 27**          *Perf. 13*
2534 A1645 80y multicolored    1.50  .35
2535 A1645 80y multicolored    1.50  .35

A1974          A1975

Designs: No. 2536, Advances of women in society, diffusion of home electrical products. No. 2537, Modern highway, railway systems.

**1996, Aug. 27   Photo.   Perf. 13**
2536 A1974 80y multicolored    1.50  .40
2537 A1975 80y multicolored    1.50  .40

51st Natl. Athletic Meet — A1976

**1996, Sept. 6   Photo.   Perf. 13½**
2538 A1976 50y Archery         1.00  .30

Community Chest, 50th Anniv. — A1977

**1996, Sept. 30**
2539 A1977 80y multicolored    1.50  .35

Intl. Music Day — A1978

**1996, Oct. 1**          *Perf. 13*
2540 A1978 80y multicolored    1.50  .35

A1979

A1980

A1980a

Intl. Letter Writing Week — A1980b

Paintings: No. 2541, Water wheel, Mt. Fuji. No. 2543, Mt. Fuji in Clear Weather (Red Fuji), by Hokusai. No. 2545, Mt. Fuji, lake.

**1996, Oct. 7**    *Perf. 13½*
2541 A1979 90y multicolored 1.75 .50
2542 A1980 90y multicolored 1.75 .50
  a.   Pair, #2541-2542 3.75 1.75
2543 A1979 110y multicolored 2.25 .55
2544 A1980a 110y multicolored 2.25 .55
  a.   Pair, #2543-2544 4.50 2.00
2545 A1979 130y multicolored 2.50 .60
2546 A1980b 130y multicolored 2.50 .60
  a.   Pair, #2545-2546 5.50 2.25
  Nos. 2541-2546 (6) 13.00 3.30

18th World Congress of Savings Banks — A1981

**1996, Oct. 23**    *Perf. 13*
2547 A1981 80y multicolored 1.50 .35

50th Postwar Memorial Year
A1982    A1983

No. 2548, Earth from space. No. 2549, Cellular telephone, fiber optic cable, satellite in orbit.

**1996, Nov. 8**    Photo.    *Perf. 13*
2548 A1982 80y multicolored 1.50 .40
2549 A1983 80y multicolored 1.50 .40

A1984    A1985

New Year 1997 (Year of the Ox)
A1986    A1987

**1996, Nov. 15**   Photo.   *Perf. 13x13½*
2550 A1984 50y multicolored 1.00 .30
2551 A1985 80y multicolored 1.50 .40

     *Perf. 13½*
2552 A1986 50y +3y multi 1.25 .40
2553 A1987 80y +3y multi 1.75 .40
  Nos. 2550-2553 (4) 5.50 1.50
  Sheets of 2 containing Nos. 2550-2551 were lottery prizes. Value $2.75.

Yujiro Ishihara, Actor — A1988

Hibari Misora, Entertainer — A1990

Osamu Tezuka, Cartoonist — A1992

**1997, Jan. 28**    Photo.    *Perf. 13*
2554   80y multicolored 1.25 .40
2555   80y multicolored 1.25 .40
  a.   A1988 Pair, #2554-2555 3.50 1.75
2556   80y multicolored 1.25 .40
2557   80y multicolored 1.25 .40
  a.   A1990 Pair, #2556-2557 3.50 1.75
2558   80y multicolored 1.25 .45
2559   80y multicolored 1.25 .45
  a.   A1992 Pair, #2558-2559 3.50 2.00
  Nos. 2554-2559 (6) 7.50 2.50

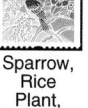

Sparrow, Rice Plant, Camellia A1994    Sparrow, Maple, Camellia A1995

***Perf. 14 Horiz. Syncopated Type A***
**1997, Apr. 10**    Photo.
2560 A1994 50y multi 1.50 .50
2560A A1994 80y multi 2.25 .50
2560B A1994 90y multi 2.50 .60
2560C A1994 120y multi 3.25 .65
2560D A1994 130y multi 28.00 7.00
2561 A1994 270y multi 7.00 1.25
  Nos. 2560-2561 (6) 44.50 10.50

Denominations of Nos. 2560-2561 were printed by machine at point of sale, and were limited to the denominations listed.

Daigo, by Okumura Dogyu (1889-1990) A1996

**1997, Apr. 18**   Litho.   *Perf. 13½*
2562 A1996 80y multicolored 1.60 .35
  Philately Week.

Supreme Court, 50th Anniv. — A1997

**1997, May 2**   Photo.   *Perf. 13*
2563 A1997 80y Main court room 1.50 .35

Doraemon — A1998

Designs: No. 2564, Shown. No. 2565, With envelope. No. 2566, Standing on hand. No. 2567, With propeller. No. 2568, In love.

**Booklet Stamps**
*Serpentine Die Cut 13½*
**1997, May 2**    Self-Adhesive
2564 A1998 80y multicolored 1.50 .40
2565 A1998 80y multicolored 1.50 .40
2566 A1998 80y multicolored 1.50 .40
2567 A1998 80y multicolored 1.50 .40
2568 A1998 80y multicolored 1.50 .40
  a.   Pane of 5, #2564-2568 8.00 8.00

Japanese Migration to Mexico, Cent. — A1999

**1997, May 12**    *Perf. 13*
2569 A1999 80y multicolored 1.50 .35
  See Mexico No. 2035.

Natl. Afforestation Campaign — A2000

50y, Miyagi bush clover.

**1997, May 16**    *Perf. 13½*
2570 A2000 50y multicolored 1.00 .30

Natl. Diet — A2001

**1997, May 20**    *Perf. 13*
2571 A2001 80y multicolored 1.50 .35
  Natl. House of Councilors, 50th anniv.

**Letter Writing Day**

A2002    A2003

A2004    A2005

**1997, July 23**   Photo.   *Perf. 13*
2572 A2002 50y multicolored 1.00 .30
2573 A2003 70y multicolored 1.25 .35
2574 A2004 80y multicolored 1.50 .35
  a.   Souvenir sheet of 1 1.75 1.75
  b.   Bklt. pane, 5 ea #2572, 2574 13.00
     Complete booklet, #2574b 13.00
2575 A2005 90y multicolored 1.75 .45
  Nos. 2572-2575 (4) 5.50 1.45

A2006

**1997, Aug. 11**   Photo.   *Perf. 13*
2576 A2006 50y multicolored 1.00 .30
  Part-time and correspondence education at upper secondary schools, 50th anniv.

Labor Standards Law, 50th Anniv. — A2007

**1997, Sept. 1**
2577 A2007 80y multicolored 1.50 .35

Friendship Between Japan and Chile, Cent. — A2008

**1997, Sept. 1**    *Perf. 13½*
2578 A2008 80y multicolored 1.50 .35
  See Chile No. 1217.

52nd Natl. Sports Festival — A2009

**1997, Sept. 12**
2579 A2009 50y multicolored 1.00 .30

A2010

A2010a

A2010b

Intl. Letter Writing Week — A2010c

Paintings of Tokaido's 53 Stations by Hiroshige: No. 2580, Hodogaya (bridge over waterway). No. 2582, Kameyama snow-covered mountain slope).

No. 2584, Sumida Riverbank Snowscape (woman in traditional attire beside river), by Hiroshige
From Scrolls of Flowers and Birds of the Four Seasons by Hoitsu Sakai: No. 2581, Bird on tree. No. 2583, Leaves and berries. No. 2585, Bird on tree branch of blossoms.

| 1997, Oct. 6 | | Photo. | Perf. 13½ | |
|---|---|---|---|---|
| 2580 | A2010 | 90y multicolored | 1.75 | .45 |
| 2581 | A2010a | 90y multicolored | 1.75 | .45 |
| a. | | Pair, #2580-2581 | 3.75 | 2.00 |
| 2582 | A2010 | 110y multicolored | 2.25 | .50 |
| 2583 | A2010b | 110y multicolored | 2.25 | .50 |
| a. | | Pair, #2582-2583 | 4.75 | 2.00 |
| 2584 | A2010 | 130y multicolored | 2.50 | .55 |
| 2585 | A2010c | 130y multicolored | 2.50 | .55 |
| a. | | Pair, #2584-2585 | 5.25 | 2.25 |
| | | Nos. 2580-2585 (6) | 13.00 | 3.00 |

Grand Opening of the Natl. Theater of Tokyo — A2011

| 1997, Oct. 9 | | | Perf. 13 | |
|---|---|---|---|---|
| 2586 | A2011 | 80y multicolored | 1.50 | .35 |

Favorite Songs
A2012    A2013

50y Departure on a Fine Day, by Tanimura Shinji. 80y, Desert Under the Moon, by Kato Masao & Sakasi Suguru.

| 1997, Oct. 24 | | | | |
|---|---|---|---|---|
| 2587 | A2012 | 50y multicolored | 1.00 | .30 |
| 2588 | A2013 | 80y multicolored | 1.50 | .40 |

**Cultural Pioneers Type of 1992**

No. 2589, Rohan Kouda (1867-1947), writer. No. 2590, Ando Hiroshige (1797-1858), artist.

| 1997, Nov. 4 | | | | |
|---|---|---|---|---|
| 2589 | A1645 | 80y multicolored | 1.50 | .35 |
| 2590 | A1645 | 80y multicolored | 1.50 | .35 |

A2016                    A2017

New Year 1997 (Year of the Tiger)
A2018    A2019

| 1997, Nov. 14 | | | Perf. 13x13½ | |
|---|---|---|---|---|
| 2591 | A2016 | 50y multicolored | 1.00 | .30 |
| 2592 | A2017 | 80y multicolored | 1.50 | .40 |
| | | Perf. 13½ | | |
| 2593 | A2018 | 50y +3y multi | 1.25 | .40 |
| 2594 | A2019 | 80y +3y multi | 1.75 | .40 |

Sheets of two containing Nos. 2591-2592 were lottery prizes. Value $2.75.

Return of Okinawa to Japan, 25th Anniv. — A2020

| 1997, Nov. 21 | | | Perf. 13 | |
|---|---|---|---|---|
| 2595 | A2020 | 80y multicolored | 1.50 | .35 |

Shibuya Family's House — A2021    Tomizawa Family's House — A2022

| | | Photo. & Engr. | | |
|---|---|---|---|---|
| 1997, Nov. 28 | | | Perf. 13½ | |
| 2596 | A2021 | 80y multicolored | 1.50 | .45 |
| 2597 | A2022 | 80y multicolored | 1.50 | .45 |

A2023

Woodprints: No. 2598, Mother Sea. No. 2599, Mother Earth.

| 1997, Dec. 1 | | Photo. | Perf. 13 | |
|---|---|---|---|---|
| 2598 | A2023 | 80y multicolored | 1.50 | .35 |
| 2599 | A2023 | 80y multicolored | 1.50 | .35 |
| a. | | Pair, #2598-2599 | 3.00 | 2.00 |

3rd Conference of the Parties to the UN Framework Convention on Climate Change, Kyoto.

A2024

| 1997, Dec. 2 | | | | |
|---|---|---|---|---|
| 2600 | A2024 | 80y multicolored | 1.50 | .35 |

Agricultural Insurance System, 50th anniv.

**Favorite Songs**

Sunayama
A2025    Jingle Bells
A2026

| 1997, Dec. 8 | | | | |
|---|---|---|---|---|
| 2601 | A2025 | 50y multicolored | 1.00 | .30 |
| 2602 | A2026 | 80y multicolored | 1.50 | .35 |

Shabondama
A2027    Kitaguni no Haru
A2028

| 1998, Jan. 26 | | Photo. | Perf. 13 | |
|---|---|---|---|---|
| 2603 | A2027 | 50y multicolored | 1.00 | .30 |
| 2604 | A2028 | 80y multicolored | 1.50 | .35 |

1998 Winter Olympic & Paralympic Games, Nagano
A2029    A2030

Paralympic logo and: No. 2605, Glaucidium palmatum. No. 2606, Ice hockey.
Olympic rings and: No. 2607: a, Gentiana nipponica. b, Caltha palustris. c, Fritillaria camtschatcensis. d, Paeonia japonica. e,

Erythronium japonicum. f, Snowboarding. g, Curling. h, Speed skating. i, Cross-country skiing. j, Downhill skiing.

| 1998, Feb. 5 | | | | |
|---|---|---|---|---|
| 2605 | A2029 | 50y multicolored | .75 | .30 |
| 2606 | A2030 | 80y multicolored | 1.25 | .35 |
| a. | | Pair, #2605-2606 | 2.50 | 1.00 |
| 2607 | | Sheet of 10 | 12.50 | 12.50 |
| a.-e. | | A2029 50y Any single | .75 | .30 |
| f.-j. | | A2030 80y Any single | 1.25 | .35 |

**Historic Houses**

A2031                    A2032

| | | Photo. & Engr. | | |
|---|---|---|---|---|
| 1998, Feb. 23 | | | Perf. 13½ | |
| 2608 | A2031 | 80y multicolored | 1.50 | .45 |
| 2609 | A2032 | 80y multicolored | 1.50 | .45 |

Japanese Fire Service, 50th Anniv. — A2033

| 1998, Mar. 6 | | Photo. | Perf. 13 | |
|---|---|---|---|---|
| 2610 | | 80y multicolored | 1.50 | .40 |
| 2611 | | 80y multicolored | 1.50 | .40 |
| a. | | A2033 Pair, #2610-2611 | 3.50 | 3.50 |

Favorite Songs
A2035    A2036

50y, Medaka-no-Gakko. 80y, Aoi Sanmyaku.

| 1998 | | Photo. | Perf. 13 | |
|---|---|---|---|---|
| 2612 | A2035 | 50y multicolored | 1.00 | .30 |
| 2613 | A2036 | 80y multicolored | 1.50 | .35 |
| | | Issued: 50y, 3/23; 80y, 3/16. | | |

Greetings Stamps
A2037

Designs: a, Puppy. b, Kitten. c, Parakeets. d, Pansies. e, Bunny.

| 1998, Mar. 13 | | Photo. | Die Cut | |
|---|---|---|---|---|
| | | Self-Adhesive | | |
| 2614 | | Sheet of 5 | 9.00 | 9.00 |
| a.-e. | | A2037 80y any single | 1.25 | .75 |

Philately Week — A2038

"Poppies," by Kokei Kobayashi (1883-1957).

| 1998, Apr. 17 | | | Perf. 13½ | |
|---|---|---|---|---|
| 2615 | A2038 | 80y multicolored | 1.50 | .35 |

1998 Year of France in Japan — A2039

"Liberty Leading the People," by Delacroix.

| 1998, Apr. 28 | | | Perf. 13½ | |
|---|---|---|---|---|
| 2616 | A2039 | 110y multicolored | 2.25 | .55 |

Natl. Afforestation Campaign — A2040

50y, Trout, Renge azalea.

| 1998, May 8 | | | | |
|---|---|---|---|---|
| 2617 | A2040 | 50y multicolored | 1.00 | .30 |

**Favorite Songs**

A2041                    A2042

Designs: 50y, "Wild Roses," by Franz Schubert. 80y, "Hill Abloom with Tangerine Flowers," by Minoru Uminuma and Shogo Kato.

| 1998, May 25 | | | Perf. 13 | |
|---|---|---|---|---|
| 2618 | A2041 | 50y multicolored | 1.00 | .30 |
| 2619 | A2042 | 80y multicolored | 1.50 | .35 |

**Historic Houses**

Kowata Residence
A2043    Kamihaga Residence
A2044

| | | Photo. & Engr. | | |
|---|---|---|---|---|
| 1998, June 22 | | | Perf. 13½ | |
| 2620 | A2043 | 80y multicolored | 1.50 | .45 |
| 2621 | A2044 | 80y multicolored | 1.50 | .45 |

**Favorite Songs**

A2045    A2046

50y, Kono Michi, "This Road." 80y, Ware Wa Umino Ko, "I'm a Boy of the Sea."

| 1998, July 6 | | Photo. | Perf. 13 | |
|---|---|---|---|---|
| 2622 | A2045 | 50y multicolored | 1.00 | .30 |
| 2623 | A2046 | 80y multicolored | 1.50 | .35 |

Letter Writing Day — A2047

Stylized drawings of children: No. 2624, Child writing letter. No. 2625, Child wearing glasses, letter on table. No. 2626, Child with ink pen, flowers overhead. No. 2627, Child with ink pen, dove overhead. No. 2628, Children holding letters, envelopes.

| 1998, July 23 | | | Perf. 13 | |
|---|---|---|---|---|
| 2624 | A2047 | 50y multi | .75 | .30 |
| 2625 | A2047 | 50y multi | .75 | .30 |
| a. | | Pair, #2624-2625 | 2.00 | 1.10 |
| 2626 | A2047 | 80y multi | 1.25 | .35 |
| 2627 | A2047 | 80y multi | 1.25 | .35 |

| 2628 | A2047 80y multi, horiz. | 1.25 | .35 |
|---|---|---|---|
| a. | Souvenir sheet of 1 | 1.75 | 1.75 |
| b. | Sheet, 4 each #2626-2627, 2 #2628 | 17.50 | 17.50 |
| c. | Bklt. pane, 2 ea #2624-2628 | 14.00 | 14.00 |
| | Complete booklet, #2628c | 15.00 | |

See Nos. 2682-2686, 2738-2742, 2779-2783, 2824-2828. See Nos. 2733h-2733j for self-adhesive stamps.

### Historic Houses

Kamio Residence A2048

Nakamura Residence A2049

**Photo. & Engr.**

**1998, Aug. 24**     **Perf. 13½**

| 2629 | A2048 80y multicolored | 1.50 | .45 |
|---|---|---|---|
| 2630 | A2049 80y multicolored | 1.50 | .45 |

53rd Natl. Sports Festival, Kanagawa — A2050

**1998, Sept. 11**   **Photo.**   **Perf. 13½**

| 2631 | A2050 50y multicolored | 1.00 | .30 |
|---|---|---|---|

A2051

A2051a

A2051b

A2051c

Intl. Letter Writing Week, Greetings — A2051c

Details or complete paintings by Jakuchu Ito: No. 2632, "Birds & Autumn Maple." No. 2633, "Parakeet in Oak Tree." No. 2634, "Mandarin Ducks in the Snow." No. 2635, "Golden Pheasant & Bamboo in Snow." No. 2636, "Leafy Peonies & Butterflies." No. 2637, "Parakeet in Rose Bush."

**1998, Oct. 6**    **Photo.**    **Perf. 13½**

| 2632 | A2051 90y multicolored | 1.75 | .45 |
|---|---|---|---|
| 2633 | A2051a 90y multicolored | 1.75 | .45 |
| a. | Pair, #2632-2633 | 3.75 | 1.50 |
| 2634 | A2051 110y multicolored | 2.25 | .55 |
| 2635 | A2051b 110y multicolored | 2.25 | .55 |
| a. | Pair, #2634-2635 | 5.00 | 1.75 |
| 2636 | A2051 130y multicolored | 2.50 | .65 |
| 2637 | A2051c 130y multicolored | 2.50 | .65 |
| a. | Pair, #2636-2637 | 5.50 | 1.75 |
| | Nos. 2632-2637 (6) | 13.00 | 3.30 |

Nos. 2632, 2634, 2636 are from "Plants and Animals" and are inscribed for Intl. Letter Writing Week. Nos. 2633, 2635, 2637 are from "Painted Woodcuts of Flowers and Birds."

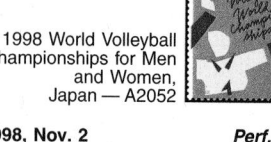

1998 World Volleyball Championships for Men and Women, Japan — A2052

**1998, Nov. 2**         **Perf. 13**

| 2638 | A2052 80y Serve | 1.25 | .35 |
|---|---|---|---|
| 2639 | A2052 80y Receive | 1.25 | .35 |
| 2640 | A2052 80y Set & spike | 1.25 | .35 |
| 2641 | A2052 80y Block | 1.25 | .35 |
| a. | Strip of 4, #2638-2641 | 6.00 | 6.00 |

### Cultural Pioneer Type of 1992 and

Yoshie Fujiwara(1898-1976) — A2053

No. 2642, Bakin Takizawa (1767-1848).

**Photo. & Engr.**

**1998, Nov. 4**        **Perf. 13**

| 2642 | A1645 80y multicolored | 1.50 | .35 |
|---|---|---|---|
| 2643 | A2053 80y multicolored | 1.50 | .35 |

See Nos. 2719, 2747-2748, 2839-2840.

A2054        A2055

New Year 1999 (Year of the Rabbit) A2056    A2057

**1998, Nov. 13**   **Photo.**   **Perf. 13x13½**

| 2644 | A2054 50y multicolored | 1.00 | .30 |
|---|---|---|---|
| 2645 | A2055 80y multicolored | 1.50 | .40 |

**Perf. 13½x13**

| 2646 | A2056 50y +3y multi | 1.25 | .40 |
|---|---|---|---|
| 2647 | A2057 80y +3y multi | 1.75 | .40 |
| | Nos. 2644-2647 (4) | 5.50 | 1.50 |

Sheets of two containing Nos. 2644-2645 were lottery prizes. Value $2.75. See No. 2655.

### Favorite Songs

A2058       A2059

50y, The Apple Song. 80y, Toys Cha-Cha-Cha at Night.

**1998, Nov. 24**     **Perf. 13x13½**

| 2648 | A2058 50y multicolored | 1.00 | .30 |
|---|---|---|---|
| 2649 | A2059 80y multicolored | 1.50 | .35 |

Japan-Argentina Friendship Treaty, Cent. — A2060

**1998, Dec. 2**    **Photo.**    **Perf. 13**

| 2650 | A2060 80y multicolored | 1.50 | .35 |
|---|---|---|---|

A2061      A2062

Universal Declaration of Human Rights, 50th Anniv. A2063    A2064

**1998, Dec. 10**

| 2651 | A2061 50y multicolored | 1.00 | .35 |
|---|---|---|---|
| 2652 | A2062 70y multicolored | 1.25 | .40 |
| 2653 | A2063 80y multicolored | 1.50 | .35 |
| 2654 | A2064 90y multicolored | 1.75 | .45 |
| | Nos. 2651-2654 (4) | 5.50 | 1.55 |

### Greetings Types of 1951, 1962, 1986 and 1998

**1998, Dec. 15**   **Photo.**   **Perf. 13x13½**

| 2655 | 50y Sheet of 8, 2 each #a.-c., 2644 | 8.00 | 8.00 |
|---|---|---|---|
| a. | A281 rose pink, like #522 | .75 | .30 |
| b. | A483 multi, like #773 | .75 | .30 |
| c. | A1273 multi, like #1708 | .75 | .30 |

### Favorite Songs

A2065      A2066

50y, Flowing Like a River. 80y, Song of the Four Seasons.

**1999, Jan. 26**   **Photo.**   **Perf. 13**

| 2656 | A2065 50y multicolored | 1.00 | .30 |
|---|---|---|---|
| 2657 | A2066 80y multicolored | 1.50 | .35 |

### Traditional Houses

Iwase Family House, Gokayama District — A2067

Gassho-Zukuri Houses, Shirakawa-mura District — A2068

Gassho-Zukuri House — A2069

**Photo. & Engr.**

**1999, Feb. 16**      **Perf. 13½**

| 2658 | A2067 80y multicolored | 1.50 | .45 |
|---|---|---|---|
| 2659 | A2068 80y multicolored | 1.25 | .45 |
| 2660 | A2069 80y multicolored | 1.25 | .45 |
| a. | Pair, #2659-2660 | 3.00 | 1.35 |
| | Nos. 2658-2660 (3) | 4.00 | 1.35 |

### Rakugo (Comic Storytellers) Stamps

Kokontei Shinshou V — A2070

Katsura Bunraku VIII — A2071

Sanyutei Enshou VI — A2072

Yanagiya Kosan V — A2073

Katsura Beichou III — A2074

**1999, Mar. 12**    **Photo.**    **Perf. 13**

| 2661 | A2070 80y multicolored | 1.25 | .50 |
|---|---|---|---|
| 2662 | A2071 80y multicolored | 1.25 | .50 |
| 2663 | A2072 80y multicolored | 1.25 | .50 |
| 2664 | A2073 80y multicolored | 1.25 | .50 |
| 2665 | A2074 80y multicolored | 1.25 | .50 |
| a. | Sheet, 2 each #2661-2665 | 16.00 | 16.00 |

### Favorite Songs

Sukiyaki Song A2075

Soushunfu A2076

**1999, Mar. 16**

| 2666 | A2075 50y multicolored | 1.00 | .30 |
|---|---|---|---|
| 2667 | A2076 80y multicolored | 1.50 | .35 |

Greetings Stamps A2077

a, Kitten, daisies. b, Checks, flowers, roses. c, Tartan, puppy. d, Flowers, brown rabbit. e, Gray and white rabbit, moon and stars.

**1999, Mar. 23**     **Die Cut**

**Self-Adhesive**

| 2668 | Sheet of 5 | 7.50 | 7.50 |
|---|---|---|---|
| a.-e. | A2077 80y Any single | 1.25 | .75 |

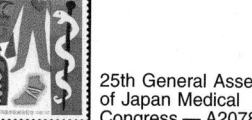

25th General Assembly of Japan Medical Congress — A2078

**1999, Apr. 2**        **Perf. 13**

| 2669 | A2078 80y multicolored | 1.50 | .35 |
|---|---|---|---|

Philately Week A2079

Rabbits Playing in the Field in Spring, by Doumoto Inshou (1891-1975): No. 2670, Three rabbits. No. 2671, Two rabbits.

**1999, Apr. 20**     **Perf. 13½**

| 2670 | 80y Three rabbits | 1.25 | .40 |
|---|---|---|---|
| 2671 | 80y Two rabbits | 1.25 | .40 |
| a. | A2079 Pair, #2670-2671 | 3.00 | 1.50 |

No. 2671a is a continuous design. No. 2671a also exists as a strip of two with central label. Value, $6.50.

A2080

**1999, May 18** **Photo.** *Perf. 13*
2672 A2080 80y multicolored 1.50 .35
Japanese migration to Peru, cent.

Natl. Afforestation Campaign — A2081

**1999, May 28** *Perf. 13¼*
2673 A2081 50y multicolored 1.00 .30

A2082

Painting: Ruins of Tholos, by Masayuki Murai.

**1999, June 1** **Photo.** *Perf. 13*
2674 A2082 80y multicolored 1.50 .35
Japanese-Greek Treaty of Commerce & Navigation, cent.

A2083

**1999, June 3**
2675 A2083 80y multicolored 1.50 .35
Japanese emigration to Bolivia, cent.

Land Improvement System, 50th Anniv. — A2084

**1999, June 4**
2676 A2084 80y multicolored 1.50 .35

Family Court, 50th Anniv. — A2085

**1999, June 16**
2677 A2085 80y multicolored 1.50 .35

Patent Attorney System in Japan, Cent. — A2086

**1999, July 1** **Photo.** *Perf. 13*
2678 A2086 80y multicolored 1.50 .35

A2087

**1999, July 1**
2679 A2087 80y multicolored 1.50 .35
Japanese Community-Based Treatment of Offenders System, 50th anniv.

A2088

Enforcement of Civil and Commercial Codes, Cent.: Masaakira Tomii (1858-1935), Kenjiro Ume (1860-1910) and Nobushige Hozumi (1856-1926), drafters of Civil and Commerical Codes.

**1999, July 19**
2680 A2088 80y multicolored 1.50 .35

Copyright System in Japan, Cent. — A2089

**1999, July 22**
2681 A2089 80y multicolored 1.50 .35

**Letter Writing Day Type of 1998**

Stylized drawings of children and toys: No. 2682, Boy and clown, letter. No. 2683, Teddy bear seated on pencil. No. 2684, Girl, ink pen. No. 2685, Clown with yellow hat, jumping up out of envelope.
No. 2686: a, Giraffes. b, Kite, bird, horiz. c, Boy holding kite string. d, Girl with pencil and paper. e, Bunny and bear. f, Boy blowing trumpet. g, Girl playing cello. h, Girl in red. i, Girl in yellow holding envelope. j, Three ducks.

**1999, July 23** **Photo.** *Perf. 13*
2682 A2047 50y multicolored .75 .30
2683 A2047 50y multicolored .75 .30
2684 A2047 50y multicolored .75 .30
2685 A2047 50y multicolored .75 .30
  *a.*    Strip of 4, #2682-2685 4.00 3.50
2686   Sheet of 10 16.00 16.00
  *a.-j.* A2047 80y any single 1.25 .35
  *k.*  Booklet pane, #2682-2685, 2
      each #2686c, 2686g, 2686i 14.00
    Complete booklet, #2686k 15.00
  *l.*  Sheet of 2, #2682, 2686g 2.75 2.75

Nos. 2686a is 53x27mm. Nos. 2686d, 2686h, 2686j are 30mm in diameter. No. 2686f is 38x39mm. Sheet numbers are in center of rectangles at top of sheets.

The 20th Century — A2090

1900-10 (Sheet 1) — No. 2687: a, 50y, 1905-06 Serialized novel "Wagahai wa Neko de aru," by Soseki Natsume (stamp 7). b, 50y, 1906 Novel "Bochan," by Natsume (stamp 8). c, 80y, 1901 Collection of poems "Midaregami," by Akiko Yosano (stamp 1). d, 80y, Opening of Denkikan movie theater in Asakusa, 1903 (stamp 2). e, 80y, Electrification of streetcars, 1903 (stamp 3). f, 80y, Otojirou Kawakami & Sadayakko, actors (stamp 4). g, 80y, Westernization of fashion

(stamp 9). h, 80y, Completion of Ryogoku Kokugikan sumo arena, 1909 (stamp 10). i, 80y, Russo-Japanese War soldiers on horseback (stamp 5). j, 80y, Russo-Japanese War soldiers in tent (stamp 6).

A2090a

1910-13 (Sheet 2) — No. 2688: a, 50y, 1st Japanese-produced airship, tail of 1st Japanese airplane (stamp 3). b, 50y, Front of 1st Japanese airplane (stamp 4). c, 80y, Elementary school song book published by Education ministry, 1910 (stamp 1). d, 80y, Antarctic expedition led by Nobu Shirase, 1910 (stamp 2). e, 80y, Dr. Hideyo Noguchi (stamp 5). f, 80y, Extinction of Japanese wolves (stamp 6). g, 80y, Runner Shizo Kanaguri at 1st participation in Olympic Games, 1912 (stamp 7). h, Takarazuka Musical Review founded, 1913 (stamp 8). i, 80y, "Song of Kachusha," by Sumako Matsui & Hogetsu Shimamura (stamp 9). j, 80y, 1st sale of caramels, 1913 (stamp 10).

A2090b

1914-20 (Sheet 3) — No. 2689: a, 50y, Painting of couple in boat by Yumeji Takehisa (stamp 9). b, 50y, Takehisa, painting of flowers (stamp 10). c, 80y, 1914 Opening of Tokyo train station (blimp in sky) (stamp 1). d, 80y, Tokyo train station main entrance (stamp 2). e, 80y, Japanese WWI seamen (stamp 3). f, 80y, Western-style women's hair styles (stamp 4). g, 80y, 1915 Poetry book "Rashomon," by Ryunosuke Akutagawa (stamp 5). h, 80y, 1916 Start of postal life insurance (goddess in clouds) (stamp 6). i, 80y, Sakuzo Yoshino, political scientist & democracy advocate, & tree (stamp 7). j, 80y, 1918 Rice riots (painting, photo of crowds) (stamp 8).

A2090c

1920-25 (Sheet 4) — No. 2690: a, 50y, Silent film star Matsunosuke Onoe (denomination at UR) (stamp 8). b, 50y, Silent film star Tsumasaburo Bandoh (denomination at UL) (stamp 9). c, 80y, 1st Hakone Relay Marathon, 1920 (stamp 1). d, 80y, Popularity of "Gondola Song" recording, spread of phonographs

(stamp 2). e, 80y, Ruins from 1923 Kanto earthquake (stamp 3). f, "Nonki na Tosan" comic strip (man with dog) (stamp 4). g, 80y, "Adventures of Sho-chan" comic strip (man with vulture). h, 80y, Japanese crane nears extinction (stamp 6). i, 80y, 1924 Opening of Koshien Stadium (stamp 7). j, 80y, Man, woman in Western-style clothing (stamp 10).

A2090d

1927-28 (Sheet 5) — No. 2691: a, 50y, 1927 Opening of Tokyo subway (close-up of car) (stamp 2). b, 50y, Subway car approaching station (stamp 3). c, 80y, Movie "Kurama Tengu" (Samurai) (stamp 1). d, 80y, Radio broadcast of "National Health Gymnastics" exercise program (stamp 4). e, 80y, Yoshiyuki Tsuruta, 1928 Olympic swimming champion (stamp 5). f, 80y, Mikio Oda, 1928 Olympic triple jump champion (stamp 6). g, 80y, Olympic Games program (stamp 7). h, 80y, Runner Kinue Hitomi, 1st female Japanese Olympic medalist (stamp 8). i, 80y, Man in Western clothing, cafe (stamp 9). j, 1928 Publishing of "Horoki," by Fumiko Hayashi (stamp 10).

A2090e

1929-32 (Sheet 6) — No. 2692: a, 50y, Mass production of Japanese automobiles (green 1932 Datsun Model 10) (stamp 4). b, 50y, Black 1936 Toyota Model AA (stamp 5). c, 80y, Volcano, Mt. Asama (stamp 1). d, 80y, Takiji Kobayashi, writer of "Kani-kosen," crane, smokestacks (stamp 2). e, 80y, Man with shirt with open collar, woman with handbag (stamp 3). f, 80y, "Norakuro" comic strip (cat, brick wall) (stamp 6). g, 80y, 1932 Nippon Derby winner Wakataka & jockey (stamp 7). h, 80y, Nippon Derby winner Kabutoyama (stamp 8). i, 80y, Song "Longing for Your Shadow" (woman with closed eyes) (stamp 9). j, 80y, 1932, 1936 Political assassinations (soldiers, truck, building) (stamp 10).

A2090f

1932-36 (Sheet 7) — No. 2693: a, 50y, Front of D51 steam locomotive (stamp 8). b, 50y, Rear of D51 (stamp 9). c, 80y, Fumihiko

Otsuki, lexicographer (Otsuki, geometric design) (stamp 1). d, 80y, Song "Tokyo Ondo" (woman, buildings) (stamp 2). e, 80y, Keinichi Enomoto, comic actor, with feather (stamp 3). f, 80y, Formation of Japanese Baseball League (catcher, umpire) (stamp 4). g, 80y, Batter (stamp 5). h, 80y, Hachiko, dog that waited for dead owner, statue of Hachiko (stamp 6). i, 80y, Eiji Yoshikawa, author of "Miyamoto Musashi." (stamp 7). j, Extinct species Okinawan pigeon (stamp 10).

A2090g

1937-40 (Sheet 8) — No. 2694: a, 50y, Nose of Kamikaze plane, tail of Nippon cargo plane (stamp 2). b, 50y, Nose of Nippon cargo plain, tail of Kamikaze plane (stamp 3). c, 80y, Helen Keller's 1st trip to Japan (stamp 1). d, 80y, Women with senninbari cloths, monpe work pants, man with kokumin-fuku uniform (stamp 4). e, 80y, Yuzo Yamamoto, author of "Robo No Ishi" (stamp 5). f, 80y, Woman & man embracing in movie, "Aizenkatsura" (stamp 6). g, 80y, Sumo wrestler Yokozuna Futabayama, winner of 69 consecutive matches (stamp 7). h, 80y, Baseball pitcher Eiji Sawamura (stamp 8). i, 80y, Song, "Dareka Kokyo" (ducks in flight) (stamp 9). j, 80y, Woodblock art of Shiko Munakata (stamp 10).

A2090h

1940-45 (Sheet 9) — No. 2695: a, 50y, "Ohgon Bat," cartoon by Ichiro Suzuki (character without hat) (stamp 9). b, 50y, "Ohgon Bat" character wearing hat (stamp 10). c, 80y, Chiune Sugihara, vice-consul in Lithuania who saved Jews from Holocaust (stamp 1). d, 80y, Start of Kokumin Gakko school system (children exercising) (stamp 2). e, 80y, Airplane in attack on Pearl Harbor (stamp 3). f, 80y, Kotaro Takamura, poet, winner of 1st Imperial Art Academy prize, & Japanese characters (stamp 4). g, 80y, Eruption of Mt. Showashinzan (stamp 5). h, 80y, Atomic Bomb Memorial Dome (stamp 6). i, 80y, Statue at Nagasaki Atomic Bomb Museum (stamp 7). j, Signing of World War II surrender documents on USS Missouri (stamp 8).

A2090i

1945-52 (Sheet 10) — No. 2696: a, 50y, "Captain Atom" cartoon by Osamu Tezuka (stamp 7). b, 50y, "Astro Boy," cartoon by Tezuka (stamp 8). c, 80y, Song, "Ringo No Uta" (Apple Song) (stamp 1). d, 80y, "Sazae San," cartoon by Machiko Hasegawa (stamp 2). e, 80y, Promulgation of Japanese Constitution (woman, child, buildings) (stamp 3). f, 80y, Swimming records by Hironoshin Furuhashi (stamp 4). g, 80y, Dr. Hideki Yukawa, Nobel laureate for Physics (stamp 5). h, 80y, New Year's Eve radio program "Kohaku Uta Gassen" on NHK (stamp 6). i, 80y, Radio soap opera "Kimino Na Wa" (woman and man) (stamp 9). j, 80y, Novel "Nijyu-Yon No Hitomi," by Sakae Tsuboi (stamp 10).

A2090j

1953-58 (Sheet 11) — No. 2697: a, 50y, Tokyo Tower (olive green panel) (stamp 9). b, 50y, Tokyo Tower from ground (stamp 10). c, 80y, Popularity of radio and television (stamp 1). d, 80y, Director Akira Kurosawa, camera, two Samurai from "Shinchinin No Samurai." (stamp 2). e, 80y, Five Samurai from "Shinchinin No Samurai." (stamp 3). f, 80y, Sumo wrestler Rikidozan and championship belt (stamp 4). g, 80y, Rikidozan in action (stamp 5). h, 80y, Movie "Godzilla" (stamp 6). i, 80y, Taiyozoku fashions (man, woman at seaside) (stamp 7), j, 80y, Portrait of Shotokutaishi from 10,000-yen bank note (stamp 8, 31x42mm oval stamp).

A2090k

1959-64 (Sheet 12) — No. 2698: a, 50y, Dog Taro, survivor of abandonment in Antarctica, ship's stern (stamp 1). b, 50y, Dog Giro, survivor of abandonment in Antarctic, ship's bow (stamp 2). c, 80y, Commemorative cake box from Wedding of Crown Prince Akihito (stamp 3). d, 80y, Weather map of Isewan Typhoon (stamp 4). e, 80y, "Sukiyaki Song," by Rokusuke Ei (stamp 5). f, 80y, Novelist Ryotaro Shiba and cover from "Ryomaga Yuku," depicting Ryoma Sakamoto (stamp 6). g, 80y, Baby doll, and song "Konnichiwa Akachan," by Ei (stamp 7). h, 80y, Inauguration of

Bullet Train (stamp 8). i, 80y, Poster depicting swimmer from Tokyo Olympics (stamp 9). j, 80y, Poster depicting torchbearer from Tokyo Olympics (stamp 10).

A2090l

1964-71 (Sheet 13) — No. 2699: a, 50y, TV show puppets Don Gabacho and Torahige (stamp 1, 31x30mm semi-oval stamp with straight side at right). b, 50y, TV show puppets Hakase and Lion (stamp 2, 31x30mm semi-oval stamp with straight side at left). c, 80y, Color television, automobile and air conditioner (stamp 3). d, 80y, TV character, Ultraman (stamp 4). e, 80y, Baltan Seijin, character from Ultraman TV series (stamp 5). f, 80y, Electric guitars (stamp 6). g, 80y, Yasunari Kawabata and Kenzaburo Oe, Nobel laureates for Literature (stamp 7). h, 80y, Scene from movie "Otokowa Tsuraiyo" (man holding basket) (stamp 8). i, 80y, Tower from Expo '70, Osaka (stamp 9). j, 80y, Youth fashions and song "Senso O Shiranai Kodomotachi" (stamp 10).

A2090m

1972-74 (Sheet 14) — No. 2700: a, 50y, Baseball player Sadaharu Oh (leg in air) (stamp 7). b, 50y, Baseball player Shigeo Nagashima (Tokyo uniform) (stamp 8). c, 80y, Two men from Takamatsu Zuka wall paintings, Asuka (stamp 1). d, 80y, Four women from Takamatsu Zuka wall paintings (stamp 2). e, 80y, Pandas Kankan and Ranran, gift from China (stamp 3). f, Shureimon, Return of Okinawa to Japanese control (stamp 4). g, 80y, Oscar, from cartoon "Roses of Versailles," by Riyoko Ikeda (stamp 5). h, 80y, Conductor Seiji Ozawa (stamp 6). i, 80y, Erimo Cape, and song "Erimo Misaki" (stamp 9). j, 80y, Space battleship Yamato from cartoon "Uchu Senkan Yamato," by Reiji Matsumoto (stamp 10).

A2090n

1975-83 (Sheet 15) — No. 2701: a, 50y, Gundam and Zaku, from TV cartoon series "Kidonsenshi Gundam" (blue background) (stamp 7). b, 50y, Amuro and Gundam, from

"Kidonsenshi Gundam" (orange background) (stamp 8). c, 80y, Guitar, and song "Jidai" (stamp 1). d, 80y, Fish character Taiyaki Kun, from children's song "Oyoge! Taiyaki Kun" (stamp 2). e, 80y, Musical notes and microphones (popularity of karaoke) (stamp 3). f, 80y, Flower, and song "Cosmos" (stamp 4). g, 80y, UFO, and song "UFO" (stamp 5). h, 80y, Students from TV series, "San Nen B Gumi Kinpachi Sensei" (stamp 6). i, 80y, Musical notes and electronic synthesizer (stamp 9). j, 80y, Oshin, from TV series "Oshin" (stamp 10).

A2090o

1986-93 (Sheet 16) — No. 2702: a, 50y, Character from cartoon show "Soreike! Anpanman" (stamp 7). b, 50y, Four characters from "Soreike! Anpanman" (stamp 4). c, 80y, Return of Halley's Comet (stamp 1, pentagonal). d, 80y, Opening of Seikan Railroad Tunnel (stamp 2). e, 80y, Watchtower excavated at Yoshinogari Iseki ruins (stamp 5). f, 80y, Singer Hibari Misora, National Medal of Honor recipient (stamp 6). g, 80y, Mascot of J-League Soccer Games (stamp 7, 34x28mm semi-oval stamp with straight side at bottom). h, 80y, Soccer ball (stamp 8, 34x28mm stamp with straight side at top). i, 80y, Selection of Dunjuang as World Heritage Site (Cliffside, stamp 9). j, 80y, Selection of Horyuji Temple as World Heritage Site (Temple and sun, stamp 10).

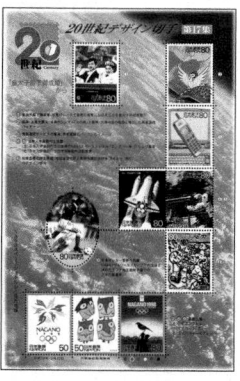

A2090p

1993-98 (Sheet 17) — No. 2703: a, 50y, Nagano Winter Olympics emblem (stamp 7). b, 50y, Four owl mascots of Nagano Winter Olympics (stamp 8). c, 80y, Wedding of Crown Prince Naruhito and Masako Owada (stamp 1). d, 80y, Phoenix and damage from Hanshin-Awaji earthquake (stamp 2). e, 80y, Cellular phone and computer (stamp 3). f, 80y, Launch of Japanese astronaut aboard Space Shuttle Endeavor (stamp 4). g, 80y, Astronaut Mamoru Mohri in space (stamp 5). h, 80y, Details from Kyoto Climate Change Conf. stamps, #2598-2599 (stamp 6). i, 80y, Poster for Nagano Winter Olympics (stamp 9). j, Soccer player at 1998 World Cup Championships (stamp 10, 42x31mm elliptical stamp).
Illustrations reduced.

| 1999-2000 | Photo. | Perf. 13x13¼ | |
|---|---|---|---|
| | Sheets of 10 | | |
| 2687 | A2090 | #a.-j. | 15.00 | 15.00 |
| a.-b. | 50y any single | | .75 | .50 |
| c.-j. | 80y any single | | 1.25 | .50 |
| 2688 | A2090a | #a.-j. | 15.00 | 15.00 |
| a.-b. | 50y any single | | .75 | .50 |
| c.-j. | 80y any single | | 1.25 | .50 |
| 2689 | A2090b | #a.-j. | 15.00 | 15.00 |
| a.-b. | 50y any single | | .75 | .50 |
| c.-j. | 80y any single | | 1.25 | .50 |
| 2690 | A2090c | #a.-j. | 15.00 | 15.00 |
| a.-b. | 50y any single | | .75 | .50 |
| c.-j. | 80y any single | | 1.25 | .50 |
| 2691 | A2090d | #a.-j. | 15.00 | 15.00 |
| a.-b. | 50y any single | | .75 | .50 |
| c.-j. | 80y any single | | 1.25 | .50 |
| 2692 | A2090e | #a.-j. | 15.00 | 15.00 |
| a.-b. | 50y any single | | .75 | .50 |
| c.-j. | 80y any single | | 1.25 | .50 |

| | | | | |
|---|---|---|---|---|
| 2693 | A2090f | #a.-j. | 15.00 | 15.00 |
| a.-b. | | 50y any single | .75 | .50 |
| c.-j. | | 80y any single | 1.25 | .50 |
| 2694 | A2090g | #a-j | 15.00 | 15.00 |
| a.-b. | | 50y any single | .75 | .50 |
| c.-j. | | 80y Any single | 1.25 | .50 |
| 2695 | A2090h | #a-j | 15.00 | 15.00 |
| a.-b. | | 50y any single | .75 | .50 |
| c.-j. | | 80y Any single | 1.25 | .50 |
| 2696 | A2090i | #a-j | 15.00 | 15.00 |
| a.-b. | | 50y any single | .75 | .50 |
| c.-j. | | 80y Any single | 1.25 | .50 |
| 2697 | A2090j | #a-j | 15.00 | 15.00 |
| a.-b. | | 50y any single | .75 | .50 |
| c.-j. | | 80y Any single | 1.25 | .50 |
| 2698 | A2090k | #a-j | 15.00 | 15.00 |
| a.-b. | | 50y any single | .75 | .50 |
| c.-j. | | 80y Any single | 1.25 | .50 |
| 2699 | A2090l | #a-j | 15.00 | 15.00 |
| a.-b. | | 50y any single | .75 | .50 |
| c.-j. | | 80y Any single | 1.25 | .50 |
| 2700 | A2090m | #a-j | | 15.00 |
| a.-b. | | 50y any single | .75 | .50 |
| c.-j. | | 80y Any single | 1.25 | .50 |
| 2701 | A2090n | #a-j | | 15.00 |
| a.-b. | | 50y any single | .75 | .50 |
| c.-j. | | 80y Any single | 1.25 | .50 |
| 2702 | A2090o | #a-j | | 15.00 |
| a.-b. | | 50y any single | .75 | .50 |
| c.-j. | | 80y Any single | 1.25 | .50 |
| 2703 | A2090p | #a-j | 15.00 | 15.00 |
| a.-b. | | 50y any single | .75 | .50 |
| c.-j. | | 80y Any single | 1.25 | .50 |
| | *Nos. 2687-2703 (17)* | | 255.00 | 255.00 |

Sheet numbers are in UR corner of sheets or in center of rectangles at top of sheet. Stamp numbers are in sheet margin.

Issued: No. 2687, 8/23; No. 2688, 9/22; No. 2689, 10/22; No. 2690, 12/22; No. 2691, 1/21/00; No. 2692, 2/9/00; No. 2693, 2/23/00; No. 2694, 3/23/00; No. 2695, 4/21/00; No. 2696, 5/23/00; No. 2697, 6/23/00; No. 2698, 7/21/00; No. 2699, 8/23/00; No. 2700, 9/22/00; No. 2701, 10/23/00; No. 2702, 11/22; No. 2703, 12/22.

Hearts and Doves A2092

Celebration A2093

Red-crowned Crane — A2094

**1999, Aug. 16**    **Photo.**    *Perf. 13¼*

| | | | | |
|---|---|---|---|---|
| 2704 | A2092 | 50y multi | 1.00 | .30 |
| 2705 | A2093 | 80y multi | 1.75 | .35 |
| 2706 | A2094 | 90y multi | 2.00 | .40 |
| | *Nos. 2704-2706 (3)* | | 4.75 | 1.05 |

54th Natl. Sports Festival — A2095

**1999, Sept. 10**

| | | | | |
|---|---|---|---|---|
| 2707 | A2095 | 50y multi | 1.00 | .30 |

A2096

**1999, Oct. 1**    *Perf. 12¾x13*

| | | | | |
|---|---|---|---|---|
| 2708 | A2096 | 80y multi | 1.50 | .35 |

Intl. Year of Older Persons.

A2097

---

A2098

A2099

Intl. Letter Writing Week — A2100

Hokusai Paintings: No. 2709, Sea Route in Kazusa Area. No. 2710, Roses & a Sparrow. No. 2711, Rain Beneath the Mountaintop. No. 2712, Chrysanthemums & a Horsefly. No. 2713, Under the Fukagawa Bridge. No. 2714, Peonies & a Butterfly.

**1999, Oct. 6**    *Perf. 13¼*

| | | | | |
|---|---|---|---|---|
| 2709 | A2097 | 90y multi | 1.75 | .45 |
| 2710 | A2098 | 90y multi | 1.75 | .45 |
| a. | | Pair, #2709-2710 | 3.50 | 1.75 |
| 2711 | A2099 | 110y multi | 2.25 | .55 |
| 2712 | A2099 | 110y multi | 2.25 | .55 |
| a. | | Pair, #2711-2712 | 4.50 | 1.75 |
| 2713 | A2097 | 130y multi | 2.50 | .60 |
| 2714 | A2100 | 130y multi | 2.50 | .60 |
| a. | | Pair, #2713-2714 | 5.25 | 1.75 |
| | *Nos. 2709-2714 (6)* | | 13.00 | 3.20 |

Central and Pacific Baseball Leagues, 50th Anniv. A2101

Mascots wearing uniforms of: a, Yokohama Bay Stars. b, Chunichi Dragons. c, Seibu Lions. d, Nippon Ham Fighters. e, Yomiuri Giants. f, Yakult Swallows g, Orix Blue Wave. h, Fukuoka Daiei Hawks. i, Hiroshima Toyo Carp. j, Hanshin Tigers. k, Kintetsu Buffaloes. l, Chiba Lotte Marines.

**1999, Oct. 22**    *Die Cut*
**Self-Adhesive**

| | | | | |
|---|---|---|---|---|
| 2715 | A2101 | Sheet of 12 | 18.00 | 18.00 |
| a.-l. | | 80y any single | 1.40 | .35 |

Natl. Science Council, 50th Anniv. — A2102

**1999, Oct. 28**    *Perf. 13x13¼*

| | | | | |
|---|---|---|---|---|
| 2716 | A2102 | 80y multi | 1.50 | .35 |

**Cultural Pioneers Types of 1992-98**

No. 2717, Hokusai (1760-1849), painter. No. 2718, Yasunari Kawabata (1899-1972), writer. No. 2719, Shoen Uemura (1875-1949), painter.

**1999, Nov. 4**    **Photo.**    *Perf. 12¾x13*

| | | | | |
|---|---|---|---|---|
| 2717 | A1645 | 80y multi | 1.50 | .35 |

**Photo. & Engr.**
*Perf. 13*

| | | | | |
|---|---|---|---|---|
| 2718 | A1645 | 80y multi | 1.50 | .35 |
| 2719 | A2053 | 80y multi | 1.50 | .35 |
| | *Nos. 2717-2719 (3)* | | 4.50 | 1.05 |

Reign of Emperor Akihito, 10th Anniv. — A2103

Designs: No. 2720, Paulownia and bamboo crest. No. 2721, Phoenix crest.

---

**1999, Nov. 12**    **Photo.**    *Perf. 12¼*

| | | | | |
|---|---|---|---|---|
| 2720 | A2103 | 80y red & multi | 1.75 | .35 |
| 2721 | A2103 | 80y yel & multi | 1.75 | .35 |
| a. | | Souvenir sheet, #2720-2721 | 3.50 | 3.00 |

A2104      A2105

New Year 2000 (Year of the Dragon)
A2106      A2107

**1999, Nov. 15**    *Perf. 13x13¼*

| | | | | |
|---|---|---|---|---|
| 2722 | A2104 | 50y multi | 1.00 | .30 |
| 2723 | A2105 | 80y multi | 1.50 | .40 |

*Perf. 13¼*

| | | | | |
|---|---|---|---|---|
| 2724 | A2106 | 50y +3y multi | 1.25 | .40 |
| 2725 | A2107 | 80y +3y multi | 1.75 | .40 |

Sheets of 2 containing Nos. 2722-2723 were lottery prizes. Value $2.75.

Children's Book Day — A2108

a, Flower with child reading, bird in flight. b, Flower with child reading, bird perched. c, Child, left half of new Intl. Library of Children's Literature. d, Child, right half of library. e, Butterfly with child's head. f, Two children, library.

*Perf. 12¾x13¼*

**2000, Mar. 31**    **Photo.**

| | | | | |
|---|---|---|---|---|
| 2726 | A2108 | Sheet of 10, #e-f, 2 each #a-d | 16.00 | 16.00 |
| a.-f. | | 80y any single | 1.25 | .35 |

Seishu Hanaoka (1760-1835), Physician, and Flower — A2109

**2000, Apr. 11**    *Perf. 12¾x13*

| | | | | |
|---|---|---|---|---|
| 2727 | A2109 | 80y multi | 1.50 | .35 |

Japan Surgical Society, 100th congress.

Japan-Netherlands Relations, 400th Anniv. — A2110

**2000, Apr. 19**    *Perf. 13*

| | | | | |
|---|---|---|---|---|
| 2728 | | 80y multi | 1.25 | .35 |
| 2729 | | 80y multi | 1.25 | .35 |
| a. | | A2110 Pair, #2728-2729 | 3.00 | 1.50 |

---

Dragon and Tiger by Gaho Hashimoto — A2112

**2000, Apr. 20**    *Perf. 13¼*

| | | | | |
|---|---|---|---|---|
| 2730 | | 80y multi | 1.25 | .40 |
| 2731 | | 80y multi | 1.25 | .40 |
| a. | | A2112 Pair, #2730-2731 | 3.00 | 1.50 |

Philately week.

Natl. Land Afforestation Campaign — A2114

**2000, Apr. 21**    *Perf. 13¼*

| | | | | |
|---|---|---|---|---|
| 2732 | A2114 | 50y multi | 1.00 | .40 |

Phila Nippon 2001, Tokyo A2115

Designs: a, Wild goose (dull green frame background). b, Wagtail (dull violet frame background). c, Goshawk (dull rose frame background). d, A Girl Blowing Glass Toy, by Utamaro. e, Kabuki Actor Ebizo Ichikawa, by Sharaku. f, Flowers. g, Dog and cat. h, Children with pen and envelope (blue background). i, Child with clown. j, Children with pen and envelope (red background).

**2000, May 19**    **Photo.**    *Die Cut*
**Self-Adhesive**

| | | | | |
|---|---|---|---|---|
| 2733 | A2115 | Sheet of 10, #a-j | 16.00 | 16.00 |
| a.-j. | | 80y any single | 1.25 | .55 |

Kyushu-Okinawa Summit — A2116

**2000, June 21**    **Photo.**    *Perf. 12¾x13*

| | | | | |
|---|---|---|---|---|
| 2734 | | 80y multi | 1.25 | .35 |
| 2735 | | 80y multi | 1.25 | .35 |
| a. | | A2116 Pair, #2734-2735 | 3.00 | 1.50 |

A2117

**2000, June 30**

| | | | | |
|---|---|---|---|---|
| 2736 | | 80y Three flowers | 1.25 | .35 |
| 2737 | | 80y Two flowers | 1.25 | .35 |
| a. | | A2117 Pair, #2736-2737 | 3.00 | 1.50 |

Crime Prevention Campaign, 50th anniv.

**Letter Writing Day Type of 1998**

Designs: No. 2738, Girl with bows in hair, pen. No. 2739, Birds, house, letter. No. 2740, Clown with red hat, open envelope. No. 2741, Boy reading letter, puppy.

No. 2742: a, Child, dog, in basket. b, Apple tree, flower (circular stamp). c, Parrots holding envelope (elliptical stamp). d, Bicycle, rabbit, flower (oval stamp). e, Boy, girl, dove. f, Girl, letter, snail, porcupine (oval stamp). g, Child playing harp. h, Child playing recorder. i, Child playing bass (semicircular stamp). j, Girl with blue hat, pen, birds holding envelope.

**2000, July 21**    *Perf. 12¾x13¼*

| | | | | |
|---|---|---|---|---|
| 2738 | A2047 | 50y multi | .80 | .35 |
| 2739 | A2047 | 50y multi | .80 | .35 |
| 2740 | A2047 | 50y multi | .80 | .35 |

| | | | | |
|---|---|---|---|---|
| 2741 | A2047 50y multi | | .80 | .35 |
| a. | Strip of 4, #2738-2741 | | 4.00 | 4.00 |
| 2742 | Sheet of 10 | | 16.00 | 16.00 |
| a.-/. | A2047 80y Any single | | 1.25 | .40 |
| k. | Booklet pane, #2738-2741, 2742g, 2742h, 2 #2742e, 2742j | | 13.00 | 13.00 |
| | Booklet, #2742k | | 15.00 | |
| l. | Souvenir sheet, #2739, 2742e | | 2.75 | 2.75 |

No. 2742b is 30mm in diameter, No. 2742c is 23x34mm, Nos. 2742d, 2742f are 28x40mm, and No. 2742i is 24x40mm.

Women's Private Higher Education, Cent. — A2118

| | | | |
|---|---|---|---|
| **2000, Sept. 22** | **Photo.** | | ***Perf. 13*** |
| 2743 | A2118 80y multi | 1.50 | .35 |

Intl. Letter Writing Week — A2119

Artwork by Hiroshige: 90y, Okabe. 110y, Maisaka. 130y, Okazaki.

| | | | |
|---|---|---|---|
| **2000, Oct. 6** | | | ***Perf. 13¼*** |
| 2744 | A2119 90y multi | 1.75 | .50 |
| 2745 | A2119 110y multi | 2.25 | .60 |
| 2746 | A2119 130y multi | 2.50 | .65 |
| | *Nos. 2744-2746 (3)* | 6.50 | 1.75 |

See Nos. 2791-2793, 2835-2837, 2865-2867, 2904-2906, 2938-2940, 2999-3001, 3064-3066. See listing of No. 4448 for images of each Hiroshige print.

### Cultural Pioneers Type of 1998 and

Ukichiro Nakaya (1900-62), Snow Crystal Researcher — A2120

Designs: No. 2747, Hantaro Nagaoka (1865-1950), physicist. No. 2748, Teijo Nakamura (1900-88), poet.

| | | | |
|---|---|---|---|
| | **Photo. & Engr.** | | |
| **2000, Nov. 6** | | | ***Perf. 13*** |
| 2747 | A2053 80y multi | 1.50 | .35 |
| 2748 | A2053 80y multi | 1.50 | .35 |
| 2749 | A2120 80y multi | 1.50 | .35 |
| | *Nos. 2747-2749 (3)* | 4.50 | 1.05 |

See No. 2841.

A2121                    A2122

New Year 2001 (Year of the Snake)
A2123             A2124

| | | | | |
|---|---|---|---|---|
| **2000, Nov. 15** | **Photo.** | | ***Perf. 13x13¼*** | |
| 2750 | A2121 50y multi | | 1.00 | .30 |
| 2751 | A2122 80y multi | | 1.50 | .40 |
| | | | ***Perf. 13¼x13½*** | |
| 2752 | A2123 50y +3y multi | | 1.25 | .40 |
| 2753 | A2124 80y +3y multi | | 1.75 | .40 |
| | *Nos. 2750-2753 (4)* | | 5.50 | 1.50 |

Sheets of 2, Nos. 2750-2751, were lottery prizes. Value, $2.75.

Diet, 110th Anniv. — A2125

| | | | |
|---|---|---|---|
| **2000, Nov. 29** | | | ***Perf. 13*** |
| 2754 | A2125 80y multi | 1.50 | .35 |

Internet Expo 2001 A2126

| | | | |
|---|---|---|---|
| **2001, Jan. 5** | | | ***Perf. 13x13¼*** |
| 2755 | 80y Denom. at L | 1.25 | .35 |
| 2756 | 80y Denom. at R | 1.25 | .35 |
| a. | A2126 Pair, #2755-2756 | 3.00 | 1.50 |

Intl. Volunteers Year — A2127

| | | | |
|---|---|---|---|
| **2001, Jan. 17** | | | ***Perf. 13½x13¼*** |
| 2757 | A2127 80y multi | 1.50 | .35 |

Administrative Scriveners System, 50th Anniv. — A2128

| | | | |
|---|---|---|---|
| **2001, Feb. 22** | **Photo.** | | ***Perf. 13¼*** |
| 2758 | A2128 80y multi | 1.50 | .35 |

### World Heritage Sites

Sheet 1 A2129

Sheet 2 A2130

Sheet 3 A2131

Sheet 4 A2132

Sheet 5 A2133

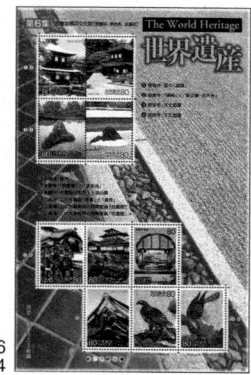

Sheet 6 A2134

No. 2759 — Nikko: a, Bridge (stamp 1). b, Shrine with pillars in foreground (stamp 2). c, Temple gate (stamp 3). d, Dragon (stamp 4). e, Peacock (stamp 5). f, Cat (stamp 6). g, Statue of blue green figure (stamp 7). h, Statue of red figure (stamp 8). i, Shrine (stamp 9). j, Shrine and walkways (stamp 10).

No. 2760 — Itsukushima: a, Marodo Jinjya and pillar in water (stamp 1). b, Marodo Jinjya (stamp 2). c, Honsha (shrine entrance with steps, stamp 3). d, Koma-inu (lion statue, stamp 4). e, Marodo Jinjya and Gojyuno-tou (stamp 5). f, Bugakumen (sculpture with blue water background, stamp 6). g, Kazari-uma (horse statue, stamp 7). h, Noubutai (building with brown eaves, stamp 8). i, Tahoutou (building with cherry blossoms, stamp 9). j, Oomoto Jinjya (building with red fence, stamp 10).

No. 2761 — Kyoto: a, Hosodono Hall, Maidono Hall and Tsuchinoya Hall, Kamowakeikazuchi Shrine (buildings with cones in foreground, stamp 1). b, Romon Gate, Kamowakeikazuchi Shrine (building with

stream, stamp 2). c, East Main Hall, Kamomioya Shrine (building with guardian dog statue on landing, stamp 3). d, Guardian dog statue, Kamomioya Shrine (stamp 4). e, South Great Gate and 5-Story Pagoda (deep blue sky, stamp 5). f, Fukuu Joju Nyorai Statue, Toji Temple (gold statue, stamp 6). g, Nyoirin Kannon, Toji Temple (painting, stamp 7). h, Daiitoku Myoo Statue, Toji Temple (stone statue, stamp 8). i, West Gate, 3-Story Pagoda, Kiyomizudera Temple (red gate and temple, stamp 9). j, Main Hall, Kiyomizudera Temple (building with cherry bloosoms, stamp 10).

No. 2762 — Kyoto: a, Konpon Chudo Hall, Enryakuji Temple (roof, stamp 1). b, Eternal Flame, Enryakuji Temple (stamp 2). c, Ninaido Hall, Enryakuji Temple (building with large trees in foreground, stamp 3). d, Sanbo-in Temple Garden, Daigoji Temple (building, one end of small bridge, stamp 4). e, Sanbo-in Temple Garden (end of bridge, trees, stamp 5). f, 5-Story Pagoda, Daigoji Temple (white sky, stamp 6). g, Goten, Ninnaji Temple (buildings with walkways, stamp 7). h, 5-Story Pagoda (cherry trees in foreground, stamp 8). i, Phoenix Hall, Byodoin Temple (black sky, stamp 9). j, Wooden carving of Bodhisattvas Floating on Clouds, Byodoin Temple (stamp 10).

No. 2763 — Kyoto: a, Ujikami Shrine (low fence around shrine with denomination at UL, stamp 1). b, Kaeru Mata, Ujikami Shrine (thin, crossing diagonal strips, stamp 2). c, Front approach to Kozanji Temple (walkway of square panels, stamp 3). d, Sekisuiin, Kozanji Temple (yellow tree blossoms in front of temple, stamp 4). e, Kasumijima Garden, Saihoji Temple (moss-covered bridge, stamp 5) f, Kojokan Garden, Saihoji Temple (Stone stairs and rocks, stamp 6). g, View of garden and pond from under roof, Tenryuji Temple (denomination at left, stamp 7). h, View of garden and pond from under roof, Tenryuji Temple (denomination at right, stamp 8). i, Rokuonji Temple in autumn (Building on lake, green leaves on trees, stamp 9). j, Rokuonji Temple in winter (snow covered roofs and trees, stamp 10).

No. 2764 — Kyoto: a, Snow-covered Silver Pavilion, Jishoji Temple (stamp 1). b, Silver Pavilion without snow (stamp 2). c, Moss-covered rock, Hojo Garden, Ryoanji Temple (stamp 3). d, Rock and snow, Hojo Garden (stamp 4). e, Karamon, Honganji Temple (gate with curved roof, stamp 5). f, Hiunkaku, Honganji Temple (building near pond, stamp 6). g, Shoin, Honganji Temple (wall with landscape, stamp 7). h, Ninomaur Palace, Nijo Castle (roof with chrysanthemum crest at peak, stamp 8). i, Detail from "Hawks on Pine," Nijo Castle (hawk looking left, stamp 9). j, Detail from "Hawks on Pine," Nijo Castle (hawk looking down, stamp 10).

| | | | | |
|---|---|---|---|---|
| **2001** | **Photo.** | | ***Perf. 13x13¼*** | |
| 2759 | A2129 | Sheet of 10 | 16.00 | 16.00 |
| a.-/. | | 80y Any single | 1.25 | .55 |
| 2760 | A2130 | Sheet of 10 | 16.00 | 16.00 |
| a.-/. | | 80y Any single | 1.25 | .55 |
| 2761 | A2131 | Sheet of 10 | 16.00 | 16.00 |
| a.-/. | | 80y Any single | 1.25 | .55 |
| 2762 | A2132 | Sheet of 10 | 16.00 | 16.00 |
| a.-/. | | 80y Any single | 1.25 | .55 |
| 2763 | A2133 | Sheet of 10 | 16.00 | 16.00 |
| a.-/. | | 80y Any single | 1.25 | .55 |
| 2764 | A2134 | Sheet of 10 | 16.00 | 16.00 |
| a.-/. | | 80y Any single | 1.25 | .55 |
| | | *Nos. 2759-2764 (6)* | 96.00 | 96.00 |

Issued: No. 2759, 2/23; No. 2760, 3/23; No. 2761, 6/22; No. 2762, 8/23. No. 2763, 12/21. No. 2764, 2/22/02.

Sheet numbers are in center of colored rectangles at top of sheet. Stamp numbers are in sheet margins.

Exhibit of Italian Art at Museum of Western Art, Tokyo — A2135

Designs: 80y, Show emblem. No. 2766, Angel, from The Annunciation, by Botticelli. No. 2767, Virgin Mary, from The Annunciation.

| | | | |
|---|---|---|---|
| **2001, Mar. 19** | **Photo.** | | ***Perf. 13*** |
| 2765 | A2135 80y multi | 1.50 | .35 |
| | **Size: 33x44mm** | | |
| | ***Perf. 13¼*** | | |
| 2766 | A2135 110y multi | 1.75 | .55 |
| 2767 | A2135 110y multi | 1.75 | .55 |
| a. | Pair, #2766-2767 | 4.50 | 3.00 |
| | *Nos. 2765-2767 (3)* | 5.00 | 1.45 |

## Japanese Dermatological Association, 100th Annual Meeting — A2136

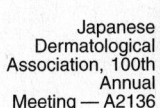

**2001, Apr. 6** — **Perf. 13¼**
**Color of Triangle Behind "0" in Denomination**

| | | | | |
|---|---|---|---|---|
| 2768 | A2136 | 80y pink | 1.25 | .35 |
| 2769 | A2136 | 80y orange | 1.25 | .35 |
| 2770 | A2136 | 80y yellow | 1.25 | .35 |
| 2771 | A2136 | 80y green | 1.25 | .35 |
| 2772 | A2136 | 80y blue | 1.25 | .35 |
| a. | | Vert. strip of 5, #2768-2772 | 8.00 | 5.00 |

## Depositing Mail, by Senseki Nakamura — A2137

**2001, Apr. 20** — **Perf. 13x13¼**
| 2773 | A2137 | 80y multi | 1.50 | .35 |
|---|---|---|---|---|

Philately Week, Cent. of red cylindrical mailboxes.

## Membership in UNESCO, 50th Anniv. — A2138

**2001, July 2** — **Perf. 13¼**
| 2774 | A2138 | 80y multi | 1.50 | .35 |
|---|---|---|---|---|

## 9th FINA World Swimming Championships, Fukuoka — A2139

Designs: No. 2775, Swimming race. No. 2776, Synchronized swimming. No. 2777, Diving. No. 2778, Water polo.

**2001, July 16** — **Perf. 13x13¼**
| 2775 | A2139 | 80y multi | 1.25 | .35 |
|---|---|---|---|---|
| 2776 | A2139 | 80y multi | 1.25 | .35 |
| 2777 | A2139 | 80y multi | 1.25 | .35 |
| 2778 | A2139 | 80y multi | 1.25 | .35 |
| a. | | Horiz. strip of 4, #2775-2778 | 6.00 | 6.00 |

### Letter Writing Day Type of 1998

Designs: No. 2779, Three rabbits, tulip background. No. 2780, Girl with pencil, pencil background. No. 2781, Boy with envelope, bird background. No. 2782, Girl, flower background.

No. 2783: a, Girl with rabbit, bird, flower (oval stamp). b, Bird in tree (circular stamp). c, Boy with pen behind back. d, Girl with envelope and dog. e, Girl on bicycle, flowers (semicircular stamp). f, Flowers, bird with envelope, insect (circular stamp). g, Bird flying, bird on roof. h, Chicken, chicks, pig (oval stamp). i, Rabbit, flowers (elliptical stamp). j, Boy with hat, rabbit (oval stamp).

**2001, July 23** — **Perf. 13x13¼**
| 2779 | A2047 | 50y multi | .80 | .30 |
|---|---|---|---|---|
| 2780 | A2047 | 50y multi | .80 | .30 |
| 2781 | A2047 | 50y multi | .80 | .30 |
| 2782 | A2047 | 50y multi | .80 | .30 |
| a. | | Horiz. strip of 4, #2779-2782 | 4.00 | 4.00 |
| 2783 | | Sheet of 10 | 16.00 | 16.00 |
| a.-j. | | A2047 80y Any single | 1.25 | .35 |
| k. | | Booklet pane, #2779-2782, 2 each #2783c, 2783d, 2783g | 13.50 | |
| | | Booklet, #2783k | 15.00 | |
| l. | | Souvenir sheet, #2780, 2783g | 2.75 | 2.75 |

Phila Nippon '01 (Nos. 2783, 2783l). Nos. 2783a and 2783e are 35x29mm; Nos. 2783b and 2783f are 29mm in diameter; No. 2783h is 40x28mm; No. 2783i is 35x23mm; No. 2783j is 34x28mm.

On No. 2783e, the bicycle appears in the selvage below the stamp.

## Phila Nippon '01 A2140

Art: a, Oniji Otani as Edobei (striped kimono), by Sharaku. b, Hanshiro Iwai as Shigenoi (flowered kimono, facing left), by Sharaku. c, Hangoro Sakata as Mizuemon Fujikawa (brown kimono), by Sharaku. d, Kikunojo Segawa as Oshizu, Bunzo Tanabe's Wife (kimono with stars), by Sharaku. e, Omezo Ichikawa as Ippei Yakko (with sword), by Sharaku. f, Beauty Looking Back (flowered kimono), by Moronobu Hishikawa. g, A Girl Whistling a Vidro (checkered kimono), by Utamaro. h, Nishiki Fuzoku Higashino Returning From a Bathhouse in the Rain (with umbrella), by Kiyonaga Torii. i, Kumesaburo Iwai as Chiyo (blue background), by Kunimasa Utagawa. j, Komazo Ichikawa as Ganryu Sasaki (with sword), by Toyokuni Utagawa.

**2001, Aug. 1** — **Perf. 13**
| 2784 | A2140 | Sheet of 10+10 labels | 12.50 | 12.50 |
|---|---|---|---|---|
| a.-e. | | 50y Any single | .80 | .50 |
| f.-j. | | 80y Any single | 1.25 | .50 |

Labels could be personalized by customers at Phila Nippon stamp exhibition.

## 2001 World Games, Akita — A2141

Designs: No. 2785, Fishing, Frisbee throwing. No. 2786, Aerobics, billiards. No. 2787, Life saving, water skiing. No. 2788, Body building, tug-of-war.

**2001, Aug. 16** — **Perf. 13**
| 2785 | A2141 | 50y multi | .80 | .30 |
|---|---|---|---|---|
| 2786 | A2141 | 50y multi | .80 | .30 |
| a. | | Pair, #2785-2786 | 2.00 | 1.00 |
| 2787 | A2141 | 80y multi | 1.25 | .35 |
| 2788 | A2141 | 80y multi | 1.25 | .35 |
| a. | | Pair, #2787-2788 | 3.25 | 1.50 |
| | | Nos. 2785-2788 (4) | 4.10 | 1.30 |

## Phila Nippon '01 A2142

Designs: a, Hanshiro Iwai as Shigenoi (figure with stick in hair), by Sharaku. b, Oniji Otani as Edobei (figure with fingers splayed), by Sharaku. c, Mandarin duck in water. d, White-eye on branch. e, Children with letters. f, Kumesaburo Iwai as Chiyo (lilac background), by Kunimasa Utagawa. g, Komazo Ichikawa as Ganryu Sasaki (brown background), by Toyokuni Utagawa. h, Turtledove (blue background). i, Greater pied kingfisher (green background). j, Japan #1.

**2001, Aug. 1** — **Photo.** — **Die Cut**
**Self-Adhesive**
| 2789 | A2142 | Sheet of 10 | 12.00 | 12.00 |
|---|---|---|---|---|
| a.-e. | | 50y Any single | .80 | .30 |
| f.-j. | | 80y Any single | 1.25 | .35 |

## San Francisco Peace Treaty, 50th Anniv. — A2143

**2001, Sept. 7** — **Perf. 13**
| 2790 | A2143 | 80y multi | 1.50 | .35 |
|---|---|---|---|---|

### Intl. Letter Writing Week Type of 2000

Hiroshige paintings from 53 Stations of the Tokaido: 90y, Hara. 110y, Oiso. 130y, Sakanoshita.

**2001, Oct. 5** — **Perf. 13¼**
| 2791 | A2119 | 90y multi | 1.75 | .50 |
|---|---|---|---|---|
| 2792 | A2119 | 110y multi | 2.25 | .55 |
| 2793 | A2119 | 130y multi | 2.50 | .60 |
| | | Nos. 2791-2793 (3) | 6.50 | 1.65 |

See listing of No. 4448 for images of each Hiroshige print.

## Town Safety Campaign A2144

Designs: No. 2794, Boy, duck chicks, owl, frogs, insects. No. 2795, Girl, dogs, cats, birds, insects.

**2001, Oct. 11** — **Perf. 13x13¼**
| 2794 | | 80y multi | 1.25 | .35 |
|---|---|---|---|---|
| 2795 | | 80y multi | 1.25 | .35 |
| a. | A2144 | Horiz. pair, #2794-2795 | 3.25 | 1.50 |

## 1st National Games for the Disabled A2145

Designs: No. 2796, Disc throwing. No. 2797, Wheelchair race.

**2001, Oct. 26** — **Perf. 12¾x13**
| 2796 | | 80y multi | 1.25 | .35 |
|---|---|---|---|---|
| 2797 | | 80y multi | 1.25 | .35 |
| a. | A2145 | Horiz. pair, #2796-2797 | 3.00 | 1.50 |

## Norinaga Motoori (1730-1801), Physician, Scholar A2146 / Gidayu Takemoto (1651-1714), Joruri Chanter A2147

**Photo. & Engr.**
**2001, Nov. 5** — **Perf. 12¾x13**
| 2798 | A2146 | 80y multi | 1.50 | .35 |
|---|---|---|---|---|
| 2799 | A2147 | 80y multi | 1.50 | .35 |

## Commercial Broadcasting, 50th Anniv. — A2148

**2001, Nov. 15** — **Photo.**
| 2800 | A2148 | 80y multi | 1.50 | .35 |
|---|---|---|---|---|

A2149 / A2150

## New Year 2002 (Year of the Horse)
A2151 / A2152

**2001, Nov. 15** — **Perf. 13x13¼**
| 2801 | A2149 | 50y multi | 1.00 | .30 |
|---|---|---|---|---|
| 2802 | A2150 | 80y multi | 1.50 | .40 |

**Perf. 13¼x13½**
| 2803 | A2151 | 50y +3y multi | 1.25 | .40 |
|---|---|---|---|---|
| 2804 | A2152 | 80y +3y multi | 1.75 | .40 |
| | | Nos. 2801-2804 (4) | 5.50 | 1.50 |

Sheets of two containing Nos. 2801-2802 were lottery prizes. Value, $3.

## Legal Aid System, 50th Anniv. — A2153

**2002, Jan. 24** — **Perf. 12¾x13**
| 2805 | A2153 | 80y multi | 1.50 | .35 |
|---|---|---|---|---|

## Japan — Mongolia Diplomatic Relations, 30th Anniv. — A2154

**2002, Feb. 15**
| 2806 | A2154 | 80y multi | 1.50 | .35 |
|---|---|---|---|---|

## Lions Clubs in Japan, 50th Anniv. — A2155

**2002, Mar. 1** — **Photo.** — **Perf. 13x13¼**
| 2807 | A2155 | 80y multi | 1.50 | .35 |
|---|---|---|---|---|

## 2002 World Figure Skating Championships, Nagano — A2156

**2002, Mar. 8**
| 2808 | | 80y Men's Singles | 1.25 | .90 |
|---|---|---|---|---|
| 2809 | | 80y Pairs | 1.25 | .90 |
| a. | A2156 | Horiz. pair, #2808-2809 | 3.00 | 1.90 |

## Diplomatic Relations Anniversaries — A2157

Designs: No. 2810, Taj Mahal, India. No. 2811, Sculpture of "Priest King," Mohenjo Daro excavations, Pakistan. No. 2812, Sigiriya goddess, Lion's Rock, Sri Lanka. No. 2813, Carving from Buddhist Vihara, Paharpur, Bangladesh.

**2002, Apr. 12**
| 2810 | A2157 | 80y multi | 1.50 | .40 |
|---|---|---|---|---|
| 2811 | A2157 | 80y multi | 1.50 | .40 |
| 2812 | A2157 | 80y multi | 1.50 | .40 |
| 2813 | A2157 | 80y multi | 1.50 | .40 |
| | | Nos. 2810-2813 (4) | 6.00 | 1.60 |

Japanese diplomatic relations with India, 50th anniv. (No. 2810); Pakistan, 50th anniv.

(No. 2811). Sri Lanka, 50th anniv. (No. 2812), and Bangladesh, 30th anniv. (No. 2813).

Philately Week A2158

Folding screen panels depicting horse racing scenes: No. 2814, Denomination at bottom. No. 2815, Denomination at top.

| 2002, Apr. 19 | | Perf. 13¼ | |
|---|---|---|---|
| 2814 | 80y multi | 1.25 | .40 |
| 2815 | 80y multi | 1.25 | .40 |
| a. | A2158 Horiz. pair, #2814-2815 | 3.00 | 1.75 |

Fulbright Exchange Program, 50th Anniv. — A2159

| 2002, May 8 | | Perf. 12¾x13 | |
|---|---|---|---|
| 2816 | A2159 80y multi | 1.50 | .35 |

Return of Okinawa, 30th Anniv. — A2160

| 2002, May 15 | | Perf. 13x13¼ | |
|---|---|---|---|
| 2817 | A2160 80y multi | 1.50 | .35 |

2002 World Cup Soccer Championships, Japan and Korea — A2161

| 2002, May 24 | | | |
|---|---|---|---|
| 2818 | 80y Soccer field | 1.25 | .35 |
| 2819 | 80y World Cup | 1.25 | .35 |
| a. | A2161 Horiz. pair, #2818-2819 | 3.00 | 1.75 |

Nos. 2818-2819 were issued in sheets of 10 stamps, containing five of each. Thirteen different sheet margins exist.

## World Heritage Sites

Sheet 7
A2162

No. 2820 — Todaiji and Koufukuji Temples, Nara: a, Great Buddha Hall, Todaiji Temple (stamp 1). b, Underside of roof of Nandaimon Gate, Todaiji Temple (stamp 2). c, Engraving on lotus petal, Todaiji Temple (stamp 3). d, Head of Koumokuten, Todaiji Temple (stamp 4). e, Hokkedo Hall and steps, Todaiji Temple (stamp 5). f, Five-story pagoda, Koufukuji Temple (stamp 6). g, Hokuendo Hall (with roof ornament), Koufukuji Temple (stamp 7). h, Ashura (statue with four arms), Koufukuji Temple (stamp 8). i, Head of Buddha, Koufukuji

Temple (stamp 9). j, Ogre under dragon lantern, Koufukuji Temple (stamp 10).

| 2002 | | Photo. | Perf. 13x13¼ | |
|---|---|---|---|---|
| 2820 | A2162 | Sheet of 10 | 16.00 | 16.00 |
| a.-j. | | 80y Any single | 1.25 | .55 |

Issued: No. 2820, 6/21.
Sheet numbers are in center of colored rectangle at top of sheet. Stamp numbers are in sheet margins.

## World Heritage Series

Sheet 8
A2163

Sheet 9
A2164

Sheet 10
A2165

No. 2821 — Nara: a, Covered passageway, Kasuga Taisha Shrine (stamp 1). b, Chumon, Kasuga Taisha Shrine (stamp 2). c, Deer in Kasuga-yama Primeval Forest (stamp 3). d, Gokurakubo Zenshitsu and Gokurakubo Hondo, Gango-ji Temple (stamp 4). e, Gokurakubo Five-story Pagoda, Gango-ji Temple (stamp 5). f, East and West Pagodas, Yakushi-ji Temple (stamp 6). g, Yakushi Nyorai (seated Buddha), Yakushi-ji Temple (stamp 7). h, Golden Hall, Toshodai-ji Temple (stamp 8). i, Senju Kannon Ryu-zo (standing image with hands together of Thousand-handed Goddess of Mercy), Toshodai-ji Temple (stamp 9). j, Suzakumon Gate, Heijo Imperial Palace (stamp 10).

No. 2822 — Villages of Shirakawa-go and Gokayama: a, House with large tree at left, Ogimachi (stamp 1). b, Two houses, trees in fall colors Ogimachi (stamp 2). c, House with flowers, Ogimachi (stamp 3). d, Myozen-ji Temple and house, Ogimachi (stamp 4). e, Two houses covered in snow at night, Ogimachi (stamp 5). f, Neighborhood of houses, Ainokura (stamp 6). g, Sonen-ji Temple with stone wall, Ainokura (stamp 7). h, Two houses, Ainokura (stamp 8). i, House with shrub in front, Suganuma (stamp 9). j, House covered in snow, Suganuma (stamp 10).

No. 2823 — Gusuku Sites of the Ryukyu Kingdom: a, Stone lion at royal mausoleum (stamp 1). b, Three steps and stone gate to Sonohyan'utaki Sanctuary (stamp 2). c,

Cherry blossoms and ruins of Nakijinjou Castle (stamp 3). d, Steps and stone gate at ruins of Zakimijou Castle (stamp 4). e, Ruins of Katsurenjou Castle walls (stamp 5). f, Ruins of Nakagusukujou Castle citadel (walls with gate, stamp 6). g, Kankaimon, main gate of Shurijou Castle (stamp 7). h, Main hall of Shurijou Castle (red building, stamp 8). i, Shikina'en, royal garden (stamp 9). j, Seifautaki Sanctuary (niche in rocks, stamp 10).

| 2002 | | Photo. | Perf. 13x13¼ | |
|---|---|---|---|---|
| 2821 | A2163 | Sheet of 10 | 16.00 | 16.00 |
| a.-j. | | 80y Any single | 1.25 | .55 |
| 2822 | A2164 | Sheet of 10 | 16.00 | 16.00 |
| a.-j. | | 80y Any single | 1.25 | .55 |
| 2823 | A2165 | Sheet of 10 | 16.00 | 16.00 |
| a.-j. | | 80y Any single | 1.25 | .55 |

Issued: No. 2821, 7/23; No. 2822, 9/20; No. 2823, 12/20. Sheet numbers are in center of colored rectangle at top of sheet. Stamp numbers are in sheet margins.

### Letter Writing Day Type of 1998

Designs: No. 2824, Girl with bows in hair holding envelope. No. 2825, Monkey in tree holding envelope. No. 2826, House and flowers. No. 2827, Boy with arms raised, fence. No. 2828: a, Cow and bird (triangular stamp). b, Boy and sheep (elliptical stamp). c, Caterpillar and ladybug under magnifying glass (round stamp). d, Girl with bows in hair, flowers (oval stamp). e, Boy with soccer ball. f, Girl with tennis racquet and ball. g, Man on bicycle. h, Girl with flower in vase (round stamp). i, Truck and automobile. j, Woman holding gift and coat, boy holding envelope

| Perf. 13x13¼, 13 (#2828a) | | | |
|---|---|---|---|
| 2002, July 23 | | Photo. | |
| 2824 | A2047 50y multi | .80 | .40 |
| 2825 | A2047 50y multi | .80 | .40 |
| 2826 | A2047 50y multi | .80 | .40 |
| 2827 | A2047 50y multi | .80 | .40 |
| a. | Strip of 4, #2824-2827 | 4.00 | 2.75 |
| 2828 | Sheet of 10 | 16.00 | 16.00 |
| a.-j. | A2047 80y Any single | 1.40 | .45 |
| k. | Booklet pane, #2824-2827, 3 each #2828g, 2828j | 16.00 | — |
| | Booklet, #2828k | 16.00 | — |
| l. | Souvenir sheet, #2825, 2828j | 2.75 | 2.75 |

No. 2828a is 34x28mm; No. 2828b is 29x26mm; No. 2828c is 29mm in diameter; No. 2828d is 28x40mm; Nos. 2828e and 2828f are 22x36mm; No. 2828h is 28mm in diameter; No. 2828i is 25x25mm.

12th World Congress of Psychiatry, Yokohama — A2166

| 2002, Aug. 1 | Photo. | Perf. 12¾x13 | |
|---|---|---|---|
| 2829 | A2166 80y multi | 1.50 | .35 |

World Wheelchair Basketball Championships, Kitakyushu — A2167

| 2002, Aug. 9 | | | |
|---|---|---|---|
| 2830 | A2167 80y multi | 1.50 | .35 |

Civil Aviation, 50th Anniv. — A2168

| 2002, Sept. 6 | | | |
|---|---|---|---|
| 2831 | A2168 80y multi | 1.50 | .35 |

Normalization of Diplomatic Relations Between Japan and People's Republic of China, 30th Anniv. — A2169

Designs: No. 2832, Purple wisteria flowers. No. 2833, Goldfish and cherry blossoms.

| 2002, Sept. 13 | | Perf. 13x13¼ | |
|---|---|---|---|
| 2832 | 80y multi | 1.25 | .55 |
| 2833 | 80y multi | 1.25 | .55 |
| a. | A2169 Horiz. pair, #2832-2833 | 3.00 | 2.50 |

Intl. Fleet Review, Tokyo Bay — A2170

| 2002, Oct. 1 | | | |
|---|---|---|---|
| 2834 | A2170 80y multi | 1.50 | .40 |

### Letter Writing Week Type of 2000

Hiroshige paintings from 53 Stations of the Tokaido Highway: 90y, Yui. 110y, Shono. 130y, Tozuka.

| 2002, Oct. 7 | | Perf. 13¼ | |
|---|---|---|---|
| 2835 | A2119 90y multi | 1.75 | .50 |
| 2836 | A2119 110y multi | 2.25 | .55 |
| 2837 | A2119 130y multi | 2.50 | .60 |
| | Nos. 2835-2837 (3) | 6.50 | 1.65 |

See listing of No. 4448 for images of each Hiroshige print.

Asian and Pacific Decade of Disabled Persons — A2171

| 2002, Oct. 10 | | Perf. 12¾x13 | |
|---|---|---|---|
| 2838 | A2171 80y multi | 1.50 | .40 |

### Cultural Pioneers Types of 1998-2000

Designs: No. 2839, Shiki Masaoka (1867-1902), poet. No. 2840, Ookawabata Yusuzumi-zu, by Kiyonaga Torii (1752-1815), artist. No. 2841, Aikitu Tanakadate (1856-1952), physicist.

| Photo. & Engr., Photo. (#2840) | | | |
|---|---|---|---|
| 2002, Nov. 5 | | Perf. 13 | |
| 2839 | A2053 80y multi | 1.50 | .40 |
| 2840 | A2053 80y multi | 1.50 | .40 |
| 2841 | A2120 80y multi | 1.50 | .40 |
| | Nos. 2839-2841 (3) | 4.50 | 1.20 |

A2172          A2173

New Year 2003 (Year of the Ram)
A2174          A2175

| 2002, Nov. 15 | Photo. | Perf. 13x13¼ | |
|---|---|---|---|
| 2842 | A2172 50y multi | 1.00 | .30 |
| 2843 | A2173 80y multi | 1.50 | .40 |
| | Perf. 13½x13¼ | | |
| 2844 | A2174 50y +3y multi | 1.25 | .40 |
| 2845 | A2175 80y +3y multi | 1.75 | .40 |
| | Nos. 2842-2845 (4) | 5.50 | 1.50 |

Sheets of two containing Nos. 2842-2843 were lottery prizes. Value, $2.75.

Kabuki, 400th Anniv. A2176

Designs: No. 2846, Shibaraku and Tsuchigumo. No. 2847, Okuni Kabuki-zu, detail from painted screen.

**2003, Jan. 15    Photo.    Perf. 13x13¼**

| 2846 | 80y multi | 1.25 | .50 |
|---|---|---|---|
| 2847 | 80y multi | 1.25 | .50 |
| a. | A2176 Horiz. pair, #2846-2847 | 3.50 | 2.00 |

Japanese Television, 50th Anniv.
A2177        A2178

**2003, Jan. 31**

| 2848 | A2177 80y multi | 1.50 | .40 |
|---|---|---|---|
| 2849 | A2178 80y multi | 1.50 | .40 |

A2179

Greetings — A2180

No. 2850: a, Roses. b, Reindeer. c, Cat and butterfly. d, Rabbits in automobile. e, White flowers.

No. 2851: a, Heart and flower. b, Dog with noisemaker. c, Bird and snowman. d, Bird and strawberries. e, Cranes and turtle.

**2003, Feb. 10    Die Cut Perf. 13½**
**Self-Adhesive**

| 2850 | A2179 | Pane of 5 + 5 labels | 7.00 | 7.00 |
|---|---|---|---|---|
| a.-e. | | 80y Any single | 1.25 | .75 |
| 2851 | A2180 | Pane of 5 + 5 labels | 7.00 | 7.00 |
| a.-e. | | 80y Any single | 1.25 | .75 |

See Nos. 2855A-2855J.

**World Heritage Series**

Sheet 11
A2181

No. 2852 — Hiroshima buildings and stamps on theme of "Peace": a, Atomic Bomb Dome (stamp 1). b, Hiroshima Prefectural Commercial Exhibit Hall (stamp 2). c, Dove over Atomic Bomb Dome, yellow denomination (stamp 3). d, Child's drawing of person with flower (stamp 4). e, Dove over Atomic Bomb Dome, blue denomination (stamp 5). f, Dove over Atomic Bomb Dome, red denomination (stamp 6). g, Doves, stylized person holding child (stamp 7). h, People on hill (stamp 8). i, Bird (stamp 9). j, Rabbit, butterflies and flowers (stamp 10).

**2003, Mar. 20    Photo.    Perf. 13x13¼**

| 2852 | A2181 | Sheet of 10 | 16.00 | 16.00 |
|---|---|---|---|---|
| a.-j. | | 80y Any single | 1.25 | .55 |

Sheet numbers are in center of colored rectangle at top of sheet. Stamp numbers are in sheet margin.

Inauguration of Japan Post — A2182

No. 2853 — Flowers: a, Adonis (yellow flowers). b, Primrose (pink flowers). c, Violets and Japanese quince (violet and red flowers). d, Field horsetail (flowerless). e, Japanese wisteria (white hanging flowers). f, Weeping cherry tree (pink buds and flowers) and swallow. g, Hydrangea (lilac flowers). h, Japanese magnolia (white and pink flowers). i, Candock (yellow flower) and moorhen. j, Peony (pink flower and bud) and butterfly.

**2003, Apr. 1    Die Cut Perf. 13¼**
**Self-Adhesive**

| 2853 | A2182 | Sheet of 10 | 16.00 | 16.00 |
|---|---|---|---|---|
| a.-j. | | 80y Any single | 1.25 | .55 |

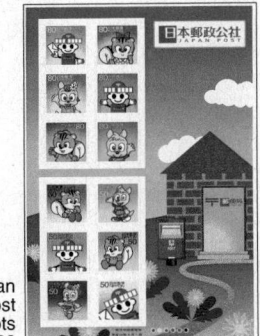

Japan Post Mascots A2183

Designs: a, Aichan (squirrel with pink bow). b, Male Kanchan (with heart on shorts). c, Posuton (with hands extended). d, Yuchan (squirrel with cap). e, Female Kanchan (with flower). f, Posuton (with letter). g, Posuton (with letter). h, Aichan (with pink bow), diff. i, Female Kanchan (with flower), diff. j, Posuton (with hands extended), diff. k, Yuchan (with cap), diff. l, Male Kanchan (waving).

**2003, Apr. 1    Die Cut Perf. 13¼**
**Self-Adhesive**

| 2854 | A2183 | Sheet of 12 | 16.00 | 16.00 |
|---|---|---|---|---|
| a.-f. | | 50y Any single | 1.25 | .40 |
| g.-l. | | 80y Any single | 1.50 | .55 |

Ram and Tree Batik Screen Design — A2184

**2003, Apr. 18    Perf. 13¼**

| 2855 | A2184 80y multi | 1.50 | .40 |
|---|---|---|---|

Philately Week.

**Greetings Type of 2003**

**2003    Photo.    Perf. 13**

| 2855A | A2180 80y Like No. 2851a + label | — |
|---|---|---|
| 2855B | A2179 80y Like No. 2850d + label | — |
| 2855D | A2179 80y Like No. 2850e + label | — |
| 2855E | A2180 80y Like No. 2851b + label | — |
| 2855F | A2180 80y Like No. 2851c + label | — |
| 2855H | A2180 80y Like No. 2851e + label | — |
| 2855I | A2179 80y Like No. 2850b + label | — |
| 2855J | A2179 80y Like No. 2850c + label | — |

Issued: Nos. 2855A, 2855B, 2855D, 4/19; Nos. 2855E, 2855F, 2855H, 2855I, 2855j, 6/11. Below each stamp was a label that could be personalized. Two additional stamps were

issued in this set. The editors would like to examine any examples.

**Edo Shogunate, 400th Anniv.**

Screen Depicting Edo A2185

Wall Decoration, Edo Castle A2186

Armor of Ieyasu Tokugawa A2187

Detail from Writing Box A2188

Noh Mask and Costume — A2189

Sheet 2
A2190

A2191

No. 2857 — Sheet 2: a, Nihonbashi, from 53 Stations of the Tokaido Road, by Hiroshige (stamp 1). b, Fireman's coat (stamp 2). c, Screen depicting Kabuki theater (stamp 3). d, Hina-matsuri fesitval doll of empress (no number). e, Hina-matsuri festival doll of emperor (stamp 4). f, Danjurou Ichikawa playing role of Goro Takenuki (stamp 5).

No. 2858 — Sheet 3: a, Stern of USS Powhatan (stamp 1). b, Bow of USS Powhatan (no number). c, Screen art depicting return of Commodore Perry's fleet to Japan (stamp 2). d, Ceramic platter for export to Europe (stamp 3). e, Portrait of a European Woman, probably by Gennai Hiraga (stamp 4). f, Perpetual clock (stamp 5).

**2003    Perf. 13x13¼**

| 2856 | Vert. strip of 5 | 7.00 | 7.00 |
|---|---|---|---|
| a. | A2185 80y multi | 1.25 | .55 |
| b. | A2186 80y multi | 1.25 | .55 |
| c. | A2187 80y multi | 1.25 | .55 |
| d. | A2188 80y multi | 1.25 | .55 |
| e. | A2189 80y multi | 1.25 | .55 |
| | Sheet, 2 #2856 (Sheet 1) | 16.50 | 16.50 |

| 2857 | A2190 | Sheet of 10, #2857d- 2857e, 2 each #2857a-2857c, 2857f | 16.50 | 16.50 |
|---|---|---|---|---|
| a.-f. | | 80y Any single | 1.25 | .55 |
| 2858 | A2191 | Sheet of 10, #2858a- 2858b, 2 each #2858c-2858f | 16.50 | 16.50 |
| a.-f. | | 80y Any single | 1.25 | .55 |

Issued: No. 2856, 5/23; No. 2857, 6/12; No. 2858, 7/1. Sheet numbers are in center of arrows at top of sheet. Stamp numbers are in sheet margins.

ASEAN — Japan Exchange Year — A2192

No. 2859: a, Omar Ali Saifuddien Mosque, Brunei (stamp 1). b, Angkor Wat, Cambodia (stamp 2). c, Borobudur Temple, Indonesia (stamp 3). d, That Luang, Laos (stamp 4). e, Sultan Abdul Samad Building, Malaysia (stamp 5). f, Shwedagon Pagoda, Myanmar (stamp 6). g, Rice terraces, Philippines (stamp 7). h, Merlion Statue, Singapore (stamp 8). i, Wat Phra Kaeo, Thailand (stamp 9). j, Van Mieu, Viet Nam (stamp 10).

**2003, June 16    Photo.    Perf. 13x13¼**

| 2859 | A2192 | Sheet of 10 | 16.50 | 16.50 |
|---|---|---|---|---|
| a.-j. | | 80y Any single | 1.25 | .55 |

Letter Writing Day — A2193

Designs: No. 2860, Bear with guitar, bird. No. 2861, Monkey with letter. No. 2862, Crocodile with accordion, bird. No. 2863, Cat with camera, letter.

No. 2864: a, Hippopotamus with umbrella, flowers, birds (oval stamp). b, Parakeet with letter. c, Owl (round stamp). d, Bear with letter, bird (oval stamp). e, Elephant with flowers. f, Giraffe with letter (oval stamp). g, Rabbit with letter, flowers (semi-circular stamp). h, Lion with letter, lantern. i, Goat with letter. j, Gorilla with koala, bird and owl.

**2003, July 23    Photo.    Perf. 13x13¼**

| 2860 | A2193 50y multi | .80 | .35 |
|---|---|---|---|
| 2861 | A2193 50y multi | .80 | .35 |
| 2862 | A2193 50y multi | .80 | .35 |
| 2863 | A2193 50y multi | .80 | .35 |
| a. | Horiz. strip of 4, #2860-2863 | 4.00 | 2.25 |
| 2864 | Sheet of 10 | 16.50 | 16.50 |
| a.-j. | A2193 80y any single | 1.25 | .55 |
| k. | Booklet pane of 10, #2860-2863, 2 each #2864b, 2864h, 2864i | 13.00 | 13.00 |
| | Complete booklet, #2864k | 15.00 | |
| l. | Souvenir sheet, #2860, #2864b | 2.75 | 2.75 |

Nos. 2864a, 2864d and 2864f are 28x40mm; No. 2864c is 30mm in diameter; No. 2864g is 40x24mm.

**Intl. Letter Writing Week Type of 2000**

Hiroshige paintings from 53 Stations of the Tokaido Highway: 90y, Kawasaki. 110y, Miya. 130y, Otsu.

**2003, Oct. 6    Perf. 13¼**

| 2865 | A2119 90y multi | 1.75 | .45 |
|---|---|---|---|
| 2866 | A2119 110y multi | 2.25 | .65 |
| 2867 | A2119 130y multi | 2.50 | .65 |
| | Nos. 2865-2867 (3) | 6.50 | 1.65 |

See listing of No. 4448 for images of each Hiroshige print.

Cultural
Pioneers — A2194

Designs: No. 2868, Mokichi Saito (1882-1953), poet. No. 2869, Shibasaburo Kitasato (1853-1931), bacteriologist.

**Photo. & Engr.**

| | | | |
|---|---|---|---|
| **2003, Nov. 4** | | | **Perf. 13** |
| 2868 | A2194 80y multi | 1.40 | .40 |
| 2869 | A2194 80y multi | 1.40 | .40 |

See Nos. 2907-2909.

Reversion of the Amami
Islands to Japanese
Control, 50th
Anniv. — A2195

| | | | |
|---|---|---|---|
| **2003, Nov. 7** | | | **Photo.** |
| 2870 | A2195 80y multi | 1.50 | .40 |

A2196　　　　　　　A2197

New Year 2004 (Year of
the Monkey)
A2198　　A2199

| | | | |
|---|---|---|---|
| **2003, Nov. 14** | | | **Perf. 13x13¼** |
| 2871 | A2196 50y multi | 1.00 | .30 |
| 2872 | A2197 80y multi | 1.50 | .40 |

**Photo. & Litho.**
**Perf. 13½x13¼**

| | | | |
|---|---|---|---|
| 2873 | A2198 50y +3y multi | 1.25 | .40 |
| 2874 | A2199 80y +3y multi | 1.75 | .40 |
| | *Nos. 2871-2874 (4)* | 5.50 | 1.50 |

Sheets of two containing Nos. 2871-2872 were lottery prizes. Value, $2.75.

Happy Face　　　　　Sky —
— A2199a　　　　　A2199b

***Serpentine Die Cut 9¼x9***

| | | | |
|---|---|---|---|
| **2003, Dec. 1** | | | **Photo.** |

**Self-Adhesive**

2874A　A2199a 80y multi + label　2.00　1.25

***Serpentine Die Cut 6½x5½***

**Stamp + Label**

**Color of Japanese Inscription**

| | | | |
|---|---|---|---|
| 2874B | A2199b 80y blue | 2.00 | 1.25 |
| 2874C | A2199b 80y red orange | 2.00 | 1.25 |
| 2874D | A2199a 80y white | — | — |
| | *Nos. 2874A-2874C (3)* | 6.00 | 3.75 |

Stamps and labels are separated by a line of rouletting on Nos. 2874B-2874D. Labels could be personalized. No. 2874A was printed in sheets of 4 stamps and 4 labels that sold for 500y, and sheets of 10 stamps and 10 labels that sold for 1000y. Nos. 2874B-2874C were

printed in sheets containing five of each stamp and 10 labels that sold for 1000y. No. 2874D was printed in sheets of 10 and 10 labels and sold for 1000y.

Bubbles —　　　　　Bubbles —
A2199c　　　　　　A2199d

Rose — A2199e

***Serpentine Die Cut 6***

| | | | |
|---|---|---|---|
| **2004, Jan. 23** | | | **Photo.** |

**Self-Adhesive**

| | | | |
|---|---|---|---|
| 2874E | A2199c 50y multi + label | 1.75 | 1.25 |
| 2874F | A2199d 50y multi + label | 1.75 | 1.25 |
| 2874G | A2199e 90y multi + label | *2.50* | 1.50 |
| | *Nos. 2874E-2874G (3)* | 6.00 | 4.00 |

Stamps and labels are separated by a line of rouletting. Labels could be personalized. Nos. 2874E-2874F were printed in sheets containing ten of each stamp and 20 labels that sold for 1200y. No. 2874G was printed in a sheet of 20 stamps and 20 labels that sold for 2000y.

**Science, Technology and Animation**

Astro
Boy — A2200

Bowman
Doll — A2201

Hantaro
Nagaoka
A2202

H-II Rocket
A2203

Morph
3 — A2204

Astro
Boy — A2205

Astro
Boy — A2206

Astro
Boy — A2207

Super Jetter
A2208

Otomo
A2210

Stratospheric
Platform
Airship
A2212

Super Jetter
A2214

Japanese
Clock
A2209

KAZ
A2211

Super Jetter
A2213

Super Jetter
A2215

| | | | |
|---|---|---|---|
| **2003-2004** | **Photo.** | | **Perf. 13x13¼** |
| 2875 | Vert. strip of 5 | 8.00 | 8.00 |
| *a.* | A2200 80y multi | 1.25 | .50 |
| *b.* | A2201 80y multi | 1.25 | .50 |
| *c.* | A2202 80y multi | 1.25 | .50 |
| *d.* | A2203 80y multi | 1.25 | .50 |
| *e.* | A2204 80y multi | 1.25 | .50 |
| | Sheet, 2 #2875 | 17.50 | 17.50 |
| 2876 | Sheet, #2875b-2875e, 2 each #2876a-2876c | 17.50 | 17.50 |
| *a.* | A2205 80y multi | 1.25 | .50 |
| *b.* | A2206 80y multi | 1.25 | .50 |
| *c.* | A2207 80y multi | 1.25 | .50 |
| 2877 | Vert. strip of 5 | 8.00 | 8.00 |
| *a.* | A2208 80y multi | 1.25 | .50 |
| *b.* | A2209 80y multi | 1.25 | .50 |
| *c.* | A2210 80y multi | 1.25 | .50 |
| *d.* | A2211 80y multi | 1.25 | .50 |
| *e.* | A2212 80y multi | 1.25 | .50 |
| | Sheet, 2 #2875 | 17.50 | 17.50 |
| 2878 | Sheet, #2877b-2877e, 2 each #2878a-2878c | 17.50 | 17.50 |
| *a.* | A2213 80y multi | 1.25 | .50 |
| *b.* | A2214 80y multi | 1.25 | .50 |
| *c.* | A2215 80y multi | 1.25 | .50 |

Issued: Nos. 2875-2876, 12/16/03; Nos. 2877-2878, 1/23/04.

**Science, Technology and Animation**

Marvelous
Melmo and
Baby
A2216

Wooden
Microscope
A2218

Seishu
Hanaoka
(1760-1835),
Surgeon
A2217

Jokichi
Takamine
(1854-1922),
Chemist
A2219

Drug Delivery
System
A2220

Marvelous
Melmo with
Man
A2222

Science Ninja
Team
Gatchaman
A2224

OHSUMI
Satellite
A2226

Tissue and
Organ
Reproduction
A2228

Science Ninja
Team
Gatchaman
A2230

Marvelous
Melmo with
Mother
A2221

Marvelous
Melmo and
Others in
Bottle
A2223

Proposed
Perpetual
Motion
Machine of
Michitaka
Kume
A2225

Conducting
Polymer
A2227

Science Ninja
Team
Gatchaman
A2229

Science Ninja
Team
Gatchaman
A2231

| | | | |
|---|---|---|---|
| **2004** | **Photo.** | | **Perf. 13x13¼** |
| 2879 | Vert. strip of 5 | 8.00 | 8.00 |
| *a.* | A2216 80y multi | 1.25 | .50 |
| *b.* | A2217 80y multi | 1.25 | .50 |
| *c.* | A2218 80y multi | 1.25 | .50 |
| *d.* | A2219 80y multi | 1.25 | .50 |
| *e.* | A2220 80y multi | 1.25 | .50 |
| | Sheet, 2 #2879 | 17.50 | 17.50 |
| 2880 | Sheet, #2879b-2879e, 2 each #2880a-2880c | 17.50 | 17.50 |
| *a.* | A2221 80y multi | 1.25 | .50 |
| *b.* | A2222 80y multi | 1.25 | .50 |
| *c.* | A2223 80y multi | 1.25 | .50 |
| 2881 | Vert. strip of 5 | 8.00 | 8.00 |
| *a.* | A2224 80y multi | 1.25 | .50 |
| *b.* | A2225 80y multi | 1.25 | .50 |
| *c.* | A2226 80y multi | 1.25 | .50 |
| *d.* | A2227 80y multi | 1.25 | .50 |
| *e.* | A2228 80y multi | 1.25 | .50 |
| | Sheet, 2 #2881 | 17.50 | 17.50 |

| 2882 | Sheet, #2881b-2881e, 2 each | | |
|---|---|---|---|
|  | #2882a-2882c | 17.50 | 17.50 |
| a. | A2229 80y multi | 1.25 | .50 |
| b. | A2230 80y multi | 1.25 | .50 |
| c. | A2231 80y multi | 1.25 | .50 |

Issued: Nos. 2879-2880, 2/23/04. Nos. 2881-2882, 3/23/04.

Hello Kitty

売価 500円
©1976, 2004 SANRIO CO., LTD.

A2232

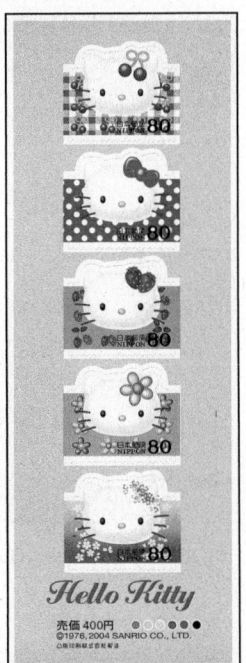

Hello Kitty
A2233

売価 400円
©1976, 2004 SANRIO CO., LTD.

No. 2883: a, Red, white and blue flowers under chin. b, Red flower under chin, beige background. c, No flower under chin. d, Blue and red flowers under chin. e, Red flower under chin. f, Two blue flowers under chin. g, White flowers with green leaves under chin. h, Two pink flowers under chin. i, One blue flower under chin. j, Pink, yellow and green flower under chin.
No. 2884 — Head of Kitty with: a, Cherries. b, Bow. c, Strawberries. d, Blue flower. e, Spray of flowers.

**Die Cut Perf. 13¼**
**2004, Feb. 6          Litho.**
**Self-Adhesive**

| 2883 | A2232 Sheet of 10 | 9.50 | 9.50 |
|---|---|---|---|
| a.-j. | 50y Any single | .80 | .80 |
| 2884 | A2233 Sheet of 5 | 7.00 | 7.00 |
| a.-e. | 80y Any single | 1.25 | .80 |

Uchu-no Sakura Gohiki-no Saru-zu, by Sosen Mori — A2234

**Perf. 12½x12¾ Syncopated**
**2004, Apr. 20          Photo.**
2885  A2234  80y multi          1.50  .45

Philatelic Week.

Japanese Racing Association, 50th Anniv. — A2235

Designs: No. 2886, Ten Point and Tosho Boy, 22nd Armia Memorial Stakes. No. 2887, Narita Brian, 61st Tolyo Yushun.

**2004, May 28          Perf. 13x13¼**
| 2886 | 80y green & multi | 1.25 | .45 |
|---|---|---|---|
| 2887 | 80y blue & multi | 1.25 | .45 |
| a. | A2235 Horiz. pair, #2886-2887 | 3.00 | 2.25 |

Police Law, 50th Anniv. A2236

**2004, June 21          Perf. 13**
| 2888 | 80y Police car | 1.25 | .45 |
|---|---|---|---|
| 2889 | 80y Police motorcycle | 1.25 | .45 |
| a. | A2236 Horiz. pair, #2888-2889 | 3.00 | 2.25 |

Letter Writing Day — A2237

Designs: No. 2890, Donkichi with pencil. No. 2891, Hime (woman with letter). No. 2892, Shouchan (man with ski cap). No. 2893, Owl with letter.
No. 2894: a, Dove with letter, rainbow. b, Squirrel with wings, rainbow. c, Stork (round stamp). d, Hime with wings (oval stamp). e, Donkichi with wings, letter. f, Kuriko (elf in pink) with wings. g, Megami (woman in white) (oval stamp). h, Shouchan with wings. i, Squirrel with flowers, letter. j, Rabbit (round stamp).

**2004, July 23   Photo.   Perf. 13x13¼**
| 2890 | A2237 50y multi | .80 | .25 |
|---|---|---|---|
| 2891 | A2237 50y multi | .80 | .25 |
| 2892 | A2237 50y multi | .80 | .25 |
| 2893 | A2237 50y multi | .80 | .25 |
| a. | Horiz. strip of 4, #2890-2893 | 4.00 | 2.75 |
| 2894 | Sheet of 10 | 16.50 | 16.50 |
| a.-j. | A2237 Any single | 1.25 | .55 |
| k. | Booklet pane of 10, #2890-2893, 2 each #2894b, 2894e, 2894f | 14.00 | — |
|  | Complete booklet, #2894k | 15.00 |  |
| l. | Souvenir sheet, #2890, #2894f | 2.75 | 2.75 |

Nos. 2894c, 2894j are 30mm in diameter; No. 2894d is 28x37mm; No. 2894g is 28x40mm; No. 2894i is 28x29mm.

2004 Summer Olympics, Athens A2238

Olympic rings and: No. 2895, Olympic Flame, Olympia. No. 2896, 2004 Athens Olympics emblem.

**2004, Aug. 6          Perf. 13**
| 2895 | 80y multi | 1.25 | .45 |
|---|---|---|---|
| 2896 | 80y multi | 1.25 | .45 |
| a. | A2238 Horiz. pair, #2895-2896 | 3.00 | 2.25 |

**Science, Technology and Animation**

Mazinger-Z A2239

Steam Locomotive A2240

New KS Steel A2241

Shinkai 6500 Research Submarine A2242

Fuel Cell A2243

Mazinger-Z A2244

Mazinger-Z A2245

Mazinger-Z A2246

**2004, Aug. 23   Photo.   Perf. 13x13¼**
| 2897 | Vert. strip of 5 | 8.00 | 8.00 |
|---|---|---|---|
| a. | A2239 80y multi | 1.25 | .40 |
| b. | A2240 80y multi | 1.25 | .40 |
| c. | A2241 80y multi | 1.25 | .40 |
| d. | A2242 80y multi | 1.25 | .40 |
| e. | A2243 80y multi | 1.25 | .40 |
|  | Sheet, 2 #2897 | 17.50 | 17.50 |
| 2898 | Sheet, #2897b-2897e, 2 each #2898a-2898c | 17.50 | 17.50 |
| a. | A2244 80y multi | 1.25 | .40 |
| b. | A2245 80y multi | 1.25 | .40 |
| c. | A2246 80y multi | 1.25 | .40 |

**Science, Technology and Animation**

Doraemon A2247

Gennai Hiraga A2248

Mechanical Netsuke A2249

Television A2250

Optical Fiber A2251

Doraemon A2252

Doraemon A2253

Doraemon A2254

**2004, Nov. 22   Photo.   Perf. 13x13¼**
| 2899 | Vert. strip of 5 | 8.00 | 8.00 |
|---|---|---|---|
| a. | A2247 80y multi | 1.25 | .40 |
| b. | A2248 80y multi | 1.25 | .40 |
| c. | A2249 80y multi | 1.25 | .40 |
| d. | A2250 80y multi | 1.25 | .40 |
| e. | A2251 80y multi | 1.25 | .40 |
|  | Sheet, 2 #2899 | 17.50 | 17.50 |
| 2900 | Sheet, #2899b-2899e, 2 each #2900a-2900c | 17.50 | 17.50 |
| a. | A2252 80y multi | 1.25 | .40 |
| b. | A2253 80y multi | 1.25 | .40 |
| c. | A2254 80y multi | 1.25 | .40 |

Japan — United States Relationships, 150th Anniv. — A2255

Designs: No. 2901, Mt. Fuji, by Frederick Harris. No. 2902, Cafe, by Yasuo Kuniyoshi.

**2004, Sept. 22          Perf. 13**
| 2901 | 80y multi | 1.25 | .50 |
|---|---|---|---|
| 2902 | 80y multi | 1.25 | .50 |
| a. | A2255 Horiz. pair, #2901-2902 | 3.00 | 2.25 |

World Medical Association General Assembly, Tokyo — A2256

**2004, Oct. 6          Perf. 12¾x13**
2903  A2256  80y multi          1.50  .40

**International Letter Writing Week Type of 2000**

Hiroshige paintings from 53 Stations of the Tokaido Highway: 90y, Hiratsuka. 110y, Yokkaichi. 130y, Tsuchiyama.

**2004, Oct. 8          Perf. 13¼**
| 2904 | A2119 90y multi | 1.75 | .45 |
|---|---|---|---|
| 2905 | A2119 110y multi | 2.25 | .55 |
| 2906 | A2119 130y multi | 2.50 | .65 |
|  | Nos. 2904-2906 (3) | 6.50 | 1.65 |

See listing of No. 4448 for images of each Hiroshige print.

**Cultural Pioneers Type of 2003**

Designs: No. 2907, Lafcadio Hearn (1850-1904), writer. No. 2908, Isamu Noguchi (1904-88), sculptor. No. 2909, Masao Koga (1904-78), composer.

**Litho. & Engr.**
**2004, Nov. 4          Perf. 12¾x13**
| 2907 | A2194 80y multi | 1.50 | .40 |
|---|---|---|---|
| 2908 | A2194 80y multi | 1.50 | .40 |
| 2909 | A2194 80y multi | 1.50 | .40 |
|  | Nos. 2907-2909 (3) | 4.50 | 1.20 |

A2257

A2258

New Year 2005 (Year of the Cock)
A2259      A2260

**2004, Nov. 15   Photo.   Perf. 13x13¼**

| | | | | |
|---|---|---|---|---|
| 2910 | A2257 | 50y multi | 1.00 | .30 |
| 2911 | A2258 | 80y multi | 1.50 | .40 |

**Photo. & Typo.   Perf. 13½x13¼**

| | | | | |
|---|---|---|---|---|
| 2912 | A2259 | 50y +3y multi | 1.25 | .40 |
| 2913 | A2260 | 80y +3y multi | 1.75 | .40 |
| | | Nos. 2910-2913 (4) | 5.50 | 1.50 |

Sheets of two containing Nos. 2910-2911 were lottery prizes. Value, $2.75.

**Miniature Sheet**

Eto Calligraphy — A2261

Word "tori" in: a, Tensho style. b, Kinbun style (red). c, Kinbun style (black). d, Pictographic tensho style. e, Kana style. f, Sousho style. g, Kobun style (denomination at UR). h, Reisho style. i, Koukotsumoji style. j, Kobun style (denomination at LR).

**Photo. & Embossed**
**2004, Dec. 1                     Perf. 13**

| | | | | |
|---|---|---|---|---|
| 2914 | A2261 | Sheet of 10 | 25.00 | 20.00 |
| a.-j. | | 80y Any single | 1.25 | .50 |

"Japan Post" —
A2261a            A2261b

A2261c            Rose —
                  A2261d

A2261e            A2261f

*Die Cut Perf. 12½*

**2004, Dec. 15                     Photo.**
**Stamp + Label**

| | | Denomination | Color | | |
|---|---|---|---|---|---|
| 2914K | A2261a | 80y | rose | 3.00 | 1.25 |
| 2914L | A2261a | 80y | blue | 3.00 | 1.25 |
| 2914M | A2261b | 80y | lilac | 3.00 | 2.00 |
| 2914N | A2261c | 80y | green | 3.00 | 2.00 |
| 2914O | A2261d | 80y | rose | 3.00 | 2.00 |
| 2914P | A2261e | 80y | gray | 3.00 | 2.00 |
| 2914Q | A2261f | 80y | rose | 3.00 | 2.00 |
| | | Nos. 2914K-2914Q (7) | | 21.00 | 12.50 |

Stamps and labels are separated by a line of rouletting. Labels could be personalized. Nos. 2914K-2914L were printed in sheets containing five of each stamp and 10 labels that sold for 1000y. Nos. 2914M-2914Q were printed in sheets of two of each stamp and 10 labels that sold for 1000y.

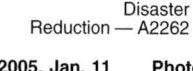

World Conference on Disaster Reduction — A2262

**2005, Jan. 11   Photo.   Perf. 13**

| | | | | |
|---|---|---|---|---|
| 2915 | A2262 | 80y multi | 1.50 | .40 |

Opening of Chubu Natl. Airport — A2263

**2005, Feb. 1**

| | | | | |
|---|---|---|---|---|
| 2916 | A2263 | 80y multi | 1.50 | .40 |

**Science, Technology and Animation**

Time Bokan            Circular Loom
A2264                 A2265

Bullet Train          Micromachines
A2266                 A2267

International          Time Bokan
Space Station         A2269
A2268

 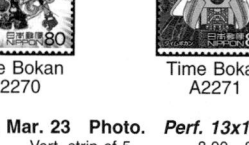

Time Bokan            Time Bokan
A2270                 A2271

**2005, Mar. 23   Photo.   Perf. 13x13¼**

| | | | | |
|---|---|---|---|---|
| 2917 | | Vert. strip of 5 | 8.00 | 8.00 |
| a. | A2264 | 80y multi | 1.25 | .50 |
| b. | A2265 | 80y multi | 1.25 | .50 |
| c. | A2266 | 80y multi | 1.25 | .50 |
| d. | A2267 | 80y multi | 1.25 | .50 |
| e. | A2268 | 80y multi | 1.25 | .50 |
| | | Sheet, 2 #2917 | 17.50 | 17.50 |
| 2918 | | Sheet, #2917b-2917e, 2 each #2918a-2918c | 17.50 | 17.50 |
| a. | A2269 | 80y multi | 1.25 | .50 |
| b. | A2270 | 80y multi | 1.25 | .50 |
| c. | A2271 | 80y multi | 1.25 | .50 |

**Pokémon**

Gonbe                 Rayquaza
A2272                 A2273

Mew                   Rizadon
A2274                 A2275

Pikachu — A2276

**2005, June 23   Litho.   Perf. 13x13¼**

| | | | | |
|---|---|---|---|---|
| 2919 | | Vert. strip of 5 | 6.50 | 6.50 |
| a. | A2272 | 50y multi | .80 | .50 |
| b. | A2273 | 50y multi | .80 | .50 |
| c. | A2274 | 80y multi | 1.25 | .50 |
| d. | A2275 | 80y multi | 1.25 | .50 |
| e. | A2276 | 80y multi | 1.25 | .50 |
| | | Sheet, 2 #2919 | 22.00 | 20.00 |

**Self-Adhesive**
**Booklet Stamps**

| | | | | |
|---|---|---|---|---|
| 2919F | A2272 | 50y multi | 1.00 | .50 |
| i. | | Booklet pane of 2 | 2.75 | 2.75 |
| 2919G | A2276 | 80y multi | 1.25 | .50 |
| 2919H | A2274 | 80y multi | 1.25 | .50 |
| j. | | Booklet pane, #2919G-2919H | 3.00 | 3.00 |
| | | Complete booklet, #2919Fi, 2919Hj + 8 postal cards | 14.00 | |

Complete booklet sold for 1000y.

**Mobile Suit Gundam**

Freedom               Justice
Gundam and            Gundam and
Kira Yamato           Athrun Zala
A2277                 A2278

Gundam                Hiiro — A2280
W — A2279

Kamille Bidan         Z Gundam
A2281                 A2282

Zaku                  Char Aznable
A2283                 A2284

Amuro Ray             Gundam
A2285                 A2286

**2005, Aug. 1**

| | | | | |
|---|---|---|---|---|
| 2920 | | Sheet of 10 | 22.00 | 22.00 |
| a. | A2277 | 50y multi | .80 | .50 |
| b. | A2278 | 50y multi | .80 | .50 |
| c. | A2279 | 50y multi | .80 | .50 |
| d. | A2280 | 50y multi | .80 | .50 |
| e. | A2281 | 80y multi | 1.25 | .50 |
| f. | A2282 | 80y multi | 1.25 | .50 |
| g. | A2283 | 80y multi | 1.25 | .50 |
| h. | A2284 | 80y multi | 1.25 | .50 |
| i. | A2285 | 80y multi | 1.25 | .50 |
| j. | A2286 | 80y multi | 1.25 | .50 |

Expo 2005, Aichi A2287

Designs: No. 2921, Earth and mammoth skull and tusks. No. 2922, Earth and mammoth.

**2005, Mar. 25   Photo.   Perf. 13x13¼**

| | | | | |
|---|---|---|---|---|
| 2921 | | 80y multi | 1.25 | .45 |
| 2922 | | 80y multi | 1.25 | .45 |
| a. | A2287 | Horiz. pair, #2921-2922 | 3.00 | 2.25 |

Daikei-shiyu-zu, by Jakuchu Itou — A2288

*Perf. 12½x12¾ Syncopated*
**2005, Apr. 20**

| | | | | |
|---|---|---|---|---|
| 2923 | A2288 | 80y multi | 1.50 | .45 |

Philately Week.

Rotary International, Cent. — A2289

**2005, Apr. 28   Litho.   Perf. 12¾x13**

| | | | | |
|---|---|---|---|---|
| 2924 | A2289 | 80y multi | 1.50 | .40 |

Hodakadake
A2290

Hakusan-
ichige
A2291

Yarigatake
A2292

Miyama-
odamaki
A2293

**2005, May 2**     **Perf. 13¼**
| | | | |
|---|---|---|---|
| 2925 | A2290 | 50y multi | .80 | .30 |
| 2926 | A2291 | 50y multi | .80 | .30 |
| 2927 | A2292 | 50y multi | .80 | .30 |
| 2928 | A2293 | 50y multi | .80 | .30 |
| a. | | Horiz. strip of 4, #2925-2928 | 4.00 | 2.00 |

Japanese Alpine Club, cent.

Letter Writing
Day — A2294

Designs: No. 2929, Owl on branch with envelope. No. 2930, Kuriko with letter. No. 2931, Squirrel with acorn. No. 2932, Rabbit and flowers.

No. 2933: a, Pigeon with pink letter. b, Donkichi in tree (round stamp). c, Castle and rainbow (oval stamp). d, Shochan with blue ski cap. e, Rabbit with pink letter (round stamp). f, Kuriko with flute on horse. g, Hime with bows in hair. h, Squirrel. i, Fox with letter (round stamp). j, Violets (oval stamp).

**2005, July 22**   **Photo.**   **Perf. 13x13¼**
| | | | |
|---|---|---|---|
| 2929 | A2294 | 50y multi | .80 | .30 |
| 2930 | A2294 | 50y multi | .80 | .30 |
| 2931 | A2294 | 50y multi | .80 | .30 |
| 2932 | A2294 | 50y multi | .80 | .30 |
| a. | | Horiz. strip of 4, #2929-2932 | 4.00 | 2.00 |
| 2933 | | Sheet of 10 | 13.00 | 13.00 |
| a.-j. | | A2294 80y Any single | 1.25 | .50 |
| k. | | Booklet pane of 10, #2929-2932, 2 each #2933d, 2933f, 2933g | 13.00 | — |
| | | Complete booklet, #2933k | 14.00 | |
| l. | | Souvenir sheet, #2932, #2933d | 2.75 | 2.75 |

Nos. 2933a, 2933h are 28x29mm, Nos. 2933b, 2933e, 2933i are 30mm in diameter; No. 2933c, 2933j are 28x40mm.

Poetry Collections — A2295

Poets: No. 2934, Ono no Komachi. No. 2935, Fujiwara no Teika.

**2005, Sept. 1**   **Litho.**   **Perf. 12¾x13**
| | | | |
|---|---|---|---|
| 2934 | | 80y multi | 1.25 | .45 |
| 2935 | | 80y multi | 1.25 | .45 |
| a. | | A2295 Horiz. pair, #2934-2935 | 3.00 | 2.25 |

Kokin Wakashu, 1100th anniv. (No. 2934), Shinkokin Wakashu, 800th anniv. (No. 2935).

Intl Astronautics Congress,
Fukuoka — A2296

Designs: No. 2936, Himawari-6 satellite. No. 2937, H-IIA rocket launch.

**2005, Oct. 3**
| | | | |
|---|---|---|---|
| 2936 | | 80y multi | 1.25 | .50 |
| 2937 | | 80y multi | 1.25 | .50 |
| a. | | A2296 Horiz. pair, #2934-2935 | 3.00 | 2.25 |

### Intl. Letter Writing Week Type of 2000

Hiroshige paintings from 53 Stations of the Tokaido Highway: 90y, Mariko. 110y, Minakuchi. 130y, Shinagawa.

**2005, Oct. 7**   **Photo.**   **Perf. 13¼**
| | | | |
|---|---|---|---|
| 2938 | A2119 | 90y multi | 1.75 | .50 |
| 2939 | A2119 | 110y multi | 2.25 | .50 |
| 2940 | A2119 | 130y multi | 2.50 | .50 |
| | | Nos. 2938-2940 (3) | 6.50 | 1.50 |

See listing of No. 4448 for images of each Hiroshige print.

### Souvenir Sheets

A2297

Greetings Stamps — A2298

No. 2941: a, Cyclamen. b, Elf and flower. c, Bear and bird. d, Owl, gorilla playing banjo. e, Snowman.
No. 2942: a, Santa Claus. b, Poinsettias and candle. c, Angel with gift. d, Hamster and strawberries. e, Owl, cat playing drums.

### Litho. With Foil Application
*Serpentine Die Cut 13¼*
**2005, Oct. 21**     **Self-Adhesive**
| | | | |
|---|---|---|---|
| 2941 | A2297 | Sheet of 5 | 6.00 | 6.00 |
| a.-e. | | 50y Any single | .80 | .80 |

*Serpentine Die Cut 13¼x13½*
| | | | |
|---|---|---|---|
| 2942 | A2298 | Sheet of 5 | 10.00 | 10.00 |
| a.-e. | | 80y Any single | 1.25 | .80 |

A2299

A2300

New Year 2006 (Year of
the Dog)
A2301     A2302

**2005, Nov. 15**   **Photo.**   **Perf. 13x13¼**
| | | | |
|---|---|---|---|
| 2943 | A2299 | 50y multi | 1.00 | .30 |
| 2944 | A2300 | 80y multi | 1.50 | .40 |

**Photo. & Typo.**
*Perf. 13¼*
| | | | |
|---|---|---|---|
| 2945 | A2301 | 50y +3y multi | 1.25 | .40 |
| 2946 | A2302 | 80y +3y multi | 1.75 | .40 |
| | | Nos. 2943-2946 (4) | 5.50 | 1.50 |

Sheets of two containing Nos. 2943-2944 were lottery prizes. Value, $2.75.

### Miniature Sheet

Germany — Japan Exchange
Year — A2303

No. 2947: a, Ludwig van Beethoven. b, Benz automobile. c, Meissen porcelain figurine of Japanese man playing drum. d, Meissen porcelain figurine of female musician. e, Meissen porcelain figurine of woman on circus horse. f, Meissen porcelain figurine of a harlequin.

**2005, Dec. 1**   **Photo.**   **Perf. 13**
| | | | |
|---|---|---|---|
| 2947 | A2303 | Sheet of 10, #a-b, 2 each #c-f | 16.00 | 16.00 |
| a.-f. | | 80y Any single | 1.25 | .50 |

### Miniature Sheet

Eto Calligraphy — A2304

Word "inu" in: a, Tensho style (connected lines). b, Kinbun style (on brown red panel). c, Pictograph (denomination at UL). d, Phonetic letters (2 lines unconnected, denomination at LR). e, Tensho style (2 red chops). f, Tensho style (blue half-circle). g, Symbolic characters (red). h, Semi-cursive style (red chop at L, denomination at LL). i, Semi-cursive style (oval chop in red at L). j, Koukotsumoji style (denomination at L, red chop at R).

**Photo. & Embossed**
**2005, Dec. 1**     **Perf. 13x13¼**
| | | | |
|---|---|---|---|
| 2948 | A2304 | Sheet of 10 | 16.00 | 16.00 |
| a.-j. | | 80y Any single | 1.25 | .50 |

### Animation

Galaxy
Express
999
A2305

No. 2949: a, Tetsuro and Galaxy Express 999 in flight. b, Matael and passenger cars. c, Claire holding book. d, The Conductor. e, Freija and Matael. f, Tetsuro and Moriki Yutaka. g, Emeraldas and Count Mecha. h, Herlock. i, Matael and galaxy. j, Galaxy Express 999.

**2006, Feb. 1**   **Litho.**   **Perf. 13x13¼**
| | | | |
|---|---|---|---|
| 2949 | A2305 | Sheet of 10 | 27.50 | 20.00 |
| a.-j. | | 80y Any single | 1.25 | .50 |

Detective
Conan
A2306

No. 2950: a, Conan in green jacket. b, Conan wearing glasses, with woman in light blue jacket. c, With Shinichi, scratching chins. d, Ran holding letter. e, Dr. Agasa, Ayumi, front of car. f, Mitushiko, Genta, rear of car. g, Haibara Ai. h, Conan with backpack. i, Mysterious Thief Kid. j, Shinichi and Conan, city in background.

**2006, Apr. 3**   **Litho.**   **Perf. 13x13¼**
| | | | |
|---|---|---|---|
| 2950 | A2306 | Sheet of 10 | 22.50 | 20.00 |
| a.-j. | | 80y Any single | 1.25 | .50 |

International
Exchanges and
Friendships — A2307

Designs: No. 2951, Rabbit and flowers. No. 2952, Children kissing. No. 2953, Bears and caught fish. No. 2954, Children's drawing of two animals. No. 2955, Chick, cat, dog, rabbit, squirrel and rocket.

**2006, Mar. 1**   **Photo.**   **Perf. 13**
| | | | |
|---|---|---|---|
| 2951 | A2307 | 80y multi | 1.25 | .50 |
| 2952 | A2307 | 80y multi | 1.25 | .50 |
| 2953 | A2307 | 80y multi | 1.25 | .50 |
| 2954 | A2307 | 80y multi | 1.25 | .50 |
| 2955 | A2307 | 80y multi | 1.25 | .50 |
| a. | | Vert. strip of 5, #2951-2955 | 8.50 | 5.00 |
| | | Sheet, 2 each #2951-2955 | 17.50 | 17.50 |

Morning Glories and Puppies, Door
Painting by Okyu Maruyama — A2308

Designs: No. 2956, Morning glories. No. 2957, Puppies.

*Perf. 13½x13 Syncopated*
**2006, Apr. 20**     **Photo.**
| | | | |
|---|---|---|---|
| 2956 | | 80y multi | 1.25 | .50 |
| 2957 | | 80y multi | 1.25 | .50 |
| a. | | A2308 Horiz. pair, #2956-2957 | 4.00 | 2.00 |

Philately Week.

## Miniature Sheet

Australia-Japan Year of
Exchange — A2309

No. 2958: a, Australian flag, Ayers Rock. b, Kangaroo and Ayers Rock. c, Sydney Opera House. d, Australian flag and Sydney Opera House. e, Fish of Great Barrier Reef. f, Heart Reef. g, Golden wattle flowers. h, Bottlebrush flowers. i, Koalas. j, Kookaburra.

| | | | | |
|---|---|---|---|---|
| **2006, May 23** | | **Photo.** | | **Perf. 13** |
| 2958 | A2309 | Sheet of 10 | 16.00 | 16.00 |
| a.-j. | 80y Any single | | 1.25 | .50 |

## Miniature Sheet

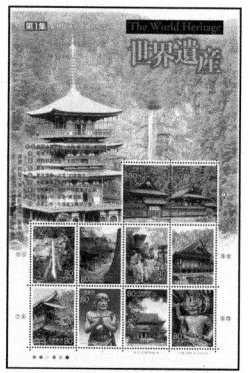

Sacred Sites and Pilgrimage Routes of
the Kii Mountains World Heritage
Site — A2310

No. 2959: a, Kumano Hongu-Taisha Shrine Building 3 (brown roof, part of stairs seen at bottom). b, Kumano Hongu-Taisha Shrine Building 4 (brown roof, full set of stairs at LR). c, Great Waterfall of Nachi. d, Overhead view of Kumano Nachi-Taisha Shrine (denomination at LL). e, Nachi Fire Festival. f, Seigantoji Temple (dark blue roof). g, Kongobuji Temple (blue green roof). h, Wooden Kongara-Doji-Ryuzo (statue, denomination at UL). i, Kinpusenji Temple (gray roof). j, Wooden Zao-Gongen-Ryuzo (statue, denomination at LL).

| | | | | |
|---|---|---|---|---|
| **2006, June 23** | | | | **Perf. 13x13¼** |
| 2959 | A2310 | Sheet of 10 | 17.50 | 17.50 |
| a.-j. | 80y Any single | | 1.25 | .50 |

## Miniature Sheets

A2311

Greetings Stamps — A2312

No. 2960: a, Fairy and flower. b, Church bell. c, Flower bouquet and ribbons. d, Dolphin. e, Hibiscus and hummingbird.
No. 2961: a, Pink cattleya orchid. b, Fairy, flowers and trees. c, Flower and oranges. d, Parrot and flowers. e, Fairy with pail and orange flowers.

### Litho. With Foil Application
*Serpentine Die Cut 13¼*

| | | | | |
|---|---|---|---|---|
| **2006, June 30** | | | | **Self-Adhesive** |
| 2960 | A2311 | Sheet of 5 | 6.00 | 6.00 |
| a.-e. | 50y Any single | | .80 | .80 |

*Serpentine Die Cut 13½*

| | | | | |
|---|---|---|---|---|
| 2961 | A2312 | Sheet of 5 | 10.00 | 10.00 |
| a.-e. | 80y Any single | | 1.25 | .80 |

No. 2960 sold for 300y; No. 2961 for 500y.

Taifu Iseno,
Poet
A2313

Sadaijin
Gotokudaijino,
Poet
A2314

Mitsune
Ooshikochino,
Poet
A2315

Akahito
Yamabeno,
Poet
A2316

Naishi Suono,
Poet — A2317

Poets
and
Poetry
A2318

No. 2963: a, Double Cherry Blossoms, by Yasuko Koyama. b, Iseno and poetry. c, Pale Morning Moon, by Keiso Mitsuoka. d, Gotokudaijino and poetry. e, White Chrysanthemum, by Shiko Miyazaki. f, Ooshikochino and poetry. g, Mt. Fuji, by Eiko Matsumoto. h, Yamabeno and poetry. i, Spring Night, by Soshu Miyake. j, Suono and poetry.

| | | | | |
|---|---|---|---|---|
| **2006, July 21** | | **Photo.** | | **Perf. 13¼** |
| 2962 | | Vert. strip of 5 | 5.00 | 3.50 |
| a. | A2313 | 50y multi | .80 | .30 |
| b. | A2314 | 50y multi | .80 | .30 |
| c. | A2315 | 50y multi | .80 | .30 |
| d. | A2316 | 50y multi | .80 | .30 |
| e. | A2317 | 50y multi | .80 | .30 |
| | | Sheet, 2 #2962 | 13.00 | 13.00 |

*Perf. 13*

| | | | | |
|---|---|---|---|---|
| 2963 | A2318 | Sheet of 10 | 16.00 | 16.00 |
| a.-j. | 80y Any single | | 1.25 | .50 |

Letter Writing Day.

Horizontal Lines and
Colored Circles —
A2318a

### Die Cut Perf. 13¼

| | | | | |
|---|---|---|---|---|
| **2006, Sept. 1** | | | | **Litho.** |
| **Self-Adhesive** | | | | |
| 2963K | A2318a | 80y multi | 1.50 | .50 |

Printed in sheets of 10 that sold for 1000y. Value, $22.50. The image portion could be personalized. The image shown is a generic image.

Blue Flowers —
A2318b

Pink Flowers —
A2318c

### Die Cut Perf. 13¼

| | | | | |
|---|---|---|---|---|
| **2006, Sept. 1** | | | | **Litho.** |
| **Self-Adhesive** | | | | |
| 2963L | A2318b | 80y multi | 1.25 | .50 |
| 2963M | A2318c | 80y multi | 1.25 | .50 |

Nos. 2963L-2963M were printed in sheets of 10, containing five of each stamp, that sold for 1000y. Value, $22.50. The image portions could be personalized. The images shown are generic images.

Accession to
the United
Nations, 50th
Anniv.
A2319

Paintings by Toshiro Sawanuki: 90y, Glorious World To Come. 110y, Eternity.

| | | | | |
|---|---|---|---|---|
| **2006, Sept. 29** | | **Litho.** | | **Perf. 13¾x14** |
| 2964 | A2319 | 90y multi | 1.75 | .50 |
| 2965 | A2319 | 110y multi | 2.25 | .50 |

## Miniature Sheet

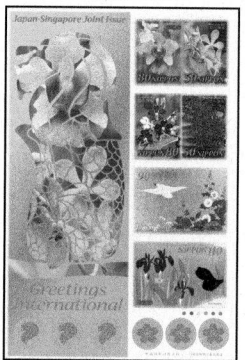

Greetings — A2320

No. 2966: a, Mokara Lion's Gold orchid. b, Renanthera Singaporean orchid. c, Vanda Miss Joaquim orchid. d, Vanda Mimi Palmer orchid. e, Hollyhocks and Egret, by Hoitsu Sakai, horiz. f, Irises and Moorhens, by Sakai, horiz.

### Litho. With Foil Application
| | | | | |
|---|---|---|---|---|
| **2006, Oct. 3** | | *Die Cut Perf. 13½x13¾* | | |
| **Self-Adhesive** | | | | |
| 2966 | A2320 | Sheet of 6 | 10.00 | *10.00* |
| a.-b. | 50y Either single | | .80 | .80 |
| c.-d. | 80y Either single | | 1.25 | .80 |
| e. | 90y multi | | 1.40 | .80 |
| f. | 110y multi | | 1.75 | .80 |

Roulettes separate adjacent 50y and 80y stamps. No. 2966 sold for 500y. See Singapore Nos. 1225-1231.

## Miniature Sheets

A2321

Scenes From Japanese
Movies — A2322

No. 2967: a, Tange Sazen (scarred samurai, green). b, Carmen Kokyo-Ni-Kaeru (women waving, lilac). c, Ugetsu Monogatari (man and woman, maroon). d, Tokyo Monogatari (man and woman, brown). e, Shichinin-No-Samurai (helmeted samurai, deep green). f, Hawaii-No-Yoru (man and woman, olive green). g, Nemuri Kyoshiro (samurai, blue green). h, Guitar-Wo-Motta-Wataridori (man with guitar, blue). i, Miyamoto Musashi (swordsman, blue gray). j, Cupola-No-Aru-Machi (girl, brown).
No. 2968: a, Sailor-Fuku-To-Kikanju (woman with gun). b, Otoko-Ha-Tsuraiyo (man in light blue kimono). c, Kamata Koshin Kyoku (Three people). d, Yomigaeru Kinro (man in chair). e, Setouchi-Shonen-Yakyu-Dan (woman with baseball glove). f, HANA-BI (man standing). g, Shitsurakuen (Woman hugging man). h, Gamera (monster, denomination at UL). i, Tasogare Seibei (woman grooming man). j, Godzilla (monster, denomination at UR).

| | | | | |
|---|---|---|---|---|
| **2006, Oct. 10** | | **Photo.** | | **Perf. 13** |
| 2967 | A2321 | Sheet of 10 | 17.50 | 17.50 |
| a.-j. | 80y Any single | | 1.25 | .50 |
| 2968 | A2322 | Sheet of 10 | 17.50 | 17.50 |
| a.-j. | 80y Any single | | 1.25 | .50 |

Ikebana
International
Ninth World
Convention
A2323

| | | | | |
|---|---|---|---|---|
| **2006, Oct. 23** | | **Litho.** | | **Perf. 13x13¼** |
| **Background Colors** | | | | |
| 2969 | 80y grn & lt grn | | 1.25 | .50 |
| 2970 | 80y red & yel | | 1.25 | .50 |
| a. | A2323 | Pair, #2969-2970 | 3.00 | 2.00 |

A2324

A2325

New Year 2007 (Year of the Pig)

A2326          A2327

**2006, Nov. 1    Photo.      Perf. 13x13¼**
2971  A2324  50y multi           1.00   .30
2972  A2325  80y multi           1.50   .40

**Photo. & Typo.**
**Perf. 13¼**
2973  A2326  50y +3y multi       1.25   .40
2974  A2327  80y +3y multi       1.75   .40
     Nos. 2971-2974 (4)          5.50  1.50

Sheets of two containing Nos. 2971-2972 were lottery prizes. Value, $3.

New Year Greetings — A2327a

Inscribed "'07 New Year"
Stamp + Label
**Panel Color**

**2006, Nov. 1    Photo.      Perf. 13¼**
2974A  A2327a  50y blue         1.50  1.50
2974B  A2327a  50y red violet   1.50  1.50
     c.  Pair, #2974A-2974B + 2 la-
         bels                    3.50  3.50

Labels could be personalized.
See Nos. 3010P-3010Q, 3074-3075.

Miniature Sheets

A2328

Greetings Stamps — A2329

No. 2975: a, Squirrel in mug. b, Bell with flowers. c, Clown with flower. d, Skating polar bear. e, Bear in Santa Claus suit, guitar, birds.
No. 2976: a, Cat in Santa Claus suit ringing bell. b, Fairy and cyclamen. c, Snowman with gift. d, Reindeer and star. e, Floral wreath.

**Litho. with Foil Application**
**Die Cut Perf. 13½x13¼**
**2006, Nov. 24         Self-Adhesive**
2975  A2328  Sheet of 5         6.00  6.00
a.-e.        50y Any single      .80   .80

**Die Cut Perf. 13**
2976  A2329  Sheet of 5        10.00 10.00
a.-e.        80y Any single      .80   .80

No. 2975 sold for 300y; No. 2976 for 500y.

---

Miniature Sheet

Eto Calligraphy — A2330

No. 2977: a, Semicursive style (white background, red chop at lower left). b, Kinbun style (blue background). c, Reisho style (red background). d, Japanese cursive syllabary (white background, red chop at lower right, character with small arc at top). e, Kinbun style (white background, red chop at lower right, character with funnel-shaped line at top). f, Kinbun style (red character). g, Kinbun style (white background, red chop at lower left, character with flat line at top. h, Kinbun style (white background. red chop at lower right, character with large blotch at top). i, Tensho style (white background, red chop at lower left, character with long curved arc and circle at top) j, Reisho style (white background, red chop at lower right, character with dot and straight line at top).

**Litho. & Embossed**
**2006, Dec. 1          Perf. 13x13¼**
2977  A2330  Sheet of 10        17.50 17.50
a.-j.        80y Any single      1.25   .50

Miniature Sheet

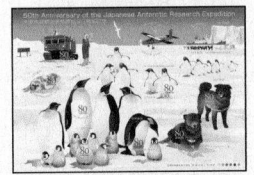

A2331

Japanese Antarctic Research
Expeditions, 50th Anniv. — A2332

No. 2978: a, Observation ship Fuji. b, Spotter plane. c, Adult emperor penguin and chick. d, Adult emperor penguins and five chicks. e, Observation ship Soya and Adelie penguins. f, Adult Adelie penguins and chick. g, Dog, Jiro, in snow, dog team. h, Dog, Taro, standing, dog sled. i, Scientist, observation ship Shirase. j, Snowmobile with cabin.

---

No. 2979: a, Snowmobile with cabin (26x28mm). b, Spotter plane (28mm diameter). c, Soya and dog sled (34x26mm). d, Weddell seal (28x23mm ellipse). e, Head of emperor penguin (26x37mm oval). f, Two Adelie penguins (26x28mm). g, Dog, Taro, standing with mouth open (28mm diameter). h, Emperor penguin chicks (28mm diameter). i, Adult emperor penguin and chick (26x28mm). j, Dog, Jiro, in snow (26x37mm oval).

**2007, Jan. 23    Litho.      Perf. 13**
2978  A2331  Sheet of 10        16.50 16.50
a.-j.        80y Any single      1.25   .40

**Self-Adhesive**
**Die Cut Perf. 13¾x13½**
2979  A2332  Sheet of 10        20.00 20.00
a.-j.        80y Any single      1.25   .55

**Animation**
Miniature Sheet

Neon Genesis Evangelion — A2333

No. 2980: a, Evangelion Unit 01. b, Shinji Ikari. c, Rei Ayanami. d, Evangelion Unit 00. e, Soryu Asuka Langley. f, Evangelion Unit 02. g, Rei Ayanami and Soryu Asuka Langley. h, Misato Katsuragi. i, Kawora Nagisa. j, Sachiel, the third angel.

**2007, Feb. 23          Perf. 13x13¼**
2980  A2333  Sheet of 10        22.50 22.50
a.-j.        80y Any single      1.25   .50

**Animation**
Miniature Sheet

Future Boy Conan A2334

No. 2981: a, Conan (with name). b, Lana (with name). c, Lana (without name). d, Conan (without name). e, Monsley and airplane. f, Lepka. g, Jimsy and Umaso. h, Dyce on running robot. i, Dr. Lao and hovering craft. j, Grandpa.

**2007, June 22   Litho.      Perf. 13x13¼**
2981  A2334  Sheet of 10        16.50 16.50
a.-j.        80y Any single      1.25   .50

---

**World Heritage Sites**
Miniature Sheet

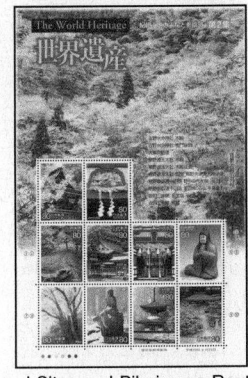

Sacred Sites and Pilgrimage Routes of the Kii Mountains World Heritage Site — A2335

No. 2982: a, Yoshino Mikumari Shrine, cherry blossoms at left. b, Pictoral and rope decoration at Yoshino Mikumari shrine. c, Omine-Okugake-Michi trail. d, Kumano Hayatama-Taisha Shrine (black-roofed building with red trim). e, Kumano Hayatama-Taisha Shrine, diff. f, Wooden icon of Kumano-Fusumino-Okami-Zazo. g, Cherry trees in bloom at Kumano Sankei-Michi Nakahechi. h, Stone sculpture of Emperor Kazan riding ox and horse. i, Kongo-Sanmaiin Temple. j, Steps to Kong-Sanmaiin Temple.

**2007, Mar. 23   Photo.      Perf. 13x13¼**
2982  A2335  Sheet of 10        16.50 16.50
a.-j.        80y Any single      1.25   .50

**World Heritage Sites**
Miniature Sheet

Shiretoko World Heritage Site A2336

No. 2983: a, Lake and mountain, cloudless sky. b, Lake and mountain, cloud in sky. c, Blakiston's fish owl. d, Sea ice, Mt. Rausu. e, Cherry blossoms. f, Brown bear. g, Harbor seal. h, Ezo deer. i, Sea eagle. j, Shiretoko violets (white and yellow flowers).

**2007, July 6    Photo.      Perf. 13x13¼**
2983  A2336  Sheet of 10        16.50 16.50
a.-j.        80y Any single      1.25   .50

Sleeping Boar, by Ippo Mori — A2337

Boar Loping Across Fields, by Mori — A2338

Sparrow, by Mori — A2339

Cherry Blossoms, by Mori — A2340

Bird Flock, by
Mori — A2341

Great Tits
Sitting In a
Japanese
Bush Clover,
by
Mori — A2342

### Perf. 13¼x13 Syncopated

| | | | |
|---|---|---|---|
| **2007, Apr. 20** | | | **Photo.** |
| 2984 | A2337 80y multi | 1.25 | .50 |
| 2985 | A2338 80y multi | 1.25 | .50 |
| a. | Horiz. pair, #2984-2985 | 3.00 | 2.00 |
| | Sheet, 5 #2985a | 16.00 | 16.00 |
| 2986 | A2339 80y multi | 1.25 | .50 |
| 2987 | A2340 80y multi | 1.25 | .50 |
| 2988 | A2341 80y multi | 1.25 | .50 |
| 2989 | A2342 80y multi | 1.25 | .50 |
| a. | Vert. strip of 4, #2986-2989 | 7.50 | 4.00 |
| | Sheet, 2 each #2985-2989 | 16.00 | 16.00 |
| | Nos. 2984-2989 (6) | 7.50 | 3.00 |

### Miniature Sheet

Japan - India Friendship
Year — A2343

No. 2990: a, Taj Mahal. b, Taj Mahal and camels. c, Bengal tiger. d, Peacock. e, Buddhist monastery, Sanchi, India. f, Statue of goddess, Sanchi. g, Painting of Indian woman facing left. h, Calico print of Indian facing right. i, Indian folk dancer. j, Character from Kathakali, Indian dance drama.

| | | | |
|---|---|---|---|
| **2007, May 23** | | | **Perf. 13** |
| 2990 | A2343 Sheet of 10 | 16.00 | 16.00 |
| a.-j. | 80y Any single | 1.25 | .50 |

Tsurayuki
Kino,
Poet — A2344

Empress Jito,
Poet — A2345

Dayu
Sarumaru,
Poet — A2346

Kanemasa
Minamotono,
Poet — A2347

Sanuki Nijoinno,
Poet — A2348

Poetry
A2349

No. 2996 — Poetry in Japanese calligraphy and: a, Plum blossoms. b, Tsurayuki Kino. c, Mount Kagu. d, Empress Jito. e, Deer. f, Dayu Sarumaru. g, Plovers. h, Kanemasa Minamotono. i, Stone in sea. j, Sanuki Nijoinno.

| | | | |
|---|---|---|---|
| **2007, July 23** | | **Photo.** | **Perf. 13½** |
| 2991 | A2344 50y multi | .80 | .30 |
| 2992 | A2345 50y multi | .80 | .30 |
| 2993 | A2346 50y multi | .80 | .30 |
| 2994 | A2347 50y multi | .80 | .30 |
| 2995 | A2348 50y multi | .80 | .30 |
| a. | Vert. strip of 5, #2991-2995 | 5.75 | 4.00 |
| | **Perf. 13** | | |
| 2996 | A2349 Sheet of 10 | 16.50 | 16.50 |
| a.-j. | 80y Any single | 1.25 | .50 |

Letter Writing Day.

### Miniature Sheet

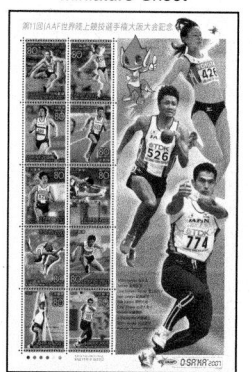

11th World Track and Field
Championships, Osaka — A2350

No. 2997: a, Dai Tamesue (athlete 545), hurdler. b, Kumiko Ikeda (athlete 426), sprinter. c, Yuzo Kanemaru (athlete 300), runner. d, Shingo Suetsugu (athlete 526), runner. e, Kayoko Fukushi (athlete 422), runner. f, Masato Naito running over hurdle. g, Naoyuki Daigo high jumping. h, Kenji Narisako (athlete 531), hurdler. i, Daichi Sawano pole vaulting. j, Koji Murofushi (athlete 774), hammer throw.

| | | | |
|---|---|---|---|
| **2007, Aug. 23** | | **Litho.** | **Perf. 13x13¼** |
| 2997 | A2350 Sheet of 10 | 16.50 | 16.50 |
| a.-j. | 80y Any single | 1.25 | .50 |

### Miniature Sheet

Diplomatic Relations Between Japan
and Thailand, 120th Anniv. — A2351

No. 2998: a, Maple leaves, bamboo. b, Cherry blossoms. c, Ratchaphruek (yellow flower) blossom. d, Rhynchostylis gigantea (purple and white orchids). e, Mother-of-pearl elephant. f, Mother-of-pearl flower. g, Thai dancer. h, Statue, Wat Phra Keo. i, Elephant with head at left, from Toshogu Shrine, Japan, horiz. j, Elephant with head at right, from Toshogu Shrine, horiz.

### Die Cut Perf. and Serpentine Die Cut

| | | | |
|---|---|---|---|
| **2007, Sept. 26** | | | **Litho.** |
| **Self-Adhesive** | | | |
| 2998 | A2351 Sheet of 10 | 16.50 | 16.50 |
| a.-j. | 80y Any single | 1.25 | .50 |

Vertical stamps are die cut perf. 13 at top and bottom, serpentine die cut 10¼ on side adjacent to another stamp, and die cut perf. 12½ on remaining side. Horizontal stamps are die cut perf. 13 at top and bottom, serpentine die cut 10¼ on side adjacent to another stamp, and die cut perf. 12¾ on remaining side.

See Thailand No. 2316.

### International Letter Writing Week Type of 2000

Hiroshige paintings from 53 Stations of the Tokaido Highway: 90y, Hodogaya. 110y, Arai. 130y, Kusatsu.

| | | | |
|---|---|---|---|
| **2007, Sept. 28** | **Litho.** | | **Perf. 14** |
| 2999 | A2119 90y multi | 1.75 | .50 |
| 3000 | A2119 110y multi | 2.25 | .50 |
| 3001 | A2119 130y multi | 2.50 | .50 |
| | Nos. 2999-3001 (3) | 6.50 | 1.50 |

See listing of No. 4448 for images of each Hiroshige print.

Mandarin
Duck
A2352

Eastern
Turtle
Dove
A2353

| | | | |
|---|---|---|---|
| **2007, Oct. 1** | **Photo.** | | **Perf. 13x13½** |
| 3002 | A2352 50y multi | 1.50 | .30 |
| 3003 | A2353 80y multi | 1.60 | .30 |

See No. 3281.

### Miniature Sheets

A2354

Establishment of Japan Post
Corporation — A2355

### Miniature Sheet

Diplomatic Relations Between Japan and Thailand 120th Anniv.

No. 3004: a, Baron Hisoka Maejima (red panels). b, Japan #2 (red panels). c, Post office counter (orange panels). d, Postal workers loading mail coach (dark red panels). e, Postal saving counter (green panels). f, People at post office counters (blue panels).

No. 3005 — Paintings of flowers: a, Sunflower, by Hoitsu Sakai. b, Confederate Roses, by Sakai. c, Chrysanthemums, by Sakai. d, Maple Leaves, by Kiitsu Suzuki (showing branch). e, Maple Leaves, by Suzuki (no branch). f, Camellia, by Sakai. g, Cherry Tree, by Sakai (bird in tree). h, Tree Peony, by Sakai. i, Iris, by Sakai. j, Hydrangeas, by Sakai.

| | | | |
|---|---|---|---|
| **2007, Oct. 1** | **Photo.** | | **Perf. 13¼** |
| 3004 | A2354 Sheet of 10, | | |
| | #a-b, 2 each | | |
| | #c-f | 16.50 | 16.50 |
| a.-f. | 80y Any single | 1.25 | .50 |
| 3005 | A2355 Sheet of 10 | 16.50 | 16.50 |
| a.-j. | 80y Any single | 1.25 | .50 |

### Miniature Sheet

Intl.
Skills
Festival
For All
A2356

No. 3006: a, Computer operator and robot. b, Computer operator. c, Plasterer and Geisha. d, Plasterer and pillar. e, Pastry chef and cake. f, Pastry chef and bowls. g, Flower arranger and flowers. h, Flower arranger holding scissors. i, Sheet metal worker and automobile. j, Sheet metal worker hammering metal.

| | | | |
|---|---|---|---|
| **2007, Oct. 23** | **Litho.** | | **Perf. 13** |
| 3006 | A2356 Sheet of 10 | 16.00 | 16.00 |
| a.-j. | 80y Any single | 1.25 | .50 |

A2357                 A2358

New Year 2008 (Year of
the Rat)
A2359            A2360

| | | | |
|---|---|---|---|
| **2007, Nov. 1** | **Photo.** | | **Perf. 13x13½** |
| 3007 | A2357 50y multi | 1.00 | .30 |
| 3008 | A2358 80y multi | 1.50 | .40 |
| | **Photo. & Typo.** | | |
| | **Perf. 13¼** | | |
| 3009 | A2359 50y +3 multi | 1.25 | .40 |
| 3010 | A2360 80y +3 multi | 1.40 | .40 |
| | Nos. 3007-3010 (4) | 5.15 | 1.50 |

Sheets of two containing stamps similar to Nos. 3009-3010 were lottery prizes. Value, $4.

Diamonds — A2360a        Diamonds — A2360b

Diamonds — A2360c

Diamonds — A2360d

***Die Cut Perf. 13¼***
**2007, Nov. 1          Litho.**
**Self-Adhesive**
**Green Diamonds**
**Color of Country Name**

| | | | | |
|---|---|---|---|---|
| 3010A | A2360a | 50y blue | 3.50 | 3.50 |
| 3010B | A2360a | 50y green | 3.50 | 3.50 |
| 3010C | A2360a | 50y red | 3.50 | 3.50 |
| 3010D | A2360a | 50y purple | 3.50 | 3.50 |
| 3010E | A2360a | 50y black | 3.50 | 3.50 |

**Blue Diamonds**

| | | | | |
|---|---|---|---|---|
| 3010F | A2360a | 80y blue | 4.00 | 4.00 |
| 3010G | A2360a | 80y green | 4.00 | 4.00 |
| 3010H | A2360a | 80y red | 4.00 | 4.00 |
| 3010I | A2360a | 80y purple | 4.00 | 4.00 |
| 3010J | A2360a | 80y black | 4.00 | 4.00 |

**Blue Diamonds**
**Color of Country Name**

| | | | | |
|---|---|---|---|---|
| 3010L | A2360b | 80y dk blue | — | — |
| 3010M | A2360b | 80y brt grn | — | — |
| 3010N | A2360b | 80y orange | — | — |
| 3010O | A2360b | 80y red violet | — | — |
| 3010S | A2360c | 80y blue, country name at LR | — | — |
| 3010T | A2360d | 80y blue, country name at LL | — | — |
| *u.* | | Sheet of 10, #3010S, 3010T, 2 each #3010L-3010O | | — |

Nos. 3010A-3010E were printed in sheets of 10, containing two of each stamp, that sold for 900y. Nos. 3010F-3010J were printed in sheets of 10, containing two of each stamp, that sold for 1200y. The image portion could be personalized. The image shown is a generic image.
The image portions of Nos. 3010L-3010o, 3010S-3010T could be personalized.

**New Year Greetings Type of 2006**
**Inscribed "'08 New Year"**
**Stamp + Label**
**Panel Color**

**2007, Nov. 1          Photo.          Perf. 13¼**

| | | | | |
|---|---|---|---|---|
| 3010P | A2327a | 50y red violet | 1.50 | 1.00 |
| 3010Q | A2327a | 50y orange | 1.50 | 1.00 |
| *r.* | | Pair, #3010P-3010Q + 2 labels | 4.00 | 4.00 |

Labels could be personalized.

**Miniature Sheets**

A2361

Greetings Stamps — A2362

No. 3011 — a, White buildings. b, Fairies on flying swans. c, Santa Claus. d, Flowers and snow-covered trees. e, Cat and candy cane.
No. 3012 — a, Santa Claus and reindeer. b, Fairy and flowers. c, Snowman with green cap. d, Strawberries. e, Snowman and flying reindeer.

**2007, Nov. 26    Litho.    *Die Cut Perf.***
**Self-Adhesive**

| | | | | |
|---|---|---|---|---|
| 3011 | A2361 | Sheet of 5 | 6.00 | 6.00 |
| *a.-e.* | | 50y Any single | .80 | .80 |

***Die Cut Perf. 13***

| | | | | |
|---|---|---|---|---|
| 3012 | A2362 | Sheet of 5 | 10.00 | 10.00 |
| *a.-e.* | | 80y Any single | 1.25 | .80 |

**Miniature Sheet**

Edo Calligraphy — A2363

No. 3013 — Charcters for "rat": a, In Kinbun style (red character). b, Black character with three long vertical lines at top, with red chop at LR. c, In Tensho style (gold character on red and brown background). d, In Reisho style (black character resembling a "3" with line through it, with red chop at LR). e, In Shoden style (gold character on blue and pink background). f, In Kana style (black characters resembling "12" with a check mark, with red chop at LR). g, In Reisho style (black characters, with red chop at LL). h, In Sosho style (black character with pink lines, with red chop at LL). i, Black character resembling stick figure with raised arms, with red chop at LR. j, In Kinbun style (black character with five short vertical lines at top, red chop at LL).

**Litho. & Embossed          Perf. 13**

| | | | | |
|---|---|---|---|---|
| 3013 | A2363 | Sheet of 10 | 16.00 | 16.00 |
| *a.-j.* | | 80y Any single | 1.25 | .50 |

Mt. Fuji — A2364

Mt. Fuji — A2365

Mt. Fuji — A2366

Mt. Fuji — A2367

Mt. Fuji — A2368

Bamboo A2369

Someiyoshino Blossoms A2370

Hydrangea Blossoms A2371

Maple Leaves A2372

Narcissuses A2373

**2008, Jan. 23    Litho.    Perf. 13¾x14**

| | | | | |
|---|---|---|---|---|
| 3014 | | Sheet of 10 | 17.50 | 17.50 |
| *a.* | A2364 | 80y multi | 1.25 | .50 |
| *b.* | A2365 | 80y multi | 1.25 | .50 |
| *c.* | A2366 | 80y multi | 1.25 | .50 |
| *d.* | A2367 | 80y multi | 1.25 | .50 |
| *e.* | A2368 | 80y multi | 1.25 | .50 |
| *f.* | A2369 | 80y multi | 1.25 | .50 |
| *g.* | A2370 | 80y multi | 1.25 | .50 |
| *h.* | A2371 | 80y multi | 1.25 | .50 |
| *i.* | A2372 | 80y multi | 1.25 | .50 |
| *j.* | A2373 | 80y multi | 1.25 | .50 |

Yokoso! Japan Weeks.

**Souvenir Sheet**

New Year 2008 (Year of the Rat) A2374

No. 3015: a, Two rats. b, One rat.

**2008, Jan. 28    Photo.    Perf. 13**

| | | | | |
|---|---|---|---|---|
| 3015 | A2374 | Sheet of 2 | 2.50 | 2.50 |
| *a.* | | 50y multi | .90 | .45 |
| *b.* | | 80y multi | 1.25 | .50 |

**Miniature Sheet**

Animated Folktales — A2375

No. 3016: a, Man on horse, cherry trees, pagoda. b, Man in cherry tree. c, Moon Princess in bamboo stump, woodsman with ax. d,

Moon Princess, flying horse and wagon, archers. e, Four statues in snow. f, Two statues in snow, man with basket. g, Boy in ship. h, Demons. i, Woman carrying roll of cloth. j, Man, woman, crane.

**2008, Feb. 22    Litho.    Perf. 13**

| | | | | |
|---|---|---|---|---|
| 3016 | A2375 | Sheet of 10 | 16.00 | 16.00 |
| *a.-j.* | | 80y Any single | 1.25 | .50 |

Folktales "The Old Man Who Made Cherry Trees Blossom" (No. 3016a-3016b), "The Moon Princess" (Nos. 3016c-3016d), "Six Little Statues" (Nos. 3016e-3016f), "The Peach Boy" (NOs. 3016g-3016h), "The Grateful Crane" (Nos. 3016i-3016j).

**Miniature Sheet**

Astronomical Society of Japan, Cent. — A2376

No. 3017: a, Jupiter. b, Saturn. c, Spiral galaxy. d, Suzaku X-ray satellite. e, Hayabusa probe. f, Asteroids and Earth. g, Subaru Telescope. h, Stars. i, Mars. j, Nobeyama Radio Telescope.

**2008, Mar. 21**

| | | | | |
|---|---|---|---|---|
| 3017 | | Sheet of 10 | 17.50 | 17.50 |
| *a.-j.* | | 80y Any single | 1.25 | .50 |

**Miniature Sheet**

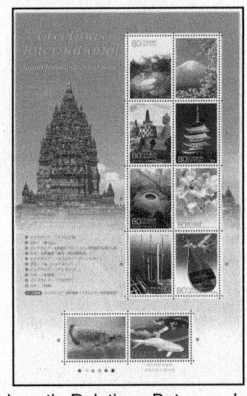

Diplomatic Relations Between Japan and Indonesia, 50th Anniv. — A2377

No. 3018: a, Kelimutu Volcano, Indonesia. b, Mt. Fuji, Japan, and cherry blossoms. c, Borobudur, Indonesia. d, Toji Temple, Kyoto. e, Rafflesia arnoldii. f, Cherry blossoms. g, Angklung (Indonesian musical instrument). h, Gaku biwa (Japanese musical instrument). i, Red arowana fish, horiz. j, Three koi, horiz.

**2008, June 23    Photo.    Perf. 13**

| | | | | |
|---|---|---|---|---|
| 3018 | A2377 | Sheet of 10 | 15.00 | 15.00 |
| *a.-j.* | | 80y Any single | 1.25 | .50 |

See Indonesia Nos. 2135-2139.

Small Bird in Cherry Blossom, by Seitei Watanabe A2378

Butterfly in Peony Branch, by Watanabe A2379

Egrets in the Rain Beneath Willow Trees, by Watanabe A2380

Grapes, by Watanabe A2381

Sea Birds on a Rocky Crag, by Watanabe — A2382

### Perf. 13½x13 Syncopated

| | | | | Photo. |
|---|---|---|---|---|
| **2008, Apr. 18** | | | | |
| 3019 | A2378 | 80y multi | 1.25 | .50 |
| 3020 | A2379 | 80y multi | 1.25 | .50 |
| 3021 | A2380 | 80y multi | 1.25 | .50 |
| 3022 | A2381 | 80y multi | 1.25 | .50 |
| 3023 | A2382 | 80y multi | 1.25 | .50 |
| a. | | Vert. strip of 5, #3019-3023 | 7.50 | 7.50 |
| | | Sheet, 2 #3023a | 15.00 | 15.00 |

Philately Week.

See note after No. Z827 in the Prefecture Stamp listings.

### Miniature Sheet

Home Towns A2383

No. 3024 — Paintings by Taiji Harada of views of towns: a, Water Shield (Yamamoto District, Akita prefecture). b, Bell of Time (Kawago, Saitama prefecture). c, Enjoying the Evening Cool (Gujo, Gifu prefecture). d, The Little Electric Train (Choshi, Chiba prefecture). e, Sea of the Heart (Shozu District, Kagawa prefecture). f, Lake in the Evening Sun (Gamo District, Shiga prefecture). g, Tanabata Dolls (Matsumoto, Nagano prefecture). h, Town of Outdoor Warehouses (Ise, Mie prefecture). i, The Farm Clock (Aki, Kochi prefecture). j, Late Summer Heat in the Street (Hakusan, Ishikawa prefecture).

| **2008, May 2** | **Photo.** | | | **Perf. 13** |
|---|---|---|---|---|
| 3024 | A2383 | Sheet of 10 | 16.00 | 16.00 |
| a.-j. | | 80y Any single | 1.25 | .50 |

Hideyo Noguchi Africa Prize A2384

| **2008, May 23** | **Litho.** | | | **Perf. 13** |
|---|---|---|---|---|
| 3025 | | 80y Noguchi | 1.25 | .50 |
| 3026 | | 80y Map of Africa | 1.25 | .50 |
| a. | | A2384 Horiz. pair, #3025-3026 | 3.00 | 2.00 |

### Miniature Sheet

National Afforestation Campaign — A2385

No. 3027 — Scenes from Akita prefecture: a, Aleutian avens and Mt. Moriyoshi, denomination at UL. b, Aleutian avens and Mt. Moriyoshi, denomination at UR. c, Fringed galax flowers, denomination at LL. d, Fringed galax flowers, denomination at LR. e, Autumn leaves, denomination at UR. g, Beech forest in autumn, denomination in UL. h, Beech forest in autumn, denomination in UR. i, Weigela. j, Waterfall.

| **2008, June 13** | **Photo.** | | | **Perf. 13** |
|---|---|---|---|---|
| 3027 | A2385 | Sheet of 10 | 8.00 | 5.00 |
| a.-j. | | 50y Any single | .80 | .40 |

### Miniature Sheet

Year of Exchange Between Japan and Brazil — A2386

No. 3028 — a, Roasted coffee beans, seal of Brazilian vice-consulate in Kobe. b, Coffee cherries, ship. c, Christ the Redeemer Statue, Rio de Janeiro. d, Sugarloaf Mountain, Rio de Janeiro. e, Iguaçu Falls, denomination at UL. f, Iguaçu Falls, denomination at UR. g, Houses, denomination at LL. h, Houses, denomination at LR. i, Butterflies. j, Toucan.

| **2008, June 18** | **Litho.** | | | **Perf. 13** |
|---|---|---|---|---|
| 3028 | A2386 | Sheet of 10 | 16.00 | 16.00 |
| a.-j. | | 80y Any single | 1.25 | .50 |

See Brazil No. 3051.

### Miniature Sheet

Publication of *Anne of Green Gables,* by Lucy Maud Montgomery, Cent. — A2387

No. 3029: a, Anne holding buttercups. b, Green Gables House. c, Matthew Cuthbert, wearing hat, vert. d, Marilla Cuthbert, wearing hat, vert. e, Anne, Diana Barry holding hands, vert. f, Diana, vert. g, Anne in black dress, vert. h, Anne and Gilbert Blythe, vert. i, Matthew Cuthbert, without hat, vert. j, Anne, Marilla Cuthbert, vert.

### Perf. 13¼x13 (#3029a-3029b), 13x13¼

| **2008, June 20** | | | | |
|---|---|---|---|---|
| 3029 | A2387 | Sheet of 10 | 12.00 | 12.00 |
| a.-j. | | 80y Any single | 1.25 | .50 |

See Canada Nos. 2276-2278.

Lily A2388

Rugosa Rose A2389

Rhododendron A2390

Safflower A2391

Gentian A2392

Lily A2393

Rugosa Rose A2394

Rhododendron A2395

Safflower A2396

Gentian A2397

| **2008, July 1** | **Photo.** | | | **Perf. 13¼** |
|---|---|---|---|---|
| 3030 | A2388 | 50y multi | .80 | .40 |
| 3031 | A2389 | 50y multi | .80 | .40 |
| 3032 | A2390 | 50y multi | .80 | .40 |
| 3033 | A2391 | 50y multi | .80 | .40 |
| 3034 | A2392 | 50y multi | .80 | .40 |
| a. | | Vert. strip of 5, #3030-3034 | 4.50 | 3.00 |

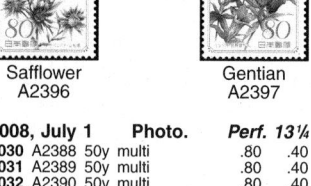

| 3035 | A2393 | 80y multi | 1.25 | .60 |
|---|---|---|---|---|
| 3036 | A2394 | 80y multi | 1.25 | .60 |
| 3037 | A2395 | 80y multi | 1.25 | .60 |
| 3038 | A2396 | 80y multi | 1.25 | .60 |
| 3039 | A2397 | 80y multi | 1.25 | .60 |
| a. | | Vert. strip of 5, #3035-3039 | 6.50 | 4.00 |
| | | Nos. 3030-3039 (10) | 10.25 | 5.00 |

Flowers of Kanagawa, Hokkaido, Fukushima, Yamagata and Nagano prefectures.

### Miniature Sheet

Hokkaido Local Autonomy Law, 60th Anniv. — A2398

No. 3040: a, Lake Toya, cranes (32x39mm). b, Goryokaku Fortress (28x33mm). c, Hills around Biei (28x33mm). d, Sea angel (28x33mm). e, Otaru Canal (28x33mm).

| **2008, July 1** | **Perf. 13¼ (#3040a), 13** | | | |
|---|---|---|---|---|
| 3040 | A2398 | Sheet of 5 | 6.50 | 3.50 |
| a.-e. | | 80y Any single | 1.25 | .55 |

### Miniature Sheet

G8 Summit, Toyako A2399

No. 3041: a, Mt. Yotei (stamp 1). b, Showa Shinzan (stamp 2). c, Mt. Yotei and Lake Toya (stamp 3). d, Mt. Yotei and Fukidashi Park (stamp 4). e, Mt. Eniwa and Lake Shikotsu (stamp 5). f, Pink Japanese wood poppies (stamp 6). g, Squirrel (stamp 7). h, Beardtongue flowers (stamp 8). i, Mountain ash leaves and berries (stamp 9). j, Northern fox (stamp 10).

| **2008, July 7** | **Litho.** | | | **Perf. 13¾x14** |
|---|---|---|---|---|
| 3041 | A2399 | Sheet of 10 | 16.00 | 16.00 |
| a.-j. | | 80y Any single | 1.25 | .50 |

Lady Shikibu Murasaki, Poet A2400

Sanekata Fujiwara, Poet A2401

Lady
Shonagon
Sei, Poet
A2402

Kinto
Dainagon,
Poet
A2403

Lady Shikibu Izumi,
Poet — A2404

Poetry
A2405

No. 3047 — Poetry in Japanese calligraphy and: a, Moon behind cloud. b, Lady Shikibu Murasaki. c, Mugwort. d, Sanekata Fujiwara. e, Waterfall. f, Lady Shonagon Sei. g, Barrier. h, Kinto Dainagon. i, Bare branches. j, Lady Shikibu Izumi.

| 2008, July 23 | | Photo. | Perf. 13¼ | |
|---|---|---|---|---|
| 3042 | A2400 | 50y multi | .80 | .30 |
| 3043 | A2401 | 50y multi | .80 | .30 |
| 3044 | A2402 | 50y multi | .80 | .30 |
| 3045 | A2403 | 50y multi | .80 | .30 |
| 3046 | A2404 | 50y multi | .80 | .30 |
| a. | | Vert. strip of 5, #3042-3046 | 5.00 | 5.00 |
| | | Perf. 12¾x13 | | |
| 3047 | A2405 | Sheet of 10 | 16.00 | 16.00 |
| a.-j. | | 80y Any single | 1.25 | .55 |

Letter Writing Day.

Miniature Sheets

A2406

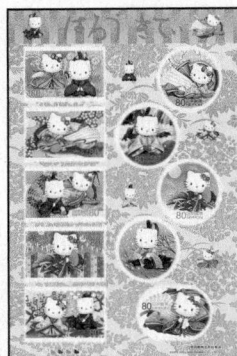
Hello
Kitty
A2407

No. 3048 — Hello Kitty characters with: a, Gold denomination at UR. b, Green denomination at UR. c, Yellow denomination at UL, Kitty with pink flowers on head. d, Yellow denomination at UR, Kitty wearing green patterned kimono. e, Green denomination at UL, Kitty wearing black kimono. f, Green denomination at UL, Kitty with pink and blue flowers on head. g, Green denomination at UL, Kitty with bow and flowers on head. h, Yellow denomination at UL, Kitty wearing dark green kimono. i, Green denomination at UL, Kitty wearing brown kimono. j, Green denomination at UL, Kitty with purple and green flowers on head.

No. 3049 — Hello Kitty characters with: a, Green denomination at LL (41x27mm). b, Gold denomination at LR, one Kitty with two pink flowers on head (41x27mm). c, Gold denomination at LR, Kitty at right with purple and green flowers on head (41x27mm). d, Green denomination at UR (41x27mm). e, Gold denomination at LR, Kitty at left with bow and flower on head (41x27mm). f, Blue denomination (34mm diameter). g, Gold denomination, Kitty wearing gray kimono (34mm diameter). h, Gold denomination, Kitty holding fan (34mm diameter). i, Gold denomination, Kitty with snowflakes in background (34mm diameter). j, Blue denomination (40x28mm oval stamp).

### Die Cut Perf. and Serpentine Die Cut (see note)

| 2008, July 23 | | | Litho. |
|---|---|---|---|
| | | Self-Adhesive | |
| 3048 | A2406 | Sheet of 10 | 9.50 9.50 |
| a.-j. | | 50y Any single | .80 .80 |

#### Die Cut Perf. 13x13¼ (#3049a-3049e), Die Cut Perf.

| 3049 | A2407 | Sheet of 10 | 12.50 12.50 |
|---|---|---|---|
| a.-j. | | 80y Any single | 1.25 .80 |

Stamps on No. 3048 are arranged in five rows of se-tenant pairs. Each pair is die cut perf. 13¾ at top and bottom, die cut perf. 13½ on the outer sides, and serpentine die cut 11¼ between the stamps in the pair.

Love That
Meets the
Night, by
Utamaro
A2408

Yatsumi
Bridge, by
Hiroshige
A2409

Mannen
Bridge,
Fukagawa,
by Hiroshige
A2410

Koshiro
Matsumoto
IV as
Gorobe
Sakanaya of
San'ya, by
Sharaku
A2411

Hanazuma
From
Hyogoya, by
Utamaro
A2412

Ayase River
at
Kanegafuchi,
by Hiroshige
A2413

Tsukiji
Hongan-ji
Temple,
Teppozu, by
Hiroshige
A2414

Hikosaburo
Bando III as
Sanai
Sagisaka, by
Sharaku
A2415

Roko of
Tatsumi, by
Utamaro
A2416

Kameido
Plum
Gardens, by
Hiroshige
A2417

| 2008, Aug. 1 | | Litho. | Perf. 13¼ | |
|---|---|---|---|---|
| 3050 | | Sheet of 10 | 16.00 | 16.00 |
| a. | A2408 | 80y multi | 1.25 | .50 |
| b. | A2409 | 80y multi | 1.25 | .50 |
| c. | A2410 | 80y multi | 1.25 | .50 |
| d. | A2411 | 80y multi | 1.25 | .50 |
| e. | A2412 | 80y multi | 1.25 | .50 |
| f. | A2413 | 80y multi | 1.25 | .50 |
| g. | A2414 | 80y multi | 1.25 | .50 |
| h. | A2415 | 80y multi | 1.25 | .50 |
| i. | A2416 | 80y multi | 1.25 | .50 |
| j. | A2417 | 80y multi | 1.25 | .50 |

Life in Edo (Tokyo).

Miniature Sheet

Hometown Festivals — A2418

No. 3051: a, Streamers for Sendai Tanabata Festival, Miyagi prefecture (light green background, denomination at UR). b, Streamers for Sendai Tanabata Festival (light green background, denomination at UL). c, Portable shrine for Kanda Festival, Tokyo prefecture (yellow background, denomination in red at LL). d, Portable shrine for Kanda Festival (yellow background, denomination in blue at UR).

e, Dancers from Awa Dance Festival, Tokushima prefecture (pink background, denomination at LR). f, Dancers from Awa Dance Festival (pink background, denomination at UR). g, Participants and lanterns for Hakata Gion Yamakasa Festival, Fukuoka prefecture (light blue background, denomination at UL). h, Participants and float for Hakata Gion Yamakasa Festival (light blue background, denomination at UR). i, Drummers for Eisa Festival, Okinawa prefecture (yellow background, denomination in red at LR). j, Drummers for Eisa Festival (yellow background, denomination in blue at UR).

| 2008, Aug. 1 | | Photo. | Perf. 13½x13¼ | |
|---|---|---|---|---|
| 3051 | A2418 | Sheet of 10 | 8.00 | 8.00 |
| a.-j. | | 50y Any single | .80 | .40 |

Miniature Sheet

Treaty of Peace and Friendship
Between Japan and People's Republic
of China, 30th Anniv. — A2419

No. 3052: a, Temple of Heaven, Beijing. b, Huangshan Mountains, China. c, Mogao Cave Shrines, China. d, Temple of the Flourishing Law, Ikaruga, Japan. e, Female mandarin duck. f, Male mandarin duck. g, Panel from painting by Wang Chuanfeng depicting three stylized fish and red Japanese apricot flower. h, Panel from painting by Wang Chuanfeng depicting two stylized fish and water lily. i, Panel from painting by Wang Chuanfeng depicting one stylized fish and autumn leaves. j, Panel from painting by Wang Chuanfeng depicting two staylized fish and white and red narcissi. Nos. 3052a-3052d, 3052g-3052j are 28x49mm; Nos. 3052e-3052f, 32x49mm.

| 2008, Aug. 12 | | Photo. | Perf. 13 | |
|---|---|---|---|---|
| 3052 | A2419 | Sheet of 10 | 16.00 | 16.00 |
| a.-j. | | 80y Any single | 1.25 | .50 |

### Animation
Miniature Sheet

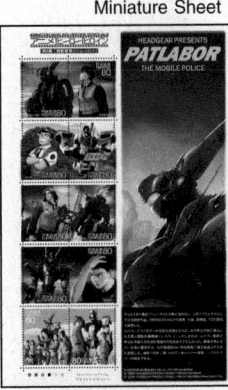
Patlabor
A2420

No. 3053: a, Ingfram Model 1 robot. b, Noa Izumimn, with "2" on sleeve patch. c, Isao Ota, with crossed arms. d, Ingram Model 2 robot. e, Shinobu Nagumo, with long hair. f, Ingram Model 3 robot. g, Robot, diff. h, Asumo Shinohara, with hand on head. i, Ingram Model 1 robot and eight characters. j, Ingram Model 2 robot and three characters.

| 2008, Aug. 22 | | Litho. | Perf. 13x13¼ | |
|---|---|---|---|---|
| 3053 | A2420 | Sheet of 10 | 16.00 | 16.00 |
| a.-j. | | 80y Any single | 1.25 | .50 |

## Miniature Sheet

Home
Towns
A2421

No. 3054 — Paintings by Taiji Harada of views of towns: a, Idyllic Village (Farmhouses, Tonami, Toyama prefecture). b, Blessing (Wedding at Yamate Catholic Church, Yokohama, Kanagawa prefecture). c, Approaching Winter (Lake Nojiri, Kamiminochi District, Nagano prefecture). d, Konjac Field (Farmers planting, Numata, Gunma prefecture). e, Vespers (Family in garden near houses, Nara, Nara prefecture). f, Cosmos (Flowers, boats and boathouses, Mikatakaminaka District, Fukui prefecture). g, Voices of Excited Children (Farmhouse and hill, Haga District, Tochigi prefecture). h, Autumn Colors Everywhere (Farmhouse and train car, Namegata, Ibaraki prefecture). i, Small Market (Family at roadside market, Asakura District, Fukuoka prefecture). j, Lullaby Village (Village and bridge, Kuma District, Kumamoto prefecture).

**2008, Sept. 1     Photo.        Perf. 13**
3054   A2421     Sheet of 10        12.50  12.50
*a.-j.*        80y Any single                1.25   .55

## Miniature Sheet

Kyoto
Travel
Scenes
A2422

No. 3055: a, Otagi Nebutsu Temple and stone sculptures (stamp 1). b, Toriimoto (stamp 2). c, Adashino Nenbutsu Temple (stamp 3). d, Gio Temple (stamp 4). e, Buddha sculptures, Nison Temple (stamp 5). f, Hut of Fallen Persimmons, persimmons on tree (stamp 6). g, Jojakko Temple (stamp 7). h, Sagano Scenic Railway bridge and trains (stamp 8). i, Rowboats on Hozu River (stamp 9). j, Togetsu Bridge (stamp 10).

**2008, Sept. 1     Litho.      Perf. 13x13¼**
3055   A2422     Sheet of 10        12.50  12.50
*a.-j.*        80y Any single                1.25   .55

Personalized
Stamp — A2423

***Die Cut Perf. 12¾ Syncopated***
**2008, Aug. 7                        Litho.**
**Self-Adhesive**
**Color of Denomination**
3056   A2423   80y blue          2.00   2.00
3057   A2423   80y red           2.00   2.00
3058   A2423   80y orange        2.00   2.00

---

3059   A2423   80y green         2.00   2.00
3060   A2423   80y black         2.00   2.00
       Nos. 3056-3060 (5)       10.00  10.00

Nos. 3056-3060 were printed in sheets of 10 containing 2 of each stamp that sold for 1200y. The image portion could be personalized. The image shown is a generic image.

A2424

A2425

A2426

A2427

A2428

A2429

A2430

A2431

A2432

The Tale of
Genji, by
Shikibu
Murasaki
A2433

**2008, Sept. 22     Photo.        Perf. 13¼**
3061              Sheet of 10      16.00  16.00
*a.*   A2424  80y multi            1.25   .50
*b.*   A2425  80y multi            1.25   .50
*c.*   A2426  80y multi            1.25   .50
*d.*   A2427  80y multi            1.25   .50
*e.*   A2428  80y multi            1.25   .50
*f.*   A2429  80y multi            1.25   .50
*g.*   A2430  80y multi            1.25   .50
*h.*   A2431  80y multi            1.25   .50
*i.*   A2432  80y multi            1.25   .50
*j.*   A2433  80y multi            1.25   .50

Kyushu Oil
Dome, Oita
Sports Park
A2435

Fencing
A2436

Hurdler
A2437

Kayaker
A2438

**2008, Sept. 26                  Perf. 13x13¼**
3062          Sheet of 10, 2 each
              #3062a, 3062b, 3062d,
              4 #3062c              9.50   9.50
*a.*   A2435  50y multi             .90    .50
*b.*   A2436  50y multi             .90    .50
*c.*   A2437  50y multi             .90    .50
*d.*   A2438  50y multi             .90    .50

## Miniature Sheet

Travel
Scenes
A2439

No. 3063: a, Sanjunoto Pagoda (stamp 1). b, Kiyomizudera Temple (stamp 2). c, Detail from painted sliding partition showing flowers from Chishaku Temple, denomination at LL (stamp 3). d, Like "c," denomination at LR (stamp 4). e, Kodai Temple (stamp 5). f, Temple garden (stamp 6). g, Sannei Hill (stamp 7). h, Yasaka Pagoda (stamp 8). i, Apprentice geisha (stamp 9). j, Kamo River and waterfront (stamp 10).

**2008, Oct. 1     Litho.     Perf. 13x13¼**
3063   A2439     Sheet of 10        12.50  12.50
*a.-j.*        80y Any single                1.25   .55

### International Letter Writing Week
### Type of 2000

Hiroshige paintings from 53 Stations of the Tokaido Highway: 90y, Kanagawa. 110y, Mishima. 130y, Ishibe.

**2008, Oct. 9   Photo.     Perf. 13¼x13½**
3064   A2119   90y multi          1.75   .50
3065   A2119   110y multi         2.25   .50
3066   A2119   130y multi         2.50   .50
       Nos. 3064-3066 (3)         6.50  1.50

See listing of No. 4448 for images of each Hiroshige print.

## World Heritage Sites
### Miniature Sheet

Iwami
Silver
Mine
World
Heritage
Site
A2440

No. 3067: a, Map of Tartary by Abraham Ortelius (stamp 1). b, Ryugenji mine shaft (stamp 2). c, Smelting plant and ruins of Shimizudani smelting works (stamp 3). d, Painting of dragon, ceiling of Kigami Shinto shrine (stamp 4). e, Rakanji Temple (stamp 5). f, Omori silver mine district (stamp 6). g, Silver guardian dog (stamp 7). h, Interior of Kumagai family residence (stamp 8). i, Silver coin for official use and picture scroll (stamp 9). j, Naito Mansion, Yunotsu (stamp 10).

**2008, Oct. 23                  Perf. 13x13¼**
3067   A2440     Sheet of 10        16.00  16.00
*a.-j.*        80y Any single                1.25   .50

### Miniature Sheet

Kyoto Prefecture Local Autonomy Law,
60th Anniv. — A2441

No. 3068: a, Scene from The Tale of Genji, by Shikibu Murasaki (33x39mm). b, Cherry blossoms, Kyoto Prefectural Botanical Garden (28x33mm). c, Thatched-roof house, Nantan (28x33mm). d, Kaijusen Pagoda, Wazuka tea plantation (28x33mm). e, Amanohashidate Sandbar (28x33mm).

***Perf. 13¼ (#3068a), 13x13¼***
**2008, Oct. 27                        Photo.**
3068   A2441     Sheet of 5         7.50   7.50
*a.-e.*        80y Any single                1.25   .50

### Miniature Sheet

Home
Towns
A2442

No. 3069 — Paintings by Taiji Harada of views of towns: a, Stove Train (train, Kitatsugaru District, Aomori prefecture). b, New Year (buildings with snow-covered roofs, man shoveling snow, Nishimurayama District, Yamagata prefecture). c, Seaside Station (train station and telephone pole, Abashiri, Hokkaido prefecture). d, Incense Waterwheel (mill with waterwheel, Tsuyama, Okayama prefecture). e, Harness Straps (horse dragging log, Kurayoshi, Tottori prefecture). f, Life in the Snow Country (postman delivering mail to people at snow-covered house, Waga District, Iwate prefecture). g, Good Friends (people on town street in snowfall, Aizu Wakamatsu, Fukushima prefecture). h, Community of Stone Walls (people walking by stone wall, Minamiuwa District, Ehime prefecture). i, Village on Steep Slope (houses on mountainside, Miyoshi, Toskushima prefecture). j, Sedge-woven Hat (woman standing outside of building in snowstorm, Nakauonuma District, Niigata prefecture).

**2008, Nov. 4** — *Perf. 13*
3069  A2442  Sheet of 10  12.50  12.50
a.-j.  80y Any single  1.25  .50

A2443  A2444

New Year 2009 (Year of the Ox)
A2445  A2446

**2008, Nov. 4  Photo.  Perf. 13x13¼**
3070  A2443  50y multi  1.00  .30
3071  A2444  80y multi  1.50  .40

*Perf. 13¼*
3072  A2445  50y +3y multi  1.25  .40
3073  A2446  80y +3y multi  1.75  .40
  Nos. 3070-3073 (4)  5.50  1.50

Sheets of two containing Nos. 3070-3071 were lottery prizes. Value, $3.25.

**New Year Greetings Type of 2006
Inscribed "'09 New Year"
Stamp + Label
Panel Color**

**2008, Nov. 4  Photo.  Perf. 13¼**
3074  A2327a  50y blue green  1.50  1.50
3075  A2327a  50y red  1.50  1.50
a.  Pair, #3074-3075 + 2 labels  3.00  3.00

Labels could be personalized.

Miniature Sheet

Keio University, 150th Anniv. — A2447

No. 3076: a, Yukichi Fukuzawa (1835-1901), founder (stamp 1). b, University emblem (stamp 2). c, Old Library, denomination at LL (stamp 3). d, Old Library, denomination at LR (stamp 4). e, Keio and Waseda University rugby players (stamp 6). f, Keio and Waseda University baseball players (stamp 6). g, Stained-glass window depicting horse's head (stamp 7). h, Stained-glass window depicting goddess with upraised arm (stamp 8). i, Stained-glass window depicting feudal warrior

(stamp 9). j, Stained-glass window with Latin inscription "Calamus Gladio Fortior" (stamp 10).

**2008, Nov. 7** — *Perf. 13*
3076  A2447  Sheet of 10  16.00  16.00
a.-j.  80y Any single  1.25  .50

Miniature Sheet

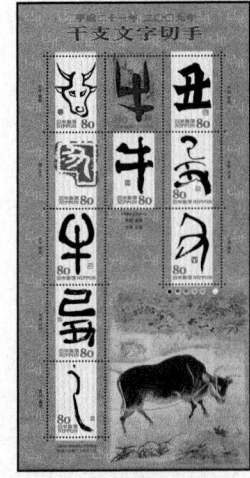

Edo Calligraphy — A2448

No. 3077 — Characters for "ox": a, Depiction of ox head (Kinbun style) with red chop at LL. b, Blue character on lilac background, in Kokotsubun style. c, Character with three horizontal lines and two vertical lines, in standard script, with red chop at LR. d, Red character in Kinbun style. e, Character with two horizontal lines and one vertical line, in standard script, with red chop at left center. f, Character in Tensho style with red chop at right center. g, Character with arc and crossed lines in Tensho style, with red chop at LR. h, Character with two crossing curves in Kokotsubun style, with red chop in center. i, Character with two components in Reisho style, with red chop at left. j, Character with dot above sinuous line in Hiragana style, with red chop at LR.

**Litho. & Embossed**
**2008, Nov. 21** — *Perf. 13x13¼*
3077  A2448  Sheet of 10  16.00  16.00
a.-j.  80y Any single  1.25  .50

A2449  A2450

A2451  A2452

A2453

Iron and Steel Industry, 150th Anniv. — A2454

**2008, Dec. 1  Photo.  Perf. 12¾x13**
3078  Sheet of 10, #3078a,
  3078b, 2 each
  #3078c-3078f  16.00  16.00
a.  A2449  80y multi  1.25  .50
b.  A2450  80y multi  1.25  .50
c.  A2451  80y multi  1.25  .50
d.  A2452  80y multi  1.25  .50
e.  A2453  80y multi  1.25  .50
f.  A2454  80y multi  1.25  .50

Daffodils
A2455

Plum
Blossoms
A2456

Fuki
A2457

Plum
Blossoms
A2458

Weeping
Cherry
Blossoms
A2459

Daffodils
A2460

Plum
Blossoms
A2461

Fuki
A2462

Plum
Blossoms
A2463

Weeping
Cherry
Blossoms
A2464

**2008, Dec. 1  Photo.  Perf. 13¼**
3079  A2455  50y multi  .80  .40
3080  A2456  50y multi  .80  .40
3081  A2457  50y multi  .80  .40
3082  A2458  50y multi  .80  .40
3083  A2459  50y multi  .80  .40
a.  Vert. strip of 5, #3079-3083  4.50  3.50
3084  A2460  80y multi  1.25  .55
3085  A2461  80y multi  1.25  .55
3086  A2462  80y multi  1.25  .55
3087  A2463  80y multi  1.25  .55
3088  A2464  80y multi  1.25  .55
a.  Vert. strip of 5, #3084-3088  7.00  5.00
  Nos. 3079-3088 (10)  10.25  4.75

Flowers of Fukui, Wakayama, Akita, Fukuoka and Kyoto prefectures.

Miniature Sheets

A2465

Greetings Stamps — A2466

No. 3089: a, Santa Claus holding star (26x30mm). b, Stylized man, woman as bell (26x30mm). c, Kittens (26x30mm). d, Teddy

bears and gift box (26x30mm). e, Chick, flowers (29mm diameter).
No. 3090: a, Kittens (34x28mm oval). b, Elf with bag of toys (25x34mm). c, Bluebirds in bouquet of roses (25x34mm). d, Santa Claus with horn (25x34mm). e, Fruit and flowers (25x34mm).

*Die Cut Perf. 13¼*
**2008, Dec. 8** — Litho.
3089  A2465  Sheet of 5  5.00  5.00
a.-e.  50y Any single  .80  .80

*Die Cut Perf. 13*
3090  A2466  Sheet of 5  7.50  7.50
a.-e.  80y Any single  1.25  .80

Miniature Sheet

Shimane Prefecture Local Autonomy Law, 60th Anniv. — A2467

No. 3091: a, Tree peony, silver coin for official use (33x39mm). b, Kuniga Coast (28x33mm). c, Matsue Castle (28x33mm). d, Tsuwano (28x33mm). e, Bronze bell (28x33mm).

**Perf. 13¼ (#3091a), 13x13¼**
**2008, Dec. 8** — Photo.
3091  A2467  Sheet of 5  6.50  6.50
a.-e.  80y Any single  1.25  .40

Miniature Sheet

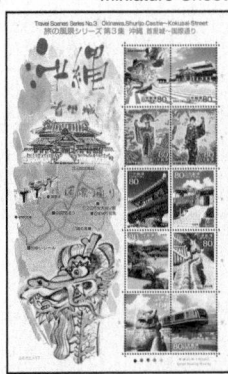

Travel
Scenes
A2468

No. 3092: a, Dragon from Shuri Castle Main Hall (stamp 1). b, Shuri Castle Main Hall (stamp 2). c, Ryukyuan dancer with arm raised at left (stamp 3). d, Ryukuan dancer with arm raised at right (stamp 4). e, Shurei Gate (stamp 5). f, Zuisen Gate and Rokoku Gate, Shuri Castle (stamp 6). g, Shikina Garden (stamp 7). h, Stone pavement, Kinjo (stamp 8). i, Guardian lion, International Street, Naha (stamp 9). j, Yui Monorail, Naha (stamp 10).

**2009, Jan. 23  Litho.  Perf. 13x13¼**
3092  A2468  Sheet of 10  12.50  12.50
a.-j.  80y Any single  1.25  .60

### Miniature Sheet

Travel
Scenes
A2469

No. 3093: a, Guardian Lion (stamp 1). b, Indian coral tree, Iejima (stamp 2). c, Fish in Okinawa Churaumi Aquarium, denomination at UR (stamp 3). d, As "c," denomination at LL (stamp 4). e, People watching fish in Okinawa Churaumi Aquarium, denomination at LL (stamp 5). f, As "e," denomination at LR (stamp 6). g, Nakijin Castle ruins (stamp 7). h, Okinawa rail (stamp 8). i, Cape Hedo, Okinawa (stamp 9). j, Mangroves, Gesashi Inlet (stamp 10).

**2009, Feb. 2**
| | | | | |
|---|---|---|---|---|
| 3093 | A2469 | Sheet of 10 | 12.50 | 12.50 |
| a.-j. | | 80y Any single | 1.25 | .60 |

Yoshino
Cherry
Blossoms
A2470

Azaleas
A2471

Tulips
A2472

Rhododendron
A2473

Nara Cherry
Blossoms
A2474

Yoshino
Cherry
Blossoms
A2475

Azaleas
A2476

Tulips
A2477

Rhododendrons
A2478

Nara Cherry
Blossoms
A2479

**2009, Feb. 2    Photo.    Perf. 13¼**
| | | | | |
|---|---|---|---|---|
| 3094 | A2470 | 50y multi | .80 | .40 |
| 3095 | A2471 | 50y multi | .80 | .40 |
| 3096 | A2472 | 50y multi | .80 | .40 |
| 3097 | A2473 | 50y multi | .80 | .40 |
| 3098 | A2474 | 50y multi | .80 | .40 |
| a. | | Vert. strip of 5, #3094-3098 | 5.00 | 3.75 |
| 3099 | A2475 | 80y multi | 1.25 | .60 |
| 3100 | A2476 | 80y multi | 1.25 | .60 |

| | | | | |
|---|---|---|---|---|
| 3101 | A2477 | 80y multi | 1.25 | .60 |
| 3102 | A2478 | 80y multi | 1.25 | .60 |
| 3103 | A2479 | 80y multi | 1.25 | .60 |
| a. | | Vert. strip of 5, #3099-3103 | 6.50 | 3.50 |
| | | Nos. 3094-3103 (10) | 10.25 | 5.00 |

Flowers of Tokyo, Tochigi, Niigata, Shiga and Nara prefectures.

### Animation
### Miniature Sheet

GeGeGe
no Kitaro
A2480

No. 3104: a, Kitaro and Otoko Nezumi. b, Daddy Eyeball in bowl. c, Kitaro kicking. d, Kitaro in fire. e, Villain with elongated head, villain with blades for arms. f, Villains with red face, villain with snake. g, Kitaro and mermaid. h, Musume Neko. i, Otoko Nezumi, Musume Neko, Babaa Sunakake and Nurikabe. j, Kitaro, Daddy Eyeball, Jijii Konaki, Momen Ittan.

**2009, Feb. 23    Litho.    Perf. 13x13¼**
| | | | | |
|---|---|---|---|---|
| 3104 | A2480 | Sheet of 10 | 16.00 | 16.00 |
| a.-j. | | 80y Any single | 1.25 | .50 |

### Miniature Sheet

Travel
Scenes
A2481

No. 3105: a, Todai Temple (stamp 1). b, Buddha, Todai Temple (stamp 2). c, Asura, Kofuku Temple (stamp 3). d, Nara National Museum (stamp 4). e, Kasuga Taisha Shrine (stamp 5). f, Roof of Kasuga Taisha Shrine and overhanging roof (stamp 6). g, Japanese deer, Wakakusa Hill (stamp 7). h, Inanuishi family residence (stamp 8). i, Gazebo, Nara Park (stamp 9). j, Bridge to gazebo, Nara Park (stamp 10).

**2009, Mar. 2**
| | | | | |
|---|---|---|---|---|
| 3105 | A2481 | Sheet of 10 | 12.50 | 12.50 |
| a.-j. | | 80y Any single | 1.25 | .60 |

### Miniature Sheet

Home
Towns
A2482

No. 3106 — Paintings by Taiji Harada of views of towns: a, Cultivating (farmer in field, Nishitama District, Tokyo prefecture). b, Children Planting Rice (children in rice paddy, Katta District, Miyagi prefecture). c, I'm Home (child running up hill to farmhouse, Yamagata District, Hiroshima prefecture). d, Northern Springtime (farmer and wheelbarrow in field of yellow flowers, Iwanai District, Hokkaido prefecture). e, Chinese Milk Vetch Field (people near farmhouse, Kyoto, Kyoto prefecture). f, Water Mortar (farmer near water mortar, Hita, Oita prefecture). g, Short Rest (woman resting on bench in front of building, Numazu, Shizuoka prefecture). h, Red Train (street scene with train in background, Izumo, Shimane prefecture). i, Oven-shaped Thatch Roofs (woman, children with toy car in front of farm house, Kishima District, Saga prefecture). j, Little Post Office (people outside of post office, Hosu District, Ishikawa prefecture).

**2009, Mar. 2    Photo.    Perf. 13**
| | | | | |
|---|---|---|---|---|
| 3106 | A2482 | Sheet of 10 | 12.50 | 12.50 |
| a.-j. | | 80y single | 1.25 | .60 |

### Miniature Sheets

Weekly
Comic
Books
For
Boys,
50th
Anniv
A2484

A2483

No. 3107: a, Osomatsu-kun (boy's face, green panel at top). b, Makoto Chan (boy with broom). c, Kamui Gaiden (swordsman with black hair). d, Gambare Genki (boxer, dark blue background). e, Paman (three characters with masks and capes). f, Urusei Yatsura (boy in cap, girl in bikini). g, Dame Oyaji (man holding radish and knife). h, Saibogu 009 (characters with galaxy in background). i, Purogorufa Saru (golfer). j, Tacchi (boy and girl looking over their shoulders).

No. 3108: a, Eitoman (android with "8" on chest). b, Taiga Masuku (caped man with tiger mask). c, Kyojin no Hoshi (Yomiuri Giants pitcher). d, Karate Baka Ichidai (karate master with green hair). e, GeGeGe no Kitaro (Kitaro, Daddy Eyeball and Otoko Nezumi). f, Ai to Makoto (girl with orange hair, boy with green hair). g, Tensai Bakabon (woman with yellow hair bow, screaming man). h, Tsurikichi Sanpei (boy holding fish). i, Ashita no Jo (boxer, pale blue background). j, Tonda Kappuru (boy, girl with green dress and orange bow).

**2009, Mar. 17    Litho.    Perf. 13**
| | | | | |
|---|---|---|---|---|
| 3107 | A2483 | Sheet of 10 | 12.50 | 12.50 |
| a.-j. | | 80y Any single | 1.25 | .60 |
| 3108 | A2484 | Sheet of 10 | 12.50 | 12.50 |
| a.-j. | | 80y Any single | 1.25 | .60 |

Wedding of
Emperor Akihito
and Empress
Michiko, 50th
Anniv. — A2485

Designs: No. 3109, Confectionery box. No. 3110, Fan.

**2009, Apr. 10    Photo.    Perf. 13¼**
| | | | | |
|---|---|---|---|---|
| 3109 | | 80y multi | 1.50 | .60 |
| 3110 | | 80y multi | 1.50 | .60 |
| a. | | A2485 Pair, #3109-3110 | 3.20 | 2.50 |
| b. | | Souvenir sheet, #3109-3110 | 3.50 | 3.50 |

### Animation
### Miniature Sheet

Detective
Conan
A2486

No. 3111: a, Ai Haibara and Conan and brick wall. b, Mitsuhiko Tsuburaya, Ayumi Yoshida, and Genta Kojima and brick wall. c, Heiji Hattori and cherry blossoms. d, Kazuha Toyama and cherry blossoms. e, Conan and night sky. f, Gin and night sky. g, Conan and fence. h, Ran Mori and fence. i, Kiddo Kaito holding Christmas gift. j, Conan, Moon and hang-glider.

**2009, Apr. 17    Litho.    Perf. 13x13¼**
| | | | | |
|---|---|---|---|---|
| 3111 | A2486 | Sheet of 10 | 16.00 | 16.00 |
| a.-j. | | 80y Any single | 1.25 | .50 |

Peonies, by Yu
Fei'an — A2487

Peonies, by Ren
Bonian — A2488

Peonies, by
Keika
Kanashima
A2489

Peonies, by
Keika
Kanashima
A2490

Peonies, by
Keika
Kanashima
A2491

Peonies, by
Keika
Kanashima
A2492

**2009, Apr. 20**  **Photo.**  **Perf. 13¼**

| 3112 | Sheet of 10, #3112c-3112f, 3 each, #3112a-3112b | 16.00 | 16.00 |
|---|---|---|---|
| a. | A2487 80y multi | 1.20 | .60 |
| b. | A2488 80y multi | 1.20 | .60 |
| c. | A2489 80y multi | 1.20 | .60 |
| d. | A2490 80y multi | 1.20 | .60 |
| e. | A2491 80y multi | 1.20 | .60 |
| f. | A2492 80y multi | 1.20 | .60 |

Philately Week.

Red Cross, 150th Anniv. A2493

Designs: No. 3113, Henri Dunant (1828-1910), founder of Red Cross. No. 3114, Japanese Red Cross Day poster, 1933.

**2009, May 8**  **Litho.**  **Perf. 13**

| 3113 | 80y multi | 1.25 | .50 |
|---|---|---|---|
| 3114 | 80y multi | 1.25 | .50 |
| a. | A2493 Pair, #3113-3114 | 3.00 | 2.50 |

**Miniature Sheet**

Nagano Prefecture Local Autonomy Law, 60th Anniv. — A2494

No. 3115: a, Kappa Bridge, Azusa River, Mt. Hodaka (33x39mm). b, Nanohana Park and Chikuma River, Iiyama City (28x33mm). c, Anraku Temple (28x33mm). d, Matsumoto Castle (28x33mm). e, Manji Buddha statue (28x33mm).

**Perf. 13¼ (#3115a), 13x13¼**

**2009, May 14**  **Photo.**

| 3115 | A2494 | Sheet of 5 | 6.50 | 6.50 |
|---|---|---|---|---|
| a.-e. | | 80y Any single | 1.25 | .60 |

Inauguration of Lay Judge System — A2495

Designs: No. 3116, Lay Judge System emblem. No. 3117, Birds on scale.

**2009, May 21**  **Litho.**  **Perf. 13x13¼**

| 3116 | 80y multi | 1.25 | .50 |
|---|---|---|---|
| 3117 | 80y multi | 1.25 | .50 |
| a. | A2495 Pair, #3116-3117 | 3.00 | 2.50 |

**Miniature Sheets**

A2496

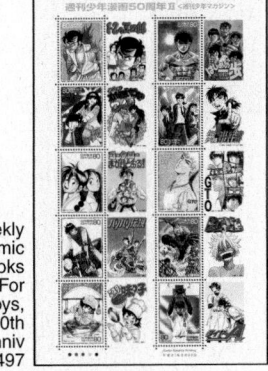

Weekly Comic Books For Boys, 50th Anniv A2497

No. 3118: a, Gu-Gu Ganmo (child and chicken-like alien). b, Major (baseball player with bat, ball and glove). c, Patlabor Mobile Police (man standing on robot). d, Rekka no Hono (boy with gloved hand raised). e, Ushio to Tora (monster and boy holding torch). f, ARMS (boy with extended hand and slash marks in background). g, GS Mikami Gakuraku Daisakusen (woman with long red hair). h, Kekkaishi (magician pointing finger forward). i, Detective Conan (boy pointing forward wearing glasses and bow tie). j, Hayate no Gotoku (girl, boy and tower).

No. 3119: a, 1, 2 no Sanshiro (judo fighter with flame in background). b, Hajime no Ippo (boxer). c, Kabocha Wain (boy and tall girl). d, Kindaichi Shonen no Jikenbo (two boys and girl). e, Kotaro Makari Tooru (boy and girl in white clothes). f, GTO (boy with GTO tattoo). g, Bari Bari Densetsu (motorcyclist). h, RAVE (swordsman and other characters). i, Misuta Ajikko (chef). j, Daiya no A (baseball pitcher).

**2009, May 22**  **Litho.**  **Perf. 13**

| 3118 | A2496 | Sheet of 10 | 16.00 | 16.00 |
|---|---|---|---|---|
| a.-j. | | 80y Any single | 1.25 | .50 |
| 3119 | A2497 | Sheet of 10 | 16.00 | 16.00 |
| a.-j. | | 80y Any single | 1.25 | .50 |

**Opening of Japanese Ports, 150th Anniv.**
**Miniature Sheets**

Nagasaki A2498

Yokohama — A2499

Hakodate — A2500

No. 3120: a, 19th century woodblock print of Nagasaki Port (denomination at left in black).

b, 19th century woodblock print of Nagasaki Port (denomination at right in black). c, Nagasaki Port at night (denomination at UL in white). d, Nagasaki Port at night (denomination at UR in black). e, Drawing of boats and ships (denomination at UL in black). f, Drawing of boats and ships (denomination at LR in white). g, Nagasaki Port at night (denomination at LL in white). h, Oura Catholic Church. i, Goddess Great Bridge, Nippon Maru cruise ship. j, Glover Garden, Nagasaki Port (lamppost in foreground).

No. 3121: a, Woodblock print of Yokohama Port, 1871 (denomination at LL in black). b, Woodblock print of Yokohama Port, 1871 (denomination at LR in black). c, Yokohama Port at night (denomination at UL in white, tall building at right). d, Yokohama Port at night (denomination at LR in white). e, Yokohama Bay Bridge. f, Yokohama City Port Opening Memorial Hall. g, Sailing ship Nippon Maru. h, Yokohama International Passenger Boat Terminal and cruise ship.

No. 3122: a, Woodblock print of Hakodate Port, 1882 (denomination at LL in black). b, Woodblock print of Hakodate Port, 1882 (denomination at UL in black). c, Hakodate Port at night (denomination at UR in white). d, Hakodate Port at night (denomination at UL in white). e, Street on Hachiman Slope, Hakodate Port at night. f, Hakodate Orthodox Christian Church. g, Ship, lamppost at Old Pier at night. h, Hakodate Park, Hakodate Port (denomination at UL in black).

**2009, June 2**  **Litho.**  **Perf. 13**

| 3120 | A2498 | Sheet of 10 | 16.00 | 16.00 |
|---|---|---|---|---|
| a.-j. | | 80y Any single | 1.25 | .50 |
| 3121 | A2499 | Sheet of 10, #3120e-3120f, 3121a-3121h | 16.00 | 16.00 |
| a.-h. | | 80y Any single | 1.25 | .50 |
| 3122 | A2500 | Sheet of 10, #3120e-3120f, 3122a-3122h | 16.00 | 16.00 |
| a.-h. | | 80y Any single | 1.25 | .50 |
| | | Nos. 3120-3122 (3) | 48.00 | 48.00 |

**Miniature Sheet**

National Afforestation Campaign — A2501

No. 3123 — Flora from Fukui Prefecture: a, Weeping cherry blossoms. b, Japanese zelkova tree. c, Japanese red pine tree. d, Japanese bird cherry tree. e, Magnolia blossoms. f, Camellia. g, Japanese horse chestnut tree. h, Kousa dogwood blossoms. i, Narcissi (denomination at UL). j, Narcissi (denomination at UR).

**2009, June 5**  **Litho.**  **Perf. 13**

| 3123 | A2501 | Sheet of 10 | 8.00 | 8.00 |
|---|---|---|---|---|
| a.-j. | | 50y Any single | .80 | .40 |

### Miniature Sheet

Home
Towns
A2502

No. 3124 — Paintings by Taiji Harada of views of towns: a, Flowers Blooming in the Rain (mother and daughter under umbrellas on path by flower field, Tone District, Gumma prefecture). b, Potato Blossoms (train car near potato field, Nakagawa District, Hokkaido prefecture). c, High Country Flowers (people in flower field, Suwa, Nagano prefecture). d, Memories on the Wind (farmer with wheelbarrow on path near farmhouse, Hagi, Yamaguchi prefecture). e, Tranquility (people near stone wall in front of house, Sumoto, Hyogo prefecture). f, Sunset Skies (adult and child on hillside path near house, Nishiusuki District, Miyazaki prefecture). g, Island Post Office (people standing in front of post office, Yaeyama District, Okinawa prefecture). h, Lotus Blossoms (field of lotus with house and large tree in background, Hakusan, Ishikawa prefecture). i, Flower Garden (two women picking flowers with house and telephone pole in background, Minamiboso, Chiba prefecture). j, Peach Blossoms (adult and child picnicking under trees, Fuefuki, Yamanashi prefecture).

**2009, June 23　Photo.　　Perf. 13**
3124　A2502　Sheet of 10　12.50　12.50
　a.-j.　　80y Any single　　　1.25　　.60

### Miniature Sheet

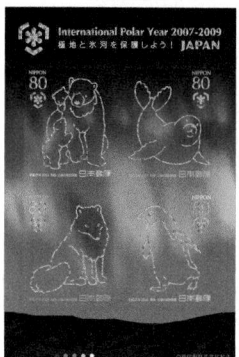

Intl.
Polar
Year
A2503

No. 3125: a, Polar bears. b, Weddell seal. c, Arctic fox. d, Adélie penguin.

**Litho. With Hologram Affixed**
**2009, June 30　　Die Cut Perf. 13**
**Self-Adhesive**
3125　A2503　Sheet of 4　7.00　7.00
　a.-d.　　80y Any single　　1.25　　.60

Gentian
A2504

Chrysanthemums
A2505

Miyagi Bush
Clover
A2506

Black Lilies
A2507

---

Japanese
Maple
A2508

Chrysanthemums
A2510

Black Lilies
A2512

Gentian
A2509

Miyagi Bush
Clover
A2511

Japanese
Maple
A2513

**2009, July 1　　Photo.　　　Perf. 13¼**
3126　A2504　50y multi　　　.80　　.40
3127　A2505　50y multi　　　.80　　.40
3128　A2506　50y multi　　　.80　　.40
3129　A2507　50y multi　　　.80　　.40
3130　A2508　50y multi　　　.80　　.40
　a.　　Vert. strip of 5, #3126-3130　4.50　4.00
3131　A2509　80y multi　　　1.25　　.60
3132　A2510　80y multi　　　1.25　　.60
3133　A2511　80y multi　　　1.25　　.60
3134　A2512　80y multi　　　1.25　　.60
3135　A2513　80y multi　　　1.25　　.60
　a.　　Vert. strip of 5, #3131-3135　6.50　6.50
　　Nos. 3126-3135 (10)　　10.25　5.00

Flora of Kumamoto, Hyogo, Miyagi, Ishikawa and Hiroshima prefectures.

### Miniature Sheet

Niigata Prefecture Local Autonomy
Law, 60th Anniv. — A2514

No. 3136: a, Japanese crested ibis over Sado Island (33x39mm). b, Cherry blossoms, Takada Castle (28x33mm). c, Fireworks over Nagaoka (28x33mm). d, Imori Pond, Mt. Myoko (28x33mm). e, Fireworks at Tokamichi Snow Festival (28x33mm).

**Perf. 13¼ (#3136a), 13x13¼**
**2009, July 8　　　　　Photo.**
3136　A2514　Sheet of 5　6.50　6.50
　a.-e.　　80y Any single　　1.25　　.60

Statue of Eki
Doji — A2515

**2009, July 23　Photo.　Perf. 13x13½**
3137　A2515　300y multi　　　8.00　　.30

---

Ono no
Komachi,
Poet
A2516

Hoshi
Jakuren,
Poet
A2518

Daini no Sanmi,
Poet — A2520

Ietaka Junii,
Poet
A2517

Sakanoue no
Korenori,
Poet
A2519

### Miniature Sheet

Poetry
A2521

No. 3143 — Poetry in Japanese calligraphy and: a, Tree with white blossoms. b, Ono no Komachi. c, Tree near pond. d, Ietaka Junii. e, Tree with green leaves. f, Hoshi Jakuren. g, House. h, Sakanoue no Korenori. i, Leaves. j, Daini no Sanmi.

**2009, July 23　　Photo.　　Perf. 13¼**
3138　A2516　50y multi　　　.80　　.30
3139　A2517　50y multi　　　.80　　.30
3140　A2518　50y multi　　　.80　　.30
3141　A2519　50y multi　　　.80　　.30
3142　A2520　50y multi　　　.80　　.30
　a.　　Vert. strip of 5, #3138-
　　　　3142　　　　　　5.00　3.50
**Perf. 12¾x13**
3143　A2521　Sheet of 10　16.00　16.00
　a.-j.　　80y Any single　　1.25　　.50

　　Letter Writing Day.

---

### Miniature Sheets

A2522

Hello
Kitty and
Dear
Daniel
A2523

No. 3144: a, Hello Kitty with envelope. b, Hello Kitty, Dear Daniel, birds in pond. c, Hello Kitty, Dear Daniel, two trees. d, Hello Kitty and Dear Daniel with envelopes. e, Hello Kitty, Dear Daniel, three trees.

No. 3145: a, Hello Kitty with envelope (35mm diameter). b, Hello Kitty, two birds (35x28mm, heart-shaped). c, Hello Kitty, tree, three birds. d, Bird carrying envelope flying over Hello Kitty. e, Hello Kitty, bird, two trees. f, Hello Kitty, Dear Daniel, bird, squirrel and rabbit.

**Die Cut Perf. 13½**
**2009, July 23　　　　　Litho.**
3144　A2522　Sheet of 10, 2
　　　　each #a-e　　9.00　9.00
　a.-e.　　50y Any single　　.80　　.80
**Die Cut Perf. (#3145a-3145b), Die
Cut Perf. 13½**
3145　A2523　Sheet of 10,
　　　　#a-b, 2 each
　　　　#c-f　　13.00　13.00
　a.-f.　　80y Any single　　1.25　　.80

Suwa Bluff,
Nippori, by
Hiroshige
A2524

Pensive
Love, by
Utamaro
A2525

Tokuji Otani
as Yakko
Sodesuke,
by Sharaku
A2526

Kumano
Junisha
Shrine, by
Hiroshige
A2527

Moon
Promontory,
by Hiroshige
A2528

Woman
Reading a
Letter, by
Utamaro
A2529

Wadaemon Nakajima as
Bodara Chozaemon and
Konozo Nakamura as
Funayado Kanagaway
no Gon, by Sharaku
A2530

Pagoda at Zojo Temple,
by Hiroshige
A2531

Clear
Weather
After
Snowfall at
Japan
Bridge, by
Hiroshige
A2532

Kameikichi
of
Sodegaura,
by Utamaro
A2533

**2009, Aug. 3   Litho.   Perf. 13¼**

| 3146 | Sheet of 10 | 13.00 | 13.00 |
|---|---|---|---|
| a. | A2524 80y multi | 1.25 | .60 |
| b. | A2525 80y multi | 1.25 | .60 |
| c. | A2526 80y multi | 1.25 | .60 |
| d. | A2527 80y multi | 1.25 | .60 |
| e. | A2528 80y multi | 1.25 | .60 |
| f. | A2529 80y multi | 1.25 | .60 |
| g. | A2530 80y multi | 1.25 | .60 |
| h. | A2531 80y multi | 1.25 | .60 |
| i. | A2532 80y multi | 1.25 | .60 |
| j. | A2533 80y multi | 1.25 | .60 |

Life in Edo (Tokyo).

Gujo Dance
(Gifu)
A2534

Fukagawa
Hachiman
Festival
(Tokyo)
A2535

Denomination at: No. 3147, Right. No.
3148, Left. No. 3149, Right. No. 3150, Left.

**2009, Aug. 10**

| 3147 | 50y multi | .80 | .40 |
|---|---|---|---|
| 3148 | 50y multi | .80 | .40 |
| a. | A2534 Horiz. pair, #3147-3148 | 1.75 | 1.25 |

| 3149 | 50y multi | .80 | .40 |
|---|---|---|---|
| 3150 | 50y multi | .80 | .40 |
| a. | A2535 Horiz. pair, #3149-3150 | 1.75 | 1.25 |
| | Nos. 3147-3150 (4) | 3.20 | 1.60 |

**Miniature Sheet**

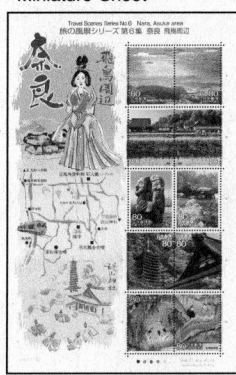

Travel
Scenes
A2536

No. 3151: a, Asuka, denomination at LL
(stamp 1). b, Asuka, denomination at LR
(stamp 2). c, Tachibana Temple, denomination
at LL (stamp 3). d, Tachibana Temple, denomination at LR (stamp 4). e, Sculpture, Asuka
Historical Museum (stamp 5). f, Stone burial
mound (stamp 6). g, Tanzan Shrine, denomination at UR (stamp 7). h, Tanzan Shrine,
denomination at UL (stamp 8). i, Picture scroll,
denomination at UL (stamp 9). j, Picture scroll,
denomination at LL (stamp 10).

**2009, Aug. 21   Perf. 13x13¼**

| 3151 | A2536 Sheet of 10 | 13.00 | 13.00 |
|---|---|---|---|
| a.-j. | 80y Any single | 1.25 | .60 |

Persimmons
and Haiku by
Shiki
Masaoka
A2537

Roofs of
Dogo Onsen
and Haiku by
Shiki
Masaoka
A2538

Mountain,
Field and
Haiku by
Kyoshi
Takahama
A2539

House and
Haiku by
Soseki
Natsume
A2540

Cherry Blossoms and
Haiku by Hekigoto
Kawahigashi — A2541

**2009, Sept. 1   Litho.**

| 3152 | A2537 80y multi | 1.25 | .40 |
|---|---|---|---|
| 3153 | A2538 80y multi | 1.25 | .40 |
| 3154 | A2539 80y multi | 1.25 | .40 |
| 3155 | A2540 80y multi | 1.25 | .40 |
| 3156 | A2541 80y multi | 1.25 | .40 |
| a. | Vert. strip of 5, #3152-3156 | 6.50 | 6.50 |

**Miniature Sheet**

National
Athletic
Meet
(Niigata)
A2542

No. 3157: a, Tohoku Electric Power Big
Swan Stadium. b, Soccer player. c, Boxer. d,
Basketball player.

**2009, Sept. 25   Perf. 13x13¼**

| 3157 | A2542 Sheet of 10, 2 each #3157a-3157c, 4 #3157d | 8.00 | 8.00 |
|---|---|---|---|
| a.-d. | 50y Any single | .80 | .40 |

Takayama
Festival
(Gifu)
A2543

Hakone
Feudal
Lord's
Procession
(Kanagawa)
A2544

Designs: No. 3158, Crowd at Night Festival.
No. 3159, Shakkyo float puppet. No. 3160,
Three men and box. No. 3161, Three men.

**2009, Oct. 1   Perf. 13¼**

| 3158 | 50y multi | .80 | .40 |
|---|---|---|---|
| 3159 | 50y multi | .80 | .40 |
| a. | A2543 Pair, #3158-3159 | 1.75 | 1.25 |
| 3160 | 50y multi | .80 | .40 |
| 3161 | 50y multi | .80 | .40 |
| a. | A2544 Horiz. pair, #3160-3161 | 1.75 | 1.60 |
| | Nos. 3158-3161 (4) | 3.20 | 1.60 |

**Miniature Sheet**

Home
Towns
A2545

No. 3162 — Paintings by Taiji Harada of
views of towns: a, Nagasaki Kunchi (palanquin
in parade, Nagasaki, Nagasaki prefecture). b,
Rice Paddy Spirit Festival (people in rice

paddy, Satsumasendai, Kagoshima prefecture). c, Carp Streamers (people making carp
streamers, Iwakura, Aichi prefecture). d, Doll
Send-off (winter parade, Waga District, Iwate
prefecture). e, Deer Dance (musicians, people
in blue, white, red and yellow costumes holding poles with banners, Kitauwa District,
Ehime prefecture). f, Business Success Festival (crowd in front of Ebisu Shrine, Naniwa
Ward, Osaka prefecture). g, Amahage Festival
(masked man visiting children and parents,
Akumi District, Yamagata prefecture). h, Lion
Dance (large crowd surrounding float with
dancers on tower, Wakayama, Wakayama prefecture). i, Floating Doll Festival (women drop-
ping dolls into Sendai River, Tottori, Tottori
prefecture). j, Gruel Doll Festival (children at
table near Kama River, Tano District, Gumma
prefecture).

**2009, Oct. 8   Photo.   Perf. 13**

| 3162 | A2545 Sheet of 10 | 13.00 | 13.00 |
|---|---|---|---|
| a.-j. | 80y Any single | 1.25 | 1.00 |

**International Letter Writing Week
Type of 2000**

Hiroshige paintings from 53 Stations of the
Tokaido Highway: 90y, Fujisawa. 110y, Okitsu.
130y, Chiryu.

**2009, Oct. 9   Photo.   Perf. 13¼**

| 3163 | A2119 90y multi | 1.75 | .50 |
|---|---|---|---|
| 3164 | A2119 110y multi | 2.25 | .50 |
| 3165 | A2119 130y multi | 2.50 | .50 |
| | Nos. 3163-3165 (3) | 6.50 | 1.50 |

See listing of No. 4448 for images of each
Hiroshige print.

**Miniature Sheet**

Diplomatic Relations Between Japan
and Austria, 140th Anniv. — A2546

No. 3166: a, Portrait of Emilie Flöge, by
Gustav Klimt (45x30mm). b, Autumn Clothing,
by Shoen Uemura (45x30mm). c, Vienna Art
History Museum and fountain (39x30mm). d,
Empress Elizabeth of Austria, by Franz Win-
terhalter (39x30mm). e, Melk Abbey (steeple
at right), Austria (39x30mm). f, Melk Abbey
(steeple at left, 39x30mm). g, Wolfgang
Amadeus Mozart and Salzburg (39x30mm). h,
Salzburg (39x30mm). i, Hallstatt waterfront
(39x30mm). j, Mountainside buildings, Hallstatt (39x30mm).

**2009, Oct. 16   Litho.   Perf. 13¼x13**

| 3166 | A2546 Sheet of 10 | 16.00 | 16.00 |
|---|---|---|---|
| a.-j. | 80y Any single | 1.25 | .50 |

See Austria No. 2227.

**Miniature Sheet**

Diplomatic Relations Between Japan
and Hungary, 140th Anniv. — A2547

No. 3167: a, Hungarian flask. b, Mount Fuji,
horiz. c, Jar from Japanese tea service. d,
Hungarian Parliament (flag above building). e,
Hungarian Parliament (building with dome). f,
Matyo folk embroidery, Hungary. g, Elizabeth
Bridge, Hungary, horiz. h, Crane and leaves
fabric pattern from Japanese kimono. i, Herend porcelain figurine (Hussar examining
sword blade). j, Herend porcelain vase.

*Perf. 13x13¼, 13¼x13*

**2009, Oct. 16**                                           **Litho.**
3167  A2547   Sheet of 10        16.00  16.00
*a.-j.*       80y Any single         1.25    .50

See Hungary No. 4141.

**Animation**
**Miniature Sheet**

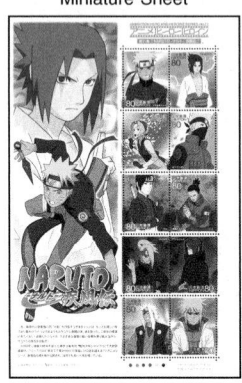

**Naruto: Hurricane Chronicles — A2548**

No. 3168: a, Naruto Uzumaki (yellow hair, black and orange shirt). b, Sasuke Uchiha (with open shirt). c, Sakura Haruno (girl with pink hair). d, Kakashi Hatake (with red spiral on sleeve). e, Sai (with sword). f, Shikamaru Nara (clasping hands). g, Deidara (girl with yellow hair and raised hand). h, Itachi Uchiha (with black hair and black and red robe). i, Jiraiya (with white hair). j, Fourth Hokage (yellow hair, white, gray and red robe).

**2009, Oct. 23   Litho.   Perf. 13x13¼**
3168  A2548   Sheet of 10        16.00  16.00
*a.-j.*       80y Any single         1.25    .50

**Miniature Sheet**

**Ibaraki Prefecture Local Autonomy**
**Law, 60th Anniv. — A2549**

No. 3169: a, H-2 rocket, Mt. Tsukuba (33x39mm). b, Fukuroda Falls (28x33mm). c, Mitsukuni Tokugawa (1628-1700), Mito daimyo (28x33mm). d, Boat on Kasumigaura (28x33mm). e, Fireworks over Tsuchiura (28x33mm).

*Perf. 13¼ (#3169a), 13x13¼*

**2009, Nov. 4**                                           **Photo.**
3169  A2549   Sheet of 5          7.50   7.50
*a.-e.*       80y Any single         1.25    .60

A2550        A2551

---

**New Year 2010 (Year of**
**the Tiger)**
A2552        A2553

**2009, Nov. 11   Photo.   Perf. 13x13½**
3170  A2550  50y multi           1.00    .30
3171  A2551  80y multi           1.50    .40

*Perf. 13¼*

3172  A2552  50y +3y multi       1.25    .40
3173  A2553  80y +3y multi       1.75    .40
    *Nos. 3170-3173 (4)*          5.50   1.50

Sheets of two containing Nos. 3170-3171 were lottery prizes. Value, $4.

**Phoenix**
**A2554**

**Kirin Facing**
**Right — A2555**

**Kirin Facing**
**Left — A2556**

**2009, Nov. 12   Photo.   Perf. 13¼**
3174  A2554  80y multi           1.25    .50
3175  A2555  80y multi           1.25    .50
3176  A2556  80y multi           1.25    .50
    *a.*     Souvenir sheet, #3175-3176   3.50  3.50
    *Nos. 3174-3176 (3)*          3.75   1.50

Enthronement of Emperor Akihito, 20th anniv. Nos. 3174-3176 were printed in sheets containing two each of Nos. 3175 and 3176 and six of No. 3174.

**Miniature Sheet**

**Calligraphy — A2557**

No. 3177 — Characters for "tiger" by calligraphers: a, Chikusei Hayashi (character in running script with red background). b, Chosho Kneko (character in clerical style, with denomination at LR, and large red chop at LL). c, Gakufu Toriyama (character in kinbun style in gold with blue green background). d, Hosen Takeuchi (character in kinbun style with denomination at LL, red chop at LR). e, Shiko Miyazaki (character in hiragana script with denomination above Japanese characters and "Nippon" at LL). f, Setsuzan Kitano (character in kokotsubun style with denomination and red

---

chop at LL). g, Masato Seki (character in kinbun style in red). h, Junichi Yanagida (characters in running script with denomination at LL above Japanese characters and "Nippon" at LR). i, Kukoku Tamura (character in clerical script in blue with light blue and white background). j, Bokushun Kito (character in kinbun style with denomination at LR and small red chop at LL).

**Litho. & Embossed**
**2009, Nov. 20**               **Perf. 13x13¼**
3177  A2557   Sheet of 10        16.00  16.00
*a.-j.*       80y Any single         1.25    .50

**Miniature Sheets**

A2558

**Greetings Stamps — A2559**

No. 3178: a, Girl and apples. b, Snowman and stars. c, Angel holding toy rabbit. d, Apple, ribbon, ring of roses. e, Figures with blue and pink faces, horiz.

No. 3179: a, Christmas wreath. b, Santa Claus playing violin on chimney. c, Oil lamp and flowers. d, Angel with gift. e, Figure made of fir branches, candle.

*Die Cut Perf. 12¾x13, 13x12¾*
**2009, Nov. 24**                             **Litho.**
**Self-Adhesive**
3178  A2558   Sheet of 5          5.00   5.00
*a.-e.*       50y Any single          .80    .80

*Die Cut Perf. 12¾x13*
3179  A2559   Sheet of 5          7.00   7.00
*a.-e.*       80y Any single         1.25    .80

**Peach**
**Blossoms**
**A2560**

**Rape**
**Blossoms**
**A2561**

**Plum**
**Blossoms**
**and**
**Primrose**
**A2562**

**Bayberry**
**A2563**

**Bungo Plum**
**Blossoms**
**A2564**

**Peach**
**Blossoms**
**A2565**

**Rape**
**Blossoms**
**A2566**

**Plum**
**Blossoms**
**and**
**Primrose**
**A2567**

---

**Bayberry**
**A2568**

**Bungo Plum**
**Blossoms**
**A2569**

**2009, Dec. 1   Photo.   Perf. 13¼**
3180  A2560  50y multi            .80    .40
3181  A2561  50y multi            .80    .40
3182  A2562  50y multi            .80    .40
3183  A2563  50y multi            .80    .40
3184  A2564  50y multi            .80    .40
    *a.*     Vert. strip of 5, #3180-3184   4.50  4.50
3185  A2565  80y multi           1.25    .60
3186  A2566  80y multi           1.25    .60
3187  A2567  80y multi           1.25    .60
3188  A2568  80y multi           1.25    .60
3189  A2569  80y multi           1.25    .60
    *a.*     Vert. strip of 5, #3185-3189   6.50  6.50
    *Nos. 3180-3189 (10)*        10.25   5.00

Flowers of Okayama, Chiba, Osaka, Kochi and Oita prefectures.

**Prefecture Types of 1991-2007**

Designs as before.

*Die Cut Perf. 13¼ at T, L and R,*
*Serpentine Die Cut 11¾ at B*
**2009**          **Litho.**   **Self-Adhesive**
3189B  ZA684  50y multi           .90    .50
*Serpentine Die Cut 11¾ at T and B,*
*Die Cut Perf. 13¼ at L and R*
3189C  ZA685  50y multi           .90    .50
3189D  ZA686  50y multi           .90    .50
3189E  ZA687  50y multi           .90    .50
*Serpentine Die Cut 11¾ at T, Die*
*Cut Perf. 13¼ at L, R and B*
3189F  ZA688  50y multi           .90    .50
    *j.*     Vert. strip of 5, #3189B-
             3189F                5.50
*Serpentine Die Cut 11½ at T, Die*
*Cut Perf. 13½ at L, R and B*
3189G  ZA115  80y multi          1.40    .90
*Serpentine Die Cut 11¾*
3189H  80y Katsura Beach         1.40    .90
3189I  80y Sakamoto Ryoma        1.40    .90
    *k.*     ZA352  Horiz. pair, #3189H-
             3189I                3.50
    *Nos. 3189B-3189I (8)*        8.70   5.20

Issued: Nos. 3189B-3189F, Oct.; No. 3189G, 3/19; Nos. 3189H-3189I, Nov.

**Animation**
**Miniature Sheet**

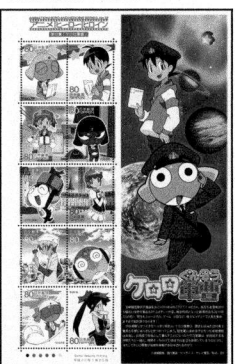

**Sergeant**
**Keroro**
**A2570**

No. 3190: a, Sergeant Keroro, wearing helmet, holding post card. b, Fuyuki Hinata holding post card. c, Natsumi Hinata holding gift. d, Corporal Giroro, wearing helmet, with arms crossed. e, Private Tamama holding gift above head. f, Momoka Nishizawa holding letter. g, Saburo holding stamps. h, Sergeant Major Kururu with stamp on forehead. i, Lance Corporal Dororo, with white helmet, holding scroll. j, Koyuki Azumaya, holding scroll.

**2010, Jan. 22   Litho.   Perf. 13**
3190  A2570   Sheet of 10        16.00  16.00
*a.-j.*       80y Any single         1.25    .50

**Miniature Sheets**

A2571

Greetings Stamps — A2572

No. 3191: a, Fairy with watering can. b, Fairy giving letter to bird. c, Fairies holding flower basket. d, Fairy with horn on back of flying bird. e, Fairy with violin on flower leaf.
No. 3192: a, Flower bouquet in red wrapping paper, butterflies. b, Woman with flute. c, Flower bouquet in white wrapping paper, butterflies. d, Flowers, G clef. e, Flowers, rabbit.

**Die Cut Perf. 12¾x13**

| 2010, Jan. 25 | | Litho. | | |
|---|---|---|---|---|
| | **Self-Adhesive** | | | |
| 3191 | A2571 | Sheet of 5 | 5.00 | 5.00 |
| a.-e. | | 50y Any single | .80 | .80 |
| 3192 | A2572 | Sheet of 5 | 7.00 | 7.00 |
| a.-e. | | 80y Any single | 1.25 | .80 |

Miniature Sheet

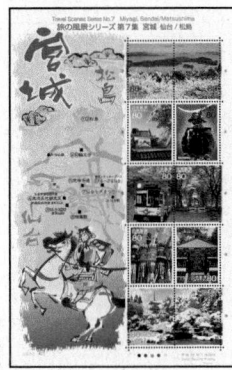

Travel Scenes A2573

No. 3193: a, Matsushima, denomination at LL (stamp 1). b, Matsushima, denomination at LR (stamp 2). c, Sendai Castle ruins (stamp 3). d, Suit of armor and crested helmet (stamp 4). e, Sendai tourist bus (stamp 5). f, A Bathing Woman, sculpture by Venanzo Crocetti, Sendai (stamp 6). g, Tanabata Festival, Sendai (stamp 7). h, Zuihoden Mausoleum (stamp 8). i, Rinno Temple, denomination at LL (stamp 9). j, Garden and pond at Rinno Temple (stamp 10).

| 2010, Jan. 29 | | Litho. | Perf. 13 | |
|---|---|---|---|---|
| 3193 | A2573 | Sheet of 10 | 13.00 | 13.00 |
| a.-j. | | 80y Any single | 1.25 | .50 |

Tulips A2574

Chinese Milk Vetch A2575

Nijisseiki Pear Blossoms A2576

Coral Tree Blossoms A2577

Fuji Cherry Blossoms A2578

Tulips A2579

Chinese Milk Vetch A2580

Coral Tree Blossoms A2582

Nijisseiki Pear Blossoms A2581

Fuji Cherry Blossoms A2583

| 2010, Feb. 1 | | Photo. | Perf. 13¼ | |
|---|---|---|---|---|
| 3194 | A2574 | 50y multi | .80 | .40 |
| 3195 | A2575 | 50y multi | .80 | .40 |
| 3196 | A2576 | 50y multi | .80 | .40 |
| 3197 | A2577 | 50y multi | .80 | .40 |
| 3198 | A2578 | 50y multi | .80 | .40 |
| a. | | Vert. strip of 5, #3194-3198 | 4.50 | 3.00 |
| 3199 | A2579 | 80y multi | 1.25 | .60 |
| 3200 | A2580 | 80y multi | 1.25 | .60 |
| 3201 | A2581 | 80y multi | 1.25 | .60 |
| 3202 | A2582 | 80y multi | 1.25 | .60 |
| 3203 | A2583 | 80y multi | 1.25 | .60 |
| a. | | Vert. strip of 5, #3199-3203 | 6.50 | 4.00 |
| | | Nos. 3194-3203 (10) | 10.25 | 5.00 |

Flowers of Toyama, Gifu, Tottori, Okinawa and Yamanashi prefectures.

Miniature Sheet

Nara Prefecture Local Autonomy Law, 60th Anniv. — A2584

No. 3204: a, Great Hall of State, cherry blossoms, kemari players (33x39mm). b, Hase Temple, peonies (28x33mm). c, Ukimodo during Nara Candlelight Festival (28x33mm). d, Muro Temple pagoda (28x33mm). e, Mt. Yoshino and cherry blossoms (28x33mm).

**Perf. 13¼ (#3204a), 13x13¼**

| 2010, Feb. 8 | | | Photo. | |
|---|---|---|---|---|
| 3204 | A2584 | Sheet of 5 | 6.50 | 6.50 |
| a.-e. | | 80y Any single | 1.25 | .60 |

Miniature Sheet

Travel Scenes A2585

No. 3205: a, Kurashiki District buildings, denomination at LL (stamp 1). b, Kurashiki District buildings, swans, denomination at UR (stamp 2). c, Ōhara Museum of Art (stamp 3). d, Belgian Girl in Kimono, painting by Torajiro Kojima (stamp 4). e, Seto Great Bridge, from distance (stamp 5). f, Arches and roadway of Seto Great Bridge (stamp 6). g, Kotohira Shrine (stamp 7). h, Mt. Iino (stamp 8). i, Bridge, Ritsurin Park, Takamatsu, denomination at LL (stamp 9). j, Bridge, Ritsurin Park, and cherry blossoms, denomination at UR (stamp 10).

| 2010, Mar. 1 | | Litho. | Perf. 13 | |
|---|---|---|---|---|
| 3205 | A2585 | Sheet of 10 | 13.00 | 13.00 |
| a.-j. | | 80y Any single | 1.25 | .60 |

Miniature Sheet

Characters From Peanuts Comic Strip — A2586

No. 3206: a, Snoopy reading letter (33x32mm). b, Woodstock reading letter under lamp (33x32mm). c, Peppermint Patty reading letter (33x32mm). d, Snoopy hugging Woodstock (35mm diameter). e, Sally reading letter (33x32mm). f, Snoopy and Woodstock on doghouse (35x29mm heart-shaped). g, Snoopy giving letter to Woodstock (33x32mm). h, Charlie Brown writing letter (33x32mm).

**Die Cut Perf. 13½**

| 2010, Mar. 3 | | Litho. | | |
|---|---|---|---|---|
| | **Self-Adhesive** | | | |
| 3206 | A2586 | Sheet of 10, #3206c-3206h, 2 each #3206a-3206b | 13.00 | 13.00 |
| a.-h. | | 80y Any single | 1.25 | .80 |

Peony A2587

Sudachi Flowers A2588

Unzen Azalea Flowers A2589

Kakitsubata Irises A2590

Camphor Blossoms A2591

Peonies A2592

Sudachi Flowers A2593

Unzen Azalea Flowers A2594

Kakitsubata Irises A2595

Camphor Blossoms A2596

| 2010, Mar. 8 | | Photo. | Perf. 13¼ | |
|---|---|---|---|---|
| 3207 | A2587 | 50y multi | .80 | .40 |
| 3208 | A2588 | 50y multi | .80 | .40 |
| 3209 | A2589 | 50y multi | .80 | .40 |
| 3210 | A2590 | 50y multi | .80 | .40 |
| 3211 | A2591 | 50y multi | .80 | .40 |
| a. | | Vert. strip of 5, #3207-3211 | 4.50 | 3.00 |
| 3212 | A2592 | 80y multi | 1.25 | .60 |
| 3213 | A2593 | 80y multi | 1.25 | .60 |
| 3214 | A2594 | 80y multi | 1.25 | .60 |
| 3215 | A2595 | 80y multi | 1.25 | .60 |
| 3216 | A2596 | 80y multi | 1.25 | .60 |
| a. | | Vert. strip of 5, #3212-3216 | 6.50 | 4.00 |
| | | Nos. 3207-3216 (10) | 10.25 | 5.00 |

Flowers of Shimane, Tokushima, Nagasaki, Aichi and Saga prefectures.

Miniature Sheet

Friendship With San Marino — A2597

No. 3217: a, La Repubblica, statue by Vittorio Pocchini, San Marino (stamp 1). b, First Tower, San Marino (stamp 2). c, Saint Marinus, angel and crowd from Appearance of Saint Marinus to His People, mural by Emilio Retrosi (stamp 3). d, Angel and crowd from Appearance of Saint Marinus to His People (stamp 4). e, Statue of Liberty, San Marino Government Building (stamp 5). f, Basilica of Saint Marinus (stamp 6). g, Second Tower, San Marino (stamp 7). h, Bell tower, First Tower (stamp 8). i, St. Mary Magdalene, painting by Francesco Menzocchi (stamp 9). j, St. Marinus, painting by unknown artist (stamp 10).

| 2010, Mar. 23 | | Litho. | Perf. 13 | |
|---|---|---|---|---|
| 3217 | A2597 | Sheet of 10 | 16.00 | 16.00 |
| a.-j. | | 80y Any single | 1.25 | .50 |

See San Marino No. 1818.

## Miniature Sheet

Hometown Festival — A2598

No. 3218 — Suwa Grand Shrine Sacred Pillar Festival, Nagano Prefecture: a, Honmiya Shrine, denomination in yellow. b, Maemiya Shrine, denomination in pink. c, Akimiya Shrine, denomination in greenish black. d, Harumiya Shrine, denomination in light blue. e, Men dragging logs to Miya River, denomination in pink. f, Nagamochi, denomination in black. g, Men dragging log down hill, denomination in blue.

**2010, Apr. 1      Litho.      Perf. 13¼**
**Self-Adhesive**
3218   A2598   Sheet of 10,
                   #3218a-
                   3218d, 2 each
                   #3218e-3218g   9.00   9.00
   a.-g.   50y Any single         .80     .40

Philately
Week
A2599

No. 3219: a, Tiger from screen painting by Gaho Hashimoto, denomination at UL. b, Peonies from screen painting by Hashimoto, denomination at LL. c, Peonies and birds from screen painting by Hashimoto, denomination at UL. d, Tiger, by Zhang Shanzi, denomination at LR.

**Perf. 12¾x12½ Syncopated**
**2010, Apr. 20                Photo.**
3219   A2599   Block of 4         6.00   6.00
   a.-d.   80y Any single         1.25    .50

## Miniature Sheet

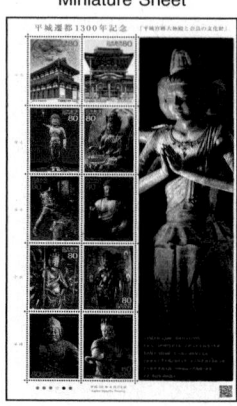

Treasures of Nara — A2600

---

No. 3220: a, Restored Heijo Palace (stamp 1). b, Inner gate, Kasuga Grand Shrine (stamp 2). c, Tanjo Shaka statue, denomination in white at UR (stamp 3). d, Aizen Myo-o statue, denomination in white at UL (stamp 4). e, Tentoki holding lantern, denomination in gold at UL (stamp 5). f, Buddha Yakushi, denomination in gold at UL (stamp 6). g, Thousand-armed Kannon statue, denomination in white at UR (stamp 7). h, Standing Bodhisattva statue, denomination in white at LR (stamp 8). i, Tamonten statue, denomination in gold at LL (stamp 9). j, Basara Taisho statue, denomination in gold at LR (stamp 10).

**2010, Apr. 23    Litho.    Perf. 14x13¾**
3220   A2600   Sheet of 10       16.00  16.00
   a.-j.   80y Any single        1.25    .50

Move of Imperial capital to Nara, 1300th anniv.

Hanashobu
Iris
A2601

Olive
Blossoms
A2602

Azalea
Flowers
A2603

Paulownia
Blossoms
A2604

Crinum
Flowers
A2605

Hanashobu
Irises
A2606

Olive
Blossoms
A2607

Azalea
Flowers
A2608

Paulownia
Blossoms
A2609

Crinum
Flowers
A2610

**2010, Mar. 8      Photo.      Perf. 13¼**
3221   A2601   50y multi         .80    .40
3222   A2602   50y multi         .80    .40
3223   A2603   50y multi         .80    .40
3224   A2604   50y multi         .80    .40
3225   A2605   50y multi         .80    .40
   a.   Vert. strip of 5, #3221-3225   4.50   3.00
3226   A2606   80y multi        1.25    .60
3227   A2607   80y multi        1.25    .60
3228   A2608   80y multi        1.25    .60
3229   A2609   80y multi        1.25    .60
3230   A2610   80y multi        1.25    .60
   a.   Vert. strip of 5, #3226-3230   6.50   4.00
   Nos. 3221-3230 (10)          10.25   5.00

Flowers of Mie, Kagawa, Gumma, Iwate and Miyazaki prefectures.

### Kobe-Awaji Expressway Prefecture Type of 1998

**Serpentine Die Cut 11½**
**2010, Aug.    Self-Adhesive    Litho.**
3230B   ZA229   80y Like No. Z237   —   2.50
3230C   ZA229   80y Like No. Z238   —   2.50
   d.   Horiz. pair, #3230B-3230C   —

---

## Miniature Sheet

A2611

Hello
Kitty
A2612

No. 3231 — Hello Kitty: a, With butterflies and flowers (28x31mm heart-shaped). b, In kimono, flowers (28x31mm heart-shaped). c, With dragon (28x28mm). d, With mountain (28x28mm). e, With peonies (28x28mm). f, With origami cranes (28x28mm).
No. 3232 — Hello Kitty: a, And Shanghai skyline (30x32mm). b, And pagoda in Shanghai (30x32mm). c, And Tiger (30x32mm). d, With peonies (31x28mm heart-shaped). e, Holding fan (31mm diameter).

**Die Cut Perf. 13½**
**2010, May 6                    Litho.**
**Self-Adhesive**
3231   A2611   Sheet of 10,
                   #3231a-
                   3231b, 2 each
                   #3231c-3231f   9.00   9.00
   a.-f.   50y Any single        .80     .80

**Die Cut Perf. 12½**
3232   A2612   Sheet of 10, 2
                   each #3232a-
                   3232e           13.00  13.00
   a.-e.   80y Any single         1.25    .80

---

## Miniature Sheet

Kochi Prefecture Local Autonomy Law,
60th Anniv. — A2613

No. 3233: a, Ryoma Sakamoto (1836-67), samurai, and Katsura Beach (33x39mm). b, Farmhouse clock, Aki (28x33mm). c, Harimaya Bridge, streetcar (28x33mm). d, Paper carp streamers (28x33mm). e, Cape Ashizuri Lighthouse (28x33mm).

**Perf. 13¼ (#3233a), 13x13¼**
**2010, May 14                   Photo.**
3233   A2613   Sheet of 5         7.00   7.00
   a.-e.   80y Any single        1.25    .60

## Miniature Sheet

Kanagawa Prefecture
Afforestation — A2614

No. 3234: a, Pinks. b, Japanese cedar. c, Sawtooth oak. d, Japanese maple. e, Golden-rayed lilies. f, Evergreen oak. g, Japanese chinquapin. h, Ginkgo. i, Beech. j, Gentians.

**2010, May 21      Litho.      Perf. 13**
3234   A2614   Sheet of 10       10.00  10.00
   a.-j.   50y Any single        .80     .40

## Miniature Sheets

A2615

2010 World Cup Soccer Championships, South Africa — A2616

No. 3235: a, Soccer ball, African animals (33x39mm). b, World Cup trophy (29x38mm). c, Poster for 2010 World Cup tournament (29x38mm). d, Emblem of 2010 World Cup (29x38mm). e, Emblem of Japan Soccer Association (29x38mm).

No. 3236 — Posters for World Cup tournaments of: a, 1930. b, 1934. c, 1938. d, 1950. e, 1954. f, 1958. g, 1962. h, 1970. i, 1978. j, 1986. k, 1990. l, 1994. m, 1998. n, 2002. o, 2006. p, Jules Rimet Cup. q, Jules Rimet Cup and hand.

**Litho., Litho. & Embossed (#3235a)**
*Perf. 13, 14x13½ (#3235a)*
**2010, May 31**
3235 A2615 Sheet of 5   8.00   8.00
*a.-e.*   80y Any single   1.25   .50

**Litho.**
*Perf. 13*
3236 A2616 Sheet of 20, #3236a-3236o, 3 #3236p, 2 #3236q   35.00   35.00
*a.-q.*   80y Any single   1.25   .50

## Miniature Sheet

Asia-Pacific Economic Cooperation Economic Leader's Meeting, Yokohama — A2617

No. 3237: a, Flowers at top and left, denomination at LR. b, Flowers at top and right, denomination at LL. c, Purple flower at center right, denomination at UR. d, Purple flower at center left, denomination at UL. e, Pink rose at center right, denomination at LL. f, Pink rose at center left, denomination at LR. g, White flowers at center right, denomination at UR. h, White flowers at center left, denomination at UL. i, Flowers at bottom and left, red flowers at LR, denomination at UR. j, Flowers at bottom and right, red flowers at LL, denomination at UL.

**2010, June 4   Litho.   Perf. 13**
3237 A2617 Sheet of 10   16.00   16.00
*a.-j.*   80y Any single   1.25   .50

Emblem of Japan Academy A2618    Certificate and Photograph of First Awards Ceremony A2619

Venue of First Awards Ceremony A2620    Former Japan Academy Hall A2621

Rooster — A2622

**2010, June 7   Litho.   Perf. 13**
3238 A2618 80y multi   1.25   .50
3239 A2619 80y multi   1.25   .50
3240 A2620 80y multi   1.25   .50
3241 A2621 80y multi   1.25   .50
3242 A2622 80y multi   1.25   .50
*a.*   Vert. strip of 5, #3238-3242   7.50   7.50
*Nos. 3238-3242 (5)*   6.25   2.50

Japan Academy Prizes, cent.

## Animation
### Miniature Sheet

Full Metal Alchemist — A2623

No. 3243: a, Edward Elric (with yellow hair and hand on his shoulder). b, Alphonse Elric (in black armor). c, Riza Hawkeye (holding gun). d, Roy Mustang with symbol on back of hand. e, Xiao Mei (panda). f, May Chang (with braided hair). g, Ling Yao holding sword. h, Lan Fan holding dagger. i, Winry Rockbell (girl in tank top). j, Edward Elric with dog, Den.

**2010, June 14   Litho.   Perf. 13x13¼**
3243 A2623 Sheet of 10   16.00   16.00
*a.-j.*   80y Any single   1.25   .50

## Miniature Sheet

Gifu Local Autonomy Law, 60th Anniv. — A2624

No. 3244: a, Cormorant fishing on Nagara River (32x39mm). b, Gifu Castle (28x33mm). c, Yokokura Temple (28x33mm). d, Art exhibition, Mino (28x33mm). e, Restored buildings, Magome (28x33mm).

*Perf. 13¼ (#3244a), 13x13¼*
**2010, June 18   Photo.**
3244 A2624 Sheet of 5   7.00   7.00
*a.-e.*   80y Any single   1.25   .60

Revision of Japan-United States Security Treaty, 50th Anniv. — A2625

Designs: No. 3245, Flags of U.S. and Japan, Japanese Prime Minister Nobusuke Kishi and U.S. President Dwight D. Eisenhower. No. 3246, Japanese Diet and U.S. Capitol.

**2010, June 23   Litho.   Perf. 13**
3245   80y multi   1.25   .50
3246   80y multi   1.25   .50
*a.*   A2625 Pair, #3245-3246   3.00   1.50

## Miniature Sheet

National Fireworks Competition, Omagari, Akita Prefecture — A2626

No. 3247 — Various fireworks with denomination in: a, Yellow green at UL, country name in Japanese characters at LL. b, Yellow green at UR. c, Pale orange at LL. d, Blue at LL. e, Rose at UL. f, Rose at LR, country name in Japanese characters at LR. g, Rose at LR, country name in Japanese characters at LL. h, Blue green at LR. i, Yellow green at UL, country name in Japanese characters at LR. j, Yellow green at LR.

**2010, July 1   Litho.   Perf. 13¼**
3247 A2626 Sheet of 10   10.00   10.00
*a.-j.*   50y Any single   .80   .40

## Miniature Sheet

Travel Scenes A2627

No. 3248: a, Kurushima-Kaikyo Great Bridge, denomination at LL (stamp 1). b, Kurushima-Kaikyo Great Bridge, denomination at LR (stamp 2). c, Jodo Temple, denomination at UR (stamp 3). d, Jodo Temple, denomination at UL (stamp 4). e, Bridge, sculptures on Mt. Shirataki (stamp 5). f, Kojoji three-story pagoda (stamp 6). g, Oyamazumi Shrine (stamp 7). h, Omishima Bridge, boat (stamp 8). i, Building with red window shutters at Imabari Castle (stamp 9). j, Six-story donjon at Imabari Castle (stamp 10).

**2010, July 8   Litho.   Perf. 13x13¼**
3248 A2627 Sheet of 10   13.00   13.00
*a.-j.*   80y Any single   1.25   .60

Emperor Koko, Poet A2628    Lady Ise, Poet A2629

Saki no
Daisojo
Gyoson,
Poet
A2630

Yushi
Naishinno-
ke no Kii,
Poet
A2631

Sutoku In, Poet — A2632

Poetry
A2633

No. 3254 — Poetry in Japanese calligraphy
and: a, Purple flowers. b, Emperor Koko. c,
Pond. d, Lady Ise. e, Hill and flowering trees. f,
Saki no Daisojo Gyoson. g, Ocean waves. h,
Yushi Naishinno-ke no Kii. i, Waterfall. j,
Sutoku In.

| 2010, July 23 | Photo. | Perf. 13¼ | |
|---|---|---|---|
| 3249 | A2628 | 50y multi | .80 | .30 |
| 3250 | A2629 | 50y multi | .80 | .30 |
| 3251 | A2630 | 50y multi | .80 | .30 |
| 3252 | A2631 | 50y multi | .80 | .30 |
| 3253 | A2632 | 50y multi | .80 | .30 |
| a. | Vert. strip of 5, #3249-3253 | | 5.00 | 3.50 |

Perf. 12¾x13

| 3254 | A2633 | Sheet of 10 | 16.00 | 16.00 |
|---|---|---|---|---|
| a.-j. | | 80y Any single | 1.25 | .50 |

Letter Writing Day.

Suruga
Street, by
Hiroshige
A2634

Woman
Reading a
Letter, by
Utamaro
A2635

Dyer's
Quarters,
Kanda, by
Hiroshige
A2636

Sojuro
Sawamura II
as Kurando
Ogishi, by
Sharaku
A2637

Asakusa
Ricefields
and
Torinomachi
Festival, by
Hiroshige
A2638

Takinogawa,
Oji, by
Hiroshige
A2640

Yamashita
Park, Ueno,
by Hiroshige
A2642

White
Uchikake,
by Utamaro
A2639

Torazo
Tanimura as
Yaheiji
Washizuka,
by Sharaku
A2641

Glass
Goblet, by
Utamaro
A2643

| 2010, Aug. 2 | Litho. | Perf. 13¼ | |
|---|---|---|---|
| 3255 | | Sheet of 10 | 13.00 | 13.00 |
| a. | A2634 80y multi | | 1.25 | .60 |
| b. | A2635 80y multi | | 1.25 | .60 |
| c. | A2636 80y multi | | 1.25 | .60 |
| d. | A2637 80y multi | | 1.25 | .60 |
| e. | A2638 80y multi | | 1.25 | .60 |
| f. | A2639 80y multi | | 1.25 | .60 |
| g. | A2640 80y multi | | 1.25 | .60 |
| h. | A2641 80y multi | | 1.25 | .60 |
| i. | A2642 80y multi | | 1.25 | .60 |
| j. | A2643 80y multi | | 1.25 | .60 |

Life in Edo (Tokyo).

Miniature Sheet

Fukui Local Autonomy Law, 60th
Anniv. — A2644

No. 3256: a, Dinosaur at Tojimbo
(32x39mm). b, Narcissus (28x33mm). c, Lake
and flowers (28x33mm). d, Ichijodani ruins,
cherry tree (28x33mm). e, Crab, Echizen-
Kaga Kaigan Quasi-National Park (28x33mm).

Perf. 13¼ (#3256a), 13x13¼

| 2010, Aug. 9 | | Photo. | |
|---|---|---|---|
| 3256 | A2644 | Sheet of 5 | 7.00 | 7.00 |
| a.-e. | | 80y Any single | 1.25 | .60 |

Miniature Sheet

Home
Towns
A2645

No. 3257 — Paintings by Taiji Harada of
views of Hokkaido prefecture towns: a,
Shiranuka Line (Farmhouses, haystack, two
cows, Shiranuka). b, Shiranuka Line (Train,
three cows, Shiranuka). c, Red-crowned
Cranes (Building near forest in snow, Tsurui).
d, Red-crowned Cranes (Woman feeding
cranes, Tsurui). e, Flowers of the Land
(Houses, trees hills, Biei). f, Flowers of the
Land (Tractor, hills, trees, Biei). g, Farm (Farm
buildings, mail box cows, Ishikari). h, Farm
(Farm buildings, silo, farmer tending cow,
Ishikari). i, Hibernation (Building in snow, fishing boats, Wakkanai). j, Canal in Spring (Boats
in canal, Otaru).

| 2010, Sept. 10 | Photo. | Perf. 13 | |
|---|---|---|---|
| 3257 | A2645 | Sheet of 10 | 16.00 | 16.00 |
| a.-j. | | 80y Any single | 1.25 | .60 |

Biplane of Henri
Farman — A2646

Aeronautical
Research
Plane — A2647

Asuka — A2648

Boeing 747-
400 — A2649

Mitsubishi
Regional
Jet — A2650

Monoplane of
Hans
Grade — A2651

YS-11 — A2652

Kawasaki T-
4 — A2653

US-2 — A2654

Supersonic
Plane — A2655

| 2010, Sept. 21 | Litho. | Perf. 13 | |
|---|---|---|---|
| 3258 | | Sheet of 10 | 16.00 | 16.00 |
| a. | A2646 80y multi | | 1.25 | .50 |
| b. | A2647 80y multi | | 1.25 | .50 |
| c. | A2648 80y multi | | 1.25 | .50 |
| d. | A2649 80y multi | | 1.25 | .50 |
| e. | A2650 80y multi | | 1.25 | .50 |
| f. | A2651 80y multi | | 1.25 | .50 |
| g. | A2652 80y multi | | 1.25 | .50 |
| h. | A2653 80y multi | | 1.25 | .50 |
| i. | A2654 80y multi | | 1.25 | .50 |
| j. | A2655 80y multi | | 1.25 | .50 |

Aviation in Japan, cent.

**Animation**
Miniature Sheet

Chibi Maruko-chan — A2656

No. 3259: a, Sakura family members,
Maruko, Sakiko, and mother Sumire (denomination in red at UL). b, Sakura family members
father Hiroshi, grandfather Tomozo, and
grandmother Kotake (denomination in white at
LL). c, Maruko blowing bubbles (holding gun).
d, Tomozo and bubbles. e, Hiroshi and Maruko
with glow worm. f, Sakiko with glow worm. g,
Sumire preparing food. h, Maruko and Kotake
preparing food. i, Hamaji and Butaro (boys and
snowflakes). j, Maruko and Tama-chan (and
snowflakes).

| 2010, Sept. 22 | Litho. | Perf. 13x13¼ | |
|---|---|---|---|
| 3259 | A2656 | Sheet of 10 | 16.00 | 16.00 |
| a.-j. | | 80y Any single | 1.25 | .50 |

Chiba Central
Sports Center
and Chiba
Marine
Stadium
A2657

Hammer
Throw
A2658

Equestrian
A2659

Rock
Climbing
A2660

Pole Vault — A2661

| 2010, Sept. 24 | Litho. | Perf. 13x13¼ | |
|---|---|---|---|
| 3260 | | Sheet of 10, 2 each | | |
| | #a-e | | 10.00 | 10.00 |
| a. | A2657 50y multi | | .80 | .40 |
| b. | A2658 50y multi | | .80 | .40 |
| c. | A2659 50y multi | | .80 | .40 |
| d. | A2660 50y multi | | .80 | .40 |
| e. | A2661 50y multi | | .80 | .40 |

65th National Athletics Meet, Chiba.

## Miniature Sheet

Travel Scenes
A2662

No. 3261: a, Akashi Strait Great Bridge, denomination in blue at UL (stamp 1). b, Akashi Strait Great Bridge, Sun Yat-sen Memorial Hall, Kobe, denomination at UR (stamp 2). c, Flowers, Awaji Island, denomination at UR to right of "Nippon" (stamp 3). d, Flowers, Awaji Island, denomination at UR below "Nippon" (stamp 4). e, Awaji puppet theater, denomination at UR (stamp 5). f, Awaji puppet theater, denomination at UL (stamp 6). g, Onaruto Bridge, denomination in white at LL (stamp 7). h, Onaruto Bridge, denomination in white at UR( stamp 8). i, Bridge, Naruto Whirlpools (stamp 9). j, Esaki Lighthouse (stamp 10).

| 2010, Oct. 1 | Litho. | Perf. 13x13¼ |
|---|---|---|
| 3261 | A2662 | Sheet of 10 | 13.00 | 13.00 |
| a.-j. | | 80y Any single | 1.25 | .60 |

## Miniature Sheet

Aichi Local Autonomy Law, 60th Anniv. — A2663

No. 3262: a, Golden dolphin sculpture at Nagoya Castle, irises, Atsumi Peninsula (32x39mm). b, Eurasian scops owl (28x33mm). c, Ginkgo leaves (28x33mm). d, Seto ceramic jar (28x33mm). e, Cherry blossoms (28x33mm).

| Perf. 13¼ (#3262a), 13x13¼ |
|---|
| 2010, Oct. 4 | Photo. |
| 3262 | A2663 | Sheet of 5 | 7.00 | 7.00 |
| a.-e. | 80y Any single | 1.25 | .60 |

Intl. Letter Writing Week — A2664

Painting details: 90y, Michitose, by Shinsui Ito. 110y, Nozaki Village, by Kiyokata Kaburagi. 130y, Botanyuki, by Shoen Uemura, horiz.

| 2010, Oct. 8 | Photo. | Perf. 13¼ |
|---|---|---|
| 3263 | A2664 | 90y multi | 1.75 | .50 |
| 3264 | A2664 | 110y multi | 2.25 | .50 |
| 3265 | A2664 | 130y multi | 2.50 | .50 |
| | Nos. 3263-3265 (3) | 8.25 | 6.25 |

## Miniature Sheet

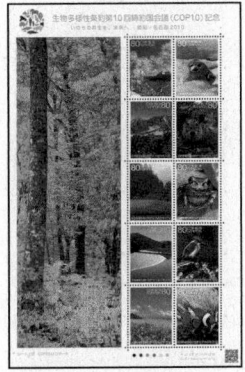

Tenth Conference of Parties to the Convention on Biological Diversity, Nagoya — A2665

No. 3266: a, Lake Mashu, frost-covered trees. b, Spotted seal. c, Mt. Tsurugi. d, Japanese antelope. e, Buildings in mountains. f, Common tree frog and flowers. g, Banks of Shimanto River. h, Common kingfisher. i, Flowers at Cape Tamatori. j, False clownfish and sea anemone.

| 2010, Oct. 18 | Litho. | Perf. 13x13¼ |
|---|---|---|
| 3266 | A2665 | Sheet of 10 | 16.00 | 16.00 |
| a.-j. | 80y Any single | 1.25 | .50 |

## Miniature Sheet

Friendship Between Japan and Portugal, 150th Anniv. — A2666

No. 3267: a, Japanese screen painting depicting bow of Portuguese ship, denomination at LL (30x45mm, stamp 1). b, Japanese screen painting depicting stern of Portuguese ship, denomination at LR (30x45mm, stamp 2). c, Belém Tower, Lisbon (30x43mm, stamp 3). d, Statue of St. Vincent (30x43mm, stamp 4). e, Monastery of the Hieronymites, Lisbon (30x43mm, stamp 5). f, Ruins of Roman Temple of Evora, Portugal (30x43mm, stamp 6). g, Oporto, Portugal, and boat (30x43mm, stamp 7). h, Batalha Monastery, Batalha, Portugal (30x43mm, stamp 8). i, Portuguese decorative tiles (30x43mm, stamp 9). j, Puppet of St. Isabel of Portugal (30x43mm, stamp 10).

| 2010, Oct. 22 | Litho. | Perf. 13¼x13 |
|---|---|---|
| 3267 | A2666 | Sheet of 10 | 16.00 | 16.00 |
| a.-j. | 80y Any single | 1.25 | .50 |

See Portugal No. 3271.

Seven People
A2667

Eight People
A2668

Congress Emblem
A2669

Peace Statue, Nagasaki
A2670

| 2010, Nov. 5 | Photo. | Perf. 13 |
|---|---|---|
| 3268 | Sheet of 10, 2 each #3268a-3268c, 4 #3268d | 16.00 | 16.00 |
| a. | A2667 80y multi | 1.25 | .50 |
| b. | A2668 80y multi | 1.25 | .50 |
| c. | A2669 80y multi | 1.25 | .50 |
| d. | A2670 80y multi | 1.25 | .50 |

Third UNI Global Union World Congress, Nagasaki.

## Miniature Sheets

A2671

A2672

Greetings — A2673

No. 3269: a, Star and Santa Claus with sack. b, Poinsettias, ribbon and bell. c, Sleigh of Santa Claus over church, horiz. d, Heart-shaped wreath. e, Reindeer and Aurora Borealis.

No. 3270: a, Santa Claus. b, Christmas tree. c, Sleigh of Santa Claus over mountain, horiz. d, Wreath with pine cones. e, Reindeer and Aurora Borealis, diff.

No. 3271: a, Fairy with horn flying above town. b, Snowman juggling snowballs. c, Children singing, horiz. d, Rose in box. e, Cakes.

### Die Cut Perf. 13

| 2010, Nov. 8 | | Litho. |
|---|---|---|
| | Self-Adhesive | |
| 3269 | A2671 | Sheet of 5 | 5.00 | 5.00 |
| a.-e. | 50y Any single | .80 | .80 |
| 3270 | A2672 | Sheet of 5 | 7.00 | 7.00 |
| a.-e. | 80y Any single | 1.25 | .80 |
| 3271 | A2673 | Sheet of 5 | 9.00 | 9.00 |
| a.-e. | 90y Any single | 1.40 | .80 |

A2674 A2675

New Year 2011 (Year of the Rabbit)
A2676 A2677

| 2010, Nov. 10 | Photo. | Perf. 13x13½ |
|---|---|---|
| 3272 | A2674 | 50y multi | 1.00 | .30 |
| 3273 | A2675 | 80y multi | 1.50 | .40 |
| | Photo. & Typo. | |
| | Perf. 13¼ | |
| 3274 | A2676 | 50y +3y multi | 1.25 | .40 |
| 3275 | A2677 | 80y +3y multi | 1.75 | .40 |
| | Nos. 3272-3275 (4) | 6.75 | 5.15 |

Sheets of two containing Nos. 3272-3273 were lottery prizes. Value, $3.25.

## Miniature Sheet

Aomori Local Autonomy Law, 60th Anniv. — A2678

No. 3276: a, Apples, Nebuta Festival floats (32x39mm). b, Hirosaki Castle and cherry blossoms (28x33mm). c, Three Shrines Festival, Hachinohe (28x33mm). d, Lake Towada (28x33mm). e, Horse and Shiriyazaki Lighthouse (28x33mm).

| Perf. 13¼ (#3276a), 13x13¼ |
|---|
| 2010, Nov. 15 | Photo. |
| 3276 | A2678 | Sheet of 5 | 7.00 | 7.00 |
| a.-e. | 80y Any single | 1.25 | .60 |

## Miniature Sheet

Edo Calligraphy — A2679

No. 3277 — Charcters for "rabbit": a, In Kinbun style (red character). b, In Six Dynasties style standard script (heavy black characters with red chop at LL, denomination at UR. c, In oracle bone script (single black character resembling animal with legs and tail, denomination at LR). d, In oracle bone script (three characters having horizontal line at UL, with red chop at LR, denomination at LR). e, In clerical script (silver character on green background). f, In small seal script (denomination at UL, "Nippon" at LR). g, In seal script (two black characters, with red chop, denomination and "Nippon" at LR). h, In Hirigana style (black character with denomination and "Nippon" at UL, red chop near center). i, In running script (black character with small dot at top, with denomination at LR and "Nippon" at LL). j, In standard script (two black characters with red chop and denomination at LR, "Nippon" at LL).

| Litho. & Embossed | |
|---|---|
| 2010, Dec. 3 | Perf. 13x13¼ |
| 3277 | A2679 | Sheet of 10 | 16.00 | 16.00 |
| a.-j. | 80y Any single | 1.25 | .50 |

Japanese Diet, 120th Anniv. A2680

Stained-glass window from Central Hall, old and new Diet buildings with entranceway of: No. 3278, New Diet. No. 3279, Old Diet.

**2010, Nov. 29**     Litho.     *Perf. 13*

| | | | | |
|---|---|---|---|---|
| 3278 | 80y multi | | 1.25 | .50 |
| 3279 | 80y multi | | 1.25 | .50 |
| *a.* | A2680 | Horiz. pair, #3278-3279 | 3.00 | 1.50 |

**Miniature Sheet**

Home Towns
A2681

No. 3280 — Paintings by Taiji Harada of views of Tohuku region towns: a, Paulownia Village (Cyclist near house, Mishima, Fukushima prefecture). b, Paulownia Village (Farmers and tree near water, Mishima). c, Bonnet Bus (White bus, Hiraizumi, Iwate prefecture). d, Bonnet Bus (Houses, people under umbrella, Hiraizumi). e, Bent House by the Sea (Mother with children near sea, Yurihonjo, Akita prefecture). f, After the Snowfall (Person and houses in snow, Akita, Akita prefecture). g, Railbus (Railbus and station, Kamikita District, Aomori prefecture). h, Railbus (People at station, Kamikita District). i, Dear Home (People on path near house, Tsuruoka, Yamagata prefecture). j, Kokeshi Doll (Children and adults near doll vendor's stall, Shiroishi, Miyagi prefecture).

**2010, Dec. 1**     Photo.     *Perf. 13*

| | | | | |
|---|---|---|---|---|
| 3280 | A2681 | Sheet of 10 | 13.00 | 13.00 |
| *a.-j.* | | 80y Any single | 1.25 | .60 |

**Mandarin Duck Type of 2007**
*Perf. 13¾x13½ Syncopated*

**2010, Jan.**              Litho.

| | | | | |
|---|---|---|---|---|
| 3281 | A2352 | 50y multi | .90 | .50 |

**Prefecture Type of 1990 Redrawn and Prefecture Types of 1991-96**

Designs as before.

*Serpentine Die Cut 10¾x11½*

| **2010** | **Litho.** | | **Self-Adhesive** | |
|---|---|---|---|---|
| 3282 | ZA85 | 80y multi | 1.25 | .60 |
| 3283 | ZA86 | 80y multi | 1.25 | .60 |
| 3284 | ZA87 | 80y multi | 1.25 | .60 |
| 3285 | ZA88 | 80y multi | 1.25 | .60 |
| *a.* | | Horiz. strip of 4, #3282-3285 | 6.00 | 6.00 |
| 3286 | ZA97 | 80y multi | 1.25 | .60 |
| 3287 | ZA98 | 80y multi | 1.25 | .60 |
| 3288 | ZA99 | 80y multi | 1.25 | .60 |
| 3289 | ZA100 | 80y multi | 1.25 | .60 |
| *a.* | | Horiz. strip of 4, #3286-3289 | 6.00 | 6.00 |

*Serpentine Die Cut 11½x11¾*

| | | | | |
|---|---|---|---|---|
| 3290 | ZA186 | 80y multi | 1.25 | .60 |
| | | Nos. 3282-3290 (9) | 11.25 | 5.40 |

Issued: Nos. 3282-3289, Mar.; No. 3290, Apr.

Hisoka Maeshima (1835-1919), Founder of Japanese Postal Service
A2682

Little Cuckoo
A2683

Mute Swan
A2684

Burial Statue of Warrior, Ota
A2686

Silver Crane
A2685

Bazara-Taisho, c. 710-794
A2687

**2010-11**     Photo.     *Perf. 13x13½*

| | | | | |
|---|---|---|---|---|
| 3293 | A2682 | 1y brown | .30 | .25 |
| 3294 | A2683 | 3y green | .30 | .25 |
| 3295 | A2684 | 5y blue & lt bl | .30 | .25 |
| 3296 | A2685 | 100y multi | 2.50 | .40 |
| 3297 | A2686 | 200y vermilion | 5.00 | .40 |
| 3298 | A2687 | 500y dark green | 14.00 | .50 |
| | | Nos. 3293-3298 (6) | 22.40 | 2.05 |

Issued: 1y, 1/7/11; 3y, 12/8; 5y, 12/6; 100y, 12/27; 200y, 2/10/11; 500y, 12/16. Compare type A2682 with types A563a and A3348, types A2683-A2687 with types A713, A714, A718a, A718d, A1013 and A1207.

**Miniature Sheet**

Saga Local Autonomy Law, 60th Anniv. — A2688

No. 3299: a, Shigenobu Okuma (1838-1922), politician, and Arita porcelain (32x39mm). b, Yoshinogari ruins (28x33mm). c, Yutoku Inari shrine and bridge (28x33mm). d, Hot-air balloons, Saga International Balloon Festival (28x33mm). e, Sea bream float, Karatsu Festival (28x33mm).

*Perf. 13¼ (#3299a), 13x13¼*

**2011, Jan. 14**              Photo.

| | | | | |
|---|---|---|---|---|
| 3299 | A2688 | Sheet of 5 | 7.00 | 7.00 |
| *a.-e.* | | 80y Any single | 1.25 | .60 |

**Miniature Sheet**

Phila Nippon'11, Yokohama — A2689

No. 3300: a, Mighty Atom (blue background, 28x48mm). b, Doraemon (green background, 28x48mm). c, Pikachu (purple background, 28x48mm). d, Hello Kitty (red background, 28x48mm). e, Rabbit riding donkey from 11th cent. scroll (28x48mm). f, Mighty Atom, diff. (28x32mm). g, Doraemon, diff. (28x32mm). h, Pikachu, diff. (28x32mm). i, Hello Kitty, diff. (28x32mm). j, Rabbit riding donkey, diff. (28x32mm).

*Die Cut Perf. 12¾x13*

**2011, Jan. 21**            Litho.
**Self-Adhesive**

| | | | | |
|---|---|---|---|---|
| 3300 | A2689 | Sheet of 10 | 16.00 | 16.00 |
| *a.-j.* | | 80y Any single | 1.50 | .60 |

**Miniature Sheet**

Friendship Between Japan and Germany, 150th Anniv. — A2690

No. 3301 — UNESCO World Heritage Sites and other landmarks: a, Old Town, Regensburg, horiz. (45x26mm, stamp 1). b, Yakushi-ji, Historic Monuments of Ancient Nara, Japan, horiz. (45x26mm, stamp 2). c, Quadriga of Brandenburg Gate, Berlin (27x38mm, stamp 3). d, Frauenkirche, Dresden (27x38mm, stamp 4). e, Schwerin Castle (two tall spires, 27x38mm, stamp 5). f, Schwerin Castle (three tall spires, 27x38mm, stamp 6). g, Old Town, Bamberg (bridge at right, 27x38mm, stamp 7). h, Old Town, Bamberg (bridge at left, 27x38mm, stamp 8). i, Neuschwanstein Castle (27x38mm, stamp 9). j, Tower at Zollverein Coal Mine Industrial Complex, Essen (27x38mm, stamp 10).

**2011, Jan. 24**     Litho.     *Perf. 13*

| | | | | |
|---|---|---|---|---|
| 3301 | A2690 | Sheet of 10 | 16.00 | 16.00 |
| *a.-j.* | | 80y Any single | 1.25 | .50 |

**Miniature Sheet**

Travel Scenes
A2691

No. 3302: a, Snow sculpture of Frauenkirche of Dresden, Germany at Sapporo Snow Festival, German and Japanese flags (stamp 1). b, Penguins walking at Asahiyama Zoo (stamp 2). c, Lamp post along canal at Otaru Snow Light Path (stamp 3). d, Building along canal in Otaru (stamp 4). e, Lake Toya in winter (stamp 5). f, Hakodate Orthodox Christian Church (stamp 6). g, Lake and snow-capped mountains at Shiretoko UNESCO World Heritage Site, denomination at LL (stamp 7). h, Lake and snow-capped mountains at Shiretoko UNESCO World Heritage Site, denomination at LR (stamp 8). i, Red-crowned cranes (stamp 9). j, Ice on Sea of Okhotsk near Abashiri (stamp 10).

**2011, Feb. 1**     Litho.     *Perf. 13x13¼*

| | | | | |
|---|---|---|---|---|
| 3302 | A2691 | Sheet of 10 | 13.00 | 13.00 |
| *a.-j.* | | 80y Any single | 1.25 | .60 |

**Miniature Sheets**

A2692

Greetings Stamps — A2693

No. 3303: a, Fawn, yellow crocuses. b, Bluebird, blue lilies. c, Rose, butterfly made of pink violets. d, Swans, blue roses. e, Hares, strawberries and flowers.
No. 3304: a, Flowers trailing from fairy's hat. b, Fairy blowing horn in daffodils. c, Fairy on back of bird delivering mail, horiz. d, Fairy with letter on rainbow. e, Fairy writing in purple flowers.

**2011, Feb. 4**     Litho.     *Die Cut Perf.*
**Self-Adhesive**

| | | | | |
|---|---|---|---|---|
| 3303 | A2692 | Sheet of 5 | 5.00 | 5.00 |
| *a.-e.* | | 50y Any single | .80 | .80 |

*Die Cut Perf. 13*

| | | | | |
|---|---|---|---|---|
| 3304 | A2693 | Sheet of 5 | 7.00 | 7.00 |
| *a.-e.* | | 80y Any single | 1.25 | .80 |

Rose
A2694

Apple Blossoms
A2695

Primroses
A2696

Japanese Grapefruit Blossoms
A2697

Kyushu Azalea Flowers
A2698

Roses
A2699

Apple Blossoms
A2700

Primroses
A2701

Japanese Grapefruit Blossoms
A2702

Kyushu Azalea Flowers
A2703

**2011, Feb. 8**     Photo.     *Perf. 13¼*

| | | | | |
|---|---|---|---|---|
| 3305 | A2694 | 50y multi | .80 | .40 |
| 3306 | A2695 | 50y multi | .80 | .40 |
| 3307 | A2696 | 50y multi | .80 | .40 |
| 3308 | A2697 | 50y multi | .80 | .40 |
| 3309 | A2698 | 50y multi | .80 | .40 |
| *a.* | | Vert. strip of 5, #3305-3309 | 4.50 | 3.00 |
| 3310 | A2699 | 80y multi | 1.25 | .60 |
| 3311 | A2700 | 80y multi | 1.25 | .60 |
| 3312 | A2701 | 80y multi | 1.25 | .60 |
| 3313 | A2702 | 80y multi | 1.25 | .60 |
| 3314 | A2703 | 80y multi | 1.25 | .60 |
| *a.* | | Vert. strip of 5, #3310-3314 | 7.50 | 4.50 |
| | | Nos. 3305-3314 (10) | 10.25 | 5.00 |

Flowers of Ibaraki, Aomori, Saitama, Yamaguchi and Kagoshima prefectures.

## Miniature Sheet

Home Towns A2704

No. 3315 — Paintings by Taiji Harada of views of towns of Kanto region: a, Rice Nursery (farmers in rice field, Hitachi, Ibaraka prefecture, denomination at UL). b, Rice Nursery (farmers in rice field, Hitachi, denomination at LL). c, Spring Breeze (woman and child near farmhouse, Kumagaya, Saitama prefecture, denomination at LL). d, Spring Breeze (farm buildings, trees in bloom in orchard, Kumagaya, denomination at UL). e,Spring Garden (tall tree, farmer with pole near shed, Tone District, Gumma prefecture). f, Spring Garden (boy with dog near mailbox near farmhouse, Tone District). g, Wheat Field (farmer and dog in field, Haga District, Tochigi prefecture). h, Home Inside a Tree Grove (house amidst trees, Kisarazu, Chiba prefecture). i, Roadside Zelkova Trees (city street with trees, Shibuya Ward, Tokyo prefecture). j, Westernized Building (building with lamp post, Yokohama, Kanagawa prefecture).

| 2011, Mar. 1 | Photo. | | Perf. 13 | |
|---|---|---|---|---|
| 3315 | A2704 | Sheet of 10 | 13.00 | 13.00 |
| a.-j. | | 80y Any single | 1.25 | .60 |

## Miniature Sheets

Characters From Children's Stories by Beatrix Potter — A2705

Scenes From *The Tale of Peter Rabbit*, by Beatrix Potter A2706

No. 3316: a, Peter Rabbit running. b, Mouse of Gloucester. c, Peter Rabbit standing. d, Benjamin Bunny. e, Pigling Bland. f, Old Mr. Brown and Nutkin. g, Mrs. Tiggy-winkle. h, Jemima Puddle-duck. i, Squirrel Nutkin. j, Tom Kitten.

No. 3317: a, Rabbit family's home under fir tree. b, Mother and younger sisters (27x37mm oval). c, Peter Rabbit and back of sisters. d, Mother dressing Peter (29mm diameter) e, Mother holding basket. f, Peter near pots in garden, robin. g, Peter going under garden fence (27x37mm oval). h, Peter eating vegetables. i, Peter encountering Mr. McGregor

(29mm diameter). j, Peter running from Mr. McGregor (29mm diameter).

| 2011, Mar. 3 | Litho. | Die Cut Perf. |
|---|---|---|

### Self-Adhesive

| 3316 | A2705 | Sheet of 10 | 11.00 | 11.00 |
|---|---|---|---|---|
| a.-j. | | 50y Any single | .80 | .80 |

### Die Cut Perf. 13¼x13¾, Die Cut Perf.

| 3317 | A2706 | Sheet of 10 | 13.00 | 13.00 |
|---|---|---|---|---|
| a.-j. | | 80y Any single | 1.25 | .80 |

## Animation
### Miniature Sheet

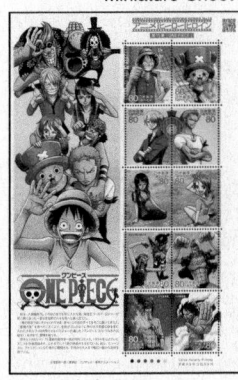

One Piece A2707

No. 3318: a, Monkey D. Luffy wearing hat and red shirt. b, Chopper wearing large top hat. c, Sanji wearing blue shirt. d, Zoro wearing white shirt. e, Robin wearing red striped blouse. f, Nami wearing beige shirt. g, Usopp and Brook. h, Franky with chain on chest. i, D Successor 1 with fire coming from hand. j, D Successor 2 with clouds.

| 2011, Mar. 23 | Litho. | | Perf. 13x13¼ | |
|---|---|---|---|---|
| 3318 | A2707 | Sheet of 10 | 16.00 | 16.00 |
| a.-j. | | 80y Any single | 1.25 | .50 |

Samisen Player A2708

Samisen Player and Children A2709

Matsubashi Parade Participants, Decorated Bamboo A2710

Matsubashi Parade A2711

| 2011, Apr. 4 | Litho. | Perf. 13¼ | |
|---|---|---|---|
| 3319 | | Block of 6, #3319c-3319d, 2 each #3319a-3319b | 6.00 6.00 |
| a. | A2708 | 50y green & multi | .80 .40 |
| b. | A2709 | 50y red violet & multi | .80 .40 |
| c. | A2710 | 50y blue & multi | .80 .40 |
| d. | A2711 | 50y blue & multi | .80 .40 |

Hakata Dontaku Port Festival, Fukuoka, Fukuoka prefecture. Printed in sheets of 10 containing Nos. 3319c-3319d and 4 each Nos. #3319a-3319b.

Administrative Counselors System, 50th Anniv. — A2712

| 2011, Apr. 15 | | Perf. 13 | |
|---|---|---|---|
| 3320 | 80y Denomination at LL | 1.25 | .50 |
| 3321 | 80y Denomination at LR | 1.25 | .50 |
| a. | A2712 Horiz. pair, #3320-3321 | 3.00 | 2.00 |

Digital Television Broadcasting Towers — A2713

Designs: No. 3322, Tokyo Sky Tree, emblem at LR. No. 3323, Tokyo Tower, emblem at LL.

| 2011, Apr. 15 | | Perf. 14x14¼ | |
|---|---|---|---|
| 3322 | 80y multi | 1.25 | .50 |
| 3323 | 80y multi | 1.25 | .50 |
| a. | A2713 Pair, #3322-3323 | 3.00 | 2.00 |

Kabuki Actor Kikugoro Onoe V as Postman, by Kunichika Toyohara — A2714

Yokkaichi Postal Communications Bureau, by Hiroshige III — A2715

A Quick Primer on Modernization, by Kunimasa Baido — A2716

### Perf. 12½x12¾ Syncopated

| 2011, Apr. 20 | | Photo. | |
|---|---|---|---|
| 3324 | A2714 80y multi | 1.25 | .50 |
| 3325 | A2715 80y multi | 1.25 | .50 |
| 3326 | A2716 80y multi | 1.25 | .50 |
| a. | Vert. strip of 3, #3324-3326 | 3.50 | 3.50 |

Philately Week. Printed in sheets of 10 containing 4 No. 3325 and 3 each Nos. 3324, 3326.

Azalea Flowers A2717

Satsuma Orange Blossoms A2718

Azalea Flowers A2719

Satsuma Orange Blossoms A2720

| 2011, May 2 | Photo. | | Perf. 13¼ | |
|---|---|---|---|---|
| 3327 | A2717 50y multi | | .80 | .40 |
| 3328 | A2718 50y multi | | .80 | .40 |
| a. | Horiz. pair, #3327-3328 | | 2.00 | 1.25 |
| b. | Sheet of 47 + label (see contents below) | | 50.00 | 50.00 |
| 3329 | A2719 80y multi | | 1.25 | .60 |
| 3330 | A2720 80y multi | | 1.25 | .60 |
| a. | Horiz. pair, #3329-3330 | | 3.00 | 2.00 |
| b. | Sheet of 47 + label (see contents below) | | 80.00 | 80.00 |
| | Nos. 3327-3330 (4) | | 4.10 | 2.00 |

Flowers of Shizuoka and Ehime prefectures. Issued: Nos. 3328b, 3330b, 7/15.

No. 3328b contains Nos. 3030-3034, 3079-3083, 3094-3098, 3126-3130, 3180-3184, 3194-3198, 3207-3211, 3221-3225, 3305-3309, 3327-3328 + label.

No. 3330b, contains Nos. 3035-3039, 3084-3088, 3099-3103, 3131-3135, 3185-3189, 3199-3203, 3212-3216, 3226-3230, 3310-3314, 3329-3330 + label.

## Miniature Sheet

Kumamoto Local Autonomy Law, 60th Anniv. — A2721

No. 3331: a, Mt. Azo (32x39mm). b, Kumamoto Castle (28x33mm). c, Kikuchi Castle (octagonal tower, 28x33mm). d, Utasebune (sailboat, 28x33mm). e, Matsushima and Maejima Bridges (28x33mm).

| Perf. 13¼ (#3331a), 13x13¼ | | | | |
|---|---|---|---|---|
| 2011, May 13 | | | Photo. | |
| 3331 | A2721 | Sheet of 5 | 7.00 | 7.00 |
| a.-e. | | 80y Any single | 1.25 | .60 |

## Miniature Sheet

Intl. Year
of
Forests
A2722

No. 3332: a, Japanese cypress (denomination in white at LL, Japanese text in green, date at UR). b, Cherry blossoms (denomination in white at UR, Japanese text in blue, date at LL). c, Persea thunbergii (denomination in white at LL, Japanese text in blue, date at LR). d, Japanese umbrella pine (denomination in blue at UR, Japanese text in green, date at UL). e, Plum blossoms (denomination in white at UR, Japanese text in green, date at LL). f, Boat oak (denomination in white at UR, Japanese text in blue, date at LL). g, Nageia nagi (denomination in white at LL, Japanese text in blue, date at UL). h, Michelia compressa blossom (denomination in white at UL, Japanese text in green, date at UL). i, Japanese Douglas fir (denomination in white at UL, Japanese text in green, date at LL). j, Intl. Year of Forests emblem.

**2011, May 20**   **Litho.**   **Perf. 13**
3332   A2722   Sheet of 10   10.00  10.00
  *a.-j.*   50y Any single      .80   .40

### Miniature Sheet

Travel
Scenes
A2723

No. 3333: a, Spotted seal (stamp 1). b, Wheat field, Biei (stamp 2). c, Lavender field, Furano, denomination at LR (stamp 3). d, Lavender field, Furano, denomination at LL (stamp 4). e, Statue of Dr. William Smith Clark, Hitsujigaoka (stamp 5). f, Cattle in pasture, Kamishihoro (stamp 6). g, Rugosa roses, Mt. Rishiri, denomination at UL (stamp 7). h, Rugosa roses, Mt. Rishiri, denomination at UR (stamp 8). i, Trees on hill at Higashimokoto Moss Pink Park, denomination at UL (stamp 9). j, Trees on hill at Higashimokoto Moss Pink Park, denomination at UR (stamp 10).

**2011, May 30**  **Litho.**  **Perf. 13x13¼**
3333   A2723   Sheet of 10  13.00  13.00
  *a.-j.*   80y Any single    1.25   .60

---

**Animation**
### Miniature Sheet

Rose of Versailles — A2724

No. 3334: a, Marie Antoinette holding rose (blue denomination at LL). b, Oscar François de Jarjayes holding sword (blue denomination at LR). c, André Grandier (pink denomination at LL). d, Jarjayes wearing green shirt (pink denomination at UR). e, Hans Axel von Fersen in brown cape (trees in background, blue denomination at LL). f, Marie Antoinette (pink denomination at LR). g, Von Fersen (bubbles in background, blue denomination at LL). h, Jarjayes in blue dress (bubbles in background, blue denomination at IR) i, Rosalie Lamorlière in pink dress ( blue denomination at UL). j, Jeanne de Valois-Saint Rémy (pink denomination at UR).

**2011, June 10**    **Perf. 13x13¼**
3334   A2724   Sheet of 10  16.00  16.00
  *a.-j.*   80y Any single    1.25   .50

### Miniature Sheet

Toyama Local Autonomy Law, 60th
Anniv. — A2725

No. 3335: a, Tateyama Mountains (32x39mm). b, Kurobe Dam (28x33mm). c, Japanese rock ptarmigan (28x33mm). d, Zuiryu Temple (28x33mm). e, Gokayama farmhouse (28x33mm).

**Perf. 13¼ (#3335a), 13x13¼**
**2011, June 15**    **Photo.**
3335   A2725   Sheet of 5  7.00  7.00
  *a.-e.*   80y Any single    1.25   .60

A2726

A2727

A2728

A2729

---

A2730

Hello
Kitty
A2731

No. 3341: a, Dear Daniel at left, and Hello Kitty, rectangular stamp with green background, denomination in green at LL. b, Hello Kitty and Dear Daniel, rectangular stamp with pink background. c, Hello Kitty, rectangular stamp with blue gray background, denomination in white at UL. d, Hello Kitty and Dear Daniel, rectangular stamp with green background, denomination in purple at LL. e, Dear Daniel and Hello Kitty, rectangular stamp with purple background, denomination in gold at LL. f, Hello Kitty, oval stamp with pink background and gold denomination at right. g, Hello Kitty, oval stamp with blue gray background, denomination in white at UR. h, Dear Daniel, oval stamp with green background. i, Hello Kitty, oval stamp with pink background and white denomination at left. j, Hello Kitty, oval stamp with purple background, denomination in purple at LR.

**Die Cut Perf. 13½**
**2011, June 22**    **Litho.**
**Self-Adhesive**
3336   A2726  50y multi    .80   .80
3337   A2727  50y multi    .80   .80
3338   A2728  50y multi    .80   .80
3339   A2729  50y multi    .80   .80
3340   A2730  50y multi    .80   .80
  *a.*   Vert. strip of 5, #3336-3340  4.50  4.50
**Die Cut Perf. 11½x13¼ (#3341a-**
**3341e), 12 (#3341f-3341j)**
3341   A2731   Sheet of 10  13.00  13.00
  *a.-j.*   80y Any single    1.25   .80

Nos. 3336-3340 were printed in sheets containing 2 of each stamp.

Adélie
Penguin
A2732

Chinstrap
Penguin
A2733

Gentoo
Penguin
A2734

Emperor
Penguin
A2735

Macaroni
Penguin
A2736

Map of
Antarctica and
Snowflakes
A2737

---

**2011, June 23**    **Perf. 13**
3342   Sheet of 10, #3342a-
      3342e, 5 #3342f  16.00  16.00
  *a.*   A2732 80y multi    1.25   .50
  *b.*   A2733 80y multi    1.25   .50
  *c.*   A2734 80y multi    1.25   .50
  *d.*   A2735 80y multi    1.25   .50
  *e.*   A2736 80y multi    1.25   .50
  *f.*   A2737 80y multi    1.25   .50

Antarctic Treaty, 50th Anniv.

### Miniature Sheet

Constellations — A2738

No. 3343: a, Libra (scales). b, Scorpius (scorpion). c, Sagittarius (archer). d, Lyra (lyre). e, Aquila (eagle). f, Cygnus (swan). g, Hercules. h, Ophiuchus and Serpens (man and snake). i, Delphinus (dolphin). j, Fishhook asterism.

**Litho. With Foil Application**
**2011, July 7**    **Die Cut Perf. 13**
**Self-Adhesive**
3343   A2738   Sheet of 10  22.00  22.00
  *a.-j.*   80y Any single    1.50   .80

### Miniature Sheet

Japan Sports Association,
Cent. — A2739

No. 3344: a, Jigoro Kano (1860-1938), and Seiichi Kishi (1867-1933), presidents of Japan Amateur Sports Association (stamp 1). b, Athletes in parade at 1912 Stockholm Olympics (stamp 2). c, Women's volleyball, horse jumping, and emblem of National Athletic Meet (stamp 3). d, Hironoshin Furuhashi (1928-2009), swimmer (stamp 4). e, Baseball players and boy with martial arts stick (stamp 5). f, Weight lifter, gymnast and women's volleyball team members from 1964 Tokyo Summer Olympics (stamp 6). g, Skiers from 1972 Sapporo Winter Olympics (stamp 7). h, Skier and skater from 1998 Nagano Winter Olympics (stamp 8). i, Emblem of Sports Masters Japan Tournament (stamp 9). j, Woman wrestler, swimmer and women's softball team members from 2008 Beijing Summer Olympics (stamp 10).

**2011, July 8**   **Litho.**   **Perf. 13**
3344   A2739   Sheet of 10  16.00  16.00
  *a.-j.*   80y Any single    1.25   .50

A2740

A2741

PhilaNippon 2011 Intl. Philatelic
Exhibition, Yokohama — A2742

No. 3345 — Woodblock prints by Hokusai
depicting Mt. Fuji: a, Shower Below the Summit (Mt. Fuji and clouds, denomination in gold
at LL). b, Fujimigahara in Owari Province
(cooper making cask). c, Hodogaya on the
Tokaido (people on road near Mt. Fuji). d,
Mishima Pass in Kai Province (large tree and
Mt. Fuji). e, The Surface of the Water at Misaka (boat and reflection of Mt. Fuji in lake). f,
Clear Day with a Southern Breeze (Mt. Fuji
and clouds, denomination in white at LR). g,
The Village of Sekiya on the Sumida River
(horsemen on road). h, Sea Route to Kazusa
(sailing ship). i, Hongan Temple at Asakusa
(kite and temple roof). j, Senju in Musashi
Province (fishermen, man with horse).

No. 3346: a, Writing box depicting rabbit,
bamboo and chrysanthemum. b, Japan #1.

No. 3347: a, Astro Boy (32x47mm). b,
Doraemon (cat, 28x47mm). c, Pikachu
(28x47mm). d, Hello Kitty (28x47mm). e,
Emblem of PhilaNippon 2011, Mt. Fuji
(28x47mm). f, Astro Boy, diff. (28x32mm). g,
Doraemon, diff. (28x32mm). h, Pikachu, diff.
(28x32mm). i, Hello Kitty, diff. (28x 32mm). j,
Emblem, diff. (28x32mm).

**2011, July 28    Litho.    Perf. 13**

| | | | |
|---|---|---|---|
| 3345 | A2740 | Sheet of 10 +<br>10 labels | 21.00 | 21.00 |
| a.-j. | | 80y Any single + label | 1.25 | .50 |

**Souvenir Sheet**

**Litho. & Embossed With Foil
Application**

**Perf. 14x13¾**

| | | | |
|---|---|---|---|
| 3346 | A2741 | Sheet of 2 | 32.50 | 32.50 |
| a.-b. | | 500y Either single | 9.50 | 9.50 |

**Self-Adhesive**

**Litho. With Foil Application**

**Die Cut Perf. 13**

| | | | |
|---|---|---|---|
| 3347 | A2742 | Sheet of 10 | 21.00 | 21.00 |
| a.-j. | | 80y Any single | 1.50 | .80 |

No. 3346 sold for 1200y inside a folder that
was sealed in plastic.

Sazae Hall,
by Hiroshige
A2743

Kisegawa of
Matsubaya,
by Utamaro
A2744

Tanabata
Festival in a
Prospering
City, by
Hiroshige
A2745

Plum Garden
at Kamata,
by Hiroshige
A2747

Yatsukoji,
Inside Sujikai
Gate, by
Hiroshige
A2749

Old Man's
Tea House,
Meguro, by
Hiroshige
A2751

Komazo
Ishikawa III
as Daishichi
Shiga, by
Sharaku
A2746

Three
Beauties of
the Present
Day, by
Utamaro
A2748

Tomisaburo
Segawa II as
Yadorigi, by
Sharaku
A2750

Hanaogi of
Ogiya, by
Utamaro
A2752

**2011, Aug. 1    Litho.    Perf. 13¼**

| | | | |
|---|---|---|---|
| 3348 | | Sheet of 10 | 15.00 | 15.00 |
| a. | A2743 | 80y multi | 1.25 | .60 |
| b. | A2744 | 80y multi | 1.25 | .60 |
| c. | A2745 | 80y multi | 1.25 | .60 |
| d. | A2746 | 80y multi | 1.25 | .60 |
| e. | A2747 | 80y multi | 1.25 | .60 |
| f. | A2748 | 80y multi | 1.25 | .60 |
| g. | A2749 | 80y multi | 1.25 | .60 |
| h. | A2750 | 80y multi | 1.25 | .60 |
| i. | A2751 | 80y multi | 1.25 | .60 |
| j. | A2752 | 80y multi | 1.25 | .60 |

Life in Edo (Tokyo).

A2753

A2755

A2754

A2756

A2757

Lantern Float Festival,
Aomori — A2758

**2011, Aug. 2**

| | | | |
|---|---|---|---|
| 3349 | | Sheet of 10, #3349a-<br>3349b, 3349e-3349f, 3<br>each #3349c-3349d | 10.00 | 10.00 |
| a. | A2753 | 50y multi | .80 | .40 |
| b. | A2754 | 50y multi | .80 | .40 |
| c. | A2755 | 50y multi | .80 | .40 |
| d. | A2756 | 50y multi | .80 | .40 |
| e. | A2757 | 50y multi | .80 | .40 |
| f. | A2758 | 50y multi | .80 | .40 |

Miniature Sheet

Tottori Local Autonomy Law, 60th
Anniv. — A2759

No. 3350: a, Tottori Sand Dunes and San'in
Coast (32x39mm). b, Japanese pear
(28x33mm). c, Kirin lion mask (28x33mm). d,
Nageire Hall, Sanbutsu Temple (28x33mm). e,
Mt. Daisen (28x33mm).

**Perf. 13¼ (#3350a), 13x13¼**

**2011, Aug. 15    Photo.**

| | | | |
|---|---|---|---|
| 3350 | A2759 | Sheet of 5 | 7.00 | 7.00 |
| a.-e. | | 80y Any single | 1.25 | .60 |

Tsushima
Leopard
Cat — A2760

Saunders's
Gull — A2761

Rebun Large-
flowered
Cypripedium
A2762

Green Sea Turtle
A2763

Shijimiaeoides
Divinus — A2764

**2011, Aug. 23    Perf. 13¼**

| | | | |
|---|---|---|---|
| 3351 | A2760 | 80y multi | 1.25 | .50 |
| 3352 | A2761 | 80y multi | 1.25 | .50 |
| 3353 | A2762 | 80y multi | 1.25 | .50 |
| 3354 | A2763 | 80y multi | 1.25 | .50 |
| 3355 | A2764 | 80y multi | 1.25 | .50 |
| a. | | Vert strip of 5, #3351-3355 | 7.50 | 5.00 |

Endangered species. Nos. 3351-3355
printed in sheets containing two vertical strips.

Airplane and
Old Control
Tower
A2765

Airplane and
New Control
Tower
A2766

Airplane and
Map of Airport
A2767

Airplane and
New Control
Tower
A2768

**2011, Aug. 25    Litho.    Perf. 13**

| | | | |
|---|---|---|---|
| 3356 | A2765 | 80y multi | 1.25 | .60 |
| 3357 | A2766 | 80y multi | 1.25 | .60 |
| 3358 | A2767 | 80y multi | 1.25 | .60 |
| 3359 | A2768 | 80y multi | 1.25 | .60 |
| a. | | Block of 4, #3356-3359 | 6.50 | 4.00 |
| | | Nos. 3356-3359 (4) | 5.00 | 2.40 |

Nos. 3356-3359 were printed in a sheet of
10 containing Nos. 3356-3357, and 4 each
Nos. 3358-3359.

Bellflower
A2769

Pink
A2770

Sweet Olive
Flowers
A2771

Cosmos
A2772

Bush Clover
A2773

Bellflowers
A2774

Pinks
A2775

Sweet Olive
Flowers
A2776

Cosmos
A2777

Bush Clover
A2778

**2011, Sept. 1    Photo.    Perf. 13¼**

| | | | |
|---|---|---|---|
| 3360 | A2769 | 50y multi | .80 | .40 |
| 3361 | A2770 | 50y multi | .80 | .40 |
| 3362 | A2771 | 50y multi | .80 | .40 |
| 3363 | A2772 | 50y multi | .80 | .40 |
| 3364 | A2773 | 50y multi | .80 | .40 |
| a. | | Vert. strip of 5, #3360-3364 | 4.50 | 3.00 |
| 3365 | A2774 | 80y multi | 1.25 | .60 |
| 3366 | A2775 | 80y multi | 1.25 | .60 |
| 3367 | A2776 | 80y multi | 1.25 | .60 |

| | | | | |
|---|---|---|---|---|
| 3368 | A2777 | 80y multi | 1.25 | .60 |
| 3369 | A2778 | 80y multi | 1.25 | .60 |
| a. | | Vert. strip of 5, #3365-3369 | 6.50 | 4.00 |
| | | Nos. 3360-3369 (10) | 10.25 | 5.00 |

### Miniature Sheet

Travel Scenes A2779

No. 3370: a, Midori Swamp, denomination at LL (stamp 1). b, Lake Mashu in autumn, denomination at LR (stamp 2). c, Old Hokkaido Central Government Building, denomination at UR (stamp 3). d, Sapporo Clock Tower, denomination at LR (stamp 4). e, Lake Toya, Nakajima and tree top in autumn, denomination at LL (stamp 5). f, Lake Toya, Nakajima and tree in autumn, denomination at LR (stamp 6). g, Hagoromo Falls (stamp 7). h, Glasswort in Lake Notoro (red plants in lake) (stamp 8). i, Ezo sable, denomination at UR (stamp 9). j, Ezo flying squirrel, denomination at UL (stamp 10).

**2011, Sept. 9**   **Litho.**   ***Perf. 13x13¼***

| | | | | |
|---|---|---|---|---|
| 3370 | A2779 | Sheet of 10 | 13.00 | 13.00 |
| a.-j. | | 80y Any single | 1.25 | .60 |

Mt. Fuji — A2780

Mt. Bandai — A2781

Hakusan A2782     Mt. Hiei A2783

Mt. Ishizuchi — A2784     Mt. Iwate — A2785

Mt. Tanigawa A2786     Mt. Akaishi A2787

Hiruzen — A2788     Mt. Aso — A2789

**2011, Sept. 22**    ***Perf. 13***

| | | | | |
|---|---|---|---|---|
| 3371 | | Sheet of 10 | 16.00 | 16.00 |
| a. | A2780 | 80y multi | 1.25 | .50 |
| b. | A2781 | 80y multi | 1.25 | .50 |
| c. | A2782 | 80y multi | 1.25 | .50 |
| d. | A2783 | 80y multi | 1.25 | .50 |
| e. | A2784 | 80y multi | 1.25 | .50 |
| f. | A2785 | 80y multi | 1.25 | .50 |
| g. | A2786 | 80y multi | 1.25 | .50 |
| h. | A2787 | 80y multi | 1.25 | .50 |
| i. | A2788 | 80y multi | 1.25 | .50 |
| j. | A2789 | 80y multi | 1.25 | .50 |

66th National Athletic Meet — A2790

**2011, Sept. 30**

| | | | | |
|---|---|---|---|---|
| 3372 | A2790 | 50y Sailing | .80 | .40 |
| 3373 | A2790 | 50y Wrestling | .80 | .40 |
| 3374 | A2790 | 50y Rock climbing | .80 | .40 |
| 3375 | A2790 | 50y Handball | .80 | .40 |
| 3376 | A2790 | 50y Softball | .80 | .40 |
| a. | | Vert. strip of 5, #3372-3376 | 4.50 | 3.00 |

2011 Artistic Gymnastics World Championships, Tokyo — A2791

Designs: No. 3377, Female gymnast. No. 3378, Male gymnast.

**2011, Oct. 6**   **Litho.**   ***Perf. 13***

| | | | | |
|---|---|---|---|---|
| 3377 | A2791 | 80y red vio & multi | 1.25 | .50 |
| 3378 | A2791 | 80y blue & multi | 1.25 | .50 |
| a. | | Horiz. pair, #3377-3378 | 3.00 | 1.50 |

Intl. Letter Writing Week — A2792

Designs: 90y, Sound of the Tsuzumi, by Shoen Uemura. 110y, Backstage, by Shinsui Ito. 130y, Midori, Heroine of Takekurabe, by Kiyokata Kaburagi.

**2011, Oct. 7**   **Photo.**   ***Perf. 13¼***

| | | | | |
|---|---|---|---|---|
| 3379 | A2792 | 90y multi | 1.75 | .50 |
| 3380 | A2792 | 110y multi | 2.25 | .50 |
| 3381 | A2792 | 130y multi | 2.50 | .50 |
| | | Nos. 3379-3381 (3) | 6.50 | 1.50 |

### Miniature Sheet

Shiga Local Autonomy Law, 60th Anniv. — A2793

No. 3382: a, Ukimido Temple, grebes on Lake Biwa (32x39mm). b, Boats in canal, Omihachiman (28x33mm). c, Boat tied to tree limb (28x33mm). d, Ishiyama Temple, Japanese red maples (28x33mm). e, Hikone Castle in winter (28x33mm).

***Perf. 13¼ (#3382a), 13x13¼***

**2011, Oct. 14**    **Photo.**

| | | | | |
|---|---|---|---|---|
| 3382 | A2793 | Sheet of 5 | 7.00 | 7.00 |
| a.-e. | | 80y Any single | 1.25 | .60 |

### Miniature Sheet

Travel Scenes A2794

No. 3383: a, Yoyogi National Gymnasium, denomination at UR (stamp 1). b, Bench in Yoyogi Park, denomination at LR (stamp 2). c, Illumination of Omotesando trees at left, denomination at LL (stamp 3). d, Illumination of Otmotesando, trees at right, denomination at LR (stamp 4). e, Sidewalk and buildings along Omotesando, denomination at UL (stamp 5). f, Meiji Memorial Picture Gallery, denomination at UL (stamp 6). g, Ginkgo trees in Meiji Shrine Outer Garden, trees at left, denomination in blue at UL (stamp 7). h, Ginkgo trees in Meiji Shrine Outer Garden, trees at right, denomination in blue at UR (stamp 8). i, Nezu Museum, denomination at LR (stamp 9). j, Irises, painted screen, by Korin Ogata, denomination at LR (stamp 10).

**2011, Oct. 21**   **Litho.**   ***Perf. 13x13¼***

| | | | | |
|---|---|---|---|---|
| 3383 | A2794 | Sheet of 10 | 13.00 | 13.00 |
| a.-j. | | 80y Any single | 1.25 | .60 |

Tokyo Metropolitan Festival Hall, 50th Anniv. — A2795

No. 3384: a, Stage and seating of Main Hall. b, Piano on stage of Small Hall. c, Ballet slippers, reflection of swan. d, Opera glasses, camellia. e, Piano keyboard. f, Violin.

**2011, Oct. 31**   **Litho.**   ***Perf. 13***

| | | | | |
|---|---|---|---|---|
| 3384 | A2795 | Block of 6 | 8.00 | 8.00 |
| a.-f. | | 80y Any single | 1.25 | .50 |

No. 3384 was pritned in a sheet of 10 containing Nos. 3384a, 3384b and 2 each Nos. 3384c-3384f.

### Miniature Sheets

A2796

A2797

Greetings — A2798

No. 3385: a, Wreath and dog (29mm diameter). b, Children and three Christmas trees (28x36mm). c, Christmas tree (28x38mm, Christmas tree-shaped). d, Santa Claus (28x36mm). e, Wreath and cat (29mm diameter).

No. 3386: a, Children starting to decorate Christmas tree. b, Children and decorated Christmas tree. c, Santa Claus, Christmas tree, children in bed. d, Santa Claus at Christmas tree. e, Children with Christmas presents.

No. 3387: a, Dog in snow (28x34mm oval). b, Flower bouquet (28x34mm oval). c, Snowman and animals on child's hat (38x28mm). d, Fairy and flowers (28x34mm oval). e, Children and cat looking at rabbit in snow (28x34mm oval).

**2011, Nov. 10**   ***Die Cut Perf. 13***
**Self-Adhesive**

| | | | | |
|---|---|---|---|---|
| 3385 | A2796 | Sheet of 5 | 5.00 | 5.00 |
| a.-e. | | 50y Any single | .80 | .80 |
| 3386 | A2797 | Sheet of 5 | 7.00 | 7.00 |
| a.-e. | | 80y Any single | 1.25 | .80 |
| 3387 | A2798 | Sheet of 5 | 9.00 | 9.00 |
| a.-e. | | 90y Any single | 1.40 | .80 |

A2799      A2800

New Year 2012 (Year of the Dragon)
A2801      A2802

**2011, Nov. 11**   **Photo.**   ***Perf. 13x13½***

| | | | | |
|---|---|---|---|---|
| 3388 | A2799 | 50y multi | 1.00 | .30 |
| 3389 | A2800 | 80y multi | 1.50 | .40 |

**Photo. & Typo.**
***Perf. 13¼***

| | | | | |
|---|---|---|---|---|
| 3390 | A2801 | 50y +3y multi | 1.25 | .40 |
| 3391 | A2802 | 80y +3y multi | 1.75 | .40 |
| | | Nos. 3388-3391 (4) | 5.50 | 1.50 |

Sheets of two containing Nos. 3388-3389 were lottery prizes. Value, $3.

### Miniature Sheet

Iwate Local Autonomy Law, 60th Anniv. — A2803

No. 3392: a, Golden Hall, Chuson-ji, lotus flower (32x39mm). b, Cherry trees in bloom (28x33mm). c, Hayachine Kagura folk performers (28x33mm). d, Rocks at Jodogahama (28x33mm). e, Joboji lacquer trees (28x33mm).

***Perf. 13¼ (#3392a), 13x13¼***

**2011, Nov. 15**    **Photo.**

| | | | | |
|---|---|---|---|---|
| 3392 | A2803 | Sheet of 5 | 7.00 | 7.00 |
| a.-e. | | 80y Any single | 1.25 | .60 |

## Miniature Sheet

Edo Calligraphy — A2804

No. 3393 — Characters for "dragon": a, In running script (black character with small red chop at LR). b, In Kinbun style (blue background). c, In Kinbun style (red background). d, In Sosho cursive style (black character with large dot, red chop at LL). e, In Kana (black character with five lines not touching each other, red chop at left). f, In Reisho script (complex black character, red chop of right angle and circle at lower left). g, In Reisho script (black character with thick diagonal line over denomination, red chop at left). h, In seal script form (black character with two thick parallel horizontal lines at top, red chop at LL). i, In Tensho seal style (in red). j, In Kana black character with thin curved line well above rest of character, red chop at left).

### Litho. & Embossed
**2011, Nov. 21**                    **Perf. 13x13¼**
3393  A2804    Sheet of 10        16.00  16.00
a.-j.    80y Any single              1.25    .50

Ministry of Agriculture, Forestry and Fisheries Festival, 50th Anniv. — A2805

Designs: No. 3394, Rice, chickens, tomatoes, fruit trees. No. 3395, Rice and fish.

**2011, Nov. 22**    **Litho.**    **Perf. 13**
3394    80y multi                    1.25    .50
3395    80y multi                    1.25    .50
a.    A2805 Horiz. pair, #3394-3395  3.00   1.50

## Miniature Sheet

Home Towns A2806

No. 3396 — Paintings by Taiji Harada of views of towns of Shinetsu region: a, Excursion (children, farmhouse, field of flowers, Iiyama, Nagano prefecture, denomination at LL). b, Excursion (children, hosue, river, field of flowers, Iiyama, denomination at UL). c, Kite Flying (three children near houses, Oshino Hakkai, Yamanashi prefecture, denomination at UL). d, Kite Flying (women and children, kites in air, Oshino Hakkai, denomination at

UL). e, Riverbank Homes (person with dog in front of house, Kashiwazaki, Niigata prefecture). f, Riverbank Homes (man on scooter in front of house, Kashiwazaki). g, Yamakoshi in Springtime (koi breeding pool and building, Nagaoka, Niigata prefecture, denomination at LL). h, Yamakoshi in Springtime (building, man along path beside breeding pool, Nagaoka, denomination at UR). i, Town with a View of Fuji (adult and child, building, Mount Fuji, Yamanashi, Yamanashi prefecture). j, Snow Removal (adults cleaning snow, children playing, Naganao, Nagano prefecture).

**2011, Dec. 1**    **Photo.**    **Perf. 13**
3396    A2806    Sheet of 10    13.00  13.00
a.-j.    80y Any single             1.25    .60

## Miniature Sheet

Akita Local Autonomy Law, 60th Anniv. — A2807

No. 3397: a, Nobu Shirase (1861-1946), Antarctic explorer, and two namahage (32x39mm). b, Korakukan Theater, Kosaka (28x33mm). c, Weeping cherry trees, Kakunodate (28x33mm). d, Statue of Tatsuko, Lake Tazawa (28x33mm). e, Kamakura Snow Festival, Yokote (28x33mm).

**Perf. 13¼ (#3397a), 13x13¼**
**2012, Jan. 13**
3397    A2807    Sheet of 5    7.00    7.00
a.-e.    80y Any single           1.25    .60

### Animation
## Miniature Sheet

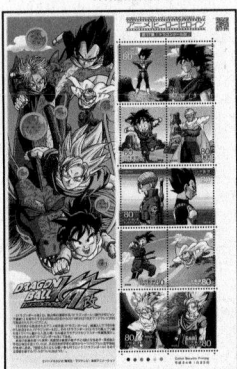

Dragon Ball Kai A2808

No. 3398: a, Vegeta on rock (white denomination at UL). b, Son Goku (purple denomination at LL). c, Son Gohan (red denomination at LL). d, Piccolo (purple denomination at LR). e, Trunks facing left(white denomination at LL). f, Vegeta facing right (white denomination at UR). g, Son Goku with fist extended(red denomination at LR). h, Piccolo flying (white denomination at LR) i, Son Gohan with white cape (white denomination at LL). j, Son Goku with brown tunic (white denomination at LR).

**2012, Jan. 23**    **Litho.**    **Perf. 13x13¼**
3398    A2808    Sheet of 10    16.00  16.00
a.-j.    80y Any single             1.25    .50

## Miniature Sheets

A2809

Greetings Stamps — A2810

No. 3399: a, Child on bird. b, Child with boxes and pail, cat, flowers. c, Tree, bear, rabbit, bird, flowers. d, Swan, flower bouquet. e, Children on cherry blossom petals.
No. 3400: a, Cat and flowers in box. b, Dog, falling cherry blossom petals. c, Bouquet of cherry blossoms. d, Birds in basket of flowers. e, Girl with letter, mailbox.

### Die Cut Perf. 13¼x13½
**2012, Feb. 1**    **Litho.**
### Self-Adhesive
3399    A2809    Sheet of 5    5.00    5.00
a.-e.    50y Any single           .80      .80
### Die Cut Perf. 13
3400    A2810    Sheet of 5    7.00    7.00
a.-e.    80y Any single           1.25    .80

Violets A2811

Flowering Dogwood A2813

Poppy A2815

Roses A2817

Muscari A2819

Rose A2812

Muscari A2814

Violets A2816

Flowering Dogwood A2818

Poppies A2820

**2012, Mar. 1**    **Photo.**    **Perf. 13¼**
3401    A2811    50y multi         .80    .40
3402    A2812    50y multi         .80    .40
3403    A2813    50y multi         .80    .40
3404    A2814    50y multi         .80    .40
3405    A2815    50y multi         .80    .40
a.    Vert. strip of 5, #3401-3405   4.50   3.00
3406    A2816    80y multi        1.25    .60
3407    A2817    80y multi        1.25    .60
3408    A2818    80y multi        1.25    .60
3409    A2819    80y multi        1.25    .60
3410    A2820    80y multi        1.25    .60
a.    Vert. strip of 5, #3406-3410   6.50   4.00
Nos. 3401-3410 (10)                 10.25   5.00

## Miniature Sheets

A2821

Disney Characters — A2822

No. 3411: a, Mickey and Minnie Mouse holding each other with arms extended (36x29mm heart-shaped stamp). b, Mickey with arm raised (27x28mm). c, Minnie with arms at side (27x28mm). d, Mickey with arms behind back (27x28mm). e, Minnie winking (27x28mm). f, Mickey with hands on hips (27x28mm). g, Minnie and Mickey, Minnie at left (36x29mm heart-shaped stamp). h, Mickey and Minnie not touching, Mickey's arm extended (36x29mm heart-shaped stamp). i, Mickey and Minnie, tails crossing (36x29mm heart-shaped stamp). j, Mickey and Minnie, Minnie's arms extended (36x29mm heart-shaped stamp).
No. 3412: a, Mickey (yellow background, 28mm diameter). b, Minnie (yellow background, 28mm diameter). c, Mickey, Minnie, Goofy, Pluto, Daisy Duck, Donald Duck (yellow background, 37mm diameter). d, Minnie and Daisy (pink background, 28mm diameter). e, Daisy (pink background, 28mm diameter). f, Donald (blue background, 28mm diameter). g, Mickey and Pluto (blue background, 28mm diameter). h, Mickey with arms raised (white, beige and blue background, oval). i, Goofy, Mickey and Donald (pink background, 37mm diameter). j, Minnie, Pluto and Mickey (blue background, 37mm diameter).

### Die Cut Perf., Die Cut Perf. 13¼x13½ (#3411b-3411f)
**2012, Mar. 2**    **Litho.**
### Self-Adhesive
3411    A2821    Sheet of 10    10.00  10.00
a.-j.    50y Any single            .80      .80
3412    A2822    Sheet of 10    13.00  13.00
a.-j.    80y Any single            1.25    .80

## Miniature Sheet

U.S. Cherry Blossom Centennial — A2823

No. 3413: a, Cherry trees in bloom, Washington Monument. b, Cherry trees in bloom, Jefferson Memorial. c, Cherry blossoms, bright blue background. d, Cherry blossoms, dark green background. e, Cherry blossoms, gray blue background. f, Cherry blossoms, olive brown background. g, Cherry blossoms, pink background.

**2012, Mar. 27**    **Perf. 13**
3413    A2823    Sheet of 10,
                    #3413a-3413f,
                    4 #3413g        16.00  16.00
a.-g.    80y Any single             1.25    .50

See U.S. Nos. 4651-4652.

## Miniature Sheet

Okinawa Local Autonomy Law, 60th Anniv. — A2824

No. 3414: a, Shuri Castle and Kumiodori dancer (32x39mm). b, Shurei Gate, Shuri Castle (28x33mm). c, Ryukyuan bingata (28x33mm). d, Ryukyuan dancers (28x33mm). e, Coral tree blossoms (28x33mm).

**Perf. 13¼ (#3414a), 13x13¼**

| | | | **2012, Apr. 13** | | **Photo.** |
|---|---|---|---|---|---|
| **3414** | A2824 | Sheet of 5 | | 7.00 | 7.00 |
| *a.-e.* | | 80y Any single | | 1.25 | .60 |

Fence with Grasses and Flowers, From Paper Partition by Unknown Artist — A2825

Dragon, From Screen by Sanraku Kano — A2826

Peonies, From Screen by Eino Kano — A2827

**Perf. 12¾ Syncopated**

| | | | **2012, Apr. 20** | | **Photo.** |
|---|---|---|---|---|---|
| **3415** | A2825 | 80y multi | | 1.25 | .50 |
| **3416** | A2826 | 80y multi | | 1.25 | .50 |
| **3417** | A2827 | 80y multi | | 1.25 | .50 |
| | | *Nos. 3415-3417 (3)* | | 3.75 | 1.50 |

Philately Week. Nos. 3415-3417 were printed in a sheet of 10 containing 3 each Nos. 3415 and 3417 and 4 No. 3416.

## Miniature Sheet

Travel Scenes A2828

No. 3418: a, Giant panda with open mouth (stamp 1). b, Giant panda with closed mouth (stamp 2). c, Shinobazo Pond, Ueno Park, Tokyo, denomination at UL (stamp 3). d, Shinobazo Pond, Ueno Park and Tokyo Buildings

in distance, denomination at UR (stamp 4). e, Thunder Gate, Senso-ji Temple, denomination at LL (stamp 5). f, Senso-ji pagodas, denomination at UL (stamp 6). g, Boat on Sumida River. buildings, denomination at UR (stamp 7). h, Asahi Beer Buildings along Sumida River, denomination at UR (stamp 8). i, Cherry blossoms, Sumida Park, denomination at UL (stamp 9). j, Fireworks display alomg Sumida River, denomination at LR (stamp 10).

| | | | **2012, Apr. 23** | **Litho.** | **Perf. 13x13¼** |
|---|---|---|---|---|---|
| **3418** | A2828 | Sheet of 10 | | 13.00 | 13.00 |
| *a.-j.* | | 80y Any single | | 1.25 | .60 |

Japanese Bush Cranberry — A2829

Yellow-flowered Toad Lily — A2830

Phedimus Sikokianus A2831

Japanese Wild Orchid A2832

Stigmatodactylus Sikokianus A2833

| | | | **2012, Apr. 24** | **Perf. 12¾x13** |
|---|---|---|---|---|
| **3419** | A2829 | 80y multi | 1.25 | .50 |
| **3420** | A2830 | 80y multi | 1.25 | .50 |
| **3421** | A2831 | 80y multi | 1.25 | .50 |
| **3422** | A2832 | 80y multi | 1.25 | .50 |
| **3423** | A2833 | 80y multi | 1.25 | .50 |
| *a.* | | Vert. strip of 5, #3419-3423 | 8.00 | 8.00 |
| | | *Nos. 3419-3423 (5)* | 6.25 | 2.50 |

Plant illustrations by Tomitaro Makino (1862-1957), botanist.

## Miniature Sheet

Return of Okinawa to Japanese Control, 40th Anniv. — A2834

No. 3424: a, Shuri Castle, denomination at LL. b, Shuri Castle, denomination at UR. c, Bitter melon, denomination at LL. d, Mangos, denomination at UR. e, Pink and white orchids, denomination at LL. f, White orchids, denomination at UR. g, Whale shark and fish, denomination at LL. h, Whale shark and fish, denomination at UR. i, Okinawa Urban Monorail, denomination at LL. j, Bridge between islands, denomination at UR.

| | | | **2012, May 15** | **Photo.** | **Perf. 13** |
|---|---|---|---|---|---|
| **3424** | A2834 | Sheet of 10 | | 16.00 | 16.00 |
| *a.-j.* | | 80y Any single | | 1.25 | .50 |

## Miniature Sheet

Yamaguchi Prefecture Afforestation — A2835

No. 3425: a, Camphor tree, denomination at UR. b, Japanese maple, denomination at LR in yellow. c, Ginkgo (yellow leaves on branch), denomination at LL in yellow. d, Wild camellia, denomination at UR. e, Citrus natsudaiidai (single white flower), denomination at UR. f, Japanese red pine, denomination at UR in green. g, Rape blossoms (yellow flowers), denomination at LR in yellow. h, Japanese cypress, denomination at LL. i, Boat oak, denomination at LL in green . j, Cherry blossoms, denomination at LL.

| | | | **2012, May 25** | **Litho.** |
|---|---|---|---|---|
| **3425** | A2835 | Sheet of 10 | 9.00 | 9.00 |
| *a.-j.* | | 50y Any single | .80 | .40 |

A2836

A2837

A2838

A2839

A2840

A2841

A2842

A2843

A2844

Ikebana, 550th Anniv. — A2845

| | | **2012, May 31** | | |
|---|---|---|---|---|
| **3426** | | Sheet of 10 | 16.00 | 16.00 |
| *a.* | A2836 | 80y multi | 1.25 | .50 |
| *b.* | A2837 | 80y multi | 1.25 | .50 |
| *c.* | A2838 | 80y multi | 1.25 | .50 |
| *d.* | A2839 | 80y multi | 1.25 | .50 |
| *e.* | A2840 | 80y multi | 1.25 | .50 |
| *f.* | A2841 | 80y multi | 1.25 | .50 |
| *g.* | A2842 | 80y multi | 1.25 | .50 |
| *h.* | A2843 | 80y multi | 1.25 | .50 |
| *i.* | A2844 | 80y multi | 1.25 | .50 |
| *j.* | A2845 | 80y multi | 1.25 | .50 |

## Miniature Sheet

Modern Art A2846

No. 3427: a, Bathhouse Girls, by Bakusen Tsuchida (detail of bird in tree). b, Bathouse Girls, by Tsuchida (detail of girl). c, Young Girl, by Kunzo Minami (girl at table writing). d, Portrait of Encho San'yutei, by Kiyokata Kaburagi (man kneeling on mat). e, Road, Cut Bank and Fence, by Ryusei Kishida. f, Mother and Child, by Shoen Uemura. g, Reading by the Window, by Kijiro Ota (woman reading book). h, Back Garden After the Rain, by Shinsen Tokuoka (bird under flowering bush). i, Portrait of a Lady, by Sotaro Yasui (woman seated in chair). j, Study of Flowers, by Heihachiro Fukuda (pond with iris shoots and fallen cherry blossoms).

| | | | **2012, June 1** | **Photo.** | **Perf. 13** |
|---|---|---|---|---|---|
| **3427** | A2846 | Sheet of 10 | | 16.00 | 16.00 |
| *a.-j.* | | 80y Any single | | 1.25 | .50 |

Wisteria A2847

Lily of the Valley A2848

Hydrangea A2849

Sunflower A2850

Morning
Glories
A2851

Wisteria
A2852

Lily of the
Valley
A2853

Hydrangea
A2854

Sunflowers
A2855

Morning
Glories
A2856

| 2012, June 7 | Photo. | Perf. 13¼ | |
|---|---|---|---|
| 3428 | A2847 | 50y multi | .80 | .40 |
| 3429 | A2848 | 50y multi | .80 | .40 |
| 3430 | A2849 | 50y multi | .80 | .40 |
| 3431 | A2850 | 50y multi | .80 | .40 |
| 3432 | A2851 | 50y multi | .80 | .40 |
| a. | | Vert. strip of 5, #3428-3432 | 4.50 | 3.00 |
| 3433 | A2852 | 80y multi | 1.25 | .60 |
| 3434 | A2853 | 80y multi | 1.25 | .60 |
| 3435 | A2854 | 80y multi | 1.25 | .60 |
| 3436 | A2855 | 80y multi | 1.25 | .60 |
| 3437 | A2856 | 80y multi | 1.25 | .60 |
| a. | | Vert. strip of 5, #3433-3437 | 6.50 | 4.00 |
| | | Nos. 3428-3437 (10) | 10.25 | 5.00 |

Tenjin
Festival
(Osaka)
A2857

| 2012, June 15 | Litho. | Perf. 13¼ | |
|---|---|---|---|
| 3438 | 50y Denomination at UR | .80 | .50 |
| 3439 | 50y Denomination at UL | .80 | .50 |
| a. | A2857 Horiz. pair, #3438-3439 | 1.75 | 1.25 |

Japanese Forces in United Nations
Peacekeeping Operations, 20th
Anniv. — A2858

| 2012, June 19 | Perf. 13 | |
|---|---|---|
| 3440 | 80y pink & multi | 1.25 | .50 |
| 3441 | 80y blue & multi | 1.25 | .50 |
| a. | A2858 Pair, #3440-3441 | 3.00 | 1.50 |

## Miniature Sheet

Ogaswara Islands UNESCO World
Heritage Site — A2859

No. 3442: a, Bonin white-eye, denomination at UL (stamp 1). b, Bonin peonies, denomination at LR (stamp 2). c, Heart Rock, denomination at UL (stamp 3). d, Snail on leaf, denomination at LL (stamp 4). e, Ogi Pond and rock arch, denomination at LL (stamp 5). f, Semi-fossilized shells, denomination at UL (stamp 6). g, Bonin camellia, denomination at LL (stamp 7). h, Chichijima Forests, denomination at LR (stamp 8). i, Southern bottlenose dolphins, denomination at UR (stamp 9). j, Pandanus boninensis, denomination at UR (stamp 10).

| 2012, June 20 | Photo. | Perf. 13x13¼ | |
|---|---|---|---|
| 3442 | A2859 Sheet of 10 | 16.00 | 16.00 |
| a.-j. | 80y Any single | 1.25 | .50 |

## Miniature Sheets

A2860

Hello
Kitty
A2861

No. 3443: a, Hello Kitty and Dear Daniel (25x38mm fan-shaped stamp). b, Hello Kitty (25x38mm fan-shaped stamp). c, Hello Kitty, pink panel (25x25mm). d, Hello Kitty, lilac panel (25x25mm). e, Hello Kitty, yellow panel (25x25mm).

No. 3444: a, Hello Kitty and Dear Daniel (42x27mm rectangular stamp). b, Hello Kitty, rabbit, building with blue roof (40x29mm building-shaped stamp). c, Hello Kitty, denomination in red at R (29mm diameter). d, Hello Kitty, bear, building with red roof (40x29mm building shaped stamp). e, Hello Kitty, white denomination at L (29mm diameter). f, Hello Kitty and Dear Daniel, building with orange roof (40x29mm building-shaped stamp). g, Hello Kitty and Dear Daniel, fireworks overhead (28x38mm oval stamp). h, Hello Kitty and Dear Daniel holding fans (28x38mm oval stamp).

**Die Cut Perf. 13¼ (#3443a-3443b),
Die Cut Perf. 13¼x13½ (#3443c-3443e)**

| 2012, June 22 | Litho. | |
|---|---|---|
| **Self-Adhesive** | | |
| 3443 | A2860 Sheet of 10, 2 each #3443a-3443e | 12.50 | 12.50 |
| a.-e. | 50y Any single | 1.25 | .80 |
| **Die Cut Perf. 13½** | | |
| 3444 | A2861 Sheet of 10, #3444a-3444f, 2 each #3444g-3444h | 16.00 | 16.00 |
| a.-h. | 80y Any single | 1.25 | .80 |

## Miniature Sheet

Hiraizumi UNESCO World Heritage
Site — A2862

No. 3445: a, Golden Hall, Chuson-ji, denomination at LR in gold (stamp 1). b, Hanging ornament, denomination at LL (stamp 2). c, Kyozo buildings, Chuson-ji, denomination at UL (stamp 3). d, People under umbrellas at Motsuji, denomination at LL (stamp 4). e, Motsuji Jodo Garden and pond, denomination at UL (stamp 5). f, Motsuji Jodo Garden and pond, denomination at UR (stamp 6). g, Kanjizaio-in temple garden and pond, denomination at LR (stamp 7). h, Kanjizaio-in temple garden and pond, denomination at LL (stamp 8). i, Muryoko-in ruins, trees and mountain, denomination at LR (stamp 9). j, Lotus blossoms, denomination at LL (stamp 10).

| 2012, June 29 | Photo. | Perf. 13x13¼ | |
|---|---|---|---|
| 3445 | A2862 Sheet of 10 | 16.00 | 16.00 |
| a.-j. | 80y Any single | 1.25 | .80 |

Adder's
Tongue Lily
A2863

Bazara-
Taisho (c.
710-794)
A2864

| 2012, July 2 | Photo. | Perf. 13x13¼ | |
|---|---|---|---|
| 3446 | A2863 350y multi | 9.00 | .50 |
| 3447 | A2864 500y multi | 11.00 | .50 |

No. 3446 has a vignette different from No. 2166.

## Miniature Sheet

Season's Memories in My
Heart — A2865

No. 3448: a, Woman on bench near water, denomination at UL (stamp 1). b, Street vendor booths at festival, denomination at LR in gold (stamp 2). c, Child running stick against fence posts, denomination at UR (stamp 3). d, Children and animals in fog, denomination at UR (stamp 4). e, Girl with flower, boy with fishing pole and bucket, denomination at UL (stamp 5). f, Children on steps near sea, denomination at LR (stamp 6). g, Children, boats on shore, flying gull, denomination at UL (stamp 7). h, Children on hill looking at boat, denomination at UL in gold (stamp 8). i, Boat on shore, children looking at jellyfish, denomination at UL (stamp 9). j, Cricket with leaf cello, child, bottle, denomination at UL in gold (stamp 10).

| 2012, July 3 | Photo. | Perf. 13 | |
|---|---|---|---|
| 3448 | A2865 Sheet of 10 | 16.00 | 16.00 |
| a.-j. | 80y Any single | 1.25 | .50 |

## Miniature Sheet

Constellations — A2866

No. 3449: a, Capricornus (goat). b, Aquarius (water bearer). c, Pisces (fish). d, Cassiopeia (woman in chair). e, Pegasus. f, Andromeda (woman in chains). g, Perseus (swordsman). h, Cepheus (king with scepter). i, Cetus (creature with two front legs and tail). j, Cassiopeia (anchor).

**Litho. With Foil Application**

| 2012, July 6 | Die Cut Perf. 13 | |
|---|---|---|
| **Self-Adhesive** | | |
| 3449 | A2866 Sheet of 10 | 16.00 | 16.00 |
| a.-j. | 80y Any single | 1.50 | .80 |

Miniature Sheet

Kanagawa Local Autonomy Law, 60th Anniv. — A2867

No. 3450: a, Tsurugaoka Hachimangu, Kamakura, and mounted archer (32x39mm). b, Minato Mirai 21 buildings, Yokohama (28x33mm). c, Jogashima Lighthouse (28x33mm). d, Tanzawa Mountains and Lake Miyagase (28x33mm). e, Lake Ashi (28x33mm).

Perf. 13¼ (#3450a), 13x13¼

2012, July 13			**Photo.**	
3450	A2867	Sheet of 5	7.00	7.00
a.-e.		80y Any single	1.25	.60

Susanoo, Shinto God of the Sea A2868

Legendary Princess Inada A2869

Legendary Princess Konohanasakuya A2870

Legendary Prince Yamatotakeru A2871

2012, July 20	**Litho.**		***Perf. 13***	
3451	A2868	80y multi	1.25	.50
3452	A2869	80y multi	1.25	.50
3453	A2870	80y multi	1.25	.50
3454	A2871	80y multi	1.25	.50
a.		Block of 4, #3451-3454	7.00	7.00
		Nos. 3451-3454 (4)	5.00	2.00

Nos. 3451-3454 were printed in sheets of 10 containing 3 each Nos. 3451-3452 and 2 each Nos. 3453-3454.

Inpumon In no Taifu, Poet A2872

Fujiwara no Toshiyuki Ason, Poet A2873

Shune-hoshi, Poet A2874

Kokamon In no Betto, Poet A2875

Sone no Yoshitada, Poet — A2876

Poetry A2877

No. 3460 — Poetry in Japanese calligraphy and: a, Boat in lake, denomination at LL. b, Inpumon In no Taifu. c, Hill near water, denomination at UL. d, Fujiwara no Toshiyuki Ason. e, Building and tree. f, Shune-hoshi. g, Eddies in river, denomination at UR. h, Kokamon In no Betto. i, Man rowing boat. j, Sone no Yoshitada.

2012, July 23	**Photo.**		***Perf. 13¼***	
3455	A2872	50y multi	.80	.30
3456	A2873	50y multi	.80	.30
3457	A2874	50y multi	.80	.30
3458	A2875	50y multi	.80	.30
3459	A2876	50y multi	.80	.30
a.		Vert. strip of 5, #3455-3459	5.00	5.00
		Nos. 3455-3459 (5)	4.00	1.50
		Perf. 12¾x13		
3460	A2877	Sheet of 10	16.00	16.00
a.-j.		80y Any single	1.25	.50

Hanaogi of the Ogi Establishment Going Elsewhere, by Eisho Chokosai A2878

The Moon Crossing Bridge at Arashiyama in Yamashiro Province, by Hiroshige A2879

Tosei Onna Fuzuoku Tsuu Hokkoku no Keisei, by Utamaro A2880

The Brocade Bridge at Iwakuni in Suo Province, by Hiroshige A2881

Furyu Setsugekka Tsuki, by Eizan Kikukawa A2882

Mt. Kyodai and the Moon Reflected in the Rice Fields at Sarashina in Shinano Province, by Hiroshige A2883

Ogiya Uchi Hanaogi Yoshino Tatsuta, by Utamaro A2884

Rough Sea at Naruto in Awa Province, by Hiroshige A2885

Furyu Mutamagawa Chofu no Tamagawa, by Eizan Kikukawa A2886

The Monkey Bridge in Kai Province, by Hiroshige A2887

2012, Aug. 1	**Litho.**	***Perf. 13***	
3461	Sheet of 10	16.00	16.00
a.	A2878 80y multi	1.25	.50
b.	A2879 80y multi	1.25	.50
c.	A2880 80y multi	1.25	.50
d.	A2881 80y multi	1.25	.50
e.	A2882 80y multi	1.25	.50
f.	A2883 80y multi	1.25	.50
g.	A2884 80y multi	1.25	.50
h.	A2885 80y multi	1.25	.50
i.	A2886 80y multi	1.25	.50
j.	A2887 80y multi	1.25	.50

Miniature Sheet

Miyazaki Local Autonomy Law, 60th Anniv. — A2888

No. 3462: a, Miyazaki Prefectural Office and dancer (32x39mm). b, Koibitono-oka (hill with gazebo) (28x33mm). c, Yellow flowers, Saitobaru Burial Grounds (28x33mm). d, Pink flowers, Ebino-kogen Highlands (28x33mm). e, Terraced rice fields (28x33mm).

Perf. 13¼ (#3462a), 13x13¼

2012, Aug. 15			**Photo.**	
3462	A2888	Sheet of 5	7.00	7.00
a.-e.		80y Any single	1.25	.60

Sorex Minutissimus A2889

Aquila Chrysaetos A2890

Paeonia Obovata — A2891

Oryzias Latipes — A2892

Tachypleus Tridentatus A2893

2012, Aug. 23			***Perf. 13¼***	
3463	A2889	80y multi	1.25	.50
3464	A2890	80y multi	1.25	.50
3465	A2891	80y multi	1.25	.50
3466	A2892	80y multi	1.25	.50
3467	A2893	80y multi	1.25	.50
a.		Vert. strip of 5, #3463-3467	7.50	5.00
		Nos. 3463-3467 (5)	6.25	2.50

Normalization of Diplomatic Relations Between Japan and People's Republic of China, 40th Anniv. — A2894

2012, Sept. 4			***Perf. 13***	
3468	A2894	80y multi	1.50	.50

Miniature Sheet

Travel Scenes A2895

No. 3469 — Sites in Nagasaki: a, Urakami Cathedral, denomination at UR (stamp 1). b, Peace Statue, Nagasaki (stamp 2). c, Megane Bridge, denomination at LL (stamp 3). d, Megane Bridge, denomination at LR (stamp 4). e, Lantern Festival, denomination at UL below country name (stamp 5). f, Sofuku Temple, denomination at UL, to left of country name (stamp 6). g, Glover House, Glover Gardens, denomination at UR (stamp 7). h, Glover House , Glover Gardens, denomination at LR (stamp 8). i, People carrying dragon at Kunchi Festival, denomination at LL (stamp 9). j, Tall Ships Festival, denomination at UR (stamp 10).

2012, Sept. 11	**Litho.**		***Perf. 13x13¼***	
3469	A2895	Sheet of 10	13.00	13.00
a.-j.		80y Any single	1.25	.60

## Miniature Sheets

Greetings:Autumn

A2896

Greetings:Autumn

Teddy Bears A2897

No. 3470 — Teddy bear with: a, Blue cap, pink background, red bow at top (28x28mm). b, Blue cap, light blue background, blue bow at top (28x28mm). c, Blue and white box with red ribbon, pink background, pink bow at top (28x28mm). d, Gold box with yellow ribbon, yellow background, yellow bow at top (28x28mm). e, Card with red ribbon, lilac background, red bow at top (28x28mm). f, Card with blue ribbon, light green background, gray green bow at top (28x28mm). g, Red box with white ribbon, plaid bow around neck (26x30mm). h, Blue box with red ribbon, dark blue bow around neck (26x30mm). i, Card with red ribbon, green bow around neck (26x30mm). j, Blue and white box with red ribbon, blue bow around neck (26x30mm).

No. 3471: a, Bear with blue and white box with yellow ribbon (26x38mm). b, Bear with green box with red ribbon (26x38mm). c, Bear with card with red ribbon (26x38mm). d, Two bears, lilac denomination (42x27mm). e, Two bears, blue denomination (27x38mm oval). f, Two bears, red denomination (27x38mm oval). g, Bear with black and brown bow around neck, red denomination (27x38mm oval). h, Bear with card with red ribbon, red denomination (27x38mm oval). i, Bear with flower (27x38mm oval). j, Bear with cap, two boxes (42x27mm).

***Die Cut Perf. 14, Die Cut Perf.***
***(#3470g-3470j)***
**2012, Sept. 21**      Litho.
**Self-Adhesive**
3470   A2896    Sheet of 10    10.00   10.00
   *a.-j.*    50y Any single         .80     .80
***Die Cut Perf. 14½x14 (#3471a-***
***3471c), 11¼x13½ (#3471d, 3471j),***
***13¾***
3471   A2897    Sheet of 10    13.00   13.00
   *a.-j.*    80y Any single       1.25     .80

---

Badminton
A2898

Rhythmic Gymnastics
A2899

Rowing
A2900

Cycling
A2901

Field Hockey — A2902

**2012, Sept. 28**   Litho.   ***Perf. 13***
3472   A2898   50y multi      .80    .40
3473   A2899   50y multi      .80    .40
3474   A2900   50y multi      .80    .40
3475   A2901   50y multi      .80    .40
3476   A2902   50y multi      .80    .40
   *a.*     Vert. strip of 5, #3472-3476   4.50   3.00

67th National Athletic Meet, Gifu. Compare with type A2790.

### Miniature Sheet

Horse Racing in Japan, 150th Anniv. — A2903

No. 3477: a, Orfevre (horse #9, jockey with green helmet). b, Apapane (horse #9, jockey with yellow helmet, blue and yellow silks). c, Deep Impact (horse #5, jockey with red helmet, yellow and gray silks). d, Still in Love (horse #9, jockey with yellow helmet, red and blue silks). e, Narita Brian (horse #4, jockey with red helmet). f, Mejiro l'Amone (horse #13). g, Symboli Rudolf (horse #5, jockey with red helmet, blue and red silks). h, Mr. C.B. (horse #12, jockey with green and white silks). i, Shinzan (horse #4, jockey with brown helmet). j, Saint Lite (horse #12, black-and-white photograph).

**2012, Oct. 2**    Photo.    ***Perf. 13***
3477   A2903    Sheet of 10    16.00   16.00
   *a.-j.*    80y Any single      1.40    .90

Intl. Letter Writing Week — A2904

Designs: 90y, Hatsugochi, by Kiyokata Kaburaki. 110y, Shunpo, by Shoen Uemura. 130y, Hubuki, by Shinsui Ito.

**2012, Oct. 9**    Photo.    ***Perf. 13¼***
3478   A2904   90y multi     1.75    .50
3479   A2904   110y multi    2.25    .50
3480   A2904   130y multi    2.50    .50
   Nos. 3478-3480 (3)      6.50   1.50

---

### Miniature Sheet

Annual Meeting of Intl. Monetary Fund and World Bank Group, Tokyo A2905

No. 3481: a, Silver and copper Wado Kaichin coins, 708 (gold frame). b, Oval copper Tempo Tsuho coin, 1835, round Kanei Tsuho coin, 1636 (gold frame). c, Six round Chinese copper coins, 12th-15th cent. (silver frame) d, Moneychanger's balance, 19th cent. (silver frame). e, Hirumokin gold slug, Sekishugin silver slug, Yuzurihakin gold plate, 16th cent. (gold frame). f, Yamada Hagaki paper money, 17th-19th cent. (gold frame). g, Gold Keicho Oban, 1601 (silver frame). h, Molded coins attached to sprues, c. 1863 (silver frame). i, Silver Keicho Chogin coin and five Silver Keicho Mameitagin coins, 1601 (silver frame). j, 1871 gold 20-yen, silver 50-yen and copper 2-sen coins (gold frame).

**2012, Oct. 12**    Photo.    ***Perf. 13***
3481   A2905    Sheet of 10    16.00   16.00
   *a.-j.*    80y Any single      1.25    .60

### Miniature Sheet

Tochigi Local Autonomy Law, 60th Anniv. — A2906

No. 3482: a, Yomei Gate, Toshogu Shrine (32x39mm). b, Gate at Ashikaga School (28x33mm). c, Carp amulets on sticks (28x33mm). d, Moka Railway steam locomotive and flowers (28x33mm). e, Cherry blossoms and mountain, Nasu Kogen (28x33mm).

***Perf. 13¼ (#3482a), 13x13¼***
**2012, Oct. 15**           Photo.
3482   A2906    Sheet of 5    7.00   7.00
   *a.-e.*    80y Any single    1.25    .60

---

### Animation
### Miniature Sheet

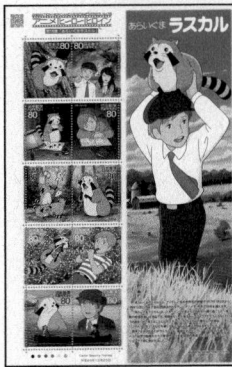

Rascal
A2907

No. 3483: a, Rascal the Raccoon on tree (white denomination at UR). b, Sterling and Alice (white denomination at UL). c, Rascal with book and lamp (white denomination at UL). d, Sterling and book (white denomination at UR). e, Three raccoon babies, butterflies (black denomination at UL). f, Rascal facing left (black denomination at UR). g, Rascal drinking from bottle (white denomination at UL). h, Sterling drinking from bottle (white denomination at UL). i, Rascal, Rascal in canoe (black denomination at UR). j, Sterling, Sterling in canoe (white denomination at UR).

**2012, Oct. 23**   Litho.   ***Perf. 13x13¼***
3483   A2907    Sheet of 10    16.00   16.00
   *a.-j.*    80y Any single      1.25    .50

### Miniature Sheet

Traditional Crafts — A2908

No. 3484: a, Hakata doll depicting man holding fan (Fukuoka Prefecture). b, Black rectangular inkstone and lid (Miyagi Prefecture). c, Banana-fiber handbag (Okinawa Prefecture). d, Container and two cups (Fukushima Prefecture). e, Two lacquerware bowls (Aomori Prefecture). f, Folding fan (Kyoto Prefecture). g, Kaga dyed screen (Ishikawa Prefecture). h, Decorated Kutani plate (Ishikawa Prefecture). i, Cast-iron kettle (Iwate Prefecture). j, Tsuboya ceramic urn with handles (Okinawa Prefecture).

**2012, Oct. 25**    Photo.    ***Perf. 13½***
3484   A2908    Sheet of 10    16.00   16.00
   *a.-j.*    80y Any single      1.25    .60

### Miniature Sheets

Greetings:Winter

A2909

A2910

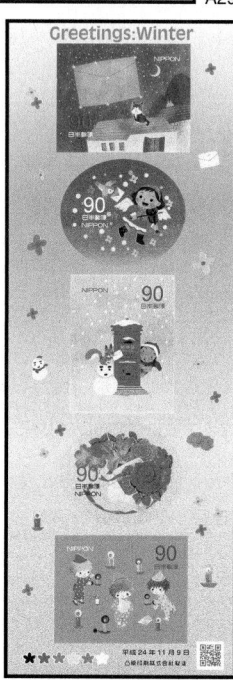

Greetings — A2911

No. 3485: a, Star, Santa Clauses, gift (29x39mm). b, Kitten in stocking (26x34mm). c, Wreath, children, squirrel (29mm diameter). d, Puppy in stocking (26x34mm). e, Christmas tree and cardinal (29x39mm).

No. 3486: a, Santa Claus and reindeer on building roof. b, Fireplace, Christmas tree, two children, cat and bird. c, Fireplace, three children, bird. d, Fireplace, Christmas tree, two children, two cats, bird. e, Fireplace, two children, Christmas tree being decorated, bird.

No. 3487: a, Cat on roof, envelope in night sky (37x28mm). b, Angel with violin, bird carrying letter (35x28mm ellipse). c, Snowman, squirrel, mailbox, child (28x37mm). d, Roses and open letter (35x28mm ellipse). e, three children in pajamas, candles (37x28mm).

**Self-Adhesive**

*Die Cut Perf. 13*

| | | | | |
|---|---|---|---|---|
| **2012, Nov. 9** | | | | **Litho.** |
| **3485** | A2909 | Sheet of 5 | 5.00 | 5.00 |
| *a.-e.* | | 50y Any single | .80 | .80 |
| **3486** | A2910 | Sheet of 5 | 7.00 | 7.00 |
| *a.-e.* | | 80y Any single | 1.25 | .80 |
| **3487** | A2911 | Sheet of 5 | 8.00 | 8.00 |
| *a.-e.* | | 90y Any single | 1.50 | .80 |

A2912    A2913

A2914    A2915

**New Year 2013 (Year of the Snake)**
A2914    A2915

| | | | | |
|---|---|---|---|---|
| **2012, Nov. 12** | **Photo.** | | **Perf. 13x13½** | |
| **3488** | A2912 | 50y multi | 1.00 | .30 |
| **3489** | A2913 | 80y multi | 1.50 | .40 |

**Photo. & Typo.**
**Perf. 13¼**

| | | | | |
|---|---|---|---|---|
| **3490** | A2914 | 50y +3y multi | 1.25 | .40 |
| **3491** | A2915 | 80y +3y multi | 1.75 | .40 |
| | Nos. 3488-3491 (4) | | 5.50 | 1.50 |

Sheets of two containing Nos. 3488-3489 were lottery prizes. Value, $4.

**Miniature Sheet**

**Oita Local Autonomy Law, 60th Anniv. — A2916**

No. 3492: a, Usa Jingu Shrine, Oita, Futabayama (1912-68), sumo wrestler (32x39mm). b, Plum blossoms, Japanese white-eye (28x33mm). c, Fukiji Temple (28x33mm). d, Hita Gion Festival (28x33mm). e, Sunrise at Bungofutamigaura (28x33mm).

*Perf. 13¼ (#3492a), 13x13¼*

| | | | | |
|---|---|---|---|---|
| **2012, Nov. 15** | | | **Photo.** | |
| **3492** | A2916 | Sheet of 5 | 7.00 | 7.00 |
| *a.-e.* | | 80y Any single | 1.25 | .60 |

**Miniature Sheets**

A2917

**Disney Characters — A2918**

No. 3493: a, Winnie the Pooh (27x27mm). b, Piglet (27x27mm). c, Alice in Wonderland (27x38mm oval). d, Donald Duck (26x34mm). e, Daisy Duck (26x34mm). f, Cinderella (27x38mm oval). g, Dumbo (29mm diameter). h, Marie the Cat (26x34mm). i, Goofy (26x34mm). j, Three Dalmatians (29mm diameter).

No. 3494: a, Tinker Bell (27x27mm). b, Mickey Mouse (27x38mm oval). c, Minnie Mouse (27x38mm oval). d, Bambi (27x27mm). e, Pinocchio (27x35mm). f, Snow White (27x38mm oval). g, Pluto (27x35mm). h, Ariel (35x27mm). i, Stitch (29mm diameter). j, Three Little Pigs (35x27mm).

*Die Cut Perf. 13½, Die Cut Perf. 13 (#3493d, 3493e, 3493h, 3493i), Die Cut Perf. 13¼x13¾ (#3494e, 3494g), Die Cut Perf. 13¾x13¼ (#3494h, 3494j) Die Cut Perf. (#3493g, 3493j, 3494i)*

| | | | | |
|---|---|---|---|---|
| **2012, Nov. 20** | | | **Litho.** | |
| **Self-Adhesive** | | | | |
| **3493** | A2917 | Sheet of 10 | 10.00 | 10.00 |
| *a.-j.* | | 50y Any single | .80 | .80 |
| **3494** | A2918 | Sheet of 10 | 13.00 | 13.00 |
| *a.-j.* | | 80y Any single | 1.25 | .80 |

**Miniature Sheet**

**Edo Calligraphy — A2919**

No. 3495 — Characters for "snake": a, In Gyosho style (red background). b, In Reisho style (black character with red chop at bottom center). c, From Qing Dynaasty seal (black curved character with circle with small red chop at left). d, In Reisho style (pink background, red chop at bottom center). e, In Kana (black character similar to "3", red chop at LR). f, In Kaisho script (black character, red chop at LL). g, In Sosho stylet (black character with thick line similar to "2" and thin curved line, red chop at LR). h, In Gyosho style (green background). i, In small seal cutting (character in red). j, In Kinbun style (character in gold, brown background).

**Litho. & Embossed**

| | | | | |
|---|---|---|---|---|
| **2012, Nov. 21** | | | **Perf. 13x13¼** | |
| **3495** | A2919 | Sheet of 10 | 16.00 | 16.00 |
| *a.-j.* | | 80y Any single | 1.25 | .50 |

Camellia
A2920

Plum Blossom
A2921

Adonis Flower
A2922

Cyclamen
A2923

Hellebore
A2924

Camellia
A2925

Plum Blossoms
A2926

Adonis Flowers
A2927

Cyclamen
A2928

Hellebores
A2929

| | | | | |
|---|---|---|---|---|
| **2012, Dec. 3** | **Photo.** | | **Perf. 13¼** | |
| **3496** | A2920 | 50y multi | .80 | .40 |
| **3497** | A2921 | 50y multi | .80 | .40 |
| **3498** | A2922 | 50y multi | .80 | .40 |
| **3499** | A2923 | 50y multi | .80 | .40 |
| **3500** | A2924 | 50y multi | .80 | .40 |
| *a.* | | Vert. strip of 5, #3496-3500 | 4.50 | 3.00 |
| **3501** | A2925 | 80y multi | 1.25 | .60 |
| **3502** | A2926 | 80y multi | 1.25 | .60 |
| **3503** | A2927 | 80y multi | 1.25 | .60 |
| **3504** | A2928 | 80y multi | 1.25 | .60 |
| **3505** | A2929 | 80y multi | 1.25 | .60 |
| *a.* | | Vert. strip of 5, #3501-3505 | 6.50 | 4.00 |
| | Nos. 3496-3505 (10) | | 10.25 | 5.00 |

**Miniature Sheet**

**Hyogo Local Autonomy Law, 60th Anniv. — A2930**

No. 3506: a, Flying crane, Himeji Castle (32x39mm). b, Meriken Park, Kobe, and waterfront buildings (28x33mm). c, Shinkoro Tower, Izushi (28x33mm). d, Shinmaiko Beach (28x33mm). e, Narcissuses, Awaji-shima (28x33mm).

## Perf. 13¼ (#3506a), 13x13¼
**2013, Jan. 15**

| | | | | |
|---|---|---|---|---|
| 3506 | A2930 | Sheet of 5 | 7.00 | 7.00 |
| a.-e. | | 80y Any single | 1.25 | .60 |

### Animation
### Miniature Sheet

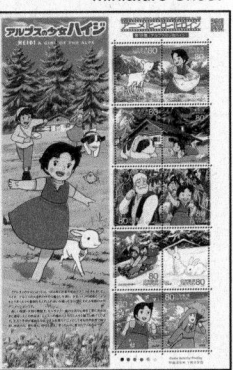

Heidi,
Girl of
the Alps
A2931

No. 3507: a, Lamb and flowers. b, Heidi picking flowers). c, Dog and chalet. d, Heidi and chalet. e, Heidi's grandfather. f, Heidi pointing. g, Heidi and Peter on sled. h, Rabbits. i, Heidi running, mountain in background. j, Clara in blue dress.

**2013, Jan. 23    Litho.    Perf. 13x13¼**

| | | | | |
|---|---|---|---|---|
| 3507 | A2931 | Sheet of 10 | 16.00 | 16.00 |
| a.-j. | | 80y Any single | 1.25 | .50 |

### Miniature Sheets

A2932

Greetings — A2933

No. 3508: a, Cherry blossom, boy, birds with letter (30x29mm flower-shaped stamp). b, Wreath with strawberries (29mm diameter). c, Boy, girl, cat, wreath of cherry blossoms (29mm diameterl). d, Tulips, cats and rabbit (28x28mm). e, Girl carrying potted plant up stairs, cat with broom (28x28mm).

No. 3509: a, Gril with letter, cherry blossoms (30x29mm flower shaped stamp). b, Bouquet of red and pink flowerst (24x34mm oval). c, Bouquet of blue and white flowers (24x34mm oval). d, Bouquet of yellow and orange flowers (24x34mm oval). e, Teddy bear with letter and mail bag, mail box (23x30mm).

### Die Cut Perf., Die Cut Perf 13¼ (#3508d, 3508e, 3509b-3509d), Die Cut Perf. 13¼x12¾ (#3509e)
**2013, Feb. 1**
### Self-Adhesive

| | | | | |
|---|---|---|---|---|
| 3508 | A2932 | Sheet of 5 | 5.00 | 5.00 |
| a.-e. | | 50y Any single | .80 | .80 |
| 3509 | A2933 | Sheet of 5 | 7.00 | 7.00 |
| a.-e. | | 80y Any single | 1.25 | .80 |

Dianthus
Caryophyllus
A2934

Tulip
A2935

Cherry
Blossoms
A2936

Gerbera
Daisy
A2937

Myosotis
Scorpioides
A2938

Dianthus
Caryophyllus
A2939

Tulip
A2940

Cherry
Blossoms
A2941

Gerbera
Daisy
A2942

Myosotis
Scorpioides
A2943

**2013, Feb. 8    Photo.    Perf. 13¼**

| | | | | |
|---|---|---|---|---|
| 3510 | A2934 | 50y multi | .80 | .40 |
| 3511 | A2935 | 50y multi | .80 | .40 |
| 3512 | A2936 | 50y multi | .80 | .40 |
| 3513 | A2937 | 50y multi | .80 | .40 |
| 3514 | A2938 | 50y multi | .80 | .40 |
| a. | | Vert. strip of 5, #3510-3514 | 4.50 | 3.00 |
| 3515 | A2939 | 80y multi | 1.25 | .60 |
| 3516 | A2940 | 80y multi | 1.25 | .60 |
| 3517 | A2941 | 80y multi | 1.25 | .60 |
| 3518 | A2942 | 80y multi | 1.25 | .60 |
| 3519 | A2943 | 80y multi | 1.25 | .60 |
| a. | | Vert. strip of 5, #3515-3519 | 6.50 | 4.00 |
| | | Nos. 3510-3519 (10) | 14.25 | 11.25 |

Mt. Fuji
A2944

Mt. Tsukuba
A2945

Mt.
Kasa — A2946

Mt.
Ibuki — A2947

Mt. Iino — A2948

Mt. Zao — A2949

Mt. Gassan
A2950

Mt. Ryokami
A2951

Mt. Nijo — A2952

Mt.
Kuju — A2953

**2013, Feb. 22    Litho.    Perf. 13¼x13**

| | | | | |
|---|---|---|---|---|
| 3520 | | Sheet of 10 | 16.00 | 16.00 |
| a. | A2944 | 80y multi | 1.25 | .50 |
| b. | A2945 | 80y multi | 1.25 | .50 |
| c. | A2946 | 80y multi | 1.25 | .50 |
| d. | A2947 | 80y multi | 1.25 | .50 |
| e. | A2948 | 80y multi | 1.25 | .50 |
| f. | A2949 | 80y multi | 1.25 | .50 |
| g. | A2950 | 80y multi | 1.25 | .50 |
| h. | A2951 | 80y multi | 1.25 | .50 |
| i. | A2952 | 80y multi | 1.25 | .50 |
| j. | A2953 | 80y multi | 1.25 | .50 |

A2954

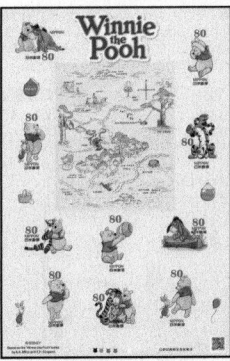

Winnie
the Pooh
A2955

No. 3521: a, Winnie, Piglet, two beamed sixteenth notes in blue, eighth note in black. b, Winnie, sixteenth notes in black and green. c, Winnie, staff in pink, two beamed eighth notes in black. d, Tigger, staff in pink, eighth note in black. e, Winnie, staff in yellow, black and red sixteenth notes. f, Tigger, staff in yellow, two beamed eighth notes in black, eighth note in blue. g, Piglet, staff in yellow, three beamed sixteenth notes, eighth notes in black and pink, half note. h, Eeyore, staff in yellow, sixteenth note and two beamed sixteenth notes in black, eighth note in lilac. i, Winnie, staff in pink, sixteenth note and two beamed sixteenth notes in black. j, Winnie, staff in pink, eighth note, sixteenth note and two beamed sixteenth notes in black.

No. 3522, oval stamps: a, Winnie and Eeyore. b, Winnie seated, touching his nose and with arm wrapped over his head, vert. c, Winnie and Piglet standing, vert. d, Tigger, vert. e, Winnie and Tigger. f, Winnie and honey jar, vert. g, Eeyore and log. h, Winnie standing with arm near mouth. i, Tigger, Eeyore and Winnie. j, Winnie and Piglet walking, vert.

**2013, Mar. 1    Die Cut Perf. 13x12¾**
### Self-Adhesive

| | | | | |
|---|---|---|---|---|
| 3521 | A2954 | Sheet of 10 | 9.00 | 9.00 |
| a.-j. | | 50y Any single | .80 | .80 |

### Die Cut Perf. 13

| | | | | |
|---|---|---|---|---|
| 3522 | A2955 | Sheet of 10 | 13.00 | 13.00 |
| a.-j. | | 80y Any single | 1.25 | .80 |

Grand Canyon,
United
States — A2956

Pyramids,
Egypt — A2957

Mont-Saint-Michel,
France — A2958

Macchu Picchu,
Peru
A2959

Angkor Wat,
Cambodia
A2960

**2013, Mar. 14**        **Perf. 13¼x13**

| | | | |
|---|---|---|---|
| 3523 | A2956 | 80y multi | 1.25 .50 |
| 3524 | A2957 | 80y multi | 1.25 .50 |
| 3525 | A2958 | 80y multi | 1.25 .50 |
| 3526 | A2959 | 80y multi | 1.25 .50 |
| 3527 | A2960 | 80y multi | 1.25 .50 |
| a. | | Horiz. strip of 5, #3523-3527 | 7.50 4.00 |
| | | Nos. 3523-3527 (5) | 6.25 2.50 |

Foreign UNESCO World Heritage Sites.

Hiroaki Cherry Blossom Festival (Aomori) A2961

Designs: No. 3528, Weeping cherry branch, Mt. Iwaki (denomination in green). No. 3529, Yoshino cherry blossoms, Hirosaki Castle (denomination in lilac).

**2013, Mar. 22**        **Perf. 13¼**

| | | | |
|---|---|---|---|
| 3528 | 50y multi | | .80 .40 |
| 3529 | 50y multi | | .80 .40 |
| a. | A2961 Horiz. pair, #3528-3529 | | 1.75 1.25 |

### Miniature Sheet

Season's Memories in My Heart — A2962

No. 3530: a, Girl in yellow dress staring at cherry blossom petals (stamp 1). b, Two children and flower cart (stamp 2). c, Three children, falling cherry blossom petals (stamp 3). d, Girl holding fiddlehead fern in field (stamp 4). e, Girl and flowers (stamp 5). f, Boy and girl looking at flowers (stamp 6). g, Boy in tulips, cat (stamp 7). h, Boy playing flute, girl reading book, flowers (stamp 8). i, Girl with doll, girl with dog, flowers (stamp 9). j, Girls playing house with doll, lawn chair (stamp 10).

**2013, Apr. 3**    **Photo.**      **Perf. 13**

| | | | |
|---|---|---|---|
| 3530 | A2962 | Sheet of 10 | 16.00 16.00 |
| a.-j. | | 80y Any single | 1.25 .50 |

### Miniature Sheet

Travel Scenes A2963

No. 3531 — Sites in Tateyama and Kurobe areas of Toyama: a, Ptarmigan (stamp 1). b, Bus and tourists in Great Snow Valley (stamp 2). c, Shomyo Falls (stamp 3). d, Tateyama gentians, denomination at LL (stamp 4). e, Midagahara Wetlands, denomination at UL (stamp 5). f, Midagahara Wetlands, denomination at UR (stamp 6). g, Murodo Highland, yellow day lilies (stamp 7). h, Stoat (stamp 8). i, Aleutian avens flowers, denomination at LR (stamp 9). j, Cable car at Daikanbo (stamp 10).

---

**2013, Apr. 16**   **Litho.**   **Perf. 13x13¼**

| | | | |
|---|---|---|---|
| 3531 | A2963 | Sheet of 10 | 13.00 13.00 |
| a.-j. | | 80y Any single | 1.25 .60 |

A2964

A2965

A2966

A2967

A2968

A2969

A2970

A2971

Sections of Painted Screen by Motonobu Kano (1476-1559) A2972    A2973

**2013, Apr. 19**   **Photo.**   **Perf. 13¼**

| | | | |
|---|---|---|---|
| 3532 | | Sheet of 10 | 16.00 16.00 |
| a. | A2964 | 80y multi | 1.25 .50 |
| b. | A2965 | 80y multi | 1.25 .50 |
| c. | A2966 | 80y multi | 1.25 .50 |
| d. | A2967 | 80y multi | 1.25 .50 |
| e. | A2968 | 80y multi | 1.25 .50 |
| f. | A2969 | 80y multi | 1.25 .50 |
| g. | A2970 | 80y multi | 1.25 .50 |
| h. | A2971 | 80y multi | 1.25 .50 |
| i. | A2972 | 80y multi | 1.25 .50 |
| j. | A2973 | 80y multi | 1.25 .50 |

Philately Week.

Lily A2974

Day Lily A2975

---

Lilac A2976

Clematis A2977

Skunk Cabbage A2978

Lilies A2979

Day Lilies A2980

Lilac A2981

Clematis A2982

Skunk Cabbages A2983

**2013, Apr. 24**        **Perf. 13¼**

| | | | |
|---|---|---|---|
| 3533 | A2974 | 50y multi | .80 .40 |
| 3534 | A2975 | 50y multi | .80 .40 |
| 3535 | A2976 | 50y multi | .80 .40 |
| 3536 | A2977 | 50y multi | .80 .40 |
| 3537 | A2978 | 50y multi | .80 .40 |
| a. | | Vert. strip of 5, #3533-3537 | 4.50 3.00 |
| 3538 | A2979 | 80y multi | 1.25 .60 |
| 3539 | A2980 | 80y multi | 1.25 .60 |
| 3540 | A2981 | 80y multi | 1.25 .60 |
| 3541 | A2982 | 80y multi | 1.25 .60 |
| 3542 | A2983 | 80y multi | 1.25 .60 |
| a. | | Vert. strip of 5, #3538-3542 | 6.50 4.00 |

### Miniature Sheet

Miyagi Local Autonomy Law, 60th Anniv. — A2984

No. 3543: a, Statue of Masamune Date, replica of Date Maru ship (32x39mm). b, Mt. Kurikoma and cherry tree (28x33mm). c, Sendai Tanabata Festival (28x33mm). d, Bridge, Narukokyo Gorge (28x33mm). e, Sendai Pageant of Starlight (28x33mm).

**Perf. 13¼ (#3543a), 13x13¼**

**2013, May 15**        **Photo.**

| | | | |
|---|---|---|---|
| 3543 | A2984 | Sheet of 5 | 7.00 7.00 |
| a.-e. | | 80y Any single | 1.25 .60 |

---

Martes Zibellina Brachyura A2985

Luscinia Komadori Namiyei A2986

Primula Kisoana Miquel — A2987

Neolucanus Insulicola Donan — A2988

Meretrix Lusoria — A2989

**2013, May 23**        **Perf. 13¼**

| | | | |
|---|---|---|---|
| 3544 | A2985 | 80y multi | 1.25 .50 |
| 3545 | A2986 | 80y multi | 1.25 .50 |
| 3546 | A2987 | 80y multi | 1.25 .50 |
| 3547 | A2988 | 80y multi | 1.25 .50 |
| 3548 | A2989 | 80y multi | 1.25 .50 |
| a. | | Vert. strip of 5, #3544-3548 | 7.50 4.00 |
| | | Nos. 3544-3548 (5) | 6.25 2.50 |

### Miniature Sheet

Tottori Prefecture Afforestation — A2990

No. 3549: a, Quercus serrata (tree), denomination at LL. b, Lilium japonicum (pink flower), denomination at LL. c, Prunus jamasakura (cherry blossoms), denomination at LR. d, Taxus cuspidata (Japanese yew with red arils), denomination at LR. e, Castanopsis sieboldii (tree), denomination at UR. f, Iris sanguinea (purple flowers), denomination at UL. g, Nijisseiki pear tree blossoms, denomination at LR. h, Japanese persimmons on branch, denomination at LR. i, Castanea crenata (Japanese chestnut), denomination at UR. j, Magnolia obovata flower, denomination at LL.

**2013, May 24**   **Litho.**    **Perf. 13**

| | | | |
|---|---|---|---|
| 3549 | A2990 | Sheet of 10 | 10.00 10.00 |
| a.-j. | | 50y Any single | .80 .40 |

Second Hideyo Noguchi Africa Prize A2991

Noguchi (1876-1928), bacteriologist, and: No. 3550, Microscope and flowers. No. 3551, Globe.

**2013, May 31**      **Photo.**
| 3550 | 80y multicolored | 1.25 | .50 |
| 3551 | 80y multicolored | 1.25 | .50 |
| a. | A2991 Horiz. pair, #3550-3551 | 3.00 | 1.50 |

## Animation

Doraemon — A2992

No. 3552: a, Doraemon with wings, two children with wings. b, Three children with wings. c, Doraemon paddling raft. d, Children on fish. e, Doraemon, machine, woman near doorway carrying tray with bottles and glasses. f, Man and boy in indoor fountain. g, Three children with helicopter rotor on head flying. h, Doraemon and child with helicopter rotor on head flying. i, Boy and girl on orse, boy with smokestack on head, boy with umbrella in flight. j, Doraemon and cat on flying seahorses.

**2013, June 4**    **Litho.**    **Perf. 13x13¼**
| 3552 | A2992 Sheet of 10 | 16.00 | 16.00 |
| a.-j. | 80y Any single | 1.25 | .50 |

Miniature Sheet

Hiroshima Local Autonomy Law, 60th Anniv. — A2993

No. 3553: a, Itsukushima Shrine, Bugaku dancer, maple leaves (32x39mm). b, Mibo no Hana Taue rice-planting ritual (28x33mm). c, Taishakukyo Valley (28x33mm). d, Lemons (28x33mm). e, Lighthouse and street, Tomonoura (28x33mm).

**Perf. 13¼ (#3553a), 13x13¼**
**2013, June 14**      **Photo.**
| 3553 | A2993 Sheet of 5 | 7.00 | 7.00 |
| a.-e. | 80y Any single | 1.25 | .60 |

Japan Women's Association for Rehabilitation Aid, 50th Anniv. — A2994

Designs: No. 3554, Two women. No. 3555, Three women.

---

**2013, June 18**    **Litho.**    **Perf. 13**
| 3554 | 80y multicolored | 1.25 | .50 |
| 3555 | 80y multicolored | 1.25 | .50 |
| a. | A2994 Horiz. pair, #3554-3555 | 3.00 | 1.50 |

Miniature Sheets

A2995

Greetings — A2996

No. 3556: a, Hello Kitty reading book (30x27mm heart-shaped stamp). b, Hello Kitty and house (27x30mm house-shaped stamp). c, Mimmy riding tricycle (23x23mm). d, Dear Daniel with letter at mailbox (22x30mm oval stamp). e, My Melody receiving kiss from mouse on tree stump (28mm diameter). f, Hello Kitty watering flowers (27x21mm). g, My Melody, bird in mailbox holding letter (21x27mm). h, My Melody and mouse jumping (30x27mm heart-shaped stamp). i, Little Twin Stars on crescent moon (28mm diameter). j, Little Twin Stars with music book and harp (23x23mm).

No. 3557: a, Little Twin Stars on cloud (27x21mm). b, Little Twin Stars, stars (24x28mm). c, Hello Kitty in airplane (28mm diameter). d, Hello Kitty holding teddy bear and letter (23x23mm). e, Hello Kitty on back of envelope (27x21mm). f, Hello Kitty and Mimmy on tricycles (27x21mm). g, Dear Daniel reaching to insert letter in mailbox (26x29mm). h, Hello Kitty holding apple (29x27mm heart-shaped stamp). i, My Melody receiving letter from bird in mailbox (29x26mm). j, My Melody

---

receiving kiss from mouse (30x27mm oval stamp).

*Die Cut Perf. 13¼, Die Cut Perf. 14 (#3556c, 3556j, 3557d), Die Cut Perf. 13¼x14 (#3556f, 3557a, 3557e, 3557f), Die Cut Perf. 14x13¾ (#3556g), Die Cut Perf. (#3556e, 3556i, 3557b, 3557c)*

**2013, June 21**      **Litho.**
**Self-Adhesive**
| 3556 | A2995 Sheet of 10 | 9.00 | 9.00 |
| a.-j. | 50y Any single | .80 | .80 |
| 3557 | A2996 Sheet of 10 | 13.00 | 13.00 |
| a.-j. | 80y Any single | 1.25 | .80 |

Miniature Sheet

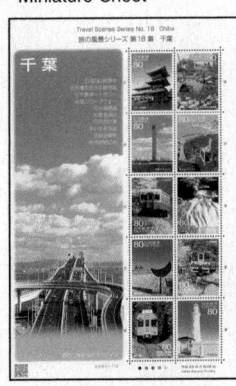

Travel Scenes A2997

No. 3558 — Sites in Chiba: a, Narita-san Temple (stamp 1). b, Tourists in boat, flowers at Suigo Sarawa Aquatic Botanical Gardens (stamp 2). c, Chiba Port Tower (stamp 3). d, Nokogiriyama Cable Car (stamp 4). e, Yellow and red Kominato Railway train car (stamp 5). f, Waterfall, Yoro-keikoku Valley (stamp 6). g, Tsuki-no-Sabaku Statues, Onjuku Beach (stamp 7). h, Yellow and green Isumi Railway train car (stamp 8). i, Light green Choshi Electric Railway train car (stamp 9). j, Inubosaki Lighthouse (stamp 10).

**2013, June 25**    **Litho.**    **Perf. 13x13¼**
| 3558 | A2997 Sheet of 10 | 13.00 | 13.00 |
| a.-j. | 80y Any single | 1.25 | .60 |

Gion Festival, Kyoto A2998

Various festival scenes with denomination in purple at: No. 3559, UL. No. 3560, UR. No. 3561, LL. No. 3562, LR.

**2013, July 1**      **Perf. 13¼**
| 3559 | 50y multi | .80 | .40 |
| 3560 | 50y multi | .80 | .40 |
| 3561 | 50y multi | .80 | .40 |
| 3562 | 50y multi | .80 | .40 |
| a. | A2998 Block of 4, #3559-3562 | 3.50 | 2.50 |
| | Nos. 3559-3562 (4) | 3.20 | 1.60 |

Miniature Sheet

Constellations — A2999

---

No. 3563: a, Cancer (crab). b, Leo (lion). c, Virgo (virgin). d, Ursa Major (large bear, tail at left). e, Ursa Minor (small bear, tail at top). f, Boötes (herdsman). g, Corvus (crow). h, Corona Borealis (crown). i, Canes Venatici (hunting dogs). j, Big Dipper asterism.

## Litho. With Foil Application
**2013, July 5**    **Die Cut Perf. 13**
**Self-Adhesive**
| 3563 | A2999 Sheet of 10 | 16.00 | 16.00 |
| a.-j. | 80y Any single | 1.50 | .60 |

Miniature Sheet

Gunma Local Autonomy Law, 60th Anniv. — A3000

No. 3564: a, Tomioka Silk Mill, woman (32x39mm). b, Red rhododendrons (28x33mm). c, Usui Railway Bridge (28x33mm). d, Fukiware Falls (28x33mm). e, Yellow day lilies (28x33mm).

**Perf. 13¼ (#3564a), 13x13¼**
**2013, July 12**      **Photo.**
| 3564 | A3000 Sheet of 5 | 7.00 | 7.00 |
| a.-e. | 80y Any single | 1.25 | .60 |

Boy Writing Postcard A3001

Goldfish in Bowl A3002

Mailbox, Dragonfly, Net A3003

Japanese Morning Glories and Trellis A3004

Cucumbers, Eggplants, and Tomatoes — A3005

A3006

No. 3570: a, Girl writing a letter. b, Mailbox, dragonfly, net, diff. c, Beans and bowl of rice. d, Tea kettle and glasses. e, Corn. f, Japanese morning glories and trellis, diff. g, Postal truck on bridge. h, Spiral mosquito repellent coils. i, Bowls of noodles and sauce. j, Tomatoes.

| 2013, July 23 | | | Perf. 13¼ | |
|---|---|---|---|---|
| 3565 | A3001 | 50y multi | .80 | .30 |
| 3566 | A3002 | 50y multi | .80 | .30 |
| 3567 | A3003 | 50y multi | .80 | .30 |
| 3568 | A3004 | 50y multi | .80 | .30 |
| 3569 | A3005 | 50y multi | .80 | .30 |
| a. | | Vert strip of 5, #3565-3569 | 4.50 | 3.00 |
| | | Nos. 3565-3569 (5) | 4.00 | 1.50 |
| | | *Perf. 13* | | |
| 3570 | A3006 | Sheet of 10 | 16.00 | 16.00 |
| a.-j. | | 80y Any single | 1.25 | .50 |

Letter Writing Day.

Kisegawa of Matsubaya, by Eishi Chobunsai
A3007

Pine Grove at Miho, by Hiroshige
A3008

Midorigi of the Wakamatsu House, by Eisho Chokosai
A3009

Oyashirazu, by Hiroshige
A3010

Woman Holding an Umbrella, by Eizan Kikukawa
A3011

Waka Bay, by Hiroshige
A3012

Koito of Itoya, by Utamaro
A3013

Festival at the Itsukushima Shrine, by Hiroshige
A3014

Geisha of Tachibana Street, by Kiyonaga Torii
A3015

Amanohashidate, by Hiroshige
A3016

| 2013, Aug. 1 | | | Litho. | Perf. 13 | |
|---|---|---|---|---|---|
| 3571 | | Sheet of 10 | | 16.00 | 16.00 |
| a. | A3007 | 80y multi | | 1.25 | .50 |
| b. | A3008 | 80y multi | | 1.25 | .50 |
| c. | A3009 | 80y multi | | 1.25 | .50 |
| d. | A3010 | 80y multi | | 1.25 | .50 |
| e. | A3011 | 80y multi | | 1.25 | .50 |
| f. | A3012 | 80y multi | | 1.25 | .50 |
| g. | A3013 | 80y multi | | 1.25 | .50 |
| h. | A3014 | 80y multi | | 1.25 | .50 |
| i. | A3015 | 80y multi | | 1.25 | .50 |
| j. | A3016 | 80y multi | | 1.25 | .50 |

Miniature Sheets

A3017

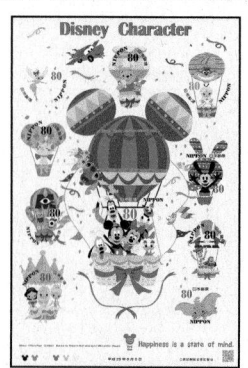

Disney Characters — A3018

No. 3572: a, Mickey Mouse on blue box. b, Minnie Mouse on pink box. c, Donald Duck on blue box. d, Daisy Duck on pink box. e, Tinker Bell on pink box. f, Marie the Cat on blue box. g, Buzz Lightyear and Woody on pink box. h, Lightning McQueen on blue box. i, Winnie the Pooh on blue box. j, Alice on pink box.

No. 3573: a, Tinker Bell (29mm diameter). b, Winnie the Pooh and Piglet in balloon gondola (21x30mm oval). c, Alice in balloon gondola (29mm diameter). d, Marie the Cat in balloon gondola (21x30mm oval). e, Oswald the Rabbit in balloon gondola (23x23mm). f, Mike Wazowski and James P. Sullivan in balloon gondola (21x30mm oval). g, Goofy, Chip, Donald Duck, Pluto, Mickey Mouse, Minnie Mouse, Daisy Duck in balloon gondola (44x35mm). h, Woody and Buzz Lightyear in balloon gondola (21x30mm oval). i, Snow White, Rapunzel and Cinderella in balloon gondola (29mm diameter). j, Dumbo (30x21mm oval).

*Die Cut Perf. 13¼*

| 2013, Aug. 8 | | | Litho. | |
|---|---|---|---|---|
| | | **Self-Adhesive** | | |
| 3572 | A3017 | Sheet of 10 | 9.00 | 9.00 |
| a.-j. | | 50y Any single | .80 | .80 |

*Die Cut Perf., Die Cut Perf. 13¼ (oval stamps), Die Cut Perf. 14 (#3573e), Die Cut Perf. 13½ (#3573g)*

| 3573 | A3018 | Sheet of 10 | 13.00 | 13.00 |
|---|---|---|---|---|
| a.-j. | | 80y Any single | 1.25 | .80 |

Kayak on Tama River
A3019

Sailboats Near Tokyo Gate Bridge
A3020

Bonin Islands
A3021

Tokyo Skyline
A3022

Tokyo Stadium — A3023

| 2013, Aug. 25 | | | Litho. | Perf. 13 | |
|---|---|---|---|---|---|
| 3574 | A3019 | 80y multi | | 1.25 | .60 |
| 3575 | A3020 | 80y multi | | 1.25 | .60 |
| 3576 | A3021 | 80y multi | | 1.25 | .60 |
| 3577 | A3022 | 80y multi | | 1.25 | .60 |
| 3578 | A3023 | 80y multi | | 1.25 | .60 |
| a. | | Vert. strip of 5, #3574-3578 | | 6.50 | 4.00 |
| | | Nos. 3574-3578 (5) | | 6.25 | 3.00 |

68th National Athletic Meet, Tokyo.

Persimmon
A3024

Bok Choy
A3025

Chestnut
A3026

Sweet Potato
A3027

Pear
A3028

Apple
A3029

Taro Roots
A3030

Japanese Pears
A3031

Turnip Greens
A3032

Grapes
A3033

*Die Cut Perf. 13x13¼, 13¼x13*

| 2013, Aug. 30 | | | Photo. | |
|---|---|---|---|---|
| | | **Self-Adhesive** | | |
| 3579 | | Sheet of 10, 2 each #3579a-3579e | 10.00 | 10.00 |
| a. | A3024 | 50y multi | 1.00 | .75 |
| b. | A3025 | 50y multi | 1.00 | .75 |
| c. | A3026 | 50y multi | 1.00 | .75 |
| d. | A3027 | 50y multi | 1.00 | .75 |
| e. | A3028 | 50y multi | 1.00 | .75 |
| 3580 | | Sheet of 10, 2 each #3580a-3580e | 16.00 | 16.00 |
| a. | A3029 | 80y multi | 1.60 | .80 |
| b. | A3030 | 80y multi | 1.60 | .80 |
| c. | A3031 | 80y multi | 1.60 | .80 |
| d. | A3032 | 80y multi | 1.60 | .80 |
| e. | A3033 | 80y multi | 1.60 | .80 |

Dahlia
A3034

Chrysanthemu
A3035

Cockscomb
A3036

Asiatic Dayflower
A3037

Rose
A3038

Dahlias
A3039

Chrysanthemums
A3040

Cockscombs
A3041

Asiatic Dayflowers
A3042

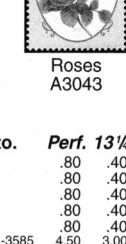

Roses
A3043

| 2013, Sept. 13 | | | Photo. | Perf. 13¼ | |
|---|---|---|---|---|---|
| 3581 | A3034 | 50y multi | | .80 | .40 |
| 3582 | A3035 | 50y multi | | .80 | .40 |
| 3583 | A3036 | 50y multi | | .80 | .40 |
| 3584 | A3037 | 50y multi | | .80 | .40 |
| 3585 | A3038 | 50y multi | | .80 | .40 |
| a. | | Vert. strip of 5, #3581-3585 | | 4.50 | 3.00 |
| 3586 | A3039 | 80y multi | | 1.25 | .60 |
| 3587 | A3040 | 80y multi | | 1.25 | .60 |
| 3588 | A3041 | 80y multi | | 1.25 | .60 |
| 3589 | A3042 | 80y multi | | 1.25 | .60 |
| 3590 | A3043 | 80y multi | | 1.25 | .60 |
| a. | | Vert. strip of 5, #3586-3590 | | 6.50 | 4.00 |
| | | Nos. 3581-3590 (10) | | 10.25 | 5.00 |

Ambulance Service Legislation, 50th Anniv. — A3044

**2013, Sept. 9　Litho.　Perf. 13**
| | | | | |
|---|---|---|---|---|
| 3591 | 80y | Helicopter ambulance | 1.25 | .50 |
| 3592 | 80y | Ambulance | 1.25 | .50 |
| a. | A3044 | Horiz. pair, #3591-3592 | 3.00 | 1.50 |

**Miniature Sheets**

A3045

Greetings — A3046

No. 3593 — Teddy bear wearing postman's cap: a, In bed (21x30mm oval). b, Alone at table (21x30mm oval). c, At right of pillar box (23x23mm). d, At left of pillar box (23x23mm). e, Delivering letter to large teddy bear (23x23mm). f, Delivering gift to large teddy bear (23x23mm). g, Holding flower bouquet with light blue ribbon (27x30mm). h, Holding flower bouquet with yellow ribbon (27x30mm). i, With two other teddy bears at table (21x30mm oval). j, Reading book in bed (21x30mm oval).

No. 3594: a, Teddy bear delivering letter to large teddy bear (27x21mm). b, Teddy bear walking on path, holding letter (21x30mm oval). c, Teddy bear delivering gift to large teddy bear (27x21mm). d, Teddy bear delivering letter to bird (21x30mm oval). e, Teddy bear on bicycle (27x21mm). f, Teddy bear delivering letter to bear with pail and fishing pole (27x21mm). g, Small teddy bear without cap holding letter near pillar box (21x30mm oval). h, Teddy bear with cap, small teddy bear with flower bouquet (27x21mm). i, Teddy bear with cap lifting small teddy bear to slot of pillar box (21x27mm). j, Small teddy bear behind teddy bear with cap (29mm diameter).

---

***Die Cut Perf. 13¼ (oval stamps), Die Cut Perf. 14 (square stamps), Die Cut Perf. (#3593g, 3593h)***
**2013, Sept. 19　　　Litho.**
**Self-Adhesive**
| | | | | |
|---|---|---|---|---|
| 3593 | A3045 | Sheet of 10 | 9.00 | 9.00 |
| a.-j. | | 50y Any single | .80 | .80 |

***Die Cut Perf. 13¼x13¾, Die Cut Perf. 13¼ (oval stamps), Die Cut Perf. 13¾x13¼ (#3594i), Die Cut Perf. (#3594j)***
| | | | | |
|---|---|---|---|---|
| 3594 | A3046 | Sheet of 10 | 13.00 | 13.00 |
| a.-j. | | 80y Any single | 1.25 | .80 |

Baby Elephant A3047

Baby and Adult Killer Whales A3048

Black-tailed Prairie Dog A3049

Adult and Juvenile Gentoo Penguins A3050

Kangaroo A3051

Amur Tiger Cub A3052

Timber Wolf Pups — A3053

Ring-tailed Lemurs — A3054

Polar Bear A3055

White Oryx A3056

***Die Cut Perf. 13¼***
**2013, Sept. 20　　　Litho.**
**Self-Adhesive**
| | | | | |
|---|---|---|---|---|
| 3595 | | Sheet of 10, 2 each | | |
| | | #3595a-3595e | 10.00 | 10.00 |
| a. | A3047 | 50y multi | 1.00 | .75 |
| b. | A3048 | 50y multi | 1.00 | .75 |
| c. | A3049 | 50y multi | 1.00 | .75 |
| d. | A3050 | 50y multi | 1.00 | .75 |
| e. | A3051 | 50y multi | 1.00 | .75 |
| 3596 | | Sheet of 10, 2 each | | |
| | | #3596a-3596e | 16.00 | 16.00 |
| a. | A3052 | 80y multi | 1.60 | .75 |
| b. | A3053 | 80y multi | 1.60 | .75 |
| c. | A3054 | 80y multi | 1.60 | .75 |
| d. | A3055 | 80y multi | 1.60 | .75 |
| e. | A3056 | 80y multi | 1.60 | .75 |

---

**Miniature Sheet**

Diplomatic Relations Between Japan and Spain, 400th Anniv. — A3057

No. 3597: a, Potted geraniums on decorative shelf. b, Japanese bush clover. c, Guggenheim Museum, Bilbao, Spain (white denomination at UR, numeral to right of "Nippon.") d, Santiago de Compostela Cathedral (gold denomination at UR). e, Museum of Contemporary Art, León, Spain (white denomination at UR, numeral below "Nippon."). f, Alcazar of Segovia (castle with spires). g, Royal Palace, Madrid (building with dome). h, Arches and columns, Córdoba Cathedral, Spain. i, Courtyard and archway, Palace of Generalife, Granada, Spain. j, Field of sunflowers.

**2013, Oct. 1　Litho.　Perf. 13**
| | | | | |
|---|---|---|---|---|
| 3597 | A3057 | Sheet of 10 | 16.00 | 16.00 |
| a.-j. | | 80y Any single | 1.25 | .50 |

See Spain No. 3944.

**Miniature Sheet**

Okayama Local Autonomy Law, 60th Anniv. — A3058

No. 3598: a, Korakuen Gardens, Momotaro with animals (32x39mm). b, Bridge and buildings, Kurashiki Bikan (28x33mm). c, Shizutani School (28x33mm). d, Cattle grazing, Hiruzenkogen Highlands (28x33mm). e, Tsuyama Castle and cherry blossoms (28x33mm).

***Perf. 13¼ (#3598a), 13x13¼***
**2013, Oct. 4　　　　　Photo.**
| | | | | |
|---|---|---|---|---|
| 3598 | A3058 | Sheet of 5 | 7.00 | 7.00 |
| a.-e. | | 80y Any single | 1.25 | .60 |

Intl. Letter Writing Week — A3059

Posting stations from The Fifty-three Stations of the Tokaido, by Hiroshige: 70y, Shirasuka. 90y, Odawara. 110y, Hamamatsu. 130y, Ishiyakushi.

---

**2013, Oct. 9　Photo.　Perf. 13**
| | | | | |
|---|---|---|---|---|
| 3599 | A3059 | 70y multi | 1.25 | .50 |
| 3600 | A3059 | 90y multi | 1.75 | .50 |
| 3601 | A3059 | 110y multi | 2.25 | .50 |
| 3602 | A3059 | 130y multi | 2.60 | .50 |
| | | Nos. 3599-3602 (4) | 7.85 | 2.00 |

See listing of No. 4448 for images of each Hiroshige print.

Tokyo Railroad Station A3060

Odakyu 3000 Series Locomotive A3061

JNR 151 Series Locomotive A3062

Kintetsu 10100 Series Locomotive A3063

JNR Kiha 81 Series Locomotive A3064

Meitetsu 7000 Series Locomotive A3065

Kintetsu 20100 Series Locomotive A3066

Odakyu 3100 Series Locomotive A3067

JNR Shinkansen 0 Series Locomotive A3068

Shinkansen E5 Series Locomotive A3069

**2013, Oct. 11　Photo.　Perf. 13¼x13**
| | | | | |
|---|---|---|---|---|
| 3603 | | Sheet of 10 | 16.00 | 16.00 |
| a. | A3060 | 80y multi | 1.25 | .50 |
| b. | A3061 | 80y multi | 1.25 | .50 |
| c. | A3062 | 80y multi | 1.25 | .50 |
| d. | A3063 | 80y multi | 1.25 | .50 |
| e. | A3064 | 80y multi | 1.25 | .50 |
| f. | A3065 | 80y multi | 1.25 | .50 |
| g. | A3066 | 80y multi | 1.25 | .50 |
| h. | A3067 | 80y multi | 1.25 | .50 |
| i. | A3068 | 80y multi | 1.25 | .50 |
| j. | A3069 | 80y multi | 1.25 | .50 |

### Miniature Sheet

Shizuoka Local Autonomy Law, 60th Anniv. — A3070

No. 3604: a, Mount Fuji and clouds (32x39mm). b, Mount Fuji and yellow flowers (28x33mm). c, Mount Fuji reflected in Lake Tanuki (28x33mm). d, Mount Fuji and trees (28x33mm). e, Mount Fuji, ships and coastal rocks (28x33mm).

**Perf. 13¼ (#3604a), 13x13¼**

| 2013, Oct. 15 | | Photo. | | |
|---|---|---|---|---|
| 3604 | A3070 | Sheet of 5 | 7.00 | 7.00 |
| a.-e. | | 80y Any single | 1.25 | .60 |

Tortoise on Galapagos Islands, Ecuador A3071

Taj Mahal, India A3072

Venice, Italy A3073

Victoria Falls, Zambia and Zimbabwe A3074

Cologne Cathedral, Germany — A3075

| 2013, Oct. 23 | | Litho. | Perf. 13¼x13 | |
|---|---|---|---|---|
| 3605 | A3071 | 80y multi | 1.25 | .50 |
| 3606 | A3072 | 80y multi | 1.25 | .50 |
| 3607 | A3073 | 80y multi | 1.25 | .50 |
| 3608 | A3074 | 80y multi | 1.25 | .50 |
| 3609 | A3075 | 80y multi | 1.25 | .50 |
| a. | | Horiz. strip of 5, #3605-3609 | 7.50 | 4.50 |
| | | Nos. 3605-3609 (5) | 6.25 | 2.50 |

Foreign UNESCO World Heritage Sites.

### Miniature Sheet

Traditional Crafts — A3076

No. 3610: a, Kishu lacquerware vase (Wakayama Prefecture). b, Two Edo Kiriko glasses (Tokyo Prefecture). c, Owari Shippo porcelain bowl with lid (Aichi Prefecture). d, Two Kyo Kumihimo braids (Kyoto Prefecture). e, Chibana Okinawa weavings (Okinawa Prefecture). f, Ainu ceremonial costume (Hokkaido Prefecture). g, Kishu lacquered utensil handles (Wakayama Prefecture). h, Mashiko-yaki pottery bowl (Tochigi Prefecture). i, Kokeshi dolls (Miyagi Prefecture). j, Takaoka copper vessel (Toyama Prefecture).

| 2013, Oct. 25 | | Litho. | Perf. 13½ | |
|---|---|---|---|---|
| 3610 | A3076 | Sheet of 10 | 16.00 | 16.00 |
| a.-j. | | 80y Any single | 1.25 | .50 |

A3077　A3078

New Year 2014 (Year of the Horse) A3079　A3080

| 2013, Nov. 1 | | Photo. | Perf. 13x13½ | |
|---|---|---|---|---|
| 3611 | A3077 | 50y multi | 1.00 | .30 |
| 3612 | A3078 | 80y multi | 1.50 | .40 |

**Photo. & Typo. Perf. 13¼**

| 3613 | A3079 | 50y +3y multi | 1.25 | .40 |
|---|---|---|---|---|
| 3614 | A3080 | 80y +3y multi | 1.75 | .40 |
| | | Nos. 3611-3614 (4) | 5.50 | 1.50 |

Sheets of two containing Nos. 3611-3612 were lottery prizes. Value, $3.

### Miniature Sheet

Edo Calligraphy — A3081

No. 3615 — Characters for "horse": a, In Manyo-kana style (black character with dot at top, red chop at center left). b, In oracle bone script (red character). c, In Qin Dynasty bamboo roll calligraphy (black character with curved arc crossing center line, red chop at center left). d, In Western Zhou Dynasty Kinbun style (black character with teardrop shaped top with dot in center, red chop at LL). e, In Sosho style (black character of one continuous curved line, red chop at LL). f, In Kaisho style (black character, red chop at bottom center). g, In Gyosho style (black character with red chop at LR. h, In Kana (black character with lilac background). i, In Seal style calligraphy (black character with two horizontal lines at bottom, red chop at center right). j, In Katakana (gold character on blue violet background).

**Litho. & Embossed**

| 2013, Nov. 1 | | | Perf. 13x13¼ | |
|---|---|---|---|---|
| 3615 | A3081 | Sheet of 10 | 16.00 | 16.00 |
| a.-j. | | 80y Any single | 1.25 | .50 |

Two Snowmen A3082

Snowman With Broom A3083

Three Snowmen A3084

Snowman on Skis A3086

Snowflake Jewelry With Emeralds A3088

Snowflake Jewelry With Peridots A3090

Two Wine Glasses A3092

Two Champagne Flutes A3094

Two Martini Glasses — A3096

Snowman With Gift A3085

Snowflake Jewelry With Sapphires A3087

Snowflake Jewelry With Aquamarines A3089

Snowflake Jewelry With Rubies A3091

Two Candles A3093

Candle A3095

**Die Cut Perf. 13¼**

| 2013, Nov. 7 | | | Litho. | |
|---|---|---|---|---|

**Self-Adhesive**

| 3616 | | Sheet of 10, 2 each #3616a-3616e | 9.00 | 9.00 |
|---|---|---|---|---|
| a. | A3082 | 50y multi | .80 | .80 |
| b. | A3083 | 50y multi | .80 | .80 |
| c. | A3084 | 50y multi | .80 | .80 |
| d. | A3085 | 50y multi | .80 | .80 |
| e. | A3086 | 50y multi | .80 | .80 |
| 3617 | | Sheet of 10 | 13.00 | 13.00 |
| a. | A3087 | 80y multi | 1.25 | .80 |
| b. | A3088 | 80y multi | 1.25 | .80 |
| c. | A3089 | 80y multi | 1.25 | .80 |
| d. | A3090 | 80y multi | 1.25 | .80 |
| e. | A3091 | 80y multi | 1.25 | .80 |
| f. | A3092 | 80y multi | 1.25 | .80 |
| g. | A3093 | 80y multi | 1.25 | .80 |
| h. | A3094 | 80y multi | 1.25 | .80 |
| i. | A3095 | 80y multi | 1.25 | .80 |
| j. | A3096 | 80y multi | 1.25 | .80 |

### Miniature Sheet

Yamanashi Local Autonomy Law, 60th Anniv. — A3097

No. 3618: a, Mount Fuji, grapes, and maglev test train (32x39mm). b, Shosenkyo Gorges (28x33mm). c, Nishizawa Valley waterfalls (28x33mm). d, Pagoda and cherry blossoms (28x33mm). e, Saruhashi Bridge (28x33mm).

**Perf. 13¼ (#3618a), 13x13¼**

| 2013, Nov. 15 | | | Photo. | |
|---|---|---|---|---|
| 3618 | A3097 | Sheet of 5 | 7.00 | 7.00 |
| a.-e. | | 80y Any single | 1.25 | .60 |

Mt. Iwakisan A3098

Mt. Tsurugidake A3099

Mt. Hirugatake A3100

Mt. Gozaishodake A3101

Mt. Daisen A3102

Mt. Myokosan A3103

Mt. Aobasan A3104

Mt. Kaikomagatake A3105

Mt. Oodaigahara A3106

Mt. Tenzan A3107

| 2013, Nov. 19 | | Litho. | Perf. 13¼x13 | |
|---|---|---|---|---|
| 3619 | | Sheet of 10 | 16.00 | 16.00 |
| a. | A3098 | 80y multi | 1.25 | .50 |
| b. | A3099 | 80y multi | 1.25 | .50 |
| c. | A3100 | 80y multi | 1.25 | .50 |
| d. | A3101 | 80y multi | 1.25 | .50 |
| e. | A3102 | 80y multi | 1.25 | .50 |
| f. | A3103 | 80y multi | 1.25 | .50 |
| g. | A3104 | 80y multi | 1.25 | .50 |
| h. | A3105 | 80y multi | 1.25 | .50 |
| i. | A3106 | 80y multi | 1.25 | .50 |
| j. | A3107 | 80y multi | 1.25 | .50 |

Volunteer
Fire
Service,
120th
Anniv.
A3108

Paintings by Kunichida Toyohara of Kabuki actors wearing costumes of fire fighters: No. 3620, Jyuzaburo Nakamura (denomination at right). No. 3621, Hikosaburo Bando (denomination at left).

**2013, Nov. 25**    Litho.    Perf. 13
| | | | | |
|---|---|---|---|---|
| 3620 | 80y multi | | 1.25 | .50 |
| 3621 | 80y multi | | 1.25 | .50 |
| a. | A3108 Horiz. pair, #3620-3621 | | 3.00 | 1.50 |

Japanese Allspice A3109

Snowdrop A3110

Christmas Camellia A3111

Narcissus A3112

Leopard Plant Flowers A3113

Japanese Allspice A3114

Snowdrops A3115

Christmas Camellias A3116

Narcissi A3117

Leopard Plant Flowers A3118

**2013, Dec. 3**    Photo.    Perf. 13¼
| | | | |
|---|---|---|---|
| 3622 | A3109 50y multi | .80 | .40 |
| 3623 | A3110 50y multi | .80 | .40 |
| 3624 | A3111 50y multi | .80 | .40 |
| 3625 | A3112 50y multi | .80 | .40 |
| 3626 | A3113 50y multi | .80 | .40 |
| a. | Vert. strip of 5, #3622-3626 | 4.50 | 3.00 |
| 3627 | A3114 80y multi | 1.25 | .60 |
| 3628 | A3115 80y multi | 1.25 | .60 |
| 3629 | A3116 80y multi | 1.25 | .60 |
| 3630 | A3117 80y multi | 1.25 | .60 |
| 3631 | A3118 80y multi | 1.25 | .60 |
| a. | Vert. strip of 5, #3627-3631 | 6.50 | 4.00 |
| | Nos. 3622-3631 (10) | 10.25 | 5.00 |

Miniature Sheet

Constellations — A3119

No. 3632: a, Aries (ram). b, Taurus (bull). c, Gemini (twins). d, Orion (hunter with shield). e, Auriga (man holding goat). f, Canis Major (dog on hind legs). g, Canis Minor (dog on four legs). h, Lepus (rabbit). i, Monoceros (unicorn). j, Tsuzumiboshi (Japanese drum, Japanese version of Orion).

**Litho. With Foil Application**
**2013, Dec. 4**    Die Cut Perf. 13
**Self-Adhesive**
| | | | | |
|---|---|---|---|---|
| 3632 | A3119 | Sheet of 10 | 16.00 | 16.00 |
| a.-j. | 80y Any single | | 1.50 | .80 |

Wakamatsu Castle A3120

Odawara Castle A3121

Hikone Castle A3122

Nijo Castle A3123

Okayama Castle — A3124

**2013, Dec. 10**    Litho.    Perf. 13
| | | | | |
|---|---|---|---|---|
| 3633 | A3120 80y multi | | 1.25 | .50 |
| 3634 | A3121 80y multi | | 1.25 | .50 |
| 3635 | A3122 80y multi | | 1.25 | .50 |
| 3636 | A3123 80y multi | | 1.25 | .50 |
| 3637 | A3124 80y multi | | 1.25 | .50 |
| a. | Vert. strip of 5, #3633-3637 | | 8.00 | 4.00 |
| | Nos. 3633-3637 (5) | | 6.25 | 2.50 |

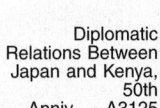

Diplomatic Relations Between Japan and Kenya, 50th Anniv. — A3125

African wildlife: No. 3638, Giraffes. No. 3639, Cheetahs. No. 3640, Elephants. No. 3641, Zebras. No. 3642, Lion.

**2013, Dec. 12**    Litho.    Perf. 13¼x13
| | | | | |
|---|---|---|---|---|
| 3638 | A3125 80y multi | | 1.25 | .50 |
| 3639 | A3125 80y multi | | 1.25 | .50 |
| 3640 | A3125 80y multi | | 1.25 | .50 |
| 3641 | A3125 80y multi | | 1.25 | .50 |
| 3642 | A3125 80y multi | | 1.25 | .50 |
| a. | Horiz. strip of 5, #3638-3642 | | 8.00 | 4.00 |
| | Nos. 3638-3642 (5) | | 6.25 | 2.50 |

Miniature Sheet

Kagoshima Local Autonomy Law, 60th Anniv. — A3126

No. 3643: a, Jomon Sugi tree, rhododendrons (32x39mm). b, Sakurajima Volcano (28x33mm). c, Kaimondake Volcano and coastal rocks (28x33mm). d, Flowers on Kirishima Mountains (28x33mm). e, Cranes (28x33mm).

**Perf. 13¼ (#3643a), 13x13¼**
**2013, Dec. 13**    Photo.
| | | | | |
|---|---|---|---|---|
| 3643 | A3126 | Sheet of 5 | 7.00 | 7.00 |
| a.-e. | 80y Any single | | 1.25 | .60 |

Teddy Bear, Gift and Dog A3127

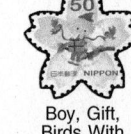

Boy, Gift, Birds With Ribbon A3128

Girl With Broom, Squirrel and Turtle A3129

Animals, Gift, Flowers and Strawberries A3130

Roses A3131

Cherry Blossoms A3132

Mt. Fuji and Cherry Blossoms A3133

Rose Bouquet A3134

Tulips and Girl With Letter and Flower Bouquet A3135

Teddy Bears, Flowers and Mailbox A3136

**Die Cut Perf., Die Cut Perf. 13**
**(#3644d, 3644e, 3645e)**
**2014, Jan. 16**    Litho.
**Self-Adhesive**
| | | | | |
|---|---|---|---|---|
| 3644 | Sheet of 10, 2 each | | | |
| | #3644a-3644e | | 9.00 | 9.00 |
| a. | A3127 50y multi | | .80 | .80 |
| b. | A3128 50y multi | | .80 | .80 |
| c. | A3129 50y multi | | .80 | .80 |
| d. | A3130 50y multi | | .80 | .80 |
| e. | A3131 50y multi | | .80 | .80 |
| 3645 | Sheet of 10, 2 each | | | |
| | #3645a-3645e | | 12.00 | 12.00 |
| a. | A3132 80y multi | | 1.25 | .80 |
| b. | A3133 80y multi | | 1.25 | .80 |
| c. | A3134 80y multi | | 1.25 | .80 |
| d. | A3135 80y multi | | 1.25 | .80 |
| e. | A3136 80y multi | | 1.25 | .80 |

Miniature Sheet

Diplomatic Relations Between Japan and Switzerland, 150th Anniv. — A3137

No. 3646: a, Swiss mountains in spring. b, Mount Fuji and cherry blossoms. c, Aletsch Glacier, Switzerland. d, Bern, Switzerland. e, Lavaux Vineyard Terraces. f, Rhaetian Railway train on bridge. g, Jungfrau Railway train, flowers and mountains. h, Narcissus Path, Les Avants, Switzerland. i, Fluhalp Mountain Lodge. j, Meadow in Bernina Alps.

**2014, Feb. 6**    Litho.    Perf. 13
| | | | | |
|---|---|---|---|---|
| 3646 | A3137 | Sheet of 10 | 16.00 | 16.00 |
| a.-j. | 80y Any single | | 1.25 | .50 |

See Switzerland Nos. 1507-1508.

Hokkaido Mountain Hare A3138

Cherry Blossoms A3139

Plum Blossoms A3140

Violets A3141

Cedar Tree A3142

Nachi Falls A3143

Rishiri Island — A3144

**2014, Mar. 3**    Photo.    Perf. 13x13¼
| | | | | |
|---|---|---|---|---|
| 3647 | A3138 | 2y multi | .30 | .25 |
| 3648 | A3139 | 52y multi | 1.00 | .75 |
| 3649 | A3140 | 82y multi | 1.60 | 1.25 |
| 3650 | A3141 | 92y multi | 1.90 | 1.40 |
| 3651 | A3142 | 205y multi | 4.00 | 3.00 |
| 3652 | A3143 | 280y multi | 5.50 | 4.25 |
| 3653 | A3144 | 310y multi | 6.00 | 4.50 |
| | Nos. 3647-3653 (7) | | 20.30 | 15.40 |

Flowers For
Mourning — A3145

**2014, Mar. 3   Photo.   *Perf. 13x13¼***
3654  A3145  52y multi          1.00  .75
See No. 4106.

Fan With
Plum
Blossoms
A3146

Fan With
Bamboo
A3147

Fan With Tree
Branches — A3148

**2014, Mar. 3   Photo.   *Perf. 13x13¼***
3655  A3146  52y multi          1.00  .75
3656  A3147  82y multi          1.60  1.25
3657  A3148  92y multi          1.90  1.40
      Nos. 3655-3657 (3)         4.50  3.40
Compare with type A3914.

A3149          A3150

A3151          A3152

A3153          A3154

A3155          A3156

A3157          Takarazuka
               Revue, 100th
               Anniv. — A3158

**2014, Apr. 1   Litho.   *Perf. 13***
3658  Sheet of 10           16.00  16.00
  a.  A3149  82c multi         1.25  .50
  b.  A3150  82c multi         1.25  .50
  c.  A3151  82c multi         1.25  .50
  d.  A3152  82c multi         1.25  .50
  e.  A3153  82c multi         1.25  .50
  f.  A3154  82c multi         1.25  .50
  g.  A3155  82c multi         1.25  .50
  h.  A3156  82c multi         1.25  .50
  i.  A3157  82c multi         1.25  .50
  j.  A3158  82c multi         1.25  .50

Organization for Economic
Cooperation, 50th Anniv. — A3159

Designs: No. 3659, Emblem, Organization
Headquarters, Paris. No. 3660, Symbols for
cooperation and development.

**2014, Apr. 2   Litho.   *Perf. 13***
3659  82y multi               1.25  .50
3660  82y multi               1.25  .50
  a.  A3159  Pair, #3659-3660   3.00  1.50

Daisy and
Sweet
Peas
A3160

Lily
A3161

Cherry
Blossoms
A3162

Water Lily
A3163

Poppies
and
Ranunculus
A3164

Peony
A3165

Roses
A3166

Magnolias
A3167

**2014, Apr. 3   Litho.   *Perf. 14x14¼***
3661  A3160  52y multi          .80  .30
3662  A3161  52y multi          .80  .30
3663  A3162  52y multi          .80  .30
3664  A3163  52y multi          .80  .30
  a.  Horiz. strip of 4, #3661-3664   4.00  2.00
3665  A3164  82y multi         1.25  .50
3666  A3165  82y multi         1.25  .50
3667  A3166  82y multi         1.25  .50
3668  A3167  82y multi         1.25  .50
  a.  Horiz. strip of 4, #3665-3668   6.00  3.00
      Nos. 3661-3668 (8)        8.20  3.20

**Miniature Sheet**

Ehime Local Autonomy Law, 60th
Anniv. — A3168

No. 3669: a, Oranges, Dogo Hot Springs
Building (32x39mm). b, Matsuyama Castle
(28x33mm). c, Mount Ichizuchi (28x33mm). d,
Terraced fields, Yusumizugaura (28x33mm).
e, Sadamisaki Lighthouse (28x33mm).

**Perf. 13¼ (#3669a), 13x13¼**
**2014, Apr. 17              Photo.**
3669  A3168  Sheet of 5        7.00  7.00
  a.-e.  82y Any single        1.25  .60

Philatelic
Week
A3169

Details from folding screens by Eishuku
Kano: No. 3670, Seven small birds near tree.
No. 3671, Two birds below tree branch. No.
3672, Three adult and three juvenile cranes,
white and yellow flowers. No. 3673, Adult
cranes and flowers.

**2014, Apr. 18   Photo.   *Perf. 13¼***
3670  82y multi               1.25  .50
3671  82y multi               1.25  .50
3672  82y multi               1.25  .50
3673  82y multi               1.25  .50
  a.  A3169  Block of 4, #3670-3673   6.00  3.00
      Nos. 3670-3673 (4)       5.00  2.00
Nos. 3670-3673 were printed in sheets of 10
containing 3 each of Nos. 3670-3671 and 2
each of Nos. 3672-3673.

Mount Akita-
Komagatake
A3170

Mount Iyo
A3171

Mount Oku-
Hotakadake
A3172

Mount Fuji
A3173

Mount
Rokko — A3174

Mount
Mikura — A3175

Mount
Tsurugi — A3176

Mount
Unzen — A3177

Mount
Okue — A3178

Mount
Tama — A3179

**2014, May 1   Litho.   *Perf. 13¼x13***
3674  Sheet of 10           16.00  16.00
  a.  A3170  82y multi         1.25  .50
  b.  A3171  82y multi         1.25  .50
  c.  A3172  82y multi         1.25  .50
  d.  A3173  82y multi         1.25  .50
  e.  A3174  82y multi         1.25  .50
  f.  A3175  82y multi         1.25  .50
  g.  A3176  82y multi         1.25  .50
  h.  A3177  82y multi         1.25  .50
  i.  A3178  82y multi         1.25  .50
  j.  A3179  82y multi         1.25  .50

**Souvenir Sheets**

A3180

A3181

2014 World Cup Soccer
Championships, Brazil — A3182

No. 3675 — Trophy with: a, Denomination at
UL, "Nippon" at UR. b, Denomination at LR. c,
Denomination and "Nippon" at UL.
No. 3676: a, Emblem. b, Emblem, design
with stylized soccer player dribbling ball at left.
c, Emblem, design with stylized goalie making
save at right.
No. 3677 — Mascot: a, Carrying flag. b,
Holding soccer ball. c, Dribbling soccer ball.

**2014, May 12   Litho.   *Perf. 13***
3675  A3180  Sheet of 3        5.00  5.00
  a.-c.  82y Any single        1.25  .50
3676  A3181  Sheet of 3        5.00  5.00
  a.-c.  82y Any single        1.25  .50
3677  A3182  Sheet of 3        5.00  5.00
  a.-c.  82y Any single        1.25  .50
      Nos. 3675-3677 (3)      15.00  15.00

**Miniature Sheet**

Yamagata Local Autonomy Law, 60th
Anniv. — A3183

No. 3678: a, Mogami River and cherries
(32x39mm). b, Mt. Haguro five-story pagoda
(28x33mm). c, Kubo cherry tree blossoming
(28x33mm). d, Hayashi Family court dancer
(28x33mm). e, Shinjo Festival (28x33mm).

**Perf. 13¼ (#3678a), 13x13¼**
**2014, May 14              Photo.**
3678  A3183  Sheet of 5        8.00  8.00
  a.-e.  82y Any single        1.25  .60

Pentalagus
Furnessi
A3184

Lagopus Muta
Japonica
A3185

Polemonium
Kiushianum
A3186

Tanakia Tanago
A3187

Cuora
Flavomarginata
Evelynae — A3188

**2014, May 15    Litho.    Perf. 13¼**

| | | | | |
|---|---|---|---|---|
| 3679 | A3184 | 82y multi | 1.25 | .50 |
| 3680 | A3185 | 82y multi | 1.25 | .50 |
| 3681 | A3186 | 82y multi | 1.25 | .50 |
| 3682 | A3187 | 82y multi | 1.25 | .50 |
| 3683 | A3188 | 82y multi | 1.25 | .50 |
| a. | | Vert. strip of 5, #3679-3683 | 8.00 | 4.00 |
| | | Nos. 3679-3683 (5) | 6.25 | 2.50 |

### Miniature Sheets

A3189

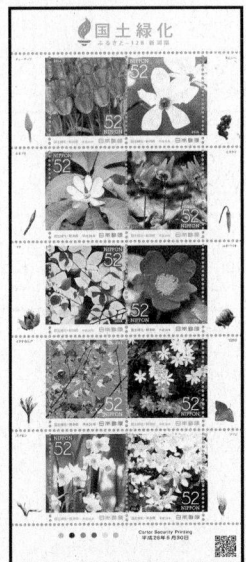

Characters From Disney Animated
Films — A3190

No. 3684: a, Snow White and bird. b, Sleeping Beauty. c, Cinderella. d, Peter Pan with Wendy, John and Michael Darling. e, March Hare, Alice and Mad Hatter. f, Dumbo and Timothy. g, Thumper, Bambi and Flower. h, Lady and the Tramp. i, 101 Dalmatians. j, Geppetto and Pinocchio.

No. 3685: a, Winnie the Pooh seated, looking in honey jar. b, Winnie standing, looking in honey jar. c, Winnie and Eeyore. d, Winnie and Tigger. e, Winnie, Kanga and Roo. f, Winnie and Piglet. g, Winnie holding note. h, Winnie reaching for honey jar. i, Winnie turning over honey jar. j, Winnie standing in large honey pot.

**Die Cut Perf. 14**

**2014, May 23                             Litho.**

**Self-Adhesive**

| | | | | |
|---|---|---|---|---|
| 3684 | A3189 | Sheet of 10 | 10.00 | 10.00 |
| a.-j. | | 52y Any single | 1.00 | .75 |
| 3685 | A3190 | Sheet of 10 | 16.00 | 16.00 |
| a.-j. | | 82y Any single | 1.25 | .80 |

### Miniature Sheet

National Afforestation — A3191

No. 3686: a, Tulipa gesneria. b, Magnolia salicifolia flowers. c, Magnolia obovata flowers. d, Erythronium japonicum. e, Fagus crenata leaves. f, Camellia rusticana. g, Maple leaves on branches. h, Hepatica nobilis. i, Narcissus tazetta. j, Azalea flowers.

**2014, May 30    Litho.    Perf. 13**

| | | | | |
|---|---|---|---|---|
| 3686 | A3191 | Sheet of 10 | 10.00 | 10.00 |
| a.-j. | | 52y Any single | 1.00 | .75 |

Palace of
Versailles,
France — A3192

Thebes,
Egypt — A3193

Roman
Colosseum, Italy
A3194

Great Barrier
Reef, Australia
A3195

La Pedrera,
Barcelona,
Spain — A3196

**2014, June 3    Litho.    Perf. 13¼x13**

| | | | | |
|---|---|---|---|---|
| 3687 | A3192 | 82y multi | 1.25 | .50 |
| 3688 | A3193 | 82y multi | 1.25 | .50 |
| 3689 | A3194 | 82y multi | 1.25 | .50 |
| 3690 | A3195 | 82y multi | 1.25 | .50 |
| 3691 | A3196 | 82y multi | 1.25 | .50 |
| a. | | Horiz. strip of 5, #3687-3691 | 8.00 | 4.00 |
| | | Nos. 3687-3691 (5) | 6.25 | 2.50 |

UNESCO World Heritage sites.

 Cherries
A3197

 Bell
Peppers
A3198

 Japanese
Plums
A3199

 Corn
A3200

 Watermelons
A3201

Tomato
A3202

 Japanese
Apricots
A3203

 Eggplants
A3204

 Cucumbers
A3205

Peach
A3206

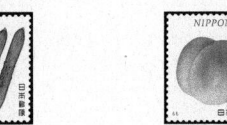

**Die Cut Perf. 13x13¼, 13¼x13**

**2014, June 4                             Litho.**

**Self-Adhesive**

| | | | | |
|---|---|---|---|---|
| 3692 | | Sheet of 10, 2 each #3692a-3692e | 10.00 | 10.00 |
| a. | A3197 | 52y multi | .80 | .80 |
| b. | A3198 | 52y multi | .80 | .80 |
| c. | A3199 | 52y multi | .80 | .80 |
| d. | A3200 | 52y multi | .80 | .80 |
| e. | A3201 | 52y multi | .80 | .80 |
| 3693 | | Sheet of 10, 2 each #3693a-3693e | 16.00 | 16.00 |
| a. | A3202 | 82y multi | 1.25 | .80 |
| b. | A3203 | 82y multi | 1.25 | .80 |

| | | | | |
|---|---|---|---|---|
| c. | A3204 | 82y multi | 1.25 | .80 |
| d. | A3205 | 82y multi | 1.25 | .80 |
| e. | A3206 | 82y multi | 1.25 | .80 |

### Miniature Sheet

Mie Local Autonomy Law, 60th
Anniv. — A3207

No. 3694: a, Uji Bridge and Isuzu River (32x39mm). b, Iris ensata (28x33mm). c, Wedded Rocks, Ise-Shima National Park (28x33mm). d, Lion Rock and fireworks (28x33mm). e, Ago Bay (28x33mm).

**Perf. 13¼ (#3694a), 13x13¼**

**2014, June 19                             Photo.**

| | | | | |
|---|---|---|---|---|
| 3694 | A3207 | Sheet of 5 | 8.00 | 8.00 |
| a.-e. | | 82y Any single | 1.25 | .60 |

### Miniature Sheets

A3208

Sanrio Cartoon Characters — A3209

No. 3695: a, Hello Kitty on bicycle (29x26mm heart-shaped stamp). b, Hello Kitty on elephant (29mm diameter). c, Hello Kitty and Mimmy on telephone (23x23mm). d, Hello Kitty and Mimmy on see-saw (22x30mm oval stamp). e, Hello Kitty in airplane (23x23mm). f, Hello Kitty on scale (27x22mm). g, My Melody on swing with squirrel, Blanco (22x27mm). h, My Melody on ground with mouse, Flat (29x26mm heart-shaped stamp). i, Pompompurin and Macaroon (29mm diameter). j, Pompompurin and stuffed toys (23x23mm).

No. 3696: a, Hello Kitty, umbrella, cherries, pencils and candy bag (22x27mm). b, Hello Kitty with balloon (29x26mm heart-shaped stamp). c, Hello Kitty and Mimmy on telephone with apples (29mm diameter). d, Hello Kitty with watering can (27x22mm). e, Hello Kitty and Mimmy in go-karts (23x23mm). f, Hello Kitty with hair brush (22x30mm oval stamp). g, My Melody at mailbox (27x22mm). h, My Melody reading letter (30x22mm oval stamp). i, Pompompurin and Muffin (29x26mm heart-shaped stamp). j, Pompompurin and "PURIN" (27x22mm).

***Die Cut Perf. 14 (square stamps), 13¼x13¾, 13¾x13¼ (rectangular stamps), 13¼ (oval stamps), Die Cut Perf.***

**2014, June 23**      **Litho.**
**Self-Adhesive**

| | | | | |
|---|---|---|---|---|
| 3695 | A3208 | Sheet of 10 | 10.00 | 10.00 |
| a.-j. | | 52y Any single | 1.00 | .75 |
| 3696 | A3209 | Sheet of 10 | 16.00 | 16.00 |
| a.-j. | | 82y Any single | 1.25 | .75 |

**Miniature Sheet**

Mount Fuji UNESCO World Heritage Site — A3210

No. 3697 — Various views of Mount Fuji: a, Clouds above mountain, denomination at LR. b, Clouds obscuring base, denomination at LR. c, Framed by cherry trees in bloom, denomination at UL. d, With farm fields below, denomination at LL. e, With cherry blossoms at top, denomination at UL. f, In winter, with

hills below, denomination at LL. g, With lake below, denomination at UL. h, With clouds and forest below, denomination at LL. i, With forest and waterfall below, denomination at LL. j, With swan on lake below, denomination at UR.

**2014, June 26**   **Photo.**   **Perf. 13x13¼**

| | | | | |
|---|---|---|---|---|
| 3697 | A3210 | Sheet of 10 | 16.00 | 16.00 |
| a.-j. | | 82y Any single | 1.25 | .50 |

**Miniature Sheet**

Constellations — A3211

No. 3698: a, Cancer. b, Leo. c, Virgo. d, Vega (without white frame).

**Litho. With Foil Application**
**2014, July 7**   ***Die Cut Perf. 13x13¼***
**Self-Adhesive**

| | | | | |
|---|---|---|---|---|
| 3698 | A3211 | Sheet of 10, 3 each #3698a- 3698c, 1 #3698d | 16.00 | 16.00 |
| a.-d. | | 82y Any single | 1.25 | .80 |

Matsumae Castle A3212

Inuyama Castle A3213

Matsue Castle A3214

Takamatsu Castle A3215

Kumamoto Castle — A3216

**2014, July 15**    **Litho.**    **Perf. 13**

| | | | | |
|---|---|---|---|---|
| 3699 | A3212 | 82y multi | 1.25 | .50 |
| 3700 | A3213 | 82y multi | 1.25 | .50 |
| 3701 | A3214 | 82y multi | 1.25 | .50 |
| 3702 | A3215 | 82y multi | 1.25 | .50 |
| 3703 | A3216 | 82y multi | 1.25 | .50 |
| a. | | Vert. strip of 5, #3699-3703 | 8.00 | 4.00 |
| | | Nos. 3699-3703 (5) | 6.25 | 2.50 |

Irises A3217

Goldfish A3218

Flowers A3219

Birds in Plum Tree A3221

Morning Glories A3223

Cranes A3225

Geometric Pattern A3227

Grapevines A3229

Rape Blossoms A3231

Morning Glory and Fan A3233

Pine Trees A3235

Rabbits A3220

Raspberries A3222

Gourds A3224

Cherry Blossoms and Water Wheels A3226

Poppies A3228

Flowers A3230

Loquats A3232

Leaves and Nuts A3234

Cherry Blossoms A3236

***Die Cut Perf. 13x13½***
**2014, July 23**      **Litho.**
**Booklet Stamps**
**Self-Adhesive**

| | | | | |
|---|---|---|---|---|
| 3704 | A3217 | 52y multi | .80 | .75 |
| 3705 | A3218 | 52y multi | .80 | .75 |
| 3706 | A3219 | 52y multi | .80 | .75 |
| 3707 | A3220 | 52y multi | .80 | .75 |
| 3708 | A3221 | 52y multi | .80 | .75 |
| 3709 | A3222 | 52y multi | .80 | .75 |
| 3710 | A3223 | 52y multi | .80 | .75 |
| 3711 | A3224 | 52y multi | .80 | .75 |
| 3712 | A3225 | 52y multi | .80 | .75 |
| 3713 | A3226 | 52y multi | .80 | .75 |
| a. | | Booklet pane of 10, #3704-3713 | 10.00 | 10.00 |

| | | | | |
|---|---|---|---|---|
| 3714 | A3227 | 82y multi | 1.25 | .80 |
| 3715 | A3228 | 82y multi | 1.25 | .80 |
| 3716 | A3229 | 82y multi | 1.25 | .80 |
| 3717 | A3230 | 82y multi | 1.25 | .80 |
| 3718 | A3231 | 82y multi | 1.25 | .80 |
| 3719 | A3232 | 82y multi | 1.25 | .80 |
| 3720 | A3233 | 82y multi | 1.25 | .80 |
| 3721 | A3234 | 82y multi | 1.25 | .80 |
| 3722 | A3235 | 82y multi | 1.25 | .80 |
| 3723 | A3236 | 82y multi | 1.25 | .80 |
| a. | | Booklet pane of 10, #3714-3723 | 16.00 | 16.00 |
| | | Nos. 3704-3723 (20) | 20.50 | 15.50 |

The Ide Tama River: Karuta of the Choji-ya, by Eizan Kikukawa A3237

Hitomoto of the Mojiro, by Utamaro Kitagawa A3239

Washing and Starching Fabric, by Eizan Kikukawa A3241

Girl with a Fan, by Utamaro Kitagawa A3243

The Doll Festival, by Eisho Chokosai A3245

Karokoyama, by Hiroshige Utagawa A3238

Fishing Boats Netting Flounder, by Hiroshige Utagawa A3240

Tsushima Tenno Festival, by Hiroshige Utagawa A3242

Cherry Island, by Hiroshige Utagawa A3244

Basket Ferry, by Hiroshige Utagawa A3246

**2014, Aug. 1**    **Litho.**    **Perf. 13½**

| | | | | |
|---|---|---|---|---|
| 3724 | | Sheet of 10 | 16.00 | 16.00 |
| a. | A3237 | 82y multi | 1.25 | .50 |
| b. | A3238 | 82y multi | 1.25 | .50 |
| c. | A3239 | 82y multi | 1.25 | .50 |
| d. | A3240 | 82y multi | 1.25 | .50 |
| e. | A3241 | 82y multi | 1.25 | .50 |
| f. | A3242 | 82y multi | 1.25 | .50 |
| g. | A3243 | 82y multi | 1.25 | .50 |
| h. | A3244 | 82y multi | 1.25 | .50 |
| i. | A3245 | 82y multi | 1.25 | .50 |
| j. | A3246 | 82y multi | 1.25 | .50 |

Mount Asahi — A3247

Mount Sanbe — A3248

Mount Nantai — A3249

Mount Tokusa — A3250

Mount Takao — A3251

Mount Hiko — A3252

Mount Mitsuse-Myojin A3253

Mount Miune A3254

Kumano Kodo A3255

Mount Shinmoe A3256

**2014, Aug. 11  Litho.    Perf. 13¼x13**
3725      Sheet of 10          16.00  16.00
a.  A3247 82y multi                1.25   .50
b.  A3248 82y multi                1.25   .50
c.  A3249 82y multi                1.25   .50
d.  A3250 82y multi                1.25   .50
e.  A3251 82y multi                1.25   .50
f.  A3252 82y multi                1.25   .50
g.  A3253 82y multi                1.25   .50
h.  A3254 82y multi                1.25   .50
i.  A3255 82y multi                1.25   .50
j.  A3256 82y multi                1.25   .50

**Miniature Sheets**

A3257

Characters From Peanuts Comic Strip — A3258

No. 3726: a, Sally, Woodstock and Snoopy drawing (26x22mm). b, Snoopy and heart (26x25mm). c, Snoopy holding slice of bread, Woodstock near mug (26x22mm). d, Snoopy, Linus, Woodstock and cookies (26x22mm). e, Snoopy on Charlie Brown's head, woodstock on books (26x22mm). f, Sally and Snoopy eating (26x22mm). g, Snoopy, Lucy and Woodstock with flowers (26x22mm). h, Woodstock flying, Snoopy attempting to fly (26x22mm). i, Snoopy and Woodstock on dog house roof (29x36mm). j, Snoopy, Woodstock, umbrella and musical notes (26x22mm).

No. 3727: a, Snoopy and Woodstock with letters, bird flying (22x27mm). b, Charlie Brown with letter near mailbox (22x27mm). c, Snoopy wearing mailman's uniform (22x27mm). d, Snoopy with nose in mailbox (22x27mm). e, Snoopy reading letter near mailbox (27x22mm). f, Snoopy and Woodstock at typewriter (27x22mm). g, Snoopy watching Sally write letter (27x22mm). h, Snoopy sitting and reading letter with Woodstock (27x22mm). i, Charlie Brown and stream of letters in mailbox (27x22mm). j, Charlie Brown and Sally looking at letter (27x22mm).

***Die Cut Perf. 14, 12¼ (#3726b, 3726i)***

**2014, Aug. 19                       Litho.**
           **Self-Adhesive**
3726  A3257    Sheet of 10     10.00  10.00
a.-j.      52y Any single            1.00    .75

***Die Cut Perf. 14x13½, 13½x14***
3727  A3258    Sheet of 10     16.00  16.00
a.-j.      52y Any single            1.25    .75

Miniature Sheet

Japan Society of Civil Engineers, Cent. — A3259

No. 3728: a, Tunnel, sun over mountains. b, Dam. c, Ships and jetties, airport runway. d, Harbor and airport. e, Floodgate ar mouth of river. f, Bridges over river and interchange. g, Farm fields near coast, rocks in water. h, Small harbor and highway tunnel. i, Terraces and irrigation canal. j, Train and irrigation canal.

**2014, Sept. 1    Litho.     Perf. 13**
3728  A3259   Sheet of 10        16.00  16.00
a.-j.     82y Any single              1.25    .50

Miniature Sheet

Season's Memories in My Heart — A3260

No. 3729: a, Houses near water, denomination in black at LL. b, Farm houses, denomination in white at LR. c, Farm house near river, denomination in white at UL. d, Sunset, denomination in white at UL. e, Village in mist, denomination in white at LL. f, Cars near church and building, denomination in black at UR. g, Church at end of path, denomination in white at left. h, Large cloud over church, flowers in air, denomination in white at UL. i, House near water, denomination in black at UR. j, Houses and path, denomination in black at UR.

**2014, Sept. 2   Photo.      Perf. 13**
3729  A3260   Sheet of 10        16.00  16.00
a.-j.     82y Any single              1.25    .50

A3261

Teddy Bears A3262

No. 3730: a, Bear with gray fur and pearl necklace, pink rose (22x30mm). b, Bear with brown fur and red ribbon, yellow flowers (22x30mm). c, Bear with light brown fur and blue bow tie, red rose (22x30mm). d, Bear with beige fur and yellow bow tie, pink flower (22x30mm). e, Bear with light brown fur, wearing cap and red ribbon, with flower bouquet (22x30mm). f, Bear with light brown fur and green ribbon, with pink lily (22x30mm). g, Three bears wearing caps, pink flowers (28x28mm). h, Five bears and yellow flowers (28x28mm). i, Two bears, pink flowers, red ribbon at top (28x28mm). j, Two bears, pink flowers, blue ribbon at top (28x28mm).

No. 3731: a, Bear with letter, yellow door (23x30mm). b, Bear with gift, green door (23x30mm). c, Bear with cap, mail bag and letter, blue door (23x30mm). d, Bear with letter, white door (23x30mm). e, Bear with cap in yellow envelope (25x25mm). f, Bear in light blue envelope (25x25mm). g, Four bears and mail box (23x30mm). h, Bear with letter at mail box (23x30mm). i, Pink bear with pink gift (27x30mm). j, Bear with blue gift (27x30mm).

***Die Cut Perf. 13¼x13¾, 13¾x13½***
**2014, Sept. 5                       Litho.**
          **Self-Adhesive**
3730  A3261    Sheet of 10     10.00  10.00
a.-j.      52y Any single            1.00    .75

*Die Cut Perf. 13x12¾, 13 (#3731e, 3731f)*

| | | | |
|---|---|---|---|
| 3731 | A3262 | Sheet of 10 | 15.00 15.00 |
| a.-j. | | 82y Any single | 1.25 .75 |

Miniature Sheet

Kagawa Local Autonomy Law, 60th Anniv. — A3263

No. 3732: a, Ritsurin Koen Park (32x39mm). b, Gennai Hiraga and his electrostatic generator (28x33mm). c, Marugame Castle (28x33mm). d, Kotohiki Park (28x33mm). e, Olives (28x33mm).

*Perf. 13¼ (#3732a), 13x13¼*

**2014, Sept. 10** Photo.

| | | | |
|---|---|---|---|
| 3732 | A3263 | Sheet of 5 | 7.50 7.50 |
| a.-e. | | 82y Any single | 1.50 .60 |

Intl. Congress on Child Abuse and Neglect, Nagoya — A3264

**2014, Sept. 12** Litho. *Perf. 13*

| | | | |
|---|---|---|---|
| 3733 | A3264 | 82y multi | 1.50 .50 |

Miniature Sheet

69th National Sports Festival A3265

No. 3734: a, Gymnast on rings. b, Blue hydrangeas. c, Runner in starting blocks. d, Pink rhododendrons. e, Archer. f, Pink day lily. g, Soccer players. h, Lilac pink rhododendrons. i, Kendoka. j, Red camellias.

**2014, Sept. 12** Litho. *Perf. 13*

| | | | |
|---|---|---|---|
| 3734 | A3265 | 82y Sheet of 10 | 16.00 16.00 |
| a.-j. | | 82y Any single | 1.25 .50 |

Tortoise A3266

Tapir A3268

Orangutans A3270

Giant Pandas A3272

Lion A3274

Spotted Seals A3267

Giraffes A3269

Koalas A3271

Capybara A3273

Fennec Fox A3275

*Die Cut Perf. 13x13¼*

**2014, Sept. 19** Litho.

Self-Adhesive

| | | | |
|---|---|---|---|
| 3735 | | Sheet of 10, 2 each | |
| | | #3735a-3735e | 10.00 10.00 |
| a. | A3266 | 52y multi | .80 .75 |
| b. | A3267 | 52y multi | .80 .75 |
| c. | A3268 | 52y multi | .80 .75 |
| d. | A3269 | 52y multi | .80 .75 |
| e. | A3270 | 52y multi | .80 .75 |

*Die Cut Perf. 13¼*

| | | | |
|---|---|---|---|
| 3736 | | Sheet of 10, 2 each | |
| | | #3736a-3736e | 15.00 15.00 |
| a. | A3271 | 82y multi | 1.25 .75 |
| b. | A3272 | 82y multi | 1.25 .75 |
| c. | A3273 | 82y multi | 1.25 .75 |
| d. | A3274 | 82y multi | 1.25 .75 |
| e. | A3275 | 82y multi | 1.25 .75 |

Miniature Sheet

Shinkansen High-Speed Rail Lines, 50th Anniv. — A3276

No. 3737: a, Train with thick blue stripe (Tokaido and Sanyo 0 series). b, Three trains (Tokaido and Sanyo 100, 0 and 300 series), top train with thick blue stripe above thin blue stripe, bottom train with thin blue strip over thick blue stripe. c, Train with two thin blue stripes (Tokaido and Sanyo N700A). d, Three trains (Tokaido and Sanyo 700 series, N700A, and T4 model), top train with two thin blue stripes, bottom train yellow with two blue stripes. e, Light blue train with one blue stripe (Sanyo and Kyushu N700). f, Three trains (Sanyo 700 series Rail Star, Sanyo and Kyushu N700, Sanyo 500 series), top train with gray and yellow stripes along windows. g, Train with thin red stripe (Kyushu New 800 series). h, Three trains (Tohuku E2 series, Kyushu New 800 series, Yamagata 400 series), top train with red stripe under window

above blue along bottom of train. i, Train with blue green top and red stripe (Tohuku E5 series). j, Three trains (Joetsu E1 series, Tohuku E5 series, Akita E6 series, light blue top train with blue green stripe).

**2014, Oct. 1** Litho. *Perf. 13½x13¼*

| | | | |
|---|---|---|---|
| 3737 | A3276 | Sheet of 10 | 16.00 16.00 |
| a.-j. | | 82y Any single | 1.25 .50 |

Miniature Sheet

Saitama Local Autonomy Law, 60th Anniv. — A3277

No. 3738: a, Eiichi Shibusawa, industrialist, Bell of Time (32x39mm). b, Saitama Stadium (28x33mm). c, Chichibu Night Festival (28x33mm). d, Shoden Hall, Kangi Temple (28x33mm). e, Stairway at Sakitama ancient tomb complex (28x33mm).

*Perf. 13¼ (#3738a), 13x13¼*

**2014, Oct. 8** Photo.

| | | | |
|---|---|---|---|
| 3738 | A3277 | Sheet of 5 | 7.50 7.50 |
| a.-e. | | 82y Any single | 1.25 .60 |

A3278

International Letter Writing Week — A3279

Paintings by Hiroshige: 70y, Sparrows and Camellia in the Snow. 90y, The Fifty-three Stations of the Tokaido: Ejiri. 110y, The Fifty-three Stations of the Tokaido: Kanaya. 130y, The Fifty-three Stations of the Tokaido: Fukuroi.

**2014, Oct. 9** Photo. *Perf. 13¼*

| | | | |
|---|---|---|---|
| 3739 | A3278 | 70y multi | 1.25 .50 |

*Perf. 13*

| | | | |
|---|---|---|---|
| 3740 | A3279 | 90y multi | 1.75 .50 |
| 3741 | A3279 | 110y multi | 2.25 .50 |
| 3742 | A3279 | 130y multi | 2.75 .50 |
| | Nos. 3739-3742 (4) | | 8.00 2.00 |

See listing of No. 4448 for images of each Hiroshige print.

Fronts of Five Passenger Train Cars A3280

Kintetsu 18200 Series Locomotive A3282

Nagoya Railroad KiHa 8000 Series Locomotive A3281

Japan National Railways 581 Series Locomotive A3283

Japan National Railways Class EF66 Locomotive A3284

Japan National Railways 14 Series Sleeping Car A3286

Keisei Electric Railway AE Series Locomotive A3288

Seibu Railways 5000 Series Locomotive A3285

East Japan Railway E259 Series Locomotive A3287

Tokyo Underground Railway 1000 Series Train A3289

**2014, Oct. 10** Photo. *Perf. 13¼x13*

| | | | |
|---|---|---|---|
| 3743 | | Sheet of 10 | 16.00 16.00 |
| a. | A3280 | 82y multi | 1.25 .50 |
| b. | A3281 | 82y multi | 1.25 .50 |
| c. | A3282 | 82y multi | 1.25 .50 |
| d. | A3283 | 82y multi | 1.25 .50 |
| e. | A3284 | 82y multi | 1.25 .50 |
| f. | A3285 | 82y multi | 1.25 .50 |
| g. | A3286 | 82y multi | 1.25 .50 |
| h. | A3287 | 82y multi | 1.25 .50 |
| i. | A3288 | 82y multi | 1.25 .50 |
| j. | A3289 | 82y multi | 1.25 .50 |

Sandalwood Go Game Board and Pieces A3290

Glass Goblet A3292

Sandalwood Lute — A3294

Gold and Silver Inlaid Lacquered Kin A3291

Decorated Catapult Sticks A3293

**2014, Oct. 17** Photo. *Perf. 13*

| | | | |
|---|---|---|---|
| 3744 | A3290 | 82y multi | 1.25 .50 |
| 3745 | A3291 | 82y multi | 1.25 .50 |
| 3746 | A3292 | 82y multi | 1.25 .50 |
| 3747 | A3293 | 82y multi | 1.25 .50 |
| 3748 | A3294 | 82y multi | 1.25 .50 |
| a. | Vert. strip of 5, #3744-3748 | | 7.50 4.00 |
| | Nos. 3744-3748 (5) | | 6.25 2.50 |

Treasures of the Shosoin.

Fish
A3295

"Happy"
and Stars
A3296

**2014, Oct. 23    Litho.    Perf. 13x13¼**

| | | | |
|---|---|---|---|
| 3749 | A3295 | 52y multi | 1.00 | .30 |

**Background Color**

| | | | | |
|---|---|---|---|---|
| 3750 | A3296 | 52y rose lilac | .90 | .30 |
| 3751 | A3296 | 52y orange | .90 | .30 |
| a. | Vert. pair, #3750-3751 | | 1.80 | 1.00 |
| | Nos. 3749-3751 (3) | | 2.80 | .90 |

**Miniature Sheet**

Traditional Crafts — A3297

No. 3752: a, Imari-Arita ceramic ware (Saga Prefecture). b, Inshu hand-made paper (Tottori Prefecture). c, Echizen chest of drawers (Fukui Prefecture). d, Chichibu-meisen silk textiles (Saitama Prefecture). e, Kagawa lacquered container (Kagawa Prefecture). f, Ise katagami paper stencils (Mie Prefecture). g, Yamaga lantern (Kumamoto Prefecture). h, Koshu carved crystal (Yamanashi Prefecture). i, Hakone parquet containers (Kanagawa Prefecture). j. Arimatsu-Narumi tie-dyed fabrics (Aichi Prefecture).

**2014, Oct. 24    Litho.    Perf. 13½**

| | | | | |
|---|---|---|---|---|
| 3752 | A3297 | Sheet of 10 | 16.00 | 16.00 |
| a.-j. | 82y Any single | | 1.25 | .50 |

**Miniature Sheet**

Edo Calligraphy — A3298

No. 3753 — Characters for "sheep": a, In Kobun style (blue character). b, In Han Dynasty document style (character in black with two red chops at left). c, In small seal script (character in black with thick lines, small red chop at LR. d, In cursive script (character in black with small red chop at LL). e, In running script (Black character on brown red background). f, In Kana characters (surved black character with dots with large red chop at LR). g, In oracle bone script (black character with curved and straight lines, large red chop at LR). h, In Chou Dyansty bronze vessel style (character in thick black lines with small red chop at LL). i, In seal script (character in red). j, In clerical script (character in thick black lines with large red chop at LL).

**Litho. & Embossed**

**2014, Oct. 30    Perf. 13x13¼**

| | | | | |
|---|---|---|---|---|
| 3753 | A3298 | Sheet of 10 | 16.00 | 16.00 |
| a.-j. | 82y Any single | | 1.25 | .80 |

New Year 2014 Japanese Foods
A3299

Designs: No. 3754, Sushi (denomination at LL). No. 3755, Tempura (denomination at LR).

---

**2014, Oct. 30    Litho.    Perf. 13¼x13**

| | | | | |
|---|---|---|---|---|
| 3754 | 18y multi | | .35 | .30 |
| 3755 | 18y multi | | .35 | .30 |
| a. | A3299 Horiz. pair, #3754-3755 | | .90 | .90 |

A3300          A3301

A3302          A3303

New Year 2015 (Year of the Ram)

**2014, Oct. 30    Photo.    Perf. 13x13¼**

| | | | | |
|---|---|---|---|---|
| 3756 | A3300 | 52y multi | 1.00 | .30 |
| 3757 | A3301 | 82y multi | 1.50 | .40 |

**Photo. & Typo.**

**Perf. 13¼**

| | | | | |
|---|---|---|---|---|
| 3758 | A3302 | 52y +3y multi | 1.25 | .40 |
| 3759 | A3303 | 82y +3y multi | 1.75 | .40 |
| | Nos. 3756-3759 (4) | | 5.50 | 1.50 |

Sheets of two containing Nos. 3756-3757 were lottery prizes. Value, $4.

Lady Shikibu          Flower
Murasaki              Arrangement
Scroll and            and Go
Books                 Players
A3304                 A3305

Noh and               Lute Player
Bunraku               and
Theater               Entertainers
A3306                 A3307

Tale of the Genji
Scroll — A3308

**2014, Oct. 31    Litho.    Perf. 13**

| | | | | |
|---|---|---|---|---|
| 3760 | A3304 | 82y multi | 1.25 | .50 |
| 3761 | A3305 | 82y multi | 1.25 | .50 |
| 3762 | A3306 | 82y multi | 1.25 | .50 |
| 3763 | A3307 | 82y multi | 1.25 | .50 |
| 3764 | A3308 | 82y multi | 1.25 | .50 |
| a. | Vert. strip of 5, #3760-3764 | | 7.50 | 4.00 |
| | Nos. 3760-3764 (5) | | 6.25 | 2.50 |

Classics Day.

Narcissus             Plum
A3309                 Blossoms
                      A3310

---

Adonis                Cyclamen
Ramosa                A3312
A3311

Matthiola             Camellia
Incana                Japonica
A3313                 A3314

Brassica              Poinsettia
Oleracea              A3316
A3315

**2014, Nov. 6    Litho.    Perf. 14x14¼**

| | | | | |
|---|---|---|---|---|
| 3765 | A3309 | 52y multi | .80 | .30 |
| 3766 | A3310 | 52y multi | .80 | .30 |
| 3767 | A3311 | 52y multi | .80 | .30 |
| 3768 | A3312 | 52y multi | .80 | .30 |
| a. | Horiz. strip of 4, #3765-3768 | | 4.00 | 2.00 |
| 3769 | A3313 | 82y multi | 1.25 | .50 |
| 3770 | A3314 | 82y multi | 1.25 | .50 |
| 3771 | A3315 | 82y multi | 1.25 | .50 |
| 3772 | A3316 | 82y multi | 1.25 | .50 |
| a. | Horiz. strip of 4, #3769-3772 | | 6.00 | 3.50 |
| | Nos. 3765-3772 (8) | | 8.20 | 3.20 |

**Miniature Sheets**

A3317

Winter Greetings — A3318

No. 3773: a, Cookie with snowman design. b, Cookies in shape of man and woman. c, Cookie with mailbox design. d, Cookie with polar bear design. e, Cookie in shape of rabbit. f, Cookie with Christmas tree design. g, Cookie in shape of horse. h, Cookie in shape of woman. i, Cookie with poinsettia design. j, Cookie in shape of man.
No. 3774 — Needlepoint designs: a, House with brown door standing in front of trees. b, Post office with red mailbox at left. c, House with red door. d, House with brown door and shrubbery. e, Automobile. f, Snowman. g, One sheep. h, Two sheep. i, Boy and dog. j, Mailbox and fence.

**Die Cut Perf. 13x13¼**

**2014, Nov. 7    Litho.**

**Self-Adhesive**

| | | | | |
|---|---|---|---|---|
| 3773 | A3317 | Sheet of 10 | 10.00 | 10.00 |
| a.-j. | 52y Any single | | .90 | .70 |
| 3774 | A3318 | Sheet of 10 | 15.00 | 15.00 |
| a.-j. | 82y Any single | | 1.25 | .80 |

**Miniature Sheet**

Season's Memories in My
Heart — A3319

---

No. 3775 — Illustrations from children's book *Guri and Gura*, by Yuriko Yamawaki: a, Guri, Gura and rabbits on sled. b, Child looking out of window. c, Guri and Gura making snowman. d, Guri and Gura reading near fireplace. e, Guri picking strawberries. f, Guri cooking. g, Gura looking at head-shaped cake. h, Guri and Gura holding basket. i, Stove and various animals. j, Guri, Gura, various animals and table.

**2014, Nov. 20    Litho.    Perf. 13½**

| | | | | |
|---|---|---|---|---|
| 3775 | A3319 | Sheet of 10 | 16.00 | 16.00 |
| a.-j. | 82y Any single | | 1.25 | .50 |

**Miniature Sheet**

Ishikawa Local Autonomy Law, 60th
Anniv. — A3320

No. 3776: a, Stone lantern, trees in Kenrokuen Garden (32x39mm). b, Terraced rice fields at sunset (28x33mm). c, Mitsukejima (28x33mm). d, Mount Hakusan (28x33mm). e, Fritillaria cantschatcensis (28x33mm).

**Perf. 13¼ (#3776a), 13x13¼**

**2014, Nov. 26    Photo.**

| | | | | |
|---|---|---|---|---|
| 3776 | A3320 | Sheet of 5 | 8.00 | 8.00 |
| a.-e. | 82y Any single | | 1.25 | .60 |

Matsumoto             Takeda
Castle                Castle
A3321                 A3322

Nagoya
Castle — A3323

Bitchu-Matsuyama
Castle — A3324

Shuri Castle — A3325

**2014, Dec. 10    Litho.    Perf. 12¾x13**

| | | | | |
|---|---|---|---|---|
| 3777 | A3321 | 82y multi | 1.25 | .50 |
| 3778 | A3322 | 82y multi | 1.25 | .50 |
| 3779 | A3323 | 82y multi | 1.25 | .50 |
| 3780 | A3324 | 82y multi | 1.25 | .50 |
| 3781 | A3325 | 82y multi | 1.25 | .50 |
| a. | Vert. strip of 5, #3777-3781 | | 7.50 | 4.00 |
| | Nos. 3777-3781 (5) | | 6.25 | 2.50 |

## Miniature Sheets

A3326

Illustrations From *Peter Rabbit,* by
Beatrix Potter — A3327

No. 3782: a, Jemima Puddleduck. b, Peter
Rabbit holding placard. c, Squirrel Nutkin. d,
Owl reading "Squirrel Nutkin" book. e, Tom Kitten. f, Benjamin Bunny. g, Peter holding
shovel. h, Peter and Benjamin Bunny. i,
Mother Rabbit and young. j, Rabbits holding
towel.

No. 3783: a, Peter with shovel and flower
box. b, Peter posting letter. c, Rabbit with mail
bag, facing forward. d, Rabbit with mail bag,
facing backward. e, Rabbit holding letter and
cauliflower. f, Rabbits with basket. g, Peter and
female rabbit on windy day. h, Cat, Peter with
daffodil. i, Peter and Benjamin carrying sticks.
j, Peter and Benjamin harvesting apples.

**2015, Jan. 9   Litho.   Die Cut Perf. 14**
**Self-Adhesive**
| | | | | |
|---|---|---|---|---|
| 3782 | A3326 | Sheet of 10 | 10.00 | 10.00 |
| a.-j. | | 52y Any single | .90 | .70 |

**Die Cut Perf. 14x13¼**
| | | | | |
|---|---|---|---|---|
| 3783 | A3327 | Sheet of 10 | 15.00 | 15.00 |
| a.-j. | | 82y Any single | 1.25 | .75 |

---

Flowers,
Musical
Notes, Clef
and Staff
A3328

Four Teddy
Bears
A3330

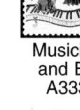

Animals
With
Musical
Instruments
A3332

Roses
A3334

Girl and
Carnations
A3336

**Die Cut Perf. 14**
**2015, Jan. 16   Litho.**
**Self-Adhesive**
| | | | |
|---|---|---|---|
| 3784 | | Sheet of 10, 2 each #3784a-3784e | 10.00 10.00 |
| a. | A3328 52y multi | | .90 .70 |
| b. | A3329 52y multi | | .90 .70 |
| c. | A3330 52y multi | | .90 .70 |
| d. | A3331 52y multi | | .90 .70 |
| e. | A3332 52y multi | | .90 .70 |

**Die Cut Perf. 14x13¼, 13¼x14**
| | | | |
|---|---|---|---|
| 3785 | | Sheet of 10, 2 each #3785a-3785e | 15.00 15.00 |
| a. | A3333 82y multi | | 1.25 .80 |
| b. | A3334 82y multi | | 1.25 .80 |
| c. | A3335 82y multi | | 1.25 .80 |
| d. | A3336 82y multi | | 1.25 .80 |
| e. | A3337 82y multi | | 1.25 .80 |

Wombats
A3338

Baby
Rhinoceros
A3340

Porcupines
A3342

---

Flowers in
Music Box
A3329

Musicians
and Bird
A3331

Cherry
Blossoms and
Bird
A3333

Violas
A3335

Teddy Bear
and Flowers
A3337

Lamb
A3339

Chick
A3341

Red
Pandas
A3343

---

Puppy
A3344

Snow
Leopard
A3346

Japanese
Macaque
A3345

California
Sea Lions
A3347

**Die Cut Perf. 13¼**
**2015, Jan. 23   Litho.**
**Self-Adhesive**
| | | | |
|---|---|---|---|
| 3786 | | Sheet of 10, 2 each #3786a-3786e | 10.00 10.00 |
| a. | A3338 52y multi | | .90 .70 |
| b. | A3339 52y multi | | .90 .70 |
| c. | A3340 52y multi | | .90 .70 |
| d. | A3341 52y multi | | .90 .70 |
| e. | A3342 52y multi | | .90 .70 |
| 3787 | | Sheet of 10, 2 each #3787a-3787e | 16.00 16.00 |
| a. | A3343 82y multi | | 1.25 .80 |
| b. | A3344 82y multi | | 1.25 .80 |
| c. | A3345 82y multi | | 1.25 .80 |
| d. | A3346 82y multi | | 1.25 .80 |
| e. | A3347 82y multi | | 1.25 .80 |

Hisoka Maejima (1835-
1919), Founder of
Japanese Postal Service
A3348

Siberian Chipmunk
A3349

Japanese
Macaque
A3350

Sika Deer
A3352

Japanese
Serow
A3354

Japanese
Wisteria
A3356

Crested
Ibis
A3351

Red Fox
A3353

Japanese
Primrose
A3355

Kerria
Japonica
A3357

Stream, Towada-
Hachimantai National
Park — A3358

Mt. Fuji, by Chikuden
Tanomura — A3359

---

**2015, Feb. 2   Photo.   Perf. 13x13¼**
| | | | | |
|---|---|---|---|---|
| 3788 | A3348 | 1y brown | .30 | .25 |
| 3789 | A3349 | 3y multi | .30 | .25 |
| a. | | Souvenir sheet of 2, #3648, 3789 | .50 | .50 |
| 3790 | A3350 | 5y multi | .30 | .25 |
| 3791 | A3351 | 10y multi | .30 | .25 |
| 3792 | A3352 | 20y multi | .35 | .25 |
| 3793 | A3353 | 30y multi | .50 | .40 |
| 3794 | A3354 | 50y multi | .55 | .45 |
| 3795 | A3355 | 100y multi | 1.10 | .50 |
| 3796 | A3356 | 120y multi | 1.40 | .50 |
| 3797 | A3357 | 140y multi | 1.60 | .50 |
| 3798 | A3358 | 500y multi | 6.50 | 1.00 |

**Photo. & Engr.**
**Perf. 13¼**
| | | | | |
|---|---|---|---|---|
| 3799 | A3359 | 1000y multi | 13.00 | 5.00 |
| a. | | Imperf. | 30.00 | 30.00 |
| b. | | Souvenir sheet of 2, #2485a, 3799a | 60.00 | 60.00 |
| | | *Nos. 3788-3799 (12)* | 26.20 | 9.60 |

Compare type A3348 with types A563a and
A2682.

Cabbage
A3360

Satsuma
Orange
A3361

Peas
A3362

Mango
A3363

Onion
A3364

Oranges
A3365

Asparagus
A3366

Strawberries
A3367

Lettuce
A3368

Pineapple
A3369

**Die Cut Perf. 13¼x13, 13x13¼**
**2015, Feb. 23   Litho.**
**Self-Adhesive**
| | | | |
|---|---|---|---|
| 3800 | | Sheet of 10, 2 each #3800a-3800e | 10.00 10.00 |
| a. | A3360 52y multi | | .80 .70 |
| b. | A3361 52y multi | | .80 .70 |
| c. | A3362 52y multi | | .80 .70 |
| d. | A3363 52y multi | | .80 .70 |
| e. | A3364 52y multi | | .80 .70 |
| 3801 | | Sheet of 10, 2 each #3801a-3801e | 16.00 16.00 |
| a. | A3365 82y multi | | 1.25 .80 |
| b. | A3366 82y multi | | 1.25 .80 |
| c. | A3367 82y multi | | 1.25 .80 |
| d. | A3368 82y multi | | 1.25 .80 |
| e. | A3369 82y multi | | 1.25 .80 |

A3370

No. 3802 — Arcs of color and map of Japan
made of flowers, with denomination in: a,
Orange. b, Carmine. c, Purple. d, Blue. e, Turquoise green.

## Perf. 13½x13¼

**2015, Mar. 13**     Photo.
3802    Horiz. strip of 5    7.00   5.00
a.-e.   A3370 82y Any single    1.25   .50
United Nations World Conference on disaster risk reduction, Sendai.

Kanazawa Railroad Station — A3371

Tateyama Mountain Range — A3372

Takada Park — A3373

Zenkoji Temple — A3374

Marunouchi Railroad Station, Tokyo — A3375

Series W7, E2 and E7 Trains — A3376

Series W7 Train — A3377

Series E7 Train — A3378

**2015, Mar. 13**    Litho.    Perf. 13¼x13
3803    Sheet of 10, #3803a-
      3803f, 2 each
      #3803g-3803h    16.00   16.00
a.   A3371 82y multi    1.25   .50
b.   A3372 82y multi    1.25   .50
c.   A3373 82y multi    1.25   .50
d.   A3374 82y multi    1.25   .50
e.   A3375 82y multi    1.25   .50
f.   A3376 82y multi    1.25   .50
g.   A3377 82y multi    1.25   .50
h.   A3378 82y multi    1.25   .50

Canadian Rocky Mountain Parks — A3379

Historic Areas of Istanbul, Turkey — A3380

Stonehenge, Great Britain A3381

Historic Center of Prague, Czech Republic A3382

Ha Long Bay, Viet Nam — A3383

**2015, Mar. 26**    Litho.    Perf. 13¼x13
3804   A3379 82y multi    1.25   .50
3805   A3380 82y multi    1.25   .50
3806   A3381 82y multi    1.25   .50
3807   A3382 82y multi    1.25   .50
3808   A3383 82y multi    1.25   .50
a.    Horiz. strip of 5, #3804-3808   7.00   4.50
    Nos. 3804-3808 (5)    6.25   2.50

UNESCO World Heritage Sites.

Hirosaki Castle A3384

Kanazawa Castle A3385

Himeji Castle A3386

Fukuyama Castle A3387

Fukuoka Castle — A3388

**2015, Apr. 3**    Litho.    Perf. 13
3809   A3384 82y multi    1.25   .50
3810   A3385 82y multi    1.25   .50
3811   A3386 82y multi    1.25   .50
3812   A3387 82y multi    1.25   .50
3813   A3388 82y multi    1.25   .50
a.    Vert. strip of 5, #3809-3813   7.50   3.00
    Nos. 3809-3813 (5)    6.25   2.50

Japanese Diet, Tokyo, and Cherry Blossoms A3389

Clock Tower, Tokyo, and Dogwood Blossoms A3390

Lincoln Memorial and Cherry Blossoms A3391

U. S. Capitol and Dogwood Blossoms A3392

White Dogwood Blossoms A3393

Cherry Blossoms A3394

Red Dogwood Blossoms A3395

**2015, Apr. 10**    Photo.    Perf. 13x12¾
3814    Sheet of 10, #3814a-
      3814d, 2 each
      #3814e-3814g    16.00   16.00
a.   A3389 82y multi    1.25   .50
b.   A3390 82y multi    1.25   .50
c.   A3391 82y multi    1.25   .50
d.   A3392 82y multi    1.25   .50
e.   A3393 82y multi    1.25   .50
f.   A3394 82y multi    1.25   .50
g.   A3395 82y multi    1.25   .50

See United States Nos. 4982-4985.

Mount Rishiri — A3396

Mount Adatara — A3397

Mount Shibutu — A3398

Shirouma Sanzan — A3399

Mount Tateyama A3400

Yarigatake A3401

Yatsugatake A3402

Mount Fuji A3403

Kitadake A3404

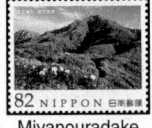

Miyanouradake A3405

**2015, Apr. 17**    Litho.    Perf. 13¼x13
3815    Sheet of 10    16.00   16.00
a.   A3396 82y multi    1.25   .50
b.   A3397 82y multi    1.25   .50
c.   A3398 82y multi    1.25   .50
d.   A3399 82y multi    1.25   .50
e.   A3400 82y multi    1.25   .50
f.   A3401 82y multi    1.25   .50
g.   A3402 82y multi    1.25   .50
h.   A3403 82y multi    1.25   .50
i.   A3404 82y multi    1.25   .50
j.   A3405 82y multi    1.25   .50

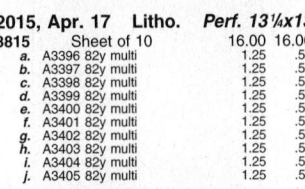

Japan Overseas Cooperation Volunteers, 50th Anniv. — A3406

**2015, Apr. 20**    Litho.    Perf. 13
**Denomination Color**

3816    82y blue    1.25   .50
3817    82y crimson    1.25   .50
a.   A3406 Horiz. pair, #3816-3817   3.00   1.50

Phoenixes by Pawlonia Trees, Screen Painting by Kano Tan'yu — A3407

Designs: No. 3818, White phoenix facing left, denomination at LL. No. 3819, Phoenix facing left, denomination at UR. No. 3820, White phoenix facing right, denomination at UR. No. 3821, Phoenix with tail raised facing right, denomination at LL.

**2015, Apr. 20**    Photo.    Perf. 13¼
3818    82y multi    1.25   .50
3819    82y multi    1.25   .50
3820    82y multi    1.25   .50
3821    82y multi    1.25   .50
a.   A3407 Block of 4, #3818-3821   5.60   3.50
    Nos. 3818-3821 (4)    5.00   2.00

Philatelic Week.

**Miniature Sheets**

A3408

Moomins A3409

No. 3822: a, Moomin standing, bright blue background. b, Little My, red background. c, Moomin, yellow background. d, Snufkin, green background. e, Moomin, red violet background. f, Moominpappa, dark blue background. g, Moomin running, bright blue background. h, Moominmamma, pink background. i, Moomin, yellow brown background. j, Snork Maiden, rose background.

No. 3823: a, Moomin characters, Snufkin with accordion. b, Moomin and Snufkin (29mm diameter). c, Moomin, Snork Maiden, ship, flowers. d, Moomin characters, Little My at left. e, Moomin characters and hammock. f, Moomin characters hugging. g, Little My in teapot. h, Moomin, Snork Maiden and Little My. i, Moominmamma and Moominpappa. j, Hattifatteners and top hat.

**2015, May 1**    Litho.    Die Cut Perf. 14
3822   A3408   Sheet of 10    10.00   10.00
a.-j.    52y Any single    .90   .70

**Die Cut Perf. 13¼x13¾**
3823   A3409   Sheet of 10    15.00   15.00
a.-j.    82y Any single    1.25   .80

## Miniature Sheet

Yamaguchi Local Autonomy Law, 60th Anniv. — A3410

No. 3824: a, Kintaikyo Bridge, Akiyoshidai (32x39mm). b, Goldfish lantern and buildings (28x33mm). c, Hooded crane (28x33mm). d, Shokasonjuku Academy and citrons (28x33mm). e, Misuzu Street (28x33mm).

### Perf. 13¼ (#3824a), 13x13¼

| 2015, May 12 | | | Photo. | |
|---|---|---|---|---|
| 3824 | A3410 | Sheet of 5 | 7.00 | 7.00 |
| a.-e. | | 82y Any single | 1.25 | .60 |

## Miniature Sheet

National Afforestation — A3411

No. 3825: a, Crepe myrtle blossoms. b, Ate cypress. c, Horse chestnut blossoms. d, Freesia. e, Japanese black pine. f, Plum blossoms. g, Wild cherry blossoms. h, Azalea blossoms. i, Zelkova tree. j, Chocolate lily.

| 2015, May 15 | | Litho. | | Perf. 13 |
|---|---|---|---|---|
| 3825 | A3411 | Sheet of 10 | 10.00 | 10.00 |
| a.-j. | | 52y Any single | 1.00 | .40 |

Crepe Myrtle A3412

Sunflowers A3413

Southern Stars A3414

Eustomas A3415

Gladiolus A3416

Marigolds A3417

Salvia A3418

Hydrangeas A3419

Gymnaster Savatieri A3420

Delphinium and Calla Lily A3421

### Die Cut Perf. 14

**2015, May 29**      **Litho.**

**Self-Adhesive**

| 3826 | | Sheet of 10, 2 each | | |
|---|---|---|---|---|
| | | #3826a-3826e | 10.00 | 10.00 |
| a. | A3412 | 52y multi | .85 | .65 |
| b. | A3413 | 52y multi | .85 | .65 |
| c. | A3414 | 52y multi | .85 | .65 |
| d. | A3415 | 52y multi | .85 | .65 |
| e. | A3416 | 52y multi | .85 | .65 |
| 3827 | | Sheet of 10, 2 each | | |
| | | #3827a-3827e | 16.00 | 16.00 |
| a. | A3417 | 82y multi | 1.25 | .80 |
| b. | A3418 | 82y multi | 1.25 | .80 |
| c. | A3419 | 82y multi | 1.25 | .80 |
| d. | A3420 | 82y multi | 1.25 | .80 |
| e. | A3421 | 82y multi | 1.25 | .80 |

## Miniature Sheet

Tokushima Local Autonomy Law, 60th Anniv. — A3422

No. 3828: a, Naruto Whirlpools, Naruto Bridge, Awa Dance Festival dancer, sudachi flower (32x39mm). b, Awa Puppet Theater (28x33mm). c, Yoshino River and Mount Bizan (28x33mm). d, Vine bridges in Iya Valley (28x33mm). e, Sea turtle on Ohama Beach (28x33mm).

### Perf. 13¼ (#3828a), 13x13¼

| 2015, June 2 | | | Photo. | |
|---|---|---|---|---|
| 3828 | A3422 | Sheet of 5 | 7.00 | 7.00 |
| a.-e. | | 82y Any single | 1.25 | .60 |

Shells — A3423

No. 3829: a, Conus ammiralis (23x35mm). b, Mimachlamys nobilis (23x30mm). c, Terebridae (22x29mm). d, Babelomurex gemmatus (22x26mm). e, Scutarcopagia linguafelis (27x23mm).
No. 3830: a, Columbarium pagoda (22x36mm). b, Phalium flammiferum (22x30mm). c, Neocancilla papilio (22x30mm). d, Spondylus sanguineus (24x27mm). e, Architectonica perspectiva (29x25mm).

### Die Cut Perf. 13x13¼, 13¼x13 (#3829e, 3830e)

| 2015, June 5 | | | Litho. | |
|---|---|---|---|---|
| 3829 | | Sheet of 10, 2 each | | |
| | | #3829a-3829e | 10.00 | 10.00 |
| a.-e. | A3423 | 52y Any single | .85 | .65 |
| 3830 | | Sheet of 10, 2 each | | |
| | | #3830a-3830e | 16.00 | 16.00 |
| a.-e. | A3423 | 82y Any single | 1.25 | .80 |

## Miniature Sheet

Fukuoka Local Autonomy Law, 60th Anniv. — A3424

No. 3831: a, Okinoshima Island, Munakata Taisha Shrine, gold ring (32x39mm). b, Kokura Castle (28x33mm). c, Triple water wheel, Asakura (28x33mm). d, Boat on Yanagawa River (28x33mm). e, Kane-no Torii and steps (28x33mm).

### Perf. 13¼ (#3831a), 13x13¼

| 2015, June 16 | | | Photo. | |
|---|---|---|---|---|
| 3831 | A3424 | Sheet of 5 | 7.00 | 7.00 |
| a.-e. | | 82y Any single | 1.25 | .60 |

Normalization of Diplomatic Relations Between Japan and South Korea, 50th Anniv. — A3425

Designs: No. 3832, Japanese woman in kimono, Korean woman in hanbok. No. 3833, Rose of Sharon and cherry blossoms.

| 2015, June 22 | | Litho. | Perf. 13½ | |
|---|---|---|---|---|
| 3832 | | 82y multi | 1.25 | .50 |
| 3833 | | 82y multi | 1.25 | .50 |
| a. | A3425 | Vert. pair, #3832-3833 | 3.00 | 1.50 |

## Miniature Sheet

Tomioka Silk Mill UNESCO World Heritage Site — A3426

No. 3834: a, Joshu Tomioka Silk Mill, woodblock print by Kuniteru Ichiyosai, denomination at UR (stamp 1). b, Joshu Tomioka Silk Mill,

denomination at UL (stamp 2). c, The Diligence of Women Workers at Tomioka Spinning Mill, woodblock print by Asataka, denomination at LR (stamp 3). d, East Cocoon Warehouse, denomination at UL (stamp 4). e, Silk-reeling mill, denomination at UL (stamp 5). f, Illustration from Tomioka Diary, denomination at LL (stamp 6). g, Tajima Yahei Sericulture Farm, denomination at UR (stamp 7). h, Takayama-sha Sericulture School, denomination at LL (stamp 8). i, Arafune Cold Storage, denomination at LL (stamp 9). j, Keystone of Tomioka Silk Mill, denomination at UL (stamp 10).

| 2015, June 25 | Photo. | Perf. 13x13¼ | | |
|---|---|---|---|---|
| 3834 | A3426 | Sheet of 10 | 16.00 | 16.00 |
| a.-j. | | 82y Any single | 1.25 | .50 |

Yosemite National Park, United States — A3427

Acropolis, Athens, Greece — A3428

Chichen Itza, Mexico — A3429

Saint Petersburg, Russia — A3430

Borobudur Temple Compounds, Indonesia — A3431

| 2015, July 10 | Litho. | Perf. 13¼x13 | | |
|---|---|---|---|---|
| 3835 | A3427 | 82y multi | 1.25 | .50 |
| 3836 | A3428 | 82y multi | 1.25 | .50 |
| 3837 | A3429 | 82y multi | 1.25 | .50 |
| 3838 | A3430 | 82y multi | 1.25 | .50 |
| 3839 | A3431 | 82y multi | 1.25 | .50 |
| a. | | Horiz. strip of 5, #3835-3839 | 7.00 | 4.50 |
| | | Nos. 3835-3839 (5) | 6.25 | 2.50 |

UNESCO World Heritage Sites.

Boy With Pencil and Postcard A3432

Penguins A3433

Squashes A3434

Snow on Camellias A3435

Cherry Blossoms and Birds A3436

Boy Putting Letter in Mailbox A3437

Hollyhocks A3438

Sparrows A3439

Chrysanthemums and Noshi — A3440

Carp
Streamer
A3441

Hydrangeas
A3443

Crane
A3445

Child,
Coins,
Letter and
Stamp
A3447

Dried
Persimmons
A3449

Child
Swimming
A3442

Flowers
A3444

Cranes,
Turtle and
Flowers
A3446

Paper
Balloons
A3448

Ume
Blossoms
A3450

Horsetails — A3451

**Die Cut Perf. 13x13½**
**2015, July 23          Litho.**
**Booklet Stamps**
**Self-Adhesive**

| | | | |
|---|---|---|---|
|3840|A3432 52y multi|.85|.65|
|3841|A3433 52y multi|.85|.65|
|3842|A3434 52y multi|.85|.65|
|3843|A3435 52y multi|.85|.65|
|3844|A3436 52y multi|.85|.65|
|3845|A3437 52y multi|.85|.65|
|3846|A3438 52y multi|.85|.65|
|3847|A3439 52y multi|.85|.65|
|3848|A3440 52y multi|.85|.65|
|3849|A3441 52y multi|.85|.65|
|a.|Booklet pane of 10, #3840-3849|10.00|10.00|
|3850|A3442 82y multi|1.25|.80|
|3851|A3443 82y multi|1.25|.80|
|3852|A3444 82y multi|1.25|.80|
|3853|A3445 82y multi|1.25|.80|
|3854|A3446 82y multi|1.25|.80|
|3855|A3447 82y multi|1.25|.80|
|3856|A3448 82y multi|1.25|.80|
|3857|A3449 82y multi|1.25|.80|
|3858|A3450 82y multi|1.25|.80|
|3859|A3451 82y multi|1.25|.80|
|a.|Booklet pane of 10, #3850-3859|16.00|16.00|
|   |Nos. 3840-3859 (20)|21.00|14.50|

Letter Writing Day.

23rd World Scout Jamboree, Kirara-hama — A3452

Designs: No. 3860, Three scouts, denomination at UL. No. 3861, Three scouts, denomination at UR. No. 3862, Male scout, denomination at UL. No. 3863, Female scout, denomination at UR.

**2015, July 28  Litho.  Perf. 13¾x13½**

| | | | |
|---|---|---|---|
|3860|82y multi|1.25|.50|
|3861|82y multi|1.25|.50|
|3862|82y multi|1.25|.50|
|3863|82y multi|1.25|.50|
|a.|A3452 Block of 4, #3860-3863|6.00|3.50|
|   |Nos. 3860-3863 (4)|5.00|2.00|

Roses
A3453

Chrysanthemums
A3454

Gerbera
Daisies
A3455

Freesias
A3457

Lilies and
Baby's
Breath
A3459

Moth
Orchids
A3461

Ranunculus
A3456

Cosmos
and
Dahlias
A3458

Pansies
A3460

Christmas
Cactus
A3462

**Die Cut Perf. 14**
**2015, July 31          Litho.**
**Self-Adhesive**

| | | | |
|---|---|---|---|
|3864|Sheet of 10, 2 each #3864a-3864e|10.00|10.00|
|a.|A3453 52y multi|.85|.65|
|b.|A3454 52y multi|.85|.65|
|c.|A3455 52y multi|.85|.65|
|d.|A3456 52y multi|.85|.65|
|e.|A3457 52y multi|.85|.65|
|3865|Sheet of 10, 2 each #3865a-3865e|16.00|16.00|
|a.|A3458 82y multi|1.25|.80|
|b.|A3459 82y multi|1.25|.80|
|c.|A3460 82y multi|1.25|.80|
|d.|A3461 82y multi|1.25|.80|
|e.|A3462 82y multi|1.25|.80|

Edo Castle
A3463

Hiroshima
Castle
A3465

Maruoka
Castle
A3464

Kochi Castle
A3466

Uwajima
Castle — A3467

**2015, Aug. 7     Litho.     Perf. 13**

| | | | |
|---|---|---|---|
|3866|A3463 82y multi|1.25|.50|
|3867|A3464 82y multi|1.25|.50|
|3868|A3465 82y multi|1.25|.50|
|3869|A3466 82y multi|1.25|.50|
|3870|A3467 82y multi|1.25|.50|
|a.|Vert. strip of 5, #3866-3870|7.00|4.50|
|   |Nos. 3866-3870 (5)|6.25|2.50|

**Nagano Flora Prefecture Type of 2003**

Designs: No. 3871, Dogtooth violet (pink flowers) and mountain. No. 3872, Skunk cabbage (white flower). No. 3873, Nikko daylily (yellow flower). No. 3874, Cosmos (white, pink and red flowers).

**2015, Aug. 21    Photo.    Perf. 13¼**

| | | | |
|---|---|---|---|
|3871|82y multi|1.25|.50|
|3872|82y multi|1.25|.50|
|3873|82y multi|1.25|.50|
|3874|82y multi|1.25|.50|
|a.|ZA510 Horiz. strip of 4, #3871-3874|6.50|3.50|
|   |Nos. 3871-3874 (4)|5.00|2.00|

**Owara Wind Festival Prefecture Type of 2007**

No. 3875, Night Light. No. 3876, Lattice Door. No. 3877, Saotome Dancers. No. 3878, Limelight. No. 3879, Moonlight Night.

**2015, Aug. 21    Litho.    Perf. 13¼**

| | | | |
|---|---|---|---|
|3875|ZA710 82y multi|1.25|.50|
|3876|ZA711 82y multi|1.25|.50|
|3877|ZA712 82y multi|1.25|.50|
|3878|ZA713 82y multi|1.25|.50|
|3879|ZA714 82y multi|1.25|.50|
|a.|Vert. strip of 5, #3875-3879|6.50|3.50|

See Nos. Z807-Z811.

Greetings: Characters
SANRIO CHARACTERS
HELLO KITTY MY MELODY Little Twin Stars

A3468

 A3469
 A3470
 A3471
A3472
 A3473
A3474
 A3475
 A3476
A3477
A3478
 A3479
A3480
 A3481
 A3482
 A3483
 A3484

A3485

A3486

A3487

A3488

A3489

A3490

A3491

A3492

A3493

A3494

A3495

A3496

A3497

A3498

A3499

A3500

A3501

A3502

A3503

A3505

A3504

A3506

Sanrio
Characters — A3507

No. 3880: a, Hello Kitty, Mimmy, playing cards, pink background (29mm diameter). b, Hello Kitty, Teddy bear in window, blue background (23x23mm). c, Hello Kitty, Mimmy, flowers, green background (23x23mm). d, Hello Kitty, Mimmy, bucket, flowers, bows, pink background (22x30mm oval). e, Hello Kitty, Mimmy, drum, cymbals, musical symbols, yellow background (29x26mm heart). f, Hello Kitty, Teddy bear, scale, blue background (27x22mm). g, Little Twin Stars, cat, blue & pink background (29mm diameter). h, Little Twin Stars, cream background (23x23mm). i, My Melody and Piano, yellow brown background with polka dots (22x27mm). j, My Melody and Piano, blue background with polka dots (29x26mm heart).

No. 3894: a, Hello Kitty, Mimmy, flowers, yellow background (27x22mm). b, Hello Kitty, Mimmy on carousel, pink background (22x30mm oval). c, Hello Kitty, Mimmy, Teddy bear in umbrella, pale lilac background (29mm diameter). d, Hello Kitty, Teddy bear, bird, berries and mushrooms, buff background (23x23mm). e, Hello Kitty, Mimmy, Teddy bear, swan, blue background (22x27mm). f, Hello Kitty, Mimmy in coffee mug, light green background (29x26mm heart). g, My Melody and mouse, pale sage green background (23x23mm). h, My Melody and mouse, pink background (29mm diameter). i, Little Twin Stars, white & rose background (29x26mm heart). j, Little Twin Stars on swan, blue & rose background (27x22mm).

**Die Cut Perf. 14 (#3880b, 3880c, 3880d, 3880h), Die Cut Perf. 13½x13¾ (#3880f), Die Cut Perf. 13¾x13½ (#3880i), Die Cut Perf.**
**2015, Aug. 21**     Litho.
**Self-Adhesive**
**Die Cut Perf. (A3469-A3474), Die Cut Perf. 13 (A3475-A3487)**

| | | | | |
|---|---|---|---|---|
| 3880 | A3468 | Sheet of 10 | 10.00 | 10.00 |
| a.-j. | | 52y Any single | .90 | .70 |
| 3881 | | Sheet of 10, #3881a-3881f, 4 #3881g | 10.00 | 10.00 |
| a. | A3469 | 52y multi | .90 | .70 |
| b. | A3470 | 52y multi | .90 | .70 |
| c. | A3471 | 52y multi | .90 | .70 |
| d. | A3472 | 52y multi | .90 | .70 |
| e. | A3473 | 52y multi | .90 | .70 |
| f. | A3474 | 52y multi | .90 | .70 |
| g. | A3475 | 52y multi | .90 | .70 |
| 3882 | | Sheet of 10, #3881a-3881f, 4 #3882a | 10.00 | 10.00 |
| a. | A3476 | 52y multi | .90 | .70 |
| 3883 | | Sheet of 10, #3881a-3881f, 4 #3883a | 10.00 | 10.00 |
| a. | A3477 | 52y multi | .90 | .70 |
| 3884 | | Sheet of 10, #3881a-3881f, 4 #3884a | 10.00 | 10.00 |
| a. | A3478 | 52y multi | .90 | .70 |
| 3885 | | Sheet of 10, #3881a-3881f, 4 #3885a | 10.00 | 10.00 |
| a. | A3479 | 52y multi | .90 | .70 |
| 3886 | | Sheet of 10, #3881a-3881f, 4 #3886a | 10.00 | 10.00 |
| a. | A3480 | 52y multi | .90 | .70 |
| 3887 | | Sheet of 10, #3881a-3881f, 4 #3887a | 10.00 | 10.00 |
| a. | A3481 | 52y multi | .90 | .70 |
| 3888 | | Sheet of 10, #3881a-3881f, 4 #3888a | 10.00 | 10.00 |
| a. | A3482 | 52y multi | .90 | .70 |
| 3889 | | Sheet of 10, #3881a-3881f, 4 #3889a | 10.00 | 10.00 |
| a. | A3483 | 52y multi | .90 | .70 |
| 3890 | | Sheet of 10, #3881a-3881f, 4 #3890a | 10.00 | 10.00 |
| a. | A3484 | 52y multi | .90 | .70 |
| 3891 | | Sheet of 10, #3881a-3881f, 4 #3891a | 10.00 | 10.00 |
| a. | A3485 | 52y multi | .90 | .70 |
| 3892 | | Sheet of 10, #3881a-3881f, 4 #3892a | 10.00 | 10.00 |
| a. | A3486 | 52y multi | .90 | .70 |
| 3893 | | Sheet of 10, #3881a-3881f, 4 #3893a | 10.00 | 10.00 |
| a. | A3487 | 52y multi | .90 | .70 |

**Die Cut Perf. 13½x13¾ (#3894a, 3894j), Die Cut Perf. 14 (#3894b, 3894d, 3894g), Die Cut Perf. 13¾x13½ (#3894e), Die Cut Perf.**

| | | | | |
|---|---|---|---|---|
| 3894 | A3488 | Sheet of 10 | 15.00 | 15.00 |
| a.-j. | | 82y Any single | 1.40 | .80 |

**Die Cut Perf. 14 (A3489-A3494), Die Cut Perf. 13½x13¾ (A3495-A3507)**

| | | | | |
|---|---|---|---|---|
| 3895 | | Sheet of 10, #3895a-3895f, 4 #3895g | 15.00 | 15.00 |
| a. | A3489 | 82y multi | 1.40 | .80 |
| b. | A3490 | 82y multi | 1.40 | .80 |
| c. | A3491 | 82y multi | 1.40 | .80 |
| d. | A3492 | 82y multi | 1.40 | .80 |
| e. | A3493 | 82y multi | 1.40 | .80 |
| f. | A3494 | 82y multi | 1.40 | .80 |
| g. | A3495 | 82y multi | 1.40 | .80 |
| 3896 | | Sheet of 10, #3895a-3985f, 4 #3896a | 15.00 | 15.00 |
| a. | A3496 | 82y multi | 1.40 | .80 |
| 3897 | | Sheet of 10, #3895a-3985f, 4 #3897a | 15.00 | 15.00 |
| a. | A3497 | 82y multi | 1.40 | .80 |
| 3898 | | Sheet of 10, #3895a-3985f, 4 #3898a | 15.00 | 15.00 |
| a. | A3498 | 82y multi | 1.40 | .80 |
| 3899 | | Sheet of 10, #3895a-3985f, 4 #3899a | 15.00 | 15.00 |
| a. | A3499 | 82y multi | 1.40 | .80 |
| 3900 | | Sheet of 10, #3895a-3985f, 4 #3900a | 15.00 | 15.00 |
| a. | A3500 | 82y multi | 1.40 | .80 |
| 3901 | | Sheet of 10, #3895a-3985f, 4 #3901a | 15.00 | 15.00 |
| a. | A3501 | 82y multi | 1.40 | .80 |
| 3902 | | Sheet of 10, #3895a-3985f, 4 #3902a | 15.00 | 15.00 |
| a. | A3502 | 82y multi | 1.40 | .80 |
| 3903 | | Sheet of 10, #3895a-3985f, 4 #3903a | 15.00 | 15.00 |
| a. | A3503 | 82y multi | 1.40 | .80 |
| 3904 | | Sheet of 10, #3895a-3985f, 4 #3904a | 15.00 | 15.00 |
| a. | A3504 | 82y multi | 1.40 | .80 |
| 3905 | | Sheet of 10, #3895a-3985f, 4 #3905a | 15.00 | 15.00 |
| a. | A3505 | 82y multi | 1.40 | .80 |
| 3906 | | Sheet of 10, #3895a-3985f, 4 #3906a | 15.00 | 15.00 |
| a. | A3506 | 82y multi | 1.40 | .80 |
| 3907 | | Sheet of 10, #3895a-3985f, 4 #3907a | 15.00 | 15.00 |
| a. | A3507 | 82y multi | 1.40 | .80 |
| | | Nos. 3880-3907 (28) | 350.00 | |

**Miniature Sheet**

70th National Sports Festival,
Wakayama — A3508

No. 3908: a, Kayaking. b, Sailing. c, Basketball. d, Field hockey. e, Cycling. f, Gymnastics. g, Fencing. h, Soccer. i, Naginata. j, Volleyball.

| | | | | |
|---|---|---|---|---|
| **2015, Aug. 28** | | **Litho.** | | **Perf. 13** |
| 3908 | A3508 | Sheet of 10 | 16.00 | 16.00 |
| a.-j. | | 82y Any single | 1.25 | .60 |

**Niigata Flowers Prefecture Type of 2002**

Designs: No. 3909, Red camellias, Kamoyama Kouen Park. No. 3910, Yellow daylilies, Oonogame. No. 3911, Irises, Ijimino Kouen Park. No. 3912, Pink iwakagami flowers, Mt. Myoukousan.

| | | | | |
|---|---|---|---|---|
| **2015, Aug. 28** | | **Photo.** | | **Perf. 13¼** |
| 3909 | | 82y multi | 1.25 | .50 |
| 3910 | | 82y multi | 1.25 | .50 |
| 3911 | | 82y multi | 1.25 | .50 |
| 3912 | | 82y multi | 1.25 | .50 |
| a. | ZA488 | Horiz. strip of 4, #3909-3912 | 6.00 | 3.50 |
| | | Nos. 3909-3912 (4) | 5.00 | 2.00 |

**Hokkaido Flowers Prefecture Type of 1991**

Designs as before.

| | | | | |
|---|---|---|---|---|
| **2015, Aug. 28** | | **Photo.** | | **Perf. 13** |
| 3913 | ZA97 | 82y multi | 1.25 | .50 |
| 3914 | ZA98 | 82y multi | 1.25 | .50 |
| 3915 | ZA99 | 82y multi | 1.25 | .50 |
| 3916 | ZA100 | 82y multi | 1.25 | .50 |
| a. | | Horiz. strip of 4, #3913-3916 | 6.00 | 3.50 |
| | | Nos. 3913-3916 (4) | 5.00 | 2.00 |

**Hokkaido Flowers Prefecture Type of 2005**

Designs as before.

| | | | | |
|---|---|---|---|---|
| **2015, Aug. 28** | | **Photo.** | | **Perf. 13¼** |
| 3917 | ZA569 | 82y multi | 1.25 | .50 |
| 3918 | ZA570 | 82y multi | 1.25 | .50 |
| 3919 | ZA571 | 82y multi | 1.25 | .50 |
| 3920 | ZA572 | 82y multi | 1.25 | .50 |
| a. | | Horiz. strip of 4, #3917-3920 | 6.00 | 3.50 |
| | | Nos. 3917-3920 (4) | 5.00 | 2.00 |

Plums
A3509

Lemon and Lime
A3510

Okra
A3511

Olives
A3512

Mustard Spinach
A3513

Celery
A3514

Lotus Root
A3515

Loquats
A3516

Soybeans
A3517

Fig
A3518

**Die Cut Perf. 13¼x13, 13x13¼**
**2015, Aug. 31**     Litho.
**Self-Adhesive**

| | | | | |
|---|---|---|---|---|
| 3921 | | Sheet of 10, 2 each #3921a-3921e | 10.00 | 10.00 |
| a. | A3509 | 52y multi | .90 | .70 |
| b. | A3510 | 52y multi | .90 | .70 |
| c. | A3511 | 52y multi | .90 | .70 |
| d. | A3512 | 52y multi | .90 | .70 |
| e. | A3513 | 52y multi | .90 | .70 |
| 3922 | | Sheet of 10, 2 each #3922a-3922e | 15.00 | 15.00 |
| a. | A3514 | 82y multi | 1.25 | .80 |
| b. | A3515 | 82y multi | 1.25 | .80 |

| c. | A3516 82y multi | 1.25 | .80 |
| d. | A3517 82y multi | 1.25 | .80 |
| e. | A3518 82y multi | 1.25 | .80 |

## Miniature Sheets

A3519

A3520

Greetings — A3521

No. 3923: a, Sea bream. b, Turtle and crane. c, Mount Fuji. d, Noshi. e, Clouds, rainbow and musical notes. f, Dove, horiz. g, "Happy" and shamrocks, horiz. h, Rose, horiz. i, Flowers and "For You," horiz. j, "Happy," birthday cake and candles, horiz.

No. 3924: a, Sea bream, diff. b, Gourds. c, Gift box with bow. d, Pine, bamboo and plum. e, Party hat, streamers and confetti. f, Bird, horiz. g, "Happy" and shamrocks, diff., horiz. h, Two roses, horiz. i, Bow and "For You," horiz. j, "Happy" and slice of birthday cake, horiz.

No. 3925: a, Sea bream, diff. b, Fans. c, Mount Fuji, diff. d, Mallet of luck. e, "Happy," heart with bow. f, Bird, diff., horiz. g, "Happy" and shamrocks, diff., horiz. h, Five roses, horiz. i, Envelope, "For You," feather, horiz. j, "Happy" and cup, horiz.

### Die Cut Perf. 13x13¼, 13¼x13
**2015, Sept. 4**          **Litho.**
#### Self-Adhesive

| 3923 | A3519 | Sheet of 10 | 10.00 | 10.00 |
| a.-j. | | 52y Any single | .90 | .70 |
| 3924 | A3520 | Sheet of 10 | 15.00 | 15.00 |
| a.-j. | | 82y Any single | 1.25 | .80 |
| 3925 | A3521 | Sheet of 10 | 17.00 | 17.00 |
| a.-j. | | 92y Any single | 1.25 | .80 |
| | | Nos. 3923-3925 (3) | 42.00 | |

## Miniature Sheet

Wakayama Local Autonomy Law, 60th Anniv. — A3522

No. 3926: a, Koyasan Danjo Garan (32x39mm). b, Wakayama Castle (28x33mm). c, Shirahama and beach (28x33mm). d, Hashikuiiwa Rocks (28x33mm). e, Nachi Waterfall and pagoda (28x33mm).

### Perf. 13¼ (#3926a), 13x13¼
**2015, Sept. 8**          **Photo.**

| 3926 | A3522 | Sheet of 5 | 7.00 | 7.00 |
| a.-e. | | 82y Any single | 1.25 | .60 |

## Miniature Sheets

A3523

Greetings — A3524

No. 3927: a, Koala bear on tree (23x23mm). b, Bird with letter (23x23mm). c, Bees holding heart (23x23mm). d, Owl holding letter (23x23mm). e, Brown Teddy bear with mail bag and flowers (22x30mm oval). f, White Teddy bear with mail bag and gift box (22x30mm oval). g, Pink Teddy bear with flowers (22x30mm oval). h, Dark brown Teddy bear with mail bag and gift box (22x30mm oval). i, Light green Teddy bear with mail bag and flowers (22x30mm oval). j, Teddy bear with envelope (25x22mm heart).

No. 3928: a, Teddy bear, cup on table (26x29mm). b, Teddy bear holding honey jar (25mm diameter). c, Teddy bear holding gift box (25mm diameter). d, Birthday cake, gifts and envelope (22x30mm oval). e, Pink Teddy bear holding flowers, cup and dessert bowl on table (25mm diameter). f, Light green Teddy bear holding flowers, drinking glass with straw on table (25mm diameter). g, Flowers, gifts and envelope (25mm diameter). h, Owl (25mm diameter). i, Gray Teddy bear holding lollipop (25mm diameter). j, Teddy bear with party hat, streamers and confetti (25mm diameter).

### Die Cut Perf. 14
**2015, Sept. 11**          **Litho.**
#### Self-Adhesive

| 3927 | A3523 | Sheet of 10 | 10.00 | 10.00 |
| a.-j. | | 52y Any single | .90 | .70 |
| 3928 | A3524 | Sheet of 10 | 15.00 | 15.00 |
| a.-j. | | 82y Any single | 1.25 | .80 |

### Okinawa Fish Prefecture Type of 2007

Designs as before.

**2015, Sept. 16    Litho.    Perf. 13¼**

| 3929 | ZA704 | 82y multi | 1.25 | .60 |
| 3930 | ZA705 | 82y multi | 1.25 | .60 |
| 3931 | ZA706 | 82y multi | 1.25 | .60 |
| 3932 | ZA707 | 82y multi | 1.25 | .60 |
| 3933 | ZA708 | 82y multi | 1.25 | .60 |
| a. | | Horiz. strip of 5, #3929-3933 | 7.00 | 4.50 |
| | | Nos. 3929-3933 (5) | 6.25 | 3.00 |

## Miniature Sheet

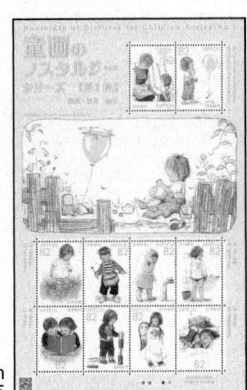

Children A3525

No. 3934: a, Mother, girl and balloon. b, Girl and balloon. c, Child holding flowers. d, Boy with drum. e, Girl in raincoat looking at snail. f, Girl on beach. g, Children reading book. h, Child playing with blocks. i, Child in angel costume. j, Child sleeping with stuffed animal.

**2015, Sept. 18    Photo.    Perf. 13**

| 3934 | A3525 | Sheet of 10 | 16.00 | 16.00 |
| a.-j. | | 82y Any single | 1.25 | .50 |

A sheet of five 82y self-adhesive stamps depicting Hello Kitty characters was printed in limited quantities and sold only in a package containing stationery. Value, $20.

Astronomy — A3526

No. 3935: a, Moon (25x34mm). b, Libra and scales (22x25mm). c, Scorpio and scorpion (22x25mm). d, Sagittarius, bow and arrow (22x25mm).

### Litho. With Foil Application
### Die Cut Perf. 13x13¼
**2015, Sept. 25          Self-Adhesive**

| 3935 | A3526 | Sheet of 10, #3935a, 3 each #3935b-3935d | 16.00 | 16.00 |
| a.-d. | | 82y Any single | 1.25 | .80 |

## Miniature Sheet

Osaka Local Autonomy Law, 60th Anniv. — A3527

No. 3936: a, Bunraku puppet, Osaka Castle (32x39mm). b, Interior of Osaka Prefectural Government Building (28x33mm). c, Tower of the Sun (28x33mm). d, Jinai-machi Town, Tondabayashi (28x33mm). e, Eggplant (28x33mm).

### Perf. 13¼ (#3936a), 13x13¼
**2015, Oct. 6**          **Photo.**

| 3936 | A3527 | Sheet of 5 | 7.00 | 7.00 |
| a.-e. | | 82y Any single | 1.25 | .80 |

A3528

International Letter Writing Week — A3529

Paintings by Hiroshige: 70y, Thoroughwort and Pink. 90y, The Fifty-three Stations of the Tokaido: Yoshiwara. 110y, The Fifty-three Stations of the Tokaido: Yoshida. 130y, The Fifty-three Stations of the Tokaido: Fujikawa.

**2015, Oct. 9    Photo.    Perf. 13¼**
| 3937 | A3528 | 70y multi | 1.25 | .50 |
| | | **Perf. 13** | | |
| 3938 | A3529 | 90y multi | 1.75 | .50 |
| 3939 | A3529 | 110y multi | 2.25 | .50 |
| 3940 | A3529 | 130y multi | 2.50 | .50 |
| | | Nos. 3937-3940 (4) | 7.75 | 2.00 |

See listing of No. 4448 for images of each Hiroshige print.

Front Ends of Tokaido Shinkansen Rail Cars A3530

Japan National Railways 183 Series Locomotive A3531

Keisei Class AE Locomotive A3532

Hankyu 6300 Series Locomotive A3533

Meitetsu 6000 Series Locomotive A3534

Kintetsu 12400 Series Locomotive A3535

Japan Railways West 500 Series Locomotive A3536

Japan Railways Tokai and Japan Railways West N700 Series Locomotive A3537

Odakyu 60000 Series Locomotive A3538

Kintetsu 50000 Series Locomotive A3539

Front Ends of Tokaido Shinkansen Rail Cars A3540

Kintetsu 12400 Series Locomotive A3541

Japan
National
Railways 183
Series
Locomotive
A3542

Japan
Railways
West 500
Series
Locomotive
A3543

Keisei Class
AE
Locomotive
A3544

Japan
Railways
Tokai and
Japan
Railways
West N700
Series
Locomotive
A3545

Hankyu 6300
Series
Locomotive
A3546

Odakyu
60000 Series
Locomotive
A3547

Meitetsu
6000 Series
Locomotive
A3548

Kintetsu
50000 Series
Locomotive
A3549

**2015, Oct. 9  Photo.      Perf. 13¼x13**
| | | | |
|---|---|---|---|
| 3941 | | Sheet of 10 | 16.00 16.00 |
| a. | A3530 | 82y multi | 1.25 .50 |
| b. | A3531 | 82y multi | 1.25 .50 |
| c. | A3532 | 82y multi | 1.25 .50 |
| d. | A3533 | 82y multi | 1.25 .50 |
| e. | A3534 | 82y multi | 1.25 .50 |
| f. | A3535 | 82y multi | 1.25 .50 |
| g. | A3536 | 82y multi | 1.25 .50 |
| h. | A3537 | 82y multi | 1.25 .50 |
| i. | A3538 | 82y multi | 1.25 .50 |
| j. | A3539 | 82y multi | 1.25 .50 |

**Perf. 13x13¼**
| | | | |
|---|---|---|---|
| 3942 | | Sheet of 10 + 10 labels | 16.00 16.00 |
| a. | A3540 | 82y multi | 1.25 .50 |
| b. | A3541 | 82y multi | 1.25 .50 |
| c. | A3542 | 82y multi | 1.25 .50 |
| d. | A3543 | 82y multi | 1.25 .50 |
| e. | A3544 | 82y multi | 1.25 .50 |
| f. | A3545 | 82y multi | 1.25 .50 |
| g. | A3546 | 82y multi | 1.25 .50 |
| h. | A3547 | 82y multi | 1.25 .50 |
| i. | A3548 | 82y multi | 1.25 .50 |
| j. | A3549 | 82y multi | 1.25 .50 |

Chinese Style
Sword
A3550

Folding
Screen
Depicting
Lady of the
Court
A3551

Circular
Mirror With
Inlaid
Decorations
A3552

Batik Folding
Screen
A3553

Lacquer Ewer — A3554

**2015, Oct. 16   Photo.         Perf. 13**
| | | | |
|---|---|---|---|
| 3943 | A3550 | 82y multi | 1.25 .50 |
| 3944 | A3551 | 82y multi | 1.25 .50 |
| 3945 | A3552 | 82y multi | 1.25 .50 |
| 3946 | A3553 | 82y multi | 1.25 .50 |
| 3947 | A3554 | 82y multi | 1.25 .50 |
| a. | | Vert. strip of 5, #3943-3947 | 7.00 4.50 |
| | | Nos. 3943-3947 (5) | 6.25 2.50 |

Treasures of the Shosoin.

Chihuahua
A3555

Shiba
A3556

Yorkshire
Terrier
A3557

French
Bulldog
A3558

Cavalier
King
Charles
Spaniel
A3559

Jack
Russell
Terriers
A3560

Papillon
A3561

Golden
Retriever
A3562

Beagles
A3563

American
Cocker
Spaniel
A3564

Toy Poodles
A3565

Dachshund
A3566

Pomeranians
A3567

Maltese
A3568

Miniature
Schnauzer
A3569

Shih Tzu
A3570

Pembroke
Welsh
Corgi
A3571

Pug
A3572

Miniature
Pinscher
A3573

Bichon
Frise
A3574

### Die Cut Perf. 13x13¼
**2015, Oct. 23                     Litho.**
**Self-Adhesive**
| | | | |
|---|---|---|---|
| 3948 | | Sheet of 10 | 10.00 10.00 |
| a. | A3555 | 52y multi | .90 .70 |
| b. | A3556 | 52y multi | .90 .70 |
| c. | A3557 | 52y multi | .90 .70 |
| d. | A3558 | 52y multi | .90 .70 |
| e. | A3559 | 52y multi | .90 .70 |
| f. | A3560 | 52y multi | .90 .70 |
| g. | A3561 | 52y multi | .90 .70 |
| h. | A3562 | 52y multi | .90 .70 |
| i. | A3563 | 52y multi | .90 .70 |
| j. | A3564 | 52y multi | .90 .70 |
| 3949 | | Sheet of 10 | 16.00 16.00 |
| a. | A3565 | 82y multi | 1.25 .80 |
| b. | A3566 | 82y multi | 1.25 .80 |
| c. | A3567 | 82y multi | 1.25 .80 |
| d. | A3568 | 82y multi | 1.25 .80 |
| e. | A3569 | 82y multi | 1.25 .80 |
| f. | A3570 | 82y multi | 1.25 .80 |
| g. | A3571 | 82y multi | 1.25 .80 |
| h. | A3572 | 82y multi | 1.25 .80 |
| i. | A3573 | 82y multi | 1.25 .80 |
| j. | A3574 | 82y multi | 1.25 .80 |

### Miniature Sheet

Edo Calligraphy — A3575

No. 3950 — Characters for "monkey": a, In Kinbun style of Western Zhou period (character with large red chop at LL). b, In Kinbuntai seal engraving style (red character). c, In Yin Dynasty oracle bone script style (white character with purple and black background). d, In Yin Dynasty oracle bone script style (character in black with light green background). e, In Shoten style (Black character with large central vertical line and large red chop at LL). f, In Hiragana style (black character, denomination at center left). g, In Gyosho style (black character with large central vertical line, small red chop at LR). h, In Gyosho style (black character with salmon pink background). i, In oracle bone script (black character with curved lines, small red chop at LL above denomination). j, In Tenreitai style (three-part black character with small red chop at LL).

### Litho. & Embossed
**2015, Oct. 29              Perf. 13x13¼**
| | | | |
|---|---|---|---|
| 3950 | A3575 | Sheet of 10 | 16.00 16.00 |
| a.-j. | | 82y Any single | 1.125 .80 |

Japanese
Foods
A3576

Designs: No. 3951, Ramen noodles (denomination at LL). No. 3952, Sukiyaki (denomination at UL).

**2015, Oct. 29   Photo.    Perf. 13¼x13**
| | | | |
|---|---|---|---|
| 3951 | | 18y multi | .30 .25 |
| 3952 | | 18y multi | .30 .25 |
| a. | A3576 | Horiz. pair, #3951-3952 | .60 .45 |

A3577          A3578

New Year 2016 (Year of
the Monkey)
A3579          A3580

**2015, Oct. 29   Photo.    Perf. 13¼x13**
| | | | |
|---|---|---|---|
| 3953 | A3577 | 52y multi | 1.00 .30 |
| 3954 | A3578 | 82y multi | 1.50 .40 |

**Photo. & Typo.**
**Perf. 13¼**
| | | | |
|---|---|---|---|
| 3955 | A3579 | 52y +3y multi | 1.25 .40 |
| 3956 | A3580 | 82y +3y multi | 1.75 .40 |
| | | Nos. 3953-3956 (4) | 5.50 1.50 |

Sheets of two containing Nos. 3953-3954 were lottery prizes. Value, $3.50.

Establishment of
Tsunami Preparedness
Day — A3581

**2015, Nov. 5   Litho.       Perf. 13**
| | | | |
|---|---|---|---|
| 3957 | A3581 | 82y multi | 1.40 .50 |

### Miniature Sheet

Traditional Crafts — A3582

No. 3758: a, Takaoka Shikki lacquer box (Toyama Prefecture). b, Makabe Ishidoro stone lantern (Ibaraki Prefecture). c, Edo glassware (Tokyo Prefecture). d, Tokoname Yaki pottery (Aichi Prefecture). e, Mino Washi Japanese paper (Gifu Prefecture). f, Kyo Yuzen dyed fabric (Kyoto Prefecture). g, Osaka Naniwa Suzuki tin container (Osaka Prefecture). h, Kumano Fude brushes (Hiroshima Prefecture). i, Awa Sho-ai Shijira-ori weaving (Tokushima Prefecture). j, Beppu Takesaiku bamboo basket (Oita Prefecture).

**2015, Nov. 5      Litho.       Perf. 13½**
| | | | |
|---|---|---|---|
| 3958 | A3582 | Sheet of 10 | 16.00 16.00 |
| a.-j. | | 82y Any single | 1.40 .50 |

## Miniature Sheets

A3583

Disney Characters — A3584

No. 3959: a, Winnie the Pooh, honey jar at his side. b, Winnie the pooh sticking snout in honey jar. c, Winnie the Pooh standing with head stuck in honey jar. d, Winnie the Pooh writing list. e, Winnie the Pooh in grass carrying honey jar. f, Winnie the Pooh scratching. g, Winnie the Pooh and Piglet. h, Christopher Robin draggin Winnie the Pooh down stairs. i, Winnie the Pooh next to Christopher Robin putting boots on feet. j, Christopher Robin and Winnie the Pooh reading sign.

No. 3960: a, Princess Aurora and pink roses (22x27mm). b, Princess Aurora and pink roses (27x22mm). c, Cinderella and lilies (22x27mm). d, Cinderella and lilies (27x22mm). e, Snow White and pink roses (22x27mm). f, Snow White, animals and pink roses (27x22mm). g, Ariel and red flowers (22x27mm). h, Rapunzel, lizard and pink flowers (27x22mm). i, Belle and pink rose (22x27mm). j, Jasmine and white flowers (27x22mm).

### Die Cut Perf. 11¼
**2015, Nov. 6          Litho.**
**Self-Adhesive**
3959   A3583   Sheet of 10      10.00 10.00

### Die Cut Perf. 14x13½, 13½x14
| | | | |
|---|---|---|---|
| a.-j. | 52y Any single | 1.00 | .80 |
| 3960 | A3584 Sheet of 10 | 16.00 | 16.00 |
| a.-j. | 82y Any single | 1.25 | .80 |

## Miniature Sheet

Nagasaki Local Autonomy Law, 60th Anniv. — A3585

No. 3961: a, Oura Church and camellias (32x39mm). b, Nagasaki Kunchi Festival (28x33mm). c, Hashima (28x33mm). d, Mount Heisei-shinzan (28x33mm). e, Golden tiger lily (28x33mm).

### Perf. 13¼ (#3961a), 13x13¼
**2015, Nov. 17                Photo.**
3961   A3585   Sheet of 5      7.00 7.00
a.-e.   82y Any single      1.25   .60

Iyokan Orange A3586

Carrot A3587

Yuzus A3588

Daikon Radish A3589

Green Onions A3590

Chinese Cabbage A3591

Broccoli A3592

Tangerines A3593

Spinach A3594

Kiwi A3595

### Die Cut Perf. 13¼
**2015, Nov. 20                Litho.**
**Self-Adhesive**
3962   Sheet of 10, 2 each #3962a-3962e    10.00 10.00
| a. | A3586 52y multi | .85 | .65 |
| b. | A3587 52y multi | .85 | .65 |
| c. | A3588 52y multi | .85 | .65 |
| d. | A3589 52y multi | .85 | .65 |
| e. | A3590 52y multi | .85 | .65 |

3963   Sheet of 10, 2 each #3963a-3963e    16.00 16.00
| a. | A3591 82y multi | 1.25 | .80 |
| b. | A3592 82y multi | 1.25 | .80 |
| c. | A3593 82y multi | 1.25 | .80 |
| d. | A3594 82y multi | 1.25 | .80 |
| e. | A3595 82y multi | 1.25 | .80 |

## Miniature Sheet

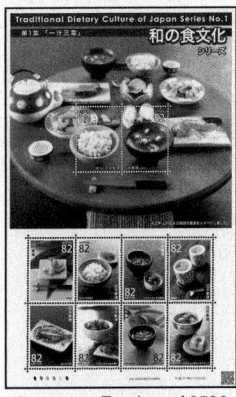

Japanese Foods — A3596

No. 3964: a, Chestnuts and rice. b, Miso soup. c, Shrimp tempura. d, Rice and Narazuke pickles. e, Miso soup and simmered seaweed. f, Steamed egg custard. g, Dried mackerel. h, Rice and Nukazuke pickles. i, Vegetable soup. j, Simmered pumpkin and cold tofu.

**2015, Nov. 24   Litho.   Perf. 13½**
3964   A3596   Sheet of 10      16.00 16.00
a.-j.   82y Any single      1.25   .50

## Miniature Sheet

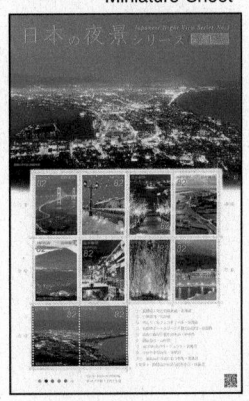

Japan at Night A3597

No. 3965: a, Hakucho Bridge (stamp 1). b, Streetlight and buildings at Otaru Canal (stamp 2). c, Lighted trees at Hakodate Winter Festival, denomination at LR (stamp 3). d, Port of Akita and highway (stamp 4). e, Mount Iwate (stamp 5). f, Ginzan Onsen (stamp 6). g, Sendai Pageant of Starlight, denomination at UR (stamp 7). h, Nakayam Setsugekka (stamp 8). i, Center of Mutsu City (stamp 9). j, Mutsu City and harbor (stamp 10).

**2015, Nov. 27   Litho.   Perf. 13**
3965   A3597   Sheet of 10      16.00 16.00
a.-j.   82y Any single      1.25   .50

## Miniature Sheet

Chiba Local Autonomy Law, 60th Anniv. — A3598

No. 3966: a, Tokyo Bay Aqua-line, rape blossoms (32x39mm). b, Character from Nanso Satomi Hakkenden (28x33mm). c, Inubosaki Lighthouse (28x33mm). d, Narita International Airport (28x33mm). e, Suigo Sawara Aquatic Botanical Garden (28x33mm).

### Perf. 13¼ (#3966a), 13x13¼
**2015, Dec. 8                Photo.**
3966   A3598   Sheet of 5      7.00 7.00
a.-e.   82y Any single      1.25   .60

 A3599
 A3600
 A3601
 A3602
 A3603
 A3604
 A3605
 A3606
 A3607
 A3608
 Candles A3609
 Girl Looking at Frosted Window A3610
 Snowglobe A3611
 House and Snowflakes A3612

Snow-covered Trees
A3613

Bird in Cage
A3614

Poinsettia
A3615

Polar Bear
A3616

Reindeer in Forest
A3617

Ice Skater
A3618

**Die Cut Perf. 13x13¼**
2015, Dec. 11          Litho.
**Self-Adhesive**

| | | | |
|---|---|---|---|
| 3967 | | Sheet of 10 | 10.00 10.00 |
| a. | A3599 52y multi | | .90 .70 |
| b. | A3600 52y multi | | .90 .70 |
| c. | A3601 52y multi | | .90 .70 |
| d. | A3602 52y multi | | .90 .70 |
| e. | A3603 52y multi | | .90 .70 |
| f. | A3604 52y multi | | .90 .70 |
| g. | A3605 52y multi | | .90 .70 |
| h. | A3606 52y multi | | .90 .70 |
| i. | A3607 52y multi | | .90 .70 |
| j. | A3608 52y multi | | .90 .70 |
| 3968 | | Sheet of 10 | 15.00 15.00 |
| a. | A3609 82y multi | | 1.25 .80 |
| b. | A3610 82y multi | | 1.25 .80 |
| c. | A3611 82y multi | | 1.25 .80 |
| d. | A3612 82y multi | | 1.25 .80 |
| e. | A3613 82y multi | | 1.25 .80 |
| f. | A3614 82y multi | | 1.25 .80 |
| g. | A3615 82y multi | | 1.25 .80 |
| h. | A3616 82y multi | | 1.25 .80 |
| i. | A3617 82y multi | | 1.25 .80 |
| j. | A3618 82y multi | | 1.25 .80 |

Phoenix Hall, Kyoto — A3619

State Guest House, Tokyo — A3620

**Photo. & Engr.**
2016, Jan. 8          Perf. 13¼

| | | | |
|---|---|---|---|
| 3969 | A3619 82y multi | 1.25 | .50 |
| 3970 | A3620 82y multi | 1.25 | .50 |
| a. | Vert. pair, #3969-3970 | 3.00 | 1.50 |

**Miniature Sheet**

Astronomy — A3621

---

No. 3971: a, Morning star (26x36mm). b, Aries and ram (22x25mm). c, Taurus and bull (22x25mm). d, Gemini and twins (22x25mm).

**Die Cut Perf. 11 (#3971a), Die Cut Perf. 13x13¼**
**Litho. With Foil Application**
2016, Jan. 22          **Self-Adhesive**

| | | | |
|---|---|---|---|
| 3971 | A3621 | Sheet of 10, #3971a, 3 each #3971b-3971d | 16.00 16.00 |
| a.-d. | 82y Any single | | 1.25 .60 |

**Souvenir Sheets**

Red Fuji, by Hokusai
A3622

Great Wave of Kanagawa, by Hokusai — A3623

No. 3972: a, Detail of Mount Fuji. b, Entire print.
No. 3973: a, Detail of wave. b, Entire print.

**Litho. & Embossed With Foil Application**
2016, Jan. 29          Perf. 13¾x14

| | | | |
|---|---|---|---|
| 3972 | A3622 Sheet of 2 | 70.00 70.00 |
| a.-b. | 1000y Either single | 25.00 5.00 |
| 3973 | A3623 Sheet of 2 | 70.00 70.00 |
| a.-b. | 1000y Either single | 25.00 5.00 |

Nos. 3972-3973 were only sold mounted in a booklet that sold for 8000y.

**Miniature Sheet**

Children A3624

No. 3974: a, Girl wearing dark brown hat. b, Cat and girl with red backpack. c, Child and tulips. d, Girl, peas and pea plant. e, Girl and irises. f, Child wearing blue bonnet. g, Four children with puppets. h, Girl wearing red hat, sea shells. i, Girl wearing red boots, hide and seek. j, Child wearing scarf and white knitted hat.

2016, Jan. 29          Litho.          Perf. 13

| | | | |
|---|---|---|---|
| 3974 | A3624 Sheet of 10 | 16.00 16.00 |
| a.-j. | 82y Any single | 1.25 .60 |

**Miniature Sheets**

Miffy A3626

No. 3975: a, Miffy and Auntie Alice, plate of food (29x26mm). b, Miffy on bicycle

---

(24x24mm). c, Miffy with hat over ears (23x29mm). d, Miffy with uncovered ears (23x29mm). e, Miffy and parents in car (24x24mm). f, Miffy writing letter (25mm diameter). g, Miffy and toys (24x24mm). h, Miffy and parent on chair (25mm diameter). i, Miffy holding plate of food (24x24mm). j, Miffy and other rabbits (35x20mm).

No. 3976: a, Miffy wearing orange dress (25x48mm). b, Miffy's father watering flowers (27x27mm). c, Miffy's mother with basket (27x27mm). d, Miffy wearing flowered dress (25mm diameter). e, Three rabbits and ball (25mm diameter). f, Angel (25mm diameter). g, Miffy wearing orange dress (25mm diameter). h, Miffy and father at dinner table (27x27mm). i, Miffy holding teddy bear (27x27mm). j, Miffy wearing flowered dress (25x48mm).

**Die Cut Perf. 12½ (#3975a, 3975j), Die Cut Perf. (3975c, 3975d, 3975f, 3975h), Die Cut Perf. 13¼x12½ (square stamps)**
2016, Feb. 12          Litho.
**Self-Adhesive**

| | | | |
|---|---|---|---|
| 3975 | A3625 Sheet of 10 | 10.00 10.00 |
| a.-j. | 52y Any single | .95 .70 |

**Die Cut Perf. 12¼ (#3976a, 3976f), Die Cut Perf. (round stamps), Die Cut Perf. 13¼ (square stamps)**

| | | | |
|---|---|---|---|
| 3976 | A3626 Sheet of 10 | 15.00 15.00 |
| a.-j. | 82y Any single | 1.25 .80 |

Kototsuru of Nishizuchiya in Shinmachi, by Kiyonaga Torii
A3627

Idemi Beach at Sumiyoshi, Settsu Province, by Hiroshige Utagawa
A3628

Karakoto of the Chojiya, by Utamaro Kitagawa
A3629

Urami Waterfall at Nikko, Shimotsuke Province, by Hiroshige Utagawa
A3630

Eight Views of Genji: Komurasaki of the Tamaya, by Eizan Kikukawa
A3631

Cave Entrance at Enoshima, Sagami Province, by Hiroshige Utagawa
A3632

Hinazuru of Keizetsuro House, by Utamaro Kitagawa
A3633

Gokanosho, Higo Province, by Hiroshige Utagawa
A3634

---

Collection of Elegant Beauties: Mirror Stand, by Eizan Kikukawa
A3635

Maiko Beach, Harima Province, by Hiroshige Utagawa
A3636

2016, Feb. 26          Litho.          Perf. 13

| | | | |
|---|---|---|---|
| 3977 | | Sheet of 10 | 16.00 16.00 |
| a. | A3627 82y multi | | 1.25 .50 |
| b. | A3628 82y multi | | 1.25 .50 |
| c. | A3629 82y multi | | 1.25 .50 |
| d. | A3630 82y multi | | 1.25 .50 |
| e. | A3631 82y multi | | 1.25 .50 |
| f. | A3632 82y multi | | 1.25 .50 |
| g. | A3633 82y multi | | 1.25 .50 |
| h. | A3634 82y multi | | 1.25 .50 |
| i. | A3635 82y multi | | 1.25 .50 |
| j. | A3636 82y multi | | 1.25 .50 |

Cherry Blossom
A3637

Dumplings on Stick
A3638

Blackberries and Blueberries
A3639

Blueberries and Raspberries
A3640

Teddy Bears
A3641

Cherry Blossom
A3642

Peach Blossoms
A3643

Letters and Bird
A3644

Strawberries
A3645

Owl and Teddy Bears
A3646

**Die Cut Perf. (#3978a), Die Cut Perf. 13 (#3978b); Die Cut Perf. 14**
2016, Mar. 3          Litho.
**Self-Adhesive**

| | | | |
|---|---|---|---|
| 3978 | | Sheet of 10, 2 each #3978a-3978e | 10.00 10.00 |
| a. | A3637 52y multi | | .95 .70 |
| b. | A3638 52y multi | | .95 .70 |
| c. | A3639 52y multi | | .95 .70 |
| d. | A3640 52y multi | | .95 .70 |
| e. | A3641 52y multi | | .95 .70 |

**Die Cut Perf. (#3979a, 3979b, 3979d), Die Cut Perf. 14x13¼ (#3979c)**

| | | | |
|---|---|---|---|
| 3979 | | Sheet of 10, 2 each #3979a-3979e | 15.00 15.00 |
| a. | A3642 82y multi | | 1.25 .80 |
| b. | A3643 82y multi | | 1.25 .80 |
| c. | A3644 82y multi | | 1.25 .80 |
| d. | A3645 82y multi | | 1.25 .80 |
| e. | A3646 82y multi | | 1.25 .80 |

Hokkaido
Shinkansen Train
Facing
Left — A3647

Port of Aomori,
Hokkaido
Shinkansen
Train — A3648

Hirosaki Castle,
Hokkaido
Shinkansen
Train — A3649

Cape Tappi,
Hokkaido
Shinkansen
Train — A3650

Hokkaido
Shinkansen Train
Facing
Right — A3651

Matsumae
Castle, Hokkaido
Shinkansen
Train — A3652

Moss Phlox on
Mt. Yakushi,
Hokkaido
Shinkansen
Train — A3653

Tree-Lined Road
and Trappist
Monastery,
Hokkaido
Shinkansen
Train — A3654

Hakodate,
Hokkaido
Shinkansen
Train — A3655

Onuma Quasi-
National Park,
Hokkaido
Shinkansen
Train — A3656

**Perf. 13¼x12¾**

| 2016, Mar. 25 | | Litho. | |
|---|---|---|---|
| 3980 | Sheet of 10 | 16.00 | 16.00 |
| a. | A3647 82y multi | 1.25 | .50 |
| b. | A3648 82y multi | 1.25 | .50 |
| c. | A3649 82y multi | 1.25 | .50 |
| d. | A3650 82y multi | 1.25 | .50 |
| e. | A3651 82y multi | 1.25 | .50 |
| f. | A3652 82y multi | 1.25 | .50 |
| g. | A3653 82y multi | 1.25 | .50 |
| h. | A3654 82y multi | 1.25 | .50 |
| i. | A3655 82y multi | 1.25 | .50 |
| j. | A3656 82y multi | 1.25 | .50 |

Opening of Hokkaido Shinkansen Line From
Aomori to Hakodate

Columbines
A3657

Scabiosa
A3658

Moss
Phlox
A3659

Cymbidium
A3660

Irises
A3661

Agapanthus
A3662

Carnations
A3663

Reeve's
Spirea
A3664

Peruvian
Lilies
A3665

Clematis
A3666

**Die Cut Perf. 14x14¼**

| 2016, Apr. 1 | | Litho. | |
|---|---|---|---|
| | **Self-Adhesive** | | |
| 3981 | Sheet of 10, 2 each | 10.00 | 10.00 |
| | #3981a-3981e | | |
| a. | A3657 52y multi | .95 | .70 |
| b. | A3658 52y multi | .95 | .70 |
| c. | A3659 52y multi | .95 | .70 |
| d. | A3660 52y multi | .95 | .70 |
| e. | A3661 52y multi | .95 | .70 |
| 3982 | Sheet of 10, 2 each | 16.00 | 16.00 |
| | #3982a-3982e | | |
| a. | A3662 82y multi | 1.25 | .80 |
| b. | A3663 82y multi | 1.25 | .80 |
| c. | A3664 82y multi | 1.25 | .80 |
| d. | A3665 82y multi | 1.25 | .80 |
| e. | A3666 82y multi | 1.25 | .80 |

**Miniature Sheet**

Castles
A3667

No. 3983: a, Goryokaku. b, Matsumoto Castle. c, Ueda Castle. d, Inuyama Castle. e,
Osaka Castle. f, Hikone Castle. g, Marugame
Castle. h, Himeji Castle. i, Matsuyama Castle.
j, Matsue Castle.

| 2016, Apr. 8 | Litho. | **Perf. 13** | |
|---|---|---|---|
| 3983 | A3667 | Sheet of 10 | 16.00 | 16.00 |
| a.-j. | | 82y Any single | 1.25 | .50 |

**Miniature Sheet**

2016 G-
7
Summit
Ministers
Meeting
A3668

No. 3984: a, Hiroshima Peace Memorial,
Hiroshima. b, Shinano River and Bandai
Bridge, Niigata. c, Ritsurin Garden, Taka-
matsu. d, Moji Port. e, Kurashiki Bikan Histori-
cal Quarter. f, Toyama Castle. g, Tsukuba
Space Center. h, Equestrian statue, Sendai
Castle Ruins. i, Port of Kobe. j, Shiraito Falls.

| 2016, Apr. 8 | Photo. | **Perf. 13** | |
|---|---|---|---|
| 3984 | A3668 | Sheet of 10 | 18.00 | 18.00 |
| a.-j. | | 82y Any single | 1.25 | .60 |

**Miniature Sheet**

Philately
Week
A3669

No. 3985 — Various details of 16th century
folding screen depicting Kyoto, by Eitoku
Kano.

| 2016, Apr. 20 | Photo. | **Perf. 13¼** | |
|---|---|---|---|
| 3985 | A3669 | Sheet of 10 | 16.00 | 16.00 |
| a.-j. | | 82y Any single | 1.25 | .50 |

**Miniature Sheets**

A3670

Cats
A3671

No. 3986: a, Scottish Fold cat (30x27mm).
b, Russian Blue cat (22x26mm). c, Maine
Coon cat (22x26mm). d, Abyssinian cat
(22x26mm). e, Ragdoll cat (22x26mm). f, Oci-
cat (22x26mm). g, Munchkin cat (22x26mm).
h, Persian cat (22x26mm). i, Two Tonkinese
cats (22x26mm). j, American curl cat
(22x26mm).

No. 3987: a, American shorthair cat
(30x27mm). b, British shorthair cat
(22x26mm). c, Norwegian Forest cat
(22x26mm). d, Himalayan cat (22x26mm). e,
Bengal cat (22x26mm). f, Singapura cats
(22x26mm). g, Somali cat (22x26mm). h,
Chartreux cat (22x26mm). i, Ragamuffin cat
(22x26mm). j, Siamese cat (22x26mm).

**Die Cut Perf. (#3986a, 3987a), Die
Cut Perf. 13x13¼**

| 2016, Apr. 22 | | Litho. | |
|---|---|---|---|
| | **Self-Adhesive** | | |
| 3986 | A3670 | Sheet of 10 | 10.00 | 10.00 |
| a.-j. | | 52y Any single | 1.00 | .75 |
| 3987 | A3671 | Sheet of 10 | 16.00 | 16.00 |
| a.-j. | | 82y Any single | 1.25 | .80 |

**Miniature Sheet**

2016 G-
7
Summit
A3672

No. 3988: a, Pearls and Ago Bay, denomination at UL. b, Pearls and Ago Bay, denomination at UR. c, Snowy plover. d, Uji Bridge. e,
Uji Bridge and Isuzu River. f, Japanese iris. g,
Japanese spiny lobster. h, Wedded Rocks,
Ise-Shima National Park. i, Cape Daio Lighthouse. j, Ise katagami and Iga kumihimo fabric
crafting.

| 2016, Apr. 26 | Photo. | **Perf. 13½** | |
|---|---|---|---|
| 3988 | A3672 | Sheet of 10 | 16.00 | 16.00 |
| a.-j. | | 82y Any single | 1.25 | .50 |

99th Lions Club
International
Convention,
Fukuoka — A3673

| 2016, May 6 | Litho. | **Perf. 13** | |
|---|---|---|---|
| 3989 | A3673 82y multi | | 1.50 | .50 |

**Miniature Sheet**

Fukushima Local Autonomy Law, 60th
Anniv. — A3674

No. 3990: a, Hideyo Noguchi (1876-1928),
bacteriologist, Mt. Bandai, Lake Inawashiro
(32x39mm). b, Red cow and Okiagari-koboshi
dolls (28x33mm). c, Waterfall cherry tree,
Miharu (28x33mm). d, Obori Soma pottery
(28x33mm). e, Aquamarine Fukushima
(28x33mm).

**Perf. 13¼ (#3990a), 13x13¼**

| 2016, May 11 | | Litho. | |
|---|---|---|---|
| 3990 | A3674 | Sheet of 5 | 7.50 | 7.50 |
| a.-e. | | 82y Any single | 1.50 | .60 |

**Miniature Sheets**

A3675

Sanrio Characters — A3676

No. 3991: a, Hello Kitty, lavender gray stripes (29x26mm heart). b, Hello Kitty, pale blue stripes (23x23mm). c, Hello Kitty, rose pink stripes (27x22mm). d, Hello Kitty, doily (29mm diameter). e, My Melody (22x30mm oval). f, My Melody, rose pink background (23x23mm). g, Little Twin Stars (22x28mm). h, Little Twin Stars, diff, (29x26mm heart). i, Pompompurin, rose pink background (29mm diameter). j, Pompompurin, pale blue background (23x23mm).

No. 3992: a, Hello Kitty, pale blue stripes (22x28mm). b, Hello Kitty, rose pink stripes (22x30mm oval). c, Hello Kitty, rose red background (29x26mm heart). d, Hello Kitty, rose pink stripes and pale blue circle (29mm diameter). e, My Melody, rose pink stripes (23x23mm). f, My Melody (29x26mm heart). g, Little Twin Stars, (27x22mm). h, Little Twin Stars (23x23mm). i, Pompompurin (29mm diameter). j, Pompompurin, pale orange stripes (27x22mm).

***Die Cut Perf. (#3991a, 3991c, 3991h, 3991i), Die Cut Perf. 14 (#3991b, 3991f, 3991j), Die Cut Perf. 12¼x11¾ (#3991c), Die Cut Perf. 13 (#3991e), Die Cut Perf12¾x13¼ (#3991g)***
**2016, May 13**         **Litho.**
**Self-Adhesive**
3991　A3675　Sheet of 10　10.00　10.00
　　*a.-j.*　52y Any single　　　.95　.70

***Die Cut Perf. 13¼x12¾ (#3992a), Die Cut Perf. 13 (#3992b), Die Cut Perf. 14 (#3992e), Die Cut Perf. 13¼x14 (#3992g, 3992j), Die Cut Perf. 13½ (#3992h), Die Cut Perf.***
3992　A3676　Sheet of 10　15.00　15.00
　　*a.-j.*　82y Any single　　　1.25　.80

Tangerine
A3677

Japanese Ginger
A3678

Perilla Leaf
A3679

Ginkgo Nuts
A3680

Potato
A3681

Kabocha Squash
A3682

Red and Yellow Peppers
A3683

Fava Beans
A3684

Kumquats
A3685

Blueberries
A3686

***Die Cut Perf, 13¼x13 (#3993a, 3994a, 3994b), Die Cut Perf. 13x13¼***
**2016, May 20**         **Litho.**
**Self-Adhesive**
3993　Sheet of 10, 2 each
　　　#3993a-3993e　10.00　10.00
　*a.*　A3677　52y multi　.95　.70
　*b.*　A3678　52y multi　.95　.70
　*c.*　A3679　52y multi　.95　.70
　*d.*　A3680　52y multi　.95　.70
　*e.*　A3681　52y multi　.95　.70
3994　Sheet of 10, 2 each
　　　#3994a-3994e　16.00　16.00
　*a.*　A3682　82y multi　1.25　.80
　*b.*　A3683　82y multi　1.25　.80
　*c.*　A3684　82y multi　1.25　.80
　*d.*　A3685　82y multi　1.25　.80
　*e.*　A3686　82y multi　1.25　.80

**Souvenir Sheet**

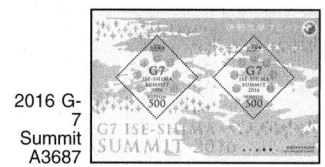

2016 G-7 Summit A3687

No. 3995 — Pearls and Ago Bay with denomination over: a, White area, b, Colored area.

**Litho. With Foil Application**
**2016, May 26**       **Perf. 14¼**
**Printed on Silk**
3995　A3687　Sheet of 2　40.00　40.00
　*a.-b.*　　500y Either single　10.00　10.00

No. 3995 sold for 1300y.

**Miniature Sheet**

Children A3688

No. 3996: a, Child with milk container. b, Girl hugging puppy. c, Children on bicycles with training wheels. d, Child poking mushrooms with stick. e, Girl crouched in foliage. f, Child holding doll opening curtain. g, Chick under tree. h, Child opening door. i, Grandmother repairing teddy bear for girl. j, Child in too-large orange kimono.

**2016, May 27**    **Litho.**    **Perf. 12¾x13**
3996　A3688　Sheet of 10　16.00　16.00
　*a.-j.*　82y Any single　1.25　.50

**Miniature Sheet**

National Afforestation — A3689

No. 3825: a, Takato winter-flowering cherry blossoms. b, Nikko fir. c, Chestnut. d, Gentian. e, Lisianthus. f, Japanese rowan. g, Japanese larch. h, Japanese white birch trees. i, Rape blossoms. j, Apple blossoms.

**2016, June 3**     **Litho.**     **Perf. 13**
3997　A3689　Sheet of 10　10.00　10.00
　*a.-j.*　52y Any single　1.00　.75

**Miniature Sheet**

Tokyo Local Autonomy Law, 60th Anniv. — A3690

No. 3998: a, Tokyo Tower, Rainbow Bridge and gulls (32x39mm). b, Eastern Sea Road 53 Stations, Morning Scene at Nihonbashi, by Hiroshige (28x33mm). c, Mt. Takao Yakuoin Izuna Gongen Hall (28x33mm). d, Camellia, Mt. Mihara (28x33mm). e, Ogasawara Islands and Ogi Pond (28x33mm).

***Perf. 13¼ (#3998a), 13x13¼***
**2016, June 7**        **Litho.**
3998　A3690　Sheet of 5　8.00　8.00
　*a.-e.*　　82y Any single　1.60　1.25

White Frangipani Flower
A3695

White and Red Frangipani Flowers
A3696

Sunlight Reflected Off Water
A3697

Palm Trees
A3698

Hibiscus
A3699

Sunflower
A3700

Two Seashells
A3701

Seashell
A3702

Drink in Glass
A3703

Palm Trees
A3704

Hibiscus
A3705

Clouds
A3706

***Die Cut Perf. 13¼, Die Cut Perf. 12 (#4000e, 4000f, 4001a, 4001b)***
**2016, June 10**        **Litho.**
**Self-Adhesive**
4000　Sheet of 10, 2 each
　　　#4000a-4000d, 1
　　　each #4000e, 4000f　10.00　10.00
　*a.*　A3695　52y multi　1.00　.75
　*b.*　A3696　52y multi　1.00　.75
　*c.*　A3697　52y multi　1.00　.75
　*d.*　A3698　52y multi　1.00　.75
　*e.*　A3699　52y multi　1.00　.75
　*f.*　A3700　52y multi　1.00　.75
4001　Sheet of 10, 1 each
　　　#4001a, 4001b, 2
　　　each #4001c-4001f　16.00　16.00
　*a.*　A3701　82y multi　1.25　.80
　*b.*　A3702　82y multi　1.25　.80
　*c.*　A3703　82y multi　1.25　.80
　*d.*　A3704　82y multi　1.25　.80
　*e.*　A3705　82y multi　1.25　.80
　*f.*　A3706　82y multi　1.25　.80

## Miniature Sheets

A3707

Traditional Japanese Designs — A3708

No. 4002: a, Fan with Mt. Fuji, dull green background (33x19mm). b, As "a," light purple background (33x19mm). c, Birds and waves, blue bottom panel (23x23mm). d, As "c," purple bottom panel (23x23mm). e, Octagon, apple green background (23x23mm). f, As "e," pale peach background (23x23mm). g, Flowers, blue green, light blue and gold petals (23x23mm). h, As "g," blue green, rose pink and gold petals (23x23mm). i, Eggplants and wavy lines, light blue background (22x26mm). j, As "i," lilac background (22x26mm).

No. 4003: a, Dark blue Mt. Fuji (30x25mm). b, Bright blue Mt. Fuji (30x25mm). c, Bird and waves, light blue background (22x26mm). d, As "c," pink panel (22x26mm). e, Octagons, sage green background (22x26mm). f, As "e," pink background (22x26mm). g, Interlocking circles, beige background (22x26mm). h, As "g," light blue background (22x26mm). i, Eggplants and wavy lines, pink background (22x26mm). j, As "i," orange yellow background (22x26mm).

---

**Die Cut Perf. 12¾ (#4002a, 4002b), Die Cut Perf. 14, Die Cut Perf. 13¼ (#4002i, 4002j)**

**2016, June 17**     Litho.

**Self-Adhesive**

| | | | | |
|---|---|---|---|---|
| 4002 | A3707 | Sheet of 10 | 10.00 | 10.00 |
| a.-j. | | 52y Any single | 1.00 | .75 |

**Die Cut Perf. 13 (#4003a, 4003b), Die Cut Perf. 13x13¼**

| | | | | |
|---|---|---|---|---|
| 4003 | A3708 | Sheet of 10 | 16.00 | 16.00 |
| a.-j. | | 82y Any single | 1.25 | .80 |

## Miniature Sheets

A3709

Doraemon Characters — A3710

No. 4004: a, Doraemon carrying mailbox (19x27mm oval ). b, Doraemon holding stamp (20x23mm). c, Doraemon delivering letter (20x24mm). d, Dorami, yellow background with white polka dots (25mm diameter). e, Doraemon, Nobita and Shizuka (31x31mm). f, Doraemon eating (20x23mm). g, Dorami winking (20x23mm). h, Nobita writing letter (20x23mm). i, Shizuka reading letter (20x23mm). j, Doraemon licking lips (19x27mm oval).

No. 4005: a, Doraemon with bamboo helicopter on head (21x29mm oval). b, Doraemon and time cloth (21x29mm oval). c, Doraemon in pass-through loop (22x26mm). d, Doraemon shining light on Nobita (22x26mm). e, Doraemon and Nobita on time machine (31x28mm). f, Doraemon in Anywhere Door (30x37mm). g, Doraemon with open mouth (25mm diameter). h, Doraemon with closed mouth (25mm diameter). i, Doraemon with raised paws (25mm diameter). j, Doraemon licking lips (25mm diameter).

**Die Cut Perf. 13 (#4004a, 4004j), Die Cut Perf. 14¼x14½, Die Cut Perf. 12½ (#4004c, 4004e), Die Cut Perf. (#4004d)**

**2016, July 1**     Litho.

**Self-Adhesive**

| | | | | |
|---|---|---|---|---|
| 4004 | A3709 | Sheet of 10 | 10.00 | 10.00 |
| a.-j. | | 52y Any single | 1.00 | .75 |

**Die Cut Perf. 13¾ (#4005a, 4005b), Die Cut Perf. 13x13¼ (#4005c, 4005d), Die Cut Perf. 13 (#4005e), Die Cut Perf. 12¾x13 (#4005f), Die Cut Perf.**

**2016, July 1**     Litho.

| | | | | |
|---|---|---|---|---|
| 4005 | A3710 | Sheet of 10 | 16.00 | 16.00 |
| a.-j. | | 82y Any single | 1.25 | .80 |

Personalized Stamp — A3710a

**Die Cut Perf. 13¼x12¾ Syncopated**
**2016, July 1**     Litho.

**Self-Adhesive**

| | | | |
|---|---|---|---|
| 4005K | A3710a | 82y gldn brn + label | 5.50 5.50 |

No. 4005K was printed in sheets of 5 that sold for 1400y. The labels, separated from the stamp by a row of rouletting, could be personalized. The image shown on the label above is a generic image. Six additional stamps were issued in this set. The editors would like to examine any examples.

## Miniature Sheet

Japan's Meiji Industrial Revolution Iron, Steel, Shipbuilding and Coal Mining UNESCO World Heritage Site — A3711

No. 4006: a, Former office of Yawata Steel Works, denomination at UR (stamp 1). b, Onga River Pumping Station, denomination at LL (stamp 2). c, Hagi Reverberatory Furnace, denomination at UL (stamp 3). d, Shuseikan Industrial Complex, denomination at LL (stamp 4). e, Nirayama Reverberatory Furnace, denomination at UR (stamp 5). f, Hashino Iron Mining and Smelting Site, denomination at UR (stamp 6). g, Mietsu Naval Dock Ruins, denomination at LL (stamp 7). h, Kosuge Slip Dock, denomination at LL (stamp 8). i, Misumi West Port, denomination at UL (stamp 9). j, Aerial view of Miike Port, denomination at UR (stamp 10).

**2016, July 8**   Litho.   **Perf. 13**

| | | | | |
|---|---|---|---|---|
| 4006 | A3711 | Sheet of 10 | 16.00 | 16.00 |
| a.-j. | | 82y Any single | 1.25 | .50 |

Amaryllises
A3712

Narcissi
A3713

Pine Tree, Sarcandra Glabra, and Ornamental Kale
A3714

Statice and Dendrobium Orchids
A3715

Dahlias
A3716

Roses
A3717

Cockscombs
A3718

Hyacinths
A3719

Chrysanthemums
A3720

Nerines
A3721

**Die Cut Perf. 14**

**2016, July 15**     Litho.

**Self-Adhesive**

| | | | | |
|---|---|---|---|---|
| 4007 | | Sheet of 10, 2 each | | |
| | | #4007a-4007e | 10.00 | 10.00 |
| a. | A3712 | 52y multi | 1.00 | .75 |
| b. | A3713 | 52y multi | 1.00 | .75 |
| c. | A3714 | 52y multi | 1.00 | .75 |
| d. | A3715 | 52y multi | 1.00 | .75 |
| e. | A3716 | 52y multi | 1.00 | .75 |

| | | | | |
|---|---|---|---|---|
| 4008 | | Sheet of 10, 2 each | | |
| | | #4008a-4008e | 16.00 | 16.00 |
| a. | A3717 | 82y multi | 1.25 | .80 |
| b. | A3718 | 82y multi | 1.25 | .80 |
| c. | A3719 | 82y multi | 1.25 | .80 |
| d. | A3720 | 82y multi | 1.25 | .80 |
| e. | A3721 | 82y multi | 1.25 | .80 |

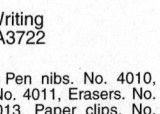

Letter Writing Day — A3722

Designs: No. 4009, Pen nibs. No. 4010, Tape rolls and strips. No. 4011, Erasers. No. 4012, Pencils. No. 4013, Paper clips. No. 4014, Three envelopes. No. 4015, Crayons. No. 4016, Fountain pens. No. 4017, Colored pencils. No. 4018, Two long envelopes.

**Die Cut Perf. 13x13¼**

**2016, July 22**     Litho.

**Booklet Stamps**
**Self-Adhesive**

| | | | | |
|---|---|---|---|---|
| 4009 | A3722 | 52y multi | 1.00 | .75 |
| 4010 | A3722 | 52y multi | 1.00 | .75 |
| 4011 | A3722 | 52y multi | 1.00 | .75 |
| 4012 | A3722 | 52y multi | 1.00 | .75 |
| 4013 | A3722 | 52y multi | 1.00 | .75 |
| a. | | Booklet pane of 10, 2 each | | |
| | | #4009-4013 | 10.00 | 10.00 |
| 4014 | A3722 | 82y multi | 1.25 | .80 |
| 4015 | A3722 | 82y multi | 1.25 | .80 |
| 4016 | A3722 | 82y multi | 1.25 | .80 |
| 4017 | A3722 | 82y multi | 1.25 | .80 |
| 4018 | A3722 | 82y multi | 1.25 | .80 |
| a. | | Booklet pane of 10, 2 each | | |
| | | #4014-4018 | 16.00 | 16.00 |
| | | Nos. 4009-4018 (10) | 11.25 | 7.75 |

Toji of the Ogiya, Kamuro, Satoji and Uraji, by Kiyonaga Torii
A3723

Mt. Otoko at Hirakata, Kawachi Province, by Hiroshige Utagawa
A3724

The Maiden at the Dojo Temple, by Yukimaro Kitagawa
A3725

Bonito Fishing at Sea, Tosa Province, by Hiroshige Utagawa
A3726

The Brine Maidens, by Kiyonaga Torii
A3727

Mt. Asama, Teahouse on the Mountain Pass, Ise Province, by Hiroshige Utagawa
A3728

Tsukioka of
the Hyogo
House, by
Eisui
Ichirakutei
A3729

The Takuhi
Shrine, Oki
Province, by
Hiroshige
Utagawa
A3730

Good
Relations
Between
Siblings, by
Utamaro
Kitagawa
A3731

The Weir in
the Shallows,
Chikugo
Province, by
Hiroshige
Utagawa
A3732

**2016, July 29    Litho.    Perf. 13**
| | | | |
|---|---|---|---|
| 4019 | Sheet of 10 | 16.00 | 16.00 |
| a. | A3723 82y multi | 1.25 | .50 |
| b. | A3724 82y multi | 1.25 | .50 |
| c. | A3725 82y multi | 1.25 | .50 |
| d. | A3726 82y multi | 1.25 | .50 |
| e. | A3727 82y multi | 1.25 | .50 |
| f. | A3728 82y multi | 1.25 | .50 |
| g. | A3729 82y multi | 1.25 | .50 |
| h. | A3730 82y multi | 1.25 | .50 |
| i. | A3731 82y multi | 1.25 | .50 |
| j. | A3732 82y multi | 1.25 | .50 |

### Miniature Sheet

Diplomatic Relations Between Japan
and Belgium, 150th Anniv. — A3733

No. 4006: a, Grand Place, Brussels, at night, denomination at LL. b, Grand Place, at night, denomination at LR. c, Cut diamond. d, Begonia. e, Notre Dame Cathedral, Tournai, Belgium, denomination at LL. f, Notre Dame Cathedral, Tournai, denomination at UR. g, Belgian waffles. h, Beer. i, Historic Center of Bruges, denomination at LL. j, Historic Center of Bruges, denomination at LR.

**2016, Aug. 1    Litho.    Perf. 13**
| | | | |
|---|---|---|---|
| 4020 | A3733 Sheet of 10 | 16.00 | 16.00 |
| a.-j. | 82y Any single | 1.25 | .50 |

### Miniature Sheets

A3734

Colors in
Daily Life
A3735

No. 4021: a, Japanese irises. b, Eggplants. c, Wisteria. d, Bellflowers. e, Blue birds. f, Hanten (short coat). g, Mt. Fuji. h, Bamboo boat and cherry blossoms in water. i, Asiatic dayflower. j, Octopus arabesque pattern.
No. 4022: a, Yarn on holders. b, Green onions. c, Mallards. d, Wasabi and grater. e, Bamboo. f, Bird and willow tree. g, Green tea and confection. h, Old Japanese coins. i, Dandelions, fiddleheads and horsetails. j, Pine tree.

**Die Cut Perf. 13x13¼**
**2016, Aug. 5    Litho.**
**Self-Adhesive**
| | | | |
|---|---|---|---|
| 4021 | A3734 Sheet of 10 | 10.00 | 10.00 |
| a.-j. | 52y Any single | 1.00 | .75 |
| 4022 | A3735 Sheet of 10 | 16.00 | 16.00 |
| a.-j. | 82y Any single | 1.25 | .80 |

### Miniature Sheet

Mountain
Day
A3736

No. 4023: a, Daisetsuzan. b, Hokkaido crying rabbit. c, Mt. Iwate. d, Komakusa flowers. e, Mt. Yari. f, Yarigatake Eastern Blue butterfly. g, Daisen. h, Daisen yellow violet. i, Kuju Mountain Range. j, Hooaka bird.

**2016, Aug. 10    Litho.    Perf. 13x13¼**
| | | | |
|---|---|---|---|
| 4023 | A3736 Sheet of 10 | 16.00 | 16.00 |
| a.-j. | 82y Any single | 1.25 | .50 |

### Miniature Sheets

A3737

Kyoto Area Tourist
Attractions — A3738

No. 4024: a, Kiyomizudera, denomination in white at LL. b, Kiyomizudera, denominaiton in white at LR, horiz. c, Sannenzaka, denomination in orange red at LL, horiz. d, Sannenzaka, denomination in white at LR, horiz. e, Nanzenji interior, denomination in pink at UR. f, Nanzen-ji exterior, denomination at LL, horiz. g, Shisen-do sands, denomination in magenta at LR, horiz. h, Shisen-do, denomination in yellow green at LR. i, Hanamikoji Dori, denomination in black at LL. j, Hanamikoji Dori at night, denomination in white at LL.
No. 4025: a, Togetsu-kyo, denomination in white at LR, horiz. b, Togetsu-kyo, denominaiton in white at UL. c, Daigo-ji statue of Buddha, denomination in white at LR. d, Daigo-ji hall, denomination in rose at LL, horiz. e, Sanzen-in, denomination in white at UR. f, Sanzen-in, denomination in white at LL, horiz. g, Nakagyo Post Office doorway, denomination in red at LR, horiz. h, Nakagyo Post Office, denomination in red at UR, horiz. i, Shoden-ji at night, denomination in azure at right, horiz. j, Shoden-ji, denomination in red at UL.

**Die Cut Perf. 13x13¼ (vert. stamps),**
**Die Cut Perf. 13¼x13**
**2016, Aug. 19    Litho.**
**Self-Adhesive**
| | | | |
|---|---|---|---|
| 4024 | A3737 Sheet of 10 | 10.00 | 10.00 |
| a.-j. | 52y Any single | 1.00 | .75 |
| 4025 | A3738 Sheet of 10 | 16.00 | 16.00 |
| a.-j. | 82y Any single | 1.25 | .80 |

## Miniature Sheet

**Diplomatic Relations Between Japan and Italy, 150th Anniv. — A3739**

No. 4026: a, Silkworm cocoons on mulberry leaves. b, Red silk. c, Madonna of the Yarnwinder, by Leonardo da Vinci. d, Maria de'Medici, by Agnolo Bronzino. e, Basil leaves and mozzarella cheese. f, Mozzarella cheese and tomatoes. g, Madonna of the Book, by Sandro Botticelli. h, Boy with a Basket of Fruit, by Caravaggio. i, Val d'Orcia, Trulli of Alberobello. j, Trulli of Alberobello, Florence Cathedral.

**2016, Aug. 25    Litho.    Perf. 13**
| | | | | |
|---|---|---|---|---|
| 4026 | A3739 | Sheet of 10 | 16.00 | 16.00 |
| a.-j. | | 82y Any single | 1.25 | .50 |

Fish
A3740

Crane and Tortoise
A3741

Mt. Fuji in Blue
A3742

Fish
A3743

Owl
A3744

Mt. Fuji in Gold
A3745

Bird and Flowers
A3746

Balloons
A3747

Bird of Ribbon
A3748

G Clef, Notes and Stars
A3749

---

Rose
A3750

Flower Bouquet
A3751

Bells
A3752

Lilies and Ribbon
A3753

**Die Cut Perf. 14, Die Cut Perf.**
**(#4030a, 4030c)**
**2016, Aug. 26        Litho.**
**Self-Adhesive**

| | | | | |
|---|---|---|---|---|
| 4027 | | Sheet of 10, 4 each #4027a-4027b, 2 #4027c | 10.00 | 10.00 |
| a. | A3740 52y multi | | 1.00 | .75 |
| b. | A3741 52y multi | | 1.00 | .75 |
| c. | A3742 52y multi | | 1.00 | .75 |
| 4028 | | Sheet of 10, 4 each #4028a-4028b, 2 #4028c | 16.00 | 16.00 |
| a. | A3743 82y multi | | 1.25 | .80 |
| b. | A3744 82y multi | | 1.25 | .80 |
| c. | A3745 82y multi | | 1.25 | .80 |
| 4029 | | Sheet of 10, 4 #4029b, 2 each #4029a, 4029c, 4029d | 16.00 | 16.00 |
| a. | A3746 82y multi | | 1.25 | .80 |
| b. | A3747 82y multi | | 1.25 | .80 |
| c. | A3748 82y multi | | 1.25 | .80 |
| d. | A3749 82y multi | | 1.25 | .80 |
| 4030 | | Sheet of 10, 4 #4030a, 2 each #4030b, 4030c, 4030d | 17.00 | 17.00 |
| a. | A3750 92y multi | | 1.40 | .80 |
| b. | A3751 92y multi | | 1.40 | .80 |
| c. | A3752 92y multi | | 1.40 | .80 |
| d. | A3753 92y multi | | 1.40 | .80 |

## Miniature Sheet

**71st National Athletic Meet, Iwate — A3754**

No. 4026: a, Rugby. b, Field hockey. c, Triathlon. d, Wrestling. e, Naginatajutsu. f, Boxing. g, Soccer. h, Tennis. i, Basketball. j, Baseball.

**2016, Sept. 1    Litho.    Perf. 13**
| | | | | |
|---|---|---|---|---|
| 4031 | A3754 | Sheet of 10 | 16.00 | 16.00 |
| a.-j. | | 82y Any single | 1.25 | .50 |

Flower Pots on Trellis
A3755

Potted Tree and Flowers
A3756

---

Trellis, Potted Plants, Watering Can
A3757

Watering Can, Plant Labels, Shovel, Gloves
A3759

Hanging Flower Basket
A3761

Rose Trellis
A3763

**Die Cut Perf. 14, Die Cut Perf.**
**(#4033a, 4033b)**
**2016, Sept. 9        Litho.**
**Self-Adhesive**

| | | | | |
|---|---|---|---|---|
| 4032 | | Sheet of 10, 2 each #4032a-4032e | 10.00 | 10.00 |
| a. | A3755 52y multi | | 1.00 | .75 |
| b. | A3756 52y multi | | 1.00 | .75 |
| c. | A3757 52y multi | | 1.00 | .75 |
| d. | A3758 52y multi | | 1.00 | .75 |
| e. | A3759 52y multi | | 1.00 | .75 |
| 4033 | | Sheet of 10, 2 each #4033a-4033e | 16.00 | 16.00 |
| a. | A3760 82y multi | | 1.25 | .80 |
| b. | A3761 82y multi | | 1.25 | .80 |
| c. | A3762 82y multi | | 1.25 | .80 |
| d. | A3763 82y multi | | 1.25 | .80 |
| e. | A3764 82y multi | | 1.25 | .80 |

Teddy Bear Postman Delivering Letter
A3765

Owl at Table
A3767

Two Teddy Bears
A3769

---

Seeds, Lantern, Gardening Tools
A3758

Roses, Pastry Carrier, Tea Cup
A3760

Garden
A3762

Potted Tree and Roses
A3764

Teddy Bear Holding Letter
A3766

Teddy Bear at Table
A3768

Beige Teddy Bear
A3770

---

Gray Teddy Bear
A3771

Brown Teddy Bear
A3772

Blue Teddy Bear
A3773

Teddy Bears and Mailbox
A3774

**Die Cut Perf. 12, Die Cut Perf.**
**(#4034e)**
**2016, Sept. 16        Litho.**
**Self-Adhesive**

| | | | | |
|---|---|---|---|---|
| 4034 | | Sheet of 10, 2 each #4034a-4034e | 10.00 | 10.00 |
| a. | A3765 52y multi | | 1.00 | .75 |
| b. | A3766 52y multi | | 1.00 | .75 |
| c. | A3767 52y multi | | 1.00 | .75 |
| d. | A3768 52y multi | | 1.00 | .75 |
| e. | A3769 52y multi | | 1.00 | .75 |

**Die Cut Perf. 12½, Die Cut Perf.**
**12x11¾ (#4035e)**

| | | | | |
|---|---|---|---|---|
| 4035 | | Sheet of 10, 2 each #4035a-4035e | 16.00 | 16.00 |
| a. | A3770 82y multi | | 1.25 | .80 |
| b. | A3771 82y multi | | 1.25 | .80 |
| c. | A3772 82y multi | | 1.25 | .80 |
| d. | A3773 82y multi | | 1.25 | .80 |
| e. | A3774 82y multi | | 1.25 | .80 |

A sheet of five self-adhesive stamps depicting teddy bears (three denominated 82y and two denominated 120y) was printed in limited quantities and sold only in a package containing stationery. Value, $20.

## Miniature Sheet

**Kamikochi Natural Monument — A3775**

No. 4036: a, Japanese rock ptarmigan (stamp 1). b, Japanese robin (stamp 2). c, Japanese dormouse (stamp 3). d, Japanese serow (stamp 4). e, Lilium medeoloides (stamp 5). f, Trollius riederianus var. japonicus (stamp 6). g, Chickweed wintergreen (stamp 7). h, Poplar admiral butterfly (stamp 8). i, Orange tip butterfly (stamp 9). j, Moorland clouded yellow butterfly (stamp 10).

## 2016, Sept. 23    Litho.    Perf. 13

| | | | |
|---|---|---|---|
| 4036 | A3775 | Sheet of 10 | 16.00 16.00 |
| a.-j. | | 82y Any single | 1.25 .50 |

### Miniature Sheet

Postal Life Insurance Service, Cent. — A3776

No. 4037 — Heart-shaped flowers: a, Blue denomination, pink flower at bottom. b, Blue denomination, pink flower at top. c, Blue denomination, pink flower left of center. d, Blue denomination, pink flower at center. e, Blue denomination, pink flower at right. f, White denomination, pink flower at LL. below dark blue flower. g, White denomination, pink flower at bottom to right of white flower. h, White denomination, pink flower partly covered by dark blue flower. i, White denomination, pink flower at UR. j, White denomination, pink flower at LR.

## 2016, Sept. 30    Photo.    Perf. 13

| | | | |
|---|---|---|---|
| 4037 | A3776 | Sheet of 10 | 16.00 16.00 |
| a.-j. | | 82y Any single | 1.25 .50 |

Fox
A3777

Purple Grapes
A3778

Rabbit
A3779

Akebia
A3780

Moose
A3781

Bear
A3782

Snake Gourds
A3783

Squirrel
A3784

White Grapes
A3785

Japanese Raccoon Dog
A3786

### Die Cut Perf. 13x13¼, Die Cut Perf. (#4038e, 4039e)

## 2016, Oct. 3     Litho.

### Self-Adhesive

| | | | |
|---|---|---|---|
| 4038 | | Sheet of 10, 2 each | |
| | | #4038a-4038e | 10.00 10.00 |
| a. | A3777 | 52y multi | 1.00 .75 |
| b. | A3778 | 52y multi | 1.00 .75 |
| c. | A3779 | 52y multi | 1.00 .75 |
| d. | A3780 | 52y multi | 1.00 .75 |
| e. | A3781 | 52y multi | 1.00 .75 |
| 4039 | | Sheet of 10, 2 each | |
| | | #4039a-4039e | 16.00 16.00 |
| a. | A3782 | 82y multi | 1.25 .80 |
| b. | A3783 | 82y multi | 1.25 .80 |
| c. | A3784 | 82y multi | 1.25 .80 |
| d. | A3785 | 82y multi | 1.25 .80 |
| e. | A3786 | 82y multi | 1.25 .80 |

Map and Trains of Hokuriku Shinkansen Line
A3787

Kintetsu 30000 Series Locomotive
A3788

Enoden 1000 Series Locomotive
A3789

Odakyu Electric Railway 7000 Series Locomotive
A3790

Hakone Tozan 1000 Series Locomotive
A3791

Keikyu 2000 Series Locomotive
A3792

Nankai Electric Railway 5000 Series Locomotive
A3793

East Japan Railway E26 Series Locomotive
A3794

Kyushu Railway 885 Series Locomotive
A3795

Toyama Light Rail TLR0600 Series Train
A3796

Hokuriku Shinkansen Line Locomotives
A3797

Keikyu 2000 Series Locomotive
A3798

Kintetsu 30000 Series Locomotive
A3799

Nankai Electric Railway 5000 Series Locomotive
A3800

Enoden 1000 Series Locomotive
A3801

East Japan Railway E26 Series Locomotive
A3802

Odakyu Electric Railway 7000 Series Locomotive
A3803

Kyushu Railway 885 Series Locomotive
A3804

Hakone Tozan 1000 Series Locomotive
A3805

Toyama Light Rail TLR0600 Series Train
A3806

## 2016, Oct. 7    Litho.    Perf. 13¼x12¾

| | | | |
|---|---|---|---|
| 4040 | | Sheet of 10 | 16.00 16.00 |
| a. | A3787 | 82y multi | 1.25 .50 |
| b. | A3788 | 82y multi | 1.25 .50 |
| c. | A3789 | 82y multi | 1.25 .50 |
| d. | A3790 | 82y multi | 1.25 .50 |
| e. | A3791 | 82y multi | 1.25 .50 |
| f. | A3792 | 82y multi | 1.25 .50 |
| g. | A3793 | 82y multi | 1.25 .50 |
| h. | A3794 | 82y multi | 1.25 .50 |
| i. | A3795 | 82y multi | 1.25 .50 |
| j. | A3796 | 82y multi | 1.25 .50 |

### Perf. 12¾x13¼

| | | | |
|---|---|---|---|
| 4041 | | Sheet of 10 | 16.00 16.00 |
| a. | A3797 | 82y multi | 1.25 .50 |
| b. | A3798 | 82y multi | 1.25 .50 |
| c. | A3799 | 82y multi | 1.25 .50 |
| d. | A3800 | 82y multi | 1.25 .50 |
| e. | A3801 | 82y multi | 1.25 .50 |
| f. | A3802 | 82y multi | 1.25 .50 |
| g. | A3803 | 82y multi | 1.25 .50 |
| h. | A3804 | 82y multi | 1.25 .50 |
| i. | A3805 | 82y multi | 1.25 .50 |
| j. | A3806 | 82y multi | 1.25 .50 |

A3807

International Letter Writing Week — A3808

Paintings by Hiroshige: 70y, Wild Duck Among Snow-Covered Reeds. 90y, Travelers Walking Towards Numazu. 110y, Changing of Horses and Porters at Fujieda Relay Station. 130y, Futagawa Station.

## 2016, Oct. 7    Photo.    Perf. 13¼

| | | | |
|---|---|---|---|
| 4042 | A3807 | 70y multi | 1.40 .50 |

### Perf. 13

| | | | |
|---|---|---|---|
| 4043 | A3808 | 90y multi | 1.75 .50 |
| 4044 | A3808 | 110y multi | 2.25 .50 |
| 4045 | A3808 | 130y multi | 2.50 .50 |
| | | Nos. 4042-4045 (4) | 7.90 2.00 |

See listing of No. 4448 for images of each Hiroshige print.

### Miniature Sheet

Japan at Night
A3809

No. 4046: a, Rainbow Bridge (stamp 1). b, Tokyo Sky Tree (stamp 2). c, Tokyo tower (stamp 3). d, Yokohama Minata Mirai 21 (stamp 4). e, Kanto Plain (stamp 5). f,

Chichibu Night Festival (stamp 6). g, Gunman Flower Park (stamp 7). h, Ashikaga Flower Park (stamp 8). i, Tokyo German Village (stamp 9). j, Fuefukigawa Fruit Park (stamp 10).

## 2016, Oct. 14    Litho.    Perf. 13

| | | | |
|---|---|---|---|
| 4046 | A3809 | Sheet of 10 | 16.00 16.00 |
| a.-j. | | 82y Any single | 1.25 .50 |

Banner Decoration
A3810

Silver Platter
A3811

Incense Burner
A3812

Lacquered Wooden Box
A3813

Detail of Incense Burner — A3814

## 2016, Oct. 21    Photo.    Perf. 13

| | | | |
|---|---|---|---|
| 4047 | A3810 | 82y multi | 1.25 .50 |
| 4048 | A3811 | 82y multi | 1.25 .50 |
| 4049 | A3812 | 82y multi | 1.25 .50 |
| 4050 | A3813 | 82y multi | 1.60 .50 |
| 4051 | A3814 | 82y multi | 1.25 .50 |
| a. | | Vert. strip of 5, #4047-4051 | 8.00 6.25 |
| | | Nos. 4047-4051 (5) | 6.60 2.50 |

### Miniature Sheet

Japanese Foods — A3815

No. 4052: a, Rice cake in ceremonial display. b, Tray of New Year foods. c, Box of beans, hiirage and sardine heads. d, Dolls and crackers. e, Mochi wrapped in cherry leaves. f, Rice in bamboo leaves. g, Noodles. h, Tsukimi dumplings. i, Chrysanthemum petal in saki. j, Kabocha squash and yuzu.

## 2016, Oct. 24    Litho.    Perf. 13½

| | | | |
|---|---|---|---|
| 4052 | A3815 | Sheet of 10 | 16.00 16.00 |
| a.-j. | | 82y Any single | 1.25 .50 |

## Miniature Sheet

Astronomy — A3816

No. 4053: a, Saturn (35x30mm). b, Capricorn and goat (22x25mm). c, Aquarius and water urn (22x25mm). d, Pisces and fish (22x25mm).

***Die Cut Perf. 9¾x10 (#4053a), Die Cut Perf. 13x13¼***
**Litho. With Foil Application**
**2016, Oct. 28**      **Self-Adhesive**

| | | | | |
|---|---|---|---|---|
| 4053 | A3816 | Sheet of 10, | | |
| | | #4053a, 3 each | | |
| | | #4053b-4053d | 16.00 | 16.00 |
| a.-d. | | 82y Any single | 1.25 | .80 |

Japanese Foods A3817

Designs: No. 4054, Soba noodles on square plate. No. 4055, Oyakodon soup in bowl.

**2016, Nov. 1**    **Litho.**    ***Perf. 13¼x13***

| | | | | |
|---|---|---|---|---|
| 4054 | | 18y multi | .25 | .25 |
| 4055 | | 18y multi | .25 | .25 |
| a. | A3817 | Horiz. pair, #4054-4055 | .55 | .45 |

A3818     A3819

New Year 2017 (Year of the Rooster)
A3820     A3821

**2016, Nov. 1**    **Photo.**    ***Perf. 13x13¼***

| | | | | |
|---|---|---|---|---|
| 4056 | A3818 | 52y multi | 1.00 | .30 |
| 4057 | A3819 | 82y multi | 1.50 | .40 |

**Photo. & Typo.**
***Perf. 13¼***

| | | | | |
|---|---|---|---|---|
| 4058 | A3820 | 52y +3y multi | 1.25 | .40 |
| 4059 | A3821 | 82y +3y multi | 1.75 | .40 |
| | | Nos. 4056-4059 (4) | 5.50 | 1.50 |

## Miniature Sheet

Traditional Crafts — A3822

No. 4060: a, Echizen lacquerware (Fukui Prefecture). b, Sendai storage cabinet (Miyagi Prefecture). c, Edo tortoiseshell eyeglasses (Tokyo Prefecture). d, Tokyo antimony jewelry box (Tokyo Prefecture). e, Tosa paper (Kochi Prefecture). f, Seto underglazed pottery (Aichi

---

Prefecture). g, Nishijin textiles (Kyoto Prefecture). h, Banshu abacus (Hyogo Prefecture). i, Ouchi lacquerware (Yamaguchi Prefecture). j, Yamagata metal cast kettle (Yamagata Prefecture).

**2016, Nov. 4**    **Litho.**    ***Perf. 13¼***

| | | | | |
|---|---|---|---|---|
| 4060 | A3822 | Sheet of 10 | 16.00 | 16.00 |
| a.-j. | | 82y Any single | 1.25 | .50 |

## Miniature Sheet

World Tsunami Awareness Day — A3823

No. 4061: a, Earth and ocean. b, Man running from tsunami. c, Burning rice sheaves, man with torch. d, Miracle Pine of Rikuzentakata. e, Winning children's art in tsunami awareness poster contest.

**2016, Nov. 4**    **Litho.**    ***Perf. 13***

| | | | | |
|---|---|---|---|---|
| 4061 | A3823 | Sheet of 10, 2 | | |
| | | each #4053a- | | |
| | | 4053e | 16.00 | 16.00 |
| a.-e. | | 82y Any single | 1.25 | .50 |

## Miniature Sheets

A3824

Animals A3825

No. 4062: a, Netherland Dwarf rabbit (30x28mm heart). b, Flying squirrel (22x26mm). c, Hamster (22x26mm). d, Chipmunk (22x26mm). e, Guinea pig (22x26mm). f, White birds on fence (30x28mm heart). g, Zebra finches (22x26mm). h, Cockatiel (22x26mm). i, Canaries (22x26mm). j, Parakeets (22x26mm).
No. 4063: a, Hedgehogs (30x28mm heart). b, Djungarian hamster (22x26mm). c, Lop-eared rabbit (22x26mm). d, Ferret (22x26mm). e, Chinchilla (22x26mm). f, Budgerigars (30x28mm heart). g, Rosy-faced lovebirds (22x26mm). h, Society finches (22x26mm). i, Sulphur-crested cockatoo (22x26mm). j, Java sparrows (22x26mm).

***Die Cut Perf. 11¼x11, Die Cut Perf.***
***(#4062a, 4062f, 4063a, 4063f)***
**2016, Nov. 11**       **Litho.**
**Self-Adhesive**

| | | | | |
|---|---|---|---|---|
| 4062 | A3824 | Sheet of 10 | 10.00 | 10.00 |
| a.-j. | | 52y Any single | .95 | .70 |
| 4063 | A3825 | Sheet of 10 | 16.00 | 16.00 |
| a.-j. | | 82y Any single | 1.25 | .80 |

---

## Miniature Sheet

Illustrations From Children's Books by Mitsumasa Anno — A3826

No. 4064: a, People and horses on path (stamp 1). b, People gathered near buildings, man near tricycle, man with delivery bicycle (stamp 2). c, Anno's Counting house (stamp 3). d, Anno's medieval world (stamp 4). e, Anno's flea market (stamp 5). f, Anno's Aesop: A book of fables by Aesop & Mr. Fox (stamp 6). g, Anno's Journey, scene 15 (stamp 7). h, Anno's Journey III, scene 10 (stamp 8). i, Anno's Journey IV, scene 11 (stamp 9). j, Anno's Journey VIII, scene 2 (stamp 10).

**2016, Nov. 25**    **Photo.**    ***Perf. 13***

| | | | | |
|---|---|---|---|---|
| 4064 | A3826 | Sheet of 10 | 16.00 | 16.00 |
| a.-j. | | 82y Any single | 1.25 | .50 |

## Miniature Sheet

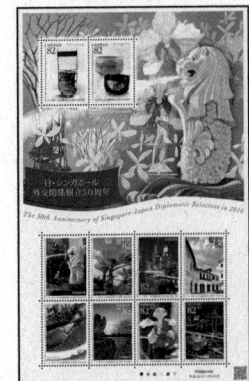

Diplomatic Relations Between Japan and Singapore, 50th Anniv. — A3827

No. 4065: a, Three Singaporean pots with handle. b, Two Japanese bowls. c, Merlion, Singapore. d, Gardens by the Bay, Singapore. e, Singapore at night. f, Singapore Art Museum. g, Plate of chili crab. h, Marina Bay at dusk. i, Orchid. j, Singapore Flyer Ferris Wheel and ArtScience Museum at night.

**2016, Nov. 29**    **Litho.**    ***Perf. 13***

| | | | | |
|---|---|---|---|---|
| 4065 | A3827 | Sheet of 10 | 16.00 | 16.00 |
| a.-j. | | 82y Any single | 1.25 | .50 |

See Singapore Nos. 1812-1813.

Fireplace A3828

Stew Pot and Bowl A3829

Snow-Covered House A3830

Snowman and Mailbox A3831

---

Child Rolling Large Snowball A3832

Trees A3833

Concert, Bows on Instruments A3834

Piano A3835

Trees With Lights at Night A3836

Shoppers With Packages A3837

Concert, Bows Raised A3838

Window and Door in Winter A3839

***Die Cut Perf. 11¼x11¾, Die Cut***
***Perf. 11½x11 (#4066c)***
**2016, Dec. 2**      **Litho.**
**Self-Adhesive**

| | | | | |
|---|---|---|---|---|
| 4066 | | Sheet of 10, 2 each | | |
| | | #4066a-4066d, 1 | | |
| | | each #4066e, 4066f | 10.00 | 10.00 |
| a. | A3828 | 52y multi | .95 | .70 |
| b. | A3829 | 52y multi | .95 | .70 |
| c. | A3830 | 52y multi | .95 | .70 |
| d. | A3831 | 52y multi | .95 | .70 |
| e. | A3832 | 52y multi | .95 | .70 |
| f. | A3833 | 52y multi | .95 | .70 |
| 4067 | | Sheet of 10, #4067a, | | |
| | | 4067e, 2 each | | |
| | | #4067b-4067d, | | |
| | | 4067f | 16.00 | 16.00 |
| a. | A3834 | 82y multi | 1.25 | .80 |
| b. | A3835 | 82y multi | 1.25 | .80 |
| c. | A3836 | 82y multi | 1.25 | .80 |
| d. | A3837 | 82y multi | 1.25 | .80 |
| e. | A3838 | 82y multi | 1.25 | .80 |
| f. | A3839 | 82y multi | 1.25 | .80 |

A3840

A3841

A3842

A3843

A3844

A3845

A3846

A3847

A3848

A3849

A3850

A3851

A3852

A3853

Flowers — A3854

### Die Cut Perf. 13x13¼
**2016, Dec. 9**                              **Litho.**
#### Self-Adhesive

| | | | |
|---|---|---|---|
| 4068 | | Sheet of 10 | 10.00 10.00 |
| a. | A3840 | 52y multi | .90 .70 |
| b. | A3841 | 52y multi | .90 .70 |
| c. | A3842 | 52y multi | .90 .70 |
| d. | A3843 | 52y multi | .90 .70 |
| e. | A3844 | 52y multi | .90 .70 |
| f. | A3845 | 52y multi | .90 .70 |
| g. | A3846 | 52y multi | .90 .70 |
| h. | A3847 | 52y multi | .90 .70 |
| i. | A3848 | 52y multi | .90 .70 |
| j. | A3849 | 52y multi | .90 .70 |
| 4069 | | Sheet of 10, 2 each | 16.00 16.00 |
| | | #4069a-4069e | |
| a. | A3850 | 82y multi | 1.25 .80 |
| b. | A3851 | 82y multi | 1.25 .80 |
| c. | A3852 | 82y multi | 1.25 .80 |
| d. | A3853 | 82y multi | 1.25 .80 |
| e. | A3854 | 82y multi | 1.25 .80 |

Five-Story
Pagoda at Kyo-
o-gokoku-ji
Temple,
Kyoto — A3855

Tokyo
Tower — A3856

#### Photo. & Engr.
**2017, Jan. 6**                             **Perf. 13¼**

| | | | |
|---|---|---|---|
| 4070 | A3855 | 82y multi | 1.25 .50 |
| 4071 | A3856 | 82y multi | 1.25 .50 |
| a. | | Horiz. pair, #4070-4071 | 3.00 2.25 |

Monocolor (green, red, orange brown and blue) engraved examples of Nos. 4070-4071 were printed in two sheets of ten that were in booklets produced in limited quantities that sold for 2500y.

---

### Miniature Sheets

A3857

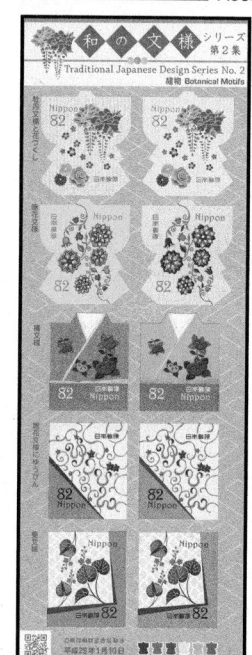

Traditional Japanese Designs — A3858

No. 4072: a, Fan with pine trees, lilac background (30x21mm). b, As "a," buff background (30x21mm). c, Pomegranates and tied rope, dull green background (27x24mm). d, As "c," rose background (27x24mm). e, Blue box with gourd pattern and bow (26x22mm), f, As "e," red violet box (26x22mm). g, Nandina berries, pink background (26x22mm). h, As "g," pale yellow background (26x22mm). i, Pine needles, dull green background (22x26mm). j, As "i," light yellow background (22x26mm).

No. 4073: a, Peonies, pink background (26x27mm). b, As "a," pale orange background (26x27mm). c, Flowers, yellow orange background (26x27mm). d, As "c," light blue background (26x27mm). e, Flowers on salmon kimono (22x23mm). f, As "e," pale green kimono (22x23mm). g, Flowers, mauve triangular panel (22x26mm). h, As "g," turquoise blue triangular panel (22x26mm). i, Flowers and leaves, light green background (22x26mm). j, As "i," lilac background (22x26mm).

---

### Die Cut Perf. 11 (#4072a, 4072b), Die Cut Perf. (#4072c, 4072d), Die Cut Perf. 11½x11, Die Cut Perf. 11¼x11¾ (#4072i, 4072j)
**2017, Jan. 10**                            **Litho.**
#### Self-Adhesive

| | | | |
|---|---|---|---|
| 4072 | A3857 | Sheet of 10 | 10.00 10.00 |
| a.-j. | | 52y Any single | .95 .70 |
| 4073 | A3858 | Sheet of 10 | 16.00 16.00 |
| a.-j. | | 82y Any single | 1.25 .80 |

#### Souvenir Sheet

New
Year
2017
(Year of
the
Rooster)
A3859

No. 4074 — Rooster facing: a, Right. b, Left.

**2017, Jan. 16    Litho.     Perf. 13x13¼**

| | | | |
|---|---|---|---|
| 4074 | A3859 | Sheet of 2 | 2.75 2.75 |
| a. | | 52y multi | 1.00 .30 |
| b. | | 82y multi | 1.50 .40 |

No. 4074 was sold to customers as well as being a lottery prize.

Skiing
A3860

Biathlon
A3861

Skating
A3862

Ice Hockey
A3863

Curling — A3864

**2017, Jan. 19     Photo.     Perf. 13**

| | | | |
|---|---|---|---|
| 4075 | A3860 | 82y multi | 1.50 .50 |
| 4076 | A3861 | 82y multi | 1.50 .50 |
| 4077 | A3862 | 82y multi | 1.50 .50 |
| 4078 | A3863 | 82y multi | 1.50 .50 |
| 4079 | A3864 | 82y multi | 1.50 .50 |
| a. | | Horiz. strip of 5, #4075-4079 | 7.50 5.50 |
| | | Nos. 4075-4079 (5) | 7.50 2.50 |

2017 Sapporo Asian Winter Games.

---

A sheet of six heart-shaped self-adhesive stamps (three denominated 52y and three deniomatied 82y) was printed in limited quantities and sold only in a package containing stationery that sold for 1200y.

---

### Miniature Sheets

A3865

Disney Characters — A3866

No. 4080: a, Mickey Mouse, orange yellow background (23x23mm). b, Minnie Mouse, orange yellow background (23x23mm). c, Mickey Mouse, apple green background (23x23mm). d, Minnie Mouse, apple green background (23x23mm). e, Mickey Mouse, lilac background (23x23mm). f, Minnie Mouse, lilac background (23x23mm). g, Mickey Mouse, rose background (22x26mm). h, Minnie Mouse, rose background (22x26mm). i, Mickey Mouse, light blue background (22x26mm). j, Minnie Mouse, light blue background (22x26mm).

No. 4081: a, Winnie the Pooh and Piglet looking at book (23x23mm). b, Winnie the Pooh in light blue frame (23x23mm). c, Winnie the Pooh and Piglet reading books (23x23mm). d, Piglet and Winnie the Pooh holding butterfly (23x23mm). e, Piglet with Winnie the Pooh holding "A," "B" and "C" (23x23mm). f, Piglet sitting on Winnie the Pooh's leg (23x23mm). g, Winnie the Pooh and letter "P" (23x23mm). h, Winnie the Pooh and Tigger (23x23mm). i, Tigger, Winnie the Pooh and Eeyore sleeping (25x22mm). j Winnie the Pooh with toys and honey pot (22x25mm).

## Die Cut Perf. 14

**2017, Feb. 9** **Litho.**
**Self-Adhesive**

| | | | | |
|---|---|---|---|---|
| 4080 | A3865 | Sheet of 10 | 16.00 | 16.00 |
| a.-j. | | 82y Any single | 1.25 | .80 |
| 4081 | A3866 | Sheet of 10 | 16.00 | 16.00 |
| a.-j. | | 82y Any single | 1.25 | .80 |

Cherry Blossoms
A3867

Plum Blossoms
A3868

Pansies and Sweet Alyssum
A3869

Snapdragons
A3870

Lupines
A3871

Cherry Blossoms
A3872

Mimosa Blossoms
A3873

Bellflowers
A3874

Ornithogalum
A3875

Anemones
A3876

## Die Cut Perf. 14

**2017, Feb. 15** **Litho.**
**Self-Adhesive**

| | | | |
|---|---|---|---|
| 4082 | Sheet of 10, 2 each #4082a-4082e | 10.00 | 10.00 |
| a. | A3867 52y multi | .95 | .70 |
| b. | A3868 52y multi | .95 | .70 |
| c. | A3869 52y multi | .95 | .70 |
| d. | A3870 52y multi | .95 | .70 |
| e. | A3871 52y multi | .95 | .70 |
| 4083 | Sheet of 10, 2 each #4083a-4083e | 16.00 | 16.00 |
| a. | A3872 82y multi | 1.25 | .80 |
| b. | A3873 82y multi | 1.25 | .80 |
| c. | A3874 82y multi | 1.25 | .80 |
| d. | A3875 82y multi | 1.25 | .80 |
| e. | A3876 82y multi | 1.25 | .80 |

Cherry Blossoms
A3877

Dandelions and Clover
A3878

Vegetables in Basket
A3879

Bamboo Shoots
A3880

Cherry Blossoms
A3881

Strawberries and Mailbox
A3882

Field Mustard
A3883

Wreath of Flowers
A3884

## Die Cut Perf. (#4085a-4085b, 4086a, 4086b), Die Cut Perf. 14

**2017, Feb. 24** **Litho.**
**Self-Adhesive**

| | | | |
|---|---|---|---|
| 4084 | Sheet of 10, 4 #4084a, 2 each #4084b-4084d | 10.00 | 10.00 |
| a. | A3877 52y multi | .95 | .70 |
| b. | A3878 52y multi | .95 | .70 |
| c. | A3879 52y multi | .95 | .70 |
| d. | A3880 52y multi | .95 | .70 |
| 4085 | Sheet of 10, 4 #4085a, 2 each #4085b-4085d | 16.00 | 16.00 |
| a. | A3881 82y multi | 1.25 | .80 |
| b. | A3882 82y multi | 1.25 | .80 |
| c. | A3883 82y multi | 1.25 | .80 |
| d. | A3884 82y multi | 1.25 | .80 |

**Miniature Sheet**

Southern Hemisphere Constellations — A3885

No. 4086: a, Grus and goose. b, Telescopium and telescope. c, Centaurus and centaur. d, Tucana and toucan. e, Pavo and peacock. f, Crux and cross. g, Volans and flying fish. h, Dorado and dolphinfish. i, Chamaeleon and chameleon. j, Carina and ship.

## Litho. With Foil Application
**2017, Mar. 3** **Die Cut Perf. 13x13¼**
**Self-Adhesive**

| | | | | |
|---|---|---|---|---|
| 4086 | A3885 | Sheet of 10 | 16.00 | 16.00 |
| a.-j. | | 82y Any single | 1.25 | .80 |

This self-adhesive sheet depicting Zodiac constellations, issued Mar. 3, 2017, was printed in limited quantities and was mounted in a booklet, which was only sold together with writing paper and envelopes for 1500y.

Hydrangea
A3890

Daisies
A3891

Peony
A3892

Lantana
A3893

Hibiscus
A3894

Hydrangea
A3895

Sunflowers and Roses
A3896

Carnations
A3897

Gardenias
A3898

Tulips
A3899

### Die Cut Perf. 10¼

**2017, Apr. 4** **Litho.**
**Self-Adhesive**

| | | | |
|---|---|---|---|
| 4091 | Sheet of 10, 2 each #4091a-4091e | 10.00 | 10.00 |
| a. | A3890 52y multi | .95 | .70 |
| b. | A3891 52y multi | .95 | .70 |
| c. | A3892 52y multi | .95 | .70 |
| d. | A3893 52y multi | .95 | .70 |
| e. | A3894 52y multi | .95 | .70 |
| 4092 | Sheet of 10, 2 each #4092a-4092e | 16.00 | 16.00 |
| a. | A3895 82y multi | 1.25 | .80 |
| b. | A3896 82y multi | 1.25 | .80 |
| c. | A3897 82y multi | 1.25 | .80 |
| d. | A3898 82y multi | 1.25 | .80 |
| e. | A3899 82y multi | 1.25 | .80 |

**Miniature Sheets**

A3900

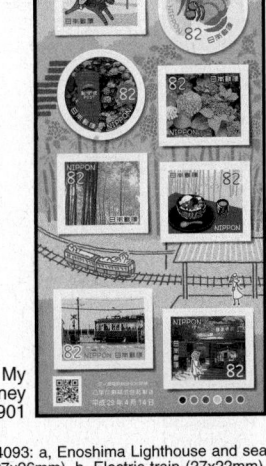
My Journey
A3901

No. 4093: a, Enoshima Lighthouse and sea gulls (27x26mm). b, Electric train (27x22mm). c, Enoshima (27x22mm). d, Electric train in station (27x22mm). e, Drink with lime and kiwifruit (22x26mm). f, Hamburger (22x26mm). g, Girl on beach, three sailboats (27x22mm). h, Dog on surfboard (27x22mm). i, Enoshima at night and shooting star (22x26mm). j, Rocky beach at sunset (27x22mm).

No. 4094: a, Great Buddha at Kamakura (25x31mm). b, Bicycle on sidewalk (26x22mm). c, Archer on horseback (26x22mm). d, Vegetables (25mm diameter). e, Mailbox and hydrangeas (25mm diameter). f, Hydrangeas (26x22mm). g, Bamboo grove (26x22mm). h, Bowl of anmitsu (26x22mm). i, Electric train and railroad crossing sign (26x22mm). j, Girl at Gokurakuji railroad station (26x22mm).

### Die Cut Perf. 10¾ (#4093a), Die Cut Perf. (#4093f), Die Cut Perf. 10¼

**2017, Apr. 14** **Litho.**

| | | | | |
|---|---|---|---|---|
| 4093 | A3900 | Sheet of 10 | 10.00 | 10.00 |
| a.-j. | | 52y Any single | .95 | .70 |

### Die Cut Perf. (#4094a, 4094d, 4094e), Die Cut Perf. 10¼

| | | | | |
|---|---|---|---|---|
| 4094 | A3901 | Sheet of 10 | 16.00 | 16.00 |
| a.-j. | | 82y Any single | 1.25 | .80 |

A sheet of seven self-adhesive stamps (five denominated 82y and two denominated 120y) was printed in limited quantities and sold only in a package containing stationery that sold for 1200y. Value, 22.50.

Irises, by Korin Ogata
A3902

Various details of the screen painting, as shown.

**2017, Apr. 20** **Photo.** **Perf. 13x13¼**

| | | | | |
|---|---|---|---|---|
| 4095 | A3902 | Sheet of 10 | 16.00 | 16.00 |
| a.-j. | | 82y Any single | 1.25 | .80 |

Philately Week.

Products of
Institute of
Physical and
Chemical
Research
A3903

K
Supercomputer
A3904

Discovery of Element
113 (Nihonium) — A3905

Photomicrographs of
Plant and Animal
Tissue — A3906

Cherry Blossom
Mutations From Heavy
Ion Beam Breeding
Technique — A3907

**2017, Apr. 26    Photo.    Perf. 13¼**

| | | | | |
|---|---|---|---|---|
| 4096 | A3903 | 82y multi | 1.25 | .50 |
| 4097 | A3904 | 82y multi | 1.25 | .50 |
| 4098 | A3905 | 82y multi | 1.25 | .50 |
| 4099 | A3906 | 82y multi | 1.25 | .50 |
| 4100 | A3907 | 82y multi | 1.25 | .50 |
| *a.* | Horiz. strip of 5, #4096-4100 | | 7.50 | 5.50 |
| | Nos. 4096-4100 (5) | | 6.25 | 2.50 |

Institute of Physical and Chemical Research
(RIKEN), cent.

### Miniature Sheet

Flora and Fauna of Oze Natural
Monument — A3908

No. 4101: a, Allium schoenoprasum var.
shibutuense (purple flower, stamp 1). b,
Leontopodium fauriei var. angustifolium (white
flower, stamp 2). c, Nuphar pumilum var.
ozeense (yellow flower, stamp 3). d, Potentilla
palustris (red flower, stamp 4). e, Lysichiton
camtschatcense (two white flowers, stamp 5).
f, Hemerocallis dumortieri (orange flower,
stamp 6). g, Dragonfly (stamp 7). h, Latham's
snipe on thick branch (stamp 8). i, Red-flanked
bluetail on thin branch (stamp 9). j, Stoat
(stamp 10).

---

**2017, Apr. 28    Litho.    Perf. 13**

| | | | | |
|---|---|---|---|---|
| 4101 | A3908 | Sheet of 10 | 16.00 | 16.00 |
| *a.-j.* | | 82y Any single | 1.25 | .80 |

### Miniature Sheet

Diplomatic Relations Between Japan
and Denmark, 150th Anniv. — A3909

No. 4102: a, Nyhavn, Copenhagen with red
boat. b, Nyhavn with green boat. c, Tivoli Gar-
dens and swans. d, Pigs and vegetables. e,
Cyclists. f, Wind generators. g, Ship and Little
Mermaid. h, Thumbelina in flower. i, Kronborg
Castle. j, Amalienborg and guards.

**2017, May 2    Litho.    Perf. 13**

| | | | | |
|---|---|---|---|---|
| 4102 | A3909 | Sheet of 10 | 16.00 | 16.00 |
| *a.-j.* | | 82y Any single | 1.25 | .50 |

### Miniature Sheets

A3910

---

Characters From *Peanuts* Comic
Strip — A3911

No. 4103: a, Snoopy with blue box (29mm
diameter). b, Snoopy driving truck facing left
(24x26mm). c, Snoopy in gift box (26x25mm).
d, Snoopy driving truck facing right
(28x23mm). e, Charlie Brown and Snoopy
exchanging gifts (26x22mm). f, Snoopy pushing gift on cart (26x22mm). g, Snoopy and
Woodstock carrying boxes (26x22mm). h,
Snoopy with red box (23x25mm). i, Snoopy on
dog house (28x36mm). j, Snoopy holding red
heart (25x30mm).

No. 4104: a, Snoopy reading Valentine's
Day card (29x26mm). b, Snoopy holding yellow envelope (29mm diameter). c, Snoopy
dancing (32x25mm). d, Woodstock and birds
in hot air balloon (24x28mm). e, Woodstock on
bicycle (26x24mm). f, Snoopy, Charlie Brown
and mailbox (27x23mm). g, Snoopy, Woodstock and bird with umbrellas (22x26mm). h,
Woodstock and Snoopy at mailbox
(26x26mm). i, Snoopy typing (26x27mm). j,
Snoopy delivering letter (22x26mm).

*Die Cut Perf. (#4103a), Die Cut Perf.*
*12¾x13 (#4103b, 4103h), Die Cut*
*Perf. 13x12¾ (#4103c), Die Cut Perf.*
*13 (#4103d), Die Cut Perf. 14*
*(#4103e, 4103f, 4103g), Die Cut Perf.*
*12 (#4103i, 4103j)*

**2017, May 10    Litho.**
**Self-Adhesive**

| | | | | |
|---|---|---|---|---|
| 4103 | A3910 | Sheet of 10 | 16.00 | 16.00 |
| *a.-j.* | | 82y Any single | 1.25 | .80 |

*Die Cut Perf. 12½ (#4104a, 4104h),*
*Die Cut Perf. (#4104b, 4104d), Die*
*Cut Perf. 12¾x12 (#4104c), Die Cut*
*Perf 12½x12¼ (#4104e), Die Cut Perf.*
*13½x13 (#4104f), Die Cut Perf.*
*13¾x14 (#4104g), Die Cut Perf. 12¾*
*(#4104i), Die Cut Perf. 13¾x13½*
*(#4104j)*

| | | | | |
|---|---|---|---|---|
| 4104 | A3911 | Sheet of 10 | 16.00 | 16.00 |
| *a.-j.* | | 82y Any single | 1.25 | .80 |

Volunteer Welfare
Commisioners System,
Cent. — A3912

**2017, May 12    Litho.    Perf. 13**

| | | | | |
|---|---|---|---|---|
| 4105 | A3912 | 82y multi | 1.50 | .50 |

---

**Flowers For Mourning Type of 2014**
**and**

Cherry
Blossoms
A3913

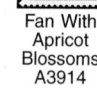

Fan With
Apricot
Blossoms
A3914

**2017, May 15    Photo.    Perf. 13x13¼**

| | | | | |
|---|---|---|---|---|
| 4106 | A3145 | 62y multi | 1.10 | .40 |
| 4107 | A3913 | 62y multi | 1.10 | .40 |
| 4108 | A3914 | 62y multi | 1.10 | .40 |
| | Nos. 4106-4108 (3) | | 3.30 | 1.20 |

Compare type A3914 with types A3146-
A3148.

"82" — A3915

**Die Cut Perf. 13x13¼**
**2017, May 17    Litho.**
**Self-Adhesive**

| | | | | |
|---|---|---|---|---|
| 4109 | A3915 | 82y multi | 1.25 | .80 |

A3916

A3917

A3918

A3919

Lions Clubs
International,
Cent. — A3920

Design: No. 4110, Logo of Lions Club International. No. 4111, Engaging our youth. No.
4112, Sharing the vision. No. 4113, Relieving
the hunger. No. 4114, Protecting our
environment.

**2017, May 24    Litho.    Perf. 13**

| | | | | |
|---|---|---|---|---|
| 4110 | A3916 | 82y multi | 1.50 | .50 |
| 4111 | A3917 | 82y multi | 1.50 | .50 |
| 4112 | A3918 | 82y multi | 1.50 | .50 |
| 4113 | A3919 | 82y multi | 1.50 | .50 |
| 4114 | A3920 | 82y multi | 1.50 | .50 |
| *a.* | Vert. strip of 5, #4110-4114 | | 7.50 | 5.50 |
| | Nos. 4110-4114 (5) | | 7.50 | 2.50 |

## Miniature Sheet

National Afforestation — A3921

No. 4115: a, Cherry blossoms. b, North Kobushi magnolia flower. c, Gentian. d, Tulips. e, Japanese bigleaf magnolia. f, Cherry blossoms, diff. g, Adder's tongue lilies. h, Kanoko lily. i, Japanese bay tree, j, Tateyama cedar tree.

**2017, May 26**    Litho.    **Perf. 13**
4115   A3921    Sheet of 10    11.00   11.00
*a.-j.*     62y Any single     .85    .40

Clouds
A3922

Shells and
Ramune
Bottles
A3923

Water
Balloons
A3924

Sunflowers
A3925

Sunflowers
A3926

Goldfish in
Bowl
A3927

Bowl of
Shaved
Ice
A3928

Beach
A3929

Shell
A3930

Shell
A3931

Marbles
A3932

Watermelon
Slice
A3933

*Die Cut Perf. 13x13¼, Die Cut Perf. 13¼x13 (#4116d, 4116e), Die Cut Perf. (#4116f)*

**2017, June 2**      Litho.
     **Self-Adhesive**
4116     Sheet of 10, #4116d,
     4116e, 2 each
     #4116a-4116c,
     4116f       12.00   12.00
  *a.*   A3922 62y multi    1.10    .85
  *b.*   A3923 62y multi    1.10    .85
  *c.*   A3924 62y multi    1.10    .85
  *d.*   A3925 62y multi    1.10    .85
  *e.*   A3926 62y multi    1.10    .85
  *f.*   A3927 62y multi    1.10    .85

*Die Cut Perf. 13x13¼ (#4117a, 4117b), Die Cut Perf. 13 (#4117c, 4117d, 4117f), Die Cut Perf. 13¼ (#4117e)*

4117     Sheet of 10, #4117c,
     4117d, 2 each
     #4117a-4117b,
     4117e-4117f     16.00   16.00
  *a.*   A3928 82y multi    1.25    .85
  *b.*   A3929 82y multi    1.25    .85
  *c.*   A3930 82y multi    1.25    .85
  *d.*   A3931 82y multi    1.25    .85
  *e.*   A3932 82y multi    1.25    .85
  *f.*   A3933 82y multi    1.25    .85

### Miniature Sheet

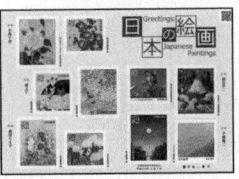

Paintings
A3934

No. 4118: a, Sunflowers, by Chinami Nakajima (stamp 5, 32x39mm). b, Morning Glories, by Nakajima (stamp 6, 32x28mm). c, Chinese Bellflowers, by Fumiko Hori (stamp 7, 30x32mm). d, The Flow of Mountain Seasons, by Hori (stamp 8, 32x39mm). e, Angela and the Blue Sky II, by Koji Kinutani (stamp 1, 32x28mm). f, Celebration - Flying Dragon, Sacred Gateway of Fuji, by Kinutani (stamp 2, 32x39mm). g, Early Summer, by Rieko Morita (stamp 9, 32x39mm). h, Autumn Flowers, by Morita (stamp 10, 32x28mm). i, Nachi Waterfall in the Moonlight, by Yuji Tezuka (stamp 3, 32x39mm). j, Beautiful Sky, by Tezuka (stamp 4, 32x32mm).

*Die Cut Perf. 12½x13, Die Cut Perf. 13x12 (#4118b, 4118e, 4118h), Die Cut Perf. 12½ (#4118c, 4118j)*

**2017, June 7**      Litho.
     **Self-Adhesive**
4118   A3934    Sheet of 10    16.00   16.00
*a.-j.*     82y Any single     1.25    .80

### Miniature Sheet

Japan at
Night
A3935

No. 4119: a, Sky Gate Bridge R, Osaka Prefecture (stamp 1). b, Meriken Park, Hyogo Prefecture (stamp 2). c, Kodaiji in autumn, Kyoto Prefecture (stamp 3). d, Nagoya Television Tower, Aichi Prefecture (stamp 4). e, Gifu Castle and Gifu, Gifu Prefecture (stamp 5). f, Shimizu Port and Mount Fuji, Shizuoka Prefecture (stamp 6). g, Lake Suwa Fireworks

Festival, Nagano Prefecture (stamp 7). h, Ishiyama-dera Autumn Moon Viewing Festival, Shiga Prefecture (stamp 8). i, Echigo Hillside National Government Park, Niigata Prefecture (stamp 9). j, Seki-juku, Mie Prefecture (stamp 10).

**2017, June 9**      Litho.    **Perf. 13**
4119   A3935    Sheet of 10    16.00   16.00
*a.-j.*     82y Any single     1.25    .50

Dragées
A3936

Jordan
Almonds
A3937

Dragées
A3938

Macarons
A3939

Dragées
A3940

Konpeito
Candy
A3941

*Die Cut Perf. 13x13¼*

**2017, June 23**      **Photo.**
     **Self-Adhesive**
4120     Sheet of 10, 5 each
     #4120a-4120b    12.00   12.00
  *a.*   A3936 62y multi    1.25    .85
  *b.*   A3937 62y multi    1.25    .85
4121     Sheet of 10, 5 each
     #4121a-4121b    16.00   16.00
  *a.*   A3938 82y multi    1.25    .85
  *b.*   A3939 82y multi    1.25    .85
4122     Sheet of 10, 5 each
     #4122a-4122b    17.50   17.50
  *a.*   A3940 92y multi    1.40    .80
  *b.*   A3941 92y multi    1.40    .80
    *Nos. 4120-4122 (3)*    45.50   45.50

### Miniature Sheet

Characters From *Super Mario* Video
Games — A3942

No. 4123: a, Mario with fist and leg raised (22x33mm). b, Mario mailing letter (24x25mm). c, Mario seated, reading letter (24x27mm). d, Princess Peach writing letter (23x25mm). e, Mario on Yoshi (25x23mm). f, Luigi removing letter from mailbox (23x25mm). g, Toad with mail bag (25x23mm). h, Mario pointing (24x24mm). i, Mario and Princess Peach (26x25mm). j, Princess Peach (24x24mm).

*Die Cut Perf. 11¾ (#4123a), Die Cut Perf. 11 (#4123b, 4123c), Die Cut Perf. 11½x11 (#4123d, 4123f, 4123i), Die Cut Perf. 11x11½ (#4123e, 4123g), Die Cut Perf. 11½ (#4123h, 4123j)*

**2017, June 28**      Litho.
     **Self-Adhesive**
4123   A3942    Sheet of 10    16.00   16.00
*a.-j.*     82y Any single     1.25    .80

A3943

A3944

A3945

A3946

A3947

A3948

A3949

A3950

A3951

Penguins — A3952

**Litho. With Foil Application**
**2017, July 5**    *Die Cut Perf. 10¼*
     **Self-Adhesive**
4124     Sheet of 10     16.00   16.00
  *a.*   A3943 82y multi    1.25    .80
  *b.*   A3944 82y multi    1.25    .80
  *c.*   A3945 82y multi    1.25    .80
  *d.*   A3946 82y multi    1.25    .80
  *e.*   A3947 82y multi    1.25    .80
  *f.*   A3948 82y multi    1.25    .80
  *g.*   A3949 82y multi    1.25    .80
  *h.*   A3950 82y multi    1.25    .80
  *i.*   A3951 82y multi    1.25    .80
  *j.*   A3952 82y multi    1.25    .80

### Miniature Sheet

National Museum of Western Art
UNESCO World Heritage
Site — A3953

No. 4125: a, Entrance to Main building (stamp 1). b, 19th Century Hall (stamp 2). c, Aerial view of Main building (stamp 3). d, Main building's second-floor exhibition room (stamp 4). e, Entrance to Main building, diff (stamp 5). f, The Thinker, statue by Auguste Rodin (stamp 6). g, Roses, by Vincent van Gogh (stamp 7). h, Boy in Flowers (Jacques Hoschedé), by Edouard Manet (stamp 8). i, The Port of Saint-Tropez, by Paul Signac (stamp 9). j, Water Lilies, by Claude Monet (stamp 10).

**2017, July 14**   Litho.    **Perf. 13¾x14¼**
4125   A3953    Sheet of 10    16.00   16.00
*a.-j.*     82y Any single     1.25    .50

Flowers
and
"Thank
You"
A3954

Cupcake
A3955

Tea Cup
and Tea Pot
A3956

Stars
A3957

Swan
Holding
Letter
A3958

Stars
A3959

Dots and
"Thank
You"
A3960

Elephant
and Flower
A3961

Gift
A3962

Ribbon With
Bow
A3963

**Die Cut Perf. 13x13¼ (#4126), Die Cut Perf. 13x12¾ (#4127, 4129, 4132, 4134), Die Cut Perf. 13½x13¼ (#4128, 4130, 4133, 4135), Die Cut Perf. 10¾ (#4131)**

2017, July 21      Litho.
**Booklet Stamps**
**Self-Adhesive**

| | | | |
|---|---|---|---|
| 4126 | A3954 62y multi | 1.10 | .80 |
| 4127 | A3955 62y multi | 1.10 | .80 |
| 4128 | A3956 62y multi | 1.10 | .80 |
| 4129 | A3957 62y multi | 1.10 | .80 |
| 4130 | A3958 62y multi | 1.10 | .80 |
| a. | Booklet pane of 5, #4126-4130 | 6.00 | 6.00 |
| 4131 | A3959 82y multi | 1.25 | .80 |
| 4132 | A3960 82y multi | 1.25 | .80 |
| 4133 | A3961 82y multi | 1.25 | .80 |
| 4134 | A3962 82y multi | 1.25 | .80 |
| 4135 | A3963 82y multi | 1.25 | .80 |
| a. | Booklet pane of 5, #4131-4135 | 8.00 | 8.00 |
| | Nos. 4126-4135 (10) | 11.75 | 8.00 |

Letter Writing Day.

Rilakkuma
A3964

Kiiroitori
and
Korilakkuma
A3965

Characters
Picking
Strawberries
A3966

Kiiroitori,
Korilakkuma
and
Rilakkuma
A3967

Characters
With
Flowers
A3968

Characters
in Tub
A3970

Chairoikoguma
and
Rilakkuma
A3972

Rilakkuma
and
Kiiroitori
A3974

Kiiroitori
A3976

Rilakkuma
Holding
Letter
A3978

Rilakkuma
Eating
A3980

Rilakkuma
and
Kiiroitori
A3982

**Die Cut Perf. 13x13¼ (#4136a, 4136b, 4136d, 4136e), Die Cut Perf. (#4136c, 4136i, 4136j), Die Cut Perf. 11½x11¼ (#4136f), Die Cut Perf. 11½ (#4136g), Die Cut Perf. 13¼x13 (#4136h)**

2017, July 26
**Self-Adhesive**      Litho.

| | | | |
|---|---|---|---|
| 4136 | Sheet of 10 | 12.00 | 12.00 |
| a. | A3964 62y multi | 1.10 | .80 |
| b. | A3965 62y multi | 1.10 | .80 |
| c. | A3966 62y multi | 1.10 | .80 |
| d. | A3967 62y multi | 1.10 | .80 |
| e. | A3968 62y multi | 1.10 | .80 |
| f. | A3969 62y multi | 1.10 | .80 |
| g. | A3970 62y multi | 1.10 | .80 |
| h. | A3971 62y multi | 1.10 | .80 |
| i. | A3972 62y multi | 1.10 | .80 |
| j. | A3973 62y multi | 1.10 | .80 |

**Die Cut Perf. 13x13¼ (#4137a, 4137g, 4137h, 4137i), Die Cut Perf 11¾ (#4137b, 4137d), Die Cut Perf.**

Characters and
Skerwered
Dumplings
A3969

Characters
and Lemon
A3971

Characters
With Toy
A3973

Korilakkuma
A3975

Rilakkuma
A3977

Characters
and Yellow
Dots
A3979

Korilakkuma
and Toys
A3981

Rilakkuma
A3983

**11 (#4132c), Die Cut Perf. 13¼x13 (#4137e, 4137j), Die Cut Perf. (#4137f)**

| | | | |
|---|---|---|---|
| 4137 | Sheet of 10 | 16.00 | 16.00 |
| a. | A3974 82y multi | 1.25 | .80 |
| b. | A3975 82y multi | 1.25 | .80 |
| c. | A3976 82y multi | 1.25 | .80 |
| d. | A3977 82y multi | 1.25 | .80 |
| e. | A3978 82y multi | 1.25 | .80 |
| f. | A3979 82y multi | 1.25 | .80 |
| g. | A3980 82y multi | 1.25 | .80 |
| h. | A3981 82y multi | 1.25 | .80 |
| i. | A3982 82y multi | 1.25 | .80 |
| j. | A3983 82y multi | 1.25 | .80 |

Miniature Sheet

Kimonos
A3984

No. 4138: a, Green and red kimono (26x27mm). b, Woman in Heian era kimono (light green background, 22x28mm). c, Beige and brown kimono (26x27mm). d, Woman in Muromachi era kimono (light brown and brown background, 22x28mm). e, Beige and brown kimono with checkerboard pattern and flowers (26x27mm). f, Woman in Azuchi-Momoyama era kimono (pale orange background, 22x28mm). g, Blue and red kimono with flowers (26x27mm). h, Woman in Edo era kimono (light blue background, 22x28mm). i, Purple kimono with flowers and cart (26x27mm). j, Modern kimono (buff background, 22x28mm).

**Die Cut Perf. 11x10¼ (#4138a, 4138c, 4138e, 4138g, 4138i), Die Cut Perf. 11¾x11½ (#4138b, 4138d, 4138f, 4138h, 4138j)**

2017, Aug. 4      Litho.
**Self-Adhesive**

| | | | |
|---|---|---|---|
| 4138 | A3984 Sheet of 10 | 16.00 | 16.00 |
| a.-j. | 82y Any single | 1.25 | .80 |

A3985

A3986

A3987

A3988

A3989

A3990

A3991

A3992

A3993

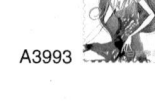

Women's
Fashion — A3994

**Die Cut Perf. 11¼x11**

2017, Aug. 9      Litho.
**Self-Adhesive**

| | | | |
|---|---|---|---|
| 4139 | Sheet of 10 | 16.00 | 16.00 |
| a. | A3985 82y multi | 1.25 | .80 |
| b. | A3986 82y multi | 1.25 | .80 |
| c. | A3987 82y multi | 1.25 | .80 |
| d. | A3988 82y multi | 1.25 | .80 |
| e. | A3989 82y multi | 1.25 | .80 |
| f. | A3990 82y multi | 1.25 | .80 |
| g. | A3991 82y multi | 1.25 | .80 |
| h. | A3992 82y multi | 1.25 | .80 |
| i. | A3993 82y multi | 1.25 | .80 |
| j. | A3994 82y multi | 1.25 | .80 |

Butterflies
A3995

Deer
A3996

Rabbits
A3997

Horses
A3998

Dragonflies
A3999

Peacock and
Peony
A4000

Geese
and
Clover
A4001

Mandarin
Ducks
A4002

Egrets
A4003

Plovers
A4004

*Die Cut Perf. (#4140a), Die Cut Perf.*
*11¼x11¾ (#4140b, 4140e, 4141b,*
*4141d, 4141e), Die Cut Perf.*
*11¾x11¼ (#4140c, 4140d, 4141c),*
*Die Cut Perf. 11¼ (#4141a)*

**2017, Aug. 18**      **Litho.**
**Self-Adhesive**
| | | | |
|---|---|---|---|
| 4140 | Sheet of 10, 2 each | | |
| | #4140a-4140e | 12.00 | 12.00 |
| a. | A3995 62y multi | 1.00 | .80 |
| b. | A3996 62y multi | 1.00 | .80 |
| c. | A3997 62y multi | 1.00 | .80 |
| d. | A3998 62y multi | 1.00 | .80 |
| e. | A3999 62y multi | 1.00 | .80 |
| 4141 | Sheet of 10, 2 each | | |
| | #4141a-4141e | 16.00 | 16.00 |
| a. | A4000 82y multi | 1.25 | .80 |
| b. | A4001 82y multi | 1.25 | .80 |
| c. | A4002 82y multi | 1.25 | .80 |
| d. | A4003 82y multi | 1.50 | .80 |
| e. | A4004 82y multi | 1.25 | .80 |

Mailbox in Autumn A4005

Chestnuts A4007

Girl Raking Leaves A4009

Rabbits Pounding Rice A4011

Mushrooms on Brazier A4013

Dragonflies Over Rice Field A4015

Girl and Mushrooms A4006

Baked Sweet Potato A4008

House and Trees A4010

Child Reading in Moonlight A4012

Girl in Library A4014

Mailbox in Autumn A4016

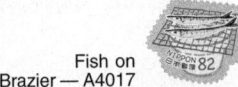
Fish on Brazier — A4017

*Die Cut Perf. 13x13¼ (#4142a,*
*4142b, 4142e, 4142f, 4143b, 4143d,*
*4143f), Die Cut Perf. (#4142c, 4143a,*
*4143c), Die Cut Perf. 13¼x13*
*(#4142d, 4143e), Die Cut Perf. 12*
*(#4143g)*

**2017, Aug. 23**      **Litho.**
**Self-Adhesive**
| | | | |
|---|---|---|---|
| 4142 | Sheet of 10, #4142a, | | |
| | 4142b, 2 each | | |
| | #4142c-4142f | 12.50 | 12.50 |
| a. | A4005 62y multi | 1.00 | .80 |
| b. | A4006 62y multi | 1.00 | .80 |
| c. | A4007 62y multi | 1.00 | .80 |
| d. | A4008 62y multi | 1.00 | .80 |

| | | | |
|---|---|---|---|
| e. | A4009 62y multi | 1.00 | .80 |
| f. | A4010 62y multi | 1.00 | .80 |
| 4143 | Sheet of 10, #4143a, | | |
| | 4143c, 4143f, | | |
| | 4143g, 2 each | | |
| | #4143b, 4143d, | | |
| | 4143e | 16.00 | 16.00 |
| a. | A4011 82y multi | 1.25 | .80 |
| b. | A4012 82y multi | 1.25 | .80 |
| c. | A4013 82y multi | 1.25 | .80 |
| d. | A4014 82y multi | 1.25 | .80 |
| e. | A4015 82y multi | 1.25 | .80 |
| f. | A4016 82y multi | 1.25 | .80 |
| g. | A4017 82y multi | 1.25 | .80 |

**Miniature Sheet**

72nd National Athletic Meet, Ehime A4018

No. 4144: a, Kendo. b, Mount Ishizuchi. c, Rowing. d, Shimanami Kaido and bridge. e, Weight lifting. f, Bathhouse at Dogo Onsen Hot Springs. g, Archery. h, Mikan oranges. i, Basketball. j, Red seabream.

**2017, Aug. 30**   **Litho.**   **Perf. 13½**
| | | | | |
|---|---|---|---|---|
| 4144 | A4018 | Sheet of 10 | 16.00 | 16.00 |
| a.-j. | | 82y Any single | 1.25 | .80 |

The Koya Tama River, Kii Province, by Eizan Kikukawa A4019

Mount Hiyori and Toba Bay, Shima Province, by Hiroshige Utagawa A4020

Yosooi and Matsumura of the Matsubaya, by Utamaro Kitagawa A4021

Mount Inasa at Nagasaki, Hizen Province, by Hiroshige Utagawa A4022

Kisegawa of the Matsubaya, by Utamaro Kitagawa A4023

Beauty with Ball and Fan, by Utamaro Kitagawa A4025

Hanaogi of the Ogiya, by Eishi Chobunsai A4027

Daijingu Shrine at Kashima, Hitachi Province, by Hiroshige Utagawa A4024

Kanegasaka, Tanba Province, by Hiroshige Utagawa A4026

Clear Evening on the Coast, Tsushima Province, by Hiroshige Utagawa A4028

**2017, Sept. 6**   **Litho.**   **Perf. 13½**
| | | | |
|---|---|---|---|
| 4145 | Sheet of 10 | 16.00 | 16.00 |
| a. | A4019 82y multi | 1.25 | .80 |
| b. | A4020 82y multi | 1.25 | .80 |
| c. | A4021 82y multi | 1.25 | .80 |
| d. | A4022 82y multi | 1.25 | .80 |
| e. | A4023 82y multi | 1.25 | .80 |
| f. | A4024 82y multi | 1.25 | .80 |
| g. | A4025 82y multi | 1.25 | .80 |
| h. | A4026 82y multi | 1.25 | .80 |
| i. | A4027 82y multi | 1.25 | .80 |
| j. | A4028 82y multi | 1.25 | .80 |

**Miniature Sheets**

A4029

Posukuma and Friends — A4030

No. 4146: a, Two bears near mailbox. b, Two bears, one with letter, near mailbox. c, Three bears. d, Large bear delivering letter to small bear. e, Bear and flowers. f, Two bears, tree, letter in mailbox. g, Bear with violin. h, Mailbox, bear licking envelope. i, Two bears on swings. j, Crying bear and letter.

No. 4147 — Tree and: a, Two bears with raised arms, two beamed yellow sixteenth notes. b, Bear and owl, red orange eighth note. c, Two bears, one with mail bag, with arms crossed, green eighth note. d, Two bears, one with crossed arms, two beamed yellow sixteenth notes. e, Two bears waving, red orange eighth note. f, Two bears with mail bags waving, red eighth note. g, Two bears, one with mail bag, sitting, red eighth note. h, Two bears sitting, green eighth note. i, Two bears waving, two beamed blue sixteenth notes. j, Seven bears and owl, red orange eighth note and two beamed blue sixteenth notes.

*Die Cut Perf. 13½x13¼*
**2017, Sept. 15**      **Litho.**
**Self-Adhesive**
| | | | | |
|---|---|---|---|---|
| 4146 | A4029 | Sheet of 10 | 12.00 | 12.00 |
| a.-j. | | 62y Any single | 1.00 | .80 |
| 4147 | A4030 | Sheet of 10 | 16.00 | 16.00 |
| a.-j. | | 82y Any single | 1.25 | .80 |

Fringed Pinks A4031

Mandarin Oranges A4033

Grapes A4035

Gentian Flowers A4032

Straw Sandals A4034

Patrinia Flowers A4036

Morning
Glories
A4037

Rough
Horsetails
A4039

Red
Maple
Leaves
A4041

Mouse,
Rice and
Rice Bags
A4043

Bush
Clover
A4045

Persimmon
A4047

Grass
A4049

Dragonflies
A4038

Fallen
Leaves
A4040

Moon,
Rabbit
and
Flowers
A4042

Chestnuts
A4044

Hen and
Chicks
A4046

Walnuts
A4048

Eurasian
Siskin
A4050

### Die Cut Perf. 13x13¼
**2017, Sept. 20**    Litho.
#### Self-Adhesive

```
4148        Sheet of 10        12.00  12.00
  a.  A4031 62y multi            1.00    .80
  b.  A4032 62y multi            1.00    .80
  c.  A4033 62y multi            1.00    .80
  d.  A4034 62y multi            1.00    .80
  e.  A4035 62y multi            1.00    .80
  f.  A4036 62y multi            1.00    .80
  g.  A4037 62y multi            1.00    .80
  h.  A4038 62y multi            1.00    .80
  i.  A4039 62y multi            1.00    .80
  j.  A4040 62y multi            1.00    .80
4149        Sheet of 10        16.00  16.00
  a.  A4041 82y multi            1.25    .80
  b.  A4042 82y multi            1.25    .80
  c.  A4043 82y multi            1.25    .80
  d.  A4044 82y multi            1.25    .80
  e.  A4045 82y multi            1.25    .80
  f.  A4046 82y multi            1.25    .80
  g.  A4047 82y multi            1.25    .80
  h.  A4048 82y multi            1.25    .80
  i.  A4049 82y multi            1.25    .80
  j.  A4050 82y multi            1.25    .80
```

### Miniature Sheet
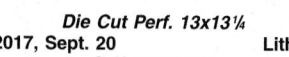
Japan at
Night
A4051

No. 4150: a, Kobe and Osaka Bay (stamp 1). b, Kobe and Osaka Bay, diff (stamp 2). c, Fireworks at Grass Burning Festival (stamp 3). d, Nabana no Sato (stamp 4). e, Hashigui Rocks (stamp 5). f, Unazzuki Onsen (stamp 6). g, Laguna Ten Bosch Amusement Park (stamp 7). h, Shiroyone Senmaida (stamp 8). i, Echizen City and Sabae (stamp 9). j, Gakunan electric train at station (stamp 10).

**2017, Sept. 29**    Litho.    *Perf. 13*
```
4150   A4051  Sheet of 10     16.00  16.00
  a.-j.   82y Any single        1.25    .80
```

Kyoto Railway Museum, Class 230 Steam Locomotive A4052

Japan National Railways 14-700 Series Locomotive A4053

Nagoya Railroad 8800 Panorama DX Series Locomotive A4054

Izukyu 2100 Series Locomotive A4055

Hokkaido Railway Company KiHa 84/83 Series Locomotive A4056

Odakyu Electric Railway 10000 Series Locomotive A4057

Tobu Railway 100 Series Locomotive A4058

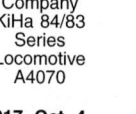
Kyushu Railway 787 Series Locomotive A4059

Central and West Japan Railways 285 Series Locomotive A4060

Hanshin 5700 Series Locomotive A4061

**2017, Oct. 4**    Litho.    *Perf. 13*
```
4151        Sheet of 10        16.00  16.00
  a.  A4052 82y multi            1.25    .50
  b.  A4053 82y multi            1.25    .50
  c.  A4054 82y multi            1.25    .50
  d.  A4055 82y multi            1.25    .50
  e.  A4056 82y multi            1.25    .50
  f.  A4057 82y multi            1.25    .50
  g.  A4058 82y multi            1.25    .50
  h.  A4059 82y multi            1.25    .50
  i.  A4060 82y multi            1.25    .50
  j.  A4061 82y multi            1.25    .50
4152        Sheet of 10        16.00  16.00
  a.  A4062 82y multi            1.25    .50
  b.  A4063 82y multi            1.25    .50
  c.  A4064 82y multi            1.25    .50
  d.  A4065 82y multi            1.25    .50
  e.  A4066 82y multi            1.25    .50
  f.  A4067 82y multi            1.25    .50
  g.  A4068 82y multi            1.25    .50
  h.  A4069 82y multi            1.25    .50
  i.  A4070 82y multi            1.25    .50
  j.  A4071 82y multi            1.25    .50
```

Class 230 Steam Locomotive A4062

Japan National Railways 14-700 Series Locomotive A4064

Nagoya Railroad 8800 Panorama DX Series Locomotive A4066

Izukyu 2100 Series Locomotive A4068

Hokkaido Railway Company KiHa 84/83 Series Locomotive A4070

Odakyu Electric Railway 10000 Series Locomotive A4063

Tobu Railway 100 Series Locomotive A4065

Kyushu Railway 787 Series Locomotive A4067

Central and West Japan Railways 285 Series Locomotive A4069

Hanshin 5700 Series Locomotive A4071

A4072

International Letter Writing Week — A4073

Art by Hirogshige: No. 4153, Drooping Cherry Tree with Small Bird (upper half, denomination at UR). b, Drooping Cherry Trees with Small Bird (lower half, denomination at LL).

90y, Travelers Crossing the Abe River West of the Fuchu Station. 110y, Goyu Station at Nightfall. 130y, Travelers at the Oi River.

**2017, Oct. 6**   Litho.   *Perf. 14x14¼*
```
4153        70y  multi            1.10    .50
4154        70y  multi            1.10    .50
  a.    A4072 Vert. pair, #4153-4154  2.50  1.90
             Perf. 13
4155  A4073   90y multi           1.75    .50
4156  A4073  110y multi           2.25    .50
4157  A4073  130y multi           2.50    .50
      Nos. 4153-4157 (5)          8.70   2.50
```
See listing of No. 4448 for images of each Hiroshige print.

### Miniature Sheets

Puppies A4074

Adult Dogs A4075

Nos. 4158 and 4159: a, Labrador retriever. b, Bernese Mountain dog. c, Akita. d, Old English sheepdog. e, Chow chow. f, German shepherd. g, Border collie. h, Siberian husky. i, Bulldog. j, Dalmatian.

### *Die Cut Perf. 11*
**2017, Oct. 11**    Litho.
#### Self-Adhesive
```
4158  A4074  Sheet of 10       12.00  12.00
  a.-j.   62y Any single         1.00    .80
4159  A4075  Sheet of 10       16.00  16.00
  a.-j.   82y Any single         1.25    .80
```

A4076    A4077

Flowers
A4078    A4079

A4080    A4081

Lace Flowers
A4082    A4083

*Die Cut Perf. 13x13¼ (#4160a-4160b), Die Cut Perf. 13 (#4161a-4161c), Die Cut Perf. (#4160c-4160d, 4161d)*

**2017, Oct. 20**      **Litho.**

**Self-Adhesive**

| | | | | |
|---|---|---|---|---|
| 4160 | | Sheet of 10, 3 each #4160a-4160b, 2 each #4160c-4160d | 12.00 | 12.00 |
| a. | A4076 | 62y multi | 1.00 | .80 |
| b. | A4077 | 62y multi | 1.00 | .80 |
| c. | A4078 | 62y multi | 1.00 | .80 |
| d. | A4079 | 62y multi | 1.00 | .80 |
| 4161 | | Sheet of 10, 3 each #4161a-4161b, 2 each #4161c-4161d | 16.00 | 16.00 |
| a. | A4080 | 82y multi | 1.25 | .80 |
| b. | A4081 | 82y multi | 1.25 | .80 |
| c. | A4082 | 82y multi | 1.25 | .80 |
| d. | A4083 | 82y multi | 1.25 | .80 |

Rice Balls and Sushi A4084

No. 4162: a, Futomaki sushi (27mm diameter). b, Rice ball with kelp (30x27mm). c, Rice ball with pickled plum (30x27mm). d, Rice ball with salmon (30x27mm). e, Rice ball with baby sardines (33x20mm). f, Tofu pockets with sushi rice (33x20mm). g, Rice ball with red beans (30x27mm). h, Tempura rice ball (30x28mm). i, Rice ball with sesame seeds and salt (30x27mm). j, Rice ball with edamame beans (30mm diameter).

*Die Cut Perf. 12¾ (#4162b-4162d, 4162g-4162i), Die Cut Perf. 12½ (#4162e-4162f), Die Cut Perf. (#4162a, 4162j)*

**2017, Oct. 24**      **Litho.**

**Self-Adhesive**

| | | | | |
|---|---|---|---|---|
| 4162 | A4084 | Booklet pane of 10 | 16.00 | 16.00 |
| a.-j. | | 82y Any single | 1.25 | .80 |

Japanese Foods A4085

Designs: No. 4163, Dango (dumplings on skewers). No. 4164, Taiyaki (fish-shaped bean paste cake).

**2017, Nov. 1**      **Litho.**      **Perf. 13¼x13**

| | | | | |
|---|---|---|---|---|
| 4163 | | 18y multi | .35 | .25 |
| 4164 | | 18y multi | .35 | .25 |
| a. | A4085 | Horiz. pair, #4163-4164 | .70 | .55 |

A4086      A4087

New Year 2018 (Year of the Dog) A4088      A4089

**2017, Nov. 1**    **Litho.**    **Perf. 13x13¼**

| | | | | |
|---|---|---|---|---|
| 4165 | A4086 | 52y gold & multi | .95 | .30 |
| 4166 | A4087 | 82y gold & multi | 1.50 | .40 |

**Photo. & Typo.**

**Perf. 13¼**

| | | | | |
|---|---|---|---|---|
| 4167 | A4088 | 52y +3y multi | 1.25 | .40 |
| 4168 | A4089 | 82y +3y gold & multi | 1.75 | .40 |
| | | Nos. 4165-4168 (4) | 5.45 | 1.50 |

The stamps shown above were printed in a sheet offered as a prize for the 2018 New Year lottery. This sheet was not sold to the public.

Miniature Sheets

A4090

Gifts From the Forest A4091

No. 4169: a, Bird in tree. b, Hardwood trees (trees with yellowed leaves in foreground). c, Conifers. d, Conifer branch with cones. e, Hardwood trees with conifers in background. f, Conifers with hardwood tree in background. g, Purple berries on tree. h, Man preparing to chop down tree. i, Flying squirrel and trees. j, Conifers in fog.

No. 4170: a, Three trees (22x26mm). b, Bird and tree (22x26mm). c, Two birds on tree branches (22x26mm). d, Hawk in flight (30x30mm). e, Magnolia blossom (30x30mm). f, Woodpecker (22x26mm). g, Yew tree branches and berries (22x26mm). h, Flying squirrel (22x26mm). i, Tree in winter (30x30mm). j, Maple samaras (30x30mm).

*Die Cut Perf. 13x13¼ (#4169a-4169j, 4170a-4170c, 4170f-4170h), Die Cut Perf. 13¼ (#4170d-4170e, 4170i-4170j)*

**2017, Nov. 8**      **Litho.**

**Self-Adhesive**

| | | | | |
|---|---|---|---|---|
| 4169 | A4090 | Sheet of 10 | 12.00 | 12.00 |
| a.-j. | | 62y Any single | 1.00 | .80 |
| 4170 | A4091 | Sheet of 10 | 16.00 | 16.00 |
| a.-j. | | 82y Any single | 1.25 | .80 |

Miniature Sheet

Diplomatic Relations Between Japan and the Maldive Islands, 50th Anniv. — A4092

No. 4171: a, Atolls. b, Shadows of palm trees. c, Beach at tourist resort. d, Clouds over island. e, Palm tree on beach. f, Maldives anemonefish. g, Manta ray. i, Aerial view of Malé. j, Coconuts. k, Palm trees and ocean with sun approaching horizon.

**2017, Nov. 14**    **Litho.**    **Perf. 13**

| | | | | |
|---|---|---|---|---|
| 4171 | A4092 | Sheet of 10 | 16.00 | 16.00 |
| a.-j. | | 82y Any single | 1.25 | .80 |

Miniature Sheets

A4093

A4094

Greetings — A4095

No. 4172: a, Sun with circle of blue diamonds. b, Sun with circle of orange diamonds. c, Girl, cat, shooting star, horiz. d, Girl, guitar and cat. e, Girl and cat at table, rainbow. f, Dove carrying letter.

No. 4173: a, Gifts, letters on blue pennants, horiz. b, Gifts, letters on pink pennants, horiz. c, Birthday cake. d, Dog wearing birthday hat. e, Balloons. f, Cracker and streamers, horiz.

No. 4174: a, Tuxedo and tie (22x26mm). b, Gown and necklace (22x26mm). c, Champagne bottle and flutes (22x26mm). d, Cut jewel (22x26mm). e, Tray of canapés (22x26mm). f, Flowers in vase (22x32mm).

*Die Cut Perf. 13x13¼, 13¼x13, Die Cut Perf. 13 (#4174f)*

**2017, Nov. 22**      **Litho.**

**Self-Adhesive**

| | | | | |
|---|---|---|---|---|
| 4172 | A4093 | Sheet of 10, #4172a-4172b, 2 each #4172c-4172f | 12.00 | 12.00 |
| a.-f. | | 62y Any single | 1.00 | .80 |
| 4173 | A4094 | Sheet of 10, #4173a-4173b, 2 each #4173c-4173f | 16.00 | 16.00 |
| a.-f. | | 82y Any single | 1.25 | .80 |
| 4174 | A4095 | Sheet of 10, #4174a-4174b, 2 each #4174c-4174f | 17.00 | 17.00 |
| a.-f. | | 92y Any single | 1.40 | .80 |
| | | Nos. 4172-4174 (3) | 45.00 | |

Miniature Sheets

A4096

Winter Greetings — A4097

No. 4175: a, Buildings in snow (22x26mm). b, Boy holding hot drink in snow (22x26mm). c, Cup of coffee with cream snowman (22x24mm). d, Wood stove (22x26mm). e, Woman holding shopping bag (22x26mm). f, Street lamps in snow (22x26mm).

No. 4176: a, Rabbit facing left (22x26mm). b, Rabbit facing right (22x26mm). c, Snowman with stick hands and shovel (22x26mm). d, Snowman with mitten on stick hand and shovel (22x26mm). e, Snow-covered house (22x26mm). f, Child with telescope, mountains in background (22x26mm). g, Snow globe (23x22mm). h, Child and starry night (22x26mm).

*Die Cut Perf. 13x13¼, Die Cut Perf. (#4175c, 4176g)*

**2017, Dec. 1**      **Litho.**

**Self-Adhesive**

| | | | | |
|---|---|---|---|---|
| 4175 | A4096 | Sheet of 10, #4175a-4175b, 2 each #4175c-4175f | 12.00 | 12.00 |
| a.-f. | | 62y Any single | 1.00 | .80 |
| 4176 | A4097 | Sheet of 10, #4176a-4176f, 2 each #4176g-4176h | 16.00 | 16.00 |
| a.-h. | | 82y Any single | 1.25 | .80 |

Thunberg Spirea A4098      Ranunculus A4099

Freesia and Leucocoryne A4100      Camellias A4101

Plum Blossoms A4102      Forsythia A4103

Cyclamen A4104      Violas A4105

Camellias A4106      Plum Blossoms A4107

*Die Cut Perf. 13x13¼*

**2017, Dec. 13**      **Litho.**

**Self-Adhesive**

| | | | | |
|---|---|---|---|---|
| 4177 | | Sheet of 10, 2 each #4177a-4177e | 12.00 | 12.00 |
| a. | A4098 | 62y multi | 1.00 | .80 |
| b. | A4099 | 62y multi | 1.00 | .80 |
| c. | A4100 | 62y multi | 1.00 | .80 |
| d. | A4101 | 62y multi | 1.00 | .80 |
| e. | A4102 | 62y multi | 1.00 | .80 |
| 4178 | | Sheet of 10, 2 each #4178a-4178e | 16.00 | 16.00 |
| a. | A4103 | 82y multi | 1.25 | .80 |
| b. | A4104 | 82y multi | 1.25 | .80 |
| c. | A4105 | 82y multi | 1.25 | .80 |
| d. | A4106 | 82y multi | 1.25 | .80 |
| e. | A4107 | 82y multi | 1.25 | .80 |

Miniature Sheet

Illustrations from Children's Book, *Where's the Fish?* by Taro Gomi — A4108

No. 4179: a, Three fish (33mm diameter). b, Fish facing left (32x24mm). c, Fish facing right (32x24mm). d, Fish in water facing right (29x23mm). e, Fish on television screen (30x30mm). f, Fish and children's toys (30x30mm). g, Fish on curtain (30x30mm). h, Fish on flower stem (28x30mm). i, Fish in candy jar (23x30mm). j, Fish in fruit bowl (30x30mm).

*Die Cut Perf. (#4179a-4179d), Die Cut Perf. 13¼x13½ (#4169e-4169g, 4169j), Die Cut Perf. 13x12¾ (#4169h)*

**2017, Dec. 20**      **Litho.**

**Self-Adhesive**

| | | | | |
|---|---|---|---|---|
| 4179 | A4108 | Sheet of 10 | 16.00 | 16.00 |
| a.-j. | | 82y Any single | 1.25 | .80 |

Kangi Temple
Shoden Hall,
Kumagaya
A4109

Main Hall of
Tsukiji Hongan-
ji,
Tokyo — A4110

### Photo. & Engr.

**2018, Jan. 5**      **Perf. 13¼**

| | | | | |
|---|---|---|---|---|
| 4180 | A4109 | 82y multi | 1.25 | .50 |
| 4181 | A4110 | 82y multi | 1.25 | .50 |
| a. | Vert. pair, #4180-4181 | | 3.00 | 2.25 |

### Miniature Sheets

A4111

Moomins
A4112

No. 4182: a, Moominpappa at typewwriter.
b, Moominmamma cooking. c, Snork Maiden
knitting. d, Hemulen with stamp album. e, Too-
Ticky with hammer. f, Snufkin with shell at ear.
g, Little My and eyeglasses. h, Moomin with

pencil and drawing. i, Moomin and Snufkin in
tree. j, Moomin family creating picture.
No. 4183: a, Moomin in chair reading letter.
b, Snufkin reading letter. c, Sniff reading letter.
d, Snork Maiden holding flower and letter. e,
Little My holding letter. f, Mymble sitting near
flowers reading letter. g, Little My handing letter to Moomin. h, Moominpappa holding letter
and bottle. i, Moominmamma holding letter
and handbag. j, Hattifatteners with letters.

**2018, Jan. 10**    **Litho.**    *Die Cut Perf.*
### Self-Adhesive

| | | | | |
|---|---|---|---|---|
| 4182 | A4111 | Sheet of 10 | 12.00 | 12.00 |
| a.-j. | | 62y Any single | 1.00 | .80 |

*Die Cut Perf. 13x13¼*

| | | | | |
|---|---|---|---|---|
| 4183 | A4112 | Sheet of 10 | 16.00 | 16.00 |
| a.-j. | | 82y Any single | 1.25 | .80 |

A4113

A4114

A4115

A4116

A4117

A4118

A4119

A4120

A4121

Traditional Japanese
Designs — A4122

*Die Cut Perf. 13*
**2018, Jan. 23**     **Litho.**
### Self-Adhesive

| | | | |
|---|---|---|---|
| 4184 | Sheet of 10, 2 each | | |
| | #4184a-4184e | 12.00 | 12.00 |
| a. | A4113 62y multi | 1.00 | .80 |
| b. | A4114 62y multi | 1.00 | .80 |
| c. | A4115 62y multi | 1.00 | .80 |
| d. | A4116 62y multi | 1.00 | .80 |
| e. | A4117 62y multi | 1.00 | .80 |

*Die Cut Perf. 12x12¼*

| | | | |
|---|---|---|---|
| 4185 | Sheet of 10, 2 each | | |
| | #4185a-4185e | 16.00 | 16.00 |
| a. | A4118 82y multi | 1.25 | .80 |
| b. | A4119 82y multi | 1.25 | .80 |
| c. | A4120 82y multi | 1.25 | .80 |
| d. | A4121 82y multi | 1.25 | .80 |
| e. | A4122 82y multi | 1.25 | .80 |

### Miniature Sheet

Heavenly
Bodies
A4123

No. 4186: a, Horsehead Nebula
(22x27mm). b, Orion Nebula (Messier 42)
(22x27mm). c, Pillars of Creation in Eagle
Nebula (22x27mm). d, S106 star-forming
region (22x27mm). e; Orion Nebula, diff.
(22x27mm). f, Iota Orionis star cluster
(22x27mm). g, Hale-Bopp Comet (26x30mm
oval). h, Sun and solar flare (22x27mm). i,
Mercury (22x27mm). j, Venus (22x27mm).

*Die Cut Perf. (#4186g), Die Cut Perf.
13x13¼*
**Litho. With Holographic Foil Affixed**
**2018, Feb. 7**     **Self-Adhesive**

| | | | | |
|---|---|---|---|---|
| 4186 | A4123 | Sheet of 10 | 16.00 | 16.00 |
| a.-j. | | 82y Any single | 1.25 | .80 |

Cat
A4124

Cat on Roof
A4125

Cat
A4126

Cat's Paw
Prints
A4127

Cat on
Tree
A4128

Cat's Tail
A4129

Cat
A4130

Cat
A4131

Cat in
Tree
A4132

Cat and
Kitten
A4133

Sleeping
Cat
A4134

Cat
A4135

Cat Under
Chair
A4136

Cat in Bag
A4137

Cat and
Cards
A4138

Kittens in
Bowl
A4139

Sleeping
Cat
A4140

Cat and
Flowers
A4141

Sleeping
Cat
A4142

Cat's Paw
A4143

*Die Cut Perf. 13¼x13 (horiz.
stamps), Die Cut Perf. 13x13¼ (vert.
stamps), Die Cut Perf. (#4187f,
4188j)*
**2018, Feb. 22**     **Litho.**
### Self-Adhesive

| | | | |
|---|---|---|---|
| 4187 | Sheet of 10 | 12.50 | 12.50 |
| a. | A4124 62y multi | 1.00 | .80 |
| b. | A4125 62y multi | 1.00 | .80 |
| c. | A4126 62y multi | 1.00 | .80 |
| d. | A4127 62y multi | 1.00 | .80 |
| e. | A4128 62y multi | 1.00 | .80 |
| f. | A4129 62y multi | 1.00 | .80 |
| g. | A4130 62y multi | 1.00 | .80 |
| h. | A4131 62y multi | 1.00 | .80 |
| i. | A4132 62y multi | 1.00 | .80 |
| j. | A4133 62y multi | 1.00 | .80 |
| 4188 | Sheet of 10 | 16.00 | 16.00 |
| a. | A4134 82y multi | 1.25 | .80 |
| b. | A4135 82y multi | 1.25 | .80 |
| c. | A4136 82y multi | 1.25 | .80 |
| d. | A4137 82y multi | 1.25 | .80 |
| e. | A4138 82y multi | 1.25 | .80 |
| f. | A4139 82y multi | 1.25 | .80 |
| g. | A4140 82y multi | 1.25 | .80 |
| h. | A4141 82y multi | 1.25 | .80 |
| i. | A4142 82y multi | 1.25 | .80 |
| j. | A4143 82y multi | 1.25 | .80 |

### Miniature Sheets

A4144

My Journey
A4145

No. 4189: a, Nagoya Castle, vert. b,
Shinkansen train and Mt. Fuji. c, Cherry blossoms and Mt. Fuji. d, Terraced tea fields and
Mt. Fuji. e, Tea service. f, Pine tree and Mt.
Fuji. g, Shrine and cherry blossoms. h, Torii
and Mt. Fuji. i, Waterfall. j, Cattle in pasture
and Mt. Fuji.

No. 4190: a, Cherry blossoms and Mt. Fuji
(22x30mm). b, Peach tree and Mt. Fuji
(26x22mm). c, Peach blossoms (26x22mm).
d, Grapes (22x26mm). e, Table with food and
wine, Mt. Fuji (22x26mm). f, Hot spring and
Mt. Fuji (22x26mm). g, Sun over Mt. Fuji and
Lake Tanuki (22x26mm). h, Temples by pond,
Mt. Fuji (22x26mm). i, Swan Lake Ferry on
Lake Yamanaka, Mt. Fuji (22x26mm). j, Phlox
flowers near lake, Mt. Fuji (22x26mm)

**Die Cut Perf. 13¼ (#4189a), Die Cut
Perf. 13x13¼ (#4190a, 4190d), Die
Cut Perf. 13¼x13**

**2018, Mar. 2** **Photo.**
**Self-Adhesive**

| 4189 | A4144 | Sheet of 10 | 12.50 | 12.50 |
| a.-j. | | 62y Any single | 1.00 | .80 |
| 4190 | A4145 | Sheet of 10 | 16.00 | 16.00 |
| a.-j. | | 82y Any single | 1.25 | .80 |

Cherry Blossoms A4146 / Plants A4147

Tulips A4148 / Rape Blossoms A4149

Strawberry Plant and Flowers A4150 / Cherry Blossoms A4151

Flowers A4152 / Dandelions A4153

Strawberries A4154

Sprout A4155

**Die Cut Perf. (#4191a-4191b, 4192a-
4192b), Die Cut Perf. 13x13¼**

**2018, Mar. 9** **Litho.**
**Self-Adhesive**

| 4191 | | Sheet of 10, 2 each #4191a-4191e | 12.50 | 12.50 |
| a. | A4146 | 62y gold & multi | 1.00 | .80 |
| b. | A4147 | 62y gold & multi | 1.00 | .80 |
| c. | A4148 | 62y gold & multi | 1.00 | .80 |
| d. | A4149 | 62y gold & multi | 1.00 | .80 |
| e. | A4150 | 62y gold & multi | 1.00 | .80 |
| 4192 | | Sheet of 10, 2 each #4192a-4192e | 16.00 | 16.00 |
| a. | A4151 | 82y gold & multi | 1.25 | .80 |
| b. | A4152 | 82y gold & multi | 1.25 | .80 |
| c. | A4153 | 82y gold & multi | 1.25 | .80 |
| d. | A4154 | 82y gold & multi | 1.25 | .80 |
| e. | A4155 | 82y gold & multi | 1.25 | .80 |

Roses A4156 / Roses A4157

Hydrangea A4158 / Hollyhocks A4159

Curcuma and Bouvardia Bouquet A4160 / Roses A4161

Pink Rose A4162 / Hydrangea Bouquet A4163

Carnations A4164 / Chinese Bellflowers A4165

**Die Cut Perf. 13x13¼**

**2018, Apr. 2** **Litho.**
**Self-Adhesive**

| 4193 | | Sheet of 10, 2 each #4193a-4193e | 12.50 | 12.50 |
| a. | A4156 | 62y multi | 1.00 | .80 |
| b. | A4157 | 62y multi | 1.00 | .80 |
| c. | A4158 | 62y multi | 1.00 | .80 |
| d. | A4159 | 62y multi | 1.00 | .80 |
| e. | A4160 | 62y multi | 1.00 | .80 |
| 4194 | | Sheet of 10, 2 each #4194a-4194e | 16.00 | 16.00 |
| a. | A4161 | 82y multi | 1.25 | .80 |
| b. | A4162 | 82y multi | 1.25 | .80 |
| c. | A4163 | 82y multi | 1.25 | .80 |
| d. | A4164 | 82y multi | 1.25 | .80 |
| e. | A4165 | 82y multi | 1.25 | .80 |

**Miniature Sheet**

Flora and Fauna of Daisetsuzan National Park — A4166

No. 4195: a, Northern fox (32x28mm). b,
Hokkaido chipmunk (32x28mm). c, Hokkaido
Crying Rabbit (32x28mm). d, Hokkaido flying
squirrel (32mm diameter). e, Purple mountain
heather (23x26mm). f, Primula flowers
(23x26mm). g, Mountain avens (23x26mm). h,
Mountain avens, diff. (23x26mm). i, Arctic
gentians (23x26mm). j, Aleutian bellflowers
(23x26mm).

**Die Cut Perf. 13x12¼ (#4195a-
4195c), Die Cut Perf. (#4195d), Die
Cut Perf. 13x13¼**

**2018, Apr. 11** **Litho.**
**Self-Adhesive**

| 4195 | A4166 | Sheet of 10 | 16.00 | 16.00 |
| a.-j. | | 82y Any single | 1.25 | .80 |

Philately Week — A4167

Screen art by Tawaraya Sotatsu (c. 1570-
c.1640): No. 4196, Raijin (Thunder God). No.
4197, Fujin (Wind God).

**Photo. & Engr.**
**2018, Apr. 20** **Perf. 13¼**
| 4196 | | 82y gold & multi | 1.25 | .50 |
| 4197 | | 82y gold & multi | 1.25 | .50 |
| a. | A4167 | Vert. pair, #4196-4197 | 3.00 | 2.20 |

A4168 / A4169

A4170 / A4171

A4172 / A4173

A4174 / A4175

Greetings — A4176

**Die Cut Perf. 13¼, Die Cut Perf.
(#4198a), Die Cut Perf. 13 (#4199a,
4200a),
Litho. With Foil Application**
**2018, Apr. 23** **Self-Adhesive**
| 4198 | | Sheet of 10, #4198a, 5 #4198b, 4 #4198c, + 3 stickers | 12.00 | 12.00 |
| a. | A4168 | 62y gold & multi | 1.00 | .80 |
| b. | A4169 | 62y gold & multi | 1.00 | .80 |
| c. | A4170 | 62y gold & multi | 1.00 | .80 |
| 4199 | | Sheet of 10, 5 #4199b, 4 #4199c, + 3 stickers | 16.00 | 16.00 |
| a. | A4171 | 82y gold & multi | 1.25 | .80 |
| b. | A4172 | 82y gold & multi | 1.25 | .80 |
| c. | A4173 | 82y gold & multi | 1.25 | .80 |

| 4200 | | Sheet of 10, #4200a, 5 #4200b, 4 #4200c, + 3 stickers | 17.50 | 17.50 |
| a. | A4174 | 92y gold & multi | 1.40 | .80 |
| b. | A4175 | 92y gold & multi | 1.40 | .80 |
| c. | A4176 | 92y gold & multi | 1.40 | .80 |
| | | Nos. 4198-4200 (3) | 45.50 | |

Envelopes — A4177

**Die Cut Perf. 13x13¼**
**2018, May 7** **Litho.**
**Self-Adhesive**
| 4201 | A4177 | 82y sil & multi | 1.25 | .80 |

**Miniature Sheets**

A4178

Kabuki A4179

No. 4202: a, Dancer from The Wisteria
Maiden (lilac background color). b, Character
from Sugawara and the Secrets of Calligraphy
(pink background color). c, Face makeup
(green panel at bottom). d, Character from
The Fight of the Carriage (rose pink background color). e, Character from Tales of the
Licensed Quarter (pale green background
color). f, Character from The Gion Festival
Chronicle of Faith (light blue background
color). g, Face makeup (pink panel at bottom.
h, Character from Sugawara and the Secrets
of Calligraphy (blue green background color).
i, Face makeup (red panel at bottom). j, Character from Kotobuki Soga no Taimen (buff
background).

No. 4203: a, Character with umbrella from
The Flower of Edo (32x43mm). b, Courtesan
character from The Flower of Edo (26x48mm).
c, Face makeup (purple panels at top and left)
(28x36mm). d, Face makeup (striped panel at
left) (28x36mm). e, Character from Yoshitsune
and the Thousand Cherry Trees (31x38mm). f,
Character from Twenty-four Paragons of Filial
Piety in This Land (31x39mm). g, Face
makeup (dark red panels at top and sides)
(28x36mm). h, Two characters from The Pair
of Lions (39x33mm). i, Face makeup (light
gray panels at top and sides (28x36mm). j,
Princess character from Twenty-four Paragons
of Filial Piety in This Land (28x51mm).

**Die Cut Perf. 13x13¼**
**2018, May 9** **Litho.**
**Self-Adhesive**
| 4202 | A4178 | Sheet of 10 | 12.00 | 12.00 |
| a.-j. | | 62y Any single | 1.00 | .80 |
**Die Cut Perf. 13**
| 4203 | A4179 | Sheet of 10 | 16.00 | 16.00 |
| a.-j. | | 62y Any single | 1.25 | .80 |

Flowers A4180

Designs: No. 4204, Daisies and rhododendrons, white, red and blue ribbon. No. 4205,
Chrysanthemums and cherry blossoms, red
and white polka-dotted ribbon.

**2018, May 16** **Litho.** **Perf. 13x13¼**
| 4204 | | 82y multi | 1.25 | .80 |
| 4205 | | 82y multi | 1.25 | .80 |
| a. | A4180 | Horiz. pair, #4204-4205 | 3.00 | 2.20 |

Japan-Russia Exchange Year. See Russia
No. 7923.

## Miniature Sheets

A4181

Hello
Kitty
A4182

No. 4206 — Hello Kitty: a, With tray of cookies (29x26mm). b, In airplane (26x25mm). c, Holding opened stamped letter (23x25mm). d, Blowing up blue balloon (27x24mm). e, Holding red balloon (22x32mm). f, With Mimmy in basket (30x24mm). g, At easel (27x23mm). h, On elephant (24x28mm). i, On apple (23x27mm). j, Holding teddy bear (23x29mm).

No. 4207 — Hello Kitty: a, At mailbox (27x23mm). b, Holding sealed letter (24x26mm). c, With Mimmy reading letter (26x24mm). d, Holding gift (22x27mm). e, Holding letter and fountain pen (23x28mm). f, Writing letter with quill pen (23x24mm). g, Holding letter and quill pen (26x24mm). h, With mouse, Joey (25x26mm). i, Holding large stamp (23x27mm). j, With bird holding letter (22x26mm).

**Die Cut Perf. 12¼, Die Cut Perf. 11¾ (#4207f)**

**2018, May 23**      **Litho.**
### Self-Adhesive
| | | | | |
|---|---|---|---|---|
| 4206 | A4181 | Sheet of 10 | 12.00 | 12.00 |
| *a.-j.* | | 62y Any single | 1.00 | .80 |
| 4207 | A4182 | Sheet of 10 | 16.00 | 16.00 |
| *a.-j.* | | 82y Any single | 1.25 | .80 |

---

Fish in Bowl
A4183

Electric Fan
Blades
A4185

Wind
Chimes
A4184

Mosquito
Coil
A4186

Watermelon
A4187

Fan
A4189

Fan
A4188

Yukata,
Morning
Glory
Design
A4190

Yukata,
Goldfish
Design
A4191

Fireworks
A4192

Water
Balloons
A4193

Boats,
Crabs,
Beach
Umbrella
and Chair
A4194

**2018, June 1**    **Litho.**    **Die Cut Perf.**
### Self-Adhesive
| | | | | |
|---|---|---|---|---|
| 4208 | | Sheet of 10, 2 each | | |
| | | #4208a-4208e | 12.00 | 12.00 |
| *a.* | A4183 | 62y multi | 1.00 | .80 |
| *b.* | A4184 | 62y multi | 1.00 | .80 |
| *c.* | A4185 | 62y multi | 1.00 | .80 |
| *d.* | A4186 | 62y multi | 1.00 | .80 |
| *e.* | A4187 | 62y multi | 1.00 | .80 |

**Die Cut Perf. 13x13¼ (#4209a-4209b), 12¼ (#4209c-4209d), 12¾x13 (#4209e-4209g)**
| | | | | |
|---|---|---|---|---|
| 4209 | | Sheet of 10, #4209a- | | |
| | | 4209d, 2 each | | |
| | | #4209e-4209g | 16.00 | 16.00 |
| *a.* | A4188 | 82y multi | 1.25 | .80 |
| *b.* | A4189 | 82y multi | 1.25 | .80 |
| *c.* | A4190 | 82y multi | 1.25 | .80 |
| *d.* | A4191 | 82y multi | 1.25 | .80 |
| *e.* | A4192 | 82y multi | 1.25 | .80 |
| *f.* | A4193 | 82y multi | 1.25 | .80 |
| *g.* | A4194 | 82y multi | 1.25 | .80 |

---

## Miniature Sheet

National Afforestation — A4195

No. 4210: a, Rhododendrons. b, Day lilies. c, Peach blossoms. d, Heartleaf false pickerelweed. e, Japanese black pine. f, Mountain cherry blossoms. g, Wheeping cherry blossoms. h, Castanopsis sieboldii. i, Japanese zelkova. j, Rhaphiolepis umbellata.

**2018, June 6**    **Litho.**    **Perf. 13¼**
| | | | | |
|---|---|---|---|---|
| 4210 | A4195 | Sheet of 10 | 12.00 | 12.00 |
| *a.-j.* | | 62y Any single | 1.00 | .80 |

## Miniature Sheets

A4196

---

Greetings — A4197

No. 4211: a, Large red flower, stem and leaves at UR. b, Two small orange and pink flowers, striped pink flower. c, Two small orange flowers, d, Two violet flowers. e, Two small orange flowers, one violet flower. f, Large red flower stem and leaves at left. g, Pink flower and small orange and pink flower. h, Violet flower, pink striped flower, small orange flower. i, Pink flower, small orange flower, violet flower, stem and leaves at top. j, Dark pink flower, stem and flowers at top.

No. 4212: a, Large orange flower, small yellow flower. b, Two small yellow flowers. c, Large yellow flower and pale blue flower. d, Small peach flower and two pale blue flowers. e, Two small yellow flowers and part of large yellow flower. f, Pale blue flower and large red flower. g, Small yellow flower and pale blue flower. h, Three yellow flowers. i, Two peach flowers at left and part of large violet blue flower at right. j, Large violet blue flower at left, two small yellow flowers at right.

**Die Cut Perf. 13**

**2018, June 13**    **Litho.**
### Self-Adhesive
| | | | | |
|---|---|---|---|---|
| 4211 | A4196 | Sheet of 10 | 12.00 | 12.00 |
| *a.-j.* | | 62y Any single | 1.00 | .80 |
| 4212 | A4197 | Sheet of 10 | 16.00 | 16.00 |
| *a.-j.* | | 82y Any single | 1.25 | .80 |

## Miniature Sheet

100th National High School Baseball
Championship — A4198

No. 4213: a, Cap, bat, glove, home plate. b, Base and baseball. c, Batter holding bat. d, Pitcher. e, Batter swinging at ball. f, Cheerleaders. g, Recording statistics in dugout. h, Player sliding home. i, Scoreboard. j, Fielder diving for ball.

**2018, June 15**    **Litho.**    **Perf. 13**
| | | | | |
|---|---|---|---|---|
| 4213 | A4198 | Sheet of 10 | 16.00 | 16.00 |
| *a.-j.* | | 82y Any single | 1.25 | .80 |

## Miniature Sheet

Return of Ogasawara (Bonin) Islands to Japan, 50th Anniv. — A4199

No. 4214: a, Military at return ceremony, tower in background. b, Military at return ceremony, Japanese flag on pole. c, Man, girl and boy on beach. d, Two women and girl on beach. e, People waving at boats, man at left. f, People waving at boats, woman at left. g, Two Meguro birds on branch. h, One Meguro bird on branch. i, Palm tree and Sun. j, Outrigger canoe and palm tree.

| 2018, June 26 | | Litho. | Perf. 13 |
|---|---|---|---|
| 4214 | A4199 | Sheet of 10 | 16.00 16.00 |
| a.-j. | | 82y Any single | 1.25 .80 |

## Miniature Sheet

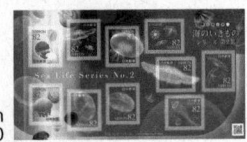

Jellyfish
A4200

No. 4215 — Various unnamed jellyfish as shown. Nos. 4215d, 4215e and 4215j are horiz.

| Litho. & Embossed | | | |
|---|---|---|---|
| 2018, July 4 | | Die Cut Perf. 13¼ | |
| Self-Adhesive | | | |
| 4215 | A4200 | Sheet of 10 | 15.00 15.00 |
| a.-j. | | 82y Any single | 1.50 1.10 |

## Miniature Sheet

Okinoshima UNESCO World Heritage Sites — A4201

No. 4216: a, Aerial view of northwest coast of Fukuoka Prefecture, denomination at UL (stamp 1). b, Aerial view of northwest coast of Fukuoka Prefecture, denomination at UR (stamp 2). c, Okitsu-miya of Munakata Grand Shrine (stamp 3). d, Nakatsu-miya of Munakata Grand Shrine (stamp 4). e, Hetsu-miya of Munataka Grand Shrine (stamp 5). f, Shinbaru-Nuyama Mounded Tomb Group (stamp 6). g, Gold ring (stamp 7). h, Gilt-bronze dragon's head (stamp 8). i, Nara style

jar (stamp 9). j, Deity and beast mirror (stamp 10).

| 2018, July 11 | | Litho. | Perf. 13 |
|---|---|---|---|
| 4216 | A4201 | Sheet of 10 | 15.00 15.00 |
| a.-j. | | 82y Any single | 1.50 1.10 |

## Miniature Sheet

Hokkaido, 150th Anniv. — A4202

No. 4217: a, Hokkaido Naming Place Monument. b, Nibutani Attush. c, Clock Tower, Sapporo. d, Former Hokkaido Central Government Building, Sapporo. e, Hanada Family Fisherman's Lodge. f, Former Branch Office of NYK Shipping Line, Otaru. g, Old Public Hall, Hakodate Ward. h, Former Court of Appeals, Sapporo. i, Aerial view of Shiretoko Peninsula. j, Hokkaido Shinkansen train leaving tunnel.

| 2018, July 13 | | Litho. | Perf. 12¾x13 |
|---|---|---|---|
| 4217 | A4202 | Sheet of 10 | 15.00 15.00 |
| a.-j. | | 82y Any single | 1.50 1.10 |

Leaves
A4203

Blue Bird Holding Letter
A4204

Green Bird Holding Letter Near Pillar Box
A4205

Birds Flying to Left With Letter
A4206

Birds Flying to Right With Letter
A4207

Yellow Bird With Letter and Mail Bag
A4208

Open Letter and Flowers
A4209

Owl, Letter and Open Mailbox
A4210

Flowers, Letter, Pen and Ink Bottle
A4211

Envelopes, Gift, Ribbons and Cat
A4212

| Die Cut Perf. 13x13¼ | | | |
|---|---|---|---|
| 2018, July 23 | | | Litho. |
| Self-Adhesive | | | |
| 4218 | | Booklet pane of 5 | 5.50 |
| a. | A4203 | 62y multi | 1.10 .85 |
| b. | A4204 | 62y multi | 1.10 .85 |
| c. | A4205 | 62y multi | 1.10 .85 |
| d. | A4206 | 62y multi | 1.10 .85 |
| e. | A4207 | 62y multi | 1.10 .85 |
| 4219 | | Sheet of 10, 2 each #4219a-4219e | 15.00 |
| a. | A4208 | 82y multi | 1.50 1.10 |
| b. | A4209 | 82y multi | 1.50 1.10 |
| c. | A4210 | 82y multi | 1.50 1.10 |
| d. | A4211 | 82y multi | 1.50 1.10 |
| e. | A4212 | 82y multi | 1.50 1.10 |

## Miniature Sheets

Animals
A4214

No. 4220: a, Deer (22x26mm). b, Flamingo (22x32mm). c, Hedgehog (23x26mm oval). d, Chipmunk (23x26mm oval). e, Snakes (22x32mm). f, Turtle (22x26mm). g, Crocodiles (25x26mm). h, Zebra (25x26mm). i, Frog (23x26mm oval). j, Birds and two capybaras (25x26mm).
No. 4221: a, Elephant (30x30mm). b, Panda (30mm diameter). c, Adult and juvenile pandas (36x36mm). d, Adult and juvenile koalas (30x30mm). e, Giraffe (19x40mm). f, Shoebill (19x40mm). g, Seal (26mm diameter). h, Chameleon (26mm diameter). i, Adult and juvenile otter (22x26mm). j, Lion (30x30mm).

| Die Cut Perf. 12¼x12½ (#4220a, 4220f), 12¼x12 (#4220b, 4220c), 12x12½ (#4220g, 4220h, 4220j), Die Cut Perf. (#4220c, 4220d, 4220i) | | | |
|---|---|---|---|
| 2018, July 27 | | | Litho. |
| Self-Adhesive | | | |
| 4220 | A4213 | Sheet of 10 | 11.00 |
| a.-j. | | 62y Any single | 1.10 .85 |

| Die Cut Perf. 12 (#4221a, 4221d, 4221j), 11½x12½ (#4221e, 4221f), 12x12½ (#4221i), Die Cut Perf. (#4221b, 4221c, 4221g, 4221h) | | | |
|---|---|---|---|
| 2018, July 27 | | | Litho. |
| 4221 | A4214 | Sheet of 10 | 15.00 |
| a.-j. | | 82y Any single | 1.50 1.10 |

## Miniature Sheet

Diplomatic Relations Between Japan and Sweden, 150th Anniv. — A4215

No. 4222: a, City Hall, Stockholm. b, Mt. Fuji and cherry blossoms. c, Swedish people in traditional costumes. d, Japanese people in traditional costumes. e, Swedish house and twinflowers. f, Japanese house. g, Coffee and fika, Sweden. h, Tea, tea whisk and yokan, Japan. i, Houses, Gamlestaden, Sweden. j, Bridge and poetry line by Basho, Japan.

| 2018, Aug. 2 | | Litho. | Perf. 12¾x13 |
|---|---|---|---|
| 4222 | A4215 | Sheet of 10 | 15.00 15.00 |
| a.-j. | | 82y Any single | 1.50 1.10 |

## Miniature Sheets

A4216

Disney Characters — A4217

No. 4223 — Winnie the Pooh characters: a, Winnie and dripping honey (30x26mm hexagonal). b, Winnie and Tigger at pond (30x26mm hexagonal). c, Winnie sitting on honey pot (30x26mm hexagonal), d, Tigger on Winnie (30x26mm hexagonal). e, Winnie and Piglet (30x26mm hexagonal). f, Winnie and Eeyore (30x26mm hexagonal). g, Winnie, Piglet and ducklings (30x26mm hexagonal). h, Winnie and Christopher Robin (30x26mm hexagonal). i, Tigger and Piglet (23x26mm). j, Winnie, with trumpet, and Eeyore (26x23mm).

No. 4224 — Mickey Mouse characters: a, Mickey at ship's wheel, in *Steamboat Willie* (26x22mm). b, Minnie Mouse, in *Steamboat Willie* (26x22mm). c, Mickey (22x26mm). d, Minnie running (22x26mm). e, Mickey wearing brown pants (26x22mm). f, Minnie touching bow (26x22mm). g, Mickey holding hat (22x26mm). h, Minnie holding umbrella (22x26mm). i, Mickey wearing wizard's hat (26x22mm). j, Minnie wearing red bow (26x22mm).

**Die Cut Perf. 13¼ (hexagonal stamps), 13x13¼ (#4223i), 13¼x13 (#4223j)**

**2018, Aug. 8**        **Litho.**
**Self-Adhesive**

| 4223 | A4216 | Sheet of 10 | 11.00 | |
| *a.-j.* | | 62y Any single | 1.10 | .85 |

**Die Cut Perf. 13¼x13 (#4224a, 4224b, 4224e, 4224f, 4224i, 4224j), 13x13¼ (#4224c, 4224d, 4224g, 4224h)**

| 4224 | A4217 | Sheet of 10 | 15.00 | |
| *a.-j.* | | 82y Any single | 1.50 | 1.10 |

Red Maple Leaves A4218

Leaves in Rocky Stream A4219

Grapes A4220

Blossoms on Tree Branch A4221

Mushrooms A4222

Red, Yellow and Orange Leaves A4224

Wreath A4226

Chipmunk and Mushrooms A4228

Flowers A4230

Bird Holding Berry A4232

Chestnuts A4234

Gourds A4236

Leaves Changing Color A4223

Flowers and Leaves A4225

Acorns A4227

Red Maple Tree A4229

Fallen Leaves and Mushrooms A4231

Leaves A4233

Pumpkin Soup A4235

Flowers A4237

**Die Cut Perf. 13¼x13 (#4225a, 4225d), 13x13¼ (#4225f, 4225c, 4225f, 4225g, 4225h, 4225i), Die Cut Perf. (#4225e, 4225j)**

**2018, Aug. 23**       **Litho.**
**Self-Adhesive**

| 4225 | | Sheet of 10 | 11.00 | |
| *a.* | A4218 | 62y multi | 1.10 | .85 |
| *b.* | A4219 | 62y multi | 1.10 | .85 |
| *c.* | A4220 | 62y multi | 1.10 | .85 |
| *d.* | A4221 | 62y multi | 1.10 | .85 |
| *e.* | A4222 | 62y multi | 1.10 | .85 |
| *f.* | A4223 | 62y multi | 1.10 | .85 |
| *g.* | A4224 | 62y multi | 1.10 | .85 |
| *h.* | A4225 | 62y multi | 1.10 | .85 |
| *i.* | A4226 | 62y multi | 1.10 | .85 |
| *j.* | A4227 | 62y multi | 1.10 | .85 |

**Die Cut Perf. (#4226a, 4226d), Die Cut Perf. 13x13¼ (#4226b, 4226c,**

**4226f, 4226g, 4226h, 4226i), 13¼x13 (#4226e, 4226j)**

| 4226 | | Sheet of 10 | 15.00 | |
| *a.* | A4228 | 82y multi | 1.50 | 1.10 |
| *b.* | A4229 | 82y multi | 1.50 | 1.10 |
| *c.* | A4230 | 82y multi | 1.50 | 1.10 |
| *d.* | A4231 | 82y multi | 1.50 | 1.10 |
| *e.* | A4232 | 82y multi | 1.50 | 1.10 |
| *f.* | A4233 | 82y multi | 1.50 | 1.10 |
| *g.* | A4234 | 82y multi | 1.50 | 1.10 |
| *h.* | A4235 | 82y multi | 1.50 | 1.10 |
| *i.* | A4236 | 82y multi | 1.50 | 1.10 |
| *j.* | A4237 | 82y multi | 1.50 | 1.10 |

**Miniature Sheet**

73rd National Athletic Meet, Fukui Prefecture — A4238

No. 4227: a, Gymnast on rings. b, Snow crabs. c, Wall climbing. d, Eyeglass frames. e, Cyclist. f, Narcissi. g, Field hockey. h, Mikata Five Lakes. i, Rowing. j, Tojinbo Cliffs.

**2018, Aug. 29**   **Photo.**   **Perf. 12¾x13**

| 4227 | A4238 | Sheet of 10 | 15.00 | 15.00 |
| *a.-j.* | | 82y Any single | 1.50 | 1.10 |

Cape Kannon Lighthouse A4239

Mikomotoshima Lighthouse A4240

Cape Muroto Lighthouse A4241

Hesaki Lighthouse A4242

Original Cape Kannon Lighthouse — A4243

**2018, Sept. 3**    **Litho.**     **Perf. 13½**

| 4228 | A4239 | 82y multi | 1.50 | 1.10 |
| 4229 | A4240 | 82y multi | 1.50 | 1.10 |
| 4230 | A4241 | 82y multi | 1.50 | 1.10 |
| 4231 | A4242 | 82y multi | 1.50 | 1.10 |
| 4232 | A4243 | 82y multi | 1.50 | 1.10 |
| *a.* | | Horiz. strip of 5, #4228-4232 | 7.50 | 5.50 |
| | | Nos. 4228-4232 (5) | 7.50 | 5.50 |

Japanese lighthouses, 150th anniv. Nos. 4228-4232 comes in sheets of 10, 2 horiz. strips of 5.

A4244

My Journey A4245

No. 4233: a, Nishi-Oyama Railroad Station (26x22mm). b, Sakurajima (26x22mm). c, Bowl of shaved ice with condensed milk and fruit (26x22mm). d, Pillar box at Nishi-Oyama Railroad Station (26x22mm). e, Boat in Takachiho Gorge (26x22mm). f, Takachiho Gorge (22x26mm). g, Mangos (26x22mm). h, Japanese macaques, Mt. Takasaki (26x22mm). i, Lake Kinrin (26x22mm). j, Steam rising from Hells of Beppu hot spring (26x22mm).

No. 4234: a, Tenman-gu Shrine, Dazaifu (26x22mm). b, Mentaiko (pollock roe) and rice (22x26mm). c, Bowl of Hakata ramen noodles (26x22mm). d, Karatsu Castle (26x22mm). e, Arita ware plate on stand (25x26mm). f, Nagasaki at night (26x22mm). g, Glover House, Nagasaki (26x22mm). h, Oura Catholic Church (22x30mm). i, Kokin Denju no Ma Teahouse, Kumamoto (26x22mm). j, Mt. Aso (26x24mm).

**Die Cut Perf. 13¼x13, 13x13¼ (#4233f)**

**2018, Sept. 5**        **Litho.**
**Self-Adhesive**

| 4233 | A4244 | Sheet of 10 | 11.00 | |
| *a.-j.* | | 62y Any single | 1.10 | .85 |

**Die Cut Perf. 13¼x13 (#4234a, 4234c, 4234d, 4234f, 4234g, 4234i),**

*13x13¼ (#4234b, 4324h), 12½ (#4234e), 13¼x12 (#4234j)*

| 4234 | A4245 | Sheet of 10 | 15.00 | |
|---|---|---|---|---|
| a.-j. | | 82y Any single | 1.50 | 1.10 |

This sheet of four 62y stamps, four 82y stamps and two 120y stamps, issued Sept. 5, 2018, was printed in limited quantities and sold only with a set of stationery, postcards and envelopes for 2000y.

## Miniature Sheets

A4246

**Posukuma and Kumamon — A4247**

No. 4235 — Teddy bear mascot of Japan Post wearing cap and black bear mascot of Kumamoto Prefecture: a, Facing each other. b, Waving. c, With musical notes. d, Jumping. e, With one paw raised. f, With cherry blossoms. g, Holding tags on tree. h, Sitting on bench. i, Ice skating. j, With hearts.

No. 4236: a, Head of Japan Post mascot in thought bubble. b, Head of Kumamoto Prefecture mascot in thought bubble, Japan Post mascot with paws crossed. c, Japan Post mascot and pillar box in thought bubble. d, Head of Kumamoto Prefecture mascot in thought bubble, Japan Post mascot with one paw raised. e, Japan Post mascot carrying letter in thought bubble. f, Kumamoto Prefecture mascot leaning in thought bubble. g, Kumamoto Prefecture mascot writing, Japan Post mascot sitting in thought bubble. h, Japan Post mascot at table with envelopes, Kumamoto Prefecture mascot in thought bubble. i, Kumamoto Prefecture mascot presenting letter to Japan Post mascot. j, Japan Post mascot presenting letter to Kumamoto Prefecture mascot.

### Die Cut Perf. 12½x13
**2018, Sept. 14**      Litho.
**Self-Adhesive**

| 4235 | A4246 | Sheet of 10 | 11.00 | |
|---|---|---|---|---|
| a.-j. | | 62y Any single | 1.10 | .85 |
| 4236 | A4247 | Sheet of 10 | 15.00 | |
| a.-j. | | 82y Any single | 1.50 | 1.10 |

This sheet of three 82y stamps and two 120y stamps + 23 stickers depicting the teddy bear mascot of Japan Post, issued Sept. 14, 2018, was printed in limited quantities and sold only with a set of envelopes and cards for 1200y.

**Fashion
A4248**

No. 4237: a, Six eyeglass frames, hat and pair of gloves (28mm diameter). b, Four t-shirts, blue green background (22x26mm). c, Four blouses, blue background (22x26mm). d, Four jackets, purple background (22x26mm). e, Six handbags (28mm diameter). f, Lipsticks, necklaces and make-up (28mm diameter). g, Four pairs of jeans and pair of shorts (22x26mm). h, Three dresses (22x26mm). i, Scarf, winter cap and three sweaters (22x26mm). j, Four pairs of high-heeled shoes (28mm diameter).

### Die Cut Perf. (circular stamps), Die Cut Perf. 13x13¼ (rectangular stamps)
**2018, Sept. 19**      Litho.
**Self-Adhesive**

| 4237 | A4248 | Booklet pane of 10 | 15.00 | |
|---|---|---|---|---|
| a.-j. | | 82y Any single | 1.50 | 1.10 |

### Miniature Sheet

**Japan at Night
A4249**

No. 4238: a, Mizushima Coastal Industrial Area, Okayama Prefecture (stamp 1). b, Lake Togo area, Tottori Prefecture (stamp 2). c, Matsue water lanterns, Shimane Prefecture (stamp 3). d, Itsukushima Shrine, Hiroshima Prefecture (stamp 4). e, Kochi City, Kochi Prefecture (stamp 5). f, Matsuyama Castle, Ehime Prefecture (stamp 6). g, Karatsu, Saga Prefecture (stamp 7). h, Shuri Castle, Okinawa Prefecture (stamp 8). i, Huis Ten Bosch Theme Park (denomination at LL), Nagasaki Prefecture (stamp 9). j, Huis Ten Bosch Theme Park (denomination at LR), Nagasaki Prefecture (stamp 10).

**2018, Sept. 26**    Photo.    **Perf. 13**

| 4238 | A4249 | Sheet of 10 | 15.00 | 15.00 |
|---|---|---|---|---|
| a.-j. | | 82y Any single | 1.50 | 1.10 |

**Tokyo Metro Cars
A4250**

**Kintetsu 21000 and 21020 Series Locomotives
A4251**

**East Japan Railways 651 Series Locomotive
A4252**

**Odakyu Electric Railway 20000 Series Locomotive
A4253**

**Kyushu Railway 883 Series Locomotive
A4254**

**East Japan Railways E257 Series Locomotive
A4255**

**Japan Freight Railway M250 Series Locomotive
A4257**

**Shikoku Railway 5100 Series Locomotive
A4256**

**Odakyu Electric Railway 50000 Series Locomotive
A4258**

**Kyushu Railway BEC819 Series Locomotive
A4259**

**Tokyo Metro Car
A4260**

**East Japan Railways E257 Series Locomotive
A4261**

**Kintetsu 21000 and 21020 Series Locomotives
A4262**

**Shikoku Railway 5100 Series Locomotive
A4263**

**East Japan Railways 651 Series Locomotive
A4264**

**Japan Freight Railway M250 Series Locomotive
A4265**

**Odakyu Electric Railway 20000 Series Locomotive
A4266**

**Odakyu Electric Railway 50000 Series Locomotive
A4267**

Kyushu
Railway 883
Series
Locomotive
A4268

Kyushu
Railway
BEC819
Series
Locomotive
A4269

**2018, Oct. 4**    Litho.    *Perf. 13x12¾*

| 4239 | | Sheet of 10 | 15.00 | 15.00 |
|---|---|---|---|---|
| a. | A4250 | 82y multi | 1.50 | 1.10 |
| b. | A4251 | 82y multi | 1.50 | 1.10 |
| c. | A4252 | 82y multi | 1.50 | 1.10 |
| d. | A4253 | 82y multi | 1.50 | 1.10 |
| e. | A4254 | 82y multi | 1.50 | 1.10 |
| f. | A4255 | 82y multi | 1.50 | 1.10 |
| g. | A4256 | 82y multi | 1.50 | 1.10 |
| h. | A4257 | 82y multi | 1.50 | 1.10 |
| i. | A4258 | 82y multi | 1.50 | 1.10 |
| j. | A4259 | 82y multi | 1.50 | 1.10 |

*Perf. 12¾x13*

| 4240 | | Sheet of 10 | 15.00 | 15.00 |
|---|---|---|---|---|
| a. | A4260 | 82y multi | 1.50 | 1.10 |
| b. | A4261 | 82y multi | 1.50 | 1.10 |
| c. | A4262 | 82y multi | 1.50 | 1.10 |
| d. | A4263 | 82y multi | 1.50 | 1.10 |
| e. | A4264 | 82y multi | 1.50 | 1.10 |
| f. | A4265 | 82y multi | 1.50 | 1.10 |
| g. | A4266 | 82y multi | 1.50 | 1.10 |
| h. | A4267 | 82y multi | 1.50 | 1.10 |
| i. | A4268 | 82y multi | 1.50 | 1.10 |
| j. | A4269 | 82y multi | 1.50 | 1.10 |

A4270      A4271

International Letter
Writing
Week — A4272

Art by Hiroshige (1797-1858): 8y, Hawk at Sunrise. No. 4242, Camellia from Camellias with Small Birds. No. 4243, Camellia and bird from Camellias with Small Birds. 90y, Travelers on Bridge Over Kake River Near the Tokaido Station. 110y, Sandbank in the Tenryu River Near the Mitsuke Station. 130y, Travelers and Hostesses at an Inn.

**2018, Oct. 9**    Litho.    *Perf. 14*

| 4241 | A4270 | 8y multi | .30 | .25 |
|---|---|---|---|---|
| 4242 | | 70y multi | 1.25 | .95 |
| 4243 | | 70y multi | 1.25 | .95 |
| a. | | Vert. pair, #4242-4243 | 2.50 | 1.90 |

*Perf. 12¾x13*

| 4244 | A4272 | 90y multi | 1.60 | 1.25 |
|---|---|---|---|---|
| 4245 | A4272 | 110y multi | 2.00 | 1.50 |
| 4246 | A4272 | 130y multi | 2.40 | 1.75 |
| | | Nos. 4241-4246 (6) | 8.80 | 6.65 |

See listing for No. 4448 for images of each Hiroshige print.

## Miniature Sheets

A4273

Gifts
From the
Forest
A4274

No. 4247: a, Fruit hanging from tree (22x26mm). b, Faces of flying squirrels (22x26mm). c, Berries on stem and leaves (22x26mm). d. Flowers (22x26mm). e, Two birds (34x34mm diamond-shaped). f, Tree bark (22x26mm). g, Birds and bird house (22x26mm). h, Vine (22x26mm). i, Animal climbing tree (22x26mm). j, Deer (34x34mm diamond-shaped).

No. 4248: a, Red flowers (22x26mm). b, Pink flowers (22x26mm). c, Two stylized birds

(22x26mm). d, Tree, flowers, and leaves (27mm diameter). e, Monkey in tree (27mm diameter). f, Insect (22x26mm). g, Vine, diff. (22x26mm). h, Leaves and fruit clusters (22x26mm). i, Fruits (27mm diameter). j, Berries on stem (27mm diameter).

*Die Cut Perf. 13x13¼, 13¼, 13¼ (#4247e, 4247j)*

**2018, Oct. 17**    Litho.

**Self-Adhesive**

| 4247 | A4273 | Sheet of 10 | 11.00 | |
|---|---|---|---|---|
| a.-j. | | 62y Any single | 1.10 | .85 |

*Die Cut Perf. 13x13¼, Die Cut Perf. (circular stamps)*

| 4248 | A4274 | Sheet of 10 | 15.00 | |
|---|---|---|---|---|
| a.-j. | | 82y Any single | 1.50 | 1.10 |

## Miniature Sheet

Start of
Meiji
Era,
150th
Anniv.
A4275

No. 4249 — Woodblock prints: a, View of Waiting Room at the Shiodome Railway Station (ceiling lamp in foreground), by Hiroshige III. b, As "a," (steam locomotive). c, View of the Opening Ceremonies at the Yokohama Post Office (one flag), by Hiroshige III. d, As "c," (four flags). e, Prominent Sights in Tokyo: Cherry Blossoms in Full Bloom at Ueno Park (women with blue umbrellas), by Hiroshige III. f, As "e," (women with beige umbrellas). g, Prominent Sights in Tokyo: Brick Buildings Along Ginza Street, Horse-Drawn Trams (horses), by Hiroshige III. h, As "g," (no horses). i, View of a European-style Musical Concert (four musicians with string instruments), by Chikanobu Yoshu. j, As "i," (pianist).

**2018, Oct. 23**    Litho.    *Perf. 12¾x13*

| 4249 | A4275 | Sheet of 10 | 15.00 | 15.00 |
|---|---|---|---|---|
| a.-j. | | 82y Any single | 1.50 | 1.10 |

Japanese Cuisine — A4276

No. 4250 — Confections: a, Jonamagashi (chrysanthemum shaped) (32x27mm). b, Kinton (shredded sweet potato) (27x32mm). c, Flower petal mochi (white folded rice cake) (27x32mm). d, Jonamagashi (red and white, flower-shaped) (27x32mm). e, Higashi (red maple, ginkgo leaves and mushroom-shaped) (27x32mm). f, Higashi (butterfly, plants and knot-shaped) (27x32mm). g, Jonamagashi (pink folded square) (26x26mm). h, Jonamagashi (green, white and dark brown) (32x27mm). i, Oribe manju (white filled bun with brown and green decorations (27x32mm). j, Jonamagashi (cherry blossom shaped) (26x26mm).

*Die Cut Perf. 12½x12¾ (#4250a, 4250h), 12¾x12½ (#4250b-4250f, 4250i), 12¾ (#4250g, 4250j)*

**2018, Oct. 24**    Litho.

**Self-Adhesive**

| 4250 | A4276 | Booklet pane of 10 | 15.00 | |
|---|---|---|---|---|
| a.-j. | | 82y Any single | 1.50 | 1.10 |

This sheet of 24 82y stamps, depicting various confections, issued Oct. 24, 2018, was printed in limited quantities and sold only with a set of stationery and envelopes for 2500y. Value, $30.

Great Wave
of
Kanagawa,
by Hokusai
A4277

Red Fuji, by
Hokusai
A4278

**2018, Nov. 1**    Litho.    *Perf. 13¼x13*

| 4251 | A4277 | 8y multi | .30 | .25 |
|---|---|---|---|---|
| 4252 | A4278 | 8y multi | .30 | .25 |
| a. | | Horiz. pair, #4251-4252 | .35 | .25 |

A4279      A4280

New Year 2019 (Year of
the Pig)
A4281      A4282

**2018, Nov. 1**    Litho.    *Perf. 13x13¼*

| 4253 | A4279 | 62y multi | 1.10 | .85 |
|---|---|---|---|---|
| 4254 | A4280 | 82y multi | 1.50 | 1.10 |

**Litho. & Typo.**

*Perf. 13¼*

| 4255 | A4281 | 62y+3y multi | 1.25 | .95 |
|---|---|---|---|---|
| 4256 | A4282 | 82y+3y multi | 1.50 | 1.10 |
| | | Nos. 4253-4256 (4) | 5.35 | 4.00 |

A4283

A4284

A4285      A4286

A4287      A4288

A4289      A4290

A4291      A4292

A4293      A4294

A4295      A4296

A4297      A4298

A4299      A4300

A4301

Plants and Fruits in Glass
Jars — A4302

*Die Cut Perf. 13x13¼*

**2018, Nov. 14**    Photo.

**Self-Adhesive**

| 4257 | | Sheet of 10 | 11.00 | |
|---|---|---|---|---|
| a. | A4283 | 62y multi | 1.10 | .85 |
| b. | A4284 | 62y multi | 1.10 | .85 |
| c. | A4285 | 62y multi | 1.10 | .85 |
| d. | A4286 | 62y multi | 1.10 | .85 |
| e. | A4287 | 62y multi | 1.10 | .85 |
| f. | A4288 | 62y multi | 1.10 | .85 |
| g. | A4289 | 62y multi | 1.10 | .85 |
| h. | A4290 | 62y multi | 1.10 | .85 |
| i. | A4291 | 62y multi | 1.10 | .85 |
| j. | A4292 | 62y multi | 1.10 | .85 |

*Die Cut Perf. 13x13¼ (#4258a-4258e, 4258j), 13¼x13 (#4258f-4258i)*

| 4258 | | Sheet of 10 | 15.00 | |
|---|---|---|---|---|
| a. | A4293 | 82y multi | 1.50 | 1.10 |
| b. | A4294 | 82y multi | 1.50 | 1.10 |
| c. | A4295 | 82y multi | 1.50 | 1.10 |
| d. | A4296 | 82y multi | 1.50 | 1.10 |
| e. | A4297 | 82y multi | 1.50 | 1.10 |
| f. | A4298 | 82y multi | 1.50 | 1.10 |
| g. | A4299 | 82y multi | 1.50 | 1.10 |
| h. | A4300 | 82y multi | 1.50 | 1.10 |
| i. | A4301 | 82y multi | 1.50 | 1.10 |
| j. | A4302 | 82y multi | 1.50 | 1.10 |

Labor and Social
Security Attorney
System, 50th
Anniv. — A4303

Designs: No. 4259, Flowers. No. 4260, Bird carrying heart-shaped balloons.

**2018, Nov. 28**    Litho.    *Perf. 13*

| 4259 | | 82y multi | 1.50 | 1.10 |
|---|---|---|---|---|
| 4260 | | 82y multi | 1.50 | 1.10 |
| a. | A4303 | Vert. pair, #4259-4260 | 3.00 | 2.20 |

## Miniature Sheet

Illustrations From *The Very Hungry Caterpillar*, by Eric Carle — A4304

No. 4261: a, Butterfly (41x24mm). b, Caterpillar ("Nippon" at bottom) (30mm diameter). c, Caterpillar ("Arigato" at bottom) (30mm diameter). d, Caterpillar and two pears (30x30mm). e, Caterpillar and three plums (30x30mm). f, Caterpillar and five oranges (30x30mm). g, Moon and egg (32x23mm). h, Sun, caterpillar on leaf (30x30mm). i, Sun and caterpillar (30x30mm). j, Caterpillar (30x30mm).

*Die Cut Perf. (#4261a-4261c), Die Cut Perf. 13¼ (#4261d-4261f, 4261h-4261j), 11¼ (#4261g)*

**2018, Nov. 30**      Litho.

**Self-Adhesive**

| 4261 | A4304 | Sheet of 10 + 16 stickers | 15.00 | |
| a.-j. | | 82y Any single | 1.50 | 1.10 |

Harp and Harpist A4305

Bassoon and Bassoonist A4306

Trumpet and Trumpeter A4307

Cymbals and Percussionist A4308

Violin and Violinist — A4309

Musical Instruments — A4310

No. 4263: a, Harp (22x30mm). b, Celesta (22x30mm). c, Trombone (30x22mm). d, French horn (24x28mm). e, Timpani (22x28mm). f, Violin (22x26mm). g, Flute and piccolo (30x22mm). h, Clarinet (22x30mm). i, Cello, pink F-clef (22x30mm). j, Bass, gray F-clef (22x33mm).

*Die Cut Perf. 13x13¼ (#4262a, 4262d), 13½x13¼ (#4262b), 14¾x13 (#4262c), 12½x13¼ (#4262e)*

**2018, Dec. 6**      Litho.

**Self-Adhesive**

| 4262 | | Sheet of 10, 2 each #4262a-4262e | 11.00 | |
| a. | A4305 | 62y multi | 1.10 | .85 |
| b. | A4306 | 62y multi | 1.10 | .85 |
| c. | A4307 | 62y multi | 1.10 | .85 |
| d. | A4308 | 62y multi | 1.10 | .85 |
| e. | A4309 | 62y multi | 1.10 | .85 |

*Die Cut Perf. 13x13¼ (#4263a, 4263b, 4263f, 4263h, 4263i, 4263j), 13¼x13 (#4263c, 4263g), 12x12¼ (#4263d), 13x12¼ (#4263e)*

| 4263 | A4310 | Sheet of 10 | 15.00 | |
| a.-j. | | 82y Any single | 1.50 | 1.10 |

Circles of Dots A4311

Triangles A4312

Squares and Parallel Lines A4313

Squares A4314

Lines and Dots A4315

Flowers A4316

Flowers A4317

Flowers A4318

Flowers A4319

Flowers A4320

A4321

A4322

A4323

A4324

A4325

**Litho. With Foil Application**

**2018, Dec. 10**    *Die Cut Perf. 13*

**Self-Adhesive**

| 4264 | | Sheet of 10, 2 each #4264a-4264e | 11.00 | |
| a. | A4311 | 62y gold & multi | 1.10 | .85 |
| b. | A4312 | 62y gold & multi | 1.10 | .85 |
| c. | A4313 | 62y gold & multi | 1.10 | .85 |
| d. | A4314 | 62y gold & multi | 1.10 | .85 |
| e. | A4315 | 62y gold & multi | 1.10 | .85 |

*Die Cut Perf. 13¼*

| 4265 | | Sheet of 10, 2 each #4265a-4265e | 15.00 | |
| a. | A4316 | 82y gold & multi | 1.50 | 1.10 |
| b. | A4317 | 82y gold & multi | 1.50 | 1.10 |
| c. | A4318 | 82y gold & multi | 1.50 | 1.10 |
| d. | A4319 | 82y gold & multi | 1.50 | 1.10 |
| e. | A4320 | 82y gold & multi | 1.50 | 1.10 |
| 4266 | | Sheet of 10, 2 each #4266a-4266e | 17.50 | |
| a. | A4321 | 92y silver & multi | 1.75 | 1.40 |
| b. | A4322 | 92y silver & multi | 1.75 | 1.40 |
| c. | A4323 | 92y silver & multi | 1.75 | 1.40 |
| d. | A4324 | 92y silver & multi | 1.75 | 1.40 |
| e. | A4325 | 92y silver & multi | 1.75 | 1.40 |
| | | Nos. 4264-4266 (3) | 43.50 | |

Background colors differ on the two examples on the sheet of Nos. 4264a-4264e and 4266a-4266e.

Tulips and Sweet Peas A4326

Roses A4327

Narcssi A4328

Adonis Flowers A4329

Snowdrops A4330

Cherry Blossoms A4331

Roses A4332

Fuchsias A4333

Nemophila A4334

Christmas Roses A4335

*Die Cut Perf. 13x13¼*

**2018, Dec. 14**      Litho.

**Self-Adhesive**

| 4267 | | Sheet of 10, 2 each #4267a-4267e | 11.00 | |
| a. | A4326 | 62y multi | 1.10 | .85 |
| b. | A4327 | 62y multi | 1.10 | .85 |
| c. | A4328 | 62y multi | 1.10 | .85 |
| d. | A4329 | 62y multi | 1.10 | .85 |
| e. | A4330 | 62y multi | 1.10 | .85 |
| 4268 | | Sheet of 10, 2 each #4268a-4268e | 15.00 | |
| a. | A4331 | 82y multi | 1.50 | 1.10 |
| b. | A4332 | 82y multi | 1.50 | 1.10 |
| c. | A4333 | 82y multi | 1.50 | 1.10 |
| d. | A4334 | 82y multi | 1.50 | 1.10 |
| e. | A4335 | 82y multi | 1.50 | 1.10 |

A4336

Gaspard and Lisa, Children's Book Characters by Anne Gutman and Georg Hallensleben — A4337

No. 4269: a, Lisa (white animal) and red balloon (30x35mm). b, Gaspard (black animal) and yellow balloon (32x32mm). c, Gaspard and Lisa with ice cream sundaes (24x24mm). d, Gaspard and Lisa with sushi plates and chopsticks (24x24mm). e, Gaspard in bed (24x24mm). f, Lisa in bed (24x24mm). g, Gaspard and Lisa on slide (24x24mm). h, Gaspard and Lisa on scooters (24x24mm). i, Gaspard and Lisa at desk with open books (24x24mm). j, Gaspard and Lisa with backpacks (24x24mm).

No. 4270: a, Lisa with dessert bowl (28x37mm). b, Gaspard with dessert bowl (28x37mm). c, Gaspard and Lisa at Eiffel Tower (24x24mm). d, Gaspard and Lisa on bridge over River Seine (24x24mm). e, Gaspard and Lisa picnicking (24x24mm). f, Gaspard and Lisa in gondola of hot air balloon (24x24mm). g, Gaspard and Lisa with puppy and kitten (24x24mm). h, Gaspard and Lisa on balcony (24x24mm). i, Gaspard and Lisa rollerblading (24x24mm). j, Gaspard and Lisa sitting on benches (24x24mm).

*Die Cut Perf. 13¼, Die Cut Perf. (#4269a, 4269b), Die Cut Perf. 13½x13¼ (#4270a, 4270b)*

**2019, Jan. 16**      Litho.

**Self-Adhesive**

| 4269 | A4336 | Sheet of 10 | 11.00 | |
| a.-j. | | 62y Any single | 1.10 | .85 |
| 4270 | A4337 | Sheet of 10 | 15.00 | |
| a.-j. | | 82y Any single | 1.50 | 1.10 |

**Souvenir Sheet**

New Year 2019 A4338

No. 4271: a, Cat holding postcard. b, Cat holding envelope.

| 2019, Jan. 21 | Litho. | *Perf. 13x13¼* | | |
| 4271 | A4338 | Sheet of 2 | 2.60 | 2.60 |
| a. | | 62y multi | 1.10 | .85 |
| b. | | 82y multi | 1.50 | 1.10 |

No. 4271 was also a prize in the New Year lottery.

Rolled
Cookies
A4339

Sandwich
Cookies
A4340

Rice
Dumplings
A4341

Filled
Wheat
Cakes
A4342

Lemon
Cakes
A4343

Filled Rice
Dumplings
A4344

Canelés
A4345

Strawberry
Shortcake
A4346

Layered
Cake Roll
Slices
A4347

Fruit
Sandwiches
A4348

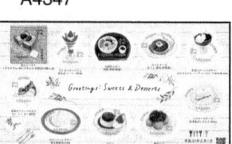

Desserts
A4349

No. 4273: a, Sweet bean paste on toast (23x23mm). b, Strawberry parfait (23x27mm). c, Bowl of fruit and syrup (28x22mm). d, Pancake (28x21mm oval). e, Bowl of coffee jelly (24x27mm). f, Fruit tart (25x22mm oval). g, Chantilly cream (30x20mm oval). h, Custard with whipped cream, syrup and fruit (28x23mm oval). i, Rice dumplings (29x22mm oval). j, Slice of cheesecake (30x22mm oval).

### Die Cut Perf. 12½
2019, Feb. 1　　　　　Litho.
**Self-Adhesive**

| | | | |
|---|---|---|---|
| 4272 | Sheet of 10 | 11.00 | |
| a. | A4339 62y multi | 1.10 | .85 |
| b. | A4340 62y multi | 1.10 | .85 |
| c. | A4341 62y multi | 1.10 | .85 |
| d. | A4342 62y multi | 1.10 | .85 |
| e. | A4343 62y multi | 1.10 | .85 |
| f. | A4344 62y multi | 1.10 | .85 |
| g. | A4345 62y multi | 1.10 | .85 |
| h. | A4346 62y multi | 1.10 | .85 |
| i. | A4347 62y multi | 1.10 | .85 |
| j. | A4348 62y multi | 1.10 | .85 |

### Die Cut Perf., Die Cut Perf. 14 (#4273a), Die Cut Perf. 13¼ (#4273c)

| | | | |
|---|---|---|---|
| 4273 | A4349 Sheet of 10 | 15.00 | |
| a.-j. | 82y Any single | 1.50 | 1.10 |

---

Miniature Sheet

Astronomy — A4350

No. 4247: a, Star cluster (red at right, 32mm diameter). b, Pleaides (32mm diameter). c, Mars (denomination at LR, 22x26mm). d, Ceres (denomination at UL, 22x26mm). e, Sirius (denomination at LL, 22x26mm). f, Moon (denomination at UL, 22x26mm). g, Io (denomination at UL, 22x26mm). h, Europa and Jupiter denomination at LL, 22x26mm). i, Earth (43mm diameter). j, Great Red Spot of Jupiter (32mm diameter).

### Die Cut Perf. 13x13¼, Die Cut Perf. (round stamps)
### Litho. With Hologram Affixed
2019, Feb. 6　　　　　Self-Adhesive

| | | | |
|---|---|---|---|
| 4274 | A4350　Sheet of 10 | 15.00 | |
| a.-j. | 82y Any single | 1.50 | 1.10 |

Cherry
Blossoms
A4351

Bird
A4352

Flowers
and
Butterfly
A4353

Poppies
A4354

Dandelions
A4355

Cherry
Blossoms
A4356

Rape
Blossoms and
Butterfly
A4357

Strawberries
A4358

Clover
Flowers and
Leaves
A4359

Tulips
A4360

---

### Die Cut Perf., Die Cut Perf. 13x13¼ (#4275c, 4275d, 4276c, 4276e), Die Cut Perf. 13¼x13¾ (#4275e), Die Cut Perf. 13¼ (#4276e)
2019, Feb. 20　　　　Litho.
**Self-Adhesive**

| | | | |
|---|---|---|---|
| 4275 | Sheet of 10, 2 each #4275a-4275e | 11.00 | |
| a. | A4351 62y multi | 1.10 | .85 |
| b. | A4352 62y multi | 1.10 | .85 |
| c. | A4353 62y multi | 1.10 | .85 |
| d. | A4354 62y multi | 1.10 | .85 |
| e. | A4355 62y multi | 1.10 | .85 |
| 4276 | Sheet of 10, 2 each #4276a-4276e | 11.00 | |
| a. | A4356 82y multi | 1.50 | 1.10 |
| b. | A4357 82y multi | 1.50 | 1.10 |
| c. | A4358 82y multi | 1.50 | 1.10 |
| d. | A4359 82y multi | 1.50 | 1.10 |
| e. | A4360 82y multi | 1.50 | 1.10 |

Crane and
Tortoise
A4361

Chrysanthemums
A4362

2019, Feb. 22　　Photo.　　Perf. 13¼

| | | | |
|---|---|---|---|
| 4277 | A4361 82y multi | 1.50 | 1.10 |
| 4278 | A4362 82y multi | 1.50 | 1.10 |
| a. | Pair, #4277-4278 | 3.00 | 2.20 |

Reign of Emperor Akihito, 30th anniv.

Dandelions
A4363

Water
Wheels
A4364

Wisteria
A4365

Rape
Blossoms
A4366

Tadpoles
A4367

Azaleas
A4368

Daffodils
A4369

Leaves
A4370

Peach and
Peach
Blossoms
A4371

Seaweed
A4372

Bush
Warblers
A4373

Bluets
A4374

---

Violets
A4375

Sea Shells
A4376

Parasol
A4377

Rice
Seedlings
A4378

Cherry
Blossoms
A4379

Kerria
Flowers
A4380

Mountains
A4381

Pussy
Willows
A4382

### Die Cut Perf. 13x13¼
2019, Mar. 6　　　　　Litho.
**Self-Adhesive**

| | | | |
|---|---|---|---|
| 4279 | Sheet of 10 | 11.00 | |
| a. | A4363 62y multi | 1.10 | .85 |
| b. | A4364 62y multi | 1.10 | .85 |
| c. | A4365 62y multi | 1.10 | .85 |
| d. | A4366 62y multi | 1.10 | .85 |
| e. | A4367 62y multi | 1.10 | .85 |
| f. | A4368 62y multi | 1.10 | .85 |
| g. | A4369 62y multi | 1.10 | .85 |
| h. | A4370 62y multi | 1.10 | .85 |
| i. | A4371 62y multi | 1.10 | .85 |
| j. | A4372 62y multi | 1.10 | .85 |
| 4280 | Sheet of 10 | 15.00 | |
| a. | A4373 82y multi | 1.50 | 1.10 |
| b. | A4374 82y multi | 1.50 | 1.10 |
| c. | A4375 82y multi | 1.50 | 1.10 |
| d. | A4376 82y multi | 1.50 | 1.10 |
| e. | A4377 82y multi | 1.50 | 1.10 |
| f. | A4378 82y multi | 1.50 | 1.10 |
| g. | A4379 82y multi | 1.50 | 1.10 |
| h. | A4380 82y multi | 1.50 | 1.10 |
| i. | A4381 82y multi | 1.50 | 1.10 |
| j. | A4382 82y multi | 1.50 | 1.10 |

Dahlias
and
Cosmos
A4383

Apple
Blossoms
A4384

Roses
A4385

Osmanthus
A4386

Petunias
A4387

Carnations
and Roses
A4388

Queen of
the Night
A4389

Roses
A4390

Sunflowers and Cockscombs A4391

Irises A4392

### Die Cut Perf. 13x13¼
**2019, Apr. 1**    Litho.
**Self-Adhesive**

| | | |
|---|---|---|
| 4281 | Sheet of 10, 2 each | |
| | #4281a-4281e | 11.00 |
| a. | A4383 62y multi | 1.10 .85 |
| b. | A4384 62y multi | 1.10 .85 |
| c. | A4385 62y multi | 1.10 .85 |
| d. | A4386 62y multi | 1.10 .85 |
| e. | A4387 62y multi | 1.10 .85 |
| 4282 | Sheet of 10, 2 each | |
| | #4282a-4282e | 15.00 |
| a. | A4388 82y multi | 1.50 1.10 |
| b. | A4389 82y multi | 1.50 1.10 |
| c. | A4390 82y multi | 1.50 1.10 |
| d. | A4391 82y multi | 1.50 1.10 |
| e. | A4392 82y multi | 1.50 1.10 |

**Miniature Sheet**

Flora and Fauna of Kurobe Gorge A4393

No. 4283: a, Red-flanked bluetail (28x32mm). b, Japanese rowan (22x26mm). c, Japanese serow (28x32mm). d, Blue-and-white flycatcher (28x32mm). e, Tiger lily (22x26mm). f, Hosta flowers (22x26mm). g, Japanese macaque (32x28mm). h, Potentilla dickinsii (22x26mm). i, White-spotted char (32mm diameter). j, Alpine accentor (32x28mm).

### Die Cut Perf. 12¼x13 (#4283a, 4283c, 4283d); Die Cut Perf. 13x13¼ (#4283b, 4283e, 4283f, 4283h); Die Cut Perf. 13x12¼ (#4283g, 4283j); Die Cut Perf. (#4283h)
**2019, Apr. 12**    Litho.
**Self-Adhesive**

| | | |
|---|---|---|
| 4283 | A4393 Sheet of 10 | 15.00 |
| a.-j. | 82y Any single | 1.50 1.10 |

A4394    A4395

A4396    A4397

A4398    A4399

A4400    A4401

Morning Glories, by Kiitsu Suzuki (1796-1858)
A4402    A4403

### Photo. & Engr.
**2019, Apr. 19**    Perf. 13x13¼

| | | |
|---|---|---|
| 4284 | Sheet of 10 | 15.00 15.00 |
| a. | A4394 82y multi | 1.50 1.10 |
| b. | A4395 82y multi | 1.50 1.10 |
| c. | A4396 82y multi | 1.50 1.10 |
| d. | A4397 82y multi | 1.50 1.10 |
| e. | A4398 82y multi | 1.50 1.10 |
| f. | A4399 82y multi | 1.50 1.10 |
| g. | A4400 82y multi | 1.50 1.10 |
| h. | A4401 82y multi | 1.50 1.10 |
| i. | A4402 82y multi | 1.50 1.10 |
| j. | A4403 82y multi | 1.50 1.10 |

Philately Week.

A4404    A4405

A4406    A4407

A4408    A4409

Jewelry A4408 A4409

### Litho. With Foil Application
### Die Cut Perf. 12¾x13½
**2019, Apr. 23**    Self-Adhesive

| | | |
|---|---|---|
| 4285 | Sheet of 10, 5 each | |
| | #4285a-4285b | 11.00 |
| a. | A4404 62y multi | 1.10 .85 |
| b. | A4405 62y multi | 1.10 .85 |
| 4286 | Sheet of 10, 5 each | |
| | #4286a-4286b | 15.00 |
| a. | A4406 82y multi | 1.50 1.10 |
| b. | A4407 82y multi | 1.50 1.10 |
| 4287 | Sheet of 10, 5 each | |
| | #4287a-4287b | 17.50 |
| a. | A4408 92y multi | 1.75 1.40 |
| b. | A4409 92y multi | 1.75 1.40 |
| | Nos. 4285-4287 (3) | 43.50 |

Simple — A4410

### Die Cut Perf. 13x13¼
**2019, May 8**    Litho.
**Self-Adhesive**

| | | |
|---|---|---|
| 4288 | A4410 82y multi | 1.50 1.10 |

Greeting Stamp.

**Souvenir Sheet**

Paintings of Mount Fuji A4411

No. 4289: a, The Sacred Peak in the Morning Sun, by Taikan Yokoyama (1868-1958) (denomination at LR). b, The Bay at Tago no Ura, by Yoshimatsu Goseda (1855-1925) (denomination at UR).

**2019, May 20**    Photo.    Perf. 13¼
**Without Serial Number**

| | | |
|---|---|---|
| 4289 | A4411 Sheet of 2 | 18.50 18.50 |
| a.-b. | 500y Either single | 9.25 7.00 |

In the sheet margins of No. 4289 there are holographic images of two birds.
Sheets with serial numbers were prizes for lottery held Jan. 20, 2019.

**Miniature Sheet**

Diplomatic Relations Between Japan and Finland, Cent. — A4412

No. 4290: a, People chopping logs near log cabin. b, Sauna. c, Boy fishing at lake. d, Children swimming in lake. e, Children gathering berries, kayak on shore. f, Kayakers and bicyclists. g, Children gathering mushrooms, bears. h, People, reindeer, Santa Claus. i, Woman bringing food to table. j, Table, child in hammock.

**2019, May 24**    Litho.    Perf. 13

| | | |
|---|---|---|
| 4290 | A4412 Sheet of 10 | 15.00 15.00 |
| a.-j. | 82y Any single | 1.50 1.10 |

Japanese Cypress A4413

Star Magnolia A4414

Mongolian Oak A4415

Chinese Fringe Tree A4416

Japanese Irises — A4417

**2019, May 28**    Litho.    Perf. 13¼

| | | |
|---|---|---|
| 4291 | A4413 62y multi | 1.25 .95 |
| 4292 | A4414 62y multi | 1.25 .95 |
| 4293 | A4415 62y multi | 1.25 .95 |
| 4294 | A4416 62y multi | 1.25 .95 |
| 4295 | A4417 62y multi | 1.25 .95 |
| a. | Vert. strip of 5, #4291-4295 | 6.25 4.75 |
| | Nos. 4291-4295 (5) | 6.25 4.75 |

Sun A4418

Starfish and Shells A4419

Pineapple and Lemons A4420

Fish A4421

Hibiscus Flower A4422

Morning Glories A4423

Fireworks A4424

Wind Chimes A4425

Watermelons A4426

Goldfish A4427

### Die Cut Perf. 13x13¼
**2019, May 30**    Litho.
**Self-Adhesive**

| | | |
|---|---|---|
| 4296 | Sheet of 10, 2 each | |
| | #4296a-4296e | 12.50 |
| a. | A4418 62y multi | 1.25 .95 |
| b. | A4419 62y multi | 1.25 .95 |
| c. | A4420 62y multi | 1.25 .95 |
| d. | A4421 62y multi | 1.25 .95 |
| e. | A4422 62y multi | 1.25 .95 |
| 4297 | Sheet of 10, 2 each | |
| | #4297a-4297e | 15.00 |
| a. | A4423 82y multi | 1.50 1.10 |
| b. | A4424 82y multi | 1.50 1.10 |
| c. | A4425 82y multi | 1.50 1.10 |
| d. | A4426 82y multi | 1.50 1.10 |
| e. | A4427 82y multi | 1.50 1.10 |

Ishioka Geodetic Station — A4428

Survey Airplane — A4429

Mountain Summit Triangulation With Global Navigational Satellite System — A4430

Surveyors Leveling — A4431

Japanese Sea
Level Reference
Point — A4432

Surveyor Using
Drone — A4433

Digital Plotting
A4434

Analog
Stereoplotting
A4435

Y Level
A4436

Theodolite
A4437

**2019, June 3    Litho.    Perf. 13x12¾**
| | | | |
|---|---|---|---|
| 4298 | | Sheet of 10 | 15.00 | 15.00 |
| a. | A4428 82y multi | | 1.50 | 1.10 |
| b. | A4429 82y multi | | 1.50 | 1.10 |
| c. | A4430 82y multi | | 1.50 | 1.10 |
| d. | A4431 82y multi | | 1.50 | 1.10 |
| e. | A4432 82y multi | | 1.50 | 1.10 |
| f. | A4433 82y multi | | 1.50 | 1.10 |
| g. | A4434 82y multi | | 1.50 | 1.10 |
| h. | A4435 82y multi | | 1.50 | 1.10 |
| i. | A4436 82y multi | | 1.50 | 1.10 |
| j. | A4437 82y multi | | 1.50 | 1.10 |

Modern surveying in Japan, 150th anniv.

Plum Knot
and Umeda
Sky Building,
Osaka
A4438

Plum Knot
and Osaka
Castle
A4439

Plum Knot
and
International
Exhibition
Center,
Osaka
A4440

Plum Knot
and Osaka
Central City
Public Hall
A4441

Plum Knot and
Tsutenkaku Tower,
Osaka — A4442

**2019, June 14    Litho.    Perf. 12¾x13**
| | | | |
|---|---|---|---|
| 4299 | A4438 82y multi | 1.50 | 1.10 |
| 4300 | A4439 82y multi | 1.50 | 1.10 |
| 4301 | A4440 82y multi | 1.50 | 1.10 |
| 4302 | A4441 82y multi | 1.50 | 1.10 |
| 4303 | A4442 82y multi | 1.50 | 1.10 |
| a. | Horiz. strip of 5, #4299-4303 | 7.50 | 5.50 |
| | Nos. 4299-4303 (5) | 7.50 | 5.50 |

G20 Summit, Osaka.

A4443

A4444

A4445    A4446

A4447    A4448

A4449    A4450

A4451    A4452

Flowers
A4453    A4454

**Die Cut Perf. 13x13¼**
**2019, June 19                    Litho.**
**Self-Adhesive**
| | | | |
|---|---|---|---|
| 4304 | | Sheet of 10, #4304c, 4304f, 2 each #4304a-4304b, 4304d-4304e | 12.50 | |
| a. | A4443 62y multi | | 1.25 | .95 |
| b. | A4444 62y multi | | 1.25 | .95 |
| c. | A4445 62y multi | | 1.25 | .95 |
| d. | A4446 62y multi | | 1.25 | .95 |
| e. | A4447 62y multi | | 1.25 | .95 |
| f. | A4448 62y multi | | 1.25 | .95 |
| 4305 | | Sheet of 10, #4305c, 4305f, 2 each #4305a-4305b, 4305d-4305e | 15.00 | |
| a. | A4449 82y multi | | 1.50 | 1.10 |
| b. | A4450 82y multi | | 1.50 | 1.10 |
| c. | A4451 82y multi | | 1.50 | 1.10 |
| d. | A4452 82y multi | | 1.50 | 1.10 |
| e. | A4453 82y multi | | 1.50 | 1.10 |
| f. | A4454 82y multi | | 1.50 | 1.10 |

Miniature Sheet

International Labor Organization,
Cent. — A4455

No. 4306: a, People, factory, wind generators. b, Farm and fishing boat. c, Cargo ship,
hospital, ambulance, police car and fire
engine. d, City, train, bus, bicyclist. e, Workers
at construction site. f, Gears, test tubes, knife
sharpener, hand, microscope beaker, can of
fish, sewing machine. g, Frying pan, kitchen
utensils, chef's toque, coffee pot, cutting
board, corkscrew, goblet, meal on plate. h,
Medical and dental items. i, Makeup, lipstick,
shaver, socks, eyeglasses, scissors, comb,
shirt, bag, groceries, shopping basket, cash
register. j, Carpenter's square, triangle, compass, file, chisel, hammer, pencil, hard hat,
camera, tape measure, paint brush and roller.

**2019, June 27    Litho.    Perf. 14**
| | | | |
|---|---|---|---|
| 4306 | A4455 | Sheet of 10 | 15.00 | 15.00 |
| a.-j. | | 82y Any single | 1.50 | 1.10 |

A4457

A4458

A4459

A4460

A4461

A4462

A4463

A4464

A4465

Dolphins — A4466

**Die Cut Perf. 13x13¼, 13¼x13**
**(horiz. stamps)**
**2019, July 3                    Litho.**
**Self-Adhesive**
| | | | |
|---|---|---|---|
| 4307 | | Sheet of 10 | 15.00 | |
| a. | A4457 82y multi | | 1.50 | 1.10 |
| b. | A4458 82y multi | | 1.50 | 1.10 |
| c. | A4459 82y multi | | 1.50 | 1.10 |
| d. | A4460 82y multi | | 1.50 | 1.10 |
| e. | A4461 82y multi | | 1.50 | 1.10 |
| f. | A4462 82y multi | | 1.50 | 1.10 |
| g. | A4463 82y multi | | 1.50 | 1.10 |
| h. | A4464 82y multi | | 1.50 | 1.10 |
| i. | A4465 82y multi | | 1.50 | 1.10 |
| j. | A4466 82y multi | | 1.50 | 1.10 |

Miniature Sheet

Hidden Christian Sites in the Nagasaki
Region UNESCO World Heritage
Sites — A4467

No. 4308: a, Aerial view of Hara Castle
ruins. b, Kasugu, terraced fields and Mount
Yasuman, Hirado Island. c, Nakano Island. d,
Wooden church and village of Sakitsu,
Amakusa Islands. e, Church and bell tower,
Sotome. f, Church and statue, Ono. g, Ruins
of village on Nozaki Island. h, Village and pier
on Kashiraga Island. i, Church and stone wall,
Hisaka Island. i, Church with blue shutters,
Egami, Naru Island.

**2019, July 12    Litho.    Perf. 13¼x13**
| | | | |
|---|---|---|---|
| 4308 | A4467 | Sheet of 10 | 15.00 | 15.00 |
| a.-j. | | 82y Any single | 1.50 | 1.10 |

Child
Mailing
Letter
A4468

Potted
Plant
A4469

Squash
and
Flowers
A4470

Bicycle
A4471

Books,
Lamp,
Cup,
Saucer,
Pen and
Ink Bottle
A4472

Woman
Writing
Letter
A4473

Pigeon
With
Letter
A4474

Sunflowers
A4475

Ice Cream
Soda
A4476

Cat and
Mailbox
A4477

**Die Cut Perf. 13x13¼**
**2019, July 23                    Litho.**
**Self-Adhesive**
| | | | |
|---|---|---|---|
| 4309 | | Sheet of 10, 2 each #4309a-4309e | 12.50 | |
| a. | A4468 62y multi | | 1.25 | .95 |
| b. | A4469 62y multi | | 1.25 | .95 |
| c. | A4470 62y multi | | 1.25 | .95 |
| d. | A4471 62y multi | | 1.25 | .95 |
| e. | A4472 62y multi | | 1.25 | .95 |
| 4310 | | Sheet of 10, 2 each #4310a-4310e | 15.00 | |
| a. | A4473 82y multi | | 1.50 | 1.10 |
| b. | A4474 82y multi | | 1.50 | 1.10 |
| c. | A4475 82y multi | | 1.50 | 1.10 |
| d. | A4476 82y multi | | 1.50 | 1.10 |
| e. | A4477 82y multi | | 1.50 | 1.10 |

Letter Writing Day.

Monkeys
A4478

Hawks
A4479

Ray
A4480

Rabbits
A4481

Japanese
Raccoon
Dogs
A4482

Sparrows
A4483

Frogs
A4484

Mole
A4485

Quails
A4486

Foxes
A4487

Ducks and
Geese
A4488

Owl
A4489

Cats
A4490

Squirrel
A4491

Geese
A4492

Deer
A4493

Tigers
A4494

Tilefish
A4495

Cranes
A4496

Elephants
A4497

**Die Cut Perf. 13x13¼ (#4311a, 4311c, 4311d); Die Cut Perf. 13x12¾ (#4311b, 4311e); Die Cut Perf. 13¼x13 (#4311f, 4311h); Die Cut Perf. (#4311g, 4311i); Die Cut Perf. 12¾ (#4311j)**

**2019, July 30**     **Litho.**
**Self-Adhesive**

| 4311 | | Sheet of 10 | 12.50 | |
|---|---|---|---|---|
| a. | A4478 | 62y multi | 1.25 | .85 |
| b. | A4479 | 62y multi | 1.25 | .85 |
| c. | A4480 | 62y multi | 1.25 | .85 |
| d. | A4481 | 62y multi | 1.25 | .85 |
| e. | A4482 | 62y multi | 1.25 | .85 |
| f. | A4483 | 62y multi | 1.25 | .85 |
| g. | A4484 | 62y multi | 1.25 | .85 |
| h. | A4485 | 62y multi | 1.25 | .85 |
| i. | A4486 | 62y multi | 1.25 | .85 |
| j. | A4487 | 62y multi | 1.25 | .85 |

**Die Cut Perf. 13 (#4312a, 4312e); Die Cut Perf. (#4312b, 4312d); Die Cut Perf. 13¼ (#4312c); Die Cut Perf. 12¾ (#4312f, 4312j); Die Cut Perf. 12¾x13 (#4312g, 4312i); Die Cut Perf. 13¼x13 (#4312h)**

| 4312 | | Sheet of 10 | 15.00 | |
|---|---|---|---|---|
| a. | A4488 | 82y multi | 1.50 | 1.10 |
| b. | A4489 | 82y multi | 1.50 | 1.10 |
| c. | A4490 | 82y multi | 1.50 | 1.10 |
| d. | A4491 | 82y multi | 1.50 | 1.10 |
| e. | A4492 | 82y multi | 1.50 | 1.10 |
| f. | A4493 | 82y multi | 1.50 | 1.10 |
| g. | A4494 | 82y multi | 1.50 | 1.10 |
| h. | A4495 | 82y multi | 1.50 | 1.10 |
| i. | A4496 | 82y multi | 1.50 | 1.10 |
| j. | A4497 | 82y multi | 1.50 | 1.10 |

Hybrid
Cherry
Blossoms
A4498

Plum
Blossoms
A4499

Violets — A4500

Iriomote-Ishigaki National
Park — A4501

Nikko
National
Park
A4502

Seto
Inland Sea
National
Park
A4503

**2019, Aug. 20  Photo.   Perf. 13x13¼**

| 4313 | A4498 | 63y multi | 1.25 | .95 |
|---|---|---|---|---|
| 4314 | A4499 | 84y multi | 1.60 | 1.25 |
| 4315 | A4500 | 94y multi | 1.75 | 1.40 |
| 4316 | A4501 | 210y multi | 4.00 | 3.00 |
| 4317 | A4502 | 290y multi | 5.50 | 4.25 |
| 4318 | A4503 | 320y multi | 6.00 | 4.50 |
| | | Nos. 4313-4318 (6) | 20.10 | 15.35 |

A4504

Red-crowned Cranes
A4505      A4506

**2019, Aug. 20  Photo.   Perf. 13x13¼**

| 4319 | A4504 | 63y multi | 1.25 | .95 |
|---|---|---|---|---|
| 4320 | A4505 | 84y multi | 1.60 | 1.25 |
| 4321 | A4506 | 94y multi | 1.75 | 1.40 |
| | | Nos. 4319-4321 (3) | 4.60 | 3.60 |

Flowers — A4507

**2019, Aug. 20  Photo.   Perf. 13x13¼**

| 4322 | A4507 | 63y multi | 1.25 | .95 |
|---|---|---|---|---|

**Miniature Sheets**

A4508

Miffy
A4509

No. 4323 — Miffy: a, In house (25x35mm). b, On bicycle (26x31mm). c, With pilot in airplane (25x25mm). d, Viewing heads of rabbits on wall (25x25mm). e, On swing (25x25mm). f, With three elephants (25x25mm). g, Wearing yellow headdress (25x25mm). h, In tree

(25x25mm). i, With paint brushes (25x25mm). j, With chicks (25x25mm).

No. 4324: a, Miffy writing letter (26x30mm). b, Head of Miffy (23x33mm). c, Miffy wearing red dress (26x26mm). d, Miffy and flowers (26x26mm). e, Miffy holding teddy bear (26x26mm). f, Miffy and pen (26x26mm). g, Miffy and five other rabbits (26x26mm). h, Miffy, other rabbit and beach ball (26x26mm). i, Miffy and stuffed animals (26x26mm). j, Miffy and pig wearing rabbit ears (26x26mm).

**Die Cut Perf. 14½; Die Cut Perf. 13 (#4323a); Die Cut Perf. (#4323b)**

**2019, Aug. 20**     **Litho.**
**Self-Adhesive**

| 4323 | A4508 | Sheet of 10 + 5 stickers | 12.50 | |
|---|---|---|---|---|
| a.-j. | | 63y Any single | 1.25 | .95 |

**Die Cut Perf. 14; Die Cut Perf. 13 (#4324a, 4324b)**

| 4324 | A4509 | Sheet of 10 + 6 stickers | 16.00 | |
|---|---|---|---|---|
| a.-j. | | 84y Any single | 1.60 | 1.25 |

**Miniature Sheets**

A4510

Autumn Greetings — A4511

No. 4325: a, Squirrel with acorn. b, Walnut. c, Pine cone (denomination at right in white and brown). d, Bird, walnut and pine cone. e,

Pine cones (green denomination). f, Pine cones (denomination at UL in white and red). g, Yew aril and pine cone. h, Squirrel and pine cone. i, Bird and acorn. j, Cedar rose pine cones (denomination at LL in white and brown).

No. 4326: a, Mushrooms. b, Cardinal and apple. c, Flowers. d, Grapes and melon. e, Autumn leaves and berries. f, Squirrel, squash and berries. g, Carrots, squash and berries. h, Apples, flowers and pumpkin. i, Mouse and beet. j, Mouse and pumpkin.

**Die Cut Perf. 13x13¼**

**2019, Aug. 23**     **Litho.**
**Self-Adhesive**

| 4325 | A4510 | Sheet of 10 | 12.50 | |
|---|---|---|---|---|
| a.-j. | | 63y Any single | 1.25 | .95 |
| 4326 | A4511 | Sheet of 10 | 16.00 | |
| a.-j. | | 84y Any single | 1.60 | 1.25 |

**Miniature Sheet**

74th National Athletic Meet, Ibaraki
Prefecture — A4512

No. 4327: a, Golf. b, Kairaku-en Gardens, Mito. c, Sailboats. d, Mount Tsukuba. e, Show jumping. f, Hitachi Seaside Park. g, Wall climbing. h, Fukuroda Falls. i, Rifle shooting. j, Ryujin Gorge.

**2019, Aug. 28   Litho.   Perf. 13**

| 4327 | A4512 | Sheet of 10 | 16.00 | 16.00 |
|---|---|---|---|---|
| a.-j. | | 84y Any single | 1.60 | 1.25 |

**Souvenir Sheet**

Moon and Plum Blossoms — A4513

No. 4328: a, Moon. b, Plum blossoms.

**2019, Sept. 3   Litho.   Perf. 13x13¼**

| 4328 | A4513 | Sheet of 2 | 3.00 | 3.00 |
|---|---|---|---|---|
| a. | | 63y multi | 1.25 | .95 |
| b. | | 84y multi | 1.60 | 1.25 |

No. 4328 was sold to the public, but also was awarded as a lottery prize.

## Miniature Sheets

A4514

My Journey
A4515

No. 4329: a, Lantern, Kenroku-en Garden (23x19mm). b, Illuminated trees at night, Kenroku-en Garden (19x24mm). c, Higasahi Chaya District at twilight, Kanazawa (23x19mm). d, Plum knot (26x25mm). e, Kutani porcelain plate (26mm diameter). f, Shima Teahouse, Higashi Chaya District (23x19mm). g, Exterior of houses, Nagamachi Samurai House District (23x19mm). h, Confections (23x19mm). i, Dyed textile with floral design (19x23mm). j, Stream near Samurai house (23x19mm).

No. 4330: a, Oyama Shrine, Kanazawa (19x23mm). b, Tsuzumi Gate (23x19mm). c, Lanterns, Kenroku-en Garden (23x19mm). d, Illuminated trees in daylight, Kenroku-en Garden (23x19mm). e, Higashi Chaya District in daylight (23x19mm). f, Doll (23x25mm). g, Temari ball (24mm diameter). h, Kanazawa Castle (23x19mm). i, Bridge, Gyokusen-in Garden (23x19mm). j, Shrimp and rice bowl (25mm diameter).

*Die Cut Perf. 13¼x13; Die Cut Perf. 13x12¾ (#4329b); Die Cut Perf. (#4329d, 4329e, 4330f, 4330g, 4330j); Die Cut Perf. 13x13¼ (#4329i, 4330a)*

**2019, Sept. 4**       Litho.
**Self-Adhesive**

| | | | | |
|---|---|---|---|---|
| 4329 | A4514 | Sheet of 10 | 12.50 | |
| a.-j. | | 63y Any single | 1.25 | .95 |
| 4330 | A4515 | Sheet of 10 | 16.00 | |
| a.-j. | | 84y Any single | 1.60 | 1.25 |

## Miniature Sheet

2019 Rugby World Cup, Japan
A4516

No. 4331 — Emblem or flag of teams from: a, Ireland, New Zealand. b, Scotland, South Africa. c, Japan, Italy. d, Russia, Namibia. e, Samoa, Canada. f, England, Australia. g, France, Wales. h, Argentina, Georgia. i, United States, Fiji. j, Tonga, Uruguay.

**2019, Sept. 6**   Litho.   *Perf. 14¼*

| | | | | |
|---|---|---|---|---|
| 4331 | A4516 | Sheet of 10 | 16.00 | 16.00 |
| a.-j. | | 84y Any single | 1.60 | 1.25 |

## Miniature Sheets

A4517

Posukuma — A4518

No. 4332 — Japan Post teddy bear mascot with: a. Other teddy bear, yellow pom-poms. b, Other teddy bear, red batons. c, Other teddy bear, megaphones. d, Other teddy bear, blue and yellow pom-poms. e, Other teddy bear, blue batons. f, Checkered flag. g, Owl. h, Balloons. i, Other teddy bear, musical notes. j, Streamers and confetti.

No. 4333 — Stuffed animals and: a, Oranges. b, Honeydew melons. c, Kiwis. d, Peaches. e, Strawberries. f, Apples. g, Lemons. h, Grapes. i, Cherries. j, Chestnuts.

**2019, Sept. 13**   Litho.   *Die Cut Perf.*
**Self-Adhesive**

| | | | | |
|---|---|---|---|---|
| 4332 | A4517 | Sheet of 10 | 12.50 | |
| a.-j. | | 63y Any single | 1.25 | .95 |

*Die Cut Perf. 10¼x12¼*

| | | | | |
|---|---|---|---|---|
| 4333 | A4518 | Sheet of 10 | 16.00 | |
| a.-j. | | 84y Any single | 1.60 | 1.25 |

## Miniature Sheet

Japan Art Academy, Cent. — A4519

No. 4334 — Paintings: a, The Charcoal Kiln, by Somei Yuki (stamp #1). b, The White Horse, by Kayo Yamaguchi (stamp #2). c, Evening Glow, by Kaii Higashiyama (stamp #3). d, Silence, by Manyo Ito (stamp #4). e, By the Window, by Gakuryo Nakamura (stamp #5). f, Forest Light, by Kan Hamada (stamp #6). g, Portrait of a Lady, by Keizo Koyama (stamp #7). h, Wall on the Rue St. Jacques, by Shinichi Nishiyama (stamp #8). i, Clematis, by Chikuma Suzuki (stamp #9). j, Interior with Female Figure, by Takanori Kinoshita (stamp #10).

**2019, Sept. 20**   Litho.   *Perf. 13*

| | | | | |
|---|---|---|---|---|
| 4334 | A4519 | Sheet of 10 | 16.00 | 16.00 |
| a.-j. | | 84y Any single | 1.60 | 1.25 |

Stars
A4520

Leaves
A4521

Birds — A4522

*Die Cut Perf. 13x13¼*

**2019, Sept. 25**      Litho.
**Self-Adhesive**

| | | | | |
|---|---|---|---|---|
| 4335 | A4520 | 63y multi | 1.25 | .95 |
| 4336 | A4521 | 84y multi | 1.60 | 1.25 |
| 4337 | A4522 | 94y multi | 1.75 | 1.40 |
| | Nos. 4335-4337 (3) | | 4.60 | 3.60 |

## Miniature Sheet

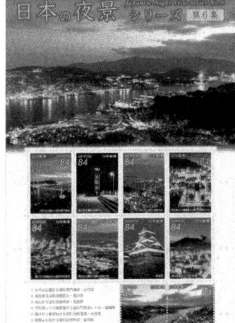

Chugoku Region, Honshu, at Night
A4523

No. 4338: a, Bridge over Kanmon Straits (stamp #1). b, Breakwater Lighthouse, Takamatsu (stamp #2). c, Tokushima (stamp #3). d, Moji (stamp #4). e, Beppu Hot Springs (stamp #5). f, Nobeoka (stamp #6). g, Kumamoto Castle (stamp #7). h, Sakurajima (stamp #8). i, Onomichi Channel, denomination at UL. j, Onomichi Channel, denomination at UR.

**2019, Sept. 27**   Litho.   *Perf. 13*

| | | | | |
|---|---|---|---|---|
| 4338 | A4523 | Sheet of 10 | 16.00 | 16.00 |
| a.-j. | | 84y Any single | 1.60 | 1.25 |

Origami Pinwheel
A4524

Origami Dove
A4525

Origami Swallow
A4526

Origami Houses
A4527

Origami Dahlia
A4528

Origami Airplane
A4529

Origami Birds
A4530

Origami Goldfish
A4531

Origami
Crane and
Tortoise
A4532

Origami
Camellia
A4533

Playthings — A4534

No. 4340: a, Paper balloon (30mm diameter). b, Kite (42x38mm). c, Party favors (30x30mm). d, Paddle and shuttlecock (25x42mm). e, Stick helicopter (30x30mm). f, Boats (30x30mm). g, Shogi piece (30x35mm). h, Top (30x39mm oval). i, Marbles (30x30mm). j, Ball and cup (24x44mm).

**Die Cut Perf. 13¼**

| 2019, Oct. 2 | | Self-Adhesive | Litho. | |
|---|---|---|---|---|
| 4339 | | Sheet of 10 | 12.50 | |
| a. | A4524 | 63y multi | 1.25 | .95 |
| b. | A4525 | 63y multi | 1.25 | .95 |
| c. | A4526 | 63y multi | 1.25 | .95 |
| d. | A4527 | 63y multi | 1.25 | .95 |
| e. | A4528 | 63y multi | 1.25 | .95 |
| f. | A4529 | 63y multi | 1.25 | .95 |
| g. | A4530 | 63y multi | 1.25 | .95 |
| h. | A4531 | 63y multi | 1.25 | .95 |
| i. | A4532 | 63y multi | 1.25 | .95 |
| j. | A4533 | 63y multi | 1.25 | .95 |

**Die Cut Perf. 12½; Die Cut Perf. 12¼
(#4340b, 4340d, 4340j), Die Cut Perf.
(#4340a, 4340h)**

| 4340 | A4534 | Sheet of 10 | 16.00 | |
|---|---|---|---|---|
| a.-j. | | 84y Any single | 1.60 | 1.25 |

A4535

A4536

International Letter
Writing
Week — A4537

Art by Hiroshige: 7y, Mandarin Duck. No. 4342, Flowering Apple Tree with Small Birds (apple tree). No. 4343, Flowering Apple Tree with Small Birds (bird). 90y, Travelers to Nissaka Near Night Weeping Stone. 110y, Travelers in Narumi. 130y, Seki, Early Departure from the Headquarters Inn.

| 2019, Oct. 9 | | Litho. | Perf. 13x13¼ | |
|---|---|---|---|---|
| 4341 | A4535 | 7y multi | .25 | .25 |
| 4342 | A4536 | 70y multi | 1.30 | 1.00 |
| 4343 | | 70y multi | 1.30 | 1.00 |
| a. | A4536 | Vert. pair, #4342-4343 | 2.60 | 2.00 |
| 4344 | A4537 | 90y multi | 1.75 | 1.40 |
| 4345 | A4537 | 110y multi | 2.10 | 1.60 |
| 4346 | A4537 | 130y multi | 2.40 | 1.75 |
| | | Nos. 4341-4346 (6) | 9.10 | 7.00 |

See listing of No. 4448 for images of each Hiroshige print.

**Miniature Sheet**

Diplomatic Relations Between Japan
and Hungary, 150th Anniv. — A4538

No. 4347: a, Hungarian Parliament Building. b, Mount Fuji. c, White and yellow chamomile flowers. d, Pink and white cherry blossoms. e, Hungarian woman's traditional costume from Kalocsa. f, Japanese kimono. g, Pot of Hungarian goulash. h, Sushi. i, Puli (white dog). j, Shiba (brown dog).

| 2019, Oct. 15 | | Litho. | Perf. 13 | |
|---|---|---|---|---|
| 4347 | A4538 | Sheet of 10 | 16.00 | 16.00 |
| a.-j. | | 84y Any single | 1.60 | 1.25 |

See Hungary No. 4535.

**Miniature Sheet**

Diplomatic Relations Between Japan
and Austria, 150th Anniv. — A4539

No. 4348: a, Hofburg Palace, Vienna. b, St. Stephen's Cathedral, Vienna. c, Schönbrunn Palace, Vienna. d, Christmas Market at Vienna City Hall. e, Wolfgang Amadeus Mozart (1756-91), composer. f, The Kiss, by Gustav Klimt (1862-1918). g, Sachertorte and coffee. h, Alps. i, Vienna Philharmonic Orchestra. j, Vienna Boys' Choir.

| 2019, Oct. 16 | | Litho. | Perf. 13 | |
|---|---|---|---|---|
| 4348 | A4539 | Sheet of 10 | 16.00 | 16.00 |
| a.-j. | | 84y Any single | 1.60 | 1.25 |

Phoenix
A4540

Floral
Arabesque
A4541

| 2019, Oct. 18 | | Photo. | Perf. 13¼ | |
|---|---|---|---|---|
| 4349 | A4540 | 84y multi | 1.60 | 1.25 |
| 4350 | A4541 | 84y multi | 1.60 | 1.25 |
| a. | | Pair, #4349-4350 | 3.20 | 2.50 |

Enthronement of Emperor Naruhito. Printed in sheet that contains 5 of No. 4350a.

Mushrooms
A4542

Nuts and
Pine Cone
A4543

Ladybugs
A4544

Animal
Tracks
A4545

Moss-
covered
Rocks
A4546

Leaves
A4547

Japanese
Raccoon
Dog
A4548

Leaves
and Bears
A4549

Pinecone
Detail
A4550

Fish
A4551

Acorns,
Nuts and
Seeds
A4552

Pine
Needles
A4553

Flowers
A4554

Animals
A4555

Squirrel
A4556

Leaves
A4557

Mushrooms
A4558

Tree
Growth
Rings
A4559

Rabbit
A4560

Animals
A4561

**Die Cut Perf. 13x13¼; Die Cut Perf.
13¼ (#4352d, 4352e, 4352i, 4352j)**

| 2019, Oct. 23 | | Self-Adhesive | Litho. | |
|---|---|---|---|---|
| 4351 | | Sheet of 10 | 12.50 | |
| a. | A4542 | 63y multi | 1.25 | .95 |
| b. | A4543 | 63y multi | 1.25 | .95 |
| c. | A4544 | 63y multi | 1.25 | .95 |
| d. | A4545 | 63y multi | 1.25 | .95 |
| e. | A4546 | 63y multi | 1.25 | .95 |
| f. | A4547 | 63y multi | 1.25 | .95 |
| g. | A4548 | 63y multi | 1.25 | .95 |
| h. | A4549 | 63y multi | 1.25 | .95 |
| i. | A4550 | 63y multi | 1.25 | .95 |
| j. | A4551 | 63y multi | 1.25 | .95 |
| 4352 | | Sheet of 10 | 16.00 | |
| a. | A4552 | 84y multi | 1.60 | 1.25 |
| b. | A4553 | 84y multi | 1.60 | 1.25 |
| c. | A4554 | 84y multi | 1.60 | 1.25 |
| d. | A4555 | 84y multi | 1.60 | 1.25 |
| e. | A4556 | 84y multi | 1.60 | 1.25 |
| f. | A4557 | 84y multi | 1.60 | 1.25 |
| g. | A4558 | 84y multi | 1.60 | 1.25 |
| h. | A4559 | 84y multi | 1.60 | 1.25 |
| i. | A4560 | 84y multi | 1.60 | 1.25 |
| j. | A4561 | 84y multi | 1.60 | 1.25 |

A4562      A4563

New Year 2020 (Year of
the Rat)
A4564      A4565

| 2019, Nov. 1 | | Litho. | Perf. 13x13¼ | |
|---|---|---|---|---|
| 4353 | A4562 | 63y multi | 1.25 | .95 |
| 4354 | A4563 | 84y multi | 1.60 | 1.25 |

**Litho. & Typo.
Perf. 13¼**

| 4355 | A4564 | 63y+3y multi | 1.25 | .95 |
|---|---|---|---|---|
| 4356 | A4565 | 84y+3y multi | 1.60 | 1.25 |
| | | Nos. 4353-4356 (4) | 5.70 | 4.40 |

Plants
A4566

Salmon
A4568

Cast Iron
Teapot
A4567

Pine
Branches
A4569

New Year's Decoration
A4570

Bobblehead Cat Doll
A4571

Lobster
A4572

Mice With Gold Coins
A4573

Red-crowned Cranes
A4574

Sparrows
A4575

Plum Blossoms
A4576

Charcoal
A4577

Decorative Carrot Slices
A4578

Igloo
A4579

Bean Soup
A4580

Yu Instrument
A4581

Mountain
A4582

Pine Needles
A4583

Comb and Hair Stick
A4584

Rolled Omelet
A4585

Die Cut Perf. 13x13¼

2019, Nov. 6 **Litho.**

Self-Adhesive

4357		Sheet of 10	12.50	
a.	A4566	63y multi	1.25	.95
b.	A4567	63y multi	1.25	.95
c.	A4568	63y multi	1.25	.95
d.	A4569	63y multi	1.25	.95
e.	A4570	63y multi	1.25	.95
f.	A4571	63y multi	1.25	.95
g.	A4572	63y multi	1.25	.95
h.	A4573	63y multi	1.25	.95
i.	A4574	63y multi	1.25	.95
j.	A4575	63y multi	1.25	.95
4358		Sheet of 10	16.00	
a.	A4576	84y multi	1.60	1.25
b.	A4577	84y multi	1.60	1.25
c.	A4578	84y multi	1.60	1.25
d.	A4579	84y multi	1.60	1.25
e.	A4580	84y multi	1.60	1.25
f.	A4581	84y multi	1.60	1.25
g.	A4582	84y multi	1.60	1.25
h.	A4583	84y multi	1.60	1.25
i.	A4584	84y multi	1.60	1.25
j.	A4585	84y multi	1.60	1.25

Miniature Sheets

A4586

Winter Greetings — A4587

No. 4359: a, Candles and snow globe (24x24mm). b, Cat and flower vase (24x24mm). c, Books, eyeglasses, unfinished woolen sock (24x24mm). d, Fruit bowl, teapot and cup (24x24mm). e, Mouse in yarn basket (24x24mm). f, Cat and sweater (26x24mm). g, Mice, mitten and sock (24x24mm). h, Knitted sweater and knitting needles (25x26mm). i, Cat and mitten (24x24mm). j, Cat and ball of yarn (27mm diameter).

No. 4360: a, Chair lift (30x21mm). b, Skiers (21x30mm). c, Deer, fox and trees (27x27mm). d, House (30x21mm). e, Snowman, rabbit and dog (27x27mm). f, People making snowman (27x27mm). g, Man pulling children on sled (30x21mm). h, Ice skater (21x30mm). i, Two ice skaters (21x30mm). j, Ice fisherman (27x27mm).

Die Cut Perf. 13¼; Die Cut Perf. (#4359h, 4359j)

2019, Nov. 22 **Litho. & Embossed**

Self-Adhesive

4359	A4586	Sheet of 10 + 2 stickers	12.50	
a.-j.		63y Any single	1.25	.95

Die Cut Perf. 13¼x13 (#4360a, 4360d, 4360g); Die Cut Perf. 13x13¼ (#4360b, 4360h, 4360i); Die Cut Perf. 13¼ (#4360c, 4360e, 4360f, 4360j)

4360	A4587	Sheet of 10 + 5 stickers	16.00	
a.-j.		84y Any single	1.60	1.25

Miniature Sheet

Guri and Gura, Children's Book Characters by Rieko Nakagawa — A4588

No. 4361: a, Guri and Gura with backpacks (34x29mm). b, Guri and Gura on log with other animals (38x28mm). c, Guri and Gura in cracked egg car (38x28mm). d, Guri whisking food in bowl (32x27mm). e, Gura lifting lid of frying pan (38x28mm). f, Guri and Gura writing (34x29mm). g, Guri and Gura carrying basket (28x28mm). h, Guri and Gura lifting egg (39x31mm oval). i, Guri and Gura on log (39x31mm oval). j, Guri lifting lid on frying pan (27x32mm).

Die Cut Perf. 13x13¼ (#4361a, 4361d, 4361f); Die Cut Perf. 13¼x13 (#4361b, 4361e, 4361j); Die Cut Perf. 13 (#4361c, 4361g); Die Cut Perf. (#4361h, 4361i)

2019, Nov. 28 **Litho.**

Self-Adhesive

4361	A4588	Sheet of 10 + 4 stickers	16.00	
a.-j.		84y Any single	1.60	1.25

Upright Piano
A4589

Bass Drum
A4590

Banjo
A4591

Sousaphone
A4592

Trumpet — A4593

Musical Instruments — A4594

No. 4363: a, Vibraphone (28x23mm). b, Drum set (32x22mm). c, Electric guitar (30x25mm). d, Two trumpets (28x23mm). e, Three trombones (32x32mm). f, Grand piano (26x33mm). g, Bass (23x32mm). h, Alto saxophone (22x30mm). i, Tenor saxophone (21x32mm). j, Baritone saxophone (21x42mm).

Die Cut Perf. 13x12¾ (#4362a), 13¼x13 (#4362b), 13¾x13¼ (#43623c), 13 (#4362d), 13x13¾ (#4362e)

2019, Dec. 6 **Litho.**

Self-Adhesive

4362		Sheet of 10, 2 each #4362a-4362e	12.50	
a.	A4589	63y multi	1.25	.95
b.	A4590	63y multi	1.25	.95
c.	A4591	63y multi	1.25	.95
d.	A4592	63y multi	1.25	.95
e.	A4593	63y multi	1.25	.95

Die Cut Perf. 12¾x12½ (#4363a), 12¾x13 (#4363b), 13 (#4363c), 12¾x12¼ (#4363d, 4363h),13¼x13 (#4363e, 4363i), 13x13¼ (#4363f), 13½ (#4363g), 13¼ (#4363j)

4363	A4594	Sheet of 10	16.00	
a.-j.		84y Any single	1.60	1.25

A4595

A4596

A4597

A4598

A4599

The Little Prince, by Antoine de Saint-Exupery (1900-44) — A4600

No. 4365 — The Little Prince: a, With sword (37x41mm). b, Standing near two flowers (24x45mm). c, With shovel (28x27mm). d, Carried by birds (28x38mm). e, Under star (28x38mm). f, Standing near flower bushes (38x27mm). g, On ground, looking at flowers (27x27mm). h, Looking at fox (38x27mm). i, At well (27x27mm). j, Bending backwards (27x27mm).

Die Cut Perf. (#4364a, 4364e), Die Cut Perf. 13¼ (#4364b-4364d, 4365b-4365c, 4365f-4365j), 13 (#4365a), 13x13¼ (#4365d-4365e)

2019, Dec. 11 **Litho.**

Self-Adhesive

4364		Sheet of 10, 2 each #4364a-4364e	12.50	
a.	A4595	63y multi	1.25	.95
b.	A4596	63y multi	1.25	.95
c.	A4597	63y multi	1.25	.95
d.	A4598	63y multi	1.25	.95
e.	A4599	63y multi	1.25	.95
4365	A4600	Sheet of 10	16.00	
a.-j.		84y Any single	1.60	1.25

A4601

Food
A4602

No. 4366: a, Dried fish and garlic bulbs. b, Steamed buns shaped like chicks, jars. c, Bottle of soy sauce, salt shaker and pepper mill. d, Bowl of rice with pollock roe, kitchen utensils. e, Package of ramen noodles. f, Rice crackers and bowl of strawberries. g, Sea bream and mackerel on plate. h, Vegetables. i, Bottle of pepper and lemons. j, Rice balls.

No. 4367: a, Bowl of soup with rice cakes and vegetables. b, Plate of pork, egg, vegetables and ramen noodles. c, Hot pot with vegetables. d, Dish of raw mackerel with soy sauce and vegetables. e, Rectangular plate with steamed eel. f, Rice cake, tea pot and tea cup. g, Bowl of seaweed, plate of chicken strips on skewers. h, Dumplings in pan. i, Hot pot with chicken and vegetables. j, Bowl of burdock root tempura noodle soup.

Die Cut Perf. 13¼

2020, Jan. 15 **Litho.**

Self-Adhesive

4366	A4601	Booklet pane of 10, #4366a-4366j	12.50	
a.-j.		63y Any single	1.25	.95
4367	A4602	Booklet pane of 10, #4367a-4367j	16.00	
a.-j.		84y Any single	1.60	1.25

## Souvenir Sheet

New Year 2020 (Year of the Rat) A4603

No. 4368: a, Rat, flower and Japanese character for "good fortune." b, Flower and Japanese character for "best wishes."

**2020, Jan. 20 Photo. *Perf. 13x13¼***
| | | | |
|---|---|---|---|
| 4368 | A4603 | Sheet of 2 | 3.00 3.00 |
| a. | | 63y multi | 1.25 .95 |
| b. | | 84y multi | 1.60 1.25 |

No. 4368 was sold to the public, but also was awarded as a lottery prize.

Roses A4604

Roses A4605

Flowers A4606

Flowers A4607

Orchids A4608

Orchids A4609

**Die Cut Perf. 12¾x13 (#4369a), 13 (#4370a, 4371a), Die Cut Perf. (#4369b, 4370b, 4371b)**
**Litho. With Foil Application**
**2020, Jan. 23**
**Self-Adhesive**
| | | | |
|---|---|---|---|
| 4369 | | Sheet of 10, 5 each #4369a-4369b | 12.50 |
| a. | A4604 | 63y gold & multi | 1.25 .95 |
| b. | A4605 | 63y gold & multi | 1.25 .95 |
| 4370 | | Sheet of 10, 5 each #4370a-4370b | 16.00 |
| a. | A4606 | 84y gold & multi | 1.60 1.25 |
| b. | A4607 | 84y gold & multi | 1.60 1.25 |
| 4371 | | Sheet of 10, 5 each #4371a-4371b | 17.50 |
| a. | A4608 | 94y gold & multi | 1.75 1.40 |
| b. | A4609 | 94y gold & multi | 1.75 1.40 |
| | | Nos. 4369-4371 (3) | 46.00 |

## Miniature Sheet

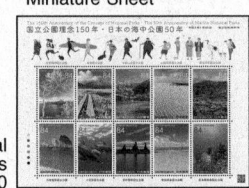

National Parks A4610

No. 4372: a, Akan-Mashu National Park. b, Oze National Park. c, Chibu Sangaku National Park. d, San'in Kaigan National Park. e, Unzen-Amakusa National Park. f, Sanriku Fukko National Park. g, Dolphins at Ogasawara National Park. h, Yoshino-Kumano National Park. i, Amami Gunto National Park. j, Fish at Kerama Shoto National Park.

**2020, Jan. 28 Litho. *Perf. 12¾x13***
| | | | |
|---|---|---|---|
| 4372 | A4610 | Sheet of 10 | 16.00 16.00 |
| a.-j. | | 84y Any single | 1.60 1.25 |

## Miniature Sheet

Astronomy — A4611

No. 4373: a, Star cluster (32mm diameter). b, Crab Nebula (32mm diameter. c, Ring Nebula (26x22mm). d, Butterfly Nebula (21x32mm oval). e, Titan (22x26mm). f, Amalthea (22x26mm). g, Thebe (22x26mm). h, Enceladus (22x26mm). i, Ganymede (32mm diameter). j, Callisto (32mm diameter).

**Die Cut Perf. (#4373a-4373b, 4373d, 4373i-4373j), Die Cut Perf. 13¼x13 (#4373c); 13x13¼ (#4373e-4373h)**
**Litho. With Holographic Foil Affixed**
**2020, Feb. 5**
**Self-Adhesive**
| | | | |
|---|---|---|---|
| 4373 | A4611 | Sheet of 10 | 16.00 |
| a.-j. | | 84y Any single | 1.60 1.25 |

## Miniature Sheets

Hakodate Tourist Attractions — A4612

Miyakojima Tourist Attractions — A4613

No. 4374: a, Hakodate Orthodox Christian Church (28x28mm). b, Old Public Hall (38x28mm). c, Tram (32mm diameter). d, Goryokaku Tower (32x31mm pentagonal), e, Red brick warehouses (38x28mm).
No. 4375: a, Guardian lion (28x28mm). b, Ruddy kingfisher (38x28mm). c, Hibiscus (32mm diameter). d, Clownfish (28x28mm). e, Green sea turtle (38x28mm).

**Die Cut Perf. 13x13½ (#4374a, 4375a, 4375d), 13¼ (#4374b, 4374e, 4375b, 4375e), 13 (4374d); Die Cut Perf. (4374c, 4375c)**
**2020, Feb. 7 Litho.**
**Self-Adhesive**
| | | | |
|---|---|---|---|
| 4374 | A4612 | Sheet of 5 | 8.00 |
| a.-e. | | 84y Any single | 1.60 1.25 |
| 4375 | A4613 | Sheet of 5 | 8.00 |
| a.-e. | | 84y Any single | 1.60 1.25 |

## Miniature Sheets

A4614

Flowers A4615

No. 4376: a, Dandelions. b, Nemophila. c, Strawberries. d, Primroses. e, Daisies and ladybug. f, Winter daphnes and bee. g, Peonies. h, Poppies. i, Pansies, j, Clover and cat.
No. 4377: a, White cherry blossoms and cat. b, White cherry blossoms and bird. c, Pink peach blossoms. d, White cherry blossoms. e, Mimosa. f, Rose of Sharon and swallow. g, Spirea and bee. h, Camellia. i, Tulips and ducklings. j, Rape blossoms.

**2020, Feb. 21 Litho. *Die Cut Perf.***
**Self-Adhesive**
| | | | |
|---|---|---|---|
| 4376 | A4614 | Sheet of 10 | 12.50 |
| a.-j. | | 63y Any single | 1.25 .95 |

**Die Cut Perf. 13¼**
| | | | |
|---|---|---|---|
| 4377 | A4615 | Sheet of 10 | 16.00 |
| a.-j. | | 84y Any single | 1.60 1.25 |

Cherry Blossoms A4616

Asian Fawnlily A4617

Safflower A4618

Hydrangea A4619

Japanese Irises A4620

Citrus Blossoms A4621

Tulips A4622

Cherry Blossoms A4623

Hydrangea A4624

Carnations A4625

**Die Cut Perf. 13x13¼**
**2020, Mar. 3 Litho.**
**Self-Adhesive**
| | | | |
|---|---|---|---|
| 4378 | | Sheet of 10, 2 each #4378a-4378e | 12.50 |
| a. | A4616 | 63y multi | 1.25 .95 |
| b. | A4617 | 63y multi | 1.25 .95 |
| c. | A4618 | 63y multi | 1.25 .95 |
| d. | A4619 | 63y multi | 1.25 .95 |
| e. | A4620 | 63y multi | 1.25 .95 |
| 4379 | | Sheet of 10, 2 each #4379a-4379e | 16.00 |
| a. | A4621 | 84y multi | 1.60 1.25 |
| b. | A4622 | 84y multi | 1.60 1.25 |
| c. | A4623 | 84y multi | 1.60 1.25 |
| d. | A4624 | 84y multi | 1.60 1.25 |
| e. | A4625 | 84y multi | 1.60 1.25 |

Torch and Torch Bearer for 2020 Summer Olympics, Tokyo — A4626

Torch, torch bearer and: No. 4380, Olympic rings. No. 4381, Paralympics emblem.

**2020, Mar. 10 Litho. *Perf. 14***
| | | | |
|---|---|---|---|
| 4380 | | 84y multi | 1.60 1.25 |
| 4381 | | 84y multi | 1.60 1.25 |
| a. | A4626 | Vert. pair, #4380-4381 | 3.20 2.50 |

The 2020 Summer Olympics and Paralympics were postponed until 2021 because of the coronavirus pandemic.

## Miniature Sheets

A4627

162    JAPAN

Art
A4628

No. 4382: a, Rabbits and flowers from Edo period porcelain plate (27x28mm). b, Irises from Scroll of Flowers and Plants of the Four Seasons, by Hoitsu Sakai (1761-1829) (27x28mm). c, Fisherman from Kajikazawa in Kai Provimce, by Hokusai Katsushika (1760-1849) (25x28mm). d, Woman Waiting for the Moon to Rise, by Shoen Uemura (1875-1949) (25x26mm). e, Hydrangea from Cloisonné vase, by Yasuyuki Namikawai (1845-1927) (22x30mm). f, The Lakeside, by Seiki Kuroda (1866-1924) (25x30mm). g, Mount Fuji Above the Clouds, by Taikan Yokoyama (1868-1958) (31x25mm). h, Pegasus, by Odilon Redon (1840-1916) (22x30mm). i, Portrait of Valentine Tessier, by Marie Laurencin (1883-1956) (22x30mm). j, Water Lilies, by Claude Monet (1846-1926) (27x25mm).

No. 4383: a, Rabbits and flowers from Edo period porcelain plate (31x35mm). b, Irises from Scroll of Flowers and Plants of the Four Seasons, by Sakai (36x30mm). c, Fisherman from Kajikazawa in Kai Provimce, by Hokusai (36x30mm). d, Oh, an Evening Shower, by Seiho Takeuchi (1864-1942) (23x45mm). e, The Lakeside, by Kuroda (33x32mm). f, Mount Fuji Above the Clouds, by Yokoyama (36x30mm). g, Grand Bouquet, by Redon (33x39mm). h, Portrait of Valentine Tessier, by Laurencin (28x39mm). i, Water Lilies, by Monet (33x395mm). j, Cloisonné vase depicting hydrangeas, by Namikawai (23x45mm).

**Die Cut Perf. 12¾ (#4382a, 4382b, 4382c, 4382j), 12¾x13 (#4382d), 13x13¼ (#4382e, 4382f), 13x12½ (#4382g), 13 (#4382h, 4382i)**
2020, Mar. 19                    Litho.
**Self-Adhesive**
4382  A4627   Sheet of 10        12.50
a.-j.        63y Any single       1.25   .95

**Die Cut Perf. 13x12¾ (#4383a), 13x13¼ (#4383b, 4383c, 4383d, 4383e, 4383f, 4383j), 13 (#4383g, 4383h, 4383i)**
4383  A4628   Sheet of 10        16.00
a.-j.        84y Any single       1.60  1.25

White Roses
A4629

Pink Roses
A4630

Purple Roses
A4631

Orange Roses
A4632

Red Roses
A4633

Pink Roses
A4634

Pale Orange Roses
A4635

Magenta Roses
A4636

Peach Roses
A4637

White Roses
A4638

**Die Cut Perf. 13½x13, 13½ (#4385e)**
2020, Apr. 1                     Litho.
**Self-Adhesive**
4384       Sheet of 10, 2 each
           #4384a-4384e          12.50
a.  A4629 63y multi              1.25  .95
b.  A4630 63y multi              1.25  .95
c.  A4631 63y multi              1.25  .95
d.  A4632 63y multi              1.25  .95
e.  A4633 63y multi              1.25  .95
4385       Sheet of 10, 2 each
           #4385a-4385e          16.00
a.  A4634 84y multi              1.60  1.25
b.  A4635 84y multi              1.60  1.25
c.  A4636 84y multi              1.60  1.25
d.  A4637 84y multi              1.60  1.25
e.  A4638 84y multi              1.60  1.25

Miniature Sheet

14th United Nations Congress on Crime Prevention and Criminal Justice, Kyoto — A4639

No. 4386: a, Birds and feathers. b, Congress emblem depicting cherry blossoms. c, Golden Pavilion, Kyoto. d, Kyoto Congress Youth Forum emblem depicting crane. e, Homes, woman and child. f, Buildings, four people.

2020, Apr. 6       Litho.   Perf. 13½
4386  A4639   Sheet of 10,
              #4386e,
              4386f, 2 each
              #4386a-4386d    16.00 16.00
a.-f.        84y Any single    1.60  1.25

Stylized Tree
A4640

Stylized Tree
A4641

Stylized Tree — A4642

**Die Cut Perf. 13x13¼**
2020, Apr. 15                    Litho.
**Self-Adhesive**
4387  A4640 63y blue & multi    1.25  .95
4388  A4641 84y emerald & multi 1.60 1.25
4389  A4642 94y red violet & mul-
            ti                   1.75 1.40
      Nos. 4387-4389 (3)        4.60 3.60

Red and White Plum Blossoms, Screen Painting by Korin Ogata (1658-1716) — A4643

Plum tree with: No. 4390, White blossoms. No. 4391, Red blossoms.

**Photo. & Engr.**
2020, Apr. 20              Perf. 13¼
4390  84y gold & black          1.60  1.25
4391  84y gold & black          1.60  1.25
a.  A4643 Horiz. pair (#4390-4391) 3.20 2.50
Philatelic Week.
No. 4391a was printed in sheets of 5 pairs.

Miniature Sheet

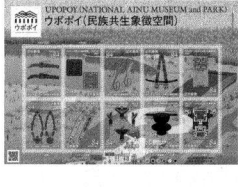
Upopoy National Ainu Musuem and Park
A4644

No. 4392: a, Sheathed knives. b, Square carved wood trays. c, Idiophones. d, Sword and sword belt. e, Pink and blue elm bark robe. f, Necklaces with medallions. g, Tonkoris (stringed instruments). h, Three Ainu dancers. i, Sake paddle and cup. j, Black, white, green and red ruunpe (garment).

2020, Apr. 21  Litho.  Perf. 14¼x13¾
4392  A4644  Sheet of 10     16.00 16.00
a.-j.       84y Any single    1.60  1.25

A4645

Sumo Wresting
A4646

No. 4393: a, Two wrestlers in Yorikiri move (22x26mm). b, Two wrestlers and referee (22x26mm). c, Wrestler squatting with one arm extended (32x26mm), d, Wrestler squatting with both arms extended (33x26mm). e, Wrestler receiving prize money from referee (22x26mm). f, Two wrestlers in Uwatenage move (22x26mm). g, Two wrestlers in Harimanage move (22x26mm). h, Three wrestlers standing wearing ceremonial ropes and aprons (34x30mm). i, Two wrealters with arms extended in ring with referee (34x30mm). j, Two wrestlers in Tsuridashi move (22x26mm).
No. 4394 — Edo era woodblock prints of sumo wrestlers: a, Dohyoiri at a Sumo Match with the Emperor in the Audience (three wrestlers, referee and spectators), by Toyonobu Utagawa (1859-86) (32x34mm). b, A Benefit Match (wrestlers in action in ring, referee and spectators in background and ringside), by Kunitoshi Utagawa (1847-99) (32x34mm). c, The Yokozuna Reigoro Hidenoyama Performing Dohyoiri (wrestler with arms extended), by Toyokuni Utagawa III (1786-1865) (30x35mm). d, A Mirror of Japan's Great Sumo Wrestlers (group of wrestlers, denomination at LL), by Yoshiiku Ochiai (1833-1904) (26x30mm). e, A Mirror of Japan's Great Sumo Wrestlers (different group of wrestlers, denomination at LR), by Ochiai (26x30mm). f, A Benefit O-zumo Match Featuring Rikishi Koyanagi and Arauma (two wrestlers in and referee in ring, three ringside spectators), by Toyokuni Utagawa III (34x35mm). g, Group of wrestlers from A Benefit O-zumo Match Featuring Rikishi Koyanagi and Arauma (23x27mm). h, Two wrestlers in ring bent over with heads touching, from A Benefit O-zumo Match Featuring Rikishi Koyanagi and Arauma (22x26mm). i, Dohyoiri from the East League (four wrestlers, denomination at UL), by Toyokuni Utagawa III (28x36mm). j, Four different wrestlers from Dohyoiri from the East League (denominiation at top center) (28x36mm).

**Die Cut Perf. 13x13¼ (#4393a, 4393b, 4393e, 4393f, 4393g, 4393j), 13 (#4393c, 4393d), 13½ (#4393h, 4393i)**
2020, May 8                      Litho.
**Self-Adhesive**
4393  A4645  Sheet of 10         12.50
a.-j.       63y Any single        1.25  .95

**Die Cut Perf. 13¼x13 (#4394a, 4394b, 4394c), 13¼ (#4394d, 4394e), 13 (#4394f), 13x13¼ (#4394g, 4394h), 12¾x13 (#4394i, 4394j)**
4394  A4646  Sheet of 10         16.00
a.-j.       84y Any single        1.60  1.25

Snail Shell
A4647

Shell Spiral
A4648

Starfish
A4649

Conch Shell
A4650

Scallop Shell
A4651

Flowers
A4652

Flowers
A4653

Flowers
A4654

Flowers
A4655

Flowers
A4656

Flowers
A4657

Flowers
A4658

**Litho. With Foil Application**
2020, May 14      Die Cut Perf. 13¼
**Self-Adhesive**
4395       Sheet of 10, 2 each
           #4395a-4395e          12.50
a.  A4647 63y multi              1.25  .95
b.  A4648 63y multi              1.25  .95
c.  A4649 63y multi              1.25  .95
d.  A4650 63y multi              1.25  .95
e.  A4651 63y multi              1.25  .95
4396       Sheet of 10, 2 each
           #4396a-4396e          16.00
a.  A4652 84y multi              1.60  1.25
b.  A4653 84y multi              1.60  1.25
c.  A4654 84y multi              1.60  1.25
d.  A4655 84y multi              1.60  1.25
e.  A4656 84y multi              1.60  1.25
4397       Sheet of 10, 5 each
           #4397a-4397b          17.50
a.  A4657 94y multi              1.75  1.40
b.  A4658 94y multi              1.75  1.40
      Nos. 4395-4397 (3)        46.00

Doraemon at Festival
A4659

Doraemon Fishing
A4660

Doraemon
and Mount
Fuji
A4661

Doraemon
on Picnic
A4663

Doraemon
as
Japanese
Mailman
A4665

Doraemon
Under
Umbrella
A4667

Doraemon
and Bridge
A4662

Doraemon
Harvesting
Rice
A4664

Doraemon
Picking Tea
Leaves
A4666

Doraemon
and
Bamboo
A4668

Doraemon — A4669

No. 4399 — Doraemon: a, Standing and smiling (27x30mm). b, In desk drawer (30x30mm). c, Eating (27x30mm). d, Flying with Nobita Nobi (30x30mm). e, Walking with Nobita Nobi (30x30mm). f, On telephone (27x30mm). g, Unfurling time kerchief (30x30mm). h, Laughing with arm and leg raised (27x30mm). i, Seated in time machine (30x30mm). j, Dancing with Nobita Nobi (27x30mm).

### *Die Cut Perf. 12¾x12½*
**2020, May 20**     **Litho.**
**Self-Adhesive**

| 4398 | | Booklet pane of 10 | 12.50 | |
|------|--|--------------------|-------|--|
| a. | A4659 | 63y multi | 1.25 | .95 |
| b. | A4660 | 63y multi | 1.25 | .95 |
| c. | A4661 | 63y multi | 1.25 | .95 |
| d. | A4662 | 63y multi | 1.25 | .95 |
| e. | A4663 | 63y multi | 1.25 | .95 |

| f. | A4664 | 63y multi | 1.25 | .95 |
|----|-------|-----------|------|-----|
| g. | A4665 | 63y multi | 1.25 | .95 |
| h. | A4666 | 63y multi | 1.25 | .95 |
| i. | A4667 | 63y multi | 1.25 | .95 |
| j. | A4668 | 63y multi | 1.25 | .95 |
| 4399 | A4669 | Sheet of 10 | 16.00 | |
| a.-j. | | 84y Any single | 1.60 | 1.25 |

### Miniature Sheets

A4670

### National Treasures — A4671

No. 4400: a, Jomon Venus (pink background, 22x30mm). b, Hollow Dogu (orange background, 22x30mm). c, Gassho Dogu (yellow background, 22x30mm). d, Jomon Goddess (green background, 22x30mm). e, Masked Goddess (blue background, 22x30mm). f, Haniwa Armored Male statue (tan background, 24x39mm). g, Bronze ritual bell (lt blue background, 24x39mm). h, Bronze mirror (pink background, 32x36mm). i, Flame-shpaed piece of pottery (dark red background, 32x32mm). j, Saddle fittings (gray background, 39x28mm).

No. 4401: a, Engaku-ji Reliquary Hall (two roofs and steps, 39x28mm). b, Todai-ji Belfry (with one roof, 39x33mm). c, Daigo-ji Five-story Pagoda (24x45mm). d, Chuson-ji Golden Hall at night (39x28mm). e, Ishiyamadera Tahoto (with two roofs, 39x33mm). f, Kofuku-ji Octagonal Hall (39x33mm). g, Mt. Haguro Five-story Pagoda (24x45mm). h, Mt. Mitoku Sanbutsu-ji Nageiredo on rock face (39x33mm). i, Jodo-ji Treasure Tahoto (denomination at UL, 39x33mm). j, Shosoin Repository (one roof, 39x28mm).

### *Die Cut Perf. 14 (#4400a, 4400b, 4400c, 4400d, 4400e), 13¼ (#4400f), 13¼x13½ (#4400g), 13¾x13¼ (#4400h), 13x13¼ (#4400i), 13 (#4400j)*
**2020, May 29**     **Litho.**
**Self-Adhesive**

| 4400 | A4670 | Sheet of 10 | 12.50 | |
|------|-------|-------------|-------|--|
| a.-j. | | 63y Any single | 1.25 | .95 |

### *Die Cut Perf. 12½x13 (#4401a, 4401d, 4401j), 13 (#4401b, 4401e, 4401f, 4401h, 4401i), 13¼ (#4401c, 4401g)*

| 4401 | A4671 | Sheet of 10 | 16.00 | |
|------|-------|-------------|-------|--|
| a.-j. | | 84y Any single | 1.60 | 1.25 |

### Miniature Sheets

A4672

### Summer Greetings — A4673

No. 4402: a, Red ginger flower (22x30mm). b, Palm tree, pink sky (22x26mm). c, Palm tree, lilac sky (22x26mm). d, Papaya (23x27mm). e, Sunflower (22x30mm). f, Bird-of-paradise flower (22x36mm). g, Hibiscus flower (22x26mm). h, Frangipani flower (27x23mm). i, Sea shell (29x22mm). j, Hibiscus flowers (29x22mm).

No. 4403: a, Palm tree reflected in drink glass (22x26mm). b, Red frangipani flowers (22x26mm). c, Palm tree, blue sky (22x26mm). d, Cloud (22x26mm). e, Red ginger flower, diff. (22x26mm). f, Seagull (29x22mm). g, White frangipani flowers (28x23mm). h, People at beach (23x27mm). i, Shadow of palm tree (22x26mm). j, Lei (29x22mm).

### *Die Cut Perf. 13x13¼ (#4402a, 4402b, 4402c, 4402e, 4402f, 4402g), 13¼ (#4402d), 13¼x13 (#4402h, 4402i, 4402j)*
**2020, June 1**     **Litho.**
**Self-Adhesive**

| 4402 | A4672 | Sheet of 10 | 12.50 | |
|------|-------|-------------|-------|--|
| a.-j. | | 63y Any single | 1.25 | .95 |

### *Die Cut Perf. 13x13¼ (#4403a, 4403b, 4403c, 4403d, 4403e, 4403h, 4403i), 13¼x13 (#4403f, 4403g, 4403j)*

| 4403 | A4673 | Sheet of 10 | 16.00 | |
|------|-------|-------------|-------|--|
| a.-j. | | 84y Any single | 1.60 | 1.25 |

### Miniature Sheet

### Flora and Fauna of Iriomote Island A4674

No. 4404: a, Crested serpent eagle (29x36mm). b, Ruddy kingfisher (29x33mm). c, Ryukyu scops owl (28x32mm). d, Iriomote wild cat (29x36mm). e, Chinese box turtle (32mm diameter). f, Large tree nymph butterfly (22x26mm). g, Bamboo orchid (22x26mm). h, Screw pine cone (22x26mm). i, Powder-puff tree (22x26mm). j, Loop-root mangrove (29x36mm).

### *Die Cut Perf. 13¼ (#4404a, 4404d, 4404j), 12x13 (#4404b, 4404c), 13x13¼ (#4404f, 4404g, 4404h, 4404i), Die Cut Perf. (#4404e)*
**2020, June 10**     **Litho.**
**Self-Adhesive**

| 4404 | A4674 | Sheet of 10 | 16.00 | |
|------|-------|-------------|-------|--|
| a.-j. | | 84y Any single | 1.60 | 1.25 |

### Miniature Sheets

A4675

### Items of Nihonbashi Business District of Tokyo — A4676

No. 4405: a, Kitchen utensils, b, Dried seaweed, fish and mushrooms. c, Fork, spoon and desserts. d, Calligraphy brush, fan and paper products. e, Kimono, sandals, umbrella and handbag. f, Lunch food and chopsticks. g, Toothpicks and toothpick boxes. h, Brushes, sewing scissors, tongs and knife. i, Tags, coin and shrine gifts. j, Bowl of rice with chicken and egg, spoon, dish and glass.

No. 4406: a, Entrance of Mitsukoshi-Isetan Department Store (denomination at LR, 27x27mm). b, Woman drinking from cup, pot and dried food (27x27mm). c, Entrance to specialty brush shop (denomination at UL, 27x27mm). d, Entrance to specialty knife shop (24x30mm). e, Bridge (30x21mm). f, Tamahide chicken restaurant (30x21mm). g, Fans and items on stationery store shelves (27x27mm). h, Postman, letter, stamp, pen, stationery, bust of Hisoka Maeshima (1835-1919), founder of Japanese Postal Service (27x27mm). i, Festival participants (27x27mm). j, People at Koami Shrine (27x27mm).

### *Die Cut Perf. 13¼*
**2020, June 16**     **Litho.**
**Self-Adhesive**

| 4405 | A4675 | Sheet of 10 | 12.50 | |
|------|-------|-------------|-------|--|
| a.-j. | | 63y Any single | 1.25 | .95 |
| 4406 | A4676 | Sheet of 10 | 16.00 | |
| a.-j. | | 84y Any single | 1.60 | 1.25 |

Soft Drink
Bottle
A4679

Bowl of
Flavored
Shaved
Ice
A4681

Pea Pod
A4683

Dianthus
Flowers
A4685

Glass and
Bottle
A4687

Bowl of
Curry
A4689

Fishing
With
Cormorants
A4691

Cloud,
Airplane
and
Flowers
A4693

Sunflowers
A4695

Two
Goldfish
A4680

Bowl of
Ice Cream
A4682

Kingfisher
A4684

Roses
A4686

Fan
A4688

Straw Hat
A4690

Jellyfish
A4692

Ear of
Corn
A4694

Beetles
A4696

Mulberries
A4677

Bitter
Melon
A4678

### *Die Cut Perf. 13x13¼*
**2020, June 19**     **Litho.**
**Self-Adhesive**

| 4407 | | Sheet of 10 | 12.50 | |
|------|--|-------------|-------|--|
| a. | A4677 | 63y multi | 1.25 | .95 |
| b. | A4678 | 63y multi | 1.25 | .95 |
| c. | A4679 | 63y multi | 1.25 | .95 |
| d. | A4680 | 63y multi | 1.25 | .95 |
| e. | A4681 | 63y multi | 1.25 | .95 |
| f. | A4682 | 63y multi | 1.25 | .95 |
| g. | A4683 | 63y multi | 1.25 | .95 |
| h. | A4684 | 63y multi | 1.25 | .95 |
| i. | A4685 | 63y multi | 1.25 | .95 |
| j. | A4686 | 63y multi | 1.25 | .95 |

| 4408 | Sheet of 10 | 16.00 | |
|---|---|---|---|
| a. | A4687 84y multi | 1.60 | 1.25 |
| b. | A4688 84y multi | 1.60 | 1.25 |
| c. | A4689 84y multi | 1.60 | 1.25 |
| d. | A4690 84y multi | 1.60 | 1.25 |
| e. | A4691 84y multi | 1.60 | 1.25 |
| f. | A4692 84y multi | 1.60 | 1.25 |
| g. | A4693 84y multi | 1.60 | 1.25 |
| h. | A4694 84y multi | 1.60 | 1.25 |
| i. | A4695 84y multi | 1.60 | 1.25 |
| j. | A4696 84y multi | 1.60 | 1.25 |

### Miniature Sheet

Fish
A4697

No. 4409: a, Pacific double-saddle butterf-lyfish, Moorish idol, Blue-green chromis. b, Two Blue devils, Blue-green chromis. c, Blue tang. d, Shepard's angelfish, Yellow tang, Blue-green chromis, coral. e, Two Moorish idols. f, Two Forceps butterflyfish. g, Two fire gobies, horiz. h, Saddle butterflyfish, Yellow boxfish. i, Clownfish, horiz. j, Two Clownfish in anemone, horiz.

### Die Cut Perf. 13x13¼ (vert. stamps), 13¼x13 (horiz. stamps)
**2020, July 1**          Litho.
#### Self-Adhesive

| 4409 | A4697 | Sheet of 10 | 16.00 | |
|---|---|---|---|---|
| a.-j. | | 84y Any single | 1.60 | 1.25 |

Emperor Ninkoku
Kofun — A4698

Emperor Richu
Kofun — A4699

Haniwa Helmet
from Itasuke
Kofun — A4700

Itasuke
Kofun — A4701

Gobyoyama
Kofun — A4702

Emperor Ojin
Kofun — A4703

Nakatsuhime-no-Mikoto
Kofun — A4704

Waterfowl-shaped
Haniwas from
Tsudo Shiroyama
Kofun — A4705

Emperor Chuai
Kofun — A4706

Hakuchoryo
Kofun — A4707

**2020, July 8**   Litho.   *Perf. 13¾x14¼*

| 4410 | Sheet of 10 | 16.00 | 16.00 |
|---|---|---|---|
| a. | A4698 84y multi | 1.60 | 1.25 |
| b. | A4699 84y multi | 1.60 | 1.25 |
| c. | A4700 84y multi | 1.60 | 1.25 |
| d. | A4701 84y multi | 1.60 | 1.25 |
| e. | A4702 84y multi | 1.60 | 1.25 |
| f. | A4703 84y multi | 1.60 | 1.25 |
| g. | A4704 84y multi | 1.60 | 1.25 |
| h. | A4705 84y multi | 1.60 | 1.25 |
| i. | A4706 84y multi | 1.60 | 1.25 |
| j. | A4707 84y multi | 1.60 | 1.25 |

Mozo-Furuichi Kofun Group UNESCO World Heritage Site.

### Miniature Sheet

Protection of Historic Sites and Natural Monuments — A4708

No. 4411: a, Goryokaku. b, Nakijin Castle ruins. c, East Palace Garden of Heijo Palace. d, Yohinogari Archaeological Site. e, Kamikochi Valley (Japanese inscription at UR). f, Kamikochi Valley (Japanese inscription at UL). g, Kenroku-en. h, Amanohashidate. i, Japanese serow. j, Oriental white storks.

**2020, July 17**   Litho.   *Perf. 13*

| 4411 | A4708 | Sheet of 10 | 16.00 | 16.00 |
|---|---|---|---|---|
| a.-j. | | 84y Any single | 1.60 | 1.25 |

First Japanese Natural Monument, cent.

House,
Mailbox
and Van
A4709

Fruit
Basket
A4710

House
and
Clothes
Drying on
Line
A4711

Chicken
and Goat
A4712

Child
Reading
Letter
Near
Mailbox
A4713

Jar of
Fruit
A4715

Sandwiches,
Jars and
Utensils
A4717

Child
Writing
Letter
A4714

Iron and
Folded
Clothes
A4716

Child
Mailing
Letter
A4718

### Die Cut Perf. 13x13¼
**2020, July 22**          Litho.
#### Booklet Stamps
#### Self-Adhesive

| 4412 | A4709 63y multi | 1.25 | .95 |
|---|---|---|---|
| 4413 | A4710 63y multi | 1.25 | .95 |
| 4414 | A4711 63y multi | 1.25 | .95 |
| 4415 | A4712 63y multi | 1.25 | .95 |
| 4416 | A4713 63y multi | 1.25 | .95 |
| a. | Booklet pane of 10, 2 each #4412-4416 | 12.50 | |
| 4417 | A4714 84y multi | 1.60 | 1.25 |
| 4418 | A4715 84y multi | 1.60 | 1.25 |
| 4419 | A4716 84y multi | 1.60 | 1.25 |
| 4420 | A4717 84y multi | 1.60 | 1.25 |
| 4421 | A4718 84y multi | 1.60 | 1.25 |
| a. | Booklet pane of 10, 2 each #4417-4421 | 16.00 | |
| | Nos. 4412-4421 (10) | 14.25 | 11.00 |

Letter Writing Day.

### Miniature Sheet

Philanippon 2021 World Stamp Championship Exhibition, Yokohama — A4719

No. 4422 — Mount Fuji and: a, Yokohama buildings at night. b, Cherry blossoms. c, Lake Yamanaka. d, Kochia and cosmos flowers. e, Larch forest. f, Cherry blossoms, vert. g, Tea plantation, vert. h, Azalea garden, vert. i, Small building and cosmos flower field, vert. j, Lake Kawaguchi, vert.

### Die Cut Perf. 13¼
**2020, Aug. 3**          Litho.
#### Self-Adhesive

| 4422 | A4719 | Sheet of 10 | 16.00 | |
|---|---|---|---|---|
| a.-j. | | 84y Any single | 1.60 | 1.25 |

Ginkgo
Branch
and
Leaves
A4720

Dahlia and
Cosmos
Flowers
A4721

Gentian Flowers
A4722

Chrysanthemums
A4723

Roses
A4724

Dahlia and
Cosmos
Flowers
A4726

Cockscomb
Flowers
A4728

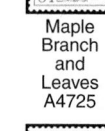

Maple
Branch
and
Leaves
A4725

Chinese
Bellflowers
A4727

Roses
A4729

### Die Cut Perf. 13x13¼
**2020, Aug. 18**          Litho.
#### Self-Adhesive

| 4423 | Sheet of 10, 2 each #4423a-4423e | 12.50 | |
|---|---|---|---|
| a. | A4720 63y multi | 1.25 | .95 |
| b. | A4721 63y multi | 1.25 | .95 |
| c. | A4722 63y multi | 1.25 | .95 |
| d. | A4723 63y multi | 1.25 | .95 |
| e. | A4724 63y multi | 1.25 | .95 |
| 4424 | Sheet of 10, 2 each #4424a-4424e | 16.00 | |
| a. | A4725 84y multi | 1.60 | 1.25 |
| b. | A4726 84y multi | 1.60 | 1.25 |
| c. | A4727 84y multi | 1.60 | 1.25 |
| d. | A4728 84y multi | 1.60 | 1.25 |
| e. | A4729 84y multi | 1.60 | 1.25 |

### Miniature Sheets

A4730

Autumn Greetings — A4731

No. 4425: a, Maple leaf (33x33mm). b, Pine cone (27x29mm). c, Pear (27x33mm). d, Red leaf (33x30mm). e, Oak leaf (32x31mm). f, Persimmon (28x28mm). g, Pumpkin (27x33mm). h, Orange leaf (27x27mm). i, Acorns (28x31mm). j, Fig (25x31mm).

No. 4426: a, Acorns. b, Ginkgo leaves. c, Squashes. d, Pine cones. e, Persimmons. f, Rambutans. g, Six leaves. h, Pears. i, Figs. j, Red and brown leaves.

**2020, Aug. 21**   Litho.   *Die Cut Perf.*
#### Self-Adhesive

| 4425 | A4730 | Sheet of 10 + 2 stickers | 12.50 | |
|---|---|---|---|---|
| a.-j. | | 63y Any single | 1.25 | .95 |

### *Die Cut Perf. 13¼*

| 4426 | A4731 | Sheet of 10 | 16.00 | |
|---|---|---|---|---|
| a.-j. | | 84y Any single | 1.60 | 1.25 |

People of
1920 and Bar
Graphs
A4732

Woman and
Tabulating
Machine
A4733

Japanese Statistics Bureau, Koji Sugi (1828-1917), Statistician and Prime Ministers Shigenobu Okuma (1838-1922) and Takashi Hara (1856-1921) A4734

Woman Providing Data by Smartphone A4735

People of 2020 and Bar Graphs — A4736

**2020, Sept. 1**  **Litho.**  **Perf. 13**

| | | | | |
|---|---|---|---|---|
| 4427 | A4732 | 84y multi | 1.60 | 1.25 |
| 4428 | A4733 | 84y multi | 1.60 | 1.25 |
| 4429 | A4734 | 84y multi | 1.60 | 1.25 |
| 4430 | A4735 | 84y multi | 1.60 | 1.25 |
| 4431 | A4736 | 84y multi | 1.60 | 1.25 |
| a. | Vert. strip of 5, #4427-4431 | | 8.00 | 6.25 |
| | Nos. 4427-4431 (5) | | 8.00 | 6.25 |

**Miniature Sheets**

A4737

Japan Post Teddy Bears A4738

No. 4432 — Teddy bear: a, With cup of tea (26x23mm). b, With three other teddy bears (22x33mm). c, With cat (26x23mm). d, With owl (34x21mm fan-shaped stamp). e, With two other teddy bears (27mm diameter).
No. 4433 — Teddy bear: a, With knotted cord (22x23mm). b, With other teddy bear, owl and mountain (23x45mm). c, On paper lantern (27mm diameter). d, Coming through curtain (26x22mm). e, With koala in hot spring (26x22mm).

***Die Cut Perf. 13¼x13 (#4432a, 4432c, 4433d, 4433e), Die Cut Perf. 13¼ (4432b, 4432d), Die Cut Perf. (#4432e, 4433c), Die Cut Perf. 13½x13 (#4433a), 13x13½ (#4433b)***

**2020, Sept. 15**  **Litho.**
**Self-Adhesive**

| | | | | |
|---|---|---|---|---|
| 4432 | A4737 | Sheet of 10, 2 each #4432a-4432e | 12.50 | |
| a.-e. | 63y Any single | | 1.25 | .95 |
| 4433 | A4738 | Sheet of 10, 2 each #4433a-4433e | 16.00 | |
| a.-e. | 84y Any single | | 1.60 | 1.25 |

First Rotary Club in Japan, Cent. — A4739

"Rotary," Rotary International emblem and: No. 4434, Dove. No. 4435, Stethoscopes. No. 4436, Water droplets. No. 4437, Stylized mother and child. No. 4438, Open books.

**2020, Sept. 18**  **Photo.**  **Perf. 13**
**Denomination Color**

| | | | | |
|---|---|---|---|---|
| 4434 | A4739 | 84y magenta | 1.60 | 1.25 |
| 4435 | A4739 | 84y dk brown | 1.60 | 1.25 |
| 4436 | A4739 | 84y blue | 1.60 | 1.25 |
| 4437 | A4739 | 84y orange | 1.60 | 1.25 |
| 4438 | A4739 | 84y emerald | 1.60 | 1.25 |
| a. | Horiz. strip of 5, #4434-4438 | | 8.00 | 6.25 |
| | Nos. 4434-4438 (5) | | 8.00 | 6.25 |

Sofa Cushion A4740

Sofa Cushion A4741

Mirror A4742

Tiles A4744

Tiles A4746

Perfume Bottles A4743

Tiles A4745

Tiles A4747

Tiles — A4748

**Litho. & Embossed**
**2020, Sept. 25**  **Die Cut Perf. 11**
**Self-Adhesive**

| | | | | |
|---|---|---|---|---|
| 4439 | | Sheet of 10, 2 each #4439a-4439e | 12.50 | |
| a. | A4740 | 63y lt blue sofa cushion | 1.25 | .85 |
| b. | A4741 | 63y lt brown sofa cushion | 1.25 | .85 |
| c. | A4740 | 63y green sofa cushion | 1.25 | .85 |
| d. | A4741 | 63y claret sofa cushion | 1.25 | .85 |
| e. | A4740 | 63y blue green sofa cushion | 1.25 | .85 |

**Litho. With Foil Application**

| | | | | |
|---|---|---|---|---|
| 4440 | | Sheet of 10, 5 each #4440a-4440b | 16.00 | |
| a. | A4742 | 84y gold & multi | 1.60 | 1.25 |
| b. | A4743 | 84y gold & multi | 1.60 | 1.25 |

**Litho.**

| | | | | |
|---|---|---|---|---|
| 4441 | | Sheet of 10, 2 each #4441a-4441e | 17.50 | |
| a. | A4744 | 94y multi | 1.75 | 1.40 |
| b. | A4745 | 94y multi | 1.75 | 1.40 |
| c. | A4746 | 94y multi | 1.75 | 1.40 |
| d. | A4747 | 94y multi | 1.75 | 1.40 |
| e. | A4748 | 94y multi | 1.75 | 1.40 |
| | Nos. 4439-4441 (3) | | 46.00 | |

**Miniature Sheet**

International Year of Plant Health — A4749

No. 4442: a, Airport baggage carousel opening and red suitcase. b, Baggage claim sign, baggage carousel with green and light blue suitcases. c, Child near baggage carousel, red, yellow and blue suitcases. d, Man and woman near baggage carousel with retrieved suitcases. e, Woman with red suitcase at customs counter. f, Man with green suitcase at customs counter. g, Male customs agent inspecting fruit. h, Female customs agent inspecting flowers. i, Man and girl with fruit. j, Woman and child with flowers.

**2020, Oct. 5**  **Photo.**  **Perf. 13**

| | | | | |
|---|---|---|---|---|
| 4442 | A4749 | Sheet of 10 | 16.00 | 16.00 |
| a.-j. | 84y Any single | | 1.60 | 1.25 |

Peonies and Canary, Detail of Print by Hokusai (1760-1849) A4750

Peonies and Canary, Detail of Print by Hokusai A4751

Fuji from Ushibori in Hitachi Province, Print by Hokusai — A4752

In the Mountains of Totomi Province, Print by Hokusai — A4753

Nihonbashi in Edo, Print by Hokusai — A4754

**2020, Oct. 9**  **Litho.**  **Perf. 13x13¼**

| | | | | |
|---|---|---|---|---|
| 4443 | A4750 | 7y multi | .30 | .25 |
| 4444 | A4751 | 70y multi | 1.40 | 1.10 |

**Perf. 13**

| | | | | |
|---|---|---|---|---|
| 4445 | A4752 | 90y multi | 1.75 | 1.40 |
| 4446 | A4753 | 110y multi | 2.10 | 1.60 |
| 4447 | A4754 | 130y multi | 2.50 | 1.90 |
| | Nos. 4443-4447 (5) | | 8.05 | 6.25 |

International Letter Writing Week.

Nihonbashi (Print Shown on No. 769) — A4755

Shinagawa (Print Shown on No. 2940) — A4756

Kawasaki (Print Shown on No. 2865) — A4757

Kanagawa (Print Shown on No. 3064) — A4758

Hodogaya (Print Shown on No. 2999) — A4759

Totsuka (Print Shown on No. 2837) — A4760

Fujisawa (Print Shown on No. 3163) — A4761

Hirutsuka (Print Shown on No. 2904) — A4762

Oiso (Print Shown on No. 2792) — A4763

Odawara (Print Shown on No. 3600) — A4764

Hakone (Print Shown on No. 735) — A4765

Mishima (Print Shown on No. 3065) — A4766

Maisaka (Print Shown on No. 2745) — A4785

Arai (Print Shown on No. 3000) — A4786

Minakuchi (Print Shown on No. 2939) — A4805

Ishibe (Print Shown on No. 3066) — A4806

Numazu (Print Shown on No. 4043) — A4767

Hara (Print Shown on No. 2791) — A4768

Shirasuka (Print Shown on No. 3599) — A4787

Futagawa (Print Shown on No. 4045) — A4788

Kusatsu (Print Shown on No. 3001) — A4807

Otsu (Print Shown on No. 2867) — A4808

Yoshiwara (Print Shown on No. 3938) — A4769

Kanbara (Print Shown on No. 704) — A4770

Yoshida (Print Shown on No. 3939) — A4789

Goyu (Print Shown on No. 4156) — A4790

Kyoto (Print Shown on No. 656) — A4809

Yui (Print Shown on No. 2835) — A4771

Okitsu (Print Shown on No. 3164) — A4772

Akasaka (Print Shown on No. 4246) — A4791

Fujikawa (Print Shown on No. 3940) — A4792

**2020, Oct. 9    Litho.    Perf. 13**

| | | | |
|---|---|---|---|
| 4448 | | Sheet of 55 | 105.00  105.00 |
| a. | A4755 | 70y multi | 1.90  1.90 |
| b. | A4756 | 70y multi | 1.90  1.90 |
| c. | A4757 | 70y multi | 1.90  1.90 |
| d. | A4758 | 70y multi | 1.90  1.90 |
| e. | A4759 | 70y multi | 1.90  1.90 |
| f. | A4760 | 70y multi | 1.90  1.90 |
| g. | A4761 | 70y multi | 1.90  1.90 |
| h. | A4762 | 70y multi | 1.90  1.90 |
| i. | A4763 | 70y multi | 1.90  1.90 |
| j. | A4764 | 70y multi | 1.90  1.90 |
| k. | A4765 | 70y multi | 1.90  1.90 |
| l. | A4766 | 70y multi | 1.90  1.90 |
| m. | A4767 | 70y multi | 1.90  1.90 |
| n. | A4768 | 70y multi | 1.90  1.90 |
| o. | A4769 | 70y multi | 1.90  1.90 |
| p. | A4770 | 70y multi | 1.90  1.90 |
| q. | A4771 | 70y multi | 1.90  1.90 |
| r. | A4772 | 70y multi | 1.90  1.90 |
| s. | A4773 | 70y multi | 1.90  1.90 |
| t. | A4774 | 70y multi | 1.90  1.90 |
| u. | A4775 | 70y multi | 1.90  1.90 |
| v. | A4776 | 70y multi | 1.90  1.90 |
| w. | A4777 | 70y multi | 1.90  1.90 |
| x. | A4778 | 70y multi | 1.90  1.90 |
| y. | A4779 | 70y multi | 1.90  1.90 |
| z. | A4780 | 70y multi | 1.90  1.90 |
| aa. | A4781 | 70y multi | 1.90  1.90 |
| ab. | A4782 | 70y multi | 1.90  1.90 |
| ac. | A4783 | 70y multi | 1.90  1.90 |
| ad. | A4784 | 70y multi | 1.90  1.90 |
| ae. | A4785 | 70y multi | 1.90  1.90 |
| af. | A4786 | 70y multi | 1.90  1.90 |
| ag. | A4787 | 70y multi | 1.90  1.90 |
| ah. | A4788 | 70y multi | 1.90  1.90 |
| ai. | A4789 | 70y multi | 1.90  1.90 |
| aj. | A4790 | 70y multi | 1.90  1.90 |
| ak. | A4791 | 70y multi | 1.90  1.90 |
| al. | A4792 | 70y multi | 1.90  1.90 |
| am. | A4793 | 70y multi | 1.90  1.90 |
| an. | A4794 | 70y multi | 1.90  1.90 |
| ao. | A4795 | 70y multi | 1.90  1.90 |
| ap. | A4796 | 70y multi | 1.90  1.90 |
| aq. | A4797 | 70y multi | 1.90  1.90 |
| ar. | A4798 | 70y multi | 1.90  1.90 |
| as. | A4799 | 70y multi | 1.90  1.90 |
| at. | A4800 | 70y multi | 1.90  1.90 |
| au. | A4801 | 70y multi | 1.90  1.90 |
| av. | A4802 | 70y multi | 1.90  1.90 |
| aw. | A4803 | 70y multi | 1.90  1.90 |
| ax. | A4804 | 70y multi | 1.90  1.90 |
| ay. | A4805 | 70y multi | 1.90  1.90 |
| az. | A4806 | 70y multi | 1.90  1.90 |
| ba. | A4807 | 70y multi | 1.90  1.90 |
| bb. | A4808 | 70y multi | 1.90  1.90 |
| bc. | A4809 | 70y multi | 1.90  1.90 |

Completion of depicting each of the prints from Hiroshige's "The Fifty-three Stations of the Tokaido" on International Letter Writing Week stamps, 1st anniv. Nos. 4448a and 4448bc depict prints by Hiroshige of the Eastern (Nihonbashi) and Western (Kyoto) terminals of the Tokaido route. No. 4448 sold for 5000y.

Ejiri (Print Shown on No. 3740) — A4773

Fuchu (Print Shown on No. 4155) — A4774

Okazaki (Print Shown on No. 2746) — A4793

Chiryu (Print Shown on No. 3165) — A4794

Mariko (Print Shown on No. 2938) — A4775

Okabe (Print Shown on No. 2744) — A4776

Narumi (Print Shown on No. 4345) — A4795

Atsuta (Print Shown on No. 2866) — A4796

### Miniature Sheets

A4810

Art A4811

Fujieda (Print Shown on No. 4044) — A4777

Shimada (Print Shown on No. 4157) — A4778

Kuwana (Print Shown on No. 679) — A4797

Yokkaichi (Print Shown on No. 2905) — A4798

Kanaya (Print Shown on No. 3741) — A4779

Nissaka (Print Shown on No. 4344) — A4780

Ishiyakushi (Print Shown on No. 3602) — A4799

Shono (Print Shown on No. 2836) — A4800

No. 4449: a, Detail of 17th century overglazed enamel tea jar with Moon and plum branches design, by Ninsei Nonomura (25x28mm). b, Devotion, detail of painting by Ryushi Kawabata (1885-1966) (27x26mm). c, The Sound of the Hand Drum, painting by

Kakegawa (Print Shown on No. 4244) — A4781

Fukuroi (Print Shown on No. 3742) — A4782

Kameyama (Print Shown on No. 2582) — A4801

Seki (Print Shown on No. 4346) — A4802

Mitsuke (Print Shown on No. 4245) — A4783

Hamamatsu (Print Shown on No. 3601) — A4784

Sakanoshita (Print Shown on No. 2793) — A4803

Tsuchiyama (Print Shown on No. 2906) — A4804

Shoen Uemura (1875-1949) (27x27mm). d, Dusk at the Ferry Crossing, painting by Eisaku Wada (1874-1959) (31x26mm). e, Peony and swallow fabric design from 19th century cotton robe (22x32mm). f, Thirty-six Views of Fuji, South Wind and Clear Skies, detail of woodblock print by Hokusai (1760-1849) (24x34mm). g, Birds and Flowers of the Four Seasons, Autumn, painting by Jippo Araki (1872-1944) (23x34mm). h, Girl with Braids, detail of painting by Amadeo Modigliani (1884-1920) (25x30mm). i, La France, painting by Henri Matisse (1869-1954) (24x33mm). j, Peony Garden, painting by Claude Monet (1840-1926) (30x26mm).

No. 4450: a, 17th century overglazed enamel tea jar with Moon and plum branches design, by Nonomura (28x35mm). b, Devotion, by Kawabata (35x29mm). c, The Prelude, painting by Uemura (31x38mm). d, Salmon, painting by Yuichi Takahashi (1828-94) (23x45mm). e, Thirty-six Views of Fuji, South Wind and Clear Skies, by Hokusai (36x30mm). f, Fire Dance, painting by Gyoshu Hayami (1894-1935) (27x43mm). g, Girl with Braids, by Modigliani (26x39mm). h, Haystacks at Giverny, Sunset, painting by Monet (36x31mm). i, The Lute, painting by Matisse (34x31mm). j, 19th century cotton robe with peony and swallow design (32x42mm).

*Die Cut Perf. 12¾ (#4449a), Die Cut Perf. 13¼x13¾ (#4449b), Die Cut Perf. 13¼ (#4449c, 4449d, 4449j, 4450b), Die Cut Perf. 12x12½ (#4449e, 4450f), Die Cut Perf. 12x13 (#4449f, 4449i), Die Cut Perf. 12½x13 (#4449g), Die Cut Perf. 13x12¾ (#4449h, 4450d, 4450h), Die Cut Perf. 12¼ (#4450a), Die Cut Perf. 13x12 (#4450c), Die Cut Perf. 13x13½ (#4450e), Die Cut Perf. 13¼x13 (#4450g), Die Cut Perf. 12¼x12¾ (#4450i), Die Cut Perf. 12½x11½ (#4450j)*

**2020, Oct. 16    Litho.**

**Self-Adhesive**

| | | | |
|---|---|---|---|
| 4449 | A4810 | Sheet of 10 | 12.50 |
| a.-j. | | 63y Any single | 1.25  .95 |
| 4450 | A4811 | Sheet of 10 | 16.00 |
| a.-j. | | 84y Any single | 1.60  1.25 |

### Souvenir Sheet

Summer Greetings — A4812

No. 4451: a, Boy writing postcard. b, Mailbox, insect and net.

**2020, Oct. 23    Litho.    Perf. 13x13¼**

| | | | |
|---|---|---|---|
| 4451 | A4812 | Sheet of 2 | 3.00  3.00 |
| a. | | 63y multi | 1.25  .95 |
| b. | | 84y multi | 1.60  1.25 |

No. 4451 was sold to the public, but also was awarded as a lottery prize.

A4813          A4814

A4815          A4816

New Year 2021 (Year of the Ox)

**2020, Oct. 29    Litho.    Perf. 13x13¼**

| | | | |
|---|---|---|---|
| 4452 | A4813 | 63y multi | 1.25  .95 |
| 4453 | A4814 | 84y multi | 1.60  1.25 |

## Photo. & Typo.
### Perf. 13¼

| | | | |
|---|---|---|---|
| 4454 | A4815 | 63y+3y multi | 1.25 .95 |
| 4455 | A4816 | 84y+3y multi | 1.75 1.30 |
| | *Nos. 4452-4455 (4)* | | 5.85 4.45 |

Coffee
Grinder,
Cup and Pot
A4817

Sliced
Melon and
Blue
Honeysuckle
A4818

Carved Bear
and Ice
Cream
Cone
A4819

Gyoza Curry
A4820

Cheesecake and Cup of
Coffee — A4821

Packaged Cookies and
Chocolate-Covered
Potato Chips — A4822

Milk Bottle
and Stuffed
Rolls
A4823

Cheese
Board and
Butter
A4824

Grilled Corn
and Potato
A4825

Stir-fried
Yakisoba
Noodles
A4826

Rice with
Sea Urchin
and Salmon
Roe
A4827

Ramen with
Miso
A4828

Mutton and
Vegetables
A4829

Dried
Mackerel
A4830

Grilled
Scallop
A4831

Curry Soup
A4832

Salmon Hot
Pot
A4833

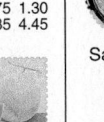

Salmon
Soup with
Vegetables
A4834

Fried
Chicken
A4835

Squid
Sashimi and
Ramen
Salad
A4836

### Die Cut Perf. 13¼
**2020, Nov. 11**  Litho.
#### Self-Adhesive

| 4456 | | Sheet of 10 | 12.50 | |
|---|---|---|---|---|
| a. | A4817 | 63y multi | 1.25 | .95 |
| b. | A4818 | 63y multi | 1.25 | .95 |
| c. | A4819 | 63y multi | 1.25 | .95 |
| d. | A4820 | 63y multi | 1.25 | .95 |
| e. | A4821 | 63y multi | 1.25 | .95 |
| f. | A4822 | 63y multi | 1.25 | .95 |
| g. | A4823 | 63y multi | 1.25 | .95 |
| h. | A4824 | 63y multi | 1.25 | .95 |
| i. | A4825 | 63y multi | 1.25 | .95 |
| j. | A4826 | 63y multi | 1.25 | .95 |

### Die Cut Perf.

| 4457 | | Sheet of 10 | 16.00 | |
|---|---|---|---|---|
| a. | A4827 | 84y multi | 1.60 | 1.25 |
| b. | A4828 | 84y multi | 1.60 | 1.25 |
| c. | A4829 | 84y multi | 1.60 | 1.25 |
| d. | A4830 | 84y multi | 1.60 | 1.25 |
| e. | A4831 | 84y multi | 1.60 | 1.25 |
| f. | A4832 | 84y multi | 1.60 | 1.25 |
| g. | A4833 | 84y multi | 1.60 | 1.25 |
| h. | A4834 | 84y multi | 1.60 | 1.25 |
| i. | A4835 | 84y multi | 1.60 | 1.25 |
| j. | A4836 | 84y multi | 1.60 | 1.25 |

#### Miniature Sheets

Juvenile
Animals
A4837

Adult
and
Juvenile
Animals
A4838

No. 4458: a, Kitten (26x25mm). b, Chicks (26x23mm oval). c, Rabbit kit (23x26mm oval). d, Hedgehog pup with adult (26x23mm oval). e, Puppy (26x25mm). f, Chipmunk (22x26mm). g, Piglets (26x22mm). h, Long-tailed tit (26x22mm). i, Wild piglets (26x22mm). j, Hamster pup (22x26mm).

No. 4459: a, Elephant and calf (37x24mm). b, Panda and cub (37x26mm). c, Koala and joey (30x24mm). d, Polar bear and cub (28x37mm). e, Penguin and chick (25x36mm). f, Zebra and foal (28x23mm). g, Indian spot-billed duck and ducklings (26x22mm). h, Kangaroo and joey (28x37mm). i, Deer and fawn (28x23mm). j, Macaque and infant (22x32mm).

*Die Cut Perf. 12¾ (#4458a, 4458e, 4459e), Die Cut Perf. (#4458b, 4458c, 4458d), Die Cut Perf. 13x13¼ (#4458f, #4458j), Die Cut Perf. 13¼x13 (#4458g, 4458h, 4458i), Die Cut Perf. 13x12½ (#4459a, 4459j), Die Cut Perf. 13 (#4459b), Die Cut Perf. 12½ (#4459c), Die Cut Perf. 12¾x13 (#4459d, 4459f, 4459h, 4459i), Die Cut Perf. 13½x13 (#4459g)*

**2020, Nov. 16**  Litho.
#### Self-Adhesive

| 4458 | A4837 | Sheet of 10 | 12.50 | |
|---|---|---|---|---|
| a.-j. | | 63y Any single | 1.25 | .95 |
| 4459 | A4838 | Sheet of 10 | 16.00 | |
| a.-j. | | 84y Any single | 1.60 | 1.25 |

Snowflakes
A4839

Snowflakes
A4841

Trees and
Snowflakes
A4843

Snowflakes
and Trees
A4845

Fox and
Snow-
covered
Trees
A4847

Snowflakes
A4849

Squirrel and
Snow-covered
Trees
A4851

Robin and Snow-
covered
Trees — A4853

Tree,
Buildings
and
Snowflakes
A4840

Buildings,
Tree and
Snowflakes
A4842

Snowflakes
A4844

Snow-
covered
House and
Tree
A4846

Deer and
Snow-
covered
Trees
A4848

Rabbits and
Snow-covered
Trees
A4850

Owl and
Snow-covered
Trees
A4852

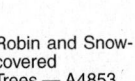

#### Litho. With Foil Application
**2020, Nov. 20**  *Die Cut Perf. 13x13½*
#### Self-Adhesive

| 4460 | | Sheet of 10, 2 each #4460a-4460e, + 4 stickers | 12.50 | |
|---|---|---|---|---|
| a. | A4839 | 63y sil & multi | 1.25 | .95 |
| b. | A4840 | 63y sil & multi | 1.25 | .95 |
| c. | A4841 | 63y sil & multi | 1.25 | .95 |
| d. | A4842 | 63y sil & multi | 1.25 | .95 |
| e. | A4843 | 63y sil & multi | 1.25 | .95 |

*Die Cut Perf. 13¼ (#4461a-4461f), Die Cut Perf. 12¾x13 (#4461g-4461j)*

| 4461 | | Sheet of 10 + 2 stickers | 16.00 | |
|---|---|---|---|---|
| a. | A4844 | 84y sil & multi | 1.60 | 1.25 |
| b. | A4845 | 84y sil & multi | 1.60 | 1.25 |
| c. | A4846 | 84y sil & multi | 1.60 | 1.25 |
| d. | A4847 | 84y sil & multi | 1.60 | 1.25 |
| e. | A4848 | 84y sil & multi | 1.60 | 1.25 |
| f. | A4849 | 84y sil & multi | 1.60 | 1.25 |
| g. | A4850 | 84y sil & multi | 1.60 | 1.25 |
| h. | A4851 | 84y sil & multi | 1.60 | 1.25 |
| i. | A4852 | 84y sil & multi | 1.60 | 1.25 |
| j. | A4853 | 84y sil & multi | 1.60 | 1.25 |

#### Miniature Sheet

 (top sheet, A4854)

Children's Book Illustrations by Leo
Lionni (1910-99) — A4854

No. 4462: a, Black fish, rocks and seaweed (38x28mm). b, Black fish approaching school of fish (38x28mm). c, Black fish as eye of fish-shaped school of fish (38x28mm). d, Close-up of head of fish-shaped school (38x28mm). e, Five mice (38x28mm). f, Mouse, wind-up mouse, bird and teddy bear (38x28mm). g, Mouse holding flower (32x37mm). h, Mouse, wind-up mouse and nesting doll (32x37mm). i, Mouse in boot (32x37mm). j, Mouse, box containing gifts and wind-up mouse (32x37mm).

### Die Cut Perf. 13¼x13½
**2020, Nov. 27**  Litho.
#### Self-Adhesive

| 4462 | A4854 | Sheet of 10 | 16.00 | |
|---|---|---|---|---|
| a.-j. | | 84y Any single | 1.60 | 1.25 |

#### Miniature Sheets

A4855

Japanese Musical
Instruments — A4856

No. 4463: a, Satsuma biwa (light green background, 22x26mm). b, Sanshin (yellow background, 22x26mm). c, Man beating odaiko (light blue background, 26x27mm). d, Surigane and shinobue (light blue background, 22x26mm). e, Shimedaiko (light brown background, 22x26mm). f, Otsuzumi (light brown background, 26x22mm). g, Nokan and kotsuzumi (tan and pale orange background, 22x26mm). h, Woman playing so (orange yellow and rose background, 29x23mm). i, Samisen (orange yellow and rose background, 22x26mm). j, Shakuhachi (orange yellow and rose background, 21x29mm).

No. 4464: a, Furitsuzumi (22x31mm, denomination at LR above country name). b, Man playing gakuso (24x27mm). c, Hichiriki and ryuteki (22x30mm, denomination at UL). d, Sho (22x32mm, denomination at LR). e, Man holding and playing gakubiwa (27x26mm, denomination at UR under country name). f, Dadaiko (30x40mm). g, Shoko (22x32mm, denomination at UR above country name). h, Gakudaiko (24x32mm, denomination at UR above country name). i, Kakko (26x29mm, denomination at UL). j, San no Tsuzumi and Ikko (26x28mm, denomination at LR above country name).

*Die Cut Perf. 13x13¼ (#4463a-4463e, 4463g, 4463i, 4464c, 4464d, 4464g), Die Cut Perf. 13¼x13 (#4463f, 4464i, 4464j), Die Cut Perf. 12½x13 (#4463h), Die Cut Perf. 13x12½ (#4463j), Die Cut Perf. 13 (#4464a, 4464f), Die Cut Perf. 12¾ (#4464b), Die Cut Perf. 12¾x13 (#4464e), Die Cut Perf. 13¼ (#4464h)*

**2020, Dec. 4**  Litho.
#### Self-Adhesive

| 4463 | A4855 | Sheet of 10 | 12.50 | |
|---|---|---|---|---|
| a.-j. | | 63y Any single | 1.25 | .95 |
| 4464 | A4856 | Sheet of 10 | 16.00 | |
| a.-j. | | 84y Any single | 1.60 | 1.25 |

 (top sheet, A4856)

Forsythia
A4857

Anemones
A4858

Coralberry
A4859

Narcissi
A4860

Roses
A4861

Magnolia
A4862

Poppies
A4863

Plum
Blossoms
A4864

Cherry
Blossoms
A4865

Rapeseed
and Peach
Blossoms
A4866

### Die Cut Perf. 13x13¼
**2020, Dec. 14**     Litho.
#### Self-Adhesive

| | | | |
|---|---|---|---|
| 4465 | Sheet of 10, 2 each | 12.50 | |
| | #4465a-4465e | | |
| a. | A4857 63y multi | 1.25 | .95 |
| b. | A4858 63y multi | 1.25 | .95 |
| c. | A4859 63y multi | 1.25 | .95 |
| d. | A4860 63y multi | 1.25 | .95 |
| e. | A4861 63y multi | 1.25 | .95 |
| 4466 | Sheet of 10, 2 each | 16.00 | |
| | #4466a-4466e | | |
| a. | A4862 84y multi | 1.60 | 1.25 |
| b. | A4863 84y multi | 1.60 | 1.25 |
| c. | A4864 84y multi | 1.60 | 1.25 |
| d. | A4865 84y multi | 1.60 | 1.25 |
| e. | A4866 84y multi | 1.60 | 1.25 |

Sunrise on
Mitsukejima
A4867

Sun and
Clouds
Over
Kujuku
Islands
A4868

Cherry Tree
in Bloom,
Maniwa
A4869

Cherry
Blossoms
on Water
A4870

Frost
Flowers on
Ice
A4871

Nomizo
Falls,
Kameiwa
Cave
A4872

Naruto
Strait
Whirlpool
A4873

Frozen
Kiyotaki
Waterfall
A4874

Rainstorm,
Amaharashi
Beach
A4875

Clouds Over
Mount Fuji
A4877

Cherry
Blossoms
on Mt,
Yoshino
A4879

Frost-
covered
Trees on Mt.
Zao
A4881

Flukes of
Humpback
Whale
A4883

Shodo
Island Angel
Road
A4885

### Die Cut Perf. 13¼
**2021, Jan. 12**     Litho.
#### Self-Adhesive

| | | | |
|---|---|---|---|
| 4467 | Sheet of 10 | 12.50 | |
| a. | A4867 63y multi | 1.25 | .95 |
| b. | A4868 63y multi | 1.25 | .95 |
| c. | A4869 63y multi | 1.25 | .95 |
| d. | A4870 63y multi | 1.25 | .95 |
| e. | A4871 63y multi | 1.25 | .95 |
| f. | A4872 63y multi | 1.25 | .95 |
| g. | A4873 63y multi | 1.25 | .95 |
| h. | A4874 63y multi | 1.25 | .95 |
| i. | A4875 63y multi | 1.25 | .95 |
| j. | A4876 63y multi | 1.25 | .95 |
| 4468 | Sheet of 10 | 16.00 | |
| a. | A4877 84y multi | 1.60 | 1.25 |
| b. | A4878 84y multi | 1.60 | 1.25 |
| c. | A4879 84y multi | 1.60 | 1.25 |
| d. | A4880 84y multi | 1.60 | 1.25 |
| e. | A4881 84y multi | 1.60 | 1.25 |
| f. | A4882 84y multi | 1.60 | 1.25 |
| g. | A4883 84y multi | 1.60 | 1.25 |
| h. | A4884 84y multi | 1.60 | 1.25 |
| i. | A4885 84y multi | 1.60 | 1.25 |
| j. | A4886 84y multi | 1.60 | 1.25 |

Snork
Maiden,
Mymble,
Little My
A4887

Hornfels on
Susa Bay
A4876

Fog Near
Takeda
Castle
Ruins
A4878

Tree and
Nemophila
Flowers,
Hitachi
Seaside
Park
A4880

Inazumi
Underwater
Cave
A4882

Snow on
Trees,
Okutama
A4884

Sunrise at
Shishi-Iwa
A4886

Little My,
Moomin,
Snork
Maiden
A4888

Moominmamma,
Moominpappa, Little
My — A4889

Moominmamma, Little
My — A4890

Snufkin,
Little My,
Moomin
A4891

Moomin,
Little My,
Stinky
A4892

Little My
Spraying
Hattifatteners
A4893

Little My
With Large
Eyeglasses
A4894

Little My,
Shadow on
Floating Box
of Seeds
A4895

Moominpappa,
Little My,
Moominmamma
A4896

Stinky, Sniff
A4897

Little My on
Tree Branch
A4898

Moominmamma, Too-
Ticky Planting
Seedling — A4899

Moominpappa, and
Plate of Fruit — A4900

Moominhouse
A4901

Mymble
Reading
A4902

Snufkin With
Accordion
A4903

Moomin
Picking
Flowers
A4904

Snork
Maiden in
Flowers
A4905

Police
Inspector
Watering
Flowers
A4906

### Die Cut Perf. 13¼
**2021, Jan. 15**     Litho.
#### Self-Adhesive

| | | | |
|---|---|---|---|
| 4469 | Sheet of 10 | 12.50 | |
| a. | A4887 63y multi | 1.25 | .95 |
| b. | A4888 63y multi | 1.25 | .95 |
| c. | A4889 63y multi | 1.25 | .95 |
| d. | A4890 63y multi | 1.25 | .95 |
| e. | A4891 63y multi | 1.25 | .95 |
| f. | A4892 63y multi | 1.25 | .95 |
| g. | A4893 63y multi | 1.25 | .95 |
| h. | A4894 63y multi | 1.25 | .95 |
| i. | A4895 63y multi | 1.25 | .95 |
| j. | A4896 63y multi | 1.25 | .95 |
| 4470 | Sheet of 10 | 16.00 | |
| a. | A4897 84y multi | 1.60 | 1.25 |
| b. | A4898 84y multi | 1.60 | 1.25 |
| c. | A4899 84y multi | 1.60 | 1.25 |
| d. | A4900 84y multi | 1.60 | 1.25 |
| e. | A4901 84y multi | 1.60 | 1.25 |
| f. | A4902 84y multi | 1.60 | 1.25 |
| g. | A4903 84y multi | 1.60 | 1.25 |
| h. | A4904 84y multi | 1.60 | 1.25 |
| i. | A4905 84y multi | 1.60 | 1.25 |
| j. | A4906 84y multi | 1.60 | 1.25 |

#### Souvenir Sheet

New
Year
2021
A4907

No. 4471: a, Red-crowned crane. b, Turtle.

**2021, Jan. 18**   Photo.   Die Cut Perf.
#### Self-Adhesive

| | | | | |
|---|---|---|---|---|
| 4471 | A4907 | Sheet of 2 | 3.00 | |
| a. | | 63y gold & multi | 1.25 | .95 |
| b. | | 84y gold & multi | 1.60 | 1.25 |

Noble
Orchids
A4908

Star
Magnolias
A4909

Violets
A4910

Winter
Chrysanthemum
A4911

Narcissi
A4912

Hydrangea
A4913

Roses
A4914

Fringed
Irises
A4915

Reeve's
Spiraea
A4916

Yoraku
Azalea
A4917

## Die Cut Perf. 13¼

**2021, Jan. 22**      Litho.

### Self-Adhesive

| | | | |
|---|---|---|---|
| 4472 | Sheet of 10 | 16.00 | |
| a. | A4908 84y multi | 1.60 | 1.25 |
| b. | A4909 84y multi | 1.60 | 1.25 |
| c. | A4910 84y multi | 1.60 | 1.25 |
| d. | A4911 84y multi | 1.60 | 1.25 |
| e. | A4912 84y multi | 1.60 | 1.25 |
| f. | A4913 84y multi | 1.60 | 1.25 |
| g. | A4914 84y multi | 1.60 | 1.25 |
| h. | A4915 84y multi | 1.60 | 1.25 |
| i. | A4916 84y multi | 1.60 | 1.25 |
| j. | A4917 84y multi | 1.60 | 1.25 |

### Miniature Sheeta

A4918

Astronomical Objects — A4919

No. 4473: a, Neutron star (22x26mm). b, Black hole (26x22mm). c, Oumuamua (22x26mm). d, Saturn and its moon, Mimas (44x32mm irregular shape). e, 486958 Arrokoth (26x22mm). f, Saturn's moon, Rhea (32x22mm oval). g, Pluto (32mm diameter). h, Uranus and its moon, Miranda (32mm diameter). i, Neptune (22x32mm oval). j, Neptune's moon, Triton (22x32mm oval).

No. 4474: a, Mars (32mm diameter). b, Saturn's moon, Titan (26x22mm). c, Saturn and its moon, Mimas (32mm diameter). d, Pluto's moon, Charon (22x26mm). e, Hale-Bopp Comet (22x32mm oval). f, Venus (32mm diameter). g, Dwarf planet Ceres (32x22mm oval). h, Saturn's rings and its moon, Enceladus (32x22mm oval). i, Saturn's moon, Rhea (26x22mm). j, Uranus's moon, Titania (22x32mm oval). k, Pluto (22x26mm). l, Mercury (32mm diameter). m, Moon (32x22mm oval). n, Jupiter's moon, Io (26x22mm). o, Jupiter's moon, Europa (22x26mm). p, Jupiter's moons, Thebe and Amalthea (22x26mm). q, Uranus (22x32mm oval). r, Uranus's moon, Miranda (32x22mm oval). s, Sun (32mm diameter). t, Earth (43mm diameter). u, Great Red Spot of Jupiter (32mm diameter). v, Jupiter's moon, Ganymede (32mm diameter). w, Jupiter's moon, Callisto (32mm diameter). x, Neptune (32mm diameter). y, Neptune's moon, Triton (32x22mm oval).

## Die Cut Perf. 13x13¼ (#4473a, 4473c, 4474k, 4474m, 4474o, 4474p), Die Cut Perf. 13¼x13 (#4473b, 4473e, 4474b, 4474d, 4474i, 4474n), Die Cut Perf. (others)
## Litho. With Hologram Affixed
**2021, Feb. 3**

### Self-Adhesive

| | | | |
|---|---|---|---|
| 4473 | A4918 Sheet of 10 | 16.00 | |
| a.-j. | 84y Any single | 1.60 | 1.25 |

### Litho With Silver Foil Application

| | | | |
|---|---|---|---|
| 4474 | A4919 Sheet of 25 | 57.00 | |
| a.-y. | 84y Any single | 2.25 | 2.25 |

No. 4474 sold for 3000y.

Fiddlehead Ferns
A4920

Poppies
A4921

---

Bee and Rape Blossoms
A4922

Rabbits
A4924

Tulips
A4926

Wisteria
A4928

Camellias and Birds
A4930

Strawberries
A4923

Cat, Flowers and Butterfly
A4925

Dandelions
A4927

Pansies
A4929

Dog and Cherry Blossoms
A4931

## Die Cut Perf. 13x13¼

**2021, Feb. 19**      Photo.

### Self-Adhesive

| | | | |
|---|---|---|---|
| 4475 | Sheet of 10, #4475c, 4475f, 2 each #4475a-4475b, 4475d-4475e | 12.50 | |
| a. | A4920 63y multi | 1.25 | .95 |
| b. | A4921 63y multi | 1.25 | .95 |
| c. | A4922 63y multi | 1.25 | .95 |
| d. | A4923 63y multi | 1.25 | .95 |
| e. | A4924 63y multi | 1.25 | .95 |
| f. | A4925 63y multi | 1.25 | .95 |
| 4476 | Sheet of 10, #4476c, 4476f, 2 each #4476a-4476b, 4476d-4476e | 16.00 | |
| a. | A4926 84y multi | 1.60 | 1.25 |
| b. | A4927 84y multi | 1.60 | 1.25 |
| c. | A4928 84y multi | 1.60 | 1.25 |
| d. | A4929 84y multi | 1.60 | 1.25 |
| e. | A4930 84y multi | 1.60 | 1.25 |
| f. | A4931 84y multi | 1.60 | 1.25 |

---

### Miniature Sheets

A4932

My Journey
A4933

No. 4477: a, Hirosaki Park, Hirosaki (26x22mm). b, Lake Towada (26x22mm). c, Bowl of Kiritanpo (22x26mm). d, Namahage (26x22mm). e, Nambu iron kettle (23x27 oval). f, Cherries (25mm diameter). g, Plate of beef tongue (22x26mm). h, Matsushima (26x22mm). i, Red cow toys with bobbling heads (23x27mm oval). j, Weeping cherry tree, Miharu (26x22mm).

No. 4478: a, Lake Inawashiro and Mt. Bandai (26x22mm). b, Crane Castle, Wakamatsu (26x22mm). c, Statue of Masamune Date (1567-1636), warrior, Sendai (22x26mm). d, Kokeshi dolls (23x27mm oval). e, Game pieces for Shogi (23x28mm pentagonal). f, Yamagata Prefectural Local History Museum (26x22mm). g, Jodogahama Beach (26x22mm). h, Soba bowls (26x22mm). i, Akita dog (23x27mm oval). j, Forest in Shirakami Mountain Range (22x27mm).

---

## Die Cut Perf. 13¼x13 (#4477a, 4477b, 4477d, 4477h, 4477j, 4478a, 4478b, 4478f, 4478g, 4478h), Die Cut Perf. 13x13¼ (#4477c, 4477g, 4478c), Die Cut Perf 13x12¾ (#4478e), Die Cut Perf. (others)

**2021, Mar. 9**      Litho.

### Self-Adhesive

| | | | |
|---|---|---|---|
| 4477 | A4932 Sheet of 10 | 12.50 | |
| a.-j. | 63y Any single | 1.25 | .95 |
| 4478 | A4933 Sheet of 10 | 15.00 | |
| a.-j. | 84y Any single | 1.50 | 1.10 |

This sheet of self-adhesive stamps containing four 63y, four 84y and two 120y stamps was produced in limited quantities and sold in a package with post cards, envelopes and stationery for 2000y.

Survey Ship Kasuba and First Japanese Nautical Chart
A4934

Echo Sounding Survey of Sea Bottom
A4935

Nautical Chart and Naval Surveying Tools
A4936

Airplane Conducting Laser Survey of Sea Bottom
A4937

Japanese Coast Guard Ship Heiyo and Nautical Chart of Kamaishi Bay — A4938

**2021, Mar. 12 Litho. Perf. 13½**

| | | | |
|---|---|---|---|
| 4479 | A4934 84y multi | 1.50 | 1.10 |
| 4480 | A4935 84y multi | 1.50 | 1.10 |
| 4481 | A4936 84y multi | 1.50 | 1.10 |
| 4482 | A4937 84y multi | 1.50 | 1.10 |
| 4483 | A4938 84y multi | 1.50 | 1.10 |
| a. | Horiz. strip of 5, #4479-4483 | 7.50 | 5.50 |
| | *Nos. 4479-4483 (5)* | 7.50 | 5.50 |

Nautical chart production in Japan, 150th anniv.

Hostas
A4939

Sunflowers
A4940

Blue Passionflowers
A4941

Hydrangea and Roses
A4942

Gloriosas
A4943

Jasmines
A4944

Marigolds
A4945

Delphiniums and Carnations
A4946

Peonies
A4947

Roses
A4948

**Die Cut Perf. 13x13¼**
**2021, Apr. 1 Litho.**
**Self-Adhesive**

| | | | |
|---|---|---|---|
| 4484 | Sheet of 10, 2 each #4484a-4484e | 12.50 | |
| a. | A4939 63y multi | 1.25 | .95 |
| b. | A4940 63y multi | 1.25 | .95 |
| c. | A4941 63y multi | 1.25 | .95 |
| d. | A4942 63y multi | 1.25 | .95 |
| e. | A4943 63y multi | 1.25 | .95 |
| 4485 | Sheet of 10, 2 each #4485a-4485e | 15.00 | |
| a. | A4944 84y multi | 1.50 | 1.10 |
| b. | A4945 84y multi | 1.50 | 1.10 |
| c. | A4946 84y multi | 1.50 | 1.10 |
| d. | A4947 84y multi | 1.50 | 1.10 |
| e. | A4948 84y multi | 1.50 | 1.10 |

**Flowers Types of 2015, Violets Type of 2019 and**

Oze National Park — A4949

**2021 Photo. Perf. 13x13¼**
**With Iridescent Security Images**
**Overprinted at UR and LL**

| | | | |
|---|---|---|---|
| 4486 | A4500 94y multi | 1.75 | 1.30 |
| 4487 | A3355 100y multi | 1.90 | 1.40 |
| 4488 | A3356 120y multi | 2.25 | 1.75 |
| 4489 | A3357 140y multi | 2.60 | 2.00 |
| 4490 | A4949 260y multi | 4.75 | 3.75 |
| | *Nos. 4486-4490 (5)* | 13.25 | 10.20 |

Issued: Nos. 4486-4489, 4/13; 260y, 9/1. The security image at the upper right is a Japanese character that looks like a capital "T" with a line above it. The security image at the lower left is a five-petaled cherry blossom.

Posukuma Teddy Bear
A4950

Numeral in Rectangle
A4951

**Die Cut Perf. 13x13¼**
**2021, Apr. 14 Litho.**
**Self-Adhesive**

| | | | |
|---|---|---|---|
| 4491 | A4950 1y multi | .25 | .25 |
| 4492 | A4951 84y multi | 1.60 | 1.25 |

 A4952
 A4953
 A4954
 A4955
 A4956
 A4957
 A4958
 A4959
 A4960

Scenes From *The Postal Operations Picture Scrolls,* Silk Paintings by Shinsai Shibata (1858-95)
A4961

**Photo. & Engr.**
**2021, Apr. 20 Perf. 13**

| | | | |
|---|---|---|---|
| 4493 | Sheet of 10 | 16.00 | 16.00 |
| a. | A4952 84y gold & multi | 1.60 | 1.25 |
| b. | A4953 84y gold & multi | 1.60 | 1.25 |
| c. | A4954 84y gold & multi | 1.60 | 1.25 |
| d. | A4955 84y gold & multi | 1.60 | 1.25 |
| e. | A4956 84y gold & multi | 1.60 | 1.25 |
| f. | A4957 84y gold & multi | 1.60 | 1.25 |
| g. | A4958 84y gold & multi | 1.60 | 1.25 |
| h. | A4959 84y gold & multi | 1.60 | 1.25 |
| i. | A4960 84y gold & multi | 1.60 | 1.25 |
| j. | A4961 84y gold & multi | 1.60 | 1.25 |

Hummingbird and Flowers
A4962

Bird on Branch
A4963

Bird and Flora
A4964

Bird and Wreath
A4965

Peacock
A4966

Peacock
A4967

**Litho. With Foil Application**
**2021, Apr. 23 Self-Adhesive**
**Die Cut Perf. 12¾x13 (#4494a, 4494b), 13¼x13½ (#4495a, 4496a), Die Cut Perf. (#4495b, 4496b)**

| | | | |
|---|---|---|---|
| 4494 | Sheet of 10, 5 each #4494a-4494b + sticker | 12.50 | |
| a. | A4962 63y gold & multi | 1.25 | .95 |
| b. | A4963 63y gold & multi | 1.25 | .95 |
| 4495 | Sheet of 10, 5 each #4495a-4495b + sticker | 16.00 | |
| a. | A4964 84y gold & multi | 1.60 | 1.25 |
| b. | A4965 84y gold & multi | 1.60 | 1.25 |
| 4496 | Sheet of 10, 5 each #4496a-4496b + sticker | 17.50 | |
| a. | A4966 94y gold & multi | 1.75 | 1.30 |
| b. | A4967 94y gold & multi | 1.75 | 1.30 |
| | *Nos. 4494-4496 (3)* | 46.00 | |

**Miniature Sheet**

Flora, Fauna and Scenery of Lake Towada and Oirase Gorge
A4968

No. 4497: a, Ruddy kingfisher facing left (28x32mm). b, Gray wagtail facing right (32x28mm). c, Narcissus flycatcher facing left (32x28mm). d, Japanese dwarf flying squirrel (22x26mm). e, Flaccid anemone (22x26mm). f, Japanese serow (32mm diameter). g, Anemone pseudoaltaica (22x26mm). h, Oirase River and feather moss (29x36mm). i, Blue-and-white flycatcher (32x28mm). j, Japanese marten (29x36mm).

**Die Cut Perf. 12¼x13 (#4497a), 13x12¼ (#4497b, 4497c, 4497i), 13x13¼ (#4497d, 4497e, 4497g), 13¼ (#4497h, 4497j), Die Cut Perf. (#4497f)**
**2021, May 10 Litho.**
**Self-Adhesive**

| | | | |
|---|---|---|---|
| 4497 | A4968 Sheet of 10 | 16.00 | |
| a.-j. | 84y Any single | 1.60 | 1.25 |

 A4969
 A4970
 A4971
 A4972
 A4973
 A4974
 A4975
 A4976

 A4977
 A4978
 A4979
 A4980
 A4981
 A4982
 A4983
 A4984
 A4985, A4986

Flowers and Plants
A4987    A4988

**Die Cut Perf. 13¼x13 (#4498j, 4499g, 4499h), 13x13¼ (others)**
**2021, May 17 Litho.**
**Self-Adhesive**

| | | | |
|---|---|---|---|
| 4498 | Sheet of 10 | 12.50 | |
| a. | A4969 63y multi | 1.25 | .95 |
| b. | A4970 63y multi | 1.25 | .95 |
| c. | A4971 63y multi | 1.25 | .95 |
| d. | A4972 63y multi | 1.25 | .95 |
| e. | A4973 63y multi | 1.25 | .95 |
| f. | A4974 63y multi | 1.25 | .95 |
| g. | A4975 63y multi | 1.25 | .95 |
| h. | A4976 63y multi | 1.25 | .95 |
| i. | A4977 63y multi | 1.25 | .95 |
| j. | A4978 63y multi | 1.25 | .95 |
| 4499 | Sheet of 10 | 16.00 | |
| a. | A4979 84y multi | 1.60 | 1.25 |
| b. | A4980 84y multi | 1.60 | 1.25 |
| c. | A4981 84y multi | 1.60 | 1.25 |
| d. | A4982 84y multi | 1.60 | 1.25 |
| e. | A4983 84y multi | 1.60 | 1.25 |
| f. | A4984 84y multi | 1.60 | 1.25 |
| g. | A4985 84y multi | 1.60 | 1.25 |
| h. | A4986 84y multi | 1.60 | 1.25 |
| i. | A4987 84y multi | 1.60 | 1.25 |
| j. | A4988 84y multi | 1.60 | 1.25 |

 A4989
 A4990
 A4991, A4992
 A4993
 A4994
 A4995, A4996

**Fabric Designs for Kimonos**
A4997      A4998

**Kimonos and Fabric Designs**
A4999

No. 4501: a, Kimono with black and white background colors and plum blossom design (30x42mm). b, Blue and white kimono with flower garden design (30x42mm). c, Red kimono with fans and flowers design (30x42mm). d, White and pink kimono with tree and dandelions design (30x42mm). e, Yellow kimono with picture frames design (30x42mm). f, Fabric design of yellow and red flowers on arbor (30x36mm). g, Fabric designs of water and flowers (30x36mm). h, Fabric design of pine trees and flowers (30mm diameter). i, Fabric design of palace decorations and ornate fence (30x36mm). j, Fabric desgin of peonies and waterfalls (30x36mm).

**Die Cut Perf. 13¼**

2021, May 21                         Litho.

**Self-Adhesive**

| 4500 | Sheet of 10 | 12.50 | |
|------|-------------|-------|---|
| a. | A4989 63y gold & multi | 1.25 | .95 |
| b. | A4990 63y gold & multi | 1.25 | .95 |
| c. | A4991 63y gold & multi | 1.25 | .95 |
| d. | A4992 63y gold & multi | 1.25 | .95 |
| e. | A4993 63y gold & multi | 1.25 | .95 |
| f. | A4994 63y gold & multi | 1.25 | .95 |
| g. | A4995 63y gold & multi | 1.25 | .95 |
| h. | A4996 63y gold & multi | 1.25 | .95 |
| i. | A4997 63y gold & multi | 1.25 | .95 |
| j. | A4998 63y gold & multi | 1.25 | .95 |

**Die Cut Perf. 13¼ (#4501a-4501e), 13¼x13 (#4501f, 4501g, 4501i, 4501j), Die Cut Perf. (#4501h)**

| 4501 | A4999 Sheet of 10 | 16.00 | |
|------|-------------------|-------|---|
| a.-j. | 84y Any single | 1.60 | 1.25 |

A5000      A5001

A5002      A5003

**National Afforestation (Shimane) — A5004**

2021, May 26    Litho.    Perf. 13½x14

| 4502 | A5000 84y multi | 1.60 | 1.25 |
|------|-----------------|------|------|
| 4503 | A5001 84y multi | 1.60 | 1.25 |
| 4504 | A5002 84y multi | 1.60 | 1.25 |
| 4505 | A5003 84y multi | 1.60 | 1.25 |
| 4506 | A5004 84y multi | 1.60 | 1.25 |
| a. | Vert. strip of 5, #4502-4506 | 8.00 | 6.25 |
| | Nos. 4502-4506 (5) | 8.00 | 6.25 |

**Ice Cream Cone and Bar**
A5005

**Food on Cutting Board**
A5006

**Food Basket**
A5007

**Sandals and Crab**
A5009

**Sunglasses**
A5011

**Avocado, Tomato and Banana**
A5013

**Bowl of Shaved Ice**
A5015

**Fan and Mosquito Coil**
A5017

**Japanese Rice Fish**
A5019

**Plums**
A5021

**Ramune Bottles**
A5023

**Cacti**
A5008

**Starfish, Shells and Coral**
A5010

**Fish and Seahorse**
A5012

**Lemon Drink**
A5014

**Fireworks**
A5016

**Bitter Melons**
A5018

**Watermelon Slice and Beetle**
A5020

**Ginger, Perilla and Japanese Ginger**
A5022

**Beans and Corn**
A5024

2021, June 1    Litho.    Die Cut Perf.

**Self-Adhesive**

| 4507 | Sheet of 10 | 12.50 | |
|------|-------------|-------|---|
| a. | A5005 63y multi | 1.25 | .95 |
| b. | A5006 63y multi | 1.25 | .95 |
| c. | A5007 63y multi | 1.25 | .95 |
| d. | A5008 63y multi | 1.25 | .95 |
| e. | A5009 63y multi | 1.25 | .95 |
| f. | A5010 63y multi | 1.25 | .95 |
| g. | A5011 63y multi | 1.25 | .95 |
| h. | A5012 63y multi | 1.25 | .95 |
| i. | A5013 63y multi | 1.25 | .95 |
| j. | A5014 63y multi | 1.25 | .95 |

**Die Cut Perf. 13¼**

| 4508 | Sheet of 10 | 16.00 | |
|------|-------------|-------|---|
| a. | A5015 84y multi | 1.60 | 1.25 |
| b. | A5016 84y multi | 1.60 | 1.25 |
| c. | A5017 84y multi | 1.60 | 1.25 |
| d. | A5018 84y multi | 1.60 | 1.25 |
| e. | A5019 84y multi | 1.60 | 1.25 |
| f. | A5020 84y multi | 1.60 | 1.25 |
| g. | A5021 84y multi | 1.60 | 1.25 |
| h. | A5022 84y multi | 1.60 | 1.25 |
| i. | A5023 84y multi | 1.60 | 1.25 |
| j. | A5024 84y multi | 1.60 | 1.25 |

**Merrymaking Under the Cherry Blossoms (Detail), Screen Painting by Naganobu Kano (1577-1654)**
A5025

**Thunder God Raijin (Detail), Screen Painting by Tawaraya Sotatsu (c. 1570-c.1640)**
A5027

**Viewing Maple Leaves (Detail), Screen Painting by Hideyori Kano (fl. 16th Cent)**
A5029

**Kamakura Period Gilt Copper Reliquary**
A5031

**12th-13 Cent. Tea Bowl**
A5033

**Merrymaking Under the Cherry Blossoms (Detail), Screen Painting by Naganobu Kano**
A5026

**Wind God Fujin (Detail), Screen Painting by Sotatsu**
A5028

**Heian Period Sutra Box**
A5030

**17th Cent. Tea Jar, by Ninsei Nonmura**
A5032

**Heian Period Leather Ornament**
A5034

**Negoro-ji Daito, Iwade — A5035**

**Tamaudun Royal Mausoleum, Shuri — A5036**

**Flying Cloud Pavilion, Kyoto**
A5037

**Ruriko-ji Five-Story Pagoda, Yamaguchi**
A5038

**Osaki Hachimangu Shrine, Sendai — A5039**

**Matsue Castle, Matsue — A5040**

**Ninna-ji Temple, Kyoto**
A5041

**Kunozan Tosho-ga Shrine, Shizuoka**
A5042

**Iwashimizu Hachimangu Main Shrine, Yawata**
A5043

**Siofuku-ji Temple Main Hall, Nagasaki**
A5044

**Die Cut Perf. 13¼**

2021, June 16                         Litho.

**Self-Adhesive**

| 4509 | Sheet of 10 | 12.50 | |
|------|-------------|-------|---|
| a. | A5025 63y multi | 1.25 | .95 |
| b. | A5026 63y multi | 1.25 | .95 |
| c. | A5027 63y multi | 1.25 | .95 |
| d. | A5028 63y multi | 1.25 | .95 |
| e. | A5029 63y multi | 1.25 | .95 |
| f. | A5030 63y multi | 1.25 | .95 |
| g. | A5031 63y multi | 1.25 | .95 |
| h. | A5032 63y multi | 1.25 | .95 |
| i. | A5033 63y multi | 1.25 | .95 |
| j | A5034 63y multi | 1.25 | .95 |

**Die Cut Perf. 13 (#4510a, 4510b, 4510e-4510j), 12½x13 (#4510c), 13¼ (#4510d)**

| 4510 | Sheet of 10 | 15.00 | |
|------|-------------|-------|---|
| a. | A5035 84y multi | 1.50 | 1.10 |
| b. | A5036 84y multi | 1.50 | 1.10 |
| c. | A5037 84y multi | 1.50 | 1.10 |
| d. | A5038 84y multi | 1.50 | 1.10 |
| e. | A5039 84y multi | 1.50 | 1.10 |
| f. | A5040 84y multi | 1.50 | 1.10 |
| g. | A5041 84y multi | 1.50 | 1.10 |
| h. | A5042 84y multi | 1.50 | 1.10 |
| i. | A5043 84y multi | 1.50 | 1.10 |
| j. | A5044 84y multi | 1.50 | 1.10 |

**3-on-3 Basketball**
A5045

**Archery**
A5046

172                                                                                              JAPAN

Gymnastics
A5047

Artistic
Swimming
A5048

Diving
A5063

Equestrian
Dressage
A5064

Rowing
A5078

Rugby
A5079

Paralympics
Archery
A5095

Paralympics
Track and
Field
A5096

Track and
Field
A5049

Badminton
A5050

Equestrian
Eventing
A5065

Equestrian
Jumping
A5066

Sailing
A5080

Shooting
A5081

Paralympics
Badminton
A5097

Paralympics
Bocce
A5098

Baseball
A5051

Softball
A5052

Fencing
A5067

Soccer
A5068

Skateboarding
A5082

Sport
Climbing
A5083

Paralympics
Canoeing
A5099

Paralympics
Road Cycling
A5100

Basketball
A5053

Beach
Volleyball
A5054

Golf — A5069

Surfing
A5084

Swimming
A5085

Paralympics
Track Cycling
A5101

Paralympics
Equestrian
A5102

Boxing
A5055

Canoe
Slalom
A5056

Handball
A5070

Field Hockey
A5071

Table Tennis
A5086

Taekwondo
A5087

Paralympics
5-on-5
Soccer
A5103

Paralympics
Goalball
A5104

Canoe Sprint
A5057

BMX
Freestyle
Bicycling
A5058

Judo
A5072

Karate Kata
A5073

Tennis
A5088

Trampolining
A5089

Paralympics
Judo
A5105

Emblem of
2020
Summer
Paralympics
A5106

BMX Racing
A5059

Mountain
Biking
A5060

Karate
Kumite
A5074

Marathon
Swimming
A5075

Triathlon
A5090

Volleyball
A5091

Paralympics
Powerlifting
A5107

Paralympics
Rowing
A5108

Road Cycling
A5061

Track Cycling
A5062

Modern
Pentathlon
A5076

Rhythmic
Gymnastics
A5077

Water Polo
A5092

Weight Lifting
A5093

Paralympics
Shooting
A5109

Paralympics
Sitting
Volleyball
A5110

Wrestling — A5094

Paralympics
Swimming
A5111

Paralympics
Table Tennis
A5112

Paralympics
Taekwondo
A5113

Paralympics
Triathlon
A5114

Paralympics
Wheelchair
Basketball
A5115

Paralympics
Wheelchair
Fencing
A5116

Paralympics
Wheelchair
Rugby
A5117

Paralympics
Wheelchair
Tennis
A5118

**2021, June 23    Litho.    Perf. 13**

| | | | |
|---|---|---|---|
| 4511 | | Sheet of 25 | 37.50 | 37.50 |
| a. | A5045 84y multi | 1.50 | 1.10 |
| b. | A5046 84y multi | 1.50 | 1.10 |
| c. | A5047 84y multi | 1.50 | 1.10 |
| d. | A5048 84y multi | 1.50 | 1.10 |
| e. | A5049 84y multi | 1.50 | 1.10 |
| f. | A5050 84y multi | 1.50 | 1.10 |
| g. | A5051 84y multi | 1.50 | 1.10 |
| h. | A5052 84y multi | 1.50 | 1.10 |
| i. | A5053 84y multi | 1.50 | 1.10 |
| j. | A5054 84y multi | 1.50 | 1.10 |
| k. | A5055 84y multi | 1.50 | 1.10 |
| l. | A5056 84y multi | 1.50 | 1.10 |
| m. | A5057 84y multi | 1.50 | 1.10 |
| n. | A5058 84y multi | 1.50 | 1.10 |
| o. | A5059 84y multi | 1.50 | 1.10 |
| p. | A5060 84y multi | 1.50 | 1.10 |
| q. | A5061 84y multi | 1.50 | 1.10 |
| r. | A5062 84y multi | 1.50 | 1.10 |
| s. | A5063 84y multi | 1.50 | 1.10 |
| t. | A5064 84y multi | 1.50 | 1.10 |
| u. | A5065 84y multi | 1.50 | 1.10 |
| v. | A5066 84y multi | 1.50 | 1.10 |
| w. | A5067 84y multi | 1.50 | 1.10 |
| x. | A5068 84y multi | 1.50 | 1.10 |
| y. | A5069 84y multi | 1.50 | 1.10 |
| 4512 | | Sheet of 25 | 37.50 | 37.50 |
| a. | A5070 84y multi | 1.50 | 1.10 |
| b. | A5071 84y multi | 1.50 | 1.10 |
| c. | A5072 84y multi | 1.50 | 1.10 |
| d. | A5073 84y multi | 1.50 | 1.10 |
| e. | A5074 84y multi | 1.50 | 1.10 |
| f. | A5075 84y multi | 1.50 | 1.10 |
| g. | A5076 84y multi | 1.50 | 1.10 |
| h. | A5077 84y multi | 1.50 | 1.10 |
| i. | A5078 84y multi | 1.50 | 1.10 |
| j. | A5079 84y multi | 1.50 | 1.10 |
| k. | A5080 84y multi | 1.50 | 1.10 |
| l. | A5081 84y multi | 1.50 | 1.10 |
| m. | A5082 84y multi | 1.50 | 1.10 |
| n. | A5083 84y multi | 1.50 | 1.10 |
| o. | A5084 84y multi | 1.50 | 1.10 |
| p. | A5085 84y multi | 1.50 | 1.10 |
| q. | A5086 84y multi | 1.50 | 1.10 |
| r. | A5087 84y multi | 1.50 | 1.10 |
| s. | A5088 84y multi | 1.50 | 1.10 |
| t. | A5089 84y multi | 1.50 | 1.10 |
| u. | A5090 84y multi | 1.50 | 1.10 |
| v. | A5091 84y multi | 1.50 | 1.10 |
| w. | A5092 84y multi | 1.50 | 1.10 |
| x. | A5093 84y multi | 1.50 | 1.10 |
| y. | A5094 84y multi | 1.50 | 1.10 |
| 4513 | | Sheet of 25, #4513a-4513k, 4513l-4513x, 2 #4513l | 37.50 | 37.50 |
| a. | A5095 84y multi | 1.50 | 1.10 |
| b. | A5096 84y multi | 1.50 | 1.10 |
| c. | A5097 84y multi | 1.50 | 1.10 |
| d. | A5098 84y multi | 1.50 | 1.10 |
| e. | A5099 84y multi | 1.50 | 1.10 |
| f. | A5100 84y multi | 1.50 | 1.10 |
| g. | A5101 84y multi | 1.50 | 1.10 |
| h. | A5102 84y multi | 1.50 | 1.10 |
| i. | A5103 84y multi | 1.50 | 1.10 |
| j. | A5104 84y multi | 1.50 | 1.10 |
| k. | A5105 84y multi | 1.50 | 1.10 |
| l. | A5106 84y multi | 1.50 | 1.10 |
| m. | A5107 84y multi | 1.50 | 1.10 |
| n. | A5108 84y multi | 1.50 | 1.10 |
| o. | A5109 84y multi | 1.50 | 1.10 |
| p. | A5110 84y multi | 1.50 | 1.10 |
| q. | A5111 84y multi | 1.50 | 1.10 |
| r. | A5112 84y multi | 1.50 | 1.10 |
| s. | A5113 84y multi | 1.50 | 1.10 |
| t. | A5114 84y multi | 1.50 | 1.10 |
| u. | A5115 84y multi | 1.50 | 1.10 |
| v. | A5116 84y multi | 1.50 | 1.10 |
| w. | A5117 84y multi | 1.50 | 1.10 |
| x. | A5118 84y multi | 1.50 | 1.10 |
| | Nos. 4511-4513 (3) | 112.50 | 112.50 |

Sports of the 2020 Summer Olympics and Paralympics, Tokyo. The 2020 Summer Olympics and Paralympics were postponed until 2021 because of the COVID-19 pandemic.

**Souvenir Sheet**

Japan National Stadium, Tokyo A5119

**2021, June 23    Photo.    Perf. 13¼**
4514  A5119 500y multi    75.00  75.00

2020 Summer Olympics and Paralympics, which were postponed until 2021 because of the COVID-19 pandemic.

No. 4514 was included in a booklet that also contained Nos. 4511-4513, which sold for 10,000y.

Japan Mint Gas Lamps A5120

Early Coinage Press A5121

Original Entrance to Japan Mint A5122

Balance Scale A5123

Shigenobu Okuma (1838-1922), Prime Minister A5124

Coin Commemorating 150th Anniv. of Modern Currency System A5125

Silver 1-yen Coin — A5126

Gold 1-yen Coin — A5127

Copper 1-yen Coin A5128

Wadokaichin Coin, c. 7th-10th Cent. A5129

**2021, June 25    Litho.    Die Cut Perf.**
**Self-Adhesive**

| | | | |
|---|---|---|---|
| 4515 | | Sheet of 10 | 15.00 | |
| a. | A5120 84y sil & multi | 1.50 | 1.10 |
| b. | A5121 84y sil & multi | 1.50 | 1.10 |
| c. | A5122 84y sil & multi | 1.50 | 1.10 |
| d. | A5123 84y sil & multi | 1.50 | 1.10 |
| e. | A5124 84y sil & multi | 1.50 | 1.10 |
| f. | A5125 84y sil & multi | 1.50 | 1.10 |
| g. | A5126 84y sil & multi | 1.50 | 1.10 |
| h. | A5127 84y sil & multi | 1.50 | 1.10 |
| i. | A5128 84y sil & multi | 1.50 | 1.10 |
| j. | A5129 84y sil & multi | 1.50 | 1.10 |

Modern currency system, 150th anniv.

Reef Manta Ray A5130

Spotted Eagle Ray A5131

Double-lined Fusilier A5132

Devil Ray and Double-lined Fusiliers A5133

Whale Shark and Remora A5134

Head of Whale Shark and Three Golden Trevallies A5135

Gills of Whale Shark A5136

Two Golden Trevallies and Fin of Whale Shark A5137

Giant Trevallies A5138

Whale Shark A5139

**Die Cut Perf. 13¼x13 (#4516a, 4516c, 4516e, 4516f, 4516g, 4516j), 13x13¼ (#4516b, 4516d, 4516h, 4516i)**

**2021, July 1    Litho.**
**Self-Adhesive**

| | | | |
|---|---|---|---|
| 4516 | | Sheet of 10 | 15.00 | |
| a. | A5130 84y multi | 1.50 | 1.10 |
| b. | A5131 84y multi | 1.50 | 1.10 |
| c. | A5132 84y multi | 1.50 | 1.10 |
| d. | A5133 84y multi | 1.50 | 1.10 |
| e. | A5134 84y multi | 1.50 | 1.10 |
| f. | A5135 84y multi | 1.50 | 1.10 |
| g. | A5136 84y multi | 1.50 | 1.10 |
| h. | A5137 84y multi | 1.50 | 1.10 |
| i. | A5138 84y multi | 1.50 | 1.10 |
| j. | A5139 84y multi | 1.50 | 1.10 |

Sand was applied to parts of the designs of Nos. 4516a-4516j.

Pokémon Game Card Depicting Butterfree A5140

Pokémon Game Card Depicting Aceburn A5141

Pokémon Game Card Depicting Magikarp A5142

Back of Pokémon Game Card A5143

Pokémon Game Card Depicting Pikachu A5144

Pokémon Game Card Depicting Eevee A5145

Pokémon Game Card Depicting Mewtwo A5146

Pokémon Game Card Depicting Lucario A5147

Pokémon Game Card Depicting Liepard A5148

Pokémon Game Card Depicting Jirachi A5149

Various Pokémon Characters — A5150

No. 4518 — Pikachu and other Pokémon characters: a: Running on hilltop with streamer in air (26x27mm). b, With cherry blossoms in background (29x30mm). c, With Pikachu holding fishing rod (26x27mm). d, Taking shelter from the rain (26x26mm). e, At beach (26x27mm). f, With pile of fruits (26x29mm). g, Sleeping on hilltop (26x27mm). h, Soaking in natural pool (26x27mm). i, Running near tree in autumn (26x27mm). j, By fire in cave (22x26mm).

**Die Cut Perf. 13¼**
**2021, July 7    Litho.**
**Self-Adhesive**

| | | | |
|---|---|---|---|
| 4517 | | Sheet of 10 | 12.50 | |
| a. | A5140 63y multi | 1.25 | .95 |
| b. | A5141 63y multi | 1.25 | .95 |
| c. | A5142 63y multi | 1.25 | .95 |
| d. | A5143 63y multi | 1.25 | .95 |
| e. | A5144 63y multi | 1.25 | .95 |
| f. | A5145 63y multi | 1.25 | .95 |
| g. | A5146 63y multi | 1.25 | .95 |
| h. | A5147 63y multi | 1.25 | .95 |
| i. | A5148 63y multi | 1.25 | .95 |
| j. | A5149 63y multi | 1.25 | .95 |

**Die Cut Perf. 13½ (#4518j), 13¼ (others)**

| | | | |
|---|---|---|---|
| 4518 | A5150 | Sheet of 10 | 16.00 | |
| a.-j. | | 84y Any single | 1.60 | 1.25 |

Child
Mailing
Letter
A5151

Cyclist
A5152

House
and Mail
Van
A5153

Motorcyclist
A5154

Mail Van
Passing
Farm Field
A5155

Store
A5156

Barbershop
A5157

Coffeeshop
A5158

Cyclist
Near
Public
Bathhouse
A5159

House,
Mailbox
and
Delivery
Bike
A5160

*Die Cut Perf. 13¼*

2021, July 21                                    Litho.

**Booklet Stamps**
**Self-Adhesive**

| | | | | |
|---|---|---|---|---|
| 4519 | A5151 | 63y multi | 1.25 | .95 |
| 4520 | A5152 | 63y multi | 1.25 | .95 |
| 4521 | A5153 | 63y multi | 1.25 | .95 |
| 4522 | A5154 | 63y multi | 1.25 | .95 |
| 4523 | A5155 | 63y multi | 1.25 | .95 |
| *a.* | | Booklet pane of 10, 2 each | | |
| | | #4519-4523 | 12.50 | |
| 4524 | A5156 | 84y multi | 1.60 | 1.25 |
| 4525 | A5157 | 84y multi | 1.60 | 1.25 |
| 4526 | A5158 | 84y multi | 1.60 | 1.25 |
| 4527 | A5159 | 84y multi | 1.60 | 1.25 |
| 4528 | A5160 | 84y multi | 1.60 | 1.25 |
| *a.* | | Booklet pane of 10, 2 each | | |
| | | #4524-4528 | 16.00 | |
| | | *Nos. 4519-4528 (10)* | 14.25 | 11.00 |

Letter Writing Day.

A5161

A5162

A5163

A5164

A5165

A5166

A5167

A5168

A5169

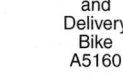

Flowers — A5170

*Die Cut Perf. 12¾x13*

2021, Aug. 16                                     Litho.

**Self-Adhesive**

| | | | |
|---|---|---|---|
| 4529 | | Sheet of 10, 2 each | |
| | | #4529a-4529e | 12.50 |
| *a.* | A5161 | 63y multi | 1.25 | .95 |
| *b.* | A5162 | 63y multi | 1.25 | .95 |
| *c.* | A5163 | 63y multi | 1.25 | .95 |
| *d.* | A5164 | 63y multi | 1.25 | .95 |
| *e.* | A5165 | 63y multi | 1.25 | .95 |
| 4530 | | Sheet of 10, 2 each | |
| | | #4530a-4530e | 16.00 |
| *a.* | A5166 | 84y multi | 1.60 | 1.25 |
| *b.* | A5167 | 84y multi | 1.60 | 1.25 |
| *c.* | A5168 | 84y multi | 1.60 | 1.25 |
| *d.* | A5169 | 84y multi | 1.60 | 1.25 |
| *e.* | A5170 | 84y multi | 1.60 | 1.25 |

Miniature Sheet

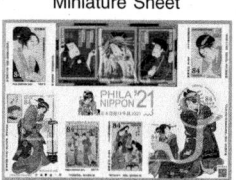

Phila Nippon 21 Philatelic Exhibition,
Yokohama — A5171

No. 4531: a, Love that Meets Each Night,
print by Utamaro Kitigawa (c. 1753-1806)
(30x49mm). b, Kabuki Actor Jingoro Hidari
Holding Cup, print by Kunichika Toyohara
(1835-1900) (30x40mm). c, Satemo Migoto
Nadai No Horimono Kabuki Actor Wearing
White Kimono with Irises, print by Kunichika
(28x40mm). d, Kabuki Actor Kikugoro Onoe V
as Postman, print by Kunichika (28x40mm). e,
The Courtesan Hanaogi of Ogiya, print by
Utamaro (30x42mm). f, Woman Holding
Scroll, print by Eisen Keisai (1790-1848)
(28x36mm). g, Two Women Readeing a Letter, print by Harunobu Suzuki (c. 1725-70)
(30x42mm). h, A Mirror of the Ages (three
women), print by Chikanobu Yoshu (1838-
1912) (30x42mm). i, A Sigh of Amazement at
the Prosperity of Great Edo, Where 3,000 Ryo
Changes Hands Every Day (detail of woman
looking upwards), print by Kunisawa Utagawa
(1786-1865) (24x30mm). j, A Sigh of Amazement at the Prosperity of Great Edo, Where
3,000 Ryo Changes Hands Every Day (detail
of woman looking downwards), print by Utagawa (1786-1865) (35mm diameter).

*Die Cut Perf. 13¼ (#4531a, 4531e,
4531g, 4531h, 4531i), 12¾x13
(#4531b, 4531c, 4531d), 12¾x13¼
(#4531f), Die Cut Perf. (#4531j)*

2021, Aug. 25                                     Litho.

**Self-Adhesive**

| | | | |
|---|---|---|---|
| 4531 | A5171 | Sheet of 10 | 16.00 |
| *a.-j.* | | 84y Any single | 1.60 | 1.25 |

Souvenir Sheets

A5172

Modern
Postal
Service
of Japan,
150th
Anniv.
A5174

No. 4532: a, Beauty Looking Back, print by
Moronobu Hishikawa (1618-94). b, Moon and
Geese, print by Hiroshige Utagawa (1797-
1858).
No. 4533: a, Koshaku-Musume, print by
Kunisada Utagawa (1786-1865). b, View of the
Opening Ceremonies of the Yokohama Post
Office, print by Hiroshige II (c. 1842-94), horiz.
No. 4534 — Hisoka Maeshima (1835-1919),
founder of Japanese postal service, in: a, Red.
b, Green, c, Blue. d, Purple. e, Red violet. f,
Orange.

*Die Cut Perf. 13¼*

2021, Aug. 25                                    Photo.

**Self-Adhesive**

| | | | |
|---|---|---|---|
| 4532 | A5172 | Sheet of 2 | 27.50 |
| *a.-b.* | | 500y Either single | 13.50 | 13.50 |

*Die Cut Perf. 13¼ (#4533a), 13¼x13
(#4533b)*

| | | | |
|---|---|---|---|
| 4533 | A5173 | Sheet of 2 | 23.00 |
| *a.-b.* | | 500y Either single | 11.50 | 11.50 |

*Die Cut Perf. 13*

| | | | |
|---|---|---|---|
| 4534 | A5174 | Sheet of 6 | 68.00 |
| *a.-b.* | | 500y Any single | 11.00 | 11.00 |

No. 4532 was sold in a folder for 1500y.
Nos. 4533 and 4534 were sold together in a
folder for 5000y. Nos. 4532-4534 were printed
on a machine made paper that mimics traditional Japanese hand-crafted paper.

On Aug. 25, 2021, a sheet of 10
stamps (eight 84y stamps depicting
Pokémon game cards and two 120y
stamps depicting the artwork depicted
on Nos. 4532a and 4532b) was offered
for sale in a package that contained the
sheet, a Pokémon game and other pro-
motional material at a price of 4000y.
The sheet was not offered for sale without the other contents of the package.

Miniature Sheets

A5175

Jspanese Art Using Green
Shades — A5176

No. 4535: a, Detail of 7th cent. glazed lidded
jar with plum blossom design (25x28mm). b,
Detail from folding screen from Amanosan
Kongoji Termple depicting Moon over valley
(25x28mm). c, Detail of folding screen by
Kiitsu Suzuki (1796-1858) depicting mountain
stream (25x28mm). d, Road, painting by Kaii
Higashiyama (1908-99) (27x27mm). e, Detail
of celadon incense burner (22x32mm). f, Brindled Cat, detail of painting by Seiho Takeuchi
(1864-1942) (23x32mm). g, A Tour of Waterfalls Around the Country — Oku-Amida Falls
on the Kiso Road, detail of print by Hokusai

Katsushika (1760-1849) (23x32mm). h, Needlework, painting by Seiki Kuroda (1866-1924)
(23x32mm). i, Daubigny's Garden, detail of
painting by Vincent van Gogh (1853-90)
(23x33mm). j, Eve in the Garden of Eden,
painting by Henri Rousseau (1844-1910
(29x27mm))
No. 4536: a, Entire 7th cent. glazed lidded
jar with plum blossom design (28x36mm). b,
Detail from folding screen from Amanosan
Kongoji Termple depicting Moon over valley,
diff. (39x26mm). c, Detail of folding screen by
Kiitsu depicting mountain stream, diff.
(37x27mm). d, Echoes of Green, painting by
Kaii (34x31mm). e, A Tour of Waterfalls
Around the Country — Oku-Amida Falls on the
Kiso Road, detail of print by Hokusai , diff.
(32x36mm). f, Brindled Cat, detail of painting
by Seiho (34x36mm). g, Ducklings, painting by
John Everett Millais (1829-96) (31x38mm). h,
Daubigny's Garden, detail of painting by van
Gogh, diff. (39x27mm). i, Water Lily Pond,
painting by Claude Monet (1840-1926)
(30x35mm). j, Entire celadon incense burner
(32x33mm).

*Die Cut Perf. 12¾x13 (#4535a,
4536f), 12¾ (#4535b, 4535c, 4535d),
12¾x12½ (#4535e, 4536a, 4536h),
12¼x12½ (#4535f), 12x12¾ (#4535g),
13 (#4535h, 4536d), 12¼x12¾
(#4535i), 12½ (#4535j, 4536g),
13x12½ (#4536b), 13x13¼ (#4536c),
12½x12¾ (#4536e), 13¼x12¾
(#4536i), 13¼ (#4536j)*

2021, Sept. 8                                     Litho.

**Self-Adhesive**

| | | | |
|---|---|---|---|
| 4535 | A5175 | Sheet of 10 | 12.50 |
| *a.-j.* | | 63y Any single | 1.25 | .95 |
| 4536 | A5176 | Sheet of 10 | 15.00 |
| *a.-j.* | | 84y Any single | 1.50 | 1.10 |

Miniature Sheets

A5177

Teddy Bear Mascot of Japan Post
A5178

No. 4537: a, Head of mascot. b, Mascot with fishing rod and bucket, horiz. c, Mascot holding camera, horiz. d, Mascot playing bagpipes, horiz. e, Mascot holding airmail letter, horiz. f, Mascot holding shovel, horiz. g, Mascot watering flowers, horiz. h, Mascot, owl, koala, another teddy bear, table, horiz. h, Mascot, other teddy bears, table, horiz.

No. 4538: a, Head of mascot, diff. b, Teddy bears crossing street, horiz. c, Mascot and another teddy bear holding letters, horiz. d, Mascot and double-decker bus. e, Mascot holding magnifying glass at British House of Parliament, horiz. f, Mascot holding honey pot, horiz. g, Mascot holding bowl, another teddy bear near statue, horiz. h, Teddy bear holding basket of flowers, horiz. i, Mascot with wheeled suitcase, horiz.

***Die Cut Perf. 13x13¼ (#4537a, 4538a), 13¼x13 (others)***
**2021, Sept. 15**                          **Litho.**
**Self-Adhesive**
4537  A5177  Sheet of 10,
             #4537b-4537i,
             2 #4537a        12.50
a.-i.  63y Any single        1.25   .95
4538  A5178  Sheet of 10,
             #4538b-4538i,
             2 #4538a        15.00
a.-i.  84y Any single        1.50  1.10

A5179  A5180

A5181  A5182

A5183  A5184

A5185  A5186

Gift Boxes with Ribbons
A5187   A5188

A5189   A5190

A5191   A5192

A5193   A5194

A5195   A5196
Cookies
A5197   A5198

A5199   A5200

A5201   A5202

A5203   A5204

A5205   A5206

A5207

Flowers — A5208

**Litho. With Foil Application**
**2021, Sept. 22**    ***Die Cut Perf. 13¼***
**Self-Adhesive**
4539  Sheet of 10            12.50
a.  A5179 63y gold & multi   1.25   .95
b.  A5180 63y gold & multi   1.25   .95
c.  A5181 63y gold & multi   1.25   .95
d.  A5182 63y gold & multi   1.25   .95
e.  A5183 63y gold & multi   1.25   .95
f.  A5184 63y gold & multi   1.25   .95
g.  A5185 63y gold & multi   1.25   .95
h.  A5186 63y gold & multi   1.25   .95
i.  A5187 63y gold & multi   1.25   .95
j.  A5188 63y gold & multi   1.25   .95
4540  Sheet of 10            15.00
a.  A5189 84y gold & multi   1.50  1.10
b.  A5190 84y gold & multi   1.50  1.10
c.  A5191 84y gold & multi   1.50  1.10
d.  A5192 84y gold & multi   1.50  1.10
e.  A5193 84y gold & multi   1.50  1.10
f.  A5194 84y gold & multi   1.50  1.10
g.  A5195 84y gold & multi   1.50  1.10
h.  A5196 84y gold & multi   1.50  1.10
i.  A5197 84y gold & multi   1.50  1.10
j.  A5198 84y gold & multi   1.50  1.10
4541  Sheet of 10            17.50
a.  A5199 94y gold & multi   1.75  1.30
b.  A5200 94y gold & multi   1.75  1.30
c.  A5201 94y gold & multi   1.75  1.30
d.  A5202 94y gold & multi   1.75  1.30
e.  A5203 94y gold & multi   1.75  1.30
f.  A5204 94y gold & multi   1.75  1.30
g.  A5205 94y gold & multi   1.75  1.30
h.  A5206 94y gold & multi   1.75  1.30
i.  A5207 94y gold & multi   1.75  1.30
j.  A5208 94y gold & multi   1.75  1.30
     Nos. 4539-4541 (3)      45.00

Miniature Sheet

Diplomatic Relations Between Japan and Uruguay, Cent. — A5209

No. 4542: a, Salvo Palace, Montevideo, Uruguay (30x36mm). b, Piriápolis, Uruguay waterfront (40x26mm). c, Casapueblo and its swimming pool, Punta Ballena, Uruguay (38x28mm). d, Buildings, Colonia del Sacramento, Uruguay (38x28mm). e, Maté pot and cups (24x32mm). f, Southern lapwing (24x32mm). g, Cows grazing (24x32mm). h, Carnival drummers (24x32mm). i, Gaucho with flag of Uruguay (24c32mm). j, Children playing soccer (24x32mm).

***Die Cut Perf. 13¼x12¾ (#4542c, 4542d), 13½x13¼ (others)***
**2021, Sept. 24**                         **Litho.**
**Self-Adhesive**
4542  A5209  Sheet of 10     15.00
a.-j.  84y Any single        1.50  1.10

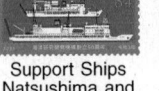
Support Ships          Drilling Vessel
Natsushima and            Chikyu
Yokosuka                  A5211
A5210

Research               Underwater
Submarine              Vehicles
Shinkai 2000           Jinbei and
A5212                  Yumeiruka
                       A5213

Research Submarine
Shinkai 6500 — A5214

***Die Cut Perf. 13¼x11 (#4543a), 13¼x10¾ (#4543b), Die Cut Perf. (circular stamps)***
**2021, Oct. 1**                           **Litho.**
**Self-Adhesive**
4543  Sheet of 10, 2 each
      #4543a-4543e, + 3
      stickers              15.00
a.  A5210 84y multi          1.50  1.10
b.  A5211 84y multi          1.50  1.10
c.  A5212 84y multi          1.50  1.10
d.  A5213 84y multi          1.50  1.10
e.  A5214 84y multi          1.50  1.10

Japan Agency for Marine-Earth Science and Technology, 50th anniv.

Hawfinch               Marvel-of-
A5215                  Peru
                       A5216
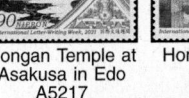
Hongan Temple at       Honjo Tatekawa
Asakusa in Edo         A5218
A5217

Sunset Across the Ryogoku Bridge From the Bank of the Sumida Riverat Onmya Embankment
A5219

**2021, Oct. 8   Photo.   Perf. 13x13¼**
4544  A5215  7y multi        .25    .25
4545  A5216  70y multi      1.25    .95
              **Perf. 13**
4546  A5217  90y multi      1.60  1.25
4547  A5218  110y multi     2.00  1.50
4548  A5219  130y multi     2.25  1.75
      Nos. 4544-4548 (5)    7.35  5.70

Details from prints by Hokusai (1760-1849), International Letter-Writing Week.

Mailboxes — A5220

Designs: No. 4549, Yellow mailbox of France. No. 4550, Red mailbox of Japan.

**2021, Oct. 8   Litho.   Perf. 13**
4549  70y multi             1.25   .95
4550  70y multi             1.25   .95
a.  A5220 Pair, #4549-4550  2.50  1.90

Joint issue between Japan and France. See France Nos. 6101-6102.
International Letter-Writing Week.

Landscape,             Clouds from
Shiga                  Waterfall,
Prefecture             Niigata
A5221                  Prefecture
                       A5222

Field in               Hamarikyu
Kanagawa               Gardens,
Prefecture             Tokyo
A5223                  Prefecture
                       A5224

Nabegataki
Falls,
Kumamoto
Prefecture
A5225

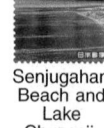

Senjugahama
Beach and
Lake
Chuzenji,
Tochigi
Prefecture
A5226

Yodo River,
Aichi
Prefecture
A5227

Rocks Off
Jodogahama
Beach,
Iwate
Prefecture
A5228

Sunset
Over
Sukumo
Bay, Kochi
Prefecture
A5229

Trees and
Islands,
Hokkaido
Prefecture
A5230

**Die Cut Perf. 13¼**

2021, Oct. 13                    Litho.

**Self-Adhesive**

| 4551 | | Sheet of 10 | 15.00 | |
|---|---|---|---|---|
| | a. | A5221 84y multi | 1.50 | 1.10 |
| | b. | A5222 84y multi | 1.50 | 1.10 |
| | c. | A5223 84y multi | 1.50 | 1.10 |
| | d. | A5224 84y multi | 1.50 | 1.10 |
| | e. | A5225 84y multi | 1.50 | 1.10 |
| | f. | A5226 84y multi | 1.50 | 1.10 |
| | g. | A5227 84y multi | 1.50 | 1.10 |
| | h. | A5228 84y multi | 1.50 | 1.10 |
| | i. | A5229 84y multi | 1.50 | 1.10 |
| | j. | A5230 84y multi | 1.50 | 1.10 |

Plum Blossoms
A5231

Chrysanthemums
A5232

Camellias
A5233

Narcissi
A5234

Roses
A5235

Violas
A5236

Cyclamen
A5237

Mitsumata
Blossoms
A5238

Poinsettias
A5239

Roses
A5240

**Die Cut Perf. 13x13¼**

2021, Oct. 20                    Litho.

**Self-Adhesive**

| 4552 | | Sheet of 10, 2 each | | |
|---|---|---|---|---|
| | | #4552a-4552e | 11.00 | |
| | a. | A5231 63y multi | 1.10 | .85 |
| | b. | A5232 63y multi | 1.10 | .85 |
| | c. | A5233 63y multi | 1.10 | .85 |
| | d. | A5234 63y multi | 1.10 | .85 |
| | e. | A5235 63y multi | 1.10 | .85 |
| 4553 | | Sheet of 10, 2 each | | |
| | | #4553a-4553e | 15.00 | |
| | a. | A5236 84y multi | 1.50 | 1.10 |
| | b. | A5237 84y multi | 1.50 | 1.10 |
| | c. | A5238 84y multi | 1.50 | 1.10 |
| | d. | A5239 84y multi | 1.50 | 1.10 |
| | e. | A5240 84y multi | 1.50 | 1.10 |

A5241

A5242          A5243

New Year 2022 (Year of
the Tiger) — A5244

2021, Nov. 1    Litho.    Perf. 13x13¼
4554  A5241    84y gold & multi  1.50 1.10

**Litho. & Typo.**
**Perf. 13¼**

| 4555 | A5242 | 63y+3y gold & multi | 1.25 | .95 |
|---|---|---|---|---|
| 4556 | A5243 | 84y+3y gold & multi | 1.60 | 1.25 |
| | | Nos. 4554-4556 (3) | 4.35 | 3.30 |

**Litho.**
**Die Cut Perf. 13x13¼**

| 4557 | A5244 | 63y gold & multi | 1.10 | .85 |
|---|---|---|---|---|

Numerals — A5245

**Die Cut Perf. 13x13¼**

2021, Nov. 5                    Litho.

**Self-Adhesive**
4558  A5245 84y multi          1.50 1.10

Fried
Shrimp
Sandwich
A5246

Spaghetti
A5247

Shiro-Noir
A5248

Toast With
Bean
Spread and
Pudding
A5249

Tea and
Cookies
A5250

Rice Balls
With Nori,
Pickled
Radishes
A5251

Ramen
Noodles and
Red Bean
Soup
A5252

Rice Flour
Cake and
Devil's Food
Cake
A5253

Shrimp Rice
Crackers
and
Steamed
Rice Flour
Cakes
A5254

Packaged
Food and
Candies
A5255

Grilled Eel
on Rice
A5256

Ramen
Noodles With
Pork and
Onions
A5257

Noodles
A5258

Chicken
Wings
A5259

Pork Cutlets
and Miso
Sauce
A5260

Rice With
Vegetables
and Red
Miso Tofu
A5261

Udon Noodle
Soup
A5262

Chicken Hot
Pot
A5263

Beef Stewed
in Miso
A5264

Miso Stew
A5265

**Die Cut Perf. 13¼**

2021, Nov. 11                   Litho.

**Self-Adhesive**

| 4559 | | Sheet of 10 | 11.00 | |
|---|---|---|---|---|
| | a. | A5246 63y multi | 1.10 | .85 |
| | b. | A5247 63y multi | 1.10 | .85 |
| | c. | A5248 63y multi | 1.10 | .85 |
| | d. | A5249 63y multi | 1.10 | .85 |
| | e. | A5250 63y multi | 1.10 | .85 |
| | f. | A5251 63y multi | 1.10 | .85 |
| | g. | A5252 63y multi | 1.10 | .85 |
| | h. | A5253 63y multi | 1.10 | .85 |
| | i. | A5254 63y multi | 1.10 | .85 |
| | j. | A5255 63y multi | 1.10 | .85 |

**Die Cut Perf.**

| 4560 | | Sheet of 10 | 15.00 | |
|---|---|---|---|---|
| | a. | A5256 84y multi | 1.50 | 1.10 |
| | b. | A5257 84y multi | 1.50 | 1.10 |
| | c. | A5258 84y multi | 1.50 | 1.10 |
| | d. | A5259 84y multi | 1.50 | 1.10 |
| | e. | A5260 84y multi | 1.50 | 1.10 |
| | f. | A5261 84y multi | 1.50 | 1.10 |
| | g. | A5262 84y multi | 1.50 | 1.10 |
| | h. | A5263 84y multi | 1.50 | 1.10 |
| | i. | A5264 84y multi | 1.50 | 1.10 |
| | j. | A5265 84y multi | 1.50 | 1.10 |

Candle
Stand
A5266

Wolf
A5268

Reindeer
A5270

Lanterns
A5272

Quill Pen
and
Envelope
A5274

Sleigh
A5267

Gift Bag
A5269

Bird
A5271

Poinsettia
A5273

Apple
A5275

**Litho. With Foil Application**
2021, Nov. 19   *Die Cut Perf. 13x13¼*
**Self-Adhesive**

| 4561 | | Sheet of 10, 2 each | | |
|---|---|---|---|---|
| | | #4561a-4561e | 11.00 | |
| | a. | A5266 63y met bl & pale bl | 1.10 | .85 |
| | b. | A5267 63y met bl & pale bl | 1.10 | .85 |
| | c. | A5268 63y met bl & pale bl | 1.10 | .85 |
| | d. | A5269 63y met bl & pale bl | 1.10 | .85 |
| | e. | A5270 63y met bl & pale bl | 1.10 | .85 |
| 4562 | | Sheet of 10, 2 each | | |
| | | #4562a-4562e | 15.00 | |
| | a. | A5271 84y met red & pink | 1.50 | 1.10 |
| | b. | A5272 84y met red & pink | 1.50 | 1.10 |
| | c. | A5273 84y met red & pink | 1.50 | 1.10 |
| | d. | A5274 84y met red & pink | 1.50 | 1.10 |
| | e. | A5275 84y met red & pink | 1.50 | 1.10 |

A5276

A5277

A5278

A5279

A5280

A5281

A5282

A5283

A5284

Children's Book Illustrations by Ken Wakayama (1930-2015) — A5285

**Die Cut Perf. 13x13¼**

2021, Nov. 26          Litho.
**Self-Adhesive**

| 4563 | | Sheet of 10 + 9 stickers | 15.00 | |
|---|---|---|---|---|
| a. | A5276 | 84y multi | 1.50 | 1.10 |
| b. | A5277 | 84y multi | 1.50 | 1.10 |
| c. | A5278 | 84y multi | 1.50 | 1.10 |
| d. | A5279 | 84y multi | 1.50 | 1.10 |
| e. | A5280 | 84y multi | 1.50 | 1.10 |
| f. | A5281 | 84y multi | 1.50 | 1.10 |
| g. | A5282 | 84y multi | 1.50 | 1.10 |
| h. | A5283 | 84y multi | 1.50 | 1.10 |
| i. | A5284 | 84y multi | 1.50 | 1.10 |
| j. | A5285 | 84y multi | 1.50 | 1.10 |

Nezuko Kamado A5286

Tanjiro Kamado A5287

Inosuke Hashibira A5288

Zenitsu Agatsuma A5289

Tanjiro Kamado — A5290

Giyu Tomioka A5291

Shinobu Kocho — A5292

Kyojuro Rengoku A5293

Mitsuri Kanroji A5294

Tengen Uzui — A5295

Kyojuro Rengoku A5296

Sanemi Shinazugsawa A5297

Obanai Iguro — A5298

Muichiro Tokito — A5299

Gyomei Himejima A5300

**Die Cut Perf. 11¾**

2021, Dec. 6          Litho.
**Self-Adhesive**

| 4564 | | Sheet of 15 | 22.50 | |
|---|---|---|---|---|
| a. | A5286 | 84y multi | 1.50 | 1.10 |
| b. | A5287 | 84y multi | 1.50 | 1.10 |
| c. | A5288 | 84y multi | 1.50 | 1.10 |
| d. | A5289 | 84y multi | 1.50 | 1.10 |
| e. | A5290 | 84y multi | 1.50 | 1.10 |
| f. | A5291 | 84y multi | 1.50 | 1.10 |
| g. | A5292 | 84y multi | 1.50 | 1.10 |
| h. | A5293 | 84y multi | 1.50 | 1.10 |
| i. | A5294 | 84y multi | 1.50 | 1.10 |
| j. | A5295 | 84y multi | 1.50 | 1.10 |
| k. | A5296 | 84y multi | 1.50 | 1.10 |
| l. | A5297 | 84y multi | 1.50 | 1.10 |
| m. | A5298 | 84y multi | 1.50 | 1.10 |
| n. | A5299 | 84y multi | 1.50 | 1.10 |
| o. | A5300 | 84y multi | 1.50 | 1.10 |

Characters from *Demon Slayer: Kimetsu no Yaiba,* manga by Koyoharu Gotouge.

**Miniature Sheet**

Fruits and Vegetables With Rabbits from *Peter Rabbit,* by Beatrix Potter (1866-1943) — A5301

No. 4565 — Various rabbits and: a, Lemons (22x30mm). b, Pepper (22x30mm). c, Apple (22x26mm). d, Grapes (22x26mm). e, Oranges (22x36mm). f, Strawberry (22x30mm). g, Grapefruit (22x30mm). h, Fruit and vegetable basket (32mm diameter). i, Mushrooms (22x36mm). j, Blueberries (22x36mm).

**Die Cut Perf. (#4565h), Die Cut Perf. 13x13¼ (others)**

2021, Dec. 10          Litho.
**Self-Adhesive**

| 4565 | A5301 | Sheet of 10 | 15.00 | |
|---|---|---|---|---|
| a.-j. | | 84y Any single | 1.50 | 1.10 |

**Miniature Sheets**

A5302

My Journey A5303

No. 4566: a, Tenneiji Temple pagoda (26x22mm). b, Onomichi Channel (26x22mm). c, Bowl of Onomichi ramen (23x25mm). d, Setoda Sunset Beach (26x22mm). e, Innoshima Suigun Castle (22x27mm). f, Building and bridge, Kurashiki Bikan Historical Quarter (26x22mm). g, Waterfront trees and buildings, Kurashiki Bikan Historical Quarter (26x22mm). h, Peach and muscat grapes (22x27mm). i, Pair of blue jeans (22x30mm). j, Great Seto Bridge (26x22mm).

No. 4567: a, Drawing of houses, Kurashiki Bikan Historical Quarter (30x24mm). b, Fruit parfait and cookie (22x28mm). c, Kurashiki Ivy Square (26x22mm). d, Bridge and building, Kurashiki Bikan Historical Quarter, diff. (26x22mm). e, Okayama Barazushi (dish with shrimp) (23x25mm). f, Senkoji Temple aerial tramway (26x22mm). g, Senko-ji Temple (22x29mm). h, Cat on steps (22x27mm). i, Lemons and jar of lemon curd (22x27mm). j, Lemon orchard, Tatara Bridge (22x27mm).

**Die Cut Perf. 13¼x13 (#4566a, 4566b, 4566d, 4566e, 4566f, 4566g, 4566j, 4567c, 4567d, 4567f), 12½x13 (#4566c, 4566h), 12 (#4566i, 4567b), 12¾x12½ (#4567a), 12¼x12¾ (#4567e), 13 (#4567g, 4567j), 12¼x13 (#4567h, 4567i)**

2022, Jan. 14          Litho.
**Self-Adhesive**

| 4566 | A5302 | Sheet of 10 | 11.00 | |
|---|---|---|---|---|
| a.-j. | | 63y Any single | 1.10 | .85 |
| 4567 | A5303 | Sheet of 10 | 15.00 | |
| a.-j. | | 84y Any single | 1.50 | 1.10 |

**Souvenir Sheet**

New Year 2022 (Year of the Tiger) A5304

No. 4568 — Tiger with: a, Scroll (24x40mm). b, Envelope (29x33mm).

2022, Jan. 17   Litho.   **Die Cut Perf.**
**Self-Adhesive**

| 4568 | A5304 | Sheet of 2 | 2.60 | |
|---|---|---|---|---|
| a. | | 63y multi | 1.10 | .85 |
| b. | | 84y multi | 1.50 | 1.10 |

Blue-and-White Flycatcher A5305

Ruddy and Common Kingfishers A5306

Java Sparrow A5307

Great Spotted Woodpecker A5308

Green Peacock A5309

Horned Owl A5310

Yellow-Crested Cockatoo A5311

Bantam Chicken A5312

White's Thrush A5313

Mandarin Duck A5314

**Die Cut Perf. 13¼, 13¼x13 (#4569e)**

2022, Jan. 24          Litho.
**Self-Adhesive**

| 4569 | | Sheet of 10 | 15.00 | |
|---|---|---|---|---|
| a. | A5305 | 84y multi | 1.50 | 1.10 |
| b. | A5306 | 84y multi | 1.50 | 1.10 |
| c. | A5307 | 84y multi | 1.50 | 1.10 |
| d. | A5308 | 84y multi | 1.50 | 1.10 |
| e. | A5309 | 84y multi | 1.50 | 1.10 |
| f. | A5310 | 84y multi | 1.50 | 1.10 |

| | | | | |
|---|---|---|---|---|
| *g.* | A5311 | 84y multi | 1.50 | 1.10 |
| *h.* | A5312 | 84y multi | 1.50 | 1.10 |
| *i.* | A5313 | 84y multi | 1.50 | 1.10 |
| *j.* | A5314 | 84y multi | 1.50 | 1.10 |

### Miniature Sheets

A5315

Flora
A5316

No. 4570: a, Dahlias (22x31mm). b, Dandelions (22x31mm). c, Evening primrose and Sun (22x26mm). d, Camellia (22x26mm). e, White flowers on red orange background (26x22mm). f, Flowers and bird (26x22mm). g, Roses (26x26mm). h, Primroses (26x26mm). i, Ginkgo tree leaves (26x26mm). j, Asiatic dayflower (26x26mm).

No. 4571: a, Flowers on vines (22x26mm). b, Camellias (22x26mm). c, Red flowers (22x26mm). d, Strawberries (22x26mm). e, Rose (19x48mm). f, Chameleon plant, light blue background (19x48mm). g, Lily of the valley, light green background (19x48mm). h, Oriental lady's thumb, dark green background (19x48mm). i, Rape blossoms, pink background (19x48mm). j, Flowers, yellow background (19x48mm).

***Die Cut Perf. 13x13¼ (#4570a, 4570b, 4570c, 4570d), 13¼x13 (#4570e, 4570f), 13¼ (#4570g, 4570h, 4570i, 4570j)***

**2022, Feb. 1**        Litho.

#### Self-Adhesive

| | | | | |
|---|---|---|---|---|
| 4570 | A5315 | Sheet of 10 | 11.00 | |
| *a.-j.* | | 63y Any single | 1.10 | .85 |

**Die Cut Perf. 13x13¼**

| | | | | |
|---|---|---|---|---|
| 4571 | A5316 | Sheet of 10 | 15.00 | |
| *a.-j.* | | 84y Any single | 1.50 | 1.10 |

Pink Flowers
A5317

Yellow Flowers
A5318

Pink and White Flowers
A5319

Light Purple Flowers
A5320

Pink Flowers
A5321

Orange and Yellow Flowers
A5322

White, Pink and Purple Flowers
A5323

Pink Flowers
A5324

Red Violet Flowers
A5325

Blue Flowers
A5326

***Die Cut Perf. 12¾x13 (#4572a, 4572c); 13x12¾ (#4572b, 4572d, 4572e)***

**2022, Feb. 15**        Litho.

#### Self-Adhesive

| | | | | |
|---|---|---|---|---|
| 4572 | | Sheet of 10, 2 each | | |
| | | #4572a-4572e | 11.00 | |
| *a.* | A5317 | 63y multi | 1.10 | .85 |
| *b.* | A5318 | 63y multi | 1.10 | .85 |
| *c.* | A5319 | 63y multi | 1.10 | .85 |
| *d.* | A5320 | 63y multi | 1.10 | .85 |
| *e.* | A5321 | 63y multi | 1.10 | .85 |

**Die Cut Perf. 13**

| | | | | |
|---|---|---|---|---|
| 4573 | | Sheet of 10, 2 each | | |
| | | #4573a-4573e | 15.00 | |
| *a.* | A5322 | 84y multi | 1.50 | 1.10 |
| *b.* | A5323 | 84y multi | 1.50 | 1.10 |
| *c.* | A5324 | 84y multi | 1.50 | 1.10 |
| *d.* | A5325 | 84y multi | 1.50 | 1.10 |
| *e.* | A5326 | 84y multi | 1.50 | 1.10 |

### Miniature Sheets

A5327

Gems and Minerals
A5328

No. 4574 — Unprocessed gems: a, Red beryl. b, Tanzanite. c, Emerald. d, Citrine. e,

Pearl, horiz. f, Mandarin garnet, horiz. g, Fluorite. h, Rhodochrosite. i, Aquamarine. j, Tourmaline.

No. 4575 — Cut gems: a, Fire opal (26x23mm). b, Blue sapphire (23x26mm). c, Diamond (26x27mm). d, Ruby (23x26mm). e, Jadeite (26x23mm). f, Peridot (25x26mm). g, Pink spinel (23x26mm). h, Paraiba tourmaline (24x26mm). i, Amethyst (25x26mm). j, Imperial topaz (22x27mm).

***Die Cut Perf. 13x13¼, 13¼x13 (#4574e, 4574f)***

**2022, Feb. 22**        Litho.

#### Self-Adhesive

| | | | | |
|---|---|---|---|---|
| 4574 | A5327 | Sheet of 10 | 11.00 | |
| *a.-j.* | | 63y Any single | 1.10 | .85 |

***Die Cut Perf. 13¼x13 (#4575a, 4575c, 4575e), 13 (others)***

| | | | | |
|---|---|---|---|---|
| 4575 | A5328 | Sheet of 10 | 15.00 | |
| *a.-j.* | | 84y Any single | 1.50 | 1.10 |

Names of gems are found in margin below stamps on No. 4574, and above stamps on No. 4575.

### Miniature Sheets

A5329

Sites, Scenes and Items From Asakusa District of Edo and Tokyo
A5330

No. 4576: a, Wooden spice bottle (27x25mm). b, Bowl of soba noodles and tempura (32x22mm). c, Folding fan (29x22mm). d, Animal-shaped toy (23x30mm). e, Cut glass (23x26mm). f, Puffed millet candy (29x26mm). g, Covered bowl with sweet bean paste and millet (28x26mm). h, Braided cord (26x26mm). i, Socks (25x28mm). j, Tortoiseshell hair pin (25x26mm).

No. 4577: a, Kitchen Supply District buildings (21x30mm). b, Theater entrance (27x27mm). c, Panda sculpture at entrance to flower garden (27x27mm). d, Sensoji Temple pagoda (21x30mm). e, Maneki-neko (beckoning cat) at Imado pottery factory building (27x27mm). f, Paper lanterns (30x21mm). g, Teapot, cup and dessert dish (27x27mm). h, Thunder Gate of Sensoji (30x21mm). i, Hot pot of loach soup, chopsticks, boxes (27x27mm). j, Bridge over Sumida River (27x27mm).

**2022, Mar. 3**    Litho.    **Die Cut Perf.**

#### Self-Adhesive

| | | | | |
|---|---|---|---|---|
| 4576 | A5329 | Sheet of 10 | 11.00 | |
| *a.-j.* | | 63y Any single | 1.10 | .85 |

**Die Cut Perf. 13¼**

| | | | | |
|---|---|---|---|---|
| 4577 | A5330 | Sheet of 10 | 14.00 | |
| *a.-j.* | | 84y Any single | 1.40 | 1.10 |

A5331

A5332

A5333

A5334

**2022**    Litho.    **Die Cut Perf. 13x13¼**

#### Self-Adhesive

| | | | | |
|---|---|---|---|---|
| 4578 | A5331 | 84y multi | 1.30 | 1.00 |
| 4579 | A5332 | 94y multi | 1.50 | 1.10 |
| 4580 | A5333 | 120y multi | 2.00 | 1.50 |
| 4581 | A5334 | 140y multi | 2.40 | 1.75 |
| | | Nos. 4578-4581 (4) | 7.20 | 5.35 |

Issued: Nos. 4578-4579, 5/18; Nos. 4580-4581, 3/17.

Carnations
A5335

Bougainvillea
A5337

Roses
A5339

Sunflowers
A5341

Azaleas
A5343

Begonias
A5336

Columbines
A5338

Carnations and Baby's Breath
A5340

Handkerchief Tree Flowers
A5342

Roses
A5344

**Die Cut Perf. 13x13¼**

**2022, Apr. 6**        Litho.

#### Self-Adhesive

| | | | | |
|---|---|---|---|---|
| 4582 | | Sheet of 10, 2 each | | |
| | | #4582a-4582e | 10.00 | |
| *a.* | A5335 | 63y multi | 1.00 | .75 |
| *b.* | A5336 | 63y multi | 1.00 | .75 |
| *c.* | A5337 | 63y multi | 1.00 | .75 |
| *d.* | A5338 | 63y multi | 1.00 | .75 |
| *e.* | A5339 | 63y multi | 1.00 | .75 |
| 4583 | | Sheet of 10, 2 each | | |
| | | #4583a-4583e | 13.00 | |
| *a.* | A5340 | 84y multi | 1.30 | 1.00 |
| *b.* | A5341 | 84y multi | 1.30 | 1.00 |
| *c.* | A5342 | 84y multi | 1.30 | 1.00 |
| *d.* | A5343 | 84y multi | 1.30 | 1.00 |
| *e.* | A5344 | 84y multi | 1.30 | 1.00 |

Flowers
A5345

Owl
A5346

Flowers
A5347

Dove
A5348

Flowers
A5349

Rabbit
A5350

***Die Cut Perf. 13¼ (#4584a, 4585a, 4586a), Die Cut Perf. (#4584b, 4585b, 4586b)***

**Litho. With Foil Application**

**2022, Apr. 13**

#### Self-Adhesive

| | | | | |
|---|---|---|---|---|
| 4584 | | Sheet of 10, 6 | | |
| | | #4584a, 4 #4584b | 10.00 | |
| *a.* | A5345 | 63y multi | 1.00 | .75 |
| *b.* | A5346 | 63y multi | 1.00 | .75 |

| 4585 | Sheet of 10, 6 | | |
|---|---|---|---|
| | #4585a, 4 #4585b | 13.00 | |
| a. | A5347 84y multi | 1.30 | 1.00 |
| b. | A5348 84y multi | 1.30 | 1.00 |
| 4586 | Sheet of 10, 6 | | |
| | #4586a, 4 #4586b | 15.00 | |
| a. | A5349 94y multi | 1.50 | 1.10 |
| b. | A5350 94y multi | 1.50 | 1.10 |
| | Nos. 4584-4586 (3) | 38.00 | |

Beauty Blowing a Biidoro, by Utamaro (1753-1806) A5351

Ebizo Ichikawa (1741-1806), Actor, by Sharaku A5352

Playing With a Temari Ball, by Harunobu Suzuki (c. 1725-70) — A5353

**Litho. & Engr.**

| 2022, Apr. 20 | | **Perf. 13½** | |
|---|---|---|---|
| 4587 | Horiz. strip of 3 | 3.90 | 3.00 |
| a. | A5351 84y multi | 1.30 | 1.00 |
| b. | A5352 84y multi | 1.30 | 1.00 |
| c. | A5353 84y multi | 1.30 | 1.00 |

Philately Week. Printed in sheets of 10 containing 4 each Nos. 4587a-4587b and 2 No. 4587c.

Bitter Melon, Fish and Pottery Flask A5354

Drums and Lion Dance Costume A5355

Phoenix and Shuri Castle A5356

Okinawa Rail, Hibiscus Flower and Indian Coral Tree A5357

Airplane, Whale Shark and Irabu Bridge — A5358

**Die Cut Perf. 12¾x13¼**

| 2022, May 13 | | **Litho.** | |
|---|---|---|---|
| **Self-Adhesive** | | | |
| 4588 | Sheet of 10, 2 each | | |
| | #4588a-4588e | 13.00 | |
| a. | A5354 84y multi | 1.30 | 1.00 |
| b. | A5355 84y multi | 1.30 | 1.00 |
| c. | A5356 84y multi | 1.30 | 1.00 |
| d. | A5357 84y multi | 1.30 | 1.00 |
| e. | A5358 84y multi | 1.30 | 1.00 |

Return to Japan of Ryukyu Islands, 50th anniv.

 Horse Chestnut Tree A5359

 Black Pine Tree and Lake Biwa A5361

 Japanese Maple Tree A5360

 Rhododendrons A5362

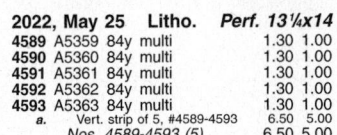 Japanese Evergreen Oak Tree — A5363

| **2022, May 25** | **Litho.** | **Perf. 13¼x14** | |
|---|---|---|---|
| 4589 | A5359 84y multi | 1.30 | 1.00 |
| 4590 | A5360 84y multi | 1.30 | 1.00 |
| 4591 | A5361 84y multi | 1.30 | 1.00 |
| 4592 | A5362 84y multi | 1.30 | 1.00 |
| 4593 | A5363 84y multi | 1.30 | 1.00 |
| a. | Vert. strip of 5, #4589-4593 | 6.50 | 5.00 |
| | Nos. 4589-4593 (5) | 6.50 | 5.00 |

National Afforestation (Shiga).

 Hydrangea A5364

 Morning Glories A5366

 Oriental Lily A5368

 Goldfish A5370

 Bowl of Shaved Ice A5372

 Beach A5374

 Lavender A5365

 Day Lilies and Rainbow A5367

 Sunflowers A5369

 Watermelon and Beverage A5371

 Wind Chimes A5373

 Coral and Fish A5375

 Fish in Sea Anemone A5376

 Morning Glories A5378

 Cloud and Rainbow A5380

 Lily A5382

 Bindweed A5377

 Frog A5379

 Sunflowers A5381

 Fireworks A5383

**Die Cut Perf. 13x13¼**

| 2022, June 1 | | **Litho.** | |
|---|---|---|---|
| **Self-Adhesive** | | | |
| 4594 | Sheet of 10 | 10.00 | |
| a. | A5364 63y multi | 1.00 | .75 |
| b. | A5365 63y multi | 1.00 | .75 |
| c. | A5366 63y multi | 1.00 | .75 |
| d. | A5367 63y multi | 1.00 | .75 |
| e. | A5368 63y multi | 1.00 | .75 |
| f. | A5369 63y multi | 1.00 | .75 |
| g. | A5370 63y multi | 1.00 | .75 |
| h. | A5371 63y multi | 1.00 | .75 |
| i. | A5372 63y multi | 1.00 | .75 |
| j. | A5373 63y multi | 1.00 | .75 |
| 4595 | Sheet of 10 | 13.00 | |
| a. | A5374 84y multi | 1.30 | 1.00 |
| b. | A5375 84y multi | 1.30 | 1.00 |
| c. | A5376 84y multi | 1.30 | 1.00 |
| d. | A5377 84y multi | 1.30 | 1.00 |
| e. | A5378 84y multi | 1.30 | 1.00 |
| f. | A5379 84y multi | 1.30 | 1.00 |
| g. | A5380 84y multi | 1.30 | 1.00 |
| h. | A5381 84y multi | 1.30 | 1.00 |
| i. | A5382 84y multi | 1.30 | 1.00 |
| j. | A5383 84y multi | 1.30 | 1.00 |

 A5384

 A5386

 A5388

 A5390

 A5392

 A5394

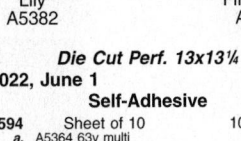 A5385

A5387

A5389

A5391

A5393

A5395

 A5396

 A5398

A5400

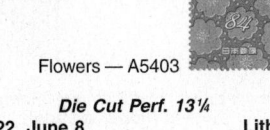 A5397

A5399

A5401

A5402

Flowers — A5403

**Die Cut Perf. 13¼**

| 2022, June 8 | | **Litho.** | |
|---|---|---|---|
| **Self-Adhesive** | | | |
| 4596 | Sheet of 10 | 9.50 | |
| a. | A5384 63y multi | .95 | .75 |
| b. | A5385 63y multi | .95 | .75 |
| c. | A5386 63y multi | .95 | .75 |
| d. | A5387 63y multi | .95 | .75 |
| e. | A5388 63y multi | .95 | .75 |
| f. | A5389 63y multi | .95 | .75 |
| g. | A5390 63y multi | .95 | .75 |
| h. | A5391 63y multi | .95 | .75 |
| i. | A5392 63y multi | .95 | .75 |
| j. | A5393 63y multi | .95 | .75 |
| 4597 | Sheet of 10 | 12.50 | |
| a. | A5394 84y multi | 1.25 | .95 |
| b. | A5395 84y multi | 1.25 | .95 |
| c. | A5396 84y multi | 1.25 | .95 |
| d. | A5397 84y multi | 1.25 | .95 |
| e. | A5398 84y multi | 1.25 | .95 |
| f. | A5399 84y multi | 1.25 | .95 |
| g. | A5400 84y multi | 1.25 | .95 |
| h. | A5401 84y multi | 1.25 | .95 |
| i. | A5402 84y multi | 1.25 | .95 |
| j. | A5403 84y multi | 1.25 | .95 |

**Miniature Sheet**

Diplomatic Relations Between Japan and Mongolia, 50th Anniv. — A5404

No. 4598: a, Altai Tavan Bogd National Park, Mongolia (40x32mm). b, Hunter with eagle (33x38mm). c, Reindeer (40x32mm). d, Eurasian wolf (38x31mm). e, Pincushion flowers (38x31mm). f, Yurt (41x30mm pentagonal). g, Taimen (42x26mm). h, Shepherd on horseback, grazing sheep (40x32mm). i, Rider on Bactrian camel (40x32mm). j, Saurolophus (42x31mm).

**Die Cut Perf. 13 (#4598a, 4598d, 4598e, 4598h, 4598i, 4598j), 13¼ (#4598b, 4598f), 13x13¼ (#4598c), 12¾x13 (#4598g)**

| 2022, June 15 | | **Litho.** | |
|---|---|---|---|
| **Self-Adhesive** | | | |
| 4598 | A5404 Sheet of 10 | 12.50 | |
| a.-j. | 84y Any single | 1.25 | .95 |

 A5405

 A5406

A5407

A5408

A5409

A5410

A5411

A5412

A5413

Sea Otters — A5414

**Die Cut Perf. 13x13¼ (vert. stamps),
13¼x13 (horiz. stamps)**

2022, June 22          Litho. & Engr.
**Self-Adhesive**

| | | | |
|---|---|---|---|
| 4599 | | Sheet of 10 | 12.50 |
| a. | A5405 84y multi | 1.25 | .95 |
| b. | A5406 84y multi | 1.25 | .95 |
| c. | A5407 84y multi | 1.25 | .95 |
| d. | A5408 84y multi | 1.25 | .95 |
| e. | A5409 84y multi | 1.25 | .95 |
| f. | A5410 84y multi | 1.25 | .95 |
| g. | A5411 84y multi | 1.25 | .95 |
| h. | A5412 84y multi | 1.25 | .95 |
| i. | A5413 84y multi | 1.25 | .95 |
| j. | A5414 84y multi | 1.25 | .95 |

Miniature Sheets

A5415

Characters From *Toy Story*
Movies — A5416

No. 4600: a, Buzz Lightyear. b, Jessie, vert.
c, Woody, vert. d, Bo Peep, vert. e, Rex, vert.
f, Hamm. g, Aliens. h, Mr. Potato Head. i, Mrs.
Potato Head. j, Slinky Dog.
No. 4601 — Envelopes and: a, Woody. b,
Buzz Lightyear, vert. c, Woody and Buzz
Lightyear. d, Bo Peep, vert. e, Hamm. f,
Aliens. g, Jessie, vert. h, Mr. and Mrs. Potato
Head. i, Rex, vert. j, Slinky Dog.

**Die Cut Perf. 13**

2022, July 13          Litho.
**Self-Adhesive**

| | | | |
|---|---|---|---|
| 4600 | A5415 | Sheet of 10 | 9.50 |
| a.-j. | | 63y Any single | .95 | .75 |
| 4601 | A5416 | Sheet of 10 | 13.00 |
| a.-j. | | 84y Any single | 1.30 | 1.00 |

A5417

A5418

A5419

---

Letter Writing
Day — A5420

**Die Cut Perf. 12¾**

2022, July 22          Litho.
**Self-Adhesive**

| | | | |
|---|---|---|---|
| 4602 | | Sheet of 10, 5 each | |
| | | #4602a-4602b | 9.50 |
| a. | A5417 63y multi | .95 | .75 |
| b. | A5418 63y multi | .95 | .75 |
| 4603 | | Sheet of 10, 5 each | |
| | | #4603a-4603b | 13.00 |
| a. | A5419 84y multi | 1.30 | 1.00 |
| b. | A5420 84y multi | 1.30 | 1.00 |

Scout's Hat
A5421

Scouts Saluting
A5422

Boy Scout
Tent — A5423

Scout's
Mess
Kit — A5424

Scouts Around
Campfire — A5425

**Die Cut Perf. 13**

2022, July 27          Litho.
**Self-Adhesive**

| | | | |
|---|---|---|---|
| 4604 | | Sheet of 10, 2 each | |
| | | #4604a-4604e | 13.00 |
| a. | A5421 84y multi | 1.30 | 1.00 |
| b. | A5422 84y multi | 1.30 | 1.00 |
| c. | A5423 84y multi | 1.30 | 1.00 |
| d. | A5424 84y multi | 1.30 | 1.00 |
| e. | A5425 84y multi | 1.30 | 1.00 |

Scouting in Japan, cent.

Ko-Kutani
Bowl
Decorated
With
Peonies
A5426

Muromachi
Period
Folding
Screen
Depicting
Beach and
Pines
A5427

Beautiful
Vessel,
Painting by
Yuki Ogura
(1895-2000)
A5428

Sunflowers,
Painting by
Kiitsu
Suzuki
(1796-
1858)
A5429

---

Writing Box
Cover
Depicting
Deer
A5430

A Tour of
Bridges
Around the
Country -
Rope
Bridge on
the Hietsu
Border,
Print by
Hokusai
(1760-
1849)
A5432

Portrait of
Eugenia
Primavesi,
Painting by
Gustav
Klimt (1862-
1918)
A5434

Ko-Kutani
Bowl
Decorated
With Peonies
A5436

The Path,
Painting by
Ogura
A5438

Folding
Screen With
Dragon and
Tiger, by
Hashimoto
A5440

---

Folding
Screen
With
Dragon
and Tiger,
by Gaho
Hashimoto
(1835-
1908)
A5431

Morning at
Etretat,
Painting by
Claude
Monet
(1840-1926)
A5433

Sunflowers,
Painting by
Vincent van
Gogh
(1853-90)
A5435

Muromachi
Period Folding
Screen
Depicting
Beach and
Pines
A5437

Sunflowers,
by Suzuki
A5439

A Tour of
Bridges Around
the Country -
Rope Bridge on
the Hietsu
Border, by
Hokusai
A5441

---

Sunflowers, by
van
Gogh — A5442

Life is a
Struggle
(Golden
Knight),
Painting by
Klimt — A5443

Yellow Irises,
Painting by
Monet
A5444

Writing Box
Cover
Depicting
Deer
A5445

**Die Cut Perf. 13 (#4605a, 4605c),
13x12¼ (#4605b), 13¼x12¼
(#4605d), 12¾x12½ (#4605e, 4605f,
4605g), 12¾ (#4605h), 13x12½
(#4605i), 12½x12¾ (#4605j)**

2022, Aug. 3          Litho.
**Self-Adhesive**

| | | | |
|---|---|---|---|
| 4605 | | Sheet of 10 | 9.00 |
| a. | A5426 63y multi | .90 | .70 |
| b. | A5427 63y multi | .90 | .70 |
| c. | A5428 63y multi | .90 | .70 |
| d. | A5429 63y multi | .90 | .70 |
| e. | A5430 63y multi | .90 | .70 |
| f. | A5431 63y multi | .90 | .70 |
| g. | A5432 63y multi | .90 | .70 |
| h. | A5433 63y multi | .90 | .70 |
| i. | A5434 63y multi | .90 | .70 |
| j. | A5435 63y multi | .90 | .70 |

**Die Cut Perf. 13 (#4606a), 13½x13
(#4606b), 13x12½ (#4606c, 4606i),
12½x13 (#4606d), 13¼x13 (#4606e,
4606f), 13½x12¾ (#4306g), 13½x13¼
(#4606h), 12¾x12¼ (#4606j)**

2022, Aug. 3
| | | | |
|---|---|---|---|
| 4606 | | Sheet of 10 | 12.50 |
| a. | A5436 84y multi | 1.25 | .95 |
| b. | A5437 84y multi | 1.25 | .95 |
| c. | A5438 84y multi | 1.25 | .95 |
| d. | A5439 84y multi | 1.25 | .95 |
| e. | A5440 84y multi | 1.25 | .95 |
| f. | A5441 84y multi | 1.25 | .95 |
| g. | A5442 84y multi | 1.25 | .95 |
| h. | A5443 84y multi | 1.25 | .95 |
| i. | A5444 84y multi | 1.25 | .95 |
| j. | A5445 84y multi | 1.25 | .95 |

Miniature Sheet

Flora and Fauna of Amami-Oshima
Island, Tokunoshima Island, Northern
Part of Okinawa Island and Iriomote
Island UNESCO World Heritage
Site — A5446

No. 4607: a, Amami rabbit (37x28mm). b,
Crested serpent eagle (28x37mm). c, Yanbaru
long-armed scarab beetle (28x37mm). d,
Amami violet (28x37mm). e, Lidth's jay (28mm
diameter). f, Okinawa rail (28mm diameter). g,
Yaeyama Chinese box turtle (28mm diameter).
h, Amami Ishikawa's frog (28x37mm). i, Iriomote cat (28x37mm). j, Banded ground
gecko (28x37mm).

**Die Cut Perf. 13x12¾ (#4607a),
12¾x13 (#4607b, 4607c, 4607d,
4607h, 4607i, 4607j), Die Cut Perf.
(#4607e, 4607f, 4607g)**

2022, Aug. 10          Litho.
**Self-Adhesive**

| | | | |
|---|---|---|---|
| 4607 | A5446 | Sheet of 10 | 12.50 |
| a.-j. | | 84y Any single | 1.25 | .95 |

## Miniature Sheet

**Items From Jomon Prehistoric Sites in Northern Japan UNESCO World Heritage Site — A5447**

No. 4608: a, Clay figurine with large eyes (28x37mm). b, Lacquered spouted earthenware vessel (28x37mm). c, Bowl with ornamental projections (28x37mm). d, Daigi pottery (28x37mm). e, Triangular flat stones (28x37mm). f, Clay figurine with open mouth (28x37mm). g, Deer-horn comb (37x28mm). h, Obsidian spearheads (37x28mm). i, Jade bead (37x28mm). j, Ceremonial spoons (37x28mm).

***Die Cut Perf. 12¾x13 (vert. stamps), 13x12¾ (horiz. stamps)***

**2022, Aug. 17**     Litho.

**Self-Adhesive**

| | | | | |
|---|---|---|---|---|
| 4608 | A5447 | Sheet of 10 | 12.50 | |
| a.-j. | | 84y Any single | 1.25 | .95 |

Ginkgo Tree Branch A5448 — Persimmons on Tree A5449

Dahlias A5450 — Cosmos A5451

Chrysanthemums A5452 — Japanese Maple Tree Branch A5453

Konara Acorns A5454 — Wild Grapes A5455

Winter Cosmos A5456 — Marigolds A5457

***Die Cut Perf. 13x12¾***

**2022, Aug. 24**     Litho.

**Self-Adhesive**

| | | |
|---|---|---|
| 4609 | Sheet of 10, 2 each #4609a-4609e | 9.00 |
| a. | A5448 63y multi | .90 .70 |
| b. | A5449 63y multi | .90 .70 |
| c. | A5450 63y multi | .90 .70 |
| d. | A5451 63y multi | .90 .70 |
| e. | A5452 63y multi | .90 .70 |
| 4610 | Sheet of 10, 2 each #4610a-4610e | 12.50 |
| a. | A5453 84y multi | 1.25 .95 |
| b. | A5454 84y multi | 1.25 .95 |
| c. | A5455 84y multi | 1.25 .95 |
| d. | A5456 84y multi | 1.25 .95 |
| e. | A5457 84y multi | 1.25 .95 |

## Miniature Sheet

77th National Athletic Meet, Tochigi A5458

No. 4611: a, Field hockey. b, Kegon Falls. c, Equestrian. d, Mt. Chausu. e, Diving. f, Plate of gyoza (potstickers). g, Softball. h, Ashikaga Flower Park. i, Climbing. j, Moka Railway.

**2022, Sept. 1** Litho. **Perf. 12¾x13**

| | | | |
|---|---|---|---|
| 4611 | A5458 | Sheet of 10 | 12.50 12.50 |
| a.-j. | | 84y Any single | 1.25 .95 |

### Miniature Sheets

A5459

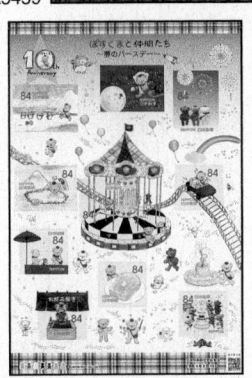

**Posukuma and Friends — A5460**

No. 4612: a, Small teddy bear reading letter in bed. b, Small teddy bear waving in window. c, Posukuma holding mail bag and waving. d, Posukuma, pillar box, small teddy bear with envelope. e, Posukuma, two other teddy bears with mailbags, house. f, Posukuma, three other teddy bears, owl. g, Posukuma, small teddy bear, near pillar box with statue of Posukuma. h, Posukuma, six other teddy bears, owl. i, Posukuma carrying tray of food. j, Posukuma waving, Parliament Building, London in background.

No. 4613: a, Posukuma delivering letter to penguins (33x23mm). b, Posukuma in space, delivering letter to planet (33x23mm). c, Posukuma and other teddy bears watching fireworks display (23x33mm). d, Posukuma bathing in hot spring (33x23mm). e, Posukuma on merry-go-round (25x23mm). f, Posukuma and small teddy bear on roller coaster (25x23mm). g, Posukuma and small

teddy bear at tea ceremony (25x23mm). h, Posukuma and buttered bread (25x23mm). i, Posukuma making meal (25x23mm). j, Posukuma and friends around 10th anniversary cake (25x23mm).

**Litho. With Foil Application**

**2022, Sept. 14**    ***Die Cut Perf.***

**Self-Adhesive**

| | | | |
|---|---|---|---|
| 4612 | A5459 | Sheet of 10 + 23 stickers | 9.00 |
| a.-j. | | 63y Any single | .90 .70 |

***Die Cut Perf. 13x13¼ (#4613c), 13¼x13 (others)***

| | | | |
|---|---|---|---|
| 4613 | A5460 | Sheet of 10 + 15 stickers | 12.50 |
| a.-j. | | 84y Any single | 1.25 .95 |

This sheet of three 120y stamps + 6 stickers, issued Sept. 14, 2022, was printed in limited quantities and sold only with a set of postcards for 1000y.

 Locomotive No. 1 — A5461
 Tokyo Subway 1000 Series Car 1001 — A5462

 Type C62 Locomotive A5463
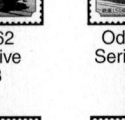 Odakyu 3000 Series Express Train A5464

 Japan National Railways 101 Series Train — A5465
  Japan National Railways 151 Series Train — A5466

 Japan National Railways KiHa58 Series Diesel Train — A5467
  Japan National Railways / Japan Railways ED75 Series Locomotive and KoKi 5500 Series Freight Cars — A5468

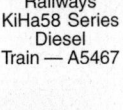 0 Series Shinkansen Train A5469
  Japan Railways Sleeper Express "Hokutosei" A5470

**Die Cut Perf. 13¼**

**2022, Sept. 21**    Litho.

**Self-Adhesive**

| | | |
|---|---|---|
| 4614 | Sheet of 10 | 12.50 |
| a. | A5461 84y multi | 1.25 .95 |
| b. | A5462 84y multi | 1.25 .95 |
| c. | A5463 84y multi | 1.25 .95 |

| | | |
|---|---|---|
| d. | A5464 84y multi | 1.25 .95 |
| e. | A5465 84y multi | 1.25 .95 |
| f. | A5466 84y multi | 1.25 .95 |
| g. | A5467 84y multi | 1.25 .95 |
| h. | A5468 84y multi | 1.25 .95 |
| i. | A5469 84y multi | 1.25 .95 |
| j. | A5470 84y multi | 1.25 .95 |

Railways in Japan, 150th anniv.

  A5471

 Normalization of Diplomatic Relations Between Japan and People's Republic of China, 50th Anniv. — A5472

***Die Cut Perf. 12¾x13***

**2022, Sept. 29**    Litho.

**Self-Adhesive**

| | | |
|---|---|---|
| 4615 | Sheet of 10, 5 each #4615a-4615b | 12.50 |
| a. | A5471 84y multi | 1.25 .95 |
| b. | A5472 84y multi | 1.25 .95 |

 Factory and Trees A5473
 Calculator, Piggy Bank, Currency, Change Purse A5474

 Family and House A5475
  Tree and House A5476

 Bicyclist, Scooter Rider and Automobiles — A5477

**2022, Oct. 3** Litho. ***Die Cut Perf. 13***

**Self-Adhesive**

| | | |
|---|---|---|
| 4616 | Sheet of 10, 2 each #4616a-4616e | 12.50 |
| a. | A5473 84y multi | 1.25 .95 |
| b. | A5474 84y multi | 1.25 .95 |
| c. | A5475 84y multi | 1.25 .95 |
| d. | A5476 84y multi | 1.25 .95 |
| e. | A5477 84y multi | 1.25 .95 |

Conciliation system in Japan, cent.

 Black-naped Oriole and Shrubby Chinese Rose, Detail of Print by Hokusai (1760-1849) A5478

 Black-naped Oriole and Shrubby Chinese Rose, Detail of Print by Hokusai A5479

Snowy Morning in Koishikawa, Print by Hokusai — A5480

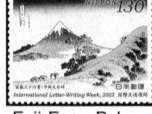

Fuji From Palace Hill, Shinagawa, Tokaido, Print by Hokusai — A5481

Inume Pass in Kai Province, Print by Hokusai — A5482

**2022, Oct. 7**    **Photo.**    *Perf. 13x13¼*

| | | | | |
|---|---|---|---|---|
| 4617 | A5478 | 7y multi | .30 | .30 |
| 4618 | A5479 | 70y multi | .95 | .70 |

*Perf. 13*

| | | | | |
|---|---|---|---|---|
| 4619 | A5480 | 90y multi | 1.25 | .85 |
| 4620 | A5481 | 110y multi | 1.50 | 1.10 |
| 4621 | A5482 | 130y multi | 1.75 | 1.30 |
| | *Nos. 4617-4621 (5)* | | 5.75 | 4.25 |

International Letter Writing Week.

Haniwa Armored Man Clay Figurine, c. 6th Cent. A5483

Bronze Mirror with Beach Scene Decoration, c. 8th Cent. A5484

Lacquered Wooden Box With Mother of Pearl Inlay, 13th Cent. A5485

Cinerary Urn, 8th Cent. A5486

Ewer With Dragon Head Spout, 7th Cent. A5487

Autumn Landscape, Painting on Silk by Toyo Sesshu (1420-c. 1506) A5488

Detail of Painted Folding Screen by Eitoku Kano (1543-90) A5489

Detail of Painted Folding Screen by Eitoku Kano A5490

Red and White Cotton Roses, Painting on Silk by Li Di (c. 1100-c. 1197) — A5491

Red and White Cotton Roses, Painting on Silk by Li Di — A5492

16 Arhats, Ninth Arhat (Svaka), Painting on Silk, 11th Cent. A5493

Image of Bodhisattva Akasagarbha, Painting on Silk, 12th Cent. A5494

Snow Landscape, Painting on Silk by Liang Kai (c. 1140-c.1210) A5495

Sakyamuni Coming Down From the Mountain, Painting on Silk by Liang Kai A5496

Snow Landscape, Painting on Silk by Liang Kai A5497

Portrait of Senseki Takami, Painting on Silk by Kazan Watanabe (1793-1841) A5498

Image of Mahamayuri-vidya-rajni, Painting on Silk, 12th Cent. — A5499

Screen Painting Depicting Kyoto City Scenes, 17th Cent. A5500

Screen Painting Depicting Kyoto City Scenes, 17th Cent. A5501

Detail From Heiji Monogatari Scroll, 13th Cent. — A5502

*Die Cut Perf. 13¼ (#4622a, 4622b, 4622c, 4622d, 4622e, 4622i, 4622j), 13 (#4622f, 4622g, 4622h)*

**2022, Oct. 12**      **Litho.**

**Self-Adhesive**

| | | | | |
|---|---|---|---|---|
| 4622 | | Sheet of 10 | 8.50 | |
| a. | A5483 | 63y multi | .85 | .65 |
| b. | A5484 | 63y multi | .85 | .65 |
| c. | A5485 | 63y multi | .85 | .65 |
| d. | A5486 | 63y multi | .85 | .65 |
| e. | A5487 | 63y multi | .85 | .65 |
| f. | A5488 | 63y multi | .85 | .65 |
| g. | A5489 | 63y multi | .85 | .65 |
| h. | A5490 | 63y multi | .85 | .65 |
| i. | A5491 | 63y multi | .85 | .65 |
| j. | A5492 | 63y multi | .85 | .65 |

*Die Cut Perf. 13¼ (#4623a, 4623b, 4623c, 4623d, 4623e, 4623h, 4623i), 13 (#4623f, 4623g, 4623j)*

| | | | | |
|---|---|---|---|---|
| 4623 | | Sheet of 10 | 11.00 | |
| a. | A5493 | 84y multi | 1.10 | .85 |
| b. | A5494 | 84y multi | 1.10 | .85 |
| c. | A5495 | 84y multi | 1.10 | .85 |
| d. | A5496 | 84y multi | 1.10 | .85 |
| e. | A5497 | 84y multi | 1.10 | .85 |
| f. | A5498 | 84y multi | 1.10 | .85 |
| g. | A5499 | 84y multi | 1.10 | .85 |
| h. | A5500 | 84y multi | 1.10 | .85 |
| i. | A5501 | 84y multi | 1.10 | .85 |
| j. | A5502 | 84y multi | 1.10 | .85 |

Tokyo National Museum, 150th anniv.

Japanese Apricot Blossoms A5503

Sarcandra A5505

Roses A5507

Pieris A5509

Rosemary A5511

Narcissi A5504

Tulips and Pansies A5506

Christmas Roses A5508

Roses A5510

Ornamental Cabbages A5512

*Die Cut Perf. 13x13¼*

**2022, Oct. 26**      **Litho.**

**Self-Adhesive**

| | | | | |
|---|---|---|---|---|
| 4624 | | Sheet of 10, 2 each | | |
| | | #4624a-4624e | 8.50 | |
| a. | A5503 | 63y multi | .85 | .65 |
| b. | A5504 | 63y multi | .85 | .65 |
| c. | A5505 | 63y multi | .85 | .65 |
| d. | A5506 | 63y multi | .85 | .65 |
| e. | A5507 | 63y multi | .85 | .65 |
| 4625 | | Sheet of 10, 2 each | | |
| | | #4625a-4625e | 11.00 | |
| a. | A5508 | 84y multi | 1.10 | .85 |
| b. | A5509 | 84y multi | 1.10 | .85 |
| c. | A5510 | 84y multi | 1.10 | .85 |
| d. | A5511 | 84y multi | 1.10 | .85 |
| e. | A5512 | 84y multi | 1.10 | .85 |

A5513

A5514

A5515

New Year 2023 (Year of the Rabbit) — A5516

**2022, Nov. 1**    **Photo.**    *Perf. 13x13¼*

| | | | | |
|---|---|---|---|---|
| 4626 | A5513 | 84y multi | 1.10 | .85 |

**Photo. & Typo.**

*Perf. 13¼*

| | | | | |
|---|---|---|---|---|
| 4627 | A5514 | 63y+3y multi | .90 | .70 |
| 4628 | A5515 | 84y+3y multi | 1.25 | .95 |
| | *Nos. 4626-4628 (3)* | | 3.25 | 2.50 |

**Photo.**

*Die Cut Perf. 13x13¼*

**Self-Adhesive**

| | | | | |
|---|---|---|---|---|
| 4629 | A5516 | 63y multi | .85 | .65 |

Child and Dog Near Pond A5517

Cup of Cocoa A5518

House in Winter A5519

Heater and Cat A5520

Snowman A5521

House in Snow Globe A5522

Child Carrying Gifts in Snow Globe A5523

Deer and Rabbit in Snow Globe A5524

Child Making Snowman in Snow Globe A5525

Child Looking at Star in Snow Globe A5526

## Die Cut Perf. 13x12½

**2022, Nov. 16**    Litho.

**Self-Adhesive**

| | | | |
|---|---|---|---|
| 4630 | Sheet of 10, 2 each #4630a-4630e | 9.00 | |
| a. | A5517 63y multi | .90 | .70 |
| b. | A5518 63y multi | .90 | .70 |
| c. | A5519 63y multi | .90 | .70 |
| d. | A5520 63y multi | .90 | .70 |
| e. | A5521 63y multi | .90 | .70 |
| 4631 | Sheet of 10, 2 each #4631a-4631e | 12.50 | |
| a. | A5522 84y multi | 1.25 | .95 |
| b. | A5523 84y multi | 1.25 | .95 |
| c. | A5524 84y multi | 1.25 | .95 |
| d. | A5525 84y multi | 1.25 | .95 |
| e. | A5526 84y multi | 1.25 | .95 |

## PREFECTURE ISSUES

Japan has 47 prefectures (political subdivisions) and 13 postal regions (12 until 2004). Since 1989, the national postal ministry has issued stamps to publicize each prefecture. These prefectural stamps are valid throughout Japan and were issued not only in the prefecture named on the stamp but in all other prefectures in the postal region, and in one or more post offices in the other 11 or 12 postal regions. Prefectural stamps are distinguishable from other Japanese stamps by the style of the ideographic characters of "Nippon yubin" on each stamp:

Inscr. on National Stamps since 1948

Inscr. on Prefectural Stamps

Monkeys (Nagano) ZA1

Cherries on Tree (Yamagata) ZA2

*Shurei-mon,* Gate of Courtesy (Okinawa) ZA3

Dogo Hot Spa (Ehime) ZA4

Blue-eyed Doll (Kanagawa) — ZA5

Seto Inland Sea (Hiroshima) — ZA6

Memorial Hall and Mandai Bridge (Niigata) ZA8

Nagoya Castle and *Shachihoko* (Aichi) ZA9

Mt. Takasaki Monkey Holding Perilla Leaf, Fruit (Oita) ZA10

City Hall, 1888 (Hokkaido) ZA11

Runner, Flower (Hokkaido) ZA12

Kumamoto Castle (Kumamoto) ZA13

Stone Lantern, Kenroku-en Park (Ishikawa) ZA14

Bunraku Puppets and Theater (Osaka) ZA15

Shigaraki Ware Raccoon Dog and Lake Biwa (Shiga) ZA16

Apples and Blossoms (Aomori) ZA17

Raccoon Dogs Dancing (Chiba) ZA18

Blowfish Lanterns (Yamaguchi) ZA19

Tokyo Station (Tokyo) ZA20

2nd Asian Winter Olympics (Hokkaido) ZA21

Waterfalls (Toyama) — ZA22

### Perf. 13, 13½ (#Z4, Z11, Z20), 13x13½ (#Z12-Z19)

**1989-90**    Photo., Litho. (#Z16-Z17)

| | | | | |
|---|---|---|---|---|
| Z1 | ZA1 | 62y multicolored | 1.10 | .70 |
| Z2 | ZA2 | 62y multicolored | 1.10 | .70 |
| Z3 | ZA3 | 62y multicolored | 1.10 | .70 |
| Z4 | ZA4 | 62y multicolored | 1.10 | .70 |
| Z5 | ZA5 | 62y multicolored | 1.10 | .70 |
| Z6 | ZA6 | 62y sampan, bridge | 1.10 | .70 |
| Z7 | ZA7 | 62y islands, stairs, starbursts | 1.10 | .70 |
| a. | ZA6 | Pair, #Z6-Z7 | 2.25 | 2.25 |
| Z8 | ZA8 | 62y multicolored | 1.10 | .70 |
| Z9 | ZA9 | 62y multicolored | 1.10 | .70 |
| Z10 | ZA10 | 62y multicolored | 1.10 | .70 |
| Z11 | ZA11 | 62y multicolored | 1.10 | .70 |
| Z12 | ZA12 | 62y multicolored | 1.10 | .70 |
| Z13 | ZA13 | 62y multicolored | 1.10 | .70 |
| Z14 | ZA14 | 62y multicolored | 1.10 | .70 |
| Z15 | ZA15 | 62y multicolored | 1.10 | .70 |
| Z16 | ZA16 | 62y multicolored | 1.10 | .70 |
| Z17 | ZA17 | 62y multicolored | 1.10 | .70 |
| Z18 | ZA18 | 62y multicolored | 1.10 | .70 |
| Z19 | ZA19 | 62y multicolored | 1.10 | .70 |
| Z20 | ZA20 | 62y multicolored | 1.10 | .70 |
| Z21 | ZA21 | 62y multicolored | 1.10 | .70 |
| Z22 | ZA22 | 62y multicolored | 1.10 | .70 |
| | | Nos. Z1-Z22 (22) | 24.20 | 15.40 |

Sheets containing 4 Nos. Z1, Z2, Z4, Z11 or 3 No. Z14 + label, 3 No. Z19 + label were lottery prizes.

Issued: Nos. Z1-Z2, 4/1; No. Z3, 5/15; No. Z4, 6/1; No. Z5, 6/2; NOs. Z6-Z7, 7/7; No. Z8, 7/14; No. Z9, 8/1; Nos. Z10-Z11, 8/15; No. Z12, 9/1; No. Z13, 9/29; Nos. Z14-Z17, 10/2; No. Z18, 10/27; Nos. Z19-Z20, 11/1; No. Z21, 3/1/90; No. Z22, 4/18/90.

See Nos. Z263, Z285, Z363.

Nos. Z23-Z69 were issued as one set. It is broken into sections for ease of reference. See No. Z69a for sheet containing all 47 stamps.

Hokkaido ZA23

Iwate ZA25

Akita ZA27

Fukushima ZA29

Aomori ZA24

Miyagi ZA26

Yamagata ZA28

Ibaraki ZA30

Flowers of the Prefectures: No. Z23, Sweet briar. No. Z24, Apple blossom. No. Z25, Paulowina. No. Z26, Japanese bush clover. No. Z27, Butterbur flower. No. Z28, Safflower. No. Z29, Alpine rose. No. Z30, Rose.

**1990, Apr. 27**    Litho.    Perf. 13½

| | | | | |
|---|---|---|---|---|
| Z23 | ZA23 | 62y multicolored | 3.50 | .70 |
| Z24 | ZA24 | 62y multicolored | 1.25 | .70 |
| Z25 | ZA25 | 62y multicolored | 1.25 | .70 |
| Z26 | ZA26 | 62y multicolored | 1.25 | .70 |
| Z27 | ZA27 | 62y multicolored | 1.25 | .70 |
| Z28 | ZA28 | 62y multicolored | 1.25 | .70 |
| Z29 | ZA29 | 62y multicolored | 1.25 | .70 |
| Z30 | ZA30 | 62y multicolored | 1.25 | .70 |
| | | Nos. Z23-Z30 (8) | 12.25 | 5.60 |

See Nos. Z190, Z614-Z619.

Tochigi ZA31

Saitama ZA33

Tokyo ZA35

Yamanashi ZA37

Niigata ZA39

Gunma ZA32

Chiba ZA34

Kanagawa ZA36

Nagano ZA38

Toyama ZA40

No. Z31, Yashio azalea. No. Z32, Japanese azalea. No. Z33, Primrose. No. Z34, Rape blossom. No. Z35, Cherry blossom. No. Z36, Gold-banded lily. No. Z37, Cherry blossom. No. Z38, Autumn bellflower. No. Z39, Tulip. No. Z40, Tulip.

| | | | | |
|---|---|---|---|---|
| Z31 | ZA31 | 62y multicolored | 1.25 | .70 |
| Z32 | ZA32 | 62y multicolored | 1.25 | .70 |
| Z33 | ZA33 | 62y multicolored | 1.25 | .70 |
| Z34 | ZA34 | 62y multicolored | 1.25 | .70 |
| Z35 | ZA35 | 62y multicolored | 1.25 | .70 |
| Z36 | ZA36 | 62y multicolored | 1.25 | .70 |
| Z37 | ZA37 | 62y multicolored | 1.25 | .70 |
| Z38 | ZA38 | 62y multicolored | 3.50 | .70 |
| Z39 | ZA39 | 62y multicolored | 1.25 | .70 |
| Z40 | ZA40 | 62y multicolored | 1.25 | .70 |
| | | Nos. Z31-Z40 (10) | 14.75 | 7.00 |

See No. Z197.

Ishikawa ZA41

Gifu ZA43

Aichi ZA45

Fukui ZA42

Shizuoka ZA44

Mie ZA46

Shiga
ZA47

Kyoto
ZA48

Osaka
ZA49

Hyogo
ZA50

Kochi
ZA61

Fukuoka
ZA62

No. Z41, Black lily. No. Z42, Daffodil. No. Z43, Chinese milk vetch. No. Z44, Azalea. No. Z45, Rabbit-ear iris. No. Z46, Iris. No. Z47, Alpine rose. No. Z48, Drooping cherry blossom. No. Z49, Japanese apricot and primrose. No. Z50, Chrysanthemum.

| | | | | |
|---|---|---|---|---|
| Z41 | ZA41 | 62y multicolored | 1.25 | .70 |
| Z42 | ZA42 | 62y multicolored | 1.25 | .70 |
| Z43 | ZA43 | 62y multicolored | 1.50 | .70 |
| Z44 | ZA44 | 62y multicolored | 2.00 | .70 |
| Z45 | ZA45 | 62y multicolored | 1.25 | .70 |
| Z46 | ZA46 | 62y multicolored | 1.25 | .70 |
| Z47 | ZA47 | 62y multicolored | 3.00 | .70 |
| Z48 | ZA48 | 62y multicolored | 3.00 | .70 |
| Z49 | ZA49 | 62y multicolored | 1.25 | .70 |
| Z50 | ZA50 | 62y multicolored | 1.25 | .70 |
| | | Nos. Z41-Z50 (10) | 17.00 | 7.00 |

Nara
ZA51

Wakayama
ZA52

Tottori
ZA53

Shimane
ZA54

Okayama
ZA55

Hiroshima
ZA56

Yamaguchi
ZA57

Tokushima
ZA58

Kagawa
ZA59

Ehime
ZA60

No. Z51, Double cherry blossom. No. Z52, Japanese apricot. No. Z53, Pear blossom. No. Z54, Peony. No. Z55, Peach blossom. No. Z56, Japanese Maple. No. Z57, Summer orange blossom. No. Z58, Sudachi orange blossom. No. Z59, Olive blossom. No. Z60, Mandarin orange blossom.

| | | | | |
|---|---|---|---|---|
| Z51 | ZA51 | 62y multicolored | 2.00 | .70 |
| Z52 | ZA52 | 62y multicolored | 1.50 | .70 |
| Z53 | ZA53 | 62y multicolored | 1.25 | .70 |
| Z54 | ZA54 | 62y multicolored | 1.25 | .70 |
| Z55 | ZA55 | 62y multicolored | 1.25 | .70 |
| Z56 | ZA56 | 62y multicolored | 1.25 | .70 |
| Z57 | ZA57 | 62y multicolored | 1.25 | .70 |
| Z58 | ZA58 | 62y multicolored | 1.50 | .70 |
| Z59 | ZA59 | 62y multicolored | 5.00 | .70 |
| Z60 | ZA60 | 62y multicolored | 2.50 | .70 |
| | | Nos. Z51-Z60 (10) | 18.75 | 7.00 |

Saga
ZA63

Nagasaki
ZA64

Kumamoto
ZA65

Oita
ZA66

Miyazaki
ZA67

Kagoshima
ZA68

Okinawa — ZA69

No. Z61, Myrica. No. Z62, Japanese apricot. No. Z63, Laurel. No. Z64, Unzen azalea. No. Z65, Autumn bellflower. No. Z66, Japanese apricot of bungo. No. Z67, Crinum. No. Z68, Rosebay. No. Z69, Coral tree.

| | | | | |
|---|---|---|---|---|
| Z61 | ZA61 | 62y multicolored | 2.00 | .70 |
| Z62 | ZA62 | 62y multicolored | 1.25 | .70 |
| Z63 | ZA63 | 62y multicolored | 1.25 | .70 |
| Z64 | ZA64 | 62y multicolored | 1.25 | .70 |
| Z65 | ZA65 | 62y multicolored | 1.25 | .70 |
| Z66 | ZA66 | 62y multicolored | 1.25 | .70 |
| Z67 | ZA67 | 62y multicolored | 1.25 | .70 |
| Z68 | ZA68 | 62y multicolored | 1.25 | .70 |
| Z69 | ZA69 | 62y multicolored | 1.25 | .70 |
| a. | | Sheet of 47 + 3 labels, #Z23-Z69 | 110.00 | |
| | | Nos. Z61-Z69 (9) | 12.00 | 6.30 |

Nos. Z23-Z69 were issued in sheets of 20. No. Z69a was released in all prefectures.

Seven Baby Crows (Ibaraki) — ZA70

Inns of Tsumago & Magome (Nagano)
ZA71          ZA72

Mt. Fuji and Tea Picking (Shizuoka)
ZA73

Two Peaches (Fukushima)
ZA74

Mt. Sakurajima (Kagoshima)
ZA75

Fireworks Festival of Omagari (Akita)
ZA76

Travel Expo '90, Nagasaki (Nagasaki)
ZA77

Tokyo Shin Post Office (Tokyo)
ZA78

Yasukibushi Folk Song (Shimane)
ZA79

Ryukyu Dancer (Okinawa)
ZA80

### Litho., Litho. & Engr. (#Z70-Z71)

1990                          Perf. 13

| | | | | |
|---|---|---|---|---|
| Z70 | ZA70 | 62y multicolored | 1.10 | .70 |
| Z71 | ZA71 | 62y blk & buff | 1.10 | .70 |
| Z72 | ZA72 | 62y blk & pale grn | 1.10 | .70 |
| a. | | Pair, #Z71-Z72 | 2.25 | 2.25 |
| Z73 | ZA73 | 62y multicolored | 1.10 | .70 |
| Z74 | ZA74 | 62y multicolored | 1.10 | .70 |
| Z75 | ZA75 | 62y multicolored | 1.10 | .70 |
| Z76 | ZA76 | 62y multicolored | 1.10 | .70 |
| Z77 | ZA77 | 62y multicolored | 1.10 | .70 |
| Z78 | ZA78 | 62y multicolored | 1.10 | .70 |
| Z79 | ZA79 | 62y multicolored | 1.10 | .70 |
| Z80 | ZA80 | 62y multicolored | 1.10 | .70 |
| | | Nos. Z70-Z80 (11) | 12.10 | 7.70 |

Issued: Nos. Z70-Z72, 5/1; No. Z73, 5/2; No. Z74, 6/1; Nos. Z75-Z76, 7/2; No. Z77, 8/1; No. Z78, 8/6; Nos. Z79-Z80, 8/15.
Sheets of 3 + label of Nos. Z70, Z73, Z80 were lottery prizes. Value, each $3.25.
See Nos. Z332-Z333.

Dancing Girl (Kyoto)
ZA81

Old Path of Kumano (Wakayama)
ZA82

45th Natl. Athletic Meet (Fukuoka)
ZA83

Izu Swamp, Swans (Miyagi)
ZA84

Spring (Gifu)
ZA85

Summer (Gifu)
ZA86

Autumn (Gifu)
ZA87

Winter (Gifu)
ZA88

Nursery Rhyme, Toryanse (Saitama)
ZA89

Japanese Cranes (Hokkaido)
ZA90

1990

| | | | | |
|---|---|---|---|---|
| Z81 | ZA81 | 62y multicolored | 1.10 | .70 |
| Z82 | ZA82 | 62y multicolored | 1.10 | .70 |
| Z83 | ZA83 | 62y multicolored | 1.10 | .70 |
| Z84 | ZA84 | 62y multicolored | 1.10 | .70 |
| Z85 | ZA85 | 62y multicolored | 1.10 | .70 |
| Z86 | ZA86 | 62y multicolored | 1.10 | .70 |
| Z87 | ZA87 | 62y multicolored | 1.10 | .70 |
| Z88 | ZA88 | 62y multicolored | 1.10 | .70 |
| a. | | Strip of 4, #Z85-Z88 | 4.50 | 4.50 |
| Z89 | ZA89 | 62y multicolored | 1.10 | .70 |
| Z90 | ZA90 | 62y multicolored | 1.10 | .70 |
| | | Nos. Z81-Z90 (10) | 11.00 | 7.00 |

Issued: Nos. Z81-Z83, 9/3; No. Z84, 10/1; Nos. Z85-Z88, 10/9; No. Z89, 10/12; No. Z90, 10/30.
Sheets of 3 No. Z82 + label were lottery prizes. Value, $3.25.
See Nos. 3282-3285, Z171-Z174.

Bizen Ware (Okayama) — ZA92

Battle of Yashima (Kagawa)
ZA91

Yoshinogari Ruins (Saga)
ZA94

Bride Under Cherry Blossoms (Yamanashi)
ZA95

Carp (Niigata)
ZA96

Lily of the Valley (Hokkaido)
ZA97

Lilac (Hokkaido)
ZA98

Daylily
(Hokkaido)
ZA99

Rowanberry
(Hokkaido)
ZA100

### Litho., Photo. (#Z94-Z95)
**1991**     *Perf. 13*

| | | | | |
|---|---|---|---|---|
| **Z91** | ZA91 | 62y multicolored | 1.10 | .70 |
| **Z92** | | 62y pedestal | 1.10 | .70 |
| **Z93** | | 62y bowl | 1.10 | .70 |
| *a.* | | ZA92 Pair, #Z92-Z93 | 2.25 | 2.25 |
| **Z94** | ZA94 | 62y multicolored | 1.10 | .70 |
| **Z95** | ZA95 | 62y multicolored | 1.10 | .70 |
| **Z96** | ZA96 | 62y multicolored | 1.10 | .70 |
| **Z97** | ZA97 | 62y multicolored | 1.10 | .70 |
| **Z98** | ZA98 | 62y multicolored | 1.10 | .70 |
| **Z99** | ZA99 | 62y multicolored | 1.10 | .70 |
| **Z100** | ZA100 | 62y multicolored | 1.10 | .70 |
| *a.* | | Strip of 4, #Z97-Z100 | 4.50 | 4.50 |
| | *Nos. Z91-Z100 (10)* | | 11.00 | 7.00 |

Issued: No. Z91, 2/19; Nos. Z92-Z93, 4/5; No. Z94, 4/12; No. Z95, 4/18; No. Z96, 5/1; Nos. Z97-Z100, 5/31.
See Nos. 3286-3289, 3913-3916, Z304-Z307.

Nikkou
Mountains
(Tochigi)
ZA101

Mt. Iwate by
Yaoji
Hashimoto
(Iwate)
ZA102

Wooden
Puppet
(Tokushima)
ZA103

Whales
(Kochi)
ZA104

Fringed
Orchids
(Tokyo)
ZA105

Cape Toi,
Horses
(Miyazaki)
ZA106

Black Pearls
of Kabira Bay
(Okinawa)
ZA107

Japanese
Pears
(Tottori)
ZA108

Tsujun-kyo Bridge
(Kumamoto)
ZA109

**1991**    **Photo.**

| | | | | |
|---|---|---|---|---|
| **Z101** | ZA101 | 62y multicolored | 1.10 | .70 |
| **Z102** | ZA102 | 62y multicolored | 1.10 | .70 |
| *a.* | Booklet pane of 10 | | 11.00 | |
| | Complete booklet, #Z102a | | 11.00 | |
| **Z103** | ZA103 | 62y multicolored | 1.10 | .70 |
| *a.* | Pane of 10 | | 11.00 | |
| **Z104** | ZA104 | 62y multicolored | 1.10 | .70 |
| *a.* | Pane of 10 | | 11.00 | |
| **Z105** | ZA105 | 41y multicolored | 2.50 | 1.00 |
| *a.* | Booklet pane of 10 | | 15.00 | |
| | Complete booklet, #Z105a | | 15.00 | |

| | | | | |
|---|---|---|---|---|
| **Z106** | ZA106 | 62y multicolored | 1.10 | .70 |
| *a.* | Booklet pane of 10 | | 15.00 | |
| | Complete booklet, #Z106a | | 15.00 | |
| **Z107** | ZA107 | 41y multicolored | .80 | .50 |
| **Z108** | ZA108 | 62y multicolored | 1.10 | .70 |
| **Z109** | ZA109 | 62y multicolored | 1.10 | .70 |
| *a.* | Booklet pane of 10 | | 15.00 | |
| | Complete booklet, #Z108a | | 15.00 | |
| | *Nos. Z101-Z109 (9)* | | 11.00 | 6.40 |

Issued: No. Z101, 5/29; No. Z102, 6/10; Nos. Z103-Z104, 6/26; Nos. Z105-Z106, 7/1; Nos. Z107-Z108, 8/1; No. Z109, 8/26.
Sheets of 3 No. Z106 + label were lottery prizes. Value, $3.

Ninja, Iga Ueno
Castle (Mie)
ZA111

46th Natl.
Athletic
Meet
(Ishikawa)
ZA110

Eyeglass
Industry
(Fukui)
ZA112

Nursery
Rhyme,
Tortoise and
the Hare
ZA113

Kobe City
Weathervane
(Hyogo)
ZA114

Spring (Nara)
ZA115

Autumn (Nara,
Gunma) — ZA116

### Litho., Photo. (#Z110, Z112)
**1991**    *Perf. 13, 13½ (#Z110)*

| | | | | |
|---|---|---|---|---|
| **Z110** | ZA110 | 41y multicolored | .80 | .50 |
| *a.* | Pane of 10 | | 8.00 | |
| **Z111** | ZA111 | 62y multicolored | 1.10 | .70 |
| *a.* | Booklet pane of 10 | | 14.00 | |
| | Complete booklet, #Z111a | | 14.00 | |
| **Z112** | ZA112 | 62y multicolored | 1.10 | .70 |
| *a.* | Booklet pane of 10 | | 14.00 | |
| | Complete booklet, #Z112a | | 14.00 | |
| **Z113** | ZA113 | 62y multicolored | 1.10 | .70 |
| *a.* | Booklet pane of 10 | | 14.00 | |
| | Complete booklet, #Z113a | | 14.00 | |
| **Z114** | ZA114 | 62y multicolored | 1.10 | .70 |
| *a.* | Booklet pane of 10 | | 14.00 | |
| | Complete booklet, #Z114a | | 14.00 | |
| **Z115** | ZA115 | 62y multicolored | 1.10 | .70 |
| **Z116** | ZA116 | 62y multicolored | 1.10 | .70 |
| *a.* | Pair, #Z115-Z116 | | 2.25 | 2.25 |
| *b.* | Booklet pane, 5 #Z116a | | 14.00 | |
| | Complete booklet, #Z116b | | 14.00 | |
| | *Nos. Z110-Z116 (7)* | | 7.40 | 4.70 |

Issued: No. Z110, 9/2; No. Z111, 9/10; No. Z112, 10/1; No. Z113, 10/23; Nos. Z114-Z116, 10/25.
See Nos. 3189G, Z177-Z178.

Gogo-An
Temple, Sea
of Japan
(Niigata)
ZA117

Natl. Land
Afforestation
Campaign
(Fukuoka)
ZA118

Arctic Fox
(Hokkaido)
ZA119

Tateyama
Mountain
Range
(Toyama)
ZA120

Rikuchu
Coast
(Iwate)
ZA121

Kurushima Strait
(Ehime)
ZA122

Tsurusaki
Dance
(Oita)
ZA123

Tanabata
Lantern
Festival
(Yamaguchi)
ZA124

Shasui-no-
taki
Waterfall
(Kanagawa)
ZA125

Kurodabushi
Dance
(Fukuoka)
ZA126

Boat Race
(Okinawa)
ZA127

Osaka
Castle,
Business
Park
(Osaka)
ZA128

Owl, Mt. Horaiji
(Aichi) — ZA129

**1992**    **Litho.**    *Perf. 13½*

| | | | | |
|---|---|---|---|---|
| **Z117** | ZA117 | 41y multicolored | .80 | .50 |
| *a.* | Pane of 10 | | 8.00 | |

**Photo.**

| | | | | |
|---|---|---|---|---|
| **Z118** | ZA118 | 41y multicolored | .80 | .50 |
| **Z119** | ZA119 | 62y multicolored | 1.10 | .70 |
| *a.* | Souvenir sheet of 3 | | 3.50 | 3.50 |

**Litho.**

| | | | | |
|---|---|---|---|---|
| **Z120** | ZA120 | 62y multicolored | 1.10 | .70 |
| *a.* | Pane of 10 | | 11.00 | |

**Photo.**

| | | | | |
|---|---|---|---|---|
| **Z121** | ZA121 | 62y multicolored | 1.10 | .70 |
| *a.* | Pane of 10 | | 11.00 | |
| **Z122** | ZA122 | 62y multicolored | 1.10 | .70 |
| *a.* | Pane of 10 | | 11.00 | |
| **Z123** | ZA123 | 62y multicolored | 1.10 | .70 |
| **Z124** | ZA124 | 62y multicolored | 1.10 | .70 |
| **Z125** | ZA125 | 62y multicolored | 1.10 | .70 |
| *a.* | Pane of 10 | | 11.00 | |
| *b.* | Souvenir sheet of 3 | | 3.50 | 3.50 |

**Litho.**

| | | | | |
|---|---|---|---|---|
| **Z126** | ZA126 | 62y multicolored | 1.10 | .70 |
| **Z127** | ZA127 | 62y multicolored | 1.10 | .70 |
| **Z128** | ZA128 | 41y multicolored | .80 | .60 |

**Photo.**

| | | | | |
|---|---|---|---|---|
| **Z129** | ZA129 | 62y multicolored | 1.10 | .70 |
| *a.* | Souvenir sheet of 3 | | 3.50 | 3.50 |
| *b.* | Pane of 10 | | 11.00 | |
| | *Nos. Z117-Z129 (13)* | | 13.40 | 8.60 |

Issued: No. Z117, 5/1; No. Z118, 5/8; No. Z119, 5/29; No. Z120, 6/10; Nos. Z121-Z122, 6/23; No. Z124, 7/7; No. Z123, 7/23; No. Z125, 7/24; No. Z126, 8/3; No. Z127, 8/17; No. Z129, 10/15.
See also No. Z320.

Oga
Peninsula
(Akita)
ZA130

Fukuroda
Waterfall
(Ibaraki)
ZA131

Notojima Bridge,
Nanao Bay
(Ishikawa)
ZA132

Tama District
Mountains
(Metropolitan
Tokyo)
ZA133

Harbor Seal
(Hokkaido)
ZA134

Peace Statue
(Kagawa)
ZA135

Hana Ta'ue
Rice
Planting
Festival
(Hiroshima)
ZA136

Paradise
Flycatcher
and Mt. Fuji
(Shizuoka)
ZA137

Sailboats on
Lake Biwa
(Shiga)
ZA138

Matumoto
Castle &
Japan Alps
(Nagano)
ZA139

Ohara
Festival
(Kagoshima)
ZA140

Oirase
Mountain
Stream
(Aomori)
ZA141

Yourou Valley
(Chiba) — ZA142

**1993**    **Litho.**    *Perf. 13½*

| | | | | |
|---|---|---|---|---|
| **Z130** | ZA130 | 41y multicolored | .80 | .50 |
| *a.* | Pane of 10 | | 8.00 | |

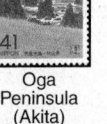

| | | | | |
|---|---|---|---|---|
| **Z131** | ZA131 | 62y multicolored | 1.10 | .70 |
| *a.* | | Pane of 10 | 11.00 | |

**Photo.**

| | | | | |
|---|---|---|---|---|
| **Z132** | ZA132 | 62y multicolored | 1.10 | .70 |
| *a.* | | Pane of 10 | 11.50 | |
| **Z133** | ZA133 | 62y multicolored | 1.10 | .70 |
| *a.* | | Booklet pane of 10 | 11.50 | |
| | | Complete booklet, #Z133a | 11.50 | |
| **Z134** | ZA134 | 62y multicolored | 1.10 | .70 |
| **Z135** | ZA135 | 62y multicolored | 1.10 | .70 |
| *a.* | | Pane of 10 | 11.50 | |
| **Z136** | ZA136 | 62y multicolored | 1.25 | .70 |
| **Z137** | ZA137 | 41y multicolored | .80 | .50 |
| *a.* | | Pane of 10 | 12.00 | |
| **Z138** | ZA138 | 62y multicolored | 1.25 | .70 |
| *a.* | | Pane of 10 | 12.00 | |
| **Z139** | ZA139 | 62y multicolored | 1.25 | .70 |
| *a.* | | Pane of 10 | 12.00 | |
| **Z140** | ZA140 | 41y multicolored | .80 | .50 |
| *a.* | | Pane of 10 | 8.00 | |

**Perf. 13x13½**

| | | | | |
|---|---|---|---|---|
| **Z141** | ZA141 | 62y multicolored | 1.10 | .70 |
| *a.* | | Pane of 10 | 11.00 | |

**Perf. 13½**

| | | | | |
|---|---|---|---|---|
| **Z142** | ZA142 | 41y multicolored | .80 | .50 |
| *a.* | | Pane of 10 | 8.00 | |
| | | *Nos. Z130-Z142 (13)* | 13.55 | 8.30 |

Issued: No. Z130, 2/12; No. Z131, 3/26; No. Z132, 4/2; No. Z133, 4/23; No. Z134, 5/17; No. Z135, 5/21; No. Z136, 6/4; No. Z137, 6/23; No. Z138, 7/1; No. Z139, 7/16; No. Z140, 9/1; No. Z141, 9/22; No. Z142, 10/1.
See also No. Z321.

Dream Bridge (Metropolitan Tokyo) ZA143

Kurobe Canyon & Dam (Toyama) ZA144

Haiku, Storehouse of Poet Issa (1763-1827) (Nagano) ZA145

Okuni, Izumo Great Shrine, Taisha (Shimane) ZA146

Fukiwari Falls (Gunma) ZA147

Ezoshika (Hokkaido) ZA148

Watch Tower, Festival in Tajima (Hyogo) ZA149

Wakura Coast (Wakayama) ZA150

**1994**      **Photo.**      **Perf. 13**

| | | | | |
|---|---|---|---|---|
| **Z143** | ZA143 | 50y multicolored | .90 | .50 |
| *a.* | | Pane of 10 | 9.50 | |
| **Z144** | ZA144 | 80y multicolored | 1.40 | .90 |
| *a.* | | Pane of 10 | 15.00 | |
| **Z145** | ZA145 | 80y multicolored | 1.40 | .90 |
| *a.* | | Pane of 10 | 15.00 | |
| **Z146** | ZA146 | 80y multicolored | 1.40 | .90 |
| *a.* | | Pane of 10 | 15.00 | |

**Litho.**

| | | | | |
|---|---|---|---|---|
| **Z147** | ZA147 | 80y multicolored | 1.40 | .90 |
| *a.* | | Pane of 10 | 15.00 | |
| **Z148** | ZA148 | 50y multicolored | .90 | .50 |
| *a.* | | Pane of 10 | 10.00 | |
| **Z149** | ZA149 | 50y multicolored | .90 | .50 |
| *a.* | | Pane of 10 | 10.00 | |

| | | | | |
|---|---|---|---|---|
| **Z150** | ZA150 | 80y multicolored | 1.40 | .90 |
| *a.* | | Pane of 10 | 15.00 | |
| | | *Nos. Z143-Z150 (8)* | 9.70 | 6.00 |

Issued: No. Z143, 3/23; No. Z144, 4/25; Nos. Z145-Z146, 5/2; No. Z147, 6/6; No. Z148, 6/7; No. Z149, 6/23; No. Z150, 7/15.

Kentish Plovers (Mie) ZA151

Awaodori Dance (Tokushima) ZA152

Tug-of-War (Okinawa) ZA153

Kehi Pine Wood (Fukui) ZA154

Matsushima (Miyagi) ZA155

Kunchi Festival (Nagasaki) ZA156

**1994**      **Photo.**      **Perf. 13**

| | | | | |
|---|---|---|---|---|
| **Z151** | ZA151 | 80y multicolored | 1.40 | .90 |
| *a.* | | Pane of 10 | 15.00 | |
| **Z152** | ZA152 | 50y multicolored | .90 | .50 |
| *a.* | | Pane of 10 | 10.00 | |
| **Z153** | ZA153 | 50y multicolored | .90 | .50 |
| **Z154** | ZA154 | 50y multicolored | .90 | .50 |
| *a.* | | Pane of 10 | 10.00 | |
| **Z155** | ZA155 | 80y multicolored | 1.40 | .90 |
| *a.* | | Pane of 10 | 16.50 | |
| **Z156** | ZA156 | 80y multicolored | 1.40 | .90 |
| *a.* | | Pane of 10 | 16.50 | |
| | | *Nos. Z151-Z156 (6)* | 6.90 | 4.20 |

Issued: No. Z151, 7/22; Nos. Z152-Z153, 8/1; No. Z154, 9/1; No. Z155, 9/20; No. Z156, 10/3.

Hokkaido Chipmunks (Hokkaido) ZA157

Ushiwakamaru and Benkei (Kyoto) ZA158

Utopia Flower (Gifu) ZA159

Jade Bead, Gyofu Soma (1883-1950), Lyricist (Niigata) ZA160

Cape Ashizuri-Misaki Lighthouse (Kochi) ZA161

Ishikawamon Gate, Kanazawa Castle (Ishikawa) ZA162

Akamon Gate, University of Tokyo (Tokyo) ZA163

Three Waterfalls, Kuroyama (Saitama) ZA164

Lady's Slipper, Rebun Island (Hokkaido) ZA165

Street with Zelkova Trees (Miyagi) ZA166

Eisa Festival (Okinawa) — ZA167

**1995**      **Photo.**      **Perf. 13**

| | | | | |
|---|---|---|---|---|
| **Z157** | ZA157 | 80y multicolored | 1.40 | .90 |
| *a.* | | Pane of 10 | 19.00 | |

**Perf. 13½**

| | | | | |
|---|---|---|---|---|
| **Z158** | ZA158 | 80y multicolored | 1.40 | .90 |
| *a.* | | Pane of 10 | 19.00 | |
| **Z159** | ZA159 | 80y multicolored | 1.40 | .90 |
| *a.* | | Pane of 10 | 19.00 | |
| **Z160** | ZA160 | 80y multicolored | 1.40 | .90 |
| *a.* | | Pane of 10 | 19.00 | |
| **Z161** | ZA161 | 80y multicolored | 1.40 | .90 |
| *a.* | | Pane of 10 | 19.00 | |
| **Z162** | ZA162 | 80y multicolored | 1.40 | .90 |
| *a.* | | Pane of 10 | 19.00 | |
| **Z163** | ZA163 | 50y multicolored | .90 | .50 |
| *a.* | | Pane of 10 | 11.00 | |
| **Z164** | ZA164 | 80y multicolored | 1.40 | .90 |
| *a.* | | Pane of 10 | 17.50 | |
| **Z165** | ZA165 | 80y multicolored | 1.40 | .90 |
| *a.* | | Pane of 10 | 17.50 | |
| **Z166** | ZA166 | 50y multicolored | .90 | .50 |
| *a.* | | Pane of 10 | 10.00 | |
| **Z167** | ZA167 | 80y multicolored | 1.40 | .90 |
| | | *Nos. Z157-Z167 (11)* | 14.40 | 9.10 |

Issued: No. Z157, 3/3; No. Z158, 4/3; No. Z159, 4/26; No. Z160, 5/1; Nos. Z161-Z162, 6/1; Nos. Z163-Z165, 7/7; Nos. Z166-Z167, 8/1.

**Seasons Types of 1990-91 Redrawn and**

Kishiwada Danjiri Festival (Osaka) ZA168

Yamadera Temple (Yamagata) ZA169

Karatsu Kunchi Festival (Saga) ZA170

Niimi-No-Shou Festival (Okayama) ZA171

Kirifuri Waterfall (Tochigi) ZA172

10th All-Japan Holstein Show (Chiba) ZA173

Nos. Z171-Z174: (Gifu). No. Z177, (Nara). No. Z178, (Nara, Gunma).

**1995**      **Photo.**      **Perf. 13½**

| | | | | |
|---|---|---|---|---|
| **Z168** | ZA168 | 80y multicolored | 1.40 | .90 |
| *a.* | | Pane of 10 | 16.00 | |
| **Z169** | ZA169 | 80y multicolored | 1.40 | .90 |
| *a.* | | Pane of 10 | 16.00 | |
| **Z170** | ZA170 | 80y multicolored | 1.40 | .90 |
| *a.* | | Pane of 10 | 16.00 | |

**Perf. 13**

| | | | | |
|---|---|---|---|---|
| **Z171** | ZA85 | 80y Spring | 1.40 | .90 |
| **Z172** | ZA86 | 80y Summer | 1.40 | .90 |
| **Z173** | ZA87 | 80y Autumn | 1.40 | .90 |
| **Z174** | ZA88 | 80y Winter | 1.40 | .90 |
| *a.* | | Strip of 4, #Z171-Z174 | 6.50 | 6.50 |

**Perf. 13½**

| | | | | |
|---|---|---|---|---|
| **Z175** | ZA171 | 80y multicolored | 1.40 | .90 |
| **Z176** | ZA172 | 50y multicolored | .90 | .50 |
| *a.* | | Pane of 10 | 10.00 | |
| **Z177** | ZA115 | 80y Spring | 1.40 | .90 |
| **Z178** | ZA116 | 80y Autumn | 1.40 | .90 |
| *a.* | | Pair, #Z177-Z178 | 3.00 | 3.00 |
| **Z179** | ZA173 | 80y multicolored | 1.40 | .90 |
| *a.* | | Pane of 10 | 15.00 | |
| | | *Nos. Z168-Z179 (12)* | 16.30 | 10.40 |

Issued: No. Z168, 9/1; No. Z169, 9/15; Nos. Z170-Z174, 10/2; No. Z175, 10/13; No. Z176, 10/27; Nos. Z177-Z178, 11/6; No. Z179, 11/21.

For self-adhesives, see Nos. 3282-3285.

Clione Limancia (Hokkaido) ZA174

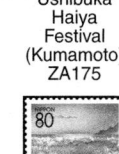

Ushibuka Haiya Festival (Kumamoto) ZA175

Peony of Sukagawa (Fukushima) ZA176

Hamayu (Mie) ZA177

Ama Divers (Mie) ZA178

World Ceramics Expo '96 (Saga) ZA179

Shosenkyo Gorge (Yamanashi) ZA180

Murasaki Shikibu of Takefu (Fukui) ZA181

**1996**      **Litho.**      **Perf. 13½x13**

| | | | | |
|---|---|---|---|---|
| **Z180** | ZA174 | 80y multicolored | 1.40 | .90 |
| *a.* | | Pane of 10 | 11.50 | |

## Photo.

| | | | | |
|---|---|---|---|---|
| **Z181** | ZA175 | 80y multicolored | 1.40 | .90 |
| a. | | Pane of 10 | 15.00 | |
| **Z182** | ZA176 | 80y multicolored | 1.40 | .90 |
| a. | | Pane of 10 | 15.00 | |
| **Z183** | ZA177 | 80y multicolored | 1.40 | .90 |
| **Z184** | ZA178 | 80y multicolored | 1.40 | .90 |
| a. | | Pair, #Z183-Z184 | 3.00 | 3.00 |
| b. | | Pane, 5 #Z184a | 15.00 | |
| **Z185** | ZA179 | 80y multicolored | 1.40 | .90 |

### Perf. 13½

| | | | | |
|---|---|---|---|---|
| **Z186** | ZA180 | 50y multicolored | .90 | .50 |
| a. | | Pane of 10 | 9.50 | |
| **Z187** | ZA181 | 80y multicolored | 1.40 | .90 |
| a. | | Pane of 10 | 15.00 | |
| | | *Nos. Z180-Z187 (8)* | 10.70 | 6.80 |

Issued: No. Z180, 2/6; No. Z181, 4/1; No. Z182, 4/26; Nos. Z183-Z184, 5/1; No. Z185, 5/17; No. Z186, 6/3; No. Z187, 6/24.

## Flower Types of 1990 and

Ancient Trees, Komponchudo of Mt. Hiei (Shiga) ZA182

Nishiumi Marine Park (Ehime) ZA183

Nebuta Festival (Aomori) #ZA184

Main Palace, Shuri Castle (Okinawa) ZA186

Shimozuru Usudaiko Odori Folk Dance (Miyazaki) ZA185

Asakusa Kaminarimon Gate (Metropolitan Tokyo) ZA187

Tottori Shanshan Festival (Tottori) ZA188

Saito Kinen Festival Matsumoto (Nagano) ZA189

No. Z190, (Hokkaido). No. Z197, (Nagano).

## 1996    Photo.    Perf. 13½

| | | | | |
|---|---|---|---|---|
| **Z188** | ZA182 | 80y multicolored | 1.40 | .90 |
| a. | | Pane of 10 | 15.00 | |
| **Z189** | ZA183 | 80y multicolored | 1.40 | .90 |
| a. | | Pane of 10 | 15.00 | |
| **Z190** | ZA23 | 80y Sweetbriar | 1.40 | .90 |
| **Z191** | ZA184 | 80y multicolored | 1.40 | .90 |
| a. | | Pane of 10 | 15.00 | |
| **Z192** | ZA185 | 80y multicolored | 1.40 | .90 |
| a. | | Pane of 10 | 15.00 | |
| **Z193** | ZA186 | 80y multicolored | 1.40 | .90 |
| **Z194** | ZA187 | 80y multicolored | 1.40 | .90 |
| a. | | Pane of 10 | 15.00 | |
| **Z195** | ZA188 | 80y multicolored | 1.40 | .90 |
| **Z196** | ZA189 | 80y multicolored | 1.40 | .90 |
| a. | | Pane of 10 | 15.00 | |
| **Z197** | ZA38 | 80y Autumn bell-flower | 1.40 | .90 |
| | | *Nos. Z188-Z197 (10)* | 14.00 | 9.00 |

Issued: Nos. Z188-Z189, 7/1; No. Z190, 7/5; No. Z191, 7/23; Nos. Z192-Z193, 8/1; No. Z194, 8/8; No. Z195, 8/16; Nos. Z196-Z197, 8/22.

For self-adhesive, see No. 3290.

---

Sengokubara Marsh (Kanagawa) ZA190

Nagoya Festival (Aichi) ZA191

Grass-burning Rite on Mt. Wakakusa (Nara) ZA193

1997 Men's Handball World Championships (Kumamoto) ZA194

Tea Picking (Shizuoka) ZA195

Dahurian Rhododendron (Hokkaido) ZA196

Mt. Fuji (Shizuoka) ZA197

## 1996-97    Photo.    Perf. 13½

| | | | | |
|---|---|---|---|---|
| **Z198** | ZA190 | 80y multicolored | 1.40 | .90 |
| a. | | Pane of 10 | 15.00 | |
| **Z199** | | 80y horse, rider | 1.40 | .90 |
| **Z200** | | 80y two floats | 1.40 | .90 |
| a. | ZA191 | Pair, #Z199-Z200 | 3.00 | 3.00 |
| b. | | Pane, 5 #Z200a | 15.00 | |
| **Z201** | ZA193 | 50y multicolored | .90 | .50 |
| a. | | Pane of 10 | 9.50 | |
| **Z202** | ZA194 | 80y multicolored | 1.40 | .90 |
| a. | | Pane of 10 | 15.00 | |
| **Z203** | ZA195 | 50y multicolored | .90 | .50 |
| a. | | Pane of 10 | 9.50 | |
| **Z204** | ZA196 | 80y multicolored | 1.40 | .90 |
| a. | | Pane of 10 | 15.00 | |
| **Z205** | | 80y cattle | 1.40 | .90 |
| **Z206** | | 80y orange grasses | 1.40 | .90 |
| a. | ZA197 | Pair, #Z205-Z206 | 2.50 | 2.50 |
| b. | | Pane, 5 #Z206a | 12.50 | |
| | | *Nos. Z198-Z206 (9)* | 11.60 | 7.30 |

Issued: No. Z198, 9/6; Nos. Z199-Z200, 10/1; No. Z201, 11/15; No. Z202, 4/17/97; Nos. Z203-Z206, 4/25/97.

Marugame Castle (Kagawa) ZA199

Hokkaido Ermine (Hokkaido) ZA200

Okayama Castle (Okayama) ZA201

Okinawan Fruits (Okinawa) ZA202

---

ZA204    ZA205

ZA206    ZA207

Nagasaki Kaido Highway (Nagasaki, Saga, Fukuoka)

Fukiya Koji's Hanayome Ningyo, Doll of Bride (Niigata) ZA208

The Clock Tower of Kyoto University (Kyoto) ZA209

## 1997    Photo.    Perf. 13½

| | | | | |
|---|---|---|---|---|
| **Z207** | ZA199 | 80y multicolored | 1.40 | .90 |
| a. | | Pane of 10 | 15.00 | |
| **Z208** | ZA200 | 50y multicolored | .90 | .50 |
| a. | | Pane of 10 | 9.50 | |
| **Z209** | ZA201 | 80y multicolored | 1.40 | .90 |
| a. | | Pane of 10 | 15.00 | |
| **Z210** | ZA202 | 50y pineapple | .90 | .50 |
| **Z211** | ZA202 | 50y mango | .90 | .50 |
| a. | | Pair, #Z210-Z211 | 1.90 | 1.90 |
| **Z212** | ZA204 | 80y multicolored | 1.40 | .90 |
| **Z213** | ZA205 | 80y multicolored | 1.40 | .90 |
| **Z214** | ZA206 | 80y multicolored | 1.40 | .90 |
| **Z215** | ZA207 | 80y multicolored | 1.40 | .90 |
| a. | | Strip of 4, #Z212-Z215 | 6.00 | 6.00 |
| **Z216** | ZA208 | 50y multicolored | .90 | .50 |
| a. | | Pane of 10 | 9.50 | |
| **Z217** | ZA209 | 80y multicolored | 1.40 | .90 |
| a. | | Pane of 10 | 15.00 | |
| | | *Nos. Z207-Z217 (11)* | 13.40 | 8.30 |

Issued: No. Z207, 5/15; Nos. Z208-Z209, 5/30; Nos. Z210-Z211, 6/2; Nos. Z212-Z215, 6/3; Nos. Z216-Z217, 6/18.

Kanto Festival (Akita) ZA210

San-in Yume Minato Exposition (Tottori) ZA211

Waterwheel Plant, Hozoji-numa Pond (Saitama) ZA212

Lake Kasumigaura (Ibaraki) ZA215

Bon Wind Festival, Owara (Toyama) ZA213

Tokyo Big Site (Tokyo) ZA216

---

Telecom Center (Tokyo) ZA217

Rainbow Bridge (Tokyo) ZA218

Intl. Forum (Tokyo) ZA219

Tokyo Museum (Tokyo) ZA220

First World Walking Festival (Saitama) — ZA221

## 1997    Photo.    Perf. 13½

| | | | | |
|---|---|---|---|---|
| **Z218** | ZA210 | 80y multicolored | 1.40 | .90 |
| a. | | Pane of 10 | 15.00 | |
| **Z219** | ZA211 | 80y multicolored | 1.40 | .90 |
| a. | | Pane of 10 | 15.00 | |
| **Z220** | ZA212 | 50y multicolored | .90 | .50 |
| a. | | Pane of 10 | 9.50 | |
| **Z221** | | 80y woman | 1.40 | .90 |
| **Z222** | | 80y man | 1.40 | .90 |
| a. | ZA213 | Pair, #Z221-Z222 | 3.00 | 3.00 |
| b. | | Pane, 5 #Z222a | 15.00 | |
| **Z223** | ZA215 | 80y multicolored | 1.40 | .90 |
| a. | | Pane of 10 | 15.00 | |
| **Z224** | ZA216 | 80y multicolored | 1.40 | .90 |
| **Z225** | ZA217 | 80y multicolored | 1.40 | .90 |
| **Z226** | ZA218 | 80y multicolored | 1.40 | .90 |
| **Z227** | ZA219 | 80y multicolored | 1.40 | .90 |
| **Z228** | ZA220 | 80y multicolored | 1.40 | .70 |
| a. | | Strip of 5, #Z224-Z228 | 7.50 | 7.50 |
| b. | | Pane, 2 #Z228a | 15.00 | |
| **Z229** | ZA221 | 80y multicolored | 1.40 | .70 |
| a. | | Pane of 10 | 15.00 | |
| | | *Nos. Z218-Z229 (12)* | 16.30 | 10.00 |

Issued: No. Z218, 7/7; No. Z219, 7/11; No. Z220, 8/1; Nos. Z221-Z222, 8/20; No. Z223, 9/1; Nos. Z224-Z228, 10/1; No. Z229, 10/28.

Kanagawa-Chiba Bridge Tunnel (Chiba, Kanagawa) ZA222

Snow-Covered Tree (Hokkaido) ZA224

Flower in a Dream (Hokkaido) ZA225

Hiyoshi Dam (Kyoto) ZA226

Sanshin (Okinawa) ZA227

Okoshi Daiko (Gifu) ZA228

Kobe-Awaji
Expressway
(Tokushima,
Hyogo)
ZA229

| | | 1997-98 | Litho. | Perf. 13½ | |
|---|---|---|---|---|---|
| Z230 | | 80y denomination upper right | | 1.40 | .90 |
| Z231 | | 80y denomination lower left | | 1.40 | .90 |
| a. | ZA222 | Pair, #Z230-Z231 | | 3.00 | 3.00 |
| b. | | Pane, 5 #Z231a | | 15.00 | |

**Photo.**
**Perf. 13**

| Z234 | ZA226 | 80y multicolored | | 1.40 | .90 |
|---|---|---|---|---|---|
| a. | | Pane of 10 | | 15.00 | |

**Perf. 13½**

| Z235 | ZA227 | 80y multicolored | | 1.40 | .90 |
|---|---|---|---|---|---|
| a. | | Pane of 10 | | 15.00 | |
| Z236 | ZA228 | 80y multicolored | | 1.40 | .90 |
| a. | | Pane of 10 | | 15.00 | |
| Z237 | | 80y bridge, whirl-pool | | 1.40 | .90 |
| Z238 | | 80y bridge, flow-ers | | 1.40 | .90 |
| a. | ZA229 | Pair, #Z237-Z238 | | 3.00 | 3.00 |
| b. | | Pane, 5 #Z238a | | 15.00 | |

Issued: Nos. Z230-Z231, 12/18; Nos. Z232-Z233, 2/5/98; No. Z234, 3/2/98; No. Z235, 3/4/98; No. Z236, 3/19/98; Nos. Z237-Z238, 3/20/98.
See Nos. 3230B-3230C.

Jomon
Figurine
(Nagano)
ZA231

Chaguchagu
Umakko, Mt.
Iwate
(Iwate)
ZA232

Tokyo '98
Business
Show
(Tokyo)
ZA233

Mt. Heisei
Shinzan
(Nagasaki)
ZA234

Oze
(Gunma)
ZA235

Hanagasa
Matsuri
(Yamagata)
ZA237

9th
Women's
World
Softball
Championships
(Shizuoka)
ZA238

| | | 1998 | Photo. | Perf. 13½ | |
|---|---|---|---|---|---|
| Z239 | ZA231 | 80y multicolored | | 1.40 | .90 |
| a. | | Pane of 10 | | 15.00 | |
| Z240 | ZA232 | 80y multicolored | | 1.40 | .90 |
| a. | | Pane of 10 | | 15.00 | |
| Z241 | ZA233 | 80y multicolored | | 1.40 | .90 |
| a. | | Pane of 10 | | 15.00 | |
| Z242 | ZA234 | 80y multicolored | | 1.40 | .90 |
| a. | | Pane of 10 | | 15.00 | |
| Z243 | | 80y blue & multi | | 1.40 | .90 |
| Z244 | | 80y brown & multi | | 1.40 | .90 |
| a. | ZA235 | Pair, #Z243-Z244 | | 3.00 | 3.00 |
| b. | | Pane, 5 #Z244a | | 15.00 | |

| | | | | | |
|---|---|---|---|---|---|
| Z245 | ZA237 | 50y multicolored | | .90 | .50 |
| a. | | Pane of 10 | | 9.50 | |
| Z246 | ZA238 | 80y multicolored | | 1.40 | .90 |
| a. | | Pane of 10 | | 15.00 | |
| | | Nos. Z239-Z246 (8) | | 10.70 | 6.80 |

Issued: No. Z239, 4/1; No. Z240, 4/24; No. Z241, 5/19; No. Z242, 5/20/98; Nos. Z243-Z244, 5/21; No. Z245, 6/5; No. Z246, 6/22.

Mt. Hakusan
(Ishikawa)
ZA239

Hita Gion
(Ohita)
ZA240

World
Puppetry
Festival
(Nagano)
ZA241

Views of
Seto
(Hiroshima)
ZA243

First Postage
Stamps of
Ryukyu
Islands, 50th
Anniv.
(Ryukyu
Islands)
ZA245

| | | 1998 | Photo. | Perf. 13½ | |
|---|---|---|---|---|---|
| Z247 | ZA239 | 50y multicolored | | .90 | .50 |
| a. | | Pane of 10 | | 9.50 | |
| Z248 | ZA240 | 50y multicolored | | .90 | .50 |
| a. | | Pane of 10 | | 9.50 | |
| Z249 | | 50y stage left | | .90 | .50 |
| Z250 | | 50y stage right | | .90 | .50 |
| a. | ZA241 | Pair, #Z249-Z250 | | 1.90 | 1.90 |
| b. | | Pane, 5 #Z250a | | 9.50 | |
| Z251 | | 80y harbor | | 1.40 | .90 |
| Z252 | | 80y highway | | 1.40 | .90 |
| a. | ZA243 | Pair, #Z251-Z252 | | 3.00 | 3.00 |
| b. | | Pane, 5 #Z252a | | 15.00 | |
| Z253 | | 80y Ryukyu Is-lands #1 | | 1.40 | .90 |
| Z254 | | 80y Ryukyu Is-lands #228 | | 1.40 | .90 |
| a. | ZA245 | Pair, #Z253-Z254 | | 3.00 | 3.00 |
| | | Nos. Z247-Z254 (8) | | 9.20 | 5.60 |

Issued: Nos. Z247-Z248, 7/1; Nos. Z249-Z252, 7/17; Nos. Z253-Z254, 7/23.

Satsuma
Pottery,
400th Anniv.
(Kogoshima)
ZA247

Seto Ohashi
Bridge
(Kagawa)
ZA249

Kobe
Luminaries
(Hyogo)
ZA250

Apples
(Aomori)
ZA251

Kumano Path
(Wakayama)
ZA252

Tama Monorail
(Tokyo) — ZA253

| | | 1998 | Photo. | Perf. 13½ | |
|---|---|---|---|---|---|
| Z255 | | 80y bowl | | 1.40 | .90 |
| Z256 | | 80y vase | | 1.40 | .90 |
| a. | ZA247 | Pair, #Z255-Z256 | | 3.00 | 3.00 |
| b. | | Pane, 5 #Z256a | | 15.00 | |
| Z257 | ZA249 | 80y multicolored | | 1.40 | .90 |
| a. | | Pane of 10 | | 15.00 | |
| Z258 | ZA250 | 80y multicolored | | 1.40 | .90 |
| a. | | Pane of 10 | | 15.00 | |

**Perf. 13**

| Z259 | ZA251 | 80y multicolored | | 1.40 | .90 |
|---|---|---|---|---|---|
| a. | | Pane of 10 | | 15.00 | |
| Z260 | ZA252 | 80y multicolored | | 1.40 | .90 |

**Perf. 13½**

| Z261 | ZA253 | 80y multicolored | | 1.40 | .90 |
|---|---|---|---|---|---|
| a. | | Pane of 10 | | 15.00 | |
| | | Nos. Z255-Z261 (7) | | 9.80 | 6.30 |

Issued: Nos. Z255-Z256, 10/1; Nos. Z257-Z258, 11/9; Nos. Z259-Z260, 11/13; No. Z261, 11/26.

**Dogo Hot Spa (Ehime) Type of 1989
and**

Ibara Line (Okayama,
Hiroshima) — ZA254

ZA255

Ao-no-Domon
(Oita) — ZA256

ZA257       ZA258

Snow World (Hokkaido)
ZA259       ZA260

Tokamachi
Snow
Festival
(Niigata)
ZA261

Orchids (Tokyo)
ZA262

Dinosaurs
(Fukui)
ZA264

| | | 1999 | Photo. | Perf. 13½ | |
|---|---|---|---|---|---|
| Z262 | ZA254 | 80y multicolored | | 1.40 | .70 |
| a. | | Pane of 10 | | 15.00 | |
| Z263 | ZA4 | 80y multicolored | | 1.40 | .70 |
| Z264 | ZA255 | 80y multicolored | | 1.40 | .70 |
| Z265 | ZA256 | 80y multicolored | | 1.40 | .70 |
| a. | | Vert. pair, #Z264-Z265 | | 3.00 | 3.00 |
| b. | | Pane, 5 #Z265a | | 15.00 | |

| | | | | | |
|---|---|---|---|---|---|
| Z266 | ZA257 | 50y multicolored | | .90 | .50 |
| Z267 | ZA258 | 50y multicolored | | .90 | .50 |
| Z268 | ZA259 | 80y multicolored | | 1.40 | .70 |
| Z269 | ZA260 | 80y multicolored | | 1.40 | .70 |
| a. | | Strip of 4, #Z266-Z269 | | 5.00 | 3.50 |
| Z270 | ZA261 | 80y multicolored | | 1.40 | .70 |
| a. | | Pane of 10 | | 15.00 | |
| Z271 | | 80y white flowers | | 1.40 | .70 |
| Z272 | | 80y purple flowers | | 1.40 | .70 |
| a. | ZA262 | Pair, #Z271-Z272 | | 3.00 | 3.00 |
| b. | | Pane, 5 #Z272a | | 15.00 | |
| Z273 | | 80y denomination upper left | | 1.40 | .70 |
| Z274 | | 80y denomination lower left | | 1.40 | .70 |
| a. | ZA264 | Pair, #Z273-Z274 | | 3.00 | 3.00 |
| b. | | Pane, 5 #Z274a | | 15.00 | |
| | | Nos. Z262-Z274 (13) | | 17.20 | 8.70 |

Issued: No. Z262, 1/1; Nos. Z263-Z265, 2/1; Nos. Z266-Z269, 2/5; Nos. Z270-Z272, 2/12; Nos. Z273-Z274, 2/22.

Lake
Chuzenji
(Tochigi)
ZA266

Renowned
Cherry Tree
(Gifu)
ZA268

Kiso
Observatory,
Mt. Ontake
(Nagano)
ZA271

Postal Service in
Okinawa, 125th Anniv.
(Okinawa) — ZA269

ZA272

ZA273

ZA274

The Old Path for
Kumano (Mie) — ZA275

No. Z275, Spring. No. Z276, Fall. No. Z278, Traditional costume. No. Z279, Laughing lions. No. Z281, Tsuzurato Pass. No. Z282, Matsumoto Pass. No. Z283, Umagoshi Pass. No. Z284, Touri Pass.

| | | 1999 | Photo. | Perf. 13½ | |
|---|---|---|---|---|---|
| Z275 | | 80y multicolored | | 1.40 | .90 |
| Z276 | | 80y multicolored | | 1.40 | .90 |
| a. | ZA266 | Pair, #Z275-Z276 | | 3.00 | 3.00 |
| b. | | Pane, 5 #Z276a | | 15.00 | |
| Z277 | ZA268 | 80y multicolored | | 1.40 | .90 |
| a. | | Pane of 10 | | 15.00 | |
| Z278 | | 80y multicolored | | 1.40 | .90 |
| Z279 | | 80y multicolored | | 1.40 | .90 |
| a. | ZA269 | Pair, #Z278-Z279 | | 3.00 | 3.00 |
| b. | | Pane, 5 #Z279a | | 15.00 | |
| Z280 | ZA271 | 80y multicolored | | 1.40 | .90 |
| a. | | Pane of 10 | | 15.00 | |
| Z281 | ZA272 | 80y multicolored | | 1.40 | .70 |
| Z282 | ZA273 | 80y multicolored | | 1.40 | .70 |
| Z283 | ZA274 | 80y multicolored | | 1.40 | .70 |
| Z284 | ZA275 | 80y multicolored | | 1.40 | .70 |
| a. | | Strip of 4, #Z281-Z284 | | 6.00 | 6.00 |
| | | Nos. Z275-Z284 (10) | | 14.00 | 8.20 |

Issued: Nos. Z275-Z276, 3/1. No. Z277, 3/16. Nos. Z278-Z279, 3/23. No. Z280, 4/9. Nos. Z281-Z284, 4/16.

## Cherries (Yamagata) Type of 1989 and

Taiko-Mon Gate, Matsumoto Castle (Nagano) ZA276

Firefly Squid (Toyama) ZA277

ZA278  ZA279

Four Seasons, Kenrokuen Garden (Ishikawa)
ZA280     ZA281

No. Z288, Kaisekitou Pagoda, Spring. No. Z289, Fountain, Summer. No. Z290, Kinjoureitaku spring, Autumn. No. Z291, Kotoji stone lantern and yukitsuri, Winter.

**1999, Apr. 26    Photo.    Perf. 13**

| | | | | |
|---|---|---|---|---|
| Z285 | ZA2 | 80y like #Z2 | 1.40 | .90 |

**Perf. 13½**

| | | | | |
|---|---|---|---|---|
| Z286 | ZA276 | 80y multicolored | 1.40 | .90 |
| a. | | Pane of 10 | 15.00 | |
| Z287 | ZA277 | 80y multicolored | 1.40 | .90 |
| a. | | Pane of 10 | 15.00 | |
| Z288 | ZA278 | 80y multicolored | 1.40 | .90 |
| Z289 | ZA279 | 80y multicolored | 1.40 | .90 |
| Z290 | ZA280 | 80y multicolored | 1.40 | .90 |
| Z291 | ZA281 | 80y multicolored | 1.40 | .90 |
| a. | | Strip of 4, #Z288-Z291 | 6.00 | 6.00 |
| b. | | Souvenir sheet, #Z288-Z291 | 6.00 | 6.00 |
| | | Nos. Z285-Z291 (7) | 9.80 | 6.30 |

ZA282     ZA283

ZA284     ZA285

ZA286     ZA287

ZA288     ZA289

Opening of Shimanami Seaside Highway (Hiroshima & Ehime)
ZA290     ZA291

Designs: No. Z292, Onomichi-suido Channel. No. Z293, Kurushima-kaikyo Straits. No. Z294, Old, new Onomichi-oohashi Bridges. No. Z295, Kurushima-kaikyo-oohashi Bridge. No. Z296, Innoshima-oohashi Bridge. No. Z297, Kurushima-kaikyo-oohashi Bridge, diff. No. Z298, Ikuchibashi Bridge. No. Z299, Hakatabashi, Ooshima-oohashi Bridges. No. Z300, Tatara-oohashi Bridge. No. Z301, Oom-ishimabashi Bridge.

**1999, Apr. 26    Photo.    Perf. 13½**

| | | | | |
|---|---|---|---|---|
| Z292 | ZA282 | 80y multicolored | 1.40 | .90 |
| Z293 | ZA283 | 80y multicolored | 1.40 | .90 |
| Z294 | ZA284 | 80y multicolored | 1.40 | .90 |
| Z295 | ZA285 | 80y multicolored | 1.40 | .90 |
| Z296 | ZA286 | 80y multicolored | 1.40 | .90 |
| Z297 | ZA287 | 80y multicolored | 1.40 | .90 |
| Z298 | ZA288 | 80y multicolored | 1.40 | .90 |
| Z299 | ZA289 | 80y multicolored | 1.40 | .90 |
| Z300 | ZA290 | 80y multicolored | 1.40 | .90 |
| Z301 | ZA291 | 80y multicolored | 1.40 | .90 |
| a. | | Block of 10, #Z292-Z301 | 15.00 | 15.00 |
| b. | | Sheet of 8, # Z294-Z301 | 12.00 | 12.00 |

## Flora (Hokkaido) Type of 1991 and

Southern Kii Peninsula (Wakayama) ZA292

Designs: No. Z302, Nachi-no-taki Falls. No. Z303, Engetsutou Island.

**1999, Apr. 28    Photo.    Perf. 13½**

| | | | | |
|---|---|---|---|---|
| Z302 | | 80y multicolored | 1.40 | .90 |
| Z303 | | 80y multicolored | 1.40 | .90 |
| a. | | ZA292 Pair, #Z302-Z303 | 3.00 | 3.00 |
| b. | | Pane, 5 #Z303a | 15.00 | |

**Perf. 13**

| | | | | |
|---|---|---|---|---|
| Z304 | ZA97 | 80y Lily bell | 1.40 | .90 |
| Z305 | ZA98 | 80y Lilac | 1.40 | .90 |
| Z306 | ZA99 | 80y Daylily | 1.40 | .90 |
| Z307 | ZA100 | 80y Rowanberry | 1.40 | .90 |
| a. | | Strip of 4, #Z304-Z307 | 6.00 | 6.00 |

Sendai Tanabata Festival (Miyagi) ZA294

Souma Nomaoi Festival (Fukushima) ZA295

**1999, May 14    Photo.    Perf. 13½**

| | | | | |
|---|---|---|---|---|
| Z310 | ZA294 | 80y multicolored | 1.40 | .90 |
| Z311 | ZA295 | 80y multicolored | 1.40 | .90 |
| a. | | Pair, #Z310-Z311 | 3.00 | 3.00 |
| b. | | Pane, 5 #Z311a | 15.00 | |

Ryukyu Dance (Okinawa) — ZA296

**1999, May 14**

| | | | | |
|---|---|---|---|---|
| Z312 | ZA296 | 80y multicolored | 1.40 | .90 |
| a. | | Pane of 10 | 15.00 | |

ZA297

 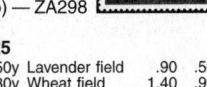

Northern Paradise (Hokkaido) — ZA298

**1999, May 25**

| | | | | |
|---|---|---|---|---|
| Z313 | ZA297 | 50y Lavender field | .90 | .50 |
| Z314 | ZA298 | 80y Wheat field | 1.40 | .90 |

Kurashiki Sightseeing District (Okayama) — ZA299

**1999, May 25    Photo.    Perf. 13½**

| | | | | |
|---|---|---|---|---|
| Z316 | ZA299 | 80y multicolored | 1.40 | .90 |
| a. | | Pane of 10 | 15.00 | |

Shirone Big Kite Battle (Niigata)
ZA300     ZA301

**1999, June 1    Litho.    Perf. 13½**

| | | | | |
|---|---|---|---|---|
| Z317 | ZA300 | 80y multicolored | 1.40 | .90 |
| Z318 | ZA301 | 80y multicolored | 1.40 | .90 |
| a. | | Pair, #Z317-Z318 | 3.00 | 3.00 |
| b. | | Pane, 5 #Z318a | 15.00 | |

Noto Kiriko Festival (Ishikawa) — ZA302

**1999, June 11**

| | | | | |
|---|---|---|---|---|
| Z319 | ZA302 | 80y multicolored | 1.40 | .90 |
| a. | | Pane of 10 | 15.00 | |

### Hokkaido Types of 1992-93

**1999, June 25    Photo.    Perf. 13½**

| | | | | |
|---|---|---|---|---|
| Z320 | ZA119 | 80y Arctic fox | 1.40 | .90 |

**Litho.**

| | | | | |
|---|---|---|---|---|
| Z321 | ZA134 | 80y Largha seals | 1.40 | .90 |

ZA303

Tokyo: No. Z323, morning glories. No. Z324, starburst fireworks over Sumida River. No. Z325, flower burst fireworks.

**1999, July 1    Photo.    Perf. 13½**

| | | | | |
|---|---|---|---|---|
| Z323 | | 80y multicolored | 1.40 | .90 |
| Z324 | | 80y multicolored | 1.40 | .90 |
| Z325 | | 80y multicolored | 1.40 | .90 |
| a. | | ZA303 Block of 3, #Z323-Z325 | 4.50 | 4.50 |
| b. | | Souv. sheet of 2, #Z324-Z325 | 3.00 | 3.00 |

Hakata Gion Yamagasa Festival (Fukuoka) — ZA306

**1999, July 1    Litho.**

| | | | | |
|---|---|---|---|---|
| Z326 | ZA306 | 80y multicolored | 1.40 | .90 |
| a. | | Pane of 10 | 15.00 | |

ZA307     ZA308

ZA309     ZA310

Five Fuji Lakes (Yamanashi) — ZA311

**1999, July 1**

| | | | | |
|---|---|---|---|---|
| Z327 | ZA307 | 80y Yamanakako | 1.40 | .90 |
| Z328 | ZA308 | 80y Kawaguchiko | 1.40 | .90 |
| Z329 | ZA309 | 80y Saiko | 1.40 | .90 |
| Z330 | ZA310 | 80y Shoujiko | 1.40 | .90 |
| Z331 | ZA311 | 80y Motosuko | 1.40 | .90 |
| a. | | Strip of 5, #Z327-Z331 | 7.70 | 7.50 |
| b. | | Pane, 2 #Z331a | 15.00 | |

### Inns of Tsumago, Magome Types of 1990

**Photo. & Engr.**

**1999, July 16    Perf. 13**

| | | | | |
|---|---|---|---|---|
| Z332 | ZA71 | 80y like #Z71 | 1.40 | .90 |
| Z333 | ZA72 | 80y like #Z72 | 1.40 | .90 |
| a. | | Pair, #Z332-Z333 | 3.00 | 3.00 |

ZA312

Toki (Japanese Crested Ibis) (Niigata) — ZA313

No. Z334, Youyou, Yangyang. No. Z335, Kin.

**1999, July 16    Litho.    Perf. 13½**

| | | | | |
|---|---|---|---|---|
| Z334 | ZA312 | 80y multicolored | 1.40 | .90 |
| Z335 | ZA313 | 80y multicolored | 1.40 | .90 |
| a. | | Pair, #Z334-Z335 | 3.00 | 3.00 |
| b. | | Pane, 5 #Z335a | 15.00 | |

ZA314

Design: Amanohashidate sandbar, Miyatsu Bay (Kyoto).

**1999, July 16**

| | | | | |
|---|---|---|---|---|
| Z336 | ZA314 | 80y multicolored | 1.40 | .90 |

ZA315

Design: Ooga lotus (Chiba).

**1999, July 16**

| | | | | |
|---|---|---|---|---|
| Z337 | ZA315 | 80y multicolored | 1.40 | .90 |
| a. | | Pane of 10 | 15.00 | |

# JAPAN

ZA316

ZA317

ZA318

ZA319

Birds (Hokkaido): No. Z338, Steller's sea-eagle. No. Z339, Tufted puffin. No. Z340, Blakiston's fish owl. No. Z341, Red-crowned crane.

| 1999, July 23 | Photo. | Perf. 13½ | |
|---|---|---|---|
| **Z338** | ZA316 50y multicolored | .90 | .50 |
| **Z339** | ZA317 50y multicolored | .90 | .50 |
| **Z340** | ZA318 50y multicolored | .90 | .50 |
| **Z341** | ZA319 50y multicolored | .90 | .50 |
| *a.* | Strip of 4, #Z337-Z340 | 4.00 | 4.00 |

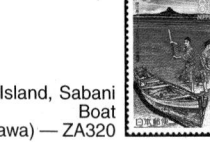

Hill on Ie Island, Sabani Boat (Okinawa) — ZA320

| 1999, July 23 | Litho. | Perf. 13¼ | |
|---|---|---|---|
| **Z343** | ZA320 80y multicolored | 1.40 | .90 |
| *a.* | Pane of 10 | 15.00 | |

National Treasures (Wakayama) ZA321

No. Z344, Kouyasan, Buddhist monastic complex. No. Z345, Natl. treasure, Kongara-douji.

| 1999, July 26 | | Perf. 13½ | |
|---|---|---|---|
| **Z344** | 80y multicolored | 1.40 | .90 |
| **Z345** | 80y multicolored | 1.40 | .90 |
| *a.* | ZA321 Pair, #Z344-Z345 | 3.00 | 3.00 |
| *b.* | Pane, 5 #Z345a | 15.00 | |

Autumn Bellflowers (Iwate) — ZA323

| 1999, July 30 | | | |
|---|---|---|---|
| **Z346** | ZA323 50y multicolored | .90 | .50 |
| *a.* | Pane of 10 | 9.50 | |

Shimizu Port, Cent. (Shizuoka) ZA324

Fishing Boat (Kumamoto) ZA325

| 1999, Aug. 2 | Litho. | Perf. 13¼ | |
|---|---|---|---|
| **Z347** | ZA324 80y multi | 1.40 | .90 |
| *a.* | Pane of 10 | 15.00 | |
| **Z348** | ZA325 80y multi | 1.40 | .90 |
| *a.* | Pane of 10 | 15.00 | |

Ritsurin Park (Kagawa) — ZA326

---

| 1999, Aug. 2 | | Perf. 13¼ | |
|---|---|---|---|
| **Z349** | ZA326 80y multi | 1.40 | .90 |
| *a.* | Pane of 10 | 15.00 | |

Artificial Island, Dejima (Nagasaki) — ZA327

| 1999, Sept. 1 | | Photo. | |
|---|---|---|---|
| **Z350** | ZA327 80y multi | 1.40 | .90 |
| *a.* | Pane of 10 | 15.00 | |

Yoritomo Minamotono (1174-99), Shogun (Kanagawa) — ZA328

| 1999, Sept. 2 | | Litho. | |
|---|---|---|---|
| **Z351** | ZA328 80y multi | 1.40 | .90 |
| *a.* | Pane of 10 | 15.00 | |

Shirakami Mountains (Aomori) — ZA329

| 1999, Sept. 6 | | | |
|---|---|---|---|
| **Z352** | ZA329 80y multi | 1.40 | .90 |
| *a.* | Pane of 10 | 15.00 | |

Gassho-zukuri Farmhouses and Kokiriko Dance (Toyama) — ZA330

| 1999, Sept. 14 | | Photo. | |
|---|---|---|---|
| **Z353** | ZA330 80y multi | 1.40 | .90 |
| *a.* | Pane of 10 | 15.00 | |

Corn (Hokkaido) ZA331

Potatoes (Hokkaido) ZA332

Asparagus (Hokkaido) ZA333

Muskmelon (Hokkaido) ZA334

| 1999, Sept. 17 | | Litho. | |
|---|---|---|---|
| **Z354** | ZA331 50y multi | .90 | .50 |
| **Z355** | ZA332 50y multi | .90 | .50 |
| **Z356** | ZA333 50y multi | .90 | .50 |
| **Z357** | ZA334 50y multi | .90 | .50 |
| *a.* | Strip, #Z354-Z357 | 4.00 | 4.00 |

(Gumma) — ZA335

| 1999, Sept. 17 | | Perf. 13¼ | |
|---|---|---|---|
| **Z358** | ZA335 80y multi | 1.40 | .90 |
| *a.* | Pane of 10 | 15.00 | |

Iwajuku Paleolithic Site Excavations, 50th anniv.

---

(Osaka) — ZA336

| 1999, Sept. 27 | | | |
|---|---|---|---|
| **Z359** | ZA336 80y multi | 1.40 | .90 |

23rd Rhythmic Gymnastics World Championships.

Nihonmatsu Chrysanthemum Exhibition (Fukushima) — ZA337

| 1999, Oct. 1 | | | |
|---|---|---|---|
| **Z360** | ZA337 80y multi | 1.40 | .90 |

Town of Obi (Miyazaki) ZA338

Designs: No. Z361, Taihei dance, front gate of Obi Castle. No. Z362, Shintokudou School, Komura Jutarou (1855-1911).

| 1999, Oct. 1 | | Perf. 13¼ | |
|---|---|---|---|
| **Z361** | 80y multi | 1.40 | .90 |
| **Z362** | 80y multi | 1.40 | .90 |
| *a.* | ZA338 Pair, #Z361-Z362 | 3.00 | 3.00 |
| *b.* | Pane, 5 #Z362a | 15.00 | |

### Nagano Monkey Type of 1989

| 1999, Oct. 13 | Photo. | Perf. 12¾x13 | |
|---|---|---|---|
| **Z363** | ZA1 80y multi | 1.50 | .75 |

(Aichi) ZA340

No. Z364, Ichiei Sato. No. Z365, "Beautiful Yamato."

| 1999, Oct. 13 | Photo. | Perf. 13¼ | |
|---|---|---|---|
| **Z364** | 80y multi | 1.40 | .90 |
| **Z365** | 80y multi | 1.40 | .90 |
| *a.* | ZA340 Pair, #Z364-Z365 | 3.00 | 3.00 |
| *b.* | Pane, 5 #Z365a | 15.00 | |

ZA342

No. Z366, Hagi (Yamaguchi). No. Z367, Tsuwano (Shimane).

| 1999, Oct. 13 | | | |
|---|---|---|---|
| **Z366** | 80y multi | 1.40 | .90 |
| **Z367** | 80y multi | 1.40 | .90 |
| *a.* | ZA342 Vert. pair, #Z366-Z367 | 3.00 | 3.00 |
| *b.* | Pane, 5 #Z367a | 15.00 | |

(Nara) ZA344

No. Z368, Yamato Three Mountains. No. Z369, Ishibutai Tomb.

---

| 1999, Oct. 28 | Litho. | Perf. 13¼ | |
|---|---|---|---|
| **Z368** | 80y multi | 1.40 | .90 |
| **Z369** | 80y multi | 1.40 | .90 |
| *a.* | ZA344 Pair, #Z368-Z369 | 3.00 | 3.00 |
| *b.* | Pane, 5 #Z369a | 15.00 | |

Shikina-en Garden (Okinawa) ZA346

| 1999, Oct. 28 | | | |
|---|---|---|---|
| **Z370** | 50y multi | .90 | .50 |
| **Z371** | 50y multi | .90 | .50 |
| *a.* | ZA346 Pair, #Z370-Z371 | 1.90 | 1.90 |
| *b.* | Pane, 5 #Z371a | 9.50 | |

(Fukui) ZA348

No. Z372, Echizen Crab. No. Z373, Tojinbou Cliff.

| 1999, Nov. 4 | | | |
|---|---|---|---|
| **Z372** | 80y multi | 1.40 | .90 |
| **Z373** | 80y multi | 1.40 | .90 |
| *a.* | ZA348 Pair, #Z372-Z373 | 3.00 | 3.00 |
| *b.* | Pane, 5 #Z373a | 15.00 | |

Children in Santa's Sleigh (Hokkaido) ZA350

Yoshinogari Dig Site (Saga) ZA351

| 1999, Nov. 11 | | Perf. 13¼ | |
|---|---|---|---|
| **Z374** | ZA350 80y multi | 1.40 | .90 |
| *a.* | Pane of 10 | 15.00 | |
| **Z375** | ZA351 80y multi | 1.40 | .90 |
| *a.* | Pane of 10 | 15.00 | |

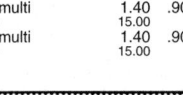

(Kochi) ZA352

No. Z376, Katsura Beach. No. Z377, Sakamoto Ryoma.

| 1999, Nov. 15 | | Photo. | |
|---|---|---|---|
| **Z376** | 80y multi | 1.40 | .90 |
| **Z377** | 80y multi | 1.40 | .90 |
| *a.* | ZA352 Pair, #Z376-Z377 | 3.00 | 3.00 |
| *b.* | Pane, 5 #Z377a | 15.00 | |

For self-adhesives, see Nos. 3189H-3189I.

Samurai House, Kakunodate (Akita) — ZA354

| 1999, Dec. 17 | Litho. | Perf. 13¼ | |
|---|---|---|---|
| **Z378** | ZA354 80y multi | 1.40 | .90 |
| *a.* | Pane of 10 | 15.00 | |

ZA355

ZA356

ZA357

ZA358

Tokyo Scenes
(Tokyo) — ZA359

**2000, Jan. 12    Litho.    Perf. 13¼**
Z379  ZA355 50y multi ..... .90  .50
Z380  ZA356 50y multi ..... .90  .50
Z381  ZA357 50y multi ..... .90  .50
Z382  ZA358 50y multi ..... .90  .50
Z383  ZA359 50y multi ..... .90  .50
  a.  Horiz. strip, #Z379-Z383 ..... 4.75  4.75
  b.  Pane, 2 each #Z379-Z383 ..... 9.50

ZA360    ZA361
ZA362    ZA363
Snow World (Hokkaido)

**2000, Feb. 7    Photo.**
Z384  ZA360 80y multi ..... 1.40  .90
Z385  ZA361 80y multi ..... 1.40  .90
Z386  ZA362 80y multi ..... 1.40  .90
Z387  ZA363 80y multi ..... 1.40  .90
  a.  Strip, #Z384-Z387 ..... 6.00  6.00

ZA364

Japan Flora 2000
(Hyogo) — ZA365

**2000, Mar. 1    Litho.    Perf. 13¼**
Z388  ZA364 50y multi ..... .90  .50
Z389  ZA365 80y multi ..... 1.40  .90
  a.  Pane, 5 each #Z388-Z389 ..... 12.50

ZA366    ZA367
ZA368    ZA369
Korakuen Gardens, 300th
Anniv. (Okayama)

**2000, Mar. 2    Photo.**
Z390  ZA366 80y multi ..... 1.40  .70
Z391  ZA367 80y multi ..... 1.40  .70
Z392  ZA368 80y multi ..... 1.40  .70

Z393  ZA369 80y multi ..... 1.40  .70
  a.  Strip, #Z390-Z393 ..... 6.00  6.00
  b.  Souvenir sheet, #Z390-Z393 ..... 6.00  6.00

Cherry Blossoms in
Takato
(Nagano) — ZA370

**2000, Mar. 3**
Z394  ZA370 80y multi ..... 1.40  .90
  a.  Pane of 10 ..... 15.00

Dyed Fabrics
(Okinawa) — ZA371

**2000, Mar. 17    Litho.**
Z395  ZA371 50y multi ..... .90  .50
  a.  Pane of 10 ..... 9.50

Azumino (Nagano) — ZA372

**2000, Mar. 23    Photo.**
Z396  ZA372 80y multi ..... 1.40  .90
  a.  Pane of 10 ..... 15.00

Cherry Blossoms
(Aomori)
ZA373

Cherry Blossoms
(Fukushima)
ZA374

Cherry Blossoms
(Iwate)
ZA375

Cherry Blossoms
(Miyagi)
ZA376

Cherry Blossoms
(Akita)
ZA377

Cherry Blossoms
(Yamagata)
ZA378

**2000, Apr. 3    Litho.**
Z397  ZA373 80y multi ..... 1.40  .90
  a.  Pair, #Z397, Z399 ..... 3.00  3.00
  b.  Pair, #Z397, Z400 ..... 3.00  3.00
  c.  Pair, #Z397, Z401 ..... 3.00  3.00
  d.  Pair, #Z397, Z402 ..... 3.00  3.00
Z398  ZA374 80y multi ..... 1.40  .90
  a.  Pair, #Z398, Z399 ..... 3.00  3.00
  b.  Pair, #Z398, Z400 ..... 3.00  3.00
  c.  Pair, #Z398, Z401 ..... 3.00  3.00
  d.  Pair, #Z398, Z402 ..... 3.00  3.00
Z399  ZA375 80y multi ..... 1.40  .90
Z400  ZA376 80y multi ..... 1.40  .90
Z401  ZA377 80y multi ..... 1.40  .90
Z402  ZA378 80y multi ..... 1.40  .90
  a.  Vert. strip, #Z399-Z402 ..... 6.00  6.00
  *Nos. Z397-Z402 (6)* ..... 8.40  5.40

Printed in sheets containing one column of
four stamps of Nos. Z397 and Z398 at left and
right respectively with 3 No. Z402a between.

Tulips
(Toyama)
ZA379

**2000, Apr. 28    Photo.    Perf. 13¼**
Z403    50y multi ..... .90  .50
Z404    80y multi ..... 1.40  .90
  a.  ZA379 Pair, #Z403-Z404 ..... 2.50  2.50
  b.  Pane, 5 #Z404a ..... 12.50

Uwajima Castle
(Ehime) — ZA381

**2000, Apr. 28    Perf. 13½x13¼**
Z405  ZA381 80y multi ..... 1.40  .90

New Urban
Center
(Saitama)
ZA382

**2000, May 1    Perf. 13¼**
Z406    50y multi ..... .90  .50
Z407    50y multi ..... .90  .50
  a.  ZA382 Pair, #Z406-Z407 ..... 1.90  1.90
  b.  Pane, 5 #Z407a ..... 9.50

### Flowers of the Chugoku Region

(Tottori)
ZA384

(Shimane)
ZA385

(Okayama)
ZA386

(Hiroshima)
ZA387

(Yamaguchi) — ZA388

**2000, May 1    Litho.    Perf. 13¼**
Z408  ZA384 50y multi ..... .90  .50
Z409  ZA385 50y multi ..... .90  .50
Z410  ZA386 50y multi ..... .90  .50
Z411  ZA387 50y multi ..... .90  .50
Z412  ZA388 50y multi ..... .90  .50
  a.  Vert. strip, #Z408-Z412 ..... 4.75  4.75
  b.  Pane, 2# Z412a ..... 9.50

Cosmos
(Tokyo)
ZA389

Roses
(Tokyo)
ZA390

Bird of
Paradise
Flowers
(Tokyo)
ZA391

Sasanquas
(Tokyo)
ZA392

Freesias
(Tokyo) — ZA393

**2000, June 1    Photo.    Perf. 13¼**
Z413  ZA389 50y multi ..... .90  .50
Z414  ZA390 50y multi ..... .90  .50
Z415  ZA391 50y multi ..... .90  .50
Z416  ZA392 50y multi ..... .90  .50
Z417  ZA393 50y multi ..... .90  .50
  a.  Vert. strip of 5, #Z413-Z417 ..... 4.75  4.75
  b.  Pane, 2 #Z417a ..... 9.50

Shonan
Hiratsuka
Tanabata
Festival
(Kanagawa)
ZA394

**2000, June 2    Litho.**
Z418    50y multi ..... .90  .50
Z419    50y multi ..... .90  .50
  a.  ZA394 Pair, #Z418-Z419 ..... 1.90  1.90
  b.  Pane, 5 #Z419a ..... 9.50

Bankoku Shinryokan
(Okinawa) — ZA396

**2000, June 21    Photo.    Perf. 13¼**
Z420  ZA396 80y multi ..... 1.40  .90
  a.  Pane of 10 ..... 15.00

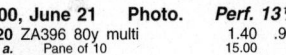

World Performing Arts
Festival
(Osaka) — ZA397

**2000, June 28    Litho.**
Z421  ZA397 80y multi ..... 1.40  .90
  a.  Pane of 10 ..... 15.00

Kujuku Islands
(Akita) — ZA398

**2000, July 7    Photo.**
Z422  ZA398 80y multi ..... 1.40  .90
  a.  Pane of 10 ..... 15.00

Potato Field
(Hokkaido)
ZA399

Hillside and
Hay Rolls
(Hokkaido)
ZA400

**2000, July 19**
Z423    50y Flowers, barn ..... .90  .50
Z424    50y Barn, silo ..... .90  .50
  a.  ZA399 Pair, #Z423-Z424 ..... 1.90  1.90
Z425    80y + 20y Hayrolls, houses ..... 1.90  1.00
Z426    80y + 20y Hayrolls, barns ..... 1.90  1.00
  a.  ZA400 Pair, #Z425-Z426 ..... 4.00  4.00
  *Nos. Z423-Z426 (4)* ..... 5.60  3.00

Surtax on Nos. Z425-Z426 for refugees of
eruption of Mt. Usu.

Awa-odori
(Tokushima) — ZA401

**2000, July 31**                    **Litho.**
Z427    ZA401  80y multi        1.40    .90
  *a.*      Pane of 10              15.00

Golden Hall of Chusonji
Temple (Iwate) — ZA402

**2000, Aug. 1**
Z428    ZA402  80y multi        1.40    .90
  *a.*      Pane of 10              15.00

Hakata Doll
(Fukuoka) — ZA403

**2000, Aug. 2**
Z429    ZA403  80y multi        1.40    .90
  *a.*      Pane of 10              15.00

55th Natl. Athletic Meet
(Toyama) — ZA404

**2000, Sept. 1**                    **Photo.**
Z430    ZA404  50y multi         .90    .50
  *a.*      Pane of 10               9.50

25th World Parachuting
Championships (Mie) — ZA405

No. Z431, 2 skydivers. No. Z432, 3
skydivers.

**2000, Sept. 13**
Z431    80y multicolored        1.40    .90
Z432    80y multicolored        1.40    .90
  *a.*      ZA405 Pair, #Z431-Z432   3.00   3.00
  *b.*      Pane, 5 #Z432a           15.00

Friendly Tokyo
(Tokyo) — ZA406

**2000, Sept. 29**                    **Litho.**
Z433    ZA406  80y multi        1.40    .90
  *a.*      Pane of 10              15.00

Iwakuni Kintaikyo Bridge
(Yamaguchi) — ZA407

**2000, Oct. 10**
Z434    ZA407  80y multi        1.40    .90
  *a.*      Pane of 10              15.00

Intl. Wheelchair
Marathon
(Oita) — ZA408

**2000, Oct. 11**
Z435    ZA408  80y multi        1.40    .90
  *a.*      Pane of 10              15.00

Willow and Frog
(Aichi) — ZA409

**2000, Oct. 20**                    **Photo.**
Z436    ZA409  80y multi        1.40    .90
  *a.*      Pane of 10              15.00

ZA410         ZA411

ZA412         ZA413
Four Seasons (Kyoto)

**2000, Oct. 20**                    **Litho.**
Z437    ZA410  80y multi        1.40    .90
Z438    ZA411  80y multi        1.40    .90
  *a.*      Pane, 5 each #Z437-Z438   15.00
Z439    ZA412  80y multi        1.40    .90
Z440    ZA413  80y multi        1.40    .90
  *a.*      Horiz. strip, #Z437-Z440   6.00   3.50
  *b.*      Pane, 5 each #Z439-Z440   15.00

Odawarajo
Castle
(Kanagawa)
ZA414

**2000, Oct. 27**                    **Perf. 13¼**
Z441    50y multi                .90    .50
Z442    50y multi                .90    .50
  *a.*      ZA414 Pair, #Z441-Z442   1.90   1.90
  *b.*      Pane, 5 #Z442a           9.50

Intl. Balloon Festival
(Saga) — ZA415

**2000, Nov. 1**    **Litho.**    **Perf. 13¼**
Z443    ZA415  80y multi        1.40    .90
  *a.*      Pane of 10              15.00

Chichibu
Night
Festival
(Saitama)
ZA416

**2000, Nov. 1**                    **Photo.**
Z444    80y Yatai, fireworks    1.40    .90
Z445    80y Kasahoko            1.40    .90
  *a.*      ZA416 Pair, #Z444-Z445   3.00   3.00
  *b.*      Pane, 5 #Z445a           15.00

Scenic Izu
(Shizuoka)
ZA417

**2000, Nov. 29**                    **Litho.**
Z446    50y Garden               .90    .50
Z447    50y Waterfall            .90    .50
  *a.*      ZA417 Pair, #Z446-Z447   1.90   1.90
  *b.*      Pane, 5 #Z447a           9.50

Hata Festival, Kohata
(Fukushima) — ZA418

**2000, Dec. 1**                    **Photo.**
Z448    ZA418  80y multi        1.40    .90
  *a.*      Pane of 10              15.00

Sekino'o-taki
Falls and
Kirishima
(Miyazaki)
ZA419

**2000, Dec. 12**                    **Photo.**
Z449    80y Waterfall           1.40    .90
Z450    80y Mountain            1.40    .90
  *a.*      ZA419 Pair, #Z449-Z450   3.00   3.00
  *b.*      Pane, 5 #Z450a           15.00

Megane-bashi Bridge
(Gunma) — ZA420

**2000, Dec. 15**                    **Litho.**
Z451    50y Bridge               .90    .50
Z452    50y Transformer substa-
        tion                     .90    .50
  *a.*      ZA420 Pair, #Z451-Z452   1.90   1.90

Song
"Shinano-no
Kuni"
(Nagano)
ZA421

**2000, Dec. 15**                    **Photo.**
Z453    50y Denom. at L          .90    .50
Z454    50y Denom. at R          .90    .50
  *a.*      ZA421 Pair, #Z453-Z454   1.90   1.90

Kobe
Earthquake
Restoration
(Hyogo)
ZA422

**2001, Jan. 17**    **Photo.**    **Perf. 13¼**
Z455    50y Pandas               .90    .50
Z456    80y Kobe Port           1.40    .90
  *a.*      ZA422 Pair, #Z455-Z456   2.50   2.50
  *b.*      Pane, 5 #Z456a           12.50

Ooe Kouwaka-mai
(Fukuoka) — ZA423

**2001, Jan. 19**                    **Litho.**
Z457    ZA423  80y multi        1.40    .90
  *a.*      Pane of 10              15.00

Kairakuen Garden (Ibaraki) — ZA424

Designs: No. Z458, Koubuntei Pavilion, tree
blossoms. No. Z459, Path, Chumon Gate. No.
Z460, Togyokusen Spring, path. No. Z461,
Koubuntei Pavilion in winter.

**2001, Feb. 1**                    **Photo.**
Z458    50y multi                .90    .50
Z459    50y multi                .90    .50
Z460    50y multi                .90    .50
Z461    50y multi                .90    .50
  *a.*      ZA424 Horiz. strip, #Z458-Z461   4.00   4.00
  *b.*      Souvenir sheet, #Z461a   4.00   4.00

Ezo Sable
(Hokkaido) — ZA425

**2001, Feb. 6**                    **Litho.**
Z462    ZA425  80y multi        1.40    .90
  *a.*      Pane of 10              15.00
  *b.*      Horiz. pair, #Z321, Z462   3.00   3.00

Issued: No. Z462b, Sept. 2007.

Kochi
Castle and
Sunday
Market
(Kochi)
ZA426

**2001, Mar. 1**    **Photo.**    **Perf. 13¼**
Z463    80y multi               1.40    .90
Z464    80y multi               1.40    .90
  *a.*      ZA426 Pair, #Z463-Z464   3.00   3.00
  *b.*      Pane, 5 #Z464a           15.00

Takarazuka              Violets
Revue                   (Hyogo)
Dancers                 ZA428
(Hyogo)
ZA427

**2001, Mar. 21**                    **Litho.**
Z465    ZA427  80y multi        1.40    .90
Z466    ZA428  80y multi        1.40    .90
  *a.*      Pane, 5 each #Z465-Z466   15.00

Matsue
Castle and
Meimei-an
Teahouse
(Shimane)
ZA429

**2001, Mar. 21**
Z467    80y multi               1.40    .90
Z468    80y multi               1.40    .90
  *a.*      ZA429 Pair, #Z467-Z468   3.00   3.00
  *b.*      Pane, 5 #Z468a           15.00

Grapes, Jewelry and Mt.
Fuji
(Yamanashi) — ZA430

**2001, Mar. 30**                    **Photo.**
Z469    ZA430  80y multi        1.40    .90
  *a.*      Pane of 10              15.00

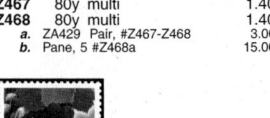

Sports
Paradise
(Osaka)
ZA431

Designs: No. Z470, Thunder god (red) playing table tennis. No. Z471, Wing god (green) playing table tennis. No. Z472, Bowling. No. Z473, Taekwondo.

**2001, Apr. 3**
| | | | |
|---|---|---|---|
| Z470 | 50y multi | .90 | .50 |
| Z471 | 50y multi | .90 | .50 |
| Z472 | 50y multi | .90 | .50 |
| Z473 | 50y multi | .90 | .50 |
| a. | ZA431 Horiz. strip, #Z470-Z473 | 4.00 | 4.00 |

Beautiful Fukushima Future Expo (Fukushima) — ZA432

**2001, Apr. 10**
| | | | |
|---|---|---|---|
| Z474 | ZA432 80y multi | 1.40 | .90 |
| a. | Pane of 10 | 15.00 | |

Cherry Blossoms at Takada Castle (Niigata) — ZA433

**2001, Apr. 10** Litho.
| | | | |
|---|---|---|---|
| Z475 | ZA433 80y multi | 1.40 | .90 |
| a. | Pane of 10 | 15.00 | |

Hamamatsu Festival (Shizuoka) — ZA434

Designs: No. Z476, Palace Festival. No. Z477, Kite fighting.

**2001, May 1**
| | | | |
|---|---|---|---|
| Z476 | 80y multi | 1.40 | .90 |
| Z477 | 80y multi | 1.40 | .90 |
| a. | ZA434 Pair, #Z476-Z477 | 3.00 | 3.00 |
| b. | Pane, 5 #Z477a | 15.00 | |

Ashikaga School Gate (Tochigi) ZA435 — Ashikaga School (Tochigi) ZA436

**2001, May 11** Photo.
| | | | |
|---|---|---|---|
| Z478 | ZA435 80y multi | 1.40 | .90 |
| Z479 | ZA436 50y multi | 1.40 | .90 |
| a. | Pane, 5 each #Z478-Z479 | 15.00 | |

Natl. Afforestation Campaign (Yamanashi) — ZA437

**2001, May 18**
| | | | |
|---|---|---|---|
| Z480 | ZA437 50y multi | .90 | .50 |
| a. | Pane of 10 | 9.50 | |

Sendai, 400th Anniv. (Miyagi) — ZA438

**2001, May 18** Litho.
| | | | |
|---|---|---|---|
| Z481 | ZA438 80y multi | 1.40 | .90 |
| a. | Pane of 10 | 15.00 | |

Zenkoji Temple and Mt. Iizunayama (Nagano) ZA439

**2001, May 23**
| | | | |
|---|---|---|---|
| Z482 | 80y multi | 1.40 | .90 |
| Z483 | 80y multi | 1.40 | .90 |
| a. | ZA439 Pair, #Z482-Z483 | 3.00 | 3.00 |
| b. | Pane, 5 #Z483a | 15.00 | |

Ducks (Yamaguchi) ZA440

Kirara Band, Japan Expo Site (Yamaguchi) ZA441

**2001, May 25**
| | | | |
|---|---|---|---|
| Z484 | ZA440 50y multi | .90 | .50 |
| Z485 | ZA441 80y multi | 1.40 | .90 |
| a. | Pane, 5 each #Z484-Z485 | 12.25 | |

Cherry Blossoms (Tokyo) ZA442

Hydrangea (Tokyo) ZA443

Salvia (Tokyo) — ZA444

Chrysanthemums (Tokyo) — ZA445

Camellias (Tokyo) — ZA446

**2001, June 1** Photo.
| | | | |
|---|---|---|---|
| Z486 | ZA442 50y multi | .90 | .50 |
| Z487 | ZA443 50y multi | .90 | .50 |
| Z488 | ZA444 50y multi | .90 | .50 |
| Z489 | ZA445 50y multi | .90 | .50 |
| Z490 | ZA446 50y multi | .90 | .50 |
| a. | Vert. strip, #Z486-Z490 | 4.75 | 4.75 |
| b. | Pane, 2 #Z490a | 9.50 | |

ZA447

Sites (Tottori) ZA448

Designs: No. Z491, Snow crab, Uradome Coast. No. Z492, Tottori Dunes. No. Z493, Paper Hina dolls in river. No. Z494, Mt. Daisen. No. Z495, Nageiredo Hall. No. Z496, Mukibanda Yayoi Period. Illustration ZA447 reduced.

**2001, June 1**
| | | | |
|---|---|---|---|
| Z491 | 50y multi | .90 | .50 |
| Z492 | 50y multi | .90 | .50 |
| Z493 | 50y multi | .90 | .50 |
| Z494 | 50y multi | .90 | .50 |
| a. | ZA447 Horiz. strip, #Z491-Z494 | 4.00 | 4.00 |
| Z495 | 80y multi | 1.40 | .90 |
| Z496 | 80y multi | 1.40 | .90 |
| a. | ZA448 Horiz. pair, #Z495-Z496 | 3.00 | 3.00 |
| | Nos. Z491-Z496 (6) | 6.40 | 3.80 |

Prosperity in Kaga (Ishikawa) — ZA449

**2001, June 4**
| | | | |
|---|---|---|---|
| Z497 | ZA449 80y multi | 1.40 | .90 |
| a. | Pane of 10 | 15.00 | |

Poppies (Hokkaido) ZA450

Calanthe (Hokkaido) ZA451

**2001, June 22** Litho.
| | | | |
|---|---|---|---|
| Z498 | ZA450 50y multi | .90 | .50 |
| a. | Pane of 10 | 9.50 | |
| Z499 | ZA451 50y multi | .90 | .50 |
| a. | Pane of 10 | 9.50 | |

Cornerstone of Peace (Okinawa) — ZA452

**2001, June 22** Photo.
| | | | |
|---|---|---|---|
| Z500 | ZA452 80y multi | 1.40 | .90 |

Peach Blossoms, Shirane-sanzan Mountains (Yamanashi) ZA453

Irises, Mt. Kitadake (Yamanashi) ZA454

Horses. Mt. Yatsugatake (Yamanashi) ZA455 — Oshino-hakkai Pond (Yamanashi) ZA456

Cherry Blossoms, Minobu (Yamanashi) — ZA457

**2001, July 2**
| | | | |
|---|---|---|---|
| Z501 | ZA453 50y multi | .90 | .50 |
| Z502 | ZA454 50y multi | .90 | .50 |
| Z503 | ZA455 50y multi | .90 | .50 |
| Z504 | ZA456 50y multi | .90 | .50 |
| Z505 | ZA457 50y multi | .90 | .50 |
| a. | Vert. strip, #Z501-Z505 | 4.75 | 4.75 |
| b. | Pane, 2 #Z505a | 9.50 | |

Automobile City, Toyota (Aichi) ZA458

Designs: No. Z506, Toyota-oohashi Bridge. No. Z507, Toyota Stadium.

**2001, July 2**
| | | | |
|---|---|---|---|
| Z506 | 50y multi | .90 | .50 |
| Z507 | 50y multi | .90 | .50 |
| a. | ZA458 Pair, #Z506-Z507 | 1.90 | 1.90 |
| b. | Pane, 5 #Z507a | 9.50 | |

Kitakyushu Expo Festival (Fukuoka) — ZA459

**2001, July 4**
| | | | |
|---|---|---|---|
| Z508 | ZA459 80y multi | 1.40 | .90 |
| a. | Pane of 10 | 15.00 | |

World Trade Organization, 14th General Assembly (Osaka) — ZA460

Designs: No. Z509, Namdaemun, Seoul, and Doton-bori, Osaka. No. Z510, Bunraku, Nong-ak.

**2001, July 6** Litho.
| | | | |
|---|---|---|---|
| Z509 | 80y multi | 1.40 | .90 |
| Z510 | 80y multi | 1.40 | .90 |
| a. | ZA460 Pair, #Z509-Z510 | 3.00 | 3.00 |

Grand Fireworks of Nagaoka (Niigata) ZA461

**2001, July 23**
| | | | |
|---|---|---|---|
| Z511 | 50y yel & multi | .90 | .50 |
| Z512 | 50y pink & multi | .90 | .50 |
| a. | ZA461 Pair, #Z511-Z512 | 1.90 | 1.90 |
| b. | Pane, 5 #Z512a | 9.50 | |

Poplars (Hokkaido) ZA462

Statue, Sheep (Hokkaido) ZA463

**2001, Sept. 3** Litho. *Perf. 13¼*
| | | | |
|---|---|---|---|
| Z513 | ZA462 80y multi | 1.40 | .90 |
| Z514 | ZA463 80y multi | 1.40 | .90 |
| a. | Pane, 5 each #Z513-Z514 | 15.00 | |

56th Natl. Athletic Meets (Miyagi) — ZA464

**2001, Sept. 7** Photo.
| | | | |
|---|---|---|---|
| Z515 | ZA464 50y multi | .90 | .50 |
| a. | Pane of 10 | 9.50 | |

Matsuyama Castle, Masaoki Shiki (1867-1902), Poet (Ehime) ZA465

**2001, Sept. 12**
| | | | |
|---|---|---|---|
| Z516 | 50y Castle | .90 | .50 |
| Z517 | 50y Poet | .90 | .50 |
| *a.* | ZA465 Horiz. pair, #Z516-Z517 | 1.90 | 1.90 |

Ibi Traditions (Gifu) ZA466

Designs: No. Z518, Tanigumi-Odori dance. No. Z519, Train, persimmons.

**2001, Sept. 28　Photo.　Perf. 13¼**
| | | | |
|---|---|---|---|
| Z518 | 50y multi | .90 | .50 |
| Z519 | 50y multi | .90 | .50 |
| *a.* | ZA466 Horiz. pair, #Z518-Z519 | 1.90 | 1.90 |
| *b.* | Pane, 5 #Z519a | 9.50 | |

Kamakura Igloo (Akita) — ZA467

**2001, Oct. 1　　　　　Litho.**
| | | | |
|---|---|---|---|
| Z520 | ZA467 80y multi | 1.40 | .90 |
| *a.* | Pane of 10 | 15.00 | |

9th Intl. Conference on Lake Conservation & Management (Shiga) — ZA468

**2001, Oct. 1**
| | | | |
|---|---|---|---|
| Z521 | ZA468 50y multi | .90 | .50 |
| *a.* | Pane of 10 | 9.50 | |

World Indoor Cycling Championships (Kagoshima) — ZA469

**2001, Oct. 1**
| | | | |
|---|---|---|---|
| Z522 | ZA469 80y multi | 1.40 | .90 |

Okuma Auditorium, Waseda University (Tokyo) — ZA470

**2001, Oct. 19**
| | | | |
|---|---|---|---|
| Z523 | ZA470 80y multi | 1.40 | .90 |
| *a.* | Pane of 10 | 15.00 | |

Wild Narcissi (Fukui) ZA471

Echizen Coast and Wild Narcissi (Fukui) ZA472

**2001, Nov. 6**
| | | | |
|---|---|---|---|
| Z524 | ZA471 50y multi | .90 | .50 |
| *a.* | Pane of 10 | 9.50 | |
| Z525 | ZA472 80y multi | 1.40 | .90 |
| *a.* | Pane of 10 | 15.00 | |

Tokyo Millenalio (Tokyo) — ZA473

**2001, Dec. 3　　　　　Photo.**
| | | | |
|---|---|---|---|
| Z526 | ZA473 80y multi | 1.40 | .90 |
| *a.* | Pane of 10 | 15.00 | |

Ezo Flying Squirrels (Hokkaido) — ZA474

**2002, Feb. 5**
| | | | |
|---|---|---|---|
| Z527 | ZA474 80y multi | 1.40 | .90 |

Scenes North of Hiroshima (Hiroshima) ZA475

Designs: No. Z528, Nukui Dam. No. Z529, On-bashi Bridge.

**2002, Feb. 22　　　　Litho.**
| | | | |
|---|---|---|---|
| Z528 | 80y multi | 1.40 | .90 |
| Z529 | 80y multi | 1.40 | .90 |
| *a.* | ZA475 Horiz. pair, #Z528-Z529 | 3.00 | 3.00 |

Azaleas (Wakayama) — ZA476

**2002, Mar. 1　Photo.　Perf. 13¼**
| | | | |
|---|---|---|---|
| Z530 | ZA476 80y multi | 1.40 | .90 |

Glover Garden (Nagasaki) ZA477

Designs: No. Z531, Houses, fountain, roses. No. Z532, House, tulips.

**2002, Mar. 1　　　　　Litho.**
| | | | |
|---|---|---|---|
| Z531 | 50y multi | .90 | .50 |
| Z532 | 50y multi | .90 | .50 |
| *a.* | ZA477 Horiz. pair, #Z531-Z532 | 1.90 | 1.90 |

Cherry Blossoms, Hiikawa River (Shimane) ZA478

Cherry Blossoms, Bicchu-Kokubunji Temple (Okayama) ZA479

**2002, Mar. 18**
| | | | |
|---|---|---|---|
| Z533 | ZA478 50y multi | .90 | .50 |
| Z534 | ZA479 50y multi | .90 | .50 |
| *a.* | Horiz. pair, #Z533-Z534 | 1.90 | 1.90 |
| *b.* | Pane, 5 #Z534a | 9.50 | — |

Tangerine, Sata Cape (Ehime) ZA480

Citrus Fruit, Mt. Tsurugisan (Tokushima) ZA481

Bayberry, Tengu Highlands (Kochi) ZA482

Olives, Shodo Island (Kagawa) ZA483

**2002, Mar. 20　　　　Photo.**
| | | | |
|---|---|---|---|
| Z535 | ZA480 50y multi | .90 | .50 |
| Z536 | ZA481 50y multi | .90 | .50 |
| Z537 | ZA482 50y multi | .90 | .50 |
| Z538 | ZA483 50y multi | .90 | .50 |
| *a.* | Horiz. strip of 4, #Z535-Z538 | 4.00 | 4.00 |

Flowers (Hokkaido) ZA484

No. Z539, Tulips, windmills. No. Z540, Sunflowers, field.

**2002, Apr. 25　　　　Litho.**
| | | | |
|---|---|---|---|
| Z539 | 80y multicolored | 1.40 | .90 |
| Z540 | 80y multicolored | 1.40 | .90 |
| *a.* | ZA484 Horiz. pair, #Z539-Z540 | 3.00 | 3.00 |

54th Intl. Whaling Commission (Yamaguchi) — ZA485

**2002, Apr. 25**
| | | | |
|---|---|---|---|
| Z541 | ZA485 80y multi | 1.40 | .90 |

Bonsai Village (Saitama) — ZA486

**2002, Apr. 26　　　　Photo.**
| | | | |
|---|---|---|---|
| Z542 | ZA486 80y multi | 1.40 | .90 |

Yokohama (Kanagawa) ZA487

Designs: No. Z543, Sailing ships. No. Z544, Modern ship, skyline, woman.

**2002, May 1**
| | | | |
|---|---|---|---|
| Z543 | 50y multi | .90 | .50 |
| Z544 | 50y multi | .90 | .50 |
| *a.* | ZA487 Horiz. pair, #Z543-Z544 | 1.90 | 1.90 |
| *b.* | Pane, 5 #Z544a | 9.50 | |

Flowers (Niigata) ZA488

Designs: No. Z545, Red camellias. No. Z546, Yellow daylilies. No. Z547, Purple and pink irises. No. Z548, Pink iwakagami flowers.

**2002, May 1　　　　　Litho.**
| | | | |
|---|---|---|---|
| Z545 | 50y multi | .90 | .50 |
| Z546 | 50y multi | .90 | .50 |
| Z547 | 50y multi | .90 | .50 |
| Z548 | 50y multi | .90 | .50 |
| *a.* | ZA488 Horiz. strip of 4, #Z545-Z548 | 4.00 | 4.00 |

See Nos. 3909-3912.

Natl. Afforestation Campaign (Yamagata) — ZA489

**2002, May 31　　　　Photo.**
| | | | |
|---|---|---|---|
| Z549 | ZA489 50y multi | .90 | .50 |
| *a.* | Pane of 10 | 9.50 | — |

Oze (Fukushima) ZA490

Designs: No. Z550, Flowers, bare trees, walkway. No. Z551, Flowers, evergreens.

**2002, June 28　　　　Litho.**
| | | | |
|---|---|---|---|
| Z550 | 50y multi | .90 | .50 |
| Z551 | 50y multi | .90 | .50 |
| *a.* | ZA490 Horiz. pair, #Z550-Z551 | 1.90 | 1.90 |

Mt. Tanigawadake (Gunma) ZA491

Mountains and: No. Z552, Rhododendrons. No. Z553, Trees in autumn.

**2002, June 28**
| | | | |
|---|---|---|---|
| Z552 | 80y multi | 1.40 | .90 |
| Z553 | 80y multi | 1.40 | .90 |
| *a.* | ZA491 Horiz. pair, #Z552-Z553 | 3.00 | 3.00 |

Tokyo Fair and Market (Tokyo) ZA492

Designs: No. Z554, Morning Glory Fair. No. Z555, Hozuki Fair.

**2002, June 28　　　　Photo.**
| | | | |
|---|---|---|---|
| Z554 | 80y multi | 1.40 | .90 |
| Z555 | 80y multi | 1.40 | .90 |
| *a.* | ZA492 Horiz. pair, #Z554-Z555 | 3.00 | 3.00 |

Alpine Flora (Ishikawa) — ZA493

**2002, July 1　　　Flower Color**
| | | | |
|---|---|---|---|
| Z556 | 50y Purple | .90 | .50 |
| Z557 | 50y Brown | .90 | .50 |
| Z558 | 50y Bright pink | .90 | .50 |
| Z559 | 50y White | .90 | .50 |
| *a.* | ZA493 Horiz. strip of 4, #Z556-Z559 | 4.00 | 4.00 |

Gujou-odori Dance (Gifu) — ZA494

**2002, July 1**
| | | | |
|---|---|---|---|
| Z560 | ZA494 50y multi | .90 | .50 |

85th Lions Club Intl. Convention (Osaka) — ZA495

**2002, July 1**
Z561 ZA495 80y multi     1.40 .90

23rd Asia-Pacific Scout Jamboree (Osaka) — ZA496

**2002, July 15**
Z562 ZA496 50y multi     .90 .50

Yachiyoza Theater (Kumamoto) — ZA497

**2002, July 15**     **Litho.**
Z563 ZA497 80y multi     1.40 .90

Hikan-zakura, Iejima (Okinawa) ZA498

Hibiscus, Kaichudouro Highway (Okinawa) ZA499

Bougainvillea, House in Tsuboya (Okinawa) ZA500

Lily, Higashihennazaki (Okinawa) ZA501

Seishika Flower, Seishika Bridge (Okinawa) — ZA502

**2002, Aug. 23**     **Photo.**     **Perf. 13¼**
Z564 ZA498 50y multi     .90 .50
Z565 ZA499 50y multi     .90 .50
Z566 ZA500 50y multi     .90 .50
Z567 ZA501 50y multi     .90 .50
Z568 ZA502 50y multi     .90 .50
   *a.*    Vert. strip of 5, #Z564-Z568     4.75 4.75
Printed in sheets containing two No. Z568a.

Flora (Tokyo) ZA503

Designs: No. Z569, Azalea (pink flower, blue denomination). No. Z570, Lily. No. Z571, Crape myrtle (pink flower and denomination). No. Z572, Ginkgo leaves.

**2002, Sept. 2**
Z569 50y multi     .90 .50
Z570 50y multi     .90 .50
Z571 50y multi     .90 .50
Z572 50y multi     .90 .50
   *a.*   ZA503 Horiz. strip of 4, #Z569-Z572     4.00 4.00

57th Natl. Athletic Meet (Kochi) — ZA504

**2002, Sept. 5**
Z573 ZA504 50y multi     .90 .50

Iga-Ueno (Mie) ZA505

Designs: No. Z574, Basho Matsuo, Iga-Ueno Castle. No. Z575, Iga-Ueno Castle, Haisei-den Hall.

**2002, Sept. 10**     **Litho.**
Z574 80y multi     1.40 .90
Z575 80y multi     1.40 .90
   *a.*   ZA505 Horiz. pair, #Z574-Z575     3.00 3.00

Tohoku's Four Season Story (Aomori) — ZA506

**2002, Oct. 23**     **Photo.**     **Perf. 13¼**
Z576 ZA506 80y multi     1.40 .90

Fifth Winter Asian Games (Aomori) — ZA507

**2003, Jan. 24**     **Photo.**     **Perf. 13¼**
Z577 ZA507 50y multi     1.40 .90

Nobeoka, City of Noh Theater (Miyazaki) ZA508

Designs: No. Z578, Actor on stage, audience. No. Z579, Actor with red kimono.

**2003, Feb. 3**
Z578 80y multi     1.40 .90
Z579 80y multi     1.40 .90
   *a.*   ZA508 Horiz. pair, #Z578-Z579     3.00 3.00

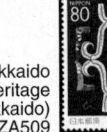

Hokkaido Heritage (Hokkaido) ZA509

**2003, Feb. 5**     **Photo.**     **Perf. 13¼**
Z580 80y Ainu design     1.40 .90
Z581 80y Lake Mashuko     1.40 .90
   *a.*   ZA509 Horiz. pair, #Z580-Z581     3.00 3.00

Flora (Nagano) ZA510

Designs: No. Z582, Dogtooth violet (pink flowers) and mountain. No. Z583, Skunk cabbage (white flower). No. Z584, Nikko day lily (yellow flower). No. Z585, Cosmos (white, pink and red flowers).

**2003, Mar. 5**     **Photo.**     **Perf. 13¼**
Z582 50y multi     .85 .50
Z583 50y multi     .85 .50
Z584 50y multi     .85 .50
Z585 50y multi     .85 .50
   *a.*   ZA510 Horiz. strip of 4, #Z582-Z585     3.50 3.50

See Nos. 3871-3874.

Kibitsu Shrine (Okayama) — ZA511

**2003, Mar. 5**
Z586 ZA511 80y multi     1.40 .90

Kompira-Ohshibai Theater (Kagawa) — ZA512

**2003, Mar. 24**     **Litho.**
Z587 ZA512 80y multi     1.40 .90

Imari-Arita Ceramics (Saga) — ZA513

**2003, Apr. 10**
Z588 ZA513 80y multi     1.40 .90

Kaneko Misuzu and Poem "Tairyo" (Yamaguchi) ZA514

**2003, Apr. 11**     **Photo.**
Z589 80y Misuzu     1.40 .90
Z590 80y Poem     1.40 .90
   *a.*   ZA514 Horiz. pair, #Z589-Z590     2.80 2.80

Cormorant Fishing and Gifu Castle (Gifu) ZA515

**2003, May 1**     **Perf. 13¼**
Z591 50y Fishermen     .85 .50
Z592 50y Castle     .85 .50
   *a.*   ZA515 Horiz. pair, #Z591-Z592     1.75 1.75

Traditional Events (Kyoto) — ZA516

Designs: No. Z593, Aoi-matsuri (wagon decorated with flowers). No. Z594, Gion-matsuri festival float (tower on wheels). No. Z595, Okuribi (fire on mountain). No. Z596, Jidai-matsuri (parade procession).

**2003, May 1**     **Litho.**
Z593 50y multi     .85 .50
Z594 50y multi     .85 .50
Z595 50y multi     .85 .50
Z596 50y multi     .85 .50
   *a.*   ZA516 Horiz. strip of 4, #Z593-Z596     3.50 3.50

Natl. Afforestation Campaign (Chiba) — ZA517

**2003, May 16**     **Photo.**
Z597 ZA517 50y multi     .85 .50

Mt. Tsukuba and Iris (Ibaraki) — ZA518

**2003, May 20**     **Litho.**
Z598 ZA518 80y multi     1.40 .90

Tsurugajou Castle, Persimmons (Fukushima) — ZA519

**2003, July 1**     **Photo.**     **Perf. 13¼**
Z599 ZA519 80y multi     1.40 .90

Kyuya Fukada, Mountineer, Birth Cent. (Ishikawa) — ZA520

**2003, July 1**     **Litho.**
Z600 ZA520 80y multi     1.40 .90

Okinawa Urban Monorail (Okinawa) ZA521

**2003, Aug. 8**
Z601 50y Shurijo Castle     .85 .50
Z602 50y Naha Airport     .85 .50
   *a.*   ZA521 Horiz. pair, #Z601-Z602     1.75 1.75

58th Natl. Athletics Meets (Shizuoka) — ZA522

**2003, Aug. 29**     **Photo.**
Z603 ZA522 50y multi     .85 .65

Sweet Briar (Tokyo) ZA523

Wisterias (Tokyo) ZA524

Irises (Tokyo) ZA525

Tea Blossoms (Tokyo) ZA526

**2003, Sept. 1**
Z604 ZA523 50y multi     .85 .50
Z605 ZA524 50y multi     .85 .50
Z606 ZA525 50y multi     .85 .50
Z607 ZA526 50y multi     .85 .50
   *a.*   Horiz. strip, #Z604-Z607     3.50 3.50

Chiyojo, Haiku Poet (Ishikawa) ZA527

**2003, Oct. 3**     **Litho.**
Z608   80y   Haiku text    1.40   .90
Z609   80y   Chiyojo      1.40   .90
   *a.*   ZA527 Horiz. pair, #Z608-Z609   3.00   3.00

Yasujiro Ozu (1903-63),
Film Director
(Mie) — ZA528

**2003, Oct. 23**       **Photo.**
Z610   ZA528 80y multi     1.40   .90

Kiritappu
Wetland
and Wakka
Primeval
Garden
(Hokkaido)
ZA529

**2004, Feb. 5**   **Litho.**   *Perf. 13¼*
Z611   80y   Yellow flowers    1.40   .90
Z612   80y   Orange flowers   1.40   .90
   *a.*   ZA529 Horiz. pair, #Z611-Z612   3.00   3.00

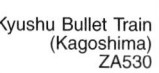

Kyushu Bullet Train
(Kagoshima)
ZA530

**2004, Mar. 12**   **Photo.**   *Perf. 13¼*
Z613   ZA530 50y multi      .90   .65

### Flower Types of 1990
Designs as before.

**2004, Mar. 19**
Z614   ZA24 50y multi      .90   .50
Z615   ZA25 50y multi      .90   .50
Z616   ZA26 50y multi      .90   .50
Z617   ZA27 50y multi      .90   .50
Z618   ZA28 50y multi      .90   .50
Z619   ZA29 50y multi      .90   .50
   *Nos. Z614-Z619 (6)*     5.40   3.00

Zuiryuji Temple
(Toyama) — ZA531

**2004, Mar. 19**      **Litho.**
Z620   ZA531 80y multi     1.40   .90

Hana-Kairou Flower
Park (Tottori) — ZA532

**2004, Mar. 23**
Z621   ZA532 80y multi     1.40   .90

Gerbera
(Shizuoka)
ZA533

Carnation
(Shizuoka)
ZA534

Rose
(Shizuoka)
ZA535

Lisianthus
(Shizuoka)
ZA536

---

**2004, Apr. 8**
Z622   ZA533 80y multi     1.40   .90
Z623   ZA534 80y multi     1.40   .90
Z624   ZA535 80y multi     1.40   .90
Z625   ZA536 80y multi     1.40   .90
   *a.*   Horiz. strip of 4, #Z622-Z625   6.00   6.00
     Pacific Flora 2004.

National Afforestation
Campaign
(Miyazaki) — ZA537

**2004, Mar. 23**       **Photo.**
Z626   ZA537 50y multi      .90   .50

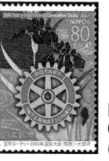

Murouji's Five Story
Pagoda (Nara) — ZA538

**2004, Apr. 26**
Z627   ZA538 80y multi     1.40   .90

Rotary International
Convention
(Osaka) — ZA539

**2004, May 21**
Z628   ZA539 80y multi     1.40   .90

Ice Breaker Garinko-go,
Steller's Sea Eagle
(Hokkaido) — ZA540

**2004, May 28**
Z629   ZA540 80y multi     1.40   .90

Kanto
Festival
Performer,
Namahage
(Akita)
ZA541

**2004, June 1**      **Litho.**
Z630   50y blue & multi     .90   .50
Z631   50y red & multi      .90   .50
   *a.*   ZA541 Horiz. pair, #Z630-Z631   1.80   1.80
     Akita City, 400th anniv.

Magnolia
(Tokyo)
ZA542

Azalea
(Tokyo)
ZA543

Wildflower
(Tokyo)
ZA544

Bush Clover
(Tokyo)
ZA545

**2004, June 1**       **Photo.**
Z632   ZA542 50y multi      .90   .50
Z633   ZA543 50y multi      .90   .50
Z634   ZA544 50y multi      .90   .50
Z635   ZA545 50y multi      .90   .50
   *a.*   Horiz. strip of 4, #Z632-Z635   3.75   3.75

---

Roses and
Buildings
(Kanagawa)
ZA546

Gold-
banded Lily
and
Buildings
(Kanagawa)
ZA547

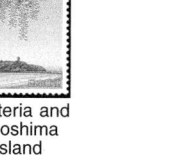

Wisteria and
Enoshima
Island
(Kanagawa)
ZA548

Hydrangea
and Lake
Ashinoko
(Kanagawa)
ZA549

**2004, June 1**
Z636   ZA546 50y multi      .90   .50
Z637   ZA547 50y multi      .90   .50
Z638   ZA548 50y multi      .90   .50
Z639   ZA549 50y multi      .90   .50
   *a.*   Horiz. strip of 4, #Z636-Z639   3.75   3.75

Daimyo
Processions
of Lord
Takachika
Mouri
(Yamaguchi)
ZA550

**2004, June 21**      **Litho.**
Z640   80y red & multi     1.40   .90
Z641   80y green & multi    1.40   .90
   *a.*   ZA550 Horiz. pair, #Z640-Z641   3.00   3.00

Rose, Mt.
Tsukubasan
(Ibaraki)
ZA551

Yashio-
tsutsuji and
Lake
Chuzenjiko
(Tochigi)
ZA552

Renge-
tsutsuji and
Mt. Akagisan
(Gunma)
ZA553

Primrose
and
Tajimagahara
Native
Primrose
Field
(Saitama)
ZA554

Rape Blossoms and
Nojimazaki Lighthouse
(Chiba) — ZA555

**2004, June 23**       **Photo.**
Z642   ZA551 50y multi      .90   .50
Z643   ZA552 50y multi      .90   .50
Z644   ZA553 50y multi      .90   .50
Z645   ZA554 50y multi      .90   .50
Z646   ZA555 50y multi      .90   .50
   *a.*   Vert. strip of 5, #Z642-Z646   4.75   4.75

---

Owara
Dance
(Toyama)
ZA556

Designs: No. Z647, Children. No. Z648,
Dancers in pink kimonos. No. Z649, Dancers
in black clothes. No. Z650, Dancers in blue
kimonos.

**2004, Aug. 20**       **Litho.**
Z647   50y multi      .90   .50
Z648   50y multi      .90   .50
Z649   50y multi      .90   .50
Z650   50y multi      .90   .50
   *a.*   ZA556 Horiz. strip of 4, #Z647-Z650   3.75   3.75

59th National Athletic
Meets
(Saitama) — ZA557

**2004, Sept. 10**   **Photo.**   *Perf. 13¼*
Z651   ZA557 50y multi      .90   .50

### Miniature Sheet

88
Temples
(Shikoku)
ZA558

No. Z652: a, Ryozenji (Temple 1). b,
Gokurakuji (Temple 2). c, Konsenji (Temple 3).
d, Dainchiji (Temple 4). e, Tatsueji (Temple
19). f, Kakurinji (Temple 20). g, Tairyuji (Temple 21). h, Byoudouji (Temple 22). i, Iwamotoji
(Temple 37). j, Kongoufukuji (Temple 38). k,
Enkouji (Temple 39). l, Kanjizaiji (Temple 40).
m, Nankoubou (Temple 55). n, Taizanji (Temple 56). o, Eifukuji (Temple 57). p, Senyuji
(Temple 58). q, Shusshakaji (Temple 73). r,
Kouyamaji (Temple 74). s, Zentsuji (Temple
75). t, Kouzouji (Temple 76).

**2004, Nov. 5**
Z652   ZA558   Sheet of 20   30.00   30.00
   *a.-t.*   80y Any single     1.40   .90

Temple numbers are found in the first group
of small Japanese characters on each stamp.
The numbers used are the same as those
found under "China" in the Illustrated Identifier
at the back of the book. The left and right
Japanese characters in this first group of small
characters, which ranges from 3 to 5 characters in length, are the same on each stamp.
The characters between these two constant
characters represent the temple number. As
there is no character for zero, the number "20"
will show the character for "2" (=) to the left of
the character for "10" (+). Numbers 11-19 will
have the unit's character to the right of the
character for "10." Thus, the numbers "12" and
"20" will have the same characters, just in a
different order. Two-digit numbers beginning
with 21 that are not divisible by 10 will be three
characters long. Number 21, as an example,
will show the characters for "2," "10," and "1"
reading from left to right ( = + - ).

National Theater
(Okinawa) — ZA559

**2005, Jan. 21**   **Litho.**   *Perf. 13¼*
Z653   ZA559 50y multi      .90   .50

Apple
Blossoms
(Nagano)
ZA560

Renge
Azalea
(Nagano)
ZA561

Lily of the
Valley
(Nagano)
ZA562

Gentian
(Nagano)
ZA563

**2005, Apr. 1        Litho.        Perf. 13¼**

| | | | | |
|---|---|---|---|---|
| Z654 | ZA560 | 50y multi | .90 | .50 |
| Z655 | ZA561 | 50y multi | .90 | .50 |
| Z656 | ZA562 | 50y multi | .90 | .50 |
| Z657 | ZA563 | 50y multi | .90 | .50 |
| a. | Horiz. strip of 4, #Z654-Z657 | | 3.75 | 3.75 |

Tulip
(Toyama,
Ishikawa,
Fukui)
ZA564

Hydrangea
(Toyama,
Ishikawa,
Fukui)
ZA565

Rhododendron
(Toyama,
Ishikawa,
Fukui)
ZA566

Lily (Toyama,
Ishikawa,
Fukui)
ZA567

**2005, Apr. 1**

| | | | | |
|---|---|---|---|---|
| Z658 | ZA564 | 50y multi | .90 | .50 |
| Z659 | ZA565 | 50y multi | .90 | .50 |
| Z660 | ZA566 | 50y multi | .90 | .50 |
| Z661 | ZA567 | 50y multi | .90 | .50 |
| a. | Horiz. strip of 4, #Z658-Z661 | | 3.75 | 3.75 |

Peace
Memorial
Park
(Hiroshima)
ZA568

Designs: No. Z662, Birds, Cenotaph for
Atomic Bomb Victims. No. Z663, Fountains,
Hiroshima Peace Memorial Museum.

**2005, Apr. 22**

| | | | |
|---|---|---|---|
| Z662 | 50y multi | .90 | .50 |
| Z663 | 50y multi | .90 | .50 |
| a. | ZA568 Horiz. pair, #Z662-Z663 | 1.90 | 1.90 |

Sweetbrier
(Hokkaido)
ZA569

Lavender
(Hokkaido)
ZA570

Cowslip
(Hokkaido)
ZA571

Lily of the
Valley
(Hokkaido)
ZA572

**2005, Apr. 26**

| | | | | |
|---|---|---|---|---|
| Z664 | ZA569 | 50y multi | .90 | .50 |
| Z665 | ZA570 | 50y multi | .90 | .50 |
| Z666 | ZA571 | 50y multi | .90 | .50 |
| Z667 | ZA572 | 50y multi | .90 | .50 |
| a. | Horiz. strip of 4, #Z664-Z667 | | 3.75 | 3.75 |

See Nos. 3917-3920.

Momordica Charantia
(Okinawa) — ZA573

**2005, May 6**

| | | | | |
|---|---|---|---|---|
| Z668 | ZA573 | 50y multi | | .90 | .50 |

Sunflower,
Mt.
Yatsugatake
(Yamanashi)
ZA574

Gentian, Mt.
Kitadake
(Yamanashi)
ZA575

Evening
Primrose,
Mt. Fuji
(Yamanashi)
ZA576

Lady's
Slipper, Mt.
Fuji
(Yamanashi)
ZA577

**2005, May 16        Litho.        Perf. 13¼**

| | | | | |
|---|---|---|---|---|
| Z669 | ZA574 | 80y multi | 1.40 | .90 |
| Z670 | ZA575 | 80y multi | 1.40 | .90 |
| Z671 | ZA576 | 80y multi | 1.40 | .90 |
| Z672 | ZA577 | 80y multi | 1.40 | .90 |
| a. | Horiz. strip of 4, #Z669-Z672 | | 6.00 | 6.00 |

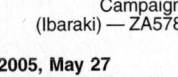

National Afforestation
Campaign
(Ibaraki) — ZA578

**2005, May 27        Photo.**

| | | | | |
|---|---|---|---|---|
| Z673 | ZA578 | 50y multi | | .90 | .50 |

Orchid
(Tokyo)
ZA579

Crinum
(Tokyo)
ZA580

Kerria
(Tokyo)
ZA581

Azalea
(Tokyo)
ZA582

**2005, June 1**

| | | | | |
|---|---|---|---|---|
| Z674 | ZA579 | 50y multi | .90 | .50 |
| Z675 | ZA580 | 50y multi | .90 | .50 |
| Z676 | ZA581 | 50y multi | .90 | .50 |
| Z677 | ZA582 | 50y multi | .90 | .50 |
| a. | Horiz. strip of 4, #Z674-Z677 | | 3.75 | 3.75 |

Une,
Dazaifu-
Tenmangu
(Fukuoka)
ZA583

Cherry
Blossoms,
Kanmon
Bridge
(Fukuoka)
ZA584

Camphor
Blossoms,
Ariake Sea
(Saga)
ZA585

Azaleas, Mt.
Fugendake
(Nagasaki)
ZA586

Tulips, Huis
Ten Bosch
(Nagasaki)
ZA587

Gentians,
Mt. Aso
(Kumamoto)
ZA588

Bungo-ume,
Mt. Takasaki
(Oita)
ZA589

Crinums,
Nichinan
Beach
(Miyazaki)
ZA590

Azaleas,
Kirishima
Mountains
(Kagoshima)
ZA591

Hibiscus,
Screw Pine
(Kagoshima)
ZA592

**2005, June 1**

| | | | | |
|---|---|---|---|---|
| Z678 | ZA583 | 50y multi | .90 | .50 |
| Z679 | ZA584 | 50y multi | .90 | .50 |
| Z680 | ZA585 | 50y multi | .90 | .50 |
| Z681 | ZA586 | 50y multi | .90 | .50 |
| Z682 | ZA587 | 50y multi | .90 | .50 |
| Z683 | ZA588 | 50y multi | .90 | .50 |
| Z684 | ZA589 | 50y multi | .90 | .50 |
| Z685 | ZA590 | 50y multi | .90 | .50 |
| Z686 | ZA591 | 50y multi | .90 | .50 |
| Z687 | ZA592 | 50y multi | .90 | .50 |
| a. | Block of 10, #Z678-Z687 | | 9.50 | 9.50 |

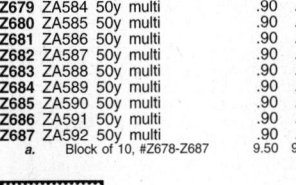

Reintroduction of
Oriental White Stork
(Hyogo) — ZA593

**2005, June 6        Litho.**

| | | | | |
|---|---|---|---|---|
| Z688 | ZA593 | 80y multi | | 1.40 | .90 |

Azaleas,
Tsutsujigaoka
Park
(Gunma)
ZA594

Nikko Day
Lily, Kirifuri
Heights
(Tochigi)
ZA595

Sunflowers,
Hana-hotaru
(Chiba)
ZA596

Bush Clover,
Kairakuen
Garden
(Ibaraki)
ZA597

Allspice, Mt. Bukosan
(Saitama) — ZA598

**2005, June 23**

| | | | | |
|---|---|---|---|---|
| Z689 | ZA594 | 50y multi | .90 | .50 |
| Z690 | ZA595 | 50y multi | .90 | .50 |
| Z691 | ZA596 | 50y multi | .90 | .50 |
| Z692 | ZA597 | 50y multi | .90 | .50 |
| Z693 | ZA598 | 50y multi | .90 | .50 |
| a. | Vert. strip of 5, #Z689-Z693 | | 4.50 | 4.50 |

Apples
(Aomori)
ZA599

Apples
(Iwate)
ZA600

Cherries
(Yamagata)
ZA601

Peaches
(Fukushima)
ZA602

**2005, June 28        Litho.**

| | | | | |
|---|---|---|---|---|
| Z694 | ZA599 | 50y multi | .90 | .50 |
| Z695 | ZA600 | 50y multi | .90 | .50 |
| Z696 | ZA601 | 50y multi | .90 | .50 |
| Z697 | ZA602 | 50y multi | .90 | .50 |
| a. | Horiz. strip of 4, #Z694-Z697 | | 3.75 | 3.75 |

Miniature Sheet

88
Temples
(Shikoku)
ZA603

No. Z698: a, Zizouji (Temple 5). b, Anrakuji
(Temple 6). c, Juurakuji (Temple 7). d,
Kumadaniji (Temple 8). e, Yakuooji (Temple
23). f, Hotsumisakiji (Temple 24). g, Shinjouji
(Temple 25). h, Kongouchouji (Temple 26). i,
Ryukouji (Temple 41). j, Butsumokuji (Temple
42). k, Meisekiji (Temple 43). l, Daihouji (Tem-
ple 44). m, Kokubunji (Temple 59). n,
Yokomineji (Temple 60). o, Kouonji (Temple
61). p, Houjuji (Temple 62). q, Douryuji (Tem-
ple 77). r, Goushouji (Temple 78). s, Tennouji
(Temple 79). t, Kokubunji (Temple 80).

**2005, July 8        Photo.**

| | | | | |
|---|---|---|---|---|
| Z698 | ZA603 | Sheet of 20 | 30.00 | 30.00 |
| a.-t. | 80y Any single | | 1.40 | .90 |

See note under No. Z652 for information on
identifying temple numbers.

Swwtbriar, Old Shana Post Office (Hokkaido) ZA604

Sea Otter (Hokkaido) ZA605

Cherry Blossoms (Hokkaido) ZA606

Tufted Puffins (Hokkaido) ZA607

**2005, Aug. 22**

| | | | |
|---|---|---|---|
| Z699 | ZA604 80y multi | 1.40 | .90 |
| Z700 | ZA605 80y multi | 1.40 | .90 |
| Z701 | ZA606 80y multi | 1.40 | .90 |
| Z702 | ZA607 80y multi | 1.40 | .90 |
| *a.* | Horiz. strip of 4, #Z699-Z702 | 6.00 | 6.00 |

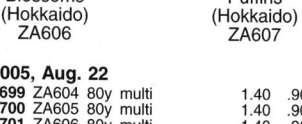
60th Natl. Athletic Meets (Okayama) — ZA608

**2005, Sept. 1**

| | | | |
|---|---|---|---|
| Z703 | ZA608 50y multi | .90 | .50 |

Kobe Luminarie (Hyogo) ZA609

**2005, Dec. 9**     **Litho.**

| | | | |
|---|---|---|---|
| Z704 | 50y Yellow denomination | .85 | .50 |
| Z705 | 50y Blue denomination | .85 | .50 |
| *a.* | ZA609 Horiz. pair, #Z704-Z705 | 1.75 | 1.75 |

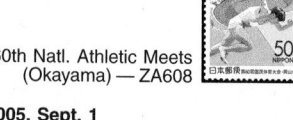
Kawazu Cherry Blossoms (Shizuoka) ZA610

**2006, Feb. 1**    **Photo.**    **Perf. 13¼**

| | | | |
|---|---|---|---|
| Z706 | 50y With bird | .85 | .50 |
| Z707 | 50y Without bird | .85 | .50 |
| *a.* | ZA610 Horiz. pair, #Z706-Z707 | 1.75 | 1.75 |

Japanese Characters (Fukui) ZA611

Maruoka Castle, Hills (Fukui) ZA612

Maruoka Castle, Clouds (Fukui) ZA613

Maruoka Castle, Sun (Fukui) ZA614

Maruoka Castle, Moon (Fukui) — ZA615

**2006, Apr. 3**     **Litho.**

| | | | |
|---|---|---|---|
| Z708 | ZA611 80y multi | 1.40 | .90 |
| Z709 | ZA612 80y multi | 1.40 | .90 |
| Z710 | ZA613 80y multi | 1.40 | .90 |
| Z711 | ZA614 80y multi | 1.40 | .90 |
| Z712 | ZA615 80y multi | 1.40 | .90 |
| *a.* | Horiz. strip of 4, #Z709-Z712 | 5.75 | 5.75 |
| | *Nos. Z708-Z712 (5)* | 7.00 | 4.50 |

Printed in sheets of 20 consisting of 12 No. ZA708, and 2 each Nos. Z709-Z712.

Primroses (Osaka) ZA616

Cherry Blossoms (Nara) ZA617

Wild Chrysanthemums (Hyogo) ZA618

Rhododendrons (Shiga) ZA619

Ume Blossoms (Wakayama) ZA620

Weeping Cherry Blossoms (Kyoto) ZA621

**2006, Apr. 3**

| | | | |
|---|---|---|---|
| Z713 | ZA616 50y multi | .85 | .50 |
| Z714 | ZA617 50y multi | .85 | .50 |
| Z715 | ZA618 50y multi | .85 | .50 |
| Z716 | ZA619 50y multi | .85 | .50 |
| Z717 | ZA620 50y multi | .85 | .50 |
| *a.* | Horiz. strip of 4, #Z714-Z717 | 3.50 | 3.50 |
| Z718 | ZA621 50y multi | .85 | .50 |
| | *Nos. Z713-Z718 (6)* | 5.10 | 3.00 |

Printed in sheets containing 4 each nos. Z713, Z718, 3 each Nos. Z714-Z717.

Pear Blossoms, Yumigahama Beach (Tottori) ZA622

Peonies, Hinomisaki Lighthouse (Shimane) ZA623

Peach Blossoms, Seto-oohashi Bridge (Okayama) ZA624

Scarlet Maple Leaves, Miyajima Shrine (Hiroshima) ZA625

Citron Blossoms, Oomi Island (Yamaguchi) — ZA626

**2006, May 1**     **Photo.**

| | | | |
|---|---|---|---|
| Z719 | ZA622 50y multi | .90 | .50 |
| Z720 | ZA623 50y multi | .90 | .50 |
| Z721 | ZA624 50y multi | .90 | .50 |
| Z722 | ZA625 50y multi | .90 | .50 |
| Z723 | ZA626 50y multi | .90 | .50 |
| *a.* | Vert. strip of 5, #Z719-Z723! | 4.50 | 4.50 |
| | *Nos. Z719-Z723 (5)* | 4.50 | 2.50 |

National Afforestation Campaign (Gifu) — ZA627

**2006, May 19**

| | | | |
|---|---|---|---|
| Z724 | ZA627 50y multi | .90 | .50 |

Mt. Echigo (Niigata, Nagano) ZA628

Mt. Asama (Niigata, Nagano) ZA630

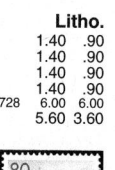
Sankayou Flowers (Niigata, Nagano) ZA629

Sakurasou Flowers (Niigata, Nagano) ZA631

**2006, June 1**     **Litho.**

| | | | |
|---|---|---|---|
| Z725 | ZA628 80y multi | 1.40 | .90 |
| Z726 | ZA629 80y multi | 1.40 | .90 |
| Z727 | ZA630 80y multi | 1.40 | .90 |
| Z728 | ZA631 80y multi | 1.40 | .90 |
| *a.* | Horiz. strip of 4, #Z725-Z728 | 6.00 | 6.00 |
| | *Nos. Z725-Z728 (4)* | 5.60 | 3.60 |

Daffodils, Nokonoshima Island (Fukuoka) ZA632

Bellflowers, Hirodai (Fukuoka) ZA633

Hydrangeas, Mikaerinotaki Falls (Saga) ZA634

Cosmos, Kujukushima Islands (Nagasaki) ZA635

Camellias, Amakusa Bridges (Kumamoto) ZA636

Flowers, Mt. Aso (Kumamoto) ZA637

Primroses, Mt. Yufudake (Oita) ZA638

Lavender, Kujurenzan (Oita) ZA639

Poppies, Mt. Hinamoridake (Miyazaki) ZA640

Nanohana, Mt. Kaimondake (Kagoshima) ZA641

**2006, June 1**     **Photo.**

| | | | |
|---|---|---|---|
| Z729 | ZA632 80y multi | 1.40 | .90 |
| Z730 | ZA633 80y multi | 1.40 | .90 |
| Z731 | ZA634 80y multi | 1.40 | .90 |
| Z732 | ZA635 80y multi | 1.40 | .90 |
| Z733 | ZA636 80y multi | 1.40 | .90 |
| Z734 | ZA637 80y multi | 1.40 | .90 |
| Z735 | ZA638 80y multi | 1.40 | .90 |
| Z736 | ZA639 80y multi | 1.40 | .90 |
| Z737 | ZA640 80y multi | 1.40 | .90 |
| Z738 | ZA641 80y multi | 1.40 | .90 |
| *a.* | Block of 10, #Z729-Z738 | 15.00 | 15.00 |
| | *Nos. Z729-Z738 (10)* | 14.00 | 9.00 |

Fox (Hokkaido) ZA642

Bears (Hokkaido) ZA643

Squirrel (Hokkaido) ZA644

Owl (Hokkaido) ZA645

**2006, June 3**

| | | | |
|---|---|---|---|
| Z739 | ZA642 50y multi | .90 | .50 |
| Z740 | ZA643 50y multi | .90 | .50 |
| Z741 | ZA644 50y multi | .90 | .50 |
| Z742 | ZA645 50y multi | .90 | .50 |
| *a.* | Horiz. strip of 4, #Z739-Z742 | 3.75 | 3.75 |
| | *Nos. Z739-Z742 (4)* | 3.60 | 2.00 |

Aomori Nebuta Festival (Aomori) ZA646

Akita Kanto Festival (Akita) ZA647

Yamagata
Hanagasa
Festival
(Yamagata)
ZA648

Sendai
Tanabata
Festival
(Miyagi)
ZA649

**2006, June 3** **Litho.**
Z743 ZA646 80y multi 1.40 .90
Z744 ZA647 80y multi 1.40 .90
Z745 ZA648 80y multi 1.40 .90
Z746 ZA649 80y multi 1.40 .90
a. Horiz. strip of 4, #Z743-Z746 5.75 5.75
Nos. Z743-Z746 (4) 5.60 3.60

Azaleas,
Eboshi-iwa,
Mt. Fuji
(Kanagawa)
ZA650

Daffodils,
Sakawagawa
River
(Kanagawa)
ZA651

Pinks,
Tanzawa
Mountains
(Kanagawa)
ZA652

Balloon
Flowers, Mt.
Fuji
(Kanagawa)
ZA653

**2006, Aug. 1** **Photo.**
Z747 ZA650 80y multi 1.40 .90
Z748 ZA651 80y multi 1.40 .90
Z749 ZA652 80y multi 1.40 .90
Z750 ZA653 80y multi 1.40 .90
a. Horiz. strip of 4, #Z747-Z750 5.75 5.75
Nos. Z747-Z750 (4) 5.60 3.60

**Miniature Sheet**

88
Temples
(Shikoku)
ZA654

No. Z751: a, Hourinji (Temple 9). b, Kirihata (Temple 10). c, Fujiidera (Temple 11). d, Shouzanji (Temple 12). e, Kounomineji (Temple 27). f, Dainichiji (Temple 28). g, Kokubunji (Temple 29). h, Zenrakuji (Temple 30). i, Iwayaji (Temple 45). j, Joururiji (Temple 46). k, Yasakaji (Temple 47). l, Sairinji (Temple 48). m, Kichijouji (Temple 63). n, Maegamiji (Temple 64). o, Sankakuji (Temple 65). p, Unbenji (Temple 66). q, Shiromineji (Temple 81). r, Negoroji (Temple 82). s, Ichinomiyaji (Temple 83). t, Yashimaji (Temple 84).

**2006, Aug. 1**
Z751 ZA654 Sheet of 20 28.00 28.00
a.-t. 80y Any single 1.40 .90

See note under No. Z652 for information on identifying temple numbers.

61st National Athletic
Meets (Hyogo) — ZA655

**2006, Sept. 1**
Z752 ZA655 50y multi .85 .50

Loquats,
Byobugaura
(Chiba)
ZA656

Umes,
Fukuroda
Waterfall
(Ibaraki)
ZA657

Apples, Oze
(Gunma)
ZA658

Japanese
Pears,
Nagatoro
(Saitama)
ZA659

Strawberries, Kegon
Waterfall
(Tochigi) — ZA660

**2006, Sept. 1**
Z753 ZA656 80y multi 1.40 .90
Z754 ZA657 80y multi 1.40 .90
Z755 ZA658 80y multi 1.40 .90
Z756 ZA659 80y multi 1.40 .90
Z757 ZA660 80y multi 1.40 .90
a. Vert. strip of 5, #Z753-Z757 7.00 7.00
Nos. Z753-Z757 (5) 7.00 4.50

Roses (Aichi) — ZA661

Chrysanthemums
(Aichi) — ZA662

Orchids
(Aichi)
ZA663

Cyclamen
(Aichi)
ZA664

**2006, Oct. 2** **Litho.**
Z758 ZA661 50y multi .85 .50
Z759 ZA662 50y multi .85 .50
Z760 ZA663 50y multi .85 .50
Z761 ZA664 50y multi .85 .50
a. Horiz. strip of 4, #Z758-Z761 3.50 3.50
Nos. Z758-Z761 (4) 3.40 2.00

Cherry
Blossoms,
Chidorigafuchi
(Tokyo)
ZA665

Roses,
Akasaka
Palace
(Tokyo)
ZA666

Cosmos,
Shouwa
Kinen Park
(Tokyo)
ZA667

Japanese
Apricot
Blossoms,
Yushima
Tenjin Shrine
(Tokyo)
ZA668

**2006, Oct. 2** **Photo.**
Z762 ZA665 80y multi 1.40 .90
Z763 ZA666 80y multi 1.40 .90
Z764 ZA667 80y multi 1.40 .90
Z765 ZA668 80y multi 1.40 .90
a. Horiz. strip of 4, #Z762-Z765 5.75 5.75
Nos. Z762-Z765 (4) 5.60 3.60

Iris,
Takeshima
(Aichi, Mie,
Gifu,
Shizuoka)
ZA669

Chinese
Milk Vetch,
Shirakawa
Village
(Aichi, Mie,
Gifu,
Shizuoka)
ZA670

Lily, Nagoya
Castle
(Aichi, Mie,
Gifu,
Shizuoka)
ZA671

Japanese
Iris, Couple
Rock (Aichi,
Mie, Gifu,
Shizuoka)
ZA672

Azalea, Jogasaki Coast
(Aichi, Mie, Gifu,
Shizuoka) — ZA673

**2007, Apr. 2** **Photo.** *Perf. 13¼*
Z766 ZA669 80y multi 1.40 .90
Z767 ZA670 80y multi 1.40 .90
Z768 ZA671 80y multi 1.40 .90
Z769 ZA672 80y multi 1.40 .90
Z770 ZA673 80y multi 1.40 .90
a. Vert. strip of 5, #Z766-Z770 7.00 7.00

Cherry
Blossom,
Yatsugatake
(Yamanashi)
ZA674

Grapes,
Katsunuma
Vineyard
(Yamanashi)
ZA675

Azalea,
Syosenkyo
(Yamanashi)
ZA676

Lavender,
Mt. Fuji
(Yamanashi)
ZA677

Peaches, Southern
Japanese Alps
(Yamanashi) — ZA678

**2007, Apr. 2**
Z771 ZA674 80y multi 1.40 .90
Z772 ZA675 80y multi 1.40 .90
Z773 ZA676 80y multi 1.40 .90
Z774 ZA677 80y multi 1.40 .90
Z775 ZA678 80y multi 1.40 .90
a. Vert. strip of 5, #Z771-Z775 7.00 7.00

Tulips
(Niigata)
ZA679

Rice
(Niigata)
ZA680

Pears
(Niigata)
ZA681

Mealy
Primrose
(Niigata)
ZA682

Iris (Niigata) — ZA683

**2007, Apr. 2** **Litho.**
Z776 ZA679 80y multi 1.40 .90
Z777 ZA680 80y multi 1.40 .90
Z778 ZA681 80y multi 1.40 .90
Z779 ZA682 80y multi 1.40 .90
Z780 ZA683 80y multi 1.40 .90
a. Vert. strip of 5, #Z776-Z780 7.00 7.00

Cherry
Blossom
(Saitama)
ZA684

Japanese
Rose
(Ibaraki)
ZA685

Skunk
Cabbage
(Gunma)
ZA686

Adder's
Tongue Lily
(Tochigi)
ZA687

Poppies
(Chiba) — ZA688

**2007, May 1**    Photo.    *Perf. 13¼*

| | | | | |
|---|---|---|---|---|
| Z781 | ZA684 | 50y multi | .85 | .50 |
| Z782 | ZA685 | 50y multi | .85 | .50 |
| Z783 | ZA686 | 50y multi | .85 | .50 |
| Z784 | ZA687 | 50y multi | .85 | .50 |
| Z785 | ZA688 | 50y multi | .85 | .50 |
| a. | | Vert. strip of 5, #Z781-Z785 | 4.25 | 4.25 |

For self-adhesives, see Nos. 3189B-3189F.

Mandarin Ducks (Tottori) ZA689

Swans (Shimane) ZA690

Pheasants (Okayama) ZA691

Red-throated Loons (Hiroshima) ZA692

Hooded Cranes (Yamaguchi) — ZA693

**2007, May 1**           Litho.

| | | | | |
|---|---|---|---|---|
| Z786 | ZA689 | 80y multi | 1.40 | .90 |
| Z787 | ZA690 | 80y multi | 1.40 | .90 |
| Z788 | ZA691 | 80y multi | 1.40 | .90 |
| Z789 | ZA692 | 80y multi | 1.40 | .90 |
| Z790 | ZA693 | 80y multi | 1.40 | .90 |
| a. | | Vert. strip of 5, #Z786-Z790 | 7.00 | 7.00 |

Japanese Cranes (Hokkaido) ZA694

Hokkaido Mountain Hares (Hokkaido) ZA695

Flying Squirrels (Hokkaido) ZA696

Hokkaido Deer (Hokkaido) ZA697

Spotted Seals (Hokkaido) — ZA698

**2007, May 1**           Litho.

| | | | | |
|---|---|---|---|---|
| Z791 | ZA694 | 80y multi | 1.40 | .90 |
| Z792 | ZA695 | 80y multi | 1.40 | .90 |
| Z793 | ZA696 | 80y multi | 1.40 | .90 |
| Z794 | ZA697 | 80y multi | 1.40 | .90 |
| Z795 | ZA698 | 80y multi | 1.40 | .90 |
| a. | | Horiz. strip of 5, #Z791-Z795 | 7.00 | 7.00 |

Koriyama Castle (Nara) ZA699

Hikone Castle (Shiga) ZA700

---

Himeji Castle (Hyogo) ZA701

Osaka Castle (Osaka) ZA702

Wakayama Castle (Wakayama) — ZA703

**2007, June 1**           Photo.

| | | | | |
|---|---|---|---|---|
| Z796 | ZA699 | 50y multi | .85 | .50 |
| Z797 | ZA700 | 50y multi | .85 | .50 |
| Z798 | ZA701 | 50y multi | .85 | .50 |
| Z799 | ZA702 | 50y multi | .85 | .50 |
| Z800 | ZA703 | 50y multi | .85 | .50 |
| a. | | Vert. strip of 5, #Z796-Z800 | 4.25 | 4.25 |

Whale Shark (Okinawa) ZA704

Longfin Bannerfish (Okinawa) ZA705

False Clownfish (Okinawa) ZA706

Blue Damselfish (Okinawa) ZA707

Manta Ray (Okinawa) — ZA708

**2007, June 1**           Photo.

| | | | | |
|---|---|---|---|---|
| Z801 | ZA704 | 80y multi | 1.40 | .90 |
| Z802 | ZA705 | 80y multi | 1.40 | .90 |
| Z803 | ZA706 | 80y multi | 1.40 | .90 |
| Z804 | ZA707 | 80y multi | 1.40 | .90 |
| Z805 | ZA708 | 80y multi | 1.40 | .90 |
| a. | | Horiz. strip of 5, #Z801-Z805 | 7.00 | 7.00 |

See Nos. 3929-3933.

National Afforestation Campaign (Hokkaido) — ZA709

**2007, June 22**      *Perf. 12½x12¾*

| | | | | |
|---|---|---|---|---|
| Z806 | ZA709 | 50y multi | .85 | .60 |

Dancers, Owara Wind Festival (Toyama) ZA710

Dancers, Owara Wind Festival (Toyama) ZA711

---

Dancers, Owara Wind Festival (Toyama) ZA712

Dancers, Owara Wind Festival (Toyama) ZA713

Dancers, Owara Wind Festival (Toyama) — ZA714

**2007, July 2**    Litho.    *Perf. 13¼*

| | | | | |
|---|---|---|---|---|
| Z807 | ZA710 | 80y multi | 1.40 | .90 |
| Z808 | ZA711 | 80y multi | 1.40 | .90 |
| Z809 | ZA712 | 80y multi | 1.40 | .90 |
| Z810 | ZA713 | 80y multi | 1.40 | .90 |
| Z811 | ZA714 | 80y multi | 1.40 | .90 |
| a. | | Vert. strip of 5, #Z807-Z811 | 7.00 | 7.00 |

See Nos. 3875-3879.

Tokyo Tower, Japanese Allspice (Tokyo) ZA715

Double Bridge, Chinese Violet Cress (Tokyo) ZA716

Meiji shrine Outer Garden, Sweet Olive (Tokyo) ZA717

Lake Okutama, Gentian (Tokyo) ZA718

Japan Bridge, Camellia (Tokyo) — ZA719

**2007, July 2**           Photo.

| | | | | |
|---|---|---|---|---|
| Z812 | ZA715 | 80y multi | 1.40 | .90 |
| Z813 | ZA716 | 80y multi | 1.40 | .90 |
| Z814 | ZA717 | 80y multi | 1.40 | .90 |
| Z815 | ZA718 | 80y multi | 1.40 | .90 |
| Z816 | ZA719 | 80y multi | 1.40 | .90 |
| a. | | Vert. strip of 5, #Z812-Z8161 | 7.00 | 7.00 |

Oirase Mountain Stream (Aomori) ZA720

Hirosaki Castle (Aomori) ZA721

Chuson Temple (Iwate) ZA722

Jodogahama (Iwate) ZA723

---

Matsushima (Miyagi) ZA724

Mt. Zao Crater Lake (Miyagi, Yamagata) ZA725

Oga Peninsula (Akita) ZA726

Mt. Chokai (Akita, Yamagata) ZA727

Oze (Fukushima) ZA728

Gassan Volcano (Yamagata) ZA729

**2007, July 2**

| | | | | |
|---|---|---|---|---|
| Z817 | | Sheet of 10 | 14.00 | 14.00 |
| a. | ZA720 | 80y multi | 1.40 | .90 |
| b. | ZA721 | 80y multi | 1.40 | .90 |
| c. | ZA722 | 80y multi | 1.40 | .90 |
| d. | ZA723 | 80y multi | 1.40 | .90 |
| e. | ZA724 | 80y multi | 1.40 | .90 |
| f. | ZA725 | 80y multi | 1.40 | .90 |
| g. | ZA726 | 80y multi | 1.40 | .90 |
| h. | ZA727 | 80y multi | 1.40 | .90 |
| i. | ZA728 | 80y multi | 1.40 | .90 |
| j. | ZA729 | 80y multi | 1.40 | .90 |

Main Tower, Kumamoto Castle, Cherry Blossoms (Kumamoto) ZA730

Uto Turret, Kumamoto Castle, in Summer (Kumamoto) ZA731

Main Tower, Kumamoto Castle, Gingko Trees (Kumamoto) ZA732

Uto Turret, Kumamoto Castle, in Winter (Kumamoto) ZA733

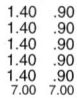

Three Towers, Kumamoto Castle (Kumamoto) — ZA734

**2007, Aug. 1**           Litho.

| | | | | |
|---|---|---|---|---|
| Z818 | ZA730 | 80y multi | 1.40 | .90 |
| Z819 | ZA731 | 80y multi | 1.40 | .90 |
| Z820 | ZA732 | 80y multi | 1.40 | .90 |
| Z821 | ZA733 | 80y multi | 1.40 | .90 |
| Z822 | ZA734 | 80y multi | 1.40 | .90 |
| a. | | Vert. strip of 5, #Z818-Z822 | 7.00 | 7.00 |

Edo Bridge from Japan Bridge, by Hiroshige (Tokyo) ZA735

Ohisa Takashima, by Utamaro (Tokyo) ZA736

Yaozo Ichikawa II as Bunzo Tanabe, by Sharaku (Tokyo) ZA737

Horikiri Irises, by Hiroshige (Tokyo) ZA738

Kinryuzan Temple, by Hiroshige (Tokyo) ZA739

Seven Women Applying Makeup Using a Full Length Mirror, by Utamaro (Tokyo) ZA740

Ryuzo Arashi II as Kinkichi Ishibe, Moneylender, by Sharaku (Tokyo) ZA741

Suido Bridge and Surugadai, by Hiroshige (Tokyo) ZA742

Moon Pine, Ueno Temple, by Hiroshige (Tokyo) ZA743

Hanaogi from Ogiya, No. 1 District, Edo Town, by Utamaro (Tokyo) ZA744

**2007, Aug. 1**

| Z823 | Sheet of 10 | 14.00 | 14.00 |
|---|---|---|---|
| a. | ZA735 80y multi | 1.40 | .90 |
| b. | ZA736 80y multi | 1.40 | .90 |
| c. | ZA737 80y multi | 1.40 | .90 |
| d. | ZA738 80y multi | 1.40 | .90 |
| e. | ZA739 80y multi | 1.40 | .90 |
| f. | ZA740 80y multi | 1.40 | .90 |
| g. | ZA741 80y multi | 1.40 | .90 |
| h. | ZA742 80y multi | 1.40 | .90 |
| i. | ZA743 80y multi | 1.40 | .90 |
| j. | ZA744 80y multi | 1.40 | .90 |

ZA745

88 Temples (Shikoku) ZA746

No. Z824: a, Dainchiji (Temple 13). b, Jorakuji (Temple 14). c, Kokubunji (Temple 15). d, Kanonji (Temple 16). e, Chikurinji (Temple 31). f, Zenjibuji (Temple 32). g, Sekkeiji (Temple 33). h, Tanemaji (Temple 34). i, Jodoji (Temple 49). j, Hantaji (Temple 50). k, Ishiteji (Temple 51). l, Taisanji (Temple 52). m, Daikoji (Temple 67). n, Jinnein (Temple 68). o, Kannonji (Temple 69). p, Motoyamaji (Temple 70). q, Yakuriji (Temple 85). r, Shidoji (Temple 86). s, Nagaoji (Temple 87). t, Okuboji (Temple 88).
No. Z825: a, Idoji (Temple 17). b, Onzanji (Temple 18). c, Kiyotakiji (Temple 35). d, Shoryuji (Temple 36). e, Emmyoji (Temple 53). f, Emmeiji (Temple 54). g, Iyadaniji (Temple 71). h, Mandaraji (Temple 72). i, Deities Cave (no temple number). j, Painting of Daishi Kobo (no temple number).

**2007, Aug. 1**    **Photo.**    **Perf. 13¼**

| Z824 | ZA745 | Sheet of 20 | 28.00 | 28.00 |
|---|---|---|---|---|
| a.-t. | | 80y Any single | 1.40 | .90 |
| Z825 | ZA746 | Sheet of 10 | 14.00 | 14.00 |
| a.-j. | | 80y Any single | 1.40 | .90 |

See note under No. Z652 for information on identifying temple numbers.

62nd National Athletic Meet (Akita) — ZA747

**2007, Sept. 3**      **Litho.**

| Z826 | ZA747 50y multi | .90 | .50 |
|---|---|---|---|

---

Miniature Sheet

Nagoya Port (Aichi) ZA748

No. Z827: a, Hibiscus and Antarctic survey. b, Hibiscus and Port Tower. c, Azaleas, killer whale at Nagoya Aquarium. d, Azaleas, dolphins at Nagoya Aquarium. e, Yellow chrysanthemums, Meiko Triton Bridge. f, Orange and yellow chrysanthemums, two bridges. g, Snapdragons and fireworks. h, Sailing ship and snapdragons. i, Azaleas, bridge, Nagoya Aquarium and half of Ferris wheel. j, Azaleas, Port Tower, Nagoya Castle, and half of Ferris wheel.

**2007, Nov. 5**    **Litho.**    **Perf. 13¼**

| Z827 | ZA748 | Sheet of 10 | 15.00 | 15.00 |
|---|---|---|---|---|
| a.-j. | | 80y Any single | 1.40 | .90 |

Beginning in 2008 the planning and design of prefecture stamps, previously done by regional postal authorities, was taken over by national postal authorities. The national authorities planned issues for 2008 that would be available in more of postal regions, thus making prefectural issues more nationwide and less local in scope. Additionally, the style of the "Nippon yubin" ideographic characters that had been used solely for prefecture stamps reverted to the style used on the national issues for most issues. Because of these changes, prefecture stamps will be listed in the regular postage listings starting with the 2008 issues.

---

**PREFECTURE SEMI-POSTAL STAMPS**

Earthquake and Volcano Eruption Refugee Relief (Tokyo) ZSP1

**2000, Nov. 15**      **Photo.**

| ZB1 | 80y +20y Pink ribbon | 1.75 | 1.25 |
|---|---|---|---|
| ZB2 | 80y +20y Blue ribbon | 1.75 | 1.25 |
| a. | ZSP1 Pair, #ZB1-ZB2 | 4.00 | 4.00 |

---

# SEMI-POSTAL STAMPS

Douglas Plane over Japan Alps — SP1

**Wmk. Zigzag Lines (141)**
**1937, June 1**    **Photo.**    **Perf. 13**

| B1 | SP1 2s + 2s rose carmine | 2.50 | 1.50 |
|---|---|---|---|
| B2 | SP1 3s + 2s purple | 2.50 | 2.00 |
| B3 | SP1 4s + 2s green | 3.00 | 1.50 |
| | Nos. B1-B3 (3) | 8.00 | 5.00 |
| | Set, never hinged | 13.00 | |

The surtax was for the Patriotic Aviation Fund to build civil airports.

Nos. 259 and 261 Surcharged in Blue or Red

**1942, Feb. 16**    **Wmk. 257**    **Perf. 13**

| B4 | A84 2s +1s crimson (Bl) | 1.25 | 2.50 |
|---|---|---|---|
| B5 | A86 4s +2s dk grn (R) | 1.25 | 2.50 |
| | Set, never hinged | 4.25 | |

Fall of Singapore to Japanese forces.

Tank Corps Attack, Bataan — SP2

Pearl Harbor Under Japanese Attack — SP3

**Unwmk.**
**1942, Dec. 8**    **Photo.**    **Perf. 12**

| B6 | SP2 2s +1s rose brown | 2.00 | 2.00 |
|---|---|---|---|
| B7 | SP3 5s +2s sapphire | 2.25 | 3.50 |
| | Set, never hinged | 7.00 | |

1st anniv. of the "Greater East Asia War." The surtax was for national defense.

> **Catalogue values for unused stamps in this section, from this point to the end of the section, are for Never Hinged items.**

SP4

**1947, Nov. 25   Wmk. 257   Perf. 12½**

| B8 | SP4 1.20y + 80s dk rose red | 2.00 | 2.00 |
|---|---|---|---|

Japan's 1st Community Chest drive. The surtax was for charitable purposes.

Nurse SP5

Bird Feeding Young SP6

**1948, Oct. 1**    **Unwmk.**    **Perf. 12½**

| B9 | SP5 5y + 2.50y bright red | 12.00 | 15.00 |
|---|---|---|---|
| B10 | SP6 5y + 2.50y emerald | 12.00 | 17.00 |

**Souvenir Sheet**
**Wmk. 257**
*Imperf*
**Without Gum**

| B11 | Sheet of 2 | 65.00 | 65.00 |
|---|---|---|---|

The surtax on Nos. B9-B11 was divided between the Red Cross and Community Chest organizations.
No. B11 contains Nos. B9-B10, imperf.

Javelin
Thrower — SP8

No. B13, Wrestlers. No. B14, Diver. No. B15, Water polo. No. B16, Woman gymnast. No. B17, Judo. No. B18, Fencing. No. B19, Basketball. No. B20, Rowing. No. B21, Sailing. No. B22, Boxing. No. B23, Volleyball. No. B24, Bicyclist. No. B25, Equestrian. No. B26, Field hockey. No. B27, Pistol shooting. No. B28, Modern pentathlon. No. B29, Weight lifter. No. B30, Women's kayak doubles. No. B31, Soccer.

**Perf. 13½**

**1961, Oct. 11     Unwmk.          Engr.**
B12 SP8 5y + 5y bister          1.00  1.50
B13 SP8 5y + 5y dk green        1.00  1.50
B14 SP8 5y + 5y carmine         1.00  1.50
  *a.*  Souvenir sheet of 3 ('64)  6.00  7.00

**1962, June 23**
B15 SP8 5y + 5y green            .65  1.25
B16 SP8 5y + 5y dk purple        .65  1.25
B17 SP8 5y + 5y dk carmine       .65  1.25
  *a.*  Souvenir sheet of 3 ('64)  4.00  5.00

**1962, Oct. 10**
B18 SP8 5y + 5y brick red        .55   .65
B19 SP8 5y + 5y slate grn        .55   .65
B20 SP8 5y + 5y violet           .55   .65
  *a.*  Souvenir sheet of 3 ('64)  3.00  4.00

**1963, June 23**
B21 SP8 5y + 5y blue             .55   .65
B22 SP8 5y + 5y dk brown         .55   .65
B23 SP8 5y + 5y brown            .55   .65
  *a.*  Souvenir sheet of 3 ('64)  6.50  7.50

**1963, Nov. 11**
B24 SP8 5y + 5y dk blue          .50   .50
B25 SP8 5y + 5y olive            .50   .50
B26 SP8 5y + 5y black            .50   .50
B27 SP8 5y + 5y claret           .50   .50
  *a.*  Souvenir sheet of 4 ('64)  6.50  7.50

**1964, June 23**
B28 SP8 5y + 5y bluish vio       .40   .40
B29 SP8 5y + 5y dp olive         .40   .40
B30 SP8 5y + 5y grnsh blue       .40   .40
B31 SP8 5y + 5y rose claret      .40   .40
  *a.*  Souvenir sheet of 4 ('64)  6.50  7.50
     Nos. B12-B31 (20)          11.85 15.75

Issued to raise funds for the 1964 Olympic Games in Tokyo.

The souvenir sheets were issued Aug. 20, 1964. Each contains one each of the stamps in the set it follows. Nos. B14a, B20a, B23a and B27a, exist imperf.

Cobalt Treatment Unit SP9

Early Cancer Detection with X-rays SP10

**1966, Oct. 21     Photo.      Perf. 13**
B32 SP9 7y + 3y yel org & blk    .25   .25
B33 SP10 5y + 5y multicolored    .40   .25

9th Intl. Anticancer Congress, Tokyo, Oct. 23-29. The surtax was for the fight against cancer and for research.

EXPO '70 Emblem and Globe SP11

Cherry Blossoms, Screen, Chishakuin Temple SP12

**1969, Mar. 15     Photo.      Perf. 13**
B34 SP11 15y + 5y bl, ocher & ver              .60   .60
B35 SP12 50y + 10y gold, brn & grn            1.25  1.25

Issued to publicize EXPO '70, International Exhibition, Osaka, 1970.

Ice Hockey, Sapporo Olympic Emblem — SP13

Design: No. B37, Ski jump and Sapporo Olympic Games emblem, vert.

**1971, Feb. 6      Photo.      Perf. 13**
B36 SP13 15y + 5y multi          .40   .25
B37 SP13 15y + 5y multi          .40   .25

To promote the 11th Winter Olympic Games, Sapporo, Japan, 1972.

Blue Dragon, East Wall — SP14

Murals from ancient tomb mound: No. B39, Two men, east wall, vert. 50y+10y, Four women, west wall, vert.

**1973, Mar. 26     Photo.      Perf. 13**
**Size: 48x27mm, 27x48mm**
B38 SP14 20y + 5y multi          .50   .40
B39 SP14 20y + 5y multi          .50   .40

**Photogravure and Engraved**
**Size: 33x48mm**
B40 SP14 20y + 10y multi        1.10  1.10
     Nos. B38-B40 (3)           2.10  1.90

Surtax was for restoration work on the murals of the Takamatsu-zuka tomb mound, discovered in March, 1972, and excavated in Nara Prefecture.

Reefs, by Hyakusui Hirafuku SP15

**1974, Mar. 2      Photo.      Perf. 13**
B41 SP15 20y + 5y multi          .50   .30

The surtax was for the International Ocean Exposition, Okinawa, 1975.

Intl. Year of the Disabled — SP16

**Photogravure and Embossed**
**1981, Sept. 1                 Perf. 13½**
B42 SP16 60y + 10y multi        1.00   .35

Surtax was for education of the disabled.

TSUKUB'85 Intl. Exposition, Mar. 17-Sept. 16, 1985 — SP17

**1984, Feb. 19     Photo.      Perf. 13½**
B43 SP17 60y + 10y multi        1.00   .35

Intl. Garden and Greenery Exposition, Osaka — SP18

**1989, June 1      Photo.      Perf. 13**
B44 SP18 62y + 10y multi        1.40   .40

Surtax for the preparation and management of the exposition.

Intl. Garden and Greenery Exposition, Osaka — SP19

**1990, Mar. 30**
B45 SP19 41y +4y multi           .75   .25

SP20

**1991, July 5      Photo.      Perf. 13**
B46 SP20 62y +10y multi         1.25   .40

11th World Congress of the World Federation of the Deaf.

SP21

**1995, Apr. 20     Photo.      Perf. 13**
B47 SP21 80y +20y multi         2.00   .60

Philately week. Surtax for benefit of victims of Kobe earthquake.

1998 Winter Olympic Games, Nagano SP22

**1997, Feb. 7      Photo.      Perf. 13**
B48     80y +10y Emblem        1.75   .60
B49     80y +10y Stylized owls 1.75   .60
  *a.*  SP22 Pair, #B48-B49    3.50  2.25

2002 Soccer World Cup, Japan and Korea — SP23

Colors of mascots: No. B50, Purple, yellow and blue. No. B51, Purple. No. B52, Blue.

**2001, May 31   Photo.   Perf. 13x13¼**
B50 SP23 80y +10y multi         1.75   .50
B51 SP23 80y +10y multi         1.75   .50
B52 SP23 80y +10y multi         1.75   .50
  *a.*  Horiz. pair, #B51-B52   3.50  2.20

Wall Paintings, Kitora Tumulus, Asuka SP24

Designs: No. B53, White Tiger of the West. No. B54, Red Bird fo the South.

**2003, Oct. 15     Photo.      Perf. 13**
B53     80y +10y multi          1.50   .60
B54     80y +10y multi          1.50   .60
  *a.*  SP24 Horiz. pair, #B53-B54  3.50  2.50

2005 World Exposition, Aichi — SP25

Exposition mascots and: No. B55, Earth. No. B56, Cherry blossoms.

**2004, Mar. 25   Photo.   Perf. 13x13¼**
B55     80y +10y multi          1.75  1.25
B56     80y +10y multi          1.75  1.25
  *a.*  SP25 Horiz. pair, #B55-B56  3.50  3.50

**Miniature Sheet**

Be Kind to Animals Week SP26

No. B57: a, Dog, flower background. b, White cat, red background. c, White Yorkshire terrier, green curtain. d, Cat, bubbles in background. e, Black Labrador retriever puppy sitting. f, Cat, brown striped background. g, Shiba puppy standing. h, Scottish Fold cat, dots and stripes in background. i, Dog in doorway. j, Cat, crescent moon.

**2009, Sept. 18   Litho.     Perf. 13¼**
B57 SP26  Sheet of 10         11.00 11.00
  *a.-j.*  50y+5y Any single   1.00   .40

Surtax for animal welfare organizations.

SP27

SP28

SP29

SP30

Mar. 11, 2011 Earthquake and Tsunami Relief — SP31

**2011, June 21     Photo.      Perf. 13**
B58 SP27 80y+20y multi          1.50   .60
B59 SP28 80y+20y multi          1.50   .60
B60 SP29 80y+20y multi          1.50   .60
B61 SP30 80y+20y multi          1.50   .60
B62 SP31 80y+20y multi          1.50   .60
  *a.*  Vert. strip of 5, #B58-B62  12.50 12.50

Nos. B58-B62 were printed in sheets containing two strips.

## Miniature Sheet

2019 Rugby World Cup, Japan SP32

No. B63: a, Mount Fuji in blue rugby ball. b, Mount Fuji in red rugby ball. c, Mount Fuji in yellow rugby ball. d, Mount Fuji in purple rugby ball. e, World Cup. f, Rugby World Cup emblem in rugby ball. g, Mascots.

**2018, Aug. 20      Litho.      Perf. 13½**

| B63 | SP32 | Sheet of 10, #B63a-B63d, 2 each #B63e-B63g | 17.50 | 17.50 |
| a.-g. | | 82y+10y Any single | 1.75 | 1.75 |

Surtax for preparation and management of 2019 Rugby World Cup.

## Miniature Sheet

2020 Summer Olympics and Paralympics, Tokyo — SP33

No. B64: a, Dark blue mascot with raised fist. b, Dark blue 2020 Olympics emblem (circular) and Olympic rings in color. c, Aerial view of New National Stadium, Tokyo. d, Dark blue 2020 Paralympics emblem (crescent) and Paralympics crescents in color. e, Magenta mascot with arm extended. f, Dark blue mascot with arms extended. g, Red 2020 Olympics emblem and Olympic rings in magenta. h, Yoyogi Nation Stadium exterior, Tokyo. i, Carmine 2020 Paralympics emblem and carmine Paralympics crescents in color. j, Magenta mascot with fists raised.

**Litho., Litho. & Embossed (#B64b, B64d, B64g, B64i)**

**2019, Mar. 12                   Perf. 13½**

| B64 | SP33 | Sheet of 10 | 17.50 | 17.50 |
| a.-j. | | 82y+10y Any single | 1.75 | 1.75 |

Surtax for preparation and management of 2020 Summer Olympics and Paralympics. The 2020 Summer Olympics and Paralympics were postponed to 2021 due to the Coronavirus pandemic.

## Miniature Sheet

2020 Summer Olympics and Paralympics, Tokyo — SP34

No. B65: a, Circular 2020 Olympics emblem, Olympic rings, silver background. b, As "a," gold background. c, As "a," bronze background. d, Crescent-shaped 2020 Paralympics emblem, Paralympics crescents, silver background. e, As "e," gold background. f, As "e," bronze background. g, Dark blue 2020 Olympics emblem and Olympic rings in color. h, Dark blue 2020 Paralympics emblem and Paralympics crescents in color.

**Litho. & Embossed**

**2019, Aug. 26                   Perf. 13½**

| B65 | SP34 | Sheet of 10, #B65a-B65f, 2 each #B65g-B65h | 17.50 | 17.50 |
| a.-h. | | 84y+10y Any single | 1.75 | 1.75 |

Surtax for preparation and management of 2020 Summer Olympics and Paralympics. The 2020 Summer Olympics and Paralympics were postponed to 2021 due to the Coronavirus pandemic.

---

## AIR POST STAMPS

Regular Issue of 1914 Overprinted in Red or Blue

**Wmk. Zigzag Lines (141)**
**1919, Oct. 3           Perf. 13x13½**
**Granite Paper**

| C1 | A34 | 1½s blue (R) | 400.00 | 150.00 |
| C2 | A34 | 3s rose (Bl) | 900.00 | 500.00 |

Excellent counterfeits exist.

Passenger Plane over Lake Ashi — AP1

**Granite Paper**
**1929-34      Engr.      Perf. 13½x13**

| C3 | AP1 | 8½s orange brn | 45.00 | 45.00 |
| C4 | AP1 | 9½s rose | 15.00 | 10.00 |
| C5 | AP1 | 16½s yellow grn | 20.00 | 20.00 |
| C6 | AP1 | 18s ultra | 25.00 | 10.00 |
| C7 | AP1 | 33s gray | 45.00 | 10.00 |
| | | Nos. C3-C7 (5) | 150.00 | 95.00 |
| | | Set, never hinged | 225.00 | |

**Souvenir Sheet**

| C8 | AP1 | Sheet of 4, #C4-C7 | 1,300. | 1,300. |
| | | Never hinged | 2,000. | |

Issued: 9½s, 3/1/34; No. C8, 4/20/34; others, 10/6/29. No. C8 for Communications Commemoration Day (1st observance of establishment of the postal service and issuance of stamps) sold only at Phil. Exhib. p.o., Tokyo, 4/20-27. Size: 110x100mm.

> Catalogue values for unused stamps in this section, from this point to the end of the section, are for Never Hinged items.

Southern Green Pheasant — AP3

**Perf. 13x13½**
**1950, Jan. 10      Engr.      Unwmk.**

| C9 | AP3 | 16y gray | 35.00 | 10.00 |
| C10 | AP3 | 34y brown violet | 60.00 | 12.00 |
| C11 | AP3 | 59y carmine | 80.00 | 7.00 |
| C12 | AP3 | 103y orange yellow | 55.00 | 20.00 |
| C13 | AP3 | 144y olive | 65.00 | 22.50 |
| | | Nos. C9-C13 (5) | 295.00 | 71.50 |
| | | Set, hinged | 125.00 | |

Pagoda and Plane AP4

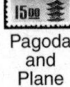

Plane and Mt. Tsurugi-dake AP5

**1951-52                             Photo.**

| C14 | AP4 | 15y purple | 5.00 | 4.00 |
| C15 | AP4 | 20y blue | 35.00 | 3.00 |
| C16 | AP4 | 25y yellow grn | 35.00 | .45 |
| C17 | AP4 | 30y brown red | 25.00 | .45 |
| C18 | AP4 | 40y gray blk | 9.00 | .55 |
| C19 | AP5 | 55y brt blue | 230.00 | 40.00 |
| C20 | AP5 | 75y brnsh red | 175.00 | 25.00 |
| C21 | AP5 | 80y magenta | 30.00 | 3.00 |
| C22 | AP5 | 85y black | 50.00 | 10.00 |
| C23 | AP5 | 125y olive bis | 15.00 | 5.00 |
| C24 | AP5 | 160y Prus green | 40.00 | 5.00 |
| | | Nos. C14-C24 (11) | 649.00 | 96.45 |
| | | Set, hinged | 300.00 | |

Issue dates: 25y, 30y, Dec. 20; 15y, 20y, 40y, Sept. 1; 55y-160y, Feb. 11, 1952.

**Redrawn; Underlined Zeros Omitted**
**1952-62**

| C25 | AP4 | 15y purple ('62) | 2.50 | .90 |
| C26 | AP4 | 20y blue | 75.00 | 6.00 |
| C27 | AP4 | 25y yel grn ('53) | 1.25 | .30 |
| C28 | AP4 | 30y brown red | 6.00 | .30 |
| C29 | AP4 | 40y gray blk ('53) | 5.25 | .40 |
| C30 | AP5 | 55y brt blue | 70.00 | 4.00 |

---

| C32 | AP5 | 75y brnsh red | 160.00 | 15.00 |
| C33 | AP5 | 80y magenta | 120.00 | 4.00 |
| C34 | AP5 | 85y black | 5.50 | 3.00 |
| C36 | AP5 | 125y olive bis | 12.50 | 3.00 |
| C38 | AP5 | 160y Prus green | 40.00 | 4.00 |
| | | Nos. C25-C38 (11) | 498.00 | 40.90 |
| | | Set, hinged | 185.00 | |

See No. C43.

Great Buddha of Kamakura — AP6

**1953, Aug. 15                   Perf. 13½**

| C39 | AP6 | 70y red brown | 3.50 | .25 |
| C40 | AP6 | 80y blue | 5.00 | .25 |
| C41 | AP6 | 115y olive green | 3.00 | .40 |
| C42 | AP6 | 145y Prus green | 20.00 | 2.50 |
| | | Nos. C39-C42 (4) | 31.50 | 3.40 |

**Redrawn Type of 1952-62 Coil Stamp**
**1961, Oct. 2                 Perf. 13 Horiz.**

| C43 | AP4 | 30y brown red | 40.00 | 27.50 |

---

## MILITARY STAMPS

Nos. 98, 119, 131 Overprinted

**1910-14   Unwmk.   Perf. 11½ to 13½**

| M1 | A26 | 3s rose | 200.00 | 35.00 |
| M2 | A34 | 3s rose ('13) | 325.00 | 140.00 |

**Wmk. 141**

| M3 | A34 | 3s rose ('14) | 30.00 | 16.00 |
| | | Nos. M1-M3 (3) | 555.00 | 191.00 |

Nos. M1-M3 overprint type I has 3.85mm between characters; type II, 4-4.5mm (movable type).

**1921          On Offices in China No. 37**

| M4 | A34 | 3s rose | 5,750. | 4,750. |

No. M4 is a provisional military stamp issued at the Japanese Post Office, Tsingtao, China. The overprint differs from the illustration, being 12mm high with thicker characters. Counterfeits are plentiful.

**Overprint 16mm High**

**1924                     On No. 131**

| M5 | A34 | 3s rose | 90.00 | 72.50 |
| a. | | 3s rose (#131b) | 90.00 | 75.00 |

Excellent forgeries exist of Nos. M1-M5.

---

## JAPANESE OFFICES ABROAD

### Offices in China

1899-1907 Regular Issues of Japan Overprinted in Red or Black

**Perf. 11½, 12, 12½, 13½, 13x13½**
**1900-06                          Unwmk.**

| 1 | A26 | 5r gray (R) | 3.25 | 2.50 |
| 2 | A26 | ½s gray (R) ('01) | 2.00 | .70 |
| 3 | A26 | 1s lt red brn (R) | 2.00 | .70 |
| 4 | A26 | 1½s ultra | 9.00 | 2.00 |
| 5 | A26 | 1½s vio ('06) | 5.00 | .95 |
| 6 | A26 | 2s lt grn (R) | 5.00 | .70 |
| 7 | A26 | 3s violet brn | 5.50 | .70 |
| 8 | A26 | 3s rose ('06) | 4.00 | .50 |
| 9 | A26 | 4s rose | 4.50 | 1.25 |
| 10 | A26 | 5s org yel (R) | 9.00 | 1.25 |
| 11 | A27 | 6s maroon ('06) | 16.00 | 11.00 |
| 12 | A27 | 8s ol grn (R) | 9.00 | 5.50 |
| 13 | A27 | 10s deep blue | 9.00 | 1.00 |
| 14 | A27 | 15s purple | 18.00 | 1.75 |
| 15 | A27 | 20s red org | 16.00 | 1.00 |
| 16 | A28 | 25s blue grn (R) | 32.50 | 3.50 |
| 17 | A28 | 50s red brown | 35.00 | 2.50 |
| 18 | A29 | 1y carmine | 55.00 | 2.50 |
| | | Nos. 1-18 (18) | 239.75 | 40.00 |

No. 6 with black overprint is bogus.

---

Nos. 5, 6, 8, 9 and 13 exist as booklet panes of 6, made from sheet stamps. They are rare.

**1900**

| 19 | A30 | 3s carmine | 25.00 | 15.00 |

Wedding of Crown Prince Yoshihito and Princess Sadako.

Japan Nos. 113 & 114 Overprinted

**1908**

| 20 | A33 | 5y green | 400.00 | 47.50 |
| 21 | A33 | 10y dark violet | 700.00 | 110.00 |

On #20-21 the space between characters of the overprint is 6½mm instead of 1½mm.

Stamps of 1913-33 Issues Overprinted

**1913          Perf. 12, 12x13, 13x13½**

| 22 | A34 | ½s brown | 14.00 | 14.00 |
| 23 | A34 | 1s orange | 15.00 | 15.00 |
| 24 | A34 | 1½s lt blue | 40.00 | 18.00 |
| 25 | A34 | 2s green | 45.00 | 20.00 |
| 26 | A34 | 3s rose | 22.50 | 8.00 |
| 27 | A35 | 4s red | 62.50 | 62.50 |
| 28 | A35 | 5s violet | 62.50 | 50.00 |
| 29 | A35 | 10s deep blue | 62.50 | 21.00 |
| 30 | A35 | 20s claret | 250.00 | 140.00 |
| 31 | A35 | 25s olive green | 90.00 | 21.00 |
| 32 | A36 | 1y yel grn & mar | 750.00 | 500.00 |
| | | Nos. 22-32 (11) | 1,414. | 869.50 |

Nos. 24, 25, 26, 27 and 29 exist in booklet panes of 6, made from sheet stamps. The No. 26 pane is very rare.

**Japan Nos. 127-137, 139-147 Overprinted**
**1914-21                          Wmk. 141**
**Granite Paper**

| 33 | A34 | ½s brown | 3.25 | .80 |
| 34 | A34 | 1s orange | 3.75 | .80 |
| 35 | A34 | 1½s blue | 4.25 | .80 |
| 36 | A34 | 2s green | 2.75 | .95 |
| 37 | A34 | 3s rose | 2.40 | .80 |
| 38 | A35 | 4s red | 10.00 | 4.75 |
| 39 | A35 | 5s violet | 17.50 | 1.75 |
| 40 | A35 | 6s brown ('20) | 30.00 | 18.00 |
| 41 | A35 | 8s gray ('20) | 37.50 | 20.00 |
| 42 | A35 | 10s dp blue | 12.00 | 1.25 |
| 43 | A35 | 20s claret | 42.50 | 3.25 |
| 44 | A35 | 25s olive grn | 50.00 | 3.50 |
| 45 | A36 | 30s org brn ('20) | 75.00 | 27.50 |
| 46 | A35 | 50s dk brn ('20) | 90.00 | 30.00 |
| 47 | A36 | 1y yel grn & mar ('18) | 130.00 | 6.75 |
| 48 | A33 | 5y green | 1,850. | 525.00 |
| 49 | A33 | 10y violet ('21) | 2,650. | 1,600. |
| | | Nos. 33-49 (17) | 5,011. | 2,246. |

On Nos. 48-49 the space between characters of overprint is 4½mm, instead of 6½mm on Nos. 20-21 and 1½mm on all lower values. See No. M4.

No. 42 exists as a booklet pane of 6, made from sheet stamps. It is very rare.

Counterfeit overprints exist of Nos. 1-49.

---

### Offices in Korea

Regular Issue of Japan Overprinted in Red or Black

**1900      Unwmk.      Perf. 11½, 12, 12½**

| 1 | A26 | 5r gray (R) | 19.00 | 8.75 |
| 2 | A26 | 1s lt red brn (R) | 20.00 | 5.00 |
| 3 | A26 | 1½s blue | 250.00 | 130.00 |
| 4 | A26 | 2s lt green (R) | 19.00 | 10.00 |
| 5 | A26 | 3s violet brn | 17.00 | 4.75 |
| 6 | A26 | 4s rose | 65.00 | 27.50 |
| 7 | A26 | 5s org yel (R) | 67.50 | 27.50 |
| 8 | A27 | 8s ol grn (R) | 250.00 | 120.00 |
| 9 | A27 | 10s deep blue | 35.00 | 9.00 |
| 10 | A27 | 15s purple | 62.50 | 6.00 |
| 11 | A27 | 20s red orange | 62.50 | 5.00 |
| 12 | A28 | 25s blue grn (R) | 220.00 | 55.00 |

| 13 | A28 | 50s red brown | 175.00 | 18.00 |
|----|-----|---------------|--------|-------|
| 14 | A29 | 1y carmine | 475.00 | 14.00 |
| | | Nos. 1-14 (14) | 1,738. | 440.50 |

**1900**

| 15 | A30 | 3s carmine | 125.00 | 55.00 |
|----|-----|------------|--------|-------|

Wedding of Crown Prince Yoshihito and Princess Sadako.

Counterfeit overprints exist of Nos. 1-15.

### Taiwan (Formosa)

Numeral of Value and Imperial Crest — A1

**1945    Unwmk.    Litho.    Imperf.**
**Without Gum**

| 1 | A1 | 3s carmine | 30.00 | 30.00 |
|---|-----|------------|-------|-------|
| 2 | A1 | 5s blue green | 24.00 | 24.00 |
| 3 | A1 | 10s pale blue | 35.00 | 35.00 |
| | | Nos. 1-3 (3) | 89.00 | 89.00 |

Additional values, prepared, but not issued, were: 30s, 40s, 50s, 1y, 5y and 10y. The entire set of nine was overprinted by Chinese authorities after World War II and issued for use in Taiwan.

For overprints see China-Taiwan Nos. 1-7.

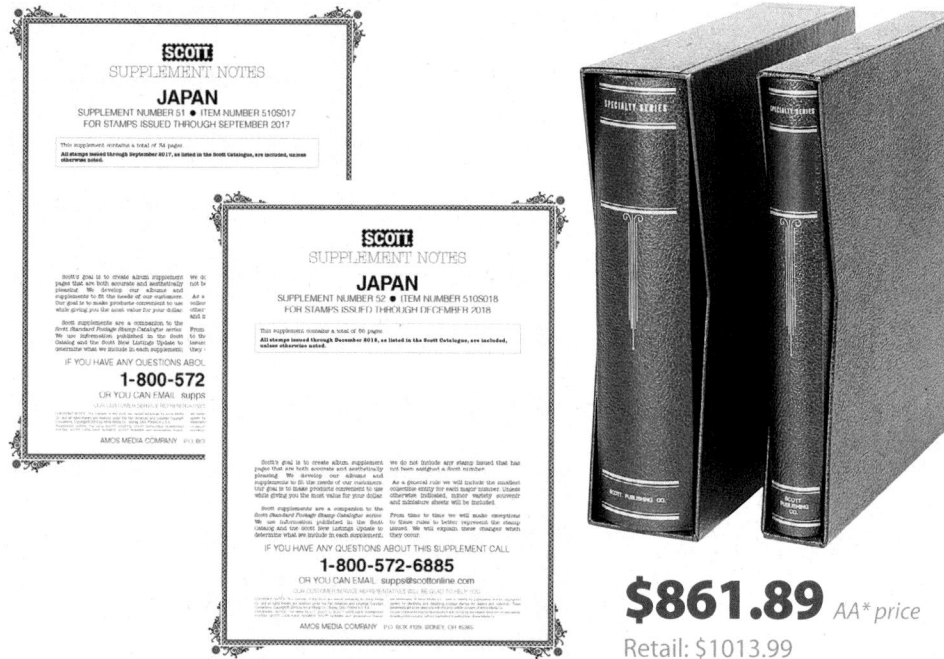

# JORDAN

'jor-dən

## Trans-Jordan

LOCATION — In the Near East, separated from the Mediterranean Sea by Israel
GOVT. — Kingdom
AREA — 38,400 sq. mi.
POP. — 4,561,147 (1999 est.)
CAPITAL — Amman

The former Turkish territory was mandated to Great Britain following World War I. It became an independent state in 1946.

10 Milliemes = 1 Piaster
1000 Mils = 1 Palestine Pound (1930)
1000 Fils = 100 piasters = 1 Jordan Dinar (1951)

Catalogue values for unused stamps in this country are for Never Hinged items, beginning with Scott 221 in the regular postage section, Scott B13 in the semi-postal section, Scott C1 in the air post section, Scott J47 in the postage due section, Scott RA1 in the postal tax section, Scott N1 in the occupation section, Scott NJ1 in the occupation postage due section, and Scott NRA1 in the occupation postal tax section.

### Watermarks

Wmk. 305 — Roman and Arabic Initials

Wmk. 328 — UAR

Wmk. 388 — Multiple "SPM"

### British Mandate

Stamps and Type of Palestine 1918 Overprinted in Black or Silver

Type I    Type II

**1920, Nov.    Wmk. 33    Perf. 15x14**

| | | | | |
|---|---|---|---|---|
| 1 | A1 | 1m dark brown | 3.75 | 6.00 |
| a. | | Inverted overprint | 150.00 | 300.00 |
| 2 | A1 | 2m blue green | 25.00 | 27.50 |
| 3 | A1 | 3m light brown (I) | 3.75 | 4.75 |
| a. | | Overprint type II | 1,200. | |
| 4 | A1 | 4m scarlet | 4.50 | 4.50 |
| a. | | Arabic "40" | 82.50 | |
| 5 | A1 | 5m orange | 10.00 | 3.50 |
| 6 | A1 | 1pi dark blue (S) | 2,200. | |
| 7 | A1 | 2pi olive green (I) | 14.00 | 16.00 |
| a. | | Overprint type II | 950.00 | |
| 8 | A1 | 5pi plum | 55.00 | 82.50 |
| a. | | Overprint type II | 1,500. | |
| 9 | A1 | 9pi bister | 100.00 | 120.00 |
| | | Nos. 1-9 (9) | 2,416. | 264.75 |

**Perf. 14**

| | | | | |
|---|---|---|---|---|
| 1B | A1 | 1m dark brown | 1.40 | 5.00 |
| a. | | Inverted overprint | 190.00 | |
| 2B | A1 | 2m blue green | 3.00 | 4.50 |
| a. | | Silver overprint | 625.00 | 675.00 |
| 3B | A1 | 3m light brown | 22.50 | 30.00 |
| 4B | A1 | 4m scarlet | 19.00 | 50.00 |
| a. | | Arabic "40" | 160.00 | |
| 5B | A1 | 5m orange | 2.75 | 3.50 |
| 6B | A1 | 1pi dark blue (S) | 3.75 | 4.25 |
| 7B | A1 | 2pi olive green | 13.00 | 13.00 |
| 8B | A1 | 5pi plum | 8.00 | 16.00 |
| 9B | A1 | 9pi bister | 8.00 | 55.00 |
| 10 | A1 | 10pi ultramarine | 22.50 | 60.00 |
| 11 | A1 | 20pi gray | 25.00 | 100.00 |
| | | Nos. 1B-11 (11) | 128.90 | 341.25 |

The overprint reads "Sharqi al-ardan" (East of Jordan).
For overprints see Nos. 12-73, 83A.

Moab District Seal

**1920, Nov.  Handstamped  Imperf.**

| | | | | |
|---|---|---|---|---|
| 12 | A2 | (1p) pale blue | 4,000. | 4,500. |

No. 12 was issued at Kerak by the political officer for the Moab District and was used until March 1921 pending the arrival of Nos. 1//11.

Stamps of 1920 Issue Handstamp Surcharged "Ashir el qirsh" (tenth of piaster) and numeral in Black, Red or Violet

**On Nos. 1-9 (Perf. 15x14)**

**1922, Nov.**

| | | | | |
|---|---|---|---|---|
| 13 | A1 | 1/10pi on 1m dk brn | 32.50 | 55.00 |
| 14 | A1 | 1/10pi on 1m dk brn (R) | 77.50 | 77.50 |
| 15 | A1 | 1/10pi on 1m dk brn (V) | 77.50 | 77.50 |
| 16 | A1 | 2/10pi on 2m bl grn | 37.50 | 37.50 |
| a. | | 2/10pi on 2m bl grn (error) | 140.00 | 120.00 |
| 17 | A1 | 2/10pi on 2m bl grn (R) | 87.50 | 87.50 |
| 18 | A1 | 2/10pi on 2m bl grn (V) | 110.00 | 110.00 |
| 19 | A1 | 2/10pi on 3m lt brn | 16.00 | 16.00 |
| a. | | Pair, one without surcharge | 925.00 | |
| b. | | On #3a (type II) | 1,400. | 1,400. |
| 20 | A1 | 2/10pi on 3m lt brn | 160.00 | 160.00 |
| a. | | On #3a (type II) | 3,000. | |
| 21 | A1 | 1/10pi on 4m scar | 65.00 | 70.00 |
| 22 | A1 | 5/10pi on 5m org | 200.00 | 110.00 |
| 23 | A1 | 5/10pi on 5m dp org (V) | 275.00 | 275.00 |

Handstamp Surcharged "El qirsh" (piaster) and numeral in Black, Red or Violet

| | | | | |
|---|---|---|---|---|
| 24 | A1 | 2pi on 2pi ol grn | 275.00 | 82.50 |
| a. | | On #7a (type II) | 1,500. | |
| 25 | A1 | 2pi on 2pi ol grn (R) | 350.00 | 87.50 |
| 26 | A1 | 2pi on 2pi ol grn (V) | 325.00 | 100.00 |
| 27 | A1 | 5pi on 5pi plum | 70.00 | 87.50 |
| a. | | On #8a (type II) | 1,750. | |
| 28 | A1 | 9pi on 9pi bister | 325.00 | 375.00 |
| 29 | A1 | 9pi on 9pi bister (R) | 140.00 | 150.00 |

For overprint see No. 83B.

**On Nos. 1B-11 (Perf. 14)**

| | | | | |
|---|---|---|---|---|
| 13C | A1 | 1/10pi on 1m dk brn | 27.50 | 32.50 |
| a. | | Pair, one without surcharge | 1,700. | |
| 14C | A1 | 1/10pi on 1m dk brn (R) | 65.00 | 65.00 |
| 15C | A1 | 1/10pi on 1m dk brn (V) | 275.00 | 325.00 |
| 16C | A1 | 2/10pi on 2m bl grn | 32.50 | 32.50 |
| a. | | Pair, one without surcharge | 1,700. | |
| b. | | 2/10pi on 2m bl grn (error) | 120.00 | 120.00 |
| 17C | A1 | 2/10pi on 2m bl grn (R) | 87.50 | 87.50 |
| 18C | A1 | 2/10pi on 2m bl grn (V) | 87.50 | 87.50 |
| 22C | A1 | 5/10pi on 5m org | 250.00 | 110.00 |
| a. | | Pair, one without surcharge | 2,350. | |
| 23C | A1 | 5/10pi on 5m org (V) | 300.00 | |
| 23D | A1 | 1pi on 1pi dk blue (R) | 225.00 | 65.00 |
| a. | | Pair, one without surcharge | 2,000. | |
| 23E | A1 | 1pi on 1pi dk blue (V) | 450.00 | |
| 29C | A1 | 9pi on 9pi bister | 600.00 | 600.00 |
| 31 | A1 | 10pi on 10pi ultra | 925.00 | 1,100. |
| 32 | A1 | 20pi on 20pi gray | 700.00 | 825.00 |
| 33 | A1 | 20pi on 20pi gray (V) | 1,000. | 1,050. |

Surcharge in Black on Palestine Nos. 13-14

| | | | | |
|---|---|---|---|---|
| 34 | A1 | 10pi on 10pi ultra | 2,000. | 2,750. |
| 35 | A1 | 20pi on 20pi gray | 2,750. | 3,250. |

Nos. 13-35 are handstamped, and the overprints exist double on most values. They have been extensively forged. Values above are for expertized examples.

Stamps of 1920 Handstamped in Violet, Black or Red

**1922, Dec.    Perf. 14**
**On Nos. 1-5, 7-9 (Perf. 15x14)**

| | | | | |
|---|---|---|---|---|
| 36 | A1 | 1m dk brn (R) | 32.50 | 32.50 |
| 37 | A1 | 1m dk brn (V) | 32.50 | 37.50 |
| 38 | A1 | 1m dk brn (Blk) | 27.50 | 27.50 |
| 39 | A1 | 2m bl grn (R) | 30.00 | 30.00 |
| 40 | A1 | 2m bl grn (V) | 26.00 | 26.00 |
| 41 | A1 | 2m bl grn (Blk) | 25.00 | 25.00 |
| 42 | A1 | 3m lt brn (R) | 52.50 | 52.50 |
| a. | | On #3a (type II) | 1,750. | |
| 43 | A1 | 3m lt brn (V) | 10.00 | 10.00 |
| a. | | Pair, one without surcharge | 1,500. | |
| b. | | On #3a (type II) | 1,600. | 1,600. |
| 44 | A1 | 3m lt brn (Blk) | 11.00 | 11.00 |
| 45 | A1 | 4m scar (R) | 65.00 | 70.00 |
| 46 | A1 | 4m scar (V) | 65.00 | 70.00 |
| 47 | A1 | 4m scar (Blk) | 65.00 | 65.00 |
| 48 | A1 | 5m orange (R) | 50.00 | 13.00 |
| 49 | A1 | 5m orange (V) | 20.00 | 13.00 |
| 50 | A1 | 5m orange (Blk) | 65.00 | 50.00 |
| a. | | On #7a (type II) | 1,600. | |
| 52 | A1 | 2pi ol grn (V) | 27.50 | 20.00 |
| a. | | On #7a (type II) | 1,600. | 1,400. |
| 53 | A1 | 2pi ol grn (Blk) | 18.00 | 13.00 |
| 54 | A1 | 5pi plum (R) | 110.00 | 130.00 |
| a. | | Pair, one without surcharge | 1,750. | |
| 55 | A1 | 5pi plum (V) | 70.00 | 90.00 |
| 56 | A1 | 9pi bister (R) | 450.00 | 500.00 |
| 57 | A1 | 9pi bister (V) | 225.00 | 275.00 |
| a. | | Type II overprint | 2,500. | |
| 58 | A1 | 9pi bister (Blk) | 75.00 | 90.00 |

**On #1B//11 (Perf. 14)**

| | | | | |
|---|---|---|---|---|
| 36C | A1 | 1m dk brn | 17.50 | 22.00 |
| a. | | Pair, one without ovpt. | 1,500. | |
| 37C | A1 | 1m dk brn (V) | 27.50 | 25.00 |
| 38C | A1 | 1m dk brn (Blk) | 25.00 | 25.00 |
| 39C | A1 | 2m bl grn (V) | 35.00 | 35.00 |
| 40C | A1 | 2m bl grn (V) | 11.00 | 11.00 |
| 41C | A1 | 2m bl grn (Blk) | 17.50 | 17.50 |
| 43C | A1 | 3m lt brn (V) | 850.00 | 375.00 |
| 48C | A1 | 5m orange (R) | 325.00 | 80.00 |
| 49C | A1 | 5m orange (V) | 35.00 | 25.00 |
| 51 | A1 | 1pi dark blue (R) | 40.00 | 19.00 |
| 51C | A1 | 1pi dark blue (V) | 25.00 | 12.50 |
| 52C | A1 | 2pi ol grn (V) | 85.00 | 90.00 |
| 54C | A1 | 5pi plum (R) | 110.00 | 120.00 |
| 55C | A1 | 5pi plum (V) | 110.00 | 130.00 |
| 57C | A1 | 9pi bister (V) | 1,000. | 1,100. |
| 59 | A1 | 10pi ultra (R) | 2,000. | 2,100. |
| 60 | A1 | 10pi ultra (V) | 1,500. | 1,750. |
| 61 | A1 | 20pi gray (R) | 1,750. | 2,200. |
| 62 | A1 | 20pi gray (V) | 1,200. | 2,000. |

The overprint reads "Hukumat al Sharqi al Arabia" (Arab Government of the East) and date, 1923. The surcharges or overprints on Nos. 12 to 61 inclusive are handstamped and, as usual, are found inverted and double.
Ink pads of several colors were in use at the same time and the surcharges and overprints frequently show a mixture of two colors.
For overprints see Nos. 84, 87, 89, 92-93, 95-96.

Stamps of 1920 Overprinted in Gold or Black

**1923, Mar. 1    Perf. 15x14**

| | | | | |
|---|---|---|---|---|
| 63 | A1 | 1m dark brn (G) | 1,600. | 1,900. |
| 64 | A1 | 2m blue grn (G) | 25.00 | 27.50 |
| 65 | A1 | 3m lt brn (G) | 19.00 | 20.00 |
| a. | | Double overprint | 550.00 | |
| b. | | Inverted overprint | 600.00 | |
| c. | | Black overprint | 87.50 | 100.00 |
| 66 | A1 | 4m scarlet (Blk) | 22.50 | 20.00 |
| 67 | A1 | 5m orange (Blk) | 65.00 | 55.00 |
| a. | | Original ovpt. albino | 1,300. | 1,500. |
| 69 | A1 | 2pi ol grn (G) | 25.00 | 22.50 |
| a. | | On #7a (type II) | 1,300. | 1,100. |
| b. | | Black overprint | 275.00 | 275.00 |
| 70 | A1 | 5pi plum (G) | 80.00 | 110.00 |
| a. | | Inverted overprint | 240.00 | |
| b. | | On #8a (type II) | 2,200. | |
| c. | | As "b," inverted ovpt. | 2,750. | |
| d. | | Black overprint inverted | 1,600. | |

**Perf. 14**

| | | | | |
|---|---|---|---|---|
| 63E | A1 | 1m dark brn (R) | 21.00 | 35.00 |
| a. | | Inverted overprint | 800.00 | |
| 64E | A1 | 2m blue grn (R) | 20.00 | 22.50 |
| a. | | Double overprint | 325.00 | |
| b. | | Inverted overprint | 375.00 | 375.00 |
| c. | | Black overprint | 325.00 | |
| d. | | As "c," inverted overprint | 1,600. | |
| 67E | A1 | 5m orange (Blk) | 15.00 | 15.00 |
| 68 | A1 | 1pi dk blue (G) | 15.00 | 20.00 |
| a. | | Double overprint | 550.00 | 600.00 |
| b. | | Black overprint | 850.00 | 900.00 |
| 71 | A1 | 9pi bister (Blk) | 100.00 | 140.00 |
| a. | | Gold overprint | 3,250. | |
| 72 | A1 | 10pi ultra (G) | 90.00 | 140.00 |
| 73 | A1 | 20pi gray (G) | 90.00 | 140.00 |
| a. | | Inverted overprint | 400.00 | |
| b. | | Double overprint | 500.00 | |
| c. | | Double ovpt., one inverted | 500.00 | |
| d. | | Double ovpt., one inverted, one gold, one black, black ovpt. inverted | 800.00 | |
| e. | | Triple overprint, one inverted | 1,200. | |
| f. | | Black overprint | 900.00 | |
| g. | | As "f," inverted overprint | 1,200. | |
| h. | | As "f," double overprint, one inverted | 1,400. | |

The overprint reads "Hukumat al Sharqi al Arabia, Nissan Sanat 921" (Arab Government of the East, April, 1921).
For overprints see Nos. 85, 99, 100, 102.

Stamps of Hejaz, 1922, Overprinted in Black

Coat of Arms (Hejaz A7)

**1923, Apr.   Unwmk.   Perf. 11½**

| | | | | |
|---|---|---|---|---|
| 74A | A7 | 1/8pi orange brn | 5.75 | 4.50 |
| a. | | Double overprint | 225.00 | |
| b. | | Inverted overprint | 120.00 | |
| 74B | A7 | 1/8pi red | 5.75 | 4.50 |
| a. | | Inverted overprint | 125.00 | |
| 74C | A7 | 1pi dark blue | 4.50 | 1.50 |
| a. | | Inverted overprint | 140.00 | 140.00 |
| 74D | A7 | 1½pi violet | 4.75 | 2.75 |
| a. | | Double overprint | 160.00 | |
| b. | | Pair, one without overprint | 250.00 | |
| c. | | Pair, imperf. between | 175.00 | |
| 74E | A7 | 2pi orange | 6.00 | 8.50 |
| 74F | A7 | 3pi olive brn | 15.00 | 20.00 |
| a. | | Inverted overprint | 250.00 | |
| b. | | Double overprint | 250.00 | 250.00 |
| c. | | Pair, one without overprint | 400.00 | |
| 74G | A7 | 9pi olive green | 35.00 | 47.50 |
| | | Nos. 64-70 (7) | 76.75 | 89.25 |

The overprint is similar to that on the preceding group but is differently arranged. There are numerous varieties in the Arabic letters.
For overprints see Nos. 71-72, 91, J1-J5.

With Additional Surcharge of New Value in Arabic

a        b

| | | | | |
|---|---|---|---|---|
| 74H | A7(a) | 1/4pi on 1/8pi | 16.00 | 11.00 |
| a. | | Inverted surcharge | 175.00 | |
| b. | | Surcharge doubled | | 200.00 |
| c. | | Inverted surch. & ovpt. | 425.00 | |
| 74I | A7(b) | 10pi on 5pi | 37.50 | 42.50 |

### Independence Issue

Palestine Stamps and Type of 1918 Overprinted Vertically in Black or Gold

**1923, May   Wmk. 33   Perf. 15x14**

| | | | | |
|---|---|---|---|---|
| 74J | A1 | 1m dark brn (Bk) | 24.00 | 24.00 |
| a. | | Double ovpt., one reversed | 725.00 | 650.00 |
| 74K | A1 | 1m dark brn (G) | 175.00 | 175.00 |
| c. | | Double ovpt., one reversed | 1,000. | |
| 74 | A1 | 2m blue grn | 42.50 | 50.00 |
| 75 | A1 | 3m lt brown | 14.00 | 17.50 |
| 76 | A1 | 4m scarlet | 14.00 | 17.50 |
| 77 | A1 | 5m orange | 70.00 | 80.00 |
| 78 | A1 | 1pi dk blue (G) | 95.00 | 110.00 |
| a. | | Double overprint | 750.00 | 850.00 |
| 79 | A1 | 2pi olive grn | 70.00 | 90.00 |
| 80 | A1 | 5pi plum (G) | 80.00 | 90.00 |
| a. | | Double overprint (G) | 725.00 | |
| b. | | Double overprint (Bk) | 1,500. | |
| 81 | A1 | 9pi bis, perf. 14 | 80.00 | 85.00 |
| 82 | A1 | 10pi ultra, perf. 14 | 80.00 | 100.00 |
| 83 | A1 | 20pi gray | 85.00 | 110.00 |
| | | Nos. 73-83 (12) | 819.50 | 949.00 |

The overprint reads, "Arab Government of the East (abbreviated), Souvenir of Independence, 25th, May, 1923 ('923')."
There were printed 480 complete sets with a larger number of the 1, 2, 3 and 4m. A large number of these sets were distributed to high officials. The overprint was in a setting of twenty-four and the error "933" instead of "923" occurs once in the setting. Value about five times the "923" stamps.

The overprint exists reading downward on all values, as illustrated, and reading upward on all except the 5m and 2pi.
Forged overprints exist.
For overprint see No. 101.

## Stamps of Preceding Issues, Handstamp Surcharged

| | | | | |
|---|---|---|---|---|
| 83A | A1 | 2½ 10ths pi on 5m dp org | 240.00 | 240.00 |
| 83B | A1 | ⁵⁄₁₀pi on 3m (#17) | — | 120.00 |
| 84 | A1 | ⁵⁄₁₀pi on 3m (#36) | 100.00 | 60.00 |
| 85 | A1 | ⁵⁄₁₀pi on 3m (#55) | 27.50 | 40.00 |
| 86 | A1 | ⁵⁄₁₀pi on 5pi (#23) | 85.00 | 100.00 |
| 87 | A1 | ⁵⁄₁₀pi on 5pi (#48) | 10.00 | 17.50 |
| 88 | A1 | 1pi on 5pi (#23) | 75.00 | 140.00 |
| 89 | A1 | 1pi on 5pi (#48) | 2,500. | 2,750. |

### Same Surcharge on Palestine Stamp of 1918

| | | | |
|---|---|---|---|
| 90 | A1 | ⁵⁄₁₀pi on 3m lt brn | 17,000. |

No. 90 is valued in the grade of fine-very fine. Very fine examples are not known.
As is usual with handstamped surcharges these are found double, inverted, etc.

## No. 67 Surcharged by Handstamp

| | | | Unwmk. | Perf. 11½ |
|---|---|---|---|---|
| 91 | A7 | ½pi on 1½pi vio | 12.00 | 14.00 |
| a. | | Surcharge typographed | 55.00 | 55.00 |
| b. | | As "a," inverted surcharge | 150.00 | |
| c. | | As "a," double surcharge | 180.00 | |
| d. | | As "a," pair, one with surcharge | 500.00 | |

The surcharge reads: "Nusf el qirsh" (half piastre). See note after No. 90.
Handstamped surcharge exists double; inverted; double, one inverted, etc.

## Stamps of Preceding Issues Surcharged by Handstamp

No. 92

| | | | Perf. 14, 15x14 | |
|---|---|---|---|---|
| **1923, Nov.** | | | **Wmk. 33** | |
| 92 | A1 | ½pi on 2pi (#45) | 70.00 | 85.00 |
| 93 | A1 | ½pi on 2pi (#47) | 110.00 | 125.00 |
| 94 | A1 | ½pi on 5pi (#23) | 75.00 | 85.00 |
| 95 | A1 | ½pi on 5pi (#48) | 3,000. | 2,000. |
| 96 | A1 | ½pi on 5pi (#49) | 2,000. | 2,750. |
| 97 | A1 | ½pi on 9pi (#24) | 6,500. | |
| 98 | A1 | ½pi on 9pi (#25) | 95.00 | 160.00 |
| 99 | A1 | ½pi on 9pi (#61) | 200.00 | 160.00 |

## Surcharged by Handstamp

No. 102

| | | | | |
|---|---|---|---|---|
| 100 | A1 | 1pi on 10pi (#62) | 2,250. | 2,500. |
| 101 | A1 | 1pi on 10pi (#82) | 3,000. | 3,000. |
| 102 | A1 | 2pi on 20pi (#63) | 70.00 | 95.00 |

Of the 25 examples of No. 100, a few were handstamped in violet. Value, unused $2,750.

## Stamp of Hejaz, 1922, Overprinted by Handstamp

| | | | Unwmk. | Perf. 11½ |
|---|---|---|---|---|
| **1923, Dec.** | | | | |
| 103 | A7 | ½pi red | 9.00 | 5.00 |

Two settings of No. 103 exist. They differ in the spacing of the characters and the position

---

of the bottom line of the overprint, either to the left or centered.
Nos. 92-103 handstamps exist inverted, doubled, etc.

## Stamp of Hejaz, 1922, Overprinted

| | | Typo. | |
|---|---|---|---|
| **1924** | | | |
| 104 | A7 | ½pi red | 14.00 | 16.00 |

### King Hussein Issue

## Stamps of Hejaz, 1922, Overprinted

| | | | Gold Overprint | |
|---|---|---|---|---|
| **1924** | | | | |
| 105 | A7 | ½pi red | 4.00 | 4.00 |
| 106 | A7 | 1pi dark blue | 4.25 | 3.25 |
| 107 | A7 | 1½pi violet | 5.00 | 4.50 |
| 108 | A7 | 2pi orange | 12.00 | 13.00 |

| | | | Black Overprint | |
|---|---|---|---|---|
| 109 | A7 | ½pi red | 3.00 | 3.00 |
| 110 | A7 | 1pi dark blue | 3.75 | 3.75 |
| 111 | A7 | 1½pi violet | 5.50 | 5.50 |
| 112 | A7 | 2pi orange | 13.00 | 13.00 |
| | | Nos. 105-112 (8) | 50.50 | 50.00 |

The overprint reads: "Arab Government of the East. In commemoration of the visit of H. M. the King of the Arabs, 11 Jemad el Than i 1342 (17th Jan. 1924)." The overprint was in a setting of thirty-six and the error "432" instead of "342" occurs once in the setting and is found on all values. Value, $75 each.

## Stamps of Hejaz, 1922-24, Overprinted in Black or Red

Coat of Arms (Hejaz A8)

| | | | | |
|---|---|---|---|---|
| **1924** | | | | |
| 113 | A7 | ⅛pi red brown | 2.00 | 1.75 |
| a. | | Inverted overprint | 130.00 | |
| 114 | A7 | ¼pi yellow green | 2.00 | 1.00 |
| a. | | Tête bêche pair | 15.00 | 35.00 |
| b. | | As "a," one overprint inverted | 300.00 | — |
| c. | | Inverted overprint | 85.00 | — |
| 115 | A7 | ½pi red | 2.00 | .90 |
| 116 | A7 | 1pi dark blue | 11.00 | 1.50 |
| a. | | Inverted overprint | — | |
| 117 | A7 | 1½pi violet | 7.00 | 7.00 |
| 118 | A7 | 2pi orange | 5.00 | 3.50 |
| a. | | Double overprint | — | |
| 119 | A7 | 3pi red brown | 5.00 | 5.00 |
| a. | | Double overprint | 100.00 | |
| b. | | Inverted overprint | 100.00 | |
| 120 | A7 | 5pi olive green | 7.00 | 7.00 |
| 121 | A8 | 10pi vio & dk brn (R) | 15.00 | 17.50 |
| a. | | Pair, one without overprint | 250.00 | |
| b. | | Black overprint | | |
| | | Nos. 113-121 (9) | 56.00 | 45.15 |

The overprint reads: "Hukumat al Sharqi al Arabia, 1342." (Arab Government of the East, 1924).

## Stamps of Hejaz, 1925, Overprinted in Black or Red

(Hejaz A9)     (Hejaz A10)

(Hejaz A11)

| | | | | |
|---|---|---|---|---|
| **1925, Aug.** | | | | |
| 122 | A9 | ⅛pi chocolate | 1.25 | 3.50 |
| a. | | Inverted overprint | 70.00 | — |
| 123 | A9 | ¼pi ultramarine | 2.25 | 5.00 |
| a. | | Inverted overprint | 70.00 | — |
| 124 | A9 | ½pi carmine rose | 1.75 | 1.50 |
| a. | | Inverted overprint | 70.00 | — |

---

| | | | | |
|---|---|---|---|---|
| 125 | A10 | 1pi yellow green | 1.75 | 4.00 |
| 126 | A10 | 1½pi orange | 4.00 | 6.50 |
| a. | | Inverted overprint | 70.00 | |
| 127 | A10 | 2pi deep blue | 5.00 | 9.00 |
| 128 | A11 | 3pi dark green (R) | 5.50 | 14.00 |
| a. | | Inverted overprint | 90.00 | |
| 129 | A11 | 5pi orange brn | 8.00 | 22.00 |
| a. | | Inverted overprint | 85.00 | — |
| | | Nos. 122-129 (8) | 29.50 | 65.50 |

The overprint reads: "Hukumat al Sharqi al Arabi. 1343 Sanat." (Arab Government of the East, 1925). Nos. 122-129 exist imperforate, and with overprint double.

## Type of Palestine, 1918

| | | | Wmk. 4 | Perf. 14 |
|---|---|---|---|---|
| **1925, Nov. 1** | | | | |
| 130 | A1 | 1m dark brown | .60 | 3.50 |
| 131 | A1 | 2m yellow | .85 | .65 |
| 132 | A1 | 3m Prussian bl | 2.75 | 1.60 |
| 133 | A1 | 4m rose | 2.75 | 3.75 |
| 134 | A1 | 5m orange | 3.25 | .60 |
| 135 | A1 | 6m blue green | 2.75 | 2.75 |
| 136 | A1 | 7m yel brown | 2.75 | 2.75 |
| 137 | A1 | 8m red | 2.75 | 1.60 |
| 138 | A1 | 1pi gray | 2.75 | .75 |
| 139 | A1 | 13m ultramarine | 3.50 | 3.50 |
| 140 | A1 | 2pi olive green | 4.50 | 5.00 |
| 141 | A1 | 5pi plum | 9.50 | 10.00 |
| 142 | A1 | 9pi bister | 14.00 | 27.50 |
| 143 | A1 | 10pi light blue | 30.00 | 40.00 |
| 144 | A1 | 20pi violet | 50.00 | 90.00 |
| | | Nos. 130-144 (15) | 132.70 | 193.95 |

This overprint reads: "Sharqi al-ardan" (East of Jordan).
For overprints see Nos. J12-J23.

| | | | Perf. 15x14 | |
|---|---|---|---|---|
| 142a | A1 | 9pi | 950. | 1,500. |
| 143a | A1 | 10pi | 100. | 110. |
| 144a | A1 | 20pi | 1,100. | 1,100. |
| | | Nos. 142a-144a (3) | 2,150. | 2,710. |

Amir Abdullah ibn Hussein
A1     A2

| | | | Engr. | Perf. 14 |
|---|---|---|---|---|
| **1927-29** | | | | |
| 145 | A1 | 2(m) Prus blue | 2.50 | 1.25 |
| 146 | A1 | 3(m) rose | 3.75 | 3.00 |
| 147 | A1 | 4(m) green | 4.50 | 6.50 |
| 148 | A1 | 5(m) orange | 2.75 | .35 |
| 149 | A1 | 10(m) red | 3.75 | 6.50 |
| 150 | A1 | 15(m) ultra | 3.50 | .50 |
| 151 | A1 | 20(m) olive grn | 3.75 | 4.00 |
| 152 | A2 | 50(m) claret | 3.75 | 12.00 |
| 153 | A2 | 90(m) bister | 9.00 | 27.50 |
| 154 | A2 | 100(m) lt blue | 10.00 | 22.50 |
| 155 | A2 | 200(m) violet | 17.50 | 45.00 |
| 156 | A2 | 500(m) dp brn ('29) | 70.00 | 100.00 |
| 157 | A2 | 1000(m) gray ('29) | 165.00 | 190.00 |
| | | Nos. 145-157 (13) | 299.75 | 419.10 |

For overprints see Nos. 158-168, B1-B12, J24-J29.

## Stamps of 1927 Overprinted in Black

| | | | | |
|---|---|---|---|---|
| **1928, Sept. 1** | | | | |
| 158 | A1 | 2(m) Prus blue | 3.00 | 3.50 |
| 159 | A1 | 3(m) rose | 3.50 | 4.50 |
| 160 | A1 | 4(m) green | 3.50 | 5.25 |
| 161 | A1 | 5(m) orange | 3.50 | 2.50 |
| 162 | A1 | 10(m) red | 3.75 | 5.75 |
| 163 | A1 | 15(m) ultra | 3.75 | 2.75 |
| 164 | A1 | 20(m) olive grn | 8.50 | 14.00 |
| 165 | A2 | 50(m) claret | 12.00 | 15.00 |
| 166 | A2 | 90(m) bister | 22.50 | 45.00 |
| 167 | A2 | 100(m) lt blue | 27.50 | 65.00 |
| 168 | A2 | 200(m) violet | 85.00 | 160.00 |
| | | Nos. 158-168 (11) | 176.50 | 323.25 |

The overprint is the Arabic word "Dastour," meaning "Constitution." The stamps were in commemoration of the enactment of the law setting forth the Constitution.

A3

---

"MILS" or "L. P." at lower right and Arabic equivalents at upper left.

| | | | Engr. | Perf. 14 |
|---|---|---|---|---|
| **1930-36** | | | | |
| | | **Size: 17¼x21mm** | | |
| 169 | A3 | 1m red brn ('34) | 2.00 | 1.00 |
| 170 | A3 | 2m Prus blue | 1.00 | .60 |
| 171 | A3 | 3m rose | 1.75 | 1.00 |
| 172 | A3 | 3m green ('34) | 2.50 | 1.25 |
| 173 | A3 | 4m green | 2.00 | 4.00 |
| 174 | A3 | 4m rose ('34) | 4.00 | 1.50 |
| 175 | A3 | 5m orange | 1.50 | .45 |
| a. | | Perf. 13½x14 (coil) ('36) | 35.00 | 20.00 |
| 176 | A3 | 10m red | 2.25 | .25 |
| 177 | A3 | 15m ultra | 2.25 | .30 |
| a. | | Perf. 13½x14 (coil) ('36) | 32.50 | 17.50 |
| 178 | A3 | 20m olive grn | 3.25 | .55 |
| | | **Size: 19¼x23½mm** | | |
| 179 | A3 | 50m red violet | 4.50 | 2.25 |
| 180 | A3 | 90m bister | 4.25 | 6.25 |
| 181 | A3 | 100m light blue | 5.00 | 6.00 |
| 182 | A3 | 200m violet | 17.50 | 18.00 |
| 183 | A3 | 500m deep brown | 32.50 | 57.50 |
| 184 | A3 | £1 gray | 77.50 | 120.00 |
| | | Nos. 169-184 (16) | 163.75 | 220.90 |

See Nos. 199-220, 230-235. For overprint see No. N15a.

| | | | Perf. 13½x13 | |
|---|---|---|---|---|
| **1939** | | | | |
| | | **Size: 17¼x21mm** | | |
| 169a | A3 | 1m red brown | 6.50 | 4.50 |
| 170a | A3 | 2m Prussian blue | 16.00 | 4.50 |
| 172a | A3 | 3m green | 25.00 | 7.00 |
| 174a | A3 | 4m rose | 90.00 | 29.00 |
| 175b | A3 | 5m orange | 75.00 | 4.50 |
| 176a | A3 | 10m red | 150.00 | 5.75 |
| 177b | A3 | 15m ultramarine | 47.50 | 6.00 |
| 178a | A3 | 20m olive green | 72.50 | 17.50 |
| | | Nos. 169a-178a (8) | 482.50 | 78.25 |

For overprint see No. N3a.

Mushetta — A4     Nymphaeum, Jerash — A5

Kasr Kharana — A6     Kerak Castle — A7

Temple of Artemis, Jerash — A8     Aijalon Castle — A9

Khazneh, Rock-hewn Temple, Petra — A10     Allenby Bridge, River Jordan — A11

Ancient Threshing Floor A12     Amir Abdullah ibn Hussein A13

| | | | | |
|---|---|---|---|---|
| **1933, Feb. 1** | | | **Perf. 12** | |
| 185 | A4 | 1m dk brn & blk | 1.75 | 1.40 |
| 186 | A5 | 2m claret & blk | 4.00 | 1.00 |
| 187 | A6 | 3m blue green | 4.25 | 1.50 |
| 188 | A7 | 4m bister & blk | 6.50 | 3.75 |
| 189 | A8 | 5m orange & blk | 4.50 | 3.75 |
| 190 | A9 | 10m brown red | 7.00 | 3.50 |
| 191 | A10 | 15m dull blue | 4.75 | 1.75 |
| 192 | A11 | 20m ol grn & blk | 6.75 | 5.50 |
| 193 | A12 | 50m brn vio & blk | 20.00 | 17.50 |
| 194 | A6 | 90m yel & black | 25.00 | 27.50 |
| 195 | A8 | 100m blue & blk | 27.50 | 35.00 |
| 196 | A9 | 200m dk vio & blk | 60.00 | 80.00 |

| | | | | | |
|---|---|---|---|---|---|
| 197 | A10 | 500m brn & ver | | 190.00 | 275.00 |
| 198 | A13 | £1 green & blk | | 650.00 | 950.00 |
| | | Nos. 185-198 (14) | | 1,012. | 1,407. |

Nos. 194-197 are larger than the lower values in the same designs.

**Amir Abdullah ibn Hussein — A14**

### *Perf. 13x13½*
**1942, May 18    Litho.    Unwmk.**

| | | | | |
|---|---|---|---|---|
| 199 | A14 | 1m dull red brn | 1.10 | 4.00 |
| 200 | A14 | 2m dull green | 2.00 | 2.25 |
| 201 | A14 | 3m dp yel green | 2.50 | 4.50 |
| 202 | A14 | 4m rose pink | 2.50 | 4.50 |
| 203 | A14 | 5m orange yel | 4.25 | 1.00 |
| 204 | A14 | 10m dull ver | 6.00 | 3.25 |
| 205 | A14 | 15m deep blue | 12.50 | 4.00 |
| 206 | A14 | 20m dull ol grn | 22.50 | 22.50 |
| | | Nos. 199-206 (8) | 53.35 | 46.00 |

Type A14 differs from A3 in the redrawn inscription above the head and in the form of the "millieme" character at upper left.
For overprint see No. N1.

**Abdullah Type of 1930-39**
**White Paper**
**1943-44   Engr.   Wmk. 4   *Perf. 12***
**Size: 17¾x21½mm**

| | | | | |
|---|---|---|---|---|
| 207 | A3 | 1m red brown | .30 | .70 |
| 208 | A3 | 2m Prussian grn | 1.50 | 1.25 |
| 209 | A3 | 3m blue green | 1.25 | 1.25 |
| 210 | A3 | 4m deep rose | 1.25 | 1.25 |
| 211 | A3 | 5m orange | 1.25 | .30 |
| 212 | A3 | 10m scarlet | 2.25 | 1.25 |
| 213 | A3 | 15m blue | 2.25 | 1.50 |
| 214 | A3 | 20m olive ('44) | 2.25 | 1.00 |

**Size: 20x24mm**

| | | | | |
|---|---|---|---|---|
| 215 | A3 | 50m red lil ('44) | 2.50 | 1.25 |
| 216 | A3 | 90m ocher | 5.00 | 6.00 |
| 217 | A3 | 100m dp bl ('44) | 6.50 | 3.00 |
| 218 | A3 | 200m dk vio ('44) | 8.00 | 10.00 |
| 219 | A3 | 500m dk brn ('44) | 11.00 | 12.50 |
| 220 | A3 | £1 black ('44) | 20.00 | 27.50 |
| | | Nos. 207-220 (14) | 65.30 | 68.75 |

See Nos. 230-235. For overprints see Nos. 255-256, 259, 264-269, RA23, N2-N4, N7, N12-N17.

> **Catalogue values for unused stamps in this section, from this point to the end of the section, are for Never Hinged items.**

### Independent Kingdom

**Symbols of Peace and Liberty — A15**

### *Perf. 11½*
**1946, May 25    Unwmk.    Litho.**

| | | | | |
|---|---|---|---|---|
| 221 | A15 | 1m sepia | .30 | .25 |
| 222 | A15 | 2m yel orange | .30 | .25 |
| 223 | A15 | 3m dl ol grn | .30 | .25 |
| 224 | A15 | 4m lt violet | .30 | .25 |
| 225 | A15 | 10m orange brn | .30 | .25 |
| 226 | A15 | 12m rose red | .30 | .25 |
| 227 | A15 | 20m dark blue | .35 | .25 |
| 228 | A15 | 50m ultra | .90 | .75 |
| 229 | A15 | 200m green | 3.00 | 3.00 |
| | | Nos. 221-229 (9) | 6.05 | 5.50 |

Independence of the Kingdom of Trans-Jordan.
Nos. 221-229 exist imperforate.

**Abdullah Type of 1930-39**
**1947   Wmk. 4   Engr.   *Perf. 12***

| | | | | |
|---|---|---|---|---|
| 230 | A3 | 3m rose carmine | .40 | .30 |
| 231 | A3 | 4m deep yel green | .40 | .30 |
| 232 | A3 | 10m violet | .60 | .30 |
| 233 | A3 | 12m deep rose | 1.10 | .80 |
| 234 | A3 | 15m dull olive grn | 1.25 | .90 |
| 235 | A3 | 20m deep blue | 1.40 | 1.00 |
| | | Nos. 230-235 (6) | 5.15 | 3.60 |

For overprints see Nos. 257-258, 260-263, RA24-RA25, N5-N6, N8-N11.

---

**Parliament Building, Amman — A16**

**1947, Nov. 1    Engr.    Unwmk.**

| | | | | |
|---|---|---|---|---|
| 236 | A16 | 1m purple | .40 | .25 |
| 237 | A16 | 3m red orange | .40 | .25 |
| 238 | A16 | 4m yel green | .40 | .25 |
| 239 | A16 | 10m dk vio brn | .40 | .25 |
| 240 | A16 | 12m carmine | .40 | .25 |
| 241 | A16 | 20m deep blue | .50 | .25 |
| 242 | A16 | 50m red vio | .80 | .35 |
| 243 | A16 | 100m rose | 1.00 | .65 |
| 244 | A16 | 200m dark green | 1.60 | 1.50 |
| | | Nos. 236-244 (9) | 5.90 | 4.00 |

Founding of the new Trans-Jordan parliament, 1947.
Nos. 236-244 exist imperforate.

**Symbols of the UPU — A17**

**King Abdullah ibn Hussein — A18**

**1949, Aug. 1    Wmk. 4    *Perf. 13***

| | | | | |
|---|---|---|---|---|
| 245 | A17 | 1m brown | .40 | .40 |
| 246 | A17 | 4m green | .75 | .75 |
| 247 | A17 | 10m red | .95 | .95 |
| 248 | A17 | 20m ultramarine | 1.60 | 1.60 |
| 249 | A18 | 50m dull green | 2.50 | 2.50 |
| | | Nos. 245-249 (5) | 6.20 | 6.20 |

UPU, 75th anniv. For overprints see Nos. N18-N22.

**Nos. 207-208, 211, 215-220, 230-235 Surcharged in Carmine, Black or Green**

**1952    Wmk. 4    *Perf. 12***
**Size: 17¾x21½mm**

| | | | | |
|---|---|---|---|---|
| 255 | A3 | 1f on 1m red brn (Bk) | .50 | .50 |
| 256 | A3 | 2f on 2m Prus grn (Bk) | .50 | .50 |
| 257 | A3 | 3f on 3m rose car | .50 | .50 |
| 258 | A3 | 4f on 4m dp yel grn | .50 | .50 |
| 259 | A3 | 5f on 5m org (G) | .75 | .75 |
| 260 | A3 | 10f on 10m vio | 1.10 | 1.00 |
| 261 | A3 | 12f on 12m dp rose (Bk) | 1.10 | 1.00 |
| 262 | A3 | 15f on 15m dl ol grn | 1.40 | .75 |
| 263 | A3 | 20f on 20m dp bl | 2.25 | 1.10 |

**Size: 20x24mm**

| | | | | |
|---|---|---|---|---|
| 264 | A3 | 50f on 50m red lil (G) | 2.25 | 1.75 |
| 265 | A3 | 90f on 90m ocher (G) | 16.00 | 11.50 |
| 266 | A3 | 100f on 100m dp bl | 9.00 | 3.75 |
| 267 | A3 | 200f on 200m dk vio | 14.00 | 4.75 |
| 268 | A3 | 500f on 500m dk brn | 30.00 | 15.00 |
| 269 | A3 | 1d on £1 black | 75.00 | 20.00 |
| | | Nos. 255-269 (15) | 154.85 | 63.35 |

This surcharge also exists on Nos. 199-203, 205, 209-210, 212-214. Numerous inverted, double and wrong color surcharges exist.

**Relief Map — A19**

### *Perf. 13½x13*
**1952, Apr. 1    Engr.    Wmk. 4**

| | | | | |
|---|---|---|---|---|
| 270 | A19 | 1f red brn & yel grn | .45 | .45 |
| 271 | A19 | 2f dk bl grn & red | .45 | .45 |
| 272 | A19 | 3f car & gray blk | .45 | .45 |
| 273 | A19 | 4f green & orange | .50 | .50 |
| 274 | A19 | 5f choc & rose vio | .55 | .55 |
| 275 | A19 | 10f violet & brown | .55 | .55 |
| 276 | A19 | 20f dark bl & blk | 1.50 | .80 |
| 277 | A19 | 100f dp blue & brn | 5.50 | 3.50 |
| 278 | A19 | 200f purple & orange | 13.00 | 6.75 |
| | | Nos. 270-278 (9) | 22.95 | 14.00 |

Unity of Jordan, Apr. 24, 1950.

---

For overprints see Nos. 297-305.

**Amir Abdullah ibn Hussein — A20**

**1952    Wmk. 4    *Perf. 11½***

| | | | | |
|---|---|---|---|---|
| 279 | A20 | 5f orange | .50 | .50 |
| 280 | A20 | 10f violet | .50 | .50 |
| 281 | A20 | 12f carmine | 2.00 | 1.25 |
| 282 | A20 | 15f olive | 1.25 | .50 |
| 283 | A20 | 20f deep blue | 1.25 | .60 |

**Size: 20x24½mm**
**Perf. 12x12½**

| | | | | |
|---|---|---|---|---|
| 284 | A20 | 50f plum | 2.75 | 1.00 |
| 285 | A20 | 90f brn orange | 7.50 | 3.75 |
| 286 | A20 | 100f deep blue | 8.00 | 2.50 |
| | | Nos. 279-286 (8) | 23.75 | 10.60 |

**Nos. RA5-RA7 Overprinted in Black or Carmine**

### *Perf. 11½x12½*
**1953    Unwmk.    Engr.**

| | | | | |
|---|---|---|---|---|
| 286A | PT1 | 10m carmine | 57.50 | 47.50 |
| 286B | PT1 | 15m gray (C) | 4.00 | 2.00 |
| 286C | PT1 | 20m dark brown | 125.00 | 95.00 |

**Same Overprint on Nos. NRA4-NRA7**

| | | | | |
|---|---|---|---|---|
| 286D | PT1 | 5m plum | 80.00 | 47.50 |
| 286E | PT1 | 10m carmine | 80.00 | 47.50 |
| 286F | PT1 | 15m gray (C) | 80.00 | 47.50 |
| 286G | PT1 | 20m dk brn (C) | 80.00 | 47.50 |
| | | Nos. 286A-286G (7) | 506.50 | 334.50 |

In addition a few sheets of Nos. RA9, NRA1, NRA3, NRA8-NRA9 and RA37-RA41 have been reported with this overprint. It is doubtful whether they were regularly issued. See Nos. 344-347.

**1953    Wmk. 4    *Perf. 11½x12½***

| | | | | |
|---|---|---|---|---|
| 287 | PT1 | 5f plum | .45 | .25 |
| 288 | PT1 | 10f carmine | .55 | .25 |
| 289 | PT1 | 15f gray (C) | 1.25 | 1.00 |
| 290 | PT1 | 20f dark brown (C) | 2.75 | 1.50 |
| | | Nos. 287-290 (4) | 5.00 | 3.00 |

**King Hussein — A21**

**Unwmk.**
**1953, Oct. 1    Engr.    *Perf. 12***
**Portrait in Black**

| | | | | |
|---|---|---|---|---|
| 291 | A21 | 1f dark green | .35 | .25 |
| 292 | A21 | 4f deep plum | .35 | .25 |
| 293 | A21 | 15f deep ultra | 2.00 | .40 |
| 294 | A21 | 20f dark purple | 3.25 | .40 |
| 295 | A21 | 50f dark blue grn | 7.00 | 3.25 |
| 296 | A21 | 100f dark blue | 12.50 | 9.00 |
| | | Nos. 291-296 (6) | 25.45 | 13.55 |

Accession of King Hussein, May 2, 1953.

**Nos. 270-278 Overprinted in Black**

1½mm Spacing

**Nos. RA28-RA31 Overprinted in Black or Carmine ½mm Spacing**

**1953    Wmk. 4    *Perf. 13½x13***

| | | | | |
|---|---|---|---|---|
| 297 | A19 | 1f red brn & yel grn | .40 | .40 |
| 298 | A19 | 2f dk bl grn & red | .40 | .40 |
| 299 | A19 | 3f car & gray blk | .40 | .40 |
| 300 | A19 | 4f green & orange | .40 | .40 |
| 301 | A19 | 5f choc & rose vio | .40 | .40 |
| 302 | A19 | 10f violet & brown | 1.25 | .75 |
| 303 | A19 | 20f dark bl & blk | 1.25 | .95 |

---

| | | | | |
|---|---|---|---|---|
| 304 | A19 | 100f dp blue & brn | 7.25 | 1.75 |
| 305 | A19 | 200f purple & org | 10.00 | 6.50 |
| | | Nos. 297-305 (9) | 21.75 | 11.95 |

Two main settings of the bars exist on Nos. 297-300 and 304 — the "normal" 1½mm spacing, and the "narrow" ½mm spacing. Values above are for normal spacing. Value of set with narrow spacing, $150.

**El Deir Temple, Petra — A22**

**King Hussein — A22a**

**Dome of the Rock — A23**

**Al Aqsa Mosque — A23a**

Designs: 4f, 500f, 1d, King Hussein. 3f, 5f, Treasury Bldg., Petra. 50f, 100f, 200f, Al Aqsa Mosque. 20f, Dome of the Rock.

**1954    Unwmk.    Engr.    *Perf. 12½***

| | | | | |
|---|---|---|---|---|
| 306 | A22 | 1f dk bl grn & red brn | .35 | .25 |
| 307 | A22 | 2f red & black | .35 | .25 |
| 308 | A22 | 3f dp redsh pur & vio bl | .35 | .25 |
| 309 | A22a | 4f org brn & dk grn | .50 | .30 |
| 310 | A22 | 5f vio & dk grn | .50 | .30 |
| 311 | A23 | 10f pur & dk grn | .75 | .75 |
| 312 | A23a | 12f car rose & sep | 1.75 | .70 |
| 313 | A23 | 20f bl & gray grn | 1.75 | .35 |
| 314 | A23a | 50f dk bl & dp rose | 3.75 | 1.25 |
| 315 | A23a | 100f dk grn & bl | 3.25 | .75 |
| 316 | A23a | 200f dp cl & pck bl | 13.00 | 2.25 |
| 317 | A22a | 500f choc & purple | 37.50 | 12.50 |
| 318 | A22a | 1d dk ol grn & rose brn | 55.00 | 22.50 |
| | | Nos. 306-318 (13) | 118.80 | 42.40 |

See Nos. 324-337. For overprint see No. 425.

**Globe — A23b**

### *Perf. 13½x13*
**1955, Jan. 1    Photo.    Wmk. 195**

| | | | | |
|---|---|---|---|---|
| 319 | A23b | 15f green | .60 | .45 |
| 320 | A23b | 20f violet | .60 | .45 |
| 321 | A23b | 25f yellow brown | .75 | .70 |
| | | Nos. 319-321 (3) | 1.95 | 1.60 |

Founding of the APU, July 1, 1954.

**Princess Dina Abdul Hamid and King Hussein**
**A24**

**1955, Apr. 19    *Perf. 11x11½***

| | | | | |
|---|---|---|---|---|
| 322 | A24 | 15f ultramarine | 2.25 | .95 |
| 323 | A24 | 100f rose brown | 8.50 | 3.75 |

Marriage of King Hussein and Princess Dina Abdul Hamid.

**Types of 1954**
Design: 15f, Dome of the Rock.

**Wmk. 305**
**1955-64    Engr.    *Perf. 12½***

| | | | | |
|---|---|---|---|---|
| 324 | A22 | 1f dk grn & red brn ('57) | .40 | .25 |
| 325 | A22 | 2f red & blk ('57) | .40 | .25 |
| 326 | A22 | 3f dp plum & vio bl ('56) | .40 | .25 |
| 327 | A22 | 4f org brn & dk grn ('56) | .40 | .25 |

| 328 | A22 | 5f vio & dk grn ('56) | .40 | .25 |
| 329 | A23 | 10f pur & grn ('57) | 3.75 | 2.25 |
| 330 | A23 | 12f car rose & sep | 1.50 | 1.00 |
| 331 | A23 | 15f dp brn & rose red | .90 | .25 |
| 332 | A23 | 20f dp bl & dk grn ('57) | .75 | .25 |
| 333 | A23 | 50f dk bl & dp rose | 1.40 | .35 |
| 334 | A23 | 100f grn & dp bl ('62) | 3.50 | 1.25 |
| 335 | A23 | 200f dp cl & pck bl ('65) | 9.50 | 2.25 |
| 336 | A22 | 500f choc & pur ('65) | 32.50 | 12.00 |
| 337 | A22 | 1d dk ol grn & rose brn ('65) | 57.50 | 20.00 |
| | | Nos. 324-337 (14) | 113.30 | 40.85 |

Envelope — A25

### Wmk. 305
**1956, Jan. 15     Engr.     Perf. 14**
**"Postmarks" in Black**

| 338 | A25 | 1f light brown | .35 | .30 |
| 339 | A25 | 4f dark car rose | .35 | .30 |
| 340 | A25 | 15f blue | .35 | .30 |
| 341 | A25 | 20f yellow olive | .35 | .30 |
| 342 | A25 | 50f slate blue | .75 | .40 |
| 343 | A25 | 100f vermilion | 1.10 | .70 |
| | | Nos. 338-343 (6) | 3.25 | 2.30 |

1st Arab Postal Congress in Amman.

Nos. RA1, RA3, RA8 and RA33 Overprinted in Carmine or Black

### Perf. 11½x12½
**1956, Jan. 5     Unwmk.**

| 344 | PT1 | 1m ultramarine | .45 | .45 |
| 345 | PT1 | 3m emerald | .45 | .45 |
| 346 | PT1 | 50m purple | 1.10 | 1.00 |

**Wmk. 4**
| 347 | PT1 | 100f orange (Bk) | 6.75 | 3.50 |
| | | Nos. 344-347 (4) | 8.75 | 5.40 |

Numerous inverted, double and wrong color surcharges exist.

Torch of Liberty — A26

**1958     Wmk. 305     Engr.     Perf. 12½**

| 348 | A26 | 5f blue & red brown | .35 | .35 |
| 349 | A26 | 15f bister brn & blk | .45 | .40 |
| 350 | A26 | 35f blue grn & plum | 1.00 | .90 |
| 351 | A26 | 45f car & olive grn | 3.25 | 1.00 |
| | | Nos. 348-351 (4) | 5.05 | 2.65 |

10th anniv. of the Universal Declaration of Human Rights.

King Hussein — A27

### Perf. 12x11½
**1959     Wmk. 305     Engr.**
**Centers in Black**

| 352 | A27 | 1f deep green | .35 | .25 |
| 353 | A27 | 2f violet | .35 | .25 |
| 354 | A27 | 3f deep carmine | .40 | .25 |
| 355 | A27 | 4f brown black | .45 | .25 |
| 356 | A27 | 7f dark green | .55 | .25 |
| 357 | A27 | 12f deep carmine | .75 | .25 |
| 358 | A27 | 15f dark red | .80 | .25 |
| 359 | A27 | 21f green | .90 | .25 |
| 360 | A27 | 25f ocher | 1.10 | .25 |
| 361 | A27 | 35f dark blue | 1.75 | .30 |
| 362 | A27 | 40f olive green | 2.50 | .30 |
| 363 | A27 | 50f red | 3.00 | .30 |
| 364 | A27 | 100f blue green | 4.00 | .75 |
| 365 | A27 | 200f rose lake | 11.00 | 3.00 |

| 366 | A27 | 500f gray blue | 26.00 | 12.00 |
| 367 | A27 | 1d dark purple | 50.00 | 30.00 |
| | | Nos. 352-367 (16) | 103.90 | 48.90 |

For overprints see Nos. 423-424, 425a, 426-427.

Arab League Center, Cairo, and King Hussein — A28

### Perf. 13x13½
**1960, Mar. 22     Photo.     Wmk. 328**
| 368 | A28 | 15f dull green & blk | .35 | .25 |

Opening of the Arab League Center and the Arab Postal Museum in Cairo.

World Refugee Year Emblem — A29

### Wmk. 305
**1960, Apr. 7     Litho.     Perf. 13½**
| 369 | A29 | 15f pale blue & red | .35 | .25 |
| 370 | A29 | 35f bister & blue | .60 | .45 |

World Refugee Year, 7/1/59-6/30/60.
For overprints see Nos. 377-378.

Shah of Iran, King Hussein and Flags — A30

### Perf. 13x13½
**1960, May 15     Wmk. 305**
**Flags in Green, Red & Black**

| 371 | A30 | 15f yellow & black | .55 | .55 |
| 372 | A30 | 35f blue & black | .80 | .80 |
| 373 | A30 | 50f salmon & black | 1.10 | 1.10 |
| | | Nos. 371-373 (3) | 2.45 | 2.45 |

Visit of Mohammed Riza Pahlavi, Shah of Iran, to Jordan, Nov. 2, 1959.

Oil Refinery, Zarka — A31

**1961, May 1     Engr.     Perf. 14x13**
| 374 | A31 | 15f dull vio & blue | .35 | .25 |
| 375 | A31 | 35f dl vio & brick red | .55 | .40 |

Opening of oil refinery at Zarka.

Urban and Nomad Families and Chart — A32

### Perf. 13x13½
**1961, Oct. 15     Photo.     Unwmk.**
| 376 | A32 | 15f orange brown | .30 | .25 |

First Jordanian census, 1961.

**Nos. 369-370 Overprinted in English and Arabic, "In Memorial of Dag Hammarskjoeld 1904-1961," and Laurel Leaf Border**

**1961     Wmk. 305     Litho.     Perf. 13½**
| 377 | A29 | 15f pale blue & red | 4.00 | 3.75 |
| 378 | A29 | 35f bister & blue | 4.50 | 4.00 |

Dag Hammarskjold, Secretary General of the UN, 1953-1961.

Malaria Eradication Emblem — A33

### Perf. 11x11½
**1962, Apr. 15     Unwmk.**
| 379 | A33 | 15f bright pink | .35 | .25 |
| 380 | A33 | 35f blue | .45 | .30 |

WHO drive to eradicate malaria. A souvenir sheet exists perf. and imperf. with one each of Nos. 379-380. Value, $5.50, perf. and imperf.

Dial and Exchange Building, Amman — A34

**1962, Dec. 11     Engr.     Wmk. 305**
| 381 | A34 | 15f blue & lilac | .30 | .25 |
| 382 | A34 | 35f lilac & emer | .35 | .25 |

Telephone automation in Amman (in 1960).

Opening of the Port of 'Aqaba — A35

**1962, Dec. 11**
| 383 | A35 | 15f lilac & blk | .40 | .25 |
| 384 | A35 | 35f violet bl & blk | .60 | .30 |
| a. | | Souvenir sheet of 2, #383-384 | 5.00 | 5.00 |

No. 384a imperf., same value.

Dag Hammarskjold and UN Headquarters, NY — A36

### Perf. 14x14½
**1963, Jan. 24     Photo.     Unwmk.**
| 385 | A36 | 15f ultra, ol grn & brn red | .45 | .25 |
| 386 | A36 | 35f ol, brn red & ultra | .80 | .45 |
| 387 | A36 | 50f brn red, ol & ultra | 1.25 | .80 |
| | | Nos. 385-387 (3) | 2.50 | 1.50 |

17th anniv. of the UN and in memory of Dag Hammarskjold, Secretary General of the UN, 1953-61. An imperf. souvenir sheet contains one each of Nos. 385-387 with simulated perforations. Value $9.

### Imperforates
Starting with No. 385, imperforates exist of many Jordanian stamps.

Church of St. Virgin's Tomb, Jerusalem — A37

Designs: No. 389, Basilica of the Agony, Gethsemane. No. 390, Church of the Holy Sepulcher, Bethlehem. No. 391, Church of the Nativity, Bethlehem. No. 392, Haram el-Khalil (tomb of Abraham), Hebron. No. 393, Dome of the Rock, Jerusalem. No. 394, Mosque of Omar el-Khatab, Jerusalem. No. 395, Al Aqsa Mosque, Jerusalem.

**1963, Feb. 5     Perf. 14½x14**
**Center Multicolored**

| 388 | A37 | 50f blue | 1.50 | 1.00 |
| 389 | A37 | 50f dull red | 1.50 | 1.00 |
| 390 | A37 | 50f bright blue | 1.50 | 1.00 |
| 391 | A37 | 50f olive green | 1.50 | 1.00 |
| a. | | Vert. strip of 4, #388-391 | 15.00 | |
| 392 | A37 | 50f gray | 1.50 | 1.00 |
| a. | | Yellow (in center) omitted | — | |
| 393 | A37 | 50f purple | 1.50 | 1.00 |
| a. | | Yellow (in center) omitted | — | |
| 394 | A37 | 50f dull red | 1.50 | 1.00 |
| a. | | Yellow (in center) omitted | — | |
| 395 | A37 | 50f light purple | 1.50 | 1.00 |
| a. | | Vert. strip of 4, #392-395 | 15.00 | |
| b. | | Yellow (in center) omitted | — | |
| | | Nos. 388-395 (8) | 12.00 | 8.00 |

Arab League Building, Cairo — A38

**1963, July 16     Photo.     Perf. 13½x13**
| 396 | A38 | 15f slate blue | .45 | .25 |
| 397 | A38 | 35f orange red | .65 | .25 |

Arab League.

Wheat and UN Emblem — A39

### Perf. 11½x12½
**1963, Sept. 15     Litho.     Wmk. 305**
| 398 | A39 | 15f lt bl, grn & black | .30 | .25 |
| 399 | A39 | 35f lt grn, grn & blk | .30 | .25 |
| a. | | Souvenir sheet of 2, #398-399 | 1.50 | 1.50 |

FAO "Freedom from Hunger" campaign. No. 399a imperf., same value.

East Ghor Canal, Pylon, Gear Wheel and Wheat — A40

**1963, Sept. 20     Perf. 14½x14**
| 400 | A40 | 1f dull yel & black | .35 | .25 |
| 401 | A40 | 4f blue & black | .35 | .25 |
| 402 | A40 | 5f lilac & black | .35 | .25 |
| 403 | A40 | 10f brt yel grn & blk | .40 | .25 |
| 404 | A40 | 35f orange & black | 1.25 | .50 |
| | | Nos. 400-404 (5) | 2.70 | 1.50 |

East Ghor Canal Project.

UNESCO Emblem, Scales and Globe — A41

### Perf. 13½x13
**1963, Dec. 10     Unwmk.**
| 405 | A41 | 50f pale vio bl & red | .70 | .60 |
| 406 | A41 | 50f rose red & blue | .70 | .60 |

15th anniv. of the Universal Declaration of Human Rights.

Red Crescent and King Hussein A42

**1963, Dec. 24     Photo.     Perf. 14x14½**
| 407 | A42 | 1f red & red lilac | .30 | .25 |
| 408 | A42 | 2f red & bl green | .30 | .25 |
| 409 | A42 | 3f red & dk blue | .30 | .25 |
| 410 | A42 | 4f red & dk green | .30 | .25 |
| 411 | A42 | 5f red & dk brown | .30 | .25 |
| 412 | A42 | 85f red & dp green | 1.10 | .95 |

**Design: Red Cross at right, no portrait**
| 413 | A42 | 1f red lilac & red | .30 | .25 |
| 414 | A42 | 2f blue grn & red | .30 | .25 |
| 415 | A42 | 3f dk blue & red | .30 | .25 |
| 416 | A42 | 4f dk green & red | .30 | .25 |
| 417 | A42 | 5f dk brown & red | .30 | .25 |
| 418 | A42 | 85f dp green & red | 4.00 | 1.50 |
| | | Nos. 407-418 (12) | 8.10 | 4.95 |

Centenary of the Intl. Red Cross. Two 100f imperf. souvenir sheets, red and red lilac, exist in the Red Crescent and Red Cross designs. Value, pair of sheets $50.

Hussein ibn Ali and King Hussein — A43

## Perf. 11x11½

**1963, Dec. 25**    **Litho.**    **Unwmk.**
| | | | |
|---|---|---|---|
| 419 | A43 | 15f yellow & multi | .50 | .25 |
| 420 | A43 | 25f multicolored | .75 | .35 |
| 421 | A43 | 35f brt pink & multi | 1.75 | .85 |
| 422 | A43 | 50f lt blue & multi | 2.75 | 2.00 |
| | | *Nos. 419-422 (4)* | 5.75 | 3.45 |

Arab Renaissance Day, June 10, 1916. Perf. and imperf. souvenir sheets exist containing one each of Nos. 419-422. Value: perf, $6.50; imperf, $9.

Nos. 359, 312, 357 and 361 Surcharged

**Wmk. 305, Unwmk.**
**Perf. 12x11½, 12½**

**1963, Dec. 16**          **Engr.**
| | | | | |
|---|---|---|---|---|
| 423 | A27 | 1f on 21f grn & blk | .40 | .30 |
| 424 | A27 | 2f on 21f grn & blk | .40 | .30 |
| 425 | A23 | 4f on 12f car rose & sepia | .45 | .40 |
| a. | | 4f on 12f dp car & blk (#357) | 19.00 | 22.50 |
| 426 | A27 | 5f on 21f grn & blk | .85 | .50 |
| 427 | A27 | 25f on 35f dk bl & blk | 3.25 | 1.50 |
| | | *Nos. 423-427 (5)* | 5.35 | 3.00 |

Pope Paul VI, King Hussein and Al Aqsa Mosque, Jerusalem — A44

Portraits and: 35f, Dome of the Rock. 50f, Church of the Holy Sepulcher. 80f, Church of the Nativity, Bethlehem.

**1964, Jan. 4**    **Litho.**    **Perf. 13x13½**
| | | | | |
|---|---|---|---|---|
| 428 | A44 | 15f emerald & blk | .80 | .30 |
| 429 | A44 | 35f car rose & blk | 1.00 | .40 |
| a. | | Black omitted | | |
| 430 | A44 | 50f brown & black | 1.75 | .90 |
| 431 | A44 | 80f vio bl & blk | 3.25 | 2.00 |
| | | *Nos. 428-431 (4)* | 6.80 | 3.60 |

Visit of Pope Paul VI to the Holy Land, Jan. 4-6. An imperf. souvenir sheet contains 4 stamps similar to Nos. 428-431. Value $27.50.

A45

Crown Prince Abdullah ben Al-Hussein A46

Design: 5f, Crown Prince standing, vert.

**1964, Mar. 30**    **Photo.**    **Perf. 14**
| | | | | |
|---|---|---|---|---|
| 432 | A46 | 5f multicolored | .55 | .25 |
| 433 | A46 | 10f multicolored | .65 | .50 |
| 434 | A46 | 35f multicolored | 1.50 | 1.00 |
| | | *Nos. 432-434 (3)* | 2.70 | 1.75 |

2nd birthday of Crown Prince Abdullah ben Al-Hussein (b. Jan. 30, 1962).
Nos. 433 and 434 exist with gold color omitted.

A47

---

Mercury Astronauts, Spacecraft — A48

Designs: b, M. Scott Carpenter. c, Entering space. d, Alan Shepard. e, At launch pad. f, Virgil Grissom. g, After separation. h, Walter Schirra. i, Lift-off. j, John Glenn. Stamp has point down on b, d, f, h, j.

**1964, Mar. 25**    **Photo.**    **Perf. 14**
| | | | | |
|---|---|---|---|---|
| 435 | A47 | 20f Block of 10, #a.-j. | 12.00 | 6.50 |

*Imperf*
**Size: 111x80mm**
| | | | | |
|---|---|---|---|---|
| 436 | A48 | 100f multicolored | 20.00 | 20.00 |

1964 Olympic Games, Tokyo — A49

Designs: 1f, 2f, 3f, 5f vertical.

**Perf. 14½x14, 14x14½**
**1964, June 1**    **Litho.**    **Unwmk.**
| | | | | |
|---|---|---|---|---|
| 446 | A49 | 1f Basketball | .50 | .25 |
| 447 | A49 | 2f Volleyball | .50 | .25 |
| 448 | A49 | 3f Soccer | .50 | .25 |
| 449 | A49 | 4f Table Tennis | .50 | .25 |
| 450 | A49 | 5f Running | .50 | .25 |
| 451 | A49 | 35f Bicycling | 1.75 | 1.10 |
| 452 | A49 | 50f Fencing | 2.50 | 1.50 |
| 453 | A49 | 100f Pole vault | 4.50 | 2.75 |
| | | *Nos. 446-453 (8)* | 11.25 | 6.60 |

Oct. 10-25. An imperf. 200f greenish blue souvenir sheet in design of 100f exists. Value $35.

Mother and Child — A50

**1964, June 1**    **Wmk. 305**    **Perf. 14**
| | | | | |
|---|---|---|---|---|
| 454 | A50 | 5f multicolored | .30 | .25 |
| 455 | A50 | 10f multicolored | .30 | .25 |
| 456 | A50 | 25f multicolored | .30 | .25 |
| | | *Nos. 454-456 (3)* | .90 | .75 |

Social Studies Seminar, fourth session.

Pres. John F. Kennedy A51

**1964, July 15**        **Unwmk.**
| | | | | |
|---|---|---|---|---|
| 457 | A51 | 1f brt violet | .50 | .40 |
| 458 | A51 | 2f carmine rose | .50 | .40 |
| 459 | A51 | 3f ultramarine | .50 | .40 |
| 460 | A51 | 4f orange brown | .50 | .40 |
| 461 | A51 | 5f bright green | .50 | .40 |
| 462 | A51 | 85f rose red | 18.50 | 11.00 |
| | | *Nos. 457-462 (6)* | 21.00 | 13.00 |

President John F. Kennedy (1917-1963). An imperf. 100f brown souvenir sheet exists. Size of stamp: 58x83mm. Value $18.50.

Ramses II — A52

**Perf. 14½x14**
**1964, July**    **Litho.**    **Wmk. 305**
| | | | | |
|---|---|---|---|---|
| 463 | A52 | 4f lt blue & dark brn | .30 | .25 |
| 464 | A52 | 15f yellow & violet | .30 | .25 |
| 465 | A52 | 25f lt yel grn & dk red | .30 | .25 |
| | | *Nos. 463-465 (3)* | .90 | .75 |

UNESCO world campaign to save historic monuments in Nubia.

---

King Hussein and Map of Jordan and Israel — A53

**1964, Sept. 5**    **Unwmk.**    **Perf. 12**
| | | | | |
|---|---|---|---|---|
| 466 | A53 | 10f multicolored | .40 | .25 |
| 467 | A53 | 15f multicolored | .40 | .25 |
| 468 | A53 | 25f multicolored | .40 | .25 |
| 469 | A53 | 50f multicolored | .70 | .25 |
| 470 | A53 | 80f multicolored | 1.00 | .45 |
| | | *Nos. 466-470 (5)* | 2.90 | 1.45 |

Council of the Heads of State of the Arab League (Arab Summit Conference), Cairo, Jan. 13, 1964. An imperf. souvenir sheet contains Nos. 466-470 with simulated perforations. Value $4.

Pope Paul VI, King Hussein and Patriarch Athenagoras; Church of St. Savior, Church of the Holy Sepulcher and Dome of the Rock — A54

**1964, Aug. 17**        **Litho.**
| | | | | |
|---|---|---|---|---|
| 471 | A54 | 10f dk grn, sep & org | .50 | .25 |
| 472 | A54 | 15f claret, sep & org | .50 | .25 |
| 473 | A54 | 25f choc, sepia & org | .50 | .25 |
| 474 | A54 | 50f blue, sepia & org | 1.00 | .70 |
| 475 | A54 | 80f brt grn, sep & org | 2.25 | .60 |
| | | *Nos. 471-475 (5)* | 4.75 | 2.05 |

Meeting between Pope Paul VI and Patriarch Athenagoras of the Greek Orthodox Church in Jerusalem, Jan. 5, 1964. An imperf. souvenir sheet contains Nos. 471-475 with simulated perforations. Value $12.
A two-line bilingual overprint, "Papa Paulus VI World Peace Visit to United Nations 1965", was applied to Nos. 471-475 and the souvenir sheet. These overprints were issued Apr. 27, 1966. Value, unused: set, $6; souvenir sheet, $12.

Pagoda, Olympic Torch and Emblem A55

**1964, Nov. 21**    **Litho.**    **Perf. 14**
| | | | | |
|---|---|---|---|---|
| 476 | A55 | 1f dark red | .45 | .25 |
| 477 | A55 | 2f bright violet | .55 | .25 |
| 478 | A55 | 3f blue green | .65 | .25 |
| 479 | A55 | 4f brown | .75 | .30 |
| 480 | A55 | 5f henna brown | .85 | .35 |
| 481 | A55 | 35f indigo | 1.25 | 1.00 |
| 482 | A55 | 50f olive | 2.00 | 1.50 |
| 483 | A55 | 100f violet blue | 4.25 | 3.00 |
| | | *Nos. 476-483 (8)* | 10.75 | 6.90 |

18th Olympic Games, Tokyo, Oct. 10-25. An imperf. 100f carmine rose souvenir sheet exists. Size of stamp: 82mm at the base. Value $20.

Scouts Crossing Stream on Log Bridge A56

Designs: 2f, First aid. 3f, Calisthenics. 4f, Instruction in knot tying. 5f, Outdoor cooking. 35f, Sailing. 50f, Campfire.

**1964, Dec. 7**        **Unwmk.**
| | | | | |
|---|---|---|---|---|
| 484 | A56 | 1f brown | .70 | .25 |
| 485 | A56 | 2f bright violet | .70 | .25 |
| 486 | A56 | 3f ocher | .70 | .25 |
| 487 | A56 | 4f maroon | .70 | .25 |
| 488 | A56 | 5f yellow green | .70 | .25 |
| 489 | A56 | 35f bright blue | 2.00 | 1.25 |
| 490 | A56 | 50f dk slate green | 3.50 | 1.75 |
| | | *Nos. 484-490 (7)* | 9.00 | 4.25 |

Jordanian Boy Scouts. An imperf. 100f dark blue souvenir sheet in campfire design exists. Size of stamp: 104mm at the base. Value $22.50.

---

Russian Cosmonauts — A57

Designs: No. 491, Yuri Gagarin. No. 492, Gherman Titov. No. 493, Andrian G. Nikolayev. No. 494, Pavel R. Popovich. No. 495, Valeri Bykovski. No. 496, Valentina Tereshkova.

**1965, Jan. 20**    **Litho.**    **Perf. 14**
| | | | | |
|---|---|---|---|---|
| 491 | A57 | 40f sepia & vio bl | 1.25 | .75 |
| 492 | A57 | 40f pink & dk grn | 1.25 | .75 |
| 493 | A57 | 40f lt bl & vio blk | 1.25 | .75 |
| 494 | A57 | 40f olive & dk vio | 1.25 | .75 |
| 495 | A57 | 40f lt grn & red brn | 1.25 | .75 |
| 496 | A57 | 40f chlky bl & blk | 1.25 | .75 |
| | | *Nos. 491-496 (6)* | 7.50 | 4.50 |

Russian cosmonauts. A blue 100f souvenir sheet exists showing portraits of the 6 astronauts and space-ship circling globe. This sheet received later an additional overprint honoring the space flight of Komarov, Feoktistov and Yegorov. Value $20, each.
For overprints see Nos. 527-527E.

UN Headquarters and Emblem A58

**1965, Feb. 15**        **Perf. 14x15**
| | | | | |
|---|---|---|---|---|
| 497 | A58 | 30f yel brn, pur & lt bl | .60 | .25 |
| 498 | A58 | 70f vio, lt bl & yel brn | 1.00 | .70 |

19th anniv. of the UN (in 1964). A souvenir sheet contains Nos. 497-498, imperf. Value $14.

Dagger in Map of Palestine — A59

**1965, Apr. 9**    **Photo.**    **Perf. 11x11½**
| | | | | |
|---|---|---|---|---|
| 499 | A59 | 25f red & olive | 4.50 | 1.25 |
| a. | | Red omitted | | |

Deir Yassin massacre, Apr. 9, 1948.
See Iraq Nos. 372-373 and Kuwait Nos. 281-282.

Volleyball Player and Cup — A60

**1965, June**    **Litho.**    **Perf. 14½x14**
| | | | | |
|---|---|---|---|---|
| 500 | A60 | 15f lemon | 1.25 | .25 |
| 501 | A60 | 35f rose brown | 1.50 | .25 |
| 502 | A60 | 50f greenish blue | 2.25 | .75 |
| | | *Nos. 500-502 (3)* | 5.00 | 1.25 |

Arab Volleyball Championships. An imperf. 100f orange brown souvenir sheet exists. Size of stamp: 33x57mm. Value $22.50.

Cavalry Horsemanship — A61

Army Day: 10f, Tank. 35f, King Hussein and aides standing in army car.

**1965, May 24**
| | | | | |
|---|---|---|---|---|
| 503 | A61 | 5f green | .50 | .25 |
| 504 | A61 | 10f violet blue | .55 | .25 |
| 505 | A61 | 35f brown red | 1.50 | .55 |
| | *Nos. 503-505 (3)* | | 2.55 | 1.05 |

John F. Kennedy A62

**1965, June 1    Wmk. 305    Perf. 14**
| | | | | |
|---|---|---|---|---|
| 506 | A62 | 10f black & brt green | .30 | .25 |
| 507 | A62 | 15f violet & orange | .50 | .25 |
| 508 | A62 | 25f brown & lt blue | .50 | .30 |
| 509 | A62 | 50f deep claret & emer | 1.50 | .60 |
| | *Nos. 506-509 (4)* | | 2.80 | 1.40 |

John F. Kennedy (1917-63). An imperf. 50f salmon and dark blue souv. sheet exists. Value $17.50.

Pope Paul VI, King Hussein and Dome of the Rock — A63

**Perf. 13½x14**
**1965, June 15    Litho.    Wmk. 305**
| | | | | |
|---|---|---|---|---|
| 510 | A63 | 5f brown & rose lil | .50 | .25 |
| 511 | A63 | 10f vio brn & lt yel grn | .90 | .40 |
| 512 | A63 | 15f ultra & salmon | 1.10 | .50 |
| 513 | A63 | 50f black & rose | 3.25 | 1.60 |
| | *Nos. 510-513 (4)* | | 5.75 | 2.75 |

1st anniversary of the visit of Pope Paul VI to the Holy Land. An imperf. 50f violet and light blue souvenir sheet exists with simulated perforations. Value $25.

Jordan's Pavilion and Unisphere — A64

**Perf. 14x13½**
**1965, Aug.    Unwmk.    Photo.**
| | | | | |
|---|---|---|---|---|
| 514 | A64 | 15f silver & multi | .45 | .25 |
| 515 | A64 | 25f bronze & multi | .45 | .25 |
| 516 | A64 | 50f gold & multi | .85 | .40 |
| a. | Souvenir sheet of 1, 100f | 3.25 | 3.00 |
| | *Nos. 514-516 (3)* | | 1.75 | .90 |

New York World's Fair, 1964-65.
No. 516a contains a 100f gold and multicolored stamp, type A64, imperf.

Library Aflame and Lamp — A64a

**1965, Aug.    Wmk. 305    Perf. 11½x11**
| | | | | |
|---|---|---|---|---|
| 517 | A64a | 25f black, grn & red | .50 | .25 |

Burning of the Library of Algiers, 6/7/62.

ITU Emblem, Old and New Telecommunication Equipment — A65

**1965, Aug.    Litho.    Perf. 14x13½**
| | | | | |
|---|---|---|---|---|
| 518 | A65 | 25f lt blue & dk bl | .40 | .25 |
| 519 | A65 | 45f grnsh gray & blk | .60 | .35 |

ITU, centenary. An imperf. 100f salmon and carmine rose souvenir sheet exists with carmine rose border. Size of stamp: 39x32mm. Value $3.

Syncom Satellite over Pagoda — A66

Designs: 10f, 20f, Rocket in space. 15f, Astronauts in cabin.

**1965, Sept.    Perf. 14**
| | | | | |
|---|---|---|---|---|
| 521 | A66 | 5f multicolored | .30 | .25 |
| 521A | A66 | 10f multicolored | .30 | .25 |
| 521B | A66 | 15f multicolored | .50 | .25 |
| 521C | A66 | 20f multicolored | .60 | .30 |
| 521D | A66 | 50f multicolored | 1.50 | .75 |
| | *Nos. 521-521D (5)* | | 3.20 | 1.80 |

Achievements in space research. A 50f multicolored imperf. souvenir sheet shows earth and Syncom satellite. Value $17.50.

Dead Sea — A66a

Designs: b, Qumran Caves. c, Dead Sea. d, Dead Sea Scrolls.

**1965, Sept. 23    Photo.    Perf. 14**
| | | | | |
|---|---|---|---|---|
| 522 | A66a | 35f Strip of 4, #a.-d. | 6.00 | 6.00 |

Visit of King Hussein to France and U.S. — A66b

10f, With Charles DeGaulle. 20f, With Lyndon Johnson.

**Wmk. 305**
**1965, Oct. 5    Litho.    Perf. 14**
| | | | | |
|---|---|---|---|---|
| 523 | A66b | 5f shown | .30 | .25 |
| 523A | A66b | 10f multicolored | .30 | .25 |
| 523B | A66b | 20f multicolored | .65 | .50 |
| 523C | A66b | 50f like #523 | 1.50 | 1.10 |
| | *Nos. 523-523C (4)* | | 2.75 | 2.10 |

No. 523C exists in a 50f imperf. souvenir sheet. Value $12.

Intl. Cooperation Year — A66c

**1965, Oct. 24    Perf. 14x13½**
| | | | | |
|---|---|---|---|---|
| 524 | A66c | 5f brt org & dk org | .40 | .25 |
| 524A | A66c | 10f brt bl & dk bl | .75 | .35 |
| 524B | A66c | 45f brt grn & dk violet | 2.10 | 1.40 |
| | *Nos. 524-524B (3)* | | 3.25 | 2.00 |

Arab Postal Union, 10th Anniv. — A66d

**1965, Nov. 5    Perf. 15x14**
| | | | | |
|---|---|---|---|---|
| 525 | A66d | 15f violet bl & blk | .30 | .25 |
| 525A | A66d | 25f brt yel grn & blk | .50 | .35 |

Dome of the Rock — A66e

**1965, Nov. 20    Perf. 14x15**
| | | | | |
|---|---|---|---|---|
| 526 | A66e | 15f multicolored | 1.10 | 1.10 |
| 526A | A66e | 25f multicolored | 1.60 | 1.60 |

**Nos. 491-496 with Spaceship & Bilingual Ovpt. in Blue**

**1966, Jan. 15    Litho.    Perf. 14**
| | | | | |
|---|---|---|---|---|
| 527 | A57 | 40f on No. 491 | 3.75 | 3.50 |
| 527A | A57 | 40f on No. 492 | 3.75 | 3.50 |
| 527B | A57 | 40f on No. 493 | 3.75 | 3.50 |
| 527C | A57 | 40f on No. 494 | 3.75 | 3.50 |
| 527D | A57 | 40f on No. 495 | 3.75 | 3.50 |
| 527E | A57 | 40f on No. 496 | 3.75 | 3.50 |
| | *Nos. 527-527E (6)* | | 22.50 | 21.00 |

Both souvenir sheets mentioned after No. 496 exist overprinted in red violet. Value, $50 each.

King Hussein A67

**Perf. 14½x14**
**1966, Jan. 15    Photo.    Unwmk.**
**Portrait in Slate Blue**
| | | | | |
|---|---|---|---|---|
| 528 | A67 | 1f orange | .40 | .25 |
| 528A | A67 | 2f ultramarine | .40 | .25 |
| 528B | A67 | 3f dk purple | .40 | .25 |
| 528C | A67 | 4f plum | .40 | .25 |
| 528D | A67 | 7f brn orange | .40 | .25 |
| 528E | A67 | 12f cerise | .40 | .25 |
| 528F | A67 | 15f olive brn | .40 | .25 |

**Portrait in Violet Brown**
| | | | | |
|---|---|---|---|---|
| 528G | A67 | 21f green | .55 | .25 |
| 528H | A67 | 25f greenish bl | .55 | .25 |
| 528I | A67 | 35f yel bister | .80 | .35 |
| 528J | A67 | 40f orange yel | 1.00 | .35 |
| 528K | A67 | 50f olive grn | 1.10 | .25 |
| 528L | A67 | 100f lt yel grn | 2.10 | .40 |
| 528M | A67 | 150f violet | 3.00 | 1.00 |
| | *Nos. 528-528M,C43-C45 (17)* | | 46.90 | 27.10 |

Anti-tuberculosis Campaign — A67a

**1966, May 17    Photo.    Perf. 14x15**
**Blue Overprint**
| | | | | |
|---|---|---|---|---|
| 529 | A67a | 15f multicolored | .65 | .50 |
| 529A | A67a | 35f multicolored | 1.10 | .95 |
| 529B | A67a | 50f multicolored | 1.50 | 1.25 |
| | *Nos. 529-529B (3)* | | 3.25 | 2.70 |

Unissued Freedom from Hunger stamps overprinted. Two imperf. souvenir sheets exist, one with simulated perforations. Value, each $10.

**Nos. 529-529B with Added Surcharge Obliterated with Black Bars**

**1966, May 17    Photo.    Perf. 14x15**
| | | | | |
|---|---|---|---|---|
| 530 | A67a | 15f on 15f + 15f | .75 | .30 |
| 530A | A67a | 35f on 35f + 35f | 1.50 | .75 |
| 530B | A67a | 50f on 50f + 50f | 2.75 | 1.25 |
| | *Nos. 530-530B (3)* | | 5.00 | 2.30 |

A67b

Stations on Jesus' walk to Calvary along Via Dolorosa (Stations of the Cross): 1f, Condemned to death. 2f, Takes up cross. 3f, Falls the 1st time. 4f, Meets His mother. 5f, Simon helps carry cross. 6f, Woman wipes Jesus' brow. 7f, Falls 2nd time. 8f, Tells women not to weep. 9f, Falls 3rd time. 10f, Stripped of His garment. 11f, Nailed to cross. 12f, Death on cross. 13f, Removal from cross. 14f, Burial.
Denominations expressed in Roman numerals.

**1966, Sept. 14    Photo.    Perf. 15x14**
| | | | | |
|---|---|---|---|---|
| 531 | A67b | 1f multi | .40 | .25 |
| 531A | A67b | 2f multi | .40 | .25 |
| 531B | A67b | 3f multi | .40 | .25 |
| 531C | A67b | 4f multi | .50 | .25 |
| 531D | A67b | 5f multi | .60 | .30 |
| 531E | A67b | 6f multi | .60 | .30 |
| 531F | A67b | 7f multi | .80 | .40 |
| 531G | A67b | 8f multi | .90 | .45 |
| 531H | A67b | 9f multi | 1.00 | .50 |
| 531I | A67b | 10f multi | 1.10 | .55 |
| 531J | A67b | 11f multi | 1.25 | .60 |
| 531K | A67b | 12f multi | 1.40 | .65 |
| 531L | A67b | 13f multi | 1.50 | .70 |
| 531M | A67b | 14f multi | 1.60 | .75 |
| | *Nos. 531-531M (14)* | | 12.45 | 6.20 |

**Souvenir Sheet**
**Imperf**
| | | | | |
|---|---|---|---|---|
| 531N | A67b | 100f like #531 | 30.00 | 27.50 |

A67c

Astronauts and spacecraft from Gemini Missions 6-8: 1f, Walter M. Schirra. 2f, Thomas P. Stafford. 3f, Frank Borman. 4f, James A. Lovell. 30f, Neil Armstrong. 60f, David R. Scott.
100f, Gemini 6-8 astronauts.

**1966, Nov. 15    Photo.    Perf. 15x14**
| | | | | |
|---|---|---|---|---|
| 532 | A67c | 1f multi | .35 | .25 |
| 532A | A67c | 2f multi | .35 | .25 |
| 532B | A67c | 3f multi | .35 | .25 |
| 532C | A67c | 4f multi | .35 | .25 |
| 532D | A67c | 30f multi | 1.50 | .90 |
| 532E | A67c | 60f multi | 2.10 | 1.50 |
| | *Nos. 532-532E (6)* | | 5.00 | 3.20 |

**Imperf**
**Size: 119x89mm**
| | | | | |
|---|---|---|---|---|
| 532F | A67c | 100f multi | 22.50 | 20.00 |

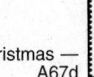

Christmas — A67d

5f, Magi following star. 10f, Adoration of the Magi. 35f, Flight to Egypt, vert.

**Perf. 14x15, 15x14**

| 1966, Dec. 21 | | | Photo. | |
|---|---|---|---|---|
| 533 | A67d | 5f multi | .35 | .25 |
| 533A | A67d | 10f multi | .35 | .25 |
| 533B | A67d | 35f multi | 3.25 | 1.10 |
| | | Nos. 533-533B (3) | 3.95 | 1.60 |

**Souvenir Sheet**
*Imperf*

| 533C | A67d | 50f like #533A | 22.50 | 20.00 |
|---|---|---|---|---|

King Hussein — A67e

Builders of World Peace: No. 534, Dag Hammarskjold. No. 534A, U Thant. No. 534B, Jawaharlal Nehru. No. 534C, Charles DeGaulle. No. 534D, John F. Kennedy. No. 534E, Lyndon B. Johnson. No. 534F, Pope John XXIII. No. 534G, Pope Paul VI. No. 534H, King Abdullah of Jordan.

| 1967, Jan. 5 | | Photo. | Perf. 15x14 | |
|---|---|---|---|---|
| | | **Background Color** | | |
| 534 | A67e | 5f gray | .35 | .25 |
| 534A | A67e | 5f brt yel grn | .35 | .25 |
| 534B | A67e | 10f rose lilac | .35 | .25 |
| a. | | "FILS" omitted | | |
| 534C | A67e | 10f red brown | .35 | .25 |
| 534D | A67e | 35f olive green | .95 | .70 |
| 534E | A67e | 35f orange | .95 | .70 |
| a. | | Gold (frame) omitted | | |
| 534F | A67e | 50f rose claret | 1.10 | 1.00 |
| 534G | A67e | 50f yel bister | 1.10 | 1.00 |
| 534H | A67e | 100f brt blue | 2.50 | 2.10 |
| 534I | A67e | 100f dull blue | 2.50 | 2.10 |
| | | Nos. 534-534I (10) | 10.50 | 8.60 |

**Imperf**
**Size: 99x64mm**

| 534J | A67e | 100f Kennedy, etc. | 22.50 | 22.50 |
|---|---|---|---|---|
| 534K | A67e | 100f DeGaulle, etc. | 22.50 | 22.50 |

King Hussein — A67f

**Photo. & Embossed**

| 1967, Feb. 7 | | | Imperf. | |
|---|---|---|---|---|
| | **Gold Portrait and Border** | | | |
| Diameter: 50f, 100f, 48mm; 200f, 54mm | | | | |
| | **Portrait of King Hussein** | | | |
| 535 | A67f | 5f dk bl & sal | .75 | .75 |
| 535A | A67f | 10f pur & sal | .75 | .75 |
| 535B | A67f | 50f blk brn & vio | 4.25 | 4.25 |
| 535C | A67f | 100f dk ol grn & pink | 5.00 | 5.00 |
| 535D | A67f | 200f dp bl & bl | 7.75 | 7.75 |
| | **Portrait of Crown Prince Hassan** | | | |
| 536 | A67f | 5f brt yel grn & blk | .75 | .75 |
| 536A | A67f | 10f vio & blk | .75 | .75 |
| 536B | A67f | 50f bl & blk | 4.25 | 4.25 |
| 536C | A67f | 100f bister & blk | 5.00 | 5.00 |
| 536D | A67f | 200f brt pink & blk | 7.75 | 7.75 |
| | **Portrait of John F. Kennedy** | | | |
| 537 | A67f | 5f brt bl & lt grn | .75 | .75 |
| 537A | A67f | 10f dp grn & pink | .75 | .75 |
| 537B | A67f | 50f brt rose & org yel | 3.25 | 3.25 |
| 537C | A67f | 100f brn & app grn | 4.25 | 4.25 |
| 537D | A67f | 200f dk pur & pale grn | 5.00 | 5.00 |
| | | Nos. 535-537D (15) | 51.00 | 51.00 |

1968 Summer Olympic Games, Mexico A67g

Olympic torch and: 1f, Natl. University Library with O'Gormans mosaics, statue, Mexico City. 2f, Fishermen on Lake Patzcuaro. 3f, Natl. University buildings. 4f, Paseo de la Reforma, Mexico City. 30f, Guadalajara Cathedral. 60f, 100f, Palace of Fine Arts, Mexico City.

**Perf. 14x15**

| 1967, Mar. | | Photo. | Unwmk. | |
|---|---|---|---|---|
| 538 | A67g | 1f lake, dk bl vio & blk | .30 | .25 |
| 538A | A67g | 2f blk, lake & dk bl vio | .30 | .25 |
| 538B | A67g | 3f dark bl vio, blk & lake | .30 | .25 |
| 538C | A67g | 4f bl, grn & brn | .30 | .25 |
| 538D | A67g | 30f grn, brn & bl | .60 | .60 |
| 538E | A67g | 60f brn, bl & grn | 1.10 | 1.10 |
| | | Nos. 538-538E (6) | 2.90 | 2.70 |

**Souvenir Sheet**
*Imperf*

| 538F | A67g | 100f brn, dark bl & grn | 22.50 | 22.50 |
|---|---|---|---|---|

Symbolic Water Cycle — A68

**Perf. 14½x14**

| 1967, Mar. 1 | | Litho. | Wmk. 305 | |
|---|---|---|---|---|
| 539 | A68 | 10f dp org, blk & gray | .50 | .25 |
| 540 | A68 | 15f grnsh bl, blk & gray | .50 | .35 |
| 541 | A68 | 25f brt rose lil, blk & gray | .75 | .50 |
| | | Nos. 539-541 (3) | 1.75 | 1.10 |

Hydrological Decade (UNESCO), 1965-74.

UNESCO Emblem — A69

| 1967, Mar. 16 | | | | |
|---|---|---|---|---|
| 542 | A69 | 100f multicolored | 1.10 | 1.10 |

20th anniv. of UNESCO.

Dromedary A70

Animals: 2f, Karakul. 3f, Angora goat.

**Perf. 14x15**

| 1967, Feb. 11 | | Photo. | Unwmk. | |
|---|---|---|---|---|
| 543 | A70 | 1f dark brn & multi | 1.10 | .25 |
| 544 | A70 | 2f yellow & multi | 1.10 | .25 |
| 545 | A70 | 3f lt blue & multi | 1.10 | .25 |
| | | Nos. 543-545,C46-C48 (6) | 12.30 | 3.15 |

A souvenir sheet exists with a 100f in design and colors of No. C47, simulated perforation and marginal animal design. Value $35.

Inauguration of WHO Headquarters, Geneva — A71

| 1967, Apr. 7 | | | Wmk. 305 | |
|---|---|---|---|---|
| 546 | A71 | 5f emerald & blk | .40 | .25 |
| 547 | A71 | 45f dl orange & blk | .50 | .30 |

Arab League Emblem and Hands Reaching for Knowledge — A72

| 1968, May 5 | | Unwmk. | Perf. 11 | |
|---|---|---|---|---|
| 548 | A72 | 20f org & slate grn | .45 | .25 |
| 549 | A72 | 20f brt pink & dk bl | .45 | .25 |

Issued to publicize the literacy campaign.

"20" and WHO Emblem — A73

**Perf. 14½x14**

| 1968, Aug. 10 | | | Wmk. 305 | |
|---|---|---|---|---|
| 550 | A73 | 30f multicolored | .60 | .25 |
| 551 | A73 | 100f multicolored | 1.75 | 1.10 |

20th anniv. of the WHO.

European Goldfinch A74

Protected Game: 10f, Rock partridge, vert. 15f, Ostriches, vert. 20f, Sand partridge. 30f, Dorcas gazelle. 40f, Oryxes. 50f, Houbara bustard.

| 1968, Oct. 5 | | Unwmk. | Perf. 13½ | |
|---|---|---|---|---|
| 552 | A74 | 5f multicolored | 3.25 | 1.25 |
| 553 | A74 | 10f multicolored | 6.50 | 1.25 |
| 554 | A74 | 15f multicolored | 8.50 | 1.50 |
| 555 | A74 | 20f multicolored | 8.50 | 1.75 |
| 556 | A74 | 30f multicolored | 5.25 | 1.25 |
| 557 | A74 | 40f multicolored | 8.00 | 1.50 |
| 558 | A74 | 50f multicolored | 12.50 | 3.00 |
| | | Nos. 552-558,C49-C50 (9) | 77.00 | 25.50 |

Human Rights Flame — A75

| 1968, Dec. 10 | | Litho. | Perf. 13 | |
|---|---|---|---|---|
| 559 | A75 | 20f dp org, lt org & blk | .40 | .25 |
| 560 | A75 | 60f grn, lt blue & blk | .75 | .45 |

International Human Rights Year.

Dome of the Rock, Jerusalem — A76

5f, 45f, Holy Kaaba, Mecca, & Dome of the Rock.

| 1969, Oct. 8 | | Photo. | Perf. 12 | |
|---|---|---|---|---|
| | | **Size: 56x25mm** | | |
| 561 | A76 | 5f dull vio & multi | .80 | .25 |
| | | **Size: 36x25mm** | | |
| 562 | A76 | 10f vio blue & multi | .80 | .50 |
| 563 | A76 | 20f Prus bl & multi | 1.25 | .60 |
| | | **Size: 56x25mm** | | |
| 564 | A76 | 45f Prus bl & multi | 2.10 | .70 |
| | | Nos. 561-564 (4) | 4.95 | 2.05 |

ILO Emblem — A77

| 1969, June 10 | | | Perf. 13½x14 | |
|---|---|---|---|---|
| 565 | A77 | 10f blue & black | .35 | .25 |
| 566 | A77 | 20f bister brn & blk | .35 | .25 |
| 567 | A77 | 25f lt olive & black | .35 | .25 |
| 568 | A77 | 45f lil rose & black | .50 | .30 |
| 569 | A77 | 60f orange & black | .75 | .25 |
| | | Nos. 565-569 (5) | 2.30 | 1.40 |

ILO, 50th anniversary.

Horses — A78

20f, White stallion. 45f, Mare and foal.

| 1969, July 6 | | Unwmk. | Perf. 13½ | |
|---|---|---|---|---|
| 570 | A78 | 10f dark bl & multi | 1.50 | .25 |
| 571 | A78 | 20f dl green & multi | 3.50 | .60 |
| 572 | A78 | 45f red & multi | 6.50 | 1.75 |
| | | Nos. 570-572 (3) | 11.50 | 2.60 |

Prince Hassan and Princess Tharwat — A79

Designs: 60f, 100f, Prince Hassan and bride in western bridal gown.

| 1969, Dec. 2 | | Photo. | Perf. 12½ | |
|---|---|---|---|---|
| 573 | A79 | 20f gold & multi | .50 | .25 |
| 573A | A79 | 60f gold & multi | 1.00 | .65 |
| 573B | A79 | 100f gold & multi | 1.50 | 1.25 |
| c. | | Strip of 3, #573-573B | 3.25 | 3.25 |

Wedding of Crown Prince Hassan, 11/14/68.

The Tragedy and the Flight of the Refugees — A79a

Different design on each stamp. Each strip of 5 has five consecutive denominations.

**Perf. 14½x13½**

| 1969, Dec. 10 | | | Photo. | |
|---|---|---|---|---|
| 574 | A79a | 1f-5f Strip of 5 | 11.00 | 11.00 |
| f.-j. | | 1f-5f Any single | | |
| 574A | A79a | 6f-10f Strip of 5 | 11.00 | 11.00 |
| a.-e. | | 6f-10f Any single | | |
| 574B | A79a | 11f-15f Strip of 5 | 11.00 | 11.00 |
| a.-e. | | 11f-15f Any single | | |
| 574C | A79a | 16f-20f Strip of 5 | 11.00 | 11.00 |
| a.-e. | | 16f-20f Any single | | |
| 574D | A79a | 21f-25f Strip of 5 | 11.00 | 11.00 |
| a.-e. | | 21f-25f Any single | | |
| 574E | A79a | 26f-30f Strip of 5 | 11.00 | 11.00 |
| a.-e. | | 26f-30f Any single | | |

For surcharges see Nos. 870-875.

**Inscribed: Tragedy in the Holy Lands**

Different design on each stamp. Each strip of 5 has five consecutive denominations.

**Perf. 14½x13½**

| 1969, Dec. 10 | | | Photo. | |
|---|---|---|---|---|
| 575 | A79a | 1f-5f Strip of 5 | 5.00 | 5.00 |
| f.-j. | | 1f-5f Any single | | |
| 575A | A79a | 6f-10f Strip of 5 | 5.00 | 5.00 |
| a.-e. | | 6f-10f Any single | | |
| 575B | A79a | 11f-15f Strip of 5 | 5.00 | 5.00 |
| a.-e. | | 11f-15f Any single | | |
| 575C | A79a | 16f-20f Strip of 5 | 5.00 | 5.00 |
| a.-e. | | 16f-20f Any single | | |
| 575D | A79a | 21f-25f Strip of 5 | 5.00 | 5.00 |
| a.-e. | | 21f-25f Any single | | |
| 575E | A79a | 26f-30f Strip of 5 | 5.00 | 5.00 |
| a.-e. | | 26f-30f Any single | | |

For surcharges see Nos. 876-881.

Pomegranate
Flower
(inscribed
"Desert
Scabius")
A80

Oranges
A81

Black Bush
Robin — A82

Designs: 15f, Wattle flower ("Caper"). 20f, Melon. 25f, Caper flower ("Pomegranate"). 30f, Lemons. 35f, Morning glory. 40f, Grapes. 45f, Desert scabius ("Wattle"). 50f, Olive-laden branch. 75f, Black iris. 100f, Apples. 180f, Masked shrike. 200f, Palestine sunbird. (Inscriptions incorrect on 5f, 15f, 25f and 45f.)

**Perf. 14x13½ (flowers), 12 (fruit), 13½x14 (birds)**

| 1969-70 | | | Photo. | |
|---|---|---|---|---|
| 576 | A80 | 5f yel & multi ('70) | .40 | .25 |
| 577 | A81 | 10f blue & multi | .40 | .25 |
| 578 | A81 | 15f tan & multi ('70) | .70 | .25 |
| 579 | A81 | 20f sepia & multi | .60 | .25 |
| 580 | A80 | 25f multi ('70) | 1.00 | .25 |
| 581 | A81 | 30f vio bl & multi | 1.00 | .25 |
| 582 | A81 | 35f multi ('70) | 1.50 | .25 |
| 583 | A81 | 40f dull yel & multi | 1.50 | .25 |
| 584 | A81 | 45f gray & multi ('70) | 2.00 | .25 |
| 585 | A81 | 50f car rose & multi | 2.00 | .40 |
| 586 | A80 | 75f multi ('70) | 3.00 | 1.00 |
| 587 | A81 | 100f dk gray & multi | 3.25 | 1.25 |
| 588 | A82 | 120f org & multi ('70) | 10.00 | 2.00 |
| 589 | A82 | 180f multi ('70) | 17.50 | 4.75 |
| 590 | A82 | 200f multi ('70) | 20.00 | 7.00 |
| | | Nos. 576-590 (15) | 64.85 | 18.65 |

Issued: Fruits, 11/22; flowers, 3/21; birds, 9/1.

Soccer — A83

Designs: 10f, Diver. 15f, Boxers. 50f, Runner. 100f, Bicyclist, vert. 150f, Basketball, vert.

| 1970, Aug. | | | Perf. 13½x14, 14x13½ | |
|---|---|---|---|---|
| 651 | A83 | 5f green & multi | 1.00 | .25 |
| 652 | A83 | 10f lt bl & multi | 1.00 | .25 |
| 653 | A83 | 15f gray & multi | 1.00 | .25 |
| 654 | A83 | 50f gray & multi | 1.50 | .65 |
| 655 | A83 | 100f yellow & multi | 2.25 | 1.25 |
| 656 | A83 | 150f multicolored | 3.25 | 2.25 |
| | | Nos. 651-656 (6) | 10.00 | 4.90 |

Refugee
Children — A84

Emblems and: 10F, Boy Fetching Water, UNICEF and Refugee Emblems. 15f, Girl and tents. 20f, Boy in front of tent.

**1970, Aug.**

| 657 | A84 | 5f multicolored | .30 | .25 |
|---|---|---|---|---|
| 658 | A84 | 10f multicolored | .40 | .25 |
| 659 | A84 | 15f multicolored | .50 | .25 |
| 660 | A84 | 20f multicolored | .70 | .25 |
| | | Nos. 657-660 (4) | 1.90 | 1.00 |

Issued for Childhood Day.

Nativity Grotto,
Bethlehem
A85

Church of the Nativity, Bethlehem: 10f, Manger. 20f, Altar. 25f, Interior.

| 1970, Dec. 25 | | | Photo. | Perf. 13½ | |
|---|---|---|---|---|---|
| 661 | A85 | 5f blue & multi | .45 | .25 |
| 662 | A85 | 10f scarlet & multi | .45 | .25 |
| 663 | A85 | 20f rose lilac & multi | .80 | .30 |
| 664 | A85 | 25f green & multi | 1.00 | .35 |
| | | Nos. 661-664 (4) | 2.70 | 1.15 |

Christmas.

Flag and Map of
Arab League
Countries
A85a

| 1971, May 10 | | | Photo. | Perf. 11½x11 | |
|---|---|---|---|---|---|
| 665 | A85a | 10f orange & multi | .40 | .25 |
| 666 | A85a | 20f lt blue & multi | .40 | .25 |
| 667 | A85a | 30f olive & multi | .40 | .25 |
| | | Nos. 665-667 (3) | 1.20 | .75 |

25th anniversary of the Arab League.

Emblem and
Doves — A86

Designs: 5f, Emblem and 4 races, vert. 10f, Emblem as flower, vert.

**1971, July**

| 668 | A86 | 5f green & multi | .35 | .30 |
|---|---|---|---|---|
| 669 | A86 | 10f brick red & multi | .40 | .30 |
| 670 | A86 | 15f dk blue & multi | .50 | .30 |
| | | Nos. 668-670 (3) | 1.25 | .90 |

Intl. Year Against Racial Discrimination.

Dead Sea — A87

Views of the Holy Land: 30f, Excavated building, Petra. 45f, Via Dolorosa, Jerusalem, vert. 60f, Jordan River. 100f, Christmas bell, Bethlehem, vert.

| 1971, Aug. | | | Perf. 14x13½, 13½x14 | |
|---|---|---|---|---|
| 671 | A87 | 5f blue & multi | .90 | .30 |
| 672 | A87 | 30f pink & multi | 1.75 | .60 |
| 673 | A87 | 45f blue & multi | 2.25 | .90 |
| 674 | A87 | 60f gray & multi | 3.75 | 1.50 |
| 675 | A87 | 100f gray & multi | 5.50 | 3.00 |
| | | Nos. 671-675 (5) | 14.15 | 6.30 |

Tourist publicity.

Opening of UPU
Headquarters,
Bern in
1970 — A88

| 1971, Oct. | | | Perf. 11 | |
|---|---|---|---|---|
| 676 | A88 | 10f brn, brn & yel grn | .40 | .25 |
| 677 | A88 | 20f dk vio, grn & yel grn | .70 | .25 |

Averroes (1126-
1198) — A89

Arab Scholars: 5f, Avicenna (980-1037). 20f, ibn-Khaldun (1332-1406). 25f, ibn-Tufail (?-1185). 30f, Alhazen (965?-1039?).

| 1971, Sept. | | | Perf. 12 | |
|---|---|---|---|---|
| 678 | A89 | 5f gold & multi | .35 | .25 |
| 679 | A89 | 10f gold & multi | .35 | .25 |
| 680 | A89 | 20f gold & multi | .65 | .25 |
| 681 | A89 | 25f gold & multi | 1.00 | .35 |
| 682 | A89 | 30f gold & multi | 1.50 | .75 |
| | | Nos. 678-682 (5) | 3.85 | 1.85 |

Child Learning to
Write — A90

| 1972, Feb. 9 | | | Photo. | Perf. 11 | |
|---|---|---|---|---|---|
| 683 | A90 | 5f ultra, brn & grn | .35 | .25 |
| 684 | A90 | 15f mag, brn & blue | .35 | .25 |
| 685 | A90 | 20f grn, brn & blue | .35 | .25 |
| 686 | A90 | 30f org, brn & blue | .75 | .30 |
| | | Nos. 683-686 (4) | 1.80 | 1.05 |

International Education Year.

Arab Mother and
Child — A91

Mother's Day: 10f, Mothers and children, horiz. 20f, Mother and child.

| 1972, Mar. | | | Perf. 14x13½ | |
|---|---|---|---|---|
| 687 | A91 | 10f lt grn & multi | .50 | .25 |
| 688 | A91 | 20f red brown & blk | .50 | .25 |
| 689 | A91 | 30f blue, brn & blk | .75 | .25 |
| | | Nos. 687-689 (3) | 1.75 | .75 |

Pope Paul VI and Holy
Sepulcher — A92

| 1972, Apr. | | | Photo. | Perf. 14x13½ | |
|---|---|---|---|---|---|
| 690 | A92 | 30f black & multi | 1.00 | .25 |

Easter. See Nos. C51-C52.

UNICEF
Emblem,
Children — A93

UNICEF Emblem and: 20f, Child playing with blocks spelling "UNICEF," vert. 30f, Mother and child.

| 1972, May | | | Perf. 11½x11, 11x11½ | |
|---|---|---|---|---|
| 691 | A93 | 10f bl, vio bl & blk | .40 | .25 |
| 692 | A93 | 20f multicolored | .40 | .25 |
| 693 | A93 | 30f blue & multi | .50 | .25 |
| | | Nos. 691-693 (3) | 1.30 | .75 |

25th anniv. (in 1971) of UNICEF.

UN Emblem, Dove and
Grain — A94

| 1972, July | | | Perf. 11x11½ | |
|---|---|---|---|---|
| 694 | A94 | 5f vio & multi | .50 | .25 |
| 695 | A94 | 10f multicolored | .50 | .25 |
| 696 | A94 | 15f black & multi | .50 | .25 |
| 697 | A94 | 20f green & multi | .50 | .25 |
| 698 | A94 | 30f multicolored | .85 | .50 |
| | | Nos. 694-698 (5) | 2.85 | 1.50 |

25th anniv. (in 1970) of the UN.

Al Aqsa
Mosque,
Jerusalem
A95

Designs: 60f, Al Aqsa Mosque on fire. 100f, Al Aqsa Mosque, interior.

| 1972, Aug. 21 | | | Litho. | Perf. 14½ | |
|---|---|---|---|---|---|
| 699 | A95 | 30f green & multi | 1.60 | .25 |
| 700 | A95 | 60f blue & multi | 3.50 | .85 |
| 701 | A95 | 100f ocher & multi | 5.50 | 1.50 |
| | | Nos. 699-701 (3) | 10.60 | 2.60 |

3rd anniversary of the burning of Al Aqsa Mosque, Jerusalem.

House in
Desert — A96

5f, Falconer, vert. 15f, Man on camel. 20f, Pipe line construction. 25f, Shepherd. 30f, Camels at water trough. 35f, Chicken farm. 45f, Irrigation canal.

| 1972, Nov. | | | Perf. 14x13½, 13½x14 | |
|---|---|---|---|---|
| 702 | A96 | 5f multicolored | .55 | .25 |
| 703 | A96 | 10f shown | .55 | .25 |
| 704 | A96 | 15f multicolored | .55 | .25 |
| 705 | A96 | 20f multicolored | .95 | .25 |
| 706 | A96 | 25f multicolored | .95 | .25 |
| 707 | A96 | 30f multicolored | 1.25 | .45 |
| 708 | A96 | 35f multicolored | 1.50 | .65 |
| 709 | A96 | 45f multicolored | 2.00 | 1.10 |
| | | Nos. 702-709 (8) | 8.30 | 3.45 |

Life in the Arab desert.

Wasfi el Tell and
Dome of the
Rock — A97

Wasfi el Tell,
Map of
Palestine and
Jordan — A98

| 1972, Dec. | | | Perf. 13x13½, 13½x13 | Photo. | |
|---|---|---|---|---|---|
| 710 | A97 | 5f citron & multi | .45 | .25 |
| 711 | A98 | 10f red & multi | .50 | .25 |
| 712 | A97 | 20f dl blue & multi | 1.00 | .85 |
| 713 | A98 | 30f green & multi | 1.10 | .85 |
| | | Nos. 710-713 (4) | 3.05 | 1.60 |

In memory of Prime Minister Wasfi el Tell, who was assassinated in Cairo by Black September terrorists.

Trapshooting — A99

Designs: 75f, Trapshooter facing right, horiz. 120f, Trapshooter facing left, horiz.

| 1972, Dec. | | | Perf. 14x13½, 13½x14 | |
|---|---|---|---|---|
| 714 | A99 | 25f multicolored | .80 | .25 |
| 715 | A99 | 75f multicolored | 1.10 | .80 |
| 716 | A99 | 120f multicolored | 2.10 | 1.00 |
| | | Nos. 714-716 (3) | 4.00 | 2.05 |

World Trapshooting Championships.

Aero Club
Emblem — A100

| 1973, Jan. | | | Photo. | Perf. 13½x14 | |
|---|---|---|---|---|---|
| 717 | A100 | 5f blue, blk & yel | .50 | .25 |
| 718 | A100 | 10f lt blue, blk & yel | .50 | .25 |
| | | Nos. 717-718,C53-C55 (5) | 4.10 | 2.05 |

Royal Jordanian Aero Club.

Peace Dove and Jordanian Flag — A101

10f, Emblem. 15f, King Hussein. 30f, Map of Jordan.

**1973, Mar.** *Perf. 11½*
| | | | | |
|---|---|---|---|---|
| 719 | A101 | 5f blue & multi | .45 | .25 |
| 720 | A101 | 10f pale grn & multi | .45 | .25 |
| 721 | A101 | 15f olive & multi | .45 | .25 |
| 722 | A101 | 30f yel grn & multi | .90 | .45 |
| | | *Nos. 719-722 (4)* | 2.25 | 1.20 |

Hashemite Kingdom of Jordan, 50th anniv.

Battle, Flag and Map of Palestine A102

10f, 2 soldiers in combat, map of Palestine. 15f, Map of Palestine, olive branch, soldier on tank.

**1973, Apr. 10** **Photo.** *Perf. 11*
| | | | | |
|---|---|---|---|---|
| 723 | A102 | 5f crimson & multi | 1.00 | .40 |
| 724 | A102 | 10f crimson & multi | 1.50 | .60 |
| 725 | A102 | 15f crim, blue & brn | 2.25 | 1.25 |
| | | *Nos. 723-725 (3)* | 4.75 | 2.25 |

5th anniversary of Karama Battle.

Father and Child — A103

Father's Day: 20f, Father & infant. 30f, Family.

**1973, Apr. 20** *Perf. 13½*
| | | | | |
|---|---|---|---|---|
| 726 | A103 | 10f citron & multi | .50 | .25 |
| 727 | A103 | 20f lt blue & multi | .75 | .25 |
| 728 | A103 | 30f multicolored | 1.25 | .55 |
| | | *Nos. 726-728 (3)* | 2.50 | 1.05 |

Phosphate Mine — A104

10f, Cement factory. 15f, Sharmasil Dam. 20f, Kafrein Dam.

**1973, June 25** **Litho.** *Perf. 13½x14*
| | | | | |
|---|---|---|---|---|
| 729 | A104 | 5f shown | .40 | .25 |
| 730 | A104 | 10f multicolored | .40 | .25 |
| 731 | A104 | 15f multicolored | .50 | .25 |
| 732 | A104 | 20f multicolored | .70 | .25 |
| | | *Nos. 729-732 (4)* | 2.00 | 1.00 |

Development projects.

Camel Racer — A105

Designs: Camel racing.

**1973, July 21**
| | | | | |
|---|---|---|---|---|
| 733 | A105 | 5f multicolored | .80 | .25 |
| 734 | A105 | 10f multicolored | .80 | .25 |
| 735 | A105 | 15f multicolored | .80 | .25 |
| 736 | A105 | 20f multicolored | .80 | .25 |
| | | *Nos. 733-736 (4)* | 3.20 | 1.00 |

Book Year Emblem A106

**1973, Aug. 25** **Photo.** *Perf. 13x13½*
| | | | | |
|---|---|---|---|---|
| 737 | A106 | 30f dk grn & multi | .75 | .25 |
| 738 | A106 | 60f purple & multi | 1.00 | .35 |

Intl. Book Year. For overprints see Nos. 781-782.

Family — A107

Family Day: 30f, Family around fire. 60f, Large family outdoors.

**1973, Sept. 18** **Litho.** *Perf. 13½*
| | | | | |
|---|---|---|---|---|
| 739 | A107 | 20f multicolored | .50 | .25 |
| 740 | A107 | 30f multicolored | .50 | .25 |
| 741 | A107 | 60f multicolored | 1.00 | .35 |
| | | *Nos. 739-741 (3)* | 2.00 | .85 |

Kings of Iran and Jordan, Tomb of Cyrus the Great and Mosque of Omar A108

**1973, Oct.** **Litho.** *Perf. 13*
| | | | | |
|---|---|---|---|---|
| 742 | A108 | 5f ver & multi | .50 | .25 |
| 743 | A108 | 10f brown & multi | .50 | .25 |
| 744 | A108 | 15f gray & multi | .75 | .25 |
| 745 | A108 | 30f blue & multi | 1.00 | .40 |
| | | *Nos. 742-745 (4)* | 2.75 | 1.15 |

2500th anniversary of the founding of the Persian Empire by Cyrus the Great.

Palestine Week Emblem — A109

Palestine Week: 10f, Torch and laurel. 15f, Refugee family behind barbed wire, vert. 30f, Children, Map of Palestine, globe. Sizes: 5f, 10f, 30f; 38½x22mm. 15f, 25x46mm.

**1973, Nov. 17** **Photo.** *Perf. 11*
| | | | | |
|---|---|---|---|---|
| 746 | A109 | 5f multicolored | .50 | .25 |
| 747 | A109 | 10f dl bl & multi | .65 | .25 |
| 748 | A109 | 15f yel grn & multi | .85 | .25 |
| 749 | A109 | 30f brt grn & multi | 1.50 | .40 |
| | | *Nos. 746-749 (4)* | 3.50 | 1.15 |

Traditional Harvest — A110

Traditional and modern agricultural methods: 10f, Harvesting machine. 15f, Traditional seeding. 20f, Seeding machine. 30f, Ox plow. 35f, Plowing machine. 45f, Pest control. 60f, Horticulture.

**1973, Dec. 25** *Perf. 13½*
| | | | | |
|---|---|---|---|---|
| 750 | A110 | 5f shown | .65 | .25 |
| 751 | A110 | 10f multicolored | .65 | .25 |
| 752 | A110 | 15f multicolored | .65 | .25 |
| 753 | A110 | 20f multicolored | .65 | .25 |
| 754 | A110 | 30f multicolored | 1.00 | .25 |
| 755 | A110 | 35f multicolored | 1.10 | .25 |
| 756 | A110 | 45f multicolored | 1.25 | .25 |
| 757 | A110 | 60f multicolored | 1.75 | 1.10 |
| | | *Nos. 750-757,C56 (9)* | 10.20 | 4.60 |

Red Sea Fish — A111

Designs: Various Red Sea fishes.

**1974, Feb. 15** **Photo.** *Perf. 14*
| | | | | |
|---|---|---|---|---|
| 758 | A111 | 5f multicolored | .50 | .25 |
| 759 | A111 | 10f multicolored | .60 | .25 |
| 760 | A111 | 15f multicolored | .75 | .25 |
| 761 | A111 | 20f multicolored | .90 | .35 |
| 762 | A111 | 25f multicolored | 1.25 | .40 |
| 763 | A111 | 30f multicolored | 2.00 | .50 |
| 764 | A111 | 35f multicolored | 2.25 | .80 |
| 765 | A111 | 40f multicolored | 2.75 | 1.00 |
| 766 | A111 | 45f multicolored | 3.00 | 1.10 |
| 767 | A111 | 50f multicolored | 5.00 | 1.25 |
| 768 | A111 | 60f multicolored | 6.25 | 1.75 |
| | | *Nos. 758-768 (11)* | 25.25 | 7.90 |

Battle of Muta, 1250 — A112

20f, Yarmouk Battle, 636. 30f, Hitteen Battle, 1187.

**1974, Mar. 15** **Photo.** *Perf. 13½*
| | | | | |
|---|---|---|---|---|
| 769 | A112 | 10f shown | .65 | .25 |
| 770 | A112 | 20f multicolored | 1.25 | .40 |
| 771 | A112 | 30f multicolored | 1.60 | .65 |
| | | *Nos. 769-771 (3)* | 3.50 | 1.30 |

Clubfooted Boy, by Murillo — A113

Paintings: 10f, Praying Hands, by Dürer. 15f, St. George and the Dragon, by Paolo Uccello. 20f, Mona Lisa, by Da Vinci. 30f, Hope, by Frederic Watts. 40f, Angelus, by Jean F. Millet, horiz. 50f, The Artist and her Daughter, by Angelica Kauffmann. 60f, Portrait of my Mother, by James Whistler, horiz. 100f, Master Hare, by Reynolds.

*Perf. 14x13½, 13½x14*
**1974, Apr. 15** **Litho.**
| | | | | |
|---|---|---|---|---|
| 772 | A113 | 5f black & multi | 1.50 | .25 |
| 773 | A113 | 10f black & gray | 1.50 | .25 |
| 774 | A113 | 15f black & multi | 1.50 | .25 |
| 775 | A113 | 20f black & multi | 1.50 | .25 |
| 776 | A113 | 30f black & multi | 1.50 | .25 |
| 777 | A113 | 40f black & multi | 1.75 | .25 |
| 778 | A113 | 50f black & multi | 2.00 | .95 |
| 779 | A113 | 60f black & multi | 2.50 | 1.00 |
| 780 | A113 | 100f black & multi | 3.50 | 1.75 |
| | | *Nos. 772-780 (9)* | 17.25 | 5.20 |

**Nos. 737-738 Overprinted**

**1974, Apr. 20** **Photo.** *Perf. 13x13½*
| | | | | |
|---|---|---|---|---|
| 781 | A106 | 30f dk grn & multi | .70 | .25 |
| 782 | A106 | 60f purple & multi | 1.00 | .50 |

Intl. Conf. for Damascus History, Apr. 20-25.

UPU Emblem — A114

**1974** *Perf. 13x12½*
| | | | | |
|---|---|---|---|---|
| 783 | A114 | 10f yel grn & multi | .40 | .25 |
| 784 | A114 | 30f blue & multi | .50 | .25 |
| 785 | A114 | 60f multicolored | .85 | .30 |
| | | *Nos. 783-785 (3)* | 1.75 | .80 |

Centenary of Universal Postal Union.

Camel Caravan at Sunset — A115

3f, 30f, Palm at shore of Dead Sea. 4f, 40f, Hotel at shore. 5f, 50f, Jars from Qumran Caves. 6f, 60f, Copper scrolls, vert. 10f, 100f, Cracked cistern steps, vert. 20f, like 2f.

**1974, June 25** **Photo.** *Perf. 14*
| | | | | |
|---|---|---|---|---|
| 786 | A115 | 2f multicolored | .50 | .25 |
| 787 | A115 | 3f multicolored | .50 | .25 |
| 788 | A115 | 4f multicolored | .50 | .25 |
| 789 | A115 | 5f multicolored | .75 | .25 |
| 790 | A115 | 6f multicolored | .75 | .25 |
| 791 | A115 | 10f multicolored | .75 | .25 |
| 792 | A115 | 20f multicolored | .50 | .25 |
| 793 | A115 | 30f multicolored | .65 | .25 |
| 794 | A115 | 40f multicolored | .75 | .50 |
| 795 | A115 | 50f multicolored | 1.75 | .40 |
| 796 | A115 | 60f multicolored | 2.25 | .50 |
| 797 | A115 | 100f multicolored | 3.50 | .85 |
| | | *Nos. 786-797 (12)* | 13.15 | 4.25 |

WPY Emblem — A116

**1974, Aug. 20** **Photo.** *Perf. 11*
| | | | | |
|---|---|---|---|---|
| 798 | A116 | 5f lt green, blk & pur | .30 | .25 |
| 799 | A116 | 10f lt green, blk & car | .30 | .25 |
| 800 | A116 | 20f lt green, blk & org | .40 | .25 |
| | | *Nos. 798-800 (3)* | 1.00 | .75 |

World Population Year.

Water Skiing — A117

Water Skiing: 10f, 100f, Side view, horiz. 20f, 200f, Turning, horiz. 50f, like 5f.

*Perf. 14x13½, 13½x14*
**1974, Sept. 20**
| | | | | |
|---|---|---|---|---|
| 801 | A117 | 5f multicolored | .50 | .25 |
| 802 | A117 | 10f multicolored | .50 | .25 |
| 803 | A117 | 20f multicolored | .50 | .25 |
| 804 | A117 | 50f multicolored | .65 | .25 |
| 805 | A117 | 100f multicolored | 1.25 | .50 |
| 806 | A117 | 200f multicolored | 2.10 | .95 |
| | | *Nos. 801-806 (6)* | 5.50 | 2.45 |

Holy Kaaba, Mecca, and Pilgrims A118

**1974, Nov.** **Photo.** *Perf. 11*
| | | | | |
|---|---|---|---|---|
| 807 | A118 | 10f blue & multi | .75 | .25 |
| 808 | A118 | 20f yellow & multi | .80 | .25 |

Pilgrimage season.

Amrah Palace — A119

Ruins: 20f, Hisham Palace. 30f, Kharraneh Castle.

**1974, Nov. 25** **Photo.** *Perf. 14x13½*
| | | | | |
|---|---|---|---|---|
| 809 | A119 | 10f black & multi | .50 | .25 |
| 810 | A119 | 20f black & multi | .75 | .30 |
| 811 | A119 | 30f black & multi | 1.25 | .50 |
| | | *Nos. 809-811 (3)* | 2.50 | 1.05 |

Jordanian Woman — A120

Designs: Various women's costumes.

**1975, Feb. 1** **Photo.** *Perf. 12*
| | | | | |
|---|---|---|---|---|
| 812 | A120 | 5f lt green & multi | .45 | .25 |
| 813 | A120 | 10f yellow & multi | .50 | .25 |
| 814 | A120 | 15f lt blue & multi | .75 | .30 |

| 815 | A120 | 20f ultra & multi | 1.10 | .40 |
|---|---|---|---|---|
| 816 | A120 | 25f green & multi | 1.50 | .85 |
| | | Nos. 812-816 (5) | 4.30 | 2.05 |

Additional denominations of 30f, 35f, 40f, 50f, and 60f were produced but not issued.

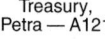

Treasury, Petra — A121

Ommayyad Palace, Amman — A122

Designs: 30f, Dome of the Rock, Jerusalem. 40f, Columns, Forum of Jerash.

### Perf. 14x13½, 13½x14

**1975, Mar. 1**       Photo.

| 824 | A121 | 15f lt blue & multi | 1.00 | .25 |
|---|---|---|---|---|
| 825 | A122 | 20f pink & multi | 1.00 | .25 |
| 826 | A122 | 30f yellow & multi | 1.25 | .25 |
| 827 | A122 | 40f lt blue & multi | 1.60 | .25 |
| | | Nos. 824-827,C59-C61 (7) | 10.25 | 3.25 |

King Hussein — A123

**1975, Apr. 8**     Photo.     Perf. 14
### Size: 19x23mm

| 831 | A123 | 5f green & ind | .50 | .25 |
|---|---|---|---|---|
| 832 | A123 | 10f vio & indigo | .50 | .25 |
| 833 | A123 | 15f car & indigo | .50 | .25 |
| 834 | A123 | 20f brn ol & ind | .50 | .25 |
| 835 | A123 | 25f vio bl & ind | .50 | .25 |
| 836 | A123 | 30f brown & ind | .50 | .25 |
| 837 | A123 | 35f vio & indigo | .50 | .25 |
| 838 | A123 | 40f orange & ind | .50 | .25 |
| 839 | A123 | 45f red lil & ind | .50 | .25 |
| 840 | A123 | 50f bl green & ind | .65 | .25 |
| | | Nos. 831-840,C62-C68 (17) | 21.00 | 13.00 |

Globe, "alia" and Plane — A125

Designs: 30f, Boeing 727 connecting Jordan with world, horiz. 60f, Globe and "alia."

**1975, June 15**    Photo.    Perf. 11

| 853 | A125 | 10f multicolored | .70 | .25 |
|---|---|---|---|---|
| 854 | A125 | 30f multicolored | .75 | .25 |
| 855 | A125 | 60f multicolored | 1.40 | .85 |
| | | Nos. 853-855 (3) | 2.85 | 1.35 |

Royal Jordanian Airline, 30th anniversary.

Satellite Transmission System, Map of Mediterranean — A126

**1975, Aug. 1**    Photo.    Perf. 11

| 856 | A126 | 20f vio bl & multi | .90 | .25 |
|---|---|---|---|---|
| 857 | A126 | 30f green & multi | 1.10 | .75 |

Opening of satellite earth station.

Chamber of Commerce Emblem — A127

---

**1975, Oct. 15**    Photo.    Perf. 11

| 858 | A127 | 10f yellow & blue | .35 | .25 |
|---|---|---|---|---|
| 859 | A127 | 15f yel, red & blue | .35 | .25 |
| 860 | A127 | 20f yel, grn & blue | .35 | .25 |
| | | Nos. 858-860 (3) | 1.05 | .75 |

Amman Chamber of Commerce, 50th anniv.

Hand Holding Wrench, Wall and Emblem A128

**1975, Nov.**    Photo.    Perf. 11½

| 861 | A128 | 5f green, car & blk | .35 | .25 |
|---|---|---|---|---|
| 862 | A128 | 10f car, green & blk | .35 | .25 |
| 863 | A128 | 20f blk, green & car | .35 | .25 |
| | | Nos. 861-863 (3) | 1.05 | .75 |

Three-year development plan.

Family and IWY Emblem — A129

IWY Emblem and: 25f, Woman scientist with microscope. 60f, Woman graduate.

**1976, Apr. 27**    Litho.    Perf. 14x13½

| 864 | A129 | 5f multicolored | .50 | .25 |
|---|---|---|---|---|
| 865 | A129 | 25f multicolored | .50 | .25 |
| 866 | A129 | 60f multicolored | 1.00 | .40 |
| | | Nos. 864-866 (3) | 2.00 | .90 |

International Women's Year.

Salt Industry — A130

Arab Labor Organization Emblem and: 30f, Welders. 60f, Ship at 'Aqaba.

**1976, June 1**    Litho.    Perf. 13½x14

| 867 | A130 | 10f gray & multi | .50 | .25 |
|---|---|---|---|---|
| 868 | A130 | 30f bister & multi | .50 | .25 |
| 869 | A130 | 60f brown & multi | .75 | .40 |
| | | Nos. 867-869 (3) | 1.75 | .90 |

Arab Labor Organization.

Nos. 574-574E Srchd.

### Perf. 14½x13½

**1976, July 18**   Strips of 5   Photo.

| 870 | A79a | 25f on 1f-5f | 32.50 | 32.50 |
|---|---|---|---|---|
| a.-e. | | Any single, 1f-5f | | |
| 871 | A79a | 25f on 6f-10f | 32.50 | 32.50 |
| a.-e. | | Any single, 6f-10f | | |
| 872 | A79a | 40f on 11f-15f | 32.50 | 32.50 |
| a.-e. | | Any single, 11f-15f | | |
| 873 | A79a | 50f on 16f-20f | 32.50 | 32.50 |
| a.-e. | | Any single, 16f-20f | | |
| 874 | A79a | 75f on 21f-25f | 32.50 | 32.50 |
| a.-e. | | Any single, 21f-25f | | |
| 875 | A79a | 125f on 26f-30f | 32.50 | 32.50 |
| a.-e. | | Any single, 26f-30f | | |

### Nos. 575-575E Surcharged Same as Nos. 870-875

| 876 | A79a | 25f on 1f-5f | 32.50 | 32.50 |
|---|---|---|---|---|
| a.-e. | | Any single, 1f-5f | | |
| 877 | A79a | 25f on 6f-10f | 32.50 | 32.50 |
| a.-e. | | Any single, 6f-10f | | |
| 878 | A79a | 40f on 11f-15f | 32.50 | 32.50 |
| a.-e. | | Any single, 11f-15f | | |
| 879 | A79a | 50f on 16f-20f | 32.50 | 32.50 |
| a.-e. | | Any single, 16f-20f | | |
| 880 | A79a | 75f on 21f-25f | 32.50 | 32.50 |
| a.-e. | | Any single, 21f-25f | | |
| 881 | A79a | 125f on 26f-30f | 32.50 | 32.50 |
| a.-e. | | Any single, 26f-30f | | |

---

Tennis — A132

Designs: 10f, Athlete and wreath. 15f, Soccer. 20f, Equestrian and Jordanian flag. 30f, Weight lifting. 100f, Stadium, Amman.

**1976, Nov. 1**    Litho.    Perf. 14x13½

| 990 | A132 | 5f buff & multi | .75 | .25 |
|---|---|---|---|---|
| 991 | A132 | 10f lt bl & multi | .75 | .25 |
| 992 | A132 | 15f green & multi | .75 | .25 |
| 993 | A132 | 20f green & multi | .75 | .25 |
| 994 | A132 | 30f green & multi | 1.00 | .25 |
| 995 | A132 | 100f multicolored | 2.00 | 1.25 |
| | | Nos. 990-995 (6) | 6.00 | 2.50 |

Sports and youth.

Dam — A133

Designs: Various dams.

**1976, Dec. 7**    Litho.    Perf. 14x13½

| 996 | A133 | 30f multicolored | 1.00 | .25 |
|---|---|---|---|---|
| 997 | A133 | 60f multicolored | 1.25 | .70 |
| 998 | A133 | 100f multicolored | 2.25 | 1.10 |
| | | Nos. 996-998 (3) | 4.50 | 2.05 |

Telephones, 1876 and 1976 — A134

125f, 1876 telephone and 1976 receiver.

**1977, Feb. 17**    Litho.    Perf. 11½x12

| 999 | A134 | 75f rose & multi | 1.50 | .95 |
|---|---|---|---|---|
| 1000 | A134 | 125f blue & multi | 2.00 | 1.25 |

Centenary of first telephone call by Alexander Graham Bell, Mar. 10, 1876.

Street Crossing, Traffic Light — A135

Designs: 75f, Traffic circle and light. 125f, Traffic light and signs, motorcycle policeman.

**1977, May 4**    Litho.    Perf. 11x12

| 1001 | A135 | 5f rose & multi | .55 | .25 |
|---|---|---|---|---|
| 1002 | A135 | 75f black & multi | 1.50 | .85 |
| 1003 | A135 | 125f yellow & multi | 2.25 | 1.40 |
| | | Nos. 1001-1003 (3) | 4.30 | 2.50 |

International Traffic Day.

Plane over Ship — A136

Coat of Arms and: 25f, Factories and power lines. 40f, Fertilizer plant and trucks. 50f, Ground to air missile. 75f, Mosque and worshippers. 125f, Radar station and TV emblem.

**1977, Aug. 11**    Litho.    Perf. 11½x12

| 1004 | A136 | 10f sil & multi | .40 | .25 |
|---|---|---|---|---|
| 1005 | A136 | 25f sil & multi | .40 | .25 |
| 1006 | A136 | 40f sil & multi | .70 | .35 |
| 1007 | A136 | 50f sil & multi | .80 | .40 |
| 1008 | A136 | 75f sil & multi | .95 | .60 |
| 1009 | A136 | 125f sil & multi | 1.75 | 1.00 |
| | | Nos. 1004-1009 (6) | 5.00 | 2.85 |

### Imperf
### Size: 100x70mm

| 1009A | A136 | 100f multicolored | 8.50 | 8.50 |
|---|---|---|---|---|

25th anniv. of the reign of King Hussein.

Child with Toy Bank — A137

---

Postal Savings Bank: 25f, Boy with piggy bank. 50f, Postal Savings Bank emblem. 75f, Boy talking to teller.

**1977, Sept. 1**    Litho.    Perf. 11½x12

| 1010 | A137 | 10f multicolored | .40 | .25 |
|---|---|---|---|---|
| 1011 | A137 | 25f multicolored | .60 | .25 |
| 1012 | A137 | 50f multicolored | .75 | .40 |
| 1013 | A137 | 75f multicolored | 1.10 | .65 |
| | | Nos. 1010-1013 (4) | 2.85 | 1.55 |

King Hussein and Queen Alia — A138

**1977, Nov. 1**    Litho.    Perf. 11½x12

| 1014 | A138 | 10f lt grn & multi | .40 | .25 |
|---|---|---|---|---|
| 1015 | A138 | 25f rose & multi | .40 | .25 |
| 1016 | A138 | 40f yellow & multi | .50 | .25 |
| 1017 | A138 | 50f blue & multi | .70 | .25 |
| | | Nos. 1014-1017 (4) | 2.00 | 1.00 |

Queen Alia — A139

**1977, Dec. 1**    Litho.    Perf. 11½x12

| 1018 | A139 | 10f green & multi | .50 | .25 |
|---|---|---|---|---|
| 1019 | A139 | 25f brown & multi | .50 | .25 |
| 1020 | A139 | 40f blue & multi | .70 | .25 |
| 1021 | A139 | 50f yellow & multi | .95 | .25 |
| | | Nos. 1018-1021 (4) | 2.65 | 1.00 |

Queen Alia, died in 1977 air crash.

Jinnah, Flags of Pakistan and Jordan — A140

**1977, Dec. 20**       Perf. 11½

| 1022 | A140 | 25f multicolored | .30 | .25 |
|---|---|---|---|---|
| 1023 | A140 | 75f multicolored | .70 | .40 |

Mohammed Ali Jinnah (1876-1948), 1st Governor General of Pakistan.

APU Emblem, Members' Flags — A141

**1978, Apr. 12**    Litho.    Perf. 12x11½

| 1024 | A141 | 25f yellow & multi | .75 | .50 |
|---|---|---|---|---|
| 1025 | A141 | 40f buff & multi | 1.25 | .75 |

25th anniv. (in 1977), of Arab Postal Union.

Copper Coffee Set — A142

Handicraft: 40f, Porcelain plate and ashtray. 75f, Vase and jewelry. 125f, Pipe holder.

**1978, May 30**    Photo.    Perf. 11½x12

| 1026 | A142 | 25f olive & multi | .50 | .25 |
|---|---|---|---|---|
| 1027 | A142 | 40f lilac & multi | .65 | .25 |
| 1028 | A142 | 75f ultra & multi | 1.10 | .65 |
| 1029 | A142 | 125f orange & multi | 1.75 | 1.00 |
| | | Nos. 1026-1029 (4) | 4.00 | 2.15 |

Roman Amphitheater, Jerash — A143

Tourist Views: 20f, Roman Columns, Jerash. 40f, Goat, grapes and man, Roman mosaic, Madaba. 75f, Rock formations, Rum, and camel rider.

**1978, July 30   Litho.   Perf. 12**
| | | | | |
|---|---|---|---|---|
| 1030 | A143 | 5f | multicolored | .55 | .25 |
| 1031 | A143 | 20f | multicolored | .55 | .25 |
| 1032 | A143 | 40f | multicolored | 1.00 | .25 |
| 1033 | A143 | 75f | multicolored | 1.40 | .75 |
| | | *Nos. 1030-1033 (4)* | | 3.50 | 1.50 |

King Hussein and Pres. Sadat — A144

Designs: No. 1035, King Hussein and Pres. Assad, Jordanian and Syrian flags, horiz. No. 1036, King Hussein, King Khalid, Jordanian and Saudi Arabian flags, horiz.

**1978, Aug. 20   Perf. 11½x12**
| | | | | |
|---|---|---|---|---|
| 1034 | A144 | 40f | multicolored | .90 | .50 |
| 1035 | A144 | 40f | multicolored | .90 | .50 |
| 1036 | A144 | 40f | multicolored | .90 | .50 |
| | | *Nos. 1034-1036 (3)* | | 2.70 | 1.50 |

Visits of Arab leaders to Jordan.

Cement Factory — A145

Designs: 10f, Science laboratory. 25f, Printing press. 75f, Artificial fertilizer plant.

**1978, Sept. 25   Litho.   Perf. 12**
| | | | | |
|---|---|---|---|---|
| 1037 | A145 | 5f | multicolored | .60 | .25 |
| 1038 | A145 | 10f | multicolored | .60 | .25 |
| 1039 | A145 | 25f | multicolored | .80 | .25 |
| 1040 | A145 | 75f | multicolored | 1.60 | .90 |
| | | *Nos. 1037-1040 (4)* | | 3.60 | 1.65 |

Industrial development.

"UNESCO" Scales and Globe — A146

**1978, Dec. 5   Litho.   Perf. 12x11½**
| | | | | |
|---|---|---|---|---|
| 1041 | A146 | 40f | multicolored | .75 | .35 |
| 1042 | A146 | 75f | multicolored | 1.25 | .70 |

30th anniversary of UNESCO.

1976-1980 Development Plan — A147

**1979, Oct. 25   Litho.   Perf. 12½x12**
| | | | | |
|---|---|---|---|---|
| 1043 | A147 | 25f | multicolored | .30 | .25 |
| 1044 | A147 | 40f | multicolored | .70 | .25 |
| 1045 | A147 | 50f | multicolored | .95 | .25 |
| | | *Nos. 1043-1045 (3)* | | 1.95 | .75 |

IYC Emblem, Flag of Jordan — A148

**1979, Nov. 15   Litho.   Perf. 12x12½**
| | | | | |
|---|---|---|---|---|
| 1046 | A148 | 25f | multicolored | .50 | .25 |
| 1047 | A148 | 40f | multicolored | .75 | .25 |
| 1048 | A148 | 50f | multicolored | 1.25 | .35 |
| | | *Nos. 1046-1048 (3)* | | 2.50 | .85 |

International Year of the Child.

1979 Population and Housing Census — A149

**1979, Dec. 25   Litho.   Perf. 12½x12**
| | | | | |
|---|---|---|---|---|
| 1049 | A149 | 25f | multicolored | .50 | .25 |
| 1050 | A149 | 40f | multicolored | .70 | .25 |
| 1051 | A149 | 50f | multicolored | .80 | .30 |
| | | *Nos. 1049-1051 (3)* | | 2.00 | .80 |

King Hussein — A150

**1980   Litho.   Perf. 13½x13**
| | | | | |
|---|---|---|---|---|
| 1052 | A150 | 5f | multicolored | .30 | .25 |
| b. | | Inscribed 1981 | | .30 | .25 |
| 1053 | A150 | 10f | multicolored | .30 | .25 |
| b. | | Inscribed 1981 | | .30 | .25 |
| 1055 | A150 | 20f | multicolored | .30 | .25 |
| b. | | Inscribed 1981 | | .30 | .25 |
| 1056 | A150 | 25f | multicolored | .30 | .25 |
| a. | | Inscribed 1979 | | .30 | .25 |
| b. | | Inscribed 1981 | | .30 | .25 |
| 1058 | A150 | 40f | multicolored | .60 | .25 |
| a. | | Inscribed 1979 | | .50 | .25 |
| b. | | Inscribed 1981 | | .60 | .25 |
| 1059 | A150 | 50f | multicolored | .80 | .25 |
| 1060 | A150 | 75f | multicolored | 1.00 | .30 |
| 1061 | A150 | 125f | multicolored | 1.50 | .35 |
| a. | | Complete booklet, 4 each #1056, 1058-1061 | | 17.50 | |
| | | *Nos. 1052-1061 (8)* | | 5.10 | 2.15 |

International Nursing Day — A151

**1980, May 12   Litho.   Perf. 12x12½**
| | | | | |
|---|---|---|---|---|
| 1062 | A151 | 25f | multicolored | .50 | .25 |
| 1063 | A151 | 40f | multicolored | .70 | .25 |
| 1064 | A151 | 50f | multicolored | .85 | .25 |
| | | *Nos. 1062-1064 (3)* | | 2.05 | .75 |

El Deir Temple, Petra — A152

**1980   Litho.   Perf. 14½**
| | | | | |
|---|---|---|---|---|
| 1065 | A152 | 25f | multicolored | .60 | .25 |
| 1066 | A152 | 40f | multicolored | .90 | .50 |
| 1067 | A152 | 50f | multicolored | 1.25 | .60 |
| | | *Nos. 1065-1067 (3)* | | 2.75 | 1.35 |

World Tourism Conf., Manila, Sept. 27.

Hegira (Pilgrimage Year) — A153

**1980, Nov. 11   Litho.   Perf. 14½**
| | | | | |
|---|---|---|---|---|
| 1068 | A153 | 25f | multicolored | .30 | .25 |
| 1069 | A153 | 40f | multicolored | .45 | .25 |
| 1070 | A153 | 50f | multicolored | .75 | .30 |
| 1071 | A153 | 75f | multicolored | 1.50 | .40 |
| 1072 | A153 | 100f | multicolored | 1.50 | .70 |
| | | *Nos. 1068-1072 (5)* | | 4.50 | 1.90 |

**Souvenir Sheet**
**Imperf**
| | | | | |
|---|---|---|---|---|
| 1073 | A153 | 290f | multicolored | 6.50 | 6.50 |

No. 1073 contains designs of Nos. 1068-1071.

11th Arab Summit Conference, Amman — A153a

**1980, Nov. 25   Litho.   Perf. 14½**
| | | | | |
|---|---|---|---|---|
| 1073A | A153a | 25f | multi | .40 | .25 |
| 1073B | A153a | 40f | multi | .60 | .25 |
| 1073C | A153a | 50f | multi | .80 | .30 |
| 1073D | A153a | 75f | multi | 1.00 | .45 |
| 1073E | A153a | 100f | multi | 1.10 | .65 |
| f. | | Souv. sheet of 5, #1073A-1073E, imperf. | | 6.50 | 6.50 |
| | | *Nos. 1073A-1073E (5)* | | 3.90 | 1.90 |

A154

**1981, May 8   Litho.   Perf. 14½**
| | | | | |
|---|---|---|---|---|
| 1074 | A154 | 25f | multicolored | .50 | .25 |
| 1075 | A154 | 40f | multicolored | .80 | .60 |
| 1076 | A154 | 50f | multicolored | .95 | .70 |
| | | *Nos. 1074-1076 (3)* | | 2.25 | 1.55 |

Red Crescent Society.

A155

**1981, June 17   Litho.   Perf. 14x14½**
| | | | | |
|---|---|---|---|---|
| 1077 | A155 | 25f | multicolored | .75 | .25 |
| 1078 | A155 | 40f | multicolored | .90 | .90 |
| 1079 | A155 | 50f | multicolored | 1.25 | .90 |
| | | *Nos. 1077-1079 (3)* | | 2.90 | 2.05 |

13th World Telecommunications Day.

Nos. 174 and 832 — A156

40f, Nos. 313, 189, vert. 50f, Nos. 272, 222.

**Perf. 13½x14½, 14½x13½**
**1981, July 1   Litho.**
| | | | | |
|---|---|---|---|---|
| 1080 | A156 | 25f | shown | .55 | .25 |
| 1081 | A156 | 40f | multicolored | 1.00 | .65 |
| 1082 | A156 | 50f | multicolored | 1.10 | .90 |
| | | *Nos. 1080-1082 (3)* | | 2.65 | 1.80 |

Postal Museum opening.

A157

Arab Women: 25f, Khawla Bint El-Azwar, Ancient Warrior. 40f, El-Khansa (d.645), writer. 50f, Rabia El-Adawiyeh, religious leader.

**1981, Aug. 25   Litho.   Perf. 14½x14**
| | | | | |
|---|---|---|---|---|
| 1083 | A157 | 25f | multicolored | .25 | .25 |
| 1084 | A157 | 40f | multicolored | 2.00 | 1.25 |
| 1085 | A157 | 50f | multicolored | 3.00 | 1.50 |
| | | *Nos. 1083-1085 (3)* | | 5.25 | 3.00 |

A158

**1981, Oct. 16   Litho.   Perf. 14x14½**
| | | | | |
|---|---|---|---|---|
| 1086 | A158 | 25f | multicolored | .25 | .25 |
| 1087 | A158 | 40f | multicolored | .80 | .55 |
| 1088 | A158 | 50f | multicolored | 1.00 | .65 |
| | | *Nos. 1086-1088 (3)* | | 2.05 | 1.45 |

World Food Day.

Intl. Year of the Disabled — A159

**1981, Nov. 14   Litho.   Perf. 14½x14**
| | | | | |
|---|---|---|---|---|
| 1089 | A159 | 25f | multicolored | .25 | .25 |
| 1090 | A159 | 40f | multicolored | 1.00 | .70 |
| 1091 | A159 | 50f | multicolored | 1.40 | .90 |
| | | *Nos. 1089-1091 (3)* | | 2.65 | 1.85 |

Hands Reading Braille — A160

**1981, Nov. 14   Perf. 14x14½**
| | | | | |
|---|---|---|---|---|
| 1092 | A160 | 25f | multicolored | .25 | .25 |
| 1093 | A160 | 40f | multicolored | 1.00 | .70 |
| 1094 | A160 | 50f | multicolored | 1.40 | .90 |
| | | *Nos. 1092-1094 (3)* | | 2.65 | 1.85 |

A161

Design: Hand holding jug and stone tablet.

**1982, Mar. 10   Litho.   Perf. 14x14½**
| | | | | |
|---|---|---|---|---|
| 1095 | A161 | 25f | multicolored | .50 | .25 |
| 1096 | A161 | 40f | multicolored | 1.10 | .60 |
| 1097 | A161 | 50f | multicolored | 1.25 | .80 |
| | | *Nos. 1095-1097 (3)* | | 2.85 | 1.65 |

Nos. 1095-1097 inscribed 1981.

A162

**1982, Apr. 12   Litho.   Perf. 14x14½**
| | | | | |
|---|---|---|---|---|
| 1098 | A162 | 10f | multicolored | .30 | .25 |
| 1099 | A162 | 25f | multicolored | .65 | .25 |
| 1100 | A162 | 40f | multicolored | .90 | .65 |
| 1101 | A162 | 50f | multicolored | 1.10 | .80 |
| 1102 | A162 | 100f | multicolored | 2.40 | 1.60 |
| | | *Nos. 1098-1102 (5)* | | 5.35 | 3.55 |

30th anniv. of Arab Postal Union.

King Hussein and Rockets — A163

25f, Tanks crossing bridge. 40f, Jet. 50f, Tanks, diff. 100f, Raising flag.

**1982, May 25   Litho.   Perf. 14½x14**
| | | | | |
|---|---|---|---|---|
| 1103 | A163 | 10f | shown | .30 | .25 |
| 1104 | A163 | 25f | multicolored | .65 | .25 |
| 1105 | A163 | 40f | multicolored | .90 | .65 |
| 1106 | A163 | 50f | multicolored | 1.25 | .75 |
| 1107 | A163 | 100f | multicolored | 2.25 | 1.50 |
| | | *Nos. 1103-1107 (5)* | | 5.35 | 3.40 |

Independence and Army Day; 30th anniv. of King Hussein's accession to the throne.

Salt Secondary School — A164

**1982, Sept. 12   Litho.   Perf. 14½x14**
| | | | | |
|---|---|---|---|---|
| 1108 | A164 | 10f | multicolored | .30 | .25 |
| 1109 | A164 | 25f | multicolored | .60 | .25 |
| 1110 | A164 | 40f | multicolored | .85 | .60 |
| 1111 | A164 | 50f | multicolored | 1.10 | .65 |
| 1112 | A164 | 100f | multicolored | 2.25 | 1.25 |
| | | *Nos. 1108-1112 (5)* | | 5.10 | 3.00 |

International Heritage of Jerusalem — A165

10f, Gate to Old City. 25f, Minaret. 40f, Al Aqsa. 50f, Dome of the Rock. 100f, Dome of the Rock, diff.

**1982, Nov. 14   Litho.   Perf. 14x14½**
| | | | |
|---|---|---|---|
| 1113 | A165 | 10f multicolored | .30 .25 |
| 1114 | A165 | 25f multicolored | 1.00 .45 |
| 1115 | A165 | 40f multicolored | 1.25 .80 |
| 1116 | A165 | 50f multicolored | 1.60 .90 |
| 1117 | A165 | 100f multicolored | 3.25 1.75 |
| | | Nos. 1113-1117 (5) | 7.40 4.15 |

Yarmouk Forces — A166

No. 1123, Armed Forces emblem.

**1982, Nov. 14   Perf. 14½x14**
| | | | |
|---|---|---|---|
| 1118 | A166 | 10f pink & multi | .30 .25 |
| 1119 | A166 | 25f buff & multi | .45 .25 |
| 1120 | A166 | 40f yel & multi | .80 .45 |
| 1121 | A166 | 50f lt blue & multi | .95 .60 |
| 1122 | A166 | 100f pale grn & multi | 2.10 1.40 |
| | | Nos. 1118-1122 (5) | 4.60 2.95 |

**Size: 71x51mm**
**Imperf**
| | | | |
|---|---|---|---|
| 1123 | A166 | 100f tan & multi | 15.00 15.00 |

2nd UN Conf. on Peaceful Uses of Outer Space, Vienna, Aug. 9-21 — A167

**1982, Dec. 1   Perf. 14½x14**
| | | | |
|---|---|---|---|
| 1124 | A167 | 10f multicolored | .30 .25 |
| 1125 | A167 | 25f multicolored | .50 .25 |
| 1126 | A167 | 40f multicolored | .75 .50 |
| 1127 | A167 | 50f multicolored | .95 .60 |
| 1128 | A167 | 100f multicolored | 2.00 1.25 |
| | | Nos. 1124-1128 (5) | 4.50 2.85 |

Birth Centenary of Amir Abdullah ibn Hussein — A168

**1982, Dec. 13   Litho.   Perf. 14½**
| | | | |
|---|---|---|---|
| 1129 | A168 | 10f multicolored | .30 .25 |
| 1130 | A168 | 25f multicolored | .40 .25 |
| 1131 | A168 | 40f multicolored | .60 .45 |
| 1132 | A168 | 50f multicolored | .95 .80 |
| 1133 | A168 | 100f multicolored | 2.25 1.40 |
| | | Nos. 1129-1133 (5) | 4.50 3.15 |

Roman Ruins of Jerash — A169

10f, Temple colonnade. 25f, Arch. 40f, Columns. 50f, Ampitheater. 100f, Hippodrome.

**1982, Dec. 29   Litho.   Perf. 15**
| | | | |
|---|---|---|---|
| 1134 | A169 | 10f multicolored | .30 .25 |
| 1135 | A169 | 25f multicolored | .90 .25 |
| 1136 | A169 | 40f multicolored | 1.40 .90 |
| 1137 | A169 | 50f multicolored | 1.75 1.00 |
| 1138 | A169 | 100f multicolored | 3.25 2.10 |
| | | Nos. 1134-1138 (5) | 7.60 4.50 |

King Hussein — A170

**1983   Litho.   Perf. 14½x14**
| | | | |
|---|---|---|---|
| 1139 | A170 | 10f multicolored | .30 .25 |
| 1140 | A170 | 25f multicolored | .30 .25 |
| 1141 | A170 | 40f multicolored | .40 .30 |
| 1142 | A170 | 60f multicolored | .60 .40 |
| 1143 | A170 | 100f multicolored | 1.00 .65 |
| 1144 | A170 | 125f multicolored | 1.25 .70 |
| | | Nos. 1139-1144 (6) | 3.85 2.55 |

Issue dates: 10f, 60f, Feb. 1; 40f, Feb. 8; 25f, 100f, 125f, Mar. 3. Inscribed 1982.

Massacre at Shatilla and Sabra Palestinian Refugee Camps — A171

10f, 25f, 50f, No. 1149, Various victims. 40f, Children. No. 1150, Wounded child.

**1983, Apr. 9   Litho.   Perf. 14½**
| | | | |
|---|---|---|---|
| 1145 | A171 | 10f multicolored | .50 .25 |
| 1146 | A171 | 25f multicolored | 1.00 .70 |
| 1147 | A171 | 40f multicolored | 1.50 .90 |
| 1148 | A171 | 50f multicolored | 2.00 1.25 |
| 1149 | A171 | 100f multicolored | 3.00 2.00 |
| | | Nos. 1145-1149 (5) | 8.00 5.10 |

**Souvenir Sheet**
**Imperf**
| | | | |
|---|---|---|---|
| 1150 | A171 | 100f multicolored | 18.00 |

Opening of Queen Alia Intl. Airport — A172

10f, Aerial view. 25f, Terminal buildings. 40f, Hangar. 50f, Terminal buildings, diff. 100f, Embarkation Bridge.

**1983, May 25   Litho.   Perf. 12½**
| | | | |
|---|---|---|---|
| 1151 | A172 | 10f multicolored | .30 .25 |
| 1152 | A172 | 25f multicolored | .80 .25 |
| 1153 | A172 | 40f multicolored | 1.10 .80 |
| 1154 | A172 | 50f multicolored | 1.40 .90 |
| 1155 | A172 | 100f multicolored | 2.75 1.75 |
| | | Nos. 1151-1155 (5) | 6.35 3.95 |

Royal Jordanian Radio Amateurs' Society — A173

**1983, Aug. 11   Litho.   Perf. 12**
| | | | |
|---|---|---|---|
| 1156 | A173 | 10f multicolored | .30 .25 |
| 1157 | A173 | 25f multicolored | .65 .25 |
| 1158 | A173 | 40f multicolored | .90 .65 |
| 1159 | A173 | 50f multicolored | 1.25 .75 |
| 1160 | A173 | 100f multicolored | 2.40 1.50 |
| | | Nos. 1156-1160 (5) | 5.50 3.40 |

Royal Academy for Islamic Cultural Research A174

10f, Academy Building. 25f, Silk carpet. 40f, Mosque, Amman. 50f, Dome of the Rock. 100f, Islamic city views.

**1983, Sept. 16   Litho.   Perf. 12**
| | | | |
|---|---|---|---|
| 1161 | A174 | 10f multicolored | .30 .25 |
| 1162 | A174 | 25f multicolored | .70 .50 |
| 1163 | A174 | 40f multicolored | 1.10 .70 |
| 1164 | A174 | 50f multicolored | 1.50 .90 |
| 1165 | A174 | 100f multicolored | 2.75 1.75 |
| | | Nos. 1161-1165 (5) | 6.35 4.10 |

A 100f souvenir sheet shows letter from Mohammed. Value $15.

World Food Day — A175

10f, Irrigation canal. 25f, Greenhouses. 40f, Light-grown crops. 50f, Harvest. 100f, Sheep farm.

**1983, Oct. 16   Litho.   Perf. 12**
| | | | |
|---|---|---|---|
| 1166 | A175 | 10f multicolored | .30 .25 |
| 1167 | A175 | 25f multicolored | .60 .25 |
| 1168 | A175 | 40f multicolored | 1.00 .60 |
| 1169 | A175 | 50f multicolored | 1.25 .70 |
| 1170 | A175 | 100f multicolored | 2.50 1.40 |
| | | Nos. 1166-1170 (5) | 5.65 3.20 |

World Communications Year — A176

10f, Radio switchboard operators. 25f, Earth satellite station. 40f, Symbols of communication. 50f, Emblems. 100f, Airmail letter.

**1983, Nov. 14**
| | | | |
|---|---|---|---|
| 1171 | A176 | 10f multicolored | .30 .25 |
| 1172 | A176 | 25f multicolored | 1.00 .25 |
| 1173 | A176 | 40f multicolored | 1.25 1.00 |
| 1174 | A176 | 50f multicolored | 1.50 1.00 |
| 1175 | A176 | 100f multicolored | 3.25 1.75 |
| | | Nos. 1171-1175 (5) | 7.30 4.25 |

Intl. Palestinian Solidarity Day — A177

Dome of the Rock, Jerusalem.

**1983, Nov. 29   Perf. 12**
| | | | |
|---|---|---|---|
| 1176 | A177 | 5f multicolored | .90 .45 |
| 1177 | A177 | 10f multicolored | 1.50 .70 |

35th Anniv. of UN Declaration of Human Rights — A178

**1983, Dec. 10**
| | | | |
|---|---|---|---|
| 1178 | A178 | 10f multicolored | .30 .25 |
| 1179 | A178 | 25f multicolored | .65 .25 |
| 1180 | A178 | 40f multicolored | .75 .65 |
| 1181 | A178 | 50f multicolored | 1.25 .75 |
| 1182 | A178 | 100f multicolored | 2.50 1.50 |
| | | Nos. 1178-1182 (5) | 5.45 3.40 |

Anti-Paralysis A179

**1984, Apr. 7   Perf. 13½x11½**
| | | | |
|---|---|---|---|
| 1183 | A179 | 40f multicolored | 1.10 .70 |
| 1184 | A179 | 60f multicolored | 1.60 .95 |
| 1185 | A179 | 100f multicolored | 2.75 1.60 |
| | | Nos. 1183-1185 (3) | 5.45 3.25 |

Anti-Polio Campaign.

Israeli Bombing of Iraq Nuclear Reactor A180

Various designs.

**1984, June 7   Litho.   Perf. 13½x11½**
| | | | |
|---|---|---|---|
| 1186 | A180 | 40f multicolored | 1.60 .55 |
| 1187 | A180 | 60f multicolored | 2.00 .70 |
| 1188 | A180 | 100f multicolored | 3.25 1.25 |
| | | Nos. 1186-1188 (3) | 6.85 2.50 |

Independence and Army Day — A181

King Hussein and various armed forces.

**1984, June 10**
| | | | |
|---|---|---|---|
| 1189 | A181 | 10f multicolored | .30 .25 |
| 1190 | A181 | 25f multicolored | .65 .25 |
| 1191 | A181 | 40f multicolored | 1.00 .65 |
| 1192 | A181 | 60f multicolored | 1.60 .90 |
| 1193 | A181 | 100f multicolored | 2.75 1.60 |
| | | Nos. 1189-1193 (5) | 6.30 3.65 |

1984 Summer Olympics, Los Angeles A182

40f, Swimming. 60f, Shooting, archery. 100f, Gymnastics.

**1984, July 28**
| | | | |
|---|---|---|---|
| 1194 | A182 | 25f shown | .30 .25 |
| 1195 | A182 | 40f multicolored | .50 .30 |
| 1196 | A182 | 60f multicolored | 1.10 .45 |
| 1197 | A182 | 100f multicolored | 1.60 .75 |
| | | Nos. 1194-1197 (4) | 3.50 1.75 |

An imperf. 100f souvenir sheet exists picturing pole vaulting. Value $14.

Water and Electricity Year — A183

25f, Power lines, factory. 40f, Amman Power Station. 60f, Irrigation. 100f, Hydro-electric dam.

**1984, Aug. 11**
| | | | |
|---|---|---|---|
| 1198 | A183 | 25f multicolored | .45 .25 |
| 1199 | A183 | 40f multicolored | .70 .45 |
| 1200 | A183 | 60f multicolored | 1.10 .60 |
| 1201 | A183 | 100f multicolored | 1.75 1.10 |
| | | Nos. 1198-1201 (4) | 4.00 2.40 |

Coins — A184

40f, Omayyad gold dinar. 60f, Abbasid gold dinar. 125f, Hashemite silver dinar.

**1984, Sept. 26   Photo.   Perf. 13**
| | | | |
|---|---|---|---|
| 1202 | A184 | 40f multicolored | 1.10 .60 |
| 1203 | A184 | 60f multicolored | 1.40 .80 |
| 1204 | A184 | 125f multicolored | 3.00 1.75 |
| | | Nos. 1202-1204 (3) | 5.50 3.15 |

Royal Society for the Conservation of Nature — A185

25f, Four antelopes. 40f, Grazing. 60f, Three antelopes. 100f, King Hussein, Queen Alia, Duke of Edinburgh.

**1984, Oct. 18**
| | | | |
|---|---|---|---|
| 1205 | A185 | 25f multicolored | .70 .25 |
| 1206 | A185 | 40f multicolored | 1.10 .70 |
| 1207 | A185 | 60f multicolored | 1.60 .95 |
| 1208 | A185 | 100f multicolored | 2.75 1.60 |
| | | Nos. 1205-1208 (4) | 6.15 3.50 |

Natl. Universities A186

Designs: 40f, Mu'ta Military University, Karak. 60f, Yarmouk University, Irbid. 125f, Jordan University, Amman.

**1984, Nov. 14   Perf. 13x13½**
| | | | |
|---|---|---|---|
| 1209 | A186 | 40f multicolored | .55 .40 |
| 1210 | A186 | 60f multicolored | .95 .55 |
| 1211 | A186 | 125f multicolored | 2.00 1.10 |
| | | Nos. 1209-1211 (3) | 3.50 2.05 |

Al Sahaba
Tombs — A187

Designs: 10f, El Harath bin Omier el-Azdi
and Derer bin El-Azwar. 25f, Sharhabil bin
Hasna and Abu Obaidah Amer bin el-Jarrah.
40f, Muath bin Jabal. 50f, Zaid bin Haretha
and Abdullah bin Rawaha. 60f, Amer bin Abi
Waqqas. 100f, Jafar bin Abi Taleb.

**1984, Dec. 5   Litho.   Perf. 13½x11½**
| | | | | |
|---|---|---|---|---|
| 1212 | A187 | 10f multicolored | .30 | .25 |
| 1213 | A187 | 25f multicolored | .50 | .25 |
| 1214 | A187 | 40f multicolored | .75 | .50 |
| 1215 | A187 | 50f multicolored | .95 | .55 |
| 1216 | A187 | 60f multicolored | 1.25 | .65 |
| 1217 | A187 | 100f multicolored | 2.00 | 1.25 |
| | | Nos. 1212-1217 (6) | 5.75 | 3.45 |

Independence
and Army
Day — A188

Designs: 25f, King Hussein, soldier
descending mountain. 40f, King Hussein,
Arab revolt flag, globe, Sharif Hussein. 60f,
Flag, natl. arms, equestrian. 100f, Natl. flag,
arms, Sharif Hussein.

**1985, June 10      Perf. 13x13½**
| | | | | |
|---|---|---|---|---|
| 1218 | A188 | 25f multicolored | .45 | .25 |
| 1219 | A188 | 40f multicolored | .90 | .45 |
| 1220 | A188 | 60f multicolored | 1.40 | .75 |
| 1221 | A188 | 100f multicolored | 2.25 | 1.40 |
| | | Nos. 1218-1221 (4) | 5.00 | 2.85 |

Men in Postal
History — A189

40f, Sir Rowland Hill. 60f, Heinrich von Stephan. 125f, Yacoub al-Sukkar.

**1985, July 1**
| | | | | |
|---|---|---|---|---|
| 1222 | A189 | 40f multicolored | .75 | .45 |
| 1223 | A189 | 60f multicolored | 1.10 | .65 |
| 1224 | A189 | 125f multicolored | 2.40 | 1.40 |
| | | Nos. 1222-1224 (3) | 4.25 | 2.50 |

1st Convention of
Jordanian
Expatriates
A190

Various designs.

**1985, July 20      Photo.**
| | | | | |
|---|---|---|---|---|
| 1225 | A190 | 40f multicolored | .75 | .45 |
| 1226 | A190 | 60f multicolored | 1.10 | .65 |
| 1227 | A190 | 125f multicolored | 2.40 | 1.40 |
| | | Nos. 1225-1227 (3) | 4.25 | 2.50 |

Intl. Youth
Year — A191

Various designs.

**1985, Aug. 11   Litho.   Perf. 13½x13**
| | | | | |
|---|---|---|---|---|
| 1228 | A191 | 10f multicolored | .30 | .25 |
| 1229 | A191 | 25f multicolored | .50 | .25 |
| 1230 | A191 | 40f multicolored | .80 | .50 |
| 1231 | A191 | 60f multicolored | 1.25 | .70 |
| 1232 | A191 | 125f multicolored | 2.50 | 1.50 |
| | | Nos. 1228-1232 (5) | 5.35 | 3.20 |

World Tourism
Organization,
10th
Anniv. — A192

10f, Ruins of the Treasury, Petra. 25f, Jerash Temple. 40f, Roman baths. 50f, Jordanian
valley town. 60f, Aqaba Bay. 125f, Roman
amphitheater.

**1985, Sept. 13      Perf. 13½x13**
| | | | | |
|---|---|---|---|---|
| 1233 | A192 | 10f multicolored | .30 | .25 |
| 1234 | A192 | 25f multicolored | .50 | .25 |
| 1235 | A192 | 40f multicolored | .80 | .50 |
| 1236 | A192 | 50f multicolored | 1.00 | .60 |
| 1237 | A192 | 60f multicolored | 1.25 | .70 |
| 1238 | A192 | 125f multicolored | 2.50 | 1.40 |
| | | Nos. 1233-1238 (6) | 6.35 | 3.70 |

An imperf. 100f souvenir sheet exists picturing flower, 10 and natl. flag. Value $6.50.

UN Child Survival
Campaign — A193

Various designs.

**1985, Oct. 7**
| | | | | |
|---|---|---|---|---|
| 1239 | A193 | 25f multicolored | .50 | .25 |
| 1240 | A193 | 40f multicolored | .75 | .50 |
| 1241 | A193 | 60f multicolored | 1.25 | .70 |
| 1242 | A193 | 125f multicolored | 2.50 | 1.50 |
| | | Nos. 1239-1242 (4) | 5.00 | 2.95 |

An imperf. 100f souvenir sheet exists picturing campaign emblem and the faces of healthy
children. Value $12.

5th Jerash
Festival
A194

10f, Opening ceremony, 1980. 25f, Folk
dancers. 40f, Dancers. 60f, Choir, Roman theater. 100f, King and Queen.

**1985, Oct. 21**
| | | | | |
|---|---|---|---|---|
| 1243 | A194 | 10f multicolored | .30 | .25 |
| 1244 | A194 | 25f multicolored | .45 | .25 |
| 1245 | A194 | 40f multicolored | .90 | .45 |
| 1246 | A194 | 60f multicolored | 1.50 | .75 |
| 1247 | A194 | 100f multicolored | 2.40 | 1.50 |
| | | Nos. 1243-1247 (5) | 5.55 | 3.20 |

UN, 40th
Anniv. — A195

**1985, Oct. 25   Photo.   Perf. 13x13½**
| | | | | |
|---|---|---|---|---|
| 1248 | A195 | 60f multicolored | 1.25 | 1.00 |
| 1249 | A195 | 125f multicolored | 2.50 | 2.00 |

King Hussein,
50th Birthday
A196

Various photos of King.

**1985, Nov. 14   Litho.   Perf. 14½**
| | | | | |
|---|---|---|---|---|
| 1250 | A196 | 10f multicolored | .30 | .25 |
| 1251 | A196 | 25f multicolored | .50 | .25 |
| 1252 | A196 | 40f multicolored | .90 | .50 |
| 1253 | A196 | 60f multicolored | 1.50 | .75 |
| 1254 | A196 | 100f multicolored | 2.40 | 1.50 |
| | | Nos. 1250-1254 (5) | 5.60 | 3.25 |

An imperf. 200f souvenir sheet exists picturing flags, King Hussein and Dome of the Rock.
Value $15.

Restoration of Al
Aqsa Mosque,
Jerusalem
A196a

**1985, Nov. 25   Litho.   Perf. 13x13½**
| | | | | |
|---|---|---|---|---|
| 1254A | A196a | 5f multicolored | 1.10 | 1.10 |
| 1254B | A196a | 10f multicolored | 2.40 | 2.25 |

Police — A197

**1985, Dec. 18**
| | | | | |
|---|---|---|---|---|
| 1255 | A197 | 40f Patrol car | 1.10 | .25 |
| 1256 | A197 | 60f Crossing guard | 1.40 | 1.10 |
| 1257 | A197 | 125f Police academy | 3.00 | 2.00 |
| | | Nos. 1255-1257 (3) | 5.50 | 3.35 |

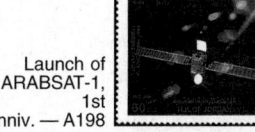

Launch of
ARABSAT-1,
1st
Anniv. — A198

60f, Satellite in orbit. 100f, Over map of Arab
countries.

**1986, Feb. 8   Litho.   Perf. 13½x13**
| | | | | |
|---|---|---|---|---|
| 1258 | A198 | 60f multicolored | .85 | .25 |
| 1259 | A198 | 100f multicolored | 1.40 | .85 |

Arabization of the
Army, 30th
Anniv. — A199

40f, King Hussein presenting flag. 60f,
Greeting army sergeant. 100f, Hussein
addressing army.

**1986, Mar. 1      Perf. 11½x12½**
| | | | | |
|---|---|---|---|---|
| 1260 | A199 | 40f multicolored | .75 | .25 |
| 1261 | A199 | 60f multicolored | .90 | .25 |
| 1262 | A199 | 100f multicolored | 1.60 | .90 |
| | | Nos. 1260-1262 (3) | 3.25 | 1.40 |

An imperf. souvenir sheet exists with design
of 100f. Value $10.

Natl. Independence, 40th
Anniv. — A200

Design: King Abdullah decorating soldier.

**1986, May 25      Perf. 12½x11½**
| | | | | |
|---|---|---|---|---|
| 1263 | A200 | 160f multicolored | 2.75 | 2.10 |

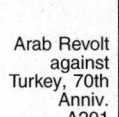

Arab Revolt
against
Turkey, 70th
Anniv.
A201

Unattributed paintings (details): 40f, The
four sons of King Hussein, Prince of Mecca,
vert. 60f, Sharif Hussein, retainers and bodyguard. 160f, Abdullah and followers on
horseback.

**Perf. 12½x11½, 11½x12½**
**1986, June 10**
| | | | | |
|---|---|---|---|---|
| 1264 | A201 | 40f multicolored | .65 | .25 |
| 1265 | A201 | 60f multicolored | .85 | .25 |
| 1266 | A201 | 160f multicolored | 2.50 | 1.25 |
| | | Nos. 1264-1266 (3) | 4.00 | 1.75 |

An imperf. 200f souvenir sheet exists picturing the Arab Revolt flag, Sharif Hussein and
text from independence declaration. Value $9.

Intl. Peace
Year — A202

**1986, July 1   Litho.   Perf. 13½x13**
| | | | | |
|---|---|---|---|---|
| 1267 | A202 | 160f multicolored | 2.25 | 1.25 |
| 1268 | A202 | 240f multicolored | 3.25 | 1.90 |

King Hussein
Medical City
Cardiac
Center — A203

**1986, Aug. 11**
| | | | | |
|---|---|---|---|---|
| 1269 | A203 | 40f Cardiac Center | .90 | .25 |
| 1270 | A203 | 60f Surgery | 1.10 | .90 |
| 1271 | A203 | 100f Surgery, diff. | 1.75 | .95 |
| | | Nos. 1269-1271 (3) | 3.75 | 2.10 |

UN, 40th
Anniv.
A204

Excerpts from King Hussein's speech: 40f,
In Arabic. 80f, Arabic, diff. 100f, English.

**1986, Sept. 27      Perf. 12½x11½**
| | | | | |
|---|---|---|---|---|
| 1272 | A204 | 40f multicolored | .75 | .25 |
| 1273 | A204 | 80f multicolored | 1.25 | .85 |
| 1274 | A204 | 100f multicolored | 1.60 | .85 |
| | | Nos. 1272-1274 (3) | 3.60 | 1.95 |

An imperf. 200f stamp 90x70mm exists picturing speech in Arabic and English, King Hussein at podium. Value $8.50.

Arab Postal
Union, 35th
Anniv. — A205

**1987, Apr. 12   Litho.   Perf. 13½x13**
| | | | | |
|---|---|---|---|---|
| 1275 | A205 | 80f Old post office | .85 | .60 |
| 1276 | A205 | 160f New post office | 1.90 | 1.10 |

Chemical Soc.
Emblem and
Chemists
A206

Designs: 60f, Jaber ibn Hayyan al-Azdi
(720-813). 80f, Abu-al-Qasem al-Majreeti
(950-1007). 240f, Abu-Bakr al-Razi (864-932).

**1987, Apr. 24**
| | | | | |
|---|---|---|---|---|
| 1277 | A206 | 60f multicolored | .75 | .50 |
| 1278 | A206 | 80f multicolored | 1.00 | .60 |
| 1279 | A206 | 240f multicolored | 2.75 | 1.60 |
| | | Nos. 1277-1279 (3) | 4.50 | 2.70 |

SOS Children's
Village — A207

80f, Village in Amman. 240f, Child, bird mural.

**1987, May 7**
| | | | | |
|---|---|---|---|---|
| 1280 | A207 | 80f multicolored | 1.25 | .70 |
| 1281 | A207 | 240f multicolored | 3.25 | 1.90 |

4th Brigade, 40th Anniv. — A208

80f, Soldiers in armored vehicle. 160f, Four veterans.

**1987, June 10**
| | | | | |
|---|---|---|---|---|
| 1282 | A208 | 60f shown | 1.40 | .95 |
| 1283 | A208 | 80f multicolored | 1.60 | 1.10 |

**Size: 70x91mm**
*Imperf*
| | | | | |
|---|---|---|---|---|
| 1284 | A208 | 160f multicolored | 8.00 | 7.50 |
| | *Nos. 1282-1284 (3)* | | 11.00 | 9.55 |

Indigenous Birds — A209

10f, Hoopoe. 40f, Palestine sunbird. 50f, Black-headed bunting. 60f, Spur-winged plover. 80f, Greenfinch. 100f, Black-winged stilt.

**1987, June 24**
| | | | | |
|---|---|---|---|---|
| 1285 | A209 | 10f multicolored | 1.60 | .55 |
| 1286 | A209 | 40f multicolored | 1.60 | .55 |
| 1287 | A209 | 50f multicolored | 2.00 | .60 |
| 1288 | A209 | 60f multicolored | 2.50 | .90 |
| 1289 | A209 | 80f multicolored | 3.00 | 1.25 |
| 1290 | A209 | 100f multicolored | 4.00 | 1.75 |
| | *Nos. 1285-1290 (6)* | | 14.70 | 5.60 |

King Hussein — A210

**1987, June 24   Litho.   Perf. 13x13½**
| | | | | |
|---|---|---|---|---|
| 1291 | A210 | 60f multicolored | .40 | .30 |
| 1292 | A210 | 80f multicolored | .85 | .40 |
| 1293 | A210 | 160f multicolored | 1.75 | 1.10 |
| 1294 | A210 | 240f multicolored | 2.50 | 1.75 |
| | *Nos. 1291-1294 (4)* | | 5.50 | 3.55 |

Battle of Hittin, 800th Anniv. — A211

Dome of the Rock and Saladin (1137-1193), Conqueror of Jerusalem — A212

60f, Battle, Jerusalem. 80f, Horseman, Jerusalem, Dome of the Rock. No. 1297, 100f, Saladin.

**1987, July 4**
| | | | | |
|---|---|---|---|---|
| 1295 | A211 | 60f multicolored | .75 | .70 |
| 1296 | A211 | 80f multicolored | 1.50 | .85 |
| 1297 | A211 | 100f multicolored | 2.25 | 1.50 |
| | *Nos. 1295-1297 (3)* | | 4.50 | 3.05 |

**Souvenir Sheet**
**Perf. 12x12½**
| | | | | |
|---|---|---|---|---|
| 1298 | A212 | 100f shown | 8.00 | 7.75 |

No. 1298 exists imperf.

Natl. Coat of Arms — A213

**Perf. 11½x12½**
**1987, Aug. 11          Litho.**
| | | | | |
|---|---|---|---|---|
| 1299 | A213 | 80f multicolored | 1.00 | .65 |
| 1300 | A213 | 160f multicolored | 2.00 | 1.25 |

Amman Industrial Park at Sahab — A214

**1987, Aug. 11          Perf. 13½x13**
| | | | | |
|---|---|---|---|---|
| 1301 | A214 | 80f multicolored | 1.00 | .80 |

University Crest — A215

University Entrance A216

**Perf. 11½x11, 12½x11½**
**1987, Sept. 2**
| | | | | |
|---|---|---|---|---|
| 1302 | A215 | 60f multicolored | .80 | .50 |
| 1303 | A216 | 80f multicolored | .95 | .65 |

University of Jordan, 25th anniv.

UN Child Survival Campaign — A217

60f, Oral vaccine. 80f, Natl. flag, child. 160f, Growth monitoring.

**1987, Oct. 5          Litho.          Perf. 13½x13½**
| | | | | |
|---|---|---|---|---|
| 1304 | A217 | 60f multicolored | .75 | .60 |
| 1305 | A217 | 80f multicolored | 1.25 | .80 |
| 1306 | A217 | 160f multicolored | 2.50 | 1.60 |
| | *Nos. 1304-1306 (3)* | | 4.50 | 3.00 |

Parliament, 40th Anniv. — A218

60f, Opening ceremony, 1947. 80f, In session, 1987.

**1987, Oct. 20          Perf. 13½x13**
| | | | | |
|---|---|---|---|---|
| 1307 | A218 | 60f dp mag & gold | 1.00 | .60 |
| 1308 | A218 | 80f multi & gold | 1.25 | .80 |

A219

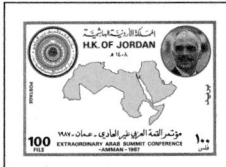

Special Arab Summit Conference, Amman — A220

**1987, Nov. 8**
| | | | | |
|---|---|---|---|---|
| 1309 | A219 | 60f multicolored | .55 | .50 |
| 1310 | A219 | 80f multicolored | .90 | .55 |
| 1311 | A219 | 160f multicolored | 2.00 | 1.25 |
| 1312 | A219 | 240f multicolored | 2.75 | 2.00 |
| | *Nos. 1309-1312 (4)* | | 6.20 | 4.30 |

**Size: 90x66mm**
*Imperf*
| | | | | |
|---|---|---|---|---|
| 1313 | A220 | 100f multicolored | 7.50 | 7.50 |

King Hussein, Dag Hammarskjold Peace Prize Winner for 1987 — A221

80f, Hussein, woman, vert.

**1988, Feb. 6          Litho.          Perf. 12½**
| | | | | |
|---|---|---|---|---|
| 1314 | A221 | 80f multicolored | .95 | .75 |
| 1315 | A221 | 160f shown | 1.90 | 1.25 |

Natl. Victory at the 1987 Arab Military Basketball Championships A222

60f, Golden Sword Award. 80f, Hussein congratulating team. 160f, Jump ball.

**1988, Mar. 1          Perf. 13½x13**
| | | | | |
|---|---|---|---|---|
| 1316 | A222 | 60f multicolored | .80 | .50 |
| 1317 | A222 | 80f multicolored | 1.10 | .65 |
| 1318 | A222 | 160f multicolored | 2.10 | 1.25 |
| | *Nos. 1316-1318 (3)* | | 4.00 | 2.40 |

WHO, 40th Anniv. — A223

**1988, Apr. 7          Photo.          Perf. 13½x13½**
| | | | | |
|---|---|---|---|---|
| 1319 | A223 | 60f multicolored | 1.00 | .70 |
| 1320 | A223 | 80f multicolored | 1.25 | .90 |

Arab Scouts, 75th Anniv. — A224

**1988, July 2          Litho.          Perf. 13½x13**
| | | | | |
|---|---|---|---|---|
| 1321 | A224 | 60f multicolored | 1.00 | .90 |
| 1322 | A224 | 80f multicolored | 1.25 | 1.10 |

Birds — A225

10f, Crested lark. 20f, Stone curlew. 30f, Redstart. 40f, Blackbird. 50f, Rock dove. 160f, Smyrna kingfisher.
310f, Six species.

**1988, July 21          Litho.          Perf. 11½x12**
| | | | | |
|---|---|---|---|---|
| 1323 | A225 | 10f multi | 2.25 | .70 |
| 1324 | A225 | 20f multi | 2.25 | .80 |
| 1325 | A225 | 30f multi | 2.25 | .90 |
| 1326 | A225 | 40f multi | 3.25 | 1.00 |
| 1327 | A225 | 50f multi | 4.00 | 1.10 |
| 1328 | A225 | 160f multi | 11.00 | 1.75 |
| | *Nos. 1323-1328 (6)* | | 25.00 | 6.25 |

**Size: 71x90mm**
*Imperf*
| | | | | |
|---|---|---|---|---|
| 1328A | A225 | 310f multi | 17.50 | 15.00 |

Restoration of San'a, Yemen Arab Republic — A226

**1988, Aug. 11          Litho.          Perf. 12x11½**
| | | | | |
|---|---|---|---|---|
| 1329 | A226 | 80f multicolored | .95 | .70 |
| 1330 | A226 | 160f multicolored | 1.90 | 1.50 |

Historic Natl. Sites — A227

**1988, Aug. 11          Perf. 13½x13**
| | | | | |
|---|---|---|---|---|
| 1331 | A227 | 60f Umm Al-rasas | .70 | .50 |
| 1332 | A227 | 80f Umm Qais | .90 | .70 |
| 1333 | A227 | 160f Iraq Al-amir | 1.90 | 1.50 |
| | *Nos. 1331-1333 (3)* | | 3.50 | 2.70 |

An imperf. souvenir sheet of 3 exists containing one each Nos. 1331-1333. Value $5.

1988 Summer Olympics, Seoul — A228

10f, Tennis. 60f, Character trademark. 80f, Running, swimming. 120f, Basketball. 160f, Soccer.
100f, Emblems.

**1988, Sept. 17          Litho.          Perf. 13x13½**
| | | | | |
|---|---|---|---|---|
| 1334 | A228 | 10f multi | .30 | .25 |
| 1335 | A228 | 60f multi | .90 | .70 |
| 1336 | A228 | 80f multi | 1.40 | .90 |
| 1337 | A228 | 120f multi | 1.75 | 1.50 |
| 1338 | A228 | 160f multi | 2.50 | 1.75 |
| | *Nos. 1334-1338 (5)* | | 6.85 | 5.10 |

**Size: 70x91mm**
*Imperf*
| | | | | |
|---|---|---|---|---|
| 1339 | A228 | 100f multi | 17.50 | 17.50 |

Royal Jordanian Airlines, 25th Anniv. — A229

60f, Ruins of Petra. 80f, Aircraft, world map.

**1988, Dec. 15          Litho.          Perf. 11½x12**
| | | | | |
|---|---|---|---|---|
| 1340 | A229 | 60f multicolored | 1.00 | .75 |
| 1341 | A229 | 80f multicolored | 1.25 | 1.00 |

UN Declaration of Human Rights, 40th Anniv. — A230

**1988, Dec. 10**
| | | | | |
|---|---|---|---|---|
| 1342 | A230 | 80f multicolored | .75 | .60 |
| 1343 | A230 | 160f multicolored | 1.75 | 1.10 |

Arab Cooperation Council, Feb. 16 — A231

| 1989 | | Litho. | Perf. 13½x13 | |
|---|---|---|---|---|
| 1344 | A231 | 10f shown | .30 | .25 |
| 1345 | A231 | 30f multi, diff. | .30 | .25 |
| 1346 | A231 | 40f multi, diff. | .30 | .25 |
| 1347 | A231 | 60f multi, diff. | 1.00 | .95 |
| | | Nos. 1344-1347 (4) | 1.90 | 1.70 |

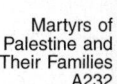

Martyrs of Palestine and Their Families A232

| 1989 | | | Perf. 14½ | |
|---|---|---|---|---|
| 1348 | A232 | 5f multicolored | .90 | .30 |
| 1349 | A232 | 10f multicolored | .90 | .30 |

Interparliamentary Union, Cent. — A233

| 1989 | | Litho. | Perf. 12 | |
|---|---|---|---|---|
| 1350 | A233 | 40f multicolored | .35 | .25 |
| 1351 | A233 | 60f multicolored | .55 | .35 |

Arab Housing Day and World Refuge Day — A234

Designs: 5f, Housing complex, emblems, vert. 60f, Housing complex, emblem.

| 1989 | | | | |
|---|---|---|---|---|
| 1352 | A234 | 5f multicolored | .30 | .25 |
| 1353 | A234 | 40f shown | .55 | .25 |
| 1354 | A234 | 60f multicolored | .75 | .55 |
| | | Nos. 1352-1354 (3) | 1.60 | 1.05 |

Ministry of Agriculture, 50th Anniv. — A235

40f, Tree, anniv. emblem. 60f, Fruit tree, emblem, apiary.

| 1989 | | Litho. | Perf. 12 | |
|---|---|---|---|---|
| 1355 | A235 | 5f shown | .30 | .25 |
| 1356 | A235 | 40f multicolored | .30 | .25 |
| 1357 | A235 | 60f multicolored | 2.25 | .25 |
| | | Nos. 1355-1357 (3) | 2.85 | .75 |

Arabian Horse Festival A236

40f, Horse, building facade. 60f, Horse's head, vert. 100f, Mare and foal.

| 1989 | | | Perf. 12 | |
|---|---|---|---|---|
| 1358 | A236 | 5f shown | .40 | .25 |
| 1359 | A236 | 40f multicolored | .85 | .25 |
| 1360 | A236 | 60f multicolored | 2.40 | .25 |
| | | Nos. 1358-1360 (3) | 3.65 | .75 |

### Size: 90x70mm
### Imperf

| 1361 | A236 | 100f multicolored | 25.00 | 22.50 |
|---|---|---|---|---|

Natl. Library Assoc. — A237

| 1989 | | | Perf. 12 | |
|---|---|---|---|---|
| 1362 | A237 | 40f multicolored | .30 | .25 |
| 1363 | A237 | 60f multicolored | 1.00 | .25 |

Mosque of the Martyr King Abdullah A238

| 1989 | | | Perf. 12 | |
|---|---|---|---|---|
| 1364 | A238 | 40f multicolored | .30 | .25 |
| 1365 | A238 | 60f multicolored | 1.00 | .25 |

### Size: 90x70mm
### Imperf

| 1366 | A238 | 100f multicolored | 6.75 | 6.75 |
|---|---|---|---|---|

Mosaics — A239

5f, Man with Basket. 10f, Building. 40f, Deer. 60f, Man with stick. 80f, Town, horiz.

| 1989, Dec. 23 | | Litho. | Perf. 12 | |
|---|---|---|---|---|
| 1367 | A239 | 5f multi | .60 | .30 |
| 1368 | A239 | 10f multi | .60 | .30 |
| 1369 | A239 | 40f multi | 1.50 | .50 |
| 1370 | A239 | 60f multi | 2.00 | .65 |
| 1371 | A239 | 80f multi | 2.50 | .90 |
| | | Nos. 1367-1371 (5) | 7.20 | 2.65 |

### Size: 90x70mm
### Imperf

| 1372 | A239 | 100f like #1371, horiz. | 17.50 | 17.50 |
|---|---|---|---|---|

Arab Cooperation Council, 1st Anniv. A240

| 1990, Feb. 16 | | | Perf. 13 | |
|---|---|---|---|---|
| 1373 | A240 | 5f multicolored | .30 | .25 |
| 1374 | A240 | 20f multicolored | .30 | .25 |
| 1375 | A240 | 60f multicolored | .75 | .45 |
| 1376 | A240 | 80f multicolored | 1.00 | .65 |
| | | Nos. 1373-1376 (4) | 2.35 | 1.60 |

Nature Conservation A241

| 1990, Apr. 22 | | | | |
|---|---|---|---|---|
| 1377 | A241 | 40f Horses | .30 | .25 |
| 1378 | A241 | 60f Mountain | .50 | .25 |
| 1379 | A241 | 80f Oasis | .65 | .35 |
| | | Nos. 1377-1379 (3) | 1.45 | .85 |

Prince Abdullah's Arrival in Ma'an, 70th Anniv. A243

| 1990 | | Litho. | Perf. 13½x13 | |
|---|---|---|---|---|
| 1382 | A243 | 40f org & multi | .30 | .25 |
| 1383 | A243 | 60f grn & multi | .40 | .25 |

### Size: 90x70mm
### Imperf

| 1384 | A243 | 200f multicolored | 7.00 | 7.00 |
|---|---|---|---|---|

UN Development Program, 40th Anniv. — A244

| 1990 | | | Perf. 13 | |
|---|---|---|---|---|
| 1385 | A244 | 60f multicolored | .30 | .25 |
| 1386 | A244 | 80f multicolored | .55 | .25 |

King Hussein — A245

| 1990-92 | | Litho. | Perf. 12x13½ | |
|---|---|---|---|---|
| 1387 | A245 | 5f yel org & multi | .30 | .25 |
| a. | | Slightly larger vignette, inscr. 1991 | .30 | .25 |
| 1390 | A245 | 20f bl grn & multi | .30 | .25 |
| 1391 | A245 | 40f orange & multi | .30 | .25 |
| 1393 | A245 | 60f blue & multi | .45 | .45 |
| 1395 | A245 | 80f pink & multi | .70 | .70 |
| a. | | Slightly larger vignette, inscr. 1991 | .70 | .70 |
| 1397 | A245 | 240f brown & multi | 1.25 | .90 |
| 1398 | A245 | 320f red lilac & multi | 1.75 | 1.25 |
| 1399 | A245 | 1d yel green & multi | 2.75 | 2.40 |
| | | Nos. 1387-1399 (8) | 7.80 | 6.45 |

No. 1390 dated 1991.
Issued: 20f, 1992; 5f, 60f, 80f 1990; others 1991.

Endangered Animals — A246

| 1991, Sept. 1 | | Litho. | Perf. 13x13½ | |
|---|---|---|---|---|
| 1401 | A246 | 5f Nubian ibex | .30 | .25 |
| 1402 | A246 | 40f Onager | .50 | .25 |
| 1403 | A246 | 80f Arabian gazelle | 2.25 | .40 |
| 1404 | A246 | 160f Arabian oryx | 1.60 | 1.10 |
| | | Nos. 1401-1404 (4) | 4.65 | 2.00 |

Energy Rationalization Program A247

Designs: 5f, Light bulbs. 40f, Solar panels, sun, vert. 80f, Electric table lamp, vert.

### Perf. 13½x13, 13x13½

| 1991, Oct. 3 | | | Litho. | |
|---|---|---|---|---|
| 1405 | A247 | 5f multicolored | .30 | .25 |
| 1406 | A247 | 40f multicolored | .30 | .25 |
| 1407 | A247 | 80f multicolored | .70 | .25 |
| | | Nos. 1405-1407 (3) | 1.30 | .75 |

Grain Production for Food Security A248

5f, Different grains. 80f, Wheat stalk, kernels.

| 1991, Oct. 16 | | | Perf. 13½x13 | |
|---|---|---|---|---|
| 1408 | A248 | 5f multicolored | .30 | .25 |
| 1409 | A248 | 40f shown | .30 | .25 |
| 1410 | A248 | 80f multicolored | .70 | .25 |
| | | Nos. 1408-1410 (3) | 1.30 | .75 |

Palestinian Uprising A249

| 1991, Nov. 29 | | Litho. | Perf. 11 | |
|---|---|---|---|---|
| 1411 | A249 | 20f multicolored | 2.00 | .75 |

Blood Donation Campaign A250

| 1991, Nov. 14 | | Litho. | Perf. 13½x13 | |
|---|---|---|---|---|
| 1412 | A250 | 80f multicolored | .75 | .25 |
| 1413 | A250 | 160f multicolored | 1.50 | .75 |

Expo '92, Seville — A251

| 1992, Feb. 20 | | | | |
|---|---|---|---|---|
| 1414 | A251 | 80f multicolored | .65 | .25 |
| 1415 | A251 | 320f multicolored | 1.60 | .95 |

Healthy Hearts — A252

80f, Man & woman, heart at center of scale, vert.

### Perf. 13x13½, 13½x13

| 1992, Apr. 7 | | | Litho. | |
|---|---|---|---|---|
| 1416 | A252 | 80f multicolored | .70 | .25 |
| 1417 | A252 | 125f multicolored | .80 | .50 |

SOS Children's Village, 'Aqaba — A253

| 1992, Apr. 30 | | Litho. | Perf. 13½x13 | |
|---|---|---|---|---|
| 1418 | A253 | 80f shown | .70 | .25 |
| 1419 | A253 | 125f Village | .80 | .50 |

1992 Summer Olympics, Barcelona A254

Stylized designs with Barcelona Olympic emblem: 5fr, Judo. 40f, Runner, vert. 80f, Diver. 125f, Flag, Cobi, map, vert. 160f, Table tennis.
100f, Incorporates all designs of set.

### Perf. 13½x13, 13x13½

| 1992, July 25 | | | Litho. | |
|---|---|---|---|---|
| 1420 | A254 | 5f multicolored | .30 | .25 |
| 1421 | A254 | 40f multicolored | .30 | .25 |
| 1422 | A254 | 80f multicolored | .50 | .25 |
| 1423 | A254 | 125f multicolored | .75 | .35 |
| 1424 | A254 | 160f multicolored | 1.10 | .50 |
| | | Nos. 1420-1424 (5) | 2.95 | 1.60 |

### Size: 70x90mm
### Imperf

| 1425 | A254 | 100f multicolored | 15.00 | 12.00 |
|---|---|---|---|---|

King Hussein, 40th Anniv. of Accession A255

Designs: 40f, Flags, King in full dress uniform, vert. 125f, King wearing headdress, flags. 160f, King in business suit, crown. 200f, Portrait.

**1992, Aug. 11**     *Perf. 13x13½*
| | | | | |
|---|---|---|---|---|
| 1426 | A255 | 40f multicolored | .30 | .25 |

*Perf. 13½x13*
| | | | | |
|---|---|---|---|---|
| 1427 | A255 | 80f shown | .45 | .25 |
| 1428 | A255 | 125f multicolored | .75 | .35 |
| 1429 | A255 | 160f multicolored | 1.10 | .50 |
| | | Nos. 1426-1429 (4) | 2.60 | 1.35 |

*Size: 90x70mm*
*Imperf*
| | | | | |
|---|---|---|---|---|
| 1430 | A255 | 200f multicolored | 7.25 | 7.25 |

Butterflies A256

5f, Danaus chrysippus. 40f, Aporia cartaegi. 80f, Papilio machaon. 160f, Pseudochazara telephassa. 200f, Same as Nos. 1431-1434.

**1992, Dec. 20**    Litho.    *Perf. 13½x13*
| | | | | |
|---|---|---|---|---|
| 1431 | A256 | 5f multicolored | .50 | .25 |
| 1432 | A256 | 40f multicolored | 1.00 | .25 |
| 1433 | A256 | 80f multicolored | 2.00 | .50 |
| 1434 | A256 | 160f multicolored | 4.50 | 1.25 |
| | | Nos. 1431-1434 (4) | 8.00 | 2.25 |

*Imperf*
*Size: 90x70mm*
| | | | | |
|---|---|---|---|---|
| 1435 | A256 | 200f multicolored | 17.50 | 17.50 |

See Nos. 1448-1452.

Intl. Customs Day — A257

**1993, Jan. 26**    Litho.    *Perf. 13½x13*
| | | | | |
|---|---|---|---|---|
| 1436 | A257 | 80f green & multi | .60 | .25 |
| 1437 | A257 | 125f pale org & multi | .90 | .45 |

Royal Scientific Society — A258

**1993, June 10**    Litho.    *Perf. 12½x13*
| | | | | |
|---|---|---|---|---|
| 1438 | A258 | 80f multicolored | .50 | .25 |

Es Salt Municipality, Cent. — A259

**1993, Sept. 1**    Litho.    *Perf. 12*
| | | | | |
|---|---|---|---|---|
| 1439 | A259 | 80f pink & multi | .60 | .25 |
| 1440 | A259 | 125f green & multi | .90 | .45 |
| a. | | Souvenir sheet of 2, #1439-1440, imperf. | 6.25 | 6.25 |

No. 1440a sold for 200f.

Great Arab Revolt and Army Day — A260

Designs: 5f, Rockets, planes, tank, King Hussein, 40f, King Hussein, military activities. 80f, Amir Abdullah ibn Hussein, Dome of the Rock, map, flags. 125f, Amir Abdullah ibn Hussein, Dome of the Rock, riders. 100f, King Hussein, flags.

**1993, June 10**
| | | | | |
|---|---|---|---|---|
| 1441 | A260 | 5f multicolored | .30 | .25 |
| 1442 | A260 | 40f multicolored | .30 | .25 |
| 1443 | A260 | 80f multicolored | .50 | .25 |
| 1444 | A260 | 125f multicolored | .85 | .35 |
| | | Nos. 1441-1444 (4) | 1.95 | 1.10 |

*Size: 90x70mm*
*Imperf*
| | | | | |
|---|---|---|---|---|
| 1445 | A260 | 100f multicolored | 6.00 | 6.00 |

White Cane Day — A261

Design: 125f, Lighted world, cane, eye, vert.

**1993, Oct. 23**    Litho.    *Perf. 12*
| | | | | |
|---|---|---|---|---|
| 1446 | A261 | 80f shown | .60 | .25 |
| 1447 | A261 | 125f multicolored | .90 | .45 |

**Butterfly Type of 1992**

Designs: 5f, Lampides boeticus. 40f, Melanargria titea. 80f, Allancastria deyrollei. 160f, Gonepteryx cleopatra. 100f, Same designs as Nos. 1448-1451.

**1993, Oct. 10**    Litho.    *Perf. 12*
| | | | | |
|---|---|---|---|---|
| 1448 | A256 | 5f multicolored | .40 | .25 |
| 1449 | A256 | 40f multicolored | .75 | .30 |
| 1450 | A256 | 80f multicolored | 1.00 | .40 |
| 1451 | A256 | 160f multicolored | 2.50 | 1.00 |
| | | Nos. 1448-1451 (4) | 4.65 | 1.95 |

*Size: 83x65mm*
*Imperf*
| | | | | |
|---|---|---|---|---|
| 1452 | A256 | 100f multicolored | 25.00 | 25.00 |

UN Declaration of Human Rights, 45th Anniv. — A262

**1993, Dec. 10**    *Perf. 12*
| | | | | |
|---|---|---|---|---|
| 1453 | A262 | 40f yellow & multi | .30 | .25 |
| 1454 | A262 | 160f red & multi | 1.10 | .75 |

Recovery & Homecoming, 1st Anniv. — A263

King Hussein: 80f, Crowd. 125f, Waving to people. 160f, Embracing woman. 100f, Standing on airplane ramp.

**1993, Nov. 25**
| | | | | |
|---|---|---|---|---|
| 1455 | A263 | 80f multicolored | .50 | .25 |
| 1456 | A263 | 125f multicolored | .85 | .40 |
| 1457 | A263 | 160f multicolored | 1.00 | .50 |
| | | Nos. 1455-1457 (3) | 2.35 | 1.15 |

*Size: 85x65*
*Imperf*
| | | | | |
|---|---|---|---|---|
| 1458 | A263 | 100f multicolored | 5.50 | 3.75 |

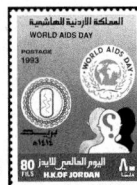

World AIDS Day — A264

**1993, Dec. 1**    *Perf. 12*
| | | | | |
|---|---|---|---|---|
| 1459 | A264 | 80f red & multi | .50 | .25 |
| 1460 | A264 | 125f green & multi | .85 | .45 |

*Size: 83x70mm*
*Imperf*
| | | | | |
|---|---|---|---|---|
| 1461 | A264 | 200f like #1459-1460 | 6.25 | 4.50 |

King Hussein — A265

King Hussein wearing: 40f, Military uniform. 80f, Traditional costume. 125f, Business suit. 160f, 100f, Dress uniform in portrait with Queen Noor.

**1993, Nov. 14**    *Perf. 12*
| | | | | |
|---|---|---|---|---|
| 1462 | A265 | 40f multicolored | .30 | .25 |
| 1463 | A265 | 80f multicolored | .50 | .25 |
| 1464 | A265 | 125f multicolored | .80 | .35 |
| 1465 | A265 | 160f multi, horiz. | 1.25 | .50 |
| | | Nos. 1462-1465 (4) | 2.85 | 1.35 |

*Size: 82x68mm*
*Imperf*
| | | | | |
|---|---|---|---|---|
| 1466 | A265 | 100f multicolored | 8.00 | 5.75 |

Assumption of Constitutional Powers by King Hussein, 40th anniv.

Saladin (1138-1193), Dome of the Rock — A266

**1993, Nov. 25**    *Perf. 12*
| | | | | |
|---|---|---|---|---|
| 1467 | A266 | 40f blue & multi | .30 | .25 |
| 1468 | A266 | 80f gray & multi | .55 | .25 |
| 1469 | A266 | 125f yellow & multi | .75 | .40 |
| | | Nos. 1467-1469 (3) | 1.60 | .90 |

Triumphal Arch, Jerash — A267

*Perf. 12x13½ (5f, No. 80f, 1473A, 1475, 160f, 320f, 1d), 12 (25f, 40f, 50f, #1474C, 240f, No. 1478C, No. 1479), 14x13½ (75f, No. 1474, 150f, 200f, 300f, 400f), 13½x14 (#120f), 12¾x13¼ (#1479B)*

**1993-2003**       Litho.
| | | | | |
|---|---|---|---|---|
| 1470 | A267 | 5f blue & multi | .30 | .25 |
| 1471 | A267 | 25f pale vio & multi | .30 | .25 |
| b. | | Perf 12¾x13¼, inscr. "2003" | .30 | .25 |
| 1471A | A267 | 40f grn & multi | .30 | .25 |
| 1472 | A267 | 50f yel & multi | .30 | .25 |
| a. | | Perf 12, inscr. "1996" | .30 | .25 |
| b. | | Perf 12¾x13¼ | .30 | .25 |
| c. | | Perf 13½x14 | .30 | .25 |
| d. | | As "b," inscr. "2003" | .30 | .25 |
| 1472E | A267 | 75f buff & multi | .40 | .40 |
| 1473 | A267 | 80f grn & multi | .35 | .25 |
| 1473A | A267 | 100f red & multi | .40 | .25 |
| b. | | Perf. 12 | .40 | .25 |
| c. | | As "b," inscribed "1996" | .40 | .25 |
| 1474 | A267 | 100f apple grn & multi | .50 | .50 |
| a. | | Perf. 12 | .50 | .50 |
| b. | | As "a," inscr. "1996" | .50 | .50 |
| 1474B | A267 | 120f bl grn & multi | .65 | .65 |
| 1474C | A267 | 125f lt bl & multi | .60 | .60 |
| 1475 | A267 | 125f buff & multi | .50 | .25 |
| a. | | Perf. 12 | .50 | .25 |
| 1475B | A267 | 150f sal pink & multi | .90 | .90 |
| 1476 | A267 | 160f yel & multi | .65 | .25 |
| b. | | Perf. 12 | .75 | .25 |
| c. | | As "b," inscribed "1994" | .75 | .25 |
| 1476A | A267 | 200f gray & multi | 1.10 | 1.10 |
| d. | | Perf. 12 | 1.10 | 1.10 |
| 1477 | A267 | 240f pink & multi | 1.00 | .25 |
| a. | | Perf. 12x13½ | .90 | .25 |
| c. | | perf 12, inscribed "1994" | 1.25 | 1.25 |
| 1477A | A267 | 300f pink & multi | 1.75 | 1.75 |
| d. | | Perf. 12 | 1.75 | 1.75 |
| 1478 | A267 | 320f brn & multi | 1.25 | .35 |
| 1478A | A267 | 320f sal & multi | 1.25 | .35 |
| 1478C | A267 | 400f brt blue & multi | 2.50 | 2.50 |
| b. | | Perf. 13x13¼ | 2.50 | 2.50 |
| 1479 | A267 | 500f bister & multi | 2.00 | .85 |
| d. | | Perf 12x13½ | 2.00 | .85 |
| 1479B | A267 | 500f yel & multi | 2.50 | 2.50 |
| 1480 | A267 | 1d olive & multi | 4.00 | 1.25 |
| a. | | Perf. 12¾x13¼ | 5.00 | 1.25 |
| | | Nos. 1470-1480 (22) | 23.50 | 15.95 |

Nos. 1472E, 1473, 1473A, 1477b, 1479a are dated 1992; Nos. 1471A, 1473Ab, 1476b, 1993; No. 1474, 1994; No. 1477Ac, 1995; Nos. 1478Cb, 1479B, 1480a, 1997.

Issued: 5f, 320f, 1/13/93 (dated 1992); 25f, 1/18/96 (dated 1995); 40f, 1994; 80f, 125f, 160f, 1d, Nos. 1473A, 1477b, 1479a, 1/13/93; No. 1478C, 1993; Nos. 1473Ab, 1476b, 240f, 3/23/94; 50f, 1995; No. 1474C, 2/13/95; 75f, 100f, 120f, 150f, 200f, 300f, 400f, 5/15/96; Nos. 1476Ad, 1477Ad, 1/18/96; 500f, 10/25/96; No. 1478Cb, 5/10/98; Nos. 1479B, 1480a, 5/10/98.
For surcharges, see Nos. 2018, 2305-2314, 2384.

Hashemite Charity Organization A268

Designs: 80f, Loading supplies into plane. 125f, People gathering at plane.

**1994, Mar. 20**    Litho.    *Perf. 12*
| | | | | |
|---|---|---|---|---|
| 1481 | A268 | 80f multicolored | .55 | .25 |
| 1482 | A268 | 125f multicolored | .80 | .50 |

Third Hashemite Restoration of Al Aqsa Mosque, Dome of the Rock A269

King Hussein with various scenes of restoration.

**1994, Apr. 18**    Litho.    *Perf. 12x12½*
| | | | | |
|---|---|---|---|---|
| 1483 | A269 | 80f yellow & multi | .40 | .25 |
| 1484 | A269 | 125f lt orange & multi | .70 | .35 |
| 1485 | A269 | 240f lilac & multi | 1.25 | .60 |
| | | Nos. 1483-1485 (3) | 2.35 | 1.20 |

*Imperf*
*Size: 90x70mm*
| | | | | |
|---|---|---|---|---|
| 1486 | A269 | 100f green & multi | 8.00 | 5.50 |

ILO, 75th Anniv. — A270

**1994, June 13**    Litho.    *Perf. 12*
| | | | | |
|---|---|---|---|---|
| 1487 | A270 | 80f yellow & multi | .45 | .25 |
| 1488 | A270 | 125f brt pink & multi | .70 | .35 |

Intl. Red Cross and Red Crescent Societies, 75th Anniv. — A271

160f, Doves, emblems, vert.

**1994, May 8**    *Perf. 12*
| | | | | |
|---|---|---|---|---|
| 1489 | A271 | 80f shown | .45 | .25 |
| 1490 | A271 | 160f multicolored | .80 | .45 |

*Size: 61x78mm*
*Imperf*
| | | | | |
|---|---|---|---|---|
| 1491 | A271 | 200f #1489-1490 | 11.00 | 8.25 |

Intl. Year of the Family — A272

**1994, Aug. 11**    Litho.    *Perf. 12*
| | | | | |
|---|---|---|---|---|
| 1492 | A272 | 80f green & multi | .45 | .25 |
| 1493 | A272 | 125f pink & multi | .80 | .40 |
| 1494 | A272 | 160f yellow & multi | 1.00 | .45 |
| | | Nos. 1492-1494 (3) | 2.25 | 1.10 |

Intl. Olympic Committee, Cent. — A273

Olympic rings and: 80f, Globe, venue symbols, vert. 100f, Jordanian colors. 125f, Venue symbols, diff., vert. 160f, shown. 240f, Torch.

**1994, June 23**
| | | | | |
|---|---|---|---|---|
| 1495 | A273 | 80f blue & multi | .40 | .25 |
| 1496 | A273 | 125f multicolored | .65 | .30 |
| 1497 | A273 | 160f multicolored | 1.10 | .40 |
| 1498 | A273 | 240f multicolored | 1.60 | .65 |
| | *Nos. 1495-1498 (4)* | | 3.75 | 1.60 |

**Size: 90x70mm**
*Imperf*
| | | | | |
|---|---|---|---|---|
| 1499 | A273 | 100f multicolored | 8.50 | 8.50 |

Jordanian Participation in UN Peacekeeping Forces — A274

Designs: 80f, King Hussein greeting troops. 125f, King inspecting troops. 160f, Checkpoint.

**1994, Aug. 11    Litho.    Perf. 14**
| | | | | |
|---|---|---|---|---|
| 1500 | A274 | 80f multicolored | .45 | .25 |
| 1501 | A274 | 125f multicolored | .70 | .35 |
| 1502 | A274 | 160f multicolored | .85 | .45 |
| | *Nos. 1500-1502 (3)* | | 2.00 | 1.05 |

Water Conservation Day — A275

80f, Hands, water droplet. 125f, Water faucet, foods, factory. 160f, Child, rain drops.

**1994, Nov. 14    Litho.    Perf. 14**
| | | | | |
|---|---|---|---|---|
| 1503 | A275 | 80f multicolored | .60 | .25 |
| 1504 | A275 | 125f multicolored | 1.00 | .55 |
| 1505 | A275 | 160f multicolored | 1.25 | .60 |
| | *Nos. 1503-1505 (3)* | | 2.85 | 1.40 |

ICAO, 50th Anniv. — A276

**1994, Oct. 25    Perf. 12**
| | | | | |
|---|---|---|---|---|
| 1506 | A276 | 80f green & multi | .45 | .25 |
| 1507 | A276 | 125f red & multi | .70 | .35 |
| 1508 | A276 | 160f blue & multi | .85 | .45 |
| | *Nos. 1506-1508 (3)* | | 2.00 | 1.05 |

Crown Prince's Award, 10th Anniv. — A277

**1994, Dec. 11    Litho.    Perf. 12**
| | | | | |
|---|---|---|---|---|
| 1509 | A277 | 80f yel grn & multi | .70 | .25 |
| 1510 | A277 | 125f org brn & multi | .90 | .55 |
| 1511 | A277 | 160f vio bl & multi | 1.25 | .70 |
| | *Nos. 1509-1511 (3)* | | 2.85 | 1.50 |

UN, 50th Anniv. — A278

**1995, Apr. 1    Litho.    Perf. 14**
| | | | | |
|---|---|---|---|---|
| 1512 | A278 | 80f green & multi | .65 | .25 |
| 1513 | A278 | 125f pink & multi | .95 | .55 |

May Day — A279

80f, Emblem, workers, flag. 125f, Emblem, world map, worker. 160f, Hands holding wrench, torch, Jordanian map, emblem.

**1995, May 1**
| | | | | |
|---|---|---|---|---|
| 1514 | A279 | 80f multicolored | .45 | .25 |
| 1515 | A279 | 125f multicolored | .65 | .40 |
| 1516 | A279 | 160f multicolored | .90 | .45 |
| | *Nos. 1514-1516 (3)* | | 2.00 | 1.10 |

Jordan Week in Japan — A280

Globe in two hemispheres with olive branches and: 125f, Japanese, Jordanian flags. 160f, Flags above wall.

**1995, May 22    Litho.    Perf. 14**
| | | | | |
|---|---|---|---|---|
| 1517 | A280 | 80f green & multi | .45 | .25 |
| 1518 | A280 | 125f pink & multi | .70 | .30 |
| 1519 | A280 | 160f gray & multi | .85 | .45 |
| | *Nos. 1517-1519 (3)* | | 2.00 | 1.00 |

Opening of Al al-Bayt University — A281

**1995, Feb. 8    Litho.    Perf. 12**
| | | | | |
|---|---|---|---|---|
| 1520 | A281 | 80f aqua & multi | .50 | .25 |
| 1521 | A281 | 125f ol grn & multi | .75 | .40 |
| | *a.* | Souvenir sheet, #1520-1521, imperf. | 3.75 | 3.25 |

No. 1521a sold for 200f. Nos. 1520-1521 are dated 1994.

Petra, the Rose City — A282

Archaeological discoveries: 50f, Amphitheater. 75f, Facial carvings, bowl, pitcher. 80f, Columns of building, vert. 160f, Front of building with columns, vert. 200f, Building in side of mountain.

**1995, Aug. 11    Litho.    Perf. 14**
| | | | | |
|---|---|---|---|---|
| 1524 | A282 | 50f multicolored | .30 | .25 |
| 1525 | A282 | 75f multicolored | .85 | .25 |
| 1526 | A282 | 80f multicolored | .95 | .25 |
| 1527 | A282 | 160f multicolored | 1.75 | .95 |
| | *Nos. 1524-1527 (4)* | | 3.85 | 1.70 |

**Size: 90x70mm**
*Imperf*
| | | | | |
|---|---|---|---|---|
| 1528 | A282 | 200f multicolored | 20.00 | 20.00 |

Arab League, 50th Anniv. — A283

**1995, Sept. 20    Litho.    Perf. 14**
| | | | | |
|---|---|---|---|---|
| 1529 | A283 | 80f green & multi | .45 | .25 |
| 1530 | A283 | 125f pink & multi | .70 | .25 |
| 1531 | A283 | 160f gray & multi | .85 | .45 |
| | *Nos. 1529-1531 (3)* | | 2.00 | .95 |

FAO, 50th Anniv. — A284

Designs: 125f, "50," FAO emblem, shafts of grain. 160f, UN, FAO emblems, "50."

**1995, Oct. 16    Litho.    Perf. 14**
| | | | | |
|---|---|---|---|---|
| 1532 | A284 | 80f shown | .50 | .25 |
| 1533 | A284 | 125f multicolored | .85 | .40 |
| 1534 | A284 | 160f multicolored | 1.00 | .50 |
| | *Nos. 1532-1534 (3)* | | 2.35 | 1.15 |

Middle East and North Africa Economic Summit, Amman — A285

**1995, Oct. 29    Perf. 12**
| | | | | |
|---|---|---|---|---|
| 1535 | A285 | 80f brt pink & multi | .50 | .25 |
| 1536 | A285 | 125f org yel & multi | .75 | .40 |

The Deaf — A286

125f, Emblems, hand sign.

**1995, Nov. 30    Perf. 14**
| | | | | |
|---|---|---|---|---|
| 1537 | A286 | 80f shown | .50 | .25 |
| 1538 | A286 | 125f multicolored | .75 | .35 |

King Hussein, 60th Birthday A287

Designs: 40f, Crown over King's picture in business suit. 80f, Crown, flag, dove, ruins of Petra, King in traditional head wear, military uniform. 100f, King in dress uniform, crown, "60." 125f, King in traditional head wear, business suit, crown, flag, olive branch. 160f, Flag, King in business suit. 200f, "60," Dome of the Rock, King in dress uniform, olive branch.

**1995, Nov. 14**
| | | | | |
|---|---|---|---|---|
| 1539 | A287 | 25f multicolored | .30 | .25 |
| 1540 | A287 | 40f multicolored | .30 | .25 |
| 1541 | A287 | 80f multicolored | .45 | .25 |
| 1542 | A287 | 100f multicolored | .50 | .25 |
| 1543 | A287 | 125f multicolored | 1.00 | .35 |
| 1544 | A287 | 160f multicolored | 1.25 | .45 |
| | *Nos. 1539-1544 (6)* | | 3.80 | 1.80 |

**Size: 83x63mm**
*Imperf*
| | | | | |
|---|---|---|---|---|
| 1545 | A287 | 200f multicolored | 6.25 | 6.25 |

Independence, 50th Anniv. — A288

King Hussein and: No. 1547, Outline map of Jordan, crown, dove of peace, Amir Abdullah ibn Hussein. 300f, Jordanian monuments, flag. No. 1549, Map of Jordan surrounded by wreath, dove, national flags.

**1996, May 25    Litho.    Perf. 12**
| | | | | |
|---|---|---|---|---|
| 1546 | A288 | 100f multicolored | .55 | .25 |
| 1547 | A288 | 200f multicolored | 1.10 | .40 |
| 1548 | A288 | 300f multicolored | 1.75 | .65 |
| | *Nos. 1546-1548 (3)* | | 3.40 | 1.30 |

**Size: 86x66mm**
| | | | | |
|---|---|---|---|---|
| 1549 | A288 | 200f multicolored | 7.50 | 7.50 |

1996 Summer Olympic Games, Atlanta — A289

1996 Olympic Games Emblem and: 50f, Natl. flag, Olympic rings, sports pictograms. 100f, Sports pictograms. 200f, Hands. 300f, Torch, Olympic rings, natl. flag.

**1996, July 19    Litho.    Perf. 12**
| | | | | |
|---|---|---|---|---|
| 1550 | A289 | 50f multicolored | .30 | .25 |
| 1551 | A289 | 100f multicolored | .70 | .25 |
| 1552 | A289 | 200f multicolored | 1.60 | .70 |
| 1553 | A289 | 300f multicolored | 2.50 | 1.10 |
| | *Nos. 1550-1553 (4)* | | 5.10 | 2.30 |

Protection of the Ozone Layer — A290

**1996, Sept. 16**
| | | | | |
|---|---|---|---|---|
| 1554 | A290 | 100f multicolored | 1.25 | .25 |

UNICEF, 50th Anniv. — A291

**1996, Dec. 11    Litho.    Perf. 12**
| | | | | |
|---|---|---|---|---|
| 1555 | A291 | 100f green & multi | .60 | .25 |
| 1556 | A291 | 200f gray lilac & multi | 1.00 | .60 |

Crown Prince El-Hassan, 50th Birthday A292

Designs: 50f, On horseback. 100f, Wearing suit & tie, vert. No. 1559, Natl. flag, wearing traditional attire. No. 1560, Wearing graduation cap.

**1997, Mar. 20    Litho.    Perf. 12**
| | | | | |
|---|---|---|---|---|
| 1557 | A292 | 50f multicolored | .30 | .25 |
| 1558 | A292 | 100f multicolored | .70 | .25 |
| 1559 | A292 | 200f multicolored | 1.10 | .70 |
| | *Nos. 1557-1559 (3)* | | 2.10 | 1.20 |

**Size: 84x64mm**
*Imperf*
| | | | | |
|---|---|---|---|---|
| 1560 | A292 | 200f multicolored | 8.25 | 8.25 |

Heinrich von Stephan (1831-97) — A293

**1997, Apr. 8    Litho.    Perf. 12**
| | | | | |
|---|---|---|---|---|
| 1561 | A293 | 100f multicolored | .90 | .25 |
| 1562 | A293 | 200f multicolored | 1.60 | .80 |

Discovery of the Madeba Mosaic Map, Cent. — A294

100f, Karak, vert. 200f, River Jordan. 300f, Jerusalem, vert. No. 1566, Entire map.

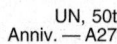

**1997, Apr. 7**
| | | | | |
|---|---|---|---|---|
| 1563 | A294 | 100f multicolored | .75 | .35 |
| 1564 | A294 | 100f multicolored | 1.50 | .50 |
| 1565 | A294 | 300f multicolored | 2.50 | .90 |
| | | Nos. 1563-1565 (3) | 4.75 | 1.75 |

**Size: 86x67mm**
*Imperf*
| | | | | |
|---|---|---|---|---|
| 1566 | A294 | 100f multi | 15.00 | 15.00 |

Jordanian Rosefinch A295

**1997, May 25    Litho.    Perf. 12**
| | | | | |
|---|---|---|---|---|
| 1567 | A295 | 50f multicolored | .30 | .25 |
| 1568 | A295 | 100f multi, diff. | .65 | .25 |
| 1569 | A295 | 150f multi, diff. | 1.00 | .45 |
| 1570 | A295 | 200f multi, diff. | 1.50 | .65 |
| | | Nos. 1567-1570 (4) | 3.45 | 1.60 |

Jerash Festival, 15th Anniv. — A296

Designs: 50f, Couples in traditional costumes, ruins. 100f, Symphony orchestra, silhouettes of buildings. 150f, Pillars, parade of dignitaries. 200f, Women in traditional costumes, crowd, ruins.
15d, Queen Noor lighting torch.

**1997, July 23    Litho.    Perf. 12**
| | | | | |
|---|---|---|---|---|
| 1571 | A296 | 50f multicolored | .30 | .25 |
| 1572 | A296 | 100f multicolored | .60 | .25 |
| 1573 | A296 | 150f multicolored | .95 | .45 |
| 1574 | A296 | 200f multicolored | 1.50 | .65 |
| | | Nos. 1571-1574 (4) | 3.35 | 1.60 |

**Size: 90x70mm**
*Imperf*
| | | | | |
|---|---|---|---|---|
| 1575 | A296 | 15d multicolored | 8.50 | 8.50 |

Natl. Forum for Women — A297

Emblem and: 50f, Women in tradtional and modern dress, vert. 100f, Natl. flag, flame, book. 150fr, Natl. flag, women seated at conference table.

**1997, Dec. 20    Litho.    Perf. 12**
| | | | | |
|---|---|---|---|---|
| 1576 | A297 | 50f multicolored | .30 | .25 |
| 1577 | A297 | 100f multicolored | .50 | .25 |
| 1578 | A297 | 150f multicolored | .80 | .35 |
| | | Nos. 1576-1578 (3) | 1.60 | .85 |

Jordanian Team, 1997 Arab Soccer Champions A298

Designs: 50f, Team parading in stadium. 75f, Team in red uniforms. 100f, Team in white uniforms, ceremony.
200f, Formal presentation to King Hussein, motorcade.

**1997, Dec. 15**
| | | | | |
|---|---|---|---|---|
| 1579 | A298 | 50f multicolored | .30 | .25 |
| 1580 | A298 | 75f multicolored | .40 | .25 |
| 1581 | A298 | 100f multicolored | .55 | .25 |
| | | Nos. 1579-1581 (3) | 1.25 | .75 |

**Size: 91x70mm**
*Imperf*
| | | | | |
|---|---|---|---|---|
| 1582 | A298 | 200f multicolored | 9.00 | 7.50 |

House of Parliament, 50th Anniv. — A299

100f, Outside view of building, drawing. 200f, Speaker, members assembled in chamber.

**1997, Nov. 1    Perf. 12½**
| | | | | |
|---|---|---|---|---|
| 1583 | A299 | 100f multicolored | .60 | .25 |
| 1584 | A299 | 200f multicolored | .90 | .60 |

53rd General Meeting of Intl. Air Transport Association — A300

**1997, Nov. 3    Litho.    Perf. 13x13½**
| | | | | |
|---|---|---|---|---|
| 1585 | A300 | 100f lt blue & multi | 1.00 | 1.00 |
| 1586 | A300 | 200f red & multi | 1.00 | 1.00 |
| 1587 | A300 | 300f gray & multi | 1.00 | 1.00 |

Two additional stamps were issued in this set. The editors would like to examine them.

King Hussein II, 62nd Birthday — A301

**1997, Nov. 14    Litho.    Perf. 13x13½**
**Frame Color**
| | | | | |
|---|---|---|---|---|
| 1588 | A301 | 100f red | 1.00 | 1.00 |
| 1589 | A301 | 200f gold | 1.00 | 1.00 |
| 1590 | A301 | 300f gold | 1.00 | 1.00 |

**Souvenir Sheet**
**Perf. 12**
| | | | | |
|---|---|---|---|---|
| 1590A | A301 | 200f gold | 8.50 | 8.50 |

No. 1590A contains one 44x60mm stamp.

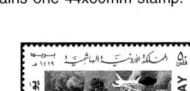
Earth Day — A302

Children's drawings: 50f, Various ways of polluting air and water. 100f, Pollution from factory smoke, automobiles. 150f, Earth chained to various methods of pollution, vert.

**1998, Apr. 29    Litho.    Perf. 14**
| | | | | |
|---|---|---|---|---|
| 1591 | A302 | 50f multicolored | .30 | .25 |
| 1592 | A302 | 100f multicolored | .50 | .25 |
| 1593 | A302 | 150f multicolored | .80 | .50 |
| | | Nos. 1591-1593 (3) | 1.60 | 1.00 |

Trans-Jordan Emirate, 75th Anniv. — A303

Designs: 100f, Camel rider holding flag, Amir Abdullah ibn Hussein. 200f, Camel rider holding flag, King Hussein. 300f, King Hussein, arms, #81, Amir Abdullah ibn Hussein.

**1998, May 25    Perf. 12**
| | | | | |
|---|---|---|---|---|
| 1594 | A303 | 100f multicolored | .50 | .50 |
| 1595 | A303 | 200f multicolored | 1.00 | 1.00 |
| 1596 | A303 | 300f multicolored | 1.75 | 1.75 |
| | | Nos. 1594-1596 (3) | 3.25 | 3.25 |

**Size: 80x70mm**
*Imperf*
| | | | | |
|---|---|---|---|---|
| 1597 | A303 | 300f like #1596 | 8.50 | 8.50 |

Mosaics, Um Ar-Rasas — A304

**1998, July 22    Litho.    Perf. 14**
| | | | | |
|---|---|---|---|---|
| 1598 | A304 | 100f multicolored | .50 | .50 |
| 1599 | A304 | 200f multi, diff. | 1.00 | 1.00 |
| 1600 | A304 | 300f multi, diff. | 1.75 | 1.75 |
| | | Nos. 1598-1600 (3) | 3.25 | 3.25 |

Flowers — A305

50f, Purple & white, thorns. 100f, Poppies. 200f, Flower, map of Jordan.

**1998, July 7**
| | | | | |
|---|---|---|---|---|
| 1601 | A305 | 50f multicolored | .30 | .25 |
| 1602 | A305 | 100f multicolored | .60 | .55 |
| 1603 | A305 | 150f shown | 1.00 | .75 |
| | | Nos. 1601-1603 (3) | 1.90 | 1.55 |

**Size: 60x80mm**
*Imperf*
| | | | | |
|---|---|---|---|---|
| 1604 | A305 | 200f multicolored | 8.50 | 8.50 |

2nd Arab Beekeepers Conference A306

Various pictures of bees, flowers, honeycomb.

**1998, Aug. 3    Litho.    Perf. 14**
| | | | | |
|---|---|---|---|---|
| 1605 | A306 | 50f multicolored | .50 | .40 |
| 1606 | A306 | 100f multi, vert. | .85 | .50 |
| 1607 | A306 | 150f multicolored | 1.25 | .60 |
| | | Nos. 1605-1607 (3) | 2.60 | 1.50 |

**Size: 80x60mm**
*Imperf*
| | | | | |
|---|---|---|---|---|
| 1608 | A306 | 200f Bees, flowers, emblem | 9.00 | 9.00 |

World Stamp Day — A307

100f, World map, emblems. 150f, Globe, stamps.

**1998, Oct. 9    Litho.    Perf. 14**
| | | | | |
|---|---|---|---|---|
| 1609 | A307 | 50f shown | .30 | .25 |
| 1610 | A307 | 100f multicolored | .90 | .90 |
| 1611 | A307 | 150f multicolored | 1.75 | 1.75 |
| | | Nos. 1609-1611 (3) | 2.95 | 2.90 |

Universal Declaration of Human Rights, 50th Anniv. — A308

200f, Emblems, people.

**1998, Dec. 10**
| | | | | |
|---|---|---|---|---|
| 1612 | A308 | 100f shown | .60 | .60 |
| 1613 | A308 | 200f multicolored | 1.00 | 1.00 |

King Hussein, 63rd Birthday A309

**1998, Nov. 14    Litho.    Perf. 14x14½**
| | | | | |
|---|---|---|---|---|
| 1614 | A309 | 100f green & multi | .65 | .45 |
| 1615 | A309 | 200f violet & multi | 1.25 | 1.00 |
| 1616 | A309 | 300f vio blue & multi | 2.25 | 1.50 |
| | | Nos. 1614-1616 (3) | 4.15 | 2.95 |

**Size: 90x70mm**
*Imperf*
| | | | | |
|---|---|---|---|---|
| 1617 | A309 | 300f gold & multi | 8.50 | 8.50 |

Arab Police and Security Chiefs Meeting, 25th Anniv. (in 1997) — A310

Map of Arab world and: 100f, King Hussein, emblem. 200f, Flags of Arab countries, emblem, flame, vert. 300f, Beret.

**1998, Nov. 18    Perf. 14**
| | | | | |
|---|---|---|---|---|
| 1618 | A310 | 100f multicolored | .65 | .65 |
| 1619 | A310 | 200f multicolored | 1.10 | 1.10 |
| 1620 | A310 | 300f multicolored | 2.00 | 1.75 |
| | | Nos. 1618-1620 (3) | 3.75 | 3.50 |

Mustafa Wahbi (1899-1949), Poet — A311

**1999, May 25    Litho.    Perf. 14¼**
| | | | | |
|---|---|---|---|---|
| 1621 | A311 | 100f multicolored | .90 | .90 |

Environmental Protection A312

Designs: 100f, Children, bandaged Earth. 200f, Earth as fruit in hands.

**1999, Oct. 14    Litho.    Perf. 13¼x13¾**
| | | | | |
|---|---|---|---|---|
| 1622 | A312 | 100f multi | .50 | .50 |
| 1623 | A312 | 200f multi | 1.00 | 1.00 |

Hijazi Railway Museum A313

Train and: 100f, Map of Jordan, museum building. 300f, Museum building.

**1999, Sept. 7    Litho.    Perf. 13½x13¾**
| | | | | |
|---|---|---|---|---|
| 1624-1626 | A313 | Set of 3 | 6.00 | 6.00 |

9th Arab Sports Tournament A314

Bird mascot, emblem and: 50f, Weight lifting, tennis, wrestling, soccer. 100f, Torch. No. 1629, Shooting, fencing, swimming, track & field, vert. 300f, Flag, map, discus thrower, tennis player.
No. 1631, Basketball, volleyball, boxing, swimming.

**Perf. 13¼x13¾, 13¾x13¼**
**1999, Aug. 15    Litho.**
| | | | | |
|---|---|---|---|---|
| 1627 | A314 | 50f multi | .30 | .25 |
| 1628 | A314 | 100f multi | .65 | .65 |
| 1629 | A314 | 200f multi | 1.40 | 1.40 |
| 1630 | A314 | 300f multi | 2.25 | 2.25 |
| | | Nos. 1627-1630 (4) | 4.60 | 4.55 |

*Imperf*
**Size: 90x70mm**
| | | | | |
|---|---|---|---|---|
| 1631 | A314 | 200f multi | 3.25 | 3.25 |

UPU, 125th Anniv. — A315

Designs: 100f, "125," UPU emblems, stripes of airmail envelope. No. 1633, Airmail envelope with UPU emblem.

No. 1634, Like No. 1633, yellow background.

**1999, Oct. 9**     **Perf. 13¼x13¾**
1632 A315 100f multi     .65 .65
1633 A315 200f multi     1.10 1.10
*Imperf*
**Size: 90x70mm**
1634 A315 200f multi     2.50 2.50

Gulf of Aqaba Corals — A316

Designs: 50f, Pachyseris speciosa. 100f, Acropora digitifera. No. 1637, 200f, Oxypora lacera. 300f, Fungia echinata. No. 1639, 200f, Gorgonia.

**1999, Oct. 2**   **Litho.**   **Perf. 13½x13¾**
1635-1638 A316 Set of 4     4.00 4.00
*Imperf*
**Size: 90x70mm**
1639 A316 200f multi     12.00 12.00

Cradle of Civilizations A317

Archaeological sites — Petra: No. 1640, 100f, Al-Deir. No. 1641, 200f, Khazneh. No. 1642, 300f, Obelisk tomb.
Jerash: No. 1643, 100f, Cardo Maximus. No. 1644, 200f, Temple of Artemis. No. 1645, 300f, Nymphaeum.
Amman: No. 1646, 100f, Roman Theater. No. 1647, 200f, Citadel. No. 1648, 300f, Ain Ghazal statues.
Wadi Rum and Aqaba: No. 1649, 100f, Camel riders, Wadi Rum. No. 1650, 200f, House, Aqaba. No. 1651, Ruins, Aqaba.
Madaba: No. 1652, 100f, Mosaic. No. 1653, 200f, Church. No. 1654, 300f, Mosaic map of Jerusalem.
Baptism Site (Bethany): No. 1655, Plant life near water. No. 1656, 200f, Aerial view. No. 1657, 300f, Excavation site.
Aljoun: No. 1658, 100f, Ruins. No. 1659, 200f, Ruins diff. No. 1660, 300f, Ruins diff.
Pella: No. 1661, 100f, Ruins of Byzantine cathedral. No. 1662, 200f, Three large pillars. No. 1663, 300f, Ruins.

**1999-2000**   **Litho.**   **Perf. 13½x14**
1640-1663 A317 Set of 24     23.00 23.00
Issued: Nos. 1640-1645, 10/24; Nos. 1646-1651, 10/31; Nos. 1652-1654, 12/22; Nos. 1655-1657, 12/23; Nos. 1658-1663, 3/7/00.
See Nos. 1688-1693. For surcharges, see Nos. 2317-2321, 2324-2325, 2378-2381.

Museum of Political History — A318

100f, Building interior. 200f, Museum entrance and plaza. 300f, Museum entrance.

**1999, Nov. 14**   **Litho.**   **Perf. 13½x14**
1664-1666 A318 Set of 3     3.75 3.75

Jordan Philatelic Club, 20th Anniv. A318a

Designs: 100f, #534H and other stamps. 200f, #284 and other stamps.

**1999, Nov. 14**     **Perf. 14¼**
1666A-1666B A318a Set of 2     1.50 1.50

SOS Children's Village, Irbid — A318b

100f, SOS Children's Village 50th anniv. emblem, Jordanian flag. 200f, Woman, children.

**1999, Nov. 23**
1666C-1666D A318b Set of 2     1.50 1.50

Coronation of King Abdullah II — A319

**1999, Dec. 27**   **Litho.**   **Perf. 11¾**
**Frame Color**
1667 A319 100f red     .90 .90
1668 A319 200f green     .90 .90
1669 A319 300f blue     .90 .90
**Souvenir Sheet**
1670 A319 200f gold     1.00 1.00

King Abdullah II and Queen Rania A319a

**1999, Dec. 27**   **Litho.**   **Perf. 11¾**
1670A A319a 100f red     .95 .95
1670B A319a 200f green     .95 .95
1670C A319a 300f blue     .95 .95
**Souvenir Sheet**
1670D A319a 200f gold     5.25 5.25
Issued: 1670D, 12/27/99.
Numbers have been reserved for three additional stamps in this set. The editors would like to examine any examples of them.

King Abdullah II, 38th Birthday — A320

King, crown and: 100f, Olive branches. 200f, Nos. #1672 #1674, Flag, "38," horiz. 300f, Flag, "38," eagle, olive branch, horiz.

**Perf 12, Imperf (#1674)**
**2000, Jan. 30**     **Litho.**
1671-1673 A320 Set of 3     3.00 3.00
**Size: 90x74mm**
1674 A320 200f multi     3.50 3.50

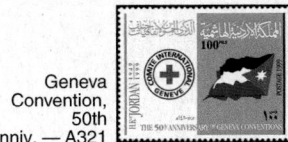

Geneva Convention, 50th Anniv. — A321

**Perf. 13½x13¾**
**2000, Feb. 15**     **Litho.**
1675 Horiz. strip of 3     3.50 3.50
   a. A321 100f lt bl & multi     .50 .50
   b. A321 200f ocher & multi     1.00 1.00
   c. A321 300f gray & multi     1.50 1.50
Dated 1999.

Millennium — A322

No. 1678: a, Jordanian flag, "Jordan, The River & The Land of the Baptism" in English. b, Fish in river. c, As "a," with Arabic inscription.

**2000, Feb. 22**   **Perf. 13¼x13¾**     **Litho.**
1678 Strip of 3     3.25 3.25
   a. A322 100f multi     .45 .45
   b. A322 200f multi     .90 .90
   c. A322 300f multi     1.25 1.25

King Abdullah II, Houses of Worship and Pope John Paul II — A323

Color of lower panel: 100f, Dull blue green. 200f, Lilac. 300f, Bright yellow green.

**2000, Mar. 20**   **Litho.**   **Perf. 12**
1679-1681 A323 Set of 3     3.25 3.25
Visit of Pope Paul VI to Jordan, 36th anniv.

Visit of Pope John Paul II to Jordan — A324

Pope John Paul II, King Abdullah II and: 100f, "2000." 200f, River. 300f, Vatican and Jordanian flags, map of Jordan. No. 1685, Pope, baptism of Christ, vert.

**Perf 12, Imperf (#1685)**
**2000, Mar. 20**
1682-1684 A324 Set of 3     3.25 3.25
**Size: 70x90mm**
1685 A324 200f multi     17.50 17.50

World Meteorological Organization, 50th Anniv. — A325

Designs: 100f, Globe, emblem, anniversary emblem. 200f, Globe with arrows, emblem, anniversary emblem.

**2000, Mar. 23**   **Litho.**   **Perf. 12**
1686 A325 100f multi     .75 .75
1687 A325 200f multi     1.25 1.25

**Cradle of Civilizations Type of 1999**

Archaeological sites — Palaces: No. 1688, 100f, Mushatta. No. 1689, 200f, Kharaneh. No. 1690, 300f, Amra.
Um Qais: No. 1691, 100f, Decumanus. No. 1692, 200f, Amphitheater. No. 1693, 300f, Ruins.

**2000, Apr. 7**   **Litho.**   **Perf. 13½x14**
**Palaces**
1688-1690 A317 Set of 3     4.00 4.00
**Um Qais**
1691-1693 A317 Set of 3     4.00 4.00
   a. Sheet, #1640-1663, 1688-1693     40.00 —
For surcharges, see Nos. 2322-2323, 2382-2383.

Scouting in Jordan, 90th Anniv. — A326

"90" and: 100f, Emblem, Jordanian flag. 200f, Tents. 300f, Tents, Jordanian flag. No. 1697, Like No. 1694.

**Perf 12, Imperf (#1697)**
**2000, May 11**     **Litho.**
1694-1696 A326 Set of 3     5.00 5.00
**Size: 90x70mm**
1697 A326 200f multi     7.50 7.50

Expo 2000, Hanover — A327

Designs: No. 1698, 200f, Inscribed clay tablet. 300f, Artifact with two heads. No. 1700, 200f, King, Queen, Jordan pavilion interior.

**2000, June 1**   **Litho.**   **Perf. 11¾**
**Granite Paper**
1698-1699 A327 Set of 2     3.50 3.50
*Imperf*
**Size: 90x70mm**
1700 A327 200f multi     3.00 3.00

Palace of Justice — A328

Palace and: 100f, Scales of justice. 200f, Scales, Jordanian flag.

**2000, June 25**   **Unwmk.**   **Perf. 12**
1701 A328 100f multi     .75 .75
**Wmk. 388**
1702 A328 200f multi     1.25 1.25
A number has been reserved for an additional stamp in this set. The editors would like to examine it.

Al-Amal Cancer Center — A329

Emblem and: 200f, Building. 300f, Family.

**Perf. 11¾**
**2000, July 17**   **Litho.**   **Unwmk.**
**Granite Paper**
1704-1705 A329 Set of 2     3.75 3.75

Flora and Fauna — A330

Designs: 50f, Dove. 100f, Arabian oryx. 150f, Caracal. 200f, Red fox. 300f, Jal'ad iris. 400f, White broom.

**2000, Sept. 28**     **Perf. 14¼**
**Booklet Stamps**
1706 A330 50f multi     .35 .30
1707 A330 100f multi     .75 .50
   a. Booklet pane, 2 each #1706-1707     4.00 —

| | | | | |
|---|---|---|---|---|
| **1708** | A330 | 150f multi | 1.25 | .60 |
| **1709** | A330 | 200f multi | 1.50 | .80 |
| *a.* | Booklet pane, 2 each #1708-1709 | | 7.00 | — |
| **1710** | A330 | 300f multi | 2.50 | 1.75 |
| **1711** | A330 | 400f multi | 3.00 | 1.90 |
| *a.* | Booklet pane, 2 each #1710-1711 | | 13.00 | — |
| | Booklet, #1707a, 1709a, 1711a | | 30.00 | |

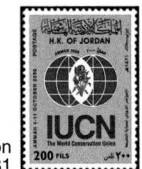

World Conservation
Union — A331

Background color: 200f, Green. 300f, Blue.

**2000, Oct. 4**      *Perf. 11¾*
**Granite Paper**
**1712-1713** A331   Set of 2    3.50 3.50

Tourist
Sites — A332

Designs: 50f, Petra. 100f, Jerash. 150f, Mount Nebo. 200f, Dead Sea. 300f, Aqaba. 400f, Wadi Rum.

**2000, Oct. 9**      *Perf. 14¼*
**Booklet Stamps**

| | | | | |
|---|---|---|---|---|
| **1714** | A332 | 50f multi | .35 | .35 |
| **1715** | A332 | 100f multi | .75 | .60 |
| *a.* | Booklet pane, 2 each #1714-1715 | | 2.25 | |
| **1716** | A332 | 150f multi | 1.25 | .90 |
| **1717** | A332 | 200f multi | 1.75 | 1.10 |
| *a.* | Booklet pane, 2 each #1716-1717 | | 6.00 | — |
| **1718** | A332 | 300f multi | 2.25 | 1.50 |
| **1719** | A332 | 400f multi | 2.75 | 2.25 |
| *a.* | Booklet pane, 2 each #1718-1719 | | 10.00 | — |
| | Booklet, #1715a, 1717a, 1719a | | 22.50 | |

King Hussein
(1935-99) — A333

Designs: 50f, King, vert. No. 1721, 150f, No. 1723, 200f, King and wreath. No. 1722, 200f, King, symbols of industry and agriculture.

**2000, Nov. 14**   **Litho.**   *Perf. 11¾*
**Granite Paper**
**1720-1722** A333   Set of 3    *2.75 2.75*
**Size: 90x70mm**
*Imperf*
**1723** A333 200f multi    *4.50 4.50*

UN High
Commissioner for
Refugees, 50th
Anniv. — A334

Designs: 200f, Man, women, child. 300f, Emblem.

**2000, Dec. 3**   **Litho.**   *Perf. 11¾*
**Granite Paper**
**1724-1725** A334   Set of 2    3.50 3.50

13th Arab Summit
Conference
A335

Emblem, map of Middle East and: 50f, Jordanian flag. 200f, Jordanian flags. 250f, King Abdullah II.

**2001, Aug. 1**      *Perf. 14*
**1726-1728** A335   Set of 3    3.00 3.00

---

Palestinian
Intifada — A336

Dome of the Rock and: 200f, Rock throwers, man carrying flag. 300f, Rock throwers, Israeli troops.

**2001, Aug. 5**
**1729-1730** A336   Set of 2    3.00 3.00

Mohammed Al-
Dorra, Boy Killed
in Intifada
Crossfire — A337

Designs: 200f, Al-Dorra and father, Dome of the Rock. 300f, Close-up of Al-Dorra, Al-Dorra dead on father's lap.

**2001, Aug. 5**
**1731-1732** A337   Set of 2    3.00 3.00

Healthy Non-
smoking
Students — A338

Designs: 200f, Students. 300f, Cartoon character, vert.

**2001, Sept. 1**
**1733-1734** A338   Set of 2    3.00 3.00

Sports For People With
Special Needs — A339

Stylized figures and: 200f, Man in wheelchair. 300f, Woman.

**2001, Sept. 15**
**1735-1736** A339   Set of 2    3.00 3.00

Olive
Trees — A340

Designs: 200f, Olives on branch, tree, map of Jordan. 300f, Woman picking olives, vert.

**2001, Oct. 1**
**1737-1738** A340   Set of 2    3.00 3.00

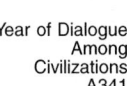

Year of Dialogue
Among
Civilizations
A341

Emblem and: 200f, Family, handshake, world map. 300f, Other stylized drawings.

**2001, Oct. 21**
**1739-1740** A341   Set of 2    3.00 3.00

Cooperation
Between Jordan
and
Japan — A342

Designs: 200f, Sheikh Hussein Bridge, flags. 300f, King Hussein Bridge, handshake.

**2001, Nov. 12**   **Litho.**   *Perf. 14¼*
**1741-1742** A342   Set of 2    3.00 3.00

---

Jordan - People's
Republic of China
Diplomatic
Relations, 25th
Anniv. — A343

Designs: 200f, Dove with envelope. 300f, King Abdullah II and Chinese Pres. Jiang Zemin.

**2002**      *Perf. 12*
**1743-1744** A343   Set of 2    2.25 2.25

Amman, 2002
Arab Cultural
Capital — A344

Designs: 100f, Arabic script, star. 200f, Pen, torch. 300f, Amphitheater.

**2002**      *Perf. 14¼*
**1745-1747** A344   Set of 3    3.00 3.00

Paintings — A345

Paintings by, 100f, Rafiq Laham. 150f, Mahmoud Taha, horiz. 200f, Mohanna Durra. 300f, Wijdan, horiz.

**2002, July 2**      *Perf. 13¼*
**1748-1751** A345   Set of 4    4.50 4.50

Vision 2020 — A346

Designs: 200f, Symbols of business and technology. 300f, Fingers, electronic device.

**2002**   **Litho.**   *Perf. 13¼*
**1752-1753** A346   Set of 2    2.25 2.25

Migratory
Birds — A347

Designs: 100f, Goldfinch. No. 1755, 200f, Rufous bush robin. 300f, White stork.
No. 1757, 200f, Golden oriole, goshawk, ortolan bunting, hoopoe.

**2002**      *Perf. 13¼*
**1754-1756** A347   Set of 3    4.00 4.00
*Imperf*
**Size: 70x90mm**
**1757** A347 200f multi    *8.50 8.50*

Hashemite
Rulers — A348

No. 1758: a, Sherif Hussein bin Ali. b, King Abdullah. c, King Talal bin Abdullah. d, King Hussein bin Talal. e, King Abdullah II.

---

**2003, July 2**   **Litho.**   *Perf. 14*
**1758**    Miniature sheet of 5    4.50 4.50
*a.-e.*   A348 200f Any single    .75 .75

Salt
Museum — A349

Views of building exterior: 150f, 250f.

**2003, July 2**
**1759-1760** A349   Set of 2    1.75 1.75

Trees — A350

Designs: 50f, Cupressus sempervirens. 100f, Pistacia atlantica. 200f, Quercus aegilops.

**2003, Aug. 7**
**1761-1763** A350   Set of 3    2.25 2.25

Flowers — A351

Designs: 50f, Cistanche tubulosa. 100f, Ophioglossum polyphyllum, vert. 150f, Narcissus tazetta. 200f, Gynandriris sisyrinchium, vert.

**2003, Aug. 7**
**1764-1767** A351   Set of 4    3.00 3.00

Birds of Prey — A352

Designs: 100f, Ciraetus gallicus. No. 1769, 200f, Falco peregrinus. 300f, Accipiter nisus. No. 1771, 200f, Ciraetus gallicus, diff.

**2003, Dec. 9**   **Litho.**   *Perf. 14*
**1768-1770** A352   Set of 3    3.50 3.50
**Size: 70x90mm**
*Imperf*
**1771** A352 200f multi    6.00 6.00

Royal Cars
Museum — A353

Designs: 100f, Red sports car. 150f, Black limousine. 300f, White limousine. 200f, Three automobiles.

**2003, Dec. 23**   **Litho.**   *Perf. 14*
**1772-1774** A353   Set of 3    3.50 3.50
**Size: 90x70mm**
*Imperf*
**1775** A353 200f multi    4.50 4.50

Jordan Post
Company
A354

Emblem and: 50f, Arch. 100f, Pillars, vert.

**2003, Dec. 23**   **Litho.**   *Perf. 14*
**1776-1777** A354   Set of 2    1.00 1.00

## Triumphal Arch Type of 1993-98
**2003** **Litho.** **Perf. 12¾x13¼**
**Granite Paper**
1777A A267 25f gray & multi — —

Arabian
Horses — A355

Various horses: 5pi, 7.50pi, 12.50pi, 15pi, 25pi.
10pi, Two horses, horiz.

**2004, Dec. 27** **Litho.** **Perf. 14¼**
**Granite Paper**
1778-1782 A355 Set of 5 3.25 3.25
*Imperf*
**Size: 90x70mm**
1783 A355 10pi multi 8.50 8.50

Ain Ghazal
Statues — A356

Various statues: 5pi, 7.50pi, 12.50pi, 15pi, 25pi.
10pi, Two statues.

**2004, Dec. 29** **Granite Paper**
1784-1788 A356 Set of 5 3.00 3.00
*Imperf*
**Size: 70x90mm**
1789 A356 10pi multi 5.00 5.00

Children's
Paintings
A357

Various paintings: 5pi, 7.50pi, 12.50pi, 15pi, 25pi.
10pi, Parts of various paintings.

**2004, Dec. 27** **Granite Paper**
1790-1794 A357 Set of 5 2.75 2.75
*Imperf*
**Size: 90x70mm**
1795 A357 10pi multi 5.50 5.50

**Miniature Sheet**

Nazareth
Iris
A358

No. 1796 — Various photographs of Nazareth Iris: a, 5pi. b, 7.50pi. c, 10pi (70x90mm). d, 12.50pi. e, 15pi. f, 25pi.

**2004, Dec. 29** **Perf. 14¼**
**Granite Paper**
1796 A358 Sheet of 6, #a-f 6.00 6.00

**Miniature Sheet**

Details From Mosaic Floor of Church
of the Holy Martyrs Lot and Procopius,
Mount Nebo — A359

No. 1797: a, 10pi, Man with scythe (68x90mm). b, 10pi, Man with flute, grapes. c, 15pi, Building. d, 25pi, Man with Basket.

**2004, Dec. 27** **Litho.**
**Granite Paper**
1797 A359 Sheet of 4, #a-d 6.00 6.00

Expo 2005, Aichi,
Japan — A360

No. 1798: a, Dead Sea salt crystal. b, Dead Sea salt crystal, diff. c, Dead Sea salt crystal, diff. d, Dead Sea (70x70mm).

**2005, Aug. 7** **Litho.** **Perf. 13¾**
1798 Sheet of 4 3.25 3.25
a. A360 5pi multi .30 .30
b. A360 7.50pi multi .45 .45
c. A360 12.50pi multi .75 .75
d. A360 20pi multi .90 .90

Fish — A361

Various Red Sea fish: 5f, 5pi, 7.50pi, 12.50pi.

**Perf. 13½x13¾**
**2005, Dec. 27** **Litho.**
1799-1802 A361 Set of 4 2.50 2.50
**Souvenir Sheet**
1803 A361 20pi Lionfish 5.00 5.00

Intl. Sports
Year — A362

Children's drawings of: 1pi, Tennis player. 10pi, Medal winner. 15pi, Soccer game, horiz. No. 1807, 20pi, Swimmer, horiz.
No. 1808, Basketball player.

**Perf. 13½x13¾, 13¾x13½**
**2005, Dec. 27**
1804-1807 A362 Set of 4 3.50 3.50
**Size: 71x90mm**
*Imperf*
1808 A362 20pi multi 6.00 6.00

Worldwide
Fund for
Nature — A363

Arabian oryx: 1.50pi, Grazing. 5pi, Three oryx. 7.50pi, Adults and juvenile. 12.50pi, Two adults.
20pi, Adult, three oryx in background.

**2005, Dec. 27** **Perf. 13¾x13½**
1809-1812 A363 Set of 4 7.25 7.25
**Souvenir Sheet**
1813 A363 20pi multi 22.50 22.50

Child
Protection
A364

Designs: 7.50pi, Hands of adult and child. 10pi, Mother holding infant. 12.50pi, Adult hugging child.
20pi, Child.

**2005, Dec. 27** **Perf. 13¾**
1814-1816 A364 Set of 3 3.00 3.00
**Size: 70x90mm**
*Imperf*
1817 A364 20pi multi 6.50 6.50

Friendship of
Jordan and
Japan — A365

Design: 7.50pi, Gallery of Japanese calligraphy. 12.50pi, Building. 15pi, Building at night. 20pi, Pottery in museum gallery.

**2005, Dec. 27** **Perf. 13¾x13½**
1818-1820 A365 Set of 3 2.75 2.75
**Size: 70x90mm**
*Imperf*
1821 A365 20pi multi 5.75 5.75

Islamic Art
Revival — A366

Designs: 5pi, Woodworker. 7.50pi, Engraver. 10pi, Calligrapher. 15pi, Woodworker, diff.
20pi, Calligrapher, diff.

**2005, Dec. 27** **Perf. 13¾x13½**
1822-1825 A366 Set of 4 3.00 3.00
**Size: 90x71mm**
*Imperf*
1826 A366 20pi multi 6.00 6.00

Modern
Architecture — A367

Various buildings with panel color of: 7.50pi, Green. 10pi, Lemon, horiz. 12.50pi, Red brown.
20pi, Brown, horiz.

**2006, Jan. 1** **Litho.** **Perf. 14**
1827-1829 A367 Set of 3 3.50 3.50
*Imperf*
**Size: 90x70mm**
1830 A367 20pi multi 4.50 4.50

Government
Vehicles — A368

Designs: 10pi, Police car. 12.50pi, Fire truck. 17.50pi, Garbage truck. No. 1834, 20pi, Mail vans.
No. 1835, 20pi, Ambulance.

**2006, Jan. 1** **Perf. 14**
1831-1834 A368 Set of 4 3.75 3.75
*Imperf*
**Size: 90x70mm**
1835 A368 20pi multi 4.50 4.50

Ancient
Coins — A369

Various coins with background color of: 5pi, Purple. 7.50pi, Yellow brown. 10pi, Gray. 12.50pi, Blue. 15pi, Dark red.
30pi, Dark blue, horiz.

**2006, Jan. 1** **Perf. 13¾**
1836-1840 A369 Set of 5 4.50 4.50

*Imperf*
**Size: 90x70mm**
1841 A369 30pi multi 6.50 6.50

2006 World Cup
Soccer
Championships,
Germany — A370

Background color: 5pi, Light blue. 7.50pi, Yellow. 10pi, Tan. 12.50pi, Green. 15pi, Blue. 30pi, Yellow green, horiz.

**2006, Jan. 1** **Perf. 14**
1842-1846 A370 Set of 5 4.50 4.50
*Imperf*
**Size: 90x70mm**
1847 A370 30pi multi 5.50 5.50

Art — A371

Various works of art by unnamed artists: 5pi, 10pi, 15pi. 20pi.
No. 1852, Four works of art, horiz.

**2006, Oct. 21** **Litho.** **Perf. 14¼**
**Granite Paper**
1848-1851 A371 Set of 4 3.50 3.50
*Imperf*
**Size: 90x70mm**
1852 A371 20pi multi 6.00 6.00

Desert
Reptiles — A372

Designs: 5pi, Lizard. 7.50pi, Snake. 10pi, Lizards. 12.50pi, Lizard, diff. 15pi, Lizard, horiz. 20pi, Snake, diff.
No. 1859, Lizard, diff., horiz.

**2006, Oct. 21** **Perf. 14¼**
**Granite Paper**
1853-1858 A372 Set of 6 3.25 3.25
*Imperf*
**Size: 90x70mm**
1859 A372 20pi multi 5.25 5.25

Information and
Communications
Technology in
Education — A373

Design: 7.50pi, Man at computer. 12.50pi, Woman punching keys on keypad. 15pi, Man and computer screen. 20pi, Man using cellular phone.
No. 1864, Circuit board, design of unissued 50f stamp showing finger punching keypad.

**2006, Nov. 11** **Perf. 14¼**
**Granite Paper**
1860-1863 A373 Set of 4 2.75 2.75
*Imperf*
**Size: 70x90mm**
1864 A373 20pi multi 5.50 5.50

National Symbols — A374

Designs: 5pi, King Abdullah II in dress uniform. 7.50pi, King Abdullah II in suit and tie. 10pi, Jordanian soldiers, horiz. 12.50pi, King Abdullah II in camouflage uniform. 15pi, Flag, horiz. 20pi, Men in army uniforms and native garb, horiz. 25pi, Parade of tanks, horiz. 30pi, Flag and rose, horiz.

**2006, Nov. 11**     **Perf. 14¼**
**Granite Paper**
1865-1872 A374   Set of 8    6.25 6.25

Pitchers and Spouted Pots — A375

Designs: 10pi, Spouted pot. 20pi, Spouted pot with legs. 30pi, Pitcher.
25pi, Spouted pot, horiz.

          **Perf. 13½x13¾**
**2007, Dec. 31**     **Litho.**
1873-1875 A375   Set of 3    1.75 1.75
**Imperf**
**Size: 90x70mm**
1876 A375 25pi multi      2.25 2.25

Culture and Identity — A376

Designs: 10pi, Books. No. 1878, 20pi, Lute. 25pi, Bottle. 30pi, Arabic text.
No. 1881, 20pi, Arabic text, paint brushes, bottle, lute, books.

**2007, Dec. 31**     **Perf. 13½x13¾**
1877-1880 A376   Set of 4    2.40 2.40
**Imperf**
**Size: 70x90mm**
1881 A376 20pi multi      1.50 1.50

Butterflies — A377

Various butterflies with denomination color of: 10pi, Orange. 15pi, Yellow green. 20pi, Gray. 25pi, Olive gray, horiz. 30pi, Orange, horiz.
40pi, Olive green, horiz.

    **Perf. 13½x13¾, 13¼x13½**
**2007, Dec. 31**
1882-1886 A377   Set of 5    3.00 3.00
**Imperf**
**Size: 90x70mm**
1887 A377 40pi multi      4.50 4.50

Aqaba — A378

---

Designs: 10pi, Arch and beach. 15pi, Scuba diver. 20pi, Motor boats. 30pi, Double-masted ship.

**2008, July 16**     **Litho.**     **Perf. 14¼**
**Granite Paper**
1888-1891 A378   Set of 4    2.10 2.10

Traditional Women's Clothing — A379

Designs: 10pi, Mafraq. 15pi, Ma'an. 20pi, Amman. 25pi, Jerash. 30pi, Salt.

**2008, July 16**     **Granite Paper**
1892-1896 A379   Set of 5    3.00 3.00

Fruit — A380

Designs: 10pi, Oranges. 15pi, Cherries. 20pi, Figs. 25pi, Pomegranates. 30pi, Grapes.

**2008, July 16**     **Granite Paper**
1897-1901 A380   Set of 5    3.00 3.00

Petra — A381

Designs: 10pi, Sculpture of face. 15pi, Ceramic plate. 20pi, Sculpture of grapevine. 25pi, Siq al Barid fresco. 30pi, Rock formations. 40pi, Treasury.

**2008, July 16**     **Litho.**     **Perf. 14¼**
**Granite Paper**
1902-1906 A381   Set of 5    3.00 3.00
**Size: 66x86mm**
1907 A381 40pi multi      1.25 1.25
**Imperf**
1908 A381 40pi multi      1.25 1.25

Bridge — A382

50th Anniversary Emblem of Engineer's Association — A383

**2008, Sept. 22**     **Litho.**     **Perf. 14¼**
**Granite Paper**
1909 A382 15pi shown      .45 .45
1910 A382 20pi shown      .60 .60
1911 A382 25pi Power station    .70 .70
    Nos. 1909-1911 (3)     1.75 1.75

---

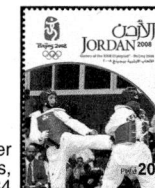

2008 Summer Olympics, Beijing — A384

Designs: 20pi, Taekwondo. 30pi, Equestrian. 40pi, Table tennis. 50pi, Running.

**2008, Sept. 22**     **Litho.**
**Granite Paper**
1912-1915 A384   Set of 4    4.00 4.00

Musical Instruments A385

Designs: 20pi, Oud. 40pi, Rebab. 60pi, Zither. 80pi, Flutes. 100pi, Tambourine and drum.
50pi, Oud, rebab, zither, flutes, tambourine and drum, horiz.

**2008, Sept. 22**     **Perf. 14¼**
**Granite Paper**
1916-1920 A385   Set of 5    8.50 8.50
**Imperf**
**Size: 90x70mm**
1921 A385 50pi multi      1.40 1.40

Flowers — A386

Designs: 5pi, Egyptian catchfly. 10pi, Lupine. 15pi, Judean viper's bugloss. 20pi, Pimpernel. 30pi, Asiatic crowfoot. 40pi, Grape hyacinth. No. 1928, 50pi, Large flowered sage. 60pi, Star of Bethlehem. 80pi, Pyramidalis. 100pi, Calotropis.
No. 1932, 50pi, Cyclamen, horiz.

**2008, Nov. 25**     **Litho.**     **Perf. 14¼**
**Granite Paper**
1922-1931 A386   Set of 10    12.00 12.00
**Imperf**
**Size: 90x70mm**
1932 A386 50pi multi      1.40 1.40

Art From Quseir Amra UNESCO World Heritage Site — A387

Designs: 40pi, Woman with arm raised. 60pi, Grapes. 80pi, Hunters on horseback, bath. 100pi, Face of woman.
50pi, Quseir Amra Palace.

**2008, Nov. 25**     **Perf. 14¼x14**
**Granite Paper**
1933-1936 A387   Set of 4    8.00 8.00
**Imperf**
**Size: 90x69mm**
1937 A387 50pi multi      1.40 1.40

Hejaz Railway, Cent. — A388

Designs: 20pi, Train on bridge. 30pi, Locomotive and tender. 50pi, Station and road.

---

**2009, Feb. 1**     **Litho.**     **Perf. 14¼**
**Granite Paper**
1938-1940 A388   Set of 3    3.00 3.00
    Dated 2008.

Birds — A389

Designs: 10pi, Mallard duck. 15pi, Saker. 20pi, Crouser cream. 30pi, Palestine sunbird. 40pi, Hoopoe. No. 1946, 50pi, Black francolin. 60pi, Little green bee-eater. 80pi, Sinai rosefinch.
No. 1949, 50pi, Kingfisher.

**2009, Feb. 1**     **Perf. 14¼**
**Granite Paper**
1941-1948 A389   Set of 8    8.75 8.75
**Imperf**
**Size: 90x70mm**
1949 A389 50pi multi      4.75 4.75
    Dated 2008.

Arabian Coffee Tools — A390

Designs: 40pi, Mortar and pestle. 60pi, Coffee pots and roasting pan. 80pi, Coffee pot and cups. 100pi, Bowl, roasting pan and shovel.
50pi, Mortar, pestle, coffee pot, bowl, roasting pan and shovel.

**2009, Mar. 1**     **Perf. 14¼**
**Granite Paper**
1950-1953 A390   Set of 4    8.00 8.00
**Imperf**
**Size: 70x90mm**
1954 A390 50pi multi      4.25 4.25
    Dated 2008.

Traditional Costumes — A391

Close-ups of costumes and: 40pi, Woman. 60pi, Woman, diff. 80pi, Woman, diff. 100pi, Man and woman.
50pi, Woman only.

**2009, Mar. 1**     **Perf. 14¼**
**Granite Paper**
1955-1958 A391   Set of 4    8.00 8.00
**Imperf**
**Size: 70x90mm**
1959 A391 50pi multi      4.25 4.25

Visit of Pope Benedict XVI to Jordan — A392

Designs: 20pi, Pope Benedict XVI, King Abdullah II, walkway to river. 30pi, Pope Benedict XVI. 40pi, Pope and King shaking hands.
50pi, Pope and King shaking hands, walkway to river, crucifix.

**2009, May 8**     **Perf. 14¼**
**Granite Paper**
1960-1962 A392   Set of 3    2.60 2.60
**Imperf**
**Size: 90x70mm**
1963 A392 50pi multi      4.75 4.75

King Abdullah II, 10th
Anniv. of Accession to
Throne — A393

**2009, June 9**     *Perf. 13¾*
**Granite Paper**
**Background Color**

| 1964 | A393 | 10pi maroon | .30 | .30 |
|---|---|---|---|---|
| 1965 | A393 | 15pi dark blue | .45 | .45 |
| 1966 | A393 | 20pi bright blue | .60 | .60 |
| 1967 | A393 | 25pi tan | .70 | .70 |
| 1968 | A393 | 30pi dark green | .85 | .85 |
| 1969 | A393 | 35pi blue | 1.00 | 1.00 |
| 1970 | A393 | 40pi purple | 1.10 | 1.10 |
| 1971 | A393 | 45pi black | 1.25 | 1.25 |
| 1972 | A393 | 50pi brown | 1.40 | 1.40 |
| 1973 | A393 | 1d blue gray | 3.00 | 3.00 |
| | *Nos. 1964-1973 (10)* | | 10.65 | 10.65 |

E-Government — A394

Designs: 20pi, Computer cables. 30pi, Spiral emblem. 40pi, Internet address of Jordanian government. 50pi, Letter, compass, Earth.

**2009, Aug. 25**   **Litho.**   *Perf. 13¼*
**Granite Paper**

| 1974-1977 | A394 | Set of 4 | 4.00 | 4.00 |
|---|---|---|---|---|

A395     A396

A397     A398

A399

University emblems: No. 1983, Al-Hussein Bin Jalal University. No. 1984, Tafila Technical University. No. 1985, German-Jordanian University. No. 1986, Al-Balqa Applied University. No. 1987, Yarmouk University.

**2009, Aug. 25**     *Perf. 13¼*
**Granite Paper**

| 1978 | A395 | 20pi multi | .60 | .60 |
|---|---|---|---|---|
| 1979 | A396 | 20pi multi | .60 | .60 |
| 1980 | A397 | 20pi multi | .60 | .60 |
| 1981 | A398 | 20pi multi | .60 | .60 |
| 1982 | A399 | 20pi multi | .60 | .60 |
| 1983 | A399 | 20pi multi | .60 | .60 |
| 1984 | A399 | 20pi multi | .60 | .60 |
| 1985 | A399 | 20pi multi | .60 | .60 |
| 1986 | A399 | 20pi multi | .60 | .60 |
| 1987 | A399 | 20pi multi | .60 | .60 |
| | *Nos. 1978-1987 (10)* | | 6.00 | 6.00 |

Waterfalls,
Ma'een — A400

Designs: 10pi, Waterfall, orange brown panel. 20pi, Building and mountain, fawn panel. 30pi, Waterfall, black panel. 40pi, Waterfall, gray green panel. 50pi, Waterfall, olive brown panel.
60pi, Waterfall, blue panel.

**2009, Aug. 25**     **Litho.**
**Granite Paper**

| 1988-1992 | A400 | Set of 5 | 4.25 | 4.25 |
|---|---|---|---|---|

**Size: 70x91mm**
*Imperf*

| 1993 | A400 | 60pi multi | 1.75 | 1.75 |
|---|---|---|---|---|

Animals — A401

Designs: 10pi, Horse. 20pi, Rabbits. 30pi, Fox. 40pi, Maha gazelle. 50pi, Gazelle. 60pi, Camel.

**2009, Aug. 25**     **Litho.**
**Granite Paper**

| 1994-1998 | A401 | Set of 5 | 4.25 | 4.25 |
|---|---|---|---|---|

**Size: 70x91mm**
*Imperf*

| 1999 | A401 | 60pi multi | 1.75 | 1.75 |
|---|---|---|---|---|

Vegetables — A402

No. 2000: a, Corn. b, Onions, garlic. c, Beans, peas, okra. d, Cabbages. e, Eggplants. f, Pumpkins. g, Bell peppers. h, Hot peppers. i, Radishes, turnips, beets. j, Tomatoes, zucchini.

**2009, Aug. 25**     *Perf. 13¼*
**Granite Paper**

| 2000 | | Sheet of 10 | 6.00 | 6.00 |
|---|---|---|---|---|
| a.-j. | A402 | 20pi Any single | .60 | .60 |

Environmental
Protection — A403

Designs: 20pi, Tree, shrub, flower. 30pi, Man and fire. 40pi, Animals grazing. 50pi, Litter in stream.

**2009**    **Granite Paper**    **Litho.**

| 2001-2004 | A403 | Set of 4 | 4.00 | 4.00 |
|---|---|---|---|---|

Insects — A404

Designs: 10pi, Beetle. 15pi, Butterfly. 20pi, Ladybug. 25pi, Bee. 30pi, Mantis. 40pi, Moth. 50pi, Dragonfly. 60pi, Fly. 80pi, Grasshopper. 100pi, Dragonflies.

**2009, Dec. 13**   **Litho.**   *Perf. 13¼*
**Granite Paper**

| 2005-2014 | A404 | Set of 10 | 12.50 | 12.50 |
|---|---|---|---|---|

Nos. 588-590
Surcharged

**Methods and Perfs As Before**
**2009, Dec. 20**

| 2015 | A82 | 80pi on 120f #588 | 2.25 | 2.25 |
|---|---|---|---|---|
| 2016 | A82 | 80pi on 180f #589 | 2.25 | 2.25 |
| 2017 | A82 | 80pi on 200f #590 | 2.25 | 2.25 |
| | *Nos. 2015-2017 (3)* | | 6.75 | 6.75 |

No. 1471b Surcharged

    *Perf. 12¾x13¼*
**2009, Dec. 20**     **Litho.**

| 2018 | A267 | 80pi on 25f multi | 2.25 | 2.25 |
|---|---|---|---|---|

Tourism — A405

Sites in: 10pi, Ajlun. 20pi, Amman. 30pi, Karak. 40pi, Showbak. 50pi, Jerash.

**2010, Oct. 3**     *Perf. 14*

| 2019-2022 | A405 | Set of 4 | 3.00 | 3.00 |
|---|---|---|---|---|

**Size: 90x70mm**
*Imperf*

| 2023 | A405 | 50pi multi | 1.50 | 1.50 |
|---|---|---|---|---|

**Miniature Sheet**

Mushrooms — A406

No. 2024: a, Cortinarius balteatus. b, Russula bicolor. c, Red fly agaric. d, Amanita muscaria. e, Boletus edulis. f, Amanita albocreata. g, Agaricus anderwij. h, Agaricus bisporus.

**2010, Oct. 3**     *Perf. 14*

| 2024 | A406 | 20pi Sheet of 8, #a-h | 4.50 | 4.50 |
|---|---|---|---|---|

Mosques in
Jordan — A407

Designs: 10pi, Jordan University Mosque. 20pi, Abu-Darwiesh Mosque. 30pi, Al Hussainy Mosque. 40pi, King Abdullah Mosque. 50pi, King Hussein bin Talal Mosque.

**2010, Nov. 30**

| 2025-2029 | A407 | Set of 5 | 4.25 | 4.25 |
|---|---|---|---|---|

Sports — A408

Designs: 10pi, Skydiving. 20pi, Swimming. 30pi, Hot-air ballooning. 40pi, Racing boats. 50pi, Jordan Rally.

**2010, Nov. 30**     *Perf. 14*

| 2030-2033 | A408 | Set of 4 | 3.00 | 3.00 |
|---|---|---|---|---|

**Size: 70x90mm**
*Imperf*

| 2034 | A408 | 50pi multi | 1.50 | 1.50 |
|---|---|---|---|---|

Old Farming
Tools — A409

Designs: 20pi, Millstone. 30pi, Flail. 40pi, Pitchfork. 50pi, Olive crushing wheel.

**2011, Feb. 27**     *Perf. 14*

| 2035-2038 | A409 | Set of 4 | 4.00 | 4.00 |
|---|---|---|---|---|

Dated 2010.

Development
Zones — A410

Emblem of: No. 2039, 20pi, Dead Sea Development Zone. No. 2040, 20pi, Irbid Development Zone. No. 2041, 20pi, Jabal Ajloun Development Area. No. 2042, 20pi, King Hussein Bin Talal Development Area. No. 2043, 20pi, Ma'an Development Area.

**2011, Feb. 27**

| 2039-2043 | A410 | Set of 5 | 3.00 | 3.00 |
|---|---|---|---|---|

Dated 2010.

Wild Herbs — A411

Designs: No. 2044, 20pi, Artemisia herba alba. No. 2045, 20pi, Capparis spinosa. No. 2046, 20pi, Lavandula vera. No. 2047, 20pi, Matricaria chamomilla. No. 2048, 20pi, Ocimum basilicum. No. 2049, 20pi, Salvia officinalis. No. 2050, 20pi, Thymus serpyllum. No. 2051, 20pi, Trigonella foenum-graecum.

**2011, Feb. 27**

| 2044-2051 | A411 | Set of 8 | 4.50 | 4.50 |
|---|---|---|---|---|

Dated 2010. Latin names of plants are misspelled on Nos. 2044, 2045, 2046, 2050 and 2051.

Junior and Cadet World Fencing
Championships, Jordan — A412

Fencers and stylized fencer in panel in: 10pi, Red brown. 20pi, Blue violet. 30pi, Greenish blue. 40pi, Olive green. No. 2056, 50pi, Gray.
No. 2057, 50pi, Fencers, vert.

**2011, Apr. 6**     *Perf. 13x12¾*

| 2052-2056 | A412 | Set of 5 | 4.25 | 4.25 |
|---|---|---|---|---|

**Size: 75x94mm**
*Imperf*

| 2057 | A412 | 50pi multi | 6.00 | 6.00 |
|---|---|---|---|---|

Jordan
Rally
A413

Various race cars: 10pu, 20pi, 30pi, 40pi, 50pi.
No. 2063, 50pi, Race car, ruins, helicopter.

**2011, Apr. 14**     *Perf. 13x12¾*

| 2058-2062 | A413 | Set of 5 | 4.25 | 4.25 |
|---|---|---|---|---|

**Size: 95x74mm**
*Imperf*

| 2063 | A413 | 50pi multi | 5.75 | 5.75 |
|---|---|---|---|---|

Jewelry — A414

Designs: 20pi, Pendant on necklace. No. 2065, 30pi, Pendants, necklace and bracelet. 40pi, Ring. 50i, Necklace with pendants. No. 2068, 30pi, Ring, diff.

**2011, May 10**     **Perf. 13¼x13**
**Granite Paper**
2064-2067 A414 Set of 4    4.00 4.00
**Size: 77x77mm**
*Imperf*
2068 A414 30pi multi     5.00 5.00
Dated 2010.

A415

A416

A417

A418

A419

A420

A421

A422

A423

Dams — A424

**2011, May 10**     **Perf. 13x13¼**
**Granite Paper**
2069 A415 20pi multi    .60 .60
2070 A416 20pi multi    .60 .60
2071 A417 20pi multi    .60 .60
2072 A418 20pi multi    .60 .60
2073 A419 20pi multi    .60 .60
2074 A420 20pi multi    .60 .60
2075 A421 20pi multi    .60 .60
2076 A422 20pi multi    .60 .60
2077 A423 20pi multi    .60 .60
2078 A424 20pi multi    .60 .60
    *Nos. 2069-2078 (10)*    6.00 6.00

---

**Size: 90x70mm**
*Imperf*
2079 A424 30pi multi    6.75 6.75
Dated 2010.

Red Sea Coral
Reefs — A425

Designs: 20pi, Brain coral. 30pi, Coral, fish. No. 2082, 40pi, Coral. 50pi, Coral, diff. 60pi, Coral, diff. No. 2085, 40p, Coral, fish, diff.

**2011, Sept. 28**   **Litho.**   **Perf. 14**
2080-2084 A425 Set of 5    5.75 5.75
**Size: 90x70mm**
*Imperf*
2085 A425 40pi multi    1.25 1.25

Ceramics — A426

Designs: 10pi, Jug with handle, head. 20pi, Item on pedestal. No. 2088, 30pi, Jug with handle. 40pi, Item with Arabic script. 50pi, Item with Arabic script and people. 60pi, Sphere on pedestal. No. 2092, 30p, Abstract tile designs.

**2011, Sept. 28**     **Perf. 14**
2086-2091 A426 Set of 5    6.00 6.00
**Size: 70x90mm**
*Imperf*
2092 A426 30pi multi    .85 .85

A427

A428

A429

A430

A431

A432

---

A433

A434

A435

Historical
Path — A436

**2011, Sept. 28**     **Perf. 14**
2093 A427 20pi multi    .60 .60
2094 A428 20pi multi    .60 .60
2095 A429 20pi multi    .60 .60
2096 A430 20pi multi    .60 .60
2097 A431 20pi multi    .60 .60
2098 A432 20pi multi    .60 .60
2099 A433 20pi multi    .60 .60
2100 A434 20pi multi    .60 .60
2101 A435 20pi multi    .60 .60
2102 A436 20pi multi    .60 .60
    *Nos. 2093-2102 (10)*    6.00 6.00

Crown Prince
Hussein — A437

Denominations: 20pi, 30pi, 50pi.

**2011**     **Perf. 13½x13¼**
**Granite Paper**
2103-2105 A437 Set of 3    3.00 3.00

Old Astronomical
Instruments — A438

Designs: 10pi, Astrolabe. 20pi, Telescope. 30pi, Sextant. 40pi, Sundial.

**2011**     **Perf. 13½x13¼**
**Granite Paper**
2106-2109 A438 Set of 4    3.00 3.00

Royal
Jordanian
Falcons
Aerobatic
Squad — A439

Designs: 10pi, Line of four airplanes. 20pi, Pilot in cockpit, three other airplanes. 30pi, Three airplanes. 40pi, Four airplanes in formation.
50pi, Four airplanes, Jordanian flag.

**2011**     **Perf. 13¼x13½**
**Granite Paper**
2110-2113 A439 Set of 4    3.00 3.00
**Size: 90x70mm**
*Imperf*
2114 A439 50pi multi    1.40 1.40

---

**Souvenir Sheet**

Preervation of Polar Regions and
Glaciers — A440

No. 2115: a, 80pi, Penguins. b, 1d, Polar bear.

**2012, Jan. 23**     **Perf. 13½**
**Granite Paper**
2115 A440 Sheet of 2, #a-b   5.25 5.25
Dated 2011.

A441

A442

A443

A444

A445

King Abdullah
II — A446

Design: 50pi, King Abdullah II and mosque, horiz.

**2012, Jan. 30**     **Perf. 13½x13¼**
**Granite Paper**
2116 A441 20pi multi    .60 .60
2117 A442 20pi multi    .60 .60
2118 A443 20pi multi    .60 .60
2119 A444 20pi multi    .60 .60
2120 A445 20pi multi    .60 .60
2121 A446 20pi multi    .60 .60
    *Nos. 2116-2121 (6)*    3.60 3.60
**Size: 90x70mm**
*Imperf*
2122 A446 50pi multi    1.40 1.40

Labor Day — A447

Designs: 20pi, Raised fists. 30pi, Man with shovel. 40pi, Man with pick, woman and child. 50pi, Man with hard hat.

**2012**     **Perf. 13½x13¼**
**Granite Paper**
2123-2126 A447 Set of 4    4.00 4.00

World Telecommunications Day — A448

Designs: 30pi, Hands holding Earth. 40pi, Dish antennas. 50pi, Computer.

2012 Granite Paper Litho.
2127-2129 A448 Set of 3 3.50 3.50

2012 Summer Olympics, London — A449

Designs: 20pi, Equestrian. 30pi, Soccer. 40pi, Tennis. 50pi, Kayaking.

2012 Granite Paper
2130-2133 A449 Set of 4 4.00 4.00

Chess — A450

Various chess pieces: 30pi, 40pi, 50pi.

2012 Litho. *Perf. 11¾*
2134-2136 A450 Set of 3 3.50 3.50

Citrus Fruits — A451

Designs: 10pi, Kumquats. 20pi, Oranges. 30pi, Lemons. 40pi, Oranges, diff. 50pi, Pomelos.

2012 Litho. *Perf. 11¾*
2137-2141 A451 Set of 5 4.25 4.25

Miniature Sheets

A452

Prehistoric Animals — A453

No. 2142: a, Pteranodon in flight, back of Apatosaurus. b, Tyrannosaurus Rex and volcano. c, Triceratops and Stegosaurus. d, Horned dinosaur, legs of Tyrannosaurus Rex.
No. 2143: a, Head of Tyrannosaurus rex, waterfall. b, Apatosauruses. c, Raptors on shore. d, Three dinosaurs in water.

2012 Litho. *Perf. 11¾*
2142 A452 20pi Sheet of 4, #a-d 2.25 2.25
2143 A453 20pi Sheet of 4, #a-d 2.25 2.25

A454

A454a

A454b

A454c

A454d

A454e

A454f

Artists — A454g

2012 Litho. *Perf. 11¾*

2144	A454	20pi	multi	.60	.60
2145	A454a	20pi	multi	.60	.60
2146	A454b	20pi	multi	.60	.60
2147	A454c	20pi	multi	.60	.60
2148	A454d	20pi	multi	.60	.60
2149	A454e	20pi	multi	.60	.60
2150	A454f	20pi	multi	.60	.60
2151	A454g	20pi	multi	.60	.60
	Nos. 2144-2151 (8)			4.80	4.80

Jordan Library and Information Association, 50th Anniv. — A455

Designs: 40pi, Association emblem. 50pi, 50th anniversary emblem.

2013 Litho. *Perf. 14*
2152-2153 A455 Set of 2 2.60 2.60

Horses — A456

Designs: 10pi, Two horses. 20pi, One horse, horiz. 30pi, Two horses, horiz. 40pi, Head of horse, horiz. No. 2158, 50pi, Horse in water, horiz.
No. 2159, 50pi, Six horses, horiz.

2013, Dec. 2 Litho. *Perf. 11¾*
2154-2158 A456 Set of 5 4.25 4.25

Size: 90x70mm

Imperf

2159 A456 50pi multi 1.40 1.40

Dated 2012.

Ships — A457

Various ships, 20pi, 30pi, 40pi, 50pi.
No. 2164, 50pi, Fleet of ships.

2013, Dec. 2 Litho. *Perf. 11¾*
2160-2163 A457 Set of 4 4.00 4.00

Size: 90x70mm

Imperf

2164 A457 50pi multi 1.40 1.40

Dated 2012.

Nature Reserves — A458

Designs: 10pi, Rocks. 20pi, Flowers, horiz. 30pi, Lake, horiz. 40pi, Plateaus, horiz. No. 2169, 50pi, Antelopes, horiz.
No. 2170, 50pi, Hillside village, horiz.

2014, Feb. 9 Litho. *Perf. 14*
2165-2169 A458 Set of 5 4.25 4.25

Size: 90x70mm

Imperf

2170 A458 50pi multi 1.40 1.40

Dated 2013.

Doors and Windows — A459

Designs: No. 2171, 20pi, Door, King Hussein's Mosque. No. 2172, 20pi, Door and window, Umayyad Palace. No. 2173, 20pi, Door, Royal Hashemite Court, vert. No. 2174, 20pi, Door and windows, Justice Palace, vert. No. 2175, 20pi, Window, Raghadan Palace, vert. No. 2176, 20pi, Door, Al-Salt School, vert. No. 2177, 20pi, Window, Al-Salt, vert.

2014, Feb. 9 Litho. *Perf. 14*
2171-2177 A459 Set of 7 4.00 4.00

Dated 2013.

A460

A461

A462

A463

A464

A465

A466

Birds — A467

2014, Feb. 9 Litho. *Perf. 14*

2178	A460	20pi	multi	.60	.60
2179	A461	20pi	multi	.60	.60
2180	A462	20pi	multi	.60	.60
2181	A463	20pi	multi	.60	.60
2182	A464	20pi	multi	.60	.60
2183	A465	20pi	multi	.60	.60
2184	A466	20pi	multi	.60	.60
2185	A467	20pi	multi	.60	.60
	Nos. 2178-2185 (8)			4.80	4.80

Dated 2013.

1933 Stamps and Map of Jordan — A468

Map of Jordan and stamp: No. 2186, 80pi, Jordan #191. No. 2187, 80pi, Jordan #197.

2014, Feb. 9 Litho. *Imperf.*
2186-2187 A468 Set of 2 4.50 4.50

Visit of Pope Francis to Jordan — A469

Designs: 20pi, Pope Francis. 30pi, Pope Francis and King Abdullah II. 40pi, Pope Francis and dove, vert.
50pi, Flags of Vatican City and Jordan, Jordan #474, 1683, 1961, 2188.

2014, May 24 Litho. *Perf. 14¼*
2188-2190 A469 Set of 3 2.60 2.60

Imperf

Size: 90x70mm

2191 A469 50pi multi 1.40 1.40

First Papal visit to Jordan, 50th anniv. (No. 2191).

A470

A471

A472

A473

Cartoons — A475

**2014, July 1**    **Litho.**    **Perf. 14**
| | | | | |
|---|---|---|---|---|
| 2192 | A470 | 20pi multi | .60 | .60 |
| 2193 | A471 | 20pi multi | .60 | .60 |
| 2194 | A472 | 20pi multi | .60 | .60 |
| 2195 | A473 | 20pi multi | .60 | .60 |
| 2196 | A474 | 20pi multi | .60 | .60 |
| 2197 | A475 | 20pi multi | .60 | .60 |
| | *Nos. 2192-2197 (6)* | | 3.60 | 3.60 |

Dated 2013.

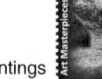

Paintings
A476

Paintings by: No. 2198, 20pi, Claude Monet. No. 2199, 20pi, Monet, diff. No. 2200, 20pi, J.M.W. Turner. No. 2201, 20pi, Joaquín Sorolla y Bastida. No. 2202, 20pi, Vincent van Gogh. No. 2203, 20pi, Peter Paul Rubens. No. 2204, 20pi, Monet, diff., vert. No. 2205, 20pi, Johannes Vermeer, vert.

**2014**    **Litho.**    **Perf. 11¾**
| | | | | |
|---|---|---|---|---|
| 2198-2205 | A476 | Set of 8 | 4.50 | 4.50 |

Dated 2013.

**Miniature Sheet**

Gems
A477

No. 2206: a, Amethyst. b, Red diamond. c, Emerald. d, Black opal. e, Pearl. f, Ruby.

**2014**    **Litho.**    **Perf. 11¾**
| | | | | |
|---|---|---|---|---|
| 2206 | A477 | 20pi Sheet of 6, #a-f | 3.50 | 3.50 |

Dated 2013.

Euromed Postal
Emblem and
Mediterranean
Sea — A478

**2014, July 9**
| | | | | |
|---|---|---|---|---|
| 2207 | A478 | 80pi multi | 2.25 | 2.25 |

Amman Chamber of
Commerce, 90th
Anniv. — A479

**2014**    **Litho.**    **Perf. 14¼**
| | | | | |
|---|---|---|---|---|
| 2208 | A479 | 40pi multi | 1.25 | 1.25 |

Economic and
Social
Foundation for
Military Retirees
and Veterans
A480

**2014**    **Litho.**    **Perf. 14¼**
| | | | | |
|---|---|---|---|---|
| 2209 | A480 | 40pi multi | 1.25 | 1.25 |

Arab Lawyers
Union — A481

**2014**    **Litho.**    **Perf. 14¼**
| | | | | |
|---|---|---|---|---|
| 2210 | A481 | 40pi multi | 1.25 | 1.25 |

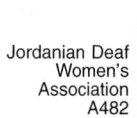

Jordanian Deaf
Women's
Association
A482

**2015**    **Litho.**    **Perf. 14¼**
| | | | | |
|---|---|---|---|---|
| 2211 | A482 | 40pi multi | 1.25 | 1.25 |

United Nations,
70th
Anniv. — A483

**Perf. 14¼x14½ Syncopated**
**2015, Dec. 13**    **Litho.**
| | | | | |
|---|---|---|---|---|
| 2212 | A483 | 80pi multi | 2.25 | 2.25 |

Jordanian
Banknotes
A484

Designs: 10pi, 1-dinar note. 20pi, 5-dinar note. 40pi, 10-dinar note. 60pi, 20-dinar note. 80pi, 50-dinar note.

**Perf. 14¼x14½ Syncopated**
**2015, Dec. 13**    **Litho.**
| | | | | |
|---|---|---|---|---|
| 2213-2217 | A484 | Set of 5 | 6.00 | 6.00 |

Order of the
Renaissance
A485

Order of the
Renaissance
A486

Order of
Independence
A487

Al-Hussein
Order of Military
Merit — A488

Order of the
Star of
Jordan — A489

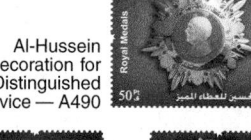

Al-Hussein
Decoration for
Distinguished
Service — A490

Order of
Hussein ibn
Ali — A491

Medal of
Honor — A492

Order of the
Hashemite
Star — A493

Royal
Medal — A494

**Perf. 14¼x14½ Syncopated**
**2015, Dec. 13**    **Litho.**
| | | | | |
|---|---|---|---|---|
| 2218 | A485 | 50pi multi | 1.40 | 1.40 |
| 2219 | A486 | 50pi multi | 1.40 | 1.40 |
| 2220 | A487 | 50pi multi | 1.40 | 1.40 |
| 2221 | A488 | 50pi multi | 1.40 | 1.40 |
| 2222 | A489 | 50pi multi | 1.40 | 1.40 |
| 2223 | A490 | 50pi multi | 1.40 | 1.40 |

**Perf. 14½x14¼ Syncopated**
| | | | | |
|---|---|---|---|---|
| 2224 | A491 | 50pi multi | 1.40 | 1.40 |
| 2225 | A492 | 50pi multi | 1.40 | 1.40 |
| 2226 | A493 | 50pi multi | 1.40 | 1.40 |
| 2227 | A494 | 50pi multi | 1.40 | 1.40 |
| | *Nos. 2218-2227 (10)* | | 14.00 | 14.00 |

Decapolis
A495

Designs: No. 2228, 50pi, Beit Ras. No. 2229, 50pi, Gerasa. No. 2230, 50pi, Quwayliba. No. 2231, 50pi, Umm Aljemal. No. 2232, 50pi, Umm Qais.

**Perf. 14¼x14½ Syncopated**
**2015, Dec. 28**    **Litho.**
| | | | | |
|---|---|---|---|---|
| 2228-2232 | A495 | Set of 5 | 7.00 | 7.00 |

A496

A497

A498

Mosaics
A499

Design: 60pi, Thalassa.

**Perf. 14¼x14½ Syncopated**
**2015, Dec. 28**    **Litho.**
| | | | | |
|---|---|---|---|---|
| 2233 | A496 | 30pi multi | .85 | .85 |
| 2234 | A497 | 30pi multi | .85 | .85 |
| 2235 | A498 | 30pi multi | .85 | .85 |
| 2236 | A499 | 30pi multi | .85 | .85 |
| | *Nos. 2233-2236 (4)* | | 3.40 | 3.40 |

**Size: 90x70mm**
**Imperf**
| | | | | |
|---|---|---|---|---|
| 2237 | A499 | 60pi multi | 1.75 | 1.75 |

A500

A501

A502

A503

Handicrafts
A504

Design: 60pi, Sand bottles.

**Perf. 14¼x14½ Syncopated**
**2015, Dec. 28**    **Litho.**
| | | | | |
|---|---|---|---|---|
| 2238 | A500 | 30pi multi | .85 | .85 |
| 2239 | A501 | 30pi multi | .85 | .85 |
| 2240 | A502 | 30pi multi | .85 | .85 |
| 2241 | A503 | 30pi multi | .85 | .85 |
| 2242 | A504 | 30pi multi | .85 | .85 |
| | *Nos. 2238-2242 (5)* | | 4.25 | 4.25 |

**Size: 90x70mm**
**Imperf**
| | | | | |
|---|---|---|---|---|
| 2243 | A504 | 60pi multi | 1.75 | 1.75 |

Traditional Women's
Clothing — A505

Woman from: No. 2244, 20pi, Ajloun. No. 2245, 20pi, Amman. No. 2246, 20pi, Badawi. No. 2247, 20pi, Jerash. No. 2248, 20pi, Karak. No. 2249, 20pi, Ma'an. No. 2250, 20pi, Madaba. No. 2251, 20pi, Mafraq. No. 2252, 20pi, Salt. No. 2253, 20pi, Tafilah. No. 2254, 20pi, Um Qais. No. 2255, 20pi, Wadi Rum.

**Perf. 14½x14¼ Syncopated**
**2015, Dec. 28**    **Litho.**
| | | | | |
|---|---|---|---|---|
| 2244-2255 | A505 | Set of 12 | 6.75 | 6.75 |

## Miniature Sheet

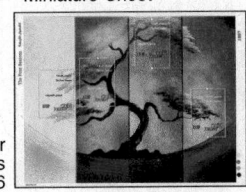

Four Seasons A506

No. 2256 — Tree leaves in: a, Spring (yellow background). b, Summer (green background). c, Autumn (orange brown background). d, Winter (blue background).

**Perf. 14½x14¼ Syncopated**
**2015, Dec. 28**                    **Litho.**
2256 A506 30pi Sheet of 4, #a-d    3.50 3.50

Great Arab Revolt, Cent. — A507

Centenary emblem and: 10pi, Soldiers on camels. 20pi, Soldier on horse. 30pi, Jordanian kings. 50pi, Kingh Abdullah II. 100pi, Sharif Hussein.
40pi, Centenary emblem, vert.

**Perf. 14¼x14½ Syncopated**
**2016, June 10**                   **Litho.**
2257-2261 A507   Set of 5          6.00 6.00
           **Size: 70x90mm**
           **Imperf**
2262 A507 40pi multi               1.25 1.25

Fish of the Mediterranean Sea — A508

Designs: No. 2263, 40pi, Axillary wrasse. No. 2264, 40pi, Blackback butterflyfish. No. 2265, 40pi, Butterfly blenny. No. 2266, 40pi, Lionfish. 40pi, Scorpionfish.

**Perf. 14¼x14½ Syncopated**
**2016, June 30**                   **Litho.**
2263-2267 A508   Set of 5          5.75 5.75

First International Numismatic and Philatelic Fair, Amman A509

Background colors: 30pi, Yellow. 50pi, Dark red and red.

**Perf. 14¼x14½ Syncopated**
**2016, July 28**                   **Litho.**
2268-2269 A509   Set of 2          2.25 2.25

Hiking Destinations A510

Designs: No. 2270, 40pi, Karak. No. 2271, 40pi, Ma'in. No. 2272, 40pi, Madaba. No. 2273, 40pi, Wadi Rum. No. 2274, 40pi, Ajlun, vert. No. 2275, 40pi, Madaba, vert. No. 2276, 40pi, Wadi Al Dab, vert.

**Perf. 14¼x14½ Syncopated,**
**14½x14¼ Syncopated**
**2016, July 28**                   **Litho.**
2270-2276 A510   Set of 7          8.00 8.00

Arab Postal Day — A511

Background color: No. 2277, 40pi, Blue, denomination at LR. No. 2278, 40pi, Green, denomination at LL.

**Perf. 14¼x14½ Syncopated**
**2016, Aug. 3**                    **Litho.**
2277-2278 A511   Set of 2          2.25 2.25

Women's Under-17 World Cup Soccer Tournament, Jordan — A512

Jordanian flag and silhouettes of players: 40pi, Dribbling ball (white silhouette). 50pi, Chasing ball (gray and white silhouettes). 60pi, Dribbling ball (black silhouette). 70pi, Kicking ball (black silhouette).

**Perf. 14¼x14½ Syncopated**
**2016, Sept. 25**                  **Litho.**
2279-2282 A512   Set of 4          3.25 3.25

Ancient Castles and Palaces — A513

Designs: No. 2283, 30pi, Ajlun Castle. No. 2284, 30pi, Al-azraq Castle. No. 2285, 30pi, Umayyad Palace. No. 2286, 40pi, Aqaba Castle. No. 2287, 40pi, Karak Castle. No. 2288, 40pi, Shobak Castle.

**Perf. 14¼x14½ Syncopated**
**2016, Oct. 20**                   **Litho.**
2283-2288 A513   Set of 6          6.00 6.00

Museum of Parliamentary Life, Amman — A514

Designs: 20pi, Emblem. 30pi, Museum gate and entrance. 40pi, Room. 50pi, Dais. 60pi, King Abdullah II.

**Perf. 14¼x14½ Syncopated**
**2016, Nov. 7**                    **Litho.**
2289-2293 A514   Set of 5          5.75 5.75

28th Arab League Summit, Amman A515

Designs: 10pi, Map and flags of Arab League countries. 20pi, Summit venue. 30pi, Umayyad Palace, map and flag of Jordan. 40pi, "28th."
50pi, King Abdullah II.

**2017, Mar. 29      Litho.      Perf. 10**
           **Granite Paper**
2294-2297 A515   Set of 4          3.00 3.00
           **Size: 96x80mm**
           **Imperf**
2298 A515 50pi multi               1.40 1.40

1996 Half-Piaster Coin — A516

1978 10-Fils Coin — A517

1949 100-Fils Coin — A518

2000 10-Piaster Coin — A519

1970 Quarter-Dinar Coin — A520

1977 Quarter-Dinar Coin — A521

**2017, May 4      Litho.      Perf. 10**
           **Granite Paper**
2299 A516 40pi multi               1.10 1.10
2300 A517 40pi multi               1.10 1.10
2301 A518 40pi multi               1.10 1.10
2302 A519 40pi multi               1.10 1.10
2303 A520 40pi multi               1.10 1.10
2304 A521 40pi multi               1.10 1.10
   Nos. 2299-2304 (6)              6.60 6.60

No. 1472d Surcharged in Red Brown and Gray

**Methods and Perfs. As Before**
**2017, July 20**
           **Granite Paper**
2305 A267 10pi on 50f #1472d       .30 .30
2306 A267 15pi on 50f #1472d       .45 .45
2307 A267 20pi on 50f #1472d       .60 .60
2308 A267 25pi on 50f #1472d       .70 .70
2309 A267 30pi on 50f #1472d       .85 .85
2310 A267 35pi on 50f #1472d      1.00 1.00
2311 A267 40pi on 50f #1472d      1.10 1.10
2312 A267 45pi on 50f #1472d      1.25 1.25
2313 A267 50pi on 50f #1472d      1.40 1.40
2314 A267 60pi on 50f #1472d      1.75 1.75
   Nos. 2305-2314 (10)            9.40 9.40

Trees — A522

Designs: 30pi, Spanish fir. 50pi, Turkey oak.

**Perf. 14¾x14¼ Syncopated**
**2017, July 10**                   **Litho.**
2315-2316 A522   Set of 2          2.25 2.25

Nos. 1640, 1643, 1649, 1658, 1661, 1688, 1691 Surcharged in Black and Red and No. 1648 Surcharged in Black, Red and Green

c

d

**Methods and Perfs. As Before**
**2017, Oct. 12**
2317 A317(c) 20pi on 100f #1640    .60 .60
2318 A317(c) 20pi on 100f #1643    .60 .60
2319 A317(c) 20pi on 100f #1649    .60 .60
2320 A317(c) 20pi on 100f #1658    .60 .60
2321 A317(c) 20pi on 100f #1661    .60 .60
2322 A317(c) 20pi on 100f #1688    .60 .60
2323 A317(c) 20pi on 100f #1691    .60 .60
2324 A317(d) 30pi on 300f #1648    .85 .85
2325 A317(d) 50pi on 300f #1648   1.40 1.40
   Nos. 2317-2325 (9)             6.45 6.45

Fruit — A523

Designs: No. 2326, 20pi, Plums. No. 2327, 20pi, Pomegranate. No. 2328, 20pi, Peaches. No. 2329, 20pi, Figs. No. 2330, 20pi, Cactus fruit. No. 2331, 20pi, Grapes. No. 2332, 20pi, Blackberries. No. 2333, 20pi, Strawberries. No. 2334, 20pi, Cantaloupe. No. 2335, 20pi, Watermelon.

**Perf. 14¼x14¾ Syncopated**
**2017, Oct. 12**                   **Litho.**
2326-2335 A523   Set of 10         5.75 5.75

## Miniature Sheet

Birds A524

No. 2336: a, Carrier pigeon. b, Goldfinch. c, Buteo rufinus. d, Blackbird. e, Shunnarbird (rock partridge). f, Sinai rosefinch.

**Perf. 14¼x14¾ Syncopated**
**2017, Oct. 12**                   **Litho.**
2336 A524 30pi Sheet of 6, #a-f    5.25 5.25

Medical Tourism Sites — A525

Designs: No. 2337, 40pi, Maeen Baths. No. 2338, 40pi, Afra Baths. No. 2339, 40pi, Dead Sea. No. 2340, 40pi, Jordan's Springs.

**Perf. 14¼x14¾ Syncopated**
**2017, Nov. 21**                   **Litho.**
2337-2340 A525   Set of 4          4.50 4.50

UNESCO World
Heritage Sites
in
Jordan — A526

Designs: No. 2341, 40pi, Baptism Site. No.
2342, 40pi, Petra. No. 2343, 40pi, Qusayr
Amra. No. 2344, 40pi, Um er-Rasas. No.
2345, 40pi, Wadi Rum.

**Perf. 14¼x14¾ Syncopated**

| 2017, Nov. 21 | | Litho. | |
|---|---|---|---|
| 2341-2345 A526 | Set of 5 | 5.75 | 5.75 |

A527

A528

A529

A530

A531

A532

Military
Uniforms of
Jordan — A533

**Perf. 14¼x14¾ Syncopated**

| 2017, Nov. 21 | | | Litho. | |
|---|---|---|---|---|
| 2346 A527 | 30pi multi | | .85 | .85 |
| 2347 A528 | 30pi multi | | .85 | .85 |
| 2348 A529 | 30pi multi | | .85 | .85 |
| 2349 A530 | 30pi multi | | .85 | .85 |
| 2350 A531 | 30pi multi | | .85 | .85 |
| 2351 A532 | 30pi multi | | .85 | .85 |
| 2352 A533 | 30pi multi | | .85 | .85 |
| | Nos. 2346-2352 (7) | | 5.95 | 5.95 |

A534

A535

A536

A537

Battle of Al-Karameh, 50th
Anniv. — A538

| 2018, Mar. 21 | | Litho. | Perf. 12 | |
|---|---|---|---|---|
| 2353 A534 | 30pi multi | | .85 | .85 |
| 2354 A535 | 30pi multi | | .85 | .85 |
| 2355 A536 | 30pi multi | | .85 | .85 |
| 2356 A537 | 30pi multi | | .85 | .85 |
| | Nos. 2353-2356 (4) | | 3.40 | 3.40 |

**Souvenir Sheet**
**Imperf**

| 2357 A538 | 50pi multi | | 1.40 | 1.40 |
|---|---|---|---|---|

Hashemite
Restoration of
Holy
Places — A539

Designs: No. 2358, 40pi, Church of the Holy
Sepulcher. No. 2359, 40pi, Saladin Pulpit. No.
2360, 40pi, Dome of the Rock.

| 2018, Apr. 23 | | Litho. | Perf. 12 | |
|---|---|---|---|---|
| 2358-2360 A539 | Set of 3 | | 3.50 | 3.50 |

**Miniature Sheet**

Adventure Tourism — A540

No. 2361: a, Parachuting above Dead Sea.
b, Rock climbing, Wadi Balua. c, Ultralight airplane flying, Wadi Rum. d, Tourists looking at
waterfall, Wadi Mujib. e, Jet skiing, Aqaba. f,
Rock climbing, Ajloun.

| 2018, May 24 | | Litho. | Perf. 12 | |
|---|---|---|---|---|
| 2361 A540 | 20pi Sheet of 6, #a-f, | | | |
| | + label | | 3.50 | 3.50 |

**Miniature Sheet**

Vegetables — A541

No. 2362: a, Spinach. b, Common mallow.
c, Watercress. d, Broccoli. e, Cauliflower. f,
Corchorus. g, Dandelion. h, Fava beans. i,
Green beans. j, Chard.

| 2018, June 28 | | Litho. | Perf. 12 | |
|---|---|---|---|---|
| 2362 A541 | 20pi Sheet of 10, #a-j | 5.75 | 5.75 | |

**Miniature Sheet**

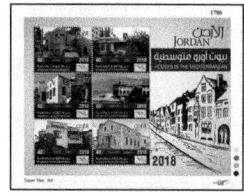

European and Mediterranean Style
Houses — A542

No. 2363: a, House with telephone pole and
light on pole at left. b, House with chimney and
satellite dish on roof. c, House with large light
on roof at left. d, House overlooking water. e,
House with tile shingles. f, Stone house with
green door and shutters.

| 2018, July 9 | | Litho. | Perf. 12 | |
|---|---|---|---|---|
| 2363 A542 | 40pi Sheet of 6, #a-f | 6.75 | 6.75 | |

A543

A544

A545

A546

A547

Jerash
Festival
A548

| 2018, Aug. 2 | | Litho. | Perf. 12 | |
|---|---|---|---|---|
| 2364 A543 | 30pi multi | | .85 | .85 |
| 2365 A544 | 30pi multi | | .85 | .85 |
| 2366 A545 | 30pi multi | | .85 | .85 |
| 2367 A546 | 30pi multi | | .85 | .85 |
| 2368 A547 | 30pi multi | | .85 | .85 |
| | Nos. 2364-2368 (5) | | 4.25 | 4.25 |

**Imperf**
**Size: 90x71mm**

| 2369 A548 | 50pi multi | | 1.40 | 1.40 |
|---|---|---|---|---|

A549

A550

A551

A552

A553

A554

A555

Traditional
Foods — A556

| 2018, Sept. 30 | | Litho. | Perf. 12 | |
|---|---|---|---|---|
| 2370 | | Sheet of 8 | 4.80 | 4.80 |
| a. A549 | 20pi multi | | .60 | .60 |
| b. A550 | 20pi multi | | .60 | .60 |
| c. A551 | 20pi multi | | .60 | .60 |
| d. A552 | 20pi multi | | .60 | .60 |
| e. A553 | 20pi multi | | .60 | .60 |
| f. A554 | 20pi multi | | .60 | .60 |
| g. A555 | 20pi multi | | .60 | .60 |
| h. A556 | 20pi multi | | .60 | .60 |

Churches
A557

Designs: No. 2371, 30pi, Church of Christ, Khalda. No. 2372, 30pi, Church of the Latin, Kerak. No. 2373, 30pi, Church of Mount Nebo, Madaba. No. 2374, 30pi, Church of the Map, Madaba. No. 2375, 30pi, Coptic Church, Alabdali. No. 2376, 30pi, St. Ephrem Church, Sweifieh.

**2018, Oct. 4        Litho.        Perf. 12**
2371-2376 A557    Set of 6        5.25 5.25

Jordan Museum Artifacts
A558

No. 2377: a, Double-headed statue from Ayn Ghazal. b, Box from Pella. c, Statue of Ammonite king. d, Architectural relief depicting Melpomene. e, Rosette from Qaser Al-Mushatta.

**2018, Nov. 15       Litho.        Perf. 12**
2377 A558 30pi Sheet of 5, #a-e    4.25 4.25

**Nos. 1644, 1653, 1659, 1662, 1689, 1692 Surcharged in Red and Black**

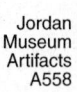

**Methods and Perfs. As Before**
**2018, Nov. 15**
2378 A317 20pi on 200f #1644    .60  .60
2379 A317 20pi on 200f #1653    .60  .60
2380 A317 20pi on 200f #1659    .60  .60
2381 A317 20pi on 200f #1662    .60  .60
2382 A317 20pi on 200f #1689    .60  .60
2383 A317 20pi on 200f #1692    .60  .60
    Nos. 2378-2383 (6)          3.60 3.60

No. 1472d Surcharged in Red and Black

**Method and Perf. As Before**
**2018, Nov. 15**
2384 A267 50pi on 50f #1472d    1.40 1.40

Miniature Sheet

Universal Declaration of Human Rights, 70th Anniv. — A559

No. 2385 — Emblem with: a, Violet background. b, White background, text in green. c, White background, text in violet. d, Green background.

**2018, Dec. 10       Litho.        Perf. 12**
2385 A559 50pi Sheet of 4, #a-d    5.75 5.75

A560

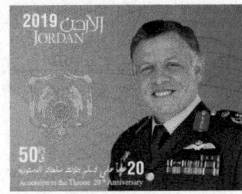

King Abdullah II's Accession to the Throne, 20th Anniv. — A561

Various photographs of King Abdullah II: 5pi, 10pi, 15pi, 20pi, 25pi, 30pi, 35pi, 40pi, 45pi, 50pi.
No. 2396, King Abdullah II in military uniform, coat of arms of Jordan.

**Litho. With Foil Application**
**2019, Feb. 21        Perf. 14x12**
2386-2395 A560    Set of 10        7.75 7.75
**Imperf**
**Size: 91x70mm**
2396 A561 50pi multi              1.40 1.40

A562

A563

A564

A565

A566

Humanitarian Roles of the Army — A567

**2019, Mar. 31       Litho.        Perf. 12**
2397 A562 30pi multi       .85  .85
2398 A563 30pi multi       .85  .85
2399 A564 30pi multi       .85  .85
2400 A565 30pi multi       .85  .85
2401 A566 30pi multi       .85  .85
2402 A567 30pi multi       .85  .85
    Nos. 2397-2402 (6)     5.10 5.10

Dead Sea Ultra Marathon, 25th Anniv. — A568

Various marathon runners: 30pi, 40pi, 50pi, 60pi.

**2019, Apr. 1        Litho.        Perf. 12**
2403-2406 A568    Set of 4        5.25 5.25

Souvenir Sheet

Dome of the Rock, Jerusalem — A569

**2019, June 16       Litho.        Perf. 12**
2407 A569 80pi multi              2.25 2.25

A570

A571

A572

A573

Traditional Clothing — A574

**2019, July 8        Litho.        Perf. 12**
2408 A570 40pi multi       1.10 1.10
2409 A571 40pi multi       1.10 1.10
2410 A572 40pi multi       1.10 1.10
2411 A573 40pi multi       1.10 1.10
    Nos. 2408-2411 (4)     4.40 4.40
**Imperf**
2412 A574 50pi multi       1.40 1.40

Wonders of the World
A575

Designs: No. 2413, 40pi, Christ the Redeemer Statue, Brazil. No. 2414, 40pi, Great Wall of China, People's Republic of China. No. 2415, 40pi, Taj Mahal, India. No. 2416, 40pi, Colosseum, Italy. No. 2417, 40pi, Petra, Jordan. No. 2418, 40pi, Chichen Itza, Mexico. No. 2419, 40pi, Machu Picchu, Peru.

**2019, July 8        Litho.        Perf. 13¾x12**
2413-2419 A575    Set of 7        8.00 8.00

Miniature Sheet

Jordanian Heritage — A576

No. 2420: a, Earthenware urn in frame. b, Teapot. c, Tent, horiz. d, Weaver at loom, horiz. e, Dead birds hanging from branch, horiz. f, Images of rees carved in stone, horiz. g, Grain mill, horiz. h, Animal skin hanging from rope, horiz. i, Calligraphy brush and ink pot. j, Stringed instrument and bow.

**2019, Aug. 8        Litho.        Perf. 12**
2420 A576 20pi Sheet of 10, #a-j, + central label    5.75 5.75

Express Mail Service, 20th Anniv.
A577

**2019, Oct. 9        Litho.        Perf. 13¾x12**
2421 A577 80pi multi              2.25 2.25

Miniature Sheet

Y1SAT, First Jordanian Satellite — A578

No. 2422: a, Technicians wearing hair nets. b, Technician soldering. c, Technical team. d, Assembled Y1SAT. e, Finger and circuit board. f, Y1SAT in space.

**2019, Oct.        Litho.        Perf. 12**
2422 A578 40pi Sheet of 6, #a-f    6.75 6.75

Miniature Sheet

Olive Picking
A579

No. 2423: a, 30pi, Man on ladder picking olives. b, 40pi, Two women picking olives. c, 50pi, Man using picking tool. d, 60pi, Three olive pickers.

**2019, Nov. 28       Litho.        Perf. 12**
2423 A579 Sheet of 4, #a-d        5.25 5.25

Flag of Palestinian Authority, Doves, and Dome of the Rock, Jerusalem
A580

**Litho. & Embossed With Foil Application**
**2019, Dec. 24        Perf. 12**
2424 A580 120pi gold & multi      3.50 3.50
Jerusalem, capital of Palestinian Authority.

Arab League, 75th Anniv. — A581

**2020, Mar. 21       Litho.        Perf. 12**
2425 A581 120pi multi             3.50 3.50

Campaign Against COVID-19 Pandemic — A582

234                           JORDAN

No. 2426: a, Police officer and police car. b,
People participating in teleconference. c, People in meeting with leader at easel. d, People seated at table. e, Health care workers and ambulance. f, Delivery man with boxes. g, Soldier and military vehicle.

| 2021, Mar. 31 | Litho. | Perf. 12 | |
|---|---|---|---|
| 2426 | Sheet of 7 | 6.00 | 6.00 |
| a.-g. | A582 30pi Any single | .85 | .85 |

A583

A584

A585

A586

A587

A588

A589

A590

A591

A592

Establishment of the Emirate of
Transjordan, Cent. — A603

### Litho. & Embossed With Foil Application

| 2021, Apr. | | Perf. 12 | |
|---|---|---|---|
| 2427 | A583 100pi multi | — | — |
| 2428 | A584 100pi multi | — | — |
| 2429 | A585 100pi multi | — | — |
| 2430 | A586 100pi multi | — | — |
| 2431 | A587 100pi multi | — | — |
| 2432 | A588 100pi multi | — | — |
| 2433 | A589 100pi multi | — | — |
| 2434 | A590 100pi multi | — | — |
| 2435 | A591 100pi multi | — | — |
| 2436 | A592 100pi multi | — | — |

### Imperf
### Litho. & Embossed With Foil Application

| 2438 | A603 100pi multi | — | — |

A608

The
Martyr — A609

### Litho. & Embossed With Foil Application

| 2021, June 23 | | Perf. 12 | |
|---|---|---|---|
| 2443 | A608 100pi gold & multi | 3.00 | 3.00 |
| 2444 | A609 100pi gold & multi | 3.00 | 3.00 |

A610

A611

A612

A613

A614

A615

A616

Jordanian Nature Reserves — A617

| 2021, June 23 | Litho. | Perf. 14 | |
|---|---|---|---|
| 2445 | Sheet of 8 | — | — |
| a. | A610 35pi multi | | |
| b. | A611 35pi multi | | |
| c. | A612 35pi multi | | |
| d. | A613 35pi multi | | |
| e. | A614 35pi multi | | |
| f. | A615 35pi multi | | |
| g. | A616 35pi multi | | |
| h. | A617 35pi multi | | |

### Miniature Sheet

Handicrafted Jewelry — A618

No. 2446: a, Beaded necklace. b, Necklace and pendant. c, Earrings. d, Pendant.

### Litho. & Embossed With Foil Application

| 2021, July 12 | | Perf. 12 | |
|---|---|---|---|
| 2446 | A618 50pi Sheet of 4, #a-d | 5.75 | 5.75 |

A619

A620

A621

A622

A623

A624

A625

Purebred Arabian Horses
A626

| 2021, Aug. 31 | Litho. | Perf. 12 | |
|---|---|---|---|
| 2447 | A619 30pi multi | .85 | .85 |
| 2448 | A620 30pi multi | .85 | .85 |
| 2449 | A621 30pi multi | .85 | .85 |
| 2450 | A622 30pi multi | .85 | .85 |
| 2451 | A623 30pi multi | .85 | .85 |
| 2452 | A624 30pi multi | .85 | .85 |
| 2453 | A625 30pi multi | .85 | .85 |
| | Nos. 2447-2453 (7) | 5.95 | 5.95 |
| | Size:120x70mm | | |
| | Imperf | | |
| 2454 | A626 50pi multi | 1.40 | 1.40 |

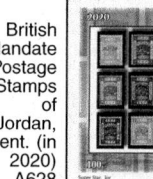
Musical Instruments — A627

Designs: No. 2455, 30pi, Zither. No. 2456, 30pi, Tambourine. No. 2457, 30pi, Piano. No. 2458, 30pi, Bouzouki. No. 2459, 30pi, Cello. No. 2460, 30pi, Clarinet. No. 2461, 30pi, Accordion. No. 2462, 30pi, Flute. No. 2463, 30pi, Violin. No. 2464, 30pi, Oud.

| 2021, Oct. 25 | Litho. | Perf. 12 | |
|---|---|---|---|
| 2455-2464 | A627 Set of 10 | 8.50 | 8.50 |

British Mandate Postage Stamps of Jordan, Cent. (in 2020)
A628

| 2021, Oct. 26 | Litho. | Imperf. | |
|---|---|---|---|
| 2465 | A628 100pi multi + label | 3.00 | 3.00 |

A629

A630

A631

Inclusion of People with Disabilities in
Society — A632

**2021, Nov. 29    Litho.    Perf. 12**
2466 A629 50pi multi          1.40 1.40
2467 A630 50pi multi          1.40 1.40
2468 A631 50pi multi          1.40 1.40
2469 A632 50pi multi          1.40 1.40
     Nos. 2466-2469 (4)        5.60 5.60

A633

A634

A635

Return of Al
Baqoura and
Al Ghamr to
Jordanian
Control
A636

**Litho. & Embossed With Foil
Application**
**2021, Nov. 29       Perf. 12x14**
2470 A633 50pi sil & multi    1.40 1.40
2471 A634 50pi sil & multi    1.40 1.40
2472 A635 50pi sil & multi    1.40 1.40
2473 A636 50pi sil & multi    1.40 1.40
     Nos. 2470-2473 (4)        5.60 5.60

**Miniature Sheet**

Aerial
Views of
Cities
A637

No. 2474: a, Al Shoubak. b, Ajlun. c,
Amman. d, As Salt. e, Aqaba. f, Umm Qais.

**Litho. & Embossed With Foil
Application**
**2021, Nov. 29       Perf. 12**
2474 A637 40pi Sheet of 6, #a-f  6.75 6.75

Madaba,
2022
Capital of
Arab
Tourism
A638

Designs: No. 2475, 40pi, Fortress of
Mukawir. No. 2476, 40pi, Ma'in Hot Springs.
No. 2477, 40pi, Mount Nebo. No. 2478, 40pi,
Tourist Street. No. 2479, 40pi, Wadi Al-Hidan.
No. 2480, 40pi, St. George Church.
50pi, Mosaic map of Jerusalem.

**2022, June 27    Litho.    Perf. 12**
2475-2480 A638  Set of 6     6.75 6.75
          Size: 111x55mm
          *Imperf*
2481 A638 50pi multi         1.40 1.40

A639

A640

A641

A642

A643

A644

A645

A646

Royal
Tank
Museum,
Amman
A647

**Litho. & Embossed With Foil
Application**
**2022, July 27               Perf. 14**
2482 A639 40pi multi         — —
2483 A640 40pi multi         — —
2484 A641 40pi multi         — —
2485 A642 40pi multi         — —
2486 A643 40pi multi         — —
2487 A644 40pi multi         — —
2488 A645 40pi multi         — —
2489 A646 40pi multi         — —
          *Imperf*
2490 A647 50pi multi         — —

A648

A649

A650

A651

A652

A653

A654

A655

A656

Wildflowers
A657

          *Perf. 13¼x13½*
**2022, Aug. 18              Litho.**
2491 A648 30pi multi         .85 .85
2492 A649 30pi multi         .85 .85
2493 A650 30pi multi         .85 .85
2494 A651 30pi multi         .85 .85
2495 A652 30pi multi         .85 .85
2496 A653 30pi multi         .85 .85
2497 A654 30pi multi         .85 .85
2498 A655 30pi multi         .85 .85
2499 A656 30pi multi         .85 .85
2500 A657 30pi multi         .85 .85
     Nos. 2491-2500 (10)      8.50 8.50

**SEMI-POSTAL STAMPS**

**Locust Campaign Issue**

Nos. 145-156 Overprinted

**1930, Apr. 1    Wmk. 4    Perf. 14**
B1  A1   2(m) Prus blue      2.50   4.00
a.    Inverted overprint    225.00
B2  A1   3(m) rose           2.00   4.00
B3  A1   4(m) green          2.75   5.00
B4  A1   5(m) orange        22.50  17.50
a.    Double overprint      400.00
B5  A1  10(m) red            2.25   3.75
B6  A1  15(m) ultra          2.25   3.50
a.    Inverted overprint    225.00
B7  A1  20(m) olive grn      2.75   4.50
B8  A2  50(m) claret         5.50  11.00
B9  A2  90(m) bister        16.00  47.50
B10 A2 100(m) lt blue       17.50  50.00
B11 A2 200(m) violet        37.50 100.00
B12 A2 500(m) brown        100.00 160.00
a.   "C" of "Locust" omitted 750.00
     Nos. B1-B12 (12)       213.50 410.75

These stamps were issued to raise funds to
help combat a plague of locusts.

Catalogue values for unused
stamps in this section, from this
point to the end of the section, are
for Never Hinged items.

Jerusalem
SP1

**1997, Nov. 29   Litho.   Perf. 13½x13**
B13 SP1 100f +10f bl & multi   .90  .75
B14 SP1 200f +20f yel & multi 1.90 1.75
B15 SP1 300f +30f bl grn &
         multi                2.75 2.50
     Nos. B13-B15 (3)         5.55 5.00

Breast Cancer
Prevention — SP2

**2009, Aug. 25   Litho.   Perf. 13¼**
          **Granite Paper**
B16 SP2 30pi +50pi multi      3.75 3.75

Jerusalem, Capital of
Arab Culture — SP3

Panel color: 20pi+25pi, Orange. 30pi+25pi,
Purple. 40pi+25pi, Red. 50pi+25pi, Gray
green.

**2009, Dec. 13              Perf. 13¼**
          **Granite Paper**
B17-B20 SP3   Set of 4        8.00 8.00

**AIR POST STAMPS**

Catalogue values for unused
stamps in this section are for
Never Hinged items.

Plane and Globe — AP1

**Perf. 13½x13**

**1950, Sept. 16   Engr.   Wmk. 4**

| | | | | |
|---|---|---|---|---|
| C1 | AP1 | 5f org & red vio | 1.00 | .80 |
| C2 | AP1 | 10f pur & brown | 1.00 | .80 |
| C3 | AP1 | 15f ol grn & rose car | 1.00 | .80 |
| C4 | AP1 | 20f deep blue & blk | 1.25 | 1.25 |
| C5 | AP1 | 50f rose pink & dl grn | 1.75 | 1.25 |
| C6 | AP1 | 100f blue & brown | 3.00 | 3.00 |
| C7 | AP1 | 150f blk & red org | 4.50 | 4.25 |
| | | Nos. C1-C7 (7) | 13.50 | 12.15 |

Temple of Artemis, Jerash — AP2

**1954   Unwmk.   Perf. 12**

| | | | | |
|---|---|---|---|---|
| C8 | AP2 | 5f blue blk & org | .45 | .25 |
| C9 | AP2 | 10f vio brn & ver | .80 | .75 |
| C10 | AP2 | 25f bl grn & ultra | .90 | .80 |
| C11 | AP2 | 35f dp plum & grnsh bl | 1.00 | .80 |
| C12 | AP2 | 40f car rose & blk | 1.25 | .80 |
| C13 | AP2 | 50f dp ultra & org yel | 1.50 | 1.00 |
| C14 | AP2 | 100f dk bl & vio brn | 1.75 | 1.75 |
| C15 | AP2 | 150f stl bl & red brn | 3.00 | 2.25 |
| | | Nos. C8-C15 (8) | 10.65 | 8.40 |

**1958-59   Wmk. 305   Perf. 12**

| | | | | |
|---|---|---|---|---|
| C16 | AP2 | 5f blue blk & org | .45 | .25 |
| C17 | AP2 | 10f vio brn & ver | .75 | .25 |
| C18 | AP2 | 25f bl grn & ultra | .90 | .40 |
| C19 | AP2 | 35f dp plum grnsh bl | .90 | .60 |
| C20 | AP2 | 40f car rose & blk | 1.10 | .75 |
| C21 | AP2 | 50f dp ultra & org yel ('59) | 2.00 | 1.00 |
| | | Nos. C16-C21 (6) | 6.10 | 3.25 |

Stadium and Torch — AP3

**Perf. 11x11½**

**1964, July 12   Litho.   Wmk. 305**

| | | | | |
|---|---|---|---|---|
| C22 | AP3 | 1f yellow & multi | .40 | .30 |
| C23 | AP3 | 4f red & multi | .40 | .30 |
| C24 | AP3 | 10f blue & multi | .40 | .30 |
| C25 | AP3 | 35f yel grn & multi | .80 | .60 |
| a. | | Souvenir sheet of 4, #C22-C25 | 2.75 | 2.25 |
| | | Nos. C22-C25 (4) | 2.00 | 1.50 |

Opening of Hussein Sports City. No. C25a also exists imperf.

Gorgeous Bush-Shrike AP4

Birds: 500f, Ornate hawk-eagle, vert. 1d, Gray-headed kingfisher, vert.

**Perf. 14x14½**

**1964, Dec. 18   Photo.   Unwmk.**
**Birds in Natural Colors**

| | | | | |
|---|---|---|---|---|
| C26 | AP4 | 150f lt grn, blk & car | 30.00 | 13.00 |
| C27 | AP4 | 500f lt bl, blk & grn | 70.00 | 35.00 |
| C28 | AP4 | 1d ol brn & blk | 135.00 | 75.00 |
| | | Nos. C26-C28 (3) | 235.00 | 123.00 |

Nos. C26-C28 exist imperf.

Pagoda, Olympic Torch and Emblem AP5

**1965, Mar. 5   Litho.   Perf. 14**

| | | | | |
|---|---|---|---|---|
| C29 | AP5 | 10f deep rose | .40 | .40 |
| C30 | AP5 | 15f violet | .40 | .40 |
| C31 | AP5 | 20f blue | .45 | .45 |
| C32 | AP5 | 30f green | .45 | .45 |

| | | | | |
|---|---|---|---|---|
| C33 | AP5 | 40f brown | .60 | .60 |
| C34 | AP5 | 60f carmine rose | .85 | .85 |
| | | Nos. C29-C34 (6) | 3.15 | 3.15 |

18th Olympic Games, Tokyo, Oct. 10-25, 1964. An imperf. 100f violet blue souvenir sheet exists. Size of stamp: 60x60mm. Value $12.50.

For overprints see Nos. C42A-C42F.

Forum, Jerash — AP6

Antiquities of Jerash: No. C36, South Theater. No. C37, Triumphal arch. No. C38, Temple of Artemis. No. C39, Cathedral steps. No. C40, Artemis Temple, gate. No. C41, Columns. No. C42, Columns and niche, South Theater. Nos. C39-C42 are vertical.

**1965, June 22   Photo.   Perf. 14x15**
**Center Multicolored**

| | | | | |
|---|---|---|---|---|
| C35 | AP6 | 55f bright pink | 1.40 | 1.40 |
| C36 | AP6 | 55f light blue | 1.40 | 1.40 |
| C37 | AP6 | 55f green | 1.40 | 1.40 |
| C38 | AP6 | 55f black | 1.40 | 1.40 |
| C39 | AP6 | 55f light green | 1.40 | 1.40 |
| C40 | AP6 | 55f carmine rose | 1.40 | 1.40 |
| C41 | AP6 | 55f gray | 1.40 | 1.40 |
| C42 | AP6 | 55f blue | 1.40 | 1.40 |
| | | Nos. C35-C42 (8) | 11.20 | 11.20 |

Nos. C35-C38 are printed in horizontal rows of 4; Nos. C39-C42 in vertical rows of 4; sheets of 16.

**Nos. C29-C34 with Bilingual Ovpt. and Rocket in Black**

**1965, Sept. 25   Litho.   Perf. 14**

| | | | | |
|---|---|---|---|---|
| C42A | AP5 | 10f deep rose | 1.50 | 1.50 |
| C42B | AP5 | 15f violet | 2.00 | 2.00 |
| C42C | AP5 | 20f blue | 2.75 | 2.75 |
| C42D | AP5 | 30f green | 4.25 | 4.00 |
| C42E | AP5 | 40f brown | 5.50 | 5.50 |
| C42F | AP5 | 60f carmine rose | 7.50 | 7.50 |
| | | Nos. C42A-C42F (6) | 23.50 | 23.25 |

The imperf. 100f blue souvenir sheet exists overprinted. Value $21.50.

**King Hussein Type of Regular Issue**

**1966, Jan. 15   Photo.   Perf. 14½x14**
**Portrait in Brown**

| | | | | |
|---|---|---|---|---|
| C43 | A67 | 200f brt blue grn | 5.00 | 2.00 |
| C44 | A67 | 500f light green | 11.00 | 8.00 |
| C45 | A67 | 1d light ultra | 19.00 | 12.50 |
| | | Nos. C43-C45 (3) | 35.00 | 22.50 |

**Animal Type of Regular Issue, 1967**

Animals: 4f, Striped hyena. 30f, Arabian stallion. 60f, Persian gazelle.

**1967, Feb. 11   Photo.   Perf. 14x15**

| | | | | |
|---|---|---|---|---|
| C46 | A70 | 4f dk brn & multi | 2.00 | .30 |
| C47 | A70 | 30f lt bl & multi | 2.50 | .60 |
| C48 | A70 | 60f yellow & multi | 4.50 | 1.50 |
| | | Nos. C46-C48 (3) | 9.00 | 2.40 |

**Game Type of Regular Issue, 1968**

Protected Game: 60f, Nubian ibex, vert. 100f, Wild ducks.

**1968, Oct. 5   Litho.   Perf. 13½**

| | | | | |
|---|---|---|---|---|
| C49 | A74 | 60f multicolored | 9.50 | 5.00 |
| C50 | A74 | 100f multicolored | 15.00 | 9.00 |

**Easter Type of Regular Issue**

Designs: 60f, Altar, Holy Sepulcher. 100f, Feet Washing, Holy Gate, Jerusalem.

**1972, Apr.   Photo.   Perf. 14x13½**

| | | | | |
|---|---|---|---|---|
| C51 | A92 | 60f dk bl & multi | 1.40 | .70 |
| C52 | A92 | 100f multicolored | 2.00 | 1.10 |

**Aero Club Type of Regular Issue**

15f, Two Piper 140s. 20f, R.J.A.C. Beechcraft. 40f, Aero Club emblem with winged horse.

**1973, Jan.   Photo.   Perf. 13½x14**

| | | | | |
|---|---|---|---|---|
| C53 | A100 | 15f blue, blk & red | .70 | .35 |
| C54 | A100 | 20f blue, blk & red | .80 | .40 |
| C55 | A100 | 40f mag, blk & yel | 1.60 | .80 |
| | | Nos. C53-C55 (3) | 3.10 | 1.55 |

**Agriculture Type of Regular Issue**

Design: 100f, Soil conservation.

**1973, Dec. 25   Perf. 13½**

| | | | | |
|---|---|---|---|---|
| C56 | A110 | 100f multicolored | 2.50 | 1.75 |

King Hussein Driving Car — AP7

**1974, Dec. 20   Perf. 12**

| | | | | |
|---|---|---|---|---|
| C57 | AP7 | 30f multicolored | .60 | .25 |
| C58 | AP7 | 60f multicolored | 1.50 | .80 |

Royal Jordanian Automobile Club.

**Building Type of Regular Issue**

Designs: 50f, Palms, Aqaba. 60f, Obelisk tomb. 80f, Fort of Wadi Rum.

**1975, Mar. 1   Photo.   Perf. 13½x14**

| | | | | |
|---|---|---|---|---|
| C59 | A121 | 50f pink & multi | 1.40 | .65 |
| C60 | A121 | 60f lt bl & multi | 1.75 | .80 |
| C61 | A121 | 80f yellow & multi | 2.25 | .80 |
| | | Nos. C59-C61 (3) | 5.40 | 2.25 |

**Hussein Type of Regular Issue**

**1975, Apr. 8   Photo.   Perf. 14x13½**
**Size: 22x27mm**

| | | | | |
|---|---|---|---|---|
| C62 | A123 | 60f dk grn & brn | 1.25 | .35 |
| C63 | A123 | 100f org brn & brn | 2.00 | .40 |
| C64 | A123 | 120f dp bl & brn | 1.10 | .65 |
| C65 | A123 | 180f brt mag & brn | 1.75 | 1.10 |
| C66 | A123 | 200f grnsh bl & brn | 2.25 | 1.50 |
| C67 | A123 | 400f pur & brown | 3.25 | 2.50 |
| C68 | A123 | 500f orange & brn | 4.25 | 4.00 |
| | | Nos. C62-C68 (7) | 15.85 | 10.50 |

---

### POSTAGE DUE STAMPS

Stamps of Regular Issue (Nos. 69, 66-68 Surcharged with New Value like No. 91) Overprinted

This overprint reads: "Mustahaq" (Tax or Due)

**Typo. Ovpt. "Mustahaq" 10mm long**

**1923   Unwmk.   Perf. 11½**

| | | | | |
|---|---|---|---|---|
| J1 | A7 | ½pi on 3pi ol brn | 57.50 | 60.00 |
| a. | | Inverted overprint | 200.00 | 200.00 |
| b. | | Double overprint | 200.00 | 200.00 |

**Handstamped Overprint 12mm long**

| | | | | |
|---|---|---|---|---|
| J2 | A7 | ½pi on 3pi ol brn | 27.50 | 35.00 |
| a. | | Inverted overprint | 55.00 | — |
| b. | | Double overprint | 55.00 | — |
| J3 | A7 | 1pi dark blue | 18.00 | 21.00 |
| a. | | Inverted overprint | 50.00 | — |
| b. | | Double overprint | 52.50 | — |
| J4 | A7 | 1½pi violet | 21.00 | 22.50 |
| a. | | Inverted overprint | 50.00 | — |
| b. | | Double overprint | 52.50 | — |
| J5 | A7 | 2pi orange | 25.00 | 27.50 |
| a. | | Inverted overprint | 65.00 | 60.00 |
| b. | | Double overprint | 70.00 | — |
| | | Nos. J1-J5 (5) | 149.00 | 166.00 |

Stamps of Hejaz Handstamped

| | | | | |
|---|---|---|---|---|
| J6 | A7 | ½pi red | 2.50 | 6.00 |
| J7 | A7 | 1pi dark blue | 6.00 | 6.50 |
| J8 | A7 | 1½pi violet | 5.00 | 7.50 |
| J9 | A7 | 2pi orange | 8.00 | 8.00 |

| | | | | |
|---|---|---|---|---|
| J10 | A7 | 3pi olive brown | 12.50 | 17.50 |
| J11 | A7 | 5pi olive green | 15.00 | 30.00 |
| | | Nos. J6-J11 (6) | 49.00 | 75.50 |

Type of Palestine, 1918, Overprinted

**1925   Wmk. 4   Perf. 14**

| | | | | |
|---|---|---|---|---|
| J12 | A1 | 1m dark brown | 2.50 | 6.00 |
| J13 | A1 | 2m yellow | 4.25 | 4.25 |
| J14 | A1 | 4m rose | 4.75 | 6.75 |
| J15 | A1 | 8m red | 6.50 | 12.00 |
| J16 | A1 | 13m ultramarine | 9.50 | 12.00 |
| J17 | A1 | 5pi plum | 11.00 | 19.00 |
| a. | | Perf. 15x14 | 67.50 | 85.00 |
| | | Nos. J12-J17 (6) | 38.50 | 60.00 |

The overprint reads: "Mustahaq. Sharqi al'Ardan." (Tax. Eastern Jordan).

Stamps of Palestine, 1918, Surcharged

**1926**

| | | | | |
|---|---|---|---|---|
| J18 | A1 | 1m on 1m dk brn | 10.00 | 12.00 |
| J19 | A1 | 2m on 1m dk brn | 9.00 | 12.00 |
| J20 | A1 | 4m on 3m Prus bl | 10.00 | 15.00 |
| J21 | A1 | 8m on 3m Prus bl | 10.00 | 15.00 |
| J22 | A1 | 13m on 13m ultra | 13.00 | 17.00 |
| J23 | A1 | 5pi on 13m ultra | 16.00 | 25.00 |
| | | Nos. J18-J23 (6) | 68.00 | 96.00 |

The surcharge reads "Tax — Eastern Jordan" and New Value.

Stamps of Regular Issue, 1927, Overprinted

**1929**

| | | | | |
|---|---|---|---|---|
| J24 | A1 | 2m Prussian bl | 2.50 | 8.00 |
| J25 | A1 | 10m red | 2.50 | 9.00 |
| J26 | A2 | 50m claret | 7.50 | 22.50 |
| | | Nos. J24-J26 (3) | 12.50 | 39.50 |

**With Additional Surcharge**

| | | | | |
|---|---|---|---|---|
| J27 | A1 | 1(m) on 3(m) rose | 1.75 | 9.00 |
| J28 | A1 | 4(m) on 15(m) ultra | 3.00 | 11.00 |
| a. | | Inverted surch. and ovpt. | 200.00 | 350.00 |
| J29 | A2 | 20(m) on 100(m) lt bl | 7.00 | 20.00 |
| | | Nos. J27-J29 (3) | 11.75 | 40.00 |

D1

**Size: 17¼x21mm**

**1929   Engr.   Perf. 14**

| | | | | |
|---|---|---|---|---|
| J30 | D1 | 1m brown | 1.40 | 6.50 |
| a. | | Perf. 13½x13 | 160.00 | 130.00 |
| J31 | D1 | 2m orange | 2.75 | 7.00 |
| J32 | D1 | 4m green | 4.00 | 11.00 |
| J33 | D1 | 10m carmine | 7.00 | 10.00 |
| J34 | D1 | 20m olive green | 13.00 | 21.00 |
| J35 | D1 | 50m blue | 16.00 | 32.50 |
| | | Nos. J30-J35 (6) | 44.15 | 88.00 |

See Nos. J39-J43 design with larger type. For surcharge see No. J52. For overprints see Nos. NJ1a, NJ3, NJ5a, NJ6-NJ7.

D2

**1942   Unwmk.   Litho.   Perf. 13x13½**

| | | | | |
|---|---|---|---|---|
| J36 | D2 | 1m dull red brn | 3.00 | 24.00 |
| J37 | D2 | 2m dl orange yel | 9.00 | 14.00 |
| J38 | D2 | 10m dark carmine | 12.00 | 8.00 |
| | | Nos. J36-J38 (3) | 24.00 | 46.00 |

For overprints see Nos. NJ8-NJ10.

**Type of 1929**

**1943-44   Engr.   Wmk. 4   Perf. 12**
**Size: 17¾x21¼mm**

| | | | | |
|---|---|---|---|---|
| J39 | D1 | 1m orange brn | .70 | 6.50 |
| J40 | D1 | 2m yel orange | .90 | 7.00 |
| J41 | D1 | 4m yel green | .90 | 9.00 |

| | | | |
|---|---|---|---|
| J42 | D1 | 10m rose carmine | 2.50 | 12.00 |
| J43 | D1 | 20m olive green | 45.00 | 90.00 |
| | | Nos. J39-J43 (5) | 50.00 | 124.50 |

For overprints see Nos. J47-J51, NJ1-NJ2, NJ3a, NJ5, NJ6a.

> Catalogue values for unused stamps in this section, from this point to the end of the section, are for Never Hinged items.

Nos. J39-J43, J35 Srchd. "FILS" & its Arabic Equivalent in Black, Green or Carmine

| 1952 | | Wmk. 4 | Perf. 12 | |
|---|---|---|---|---|
| J47 | D1 | 1f on 1m org brn (Bk) | 2.00 | 2.00 |
| J48 | D1 | 2f on 2m yel org (G) | 2.00 | 2.00 |
| J49 | D1 | 4f on 4m yel grn | 2.50 | 2.50 |
| J50 | D1 | 10f on 10m rose car (Bk) | 4.25 | 4.75 |
| J51 | D1 | 20f on 20m ol grn | 10.00 | 10.00 |
| | | Perf. 14 | | |
| J52 | D1 | 50f on 50m blue | 9.50 | 10.50 |
| | | Nos. J47-J52 (6) | 30.25 | 31.75 |

This overprint exists on Nos. J34, J36-J38. Exists inverted, double and in wrong color.

 D3

Inscribed: "The Hashemite Kingdom of the Jordan"

| 1952 | | Engr. | Perf. 11½ | |
|---|---|---|---|---|
| J53 | D3 | 1f orange brown | .65 | .85 |
| J54 | D3 | 2f yel orange | .65 | .85 |
| J55 | D3 | 4f yel green | .65 | .85 |
| J56 | D3 | 10f rose carmine | 1.25 | 1.50 |
| J57 | D3 | 20f yel brown | 1.25 | 1.75 |
| J58 | D3 | 50f blue | 3.50 | 4.00 |
| | | Nos. J53-J58 (6) | 7.95 | 9.80 |

### Type of 1952 Redrawn
Inscribed: "The Hashemite Kingdom of Jordan"

| 1957 | | Wmk. 305 | Perf. 11½ | |
|---|---|---|---|---|
| J59 | D3 | 1f orange brown | 1.00 | .40 |
| J60 | D3 | 2f yel orange | 1.00 | .40 |
| J61 | D3 | 4f yel green | 1.00 | .60 |
| J62 | D3 | 10f rose carmine | 1.25 | .55 |
| J63 | D3 | 20f yel brown | 1.75 | 1.25 |
| | | Nos. J59-J63 (5) | 6.00 | 3.20 |

### OFFICIAL STAMP

Saudi Arabia No. L34 Overprinted

| 1924, Jan. | | Typo. | Perf. 11½ |
|---|---|---|---|
| O1 | A7 | ½pi red | 100.00 |

Overprint reads: "(Government) the Arabian East 1342."
No. O1 is not known genuine in used condition.

### POSTAL TAX STAMPS

> Catalogue values for unused stamps in this section are for Never Hinged items.

Mosque at Hebron — PT1

Designs: 10m, 15m, 20m, 50m, Dome of the Rock. 100m, 200m, 500m, £1, Acre.

| | | Perf. 11½x12½ | | |
|---|---|---|---|---|
| 1947 | | Unwmk. | Engr. | |
| RA1 | PT1 | 1m ultra | .60 | .40 |
| RA2 | PT1 | 2m carmine | .70 | .50 |
| RA3 | PT1 | 3m emerald | .80 | .75 |
| RA4 | PT1 | 5m plum | 1.00 | .85 |
| RA5 | PT1 | 10m carmine | 1.10 | 1.00 |
| RA6 | PT1 | 15m gray | 1.75 | 1.25 |
| RA7 | PT1 | 20m dk brown | 3.00 | 1.50 |
| RA8 | PT1 | 50m purple | 4.50 | 3.50 |
| RA9 | PT1 | 100m orange red | 14.00 | 9.00 |
| RA10 | PT1 | 200m dp blue | 37.50 | 22.50 |
| RA11 | PT1 | 500m green | 80.00 | 60.00 |
| RA12 | PT1 | £1 dk brown | 140.00 | 130.00 |
| | | Nos. RA1-RA12 (12) | 284.95 | 231.25 |

Issued to help the Welfare Fund for Arabs in Palestine. Required on foreign-bound letters to the amount of half the regular postage.
For overprints and surcharges see Nos. 286A-286C, 344-346, RA37-RA46, NRA1-NRA12.

Nos. 211, 232 and 234 Overprinted in Black

| 1950 | | Wmk. 4 | Perf. 12 | |
|---|---|---|---|---|
| RA23 | A3 | 5m orange | 20.00 | 22.50 |
| RA24 | A3 | 10m violet | 30.00 | 32.50 |
| RA25 | A3 | 15m dull olive grn | 35.00 | 35.00 |
| | | Nos. RA23-RA25 (3) | 85.00 | 90.00 |

Arch and Colonnade, Palmyra, Syria — PT2

Two types of 5m:
Type I — "A" with serifs. Arabic ovpt. 8mm wide.
Type II — "A" without serifs. Arabic ovpt. 5mm wide.

### Black or Carmine Overprint
| 1950-51 | | Engr. | Perf. 13½x13 | |
|---|---|---|---|---|
| RA26 | PT2 | 5m orange (I) | 25.00 | 20.00 |
| a. | | Type II ('51) | 27.50 | 2.75 |
| RA27 | PT2 | 10m violet (C) | 25.00 | 22.50 |

The overprint on No. RA27 is similar to that on RA23-RA25 but slightly bolder.

### Type of 1947
Designs: 5f, Hebron Mosque. 10f, 15f, 20f, Dome of the Rock. 100f, Acre.

| 1951 | | Wmk. 4 | Perf. 11½x12½ | |
|---|---|---|---|---|
| RA28 | PT1 | 5f plum | 1.00 | 1.00 |
| RA29 | PT1 | 10f carmine | 1.00 | 1.00 |
| RA30 | PT1 | 15f gray | 1.25 | 1.25 |
| RA31 | PT1 | 20f dk brown | 1.50 | 1.50 |
| RA33 | PT1 | 100f orange | 6.25 | 6.25 |
| | | Nos. RA28-RA33 (5) | 11.00 | 11.00 |

The tax on Nos. RA1-RA33 was for Arab aid in Palestine.
For overprints see Nos. 287-290, 347.

Postal Tax Stamps of 1947 Srchd. "FILS" or "J.D." & Their Arabic Equivalents & Bars in Carmine or Black

| 1952 | | | Unwmk. | |
|---|---|---|---|---|
| RA37 | PT1 | 1f on 1m ultra | .75 | .45 |
| RA38 | PT1 | 3f on 3m emer | 1.00 | .45 |
| RA39 | PT1 | 10f on 10m car | 1.50 | .55 |
| RA40 | PT1 | 15f on 15m gray | 2.00 | 1.25 |
| RA41 | PT1 | 20f on 20m dk brown | 3.00 | 1.75 |
| RA42 | PT1 | 50f on 50m pur | 6.00 | 3.75 |
| RA43 | PT1 | 100f on 100m org red | 17.50 | 10.00 |
| RA44 | PT1 | 200f on 200m dp blue | 45.00 | 27.50 |
| RA45 | PT1 | 500f on 500m grn | 100.00 | 75.00 |
| RA46 | PT1 | 1d on £1 dk brn | 150.00 | 140.00 |
| | | Nos. RA37-RA46 (10) | 326.75 | 260.70 |

"J.D." stands for Jordanian Dinar.

### OCCUPATION STAMPS
> Catalogue values for unused stamps in this section are for Never Hinged items.

### For Use in Palestine

Stamps of Jordan Overprinted in Red, Black, Dark Green, Green or Orange Red

### On No. 200
| 1948 | | Unwmk. | Perf. 13x13½ | |
|---|---|---|---|---|
| N1 | A14 | 2m dull green (R) | 8.00 | 8.00 |

### On #207-209, 211, 230-235, 215-220
| 1948 | | Wmk. 4 | Perf. 12, 13½x13, 14 | |
|---|---|---|---|---|
| N2 | A3 | 1m red brown | 1.00 | .80 |
| N3 | A3 | 2m Prus grn (R) | 1.00 | .80 |
| a. | | 2m Prussian blue, perf. 13½x13 (R) (#170a) | 2.50 | 2.50 |
| N4 | A3 | 3m blue grn (R) | 1.00 | 1.00 |
| N5 | A3 | 3m rose carmine | .65 | .65 |
| N6 | A3 | 4m dp yel grn (R) | .65 | .65 |
| N7 | A3 | 5m orange (G) | .65 | .65 |
| N8 | A3 | 10m violet (OR) | 1.50 | 1.50 |
| N9 | A3 | 12m deep rose | 1.50 | .90 |
| N10 | A3 | 15m dl ol grn (R) | 2.25 | 2.25 |
| N11 | A3 | 20m dp blue (R) | 3.25 | 3.25 |
| N12 | A3 | 50m red lil (Dk G) | 3.25 | 3.25 |
| N13 | A3 | 90m ocher (Dk G) | 15.00 | 3.25 |
| N14 | A3 | 100m dp blue (R) | 17.50 | 10.00 |
| N15 | A3 | 200m dk vio (R) | 9.00 | 15.00 |
| a. | | 200m vio, perf. 14 (R) (#182) | 75.00 | 50.00 |
| N16 | A3 | 500m dk brn (R) | 60.00 | 25.00 |
| N17 | A3 | £1 black (R) | 110.00 | 60.00 |
| | | Nos. N2-N17 (16) | 227.95 | 127.20 |

The first overprinting of these stamps include Nos. N1-N6, N9-N17. The second overprinting includes Nos. N1, N3, N5-N17, in inks differing in shade from the originals.
Many values exist with inverted or double overprint.

### Jordan Nos. 245-249 Overprinted in Black or Red

| 1949, Aug. | | Wmk. 4 | Perf. 13 | |
|---|---|---|---|---|
| N18 | A17 | 1m brown (Bk) | 1.75 | 1.75 |
| N19 | A17 | 4m green | 1.75 | 1.75 |
| a. | | "PLAESTINE" | 80.00 | |
| N20 | A17 | 10m red | 1.75 | 1.75 |
| N21 | A17 | 20m ultra | 1.75 | 1.75 |
| N22 | A18 | 50m dull green | 3.50 | 3.50 |
| a. | | "PLAESTINE" | 75.00 | |
| | | Nos. N18-N22 (5) | 10.50 | 10.50 |

The overprint is in one line on No. N22.
UPU, 75th anniversary.

### OCCUPATION POSTAGE DUE STAMPS
> Catalogue values for unused stamps in this section are for Never Hinged items.

Jordan Nos. J39, J30a, J40, J32, J41-J43, J34 and J35 Overprinted in Black, Red or Carmine

| 1948-49 | | Wmk. 4 | Perf. 12, 14 | |
|---|---|---|---|---|
| NJ1 | D1 | 1m org brn, perf. 12 | 3.50 | 5.00 |
| a. | | Perf. 13½x13 (#J30a) | 75.00 | 50.00 |
| NJ2 | D1 | 2m yel orange | 4.00 | 6.00 |
| NJ3 | D1 | 4m grn (R) (#J32) | 4.00 | 6.00 |
| a. | | 4m yel grn (C) (#J41) | 15.00 | 18.00 |
| NJ5 | D1 | 10m rose car (R) (#J42) | 4.00 | 5.50 |
| a. | | Perf. 14 (#J33) | 325.00 | |
| NJ6 | D1 | 20m ol grn (R), perf. 14 | 3.75 | 5.00 |
| a. | | Perf. 12 (R) (#J43) | 95.00 | 95.00 |
| NJ7 | D1 | 50m blue (R) | 4.25 | 6.00 |
| | | Nos. NJ1-NJ3, NJ5-NJ7 (6) | 23.50 | 33.50 |

The second overprinting of these stamps includes Nos. NJ1-NJ3, NJ3a and NJ5-NJ7, in inks differing in shade from the originals.
Double and inverted overprints exist.

### Same Overprint in Black on Jordan Nos. J36-J38
| 1948-49 | | Unwmk. | Perf. 13x13½ | |
|---|---|---|---|---|
| NJ8 | D2 | 1m dl red brn | 175.00 | 175.00 |
| NJ9 | D2 | 2m dl org yel ('49) | 20.00 | 25.00 |
| NJ10 | D2 | 10m dark car | 17.50 | 22.50 |

### OCCUPATION POSTAL TAX STAMPS
> Catalogue values for unused stamps in this section are for Never Hinged items.

Postal Tax Stamps of 1947 Overprinted in Red or Black

| 1950 | | | | |
|---|---|---|---|---|
| NRA1 | PT1 | 1m ultra (R) | .40 | .75 |
| NRA2 | PT1 | 2m carmine (R) | .45 | .75 |
| NRA3 | PT1 | 3m emer (R) | .75 | .85 |
| NRA4 | PT1 | 5m plum | 1.00 | .75 |
| NRA5 | PT1 | 10m carmine (R) | 1.25 | .75 |
| NRA6 | PT1 | 15m gray (R) | 2.75 | .90 |
| NRA7 | PT1 | 20m dk brn (R) | 4.50 | 1.50 |
| NRA8 | PT1 | 50m purple (R) | 6.50 | 3.00 |
| NRA9 | PT1 | 100m org red | 11.00 | 4.50 |
| NRA10 | PT1 | 200m dp blue | 27.50 | 14.50 |
| NRA11 | PT1 | 500m green (R) | 75.00 | 42.50 |
| NRA12 | PT1 | £1 dk brn | 140.00 | 75.00 |
| | | Nos. NRA1-NRA12 (12) | 271.10 | 145.75 |

For overprints see Nos. 286D-286G.

# KARELIA

kə-'rē-lə-ə

LOCATION — In northwestern Soviet Russia
GOVT. — An autonomous republic of the Soviet Union
AREA — 55,198 sq. mi. (approx.)
POP. — 270,000 (approx.)
CAPITAL — Petrozavodsk (Kalininsk)

In 1921 the Karelians rebelled and for a short period a form of sovereignty independent of Russia was maintained.

100 Pennia = 1 Markka

Bear — A1

### 1922   Unwmk.   Litho.   Perf. 11½, 12

| | | | | |
|---|---|---|---|---|
| 1 | A1 | 5p dark gray | 15.00 | 55.00 |
| 2 | A1 | 10p light blue | 15.00 | 55.00 |
| 3 | A1 | 20p rose red | 15.00 | 55.00 |
| 4 | A1 | 25p yellow brown | 15.00 | 55.00 |
| 5 | A1 | 40p magenta | 15.00 | 55.00 |
| 6 | A1 | 50p gray green | 15.00 | 55.00 |
| 7 | A1 | 75p orange yellow | 20.00 | 55.00 |
| 8 | A1 | 1m pink & gray | 20.00 | 55.00 |
| 9 | A1 | 2m yel grn & gray | 27.50 | 110.00 |
| 10 | A1 | 3m lt blue & gray | 27.50 | 140.00 |
| 11 | A1 | 5m red lil & gray | 27.50 | 175.00 |
| 12 | A1 | 10m lt brn & gray | 27.50 | 275.00 |
| 13 | A1 | 15m green & car | 27.50 | 275.00 |
| 14 | A1 | 20m rose & green | 27.50 | 275.00 |
| 15 | A1 | 25m yellow & blue | 30.00 | 275.00 |
| | | Nos. 1-15 (15) | 325.00 | 1,965. |
| | | Set, never hinged | 450.00 | |

Nos. 1-15 were valid Jan. 31-Feb. 16, 1922. Use probably ended Feb. 3, although cancellations of the 4th and 5th exist.
Nos. 7, 8, 10, 13, 14 and 15 exist imperf. Value, each pair $250 hinged; $500 never hinged. Other denominations may exist imperf. Counterfeits abound.

## OCCUPATION STAMPS

### Issued under Finnish Occupation

Issued in the Russian territory of Eastern Karelia under Finnish military administration.

### Types of Finland Stamps, 1930 Overprinted in Black

On A26                On A27-A28

### 1941   Unwmk.   Perf. 14

| | | | | |
|---|---|---|---|---|
| N1 | A26 | 50p brt yel grn | .45 | 1.00 |
| N2 | A26 | 1.75m dk gray | 1.25 | 1.75 |
| N3 | A26 | 2m dp org | 1.75 | 4.50 |
| N4 | A26 | 2.75m yel org | .85 | 1.25 |
| N5 | A26 | 3½m lt ultra | 2.50 | 4.50 |
| N6 | A27 | 5m rose vio | 6.00 | 10.00 |
| N7 | A28 | 5m pale brn | 6.75 | 12.00 |
| | | Nos. N1-N7 (7) | 19.55 | 35.00 |
| | | Set, never hinged | 32.00 | |

### Types of Finland Stamps, 1930 Overprinted in Green

On A26                On A27-A29

| | | | | |
|---|---|---|---|---|
| N8 | A26 | 50p brt yel grn | .55 | .90 |
| N9 | A26 | 1.75m dk gray | .70 | 1.00 |
| N10 | A26 | 2m dp org | 1.00 | 2.40 |
| N11 | A26 | 2.75m yel org | .65 | 1.25 |
| N12 | A26 | 3½m lt ultra | 1.25 | 2.25 |
| N13 | A27 | 5m rose vio | 2.00 | 5.00 |
| N14 | A28 | 10m pale brown | 4.25 | 8.50 |
| N15 | A29 | 25m green | 4.50 | 9.00 |
| | | Nos. N8-N15 (8) | 14.90 | 30.30 |
| | | Set, never hinged | 35.00 | |

---

### Mannerheim Type of Finland Overprinted

### 1942

| | | | | |
|---|---|---|---|---|
| N16 | A48 | 50p dk yel grn | .95 | 2.25 |
| N17 | A48 | 1.75m slate bl | .95 | 2.25 |
| N18 | A48 | 2m red org | .95 | 2.25 |
| N19 | A48 | 2.75m brn org | .80 | 2.25 |
| N20 | A48 | 3.50m brt ultra | .80 | 2.25 |
| N21 | A48 | 5m brn vio | .80 | 2.25 |
| | | Nos. N16-N21 (6) | 5.25 | 13.50 |
| | | Set, never hinged | 10.00 | |

### Same Overprint on Ryti Type of Finland

| | | | | |
|---|---|---|---|---|
| N22 | A49 | 50p dk yel grn | .80 | 2.25 |
| N23 | A49 | 1.75m slate bl | .80 | 2.25 |
| N24 | A49 | 2m red org | .80 | 2.25 |
| N25 | A49 | 2.75m brn org | .95 | 2.25 |
| N26 | A49 | 3.50m brt ultra | .95 | 2.25 |
| N27 | A49 | 5m brn vio | .95 | 2.25 |
| | | Nos. N22-N27 (6) | 5.25 | 13.50 |
| | | Set, never hinged | 10.00 | |

The overprint translates, "East Karelia Military Administration."

---

## OCCUPATION SEMI-POSTAL STAMP

Arms of East Karelia — SP1

### 1943   Unwmk.   Engr.   Perf. 14

| | | | | |
|---|---|---|---|---|
| NB1 | SP1 | 3.50m + 1.50m dk ol | .90 | 2.50 |
| | | Never hinged | 2.50 | |

This surtax aided war victims in East Karelia.

---

# KATANGA

kə-'täŋ-gə

LOCATION — Central Africa
GOVT. — Republic
CAPITAL — Elisabethville

Katanga province seceded from the Congo (ex-Belgian) Republic in July, 1960, but established nations did not recognize it as an independent state. The UN declared the secession ended in Sept, 1961. The last troops surrendered Sept. 1963.
During the secession Katanga stamps were tolerated in the international mails, but the government authorizing them was not recognized.

100 Centimes = 1 Franc

> Catalogue values for all unused stamps in this country are for Never Hinged items.

### Belgian Congo Nos. 318-322 Overprinted "KATANGA"
### Perf. 11½

### 1960, Sept. 12   Photo.   Unwmk.

| | | | | |
|---|---|---|---|---|
| 1 | A94 | 50c golden brn, ocher & red brn | | |
| 2 | A94 | 1fr dk bl, pur & red brn | | |
| 3 | A94 | 2fr gray, brt bl & red brn | | |
| | | Nos. 1-3 (3) | .65 | .65 |

### Inscription in French

| | | | | |
|---|---|---|---|---|
| 4 | A95 | 3fr gray & red | 6.50 | 6.50 |

### Inscription in Flemish

| | | | | |
|---|---|---|---|---|
| 5 | A95 | 3fr gray & red | 6.50 | 6.50 |

Inverted overprints exist on No. 1-5. Values: 1-3 $9 each; 4-5 $15 each.
For surcharges see Nos. 50-51.

---

### Animal Type of Belgian Congo, Nos. 306-317, Overprinted "KATANGA"

### 1960, Sept. 19   Granite Paper

| | | | |
|---|---|---|---|
| 6 | A92 | 10c bl & brn | |
| 7 | A93 | 20c red org & slate | |
| 8 | A92 | 40c brn & bl | |
| 9 | A93 | 50c brt ultra, red & sep | |
| 10 | A92 | 1fr brn, grn & blk | |
| 11 | A93 | 1.50fr blk & org yel | |
| 12 | A92 | 2fr crim, blk & brn | |
| 13 | A93 | 3fr blk, gray & lil rose | |
| 14 | A92 | 5fr brn, dk brn & brt grn | |
| 15 | A93 | 6.50fr bl, brn & org yel | |
| 16 | A92 | 8fr org brn, ol bis & lil | |
| 17 | A93 | 10fr multi | |
| | | Nos. 6-17 (12) | 52.50 27.50 |

Inverted overprints exist. Value $17.50 each.

### Flower Type of Belgian Congo, Nos. 263-271, 274-281, Overprinted "KATANGA"
### Flowers in Natural Colors

### 1960, Sept. 22   Granite Paper

| | | | |
|---|---|---|---|
| 18 | A86 | 10c dp plum & ocher | |
| 19 | A86 | 15c red & yel grn | |
| 20 | A86 | 20c grn & gray | |
| 21 | A86 | 25c dk grn & dl org | |
| 22 | A86 | 40c grn & sal | |
| 23 | A86 | 50c dk car & aqua | |
| 24 | A86 | 60c bl grn & pink | |
| 25 | A86 | 75c dp plum & gray | |
| 26 | A86 | 1fr car & yel | |
| 27 | A86 | 2fr ol grn & buff | |
| 28 | A86 | 3fr ol grn & pink | |
| 29 | A86 | 4fr choc & lil | |
| 30 | A86 | 5fr dp plum & lt bl grn | |
| 31 | A86 | 6.50fr dk car & lil | |
| 32 | A86 | 7fr dk grn & fawn | |
| 33 | A86 | 8fr grn & lt yel | |
| 34 | A86 | 10fr dp plum & pale ol | |
| | | Nos. 18-34 (17) | 75.00 27.50 |

Inverted overprints exist. Value $24 each.

### Carving and Mask Type of Belgian Congo, Nos. 241, 246, 254-256, Surcharged or Overprinted

### 1960, Sept. 22   Perf. 12½

| | | | | |
|---|---|---|---|---|
| 35 | A82 | 1.50fr on 1.25fr | 1.75 | .60 |
| 36 | A82 | 3.50fr on 2.50fr | 1.60 | .75 |
| 37 | A82 | 20fr red org & vio brn | 5.75 | 4.00 |
| 38 | A82 | 50fr dp org & blk | 12.50 | 10.00 |
| 39 | A82 | 100fr crim & blk brn | 80.00 | 30.00 |
| | | Nos. 35-39 (5) | 101.60 | 45.35 |

Inverted surcharges and overprints exist. Values: No. 37, $60; No. 38, $70; No. 39, $110.

### Map Type of Congo Democratic Republic, Nos. 356-365, Overprinted "11 / JUILLET / DE / L'ETAT DU KATANGA"

### 1960, Oct. 26   Perf. 11½
### Granite Paper

| | | | | |
|---|---|---|---|---|
| 40 | A93a | 20c brown | .30 | .25 |
| 41 | A93a | 50c rose red | .30 | .25 |
| 42 | A93a | 1fr green | .30 | .25 |
| 43 | A93a | 1.50fr red brn | .30 | .25 |
| 44 | A93a | 2fr rose car | .30 | .25 |
| 45 | A93a | 3.50fr lilac | .30 | .25 |
| 46 | A93a | 5fr brt bl | .30 | .25 |
| 47 | A93a | 6.50fr gray | .30 | .25 |
| 48 | A93a | 10fr orange | .30 | .25 |
| 49 | A93a | 20fr ultra | .40 | .25 |
| | | Nos. 40-49 (10) | 3.10 | 2.50 |

Inverted and double surcharges exist.

### Belgian Congo Nos. 321-322 Surcharged

### 1961, Jan. 16

| | | | | |
|---|---|---|---|---|
| 50 | A95 | 3.50fr on 3fr #321 | 3.50 | 3.50 |
| 51 | A95 | 3.50fr on 3fr #322 | 3.50 | 3.50 |

Inverted surcharges exist. Value $6.50 each.

---

A1

Preparing Meal — A1a

Family Group — A1b

Katangan Wood Carvings.

### 1961, Mar. 1   Perf. 11½
### Granite Paper

| | | | | |
|---|---|---|---|---|
| 52 | A1 | 10c grn & lt grn | .30 | .25 |
| 53 | A1 | 20c purple & lil | .30 | .25 |
| 54 | A1 | 50c blue & lt bl | .30 | .25 |
| 55 | A1 | 1.50fr ol grn & lt ol grn | .30 | .25 |
| 56 | A1 | 2fr red brn & lt brn | .30 | .25 |
| 57 | A1a | 3.50fr dk blue & lt bl | .30 | .25 |
| 58 | A1a | 5fr bl grn & lt bl grn | .30 | .25 |
| 59 | A1a | 6fr org brn & tan | .30 | .25 |
| 60 | A1a | 6.50fr bl vio & gray vio | .30 | .25 |
| 61 | A1a | 8fr claret & pink | .30 | .25 |
| 62 | A1b | 10fr brnsh blk & dull mauve | .30 | .25 |
| 63 | A1b | 20fr dk ol & lt grn | .30 | .25 |
| 64 | A1b | 50fr brn & lt brn | .60 | .35 |
| 65 | A1b | 100fr Prus bl & lt bl | 1.10 | .75 |
| | | Nos. 52-65 (14) | 5.30 | 4.10 |

A2

1fr, 5fr, Abstract vehicle. 2.50fr, 6.50fr, Gear.

### Granite Paper

### 1961, July 8   Perf. 11½

| | | | | |
|---|---|---|---|---|
| 66 | A2 | 50c blk, grn & red | .30 | .25 |
| 67 | A2 | 1fr blk & blue | .30 | .25 |
| 68 | A2 | 2.50fr blk & yellow | .30 | .25 |
| 69 | A2 | 3.50fr blk, brn & scar | .30 | .25 |
| 70 | A2 | 5fr blk & purple | .40 | .35 |
| 71 | A2 | 6.50fr blk & orange | .90 | .60 |
| | | Nos. 66-71 (6) | 2.50 | 1.95 |

Katanga International Fair.
Imperfs exist. Value, set $45.

Air Katanga — A3

Design: 6.50fr, 10fr, Plane on ground.

### 1961, Aug. 1   Perf. 11½
### Granite Paper

| | | | | |
|---|---|---|---|---|
| 72 | A3 | 3.50fr multicolored | | |
| 73 | A3 | 6.50fr multicolored | | |
| 74 | A3 | 8fr multicolored | | |
| 75 | A3 | 10fr multicolored | | |
| | | Nos. 72-75 (4) | 6.00 | 6.00 |

Imperfs exist. Value, set $60.

Katanga Gendarmerie — A4

### 1962, Oct. 1   Perf. 11½
### Granite Paper

| | | | | |
|---|---|---|---|---|
| 76 | A4 | 6fr multicolored | | |
| 77 | A4 | 8fr multicolored | | |
| 78 | A4 | 10fr multicolored | | |
| | | Nos. 76-78 (3) | 4.25 | 4.25 |

Imperfs exist. Value, set $40.

---

## SEMI-POSTAL STAMPS

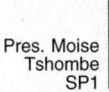

Pres. Moise
Tshombe
SP1

**1961, July 11**    **Perf. 11½**
**Granite Paper**
B1 SP1 6.50fr + 5fr multi
B2 SP1 8fr + 5fr multi
B3 SP1 10fr + 5fr multi
    *Nos. B1-B3 (3)*    7.00 5.00
Nos. B1-B3 exist imperf. Value, set $80.

## POSTAGE DUE STAMPS

Belgian Congo Nos. J8a-J10a, J16-
J19 Handstamped "KATANGA" in
Blue
**1960, Dec. 30**   **Unwmk.**   **Perf. 12½**
J1 D2 10c olive green
J2 D2 20c dark ultra
J3 D2 50c green
     **Perf. 11½**
J4 D3 1fr light blue
J5 D3 2fr vermilion
J6 D3 4fr purple
J7 D3 6fr violet blue
    *Nos. J1-J7 (7)*    30.00 30.00
This overprint also exists on Belgian Congo
Nos. J11a-J12a, J13-J15. Value, set $180.

## KAZAKHSTAN

ˌka-ˌzak-'stan

## (Kazakstan)

LOCATION — Bounded by southern
Russia, Uzbekistan, Kyrgyzstan, and
China.
GOVT. — Independent republic, mem-
ber of the Commonwealth of Inde-
pendent States.
AREA — 1,049,155 sq. mi.
POP. — 16,824,825 (1999 est.)
CAPITAL — Astana

With the breakup of the Soviet Union
on Dec. 26, 1991, Kazakhstan and ten
former Soviet republics established the
Commonwealth of Independent States.

100 Kopecks = 1 Ruble
100 Tijn = 1 Tenge (1993)

Catalogue values for all unused
stamps in this country are for
Never Hinged items.

### Overprinted Stamps
The Philatelic Club of Alma Ata,
Kazakhstan, has announced that various overprinted stamps of the USSR
were not generally available nor were
they in values reflecting actual postal
rates.

A1

**Perf. 12x12½**
**1992, Mar. 23**   **Litho.**   **Unwmk.**
1 A1 50k multicolored    .40 .30
For surcharge, see No. 667.

---

Saiga
Tatarica — A2

**1992, Sept. 11**   **Litho.**   **Perf. 12**
2 A2 75k multicolored    .40 .30

Camels and
Train, by K.
Kasteev
A3

**1992, Sept. 11**   **Litho.**   **Perf. 12½x12**
3 A3 1r multicolored    .40 .30

Day of the
Republic — A3a

**1992, Dec. 16**   **Litho.**   **Perf. 12**
4 A3a 5r multicolored    .50 .50

Space
Ship and
Yurt — A4

Natl.
Flag — A5

**1993, Jan. 24**   **Litho.**   **Perf. 13x12½**
22 A4 1r green    .30 .25
23 A4 3r red    .30 .25
24 A4 10r golden brown    .30 .30
25 A4 25r purple    .70 .70
     **Perf. 14**
26 A5 50r multicolored    1.25 1.25
    *Nos. 22-26 (5)*    2.85 2.75
See Nos. 64, 69, 108-115.

Space
Mail — A6

**1993, Mar. 5**   **Litho.**   **Perf. 13½**
35 A6 100r multicolored    1.50 1.50

New Year 1993 (Year of
the Rooster) — A7

**1993, Mar. 22**   **Litho.**   **Perf. 13x13½**
36 A7 60r yellow, black & red    1.60 1.60
See Nos. 54, 98, 141, 187A, 220, 268.

Cosmonauts' Day — A8

**1993, Apr. 12**    **Perf. 13½x13**
37 A8 90r multicolored    2.00 2.00

---

Pres. Nursultan Nazarbayev — A9

**1993, Aug. 2**   **Litho.**   **Perf. 14**
38 A9 50r multicolored    1.00 1.00

Bukar Zhirav
Kalkaman (1668-
1781),
Poet — A10

**1993, Aug. 18**    **Perf. 13½x13**
39 A10 15r multicolored    .50 .50

Map, Pres.
Nursultan
Nazarbayev
A11

**1993, Sept. 24**   **Litho.**   **Perf. 13**
40 A11 100r multicolored    1.60 1.25

Wildlife — A12

Designs: 5r, Selevinia betpakdalensis. 10r,
Hystrix leucura. 15r, Vormela peregusna. 20r,
Equis hemionus onager. 25r, Ovis orientalis.
30r, Acinonyx jubatus venaticus.

**1993, Nov. 11**    **Perf. 12x12½**
41 A12 5r multicolored    .30 .30
42 A12 10r multicolored    .35 .35
43 A12 15r multicolored    .40 .40
44 A12 20r multicolored    .45 .45
45 A12 25r multicolored    .50 .50
46 A12 30r multicolored    .55 .55
    *Nos. 41-46 (6)*    2.55 2.55

Nos. 1-46 were sold after the currency changeover as stamps denominated in one or both of the new currency units. Nos. 47-50, 54, 64 and 69
were sold as stamps denominated in
tijn, and later as tenge.

1994 Winter
Olympics,
Lillehammer — A13

**1994, Jan. 24**   **Litho.**   **Perf. 13½x13**
47 A13 15te Ice hockey    .30 .30
48 A13 25te Slalom skiing    .45 .45
49 A13 90te Ski jumping    1.25 1.25
50 A13 150te Speed skating    2.00 2.00
    *Nos. 47-50 (4)*    4.00 4.00

1994 Winter Olympics,
Lillehammer — A14

No. 53 With 2 Line Cyrillic Inscription

Designs: 2te, Skiers Vladimir Smirnov,
Kazakhstan; Bjorn Daehlie, Norway. 6.80te,
12te, Smirnov.

---

**1994, Feb. 19**   **Litho.**   **Perf. 13x13½**
51    2te multicolored    .30 .30
52    6.80te multicolored    .70 .70
a.   A14 Pair, #51-52    1.50 1.50
53 A14 12te like No. 52    1.10 1.10
    *Nos. 51-53 (3)*    2.10 2.10
No. 53 has an additional two line Cyrillic
inscription.

### New Year Type of 1993
### Size: 26x38mm
**1994, Mar. 22**    **Perf. 12**
54 A7 30te green, black & blue    .75 .50
New Year 1994 (Year of the Dog).

Space
Program — A15

**1994, Apr. 12**    **Perf. 13½x13**
55 A15 2te multicolored    .50 .50

### Souvenir Sheet

Russian Space Shuttle,
Cosmonaut — A16

**1994, July 12**    **Perf. 13**
56 A16 6.80te Sheet of 4    3.50 3.50

### Space Ship and Yurt Type of 1993
**1994, July 12**   **Litho.**   **Perf. 11½**
64 A4 15ti blue    1.10 .95
69 A4 80ti lake    2.40 1.90
For surcharges see Nos. 70-76, 122.

Nos. 64, 69 Surcharged in
Lake or Purple

**1995-2004**   **Litho.**   **Perf. 11½**
70 A4 1te on 15ti #64    .30 .30
71 A4 2te on 15ti #64    .40 .40
72 A4 3te on 80ti #69 (P)    .40 .40
73 A4 4te on 80ti #69 (P)    .50 .50
74 A4 6te on 80ti #69 (P)    .60 .60
75 A4 8te on 80ti #69 (P)    1.10 1.10
76 A4 12te on 80ti #69 (P)    .90 .90
77 A4 20te on 80ti #69 (P)    1.10 1.10
78 A4 200te on 80ti #69 (P)    10.00 10.00
    *Nos. 70-78 (9)*    15.30 15.30
Issued: 1te, 2te, 12te, 2/2/95. 3te, 4te, 6te,
20te, 2/10/95. 8te, 9/25/95. 200te, 1/29/04.
Inverted surcharges exist.

Music Competition
Festival — A18

Designs: 10te, Snow-covered mountain top.
15te, Aerial view of stadium at night.

**1994, Aug. 1**    **Perf. 13½**
81 A18 10te multicolored    .55 .55
82 A18 15te multicolored    .80 .80
For surcharges see Nos. 119A-119B.

Reptiles — A19

Designs: 1te, Agrionemys horsfieldi. 1.20te, Phrynocephalus mystaceus. 2te, Agkistrodon halys. 3te, Teratoscincus scincus. 5te, Trapelus sanguinolenta. 7te, Ophisaurus apodus. 10te, Varanus griseus.

**1994, Oct. 10**      *Perf. 12½x12*
| | | | | |
|---|---|---|---|---|
| 83 | A19 | 1te multicolored | .30 | .25 |
| 84 | A19 | 1.20te multicolored | .30 | .25 |
| 85 | A19 | 2te multicolored | .30 | .30 |
| 86 | A19 | 3te multicolored | .30 | .30 |
| 87 | A19 | 5te multicolored | .40 | .40 |
| 88 | A19 | 7te multicolored | .50 | .50 |
| | | *Nos. 83-88 (6)* | 2.10 | 2.00 |

**Souvenir Sheet**
| | | | | |
|---|---|---|---|---|
| 89 | A19 | 10te multicolored | 1.25 | 1.25 |

Prehistoric Animals — A20

1te, Entelodon. 1.20te, Saurolophus. 2te, Plesiosaurus. 3te, Sordes pilosus. 5te, Mosasaurus. 7te, Megaloceros giganteum. 10te, Koelodonta antiquitatis.

**1994, Nov. 24**   **Litho.**   *Perf. 12½x12*
| | | | | |
|---|---|---|---|---|
| 90 | A20 | 1te multicolored | .30 | .25 |
| 91 | A20 | 1.20te multicolored | .30 | .25 |
| 92 | A20 | 2te multicolored | .30 | .25 |
| 93 | A20 | 3te multicolored | .30 | .30 |
| 94 | A20 | 5te multicolored | .40 | .40 |
| 95 | A20 | 7te multicolored | .50 | .50 |
| | | *Nos. 90-95 (6)* | 2.10 | 1.95 |

**Souvenir Sheet**
| | | | | |
|---|---|---|---|---|
| 96 | A20 | 10te multicolored | 1.40 | 1.40 |

Day of the Republic — A21

**1994, Oct. 25**      *Perf. 11½*
| | | | | |
|---|---|---|---|---|
| 97 | A21 | 2te multicolored | .60 | .60 |

For surcharge see No. 160B.

**New Year Type of 1993**
**1995, Mar. 22**   **Litho.**   *Perf. 14*
**Size: 27x32mm**
| | | | | |
|---|---|---|---|---|
| 98 | A7 | 10te blue, black & ultra | 1.25 | 1.25 |

New Year 1995 (Year of the Boar).

Abai (Ibraghim) Kynanbaev (1845-1904), Poet — A22

**1995, Mar. 31**
| | | | | |
|---|---|---|---|---|
| 99 | A22 | 4te Portrait | .30 | .30 |
| 100 | A22 | 9te Portrait, diff. | .60 | .60 |

Nos. 99-100 exist with "Kazakstan" spelled "Kazakstah." Value, set $9.

Space Day — A23

Designs: 10te, Cosmonauts Malenchenko, Musabaev and Merbold.

**1995, Apr. 12**   **Litho.**   *Perf. 14*
| | | | | |
|---|---|---|---|---|
| 101 | A23 | 2te multicolored | 3.50 | 3.50 |
| 102 | A23 | 10te multicolored | 13.50 | 13.50 |

Mahatma Gandhi (1869-1948) A24

**1995, Oct. 2**
| | | | | |
|---|---|---|---|---|
| 103 | A24 | 9te multicolored | 2.50 | 2.50 |
| 104 | A24 | 22te multicolored | 6.00 | 6.00 |

End of World War II, 50th Anniv. — A25

Designs: 1te, Hero, battle scene. 3te, Heroine, tank. 5te, Dove, monument.

**1995, May 9**   **Litho.**   *Perf. 14*
| | | | | |
|---|---|---|---|---|
| 105 | A25 | 1te multicolored | 1.10 | 1.10 |
| 106 | A25 | 3te multicolored | 3.25 | 3.25 |
| 107 | A25 | 5te multicolored | 5.50 | 5.50 |
| | | *Nos. 105-107 (3)* | 9.85 | 9.85 |

**Spaceship and Yurt Type of 1993**
**1995, Mar. 24**   **Litho.**   *Perf. 14x14½*
| | | | | |
|---|---|---|---|---|
| 108 | A4 | 20ti orange | .30 | .25 |
| 109 | A4 | 25ti yellow brown | .35 | .25 |
| 110 | A4 | 50ti gray | .40 | .25 |
| 111 | A4 | 1te green | .50 | .25 |
| 112 | A4 | 2te blue | .65 | .25 |
| 113 | A4 | 4te bright pink | .85 | .50 |
| 114 | A4 | 6te gray green | 1.00 | .75 |
| 115 | A4 | 12te lilac | 2.10 | 1.50 |
| | | *Nos. 108-115 (8)* | 6.15 | 4.00 |

Nos. 108-115 are inscribed "1995."

Paintings A26

Designs: 4te, "Springtime," by S. Mambeev. 9te, "Mountains," by Z. Shchardenov. 15te, "Kulash Baiseitova in role of Kyz Zhibek," by G. Ismailova, vert. 28te, "Kokpar," by K. Telzhanov.

**1995, June 23**   **Litho.**   *Perf. 14*
| | | | | |
|---|---|---|---|---|
| 116 | A26 | 4te multicolored | .75 | .75 |
| 117 | A26 | 9te multicolored | 1.25 | 1.25 |
| 118 | A26 | 15te multicolored | 2.50 | 2.50 |
| 119 | A26 | 28te multicolored | 4.50 | 4.50 |
| | | *Nos. 116-119 (4)* | 9.00 | 9.00 |

Nos. 81-82 Ovptd.

**1995, July 25**   **Litho.**   *Perf. 13½*
| | | | | |
|---|---|---|---|---|
| 119A | A18 | 10te multicolored | 1.10 | 1.10 |
| 119B | A18 | 15te multicolored | 1.50 | 1.50 |

Dauletkerey (1820-87), Composer — A27

**1995, Sept. 1**   **Litho.**   *Perf. 14*
| | | | | |
|---|---|---|---|---|
| 120 | A27 | 2te yellow & multi | .50 | .50 |
| 121 | A27 | 28te lake & multi | 6.00 | 6.00 |

UN, 50th Anniv. — A28

**1995, Nov. 24**   **Litho.**   *Perf. 14*
| | | | | |
|---|---|---|---|---|
| 123 | A28 | 10te multicolored | 1.25 | 1.25 |
| 124 | A28 | 36te gold & lt blue | 4.75 | 4.75 |

Resurrection Cathedral A29      Circus A29a

Buildings in Alma-Ata: 2te, Culture Palace. 3te, Opera and Ballet House. 6te, Kazakh Science Academy. 48te, Dramatics Theatre.

*Perf. 14, 13x12 (#126, 129)*
**1995-96**      **Litho.**
| | | | | |
|---|---|---|---|---|
| 125 | A29 | 1te green | .50 | .40 |
| 126 | A29a | 1te green | .25 | .25 |
| 127 | A29 | 2te blue | .75 | .65 |
| 128 | A29 | 3te red | .90 | .80 |
| 129 | A29a | 6te olive | .60 | .60 |
| 130 | A29 | 48te brown | 8.00 | 7.50 |
| | | *Nos. 125-130 (6)* | 11.00 | 10.20 |

Issued: Nos. 125, 127-128, 130, 10/25/95; Nos. 126, 129, 7/5/96.

Raptors — A30

1te, Haliaeetus albicilla. 3te, Pandion haliaetus. 5te, Gypaetus barbatus. 6te, Gyps himalayensis. 30te, Falco cherrug. 50te, Aquila chrysaetus.

**1995, Dec. 20**   **Litho.**   *Perf. 14*
| | | | | |
|---|---|---|---|---|
| 131 | A30 | 1te multicolored | .30 | .25 |
| 132 | A30 | 3te multicolored | .30 | .30 |
| 133 | A30 | 5te multicolored | .50 | .50 |
| 134 | A30 | 6te multicolored | .60 | .60 |
| 135 | A30 | 30te multicolored | 2.00 | 2.00 |
| 136 | A30 | 50te multicolored | 3.50 | 3.50 |
| | | *Nos. 131-136 (6)* | 7.20 | 7.15 |

**New Year Type of 1993**
**Size: 27x32mm**
**1996, Mar. 21**      *Perf. 14*
| | | | | |
|---|---|---|---|---|
| 141 | A7 | 25te lil, blk & red | 2.25 | 2.25 |

New Year 1996 (Year of the Rat).

Space Day — A32

6te, Earth. 15te, Cosmonaut. 20te, Space station Mir.

**1996, Apr. 12**
| | | | | |
|---|---|---|---|---|
| 142 | A32 | 6te multicolored | 1.75 | 1.75 |
| 143 | A32 | 15te multicolored | 2.75 | 2.75 |
| 144 | A32 | 20te multicolored | 4.50 | 4.50 |
| | | *Nos. 142-144 (3)* | 9.00 | 9.00 |

**Souvenir Sheet**

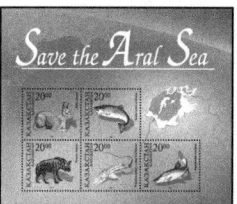

Save the Aral Sea A33

Designs: a, Felis caracal. b, Salmo trutta aralensis. c, Hyaena hyaena. d, Pseudoscaphirhynchus kaufmanni. e, Aspiolucius esocinus.

**1996, Apr. 20**   **Litho.**   *Perf. 14*
| | | | | |
|---|---|---|---|---|
| 145 | A33 | 20te Sheet of 5, #a.-e. | 4.25 | 4.25 |

See Kyrgyzstan No. 107, Tadjikistan No. 91, Turkmenistan No. 52, Uzbekistan No. 113.

1996 Summer Olympic Games, Atlanta — A34

**1996, June 19**   **Litho.**   *Perf. 14*
| | | | | |
|---|---|---|---|---|
| 146 | A34 | 4te Cycling | .60 | .60 |
| 147 | A34 | 6te Wrestling | 1.50 | 1.50 |
| 148 | A34 | 30te Boxing | 5.75 | 5.75 |
| | | *Nos. 146-148 (3)* | 7.85 | 7.85 |

**Souvenir Sheet**
| | | | | |
|---|---|---|---|---|
| 149 | A34 | 50te Hurdles | 4.00 | 4.00 |

Issued: Nos. 146-148, 6/19/96; No. 149, 7/19/96.

Architectural Sites — A35

1te, Tomb, 8-9th cent. 3te, Mausoleum, 11-12th cent. 6te, Mausoleum, 13th cent. 30te, Hadji Ahmet Yassauy's Mausoleum, 14th cent.

**1996, Sept. 27**   **Litho.**   *Perf. 14*
| | | | | |
|---|---|---|---|---|
| 150 | A35 | 1te multicolored | .50 | .50 |
| 151 | A35 | 3te multicolored | 1.50 | 1.50 |
| 152 | A35 | 6te multicolored | 3.00 | 3.00 |
| | | *Nos. 150-152 (3)* | 5.00 | 5.00 |

**Souvenir Sheet**
| | | | | |
|---|---|---|---|---|
| 153 | A35 | 30te multicolored | 2.75 | 2.75 |

World Post Day — A37

**1996, Oct. 9**   **Litho.**   *Perf. 14*
| | | | | |
|---|---|---|---|---|
| 156 | A37 | 9te shown | .85 | .85 |
| 157 | A37 | 40te UPU emblem | 2.75 | 2.75 |

Zhambyl Zhabayev (1846-1945), Folksinger — A38

**1996, Aug. 21**
| | | | | |
|---|---|---|---|---|
| 158 | A38 | 12te multicolored | 1.40 | 1.40 |

Space Station Mir — A39

**1996, Oct. 2**
| | | | | |
|---|---|---|---|---|
| 159 | | 46te multicolored | 3.00 | 2.75 |
| 160 | | 46te T. Aubakirov | 3.00 | 2.75 |
| a. | | A39 Pair, #159-160 | 6.00 | 6.00 |

T. Aubakirov, 1st Kazak cosmonaut.

No. 97 Surcharged

**1997, Oct. 25**   **Litho.**   *Perf. 11½*
| | | | | |
|---|---|---|---|---|
| 160B | A21 | 21te on 2te multi | 1.25 | 1.25 |

Surcharge adds numeral 1 to existing value to appear as 21, obliterates original date and adds new date.

Butterflies — A40

4te, Saturnia schenki. 6te, Parnassius patricius. 12te, Parnassius ariadne. 46te, Colias draconis.

**1996, Nov. 21**   **Litho.**   *Perf. 14*
| | | | | |
|---|---|---|---|---|
| 161 | A40 | 4te multicolored | .30 | .25 |
| 162 | A40 | 6te multicolored | .35 | .30 |
| 163 | A40 | 12te multicolored | .50 | .45 |
| 164 | A40 | 46te multicolored | 1.75 | 1.50 |
| a. | | Sheet of 10, 2 ea. #161-162, 3 ea. #163-164 | 9.00 | 9.00 |
| | | *Nos. 161-164 (4)* | 2.90 | 2.50 |

Hunting
Dogs — A41

**1996, Nov. 29**
165 A41   5te multicolored            .55   .55

**Souvenir Sheet**
166 A41 100te like #165              4.00  4.00
No. 166 is a continuous design.

A42

Traditional Costumes, Furnishings: a, 10te,
Woman outside tent. b, 16te, Man outside
tent. c, 45te, Interior view of furnishings.

**1996, Dec. 5**
167 A42  Strip of 3, #a.-c.          6.00  6.00
Nos. 167a-167b have continuous design.

A43

Archives, Bicent.: 4te, Quill pen, candle,
documents. 68te, Scroll, papers, book.

**1996, Dec. 24**
168 A43   4te brown                   .35   .35
169 A43  68te purple                 2.40  2.40

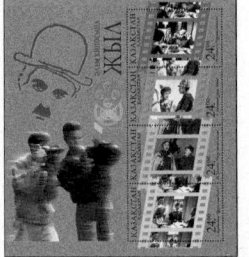

Motion Pictures, Cent. — A44

Film scenes: a, Man in hat holding up fingers. b, Horse, woman, man. c, Two men, from
"His Time Arrives." d, Woman holding paper,
boy holding hat.

**1996, Dec. 25   Litho.       Perf. 14**
170 A44 24te Sheet of 4, #a.-
         d.                          9.50  9.50

Vormela
Peregusna
A45

**1997, Feb. 12   Litho.       Perf. 14**
171 A45   6te shown                   .65   .65
172 A45  10te Adult                   .75   .75
173 A45  32te Two young              2.00  2.00
174 A45  46te Adult, tail up         2.50  2.50
  a.    Vert. strip of 4, #171-174, with
        horiz. gutters              10.00 10.00
  b.    Souv. sheet of 8, 2 ea. #171-
        174                         12.00 12.00
        Nos. 171-174 (4)             5.90  5.90

World Wildlife Fund.
Nos. 171-174 each printed in sheets of 10.
No. 174b has no gutters between stamps.

Zodiac
Constellations — A47

---

**1997, Mar. 26   Litho.       Perf. 14**
176 A47   1te Aries                   .30   .25
177 A47   2te Taurus                  .30   .25
178 A47   3te Gemini                  .30   .25
179 A47   4te Cancer                  .30   .25
180 A47   5te Leo                     .30   .25
181 A47   6te Virgo                   .30   .25
182 A47   7te Libra                   .30   .25
183 A47   8te Scorpio                 .30   .25
184 A47   9te Sagittarius             .30   .30
185 A47  10te Capricorn               .30   .35
186 A47  12te Aquarius                .40   .45
187 A47  20te Pisces                  .60   .70
  b.    Sheet of 12, #176-187        5.50  5.50

**New Year Type of 1993 With
Kazakhstan Inscribed in Both
Cyrillic & Roman Letters**

**1997, Mar. 22   Litho.       Perf. 14**
187A   A7  40te multicolored         1.75  1.75
New Year 1997 (Year of the Ox).

A48

Cosmonauts' Day: a, Earth, Sputnik. b,
Space vehicle, Saturn. c, Space shuttle, space
station.

**1997, Apr. 12**
188 A48  10te Strip of 3, #a.-c.     3.25  3.25
No. 188 has continuous design.

A49

**1997, Apr. 23**
189 A49  15te org yel & grn           .50   .50
190 A49  60te org yel & grn          2.10  2.10

UNESCO World Book Day.

Mukhtar
Auezov (1897-
1961),
Writer — A50

**1997, May**
191 A50  25te House                  1.00  1.00
192 A50  40te Auezov at his desk     1.50  1.50

Orders and
Medals — A51

Various medals.

**1997, June 30   Litho.       Perf. 14**
193 A51  15te grn & yel ribbon        .50   .50
194 A51  15te grn, red & pink rib-
         bon                          .50   .50
195 A51  20te grn bl & multi          .75   .75
196 A51  30te grn yel & multi        1.00  1.00
        Nos. 193-196 (4)             2.75  2.75

Tulips — A52

15te, Tulipa regelii. No. 198, Tulipa greigii.
No. 199, Tulipa alberti.

**1997, Aug. 7   Litho.       Perf. 13½**
197 A52  15te multicolored            .50   .50
198 A52  35te multicolored           1.40  1.40
199 A52  35te multicolored           1.40  1.40
        Nos. 197-199 (3)             3.30  3.30

---

Paintings
A53

Designs: No. 200, Roping of a Wild Horse,
by Moldakhmet S. Kenbaev. No. 201, Shepherd, by Sh. T. Sariev, vert. No. 202, Fantastic
Still Life, by Sergei I. Kalmykov, vert.

**1997, Sept. 10   Litho.       Perf. 14**
200 A53  25te multicolored           1.10  1.10
201 A53  25te multicolored           1.10  1.10
202 A53  25te multicolored           1.10  1.10
        Nos. 200-202 (3)             3.30  3.30

Agate                    Azurite
A54                      A55

**1997, Oct. 15   Litho.       Perf. 14**
203 A54  15te shown                   .70   .70
204 A54  15te Chalcedony              .70   .70
205 A54  20te shown                  1.10  1.10
206 A55  20te Malachite              1.10  1.10
  a.    Souvenir sheet, #203-206     3.75  3.75
        Nos. 203-206 (4)             3.60  3.60

Desert
Fauna — A56

Designs: No. 207, Gylippus rickmersi. No.
208, Anemelobathus rickmersi. No. 209,
Latrodectus pallidus. No. 210, Oculicosa
supermirabilis.

**1997, Nov. 26   Litho.       Perf. 14**
207 A56  30te multicolored           1.15  1.15
208 A56  30te multicolored           1.15  1.15
209 A56  30te multicolored           1.15  1.15
210 A56  30te multicolored           1.15  1.15
        Nos. 207-210 (4)             4.60  4.60

**Souvenir Sheet**

Nature
Park
A57

Designs: a, Mountain goat. b, Trees on side
of mountain. c, Rock formations, wildflowers.

**1997, Dec. 22**
211 A57  30te Sheet of 3, #a.-c.     3.00  3.00
See No. 257A.

A58

Sports — A59

Designs: No. 212, Woman, man riding horses. No. 213, Wrestling match. No. 214,
Group of men on galloping horses.

---

**1997, Dec. 30   Litho.       Perf. 14**
212 A58  20te multicolored           1.75  1.75
213 A58  20te multicolored           1.75  1.75
214 A58  20te multicolored           1.75  1.75
215 A59  20te multicolored           1.75  1.75
        Nos. 212-215 (4)             7.00  7.00

1998 Winter Olympic
Games, Nagano — A60

**1998, Mar. 13   Litho.       Perf. 14**
216 A60  15te Figure skating          .70   .50
217 A60  30te Biathlon               1.25  1.00

Children's
Paintings — A61

**1998, Mar. 20**
218 A61  15te shown                   .55   .55
219 A61  15te Outdoor scene,
         horiz.                       .55   .55

**New Year Type of 1993
with "Kazakhstan" inscribed in both
Cyrillis and Roman letters**

**1998, Mar. 22   Litho.       Perf. 14**
220 A7  30te yel, blk & brn          1.75  1.75
New Year 1998 (Year of the Tiger).

Kurmangazy Sagyrbaev
(1818-89),
Composer — A62

No. 222, Ahmet Baitursynov (1873-1937),
poet.

**1998       Litho.       Perf. 14**
221 A62  30te multicolored           1.00  1.00
222 A62  30te multicolored           1.00  1.00
Issued: No. 221, 4/10/98. No. 222, 4/28/98.

Ancient Gold
Folk Art — A63

15te, Ram's heads. 30te, Jeweled pendants, vert. 40te, Animal filigree diadem
fragment.

**1998, Apr. 30**
223 A63  15te multicolored            .55   .55
224 A63  30te multicolored            .95   .95
225 A63  40te multicolored           2.00  2.00
        Nos. 223-225 (3)             3.50  3.50

Cosmonaut's
Day — A64

No. 226, Apollo 8, moon, sun. No.227,
Apollo 8, moon, Earth. 50te, Vostok 6, Earth.

**1998, May 4**
226 A64  30te multi, vert.           1.10  1.10
227 A64  30te multi, vert.           1.10  1.10
  a.    Pair, #226-227, with tabs    4.25  4.25
228 A64  50te multi                  1.75  1.75
        Nos. 226-228 (3)             3.95  3.95

Astana, New Capital
City — A64a

A65

Buildings: 10te, Mosque. 15te, Govt., vert. 20te, Parliament, vert. 25te, Office. 100te, Presidential office.

| 1998 | | Litho. | Perf. 13½ | |
|---|---|---|---|---|
| 229 | A64a | 10te brown | .45 | .45 |
| 230 | A64a | 15te dark blue | .65 | .65 |
| 231 | A64a | 15te blue | .65 | .65 |
| 232 | A64a | 20te green blue | .80 | .80 |
| 232A | A64a | 25te purple | 1.50 | 1.50 |
| | | Nos. 229-232A (5) | 4.05 | 4.05 |

**Souvenir Sheet**

| 233 | A65 | 100te multicolored | 3.25 | 3.25 |
|---|---|---|---|---|

Issued: Nos. 229-232, 233, 6/10; 25te, 12/98. No. 230 is inscribed "AKMOLA" in Cyrillic. No. 231 is inscribed "ACTANA."

Souvenir Sheet

Climbing Mt. Everest — A67

| 1998, July 29 | | Litho. | Perf. 14 | |
|---|---|---|---|---|
| 239 | A67 | 100te multicolored | 4.25 | 4.25 |

Fauna — A68

Birds: No. 240, Ciconia nigra. No. 241, Phoenicopterus roseus. No. 242, Grus leucogeranus.
Wild cats: No. 243, Lynx lynx isabellinus. No. 244, Felis margarita. No. 245, Uncia uncia.

| 1998 | | | | |
|---|---|---|---|---|
| 240 | A68 | 15te multicolored | .70 | .70 |
| 241 | A68 | 30te multicolored | 1.25 | 1.25 |
| 242 | A68 | 50te multicolored | 2.10 | 2.10 |
| | | Nos. 240-242 (3) | 4.05 | 4.05 |
| 243 | A68 | 15te multicolored | .70 | .70 |
| 244 | A68 | 30te multicolored | 1.25 | 1.25 |
| 245 | A68 | 50te multicolored | 2.10 | 2.10 |
| | | Nos. 243-245 (3) | 4.05 | 4.05 |

Issued: Nos. 240-242, 7/31; Nos. 243-245, 8/8.

Souvenir Sheet

Admission of Kazakhstan to UPU — A69

| 1998, Oct. 9 | | Litho. | Perf. 14 | |
|---|---|---|---|---|
| 246 | A69 | 50te multicolored | 4.00 | 4.00 |

Natl. Arms
A70

World Stamp Day
A71

Republic, 5th Anniv. — A72

| 1998 | | Litho. | Perf. 13½ | |
|---|---|---|---|---|
| | | Inscribed "1998" | | |
| 247 | A70 | 1te green | .30 | .25 |
| a. | | Inscribed "1999" | .30 | .25 |
| 248 | A70 | 2te blue | .30 | .25 |
| a. | | Inscribed "1999" | .30 | .25 |
| 249 | A70 | 3te red | .30 | .25 |
| 250 | A70 | 4te bright pink | .30 | .30 |
| 251 | A70 | 5te orange yellow | .30 | .30 |
| a. | | Inscribed "1999" | .30 | .30 |
| 252 | A70 | 8te orange | .50 | .50 |
| 253 | A71 | 30te olive | 1.40 | 1.40 |
| 254 | A72 | 40te orange | 1.60 | 1.60 |
| | | Nos. 247-254 (8) | 5.00 | 4.85 |

Issued; 1te-5te, 6/29; 8te-40te, 11/12. "1999" varieties issued: 1te, 1/28/00; 2te, 9/7/99; 5te, 11/12/99.
See Nos. 296, 299. Compare with Nos. 444-455.

Natl. Epic — A73

Horseman: 20te, Holding sword. 30te, Shooting bow and arrow. 40te, Charging with spear.

| 1998, Dec. | | | Perf. 14 | |
|---|---|---|---|---|
| 255 | A73 | 20te multicolored | 1.50 | 1.50 |
| 256 | A73 | 30te multicolored | 2.25 | 2.25 |
| 257 | A73 | 40te multicolored | 2.75 | 2.75 |
| | | Nos. 255-257 (3) | 6.50 | 6.50 |

**Souvenir Sheet**
**Nature Park Type of 1997**

Designs: a, Island in middle of lake, mountains. b, Lake, mountain peaks.

| 1998, Dec. | | | Perf. 14 | |
|---|---|---|---|---|
| 257A | A57 | 30te Sheet of 2, #a.-b. | 3.00 | 3.00 |

1999
Census
A74

Space Communi-cations
A77

K. Satpayev (1899-1964)
A75          A76

| 1999 | | Litho. | Perf. 13½ | |
|---|---|---|---|---|
| 258 | A74 | 1te green | .30 | .25 |
| 259 | A75 | 15te rose lake | .50 | .50 |
| 260 | A76 | 20te brown | .65 | .65 |
| 261 | A77 | 30te olive | 1.25 | 1.25 |
| | | Nos. 258-261 (4) | 2.70 | 2.65 |

Issued: 1te, 2/5/99; 30te, 3/19/99.
See Nos. 270, 272.

Trains — A78

Map showing Orenburg-Tashkent Rail Line, 1890-1906, and: 40te, Steam train. 50te, Diesel locomotive. 60te, Bullet train. 80te, Interurban train.

| 1999 | | | Perf. 14 | |
|---|---|---|---|---|
| 262 | A78 | 40te yel & multi | 1.50 | 1.50 |
| 263 | A78 | 50te pink & multi | 2.10 | 2.10 |
| 264 | A78 | 60te grn & multi | 2.50 | 2.50 |
| 265 | A78 | 80te blue & multi | 3.00 | 3.00 |
| | | Nos. 262-265 (4) | 9.10 | 9.10 |

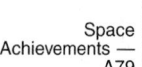

Space Achievements — A79

50te, Soviet spacecraft, vert. 90te, Apollo 11 mission.

| 1999 | | | | |
|---|---|---|---|---|
| 266 | A79 | 50te multicolored | 7.00 | 7.00 |
| 267 | A79 | 90te multicolored | 14.00 | 14.00 |

Cosmonaut Day (No. 266), first manned lunar landing, 30th anniv. (No. 267).

**New Year Type of 1993
with "Kazakhstan" inscribed in both
Cyrillis and Roman letters**

| 1999, Mar. 19 | | Litho. | Perf. 14 | |
|---|---|---|---|---|
| 268 | A7 | 40te multicolored | 3.50 | 3.50 |

New Year 1999 (Year of the Rabbit).

**Space Communications Type of
1999 and**

A79a          A79b

| 1999 | | Litho. | Perf. 13½ | |
|---|---|---|---|---|
| 270 | A77 | 3te red | .30 | .30 |
| 271 | A79a | 4te bright pink | .30 | .30 |
| 272 | A77 | 9te bright green | .50 | .50 |
| 273 | A79b | 10te purple | .75 | .75 |
| 274 | A79a | 30te olive green | 1.10 | 1.10 |
| | | Nos. 270-274 (5) | 2.95 | 2.95 |

No. 273 is for the UPU, 125th Anniv.

Flowers — A80

Designs: 20te, Pseudoeremostachys severzowii. 30te, Rhaphidophyton regelii. 90te, Niedzwedkia semiretscenskia.

| 1999, June 28 | | Litho. | Perf. 14¼x14 | |
|---|---|---|---|---|
| 276 | A80 | 20te multicolored | 1.25 | 1.25 |
| 277 | A80 | 30te multicolored | 1.50 | 1.50 |
| 278 | A80 | 90te multicolored | 4.00 | 4.00 |
| | | Nos. 276-278 (3) | 6.75 | 6.75 |

Movies
A81

No. 279: a, 15te, Film scene from 1929. b, 20te, Scenes from 1988, 1997, M. Berkovich. c, 30te, Scenes from 1935, 1938, 1957. d, 35te, Scenes from 1989, 1994, 1997. e, 50te, Alfred Hitchcock. f, 60te, Sergei Eisenstein.

| 1999 | | Litho. | Perf. 14 | |
|---|---|---|---|---|
| 279 | A81 | Sheet of 10, #e.-f., 2 each #a.-d. | 9.00 | 9.00 |

Foxes — A82

Designs: 20te, Vulpes vulpes. 30te, Cuon alpinus. 90te, Vulpes corsac.

| 1999 | | Litho. | Perf. 14x 14¼ | |
|---|---|---|---|---|
| 280 | A82 | 20te multicolored | 1.50 | 1.10 |
| 281 | A82 | 30te multicolored | 2.25 | 1.90 |
| 282 | A82 | 90te multicolored | 6.00 | 5.25 |
| | | Nos. 280-282 (3) | 9.75 | 8.25 |

Souvenir Sheet

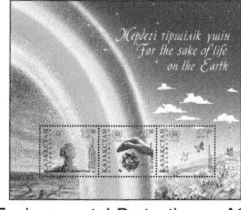

Environmental Protection — A83

Designs: a, 15te, Cessation of nuclear tests at Semipalatinsk, 10th anniv. b, 45te, Save the ozone layer. c, 60te, Save nature.

| 1999 | | Litho. | Perf. 14x13¾ | |
|---|---|---|---|---|
| 283 | A83 | Sheet of 3, #a.-c. | 4.00 | 4.00 |

Kazakhstan Hockey Team — A84

| 1999 | | Litho. | Perf. 14 | |
|---|---|---|---|---|
| 284 | A84 | 20te Face-off | 1.40 | 1.40 |
| 285 | A84 | 30te Team photo | 1.75 | 1.75 |

10th Gusman Kosanov Memorial Track & Field Meet — A85

| 1999 | | | | |
|---|---|---|---|---|
| 286 | A85 | 40te multi | 2.00 | 2.00 |

Cosmonauts A86

40te, Talgat Musabayev. 50te, Toktar Aubakirov, vert.

| 1999 | | | Perf. 14 | |
|---|---|---|---|---|
| 287 | A86 | 40te multicolored | 1.60 | 1.60 |
| 288 | A86 | 50te multicolored | 1.90 | 1.90 |

Souvenir Sheet

UPU, 125th Anniv. A87

| 1999, Dec. 20 | | Litho. | Perf. 14x13¾ | |
|---|---|---|---|---|
| 289 | A87 | 20te multi | 1.75 | 1.75 |

**Arms Type of 1998 and**

Spireanthus Schrenhianus
A88

Echo Satellite
A89

Oil Rig
A90

Mukhammed Khaidar Dulati (1499-1551), Historian
A91

Sabit Mukanov (1900-73), Writer — A92

| 2000 | | Litho. | Perf. 13½ | |
|---|---|---|---|---|
| 290 | A88 | 1te green | .30 | .25 |
| 291 | A88 | 2te bright blue | .30 | .25 |
| 291A | A89 | 5te orange yellow | .30 | .25 |
| 292 | A90 | 7te red | .40 | .40 |
| 293 | A91 | 8te dark blue | .30 | .30 |
| 294 | A92 | 10te olive green | .40 | .40 |
| 295 | A89 | 15te violet blue | .50 | .50 |
| 296 | A70 | 20te orange | .75 | .75 |
| 297 | A89 | 20te indigo | .80 | .80 |
| 299 | A70 | 50te blue | 1.90 | 1.90 |
| 300 | A88 | 50te blue | 1.75 | 1.60 |

*Nos. 290-300 (11)* 7.70 7.40

Issued: 7te, 20te, 50te, 1/18/00; 1te, 2te, No. 300, 11/24; 5te, 15te, No. 297, 9/28; 8te, 8/25; 10te, 6/30. 20te and 50te are dated 1999.

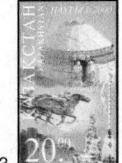

Navruz Bayram — A93

**2000, Mar. 21** Litho. *Imperf.*
301 A93 20te multi 4.00 4.00

Millennium — A94

**2000, Mar. 24** Litho. *Perf. 13½*
302 A94 30te org & blue green 2.50 2.50

Victory in World War II, 55th Anniv. — A95

**2000, May 8** Litho. *Perf. 13½*
303 A95 3te brown & red .30 .30

Souvenir Sheet

Millennium — A96

**2000, June 1** *Perf. 14x13¾*
304 A96 70te multi 3.00 3.00

Containers — A97

No. 305: a, 15te, Leather vessel for koumiss, Kazakhstan. b, 50te, Teapot, China.

**2000, June 28** *Perf. 12½x12*
305 A97 Horiz. pair, #a-b 3.00 3.00
See China (PRC) Nos. 3042-3043.

2000 Summer Olympics, Sydney — A98

Designs: 35te, Rowing. No. 307, 40te, Taekwondo. No. 308, 40te, Men's gymnastics. 50te, Triathlon.

**2000, Sept. 15** *Perf. 12*
306-309 A98 Set of 4 7.50 7.50

Souvenir Sheet

Turkistan, 1500th Anniv. — A99

Mausoleums of: a, 50te, Arystan Bab, 12th-20th cents. b, 50te, Karashash Ana, 12th-18th cents. c, 70te, Hadji Ahmet Yassauy, 14th cent.

**2000, Oct. 19** *Perf. 13½*
310 A99 Sheet of 3, #a-c 9.00 9.00
Complete booklet, #310 16.00

Bourzhan Momush-Uly (1910-82), Hero of the Soviet Union — A100

**2000, Dec. 22** *Perf. 13½*
311 A100 4te black & brown .60 .60

**No. B1 Surcharged in Dark Blue**

**Method and Perf. as Before**
**2001, Jan. 26**
**Block of 3, #a-c, + Label**
312 SP1 10te on 1te+30ti multi 1.00 1.00
No. 312 exists with double surcharge and inverted surcharge.

**New Year Type of 1993 with "Kazakhstan" Inscribed in Both Cyrillic and Roman Letters**
**2001, Mar. 2** Litho. *Perf. 13¾x14*
313 A7 40te org, blk & blue 1.60 1.60
Dated 2000. New Year 2000 (Year of the Snail).

Cosmonaut's Day — A101

Designs: 40te, Dogs Belka and Strelka. 70te, Rocket launch, vert.

**2001, Mar. 6** *Perf. 14*
314-315 A101 Set of 2 5.00 5.00
Dated 2000. Spaceflight of Belka and Strelka, 40th anniv., Baikonur Cosmodrome, 45th anniv.

**New Year Type of 1993 with "Kazakhstan" Inscribed in Both Cyrillic and Roman Letters**
**2001, Mar. 21** Litho. *Perf. 13¾x14*
316 A7 40te grn, blk & brn 1.40 1.40
New Year 2001 (Year of the Snake).

Souvenir Sheet

Ministry of Communications, 10th Anniv. — A102

**2001, Apr. 4** *Perf. 11½*
317 A102 100te multi 14.00 14.00

Cosmonaut's Day — A103

Designs: 45te, Soyuz 11 and Salyut. 60te, Yuri Gagarin, Earth.

**2001, Apr. 12** *Perf. 14*
318-319 A103 Set of 2 4.00 4.00

Aquilegia Karatavica A104

School, Almaty A105

Phodopus Roborovskii — A106

**Perf. 13½, 14 (#321, 326)**
| 2001 | | | Litho. | |
|---|---|---|---|---|
| 320 | A104 | 3te olive green | .30 | .30 |
| 321 | A105 | 7te red violet | .30 | .30 |
| 322 | A106 | 8te orange | .35 | .35 |
| 323 | A104 | 10te yellow green | .40 | .40 |
| 324 | A105 | 15te dark blue | .55 | .55 |
| 325 | A104 | 20te deep blue | .65 | .65 |
| 326 | A105 | 30te greenish gray | .85 | .85 |
| 327 | A106 | 50te brown | 1.40 | 1.40 |

*Nos. 320-327 (8)* 4.80 4.80
See Nos. 399, 403-405.
Issued: 7te, 30te, 10/19/01.

Kazakh State Khans — A107

Designs: 50te, Abulkhair Khan (1693-1748). 60te, Abylai Khan (1711-81).

**2001, May 24** Litho. *Perf. 13¾x14*
328-329 A107 Set of 2 3.75 3.75
Dated 2000.

Owls — A108

Designs: 30te, Bubo bubo. 40te, Asio otus. 50te, Surnia ulula.

**2001, June 7** *Perf. 14*
330-332 A108 Set of 3 7.75 7.75
Dated 2000.

Communications Program 2030 — A109

**2001, June 21** *Perf. 14x13¾*
333 A109 40te multi 1.40 1.40
Dated 2000.

Souvenir Sheet

Lake Markakol A110

No. 334: a, Cervus elaphus. b, Ursus arctos. c, Brachymystax lenok.

**2001, July 5** *Perf. 13¾x14*
334 A110 30te Sheet of 3, #a-c 8.50 8.50

Souvenir Sheet

Flora & Fauna A111

No. 335: a, 9te, Marmota bobac. b, 12te, Otis tarda. c, 25te, Larus relictus. d, 60te, Felis libyca. e, 90te, Nymphaea alba. f, 100te, Pelecanus crispus.

**2001, July 19** *Perf. 14x14¼*
335 A111 Sheet of 6, #a-f 6.00 6.00

Souvenir Sheet

Kazakh Railways, 10th Anniv. — A112

No. 336: a, 15te, Building. b, 20te, Turkestan-Siberia locomotive. c, 50te, Railroad workers.

**2001, Aug. 4** *Perf. 14x13¾*
336 A112 Sheet of 3, #a-c 22.50 22.50

Medicine — A113

Designs: 1te, WHO emblem, lungs (tuberculosis prevention). 5te, Ribbon, book (AIDS prevention).

**2001, Aug. 9** *Perf. 13½*
337-338 A113 Set of 2 .60 .60

Intl. Year of Mountains (in 2002) — A114

Various mountains: 35te, 60te.

**2001, Sept. 26** *Perf. 14*
339-340 A114 Set of 2 3.50 3.50

Space Achievements — A115

Designs: 50te, Alexei Leonov's walk in space, 1965, vert. 70te, Apollo-Soyuz mission, 1975.

**2001, Oct. 2**
341-342 A115 Set of 2 7.50 7.50
Dated 2000.

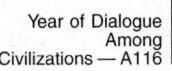

Year of Dialogue Among Civilizations — A116

**2001, Oct. 9** *Perf. 13¾x14*
343 A116 45te multi 1.75 1.75

Worldwide Fund for Nature (WWF) — A117

Various views of Equus hemionus kulan: 9te, 12te, 25te, 50te.

**2001, Nov. 1**  **Perf. 14**
344-347 A117  Set of 4    3.25 3.25

Commonwealth of Independent States, 10th Anniv. — A118

**2001, Dec. 12**  **Litho.**  **Perf. 14**
348 A118 40te multi    1.75 1.75

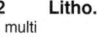

Visit of Pope John Paul II A119

No. 349: a, 20te, Pres. Nazarbayev, Pope. b, 50te, Pope, Pres. Nazarbayev.

**2001, Dec. 14**  **Perf. 11½**
349 A119  Horiz. pair, #a-b    5.50 5.50

A120

Independence, 10th Anniv. — A121

No. 351: a, 9te, Monument of Independence, Almaty. b, 25te, Parliament, Astana. c, 35te, Pres. Nazarbayev.

**2001**  **Perf. 13½**
350 A120 40te multi    1.75 1.75

**Souvenir Sheet**
**Perf. 13¾x14**
351 A121  Sheet of 3, #a-c    5.50 5.50
Issued: 40te, 12/18; No. 351, 12/16.

Native Attire A122

No. 352: a, 25te, Male attire. b, 35te, Female attire.

**2001, Dec. 25**  **Perf. 14x13¾**
352 A122  Horiz. pair, #a-b    2.75 2.75

2002 Winter Olympics, Salt Lake City — A123

Designs: 50te, Women's ice hockey. 150te, Freestyle skiing.

**2002, Feb. 14**  **Perf. 14**
353-354 A123  Set of 2    7.00 7.00
Most often collected with colored Olympic rings margin tab. Value, set $10.

---

**New Year Type of 1993 With "Kazakhstan" Inscribed in Both Cyrillic and Roman Letters**
**2002, Mar. 21**  **Perf. 11½**
355 A7 50te multi    2.00 2.00
New Year 2002 (Year of the Horse).

Horses — A124

Horses: 9te, English. 25te, Kustenai. 60te, Akhalteka.

**2002, Mar. 28**
356-358 A124  Set of 3    4.75 4.75

Pterygostemon Spathulatus A125

Gani Muratbaev (1902-25), Political Leader A126

Salpingotus Pallidus A127

Trade House, Petropavlovsk A128

Monument, Petropavlovsk A129

Gabiden Mustafin (1902-85), Writer A130

**2002**  **Litho.**  **Perf. 13½**
359 A125 1te blue green    .30 .30
360 A125 2te blue    .35 .35
361 A125 3te green    .40 .40
362 A126 3te brown    .30 .25
363 A127 5te rose lilac    .30 .25
364 A128 6te red    .30 .25
365 A128 7te lilac    .30 .25
366 A129 8te orange    .30 .30
367 A125 10te violet    .60 .60
368 A130 10te blue    .30 .30
369 A125 12te pink    .70 .70
370 A127 15te dark blue    .40 .40
371 A125 23te gray blue    .70 .70
372 A125 25te purple    .90 .90
373 A127 35te olive green    1.10 1.10
374 A127 40te bister brown    1.25 1.25
375 A127 50te brown    1.60 1.60
  Nos. 359-375 (17)    10.10 9.90

Petropavlovsk, 250th anniv. (Nos. 364-366, 371). Issued: 1te, 2te, 5/7; Nos. 361, 367, 35te, 4/30; 5te, 15te, 40te, 50te, 4/4; 6te, 7te, 8te, 23te, 7/9; 12te, 25te, 5/14; No. 362, 12/19; No. 368, 12/18.

Cosmonauts Day — A131

Designs: 30te, Cosmonauts Yuri Baturin, Talgat Musabaev and first space tourist Dennis Tito. 70te, Globe, rocket, flags of US, Kazakhstan and Russia.

**2002, Apr. 10**  **Litho.**  **Perf. 11¾**
376-377 A131  Set of 2    3.50 3.50

2002 World Cup Soccer Championships, Japan and Korea — A132

---

Two players, one with: No. 378, 10te, Jersey No. 8. No. 379, 10te, Jersey No. 7.

**2002, May 31**
378-379 A132  Set of 2    1.50 1.50

Transeurasia 2002 Conference — A133

**2002, June 6**  **Perf. 13½**
380 A133 30te multi    1.10 1.10

**Souvenir Sheet**

Flora and Fauna A134

No. 381: a, Leontopodium fedtschenkoanum. b, Mustela erminea. c, Aport Alexander apples.

**2002, June 6**  **Perf. 11¾x11½**
381 A134 30te Sheet of 3, #a-c    3.25 3.25

Art — A135

Designs: 8te, Kazakh Folk Epos, by E. Sidorkin, 1961. 9te, Makhambet, by M. Kisamedinov, 1973. 60te, Batyr, by Sidorkin, 1979.

**2002, July 19**  **Perf. 11¾**
382-384 A135  Set of 3    3.00 3.00

Birds A136

No. 385: a, 10te, Larus ichthyaetus pallas. b, 15te, Anthropoides virgo.

**2002, Aug. 29**  **Perf. 12**
385 A136  Horiz. pair, #a-b    2.00 2.00
See Russia No. 6709.

Marine Life A137

No. 386: a, 20te, Huso huso ponticus. b, 35te, Phoca caspica.

**2002, Sept. 6**
386 A137  Horiz. pair, #a-b    2.25 2.25
See Ukraine No. 483.

**Souvenir Sheet**

Taraz, 2000th Anniv. A138

**2002, Sept. 25**
387 A138 70te multi    2.25 2.25

---

**Souvenir Sheet**

International Year of Mountains — A139

**2002, Oct. 4**  **Perf. 11½x11¾**
388 A139 50te multi    1.60 1.60

Gabit Musrepov (1902-85) — A140

**2002, Dec. 30**  **Litho.**  **Perf. 11½**
389 A140 20te multi    .75 .75

Airplanes A141

Designs: 20te, Ilyushin-86. 40te, Tupolev-144 and map.

**Perf. 11½x11¾**
**2002, Dec. 23**  **Litho.**
390-391 A141  Set of 2    2.40 2.40
First Moscow to Alma Ata flight of Tupolev-144, 25th anniv. (No. 391).

**Type of 1999, Types of 2000-01 Redrawn and**

Monument to Victims of Political Reprisals A142

Selevinia Betpakdalensis A143

| **2003** | | **Litho.** | **Perf. 13½** | |
|---|---|---|---|---|
| 392 | A88 | 1te green | .30 | .25 |
| 393 | A142 | 1te red violet | .30 | .25 |
| 394 | A88 | 2te bright blue | .30 | .25 |
| 394A | A77 | 3te red | .30 | .25 |
| 395 | A143 | 4te brown | .35 | .35 |
| 396 | A143 | 5te bister | .40 | .40 |
| 397 | A143 | 6te gray green | .40 | .40 |
| 398 | A143 | 7te dull green | .40 | .40 |
| 399 | A106 | 8te orange | .30 | .25 |
| 400 | A142 | 8te red brown | .30 | .25 |
| 401 | A77 | 9te dark blue | .35 | .35 |
| 402 | A143 | 10te blue | .30 | .25 |
| 403 | A106 | 15te deep blue | .45 | .45 |
| 404 | A106 | 20te gray blue | .55 | .55 |
| 405 | A106 | 35te dark green | 1.40 | 1.40 |
| 406 | A143 | 63te fawn | 2.25 | 2.25 |
| 407 | A77 | 84te purple | 2.40 | 2.40 |
| 408 | A77 | 100te orange | 2.75 | 2.75 |
| 409 | A143 | 150te claret | 5.00 | 5.00 |
| | | Nos. 392-409 (19) | 18.80 | 18.45 |

Issued: No. 392, 2te, 2/24; Nos. 393, 400, 4/17; 4te, 5te, 6te, 7te, 10te, 63te, 150te, 1/31; No. 399, 15te, 20te, 35te, 3/28; 84te, 100te, 5/30; 3te, 9te, 9/12.

Nos. 392 and 394 are dated "2003" and have smaller Cyrillic inscription of country name, and longer Roman inscription of country name than Nos. 290-291.

Nos. 394A is dated "2003" and has a smaller denomination with thinner zeroes than No. 270.

Nos. 399, 403 and 404 are dated "2003" and have taller Cyrillic inscription of country name than Nos. 322, 324-325.

Domestic and Wild Sheep — A144

Various rams, ewes and lambs: 20te, 40te, 50te.

**2003, Feb. 26**    *Perf. 11½x11¾*
410-412 A144   Set of 3    3.50 3.50

**New Year Type of 1993 With "Kazakhstan" Inscribed in Both Cyrillic and Roman Letters**
**2003, Mar. 21**    *Perf. 11½*
413 A7 40te lt bl, blk & dk bl   1.50 1.50
New Year 2003 (Year of the Ram).

Cosmonaut's Day — A145

Designs: 40te, Pioneer 10 and Jupiter. 70te, Mir Space Station, vert.

**2003, Apr. 12**    *Perf. 11¾*
414-415 A145   Set of 2    3.50 3.50

Intl. Association of Academies of Science, 10th Anniv. — A146

**2003, Apr. 23**   Litho.   *Perf. 11½*
416 A146 50te multi    1.60 1.60

Souvenir Sheet

Ethnic Groups in Kazakhstan — A147

No. 417: a, Kazakhs (woman with red vest). b, Russians (woman with yellow blouse). c, Ukrainians (woman with blue vest).

**2003, Apr. 29**   Litho.   *Perf. 11¾x11½*
417 A147 35te Sheet of 3, #a-c   3.50 3.50

Musical Instruments — A148

Designs: 25te, Dombra. 50te, Kobyz.

**2003, May 26**
418-419 A148   Set of 2    2.25 2.25

Fairy Tales — A149

Designs: 30te, Aldar Kose and Alasha Khan. 40te, Aldar Kose and Karynbaj.

**2003, June 27**    *Perf. 11½*
420-421 A149   Set of 2    2.00 2.00

Art — A150

Designs: 20te, Chess Match, by Arturo Ricci (1854-1919). 35te, Portrait of the Shepherd,

sculpture by H. Nauryzbaev. 45te, Bowls of Koumiss, by Aisha Galimbaeva (1917- ).

**2003, July 7**    *Perf. 11¾*
422-424 A150   Set of 3    3.75 3.75

Famous Men — A151

Designs: No. 425, 60te, Tole Bey (1663-1756). No. 426, 60te, Kazybek Bey (1667-1763). No. 427, 60te, Aiteke Bey (1689-1766).

**2003, Aug. 11**    *Perf. 11¾x11½*
425-427 A151   Set of 3    4.25 4.25

Halyk Bank, 80th Anniv. — A152

**2003, Aug. 15**    *Perf. 11½x11¾*
428 A152 23te multi    .70 .70

International Transit Conference, Almaty — A153

**2003, Aug. 28**
429 A153 40te multi    1.35 1.35

World Post Day — A154

**2003, Oct. 9**    *Perf. 13½*
430 A154 23te pur & blue   .65 .65

Houses of Worship, Almaty — A155

Designs: No. 431, 50te, Cathedral. No. 432, 50te, Mosque.

**2003, Oct. 10**    *Perf. 11¾x11½*
431-432 A155   Set of 2    2.50 2.50

Tenge Currency, 10th Anniv. — A156

**2003, Nov. 15**    *Perf. 13½*
433 A156 25te blue & yel org   .65 .65

Paintings A157

No. 434: a, Baxt, by S. Ayitbaev, 1966. b, Tong. Onalik, by R. Ahmedov, 1962.

**2003, Nov. 25**    *Perf. 12*
434 A157 100te Horiz. pair, #a-b   4.75 4.75
See Uzbekistan No. 385.

Populus Diversifolia — A158

**2003, Dec. 10**    *Perf. 11½*
435 A158 100te multi    2.10 2.10

Petroglyphs, Tamgaly A159

Designs: 25te, Cows. 30te, Man as sun on bull, vert.

*Perf. 11½x11¾, 11¾x11½*
**2003, Dec. 19**
436-437 A159   Set of 2    2.10 2.10

Abylkhan Kasteev (1904-73), Artist — A160

**2004, Feb. 28**   Litho.   *Perf. 11¾*
439 A160 115te multi    3.25 3.25

**New Year Type of 1993 With "Kazakhstan" Inscribed in Both Cyrillic and Roman Letters**
**2004, Mar. 23**    *Perf. 11½*
440 A7 35te lt bl, dk bl & org   1.00 1.00
New Year 2004 (Year of the Monkey).

Cosmonaut's Day — A161

Designs: 40te, Mariner 10, vert. 50te, Luna 3.

*Perf. 11¾x11½, 11½x11¾*
**2004, Apr. 12**
441-442 A161   Set of 2    2.00 2.00

Kazakhstan Flag — A162

**2004, Apr. 19**    *Perf. 13½*
443 A162 25te yel & brt blue   .75 .75

**Arms Type of 1998 Redrawn**
**2004**    Litho.    *Perf. 13½*
444 A70 1te green    .30 .25
445 A70 2te bright blue   .30 .25
446 A70 4te bright pink   .30 .25
447 A70 5te orange yellow   .30 .30
448 A70 10te olive green   .40 .40
449 A70 16te brt purple   .50 .50
450 A70 20te purple   .60 .60
451 A70 35te bright yellow   1.00 1.00
452 A70 50te brt green   1.40 1.40
453 A70 72te orange   1.90 1.90
454 A70 100te greenish blue   2.75 2.75
455 A70 200te vermilion   5.25 5.25
Nos. 444-455 (12)   15.00 14.85

Issued: 1te, 2te, 4te, 4/19; 20te, 35te, 72te, 100te, 200te, 5/11; 5te, 10te, 16te, 50te, 6/10.
Nos. 444-455 are dated "2004," arms and "Kazakhstan" in Roman letters are larger and denominations are smaller than those features on Nos. 247-254.
No. 447 is dated "2004," arms and "Kazakhstan" in Roman letters are larger and denomination is smaller than those features on No. 251.

Souvenir Sheet

Kazakhstan Railways, Cent. — A163

**2004, Apr. 22**   Litho.   *Perf. 11¾x11½*
456 A163 150te multi    3.00 3.00

Souvenir Sheet

Ethnic Groups in Kazakhstan — A164

No. 457: a, Uzbeks (denomination at left). b, Germans (denomination at right).

**2004, May 12**
457 A164 65te Sheet of 2, #a-b   3.25 3.25

FIFA (Fédération Internationale de Football Association), Cent. — A165

FIFA emblem, soccer player and soccer ball at: No. 458, 100te, Left. No. 459, 100te, Center.

**2004, May 21**   Litho. & Embossed
458-459 A165   Set of 2    5.00 5.00

Children's Art — A166

Designs: No. 460, 45te, Yurts and sheep, by A. Sadykov. No. 461, 45te, Woman, by D. Iskhanova, vert.

**2004, June 20**   Litho.   *Perf. 11½*
460-461 A166   Set of 2    2.25 2.25

Souvenir Sheet

2004 Summer Olympics, Athens — A167

No. 462: a, 70te, Boxing. b, 115te, Shooting.

**Litho., Margin Embossed**
**2004, June 28**
462 A167   Sheet of 2, #a-b   3.75 3.75

Souvenir Sheet

Fauna in Altyn Emel Reserve A168

No. 463: a, Acgypius monacus. b, Capra sibirica. c, Gazella subgutturosa.

**2004, Aug. 11** *Perf. 11½x11¾*
463 A168 50te Sheet of 3, #a-c 4.00 4.00

Souvenir Sheet

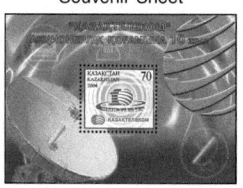

Kazaktelecom, 10th Anniv. — A169

*Perf. 11½x11¾*
**2004, Aug. 18** Litho.
464 A169 70te multi 2.00 2.00

Alkei Khakan Margulan (1904-85), Archaeologist A170

**2004, Sept. 23**
465 A170 115te multi 2.25 2.25

Flowers A171

**2004, Oct. 4** *Perf. 12¼x11½*
466 A171 25te multi + label .75 .75

Printed in sheets of 12 + 12 labels.

**World Post Day Type of 2003**
**2004, Oct. 9** *Perf. 13½*
467 A154 3te red vio & blue .30 .30
468 A154 30te yel org & blue .80 .80

New Year 2005 — A172

**2004, Nov. 23** *Perf. 13¼*
469 A172 65te multi 1.40 1.40

Musical Instruments — A173

No. 470: a, Adyma. b, Gizhak and bow.

**2004, Nov. 29** *Perf. 11½x11¾*
470 A173 100te Horiz. pair, #a-b 4.50 4.50
See Tajikistan No. 248.

Saken Seifullin (1894-1939), Writer — A174

**2004, Dec. 28**
471 A174 35te multi .75 .75

Women's Headdresses — A175

No. 472: a, Kazakh headdress, denomination at left. b, Mongol headdress, denomination at right.

**2004, Dec. 30**
472 A175 72te Horiz. pair, #a-b 3.25 3.25
See Mongolia No. 2590.

Veterinary Research Institute, Cent. — A176

**2005, Jan. 14** *Perf. 13½*
473 A176 7te multi .40 .40

Constitution, 10th Anniv. — A177

**2005, Apr. 8** Litho. *Perf. 13½*
474 A177 1te blue & brn .30 .25
475 A177 2te vio & brn .30 .25
476 A177 3te brt grn & brn .30 .25
477 A177 8te brt bl & brn .30 .25
478 A177 10te red & brn .30 .25
479 A177 (25te) red vio & brn .60 .70
480 A177 50te olive & brn 1.00 1.10
481 A177 65te bl grn & brn 1.30 1.40
  Nos. 474-481 (8) 4.40 4.45
No. 479 is inscribed "A."

Europa — A178

**2005, Apr. 14** Litho. *Perf. 11½x12¼*
482 A178 90te multi 5.00 5.00

End of World War II, 60th Anniv. — A179

**2005, Apr. 28** Litho. *Perf. 13¼x13*
483 A179 72te multi 1.75 1.75

Souvenir Sheet

Baikonur Space Complex, 50th Anniv. A180

No. 484: a, Rocket. b, Buran space shuttle. c, Capsule and parachute.

**2005, June 2** *Perf. 11½x11¾*
484 A180 72te Sheet of 3, #a-c 4.50 4.50

Peace and Harmony Palace A181

**Litho. & Embossed**
**2005, July 6** *Perf. 13¼*
485 A181 65te multi 1.50 1.50

Minerals — A182

Designs: 50te, Azurite. 70te, Agate.

**2005, July 12** Litho. *Perf. 11¾x11½*
486-487 A182 Set of 2 3.00 3.00

**Fairy Tales Type of 2003**
Designs: 35te, Aldar Kose and the Musician. 45te, Aldar Kose and the Raiser of Asses.

**2005, Aug. 11**
488-489 A149 Set of 2 1.90 1.90

Constitution, 10th Anniv. — A183

**2005, Aug. 26**
490 A183 72te multi 1.60 1.60

Souvenir Sheet

Olympic Gold Medalists — A184

No. 491: a, Zaksylik Ushkempirov, 1980, 48kg Greco-Roman wrestling. b, Vitaly Savin, 1988, 4x100m relay. c, Vasily Zhirov, 1996, light heavyweight boxing. d, Bekzat Sattarkhanov, 2000, featherweight boxing.

**2005, Sept. 22** Litho. *Perf. 11¾*
491 A184 100te Sheet of 4, #a-d 9.00 9.00

Akhmet Baitursynov (1873-1937), Writer — A185

**Litho. with Foil Application**
**2005, Oct. 6** *Perf. 13¾x14*
492 A185 30te multi .80 .80
No. 492 not issued without gold overprint.

World Post Day — A186

**2005, Oct. 8** Litho. *Perf. 13½*
493 A186 35te blue & pur .80 .80
494 A186 40te pur & red .95 .95

Dogs A187

No. 495: a, Kazakh hound (dog with curled tail). b, Estonian hound (white, black and brown dog).

**2005, Oct. 19** *Perf. 11½x11¾*
495 A187 138te Horiz. pair, #a-b 4.75 4.75
See Estonia No. 523.

United Nations, 60th Anniv. — A188

**2005, Oct. 31** *Perf. 13½*
496 A188 150te multi 3.00 3.00

New Year 2006 — A189

**2005, Nov. 10** Litho. *Perf. 13¼*
497 A189 65te multi 1.50 1.50

Evgeny Brusilovsky (1905-81), Composer A190

**2005, Nov. 18** *Perf. 11½x11¾*
498 A190 150te multi 2.75 2.75

Assembly of Peoples of Kazakhstan, 10th Anniv. — A191

**2005, Nov. 24** *Perf. 13½*
499 A191 80te multi 1.75 1.75

Souvenir Sheet

National Symbols A192

No. 500: a, 70te, Flag and eagle. b, 70te, National anthem. c, 300te, Arms.

**Litho. & Embossed**
**2005, Dec. 22** *Perf. 13¼*
500 A192 Sheet of 3, #a-c 7.00 7.00

Turgen Waterfall A193

Mountain Lake A194

**2005, Dec. 23** Litho. *Perf. 13½*
501 A193 12te multi .50 .50
502 A194 100te multi 3.00 3.00

Hans Christian Andersen (1805-75), Author — A195

**2005, Dec. 30** *Perf. 11¾x11½*
503 A195 200te multi 3.75 3.75

Parliament, 10th Anniv. — A196

**2006, Jan. 17 Litho. Perf. 11½x11¾**
504 A196 50te multi 1.25 1.25

Abylai Khan, by Aubakir Ismailov — A197

**Litho. With Foil Application**
**2006, Jan. 27 Perf. 13x13¼**
505 A197 94te multi 1.90 1.90

2006 Winter Olympics, Turin — A198

**Perf. 11½x11¾**
**2006, Feb. 20 Litho.**
506 A198 138te multi 2.50 2.50

Cosmonaut's Day — A199

Paintings of cosmonauts by: 100te, P. M. Popov. 120te, A. M. Stepanov.

**2006, Apr. 12 Perf. 11¾x11½**
507-508 A199 Set of 2 4.50 4.50

Traditional Jewelry — A200

No. 509: a, Bracelet, Kazakhstan. b, Brooch, Latvia.

**2006, Apr. 19 Perf. 11½x11¾**
509 A200 110te Horiz. pair, #a-b 4.50 4.50
See Latvia No. 650.

Saksaul Tree — A201

**2006, Apr. 27 Perf. 11¾x11½**
510 A201 25te multi .60 .60

Europa — A202

**2006, May 3**
511 A202 210te multi 3.50 3.50
a. Tete-beche pair 10.00 10.00

Turkestan-Siberia Railway, 75th Anniv. — A203

**2006, May 31 Perf. 13x13¼**
512 A203 200te multi 4.00 4.00

2006 World Cup Soccer Championships, Germany A204

**2006, June 2 Perf. 11½x11¾**
513 A204 150te multi 2.75 2.75

Intl. Year of Deserts and Desertification A205

**2006, July 7 Perf. 13¼**
514 A205 110te multi 2.10 2.10

Mosque, Astana — A206

**2006 Litho. Perf. 13½x13¾**
515 A206 5te emerald .30 .25
516 A206 8te Prus blue .40 .25
517 A206 10te olive grn .50 .25
518 A206 (25te) purple .90 .90
518A A206 100te dark blue 2.25 1.75
519 A206 110te brown 2.50 2.00
520 A206 120te green 2.75 2.25
521 A206 200te red violet 4.50 3.50
Nos. 515-521 (8) 14.10 11.15
Issued: 100te, 10/10/06; rest, 7/20/06.

Akzhan Mashani, Geologist, Cent. of Birth — A207

**2006, July 21 Litho. Perf. 11½x11¾**
522 A207 85te multi 2.00 2.00

Houses of Worship in Almaty — A208

Designs: No. 523, 25te, Catholic Church (denomination in orange). No. 524, 25te, Synagogue (denomination in white).

**2006, Aug. 17 Perf. 11¾x11½**
523-524 A208 Set of 2 1.10 1.10

**Souvenir Sheet**

Famous Men A209

No. 525: a, Chokan Valikhanov (1835-65), diplomat. b, Saken Sejfullin (1894-1938), poet.

c, Nazir Tjurjakulov (1893-1937). d, Kanysh Satpaev (1899-1964), geologist.

**2006, Aug. 20 Perf. 11½**
525 A209 90te Sheet of 4, #a-d 6.00 6.00

Third Meeting of Economic Cooperation Organization Postal Authorities, Turkey A210

**2006, Sept. 15 Perf. 12**
526 A210 210te multi 3.50 3.50
See Iran No. 2917, Pakistan No. 1101 and Turkey No. 3041.

**No. 526 Overprinted in Gold**

**2006, Sept. 22**
527 A210 210te multi 3.50 3.50
Overprint corrects site of meeting from Istanbul to Ankara.

Ahmet Zhubanov (1906-68), Composer — A211

**2006, Oct. 13 Perf. 11½**
528 A211 85te multi 1.75 1.75

Coats of Arms — A212

Arms of: 17te, Almaty. 80te, Astana.

**2006, Oct. 20 Litho. Perf. 13½x13¾**
529-530 A212 Set of 2 2.00 2.00

New Year 2007 — A213

**2006, Nov. 1 Litho. Perf. 13¼**
531 A213 25te multi .75 .75

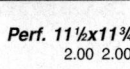
Latif Khamidi (1906-83), Composer — A214

**2006, Nov. 9 Perf. 11½x11¾**
532 A214 110te multi 2.00 2.00

Mukagali Makataev (1931-76), Writer — A215

**2006, Nov. 29 Perf. 13½x13¾**
533 A215 1te dark blue .30 .25
534 A215 4te olive grn .30 .25
535 A215 7te rose claret .30 .25
536 A215 15te red brown .30 .30
Nos. 533-536 (4) 1.20 1.05

Manash Kozybaev (1931-2002), Historian — A216

**2006, Nov. 29**
537 A216 20te brown .45 .45
538 A216 30te brn lake .65 .65

Character From Opera Silk Girl — A217

**2006, Dec. 15 Perf. 13¼**
539 A217 80te multi 1.25 1.25
Values are for stamps with surrounding selvage.

18th Century Helmet A218

**2006, Dec. 15 Perf. 13x12¾**
540 A218 85te multi 1.75 1.75

Nikolai Repinsky (1906-69), Architect — A219

**2006, Dec. 20 Perf. 13½x13¾**
541 A219 2te brown .30 .25
542 A219 3te yel brn .30 .25
543 A219 105te gray grn 2.00 2.00
544 A219 150te blue 3.00 3.00
545 A219 500te rose claret 9.00 9.00
Nos. 541-545 (5) 14.60 14.50

**Miniature Sheet**

Kurgalzhinsky Nature Reserve — A220

No. 546: a, 25te, Phoenicopterus roseus. b, 100te, Cygnus cygnus. c, 120te, Meles meles.

**2006, Dec. 29 Perf. 11½x11¾**
546 A220 Sheet of 3, #a-c 5.50 5.50

KazTransOil, 10th Anniv. A221

**2007, Apr. 12 Litho. Perf. 12¾**
547 A221 25te multi .60 .60

Cosmonaut's Day — A222

Designs: 80te, Konstantin E. Tsiolkovsky (1857-1935), rocket pioneer. 110te, Sergei P. Korolev (1906-66), aeronautical engineer.

**2007, Apr. 12**　　　　*Perf. 12¼x11¾*
548-549　A222　　Set of 2　　3.50　3.50

Europa
A223

No. 550 — Children's art: a, 25te, Scout bugler and tents. b, 65te, Scouts with backpacks, dog.

**2007, May 8**　　　　*Perf. 11½x11¾*
550　A223　　Pair, #a-b　　2.40　2.40
　　　　Scouting, cent.

63rd Session of UN Economic and Social Commission for Asia and the Pacific, Almaty
A224

**2007, May 17**　　　　*Perf. 12¾*
551　A224　25te multi　　.55　.55

Gali Ormanov (1907-78), Poet — A225

**2007, Sept. 28　Litho.**　*Perf. 11½*
552　A225　25te multi　　.55　.55

Conference on Interaction and Confidence-Building Measures in Asia, 15th Anniv. — A226

**2007, Oct. 17**　　　　*Perf. 13½*
553　A226　80te multi　　1.75　1.75

Maulen Balakaev (1907-95), Philologist — A227

**2007, Oct. 29　Litho.**　*Perf. 13½*
554　A227　1te red brown　　.30　.25
555　A227　4te green　　.30　.25
556　A227　5te dk brown　　.30　.25
　　　*Nos. 554-556 (3)*　　.90　.75

Almaty Zoo Animals
A228

No. 557: a, 25te, Zebras. b, 110te, Elephant.

**2007, Oct. 31　Litho.**　*Perf. 11½*
557　A228　Pair, #a-b　　2.75　2.75

Printed in sheets containing 4 each of Nos. 557a and 557b, with a central label.

Hirundo Rustica — A229

**2007, Nov. 15**　　　　*Perf. 13½*
558　A229　20te multi　　.65　.40
559　A229　25te multi　　.75　.50
560　A229　50te multi　　1.40　1.00
561　A229　100te multi　　3.25　2.00
　　　*Nos. 558-561 (4)*　　6.05　3.90

Saddle — A230

**2007, Nov. 27**　　　　*Perf. 12*
562　A230　80te multi　　1.75　1.75

Launch of Sputnik 1, 50th Anniv.
A231

**2007, Nov. 27**　　　*Perf. 12½x12¾*
563　A231　500te multi　　8.00　8.00

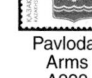
Karagand Arms
A232

Pavlodar Arms
A233

**2007, Dec. 10**　　　*Perf. 13½x13¼*
564　A232　10te multi　　.55　.55
565　A233　10te multi　　.55　.55

Miniature Sheet

Olympic Gold Medalists — A234

No. 566: a, Vladimir Smirnov, 1994, 50-kilometer skiing. b, Yuri Melinichenko, 1996, Greco-Roman wrestling. c, Olga Shishigina, 2000, 100-meter hurdles. d, Ermahan Ibraimov, 2000, boxing.

**2007, Dec. 28**　　　*Perf. 12x11½*
566　A234　150te multi, Sheet of 4, #a-d　　11.00　11.00

Souvenir Sheet

Peoples of Kazakhstan — A235

No. 567: a, Uighur man and woman (denomination at left). b, Tatar man and woman (denomination at right).

**2007, Dec. 28**　　　　*Perf. 11½*
567　A235　105te Sheet of 2, #a-b　4.25　4.25

New Year — A236

**2008, Jan. 23　Litho.**　*Perf. 13¼*
568　A236　25te multi　　.75　.75

Printed in sheets of 8 + central label.

Miniature Sheet

Women's Day
A237

No. 569 — Various flowers with: a, Denomination at LL. b, Denomination at LR. c, Denomination and country name at UL. d, Denomination and country name at UR, Kazakh text in lower panel justified at right. e, Denomination at L, country name at LL. f, Denomination and country name at UR, Kazakh text in lower panel justified at left.

**2008, Mar. 14**　　　　*Perf. 13¼*
569　A237　25te Sheet of 6, #a-f, + 3 labels　　5.25　5.25

Navruz Bayram
A238

**2008, Mar. 21**　　　　*Perf. 12¾*
570　A238　25te multi　　.70　.70

2008 Summer Olympics, Beijing — A239

**2008, Apr. 2**　　　　*Perf. 14x14¼*
571　A239　25te multi　　.70　.70

Kazakhstan Postal Service, 15th Anniv.
A240

**2008, Apr. 4**　　　　*Perf. 12¾*
572　A240　25te multi　　.70　.70

Cosmonaut's Day — A241

Designs: 100te, Space Station Mir. 150te, International Space Station.

**2008, Apr. 10**　　　　*Perf. 14x14¼*
573-574　A241　　Set of 2　　5.50　5.50

Europa
A242

No. 575 — Color of dove: a, Blue. b, Red.

**2008, May 6**　　　　*Perf. 14x14¼*
575　A242　150te Horiz. pair, #a-b　5.25　5.25

2008 Summer Olympics, Beijing — A243

No. 576: a, Judo. b, Handball.

**2008, Aug. 10　Litho.**　*Perf. 14x14¼*
576　A243　100te Horiz. pair, #a-b　4.00　4.00

Deer
A244

No. 577: a, Cervus elaphus sibiricus. b, Cervus nippon.

**2008, Sept. 18**
577　A244　110te Horiz. pair, #a-b　4.00　4.00

See Moldova No. 596.

Ancient Jewelry From Iran and Kazakhstan
A245

No. 578: a, Buckle depicting snow leopard and mountains, 4th-5th cent. B.C., Kazakhstan. b, Gold medal depicting lions, 7th cent. B.C., Iran.

**2008, Oct. 3**　　　　*Perf. 14x14¼*
578　　Horiz. pair + flanking label　　4.50　4.50
*a.*　A245　25te multi　　.55　.55
*b.*　A245　150te multi　　3.50　3.50

See Iran No. 2965.

Universal Declaration of Human Rights, 60th Anniv. — A246

*Perf. 11¾x11½*
**2008, Dec. 10**　　　　**Litho.**
579　A246　25te multi　　.70　.70

Taiyr Zharakov (1908-65), Poet — A247

**2008, Dec. 12**　　　　*Perf. 11½*
580　A247　25te multi　　.70　.70

Shakarim Kudaiberdyuly (1859-1931), Poet — A248

**2008, Dec. 12**
581　A248　25te multi　　.70　.70

Alash Movement, 90th Anniv. — A249

**2008, Dec. 18**
582　A249　25te multi　　.70　.70

Musical Instruments — A250

No. 583: a, 25te, Zhelbuaz. b, 100te, Dauylpaz.

**2008, Dec. 19**
583 A250 Pair, #a-b    2.25 2.25

Paintings A251

No. 584: a, 25te, Portrait of Kenesary, by A. Kasteev. b, 100te, Guest, by S. Aitbayev.

**2008, Dec. 19**
584 A251 Pair, #a-b    2.50 2.50

Insects A252

No. 585: a, 25te, Callisthenes semenovi. b, 100te, Dorcadion acharlense.

**2008, Dec. 22**
585 A252 Pair, #a-b    2.50 2.50

Peter Aravin (1908-79), Musicologist — A253

**Perf. 13¾x13½**
**2008, Dec. 25**    **Litho.**
586 A253 10te multi    .75 .75

Eagle — A254

**2008, Dec. 25**
587 A254 20te multi    1.00 1.00

Arms of Atyrau A255     Arms of Taraz A256

**2008, Dec. 25 Litho. Perf. 14x13½**
588 A255 (25te) multi    .80 .80
589 A256 (25te) multi    .80 .80

Preservation of Polar Regions and Glaciers A257

**2009, Mar. 12 Litho. Perf. 12¾**
590 A257 230te multi    3.75 3.75

Navruz Bayram A258

**2009, Mar. 20**
591 A258 25te multi    .50 .50

---

Louis Braille (1809-52), Educator of the Blind — A259

**2009, Mar. 26**    **Perf. 11½**
592 A259 230te multi    4.00 4.00

Europa — A260

Telescopes and: No. 593, 230te, Galileo Galilei, Moon. No. 594, 230te, Taurus constellation, Kazakhs looking at sky.

**2009, Apr. 3**
593-594 A260 Set of 2    8.00 8.00
Intl. Year of Astronomy.

Earrings — A261

No. 595 — Earring from: a, Korea, 5th-6th cent. b, Mongolia, 18th-19th cent. c, Kazakhstan, 2nd-1st cent, B.C.

**2009, June 12 Litho. Perf. 13x12¾**
595 A261 Horiz. strip of 3    9.00 9.00
a.-c.    180te Any single    2.75 2.75
See South Korea No. 2313, Mongolia No. 2674.

Astronomy — A262

Designs: 180te, Telescope. 230te, Observatories.

**2009, June 25**    **Perf. 13**
596-597 A262 Set of 2    6.25 6.25

Horsemen and Shield A263

**2009, July 9**    **Perf. 12¾x12½**
598 A263 190te multi    3.50 3.50
a.    Tête bêche pair    8.50 8.50

Maria Lizogub (1909-98), Painter — A264

**2009, Aug. 25**    **Perf. 11½**
599 A264 180te multi    3.00 3.00

Kenen Azerbaev (1884-1976), Composer — A265

**2009, Sept. 2**
600 A265 180te multi    3.00 3.00

---

Garifolla Kurmangaliev (1909-93), Singer — A266

**2009, Sept. 8**
601 A266 180te multi    3.00 3.00

18th Session of World Tourism Organization, Astana — A267

**2009, Oct. 5**
602 A267 140te multi    2.10 2.10

Miniature Sheet

Ballet A268

No. 603: a, 180te, Dancers from Giselle (woman in white, man in black). b, 180te, Dancers from Don Quixote (woman in red, man in black and white). c, 180te, Dancers from Swan Lake (man and woman in white). d, 180te, Dancer from Tilep and Sarykyz. e, 230te, Dancer in red from Legend About Love. f, 230te, Dancer in blue from Bahchisarayski Fountain.

**2009, Oct. 8**    **Perf. 13¼**
603 A268 Sheet of 6, #a-f    18.00 18.00

National Games A269

No. 604: a, 140te, Blindfolded man on horseback. b, 180te, Horsemen in competition.

**2009, Nov. 16**    **Perf. 12**
604 A269 Pair, #a-b    5.00 5.00

Abdilda Tazhibaev (1909-98), Writer — A270

**2009, Nov. 16**    **Perf. 11½**
605 A270 180te multi    3.00 3.00

Flora and Fauna — A271

Designs: No. 606, 180te, Crataegus ambigua. No. 607, 180te, Mellivora capensis.

**2009, Dec. 3 Litho. Perf. 13**
606-607 A271 Set of 2    5.50 5.50

Iskander Tynyshpaev (1909-95), Cinematographer — A272

**2009, Dec. 9**    **Perf. 11½x11¾**
608 A272 25te multi    .60 .60

---

Tuleu Basenov (1909-76), Architect — A273

**2009, Dec. 30**
609 A273 25te multi    .60 .60

Birzhan Sal Kozhagululy (1834-97), Composer — A274

**2009, Dec. 30**
610 A274 25te multi    .60 .60

Construction of Central Asian Gas Pipeline — A275

**Perf. 12½x12¾**
**2009, Dec. 30**    **Litho.**
611 A275 25te multi    .60 .60

Kazakhstan Chairmanship of Organization for Security and Cooperation in Europe — A276

**2010, Jan. 6 Litho. Perf. 12**
612 A276 230te multi    4.00 4.00

Navruz Bayram A277

**2010, Apr. 15**    **Perf. 12¾**
613 A277 32te multi    .75 .75

Victory in World War II, 65th Anniv. — A278

**2010, Apr. 15**    **Perf. 12**
614 A278 32te multi    .75 .75

2010 Winter Olympics, Vancouver A279

Designs: 32te, Ski jumper. 190te, Alpine skier.

**2010, Apr. 29 Litho. Perf. 12**
615-616 A279 Set of 2    3.75 3.75

Europa A280

**2010, May 5**    **Perf. 12¾**
617 A280 240te multi    3.75 3.75

Temirtau, 50th Anniv. — A281

**2010, June 1  Litho.  Perf. 14x14¼**
618 A281 32te multi .65 .65

Khan Shatyr Entertainment Center, Astana — A282

**2010, July 1**
619 A282 32te multi .65 .65

2010 World Cup Soccer Championships, South Africa — A283

**2010, July 12**
620 A283 240te multi 4.00 4.00

Arms of Chimkent A284  Arms of Aktyubinsk A285

**2010  Perf. 14¼ Syncopated**
621 A284 5te multi .30 .25
622 A285 10te multi .30 .25
 Issued: 5te, 8/17; 10te, 7/27.

Constitution, 15th Anniv. — A286

**2010, Aug. 20  Perf. 14x14¼**
623 A286 32te multi .60 .60

Musa Baijanuly (1835-1929), Composer — A287

**Perf. 13¾x13½ Syncopated**
**2010, Aug. 24**
624 A287 (32te) multi .60 .60

Baikonur Cosmodrome, 55th Anniv. — A288

**2010, Aug. 27  Perf. 13x13¼**
625 A288 190te multi 3.25 3.25

Mukhamedzhan Karataev (1910-95), Encyclopedia Editor — A289

**Perf. 13¾x13½ Syncopated**
**2010, Sept. 22**
626 A289 20te multi .45 .45

---

Souvenir Sheet

Baurjan Momasuhly (1910-82), World War II Hero — A290

**2010, Sept. 24  Perf. 14x14¼**
627 A290 140te multi 2.50 2.50

Shokan Valikhanov (1835-65), Diplomat, Engineer — A291

**2010, Oct. 21  Perf. 14¼x14**
628 A291 140te multi 2.50 2.50
 See Russia No. 7246.

Frédéric Chopin (1810-49), Composer — A292

**2010, Oct. 28  Perf. 14¼x14**
629 A292 240te multi 4.00 4.00

 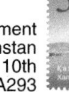

Water Agreement Between Kazakhstan and Kyrgyzstan, 10th Anniv. — A293

**2010, Nov. 17  Perf. 14x14¼**
630 A293 32te multi .65 .65

Souvenir Sheet

Organization for Security and Cooperation in Europe Summit, Astana — A294

No. 631: a, 32te, Independence Monument and Kazakhstan flag. b, 140te, Pyramid of Peace. c, 190te, Ak Orda (Presidential Palace), Pyramid of Peace.

**2010, Nov. 23  Perf. 14¼x14**
631 A294 Sheet of 3, #a-c 6.25 6.25

Birds of the Caspian Sea A295

No. 632: a, Phoenicopterus roseus. b, Ardeola ralloides.

**2010, Nov. 24  Litho.**
632 A295 140te Pair, #a-b 5.00 5.00
 See Azerbaijan No. 938.

---

Seventh Asian Winter Games, Astana and Almaty A296

No. 633: a, 190te, Games emblem. b, 190te, Mascot freestyle skiing. c, 240te, Mascot ski jumping. d, 240te, Mascot ice skating.

**2010, Dec. 21**
633 A296 Block or horiz.
strip of 4, #a-d 12.00 12.00

Mirzhakyp Dulatov (1885-1935), Poet — A297

**Perf. 13½x13¾ Syncopated**
**2010, Dec. 28**
634 A297 50te multi .80 .80

Fish in Astana Oceanarium — A298

No. 635: a, 32te, Rhinecanthus aculeatus. b, 190te, Zebrasoma veliferum.

**2010, Dec. 30  Perf. 13½x13¾**
635 A298 Pair, #a-b 3.75 3.75

Souvenir Sheet

Fauna of Bayanaul Nature Reserve A299

No. 636: a, 32te, Tadorna ferruginea. b, 140te, Mustela nivalis. c, 190te, Capreolus pygargus.

**2010, Dec. 30  Perf. 14x14¼**
636 A299 Sheet of 3, #a-c 8.00 8.00
On Nos. 636a-636c, country name is misspelled "Kazakhstah."

Souvenir Sheet

Peoples of Kazakhstan — A300

No. 637: a, 32te, Korean man and woman. b, 190te, Belarussian man and woman.

**2010, Dec. 30  Perf. 14¼x14**
637 A300 Sheet of 2, #a-b 3.50 3.50

---

First Man in Space, 50th Anniv. — A301

**2011, Feb. 28  Perf. 14x14¼**
638 A301 190te multi 3.00 3.00

Europa — A302

**2011, Apr. 21  Litho.**
639 A302 250te multi 4.00 4.00
 Intl. Year of Forests.

Shanghai Cooperation Organization, 10th Anniv. — A303

**2011, May 5  Perf. 14¼x14**
640 A303 210te multi 3.25 3.25

Campaign Against AIDS, 30th Anniv. — A304

**2011, June 3  Litho.  Perf. 14x13½**
641 A304 32te multi .70 .70

Eurasian Economic Community, 10th Anniv. — A305

**2011, June 14  Perf. 14¼x14**
642 A305 32te multi .70 .70

Kasym Amanzholov (1911-55), Poet — A306

**2011, July 14  Perf. 13½x14**
643 A306 32te multi .65 .65

Coins A307

No. 644 — Coin from: a, 7th cent. b, 13th cent. c, 14th cent. d, 16th cent.

**2011, Sept. 7  Perf. 14x14¼**
644 A307 32te Block of 4, #a-d 2.00 2.00

Orymbek Zhautykov (1911-89), Mathematician A308

**2011, Sept. 15**
645 A308 32te multi .65 .65

# KAZAKHSTAN

251

Customs Union of Eurasian Economic Community — A309

**2011, Sept. 22**     *Perf. 14¼x14*
646 A309 32te multi     .65 .65

Regional Communications Commonwealth, 20th Anniv. — A310

**2011, Sept. 22**     *Perf. 14x13½*
647 A310 150te multi     2.25 2.25

Gabdol Slanov (1911-69), Writer — A311

**2011, Sept. 30**     *Perf. 14x14¼*
648 A311 32te multi     .65 .65

National Coat of Arms — A312

*Perf. 14x14¼ Syncopated*
**2011, Oct. 5**
649 A312 (32te) multi     .50 .50
650 A312 50te multi     .85 .85
651 A312 80te multi     1.25 1.25
652 A312 100te multi     1.50 1.50
653 A312 200te multi     3.00 3.00
654 A312 500te multi     8.00 8.00
    Nos. 649-654 (6)     15.10 15.10

Umirzak Sultangazin (1936-2005), Director of Kazakhstan Space Reseach Institute — A313

**2011, Oct. 20**     *Perf. 14x14¼*
655 A313 32te multi     .65 .65

Dina Nurpeisova (1861-1955), Musician — A314

**2011, Oct. 25**     *Perf. 14x14¼*
656 A314 32te multi     .65 .65

Commonwealth of Independent States, 20th Anniv. — A315

**2011, Nov. 10**     *Perf. 14¼x14*
657 A315 150te multi     2.50 2.50

Independence, 20th Anniv. — A316

**2011, Dec. 5**
658 A316 32te multi     .65 .65

Isatai Isabayev (1936-2007), Painter — A317

**2011, Dec. 14**     *Perf. 14x14¼*
659 A317 32te multi     .65 .65

Miniature Sheet

Birds A318

No. 660: a, Turdus merula. b, Acridotheres tristis. c, Parus major. d, Corvus frugilegus. e, Pica pica. f, Columba livia. g, Corvus cornix. h, Passer domesticus.

**2011, Dec. 14**
660 A318 250te Sheet of 8,
    #a-h     30.00 30.00

Independence, 20th Anniv. — A319

**2011, Dec. 15**
661 A319 20te multi     .45 .45

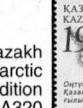

First Kazakh Antarctic Expedition A320

**2011, Dec. 16**
662 A320 190te multi     3.50 3.50

Petro Kazakhstan Kumkol Resources, 25th Anniv. — A321

**2011, Dec. 22**
663 A321 150te multi     2.25 2.25

Kazakhstan E-Government A322

**2011, Dec. 31**
664 A322 32te multi     .65 .65

Dinmukhamed Konayev (1912-93), Politician — A323

**2012, Jan. 27**     *Perf. 14¼x14*
665 A323 100te multi     1.60 1.60

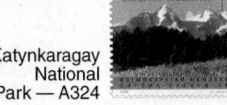

Katynkaragay National Park — A324

**2012, Mar. 20**     *Perf. 13½x13¾*
666 A324 110te multi     2.00 2.00

No. 1 Surcharged in Gold

**Method and Perf. As Before**
**2012, Apr. 4**
667 A1 50te on 50k #1     1.10 1.10

Europa — A325

**2012, Apr. 11**   **Litho.**   *Perf. 14x14¼*
668 A325 250te multi     3.50 3.50

Hedgehogs — A326

No. 669: a, Erinaceus europaeus. b, Hemiechinus auritus.

**2012, June 20**
669 A326 190te Pair, #a-b     6.50 6.50
    See Belarus Nos. 827-828.

Navruz Bayram — A327

**2012, July 25**
670 A327 190te multi     3.00 3.00

Space Vehicle — A328

**2012, July 25**
671 A328 250te multi     3.50 3.50

Ufa Ahmedsafin (1912-84), Hydrogeologist — A329

**2012, Aug. 9**     *Perf. 14¼x14*
672 A329 150te multi     2.25 2.25

Conference on a Nuclear Weapons-Free World, Astana — A330

**2012, Aug. 27**
673 A330 50te multi     1.00 1.00

Mezhit Begalin (1922-78), Film Director — A331

**2012, Oct. 4**     *Perf. 14x14¼*
674 A331 90te multi     1.40 1.40

Lev Gumilev (1912-92), Anthropologist — A332

**2012, Oct. 11**
675 A332 100te multi     1.50 1.50

Dmitri Snegin (1912-2001), Writer — A333

**2012, Oct. 17**     *Perf. 13¾ Syncopated*
676 A333 80te multi     1.50 1.50

Shara Zhienkulova (1912-91), Dancer — A334

**2012, Oct. 17**
677 A334 100te multi     1.75 1.75

Paintings — A335

No. 678: a, Warriors, by P. Zaltsman, 1973. b, Milking a Red Camel, by A. Sadykhanov, 1986-87.

**2012, Oct. 17**     *Perf. 14¼x14*
678 A335 250te Vert. pair, #a-b     7.25 7.25

Mir Broadcasting Company, 20th Anniv. — A336

**2012, Oct. 25**
679 A336 10te multi     .35 .35

Collective Security Treaty Organization, 10th Anniv. — A337

**2012, Oct. 25**
680 A337 80te multi     1.25 1.25

Zein Shashkin
(1912-66),
Writer — A338

Zhamal
Omarova (1912-
76),
Singer — A339

Zhumagali Sain
(1912-61),
Poet — A340

**Perf. 13¾ Syncopated**
**2012, Nov. 12**

| | | | | |
|---|---|---|---|---|
| 681 | A338 | 5te multi | .30 | .30 |
| 682 | A339 | 10te multi | .30 | .30 |
| 683 | A340 | 20te multi | .45 | .45 |
| | | Nos. 681-683 (3) | 1.05 | 1.05 |

Kulyash Baiseitova
(1912-57), Opera
Singer — A341

Denominations: 2te, 50te, A.

**Perf. 13¾ Syncopated**
**2012, Nov. 12**

| | | | | |
|---|---|---|---|---|
| 684-686 | A341 | Set of 3 | 2.00 | 2.00 |

No. 686 sold for 60te on day of issue.

Coat of Arms and Flag
of Kazakhstan, 20th
Anniv. — A342

**2012, Nov. 20**      **Perf. 14¼x14**

| | | | | |
|---|---|---|---|---|
| 687 | A342 | 190te multi | 2.75 | 2.75 |

Union of Designers,
25th Anniv. — A343

**2012, Nov. 22**

| | | | | |
|---|---|---|---|---|
| 688 | A343 | 80te multi | 1.40 | 1.40 |

Diplomatic Relations Between
Kazakhstan and Bulgaria, 20th
Anniv. — A344

No. 689: a, Gold buckle depicting bird and deer, 8th-7th cent. B.C. b, Gold rhyton with design of deer's head, 4th cent. B.C.

**2012, Dec. 14**      **Perf. 14¼x14**

| | | | | |
|---|---|---|---|---|
| 689 | A344 | 250te Horiz. pair, #a-b | 7.25 | 7.25 |

Printed in sheets containing 4 pairs. See Bulgaria No. 4622.

Raoul Wallenberg
(1912-47), Swedish
Diplomat Who Saved
Jews During World
War II — A345

**2012, Dec. 19**      **Perf. 14x14¼**

| | | | | |
|---|---|---|---|---|
| 690 | A345 | 250te multi | 4.00 | 4.00 |

School,
Astana
A346

Lev N.
Gumilev
University,
Astana
A347

Mangylik El Triumphal
Arch, Astana — A348

**2012, Dec. 20**

| | | | | |
|---|---|---|---|---|
| 691 | A346 | 100te multi | 1.50 | 1.50 |
| 692 | A347 | 100te multi | 1.50 | 1.50 |
| 693 | A348 | 100te multi | 1.50 | 1.50 |
| | | Nos. 691-693 (3) | 4.50 | 4.50 |

Traditional
Costumes — A349

Designs: 150te, Man and woman, emblem of Regional Communications Commonwealth. 250te, Man and woman, no emblem.

**2013, Jan. 23**      **Perf. 14¼x14**

| | | | | |
|---|---|---|---|---|
| 694-695 | A349 | Set of 2 | 6.00 | 6.00 |

**Miniature Sheet**

2012 Summer Olympics Gold
Medalists — A350

No. 696: a, Ilya Ilin, weight lifting (wearing blue and white uniform). b, Serik Sapiyev, boxing. c, Olga Rypakova, triple jump. d, Alexander Vinokourov, cycling. e, Svetlana Podobedova, weight lifting (wearing yellow uniform, with hand over heart). f, Zulfiya Chinshanlo, weight lifting (holding medal around neck, denomination at left). g, Maiya Maneza, weight lifting (holding medal around neck, denomination at right).

**2013, Jan. 23**

| | | | | |
|---|---|---|---|---|
| 696 | A350 | 150te Sheet of 7, | | |
| | | #a-g, + label | 17.50 | 17.50 |

Postman, by Nikolai
Khludov — A351

**2013, Apr. 25**

| | | | | |
|---|---|---|---|---|
| 697 | A351 | 200te multi | 3.00 | 3.00 |
| a. | | Tête bêche pair | 7.00 | 7.00 |

**Miniature Sheet**

Lunar
Calendar
Animals
A352

No. 698: a, Mouse. b, Calf. c, Snow leopard. d, Rabbit. e, Snail. f, Snake. g, Horse. h, Sheep. i, Monkey. j, Chicks. k, Dog. l, Pig.

**2013, Apr. 25**      **Perf. 14x14¼**

| | | | | |
|---|---|---|---|---|
| 698 | A352 | 100te Sheet of 12, | | |
| | | #a-l | 17.50 | 17.50 |

Rocket, Gull,
Space
Capsule and
Parachute
A353

Cosmonaut
Valentina
Tereshkova
A354

**Perf. 13½x13¾ Syncopated**
**2013, July 2**      **Litho.**

| | | | | |
|---|---|---|---|---|
| 699 | A353 | 150te multi | 2.00 | 2.00 |
| 700 | A354 | 200te multi | 3.00 | 3.00 |
| a. | | Pair, #699-700 | 6.00 | 6.00 |

Space flight of Tereshkova (first woman in space), 50th anniv. Nos. 699-700 each were printed in sheets of 6. No. 700a is from sheet containing three each of Nos. 699-700.

**Souvenir Sheets**

Pres. Nursultan Nazarbayev, Map of
Kazakhstan — A355

**Perf. 13½x13¾ Syncopated**
**2013, July 2**      **Litho.**

| | | | | |
|---|---|---|---|---|
| 701 | A355 | 250te multi | 4.00 | 4.00 |

**Litho. With Foil Application**
**Perf. 14**
**Granite Paper**

| | | | | |
|---|---|---|---|---|
| 702 | A355 | 900te multi | 13.00 | 13.00 |

Establishment of diplomatic relations with various countries, 20th anniv. No. 701 contains one 55x33mm stamp. No. 702 contains one 50x30mm stamp.

**Miniature Sheets**

A356

Renaming of Akmola to Astana, 15th
Anniv. — A357

No. 703: a, Presidential Palace. b, Palace of Independence and fountain. c, Bayterek Tower. d, Kazakh Eli Monument. No. 704: a, Pres. Nursultan Nazarbayev. b, Emblem of Astana with "1998." c, New cost of arms. d, Emblem of Expo 2017.

**Perf. 13¾x13½ Syncopated**
**2013, July 4**      **Litho.**

| | | | | |
|---|---|---|---|---|
| 703 | A356 | 100te Sheet of 4, #a-d | 6.50 | 6.50 |
| 704 | A357 | 100te Sheet of 4, #a-d | 6.50 | 6.50 |

**Miniature Sheet**

Navruz
Bayram
A358

No. 705: a, Emblem of People's Assembly of Kazakhstan. b, Pres. Nursultan Nazarbayev waving at Navruz celebrations. c, Pres. Nazarbayev playing stringed instrument at Navruz celebrations. d, Emblem of Congress of Leaders of World and Traditional Religions, Astana.

**Perf. 13¾x13½ Syncopated**
**2013, July 5**      **Litho.**

| | | | | |
|---|---|---|---|---|
| 705 | A358 | 150te Sheet of 4, | | |
| | | #a-d | 8.00 | 8.00 |

**Miniature Sheet**

Victory
Day
A359

No. 706: a, Pres. Nursultan Nazarbayev with hand over heart, floral bouquet. b, Flowers, Pres. Nazarbayev folding Kazakhstan flag. c, Eternal flame, flowers, parade. d, Pres. Nazarbayev shaking hands with veteran.

**Perf. 13½ Syncopated**
**2013, July 5**      **Litho.**

| | | | | |
|---|---|---|---|---|
| 706 | A359 | 90te Sheet of 4, #a-d, | | |
| | | + 2 labels | 5.25 | 5.25 |

**Souvenir Sheet**

Olympic Champions — A360

No. 707 — Kazakhstan flag and: a, Bakhtiyar Artayev, boxing, 2004 (denomination at UR). b, Alexander Parygin, pentathlon, 1996 (denomination at UL, Parygin not touching medal). c, Bakhyt Sarsekbayev, boxing, 2008 (denomination at UL, Sarsekbayev touching medal).

**Perf. 13½x13¾ Syncopated**
**2013, July 16**      **Litho.**

| | | | | |
|---|---|---|---|---|
| 707 | A360 | 150te Sheet of 3, #a-c, | | |
| | | + label | 6.75 | 6.75 |

**Souvenir Sheet**

Kazakhstan's Participation in 2010 and
2012 Nuclear Security
Summits — A361

No. 708: a, Pres. Nursultan Nazarbayev at lectern at 2010 summit. b, U.S. Pres. Barack Obama, Pres. Nazarbayev, and Russian Pres. Dmitry Medvedev at 2012 summit.

## Perf. 13¾x13½ Syncopated
**2013, Aug. 28**    Litho.
708 A361 150te Sheet of 2, #a-b   5.00 5.00

### Miniature Sheet

Flowers
A362

No. 709: a, 60te, Tulipa behmiana. b, 60te, Tulipa ostrowskiana. c, 100te, Papaver tianschanicum. d, 100te, Papaver pavoninum.

## Perf. 13¼x13¾ Syncopated
**2013, Oct. 4**    Litho.
709 A362   Sheet of 4, #a-d   5.25 5.25

### Souvenir Sheet

Kazakhstan Postal Service, 20th Anniv. — A363

## Perf. 13½x13¾ Syncopated
**2013, Oct. 9**    Litho.
710 A363 200te multi   3.25 3.25

### Miniature Sheet

Kazakhstan Coins — A364

No. 711: a, Obverse of 100,000-tenge gold coin. b, Reverse of 100,000-tenge gold coin of 2013. c, Obverse of 500-tenge silver coin. d, Reverse of 500-tenge silver coin of 2013.

## Perf. 13¾x13¼ Syncopated
**2013, Nov. 29**    Litho.
711 A364 60te Sheet of 4, #a-d   4.25 4.25
Introduction of tenge currency, 20th anniv.

### Miniature Sheet

Birds
A365

No. 712: a, Chettusia gregaria. b, Tetrax tetrax. c, Aquila nipalensis. d, Numenius arquata. e, Oxyura leucocephala. f, Melanocorypha yeltoniensis.

## Perf. 13½x14 Syncopated
**2013, Dec. 25**    Litho.
712 A365 150te Sheet of 6, #a-f   14.00 14.00

---

### Souvenir Sheet

Wildlife of the Ustyurt Game Reserve
A366

No. 713: a, 60te, Acinonyx jubatus. b, 150e, Saga pedo. c, 190te, Circaetus gallicus.

## Perf. 13½x14 Syncopated
**2013, Dec. 25**    Litho.
713 A366   Sheet of 3, #a-c   6.00 6.00

Mukan Tolebayev (1913-60), Composer
A367

Amre Kashaubayev (1888-1938), Singer
A368

Valentina Tereshkova, First Woman in Space
A369

Saiga
A370

## Perf. 13½x14½ Syncopated
**2013, Dec. 27**    Litho.
714 A367 1te pale yel & blk   .35 .35
715 A368 3te lt grn & blk   .35 .35
716 A369 5te lt bl & blk   .35 .35

## Perf. 14½x13½ Syncopated
717 A370 10te yel & blk   .35 .35
Nos. 714-717 (4)   1.40 1.40
Tereshkova's space flight, 50th anniv. (No. 716).

### Souvenir Sheet

Yurt Furnishings — A371

No. 718: a, Pillows and blankets on chest, edge of table. b, Trunks and chests, table with bowls and tureen. c, Curtains above bed with pillows.

## Perf. 13½ Syncopated
**2014, Jan. 15**    Litho.
718 A371 200te Sheet of 3, #a-c   8.50 8.50

### Souvenir Sheet

Communications History — A372

---

## Perf. 13½x13¾ Syncopated
**2014, Jan. 15**    Litho.
719 A372 200te multi   3.25 3.25

Kulakhmet Khodzhikov (1914-86), Artist
A373

Sabira Maykanovoy (1914-95), Actress
A374

Ilyas Dzhansugurov (1894-1938), Poet — A375

2014 World Weight Lifting Championships, Almaty — A376

## Perf. 14x14¼ Syncopated
**2014**    Litho.
720 A373 50te blk & lt bl   .50 .50
721 A374 100te yel & blk   1.00 1.00
722 A375 100te yel & blk   1.00 1.00
723 A376 200te rose & blk   2.00 2.00
Nos. 720-723 (4)   4.50 4.50
Issued: 50te, 12/31; Nos. 721-722, 12/26; 200te, 12/29.

### Souvenir Sheet

New Year 2014 (Year of the Horse)
A377

**2015, Jan. 12**    Litho.    Perf.
724 A377 200te multi   3.00 3.00
Dated 2014.

Anna Akhmatova (1889-1966), Poet
A378

Mikhail Lermontov (1814-41), Writer
A379

**2015, Jan. 12**    Litho.    Perf. 13x13½
725 A378 60te multi   .90 .90
726 A379 60te multi   .90 .90
Dated 2014.

Employment Roadmap 2020 Emblem — A380

**2015, Jan. 12**    Litho.    Perf. 12
727 A380 150te multi   2.25 2.25
Dated 2014.

---

2013 Soyuz TMA-11M Flight
A381

Voskhod Spacecraft, 50th Anniv. (in 2014)
A382

Space Flight of Talgat Musabayev, 20th Anniv. (in 2014) — A383

Space Communications, 10th Anniv. — A384

**2015, Jan. 12**    Litho.    Perf. 13x13½
728 A381 150te multi   2.25 2.25
729 A382 150te multi   2.25 2.25
730 A383 150te multi   2.25 2.25
Nos. 728-730 (3)   6.75 6.75

### Souvenir Sheet
731 A384 300te multi   4.25 4.25
Dated 2014.

### Souvenir Sheet

Statue of Batyr Zhanibek Berdauletuly (1714-92) — A385

**2015, Jan. 12**    Litho.    Perf. 13½x13
732 A385 200te multi   3.00 3.00
Dated 2014.

### Souvenir Sheet

Shaken Aimanov (1914-70), Actor — A386

**2015, Jan. 12**    Litho.    Perf. 13½x13
733 A386 200te multi   3.00 3.00
Dated 2014.

Miniature Sheet

Traditional Women's
Headdresses — A387

No. 734 — Woman from: a, Shygys, 1955.
b, Almaty, 1970. c, Karagandy, 19th cent. d,
Pavlodar, 20th cent.

**2015, Jan. 12   Litho.   *Perf. 12***
734  A387  50te Sheet of 4, #a-d   3.00 3.00
Dated 2014.

Souvenir Sheet

Naurzum
Nature
Reserve
A388

No. 735: a, Nymphaea candida. b,
Haliaeetus albicilla. c, Alces alces.

**2015, Jan. 12   Litho.   *Perf. 13½x13***
735  A388  200te Sheet of 3, #a-c   8.75 8.75
Dated 2014.

Miniature Sheet

2014 Winter Olympics, Sochi,
Russia — A389

No. 736: a, Short track speed skating. b,
Figure skating. c, Snowboarding. d, Skeleton.

**2015, Jan. 12   Litho.   *Perf. 12***
736  A389  200te Sheet of 4,
#a-d   11.50 11.50
Dated 2014.

Miniature Sheet

2014 Winter Paralympics, Sochi,
Russia — A390

No. 737: a, Alpine skiing. b, Cross-country
skiing. c, Sled hockey. d, Wheelchair curling.

**2015, Jan. 12   Litho.   *Perf. 13½x13***
737  A390  250te Sheet of 4,
#a-d   14.00 14.00
Dated 2014.

Kazakhstan
Chairmanship of
Energy Charter
Conference — A391

**2015, Jan. 15   Litho.   *Perf. 13½x13***
738  A391  100te multi   1.40 1.40
Dated 2014.

Ice Hockey — A392

**2015, Jan. 15   Litho.   *Perf. 12***
739  A392  100te multi   1.40 1.40
Dated 2014.

Nowruz
A393

**2015, Jan. 15   Litho.   *Perf. 13***
740  A393  190te multi   3.00 3.00
No. 740 is printed in sheets of 7 + label and
is dated 2014.

Europa
A394

No. 741: a, Kobyz and bow, b, Dombra.

**2015, Jan. 15   Litho.   *Perf. 12***
741  A394  200te Pair, #a-b   5.25 5.25
No. 741 was printed in sheets containing 4
pairs + 2 labels, and is dated 2014.

Children's
Art
A395

No. 742 — Drawings depicting scenes from
Kazakh fairy tales: a, Maktakyz and the Cat
(yellow panels). b, Aldar-Koze (green panels).
c, Beautiful Kunekey (blue panels). d, Alpamys
Batyr (red panels).

**2015, Jan. 15   Litho.   *Perf. 12***
742  A395  50te Block or horiz.
strip of 4, #a-d   3.00 3.00
Dated 2014.

Souvenir Sheet

Campaign to End Nuclear
Testing — A396

No. 743 — ATOM Project emblem and: a,
People. b, Landscape.

**2015, Jan. 15   Litho.   *Perf. 13½x13***
743  A396  100te Sheet of 2, #a-b   3.00 3.00
Dated 2014.

Souvenir Sheet

Charlie Chaplin (1889-1977),
Actor — A397

No. 744 — Chaplin with: a, 60te, Child actor
(30x26mm). b, 100te, Dog (37x26mm). c,
200te, Camera (37x52mm).

**2015, Jan. 15   Litho.   *Perf. 13½x13***
744  A397   Sheet of 3, #a-c   5.25 5.25
Dated 2014.

Miniature Sheet

Zhoshy Khan Mausoleum — A398

No. 745: a, Interior of dome. b, Mausoleum,
stone wall in foreground. c, Mausoleum, decorative fence in front of arch. d, Mausoleum,
grass field in foreground.

**2015, Jan. 15   Litho.   *Perf. 13½x13***
745  A398  200te Sheet of 4,
#a-d   11.00 11.00
Dated 2014.

Vaccines in Kazakhstan,
Cent. — A399

**2015, Jan. 15   Litho.   *Perf. 13x13½***
746  A399  60te multi   .80 .80

Souvenir Sheet

Victory in
World
War II,
70th
Anniv.
A400

No. 747: a, Rakhymzhan Koshkarbayev
(1924-88), damaged Reichstag Building,
medal at LL. b, Manshuk Mametova (1922-
43), gun, medal at LR. c, Ivan Panfilov (1893-
1941), Moscow buildings, medal at LL.

**Perf. 14¼x14 Syncopated**
**2015, May 6   Litho.**
747  A400  200te Sheet of 3, #a-c,
+ label   5.50 5.50

Eurasian
Economic
Union
A401

**Perf. 14¼x14 Syncopated**
**2015, May 22   Litho.**
748  A401  100te multi   1.40 1.40

Ilyas
Yesenberlin
(1915-
83),
Writer
A402

Malik
Gabdullin
(1915-
73),
Writer
A403

Emblem
of Expo
2017,
Astana
A404

Space
Walking,
50th
Anniv.
A405

**Perf. 13½x14½ Syncopated**
**2015, June 18   Litho.**
749  A402   5te lt bl & blk   .60 .60
750  A403   10te blk & stone   .60 .60
751  A404   20te blk & pink   .60 .60
752  A405   (112te) red & blue   1.25 1.25
Nos. 749-752 (4)   3.05 3.05
See No. 780.

Souvenir Sheet

Assembly of the People of
Kazakhstan, 20th Anniv. — A406

**Perf. 14¼x14 Syncopated**
**2015, June 25   Litho.**
753  A406  200te multi   2.00 2.00

Constitution, 20th
Anniv. — A407

**Perf. 14¼x14 Syncopated**
**2015, Aug. 25   Litho.**
754  A407  (112te) multi   1.40 1.40

Kazakh
Khanate,
550th Anniv.
A408

**Perf. 14¼x14 Syncopated**
**2015, Sept. 8   Litho.**
755  A408  550te multi   7.00 7.00

Navruz
Bayram — A409

## Perf. 13¼ Syncopated
**2015, Oct. 28**        **Litho.**
756 A409 140te multi      1.75 1.75

Europa — A410

No. 757: a, 200te, Asyk Atu game pieces. b, 300te, Asyk Atu players and game pieces.

## Perf. 13x13¼ Syncopated
**2015, Oct. 28**        **Litho.**
757 A410   Pair, #a-b      5.75 5.75

Diplomatic Relations Between Kazakhstan and United Arab Emirates — A411

No. 758: a, Sheikh Khalifa, flag of United Arab Emirates. b, Pres. Nursultan Nazarbayev, flag of Kazakhstan.

## Perf. 13¼x13 Syncopated
**2015, Oct. 28**        **Litho.**
758 A411 200te Horiz. pair, #a-b   5.00 5.00

See United Arab Emirates No. 1137.

Postcrossing A412

## Perf. 13x13¼ Syncopated
**2015, Nov. 7**        **Litho.**
759 A412 (140te) multi      1.75 1.75

Souvenir Sheet

Year of the Sheep A413

## Perf. Syncopated
**2015, Nov. 7**        **Litho.**
760 A413 300te multi      3.25 3.25

Cosmonaut Aidyn Aimbetov — A414

## Perf. 13¼ Syncopated
**2015, Dec. 11**        **Litho.**
761 A414 300te multi      2.50 2.50

First Spacewalk, 50th Anniv. — A415

No. 762: a, 200te, Alexei A. Leonov, first spacewalker. b, (200te), Leonov spacewalking, Voskhod 2.

## Perf. 13½x13¼ Syncopated
**2015, Dec. 11**        **Litho.**
762 A415   Horiz. pair, #a-b    3.50 3.50

Expo 2017, Astana — A416

## Perf. 13¼x13½ Syncopated
**2015, Dec. 25**        **Litho.**
763 A416 300te multi      2.50 2.50

Kenesary Street M. K. Kubrin Supermarket, Astana — A417

No. 764: a, (200te), Building in color. b, 200te, Building in Sepia.

## Perf. 13¾x13 Syncopated
**2015, Dec. 25**        **Litho.**
764 A417   Pair, #a-b      3.25 3.25

Printed in sheets of 3 horizontal pairs of Nos. 764a-764b, + 3 flanking labels.

Souvenir Sheet

Aktobe Region A418

No. 765: a, 140te, Koblandy Batyr Memorial. b, 200te, Aliya Moldagulova Monument.

## Perf. 13½x13¼ Syncopated
**2015, Dec. 30**        **Litho.**
765 A418   Sheet of 2, #a-b, + 2 labels      2.75 2.75

Kazhymukan Munaitpasov (1871-1948), Wrestler — A419

No. 766: a, 60te, Munaitpasov. b, 200te, Soviet warplane paid for by Munaitpasov, letter to Munaitpasov from Joseph Stalin.

## Perf. 13¼x13 Syncopated
**2016, Jan. 18**        **Litho.**
766 A419   Pair. #a-b      2.00 2.00

Souvenir Sheet

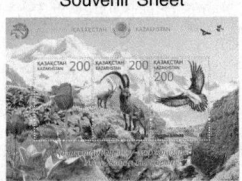

Aksu-Zhabagly Nature Reserve — A420

No. 767: a, Tulipa greigii. b, Capra sibirica. c, Gypaetus barbatus.

## Perf. 13¼x13 Syncopated
**2016, Apr. 8**        **Litho.**
767 A420 200te Sheet of 3, #a-c   5.25 5.25

Miniature Sheet

Tobet Dogs A421

No. 768: a, 60te, Two puppies (34x26mm). b, 140te, Dog, sheep, horses (37x26mm). c, 200te, Three dogs (37x26mm). d, 400te, Dog and sheep (37x52mm).

## Perf. 13¼x13 Syncopated
**2016, Apr. 27**        **Litho.**
768 A421   Sheet of 4, #a-d   7.00 7.00

Regional Communications Commonwealth, 25th Anniv. — A422

## Perf. 13¼x13 Syncopated
**2016, Apr. 29**        **Litho.**
769 A422 60te multi      .60 .60

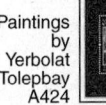

L. N. Gumilev Eurasian National University, 20th Anniv. — A423

## Perf. 13¼x13 Syncopated
**2016, May 23**        **Litho.**
770 A423 60te multi      .60 .60

Souvenir Sheet

Paintings by Yerbolat Tolepbay A424

No. 771: a, 250te, Kazakh Khans (country name at UL, 56x40mm). b, 250te, Seven Rules (country name at UR, 56x40mm). c, 500te, Pres. Nursultan Nazarbayev (28x40mm).

## Perf. 13¼ Syncopated
**2016, May 26**        **Litho.**
771 A424   Sheet of 3, #a-c   8.75 8.75

Souvenir Sheet

Pres. Nursultan Nazarbayev — A425

## Perf. 14x14¼ Syncopated
**2016, June 13**        **Litho.**
772 A425 (121te) multi      1.25 1.25

Miniature Sheet

Orders of Kazakhstan — A426

No. 773: a, Order of the Golden Eagle. b, Order of the Fatherland. c, Order of the First President of Kazakhstan Nursultan Nazarbayev. d, Order of the Leopard. e, Order of Glory. f, Order of Valor. g, Order of Nobility. h, Order of Friendship. i, Order of Honor.

## Perf. 13½x13 Syncopated
**2016, June 17**        **Litho.**
773 A426 100te Sheet of 9, #a-i   7.75 7.75

Visit of French Pres. Charles de Gaulle to Baikonur Cosmodrome, 50th Anniv. — A427

No. 774: a, Rocket launch. b, De Gaulle, Soviet Union General Secretary Leonid Brezhnev and other dignitaries watching launch.

## Perf. 13½x13¼ Syncopated
**2016, June 24**        **Litho.**
774 A427 (218te) Horiz. pair, #a-b    — —

Souvenir Sheet

Akmola Region A428

No. 775: a, 140te, Mountain and lake. b, 200te, Mosque.

## Perf. 13½ Syncopated
**2016, June 24**        **Litho.**
775 A428   Sheet of 2, #a-b, + 2 labels      2.75 2.75

Gennady Golovkin, Boxer A429

No. 776 — Golovkin with a, (121te), Championship belts (52x37mm). b, (200te), Black boxing gloves and white trunks (37x21mm). c, 200te, Black robe, assistants holding belts (37x21mm). d, 200te, Blue and red boxing gloves (37x21mm) e, (218te), Ring ropes in background (37x21mm).

## Perf. 12¾x13¼ Syncopated (#776a), Perf. 13¼x12¾ Syncopated
**2016, July 11**        **Litho.**
776 A429   Sheet of 5, #a-e   8.25 8.25

**Expo 2017 Emblem Type of 2015 and**

Alikhan Bukeikhanov (1866-1937), Statesman A430

Morali Shamenov (1916-74), Union Leader A431

Ybyrai Altynsarin (1841-89), Educator — A432

Kayim Mukhmedzhanov (1916-2004), Poet — A433

**Perf. 13½x14½ Syncopated**

| 2016 | | | Litho. |
|---|---|---|---|
| 777 A430 | 5te pale bl & black | .30 | .25 |
| 778 A431 | 50te blk & lt blue | .60 | .60 |
| 779 A432 | (121te) red & blue | 1.25 | 1.25 |
| 780 A404 | 200te pink & blk | 1.75 | 1.75 |
| 781 A433 | (218te) blk & lilac | 2.25 | 2.25 |
| *Nos. 777-781 (5)* | | 6.15 | 6.10 |

Issued: Nos. 777, 779, 781, 7/12; Nos. 778, 780, 7/22.

100 Concrete Steps for Mangilik El National Goals — A434

**Perf. 13¼ Syncopated**

**2016, Aug. 18**       **Litho.**
782 A434   100te multi      1.00 1.00

A435

**Perf. 12¾x13¼ Syncopated**

**2016, Aug. 18**       **Litho.**
783 A435   60te multi      .50 .50
    *a.*    Tete-beche pair    1.00 1.00

No. 783 was printed in sheets containing two tete-beche pairs.

**Souvenir Sheet**

Expo 2017, Astana A436

**Perf. 13¼ Syncopated**

**2016, Aug. 19**       **Litho.**
784 A436   300te multi      2.60 2.60

Traditional Foods — A437

**Perf. 13¼ Syncopated**

**2016, Aug. 26**       **Litho.**
785 A437   200te multi      1.75 1.75

**Souvenir Sheet**

Almaty Region A438

No. 786: a, 140te, Medeu skating rink. b, 200te, Tamgaly Gorge petroglyphs.

**Perf. 13½ Syncopated**

**2016, Sept. 23**       **Litho.**
786 A438   Sheet of 2, #a-b, + 2 labels    2.75 2.75

New Year — A439

**Perf. Syncopated**

**2016, Oct. 21**       **Litho.**
787 A439   100te multi      .85 .85

No. 787 was printed in sheets of 4.

**Souvenir Sheet**

New Year 2016 (Year of the Monkey) A440

**Perf. Syncopated**

**2016, Oct. 21**       **Litho.**
788 A440   300te multi      2.60 2.60

Europa A441

No. 789: a, (218te), Expo 2017 emblem and buildings. b, 300te, Buildings, cyclist and wind generators.

**Perf. 13½x13¼ Syncopated**

**2016, Oct. 21**       **Litho.**
789 A441   (218te) Pair, #a-b    — —

Kerey Khan (c.1428-70) and Zhanibek Khan (1428-80), Founders of Kazakh Khanate — A442

No. 790 — Khans: a, On scroll. b, On monument.

**Perf. 13¼ Syncopated**

**2016, Nov. 2**       **Litho.**
790 A442   200te Horiz. pair, #a-b   3.50 3.50

Printed in sheets of 8, containing 4 each Nos. 790a-790b.

2016 European Soccer Championships, France — A443

No. 791 — Soccer players, with player in red uniform at: a, Left. b, Right.

**Perf. 13¼ Syncopated**

**2016, Nov. 2**       **Litho.**
791 A443   (218te) Horiz. pair, #a-b    4.00 4.00

World Post Day — A444

**Perf. 13¼ Syncopated**

**2016, Nov. 16**       **Litho.**
792 A444   100te multi      .85 .85

No. 792 was printed in sheets of 8 + central label.

Fourth National Sports Festival A445

No. 793: a, 100te, Kyz kuu. b, 200te, Kekpar.

**Perf. 13¼ Syncopated**

**2016, Nov. 16**       **Litho.**
793 A445   Horiz. pair, #a-b    2.60 2.60

Battle of Moscow, 75th Anniv. A446

No. 794: a, Soldiers at Battle of Moscow. b, World War II Monument, Almaty.

**Perf. 13½x13¼ Syncopated**

**2016, Nov. 16**       **Litho.**
794 A446   300te Horiz. pair, #a-b    —

Joint Issue between Kazakstan and Russia. See Russia No. 7785.

**Souvenir Sheet**

Atyrau Region A447

No. 795: a, 140te, Kurmangazy Palace of Culture. b, 200te, Biplane, medal and Hiuaz Dospanova Monument.

**Perf. 13½ Syncopated**

**2016, Nov. 16**       **Litho.**
795 A447   Sheet of 2, #a-b, + 2 labels    2.75 2.75

**Miniature Sheet**

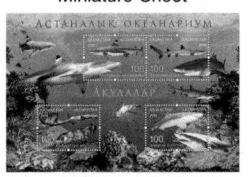

Sharks in Astana Aquarium — A448

No. 796: a, Carcharhinus melanopterus. b, Triaenodon obesus. c, Chiloscyllium plagiosum. d, Negaprion brevirostris.

**Perf. 13½ Syncopated**

**2016, Nov. 16**       **Litho.**
796 A448   100te Sheet of 4, #a-d   3.50 3.50

**Miniature Sheet**

Gold and Silver Medalists at 2016 Summer Olympics — A449

No. 797: a, Gold medalist boxer Daniyar Yeleussinov. b, Gold medalist swimmer Dmitriy Balandin. c, Gold medalist weight lifter Nijat Rahimov. d, Silver medalist boxer Vasiliy Levit. e, Silver medalist boxer Adilbek Niyazymbetov. f, Silver medalist wrestler Guzel Manyurova. g, Silver medalist judo Yeldos Smetov. h, Silver medalist weight lifter Zhazira Zhapparkul.

**Perf. 13¼ Syncopated**

**2016, Nov. 16**       **Litho.**
797 A449   200te Sheet of 8, #a-h    13.50 13.50

Independence, 25th Anniv. — A450

**Perf. 13¼x13½ Syncopated**

**2016, Dec. 5**       **Litho.**
798 A450   100te multi

Endangered Mammals — A451

No. 799: a, Martes martes. b, Martes foina.

**Perf. 13¼ Syncopated**

**2016, Dec. 5**       **Litho.**
799 A451   200te Pair, #a-b    3.50 3.50

Printed in sheets of 8, 4 each of Nos. 799a-799b.

**Souvenir Sheet**

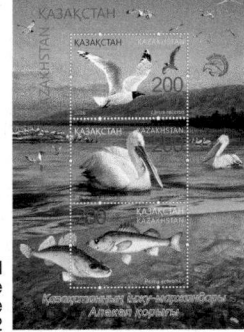

Alakol Nature Reserve A452

No. 800: a, Larus relictus. b, Pelecanus crispus. c, Perca schrenki.

**Perf. 12¾x13¼ Syncopated**

**2016, Dec. 8**       **Litho.**
800 A452   200te Sheet of 3, #a-c   5.00 5.00

## Souvenir Sheet

28th Winter Universiade, Almaty — A453

**Perf. 13¼ Syncopated**
**2016, Dec. 8** Litho.
801 A453 300te multi 2.60 2.60

Sauran Ruins — A454

**Perf. 13¼ Syncopated**
**2016, Dec. 27** Litho.
802 A454 100te multi .95 .95

No. 802 was printed in sheets of 8 + label.

Astana Circus — A455

**Perf. 13¼ Syncopated**
**2016, Dec. 27** Litho.
803 A455 150te multi 1.40 1.40

## Souvenir Sheet

Endangered Flora — A456

No. 804: a, Iridodictyum kolpokowskianum. b, Malus sieversii. c, Crocus altavicus.

**Perf. 13¼ Syncopated**
**2016, Dec. 27** Litho.
804 A456 200te Sheet of 3, #a-c 5.00 5.00

Fayzulla Galimzhanov (1891-1942) — A457

**Perf. 13¼ Syncopated**
**2016, Dec. 30** Litho.
805 A457 100te multi .95 .95

Alash Orda Provisional Government, cent. (in 2017).

Gold and Silver Medalists at the 2016 Summer Paralympics — A458

No. 806: a, Gold medalist swimmer Zulfiya Gabidullina. b, Silver medalist power lifter Raushan Koyshibayeva.

**Perf. 13½ Syncopated**
**2016, Dec. 30** Litho.
806 A458 200te Horiz. pair, #a-b 3.50 3.50

## Souvenir Sheet

New Year A459

**Perf. 13½ Syncopated**
**2016, Dec. 30** Litho.
807 A459 (218te) multi 1.90 1.90

28th Winter Universiade, Almaty — A460

**Perf. 13½ Syncopated**
**2017, Jan. 30** Litho.
808 A460 200te multi 1.90 1.90

Kazakhstan Olympic Committee, 25th Anniv. — A461

**Perf. 13½ Syncopated**
**2017, Mar. 2** Litho.
809 A461 100te multi 1.00 1.00

**Expo 2017 Emblem Type of 2015 and**

Expo 2017 Emblem
A462 A463

**2017, Mar. 7 Litho. Perf. 13½x13**
810 A404 10te blk & orange .30 .25
811 A404 50te blk & green .30 .25
812 A462 (130te) red & blue 1.25 1.25
813 A463 (218te) blk & ultra 2.10 2.10
Nos. 810-813 (4) 3.95 3.85

Nazir Tyuryakulov (1892-1937), Diplomat — A464

Kazybek (1667-1764), Bey
A465 A466

**2017, Mar. 14 Litho. Perf. 13½x13**
814 A464 1te yel & blk .30 .25
815 A465 5te lt bl & blk .30 .25
816 A466 100te org yel & blk 1.00 1.00
Nos. 814-816 (3) 1.60 1.50

Expo 2017, Astana — A467

**2017, July 12 Litho. Perf. 13¼**
817 A467 300te multi 2.75 2.75

## Souvenir Sheet

New Year 2017 (Year of the Rooster) A468

**2017, Aug. 7 Litho. Perf.**
818 A468 300te multi 2.75 2.75

KazEOSat-1 A469

**2017, Aug. 14 Litho. Perf. 12**
819 A469 (220te) multi 2.10 2.10

Kazakhstan No. 1 — A470

**2017, Aug. 21 Litho. Perf. 12**
820 A470 (220te) multi 2.00 2.00

Kazakhstan postage stamps, 25th anniv.

## Souvenir Sheet

Uncia Uncia A471

No. 821: a, Head of adult snow leopard. b, Snow leopard on rock ledge. c, Snow leopard kittens.

**2017, Aug. 28 Litho. Perf. 12**
821 A471 300te Sheet of 3, #a-c 8.50 8.50

Novruz — A472

**2017, Aug. 31 Litho. Perf.**
822 A472 300te multi 2.75 2.75

No. 822 was printed in sheets of 4.

Mausoleum of Khoja Ahmed Yasawi, Turkestan A473

**2017, Aug. 31 Litho. Perf. 13x13¼**
823 A473 750te multi 7.00 7.00

Europa.

KazTransOil, 20th Anniv. — A474

**2017, Sept. 8 Litho. Perf. 12**
824 A474 50te multi .50 .50

Diplomatic Relations Between Kazakhstan and Belarus, 25th Anniv. — A475

**2017, Sept. 16 Litho. Perf. 12**
825 A475 (140te) multi 1.40 1.40

See Belarus No. 1061.

## Souvenir Sheet

Flora A476

No. 826: a, Berberis iliensis. b, Juniperus sabina.

**2017, Sept. 25 Litho. Perf. 12**
826 A476 200te Sheet of 2, #a-b 3.75 3.75

## Miniature Sheet

2017 Automobiles — A477

No. 827: a, JAC S3. b, Hyundai Elantra. c, Peugeot 301. d, Skoda Superb. e, Lada Vesta. f, Kia Sportage.

**2017, Oct. 2 Litho. Perf. 12**
827 A477 100te Sheet of 6, #a-f 5.75 5.75

Ministry of Foreign Affairs, 25th Anniv. — A478

**2017, Oct. 10 Litho. Perf. 13x13½**
828 A478 100te pale blue & dk blue .95 .95

Bracelets, 20th Cent. — A479

**Perf. 13¾x13½ Syncopated**
**2017, Oct. 15** Litho.
829 A479 300te multi 3.00 3.00

Mir Interstate Television and Radio Company, 25th Anniv. — A480

**2017, Oct. 31 Litho. Perf. 13½x13**
830 A480 (130te) multi 1.25 1.25

See Belarus No. 1065, Russia No. 7870.

## Souvenir Sheet

Attractions of East Kazakhstan Region — A481

No. 831: a, 140te, Khalifa Altai Mosque, Oskemen. b, 200te, Kozy Korpesh and Bayan Sulu Mausoleum, Tansyk.

**2017, Nov. 3　Litho.　Perf. 12**
831　A481　Sheet of 2, #a-b, + 2
　　　　　labels　　　　　　3.25　3.25

Souvenir Sheet

Karatau
Nature
Reserve
A482

No. 832: a, Ovis ammon nigrimontana. b, Mustela erminea. c, Hedysarum mindshelkense bajt.

**2017, Nov. 6　Litho.　Perf. 13x13½**
832　A482　200te Sheet of 2, #a-b　5.75　5.75

Souvenir Sheet

Attractions of Jambyl Region — A483

No. 833: a, 140te, Karakhan Mausoleum, Taraz. b, 200te, Aisha Bibi and Babaji Khatun Mausoleums, Taraz.

**2017, Nov. 15　Litho.　Perf. 12**
833　A483　Sheet of 2, #a-b, + 2
　　　　　labels　　　　　　3.25　3.25

Diplomatic Relations Between
Kazakhstan and France, 25th
Anniv. — A484

No. 834: a, (220te), Eagle and rooster. b, 500te, Bayterek Tower, Astana, and Eiffel Tower, Paris.

**2017, Nov. 20　Litho.　Perf. 13½x13**
834　A484　Horiz. pair, #a-b　6.75　6.75

Yurt and
Decorated
Chest — A485

**2017, Nov. 23　Litho.　Perf. 13¼**
835　A485　300te multi　　　2.75　2.75

New Year
2018 — A486

**2017, Dec. 1　Litho.　Perf. 13½x13**
836　A486　(220te) multi　　　2.10　2.10

No. 836 was printed in sheets of 5, of which there were four different types of sheet margins.

Alash Autonomy,
Cent. — A487

**2017, Dec. 25　Litho.　Perf. 13½x13**
837　A487　100te multi　　　1.00　1.00

Kalaushi Begaliev
(1927-2006),
Prosecutor — A488

**2017, Dec. 25　Litho.　Perf. 13½x13**
838　A488　200te multi　　　2.00　2.00

Polish Gen. Wladyslaw Anders (1892-
1970), and His Soldiers in Kazakhstan
A489

**2017, Dec. 25　Litho.　Perf. 12**
839　A489　500te multi　　　4.50　4.50

Joint Issue between Kazakhstan & Poland. See Poland No. 4321.

Conference on Interaction and
Confidence-Building Measures in Asia,
25th Anniv. — A490

**2017, Dec. 26　Litho.　Perf. 13½x13**
840　A490　100te multi　　　1.00　1.00

Admission to the
United Nations,
25th Anniv. — A491

**2017, Dec. 26　Litho.　Perf. 13½x13**
841　A491　300te multi　　　3.00　3.00

Collective Securtiy
Treaty, 25th
Anniv. — A492

**2017, Dec. 27　Litho.　Perf. 13½x13**
842　A492　200te multi　　　1.90　1.90

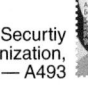

Collective Securtiy
Treaty Organization,
15th Anniv. — A493

**2017, Dec. 27　Litho.　Perf. 13½x13**
843　A493　200te multi　　　1.90　1.90

Miniature Sheet

Kazakhstan Animated Films, 50th
Anniv. — A494

No. 844 — Scenes from *Why the Swallow Has a Tail With Horns*: a, Woman feeding birds. b, Dragon and fox. c, Animals with instruments, sleeping child. d, Bird, insect, fish, flowers. e, Dragons and birds. f, Woman, child and swallow.

**2017, Dec. 27　Litho.　Perf. 13½x13**
844　A494　100te Sheet of 6, #a-f　5.75　5.75

Souvenir Sheet

Ethnic Groups in Kazakhstan — A495

No. 845: a, Polish man and woman (denomination at UL). b, Turkish man and woman (denomination at UR).

**2017, Dec. 27　Litho.　Perf. 12**
845　A495　150te Sheet of 2, #a-b　3.00　3.00

Souvenir Sheet

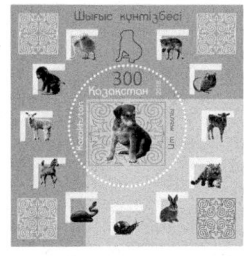

New
Year
2018
(Year of
the Dog)
A496

**2018, Jan. 1　Litho.　Perf.**
846　A496　300te multi　　　3.00　3.00

Bukhar Zhirau Kalkamanuli
(1668-1771), Poet
A497

Kurmangazy Sagyrbaey
(1818-89), Composer
A498

**2018, Jan. 1　Litho.　Perf. 13½x13**
847　A497　1te buff & black　　.30　.25
848　A498　5te lt blue & black　　.30　.25

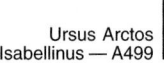

Ursus Arctos
Isabellinus — A499

**2018, Jan. 1　Litho.　Perf. 13x13½**
849　A499　10te blue vio & blk　　.30　.25
850　A499　20te green & black　　.30　.25
851　A499　100te brown & black　1.00　1.00
852　A499　200te brt blue & black　2.00　2.00
　　　　Nos. 849-852 (4)　　　3.60　3.50

Souvenir Sheet

Kazcosmos, 25th Anniv. — A500

No. 853: a, Rocket launch and satellite (40mm diameter). b, Kazakh cosmonauts (53x38mm).

**Perf. (#853a), Perf. 13x13½ (#853b)**
**Litho. With Foil Application**
**2018, May 23**
853　A500　900te Sheet of 2,
　　　　　#a-b　　　17.00　17.00

Astana as
National Capital,
20th
Anniv. — A501

**2018, June 25　Litho.　Perf. 12**
854　A501　(250te) multi　　　2.40　2.40

Magzhan
Zhumabayev
(1893-1938),
Poet — A502

**2018, June 25　Litho.　Perf. 12**
855　A502　(250te) multi　　　2.40　2.40

Souvenir Sheet

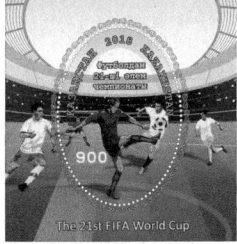

2018 World Cup Soccer
Championships, Russia — A503

**2018, July 13　Litho.　Perf.**
856　A503　900te multi　　　8.50　8.50

Ishim
River
Pedestrian
Bridge,
Astana
A504

**2018, July 30　Litho.　Perf. 12**
857　A504　800te multi　　　7.50　7.50

Europa. No. 857 was printed in sheets of 3 + label.

ATOM Project for
Abolition of Nuclear
Testing — A505

**2018, Aug. 28　Litho.　Perf. 13x13½**
858　A505　300te multi　　　2.60　2.60

Souvenir Sheet

2018 Winter Olympics, Pyeongchang,
South Korea — A506

No. 859 — Mogul skier with denomination and country name in: a, Dull rose. b, Gold.

**Litho. & Embossed With Foil**
**Application**
**2018, Sept. 3　　　　Perf. 12¼x12**
859　A506　900te Sheet of 2,
　　　　　#a-b　　　16.00　16.00

## Souvenir Sheet

West Kazakhstan Region — A507

No. 860: a, 140te, Academy Building, Oral. b, 250te, Kazakh Drama Theater, Oral.

**2018, Sept. 7    Litho.    Perf. 12**
860   A507   Sheet of 2, #a-b, + 2
            labels                        3.50  3.50

## Souvenir Sheet

Karaganda Region — A508

No. 861: a, 140te, Unity For The People Monument, Ulytau. b, 250te, Karaganda Region Central Mosque, Karaganda.

**2018, Sept. 10    Litho.    Perf. 12**
861   A508   Sheet of 2, #a-b, + 2
            labels                        3.50  3.50

## Souvenir Sheet

Aleksander Kolyadin, 2018 Paralympics Cross-country Skiing Gold Medalist — A509

No. 862 — Kolyadin: a, 800te, Standing. b, 900te, Racing.

**Litho. & Embossed With Foil Application**
**2018, Sept. 14    Perf. 12¾**
862   A509   Sheet of 2, #a-b      15.00 15.00

## Souvenir Sheet

Ursus Arctos Isabellinus — A510

No. 863: a, 500te, Bear. b, 600te, Bear, horiz.

**2018, Sept. 17    Litho.    Perf. 12**
863   A510   Sheet of 2, #a-b       9.75  9.75

Jewelry — A511

**Litho. & Embossed With Foil Application**
**2018, Sept. 21    Perf. 13x13½**
864   A511   300te sil & multi     2.60  2.60

## Miniature Sheet

Items in National Museums — A512

No. 865: a, Square piece of jewelry with large stone at center. b, Saddle, 20th cent. c, Tie belt. d, Kobyz (string instrument). e, Bracelet, 19th cent.

**Litho. & Embossed With Foil Application**
**2018, Sept. 24    Perf. 13¼**
865   A512   600te Sheet of 5,
            #a-e                   26.00 26.00

## Miniature Sheet

Industries — A513

No. 866: a, Seamstresses in shop, sewing machine. b, Cotton production. c, Textiles, thread spools, flowers, pillow. d, Shoemakers, shoes and boot, vert. e, Workers at machinery, machined parts, vert. f, Seamstresses in shop, finished garments, vert.

**Perf. 12x12¼, 12¼x12**
**2018, Sept. 28    Litho.**
866   A513   300te Sheet of 6,
            #a-f                   16.00 16.00

Nauryz (New Year) — A514

**2018, Oct. 5    Litho.    Perf. 13**
867   A514   500te multi          4.50  4.50

Old Almaty Post and Telegraph Office A515

Kazakhstan No. 1 — A516

Children's Drawings A517

Drone, Robot and Modern Postal Equipment A518

**Litho. & Embossed With Foil Application**
**2018    Perf. 12**
868   A515   (250te) gold & multi  2.25  2.25
869   A516   (250te) gold & multi  2.25  2.25
870   A517   (250te) gold & multi  2.25  2.25
871   A518   (250te) gold & multi  2.25  2.25
            Nos. 868-871 (4)       9.00  9.00

Kazakh Postal Service, 25th anniv. Issued: No. 868, 10/9; No. 869, 10/16; No. 870, 10/23; No. 871, 10/30.

Sixth Congress of Leaders of World and Traditional Religions, Astana — A519

**2018, Oct. 11    Litho.    Perf. 13½x13**
872   A519   (250te) multi        2.25  2.25

Utegen Seitov (1923-97), Prosecutor — A520

**2018, Oct. 12    Litho.    Perf. 13½x13**
873   A520   (250te) multi        2.25  2.25

## Souvenir Sheet

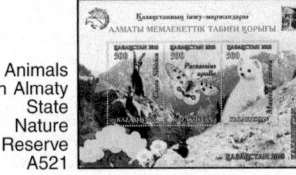

Animals in Almaty State Nature Reserve A521

No. 874: a, Capra sibirica. b, Parnassius apollo. c, Mustela erminea.

**2018, Oct. 19    Litho.    Perf. 13½x13**
874   A521   500te Sheet of 3,
            #a-c                  13.00 13.00

## Souvenir Sheet

Endangered Trees — A522

No. 875: a, 250te, Armeniaca vulgaris. b, 300te, Louiseania ulmifolia.

**2018, Oct. 26    Litho.    Perf. 12**
875   A522   Sheet of 2, #a-b      4.50  4.50

Kazakhstan's 2017-18 Seat on United Nations Security Council — A523

**2018, Nov. 26    Litho.    Perf. 12**
876   A523   (250te) multi        2.25  2.25

Portrait of Latipa Hodzhikova, by Mariya Lizogub A524

**2018, Nov. 27    Litho.    Perf. 13x13½**
877   A524   500te multi          4.50  4.50

Hodzikova (1892-1960), painter.

## Miniature Sheet

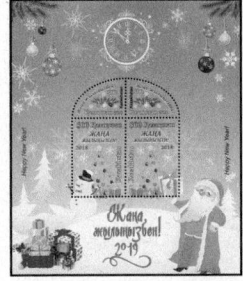

New Year 2019 A525

No. 878: a, Christmas tree ornaments, denomination at UR (28x20mm). b, Christmas tree ornaments, denomination at UL (28x20mm). c, Snowman, Christmas tree and gifts (28x40mm). d, Christmas tree and gifts (28x40mm).

**2018, Dec. 4    Litho.    Perf. 12**
878   A525   500te Sheet of 4,
            #a-d                  17.50 17.50

Ermek Serkebayev (1926-2013), Singer — A526

**2018, Dec. 11    Litho.    Perf. 13x13½**
879   A526   (250te) multi        2.25  2.25

Publication of Epic Poem "Kyz Zhibek," 125th Anniv. A527

Ayteke Bey Baybekuly (1644-1700), Poet A528

Saken Seifullin (1894-1939), Writer A529

Ilyas Zhansugurov (1894-1938), Poet A530

Turar Ryskulov (1894-1938), Communist Politician A531

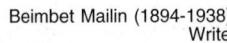

Nurken Abdirov (1919-42), Military Aviator A532

Beimbet Mailin (1894-1938), Writer A533

Lutra Lutra Seistanica
A534

| 2019 | | Litho. | Perf. 13½x13 | |
|---|---|---|---|---|
| 880 | A527 | 5te lt bl & blk | .30 | .25 |
| 881 | A528 | 10te blk & yel | .30 | .25 |
| 882 | A529 | 20te blk & pink | .30 | .25 |
| 883 | A530 | 50te blk & lt bl | .30 | .25 |
| 884 | A531 | (130te) red & blue | .70 | .70 |
| 885 | A532 | 200te pink & blk | 1.10 | 1.10 |
| 886 | A533 | 250te blk & lilac | 1.40 | 1.40 |

**Perf. 13x13½**

| 887 | A534 | 500te brt blue & blk | 2.75 | 2.75 |
|---|---|---|---|---|
| | | Nos. 880-887 (8) | 7.15 | 6.95 |

Issued: 5te, 4/22; 10te, 4/1; 20te, 4/15; 50te, 4/4; (130te), 4/18; 200te, 4/11; (250te), 4/8; 500te, 4/25.

Egemen Kazakhstan Newspaper, Cent. — A535

**2019, July 17  Litho.  Perf. 13**
888  A535  100te multi  .95  .95

Souvenir Sheet

New Year 2019 (Year of the Pig) A536

**2019, July 22  Litho.  Perf.**
889  A536  500te multi  4.25  4.25

Eurasian Economic Union, 5th Anniv. — A537

**2019, Aug. 9  Litho.  Perf. 13**
890  A537  500te multi  4.25  4.25

Universal Postal Union, 145th Anniv. — A538

**2019, Sept. 16  Litho.  Perf. 12**
891  A538  1000te multi  7.75  7.75

Souvenir Sheet

Space Communications, 15th Anniv. — A539

No. 892: a, Satellite dishes (40x28mm). b, Satellite in space (40mm diameter).

**Perf. 12 (#892a), Perf. (#892b)**
**Litho. With Foil Application**
**2019, Sept. 16**
892  A539  300te Sheet of 2, #a-b  5.00  5.00

Souvenir Sheet

Convention of the Rights of the Child, 25th Anniv. — A540

No. 893: a, Child drawing picture of astronaut holding Kazakhstan flag. b, Father, mother and daughter. c, Child in wheelchair.

**Perf. 13¼x13½ Syncopated**
**2019, Nov. 4  Litho.**
893  A540  (140te) Sheet of 3, #a-c  3.50  3.50

Mohandas K. Gandhi (1869-1948), Indian Nationalist Leader — A541

**Perf. 13½x13¼ Syncopated**
**2019, Nov. 11  Litho.**
894  A541  500te purple brn  4.25  4.25

Souvenir Sheet

Arrival in Petropavl of First Trans-Siberian Railway Train, 125th Anniv. — A542

**Litho. With Foil Application**
**2019, Nov. 14  Perf. 13¼**
895  A542  1000te multi  8.00  8.00

Souvenir Sheet

Children's Art — A543

No. 896 — Various works of children's art with large "A" at: a, UL. b, LL. c, UR.

**2019, Nov. 25  Litho.  Perf. 12**
896  A543  (130te) Sheet of 3, #a-c  2.50  2.50

Souvenir Sheet

Flowers and "Congratulations" in Various Languages — A544

**Litho. & Embossed**
**2019, Nov. 27  Perf.**
897  A544  800te multi  5.25  5.25

Scene From Animated Film Proud Girl — A545

Scene From Animated Film Sheep and Goat — A546

Scene From Animated Film Er Tostik and the Dragon — A547

**2019, Dec. 3  Litho.  Perf. 12**
898  Horiz. strip of 3  5.75  5.75
a.  A545  300te multi  1.90  1.90
b.  A546  300te multi  1.90  1.90
c.  A547  300te multi  1.90  1.90

Printed in sheets containing two each Nos. 898a-898c.

Yuri Gagarin (1934-68), First Man in Space — A548

**2019, Dec. 9  Litho.  Perf. 13x13½**
899  A548  1000te multi  6.25  6.25

Miniature Sheet

Mushrooms — A549

No. 900: a, Lactarius resimus. b, Morchella steppicola. c, Cantharellus cibarius. d, Leccinum vulpinum. e, Marasmius oreades. f, Boletus edulis.

**Litho. & Embossed**
**2019, Dec. 10  Perf. 13x13½**
900  A549  (280te) Sheet of 6, #a-f  10.50  10.50

Miniature Sheet

Butterflies — A550

No. 901: a, Papilio alexanor. b, Zerynthia polyxena. c, Iphiclides podalirius. d, Melanargia russiae. e, Vanessa atalanta. f, Pieris brassicae.

**Litho. & Embossed**
**2019, Dec. 11  Perf. 13x13½**
901  A550  (280te) Sheet of 6, #a-f  10.50  10.50

Lutra Lutra Seistanica — A551

No. 902: a, River otter on rock. b, River otter pups.

**2019, Dec. 12  Litho.  Perf. 12x12¼**
902  A551  600te Pair, #a-b  7.50  7.50

Souvenir Sheet

Europa A552

No. 903 — Aquila chrysaetos: a, In flight. b, Head. c, Chick.

**2019, Dec. 19  Litho.  Perf. 12x12¼**
903  A552  500te Sheet of 3, #a-c  9.50  9.50

Express Mail Services, 20th Anniv. A553

**2019, Dec. 31  Litho.  Perf. 13x13½**
904  A553  310te multi  2.00  2.00

Souvenir Sheet

Aquatic Flowers A554

No. 905: a, Nymphaea alba. b, Nelumbo caspica.

**2019, Dec. 31  Litho.  Perf. 12**
905  A554  310te Sheet of 2, #a-b  4.00  4.00

Miniature Sheet

Heavy Industry A555

No. 906: a, Mining. b, Iron factory. c, Nuclear power plant, smokestack, dam. d, Oil derricks. e, Train and truck factories. f, Chemical plant.

**2019, Dec. 31  Litho.  Perf. 12**
906  A555  300te Sheet of 6, #a-f  11.50  11.50

Souvenir Sheet

Barsa-Kelmes Nature Reserve — A556

No. 907: a, Saiga tatarica. b, Equus hemionus onager. c, Tragopogon porrifolius.

**2019, Dec. 31  Litho.  Perf. 13½x13**
907  A556  500te Sheet of 3, #a-c  9.75  9.75

Souvenir Sheet

Kostanay Region A557

No. 908: a, 140te, Yurt. b, 200te, Steam locomotive.

**2019, Dec. 31  Litho.  Perf. 12**
908  A557  Sheet of 2, #a-b  2.25  2.25

Space Post, 50th Anniv. A558

**2019, Dec. 31    Litho.    *Perf. 12¾***
909  A558  (310te) multi          2.50  2.50
No. 909 was printed in sheets of 4 + label.

Amina Umurazkova (1919-2006), Actress A559

Gulzkauhar Chumbalova (1919-58), Painter A560

Serali Lapin (1869-1919), Writer — A561

**2019, Dec. 31    Litho.    *Perf. 13x13½***
910  A559  (310te) multi          2.00  2.00
911  A560  (310te) multi          2.00  2.00
912  A561  (310te) multi          2.00  2.00
    *Nos. 910-912 (3)*           6.00  6.00

National Museum, Nur-Sultan A562

No. 913 — Various photographs of National Museum with denomination at: a, UR. b, UL.

**2019, Dec. 31    Litho.    *Perf. 12***
913  A562  300te Pair, #a-b        4.00  4.00
No. 913 was printed in sheets of 4 containing 2 each Nos. 913a-913b.

Souvenir Sheet

Kyzylorda Oblast — A563

No. 914: a, 140te, Baikonur Cosmodrome. b, 200te, Kyzylorda Railroad Station.

**2019, Dec. 31    Litho.    *Perf. 12***
914  A563    Sheet of 2, #a-b      2.25  2.25

---

Miniature Sheet

Puppies A564

No. 915: a, Bulldog. b, Dalmatian. c, Beagle. d, German shepherd. e, Dachshund. f, Pembroke Welsh corgi. g, Siberian husky. h, Chow chow.

**2019, Dec. 31    Litho.    *Perf. 13x13½***
915  A564  200te  Sheet of 8,
                  #a-h            10.50  10.50

Sapargali Begalin (1895-1983), Writer A565

Abai Kunanbayev (1845-1904), Poet A566

**2020, May 4    Litho.    *Perf. 13½x13***
916  A565  50te blk & lt blue      .40   .40
917  A566  (310te) blk & dull blue 2.00  2.00

A567

A568

Fish — A569

Designs: 5te, Alosa kessleri volgensis. 10te, Salmo trutta caspius. 20te, Hucho taimen. 60te, Acipenser nudiventris. (130te), Stenodus leucichthys nelma. 200te, Salmo trutta araiensis.

**2020, May 12    Litho.    *Perf. 13x13½***
918  A567    5te pale blue green
                  & blk            .30   .25
919  A568   10te blk & yellow      .30   .25
920  A568   20te blk & pink        .30   .25
921  A568   60te blk & lt blue     .45   .45
922  A569  (130te) red & blk       .95   .95
923  A568  200te rose & blk       1.40  1.40
    *Nos. 918-923 (6)*            3.70  3.55

*Kazakhstanskaya Pravda* Newspaper, Cent. — A570

**2020, June 22    Litho.    *Perf. 13x13½***
924  A570  100te lil & blk         .80   .80

Campaign Against Corruption — A571

***Perf. 13x13¼ Syncopated***
**2020, June 24                    Litho.**
925  A571  200te multi            1.60  1.60

---

United Nations, 75th Anniv. — A572

**2020, June 27    Litho.    *Perf. 13x13½***
926  A572  (280te) lt blue & blk   2.25  2.25

Souvenir Sheet

New Year 2020 (Year of the Rat) A573

**2020, Aug. 17    Litho.    *Perf.***
927  A573  500te multi            4.00  4.00

Constitution of Kazakhstan, 25th Anniv. — A574

**Litho. With Foil Application**
**2020, Aug. 25        *Perf. 13x13½***
928  A574  (130te) multi          1.10  1.10

Assembly of People of Kazakhstan, 25th Anniv. — A575

**2020, Sept. 1    Litho.    *Perf. 12¼x12***
929  A575  (130te) multi          1.10  1.10

Zhuban Moldagaliev (1920-88), Poet — A576

**2020, Sept. 24    Litho.    *Perf. 13x13½***
930  A576  200te multi            1.60  1.60

Ludwig van Beethoven (1770-1827), Composer — A577

**2020, Oct. 15    Litho.    *Perf. 13¾x13***
931  A577  800te multi            6.00  6.00
No. 931 was printed in sheets of 5 + label.

---

Souvenir Sheet

Flora and Fauna of West Altai Nature Reserve A578

No. 932: a, Bubo bubo. b, Alces alces. c, Rubus idaeus.

**2020, Oct. 21    Litho.    *Perf. 13x13½***
932  A578  500te multi  Sheet of 3,
                  #a-c            11.00  11.00

Batyrkhan Shukenov (1962-2015), Singer — A579

***Perf. 13x13¼ Syncopated***
**2020, Oct. 28                    Litho.**
933  A579  (380te) black          2.40  2.40

Movie *Kyz Zhibek,* 50th Anniv. — A580

***Perf. 13½x13 Syncopated***
**2020, Nov. 6                     Litho.**
934  A580  300te multi            2.25  2.25
No. 934 was printed in sheets of 4 + central label.

Movie *The End of Ataman,* 50th Anniv. — A581

***Perf. 13½x13 Syncopated***
**2020, Nov. 13                    Litho.**
935  A581  300te multi            2.25  2.25
No. 935 was printed in sheets of 4 + central label.

Abu Nasr al-Farabi (c. 872-c. 950), Philosopher A582

**Litho. With Foil Application**
**2020, Dec. 21        *Perf. 13x13¼***
936  A582  500te red & multi      2.50  2.50

Dauletkerey Shygayuly (1820-87), Musician — A583

***Perf. 13¼ Syncopated***
**2020, Dec. 22                    Litho.**
937  A583  300te multi            1.50  1.50
No. 937 was printed in sheets of 5 + label.

Emblems of UNESCO and Kazakhstan Man and Biosphere National Committee — A584

**2020, Dec. 23  Litho.  *Perf. 13½x13***
938  A584  310te multi        1.50  1.50

**Miniature Sheet**

Minerals
A585

No. 939: a, Gold. b, Nephrite. c, Silver. d, Iron. e, Manganese. f, Coal.

***Perf. 13¼ Syncopated***
**2020, Dec. 24                Litho.**
939  A585  300te Sheet of 6, #a-f   9.00  9.00

"Happy Postcrossing"
A586

**2020, Dec. 30  Litho.  *Perf. 13***
940  A586  (140te) multi        .70   .70

Children's Drawings — A587

**Litho. With Foil Application**
**2020, Dec. 30        *Perf. 13½x13***
941  A587  310te red & multi    1.50  1.50
Victory in World War II, 75th anniv.

Baikonur Cosmodrome, 65th Anniv. — A588

**Litho. With Foil Application**
**2020, Dec. 30     *Perf. 13½x13***
942  A588  500te sil & multi    2.50  2.50

Golden Horde, 750th Anniv. — A589

**Litho. With Foil Application**
**2020, Dec. 30         *Perf. 12***
943  A589  750te gold & multi   3.75  3.75

**Souvenir Sheet**

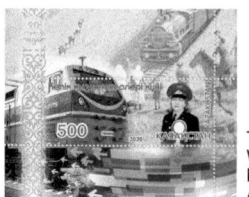

Transport Workers Day
A590

**Litho. With Foil Application**
**2020, Dec. 30     *Perf. 12x12¼***
944  A590  500te blue & multi  2.50  2.50

---

**Souvenir Sheet**

Kasym Khan (1445-1521), Uniter of Kazakh Tribes — A591

**Litho. With Foil Application**
**2020, Dec. 30           *Perf.***
945  A591  500te gold & multi   2.50  2.50

**Souvenir Sheet**

Post Riders on Horses Near Landmarks in Kazakhstan — A592

**2020, Dec. 30  Litho.  *Perf. 13½***
946  A592  800te multi      4.75  4.75
Europa. Ancient Postal Routes.

**Souvenir Sheet**

Mangystau Region — A593

No. 947: a, 140te, Mt. Sherkala. b, 250te, Beket-Ata Underground Mosque.

**2020, Dec. 30  Litho.  *Perf. 12***
947  A593  Sheet of 2, #a-b   1.90  1.90

**Miniature Sheet**

Fish
A594

No. 948: a, 500te, Hucho taimen (30x26mm). b, 600te, Alosa kessleri volgensis (37x26mm). c, 700te, Salmo trutta aralensis (30x28mm). d, 8000te, Acipenser nudiventris (40x28mm).

***Perf. 13½x13 (500te, 600te), 12
(700te, 800te)***
**2020, Dec. 30    Litho. & Embossed**
948  A594  Sheet of 4, #a-d  13.00 13.00

Independence, 30th Anniv. — A595

**Litho. With Foil Application**
**2021, Feb. 25         *Perf. 13***
949  A595  (130te) gold & multi   .65   .65

Zhambyl Zhabayev (1846-1945), Folksinger — A596

**2021, Sept. 15  Litho.  *Perf. 13x13½***
950  A596  10te dark blue     .30   .25

---

Kazhimukan Munaitpasov (1871-1948), Wrestler — A597

**2021, Sept. 15  Litho.  *Perf. 13½x13***
951  A597  50te blk & lt blue    .30   .25

L. N. Gumilyov Eurasian National University, 25th Anniv. — A598

**2021, Sept. 21  Litho.  *Perf. 13x13½***
952  A598  (300te) brt blue    1.50  1.50

Gazella Subgutturosa
A599

Ovis Ammon Karelini
A600

Cervus Elaphus Bactrianus
A601

Ovis Vignei Arcal
A602

**2021, Sept. 24  Litho.  *Perf. 13½x13***
953  A599  5te lt blue & blk     .30   .25
954  A600  20te blk & pink     .30   .25
955  A601  (130te) multi       .65   .65
956  A602  200te cerise & blk  1.00  1.00
      *Nos. 953-956 (4)*     2.25  2.15

Yuri Gagarin (1934-68), Cosmonaut — A603

**2021, Oct. 5  Litho.  *Perf. 13¼***
957  A603  1000te multi     5.00  5.00
First manned spaceflight, 60th anniv.

Radio Broadcasting in Kazakhstan, Cent. — A604

**2021, Oct. 7  Litho.  *Perf. 13x13½***
958  A604  100te black & lt blue  .50   .50

Independence of Kazakhstan, 30th Anniv. and United Arab Emirates, 50th Anniv. — A605

No. 959: a, Flags of Kazakhstan and United Arab Emirates. b, Anniversary emblems.

**Litho. With Foil Application**
**2021, Oct. 10         *Perf. 12***
959  A605  550te Horiz. pair, #a-b  5.50  5.50
See United Arab Emirates No.

---

**Souvenir Sheet**

New Year 2021 (Year of the Ox)
A606

**2021, Oct. 18    Litho.    *Perf.***
960  A606  500te multi      2.50  2.50

Regional Communications Commonwealth, 30th Anniv. — A607

**2021, Oct. 20  Litho.  *Perf. 13½x13***
961  A607  (380te) multi     1.90  1.90

Shymkent, 2200th Anniv. — A608

**2021, Oct. 29  Litho.  *Perf. 13***
962  A608  (380te) multi     1.90  1.90

**Souvenir Sheet**

Ablai Khan (1711-81), Khan of the Middle Zhuz and Kazakh Khanate — A609

**Litho. With Foil Application**
**2021, Nov. 22          *Perf.***
963  A609  500te multi      2.50  2.50

**Miniature Sheet**

Kittens
A610

No. 964: a, Maine coon. b, Abyssinian. c, British. d, Bambino. e, Oriental. f, American curl. g, Scottish fold. h, Bengal.

**2021, Nov. 24  Litho.  *Perf. 13½x13***
964  A610  200te Sheet of 8, #a-h  8.00  8.00

## Souvenir Sheet

Flora and Fauna of the Altyn-Emel Biosphere Reserve — A611

No. 965: a, Equus przewalskii. b, Mylabris quadripunctata. c, Paeonia tenuifolia.

**2021, Nov. 26   Litho.   Perf. 12x12¼**
965  A611 600te Sheet of 3, #a-c   9.00  9.00

## Souvenir Sheet

Endangered Animals — A612

No. 966: a, Capreolus pygargus. b, Sus scrofa.

**Litho. & Embossed**
**2021, Nov. 29           Perf. 13½**
966  A612 800te Sheet of 2, #a-b   8.00  8.00

Europa.

## Souvenir Sheets

Attractions of Pavlodar Region — A613

Attractions of North Kazakhstan Region — A614

No. 967: a, 140te, Balanced rock, Bayanaul State National Park. b, 250te, Mashkhur-Jusup Mosque.
No. 968: a, 140te, Karasai and Agyntai Batyrs Memorial Complex. b, 250te, Syrymbet Manor.

**2021, Dec. 14   Litho.   Perf. 12x12¼**
967  A613  Sheet of 2, #a-b   2.00  2.00
968  A614  Sheet of 2, #a-b   2.00  2.00

## Miniature Sheet

Food Processing in Kazakhstan — A615

No. 969: a, Cows, milk bottling plant, containers of milk. b, Bakery and bread, vert. c, Butchers cutting meat, meat processing plant conveyor belt. d, Canned vegetables, vegetable canning production line. e, Combine in

grain field, grain processing plant, bags of flour, vert. f, Sunflower, sunflower oil production line, bottles of oil.

**Perf. 12x12¼ (horiz. stamps),**
**12¼x12 (vert. stamps)**
**2021, Dec. 15           Litho.**
969  A615 300te Sheet of 6, #a-f   9.00  9.00

Sports of the 2020 Summer Olympics — A616

No. 970: a, Wrestling. b, Boxing.

**2021, Dec. 22   Litho.   Perf. 12x12¼**
970  A616 800te Pair, #a-b   8.00  8.00

Printed in sheets containing two each of Nos. 970a-970b. The 2020 Summer Olympics was postponed until 2021 because of the COVID-19 pandemic.

Kazakhstan  Gold Medalists at the 2020 Summer Paralympics — A617

No. 971: a, David Degtyarev, powerlifting (without cap). b, Daulet Temirzhan, judo (wearing cap).

**2021, Dec. 22   Litho.   Perf. 12¼x12**
971  A617 200te Horiz. pair, #a-b   2.00  2.00

Printed in sheets containing two pairs. The 2020 Summer Paralympics was postponed until 2021 because of the COVID-19 pandemic.

## Souvenir Sheet

Medical Workers' Day A618

**Litho. With Foil Application**
**2021, Dec. 24           Perf. 12x12¼**
972  A618 500te met blue & multi   2.50  2.50

Ungulates A619

No. 9730: a, Gazella subgutturosa. b, Cervus hanglu basctrianus.

**2021, Dec. 27   Litho.   Perf. 13x13½**
973  A619 900te Pair, #a-b   9.00  9.00

Printed in sheets containing two each of Nos. 973a-973b.

## Souvenir Sheet

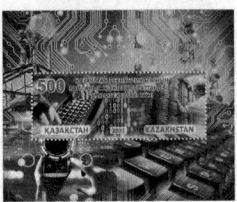

Communication and Information Workers' Day — A620

**Litho. With Foil Application**
**2021, Dec. 27           Perf. 12x12¼**
974  A620 500te met blue & multi   2.50  2.50

Closure of Semipalatinsk Nuclear Weapons Test Site, 30th Anniv. — A621

**2021, Dec. 28   Litho.   Perf. 13x13¼**
975  A621 300te multi   1.50  1.50

———

## SEMI-POSTAL STAMPS

Cartoons SP1

a, Mother and child. b, Cow, rabbit. c, Horses.

**1994, Nov. 3   Litho.   Perf. 12½x12**
B1  SP1 1te +30ti Block of 3 + label   .75  .75

# KENYA

ˈke-nyə

LOCATION — East Africa, bordering on the Indian Ocean
GOVT. — Republic
AREA — 224,960 sq. mi.
POP. — 28,808,658 (1999 est.)
CAPITAL — Nairobi

Formerly a part of the British colony of Kenya, Uganda, Tanganyika, Kenya gained independence Dec. 12, 1963.

100 Cents = 1 Shilling

**Catalogue values for all unused stamps in this country are for Never Hinged items.**

Treetop Hotel and Elephants — A1

Designs: 5c, Cattle ranching. 10c, Wood carving. 15c, Riveter. 20c, Timber industry. 30c, Jomo Kenyatta facing Mt. Kenya. 40c, Fishing industry. 50c, Flag and emblem. 65c, Pyrethrum industry (daisies). 1sh, National Assembly bldg. 2sh, Harvesting coffee. 5sh, Harvesting tea. 10sh, Mombasa port. 20sh, Royal College, Nairobi.

**Perf. 14x14½**
**1963, Dec. 12   Photo.        Unwmk.**
**Size: 21x17½mm**
1  A1  5c bl, buff & dk brn   .30  .40
2  A1  10c brown   .30  .25
a.  Booklet pane of 4   .30

3  A1  15c deep magenta   .80  .25
a.  Booklet pane of 4   4.00
4  A1  20c yel grn & dk brn   .30  .25
a.  Booklet pane of 4   .40
5  A1  30c yel & black   .30  .25
a.  Booklet pane of 4   .55
6  A1  40c blue & brown   .30  .25
7  A1  50c grn, blk & dp car   .50  .25
a.  Booklet pane of 4   2.50
8  A1  65c steel blue & yel   .45  .55

**Perf. 14½**
**Size: 41½x25½mm**
9   A1  1sh multicolored   .30  .25
10  A1  1.30sh grn, brn & blk   4.25  .25
11  A1  2sh multicolored   1.00  .30
12  A1  5sh ultra, yel grn & brn   1.00  .80
13  A1  10sh brn & dark brn   7.50  2.25
14  A1  20sh pink & grnsh blk   3.25  8.00
Nos. 1-14 (14)   20.55  14.30

President Jomo Kenyatta and Flag of Kenya — A2

Flag and: 15c, Cockerel. 50c, African lion. 1.30sh, Hartlaub's touraco. 2.50sh, Nandi flame flower.

**1964, Dec. 12   Photo.   Perf. 13x12½**
15  A2  15c lt violet & multi   .30  .25
16  A2  30c dk blue & multi   .30  .25
17  A2  50c dk brown & multi   .30  .25
18  A2  1.30sh multicolored   2.75  2.50
19  A2  2.50sh multicolored   .40  3.25
Nos. 15-19 (5)   4.05  4.50

Establishment of the Republic of Kenya, Dec. 12, 1964.

Greater Kudu — A3

Animals: 5c, Thomson's gazelle. 10c, Sable antelope. 15c, Aardvark. 20c, Senegal bush baby. 30c, Warthog. 40c, Zebra. 50c, Buffalo. 65c, Black rhinoceros. 70c, Ostrich. 1.30sh, Elephant. 1.50sh, Bat-eared fox. 2.50sh, Cheetah. 5sh, Vervet monkey. 10sh, Giant pangolin. 20sh, Lion.

**1966-69   Unwmk.   Perf. 14x14½**
**Size: 21x17mm**
20  A3  5c gray, blk & org   .30  .25
21  A3  10c blk & yel grn   .30  .25
22  A3  15c dp org & blk   .30  .25
23  A3  20c ultra, lt brn & blk   .30  .25
24  A3  30c lt ultra & blk   .30  .25
25  A3  40c ocher & blk   .45  .25
26  A3  50c dp orange & blk   .45  .25
27  A3  65c dp yel grn & blk   .85  2.00
28  A3  70c rose lake & blk   3.25  1.75

**Perf. 14½**
**Size: 41x25mm**
29  A3  1sh gray bl, ol & blk   .85  .25
30  A3  1.30sh yel grn & blk   3.00  .35
31  A3  1.50sh brn org, brn & black   2.15  3.00
32  A3  2.50sh ol bis, yel & blk   3.00  1.25
33  A3  5sh brt grn, ultra & blk   .65  .75
34  A3  10sh red brn, bis & black   2.40  3.00
35  A3  20sh ocher, bis, gold & black   6.85  12.00
Nos. 20-35 (16)   25.40  26.10

Issued: No. 28, 31, 9/15/69; others, 12/12/66.

Branched Murex — A4

Sea shells: 5c, Morning pink. 10c, Episcopal miter. 15c, Strawberry-top shell. 20c, Humpback cowrie. 30c, variable abalone. 40c, Flame-top shell. 50c, Violet sailor. 60c, Bull's-mouth helmet. 70c, Pearly nautilus. 1.50sh, Neptune's trumpet. 2.50sh, Mediterranean

264                               KENYA

tulip shell. 5sh, Fluctuating turban. 10sh, Textile cone. 20sh, Scorpion shell.

## 1971 Dec. 13   Photo.   *Perf. 14½x14*
### Size: 17x21mm

| | | | | |
|---|---|---|---|---|
| 36 | A4 | 5c bister & multi | .30 | *.55* |
| 37 | A4 | 10c dull grn & multi | .30 | .30 |
| a. | | Booklet pane of 4 | .60 | |
| 38 | A4 | 15c tan & multi | .30 | .30 |
| a. | | Booklet pane of 4 | .60 | |
| 39 | A4 | 20c tan & multi | .30 | .30 |
| a. | | Booklet pane of 4 | .75 | |
| 40 | A4 | 30c yellow & multi | .30 | .30 |
| a. | | Booklet pane of 4 | 2.25 | |
| 41 | A4 | 40c gray & multi | .30 | .30 |
| a. | | Booklet pane of 4 | 2.25 | |
| 42 | A4 | 50c buff & multi | .40 | .35 |
| | | *(Janthina globosa)* | | |
| a. | | Booklet pane of 4 | 3.50 | |
| 43 | A4 | 60c lilac & multi | .40 | *2.15* |
| 44 | A4 | 70c gray grn & multi | | |
| | | (Nautilus pompileus) | .55 | *1.85* |
| a. | | Booklet pane of 4 | 5.00 | |

### Perf. 14½
### Size: 25x41mm

| | | | | |
|---|---|---|---|---|
| 45 | A4 | 1sh ocher & multi | .40 | .45 |
| 46 | A4 | 1.50sh pale grn & multi | 1.25 | .35 |
| 47 | A4 | 2.50sh vio gray & multi | 1.75 | .35 |
| 48 | A4 | 5sh lemon & multi | 2.00 | *.30* |
| 49 | A4 | 10sh multicolored | 2.25 | *.30* |
| 50 | A4 | 20sh gray & multi | 3.25 | *.30* |
| | | *Nos. 36-50 (15)* | 14.05 | 8.45 |

Used values of Nos. 48-50 are for stamps with printed cancellations.
For surcharges see Nos. 53-55.

## Nos. 42, 44 with Revised Inscription
## 1974, Jan. 20        *Perf. 14½x14*

| | | | | |
|---|---|---|---|---|
| 51 | A4 | 50c (Janthina janthina) | 13.50 | 3.75 |
| 52 | A4 | 70c (Nautilus pompilius) | 11.75 | 7.00 |

## Nos. 46-47, 50 Surcharged with New Value and 2 Bars
## 1975, Nov. 17      Photo.   *Perf. 14½*

| | | | | |
|---|---|---|---|---|
| 53 | A4 | 2sh on 1.50sh multi | 6.75 | 5.00 |
| 54 | A4 | 3sh on 2.50sh multi | 10.25 | 19.25 |
| 55 | A4 | 40sh on 20sh multi | 6.75 | 12.00 |
| | | *Nos. 53-55 (3)* | 23.75 | 36.25 |

Microwave Tower — A5

Designs: 1sh, Cordless switchboard and operators, horiz. 2sh, Telephones of 1880, 1930 and 1976. 3sh, Message switching center, horiz.

## 1976, Apr. 15      Litho.   *Perf. 14½*

| | | | | |
|---|---|---|---|---|
| 56 | A5 | 50c blue & multi | .30 | .25 |
| 57 | A5 | 1sh red & multi | .30 | .25 |
| 58 | A5 | 2sh yellow & multi | .30 | .35 |
| 59 | A5 | 3sh multicolored | .45 | .45 |
| a. | | Souvenir sheet of 4 | 2.00 | 2.00 |
| | | *Nos. 56-59 (4)* | 1.35 | 1.30 |

Telecommunication development in East Africa. No. 59a contains 4 stamps similar to Nos. 56-59 with simulated perforations.

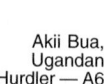

Akii Bua, Ugandan Hurdler — A6

Designs: 1sh, Filbert Bayi, Tanzanian runner. 2sh, Steve Muchoki, Kenyan boxer. 3sh, Olympic torch, flags of Kenya, Tanzania and Uganda.

## 1976, July 5       Litho.   *Perf. 14½*

| | | | | |
|---|---|---|---|---|
| 60 | A6 | 50c blue & multi | .30 | .25 |
| 61 | A6 | 1sh red & multi | .30 | .25 |
| 62 | A6 | 2sh yellow & multi | .40 | .35 |
| 63 | A6 | 3sh blue & multi | .80 | .55 |
| a. | | Souv. sheet of 4, #60-63, perf. 13 | 6.50 | 6.50 |
| | | *Nos. 60-63 (4)* | 1.80 | 1.40 |

21st Olympic Games, Montreal, Canada, July 17-Aug. 1.

Tanzania-Zambia Railway — A7

Designs: 1sh, Nile Bridge, Uganda. 2sh, Nakuru Station, Kenya. 3sh, Class A locomotive, 1896.

## 1976, Oct. 4       Litho.   *Perf. 14½*

| | | | | |
|---|---|---|---|---|
| 64 | A7 | 50c lilac & multi | .40 | .25 |
| 65 | A7 | 1sh emerald & multi | .70 | .25 |
| 66 | A7 | 2sh brt rose & multi | 1.40 | 1.00 |
| 67 | A7 | 3sh yellow & multi | 1.50 | 1.40 |
| a. | | Souv. sheet of 4, #64-67, perf. 13 | 9.00 | 9.00 |
| | | *Nos. 64-67 (4)* | 4.00 | 2.90 |

Rail transport in East Africa. No. 67a exists imperf., value $22.50.

Nile Perch — A8

Game Fish: 1sh, Tilapia. 3sh, Sailfish. 5sh, Black marlin.

## 1977, Jan. 10      Litho.   *Perf. 14½*

| | | | | |
|---|---|---|---|---|
| 68 | A8 | 50c multicolored | .30 | .25 |
| 69 | A8 | 1sh multicolored | .35 | .25 |
| 70 | A8 | 3sh multicolored | 1.10 | .60 |
| 71 | A8 | 5sh multicolored | 1.25 | 1.00 |
| a. | | Souvenir sheet of 4, #68-71 | 11.00 | 11.00 |
| | | *Nos. 68-71 (4)* | 3.00 | 2.10 |

Festival Emblem and Masai Tribesmen Bleeding Cow — A9

Festival Emblem and: 1sh, Dancers from Uganda. 2sh, Makonde sculpture, Tanzania. 3sh, Tribesmen skinning hippopotamus.

## 1977, Jan. 15        *Perf. 13½x14*

| | | | | |
|---|---|---|---|---|
| 72 | A9 | 50c multicolored | .30 | .25 |
| 73 | A9 | 1sh multicolored | .30 | .30 |
| 74 | A9 | 2sh multicolored | .65 | .65 |
| 75 | A9 | 3sh multicolored | .80 | .80 |
| a. | | Souvenir sheet of 4, #72-75 | 5.00 | 5.00 |
| | | *Nos. 72-75 (4)* | 2.05 | 2.00 |

2nd World Black and African Festival, Lagos, Nigeria, Jan. 15-Feb. 12.

Automobile Passing through Village — A10

Safari Rally Emblem and: 1sh, Winner at finish line. 2sh, Car going through washout. 5sh, Car, elephants and Mt. Kenya.

## 1977, Apr. 5       Litho.   *Perf. 14*

| | | | | |
|---|---|---|---|---|
| 76 | A10 | 50c multicolored | .30 | .25 |
| 77 | A10 | 1sh multicolored | .30 | .35 |
| 78 | A10 | 2sh multicolored | .45 | .55 |
| 79 | A10 | 5sh multicolored | 1.80 | 2.10 |
| a. | | Souvenir sheet of 4, #76-79 | 5.00 | 5.00 |
| | | *Nos. 76-79 (4)* | 2.85 | 3.25 |

25th Safari Rally, Apr. 7-11.

Rev. Canon Apolo Kivebulaya A11

1sh, Uganda Cathedral. 2sh, Early grass-topped Cathedral. 5sh, Early tent congregation, Kigezi.

## 1977, June 20      Litho.   *Perf. 14*

| | | | | |
|---|---|---|---|---|
| 80 | A11 | 50c multicolored | .30 | .25 |
| 81 | A11 | 1sh multicolored | .30 | .25 |
| 82 | A11 | 2sh multicolored | .35 | .40 |

| | | | | |
|---|---|---|---|---|
| 83 | A11 | 5sh multicolored | 1.00 | 1.25 |
| a. | | Souvenir sheet of 4, #80-83 | 1.75 | 1.75 |
| | | *Nos. 80-83 (4)* | 1.95 | 2.15 |

Church of Uganda, centenary.

Elizabeth II and Prince Philip at Sagana Lodge — A12

Designs: 5sh, "Treetops" observation hut, Aberdare Forest, and elephants, vert. 10sh, Pres. Jomo Kenyatta, Elizabeth II, crossed spears and shield. 15sh, Elizabeth II and Pres. Kenyatta in open automobile. 50sh, Elizabeth II and Prince Philip at window in Treetops.

## 1977, July 20      Litho.   *Perf. 14*

| | | | | |
|---|---|---|---|---|
| 84 | A12 | 2sh multicolored | .30 | .25 |
| 85 | A12 | 5sh multicolored | .30 | .25 |
| 86 | A12 | 10sh multicolored | .55 | .55 |
| 87 | A12 | 15sh multicolored | .65 | .65 |
| a. | | Souvenir sheet of 1 | 1.25 | 1.25 |
| | | *Nos. 84-87 (4)* | 1.80 | 1.70 |

### Souvenir Sheet

| | | | | |
|---|---|---|---|---|
| 88 | A12 | 50sh multicolored | 3.50 | 3.50 |

Reign of Queen Elizabeth II, 25th anniv.

Pancake Tortoise A13

Wildlife Fund Emblem and; 1sh, Nile crocodile. 2sh, Hunter's hartebeest. 3sh, Red colobus monkey. 5sh, Dugong.

## 1977, Sept. 26     Litho.   *Perf. 14x13½*

| | | | | |
|---|---|---|---|---|
| 89 | A13 | 50c multicolored | .50 | .25 |
| 90 | A13 | 1sh multicolored | .70 | .30 |
| 91 | A13 | 2sh multicolored | 1.75 | 1.75 |
| 92 | A13 | 3sh multicolored | 2.50 | 2.50 |
| 93 | A13 | 5sh multicolored | 2.75 | 2.75 |
| a. | | Souvenir sheet of 4, #90-93 | 9.00 | 9.00 |
| | | *Nos. 89-93 (5)* | 8.20 | 7.55 |

Endangered species.

Kenya-Ethiopia Border Point — A14

Designs: 1sh, Station wagon at Archer's Post. 2sh, Thika overpass. 5sh, Marsabit Game Lodge and elephant.

## 1977, Nov. 10      Litho.   *Perf. 14*

| | | | | |
|---|---|---|---|---|
| 94 | A14 | 50c multicolored | .30 | .25 |
| 95 | A14 | 1sh multicolored | .30 | .25 |
| 96 | A14 | 2sh multicolored | .40 | .40 |
| 97 | A14 | 5sh multicolored | .80 | .80 |
| a. | | Souvenir sheet of 4, #94-97 | 2.25 | 2.25 |
| | | *Nos. 94-97 (4)* | 1.80 | 1.70 |

Opening of Nairobi-Addis Ababa highway.

Minerals Found in Kenya — A15

A16

10c, Gypsum. 20c, Trona. 30c, Kyanite. 40c, Amazonite. 50c, Galena. 70c, Silicified wood. 80c, Fluorite. 1sh, Amethyst. 1.50sh, Agate. 2sh, Tourmaline. 3sh, Aquamarine. 5sh, Rhodolite garnet. 10sh, Sapphire. 20sh, Ruby. 40sh, Green grossular garnet.

### Perf. 14½x14, 14½ (A16)

## 1977, Dec. 13                       Photo.

| | | | | |
|---|---|---|---|---|
| 98 | A15 | 10c multicolored | 1.15 | .25 |
| 99 | A15 | 20c multicolored | 1.85 | .25 |
| 100 | A15 | 30c multicolored | 1.85 | .25 |
| 101 | A15 | 40c multicolored | 1.40 | .25 |
| 102 | A15 | 50c multicolored | 1.40 | .25 |
| 103 | A15 | 70c multicolored | 7.00 | .90 |
| 104 | A15 | 80c multicolored | 7.00 | .75 |
| 105 | A16 | 1sh multicolored | 1.40 | .25 |

| | | | | |
|---|---|---|---|---|
| 106 | A16 | 1.50sh multicolored | 1.40 | .40 |
| 107 | A16 | 2sh multicolored | 1.40 | .35 |
| 108 | A16 | 3sh multicolored | 1.65 | 1.00 |
| 109 | A16 | 5sh multicolored | 1.65 | 1.25 |
| 110 | A16 | 10sh multicolored | 1.85 | 2.00 |
| 111 | A16 | 20sh multicolored | 4.25 | 3.00 |
| 112 | A16 | 40sh multicolored | 16.50 | 20.00 |
| | | *Nos. 98-112 (15)* | 51.75 | 31.15 |

The 10c, 20c, 40c, 50c and 80c were also issued in booklet panes of 4. The 50c was also issued in a booklet pane of 2.
For surcharge see No. 242.

Soccer, Joe Kadenge and World Cup — A17

World Cup and: 1sh, Mohammed Chuma receiving trophy, and his portrait. 2sh, Shot on goal and Omari S. Kidevu. 3sh, Backfield defense and Polly Ouma.

## 1978, Apr. 10      Litho.   *Perf. 14x13½*

| | | | | |
|---|---|---|---|---|
| 113 | A17 | 50c green & multi | .30 | .25 |
| 114 | A17 | 1sh lt brown & multi | .30 | .25 |
| 115 | A17 | 2sh lilac & multi | .30 | *.70* |
| 116 | A17 | 3sh dk blue & multi | .50 | *1.00* |
| a. | | Souvenir sheet of 4, #113-116 | 3.75 | 3.75 |
| | | *Nos. 113-116 (4)* | 1.40 | 2.20 |

World Soccer Cup Championships, Argentina 78, June 1-25.

Boxing and Games' Emblem — A18

Games Emblem and: 1sh, Pres. Kenyatta welcoming 1968 Olympic team. 3sh, Javelin. 5sh, Pres. Kenyatta, boxing team and trophy.

## 1978, July 15      Photo.   *Perf. 13x14*

| | | | | |
|---|---|---|---|---|
| 117 | A18 | 50c multicolored | .30 | .25 |
| 118 | A18 | 1sh multicolored | .30 | .25 |
| 119 | A18 | 3sh multicolored | .70 | .70 |
| 120 | A18 | 5sh multicolored | .85 | .85 |
| | | *Nos. 117-120 (4)* | 2.15 | 2.05 |

Commonwealth Games, Edmonton, Canada, Aug. 3-12.

Overloaded Truck — A19

Road Safety: 1sh, Observe speed limit. 1.50sh, Observe traffic lights. 2sh, School crossing. 3sh, Passing. 5sh, Railroad crossing.

## 1978, Sept. 18     Litho.   *Perf. 13½x14*

| | | | | |
|---|---|---|---|---|
| 121 | A19 | 50c multicolored | .45 | .25 |
| 122 | A19 | 1sh multicolored | .65 | .25 |
| 123 | A19 | 1.50sh multicolored | 1.00 | 1.00 |
| 124 | A19 | 2sh multicolored | 1.55 | 1.50 |
| 125 | A19 | 3sh multicolored | 1.80 | *2.25* |
| 126 | A19 | 5sh multicolored | 2.00 | *2.50* |
| | | *Nos. 121-126 (6)* | 7.45 | 7.75 |

Pres. Kenyatta at Harambee Water Project Opening — A20

Kenyatta Day: 1sh, Prince Philip handing over symbol of independence, 1963. 2sh, Pres. Jomo Kenyatta addressing independence rally. 3sh, Stage at 15th independence anniversary celebration. 5sh, Handcuffed Kenyatta led by soldiers, 1952.

## 1978, Oct. 16      Litho.   *Perf. 14*

| | | | | |
|---|---|---|---|---|
| 127 | A20 | 50c multicolored | .35 | .35 |
| 128 | A20 | 1sh multicolored | .35 | .35 |
| 129 | A20 | 2sh multicolored | .45 | .45 |
| 130 | A20 | 3sh multicolored | .70 | .70 |
| 131 | A20 | 5sh multicolored | .95 | .95 |
| | | *Nos. 127-131 (5)* | 2.80 | 2.80 |

KENYA

Soldiers and
Emblem — A21

Anti-Apartheid Emblem and: 1sh, Anti-
Apartheid Conference. 2sh, Stephen Biko,
South African Anti-Apartheid leader. 3sh, Nel-
son Mandela, jailed since 1961. 5sh, Bishop
Lamont, expelled from Rhodesia in 1977.

**1978, Dec. 11   Litho.       Perf. 14x14½**
| 132 | A21 | 50c multicolored | .30 | .30 |
|-----|-----|------------------|-----|-----|
| 133 | A21 | 1sh multicolored | .30 | .30 |
| 134 | A21 | 2sh multicolored | .45 | .45 |
| 135 | A21 | 3sh multicolored | .65 | .65 |
| 136 | A21 | 5sh multicolored | .75 | .75 |
|     |     | Nos. 132-136 (5) | 2.45 | 2.45 |

Anti-Apartheid Year and Namibia's struggle
for independence.

Children on
School
Playground
A22

Children's Year Emblem and: 2sh, Boy
catching fish. 3sh, Children dancing and singing. 5sh, Children and camel caravan.

**1979, Feb. 5   Litho.       Perf. 14**
| 137 | A22 | 50c multicolored | .35 | .35 |
|-----|-----|------------------|-----|-----|
| 138 | A22 | 2sh multicolored | .55 | .55 |
| 139 | A22 | 3sh multicolored | .70 | .70 |
| 140 | A22 | 5sh multicolored | 1.00 | 1.00 |
|     |     | Nos. 137-140 (4) | 2.60 | 2.60 |

International Year of the Child.

"The Lion and
the
Jewel" — A23

National Theater: 1sh, Dancers and drummers. 2sh, Programs of various productions.
3sh, View of National Theater. 5sh, "Genesis,"
performed by Nairobi City Players.

**1979, Apr. 6   Litho.       Perf. 13½x14**
| 141 | A23 | 50c multicolored | .30 | .25 |
|-----|-----|------------------|-----|-----|
| 142 | A23 | 1sh multicolored | .30 | .30 |
| 143 | A23 | 2sh multicolored | .35 | .35 |
| 144 | A23 | 3sh multicolored | .55 | .55 |
| 145 | A23 | 5sh multicolored | .75 | .75 |
|     |     | Nos. 141-145 (5) | 2.25 | 2.20 |

Village
Workshop
A24

Salvation Army Emblem and: 50c, Blind
telephone operator, vert. 1sh, Care for the
aged, vert. 5sh, Vocational training (nurse).

**1979, June 4   Perf. 13½x13, 13x13½**
| 146 | A24 | 50c multicolored | .30 | .30 |
|-----|-----|------------------|-----|-----|
| 147 | A24 | 1sh multicolored | .30 | .30 |
| 148 | A24 | 3sh multicolored | .75 | .75 |
| 149 | A24 | 5sh multicolored | 1.25 | 1.25 |
|     |     | Nos. 146-149 (4) | 2.60 | 2.60 |

Salvation Army Social Services, 50th anniv.

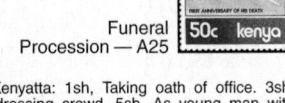

Funeral
Procession — A25

Kenyatta: 1sh, Taking oath of office. 3sh,
Addressing crowd. 5sh, As young man with
wooden trying plane.

**1979, Aug. 22   Litho.       Perf. 13½x14**
| 150 | A25 | 50c multicolored | .30 | .25 |
|-----|-----|------------------|-----|-----|
| 151 | A25 | 1sh multicolored | .30 | .25 |
| 152 | A25 | 3sh multicolored | .50 | .50 |
| 153 | A25 | 5sh multicolored | .75 | .75 |
|     |     | Nos. 150-153 (4) | 1.85 | 1.75 |

Jomo Kenyatta (1893-1978), first president
of Kenya.

British East Africa No.
2, Hill, Signature — A26

Hill, Signature and: 1sh, Kenya, Uganda and
Tanzania #54. 2sh, Penny Black. 5sh, Kenya
#19.

**1979, Nov. 27   Litho.       Perf. 14**
| 154 | A26 | 50c multicolored | .30 | .25 |
|-----|-----|------------------|-----|-----|
| 155 | A26 | 1sh multicolored | .30 | .25 |
| 156 | A26 | 2sh multicolored | .30 | .25 |
| 157 | A26 | 5sh multicolored | .65 | .65 |
|     |     | Nos. 154-157 (4) | 1.55 | 1.40 |

Sir Rowland Hill (1795-1879), originator of
penny postage.

Highways,
Globe,
Conference
Emblem
A27

Conference Emblem and: 1sh, Truck at Athi
River, New Weighbridge. 3sh, New Nyali
Bridge, Mombasa. 5sh, Jomo Kenyatta Airport
Highway.

**1980, Jan. 10   Litho.       Perf. 14**
| 158 | A27 | 50c multicolored | .30 | .25 |
|-----|-----|------------------|-----|-----|
| 159 | A27 | 1sh multicolored | .30 | .25 |
| 160 | A27 | 3sh multicolored | .60 | .60 |
| 161 | A27 | 5sh multicolored | .85 | .85 |
|     |     | Nos. 158-161 (4) | 2.05 | 1.95 |

4th IRF African Highway Conference, Nairobi, Jan. 20-25.

Patient
Airlift — A28

50c, Outdoor clinic. 1sh, Mule transport of
patient, vert.. 3sh, Surgery, vert.

**1980, Mar. 20   Litho.       Perf. 14½**
| 162 | A28 | 50c multicolored | .30 | .25 |
|-----|-----|------------------|-----|-----|
| 163 | A28 | 1sh multicolored | .30 | .25 |
| 164 | A28 | 3sh multicolored | .65 | .65 |
| 165 | A28 | 5sh shown | 1.00 | 1.00 |
| a. | | Souvenir sheet of 4, #162-165 | 2.75 | 2.75 |
|     |     | Nos. 162-165 (4) | 2.25 | 2.15 |

Flying doctor service.

Hill Statue,
Kidderminster and Mt.
Kenya — A29

**1980, May 6   Litho.       Perf. 14**
| 166 | A29 | 25sh multicolored | 1.25 | 1.25 |
|-----|-----|-------------------|------|------|
| a. | | Souvenir sheet | 1.50 | 2.00 |

London 1980 International Stamp Exhibition, May 6-14.

Pope John
Paul II and
Crowd — A30

Visit of Pope John Paul II to Kenya: 1sh,
Pope, Nairobi Cathedral, papal flag and arms,
vert. 5sh, Pope, papal and Kenya flags, dove,

vert. 10sh, Pres. arap Moi of Kenya, Pope, flag
of Kenya on map of Africa.

**1980, May 8       Perf. 13½**
| 167 | A30 | 50c multicolored | .35 | .25 |
|-----|-----|------------------|-----|-----|
| 168 | A30 | 1sh multicolored | .45 | .45 |
| 169 | A30 | 5sh multicolored | 1.00 | 1.00 |
| 170 | A30 | 10sh multicolored | 1.75 | 1.75 |
|     |     | Nos. 167-170 (4) | 3.55 | 3.45 |

Sting Ray — A31

**1980, June 27   Litho.       Perf. 14½**
| 171 | A31 | 50c shown | .50 | .25 |
|-----|-----|-----------|-----|-----|
| 172 | A31 | 2sh Alkit snapper | 1.25 | .60 |
| 173 | A31 | 3sh Sea slug | 1.40 | 1.40 |
| 174 | A31 | 5sh Hawksbill turtle | 2.50 | 2.50 |
|     |     | Nos. 171-174 (4) | 5.65 | 4.75 |

National
Archives,
1904 — A32

1sh, Commissioner's Office, Nairobi, 1913.
1.50sh, Nairobi House, 1913. 2sh, Norfolk
Hotel, 1904. 3sh, McMillan Library, 1929. 5sh,
Kipande House, 1913.

**1980, Oct. 9   Litho.       Perf. 14**
| 175 | A32 | 50c shown | .30 | .25 |
|-----|-----|-----------|-----|-----|
| 176 | A32 | 1sh multicolored | .30 | .25 |
| 177 | A32 | 1.50sh multicolored | .30 | .25 |
| 178 | A32 | 2sh multicolored | .35 | .45 |
| 179 | A32 | 3sh multicolored | .50 | .95 |
| 180 | A32 | 5sh multicolored | .60 | 1.50 |
|     |     | Nos. 175-180 (6) | 2.35 | 3.65 |

Woman in
Wheelchair and
Child — A33

1sh, Pres. arap Moi, team captain. 3sh,
Blind mountain climbers, Mt. Kenya, 1965.
5sh, Disabled artist.

**1981, Feb. 10   Litho.       Perf. 14x13½**
| 181 | A33 | 50c shown | .30 | .25 |
|-----|-----|-----------|-----|-----|
| 182 | A33 | 1sh multicolored | .30 | .25 |
| 183 | A33 | 3sh multicolored | .55 | .55 |
| 184 | A33 | 5sh multicolored | 1.00 | 1.00 |
|     |     | Nos. 181-184 (4) | 2.15 | 2.05 |

International Year of the Disabled.

Longonot
Earth Station
Complex
A34

**1981, Apr. 4   Litho.       Perf. 14x14½**
| 185 | A34 | 50c shown | .30 | .30 |
|-----|-----|-----------|-----|-----|
| 186 | A34 | 2sh Intelsat V | .40 | .40 |
| 187 | A34 | 3sh Longonot I | .50 | .50 |
| 188 | A34 | 5sh Longonot II | .85 | .85 |
|     |     | Nos. 185-188 (4) | 2.05 | 2.05 |

Conference
Center, OAU
Flag — A35

18th Organization for African Unity Conference, Nairobi: 1sh, Map of Africa showing
Panaftel earth stations. 3sh, Parliament Building, Nairobi. 5sh, Jomo Kenyatta Intl. Airport.
10sh, OAU flag.

**1981, June 24   Wmk. 373   Perf. 13½**
| 189 | A35 | 50c multicolored | .30 | .25 |
|-----|-----|------------------|-----|-----|
| 190 | A35 | 1sh multicolored | .30 | .25 |
| 191 | A35 | 3sh multicolored | .55 | .55 |
| 192 | A35 | 5sh multicolored | .70 | .70 |
| 193 | A35 | 10sh multicolored | 1.40 | 1.40 |
| a. | | Souvenir sheet of 1, perf. 14½ | 2.00 | 2.00 |
|     |     | Nos. 189-193 (5) | 3.25 | 3.15 |

St. Paul's
Cathedral — A36

50c, Charles, Pres. arap Moi. 5sh, Britannia.
10sh, Charles.
25sh, Couple.

**1981, July 29   Litho.       Perf. 14, 12**
| 194 | A36 | 50c multicolored | .30 | .25 |
|-----|-----|------------------|-----|-----|
| 195 | A36 | 3sh shown | .30 | .25 |
| 196 | A36 | 5sh multicolored | .30 | .30 |
| 197 | A36 | 10sh multicolored | .30 | .60 |
|     |     | Nos. 194-197 (4) | 1.20 | 1.40 |

**Souvenir Sheet**
| 198 | A36 | 25sh multicolored | 1.50 | 1.50 |
|-----|-----|-------------------|------|------|

Royal Wedding.
Perf. 12 comes from minisheets of 5 + label.
Value, set of 4 sheets $7.50.

Reticulated
Giraffe — A37

**1981, Aug. 31   Litho.       Perf. 14½**
| 199 | A37 | 50c shown | .30 | .30 |
|-----|-----|-----------|-----|-----|
| 200 | A37 | 2sh Bongo | .30 | .30 |
| 201 | A37 | 5sh Roan antelope | .65 | .65 |
| 202 | A37 | 10sh Mangabey | 1.90 | 1.90 |
|     |     | Nos. 199-202 (4) | 3.15 | 3.15 |

World Food Day — A38

1sh, Pres. arap Moi, team captain. 3sh,
Blind mountain climbers, Mt. Kenya, 1965.

**1981, Oct. 16   Litho.       Perf. 14**
| 203 | A38 | 50c Plowing | .25 | .25 |
|-----|-----|-------------|-----|-----|
| 204 | A38 | 1sh Rice field | .25 | .25 |
| 205 | A38 | 2sh Irrigation | .40 | .40 |
| 206 | A38 | 5sh Cattle | .90 | .90 |
|     |     | Nos. 203-206 (4) | 1.80 | 1.80 |

Ceremonial Tribal
Costumes — A39

**            Perf. 14½x13½**
**1981, Dec. 18                  Litho.**
| 207 | A39 | 50c Kamba | .45 | .25 |
|-----|-----|-----------|-----|-----|
| 208 | A39 | 1sh Turkana | .55 | .25 |
| 209 | A39 | 2sh Giriama | 1.25 | .80 |
| 210 | A39 | 3sh Masai | 1.75 | 2.25 |
| 211 | A39 | 5sh Luo | 2.00 | 4.00 |
|     |     | Nos. 207-211 (5) | 6.00 | 7.55 |

Australopithecus Boisei — A40

2sh, Homo erectus. 3sh, Homo habilis. 5sh,
Proconsul africanus.

**1982, Jan. 16   Litho.       Perf. 14**
| 212 | A40 | 50c shown | 1.75 | .40 |
|-----|-----|-----------|------|-----|
| 213 | A40 | 2sh multicolored | 2.75 | 1.50 |
| 214 | A40 | 3sh multicolored | 3.00 | 3.50 |
| 215 | A40 | 5sh multicolored | 3.50 | 5.00 |
|     |     | Nos. 212-215 (4) | 11.00 | 10.40 |

265

Scouting Year — A41

No. 216, Tree planting. No. 217, Paying homage. No. 218, Be Prepared. No. 219, Intl. friendship. No. 220, Helping disabled. No. 221, Community service. No. 222, Paxtu Cottage. No. 223, Lady Baden-Powell.

| | | | |
|---|---|---|---|
| **1982, June 2** | **Litho.** | | **Perf. 14½** |
| 216 A41 | 70c multicolored | .50 | .50 |
| 217 A41 | 70c multicolored | .50 | .50 |
| a. | Pair, #216-217 | 1.25 | 1.25 |
| 218 A41 | 3.50sh multicolored | 1.25 | 1.25 |
| 219 A41 | 3.50sh multicolored | 1.25 | 1.25 |
| a. | Pair, #218-219 | 3.00 | 3.00 |
| 220 A41 | 5sh multicolored | 1.60 | 1.60 |
| 221 A41 | 5sh multicolored | 1.60 | 1.60 |
| a. | Pair, #220-221 | 4.50 | 4.50 |
| 222 A41 | 6.50sh multicolored | 2.25 | 2.25 |
| 223 A41 | 6.50sh multicolored | 2.25 | 2.25 |
| a. | Pair, #222-223 | 6.25 | 6.25 |
| | Nos. 216-223 (8) | 11.20 | 11.20 |

**Souvenir Sheet**

| | | | |
|---|---|---|---|
| 224 | Sheet of 4 | 6.00 | 6.00 |
| a. | A41 70c like #216 | .30 | .25 |
| b. | A41 3.50sh like #218 | 1.00 | 1.00 |
| c. | A41 5sh like #220 | 1.50 | 1.50 |
| d. | A41 6.50sh like #222 | 2.00 | 2.00 |

1982 World Cup A42

Various soccer players on world map.

| | | | |
|---|---|---|---|
| **1982, July 5** | **Litho.** | | **Perf. 12½** |
| 225 A42 | 70c multicolored | 1.25 | .50 |
| 226 A42 | 3.50sh multicolored | 2.75 | 2.50 |
| 227 A42 | 5sh multicolored | 3.25 | 4.25 |
| 228 A42 | 10sh multicolored | 4.75 | 6.50 |
| | Nos. 225-228 (4) | 12.00 | 13.75 |

**Souvenir Sheet**
**Perf. 13½x14**

| | | | |
|---|---|---|---|
| 229 A42 | 20sh multicolored | 6.00 | 6.00 |

A43

| | | | |
|---|---|---|---|
| **1982, Sept. 28** | **Litho.** | | **Perf. 14½** |
| 230 A43 | 70c Cattle judging | .60 | .25 |
| 231 A43 | 2.50sh Farm machinery | 1.05 | 1.25 |
| 232 A43 | 3.50sh Musical ride | 1.65 | 2.00 |
| 233 A43 | 6.50sh Emblem | 2.50 | 4.00 |
| | Nos. 230-233 (4) | 5.80 | 7.50 |

Agricultural Society, 80th anniv.

A44

70c, Microwave radio system. 3.50sh, Ship-to-shore communication. 5sh, Rural telecommunication. 6.50sh, Emblem.

| | | | |
|---|---|---|---|
| **1982, Oct. 27** | **Photo.** | | **Perf. 11½** |
| **Granite Paper** | | | |
| 234 A44 | 70c multicolored | .50 | .25 |
| 235 A44 | 3.50sh multicolored | 1.75 | 1.75 |
| 236 A44 | 5sh multicolored | 2.25 | 2.25 |
| 237 A44 | 6.50sh multicolored | 3.00 | 3.00 |
| | Nos. 234-237 (4) | 7.50 | 7.25 |

ITU Plenipoteniaries Conf., Nairobi, Sept.

5th Anniv. of Kenya Ports Authority — A45

70c, Container cranes. 2sh, Cranes, diff. 3.50sh, Cranes, diff. 5sh, Mombasa Harbor map.

| | | | |
|---|---|---|---|
| **1983, Jan. 20** | **Litho.** | | **Perf. 14** |
| 238 A45 | 70c multicolored | .70 | .25 |
| 239 A45 | 2sh multicolored | 1.60 | 1.60 |
| 240 A45 | 3.50sh multicolored | 2.25 | 2.50 |
| 241 A45 | 5sh multicolored | 2.95 | 2.95 |
| a. | Souvenir sheet of 4, #238-241 | 7.50 | 7.50 |
| | Nos. 238-241 (4) | 7.50 | 7.30 |

**No. 104 Surcharged**

| | | | |
|---|---|---|---|
| **1983, Jan.** | **Photo.** | | **Perf. 14½x14** |
| 242 A15 | 70c on 80c multicolored | 1.50 | 1.50 |

A45a

70c, Coffee picking, vert. 2sh, Pres. arap Moi, vert. 5sh, Globe. 10sh, Masai dance.

| | | | |
|---|---|---|---|
| **1983, Mar. 14** | **Litho.** | | **Perf. 14½** |
| 243 A45a | 70c multicolored | .30 | .25 |
| 244 A45a | 2sh multicolored | .30 | .25 |
| 245 A45a | 5sh multicolored | .40 | .40 |
| 246 A45a | 10sh multicolored | .85 | .85 |
| | Nos. 243-246 (4) | 1.85 | 1.75 |

Commonwealth Day.

Dichrostachys Cinerea A46

Dombeya Burgessiae A47

20c, Rhamphicarpa montana. 30c, Barleria eranthemoides. 40c, Commelina. 50c, Canarina abyssinica. 70c, Aspilia mossambicensis. 1sh, Dombeya burgessiae. 1.50sh, Lantana trifolia. 2sh, Adenium obesum. 2.50sh, Terminalia orbicularis. 3.50sh, Ceropegia ballyana. 5sh, Ruttya fruticosa. 10sh, Pentanisia ouranogyne. 20sh, Brillantaisia nyanzarum. 40sh, Crotalaria axillaris.

**Perf. 14½x14, 14x14½**

| | | | |
|---|---|---|---|
| **1983, Feb. 15** | | | **Photo.** |
| 247 A46 | 10c shown | .50 | .40 |
| 248 A46 | 20c multicolored | .70 | .40 |
| 249 A46 | 30c multicolored | .70 | .40 |
| 250 A46 | 40c multicolored | .70 | .40 |
| 251 A46 | 50c multicolored | .70 | .30 |
| 252 A46 | 70c multicolored | .80 | .25 |
| 253 A47 | 1sh multicolored | .90 | .25 |
| 254 A47 | 1.50sh multicolored | 2.00 | .65 |
| 255 A47 | 2sh multicolored | 2.00 | .65 |
| 256 A47 | 2.50sh multicolored | 2.25 | .65 |
| 257 A47 | 3.50sh multicolored | 2.00 | 1.60 |
| 258 A47 | 5sh multicolored | 1.60 | 1.50 |
| 259 A47 | 10sh multicolored | 1.60 | 1.50 |
| 260 A47 | 20sh multicolored | 1.75 | 2.75 |
| 261 A47 | 40sh multicolored | 2.75 | 8.00 |
| | Nos. 247-261 (15) | 20.95 | 19.70 |

See Nos. 350-354.

30th Anniv. of Customs Cooperation Council — A48

70c, Parcel check. 2.50sh, Headquarters, Mombasa. 3.50sh, Headquarters, Brussels. 10sh, Patrol boat.

| | | | |
|---|---|---|---|
| **1983, May 11** | **Litho.** | | **Perf. 14½** |
| 262 A48 | 70c multicolored | .30 | .25 |
| 263 A48 | 2.50sh multicolored | .65 | .30 |
| 264 A48 | 3.50sh multicolored | .75 | .40 |
| 265 A48 | 10sh multicolored | 2.50 | 2.50 |
| | Nos. 262-265 (4) | 4.20 | 3.45 |

World Communications Year — A49

70c, Satellite, dish antenna, vert. 2.50sh, Mailbox, birthday card, telephone, vert. 3.50sh, Jet, ship. 5sh, Railroad bridge, highway.

| | | | |
|---|---|---|---|
| **1983, July 4** | **Litho.** | | **Perf. 14½** |
| 266 A49 | 70c multicolored | .65 | .25 |
| 267 A49 | 2.50sh multicolored | 1.50 | 1.50 |
| 268 A49 | 3.50sh multicolored | 2.25 | 2.25 |
| 269 A49 | 5sh multicolored | 2.50 | 2.50 |
| | Nos. 266-269 (4) | 6.90 | 6.50 |

Intl. Maritime Organization, 25th Anniv. — A50

70c, Kilindini Harbor. 2.50sh, Life preserver. 3.50sh, Mombasa Container Terminal. 10sh, Marine Park.

| | | | |
|---|---|---|---|
| **1983, Sept. 22** | **Litho.** | | **Perf. 14½** |
| 270 A50 | 70c multicolored | 1.00 | .25 |
| 271 A50 | 2.50sh multicolored | 2.00 | 1.50 |
| 272 A50 | 3.50sh multicolored | 2.50 | 2.50 |
| 273 A50 | 10sh multicolored | 3.00 | 3.75 |
| | Nos. 270-273 (4) | 8.50 | 8.00 |

29th Commonwealth Parliamentary Conference A51

2.50sh, Parliament Bldg., vert. 5sh, State Opening, vert.

| | | | |
|---|---|---|---|
| **1983, Oct. 31** | **Litho.** | | **Perf. 14** |
| 274 A51 | 70c shown | .35 | .25 |
| 275 A51 | 2.50sh multicolored | 1.25 | 1.25 |
| 276 A51 | 5sh multicolored | 1.75 | 2.25 |
| a. | Souv. sheet of 3, #274-276 + label | 3.50 | 3.50 |
| | Nos. 274-276 (3) | 3.35 | 3.75 |

Royal Visit — A52

70c, Flags. 3.50sh, Sagana State Lodge. 5sh, Tree Tops Hotel. 10sh, Elizabeth II and Daniel arap Moi.

| | | | |
|---|---|---|---|
| **1983, Nov. 10** | **Litho.** | | **Perf. 14** |
| 277 A52 | 70c multicolored | .50 | .25 |
| 278 A52 | 3.50sh multicolored | 1.70 | 1.50 |
| 279 A52 | 5sh multicolored | 1.90 | 2.25 |
| 280 A52 | 10sh multicolored | 2.95 | 4.50 |
| | Nos. 277-280 (4) | 7.05 | 8.50 |

**Souvenir Sheet**

| | | | |
|---|---|---|---|
| 281 A52 | 25sh multicolored | 5.50 | 5.50 |

No. 281 contains Nos. 277-280 without denominations showing simulated perforations.

President Daniel arap Moi, Monument A53

2sh, Tree planting. 3.50sh, Map, flag, emblem. 5sh, School, milk program. 10sh, People, flag, banner.

| | | | |
|---|---|---|---|
| **1983, Dec. 9** | **Litho.** | | **Perf. 14½** |
| 282 A53 | 70c shown | .30 | .25 |
| 283 A53 | 2sh multicolored | .30 | .25 |
| 284 A53 | 3.50sh multicolored | .35 | .35 |
| 285 A53 | 5sh multicolored | .55 | .55 |
| 286 A53 | 10sh multicolored | .95 | .95 |
| | Nos. 282-286 (5) | 2.45 | 2.35 |

**Souvenir Sheet**
*Imperf*

| | | | |
|---|---|---|---|
| 287 A53 | 25sh multicolored | 3.00 | 3.00 |

Independence, 20th Anniv. No. 287 contains Nos. 282, 284-286 without denominations.

Rare Local Birds — A54

70c, White-backed night heron. 2.50sh, Quail plover. 3.50sh, Heller's ground thrush. 5sh, Papyrus gonolek. 10sh, White-winged Apalis.

| | | | |
|---|---|---|---|
| **1984, Feb. 6** | **Litho.** | | **Perf. 14½x13½** |
| 288 A54 | 70c multicolored | 2.00 | .40 |
| 289 A54 | 2.50sh multicolored | 2.50 | 2.50 |
| 290 A54 | 3.50sh multicolored | 3.75 | 3.75 |
| 291 A54 | 5sh multicolored | 4.50 | 4.50 |
| 292 A54 | 10sh multicolored | 5.75 | 6.75 |
| | Nos. 288-292 (5) | 18.50 | 17.90 |

Intl. Civil Aviation Org., 40th Anniv. — A55

70c, Radar, vert. 2.50sh, Kenya School of Aviation. 3.50sh, Jet, Moi Intl. Airport. 5sh, Air traffic control center, vert.

| | | | |
|---|---|---|---|
| **1984, Apr. 2** | **Litho.** | | **Perf. 14** |
| 293 A55 | 70c multicolored | .30 | .25 |
| 294 A55 | 2.50sh multicolored | .50 | .50 |
| 295 A55 | 3.50sh multicolored | .80 | .80 |
| 296 A55 | 5sh multicolored | 1.25 | 1.25 |
| | Nos. 293-296 (4) | 2.85 | 2.80 |

1984 Summer Olympics A56

| | | | |
|---|---|---|---|
| **1984, May 21** | | | **Perf. 14½** |
| 297 A56 | 70c Running | .40 | .40 |
| 298 A56 | 2.50sh Hurdles | .75 | .75 |
| 299 A56 | 5sh Boxing | 1.25 | 1.25 |
| 300 A56 | 10sh Field Hockey | 4.00 | 4.00 |
| | Nos. 297-300 (4) | 6.40 | 6.40 |

**Souvenir Sheet**
*Imperf*

| | | | |
|---|---|---|---|
| 301 A56 | 25sh Torch bearers | 5.00 | 5.00 |

No. 301 contains designs of Nos. 297-300.

Bookmobile A57

70c, Emblem. 5sh, Adult library. 10sh, Children's library.

| | | | |
|---|---|---|---|
| **1984, Aug. 10** | **Litho.** | | **Perf. 14½** |
| 302 A57 | 70c multicolored | .30 | .25 |
| 303 A57 | 3.50sh shown | .45 | .45 |
| 304 A57 | 5sh multicolored | .65 | .65 |
| 305 A57 | 10sh multicolored | .95 | .95 |
| | Nos. 302-305 (4) | 2.35 | 2.30 |

Intl. Fed. of Library Associations, 50th Conf.

Kenya Export Year (KEY) — A58

| | | | |
|---|---|---|---|
| **1984, Oct. 1** | **Litho.** | | **Perf. 14** |
| 306 A58 | 70c Emblem, vert. | .30 | .30 |
| 307 A58 | 3.50sh Airport | 1.65 | 1.65 |
| 308 A58 | 5sh Harbor, vert. | 2.50 | 2.50 |
| 309 A58 | 10sh Exports | 3.50 | 3.50 |
| | Nos. 306-309 (4) | 7.95 | 7.95 |

70c, Doves, cross. 2.50sh, Doves, Hinduism symbol. 3.50sh, Doves, Sikhism symbol. 6.50sh, Doves, Islam symbol.

**1984, Aug. 23    Litho.    Perf. 14x14½**
| | | | | |
|---|---|---|---|---|
| 310 | A59 | 70c multicolored | .30 | .30 |
| 311 | A59 | 2.50sh multicolored | 1.00 | 1.00 |
| 312 | A59 | 3.50sh multicolored | 1.50 | 1.50 |
| 313 | A59 | 6.50sh multicolored | 2.75 | 2.75 |
| | | Nos. 310-313 (4) | 5.55 | 5.55 |

World Conference on Religion and Peace, Nairobi, Aug. 23-31, 1984.

Tribal Costumes — A60

**1984, Nov. 5    Litho.    Perf. 14½x13½**
| | | | | |
|---|---|---|---|---|
| 314 | A60 | 70c Luhya | .75 | .30 |
| 315 | A60 | 2sh Kikuyu | 2.00 | 1.75 |
| 316 | A60 | 3.50sh Pokomo | 2.25 | 2.00 |
| 317 | A60 | 5sh Nandi | 2.75 | 2.75 |
| 318 | A60 | 10sh Rendile | 3.50 | 4.25 |
| | | Nos. 314-318 (5) | 11.25 | 11.05 |

60th Anniv., World Chess Federation A61

70c, Nyayo Stadium, knight. 2.50sh, Fort Jesus, rook. 3.50sh, National Monument, bishop. 5sh, Parliament, queen. 10sh, Nyayo Fountain, king.

**1984, Dec. 21    Litho.    Perf. 14½**
| | | | | |
|---|---|---|---|---|
| 319 | A61 | 70c multicolored | 1.75 | .50 |
| 320 | A61 | 2.50sh multicolored | 2.50 | 1.75 |
| 321 | A61 | 3.50sh multicolored | 3.00 | 2.00 |
| 322 | A61 | 5sh multicolored | 3.50 | 3.50 |
| 323 | A61 | 10sh multicolored | 5.50 | 7.00 |
| | | Nos. 319-323 (5) | 16.25 | 14.75 |

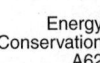

Energy Conservation A62

70c, Stove, fire pit. 2sh, Solar panel. 3.50sh, Biogas tank. 10sh, Plowing field. 20sh, Energy conservation.

**1985, Jan. 22    Litho.    Perf. 13½**
| | | | | |
|---|---|---|---|---|
| 324 | A62 | 70c multicolored | .30 | .25 |
| 325 | A62 | 2sh multicolored | .65 | .65 |
| 326 | A62 | 3.50sh multicolored | .80 | .80 |
| 327 | A62 | 10sh multicolored | 2.40 | 2.40 |
| 328 | A62 | 20sh multicolored | 4.25 | 4.25 |
| | | Nos. 324-328 (5) | 8.40 | 8.35 |

No. 328 contains Nos. 324-327 without denominations.

Girl Guides, 75th Anniv. — A63

1sh, Girl Guide, handicrafts. 3sh, Community service. 5sh, Lady Baden-Powell, Kenyan leader. 7sh, Food project.

**1985, Mar. 27    Litho.    Perf. 13½**
| | | | | |
|---|---|---|---|---|
| 329 | A63 | 1sh multicolored | .85 | .25 |
| 330 | A63 | 3sh multicolored | 1.65 | 1.00 |
| 331 | A63 | 5sh multicolored | 2.25 | 2.00 |
| 332 | A63 | 7sh multicolored | 3.25 | 4.00 |
| | | Nos. 329-332 (4) | 8.00 | 7.25 |

Intl. Red Cross Day — A64

**1985, May 8    Perf. 14½**
| | | | | |
|---|---|---|---|---|
| 333 | A64 | 1sh Emblem | .75 | .25 |
| 334 | A64 | 4sh First Aid | 2.25 | 2.25 |
| 335 | A64 | 5sh Blood donation | 2.75 | 2.75 |
| 336 | A64 | 7sh Famine relief, cornucopia | 3.75 | 4.25 |
| | | Nos. 333-336 (4) | 9.50 | 9.50 |

A65

Diseases caused by microorganisms carried by insects.

**1985, June 25**
| | | | | |
|---|---|---|---|---|
| 337 | A65 | 1sh Malaria | 1.65 | .50 |
| 338 | A65 | 3sh Leishmaniasis | 3.25 | 3.25 |
| 339 | A65 | 5sh Trypanosomiasis | 3.50 | 3.50 |
| 340 | A65 | 7sh Babesiosis | 5.75 | 9.00 |
| | | Nos. 337-340 (4) | 14.15 | 16.25 |

7th Intl. Congress on Protozoology, Nairobi, June 22-29.

UN Decade for Women — A66

1sh, Repairing water pipes. 3sh, Traditional food processing. 5sh, Basket weaving. 7sh, Dress making.

**1985, July 15**
| | | | | |
|---|---|---|---|---|
| 341 | A66 | 1sh multicolored | .35 | .25 |
| 342 | A66 | 3sh multicolored | .85 | .70 |
| 343 | A66 | 5sh multicolored | .95 | .95 |
| 344 | A66 | 7sh multicolored | 1.50 | 1.50 |
| | | Nos. 341-344 (4) | 3.65 | 3.40 |

43rd Intl. Eucharistic Congress, Nairobi, Aug. 11-18 — A67

1sh, The Last Supper. 3sh, Afro-Christian family. 5sh, Congress altar, Uhuru Park. 7sh, St. Peter Claver's Church. 25sh, Pope John Paul II.

**1985, Aug. 15    Perf. 13½**
| | | | | |
|---|---|---|---|---|
| 345 | A67 | 1sh multicolored | .70 | .30 |
| 346 | A67 | 3sh multicolored | 2.00 | 1.50 |
| 347 | A67 | 5sh multicolored | 2.25 | 2.25 |
| 348 | A67 | 7sh multicolored | 2.50 | 3.25 |
| | | Nos. 345-348 (4) | 7.45 | 7.30 |

**Souvenir Sheet**
| | | | | |
|---|---|---|---|---|
| 349 | A67 | 25sh multicolored | 9.00 | 9.00 |

**Flower Types of 1983**

1sh, Dombeya burgessiae. 3sh, Calotropis procera. 4sh, Momordica foetida. 7sh, Oncoba spinosa.

**1985    Photo.    Perf. 14½x14, 14½**
| | | | | |
|---|---|---|---|---|
| 350 | A46 | 80c like #250 | 3.00 | 4.00 |
| 351 | A46 | 1sh multicolored | 3.00 | .80 |
| 352 | A47 | 3sh multicolored | 9.00 | 8.00 |
| 353 | A47 | 4sh multicolored | 3.00 | 6.00 |
| 354 | A47 | 7sh multicolored | 4.00 | 7.50 |
| | | Nos. 350-354 (5) | 22.00 | 26.30 |

Endangered Wildlife — A68

1sh, Diceros bicornis. 3sh, Acinonyx jubatus. 5sh, Cercopithecus neglectus. 10sh, Equus greyvi. 25sh, Hunter pursuing game.

**1985, Dec. 10    Litho.    Perf. 14½**
| | | | | |
|---|---|---|---|---|
| 355 | A68 | 1sh multicolored | 2.15 | .50 |
| 356 | A68 | 3sh multicolored | 2.45 | 2.00 |
| 357 | A68 | 5sh multicolored | 2.95 | 2.75 |
| 358 | A68 | 10sh multicolored | 5.75 | 6.50 |
| | | Nos. 355-358 (4) | 13.30 | 11.75 |

**Size: 130x122mm**

*Imperf*
| | | | | |
|---|---|---|---|---|
| 359 | A68 | 25sh multicolored | 9.50 | 9.50 |

Trees — A69

1sh, Borassus aethiopum. 3sh, Acacia xanthophloea. 5sh, Ficus natalensis. 7sh, Spathodea nilotica. 25sh, Glade.

**1986, Jan. 24    Perf. 14½**
| | | | | |
|---|---|---|---|---|
| 360 | A69 | 1sh multicolored | 1.05 | .25 |
| 361 | A69 | 3sh multicolored | 2.70 | 2.00 |
| 362 | A69 | 5sh multicolored | 3.60 | 4.75 |
| 363 | A69 | 7sh multicolored | 5.25 | 6.75 |
| | | Nos. 360-363 (4) | 12.60 | 14.50 |

**Size: 117x97mm**

*Imperf*
| | | | | |
|---|---|---|---|---|
| 364 | A69 | 25sh multicolored | 6.00 | 6.00 |

Intl. Peace Year — A70

1sh, Dove, UN emblem. 3sh, UN General Assembly, horiz. 7sh, Mushroom cloud. 10sh, Isaiah 2:4, horiz.

**1986, Apr. 17    Perf. 14½**
| | | | | |
|---|---|---|---|---|
| 365 | A70 | 1sh multicolored | .55 | .55 |
| 366 | A70 | 3sh multicolored | 1.25 | 1.25 |
| 367 | A70 | 7sh multicolored | 2.40 | 2.40 |
| 368 | A70 | 10sh multicolored | 3.75 | 3.75 |
| | | Nos. 365-368 (4) | 7.95 | 7.95 |

1986 World Cup Soccer Championships, Mexico — A71

**1986, May 9**
| | | | | |
|---|---|---|---|---|
| 369 | A71 | 1sh Dribbling | .85 | .55 |
| 370 | A71 | 3sh Penalty shot | 1.70 | 1.10 |
| 371 | A71 | 5sh Tackling | 2.65 | 2.25 |
| 372 | A71 | 7sh Champions | 3.40 | 3.40 |
| 373 | A71 | 10sh Heading the ball | 4.35 | 4.35 |
| | | Nos. 369-373 (5) | 12.95 | 11.65 |

**Size: 110x86mm**

*Imperf*
| | | | | |
|---|---|---|---|---|
| 374 | A71 | 30sh Harambee Stars | 5.00 | 5.00 |

EXPO '86, Vancouver A72

1sh, Rural post office. 3sh, Container depot, Embakasi. 5sh, Plane landing. 7sh, Shipping exports. 10sh, Goods transport.

**1986, June 11    Perf. 13½x13**
| | | | | |
|---|---|---|---|---|
| 375 | A72 | 1sh multicolored | 1.05 | .60 |
| 376 | A72 | 3sh multicolored | 2.00 | 1.25 |
| 377 | A72 | 5sh multicolored | 3.10 | 2.40 |
| 378 | A72 | 7sh multicolored | 3.95 | 3.95 |
| 379 | A72 | 10sh multicolored | 5.25 | 5.25 |
| | | Nos. 375-379 (5) | 15.35 | 13.45 |

TELECOM '86, Nairobi, Sept. 16-23 — A73

1sh, Telephone-computer links. 3sh, Telephones, 1876-1986. 5sh, Satellite communications. 7sh, Switchboards.

**1986, Sept. 16    Litho.    Perf. 14½**
| | | | | |
|---|---|---|---|---|
| 380 | A73 | 1sh multicolored | .30 | .30 |
| 381 | A73 | 3sh multicolored | 1.10 | 1.10 |
| 382 | A73 | 5sh multicolored | 1.85 | 1.85 |
| 383 | A73 | 7sh multicolored | 3.00 | 3.00 |
| | | Nos. 380-383 (4) | 6.25 | 6.25 |

A74

Dhows (Ships) A75

**1986, Oct. 30    Litho.    Perf. 14½**
| | | | | |
|---|---|---|---|---|
| 384 | A74 | 1sh Mashua | .70 | .25 |
| 385 | A74 | 3sh Mtepe | 1.70 | 1.50 |
| 386 | A74 | 5sh Dau La Mwao | 2.50 | 3.00 |
| 387 | A74 | 10sh Jahazi | 5.00 | 5.00 |
| | | Nos. 384-387 (4) | 9.90 | 9.75 |

**Souvenir Sheet**
| | | | | |
|---|---|---|---|---|
| 388 | A75 | 25sh Lamu, map | 6.75 | 6.75 |

Christmas — A76

**1986, Dec. 5    Perf. 12**
| | | | | |
|---|---|---|---|---|
| 389 | A76 | 1sh Nativity, vert. | .30 | .25 |
| 390 | A76 | 3sh Shepherd boy, vert. | 1.50 | 1.50 |
| 391 | A76 | 5sh Angel, map | 2.10 | 2.00 |
| 392 | A76 | 7sh Magi | 3.15 | 3.15 |
| | | Nos. 389-392 (4) | 7.05 | 7.00 |

UNICEF, 40th Anniv. — A77

Child Survival Campaign: 1sh, Universal immunization by 1990. 3sh, Food and nutrition. 4sh, Oral rehydration. 5sh, Family planning. 10sh, Literacy of women.

**1987, Jan. 6    Litho.    Perf. 14½**
| | | | | |
|---|---|---|---|---|
| 393 | A77 | 1sh multicolored | .50 | .50 |
| 394 | A77 | 3sh multicolored | 1.00 | 1.00 |
| 395 | A77 | 4sh multicolored | 1.40 | 1.40 |
| 396 | A77 | 5sh multicolored | 1.80 | 1.80 |
| 397 | A77 | 10sh multicolored | 2.80 | 2.80 |
| | | Nos. 393-397 (5) | 7.50 | 7.50 |

A78

Tourism A79

## 1987, Mar. 25    Litho.    *Perf. 14½*

| | | | | | |
|---|---|---|---|---|---|
| 398 | A78 | 1sh | Akamba carvers | .60 | .25 |
| 399 | A78 | 3sh | Beach | 3.25 | 2.00 |
| 400 | A78 | 5sh | Escarpment | 4.00 | 4.00 |
| 401 | A78 | 7sh | Pride of lions | 6.00 | 6.00 |
| | | *Nos. 398-401 (4)* | | 13.85 | 12.25 |

### Souvenir Sheet

| | | | | | |
|---|---|---|---|---|---|
| 402 | A79 | 30sh | Kenya geysers | 12.50 | 12.50 |

Ceremonial Costumes — A80

## 1987, May 20    *Perf. 14½x13½*

| | | | | | |
|---|---|---|---|---|---|
| 403 | A80 | 1sh | Embu | 1.00 | .60 |
| 404 | A80 | 3sh | Kisii | 2.15 | 1.40 |
| 405 | A80 | 5sh | Samburu | 3.30 | 2.40 |
| 406 | A80 | 7sh | Taita | 3.70 | 3.70 |
| 407 | A80 | 10sh | Boran | 3.90 | 3.90 |
| | | *Nos. 403-407 (5)* | | 14.05 | 12.00 |

See Nos. 505-509.

Posts & Telecommunications Corp., 10th Anniv. — A81

1sh, Telecommunications satellite. 3sh, Rural post office, Kajiado. 4sh, Athletics. 5sh, Rural communication. 7sh, Speedpost. 25sh, Natl. Flag.

## 1987, July 1    Litho.    *Perf. 13½*

| | | | | | |
|---|---|---|---|---|---|
| 408 | A81 | 1sh | multicolored | .75 | .30 |
| 409 | A81 | 3sh | multicolored | 1.75 | 1.75 |
| 410 | A81 | 4sh | multicolored | 2.25 | 2.25 |
| 411 | A81 | 5sh | multicolored | 2.40 | 2.40 |
| 412 | A81 | 7sh | multicolored | 3.25 | 3.25 |
| | | *Nos. 408-412 (5)* | | 10.40 | 9.95 |

### Souvenir Sheet

| | | | | | |
|---|---|---|---|---|---|
| 413 | A81 | 25sh | multicolored | 4.00 | 4.00 |

A82

1sh, Volleyball. 3sh, Cycling. 4sh, Boxing. 5sh, Swimming. 7sh, Steeple chase. 30sh, Kasarani Sports Complex.

## 1987, Aug. 5    *Perf. 14½x14*

| | | | | | |
|---|---|---|---|---|---|
| 414 | A82 | 1sh | multicolored | .30 | .25 |
| 415 | A82 | 3sh | multicolored | .55 | .55 |
| 416 | A82 | 4sh | multicolored | .75 | .75 |
| 417 | A82 | 5sh | multicolored | .90 | .90 |
| 418 | A82 | 7sh | multicolored | 1.25 | 1.25 |
| | | *Nos. 414-418 (5)* | | 3.75 | 3.70 |

### Souvenir Sheet
### *Perf. 14x14½*

| | | | | | |
|---|---|---|---|---|---|
| 419 | A82 | 30sh | multicolored | 5.00 | 5.00 |

4th All Africa Games, Nairobi, Aug. 1-12. Nos. 414-418, vert.

Butterflies — A84

10c, Cyrestis camillus. 20c, Iolaus sidus. 40c, Vanessa cardui. 50c, Colotis euippe omphale. 70c, Precis westermanni. 80c, Colias electo. 1sh, Eronia leda. 1.50sh, Papilio dardanus planemoides. 2sh, Papilio rex. 2.50sh, Colotis phisadia. 3sh, Papilio desmondi teita. 3.50sh, Papilio demodocus. 4sh, Papilio phorcas. 5sh, Charaxes druceanus teita. 7sh, Cymothoe teita. 10sh, Charaxes zoolina. 20sh, Papilio dardanus. 40sh, Charaxes cithaeron kennethi.

## 1988-90    Photo.    *Perf. 15x14*

| | | | | | |
|---|---|---|---|---|---|
| 424A | A84 | 10c | multicolored | 1.25 | 1.25 |
| 425 | A84 | 20c | multicolored | .35 | .40 |
| 426 | A84 | 40c | multicolored | .50 | .40 |
| 427 | A84 | 50c | multicolored | .50 | .40 |
| 428 | A84 | 70c | multicolored | .50 | .40 |
| 429 | A84 | 80c | multicolored | .50 | .40 |
| 430 | A84 | 1sh | multicolored | .50 | .30 |
| 430A | A84 | 1.50sh | multicolored | 5.00 | 1.25 |

### Size: 25x41mm
### *Perf. 14½*

| | | | | | |
|---|---|---|---|---|---|
| 431 | A84 | 2sh | multicolored | .75 | .95 |
| 432 | A84 | 2.50sh | multicolored | .80 | .95 |
| 433 | A84 | 3sh | multicolored | .80 | .95 |
| 434 | A84 | 3.50sh | multicolored | .85 | .95 |
| 435 | A84 | 4sh | multicolored | .90 | *1.75* |
| 436 | A84 | 5sh | multicolored | 1.25 | .70 |
| 437 | A84 | 7sh | multicolored | 1.50 | *2.50* |
| 438 | A84 | 10sh | multicolored | 2.50 | 1.75 |
| 439 | A84 | 20sh | multicolored | 4.00 | *3.50* |
| 440 | A84 | 40sh | multicolored | 7.25 | *8.00* |
| | | *Nos. 424A-440 (18)* | | 29.70 | 26.80 |

Issued: 10c, 9/1/89; 1.50sh, 5/18/90; others, 2/14/88.

Game Lodges — A85

1sh, Samburu. 3sh, Naro Moru River. 4sh, Mara Serena. 5sh, Voi Safari. 7sh, Kilimanjaro Buffalo Lodge. 10sh, Meru Mulika.

## 1988, May 31    Litho.    *Perf. 14½*

| | | | | | |
|---|---|---|---|---|---|
| 441 | A85 | 1sh | multicolored | .75 | .35 |
| 442 | A85 | 3sh | multicolored | 1.10 | 1.10 |
| 443 | A85 | 4sh | multicolored | 1.75 | 1.75 |
| 444 | A85 | 5sh | multicolored | 1.90 | 1.90 |
| 445 | A85 | 7sh | multicolored | 2.25 | 2.25 |
| 446 | A85 | 10sh | multicolored | 2.75 | 2.75 |
| | | *Nos. 441-446 (6)* | | 10.50 | 10.10 |

World Expo '88, Brisbane — A86

EXPO '88 and Australia bicentennial emblems plus: 1sh, Stadium, site of the 1982 Commonwealth Games, and runners. 3sh, Flying Doctor Service aircraft. 4sh, HMS Sirius, a 19th cent. immigrant ship. 5sh, Ostrich and emu. 7sh, Pres. Daniel arap Moi, Queen Elizabeth II and Robert Hawke, prime minister of Australia. 30sh, Kenya Pavilion at EXPO '88.

## 1988, June 10

| | | | | | |
|---|---|---|---|---|---|
| 447 | A86 | 1sh | multicolored | .55 | .55 |
| 448 | A86 | 3sh | multicolored | 1.60 | 1.60 |
| 449 | A86 | 4sh | multicolored | 2.75 | 2.75 |
| 450 | A86 | 5sh | multicolored | 3.70 | 3.70 |
| 451 | A86 | 7sh | multicolored | 4.60 | 4.60 |
| | | *Nos. 447-451 (5)* | | 13.20 | 13.20 |

### Souvenir Sheet

| | | | | | |
|---|---|---|---|---|---|
| 452 | A86 | 30sh | multicolored | 3.75 | 3.75 |

World Health Organization, 40th Anniv. — A87

1988 Summer Olympics, Seoul — A88

## 1988, July 1    Litho.    *Perf. 14½*

| | | | | | |
|---|---|---|---|---|---|
| 453 | A87 | 1sh | shown | .30 | .25 |
| 454 | A87 | 3sh | Nutrition | 1.05 | 1.05 |
| 455 | A87 | 5sh | Immunization | 1.90 | 1.90 |
| 456 | A87 | 7sh | Water supply | 2.75 | 2.75 |
| | | *Nos. 453-456 (4)* | | 6.00 | 5.95 |

## 1988, Aug. 1    Litho.    *Perf. 14½x14*

| | | | | | |
|---|---|---|---|---|---|
| 457 | A88 | 1sh | Handball | .40 | .25 |
| 458 | A88 | 3sh | Judo | .85 | .80 |
| 459 | A88 | 5sh | Weight lifting | 1.25 | 1.25 |
| 460 | A88 | 7sh | Javelin | 1.70 | 1.70 |
| 461 | A88 | 10sh | 400-meter relay | 2.10 | 2.10 |
| | | *Nos. 457-461 (5)* | | 6.30 | 6.10 |

### Souvenir Sheet

| | | | | | |
|---|---|---|---|---|---|
| 462 | A88 | 30sh | Tennis | 4.50 | 4.50 |

Utensils — A89

1sh, Calabashes, vert. 3sh, Milk gourds, vert. 5sh, Cooking pots. 7sh, Winnowing trays. 10sh, Reed baskets. 25sh, Gourds, calabash, horn.

### *Perf. 14½x14, 14x14½*

## 1988, Sept. 20           Litho.

| | | | | | |
|---|---|---|---|---|---|
| 463 | A89 | 1sh | multicolored | .45 | .25 |
| 464 | A89 | 3sh | multicolored | .85 | .65 |
| 465 | A89 | 5sh | multicolored | 1.20 | 1.10 |
| 466 | A89 | 7sh | multicolored | 1.50 | 1.50 |
| 467 | A89 | 10sh | multicolored | 2.00 | 2.00 |
| | | *Nos. 463-467 (5)* | | 6.00 | 5.50 |

### Souvenir Sheet

| | | | | | |
|---|---|---|---|---|---|
| 468 | A89 | 25sh | multicolored | 3.00 | 3.00 |

10-Year Presidency of Daniel arap Moi — A90

Designs: 1sh, Swearing-in ceremony, 1978. 3sh, Promoting soil conservation. 3.50sh, Public transportation (bus), Nairobi. 4sh, Jua Kali artisans at market. 5sh, Moi University, Eldoret, established in 1985. 7sh, Hospital ward expansion. 10sh, British Prime Minister Margaret Thatcher and Pres. Moi inaugurating the Kapsabet Telephone Exchange, Jan. 6, 1988.

## 1988, Oct. 13    Litho.    *Perf. 13½x14½*

| | | | | | |
|---|---|---|---|---|---|
| 469 | A90 | 1sh | multicolored | .60 | .60 |
| 470 | A90 | 3sh | multicolored | 1.50 | 1.50 |
| 471 | A90 | 3.50sh | multicolored | 1.75 | 1.75 |
| 472 | A90 | 4sh | multicolored | 1.95 | 1.95 |
| 473 | A90 | 5sh | multicolored | 2.40 | 2.40 |
| 474 | A90 | 7sh | multicolored | 3.00 | 3.00 |
| 475 | A90 | 10sh | multicolored | 4.75 | 4.75 |
| | | *Nos. 469-475 (7)* | | 15.95 | 15.95 |

Independence, 25th Anniv. — A91

1sh, Natl. flag. 3sh, Coffee picking. 5sh, Model of postal headquarters. 7sh, Harambee Star Airbus A310-300. 10sh, Locomotive 9401.

## 1988, Dec. 9    Litho.    *Perf. 11½*

| | | | | | |
|---|---|---|---|---|---|
| 476 | A91 | 1sh | multicolored | .30 | .25 |
| 477 | A91 | 3sh | multicolored | 1.60 | 1.60 |
| 478 | A91 | 5sh | multicolored | 2.75 | 2.75 |
| 479 | A91 | 7sh | multicolored | 4.00 | 4.00 |
| 480 | A91 | 10sh | multicolored | 5.45 | 5.45 |
| | | *Nos. 476-480 (5)* | | 14.10 | 14.05 |

Natl. Monuments A92

1.20sh, Gedi Ruins, Malindi. 3.40sh, Vasco Da Gama Pillar, Malindi. vert. 4.40sh, Ishiakani Monument, Kiunga. 5.50sh, Ft. Jesus, Mombasa. 7.70sh, She Burnan Omwe, Lamu, vert.

## 1989, Mar. 15    Litho.    *Perf. 14½*

| | | | | | |
|---|---|---|---|---|---|
| 481 | A92 | 1.20sh | multicolored | .40 | .40 |
| 482 | A92 | 3.40sh | multicolored | 1.00 | 1.00 |
| 483 | A92 | 4.40sh | multicolored | 2.00 | 2.00 |
| 484 | A92 | 5.50sh | multicolored | 2.50 | 2.50 |
| 485 | A92 | 7.70sh | multicolored | 3.00 | 3.00 |
| | | *Nos. 481-485 (5)* | | 8.90 | 8.90 |

Red Cross, 125th Anniv. — A93

1.20sh, Anniv. and natl. soc. emblems. 3.40sh, First aid. 4.40sh, Disaster relief. 5.50sh, Jean-Henri Dunant. 7.70sh, Blood donation.

## 1989, May 8    Litho.    *Perf. 14x13½*

| | | | | | |
|---|---|---|---|---|---|
| 486 | A93 | 1.20sh | multicolored | .30 | .30 |
| 487 | A93 | 3.40sh | multicolored | 1.10 | 1.10 |
| 488 | A93 | 4.40sh | multicolored | 1.60 | 1.60 |
| 489 | A93 | 5.50sh | multicolored | 2.15 | 2.15 |
| 490 | A93 | 7.70sh | multicolored | 3.40 | 3.40 |
| | | *Nos. 486-490 (5)* | | 8.55 | 8.55 |

World Wildlife Fund — A94

Giraffes, Giraffa Camelopardalis Reticulata.

## 1989, July 12    Litho.    *Perf. 14½*

| | | | | | |
|---|---|---|---|---|---|
| 491 | A94 | 1.20sh | multicolored | 2.10 | 1.90 |
| 492 | A94 | 3.40sh | multicolored | 4.40 | 4.25 |
| 493 | A94 | 4.40sh | multicolored | 5.00 | 5.00 |
| 494 | A94 | 5.50sh | multicolored | 6.00 | *7.75* |
| | | *Nos. 491-494 (4)* | | 17.50 | 18.90 |

### Size: 80x110mm
### *Imperf*

| | | | | | |
|---|---|---|---|---|---|
| 495 | A94 | 30sh | multicolored | 10.00 | 10.00 |

No. 495 contains four labels like Nos. 491-494, perf. 14½, without denominations or WWF emblem.

Mushrooms — A95

## 1989, Sept. 6    Litho.    *Perf. 14½*

| | | | | | |
|---|---|---|---|---|---|
| 496 | A95 | 1.20sh | Oyster | 2.00 | .65 |
| 497 | A95 | 3.40sh | Chestnut | 2.90 | 2.40 |
| 498 | A95 | 4.40sh | White button | 3.30 | 3.25 |
| 499 | A95 | 5.50sh | Termite | 3.95 | 3.75 |
| 500 | A95 | 7.70sh | Shiitake | 5.50 | 6.50 |
| | | *Nos. 496-500 (5)* | | 17.65 | 16.55 |

Jawaharlal Nehru, 1st Prime Minister of Independent India — A96

1.20sh, Independence struggle. 3.40sh, Education. 5.50sh, Portrait. 7.70sh, Industry.

## 1989, Nov. 9    Litho.    *Perf. 13½x14*

| | | | | | |
|---|---|---|---|---|---|
| 501 | A96 | 1.20sh | multicolored | 1.65 | 1.50 |
| 502 | A96 | 3.40sh | multicolored | 2.10 | 2.00 |
| 503 | A96 | 5.50sh | multicolored | 3.75 | 3.75 |
| 504 | A96 | 7.70sh | multicolored | 6.25 | 6.25 |
| | | *Nos. 501-504 (4)* | | 13.75 | 13.50 |

Medicinal herbs: 1sh, Aloe volkensii. 3sh, Cassia didymobotrya. 5sh, Erythrina abyssinica. 7sh, Adenium obesum. 10sh, Herbalist's clinic.

A83

## Costume Type of 1980

**1989, Dec. 8   Litho.   Perf. 14½x13½**

| | | | | |
|---|---|---|---|---|
| 505 | A80 | 1.20sh Kipsigis | 1.05 | .45 |
| 506 | A80 | 3.40sh Rabai | 2.15 | 2.50 |
| 507 | A80 | 5.50sh Duruma | 2.75 | 2.40 |
| 508 | A80 | 7.70sh Kuria | 3.85 | 3.75 |
| 509 | A80 | 10sh Bajuni | 4.75 | 4.75 |
| | | Nos. 505-509 (5) | 14.55 | 13.85 |

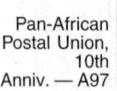

Pan-African Postal Union, 10th Anniv. — A97

1.20sh, EMS Speedpost. 3.40sh, Mail runner. 5.50sh, Mandera P.O. 7.70sh, EMS, diff., vert. 10sh, PAPU emblem, vert.

**Perf. 14x13½, 13½x14**

**1990, Jan. 31**        **Litho.**

| | | | | |
|---|---|---|---|---|
| 510 | A97 | 1.20sh multicolored | .30 | .30 |
| 511 | A97 | 3.40sh multicolored | .90 | .90 |
| 512 | A97 | 5.50sh multicolored | 1.10 | 1.10 |
| 513 | A97 | 7.70sh multicolored | 1.40 | 1.40 |
| 514 | A97 | 10sh multicolored | 1.75 | 1.75 |
| | | Nos. 510-514 (5) | 5.45 | 5.45 |

Soccer Trophies — A98

Designs:1.50sh, Moi Golden Cup. 4.50sh, East & Central Africa Challenge Cup. 6.50sh, East & Central Africa Club Championship Cup. 9sh, World Cup.

**1990, May 21   Litho.   Perf. 14½**

| | | | | |
|---|---|---|---|---|
| 515 | A98 | 1.50sh multicolored | .50 | .50 |
| 516 | A98 | 4.50sh multicolored | 3.00 | 3.00 |
| 517 | A98 | 6.50sh multicolored | 4.00 | 4.00 |
| 518 | A98 | 9sh multicolored | 5.00 | 5.00 |
| | | Nos. 515-518 (4) | 12.50 | 12.50 |

Penny Black 150th Anniv., Stamp World London '90 — A99

4.50sh, Great Britain No. 1. 6.50sh, Early British cancellations. 9sh, Main P.O.

**1990, Apr. 27   Litho.   Perf. 11½**

| | | | | |
|---|---|---|---|---|
| 519 | A99 | 1.50sh shown | .35 | .35 |
| 520 | A99 | 4.50sh multicolored | 1.30 | 1.30 |
| 521 | A99 | 6.50sh multicolored | 1.95 | 1.95 |
| 522 | A99 | 9sh multicolored | 2.85 | 2.85 |
| *a.* | | Souvenir sheet of 4, #519-522 | 7.50 | 7.50 |
| | | Nos. 519-522 (4) | 6.45 | 6.45 |

No. 522a sold for 30 shillings.

ITU, 125th Anniv. — A100

Designs: 4.50sh, Telephone assembly. 6.50sh, ITU Anniv. emblem. 9sh, Telecommunications development.

**1990, July 12**

| | | | | |
|---|---|---|---|---|
| 523 | A100 | 1.50sh multicolored | .45 | .25 |
| 524 | A100 | 4.50sh multicolored | .90 | .65 |
| 525 | A100 | 6.50sh multicolored | 1.25 | 1.10 |
| 526 | A100 | 9sh multicolored | 1.60 | 1.60 |
| | | Nos. 523-526 (4) | 4.20 | 3.60 |

Common Design Types pictured following the introduction.

## Queen Mother, 90th Birthday
### Common Design Types

10sh, Queen Mother. 40sh, At garden party, 1947.

**Perf. 14x15**

**1990, Aug. 4   Litho.   Wmk. 384**

| | | | | |
|---|---|---|---|---|
| 527 | CD343 | 10sh multicolored | 1.30 | 1.30 |

**Perf. 14½**

| | | | | |
|---|---|---|---|---|
| 528 | CD344 | 40sh multicolored | 4.75 | 4.75 |

Kenya African National Union (KANU), 50th Anniv. — A101

1.50sh, KANU flag. 2.50sh, Nyayo Monument. 4.50sh, KICC Party Headquarters. 5sh, Jomo Kenyatta. 6.50sh, Daniel T. arap Moi. 9sh, KANU mass meeting. 10sh, Voters.

**1990, June 11**

| | | | | |
|---|---|---|---|---|
| 529 | A101 | 1.50sh multicolored | .35 | .25 |
| 530 | A101 | 2.50sh multicolored | .40 | .35 |
| 531 | A101 | 4.50sh multicolored | .85 | .85 |
| 532 | A101 | 5sh multicolored | 1.00 | 1.00 |
| 533 | A101 | 6.50sh multicolored | 1.10 | 1.10 |
| 534 | A101 | 9sh multicolored | 1.75 | 1.75 |
| 535 | A101 | 10sh multicolored | 1.75 | 1.75 |
| | | Nos. 529-535 (7) | 7.20 | 7.05 |

Kenya Postage Stamps, Cent. — A102

Designs: 1.50sh, Kenya #431. 4.50sh, East Africa and Uganda Protectorates #2. 6.50sh, British East Africa #1. 9sh, Kenya and Uganda #25. 20sh, Kenya, Uganda, Tanzania #232.

**1990, Sept. 5   Litho.   Perf. 14x14½**

| | | | | |
|---|---|---|---|---|
| 536 | A102 | 1.50sh multicolored | 1.50 | .45 |
| 537 | A102 | 4.50sh multicolored | 3.00 | 2.50 |
| 538 | A102 | 6.50sh multicolored | 4.00 | 3.75 |
| 539 | A102 | 9sh multicolored | 5.25 | 4.75 |
| 540 | A102 | 20sh multicolored | 8.50 | 8.50 |
| | | Nos. 536-540 (5) | 22.25 | 19.95 |

Intl. Literacy Year — A103

1.50sh, Adult literacy class. 4.50sh, Radio teaching program. 6.50sh, Technical training. 9sh, Literacy year emblem.

**1990, Nov. 30   Litho.   Perf. 13½x14**

| | | | | |
|---|---|---|---|---|
| 541 | A103 | 1.50sh multicolored | .55 | .55 |
| 542 | A103 | 4.50sh multicolored | 1.35 | 1.35 |
| 543 | A103 | 6.50sh multicolored | 1.90 | 1.90 |
| 544 | A103 | 9sh multicolored | 2.95 | 2.95 |
| | | Nos. 541-544 (4) | 6.75 | 6.75 |

1992 Summer Olympics, Barcelona A106

**1991, Nov. 29   Litho.   Perf. 14x13½**

| | | | | |
|---|---|---|---|---|
| 554 | A106 | 2sh National flag | .45 | .45 |
| 555 | A106 | 6sh Basketball | 1.90 | 1.90 |
| 556 | A106 | 7sh Field hockey | 2.50 | 2.50 |
| 557 | A106 | 8.50sh Table tennis | 3.00 | 3.00 |
| 558 | A106 | 11sh Boxing | 4.50 | 4.50 |
| | | Nos. 554-558 (5) | 12.35 | 12.35 |

Fight AIDS — A107

2sh, You too can be infected. 6sh, Has no cure. 8.50sh, Casual sex is unsafe. 11sh, Sterilize syringe before use.

**1991, Oct. 31   Litho.   Perf. 13½x14**

| | | | | |
|---|---|---|---|---|
| 559 | A107 | 2sh multicolored | 1.25 | .25 |
| 560 | A107 | 6sh multicolored | 2.50 | 2.25 |
| 561 | A107 | 8.50sh multicolored | 3.50 | 3.00 |
| 562 | A107 | 11sh multicolored | 4.75 | 4.75 |
| | | Nos. 559-562 (4) | 12.00 | 10.25 |

## Queen Elizabeth II's Accession to the Throne, 40th Anniv.
### Common Design Type

**1992, Feb. 6   Litho.   Perf. 14x13½**

| | | | | |
|---|---|---|---|---|
| 563 | CD349 | 3sh multicolored | .30 | .25 |
| 564 | CD349 | 8sh multicolored | .95 | .95 |
| 565 | CD349 | 11sh multicolored | 1.20 | 1.20 |
| 566 | CD349 | 14sh multicolored | 1.35 | 1.35 |
| 567 | CD349 | 40sh multicolored | 4.00 | 4.00 |
| | | Nos. 563-567 (5) | 7.80 | 7.75 |

Wildlife — A108

**1992, May 8**       **Perf. 14½**

| | | | | |
|---|---|---|---|---|
| 568 | A108 | 3sh Leopard | 2.00 | .35 |
| 569 | A108 | 8sh Lion | 2.75 | 2.00 |
| 570 | A108 | 10sh Elephant | 5.75 | 3.00 |
| 571 | A108 | 11sh Buffalo | 3.50 | 3.00 |
| 572 | A108 | 14sh Rhinoceros | 9.50 | 5.00 |
| | | Nos. 568-572 (5) | 23.50 | 13.35 |

Vintage Cars — A109

Designs: 3sh, Intl. Harvester S.S. motor truck, 1926. 8sh, Fiat 509, 1924. 10sh, "R" Hupmobile, 1923. 11sh, Chevrolet Box Body, 1928. 14sh, Bentley Parkward, 1934.

**1992, June 24**      **Perf. 14½**

| | | | | |
|---|---|---|---|---|
| 573 | A109 | 3sh multicolored | 1.95 | .70 |
| 574 | A109 | 8sh multicolored | 2.65 | 1.90 |
| 575 | A109 | 10sh multicolored | 3.10 | 2.50 |
| 576 | A109 | 11sh multicolored | 3.50 | 3.50 |
| 577 | A109 | 14sh multicolored | 4.75 | 5.50 |
| | | Nos. 573-577 (5) | 15.95 | 14.10 |

1992 Summer Olympics, Barcelona — A110

3sh, Runners. 8sh, Judo. 10sh, Women's volleyball. 11sh, 4x100-meter relay. 14sh, 10,000-meter run.

**1992, July 24   Litho.   Perf. 14½**

| | | | | |
|---|---|---|---|---|
| 578 | A110 | 3sh multicolored | .45 | .45 |
| 579 | A110 | 8sh multicolored | 1.55 | 1.55 |
| 580 | A110 | 10sh multicolored | 2.60 | 2.60 |
| 581 | A110 | 11sh multicolored | 2.60 | 2.60 |
| 582 | A110 | 14sh multicolored | 3.50 | 3.50 |
| | | Nos. 578-582 (5) | 10.70 | 10.70 |

Christmas — A111

Designs: 3sh, Joseph, Jesus & animals in stable. 8sh, Mary holding Jesus in stable. 11sh, Map of Kenya, Christmas tree. 14sh, Adoration of the Magi.

**1992, Dec. 14   Litho.   Perf. 13½x14**

| | | | | |
|---|---|---|---|---|
| 583 | A111 | 3sh multicolored | .45 | .45 |
| 584 | A111 | 8sh multicolored | 1.10 | 1.10 |
| 585 | A111 | 11sh multicolored | 1.50 | 1.50 |
| 586 | A111 | 14sh multicolored | 1.75 | 1.75 |
| | | Nos. 583-586 (4) | 4.80 | 4.80 |

Lighthouses — A112

Designs: 3sh, Asembo Bay, Lake Victoria. 8sh, Ras Serani, Mombasa. 11sh, Ras Serani, Mombasa, diff. 14sh, Gingira, Lake Victoria.

**1993, Jan. 25**       **Perf. 14½**

| | | | | |
|---|---|---|---|---|
| 587 | A112 | 3sh multicolored | 2.75 | 1.10 |
| 588 | A112 | 8sh multicolored | 4.75 | 3.25 |
| 589 | A112 | 11sh multicolored | 6.00 | 5.25 |
| 590 | A112 | 14sh multicolored | 8.00 | 8.00 |
| | | Nos. 587-590 (4) | 21.50 | 17.60 |

Birds — A113

Designs: 50c, Superb starling. 1sh, Red and yellow barbet. 1.50sh, Ross's turaco. 3sh, Greater honeyguide. 5sh, African fish eagle. 6sh, Vulturine guineafowl. 7sh, Malachite kingfisher. 8sh, Speckled pigeon. 10sh, Cinnamon-chested bee-eater. 11sh, Scarlet-chested sunbird. 14sh, Reichenow's weaver. 50sh, Yellow-billed hornbill. 80sh, Lesser flamingo. 100sh, Hadada ibis.

**1993-99**    **Photo.**    **Perf. 15x14**
**Granite Paper**

| | | | | |
|---|---|---|---|---|
| 594 | A113 | 50c multi | .30 | .25 |
| 597 | A113 | 1sh multi | .30 | .25 |
| 598 | A113 | 1.50sh multi | .30 | .25 |
| 600 | A113 | 3sh multi | .30 | .25 |
| 601 | A113 | 5sh multi | .30 | .25 |
| 601A | A113 | 6sh multi | 5.00 | 1.00 |
| 602 | A113 | 7sh multi | .45 | .45 |
| 603 | A113 | 8sh multi | .55 | .55 |
| 604 | A113 | 10sh multi | .65 | .65 |
| 605 | A113 | 11sh multi | .70 | .70 |
| 606 | A113 | 14sh multi | .90 | .90 |

**Size: 25x42mm**
**Perf. 14½**

| | | | | |
|---|---|---|---|---|
| 608 | A113 | 50sh multi | 3.25 | 3.25 |
| 609 | A113 | 80sh multi | 5.00 | 5.00 |
| 610 | A113 | 100sh multi | 6.50 | 6.50 |
| | | Nos. 594-610 (14) | 24.50 | 20.25 |

Issued: 1.50sh, 5sh, 2/14/94; 6sh, 1999; others, 2/22/93.

17th World Congress of Rehabilatation Intl. — A114

3sh, Health care, vert. 8sh, Recreation. 10sh, Vocational training. 11sh, Recreation & sports. 14sh, Emblem, vert.

**1993, July 1   Litho.   Perf. 14½**

| | | | | |
|---|---|---|---|---|
| 611 | A114 | 3sh multicolored | .90 | .25 |
| 612 | A114 | 8sh multicolored | 1.40 | .75 |
| 613 | A114 | 10sh multicolored | 1.75 | 1.75 |
| 614 | A114 | 11sh multicolored | 1.75 | 1.75 |
| 615 | A114 | 14sh multicolored | 2.10 | 2.10 |
| | | Nos. 611-615 (5) | 7.90 | 6.60 |

Maendeleo ya Wanawake Organization, 42th Anniv. — A115

Designs: 3.50sh, Maendeleo House. 9sh, Planting trees. 11sh, Rural family planning services, vert. 12.50sh, Water nearer the people. 15.50sh, Maendeleo improved wood cookstove, vert.

**Perf. 14x13½, 13½x14**

**1994, Mar. 17**       **Litho.**

| | | | | |
|---|---|---|---|---|
| 616 | A115 | 3.50sh multicolored | 1.10 | 1.25 |
| 617 | A115 | 9sh multicolored | 1.60 | .60 |
| 618 | A115 | 11sh multicolored | 1.25 | 1.25 |
| 619 | A115 | 12.50sh multicolored | 2.25 | 2.25 |
| 620 | A115 | 15.50sh multicolored | 2.50 | 2.50 |
| | | Nos. 616-620 (5) | 8.70 | 6.85 |

Orchids — A116

Designs: 3.50sh, Ansellia africana. 9sh, Aerangis lutecalba. 12.50sh, Polystachya bella. 15.50sh, Brachycorythis kalbreyeri. 20sh, Eulophia guineensis.

**1994, June 27   Litho.   Perf. 13½x14**
| | | | | |
|---|---|---|---|---|
| 621 | A116 | 3.50sh multicolored | 1.85 | .25 |
| 622 | A116 | 9sh multicolored | 2.50 | 1.00 |
| 623 | A116 | 12.50sh multicolored | 2.75 | 2.50 |
| 624 | A116 | 15.50sh multicolored | 3.35 | 3.35 |
| 625 | A116 | 20sh multicolored | 4.30 | 4.30 |
| | | *Nos. 621-625 (5)* | 14.75 | 11.40 |

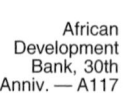

African Development Bank, 30th Anniv. — A117

**1994, Nov. 21   Litho.   Perf. 14½**
| | | | | |
|---|---|---|---|---|
| 626 | A117 | 6sh KICC, Nairobi | 1.25 | .25 |
| 627 | A117 | 25sh Isinya, Kajiado | 4.50 | 4.50 |

Intl. Year of the Family — A118

6sh, Family planning. 14.50sh, Health. 20sh, Education, horiz. 25sh, Emblem, horiz.

**1994, Dec. 22**
| | | | | |
|---|---|---|---|---|
| 628 | A118 | 6sh multi | .85 | .25 |
| 629 | A118 | 14.50sh multi | 3.10 | 1.50 |
| 630 | A118 | 20sh multi | 3.50 | 3.50 |
| 631 | A118 | 25sh multi | 3.50 | 3.50 |
| | | *Nos. 628-631 (4)* | 10.95 | 8.75 |

Rotary, 50th Anniv. — A119

Designs: 6sh, Paul P. Harris, founder. 14.50sh, Rotary Club of Mombasa. 17.50sh, Polio plus vaccine. 20sh, Water projects. 25sh, Emblem, motto.

**1994, Dec. 29   Perf. 13½x14**
| | | | | |
|---|---|---|---|---|
| 632 | A119 | 6sh multicolored | .60 | .25 |
| 633 | A119 | 14.50sh multicolored | 1.60 | .75 |
| 634 | A119 | 17.50sh multicolored | 2.00 | 2.00 |
| 635 | A119 | 20sh multicolored | 2.25 | 2.25 |
| 636 | A119 | 25sh multicolored | 2.75 | 2.75 |
| | | *Nos. 632-636 (5)* | 9.20 | 8.00 |

SPCA — A120

**1995, Jan. 13   Litho.   Perf. 14½**
| | | | | |
|---|---|---|---|---|
| 637 | A120 | 6sh Donkey | .55 | .25 |
| 638 | A120 | 14.50sh Cattle | 1.50 | .55 |
| 639 | A120 | 17.50sh Sheep | 1.90 | 1.10 |
| 640 | A120 | 20sh Dog | 2.10 | 2.10 |
| 641 | A120 | 25sh Cat | 2.60 | 2.60 |
| | | *Nos. 637-641 (5)* | 8.65 | 6.60 |

Kenya Society for Prevention of Cruelty to Animals.

Golf — A121

6sh, Man in vest. 17.50sh, Woman. 20sh, Man in red shirt. 25sh, Golf club.

**1995, Feb. 28   Litho.   Perf. 14½**
| | | | | |
|---|---|---|---|---|
| 642 | A121 | 6sh multicolored | 1.10 | .25 |
| 643 | A121 | 17.50sh multicolored | 3.50 | 1.10 |
| 644 | A121 | 20sh multicolored | 3.75 | 1.10 |
| 645 | A121 | 25sh multicolored | 5.00 | 1.60 |
| | | *Nos. 642-645 (4)* | 13.35 | 4.75 |

Traditional Crafts — A122

6sh, Perfume containers. 14.50sh, Basketry. 17.50sh, Preservation pots. 20sh, Gourds. 25sh, Wooden containers.

**1995, Mar. 24   Litho.   Perf. 14x13½**
| | | | | |
|---|---|---|---|---|
| 646 | A122 | 6sh multicolored | .50 | .25 |
| 647 | A122 | 14.50sh multicolored | 1.00 | .95 |
| 648 | A122 | 17.50sh multicolored | 1.40 | 1.40 |
| 649 | A122 | 20sh multicolored | 1.75 | 1.75 |
| 650 | A122 | 25sh multicolored | 2.40 | 2.40 |
| | | *Nos. 646-650 (5)* | 7.05 | 6.75 |

UN, 50th Anniv. — A123

Designs: 23sh, UN Headquarters, Nairobi. 26sh, People holding UN emblem. 32sh, UN Peacekeeper's helmet. 40sh, UN emblem.

**1995, Oct. 24   Litho.   Perf. 13½**
| | | | | |
|---|---|---|---|---|
| 651 | A123 | 23sh multicolored | 1.40 | .70 |
| 652 | A123 | 26sh multicolored | 1.50 | .90 |
| 653 | A123 | 32sh multicolored | 2.10 | 2.10 |
| 654 | A123 | 40sh multicolored | 2.25 | 2.25 |
| | | *Nos. 651-654 (4)* | 7.25 | 5.95 |

ICIPE, 25th Anniv. — A124

**1995, Sept. 29   Litho.   Perf. 13½**
| | | | | |
|---|---|---|---|---|
| 655 | A124 | 14sh Tse-tse fly | .75 | .35 |
| 656 | A124 | 26sh Tick | 1.40 | .90 |
| 657 | A124 | 32sh Wild silk moth | 1.75 | 1.25 |
| 658 | A124 | 33sh Maize borer | 1.90 | 1.90 |
| 659 | A124 | 40sh Locust | 2.25 | 2.25 |
| | | *Nos. 655-659 (5)* | 8.05 | 6.65 |

FAO, 50th Anniv. — A125

14sh, Maize production. 28sh, Cattle rearing. 32sh, Poultry keeping. 33sh, Fishing. 40sh, Fruits.

**1995, Oct. 16**
| | | | | |
|---|---|---|---|---|
| 660 | A125 | 14sh multicolored | .90 | .35 |
| 661 | A125 | 28sh multicolored | 2.00 | 1.00 |
| 662 | A125 | 32sh multicolored | 2.25 | 2.00 |
| 663 | A125 | 33sh multicolored | 2.25 | 2.25 |
| 664 | A125 | 40sh multicolored | 2.75 | 2.75 |
| | | *Nos. 660-664 (5)* | 10.15 | 8.35 |

Miniature Sheets

1996 Summer Olympics, Atlanta — A126

No. 665: a, 14sh, Swimming. b, 20sh, Archery. c, 32sh, Javelin. d, 40sh, Fencing. e, 50sh, Discus. f, 20sh, Weight lifting.

No. 666: a, Pole vault. b, Equestrian. c, Diving. d, Track e, Torch bearer. f, Hurdles. g, Kayak. h, Boxing. i, Gymnastics.

No. 667 — Medal winners: a, Greg Louganis, diving. b, Muhammed Ali, boxing. c, Nadia Comaneci, gymnastics. d, Daley Thompson, decathlon. e, Kipchoge "Kip" Keino, track and field. f, Kornelia Enders, swimming. g, Jackie Joyner-Kersee, track and field. h, Michael Jordan, basketball. i, Shun Fujimoto, gymnastics.

No. 668, 100sh, Torch bearer. No. 669, 100sh, Gold medalist.

**1996, Jan. 5   Litho.   Perf. 14**
| | | | | |
|---|---|---|---|---|
| 665 | A126 | Sheet of 6, #a.-f. | 10.50 | 10.50 |
| 666 | A126 | 20sh Sheet of 9, #a.-i. | 11.25 | 11.25 |
| 667 | A126 | 25sh Sheet of 9, #a.-i. | 13.50 | 13.50 |

**Souvenir Sheets**
| | | | | |
|---|---|---|---|---|
| 668-669 | A126 | Set of 2 | 11.00 | 11.00 |

World Tourism Organization, 20th Anniv. — A127

**1996, Jan. 31   Litho.   Perf. 13½**
| | | | | |
|---|---|---|---|---|
| 670 | A127 | 6sh Lions | .50 | .35 |
| 671 | A127 | 14sh Mount Kenya | 1.00 | .35 |
| 672 | A127 | 20sh Water sports | 1.50 | .80 |
| 673 | A127 | 25sh Hippopotomus | 2.00 | 2.00 |
| 674 | A127 | 40sh Culture | 3.00 | 3.00 |
| | | *Nos. 670-674 (5)* | 8.00 | 6.40 |

**Perf. 13x13½**
| | | | | |
|---|---|---|---|---|
| 675 | A127 | 50sh Giraffes, vert. | 5.00 | 5.00 |

Wild Animals — A128

No. 676, Water buck. No. 677, Rhinoceros. No. 678, Cheetah. No. 679, Oryx. No. 680, Reticulated giraffe. No. 681, Bongo.

**Booklet Stamps**

**1996   Perf. 13x13½**
| | | | | |
|---|---|---|---|---|
| 676 | A128 | 20sh multicolored | 1.40 | .75 |
| 677 | A128 | 20sh multicolored | 1.40 | .75 |
| 678 | A128 | 20sh multicolored | 1.40 | .75 |
| 679 | A128 | 20sh multicolored | 1.40 | .75 |
| 680 | A128 | 20sh multicolored | 1.40 | .75 |
| 681 | A128 | 20sh multicolored | 1.40 | .75 |
| a. | | Booklet pane of 6, #676-681 | 15.00 | |
| | | Complete booklet, 4 #681a | 70.00 | |

Nos. 676-681 appear in No. 681a in two different orders. Complete booklet contains 2 of each type of pane.

1996 Summer Olympic Games, Atlanta — A129

**1996, July 18   Litho.   Perf. 13½x14**
| | | | | |
|---|---|---|---|---|
| 682 | A129 | 6sh Woman running | .30 | .30 |
| 683 | A129 | 14sh Steeple chase | .60 | .60 |
| 684 | A129 | 20sh Victory lap | .90 | .90 |
| 685 | A129 | 25sh Boxing | 1.10 | 1.10 |
| 686 | A129 | 40sh Man running | 1.90 | 1.90 |
| | | *Nos. 682-686 (5)* | 4.80 | 4.80 |

Red Cross — A130

6sh, Emblem. 14sh, Blood donation. 20sh, Immunization. 25sh, Refugees. 40sh, Clean environment.

**1996, Aug. 30   Litho.   Perf. 14**
| | | | | |
|---|---|---|---|---|
| 687 | A130 | 6sh multicolored | .40 | .40 |
| 688 | A130 | 14sh multicolored | .80 | .80 |
| 689 | A130 | 20sh multicolored | 1.25 | 1.25 |
| 690 | A130 | 25sh multicolored | 1.50 | 1.50 |
| 691 | A130 | 40sh multicolored | 2.50 | 2.50 |
| | | *Nos. 687-691 (5)* | 6.45 | 6.45 |

East African Wildlife Society — A131

**1996, Sept. 10   Litho.   Perf. 14½**
| | | | | |
|---|---|---|---|---|
| 693 | A131 | 6sh Impala | .45 | .45 |
| 694 | A131 | 20sh Colobus monkey | 1.60 | 1.60 |
| 695 | A131 | 25sh Elephant | 2.00 | 2.00 |
| 696 | A131 | 40sh Black rhino | 3.75 | 3.75 |
| | | *Nos. 693-696 (4)* | 7.80 | 7.80 |

Lions Club Intl. — A132

**1996, Oct. 31   Litho.   Perf. 13½**
| | | | | |
|---|---|---|---|---|
| 697 | A132 | 6sh Logo | .30 | .30 |
| 698 | A132 | 14sh Eye camps | .95 | .95 |
| 699 | A132 | 20sh Wheel chair | 1.50 | 1.50 |
| 700 | A132 | 25sh Ambulance | 1.75 | 1.75 |
| | | *Nos. 697-700 (4)* | 4.50 | 4.50 |

COMESA (Common Market for Eastern and Southern Africa — A133

**1997, Jan. 15   Litho.   Perf. 13½x14**
| | | | | |
|---|---|---|---|---|
| 701 | A133 | 6sh COMESA logo | .30 | .25 |
| 702 | A133 | 20sh Natl. flag | 1.40 | 1.40 |

Fish of Lake Victoria — A134

Haplochromis: No. 703, Orange rock hunter. No. 704, Chilotes. No. 705, Cinctus. No. 706, Nigricans.

**1997, Jan. 31   Perf. 14x13½**
| | | | | |
|---|---|---|---|---|
| 703 | A134 | 25sh multicolored | 1.50 | .90 |
| 704 | A134 | 25sh multicolored | 1.50 | .90 |
| 705 | A134 | 25sh multicolored | 1.50 | .90 |
| 706 | A134 | 25sh multicolored | 1.50 | .90 |
| | | *Nos. 703-706 (4)* | 6.00 | 3.60 |

World Wildlife Fund.

Locomotives A135

**1997, Feb. 20   Litho.   Perf. 14x13½**
| | | | | |
|---|---|---|---|---|
| 707 | A135 | 6sh Class 94, 1981 | .80 | .25 |
| 708 | A135 | 14sh Class 87, 1964 | 1.25 | .45 |
| 709 | A135 | 20sh Class 59, 1955 | 1.60 | .70 |
| 710 | A135 | 25sh Class 57, 1939 | 1.60 | 1.25 |
| 711 | A135 | 30sh Class 23, 1923 | 2.00 | 2.00 |
| 712 | A135 | 40sh Class 10, 1914 | 2.25 | 2.25 |
| | | *Nos. 707-712 (6)* | 9.50 | 6.90 |

Dated 1996.

Fruits — A136

**1997, Feb. 28**          **Perf. 14½**
| | | | | |
|---|---|---|---|---|
| 713 | A136 | 6sh Orange | .30 | .25 |
| 714 | A136 | 14sh Pineapple | 2.10 | .50 |
| 715 | A136 | 20sh Mango | 3.00 | 2.00 |
| 716 | A136 | 25sh Papaya | 3.75 | 2.50 |
| | | *Nos. 713-716 (4)* | 9.15 | 5.25 |

A137

Scouting Organizations: No. 717, Girl Guides, 75th anniv. No. 718, Lord Baden Powell. No. 719, Girl scouts hiking. No. 720, Rangers camping. No. 721, Girl Guides planting trees. No. 722, Boy Scouts first aid. No. 723, Boy Scouts camping. No. 724, Brownies.

**1997, Sept. 1**    **Litho.**    **Perf. 14½**
| | | | | |
|---|---|---|---|---|
| 717 | A137 | 10sh multicolored | .35 | .35 |
| 718 | A137 | 10sh multicolored | .35 | .35 |
| a. | | Pair, #717-718 | .75 | .75 |
| 719 | A137 | 27sh multicolored | .90 | .90 |
| 720 | A137 | 27sh multicolored | .90 | .90 |
| a. | | Pair, #719-720 | 2.25 | 2.25 |
| 721 | A137 | 33sh multicolored | 1.25 | 1.25 |
| 722 | A137 | 33sh multicolored | 1.25 | 1.25 |
| a. | | Pair, #721-722 | 3.00 | 3.00 |
| 723 | A137 | 42sh multicolored | 1.50 | 1.50 |
| 724 | A137 | 42sh multicolored | 1.50 | 1.50 |
| a. | | Pair, #723-724 | 3.50 | 3.50 |
| | | *Nos. 717-724 (8)* | 8.00 | 8.00 |

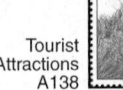

Tourist Attractions A138

Designs: 10sh, Crocodile. 27sh, Hot Springs, Lake Bogoria. 30sh, Warthogs. 33sh, Wind surfing. 42sh, Traditional huts.

**1997, Oct. 9**         **Perf. 13½**
| | | | | |
|---|---|---|---|---|
| 725 | A138 | 10sh multicolored | 1.25 | 1.25 |
| 726 | A138 | 27sh multicolored | 2.00 | 1.60 |
| 727 | A138 | 30sh multicolored | 2.00 | 1.90 |
| 728 | A138 | 33sh multicolored | 2.25 | 2.25 |
| 729 | A138 | 42sh multicolored | 2.50 | 2.50 |
| | | *Nos. 725-729 (5)* | 10.00 | 8.50 |

Vasco da Gama's Stop in Malindi, 500th Anniv. — A139

Designs: 10sh, Residents greeting ships as they arrive. 24sh, Three ships. 33sh, Map of voyage. 42sh, Ships in bay, monument.

**1998, Apr. 4**    **Litho.**    **Perf. 13**
| | | | | |
|---|---|---|---|---|
| 730 | A139 | 10sh multicolored | .60 | .30 |
| 731 | A139 | 24sh multicolored | 1.40 | .75 |
| 732 | A139 | 33sh multicolored | 2.00 | 2.00 |
| 733 | A139 | 42sh multicolored | 2.50 | 2.50 |
| | | *Nos. 730-733 (4)* | 6.50 | 5.55 |

Pan African Postal Union (PAPU) — A140

**1998, June 10**    **Litho.**    **Perf. 14½**
| | | | | |
|---|---|---|---|---|
| 734 | A140 | 10sh Lion | 1.75 | .30 |
| 735 | A140 | 24sh Buffalo | 2.25 | .85 |
| 736 | A140 | 33sh Grant's gazelle | 3.00 | 3.00 |
| 737 | A140 | 42sh Cheetah | 4.15 | 4.15 |
| | | *Nos. 734-737 (4)* | 11.15 | 8.30 |

**Souvenir Sheet**
| | | | | |
|---|---|---|---|---|
| 738 | A140 | 50sh Hirola gazelle | 4.00 | 4.00 |

Pres. Daniel arap Moi Taking Oath of Office, 1998 — A141

**1998, Dec. 8**    **Litho.**    **Perf. 13½**
| | | | | |
|---|---|---|---|---|
| 739 | A141 | 14sh multicolored | 1.50 | .80 |

Turtles — A142

Designs: 17sh, Leatherback. 20sh, Green sea. 30sh, Hawksbill. 47sh, Olive Ridley. 59sh, Loggerhead.

**2000, Apr. 13 Litho.**   **Perf. 13½x13¾**
| | | | | |
|---|---|---|---|---|
| 740 | A142 | 17sh multi | 1.00 | .35 |
| 741 | A142 | 20sh multi | 1.25 | .40 |
| 742 | A142 | 30sh multi | 1.75 | 1.00 |
| 743 | A142 | 47sh multi | 2.50 | 2.50 |
| 744 | A142 | 59sh multi | 3.00 | 3.00 |
| | | *Nos. 740-744 (5)* | 9.50 | 7.25 |

Emblems of East African Postal Administrations A143

Designs: 17sh, Postal Corporation of Kenya. 35sh, Uganda Posta Limited. 50sh, Tanzania Posts Corporation. 70sh, Postal Corporation of Kenya.

**2000, May 31**      **Perf. 13¾x13½**
| | | | | |
|---|---|---|---|---|
| 745 | A143 | 17sh multi | .85 | .35 |
| 746 | A143 | 35sh multi | 1.60 | 1.25 |
| 747 | A143 | 50sh multi | 2.25 | 2.25 |
| | | *Nos. 745-747 (3)* | 4.70 | 3.85 |

**Souvenir Sheet**
**Perf. 13¼x13**
| | | | | |
|---|---|---|---|---|
| 748 | A143 | 70sh multi | | 4.50 | 4.50 |

Crops — A144

**2001, Feb. 28 Photo.**   **Perf. 14½x14**
| | | | | |
|---|---|---|---|---|
| 749 | A144 | 2sh Cotton | .30 | .25 |
| 750 | A144 | 4sh Bananas | .30 | .25 |
| 751 | A144 | 5sh Avocados | .30 | .25 |
| 752 | A144 | 6sh Cassava | .30 | .25 |
| 753 | A144 | 8sh Arrowroot | .30 | .25 |
| 754 | A144 | 10sh Papayas | .30 | .25 |
| 755 | A144 | 19sh Oranges | .50 | .35 |
| 756 | A144 | 20sh Pyrethrum | .50 | .35 |
| 757 | A144 | 30sh Peanuts | .75 | .60 |
| 758 | A144 | 35sh Coconuts | .90 | .60 |
| 759 | A144 | 40sh Sisal | 1.00 | .75 |
| 760 | A144 | 50sh Cashews | 1.25 | .90 |

**Size: 25x42mm**
**Perf. 14¼**
| | | | | |
|---|---|---|---|---|
| 761 | A144 | 60sh Tea | 1.50 | 1.00 |
| 762 | A144 | 80sh Corn | 2.00 | 1.50 |
| 763 | A144 | 100sh Coffee | 2.50 | 1.75 |
| 764 | A144 | 200sh Finger millet | 5.00 | 3.50 |
| 765 | A144 | 400sh Sorghum | 10.00 | 7.00 |
| 766 | A144 | 500sh Sugar cane | 12.50 | 8.50 |
| | | *Nos. 749-766 (18)* | 40.20 | 28.30 |

**2001**   **Photo.**   **Perf. 14¾ Horiz.**
**Coil Stamps**
| | | | | |
|---|---|---|---|---|
| 766A | A144 | 5sh Avocados | *3.00* | *3.00* |
| 766B | A144 | 10sh Papayas | *3.00* | *3.00* |

Historic Sites of East Africa — A145

Designs: 19sh, Source of Nile River, Jinja, Uganda. 35sh, Lamu Fort, Kenya (28x28mm). 40sh, Olduvai Gorge, Tanzania. 50sh, Thimlich Ohinga, Kenya (28x28mm).

***Perf. 14¼, 13½ (35sh, 50sh)***
**2002**          **Litho.**
| | | | | |
|---|---|---|---|---|
| 767-770 | A145 | Set of 4 | 7.50 | 7.50 |

Kenya - People's Republic of China Diplomatic Relations, 40th Anniv. A146

Flags of Kenya and People's Republic of China and: 21sh, Section of Mombasa Road. 66sh, Kasarani Stadium.

**2003, Dec. 14**    **Litho.**    **Perf. 12**
| | | | | |
|---|---|---|---|---|
| 771-772 | A146 | Set of 2 | 7.50 | 7.50 |

Mammals A147

Designs: 21sh, Lioness and baby oryx. 60sh, Leopard and cub. 66sh, Zebra and calf. 88sh, Bongo and calf.

**2004, Nov. 19**    **Litho.**    **Perf. 14½**
| | | | | |
|---|---|---|---|---|
| 773-776 | A147 | Set of 4 | 10.00 | 10.00 |

Easter — A148

Designs: 25sh, Jesus with hand raised. 65sh, Jesus condemned to death. 75sh, Crucifixion. 95sh, Jesus praying.

**2005, Apr. 1**    **Litho.**    **Perf. 13½**
| | | | | |
|---|---|---|---|---|
| 777-780 | A148 | Set of 4 | 10.50 | 10.50 |

Rotary International, Cent. — A149

Rotary emblem and: 25sh, Polio vaccination. 65sh, Donation of Jaipur feet. 75sh, Don Bosco Center, Nairobi. 95sh, Donation of sewing machine.

**2005, May 26**
| | | | | |
|---|---|---|---|---|
| 781-784 | A149 | Set of 4 | 10.50 | 10.50 |

Native Costumes — A150

Designs: 21sh, Gabbra. 60sh, Pokot. 66sh, Meru. 88sh, Digo.

**2005, Dec. 6**    **Litho.**    **Perf. 14½**
| | | | | |
|---|---|---|---|---|
| 785-788 | A150 | Set of 4 | 8.00 | 8.00 |

Fish — A151

Designs: 25sh, Elephant snout fish. 55sh, Sudan catfish. 75sh, Nile perch. 95sh, Redbreast tilapia.

**2006, May 4**    **Litho.**    **Perf. 13½x13**
| | | | | |
|---|---|---|---|---|
| 789 | A151 | 25sh multi | 100.00 | 25.00 |
| 790 | A151 | 55sh multi | 30.00 | — |
| 791 | A151 | 75sh multi | 30.00 | — |
| 792 | A151 | 95sh multi | 30.00 | — |

24th Universal Postal Union Congress, Nairobi — A152

**2006, Oct. 11**    **Litho.**    **Perf. 13½**
| | | | | |
|---|---|---|---|---|
| 793 | A152 | 25sh multi | 1.25 | 1.25 |

Values are for stamps with surrounding selvage. Due to political unrest in Kenya, the UPU Congress was moved to Geneva, Switzerland.

Hippopotamus and Tortoise — A153

**2006, Dec. 15**    **Litho.**    **Perf. 12½x13**
| | | | | |
|---|---|---|---|---|
| 794 | A153 | 25sh multi | 2.00 | 2.00 |

Tourism — A155

**2006, Dec. 15**         **Perf. 13**
**Booklet Stamps**
| | | | | |
|---|---|---|---|---|
| 795 | A155 | 25sh Roan antelope | 8.00 | 4.00 |
| 796 | A155 | 25sh Weaver bird | 8.00 | 4.00 |
| 797 | A155 | 25sh Monkey | 8.00 | 4.00 |
| a. | | Booklet pane of 3, #795-797 | 25.00 | — |
| 798 | A155 | 25sh Turkana hut | 8.00 | 4.00 |
| 799 | A155 | 25sh Sports | 8.00 | 4.00 |
| 800 | A155 | 25sh Golf course | 8.00 | 4.00 |
| a. | | Booklet pane of 3, #798-800 | 25.00 | — |
| 801 | A155 | 25sh Abadares Waterfall | 8.00 | 4.00 |
| 802 | A155 | 25sh Balloon safari | 8.00 | 4.00 |
| 803 | A155 | 25sh Bull fighting | 8.00 | 4.00 |
| a. | | Booklet pane of 3, #801-803 | 25.00 | — |
| 804 | A155 | 25sh Chimpanzee | 8.00 | 4.00 |
| 805 | A155 | 25sh Maasai | 8.00 | 4.00 |
| 806 | A155 | 25sh Kit Mikaye | 8.00 | 4.00 |
| a. | | Booklet pane of 3, #804-806 | 25.00 | — |
| | | Complete booklet, #797a, 800a, 803a, 806a | 100.00 | |
| | | *Nos. 795-806 (12)* | 96.00 | 48.00 |

Mountains A156

Designs: 25sh, Mt. Kenya, Kenya. 75sh, Mt. Ruwenzori, Uganda. 95sh, Mt. Kilimanjaro, Tanzania.

**2007, Feb. 28**    **Litho.**    **Perf. 13½**
| | | | | |
|---|---|---|---|---|
| 807-809 | A156 | Set of 3 | 10.00 | 10.00 |

Breast Cancer Awareness — A157

**2007, Oct. 28**         **Perf. 13¼**
| | | | | |
|---|---|---|---|---|
| 810 | A157 | 25sh multi | 2.00 | 2.00 |

Ceremonial Costumes — A158

Men's and women's costumes: 25sh, Ogiek. 65sh, Sabaot. 75sh, Ribe. 95sh, Elmolo.

**2007, Nov. 21** — *Perf. 14½*
811-814　A158　Set of 4　　　　8.25　8.25

National Arboretum, Cent. A159

Designs: 25sh, Cape chestnut tree and blossom. 65sh, Bhutan cypress tree, Tree Center. 75sh, Nandi flame tree and blossom. 95sh, Calabash nutmeg tree and blossom.

**2007, Dec. 13　Litho.　*Perf. 13¾***
815-818　A159　Set of 4　　　　8.25　8.25

24th UPU Congress A160

Design: 25sh, Sitalunga gazelle in Saiwa Swamp. 65sh, Jackson's hartebeest at Ruma Park. 75sh, Steeplechase runner. 95sh, Kenyatta Intl. Conference Center, Nairobi.

**2008, Feb. 7　Litho.　*Perf. 14½***
819　A160　25sh multi　　　　1.00　.50
820　A160　65sh multi　　　　2.50　1.50
821　A160　75sh multi　　　　3.00　2.25
822　A160　95sh multi　　　　3.75　3.75
　　Nos. 819-822 (4)　　10.25　8.00

Because of political turmoil in Kenya, the 24th UPU Congress was moved from Nairobi to Geneva, Switzerland.

2008 Summer Olympics, Beijing — A161

Designs: 25sh, Kenyan athletes holding Kenyan flag. 65sh, Women's volleyball, vert. 75sh, Women runners. 95sh, Boxing.

**2008, Aug. 21　Litho.　*Perf. 14½***
823-826　A161　Set of 4　　　　7.50　7.50

Heroes of Kenya A162

Designs: 25sh, Vice-president Oginga Odinga (c. 1911-94), Pio Gama Pinto (1927-65), politician, Tom Mboya (1930-69), politician, Ronald Ngala (1923-72), politician. 65sh, The Kapenguria Six. 75sh, Dedan Kimathi (1920-57), rebel leader, Elijah Masinde (c. 1910-87), Bukusu tribal leader, Mekatilili Wa Menza, female leader of 1914 rebellion, Koitalel Samoei (1860-1905), Nandi chief. 95sh, Kenya Army Peacekeeping Force.

**2008, Oct. 17　　*Perf. 12¾x13¼***
827-830　A162　Set of 4　　　　8.50　8.50

Theosophical Order of Service, Cent. — A163

**2008, Nov. 17　Litho.　*Perf. 14x13¾***
831　A163　25sh multi　　　　1.25　1.25

Aga Khan, 50th Anniv.of Reign — A164

---

Designs: 25sh, Madrasa program (40x40mm). 65sh, Coastal rural support program (40x40mm). 75sh, Aga Khan Academy, Mombasa (44x30mm). 95sh, Aga Khan University Hospital, Nairobi (44x30mm).

**Perf. 13, 14½ (75sh, 95sh)**
**2008, Dec. 13**
832-835　A164　Set of 4　　　　7.50　7.50

Blind Man — A165

**2009, July 20　　*Perf. 14½***
836　A165　25sh multi　　　　.65　.65

Louis Braille (1809-52), educator of the blind.

Postal Services A166

Designs: No. 837, 25sh, Man greeting woman, PostaPay emblem. No. 838, 25sh, Parcels, Posta Parcel emblem. No. 839, 25sh, Mailman and trucks, Posta Dispatch emblem. No. 840, 25sh, Stamp collector and stamps, Posta Philately emblem. No. 841, 25sh, Open post office box, Posta Direct Mail emblem. No. 842, 25sh, Agency services, Posta Kenya emblem. No. 843, 25sh, Woman reading letter, Posta Mail emblem. No. 844, 25sh, Man at open post office box, Posta Kenya emblem. No. 845, 25sh, Financial Services clerk and client, computer, Posta Money Order emblem. No. 846, 65sh, Postal worker with package at airport, EMS Kenya emblem. No. 847, 75sh, Narok Post Office, Posta Kenya emblem. No. 848, 95sh, People at water spigot, Posta Kenya emblem.

**2009, Dec. 9　　*Perf. 14x13¾***
837-848　A166　Set of 12　　12.50　12.50
845a　　Sheet of 9, #837-845　15.00　15.00

East Africa Natural History Society, Cent. — A167

Bird on branch and: 25sh, Taita African violet, Amegilla bee. 65sh, Reed frog. 75sh, Great blue turaco. 95sh, Golden-rumped sengi.

**2010, Mar. 25　　*Perf. 13***
**Granite Paper**
849-852　A167　Set of 4　　　　6.75　6.75

Pan-African Postal Union, 30th Anniv. — A167a

**2010, Nov. 30　Litho.　*Perf. 14x13¾***
852A　A167a　25sh multi　　　　.65　.65

Insects — A168

No. 853: a, Danaus chrysippus (African monarch). b, Pontia helice. c, Junonia hierta (Yellow pansy). d, Chiasmia subcurvaria. e, Catopsilia florella (African migrant). f, Belenois thysa (False dotted border). g, Leucinodes orbonalis sp. h, Gelechioidea sp. i, Eupithecia sp. cf. festiva. j, Nymphalidae. k, Paraccra mimesa. l, Hodebertia testalis. m, Alucitidae sp. n, Anthozela sp. n. o, Eucosmini gen. n. sp. n. p, Eucosmini sp. q, Zalaca snelleni. r, Yponomeuta strigillata. s, Tortrix dinota. t, Parotis sp. nr. prasinalis. u, Precis hierta. v, Colotis antevippe. w, Cryptophlebia

---

semilunana. x, Hypolimnas misippus. y, Yponomeuta fumigatus.

No. 854: a, Oplostomus haroldi (Large hive beetle). b, Cartoblatta sp. (Cockroaches). c, Mormotomyia hirsuta. d, Cicindellidae. e, Nosognatha ruficollis. f, Hetrodinae sp. g, Helopeltis schoutedeni. h, Ceroctis sp. (Blister beetle). i, Bagrada cruciferarum. j, Popillia aeneipennis (Chafer). k, Lampetis sp. (Jewel beetle). l, Oryctes sp. (Rhinoceros beetle). m, Homoderus mellyi. n, Zonocerus variegatus. o, Leucospidae. p, Agnoscelis versicolor. q, Hispinae (Tortoise beetle). r, Curculionidae. s, Cypholoba perspicillaris. t, Lycidae. u, Milkweed bugs. v, Mylabris tristigma. w, Paederus sp. x, Pyrops turritus. y, Tenebrionidae.

No. 855: a, Fig wasp in flight. b, Ptyelus flavescens (Rain tree bug). c, Phlebotomus feeding. d, Fig wasp, head at bottom. e, Trithemis annulata (Dragonfly). f, Braconid wasp. g, Polistes sp. (Paper wasps). h, Helopeltis schoutedeni. i, Trithemis sp. (Dragonfly). j, Cicada. k, Silverfish. l, Stingless bee. m, Lipotriches sp. n, Bombyliidae. o, Bromophila caffra. p, Schistocerca gregaria. q, Plagiotryptus hippiscus. r, Reduviidae. s, Diopsidae (Stalk-eyed fly). t, Lamyra gulo and wasp prey. u, Dictyophapidae. v, Rhiniidae cf. Fainia sp. w, Locust. x, Megastigmus sp. m. y, Glossina morsitans feeding.

No. 856: a, Bactrocera invadens, head at top. b, Trirhithrum culcasiae. c, Trirhithrum coffeae. d, Bactrocera invadens, head at bottom. e, Bactrocera munroi. f, Caprophthoromyia dimidiata. g, Celidodacus obnublius. h, Ceratitis caetrata. i, Ceratitis captiata. j, Ceratitis copelandi. k, Ceratitis cosyra. l, Ceratitis cuthbertsoni. m, Ceratitis rosa. n, Ceratitis stictica. o, Ceratitis whartoni. p, Conradtina acroleuca. q, Dacus apostata. r, Dacus frontalis. s, Dacus sphaeristicus. t, Dacus telfairae. u, Munromyia whartoni. v, Craspedoxantha sp. w, Taomyia marshalli. x, Themarictera laticeps. y, Trirhithrum albomaculatum.

**2011, Nov. 16　　*Perf. 13x13¼***
853　　Sheet of 25　150.00　150.00
　a.-y.　A168 25sh Any single　5.00　5.00
854　　Sheet of 25　37.50　37.50
　a.-y.　A168 65sh Any single　1.50　1.50
855　　Sheet of 25　44.00　44.00
　a.-y.　A168 75sh Any single　1.75　1.75
856　　Sheet of 25　52.50　52.50
　a.-y.　A168 95sh Any single　2.10　2.10
　　Nos. 853-856 (4)　284.00　284.00

Intl. Center of Insect Physiology and Endocrinology, 40th anniv.

Promulgation of New Constitution — A169

**2011　　*Perf. 14½***
857　A169　25sh multi　　　　.60　.60

United Nations Environment Program, 40th Anniv. — A170

Designs: 30sh, Flags at UNEP regional office, Nairobi. 90sh, Buildings in Stockholm, Sweden. 110sh, Christ the Redeemer Statue, Rio de Janeiro.

**2012　　*Perf. 14***
858-860　A170　Set of 3　　　　5.50　5.50

United Nations Environment Program, 40th Anniv. — A171

United Nations Environment Program emblem and emblem for: 30sh, Convention on International Trade in Endangered Species of Wild Fauna and Flora. 90sh, Montreal Protocol on Substances that Deplete the Ozone Layer. 110sh, Green Economy,

**2012, June 22　Litho.　*Perf. 14***
861-863　A171　Set of 3　　　　5.50　5.50

---

Wangari Muta Maathai (1940-2011), 2004 Nobel Peace Laureate — A173

**2012, Sept. 25　Litho.　*Perf. 14***
867　A173　30sh multi　　　　.70　.70

Independence, 50th Anniv. — A174

No. 868: a, First airplane to land in Kenya, 1920. b, 1904 locomotive. c, East Africa Railway & Harbor train car. d, Jamhuri High School. e, Prince of Wales School. f, Machakos Girls School. g, Royal Technical College, University of Nairobi. h, Kenyatta University. i, Jomo Kenyatta University of Agriculture & Technology. j, Nairobi skyline. k, King George VI Hospital. l, Kenyatta National Hospital. m, Jomo Kenyatta International Airport. n, Mobile library. o, Kenya National Library, Nairobi. p, Horticulture. q, Poultry farming. r, Corn farming (maize). s, Beef farming. t, Dairy farming. u, Compulsory free primary education. v, Kenya National Adult Literacy Survey. w, Murang's Road Junction. x, Globe Cinema Complex. y, Oil prospecting.

No. 869: a, Pres. Uhuru Kenyatta and Deputy Pres. William Ruto. b, Queen Elizabeth II and Prince Philip, 1953. c, Lancaster House Conference, 1963. d, Dedan Kimathi. e, Mau Mau movement. f, Kapenguria Six. g, Kapenguria cells. h, Lowering of the Union Jack, 1963. i, Munyao Kisol hoisting Kenyan flag on Mt. Kenya, 1963. j, Promulgation of new constitution. k, First transition. l, Second transition. m, Third transition. n, Fourth transition. o, Parliament Building. p, First Cabinet, 1963. q, Colonial and current coats of arms. r, Colonial and current flags. s, Maps showing the eight provinces and 47 counties. t, Judiciary Building. u, Kenyatta Mausoleum. v, Old Provincial Commissioner's Office, 1913. w, Nyayo House. x, Baron Delamere, first governor of Nairobi. y, Kenya Defense Forces in Somalia.

No. 870: a, Fort Jesus, 1565. b, Kenya-Uganda railway line, 1896. c, Nyall Bridge, 1900. d, Gedi Ruins, 13th cent. e, First Post Office in Mombasa, 1902. f, First General Post Office in Mombasa, 1920. g, First General Post Office in Nairobi, 1944. h, Kenya National Archives, 1944. i, Macmillan Library, 1925. j, Nairobi National Museum, 1890. k, 1885 Mombasa coins. l, Maasai Morans. m, Luo traditional homestead. n, Karen Blixen Museum. o, Kipande House, 1913. p, Laikipia camel caravan. q, East Africa and Uganda Protectorates #53, Kenya #8. r, Chaka drummers. s, Obokano musical instrument. t, Vasco da Gama Pillar, Malindi. u, Naftali Temu, first Kenyan Olympic gold medalist. v, Pamela Jelimo, Janeth Jepkosgei, runners. w, Ezekiel Kemboi, 2004 Olympic steeplechase gold medalist. x, David Rudisha, 2012 Olympic 800-meter gold medalist. y, Kenya Rugby Union national team.

No. 871: a, Lion. b, Elephant. c, Leopard. d, Rhinoceros. e, Buffalo. f, Hippopotamus. g, Cheetah. h, Giraffe. i, Zebra. j, Warthog. k, Wildebeest migration. l, Bongo. m, Impala. n, Hyena. o, Jackal. p, Crocodiles on Tana River. q, Flamingos at Lake Nakuru. r, Ostriches. s, Colobus monkey. t, Falcon. u, Longonot Crater. v, Thompson Falls, Nyahururu. w, Mt. Kenya. x, Lake Turkana. y, Solar eclipse.

No. 872: a, Mail runner, 1880. b, Postman delivering letters in marketplace, 1902. c, Mail box, 1920. d, Modern postal delivery van. e, Letter boxes. f, Pillar box.

No. 873: a, East African coins, 1910-65. b, Kenyan coins, 1966-2010. c, East African bank notes, 1964. d, Kenyan banknotes, 1966.

150sh, Kenyan Presidents Jomo Kenyatta (c. 1897-1978), Daniel Arap Moi, Mwai Kibaki and Uhuru Kenyatta.

**Perf. 13½x13¼ Syncopated**
**2013, Dec. 13　　Litho.**
868　　Sheet of 25　17.50　17.50
　a.-y.　A174 30sh Any single　.70　.70
869　　Sheet of 25　44.00　44.00
　a.-y.　A174 75sh Any single　1.75　1.75
870　　Sheet of 25　52.50　52.50
　a.-y.　A174 90sh Any single　2.10　2.10
871　　Sheet of 25　75.00　75.00
　a.-y.　A174 110sh Any single　3.00　3.00
　　Nos. 868-871 (4)　189.00　189.00
872　A174　30sh Sheet of 6,
　　　　　　　#a-f　　　—　　—
873　A174　30sh Sheet of 4,
　　　　　　　#a-d　　　—　　—

## Imperf
### Size: 87x125mm

874  A174  150sh multi  — —

No. 874 has simulated perfs.

Diplomatic Relations Between Kenya and People's Republic of China, 50th Anniv.
A175

Flags of Kenya and People's Republic of China and: 30sh, Ship, Kenyan and Chinese containers. 110sh, Cranes, Kenyan Pres. Uhuru Kenyatta, Chinese Pres. Xi Jinping. 150sh, Like 110sh.

**2013, Dec. 20    Litho.    Perf. 12**
875-876  A175  Set of 2  3.25 3.25
### Souvenir Sheet
877  A175  150sh multi  3.50 3.50

No. 877 contains one 76x50mm stamp.

Birds — A176

Designs: 30sh, Red and yellow barbet. 35sh, Scarlet-chested sunbird. 50sh, Yellow-billed hornbill. 55sh, Greater honeyguide. 65sh, Superb starling. 70sh, African fish eagle. 80sh, Lesser flamingo. 100sh, Hadada ibis. 110sh, Ross's turaco.

### Perf. 13x13¼ Syncopated
**2014    Litho.**
878  A176  30sh multi  1.40  .70
879  A176  35sh multi  1.60  .80
880  A176  50sh multi  2.25  1.10
881  A176  55sh multi  2.50  1.25
882  A176  65sh multi  3.00  1.50
883  A176  70sh multi  3.25  1.60
884  A176  80sh multi  3.75  1.90
885  A176  100sh multi  4.50  2.25
886  A176  110sh multi  5.00  2.50
  *Nos. 878-886 (9)*  27.25 13.60

Nos. 878-886 have three punched holes at lower left.

St. John Bosco (1815-88) — A177

Design: 100sh, Bosco with children, horiz.

**2015, Feb. 1    Litho.    Perf. 14¼x14½**
887  A177  35sh multi + label  .80  .80
### Souvenir Sheet
### Perf. 13½ Syncopated
887A  A177  100shmulti

No. 887 was printed in sheets of 20 + 20 labels. No. 887A contains one 70x30mm stamp.

United Nations, 70th Anniv. — A178

### Perf. 13¾ Syncopated
**2015, Oct. 2    Litho.**
888  A178  35sh multi  .70  .70

---

International Telecommunication Union, 150th Anniv. — A179

Designs: 35sh, Digital and analog signals. 90sh, Terrestrial services. 105sh, 150th anniv. emblem. 130sh, Space services.

**2015    Litho.    Perf. 13x13¼**
889-892  A179  Set of 4  7.25 7.25

No. 892 the country name and denomination are smaller than on Nos. 889-891.

Big Game Animals — A180

Designs: 35sh, Elephant. 80sh, Lion, horiz. 90sh, Buffalo, horiz. 105sh, Leopard, horiz. 130sh, Rhinoceros.
175sh, Buffalo, lion, leopard, elephant and rhinoceros, horiz.

### Perf. 13¼ Syncopated
**2017, May 10    Litho.**
893-897  A180  Set of 5  8.50 8.50
### Size: 110x80mm
### Imperf
898  A180  175sh multi  3.50 3.50

Mombasa-Nairobi Standard Gauge Railway — A181

Designs: 35sh, Mombasa Terminus. 50sh, Man standing on railroad track. 110sh, Train on bridge. 130sh, Locomotive. 150sh, Nairobi Terminus.
200sh, Like 50sh.

**2017, May 31    Litho.    Perf. 14**
899-903  A181  Set of 5  9.25 9.25
### Souvenir Sheet
### Perf. 13¼x13
904  A181  200sh multi  4.00 4.00

No. 904 contains one 45x35mm stamp.

Kenya Pres. Uhuru Kenyatta and U.S. Pres. Barack Obama
A182

### Perf. 13½x13¼
**2017, Sept. 13    Litho.**
905  A182  50sh multi + label  1.00 1.00

Visit of Pres. Obama to Kenya, 2nd anniv.

United Nations Sustainable Development Goals — A183

Designs: 50sh, Goal 7. 90sh, Goal 14. 105sh, Goal 13. 130sh, Goal 15.

### Perf. 13½x13¼ Syncopated
**2017, Oct. 9    Litho.**
906-909  A183  Set of 4  7.25 7.25

---

Last Remaining Northern White Rhinoceroses
A184

Designs: 50sh, Female named Najin. 130sh, Male named Sudan, euthanized in March 2018. 160sh, Female named Fatu.
200sh, Two of the Northern white rhinoceroses, vert.

### Perf. 13½ Syncopated
**2018, May 11    Litho.**
910-912  A184  Set of 3  6.75 6.75
### Souvenir Sheet
913  A184  200sh multi  4.00 4.00

### Souvenir Sheet

Nelson Mandela (1918-2013), President of South Africa — A185

**2018, July 18    Litho.    Perf. 13½**
915  A185  100sh multi  2.00 2.00

Big Four Action Plan — A186

Designs: 30sh, Universal health coverage. 85sh, Affordable housing. 110sh, Enhancing manufacturing. 140sh, Food security and nutrition.

**2019, May 29    Litho.    Perf. 14¼**
916-919  A186  Set of 4  7.25 7.25

World Sickle Cell Day, 10th Anniv. — A187

Designs: 10sh, Family. 50sh, Children. 110sh, Mother and infant. 140sh, Father and daughter.

**2019, June 19    Litho.    Perf. 13**
920-923  A187  Set of 4  6.00 6.00

Posta House Headquarters, Nairobi — A188

**2020, Jan. 31    Litho.    Perf. 14¼**
924  A188  30sh multi  .60  .60

Postal Corporation of Kenya, 20th anniv.

Aga Khan University Hospital, Nairobi, 60th Anniv. — A189

---

Designs: 30sh, Hospital in 1963. 110sh, Hospital entrance. 140sh, Hospital campus.

**2020, Feb. 15    Litho.    Perf. 14x14¼**
925-927  A189  Set of 3  5.50 5.50

## POSTAGE DUE STAMPS

D1

### Perf. 14x13½
**1967-85    Litho.    Unwmk.**
### "POSTAGE DUE" 12½mm long
J1  D1  5c dark red  .25  2.75
J2  D1  10c green  .35  2.75
J3  D1  20c dark blue  .70  3.25
J4  D1  30c reddish brown  1.00  4.00
J5  D1  40c brt red lilac  1.25  6.75
### Perf. 14
J6  D1  80c brick red  1.00  6.25
### Perf. 14x13½
J7  D1  1sh orange  1.75  7.00
### "POSTAGE DUE" 11½mm long
### Perf. 14¾x14
J8  D1  2sh pale violet  2.25  4.00
  *Nos. J1-J8 (8)*  8.55 36.75

Issued: 80c, 1978. 2sh, 1985; others, 1/3/67. See Nos. J9-J14.

**1969-70    Perf. 14**
J1a  D1  5c  .25  5.25
J2a  D1  10c  .25  5.25
J3a  D1  20c  .45  5.75
J4a  D1  30c  .70  6.75
J5a  D1  40c  .80  22.50
J7a  D1  1sh  2.00  13.50
  *Nos. J1a-J7a (6)*  4.45 59.00

Issued: 1sh, 2/18/70; others, 12/16/69.

**1971-73    Perf. 14x15**
J1b  D1  5c  1.75  5.25
J2b  D1  10c  8.50  5.25
J3b  D1  20c  11.00  11.00
J4b  D1  30c  10.50  15.00
J5b  D1  40c  1.25  15.00
J7b  D1  1sh  17.00  40.00
  *Nos. J1b-J7b (6)*  50.00 91.50

Issued: 30c, 7/13/71; others, 2/20/73. The 10c, 20c, 1sh on chalky paper were issued 7/13/71.

**1973, Dec. 12    Perf. 15**
J1c  D1  5c  .45  4.00
J2c  D1  10c  .45  4.00
J3c  D1  20c  .45  5.00
J4c  D1  30c  .45  5.75
J5c  D1  40c  5.25  10.00
J7c  D1  1sh  1.75  12.50
  *Nos. J1c-J7c (6)*  8.80 41.25

**1983    Wmk. 373    Perf. 14x14¼**
J2d  D1  10c  .45  2.00
J3d  D1  20c  .45  2.00
J5d  D1  40c  8.50  10.00

### Nos. J5, J7-J8 Redrawn
### Perf. 14¾x14
**1987-98    Litho.    Unwmk.**
J8A  D1  30c brown  .25  .25
J9  D1  40c bright red lilac  .25  .25
J10  D1  50c dark green  .25  .25
J10A  D1  80c red brown  .25  .25
J11  D1  1sh bright orange  .80  .80
  *a.*  light orange  .25  .25
J12  D1  2sh pale violet  .25  .25
J13  D1  3sh dark blue  .45  .45
J14  D1  5sh red brown  .45  .45
J15  D1  10sh brown  .45  .45
J16  D1  20sh red lilac  .80  .80
  *Nos. J8A-J16 (10)*  4.20 4.20

"KENYA" is 9mm wide on Nos. J9, J11. "CENTS" is 4½mm wide and "SHILLING" has cross bar on "G"; both are in a new font.
"KENYA" is 8½mm wide on No. J12. "POSTAGE DUE" is 11mm wide on Nos. J10, J11a, J15, J16.
Issued: 40c, 1sh, 1987; 10sh, 20sh, 1998; others, Dec. 6, 1993.

---

## OFFICIAL STAMPS

Nos. 1-5 and 7 Overprinted

**Perf. 14x14½**

| 1964, Oct. 1 | | Photo. | Unwmk. | |
|---|---|---|---|---|
| | | **Size: 21x17½mm** | | |
| O1 | A1 | 5c blue, buff & dk brn | .25 | .25 |
| O2 | A1 | 10c brown | .25 | .25 |
| O3 | A1 | 15c dp magenta | 1.25 | .30 |
| O4 | A1 | 20c yel green & dk brn | .30 | .45 |
| O5 | A1 | 30c yellow & black | .35 | .65 |
| O6 | A1 | 50c green, blk & dp car | 2.75 | 1.10 |
| | | *Nos. O1-O6 (6)* | 5.15 | 3.00 |

# KENYA, UGANDA, & TANZANIA

'ke-nyə, ü-'gan-də, ˌtan-zə-'nē-ə

LOCATION — East Africa, bordering on the Indian Ocean
GOVT. — States in British Commonwealth
AREA — 679,802 sq. mi.
POP. — 42,760,000 (est. 1977)
CAPITAL — Nairobi (Kenya), Kampala (Uganda), Dar es Salaam (Tanzania)

Kenya became a crown colony in 1906, including the former East Africa Protectorate leased from the Sultan of Zanzibar and known as the Kenya Protectorate. In 1963 the colony became independent. Its stamps are listed under "Kenya."

The inland Uganda Protectorate, lying west of Kenya Colony, was declared a British Protectorate in 1894. Uganda became independent in 1962.

Tanganyika, a trust territory larger than Kenya or Uganda, was grouped with them postally from 1935 under the East African Posts & Telecommunications Administration. Tanganyika became independent in 1961. When it merged with Zanzibar in 1964, "Zanzibar" was added to the inscriptions on stamps issued under the E.A.P. & T. Administration. In 1965 the multiple inscription was changed to "Kenya, Uganda, Tanzania," variously arranged.

Zanzibar withdrew its own stamps in 1968, and K., U. & T. stamps became valid Jan. 1, 1968.

100 Cents = 1 Rupee
100 Cents = 1 Shilling (1922)
20 Shillings = 1 Pound

> **Catalogue values for unused stamps in this country are for Never Hinged items, beginning with Scott 90.**

## East Africa and Uganda Protectorates

King George V
A1          A2

| | | | | Perf. 14 |
|---|---|---|---|---|
| **1921** | | **Typo.** | **Wmk. 4** | |
| | | **Ordinary Paper** | | |
| 1 | A1 | 1c black | 1.00 | 1.90 |
| 2 | A1 | 3c green | 6.75 | 16.50 |
| 3 | A1 | 6c rose red | 11.00 | 22.50 |
| 4 | A1 | 10c orange | 10.00 | 1.40 |
| 5 | A1 | 12c gray | 12.50 | 150.00 |
| 6 | A1 | 15c ultramarine | 12.50 | 22.50 |
| | | **Chalky Paper** | | |
| 7 | A1 | 50c gray lilac & blk | 16.50 | 140.00 |
| 8 | A2 | 2r blk & red, *blue* | 95.00 | 190.00 |
| 9 | A2 | 3r green & violet | 160.00 | 450.00 |
| 10 | A2 | 5r gray lil & ultra | 190.00 | 350.00 |
| 11 | A2 | 50r gray grn & red | 3,750. | 9,000. |
| | | Revenue cancel | | 425.00 |
| | | *Nos. 1-10 (10)* | 515.25 | 1,345. |

The name of the colony was changed to Kenya in August, 1920, but stamps of the East Africa and Uganda types were continued in use. Stamps of types A1 and A2 watermarked Multiple Crown and C A (3) are listed under East Africa and Uganda Protectorates. Used values for Nos. 8-11 are for postally used stamps. Examples with court cancels are worth considerably less.

For stamps of Kenya and Uganda overprinted "G. E. A." used in parts of former German East Africa occupied by British forces, see Tanganyika Nos. 1-9.

## Kenya and Uganda

Nos. 18-85 were printed in various shades.

King George V
A3          A4

| | | | | |
|---|---|---|---|---|
| **1922-27** | | | | **Wmk. 4** |
| 18 | A3 | 1c brown | 1.10 | 4.75 |
| 19 | A3 | 5c violet | 7.50 | 1.00 |
| 20 | A3 | 5c grn ('27) | 2.40 | .55 |
| 21 | A3 | 10c green | 1.75 | .35 |
| 22 | A3 | 10c blk ('27) | 4.50 | .25 |
| 23 | A3 | 12c black | 16.00 | 29.00 |
| 24 | A3 | 15c car rose | 1.40 | .25 |
| 25 | A3 | 20c orange | 3.75 | .25 |
| 26 | A3 | 30c ultra | 4.50 | .60 |
| 27 | A3 | 50c gray | 2.75 | .25 |
| 28 | A3 | 75c ol bister | 11.00 | 10.00 |
| 29 | A4 | 1sh green | 7.25 | 3.00 |
| 30 | A4 | 2sh gray lil | 10.00 | 21.00 |
| 31 | A4 | 2sh50c brn ('25) | 24.00 | 125.00 |
| 32 | A4 | 3sh gray blk | 20.00 | 7.50 |
| 33 | A4 | 4sh gray ('25) | 42.50 | 135.00 |
| 34 | A4 | 5sh carmine | 27.50 | 27.50 |
| 35 | A4 | 7sh50c org ('25) | 140.00 | 350.00 |
| 36 | A4 | 10sh ultra | 82.50 | 77.50 |
| 37 | A4 | £1 grn & blk | 230.00 | 340.00 |
| | | Revenue cancel | | 30.00 |
| 38 | A4 | £2 brn vio & grn ('25) | 1,200. | 2,100. |
| | | Revenue cancel | | 170.00 |
| 39 | A4 | £3 yel & dl vio ('25) | 1,850. | — |
| | | Revenue cancel | | 275.00 |
| 40 | A4 | £4 rose lil & blk ('25) | 4,000. | — |
| | | Revenue cancel | | 300.00 |
| 41 | A4 | £5 blue & blk | 4,500. | — |
| | | Revenue cancel | | 375.00 |
| 41A | A4 | £10 grn & blk | 15,000. | — |
| | | Revenue cancel | | 475.00 |
| 41B | A4 | £20 grn & red ('25) | 34,500. | — |
| | | Revenue cancel | | 850.00 |
| 41C | A4 | £25 red & blk | 43,500. | — |
| | | Revenue cancel | | 800.00 |
| 41D | A4 | £50 brn & blk | 85,000. | — |
| | | Revenue cancel | | 900.00 |
| 41E | A4 | £75 gray & purple | 150,000. | — |
| | | Revenue cancel | | 3,500. |
| 41F | A4 | £100 blk & red | 160,000. | — |
| | | Revenue cancel | | 2,250. |
| | | *Nos. 18-37 (20)* | 640.40 | 1,134. |

High face value stamps are known with revenue cancellations removed and forged postal cancellations added.

### Common Design Types
pictured following the introduction.

### Kenya, Uganda, Tanganyika
#### Silver Jubilee Issue
Common Design Type

| | | | | |
|---|---|---|---|---|
| **1935, May** | | **Engr.** | **Perf. 13½x14** | |
| 42 | CD301 | 20c ol grn & lt bl | 2.50 | .25 |
| 43 | CD301 | 30c blue & brown | 3.50 | 3.00 |
| 44 | CD301 | 65c indigo & green | 2.00 | 3.00 |
| 45 | CD301 | 1sh brt vio & indigo | 2.25 | 5.50 |
| | | *Nos. 42-45 (4)* | 10.25 | 11.75 |
| | | Set, never hinged | 27.00 | |
| | | Set, perf. "SPECIMEN" | 175.00 | |

Kavirondo Cranes
A5

Dhow on Lake Victoria
A6

Lion
A7

Mount Kilimanjaro
A8

Jinja Bridge by Ripon Falls — A9

Mount Kenya — A10

Lake Naivasha — A11

Type I

FIVE CENTS
Type I — Left rope does not touch sail.
Type II — Left rope touches sail.

| | | | | |
|---|---|---|---|---|
| **Perf. 13, 14, 11½x13, 13x11½** | | | | |
| **Engr.; Typo. (10c, £1)** | | | | |
| **1935, May 1** | | | | |
| 46 | A5 | 1c red brn & blk | 1.50 | 3.50 |
| 47 | A6 | 5c grn & blk (I) | 4.00 | .50 |
| a. | | Type II | 42.50 | 10.00 |
| b. | | Perf. 13x11½ (I) | 9,750. | 1,000. |
| c. | | Perf. 13x11½ (II) | 875.00 | 250.00 |
| 48 | A7 | 10c black & yel | 7.50 | 1.00 |
| 49 | A8 | 15c red & black | 4.50 | .25 |
| 50 | A5 | 20c red org & blk | 4.00 | .25 |
| 51 | A9 | 30c dk ultra & blk | 5.25 | 1.25 |
| 52 | A6 | 50c blk & red vio (I) | 7.00 | .25 |
| 53 | A10 | 65c yel brn & blk | 12.50 | 3.50 |
| 54 | A11 | 1sh grn & black | 5.75 | 1.75 |
| a. | | Perf. 13x11½ ('36) | 1,600. | 150.00 |
| 55 | A8 | 2sh red vio & rose brn | 14.00 | 4.75 |
| 56 | A11 | 3sh blk & ultra | 22.50 | 17.50 |
| a. | | Perf. 13x11½ | 2,600. | |
| 57 | A9 | 5sh car & black | 27.50 | 40.00 |
| 58 | A10 | 10sh ultra & red vio | 110.00 | 135.00 |
| 59 | A7 | £1 blk & scar | 325.00 | 425.00 |
| | | *Nos. 46-59 (14)* | 551.00 | 634.50 |
| | | Set, never hinged | 900.00 | |
| | | Set, perf. "SPECIMEN" | 525.00 | |

### Coronation Issue
Common Design Type

| | | | | |
|---|---|---|---|---|
| **1937, May 12** | | **Engr.** | **Perf. 13½x14** | |
| 60 | CD302 | 5c deep green | .25 | .25 |
| 61 | CD302 | 20c deep orange | .40 | .35 |
| 62 | CD302 | 30c brt ultra | .60 | 1.75 |
| | | *Nos. 60-62 (3)* | 1.25 | 2.35 |
| | | Set, never hinged | 1.90 | |
| | | Set, perf. "SPECIMEN" | 150.00 | |

Kavirondo Cranes
A12

Dhow on Lake Victoria
A13

Lake Naivasha
A14

Jinja Bridge, Ripon Falls
A16

Mt. Kilimanjaro
A15

Lion
A17

Type II

FIFTY CENTS:

Type I — Left rope does not touch sail.
Type II — Left rope touches sail.

| | | | | |
|---|---|---|---|---|
| **1938-54** | | **Engr.** | **Perf. 13x13½** | |
| 66 | A12 | 1c vio brn & blk ('42) | .25 | .50 |
| a. | | 1c red brown & gray black, perf. 13 | 3.00 | .90 |
| | | **Perf. 13x11½** | | |
| 67 | A13 | 5c grn & blk | 3.50 | .55 |
| 68 | A13 | 5c red org & brn ('49) | 8.00 | 7.50 |
| a. | | Perf. 13x12½ ('50) | 3.00 | 4.75 |
| 69 | A14 | 10c org & brn | 1.60 | .25 |
| a. | | Perf. 14 ('41) | 95.00 | 10.00 |
| 70 | A14 | 10c grn & blk ('49) | .35 | 2.00 |
| a. | | Perf. 13x12½ ('50) | 2.75 | .25 |
| | | **Perf. 13x12½** | | |
| 71 | A14 | 10c gray & red brn ('52) | 1.00 | .60 |
| | | **Perf. 13½x13, 13x13½** | | |
| 72 | A15 | 15c car & gray blk ('43) | 4.25 | 4.00 |
| a. | | Booklet pane of 4 | 17.50 | |
| b. | | Perf. 13 | 24.00 | .60 |
| 73 | A15 | 15c grn & blk ('52) | 1.90 | 7.00 |
| 74 | A12 | 20c org & gray blk ('42) | 5.75 | .25 |
| a. | | Booklet pane of 4 | 24.00 | |
| b. | | Imperf., pair | | |
| c. | | Perf. 13 | 35.00 | .30 |
| d. | | Perf. 14 ('41) | 45.00 | 5.00 |
| | | **Perf. 13x12½** | | |
| 75 | A13 | 25c car & blk ('52) | 1.50 | 2.40 |
| | | **Perf. 13x13½** | | |
| 76 | A16 | 30c dp bl & gray blk ('42) | 2.00 | .35 |
| a. | | Perf. 14 ('41) | 130.00 | 12.50 |
| b. | | Perf. 13 | 40.00 | .45 |
| 77 | A16 | 30c brn & pur ('52) | 1.25 | .45 |
| 78 | A12 | 40c brt bl & gray blk ('52) | 1.75 | 5.00 |
| | | **Perf. 13x12½** | | |
| 79 | A13 | 50c gray blk & red vio (II) ('49) | 7.25 | .50 |
| a. | | Perf. 13x11½ (II) | 14.00 | 1.10 |
| b. | | Perf. 13x11½ (I) | 200.00 | 250.00 |
| | | **Perf. 13x11½** | | |
| 80 | A14 | 1sh yel brn & gray blk | 20.00 | .30 |
| a. | | Perf. 13x12½ ('49) | 12.00 | .65 |
| | | **Perf. 13½x13** | | |
| 81 | A15 | 2sh red vio & org brn ('44) | 30.00 | .40 |
| a. | | Perf. 13 | 120.00 | 9.00 |
| b. | | Perf. 14 ('41) | 62.50 | 19.00 |
| | | **Perf. 13x12½** | | |
| 82 | A14 | 3sh gray blk & ultra ('50) | 30.00 | 9.00 |
| a. | | Perf. 13x11½ | 30.00 | 9.00 |
| | | **Perf. 13x13½** | | |
| 83 | A16 | 5sh car rose & gray blk ('44) | 30.00 | 2.00 |
| a. | | Perf. 13 | 130.00 | 21.00 |
| b. | | Perf. 14 ('41) | 35.00 | 3.25 |
| 84 | A12 | 10sh ultra & red vio ('44) | 42.50 | 11.00 |
| a. | | Perf. 13 | 120.00 | 37.50 |
| b. | | Perf. 14 ('41) | 32.50 | 25.00 |
| | | **Typo.** | | |
| | | **Perf. 14** | | |
| 85 | A17 | £1 blk & scar ('41) | 25.00 | 27.50 |
| a. | | Perf. 11½x13 | 300.00 | 170.00 |
| b. | | Perf. 12½ ('54) | 12.00 | 42.50 |
| | | *Nos. 66-85 (20)* | 217.85 | 81.55 |
| | | Set, never hinged | 350.00 | |

Nos. 85-85b were printed on chalky paper. No. 85 also exists on ordinary paper, from a 1944 printing. Values are the same.
See Nos. 98-99.

South Africa Nos. 48, 57, 60 and 62 Surcharged

Basic stamps of Nos. 86-89 are inscribed alternately in English and Afrikaans.

| | | | | |
|---|---|---|---|---|
| **1941-42** | | **Wmk. 201** | **Perf. 15x14, 14** | |
| 86 | A6 | 5c on 1p car & gray, pair | 1.10 | 3.00 |
| a. | | Single, English | .25 | .25 |
| b. | | Single, Afrikaans | .25 | .25 |
| 87 | A17 | 10c on 3p ultra, pair | 3.50 | 10.00 |
| a. | | Single, English | .30 | .35 |
| b. | | Single, Afrikaans | .30 | .35 |
| 88 | A7 | 20c on 6p org & grn, pair | 2.50 | 3.75 |
| a. | | Single, English | .25 | .25 |
| b. | | Single, Afrikaans | .25 | .25 |
| 89 | A11 | 70c on 1sh lt bl & ol brn, pair | 15.00 | 5.50 |
| a. | | Single, English | .50 | .45 |
| b. | | Single, Afrikaans | .50 | .45 |
| | | *Nos. 86-89 (4)* | 22.10 | 22.25 |
| | | Set, never hinged | 30.00 | |

Issued: Nos. 86-88, 7/1/41; No. 89, 4/20/42.

Values are for horizontal pairs. Vertical pairs are worth substantially less.

> **Catalogue values for unused stamps in this section, from this point to the end of the section, are for Never Hinged items.**

### Peace Issue
Common Design Type
*Perf. 13½x14*

| | | | | |
|---|---|---|---|---|
| **1946, Nov. 11** | | **Engr.** | | **Wmk. 4** |
| 90 | CD303 | 20c red orange | .25 | .25 |
| 91 | CD303 | 30c deep blue | .40 | .60 |

### Silver Wedding Issue
Common Design Types

| | | | | |
|---|---|---|---|---|
| **1948, Dec. 1** | | **Photo.** | | **Perf. 14x14½** |
| 92 | CD304 | 20c orange | 1.00 | .50 |

**Engr.; Name Typo.**
*Perf. 11½x11*

| | | | |
|---|---|---|---|
| 93 | CD305 | £1 red | 50.00 | 67.50 |

### UPU Issue
Common Design Types
Engr.; Typo. on Nos. 95 and 96

| | | | | |
|---|---|---|---|---|
| **1949, Oct. 10** | | | **Perf. 13, 11x11½** | |
| 94 | CD306 | 20c red orange | .25 | .25 |
| 95 | CD307 | 30c indigo | 1.75 | 2.25 |
| 96 | CD308 | 50c gray | .40 | 1.00 |
| 97 | CD309 | 1sh red brown | .50 | .50 |
| | | Nos. 94-97 (4) | 2.90 | 4.00 |

### Type of 1949 with Added Inscription: "Royal Visit 1952"

| | | | | |
|---|---|---|---|---|
| **1952, Feb. 1** | | **Engr.** | | **Perf. 13x12½** |
| 98 | A14 | 10c green & black | .50 | 2.00 |
| 99 | A14 | 1sh yel brn & gray blk | 1.75 | 3.25 |

Visit of Princess Elizabeth, Duchess of Edinburgh, and the Duke of Edinburgh, 1952.

### Coronation Issue
Common Design Type

| | | | | |
|---|---|---|---|---|
| **1953, June 2** | | | **Perf. 13½x13** | |
| 101 | CD312 | 20c red orange & blk | .40 | .25 |

Owen Falls Dam — A18

### Inscribed "ROYAL VISIT 1954"

| | | | | |
|---|---|---|---|---|
| **1954, Apr. 28** | | | **Perf. 12½x13** | |
| 102 | A18 | 30c dp ultra & black | .50 | .25 |

Visit of Queen Elizabeth II and the Duke of Edinburgh, 1954.

Owen Falls Dam — A18a

Giraffe A19

Mt. Kilimanjaro A20

Elizabeth II — A21

5c, 30c, Owen Falls Dam (without "Royal Visit 1954"). 20c, 40c, 1sh, Lion. 15c, 1.30sh, 5sh, Elephants. 10sh, Royal Lodge, Sagana.

---

| | | | | |
|---|---|---|---|---|
| **1954-59** | | **Perf. 12½x13, 13x12½** | | |
| 103 | A18a | 5c choc & blk | 1.75 | .65 |
| a. | | Booklet pane of 4 | 7.00 | |
| b. | | Vignette (dam) inverted | | 67,500. |
| 104 | A19 | 10c carmine | 1.75 | .25 |
| a. | | Booklet pane of 4 | 7.00 | |
| 105 | A20 | 15c lt blue & blk (no period below "c") ('58) | 1.00 | 1.40 |
| a. | | Booklet pane of 4 | 4.00 | |
| 106 | A20 | 15c lt blue & blk (period below "c") ('59) | 1.00 | 1.40 |
| a. | | Booklet pane of 4 | 4.00 | |
| 107 | A19 | 20c org & black | 2.00 | .25 |
| a. | | Booklet pane of 4 | 8.00 | |
| b. | | Imperf., pair | 1,300. | 1,500. |
| 108 | A18a | 30c ultra & black | 1.25 | .25 |
| a. | | Booklet pane of 4 | 6.00 | |
| b. | | Vignette (dam) inverted | | 32,500. |
| 109 | A19 | 40c brown ('58) | 1.50 | .80 |
| 110 | A19 | 50c dp red lilac | 3.00 | .25 |
| a. | | Booklet pane of 4 | 14.00 | |
| 111 | A20 | 65c brn car & grn ('55) | 3.00 | 1.50 |
| 112 | A19 | 1sh dp mag & blk | 3.00 | .25 |
| 113 | A20 | 1.30sh pur & red org ('55) | 15.00 | .25 |
| 114 | A20 | 2sh dp grn & gray | 14.00 | 1.25 |
| 115 | A20 | 5sh black & org | 20.00 | 3.25 |
| 116 | A20 | 10sh ultra & black | 35.00 | 5.75 |
| 117 | A21 | £1 black & ver | 24.00 | 22.00 |
| | | Nos. 103-117 (15) | 127.25 | 39.50 |

No. 103b is unique.
For "Official" overprints see Tanganyika Nos. O1-O12.

Map Showing Lakes Victoria and Tanganyika — A22

*Perf. 12½x13*

| | | | | |
|---|---|---|---|---|
| **1958, July 30** | | **Engr.** | | **Wmk. 314** |
| 118 | A22 | 40c green & blue | .70 | .40 |
| 119 | A22 | 1.30sh violet & green | .70 | 1.00 |

Cent. of the discovery of Lakes Victoria and Tanganyika by Sir Richard F. Burton and Capt. J. H. Speke.

Sisal — A23

A25

Mount Kenya and Giant Plants — A24

10c, Cotton. 15c, Coffee. 20c, Gnu. 25c, Ostriches. 30c, Thompson's gazelles. 40c, Manta ray. 50c, Zebras. 65c, Cheetah. 1.30sh, Murchison Falls & hippopotamuses. 2sh, Mt. Kilimanjaro & giraffes. 2.50sh, Candelabra tree & black rhinoceroses. 5sh, Crater Lake & Mountains of the Moon. 10sh, Ngorongoro Crater & buffaloes.

*Perf. 14½x14*

| | | | | |
|---|---|---|---|---|
| **1960, Oct. 1** | | **Photo.** | | **Wmk. 314** |
| 120 | A23 | 5c dull blue | .25 | .25 |
| 121 | A23 | 10c lt olive green | .25 | .25 |
| a. | | Booklet pane of 4 | .60 | |
| 122 | A23 | 15c dull purple | .45 | .25 |
| a. | | Booklet pane of 4 | 1.75 | |
| 123 | A23 | 20c brt lilac rose | .25 | .25 |
| a. | | Booklet pane of 4 | 1.20 | |
| 124 | A23 | 25c olive gray | 3.25 | 1.25 |
| 125 | A23 | 30c brt vermilion | .25 | .25 |
| a. | | Booklet pane of 4 | .90 | |
| 126 | A23 | 40c bright blue | .25 | .25 |
| 127 | A23 | 50c dull violet | .30 | .25 |
| a. | | Booklet pane of 4 | 1.90 | |
| 128 | A23 | 65c lemon | .50 | 1.75 |

**Engr.**
*Perf. 14*

| | | | | |
|---|---|---|---|---|
| 129 | A24 | 1sh vio & red lilac | 1.50 | .25 |
| 130 | A24 | 1.30sh choc & dk car | 5.75 | .25 |
| 131 | A24 | 2sh dk bl & dull bl | 7.50 | .45 |
| 132 | A24 | 2.50sh ol grn & dull bl | 9.80 | 2.50 |
| 133 | A24 | 5sh rose red & lil | 4.25 | .60 |
| 134 | A24 | 10sh sl bl & ol grn | 13.00 | 6.00 |

---

*Perf. 13½x13*

| | | | | |
|---|---|---|---|---|
| **135** | A25 | 20sh lake & bluish violet | 25.00 | 25.00 |
| | | Nos. 120-135 (16) | 72.55 | 39.80 |

Booklets issued in 1961.
On Nos. 120-134, positions of "Kenya," "Uganda" and "Tanganyika" are rotated.
For "Official" overprints see Tanganyika Nos. O13-O20.

Agricultural Development A26

Design: 30c, 1.30sh, Farmer picking corn.

**Unwmk.**

| | | | | |
|---|---|---|---|---|
| **1963, Mar. 21** | | **Photo.** | | **Perf. 14** |
| 136 | A26 | 15c lt ol grn & ultra | .25 | .25 |
| 137 | A26 | 30c yel & red brown | .30 | .25 |
| 138 | A26 | 50c dp org & ultra | .40 | .25 |
| 139 | A26 | 1.30sh lt blue & red brn | .80 | 1.00 |
| | | Nos. 136-139 (4) | 1.75 | 1.75 |

FAO "Freedom from Hunger" campaign.

Scholars and Open Book — A27

**1963, June 28    Unwmk.    Perf. 14**

| | | | | |
|---|---|---|---|---|
| 140 | A27 | 30c multicolored | .25 | .25 |
| 141 | A27 | 1.30sh multicolored | .25 | .25 |

Inauguration of University of East Africa.

Red Cross — A28

**1963, Sept. 2**

| | | | | |
|---|---|---|---|---|
| 142 | A28 | 30c blue & red | 1.25 | .30 |
| 143 | A28 | 50c bister brown & red | 1.50 | 1.25 |

Centenary of International Red Cross.

### Kenya, Uganda, Tanganyika and Zanzibar
Issued by the East African Common Services Organization. Not used in Zanzibar.

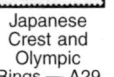

Japanese Crest and Olympic Rings — A29

Olympic Rings and Banners — A30

**Unwmk.**

| | | | | |
|---|---|---|---|---|
| **1964, Oct. 25** | | **Photo.** | | **Perf. 14** |
| 144 | A29 | 30c org & dk purple | .25 | .25 |
| 145 | A29 | 50c dk purple & org | .25 | .25 |
| 146 | A30 | 1.30sh blue, grn & org | .35 | .25 |
| 147 | A30 | 2.50sh blue, vio & lil rose | .40 | .75 |
| | | Nos. 144-147 (4) | 1.25 | 1.50 |

18th Olympic Games, Tokyo, Oct. 10-25.

### Kenya, Uganda, Tanzania
Issued by the East African Common Services Organization.

Safari Rally Emblem and Leopard — A31

---

1.30sh, 2.50sh, Car on road through national park & emblem of the East African Safari Rally.

| | | | | |
|---|---|---|---|---|
| **1965, Apr. 15** | | **Unwmk.** | | **Perf. 14** |
| 148 | A31 | 30c blue grn, yel & blk | .25 | .25 |
| 149 | A31 | 50c brown, yel & blk | .25 | .25 |
| 150 | A31 | 1.30sh lt ultra, ocher & green | .25 | .25 |
| 151 | A31 | 2.50sh blue, dk grn & dull red | .45 | 1.10 |
| | | Nos. 148-151 (4) | 1.20 | 1.85 |

13th East African Safari Rally, 4/15-19/65.

ITU Emblem, Old and Modern Communication Equipment A32

**1965, May 17    Photo.**

| | | | | |
|---|---|---|---|---|
| 152 | A32 | 30c lilac rose, gold & brn | .25 | .25 |
| 153 | A32 | 50c gray, gold & brown | .25 | .25 |
| 154 | A32 | 1.30sh lt vio bl, gold & brn | .40 | .25 |
| 155 | A32 | 2.50sh brt bl grn, gold & brn | 1.25 | 1.25 |
| | | Nos. 152-155 (4) | 2.15 | 2.00 |

Cent. of the ITU.

ICY Emblem A33

**1965, Aug. 4    Unwmk.    Perf. 14**

| | | | | |
|---|---|---|---|---|
| 156 | A33 | 30c green & gold | .25 | .25 |
| 157 | A33 | 50c slate blk & gold | .25 | .25 |
| 158 | A33 | 1.30sh ultra & gold | .40 | .25 |
| 159 | A33 | 2.50sh car & gold | 1.00 | 1.00 |
| | | Nos. 156-159 (4) | 1.90 | 1.75 |

International Cooperation Year.

Game Park Lodge — A34

Tourist Publicity: 50c, Murchison Falls, Uganda. 1.30sh, Lake Nakuru, Kenya. 2.50sh, Deep-sea fishing, Tanzania.

**1966, Apr. 4    Photo.    Perf. 14**

| | | | | |
|---|---|---|---|---|
| 160 | A34 | 30c ocher & multi | .45 | .25 |
| 161 | A34 | 50c green & multi | .55 | .25 |
| a. | | Blue omitted | 425.00 | |
| 162 | A34 | 1.30sh multicolored | 2.75 | .35 |
| 163 | A34 | 2.50sh gray & multi | 1.75 | 2.25 |
| | | Nos. 160-163 (4) | 5.50 | 3.10 |

Javelin Thrower and Games' Emblem — A35

**1966, Aug. 2    Unwmk.    Perf. 14**

| | | | | |
|---|---|---|---|---|
| 164 | A35 | 30c multicolored | .25 | .25 |
| 165 | A35 | 50c multicolored | .25 | .25 |
| 166 | A35 | 1.30sh multicolored | .25 | .25 |
| 167 | A35 | 2.50sh multicolored | .30 | 1.25 |
| | | Nos. 164-167 (4) | 1.05 | 2.00 |

8th British Commonwealth and Empire Games, Jamaica, Aug. 4-13, 1966.

UNESCO Emblem — A36

**1966, Oct. 3    Photo.    Perf. 14**

| | | | | |
|---|---|---|---|---|
| 168 | A36 | 30c rose red, brt grn & blk | .45 | .25 |
| 169 | A36 | 50c lt brn, brt grn & blk | .50 | .25 |
| 170 | A36 | 1.30sh gray, brt grn & blk | 1.25 | .25 |
| 171 | A36 | 2.50sh yel, brt grn & blk | 1.60 | 4.25 |
| | | Nos. 168-171 (4) | 3.80 | 5.00 |

20th anniv. of UNESCO.

Dragon Rapide — A37

Planes: 50c, Super VC10. 1.30sh, Comet 4. 2.50sh, F.27 Friendship.

| 1967, Jan. 23 | | Unwmk. | |
|---|---|---|---|
| 172 A37 | 30c multicolored | .30 | .25 |
| 173 A37 | 50c multicolored | .40 | .25 |
| 174 A37 | 1.30sh multicolored | .85 | .30 |
| 175 A37 | 2.50sh multicolored | 1.40 | 3.00 |
| | Nos. 172-175 (4) | 2.95 | 3.80 |

21st anniversary of East African Airways.

Pillar Tomb, East African Coast — A38

Designs: 50c, Man hunting elephant, petroglyph, Tanzania. 1.30sh, Clay head, Luzira, Uganda. 2.50sh, Proconsul skull, Rusinga Island, Kenya.

| 1967, May 2 | Photo. | Perf. 14 | |
|---|---|---|---|
| 176 A38 | 30c rose lake, blk & yel | .25 | .25 |
| 177 A38 | 50c gray, black & ver | .60 | .25 |
| 178 A38 | 1.30sh green, yel & blk | .85 | .25 |
| 179 A38 | 2.50sh cop red, yel & blk | 1.25 | 2.50 |
| | Nos. 176-179 (4) | 2.95 | 3.25 |

Archaeological relics of East Africa.

Emblems of Kenya, Tanzania and Tanganyika — A39

**Photo.; Gold Impressed**

| 1967, Dec. 1 | | Perf. 14½x14 | |
|---|---|---|---|
| 180 A39 | 5sh gray, black & gold | .50 | 1.00 |

Establishment of East African Community.

Mountain climber — A40

30c Mountain climber. 50c, Mount Kenya. 1.30sh, Mount Kilimanjaro. 2.50sh, Ruwenzori Mountains.

| 1968, Mar. 4 | Photo. | Perf. 14½ | |
|---|---|---|---|
| 181 A40 | 30c multicolored | .25 | .25 |
| 182 A40 | 50c multicolored | .35 | .25 |
| 183 A40 | 1.30sh multicolored | .60 | .25 |
| 184 A40 | 2.50sh multicolored | 1.10 | 2.00 |
| | Nos. 181-184 (4) | 2.30 | 2.75 |

Family and Rural Hospital — A41

Family and: 50c, Student nurse. 1.30sh, Microscope. 2.50sh, Mosquito and hand holding hypodermic.

| 1968, May 13 | Photo. | Perf. 13½ | |
|---|---|---|---|
| 185 A41 | 30c multicolored | .25 | .25 |
| 186 A41 | 50c rose vio, blk & brt pink | .25 | .25 |
| 187 A41 | 1.30sh brn org, blk & brt pink | .25 | .25 |
| 188 A41 | 2.50sh gray, blk & brt pink | .30 | 1.25 |
| | Nos. 185-188 (4) | 1.05 | 2.00 |

20th anniv. of the WHO.

Stadium — A42

Designs: 50c, Diving tower. 1.30sh, Pylons and tracks. 2.50sh, Boxing ring, vert.

**Perf. 14½x14, 14x14½**

| 1968, Oct. 14 | | Photo. | |
|---|---|---|---|
| 189 A42 | 30c dull pur & gray grn | .25 | .25 |
| 190 A42 | 50c brt grn, blk & gray | .25 | .25 |
| 191 A42 | 1.30sh gray grn, blk & dk car | .25 | .25 |
| 192 A42 | 2.50sh buff, brn org & brn blk | .30 | 1.00 |
| | Nos. 189-192 (4) | 1.05 | 1.75 |

19th Olympic Games, Mexico City, 10/12-27.

Railroad Ferry MV Umoja — A43

Water Transport: 50c, Transatlantic liner S.S. Harambee. 1.30sh, Lake motor vessel Victoria. 2.50sh, Ferry St. Michael.

| 1969, Jan. 20 | Photo. | Perf. 14 | |
|---|---|---|---|
| 193 A43 | 30c blue, gray & dk bl | .40 | .25 |
| 194 A43 | 50c blue, gray & scar | .45 | .25 |
| 195 A43 | 1.30sh bl, dk bl & dk green | .75 | .25 |
| 196 A43 | 2.50sh bl, dk bl & org | 1.40 | 2.50 |
| | Nos. 193-196 (4) | 3.00 | 3.25 |

Farm Workers and ILO Emblem — A44

ILO Emblem and: 50c, Construction. 1.30sh, Industry. 2.50sh, Shipping.

| 1969, Apr. 14 | Photo. | Perf. 14 | |
|---|---|---|---|
| 197 A44 | 30c green, blk & yel | .25 | .25 |
| 198 A44 | 50c car rose, blk & car | .25 | .25 |
| 199 A44 | 1.30sh dp org, blk & org | .25 | .25 |
| 200 A44 | 2.50sh grnsh bl, blk & ultra | .25 | .75 |
| | Nos. 197-200 (4) | 1.00 | 1.50 |

50th anniv. of the ILO.

Pope Paul VI, Mountains of the Moon, Papal Arms, Crested Crane — A45

| 1969, July 31 | Photo. | Perf. 14 | |
|---|---|---|---|
| 201 A45 | 30c dk blue, blk & gold | .25 | .25 |
| 202 A45 | 70c plum, blk & gold | .25 | .25 |
| 203 A45 | 1.50sh gray bl, blk & gold | .25 | .25 |
| 204 A45 | 2.50sh dp vio, blk & gold | .30 | .90 |
| | Nos. 201-204 (4) | 1.05 | 1.65 |

Visit of Pope Paul VI to Uganda, 7/31-8/2.

Euphorbia Tree in Shape of Africa, Development Bank Emblem — A46

**Perf. 14x13½**

| 1969, Dec. 8 | | Litho. | Unwmk. |
|---|---|---|---|
| 205 A46 | 30c brt grn, dk grn & gold | .25 | .25 |
| 206 A46 | 70c plum, dk grn & gold | .25 | .25 |
| 207 A46 | 1.50sh grnsh bl, dk grn & gold | .25 | .25 |
| 208 A46 | 2.50sh brn org, dk grn & gold | .35 | .60 |
| | Nos. 205-208 (4) | 1.10 | 1.35 |

African Development Bank, 5th anniv.

Amadinda, Uganda — A47

Musical Instruments: 30c, Marimba, Tanzania. 1.50sh, Nzomari (trumpet), Kenya. 2.50sh, Adeudeu, Kenya.

| 1970, Feb. 16 | Litho. | Perf. 11x12 | |
|---|---|---|---|
| 209 A47 | 30c multicolored | .25 | .25 |
| 210 A47 | 70c multicolored | .30 | .25 |
| 211 A47 | 1.50sh dk rose brn & org | .50 | .25 |
| 212 A47 | 2.50sh multicolored | .90 | 1.50 |
| | Nos. 209-212 (4) | 1.95 | 2.25 |

Satellite Earth Station — A48

Designs: 70c, Radar station by day. 1.50sh, Radar station by night. 2.50sh, Satellite transmitting communications to and from earth.

| 1970, May 18 | Litho. | Perf. 14½ | |
|---|---|---|---|
| 213 A48 | 30c multicolored | .25 | .25 |
| 214 A48 | 70c multicolored | .25 | .25 |
| 215 A48 | 1.50sh org, blk & vio | .30 | .25 |
| 216 A48 | 2.50sh dull bl & multi | .40 | 2.00 |
| | Nos. 213-216 (4) | 1.20 | 2.75 |

Opening of the East African Satellite Earth Station, Mt. Margaret, Kenya.

Runner — A49

| 1970, July 16 | Litho. | Perf. 14½ | |
|---|---|---|---|
| 217 A49 | 30c org brn, dk brn & blk | .25 | .25 |
| 218 A49 | 70c grn, dk brn & blk | .25 | .25 |
| 219 A49 | 1.50sh dull pur, dk brn & blk | .25 | .25 |
| 220 A49 | 2.50sh grnsh bl, dk brn & blk | .25 | .80 |
| | Nos. 217-220 (4) | 1.00 | 1.55 |

9th British Commonwealth Games, Edinburgh, July 16-25.

UN Emblem and People — A50

| 1970, Oct. 19 | Photo. | Perf. 14½ | |
|---|---|---|---|
| 221 A50 | 30c org brn, gold & black | .25 | .25 |
| 222 A50 | 70c bl grn, gold & black | .25 | .25 |
| 223 A50 | 1.50sh dull red brn, gold & blk | .25 | .25 |
| 224 A50 | 2.50sh olive, gold & blk | .35 | 1.50 |
| | Nos. 221-224 (4) | 1.10 | 2.25 |

25th anniversary of the United Nations.

Conversion from Pounds to Kilograms — A51

Designs: 70c, Conversion from Fahrenheit to centigrade. 1.50sh, Conversion from gallons to liters. 2.50sh, Conversion from miles to kilometers.

| 1971, Jan. 4 | Photo. | Perf. 14½ | |
|---|---|---|---|
| 225 A51 | 30c silver & multi | .25 | .25 |
| 226 A51 | 70c silver & multi | .25 | .25 |
| 227 A51 | 1.50sh silver & multi | .25 | .25 |
| 228 A51 | 2.50sh silver & multi | .25 | .80 |
| | Nos. 225-228 (4) | 1.00 | 1.55 |

Conversion to metric system of weights and measures.

Locomotive A52

Designs: Various locomotives.

| 1971, Apr. 19 | Photo. | Perf. 14½ | |
|---|---|---|---|
| 229 A52 | 30c gold & multi | .30 | .25 |
| 230 A52 | 70c gold & multi | .35 | .25 |
| 231 A52 | 1.50sh gold & multi | .80 | .25 |
| 232 A52 | 2.50sh gold & multi | 1.00 | 2.00 |
| a. | Souvenir sheet of 4, #229-232 | 8.50 | 10.00 |
| | Nos. 229-232 (4) | 2.45 | 2.75 |

70th anniversary of the completion of the Mombasa to Kisumu line.

Campaign Emblem and Cow — A53

Designs: 1.50sh, Like 30c. 70c, 2.50sh, Bull and Campaign Emblem.

| 1971, July 5 | Photo. | Perf. 14½ | |
|---|---|---|---|
| 233 A53 | 30c yel grn, blk & bis | .25 | .25 |
| 234 A53 | 70c gray bl, blk & bis | .25 | .25 |
| 235 A53 | 1.50sh mag, blk & bis | .25 | .25 |
| 236 A53 | 2.50sh red org, blk & bis | .25 | .65 |
| | Nos. 233-236 (4) | 1.00 | 1.40 |

Rinderpest campaign by the Organization for African Unity.

Meeting of Stanley and Livingstone — A54

| 1971, Oct. 28 | Litho. | Perf. 14 | |
|---|---|---|---|
| 237 A54 | 5sh multicolored | .40 | .40 |

Centenary of the meeting at Ujiji of Dr. David Livingstone, missionary, and Henry M. Stanley, journalist, who had been sent to find Livingstone.

Modern Farming Village — A55

Designs: 30c, Pres. Julius K. Nyerere carried in triumph, 1961, vert. 1.50sh, University of Dar es Salaam. 2.50sh, Kilimanjaro International Airport.

| 1971, Dec. 9 | | Perf. 14 | |
|---|---|---|---|
| 238 A55 | 30c bister & multi | .25 | .25 |
| 239 A55 | 70c lt blue & multi | .25 | .25 |
| 240 A55 | 1.50sh lt green & multi | .25 | .25 |
| 241 A55 | 2.50sh yel & multi | .50 | 1.75 |
| | Nos. 238-241 (4) | 1.25 | 2.50 |

10th anniv. of independence of Tanzania.

Flags of African Nations and Fair Emblem A56

| 1972, Feb. 23 | | Perf. 13½x14 | |
|---|---|---|---|
| 242 A56 | 30c lt bl & multi | .25 | .25 |
| 243 A56 | 70c gray & multi | .25 | .25 |
| 244 A56 | 1.50sh yel & multi | .25 | .25 |
| 245 A56 | 2.50sh multicolored | .25 | .75 |
| | Nos. 242-245 (4) | 1.00 | 1.50 |

First All-Africa Trade Fair, Nairobi, Kenya, Feb. 23-Mar. 5.

Child Drinking Milk, UNICEF Emblem — A57

25th Anniv. (in 1971) of UNICEF: 70c, Children playing ball. 1.50sh, Child writing on blackboard. 2.50sh, Boy playing with tractor.

**1972, Apr. 24    Litho.    Perf. 14½x14**
| | | | | |
|---|---|---|---|---|
| 246 | A57 | 30c brn org & multi | .25 | .25 |
| 247 | A57 | 70c lt ultra & multi | .25 | .25 |
| 248 | A57 | 1.50sh yel & multi | .25 | .25 |
| 249 | A57 | 2.50sh green & multi | .25 | .75 |
| | | *Nos. 246-249 (4)* | 1.00 | 1.50 |

Hurdles, Olympic and Motion Emblems A58

**1972, Aug. 28**
| | | | | |
|---|---|---|---|---|
| 250 | A58 | 40c shown | .25 | .25 |
| 251 | A58 | 70c Running | .25 | .25 |
| 252 | A58 | 1.50sh Boxing | .25 | .25 |
| 253 | A58 | 2.50sh Hockey | .30 | 1.50 |
| a. | | Souvenir sheet of 4, #250-253 | 6.75 | 6.75 |
| | | *Nos. 250-253 (4)* | 1.05 | 2.25 |

20th Olympic Games, Munich, 8/26-9/11.

Uganda Kob, Semliki Game Reserve A59

70c, Intl. Conf. Center. 1.50sh, Makerere Univ., Kampala. 2.50sh, Uganda arms.

**1972, Oct. 9    Litho.    Perf. 14**
| | | | | |
|---|---|---|---|---|
| 254 | A59 | 40c shown | .25 | .25 |
| 255 | A59 | 70c multicolored | .30 | .25 |
| 256 | A59 | 1.50sh multicolored | .60 | .30 |
| 257 | A59 | 2.50sh multicolored | 1.00 | 2.00 |
| a. | | Souvenir sheet of 4, #254-257, perf. 13x14 | 4.50 | 10.00 |
| | | *Nos. 254-257 (4)* | 2.15 | 2.80 |

Uganda's independence, 10th anniv. No. 256 also for 50th anniv. of Makarere University, Kampala.

Flag of East Africa A60

**1972, Dec. 1    Litho.    Perf. 14½x14**
| | | | | |
|---|---|---|---|---|
| 258 | A60 | 5sh multicolored | .85 | .85 |

5th anniv. of the East African Community.

Anemometer, Lake Victoria Station — A61

WMO Emblem and: 70c, Release of weather balloon, vert. 1.50sh, Hail suppression by meteorological rocket. 2.50sh, Meteorological satellite receiving antenna.

**1973, Mar. 5    Litho.    Perf. 14**
| | | | | |
|---|---|---|---|---|
| 259 | A61 | 40c multicolored | .25 | .25 |
| 260 | A61 | 70c ultra & multi | .25 | .25 |
| 261 | A61 | 1.50sh emer & multi | .25 | .25 |
| 262 | A61 | 2.50sh multicolored | .35 | 1.00 |
| | | *Nos. 259-262 (4)* | 1.10 | 1.75 |

Cent. of intl. meteorological cooperation.

Scouts Laying Bricks — A62

Designs: 70c, Baden-Powell's gravestone, Nyeri, Kenya. 1.50sh, World Scout emblem. 2.50sh, Lord Baden-Powell.

**1973, July 16    Litho.    Perf. 14**
| | | | | |
|---|---|---|---|---|
| 263 | A62 | 40c ocher & multi | .25 | .25 |
| 264 | A62 | 70c multicolored | .30 | .25 |
| 265 | A62 | 1.50sh multicolored | .50 | .30 |
| 266 | A62 | 2.50sh grn & ultra | 1.25 | 1.60 |
| | | *Nos. 263-266 (4)* | 2.30 | 2.40 |

24th Boy Scout World Conference (1st in Africa), Nairobi, Kenya, July 16-21.

International Bank for Reconstruction and Development and Affiliates' Emblems — A63

Designs: 40c, Arrows dividing 4 bank affiliate emblems. 70c, Vert. lines dividing 4 emblems. 1.50sh, Kenyatta Conference Center, Nairobi, vert.

**1973, Sept. 24    Litho.    Perf. 14x13½**
| | | | | |
|---|---|---|---|---|
| 267 | A63 | 40c gray, blk & grn | .25 | .25 |
| 268 | A63 | 70c brn, gray & blk | .25 | .25 |
| 269 | A63 | 1.50sh lem, gray & blk | .25 | .30 |
| 270 | A63 | 2.50sh blk, org & gray | .25 | 1.50 |
| a. | | Souvenir sheet of 4 | 2.50 | 10.00 |
| | | *Nos. 267-270 (4)* | 1.00 | 2.30 |

Intl. Bank for Reconstruction and Development and Affiliate Intl. Monetary Fund Meetings, Nairobi.

No. 270a contains stamps similar to Nos. 267-270 with simulated perforations.

INTERPOL Emblem, Policeman and Dog — A64

Designs: 70c, East African policemen and emblem. 1.50sh, INTERPOL emblem. 2.50sh, INTERPOL Headquarters, St. Cloud, France.

**1973-74    Litho.    Perf. 14x14½**
| | | | | |
|---|---|---|---|---|
| 271 | A64 | 40c yellow & multi | .55 | .25 |
| 272 | A64 | 70c multicolored | .75 | .25 |
| 273 | A64 | 1.50sh violet & multi | 1.25 | .85 |
| 274 | A64 | 2.50sh lemon & multi (St. Clans) | 3.50 | 4.75 |
| 275 | A64 | 2.50sh lemon & multi (St. Cloud) ('74) | 5.25 | 5.75 |
| | | *Nos. 271-275 (5)* | 11.30 | 11.85 |

50th anniv. of Intl. Criminal Police Org. Issued: Nos. 271-274, Oct. 24, 1973.

Tea Factory, Nandi Hills — A65

**1973, Dec. 12    Photo.    Perf. 13x14**
| | | | | |
|---|---|---|---|---|
| 276 | A65 | 40c shown | .25 | .25 |
| 277 | A65 | 70c Kenyatta Hospital | .25 | .25 |
| 278 | A65 | 1.50sh Nairobi Airport | .50 | .25 |
| 279 | A65 | 2.50sh Kindaruma hydroelectric plant | .75 | 1.50 |
| | | *Nos. 276-279 (4)* | 1.75 | 2.25 |

10th anniversary of independence.

Afro-Shirazi Party Headquarters A66

Designs: 70c, Michenzani housing development. 1.50sh, Map of East Africa and television screen with flower. 2.50sh, Amaan Stadium.

**1974, Jan. 12    Litho.    Perf. 13½x14**
| | | | | |
|---|---|---|---|---|
| 280 | A66 | 40c multicolored | .25 | .25 |
| 281 | A66 | 70c multicolored | .25 | .25 |
| 282 | A66 | 1.50sh black & multi | .35 | .25 |
| 283 | A66 | 2.50sh black & multi | .65 | 2.25 |
| | | *Nos. 280-283 (4)* | 1.50 | 3.00 |

10th anniversary of Zanzibar revolution.

Symbol of Union — A67

Designs: 70c, Map of Tanganyika and Zanzibar, and handshake. 1.50sh, Map of Tanganyika and Zanzibar, and communications symbols. 2.50sh, Flags of Tanu, Tanzania and Afro-Shirazi Party.

**1974, Apr. 24    Litho.    Perf. 14½**
| | | | | |
|---|---|---|---|---|
| 284 | A67 | 40c sepia & multi | .25 | .25 |
| 285 | A67 | 70c blue grn & multi | .25 | .25 |
| 286 | A67 | 1.50sh ultra & multi | .35 | .25 |
| 287 | A67 | 2.50sh multicolored | .65 | 2.25 |
| | | *Nos. 284-287 (4)* | 1.50 | 3.00 |

Union of Tanganyika and Zanzibar, 10th anniv.

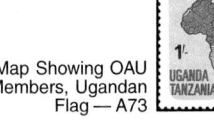

Family and Home — A68

Designs: 70c, Drummer at dawn. 1.50sh, Family hoeing, and livestock. 2.50sh, Telephonist, train, plane, telegraph lines.

**1974, July 15    Litho.    Perf. 14½**
| | | | | |
|---|---|---|---|---|
| 288 | A68 | 40c multicolored | .25 | .25 |
| 289 | A68 | 70c multicolored | .25 | .25 |
| 290 | A68 | 1.50sh multicolored | .25 | .25 |
| 291 | A68 | 2.50sh multicolored | .70 | 1.10 |
| | | *Nos. 288-291 (4)* | 1.45 | 1.85 |

17th Intl. Conf. on Social Welfare, 7/14-20.

Post and Telegraph Headquarters, Kampala — A69

Cent. of the UPU: 70c, Mail train and truck. 1.50sh, UPU Headquarters, Bern. 2.50sh, Loading mail on East African Airways VC-10.

**1974, Oct. 9    Litho.    Perf. 14**
| | | | | |
|---|---|---|---|---|
| 292 | A69 | 40c lt green & multi | .25 | .25 |
| 293 | A69 | 70c gray & multi | .25 | .25 |
| 294 | A69 | 1.50sh yel & multi | .25 | .25 |
| 295 | A69 | 2.50sh lt blue & multi | .40 | 1.10 |
| | | *Nos. 292-295 (4)* | 1.15 | 1.85 |

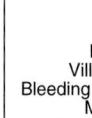

Family Planning Clinic — A70

World Population Year: 70c, "Tug of War." 1.50sh, Scales and world population figures. 2.50sh, World Population Year emblem.

**1974, Dec. 16    Litho.    Perf. 14½**
| | | | | |
|---|---|---|---|---|
| 296 | A70 | 40c multicolored | .25 | .25 |
| 297 | A70 | 70c purple & multi | .25 | .25 |
| 298 | A70 | 1.50sh multicolored | .25 | .25 |
| 299 | A70 | 2.50sh blue blk & multi | .30 | 1.25 |
| | | *Nos. 296-299 (4)* | 1.05 | 2.00 |

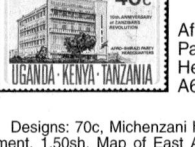

Seronera Wild Life Lodge, Tanzania — A71

Game lodges of East Africa: 70c, Mweya Safari Lodge, Uganda. 1.50sh, Ark-Aberdare Forest Lodge, Kenya. 2.50sh, Paraa Safari Lodge, Uganda.

**1975, Feb. 24    Litho.    Perf. 14½**
| | | | | |
|---|---|---|---|---|
| 300 | A71 | 40c multicolored | .25 | .25 |
| 301 | A71 | 70c multicolored | .25 | .25 |
| 302 | A71 | 1.50sh multicolored | .25 | .30 |
| 303 | A71 | 2.50sh multicolored | .75 | 1.75 |
| | | *Nos. 300-303 (4)* | 1.50 | 2.55 |

Wooden Comb, Bajun, Kenya — A72

African Artifacts: 1sh, Earring, Chaga, Tanzania. 2sh, Armlet, Acholi, Uganda. 3sh, Kamba gourd, Kenya.

**1975, May 5    Litho.    Perf. 13½**
| | | | | |
|---|---|---|---|---|
| 304 | A72 | 50c gray & multi | .25 | .25 |
| 305 | A72 | 1sh gray & multi | .25 | .25 |
| 306 | A72 | 2sh multicolored | .30 | .35 |
| 307 | A72 | 3sh multicolored | .60 | 1.25 |
| | | *Nos. 304-307 (4)* | 1.40 | 2.10 |

Map Showing OAU Members, Ugandan Flag — A73

OAU Emblem and: 50c, Entebbe Airport, horiz. 2sh, Nile Hotel, Kampala, horiz. 3sh, Ugandan Martyrs' Shrine, Namugongo.

**Perf. 11½x11, 11x11½**
**1975, July 28    Litho.**
| | | | | |
|---|---|---|---|---|
| 308 | A73 | 50c multicolored | .35 | .25 |
| 309 | A73 | 1sh multicolored | .35 | .25 |
| 310 | A73 | 2sh multicolored | .35 | .50 |
| 311 | A73 | 3sh multicolored | .55 | 1.25 |
| | | *Nos. 308-311 (4)* | 1.60 | 2.25 |

Organization for African Unity (OAU), Summit Conf., Kampala, July 28 - Aug. 1.

Elephant, Kenya — A74

Protected animals: 1sh, Albino buffalo, Uganda. 2sh, Elephant, exhibit in National Museum, Kenya. 3sh, Abbott's duiker, Tanzania.

**1975, Sept. 11    Litho.    Perf. 11x11½**
| | | | | |
|---|---|---|---|---|
| 312 | A74 | 50c multicolored | .60 | .25 |
| 313 | A74 | 1sh brown & multi | .65 | .25 |
| 314 | A74 | 2sh yel green & multi | 1.60 | 1.50 |
| 315 | A74 | 3sh blue grn & multi | 2.25 | 2.25 |
| | | *Nos. 312-315 (4)* | 5.10 | 4.25 |

Masai Villagers Bleeding Cow, Masai, Kenya — A75

Festival Emblem and: 1sh, Ugandan dancers. 2sh, Family, Makonde sculpture, Tanzania. 3sh, Skinning hippopotamus, East Africa.

**1975, Nov. 3    Litho.    Perf. 13½x14**
| | | | | |
|---|---|---|---|---|
| 316 | A75 | 50c org brown & multi | .25 | .25 |
| 317 | A75 | 1sh brt green & multi | .25 | .25 |
| 318 | A75 | 2sh dk blue & multi | .55 | .80 |
| 319 | A75 | 3sh lilac & multi | .85 | 1.25 |
| | | *Nos. 316-319 (4)* | 1.90 | 2.55 |

2nd World Black and African Festival of Arts and Culture, Lagos, Nigeria, Jan. 5 - Feb. 12.

Fokker Friendship, Nairobi
Airport — A76

East African Airways, 30th anniv.: 1sh, DC-9
Kilimanjaro Airport. 2sh, Super VC10,
Entebbe Airport. 3sh, East African Airways
emblem.

| 1976, Jan. 2 | Litho. | Perf. 11½ | |
|---|---|---|---|
| 320 | A76 50c ultra & multi | 1.10 | .75 |
| 321 | A76 1sh rose & multi | 1.25 | .75 |
| 322 | A76 2sh orange & multi | 3.25 | 3.25 |
| 323 | A76 3sh black & multi | 3.75 | 4.00 |
| | Nos. 320-323 (4) | 9.35 | 8.75 |

## POSTAGE DUE STAMPS

### Kenya and Uganda

D1

| | | Perf. 14½x14 | | |
|---|---|---|---|---|
| **1928-33** | | **Typo.** | | **Wmk. 4** |
| J1 | D1 5c deep violet | 2.50 | 1.00 |
| J2 | D1 10c orange red | 2.50 | .60 |
| J3 | D1 20c yel green | 4.00 | 4.25 |
| J4 | D1 30c ol brn ('31) | 27.50 | 20.00 |
| J5 | D1 40c dull blue | 6.50 | 15.00 |
| J6 | D1 1sh grnsh gray ('33) | 72.50 | 145.00 |
| | Nos. J1-J6 (6) | 115.50 | 185.85 |
| | Set, never hinged | 190.00 | |

### Kenya, Uganda, Tanganyika

D2

| | | Perf. 13½x14 | |
|---|---|---|---|
| **1935, May 1** | | | |
| J7 | D2 5c violet | 2.50 | 1.75 |
| J8 | D2 10c red | .35 | .45 |
| J9 | D2 20c green | .50 | .45 |
| J10 | D2 30c brown | 1.50 | .45 |
| J11 | D2 40c ultramarine | 1.60 | 3.50 |
| J12 | D2 1sh gray | 22.50 | 22.50 |
| | Nos. J7-J12 (6) | 28.95 | 29.10 |
| | Set, never hinged | 45.00 | |

### OFFICIAL STAMPS

The 1959-60 "OFFICIAL" overprints
on Nos. 103-104, 106-108, 110, 112-
117, 120-123, 125, 127, 129, 133 are
listed under Tanganyika, as they were
used by the Tanganyika government.

## KIAUCHAU

### (Kiautschou)

LOCATION — A district of China on the
south side of the Shantung
peninsula.
GOVT. — German colony
AREA — 200 sq. mi.
POP. — 192,000 (approx. 1914).

The area was seized by Germany in
1897 and through negotiations that followed was leased to Germany by
China.

100 Pfennig = 1 Mark
100 Cents = 1 Dollar (1905)

## TSINGTAU ISSUES

### Stamps of Germany, Offices in China 1898, with Additional Surcharge

a

b

c

On Nos. 1-9, a blue or violet line is drawn
through "PF. 10 PF." All exist without this line.
All examples of Nos. 1b, 2b and 3b lack the
colored line.

The three surcharge types can most easily
be distinguished by the differences in the
lower loop of the "5."

### "China" Overprint at 56 degree Angle

**1900**

| 1 | A10(a) 5pfg on 10pf car | 45.00 | 52.50 |
|---|---|---|---|
| c. | Dbl. surch., one inverted | 750.00 | |
| 2 | A10(b) 5pfg on 10pf car | 45.00 | 52.50 |
| c. | Dbl. surch., one inverted | 750.00 | |
| 3 | A10(c) 5pfg on 10pf car | 45.00 | 52.50 |
| c. | Dbl. surch., one inverted | 750.00 | |
| | Nos. 1-3 (3) | 135.00 | 157.50 |

### "China" Overprint at 45 degree Angle

| 1a | A10(a) 5pfg on 10pf car | 145.00 | 130.00 |
|---|---|---|---|
| b. | Double surcharge | 450.00 | 575.00 |
| 2a | A10(b) 5pfg on 10pf car | 145.00 | 130.00 |
| b. | Double surcharge | 450.00 | 575.00 |
| 3a | A10(c) 5pfg on 10pf car | 145.00 | 130.00 |
| b. | Double surcharge | 450.00 | 575.00 |
| | Nos. 1a-3a (3) | 435.00 | 390.00 |

### Surcharged

d

e

**5 Pf.**
f

### "China" Overprint at 48 degree Angle on Nos. 4-9

| 4 | A10(d) 5pf on 10pf car | 3,250. | 4,000. |
|---|---|---|---|
| a. | Double surcharge | 8,250. | 18,000. |
| 5 | A10(e) 5pf on 10pf car | 3,250. | 4,000. |
| a. | Double surcharge | 8,250. | 18,000. |
| 6 | A10(f) 5pf on 10pf car | 3,250. | 4,000. |
| a. | Double surcharge | 8,250. | 18,000. |
| b. | 5fP | | 18,000. |
| c. | As "b," double surcharge | — | — |

### With Add'l Handstamp **5**

| 7 | A10(d) 5pf on 10pf car | 40,000. | 50,000. |
|---|---|---|---|
| 8 | A10(f) 5pf on 10pf car | 40,000. | 50,000. |
| a. | On No. 6b | | |

### With Additional Handstamp

| 9 | A10(f) 5pf on 10pf car | 8,250. | 12,500. |
|---|---|---|---|
| a. | Double surcharge | 37,500. | |
| b. | On No. 6a | | |
| c. | On No. 6b | | |
| d. | On No. 6c | | |

Kaiser's Yacht "Hohenzollern"
A1                A2

| **1901, Jan.** | **Unwmk.** | **Typo.** | **Perf. 14** | |
|---|---|---|---|---|
| 10 | A1 3pf brown | 1.75 | 1.75 |
| 11 | A1 5pf green | 1.75 | 1.50 |
| 12 | A1 10pf carmine | 2.25 | 1.90 |
| 13 | A1 20pf ultra | 7.00 | 7.50 |
| 14 | A1 25pf org & blk, yel | 12.00 | 15.00 |
| 15 | A1 30pf org & blk, sal | 12.00 | 15.00 |
| 16 | A1 40pf lake & blk | 14.00 | 18.00 |
| 17 | A1 50pf pur & blk, sal | 14.00 | 21.00 |

| 18 | A1 80pf lake & blk, rose | 26.00 | 50.00 |
|---|---|---|---|
| | **Engr.** | **Perf. 14½x14** | |
| 19 | A2 1m carmine | 45.00 | 82.50 |
| 20 | A2 2m blue | 75.00 | 100.00 |
| 21 | A2 3m blk vio | 75.00 | 180.00 |
| 22 | A2 5m slate & car | 210.00 | 600.00 |
| | Nos. 10-22 (13) | 495.75 | 1,094. |
| | Set, never hinged | 1,350. | |

A3                A4

| **1905** | | | **Typo.** |
|---|---|---|---|
| 23 | A3 1c brown | 1.10 | 1.50 |
| 24 | A3 2c green | 1.75 | 1.50 |
| 25 | A3 4c carmine | 4.00 | 1.50 |
| 26 | A3 10c ultra | 7.50 | 5.00 |
| 27 | A3 20c lake & blk | 30.00 | 18.00 |
| 28 | A3 40c lake & blk, rose | 90.00 | 90.00 |
| | **Engr.** | | |
| 29 | A4 $½ carmine | 65.00 | 75.00 |
| 30a | A4 $1 blue | 135.00 | 120.00 |
| 31 | A4 $1½ blk vio, 26x17 holes | 1,050. | 1,400. |
| a. | blk vio, 25x16 holes | 26,000. | |
| 32 | A4 $2½ slate & car, 26x17 holes | 1,350. | 4,500. |
| a. | $2½ slate & car, 25x16 holes | 2,000. | 3,250. |
| | Nos. 23-32 (10) | 2,734. | 6,213. |
| | Set, never hinged | 7,250. | |

| **1905-16** | **Wmk. 125** | | **Typo.** |
|---|---|---|---|
| 33 | A3 1c brown ('06) | 1.10 | 1.50 |
| a. | 1c yellow brown ('16) | .45 | |
| 34 | A3 2c green ('09) | 1.10 | 1.10 |
| a. | 2c dark green ('14) | .45 | 1.75 |
| 35 | A3 4c carmine ('09) | .90 | 1.10 |
| 36 | A3 10c ultra ('09) | 1.00 | 3.25 |
| a. | 10c blue | 12.00 | 5.00 |
| 37 | A3 20c lake & blk ('08) | 2.60 | 15.00 |
| 38 | A3 40c lake & blk, rose | 3.00 | 50.00 |
| | **Engr.** | | |
| 39 | A4 $½ car, 26x17 holes ('07) | 9.00 | 65.00 |
| 40 | A4 $1 blue, 26x17 holes ('06) | 11.50 | 67.50 |
| 41 | A4 $1½ blk violet | 11.00 | 200.00 |
| 42 | A4 $2½ slate & car | 45.00 | 450.00 |
| | Nos. 33-42 (10) | 86.20 | 854.45 |
| | Set, never hinged | 460.00 | |

Four values of the design A3 and A4 stamps
in recognizably different shades were printed
and released in 1918, but by then Germany
had lost control of Kiauchau, and these
stamps are not known used. The four stamps
and their unused values are: 20c red & black,
$1.75; $½ pale rose, $5.50; $1 bright blue,
$6.75; $1½ gray violet, $20.

## KIONGA

ˈkyoŋ-gə

LOCATION — Southeast Africa and
northeast Mozambique, on Indian
Ocean south of Rovuma River
GOVT. — Part of German East Africa
AREA — 400 sq. mi.

This territory, occupied by Portuguese troops during World War I, was
allotted to Portugal by the Treaty of Versailles. Later it became part of
Mozambique.

100 Centavos = 1 Escudo

Lourenco Marques No.
149 Surcharged in Red

| **1916, May 29** | **Unwmk.** | **Perf. 11½** | |
|---|---|---|---|
| 1 | A2 ½c on 100r bl, bl | 22.00 | 17.50 |
| 2 | A2 1c on 100r bl, bl | 22.00 | 17.50 |
| 3 | A2 2½c on 100r bl, bl | 22.00 | 17.50 |
| 4 | A2 5c on 100r bl, bl | 22.00 | 17.50 |
| | Nos. 1-4 (4) | 88.00 | 70.00 |

Most of the stock of Lourenço Marques No.
149 used for these surcharges lacked gum.
Unused examples with original gum are worth
approximately 50% more than the values
shown.

# KIRIBATI

'kir-ə-ˌbas

LOCATION — A group of islands in the Pacific Ocean northeast of Australia
GOVT. — Republic
AREA — 277 sq. mi.
POP. — 85,501 (1999 est.)
CAPITAL — Tarawa

100 Cents = 1 Australian Dollar

Kiribati, former Gilbert Islands, consists of the Gilbert, Phoenix, Ocean and Line Islands.

> Catalogue values for all unused stamps in this country are for Never Hinged items.

## Watermark

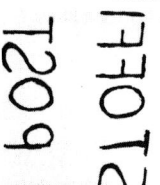

Wmk. 380 — "POST OFFICE"

Kiribati Flag — A50

Parliament, London, Assembly, Tarawa — A51

**Wmk. 373**

| | | | Perf. 14 | |
|---|---|---|---|---|
| **1979, July 12** | | **Litho.** | | |
| 325 | A50 | 10c multicolored | .30 | .30 |
| 326 | A51 | 45c multicolored | .30 | .50 |

Independence.

Training Ship Teraaka — A52

Designs: 3c, Passenger launch Tautunu. 5c, Hibiscus. 7c, Cathedral, Tarawa. 10c, House of Assembly, Bikenibeu Island. 12c, Betio harbor. 15c, Reef egret. 20c, Flamboyant tree. 25c, Moorish idol (fish). 30c, Frangipani blossoms. 35c, Chapel, Tangintebu Island. 50c, Hypolimnas bolina elliciana (butterfly). $1, Tarawa Lagoon ferry, Tabakea. $2, Sunset over lagoon. $5, Natl. flag.

| | | | Wmk. 373 | |
|---|---|---|---|---|
| **1979-80** | | | | |
| 327 | A52 | 1c multicolored | .30 | .65 |
| 328 | A52 | 3c multicolored | .30 | .35 |
| 329 | A52 | 5c multicolored | .30 | .25 |
| 330 | A52 | 7c multicolored | .30 | .25 |
| 331 | A52 | 10c multicolored | .30 | .25 |
| 332 | A52 | 12c multicolored | .30 | .25 |
| 333 | A52 | 15c multicolored | .30 | .30 |
| 334 | A52 | 20c multicolored | .30 | .30 |
| 335 | A52 | 25c multicolored | .30 | .30 |
| 336 | A52 | 30c multicolored | .30 | .30 |
| 337 | A52 | 35c multicolored | .30 | .30 |
| 338 | A52 | 50c multicolored | .70 | .55 |
| 339 | A52 | $1 multicolored | .55 | .60 |
| 340 | A52 | $2 multicolored | .55 | .70 |
| 340A | A52 | $5 multicolored | 1.25 | 3.00 |
| | *Nos. 327-340A (15)* | | 6.35 | 8.35 |

Issued: $5, 8/27/80; others, 7/12/79.

| | | | Unwmk. | |
|---|---|---|---|---|
| **1980-81** | | | | |
| 327a | A52 | 1c multi ('81) | .30 | .35 |
| 328a | A52 | 3c multi ('81) | .30 | .35 |
| 329a | A52 | 5c multi | .30 | .35 |
| 330a | A52 | 7c multi | .30 | .35 |
| 331a | A52 | 10c multi | .30 | .35 |
| 332a | A52 | 12c multi | .30 | .35 |
| 333a | A52 | 15c multi | .65 | .40 |
| 334a | A52 | 20c multi ('81) | .30 | .35 |
| 335a | A52 | 25c multi | .35 | .35 |
| 336a | A52 | 30c multi ('81) | .30 | .75 |
| 337a | A52 | 35c multi ('81) | .30 | .75 |
| 338a | A52 | 50c multi ('81) | .90 | 1.10 |

| | | | | |
|---|---|---|---|---|
| 339a | A52 | $1 multi | .75 | .75 |
| 340b | A52 | $2 multi | 1.40 | 1.05 |
| 340c | A52 | $5 multi ('80) | 2.25 | 3.75 |
| | *Nos. 327a-340c (15)* | | 9.00 | 11.30 |

For overprints see Nos. O1-O15.

Gilbert and Ellice Islands No. 1 — A53

Simulated Cancel and: 20c, Gilbert and Ellice No. 70. 25c, Great Britain No. 139. 45c, Gilbert and Ellice No. 31.

**Wmk. 373**

| | | | Perf. 14 | |
|---|---|---|---|---|
| **1979, Oct. 4** | | **Litho.** | | |
| 341 | A53 | 10c multicolored | .30 | .30 |
| 342 | A53 | 20c multicolored | .30 | .25 |
| 343 | A53 | 25c multicolored | .30 | .25 |
| 344 | A53 | 45c multicolored | .30 | .25 |
| a. | Souvenir sheet of 4, #341-344 | | 1.25 | 1.25 |
| | *Nos. 341-344 (4)* | | 1.20 | 1.00 |

Sir Rowland Hill (1795-1879), originator of penny postage.

Boy Climbing Coconut Palm, IYC Emblem — A54

IYC Emblem, Coat of Arms and: 10c, Boy and giant clam shell. 45c, Girl reading book. $1, Boy wearing sandals. All vert.

**Perf. 14x13½, 13½x14**

| | | | Litho. | |
|---|---|---|---|---|
| **1979, Nov. 28** | | | | |
| 345 | A54 | 10c multicolored | .30 | .25 |
| 346 | A54 | 20c multicolored | .30 | .25 |
| 347 | A54 | 45c multicolored | .30 | .25 |
| 348 | A54 | $1 multicolored | .30 | .25 |
| | *Nos. 345-348 (4)* | | 1.20 | 1.00 |

International Year of the Child.

Downrange Station — A55

National Space Development Agency of Japan (NASDA) Satellite Tracking: 45c, Experimental satellite trajectory (map). $1, Rocket launch, Tanegashima, Japan, vert.

| | | | Perf. 14½ | |
|---|---|---|---|---|
| **1980, Feb. 20** | | **Litho.** | | |
| 349 | A55 | 25c multicolored | .30 | .25 |
| 350 | A55 | 45c multicolored | .30 | .25 |
| 351 | A55 | $1 multicolored | .30 | .25 |
| | *Nos. 349-351 (3)* | | .90 | .75 |

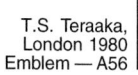

T.S. Teraaka, London 1980 Emblem — A56

25c, Air Tungaru plane, Bonriki Airport. 30c, Radio operator. $1, Bairiki post office.

| | | | Unwmk. | |
|---|---|---|---|---|
| **1980, Apr. 30** | | **Litho.** | | |
| 352 | A56 | 12c shown | .30 | .25 |
| 353 | A56 | 25c multicolored | .30 | .25 |
| 354 | A56 | 30c multicolored | .30 | .25 |
| 355 | A56 | $1 multicolored | .30 | .35 |
| a. | Souvenir sheet of 4, #352-355 | | .75 | .85 |
| | *Nos. 352-355 (4)* | | 1.20 | 1.10 |

London 1980 Intl. Stamp Exhib., May 6-14.

Achaea Janata — A57

25c, Ethmia nigroapicella. 30c, Utetheisa pulchelloides. 50c, Anua coronata.

| | | | Perf. 14 | |
|---|---|---|---|---|
| **1980, Aug. 27** | | **Litho.** | | |
| 356 | A57 | 12c shown | .30 | .25 |
| 357 | A57 | 25c multicolored | .30 | .25 |
| 358 | A57 | 30c multicolored | .30 | .30 |
| 359 | A57 | 50c multicolored | .45 | .45 |
| | *Nos. 356-359 (4)* | | 1.35 | 1.25 |

Capt. Cook Hotel — A58

| | | Wmk. 373 | Perf. 13½ | |
|---|---|---|---|---|
| **1980, Nov. 19** | | | | |
| 360 | A58 | 10c shown | .30 | .25 |
| 361 | A58 | 20c Stadium | .30 | .25 |
| 362 | A58 | 25c Intl. Airport, Bonriki | .30 | .25 |
| 363 | A58 | 30c National Library | .30 | .25 |
| 364 | A58 | $1 Otintai Hotel | .30 | .25 |
| | *Nos. 360-364 (5)* | | 1.50 | 1.25 |

Acalypha Godseffiana — A59

30c, Hibiscus schizopetalus. 35c, Calotropis gigantea. 50c, Euphorbia pulcherrima.

**Perf. 14x13½**

| | | | Wmk. 373 | |
|---|---|---|---|---|
| **1981, Feb. 18** | | **Litho.** | | |
| 365 | A59 | 12c shown | .30 | .25 |
| 366 | A59 | 30c multicolored | .30 | .25 |
| 367 | A59 | 35c multicolored | .30 | .25 |
| 368 | A59 | 50c multicolored | .30 | .25 |
| | *Nos. 365-368 (4)* | | 1.20 | 1.00 |

Abaiang and Marakei Islands, String Figures — A60

30c, Butaritari, Little Makin, house. 35c, Maiana, Coral Road. $1, Christmas Island, Resolution.

**Wmk. 380**

| | | | Perf. 14 | |
|---|---|---|---|---|
| **1981, May 6** | | **Litho.** | | |
| 369 | A60 | 12c shown | .30 | .25 |
| 370 | A60 | 30c multicolored | .30 | .25 |
| 371 | A60 | 35c multicolored | .30 | .25 |
| 372 | A60 | $1 multicolored | .45 | .45 |
| | *Nos. 369-372 (4)* | | 1.35 | 1.20 |

Prince Charles, Lady Diana, Royal Yacht Charlotte — A60a

Prince Charles and Lady Diana — A60b

No. 373, Couple, The Katherine. No. 374, Couple, No. 375, The Osborne. No. 377, Britannia.

**Wmk. 380**

| | | | Perf. 14 | |
|---|---|---|---|---|
| **1981, July 29** | | **Litho.** | | |
| 373 | A60a | 12c multi | .30 | .25 |
| a. | Bklt. pane of 4, perf. 12, unwmkd. | | .75 | |
| 374 | A60b | 12c multi | .30 | .25 |
| 375 | A60a | 50c multi | .35 | .25 |
| 376 | A60b | 50c like #374 | .40 | .25 |
| a. | Bklt. pane of 2, perf. 12, unwmkd. | | 2.25 | |
| 377 | A60a | $2 multi | 1.00 | 1.00 |
| 378 | A60b | $2 like #374 | 1.00 | .75 |
| | *Nos. 373-378 (6)* | | 3.35 | 2.50 |

**Souvenir Sheet**

| | | Perf. 12 | | |
|---|---|---|---|---|
| 379 | A60b | $1.20 like #374 | 2.00 | 2.00 |

Royal wedding.
Stamps of the same denomination issued in sheets of 7 (6 type A60a and 1 type A60b).

Bonriki Tuna Fish Bait Breeding Center — A61

| | | | | |
|---|---|---|---|---|
| **1981, Nov. 19** | | | | |
| 380 | A61 | 12c shown | .30 | .25 |
| 381 | A61 | 30c Fishing boat | .30 | .25 |
| 382 | A61 | 35c Cold storage, Betio | .30 | .25 |
| 383 | A61 | 50c Nei Manganibuka | .30 | .25 |
| a. | Souvenir sheet of 4, #380-383 | | 1.50 | 1.50 |
| | *Nos. 380-383 (4)* | | 1.20 | 1.00 |

Pomarine Jaegers — A62

2c, Mallards. 4c, Collared petrels. 5c, Blue-faced boobies. 7c, Friendly quail dove. 8c, Shovelers. 12c, Christmas Island warblers. 15c, Pacific plovers. 20c, Reef herons. 25c, Brown noddies. 30c, Brown boobies. 35c, Audubon's shearwaters. 40c, White-throated storm petrels, vert. 50c, Bristle-thighed curlews, vert. 55c, Fairy tern. $1, Scarlet-breasted lorikeets, vert. $2, Long-tailed cuckoo, vert. $5, Great frigate birds, vert.

| | | | Litho. | Perf. 14 |
|---|---|---|---|---|
| **1982-85** | | | | |
| 384 | A62 | 1c shown | .30 | .25 |
| 385 | A62 | 2c multicolored | .30 | .25 |
| 386 | A62 | 4c multicolored | .30 | .25 |
| 387 | A62 | 5c multicolored | .30 | .25 |
| 388 | A62 | 7c multicolored | .30 | .25 |
| 389 | A62 | 8c multicolored | .30 | .25 |
| 390 | A62 | 12c multicolored | .30 | .25 |
| 391 | A62 | 15c multicolored | .35 | .35 |
| 392 | A62 | 20c multicolored | .40 | .50 |
| 392A | A62 | 25c multi ('83) | 2.75 | 1.75 |
| 393 | A62 | 30c multicolored | .55 | .60 |
| 394 | A62 | 35c multicolored | .75 | .70 |
| 395 | A62 | 40c multicolored | .70 | .80 |
| 396 | A62 | 50c multicolored | .75 | .65 |
| 396A | A62 | 55c multi ('85) | 12.50 | 17.00 |
| 397 | A62 | $1 multicolored | 1.60 | .85 |
| 398 | A62 | $2 multicolored | 2.25 | 1.10 |
| 399 | A62 | $5 multicolored | 4.50 | 4.00 |
| | *Nos. 384-399 (18)* | | 29.20 | 30.05 |

Issued: 25c, 1/31/83; 55c, 11/19/85; others, 2/18/82.
For overprints see Nos. O16-O20.

Air Tungaru — A63

12c, De Havilland DH114 Heron. 30c, Britten-Norman Trislander. 35c, Casa 212 Aviocar. 50c, Boeing 727.

| | | | Wmk. 380 | |
|---|---|---|---|---|
| **1982, Feb. 18** | | | | |
| 400 | A63 | 12c multicolored | .30 | .25 |
| 401 | A63 | 30c multicolored | .30 | .25 |
| 402 | A63 | 35c multicolored | .40 | .40 |
| 403 | A63 | 50c multicolored | .40 | .40 |
| | *Nos. 400-403 (4)* | | 1.30 | 1.15 |

21st Birthday of Princess Diana, July 1 — A64

| | | | | |
|---|---|---|---|---|
| **1982, May 19** | | | | |
| 404 | A64 | 12c Mary of Teck, 1893 | .30 | .25 |
| 405 | A64 | 50c Teck arms | .40 | .40 |
| 406 | A64 | $1 Diana | .60 | .60 |
| | *Nos. 404-406 (3)* | | 1.30 | 1.25 |

**Nos. 404-406 Overprinted: "ROYAL BABY"**

| | | | | |
|---|---|---|---|---|
| **1982, July 14** | | | | |
| 407 | A64 | 12c multicolored | .30 | .25 |
| 408 | A64 | 50c multicolored | .40 | .40 |
| 409 | A64 | $1 multicolored | .60 | .60 |
| | *Nos. 407-409 (3)* | | 1.30 | 1.25 |

Birth of Prince William of Wales, June 21.

Scouting Year — A65

**1982, Aug. 12**
| | | | | |
|---|---|---|---|---|
| 410 | A65 | 12c | First aid | .30 .25 |
| 411 | A65 | 25c | Repairing boat | .30 .25 |
| 412 | A65 | 30c | Saluting | .30 .30 |
| 413 | A65 | 50c | Gilbert Islds. #304 | .40 .40 |
| | | | Nos. 410-413 (4) | 1.30 1.20 |

Visit of Queen Elizabeth II and Prince Philip — A66

**Wmk. 380**
**1982, Oct. 23    Litho.    Perf. 14**
| | | | | |
|---|---|---|---|---|
| 414 | A66 | 12c | Couple, dancer | .30 .25 |
| 415 | A66 | 25c | Couple, boat | .30 .25 |
| 416 | A66 | 35c | Philatelic Bureau | .45 .45 |
| | | | Nos. 414-416 (3) | 1.05 .95 |

**Souvenir Sheet**
| | | | | |
|---|---|---|---|---|
| 417 | A66 | 50c | Queen Elizabeth II, vert. | 1.30 1.30 |

Nos. 414-416 also issued in sheets of 6.

A67

12c, Obaia the Feathered legend. 30c, Robert Louis Stevenson Hotel, Abemama. 50c, Betio Harbor. $1, Map.

**1983, Mar. 14    Wmk. 380    Perf. 14**
| | | | | |
|---|---|---|---|---|
| 418 | A67 | 12c | multicolored | .30 .25 |
| 419 | A67 | 30c | multicolored | .30 .25 |
| 420 | A67 | 50c | multicolored | .30 .25 |
| 421 | A67 | $1 | multicolored | .30 .30 |
| | | | Nos. 418-421 (4) | 1.20 1.05 |

Commonwealth day.

Map of Beru and Nikunau Islds., Canoe — A68

25c, Abemama, Kuria, Aranuka. 35c, Nonouti, vert. 50c, Tarawa, vert.

**1983, May 19    Litho.    Perf. 14**
| | | | | |
|---|---|---|---|---|
| 422 | A68 | 12c | shown | .30 .25 |
| 423 | A68 | 25c | multicolored | .30 .25 |
| 424 | A68 | 35c | multicolored | .30 .25 |
| 425 | A68 | 50c | multicolored | .30 .25 |
| | | | Nos. 422-425 (4) | 1.20 1.00 |

See Nos. 436-439, 456-459, 475-479, 487-490.

Copra Industry — A69

Designs: 12c, Collecting fallen Coconuts. 25c, Selecting Coconuts for Copra. 30c, Removing Husk from Coconuts. 35c, Drying Copra in the Sun. 50c, Loading Copra, Betio Harbor.

**1983, Aug. 8    Litho.    Perf. 14**
| | | | | |
|---|---|---|---|---|
| 426 | A69 | 12c | multicolored | .30 .25 |
| 427 | A69 | 25c | multicolored | .35 .30 |
| 428 | A69 | 30c | multicolored | .40 .40 |
| 429 | A69 | 35c | multicolored | .45 .45 |
| 430 | A69 | 50c | multicolored | .60 .60 |
| | | | Nos. 426-430 (5) | 2.10 1.95 |

Battle of Tarawa, 40th Anniv. — A70

12c, War memorials. 30c, Battle map. 35c, Defense gun. 50c, Scenes, 1943, 1983. $1, Amphibious Assault Ship USS Tarawa.

**1983, Nov. 17    Litho.    Wmk. 380**
| | | | | |
|---|---|---|---|---|
| 431 | A70 | 12c | multicolored | .30 .25 |
| 432 | A70 | 30c | multicolored | .30 .25 |
| 433 | A70 | 35c | multicolored | .30 .25 |
| 434 | A70 | 50c | multicolored | .30 .30 |
| 435 | A70 | $1 | multicolored | .45 .45 |
| | | | Nos. 431-435 (5) | 1.65 1.50 |

**Map Type of 1983**
**1984, Feb. 14    Wmk. 380    Perf. 14**
| | | | | |
|---|---|---|---|---|
| 436 | A68 | 12c | Teraina | .30 .25 |
| 437 | A68 | 30c | Nikumaroro | .35 .35 |
| 438 | A68 | 35c | Kanton | .40 .40 |
| 439 | A68 | 50c | Banaba | .60 .60 |
| | | | Nos. 436-439 (4) | 1.65 1.60 |

Local Ships — A71

12c, Tug boat. 35c, Ferry landing craft. 50c, Ferry. $1, Cargo and passanger boat.

**1984, May 9    Litho.    Wmk. 380**
| | | | | |
|---|---|---|---|---|
| 440 | A71 | 12c | multicolored | .45 .25 |
| 441 | A71 | 35c | multicolored | .65 .50 |
| 442 | A71 | 50c | multicolored | 1.00 .75 |
| 443 | A71 | $1 | multicolored | 1.50 1.50 |
| a. | | Souvenir sheet of 4, #440-443, perf. 13½ | | 4.00 4.00 |
| | | | Nos. 440-443 (4) | 3.60 3.00 |

Ausipex '84 — A72

12c, South Tarawa sewer & water system. 30c, Fishing boat Nouamake. 35c, Overseas communications training. 50c, Intl. telecommunications link.

**1984, Aug. 21    Litho.    Perf. 14**
| | | | | |
|---|---|---|---|---|
| 444 | A72 | 12c | multicolored | .30 .25 |
| 445 | A72 | 30c | multicolored | .30 .25 |
| 446 | A72 | 35c | multicolored | .30 .25 |
| 447 | A72 | 50c | multicolored | .35 .35 |
| | | | Nos. 444-447 (4) | 1.25 1.10 |

Legends — A73

Designs: 12c, Tabakea supporting Banaba on his back. 30c, Nakaa, Judge of the Dead. 35c, Naareau and Tiku-Tiku-Tamoamoa. 50c, Whistling Ghosts.

**1984, Nov. 21    Wmk. 380    Perf. 14**
| | | | | |
|---|---|---|---|---|
| 448 | A73 | 12c | multicolored | .30 .25 |
| 449 | A73 | 30c | multicolored | .30 .25 |
| 450 | A73 | 35c | multicolored | .30 .25 |
| 451 | A73 | 50c | multicolored | .30 .25 |
| | | | Nos. 448-451 (4) | 1.20 1.00 |

See Nos. 464-467.

Reef Fish — A74

12c, Tang. 25c, White-barred triggerfish. 35c, Surgeon fish. 80c, Squirrel fish.

**1985, Feb. 19    Litho.    Perf. 14**
| | | | | |
|---|---|---|---|---|
| 452 | A74 | 12c | multicolored | .65 .30 |
| 453 | A74 | 25c | multicolored | 1.10 .70 |
| 454 | A74 | 35c | multicolored | 1.25 .90 |
| 455 | A74 | 80c | multicolored | 2.00 2.00 |
| a. | | Souvenir sheet of 4, #452-455 | | 5.50 5.50 |
| | | | Nos. 452-455 (4) | 5.00 3.90 |

See Nos. 540-554, 567.

**Map Type of 1983**
12c, Tabuaeran, frigate bird. 35c, Rawaki, coconuts. 50c, Arorae, xanthid crab. $1, Tamana, fish hook.

Intl. Youth Year — A76

**1985, May 9    Litho.    Perf. 13½**
| | | | | |
|---|---|---|---|---|
| 456 | A68 | 12c | multicolored | 1.00 .35 |
| 457 | A68 | 35c | multicolored | 1.25 .50 |
| 458 | A68 | 50c | multicolored | 1.50 .70 |
| 459 | A68 | $1 | multicolored | 2.00 1.50 |
| | | | Nos. 456-459 (4) | 5.75 3.05 |

15c, Boys playing soccer. 35c, Emblems. 40c, Girl processing fruit, vert. 55c, Intl. youth exchange.

**1985, Aug. 5**
| | | | | |
|---|---|---|---|---|
| 460 | A76 | 15c | multicolored | .75 .50 |
| 461 | A76 | 35c | multicolored | 1.00 1.00 |
| 462 | A76 | 40c | multicolored | 1.10 1.10 |
| 463 | A76 | 55c | multicolored | 1.50 1.50 |
| | | | Nos. 460-463 (4) | 4.35 4.10 |

**Legends Type of 1984**
15c, Nang Kineia & the Tickling Ghosts. 35c, Myth of Auriaria & Tituabine. 40c, First Coming of Babai at Arorae. 55c, Riiki & the Milky Way.

**1985, Nov. 19    Wmk. 380    Perf. 14**
| | | | | |
|---|---|---|---|---|
| 464 | A73 | 15c | multicolored | .50 .50 |
| 465 | A73 | 35c | multicolored | .75 .75 |
| 466 | A73 | 40c | multicolored | .90 .90 |
| 467 | A73 | 55c | multicolored | 1.10 1.10 |
| | | | Nos. 464-467 (4) | 3.25 3.25 |

Transport and Telecommunications Decade 1985-95 — A77

15c, Satellite network. 40c, Tarawa-Suva feeder service.

**1985, Dec. 9    Litho.    Perf. 14**
| | | | | |
|---|---|---|---|---|
| 468 | A77 | 15c | multicolored | 2.25 2.00 |
| 469 | A77 | 40c | multicolored | 3.25 3.00 |

Common Design Types pictured following the introduction.

**Queen Elizabeth II 60th Birthday**
**Common Design Type**
15c, Review of Girl Guides, Windsor Castle, 1938. 35c, Birthday parade, Buckingham Palace, 1980. 40c, With Prince Philip during royal tour, 1982. 55c, Banquet, Austrian embassy in London, 1966. $1, Visiting Crown Agents' offices, 1983.

**1986, Apr. 21    Perf. 14½x14**
| | | | | |
|---|---|---|---|---|
| 470 | CD337 | 15c | scar, black & sil | .30 .25 |
| 471 | CD337 | 35c | ultra & multi | .30 .25 |
| 472 | CD337 | 40c | green & multi | .30 .25 |
| 473 | CD337 | 55c | violet & multi | .40 .40 |
| 474 | CD337 | $1 | rose vio & multi | .95 .95 |
| | | | Nos. 470-474 (5) | 2.25 2.10 |

For overprints see Nos. 495-499.

**Map Type of 1983**
**1986, June 17    Wmk. 380    Perf. 14**
| | | | | |
|---|---|---|---|---|
| 475 | A68 | 15c | Manra | 2.75 1.75 |
| 476 | A68 | 30c | Birnie, McKean | 3.50 1.90 |
| 477 | A68 | 35c | Orona | 3.75 2.50 |
| 478 | A68 | 40c | Malden | 4.50 3.00 |
| 479 | A68 | 55c | Vostok, Caroline, Flint | 4.50 3.25 |
| | | | Nos. 475-479 (5) | 19.00 12.40 |

Lizards — A79

15c, Lepidodactylus lugubris. 35c, Gehyra mutilata. 40c, Hemidactylus frenatus. 55c, Gehyra oceanica.

**1986, Aug. 26    Unwmk.    Perf. 14**
| | | | | |
|---|---|---|---|---|
| 480 | A79 | 15c | multicolored | 1.50 .75 |
| 481 | A79 | 35c | multicolored | 2.25 1.75 |
| 482 | A79 | 40c | multicolored | 2.75 2.25 |
| 483 | A79 | 55c | multicolored | 3.50 2.75 |
| | | | Nos. 480-483 (4) | 10.00 7.50 |

See Nos. 491-494.

America's Cup — A80

**Perf. 14x14½**
**1986, Dec. 29    Unwmk.**
| | | | | |
|---|---|---|---|---|
| 484 | A80 | Strip of 3 | | 2.25 2.25 |
| a. | | 15c Map of Australia | | .30 .25 |
| b. | | 55c Course, trophy | | .55 .55 |
| c. | | $1.50 Australia II | | 1.30 1.30 |

No. 484 has a continuous design.

Transport and Telecommunications Decade (1985-1995) — A81

Designs: 30c, Nei Moamoa, flagship of Kiribati overseas shipping line. 55c, Manual and electronic telephone switching systems.

**1987, Mar. 31    Litho.    Perf. 14**
| | | | | |
|---|---|---|---|---|
| 485 | A81 | 30c | multicolored | 3.00 2.50 |
| 486 | A81 | 55c | multicolored | 4.00 3.50 |

**Map Type of 1983**
15c, Starbuck, red-tailed tropicbird. 30c, Enderbury, white tern. 55c, Tabiteuea, pandanus. $1, Onotoa, Okai house.

**1987, Sept. 22    Unwmk.**
| | | | | |
|---|---|---|---|---|
| 487 | A68 | 15c | multicolored | .50 .45 |
| 488 | A68 | 30c | multicolored | .60 .45 |
| 489 | A68 | 55c | multicolored | .75 .50 |
| 490 | A68 | $1 | multicolored | 1.25 1.75 |
| | | | Nos. 487-490 (4) | 3.10 3.15 |

Nos. 487-490 vert.

**Lizard Type of 1986**
**1987, Oct. 27    Perf. 15**
| | | | | |
|---|---|---|---|---|
| 491 | A79 | 15c | Emoia nigra | .30 .25 |
| 492 | A79 | 35c | Cryptoblepharus | .30 .25 |
| 493 | A79 | 40c | Emoia cyanura | .50 .50 |
| 494 | A79 | $1 | Lipinia noctua | .90 1.50 |
| a. | | Souvenir sheet of 4, #491-494 | | 2.00 2.00 |
| | | | Nos. 491-494 (4) | 2.00 2.50 |

Nos. 470-474 Overprinted in Silver

**Perf. 14½x14**
**1987, Nov. 30    Litho.    Unwmk.**
| | | | | |
|---|---|---|---|---|
| 495 | CD337 | 15c | scar, black & sil | .30 .25 |
| 496 | CD337 | 35c | ultra & multi | .30 .30 |
| 497 | CD337 | 40c | green & multi | .35 .35 |
| 498 | CD337 | 55c | violet & multi | .45 .40 |
| 499 | CD337 | $1 | rose vio & multi | .90 1.25 |
| | | | Nos. 495-499 (5) | 2.30 2.55 |

Intl. Red Cross and Red Crescent Organizations, 125th Anniv. — A83

15c, Jean Henri Dunant (1828-1910), founder. 35c, Red Cross volunteers on parade. 40c, Stretcher bearers. 55c, Gilbert and Ellice Islands #159.

**Perf. 14½x14**
**1988, May 8    Litho.    Unwmk.**
| | | | | |
|---|---|---|---|---|
| 500 | A83 | 15c | multicolored | .75 .60 |
| 501 | A83 | 35c | multicolored | 1.00 1.25 |
| 502 | A83 | 40c | multicolored | 1.25 1.40 |
| 503 | A83 | 55c | multicolored | 2.25 3.25 |
| | | | Nos. 500-503 (4) | 5.25 6.50 |

A84

SYDPEX '88, Australia
Bicentennial — A85

Emblem and: 15c, Australia-assisted cause-way construction. 35c, Capt. Cook, map of Australia and Kiribati. No. 506, Australia bicentennial banknote obverse. No. 507, Bank note reverse. $2, "Logistic Ace."

**1988, July 30    Litho.    Perf. 14½**
| | | | | |
|---|---|---|---|---|
| **504** | A84 | 15c multicolored | .30 | .30 |
| **505** | A84 | 35c multicolored | .60 | .60 |
| **506** | A84 | $1 multicolored | 1.50 | 1.50 |
| **507** | A84 | $1 multicolored | 1.50 | 1.50 |
| a. | | Pair, #506-507 | 5.00 | 5.00 |
| | | Nos. 504-507 (4) | 3.90 | 3.90 |

**Souvenir Sheet**
**Perf. 13½x14**
| | | | | |
|---|---|---|---|---|
| **508** | A85 | $2 multicolored | 6.00 | 6.00 |

Robert F. Stockton, 1st propeller-driven steamship, 150th anniv.

Transport and Telecommunications
Decade (1985-1995) — A86

35c, Telephone operator, map. 45c, Betio-Bairiki Causeway.

**Wmk. 373**
**1988, Dec. 28    Litho.    Perf. 14**
| | | | | |
|---|---|---|---|---|
| **509** | A86 | 35c multicolored | 1.25 | 1.25 |
| **510** | A86 | 45c multicolored | 1.75 | 1.75 |

Ships — A87

15c, Brigantine Hound, 1835. 30c, Brig Phantom, 1854. 40c, HMS Alacrity, 1873. $1, Whaler Charles W. Morgan, 1851.

**Wmk. 384**
**1989, May 26    Litho.    Perf. 14½**
| | | | | |
|---|---|---|---|---|
| **511** | A87 | 15c multicolored | 1.15 | .90 |
| **512** | A87 | 30c multicolored | 1.80 | 1.50 |
| **513** | A87 | 40c multicolored | 2.15 | 2.40 |
| **514** | A87 | $1 multicolored | 3.40 | 3.75 |
| | | Nos. 511-514 (4) | 8.50 | 8.55 |

See Nos. 557-561, 687-690.

A88

**Perf. 13½x14**
**1989, July 12    Litho.    Wmk. 384**
| | | | | |
|---|---|---|---|---|
| **515** | A88 | 15c House of Assembly | .35 | .35 |
| **516** | A88 | $1 Constitution | 2.20 | 2.20 |

Natl. Independence, 10th anniv.

**Moon Landing, 20th Anniv.**
Common Design Type

Apollo 10: 20c, Service and command modules, launch escape system. 50c, Eugene A. Cernan, Thomas P. Stafford and John W. Young. 60c, Mission emblem. 75c, Splashdown, Honolulu. $2.50, Apollo 11 command module in space.

**1989, July 20    Perf. 14**
**Size of Nos. 518-519: 29x29mm**
| | | | | |
|---|---|---|---|---|
| **517** | CD342 | 20c multicolored | .50 | .50 |
| **518** | CD342 | 50c multicolored | .90 | .90 |
| **519** | CD342 | 60c multicolored | 1.10 | 1.10 |
| **520** | CD342 | 75c multicolored | 1.25 | 1.25 |
| | | Nos. 517-520 (4) | 3.75 | 3.75 |

**Souvenir Sheet**
| | | | | |
|---|---|---|---|---|
| **521** | CD342 | $2.50 multicolored | 8.75 | 8.75 |

Birds — A89

No. 522, Eastern reef heron. No. 523, Brood in nest. No. 524, White-tailed tropicbird in flight. No. 525, Seated tropicbird.

**Perf. 14½x14**
**1989, June 28    Litho.    Wmk. 384**
| | | | | |
|---|---|---|---|---|
| **522** | A89 | 15c multicolored | 1.40 | 1.40 |
| **523** | A89 | 15c multicolored | 1.40 | 1.40 |
| a. | | Pair, #522-523 | 3.25 | 3.25 |
| **524** | A89 | $1 multicolored | 2.50 | 2.50 |
| **525** | A89 | $1 multicolored | 2.50 | 2.50 |
| a. | | Pair, #524-525 | 5.50 | 5.50 |
| | | Nos. 522-525 (4) | 7.80 | 7.80 |

Nos. 523a, 525a have continuous designs.
For overprints see Nos. 534-535.

**Souvenir Sheets**

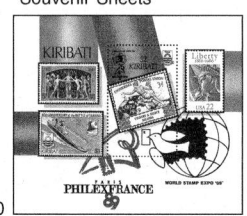

A90

**Perf. 14x13½**
**1989, Aug. 7    Litho.    Wmk. 384**
| | | | | |
|---|---|---|---|---|
| **526** | A90 | $2 Gilbert & Ellice Isls. #58 | 6.00 | 6.00 |

A91

Workmen renovating the Statue of Liberty: a, Torch. b, Drilling copper sheeting. c, Glancing at a sketch of the statue.

**Perf. 14x13½**
**1989, Sept. 25    Litho.    Unwmk.**
| | | | | |
|---|---|---|---|---|
| **527** | A91 | Sheet of 3 | 5.50 | 5.50 |
| a.-c. | | 35c any single | 1.60 | 1.60 |

World Stamp Expo '89, Washington, DC, PHILEXFRANCE '89, Paris. No. 526 margin pictures #435, France #634 and US #2224.

Transport and Telecommunications
Decade, 1985-95 — A92

**1989, Oct. 16    Wmk. 384    Perf. 14**
| | | | | |
|---|---|---|---|---|
| **528** | A92 | 30c shown | 2.50 | 2.25 |
| **529** | A92 | 75c MV Mataburo | 3.75 | 3.25 |

Christmas — A93

Paintings: 10c, Adoration of the Holy Child (detail), by Denys Calvert. 15c, Adoration of the Holy Child (entire painting). 55c, The Holy Family and St. Elizabeth, by Rubens. $1, Madonna with Child and Mary Magdalene, School of Corregio.

**1989, Dec. 1**
| | | | | |
|---|---|---|---|---|
| **530** | A93 | 10c multicolored | 1.00 | .60 |
| **531** | A93 | 15c multicolored | 1.25 | .75 |
| **532** | A93 | 55c multicolored | 2.50 | 1.25 |
| **533** | A93 | $1 multicolored | 3.75 | 6.50 |
| | | Nos. 530-533 (4) | 8.50 | 9.10 |

Nos. 524-525 Ovptd.

**1989, Oct. 21    Litho.    Perf. 14½x14**
| | | | | |
|---|---|---|---|---|
| **534** | A89 | $1 on No. 524 | 4.00 | 4.00 |
| **535** | A89 | $1 on No. 525 | 4.00 | 4.00 |
| a. | | Pair, #534-535 | 9.50 | 9.50 |

STAMPSHOW '89, Melbourne.

Penny Black
150th Anniv.,
Stamp World
London
'90 — A94

Stamps on stamps: 15c, Gilbert & Ellice #15, Great Britain #2. 50c, Gilbert & Ellice #8, Great Britain #1 canceled. 60c, Kiribati #384, Great Britain #58. $1, Gilbert Islands #269, Great Britain #3.

**1990, May 1    Litho.    Perf. 14**
| | | | | |
|---|---|---|---|---|
| **536** | A94 | 15c multicolored | 1.15 | 1.15 |
| **537** | A94 | 50c multicolored | 2.80 | 2.80 |
| **538** | A94 | 60c multicolored | 2.95 | 2.95 |
| **539** | A94 | $1 multicolored | 3.10 | 3.10 |
| | | Nos. 536-539 (4) | 10.00 | 10.00 |

**Fish Type of 1985**

Fish: 1c, Blue-barred orange parrotfish. 5c, Honeycomb rock cod. 10c, Bluefin jack. 15c, Paddle tail snapper. 20c, Variegated emperor. 25c, Rainbow runner. 30c, Black saddled coral trout. 35c, Great barracuda. 40c, Convict surgeonfish. 50c, Violet squirrelfish. 60c, Freckled hawkfish. 75c, Pennant coral fish. $1, Yellow and blue sea perch. $2, Pacific sailfish. $5, Whitetip reef shark.

**Wmk. 373**
**1990, July 12    Litho.    Perf. 14**
| | | | | |
|---|---|---|---|---|
| **540** | A74 | 1c multicolored | .40 | .40 |
| **541** | A74 | 5c multicolored | .50 | .50 |
| **542** | A74 | 10c multicolored | .65 | .65 |
| **543** | A74 | 15c multicolored | .75 | .75 |
| **544** | A74 | 20c multicolored | .90 | .90 |
| **545** | A74 | 25c multicolored | 1.00 | .95 |
| **546** | A74 | 30c multicolored | 1.10 | 1.00 |
| **547** | A74 | 35c multicolored | 1.25 | 1.10 |
| **548** | A74 | 40c multicolored | 1.50 | 1.25 |
| **549** | A74 | 50c multicolored | 1.75 | 1.75 |
| **550** | A74 | 60c multicolored | 2.00 | 2.00 |
| **551** | A74 | 75c multicolored | 2.25 | 2.25 |
| **552** | A74 | $1 multicolored | 3.00 | 2.50 |
| **553** | A74 | $2 multicolored | 4.50 | 4.50 |
| **554** | A74 | $5 multicolored | 7.75 | 9.00 |
| | | Nos. 540-554 (15) | 29.30 | 29.50 |

Dated 1990. See No. 567. For overprints see Nos. 587-590.

**Queen Mother 90th Birthday**
Common Design Types

75c, Queen Mother. $2, King, Queen & WWII bombing victim, 1940.

**1990, Aug. 4    Wmk. 384    Perf. 14x15**
| | | | | |
|---|---|---|---|---|
| **555** | CD343 | 75c multicolored | 1.50 | 1.50 |

**Perf. 14½**
| | | | | |
|---|---|---|---|---|
| **556** | CD344 | $2 multicolored | 3.25 | 3.25 |

**Ships Type of 1989**

15c, Whaling ship Herald, 1851. 50c, Bark Belle, 1849. 60c, Schooner Supply, 1851. 75c, Whaling ship Triton, 1848.
$2, Convict transport Charlotte, 1789.

**1990, Nov. 5    Litho.    Perf. 14½**
| | | | | |
|---|---|---|---|---|
| **557** | A87 | 15c multicolored | 1.00 | .75 |
| **558** | A87 | 50c multicolored | 1.60 | 1.50 |
| **559** | A87 | 60c multicolored | 1.75 | 1.75 |
| **560** | A87 | 75c multicolored | 2.25 | 2.25 |
| | | Nos. 557-560 (4) | 6.60 | 6.25 |

**Souvenir Sheet**
| | | | | |
|---|---|---|---|---|
| **561** | A87 | $2 multicolored | 8.00 | 8.00 |

Manta
Ray — A95

**1991, Jan. 17    Wmk. 373    Perf. 14**
| | | | | |
|---|---|---|---|---|
| **562** | A95 | 15c shown | 1.25 | .60 |
| **563** | A95 | 20c Manta ray, diff. | 1.50 | 1.00 |
| **564** | A95 | 30c Whale shark | 1.75 | 1.75 |
| **565** | A95 | 35c Whale shark, diff. | 2.25 | 2.25 |
| | | Nos. 562-565 (4) | 6.75 | 5.60 |

World Wildlife Fund.

**Fish Type of 1985**

Design: 23c, Bennett's pufferfish.

**1991, Apr. 30    Wmk. 384**
| | | | | |
|---|---|---|---|---|
| **567** | A74 | 23c multicolored | 1.75 | 1.75 |

For overprint see No. 587.

**Elizabeth & Philip, Birthdays**
Common Design Types

**1991, June 17    Perf. 14½**
| | | | | |
|---|---|---|---|---|
| **571** | CD345 | 65c multicolored | 1.75 | 1.75 |
| **572** | CD346 | 70c multicolored | 1.75 | 1.75 |
| a. | | Pair, #571-572 + label | 4.00 | 4.00 |

Phila Nippon
'91 — A96

Opening of new Tungaru Central Hospital: 23c, Aerial view. 50c, Traditional dancers. 60c, Main entrance. 75c, Foundation stone, plaque. $5, Ambulance, nursing staff.

**1991, Nov. 16    Perf. 13½x14**
| | | | | |
|---|---|---|---|---|
| **573** | A96 | 23c multicolored | .50 | .50 |
| **574** | A96 | 50c multicolored | 1.00 | 1.00 |
| **575** | A96 | 60c multicolored | 1.40 | 1.40 |
| **576** | A96 | 75c multicolored | 1.60 | 1.60 |
| | | Nos. 573-576 (4) | 4.50 | 4.50 |

**Souvenir Sheet**
| | | | | |
|---|---|---|---|---|
| **577** | A96 | $5 multicolored | 9.00 | 9.00 |

Christmas
A97

Designs: 23c, Island mother and child. 50c, Family in island hut. 60c, Nativity Scene. 75c, Adoration of the Shepherds.

**1991, Dec. 2    Wmk. 373**
| | | | | |
|---|---|---|---|---|
| **578** | A97 | 23c multicolored | .75 | .60 |
| **579** | A97 | 50c multicolored | 1.25 | 1.25 |
| **580** | A97 | 60c multicolored | 1.75 | 1.75 |
| **581** | A97 | 75c multicolored | 2.25 | 2.25 |
| | | Nos. 578-581 (4) | 6.00 | 5.85 |

**Queen Elizabeth II's Accession to the Throne, 40th Anniv.**
Common Design Type
**Wmk. 373**
**1992, Feb. 6    Litho.    Perf. 14**
| | | | | |
|---|---|---|---|---|
| **582** | CD349 | 23c multicolored | .35 | .35 |
| **583** | CD349 | 30c multicolored | .50 | .50 |
| **584** | CD349 | 50c multicolored | .80 | .80 |
| **585** | CD349 | 60c multicolored | 1.00 | 1.00 |
| **586** | CD349 | 75c multicolored | 1.20 | 1.20 |
| | | Nos. 582-586 (5) | 3.85 | 3.85 |

Nos. 550-551,
553, & 567
Ovptd.

**Wmk. 384, 373**
**1992, June 1    Litho.    Perf. 14**
| | | | | |
|---|---|---|---|---|
| **587** | A74 | 23c on No. 567 | .90 | .80 |
| **588** | A74 | 60c on No. 550 | 2.00 | 2.00 |
| **589** | A74 | 75c on No. 551 | 2.45 | 2.45 |
| **590** | A74 | $2 on No. 553 | 2.70 | 3.00 |
| | | Nos. 587-590 (4) | 8.05 | 8.25 |

Marine Training Center, 25th Anniv. — A98

23c, Entrance. 50c, Cadets at morning parade. 60c, Fire school. 75c, Lifeboat training.

**1992, Aug. 28**     **Perf. 14**

| | | | | |
|---|---|---|---|---|
| 591 | A98 | 23c multicolored | .65 | .65 |
| 592 | A98 | 50c multicolored | 1.00 | 1.00 |
| 593 | A98 | 60c multicolored | 1.20 | 1.20 |
| 594 | A98 | 75c multicolored | 1.50 | 1.50 |
| | | Nos. 591-594 (4) | 4.35 | 4.35 |

FAO, WHO — A99

23c, Children running. 50c, Night fishing. 60c, Fruit. 75c, Ship.

**Wmk. 373**
**1992, Dec. 1**   **Litho.**   **Perf. 14**

| | | | | |
|---|---|---|---|---|
| 595 | A99 | 23c multicolored | 1.00 | 1.00 |
| 596 | A99 | 50c multicolored | 1.10 | 1.10 |
| 597 | A99 | 60c multicolored | 1.25 | 1.25 |
| 598 | A99 | 75c multicolored | 2.00 | 2.00 |
| | | Nos. 595-598 (4) | 5.35 | 5.35 |

Water Birds — A100

No. 599, Phoenix petrel. No. 600, Cooks petrel. No. 601, Northern pintail. No. 602, Eurasian widgeon. No. 603, Spectacled tern. No. 604, Black naped tern. No. 605, Stilt wader. No. 606, Wandering tattler.

**Wmk. 373**
**1993, May 28**   **Litho.**   **Perf. 14½**

| | | | | |
|---|---|---|---|---|
| 599 | A100 | 23c multicolored | .60 | .60 |
| 600 | A100 | 23c multicolored | .60 | .60 |
| a. | | Pair, #599-600 | 1.30 | 1.30 |
| 601 | A100 | 60c multicolored | 1.15 | 1.15 |
| 602 | A100 | 60c multicolored | 1.15 | 1.15 |
| a. | | Pair, #601-602 | 2.35 | 2.35 |
| 603 | A100 | 75c multicolored | 1.40 | 1.40 |
| 604 | A100 | 75c multicolored | 1.40 | 1.40 |
| a. | | Pair, #603-604 | 3.00 | 3.00 |
| 605 | A100 | $1 multicolored | 1.60 | 1.60 |
| 606 | A100 | $1 multicolored | 1.60 | 1.60 |
| a. | | Pair, #605-606 | 3.40 | 3.40 |
| | | Nos. 599-606 (8) | 9.50 | 9.50 |

Insects — A101

23c, Chilocorus nigritus. 60c, Rodolia pumila. 75c, Rodolia cardinalis. $1, Cryptolaemus montrouzieri.

**Perf. 14½x14**
**1993, Aug. 23**   **Litho.**   **Wmk. 373**

| | | | | |
|---|---|---|---|---|
| 607 | A101 | 23c multicolored | 1.25 | 1.25 |
| 608 | A101 | 60c multicolored | 2.00 | 2.00 |
| 609 | A101 | 75c multicolored | 2.50 | 2.50 |
| 610 | A101 | $1 multicolored | 3.00 | 3.50 |
| | | Nos. 607-610 (4) | 8.75 | 9.25 |

Liberation of Kiribati, 50th Anniv. — A102

No. 611: a, Air reconnaissance of Tarawa Atoll. b, USS Nautilus surveys Tarawa. c, USS Indianapolis. d, USS Pursuit leads seaborne

---

assault. e, Kingfisher spotter plane. f, Destroyers USS Ringgold and USS Dashiell. g, Sherman tank on seabed. h, Fighter plane in lagoon. i, Naval gun on seabed. j, First US aircraft to land on Betio Island.

No. 612: a, Transports disembark landing craft. b, Marines assault Betio Island. c, Sea and air assault of Betio. d, Marines pinned down in surf. e, USS Maryland firing broadside. f, Betio from the air. g, Memorial to US Navy dead. h, Memorial to expatriates. i, Memorial to Japanese dead. j, Battle map of Betio.

**Wmk. 373**
**1993, Nov. 1**   **Litho.**   **Perf. 14**
**Sheets of 10**

| | | | | |
|---|---|---|---|---|
| 611 | A102 | 23c #a.-j. + label | 6.75 | 6.75 |
| 612 | A102 | 75c #a.-j. + label | 18.25 | 18.25 |

Christmas A103

23c, Shepherds. 40c, Three kings. 60c, Holy Family. 75c, Mother, children. $3, Madonna and Child.

**Perf. 13½x14**
**1993, Dec. 1**   **Litho.**   **Wmk. 373**

| | | | | |
|---|---|---|---|---|
| 613 | A103 | 23c multicolored | .60 | .60 |
| 614 | A103 | 40c multicolored | .90 | .90 |
| 615 | A103 | 60c multicolored | 1.25 | 1.75 |
| 616 | A103 | 75c multicolored | 1.55 | 2.10 |
| | | Nos. 613-616 (4) | 4.30 | 5.15 |

**Souvenir Sheet**

| | | | | |
|---|---|---|---|---|
| 617 | A103 | $3 multicolored | 6.50 | 6.50 |

Stampcards — A104

**Rouletted 6 on 2 or 3 Sides**
**1993, Nov. 1**     **Litho.**
**Self-Adhesive**
**Cards of 6 + 6 labels**

| | | | |
|---|---|---|---|
| 618 | A104 | 40c #a.-f. | 5.00 |
| 619 | A104 | $1 #a.-f. | 12.00 |
| 620 | A104 | $1.20 #a.-f. | 15.00 |
| 621 | A104 | $1.60 #a.-f. | 22.50 |
| | | Nos. 618-621 (4) | 54.50 |

Nos. 619-621 are airmail. Individual stamps measure 70x9mm and have a card backing. Se-tenant labels on No. 618 inscribed "economique." Se-tenant labels on Nos. 619-621 inscribed "prioritaire AIR MAIL."

It has been stated that these stamps were available only from the Philatelic Bureau and were not accepted by local post offices as valid for postage, though this is contradicted by the Controller of Postal Services.

**Souvenir Sheet**

New Year 1994 (Year of the Dog) A105

**Wmk. 373**
**1994, Feb. 18**   **Litho.**   **Perf. 14**

| | | | | |
|---|---|---|---|---|
| 622 | A105 | $3 multicolored | 6.50 | 6.50 |

Hong Kong '94.

Whales — A106

Designs: 23c, Bryde's whale. 40c, Blue whale. 60c, Humpback whale. 75c, Killer whale.

---

**1994, May 2**

| | | | | |
|---|---|---|---|---|
| 623 | A106 | 23c multicolored | 1.25 | 1.25 |
| 624 | A106 | 23c multicolored | 1.25 | 1.25 |
| a. | | Pair, #623-624 | 2.85 | 2.85 |
| 625 | A106 | 40c multicolored | 1.50 | 1.50 |
| 626 | A106 | 40c multicolored | 1.50 | 1.50 |
| a. | | Pair, #625-626 | 3.50 | 3.50 |
| 627 | A106 | 60c multicolored | 2.10 | 2.10 |
| 628 | A106 | 60c multicolored | 2.10 | 2.10 |
| a. | | Pair, #627-628 | 5.25 | 5.25 |
| 629 | A106 | 75c multicolored | 2.40 | 2.40 |
| 630 | A106 | 75c multicolored | 2.40 | 2.40 |
| a. | | Pair #629-630 | 5.75 | 5.75 |
| | | Nos. 623-630 (8) | 14.50 | 14.50 |

Value at UL on Nos. 623, 625, 627, 629; at UR on others.
Nos. 624a-630a have continuous designs.

Environmental Protection — A107

Designs: 40c, Family on beach at sunset. 60c, Fish. 75c, Frigate birds.

**1994, July 12**

| | | | | |
|---|---|---|---|---|
| 631 | A107 | 40c multicolored | 1.00 | .90 |
| 632 | A107 | 60c multicolored | 1.10 | 1.10 |
| 633 | A107 | 75c multicolored | 1.60 | 1.60 |
| | | Nos. 631-633 (3) | 3.70 | 3.60 |

Independence, 15th anniv.

Butterflies — A108

Designs: 1c, Diaphania indica. 5c, Herpetogamma licarsisalis. 10c, Parotis suralis. 12c, Sufetula sunidesalis. 20c, Aedia sericea. 23c, Anomis vitiensis. 30c, Anticarsia irrorata. 35c, Spodoptera litura. 40c, Mocis frugalis. 45c, Agrius convolvuli. 50c, Cephonodes picus. 55c, Gnathothlibus erotus. 60c, Macroglossum hirundo. 75c, Badamia exclamationis. $1, Precis villida. $2, Danaus plexippus. $3, Hypolimnas bolina (male). $5, Hypolimnas bolina (female).

**1994, Aug. 19**     **Perf. 14½x14**

| | | | | |
|---|---|---|---|---|
| 634 | A108 | 1c multicolored | .30 | .25 |
| 635 | A108 | 5c multicolored | .30 | .25 |
| 636 | A108 | 10c multicolored | .30 | .25 |
| 637 | A108 | 12c multicolored | .30 | .25 |
| 638 | A108 | 20c multicolored | .30 | .30 |
| 639 | A108 | 23c multicolored | .40 | .40 |
| 640 | A108 | 30c multicolored | .55 | .50 |
| 641 | A108 | 35c multicolored | .60 | .60 |
| 642 | A108 | 40c multicolored | .70 | .65 |
| 643 | A108 | 45c multicolored | .75 | .75 |
| 644 | A108 | 50c multicolored | .80 | .75 |
| 645 | A108 | 55c multicolored | .95 | .85 |
| 646 | A108 | 60c multicolored | .95 | .90 |
| 647 | A108 | 75c multicolored | 1.10 | 1.10 |
| 648 | A108 | $1 multicolored | 1.55 | 1.55 |
| a. | | Souvenir sheet of 1 | 2.75 | 2.75 |
| 649 | A108 | $2 multicolored | 2.90 | 3.65 |
| 650 | A108 | $3 multicolored | 4.65 | 5.50 |
| 651 | A108 | $5 multicolored | 8.00 | 9.00 |
| | | Nos. 634-651 (18) | 25.40 | 27.50 |

No. 648a issued 2/12/97 for Hong Kong '97.
For overprints see Nos. 763-767.

Flowers — A109

23c, Nerium oleander. 60c, Catharanthus roseus. 75c, Ipomea pes-caprae. $1, Calophyllum mophyllum.

**1994, Oct. 31**

| | | | | |
|---|---|---|---|---|
| 652 | A109 | 23c multicolored | .65 | .65 |
| 653 | A109 | 60c multicolored | 1.10 | 1.10 |
| 654 | A109 | 75c multicolored | 1.50 | 1.50 |
| 655 | A109 | $1 multicolored | 2.00 | 2.00 |
| | | Nos. 652-655 (4) | 5.25 | 5.25 |

---

A110

Constellations.

**1995, Jan. 31**

| | | | | |
|---|---|---|---|---|
| 656 | A110 | 50c Gemini | 1.20 | 1.20 |
| 657 | A110 | 60c Cancer | 1.30 | 1.30 |
| 658 | A110 | 75c Cassiopeia | 1.50 | 1.50 |
| 659 | A110 | $1 Southern cross | 2.00 | 2.00 |
| | | Nos. 656-659 (4) | 6.00 | 6.00 |

A111

Scenes of Kiribati: No. 660: a, Architecture. b, Men, canoe, sailboat. c, Gun emplacement, Tarawa. d, Children, shells. e, Outdoor sports.
No. 661: a, Women traditionally attired. b, Windsurfing. c, Filleting fish. d, Snorkeling, scuba diving. e, Weaving.

**Wmk. 384**
**1995, Apr. 3**   **Litho.**   **Perf. 14½**

| | | | | |
|---|---|---|---|---|
| 660 | A111 | 30c Strip of 5, #a.-e. | 4.00 | 4.00 |
| 661 | A111 | 40c Strip of 5, #a.-e. | 5.75 | 5.75 |
| f. | | Booklet pane, #660, #661 + 5 labels | 12.00 | 12.00 |
| | | Complete booklet, #661f | 13.00 | |

Visit South Pacific Year.

**End of World War II, 50th Anniv.**
**Common Design Type**

Designs: 23c, Grumman TBM-3E Avenger. 40c, Curtiss SOC. 3-1 seagull. 50c, Consolidated B-24J Liberator. 60c, Grumman Goose. 75c, Martin B-26 Marauder. $1, Northrop P-61B Black Widow. $2, Reverse of War Medal 1939-45.

**Perf. 14x13½**
**1995, May 8**     **Wmk. 373**

| | | | | |
|---|---|---|---|---|
| 662 | CD351 | 23c multicolored | .85 | .85 |
| 663 | CD351 | 40c multicolored | 1.00 | 1.00 |
| 664 | CD351 | 50c multicolored | 1.15 | 1.15 |
| 665 | CD351 | 60c multicolored | 1.30 | 1.30 |
| 666 | CD351 | 75c multicolored | 1.80 | 1.80 |
| 667 | CD351 | $1 multicolored | 2.45 | 2.45 |
| | | Nos. 662-667 (6) | 8.55 | 8.55 |

**Souvenir Sheet**
**Perf. 14**

| | | | | |
|---|---|---|---|---|
| 668 | CD352 | $2 multicolored | 4.00 | 4.00 |

For overprints see Nos. 691-697.

**Souvenir Sheet**

Environmental Protection — A112

Marine life: a, Electus parrot, great frigate bird, coconut crab. b, Red-tailed tropic bird, common dolphin, pantropical spotted dolphin. c, Yellow & blue sea perch, green turtle, blue-barred orange parrot fish. d, Pennant coral fish, red-banded wrasse, violet squirrel fish.

**Wmk. 373**
**1995, July 12**   **Litho.**   **Perf. 14**

| | | | | |
|---|---|---|---|---|
| 669 | A112 | 60c #a.-d. + 4 labels | 5.00 | 5.00 |

For overprint see No. 672.

## Souvenir Sheet

New Year 1995 (Year of the Boar) A113

$2, Sow, piglets.

| **1995, Sept. 1** | **Litho.** | | **Perf. 13** | |
|---|---|---|---|---|
| 670 | A113 | $2 multicolored | 4.25 | 4.25 |

Singapore '95.

## Souvenir Sheet

Beijing '95 A114

Design: $2, like #670.

| **1995, Sept. 14** | | | | |
|---|---|---|---|---|
| 671 | A114 | $2 multicolored | 4.25 | 4.25 |

## No. 669 Overprinted for Jakarta '95

| | | **Wmk. 373** | | |
|---|---|---|---|---|
| **1995, Aug. 19** | **Litho.** | | **Perf. 14** | |
| 672 | A112 | 60c #a.-d. + 4 labels | 10.00 | 10.00 |

Police Maritime Unit A115

Patrol boat RKS Teanoai: No. 673, In harbor. No. 674, Under way.

| | | **Wmk. 373** | | |
|---|---|---|---|---|
| **1995, Nov. 30** | **Litho.** | | **Perf. 13** | |
| 673 | | 75c multicolored | 1.90 | 1.90 |
| 674 | | 75c multicolored | 1.90 | 1.90 |
| a. | A115 | Pair, #673-674 | 4.00 | 4.00 |

Dolphins — A116

Designs: 23c, Pantropical spotted. 60c, Spinner. 75c, Fraser's. $1, Rough-toothed.

| | | **Wmk. 384** | | |
|---|---|---|---|---|
| **1996, Jan. 15** | **Litho.** | | **Perf. 14** | |
| 675 | A116 | 23c multicolored | 1.25 | .75 |
| 676 | A116 | 60c multicolored | 1.75 | 1.00 |
| 677 | A116 | 75c multicolored | 2.40 | 1.75 |
| 678 | A116 | $1 multicolored | 2.75 | 2.75 |
| | | *Nos. 675-678 (4)* | 8.15 | 6.25 |

UNICEF, 50th Anniv. A117

Portion of UNICEF emblem and: a, Water faucet, clean water. b, Documents, chilren's rights. c, Hypodermic, health care. d, Open book, education.

| | | **Wmk. 373** | | |
|---|---|---|---|---|
| **1996, Apr. 22** | **Litho.** | | **Perf. 13** | |
| 679 | A117 | 30c Block of 4, #a.-d. | 2.75 | 2.75 |

No. 679 is a continuous design.

## Souvenir Sheet

CHINA '96, 9th Intl. Philatelic Exhibition — A118

| **1996, Apr. 30** | **Wmk. 384** | | **Perf. 13½** | |
|---|---|---|---|---|
| 680 | A118 | 50c multicolored | 2.00 | 2.00 |

New Year 1996, Year of the Rat.

## Souvenir Sheet

No. 5609 Gilbert and Ellice Islands LMS Jubilee Class 4-6-0 Locomotive — A119

| | | **Wmk. 373** | | |
|---|---|---|---|---|
| **1996, June 8** | **Litho.** | | **Perf. 12** | |
| 681 | A119 | $2 multicolored | 3.75 | 3.75 |

CAPEX '96.

Sea Crabs — A120

23c, Rathbun red. 60c, Red & white painted. 75c, Red spotted. $1, Red spotted white.

| | | **Wmk. 373** | | |
|---|---|---|---|---|
| **1996, Aug. 6** | **Litho.** | | **Perf. 14** | |
| 682 | A120 | 23c multicolored | .65 | .50 |
| 683 | A120 | 60c multicolored | 1.50 | 1.10 |
| 684 | A120 | 75c multicolored | 1.75 | 1.75 |
| 685 | A120 | $1 multicolored | 2.25 | 2.75 |
| | | *Nos. 682-685 (4)* | 6.15 | 6.10 |

## Souvenir Sheet

Taipei '96 A121

| | | **Wmk. 384** | | |
|---|---|---|---|---|
| **1996, Oct. 21** | **Litho.** | | **Perf. 14½** | |
| 686 | A121 | $1.50 Outrigger canoe | 4.00 | 4.00 |

## Ships Type of 1989

23c, Whaling ship, "Potomac," 1843. 50c, Barkentine "Southern Cross IV," 1891. 60c, Bark "John Williams III," 1890. $1, HMS Dolphin, 1765.

| | | **Wmk. 384** | | |
|---|---|---|---|---|
| **1996, Dec. 2** | **Litho.** | | **Perf. 14½** | |
| 687 | A87 | 23c multicolored | .70 | .55 |
| 688 | A87 | 50c multicolored | 1.10 | 1.10 |
| 689 | A87 | 60c multicolored | 1.30 | 1.30 |
| 690 | A87 | $1 multicolored | 2.25 | 2.25 |
| | | *Nos. 687-690 (4)* | 5.35 | 5.20 |

Nos. 662-668 Ovptd.

| **Perf. 14x13½** | | | | |
|---|---|---|---|---|
| **1997, May 29** | **Litho.** | | **Wmk. 373** | |
| 691 | CD351 | 23c multicolored | .60 | .45 |
| 692 | CD351 | 40c multicolored | .85 | .75 |
| 693 | CD351 | 50c multicolored | 1.10 | 1.00 |
| 694 | CD351 | 60c multicolored | 1.35 | 1.35 |
| 695 | CD351 | 75c multicolored | 1.55 | 1.55 |
| 696 | CD351 | $1 multicolored | 2.00 | 2.00 |
| | | *Nos. 691-696 (6)* | 7.45 | 7.10 |

## Souvenir Sheet

| 697 | CD351 | $2 multicolored | 5.00 | 5.00 |
|---|---|---|---|---|

Queen Elizabeth II and Prince Philip, 50th Wedding Anniv. A122

No. 698, Queen Elizabeth II. No. 699, Horse team going down river bank. No. 700, Queen in open carriage. No. 701, Prince Philip. No. 702, Prince, Queen. No. 703, Riding horse. $2, Queen, Prince in open carriage, horiz.

| **Perf. 14½x14** | | | | |
|---|---|---|---|---|
| **1997, July 10** | **Litho.** | | **Wmk. 373** | |
| 698 | | 50c multicolored | 1.15 | 1.15 |
| 699 | | 50c multicolored | 1.15 | 1.15 |
| a. | A122 | Pair, #698-699 | 2.50 | 2.50 |
| 700 | | 60c multicolored | 1.35 | 1.35 |
| 701 | | 60c multicolored | 1.35 | 1.35 |
| a. | A122 | Pair, #700-701 | 2.90 | 2.90 |
| 702 | | 75c multicolored | 2.00 | 2.00 |
| 703 | | 75c multicolored | 2.00 | 2.00 |
| a. | A122 | Pair, #702-703 | 4.40 | 4.40 |
| | | *Nos. 698-703 (6)* | 9.00 | 9.00 |

## Souvenir Sheet

| 704 | A122 | $2 multicolored | 6.50 | 6.50 |
|---|---|---|---|---|

Birds A123

Nos. 705-706, Rock dove. Nos. 707-708, Pacific pigeon. Nos. 709-710, Micronesian pigeon.

| | | **Wmk. 373** | | |
|---|---|---|---|---|
| **1997, Dec. 1** | **Litho.** | | **Perf. 14** | |
| 705 | | 50c Immature | .90 | .90 |
| 706 | | 50c Adult | .90 | .90 |
| a. | A123 | Pair, #705-706 | 1.90 | 1.90 |
| 707 | | 60c Adult | 1.20 | 1.20 |
| 708 | | 60c Immature | 1.20 | 1.20 |
| a. | A123 | Pair, #707-708 | 2.60 | 2.60 |
| 709 | | 75c Adult | 1.40 | 1.40 |
| 710 | | 75c Immature | 1.40 | 1.40 |
| a. | A123 | Pair, #709-710 | 3.00 | 3.00 |
| | | *Nos. 705-710 (6)* | 7.00 | 7.00 |

Nos. 705-706, 709-710 With Added Inscription

| | | **Wmk. 373** | | |
|---|---|---|---|---|
| **1997, Dec. 5** | **Litho.** | | **Perf. 14** | |
| 711 | | 50c on #705 | 1.10 | 1.10 |
| 712 | | 50c on #706 | 1.10 | 1.10 |
| a. | A123 | Pair, #711-712 | 2.50 | 2.50 |
| 713 | | 75c on #709 | 1.80 | 1.80 |
| 714 | | 75c on #710 | 1.80 | 1.80 |
| a. | A123 | Pair, #713-714 | 3.80 | 3.80 |
| | | *Nos. 711-714 (4)* | 5.80 | 5.80 |

Asia '97.

Spiny Lobster — A124

No. 716, Crawling right. No. 717, Crawling left. No. 718, Looking upward. No. 719, Looking straight forward.

| | | **Wmk. 373** | | |
|---|---|---|---|---|
| **1998, Feb. 2** | **Litho.** | | **Perf. 14** | |
| 715 | A124 | 25c shown | .60 | .60 |
| 716 | A124 | 25c multicolored | .60 | .60 |
| 717 | A124 | 25c multicolored | .60 | .60 |
| 718 | A124 | 25c multicolored | .60 | .60 |
| a. | | Strip of 4, #715-718 | 2.50 | 2.50 |

## Souvenir Sheet

| 719 | A124 | $1.50 multicolored | 3.00 | 3.00 |
|---|---|---|---|---|

World Wildlife Fund.

## Diana, Princess of Wales (1961-97)
### Common Design Type

Various portraits — No. 720: a, 50c. b, 60c. c, 75c.

| **Perf. 14½x14** | | | | |
|---|---|---|---|---|
| **1998, Mar. 31** | **Litho.** | | **Wmk. 373** | |
| 719A | CD355 | 25c multicolored | .60 | .60 |

### Sheet of 4

| 720 | CD355 | #a.-c., 719A | 4.00 | 4.00 |
|---|---|---|---|---|

No. 720 sold for $2.10 + 50c, with surtax from international sales being donated to the Princess Diana Memorial Fund, and surtax from national sales being donated to designated local charity.

Intl. Year of the Ocean — A125

Whales and dolphins: No. 721, Indo-Pacific humpbacked dolphin. No. 722, Bottlenose dolphin. No. 723, Short-snouted spinner dolphin. No. 724, Risso's dolphin. No. 725, Striped dolphin. No. 726, Sei whale. No. 727, Fin whale. No. 728, Minke whale.

| | | **Wmk. 373** | | |
|---|---|---|---|---|
| **1998, Oct. 1** | **Litho.** | | **Perf. 14** | |
| 721 | | 25c multicolored | .55 | .55 |
| 722 | | 25c multicolored | .55 | .55 |
| a. | A125 | Pair, #721-722 | 1.35 | 1.35 |
| 723 | | 60c multicolored | 1.15 | 1.15 |
| 724 | | 60c multicolored | 1.15 | 1.15 |
| a. | A125 | Pair, #723-724 | 2.50 | 2.50 |
| 725 | | 75c multicolored | 1.60 | 1.60 |
| 726 | | 75c multicolored | 1.60 | 1.60 |
| a. | A125 | Pair, #725-726 | 3.40 | 3.40 |
| 727 | | $1 multicolored | 1.80 | 1.80 |
| 728 | | $1 multicolored | 1.80 | 1.80 |
| a. | A125 | Pair, #727-728 | 4.00 | 4.00 |
| | | *Nos. 721-728 (8)* | 10.20 | 10.20 |

## Souvenir Sheet

Children of Kiribati — A125a

| **1998, Sept. 15** | | | | |
|---|---|---|---|---|
| 729 | A125a | $1 multicolored | 2.00 | 2.00 |

## Souvenir Sheet

Reuben K. Uatioa Stadium A126

| | | **Wmk. 373** | | |
|---|---|---|---|---|
| **1998, Oct. 23** | **Litho.** | | **Perf. 14** | |
| 730 | A126 | $2 multicolored | 3.25 | 3.25 |

Italia '98 World Philatelic Exhibition.

Greenhouse Effect — A127

Designs: 25c, Contributors to Greenhouse gases. 50c, Explanation of the Greenhouse Effect. 60c, Greenhouse Effect on Tarawa Atoll. 75c, Greenhouse Effect on Kiritimati Island.

$1.50, People in sailboat, "Kiribati way of life."

**Wmk. 373**

**1998, Dec. 1    Litho.    Perf. 13½**
731 A127  25c multicolored      .45   .45
732 A127  50c multicolored      .70   .70
733 A127  60c multicolored      .95   .95
734 A127  75c multicolored     1.35  1.35
*Nos. 731-734 (4)*             3.45  3.45

**Souvenir Sheet**

735 A127  $1.50 multicolored   4.75  4.75

**Souvenir Sheet**

HMS Resolution at Christmas Island — A128

**Wmk. 373**

**1999, Mar. 19    Litho.    Perf. 14**
736 A128  $2 multicolored      3.75  3.75

Australia '99 World Stamp Expo.

IBRA '99, Philatelic Exhibition, Nuremberg A129

Ducks: 25c, Northern shoveller, male. 50c, Northern shoveller, female. 60c, Green-winged teal, female. 75c, Green-winged teal, female and ducklings. $3, Green winged teal, male, duckling.

**Wmk. 373**

**1999, Apr. 27    Litho.    Perf. 14**
737 A129  25c multicolored      .60   .50
738 A129  50c multicolored     1.10   .80
739 A129  60c multicolored     1.25  1.40
740 A129  75c multicolored     1.55  2.00
*Nos. 737-740 (4)*             4.50  4.70

**Souvenir Sheet**

741 A129  $3 multicolored      5.50  5.50

Independence, 20th Anniv. — A130

Designs: 25c, Millennium Island. 60c, Map of Kiribati. 75c, Map of Nikumaroro. $1, Amelia Earhart, Lockheed 10E Electra airplane.

**Wmk. 373**

**1999, July 12    Litho.    Perf. 13½**
742 A130  25c multicolored      .50   .50
743 A130  60c multicolored      .95   .95
744 A130  75c multicolored     1.25  1.25
745 A130  $1 multicolored      2.60  2.60
  a.  Souvenir sheet, #744-745  3.50  3.50
*Nos. 742-745 (4)*             5.30  5.30

**1st Manned Moon Landing, 30th Anniv.**

Common Design Type

Designs: 25c, Edwin Aldrin. 60c, Service module docks with lander. 75c, Apollo 11 on lunar surface. $1, Command module separates from service module. $2, Earth as seen from moon.

**Perf. 14x13¾**

**1999, July 20    Litho.    Wmk. 384**
746 CD357  25c multicolored     .60   .60
747 CD357  60c multicolored    1.10  1.10
748 CD357  75c multicolored    1.40  1.40
749 CD357  $1 multicolored     1.75  1.75
*Nos. 746-749 (4)*             4.85  4.85

**Souvenir Sheet**

**Perf. 14**

**1999, July 20    Litho.    Wmk. 384**
750 CD357  $2 multicolored     3.75  3.75

No. 750 contains one 40mm circular stamp 40mm.

UPU, 125th Anniv., Christmas A131

**Wmk. 373**

**1999, Oct. 9    Litho.    Perf. 13½**
751 A131  25c Santa in canoe    .50   .45
752 A131  60c Santa on dock     .85   .75
753 A131  75c Santa in sleigh  1.10  1.10
754 A131  $1 Santa at computer 1.30  1.30
*Nos. 751-754 (4)*             3.75  3.60

Millennium — A132

**Perf. 13¼x13**

**2000, Jan. 1    Litho.    Wmk. 373**
755 A132  25c Faith            .40   .35
756 A132  40c Harmony          .60   .55
757 A132  60c Hope             .80   .80
758 A132  75c Enlightenment   1.30  1.30
759 A132  $1 Peace            1.45  1.45
*Nos. 755-759 (5)*            4.55  4.45

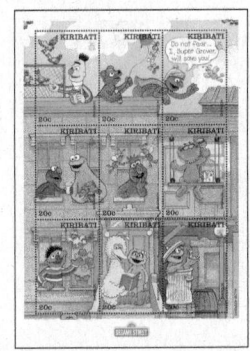

Sesame Street Characters — A133

No. 760: a, Bert. b, Baby Bear. c, Grover. d, Elmo, Cookie Monster. e, Telly Monster. f, Zoe. g, Ernie. h, Big Bird, Rosita. i, Oscar the Grouch.
No. 761, Grover as mailman.

**Perf. 14½x14¾**

**2000, Mar. 22    Litho.    Wmk. 373**
760 A133  20c Sheet of 9, #a-i  3.75  3.75

**Souvenir Sheet**

761 A133  $1.50 multi          2.75  2.75

**Souvenir Sheet**

The Stamp Show 2000, London A134

**2000, May 8    Wmk. 373    Perf. 13¾**
762 A134  $5 Queen Elizabeth II  7.50  7.50

Nos. 635, 636, 638, 648 and 650 Ovptd.

**Perf. 14½x14**

**2000, June 1    Wmk. 373**
763 A108  5c multi             .35   .35
764 A108  10c multi            .35   .35
765 A108  20c multi            .40   .40
766 A108  $1 multi            1.30  1.30
767 A108  $3 multi            3.40  3.40
*Nos. 763-767 (5)*            5.80  5.80

Prince William, 18th Birthday — A135

Various views of Prince William with Prince Charles.

**Wmk. 373**

**2000, July 24    Litho.    Perf. 12¾**
768 A135  25c multi            .40   .40
769 A135  60c multi            .90   .90
770 A135  75c multi           1.25  1.25
771 A135  $1 multi            1.50  1.50
*Nos. 768-771 (4)*            4.05  4.05

Ducks — A136

Designs: No. 772, 25c, Blue duck. No. 773, 25c, Green-winged teal. No. 774, 25c, Mallard. No. 775, 25c, Northern shoveler. No. 776, 25c, Pacific black duck. No. 777, 25c, Wandering whistling duck.

**Wmk. 373**

**2001, Jan. 22    Litho.    Perf. 14**
772-777 A136  Set of 6        8.00  8.00

**Souvenir Sheet**

778 A136  $1 Gray teal        7.75  7.75

Water Conservation A137

Children's art by: 25c, Tiare Hongkai. 50c, Gilbert Z. Tluanga. 60c, Mantokataake Tebaiuea, vert. 75c, Tokaman Karanebo, vert. $2, Taom Simon.

**2001, July 12    Litho.    Perf. 13¼**
779-783 A137  Set of 5        5.25  5.25

Phila Nippon '01 — A138

Development projects: 75c, Betio Port. $2, New Parliament House.

**2001, Aug. 1**
784-785 A138  Set of 2        5.00  5.00

Tourism A139

Designs: 75c, Norwegian Cruise Line ship, map of cruise to Fanning Island. $3, The Betsey, map of Fanning Island.

**Perf. 13¼**

**2001, Nov. 14    Litho.    Unwmk.**
786-787 A139  Set of 2        5.75  5.75

Fish — A140

Designs: 5c, Paracanthurus hepatus. 10c, Centropyge flavissimus. 15c, Anthias squamipinnis. 20c, Centropyge loriculus. 25c, Acanthurus lineatus. 30c, Oxycirrhites typus. 40c, Dascyllus trimaculatus. 50c, Acanthurus achilles. 60c, Pomacentrus coeruleus. 75c, Acanthurus glaucopareus. 80c, Thalassoma lunare. 90c, Arothron meleagris. $1, Odonus niger. $2, Cephalopholis miniatus. $5, Pomacanthus imperator. $10, Balistoides conspicillum.

**2002, Feb. 28    Unwmk.    Perf. 13**
788 A140  5c multi            .30   .25
789 A140  10c multi           .30   .30
790 A140  15c multi           .30   .30
791 A140  20c multi           .30   .30
792 A140  25c multi           .35   .35
793 A140  30c multi           .40   .40
794 A140  40c multi           .55   .55
795 A140  50c multi           .65   .65
796 A140  60c multi           .70   .70
797 A140  75c multi           .80   .80
798 A140  80c multi          1.00  1.00
799 A140  90c multi          1.30  1.30
800 A140  $1 multi           1.40  1.40
801 A140  $2 multi           2.80  2.80
802 A140  $5 multi           6.50  6.50
803 A140  $10 multi         11.50 11.50
*Nos. 788-803 (16)*         29.15 29.10

For overprints, see Nos. 988-990.

Pacific Explorers — A141

Designs: 25c, Adm. Fabian von Bellingshausen and the Vostok, 1820. 40c, Capt. Charles Wilkes and the Vincennes, 1838-42. 60c, Capt. Edmund Fanning and the Betsey, 1798. 75c, Capt. Coffin and the Transit, 1823. $1, Commodore John Byron and the Dolphin, 1765. $2, Capt. Broughton and HMS Providence, 1795. $5, Capt. James Cook, 1777, vert.

**2002, Mar. 25    Wmk. 373    Perf. 14**
804-809 A141  Set of 6        9.00  9.00

**Souvenir Sheet**

810 A141  $5 multi            8.50  8.50

In Remembrance of Sept. 11, 2001 Terrorist Attacks — A142

No. 811: a, 25c. b, $2.

**2002, May 3    Wmk. 373    Perf. 13¾**
811 A142  Vert. pair, #a-b    5.00  5.00

Issued in sheets of 2 pairs.

Reign of Queen Elizabeth II, 50th Anniv. — A143

Various photographs by Dorothy Wilding. Panel colors: 25c, Purple.
No. 812: a, Maroon. b, Purple.

**2002, June 3    Wmk. 373    Perf. 14**
812 A143  25c multi          1.25  1.25

**Souvenir Sheet**

813 A143  $2 Sheet of 2, #a-b  8.50  8.50

Christmas — A144

Ribbons and bow with various basketry weaves: 25c, 60c, 75c, $1, $2.50.

**2002, Dec. 2    Litho.    Perf. 13x13¼**
814-818 A144  Set of 5        7.00  7.00

Cowrie Shells — A145

Designs: 25c, Cypraea mappa. 50c, Cypraea eglantina. 60c, Cypraea mauritiana.

75c, Cypraea cribaria. $1, Cypraea talpa. $2.50, Cypraea depressa.

**Perf. 14½x14¼**

| 2003, May 12 | | Litho. | | Unwmk. | |
|---|---|---|---|---|---|
| 819-824 | A145 | Set of 6 | | 7.50 | 7.50 |
| 824a | | Souvenir sheet, #819-824 | | 7.50 | 7.50 |

### Coronation of Queen Elizabeth II, 50th Anniv.
### Common Design Type

Designs: Nos. 825, 25c, 827a, $2, Queen and Prince Philip waving. Nos. 826, $3, 827b, $5, Prince Philip paying homage to Queen at coronation.

**Perf. 14¼x14½**

| 2003, June 2 | | Litho. | | Wmk. 373 | |
|---|---|---|---|---|---|

**Vignettes Framed, Red Background**

| 825 | CD363 | $2 multicolored | | 1.75 | 1.75 |
|---|---|---|---|---|---|
| 826 | CD363 | $3 multicolored | | 2.50 | 2.50 |

### Souvenir Sheet
### Vignettes Without Frame, Purple Panel

| 827 | CD363 | Sheet of 2, #a-b | | 8.75 | 8.75 |
|---|---|---|---|---|---|

Powered Flight, Cent. A146

Designs: 25c, Sopwith Camel. 50c, Northrop Alpha. No. 830, 60c, DeHavilland Comet. 75c, Boeing 727. $1, English Electric Canberra. $2.50, Lockheed Martin F-22.
No. 834: a, 40c, Mitsubishi A6M-5 Zero. b, 60c, Grumman F6F Hellcat.

**Wmk. 373**

| 2003, Aug. 29 | | Litho. | | Perf. 14 | |
|---|---|---|---|---|---|

**Stamp + Label**

| 828-833 | A146 | Set of 6 | | 10.00 | 10.00 |
|---|---|---|---|---|---|

### Souvenir Sheet

| 834 | A146 | Sheet of 2, #a-b | | 3.25 | 3.25 |
|---|---|---|---|---|---|

Christmas — A147

Christmas Island scenes: 25c, Teareba Taomeka, Tabwakea. 40c, Seventh Day Adventist Church, London. 50c, St. Teresa Catholic Church, Tabakea Village. 60c, Betaera Fou, London. 75c, Children, church bells, London. $1.50, Emanuira Church, London. $2.50, Church of Christ (60x24mm).

| 2003, Dec. 20 | | Unwmk. | | Perf. 13¼ | |
|---|---|---|---|---|---|
| 835-841 | A147 | Set of 7 | | 10.00 | 10.00 |
| 841a | | Souvenir sheet, #835-841 | | 10.00 | 10.00 |

Road Safety — A148

No. 842: a, Accident. b, Automobile. c, Beverage can, drink, cigarette. d, Children.

| 2004, Apr. 7 | | Litho. | | Perf. 13x13¼ | |
|---|---|---|---|---|---|
| 842 | A148 | Horiz. strip of 4 | | 6.50 | 6.50 |
| a. | | 30c multi | | .75 | .75 |
| b. | | 40c multi | | 1.10 | 1.10 |
| c. | | 50c multi | | 1.30 | 1.30 |
| d. | | 60c multi | | 1.60 | 1.40 |
| e. | | Souvenir sheet, #842 | | 6.50 | 6.50 |

World Health Day.

Bird Life International A149

Designs: 25c, Pacific golden plover. 40c, Whimbrel. 50c, Wandering tattler. 60c, Sanderling. 75c, Bar-tailed godwit. $2.50, Ruddy turnstone.
No. 849 — Bristle-thighed curlew: a, One in tree, one at water's edge. b, Head of bird. c, Front of bird, head facing right, vert. d, Back of bird, head facing left, vert. e, Two birds at water's edge.

**Perf. 14¼x13¾**

| 2004, Apr. 29 | | Litho. | | Unwmk. | |
|---|---|---|---|---|---|
| 843-848 | A149 | Set of 6 | | 10.50 | 10.50 |

### Souvenir Sheet
**Perf. 14¼x14½**

| 849 | A149 | $1 Sheet of 5, #a-e | | 13.00 | 13.00 |
|---|---|---|---|---|---|

2004 Summer Olympics, Athens — A150

Designs: 25c, Runners. 50c, Taekwondo. 60c, Weight lifting. 75c, Women's running.

| 2004, July 12 | | Wmk. 373 | | Perf. 14 | |
|---|---|---|---|---|---|
| 850-853 | A150 | Set of 4 | | 3.75 | 3.75 |

### Souvenir Sheet

Celebration Games — A151

No. 854: a, Runners on track. b, Athletes, dancer, building.

| 2004, July 12 | | | | | |
|---|---|---|---|---|---|
| 854 | A151 | $2.50 Sheet of 2, #a-b | | 9.00 | 9.00 |

Pacific Orchids — A152

No. 855: a, Dendrobium anosmum. b, Dendrobium chrysotoxum. c, Dendrobium laevifolium. d, Dendrobium mohlianum. e, Dendrobium pseudoglomeratum. f, Dendrobium purpureum. g, Grammatophyllum speciosum. h, Dendrobium williamsianum. i, Spathoglottis plicata. j, Vanda hindsii.

| 2004, Aug. 28 | | Unwmk. | | Perf. 13½ | |
|---|---|---|---|---|---|
| 855 | A152 | Block of 10 | | 16.50 | 16.50 |
| a.-j. | | $1 Any single | | 1.60 | 1.50 |

Merchant Ships — A153

Designs: 50c, MV Montelucia. 75c, MS Pacific Princess. $2.50 MS Prinsendam. $5, MS Norwegian Wind.

| 2004, Oct. 25 | | Litho. | | Perf. 13¼ | |
|---|---|---|---|---|---|
| 856-859 | A153 | Set of 4 | | 14.50 | 14.50 |

Battle of Trafalgar, Bicent. A154

Designs: 25c, French 16-pounder cannon. 50c, San Ildefonso in action against HMS Defence. 75c, HMS Victory lashed to the Redoubtable. $1, Emperor Napoleon Bonaparte, vert. $1.50, HMS Victory. No. 865, $2.50, Vice-admiral Sir Horatio Nelson, vert.
No. 866: a, Admiral Federico Gravina. b, Santissima Trinidad.

| 2005, Mar. 29 | | Litho. | | Perf. 13¼ | |
|---|---|---|---|---|---|
| 860-865 | A154 | Set of 6 | | 12.00 | 12.00 |

### Souvenir Sheet

| 866 | A154 | $2.50 Sheet of 2, #a-b | | 8.25 | 8.25 |
|---|---|---|---|---|---|

No. 864 has particles of wood from the HMS Victory embedded in the areas covered by a thermographic process that produces a raised, shiny effect.

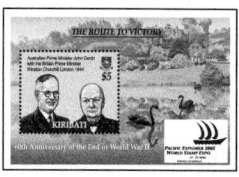

End of World War II, 60th Anniv. A155

No. 867: a, Japanese Type 95 Ha-Go tank invading Gilbert Islands. b, Japanese A6M Zero fighter on Gilbert Islands. c, USS Argonaut and Nautilus land Marines at Butaritari in Carlson Raid. d, Pacific Fleet Admiral Chester W. Nimitz. e, USS Liscome Bay sunk by Japanese submarine. f, US Higgins landing craft approaching Tarawa Red Beach. g, F6F-3 Hellcats provide air cover over Tarawa Red Beach. h, LVTs hit the shore at Tarawa Red Beach. i, Sherman tank at Tarawa Red Beach. j, US Marines take cover on Tarawa Red Beach.
$5, Australian Prime Minister John Curtin, British Prime Minister Winston Churchill.

| 2005, Apr. 21 | | | | Perf. 13¾ | |
|---|---|---|---|---|---|
| 867 | A155 | 75c Sheet of 10, #a-j | | 14.50 | 14.50 |

### Souvenir Sheet

| 868 | A155 | $5 multi | | 12.00 | 12.00 |
|---|---|---|---|---|---|

Pacific Explorer 2005 World Stamp Expo, Sydney (No. 868).

BirdLife International — A156

No. 869, 25c — Birds of Christmas Island: a, Lesser frigatebird. b, Red-tailed tropicbird. c, Blue noddy. d, Christmas shearwater. e, Sooty tern. f, Masked booby.
No. 870, $2 — Birds of Kiribati: a, White-tailed tropicbird. b, Black noddy. c, Red-footed booby. d, Wedge-tailed shearwater. e, White tern. f, Great frigatebird.

| 2005, Aug. 15 | | | | Perf. 13¼x13 | |
|---|---|---|---|---|---|

**Sheets of 6, #a-f**

| 869-870 | A156 | Set of 2 | | 25.00 | 25.00 |
|---|---|---|---|---|---|

Pope John Paul II (1920-2005) — A157

| 2005, Aug. 18 | | Litho. | | Perf. 14 | |
|---|---|---|---|---|---|
| 871 | A157 | $1 multi | | 3.00 | 3.00 |

Battle of Trafalgar, Bicent. — A158

Designs: 25c, HMS Victory. 50c, Ships, horiz. $5, Admiral Horatio Nelson.

| 2005, Oct. 18 | | Litho. | | Perf. 13½ | |
|---|---|---|---|---|---|
| 872-874 | A158 | Set of 3 | | 12.50 | 12.50 |

Worldwide Fund for Nature (WWF) — A159

Various depictions of harlequin shrimp: 50c, 60c, 75c, $5.

| 2005, Dec. 1 | | | | Perf. 14 | |
|---|---|---|---|---|---|
| 875-878 | A159 | Set of 4 | | 13.00 | 13.00 |
| 878a | | Miniature sheet, 2 each #875-878 | | 22.50 | 22.50 |

Queen Elizabeth II, 80th Birthday — A160

Queen: 50c, As young woman. 75c, Wearing tiara, sepia photograph. $1, Wearing tiara, color photograph. $2, Wearing pink hat.
No. 883: a, $1.50, Like $1. b, $2.50, Like 75c.

| 2006, Apr. 21 | | Litho. | | Perf. 14 | |
|---|---|---|---|---|---|

**Stamps With White Frames**

| 879-882 | A160 | Set of 4 | | 9.50 | 9.50 |
|---|---|---|---|---|---|

### Souvenir Sheet
**Stamps Without White Frames**

| 883 | A160 | Sheet of 2, #a-b | | 10.00 | 10.00 |
|---|---|---|---|---|---|

For surcharges, see Nos. 991-994.

Europa Stamps, 50th Anniv. — A161

Flags of European Union and Kiribati with gradiating background colors of: $2, Gray green. $2.50, Purple. $3, Yellowish brown. $5, Blue.

| 2006, May 4 | | | | Perf. 13¼ | |
|---|---|---|---|---|---|
| 884-887 | A161 | Set of 4 | | 20.00 | 20.00 |
| 887a | | Souvenir sheet, #884-887 | | 20.00 | 20.00 |

Anniversaries — A162

No. 888, 25c: a, Charles Darwin and marine life. b, Fish and marine life.
No. 889, 50c: a, Isambard Kingdom Brunel. b, Glowing rivet.
No. 890, 75c: a, Christopher Columbus. b, Ship.
No. 891, $1: a, Thomas Alva Edison. b, Tin foil phonograph.
No. 892, $1.25: a, Wolfgang Amadeus Mozart. b, Violin and quill pen.
No. 893, $1.50: a, Concorde. b, Wing of Concorde, Concorde in flight.

| 2006, May 27 | | | | Perf. 13x12½ | |
|---|---|---|---|---|---|

**Horiz. Pairs, #a-b**

| 888-893 | A162 | Set of 6 | | 22.50 | 22.50 |
|---|---|---|---|---|---|

Darwin's voyage on the Beagle, 250th anniv., Birth of Brunel, bicent., Death of Columbus, 500th anniv., Death of Edison, 75th anniv., Birth of Mozart, 250th anniv., Inaugural Concorde flights, 30th anniv.

Dinosaurs A163

Designs: 25c, Ultrasaurus. 50c, Rhamphorhynchus. 60c, Dilophosaurus. 75c, Brachiosaurus. No. 898, $1, Minmi paravertebra. No. 899, $1, Eoraptor. $1.25, Stegosaurus. $1.50, Gigantosaurus.

| 2006, Sept. 15 | | | | Perf. 13¼x13½ | |
|---|---|---|---|---|---|
| 894-901 | A163 | Set of 8 | | 11.50 | 11.50 |

Miniature Sheet

Victoria Cross, 150th Anniv. A164

No. 902: a. Troop Sergeant Major John Berryman with Captain Webb at Balaclava. b, Private W. Norman bringing in two Russian prisoners. c, Sergeant Major John Greive saving officer's life at Balaclava. d, Private Thomas Beach rescuing Colonel Carpenter at Inkerman. e, Brevet Major C. H. Lumley engaged with Russian gunners in the Redan. f, Major F. C. Elton working in trenches.

**2006, Oct. 20** Litho. **Perf. 13¼x12½**
902 A164 $1.50 Sheet of 6,
#a-f, + 6 labels          17.50 17.50

60th Wedding Anniversary of Queen Elizabeth II and Prince Philip — A165

Designs: 50c, Portrait of Elizabeth and Philip. 75c, Wedding procession. $1, Bride and groom waving. $1.50, Queen reading. $5, Wedding portrait.

**2007, Jan. 31** Litho. **Perf. 13¾**
903-906 A165 Set of 4          6.00 6.00
**Souvenir Sheet**
**Perf. 14**
907 A165 $5 multi          7.75 7.75

No. 907 contains one 42x56mm stamp

Scouting, Cent. — A166

Designs: 25c, Scouts with Kiribati flag, hands tying neckerchief. 50c, Scouts learning about AIDS, Scout saluting. 75c, Scout leaders, hand with compass. $2, 1962 Scout shelter, hands lashing rope.
No. 912, vert.: a, $1, Emblem of Kiribati Scouts. b, $1.50, Lord Robert Baden-Powell.

**Perf. 13x13¼**
**2007, Sept. 21** Litho. **Wmk. 373**
908-911 A166 Set of 4          7.50 7.50
**Souvenir Sheet**
**Perf. 13¼x13**
912 A166 Sheet of 2, #a-b          5.25 5.25

Princess Diana (1961-97) — A167

Designs: No. 913, 25c, Wearing white dress, facing right. No. 914, 25c, Wearing pink dress, facing left. 50c, Wearing pink dress, diff. No. 916, 75c, Wearing emerald necklace. No. 917, 75c, Wearing black and white dress. $1, Wearing red dress.

**Perf. 13¼x12½**
**2007, Nov. 1** Litho. **Unwmk.**
913-918 A167 Set of 6          7.00 7.00

Military Uniforms — A168

Uniforms of: 25c, Royal Engineers. 40c, 95th Rifles. 50c, 24th Regiment of Foot. 60c, New Zealand soldiers. 75c, 93rd Sutherland Highlanders. 90c, Irish Guard. $1, Japanese soldiers. $1.50, United States Marine Corps.

**2007, Nov. 20** **Wmk. 373** **Perf. 14**
919-926 A168 Set of 8          12.00 12.00

Birds — A169

Designs: 5c, Great crested tern. 10c Eurasian teal. 15c, Laughing gull. 20c, Black-tailed godwit. 25c, Pectoral sandpiper. 50c, Band-rumped storm petrel. 60c, Sharp-tailed sandpiper. 75c, Gray-tailed tattler. 90c, Red phalarope. $1, Pink-footed shearwater. $2, Ring-billed gull. $5, Bonin petrel.

**Wmk. 373**
**2008, Feb. 9** Litho. **Perf. 13¾**
927 A169 5c multi          .30 .25
928 A169 10c multi          .30 .25
929 A169 15c multi          .30 .30
930 A169 20c multi          .40 .40
931 A169 25c multi          .45 .45
932 A169 50c multi          .95 .95
933 A169 60c multi          1.10 1.10
934 A169 75c multi          1.40 1.40
935 A169 90c multi          1.75 1.75
936 A169 $1 multi          2.00 2.00
937 A169 $2 multi          4.25 4.25
 a. Souvenir sheet, #929, 933-937          10.00 10.00
938 A169 $5 multi          10.50 10.50
 a. Souvenir sheet, #927-928, 930-932, 938          12.50 12.50
 Nos. 927-938 (12)          23.70 23.60

For surcharges, see Nos. 984-987.

A170

Royal Air Force, 90th Anniv. A171

Designs: 25c, Avro Shackleton. 50c, Harrier GR3. 75c, Eurofighter Typhoon. $1, Vickers Valiant. $2.50, Dambusters Raid.

**Wmk. 373**
**2008, Apr. 1** Litho. **Perf. 14**
939-942 A170 Set of 4          5.50 5.50
**Souvenir Sheet**
943 A171 $2.50 multi          4.75 4.75

Phoenix Island Protected Area — A172

Designs: 40c, Huts. 75c, Map of Kanton Island. 80c, Map of various islands. 85c, Phoenix petrel. $1.25, Acropora nobilis and reef fish. $1.75, Blacktip reef shark.

**2008, July 12** **Perf. 13¾**
944-949 A172 Set of 6          11.50 11.50
 949a Souvenir sheet of 6, #944-949          11.50 11.50

2008 Summer Olympics, Beijing — A173

Designs: 25c, Bamboo, weight lifting. 50c, Dragon, running. 60c, Lanterns, cycling. 75c, Fish, javelin.

**Wmk. 373**
**2008, Aug. 8** Litho. **Perf. 13½**
950-953 A173 Set of 4          3.75 3.75

Christmas — A174

No. 954, 25c: a, Lady Sacred Heart Church, Bairiki. b, Kiribati Protestant Church, Bikenibeu.
No. 955, 40c: a, Kaotitaeka Roman Catholic Church, Betio. b, Mormon Church, Iesu Kristo.
No. 956, 50c: a, Moaningaina Church, Eita. b, Sacred Heart Cathedral, Tarawa.
No. 957, 75c: a, St. Paul's Millennium Church, Betio. b, Kainkatikun Kristo Church, Naninimo.

**Wmk. 406**
**2008, Dec. 8** Litho. **Perf. 13**
**Pairs, #a-b**
954-957 A174 Set of 4          5.00 5.00
 957c Souvenir sheet, #954a-954b, 955a-955b, 956a-956b, 957a-957b          5.00 5.00

Explorers — A175

Designs: 25c, Sir Ernest Shackleton (1874-1922). 40c, Robert Falcon Scott (1868-1912). 50c, Captain James Cook (1728-79). 75c, Marco Polo (1254-1324). $1.50, Matthew Flinders (1774-1814). $1.75, John Cabot (c. 1450-99).

**Wmk. 406**
**2009, Mar. 9** Litho. **Perf. 14**
958-963 A175 Set of 6          9.00 9.00

Naval Aviation, Cent. — A176

Aircraft: 40c, Grumman Avenger. 50c, Chance Vought Corsair. 75c, Westland Whirlwind helicopter. $1.25, McDonnell Douglas Phantom.
$3, Helicopter on deck of HMS Ark Royal.

**Wmk. 406**
**2009, May 12** Litho. **Perf. 14**
964-967 A176 Set of 4          4.75 4.75
**Souvenir Sheet**
968 A176 $3 multi          5.00 5.00

Nos. 964-968 each were printed in sheets of 8 + central label.

Space Exploration — A177

Designs: 40c, Mars Science Laboratory. 50c, International Space Station. 75c, Space Shuttle Endeavour and Boeing transporter plane. $1.25, Launch of Apollo 12. No. 973, $3, Luna 16.
No. 974, $3, Astronaut on Moon, painting by Capt. Alan Bean, vert.

**Wmk. 406**
**2009, July 20** Litho. **Perf. 13¼**
969-973 A177 Set of 5          9.25 9.25
**Souvenir Sheet**
**Perf. 13x13½**
974 A177 $3 multi          4.75 4.75

First man on the Moon, 40th anniv. No. 974 contains one 40x60mm stamp.

Battle of Britain, 70th Anniv. — A178

Stained-glass windows of Biggin Hill Memorial Chapel depicting: 25c, Aircraft servicing. 40c, Knight, English flag, airplanes. 50c, Parachute packing. 75c, Ground control. $1, Rescue services. $1.50, Royal Air Force emblem. $3, Photograph of Sir Douglas Bader.

**Wmk. 406**
**2010, Apr. 14** Litho. **Perf. 13**
975-980 A178 Set of 6          8.25 8.25
**Souvenir Sheet**
981 A178 $3 multi          5.75 5.75

Souvenir Sheet

Wedding of Prince William and Catherine Middleton — A179

**Perf. 14¾x14¼**
**2011, Apr. 29** Litho. **Wmk. 406**
982 A179 $5 multi          11.00 11.00

No. 871 Overprinted

Beatified 1 May 2011

**2011, June 13** Litho. **Perf. 14**
983 A157 $1 multi          2.10 2.10

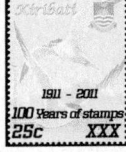

Nos. 927-930 Surcharged

**Methods, Perfs and Watermarks As Before**
**2011, July**
984 A169 25c on 5c #927          .50 .50
985 A169 30c on 10c #928          .60 .60
986 A169 50c on 20c #930          .95 .95
987 A169 75c on 15c #929          1.40 1.40
 Nos. 984-987 (4)          3.45 3.45

Nos. 794, 801 & 803 Ovptd.

## Methods and Perfs As Before
### 2011, July
| | | | | |
|---|---|---|---|---|
| 988 | A140 | 40c on #794 | .75 | .75 |
| 989 | A140 | $2 on #801 | 3.75 | 3.75 |
| 990 | A140 | $10 on #803 | 19.00 | 19.00 |
| | *Nos. 988-990 (3)* | | 23.50 | 23.50 |

### Nos. 879-882 Overprinted in Silver

## Methods and Perfs. As Before
### 2012, June 4
| | | | | |
|---|---|---|---|---|
| 991 | A160 | 50c on #879 | 1.00 | 1.00 |
| 992 | A160 | 75c on #880 | 1.50 | 1.50 |
| 993 | A160 | $1 on #881 | 2.00 | 2.00 |
| 994 | A160 | $2 on #882 | 4.00 | 4.00 |
| | *Nos. 991-994 (4)* | | 8.50 | 8.50 |

Worldwide Fund for Nature (WWF) — A180

Various views of Giant trevally.

### 2012, July 11  Litho.  Perf. 14¼x14
| 995 | | Horiz. strip of 4 | 11.50 | 11.50 |
|---|---|---|---|---|
| a. | A180 | 80c multi | 1.75 | 1.75 |
| b. | A180 | $1 multi | 2.10 | 2.10 |
| c. | A180 | $1.50 multi | 3.25 | 3.25 |
| d. | A180 | $2 multi | 4.25 | 4.25 |

Printed in sheets containing two each Nos. 995a-995d.

### Miniature Sheet

Marine Life of Phoenix Islands Protected Area — A181

No. 996: a, 40c, Manta ray. b, 50c, Napoleon wrasse. c, 60c, Yellow and blueback fusiliers. d, 75c, Rainbow runners. e, $1, Green turtle. f, $1.50, Ornate butterflyfish. g, $2, Chrysiptera albata. h, $2.50, Small giant clam.

### 2012, Sept. 12  Perf. 14¼x14
| 996 | A181 | Sheet of 8, #a-h | 19.00 | 19.00 |
|---|---|---|---|---|

Watercraft — A182

Designs: 5c, Christmas Island outrigger. 10c, Ferry to shore. 15c, Inter-island ferries. 20c, Fishing boats. 25c, Inter-island ferry. 30c, Te Tia Awaka and cargo boat. 35c, Bwaan Tetangira II. 40c, Passengers diving off outrigger Te Okarsi. 45c, Akenraoi in Abaiang Lagoon. 50c, Native house with outrigger. 55c, Moamoa. 60c, Container ship Kiribati Chief. 75c, Cruise liner Pride of Aloha. $1, Kiribati 36 yacht. $2, Pilot boat Teeitei. $5, Traditional outrigger.

### Perf. 13¾
### 2013, Oct. 5  Litho.  Unwmk.
| | | | | |
|---|---|---|---|---|
| 997 | A182 | 5c multi | .30 | .25 |
| 998 | A182 | 10c multi | .30 | .25 |
| 999 | A182 | 15c multi | .30 | .30 |
| 1000 | A182 | 20c multi | .40 | .40 |
| 1001 | A182 | 25c multi | .50 | .50 |
| 1002 | A182 | 30c multi | .60 | .60 |
| 1003 | A182 | 35c multi | .65 | .65 |
| 1004 | A182 | 40c multi | .75 | .75 |
| 1005 | A182 | 45c multi | .85 | .85 |
| 1006 | A182 | 50c multi | .95 | .95 |
| 1007 | A182 | 55c multi | 1.00 | 1.00 |
| 1008 | A182 | 60c multi | 1.10 | 1.10 |
| 1009 | A182 | 75c multi | 1.40 | 1.40 |
| 1010 | A182 | $1 multi | 1.90 | 1.90 |
| 1011 | A182 | $2 multi | 3.75 | 3.75 |

| 1012 | A182 | $5 multi | 9.50 | 9.50 |
|---|---|---|---|---|
| a. | Souvenir sheet of 16, #997-1012 | | 24.50 | 24.50 |
| | *Nos. 997-1012 (16)* | | 24.25 | 24.15 |

Mangroves A183

Designs: 45c, Building and mangroves. 75c, Man and boys on beach near mangroves. $1, People near mangroves. $3, People planting mangroves.

### 2014, June 16  Litho.  Perf. 14x14½
| 1013-1016 | A183 | Set of 4 | 10.00 | 10.00 |
|---|---|---|---|---|

2014 Commonwealth Games, Glasgow — A184

Designs: 25c, Weight lifter Davia Katoatau. 75c, Katoatau with medal.
No. 1019, horiz.: a, Kiribati team and flag-bearer. b, Scottish terrier wearing sweater with "Kiribati" sign.

### 2014, Sept. 8  Litho.  Perf. 14½
| 1017-1018 | A184 | Set of 2 | 1.75 | 1.75 |
|---|---|---|---|---|
### Souvenir Sheet
| 1019 | A184 | $2.50 Sheet of 2, #a-b | 8.75 | 8.75 |

### Souvenir Sheet

Butterflies — A185

No. 1020: a, $2, Meadow argus. b, $3, Blue moon.

### Perf. 14¼x14
### 2015, May 27  Litho.  Unwmk.
| 1020 | A185 | Sheet of 2, #a-b | 7.75 | 7.75 |
|---|---|---|---|---|

Nos. 935, 938 Surcharged | Nos. 936-937 Overprinted

## Methods, Perfs and Watermarks As Before
### 2015, July 17
| | | | | |
|---|---|---|---|---|
| 1021 | A169 | 40c on 90c #935 | .60 | .60 |
| 1022 | A169 | 60c on $5 #938 | .90 | .90 |
| 1023 | A169 | $1 on #936 | 1.50 | 1.50 |
| 1024 | A169 | $2 on #937 | 3.00 | 3.00 |
| | *Nos. 1021-1024 (4)* | | 6.00 | 6.00 |

Queen Elizabeth II, 90th Birthday — A186

Queen Elizabeth II wearing: 25c, Blue green dress and hat. 75c, Beige jacket and hat. $1, Floral dress and white hat. $2.50, Tweed jacket and hat. $3.75, Blue jacket and hat.

$5, Queen Elizabeth II and Prince Philip in Kiribati, 1982.

### Perf. 13¼x13
### 2016, Apr. 21  Litho.  Unwmk.
| 1025-1029 | A186 | Set of 5 | 13.00 | 13.00 |
|---|---|---|---|---|
### Souvenir Sheet
| 1030 | A186 | $5 multi | 7.75 | 7.75 |

2016 World Stamp Show, New York City — A187

Show emblem and: 25c, Participants in Independence celebrations. 75c, Participants in Independence celebrations, diff. $1.25, Boats on ground and in water. $3, Betio War Memorial.

### Perf. 13x13¼
### 2016, May 28  Litho.  Unwmk.
| 1031-1034 | A187 | Set of 4 | 7.75 | 7.75 |
|---|---|---|---|---|

Marine Training Center, 50th Anniv. — A188

Designs: 25c, Fisheries training. 75c, Cookery training. $1, Engine maintenance. $1.50, Transas bridge simulator.
No. 1039: a, $2, Marine Training Center. b, $3, Lifeboat training.

### Unwmk.
### 2017, July 22  Litho.  Perf. 14
| 1035-1038 | A188 | Set of 4 | 5.75 | 5.75 |
|---|---|---|---|---|
### Souvenir Sheet
| 1039 | A188 | Sheet of 2, #a-b | 8.00 | 8.00 |

Flowers — A189

Designs: 25c, Te Kanawa. 50c, Te Kaituru. 75c, Te Nikarairai. $1, Te Rooti. $2.50, Te Meeria. $4, Te Kiebu.

### Perf. 13¼x13
### 2017, Oct. 14  Litho.  Unwmk.
| 1040-1045 | A189 | Set of 6 | 14.00 | 14.00 |
|---|---|---|---|---|

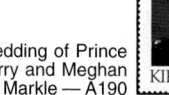

Wedding of Prince Harry and Meghan Markle — A190

Designs: 25c, Prince Harry. 75c, Meghan Markle. $1.50, Couple. $2, Couple, diff. $5, Couple, diff.

### 2018, July 20  Litho.  Perf. 14
| 1046-1049 | A190 | Set of 4 | 8.00 | 8.00 |
|---|---|---|---|---|
### Souvenir Sheet
| 1050 | A190 | $5 multi | 8.00 | 8.00 |

Military Anniversaries — A191

Designs: 25c, Map of Tarawa. 75c, Map of France.
No. 1053: a, $1, Map of Tarawa. b, $5, Map of France.

### 2018, Nov. 1  Litho.  Perf. 14
| 1051-1052 | A191 | Set of 2 | 1.50 | 1.50 |
|---|---|---|---|---|
### Souvenir Sheet
| 1053 | A191 | Sheet of 2, #a-b | 8.75 | 8.75 |

Battle of Tarawa, 75th anniv. (Nos. 1051, 1053a); End of World War I (Nos. 1052, 1053b).

Birds — A192

Designs: 40c, Long-tailed jaeger. 50c, Leach's storm petrel. 75c, Juan Fernández petrel. $2.50, Sooty shearwater.

### 2019, July 1  Litho.  Perf. 14½
| 1054-1057 | A192 | Set of 4 | 6.00 | 6.00 |
|---|---|---|---|---|
| 1057a | | Souvenir sheet of 4, #1054-1057 | 6.00 | 6.00 |

Independence, 40th anniv.

Mohandas K. Gandhi (1869-1948), Indian Nationalist Leader A193

Gandhi, flowers and quotation: 40c, "The future depends on what you do today. . ." 50c, "Where there is love there is light. . ." 75c, "Continue to grow and evolve. . ." $2.50, "My life is my message. . ."
No. 1062: a, $1.50, Spinning wheel, lotus flowers, "Life is but an endless series of experiments. . ." b, $5, Gandhi, flowers, "Speak only if it improves upon the silence. . ."

### 2019, Sept. 27  Litho.  Perf. 14½
| 1058-1061 | A193 | Set of 4 | 5.75 | 5.75 |
|---|---|---|---|---|
### Souvenir Sheet
| 1062 | A193 | Sheet of 2, #a-b | 8.75 | 8.75 |

## POSTAGE DUE STAMPS

Natl. Arms — D1

### 1981, Aug. 27  Litho.  Perf. 14
| | | | | |
|---|---|---|---|---|
| J1 | D1 | 1c brt pink & black | .30 | .25 |
| J2 | D1 | 2c greenish blue & blk | .30 | .25 |
| J3 | D1 | 5c brt yel grn & black | .30 | .25 |
| J4 | D1 | 10c lt red brown & blk | .30 | .25 |
| J5 | D1 | 20c ultra & black | .30 | .25 |
| J6 | D1 | 30c yel bister & black | .30 | .35 |
| J7 | D1 | 40c brt pur & black | .30 | .45 |
| J8 | D1 | 50c green & black | .30 | .50 |
| J9 | D1 | $1 red orange & blk | .30 | .90 |
| | *Nos. J1-J9 (9)* | | 2.70 | 3.45 |

Imperfs exist from the liquidation of Format International. They are not errors.

## OFFICIAL STAMPS
### Nos. 327a-340c Overprinted "O.K.G.S."
### 1981, May  Litho.  Unwmk.  Perf. 14
| | | | | |
|---|---|---|---|---|
| O1 | A52 | 1c multicolored | .30 | .25 |
| O2 | A52 | 3c multicolored | .30 | .25 |
| O3 | A52 | 5c multicolored | .30 | .25 |
| O4 | A52 | 7c multicolored | .30 | .25 |
| O5 | A52 | 10c multicolored | .30 | .25 |
| O6 | A52 | 12c multicolored | .30 | .25 |
| O7 | A52 | 15c multicolored | .30 | .25 |
| O8 | A52 | 20c multicolored | .30 | .25 |
| O9 | A52 | 25c multicolored | .30 | .25 |
| O10 | A52 | 30c multicolored | .30 | .25 |
| O11 | A52 | 35c multicolored | .30 | .30 |
| O12 | A52 | 50c multicolored | .40 | .40 |
| O13 | A52 | $1 multicolored | .70 | .70 |
| O14 | A52 | $2 multicolored | 1.20 | 1.20 |
| O15 | A52 | $5 multicolored | 3.00 | 3.00 |
| | *Nos. O1-O15 (15)* | | 8.60 | 8.10 |

Nos. O1-O15 have thick overprint.

**1981**                          **Wmk. 373**

| | | | | |
|---|---|---|---|---|
| O1 | A52 | 1c multi | 4.00 | 4.25 |
| O5a | A52 | 10c multi | 20.00 | 21.00 |
| O6a | A52 | 12c multi | 6.00 | 6.00 |
| O7a | A52 | 15c multi | 20.00 | 20.00 |
| O8a | A52 | 20c multi | 13.00 | 13.00 |
| O10a | A52 | 30c multi | 8.00 | 9.00 |
| O12a | A52 | 50c multi | 7.50 | 7.50 |
| O13a | A52 | $1 multi | 14.00 | 14.00 |
| O14a | A52 | $2 multi | 16.00 | 17.00 |
| O15a | A52 | $5 multi | 4.50 | 4.50 |
| | *Nos. O1a-O15a (10)* | | 113.00 | 116.25 |

**Nos. 390, 393-394, 396, 398
Overprinted "O.K.G.S."**

**1983, June 28    Litho.    Perf. 14**

| | | | | |
|---|---|---|---|---|
| O16 | A62 | 12c multicolored | .45 | .45 |
| O17 | A62 | 30c multicolored | .80 | .80 |
| O18 | A62 | 35c multicolored | .90 | .90 |
| O19 | A62 | 50c multicolored | 1.25 | 1.25 |
| O20 | A62 | $2 multicolored | 3.75 | 3.75 |
| | *Nos. O16-O20 (5)* | | 7.15 | 7.15 |

This overprint has shorter, thinner letters than the one used for Nos. O1-O15. It also exists on Nos. 327, 331-334, 336-340. These have been questioned.

# KOREA

kə-'rē-ə

## (Corea)

## (Chosen, Tyosen, Tae Han)

LOCATION — Peninsula extending from Manchuria between the Yellow Sea and the Sea of Japan (East Sea)
GOVT. — Republic
AREA — 38,221 sq. mi.
POP. — 48,860,500 (2011 est.)
CAPITAL — Seoul

Korea (or Corea) an independent monarchy for centuries under Chinese influence, came under Japanese influence in 1876. Chinese and Japanese stamps were used there as early as 1877. Administrative control was assumed by Japan in 1905 and annexation followed in 1910. Postage stamps of Japan were used in Korea from 1905 to early 1946.

At the end of World War II, American forces occupied South Korea and Russian forces occupied North Korea, with the 38th parallel of latitude as the dividing line. A republic was established in 1948 following an election in South Korea. North Korea issues its own stamps.

100 Mon = 1 Poon
5 Poon = 1 Cheun
1000 Re = 100 Cheun = Weun
100 Weun = 1 Hwan (1953)
100 Chun = 1 Won (1962)

Catalogue values for unused stamps in this country are for Never Hinged items, beginning with Scott 283 in the regular postage section, Scott B5 in the semipostal section, and Scott C23 in the airpost section.

### Watermarks

Wmk. 257 — Curved Wavy Lines

Wmk. 312 — Zigzag Lines

Wmk. 317 — Communications Department Emblem

Stylized Yin Yang
A1          A2
*Perf. 8½ to 11½*

**1884           Typo.         Unwmk.**

| | | | | |
|---|---|---|---|---|
| 1 | A1 | 5m rose | 52.50 | 10,000. |
| 2 | A2 | 10m blue | 52.50 | 10,000. |

Reprints and counterfeits of Nos. 1-2 exist.

These stamps were never placed in use. Values: 25 $5; 50 mon $6.50; 100 mon $9.
Counterfeits exist.

Yin Yang — A6

**Perf. 10¾, 11½, 11¾ 12, 13, 13¼ and Compound**

**1895                          Litho.**

| | | | | |
|---|---|---|---|---|
| 6 | A6 | 5p green (II) | 30.00 | 16.00 |
| b. | Vert. pair, imperf. horiz. | | 425.00 | — |
| c. | Horiz. pair, imperf. vert. | | 425.00 | — |
| d. | Vertical pair, imperf. between | | 425.00 | — |
| e. | Horiz. pair, imperf. btwn. | | 425.00 | — |
| 7 | A6 | 10p blue (II) | 110.00 | 37.50 |
| a. | Horiz. pair, imperf. between | | 425.00 | — |
| b. | Vert. pair, imperf. horiz. | | 425.00 | — |
| 8 | A6 | 25p maroon (II) | 70.00 | 30.00 |
| a. | Horiz. pair, imperf. between | | 375.00 | 375.00 |
| b. | Vert. pair, imperf. horiz. | | 375.00 | 375.00 |
| 9 | A6 | 50p purple (II) | 22.50 | 16.00 |
| a. | Horiz. pair, imperf. horiz. | | 400.00 | 400.00 |
| b. | Vert. pair, imperf. horiz. | | 400.00 | 400.00 |
| c. | Horiz. pair, imperf. vert. | | 400.00 | 400.00 |
| | *Nos. 6-9 (4)* | | 232.50 | 99.50 |

No. 6a exists with sewing machine perforations vertically.
For overprints and surcharges see Nos. 10-17C, 35-38.
Counterfeits exist of Nos. 6-9 and all surcharges and overprints.

Overprinted "Tae Han" in Korean and Chinese Characters

**1897                    Red Overprint**

| | | | | |
|---|---|---|---|---|
| 10 | A6 | 5p green | 87.50 | 35.00 |
| a. | 5p pale yellow green | | 200.00 | 150.00 |
| b. | Inverted overprint | | 160.00 | 160.00 |
| c. | Without ovpt. at bottom | | 150.00 | 130.00 |
| d. | Without overprint at top | | 150.00 | 130.00 |
| f. | Double overprint at top | | 140.00 | 140.00 |
| g. | Overprint at bottom in blk | | 160.00 | 160.00 |
| h. | Pair, one without overprint | | 450.00 | 450.00 |
| i. | Double overprint at top, inverted at bottom | | 550.00 | |
| 11 | A6 | 10p deep blue | 115.00 | 65.00 |
| a. | Without ovpt. at bottom | | 150.00 | 150.00 |
| b. | Without overprint at top | | 150.00 | 150.00 |
| c. | Double overprint at top | | 150.00 | 150.00 |
| d. | Bottom overprint inverted | | 140.00 | 140.00 |

| | | | | |
|---|---|---|---|---|
| e. | Top ovpt. dbl., one in blk | | 210.00 | 210.00 |
| f. | Top overprint omitted, bottom overprint inverted | | 450.00 | |
| 12 | A6 | 25p maroon | 130.00 | 65.00 |
| a. | Overprint at bottom invtd. | | 150.00 | 150.00 |
| b. | Overprint at bottom in blk | | 210.00 | 210.00 |
| c. | Bottom overprint omitted | | 150.00 | 150.00 |
| e. | Top ovpt. dbl., one in blk | | 225.00 | 225.00 |
| f. | Top and bottom overprints double, one of each in blk | | 250.00 | 250.00 |
| g. | Pair, one without overprint | | 425.00 | 425.00 |
| 13 | A6 | 50p purple | 82.50 | 50.00 |
| a. | Without ovpt. at bottom | | 120.00 | 110.00 |
| b. | Without overprint at top | | 120.00 | 110.00 |
| c. | Double overprint double | | 120.00 | 110.00 |
| e. | Pair, one without overprint | | 275.00 | 275.00 |
| | *Nos. 10-13 (4)* | | 415.00 | 215.00 |

**1897                 Black Overprint**

| | | | | |
|---|---|---|---|---|
| 13F | A6 | 5p green | 500.00 | 160.00 |
| 13G | A6 | 10p deep blue | 650.00 | 200.00 |
| h. | Without ovpt. at bottom | | 450.00 | |
| 14 | A6 | 25p maroon | 825.00 | 200.00 |
| a. | Without ovpt. at bottom | | 450.00 | |
| b. | Without overprint at top | | 450.00 | |
| c. | Double overprint at bottom | | 450.00 | |
| 15 | A6 | 50p purple | 650.00 | 160.00 |
| a. | Without ovpt. at bottom | | 450.00 | |
| | *Nos. 13F-15 (4)* | | 2,625. | |

These stamps with black overprint, also No. 16A, are said not to have been officially authorized.

Nos. 6, 6a and 8 Surcharged in Red or Black

**1900**

| | | | | |
|---|---|---|---|---|
| 15B | A6 | 1p on 5p grn (R) | 7,000. | 3,000. |
| c. | Yellow green | | | |
| 16 | A6 | 1p on 25p mar | 260.00 | 65.00 |

**Same Surcharge in Red or Black on Nos. 10, 10a, 12, 12c and 14**

| | | | | |
|---|---|---|---|---|
| 16A | A6 | 1p on 5p grn (R) | 975.00 | 550.00 |
| b. | 1p on 5p pale yellow green | | 1,050. | |
| 17 | A6 | 1p on 25p (#12) | 65.00 | 40.00 |
| a. | Figure "1" omitted | | 100.00 | |
| b. | On #12c | | 90.00 | 70.00 |
| 17C | A6 | 1p on 25p (#14) | 750.00 | 650.00 |

Counterfeit overprints and surcharges of Nos. 10-17C exist. See note after No. 15.

 A8     A9

 A10     A11

 A12     A13

 A14     A15

 A16     A17

 A18     A19

 A20     A21

**1900-01         Typo.         Perf. 11**

| | | | | |
|---|---|---|---|---|
| 18 | A8 | 2re gray | 9.75 | 8.00 |
| 19 | A9 | 1ch yellow grn | 19.50 | 10.00 |
| 20B | A11 | 2ch pale blue | 35.00 | 11.00 |
| 21 | A12 | 3ch org red | 19.50 | 16.00 |
| a. | Vert. pair, imperf. horiz. | | 200.00 | 200.00 |
| b. | Horiz. pair, imperf. btwn. | | | 500.00 |
| c. | 3c brnsh org | | 21.00 | 17.50 |
| d. | As "c," vert. pair, imperf. horiz. | | | 500.00 |
| 22 | A13 | 4ch carmine | 34.00 | 16.00 |
| 23 | A14 | 5ch pink | 27.50 | 20.00 |
| 24 | A15 | 6ch dp blue | 34.00 | 20.00 |
| 25 | A16 | 10ch pur ('01) | 40.00 | 24.00 |
| 26 | A17 | 15ch gray vio | 62.50 | 40.00 |
| 27 | A18 | 20ch red brown | 110.00 | 52.50 |
| 31 | A19 | 50ch ol grn & pink | 500.00 | 190.00 |
| a. | Pink omitted | | — | |
| 32 | A20 | 1wn rose, blk & bl | 1,050. | 325.00 |
| 33 | A21 | 2wn pur & yel grn | 1,300. | 600.00 |
| | *Nos. 18-33 (13)* | | 3,242. | 1,333. |

Nos. 22, 23, 25, 26, 33 exist imperf.
Some examples of Nos. 18-27 exist with forged Tae Han overprints in red. It is believed that Nos. 18 and 21 exist with genuine Tae Han overprints.
*Reprints of No. 24 were made in light blue, perf. 12x13, in 1905 for a souvenir booklet. Value $135. See note after No. 54.*
See Nos. 52-54.

**Perf. 10**

| | | | | |
|---|---|---|---|---|
| 18a | A8 | 2re | 17.00 | 5.25 |
| 19a | A9 | 1ch | 17.00 | 5.50 |
| 20 | A10 | 2ch blue | 75.00 | 45.00 |
| a. | Horiz. pair, imperf. btwn. | | 725.00 | — |
| 20Ba | A11 | 2ch pale blue | | — |
| 21e | A12 | 3ch | 15.50 | 9.00 |
| 22a | A13 | 4ch | 45.00 | 20.00 |
| 23a | A14 | 5ch | 40.00 | 10.00 |
| 24a | A15 | 6ch | 47.50 | 12.00 |
| 26a | A17 | 15ch | 175.00 | 150.00 |
| 27a | A18 | 20ch | 240.00 | 240.00 |
| | *Nos. 18a-27a (10)* | | 672.00 | 496.75 |

Emperor's Crown — A22

**1902, Oct. 18              Perf. 11½**

| | | | | |
|---|---|---|---|---|
| 34 | A22 | 3ch orange | 65.00 | 35.00 |

40th year of the reign of Emperor Kojong. An imperf. single was part of the 1905 souvenir booklet. Value $325. See note following No. 54.
Counterfeits exist.

**Nos. 8 and 9 Handstamp Surcharged in Black**

 1ch     2ch

 3ch    No. 37b

**Perf. 11½, 12, 12½, 13 and Compound**

**1902**

| | | | | |
|---|---|---|---|---|
| 35 | A6 | 1ch on 25p rose car | 26.00 | 20.00 |
| b. | Horiz. pair, imperf. btwn. | | 275.00 | |
| c. | Imperf. | | 90.00 | |
| d. | Vert. pair, imperf. horiz. | | 275.00 | |
| e. | On No. 12 | | — | |
| 36 | A6 | 2ch on 25p maroon | 32.50 | 30.00 |
| b. | Imperf. | | 75.00 | |
| d. | On No. 12 | | 90.00 | 90.00 |
| 36E | A6 | 2ch on 50p purple | 175.00 | 175.00 |
| f. | Character "cheun" unabbreviated (in two rows instead of one) | | 250.00 | 175.00 |
| 37 | A6 | 3ch on 50p plum | 27.50 | 20.00 |
| b. | With character "cheun" unabbreviated (in two rows instead of one) | | 2,400. | 950.00 |

|  |  |  |  |
|---|---|---|---|
| **d.** | Horiz. pair, imperf. btwn. |  | 200.00 |
| **e.** | Vert. pair, imperf. btwn. |  | 200.00 |
| **g.** | On No. 13 |  | 240.00 |
| **38** | A6 3ch on 25p maroon | 65.00 | 62.50 |
|  | *Nos. 35-38 (5)* | 326.00 | 307.50 |

There are several sizes of these surcharges. Being handstamped, inverted and double surcharges exist.

Counterfeit surcharges exist.

Falcon — A23

**1903**　　　　　　　*Perf. 13½x14*

| **39** | A23 | 2re | slate | 10.00 | 10.00 |
|---|---|---|---|---|---|
| **40** | A23 | 1ch | violet brn | 13.50 | 10.00 |
| **41** | A23 | 2ch | green | 14.00 | 10.00 |
| **42** | A23 | 3ch | orange | 12.50 | 10.00 |
| **43** | A23 | 4ch | rose | 20.00 | 10.00 |
| **44** | A23 | 5ch | yellow brn | 20.00 | 10.00 |
| **45** | A23 | 6ch | lilac | 24.00 | 11.00 |
| **46** | A23 | 10ch | blue | 29.00 | 13.50 |
| **47** | A23 | 15ch | red, *straw* | 40.00 | 20.00 |
| **48** | A23 | 20ch | vio brn, *straw* | 57.50 | 25.00 |
| **49** | A23 | 50ch | red, *grn* | 170.00 | 100.00 |
| **50** | A23 | 1wn | vio, *lav* | 425.00 | 210.00 |
| **51** | A23 | 2wn | vio, *org* | 425.00 | 210.00 |
|  |  | *Nos. 39-51 (13)* |  | 1,261. | 649.50 |

Values are for stamps with perfs touching the design.

**Types of 1901**

**1903**　　　　　　　*Perf. 12½*
**Thin, Semi-Transparent Paper**

| **52** | A19 | 50ch | pale ol grn & pale pink | 400.00 | 160.00 |
|---|---|---|---|---|---|
| **53** | A20 | 1wn | rose, blk & bl | 600.00 | 200.00 |
| **54** | A21 | 2wn | lt vio & lt grn | 875.00 | 250.00 |
|  |  | *Nos. 52-54 (3)* |  | 1,875. | 610.00 |

No. 24, perf. 12x13, No. 34 imperf. and most examples of Nos. 52-54 unused are from souvenir booklets made up in 1905 when the Japanese withdrew all Korean stamps from circulation.

**WARNING**

In 1957 the Ministry of Communications issued 4000 presentation booklets containing Nos. 1-54 reproduced on watermark 312 paper.

Other presentation booklets included full-color reproductions of Nos. 1-54 and Japan No. 110 printed on the pages. Beware of wide-margined imperfs cut from these booklets.

**Issued under US Military Rule**

Stamps of Japan Nos. 331, 268, 342, 332, 339 and 337 Surcharged in Black

**1946, Feb. 1**　**Wmk. 257**　*Perf. 13*

| **55** | A86 | 5ch on 5s brn lake | 8.00 | 17.50 |
|---|---|---|---|---|
| **56** | A93 | 5ch on 14s pur brn & pale rose | 1.20 | 3.00 |
| **a.** |  | 5ch on 40s dark violet (error) | 125.00 |  |
| **57** | A154 | 10ch on 40s dk vio | 1.20 | 3.00 |
| **58** | A147 | 20ch on 6s lt ultra | 1.20 | 3.00 |
| **a.** |  | 20ch on 27s rose brown (error) | 125.00 |  |
| **b.** |  | Double surcharge | 30.00 |  |
| **59** | A151 | 30ch on 27s rose brn | 1.20 | 3.00 |
| **a.** |  | 30ch on 6s light ultra (error) | 125.00 |  |
| **b.** |  | Double surcharge | 25.00 |  |
| **60** | A151 | 5wn on 17s gray vio | 7.25 | 17.50 |
|  |  | *Nos. 55-60 (6)* | 20.05 | 47.00 |
|  |  | Set, never hinged | 33.00 |  |

Five essays for this provisional issue exist both with and without additional overprint of two Chinese characters ("specimen") in vermilion. The essays are: 20ch on Japan No. 269; 50ch on No. 272; 1wn on No. 336; 1wn on No. 273; 10wn on No. 265. Values, each: $1,200 never hinged; $750 hinged. Other denominations have been reported.

Korean Family and Flag — A24

Arms of Korea — A25

**Wmk. 257**
**1946, May 1**　Litho.　*Perf. 10½*

| **61** | A24 | 3ch | orange yellow | .75 | 1.60 |
|---|---|---|---|---|---|
| **62** | A24 | 5ch | green | .75 | 1.60 |
| **63** | A24 | 10ch | carmine | .75 | 1.60 |
| **64** | A24 | 20ch | dark blue | .75 | 1.60 |
| **65** | A25 | 50ch | brown violet | 3.00 | 2.50 |
| **66** | A25 | 1wn | lt brown | 5.00 | 3.25 |
|  |  | *Nos. 61-66 (6)* | 11.00 | 12.15 |
|  |  | Set, never hinged | 18.50 |  |

Liberation from Japan.

Imperfs., Part Perfs.

Imperforate and part-perforate examples of a great many Korean stamps from No. 61 onward exist.

The imperfs. include Nos. 61-90, 93-97, 116-117, 119-126, 132-173, 182-186, 195, 197-199, 202A, 203, 204-205, 217, etc.

The part-perfs. include Nos. 62-65, 69, 72-73, 109, 111-113, 132, etc.

Printers waste includes printed on both sides, etc.

As the field is so extensive, the editors believe that they belong more properly in a specialized catalogue.

Dove — A26

**1946, Aug. 15**　　Unwmk.
| **67** | A26 50ch deep violet | 7.50 | 5.25 |
|---|---|---|---|
|  | Never hinged | 12.50 |  |

First anniversary of liberation.

Perforations often are rough on stamps issued between Aug. 1946 and the end of 1954. This is not considered a defect.

Flags of US and Korea — A27

**1946, Sept. 9**　　*Perf. 11*
| **68** | A27 10wn carmine | 5.75 | 4.50 |
|---|---|---|---|
|  | Never hinged | 9.50 |  |

Resumption of postal communication with the US.

Astronomical Observatory, Kyongju — A28

Hibiscus with Rice A29

Map of Korea A30

Gold Crown of Silla Dynasty A31

Admiral Li Sun-sin A32

**1946**　　　　　*Rouletted 12*
| **69** | A28 | 50ch | dark blue | .95 | 1.90 |
|---|---|---|---|---|---|
| **70** | A29 | 1wn | buff | .90 | 2.00 |
| **71** | A30 | 2wn | indigo | 1.60 | 2.75 |
| **72** | A31 | 5wn | magenta | 10.00 | 20.00 |
| **73** | A32 | 10wn | emerald | 11.00 | 18.50 |
|  |  | *Nos. 69-73 (5)* | 24.45 | 45.15 |
|  |  | Set, never hinged | 37.50 |  |

**Perf. 11**
| **70a** | A29 | 1wn | 1.75 | 3.25 |
|---|---|---|---|---|
| **71a** | A30 | 2wn | 62.50 | 120.00 |
| **72a** | A31 | 5wn | 62.50 | 120.00 |
|  |  | *Nos. 70a-72a (3)* | 126.75 | 243.25 |
|  |  | Set, never hinged | 240.00 |  |

Korean Phonetic Alphabet — A33

**1946, Oct. 9**　　*Perf. 11*
| **74** | A33 50ch deep blue | 4.50 | 4.50 |
|---|---|---|---|
|  | Never hinged | 8.50 |  |

500th anniv. of the introduction of the Korean phonetic alphabet (Hangul).

Li Jun A34

Admiral Li Sun-sin A35

**Perf. 11½x11, 11½**
**1947, Aug. 1**　Litho.　Wmk. 257
| **75** | A34 5wn lt blue green | 6.75 | 8.75 |
|---|---|---|---|
| **76** | A35 10wn light blue | 7.25 | 8.75 |
|  | Set, never hinged | 25.00 |  |

**Presentation Sheets**
Starting in 1947 with No. 75, nearly 100 Korean stamps were printed in miniature or souvenir sheets and given to government officials and others. These sheets were released in quantities of 300 to 4,000. In 1957 the Ministry of Communications began to sell the souvenir sheets at post offices at face value to be used for postage. They are listed from No. 264a onward.

Letter-encircled Globe — A36

**1947, Aug. 1**　　*Perf. 11½x11*
| **77** | A36 10wn light blue | 10.50 | 9.25 |
|---|---|---|---|
|  | Never hinged | 18.00 |  |

Resumption of international mail service between Korea and all countries of the world.

**Granite Paper**
Starting with No. 77, most Korean stamps through No. 751, except those on Laid Paper, are on Granite Paper. Granite Paper is noted above listing if the issue was printed on both ordinary and Granite Paper, such as Nos. 360a-374A.

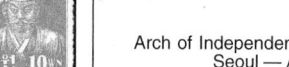
Arch of Independence, Seoul — A37

Tortoise Ship, First Ironclad War Vessel — A38

**1948, Apr.**
| **78** | A37 20wn rose | 5.00 | 4.00 |
|---|---|---|---|
| **79** | A38 50wn dull red brown | 80.00 | 40.00 |
|  | Set, never hinged | 150.00 |  |

**Republic**

Flag and Ballot A39

Woman and Man Casting Ballots A40

**Perf. 11x11½**
**1948, May 10**　Litho.　Wmk. 257
| **80** | A39 | 2wn | orange | 11.00 | 8.25 |
|---|---|---|---|---|---|
| **81** | A39 | 5wn | lilac rose | 18.50 | 11.50 |
| **82** | A39 | 10wn | lt violet | 29.00 | 20.00 |
| **83** | A40 | 20wn | carmine | 65.00 | 30.00 |
| **84** | A40 | 50wn | blue | 32.50 | 22.50 |
|  |  | *Nos. 80-84 (5)* | 156.00 | 92.25 |
|  |  | Set, never hinged | 220.00 |  |

South Korea election of May 10, 1948.

Korean Flag and Olive Branches — A41

Olympic Torchbearer and Map of Korea — A42

**1948, June 1**　*Perf. 11x11½, 11½x11*
| **85** | A41 5wn green | 120.00 | 60.00 |
|---|---|---|---|
| **86** | A42 10wn purple | 37.50 | 22.50 |
|  | Set, never hinged | 270.00 |  |

Korea's participation in the 1948 Olympic Games.

National Assembly A43

**1948, July 1**　Wmk. 257　*Perf. 11½*
| **87** | A43 4wn orange brown | 22.50 | 12.00 |
|---|---|---|---|
|  | Never hinged | 37.50 |  |

Opening of the Assembly July 1, 1948. Exists without period between "5" and "31."

Korean Family and Capitol — A44

Flag of Korea — A45

**1948, Aug. 1**                    **Litho.**
88  A44  4wn emerald          82.50  50.00
89  A45  10wn orange brown    32.50  24.00
    Set, never hinged               200.00
    Signing of the new constitution, 7/17/48.

Pres. Syngman Rhee — A46

**1948, Aug. 5**
90  A46  5wn deep blue        260.00 200.00
    Never hinged                     450.00
Inauguration of Korea's first president, Syngman Rhee.

Dove A47    Hibiscus A48

Two types of 5wn:
I — "1948" 3mm wide; top inscription 9mm wide; periods in "8.15." barely visible.
II — "1948" 4mm wide; top inscription 9½mm; periods in "8.15." bold and strong.

**1948**              **Perf. 11, 11x11½**
91  A47  4wn blue             29.00  30.00
92  A48  5wn rose lilac (II)  65.00  50.00
  a.    Type I               120.00 100.00
    Set, never hinged               160.00
Issued to commemorate the establishment of Korea's republican government.

Li Jun A49    Observatory, Kyongju A50

Types of No. 94
Type I: The top inscription is 15¼-15½mm wide. The stars are small.
Type II: The top inscription is 15¾-16mm wide. The stars are larger than Type I.

**1948, Oct. 1**          **Perf. 11½x11**
93  A49  4wn rose carmine     .75    1.20
94  A50  14wn deep blue, I    .75    1.20
  a.    light blue, I        140.00 100.00
        Never hinged         320.00
  b.    dp bl, large die, I  350.00 650.00
        Never hinged         600.00
  c.    Type II               —      —
        Never hinged          —
  d.    As a, Type II         —      —
        Never hinged          —
    Set, never hinged               3.50

For surcharges see Nos. 127, 174, 176.
Issued: No. 94, 5/1949; No. 94b, 5/1949; No. 94c, 1949; No. 94d, 10/1949.
Two die sizes were used in printing No. 94: a small die, 19¾x24mm, and a large die, 20x24mm. Small dies were used on Nos. 94 and 94c.

Doves over UN Emblem — A51

**1949, Feb. 12**  **Wmk. 257**  **Perf. 11**
95  A51  10wn blue           30.00  25.00
    Never hinged             52.50
Arrival of the UN Commission on Korea, Feb. 12, 1949.

Korean Citizen and Census Date — A52

**1949, Apr. 25**
96  A52  15wn purple         40.00  30.00
    Never hinged             72.50
Census of May 1, 1949.

Korean Boy and Girl — A53

**1949, May 5**
97  A53  15wn purple         22.50  20.00
    Never hinged             40.00
20th anniv. of Children's Day, May 5, 1949.

Postman A54

Worker and Factory A55

Rice Harvesting A56

Japanese Cranes A57

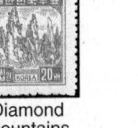
Diamond Mountains A58

Ginseng Plant A59

South Gate, Seoul A60

Tabo Pagoda, Kyongju A61

**1949**           **Litho.**    **Perf. 11**
98   A54  1wn rose            3.25   3.25
99   A55  2wn dk blue gray    3.00   3.00
100  A56  5wn yellow green    14.00  9.50
101  A57  10wn blue green     1.20   1.20
102  A58  20wn orange brown    .80   1.20
103  A59  30wn blue green      .80   1.20
104  A60  50wn violet blue     .80   1.20
105  A61  100wn dull yellow grn .80  1.20
    Nos. 98-105 (8)           24.65  21.75
    Set, never hinged         47.50

For surcharges see Nos. 129-131, 175, 177B-179, 181.

Phoenix and Yin Yang — A62

**1949, Aug. 25**
106  A62  15wn deep blue      27.50  22.50
    Never hinged              52.50
1st anniv. of Korea's independence.

Express Train "Sam Chun Li" — A63

**1949, Sept. 18**         **Perf. 11½x12**
107  A63  15wn violet blue   105.00  55.00
    Never hinged             190.00
50th anniversary of Korean railroads.

Korean Flag — A64

**Perf. 11½x11**
**1949, Oct. 15**              **Wmk. 257**
108  A64  15wn red org, yel & dk bl  14.00  15.00
    Never hinged             30.00
75th anniv. of the UPU.
No. 108 exists unwatermarked. These are counterfeit.

Hibiscus A65

Magpies and Map of Korea A66

Stylized Bird and Globe — A67

Diamond Mountains — A68

Admiral Li Sun-sin — A69

**1949**  **Wmk. 257  Litho.**  **Perf. 11**
109  A65  15wn vermilion      .60    1.10
110  A66  65wn deep blue     2.10    2.10
111  A67  200wn green         .60    1.10
112  A68  400wn brown         .60    1.10
113  A69  500wn deep blue     .60    1.10
    Nos. 109-113 (5)         4.50    6.50
    Set, never hinged        7.50

For surcharges see Nos. 128, 177, 180.

**Canceled to Order**
More than 100 Korean stamps and souvenir sheets were canceled to order, the cancellation incorporating the date "67.9.20." These include 81 stamps between Nos. 111 and 327, 18 airmail stamps between Nos. C6 and C26, and 5 souvenir sheets between Nos. 313 and 332, etc.
Also exists with later dates and on other stamps.
These c-t-o stamps and souvenir sheets are sold for much less than the values shown below, which are for postally used examples.

A70
Ancient postal medal (Ma-Pae).

**1950, Jan. 1**
114  A70  15wn yellow green   22.50  20.00
115  A70  65wn red brown      11.50   8.00
    Set, never hinged        65.00
50th anniv. of Korea's entrance into the UPU.

Revolutionists — A71

**1950, Mar. 10**              **Perf. 11½**
116  A71  15wn olive          23.00  20.00
117  A71  65wn light violet   11.50   8.00
    Set, never hinged        65.00
41st anniversary of Korea's declaration of Independence.

Korean Emblem and National Assembly — A72

**1950, May 30**
118  A72  30wn bl, red, brn & grn  15.00  10.00
    Never hinged             26.00
2nd natl. election of the Korean Republic.

Syngman Rhee A73

Korean Flag and White Mountains A74

Flags of UN and Korea, Map of Korea — A75

**1950, Nov. 20  Wmk. 257  Perf. 11**
119  A73  100wn blue          4.50   4.00
120  A74  100wn green         4.50   3.25
121  A75  200wn dark green    3.25   2.50
    Nos. 119-121 (3)         12.25  9.75
    Set, never hinged        22.00

Crane — A76

Tiger Mural — A77

Dove and Flag A78

Postal Medal A79

Mural from Ancient Tomb — A80

**1951**         **Unwmk.**      **Perf. 11**
                **Ordinary Paper**
122  A76  5wn org brn         1.60   2.00
123  A77  20wn purple         2.10   2.75
124  A78  50wn green          14.50  13.50
125  A79  100wn deep blue     27.00  13.50
126  A80  1000wn green        31.00  12.00
    Nos. 122-126 (5)         76.20  43.75
    Set, never hinged        125.00

## Rouletted 12

| | | | | |
|---|---|---|---|---|
| 122a | A76 | 5wn orange brown | 1.00 | 1.50 |
| 123a | A77 | 20wn purple | 1.00 | 1.50 |
| 124a | A78 | 50wn green | 2.75 | 4.00 |
| 125a | A79 | 100wn blue | 4.25 | 5.00 |
| | | Nos. 122a-125a (4) | 9.00 | 12.00 |
| | | Set, never hinged | 16.50 | |

No. 126 also exists perforated 12½. See Nos. 187-189.

No. 93 Surcharged in Blue

### 1951    Wmk. 257    Perf. 11½x11

| | | | | |
|---|---|---|---|---|
| 127 | A49 | 100wn on 4wn rose car | 3.25 | 5.00 |
| a. | | Inverted surcharge | 32.50 | 65.00 |
| | | Never hinged | 65.00 | |

Nos. 109, 101, 102 and 104 Surcharged in Blue or Brown

### Perf. 11

| | | | | |
|---|---|---|---|---|
| 128 | A65 | 200wn on 15wn | 3.75 | 7.00 |
| a. | | Inverted surcharge | 32.50 | 65.00 |
| | | Never hinged | 65.00 | |
| 129 | A57 | 300wn on 10wn (Br) | 5.25 | 6.00 |
| a. | | Inverted surcharge | 32.50 | |
| | | Never hinged | 65.00 | |
| 130 | A58 | 300wn on 20wn | 4.00 | 4.50 |
| a. | | Inverted surcharge | 35.00 | |
| | | Never hinged | 75.00 | |
| 131 | A60 | 300wn on 50wn (Br) | 45.00 | 4.00 |
| | | Nos. 127-131 (5) | 61.25 | 26.50 |
| | | Set, never hinged | 92.50 | |

Size and details of surcharge varies. Numeral upright on Nos. 129 and 131; numeral slanted on Nos. 175 and 179. See Nos. 174-181.

On No. 130, the zeros in "300" are octagonal; on No. 177B they are oval.

Flags of US and Korea and Statue of Liberty A81

Design (blue stamps): Flag of same country as preceding green stamp, UN emblem and doves.

### 1951-52    Wmk. 257    Perf. 11
### Flags in Natural Colors, Participating Country at Left

| | | | | |
|---|---|---|---|---|
| 132 | A81 | 500wn green | 4.50 | 8.50 |
| 133 | A81 | 500wn blue | 4.50 | 8.50 |
| 134 | A81 | 500wn grn (Australia) | 5.00 | 10.00 |
| 135 | A81 | 500wn blue | 5.00 | 10.00 |
| 136 | A81 | 500wn grn (Belgium) | 5.00 | 10.00 |
| 137 | A81 | 500wn blue | 5.00 | 10.00 |
| 138 | A81 | 500wn grn (Britain) | 5.00 | 10.00 |
| 139 | A81 | 500wn blue | 5.00 | 10.00 |
| 140 | A81 | 500wn grn (Canada) | 5.00 | 10.00 |
| 141 | A81 | 500wn blue | 5.00 | 10.00 |
| 142 | A81 | 500wn grn (Colombia) | 5.00 | 10.00 |
| 143 | A81 | 500wn grn (Denmark) | 25.00 | 35.00 |
| 144 | A81 | 500wn blue | 25.00 | 35.00 |
| 145 | A81 | 500wn grn (Ethiopia) | 5.00 | 10.00 |
| 146 | A81 | 500wn blue | 5.00 | 10.00 |
| 147 | A81 | 500wn grn (France) | 5.00 | 10.00 |
| 148 | A81 | 500wn blue | 5.00 | 10.00 |
| 149 | A81 | 500wn grn (Greece) | 5.00 | 10.00 |
| 150 | A81 | 500wn blue | 5.00 | 10.00 |
| 151 | A81 | 500wn grn (India) | 20.00 | 35.00 |
| 152 | A81 | 500wn blue | 20.00 | 35.00 |
| 153 | A81 | 500wn grn (Italy) | 5.50 | 20.00 |
| a. | | Flag without crown ('52) | 30.00 | 45.00 |
| 154 | A81 | 500wn blue | 5.50 | 20.00 |
| a. | | Flag without crown ('52) | 30.00 | 45.00 |
| 155 | A81 | 500wn grn (Luxembourg) | 20.00 | 35.00 |
| 156 | A81 | 500wn blue | 20.00 | 35.00 |
| 157 | A81 | 500wn grn (Netherlands) | 5.00 | 10.00 |
| 158 | A81 | 500wn blue | 5.00 | 10.00 |
| 159 | A81 | 500wn grn (New Zealand) | 5.00 | 10.00 |
| 160 | A81 | 500wn blue | 5.00 | 10.00 |
| 161 | A81 | 500wn grn | | |

| | | | | |
|---|---|---|---|---|
| 162 | A81 | 500wn grn (Norway) | 20.00 | 35.00 |
| 163 | A81 | 500wn blue | 20.00 | 35.00 |
| 164 | A81 | 500wn grn (Philippines) | 5.00 | 10.00 |
| 165 | A81 | 500wn blue | 5.00 | 10.00 |
| 166 | A81 | 500wn grn (Sweden) | 5.00 | 10.00 |
| 167 | A81 | 500wn blue | 5.00 | 10.00 |
| 168 | A81 | 500wn grn (Thailand) | 5.00 | 10.00 |
| 169 | A81 | 500wn blue | 5.00 | 10.00 |
| 170 | A81 | 500wn grn (Turkey) | 5.00 | 10.00 |
| 171 | A81 | 500wn blue | 5.00 | 10.00 |
| 172 | A81 | 500wn grn (Union of So. Africa) | 5.00 | 10.00 |
| 173 | A81 | 500wn blue | 5.00 | 10.00 |
| | | Nos. 132-173 (42) | 340.00 | 637.00 |
| | | Set, never hinged | 850.00 | |

Twenty-two imperf. souvenir sheets of two, containing the green and the blue stamps for each participating country (including both types of Italy) were issued. Size: 140x90mm. Value, set hinged $875; never hinged $1,400.

### Nos. 93-94, 101-105, 109-110 Surcharged Like Nos. 128-131 in Blue or Brown

### 1951    Wmk. 257    Perf. 11½x11, 11

| | | | | |
|---|---|---|---|---|
| 174 | A49 | 300wn on 4wn | 3.00 | 4.50 |
| a. | | Inverted surcharge | 32.50 | 65.00 |
| | | Never hinged | 65.00 | |
| 175 | A57 | 300wn on 10wn (Br) | 7.25 | 5.50 |
| a. | | Inverted surcharge | 32.50 | 65.00 |
| | | Never hinged | 65.00 | |
| 176 | A50 | 300wn on 14wn (Br) | 5.50 | 4.50 |
| a. | | 300wn on 14wn, #94a | 2,250. | 1,500. |
| b. | | Inverted surcharge | 32.50 | 65.00 |
| | | Never hinged | 65.00 | |
| c. | | 300wn on 14wn, #94b | — | |
| | | Never hinged | — | |
| d. | | Inverted surcharge, #94b | — | — |
| | | Never hinged | — | |
| e. | | 300wn on 14wn, #94d | — | — |
| | | Never hinged | — | |
| 177 | A65 | 300wn on 15wn | 3.00 | 4.50 |
| a. | | Inverted surcharge | 32.50 | 65.00 |
| | | Never hinged | 65.00 | |
| 177B | A58 | 300wn on 20wn | 5.25 | 5.25 |
| 178 | A59 | 300wn on 30wn (Br) | 3.25 | 4.50 |
| a. | | Inverted surcharge | 32.50 | 65.00 |
| | | Never hinged | 65.00 | |
| 179 | A60 | 300wn on 50wn (Br) | 2.75 | 4.00 |
| 180 | A66 | 300wn on 65wn (Br) | 3.25 | 4.50 |
| a. | | Inverted monad | 47.50 | 95.00 |
| | | Never hinged | 95.00 | |
| 181 | A61 | 300wn on 100wn | 3.00 | 4.50 |
| a. | | Inverted surcharge | 45.00 | 90.00 |
| | | Never hinged | 90.00 | |
| | | Nos. 174-181 (9) | 36.25 | 41.75 |
| | | Set, never hinged | 67.50 | |

"300" slanted on Nos. 175, 177B and 179; "300" upright on Nos. 129 and 131. The surcharge exists double on several of these stamps.

No. 177B differs from No. 130 in detail noted after No. 131.

Syngman Rhee and "Happiness" A82

### 1952, Sept. 10    Litho.    Perf. 12½

| | | | | |
|---|---|---|---|---|
| 182 | A82 | 1000wn dark green | 7.50 | 7.50 |
| | | Never hinged | 14.00 | |

Second inauguration of President Syngman Rhee, Aug. 15, 1952.

Sok Kul Am, Near Kyongju A83

Bool Gook Temple, Kyongju A84

Tombstone of Mu Yal Wang A85

Choong Yul Sa Shrine, Tongyung A86

### 1952    Wmk. 257    Typo.    Perf. 12½

| | | | | |
|---|---|---|---|---|
| 183 | A83 | 200wn henna brown | 1.60 | 1.40 |
| 184 | A84 | 300wn green | 1.35 | 1.00 |
| 185 | A85 | 500wn carmine | 2.10 | 1.60 |
| 186 | A86 | 2000wn deep blue | 1.60 | 1.00 |

### Rough Perf. 10-11, 11½x11 and Compound    Litho.

| | | | | |
|---|---|---|---|---|
| 186A | A83 | 200wn henna brown | 1.75 | 1.35 |
| 186B | A84 | 300wn green | 1.60 | 1.00 |
| | | Nos. 183-186B (6) | 10.00 | 7.35 |
| | | Set, never hinged | 19.50 | |

### Types of 1951
### Designs slightly smaller

### 1952-53    Rough Perf. 10-11

| | | | | |
|---|---|---|---|---|
| 187 | A77 | 20wn purple | 10.50 | 5.00 |
| 187A | A78 | 50wn green | 25.00 | 23.00 |
| 187B | A79 | 100wn deep blue | 1.60 | 1.50 |
| 187C | A80 | 1000wn green | 135.00 | 27.00 |
| | | Nos. 187-187C (4) | 172.60 | 56.50 |
| | | Set, never hinged | 340.00 | |

### Designs slightly larger    Perf. 12½

| | | | | |
|---|---|---|---|---|
| 187D | A78 | 50wn green | 2.50 | 2.40 |
| 188 | A79 | 100wn deep blue | 1.75 | 1.90 |
| 189 | A80 | 1000wn green ('53) | 5.50 | 1.10 |
| | | Nos. 187D-189 (3) | 9.75 | 5.40 |
| | | Set, never hinged | 20.00 | |

### Type of 1952

### 1953

| | | | | |
|---|---|---|---|---|
| 189A | A85 | 500wn deep blue | 24.00 | 160.00 |

All examples of No. 189A were affixed to postal cards before sale. Values are for stamps removed from the cards.
See Nos. 191-192, 203B, 248.

### Types of 1952 and

Planting Trees — A87

### Wmk. 257

### 1953, Apr. 5    Litho.    Perf. 12½

| | | | | |
|---|---|---|---|---|
| 190 | A87 | 1h aqua | .80 | .65 |
| 191 | A85 | 2h aqua | .80 | .50 |
| 192 | A85 | 5h bright green | 1.00 | .50 |
| 193 | A87 | 10h bright green | 2.75 | 1.50 |
| 194 | A86 | 20h brown | 3.75 | 2.00 |
| | | Nos. 190-194 (5) | 9.10 | 5.15 |
| | | Set, never hinged | 17.00 | |

See Nos. 203A, 247.

Map and YMCA Emblem — A88

### 1953, Oct. 25    Perf. 13½

| | | | | |
|---|---|---|---|---|
| 195 | A88 | 10h dk slate bl & red | 4.75 | 3.25 |
| | | Never hinged | 9.00 | |

50th anniv. of the Korean YMCA.

Tombstone of Mu Yal Wang — A88a

A89

Sika Deer — A90

### 1954, Apr.    Perf. 12½

| | | | | |
|---|---|---|---|---|
| 196 | A88a | 5h dark green | 1.10 | 1.20 |
| 197 | A89 | 100h brn car | 7.50 | 2.60 |
| 198 | A90 | 500h brn org | 55.00 | 10.00 |
| 199 | A90 | 1000h bister brown | 100.00 | 20.00 |
| | | Nos. 196-199 (4) | 163.60 | 33.80 |
| | | Set, never hinged | 325.00 | |

See Nos. 203C, 203D, 238-239, 248A, 250-251, 259, 261-262, 269-270, 279, 281-282.

Dok Do (Dok Island) — A91

Design: 10h, Dok Do, lateral view.

### 1954, Sept. 15

| | | | | |
|---|---|---|---|---|
| 200 | A91 | 2h claret | 2.25 | 2.40 |
| 201 | A91 | 5h blue | 4.75 | 2.40 |
| 202 | A91 | 10h blue green | 8.50 | 2.40 |
| | | Nos. 200-202 (3) | 15.50 | 7.20 |
| | | Set, never hinged | 28.00 | |

Moth and Flag — A92

Pagoda Park, Seoul — A92a

### 1954, Apr. 16    Wmk. 257    Perf. 12½

| | | | | |
|---|---|---|---|---|
| 202A | A92 | 10h brown | 8.50 | 3.00 |
| 203 | A92a | 30h dark blue | 1.00 | 1.40 |
| | | Set, never hinged | 18.50 | |

See Nos. 203E, 260, 280.

### Types of 1952-54

### 1955-56    Unwmk.    Perf. 12½
### Laid Paper

| | | | | |
|---|---|---|---|---|
| 203A | A87 | 1h aqua ('56) | .30 | .50 |
| 203B | A85 | 2h aqua ('56) | .30 | .50 |
| 203C | A88a | 5h brt grn ('56) | .40 | .50 |
| 203D | A89 | 100h brn car | 42.50 | 7.00 |
| 203E | A92a | 200h violet | 10.00 | 2.40 |
| | | Nos. 203A-203E (5) | 53.50 | 10.90 |
| | | Set, never hinged | 125.00 | |

On No. 203C the right hand character is redrawn as in illustration above No. 212D.
Nos. 203A and 203C are found on horizontally and vertically laid paper.

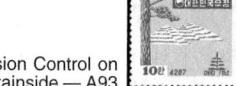

Erosion Control on Mountainside — A93

### 1954, Dec. 12    Wmk. 257

| | | | | |
|---|---|---|---|---|
| 204 | A93 | 10h dk grn & yel grn | 3.00 | 1.25 |
| 205 | A93 | 19h dk grn & yel grn | 3.50 | 1.75 |
| | | Set, never hinged | 11.00 | |

Issued to publicize the 1954 forestation campaign.

Presidents Rhee and Eisenhower Shaking Hands — A94

### 1954, Dec. 25    Perf. 13½

| | | | | |
|---|---|---|---|---|
| 206 | A94 | 10h violet blue | 1.90 | 1.60 |
| 207 | A94 | 19h brown | 2.10 | 2.00 |
| 208 | A94 | 71h dull green | 4.75 | 3.50 |
| | | Nos. 206-208 (3) | 8.75 | 7.10 |
| | | Set, never hinged | 15.50 | |

Adoption of the US-Korea mutual defense treaty.

"Reconstruction" — A95

### Wmk. 257

### 1955, Feb. 10    Litho.    Perf. 12½

| | | | | |
|---|---|---|---|---|
| 209 | A95 | 10h brown | 3.00 | 2.60 |
| 210 | A95 | 15h violet | 3.00 | 6.00 |
| 211 | A95 | 20h blue | 650.00 | 18.50 |
| | | Never hinged | 1,350. | |
| 212 | A95 | 50h plum | 7.00 | 3.00 |
| | | Nos. 209-210,212 (3) | 13.00 | |
| | | Nos. 209-212 (4) | | 26.70 |
| | | Set, #209-210, 212, never hinged | 25.00 | |

Korea's industrial reconstruction.

**1955, Oct. 19    Unwmk.    Perf. 12½**
**Laid Paper**

| | | | |
|---|---|---|---|
| 212A | A95 | 15h violet | 2.75 2.25 |
| 212B | A95 | 20h blue | 2.75 2.00 |
| 212C | A95 | 50h plum | 4.75 1.00 |
| | | *Nos. 212A-212C (3)* | 10.25 5.25 |
| | | Set, never hinged | 18.50 |

No. 212B is found on horizontally and vertically laid paper.

### Same with Right Character at Top Redrawn

Original

Redrawn

**1956, June 5    Unwmk.    Perf. 12½**
**Laid Paper**

| | | | |
|---|---|---|---|
| 212D | A95 | 10h brown | 2.75 *2.40* |
| 212E | A95 | 15h violet | 2.75 *2.40* |
| 212F | A95 | 20h blue | 2.75 1.10 |
| a. | | Booklet pane of 6 | 175.00 |
| | | *Nos. 212D-212F (3)* | 8.25 5.90 |
| | | Set, never hinged | 16.00 |

Nos. 212D-212F are found on horizontally and vertically laid paper. See Nos. 248B, 256, 272, 276.

Rotary Emblem — A96

**1955, Feb. 23    Wmk. 257    Perf. 13½**

| | | | |
|---|---|---|---|
| 213 | A96 | 20h violet | 5.00 3.50 |
| 214 | A96 | 25h dull green | 1.75 1.50 |
| 215 | A96 | 71h magenta | 1.75 1.50 |
| | | *Nos. 213-215 (3)* | 8.50 6.50 |
| | | Set, never hinged | 15.00 |

Rotary International, 50th anniversary.

Syngman Rhee, 80th Birthday, Apr. 26 — A98

**1955, Mar. 26**

| | | | |
|---|---|---|---|
| 217 | A98 | 20h deep blue | 13.50 6.75 |
| | | Never hinged | 26.00 |

Flag and Arch of Independence — A99

**1955, Aug. 15    Litho.    Perf. 13½**

| | | | |
|---|---|---|---|
| 218 | A99 | 40h Turq green | 6.00 1.60 |
| 219 | A99 | 100h brn red | 6.00 2.10 |
| | | Set, never hinged | 20.00 |

Tenth anniversary of independence.

UN Emblem in Circle of Clasped Hands — A100

**1955, Oct. 24**

| | | | |
|---|---|---|---|
| 221 | A100 | 20h bluish green | 2.50 2.00 |
| 222 | A100 | 55h aqua | 2.50 2.00 |
| | | Set, never hinged | 9.50 |

United Nations, 10th anniversary.

---

Olympic Torch and Runners — A101

**1955, Oct. 23**

| | | | |
|---|---|---|---|
| 223 | A101 | 20h claret | 3.50 2.00 |
| 224 | A101 | 55h dark green | 3.50 2.00 |
| | | Set, never hinged | 13.00 |

36th National Athletic Meet.

Adm. Li Sun-sin, Navy Flag and Tortoise Ship — A102

**Perf. 13x13½**
**1955, Nov. 11    Unwmk.**
**Laid Paper**

| | | | |
|---|---|---|---|
| 225 | A102 | 20h violet blue | 5.00 2.60 |
| | | Never hinged | 9.50 |

Korean Navy, 10th anniversary.

Rhee Monument near Seoul — A103

**1956, Mar. 26    Perf. 13½x13**

| | | | |
|---|---|---|---|
| 226 | A103 | 20h dull green | 3.25 2.60 |
| | | Never hinged | 7.00 |

81st birthday of Pres. Syngman Rhee.
No. 226 is found on horizontally and vertically laid paper.

Third Inauguration of Pres. Syngman Rhee — A104

**1956, Aug. 15    Perf. 13x13½**

| | | | |
|---|---|---|---|
| 227 | A104 | 20h brown | 72.50 30.00 |
| 228 | A104 | 55h dark blue | 27.00 12.00 |
| | | Set, never hinged | 170.00 |

Olympic Rings and Torch — A105

**1956, Nov. 1    Litho.    Perf. 12½**
**Laid Paper**

| | | | |
|---|---|---|---|
| 229 | A105 | 20h red orange | 2.75 *2.40* |
| 230 | A105 | 55h brt green | 2.75 *2.40* |
| | | Set, never hinged | 10.50 |

16th Olympic Games in Melbourne, 11/22-12/8.

Central Post Office, Seoul
A107

Stamp of 1884
A108

Mail Delivered by Donkey — A109

---

**1956, Dec. 4    Laid Paper    Unwmk.**

| | | | |
|---|---|---|---|
| 232 | A107 | 20h blue green | 6.50 2.50 |
| 233 | A108 | 50h rose carmine | 11.50 6.00 |
| 234 | A109 | 55h green | 5.00 2.00 |
| | | *Nos. 232-234 (3)* | 23.00 10.50 |
| | | Set, never hinged | 42.50 |

Issued to commemorate Postal Day.

### Types of 1954 Redrawn and

Hibiscus
A110

King Sejong
A111

Kyongju Observatory — A112

### No Hwan Symbol; Redrawn Character

**1956, Dec. 4    Unwmk.    Perf. 12½**
**Laid Paper**

| | | | |
|---|---|---|---|
| 235 | A110 | 10h lilac rose | 1.00 .75 |
| 236 | A111 | 20h lilac | 1.75 1.00 |
| 237 | A112 | 50h violet | 3.00 1.00 |
| 238 | A89 | 100h brn car | 12.50 4.00 |
| 239 | A90 | 500h brn org | 37.50 4.75 |
| | | *Nos. 235-239 (5)* | 55.75 11.50 |
| | | Set, never hinged | 100.00 |

On Nos. 238-239, the character after numeral has been omitted and the last character of the inscription has been redrawn as illustrated above No. 212D.
Nos. 235-236 are found on horizontally and vertically laid paper.
See Nos. 240-242, 253, 255, 258, 273, 275, 278, 291Bd, 291Bf, B3-B4.

### Types of 1956

**1957, Jan. 21    Wmk. 312    Perf. 12½**

| | | | |
|---|---|---|---|
| 240 | A110 | 10h lilac rose | 1.00 .65 |
| 241 | A111 | 20h red lilac | 2.25 1.05 |
| 242 | A112 | 50h violet | 3.50 .65 |
| | | *Nos. 240-242 (3)* | 6.75 2.35 |
| | | Set, never hinged | 14.00 |

Telecommunication Symbols — A117

**1957, Jan. 31    Perf. 13½**

| | | | |
|---|---|---|---|
| 243 | A117 | 40h lt ultra | 1.50 1.20 |
| 244 | A117 | 55h brt green | 1.50 1.20 |
| | | Set, never hinged | 5.00 |

5th anniv. of Korea's joining the ITU.

Boy Scout and Emblem — A118

**1957, Feb. 27    Wmk. 312**

| | | | |
|---|---|---|---|
| 245 | A118 | 40h pale purple | 1.40 *1.35* |
| 246 | A118 | 55h lt magenta | 1.40 *1.35* |
| | | Set, never hinged | 5.25 |

50th anniversary of Boy Scout movement.

### Types of 1953-56
### Top Right Character Redrawn; Hwan Symbol Retained

**1957    Wmk. 312    Perf. 12½**

| | | | |
|---|---|---|---|
| 247 | A87 | 1h aqua | .65 *.55* |
| 248 | A85 | 2h aqua | .65 *.55* |
| 248A | A88a | 5h brt green | .65 *.55* |
| 248B | A95 | 15h violet | 3.25 2.00 |
| | | *Nos. 247-248B (4)* | 5.20 3.65 |
| | | Set, never hinged | 11.50 |

---

### Redrawn Types of 1954, 1956 and

Planting Trees
A119

South Gate, Seoul
A120

Tiger
A121

Diamond Mountains
A122

### No Hwan Symbol; Redrawn Character

**1957    Wmk. 312    Litho.    Perf. 12½**

| | | | |
|---|---|---|---|
| 249 | A119 | 2h aqua | .30 .40 |
| 250 | A88a | 4h aqua | .45 .40 |
| 251 | A88a | 5h emerald | .45 .40 |
| 252 | A120 | 10h green | .50 .75 |
| 253 | A110 | 20h lilac rose | .65 .40 |
| 254 | A121 | 30h pale lilac | .65 .40 |
| 255 | A111 | 40h red lilac | .75 .35 |
| a. | | Booklet pane of 6 | 80.00 |
| 256 | A95 | 50h lake | 4.00 2.00 |
| 257 | A122 | 55h violet brn | 1.50 1.50 |
| 258 | A112 | 100h violet | 1.75 1.00 |
| 259 | A89 | 200h brown car | 2.00 1.00 |
| 260 | A92a | 400h brt violet | 32.50 4.75 |
| 261 | A90 | 500h ocher | 32.50 5.75 |
| 262 | A90 | 1000h dk ol bis | 80.00 10.50 |
| | | *Nos. 249-262 (14)* | 158.00 29.60 |
| | | Set, never hinged | 290.00 |

The "redrawn character" is illustrated above No. 212D.
See Nos. 268, 271, 274, 277, 291c, 291e.

Mercury and Flags of Korea and US — A123

**1957, Nov. 7    Wmk. 312    Perf. 13½**

| | | | |
|---|---|---|---|
| 263 | A123 | 40h dp orange | 1.00 *1.00* |
| 264 | A123 | 205h emerald | 1.90 *2.00* |
| a. | | Souv. sheet of 2, #263-264, imperf. | 850.00 |
| | | Never hinged | 1,500. |
| | | Set, never hinged | 6.25 |

Treaty of friendship, commerce and navigation between Korea and the US.

Star of Bethlehem and Pine Cone — A124

Designs: 25h, Christmas tree and tassel. 30h, Christmas tree, window and dog.

**1957, Dec. 11    Litho.    Perf. 12½**

| | | | |
|---|---|---|---|
| 265 | A124 | 15h org, brn & grn | 6.50 *2.00* |
| a. | | Souv. sheet of 1, imperf. | 650.00 |
| | | Never hinged | 1,100. |
| 266 | A124 | 25h lt grn, yel & red | 4.75 *2.00* |
| a. | | Souv. sheet of 1, imperf. | 650.00 |
| | | Never hinged | 1,100. |
| 267 | A124 | 30h bl, lt grn & yel | 14.50 3.00 |
| a. | | Souv. sheet of 1, imperf. | 650.00 |
| | | Never hinged | 1,100. |
| | | *Nos. 265-267 (3)* | 25.75 7.00 |
| | | Set, never hinged | 40.00 |

Issued for Christmas and the New Year.

### Redrawn Types of 1954-57
### Wmk. 317

**1957-59    Litho.    Perf. 12½**

| | | | |
|---|---|---|---|
| 268 | A119 | 2h aqua | .35 .45 |
| 269 | A88a | 4h aqua | .45 .45 |
| 270 | A88a | 5h emerald ('58) | .45 .45 |
| 271 | A120 | 10h green | .75 .45 |
| 272 | A95 | 15h violet ('58) | 2.50 2.25 |
| 273 | A110 | 20h lilac rose | .90 .35 |
| 274 | A121 | 30h pale lil ('58) | 1.00 .35 |
| 275 | A111 | 40h red lilac | 1.00 .35 |
| 276 | A95 | 50h lake ('58) | 5.00 .80 |
| 277 | A122 | 55h vio brn ('59) | 1.90 .85 |
| 278 | A112 | 100h violet | 1.75 .75 |

294 KOREA

| 279 | A89 | 200h brn car ('59) | 2.25 | .75 |
|---|---|---|---|---|
| 280 | A92a | 400h brt vio ('59) | 57.50 | 6.00 |
| 281 | A90 | 500h ocher ('58) | 37.50 | 6.00 |
| 282 | A90 | 1000h dk ol bis ('58) | 80.00 | 10.00 |
| | | Nos. 268-282 (15) | 193.30 | 30.25 |
| | | Set, never hinged | 425.00 | |

Nos. 268-282 have no hwan symbol, and final character of inscription is the redrawn one illustrated above No. 212D.
See No. 291B.

Catalogue values for unused stamps in this section, from this point to the end of the section, are for Never Hinged items.

Winged Envelope — A125

**1958, May 20**    **Wmk. 317**
283 A125 40h dk blue & red   2.10   .80
  *a.* Souv. sheet of 1, imperf.   *1,950.*

Issued for the Second Postal Week.

Children Looking at Industrial Growth — A126

Design: 40h, Hibiscus forming "10".

**1958, Aug. 15**    **Perf. 13½**
284 A126 20h gray   1.90   .55
285 A126 40h dk carmine   2.25   .80
  *a.* Souv. sheet of 2, # 284-285, imperf.   450.00

10th anniversary of Republic of Korea.

UNESCO Building, Paris — A127

**1958, Nov. 3**    **Wmk. 317**
286 A127 40h orange & green   1.45   .60
  *a.* Souv. sheet of 1, imperf.   170.00

Opening of UNESCO. headquarters in Paris, Nov. 3.

Children Flying Kites A128    Christmas Tree and Fortune Screen A129

Children in Costume — A130

**1958, Dec. 11**   **Litho.**   **Perf. 12½**
287 A128 15h yellow green   2.10   .70
  *a.* Souv. sheet of 1, imperf.   67.50
288 A129 25h blue, red & yel   2.10   .70
  *a.* Souv. sheet of 1, imperf.   67.50
289 A130 30h yell, ultra & red   3.00   1.05
  *a.* Souv. sheet of 1, imperf.   67.50
     Nos. 287-289 (3)   7.20   2.45
     Nos. 287a-289a (3)   202.50

Issued for Christmas and the New Year.

Flag and Pagoda Park — A131

**1959, Mar. 1**    **Perf. 13½**
290 A131 40h rose lilac & brn   1.60   .60
  *a.* Souv. sheet of 1, imperf.   115.00   115.00

40th anniv. of Independence Movement Day.

Korean Marines Landing — A132

**1959, Apr. 15**
291 A132 40h olive grn   1.60   .65
  *a.* Souv. sheet of 1, imperf.   13.00   13.00

Korean Marine Corps, 10th anniversary.

**Types of 1956-57**
**Souvenir Sheet**
**Wmk. 317**
**1959, May 20**   **Litho.**   *Imperf.*
291B   Sheet of 4   9.75   9.25
  *c.* A120 10h green   1.40   .60
  *d.* A110 20h lilac rose   1.40   .60
  *e.* A121 30h pale lilac   1.40   .60
  *f.* A111 40h red lilac   1.40   .60

3rd Postal Week, May 20-26.

WHO Emblem and Family — A133

**1959, Aug. 17**   **Wmk. 317**   **Perf. 13½**
292 A133 40h pink & rose vio   1.45   .65
  *a.* Souv. sheet of 1, imperf.   10.50   10.50

10th anniv. of Korea's joining the WHO.

Diesel Train — A134

**1959, Sept. 18**    **Litho.**
293 A134 40h brown & bister   2.25   .90
  *a.* Souv. sheet of 1, imperf.   23.00   23.00

60th anniversary of Korean railroads.

Relay Race and Emblem — A135

**1959, Oct. 3**
294 A135 40h lt bl & red brn   1.50   .70
  *a.* Souv. sheet of 1, imperf.   16.50   16.50

40th National Athletic Meet.

Red Cross and Korea Map — A136

55h, Red Cross superimposed on globe.

**1959, Oct. 27**    **Perf. 13½**
295 A136 40h red & bl grn   1.45   .60
296 A136 55h pale lilac & red   1.45   .60
  *a.* Souv. sheet of 2, #295-296, imperf.   37.50   37.50

Centenary of the Red Cross idea.

Old Postal Flag and New Communications Flag — A137

**1959, Dec. 4**
297 A137 40h blue & red   1.45   .60
  *a.* Souv. sheet of 1, imperf.   19.50   19.50

75th anniv. of the Korean postal system.

Mice and Chinese Happy New Year Character — A138

Designs: 25h, Children singing Christmas hymns. 30h, Red-crested crane.

**1959, Dec. 15**    **Perf. 12½**
298 A138 15h gray, vio bl & pink   1.45   .40
  *a.* Souv. sheet of 1, imperf.   27.00   27.00
299 A138 25h blue, red & emer   1.45   .40
  *a.* Souv. sheet of 1, imperf.   27.00   27.00
300 A138 30h lt lilac, blk & red   2.75   .55
  *a.* Souv. sheet of 1, imperf.   27.00   27.00
     Nos. 298-300 (3)   5.65   1.35
     Nos. 298a-300a (3)   81.00

Issued for Christmas and the New Year.

UPU Monument and Means of Transportation A139

**Wmk. 317**
**1960, Jan. 1**   **Litho.**   **Perf. 13½**
301 A139 40h grnsh bl & brn   1.60   .80
  *a.* Souv. sheet of 1, imperf.   32.50   32.50

60th anniv. of Korean membership in the UPU.

Bee, Honeycomb and Clover A140    Snail and Money Bag A141

**1960, Apr. 1**    **Wmk. 317**    **Perf. 12½**
302 A140 10h emer, brn & org   1.45   1.00
303 A141 20h pink, bl & brn   1.60   1.00

Issued to encourage systematic saving by children. See No. 313, souvenir sheet.
See Nos. 377-380.

Uprooted Oak Emblem and Yin Yang — A142

**1960, Apr. 7**    **Wmk. 312**    **Perf. 13½**
304 A142 40h emer, car & ultra   1.45   .60
  *a.* Souv. sheet of 1, imperf.   45.00   45.00

Issued to publicize World Refugee Year, July 1, 1959-June 30, 1960.

Dwight D. Eisenhower — A143

**1960, June 19**   **Litho.**   **Wmk. 317**
305 A143 40h bl, red & bluish grn   4.00   1.60
  *a.* Souv. sheet of 1, imperf.   30.00   30.00

Pres. Eisenhower's visit to Korea, June 19.

Children in School and Ancient Home Teaching — A144

Hibiscus and House of Councilors A145

**1960, Aug. 3**   **Wmk. 317**   **Perf. 13½**
306 A144 40h multicolored   1.45   .50
  *a.* Souv. sheet of 1, imperf.   8.25   8.25

75th anniv. of the modern educational system.

**1960, Aug. 8**
307 A145 40h blue   1.45   .50
  *a.* Souv. sheet of 1, imperf.   8.25   8.25

Inaugural session, House of Councilors.

Woman Holding Torch and Man with Flag — A146

**1960, Aug. 15**
308 A146 40h bis, lt bl & brn   1.75   .60
  *a.* Souv. sheet of 1, imperf.   8.25   8.25

15th anniversary of liberation.

Weight Lifter — A147

40h, South Gate, Seoul, & Olympic emblem.

**1960, Aug. 25**    **Litho.**
309 A147 20h brn, lt bl & sal   1.50   .70
310 A147 40h brn, lt bl & dk bl   1.50   .70
  *a.* Souv. sheet of 2, #309-310, imperf.   26.00   26.00

17th Olympic Games, Rome, 8/25-9/11.

Swallow and Telegraph Pole — A148

**1960, Sept. 28**    **Perf. 13½**
311 A148 40h lt bl, lil & gray   1.60   .70
  *a.* Souv. sheet of 1, imperf.   7.50   7.50

Establishment of telegraph service, 75th anniv.

Students and Sprout — A149

**1960, Oct. 1**    **Wmk. 317**
312 A149 40h bl, sal pink & emer   1.60   .60
  *a.* Souv. sheet of 1, imperf.   7.00   7.00

Rebirth of the Republic.

**Savings Types of 1960**
**Souvenir Sheet**
**1960, Oct. 7**    *Imperf.*
313   Sheet of two   5.00   5.00
  *a.* A140 10h emer, brn & org   2.10   1.90
  *b.* A141 20h pink, blue & brown   2.10   1.90

4th Postal Week, Oct. 7-13, and Intl. Letter Writing Week, Oct. 3-9.

Torch — A150

**1960, Oct. 15**     *Perf. 13½*
314 A150 40h dk bl, lt bl & yel   1.45   .50
   a.   Souv. sheet of 1, imperf.   6.75   6.75

Cultural Month (October).

UN Flag, Globe and Laurel — A151

**1960, Oct. 24**     *Litho.*
315 A151 40h rose lil, bl & grn   1.45   .50
   a.   Souv. sheet of 1, imperf.   6.50   6.50

15th anniversary of United Nations.

UN Emblem and Grave Markers — A152

**1960, Nov. 1**     *Wmk. 317*
316 A152 40h salmon & brn   1.45   .50
   a.   Souv. sheet of 1, imperf.   6.50   6.50

Establishment of the UN Memorial Cemetery, Tanggok, Pusan, Korea.

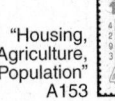

"Housing, Agriculture, Population" A153

**1960, Nov. 15**     *Perf. 13½*
317 A153 40h multicolored   1.45   .50
   a.   Souv. sheet of 1, imperf.   6.75   6.75

Issued to publicize the 1960 census.

Boy and Head of Ox — A154    Star of Bethlehem and Korean Sock — A155

Girl Giving New Year's Greeting — A156

**1960, Dec. 15**     *Litho.*   *Perf. 12½*
318 A154 15h gray, brn & org yel   2.00   .40
   a.   Souv. sheet of 1, imperf.   9.00   9.00
319 A155 25h vio bl, red & grn   2.60   .40
   a.   Souv. sheet of 1, imperf.   9.00   9.00
320 A156 30h red, vio bl & yel   3.50   .60
   a.   Souv. sheet of 1, imperf.   9.75   9.75
   Nos. 318-320 (3)   8.10   1.40
   Nos. 318a-320a (3)   27.75

Issued for Christmas and the New Year.

UN Emblem, Windsock and Ancient Rain Gauge — A157

**1961, Mar. 23**     *Perf. 13½*
321 A157 40h lt blue & ultra   1.50   .50
   a.   Souv. sheet of 1, imperf.   4.00   4.00

1st World Meteorological Day.

Children, Globe and UN Emblem — A158

**1961, Apr. 7**     *Wmk. 317*
322 A158 40h salmon & brown   1.60   .50
   a.   Souv. sheet of 1, imperf.   4.00   4.00

10th World Health Day.

Students Demonstrating A159

**1961, Apr. 19**     *Litho.*
323 A159 40h red, grn & ultra   1.90   .75
   a.   Souv. sheet of 1, imperf.   10.00   10.00

1st anniv. of the Korean April revolution.

Workers — A160

**1961, May 6**
324 A160 40h brt green   1.45   .60
   a.   Souv. sheet of 1, imperf.   6.00   6.00

International Conference on Community Development, Seoul.

Girl Scout — A161

**1961, May 10**
325 A161 40h brt green   1.90   .60
   a.   Souv. sheet of 1, imperf.   13.00   13.00

15th anniversary of Korea's Girl Scouts.

Soldier's Grave — A162

     *Wmk. 317*
**1961, June 6**    *Litho.*   *Perf. 13½*
326 A162 40h blk & ol gray   2.75   1.20
   a.   Souv. sheet of 1, imperf.   10.00   10.00

6th National Mourning Day.

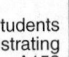

Soldier with Torch — A163

**1961, June 16**
327 A163 40h red brn & yellow   2.75   1.20
   a.   Souv. sheet of 1, imperf.   9.50   9.50

Military Revolution of May 16, 1961.

Map of Korea, Torch and Broken Chain — A164

**1961, Aug. 15**    *Wmk. 317*   *Perf. 13½*
328 A164 40h dk bl, ver & aqua   2.75   1.20
   a.   Souv. sheet of 1, imperf.   5.75   5.75

16th anniv. of liberation.

Flag and Servicemen A165

**1961, Oct. 1**     *Litho.*
329 A165 40h vio bl, red & brn   3.00   1.25
   a.   Souv. sheet of 1, imperf.   5.25   5.25

Issued for Armed Forces Day.

Kyongbok Palace Art Museum — A166

**1961, Nov. 1**    *Wmk. 317*   *Perf. 13½*
330 A166 40h beige & dk brn   1.90   .60
   a.   Souv. sheet of 1, imperf.   4.25   4.25

10th Natl. Exhibition of Fine Arts.

"UNESCO," Candle and Laurel — A167

**1961, Nov. 4**
331 A167 40h lt grn & dk bl   1.90   .60
   a.   Souv. sheet of 1, imperf.   4.00   4.00

15th anniv. of UNESCO.

Mobile X-Ray Unit — A168

**1961, Nov. 16**
332 A168 40h rose beige & red brn   1.50   .60
   a.   Souv. sheet of 1, imperf.   4.00   4.00

Tuberculosis Prevention Week.

Ginseng A169    King Sejong and Hangul Alphabet A170

Tristram's Woodpecker A171    Rice Farmer A172

Ancient Drums — A173

**1961-62**   *Unwmk.*   *Litho.*   *Perf. 12½*
338 A169 20h rose brn ('62)   2.00   1.20
339 A170 30h pale purple   5.25   1.00
340 A171 40h dk blue & red   5.00   1.00
341 A172 40h dk green ('62)   1.60
342 A173 100h red brown   11.00   2.00
   Nos. 338-342 (5)   31.75   6.80

See Nos. 363-366, 368, 388-392, 517-519, B5-B7.

Globe with Map of Korea and ITU Emblem — A175

**1962, Jan. 31**    *Unwmk.*   *Perf. 13½*
348 A175 40h ver & dk blue   1.90   .90
   a.   Souv. sheet of 1, imperf.   11.50   11.50

10th anniv. of Korea's joining the ITU.

Atomic Reactor and Atom Symbol — A176

**1962, Mar. 30**    *Litho.*   *Perf. 13½*
349 A176 40h lt bl, sl grn & ol gray 2.10   .50

Inauguration of the Triga Mark II atomic reactor.

Malaria Eradication Emblem and Mosquito — A177

**1962, Apr. 7**     *Unwmk.*
350 A177 40h green & red org   1.50   .70
   a.   Souv. sheet of 1, imperf.   3.75   3.75

WHO drive to eradicate malaria.

YWCA Emblem and Girl — A178

**1962, Apr. 20**     *Perf. 13½*
351 A178 40h pink & dk blue   3.00   .60

40th anniv. of the Korean Young Women's Christian Association.

South Gate and FPA Emblem — A179

**1962, May 12**     *Wmk. 317*
352 A179 40h lt bl, dk vio & red   3.00   .75

Meeting of the Federation of Motion Picture Producers in Asia, May 12-16.

Men Pushing Cogwheel A180    Soldiers on Hang Kang Bridge A181

Yin Yang and Factory — A182

**Wmk. 317**

**1962, May 16    Litho.    Perf. 13½**

| | | | | |
|---|---|---|---|---|
| 353 | A180 | 30h brn & pale olive | 2.75 | .85 |
| a. | | Souv. sheet of 1, Korean text | 15.00 | 15.00 |
| b. | | Souv. sheet of 1, English text | 25.00 | 20.00 |
| 354 | A181 | 40h brn, lt bl & citron | 2.75 | .85 |
| a. | | Souv. sheet of 1, Korean text | 15.00 | 15.00 |
| b. | | Souv. sheet of 1, English text | 25.00 | 20.00 |
| 355 | A182 | 200h ultra, yel & red | 32.50 | 7.75 |
| a. | | Souv. sheet of 1, Korean text | 50.00 | 50.00 |
| b. | | Souv. sheet of 1, English text | 110.00 | 100.00 |
| | | Nos. 353-355 (3) | 38.00 | 9.45 |

1st anniv. of the May 16th Revolution.
The souvenir sheets are imperf.
The sheets with English text also exist with "E" in "POSTAGE" omitted. The English-text sheets are not watermarked except those with "E" omitted. Value, $200 for set.

Tortoise Warship, 16th Century — A183

Design: 4w, Tortoise ship, heading right.

**1962, Aug. 14   Unwmk.   Perf. 13½**

| | | | | |
|---|---|---|---|---|
| 356 | A183 | 2w dk bl & turq bl | 15.00 | 1.50 |
| 357 | A183 | 4w brnsh grn, turq grn & redsh pur | 25.00 | 3.00 |

370th anniv. of Korea's victory in the naval battle with the Japanese off Hansan Island.

Flag, Scout Emblem and Tents — A184

**Wmk. 312**

**1962, Oct. 5    Litho.    Perf. 13½**

| | | | | |
|---|---|---|---|---|
| 358 | A184 | 4w brown, bl & red | 1.90 | .75 |
| a. | | Souv. sheet of 1, imperf., unwmkd. | 7.75 | 7.75 |

**Wmk. 317**

| | | | | |
|---|---|---|---|---|
| 359 | A184 | 4w green, bl & red | 1.90 | .75 |
| a. | | Souv. sheet of 1, imperf., unwmkd. | 7.75 | 7.75 |

40th anniv. of Korean Boy Scouts.

**Types of 1961-62 and**

Hanabusaya Asiatica — A185

Folk Dancers — A185a

Miruk Bosal A186

Long-horned Beetle A186a

Symbols of Thrift and Development A186b

Library of Early Buddhist Scriptures A186d

King Songdok Bell, 8th Cent. A186f

Meesun Blossoms and Fruit A186c

Sika Deer A186e

Bodhisattva in Cavern Temple, Silla Dynasty A187

Tile of Silla Dynasty — A187a

Designs: 20ch, Jin-Do dog. 1.50w, Miruk Bosal. 2w, Ginseng. 3w, King Sejong. 4w, Rice farmer. 5w, Dragon waterpot. 10w, Ancient drums. 500w, Blue dragon fresco, Koguryo dynasty.

**1962-63   Unwmk.   Litho.   Perf. 12½**
**Ordinary Paper**
**Size: 22x25mm, 25x22mm**

| | | | | |
|---|---|---|---|---|
| 360 | A186 | 20ch gldn brown | 1.40 | .40 |
| 361 | A185 | 40ch blue | 1.40 | .40 |
| 362 | A186 | 50ch claret brn | 1.40 | .40 |
| 363 | A185a | 1w brt blue ('63) | 3.25 | .40 |
| 364 | A169 | 2w red brown | 4.75 | .40 |
| 365 | A170 | 3w violet brown | 5.25 | .40 |
| 366 | A172 | 4w green | 5.50 | .40 |
| 367 | A186 | 5w grnsh blue | 6.25 | 1.00 |
| 368 | A173 | 10w red brown | 67.50 | 4.00 |
| 369 | A186c | 20w lil rose ('63) | 14.00 | 1.60 |
| 370 | A186d | 40w dl pur ('63) | 100.00 | 4.75 |
| | | Nos. 360-370 (11) | 210.70 | 14.15 |

**1964-66          Granite Paper**

| | | | | |
|---|---|---|---|---|
| 360a | A186 | 20ch org brn | .90 | .25 |
| 361a | A185 | 40ch blue | .95 | .25 |
| 362a | A186 | 50ch claret brn | .95 | .25 |
| 362B | A186a | 60ch blk ('66) | .95 | .30 |
| 363a | A185a | 1w bright blue | 3.50 | .25 |
| 363B | A186 | 1.50w dk sl grn ('66) | .70 | .30 |
| 364a | A169 | 2w red brown | 5.50 | .40 |
| 365a | A170 | 3w vio brown | 15.00 | .30 |
| 366a | A172 | 4w green | 6.75 | .30 |
| 367a | A186 | 5w grnsh blue | 32.50 | 1.50 |
| 367B | A186b | 7w lil rose ('66) | 3.25 | .75 |
| 368a | A173 | 10w red brown | 5.00 | .40 |
| 369a | A186c | 20w lilac rose | 5.00 | .40 |
| 370a | A186d | 40w vio brown | 50.00 | 2.25 |
| 371 | A186e | 50w red brn | 62.50 | 1.50 |
| 372 | A186f | 100w slate grn | 100.00 | 3.00 |
| 373 | A187 | 200w dk & lt grn ('65) | 27.50 | 3.00 |
| 374 | A187a | 300w sl grn & buff ('65) | 55.00 | 4.00 |
| 374A | A187a | 500w dk & lt bl ('65) | 27.50 | 4.00 |
| | | Nos. 360a-374A (19) | 403.45 | 23.40 |

The paper of Nos. 360a to 374A contains a few colored fibers; the paper of Nos. 385-396 contains many fibers.
Postal counterfeits exist of Nos. 369a, 370a, 371 and 372.
See Nos. 385-396, 516, 521-522, 582-584, 1076-1079, B8.

Map, Mackerel and Trawler — A188

**1962, Oct. 10      Perf. 13½**

| | | | | |
|---|---|---|---|---|
| 375 | A188 | 4w dk bl & grnsh bl | 5.00 | 1.00 |

10th anniv. of the Pacific Fishery Council.

ICAO Emblem and Plane — A189

**1962, Dec. 11      Perf. 13½**

| | | | | |
|---|---|---|---|---|
| 376 | A189 | 4w blue & brown | 2.40 | .75 |
| a. | | Souv. sheet of 1, imperf. | 9.25 | 9.25 |

10th anniv. of Korea's joining the ICAO.

**Savings Types of 1960**

**1962-64    Unwmk.    Perf. 12½**

| | | | | |
|---|---|---|---|---|
| 377 | A140 | 1w emer, brn & org ('63) | 7.25 | 1.25 |
| a. | | Granite paper | 16.00 | 12.50 |
| 378 | A141 | 2w pink, bl & brn | 12.00 | 1.50 |
| a. | | Granite paper | 14.00 | 2.50 |

**Wmk. 317**

| | | | | |
|---|---|---|---|---|
| 379 | A140 | 1w emer, brn & org ('64) | 95.00 | 10.00 |
| 380 | A141 | 2w pink, bl & brn ('64) | 14.00 | 1.75 |
| | | Nos. 377-380 (4) | 128.25 | 14.50 |

Wheat Emblem — A190

**Wmk. 317**

**1963, Mar. 21    Litho.    Perf. 13½**

| | | | | |
|---|---|---|---|---|
| 381 | A190 | 4w emer, dk bl & ocher | 1.50 | .70 |
| a. | | Souv. sheet of 1, imperf. | 4.50 | 4.50 |

FAO "Freedom from Hunger" campaign.

Globe and Letters — A191

**1963, Apr. 1**

| | | | | |
|---|---|---|---|---|
| 382 | A191 | 4w rose lil, ol & dk bl | 2.25 | .60 |
| a. | | Souv. sheet of 1, imperf. | 4.50 | 4.50 |

1st anniv. of the formation of the Asian-Oceanic Postal Union, AOPU.

Centenary Emblem and World Map — A192

**1963, May 8        Litho.**

| | | | | |
|---|---|---|---|---|
| 383 | A192 | 4w org, red & gray | 1.50 | 1.00 |
| 384 | A192 | 4w lt bl, red & gray | 1.50 | 1.00 |
| a. | | Souv. sheet of 2, #383-384, imperf. | 12.50 | 12.50 |

Cent. of the Intl. Red Cross.

**Types of 1961-63**

Designs as before.

**1963-64    Wmk. 317    Perf. 12½**
**Granite Paper**
**Size: 22x25mm, 25x22mm**

| | | | | |
|---|---|---|---|---|
| 385 | A186 | 20ch gldn brn ('64) | 1.25 | .25 |
| 386 | A185 | 40ch blue | 1.25 | .25 |
| 387 | A186 | 50ch cl brn ('64) | 1.25 | .25 |
| 388 | A185a | 1w brt blue | 3.25 | .35 |
| 389 | A169 | 2w red brown | 6.25 | .40 |
| 390 | A170 | 3w vio brown | 12.00 | .35 |
| 391 | A172 | 4w green | 6.50 | .60 |
| 392 | A173 | 10w red brown | 6.25 | 1.00 |
| 393 | A186c | 20w lil rose ('64) | 11.00 | 1.40 |
| 394 | A186d | 40w maroon | 52.50 | 2.00 |

| | | | | |
|---|---|---|---|---|
| 395 | A186e | 50w yel brown | 70.00 | 2.00 |
| 396 | A186f | 100w slate grn | 105.00 | 3.75 |
| | | Nos. 385-396 (12) | 276.50 | 12.20 |

Hibiscus and "15" — A193

**1963, Aug. 15   Wmk. 317   Perf. 13½**

| | | | | |
|---|---|---|---|---|
| 398 | A193 | 4w vio bl, pale bl & red | 3.00 | 1.20 |

15th anniversary of the Republic.

Army Nurse and Corps Emblem — A194

**1963, Aug. 26      Litho.**

| | | | | |
|---|---|---|---|---|
| 399 | A194 | 4w citron, grn & blk | 2.25 | .85 |

Army Nurses Corps, 15th anniversary.

**First Five-Year Plan Issue**

Transformer and Power Transmission Tower — A195

Irrigated Rice Fields — A196

No. 402, Cement factory. No. 403, Coal Miner. No. 404, Oil refinery. No. 405, Fishing industry (ships). No. 406, Cargo ship and cargo. No. 407, Fertilizer plant and grain. No. 408, Radar and telephone. No. 409, Transportation (plane, train, ship and map).

**1962-66    Unwmk.    Perf. 12½**

| | | | | |
|---|---|---|---|---|
| 400 | A195 | 4w org & dk vio | 27.50 | 3.00 |
| 401 | A196 | 4w turq bl & blue | 27.50 | 3.00 |

**Wmk. 317**

| | | | | |
|---|---|---|---|---|
| 402 | A195 | 4w dk bl & gray | 13.00 | 1.60 |
| 403 | A196 | 4w brnsh pink & choc | 13.00 | 1.60 |
| 404 | A195 | 4w yel ocher & bl | 5.50 | 1.15 |
| 405 | A196 | 4w turq grn & blk | 5.50 | 1.15 |

**Unwmk.**

| | | | | |
|---|---|---|---|---|
| 406 | A195 | 4w pale pink & vio bl | 1.90 | .95 |
| 407 | A196 | 4w gray brn & brn blk | 1.90 | .95 |
| 408 | A195 | 7w ol bis & blk | 3.25 | 1.00 |
| 409 | A196 | 7w turq bl & blue | 3.25 | 1.00 |
| | | Nos. 400-409 (10) | 102.30 | 15.40 |

Economic Development Five-Year Plan.
Issued: Nos. 400-401, 12/28/62; Nos. 402-403, 9/1/63; Nos. 404-405, 6/15/64; Nos. 406-407, 6/1/65; Nos. 408-409, 6/1/66.

Ramses Temple, Abu Simbel A197

**Wmk. 317**

**1963, Oct. 1    Litho.    Perf. 13½**

| | | | | |
|---|---|---|---|---|
| 410 | | 3w gray & ol gray | 5.50 | 1.75 |
| 411 | | 4w gray & ol gray | 5.50 | 1.75 |
| a. | | Souv. sheet of 2, #410-411, imperf. | 9.50 | 9.50 |
| b. | A197 | Pair, #410-411 | 11.50 | 4.25 |

UNESCO world campaign to save historic monuments in Nubia.

Rugby and Torch Bearer — A199

**1963, Oct. 4 Wmk. 317 Perf. 13½**
412 A199 4w gray, red brn & Pruss bl ... 3.75 1.30

44th National Athletic Games.

Nurse & Mobile X-Ray Unit — A200

**1963, Nov. 6 Perf. 13½**
413 A200 4w org & bluish blk ... 1.90 .75

10h anniv. of the Korean Natl. Tuberculosis Association.

Eleanor Roosevelt — A201

Design: 4w, Hands holding torch and globe.

**1963, Dec. 10 Litho. Wmk. 317**
414 A201 3w lt red brn & dk bl ... 1.60 1.00
415 A201 4w dl org, ol & dk bl ... 1.60 1.00
a. Souv. sheet of 2, 414-415, imperf. ... 5.75 5.75

Eleanor Roosevelt; 15th anniv. of the Universary Declaration of Human Rights.

Korean Flag and UN Headquarters — A202

**1963, Dec. 12 Wmk. 317 Perf. 13½**
416 A202 4w grnsh bl, ol & blk ... 1.60 .50
a. Souv. sheet of 1, imperf. ... 4.75 4.75

15th anniv. of Korea's recognition by the UN.

Tang-piri (Recorder) — A203

Musical Instruments: No. 418, Pyen-kyeng (chimes). No. 419, Chang-ko (drums). No. 420, Tai-keum (large flute). No. 421, Taipyeng-so (Chinese oboe). No. 422, Na-bal (brass trumpet). No. 423, Hyang-pipa (Chinese short lute). No. 424, Wul-keum (banjo). No. 425, Kaya-ko (zither), horiz. No. 426, Wa-kong-hu (harp), horiz.

**1963, Dec. 17 Unwmk.**
417 A203 4w pink, dk grn & mag ... 5.75 1.30
418 A203 4w lt bl, bl grn & dk bl ... 5.75 1.30
419 A203 4w pink, dk bl & brn ... 5.75 1.30
420 A203 4w tan, dk grn & dk brn ... 5.75 1.30
421 A203 4w yel, vio bl & brn ... 5.75 1.30
422 A203 4w grnsh gray, blksh brn & vio ... 5.75 1.30
423 A203 4w pink, dk bl & org brn ... 5.75 1.30
424 A203 4w turq grn, brnsh blk & bl ... 5.75 1.30
425 A203 4w rose pink, red brn & brnsh blk ... 5.75 1.30
426 A203 4w dl mauve, blk & grnsh bl ... 5.75 1.30
Nos. 417-426 (10) ... 57.50 13.00

Pres. Park and Capitol — A204

**1963, Dec. 17 Wmk. 317**
427 A204 4w black & brt grn ... 65.00 16.00

Inauguration of Pres. Park Chung Hee.

Symbols of Metric System — A205

**1964, Jan. 1 Litho.**
428 A205 4w multicolored ... 1.60 .75
a. Imperf., pair ... 75.00

Introduction of the metric system.

UNESCO Emblem and Yin Yang — A206

**1964, Jan. 30 Wmk. 317 Perf. 13½**
429 A206 4w red, lt bl & ultra ... 1.90 .75

Korean Natl. Commission for UNESCO, 10th anniv.

Industrial Census — A207

**1964, Mar. 23 Wmk. 317 Perf. 13½**
430 A207 4w gray, blk & red brn ... 1.90 .75

National Mining and Industrial Census.

YMCA Emblem and Head — A208

**1964, Apr. 12 Litho.**
431 A208 4w app grn, dk bl & red ... 1.50 .60

50th anniv. of the Korean YMCA.

Unisphere, Ginseng and Cargo Ship — A209

Design: 100w, Korean pavilion and globe.

**1964, Apr. 22 Wmk. 317 Perf. 13½**
432 A209 40w buff, red brn & grn ... 5.00 1.30
433 A209 100w bl red brn & ultra ... 45.00 8.00
a. Souv. sheet of 2, imperf. ... 97.50 70.00

New York World's Fair, 1964-65.

Secret Garden, Changdok Palace, Seoul — A210

Views: 2w, Whahong Gate, Suwon. 3w, Uisang Pavilion, Yangyang-gun. 4w, Maitreya Buddha, Bopju Temple at Mt. Songni. 5w, Paekma River and Rock of Falling Flowers. 6w, Anab Pond, Kyongju. 7w, Choksok Pavilion, Chinju. 8w, Kwanghan Pavilion. 9w, Whaom Temple, Mt. Chiri. 10w, Chonjeyon Falls, Soguipo.

**1964, May 25 Wmk. 317 Perf. 13½**
**Light Blue Background**
434 A210 1w green ... 1.40 .50
435 A210 2w blksh gray ... 1.40 .50
436 A210 3w dk green ... 1.40 .50
437 A210 4w grn ... 2.60 .85
438 A210 5w violet ... 5.25 1.35
439 A210 6w vio blue ... 7.00 1.60
a. Souv. sheet of 2 (5w, 6w) ... 16.50 16.50
440 A210 7w choc ... 11.50 2.50
a. Souv. sheet of 2 (4w, 7w) ... 16.50 16.50
441 A210 8w red brown ... 11.50 2.25
a. Souv. sheet of 2 (3w, 8w) ... 16.50 16.50
442 A210 9w lt violet ... 13.50 2.40
a. Souv. sheet of 2 (2w, 9w) ... 16.50 16.50
443 A210 10w slate grn ... 17.50 3.25
a. Souv. sheet of 2 (1w, 10w) ... 16.50 16.50
Nos. 434-443 (10) ... 73.05 15.70
Nos. 439a-443a (5) ... 82.50 82.50

The five souvenir sheets are imperf.

Globe and Wheel — A211

**1964, July 1 Litho. Perf. 13½**
444 A211 4w lt ol grn, dl brn & ocher ... 1.50 .60
a. Souv. sheet of 1, imperf. ... 4.75 4.75

Colombo Plan for co-operative economic development of south and southeast Asia.

Hands and World Health Organization Emblem — A212

**1964, Aug. 17 Wmk. 317 Perf. 13½**
445 A212 4w brt yel grn, yel grn & blk ... 1.50 .60
a. Souv. sheet of 1, imperf. ... 4.75 4.75

15th anniv. of Korea's joining the UN.

Runner — A213

**1964, Sept. 3**
446 A213 4w red lil, grn & pink ... 3.75 1.20

45th Natl. Athletic Meet, Inchon, Sept. 3-8.

UPU Monument, Bern — A214

**1964, Sept. 15**
447 A214 4w pink, red brn & bl ... 1.60 .60
a. Souv. sheet of 1, imperf. ... 5.25 5.25

1st Intl. Cong. for establishing the UPU, 90th anniv.

Crane Hook and Emblem — A215

**1964, Sept. 29 Wmk. 317 Perf. 13½**
448 A215 4w red brn & dull grn ... 1.60 .60

5th Convention of the Intl. Federation of Asian and Western Pacific Contractors' Assoc. (IFAWPCA), Seoul, Sept. 29-Oct. 7.

Marathon Runners — A216

No. 453, "V," Olympic rings, laurel & track, vert.

**1964, Oct. 10 Litho.**
449 A216 4w shown ... 3.00 1.00
450 A216 4w Equestrian ... 3.00 1.00
451 A216 4w Gymnast ... 3.00 1.00
452 A216 4w Rowing ... 3.00 1.00
453 A216 4w multicolored ... 3.00 1.00
Nos. 449-453 (5) ... 15.00 5.00

18th Olympic Games, Tokyo, Oct. 10-25.

**Souvenir Sheets of 1, Imperf., Unwmk.**
449a A216 4w ... 4.25 4.25
450a A216 4w ... 4.25 4.25
451a A216 4w ... 4.25 4.25
452a A216 4w ... 4.25 4.25
453a A216 4w ... 4.25 4.25
Nos. 449a-453a (5) ... 21.25 21.25

Stamp of 1885 — A217 / Yong Sik Hong — A218

**1964, Dec. 4 Unwmk. Perf. 13½**
454 A217 3w lilac, vio & dl bl grn ... 3.75 .95
455 A218 4w gray, vio bl & blk ... 5.25 1.20

80th anniv. of the Korean postal system. Hong Yong-Sik (1855-84) was Korea's 1st general postmaster.

Pine Branch and Cones — A219

No. 457, Plum Blossoms. No. 458, Forsythia. No. 459, Azalea. No. 460, Lilac. No. 461, Sweetbrier. No. 462, Garden balsam. No. 463, Hibiscus. No. 464, Crape myrtle. No. 465, Chrysanthemum lucidum. No. 466, Paulownia coreana. No. 467, Bamboo.

**1965 Litho. Perf. 13½**
456 A219 4w pale grn, dp grn & brn ... 2.25 .70
457 A219 4w gray, blk, rose & yel ... 2.25 .70
458 A219 4w lt bl, yel & brn ... 2.25 .70
459 A219 4w brt grn, lil rose & sal ... 2.25 .70
460 A219 4w red lil & brt grn ... 2.25 .70
461 A219 4w yel grn, grn, car & brn ... 2.25 .70
462 A219 4w bl, grn & red ... 2.25 .70
463 A219 4w bluish gray, rose red & grn ... 2.25 .70
464 A219 4w multicolored ... 2.25 .70
465 A219 4w pale grn, dk brn, grn & car rose ... 2.25 .70
466 A219 4w buff, ol grn & brn ... 2.25 .70
467 A219 4w ultra & emer ... 2.25 .70
Nos. 456-467 (12) ... 27.00 8.40

**Souvenir Sheets of 1, Imperf.**
456a A219 4w ... 3.00 3.00
457a A219 4w ... 3.00 3.00
458a A219 4w ... 3.00 3.00
459a A219 4w ... 3.00 3.00
460a A219 4w ... 3.00 3.00
461a A219 4w ... 3.00 3.00
462a A219 4w ... 3.00 3.00
463a A219 4w ... 3.00 3.00
464a A219 4w ... 3.00 3.00
465a A219 4w ... 3.00 3.00
466a A219 4w ... 3.00 3.00
467a A219 4w ... 3.00 3.00
Nos. 456a-467a (12) ... 36.00 36.00

Dancing Women, PATA Emblem and Tabo Tower — A220

**1965, Mar. 26**
468 A220 4w lt bl grn, dk brn & dk vio bl ... 1.35 .50
a. Souv. sheet of 1, imperf. ... 3.50 3.50

14th conf. of the Pacific Travel Association, Seoul, Mar. 26-Apr. 2.

Map of Viet Nam and Flag of Korean Assistance Group — A221

**1965, Apr. 20**     **Perf. 13½**
469 A221 4w blk, lt yel grn & grnsh bl   1.25 .50
  *a.* Souv. sheet of 1, imperf.   3.75 3.75

Issued to honor the Korean military assistance group in Viet Nam.

Symbols of 7-Year Plan — A222

**1965, May 1**     **Litho.**
470 A222 4w emer, dk grn & dk brn   1.25 .50

Issued to publicize the 7-year plan for increased food production.

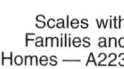

Scales with Families and Homes — A223

**1965, May 8**
471 A223 4w lt & dk grn & gray   1.25 .50
  *a.* Souv. sheet of 1, imperf.   3.25 3.25

May as Month of Family Planning.

ITU Emblem, Old and New Communication Equipment A224

**1965, May 17**
472 A224 4w lt bl, car & blk   1.25 .50
  *a.* Souv. sheet of 1, imperf.   3.25 3.25

Cent. of the ITU.

UN Emblem and Flags of Australia, Belgium, Great Britain, Canada and Colombia A225

Gen. Douglas MacArthur and Flags of Korea, UN and US — A226

UN Emblem and Flags: No. 474, Denmark, Ethiopia, France, Greece and India. No. 475, Italy, Luxembourg, Netherlands, New Zealand and Norway. No. 476, Philippines, Sweden, Thailand, Turkey and South Africa.

**1965, June 25**
**Flags in Original Colors**
473 A225 4w gray & vio bl   1.50 .75
474 A225 4w grnsh bl & vio bl   1.50 .75
475 A225 4w grnsh bl & vio bl   1.50 .75
476 A225 4w grnsh bl & vio bl   1.50 .75
477 A226 10w lt bl, blk, vio bl & red   5.00 1.50
  Nos. 473-477 (5)   11.00 4.50

15th anniv. of the participation of UN Forces in the Korean war.

**Souvenir Sheets of 1, Imperf.**
473a A225 4w   2.00 2.00
474a A225 4w   2.00 2.00
475a A225 4w   2.00 2.00

476a A225 4w   2.00 2.00
477a A226 10w   3.25 3.25
  Nos. 473a-477a (5)   11.25 11.25

Flag, Factories and "20" — A227

South Gate, Seoul, Fireworks and Yin Yang — A228

**1965, Aug. 15**     **Litho.**
478 A227 4w lt bl, vio bl & red   2.75 .60
479 A228 10w vio bl, lt bl & red   3.75 .80

20th anniv. of liberation from the Japanese.

Factory, Leaf and Ants — A229

**1965, Sept. 20**     **Perf. 13½**
480 A229 4w brt yel grn, brn & bister   1.25 .50

Issued to publicize the importance of saving.

Parabolic Antenna, Telephone Dial and Punched Tape — A230

Telegraph Operator, 1885 — A231

**1965, Sept. 28**
481 A230 3w lt bl, blk & ol   1.75 .65
482 A231 10w citron, Prus bl & blk   4.25 .85

80th anniv. of telegraph service between Seoul and Inchon.

Korean Flag and Capitol, Seoul — A232

**1965, Sept. 28**
483 A232 3w org, slate grn & bl grn   3.00 1.05

15th anniversary of recapture of Seoul.

Pole Vault — A233

**1965, Oct. 5**
484 A233 3w black, lil & sal   2.25 .90

46th Natl. Athletic Meet, Kwangju, Oct. 5-10.

ICY Emblem — A234

UN Flag and Headquarters, NY — A235

**1965, Oct. 24**     **Litho.**
485 A234 3w lt & dk grn & org brn   1.20 .55
  *a.* Souv. sheet of 1, imperf.   3.75 3.75
486 A235 10w lt bl, vio bl & grn   2.10 .75
  *a.* Souv. sheet of 1, imperf.   3.75 3.75

ICY, 1965, and 20th anniv. of the UN.

Child Posting Letter — A236

Design: 10w, Airmail envelope, telephone.

**1965, Dec. 4**     **Perf. 13½**
487 A236 3w bl grn, blk, grn & red   2.75 .95
488 A236 10w ol, dk bl & red   6.00 1.60

Tenth Communications Day.

Children with Sled — A237

Children and South Gate — A238

**1965, Dec. 11**   **Litho.**   **Perf. 12½**
489 A237 3w pale grn, vio bl & red   2.00 .65
490 A238 4w lt bl, grn, vio bl & red   3.50 1.10
  *a.* Souv. sheet of 2, #489-490, imperf.   4.25 4.25

Issued for Christmas and the New Year.

Freedom House — A239

**1966, Feb. 15**   **Unwmk.**   **Perf. 12½**
491 A239 7w brt grn, blk & cit   2.00 .70
492 A239 39w lil, blk & pale grn   13.00 3.25
  *a.* Souv. sheet of 2, #491-492, imperf.   22.50 17.50

Opening of "Freedom House" at Panmunjom.

**Wildlife Issue**

Mandarin Ducks — A240

Birds: 5w, Japanese cranes. 7w, Ring-necked pheasants.

**1966, Mar. 15**     **Litho.**   **Perf. 12½**
493 A240 3w multicolored   2.40 1.25
494 A240 5w multicolored   2.40 1.25
495 A240 7w multicolored   3.75 1.30

Alaska Pollack — A241

Fish: 5w, Manchurian trout. 7w, Yellow corvina.

**1966, June 15**
496 A241 3w bl, dk brn & yel   3.00 .90
497 A241 5w grnsh bl, blk & mag   3.50 .90
498 A241 7w brt grnsh bl, blk & yel   4.50 1.00

Firefly — A242

Insects: 5w, Grasshopper. 7w, Silk butterfly (sericinus telamon).

**1966, Sept. 15**
499 A242 3w multicolored   2.25 .90
500 A242 5w dp yellow & multi   2.75 .90
501 A242 7w lt blue & multi   3.00 1.00

Badger — A243

Animals: 5w, Asiatic black bear. 7w, Tiger.

**1966, Dec. 15**
502 A243 3w multicolored   3.00 .95
503 A243 5w multicolored   3.00 .95
504 A243 7w multicolored   3.50 .95
  Nos. 493-504 (12)   37.05 12.25

**Souvenir Sheets of 1, Imperf.**
493a A240 3w   3.75 3.75
494a A240 5w   3.75 3.75
495a A240 7w   5.75 5.75
496a A241 3w   3.25 3.25
497a A241 5w   3.75 3.75
498a A241 7w   4.25 4.25
499a A242 3w   3.25 3.25
500a A242 5w   3.25 3.25
501a A242 7w   3.75 3.75
502a A243 3w   4.50 4.50
503a A243 5w   4.50 4.50
504a A243 7w   5.00 5.00
  Nos. 493a-504a (12)   48.75 48.75

Hwansung-gun and Kwangnung Forests — A244

**1966, Apr. 5**   **Unwmk.**   **Perf. 12½**
505 A244 7w green & brown   1.50 .60

Forestation Movement.

Symbolic Newspaper Printing and Pen — A245

**1966, Apr. 7**     **Litho.**
506 A245 7w lt bl, vio brn & yel   1.35 .60

Tenth Newspaper Day.

Proper Guidance of Young People — A246

**1966, May 1**   **Unwmk.**   **Perf. 12½**
507 A246 7w Children & bell   1.35 .60

Opening of WHO Headquarters, Geneva — A247

**1966, May 3**     **Litho.**
508 A247 7w lt bl, blk & yel   1.50 .60
  *a.* Souv. sheet of 1, imperf.   4.25 4.25
509 A247 39w bluish gray, yel & red   11.00 3.00

Girl Scout and Flag — A248

**1966, May 10**
510 A248 7w yel, emer & dk bl 2.10 .80
Girl Scouts of Korea, 20th anniversary.

Pres. Park and Flags of Korea, Malaysia, Thailand and Republic of China — A249

**1966, May 10**
511 A249 7w multicolored 7.50 2.10
State visits of President Chung Hee Park.

Women's Ewha University, Seoul, and Student — A250

**1966, May 31**
512 A250 7w lt bl, vio bl & dp org 1.35 .50
80th anniv. of modern education for women.

**Types of 1961-66 Inscribed "Republic of Korea," and**

Porcelain Incense Burner, 11th-12th Centuries A253

Celadon Vessel, 12th Century A254

Unjin Miruk Buddha, Kwanchok Temple — A255

60ch, Long-horned beetle. 1w, Folk dancers. 2w, Ginseng. 3w, King Sejong. 5w, Dragon waterpot. 7w, Symbols of thrift & development.

**Perf. 12½**
**1966, Aug. 20 Unwmk. Litho.**
**Size: 22x19mm, 19x22mm**
**Granite Paper**
516 A186a 60ch gray green .70 .25
517 A185a 1w green 3.75 .35
518 A169 2w blue green 1.00 .25
519 A170 3w dull red brn .50 .25
521 A186 5w gray green 5.00 .70
522 A186b 7w grnsh blue 4.75 .50
**Size: 22x25mm**
523 A253 13w vio blue 5.00 1.00
524 A254 60w green 27.50 1.35
525 A255 80w slate grn 7.25 1.35
Nos. 516-525 (9) 55.45 6.00

**Souvenir Sheet**

Carrier Pigeons A258

**1966, July 13 Wmk. 317 Imperf.**
**Red Brown Surcharge**
534 A258 7w on 40h emer & dk grn 3.50 3.50
6th Intl. Letter Writing Week, June 13-19.
No. 534 was not issued without surcharge.

Children and World Map Projection — A259

**1966, July 28 Unwmk. Perf. 12½**
535 A259 7w pur, tan & bluish gray 2.00 .45
a. Souv. sheet of 1, imperf. 3.50 3.50
15th annual assembly of WCOTP (World Conf. of Teaching Profession), Seoul, July 28-Aug. 9.

Factory, Money Bag and Honeycomb A260

**1966, Sept. 1 Unwmk. Perf. 12½**
536 A260 7w multicolored 1.35 .50
Issued to publicize systematic saving.

Map of Korea, and People — A261

**1966, Sept. 1 Litho.**
537 A261 7w multicolored 1.35 .50
Ninth national census.

CISM Emblem and Round-Table Conference A262

**1966, Sept. 29 Unwmk. Perf. 12½**
538 A262 7w multicolored 1.35 .50
a. Souv. sheet of 1, imperf. 3.50 3.50
21st General Assembly of the Intl. Military Sports Council (CISM), Seoul, 9/29-10/9.

Flags of Korea and Viet Nam and Korean Soldiers — A263

**1966, Oct. 1**
539 A263 7w multicolored 9.00 2.10
1st anniv. of Korean combat troops in Viet Nam.

Wrestlers — A264

**1966, Oct. 10**
540 A264 7w red brn, buff & blk 2.40 1.00
47th Natl. Athletic Meet, Seoul, Oct. 10-15.

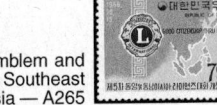
Lions Emblem and Map of Southeast Asia — A265

**1966, Oct. 15**
541 A265 7w multicolored 1.50 .90
a. Souv. sheet of 1, imperf. 3.75 3.75
5th East and Southeast Asia Lions Convention, Seoul, Oct. 15-17.

Seoul University Emblem — A266

**1966, Oct. 15 Litho.**
542 A266 7w multicolored 1.50 1.00
20th anniversary of Seoul University.

Anticommunist League Emblem — A267

**1966, Oct. 31 Unwmk. Perf. 12½**
543 A267 7w multicolored 1.50 .50
a. Souv. sheet of 1, imperf. 3.25 3.25
12th Conf. of the Asian Anticommunist League, Seoul, Oct. 31-Nov. 7.

Presidents Park and Johnson, Flags of US and Korea — A268

**1966, Oct. 31 Litho. Perf. 12½**
544 A268 7w multicolored 2.00 .75
545 A268 83w multicolored 13.00 3.50
a. Souv. sheet of 2, #544-545, imperf. 14.50 14.50
Visit of Pres. Lyndon B. Johnson to Korea.

UNESCO Emblem and Symbols of Learning — A269

**1966, Nov. 4**
546 A269 7w multicolored 1.50 .60
a. Souvenir sheets 3.50 3.50
20th anniv. of UNESCO.

Good Luck Bag and "Joy" A270

Ram and "Completion" A271

**1966, Dec. 10 Perf. 12½x13, 13x12½**
547 A270 5w multicolored 2.10 .60
a. Souv. sheet of 1, imperf. 3.75 3.75
548 A271 7w multicolored 3.75 .80
a. Souv. sheet of 1, imperf. 3.75 3.75
Issued for Christmas and the New Year.

Syncom Satellite over Globe — A272

**1967, Jan. 31 Litho. Perf. 12½**
549 A272 7w dk blue & multi 1.60 .60
a. Souv. sheet of 1, imperf. 4.00 4.00
15th anniv. of Korea's membership in the ITU.

Presidents Park and Lübke — A273

**Perf. 12½**
**1967, Mar. 2 Litho. Unwmk.**
550 A273 7w multicolored 2.40 1.15
a. Souv. sheet of 1, imperf. 4.25 4.25
Visit of Pres. Heinrich Lübke of Germany, Mar. 2-6.

Hand Holding Coin, Industrial and Private Buildings — A274

**1967, Mar. 3**
551 A274 7w lt green & blk brn 1.50 .60
1st anniv. of the Natl. Taxation Office.

**Folklore Series**

Okwangdae Clown — A275

5w, Sandi mask & dance, horiz. 7w, Hafoe mask.

**1967, Mar. 15 Litho. Perf. 12½**
552 A275 4w gray, blk & yel 2.10 .90
553 A275 5w multicolored 2.10 .90
554 A275 7w multicolored 3.00 1.00

Perfect Peace Dance — A276

Designs: 4w, Sword dance, horiz. 7w, Buddhist Monk dance.

**1967, June 15**
555 A276 4w multicolored 3.25 .90
556 A276 5w multicolored 3.75 .90
557 A276 7w multicolored 4.50 1.10

Girls on Seesaw — A277

Designs: 4w, Girls on swing, horiz. 7w, Girls dancing in the moonlight.

**1967, Sept. 15**
558 A277 4w multicolored 3.75 .90
559 A277 5w multicolored 3.75 1.00
560 A277 7w multicolored 6.00 1.20

Korean Shuttlecock — A278

Designs: 5w, Girls celebrating full moon, horiz. 7w, Archery.

**1967, Dec. 15**
561 A278 4w multicolored 3.00 .90
562 A278 5w multicolored 3.25 1.05
563 A278 7w multicolored 3.00 1.00
Nos. 552-563 (12) 41.45 11.75

**Souvenir Sheets of 1, Imperf.**
552a A275 4w 3.25 3.25
553a A275 5w 3.25 3.25
554a A275 7w 4.25 4.25
555a A276 4w 5.50 3.25
556a A276 5w 5.50 3.25
557a A276 7w 6.50 4.25
558a A277 4w 5.75 5.75
559a A277 5w 5.75 5.75
560a A277 7w 6.75 6.75
561a A278 4w 3.75 3.75
562a A278 5w 3.75 3.75
563a A278 7w 4.25 4.25
Nos. 552a-563a (12) 58.25 51.50

JCI Emblem and Kyunghoe Pavilion — A279

**1967, Apr. 13      Litho.      Perf. 12½**
564 A279 7w dk brn, brt grn, bl & red                              1.35    .60
a.      Souv. sheet of 1, imperf.                                  3.50   3.50

Intl. Junior Chamber of Commerce Conf., Seoul, Apr. 13-16.

Emblem, Map of Far East — A280

**1967, Apr. 24      Unwmk.      Perf. 12½**
565 A280 7w vio bl & multi                                         1.35    .60
a.      Souv. sheet of 1, imperf.                                  3.50   3.50

Issued to publicize the 5th Asian Pacific Dental Congress, Seoul, Apr. 24-28.

EXPO '67 Korean Pavilion — A281

**1967, Apr. 28**
566 A281  7w yel, blk & red                                        3.25    .75
567 A281 83w lt bl, blk & red                                     22.50   4.50
a.      Souv. sheet of 2, #566-567, imperf.                       18.00  18.00

EXPO '67, Intl. Exhibition, Montreal, Apr. 28-Oct. 27, 1967.

Worker, Soldier, Emblem and Buildings — A282

**1967, May 1**
568 A282 7w multicolored                                           1.50    .60
Veterans' Day, May 1.

**Second Five-Year Plan Issue**

Nut and Arrows — A283

No. 570, Iron wheel and rail. No. 571, Express highway. No. 572, Cloverleaf intersection. No. 573, Rising income for fishermen and farmers (oysters, silk worm, mushrooms and bull's head). No. 574, Machine industry (cogwheels, automobile, wrench and motor). No. 575, Harbor. No. 576, Housing projects plans. No. 577, Atomic power plant. No. 578, Four Great River Valley development.

**1967-71      Litho.      Perf. 12½**
569 A283  7w blk, red brn & dl org                                 6.50   1.20
570 A283  7w dl org, yel & blk                                     6.50   1.20
571 A283  7w grn, bl & ol                                         12.00   2.00
572 A283  7w dk brn, yel & grn                                     7.00   2.00
**                Perf. 13x12½**
573 A283  7w brn, grn, yel & org                                   1.50    .40
574 A283  7w dk bl, lil rose & buff                                1.50    .40
575 A283 10w dk bl, bl, yel & grn                                  1.50    .40
576 A283 10w lt bl, bl, grn & red                                  1.50    .40
**                Photo.      Perf. 13**
577 A283 10w blk, car & bl                                         1.50    .40
578 A283 10w blk, grn & red                                        1.50    .40
Nos. 569-578 (10)                                                 41.00   8.80

Second Economic Development Five-Year Plan.
Issued: Nos. 569-570, 6/1/67; Nos. 571-572, 12/5/68; Nos. 573-574, 12/5/69; Nos. 575-576, 12/5/70; Nos. 577-578, 12/5/71.

President Park and Phoenix — A284

**1967, July 1      Unwmk.      Perf. 12½**
579 A284 7w multicolored                                          23.00   6.00
a.      Souv. sheet of 1, imperf.                                 62.50  62.50

Inauguration of President Park Chung Hee for a 2nd term, July 1, 1967.

Korean Boy Scout, Emblem and Tents — A285

20w, Korean Boy Scout emblem, bridge & tents.

**1967, Aug. 10      Litho.      Perf. 12½**
580 A285  7w multicolored                                          1.50    .60
a.      Souv. sheet of 1, imperf.                                  4.75   4.75
581 A285 20w multicolored                                          5.00   2.25
a.      Souv. sheet of 1, imperf.                                  4.75   4.75

3rd Korean Boy Scout Jamboree, Hwarangdae, Seoul, Aug. 10-15.

**Types of 1962-66 Redrawn
(Inscribed "Republic of Korea")**

Designs: 20w, Meesun blossoms and fruit. 40w, Library of early Buddhist scriptures. 50w, Deer.

**1967, Aug. 25                Granite Paper**
582 A186c 20w green & lt bl grn                                   77.50   2.00
583 A186d 40w dk grn & lt ol                                      45.00   2.00
584 A186e 50w dk brn & bister                                      8.50   1.50
Nos. 582-584 (3)                                                 131.00   5.50

The printing of redrawn designs of the regular issue of 1962-66 became necessary upon discovery of large quantities of counterfeits, made to defraud the post. The position of the denominations was changed and elaborate fine background tracings were added.

Freedom Center and Emblem A286

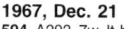

Hand Breaking Chain A287

**1967, Sept. 25      Litho.      Perf. 12½**
586 A286 5w multicolored                                           1.45    .65
a.      Souv. sheet of 1, imperf.                                  4.75   4.75
587 A287 7w multicolored                                           1.60    .65
a.      Souv. sheet of 1, imperf.                                  4.75   4.75

1st Conf. of the World Anti-Communist League, WACL, Taipei, China, Sept. 25-29.

Boxing — A288

Design: 7w, Women's basketball.

**1967, Oct. 5**
588 A288 5w tan & multi                                            2.25    .70
589 A288 7w pale rose & multi                                      3.25    .70

48th Natl. Athletic Meet, Seoul, Oct. 5-10.

Students' Memorial, Kwangjoo — A289

**1967, Nov. 3      Litho.      Perf. 12½**
590 A289 7w lt green & multi                                       1.50    .50

Issued for Student Day commemorating 1929 students' uprising against Japan.

Symbolic Water Cycle — A290

**1967, Nov. 20**
591 A290 7w multicolored                                           1.50    .60

Hydrological Decade (UNESCO), 1965-74.

Children Spinning Top A291

Monkey and Oriental Zodiac A292

**1967, Dec. 10**
592 A291 5w sal, org & vio bl                                      3.00    .75
a.      Souv. sheet of 1, imperf.                                  3.75    .75
593 A292 7w yel bis, brn & vio bl                                  3.75    .75
a.      Souv. sheet of 1, imperf.                                  3.75   3.75

Issued for Christmas and New Year.

Parabolic Antenna and Electric Waves — A293

**1967, Dec. 21**
594 A293 7w lt bl, blk & yel                                       1.50    .70
a.      Souv. sheet of 1, imperf.                                  3.75   3.75

Opening of the natl. microwave communications network, Dec. 21.

Carving from King Songdok Bell — A294

Earrings, 6th Cent. A295

Flag A296

**              Perf. 13x12½**
**1968, Feb. 1      Litho.      Unwmk.
              Granite Paper**
595 A294 1w yellow & brown                                          .80    .25
596 A295 5w dk green & yellow                                      3.25    .55
597 A296 7w dark blue & red                                        1.50    .55
Nos. 595-597 (3)                                                   5.55   1.35

WHO, 20th Anniv. — A297

**1968, Apr. 7      Unwmk.      Perf. 12½**
598 A297 7w multicolored                                           1.50    .60
a.      Souv. sheet of 1, imperf.                                  3.75   3.75

EATA Emblem and Korean Buildings — A298

**1968, Apr. 9                          Litho.**
599 A298 7w multicolored                                           1.50    .60
a.      Souv. sheet of 1, imperf.                                  4.25   4.25

2nd General Meeting of the East Asia Travel Association (EATA), Seoul, Apr. 9-13.

Door Knocker, Factories and Emblem — A299

**1968, May 6      Unwmk.      Perf. 12½**
600 A299 7w multicolored                                           1.50    .60
a.      Souv. sheet of 1, imperf.                                  4.00   4.00

2nd Conf. of the Confederation of Asian Chambers of Commerce and Industry, Seoul.

Pres. Park and Emperor Haile Selassie — A300

**1968, May 18                          Litho.**
601 A300 7w multicolored                                           3.75   1.40
a.      Souv. sheet of 1, imperf.                                  7.25   7.25

Visit of Haile Selassie I, May 18-20.

Mailman's Pouch — A301

Mailman — A302

**1968, May 31      Unwmk.      Perf. 12½**
602 A301 5w multicolored                                           1.50    .70
603 A302 7w multicolored                                           1.50    .70

First Postman's Day, May 31, 1968.

Atom Diagram and Symbols of Development A303

**1968, June 1                          Litho.**
604 A303 7w dk bl, citron & ver                                    1.50    .60

Issued to promote science and technology.

Kyung Hee University and Conference Emblem — A304

**1968, June 18                          Unwmk.**
605 A304 7w bl, pink & blk                                         1.50    .50
a.      Souv. sheet of 1, imperf.                                  5.00   5.00

2nd Conf. of the Intl. Association of University Presidents.

Liberated People — A305

**1968, July 1      Litho.      Perf. 12½**
606 A305 7w multicolored                                           1.50    .60

Issued to publicize the movement to liberate people under communist rule.

Peacock and Industrial Plant — A306

**1968, Aug. 15      Unwmk.      Perf. 12½**
607 A306 7w multicolored                                           1.50    .60

Republic of Korea, 20th anniversary.

Fair Entrance — A307

**1968, Sept. 9 Unwmk. Perf. 12½**
608 A307 7w lilac & multi 1.50 .60

Issued to publicize the first Korean Trade Fair, Seoul, Sept. 9-Oct. 18.

Assembly Emblem and Pills — A308

**1968, Sept. 16 Litho.**
609 A308 7w multicolored 1.50 .60

3rd General Assembly of the Federation of Asian Pharmaceutical Associations, Seoul, Sept. 16-21.

Soldier, Insigne and Battle Scene — A309

No. 611, Sailor, insigne & ship's guns. No. 612, Servicemen & flags. No. 613, Aviator, insigne & planes. No. 614, Marine, insigne & landing group.

**1968, Oct. 1**
610 A309 7w green & org 7.50 2.00
611 A309 7w lt & dk blue 7.50 2.00
612 A309 7w dk blue & org 7.50 2.00
613 A309 7w dk & lt blue 7.50 2.00
614 A309 7w orange & grn 7.50 2.00
 a. Vert. strip of 5, #610-614 42.50 14.00

20th anniv. of the Korean armed forces.

Colombo Plan Emblem and Globe — A310

**1968, Oct. 8 Litho. Perf. 12½**
615 A310 7w dk brn, pale sal & grn 1.50 .60

19th meeting of the Consultative Committee of the Colombo Plan, Seoul, Oct. 8-28.

Bicycling (Type I) — A311

Type II — (2nd line flush left)

No. 617, Bicycling, Type II. No. 618-619, Wrestling. No. 620-621, Boxing. No. 622-623, Olympic flame, "68" & symbols of various sports events.

**1968, Oct. 12 Unwmk. Perf. 12½**
616 A311 7w pink & multi (I) 14.00 4.25
617 A311 7w pink & multi (II) 14.00 4.25
 a. Souv. sheet of 2, #616-617, imperf. 10.50 10.50
 b. Pair, #616-617 35.00 35.00
618 A311 7w olive & multi (I) 14.00 12.00
619 A311 7w olive & multi (II) 14.00 12.00
 a. Souv. sheet of 2, #618-619, imperf. 10.50 10.50
 b. Pair, #618-619 35.00 35.00
620 A311 7w orange & multi (I) 14.00 12.00
621 A311 7w orange & multi (II) 14.00 12.00
 a. Souv. sheet of 2, #620-621, imperf. 10.50 10.50
 b. Pair, #620-621 35.00 35.00

622 A311 7w bluish grn & multi (I) 14.00 12.00
623 A311 7w bluish grn & multi (II) 14.00 12.00
 a. Souv. sheet of 2, #622-623, imperf. 10.50 10.50
 b. Pair, #622-623 35.00 35.00
 Nos. 616-623 (8) 112.00 80.50

19th Olympic Games, Mexico City, 10/12-27. The position of the "7" is reversed on Nos. 619, 621, 623 as are the designs of Nos. 619, 621.

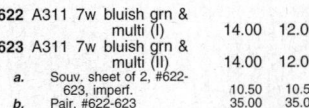

"Search for Knowledge" and School Girls — A312

**1968, Oct. 15**
624 A312 7w multicolored 1.50 .60

60th anniv. of public secondary education for women.

Coin and Statistics — A313

**1968, Nov. 1**
625 A313 7w multicolored 1.50 .50

National Wealth Survey.

Memorial to Students' Uprising — A314

**1968, Nov. 23**
626 A314 7w gray & multi 1.90 .65

Issued to commemorate the anti-communist students' uprising, Nov. 23, 1945.

Men With Banners Declaring Human Rights — A315

**1968, Dec. 10**
627 A315 7w multicolored 1.50 .60

Declaration of Human Rights, 20th anniv.

Christmas Decorations A316

Cock and Good Luck Characters A317

**1968, Dec. 11**
628 A316 5w salmon & multi 8.75 1.00
 a. Souv. sheet of 1, imperf. 7.25 7.25
629 A317 7w multicolored 9.50 1.00
 a. Souv. sheet of 1, imperf. 7.25 7.25

Issued for Christmas and the New Year.

UN Emblems and Korean House — A318

**1968, Dec. 12**
630 A318 7w lt blue & multi 1.50 .60

20th anniv. of the recognition of the Republic of Korea by the UN.

Ancient Drums — A325

Regional Boy Scout Conf. — A319

Design: Boy Scout Emblem.

**1968, Sept. 30 Litho. Perf. 12½**
631 A319 7w black & multi 2.10 .75

Sam-il Movement, 50th Anniv. — A320

Design: Torch, map and students Demonstrating against Japan, 1919.

**1969, Mar. 1 Unwmk. Perf. 12½**
632 A320 7w multicolored 1.50 .60

Hyun Choong Sa Shrine and Tortoise Ships — A321

**1969, Apr. 28 Unwmk. Perf. 12½**
633 A321 7w deep bl, grn & brn 1.50 .60

Completion of the Hyun Choong Sa Shrine at Onyang, dedicated to the memory of Adm. Li Sun-sin.

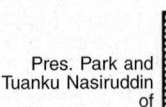

Pres. Park and Tuanku Nasiruddin of Malaysia — A322

**1969, Apr. 29 Litho.**
634 A322 7w yellow & multi 3.50 1.20
 a. Souv. sheet of 1, imperf. 57.50 57.50

Visit of Tuanku Ismail Nasiruddin, ruler of Malaysia, Apr. 29, 1969.

Hanabusaya Asiatica — A323

Old Man's Mask — A323a

Stone Lamp, 8th Cent. — A323b

Chipmunk — A323c

Flag of Korea — A324

Flag of Korea — A324a

Flag of Korea — A325a

Red-crested Cranes — A326

Tiger Lily — A326a

Highway and Farm A327

Pitcher (12-13th Centuries) A328

Ceramic Duck (Water Jar) — A329

Bee — A329a

 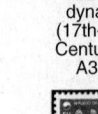

Library of Early Buddhist Scriptures A330

Vase, Yi dynasty (17th-18th Centuries) A331

Miruk Bosal A332

Gold Crown, Silla Dynasty A333

**Granite Paper (Lithographed); Ordinary Paper (Photogravure)**

*Perf. 13x12, 12x13 (Litho.); 13½x12½, 12½x13½ (Photo.)*
Litho. (40ch, Nos. 641, 650); Photo.
**1969-74 Unwmk.**
635 A323 40ch green 1.20 .35
636 A323a 1w dk rose brn ('74) .40 .25
637 A323b 5w brt plum 2.00 .25
638 A323c 5w brn red ('74) .35 .25
639 A324 7w blue ("7.00") 3.50 .50
640 A324a 7w brt blue ("7") 2.00 .30
641 A325 10w ultra 30.00 1.00
642 A325a 10w dk blue ("10") ('70) 2.00 .25
643 A326 10w bl & dk bl ('73) 1.15 .35
644 A326a 10w grn & multi ('73) .90 .25
645 A327 10w grn, red & gray ('73) .70 .25
647 A328 20w green 1.75 .50
648 A329 30w dull grn ('70) 6.75 .70
649 A329a 30w yel & dk brn ('74) .65 .25
650 A330 40w vio bl & pink 42.50 1.90
651 A331 40w ultra & lilac 1.75 .70
652 A332 100w dp claret & yel 75.00 1.90
653 A333 100w brn & yel ('74) 37.50 2.40
 Nos. 635-653 (18) 210.10 12.35

See No. 1090. For surcharge see No. B18. Counterfeits exist of No. 653.

Red Cross, Faces and Doves — A336

**1969, May 5    Litho.        Perf. 12½**
654  A336  7w multicolored          1.75    .45
 a.    Souv. sheet of 1, imperf.      5.00   5.00

50th anniv. of the League of Red Cross Societies.

Savings Bank, Factories and Highway — A337

**1969, May 20    Unwmk.    Perf. 12½**
655  A337  7w yellow grn & multi    1.50    .60

Second Economy Drive.

Pres. Park, Pres. Thieu and Flags of Korea and Viet Nam — A338

**1969, May 27                    Litho.**
656  A338  7w pink & multi          3.00   1.15
 a.    Souv. sheet of 1, imperf.     7.75   7.75

Visit of Pres. Nguyen Van Thieu of Viet Nam, May 27.

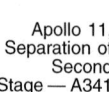

"Reforestation and Parched Fields" A339

Growing and Withering Plants A340

**1969, June 10**
657  A339  7w multicolored          1.50    .50
658  A340  7w multicolored          1.50    .50

Issued to publicize the need for prevention of damages from floods and droughts.

Apollo 11, Separation of Second Stage — A341

No. 660, Apollo 11, separation of 3rd Stage. No. 661, Orbits of command & landing modules around moon. No. 662, Astronauts gathering rock samples on moon. 40w, Spacecraft splashdown.

**1969, Aug. 15    Unwmk.    Perf. 12½**
659  A341  10w indigo, bl & red     3.50   1.30
660  A341  10w indigo, bl & red     3.50   1.30
661  A341  20w indigo, bl, red & lem  3.50  1.30
662  A341  20w indigo, bl, red & lem  3.50  1.30
663  A341  40w indigo, bl & red     3.50   1.30
 a.    Souv. sheet of 5, #659-663, imperf.  33.00  33.00
 b.    Strip of 5, #659-663         20.00  13.50

Man's 1st landing on the moon, July 20, 1969. US astronauts Neil A. Armstrong and Col. Edwin E. Aldrin, Jr., with Lieut. Col. Michael Collins piloting Apollo 11.

**Fable Issue**

Girl and Stepmother A342

Kongji and Patji (Cinderella): 7w, Sparrows help Kongji separate rice. 10w, Ox helps Kongji to weed a field. 20w, Kongji in a sedan chair on the way to the palace.

---

**1969, Sept. 1    Litho.    Perf. 12½**
664  A342  5w apple grn & multi     3.75   1.10
665  A342  7w yellow & multi        3.75   1.10
666  A342  10w lt violet & multi    6.25   1.20
667  A342  20w lt green & multi     6.25   1.20

The Sick Princess — A343

"The Hare's Liver": 7w, Hare riding to the palace on back of turtle. 10w, Hare telling a lie to the King to save his life. 20w, Hare mocking the turtle.

**1969, Nov. 1              Perf. 13x12½**
668  A343  5w yellow & multi        2.00    .85
669  A343  7w lt vio & multi        2.00    .85
670  A343  10w lt grnsh bl & multi  2.00    .95
671  A343  20w lt yel grn & multi   3.75    .95

Mother Meeting Tiger — A344

"The Sun and the Moon": 7w, Tiger disguised as mother at children's house. 10w, Tiger, and children on tree. 20w, Children safe on cloud, and tiger falling to his death.

**1970, Jan. 5**
672  A344  5w orange & multi        2.00    .65
673  A344  7w gray grn & multi      2.00    .65
674  A344  10w lt green & multi     2.00    .80
675  A344  20w gray & multi         4.00    .80

Woodcutter Stealing Fairy's Clothes — A345

Designs: No. 677, Woodcutter with wife and children. No. 678, Wife taking children to heaven. No. 679, Husband joining family in heaven.

**1970, Mar. 5**
676  A345  10w dull bl grn & multi  2.40    .95
677  A345  10w buff & multi         2.40    .95
678  A345  10w lt grnsh bl & multi  2.40    .95
679  A345  10w pink & multi         2.40   1.10

Heungbu and Wife Release Healed Swallow — A346

Designs: No. 681, Heungbu and wife finding gold treasure in gourd. No. 682, Nolbu and wife with large gourd. No. 683, Demon emerging from gourd punishing evil Nolbu and wife.

**1970, May 5                    Perf. 12½**
680  A346  10w lt grnsh bl & multi  6.50   1.20
681  A346  10w org & multi          6.50   1.20
682  A346  10w app grn & multi      6.50   1.20
683  A346  10w tan & multi          6.50   1.20
     Nos. 664-683 (20)             75.35  19.85

**Souvenir Sheets of 1, Imperf.**
664a  A342  5w                     14.50  14.50
665a  A342  7w                     14.50  14.50
666a  A342  10w                    14.50  14.50
667a  A342  20w                    14.50  14.50
668a  A343  5w                      4.50   4.50
669a  A343  7w                      4.50   4.50
670a  A343  10w                     4.50   4.50
671a  A343  20w                     4.50   4.50
672a  A344  5w                      4.25   4.25
673a  A344  7w                      4.25   4.25
674a  A344  10w                     4.25   4.25
675a  A344  20w                     4.25   4.25
676a  A345  10w                     4.25   4.25
677a  A345  10w                     4.25   4.25
678a  A345  10w                     4.25   4.25
679a  A345  10w                     4.25   4.25
680a  A346  10w                    13.50  13.50
681a  A346  10w                    13.50  13.50
682a  A346  10w                    13.50  13.50
683a  A346  10w                    13.50  13.50
     Nos. 664a-683a (20)          164.00 164.00

---

1869 Locomotive and Diesel Train — A347

Early Locomotive — A347a

**Perf. 12½**
**1969, Sept. 18    Litho.    Unwmk.**
684  A347   7w yellow & multi       1.90    .65
685  A347a  7w green & multi        1.90    .65

70th anniversary of Korean Railroads.

Formation of F-5A Planes — A348

Design: No. 687, F-4D Phantom.

**1969, Oct. 1    Photo.    Perf. 13½x13**
686  A348  10w blue, blk & car      4.75    .70

**Litho.        Perf. 13x12½**
687  A348  10w multicolored         6.75    .70

20th anniversary of Korean Air Force.

Cha-jun Game — A349

**1969, Oct. 3**
688  A349  7w ap grn, dk bl & blk   1.20    .40

10th National Festival of Traditional Skills.

Institute of Science and Technology — A350

**1969, Oct. 23**
689  A350  7w bister, grn & choc    1.20    .40

Completion of the Korean Institute of Science and Technology, Hongnung, Seoul.

Pres. Park and Diori Hamani — A351

**1969, Oct. 27**
690  A351  7w yel grn & multi       2.10    .90
 a.    Souv. sheet of 1, imperf.   12.00  12.00

Visit of Diori Hamani, Pres. of Niger, Oct. 27.

Korean Wrestling — A352

No. 692, Fencing. No. 693, Korean karate (taekwondo). No. 694, Volleyball, vert. No. 695, Soccer, vert.

**1969, Oct. 28    Perf. 13x12½, 12½x13**
691  A352  10w yel grn & multi      2.75    .85
692  A352  10w blue & multi         2.75    .85
693  A352  10w green & multi        2.75    .85
694  A352  10w olive & multi        2.75    .85
695  A352  10w ultra & multi        2.75    .85
     Nos. 691-695 (5)              13.75   4.25

50th Natl. Athletic Meet, Seoul, Oct. 28-Nov. 2.

---

Allegory of National Education Charter — A353

**1969, Dec. 5    Litho.    Perf. 12½x13**
696  A353  7w dull yel & multi      1.20    .35

1st anniv. of the proclamation of the Natl. Education Charter.

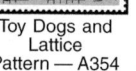

Toy Dogs and Lattice Pattern — A354

Candle, Lattice Door and Fence — A355

**1969, Dec. 11    Photo.    Perf. 13½**
697  A354  5w green & multi         1.40    .50
698  A355  7w blue & multi          1.40    .75

Issued for New Year 1970.

UPU Monument, Bern, and Korean Woman — A356

**1970, Jan. 1    Photo.    Perf. 13x13½**
699  A356  10w multicolored        10.50   3.50

70th anniv. of Korea's admission to the UPU.

Education Year Emblem and Book — A357

**1970, Mar. 10    Litho.    Perf. 12½x13**
700  A357  10w pink & multi         6.00   2.25

International Education Year 1970.

EXPO '70 Emblem, Seated Buddha, Korean Pavilion — A358

**1970, Mar. 15              Perf. 13x12½**
701  A358  10w multicolored         6.00   1.45

Issued to publicize EXPO '70 International Exhibition, Osaka, Japan, March 15-Sept. 13.

Korean Youths and 4-H Club Emblem — A359

**1970, Mar. 28              Perf. 12½x13**
702  A359  10w yellow & multi       2.75    .75

Issued to publicize the 15th Korean 4-H Club Central Contest, Suwon, March 28.

Money and Bank Emblem — A360

**1970, Apr. 9    Litho.    Perf. 13x12½**
703  A360  10w yellow & multi       1.90    .75

3rd annual Board of Governors' meeting of the Asian Development Bank, Seoul, 4/9-11.

Royal
Palanquin
A361

1899 Streetcar
A362

Historic Means of Transportation: No. 706, Emperor Sunjong's Cadillac, 1903. No. 707, Nieuport biplane, 1922.

**Perf. 13x13½, 13½x13**

| 1970, May 20 | | Photo. | |
|---|---|---|---|
| 704 | A361 10w citron & multi | 2.50 | .85 |
| 705 | A362 10w yellow & multi | 2.50 | .85 |
| 706 | A362 10w ocher & multi | 2.50 | .85 |
| 707 | A362 10w aqua & multi | 2.50 | .85 |
| | Nos. 704-707 (4) | 10.00 | 3.40 |

UPU Headquarters
A363

| 1970, May 30 | | Perf. 13½x13 | |
|---|---|---|---|
| 708 | A363 10w multicolored | 1.25 | .35 |

New UPU Headquarters in Bern, Switzerland.

Map, Radar
and Satellite
A364

| 1970, June 2 | | Perf. 13x13½ | |
|---|---|---|---|
| 709 | A364 10w sky bl, vio bl & blk | 1.90 | .75 |

Issued to commemorate the completion of the Kum San Earth Station of the International Satellite Consortium (INTELSAT).

"PEN" and Manuscript
Paper — A365

| 1970, June 28 Photo. Perf. 13x13½ | | | |
|---|---|---|---|
| 710 | A365 10w bl grn, bl & car | 1.25 | .35 |

37th Intl. P.E.N. Cong. (Poets, Playwrights, Editors, Essayists and Novelists), Seoul, June 28-July 4.

Seoul-Pusan Expressway — A366

| 1970, June 30 | | | |
|---|---|---|---|
| 711 | A366 10w multicolored | 1.90 | .75 |

Opening of Seoul-Pusan Expressway.

Postal Code Symbol and
Number — A367

| 1970, July 1 | | | |
|---|---|---|---|
| 712 | A367 10w multicolored | 1.25 | .40 |

Issued to publicize the introduction of postal zone numbers, July 1, 1970.

Mail Sorting
Machine — A368

| 1970, July 2 | | | |
|---|---|---|---|
| 713 | A368 10w lt vio & multi | 1.25 | .40 |
| a. | Souv. sheet, 2 each #712-713 | 92.50 | 92.50 |

Mechanization of Korean postal system.

Boy and Children's
Hall — A369

| 1970, July 25 | | | |
|---|---|---|---|
| 714 | A369 10w pink & multi | 1.25 | .40 |

**Paintings Issue**

Jongyangsa
Temple and
Mt.
Kumgang,
by Chong
Son (1676-
1759)
A370

The Fierce Tiger,
by Shim Sa-yung
(1707-1769)
A371

Paintings: No. 716, Mountains and Rivers, by Yi In-moon (1745-1821). No. 717, Mountains and Rivers in Moonlight, by Kim Doo-ryang (1696-1763).

**Perf. 13x13½, 13½x13**

| 1970, Aug. 31 | | Photo. | |
|---|---|---|---|
| 715 | A370 10w blue & multi | 2.25 | .75 |
| 716 | A370 10w buff & multi | 2.25 | .75 |
| 717 | A371 10w multicolored | 2.25 | .75 |

**1970, Oct. 30**

Paintings: No. 719, Cats and Sparrows, by Pyun Sang-byuk (18th century). No. 720, Dog with puppies, by Yi Am (1499-?).

| 718 | A371 30w multicolored | 8.75 | 1.60 |
|---|---|---|---|
| 719 | A371 30w multicolored | 8.75 | 1.60 |
| 720 | A371 30w multicolored | 8.75 | 1.60 |

Nos. 718-720 exist imperf. Value, set $50.

**1970, Dec. 30**

Paintings: No. 721, Cliff and Boat, by Kim Hong-do (1745-?). No. 722, Cock, Hens and Chick, by Pyun Sang-byuk (early 18th century). No. 723, Woman Playing Flute, by Shin Yun-bok (late 18th century).

| 721 | A371 10w yel brn, blk & red | 2.25 | .75 |
|---|---|---|---|
| 722 | A371 10w pale rose, blk & grn | 2.25 | .75 |
| 723 | A371 10w multicolored | 2.25 | .75 |
| | Nos. 715-723 (9) | 39.75 | 9.30 |

**Souvenir Sheets of 2**

| 715a | A370 10w | 5.00 | 5.00 |
|---|---|---|---|
| 716a | A370 10w | 5.00 | 5.00 |
| 717a | A371 10w | 5.00 | 5.00 |
| 718a | A371 30w Imperf | 31.00 | 31.00 |
| 719a | A371 30w Imperf | 31.00 | 31.00 |
| 720a | A371 30w Imperf | 31.00 | 31.00 |
| 721a | A371 10w | 8.00 | 8.00 |
| 722a | A371 10w | 8.00 | 8.00 |
| 723a | A371 10w | 8.00 | 8.00 |
| | Nos. 715a-723a (9) | 132.00 | 132.00 |

Nos. 715a-717a have simulated perforations. Background color of stamps on No. 717a is yellow instead of greenish gray as on No. 717.
Nos. 718a-720a exist perf, twice the imperf values.
Nos. 721a-723a exist imperf. Value, each $3.50.

P.T.T.I. Emblem
and Map of Far
East — A372

| 1970, Sept. 6 Litho. Perf. 13x12½ | | | |
|---|---|---|---|
| 724 | A372 10w lt yel grn, bl & dk bl | 1.60 | .50 |

Opening of the Councillors' Meeting of the Asian Chapter of the Postal, Telegraph and Telephone Intl. Org., Sept. 6-12.

Korean WAC and
Emblem — A373

| 1970, Sept. 6 Photo. Perf. 13x13½ | | | |
|---|---|---|---|
| 725 | A373 10w blue & multi | 1.60 | .50 |

20th anniv. of the founding of the Korean Women's Army Corps.

Pres. Park, Korean Flag and Means of
Transportation — A374

Pres. Park,
Highways,
Factories — A375

| 1970 | | Perf. 13x13½, 13½x13 | |
|---|---|---|---|
| 726 | A374 10w vio bl, blk & car | 8.25 | 3.00 |
| 727 | A375 10w dk bl, grnsh bl & blk | 13.50 | 3.00 |

Presidents Park
and Hernandez,
Flags of Korea,
Salvador — A376

| 1970, Sept. 28 Litho. Perf. 13x12½ | | | |
|---|---|---|---|
| 728 | A376 10w dk bl, red & blk | 3.00 | 1.45 |
| a. | Souv. sheet of 1, imperf. | 82.50 | 82.50 |

Visit of Gen. Fidel Sanchez Hernandez, President of El Salvador.
The first printing of 30,000 of No. 728a spelled "Salvadol." Second printing, also 30,000, corrected the error. Value is for first printing. Value, 2nd printing $7.50, unused or used.

People and
Houses — A377

| 1970, Oct. 1 Litho. Perf. 13x12½ | | | |
|---|---|---|---|
| 729 | A377 10w lilac & multi | 1.35 | 1.15 |

Natl. census of population & housing, Oct. 1.

Diver — A378

| 1970, Oct. 6 Photo. Perf. 12½x13½ | | | |
|---|---|---|---|
| 730 | A378 10w shown | 4.25 | .95 |
| a. | Souv. sheet of 2, imperf. | 9.25 | 9.25 |
| 731 | A378 10w Field hockey | 4.25 | .95 |
| a. | Souv. sheet of 2, imperf. | 9.25 | 9.25 |

| 732 | A378 10w Baseball | 4.25 | .95 |
|---|---|---|---|
| a. | Souv. sheet of 2, imperf. | 9.25 | 9.25 |
| | Nos. 730-732 (3) | 12.75 | 2.85 |
| | Nos. 730a-732a (3) | 27.75 | |

51st Natl. Athletic Games, Seoul, Oct. 6-11.

Police Emblem and
Activities — A379

| 1970, Oct. 21 Litho. Perf. 12½ | | | |
|---|---|---|---|
| 733 | A379 10w ultra & multi | 1.50 | .55 |

The 25th Policemen's Day.

Freedom Bell, UN
Emblem over
Globe — A380

| 1970, Oct. 24 Photo. Perf. 13x13½ | | | |
|---|---|---|---|
| 734 | A380 10w blue & multi | 1.60 | .55 |

25th anniversary of United Nations.

Kite and
Holly
A380a

Boar
A381

| 1970, Dec. 1 Litho. Perf. 13 | | | |
|---|---|---|---|
| 735 | A380a 10w lt blue & multi | 1.45 | .60 |
| a. | Souvenir sheet of 3 | 7.00 | 7.00 |
| 736 | A381 10w green & multi | 1.45 | .60 |
| a. | Souvenir sheet of 3 | 7.00 | 7.00 |

New Year 1971.

Pres. Park Quotation, Globe and
Telecommunications Emblems — A382

| 1970, Dec. 4 | | Photo. | |
|---|---|---|---|
| 737 | A382 10w multicolored | 1.60 | .55 |

For the 15th Communications Day.

Power Dam
A383

Crate
Wrapped in
World Map,
& Ships —
A383a

Irrigation Project
& Farm — A383b

Coal
Mining — A384

Cement Factory — A384a
Fertilizer Factory — A384b

Increased National Income (Scales) — A384c
Increased Savings (factories, bee & coins) — A384d

Highway Intersection — A385

| 1971 | | Perf. 13x13½, 13½x13 | | |
|------|------|------|------|------|
| 738 | A383 | 10w blue & multi | 2.25 | .55 |
| 739 | A383a | 10w pale lil & multi | 2.25 | .55 |
| 740 | A383b | 10w green & multi | 2.25 | .55 |
| 741 | A384 | 10w bl grn, lt bl & blk | 1.25 | .45 |
| 742 | A384a | 10w lt bl, vio & brt mag | 1.25 | .45 |
| 743 | A384b | 10w vio, grn & bis | 1.25 | .45 |
| 744 | A384c | 10w pink & multi | 1.40 | .65 |
| 745 | A384d | 10w lt bl grn & multi | 1.40 | .65 |
| 746 | A385 | 10w violet & multi | 1.40 | .65 |
| | | Nos. 738-746 (9) | 14.70 | 4.95 |

Economic Development.

**Souvenir Sheets of 1, Imperf.**

| 738a | A383 | 10w | 6.50 | 6.50 |
|------|------|------|------|------|
| 739a | A383a | 10w | 6.50 | 6.50 |
| 740a | A383b | 10w | 6.50 | 6.50 |

**Souvenir Sheets of 2, Imperf.**

| 741a | A384 | 10w | 6.50 | 6.50 |
|------|------|------|------|------|
| 742a | A384a | 10w | 6.50 | 6.50 |
| 743a | A384b | 10w | 6.50 | 6.50 |
| 744a | A384c | 10w | 4.75 | 4.75 |
| 745a | A384d | 10w | 4.75 | 4.75 |
| 746a | A385 | 10w | 4.75 | 4.75 |
| | | Nos. 738a-746a (9) | 53.25 | 53.25 |

No. 739a exists without date. Value $40.

Torch, Globe and Spider — A386

**1971, Mar. 1    Litho.    Perf. 12½x13**
747  A386  10w gray & multi    1.60    .45

March, the month for anti-espionage and victory over communism.

Reservist, Reserve Forces Emblem — A387

**1971, Apr. 3    Photo.    Perf. 13½x13**
748  A387  10w lt ultra & multi    1.60    .45

Home Reserve Forces Day, Apr. 3.

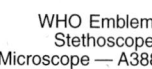

WHO Emblem, Stethoscope, Microscope — A388

**1971, Apr. 7**
749  A388  10w lt bl, pur & yel    1.60    .50

20th World Health Day, Apr. 7.

---

Subway Tunnel and Train — A389

**1971, Apr. 12    Litho.    Perf. 12½x13**
750  A389  10w multicolored    1.60    .45

Seoul subway construction start.

First Asian Soccer Games, Seoul, May 2-13 — A390

**1971, May 2**
751  A390  10w grn, dk brn & blk    1.90    .60

Veterans Flag and Veterans — A391

**1971, May 8    Photo.    Perf. 13x13½**
752  A391  10w ultra & multi    1.45    .45

20th Korean Veterans Day.

Girl Scouts and Emblem — A392

**1971, May 10**
753  A392  10w lilac & multi    1.50    .45

25th anniversary of the Korean Federation of Girl Scouts.

Torch and Development — A393

**1971, May 16**
754  A393  10w lt blue & multi    1.45    .45

10th anniversary of May 16th revolution.

"Telecommunication" A394

**1971, May 17**
755  A394  10w blue & multi    1.45    .45

3rd World Telecommunications Day.

UN Organizations A395
Korean Flag A396

No. 756, ILO. No. 757, FAO. No. 758, General Assembly (UN Headquarters). No. 759, UNESCO. No. 760, WHO. No. 761, World Bank. No. 762, Intl. Development Association (IDA). No. 763, Security Council. No. 764, Intl. Finance Corp. (IFC). No. 765, Intl. Monetary Fund. No. 766, ICAO. No. 767, Economic and Social Council. No. 768, Korean Flag. No. 769, Trusteeship Council. No. 770, UPU. No. 771,

---

ITU. No. 772, World Meteorological Org. (WMO). No. 773, Intl. Court of Justice. No. 774, Intl. Maritime Consultative Org. No. 775, UNICEF. No. 776, Intl. Atomic Energy Agency. No. 777, UN Industrial Development Org. No. 778, UN Commission for the Unification and Rehabilitation of Korea. No. 779, UN Development Program. No. 780, UN Conf. on Trade and Development.

| **1971, May 30** | | | **Perf. 13½x13** | |
|------|------|------|------|------|
| 756 | A395 | 10w grn, blk & pink | 3.75 | 1.15 |
| 757 | A395 | 10w pink, blk & bl | 3.75 | 1.15 |
| 758 | A395 | 10w bl, blk, grn & pink | 3.75 | 1.15 |
| 759 | A395 | 10w grn, blk & pink | 3.75 | 1.15 |
| 760 | A395 | 10w pink, blk & blk | 3.75 | 1.15 |
| 761 | A395 | 10w grn, blk & pink | 3.75 | 1.15 |
| 762 | A395 | 10w blue, blk & pink | 3.75 | 1.15 |
| 763 | A395 | 10w grn, blk & pink | 3.75 | 1.15 |
| 764 | A395 | 10w blue, blk & pink | 3.75 | 1.15 |
| 765 | A395 | 10w pink, blk & bl | 3.75 | 1.15 |
| 766 | A395 | 10w blue, blk & pink | 3.75 | 1.15 |
| 767 | A395 | 10w grn, blk & pink | 3.75 | 1.15 |
| 768 | A396 | 10w blue, blk & pink | 3.75 | 1.15 |
| 769 | A395 | 10w grn, blk & pink | 3.75 | 1.15 |
| 770 | A395 | 10w blue, blk & pink | 3.75 | 1.15 |
| 771 | A395 | 10w pink, blk & bl | 3.75 | 1.15 |
| 772 | A395 | 10w blue, blk & pink | 3.75 | 1.15 |
| 773 | A395 | 10w grn, blk & pink | 3.75 | 1.15 |
| 774 | A395 | 10w blue, blk & pink | 3.75 | 1.15 |
| 775 | A395 | 10w pink, blk & bl | 3.75 | 1.15 |
| 776 | A395 | 10w grn, blk & pink | 3.75 | 1.15 |
| 777 | A395 | 10w pink, blk & bl | 3.75 | 1.15 |
| 778 | A395 | 10w blue, blk & pink | 3.75 | 1.15 |
| 779 | A395 | 10w pink, blk & bl | 3.75 | 1.15 |
| 780 | A395 | 10w grn, blk & pink | 3.75 | 1.15 |
| | | Nos. 756-780 (25) | 93.75 | 28.75 |

Sheet of 50 incorporates 2 each of Nos. 756-780.

Boat Ride, by Shin Yun-bok A397

Man and Boy under Pine Tree — A398

Paintings by Shin Yun-bok: No. 782, Greeting travelers. No. 783, Sword dance. No. 784, Lady traveling with servants. No. 785, Man and woman on the road.

| **Perf. 13x13½, 13½x13** | | | | |
|------|------|------|------|------|
| **1971, June 20** | | | **Photo.** | |
| 781 | A397 | 10w multicolored | 6.25 | 1.90 |
| 782 | A397 | 10w multicolored | 6.25 | 1.90 |
| 783 | A397 | 10w multicolored | 6.25 | 1.90 |
| 784 | A397 | 10w multicolored | 6.25 | 1.90 |
| 785 | A397 | 10w multicolored | 6.25 | 1.90 |
| b. | | Vert. strip of 5, #781-785 | 40.00 | 40.00 |
| 786 | A398 | 10w multicolored | 6.00 | 1.90 |
| | | Nos. 781-786 (6) | 37.25 | 11.40 |

**Souvenir Sheets of 2**

| 781a | A397 | 10w | 11.50 | 11.50 |
|------|------|------|------|------|
| 782a | A397 | 10w | 11.50 | 11.50 |
| 783a | A397 | 10w | 11.50 | 11.50 |
| 784a | A397 | 10w | 11.50 | 11.50 |
| 785a | A397 | 10w | 11.50 | 11.50 |
| 786a | A398 | 10w | 11.50 | 11.50 |
| | | Nos. 781a-786a (6) | 69.00 | 69.00 |

**Types A397-A398 with Inscription at Left**

Paintings: No. 787, Farmyard scene, by Kim Deuk-shin. No. 788, Family living in valley, by Lee Chae-kwan. No. 789, Man reading book under pine tree, by Lee Chae-kwan.

---

**1971, July 20**

| 787 | A397 | 10w pale grn & multi | 3.25 | 1.60 |
|------|------|------|------|------|
| 788 | A398 | 10w pale grn & multi | 3.25 | 1.60 |
| 789 | A398 | 10w lt yel grn & multi | 3.25 | 1.60 |
| | | Nos. 787-789 (3) | 9.75 | 4.80 |

**Souvenir Sheets of 2**

| 787a | A397 | 10w | 8.75 | 8.75 |
|------|------|------|------|------|
| 788a | A398 | 10w | 8.75 | 8.75 |
| 789a | A398 | 10w | 8.75 | 8.75 |
| | | Nos. 787a-789a (3) | 26.25 | 26.25 |

Teacher and Students, by Kim Hong-do — A399

Paintings by Kim Hong-do (Yi Dynasty): No. 791, Wrestlers. No. 792, Dancer and musicians. No. 793, Weavers. No. 794, At the Well.

**1971, Aug. 20    Perf. 13½x13**

| 790 | A399 | 10w blk, lt grn & rose | 5.50 | 2.75 |
|------|------|------|------|------|
| 791 | A399 | 10w blk, lt grn & rose | 5.50 | 2.75 |
| 792 | A399 | 10w blk, lt grn & rose | 5.50 | 2.75 |
| 793 | A399 | 10w blk, lt grn & rose | 5.50 | 2.75 |
| 794 | A399 | 10w blk, lt grn & rose | 5.50 | 2.75 |
| b. | | Horiz. strip of 5, #790-794 | 33.00 | 33.00 |

**Souvenir Sheets of 2**

| 790a | A399 | 10w | 11.50 | 11.50 |
|------|------|------|------|------|
| 791a | A399 | 10w | 11.50 | 11.50 |
| 792a | A399 | 10w | 11.50 | 11.50 |
| 793a | A399 | 10w | 11.50 | 11.50 |
| 794a | A399 | 10w | 11.50 | 11.50 |
| | | Nos. 790a-794a (5) | 57.50 | 57.50 |

Pres. Park, Highway and Phoenix — A400

**1971, July 1    Perf. 13½x13**
795  A400  10w grn, blk & org    20.00    3.00
a.    Souvenir sheet of 2    70.00    70.00

Inauguration of President Park Chung Hee for a third term, July 1.

Campfire and Tents — A401

**1971, Aug. 2    Photo.    Perf. 13x13½**
796  A401  10w blue grn & multi    1.60    .35

13th Boy Scout World Jamboree, Asagiri Plain, Japan, Aug. 2-10.

Symbol of Conference — A402

**1971, Sept. 27    Perf. 13**
797  A402  10w multicolored    1.25    .45
a.    Souvenir sheet of 2    45.00    45.00

Asian Labor Ministers' Conference, Seoul, Sept. 27-30.

Archers A403

**1971, Oct. 8    Photo.    Perf. 13x13½**
798  A403  10w shown    2.00    .70
a.    Souvenir sheet of 3    32.00    32.00
799  A403  10w Judo    2.00    .70
a.    Souvenir sheet of 3    32.00    32.00

52nd National Athletic Meet.

Taeguk on Palette — A404

**1971, Oct. 11**    *Perf. 13½x13*
800 A404 10w yellow & multi   1.25   .50
20th National Fine Arts Exhibition.

Physician, Globe and Emblem — A405

**1971, Oct. 13**
801 A405 10w multicolored   1.25   .50
7th Congress of the Confederation of Medical Associations in Asia and Oceania.

Symbols of Contest Events — A406

**1971, Oct. 20**   **Photo.**   *Perf. 13x13½*
802 A406 10w multicolored   1.25   .50
  *a.*   Souvenir sheet of 2   37.50   37.50
2nd National Skill Contest for High School Students.

Slide Caliper and KS Emblem — A407

**1971, Nov. 11**    *Perf. 13x13½*
803 A407 10w multicolored   1.25   .50
10th anniversary of industrial standardization in Korea.

Rats A408     Japanese Crane A409

**1971, Dec. 1**
804 A408 10w multicolored   1.60   .35
  *a.*   Souvenir sheet of 3   23.00   23.00
805 A409 10w multicolored   1.60   .35
  *a.*   Souvenir sheet of 3   23.00   23.00
New Year 1972.

Emblem of Hangul Hakhoe and Hangul Letters — A410

**1971, Dec. 3**    **Photo.**
806 A410 10w dk blue & multi   1.25   .30
50th anniversary of Korean Language Research Society (Hangul Hakhoe).

Red Cross Headquarters and Map of Korea — A411

**1971, Dec. 31**    *Perf. 13½x13*
807 A411 10w multicolored   1.75   .55
  *a.*   Souvenir sheet of 2   11.50   11.50
First South and North Korean Red Cross Conference, Panmunjom, Aug. 20, 1971.

Globe and Book — A412

**1972, Jan. 5**    *Perf. 13x13½*
808 A412 10w multicolored   1.10   .35
  *a.*   Souvenir sheet of 2   11.50   11.50
International Book Year 1972.

Intelsat 4 Sending Signals to Korea — A413

**1972, Jan. 31**    *Perf. 13½x13*
809 A413 10w dk blue & multi   1.10   .35
Korea's entry into ITU, 20th anniv.

Figure Skating, Sapporo '72 Emblem — A414

Design: No. 811, Speed skating.

**1972, Feb. 3**    *Perf. 13x13½*
810 A414 10w lt & dk bl & car   1.60   .55
811 A414 10w lt & dk bl & car   1.60   .55
  *a.*   Souvenir sheet of 2, #810-811   11.50   11.50
11th Winter Olympic Games, Sapporo, Japan, Feb. 3-13.

Map of Korea with Forest Sites — A415

**1972, Mar. 10**   **Photo.**   *Perf. 13x13*
812 A415 10w buff, bl grn & red   1.20   .35
Publicity for forests planted to mark hope for re-unification of Korea.

Junior Chamber of Commerce Emblem and Beetles — A416

**1972, Mar. 19**    *Perf. 13½x13*
813 A416 10w pink & multi   1.20   .35
Junior Chamber of Commerce, 20th anniversary.

UN Emblem, Agriculture and Industry — A417

**1972, Mar. 28**    *Perf. 13x13½*
814 A417 10w violet, grn & car   1.20   .35
Economic Commission for Asia and the Far East (ECAFE), 25th anniversary.

Flags — A418

**1972, Apr. 1**    *Perf. 13½x13*
815 A418 10w blue & multi   1.20   .35
Asian-Oceanic Postal Union, 10th anniv.

Homeland Reserve Forces Flag — A419

**1972, Apr. 1**   **Photo.**   *Perf. 13x13½*
816 A419 10w yellow & multi   1.45   .40
Homeland Reserve Forces Day, Apr. 1.

YWCA Emblem, Butterflies — A420

**1972, Apr. 20**
817 A420 10w violet & multi   1.50   .40
50th anniv. of the YWCA of Korea.

Community Projects — A421

**1972, May 1**    *Perf. 13x13½*
818 A421 10w pink & multi   1.20   .35
Rural rehabilitation and construction movement.

Korean Flag & Inscription — A422

**1972, May 1**
819 A422 10w green & multi   1.20   .40
Anti-espionage and victory over communism month.

Children with Balloons — A423

**1972, May 5**    *Perf. 13½x13*
820 A423 10w yellow & multi   1.20   .40
Children's Day, May 5.

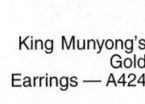

King Munyong's Gold Earrings — A424

Design: No. 822, Gold ornament from King's crown, vert.

**1972, May 10**   *Perf. 13½x13, 13x13½*
821 A424 10w green & multi   1.30   .40
822 A424 10w green & multi   1.30   .40
National treasures from tomb of King Munyong of Paekche, who reigned 501-523.

Kojo Island — A425

National parks: No. 823, Crater Lake.

**1972, May 30**    *Perf. 13½x13*
823 A425 10w blue grn & multi   3.25   .40
824 A425 10w green & multi   3.25   .40

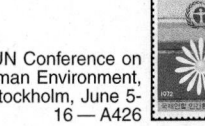

UN Conference on Human Environment, Stockholm, June 5-16 — A426

10w, Daisy, environment emblem.

**1972, May 30**   **Litho.**   *Perf. 13x13½*
825 A426 10w multicolored   1.20   .35
  *a.*   Souvenir sheet of 2   7.75   7.75

7th Meeting of Asian-Pacific Council (ASPAC) — A427

10w, Gwanghwa Gate, flags of participants.

**1972, June 14**
826 A427 10w multicolored   1.20   .35

**Third Five-Year Plan Issue**

Farm and Fish Hatchery — A428

No. 828, Steel industry and products. No. 829, Globe and cargo.

**1972, July 1**   **Photo.**   *Perf. 13½x13*
827 A428 10w shown   1.90   .50
828 A428 10w multicolored   1.90   .50
829 A428 10w multicolored   1.90   .50
   Nos. 827-829 (3)   5.70   1.50
3rd Economic Development Five-Year Plan.

Weight Lifting — A429

**1972, Aug. 26**   **Photo.**   *Perf. 13x13½*
830 A429 20w shown   1.20   .45
831 A429 20w Judo   1.20   .45
  *a.*   Souvenir sheet of 2, #830-831   5.75   5.75
  *b.*   Pair, #830-831   5.00   2.50
832 A429 20w Boxing   1.20   .45
833 A429 20w Wrestling   1.20   .45
  *a.*   Souvenir sheet of 2, #832-833   6.00   6.00
  *b.*   Pair, #832-833   5.00   2.50
   Nos. 830-833 (4)   4.80   1.80
20th Olympic Games, Munich, Aug. 26-Sept. 11. Nos. 831b, 833b each printed checkerwise.

Families Reunited by Red Cross — A430

**1972, Aug. 30**   **Photo.**   *Perf. 13½x13*
834 A430 10w lt blue & multi   1.90   .60
  *a.*   Souvenir sheet of 2   24.00   24.00
Plenary meeting of the South-North Red Cross Conference, Pyongyang, Aug. 30, 1972.

Bulkuk-sa
Temple, Kyongju
Park — A431

Bopju-sa Temple,
Mt. Sokri
Park — A432

**1972, Sept. 20  Photo.     Perf. 13½x13**
835 A431 10w brown & multi       1.35   .45
836 A432 10w blue & multi        1.35   .45
National parks.

"5" and Conference
Emblem — A433

**1972, Sept. 25          Perf. 13x13½**
837 A433 10w vio blue & multi    1.15   .35
Fifth Asian Judicial Conf., Seoul, 9/25-29.

Lions Emblem,
Taeguk Fan — A434

**1972, Sept. 28          Perf. 13½x13**
838 A434 10w multicolored        1.30   .35
11th Orient and Southeast Asian Lions Convention, Seoul, Sept. 28-30.

Scout Taking Oath,
Korean Flag and
Scout
Emblem — A435

**1972, Oct. 5**
839 A435 10w yellow & multi      1.90   .45
Boy Scouts of Korea, 50th anniversary.

Children and
Ox
A436

Children in
Balloon
A437

**1972, Dec. 1  Photo.     Perf. 13x13½**
840 A436 10w green & multi       1.30   .40
a.     Souvenir sheet of 2        4.50  4.50
841 A437 10w blue & multi        1.30   .40
a.     Souvenir sheet of 2        4.50  4.50
New Year 1973.

Mt. Naejang Park and
Temple — A438

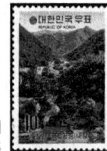

Mt. Sorang and
Madeungryong
Pass — A439

**1972, Dec. 10   Perf. 13x13½, 13½x13**
842 A438 10w multicolored        1.35   .40
843 A439 10w multicolored        1.35   .40
National parks.

Pres. Park,
Korean Flag
and Modern
Landscape
A440

**1972, Dec. 27          Perf. 13x13½**
844 A440 10w multicolored        8.50  2.00
a.     Souvenir sheet of 2       65.00 65.00
Inauguration of Park Chung Hee for a 4th term as president of Korea.

### Tourism Issue

Kyongbok Palace
(National
Museum) — A441

Mt. Sorak and
Kejo-am
Temple — A442

**1973, Feb. 20  Photo.     Perf. 13½x13**
845 A441 10w multicolored        1.25   .40
846 A442 10w multicolored        1.25   .40

Palmi Island
and Beach
A443

Sain-am
Rock, Mt.
Dokjol
A444

**1973, Apr. 20          Perf. 13x13½**
847 A443 10w multicolored        1.45   .40
848 A444 10w multicolored        1.50   .40

Shrine for
Adm. Li
Sun-sin
A445

Limestone
Cavern,
Kusan-ni
A446

**1973, June 20**
849 A445 10w multicolored        1.50   .40
850 A446 10w multicolored        1.45   .40

Namhae
Bridge — A447

Hongdo
Island — A448

**1973, Aug. 20          Perf. 13½x13**
851 A447 10w multicolored        1.45   .35
852 A448 10w multicolored        1.45   .35

Mt. Mai — A449

Tangerine
Orchard, Cheju
Island — A450

**1973, Oct. 20**
853 A449 10w multicolored         .90   .25
854 A450 10w multicolored         .90   .25
Nos. 845-854 (10)               13.10  3.60

Praying Family — A451

**1973, Mar. 1          Perf. 13x13½**
855 A451 10w yellow & multi      1.20   .50
Prayer for national unification.

Flags of Korea and
South Viet Nam, Victory
Sign — A452

**1973, Mar. 1**
856 A452 10w violet & multi      1.20   .30
Return of Korean Expeditionary Force from South Viet Nam.

Workers, Factory,
Cogwheel — A453

**1973, Mar. 10          Unwmk.**
857 A453 10w blue & multi        1.00   .30
10th Labor Day.

Satellite, WMO
Emblem — A454

**1973, Mar. 23**
858 A454 10w blue & multi        1.00   .30
a.     Souvenir sheet of 2       5.00  5.00
Cent. of Intl. Meteorological Cooperation.

King's Ceremonial
Robe — A455

Traditional Korean Costumes (Yi dynasty): No. 860, Queen's ceremonial dress. No. 861, King's robe. No. 862, Queen's robe. No. 863, Crown Prince. No. 864, Princess. No. 865, Courtier. No. 866, Royal bridal gown. No. 867, Official's wife. No. 868, Military official.

**1973          Photo.     Perf. 13½x13**
859 A455 10w ocher & multi       3.25   .70
860 A455 10w salmon & multi      3.25   .70
861 A455 10w rose lil & multi    3.00   .90
862 A455 10w apple grn &
               multi             3.00   .90
863 A455 10w lt blue & multi     2.75   .90
864 A455 10w lil rose & multi    2.75   .90
865 A455 10w yellow & multi      1.35   .50
866 A455 10w lt blue & multi     1.50   .90
867 A455 10w ocher & multi       1.50   .90
868 A455 10w lil rose & multi    1.50   .90
       Nos. 859-868 (10)        23.85  8.20

Issued: Nos. 859-860, 3/30; Nos. 861-862, 5/30; Nos. 863-864, 7/30; Nos. 865-866, 9/30; Nos. 867-868, 11/30.

### Souvenir Sheets of 2

859a  A455   10w  (#1)          7.00  7.00
860a  A455   10w  (#2)          7.00  7.00
861a  A455   10w  (#3)          7.50  7.50
862a  A455   10w  (#4)          7.50  7.50
863a  A455   10w  (#5)          7.00  7.00
864a  A455   10w  (#6)          7.00  7.00
865a  A455   10w  (#7)          4.25  4.25
866a  A455   10w  (#8)          4.25  4.25
867a  A455   10w  (#9)          4.25  4.25
868a  A455   10w  (#10)         4.25  4.25
      Nos. 859a-868a (10)      60.00 60.00

Parenthetical numbers after souvenir sheet listings appear in top marginal inscriptions.

Nurse Holding
Lamp — A456

**1973, Apr. 1          Perf. 13½x13**
869 A456 10w rose & multi        1.15   .30
50th anniv. of Korean Nurses Association.

Homeland Reservists
and Flag — A457

**1973, Apr. 7          Perf. 13½x13**
870 A457 10w yellow & multi      1.35   .30
Homeland Reserve Forces Day on 5th anniversary of their establishment.

Table Tennis
Player, and
Globe
A458

**1973, May 23          Perf. 13½x13**
871 A458 10w pink & multi        2.25   .65
Victory of Korean women's table tennis team, 32nd Intl. Table Tennis Championships, Sarajevo, Yugoslavia, Apr. 5-15.

World
Vision
Children's
Choir
A459

**1973, June 25          Perf. 13½x13**
872 A459 10w multicolored        1.30   .30
20th anniversary of World Vision International, a Christian service organization.

Converter, Pohang Steel
Works — A460

**1973, July 3          Perf. 13½x13**
873 A460 10w blue & multi         .95   .45
Inauguration of Pohang iron and steel plant.

INTERPOL
Emblem — A461

**1973, Sept. 3          Perf. 13½x13**
874 A461 10w lt violet & multi   1.10   .25
50th anniversary of the International Criminal Police Organization (INTERPOL).

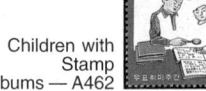

Children with
Stamp
Albums — A462

## 1973, Oct. 12 — Perf. 13½x13
875 A462 10w dp grn & multi .85 .30
  a. Souvenir sheet of 2 14.50 14.50
Philatelic Week, Oct. 12-18.

Woman Hurdler A463

## 1973, Oct. 12 — Perf. 12½x13½
876 A463 10w shown 1.10 .30
877 A463 10w Tennis player 1.10 .30
54th Natl. Athletic Meet, Pusan, Oct. 12-17.

Soyang River Dam, Map Showing Location — A464

## 1973, Oct. 15 — Perf. 13½x13
878 A464 10w blue & multi .50 .25
Inauguration of Soyang River Dam and hydroelectric plant.

Fire from Match and Cigarette — A465

## 1973, Nov. 1 — Perf. 13x13½
879 A465 10w multicolored .65 .25
10th Fire Prevention Day.

Tiger and Candles A466

Toys A467

## 1973, Dec. 1 Photo. — Perf. 13x13½
880 A466 10w emerald & multi .95 .30
  a. Souvenir sheet of 2 4.50 4.50
881 A467 10w blue & multi .95 .30
  a. Souvenir sheet of 2 4.50 4.50
New Year 1974.

Human Rights Flame, and Head — A468

## 1973, Dec. 10 — Perf. 13½x13
882 A468 10w orange & multi .70 .25
25th anniversary of Universal Declaration of Human Rights.

## Musical Instruments Issue

Komunko, Six-stringed Zither A469

Design: 30w, Nagak, shell trumpet.

## 1974, Feb. 20 Photo. — Perf. 13x13½
883 A469 10w lt bl, blk & brn 1.00 .30
884 A469 30w orange & multi 2.75 .50

## 1974, Apr. 20
Designs: 10w, Tchouk; wooden hammer in slanted box, used to start orchestra. 30w, Eu; crouching tiger, used to stop orchestra.
885 A469 10w brt blue & multi 1.10 .25
886 A469 30w lt green & multi 2.25 .35

## 1974, June 20
Designs: 10w, A-chaing, 7-stringed instrument. 30w, Kyobang-ko, drum.
887 A469 10w dull yel & multi 1.30 .25
888 A469 30w salmon pink & multi 2.25 .35

## 1974, Aug. 20
Designs: 10w, So, 16-pipe ritual instrument. 30w, Kaikeum, 2-stringed fiddle.
889 A469 10w lt blue & multi .80 .30
890 A469 30w brt pink & multi 1.60 .40

## 1974, Oct. 20
10w, Pak (clappers). 30w, Pyenchong (bell chimes).
891 A469 10w lt lilac & multi .95 .30
892 A469 30w lemon & multi 1.90 .40
  Nos. 883-892 (10) 15.90 3.40

### Souvenir Sheets of 2
883a A469 10w (#1) 4.25 4.25
884a A469 30w (#2) 7.25 7.25
885a A469 10w (#3) 3.50 3.50
886a A469 30w (#4) 5.50 5.50
887a A469 10w (#5) 3.50 3.50
888a A469 30w (#6) 5.50 5.50
889a A469 10w (#7) 2.25 2.25
890a A469 30w (#8) 3.75 3.75
891a A469 10w (#9) 2.75 2.75
892a A469 30w (#10) 5.00 5.00
  Nos. 883a-892a (10) 43.25 43.25

## Fruit Issue

Apricots — A470

## 1974, Mar. 30 Photo. — Perf. 13x13½
893 A470 10w shown .90 .30
894 A470 30w Strawberries 2.10 .40

## 1974, May 30
895 A470 10w Peaches .90 .30
896 A470 30w Grapes 2.10 .45

## 1974, July 30
897 A470 10w Pears .60 .30
898 A470 30w Apples 2.00 .45

## 1974, Sept. 30
899 A470 10w Cherries .75 .30
900 A470 30w Persimmons 1.90 .45

## 1974, Nov. 30
901 A470 10w Tangerines .60 .30
902 A470 30w Chestnuts 1.25 .35
  Nos. 893-902 (10) 13.10 3.60

### Souvenir Sheets of 2
893a A470 10w (#1) 3.25 3.25
894a A470 30w (#2) 6.75 6.75
895a A470 10w (#3) 3.25 3.25
896a A470 30w (#4) 6.00 6.00
897a A470 10w (#5) 2.75 2.75
898a A470 30w (#6) 6.50 6.50
899a A470 10w (#7) 2.10 2.10
900a A470 30w (#8) 4.25 4.25
901a A470 10w (#9) 2.40 2.40
902a A470 30w (#10) 3.00 3.00
  Nos. 893a-902a (10) 40.25 40.25

Reservist and Factory — A471

## 1974, Apr. 6 Photo. — Perf. 13½x13
903 A471 10w yellow & multi .70 .25
Homeland Reserve Forces Day.

WPY Emblem and Scales — A472

## 1974, Apr. 10 — Perf. 13x13½
904 A472 10w salmon & multi .55 .25
  a. Souvenir sheet of 2 4.25 4.25
World Population Year 1974.

Train and Communications Emblem — A473

## 1974, Apr. 22 — Perf. 13½x13
905 A473 10w multicolored .65 .25
19th Communications Day.

Emblem and Stylized Globe — A474

## 1974, May 6 Photo. — Perf. 13
906 A474 10w red lilac & multi .55 .25
22nd Session of Intl. Chamber of Commerce (Eastern Division), Seoul, May 6-8.

New Dock at Inchon — A475

## 1974, May 10
907 A475 10w yellow & multi .65 .25
Dedication of dock, Inchon.

UNESCO Emblem, "20" and Yin Yang — A476

## 1974, June 14 Photo. — Perf. 13
908 A476 10w org yel & multi .55 .25
20th anniversary of the Korean National Commission for UNESCO.

EXPLO '74 Emblems — A477

Design: No. 910, EXPLO emblem rising from map of Korea.

## 1974, Aug. 13 Photo. — Perf. 13
909 A477 10w orange & multi .50 .25
910 A477 10w blue & multi .50 .25
EXPLO '74, International Christian Congress, Yoido Islet, Seoul, Aug. 13-18.

Subway, Bus and Plane — A478

## 1974, Aug. 15
911 A478 10w green & multi .80 .25
Inauguration of Seoul subway (first in Korea), Aug. 15, 1974.

Target Shooting A479

## 1974, Oct. 8 Photo. — Perf. 13x13½
912 A479 10w shown .55 .25
913 A479 30w Rowing 1.75 .40
55th National Athletic Meet.

UPU Emblem — A480

## 1974, Oct. 9 — Perf. 13
914 A480 10w yellow & multi .45 .25
  a. Souvenir sheet of 2 4.50 4.50
Cent. of UPU. See No. C43.

International Landmarks — A481

## 1974, Oct. 11 Photo. — Perf. 13
915 A481 10w multicolored .55 .25
Intl. People to People Conf., Seoul, 10/11-14.

Korea Nos. 1-2 — A482

## 1974, Oct. 17
916 A482 10w lilac & multi .70 .25
  a. Souvenir sheet of 2 7.25 7.25
Philatelic Week, Oct. 17-23 and 90th anniversary of first Korean postage stamps.

Taekwondo and Kukkiwon Center — A483

## 1974, Oct. 18
917 A483 10w yellow grn & multi .55 .25
First Asian Taekwondo (self-defense) Games, Seoul, Oct. 18-20.

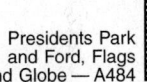
Presidents Park and Ford, Flags and Globe — A484

## 1974, Nov. 22 Photo. — Perf. 13
918 A484 10y multicolored .95 .30
  a. Souvenir sheet of 2 7.50 7.50
Visit of Pres. Gerald R. Ford to South Korea.

Yook Young Soo — A485

## 1974, Nov. 29
919 A485 10w green .95 .30
920 A485 10w orange .95 .30
921 A485 10w lilac .95 .30
922 A485 10w blue .95 .30
  a. Souvenir sheet of 4, #919-922 32.00 32.00
  b. Block of 4, #919-922 3.75 3.00
Yook Young Soo (1925-1974), wife of Pres. Park.

Rabbits A486

Good-luck Purse A487

**1974, Dec. 1    Litho.    Perf. 12½x13**
923  A486  10w multicolored                    .70    .25
 a.    Souvenir sheet of 2                     4.00   4.00
924  A487  10w multicolored                    .70    .25
 a.    Souvenir sheet of 2                     4.00   4.00
New Year 1975.

Good-luck Key and Pigeon — A488

**1975, Jan. 1    Photo.    Perf. 13**
925  A488  10w lt blue & multi                        .55    .25
Introduction of Natl. Welfare Insurance System.

UPU Emblem and "75" A489

UPU Emblem and Paper Plane A490

**1975, Jan. 1**
926  A489  10w yellow & multi                  .55    .25
927  A490  10w lt blue & multi                 .55    .25
75th anniv. of Korea's membership in UPU.

Dr. Albert Schweitzer, Map of Africa, Hypodermic Needle — A491

**1975, Jan. 14**
928  A491  10w olive                           .95    .35
929  A491  10w brt rose                        .95    .35
930  A491  10w orange                          .95    .35
931  A491  10w brt green                       .95    .35
 a.    Block of 4, #928-931                    4.75   3.00

**Folk Dance Issue**

Dancer — A492

No. 933, Dancer with fan.

**1975, Feb. 20    Photo.    Perf. 13**
932  A492  10w emerald & multi                 .70    .25
933  A492  10w brt blue & multi                .70    .25

No. 934, Woman with butterfly sleeves. No. 935, Group of Women.

**1975, Apr. 20**
934  A492  10w yel grn & multi                 .70    .25
935  A492  10w yellow & multi                  .70    .25

No. 936, Pongsan mask dance. No. 937, Pusan mask dance.

**1975, June 20**
936  A492  10w pink & multi                    .70    .25
937  A492  10w blue & multi                    .70    .25

No. 938, Buddhist drum dance. No. 939, Bara (cymbals) dance.

**1975, Aug. 20**
938  A492  20w yellow & multi                  1.25   .40
939  A492  20w salmon & multi                  1.25   .40

Bupo Nori — A492a

No. 940, Sogo dance.

**1975, Oct. 20**
940  A492  20w blue & multi                    1.35   .40
941  A492a 20w yellow & multi                  1.35   .40
     Nos. 932-941 (10)                         9.40   3.10

**Souvenir Sheets of 2**
932a  A492  10w (#1)                           1.75   1.75
933a  A492  10w (#2)                           1.75   1.75
934a  A492  10w (#3)                           1.60   1.60
935a  A492  10w (#4)                           1.60   1.60
936a  A492  10w (#5)                           1.60   1.60
937a  A492  10w (#6)                           1.60   1.60
938a  A492  20w (#7)                           2.50   2.50
939a  A492  20w (#8)                           2.50   2.50
940a  A492  20w (#9)                           2.50   2.50
941a  A492  20w (#10)                          2.50   2.50
      Nos. 932a-941a (10)                      19.90  19.90

Globe and Rotary Emblem — A493

**1975, Feb. 23**
942  A493  10w multicolored                          .60    .25
Rotary International, 70th anniversary.

Women and IWY Emblem — A494

**1975, Mar. 8**
943  A494  10w multicolored                          .60    .25
International Women's Year 1975.

**Flower Issue**

Violets A495

Anemones A496

**1975, Mar. 15**
944  A495  10w orange & multi                  .65    .25
945  A496  10w yellow & multi                  .65    .25

Clematis Patens — A496a

No. 946, Rhododendron.

**1975, May 15**
946  A495   10w dk grn & multi                 .75    .25
947  A496a  10w yel grn & multi                .75    .25

No. 948, Thistle. No. 949, Iris.

**1975, July 15**
948  A495  10w emerald & multi                 .75    .25
949  A495  10w blue & multi                    .75    .25

Broad-bell Flowers — A496b

No. 951, Bush clover.

**1975, Sept. 15**
950  A496b  20w yellow & multi                 1.30   .30
951  A495   20w blue grn & multi               1.25   .30

No. 952, Camellia. No. 953, Gentian.

**1975, Nov. 15**
952  A495  20w yellow & multi                  1.90   1.45
953  A496  20w salmon & multi                  1.75   .45
     Nos. 944-953 (10)                         10.50  4.00

Forest and Water Resources — A497

**1975, Mar. 20**
954  A497     Strip of 4                       4.50   3.00
 a.    10w Saemaeul forest                     .70    .30
 b.    10w Dam and reservoir                   .70    .30
 c.    10w Green forest                        .70    .30
 d.    10w Timber industry                     .70    .30
Natl. Tree Planting Month, Mar. 21-Apr. 20.

Map of Korea, HRF Emblem — A498

**1975, Apr. 12    Photo.    Perf. 13**
955  A498  10w blue & multi                          .65    .25
Homeland Reserve Forces Day.

Lily A499

Ceramic Jar A500

Ceramic Vase A501

Adm. Li Sun-sin A502

**1975        Photo.        Perf. 13½x13**
963  A499    6w green & bl grn                 .55    .25
964  A500   50w gray grn & brn                 .75    .25
965  A501   60w brown & yellow                 .95    .25
966  A502  100w carmine                        2.25   .50
     Nos. 963-966 (4)                          4.50   1.25
Issued: Nos. 964-965, 3/15/75; Nos. 963, 966, 10/10/75.

Metric System Symbols — A507

**1975, May 20                    Perf. 13**
975  A507  10w salmon & multi                        .60    .25
Centenary of International Meter Convention, Paris, 1875.

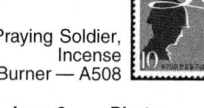
Praying Soldier, Incense Burner — A508

**1975, June 6    Photo.    Perf. 13**
976  A508  10w multicolored                          .55    .25
20th Memorial Day.

Flags of Korea, UN and US — A509

Designs (Flags of): No. 978, Ethiopia, France, Greece, Canada, South Africa. No. 979, Luxembourg, Australia, Great Britain, Colombia, Turkey. No. 980, Netherlands, Belgium, Philippines, New Zealand, Thailand.

**1975, June 25    Photo.    Perf. 13**
977  A509  10w dk blue & multi                 .70    .30
978  A509  10w dk blue & multi                 .70    .30
979  A509  10w dk blue & multi                 .70    .30
980  A509  10w dk blue & multi                 .70    .30
 a.    Strip of 4, #977-980                    4.00   2.75
25th anniv. of beginning of Korean War.

Presidents Park and Bongo, Flags of Korea and Gabon — A510

**1975, July 5**
981  A510  10w blue & multi                          .60    .25
 a.    Souvenir sheet of 2                     2.75   2.75
Visit of Pres. Albert Bongo of Gabon, 7/5-8.

Scout Emblem, Tents and Neckerchief — A511

**1975, July 29    Photo.    Perf. 13**
982  A511  10w shown                           .80    .30
983  A511  10w Pick and oath                   .80    .30
984  A511  10w Tents                           .80    .30
985  A511  10w Ax, rope and tree               .80    .30
986  A511  10w Campfire                        .80    .30
 a.    Strip of 5, #982-986                    4.75   3.50
Nordjamb 75, 14th Boy Scout Jamboree, Lillehammer, Norway, July 29-Aug. 7.

Flame and Broken Chain — A512

Balloons with Symbols of Development over Map — A513

**1975, Aug. 15                    Perf. 13½x13**
987  A512  20w gold & multi                    .75    .25
988  A513  20w silver & multi                  .75    .25
30th anniversary of liberation.

Taekwondo — A514

**1975, Aug. 26                    Perf. 13**
989  A514  20w multicolored                          .60    .25
2nd World Taekwondo Championships, Seoul, Aug. 25-Sept. 1.

National Assembly and Emblem — A515

**1975, Sept. 1    Photo.    Perf. 13½x13**
990  A515  20w multicolored                          .60    .25
Completion of National Assembly Building.

Convention Emblem and Dump Truck — A516

**1975, Sept. 7   Photo.   Perf. 13½x13**
991  A516  20w ultra & multi   .60   .25
14th Convention of the Intl. Fed. of Asian and Western Pacific Contractors.

Cassegrainian Telescope and Morse Key — A517

**1975, Sept. 28**
992  A517  20w red lil, org & blk   .60   .25
90th anniversary of Korean telecommunications system.

Stalactite Cave, Yeongweol A518    View of Mt. Sorak A519

**1975, Sept. 28**
993  A518  20w multicolored   .65   .25
994  A519  20w multicolored   .65   .25
International Tourism Day.

Armed Forces Flag and Missiles — A519a

**1975, Oct. 1   Photo.   Perf. 13**
994A  A519a  20w multicolored   .60   .25
Armed Forces Day.

Gymnastics A520    Handball A521

**1975, Oct. 7   Photo.   Perf. 13**
995  A520  20w yellow & multi   .50   .25
996  A521  20w multicolored   .50   .25
56th Natl. Athletic Meet, Taegu, Oct. 7-12.

Stamp Collecting Kangaroo — A522

**1975, Oct. 8**
997  A522  20w multicolored   .60   .25
Philatelic Week, Oct. 8-14.

Hands and UN Emblem — A523

**1975, Oct. 24**
998  A523  20w multicolored   .60   .25
United Nations, 30th anniversary.

Red Cross and Activities — A524

**1975, Oct. 30**
999  A524  20w orange, red & brn   .60   .25
Korean Red Cross, 70th anniversary.

Emblem and Dove — A525

**1975, Nov. 30   Photo.   Perf. 13**
1000  A525  20w multicolored   .60   .25
Asian Parliamentary Union, 10th anniv.

Children Playing A526    Dragon A527

**1975, Dec. 1**
1001  A526  20w multicolored   .65   .25
 a.   Souvenir sheet of 2   1.90  1.90
1002  A527  20w multicolored   .65   .25
 a.   Souvenir sheet of 2   1.90  1.90
New Year 1976.

Inchong-Bukpyong Railroad — A528

**1975, Dec. 5   Photo.   Perf. 13**
1003  A528  20w multicolored   .60   .25
Opening of electric cross-country railroad.

**Butterfly Issue**

Dilipa Fenestra — A529

Butterflies: No. 1005, Luehdorfia puziloi.

**1976, Jan. 20   Photo.   Perf. 13**
1004  A529  20w dp rose & multi   1.60   .30
1005  A529  20w dp blue & multi   1.60   .30

Butterflies: No. 1006, Papilio xuthus linne. No. 1007, Parnassius bremeri.

**1976, Mar. 20**
1006  A529  20w yellow & multi   1.60   .30
1007  A529  20w yel grn & multi   1.60   .30

Byasa Alcinous Klug — A529a

Butterflies: No. 1008, Colias erate esper.

**1976, June 20**
1008  A529  20w lt violet & multi   1.50   .30
1009  A529a  20w citron & multi   1.50   .30

Graphium Sarpedon — A529b

Butterflies: No. 1010, Hestina assimilis.

**1976, Aug. 20**
1010  A529  20w tan & multi   2.00   .70
1011  A529b  20w lt gray & multi   1.90   .70

Fabriciana Nerippe A529c    Nymphalis Xanthomelas A529d

**1976, Oct. 20**
1012  A529c  20w lt grn & multi   2.60   .80
1013  A529d  20w lilac & multi   2.60   .80
 Nos. 1004-1013 (10)   18.50  4.80

Emblems of Science, Industry and KIST — A530

**1976, Feb. 10   Photo.   Perf. 13**
1014  A530  20w multicolored   .60   .25
Korean Institute of Science and Technology (KIST), 10th anniversary.

**Birds Issue**

A531    A532

No. 1015, Siberian Bustard. No. 1016, White-naped Crane.

**1976, Feb. 20   Photo.   Perf. 13x13½**
1015  A531  20w multicolored   1.25   .35
1016  A532  20w multicolored   1.25   .35

A532a    A532b

No. 1017, Blue-winged pitta. No. 1018, Tristam's woodpecker.

**1976, May 20**
1017  A532a  20w multicolored   1.25   .35
1018  A532b  20w multicolored   1.25   .35

A532c    A532d

No. 1019, Wood pigeon. No. 1020, Oyster catcher.

**1976, July 20**
1019  A532c  20w multicolored   1.25   .35
1020  A532d  20w multicolored   1.25   .35

A532e    A532f

No. 1021, Black-faced spoonbill. No. 1022, Black stork.

**1976, Sept. 20**
1021  A532e  20w multicolored   1.25   .35
1022  A532f  20w multicolored   1.25   .35

A532g    A532h

No. 1023, Whooper swan. No. 1024, Black vulture.

**1976, Nov. 20**
1023  A532g  20w multicolored   3.25  1.15
1024  A532h  20w multicolored   3.25  1.15
 Nos. 1015-1024 (10)   16.50  5.10

1876 and 1976 Telephones, Globe — A533

**1976, Mar. 10**
1025  A533  20w multicolored   .60   .25
Centenary of first telephone call by Alexander Graham Bell, Mar. 10, 1876.

Homeland Reserves — A534

**1976, Apr. 3   Photo.   Perf. 13½x13**
1026  A534  20w multicolored   .60   .25
8th Homeland Reserve Forces Day.

"People and Eye" — A535

**1976, Apr. 7   Perf. 13x13½**
1027  A535  20w multicolored   .60   .25
World Health Day; "Foresight prevents blindness."

Pres. Park, New Village Movement Flag A536    Intellectual Pursuits A537

No. 1030, Village improvement. No. 1031, Agriculture. No. 1032, Income from production.

**1976, Apr. 22**
1028  A536  20w shown   1.45   .45
1029  A537  20w shown   1.45   .45
1030  A537  20w multicolored   1.45   .45
1031  A537  20w multicolored   1.45   .45
1032  A537  20w multicolored   1.45   .45
 a.   Strip of 5, #1028-1032   10.00  6.00
6th anniv. of Pres. Park's New Village Movement for National Prosperity.

Mohenjo-Daro A538

**1976, May 1   Perf. 13½x13**
1033  A538  20w multicolored   .60   .25
UNESCO campaign to save the Mohenjo-Daro excavations in Pakistan.

13-Star and 50-Star
Flags — A539

American Bicentennial (Bicentennial
Emblem and): No. 1035, Statue of Liberty.
No. 1036, Map of US and Mt. Rushmore monument. No. 1037, Liberty Bell. No. 1038, First
astronaut on moon.

**1976, May 8**                        ***Perf. 13x13½***
1034 A539 100w blk, dp bl &
                      red                2.60   .85
  *a.*  Souvenir sheet of 1        5.50   5.50
1035 A539 100w blk, dp bl &
                      red                2.60   .85
1036 A539 100w blk, dp bl &
                      red                2.60   .85
1037 A539 100w blk, dp bl &
                      red                2.60   .85
1038 A539 100w blk, dp bl &
                      red                2.60   .85
  *Nos. 1034-1038 (5)*            13.00  4.25

Girl Scouts, Campfire
and Emblem — A540

**1976, May 10**
1039 A540 20w orange & multi      1.00   .25
Korean Federation of Girl Scouts, 30th anniv.

Stupas, Buddha of
Borobudur — A541

**1976, June 10**
1040 A541 20w multicolored        .60   .25
UNESCO campaign to save the Borobudur
Temple, Java.

"Life Insurance" — A542

**1976, July 1   Photo.   *Perf. 13x13½***
1041 A542 20w multicolored        .60   .25
National Life Insurance policies: "Over 100
billion-won," Apr. 30, 1976.

Volleyball — A543

**1976, July 17**
1042 A543 20w shown               .50   .25
1043 A543 20w Boxing              .50   .25
21st Olympic Games, Montreal, Canada,
July 17-Aug. 1.

Children and
Books — A544

**1976, Aug. 10**                ***Perf. 13½x13***
1044 A544 20w brown & multi       .60   .25
Books for children.

Civil Defense Corps,
Flag and
Members — A545

**1976, Sept. 15**                 ***Perf. 13x13½***
1045 A545 20w multicolored        .60   .25
Civil Defense Corps, first anniversary.

Chamsungdan,              Front Gate,
Mani                       Tongdosa
Mountain — A546            Temple — A547

**1976, Sept. 28**               ***Perf. 13½x13***
1046 A546 20w multicolored        .70   .25
1047 A547 20w multicolored        .70   .25
International Tourism Day.

Cadets and
Academy — A548

**1976, Oct. 1**
1048 A548 20w multicolored        .60   .25
Korean Military Academy, 30th anniversary.

Leaves and Stones, by
Cheong Ju — A549

**1976, Oct. 5**                   ***Perf. 13x13½***
1049 A549 20w blk, gray & red     .60   .25
  *a.*  Souvenir sheet of 2         4.25   4.25
Philatelic Week, Oct. 5-11.

Snake-                    Door-pull
headed                    and Cranes
Figure, Bas-              A551
relief
A550

**1976, Dec. 1   Photo.   *Perf. 13x13½***
1050 A550 20w multicolored        .60   .25
  *a.*  Souvenir sheet of 2         2.25   2.25
1051 A551 20w multicolored        .60   .25
  *a.*  Souvenir sheet of 2         2.25   2.25
New Year 1977.

Arrows, Cogwheels,
Worker at
Lathe — A552

No. 1053, Arrows, Cogwheels, ship in dock.

**1977, Jan. 20   Photo.   *Perf. 13½x13***
1052 A552 20w multicolored        .60   .25
1053 A552 20w multicolored        .60   .25
4th Economic Development Five-Year Plan.

Satellite Antenna and
Microwaves — A553

**1977, Jan. 31**                  ***Perf. 13x13½***
1054 A553 20w multicolored        .60   .25
Membership in ITU, 25th anniv.

Korean
Broadcasting
Center — A554

**1977, Feb. 16**                  ***Perf. 13½x13***
1055 A554 20w multicolored        .60   .25
50th anniversary of broadcasting in Korea.

Parents and Two
Children — A555

**1977, Apr. 1   Photo.   *Perf. 13½x13***
1056 A555 20w brt grn & orange   2.10   .25
Family planning.

Reservist on
Duty — A556

**1977, Apr. 2**                   ***Perf. 13x13½***
1057 A556 20w multicolored        .60   .25
9th Homeland Reserve Forces Day.

Head with
Symbols — A557

**1977, Apr. 21   Photo.   *Perf. 13x13½***
1058 A557 20w dp lilac & multi    .60   .25
10th anniversary of Science Day.

Book, Map,
Syringe — A558

**1977, Apr. 25**
1059 A558 20w blue & multi        .60   .25
35th Intl. Meeting on Military Medicine.

Boy with Flowers and
Dog — A559

**1977, May 5**
1060 A559 20w multicolored        .60   .25
Proclamation of Children's Charter, 20th
anniversary.

Veteran's Emblem and
Flag — A560

**1977, May 8**
1061 A560 20w multicolored        .60   .25
25th anniversary of Korean Veterans' Day.

Buddha, 8th Century,
Sokkulam
Grotto — A561

**1977, May 25   Photo.   *Perf. 13x13½***
1062 A561 20w sepia & olive       .55   .25
  *a.*  Souvenir sheet of 2         4.50   4.50
"2600th" anniversary of birth of Buddha.

**Ceramic Issues**

Jar with                  Celadon
Grape                     Vase,
Design, 17th              Bamboo
Century                   Design, 12th
A562                      Century
                          A563

**1977, Mar. 15   Photo.   *Perf. 13x13½***
1063 A562 20w vio brn & multi    1.75   .30
1064 A563 20w gray, grn & bis    1.75   .30

Celadon Jar with          Vase with
Peonies                   Willow Reed
A564                      Peony
                          Pattern
                          A565

***Perf. 13x13½, 13½x13***
**1977, June 15**                          **Photo.**
1065 A564 20w multicolored        .95   .30
1066 A565 20w multicolored        .95   .30

Celadon Manshaped
Wine Jug — A566

Celadon Melon-shaped
Vase — A567

**1977, July 15**
1067 A566 20w multicolored        .90   .25
1068 A567 20w multicolored        .90   .25

**1977, Aug. 15**

Designs: No. 1069, White porcelain bowl
with inlaid lotus vine design. No. 1070, Black
Koryo ware vase with plum blossom vine.

1069 A564 20w multicolored        .90   .25
1070 A565 20w multicolored        .90   .25

Punch'ong Jar
A568

Celadon Cylindrical Vase
A569

**1977, Nov. 15**
1071 A568 20w multicolored .85 .25
1072 A569 20w multicolored .85 .25
Nos. 1063-1072 (10) 10.70 2.70

**Types of 1962-66**
**Designs as Before**
**1976-77     Litho.     Perf. 12½**
**Granite Paper**
1076 A187 200w brn & lt
grn 25.00 7.00
1077 A187a 300w sl grn &
sal ('76) 50.00 8.00
1078 A187a 300w brn & sal 50.00 8.00
1079 A187a 500w pur & lt
grn 100.00 10.00

Magpie
A570

Nature Protection
A571

"Family Planning"
A572

Children on Swing
A573

Ceramic Horseman
A574

Muryangsu Hall, Busok Temple
A575

Pagoda, Pobjusa Temple
A576

Gold Crown, from Chonmachong Mound
A577

Monster Mask Tile, 6th or 7th Century — A578

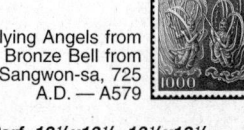

Flying Angels from Bronze Bell from Sangwon-sa, 725 A.D. — A579

**Perf. 12½x13½, 13½x12½**
**1977-79     Photo.**
1088 A570 3w lt blue & blk .60 .25
1090 A326 10w emer & blk .55 .25
1091 A571 20w multicolored .65 .25
1092 A572 20w emer & blk
('78) 1.00 .25
1093 A573 20w grn & org
('79) .45 .25
1097 A574 80w lt brn & sep 1.60 .35
1099 A575 200w salmon & brn 1.75 .50
1100 A576 300w brn purple 2.25 .60
1101 A577 500w multicolored 25.00 1.35
**Perf. 13½x13**
1102 A578 500w brown & pur 13.50 1.00

**Perf. 13**
1103 A579 1000w slate grn
('78) 7.75 1.20
Nos. 1088-1103 (11) 55.10 6.25

Ulleung Island — A580

Design: No. 1105, Haeundae Beach.

**1977, Sept. 28     Photo.     Perf. 13**
1104 A580 20w multicolored .60 .25
1105 A580 20w multicolored .60 .25
World Tourism Day.

Armed Forces Day — A581

**1977, Oct. 1     Photo.     Perf. 13**
1106 A581 20w green & multi .60 .25

Mt. Inwang after the Rain, by Chung Seon (1676-1759) A582

**1977, Oct. 4**
1107 20w mountain, clouds .85 .25
1108 20w mountain, house .85 .25
a. Souvenir sheet of 2 7.50 7.50
b. A582 Pair, #1107-1108 2.00 1.50
Philatelic Week, Oct. 4-10.

Rotary Emblem on Bronze Bell, Koryo Dynasty — A584

**1977, Nov. 10     Photo.     Perf. 13**
1109 A584 20w multicolored .55 .25
Korean Rotary Club, 50th anniversary.

Korean Flag on Mt. Everest — A585

**1977, Nov. 11**
1110 A585 20w multicolored .85 .25
Korean Mt. Everest Expedition, reached peak, Sept. 15, 1977.

Children and Kites
A586

Horse-headed Figure, Bas-relief
A587

**1977, Dec. 1     Photo.     Perf. 13**
1111 A586 20w multicolored .40 .25
a. Souvenir sheet of 2 2.00 2.00
1112 A587 20w multicolored .40 .25
a. Souvenir sheet of 2 2.00 2.00
New Year 1978.

Clay Pigeon Shooting — A588

Designs: No. 1114, Air pistol shooting. No. 1115, Air rifle shooting and target.

**1977, Dec. 3**
1113 A588 20w multicolored .50 .25
a. Souvenir sheet of 2 ('78) 4.00 4.00
1114 A588 20w multicolored .50 .25
a. Souvenir sheet of 2 ('78) 4.00 4.00
1115 A588 20w multicolored .50 .25
a. Souvenir sheet of 2 ('78) 4.00 4.00
Nos. 1113-1115 (3) 1.50 .75
Nos. 1113a-1115a (3) 12.00
42nd World Shooting Championships, Seoul, 1978.

Boeing 727 over Globe, ICAO Emblem — A589

**1977, Dec. 11**
1116 A589 20w multicolored .55 .25
25th anniv. of Korea's membership in the ICAO.

Plane, Cargo, Freighter and Globe — A590

**1977, Dec. 22     Photo.     Perf. 13**
1117 A590 20w multicolored .55 .25
Korean exports.

Ships and World Map — A591

**1978, Mar. 13     Photo.     Perf. 13**
1118 A591 20w multicolored .55 .25
Maritime Day.

**Stone Pagoda Issue**

Four Lions Pagoda, Hwaom-sa — A592

Seven-storied Pagoda, T'appyongri — A592a

**1978, Mar. 20     Photo.     Perf. 13**
1119 A592 20w lt green & multi 1.25 .30
1120 A592a 20w ocher & multi 1.25 .30

Punhwang-sa Temple — A593

Miruk-sa Temple — A593a

**1978, May 20**
1121 A593 20w lt green & blk 1.25 .30
1122 A593a 20w grn, brn & yel 1.25 .30

Tabo Pagoda, Pulguk-sa — A592b

Three-storied pagoda, Pulguk-sa — A592c

**1978, June 20**
1123 A592b 20w gray, lt grn &
blk .95 .25
1124 A592c 20w lilac & black .95 .25

Kyongch'on sa Temple — A594

Octagonal Pagoda, Wolchong-sa Temple — A594a

**1978, July 20     Perf. 13½x12½**
1125 A594 20w gray & brn 1.60 .30
1126 A594a 20w lt green & blk 1.60 .30

13-storied Pagoda, Jeonghye-sa — A592d

Three-storied Pagoda, Jinjeon-sa — A592e

**1978, Nov. 20     Perf. 13x13½**
1127 A592d 20w pale grn &
multi .55 .25
1128 A592e 20w lilac & multi .55 .25
Nos. 1119-1128 (10) 11.20 2.80

Ants and Coins — A595

**1978, Apr. 1**
1129 A595 20w multicolored .55 .25
Importance of saving.

Reservist with Flag — A596

**1978, Apr. 1**
1130 A596 20w multicolored .55 .25
10th Homeland Reserve Forces Day.

Seoul Cultural Center — A597

1978, Apr. 1

1131 A597 20w multicolored .75 .25

Opening of Seoul Cultural Center.

National Assembly in Plenary Session — A598

1978, May 31

1132 A598 20w multicolored .55 .25

30th anniversary of National Assembly.

Hands Holding Tools, Competition Emblem — A599

1978, Aug. 5 Photo. *Perf. 13*

1133 A599 20w multicolored .55 .25
a. Souvenir sheet of 2 3.25 3.25

24th World Youth Skill Olympics, Busan, Aug. 30-Sept. 15.

Bell of Joy and Crater Lake, Mt. Baegdu — A600

1978, Aug. 15

1134 A600 20w multicolored .55 .25

Founding of republic, 30th anniversary.

Nurse, Badge and Flowers — A601

1978, Aug. 26

1135 A601 20w multicolored .55 .25

Army Nurse Corps, 30th anniversary.

Sobaeksan Observatory — A602

1978, Sept. 13 Photo. *Perf. 13*

1136 A602 20w multicolored .55 .25

Opening of Sobaeksan Natl. Observatory.

Kyunghoeru Pavilion, Kyongbok Palace, Seoul — A603

Design: No. 1138, Baeg Do (island).

1978, Sept. 28

1137 A603 20w multicolored .45 .25
1138 A603 20w multicolored .45 .25

Tourist publicity.

Customs Flag and Officers — A604

1978, Sept. 28

1139 A604 20w multicolored .45 .25

Cent. of 1st Korean Custom House, Busan.

Armed Forces — A605

1978, Oct. 1 Photo. *Perf. 13*

1140 A605 20w multicolored .45 .25

Armed Forces, 30th anniversary.

Clay Figurines, Silla Dynasty — A606

1978, Oct. 1

1141 A606 20w lt green & blk .45 .25

Culture Month, October 1978.

Portrait of a Lady, by Shin Yoon-bok — A607

1978, Oct. 24

1142 A607 20w multicolored .50 .25
a. Souvenir sheet of 2 3.50 3.50

Philatelic Week, Oct. 24-29.

Young Men, YMCA Emblem — A608

1978, Oct. 28

1143 A608 20w multicolored .45 .25

75th anniv. of founding of Korean YMCA.

Hand Protecting Against Fire — A609

1978, Nov. 1 Photo. *Perf. 13*

1144 A609 20w multicolored .45 .25

Fire Prevention Day, Nov. 1.

Winter Landscape A610

Ram-headed Figure, Bas-relief A611

1978, Dec. 1 Photo. *Perf. 13x13½*

1145 A610 20w multicolored .55 .25
a. Souvenir sheet of 2 1.75 1.75
1146 A611 20w multicolored .55 .25
a. Souvenir sheet of 2 1.75 1.75

New Year 1979.

Hibiscus, Students, Globe — A612

1978, Dec. 5

1147 A612 20w multicolored .45 .25

Proclamation of National Education Charter, 10th anniversary.

President Park — A613

1978, Dec. 27

1148 A613 20w multicolored 1.00 .25
a. Souvenir sheet of 2 11.00 11.00

Inauguration of Park Chung Hee for fifth term as president.

Nature Conservation Issue

Golden Mandarinfish A614

Lace-bark Pines A615

1979, Feb. 20 Photo. *Perf. 13x13½*

1149 A614 20w multicolored 1.60 .25
1150 A615 20w multicolored 1.60 .25

Mandarin Ducks A616

Neofinettia Orchid A617

1979, May 20

1151 A616 20w multicolored 1.60 .25
1152 A617 20w multicolored 1.60 .25

Goral A618

Lilies of the Valley A619

1979, June 20

1153 A618 20w multicolored 1.60 .25
1154 A619 20w multicolored 1.60 .25

Rain Frog A620

Asian Polypody A621

1979, Nov. 25

1155 A620 20w multicolored 1.60 .25
1156 A621 20w multicolored 1.60 .25

Firefly A622

Meesun Tree A623

1980, Jan. 20

1157 A622 30w multicolored 1.60 .25
1158 A623 30w multicolored 1.60 .25
Nos. 1149-1158 (10) 16.00 2.50

Samil Monument — A624

1979, Mar. 1 Photo. *Perf. 13x13½*

1159 A624 20w multicolored .45 .25

Samil independence movement, 60th anniv.

Worker and Bulldozer — A625

1979, Mar. 10 *Perf. 13½x13*

1160 A625 20w multicolored .45 .25

Labor Day.

Hand Holding Tools, Gun and Grain — A626

1979, Apr. 1 *Perf. 13x13½*

1161 A626 20w multicolored .45 .25

Strengthening national security.

Tabo Pagoda, Pulguk-sa Temple — A627

Women, Silk Screen A628

Art Treasures: No. 1163, Statue. No. 1164, Crown. No. 1165, Celadon Vase.

1979, Apr. 1

1162 A627 20w gray bl & multi .55 .25
1163 A627 20w bister & multi .55 .25
1164 A627 20w violet & multi .55 .25
1165 A627 20w brt grn & multi .55 .25
1166 A628 60w multicolored .90 .30
a. Souvenir sheet of 2 3.75 3.75
Nos. 1162-1166 (5) 3.10 1.30

5000 years of Korean art.
See Nos. 1175-1179, 1190.

Pulguk-sa Temple and PATA Emblem — A629

1979, Apr. 16 *Perf. 13½x13*

1167 A629 20w multicolored .45 .25

28th Pacific Area Travel Association (PATA) Conf., Seoul, Apr. 16-18, and Gyeongju, Apr. 20-21.

Presidents Park and Senghor — A630

**1979, Apr. 22**     **Perf. 13½x13**
1168 A630 20w multicolored   .45 .25
a.   Souvenir sheet of 2   1.75 1.75

Visit of Pres. Leopold Sedar Senghor of Senegal.

Basketball — A631

**1979, Apr. 29**     **Perf. 13x13½**
1169 A631 20w multicolored   .45 .25

8th World Women's Basketball Championship, Seoul, Apr. 29-May 13.

Children and IYC Emblem — A632

**1979, May 5**   **Photo.**   **Perf. 13½x13**
1170 A632 20w multicolored   .45 .25
a.   Souvenir sheet of 2   1.75 1.75

International Year of the Child.

Traffic Pollution — A633

**1979, June 5**   **Photo.**   **Perf. 13x13½**
1171 A633 20w green & dk brn   .75 .25

Pollution control.

Flags, Presidents Park and Carter — A634

**1979, June 29**     **Perf. 13½x13**
1172 A634 20w multicolored   .45 .25
a.   Souvenir sheet of 2   1.75 1.75

Visit of Pres. Jimmy Carter.

Korean Exhibition Center — A635

**1979, July 3**
1173 A635 20w multicolored   .45 .25

Opening of Korean Exhibition Center.

Jet, Globe, South Gate — A636

**1979, Aug. 1**   **Photo.**   **Perf. 13½x13**
1174 A636 20w multicolored   .45 .25

10th anniversary of Korean airlines.

### Art Treasure Types

Designs: No. 1175, Porcelain jar, 17th century. No. 1176, Man on horseback, ceremonial pitcher, horiz. No. 1177, Sword Dance, by Shin Yun-bok. No. 1178, Golden Amitabha with halo, 8th century. No. 1179, Hahoe ritual mask.

---

**1979**   **Photo.**   **Perf. 13x13½, 13½x13**
1175 A627 20w lilac & multi   .60 .25
1176 A627 20w multicolored   .60 .25
1177 A627 60w multicolored   1.00 .30
a.   Souvenir sheet of 2   4.75 4.75
Nos. 1175-1177 (3)   2.20 .80

Issued: No. 1177, 9/1; Nos. 1175-1176, 10/15.

**1979, Nov. 15**
1178 A627 20w dp green & multi   .50 .25
1179 A627 20w multicolored   .50 .25

Yongdu Rock — A637

**1979, Sept. 28**
1180 A637 20w shown   .50 .25
1181 A637 20w Mt. Mai, vert.   .50 .25

World Tourism Day.

People, Blood and Heart — A637a

**1979, Oct. 1**     **Perf. 13½x13**
1182 A637a 20w multicolored   .70 .25

Blood Banks, 4th anniversary.

"My Life in the Year 2000" — A638

**1979, Oct. 30**     **Perf. 13½x13**
1183 A638 20w multicolored   .45 .25
a.   Souvenir sheet of 2   1.60 1.60

Philatelic Week, Oct. 30-Nov. 4.

Monkey-headed Figure, Bas-relief A639

Children Playing Yut A640

**1979, Dec. 1**
1184 A639 20w multicolored   .45 .25
a.   Souvenir sheet of 2   1.35 1.35
1185 A640 20w multicolored   .45 .25
a.   Souvenir sheet of 2   1.35 1.35

New Year 1980.

Inauguration of Pres. Choi Kyu-hah — A641

**1979, Dec. 21**
1186 A641 20w multicolored   .50 .25
a.   Souvenir sheet of 2   4.75 4.75

President Park — A642

**1980, Feb. 2**   **Photo.**   **Perf. 13½x13**
1187 A642 30w orange brn   .80 .25
1188 A642 30w dull purple   .80 .25
a.   Souvenir sheet of 2   3.50 3.50
b.   Pair, #1187-1188   2.00 2.00

President Park Chung Hee (1917-1979) memorial.

---

### Art Treasure Type of 1979 and

Dragon-shaped Kettle — A643

Design: 60w, Landscape, by Kim Hong-do.

**Perf. 13½x13, 13x13½**
**1980, Feb. 20**     **Photo.**
1189 A643 30w multicolored   .80 .25
1190 A628 60w multicolored   .90 .30
a.   Souvenir sheet of 2   3.75 3.75

### Art Treasure Issue

Heavenly Horse, Saddle A644

Dragon Head, Banner Staff A645

Tiger, Granite Sculpture A647

Mounted Nobleman Mural A646

Human Face, Roof Tile A648

Deva King Sculpture A650

White Tiger Mural — A649

Earthenware Ducks — A651

Tiger, Folk Painting — A653

**Perf. 13½x13, 13x13½**
**1980-83**     **Photo.**
1191 A644 30w multicolored   .70 .25
1192 A645 30w multicolored   .70 .25
1193 A646 30w multicolored   .70 .25
1194 A647 30w multicolored   .70 .25
1195 A648 30w multicolored   .70 .25
1196 A649 30w multicolored   .70 .25
**Engr.**    **Perf. 12½x13**
1197 A650 30w black   .90 .25
1198 A650 30w red   .90 .25
**1983**    **Litho.**    **Perf. 13**
1199   1000w bis brn & red brn   5.25 .80
1200   1000w bis brn & red brn   5.25 .80
a.   A651 Pair, #1199-1200   10.50 5.00
1201 A653 5000w multicolored   23.00 5.00
a.   Souvenir sheet, perf. 13½x13   30.00
Nos. 1191-1201 (11)   39.50 8.60

Issued: Nos. 1191-1192, 4/20; Nos. 1193-1194, 5/20; Nos. 1195-1196, 8/20; Nos. 1197-

---

1198, 11/20. Nos. 1199-1200, 11/25/83. No. 1201, 12/1/83.
No. 1201a for PHILAKOREA '84. No. 1201a exists imperf. Value $150.

Lotus Blossoms and Ducks A656

Tiger and Magpie A657

**1980, Mar. 10**   **Perf. 13x13½, 13½x13**
1203 A656 30w multicolored   .60 .25
1204 A657 60w multicolored   1.40 .45

Red Phoenix (in Form of Rooster) — A658

Moon Over Mt. Konryun A659

No. 1207, Sun over Mt. Konryun. No. 1207a has continuous design.

**1980, May 10**     **Perf. 13x13½**
1205 A658 30w multicolored   .55 .25
1206 A659 60w multicolored   1.60 .45
1207 A659 60w multicolored   1.60 .45
a.   Souvenir sheet of 2, #1206-1207   4.75 4.75
b.   Pair, #1206-1207   4.25 3.50
Nos. 1205-1207 (3)   3.75 1.15

Rabbits Pounding Grain in a Mortar A660

Dragon in the Clouds A661

**1980, July 10**   **Photo.**   **Perf. 13x13½**
1208 A660 30w multicolored   .65 .25
1209 A661 30w multicolored   .65 .25

Pine Tree, Pavilion, Mountain A662

Flowers and Birds, Bridal Room Screen A663

**1980, Aug. 9**   **Photo.**   **Perf. 13x13½**
1210 A662 30w multicolored   .60 .25
1211 A663 30w multicolored   .95 .30

Tortoises and Cranes — A664

Symbols of longevity: a, cranes, tortoises. b, buck. c, doe. d, waterfall.

**1980, Nov. 10  Photo.   Perf. 13½x13**
| 1212 | A664 | Strip of 4 | 6.75 | 4.50 |
| a.-d. | | 30w any single | 1.35 | .25 |

New Community Movement, 10th Anniv. — A668

**1980, Apr. 22      Perf. 13x13½**
| 1216 | A668 | 30w multicolored | .45 | .25 |

Freighters at Sea — A669

**1980, Mar. 13**
| 1217 | A669 | 30w multicolored | .45 | .25 |

Increase of Korea's shipping tonnage to 5 million tons.

Soccer — A670

**1980, Aug. 23       Perf. 13x13½**
| 1218 | A670 | 30w multicolored | .45 | .25 |

10th President's Cup Soccer Tournament, Aug. 23-Sept. 5.

Mt. Sorak
A671

Paikryung Island
A672

**Perf. 12½x13½**
**1980, Apr. 10          Photo.**
| 1219 | A671 | 15w multicolored | .35 | .25 |
| 1220 | A672 | 90w multicolored | 1.00 | .25 |

Flag — A673

**1980, Sept. 10      Perf. 13½x13**
| 1221 | A673 | 30w multicolored | .40 | .25 |

**Coil Stamp**
**Perf. Vert.**
| 1221A | A673 | 30w multicolored | 1.10 | .25 |

No. 1221A issued 2/1/87.

UN Intervention, 30th Anniv. — A674

**1980, June 25       Perf. 13x13½**
| 1222 | A674 | 30w multicolored | .50 | .25 |

Election of Miss World in Seoul — A675

**1980, July 8**
| 1223 | A675 | 30w multicolored | .50 | .25 |

---

Women's Army Corps, 30th Anniversary
A676

**1980, Sept. 6          Perf. 13½x13**
| 1224 | A676 | 30w multicolored | .50 | .25 |

Baegma River — A677

Three Peaks of Dodam — A678

**1980, Sept. 28**
| 1225 | A677 | 30w multicolored | .35 | .25 |
| 1226 | A678 | 30w multicolored | .35 | .25 |

Inauguration of Pres. Chun Doo-hwan — A679

**1980, Sept. 1**
| 1227 | A679 | 30w multicolored | .60 | .25 |
| a. | | Souvenir sheet of 2 | 3.25 | 3.25 |

Ear of Corn — A680

**1980, Oct. 20       Perf. 13x13½**
| 1228 | A680 | 30w multicolored | .50 | .25 |

12th population and housing census.

Symbolic Tree — A681

**1980, Oct. 27**
| 1229 | A681 | 30w multicolored | .50 | .25 |

National Red Cross, 75th anniversary.

"Mail-Delivering Angels" — A682

**1980, Nov. 6          Perf. 13½x13**
| 1230 | A682 | 30w multicolored | .50 | .25 |
| a. | | Souvenir sheet of 2 | 1.60 | 1.60 |

Philatelic Week, Nov. 6-11.

Korea-Japan Submarine Cable System Inauguration — A683

**1980, Nov. 28       Perf. 13x13½**
| 1231 | A683 | 30w multicolored | .50 | .25 |

Rooster
A684

Cranes
A685

---

**1980, Dec. 1**
| 1232 | A684 | 30w multicolored | .50 | .25 |
| a. | | Souvenir sheet of 2 | 1.60 | 1.60 |
| 1233 | A685 | 30w multicolored | .50 | .25 |
| a. | | Souvenir sheet of 2 | 1.60 | 1.60 |

New Year 1981.

Second Inauguration of Pres. Chun Doo-hwan — A686

**1981, Mar. 3  Photo.   Perf. 13½x13**
| 1234 | A686 | 30w multicolored | .55 | .25 |
| a. | | Souvenir sheet of 2 | 1.60 | 1.60 |

**Ship Issue**

Oil Tanker
A687

Cargo Ship
A688

**1981, Mar. 13  Perf. 13½x13, 13x13½**
| 1235 | A687 | 30w multicolored | .45 | .25 |
| 1236 | A688 | 90w multicolored | .80 | .25 |

5th Maritime Day.

Oil Tanker — A689

Cargo Ship — A690

**1981, May 10  Photo.   Perf. 13½x13**
| 1237 | A689 | 30w multicolored | .45 | .25 |
| 1238 | A690 | 90w multicolored | .85 | .30 |

Tug Boat — A691

Stern Trawler — A692

**1981, July 10          Perf. 13½x13**
| 1239 | A691 | 40w multicolored | .65 | .25 |
| 1240 | A692 | 100w multicolored | 1.05 | .30 |

Log Carrier — A693

Auto Carrier — A694

**1981, Aug. 10**
| 1241 | A693 | 40w multicolored | .65 | .25 |
| 1242 | A694 | 100w multicolored | 1.05 | .30 |

Chemical Carrier — A695

Passenger Boat — A696

**1981, Nov. 10  Engr.   Perf. 13x12½**
| 1243 | A695 | 40w black | .65 | .25 |
| 1244 | A696 | 100w dk blue | 1.10 | .30 |
| | Nos. 1235-1244 (10) | | 7.70 | 2.70 |

---

11th Natl. Assembly Opening Session — A697

**1981, Apr. 17  Photo.   Perf. 13½x13**
| 1245 | A697 | 30w gold & dk brn | .45 | .25 |

Hand Reading Braille, Helping Hands — A698

90w, Man in wheelchair.

**1981, Apr. 20  Photo.   Perf. 13x13½**
| 1246 | A698 | 30w shown | .35 | .25 |
| 1247 | A698 | 90w multicolored | .70 | .25 |

International Year of the Disabled.

Ribbon and Council Emblem — A699

**1981, June 5  Photo.   Perf. 13x13½**
| 1248 | A699 | 40w multicolored | .45 | .25 |

Advisory Council on Peaceful Unification Policy (North and South Korea) anniv.

Clena River and Mountains — A700

**1981, June 5**
| 1249 | A700 | 30w shown | .35 | .25 |
| 1250 | A700 | 90w Seagulls | .75 | .25 |

10th World Environment Day.

Pres. Chun and Pres. Suharto of Indonesia — A701

Pres. Chun Visit to Asia: b, King of Malaysia.  c, Korean, Singapore flags. d, King Bhumibol Adulyadej of Thailand. e, Pres. Marcos of Philippines.

**1981, June 25          Perf. 13½x13**
| 1251 | | Strip of 5 | 4.00 | 3.00 |
| a.-e. | | A701 40w, any single | .55 | .25 |
| f. | | Souvenir sheet of 5, imperf. | 2.50 | 2.50 |

**Size: 49x33mm**
**Perf. 13x13½**
| 1252 | A701 | 40w multicolored | .55 | .25 |
| a. | | Souvenir sheet of 2, imperf. | 2.40 | 2.40 |

36th Anniv. of Liberation — A702

**1981, Aug. 15  Photo.   Perf. 13x13½**
| 1253 | A702 | 40w multicolored | .45 | .25 |

Tolharubang, "Stone Grandfather"
A704

Rose of Sharon
A705

Porcelain Jar, 17th Cent. — A706

Chomsongdae Observatory, 7th Cent. — A707

Mounted Warrior, Earthenware Jug, 5th Cent. A708

Family Planning A709

Walking Stick A710

Ryu Kwan-soon (1904-20), Martyr A711

"Tasan" Chung Yak-yong, Lee Dynasty Scholar A712

Ahn Joong-geun (1879-1910), Martyr A713

Ahn Chang-ho (1878-1938), Independence Fighter A714

Koryo Celadon Incense Burner A715

Kim Ku (1876-1949), Statesman A716

Mountain Landscape Brick Bas-relief A717

Mandarin Duck, Celadon Incense Burner — A718

**Perf. 13½x12½ (Nos. 1256, 1257, 1266), 13, 13½x13, 13x13½**

| 1981-89 | | | Photo., Engr. | |
|---|---|---|---|---|
| 1255 | A704 | 20w multi ('86) | .45 | .25 |
| 1256 | A705 | 40w multi | .55 | .25 |
| 1257 | A706 | 60w multi | .55 | .25 |
| 1258 | A707 | 70w multi | .65 | .25 |
| 1259 | A708 | 80w multi ('83) | .70 | .25 |
| 1260 | A709 | 80w multi ('86) | .90 | .25 |
| 1261 | A710 | 80w multi ('89) | 2.25 | .25 |
| 1262 | A711 | 100w mauve | .95 | .25 |
| 1263 | A712 | 100w gray blk ('86) | 3.00 | .25 |
| 1264 | A713 | 200w lt ol grn & ol | 1.30 | .25 |
| 1265 | A714 | 300w dl lil ('83) | 1.90 | .25 |
| 1266 | A715 | 400w multi | 5.75 | .45 |
| 1267 | A715 | 400w pale grn & multi ('83) | 3.50 | .35 |

| 1268 | A716 | 450w dk vio brn ('86) | 2.40 | .35 |
|---|---|---|---|---|
| 1269 | A717 | 500w multi | 3.50 | .60 |
| 1270 | A718 | 700w multi ('83) | 4.25 | .65 |
| | Nos. 1255-1270 (16) | | 32.60 | 5.15 |

Inscription and denomination of No. 1266, colorless, No. 1267, dark brown.
See Nos. 1449, 1449C, 1594F.

**Coil Stamp**
**Photo.** **Perf. 13 Horiz.**
1271 A707 70w multicolored 2.00 .50

Girl Flying Model Plane — A721

Air Force Chief of Staff Cup, 3rd Aeronautic Competition: Various model planes.

**1981, Sept. 20** **Perf. 13½x13**
| 1272 | | Strip of 5 | 4.00 | 3.50 |
|---|---|---|---|---|
| a. | A721 | 10w multi | .50 | .25 |
| b. | A721 | 20w multi | .50 | .25 |
| c. | A721 | 40w multi | .50 | .25 |
| d. | A721 | 50w multi | .65 | .30 |
| e. | A721 | 80w multi | .80 | .35 |

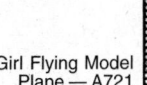
WHO Emblem, Citizens — A722

**1981, Sept. 22** **Perf. 13x13½**
1273 A722 40w multicolored .45 .25
WHO, 32nd Western Pacific Regional Committee Meeting, Seoul, Sept. 22-28.

World Tourism Day — A723

**1981, Sept. 28**
1274 A723 40w Seoul Tower .45 .25
1275 A723 40w Ulreung Isld. .45 .25

Bicycle Racing — A724

**1981, Oct. 10** **Perf. 13½x13**
1276 A724 40w shown .40 .25
1277 A724 40w Swimming .40 .25
62nd Natl. Sports Festival, Seoul, 10/10-15.

Flags, Presidents Chun and Carazo — A725

**1981, Oct. 12** **Perf. 13½x13**
1278 A725 40w multicolored .45 .25
Visit of Pres. Rodrigo Carazo Odio of Costa Rica, Oct. 12-14.

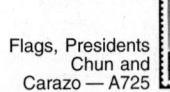
World Food Day — A726

**1981, Oct. 16** **Perf. 13x13½**
1279 A726 40w multicolored .45 .25

First Natl. Aviation Day — A727

**1981, Oct. 30** **Perf. 13½x13**
1280 A727 40w multicolored .45 .25

1988 Olympic Games, Seoul — A728

**1981, Oct. 30** **Perf. 13x13½**
1281 A728 40w multicolored .55 .25

9th Philatelic Week, Nov. 18-24 — A729

**1981, Nov. 18** **Perf. 13½x13**
1282 A729 40w multicolored .45 .25
a. Souvenir sheet of 2 1.75 1.75

Camellia and Dog — A730

Children Flying Kite — A731

**1981, Dec. 1** **Perf. 13x13½**
1283 A730 40w multicolored .55 .25
a. Souvenir sheet of 2 1.75 1.75
1284 A731 40w multicolored .55 .25
a. Souvenir sheet of 2 1.75 1.75
New Year 1982 (Year of the Dog).

Hangul Hakhoe Language Society, 60th Anniv. — A732

**1981, Dec. 3** **Perf. 13½x13**
1285 A732 40w multicolored .45 .25

Telecommunications Authority Inauguration — A733

**1982, Jan. 4** **Photo.** **Perf. 13x13½**
1286 A733 60w multicolored .45 .25

Scouting Year — A734

**1982, Feb. 22**
1287 A734 60w multicolored .45 .25

60th Anniv. of YWCA in Korea — A735

**1982, Apr. 20 Photo. Perf. 13x13½**
1288 A735 60w multicolored .45 .25

Intl. Polar Year Centenary — A736

**1982, Apr. 21** **Perf. 13½x13**
1289 A736 60w multicolored .55 .25

60th Children's Day — A737

**1982, May 5** **Perf. 13½x13**
1290 A737 60w multicolored .45 .25

Visit of Liberian Pres. Samuel K. Doe, May 9-13 — A738

**1982, May 9 Litho. Perf. 13x12½**
1291 A738 60w multicolored .55 .25
a. Souvenir sheet of 2, imperf. 1.75 1.75

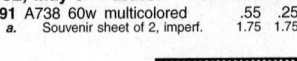
Centenary of US-Korea Treaty of Amity — A739

No. 1292, Statue of Liberty, pagoda. No. 1293, Emblem.

**1982, May 18 Photo. Perf. 13½x13**
1292 A739 60w multicolored .70 .25
1293 A739 60w multicolored .70 .25
a. Souvenir sheet of 2 3.00 3.00
b. Pair, #1292-1293 1.50 1.50

Visit of Zaire Pres. Mobutu Sese Seko, June 7-10 — A740

**1982, June 7 Litho. Perf. 13x12½**
1294 A740 60w multicolored .45 .25
a. Souvenir sheet of 2, imperf. 1.75 1.75

**Historical Painting Issue**

Gen. Kwon Yul's Victory at Haengju, by Oh Seung-woo A747

Designs: No. 1295, Territorial Expansion by Kwanggaeto the Great, by Lee Chong-sang, 1975. No. 1296, Gen. Euljimunduck's Victory at Salsoo, by Park Kak-soon, 1975. No. 1297, Shilla's Repulse of Tang's Army, by Oh Seung-woo. No. 1298, Gen. Kang Kam-chan's Victory at Kyiju, by Lee Yong-hwan. No. 1299, Admiral Yi Sun-sin's Victory at Hansan, 1592, by Kim Hyung-ku. No. 1300, Gen. Kim Chwa-jin's Battle at Chungsanri, by Sohn Soo-kwang. No. 1302, Kim Chong-suh's Exploitation of Yukjin, 1434, by Kim Tae.

**1982** **Photo.** **Perf. 13x13½**
| 1295 | A747 | 60w multicolored | .75 | .35 |
|---|---|---|---|---|
| 1296 | A747 | 60w multicolored | 1.25 | .50 |
| 1297 | A747 | 60w multicolored | .90 | .30 |
| 1298 | A747 | 60w multicolored | .90 | .30 |
| 1299 | A747 | 60w multicolored | 1.00 | .40 |
| 1300 | A747 | 60w multicolored | 1.00 | .40 |
| 1301 | A747 | 60w shown | 1.30 | .40 |
| 1302 | A747 | 60w multicolored | 1.30 | .40 |
| | Nos. 1295-1302 (8) | | 8.40 | 3.05 |

Issued: Nos. 1295-1296, 6/15; Nos. 1297-1298, 7/15; Nos. 1299-1300, 10/15; Nos. 1301-1302, 12/15.

---

55th Intl. YMCA Convention, Seoul, July 20-23 — A749

**1982, July 20**
1303 A749 60w multicolored .45 .25

Flags, Presidents Chun and Arap Moi — A750

Pres. Chun's Visit to Africa & Canada: No. 1304, Kenya (Pres. Daniel T. Arap Moi), Aug. 17-19. No. 1305, Nigeria (Pres. Alhaji Shehe Shagari), Aug. 19-22. No. 1306, Gabon (Pres. El Hadj Omar Bongo), Aug. 22-24. No. 1307, Senegal (Pres. Abdou Diouf), Aug. 24-26. No. 1308, Canada, Aug. 28-31.

**1982, Aug. 17            Perf. 13½x13**
1304 A750 60w multicolored .45 .25
1305 A750 60w multicolored .45 .25
1306 A750 60w multicolored .45 .25
1307 A750 60w multicolored .45 .25
1308 A750 60w multicolored .45 .25
Nos. 1304-1308 (5) 2.25 1.25

**Souvenir Sheets of 2**
1304a A750 60w 2.10 2.10
1305a A750 60w 2.10 2.10
1306a A750 60w 2.10 2.10
1307a A750 60w 2.10 2.10
1308a A750 60w 2.10 2.10
Nos. 1304a-1308a (5) 10.50 10.50

Natl. Flag Centenary — A751

**1982, Aug. 22**
1309 A751 60w multicolored .45 .25
a. Souvenir sheet of 2 2.40 2.40

2nd Seoul Open Intl. Table Tennis Championship, Aug. 25-31 — A752

**1982, Aug. 25**
1310 A752 60w multicolored .50 .25

27th World Amateur Baseball Championship Series, Seoul, Sept. 4-18 — A753

**1982, Sept. 4      Engr.      Perf. 13**
1311 A753 60w red brown .75 .25

Seoul Intl. Trade Fair (SITRA '82), Sept. 24-Oct. 18 — A754

**1982, Sept. 17  Photo.  Perf. 13½x13**
1312 A754 60w multicolored .45 .25

Philatelic Week, Oct. 15-21 — A755

Design: Miners reading consolatory letters.

**1982, Oct. 15**
1313 A755 60w multicolored .45 .25
a. Souvenir sheet of 2 1.60 1.60

Visit of Indonesian Pres. Suharto, Oct. 16-19 — A756

**1982, Oct. 16  Litho.  Perf. 13x12½**
1314 A756 60w multicolored .45 .25
a. Souvenir sheet of 2, imperf. 1.50 1.50

A757

**1982, Nov. 3              Perf. 13½x13**
1315 A757 60w multicolored .45 .25

37th Jaycee (Intl. Junior Chamber of Commerce) World Congress, Seoul, Nov. 3-18.

2nd UN Conference on Peaceful Uses of Outer Space, Vienna, Aug. 9-21 — A758

**1982, Nov. 20            Perf. 13x13½**
1316 A758 60w multicolored .40 .25

New Year 1983 (Year of the Boar) — A759

No. 1317, Magpies, money bag. No. 1318, Boar, bas-relief.

**1982, Dec. 1**
1317 A759 60w multicolored .45 .25
a. Souvenir sheet of 2 2.10 2.10
1318 A759 60w multicolored .45 .25
a. Souvenir sheet of 2 2.10 2.10

Flags of Korea and Turkey — A760

**1982, Dec. 20            Perf. 13**
1319 A760 60w multicolored .45 .25
a. Souvenir sheet of 2, imperf. 1.75 1.75

Visit of Pres. Kenan Evren of Turkey, Dec. 20-23.

Letter Writing Campaign — A761

**1982, Dec. 31  Photo.  Perf. 13x13½**
1320 A761 60w multicolored .45 .25

First Intl. Customs Day — A762

**1983, Jan. 26            Perf. 13½x13**
1321 A762 60w multicolored .50 .25

### Korean-made Vehicle Issue

Hyundai Pony-2 — A764     Daewoo Maepsy — A765

Super Titan Truck — A768     Flat-bed Truck — A770

**1983      Photo.      Perf. 13½x13**
1322 A764 60w Keohwa Jeep .80 .25
1323 A764 60w shown .80 .25
a. Pair, #1322-1323 2.10 2.10
1324 A765 60w shown .75 .25
1325 A765 60w Kia minibus .75 .25
a. Pair, #1324-1325 2.00 2.00
1326 A764 60w Highway bus .85 .25
1327 A768 60w shown .85 .25
1328 A764 70w Dump truck 1.15 .25
1329 A770 70w shown 1.15 .25
1330 A764 70w Cement mixer 1.10 .25
1331 A764 70w Oil truck 1.05 .25
Nos. 1322-1331 (10) 9.25 2.50

Issued: Nos. 1322-1323, 2/25; Nos. 1324-1325, 3/25; Nos. 1326-1327, 5/25; Nos. 1328-1329, 7/25; Nos. 1330-1331, 8/25.

Visit of Malaysian Seri Paduka Baginda, Mar. 22-26 — A773

**1983, Mar. 22**
1332 A773 60w multicolored .45 .25
a. Souvenir sheet of 2 1.25 1.25

### Postal Service Issue

General Bureau of Postal Administration Building — A774     Mailman, 1884 — A776

Ancient Mail Carrier — A778     Nos. 1-2 — A780

Pre-modern Period Postal Symbol, Mailbox — A782

Designs: No. 1334, Seoul Central PO. No. 1336, Mailman on motorcycle, 1983. No. 1338, Modern mail transport. No. 1340, No. 1201. No. 1342, Current postal symbol, mailbox.

**1983-84      Photo.      Perf. 13½x13**
1333 A774 60w multicolored .65 .25
1334 A774 60w multicolored .65 .25
1335 A776 70w multicolored .80 .25
1336 A776 70w multicolored .80 .25
1337 A778 70w multicolored .80 .25
1338 A778 70w multicolored .80 .25
1339 A780 70w multicolored .65 .25
1340 A780 70w multicolored .65 .25
1341 A782 70w multicolored .65 .25
1342 A782 70w multicolored .65 .25
Nos. 1333-1342 (10) 7.10 2.50

PHILAKOREA '84, Seoul, Oct. 22-31, 1984. Issued: Nos. 1333-1334, 4/22; Nos. 1335-1336, 6/10; Nos. 1337-1338, 8/10; Nos. 1339-1340, 2/10/84; Nos. 1341-1342, 3/10/84.

Teachers' Day — A784

60w, Village schoolhouse, score.

**1983, May 15  Photo.  Perf. 13x13½**
1343 A784 60w multicolored .50 .25
a. Souvenir sheet of 2 1.75 2.00

World Communications Year — A785

**1983, June 20**
1344 A785 70w multicolored .55 .25
a. Souvenir sheet of 2 1.50 1.50

Communications Life Insurance Inauguration A786

**1983, July 1  Photo.  Perf. 13½x13**
1345 A786 70w multicolored .60 .25

Science and Technology Symposium, Seoul, July 4-8 — A787

**1983, July 4**
1346 A787 70w multicolored .50 .25

Visit of Jordan's King Hussein, Sept. 10-13 — A788

70w, Pres. Hwan, King Hussein, flags.

**1983, Sept. 10  Litho.  Perf. 13x12½**
1347 A788 70w multicolored .50 .25
a. Souvenir sheet of 2, imperf. 1.60 1.60

ASTA, 53rd World Travel Congress, Seoul — A789

**1983, Sept. 25      Photo.      Perf. 13**
1348 A789 70w multicolored .55 .25

A790

**1983, Oct. 4      Photo.      Perf. 13**
1349 A790 70w multicolored .55 .25
a. Souvenir sheet of 2 1.60 1.60

70th Inter-Parliamentary Union Conference.

A791

**1983, Oct. 6    Photo.    Perf. 13**
1350 A791 70w Gymnastics    .55    .25
1351 A791 70w Soccer    .55    .25

64th National Sports Festival.

Pres. Chun and
Pres. U San Yu of
Burma — A791a

Pres. Chun's Curtailed Visit to Southwest Asia: No. 1351B, India. No. 1351C, Pres. Junius R. Jayawardene, Sri Lanka. No. 1351D, Australia, flag. No. 1351E, New Zealand, flag. Withdrawn after one day due to political assassination.

**1983, Oct. 8    Photo.    Perf. 13½x13**
1351A A791a 70w multicolored    1.30    .60
1351B A791a 70w multicolored    1.30    .60
1351C A791a 70w multicolored    1.30    .60
1351D A791a 70w multicolored    1.30    .60
1351E A791a 70w multicolored    1.30    .60
   Nos. 1351A-1351E (5)    6.50    3.00

**Souvenir Sheets of 2**
1351f A791a 70w    4.25    4.25
1351g A791a 70w    4.25    4.25
1351h A791a 70w    4.25    4.25
1351i A791a 70w    4.25    4.25
1351j A791a 70w    4.25    4.25
   Nos. 1351f-1351j (5)    21.25    21.25

Water Resource
Development — A792

**1983, Oct. 15    Litho.    Perf. 13**
1352 A792 70w multicolored    .55    .25

Newspaper Publication
Cent. — A793

**1983, Oct. 31    Litho.    Perf. 13**
1353 A793 70w multicolored    .55    .25

Natl. Tuberculosis
Assoc., 30th
Anniv. — A794

**1983, Nov. 6    Photo.    Perf. 13**
1354 A794 70w multicolored    .55    .25

Presidents Chun
and Reagan, Natl.
Flags — A795

**1983, Nov. 12    Photo.    Perf. 13**
1355 A795 70w multicolored    .65    .25
a.    Souvenir sheet of 2    2.50    2.50

Visit of Pres. Ronald Reagan, Nov. 12-14.

11th Philatelic
Week — A796

**1983, Nov. 18    Photo.    Perf. 13**
1356 A796 70w multicolored    .55    .25
a.    Souvenir sheet of 2    2.40    2.40

New Year 1984
A797    A798

No. 1357, Mouse, stone wall relief. No. 1358, Cranes, pine tree.

**1983, Dec. 1    Photo.    Perf. 13**
1357 A797 70w multicolored    .70    .25
a.    Souvenir sheet of 2    2.50    2.50
1358 A798 70w multicolored    .70    .25
a.    Souvenir sheet of 2    2.50    2.50

Bicentenary of Catholic
Church in Korea — A799

**1984, Jan. 4    Photo.    Perf. 13x13½**
1359 A799 70w Cross    .60    .25
a.    Souvenir sheet of 2    3.00    3.00

Visit of Brunei's
Sultan Bolkiah-
Apr. 7-9 — A800

**1984, Apr. 7    Litho.    Perf. 13x12½**
1360 A800 70w multicolored    .55    .25
a.    Souvenir sheet of 2, imperf.    1.75    1.75

Visit of Qatar's
Sheik Khalifa,
Apr. 20-
22 — A801

**1984, Apr. 20**
1361 A801 70w multicolored    .55    .25
a.    Souvenir sheet of 2, imperf.    1.60    1.60

Girl Mailing
Letter — A802
Mailman in
City — A803

**1984, Apr. 22    Photo.    Perf. 13½x13**
1362 A802 70w multicolored    .55    .25
a.    Souvenir sheet of 2    1.60    1.60
1363 A803 70w multicolored    .55    .25
a.    Souvenir sheet of 2    1.60    1.60

Korean postal service.

Visit of Pope John
Paul II, May 3-
7 — A808

**1984, May 3    Engr.    Perf. 12½**
1368 A808 70w dk brn    .65    .25

**Photogravure & Engraved**
1369 A808 70w multicolored    .65    .25
a.    Souvenir sheet of 2, #1368-
       1369, perf. 13½    2.40    2.40

Tools, Brushes,
Flower — A809

**1984, May 11    Photo.    Perf. 13x13½**
1370 A809 70w multicolored    .55    .25

Workers' Cultural Festival.

Jet, Ship, Asia
Map — A810

**1984, May 21    Photo.    Perf. 13x13½**
1371 A810 70w multicolored    .55    .25

Customs Cooperation Council 63rd-64th Sessions, Seoul, May 21-25.

Visit of Sri Lanka's
Pres. Jayewardene,
May 27-30 — A811

70w, Asia map, flags, flowers.

**1984, May 27    Perf. 13½x13**
1372 A811 70w multicolored    .55    .25
a.    Souvenir sheet of 2    1.50    1.50

Advertising Congress
Emblem — A812

**1984, June 18    Photo.    Perf. 13x13½**
1373 A812 70w multicolored    .55    .25

14th Asian Advertising Cong., Seoul, June 18-21.

'88 Olympic Expressway
Opening — A813

**1984, June 22**
1374 A813 70w multicolored    .60    .25

Intl. Olympic Committee,
90th Anniv. — A814

**1984, June 23**
1375 A814 70w multicolored    .55    .25

Asia-Pacific
Broadcasting
Union, 20th
Anniv. — A815

70w, Emblem, microphone.

**1984, June 30    Perf. 13½x13**
1376 A815 70w multicolored    .55    .25

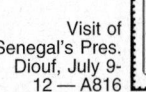

Visit of
Senegal's Pres.
Diouf, July 9-
12 — A816

70w, Flags of Korea & Senegal.

**1984, July 9    Litho.    Perf. 13x12½**
1377 A816 70w multicolored    .55    .25
a.    Souvenir sheet of 2, imperf.    1.75    1.75

1984 Summer
Olympics
A817

**Lithographed and Engraved**

**1984, July 28    Perf. 12½**
1378 A817 70w Archery    .70    .25
1379 A817 440w Fencing    2.60    .65

Korean Protestant Church
Cent. — A818

Stained glass windows.

**1984, Aug. 16    Perf. 13**
1380 A818 70w Crucifixion    .70    .25
1381 A818 70w Cross, dove    .70    .25
a.    Souvenir sheet of 2    5.25    5.25
b.    Pair, #1380-1381    1.75    1.75

Groom on
Horseback — A819

Wedding Procession: a, Lantern carrier. b, Groom. c, Musician. d, Bride in sedan chair (52x33mm).

**1984, Sept. 1    Photo.    Perf. 13x13½**
1382    Strip of 4    3.75    1.50
a.-d.    A819 70w any single    .70    .25
e.    Souvenir sheet    2.10    2.10

No. 1382e contains No. 1382d.

Pres. Chun's
Visit to Japan,
Sept. 6-
8 — A820

70w, Chun, flag, Mt. Fuji.

**1984, Sept. 6    Litho.    Perf. 13x12½**
1383 A820 70w multicolored    .55    .25
a.    Souvenir sheet of 2, imperf.    1.75    1.75

Visit of Gambia's
Pres. Jawara,
Sept. 12-
17 — A821

70w, Flags of Korea & Gambia.

**1984, Sept. 12**
1384 A821 70w multicolored    .55    .25
a.    Souvenir sheet of 2, imperf.    1.75    1.75

Visit of Gabon's Pres.
Bongo, Sept. 21-
23 — A822

70w, Flags of Korea & Gabon.

**1984, Sept. 21    Perf. 13**
1385 A822 70w multicolored    .55    .25
a.    Souvenir sheet of 2, imperf.    1.75    1.75

318                                  KOREA

Seoul Intl. Trade
Fair — A823

**1984, Sept. 18  Photo.  Perf. 13x13½**
1386  A823  70w Products           .55  .25

65th Natl. Sports
Festival, Taegu,
Oct. 11-16 — A824

**1984, Oct. 11  Photo.  Perf. 13½x13**
1387  A824  70w Badminton          .60  .25
1388  A824  70w Wrestling          .60  .25

Philakorea '84
Stamp Show,
Seoul, Oct. 22-
31 — A825

No. 1389, South Gate, stamps. No. 1390,
Emblem under magnifier, vert.

**1984, Oct. 22  Perf. 13½x13, 13x13½**
1389  A825  70w multicolored       .55  .25
 a.    Souvenir sheet of 4        3.25  3.25
1390  A825  70w multicolored       .55  .25
 a.    Souvenir sheet of 4        3.25  3.25

Visit of Maldives
Pres. Maumoon
Abdul Gayoom,
Oct. 29-Nov. 1
— A826

**1984, Oct. 29  Litho.  Perf. 13x12½**
1392  A826  70w multicolored       .55  .25
 a.    Souvenir sheet of 2, imperf. 1.90  1.90

Chamber of Commerce
and Industry
Cent. — A827

**1984, Oct. 31  Photo.  Perf. 13x13½**
1393  A827  70w "100"              .55  .25

Children Playing Jaegi-
chagi — A828

New Year 1985 (Year of the ox).

**1984, Dec. 1  Photo.  Perf. 13x13½**
1394  A828  70w Ox, bas-relief     .55  .25
 a.    Souvenir sheet of 2        1.60  1.60
1395  A828  70w shown              .55  .25
 a.    Souvenir sheet of 2        1.60  1.60

Intl. Youth
Year — A829

**1985, Jan. 25  Photo.  Perf. 13½x13**
1396  A829  70w IYY emblem         .55  .25

**Korean Folkways Series**

A830

No. 1397, Pounding rice. No. 1398, Welcoming full moon. No. 1399, Wrestling. No.
1400, Janggi, Korean chess.

**1985  Photo.  Perf. 13x13½**
1397  A830  70w multicolored       .70  .25
1398  A830  70w multicolored       .70  .25
1399  A830  70w multicolored       .85  .25
1400  A830  70w multicolored       .85  .25
 Issued: Nos. 1397-1398, 2/19; Nos. 1399-
1400, 8/20.

**Modern Art Series**

Rocky Mountain in
the Early Spring,
1915, by Shimjoen,
(Ahn Jung-shik)
A831

Still-life with a Doll,
1927, by Suhlcho,
(Lee Chong-woo)
A832

Spring Day on a
Farm, 1961, by
Eijai, (Huh Paik-
ryun, 1903-
1977) — A833

The Exorcist, 1941, by Chulma, (Kim
Chung-hyun, 1901-1953) — A834

Chunhyang-do, by
Kim Un-ho — A835

Flowers, by Lee
Sang-bum
A836

Image of A Friend,
by Ku Bon-wung
A837

Woman in a Ski
Suit, by Son Ung-
seng
A838

Valley of the Peach
Blossoms, 1964, by
Pyen Kwan-Sik
(1899-1976)
A839

Rural Landscape,
1940, by Lee Yong-
Wu (1904-1952)
A840

Male, 1932, by Lee
Ma-Dong
A841

Woman with a
Water Jar on Her
Head, 1944, by Yun
Hyo-Chung (1917-
1967)
A842

**Photo.; Litho. & Engr. (#1411-1412)**
**1985-87  Perf. 13½x13, 13x13½**
1401  A831  70w multicolored       .75  .25
1402  A832  70w multicolored       .75  .25
1403  A833  70w multicolored       .75  .25
1404  A834  70w multicolored       .75  .25
1405  A835  80w multi ('86)       1.15  .40
1406  A836  80w multi ('86)       1.15  .40
1407  A837  80w multi ('86)       1.15  .40
1408  A838  80w multi ('86)       1.15  .40
1409  A839  80w multi ('87)       3.00  .85
1410  A840  80w multi ('87)       3.00  .85
1411  A841  80w multi ('87)       3.00  .85
1412  A842  80w multi ('87)       3.00  .85
 Nos. 1401-1412 (12)            19.60  6.00
 Issued: Nos. 1401-1402, 4/10; Nos. 1403-
1404, 7/5; Nos. 1405-1408, 12/1; Nos. 1409-
1412, 6/12.

State Visit of Pres.
Chun to the
US — A843

**Photo. & Engr.**
**1985, Apr. 24  Perf. 13**
1413  A843  70w multicolored       .60  .25
 a.    Souvenir sheet of 2        1.75  1.75

**Coastal and Inland Fish Series**

Gak-si- Bung-eo
(silver
carp) — A844

Dot-sac-chi (sword
fish) — A845

Eoreumchi
A846

Sweetfish
A847

Sardine — A848

Hammerhead
Shark — A849

Cham-jung- go-
ji — A850

Swi-ri — A851

Oar Fish — A852

Devil-ray — A853

**1985-87  Photo.  Perf. 13½x13**
1414  A844  70w multicolored       .70  .25
1415  A845  70w multicolored       .70  .25
1416  A846  70w multi ('86)       1.60  .55
1417  A847  70w multi ('86)       1.60  .55
1418  A848  70w multi ('86)       1.60  .55
1419  A849  70w multi ('86)       1.60  .55
1420  A850  80w multi ('87)       2.50  1.00
1421  A851  80w multi ('87)       2.50  1.00
1422  A852  80w multi ('87)       2.50  1.00
1423  A853  80w multi ('87)       2.50  1.00
 Nos. 1414-1423 (10)            17.80  6.70
 Issued: Nos. 1414-1415, 5/30; Nos. 1416-
1423, 7/25.

Yonsei University
and Medical
School,
Cent. — A854

**Photogravure and Engraved**
**1985, May 6  Perf. 13**
1424  A854  70w Underwood Hall     .55  .25

State Visit of Pres. Mohammad Zia-Ul-Haq of Pakistan, May 6-10 — A855

**1985, May 6   Photo.   Perf. 13x13½**
1425  A855  70w multicolored        .55   .25
a.      Souvenir sheet of 2             1.60  1.60

State Visit of Pres. Luis Alberto Monge of Costa Rica, May 19-23 — A856

**1985, May 18          Perf. 13½x13**
1426  A856  70w multicolored        .55   .25
a.      Souvenir sheet of 2             1.60  1.60

State Visit of Pres. Hussain Muhammad Ershad of Bangladesh, June 15-19 — A857

**1985, June 15**
1427  A857  70w multicolored        .55   .25
a.      Souvenir sheet of 2, imperf.    1.60  1.60

State Visit of Pres. Joao Bernardo Vieira of Guinea-Bissau, June 25-28 — A858

**1985, June 25**
1428  A858  70w multicolored        .55   .25
a.      Souvenir sheet of 2, imperf.    1.60  1.60

Liberation from Japanese Occupation Forces, 40th Anniv. — A859

Heavenly Lake, Mt. Paektu, natl. flower.

**1985, Aug. 14   Litho.   Perf. 13x12½**
1429  A859  70w multicolored        .55   .25

### Music Series

The Spring of My Home, Music by Hong Nan-pa and Lyrics by Lee Won-su
A860

A Leaf Boat, Music by Yun Yong-ha and Lyrics by Park Hong-Keun
A861

Half Moon, 1924, by Yun Keuk-Young
A862

Let's Go and Pick the Moon, by Yun Seok-Jung and Park Tae Hyun
A863

**1985-86          Photo.   Perf. 13x13½**
1430  A860  70w multicolored        .80   .25
1431  A861  70w multicolored        .80   .25
1432  A862  70w multicolored        1.00  .30
1433  A863  70w multicolored        1.60  .50
        Issued: Nos. 1430-1431, 9/10; Nos. 1432-1433, 6/25/86.

### Korean Folkways Series

Korean Farm Music — A864

No. 1434 — Musicians with: a, Flag, hand gong. b, Drum flute. c, Drum, hand gong. d, Taborets, ribbons. e, Taboret, sun, woman, child. Has continuous design.

**1986, Aug. 26   Photo.   Perf. 13½x13**
1434        Strip of 5              6.75  6.75
a.-e.   A864 70w, any single          1.10  .25

### Music Series

Barley Field, by Park Wha-mok and Yun Yong-ha
A865

Magnolia, by Cho Young-Shik and Kim Dong-jin
A866

**1987, Mar. 25   Photo.   Perf. 13x13½**
1435  A865  80w multicolored        2.50  1.00
1436  A866  80w multicolored        2.50  1.00

### Korean Folkways Series

Chusok, Harvest Moon Festival
A867

No. 1437 — Harvest moon dance: a, Eight dancers, harvest moon. b, Four dancers, festival wheels, balloons. c, Three dancers, children on see-saw. d, Four dancers, women preparing meal.

**1987, Sept. 10   Photo.   Perf. 13x13½**
1437  A867  Strip of 4              16.00 16.00
a.-d.   80w any single               3.25  .85

### Folkways and Music Series

Tano, Spring Harvest Festival
A868

No. 1438: a, Woman on shore, riding a swing. b, Sweet flag coiffures. c, Boy picking flowers, girl on swing. d, Boys wrestling.

**1988, Aug. 25   Photo.   Perf. 13x13½**
1438  A868  Strip of 4              5.50  5.50
a.-d.   80w multicolored             1.10  .40

Sick for Home, by Lee Eun-sang and Kim Kong-jin
A869

Pioneer, by Yoon Hae-young and Cho Doo-nam
A870

**1988, Nov. 15**
1439  A869  80w multicolored        .70   .25
1440  A870  80w multicolored        .70   .25

Mask Dance (Talchum) — A871

No. 1441: a, Two mask dancers with scarves. b, Dancers with fans. c, Dancers with scarf and laurel or fan. d, Three dancers, first

as an animal and two more carrying fan and bells or torch.

**1989, Feb. 25**
1441  A871  Strip of 4              5.00  5.00
a.-d.   80w any single               1.10  .40

Korean Telecommunications, Cent. — A872

70w, Satellite, emblem, dish receiver.

**1985, Sept. 28          Perf. 13½x13**
1442  A872  70w multicolored        .55   .25

World Bank Conference, Seoul, Oct. 8-11 — A873

**1985, Oct. 8          Perf. 13x13½**
1443  A873  70w Emblem             .55   .25
    Intl. Bank for Reconstruction & Development, 40th Anniv.

UN, 40th Anniv. — A874

**1985, Oct. 24          Perf. 13½x13**
1444  A874  70w Emblem, doves       .55   .25

Natl. Red Cross, 80th Anniv. — A875

**1985, Oct. 26**
1445  A875  70w red, blk & bl       .55   .25

Segment of Canceled Cover — A876

**1985, Nov. 18   Photo.   Perf. 13½x13**
1446  A876  70w multicolored        .55   .25
    12th Philatelic Week, Nov. 18-23.

New Year 1986 — A877

### Lithographed and Engraved
**1985, Dec. 2          Perf. 13x13½**
1447  A877  70w multicolored        .55   .25

Mt. Fuji, Korean Airlines Jet — A878

**1985, Dec. 18          Photo.**
1448  A878  70w brt bl, blk & red   .65   .30
    Normalization of diplomatic relations between Korea and Japan, 20th anniv.
    See No. C44.

### Statesman Type of 1986 and Types of 1981-86
### Engr., Photo. (40w)
**1986-87          Perf. 13**
1449  A716  550w indigo             2.75  .40

### Coil Stamps
**Perf. 13 Vert.**
1449A  A704  20w multicolored       .65   .35
1449B  A705  40w multicolored       .75   .30
1449C  A708  80w multicolored       1.25  .55
    Nos. 1449A-1449C (3)             2.65  1.20
    Issue dates: 550w, Dec. 10; others, 1987.

Intl. Peace Year — A879

**1986, Jan. 15   Photo.   Perf. 13x13½**
1450  A879  70w multicolored        .60   .25
    See No. C45.

State Visits of Pres. Chun — A880

Portrait, natl. flags and: No. 1452, Parliament, Brussels. No. 1453, Eiffel Tower, Paris. No. 1454, Cathedral, Cologne. No. 1455, Big Ben, London.

**1986, Apr. 4   Litho.   Perf. 12½x13**
1452  A880  70w multicolored        .65   .30
1453  A880  70w multicolored        .65   .30
1454  A880  70w multicolored        .65   .30
1455  A880  70w multicolored        .65   .30
    Nos. 1452-1455 (4)               2.60  1.20
### Souvenir Sheets of 2
**Perf. 13½**
1452a  A880  70w                     3.00  3.00
1453a  A880  70w                     3.00  3.00
1454a  A880  70w                     3.00  3.00
1455a  A880  70w                     3.00  3.00
    Nos. 1452a-1455a (4)            12.00 12.00

### Science Series

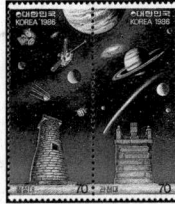

Observatories A881

Designs: No. 1456, Chomsongdae Observatory, Satellites. No. 1457, Kwanchondae Observatory, Halley's Comet.

**1986, Apr. 21          Perf. 13½x13**
1456        70w multicolored        2.60  .80
1457        70w multicolored        2.60  .80
a.      A881  Pair, #1456-1457        6.50  2.40

Weather — A883

Designs: No. 1458, Wind observatory stone foundation, Chosun Dynasty. No. 1459, Rain gauge, Sejong Period to Chosun Dynasty.

**1987, Apr. 21   Photo.   Perf. 13½**
1458        80w multicolored        2.75  .90
1459        80w multicolored        2.75  .90
a.      A883  Pair, #1458-1459        7.00  3.25

Clocks — A885

Designs: No. 1460, *Chagyokru*, water clock invented by Chang Yongshil and Kim Bin in 1434. No. 1461, *Angbuilgu*, sundial completed during King Sejong's reign (1418-1450).

**1988, Apr. 21   Photo.   Perf. 13½x13**
1460   80w multicolored   .70   .30
1461   80w multicolored   .70   .30
a.   A885 Pair, #1460-1461   1.90   1.90

Early Printing Methods — A887

Designs: No. 1462, Sutra manuscript (detail) printed from wood type, Shila Dynasty, c.704-751. No. 1463, Two characters from a manuscript printed from metal type, Koryo, c.1237.

**1989, Apr. 21**
1462   80w buff & sepia   1.45   .35
1463   80w buff & sepia   1.45   .35
a.   A887 Pair, #1462-1463   3.00   2.25

A889

Designs: No. 1464, 7th century gilt bronze Buddha. No. 1465, Bronze Age dagger, spear molds.

**1990, Apr. 21**
1464   100w multicolored   .55   .25
1465   100w multicolored   .55   .25
a.   A889 Pair, #1464-1465   1.35   1.35
Complete bklt., 2 each #1464-1465   2.50
Nos. 1456-1465 (10)   16.10   5.20

Pairs have continuous designs.

**Souvenir Booklets**
Booklets containing the stamps listed below have a stamp, pair or strip of stamps, tied to the booklet cover with a first day cancel.
1464-1465, 1523-1524, 1529-1532, 1535-1536, 1539-1540, 1553, 1559-1566, 1572-1576, 1583-1584, 1595-1608, 1613-1621, 1622-1623B, 1624, 1635-1650, 1655-1656, 1657-1668, 1669-1676, 1678-1690, 1693-1699, 1700-1702, 1713-1714, 1745-1748, 1751-1758, 1763-1764, 1767-1768, 1770-1773, 1776-1787, 1797, 1799-1802, 1803-1806, 1810-1811.

Assoc. of Natl. Olympic Committees, 5th General Assembly, Seoul, Apr. 21-25 — A891

**1986, Apr. 21   Perf. 13x13½**
1466   A891 70w multicolored   .55   .25

Souvenir Sheet

Butterflies — A892

**1986, May 22   Litho.   Perf. 13½**
1467   A892   Sheet of 6   24.00   24.00
a.   70w multicolored   2.75   1.35
b.   370w multicolored   2.75   1.35
c.   400w multicolored   2.75   1.35
d.   440w multicolored   2.75   1.35
e.   450w multicolored   2.75   1.35
f.   470w multicolored   2.75   1.35

AMERIPEX '86, Chicago, May 22-June 1. No. 1467 contains stamps of different sizes (370w, 42x41mm; 400w, 42x33mm; 440w, 39x45mm; 450w, 32x42mm; 470w, 33x44mm); margin continues the designs.

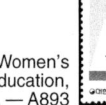

Women's Education, Cent. — A893

**1986, May 31   Perf. 13x12½**
1468   A893 70w multicolored   .55   .25

State Visit of Pres. Andre Kolingba, Central Africa — A894

**1986, June 10   Perf. 13**
1469   A894 70w multicolored   .55   .25
a.   Souvenir sheet of 2, imperf.   1.50   1.50

Completion of Han River Development Project — A895

**1986, Sept. 10   Litho.   Perf. 13**
1470   Strip of 3   4.00   4.00
a.   A895 30w Bridge   1.05   .30
b.   A895 60w Buildings   1.05   .30
c.   A895 80w Seoul Tower, buildings   1.05   .30

Printed in a continuous design.

Fireworks, Seoul Tower A896

Games Emblem A897

**1986, Sept. 20   Photo.   Perf. 13x13½**
1471   A896 80w multicolored   .65   .30
a.   Souvenir sheet of 2   6.25   6.25
1472   A897 80w multicolored   .65   .30
a.   Souvenir sheet of 2   6.25   6.25

Souvenir Sheet

10th Asian Games, Seoul, Sept. 20-Oct. 5 A898

**1986, Oct. 31**
1473   A898 550w multicolored   19.00   19.00

Juan Antonio Samaranch, Korean IOC Delegation, 1981 — A899

**1986, Sept. 30**
1474   A899 80w multicolored   .95   .40

Intl. Olympic Committee decision to hold 24th Olympic Games in Seoul, 5th anniv.

Philatelic Week — A900

**1986, Nov. 18   Photo.   Perf. 13½x13**
1475   A900 80w Boy fishing for stamp   .65   .25

New Year 1987 (Year of the Hare) — A901

**1986, Dec. 1   Photo.   Perf. 13x13½**
1476   A901 80w multicolored   .85   .30

Birds — A902

**1986, Dec. 20   Perf. 13x14**
1477   A902 80w Waxwing   1.25   .35
1478   A902 80w Oriole   1.25   .35
1479   A902 80w Kingfisher   1.25   .35
1480   A902 80w Hoopoe   1.25   .35
1481   A902 80w Roller   1.25   .35
a.   Strip of 5, #1477-1481   6.75   6.75

**Coil Stamps**
**Perf. 14 Horiz.**
1481B   A902 80w like No. 1479   2.40   .60
1481C   A902 80w like No. 1480   2.40   .60
1481D   A902 80w like No. 1481   2.40   .60
1481E   A902 80w like No. 1477   2.40   .60
1481F   A902 80w like No. 1478   2.40   .60
g.   Strip of 5, #1481B-1481F   21.00   21.00

Wildlife Conservation A903

Endangered species: No. 1482, Panthera tigris altaica. No. 1483, Felis bengalensis. No. 1484, Vulpes vulpes. No. 1485, Sus scrofa.

**1987, Feb. 25   Photo.   Perf. 13½x13**
1482   A903 80w multicolored   2.00   .60
1483   A903 80w multicolored   2.00   .60
1484   A903 80w multicolored   2.00   .60
1485   A903 80w multicolored   2.00   .60
a.   Strip of 4, #1482-1485   9.50   9.50

Flowers — A904

No. 1486, Dicentra spectabilis. No. 1487, Hanabusaya asiatica. No. 1488, Erythronium japonicum. No. 1489, Dianthus chinensis. No. 1490, Chrysanthemum zawadskii coreanum.

**1987, Mar. 20   Photo.   Perf. 14x13**
1486   A904 550w multicolored   2.25   .50
1487   A904 550w multicolored   2.25   .50
1488   A904 550w multicolored   2.25   .50
1489   A904 550w multicolored   2.25   .50
1490   A904 550w multicolored   2.25   .50
a.   Strip of 5, #1486-1490   13.50   13.50

**Coil Stamps**
**Perf. 13 Vert.**
1490B   A904 550w like No. 1486   2.40   .75
1490C   A904 550w like No. 1487   2.40   .75
1490D   A904 550w like No. 1488   2.40   .75
1490E   A904 550w like No. 1489   2.40   .75
1490F   A904 550w like No. 1490   2.40   .75
g.   Strip of 5, #1490B-1490F   16.00   16.00

State Visit of Pres. Ahmed Abdallah Abderemane of the Comoro Isls., Apr. 6-9 — A905

**1987, Apr. 6   Litho.   Perf. 13½x13**
1491   A905 80w multicolored   .55   .25
a.   Souvenir sheet of 2   2.10   2.10

Electrification of Korea, Cent. — A906

**1987, Apr. 10   Photo.**
1492   A906 80w multicolored   .55   .25

Int'l. Assoc. of Ports and Harbors, 15th General Session, Seoul — A907

**1987, Apr. 25   Photo.   Perf. 13½x13**
1493   A907 80w multicolored   .55   .25

State Visit of Pres. U San Yu of Burma — A908

**1987, June 8   Litho.   Perf. 13½x13**
1494   A908 80w multicolored   .55   .25
a.   Souvenir sheet of 2   1.90   1.90

Year of The Communications for Information Society — A909

No. 1495, Map, digital telephone. No. 1496, Emblem.

**1987, June 30   Perf. 13x13½**
1495   A909 80w multicolored   .60   .25
1496   A909 80w multicolored   .60   .25

Introduction of automatic switching telephone system.

Independence Hall, Monument to the Nation A910

Statue of Indomitable Koreans, Nat'l. Flag A911

**1987, Aug. 14    Photo.    *Perf. 13½x13***
1497  A910  80w multicolored           .95   .30
   a.    Souvenir sheet of 2          11.00  11.00
1498  A911  80w multicolored           .95   .30
   a.    Souvenir sheet of 2          11.00  11.00
Opening of Independence Hall, Aug. 15.

16th Pacific Science Congress, Seoul, Aug. 20-30 — A912

**1987, Aug. 20          *Perf. 13x13½***
1499  A912  80w multicolored           .65   .25
   a.    Souvenir sheet of 2           3.00   3.00

State Visit of Pres. Virgilio Barco of Colombia — A913

**1987, Sept. 8    Litho.    *Perf. 13½x13***
1500  A913  80w multicolored           .55   .25
   a.    Souvenir sheet of 2           2.10   2.10

Installation of 10-millionth Telephone — A914

**1987, Sept. 28          *Perf. 13½x13***
1501  A914  80w multicolored           .55   .25

Armed Forces, 39th Anniv. — A915

Armed Forces Day: Servicemen, flags of three military services.

**1987, Sept. 30    Litho.    *Perf. 13***
1502  A915  80w multicolored           .75   .25

14th Philatelic Week, Nov. 18-24 — A916

80w, Boy playing the nalrali.

**1987, Nov. 18    Photo.    *Perf. 13½***
1503  A916  80w multicolored           .65   .25

A917

**1987, Nov. 28          Litho.**
1504  A917  80w multicolored           .90   .35
Signing of the Antarctic Treaty by Korea, 1st anniv.

A918

**1987, Dec. 1          Photo.**
1505  A918  80w multicolored          1.15   .30
New Year 1988 (Year of the Dragon).

Natl. Social Security Program — A919

**1988, Jan. 4    Litho.    *Perf. 13½x13***
1506  A919  80w multicolored           .65   .25

Completion of the Korean Antarctic Base — A919a

**1988, Feb. 16    Photo.    *Perf. 13x13½***
1506A A919a 80w multicolored          1.00   .30

Inauguration of Roh Tae-Woo, 13th President — A920

**1988, Feb. 24    Photo.    *Perf. 13½x13***
1507  A920  80w multicolored          2.50   .40
   a.    Souvenir sheet of 2          20.00  20.00

World Wildlife Fund — A921

White-naped crane *(Grus vipio)* displaying various behaviors: a, Calling (1). b, Running (2). c, Spreading wings (3). d, Flying (4).

**1988, Apr. 1          *Perf. 13x13½***
1508        Strip of 4                7.00   7.00
   a.-d.  A921 80w any single          1.20   .65

Intl. Red Cross & Red Crescent Organizations, 125th Annivs. — A922

**1988, May 7    Photo.    *Perf. 13x13½***
1509  A922  80w multicolored           .65   .25

Telepress Medium, 1st Anniv. — A923

**1988, June 1          Litho.**
1510  A923  80w multicolored           .55   .25

Pierre de Coubertin, Olympic Flag — A924

Olympic Temple — A925

View of Seoul A926

Folk Dancers A927

**Litho. & Engr.**
**1988, Sept. 16          *Perf. 13½x13***
1511  A924  80w multicolored           .85   .30

1512  A925  80w multicolored           .85   .30
**Photo.**
**Perf. 13x13½**
1513  A926  80w multicolored           .85   .30
1514  A927  80w multicolored           .85   .30
   Nos. 1511-1514 (4)                3.40   1.20
1988 Summer Olympics, Seoul.

**Souvenir Sheets of 2**
1511a  A924  80w                       1.75   1.75
1512a  A925  80w                       1.75   1.75
1513a  A926  80w                       1.75   1.75
1514a  A927  80w                       1.75   1.75
   Nos. 1511a-1514a (4)             7.00   7.00
Margin inscriptions on Nos. 1511a-1512a are photo.

OLYMPHILEX '88, Sept. 19-28, Seoul — A928

**1988, Sept. 19    Photo.    *Perf. 13x13½***
1515  A928  80w multicolored           .55   .25
   a.    Souvenir sheet of 2           1.75   1.75

22nd Congress of the Intl. Iron and Steel Institute, Seoul — A929

**1988, Oct. 8          *Perf. 13½x13***
1516  A929  80w multicolored           .55   .25

A930

No. 1518, Archer seated in wheelchair.

**1988, Oct. 15          *Perf. 13x13½***
1517  A930  80w shown                  .90   .55
1518  A930  80w multicolored           .65   .30
1988 Natl. Special Olympics (Paralympics), Seoul.

A931

**1988, Dec. 1    Photo.    *Perf. 13x13½***
1519  A931  80w multicolored           .95   .25
New Year 1989 (Year of the Snake).

**Souvenir Sheet**

Successful Completion of the 1988 Summer Olympics, Seoul — A932

**1988, Dec. 20    Litho.    *Perf. 13x12½***
1520  A932  550w Opening ceremony     13.50  13.50

**Music Series**

Arirang A933          Doraji A934

Pakyon Falls A935

Chonan-Samkori A936

Natl. ballads.

**1989-90    Photo.    *Perf. 13x13½***
1521  A933  80w multicolored           .65   .25
1522  A934  80w multicolored           .65   .25
**Litho.**
1523  A935  80w multicolored           .65   .25
   Complete booklet, 4 #1523          5.50
1524  A936  80w multicolored           .65   .25
   Complete booklet, 4 #1524          5.50
Issued: Nos. 1521-1522, 3/27; Nos. 1523-1524, 2/26/90.

**Korean Folkways Series**

Willowing Bow — A937

Spinning Wheel — A938

Treating Threads — A939

Weaving Fabric — A940

**Litho. & Engr.**
**1990, Sept. 25          *Perf. 13½x13***
1525  A937  100w multicolored          .95   .30
1526  A938  100w multicolored          .95   .30
1527  A939  100w multicolored          .95   .30
1528  A940  100w multicolored          .95   .30
   a.    Strip of 4, #1525-1528      4.25   4.25

**Music Series**

Orchard Avenue A941

In Flower Garden A942

A Swing A943

Longing for Mt. Keumkang A944

**1991-92    Litho.    *Perf. 13x13½***
1529  A941  100w multicolored          .80   .30
   Complete booklet, 4 #1529          7.00
1530  A942  100w multicolored          .80   .30
   Complete booklet, 4 #1530          7.00
1531  A943  100w multicolored          .65   .25
   Complete booklet, 4 #1531          7.00
1532  A944  100w multicolored          .65   .25
   Complete booklet, 4 #1532          7.00
Issued: Nos. 1529-1530, 3/27; Nos. 1531-1532, 7/13/92.

14th Asian-Pacific Dental Congress — A945

**1989, Apr. 26    Photo.    *Perf. 13x13½***
1533  A945  80w multicolored           .55   .25

Rotary Intl. Convention, Seoul, May 21-25 — A946

**1989, May 20   Photo.   Perf. 13x13½**
1534 A946 80w multicolored      .65   .25

19th Cong. of the Intl. Council of Nurses, Seoul, May 28-June 2 — A947

**1989, May 27**
1535 A947 80w multicolored      .65   .25
   Complete booklet, 4 #1535      4.50

Information Industry Month — A948

**1989, June 1**
1536 A948 80w multicolored      .65   .25
   Complete booklet, 4 #1536      4.50

World Environment Day — A949

**1989, June 5**
1537 A949 80w multicolored      .65   .25

Asia-Pacific Telecommunity, 10th Anniv. — A950

**1989, July 1   Photo.   Perf. 13x13½**
1538 A950 80w multicolored      .65   .25

French Revolution, Bicent. — A951

**1989, July 14   Litho.   Perf. 13½x13**
1539 A951 80w multicolored      .55   .25
   Complete booklet, 4 #1539      4.50

Federation of Asian and Oceanian Biochemists 5th Congress — A952

**1989, Aug. 12                Photo.**
1540 A952 80w multicolored      .55   .25
   Complete booklet, 4 #1540      4.50

**Modern Art Series**

*A White Ox,* by Lee Joong-Sub A953

---

*A Street Stall,* by Park Lae-hyun A954

*A Little Girl,* by Lee Bong-Sang A955

*An Autumn Scene,* by Oh Ji-ho A956

**Litho. & Engr.; Photo. (#1542, 1544)**
**1989, Sept. 4   Perf. 13x13½, 13½x13**
1541 A953 80w multicolored      .70   .30
1542 A954 80w multicolored      .70   .30
1543 A955 80w multicolored      .70   .30
1544 A956 80w multicolored      .70   .30
      Nos. 1541-1544 (4)        2.80  1.20

Allegory: The Valiant Spirit of Koreans — A965

**1989, Sept. 12   Litho.   Perf. 13½x13**
1553 A965 80w multicolored      .55   .25
   Complete booklet, 4 #1553      4.50

1988 Seoul Olympics and the World Korean Sports Festival.

Personification of Justice and Ancient Codex — A966

**1989, Sept. 18**
1554 A966 80w multicolored      .65   .25

Constitutional Court, 1st anniv.

**Fish**

A967         A968

A969         A970

No. 1555, Oplegnathus fasciatus. No. 1556, Cobitis multifasciata. No. 1557, Liobagrus mediadiposalis. No. 1558, Monocentris japonicus.

**1989, Sept. 30   Photo.   Perf. 13½x13**
1555 A967 80w multicolored      .75   .30
1556 A968 80w multicolored      .75   .30
1557 A969 80w multicolored      .75   .30
1558 A970 80w multicolored      .75   .30

A971         A972

A973         A974

---

No. 1559, Hapalogenys mucronatus. No. 1560, Fugu niphobles. No. 1561, Oncorhynchus masou. No. 1562, Rhodeus ocellatus.

**1990, July 2**
1559 A971 100w multicolored     .80   .30
   Complete booklet, 4 #1559      8.75
1560 A972 100w multicolored     .80   .30
   Complete booklet, 4 #1560      8.75
1561 A973 100w multicolored     .80   .30
   Complete booklet, 4 #1561      8.75
1562 A974 100w multicolored     .80   .30
   Complete booklet, 4 #1562      8.75

A975         A976

A977         A978

No. 1563, Microphyso- gobio longidorsalis. No. 1564, Gnathopogon majimae. No. 1565, Therapon oxyrhnchus. No. 1566, Psettina ijimae.

**1991, June 8**
1563 A975 100w multicolored     .85   .25
   Complete booklet, 4 #1563      8.75
1564 A976 100w multicolored     .85   .25
   Complete booklet, 4 #1564      8.75
1565 A977 100w multicolored     .85   .25
   Complete booklet, 4 #1565      8.75
1566 A978 100w multicolored     .85   .25
   Complete booklet, 4 #1566      8.75
      Nos. 1555-1566 (12)        9.60  3.40

Light of Peace Illuminating the World — A979

**1989, Oct. 4**
1567 A979 80w multicolored      .55   .25

44th Intl. Eucharistic Cong., Seoul, Oct. 4-8.

29th World Congress of the Intl. Civil Airports Assoc., Seoul, Oct. 17-19 — A980

**1989, Oct. 17**
1568 A980 80w multicolored      .55   .25

Philatelic Week — A981

**1989, Nov. 18   Photo.   Perf. 13x13½**
1569 A981 80w multicolored      .55   .25
a.    Souvenir sheet of 2        1.90  1.90

Two Cranes A982

Folk Festival Customs A983

**1989, Dec. 1   Perf. 13x13½, 13½x13**
1570 A982 80w multicolored      .70   .25
a.    Souvenir sheet of 2        1.75  1.75
1571 A983 80w multicolored      .70   .25
a.    Souvenir sheet of 2        1.75  1.75

New Year 1990.

---

World Meteorological Day — A984

**1990, Mar. 23        Perf. 13½x13**
1572 A984 80w multicolored      .55   .25
   Complete booklet, 4 #1572      6.25

UNICEF in Korea, 40th Anniv. — A985

**1990, Mar. 24        Perf. 13x13½**
1573 A985 80w multicolored      .55   .25
   Complete booklet, 4 #1573      6.25

Cheju-Kohung Fiber Optic Submarine Cable — A986

**1990, Apr. 21        Perf. 13½x13**
1574 A986 80w multicolored      .55   .25
   Complete booklet, 4 #1574      6.25

Saemaul Movement, 20th Anniv. — A987

**1990, Apr. 21**
1575 A987 100w multicolored     .55   .25
   Complete booklet, 4 #1575      6.25

Youth Month — A988

**1990, May 1**
1576 A988 100w multicolored     .65   .25
   Complete booklet, 4 #1576      6.25

**Type of 1981 and**

Korean Flag A989

Korean Stork A990

White Magnolia A991

Korean White Pine A991a

Cart-shaped Earthenware A992

Fire Safety A993

Environmental Protection A994

Traffic Safety A995

Waiting
One's Turn
A996

Saving
Energy
A997

Child
Protection
A997a

Purification
of Language
Movement
A997b

Rose of
Sharon
A997c

Give Life
to Water
A997d

Ginger Jar — A998

Chong-IP'um-Song, Pine
Tree Natl.
Monument — A999

Drum, Drum
Dance
A1001

Mask,
Wrestlers
A1002

Hong
Yong-Sik
A1003

King
Sejong,
Korean
Alphabet
A1004

Dragon
Head,
Banner Staff
A1005

Gilt-bronze
Buddha
Triad with
Inscription of
Keymi
A1006

**Photo., Litho. (#1582), Litho. &
Engr. (#1594)**

| 1990-96 | | Perf. 13½x13, 13x13½ | | |
|---|---|---|---|---|
| 1577 | A989 | 10w multi | .40 | .25 |
| 1578 | A990 | 20w multi | .40 | .25 |
| 1579 | A991 | 30w multi | .45 | .25 |
| 1580 | A991a | 40w multi | .40 | .25 |
| 1581 | A992 | 50w multi | .55 | .25 |
| 1582 | A993 | 80w multi | 3.00 | .30 |
| 1583 | A994 | 100w multi | 8.00 | .35 |
| | | Complete booklet, 10 #1583 | 85.00 | |
| 1584 | A995 | 100w multi | 2.00 | .35 |
| | | Complete booklet, 10 #1584 | 20.00 | |
| 1585 | A996 | 100w multi | 1.90 | .25 |
| 1586 | A997 | 100w multi | 1.10 | .25 |
| 1587 | A997a | 100w multi | 1.10 | .25 |
| 1588 | A997b | 100w multi | 1.25 | .25 |
| 1589 | A997c | 110w multi | .90 | .25 |
| 1590 | A997d | 110w multi | 1.00 | .25 |
| 1591 | A998 | 150w multi | 1.30 | .25 |
| a. | | Booklet pane, 20 #1591 | 16.50 | |
| | | Complete booklet, #1591a | 19.00 | |
| 1592 | A999 | 160w multi | 1.30 | .25 |
| 1593 | A1001 | 370w multi | 2.50 | .45 |
| 1594 | A1002 | 440w multi | 3.25 | .50 |
| 1594A | A1003 | 600w multi | 4.00 | .65 |

| 1594B | A1004 | 710w multi | 4.75 | .80 |
|---|---|---|---|---|
| 1594C | A1005 | 800w multi | 5.00 | .80 |
| 1594D | A1006 | 900w multi | 5.75 | .70 |
| | | Nos. 1577-1594D (22) | 50.30 | 8.15 |

Issued: No. 1583, 6/5; 600w, 6/25; 150w,
7/2; 800w, 7/10; No. 1584, 7/25; 50w, 9/28;
80w, 11/1; No. 1585, 6/26/91; No. 1586,
11/1/91; No. 1587, 4/5/92; No. 1588, 11/2/92;
370w, 440w, 3/22/93; 10w, 3/30/93;
160w, 710w, 4/30/93; 20w, 30w, 40w, 5/24/93;
No. 1590, 7/1/93; 900w, 9/20/93; #1591a,
3/20/96.
See Nos. 1715-1738, 1846, 1851-1852,
1860, 1862.

**Coil Stamps**

| 1990 | Litho. | Perf. 13 Horiz. | | |
|---|---|---|---|---|
| 1594E | A992 | 50w multicolored | .90 | .30 |
| | | Perf. 13 Vert. | | |
| 1594F | A706 | 60w multicolored | .70 | .25 |
| 1594G | A994 | 100w multicolored | 1.50 | .60 |
| 1594H | A997c | 110w multicolored | 1.10 | .25 |
| | | Nos. 1594E-1594H (4) | 4.20 | 1.40 |

Seoul Mail
Center — A1007

| 1990, July 4 | | Litho. | Perf. 13½x13 | |
|---|---|---|---|---|
| 1595 | A1007 | 100w multicolored | .65 | .25 |
| a. | | Souvenir sheet of 2 | 2.00 | 2.00 |
| | | Complete booklet, 4 #1595 | 4.50 | |

8th Korean Boy Scout
Jamboree — A1008

| 1990, Aug. 8 | | | Perf. 13x13½ | |
|---|---|---|---|---|
| 1596 | A1008 | 100w multicolored | .65 | .25 |
| | | Complete booklet, 4 #1596 | 5.00 | |

**Wild Flowers**

Lilium
A1009

Aster
A1010

Adonis
A1011

Scabiosa
A1012

| 1990, Aug. 25 | | | Photo. | |
|---|---|---|---|---|
| 1597 | A1009 | 370w multicolored | 1.60 | .70 |
| | | Complete booklet, 4 #1597 | 15.00 | |
| 1598 | A1010 | 400w multicolored | 2.00 | .90 |
| | | Complete booklet, 4 #1598 | 19.50 | |
| 1599 | A1011 | 440w multicolored | 1.90 | .80 |
| | | Complete booklet, 4 #1599 | 18.00 | |
| 1600 | A1012 | 470w multicolored | 2.25 | .80 |
| | | Complete booklet, 4 #1600 | 21.00 | |

A1013

No. 1601, Aerides japonicum. No. 1602,
Heloniopsis orientalis. No. 1603, Aquilegia
buergeriana. No. 1604, Gentiana zollingeri.

| 1991, July 26 | | | | |
|---|---|---|---|---|
| 1601 | A1013 | 100w multicolored | .60 | .25 |
| | | Complete booklet, 4 #1601 | 4.75 | |
| 1602 | A1013 | 100w multicolored | .60 | .25 |
| | | Complete booklet, 4 #1602 | 4.75 | |
| 1603 | A1013 | 370w multicolored | 1.75 | .55 |
| | | Complete booklet, 4 #1603 | 13.50 | |
| 1604 | A1013 | 440w multicolored | 2.00 | .60 |
| | | Complete booklet, 4 #1604 | 16.00 | |

| 1992, June 22 | | Photo. | Perf. 13x13½ | |
|---|---|---|---|---|

No. 1605, Lychnis wilfordii. No. 1606,
Lycoris radiata. No. 1607, Commelina communis. No. 1608, Calanthe striata.

| 1605 | A1013 | 100w multicolored | .60 | .30 |
|---|---|---|---|---|
| | | Complete booklet, 4 #1605 | 5.00 | |
| 1606 | A1013 | 100w multicolored | .60 | .30 |
| | | Complete booklet, 4 #1606 | 5.00 | |
| 1607 | A1013 | 370w multicolored | 1.60 | .55 |
| | | Complete booklet, 4 #1607 | 13.00 | |
| 1608 | A1013 | 440w multicolored | 1.90 | .60 |
| | | Complete booklet, 4 #1608 | 15.00 | |
| | | Nos. 1597-1608 (12) | 17.40 | 6.60 |

See Nos. 1751-1762, 1869-1872, 1907-1910.

Anglican Church of
Korea, Cent. — A1021

| 1990, Sept. 29 | | Litho. | Perf. 13x13½ | |
|---|---|---|---|---|
| 1609 | A1021 | 100w | .65 | .25 |

Opening of Seoul Tower,
10th Anniv. — A1022

| 1990, Oct. 15 | | | | |
|---|---|---|---|---|
| 1610 | A1022 | 100w blk, red & bl | .65 | .25 |

National
Census — A1023

| 1990, Oct. 20 | | | Perf. 13x13½ | |
|---|---|---|---|---|
| 1611 | A1023 | 100w multicolored | .55 | .25 |

UN Development
Program, 40th
Anniv. — A1024

| 1990, Oct. 24 | | | | |
|---|---|---|---|---|
| 1612 | A1024 | 100w multicolored | .55 | .25 |

Philatelic
Week — A1025

**Litho. & Engr.**

| 1990, Nov. 16 | | | Perf. 13x13½ | |
|---|---|---|---|---|
| 1613 | A1025 | 100w multicolored | .65 | .25 |
| a. | | Souvenir sheet of 2 | 4.00 | 4.00 |
| | | Complete booklet, 4 #1613 | 5.00 | |

New Year
1991 (Year
of the
Sheep)
A1026

Two Cranes
A1027

| 1990, Dec. 1 | | Litho. | Perf. 13x13½ | |
|---|---|---|---|---|
| 1614 | A1026 | 100w multicolored | .60 | .25 |
| | | Complete booklet, 4 #1614 | 4.50 | |
| 1615 | A1027 | 100w multicolored | .60 | .25 |
| | | Complete booklet, 4 #1615 | 4.50 | |
| a. | | Souv. sheet of 2, #1614-1615 | 5.25 | 5.25 |

A1028

A1029

**Taejon Expo '93**

| 1990, Dec. 12 | | | | |
|---|---|---|---|---|
| 1616 | A1028 | 100w multicolored | .75 | .30 |
| a. | | Souvenir sheet of 2 | 1.60 | 1.60 |
| | | Complete booklet, 4 #1616 | 6.25 | |
| 1617 | A1029 | 440w multicolored | 1.90 | .75 |
| a. | | Souvenir sheet of 2 | 5.25 | 5.25 |
| | | Complete booklet, 4 #1617 | 22.50 | |

A1030

A1031

| 1991, Mar. 23 | | | | |
|---|---|---|---|---|
| 1618 | A1030 | 100w multicolored | .70 | .30 |
| a. | | Souvenir sheet of 2 | 1.60 | 1.60 |
| | | Complete booklet, 4 #1618 | 5.75 | |
| 1619 | A1031 | 100w multicolored | .70 | .30 |
| a. | | Souvenir sheet of 2 | 1.60 | 1.60 |
| | | Complete booklet, 4 #1619 | 5.75 | |

A1032

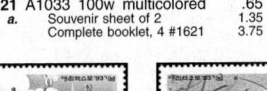

A1033

| 1992, Aug. 7 | | Photo. | Perf. 13½x13 | |
|---|---|---|---|---|
| 1620 | A1032 | 100w multicolored | .65 | .25 |
| a. | | Souvenir sheet of 2 | 1.35 | 1.35 |
| | | Complete booklet, 4 #1620 | 3.75 | |
| 1621 | A1033 | 100w multicolored | .65 | .25 |
| a. | | Souvenir sheet of 2 | 1.35 | 1.35 |
| | | Complete booklet, 4 #1621 | 3.75 | |

Government
Pavilion — A1034

Intl.
Pavilion — A1035

Recycling Art
Pavilion
A1035a

Telcom Pavilion
A1035b

| 1993, Aug. 7 | | | | |
|---|---|---|---|---|
| 1622 | A1034 | 110w multi | .70 | .25 |
| a. | | Souvenir sheet of 2 | 1.25 | 1.25 |
| | | Complete booklet, 4 #1622 | 5.00 | |
| 1623 | A1035 | 110w multi | .70 | .25 |
| c. | | Souvenir sheet of 2 | 1.25 | 1.25 |
| | | Complete booklet, 4 #1623 | 5.00 | |
| 1623A | A1035a | 110w multi | .70 | .25 |
| d. | | Souvenir sheet of 2 | 1.25 | 1.25 |
| | | Complete booklet, 4 #1623A | 5.00 | |
| 1623B | A1035b | 110w multi | .70 | .25 |
| e. | | Souvenir sheet of 2 | 1.25 | 1.25 |
| | | Complete booklet, 4 #1623B | 5.00 | |
| | | Nos. 1616-1623B (10) | 8.15 | 3.15 |

Saemaul
Minilibrary, 30th
Anniv. — A1036

| 1991, Feb. 1 | | Litho. | Perf. 13½x13 | |
|---|---|---|---|---|
| 1624 | A1036 | 100w multicolored | .60 | .25 |
| | | Complete booklet, 4 #1624 | 4.25 | |

Moth
A1037

Beetle
A1038

Butterfly
A1039

Beetle
A1040

Cicada — A1041

**1991, Apr. 8 Photo. Perf. 13½x13**
| | | | | |
|---|---|---|---|---|
| 1625 | A1037 | 100w shown | .85 | .25 |
| 1626 | A1038 | 100w shown | .85 | .25 |
| 1627 | A1039 | 100w shown | .85 | .25 |
| 1628 | A1040 | 100w shown | .85 | .25 |
| 1629 | A1041 | 100w shown | .85 | .25 |
| 1630 | A1040 | 100w Water beetle | .85 | .25 |
| 1631 | A1040 | 100w Bee | .85 | .25 |
| 1632 | A1040 | 100w Lady bug | .85 | .25 |
| 1633 | A1037 | 100w Dragonfly | .85 | .25 |
| 1634 | A1037 | 100w Grasshopper | .85 | .25 |
| a. | | Strip of 10, #1625-1634 | 11.00 | 12.00 |

Printed in sheets of 100 with each row shifted one design.

Traditional Performing
Arts Center, 40th
Anniv. — A1042

**1991, Apr. 10 Perf. 13x13½**
| | | | | |
|---|---|---|---|---|
| 1635 | A1042 | 100w multicolored | .65 | .25 |
| | | Complete booklet, 4 #1635 | 4.50 | |

Korean Provisional
Government in
Shanghai, 72nd
Anniv. — A1043

**1991, Apr. 13 Perf. 13½x13**
| | | | | |
|---|---|---|---|---|
| 1636 | A1043 | 100w multicolored | .65 | .25 |
| | | Complete booklet, 4 #1636 | 4.50 | |

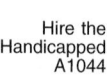
Hire the
Handicapped
A1044

**1991, Apr. 20**
| | | | | |
|---|---|---|---|---|
| 1637 | A1044 | 100w multicolored | .65 | .25 |
| | | Complete booklet, 4 #1637 | 5.00 | |

Teachers' Day, 10th
Anniv. — A1045

**1991, May 15 Litho. Perf. 13½x13½**
| | | | | |
|---|---|---|---|---|
| 1638 | A1045 | 100w multicolored | .65 | .25 |
| | | Complete booklet, 4 #1638 | 4.50 | |

A1046

**1991, Aug. 8 Litho. Perf. 13x13½**
| | | | | |
|---|---|---|---|---|
| 1639 | A1046 | 100w multicolored | .65 | .25 |
| a. | | Souvenir sheet of 2 | 1.60 | 1.60 |
| | | Complete booklet, 4 #1639 | 7.25 | |

17th World Scouting Jamboree.

---

YMCA World
Assembly — A1047

**1991, Aug. 22 Litho. Perf. 13x13½**
| | | | | |
|---|---|---|---|---|
| 1640 | A1047 | 100w multicolored | .65 | .25 |
| | | Complete booklet, 4 #1640 | 7.25 | |

Natl. Desire for
Reunification — A1048

**1991, Sept. 11 Litho. Perf. 13x13½**
| | | | | |
|---|---|---|---|---|
| 1641 | A1048 | 100w multicolored | .65 | .25 |
| | | Complete booklet, 4 #1641 | 6.50 | |

Admission to
UN — A1049

**1991, Sept. 18 Perf. 13½x13**
| | | | | |
|---|---|---|---|---|
| 1642 | A1049 | 100w multicolored | .65 | .25 |
| | | Complete booklet, 4 #1642 | 5.25 | |

**Musical Instruments**

Deerskin
Drum
(Galgo)
A1050

Mouth
Organ
(Saenghwang)
A1051

Seated
Drum
A1052

Small Gong
A1053

Designs: No. 1645, Brass chimes (Unra).
No. 1646, Large gong (Jing). No. 1649,
Dragon drum. No. 1650, Single bell chime.

**1991-92 Photo. Perf. 13x13½**
**Background color**
| | | | | |
|---|---|---|---|---|
| 1643 | A1050 | 100w gray | .75 | .30 |
| | | Complete booklet, 4 #1643 | 5.00 | |
| 1644 | A1051 | 100w tan | .75 | .30 |
| | | Complete booklet, 4 #1644 | 5.00 | |
| 1645 | A1050 | 100w lt violet | .75 | .30 |
| | | Complete booklet, 4 #1645 | 5.00 | |
| 1646 | A1050 | 100w pale green | .75 | .30 |
| | | Complete booklet, 4 #1646 | 5.00 | |
| 1647 | A1052 | 100w gray | .80 | .30 |
| | | Complete booklet, 4 #1647 | 5.00 | |
| 1648 | A1053 | 100w tan | .80 | .30 |
| | | Complete booklet, 4 #1648 | 5.00 | |
| 1649 | A1052 | 100w pale violet | .80 | .30 |
| | | Complete booklet, 4 #1649 | 5.00 | |
| 1650 | A1053 | 100w pale green | .80 | .30 |
| | | Complete booklet, 4 #1650 | 5.00 | |
| | | Nos. 1643-1650 (8) | 6.20 | 2.40 |

Issued: Nos. 1643-1646, 9/26; others,
2/24/92.

Month of
Culture — A1056

**1991, Oct. 1 Litho. Perf. 13x13½**
| | | | | |
|---|---|---|---|---|
| 1655 | A1056 | 100w multicolored | .65 | .25 |
| | | Complete booklet, 4 #1655 | 4.50 | |

---

Telecom '91 — A1057

**1991, Oct. 7 Photo.**
| | | | | |
|---|---|---|---|---|
| 1656 | A1057 | 100w multicolored | .65 | .25 |
| | | Complete booklet, 4 #1656 | 5.00 | |

Sixth World Telecommunication Exhibition &
Forum, Geneva, Switzerland.

**Beauty Series**

A1058

A1059

A1060

A1061

Kottam Architectural
Patterns
A1060    A1061

**1991, Oct. 26**
| | | | | |
|---|---|---|---|---|
| 1657 | A1058 | 100w multicolored | .85 | .30 |
| 1658 | A1059 | 100w multicolored | .85 | .30 |
| 1659 | A1060 | 100w multicolored | .85 | .30 |
| 1660 | A1061 | 100w multicolored | .85 | .30 |
| a. | | Block or strip of 4, #1657-1660 | 4.25 | 4.25 |
| | | Complete booklet, 2 #1660a | — | |

A1062

A1063

A1064

A1065

Norigae
A1064    A1065

**1992, Sept. 21 Photo. & Engr.**
| | | | | |
|---|---|---|---|---|
| 1661 | A1062 | 100w multicolored | .70 | .30 |
| 1662 | A1063 | 100w multicolored | .70 | .30 |
| 1663 | A1064 | 100w multicolored | .70 | .30 |
| 1664 | A1065 | 100w multicolored | .70 | .30 |
| a. | | Block or strip of 4, #1661-1664 | 3.75 | 3.75 |
| | | Complete booklet, 2 #1664a | — | |

A1066

A1067

A1068

A1069

Tapestries
A1068    A1069

**1993, Oct. 11 Photo. Perf. 13x13½**
| | | | | |
|---|---|---|---|---|
| 1665 | A1066 | 110w multicolored | .60 | .30 |
| 1666 | A1067 | 110w multicolored | .60 | .30 |
| 1667 | A1068 | 110w multicolored | .60 | .30 |

---

| | | | | |
|---|---|---|---|---|
| 1668 | A1069 | 110w multicolored | .60 | .30 |
| a. | | Block or strip of 4, #1665-1668 | 3.00 | 3.00 |
| | | Complete booklet, 2 #1668a | — | |

Philatelic Week — A1070

**1991, Dec. 5 Photo. Perf. 13x13½**
| | | | | |
|---|---|---|---|---|
| 1669 | A1070 | 100w multicolored | .65 | .25 |
| a. | | Souvenir sheet of 2 | 1.50 | 1.50 |
| | | Complete booklet, 4 #1669 | 4.50 | |

New Year 1992, Year of the
Monkey
A1071       A1072

**1991, Dec. 2 Photo. & Engr.**
| | | | | |
|---|---|---|---|---|
| 1670 | A1071 | 100w multicolored | .70 | .25 |
| a. | | Souvenir sheet of 2 | 1.90 | 1.90 |
| | | Complete booklet, 4 #1670 | 5.00 | |
| 1671 | A1072 | 100w multicolored | .70 | .25 |
| a. | | Souvenir sheet of 2 | 1.90 | 1.90 |
| | | Complete booklet, 4 #1671 | 5.00 | |

Hibiscus Syriacus, Natl.
Flower — A1073

**1992, Mar. 9 Photo. Perf. 13x13½**
**Background color**
| | | | | |
|---|---|---|---|---|
| 1672 | A1073 | 100w lt green | 1.10 | .40 |
| 1673 | A1073 | 100w lt blue | 1.10 | .40 |

Im-Jin War, 400th
Anniv. — A1074

**1992, May 23 Photo. Perf. 13½x13**
| | | | | |
|---|---|---|---|---|
| 1674 | A1074 | 100w multicolored | .55 | .25 |
| | | Complete booklet, 4 #1674 | 4.50 | |

Science Day, 25th
Anniv. — A1075

**1992, Apr. 21 Photo. Perf. 13½x13**
| | | | | |
|---|---|---|---|---|
| 1675 | A1075 | 100w multicolored | .55 | .25 |
| | | Complete booklet, 4 #1675 | 4.50 | |

Pong-Gil Yoon, Assassin
of Japanese Occupation
Leaders, 60th Anniv. of
Execution — A1076

**Photo. & Engr.**
**1992, Apr. 29 Perf. 13x13½**
| | | | | |
|---|---|---|---|---|
| 1676 | A1076 | 100w multicolored | .55 | .25 |
| | | Complete booklet, 4 #1676 | 4.50 | |

60th Intl. Fertilizer
Assoc. Conf. — A1077

## Photo & Engr.

**1992, May 25**      *Perf. 13x13½*
**1678** A1077 100w multicolored   .55 .25
    Complete booklet, 4 #1678   4.50

1992 Summer Olympics,
Barcelona — A1078

No. 1679, Pole vault. No. 1680, Rhythmic
gymnastics.

**1992, July 25**  **Photo.**  *Perf. 13x13½*
**1679** A1078 100w multi   .65 .25
    Complete booklet, 4 #1679   4.50
**1680** A1078 100w multi   .65 .25
    Complete booklet, 4 #1680   4.50

21st Universal
Postal Congress,
Seoul,
1994 — A1079

Designs: No. 1681, Korean Exhibition
Center, Namdae-mun Gate. No. 1682, Stone
statue of Tolharubang, Songsan Ilchulbong
Peak.

**1992, Aug. 22**  **Photo.**  *Perf. 13½x13*
**1681** A1079 100w red vio & multi   .60 .25
   a.   Souvenir sheet of 2   1.50 1.50
    Complete booklet, 4 #1681   4.50
**1682** A1079 100w brown & multi   .60 .25
   a.   Souvenir sheet of 2   1.50 1.50
    Complete booklet, 4 #1682   4.50

A1086

### Litho. & Engr.

**1992, Oct. 10**      *Perf. 13x13½*
**1683** A1086 100w sal & red brn   .55 .25
    Complete booklet, 4 #1683   4.50

Pong-Chang Yi (1900-1932), would-be
assassin of Japanese Emperor Hirohito.

A1087

Design: No. 1684, Hwang Young-Jo, 1992
Olympic marathon winner. No. 1685, Shon
Kee-Chung, 1936 Olympic Marathon Winner.

**1992, Oct. 10**      **Litho.**
**1684** A1087 100w multicolored   .70 .25
**1685** A1087 100w grn & multi   .70 .25
   a.   Pair, #1684-1685   1.90 1.90
   b.   Souv. sheet of 2, #1684-
         1685   4.00 4.00
    Complete booklet, 2 #1685a   9.00

Discovery of America,
500th Anniv. — A1088

**1992, Oct. 12**      **Photo.**
**1686** A1088 100w multicolored   .70 .25
    Complete booklet, 4 #1686   8.00

Philatelic
Week — A1089

**1992, Nov. 14**  **Photo.**  *Perf. 13½x13*
**1687** A1089 100w multicolored   .55 .25
   a.   Souvenir sheet of 2   1.60 1.60
    Complete booklet, 4 #1687   4.50

New Year 1993 (Year of
the Rooster)
A1090      A1091

**1992, Dec. 1**  **Photo.**  *Perf. 13x13½*
**1688** A1090 100w multicolored   .70 .25
   a.   Souvenir sheet of 2   1.90 1.90
    Complete booklet, 4 #1688   5.00
**1689** A1091 100w multicolored   .70 .25
   a.   Souvenir sheet of 2   1.90 1.90
    Complete booklet, 4 #1689   5.00

Intl. Conference on
Nutrition,
Rome — A1092

**1992, Dec. 5**      *Perf. 13½x13*
**1690** A1092 100w multicolored   .55 .25
    Complete booklet, 4 #1690   4.50

Seoul Art Center,
Grand
Opening — A1093

**1993, Feb. 15**  **Photo.**  *Perf. 13½x13*
**1691** A1093 110w multicolored   .55 .25
    Complete booklet, 4 #1691   4.50

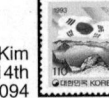

Inauguration of Kim
Young Sam, 14th
President — A1094

**1993, Feb. 24**
**1692** A1094 110w multicolored   1.00 .30
   a.   Souvenir sheet of 2   5.75 5.75

Student Inventions
Exhibition — A1095

**1993, May 27**  **Photo.**  *Perf. 13½x13*
**1693** A1095 110w lilac & silver   .55 .25
    Complete booklet, 4 #1693   5.25

A1096

**1993, June 14**  **Photo.**  *Perf. 13x13½*
**1694** A1096 110w multicolored   .55 .25
    Complete booklet, 4 #1694   5.25

UN Conference on Human Rights, Vienna.

Mushrooms — A1098

No. 1696, Ganoderma lucidum. No. 1697,
Pleurotus ostreatus. No. 1698, Lentinula
edodes. No. 1699, Tricholoma matsutake.

**1993, July 26**  **Photo.**  *Perf. 13x13½*
**1696** A1098 110w multicolored   .50 .25
    Complete booklet, 4 #1696   5.00
**1697** A1098 110w multicolored   .50 .25
    Complete booklet, 4 #1697   5.00
**1698** A1098 110w multicolored   .50 .25
    Complete booklet, 4 #1698   5.00
**1699** A1098 110w multicolored   .50 .25
    Complete booklet, 4 #1699   5.00
    Nos. 1696-1699 (4)   2.00 1.00

See Nos. 1770-1773, 1803-1806, 1883-
1886, 1912-1915, 1935.

A1099

**1993, Aug. 28**  **Photo.**  *Perf. 13x13½*
**1700** A1099 110w multicolored   .65 .25
    Complete booklet, 4 #1700   3.75

19th World Congress of Intl. Society of
Orthopedic Surgery and Trauma Study.

O-Dol-Odo-      Ong-He-Ya
Gi      A1101
A1100

**1993, Sept. 13**
**1701** A1100 110w multicolored   .65 .25
    Complete booklet, 4 #1701   3.75
**1702** A1101 110w multicolored   .65 .25
    Complete booklet, 4 #1702   3.75

Visit Korea Year '94
A1112      A1113

**1993, Sept. 27**  **Photo.**  *Perf. 13x13½*
**1713** A1112 110w multicolored   .55 .25
    Complete booklet, 4 #1713   3.75
**1714** A1113 110w multicolored   .55 .25
    Complete booklet, 4 #1714   3.75

## Type of 1993 and

Squirrel      Physalis
A1114      Alkekengi
     A1115

Scops Owl      Reduce
A1116      Garbage
     A1117

Narcissus      Little Tern
A1118      A1119

Sea Turtle      Airplane
A1120      A1122

Passenger      Porcelain
Airplane      Chicken
A1123      Water
     Dropper
     A1124

Celadon      Gilt Bronze
Water      Bongnae-
Dropper      san Incense
A1125      Burner
     A1127

Celadon
Pitcher — A1128

Designs: 300w, Van. 540w, Train. 1190w,
Passenger ship.

*Perf. 13½x13, 13x13½ (210w, 1050w,
#1728, 1732, 1734), 13½x12½ (60w,
90w), 12½x13½ (180w, 200w)*
**Photo., Litho. (#1726), Photo. &
Engr. (#1734)**

**1993-95**
**1715** A1114 60w multi   .50 .30
**1716** A1115 70w multi   .45 .25
**1717** A1116 90w multi   .65 .30
**1718** A1117 110w multi   .85 .25
**1719** A997c 120w multi   .85 .25
**1720** A1118 130w multi   .85 .30
   a.   Booklet pane of 20   16.50
    Complete booklet, #1720a   16.50
**1721** A1119 180w multi   1.25 .30
**1722** A1120 200w multi   1.60 .30
**1723** A1119 210w multi   1.40 .30
**1724** A1123 300w multi   1.90 .40
**1725** A1122 330w multi   2.75 .25
**1726** A1123 390w multi   2.50 .45
   a.   Booklet pane of 10   29.00
    Complete booklet, #1726a   29.00
**1727** A1122 400w multi   2.00 .35
   a.   Booklet pane, 10 #1727   23.00
    Complete booklet, #1727a   23.00
**1728** A1124 400w multi   2.00 .35
**1729** A1125 500w multi   2.25 .55
**1730** A1123 540w multi   3.00 .65
**1731** A1122 560w multi   3.25 .50
**1732** A1127 700w multi   3.50 .75
**1733** A1004 910w like
         #1594B   5.25 1.00
**1734** A1128 930w blue &
         multi   5.25 .85
**1735** A1128 930w tan &
         multi   5.25 1.00
   a.   Booklet pane of 10   67.50
    Complete booklet, #1735a   67.50
**1736** A1128 1050w multi   5.50 .80
**1737** A1123 1190w multi   6.00 1.10
**1738** A1122 1300w multi   7.25 .95
    Nos. 1715-1738 (24)   66.05 12.45

    Issued: No. 1718, 11/1/93;
910w, 2/15/94; 90w, 4/22/94; 130w,
8/20/94; 80w, 9/12/94; 390w, No. 1734,
1190w, 10/1/94; 540w, 11/1/94; 300w,
11/18/94; 60w, 200w, 12/19/94;
    No. 1720a, 2/28/95; 70w, 3/15/95; No.
1737, 3/11/95; No. 1735a, 3/20/95; 700w,
6/15/95; No. 1728, 8/28/95; No. 1727,
10/16/95; 1050w, 1300w, 10/25/95; 210w,
560w, 11/1/95; 500w, 11/6/95;
    120w, 330w, 11/11/95; No. 1727a, 3/27/96.
    Five versions of booklets with No. 1720a
exist with blocks of different colors at the top of
the booklet cover. The blocks of color match
color bars printed in the selvage of the
attached booklet pane.
    See Nos. 1847-1848, 1857.

### Coil Stamp

**1990**    **Litho.**    *Perf. 13 Vert.*
**1739** A1118 130w multicolored   4.50 .40

Philatelic
Week — A1144

**1993, Nov. 13   Photo.   *Perf. 13x13½***
1745  A1144  110w multicolored            .65    .25
  *a.*   Souvenir sheet of 2                 1.35   1.35
        Complete booklet, 4 #1745            8.00

21st UPU Congress,
Seoul — A1145

No. 1746, Dancer, muscians. No. 1747,
Weavers, horiz.

***Perf. 13x13½, 13½x13***
**1993, Nov. 18**
1746  A1145  110w multicolored            .55    .25
  *a.*   Souvenir sheet of 2                 1.40   1.40
        Complete booklet, 4 #1746            4.75
1747  A1145  110w multicolored            .55    .25
  *a.*   Souvenir sheet of 2                 1.40   1.40
        Complete booklet, 4 #1747            4.75

Trade Day, 30th
Anniv. — A1146

**1993, Nov. 30                *Perf. 13½x13***
1748  A1146  110w multicolored            .55    .25
        Complete booklet, 4 #1748            4.50

New Year 1994
(Year of the
Dog) — A1147

**1993, Dec. 1    *Perf. 13½x13, 13x13½***
1749  A1147  110w shown                    .90    .25
  *a.*   Souvenir sheet of 2                 1.60   1.60
1750  A1147  110w Stuffed toy
             dog, vert.                      .90    .25
  *a.*   Souvenir sheet of 2                 1.60   1.60

**Flower Type of 1991**

No. 1751, Weigela bortensis. No. 1752,
Caltha palustris. No. 1753, Iris ruthenica. No.
1754, Aceriphyllum rosii. No. 1755, Leontopodium japonicum. No. 1756, Geranium erios-
temon. No. 1757, Lycoris aurea. No. 1758,
Gentiana jamesii. No. 1759, Halenia cornicu-
lata. No. 1760, Erthyronium japonicum. No.
1761, Iris odaesanensis. No. 1762, Leontice
microrrhyncha.

**1993-95       Photo.        *Perf. 13x13½***
1751  A1013  110w multicolored            .70    .25
        Complete booklet, 4 #1751            3.50
1752  A1013  110w multicolored            .70    .25
        Complete booklet, 4 #1752            3.50
1753  A1013  110w multicolored            .70    .25
        Complete booklet, 4 #1753            3.50
1754  A1013  110w multicolored            .70    .25
        Complete booklet, 4 #1754            3.50
1755  A1013  130w multicolored            .95    .25
        Complete booklet, 4 #1755            5.00
1756  A1013  130w multicolored            .95    .25
        Complete booklet, 4 #1756            5.00
1757  A1013  130w multicolored            .95    .25
        Complete booklet, 4 #1757            5.00
1758  A1013  130w multicolored            .95    .25
        Complete booklet, 4 #1758            5.00
1759  A1013  130w multicolored            .95    .25
        Complete booklet, 6 #1759            5.00
1760  A1013  130w multicolored            .95    .25
        Complete booklet, 6 #1760            5.00
1761  A1013  130w multicolored            .95    .25
        Complete booklet, 6 #1761            5.00
1762  A1013  130w multicolored            .95    .25
        Complete booklet, 6 #1762            5.00
        *Nos. 1751-1762 (12)*              10.40  3.00

Issued: Nos. 1751-1754, 12/20/93; Nos.
1755-1758, 10/4/94; Nos. 1759-1762, 7/24/95.

Visit Korea Year
A1148           A1149

No. 1763, Masked dancer. No. 1764, Piper,
clouds.

**1994, Jan. 11   Photo.   *Perf. 13x13½***
1763  A1148  110w multicolored            .60    .25
        Complete booklet, 4 #1763            2.75
1764  A1149  110w multicolored            .60    .25
        Complete booklet, 4 #1764            2.75

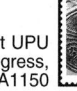

21st UPU
Congress,
Seoul — A1150

**1994, Jan. 24              *Perf. 13½x13***
1765  A1150  300w multicolored           1.30    .45
  *a.*   Souvenir sheet of 2                 3.25   3.25
  *b.*   Booklet pane of 10                  27.00
        Complete booklet, #1765b           27.00

Samil Independence
Movement, 75th
Anniv. — A1151

**1994, Feb. 28   Photo.   *Perf. 13x13½***
1766  A1151  110w multicolored            .50    .25

Wildlife
Protection — A1152

No. 1767, Sasakia charonda. No. 1768,
Allomyrina dichotoma.

**1994, Mar. 7   Photo.   *Perf. 13½x13***
1767  A1152  110w multicolored            .70    .25
  *a.*   Souvenir sheet of 2                 1.75   1.75
        Complete booklet, 4 #1767            3.75
1768  A1152  110w multicolored            .70    .25
  *a.*   Souvenir sheet of 2                 1.75   1.75
        Complete booklet, 4 #1768            3.75

Intl. Year of the
Family — A1153

**1994, May 14   Photo.       *Perf. 13***
1769  A1153  110w multicolored            .55    .25

**Mushroom Type of 1993**

No. 1770, Oudemansiella platyphylla. No.
1771, Morchella esculenta. No. 1772, Cortinarius purpurascens. No. 1773, Gomphus
floccosus.

**1994, May 30   Photo.   *Perf. 13x13½***
1770  A1098  110w multicolored            .50    .25
  *a.*   Souvenir sheet of 2                 1.35   1.35
        Complete booklet, 4 #1770            2.50
1771  A1098  110w multicolored            .50    .25
  *a.*   Souvenir sheet of 2                 1.35   1.35
        Complete booklet, 4 #1771            2.50
1772  A1098  110w multicolored            .50    .25
  *a.*   Souvenir sheet of 2                 1.35   1.35
        Complete booklet, 4 #1772            2.50
1773  A1098  110w multicolored            .50    .25
  *a.*   Souvenir sheet of 2                 1.35   1.35
        Complete booklet, 4 #1773            2.50
        *Nos. 1770-1773 (4)*               2.00   1.00
        *Nos. 1770a-1773a (4)*             5.40   5.40

Opening of War
Memorial
Center — A1154

**1994, June 10   Photo.       *Perf. 13***
1774  A1154  110w multicolored            .55    .25

PHILAKOREA '94,
Seoul — A1155

**1994, June 13                *Perf. 13***
1775  A1155  910w multicolored           3.75   1.25
  *a.*   Souvenir sheet of 1                 4.00   4.00
  *b.*   Booklet pane of 10                  37.50
        Complete booklet, #1775b           37.50

Stamps from No. 1775b have a straight
edge at either top or bottom.

**Beauty Series**

Fans
A1156

**1994, July 18   Photo.   *Perf. 13x13½***
1776       110w Taeguk                     .60    .25
1777       110w Crane                      .60    .25
1778       110w Pearl                      .60    .25
1779       110w Wheel                      .60    .25
  *a.*   A1156 Strip of 4, #1776-1779      3.00   3.00
        Complete booklet, 2 #1779a        13.50

Gates
A1160

No. 1780, Lofty Gate, traditional Yungban
residence. No. 1781, Pomosa Temple. No.
1782, Osumun (Fish Water) Gate, Changdukkung Palace. No. 1783, Pullomun Gate,
Changdukkung Palace.

**1995, May 22   Photo.   *Perf. 13x13½***
1780       130w multicolored               .60    .25
1781       130w multicolored               .60    .25
1782       130w multicolored               .60    .25
1783       130w multicolored               .60    .25
  *a.*   A1160 Strip of 4, #1780-1783      3.00   3.00
        Complete booklet, 2 #1783a        13.50

Pouches
A1164

**1996, Nov. 1   Photo.   *Perf. 13x13½***
1784       150w multicolored               .60    .25
1785       150w multicolored               .60    .25
1786       150w multicolored               .60    .25
1787       150w multicolored               .60    .25
  *a.*   A1164 Strip of 4, #1784-1787      3.00   3.00
        Complete booklet, 2 #1787a        13.50
        *Nos. 1776-1787 (12)*             7.20   3.00

A1168        PHILAKOREA
             '94 — A1169

No. 1788, Winter scene. No. 1789, Grape
vines. No. 1790, Cranes.

**1994, Aug. 16     Photo.       *Perf. 13***
1788  A1168  130w multi                   1.00    .25
  *a.*   Souvenir sheet of 2                 1.40   1.40
  *b.*   Booklet pane of 10                  10.50
        Complete booklet, #1788b           10.50
1789  A1168  130w multi                   1.00    .25
  *a.*   Souvenir sheet of 2                 1.40   1.40
  *b.*   Booklet pane of 10                  10.50
        Complete booklet, #1789b           12.50
1790  A1168  130w multi                   1.00    .25
  *a.*   Souvenir sheet of 2                 1.40   1.40
  *b.*   Booklet pane of 10                  10.50
        Complete booklet, #1790b           10.50
        *Nos. 1788-1790 (3)*               3.00    .75
        **Souvenir Sheet**
        **Litho. & Engr.**
1791         Sheet of 7                     9.75   9.00
  *a.*   A1169 130w Crane, moun-
         tains                              .40    .25
  *b.*   A1169 300w Two cranes,
         sun                                .95    .40
  *c.*   A1169 370w Two cranes in
         trees                             1.20    .50
  *d.*   A1169 400w Two deer               1.30    .55
  *e.*   A1169 440w Turtle, rapids         1.50    .60
  *f.*   A1169 470w River                  1.50    .60
  *g.*   A1169 930w Trees                  3.00   1.10

21st UPU Congress,
Seoul — A1170

No. 1792, Pens, glasses, stamps. No. 1793,
Sword dance. No. 1794, Dove holding envel-
ope. No. 1795, Hong Yong-sik, Heinrich Von
Stephan, horiz.

**1994, Aug. 22      Photo.       *Perf. 13***
1792  A1170  130w multicolored            .55    .25
  *a.*   Souvenir sheet of 2                 1.50   1.50
  *b.*   Booklet pane of 10                  6.50
        Complete booklet, #1792b            6.50
1793  A1170  130w multicolored            .55    .25
  *a.*   Souvenir sheet of 2                 1.50   1.50
  *b.*   Booklet pane of 10                  6.50
        Complete booklet, #1793b            6.50
1794  A1170  130w multicolored            .55    .25
  *a.*   Souvenir sheet of 2                 1.50   1.50
  *b.*   Booklet pane of 10                  6.50
        Complete booklet, #1794b            6.50
1795  A1170  370w multicolored           1.50    .60
  *a.*   Souvenir sheet of 2                 3.25   3.25
  *b.*   Souvenir sheet of 4, #1792-
         1795                               7.00   7.00
  *c.*   Booklet pane of 10                  45.00
        Complete booklet, #1795b           45.00
        *Nos. 1792-1795 (4)*               3.15   1.35

A1171

**1994, Sept. 27**
1796  A1171  130w multicolored            .60    .25

Seoul, Capital of Korea, 600th anniv.

A1172

**1994, Nov. 19   Photo.   *Perf. 13x13½***
1797  A1172  130w multicolored            .60    .25
  *a.*   Souvenir sheet of 2                 1.50   1.50
        Complete booklet, 4 #1797            5.25

Philatelic Week. Complete booklet has one
No. 1797 tied to cover with first day cancel.

A1173

**1994, Nov. 29**
1798  A1173  130w multicolored            .60    .25

Seoul becomes Korea's capital, 600th anniv.

New Year 1995
(Year of the
Boar) — A1174

**1994, Dec. 1                *Perf. 13½x13***
1799  A1174  130w shown                    .60    .25
  *a.*   Souvenir sheet of 2                 1.50   1.50
        Complete booklet, 4 #1799            6.00
1800  A1174  130w Family outing            .60    .25
  *a.*   Souvenir sheet of 2                 1.50   1.50
        Complete booklet, 4 #1800            6.00

Wildlife
Protection — A1175

**1995, Jan. 23   Photo.   *Perf. 13½x13***
1801  A1175  130w Rana plancyi            .70    .30
  *a.*   Souv. sheet of 2, imperf.          1.75   1.75
        Complete booklet, 4 #1801            5.50
1802  A1175  130w Bufo bufo               .70    .30
  *a.*   Souv. sheet of 2, imperf.          1.75   1.75
        Complete booklet, 4 #1802            5.50

## Mushroom Type of 1993

Designs: No. 1803, Russula virescens. No. 1804, Lentinus lepideus. No. 1805, Coprinus comalus. No. 1806, Laetiporus sulphureus.

**1995, Mar. 31  Photo.  Perf. 13x13½**

| | | | |
|---|---|---|---|
| 1803 | A1098 130w multicolored | .70 | .30 |
| a. | Souvenir sheet of 2 | 1.40 | 1.40 |
| | Complete booklet, 4 #1803 | 5.50 | |
| 1804 | A1098 130w multicolored | .70 | .30 |
| a. | Souvenir sheet of 2 | 1.40 | 1.40 |
| | Complete booklet, 4 #1804 | 5.50 | |
| 1805 | A1098 130w multicolored | .70 | .30 |
| a. | Souvenir sheet of 2 | 1.40 | 1.40 |
| | Complete booklet, 4 #1805 | 5.50 | |
| 1806 | A1098 130w multicolored | .70 | .30 |
| a. | Souvenir sheet of 2 | 1.40 | 1.40 |
| | Complete booklet, 4 #1806 | 5.50 | |
| Nos. 1803-1806 (4) | | 2.80 | 1.20 |

Completion of HANARO Research Reactor — A1176

**1995, Apr. 7  Perf. 13½x13**

| | | | |
|---|---|---|---|
| 1807 | A1176 130w multicolored | .70 | .35 |
| | Complete booklet, 4 #1807 | 5.00 | |

Modern Judicial System, Cent. — A1177

**1995, Apr. 25  Litho.  Perf. 13x13½**

| | | | |
|---|---|---|---|
| 1808 | A1177 130w multicolored | .60 | .25 |

Modern Legal Education, Cent. — A1178

**1995, Apr. 25  Perf. 13½x13**

| | | | |
|---|---|---|---|
| 1809 | A1178 130w multicolored | .60 | .25 |

Cartoons — A1179

130w, "Dooly, the Little Dinosaur," baby, porpoise. 440w, "Kochuboo," riding in airplane.

**1995, May 4**

| | | | |
|---|---|---|---|
| 1810 | A1179 130w multicolored | .65 | .35 |
| a. | Souvenir sheet of 1 | 1.45 | 1.45 |
| | Complete booklet, 4 #1810 | 5.00 | |
| 1811 | A1179 440w multicolored | 1.60 | .55 |
| a. | Souvenir sheet of 1 | 3.00 | 3.00 |
| | Complete booklet, 4 #1811 | 11.00 | |

78th Lions Clubs Intl. Convention A1180

**1995, July 4  Photo.  Perf. 13½x13**

| | | | |
|---|---|---|---|
| 1812 | A1180 130w multicolored | .70 | .25 |

Liberation Day, 50th Anniv. — A1181

Design: 440w, Mountain, yin/yang symbol.

**1995, Aug. 14  Photo.  Perf. 13½x13**

| | | | |
|---|---|---|---|
| 1813 | A1181 130w multicolored | .60 | .25 |
| a. | Booklet pane of 10 | 11.50 | |
| | Complete booklet, #1813a | 11.50 | |
| b. | Souvenir sheet of 2 | 1.45 | 1.45 |

**Size: 97x19mm**
**Perf. 13x13½**

| | | | |
|---|---|---|---|
| 1814 | A1181 440w multicolored | 1.60 | .55 |
| a. | Souvenir sheet of 1 | 2.40 | 2.40 |

Opening of Bohyunsan Optical Astronomical Observatory — A1183

**1995, Sept. 13  Litho.  Perf. 13x13½**

| | | | |
|---|---|---|---|
| 1816 | A1183 130w multicolored | .70 | .25 |
| | Complete booklet, 6 #1816 | 7.00 | |

### Literature Series

Kuji-ga Song (The Turtle's Back Song) A1184

Chongeop-sa Song A1185

A1186    A1187

Record of Travel to Five Indian Kingdoms A1188

A Poem to the Sui General Yu Zhong Wen A1189

A1190    A1191

A1192    A1193

A1194    A1195

**Perf. 13x13½, 13½x13**

**1995-99  Photo.**

| | | | |
|---|---|---|---|
| 1817 | A1184 130w multi | .65 | .25 |
| a. | Souvenir sheet of 2 | 1.40 | 1.40 |
| | Complete booklet, 6 #1817 | 5.75 | |
| 1818 | A1185 130w multi | .65 | .25 |
| a. | Souvenir sheet of 2 | 1.40 | 1.40 |
| | Complete booklet, 6 #1818 | 5.75 | |
| 1819 | A1186 150w multi | .60 | .25 |
| a. | Souvenir sheet of 2 | 1.45 | 1.45 |
| | Complete booklet, 10 #1819 | 11.50 | |
| 1820 | A1187 150w multi | .60 | .25 |
| a. | Souvenir sheet of 2 | 1.45 | 1.45 |
| | Complete booklet, 10 #1820 | 11.50 | |
| 1821 | A1188 170w multi | .65 | .25 |
| a. | Souvenir sheet of 2 | 1.35 | 1.35 |
| | Complete booklet, 10 #1821 | 9.00 | |
| 1822 | A1189 170w multi | .65 | .25 |
| a. | Sheet of 2 | 1.35 | 1.35 |
| | Complete booklet, 10 #1822 | 9.00 | |

**Photo. & Engr.**

| | | | |
|---|---|---|---|
| 1823 | A1190 170w multi | .60 | .25 |
| | Complete booklet, 10 #1823 | 9.00 | |
| a. | Souvenir sheet of 1 | 1.10 | 1.10 |

| | | | |
|---|---|---|---|
| 1824 | A1191 170w multi | .60 | .25 |
| | Complete booklet, 10 #1824 | 9.00 | |
| a. | Souvenir sheet of 1 | 1.10 | 1.10 |
| 1825 | A1192 170w multi | .60 | .30 |
| | Complete booklet, 10 #1825 | 9.00 | |
| 1826 | A1193 170w multi | .60 | .30 |
| | Complete booklet, 10 #1826 | 9.00 | |
| 1827 | A1194 170w multi | .60 | .30 |
| | Complete booklet, 10 #1827 | 9.00 | |
| 1828 | A1195 170w multi | .60 | .30 |
| | Complete booklet, 10 #1828 | 9.00 | |
| Nos. 1817-1828 (12) | | 7.40 | 3.20 |

**Souvenir Sheets**

| | | | |
|---|---|---|---|
| 1828A | A1192 340w multi | 1.60 | 1.60 |
| 1828B | A1193 340w multi | 1.60 | 1.60 |
| 1828C | A1194 340w multi | 1.60 | 1.60 |
| 1828D | A1195 340w multi | 1.60 | 1.60 |

Issued: Nos. 1817-1818, 9/25/95; Nos. 1819-1820, 9/16/96; Nos. 1821-1822, 12/12/97; Nos. 1823-1824, 9/14/98; Nos. 1825-1828D, 10/20/99.

FAO, 50th Anniv. — A1196

**Litho. & Engr.**

**1995, Oct. 16  Perf. 13**

| | | | |
|---|---|---|---|
| 1829 | A1196 150w dp vio & blk | .70 | .25 |
| | Complete booklet, 10 #1829 | 8.75 | |

Korean Bible Society, Cent. — A1197

**1995, Oct. 18  Litho.**

| | | | |
|---|---|---|---|
| 1830 | A1197 150w multicolored | .60 | .25 |
| | Complete booklet, 10 #1830 | 8.75 | |

Population and Housing Census — A1198

**1995, Oct. 20**

| | | | |
|---|---|---|---|
| 1831 | A1198 150w multicolored | .60 | .25 |
| | Complete booklet, 10 #1831 | 8.75 | |

UN, 50th Anniv. — A1199

**1995, Oct. 24  Photo.**

| | | | |
|---|---|---|---|
| 1832 | A1199 150w multicolored | .70 | .25 |
| | Complete booklet, 10 #1832 | 8.75 | |

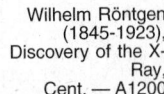

Wilhelm Röntgen (1845-1923), Discovery of the X-Ray, Cent. — A1200

**1995, Nov. 8  Perf. 13½x13**

| | | | |
|---|---|---|---|
| 1833 | A1200 150w multicolored | 1.20 | .25 |
| | Complete booklet, 10 #1833 | 16.00 | |

Philatelic Week — A1201

**1995, Nov. 18  Photo.  Perf. 13x13½**

| | | | |
|---|---|---|---|
| 1834 | A1201 150w multicolored | .70 | .25 |
| a. | Souvenir sheet of 2 | 1.45 | 1.45 |
| | Complete booklet, 10 #1834 | 8.75 | |

A1202    New Year 1996 (Year of the Rat) — A1203

**1995, Dec. 1  Perf. 13x13½, 13½x13**

| | | | |
|---|---|---|---|
| 1835 | A1202 150w multicolored | .75 | .25 |
| a. | Souvenir sheet of 2 | 1.90 | 1.90 |
| | Complete booklet, 10 #1835 | 10.00 | |
| 1836 | A1203 150w multicolored | .75 | .25 |
| a. | Souvenir sheet of 2 | 1.90 | 1.90 |
| | Complete booklet, 10 #1836 | 10.00 | |

Normalization of Korea-Japan Relations, 30th Anniv. — A1204

**1995, Dec. 18  Litho.  Perf. 13x13½**

| | | | |
|---|---|---|---|
| 1837 | A1204 420w multicolored | 1.75 | .60 |
| | Complete booklet, 4 #1837 | 8.75 | |

### Types of 1993-97 and

Gallicrex Cinerea A1206

Zosterops Japonica A1208

Luffa Cylindrica A1209

Numenius Madagascariensis A1210

Cambaroides Similis A1211

747 Airplane A1215

Mare and Colt — A1221

Soksu Stone Carving — A1223

Bronze Incense Burner in Shape of Lotus Flowers — A1224

**Photo., Photo. & Embossed (#1844)**

**1996-98  Perf. 13x13½, 13½x13**

| | | | | |
|---|---|---|---|---|
| 1839 | A1206 | 50w multi | .60 | .25 |
| 1840 | A1208 | 80w multi | .65 | .25 |
| 1841 | A1209 | 100w multi | 1.00 | .25 |
| 1842 | A1118 | 140w multi | 1.20 | .25 |

**Perf. 13**

| | | | | |
|---|---|---|---|---|
| 1843 | A1210 | 170w multi | 2.00 | .25 |
| 1844 | A1210 | 170w like #1843, braille inscription | 1.90 | .40 |

**Perf. 13x13½, 13½x13**

| | | | | |
|---|---|---|---|---|
| 1845 | A1211 | 170w multi | 1.60 | .30 |
| 1846 | A997c | 190w multi | 1.60 | .30 |
| 1847 | A1119 | 260w multi | 2.00 | .35 |

**Perf. 13x14**

| | | | | |
|---|---|---|---|---|
| 1848 | A1119 | 300w Alauda arvensis | 1.75 | .35 |

**Perf. 13½x13, 13x13½, 13 (#1855)**

| | | | | |
|---|---|---|---|---|
| 1849 | A1215 | 340w grn bl & multi | 2.10 | .40 |
| 1850 | A1215 | 380w lt lilac & multi | 2.50 | .45 |

| 1851 | A1001 | 420w like | | |
| | | #1593 | 3.00 | .40 |
| 1852 | A1002 | 480w like | | |
| | | #1594 | 3.25 | .45 |
| 1854 | A1221 | 800w multi | 3.50 | .50 |
| 1855 | A1223 | 1000w multi | 5.00 | .95 |
| 1856 | A1224 | 1170w multi | 5.75 | 1.45 |
| 1857 | A1128 | 1190w multi | 6.75 | 1.45 |
| 1858 | A1215 | 1340w brt grn & | | |
| | | multi | 8.00 | 1.20 |
| 1859 | A1215 | 1380w pink & | | |
| | | multi | 8.00 | 1.40 |
| | | Nos. 1839-1859 (20) | 62.15 | 11.60 |

### Coil Stamps
**Perf. 13 Horiz., 13 Vert. (#1860, 1862)**

**1996-97** — Photo.

| 1860 | A998 | 150w like #1591 | 1.20 | .60 |
| 1861 | A1211 | 170w like No. 1845 | 1.30 | .30 |
| 1862 | A997c | 190w like No. 1846 | 1.35 | .30 |
| | | Nos. 1860-1862 (3) | 3.85 | 1.20 |

Issued: 300w, 1/22/96; No. 1860, 2/1/96; 420w, 480w, 3/20/96; 1000w, 12/16/96; 100w, 3/5/97; 80w, 7/1/97; Nos. 1845-1846, 9/1/97; 340w, 380w, 1340w, 1380w, 9/12/97; Nos. 1842, 1847, 1856, 1857, 11/1/97; Nos. 1861, 1862, 11/18/97; No. 1843, 12/15/97; 50w, 2/19/98; 800w, 4/4/98; No. 1844, 10/15/98.

Opening of China-Korea Submarine Fiber Optic Cable System — A1229

**1996, Feb. 8  Litho.  Perf. 13½x13**

| 1863 | A1229 | 420w multicolored | 1.75 | .45 |
| | | Complete booklet, 4 #1863 | 9.25 | |

See People's Republic of China No. 2647.

Korea Institute of Science and Technology, 30th Anniv. — A1230

**1996, Feb. 10  Photo.  Perf. 13½x13**

| 1864 | A1230 | 150w multicolored | .70 | .25 |
| | | Complete booklet, 10 #1864 | 8.75 | |

Protection of Nature — A1231

No. 1865, Geoclemys reevesii. No. 1866, Scincella laterale.

**1996, Mar. 5  Photo.  Perf. 13½x13**

| 1865 | A1231 | 150w multicolored | .70 | .25 |
| a. | | Souvenir sheet of 2 | 1.75 | 1.75 |
| | | Complete booklet, 10 #1865 | 17.50 | |
| 1866 | A1231 | 150w multicolored | .70 | .25 |
| a. | | Souvenir sheet of 2 | 1.75 | 1.75 |
| | | Complete booklet, 10 #1866 | 17.50 | |

Successful Launches of Mugunghwa Satellites — A1232

**1996, Mar. 18  Photo.  Perf. 13**

| 1867 | A1232 | 150w multicolored | .70 | .25 |
| | | Complete booklet, 10 #1867 | 8.75 | |

Tongnip Shinmum, First Privately Published Newspaper, Cent. — A1233

So Chae-p'il, lead article of first issue.

### Litho. & Engr.
**1996, Apr. 6  Perf. 13**

| 1868 | A1233 | 150w multicolored | .70 | .25 |
| | | Complete booklet, 10 #1868 | 10.00 | |

### Wildflower Type of 1992

No. 1869, Cypripedium macranthum. No. 1870, Trillium tschonoskii. No. 1871, Viola variegata. No. 1872, Hypericum ascyron.

**1996, Apr. 22  Photo.  Perf. 13**

| 1869 | A1013 | 150w multicolored | .95 | .25 |
| | | Complete booklet, 10 #1869 | 11.50 | |

| 1870 | A1013 | 150w multicolored | .95 | .25 |
| | | Complete booklet, 10 #1870 | 11.50 | |
| 1871 | A1013 | 150w multicolored | .95 | .25 |
| | | Complete booklet, 10 #1871 | 11.50 | |
| 1872 | A1013 | 150w multicolored | .95 | .25 |
| | | Complete booklet, 10 #1872 | 11.50 | |
| | | Nos. 1869-1872 (4) | 3.80 | 1.00 |

Korea Military Academy, 50th Anniv. — A1234

**1996, May 1  Litho.  Perf. 13½x13**

| 1873 | A1234 | 150w multicolored | .70 | .25 |
| | | Complete booklet, 10 #1873 | 9.00 | |

Cartoons — A1235

No. 1874, Gobau running. No. 1875, Kkach'i in swordfight.

**1996, May 4  Photo.**

| 1874 | A1235 | 150w multicolored | .70 | .25 |
| a. | | Souvenir sheet of 1 | 1.45 | 1.45 |
| | | Complete booklet, 10 #1874 | 9.00 | |
| 1875 | A1235 | 150w multicolored | .70 | .25 |
| a. | | Souvenir sheet of 1 | 1.45 | 1.45 |
| | | Complete booklet, 10 #1875 | 9.00 | |

Girl Scouts of Korea, 50th Anniv. — A1236

**1996, May 10**  Litho.

| 1876 | A1236 | 150w multicolored | .70 | .25 |
| | | Complete booklet, 10 #1876 | 10.00 | |

35th IAA World Advertising Congress — A1237

**1996, June 8  Litho.  Perf. 13**

| 1877 | A1237 | 150w multicolored | .70 | .25 |
| | | Complete booklet, 10 #1877 | 8.25 | |

Campaign Against Illegal Drugs — A1238

**1996, June 26  Photo.  Perf. 13½x13**

| 1878 | A1238 | 150w multicolored | .70 | .25 |
| | | Complete booklet, 10 #1878 | 10.00 | |

Winter Universiade '97, Muju-Chonju A1239

No. 1880, Emblem, vert.

**1996, July 1  Perf. 13½x13, 13x13½**

| 1879 | A1239 | 150w shown | .70 | .25 |
| | | Complete booklet, 10 #1879 | 8.75 | |
| 1880 | A1239 | 150w multicolored | .70 | .25 |
| | | Complete booklet, 10 #1880 | 8.75 | |

1996 Summer Olympic Games, Atlanta
A1240        A1241

**1996, July 20  Perf. 13x13½**

| 1881 | A1240 | 150w multicolored | .70 | .25 |
| | | Complete booklet, 10 #1881 | 12.50 | |
| 1882 | A1241 | 150w multicolored | .70 | .25 |
| | | Complete booklet, 10 #1882 | 12.50 | |

### Mushroom Type of 1993

Designs: No. 1883, Paxillus atrotomentosus. No. 1884, Sarcodon imbricatum. No. 1885, Rhodophyllus crassipes. No. 1886, Amanita inaurata.

**1996, Aug. 19  Photo.  Perf. 13x13½**

| 1883 | A1098 | 150w multicolored | .70 | .25 |
| a. | | Souvenir sheet of 2 | 1.40 | 1.40 |
| | | Complete booklet, 10 #1883 | 12.50 | |
| 1884 | A1098 | 150w multicolored | .70 | .25 |
| a. | | Souvenir sheet of 2 | 1.40 | 1.40 |
| | | Complete booklet, 10 #1884 | 12.50 | |
| 1885 | A1098 | 150w multicolored | .70 | .25 |
| a. | | Souvenir sheet o 2 | 1.40 | 1.40 |
| | | Complete booklet, 10 #1885 | 12.50 | |
| 1886 | A1098 | 150w multicolored | .70 | .25 |
| a. | | Souvenir sheet of 2 | 1.40 | 1.40 |
| | | Complete booklet, 10 #1886 | 12.50 | |
| | | Nos. 1883-1886 (4) | 2.80 | 1.00 |

### Souvenir Sheets

2002 World Cup Soccer Championships, Korea — A1242

No. 1887, Players, Korean flag. No. 1888, 2 players.

**1996, Aug. 1  Photo.  Perf. 13½**

| 1887 | A1242 | 400w Sheet of 4 | 6.75 | 6.75 |
| 1888 | A1242 | 400w Sheet of 4 | 6.75 | 6.75 |

Korean Alphabet, 550th Anniv. — A1243

### Litho. & Engr.
**1996, Oct. 9  Perf. 13x13½**

| 1889 | A1243 | 150w multicolored | .70 | .25 |
| a. | | Souvenir sheet of 2 | 1.35 | 1.35 |
| | | Complete booklet, 10 #1889 | 10.50 | |

Suwon Castle, Bicent. — A1244

### Photo. & Engr.
**1996, Oct. 10  Perf. 13½x13**

| 1890 | A1244 | 400w multicolored | 1.90 | .55 |

Seoul Natl. University, 50th Anniv. — A1245

**1996, Oct. 15  Photo.  Perf. 13½x13**

| 1891 | A1245 | 150w multicolored | .70 | .25 |
| | | Complete booklet, 10 #1891 | 9.50 | |

Philatelic Week — A1246

Painting: Poppy and a Lizard, by Shin Saimdang.

**1996, Nov. 18  Photo.  Perf. 13x13½**

| 1892 | A1246 | 150w multicolored | .70 | .25 |
| a. | | Souvenir sheet of 2 | 1.40 | 1.40 |
| | | Complete booklet, 10 #1892 | 11.00 | |

A1247        New Year 1997 (Year of the Ox) — A1248

**1996, Dec. 2**  Perf. 13

| 1893 | A1247 | 150w multicolored | .85 | .25 |
| a. | | Souvenir sheet of 2 | 1.50 | 1.50 |
| | | Complete booklet, 10 #1893 | 13.00 | |
| 1894 | A1248 | 150w multicolored | .85 | .25 |
| a. | | Souvenir sheet of 2 | 1.50 | 1.50 |
| | | Complete booklet, 10 #1894 | 13.00 | |

Winter Universiade '97, Muju-Chonju — A1249

**1997, Jan. 24  Photo.  Perf. 13**

| 1895 | A1249 | 150w Skier | .65 | .25 |
| | | Complete booklet, 10 #1895 | 11.50 | |
| a. | | Souvenir sheet of 2 | 1.25 | 1.25 |
| 1896 | A1249 | 150w Ice skater | .65 | .25 |
| | | Complete booklet, 10 #1896 | 11.50 | |
| a. | | Souvenir sheet of 2 | 1.25 | 1.25 |

Modern Banking System in Korea, Cent. — A1250

**1997, Feb. 19  Litho.  Perf. 13½x13**

| 1897 | A1250 | 150w multicolored | .70 | .25 |
| | | Complete booklet, 10 #1897 | 11.50 | |

A1251

**1997, Apr. 10  Perf. 13x13½**

| 1898 | A1251 | 150w multicolored | .60 | .25 |
| | | Complete booklet, 10 #1898 | 10.00 | |

97th Inter-Parliamentary Conference, 160th Inter-Parliamentary Council.

World Book & Copyright Day — A1252

**1997, Apr. 23**  Litho.

| 1899 | A1252 | 150w multicolored | .70 | .25 |
| | | Complete booklet, 10 #1899 | 10.00 | |

Cartoons — A1253

No. 1900, Mother holding child from "A Long, Long Journey in Search of Mommy." No. 1901, Girl in air holding medal from "Run, Run, Hannie."

**1997, May 3  Photo.  Perf. 13½x13**

| 1900 | A1253 | 150w multicolored | .60 | .25 |
| a. | | Souvenir sheet of 1 | 1.05 | 1.05 |
| | | Complete booklet, 10 #1900 | 13.50 | |
| 1901 | A1253 | 150w multicolored | .60 | .25 |
| a. | | Souvenir sheet of 1 | 1.05 | 1.05 |
| | | Complete booklet, 10 #1901 | 13.50 | |

Nos. 1900a, 1901a are continuous designs.

2nd Pusan East Asian Games — A1254

**1997, May 10  Litho.  Perf. 13½x13**

| 1902 | A1254 | 150w multicolored | .70 | .25 |
| | | Complete booklet, 10 #1900 | 10.00 | |

2002 World Cup Soccer,
Korea/Japan
A1255          A1256

No. 1903, Jules Rimet, founder of World
Cup. No. 1904, Painting of Ch'ukkuk match.

**1997, May 31    Photo.    Perf. 13x13½**
1903 A1255 150w multicolored      .75    .25
  *a.*  Souvenir sheet of 2             1.90   1.90
    Complete booklet, 10 #1903    11.50
1904 A1256 150w multicolored      .75    .25
  *a.*  Souvenir sheet of 3             2.00   2.00
    Complete booklet, 10 #1904    11.50

Wildlife
Protection — A1257

Fish: No. 1905, Pungitius sinensis. No.
1906, Coreoperca kawamebari.

**1997, June 5                    Perf. 13**
1905 A1257 150w multicolored      .70    .25
  *a.*  Souvenir sheet of 2             1.25   1.25
    Complete booklet, 10 #1905    11.50
1906 A1257 150w multicolored      .70    .25
  *a.*  Souvenir sheet of 2             1.25   1.25
    Complete booklet, 10 #1906    11.50

**Wildflower Type of 1992**

No. 1907, Belamcanda chinensis. No. 1908,
Hylomecon ernale. No. 1909, Campanula
takesimana. No. 1910, Magnolia sieboldii.

**1997, June 19    Photo.         Perf. 13**
1907 A1013 150w multicolored      .70    .25
    Complete booklet, 10 #1907    12.50
1908 A1013 150w multicolored      .70    .25
    Complete booklet, 10 #1908    12.50
1909 A1013 150w multicolored      .70    .25
    Complete booklet, 10 #1909    12.50
1910 A1013 150w multicolored      .70    .25
    Complete booklet, 10 #1910    12.50
    *Nos. 1907-1910 (4)*          2.80   1.00

1997 Kwangju
Biennale — A1258

**1997, July 1**
1911 A1258 150w multicolored      .60    .25
    Complete booklet, 10 #1911    9.50

**Mushroom Type of 1993**

Designs: No. 1912, Inocybe fastigiata. No.
1913, Panaeolus papilionaceus. No. 1914,
Ramaria flava. No. 1915, Amanita muscaria.

**1997, July 21   Photo.    Perf. 13x13½**
1912 A1098 150w multicolored      .70    .25
  *a.*  Souvenir sheet of 2             1.30   1.30
1913 A1098 150w multicolored      .70    .25
  *a.*  Souvenir sheet of 2             1.30   1.30
1914 A1098 150w multicolored      .70    .25
  *a.*  Souvenir sheet of 2             1.30   1.30
1915 A1098 150w multicolored      .70    .25
  *a.*  Souvenir sheet of 2             1.30   1.30
    *Nos. 1912-1915 (4)*          2.80   1.00

85th World Dental
Congress,
Seoul — A1259

**1997, Sept. 5   Photo.    Perf. 13½x13**
1916 A1259 170w multicolored      .65    .25

Opening of Port of
Mokpo,
Cent. — A1260

**Litho. & Engr.**
**1997, Oct. 1              Perf. 13½x13**
1917 A1260 170w multicolored      .65    .25

---

Soongsil Academy,
Cent. — A1261

**1997, Oct. 10          Photo. & Engr.**
1918 A1261 170w multicolored      .65    .25

**Beauty Series**

Wrapping Cloths — A1262

**1997, Nov. 3   Photo.    Perf. 13x13½**
1919 170w multicolored            .85    .25
1920 170w multicolored            .85    .25
1921 170w multicolored            .85    .25
1922 170w multicolored            .85    .25
  *a.*  A1262 Strip of 4, #1919-1922   4.00   4.00

Philatelic
Week — A1266

**1997, Nov. 18**
1923 A1266 170w multicolored      .75    .25
  *a.*  Souvenir sheet of 2             1.25   1.25

New Year 1998 (Year of
the Tiger)
A1267          A1268

**1997, Dec. 1   Photo.    Perf. 13x13½**
1924 A1267 170w multicolored      .90    .25
  *a.*  Souvenir sheet of 2             1.60   1.60
1925 A1268 170w multicolored      .90    .25
  *a.*  Souvenir sheet of 2             1.60   1.60

Pulguksa
Temple
A1269

**Litho. & Engr.**
**1997, Dec. 9              Perf. 13x13½**
1926 A1269  Sheet of 14          35.00  35.00
  *a.*  170w Buddha, Sokkuram
    Grotto                          1.00   1.00
  *b.*  380w Temple                     4.00   4.00

Top part of No. 1926 contains one each
Nos. 1926a-1926b and is separated from the
bottom portion of the sheet by a row of perforations. The lower part of No. 1926 contains 9
No. 1926a and 3 No, 1926b.

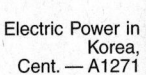

Electric Power in
Korea,
Cent. — A1271

**1998, Jan. 26   Photo.    Perf. 13½x13**
1927 A1271 170w multicolored      .70    .25

---

Inauguration of the
15th President, Kim
Dae-jung — A1272

**1998, Feb. 25   Litho.    Perf. 13½x13**
1928 A1272 170w multicolored      .90    .35
  *a.*  Souvenir sheet of 1             5.75   5.75

Protection of Wild
Animals and
Plants — A1273

Designs: a, Panthera pardus orientalis. b,
Selenarctos thibetanus ussuricus. c, Lutra
lutra. d, Moschus moschiferus.

**1998, Mar. 21               Perf. 13x13½**
1929    Sheet of 12            24.00  24.00
  *a.-d.*  A1273 340w Any single        1.50    .30

Top part of No. 1929 contains one each No.
1929a-1929d and is separated from the bottom portion of the sheet by a row of perforations. The lower part of No. 1929 contains 2
each Nos. 1929a-1929d.

Cartoons — A1274

Designs: 170w, Boy daydreaming while
holding flower, from "Aktong-i," by Lee Hi-jae.
340w, Mother on motorcycle, son making fists
from "Challenger," by Park Ki-jong.

**1998, May 4   Photo.    Perf. 13½x13**
1930 A1274 170w multicolored      .75    .25
  *a.*  Souvenir sheet of 1              .75    .75
  *b.*  Booklet pane of 10            19.00
    Complete booklet, #1930b      19.00

**Photo. & Engr.**
1931 A1274 340w multicolored     1.45   1.25
  *a.*  Souvenir sheet of 1            1.50   1.50
  *b.*  Booklet pane of 10            24.00
    Complete booklet, #1931b      24.00

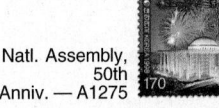

Natl. Assembly,
50th
Anniv. — A1275

**1998, May 30   Litho.    Perf. 13½x13**
1932 A1275 170w multicolored      .70    .25

2002 World Cup Soccer
Championships, Korea/Japan — A1276

Designs: a, Player. b, Two players. c, Player
heading ball. d, Player performing bicycle kick.

**1998, May 30               Perf. 13x13½**
1933    A1276   Strip of 4, #a.-d.  4.00   4.00
  *a.-d.*  170w any single                .70    .25
  *e.*  Souvenir sheet, #1933          3.25   3.25

Information Culture
Special — A1277

Communication through the ages: a, Rock
drawings. b, Horseback messenger, beacon
fire. c, Telephone, mailbox. d, Computers.

**1998, June 1   Litho.    Perf. 13½x13**
1934    Strip of 4                4.00   4.00
  *a.-c.*  A1277 170w any single        .60    .25
  *d.*  A1277 340w multicolored        1.25    .45

No. 1934d is 68x70mm.

---

**Mushroom Type of 1993**

Designs: a, Pseudocolus schellenbergiae.
b, Cyptotrama asprata. c, Laccaria
vinaceoavellanea. d, Phallus rugulosus.

**1998, July 4**
1935    Sheet of 16            17.00  17.00
  *a.-d.*  A1098 170w Any single         .75    .30

Left part of No. 1935 contains 3 each Nos.
1935a-1935d, with each strip in a different
order. This is separated from the right portion
of the sheet by a row of perforations. The right
part of No. 1935 contains 1 each Nos. 1935a-
1935d.

Republic of Korea,
50th
Anniv. — A1278

**1998, Aug. 14   Photo.    Perf. 13½x13**
1937 A1278 170w multicolored      .70    .25

Philatelic
Week — A1279

**1998, Aug. 19               Perf. 13x13½**
1938 A1279 170w multicolored      .70    .25
  *a.*  Souvenir sheet of 2             1.20   1.20

A1280

**1998, Sept. 24   Photo.    Perf. 13x13½**
1939 A1280 170w multicolored      .70    .25
    Complete booklet, 10 #1939    10.00

1998 Pusan Intl. Film Festival.

Founding of Songkyunkwan, 600th
Anniv. — A1281

**Photo. & Engr.**
**1998, Sept. 25               Perf. 13**
1940 A1281 170w multicolored      .70    .25
    Complete booklet, 5 #1940     4.50

A1282

**1998, Oct. 1**
1941 A1282 170w multicolored      .70    .25
    Complete booklet, 10 #1941    7.25

Korean Armed Forces, 50th anniv.

World Stamp
Day — A1283

**1998, Oct. 9**
1942 A1283 170w multicolored      .75    .25
    Complete booklet, 10 #1942    6.50

## Beauty Series

Ceramics — A1284

No. 1944, Box with cranes on lid. No. 1945, Fish. No. 1946, Red, white blossom with blue leaf. No. 1947, Frog. No. 1948, Dragon. No. 1949, Monkeys. No. 1950, Pagoda.

**1998, Nov. 20    Photo.    Perf. 13**
| 1943 | A1284 | 170w multicolored | .80 | .35 |
|------|-------|--------------------|-----|-----|
| 1944 | A1284 | 170w multicolored | .80 | .35 |
| 1945 | A1284 | 170w multicolored | .80 | .35 |
| 1946 | A1284 | 170w multicolored | .80 | .35 |
| 1947 | A1284 | 170w multicolored | .80 | .35 |
| 1948 | A1284 | 170w multicolored | .80 | .35 |
| 1949 | A1284 | 170w multicolored | .80 | .35 |
| 1950 | A1284 | 170w multicolored | .80 | .35 |
| *a.* | | Block of 8, #1243-1250 | 8.50 | 7.50 |

New Year 1999 (Year of the Rabbit) — A1286

**1998, Dec. 1    Perf. 13x13½**
| 1952 | A1286 | 170w multicolored | .75 | .25 |
|------|-------|--------------------|-----|-----|
| | | Complete booklet, 10 #1952 | 8.75 | |

Woodblock of Buddhist Tripitaka Koreana, Haeinsa Temple — A1287

Haeinsa Temple Changgyong P'anjon Complex — A1288

**Litho. & Engr.**
**1998, Dec. 9    Perf. 13½**
| 1953 | | Sheet of 12 | 28.00 | 28.00 |
|------|--|-------------|-------|-------|
| *a.* | A1287 | 170w multicolored | .95 | .50 |
| *b.* | A1288 | 380w multicolored | 2.75 | 1.60 |

Top part of No. 1953 contains one each Nos. 1953a-1953b and is separated from the bottom portion of the sheet by a row of perforations. The lower part of No. 1953 contains 6 No. 1953a and 4 No. 1953b.

Opening of Kunsan Port, Cent. — A1289

**1999, May 1    Litho.    Perf. 13¼**
| 1954 | A1289 | 170w multicolored | .65 | .25 |
|------|-------|--------------------|-----|-----|

Opening of Masan Port, Cent. A1290

**1999, May 1**
| 1955 | A1290 | 170w multicolored | .85 | .25 |
|------|-------|--------------------|-----|-----|

Cartoons — A1291

No. 1956, Boy and dog, "Tokgo T'ak," by Lee Sang-mu. No. 1957, Choson Dynasty robber, "Im Kkuk-jung," by Lee Du-ho. No. 1958, Fighter against alien invaders, "Rai-Fi," by Kim San-ho, vert.

**1999, May 3    Photo.    Perf. 13½**
| 1956 | A1291 | 170w multicolored | .65 | .30 |
|------|-------|--------------------|-----|-----|
| 1957 | A1291 | 170w multicolored | .65 | .30 |
| 1958 | A1291 | 170w multicolored | .65 | .30 |
| | | Nos. 1956-1958 (3) | 1.95 | .90 |

**Souvenir Sheets**
| 1959 | A1291 | 340w like #1956 | 1.45 | 1.25 |
|------|-------|------------------|------|------|
| 1960 | A1291 | 340w like #1957 | 1.45 | 1.25 |
| 1961 | A1291 | 340w like #1958 | 1.45 | 1.25 |
| | | Nos. 1959-1961 (3) | 4.35 | 3.75 |

Nos. 1959-1961 are continuous designs.

A1292

Raptors: a, Falco peregrinus. b, Accipiter soloensis. c, Bubo bubo. d, Haliaeetus pelagicus.

**1999, June 5    Litho.    Perf. 13x13¼**
| 1962 | | Sheet of 12 | 27.00 | 27.00 |
|------|--|-------------|-------|-------|
| *a.-b.* | A1292 | 170w each | 1.00 | .30 |
| *c.-d.* | A1292 | 340w each | 1.90 | .50 |

Top part of No. 1962 contains one each Nos. 1962a-1962d and is separated from the bottom portion of the sheet by a row of perforations. The lower part of No. 1962 contains 2 blocks of Nos. 1962a-1962d.

A1293

**1999, June 12    Photo.    Perf. 13x13¼**
| 1963 | A1293 | 170w multicolored | .65 | .25 |
|------|-------|--------------------|-----|-----|
| | | Complete booklet, 10 #1963 | 12.50 | |

1999 Intl. Olympic Committee Congress, Seoul.

Johann Wolfgang von Goethe, German Poet (1749-1832) — A1294

**Litho. & Engr.**
**1999, Aug. 12    Perf. 13x13½**
| 1964 | A1294 | 170w multicolored | .85 | .30 |
|------|-------|--------------------|-----|-----|

**Souvenir Sheet**
| 1965 | A1294 | 480w multicolored | 2.40 | 2.40 |
|------|-------|--------------------|------|------|

See Germany No. 2052.

Kumgang Mountain by Kyomjae (1676-1759) A1295

**1999, Aug. 13    Litho.**
| 1966 | A1295 | 170w multicolored | .75 | .30 |
|------|-------|--------------------|-----|-----|

**Souvenir Sheet**
| 1967 | A1295 | 340w multicolored | 1.25 | 1.25 |
|------|-------|--------------------|------|------|

Korean National Railroad, Cent. — A1296

**Litho. & Engr.**
**1999, Sept. 18    Perf. 13x13¼**
| 1968 | A1296 | 170w multicolored | .75 | .30 |
|------|-------|--------------------|-----|-----|
| | | Complete booklet, 10 #1968 | 10.00 | |

Millennium — A1297

A1297a

A1297b

A1297c

A1297d

A1297e

A1297f

A1297g

A1297h

A1297i

A1297j

Prehistoric sites and artifacts — No. 1969: a, Paleolithic ruins, Chungok-ri (black denomination at LL). b, Neolithic sites, Amsa-dong (white denomination at UR). c, Neolithic shell mound ruins, Tongsam-dong (black denomination at LR). d, Dolmen, Pukon-ri (black denomination at UR). e, Bronze Age artifacts and ruins, Songguk-ri. f, Rock carvings, Ulsan.

Three Countries Era artifacts — No. 1970: a, Tiger-shpaed belt buckle from tomb of Sarari, duck-shaped earthenware container, Kyongsang. b, Gold crown, silver cup from Hwangnamdae tomb. c, Wall painting of hunting scene from Tomb of the Dancers, Chibanri. d, Gold diadem ornaments, curved jade pieces from tomb of King Muryong. e, Gold crown from Koryong, armor from Kimhae. f, Decorative tiles, Anapji Pond.

Ancient Choson to Unified Shilla periods — No. 1971: a, Writing, site of Asadal, ancient capital of Choson. b, Korean wrestlers. c, King Kwanggaet'o, stone stele, and circular artifact with writing. d, Archers on horseback. e, Admiral Chang Po-go, ship.

Koryo dynasty — No. 1972: a, Writing and buildings (civil service examinations). b, Monk and Tripitaka Koreana wood blocks. c, Jade and movable metal type. d, Scholar An-hyang, writing and buildings. e, Mun Ik-jom, cotton plants and spinning wheel.

Early Choson dynasty — No. 1973: a, King Sejong and Korean alphabet. b, Korean script and Lady Shin Saimdang, calligrapher and painter. c, Yi Hwang and Yi I and Confucian academy building. d, Admiral Yi Sun-shin and turtle boat. e, Sandae-nori mask dance dramas.

Late Choson Dynasty — No. 1974: a, Tongui Pogam, medical treatises by Huh Joon (anatomic diagram, mortar and pestle) b, Dancer and Musicians, by Kim Hong-do. c, Plum Blossoms and Bird, by Chong Yak-yong and building. d, Map of Korea, by Kim Chongho and compass. e, Carved stone monument at Tongchak Peasant Uprsing Memorial Hall.

Historic relics of Koryo and Choson Dynasties — No. 1975: a, Container, pitcher, Kangjin kiln site. b, Fenced-off monument and Nirvana Hall, Pongjungsa Temple (yellow building). c, Hahoe and Pyongsan wooden masks. d, Kunjong Hall, Kyongbok Palace. e, Dream Journey to the Peach Blossom land, by An Kyon. f, Water clock of King Sejong.

Joseon Dynasty — No. 1976: a, Spring Outing, by Sin Yun-bok. b, Chusa-style calligraphy, birthplace of Kim Jeong-hui. c, Beacon Lighthouse, book of technical drawings. d, Myeongdong Cathedral. e, Wongaksa Theater, performers. f, KITSAT-1 satellite.

Vision of the Future — No. 1977: a, Bicycle with wheels represening the two Koreas. b, Rainbow (environmental protection). c, Human genome project. d, IMT 2000 and satellites. e, Children's drawing of space travel. f, Solar-powered vehicle, windmills.

Pre-independence historic events and personalities — No. 1978: a, Kim Ku. b, March 1 Independence Movement, Declaration of Independence. c, Establishment of Korean interim government. d, Ahn Ik-tae, composer of national anthem. e, Yun Dong-ju, poet.

Historic events since independence — No. 1979: a, Liberation after World War II (People with flag). b, Korean War (soldiers, barbed wire). c, Construction of Seoul-Busan Expressway. d, Saemaul Undong movement (workers and flag). e, 1988 Summer Olympics, Seoul.

| | | | |
|---|---|---|---|
| **1999-2001** | | **Litho.** | **Perf. 13x13½** |
| **1969** | A1297 | Sheet of 6 | 5.50 5.50 |
| *a.-f.* | | 170w any single | .70 .30 |
| **1970** | A1297a | Sheet of 6 | 5.50 5.50 |
| *a.-f.* | | 170w any single | .70 .30 |
| | | **Perf. 13½** | |
| **1971** | A1297b | Sheet of 5 + label | 5.75 5.75 |
| *a.-e.* | | 170w any single | .70 .30 |
| | | **Photo.** | |
| **1972** | A1297c | Sheet of 5 + label | 5.75 5.75 |
| *a.-e.* | | 170w any single | .70 .30 |
| **1973** | A1297d | Sheet of 5 + label | 5.75 5.75 |
| *a.-e.* | | 170w any single | .70 .30 |

| | | | |
|---|---|---|---|
| **1974** | A1297e | Sheet of 5 + label | 7.25 7.25 |
| *a.-e.* | | 170w Any single | .70 .30 |
| | | **Perf. 13** | |
| **1975** | A1297f | Sheet of 6 | 7.50 7.50 |
| *a.-f.* | | 170w Any single | .90 .30 |
| **1976** | A1297g | Sheet of 6 | 6.25 6.25 |
| *a.-f.* | | 170w Any single | .70 .30 |
| **1977** | A1297h | Sheet of 6 | 5.75 5.75 |
| *a.-f.* | | 170w Any single | .70 .30 |
| | | **Perf. 13½** | |
| **1978** | A1297i | Sheet of 5 + label | 7.50 7.50 |
| *a.-e.* | | 170w Any single | .90 .30 |
| **1979** | A1297j | Sheet of 5 + label | 5.50 5.50 |
| *a.-e.* | | 170w Any single | .70 .30 |
| | | Nos. 1969-1979 (11) | 68.00 68.00 |

Issued: No. 1969, 10/2; No. 1970, 11/16; No. 1971, 1/3/00; No. 1972, 3/2/00; No. 1973, 5/1/00; No. 1974, 7/1/00; No. 1975, 9/1/00; No. 1976, 11/1/00; No. 1977, 1/2/01; No. 1978, 4/2/01; No. 1979, 7/2/01.

UPU, 125th Anniv. — A1298

| | | | |
|---|---|---|---|
| **1999, Oct. 9** | | **Litho.** | **Perf. 13x13½** |
| **1980** | A1298 170w multi | | .75 .25 |

### Beauty Series

A1299

a, Purple panel, 4 orange flowers in purple and blue vase, rabbit, duck. b, Blue green panel, red jar, rooster. c, Orange panel, 4 orange flowers in yellow vase. d, Purple panel, fish, purple vase with flower decoration. e, Blue green panel, fish in net. f, Red panel, crab. g, Purple panel, birds, red flowers. h, Orange panel, deer, 3 orange flowers.

| | | | |
|---|---|---|---|
| **1999, Nov. 3** | | **Litho.** | **Perf. 13x13¼** |
| **1981** | A1299 | Sheet of 8, #a.-h. | 13.50 13.50 |
| *a.-h.* | | 340w any single | 1.60 .50 |

New Year 2000 (Year of the Dragon) — A1300

| | | | |
|---|---|---|---|
| **1999, Dec. 1** | | | **Photo.** |
| **1982** | A1300 170w multi | | .75 .30 |
| *a.* | | Souvenir sheet of 2 | 1.50 1.50 |

A1301

Registration of Korean Sites on World Heritage List — A1302

---

### Litho. & Engr.

| | | | |
|---|---|---|---|
| **1999, Dec. 9** | | | **Perf. 13x13¼** |
| **1983** | | Sheet of 10 | 17.50 17.50 |
| *a.* | A1301 170w multicolored | | 1.00 .30 |
| *b.* | A1302 340w multicolored | | 2.60 .55 |

Top part of No. 1983 contains one each Nos. 1983a-1983b. The lower part of No. 1983 contains 4 each Nos. 1983a-1983b.

Flag
A1303

Nycticorax
Nycticorax
A1304

Vitis
Amurensis
A1305

Purpuricenus
Lituratus
A1306

Eophona
Migratoria
A1307

Limenitis
Populi
A1310

Plow
A1311

Sseore
A1311a

Sowing
Basket,
Namtae
A1311b

Hoes
A1311c

Namu-
janngun,
Jaetbak
A1311d

Yongdurei
A1311e

Winnower,
Thresher
A1311f

Meongseok,
Wicker Tray
A1311g

Mortar,
Pestle,
Grindstone
A1311h

Carrier,
Rice Chest
A1311i

Hibiscus
Syriacus
A1312

Chionectes
Opilio
A1313

Falco Tinnunculus —
A1314

---

Hibiscus
Syriacus
A1314a

Hibiscus
Syriacus
A1314b

Ficedula Zanthopygia —
A1315

Hibiscus
Syriacus
A1315a

Celadon
Pitcher
A1316

Porcelain
Container
A1316a

Hong Yong-Sik,
1st General
Postmaster
A1317

Koryo Jade
Ornament
A1319

Kylin Roof-End
Tile
A1320

Ridge-End
Tile
A1321

Porcelain
Vase With
Bamboo
Design
A1322

Crown From
Tombs of
Shinch'on-ni
A1323

Malus
Asiatica
A1326

Aquilegia
Flabeliata — A1327

**Perf. 13¼x13 (#2000, 2002, 2004, 2005), 13x13¼ (#2001, 2003, 2006, 2007), 12¾x13¼ (#1984-1990, 1996), 13¾x12¾ (#1986, 1991, 1993, 1994, 1995, 1997, 1998)**

| | | | |
|---|---|---|---|
| **1999-2003** | | | **Photo.** |
| **1984** | A1303 | 10w multi | .35 .25 |
| **1985** | A1304 | 20w multi | .45 .30 |
| **1986** | A1305 | 30w multi | .45 .35 |
| **1987** | A1306 | 40w multi | .45 .30 |
| **1988** | A1307 | 60w multi | .45 .35 |
| **1989** | A1310 | 160w multi | .65 .30 |
| **1990** | | Horiz. strip of 10 | 15.50 10.00 |
| *a.* | A1311 | 170w multi | 1.00 .30 |
| *b.* | A1311a | 170w multi | 1.00 .30 |
| *c.* | A1311b | 170w multi | 1.00 .30 |
| *d.* | A1311c | 170w multi | 1.00 .30 |
| *e.* | A1311d | 170w multi | 1.00 .30 |
| *f.* | A1311e | 170w multi | 1.00 .30 |
| *g.* | A1311f | 170w multi | 1.00 .30 |
| *h.* | A1311g | 170w multi | 1.00 .30 |
| *i.* | A1311h | 170w multi | 1.00 .30 |
| *j.* | A1311i | 170w multi | 1.00 .30 |

| 1991 | A1312 | 190w multi | 1.00 | .30 |
|---|---|---|---|---|
| 1992 | A1313 | 200w multi | 1.05 | .35 |
| 1993 | A1314 | 210w multi | .90 | .30 |
| 1994 | A1314a | 220w multi | 1.00 | .30 |
| 1995 | A1314b | 240w multi | 1.45 | .40 |
| 1996 | A1315 | 280w multi | 1.10 | .40 |
| 1997 | A1315a | 310w multi | 1.30 | .60 |
| 1998 | A1316 | 400w multi | 1.45 | .80 |
| 1999 | A1316a | 500w multi | 1.90 | .85 |
| 2000 | A1317 | 600w multi | 2.60 | .85 |
| 2001 | A1319 | 700w multi | 3.25 | .85 |
| 2002 | A1320 | 1290w multi | 5.75 | 1.90 |
| 2003 | A1321 | 1310w multi | 6.00 | 1.90 |
| 2004 | A1320 | 1490w buff & multi | 6.25 | 2.60 |
| 2005 | A1321 | 1510w brn & multi | 6.25 | 2.60 |
| 2006 | A1322 | 1520w multi | 5.50 | 2.50 |
| 2007 | A1323 | 2000w multi | 7.25 | 1.20 |

**Booklet Stamps**
**Self-Adhesive**
*Serpentine Die Cut 11¼x11½,*
*11½x11¼*

| 2008 | A1326 | 190w multi | 1.45 | .75 |
|---|---|---|---|---|
| a. | | Booklet pane of 20 | 25.00 | |
| 2008A | A1327 | 190w multi | 1.45 | .75 |
| a. | | Booklet pane of 20 | 25.00 | |
| | | *Nos. 1984-2008A (26)* | 75.20 | 32.05 |

Issued: 600w, 11/15; 2000w, 11/1; 20w, 700w, 1/17/00; 40w, 6/10/00; No. 1990, 1/20/01; 200w, 3/5/01. 160w, 210w, 280w, 1290w, 1310w, 1/15/02; 10w, 3/6/03; 30w, 9/10/01; 60w, 3/15/02; 400w, 4/11/03; 1490w, 1510w, 1/1/03; Nos. 2008-2008A, 7/1/03; 500w, 7/11/03; No. 1991, 220w, 240w, 310w, 1520w, 11/1/04.

2002 World Cup Soccer
Championships, Korea &
Japan — A1328

Various players in action.

**1999, Dec. 31  Photo.  *Perf. 13x13½***
**Denomination Color**

| 2009 | | 170w | orange | .70 | .35 |
|---|---|---|---|---|---|
| 2010 | | 170w | green | .70 | .35 |
| 2011 | | 170w | red | .70 | .35 |
| 2012 | | 170w | blue | .70 | .35 |
| a. | A1328 | Strip of 4, #2009-2012 | | 3.25 | 3.25 |
| b. | | Souvenir sheet, #2009-2012 | | 3.50 | 3.50 |

Korea's Entry into
UPU,
Cent. — A1329

**2000, Jan. 3  Photo.  *Perf. 13¼x13***

| 2013 | A1329 | 170w multi | .75 | .30 |
|---|---|---|---|---|
| | | Booklet, 10 #2013 | 12.50 | |

Steam
Locomotives
A1330

Designs: No. 2014, Pashi. No. 2015, Teho. No. 2016, Mika. No. 2017, Hyouki.

**2000, Feb. 1  Photo.  *Perf. 13¾x12¾***

| 2014 | A1330 | 170w tan, blk & vio | .70 | .30 |
|---|---|---|---|---|
| 2015 | A1330 | 170w pink, blk & vio | .70 | .30 |
| 2016 | A1330 | 170w gray, blk & vio | .70 | .30 |
| 2017 | A1330 | 170w cit, blk & vio | .70 | .30 |
| a. | | Block of 4, #2014-2017 | 3.75 | 3.75 |
| | | Booklet, 2 #2017a | — | |

Endangered
Flowers — A1331

a, Lilium cernuum. b, Hibiscus hamabo. c, Sedirea japonica. d, Cypripedium japonicum.

**2000, Feb. 25        *Perf. 13x13¼***

| 2018 | | Sheet of 12 | 17.50 | 17.50 |
|---|---|---|---|---|
| a.-d. | A1331 | 170w any single | 1.10 | .30 |

Top part of No. 2018 contains one each of Nos. 2018a-2018d and the lower part contains two each. No. 2018 is impregnated with floral scent.

World Water
Day — A1332

**2000, Mar. 22  Photo.**

| 2019 | A1332 | 170w multi | .65 | .30 |
|---|---|---|---|---|
| | | Booklet, 10 #2019 | 10.00 | |

World Meteorological
Organization, 50th
Anniv. — A1333

**2000, Mar. 23        *Perf. 13x13¼***

| 2020 | A1333 | 170w multi | .75 | .30 |
|---|---|---|---|---|
| | | Booklet, 10 #2020 | 10.00 | |

Love — A1334

**2000, Apr. 20  Photo.  *Perf. 13¼***

| 2021 | A1334 | 170w multi | 1.10 | .30 |
|---|---|---|---|---|

No. 2021 has floral scent.
Value is for stamp with surrounding selvage.

Cyber Korea 21
Technology
Plan — A1335

**2000, Apr. 22  Litho.  *Perf. 13¼x13***

| 2022 | A1335 | 170w multi | .80 | .30 |
|---|---|---|---|---|
| | | Booklet, 10 #2022 | 10.50 | |

Cartoons — A1336

Designs: No. 2023: Goindol, by Park Soo-dong (cavemen). No. 2024, Youngsim-i, by Bae Gum-taek (girl with lipstick).

**2000, May 4  Photo.  *Perf. 13x13¼***

| 2023 | A1336 | 170w multi | .70 | .35 |
|---|---|---|---|---|
| a. | | Souvenir sheet of 1 | .95 | .95 |
| | | Booklet, 10 #2023 | 10.50 | |
| 2024 | A1336 | 170w multi | .70 | .35 |
| a. | | Souvenir sheet of 1 | .95 | .95 |
| | | Booklet, 10 #2024 | 10.50 | |

Summit Meeting
Between North and
South
Korea — A1337

**2000, June 12  Photo.  *Perf. 13¼x13***

| 2025 | A1337 | 170w multi | .65 | .45 |
|---|---|---|---|---|

41st Intl. Mathematical
Olympiad — A1338

**2000, July 13  Photo.  *Perf. 13x13¼***

| 2026 | A1338 | 170w multi | .85 | .35 |
|---|---|---|---|---|
| | | Booklet, 10 #2026 | 10.50 | |

**Literature Series**

The Nine Cloud
Dream, by Kim
Man-jung
A1339

From the Sea to
a Child, by Chun
Nam-seon
A1340

Tears of Blood,
by Yi In-jik
A1341

Yolha Diary,
by Park Ji-
won
A1342

The Fisherman's
Calendar, by Yun Seon-
do — A1343

**2000, Aug. 1  *Perf. 13¼x13, 13x13¼***

| 2027 | A1339 | 170w multi | .85 | .35 |
|---|---|---|---|---|
| a. | | Souvenir sheet of 1 | 1.00 | 1.00 |
| 2028 | A1340 | 170w multi | .85 | .35 |
| a. | | Souvenir sheet of 1 | 1.00 | 1.00 |
| 2029 | A1341 | 170w multi | .85 | .35 |
| a. | | Souvenir sheet of 1 | 1.00 | 1.00 |
| 2030 | A1342 | 170w multi | .85 | .35 |
| a. | | Souvenir sheet of 1 | 1.00 | 1.00 |
| 2031 | A1343 | 170w multi | .85 | .35 |
| a. | | Souvenir sheet of 1 | 1.00 | 1.00 |
| | | *Nos. 2027-2031 (5)* | 4.25 | 1.75 |

The Puljongdae
Cliff of Mt.
Kumgang, by
Chong
Son — A1344

**2000, Aug. 2  Litho.  *Perf. 13¼x13***

| 2032 | A1344 | 340w multi | 1.45 | .65 |
|---|---|---|---|---|
| a. | | Souvenir sheet of 1 | 1.60 | 1.45 |

Philately Week.

2000 Summer Olympics,
Sydney — A1345

**2000, Sept. 15  Photo.  *Perf. 13x13¼***

| 2033 | A1345 | 170w multi | .75 | .40 |
|---|---|---|---|---|

Public
Secondary
Schools,
Cent.
A1346

**2000, Oct. 2  Litho. & Engr.  *Perf. 13***

| 2034 | A1346 | 170w multi | .70 | .40 |
|---|---|---|---|---|

Third Asia-Europe
Summit Meeting,
Seoul — A1347

**2000, Oct. 20  Photo.  *Perf. 13¼x13***

| 2035 | A1347 | 170w multi | .70 | .35 |
|---|---|---|---|---|

Intl. Council of Graphic
Design Associations
Millennium
Congress — A1348

**2000, Oct. 25        *Perf. 13x13¼***

| 2036 | A1348 | 170w org & blk | .70 | .35 |
|---|---|---|---|---|

Cartoon Character Gobau. 50th Anniv.
A1349

**2000, Nov. 1  Litho.  *Perf. 13¼***

| 2037 | A1349 | 170w multi | .70 | .35 |
|---|---|---|---|---|

**Beauty Series**

Tortoise-shell Comb
A1350

Woman's
Ceremonial
Headdress
A1351

Butterfly-shaped
Hair Pin — A1352

Dragon and
Phoenix Hair
Pins — A1353

**2000, Nov. 16  Photo.  *Perf. 13¼x13***

| 2038 | | Horiz. strip of 4 | 4.25 | 4.25 |
|---|---|---|---|---|
| a. | A1350 | 170w multi | .70 | .40 |
| b. | A1351 | 170w multi | .70 | .40 |
| c. | A1352 | 170w multi | .70 | .40 |
| d. | A1353 | 170w multi | .70 | .40 |

Seoul World Cup
Stadium
A1354

Busan Sports
Complex Main
Stadium
A1355

Daegu Sports
Complex Stadium
A1356

Incheon Munhak
Stadium
A1357

Gwangju World Cup
Stadium
A1358

Daejeon World Cup
Stadium
A1359

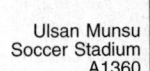

Ulsan Munsu
Soccer Stadium
A1360

Suwon World Cup
Stadium
A1361

Jeonju World Cup
Stadium
A1362

Jeju World Cup
Stadium
A1363

**2000, Nov. 24  Photo.  Perf. 13¼x13**

| | | | |
|---|---|---|---|
| 2039 | | Block of 10 | 13.50 10.00 |
| a. | A1354 170w multi | | 1.15 .35 |
| b. | A1355 170w multi | | 1.15 .35 |
| c. | A1356 170w multi | | 1.15 .35 |
| d. | A1357 170w multi | | 1.15 .35 |
| e. | A1358 170w multi | | 1.15 .35 |
| f. | A1359 170w multi | | 1.15 .35 |
| g. | A1360 170w multi | | 1.15 .35 |
| h. | A1361 170w multi | | 1.15 .35 |
| i. | A1362 170w multi | | 1.15 .35 |
| j. | A1363 170w multi | | 1.15 .35 |
| k. | Souvenir sheet, #2039a-2039b | | 2.75 2.75 |
| l. | Souvenir sheet, #2039c-2039d | | 2.75 2.75 |
| m. | Souvenir sheet, #2039e-2039f | | 2.75 2.75 |
| n. | Souvenir sheet, #2039g-2039h | | 2.75 2.75 |
| o. | Souvenir sheet, #2039i-2039j | | 2.75 2.75 |

New Year 2001
(Year of the
Snake) — A1364

**2000  Photo.  Perf. 13¼**

| | | | |
|---|---|---|---|
| 2040 | A1364 170w multi | | .95 .35 |
| a. | Souvenir sheet of 2 | | 1.75 1.75 |

**Self-Adhesive**
*Serpentine Die Cut 10¼*

| | | | |
|---|---|---|---|
| 2041 | A1364 170w multi | | 1.25 .35 |

Issued: No. 2040, 12/1; No. 241, 12/22.
No. 2041 issued in sheets of 10.

King Sejong
and Hunmin
Chongun
Manuscript
A1365

Annals of
the Choson
Dynasty and
Repository
A1365a

**Litho. & Engr.**
**2000, Dec. 9  Perf. 13x13¼**

| | | | |
|---|---|---|---|
| 2042 | | Sheet of 8 | 15.50 15.50 |
| a. | A1365 340w multi | | 1.50 .90 |
| b. | A1365a 340w multi | | 1.50 .90 |

Addition of Hunmin Chongun manuscript
and Annals of the Choson Dynasty to
UNESCO Memory of the World Register. Top
part of No. 2042 contains one each Nos.
2042a-2042b the lower part contains three
each Nos. 2042a-2042b.

Awarding of
Nobel Peace
Prize to Pres. Kim
Dae-jung
A1366

**2000, Dec. 9  Photo.**

| | | | |
|---|---|---|---|
| 2043 | A1366 170w multi | | .85 .35 |
| a. | Souvenir sheet of 1 | | 2.25 2.25 |

Oksun Peaks, by
Kim Hong-
do — A1367

**2001, Jan. 10  Photo.  Perf. 13¼**

| | | | |
|---|---|---|---|
| 2044 | A1367 170w multi | | .80 .35 |

Visit Korea Year.

A1368

A1369

A1370

Diesel and
Electric
Trains — A1371

**2001, Feb. 1  Photo.  Perf. 13¾x12¾**

| | | | |
|---|---|---|---|
| 2045 | | Block of 4 | 3.75 3.75 |
| a. | A1368 170w multi | | .85 .40 |
| b. | A1369 170w multi | | .85 .40 |
| c. | A1370 170w multi | | .85 .40 |
| d. | A1371 170w multi | | .85 .40 |

Endangered
Flowers — A1372

Designs: a, Diapensia lapponica. b, Rhododendron aureum. c, Jeffersonia dubia. d,
Sedum orbiculatum.

**2001, Feb. 26  Perf. 13x13¼**

| | | | |
|---|---|---|---|
| 2046 | | Sheet of 12 | 14.50 14.50 |
| a.-d. | A1372 170w Any single | | .80 .45 |

Top part of No. 2046 contains one each
Nos. 2046a-2046d, the lower part contains
two each Nos. 2046a-2046d.

Opening of
Inchon Intl.
Airport — A1373

**2001, Mar. 29**

| | | | |
|---|---|---|---|
| 2047 | A1373 170w multi | | .75 .40 |

Intl. Olympic Fair,
Seoul — A1374

**2001, Apr. 27  Perf. 13¼x13**

| | | | |
|---|---|---|---|
| 2048 | A1374 170w multi | | .75 .40 |
| a. | Souvenir sheet of 2 | | 1.90 1.90 |

Personalized Greetings — A1375

Designs: No. 2049, 170w, Hugging bears.
No. 2050, 170w, Carnation. No. 2051, 170w,
Congratulations. No. 2052, 170w, Birthday
cake.

**2001  Photo.  Perf. 13¼**
**Stamps + Labels**

| | | | |
|---|---|---|---|
| 2049-2052 | A1375 | Set of 4 | 7.25 3.75 |

Issued: Nos. 2049-2050, 4/30; No. 2051,
6/1; No. 2052, 7/2. Each stamp was issued in
sheets of 20+20 labels that could be personalized. Each sheet sold for 700w.

Cartoons — A1376

Designs: No. 2053, Iljimae, by Ko Woo-
young (shown). No. 2054, Kkeobeongi, by Kil
Chang-duk (student at desk).

**2001, May 4  Photo.  Perf. 13x13¼**

| | | | |
|---|---|---|---|
| 2053 | A1376 170w multi | | .70 .35 |
| a. | Souvenir sheet of 1 | | 1.60 1.60 |
| 2054 | A1376 170w multi | | .70 .35 |
| a. | Souvenir sheet of 1 | | 1.60 1.60 |

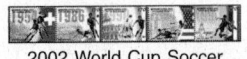

2002 World Cup Soccer
Championships, Japan and
Korea — A1377

Years of previous championships, soccer
players, flags and scenes from host countries:
a, 1954, Switzerland, mountains. b, 1986,
Mexico, Chichen Itza. c, 1990, Italy, Colosseum. d, 1994, US, World Trade Center and
Statue of Liberty. e, 1998, France, Eiffel
Tower.

**2001, May 31  Perf. 13¼x13**

| | | | |
|---|---|---|---|
| 2055 | A1377 | Horiz. strip of 5 | 4.75 4.25 |
| a.-e. | 170w Any single | | .80 .35 |
| f. | Souvenir sheet, 2 #2055a | | 1.60 1.60 |
| g. | Souvenir sheet, 2 #2055b | | 1.60 1.60 |
| h. | Souvenir sheet, 2 #2055c | | 1.60 1.60 |
| i. | Souvenir sheet, 2 #2055d | | 1.60 1.60 |
| j. | Souvenir sheet, 2 #2055e | | 1.60 1.60 |

Kkakdugi
A1378

Bossam
Kimchi — A1379

Dongchimi
A1380

Baechu
Kimchi — A1381

**2001, June 15  Perf. 13¼x13¼**

| | | | |
|---|---|---|---|
| 2056 | | Vert. strip of 4 | 3.50 3.50 |
| a. | A1378 170w multi | | .65 .35 |
| b. | A1379 170w multi | | .65 .35 |
| c. | A1380 170w multi | | .65 .35 |
| d. | A1381 170w multi | | .65 .35 |

Roses — A1382

**2001, July 18  Photo.  Perf. 13¼**

| | | | |
|---|---|---|---|
| 2057 | A1382 170w Red Queen | | .75 .35 |
| a. | Souvenir sheet of 2 | | 1.90 1.90 |
| 2058 | A1382 170w Pink Lady | | .75 .35 |
| a. | Souvenir sheet of 2 | | 1.90 1.90 |

Phila Korea 2002, (Nos. 2057a, 2058a).

Love — A1383

**2001, Aug. 2**

| | | | |
|---|---|---|---|
| 2059 | A1383 170w multi | | .70 .40 |
| a. | Souvenir sheet of 2 | | 1.75 1.75 |

World Ceramics
Exhibition — A1384

**2001, Aug. 10  Perf. 13x13¼**

| | | | |
|---|---|---|---|
| 2060 | A1384 170w multi | | .70 .35 |

53rd Session of the
Intl. Statistical
Institute — A1385

**2001, Aug. 22  Litho.  Perf. 13¼x13¼**

| | | | |
|---|---|---|---|
| 2061 | A1385 170w multi | | .70 .35 |

Korea Minting
and Security
Printing Corp.,
50th
Anniv. — A1386

**Litho. & Engr.**
**2001, Sept. 28  Perf. 13¼**

| | | | |
|---|---|---|---|
| 2062 | A1386 170w multi | | .70 .40 |

Intl. Council of Industrial
Design Societies
Congress,
Seoul — A1387

**2001, Oct. 8  Photo.  Perf. 13x13¼**

| | | | |
|---|---|---|---|
| 2063 | A1387 170w multi | | .70 .35 |

Year of Dialogue Among
Civilizations — A1388

**2001, Oct. 9  Litho.**

| | | | |
|---|---|---|---|
| 2064 | A1388 170w multi | | .70 .35 |

Intl. Organization of
Supreme Audit
Institutions, 17th
Congress — A1389

**2001, Oct. 19  Perf. 13¼x13**

| | | | |
|---|---|---|---|
| 2065 | A1389 170w blue & red | | .70 .35 |

Orchids — A1390

No. 2066: a, Habenaria radiata. b, Orchis
cyclochila. c, Dendrobium moniliforme. d,
Gymnadenia camschatica.

**2001, Nov. 12  Photo.  Perf. 13¼x13**

| | | | |
|---|---|---|---|
| 2066 | A1390 | Horiz. strip of 4 | 4.50 4.50 |
| a.-d. | 170w Any single | | .75 .40 |

No. 2066 is impregnated with orchid scent.

New Year 2002 (Year of
the Horse) — A1391

**2001, Dec. 3**     *Perf. 13x13¼*
2067 A1391 170w multi    .75 .40
   *a.*   Souvenir sheet of 2    1.90 1.90

Seonjeongjeon Hall, Changdeok
Palace — A1392

Injeongjeon
Hall,
Changdeok
Palace
A1393

**Litho. & Engr.**
**2001, Dec. 10**     *Perf. 13x13¼*
2068   Sheet of 10    17.50 14.00
   *a.*   A1392 170w multi    .85 .35
   *b.*   A1393 340w multi    1.60 .70

Top part of No. 2068 contains one each
Nos. 2068a-2068b. The lower part of No. 2068
contains 4 each Nos. 2068a-2068b.

Priority
Mail — A1394

**2002, Jan. 15 Photo.**    *Perf. 13¼x13*
**Background Color**
2069 A1394 280w orange    1.45 .45
2070 A1394 310w blue    1.60 .50
2071 A1394 1380w green    4.50 2.40
2072 A1394 1410w red    4.50 2.40
   *Nos. 2069-2072 (4)*    12.05 5.75

See Nos. 2113-2114, 2127.

Lily
A1395

Roses —
A1395a

Fish
A1396

Chick —
A1396a

**2002, Jan. 15 Photo.**    *Perf. 13¼*
**Stamp + Label**
2073   A1395   190w multi    2.00 1.00
2073A A1395a 190w multi    2.00 1.00
2074   A1396   190w multi    2.00 1.00
2074A A1396a 190w multi    2.00 1.00
   *Nos. 2073-2074A (4)*    8.00 4.00

Nos. 2073, 2073A and 2074 are impregnated with scents of items depicted. Labels
could be personalized.

---

Korea's Entrance in Intl.
Telecommunications
Union, 50th
Anniv. — A1397

**2002, Jan. 31 Photo.**    *Perf. 13x13¼*
2075 A1397 190w multi    .70 .35

Trains
A1398

No. 2076: a, Blue and white locomotive. b,
Green, yellow and white locomotive. c, Green,
yellow and white locomotive pulling cars. d,
Red, yellow and white locomotive pulling cars.

**2002, Feb. 4 Photo.**    *Perf. 13¾x12¾*
2076 A1398 190w Block of 4,
        #a-d    4.25 4.25

Dye
Plants
A1399

No. 2077: a, Carthamus tinctorius. b, Lithos-
permum erythrorhizon. c, Fraxinus
rhynchophylla. d, Persicaria tinctoria.

**2002, Feb. 25 Photo.**    *Perf. 13¼x13*
2077 A1399 190w Block of 4,
        #a-d    4.25 3.50

See No. 2117, 2140, 2170.

Intl. Flower
Exhibition, Anmyeon
Island — A1400

**2002, Apr. 26**     *Perf. 13¼*
2078 A1400 190w multi    .85 .35

Cartoons — A1401

Designs: No. 2079, Girl from "Wogdoggle
Dugdoggle," by Mi-Na Hwang. No. 2080,
Schoolmaster and children from "Mengkkong-i
Seodang Village School," by Seung-woon
Yoon.

**2002, May 4**     *Perf. 13¼x13*
2079 A1401 190w multi    .85 .35
   *a.*   Souvenir sheet of 1    1.05 1.05
2080 A1401 190w multi    .85 .35
   *a.*   Souvenir sheet of 1    1.05 1.05

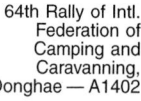

64th Rally of Intl.
Federation of
Camping and
Caravanning,
Donghae — A1402

**2002, May 16**
2081 A1402 190w multi    *1.60* .40

---

2002 World Cup Soccer
Championships, Japan and
Korea — A1403

No. 2082: a, Player with pink feet, part of
map of Europe. b, Player with blue green feet,
part of map of North and Central America. c,
Player with blue violet feet, part of map of
southeast Asia. d, Player with purple feet, part
of map of southern Africa. e, Player with brown
orange feet, part of map of South America.

**2002, May 31**     *Perf.*
2082 A1403 190w Sheet, 2
    each #a-e,
    + label    10.00 10.00
   *f.*   Souvenir sheet, 2 #2082a   1.00 .40
   *g.*   Souvenir sheet, 2 #2082b   1.00 .40
   *h.*   Souvenir sheet, 2 #2082c   1.00 .40
   *i.*   Souvenir sheet, 2 #2082d   1.00 .40
   *j.*   Souvenir sheet, 2 #2082e   1.00 .40

Korean
Cuisine
A1404

No. 2083: a, Jeolpyeon (blue background).
b, Shirutteok (red background). c, Injeolmi (tan
background). d, Songpyeon (green
background).

**2002, June 15**     *Perf. 13x13¼*
2083 A1404 190w Block of 4,
        #a-d    3.75 3.75

Women's Week — A1405

**2002, July 1 Litho.**    *Perf. 13x13¼*
2084 A1405 190w multi    .70 .35

Philakorea 2002
World Stamp
Exhibition,
Seoul — A1406

Designs: No. 2085, Children, globe. No.
2086, Child, stamps showing flags of the
world.

**2002, July 1 Photo.**    *Perf. 13¼*
2085 A1406 190w multi    .75 .35
   *a.*   Souvenir sheet of 2    1.75 1.75
2086 A1406 190w multi    .75 .35
   *a.*   Souvenir sheet of 2    1.75 1.75

**Regions of Korea**

Busan
A1407

Chungbuk — A1408

---

Chungnam — A1409

Daegu
A1410

Daejeon
A1411

Gangwon — A1412

Gwangju
A1413

Gyeongbuk — A1414

Gyeonggi — A1415

Gyeongnam — A1416

Incheon
A1417

Jeju
A1418

Jeonbuk
A1419

Jeonnam
A1420

Seoul
A1421

Ulsan
A1422

No. 2087: a, Dongnaeyaryu Festival. b,
Cliffs.
No. 2088: a, Martial arts. b, Beopju Temple.
No. 2089: a, Weaver. b, Men in sailboat.
No. 2090: a, Forest and river. b, Gwanbong
Seokjoyeorae statue.
No. 2091: a, Daeok Science Town, scientist
at work. b, Expo Science Park.
No. 2092: a, Gangneung mask drama. b,
Ulsanbawi Rock.
No. 2093: a, Men playing tug-of-war game.
b, Statues and tower at May 18th Cemetery.
No. 2094: a, Men playing game with tied
logs. b, Dokdo Island.
No. 2095: a, Yangjubyeol Sandaenori mask
dance. b, Panmunjom Freedom House.

No. 2096: a, Goseong Ogwangdae clowns performing. b, Rock formations in Hallyeo Haesang Natl. Maritime Park.

No. 2097: a, Chamseongdam dancers. b, Cliffs.

No. 2098: a, Traditional house and gate. b, Mt. Halla.

No. 2099: a, Iri folk band. b, Mt. Mai.

No. 2100: a, Ganggang Sullae circle dance. b, Odong Island.

No. 2101: a, Songpa Sandaenori mask dance. b, Heung-injimun Fortress.

No. 2102: a, Cheoyongmu mask dance. b, Cheonjeonnigakseok prehistoric inscriptions.

**2002, Aug. 1**     *Perf. 13x13¼*

| | | | |
|---|---|---|---|
| 2087 | A1407 | 190w Horiz. pair, #a-b | 1.60 .70 |
| 2088 | A1408 | 190w Horiz. pair, #a-b | 1.60 .70 |
| 2089 | A1409 | 190w Horiz. pair, #a-b | 1.60 .70 |
| 2090 | A1410 | 190w Horiz. pair, #a-b | 1.60 .70 |
| 2091 | A1411 | 190w Horiz. pair, #a-b | 1.60 .70 |
| 2092 | A1412 | 190w Horiz. pair, #a-b | 1.60 .70 |
| 2093 | A1413 | 190w Horiz. pair, #a-b | 1.60 .70 |
| 2094 | A1414 | 190w Horiz. pair, #a-b | 1.60 .70 |
| 2095 | A1415 | 190w Horiz. pair, #a-b | 1.60 .70 |
| 2096 | A1416 | 190w Horiz. pair, #a-b | 1.60 .70 |
| 2097 | A1417 | 190w Horiz. pair, #a-b | 1.60 .70 |
| 2098 | A1418 | 190w Horiz. pair, #a-b | 1.60 .70 |
| 2099 | A1419 | 190w Horiz. pair, #a-b | 1.60 .70 |
| 2100 | A1420 | 190w Horiz. pair, #a-b | 1.60 .70 |
| 2101 | A1421 | 190w Horiz. pair, #a-b | 1.60 .70 |
| 2102 | A1422 | 190w Horiz. pair, #a-b | 1.60 .70 |

*Nos. 2087-2102 (16)*    25.60 11.20

Philakorea 2002 World Stamp Exhibition, Seoul — A1423

**2002, Aug. 2**     *Perf. 13¼x13*
| 2103 | A1423 | 190w multi | .70 .35 |
|---|---|---|---|
| *a.* | | Sheet of 2, imperf. | 2.00 2.00 |

Philately Week — A1424

**2002, Aug. 2**     *Perf. 13¼*
| 2104 | A1424 | 190w multi | .70 .35 |
|---|---|---|---|
| *a.* | | Souvenir sheet of 2 | 1.90 1.90 |

South Korean Soccer Team's Fourth Place Finish at World Cup Championships — A1425

No. 2105: a, Coach Guus Hiddink. b, Goalie (jersey #1). c, Player with red shirt with white accents. d, Player with red shirt with white accents, with white sock. e, Player with white shirt with red accents, ball near shoulder. f, Player (jersey #5). g, Player (jersey #6). h, Player (jersey #7). i, Player (jersey #8.) j, Player (jersey #9). k, Player (jersey #10). l, Player with ball hiding part of head. m, Goalie with red hair, white gloves with dark trim. n, Player (jersey #13). o, Player (jersey #14). p, Player (jersey #15). q, Player with white shirt with red accents, with white sock. r, Player (jersey #17). s, Player (jersey #18). t, Player

(jersey #19). u, Player (jersey #20). v, Player (jersey #21). w, Player (jersey #22). x, Goalie with brown hair, black gloves with red trim.

**2002, Aug. 7**     *Perf. 13¼x13*
2105 A1425 190w Sheet of 24, #a-x     18.50 18.50

14th Asian Games, Busan A1426

**2002, Sept. 28   Litho.   *Perf. 13***
| 2106 | A1426 | 190w multi | .80 .40 |
|---|---|---|---|
| *a.* | | Souvenir sheet of 2 | 2.00 2.00 |

8th Far East and South Pacific Games for the Disabled, Busan — A1427

**2002, Oct. 26   Photo.   *Perf. 13x13¼***
2107 A1427 190w multi    .75 .35

Orchids — A1428

No. 2108: a, Cymbidium kanran. b, Gastrodia elata. c, Pogonia japonica. d, Cephalanthera falcata.

**2002, Nov. 12**     *Perf. 13¼x13*
| 2108 | A1428 | 190w Block of 4, #a-d | 4.00 4.00 |
|---|---|---|---|

No. 2108 is impregnated with orchid scent.

Martial Arts A1429

No. 2109: a, Taekwondo (white clothes). b, Kung Fu (red clothes).

**2002, Nov. 20**     *Perf. 13x13¼*
| 2109 | A1429 | 190w Horiz. pair, #a-b | 1.75 1.75 |
|---|---|---|---|

See People's Republic of China No. 3248.

New Year 2003 (Year of the Ram) — A1430

**2002, Dec. 2**
| 2110 | A1430 | 190w multi | .85 .40 |
|---|---|---|---|
| *a.* | | Souvenir sheet of 2 | 1.90 1.90 |

Gongsimdon Observation Tower, Hwaseong Fortress A1431

Banghwasuryu Pavilion, Hwaseong Fortress — A1432

**2002, Dec. 9**     **Litho. & Engr.**
| 2111 | | Sheet of 10 | 15.00 15.00 |
|---|---|---|---|
| *a.* | A1431 | 190w multi | .80 .40 |
| *b.* | A1432 | 280w multi | 1.25 .65 |

Top part of No. 2111 contains one each of Nos. 2111a-2111b. The lower part contains 4 each Nos. 2111a-2111b.

South Korea — Viet Nam Diplomatic Relations, 10th Anniv. — A1433

No. 2112: a, Dabo Pagoda, Gyeongju (denomination at right). b, Mot Cot Pagoda, Hanoi, Viet Nam (denomination at left).

**2002, Dec. 21   Photo.   *Perf. 13¼x13***
| 2112 | A1433 | 190w Horiz. pair, #a-b | 2.00 1.50 |
|---|---|---|---|

See Viet Nam Nos. 3167-3168.

**Priority Mail Type of 2002**
**2003, Jan. 1   Photo.   *Perf. 13¼x13***
**Background Color**
| 2113 | A1394 | 1580w lilac | 5.25 4.75 |
|---|---|---|---|
| 2114 | A1394 | 1610w brown | 5.25 4.75 |

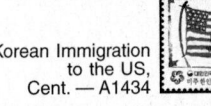

Korean Immigration to the US, Cent. — A1434

**2003, Jan. 13   Photo.   *Perf. 13¼x13***
2115 A1434 190w multi    .80 .40

Gondola Car — A1435

Box Car — A1436

Tanker Car — A1437

Hopper Car — A1438

**2003, Feb. 4**     *Perf. 13¾x13*
| 2116 | | Block of 4 | 4.00 3.25 |
|---|---|---|---|
| *a.* | A1435 | 190w multi | .70 .35 |
| *b.* | A1436 | 190w multi | .70 .35 |
| *c.* | A1437 | 190w multi | .70 .35 |
| *d.* | A1438 | 190w multi | .70 .35 |

**Dye Plants Type of 2002**

No. 2117: a, Rubia akane. b, Rhus javanica. c, Sophora japonica. d, Isatis tinctoria.

**2003, Feb. 22   Photo.   *Perf. 13¼x13***
2117 A1399   190w Horiz. strip of 4, #a-d    3.50 2.50

Inauguration of Pres. Roh Moo-hyun A1439

**2003, Feb. 25**     *Perf. 13x13¼*
| 2118 | A1439 | 190w multi | 1.35 .65 |
|---|---|---|---|
| *a.* | | Souvenir sheet of 1 | 2.00 2.00 |

**Traditional Culture**

Footwear A1440

Sedan Chairs A1441

Lighting Implements — A1442

Tables A1443

No. 2119: a, Unhye (denomination at LL, date at LR). b, Mokhwa (denomination at UR, date at L). c, Jipsin (denomination at UL, date at LR). d, Namaksin (denomination at LR, date at LL).

No. 2120: a, Eoyeon (no handles). b, Choheon (wheeled). c, Saingyo (with handles and roof). d, Nanyeo (with handles only).

No. 2121: a, Jojokdeung (round lantern). b, Deungjan (lamp oil container). c, Juchilmokje Yukgakjedeung (hexagonal lantern). d, Brass candlestick holder with butterfly design.

No. 2122: a, Gujok-ban (round table with legs connected at base. b, Punghyeol-ban (12-sided table, denomination at top). c, Iljuban (12-sided table, denomination at top). d, Haeju-ban (octagonal table).

**2003**     **Engr.**     *Perf. 12½*
| 2119 | A1440 | 190w Horiz. strip of 4, #a-d | 4.00 2.50 |
|---|---|---|---|
| 2120 | A1441 | 190w Horiz. strip of 4, #a-d | 4.00 2.50 |
| 2121 | A1442 | 190w Horiz. strip of 4, #a-d | 4.00 2.50 |
| 2122 | A1443 | 190w Horiz. strip of 4, #a-d | 4.00 2.50 |

*Nos. 2119-2122 (4)*    16.00 10.00

Issued: No. 2119, 3/19; No. 2120, 5/19; No. 2121, 7/25; No. 2122, 9/25.

Cartoons — A1444

Designs: No. 2123, The Goblin's Cap, by Shin Moon-soo (shown). No. 2124, The Sword of Fire, by Kim Hye-rin (woman with sword).

**2003, May 2   Photo.   *Perf. 13x13¼***
| 2123 | A1444 | 190w multi | .75 .35 |
|---|---|---|---|
| *a.* | | Souvenir sheet of 1 | 1.05 1.05 |
| 2124 | A1444 | 190w multi | .75 .35 |
| *a.* | | Souvenir sheet of 1 | 1.05 1.05 |

Lighthouse Construction in Korea, Cent. — A1445

**2003, May 30**     *Perf. 13¼x13*
2125 A1445 190w multi    .75 .35

Dasik — A1446

Yeot Gangjeong
A1447

Yakgwa — A1448

Yugwa — A1449

**2003, June 13**      *Perf. 13x13¼*
| 2126 | Block or strip of 4 | 2.60 | 2.10 |
|---|---|---|---|
| *a.* | A1446 190w multi | .55 | .35 |
| *b.* | A1447 190w multi | .55 | .35 |
| *c.* | A1448 190w multi | .55 | .35 |
| *d.* | A1449 190w multi | .55 | .35 |

Nos. 2126a-2126d were printed in sheets of 20 that yield four No. 2126 and one vertical strip of four of Nos. 2126a-2126d.

**Priority Mail Type of 2002**

**2003, July 1**    **Photo.**    *Perf. 13¼x13*
**Background Color**
| 2127 | A1394 420w blue green | 4.50 | 1.00 |
|---|---|---|---|

Philately
Week — A1450

**2003, Aug. 1**      *Perf. 13¼*
| 2128 | A1450 190w multi | .75 | .35 |
|---|---|---|---|
| *a.* | Souvenir sheet of 2, imperf. | 1.90 | 1.90 |

2003 Summer
Universiade,
Daegu — A1451

**2003, Aug. 21**      *Perf. 13x13¼*
| 2129 | A1451 190w multi | .75 | .35 |
|---|---|---|---|
| *a.* | Souvenir sheet of 2 | 1.90 | 1.90 |

YMCA in Korea,
Cent. — A1452

**2003, Oct. 28**    **Photo.**    *Perf. 13¼x13*
| 2130 | A1452 190w multi | .75 | .35 |
|---|---|---|---|

Soong Eui School,
Cent. — A1453

**2003, Oct. 31**      *Perf. 13x13¼*
| 2131 | A1453 190w multi | .75 | .35 |
|---|---|---|---|

Natl. Tuberculosis
Association, 50th
Anniv. — A1454

**2003, Nov. 6**      **Litho.**
| 2132 | A1454 190w black & red | .75 | .35 |
|---|---|---|---|

Orchids
A1455

No. 2133: a, Cremastra appendiculata. b, Cymbidium lancifolium. c, Orchis graminifolia. d, Bulbophyllum drymoglossum.

**2003, Nov. 12**    **Photo.**    *Perf. 13¼x13*
| 2133 | A1455 190w Block of 4, | | |
|---|---|---|---|
| | #a-d | 3.75 | 3.75 |

No. 2133 is impregnated with a floral scent.

New Year 2004 (Year of
the Monkey) — A1456

**2003, Dec. 1**      *Perf. 13x13¼*
| 2134 | A1456 190w multi | .75 | .35 |
|---|---|---|---|
| *a.* | Souvenir sheet of 2 | 1.90 | 1.90 |

A1457

Dolmens
A1458

**Litho. & Engr.**
**2003, Dec. 9**      *Perf. 13x13¼*
| 2135 | Sheet of 10 | 13.50 | 13.50 |
|---|---|---|---|
| *a.* | A1457 190w multi | .90 | .40 |
| *b.* | A1458 280w multi | 1.25 | .65 |

Top part of No. 2135 contains one each of Nos. 2135a-2135b. The lower part contains 4 each Nos. 2135a-2135b.

South Korea — India Diplomatic
Relations, 30th Anniv. — A1459

No. 2136: a, Cheomsongdae Astronomical Observatory, Gyeongju, South Korea. b, Jantar Mantar, Jaipur, India.

**2003, Dec. 10**    **Photo.**    *Perf. 13¼x13*
| 2136 | A1459 190w Horiz. pair, | | |
|---|---|---|---|
| | #a-b | 2.25 | 2.00 |

Dokdo Island Flora and
Fauna — A1460

No. 2137: a, Calystegia soldanella. b, Aster spathulifolius, butterfly. c, Calonectris laucomelas. d, Larus crassirostris.

**2004, Jan. 16**      *Perf. 13¼x13¼*
| 2137 | A1460 Horiz. strip of 4 | 15.50 | |
|---|---|---|---|
| *a.-d.* | 190w Any single | 3.75 | 3.75 |

Korean National
Commission for
UNESCO, 50th
Anniv. — A1461

**2004, Jan. 30**
| 2138 | A1461 190w multi | .75 | .30 |
|---|---|---|---|

Multiple Tie
Tamper
A1462

Ballast
Regulator
A1463

Track Inspection
Car — A1464

Ballast Cleaner
A1465

**2004, Feb. 4**      *Perf. 13¾x12¾*
| 2139 | Block of 4 | 3.50 | 3.50 |
|---|---|---|---|
| *a.* | A1462 190w brown & multi | .70 | .40 |
| *b.* | A1463 190w lilac & multi | .70 | .40 |
| *c.* | A1464 190w blue green & multi | .70 | .40 |
| *d.* | A1465 190w blue & multi | .70 | .40 |

**Dye Plants Type of 2002**

No. 2140: a, Juglans regia. b, Acer ginnala. c, Pinus densiflora. d, Punica granatum.

**2004, Feb. 25**      *Perf. 13¼x13*
| 2140 | A1399 190w Block of 4, | | |
|---|---|---|---|
| | #a-d | 3.00 | 3.00 |

12th World Water
Day — A1466

**2004, Mar. 22**    **Litho.**    *Perf. 13¼x13*
| 2141 | A1466 190w multi | .75 | .40 |
|---|---|---|---|

A1467

**2004, Mar. 25**      **Photo.**
| 2142 | A1467 190w multi | .80 | .40 |
|---|---|---|---|

Korean Meteorological Service, cent.

Inauguration of
High Speed
Railroads — A1468

**2004, Apr. 1**      *Perf. 13¼x13*
| 2143 | A1468 190w multi | .80 | .40 |
|---|---|---|---|

A1469

Winners of Future of
Science Stamp Design
Contest — A1470

*Perf. 13¼x13, 13x13¼*
**2004, Apr. 21**      **Photo.**
| 2144 | A1469 190w multi | .80 | .40 |
|---|---|---|---|
| 2145 | A1470 190w multi | .80 | .40 |

A1471

Cartoons: No. 2146, Wicked Boy Simsultong, by Lee Jeong-moon (shown). No. 2147, Nation of Winds, by Kim Jin.

**2004, May 4**    **Photo.**    *Perf. 13x13¼*
| 2146 | A1471 190w multi | .80 | .40 |
|---|---|---|---|
| *a.* | Souvenir sheet of 1 | 1.10 | 1.10 |
| 2147 | A1471 190w multi | .80 | .40 |
| *a.* | Souvenir sheet of 1 | 1.10 | 1.10 |

A1472

**2004, May 21**
| 2148 | A1472 190w multi | .55 | .35 |
|---|---|---|---|

FIFA (Fédération Internationale de Football Association), cent.

Korean
Cuisine
A1473

No. 2149: a, Sinseollo (blue background). b, Hwayangjeok (green background). c, Bibimbap (pink background). d, Gujeolpan (orange background).

**2004, June 15**
| 2149 | A1473 190w Block of 4, | | |
|---|---|---|---|
| | #a-d | 3.25 | 3.25 |

**Traditional Culture**

Needlework Equipment — A1474

Head Coverings — A1475

No. 2150: a, Octagonal storage basket. b, Thimbles with flower decorations. c, Cylindrical bobbin, bobbin and thread. d, Needle cases.
No. 2151: a, Gold crown with tassels. b, Bamboo hat with untied neck band. c, Gauze hat. d, Horsehair hat with tied neck band.

**2004**    **Engr.**    *Perf. 12½*
| 2150 | A1474 190w Horiz. strip of 4, #a-d | 3.50 | 3.50 |
|---|---|---|---|
| 2151 | A1475 190w Horiz. strip of 4, #a-d | 3.50 | 3.50 |

Issued: No. 2150, 6/24; No. 2151, 8/20.

National Academies, 50th Anniv. A1476

No. 2152: a, National Academy of Science. b, National Academy of Arts.

**2004, July 16    Litho.    Perf. 13x13¼**
2152 A1476 190w Horiz. pair, #a-
b                                 1.60    1.60

Congratulations A1477

**2004, July 22    Photo.    Perf. 13¼**
2153 A1477 190w multi            .80     .40
a.    Souvenir sheet of 2       1.75    1.75

2004 Summer Olympics, Athens — A1478

**2004, Aug. 13    Perf. 13x13¼**
2154 A1478 190w multi            .80     .40

Bridges A1479

No. 2155: a, Geumcheongyo Bridge (two arches). b, Jeongotgyo Bridge (pillars and flat slabs). c, Jincheon Nongdari Bridge (loose rocks). d, Seungseongyo Bridge (single arch).

**Perf. 13¼ Syncopated**
**2004, Sept. 24**
2155 A1479 190w Block of 4,
#a-d                             3.50    3.50

Intl. Council of Museums, 20th General Conference, Seoul — A1480

**2004, Oct. 1    Perf. 13x13¼**
2156 A1480 190w multi            .80     .40

Obaegnahan A1481

Seonjakjiwat A1482

Baengnokdam A1483

Oreum — A1484

**2004, Oct. 18**
2157    Block of 4              3.50    3.50
a.    A1481 190w multi           .70     .35
b.    A1482 190w multi           .70     .35
c.    A1483 190w multi           .70     .35
d.    A1484 190w multi           .70     .35

Flag A1485

Flowers A1486

Flower and Bee A1487

Lamb, Church and Bible A1488

Children and Lotus Flower A1489

Stylized Animals A1490

Teddy Bear A1491

Dinosaur A1492

Flower and Envelope A1493

**2004, Nov. 1    Photo.    Perf. 13¼**
2158 A1485 220w multi + label   2.10    1.35
2159 A1486 220w multi + label   2.10    1.35
2160 A1487 220w multi + label   2.10    1.35
2161 A1488 220w multi + label   2.10    1.35
2162 A1489 220w multi + label   2.10    1.35
2163    Strip of 4 + 4 alter-
        nating labels           8.75    8.75
a.    A1490 220w multi + label  2.10    2.00
b.    A1491 220w multi + label  2.10    2.00
c.    A1492 220w multi + label  2.10    2.00
d.    A1493 220w multi + label  2.10    2.00
      Nos. 2158-2163 (6)       19.25   15.50

Labels attached to Nos. 2158-2163 could be personalized.

Orchids — A1494

No. 2164: a, Goodyera maximowicziana. b, Sarcanthus scolopendrifolius. c, Calanthe sieboldii. d, Bletilla striata.

**2004, Nov. 12    Perf. 13¼x13**
2164 A1494 220w Block of 4,
#a-d                             3.50    3.50

No. 2164 is impregnated with orchid scent.

New Year 2005 (Year of the Chicken) — A1495

**2004, Dec. 1    Perf. 13x13¼**
2165 A1495 220w multi            .90     .45
a.    Souvenir sheet of 2       1.90    1.90

Daenungwon Tumuli Park, Seosuhyeong Ceramics, Royal Crown of Geumgwanchong — A1496

Anapji Pond, Scissors, Buddha, Lion Incense Burner A1497

**2004, Dec. 9    Litho. & Engr.**
2166    Sheet of 10           14.00   14.00
a.    A1496 310w multi         1.00     .55
b.    A1497 310w multi         1.00     .55

Top part of No. 2166 contains one each of Nos. 2166a-2166b. The lower part contains 4 each of Nos. 2166a-2166b.

Fish of Marado Island — A1498

No. 2167: a, Girella punctata. b, Epinephelus septemfasciatus. c, Chromis notata. d, Sebastiscus marmoratus.

**2005, Jan. 18    Photo.**
2167    Horiz. strip of 4      5.75    5.75
a.-d.  A1498 220w Any single   1.20     .50

Cloning of Human Embryonic Stem Cells, 1st Anniv. A1499

**2005, Feb. 12    Perf. 12¾x13½**
2168 A1499 220w multi           2.75    1.00

Rotary International, Cent. — A1500

**2005, Feb. 23    Perf. 13¼x13**
2169 A1500 220w multi            .80     .40

**Dye Plants Type of 2002**

No. 2170: a, Taxus cuspidata. b, Smilax china. c, Clerodendron trichotomum. d, Gardenia jasminoides.

**2005, Feb. 25**
2170 A1399 220w Block of 4,
#a-d                             3.75    3.75

Gyeonggi Province Tourism — A1501

**2005, Mar. 10    Litho.    Perf. 13x13¼**
2171 A1501 220w multi            .75     .40

A1502

Information and Communication of the Future — A1503

**2005, Apr. 22    Photo.    Perf. 13¼x13**
2172 A1502 220w multi            .75     .40
**Perf. 13x13¼**
2173 A1503 220w multi            .75     .40

Korea University, Cent. — A1504

**2005, May 4    Litho.    Perf. 13x13¼**
2174 A1504 220w multi            .85     .40

57th Intl. Whaling Commission Meeting, Ulsan — A1505

**2005, May 27    Photo.    Perf. 13¼x13**
2175 A1505 220w multi            .95     .40

Neobani (Broiled Beef) — A1506

Bindaetteok (Fried Ground Mung Beans) — A1507

Jeongol (Stew) — A1508

Hwajeon (Fried Rice Cakes and Flower Petals) — A1509

**2005, June 15**     *Perf. 13x13¼*
2176    Block of 4     3.75   3.75
   a.   A1506 220w multi    .85   .40
   b.   A1507 220w multi    .85   .40
   c.   A1508 220w multi    .85   .40
   d.   A1509 220w multi    .85   .40

Goguryeo Kingdom — A1510

No. 2177: a, Sword, armored soldier on horse. b, Armored soldiers on horses, Onyeo Fortress, Baek-am Castle.

*Perf. 13x13¼ Syncopated*
**2005, July 1**
2177 A1510 310w Vert. pair, #a-b 3.00 3.00

Strix Aluco A1513

Arctous Ruber A1514

Parus Major A1516

Crinum Asiaticum A1517

Planned City A1521

Brown Hawk Owl A1522

Rose of Sharon A1523

Sungnyemun Gate — A1524

Suwon Hwaseong Fortress — A1524a

Haeundae Dongbaek Island — A1524b

Dodamsambong Peaks — A1524c

Hongdo Island — A1524d

Cheomseongdae Observatory — A1524e

Gwanghallu Pavilion — A1524f

Gyeongpodae Pavilion — A1524g

Baengnokdam Lake — A1524h

Whistling Swans A1525

Charonia Sauliae A1526

Charonia Sauliae — A1526a

Pitta Nympha — A1526b

Celadon Incense Burner A1527

Buncheong Jar A1529

Buncheong Jar — A1530

Jar With Clay Figurines — A1530a

Jar With Clay Figurines — A1530b

Gold Earrings — A1530c

Gilt Bronze Pagoda — A1531

Vessel With Dragon's Head — A1531a

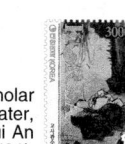

Lofty Scholar Contemplating Water, Painting by Kang Hui An — A1531b

National Seal — A1531c

Euryale Ferox A1532

Flag A1533

**2005-14**    Photo.    *Perf. 13¾x12¾*
2178 A1513 50w multi    .75   .25
2179 A1514 70w multi    .45   .25
    *Perf. 12¾x13¾*
2180 A1516 90w multi    .65   .25
    *Perf. 13¾x12¾*
2181 A1517 100w multi    .65   .25
    *Perf. 13x13¼*
2182 A1521 220w multi    .95   .25
2183 A1522 250w multi    1.05   .35
    *Perf. 13½*
2184 A1523 250w multi + label   2.00   .35
    *Perf. 13x13¾*
2185    Horiz. strip of 9   8.75   8.75
   a.   A1524 300w multi   .55   .25
   b.   A1524a 300w multi   .55   .25
   c.   A1524b 300w multi   .55   .25
   d.   A1524c 300w multi   .55   .25
   e.   A1524d 300w multi   .55   .25
   f.   A1524e 300w multi   .55   .25
   g.   A1524f 300w multi   .55   .25
   h.   A1524g 300w multi   .55   .25
   i.   A1524h 300w multi   .55   .25
    *Perf. 13¾x13*
2186 A1525   340w multi   1.00   .40
    *Perf. 12¾x13¾*
2187 A1526   360w multi   .65   .30
    *Perf. 13x13¾*
2188 A1526a   390w multi   1.00   .25
    *Perf. 13x13¼*
2189 A1526b   400w multi   .90   .35
2190 A1527   1000w multi   3.00   1.00
2191 A1529   1720w multi   4.50   1.75
    *Perf. 13x13½*
2192 A1530   1750w multi   5.50   1.90
    *Perf. 13x13¼*
2193 A1530a   1770w multi   4.00   1.50
    *Perf. 13x13½*
2194 A1530b   1930w multi   4.00   .90
    *Perf. 13¾x13½*
2195 A1530c   1930w multi   4.00   2.00
    *Perf. 13x13½*
2196 A1531   2000w multi   6.00   1.60
    *Perf. 13¾x13½*
2197 A1531a   2000w multi   4.00   1.90
2198 A1531b   3000w multi   5.75   2.75
2199 A1531c   3550w multi   7.00   3.25
   Nos. 2180-2199 (20)   65.35   30.05
    **Self-Adhesive**
    *Serpentine Die Cut 11¾x11½*
2200 A1532   250w multi   1.30   .25
    *Serpentine Die Cut 11½x11¼*
2201 A1533   270w multi   .60   .25

Issued: 50w, 9/1; 1720w, 8/1; 90w, 6/5/06; 100w, 3/2/06; 220w, 12/27/05. Nos. 2183, 2184, 2186, 2192, 11/1/06. 70w, 7/10/07. No. 2200, 6/30/08. No. 2190, 11/17/09; No. 2196, 5/25/09. Nos. 2187, 2193, 2201, 10/1/11. Nos. 2185, 2188, 2194, 11/11/13. Nos. 2189, 2197, 11/20/14. Nos. 2195, 2198, 8/7/14; No. 2199, 10/28/14.

No. 2190 was printed in sheets of 20 stamps and 20 labels that could be personalized.

Nos. 2197C, 2198A, 2198B and 2198C each have a die cut hole in the shape of the Korean Peninsula in the lower right corner of the stamp.

Happy Birthday — A1536

**2005, Aug. 3**    Photo.    *Perf. 13¼*
2203 A1536 220w multi   .85   .35
   a.   Souvenir sheet of 2   1.90   1.90

Philately Week. Portions of the design were printed with a thermochromic ink that changes color when warmed.

Liberation of Korea, 60th Anniv. — A1537

No. 2204: a, Charter and headquarters of provisional government. b, Proclamation of Korean Independence. c, Soldiers taking oath. d, Emblem of 60th anniv. of Korean liberation.

**2005, Aug. 12**     *Perf. 13¼x13*
2204    Horiz. strip of 4   7.75   7.75
   a.   A1537 480w multi   1.25   .75
   b.   A1537 520w multi   1.25   1.00
   c.   A1537 580w multi   1.50   1.10
   d.   A1537 600w multi   1.50   1.25

Fusion of Eastern and Western Cultures — A1538

**2005, Aug. 18**    Litho.    *Perf. 13x13¼*
2205 A1538 220w multi   .85   .45

Hangang Bridge A1539

Expogyo A1540

Banghwa Bridge A1541

Tongyeong Bridge A1542

*Perf. 13¼ Syncopated*
**2005, Sept. 23**     Photo.
2206    Block of 4    3.75   3.75
   a.   A1539 220w multi   .70   .40
   b.   A1540 220w multi   .70   .40
   c.   A1541 220w multi   .70   .40
   d.   A1542 220w multi   .70   .40

Ikki Falls — A1543

Piagol Valley — A1544

Cheonwangbong Peak — A1545

Baraebong Peak — A1546

**2005, Oct. 18**     *Perf. 13x13¼*
| 2207 | Horiz. strip of 4 | 5.00 | 5.00 |
| a. | A1543 220w multi | .90 | .40 |
| b. | A1544 220w multi | .90 | .40 |
| c. | A1545 220w multi | .90 | .40 |
| d. | A1546 220w multi | .90 | .40 |

Korean Red Cross, Cent. — A1547

**2005, Oct. 27**
| 2208 | A1547 220w multi | .85 | .50 |

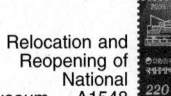
Relocation and Reopening of National Museum — A1548

**2005, Oct. 28**     *Perf. 13¼x13*
| 2209 | A1548 220w multi | .85 | .50 |

Orchids — A1549

No. 2210: a, Epipactis thunbergii. b, Cymbidium goeringii. c, Cephalanthera erecta. d, Spiranthes sinensis.

**2005, Nov. 11**
| 2210 | A1549 220w Block of 4, #a-d | 3.75 | 3.75 |

2005 Asian-Pacific Economic Cooperation Economic Leaders' Meeting, Busan — A1550

No. 2211: a, The Sun, the Moon and Five Peaks. b, Murimaru APEC House, Dongbaek Island.

**2005, Nov. 18**   Photo.   *Perf. 13x13¼*
| 2211 | A1550 220w Horiz. pair, #a-b | 1.60 | 1.60 |

New Year 2006 (Year of the Dog) — A1551

**2005, Dec. 1**
| 2212 | A1551 220w multi | .85 | .50 |
| a. | Souvenir sheet of 2 | 1.90 | 1.90 |

Jikjisimcheyojeol, Book Produced in 1377 by Movable Type — A1552

Seungjeongwon Ilgi, Diaries of the Joseon Dynasty — A1553

**2005, Dec. 9**     Litho. & Engr.
| 2213 | Sheet of 10 | 15.00 | 15.00 |
| a. | A1552 310w multi | 1.25 | .60 |
| b. | A1553 310w multi | 1.25 | .60 |

Top part of No. 2213 contains one each of Nos. 2213a-2213b. The lower part contains 4 each of Nos, 2213a-2213b.

Wildlife of Baengnyeongdo A1554

Designs: No. 2214, Phoca vitulina largha. No. 2215, Phalacrocorax pelagicus. No. 2216, Orithyia sinica. No. 2217, Ammodytes personatus.

**2006, Jan. 18**     Photo.
| 2214 | A1554 220w multi | .95 | .50 |
| 2215 | A1554 220w multi | .95 | .50 |
| 2216 | A1554 220w multi | .95 | .50 |
| 2217 | A1554 220w multi | .95 | .50 |
| a. | Horiz. strip of 4, #2214-2217 | 4.00 | 4.00 |
| b. | Sheet, 1 each #2214-2217, 3 #2217a + 2 labels | 18.50 | |
| | Nos. 2214-2217 (4) | 3.80 | 2.00 |

Designation of Cheju Island as Island of World Peace — A1555

**2006, Jan. 27**     *Perf. 13¾x12¾*
| 2218 | A1555 220w multi | .85 | .50 |

**Exports**

Automobiles A1556

Semiconductors A1557

Petrochemicals A1558

Electronics A1559

Machinery A1560

Ships — A1561

Steel — A1562

Textiles — A1563

**2006, Mar. 15**     *Perf. 13x13¼*
| 2219 | Block of 8 | 6.50 | 6.50 |
| a. | A1556 220w multi | .75 | .50 |
| b. | A1557 220w multi | .75 | .50 |
| c. | A1558 220w multi | .75 | .50 |
| d. | A1559 220w multi | .75 | .50 |
| e. | A1560 220w multi | .75 | .50 |
| f. | A1561 220w multi | .75 | .50 |
| g. | A1562 220w black | .75 | .50 |
| h. | A1563 220w multi | .75 | .50 |

Gyeongnam Goseong Dinosaur World Expo — A1564

***Serpentine Die Cut 11¼x11***
**2006, Apr. 14**
| 2220 | A1564 | Horiz. pair | 1.90 | 1.35 |
| a. | | 220w Iguanodon | .80 | .50 |
| b. | | 220w Megaraptor | .80 | .50 |

A1565

Children's Drawings on Automated World — A1566

**2006, Apr. 21**   *Perf. 13x13¼, 13¼x13*
| 2221 | A1565 220w multi | .85 | .50 |
| 2222 | A1566 220w multi | .85 | .50 |

Dongguk University, Cent. — A1567

**2006, May 8**   Litho.   *Perf. 13x13¼*
| 2223 | A1567 220w multi, *cream* | .85 | .40 |

Sookmyung Women's University, Cent. A1568

*Perf. 12¾x13¾*
**2006, May 22**     Photo.
| 2224 | A1568 220w multi | .85 | .40 |

2006 World Cup Soccer Championships, Germany — A1569

**2006, June 2**   Photo.   *Perf. 13¼*
| 2225 | A1569 220w multi + label | 4.00 | — |

No. 2225 was printed in sheets of 14 stamps + 14 labels picturing members of South Korean World Cup soccer team + one large label picturing entire team. Sheets sold for 6000w.

A1570

2006 World Cup Soccer Championships, Germany — A1571

*Perf. 12¾x13¾*
**2006, June 9**     Photo.
| 2226 | Pair | 1.75 | 1.35 |
| a. | A1570 220w multi | .75 | .45 |
| b. | A1571 220w multi | .75 | .45 |

Goguryeo Kingdom A1572

No. 2227: a, Janggun Tomb and Sanseongha Tombs. b, Sun and Moon Gods from Ohoebun Tomb No. 4.

*Perf. 13x13¼ Syncopated*
**2006, July 3**     Photo.
| 2227 | A1572 480w Vert. pair, #a-b | 3.75 | 3.75 |

No. 2227 was printed in sheets containing seven of each stamp.

Philately Week — A1573

No. 2228: a, Denomination below heart. b, Denomination above heart.

**2006, Aug. 3**   Photo.   *Perf. 13¼*
| 2228 | A1573 220w Pair, #a-b | 1.45 | 1.45 |
| c. | Souvenir sheet, #2228a-2228b | 1.90 | 1.90 |

Skateboarding — A1574

No. 2229: a, Tail stole. b, Drop in. c, Backside spin. d, Backside grab.

**Serpentine Die Cut 11¾x11¼**
**2006, Sept. 5** **Self-Adhesive**
2229 A1574 220w Block of 4, #a-
d　　　　　　　　　3.50 3.50

World Ginseng Expo,
Geumsan — A1575

**2006, Sept. 22** **Perf. 13x13¼**
2230 A1575 220w multi　　　.85 .40

Jindo Bridge
A1576

Changseon-Samcheonpo
Bridge — A1577

Olympic
Bridge
A1578

Seohae
Bridge
A1579

**Perf. 13¼ Syncopated**
**2006, Sept. 26**
2231　　Block of 4　　　3.50 3.50
　*a.* A1576 220w multi　　.70 .40
　*b.* A1577 220w multi　　.70 .40
　*c.* A1578 220w multi　　.70 .40
　*d.* A1579 220w multi　　.70 .40

Hangeul Day — A1580

**2006, Oct. 9** **Perf. 13x13¼**
2232 A1580 (220w) multi　　.85 .40
Use of Hangeul as official Korean writing system, 560th anniv.

Sahmyook University,
Cent. — A1581

**2006, Oct. 10**
2233 A1581 220w multi　　.85 .40

Lineage
A1582

Maple Story
A1583

Ragnarok
A1584

Gersang
A1585

Legend of Mir
III
A1586

Kartrider
A1587

Mu
A1588

Pangya
A1589

Fortress 2
Forever Blue
A1590

Mabinogi
A1591

**Serpentine Die Cut 11¾**
**2006, Nov. 9**
2234　　Block of 10　　10.00 10.00
　*a.* A1582 250w multi　　.90 .60
　*b.* A1583 250w multi　　.90 .60
　*c.* A1584 250w multi　　.90 .60
　*d.* A1585 250w multi　　.90 .60
　*e.* A1586 250w multi　　.90 .60
　*f.* A1587 250w multi　　.90 .60
　*g.* A1588 250w multi　　.90 .60
　*h.* A1589 250w multi　　.90 .60
　*i.* A1590 250w multi　　.90 .60
　*j.* A1591 250w multi　　.90 .60
Internet games.

Janggunbong
Peak — A1592

Ulsanbawi
Rock — A1593

Daecheongbong
Peak — A1594

Sibiseonnyeotang
Valley — A1595

**2006, Nov. 16** **Perf. 13x13¼**
2235　　Block of 4　　3.75 3.25
　*a.* A1592 250w multi　　.80 .55
　*b.* A1593 250w multi　　.80 .55
　*c.* A1594 250w multi　　.80 .55
　*d.* A1595 250w multi　　.80 .55

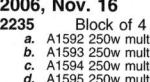

New Year 2007 (Year of
the Pig) — A1596

**2006, Dec. 1** **Photo.** **Perf. 13x13¼**
2236 A1596 250w multi　　.85 .40
　*a.* Souvenir sheet of 2　1.75 1.75

Text of
Heungboga
and Pansori
Singer
A1597

Mo Heung-
gap,
Pansori
Singer
A1598

**Litho. & Engr.**
**2006, Dec. 8** **Perf. 13x13¼**
2237　　Sheet of 10　　22.00 22.00
　*a.* A1597 480w multi　　2.10 1.75
　*b.* A1598 480w multi　　2.10 1.75
Top part of No. 2237 contains one each of Nos. 2237a-2237b. The lower part contains 4 each of Nos. 2237a-2237b.

A1599

Sharing and
Caring — A1600

**2006, Dec. 14** **Photo.** **Perf. 13x13¼**
2238 A1599 250w multi　　.85 .25
**Perf. 13¼x13**
2239 A1600 250w multi　　.85 .25
No. 2238 is impregnated with a pine scent; No. 2239 with a chocolate scent.

Nakdong
River in
Autumn
A1601

Nakdong
River in
Winter
A1602

Nakdong
River in
Spring
A1603

Nakdong
River in
Summer
A1604

**Perf. 13¼ Syncopated**
**2007, Jan. 18** **Photo.**
2240　　Block of 4　　3.25 3.00
　*a.* A1601 250w multi　　.70 .25
　*b.* A1602 250w multi　　.70 .25
　*c.* A1603 250w multi　　.70 .25
　*d.* A1604 250w multi　　.70 .25

Megatron/Matrix
A1605

TV
Buddha — A1606

The More the
Better — A1607

Oh-Mah (Mother)
A1608

**2007, Jan. 29** **Perf. 13¼**
2241　　Sheet of 12, 3 each
　　#a-d　　12.00 12.00
　*a.* A1605 250w multi　　.75 .25
　*b.* A1606 250w multi　　.75 .25
　*c.* A1607 250w multi　　.75 .25
　*d.* A1608 250w multi　　.75 .25
Art by Nam June Paik (1932-2006).

National Debt
Repayment Movement,
Cent. — A1609

**2007, Feb. 21** **Photo.** **Perf. 13x13¼**
2242 A1609 250w multi　　.85 .25

Maps of
Korea — A1610

No. 2243: a, Map from Atlas of Korea, 1780. b, Complete Territorial Map of the Great East, 19th cent. c, Map of the Eight Provinces, 1531. d, Comprehensive Map of the World and Nation's Successive Capitals, 1402.

**2007, Feb. 28** **Photo.** **Perf. 13½x13**
2243　　Sheet of 8, 2 each
　　#a-d　　17.50 17.50
　*a.* A1610 480w multi　　1.20 1.20
　*b.* A1610 520w multi　　1.50 1.50
　*c.* A1610 580w multi　　1.75 1.75
　*d.* A1610 600w multi　　1.75 1.75

Daehan Hospital, Seoul,
Cent. — A1611

**2007, Mar. 15   Litho.   *Perf. 13x13¼***
2244 A1611 250w multi          .85   .25

Ninth Asia Pacific
Orchid Conference,
Goyang — A1612

**2007, Mar. 16                 Photo.**
2245 A1612 250w multi          .85   .25

Biology
Year — A1613

**2007, Mar. 19        *Perf. 13¼x13***
2246 A1613 250w multi          .85   .25
a.      Souvenir sheet of 2    2.25  2.25

Sunflower
A1614

**2007, Mar. 21   Litho.   *Perf. 13¼***
2247 A1614 250w multi + label   2.50  2.50
Printed in sheets of 20 stamps + 20 labels
and 14 stamps + 14 labels that sold for 7500w.
Labels could be personalized.

Clover
A1615

Pig
A1616

**2007, Mar. 21   Photo.   *Perf. 13¼***
2248 A1615 250w multi + label   2.75  2.75
2249 A1616 250w multi + label   2.75  2.75
Nos. 2248-2249 were each printed in sheets
of 9 stamps + 9 labels. Each sheet sold for
4300w. Labels could be personalized.

Chinese Bride
and Groom
A1617

Indian Bride
and Groom
A1618

Malaysian
Bride and
Groom
A1619

Eurasian Bride
and Groom
A1620

No. 2250 — Korean brides and grooms
with: e, Mountains in background. f, Flowers
on orange background. g, Flowers and foliage
in background. h, Ducks in background.

**2007, Mar. 30              *Perf. 13¼x13***
2250    Block of 8         9.00  9.00
a. A1617 250w multi        .60   .40
b. A1618 250w multi        .60   .40
c. A1619 250w multi        .60   .40
d. A1620 250w multi        .60   .40
e. A1620 480w multi       1.25  1.00
f. A1620 520w multi       1.40  1.25
g. A1620 580w multi       1.75  1.50
h. A1620 600w multi       1.90  1.50

See Singapore No. 1241.

Opening of
Fortress Wall in
Mt. Bugaksan
A1621

**2007, Apr. 5   Photo.   *Perf. 13¾x12¾***
2251 A1621 250w multi          .85   .30

A1622

Internet
Culture — A1623

**2007, Apr. 20   Litho.   *Perf. 13¼x13***
2252 A1622 250w multi          .85   .30
                      **Photo.**
2253 A1623 250w multi          .85   .30

Children's Charter,
50th Anniv. — A1624

***Serpentine Die Cut***
**2007, May 4                  Photo.**
                    **Self-Adhesive**
2254 A1624 250w multi          .85   .30
No. 2254 is impregnated with a strawberry
scent.

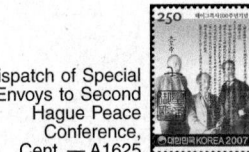

Dispatch of Special
Envoys to Second
Hague Peace
Conference,
Cent. — A1625

**Litho. & Engr.**
**2007, June 27            *Perf. 13x13¼***
2255 A1625 250w multi          .85   .30

A1626

Goguryeo
Kingdom
A1627

No. 2256: a, Cooks preparing food. b, Host
welcoming guest.

***Perf. 13 Syncopated***
**2007, July 2                 Photo.**
2256    Sheet of 14, 7 each
        #a-b           20.00  20.00
a. A1626 480w multi     1.25   .60
b. A1627 480w multi     1.25   .60

Philately
Week
A1628

No. 2257: a, Korea #1. b, Korea #2.

**2007, Aug. 1   Photo.   *Perf. 13¼x13***
2257    Horiz. pair        2.00  2.00
a.-b. A1628 250w Either single  .75  .30
c.    Souvenir sheet, #2257   2.25  2.25

Rollerblading — A1629

No. 2258: a, Drop-in. b, Flip. c, Spin. d,
Grind.

***Serpentine Die Cut 11¾x11¼***
**2007, Sept. 5                 Photo.**
                    **Self-Adhesive**
2258 A1629 250w Block of 4, #a-
     d                  4.00  4.00

Korean Bar Association,
Cent. — A1630

**2007, Sept. 21   Litho.   *Perf. 13x13¼***
2259 A1630 250w multi          .85   .30

Gwangan
Bridge
A1631

Seongsu
Bridge
A1632

Seongsan
Bridge
A1633

Yeongjong
Bridge
A1634

***Perf. 13¼x13½ Syncopated***
**2007, Sept. 28               Photo.**
2260    Block of 4         3.50  3.50
a. A1631 250w multi        .75   .30
b. A1632 250w multi        .75   .30
c. A1633 250w multi        .75   .30
d. A1634 250w multi        .75   .30

Inter-Korean Summit,
Pyongyang, North
Korea — A1635

**2007, Oct. 2        *Perf. 13¼x13***
2261 A1635 250w multi          .85   .30

Hyeongje
Falls — A1636

Rimyeongsu
Falls — A1637

Lake Samjiyeon
A1638

Lake
Chonji — A1639

**2007, Oct. 18   Photo.   *Perf. 13x13½***
2262    Block of 4         3.50  3.50
a. A1636 250w multi        .75   .30
b. A1637 250w multi        .75   .30
c. A1638 250w multi        .75   .30
d. A1639 250w multi        .75   .30

A1640

A1641

A1642

Korean
Films — A1643

No. 2263: a, Arirang, 1926. b, The Own-
erless Ferryboat, 1932. c, Looking for Love,
1928. d, Chunhyangjeon, 1935.

**2007, Oct. 26             *Perf. 13x13¼***
2263    Sheet of 16, 4 each
        #a-d          16.00  16.00
a. A1640 250w multi        .75   .30
b. A1641 250w multi        .75   .30
c. A1642 250w multi        .75   .30
d. A1643 250w multi        .75   .30

A1644

Protection of
Children's
Rights — A1645

**2007, Nov. 20　Photo.　Perf. 13x13¼**
2264　A1644　250w multi　　　　.85　.30
**Litho.**
**Perf. 13¼x13**
2265　A1645　250w multi　　　　.85　.30

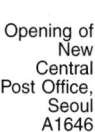

Opening of
New
Central
Post Office,
Seoul
A1646

No. 2266: a, Hanseong Post Office, 1915,
and new building. b, New building.

**2007, Nov. 22　Photo.　Perf. 13x13¼**
2266　A1646　250w Horiz. pair, #a-
b　　　　　　2.00　2.00

No. 2266 printed in sheet containing 7 pairs.

New Year 2008 (Year of
the Rat) — A1647

**2007, Nov. 30**
2267　A1647　250w multi　　　　.85　.30
　　*a.*　Souvenir sheet of 2　1.50　1.50

Tapdeunggut Exorcism, Dano Festival,
Gangneung — A1648

Gwanno
Mask
Drama,
Dano
Festival
A1649

**2007, Dec. 7　　　　Litho. & Engr.**
2268　　Sheet of 10, 5 each
　　　　#a-b　　　　　18.00　18.00
　　*a.*　A1648　480w multi　1.50　.75
　　*b.*　A1649　480w multi　1.50　.75

Top part of No. 2268 contains one each of
Nos. 2268a-2268b. The lower part contains 4
each of Nos. 2268a-2268b.

Seomjin
River in
Autumn
A1650

Seomjin
River in
Winter
A1651

Seomjin
River in
Spring
A1652

Seomjin
River in
Summer
A1653

**Perf. 13½x13¼ Syncopated**
**2008, Jan. 18　　　　　　Photo.**
2269　　Block of 4　　　3.25　3.25
　　*a.*　A1650　250w multi　.75　.30
　　*b.*　A1651　250w multi　.75　.30
　　*c.*　A1652　250w multi　.75　.30
　　*d.*　A1653　250w multi　.75　.30

Miniature Sheet

King
Sejong
Antarctic
Station
A1654

No. 2270 — Penguins and: a, Scientists on
snowmobiles. b, Station.

**2008, Feb. 15　Photo.　Perf. 13¼**
2270　A1654　250w Sheet of 10,
　　　　　　5 each #a-
　　　　　　b　　　　12.50　12.50

Inauguration of Pres. Lee Myung-
Bak — A1655

**2008, Feb. 25　Photo.　Perf. 13x13¼**
2271　A1655　250w multi　　　　.85　.30
　　*a.*　Souvenir sheet of 1　2.00　2.00

African
Savanna
A1656

No. 2272: a, African child and mask. b,
Leopard. c, Elephant. d, Zebra.

**Die Cut Perf. (outer edge) x
Serpentine Die Cut 11 (radial sides)
x Die Cut (inner edge)**
**2008, Mar. 26　　　　Self-Adhesive**
2272　A1656　250w Block of 4, #a-
　　　　　d, + central
　　　　　label　　　　4.00　4.00

Philakorea 2009 Intl.
Stamp Exhibition,
Seoul — A1657

No. 2273 — Dancers: a, Buchaechum
(orange background). b, Salpurichum (pink
background). c, Seungmu (blue background).
d, Taepyeongmu (green background).

**2008, Apr. 10　　　　Perf. 13¼x13**
2273　　Horiz. strip or block of
　　　　　4　　　　　　3.25　3.25
　　*a.-d.*　A1657　250w Any single　.75　.30
　　*e.*　Souvenir sheet, #2273a-2273d, +
　　　　label　　　　　3.00　3.00

A1658

Winning Designs in
"Mailboxes of the
Future" Children's
Stamp Design
Contest — A1659

**2008, Apr. 22　Photo.　Perf. 13¼x13**
2274　A1658　250w multi　　　　.85　.30
**Litho.**
**Perf. 13x13¼**
2275　A1659　250w multi　　　　.85　.30

Nurturing of Children
A1660　　　　A1661

**Litho., Engr. & Embossed**
**2008, May 8　　　　Perf. 13x13¼**
2276　A1660　250w multi　　　　.85　.30
**Litho.**
2277　A1661　250w multi　　　　.85　.30

Sun and
Moon
A1662

Hands
Making
Heart
A1663

Tree-lined
Path
A1664

Roses
A1665

**2008, May 19　　Photo.　　Perf. 13¼**
2278　A1662　250w multi + label　1.50　1.50
2279　A1663　250w multi + label　1.50　1.50
2280　A1664　250w multi + label　1.50　1.50
2281　A1665　250w multi + label　1.50　1.50
　　　*Nos. 2278-2281 (4)*　　6.00　6.00

Nos. 2278-2279 each were printed in sheets
of 3 stamps + 3 labels, No. 2280 was printed
in sheets of 14 stamps + 15 labels, and No.
2281 was printed in sheets of 20 stamps + 20
labels. Labels could be personalized.

Organization for Economic
Cooperation and Development
Ministerial Meeting, Seoul
A1666

**2008, June 17　　　　　Perf. 13¼**
2282　A1666　250w multi　　　　.85　.30

Yun Bong-Gil
(1908-32),
Assassin of
Japanese Colonial
Generals — A1667

**2008, June 20**
2283　A1667　250w multi　　　　.85　.30

Miniature Sheet

Dangun Wanggeom — A1668

No. 2284: a, Hwanung descending from
heavens at Taebaek Mountain. b, Bear and
tiger who prayed to become human. c, Birth of
Dangun Wanggeom. d, Dangun Wanggeom
as adult.

**2008, July 10　Photo.　Perf. 13¼x13**
2284　A1668　250w Sheet of 12, 3
　　　　　　each #a-d　　6.00　6.00

Energy Conservation — A1669

No. 2285: a, Open electrical circuit, car,
refrigerator, light bulb, fan, meter. b, Hand-
straps for public transportation. c, Electrical
plugs on flower stems. d, Thermometers.

**2008, Aug. 1　Photo.　Perf. 13¼x13**
2285　A1669　250w Block or horiz.
　　　　　　strip of 4, #a-
　　　　　　d　　　　3.00　3.00

Philately
Week
A1670

No. 2286: a, South Korea #34. b, South
Korea #176.

**2008, Aug. 7　Photo.　Perf. 13¼x13**
2286　A1670　250w Pair, #a-b　1.50　1.50
　　*c.*　Souvenir sheet, #2286a-2286b　2.00　2.00

2008 Summer
Olympics,
Beijing — A1671

**2008, Aug. 8　Photo.　Perf. 13¼x13**
2287　A1671　250w multi　　　　.85　.30

Republic of Korea, 60th Anniv. — A1672

**2008, Aug. 14**
2288 A1672 250w multi .85 .30

Korean Language Society, Cent. A1673

**2008, Aug. 29** *Perf. 12¾x13½*
2289 A1673 250w multi .85 .30

Seoul Water Works, Cent. — A1674

**2008, Sept. 1 Litho. Perf. 13x13¼**
2290 A1674 250w multi .85 .30

Amateur Radio Direction Finding Championships, Hwaseong — A1675

**2008, Sept. 2**
2291 A1675 250w multi .85 .30

Snowboarding — A1676

No. 2292: a, Carving turn. b, Indy grab. c, Nose grab. d, Air.

***Serpentine Die Cut 11¾x11¼***
**2008, Sept. 5 Photo.**
**Self-Adhesive**
2292 A1676 250w Block of 4, #a-d 3.50 3.50

Salvation Army in Korea, Cent. — A1677

**2008, Oct. 1 Photo. Perf. 13x13¼**
2293 A1677 250w multi .85 .30

Republic of Korea Armed Forces, 60th Anniv. — A1678

**2008, Oct. 1**
2294 A1678 250w multi .85 .30

Diplomatic Relations Between South Korea and Thailand, 50th Anniv. — A1679

No. 2295: a, Chakri Mahaprasat Hall, Thailand (denomination at left). b, Juhamnu Pavilion, South Korea (denomination at right).

**2008, Oct. 1 Litho. Perf. 13¼**
2295 A1679 250w Pair, #a-b 2.50 2.50
See Thailand No. 2383.

Manmulsang A1680

Gwimyeonam Rock — A1681

Outer Geumgangsan A1682

Sangpaldam Pools — A1683

**2008, Oct. 17 Photo. Perf. 13x13½**
2296 Block of 4 3.25 3.25
a. A1680 250w multi .75 .30
b. A1681 250w multi .75 .30
c. A1682 250w multi .75 .30
d. A1683 250w multi .75 .30

Korean Films A1684

No. 2297: a, A Coachman, 1961 (blue background). b, Wedding Day, 1956 (dull lilac background). c, The Seashore Village, 1965 (dull green background). d, Mother and a Guest, 1961 (gray olive background).

**2008, Oct. 27 Litho. Perf. 13x13½**
2297 A1684 250w Block of 4, #a-d 3.25 3.25

Upo Wetlands A1685

**2008, Oct. 28 Photo. Perf. 13¼**
2298 A1685 250w multi .85 .30
Tenth Ramsar Convention Meeting, Changwon.

Masks A1686

No. 2299: a, Chwibari Mask, Korea (denomination at LL). b, Big head Buddha mask, Hong Kong (denomination at LR).

**2008, Nov. 6 Perf. 13¼x13**
2299 A1686 250w Horiz. pair, #a-b 2.00 2.00
See Hong Kong Nos. 1337-1338.

New Year 2009 (Year of the Ox) — A1687

**2008, Dec. 1 Perf. 13x13¼**
2300 A1687 250w multi 1.00 .30
a. Souvenir sheet of 2 2.00 2.00

Louis Braille (1809-52), Educator of the Blind A1688

**2009, Jan. 2 Perf. 12¾x13½**
2301 A1688 250w multi .85 .30

Intl. Year of Astronomy — A1689

No. 2302: a, Whirlpool Galaxy M51. b, Planetary Nebula NGC 3132.

**2009, Jan. 15 Photo. Perf. 13x13¼**
2302 A1689 250w Horiz. pair, #a-b 1.50 1.50

Geum River in Autumn A1690

Geum River in Winter A1691

Geum River in Spring A1692

Geum River in Summer A1693

***Perf. 13¼ Syncopated***
**2009, Feb. 10**
2303 Block or horiz. strip of 4 3.25 3.25
a. A1690 250w multi .70 .30
b. A1691 250w multi .70 .30
c. A1692 250w multi .70 .30
d. A1693 250w multi .70 .30

A1694

Designs: No. 2304, 250w, Panagbenga Flower Festival, Baguio, Philippines. No. 2305, 250w, Cow Play, Hangawi, South Korea.

**2009, Mar. 3 Photo. Perf. 13x13¼**
2304-2305 A1694 Set of 2 1.50 1.50
Diplomatic relations between South Korea and the Philippines, 60th anniv.

Historic Trees A1695

No. 2306: a, Fir tree (Natural Monument No. 495) (22x50mm). b, Zelkova tree (Natural Monument No. 478), horiz. (44x25mm). c, Ginkgo tree (Natural Monument No. 30) (22x50mm). d, Seosongnyeong tree (Natural Monument No. 294), horiz. (44x25mm).

**2009, Apr. 3 Litho. Perf. 12¾**
2306 A1695 250w Block of 4, #a-d 3.25 3.25

Republic of Korea Marine Corps, 60th Anniv. — A1696

**2009, Apr. 15 Perf. 12½**
2307 A1696 250w multi .85 .30

A1697

Asia Becoming One — A1698

**2009, Apr. 22 Photo. Perf. 13¼x13**
2308 A1697 250w multi .85 .30
**Litho.**
**Perf. 13x13¼**
2309 A1698 250w multi .85 .30

A1699

Love For the Earth — A1700

**2009, Apr. 22 Litho. Perf. 13¼x13**
2310 A1699 250w multi .85 .30
**Photo.**
**Perf. 13x13¼**
2311 A1700 250w multi .85 .30

Cartooning in Korea, Cent. — A1701

**2009, June 2 Litho. Perf. 13x13¼**
2312 A1701 250w multi .85 .30

Earrings From Korea, 5th-6th Cent. — A1702

Earrings From Mongolia, 18th-19th Cent. — A1703

Earrings From Kazakhstan, 2nd-1st Cent. B.C. — A1704

**2009, June 12   Photo.   Perf. 13x13¼**

| | | | |
|---|---|---|---|
| 2313 | Strip of 3 | 2.50 | 2.50 |
| a. | A1702 250w multi | .65 | .30 |
| b. | A1703 250w multi | .65 | .30 |
| c. | A1704 250w multi | .65 | .30 |

See Kazakhstan No. 595, Mongolia No. 2674.

Cave Lake and Lava Tubes A1705

Lava Tubes, Stalactites and Stalagmite A1706

**Litho. & Engr.**

**2009, June 26   Perf. 13x13¼**

| | | | |
|---|---|---|---|
| 2314 | Sheet of 10, 5 each #a-b | 7.00 | 7.00 |
| a. | A1705 250w multi | .75 | .30 |
| b. | A1706 250w multi | .75 | .30 |

Jeju Volcanic Island and Lava Tubes UNESCO World Heritage Site.

Philately Week A1707

No. 2315: a, Korea #19. b, South Korea #639.

**2009, July 30   Photo.   Perf. 13¼x13**

| | | | |
|---|---|---|---|
| 2315 | Pair | 1.50 | 1.50 |
| a.-b. | A1707 250w Either single | .70 | .30 |
| c. | Souvenir sheet, #2315 | .70 | .30 |

 A1708    A1709

 A1710    A1711

 A1712    A1713

 A1714

Bird Drawings — A1715

**2009, July 30   Litho.   Perf. 13¼x13**

| | | | |
|---|---|---|---|
| 2316 | Block of 8 | 4.50 | 4.50 |
| a. | A1708 250w multi | .50 | .30 |
| b. | A1709 250w multi | .50 | .30 |
| c. | A1710 250w multi | .50 | .30 |
| d. | A1711 250w multi | .50 | .30 |
| e. | A1712 250w multi | .50 | .30 |
| f. | A1713 250w multi | .50 | .30 |
| g. | A1714 250w multi | .50 | .30 |
| h. | A1715 250w multi | .50 | .30 |
| i. | Souvenir sheet of 2, #2316a, 2316e | 2.00 | 2.00 |
| j. | Souvenir sheet of 2, #2316b, 2316f | 2.00 | 2.00 |
| k. | Souvenir sheet of 2, #2316c, 2316g | 2.00 | 2.00 |
| l. | Souvenir sheet of 2, #2316d, 2316h | 2.00 | 2.00 |

Philakorea 2009, Seoul.

Command From God To Move Country's Capital — A1716

Establishment of East Buyeo — A1717

Birth of King Geumwawang A1718

King Geumwawang on Throne — A1719

**2009, Aug. 18   Photo.   Perf. 13x13¼**

| | | | |
|---|---|---|---|
| 2317 | Sheet of 12, 3 each #a-d | 7.00 | 7.00 |
| a. | A1716 250w multi | .50 | .30 |
| b. | A1717 250w multi | .50 | .30 |
| c. | A1718 250w multi | .50 | .30 |
| d. | A1719 250w multi | .50 | .30 |

Legend of King Geumwawang of the Buyeo Kingdom.

Green Energy A1720

No. 2318: a, House with solar panels, bicycle. b, Automobile with solar panels. c, Wind turbines. d, Dam.

**2009, Aug. 21   Photo.   Perf. 13¼**

| | | | |
|---|---|---|---|
| 2318 | A1720 250w Block of 4, #a-d | 2.00 | 2.00 |

Groundbreaking for Taekwondo Park, Muju-gun A1721

**2009, Sept. 4   Perf. 13¾x12¾**

| 2319 | A1721 250w multi | .85 | .30 |
|---|---|---|---|

BMX Bicycling — A1722

No. 2320: a, X-up. b, No hand jump. c, One foot can can. d, Superman seat grab.

**Serpentine Die Cut 11¾x11¼**

**2009, Sept. 8   Photo.**

| 2320 | A1722 250w Block of 4, #a-d | 2.00 | 2.00 |
|---|---|---|---|

Rice A1723

No. 2321: a, Rice flowers and plants. b, Red, black and white rice grains.

**2009, Sept. 25   Litho.   Perf. 13¼**

| 2321 | Pair | 1.00 | 1.00 |
|---|---|---|---|
| a.-b. | A1723 250w Either single | .50 | .30 |

Third Organization for Economic Cooperation and Development World Forum, Busan A1724

**2009, Oct. 27   Litho.   Perf. 13¼**

| 2322 | A1724 250w multi | .75 | .30 |
|---|---|---|---|

 A1725

 A1726

 A1727

Korean Films — A1728

No. 2323: a, Chilsu and Mansu, 1988. b, Never, Never Forget Me, 1976. c, A Road to Sampo, 1975. d, Yalkae, A Joker in High School, 1976.

**2009, Oct. 27   Perf. 13x13¼**

| | | | |
|---|---|---|---|
| 2323 | Block or strip of 4 | 2.50 | 2.50 |
| a. | A1725 250w multi | .50 | .30 |
| b. | A1726 250w multi | .50 | .30 |
| c. | A1727 250w multi | .50 | .30 |
| d. | A1728 250w multi | .50 | .30 |

Diplomatic Relations Between South Korea and Brazil, 50th Anniv. — A1729

No. 2324: a, Octavio Frias de Oliveira Bridge, Brazil (denomination at UL). b, Incheon Bridge, South Korea (denomination at UR).

**2009, Oct. 30   Perf. 13¼**

| 2324 | A1729 250w Pair, #a-b | 1.25 | 1.25 |
|---|---|---|---|

See Brazil No. 3113.

New Year 2010 (Year of the Tiger) — A1730

**2009, Dec. 1   Photo.   Perf. 13x13¼**

| 2325 | A1730 250w multi | .75 | .30 |
|---|---|---|---|
| a. | Souvenir sheet of 2 | 1.25 | 1.25 |

Visit Korea Year — A1731

No. 2326: a, Stylized face, denomination in blue. b, People as Korean flag, denomination in white.

**2010, Jan. 4   Photo.   Perf. 13¼x13**

| 2326 | A1731 250w Pair, #a-b | 1.00 | 1.00 |
|---|---|---|---|

2010 Winter Olympics, Vancouver A1732

No. 2327: a, Figure skater. b, Speed skater.

**2010, Feb. 12   Perf. 12¾x13½**

| 2327 | A1732 250w Pair, #a-b | 1.00 | 1.00 |
|---|---|---|---|

Diplomatic Relations Between South Korea and Malaysia, 50th Anniv. — A1733

No. 2328: a, Panthera tigris altaica. b, Panthera tigris jacksoni.

**2010, Feb. 23   Litho.   Perf. 13¼**

| 2328 | A1733 250w Pair, #a-b | 1.00 | 1.00 |
|---|---|---|---|

Ahn Jung-geun (1879-1910), Assassin of Ito Hirobumi, Japanese Resident-General of Korea — A1734

No. 2329 — Ahn Jung-geun and: a, Handprint. b, Characters written on Korean flag with blood from his severed finger.

**Litho. & Engr.**

| 2010, Mar. 26 | | Perf. 13¼ |
|---|---|---|
| 2329 | A1734 250w Pair, #a-b | 1.00 1.00 |

Seoul National University of Technology, Cent. A1735

Jinju National University, Cent. A1736

| 2010, Apr. 1  Photo. | | Perf. 12¾x13½ |
|---|---|---|
| 2330 | A1735 250w multi | .50 .30 |
| 2331 | A1736 250w multi | .50 .30 |

Historic Trees A1737

No. 2332: a, Old Buddha's plum tree (Natural Monument No. 486) (22x50mm). b, Pine tree (Natural Monument No. 290), horiz (44x25mm). c, Entwined Chinese junipers (Natural Monument No. 88) (22x50mm). d, Three Thunbergii camphor trees (Natural Monument No. 481), horiz. (44x25mm).

| 2010, Apr. 5  Litho. | | Perf. 12¾ |
|---|---|---|
| 2332 | A1737 250w Block of 4, #a-d | 2.00 2.00 |

Mo Tae Bum — A1738

Le Sang Hwa — A1739

Lee Seung Hoon — A1740

Kim Yu Na — A1741

Kwak Yoon Gy — A1742

Kim Seoung Il — A1743

Park Seung Hi — A1744

Sung Si Bak — A1745

Lee Eun Byul — A1746

Lee Jung Su — A1747

Lee Ho Suk — A1748

| 2010, May 6  Photo. | | Perf. 13½x12¾ |
|---|---|---|
| 2333 | Sheet of 11 + label | 7.00 7.00 |
| a. | A1738 250w multi | .60 .30 |
| b. | A1739 250w multi | .60 .30 |
| c. | A1740 250w multi | .60 .30 |
| d. | A1741 250w multi | .60 .30 |
| e. | A1742 250w multi | .60 .30 |
| f. | A1743 250w multi | .60 .30 |
| g. | A1744 250w multi | .60 .30 |
| h. | A1745 250w multi | .60 .30 |
| i. | A1746 250w multi | .60 .30 |
| j. | A1747 250w multi | .60 .30 |
| k. | A1748 250w multi | .60 .30 |

Medalists at 2010 Winter Olympics, Vancouver.

Han River in Spring A1749

Han River in Summer A1750

Han River in Autumn A1751

Han River in Winter A1752

| 2010, May 11  Perf. 13½ Syncopated | | |
|---|---|---|
| 2334 | Block or strip of 4 | 2.00 2.00 |
| a. | A1749 250w multi | .50 .30 |
| b. | A1750 250w multi | .50 .30 |
| c. | A1751 250w multi | .50 .30 |
| d. | A1752 250w multi | .50 .30 |

2010 World Cup Soccer Championships, South Africa — A1753

**Perf. 13¼x13½**

| 2010, June 11 | | Photo. |
|---|---|---|
| 2335 | A1753 250w multi | .75 .30 |

World Refugee Day, 10th Anniv. A1754

| 2010, June 18 | | Perf. 13¼ |
|---|---|---|
| 2336 | A1754 250w multi | .60 .30 |

Diplomatic Relations Between South Korea and United Arab Emirates, 30th Anniv. — A1755

No. 2337: a, Flag of United Arab Emirates and air-conditioning tower. b, Flag of South Korea and Mt. Amisan Chimney, Gyeongbokgung Palace.

| 2010, June 18  Photo. | | Perf. 13x13¼ |
|---|---|---|
| 2337 | A1755 250w Pair, #a-b | 1.00 1.00 |

See United Arab Emirates No. 990.

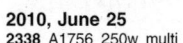

Start of Korean War, 60th Anniv. — A1756

| 2010, June 25 | | Perf. 13½x13 |
|---|---|---|
| 2338 | A1756 250w multi | .60 .30 |

Philately Week A1757

No. 2339: a, South Korea #1197. b, South Korea #1198.

| 2010, July 29 | | Perf. 13¼x13¼x13 |
|---|---|---|
| 2339 | Pair, #a-b | 1.00 1.00 |
| a.-b. | A1757 250w Either single | .50 .30 |
| c. | Souvenir sheet, #2339a-2339b | 1.25 1.25 |

Dinosaurs A1758

No. 2340: a, Herrerasaurus. b, Coelophysis. c, Plateosaurus. d, Riojasaurus.

**Perf. 13¼ Syncopated**

| 2010, Aug. 5 | | Litho. & Engr. |
|---|---|---|
| 2340 | Sheet of 12, 3 each #2340a-2340d | 7.50 7.50 |
| a.-b. | A1758 250w Either single | .50 .30 |
| c.-d. | A1758 340w Either single | .50 .30 |

23rd Intl. Union of Forest Research Organizations World Congress, Seoul — A1759

**Litho. & Embossed**

| 2010, Aug. 23 | | Perf. 12½ |
|---|---|---|
| 2341 | A1759 340w multi | .75 .30 |

Legend of Goguryeo Jumong — A1760

No. 2342: a, King Geumwa and soldiers meet woman. b, Baby Jumong, birds and animals. c, Jumong and others fleeing King Geumwa on horseback. d, Jumong on horse and followers at Jolboncheon.

| 2010, Sept. 14  Photo. | | Perf. 13x13½ |
|---|---|---|
| 2342 | A1760 250w Block of 4, #a-d | 2.00 2.00 |

A1761

A1762

A1763

Korean Films — A1764

No. 2343: a, Seopyeonje, 1993. b, Shiri, 1999. c, Tae Guk Gi: The Brotherhood of War, 2004. d, Take Off, 2009.

| 2010, Oct. 27  Litho. | | Perf. 13x13¼ |
|---|---|---|
| 2343 | Block of 4 | 2.00 2.00 |
| a. | A1761 250w multi | .50 .30 |
| b. | A1762 250w multi | .50 .30 |
| c. | A1763 250w multi | .50 .30 |
| d. | A1764 250w multi | .50 .30 |

Recycling — A1765

No. 2344: a, Flowers in pot. b, Recycling robot.

| 2010, Nov. 11  Photo. | | Perf. 13¼x13 |
|---|---|---|
| 2344 | A1765 250w Pair, #a-b | 1.00 1.00 |

**Miniature Sheet**

G20 Summit, Seoul A1766

No. 2345 — Summit emblem and: a, World map. b, Gate.

| 2010, Nov. 11 | | Perf. 13x13¼ |
|---|---|---|
| 2345 | A1766 Sheet of 14, 7 each #a-b | 10.00 10.00 |
| a.-b. | 250w Either single | .60 .35 |

New Year 2011 (Year of the Rabbit) — A1767

| 2010, Dec. 1 | | Perf. 13x13¼ |
|---|---|---|
| 2346 | A1767 250w multi | .50 .30 |
| a. | Souvenir sheet of 2 | 1.00 1.00 |

A1768 | Personalized Stamps — A1769

**2010, Dec. 1  Photo.  Perf. 13x13¼**
**Denomination Color**

| | | | | |
|---|---|---|---|---|
| 2347 | A1768 | 250w green | 2.00 | 2.00 |
| 2348 | A1768 | 250w blue | 2.00 | 2.00 |
| 2349 | A1768 | 250w red brown | 2.00 | 2.00 |

**Perf. 13¼x13½**

| | | | | |
|---|---|---|---|---|
| 2350 | A1769 | 250w green | 2.25 | 2.25 |
| 2351 | A1769 | 250w blue | 2.25 | 2.25 |
| 2352 | A1769 | 250w red brown | 2.25 | 2.25 |
| | | Nos. 2347-2352 (6) | 12.75 | 12.75 |

Nos. 2347-2349 each were available in sheets of 6 that sold for 5500w and sheets of 20 that sold for 9500w. Nos. 2350-2352 each were sold in sheets of 14 that sold for 8000y. images could be personalized.

**Miniature Sheet**

Characters in Pororo, the Little Penguin — A1770

No. 2353: a, Eddy, the Fox. b, Crong, the Baby Dinosaur on balloon. c, Pororo wearing helmet. d, Petty, the girl Penguin. e, Pipi and Popo, the Aliens. f, Poby, the Polar Bear. g, Harry, the Hummingbird on ball. h, Loopy, the Beaver with basket. i, Tong Tong, the Dragon. j, Rody, the Robot.

**2011, Feb. 22  Photo.  Die Cut**
**Self-Adhesive**

| | | | | |
|---|---|---|---|---|
| 2353 | A1770 | Sheet of 10 | 5.50 | 5.50 |
| a.-j. | | 250w Any single | .50 | .30 |

Historic Trees A1771

No. 2354: a, Japanese black pine trees at Sancheondan (Natural Monument No. 160) (22x50mm). b, Ginkgo tree at Yogwang-ri (Natural Monument No. 84), horiz. (44x25mm). c, Pine tree at Chukji-ri (Natural Monument No. 491) (22x50mm). d, Zelkova tree at Haksaru (Natural Monument No. 407), horiz. (44x25mm).

**2011, Apr. 5  Litho.  Perf. 12¾**

| | | | | |
|---|---|---|---|---|
| 2354 | A1771 | 250w Block of 4, #a-d | 2.25 | 2.25 |

Diplomatic Relations Between South Korea and Portugal, 50th Anniv. — A1772

No. 2355: a, Korean turtle ship, denomination at UL. b, Portuguese nau, denomination at UR.

**2011, Apr. 15  Photo.  Perf. 13x13¼**

| | | | | |
|---|---|---|---|---|
| 2355 | | Sheet of 14, 7 each #2355a-2355b | 12.00 | 12.00 |
| a.-b. | A1772 | 250w Either single | .75 | .30 |

See Portugal Nos. 3305-3306.

Family A1773

No. 2356: a, Stick-figure family and house. b, Heads in bunch of grapes.

**2011, May 13  Photo.  Perf. 13x13¼**

| | | | | |
|---|---|---|---|---|
| 2356 | A1773 | 250w Pair, #a-b | 1.25 | 1.25 |

Bamboo Grove, Damyang A1774

Tea Field, Boesong A1775

Upo Swamp, Changnyeong — A1776

Jusanji Pond, Cheongsong A1777

**2011, May 27  Perf. 13¼**

| | | | | |
|---|---|---|---|---|
| 2357 | | Block of 4 | 2.50 | 2.50 |
| a. | A1774 | 250w multi | .55 | .30 |
| b. | A1775 | 250w multi | .55 | .30 |
| c. | A1776 | 250w multi | .55 | .30 |
| d. | A1777 | 250w multi | .55 | .30 |

Preservation of Polar Regions and Glaciers — A1778

No. 2358: a, Polar bears. b, Penguins.

**2011, June 3  Litho.  Perf. 13x13¼**

| | | | | |
|---|---|---|---|---|
| 2358 | A1778 | 250w Pair, #a-b | 1.25 | 1.25 |

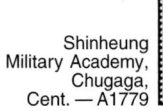

Shinheung Military Academy, Chugaga, Cent. — A1779

**2011, June 10  Photo.**

| | | | | |
|---|---|---|---|---|
| 2359 | A1779 | 250w multi | .75 | .30 |

Tomb of King Taejo A1780

Tomb of King Sejong A1781

**Litho. & Engr.**
**2011, June 30  Perf. 13x13¼**

| | | | | |
|---|---|---|---|---|
| 2360 | | Sheet of 10, 5 each #2360a-2360b | 6.50 | 6.50 |
| a. | A1780 | 250w multi | .60 | .30 |
| b. | A1781 | 250w multi | .60 | .30 |

Royal Tombs of the Joeson Dynasty UNESCO World Heritage Site.

Korea Disaster Relief Association, 50th Anniv. — A1782

**2011, July 13  Photo.  Perf. 13x13¼**

| | | | | |
|---|---|---|---|---|
| 2361 | A1782 | 250w multi | .75 | .30 |

Philately Week A1783

No. 2362 — Paintings: a, Sansu (mountain and houses), by Jo Seok-jin (denomination in green). b, Jangsongnakil (rider on horse), by Ji Woon-young (denomination in bister brown). c, Unnangjasang (portrait), by Chae Yong-sin (denomination in red brown). d, Gunmado (horses), by Kim Ki-chang (denomination in gold).

**2011, July 28  Perf. 13**

| | | | | |
|---|---|---|---|---|
| 2362 | A1783 | 250w Block of 4, #a-d | 2.50 | 2.50 |
| e. | | Souvenir sheet of 4, #2362a-2362d | 3.00 | 3.00 |

Selection of Pyeongchang as Host of 2018 Winter Olympics A1784

**2011, Aug. 3  Perf. 13x13¼**

| | | | | |
|---|---|---|---|---|
| 2363 | A1784 | 250w multi | .75 | .30 |

Dinosaurs A1785

No. 2364: a, Scelidosaurus. b, Stegosaurus. c, Allosaurus. d, Dilophosaurus.

**Perf. 13¼ Syncopated**
**2011, Aug. 11  Litho. & Engr.**

| | | | | |
|---|---|---|---|---|
| 2364 | | Sheet of 12, 3 each #2364a-2364d | 12.00 | 12.00 |
| a.-d. | A1785 | 340w Any single | .65 | .30 |

Intl. Association of Athletics Federations World Championships, Daegu — A1786

No. 2365: a, Runners. b, Pole vault.

**2011, Aug. 26  Litho.  Perf. 13¼**

| | | | | |
|---|---|---|---|---|
| 2365 | A1786 | 250w Pair, #a-b | 1.50 | 1.50 |

Tripitaka Koreana, 1000th Anniv. — A1787

**2011, Sept. 23  Photo.  Perf. 13x13¼**

| | | | | |
|---|---|---|---|---|
| 2366 | A1787 | 250w multi | .75 | .30 |

Personalized Stamp — A1788

**2011, Oct. 1  Photo.  Perf. 13x13¼**

| | | | | |
|---|---|---|---|---|
| 2367 | A1788 | 270w multi | | |

Vignette portion could be personalized. Three additional stamps were issued in this set. The editors would like to examine any examples.

Tenth Session of the Conference of the Parties to the United Nations Convention to Combat Desertification, Changwon A1792

**2011, Oct. 10  Photo.  Perf. 13¼x13**

| | | | | |
|---|---|---|---|---|
| 2371 | A1792 | 270w multi | .75 | .30 |

Ipo Weir, Han River A1793

Gongju Weir, Geum River A1794

Seungchon Weir, Yeongsan River A1795

Gangjeong-Goryeong Weir, Nakdong River — A1796

**2011, Oct. 21  Perf. 13¼**

| | | | | |
|---|---|---|---|---|
| 2372 | | Block of 4 | 2.25 | 2.25 |
| a. | A1793 | 270w multi | .55 | .30 |
| b. | A1794 | 270w multi | .55 | .30 |
| c. | A1795 | 270w multi | .55 | .30 |
| d. | A1796 | 270w multi | .55 | .30 |

Diplomatic Relations Between South Korea and Australia, 50th Anniv. — A1797

No. 2373: a, Korean woman playing haegeum. b, Australian aborigine playing didgeridoo.

**2011, Oct. 28  Photo.  Perf. 13¼x13**

| | | | | |
|---|---|---|---|---|
| 2373 | A1797 | 270w Horiz. pair, #a-b | 1.25 | 1.25 |

See Australia Nos. 3587-3588.

A1798

A1799

A1800

Daejoyong of the
Balhae
Kingdom — A1801

**2011, Nov. 17          Perf. 13x13¼**
2374       Sheet of 12, 3 each #a-
          d, + label                       6.00  6.00
  *a.*     A1798 270w multi              .50   .25
  *b.*     A1799 270w multi              .50   .25
  *c.*     A1800 270w multi              .50   .25
  *d.*     A1801 270w multi              .50   .25

New Year 2012 (Year of
the Dragon) — A1802

**2011, Dec. 1**
2375    A1802 270w multi              .75   .30
  *a.*   Souvenir sheet of 2          1.25  1.25

South Korean Achievement of One
Trillion Dollars in Trade — A1803

No. 2376: a, Automobile, computer chip,
smart phone, container ship. b, Flag of South
Korea, skyscraper.

**2011, Dec. 7**
2376    A1803 270w Horiz. pair, #a-
        b                             1.25  1.25

Diplomatic
Relations
Between South
Korea and
Mexico, 50th
Anniv.
A1804

No. 2377: a, Juvenile gray whale, denomination at right. b, Adult gray whale, denomination at left.

**2012, Jan. 26    Litho.    Perf. 13¼**
2377    A1804 270w Vert. pair, #a-b 1.25 1.25
        See Mexico Nos. 2771-2772.

Miniature Sheet

Characters in Pucca Animated
Television Series — A1805

No. 2378: a, Ssoso, with stick and birds
(blue green, light blue and gray background).
b, Abyo, with frog (green andd light green
background). c, Pucca, with heart (yellow and

---

orange background). d, Garu, with cat (orange
and light orange background. e, Ching, with
mirror (pink and light pink background). f,
Bruce, with guns (purple and gray background). g, Ho-Oh, with flame (purple and pink
background). h, Santa (bright blue and light
blue background). i, Nini, with earrings (gray
blue background). j, Woo-Wuh, with rolling
pins and dishes (dark blue and purple
background).

*Serpentine Die Cut 10¼ Vert.*
**2012, Feb. 22            Photo.**
**Self-Adhesive**
2378    A1805     Sheet of 10          6.00  6.00
  *a.-j.*     270w Any single          .55   .30

Diplomatic
Relations
Between South
Korea and
Colombia, 50th
Anniv. — A1806

No. 2379: a, Coffee beans and bush. b, Ginseng flowers and root.

**2012, Mar. 9            Perf. 13x13¼**
2379    A1806 270w Pair, #a-b    1.25  1.25
        See Colombia No. 1374.

2012 Nuclear Security Summit, Seoul
A1807

No. 2380 — Ribbon and: a, World map. b,
Dove, flag of South Korea.

**2012, Mar. 26            Perf. 13¼x13**
2380    A1807 270w Horiz. pair, #a-
        b                             1.25  1.25

Historic
Trees
A1808

No. 2381: a, Zelkova tree at Segan-ri (Natural Monument No. 493) (22x50mm). b, Trifoli-
ate orange tree at Gapgot-ri (Natural Monument No. 78), horiz. (44x25mm). c, Spring
cherry tree at Hwaeomsa Temple (Natural
Monument No. 38) (22x50mm). d, Asian fringe
trees at Gwangyang-eup (Natural Monument
No. 235), horiz. (44x25mm).

**2012, Apr. 5    Litho.    Perf. 12¾**
2381    A1808 270w Block of 4, #a-
        d                             1.90   .95

Winning Art in Stamp Design Contest
A1809

No. 2382: a, Hearts in ski cap, by Yeonju
Chung. b, Children carrying rainbow, by Glen
M. Isaac.

**2012, Apr. 25    Photo.    Perf. 13¼x13**
2382    A1809 270w Horiz. pair, #a-
        b                             .95   .50

Expo 2012,
Yeosu — A1810

Nos. 2383 and 2384 — Expo 2012 emblem
and mascot, fish and: a, Korea Pavilion. b,
Theme Pavilion. c, Big-O. d, Sky Tower.

---

**2012, May 11**
2383       Horiz. strip of 4          1.90   .95
  *a.-d.*    A1810 270w Any single     .45   .25
          **Perf. 13x13¼**
2384       Horiz. strip of 4          1.90   .95
  *a.-d.*    A1810 270w Any single,
          26x36mm                      .45   .25

No. 2383 was printed in sheets containing
five strips. No. 2384 was printed in sheets of
10 containing two strips and two additional
examples of No. 2384d.

Korea Trade Investment Promotion
Agency (KOTRA), 50th
Anniv. — A1811

No. 2385: a, 50th anniversary emblem,
world map. b, Agency headquarters.

**2012, June 14            Perf. 13¼x13**
2385    A1811 270w Horiz. pair, #a-b  .95   .50

Gungnamji
Pond, Buyeo
A1812

Daegwallyeong Sheep
Ranch — A1813

Cheonjiyeon
Waterfalls,
Jeju Island
A1814

Dinosaur
Ridge, Mt.
Seoraksan
A1815

**2012, June 20            Perf. 13¼**
2386       Block of 4                 1.90   .95
  *a.*    A1812 270w multi            .45   .25
  *b.*    A1813 270w multi            .45   .25
  *c.*    A1814 270w multi            .45   .25
  *d.*    A1815 270w multi            .45   .25

2012 Summer Olympics,
London — A1816

No. 2387: a, Swimming, Tower Bridge. b,
Archery, Big Ben.

**2012, July 27            Perf. 13x13¼**
2387    A1816 270w Vert. pair, #a-b  .95   .50

Mask and
Ogyeon
Hall, Hahoe
Village
A1817

---

Hyangdan,
Yangdong
Village
A1818

**2012, July 12    Litho.    Perf. 13x13¼**
2388       Sheet of 10, 5 each
          #2388a-2388b              4.75  4.75
  *a.*    A1817 270w multi          .45   .45
  *b.*    A1818 270w multi          .45   .45

Historic Villages of Korea UNESCO World
Heritage Site.

Dinosaurs
A1819

No. 2384: a, Pachycephalosaurus. b, Tyrannosaurus. c, Oviraptor. d, Protoceratops.

*Perf. 13¼ Syncopated*
**2012, Aug. 8                      Litho.**
2389       Sheet of 12, 3 each
          # 2389a-2389d             12.00 12.00
  *a.-d.*   A1819 360w Any single    1.00  1.00

Philately
Week
A1820

No. 2390 — Paintings: a, The Back Alley, by
Dong Jin Seo (yellow green panel). b, Namhy-
angjip (A House Facing South), by Ji Ho Oh
(blue panel). c, Tugye (Cockfighting), by Joong
Seop Lee (pink panel). d, Chodong (Early
Winter), by Sang Beom Lee (dull orange
panel).

**2012, Aug. 9    Photo.    Perf. 13**
2390    A1820 270w Block of 4, #a-
        d                             1.90   .95
  *e.*    Souvenir sheet of 4, #2390a-
        2390d                         1.90   .95

World
Conservation
Congress, Jeju
Island — A1821

**2012, Sept. 6            Perf. 13¼**
2391    A1821 270w multi              .50   .25

A1822

A1823

A1824

A1825

Park Hyeokgeose
(69 B.C.-4 A.D.),
Silla Kingdom
Monarch
A1826

**2012, Nov. 21**     *Perf. 13x13¼*
2392    Horiz. strip of 5    2.50   1.25
   *a.*   A1822 270w multi    .50   .25
   *b.*   A1823 270w multi    .50   .25
   *c.*   A1824 270w multi    .50   .25
   *d.*   A1825 270w multi    .50   .25
   *e.*   A1826 270w multi    .50   .25

New Year 2013 (Year of
the Snake)
A1827     A1828

**2012, Dec. 3**     *Perf. 13x13¼*
2393   A1827 270w multi    .50   .25
2394   A1828 270w multi    .50   .25
   *a.*   Souvenir sheet of 2, #2393-
      2394     1.00   .50

Inauguration of 18th
President, Park
Geun-hye — A1830

**2013, Feb. 25**   **Photo.**   *Perf. 13¼*
2396   A1830 270w multi    .50   .25
   *a.*   Souvenir sheet of 2

Miniature Sheet

Characters in Robocar Poli — A1831

No. 2397: a, Roy the Fire Truck. b, Amber
the Ambulance. c, Poli the Police Car. d, Helly
the Helicopter. e, Dumpoo the Dump Truck. f,
Cap the Taxi. g, Posty the Postal Van. h,
Spooky the Tow Truck. i, School B the School
Bus. j, Cleany the Street Sweeper.

*Serpentine Die Cut 11½x9*
**2013, Mar. 12**     **Self-Adhesive**
2397   A1831   Sheet of 10    5.00
   *a.-j.*    270w Any single    .50   .25

Korean
Baseball
Players
A1832

No. 2398: a, Jang Hyo-Jo (1956-2011) at
bat. b, Choi Dong-Won (1958-2011) pitching.

**2013, Mar. 29**   **Photo.**   *Perf. 13¼x13*
2398   A1832 (270w) Pair, #a-b    —   —

Diplomatic Relations Between Peru
and South Korea, 50th
Anniv. — A1833

No. 2399: a, Seongsan Ilchulbong, South
Korea, South Korean and Peruvian flags at
LR. b, Machu Picchu, Peru, South Korean and
Peruvian flags at LL.

**2013, Apr. 1**   **Photo.**   *Perf. 13x13¼*
2399   A1833 270w Horiz. pair, #a-
     b     .95   .50
   See Peru No. 1810.

Suncheon Bay
Garden Expo
2013 — A1834

**2013, Apr. 19**   **Photo.**   *Perf. 13¾x13*
2400   A1834 270w multi    .50   .25

Information and
Communication
Day — A1835

No. 2401: a, Boy and girl holding envelope
with heart, satellite, smartphone (blue background). b, Mailbox with letter in slot, robot, girl
with parcels (orange yellow background). c,
Boy on satellite dish, girl on television with
legs (yellow background). d, Girl and robot in
rocket circling Earth (purple background).

**2013, Apr. 22**   **Photo.**   *Perf. 13¼x13*
2401    Horiz. strip of 4    2.00   1.00
   *a.-d.*   A1835 270w Any single    .50   .25

Law
Day — A1836

**2013, Apr. 25**   **Photo.**   *Perf. 13x13¼*
2402   A1836 270w multi    .50   .25

Restoration of
Sungnyemun
Gate — A1837

**2013, May 10**   **Litho.**   *Perf. 13¼x13*
2403   A1837 270w multi    .50   .25

Ahn Chang-ho
(1878-1938),
Founder of Young
Korean Academy
A1838

**2013, May 13**   **Photo.**   *Perf. 13x13¼*
2404   A1838 270w multi    .50   .25

Diplomatic Relations Between Slovakia
and South Korea, 20th
Anniv. — A1839

No. 2405: a, Pansori performers, South
Korea (woman and drummer). b, Lúcnica Art
Ensemble dancers, Slovakia.

**2013, May 31**   **Photo.**   *Perf. 13x13¼*
2405   A1839 270w Pair, #a-b    1.00   .50
   See Slovakia Nos. 663-664.

Diplomatic Relations Between
Germany and Korea, 130th
Anniv. — A1840

No. 2406: a, Gyeongbokgung Palace,
Seoul. b, Temple of the Sun, Bayreuth,
Germany.

**2013, June 5**   **Litho.**   *Perf. 12¾x13*
2406   A1840 270w Horiz. pair, #a-
     b     1.00   .50
   See Germany Nos. 2739-2740.

Energy Conservation — A1841

No. 2407: a, Leaves and smokestacks. b,
Coin entering slot in piggy bank with electric
cord as tail. c, Air conditioner and fans on balance with melting iceberg. d, Boy on stylized
bicycle.

**2013, June 26**   **Photo.**   *Perf. 13¼*
2407   A1841 270w Block or horiz.
     strip of 4, #a-
     d     2.00   1.00

Philately
Week — A1846

No. 2412: a, Girl writing letter. b, Girl placing
letter in mailbox. c, Boy with magnifying glass
examining stamp. d, Boy looking at stamp
album.
600w, Combined design elements of Nos.
2412a-2412d (108x26mm).

**2013, Aug. 8**   **Photo.**   *Perf. 13¼x13*
2412    Block or horiz. strip of
     4     2.25   1.25
   *a.-d.*   A1846 270w Any single    .55   .30

**Souvenir Sheet**
2413    Sheet of 2 #2413a    2.25   1.25
   *a.*   A1846 600w Single stamp    1.10   .60
   Philakorea 2014 World Stamp Exhibition,
Seoul.

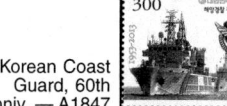

Korean Coast
Guard, 60th
Anniv. — A1847

**2013, Sept. 10**   **Photo.**   *Perf. 13x13¼*
2414   A1847 300w multi    .55   .30

Diplomatic Relations Between
Indonesia and South Korea, 40th
Anniv. — A1848

No. 2415: a, Small lion figure from Korean
folk play, large bull figure from Indonesian folk
play (denomination at left). b, Large lion figure,
small bull figure (denomination at UR).

**2013, Sept. 17**   **Photo.**   *Perf. 13x13¼*
2415   A1848 300w Pair, #a-b    1.10   .55
   See Indonesia No. 2363.

Conference on
Cyberspace,
Seoul — A1849

**2013, Oct. 17**   **Litho.**   *Perf. 13x13¼*
2416   A1849 300w multi    .55   .30

A1850

A1851

A1852

A1853

Onjo of the
Baekje
Kingdom — A1854

**2013, Nov. 20**   **Photo.**   *Perf. 13x13¼*
2417    Horiz. strip of 5    3.00   1.50
   *a.*   A1850 300w multi    .60   .30
   *b.*   A1851 300w multi    .60   .30
   *c.*   A1852 300w multi    .60   .30
   *d.*   A1853 300w multi    .60   .30
   *e.*   A1854 300w multi    .60   .30

New
Year
2014
(Year of
the
Horse)
A1855

No. 2418 — Snowflakes and: a, Close-up of
horse's head. b, Horses and heart (yellow
background). c, Line drawing of horse with
multicolored squares and rectangles in background. d, Boy inside of horse raising horse's
head.
No. 2419 — Combined designs of No. 2418
with cropped design of: a, No. 2418a at left. b,
No. 2418b at left. c, No. 2418c at left. d, No.
2418d at left.

**2013, Dec. 2**   **Photo.**   *Perf. 13¼*
2418   A1855 300w Block of 4, #a-
     d     2.40   1.25

**Souvenir Sheet**
2419   A1855 630w Sheet of 4, #a-
     d     5.00   2.50
   No. 2419 contains four 108x36mm stamps.

Miniature Sheet

Characters from *Larva* Animated
Television Series — A1856

No. 2420: a, Red at microphone. b, Pink
and flowers. c, Brown and dung ball. d, Black
with boxing gloves. e, Prussian (bird). f, Yellow
eating roll and sweating, Red. g, Red, Yellow
with open mouth. h, Yellow and Red with basketball. i, Red, Yellow holding lollipop. j, Yellow
with open mouth.

*Serpentine Die Cut 10*
**2014, Feb. 28**     **Photo.**
2420   A1856   Sheet of 10    9.50
   *a.-e.*    300w Any single    .55   .25
   *f.-h.*    390w Any single    .75   .35
   *i.*    400w multi    .75   .40
   *j.*    1930w multi    3.75   1.90

Cadastral
Resurveying
A1857

No. 2421: a, 300w, Map of South Korea, surveying equipment. b, 390w, Smart phone.

**2014, Mar. 20  Photo.  *Perf. 13¼x13***
2421  A1857  Pair, #a-b  1.40  .70

Poets
A1858

No. 2422: a, Han Yongun (1879-1944), pink background. b, Lee Yuksa (1904-44), green background. c, Yun Dongju (1917-45), blue background.

**2014, Apr. 9  Photo.  *Perf. 13x13¼***
2422  A1858  (300w) Horiz. strip of
3, #a-c  1.75  .85

Philakorea 2014 World Stamp
Exhibition, Seoul — A1859

No. 2423: a, 300w, Minhwa painting of birds and flowers. b, 300w, Hahoe wooden mask. c, 300w, Four Onggi pots. d, 300w, Neck of gayageum (stringed instrument). e, 300w, Baekja porcelain moon jar. f, 300w, Building roofs. g, 540w, Hanbok (traditional clothing). h, 540w, Hangeul (Korean text).

**2014, May 16  Litho.  *Perf. 13¼x13***
2423  A1859  Block of 8, #a-h  5.75  3.00

2014 World Cup
Soccer
Championships,
Brazil — A1860

No. 2424 — Emblem and: a, 300w, Player and ball running toward goal. b, 540w, Players and ball.

**2014, June 3  Photo.  *Perf. 13x13¼***
2424  A1860  Pair, #a-b  1.75  .85

2014 Intl. Congress
of Mathematics,
Seoul — A1861

No. 2425 — Person and: a, Pythagorean theorem. b, Leonhard Euler's trail (Seven Bridges of Königsburg problem). c, Blaise Pascal's triangle of binomial coefficients.

**2014, July 15  Photo.  *Perf. 13¼***
2425  Vert. strip of 3  2.25  1.10
a.-b.  A1861 300w Either single  .60  .30
c.  A1861 540w multi  1.00  .50

Printed in sheets containing 5 strips + 3 labels.

17th Asian Games,
Incheon — A1862

No. 2426: a, Cricket. b, Wrestling. c, Squash. d, Bowling. e, Gymnastics. f, Mascots.

**2014, July 31  Photo.  *Perf. 13¼x13***
2426  Horiz. strip of 6  4.50  2.25
a.-d.  A1862 300w Any single  .60  .30
e.-f.  A1862 540w Either single  1.00  .50

Printed in sheet containing 3 strips + 6 labels.

Arirang Dancer
A1863

No. 2427: a, Feet of Arirang dancer. b, Head and arms of Arirang dancer.

**2014, Aug. 7  Litho.  *Perf. 12¾***
**Thick Paper**
2427  A1863  Vert. pair  4.50  2.25
a.  300w multi  .60  .30
b.  1930w multi  3.75  1.90

Philately
Week
A1864

No. 2428: a, 300w, Bird with letter in tree. b, 300w, Family holding large stamps. c, 540w, Children making person out of stamps. d, 540w, Stamp train.

**2014, Aug. 8  Photo.  *Perf. 13¼***
2428  A1864  Block or horiz.
strip of 4, #a-d  3.50  1.75

Visit of
Pope
Francis
to South
Korea
A1865

No. 2429 — Pope Francis and: a, 300w, Coat of arms. b, 540w, Dove.

**2014, Aug. 8  Photo.  *Perf. 13¼x13***
2429  A1865  Pair, #a-b  1.75  .85

60th Baekje Cultural
Festival — A1866

No. 2430: a, 300w, Gold earrings, top of incense burner. b, 540w, Base of incense burner and pagoda.

**2014, Aug. 21  Photo.  *Perf. 13x13¼***
2430  A1866  Vert. pair, #a-b  1.75  .85

A1867

Conference of the parties to the Convention on biological diversity, Pyeongchang.

**2014, Sept. 16  Photo.  *Perf. 13¼x13***
2431  A1867  300w multi  .60  .30

Gwanggan
Bridge — A1868

Log Fence Near
House, Jeju
Island — A1869

Beacon
Towers — A1870

Emblem of 2014 International
Telecommunication Union
Plenipotentiary Conference,
Busan — A1871

**2014, Oct. 1  Photo.  *Perf. 13x13¼***
2432  Horiz. strip of 4  3.00  1.50
a.  A1868 300w multi  .60  .30
b.  A1869 300w multi  .60  .30
c.  A1870 300w multi  .60  .30
d.  A1871 540w multi  1.10  .55

Diplomatic
Relations
Between South
Korea and
Uruguay, 50th
Anniv. — A1872

Designs: No. 2433, Korean Nong-ak dancers and musicians. No. 2434, Uruguayan Candombe dancers and musicians.

**2014, Oct. 7  Photo.  *Perf. 13x13¼***
2433  A1872 300w multi  .55  .30
2434  A1872 540w multi  1.00  .50
a.  Horiz. pair, #2433-2434  1.60  .80

Nos. 2433-2434 were printed in sheets of 18 containing nine of each stamp. See Uruguay No. 2484.

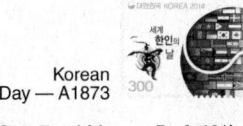

Korean
Day — A1873

**2014, Oct. 7  Litho.  *Perf. 13¼x13***
2435  A1873 300w multi  .55  .30

Period of Nine
Leaders — A1874

Turtle
Song — A1875

Six Golden
Eggs — A1876

Birth of King
Suro — A1877

Wedding of King
Suro — A1878

**2014, Nov. 20  Photo.  *Perf. 13x13¼***
2436  Horiz. strip of 5  3.75  1.75
a.  A1874 300w multi  .55  .25
b.  A1875 300w multi  .55  .25
c.  A1876 300w multi  .55  .25
d.  A1877 540w multi  1.00  .50
e.  A1878 540w multi  1.00  .50

Legend of King Suro of the Gaya Kingdom.

A1879

A1880

A1881

New Year 2015 (Year of
the Sheep) — A1882

**2014, Dec. 1  Litho.  *Perf. 14¼***
2437  Block or horiz. strip of 4  2.25  1.00
a.  A1879 300w multi  .55  .25
b.  A1880 300w multi  .55  .25
c.  A1881 300w multi  .55  .25
d.  A1882 300w multi  .55  .25
e.  Souvenir sheet of 4, #2437a-
2437d  2.25  1.00

**Miniature Sheet**

Constellations — A1883

No. 2438: a, Gemini (twins). b, Taurus (bull). c, Aries (ram). d, Pisces (fish). e, Aquarius (watere bearer). f, Capricorn (goat). g, Sagittarius (archer). h, Scorpio (scorpion). i, Libra (scales). j, Virgo (virgin). k, Leo (lion). l, Cancer (crab). m, Canis Major (dog). n, Cassiopeia (queen). o, Cygnus (swan). p, Boötes (herdsman with club).

Nos. 2438a-2438l (outer ring) are 31mm radially; Nos. 2438m-2438p are 26mm radially.

***Serpentine Die Cut 6¼ on 2 Sides***
**2015, Feb. 27  Litho.**
**Self-Adhesive**
2438  A1883  Sheet of 16 + 5
labels  9.00
a.-p.  300w Any single  .55  .25

Happy
School
Life
A1884

No. 2439 — Winning designs in stamp
design contest: a, Children at desks. b, School
roof, clock, faces of children. c, Children holding letter. d, Faces of children as puzzle
pieces.

**2015, Mar. 3        Litho.        Perf. 13¼**
2439  A1884 300w  Block of 4, #a-
                     d                        2.25  1.10

Seventh World Water
Forum, Daegu and
Gyeongbuk — A1885

**2015, Mar. 12    Litho.        Die Cut**
                    **Self-Adhesive**
2440  A1885 300w multi                 .55  .30

Endangered Wildlife — A1886

No. 2441: a, Female wolf and pups. b, Male
wolf.

**Litho. With Foil Application**
**2015, Mar. 26                    Perf. 14¼**
2441  A1886 300w Horiz. pair, #a-
                     b                        1.10  .55
   c.    Souvenir sheet of 2, #2441a-
          2441b                               1.10  .55

Scientists — A1887

No. 2442: a, Benjamin W. Lee (1935-77),
theoretical physicist (purple panel). b, Seok Ju
Myeong (1908-50), entomologist (pink panel).
c, Han Man Choon (1921-84), electrical engineer (green panel).

**Litho. With Foil Application**
**2015, Apr. 10                    Perf. 14**
2442    Horiz. strip of 3           1.75  .90
   a.-c.  A1887 (300w) Any single    .55  .30

Diplomatic
Relations
Between South
Korea and
Bolivia, 50th
Anniv. — A1888

No. 2443: a, Phibalura flavirostris. b,
Mergus squamatus.

**2015, Apr. 24    Litho.    Perf. 14x13½**
2443  A1888 (300w) Pair, #a-b      1.10  .55
          See Bolivia No. 1616.

Mangiyeoga
Seal
A1889

Ssangri Seal
A1890

Ucheonhasa
Seal — A1891

Hyangcheonsimjeongseohwajigi
Seal — A1892

**2015, May 15      Litho.       Perf. 14¼**
2444    Horiz. strip of 4          2.25  1.10
   a.   A1889 (300w) pur & multi    .55  .25
   b.   A1890 (300w) yel grn & multi .55  .25
   c.   A1891 (300w) pink & multi    .55  .25
   d.   A1892 (300w) turq grn & multi .55  .25
   e.   Souvenir sheet of 4, #2444a-
         2444d                       2.25  1.10

Seals of the Joseon Dynasty.

Major Sim Il
A1893

Captain Kim
Gyo-su
A1894

Vice Admiral
Son Won-il
(1909-80)
A1895

Brigadier
General Lee
Geun-seok
A1896

Police
Inspector
General Cha
Il-hyeok
A1897

General
James
Alward Van
Fleet (1892-
1992)
A1898

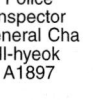

Lieutenant
Colonel
James Power
Carne (1906-
86)
A1899

First
Lieutenant
Jin Du-tae
A1900

Lieutenant
Colonel
Ralph
Monclar
(1892-1964)
A1901

Captain
William
Hamilton
Shaw (1922-
50)
A1902

**Serpentine Die Cut 6½ Vert.**
**2015, June 1                      Photo.**
                    **Self-Adhesive**
2445    Block of 10                5.50
   a.   A1893 (300w) multi          .55  .25
   b.   A1894 (300w) multi          .55  .25
   c.   A1895 (300w) multi          .55  .25
   d.   A1896 (300w) multi          .55  .25
   e.   A1897 (300w) multi          .55  .25

   f.   A1898 (300w) multi          .55  .25
   g.   A1899 (300w) multi          .55  .25
   h.   A1900 (300w) multi          .55  .25
   i.    A1901 (300w) multi          .55  .25
   j.    A1902 (300w) multi          .55  .25
          Heroes of the Korean War.

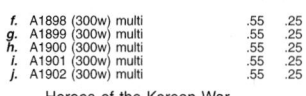

Tourist Destinations — A1903

No. 2446: a, Aerial view of Yeongwol Dong-
gang River. b, Aerial view of Chungju
Chungjuho Lake. c, Confluence of Namhan-
gang and Bukhangang Rivers. d, Rocks of
Goesan Hwayang Gugok.

**2015, June 3      Litho.      Perf. 14x13½**
2446  A1903 (300w) Block or
                     horiz. strip
                     of 4, #a-d        2.25  1.10

2015 Universiade,
Gwangju — A1904

No. 2447: a, Mascot. b, Soccer and stadium. c, Rhythmic gymnastics, Asian Culture
Complex. c, Taekwondo, Ipseokdae Rock.

**2015, June 23    Litho.     Perf. 13½x14**
2447    Horiz. strip of 4          2.25  1.00
   a.-d.  A1904 (300w) Any single    .55  .25
   e.    Souvenir sheet of 4, #2447a-
          2447d                      2.25  1.00

Silk Road
Cultural
Festival,
Gyeongju
A1905

**2015, July 10     Litho.     Perf. 14x13½**
2448  A1905 (300w) multi            .55  .25

Emblem
A1906

President Kim
Koo (1876-
1949)
A1907

**Serpentine Die Cut 10½ on 2 Sides**
**2015, Aug. 4                        Litho.**
                    **Self-Adhesive**
2449  A1906 (300w) multi            .50  .25
2450  A1907 (300w) multi            .50  .25
   a.   Horiz. pair, #2449-2450     1.00
   b.   Souvenir sheet of 2, #2449-
         2450                        1.00

Bamboo Forest
in
Snow — A1908

Bamboo
Stem — A1909

Bamboo
Forest — A1910

Bamboo
Shoots — A1911

**2015, Aug. 13      Litho.        Perf. 14**
2451    Block of 4                  2.00  1.00
   a.   A1908 (300w) multi          .50  .25
   b.   A1909 (300w) multi          .50  .25
   c.   A1910 (300w) multi          .50  .25
   d.   A1911 (300w) multi          .50  .25

   Nos. 2451a-2451d are impregnated with a
bamboo scent.

Lee Byung-chul
(1910-87),
Founder of
Samsung
Group — A1912

Chung Ju-yung
(1915-2001),
Founder of
Hyundai
Groups — A1913

**Litho. & Embossed**
**2015, Aug. 26                Perf. 14x13½**
2452    Horiz. pair                 1.00  .50
   a.   A1912 (300w) multi          .50  .25
   b.   A1913 (300w) multi          .50  .25

World Military Games,
Mungyeong — A1914

No. 2453: a, Skydivers. b, Shooting. c, Mascots. d, Pentathlon competitors scaling wall.

**2015, Sept. 16    Litho.    Perf. 13x13¼**
2453  A1914 (300w) Block or
                     horiz. strip
                     of 4, #a-d        2.10  1.10

A1915

Personalized
Stamps — A1916

**2015, Sept. 21    Photo.      Perf. 13¼**
2454  A1915 (300w) gray & black    —    —
                                **Perf. 13¼x13½**
2455  A1916 (300w) gray & black    —    —

   No. 2454 was printed in sheets of 14 + central label. No. 2455 was printed in sheets of 6
+ label and sheets of 20. Vignette area of
stamp could be personalized. The images
shown above are some of many stamps produced and sold by Korea Post on their personalized stamp creation apparatus.

Namhansanseong UNESCO World
Heritage Site — A1917

No. 2456 — Aerial view of buildings and: a,
Courtyard (49x33mm). b, Gate (49x21mm).

**Perf. 13¾x13¼**
**2015, Oct. 29          Litho. & Engr.**
2456  A1917 (300w) Vert. pair,
                     #a-b              1.10  .55

Post Culture Week
A1918

No. 2457 — Winning art in stamp design contest: a, Open envelope, musical notes, posthorn. b, People and envelope on snail. c, Children following mailman on bicycle. d, Children and large mailbox.

**2015, Nov. 18    Litho.    Perf. 13x13¼**
2457  A1918  (300w)  Block of 4,
        #a-d                    2.10 1.10

**Souvenir Sheet**

New Year 2016 (Year of the Monkey)
A1919

Designs: Nos. 2458a, 2459a, Monkey in tree. Nos. 2458b, 2459b, Six monkeys, gifts and flowers.

**2015, Dec. 1    Litho.    Perf. 14½x14¾**
2458  A1919  (300w)  Sheet of 2,
        #a-b                    1.10  .55

**Self-Adhesive**
*Serpentine Die Cut 9x9¼*
2459  A1919          Horiz. pair    1.10
  *a.-b.*  (300w) Either single      .55  .25

Korea Institute of Science and Technology, 50th Anniv. — A1920

No. 2460: a, Technician and machinery. b, Building and monument.

**2016, Feb. 4    Litho.    Perf. 13x13¼**
2460  A1920  300w  Pair, #a-b    1.00  .50

Lutra Lutra
A1921

No. 2461: a, Adult and juveniles. b, Head of animal.

**Litho. With Foil Application**
**2016, Mar. 15          Perf. 14¼x14**
2461  A1921  390w  Horiz. pair, #a-
        b                        1.40  .70
  *c.*  Souvenir sheet of 2, #2461a-
        2461b                   1.40  .70

A1922

Winning Art in International Stamp Design Contest — A1923

No. 2462: a, People painting peace dove on wall. b, Peace dove over rainbow. c, Children, trees, peace sign. d, Peace dove as balloon.
No. 2463: a, Man wearing seat belt. b, Woman and child in rain. c, Earth as person's head. d, People in floating hard hat.

**2016, Mar. 24    Litho.    Perf. 13x13¼**
2462  A1922  300w  Block of 4, #a-
        d                        2.10 1.10
2463  A1923  300w  Block of 4, #a-
        d                        2.10 1.10

Scientists — A1924

No. 2464: a, Jang Yeong-sil (1390-1443), mechanical engineer. b, Heo Jun (1538-1615), physician. c, Ree Taikyue (1902-92), chemist.

**Litho. With Foil Application**
**2016, Apr. 21          Perf. 14¼x14**
2464  A1924  300w  Horiz. strip of
        3, #a-c                 1.60  .80

Won Buddhism, Cent. — A1925

**Litho. & Embossed With Foil Application**
**2016, Apr. 28          Perf. 13x13¼**
2465  A1925  300w  multi         .55  .30

2016 Rotary International Convention, Goyang — A1926

**2016, May 2    Litho.    Perf. 13¼x13**
2466  A1926  300w  multi         .55  .30

Sorokdo National Hospital, Cent. A1927

No. 2467 — Building and: a, Statue. b, Joined hands.

**2016, May 17    Litho.    Perf. 13¾**
2467  A1927  300w  Pair, #a-b    1.00  .50

Nam Ja-hyeon (1872-1933), Female Military Leader — A1928

Ju Si-gyeong (1876-1914), Independence Activist — A1929

**Serpentine Die Cut 12 Vert.**
**2016, June 1                    Litho.**
**Self-Adhesive**
2468          Horiz. pair        1.00
  *a.*  A1928  300w multi          .50  .25
  *b.*  A1929  300w multi          .50  .25

Diplomatic Relations Betwen France and Korea, 130th Anniv. — A1930

No. 2469: a, Korean Celadon incense burner, 12th cent. b, French reliquary.

**2016, June 3    Litho.    Perf. 13¼x14**
2469  A1930  300w  Horiz. pair, #a-
        b                        1.10  .55
  See France Nos. 5043-5044.

Stephen Kim Su-hwan (1922-2009), Cardinal
A1931

Master Seongcheol (1912-93), Buddhist Monk
A1932

**Perf. 13½x12¾**
**2016, June 27                    Litho.**
2470  A1931  300w  multi         .55  .30
2471  A1932  300w  multi         .55  .30

Mailboxes of the World — A1933

No. 2472 — Mailboxes from: a, Brazil, People's Republic of China, and Canada. b, France, India, and Japan. c, Mexico, Malaysia, and New Zealand. d, Switzerland, United States, and United Kingdom.

**Serpentine Die Cut 8¾ at Right**
**2016, July 19                    Litho.**
**Self-Adhesive**
2472  A1933      Block of 4, #a-d  2.25
  *a.-d.*  300w Any single          .55  .30

Tourism
A1934

No. 2473: a, Hadong Simri Cherry Blossom Road. b, Yeongdeok Blue Road. c, Jeju Olle Trail. d, Woljeongsan Jeonnamu Forest Trail.

**2016, Aug. 12    Litho.    Perf. 13¼**
2473  A1934  300w  Block or horiz.
        strip of 4,
        #a-d                     2.25 1.10

Lighthouses — A1935

No. 2474: a, Oryukdo Lighthouse. b, Ulgi Lighthouse. c, Somaemuldo Lighthouse. d, Eocheongdo Lighthouse.

**Litho. With Foil Application**
**2016, Aug. 25          Perf. 13½**
2474  A1935  300w  Block or horiz.
        strip of 4, #a-
        d                        2.25 1.10

Painting by Lee Jung-Seop (1916-56)
A1936

**Litho. With Foil Application**
**2016, Sept. 1          Perf. 14x13¼**
2475  A1936  300w  multi         .55  .30

Gold Crowns
A1937

No. 2476 — Background color: a, Purple. b, Green. c, Red. d, Blue.

**Litho. & Embossed With Foil Application**
**2016, Sept. 21          Perf. 14x13¼**
2476  A1937  300w  Block or horiz.
        strip of 4, #a-
        d                        2.25 1.10

Kia Tigers Cap and Mascot — A1938

Nexen Heroes Cap and Mascot — A1939

Doosan Bears Cap and Mascot — A1940

Lotte Giants Cap and Mascot — A1941

Samsung Lions Cap and Mascot — A1942

NC Dinos Cap and Mascot — A1943

SK Wyverns Cap and Mascot — A1944

LG Twins Cap and Mascot — A1945

KT Wiz Cap and Mascot — A1946

Hanhwa Eagles Cap and Mascot — A1947

**Litho. & Embossed With Foil Application**
**Serpentine Die Cut 12 At Bottom**
**2016, Oct. 7          Self-Adhesive**
2477          Sheet of 10        5.50
  *a.*  A1938  300w multi          .55  .30
  *b.*  A1939  300w multi          .55  .30
  *c.*  A1940  300w multi          .55  .30
  *d.*  A1941  300w multi          .55  .30
  *e.*  A1942  300w multi          .55  .30
  *f.*  A1943  300w multi          .55  .30
  *g.*  A1944  300w multi          .55  .30
  *h.*  A1945  300w multi          .55  .30
  *i.*  A1946  300w multi          .55  .30
  *j.*  A1947  300w multi          .55  .30

Korean Baseball Organization League teams.

Baekje
Historic
Areas
UNESCO
World
Heritage
Site
A1949

**Perf. 13¾x13½**

**2016, Oct. 28      Litho. & Engr.**
| | | | |
|---|---|---|---|
| 2478 | | Sheet of 10, 5 each | |
| | | #2478a-2478b | 17.50 8.50 |
| a. | A1948 | 1000w multi | 1.75 .85 |
| b. | A1949 | 1000w multi | 1.75 .85 |

A1950

A1951

A1952

Joseon Dynasty
Seals — A1953

**2016, Nov. 10    Litho.     Perf. 14¼**
| | | | |
|---|---|---|---|
| 2479 | | Horiz. strip of 4 | 2.20 1.20 |
| a. | A1950 | 300w multi | .55 .30 |
| b. | A1951 | 300w multi | .55 .30 |
| c. | A1952 | 300w multi | .55 .30 |
| d. | A1953 | 300w multi | .55 .30 |
| e. | | Souvenir sheet of 4, #2479a-2479d | 2.20 1.20 |

Animals in the
Demilitarized
Zone — A1954

No. 2480: a, Great tit on barbed wire. b, Black-faced spoonbills.

**2016, Nov. 22   Litho.   Perf. 14x13½**
| | | | |
|---|---|---|---|
| 2480 | A1954 | 300w Pair, #a-b | 1.10 .55 |

New Year 2017 (Year of the Rooster)
A1955

No. 2481 — Rooster and: a, Snowflakes. b, Sun.

**Litho. & Embossed With Foil Application**

**2016, Dec. 1       Perf. 13¾**
| | | | |
|---|---|---|---|
| 2481 | A1955 | 300w Pair, #a-b | 1.10 .55 |
| c. | | Souvenir sheet of 4, 2 each #2481a-2481b | 2.20 1.10 |

Kim Bong-
ryong (1902-
94), Inlayer of
Mother-of-
Pearl
A1956

Kim Jeom-sun
(1918-2008),
Hemp Weaver
A1957

Lee Chi-ho
(1910-2006),
Ornament
Painter
A1958

Cheong Sang-
won (1926-
2003),
Furniture
Maker
A1959

**Litho. With Foil Application**

**2017, Jan. 25       Perf. 14¼**
| | | | |
|---|---|---|---|
| 2482 | | Block or horiz. strip of 4 | 2.20 1.20 |
| a. | A1956 | 300w multi | .55 .30 |
| b. | A1957 | 300w multi | .55 .30 |
| c. | A1958 | 300w multi | .55 .30 |
| d. | A1959 | 300w multi | .55 .30 |

**Miniature Sheet**

Webtoons — A1960

No. 2483: a, I Love You, by Kang Full (elderly couple on motorcycle, 39x36mm). b, With God, by Ju Homin (three people in traditional costumes, 35x40mm). c, Incomplete Life, by Yoon Taeho (man with briefcase, 36x37mm). d, The Sound of Your Heart, by Cho Seok (man, woman and dogs, 40x40mm).

**Serpentine Die Cut 9**

**2017, Feb. 10          Litho.**

**Self-Adhesive**
| | | | |
|---|---|---|---|
| 2483 | A1960 | Sheet of 4 | 2.20 |
| a.-d. | | 300w Any single | .55 .30 |

Nemorhaedus Caudatus — A1961

No. 2484: a, Adult and juvenile gorals. b, Head of goral.

**Litho. With Foil Application**

**2017, Feb. 20       Perf. 14¼**
| | | | |
|---|---|---|---|
| 2484 | A1961 | 300w Horiz. pair, #a-b | 1.10 .55 |
| c. | | Souvenir sheet of 2, #2484a-2484b | 1.10 .55 |

**Miniature Sheet**

Astronomy — A1962

No. 2485: a, Aurora Borealis (41x31mm curved rectangle). b, Horsehead Nebula (denomination at left above star 37x35mm oval). c, Triangulanum Galaxy (denomination just above left end of inscription, 37x35mm oval). d, Messier 81 (spiral galaxy, denomination above middle of lower inscription, 37x37mm oval). e, Messier 82 (denomination above right end of inscription, 37x35mm oval). f, Orion Nebula (denomination above middle of lower inscription, 37x35mm oval). g, Observatory (51x25mm semicircle). h, Pleaides

(36x36mm pentagon). i, Comet Lovejoy (36x36mm star). j, Rosette Nebula (37mm diameter).

***Serpentine Die Cut, Serpentine Die
Cut 11½ Vert. (#2485a), Serpentine
Die Cut 11 (#2485g), Serpentine Die
Cut 11½ (#2485h, 2485i)***
**Litho. With Foil Application**
**2017, Mar. 21       Self-Adhesive**
| | | | |
|---|---|---|---|
| 2485 | A1962 | Sheet of 10 | 5.50 |
| a.-j. | | 300w Any single | .55 .30 |

Flag
A1963

Hibiscus
A1964

Buncheong Jar — A1965

**2017, Apr. 3   Photo.   Perf. 12¾x13½**
| | | | |
|---|---|---|---|
| 2486 | A1963 | 330w multi | .60 .30 |
| 2487 | A1964 | 420w multi | .75 .40 |

**Perf. 13½**
| | | | |
|---|---|---|---|
| 2488 | A1965 | 1960w multi | 3.50 1.75 |
| | | Nos. 2486-2488 (3) | 4.85 2.45 |

**Self-Adhesive**
***Serpentine Die Cut 11½***
| | | | |
|---|---|---|---|
| 2489 | A1963 | 330w multi | .60 .30 |
| 2490 | A1964 | 420w multi | .75 .40 |

A map of the Korean Peninsula is laser cut in the lower right corner of No. 2488.

Woodang (Lee
Hoe-yeong, 1862-
1932), Nationalist
Leader — A1966

**2017, Apr. 21   Litho.   Perf. 13x12¾**
| | | | |
|---|---|---|---|
| 2491 | A1966 | 330w multi | .60 .30 |

King Sejong
(1397-1450)
A1967

Choi Mu-
seon (1325-
95), Inventor
and Military
Commander
A1968

Woo Jang-chan (1898-
1959), Botanist — A1969

**2017, Apr. 27    Litho.    Perf. 14**
| | | | |
|---|---|---|---|
| 2492 | | Strip of 3 | 1.80 .90 |
| a. | A1967 | 330w multi | .60 .30 |
| b. | A1968 | 330w multi | .60 .30 |
| c. | A1969 | 330w multi | .60 .30 |

Members of Korean Science and Technology Hall of Fame.

Winning
Art in
Postage
Stamp
Design
Contest
A1970

No. 2493: a, Love of Hedgehogs, by Lee Su-jeong. b, My Home Filled With Love, by Jeong-Seo-han. c, A Family's Laughter, by Jang-Suk-yeong. d, The Happiness a Letter Brings, by Im Yu-ra.

**2017, May 2     Litho.     Perf. 13**
| | | | |
|---|---|---|---|
| 2493 | A1970 | 330w Block of 4, #a-d | 2.40 1.25 |

Hearts are laser cut on Nos. 2493a-2493d.

Soswaewon
Garden
A1971

Mungyeongsaejae Pass — A1972

Ullimsanbang
Villa and
Gardens
A1973

Jinjuseong
Fortress
A1974

**2017, May 15     Litho.     Perf. 13¼**
| | | | |
|---|---|---|---|
| 2494 | | Block of 4 | 2.40 1.20 |
| a. | A1971 | 330w multi | .60 .30 |
| b. | A1972 | 330w multi | .60 .30 |
| c. | A1973 | 330w multi | .60 .30 |
| d. | A1974 | 330w multi | .60 .30 |

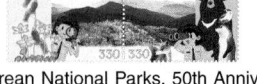

Korean National Parks, 50th Anniv.,
and National Parks Service, 30th
Anniv.
A1975

No. 2495 — Park ranger with: a, Magnifying glass and flowers. b, Binoculars, flowers and wildlife.

**Litho. With Foil Application**
**2017, May 29      Perf. 13x13¼**
| | | | |
|---|---|---|---|
| 2495 | A1975 | 330w Horiz. pair, #a-b | 1.20 .60 |

Wildlife in the
Demilitarized
Zone — A1976

No. 2496: a, Squirrel and army helmet. b, Kingfisher on barbed wire.

**2017, June 5    Litho.    Perf. 14x13½**
| | | | |
|---|---|---|---|
| 2496 | A1976 | 330w Pair, #a-b | 1.20 .60 |

Iron powder particles are affixed to No. 2496a.

2017 World
Taekwondo
Championships,
Muju — A1977

**2017, June 16   Litho.   Perf. 13x13½**
| | | | |
|---|---|---|---|
| 2497 | A1977 | 330w multi | .60 .30 |

Kim Tong-ni (1913-95), Writer — A1978

Pak Kyongni (1926-2008), Writer — A1979

**2017, June 27  Litho.   Perf. 13¼**
2498 A1978 330w multi          .60   .30
2499 A1979 330w multi          .60   .30

Korean Independence Hall, 30th Anniv. — A1980

No. 2500: a, Independence Hall and "30." b, Statue of Indomitable Koreans.

**Litho. & Embossed**
**2017, Aug. 1              Perf. 14**
2500 A1980 330w Pair, #a-b    1.20   .60

A1981

Inauguration of Pres. Moon Jae-in — A1982

**2017, Aug. 17  Photo.   Perf. 13¼x13**
2501 A1981 330w multi          .60   .30

**Souvenir Sheet**
2502 A1982 420w multi          .75   .40

A1983          A1984

A1985

Joseon Dynasty Seals — A1986

**2017, Sept. 1  Litho.   Perf. 14x14¼**
2503      Horiz. strip of 4      2.40  1.25
  a.  A1983 330y multi          .60   .30
  b.  A1984 330y multi          .60   .30
  c.  A1985 330y multi          .60   .30
  d.  A1986 330y multi          .60   .30
  e.  Souvenir sheet of 4, #2503a-
      2503d                     2.40  1.25

A1987

A1988

A1989

Highways A1990

**Litho. With Foil Application**
**2017, Sept. 28           Perf. 13½**
2504  Block or horiz. strip of 4  2.40  1.20
  a.  A1987 330w multi          .60   .30
  b.  A1988 330w multi          .60   .30
  c.  A1989 330w multi          .60   .30
  d.  A1990 330w multi          .60   .30

A1991

Namsadang Nori UNESCO Intangible Cultural Heritage A1992

**Litho. & Engr. With Foil Application**
**2017, Oct. 27         Perf. 13¾x13½**
2505      Sheet of 10, 5 each     6.00  3.00
      #2505a-2505b
  a.  A1991 330w gold & multi   .60   .30
  b.  A1992 330w gold & multi   .60   .30

**Miniature Sheets**

A1993

2018 Winter Olympics, Pyeongchang — A1994

No. 2506: a, Alpensia Ski Jumping Center. b, Mascot marching. c, Emblem of 2018 Winter Olympics. d, Mascot alpine skiing. e, Mascot in biathlon. f, Mascots in two-man bobsled. g, Mascot cross-country skiing. h, Mascot curling. i, Mascot figure skating. j, Mascot freestyle skiing.

No. 2507: a, PyeongChang Olympic Stadium. b, Mascot with arms extended. c, Mascot playing ice hockey. d, Mascot on luge. e, Mascots in Nordic combined skiing event. f, Mascot in short track speed skating event. g, Mascot on skeleton. h, Mascot ski jumping. i, Mascot snowboarding. j, Mascot speed skating.

**2017, Nov. 1  Litho.   Perf. 13x13¼**
2506 A1993    Sheet of 10        6.00  3.00
  a.-j.  330w Any single        .60   .30
2507 A1994    Sheet of 10        6.00  3.00
  a.-j.  330w Any single        .60   .30

Diplomatic Relations Between South Korea and Sri Lanka, 40th Anniv. — A1995

No. 2508: a, Korean dancer (green background). b, Sri Lankan dancer (blue background).

**2017, Nov. 14  Litho.   Perf. 13¼x13**
2508 A1995 330w Pair, #a-b    1.20   .60

See Sri Lanka Nos. 2121-2122.

Snail Mailing Letter A1996

Chrysalis on Mailbox A1997

Chrysalis Under Mailbox A1998

Mailbox, Butterfly and Snail A1999

**2017, Nov. 21  Litho.   Perf. 13¾**
2509      Horiz. strip of 4      2.40  1.20
  a.  A1996 330w multi          .60   .30
  b.  A1997 330w multi          .60   .30
  c.  A1998 330w multi          .60   .30
  d.  A1999 330w multi          .60   .30

New Year 2018 (Year of the Dog) A2000

No. 2510: a, Five dogs. b, Dog and snowflakes.

**Litho. With Holographic Foil**
**2017, Dec. 1             Perf. 13x13¼**
2510 A2000 330w Pair, #a-b    1.20   .60
  c.  Souvenir sheet of 4, 2 each
      #2510a-2510b             2.40  1.20

**Miniature Sheet**

2018 Winter Paralympics, Pyeongchang — A2001

No. 2511: a, Emblem of the 2018 Winter Paralympics. b, Torch. c, Mascot with Paralympics Alpine ski. d, Mascot in Paralympics arabiathlon. e, Mascot Paralympics cross-country skiing. f, Mascot carrying torch. g, Mascot with arm extended. h, Mascot playing Paralympics ice hockey. i, Mascot on Paralympics snowboard. j, Mascot in wheelchair curling event.

**2018, Jan. 18  Litho.   Perf. 13**
2511 A2001    Sheet of 10        6.00  3.00
  a.-j.  330w Any single        .60   .30

Opening of 2018 Winter Olympics, Pyeongchang — A2002

No. 2512: a, Olympic torch. b, Gold, silver and bronze medals.

**2018, Feb. 9  Litho.   Perf. 13x13¼**
2512 A2002 330w Horiz. pair, #a-
           b                    1.25   .60

Join Our Hands, by Chan Wing Chi A2003

From Person to Person, by Hong Seo-jeong A2004

One Flame, by Moon Seo-hyun A2005

Create the World Together, by Kim Si-hyun A2006

A Bicycle Through Which We Become One, by Park Kyeong-jin — A2007

**2018, Feb. 22  Litho.   Perf. 13¼**
2513      Horiz. strip of 5      3.00  1.50
  a.  A2003 330w multi          .60   .30
  b.  A2004 330w silver & multi .60   .30
  c.  A2005 330w silver & multi .60   .30
  d.  A2006 330w multi          .60   .30
  e.  A2007 330w multi          .60   .30

Winning art in public stamp design contest.

Members of Korea Science and Technology Hall of Fame — A2008

No. 2514: a, Gim Jeong-ho (1804-66), cartographer (orange panel). b, Yi Cheon (1376-1451), engineer (violet panel). c, Choi Hyeong-sup (1920-2004), president of Korea Institute of Science and Technology (green blue panel).

**Litho. With Foil Application**
**2018, Mar. 21            Perf. 14**
2514 A2008 330w Vert. strip of 3,
           #a-c                2.00  1.00

University of Seoul, Cent. — A2009

**2018, Apr. 2  Litho.   Perf. 14x13¼**
2515 A2009 330w multi          .65   .30

Musicians — A2010

No. 2516: a, Kim Chun-heung (1909-2007), yanggeum player (brown background). b, Shin Kwae-dong (1910-77), geomungo player (dull violet blue background). c, Kim Yun-deok (1918-78), gaygeum player (reddish purple background).

**Litho. With Foil Application**
**2018, Apr. 30**            **Perf. 13¼x14**
2516  A2010 330w Vert. strip of 3,
                  #a-c            2.00 1.00

Miniature Sheets

A2011

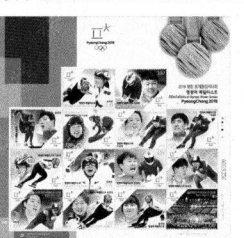

South Korean 2018 Winter Olympics Medalists — A2012

No. 2517: a, Olympic cauldron. b, Kyeong-ae Kim, curling silver medalist. c, Dong-hyun Kim, bobsledding silver medalist. d, Min-seok Kim, speed skating silver amd bronze medalist. e, Bo-reum Kim, speed skating silver medalist. f, Seon-yeong Kim, curling silver medalist. g, A-lang Kim, speed skating gold medalist. h, Yeong-mi Kim, curling silver medalist. i, Ye-jin Kim, speed skating gold medalist. j, Eun-jung Kim, curling gold medalist. k, Cho-hi Kim, curling silver medalist. l, Tae-yun Kim, speed skating bronze medalist. m, Young-woo Seo, bobsledding silver medalist. n, Yi-ra Seo, speed skating bronze medalist.
No. 2518: a, Suk-hee Shim, speed skating gold medalist. b, Yun-jong Won, bobsledding silver medalist. c, Sung-bin Yun, skeleton gold medalist. d, Sang-ho Lee, snowboarding silver medalist. e, Sang-hwa Lee, speed skating silver medalist. f, Seung-hoon Lee, speed skating gold and silver medalist. g, Yu-bin Lee, speed skating gold medalist. h, Hyo-jun Lim, speed skating gold and bronze medalist. i, Jung-lin Jun, bobsledding silver medalist. j, Jae-won chung, speed skating silver medalist. k, Min-kyu Cha, speed skating silver medalist. l, Min-jeong Choi, speed skating gold medalist. m, Dae-heon Hwang, speed skating silver medalist. n, Closing ceremony.

**2018, May 4    Photo.    Perf. 13x13¼**
2517  A2011    Sheet of 14    8.50 4.25
 *a.-n.*      330y Any single          .60   .30
2518  A2012    Sheet of 14    8.50 4.25
 *a.-n.*      330y Any single          .60   .30

Democratic Elections in South Korea, 70th Anniv. — A2013

No. 2519: a, People going to polling places. b, Building.

**Litho. With Foil Application**
**2018, May 10**            **Perf. 14x13¾**
2519  A2013 330w Pair, #a-b    1.25  .60

Mudeungsan Mountain A2014

Bukhansan Mountain A2015

Juwangsan Mountain A2016

Taebaeksan Mountain A2017

**Litho. With Stone Grit Affixed**
**2018, May 24**            **Perf. 14x13½**
2520    Block or horiz. strip of 4  2.60 1.25
 *a.*  A2014 330w multi          .65   .30
 *b.*  A2015 330w multi          .65   .30
 *c.*  A2016 330w multi          .65   .30
 *d.*  A2017 330w multi          .65   .30

Miniature Sheet

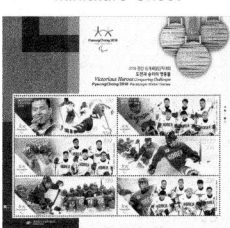

South Korean Paralympians at 2018 Winter Paralympics — A2018

No. 2521: a, Paralympian holding medal, Paralympic skiiers. b, Paralympic ice hockey players wearing white uniforms, red area at left. c, Paralympic ice hockey players, two players with helmets touching at left. d, Paralympic ice hockey players in action, puck on goal line near goal. e, Paralympic ice hockey players wearing blue uniforms, gathered near net at right. f, One Paralympic ice hockey player wearing blue uniform, six with white uniforms.

**2018, May 31    Litho.    Perf. 13x13¼**
2521  A2018    Sheet of 6    3.75 1.90
 *a.-f.*     330y Any single          .60   .30

Crafts A2019

No. 2522: a, Three Chaesang bamboo boxes. b, Embroidered flowers. c, Braided string tassels. d, Traditional clothing.

**Litho. & Embossed With Foil Application**
**2018, June 1**            **Perf. 14x14¼**
2522  A2019 330w Block of 4,
                  #a-d            2.60 1.25

Nature in the Demilitarized Zone — A2020

No. 2523: a, Flowers sprouting through crack in army helmet. b, Deer near fence.

**2018, June 25   Litho.   Perf. 14x13¼**
2523  A2020 330w Pair, #a-b    1.25  .60

Protected Wildlife — A2021

No. 2524: a, Tursiops aduncus. b, Neophocaena asiaeorientalis. c, Phoca largha. d, Callorhinus ursinus.

**Litho. With Foil Application**
**2018, July 10**            **Perf. 13¼**
2524  A2021 330w Block of 4,
                  #a-d            2.40 1.25

Painters A2022

No. 2525: a, Park Sookeun (1914-65), painting of woman. b, Chang Ucchin (1917-90), painting of bird.

**Litho. With Foil Application**
**2018, July 25**            **Perf. 14x14¼**
2525  A2022 330w Pair, #a-b    1.25  .60

Porcelain Jar — A2023

**2018, Aug. 1  Photo.  Perf. 13¾x13½**
2526  A2023 2130w multi        4.00 2.00

A map of the Korean Peninsula is laser cut in the lower right corner of No. 2526.

Yun Bong-gil (1908-32), Hongkew Park, Shanghai Bomber, and Yun Bong-gil Memorial Hall, Shanghai A2024

Ahn Chang-ho (1876-1938), Korean Independence Activist, and Korean National Association Memorial Hall, Los Angeles — A2025

Yi Jun (1859-1907), Diplomat, and Yi Jun Peace Museum, The Hague, Netherlands A2026

Ahn Jung-geun (1879-1910), Assassin of Hirobumi Ito, and Ahn Jung-geun Memorial Hall, Harbin, People's Republic of China — A2027

**Litho. With Foil Application**
**2018, Aug. 6**            **Perf. 13x13¼**
2527    Block or strip of 4    2.40 1.25
 *a.*  A2024 330w multi          .60   .30
 *b.*  A2025 330w multi          .60   .30
 *c.*  A2026 330w multi          .60   .30
 *d.*  A2027 330w multi          .60   .30

19th World Amateur Radio Direction Finding Championships, Sokcho-si A2028

                           **Perf. 13¼x13½**
**2018, Aug. 31**                    **Litho.**
2528  A2028 330w multi          .60   .30

Portions of the design were printed with thermochromic ink which changes color when warmed.

Chung-Ang University, Seoul, Cent. — A2029

**Litho. With Foil Application**
**2018, Sept. 3**            **Perf. 13¼x13½**
2529  A2029 330w multi          .60   .30

13th World Firefighters Games, Chungju — A2030

**2018, Sept. 10  Litho.   Perf. 13x13¼**
2530  A2030 330w multi          .60   .30

Summit Meeting of North Korean Chairman Kim Jong Un and South Korean Pres. Moon Jae-in — A2031

**2018, Sept. 12    Photo.    Perf. 13¼**
2531  A2031 330w multi          .60   .30

Publication of *Mokminsimseo,* and Return of Its Author, Dasan (1762-1836) From Exile, 200th Anniv. — A2032

**2018, Sept. 14    Litho.    Perf. 14¼**
2532  A2032 330w multi          .60   .30

Universal Declaration of Human Rights, 70th Anniv. — A2033

**2018, Oct. 1    Litho.    Perf. 13x13¼**
2533 A2033 330w multi              .60    .30

Postal Culture Week A2034

No. 2534 — Calligraphy with denomination at: a, LL. b, UR.

**Litho. With Foil Application**
**2018, Oct. 2        Perf. 13¾x13¼**
2534 A2034 330w Horiz. pair,
        #a-b              1.25    .60

Hong Beom-do (1868-1943), General — A2035

**2018, Oct. 12    Litho.    Perf. 14x13¼**
2535 A2035 330w multi            .60    .30

Lions A2036

No. 2536: a, Korean incense burner cover, c. 8th-9th cent. (reddish purple panel). b, Persian gold rhyton, c. 5th cent. B.C., (red violet panel)

**Litho. With Foil Application**
**2018, Oct. 23        Perf. 13¾x13¼**
2536 A2036 330w Horiz. pair,
        #a-b              1.25    .60

See Iran No. 3195.

Women Divers of Jeju UNESCO Intangible Heritage A2037

No. 2537: a, Three divers (52x24mm). b, Two divers harvesting shells (52x36mm).

**Litho. With Foil Application**
**2018, Nov. 21        Perf. 14x13¼**
2537 A2037 330w Vert. pair,
        #a-b              1.25    .60

New Year 2019 (Year of the Pig) A2038

No. 2538: a, Pig in costume. b, Pig facing left.

**Litho. With Foil Application (#2538a), Litho. With Hologram (#2438b)**
**2018, Dec. 3        Perf. 13¾**
2538 A2038 330w Pair, #a-b    1.25    .60
  c.    Souvenir sheet of 4, 2 each
        #2538a-2538b          2.50   1.25

A2039

A2040

A2041

A2042

Winning Art in Postage Stamp Design Contest — A2043

**Litho. With Foil Application**
**2019, Jan. 22        Perf. 13**
2539    Staggered horiz. strip of
        5              3.00   1.50
  a.    A2039 330w sil & multi   .60   .30
  b.    A2040 330w sil & multi   .60   .30
  c.    A2041 330w sil & multi   .60   .30
  d.    A2042 330w sil & multi   .60   .30
  e.    A2043 330w sil & multi   .60   .30

Photograph of Magnified Knee Tissues — A2044

Photograph of Magnified Pimple on Rabbit's Ear — A2045

Photograph of Magnified Intestinal Cells — A2046

Photograph of Magnified Rat Retina — A2047

**Litho. With Foil Application**
**2019, Feb. 19        Perf. 13x13¼**
2540    Block or horiz. strip of 4  2.40  1.25
  a.    A2044 330w sil & multi   .60   .30
  b.    A2045 330w sil & multi   .60   .30
  c.    A2046 330w sil & multi   .60   .30
  d.    A2047 330w sil & multi   .60   .30

March 1st Independence Movement, Cent. — A2048

**Litho. With Foil Application**
**2019, Feb. 28        Perf. 14**
2541 A2048 330w gold & multi   .60   .30

Ki-ok Kwon (1901-88), First Female Korean Aviator A2049

Cha-jeong Park (1909-44), Independence Activist A2050

Gyeong-shin Ahn (1888-?), Independence Activist A2051

Maria Kim (1892-1944), Independence Activist A2052

**Litho. With Foil Application**
**2019, Mar. 15        Perf. 13¾x13¼**
2542    Block or horiz. strip of 4  2.40  1.25
  a.    A2049 330w sil & multi   .60   .30
  b.    A2050 330w sil & multi   .60   .30
  c.    A2051 330w sil & multi   .60   .30
  d.    A2052 330w sil & multi   .60   .30

KAI KT-1 Woongbi A2053

KAI T-50 Golden Eagle — A2054

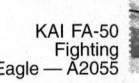

KAI FA-50 Fighting Eagle — A2055

**Litho. & Embossed With Foil Application**
**2019, Mar. 20        Perf. 13¼x13½**
2543    Horiz. strip of 3     1.80    .90
  a.    A2053 330w sil & multi   .60   .30
  b.    A2054 330w sil & multi   .60   .30
  c.    A2055 330w sil & multi   .60   .30

Korean Provisional Government, Cent. A2056

**Litho. With Foil Application**
**2019, Apr. 11        Perf. 14¼x13¾**
2544 A2056 330w gold & multi   .60   .30

Soon-ji Yi (1406-65), Astronomer A2057

Seok-jeong Choi (1646-1715), Mathematician A2058

Dong-hyuk Ahn (1907-2004), Chemical Engineer — A2059

**Litho. With Foil Application**
**2019, Apr. 19        Perf. 14**
2545    Horiz. strip of 3     1.80    .90
  a.    A2057 330w multi         .60   .30
  b.    A2058 330w multi         .60   .30
  c.    A2059 330w multi         .60   .30

Redefinition of International System of Units — A2060

**2019, May 20    Litho.    Perf. 14x13¼**
2546 A2060 330w multi          .55   .30

Miniature Sheet

Kakao Friends A2061

No. 2547 — Inscriptions: a, Muzi & Con. b, Apeach. c, Ryan. d, Frodo. e, Neo. f, Tube. g, Love. h, Friendship. i, Happiness. j, Jay-G.

**Litho. With Foil Application**
**2019, May 30        Perf. 13¼x13**
2547 A2061    Sheet of 10    6.50  3.25
  a.-j.   380w Any single        .65   .30

Corals A2062

No. 2548: a, Dendronephthya suensoni. b, Dendronephthya mollis. c, Dendronephthya putteri. d, Dendronephthya alba.

**Litho. With Foil Application**
**2019, June 5        Perf. 13**
2548 A2062    Block of 4     2.60  1.25
  a.-d.   380w Any single        .65   .30

Seol-hee Baek (1924-2010), Singer A2063

Hye-on In (1919-2002), Singer A2064

**Perf. 13¾x13½**
**2019, June 21        Litho.**
2549 A2063 380y gold & multi   .65   .30
2550 A2064 380y gold & multi   .65   .30

Flag A2065

Rose of Sharon A2066

Cat and Chrysanthemums, by Sang-byeok Byeon (1730-75) — A2067

**2019, July 1**   **Photo.**   *Perf. 12¾x13½*
2551 A2065 380w multi      .65   .35
2552 A2066 470w multi      .80   .40
               *Perf. 13½*
2553 A2067 2180wgold & multi   3.75   1.90
     Nos. 2551-2553 (3)      5.20   2.65

A map of the Korean Peninsula is laser cut in the lower right corner of No. 2553.

18th World Swimming Championships, Gwangju — A2068

**2019, July 12**   **Litho.**   *Perf. 14¼x14*
2554 A2068 380w multi      .65   .30

Hwang-ok Heo, Legendary Queen of Korea — A2069

Princess Suriratra (Later Queen Heo) — A2070

**2019, July 30**   **Litho.**   *Perf. 14x14¼*
2555    Pair            1.30   .60
   *a.*   A2069 380w multi    .65   .60
   *b.*   A2070 380w multi    .65   .30

     See India Nos. 3123-3124.

Songho Beach, Haenam A2071

Chaeseokgang, Buan — A2072

Jeongdongjin Beach, Gangneung A2073

Kkotji Beach, Taean A2074

**2019, Aug. 6**   **Litho.**   *Perf. 14x13¼*
2556    Block or horiz. strip of 4   2.60   1.25
   *a.*   A2071 380w multi    .65   .30
   *b.*   A2072 380w multi    .65   .30
   *c.*   A2073 380w multi    .65   .30
   *d.*   A2074 380w multi    .65   .30

A2075          A2076

A2077          A2078

A2079          A2080

A2081          A2082

A2083          A2084

A2085          A2086

A2087          A2088

A2089          Evolution of the South Korean Flag — A2090

**2019, Aug. 14**   **Litho.**   *Perf. 14½*
2557    Sheet of 16      10.50   5.00
   *a.*   A2075 380w multi    .65   .30
   *b.*   A2076 380w multi    .65   .30
   *c.*   A2077 380w multi    .65   .30
   *d.*   A2078 380w multi    .65   .30
   *e.*   A2079 380w multi    .65   .30
   *f.*   A2080 380w multi    .65   .30
   *g.*   A2081 380w multi    .65   .30
   *h.*   A2082 380w multi    .65   .30
   *i.*   A2083 380w multi    .65   .30
   *j.*   A2084 380w multi    .65   .30
   *k.*   A2085 380w multi    .65   .30
   *l.*   A2086 380w multi    .65   .30
   *m.*   A2087 380w multi    .65   .30
   *n.*   A2088 380w multi    .65   .30
   *o.*   A2089 380w multi    .65   .30
   *p.*   A2090 380w multi    .65   .30

National Parks and Flora — A2091

No. 2558: a, Seoraksan National Park, South Korea and Pinus pumila (orange panel). b, Northern Velebit National Park and Fianthus velebiticus, Croatia (green panel).

**2019, Aug. 29**   **Litho.**   *Perf. 13x13¼*
2558 A2091 380w Pair #a-b   1.30   .60

   South Korea and Croatia joint issue.
   See Croatia Nos. 1138-1139.

Evolution of the Woman's Hanbok A2092

No. 2559 — Woman in hanbok from: a, 1800s. b, 1900s. c, 1500s. d, 1600s-1700s.

**2019, Sept. 9**   **Litho.**   *Perf. 14*
2559 A2092 380w Block or horiz.
         strip of 4,
         #a-d         2.60   1.25

Republic of Korea Air Force, 70th Anniv. A2093

**Litho. With Foil Application**
**2019, Sept. 20**          *Perf. 14*
2560 A2093 380w sil & multi   .65   .30

100th National Sports Festival, Seoul — A2094

**2019, Sept. 26**   **Litho.**   *Perf. 14½*
2561 A2094 380w multi      .65   .30

Korean Motion Pictures, Cent. — A2095

**2019, Oct. 25**   **Litho.**   *Perf. 13¼*
2562 A2095 380w multi      .65   .30

Falconry, UNESCO Intangible Cultural Heritage A2096

No. 2563: a, Falcon and handler (53x24mm). b, Falcon and pheasant (53x36mm).

       *Perf. 13¾x13¼*
**2019, Nov. 27**          **Litho.**
2563 A2096 380w Vert. pair #a-b   1.30   .60

New Year 2020 (Year of the Rat) A2097

No. 2564: a, Rat in heart of flowers. b, Two rats.

**Litho. With Hologram Affixed**
**2019, Dec. 2**          *Perf. 13*
2564 A2097 380w Pair #a-b   1.30   .60
   *c.*   Souvenir sheet of 4, 2 each
       #2564a-2564b
                       2.60   1.25

Rice Growing Technology A2098

Integrated Steel Technology A2099

Ship Design and Construction Technology A2100

Dynamic Random Access Memory Semiconductor Technology A2101

Hantaan Virus Vaccine A2102

Satellite Technology A2103

Nuclear Power Plant Design Technology A2104

Lithium Ion Battery Technology A2105

**2019, Dec. 27**   **Litho.**   *Perf. 14¼x14*
2565    Block of 8      5.25   2.40
   *a.*   A2098 380w multi    .65   .30
   *b.*   A2099 380w multi    .65   .30
   *c.*   A2100 380w multi    .65   .30
   *d.*   A2101 380w multi    .65   .30
   *e.*   A2102 380w multi    .65   .30
   *f.*   A2103 380w multi    .65   .30
   *g.*   A2104 380w multi    .65   .30
   *h.*   A2105 380w multi    .65   .30

KUH-1EM Fire Fighting Helicopter A2106

KUH-1P Police Helicopter A2107

KUH-1FS Forest Service Helicopter A2108

**Litho. With Foil Application**
**2020, Mar. 20**          *Perf. 14x14¼*
2566    Horiz. strip of 3   2.00   .90
   *a.*   A2106 380w sil & multi   .65   .30
   *b.*   A2107 380w sil & multi   .65   .30
   *c.*   A2108 380w sil & multi   .65   .30

Deoksugung Seokjeojeon, Seoul — A2109

Jagyeongjeon Hall, Gyeongbokgung Palace, Seoul — A2110

Buyongjeong Pavilion, Changdeokgung Palace, Seoul — A2111

Main Hall, Changyeonggung Palace, Seoul — A2112

Royal Palaces A2113

No. 2568: a, Deoksugung Seokjojeon, Seoul. b, Main Hall, Changyeonggung Palace, Seoul. c, Buyongjeong Pavilion, Changdeokgung Palace, Seoul. d, Jagyeongjeon Hall, Gyeongbokgung Palace, Seoul.

**2020, Mar. 26      Litho.      Perf. 13**
| 2567 | Block or strip of 4 | 2.60 | 1.25 |
|---|---|---|---|
| a. | A2109 380w multi | .65 | .30 |
| b. | A2110 380w multi | .65 | .30 |
| c. | A2111 380w multi | .65 | .30 |
| d. | A2112 380w multi | .65 | .30 |

**Souvenir Sheet**
**Litho. & Embossed With Foil Application**
**Perf. 14**
| 2568 | A2113 | Sheet of 4 | 6.00 | 3.00 |
|---|---|---|---|---|
| a. | | 690w multi | 1.10 | .55 |
| b. | | 840w multi | 1.40 | .70 |
| c. | | 1010w multi | 1.60 | .80 |
| d. | | 1090w multi | 1.75 | .90 |

Duksung Women's University, Cent. — A2114

**Litho. With Foil Application**
**2020, Apr. 18      Perf. 14**
2569 A2114 380w gold & multi      .65   .30

International Year of Plant Health — A2115

**2020, May 29   Litho.   Perf. 14¼x14**
2570 A2115 380w multi      .65   .30

Battle of Bongodong, Cent. — A2116

**2020, June 5   Litho.   Perf. 14x13¼**
2571 A2116 380w multi      .65   .30

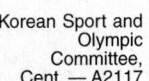

Korean Sport and Olympic Committee, Cent. — A2117

**2020, June 30   Litho.   Perf. 14**
2572 A2117 380w multi      .65   .30

Agency for Defense Development, 50th Anniv. — A2118

**2020, July 16   Litho.   Perf. 13**
2573 A2118 380w multi      .65   .30

---

Protected Marine Life — A2119

No. 2574: a, Zostera marina. b, Hippocampus kuda. c, Hippocampus trimaculata. d, Phyllospadix japonicus.

**Litho. With Foil Application**
**2020, Aug. 7      Perf. 14¼**
2574 A2119 380w Block of 4, #a-d      2.60   1.25

Evolution of the Men's Hanbok A2120

No. 2575 — Men's traditional clothing from: a, 1700s-1800s. b, 1900s. c, 1500s. d, 1600s.

**2020, Sept. 4   Litho.   Perf. 14**
2575 A2120 380w Block or horiz. strip of 4, #a-d      2.60   1.30

Warrior on Horseback Earthenware Cup — A2121

**2020, Sept. 23   Litho.   Perf. 13½**
2576 A2121 2480w multi      4.25   2.10

A map of the Korean Peninsula is laser cut in the lower right corner of No. 2576.

A2122

Yu Gwansun (1902-20), Independence Activist Killed by Japanese Colonial Authorities — A2123

**Perf. 13¼x13½**
**2020, Sept. 28            Litho.**
2577 A2122 380w multi      .65   .35

---

**Souvenir Sheet**
**On Silk-Faced Paper**
**Perf. 13¼x13**
2578 A2123 2480w multi      4.25   2.10

Ssireum (Korean Wrestling), UNESCO Intangible Cultural Heritage A2124

No. 2579 — Various wrestlers with denomination in: a, Blue panel (52x25mm). b, Red panel (52x36mm).

**2020, Oct. 8      Litho.      Perf. 14½**
2579 A2124 380w Vert. pair, #a-b   1.40   .70

Battle of Qingshanli (Cheongsanri), Cent. — A2125

**2020, Oct. 21   Litho.   Perf. 13¾x14¼**
2580 A2125 380w multi      .70   .35

Children's Book Illustrations — A2126

No. 2581 — Illustration from: a, Magic Candles (red orange denomination). b, Dokkaebi and the Rice Cake Peddler (gray blue denomination). c, When Spring Comes to the DMZ (orange yellow denomination). d, Wave (blue denomination).

**Litho. With Foil Application**
**2020, Nov. 20      Perf. 13½x13¼**
2581 A2126 380w Block or horiz. strip of 4, #a-d      2.75   1.40

Philately Week.

New Year 2021 (Year of the Ox) A2127

No. 2582: a, Cow and calf. b, Cow wearing bells.

**Litho. and Embossed With Foil Application**
**2020, Dec. 1      Perf. 13¾**
| 2582 | A2127 380w Pair #a-b | 1.40 | .70 |
|---|---|---|---|
| c. | Souvenir sheet of 4, 2 each #2582a-2582b | 2.80 | 1.40 |

Bears A2128

No. 2583: a, Ursus thibetanus ussuricus. b, Ursus arctos arctos.

**2020, Dec. 15   Litho.   Perf. 14¼**
2583 A2128 380w Pair #a-b      1.40   .70

Diplomatic relations between South Korea and Russia, 30th anniv. See Russia No. 8222.

---

Geostationary Satellites — A2129

No. 2584: a, Cheonrian 1 satellite (blue denomination at UR). b, Cheonrian 2A satellite (red denomination at UR). c, Cheonrian 2B satellite (blue denomination at UL).

**Litho. With Foil Application**
**2021, Jan. 26      Perf. 13¾x13¼**
2584 A2129 380w Horiz. strip of 3, #a-c      2.10   1.10

Korea Advanced Institute of Science and Technology, 50th Anniv. A2130

**2021, Feb. 16   Litho.   Perf. 13¼**
2585 A2130 380w multi      .70   .35

Korean Heritage Items Recently Repatriated — A2131

No. 2586: a, Empress Myeongseong Okbo (lilac background). b, Celadon monkey (orange brown background). c, Gyeonju face pattern (blue background). d, Ten-story pagoda (green background).

**Litho. & Embossed With Foil Application**
**2021, Feb. 16      Perf. 13¼**
| 2586 | A2131 | Block or horiz. strip of 4 | 2.80 | 1.40 |
|---|---|---|---|---|
| a.-d. | | 380w Any single | .70 | .35 |

Neo-Confucian Academy, Dalseong A2132

Neo-Confucian Academy, Nonsan — A2133

Neo-Confucian Academy, Andong — A2134

Neo-Confucian Academy, Jangseong A2135

Neo-Confucian Academies — A2136

No. 2588 — Academy in: a, Nonsan. b, Dalseong. c, Jangseong. d, Andong.

**2021, Mar. 11     Litho.     Perf. 13**
2587     Block or horiz. strip of 4   2.80  1.40
a. A2132 380w multi  .70  .35
b. A2133 380w multi  .70  .35
c. A2134 380w multi  .70  .35
d. A2135 380w multi  .70  .35

**Souvenir Sheet**
**Perf. 14**
2588  A2136  Sheet of 4   6.50  3.25
a. 690w sil & multi   1.25  .60
b. 840w sil & multi   1.50  .75
c. 1010w sil & multi  1.75  .90
d. 1090w sil & multi  2.00  1.00

T-50B Jet — A2137

KUH-1 Helicopter A2138

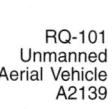
RQ-101 Unmanned Aerial Vehicle A2139

**Litho. With Foil Application**
**2021, Mar. 25     Perf. 13¼x13½**
2589     Horiz. strip of 3   2.10  1.10
a. A2137 380w multi  .70  .35
b. A2138 380w multi  .70  .35
c. A2139 380w multi  .70  .35

A2140     A2141

A2142     A2143

A2144     A2145

A2146     A2147

Painted Folding Screen Panels, by Jang Seung-up (1843-97)
A2148     A2149

**2021, Apr. 6     Litho.     Perf. 14¼**
2590     Sheet of 10 + 20 labels   7.00  3.50
a. A2140 380w multi  .70  .35
b. A2141 380w multi  .70  .35
c. A2142 380w multi  .70  .35
d. A2143 380w multi  .70  .35
e. A2144 380w multi  .70  .35
f. A2145 380w multi  .70  .35
g. A2146 380w multi  .70  .35
h. A2147 380w multi  .70  .35
i. A2148 380w multi  .70  .35
j. A2149 380w multi  .70  .35

Astronomical Clock A2150     Rain Gauge A2151

Water Clock A2152     Sundial A2153

**2021, Apr. 21   Litho.   Perf. 13¼x13½**
2591     Block or horiz. strip of 4  2.80  1.40
a. A2150 380w multi  .75  .35
b. A2151 380w multi  .75  .35
c. A2152 380w multi  .75  .35
d. A2153 380w multi  .75  .35

Astronomy and earth science of the Joseon Dynasty.

Geumgangsan Mountain, Fan Painting by Jeong Seon — A2154

Precious Vessels and Flowering Plants, Fan Painting by Lee Doyeong and Go Huidong A2155

Plum Blossoms, Fan Painting by Shin Myeongyeon A2156

Chatting Under Pine Trees by the Stream, Fan Painting by Yi Inmun A2157

Elegant Gathering in the Western Garden, Fan Painting by Kim Hongdo A2158

Gazing at a Waterfall Under a Pine Tree, Fan Painting by Yi Insang A2159

**Litho. With Foil Application**
**2021, May 17     Perf. 14¼x13¾**
2592     Block or vert. strip of 6  4.25  2.10
a. A2154 380w gold & multi  .70  .35
b. A2155 380w gold & multi  .70  .35
c. A2156 380w gold & multi  .70  .35
d. A2157 380w gold & multi  .70  .35
e. A2158 380w gold & multi  .70  .35
f. A2159 380w gold & multi  .70  .35

Protected Turtles — A2160

No. 2593: a, Eretmochelys imbricata. b, Caretta caretta. c, Dermochelys coriacea. d, Chelonia mydas.

**Litho. With Foil Application**
**2021, May 31     Perf. 14¼**
2593  A2160  Block of 4   2.80  1.40
a.-d.   380w Any single   .70  .35

A2161     A2162

A2163     Sculptures of Mythological Beasts at Gyeongbokgung Palace — A2164

**Litho. & Engr.**
**2021, June 22     Perf. 13¼**
2594     Block or horiz. strip of 4  3.50  1.60
a. A2161 470w multi  .85  .40
b. A2162 470w multi  .85  .40
c. A2163 470w multi  .85  .40
d. A2164 470w multi  .85  .40

Daecheong Lake — A2165

Hoengseong Lake — A2166

Yongdam Lake — A2167

Soyang Lake — A2168

**2021, July 1     Litho.     Perf. 14x13¼**
2595     Block or horiz. strip of 4  2.80  1.40
a. A2165 380w multi  .70  .35
b. A2166 380w multi  .70  .35
c. A2167 380w multi  .70  .35
d. A2168 380w multi  .70  .35

Baeksu Coastal Road — A2169     Heonhwa Road — A2170

Sinchang Windmill Coastal Road — A2171     Mulmi Coastal Road — A2172

**Litho. With Foil Application**
**2021, July 15     Perf. 14**
2596     Block or horiz. strip of 4  2.80  1.40
a. A2169 380w sil & multi  .70  .35
b. A2170 380w sil & multi  .70  .35
c. A2171 380w sil & multi  .70  .35
d. A2172 380w sil & multi  .70  .35

Walled Town, Gochang A2173

Walled Town, Nagan A2174

Walled town, Haemi A2175

**Litho. With Foil Application**
**2021, Aug. 4     Perf. 13¼**
2597     Horiz. strip of 3   2.00  1.10
a. A2173 380w cop & multi  .65  .35
b. A2174 380w cop & multi  .65  .35
c. A2175 380w cop & multi  .65  .35

St. Andrew Kim Taegon (1821-46), Martyred Priest — A2176

**Litho. With Foil Application**
**2021, Aug. 20     Perf. 13**
2598  A2176  380w gold & multi  .65  .35

Lycaena Dispar A2177     Yugwa (Rice Cakes) A2178

Terpsiphone Atrocaudata — A2179

Flag and Hunminjeongeum Script — A2180

Crataegus Pinnatifida
A2181

Rose of Sharon
A2182

Hangeul Alphabet
A2183

Celadon Ewer
A2184

| 2021 | | Litho. | Perf. 12¾ | |
|---|---|---|---|---|
| 2599 | A2177 | 10w multi | .30 | .30 |
| 2600 | A2178 | 50w multi | .30 | .30 |
| 2601 | A2179 | 100w multi | .30 | .30 |
| 2602 | A2180 | 430w multi | .75 | .35 |
| 2603 | A2181 | 500w multi | .85 | .40 |
| 2604 | A2182 | 520w multi | .90 | .45 |

| | | | Perf. 13½ | |
|---|---|---|---|---|
| 2605 | A2183 | 1000w multi | 1.75 | .85 |

**Litho. With Foil Application**

| 2606 | A2184 | 2530w multi | 4.50 | 2.25 |
|---|---|---|---|---|
| | | Nos. 2599-2606 (8) | 9.65 | 5.20 |

Issued: Nos. 2599-2601, 10/29; Nos. 2602, 2604, 2606, 9/1; Nos. 2603, 2605, 12/17.
A map of the Korean Peninsula is laser cut in the lower right corner of Nos. 2605 and 2606.

Oil Tanker
A2185

Container Ship — A2186

Bulk Cargo Ship — A2187

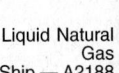
Liquid Natural Gas Ship — A2188

**Litho. With Foil Application**
**2021, Sept. 15**    *Perf. 13¼x13½*

| 2607 | | Block or horiz. strip of 4 | 3.00 | 1.40 |
|---|---|---|---|---|
| a. | A2185 | 430w sil & multi | .75 | .35 |
| b. | A2186 | 430w sil & multi | .75 | .35 |
| c. | A2187 | 430w sil & multi | .75 | .35 |
| d. | A2188 | 430w sil & multi | .75 | .35 |

Jultagi (Korean Tightrope Walking) UNESCO Intangible Cultural Property
A2189

No. 2608: a, Tightrope walker above wire (52x24mm). b, Tightrope walker on rope (52x36mm).

**Litho. With Foil Application**
**2021, Sept. 30**    *Perf. 14x13½*

| 2608 | A2189 | 430w Vert. pair. #a-b | 1.50 | .70 |
|---|---|---|---|---|

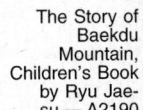
The Story of Baekdu Mountain, Children's Book by Ryu Jae-su — A2190

Half Past Four, Children's Book by Yun Seok-jung
A2191

Manhee's Home, Children's Book by Kwon Yoon-duck
A2192

Children of the Dong River, Children's Book by Kim Jae-hong
A2193

**Litho. With Foil Application**
**2021, Oct. 25**    *Perf. 14x14¼*

| 2609 | | Block or horiz. strip of 4 | 3.00 | 1.40 |
|---|---|---|---|---|
| a. | A2190 | 430w gold & multi | .75 | .35 |
| b. | A2191 | 430w gold & multi | .75 | .35 |
| c. | A2192 | 430w gold & multi | .75 | .35 |
| d. | A2193 | 430w gold & multi | .75 | .35 |

Philately Week.

Korean Jindo
A2194

Sapsali
A2195

Donggyeongi
A2196

**Litho. With Foil Application**
**2021, Oct. 29**    *Perf. 14*

| 2610 | | Horiz. strip of 3 | 2.25 | 1.10 |
|---|---|---|---|---|
| a. | A2194 | 430w gold & multi | .75 | .35 |
| b. | A2195 | 430w gold & multi | .75 | .35 |
| c. | A2196 | 430w gold & multi | .75 | .35 |

Medicinal Plants — A2197

No. 2611: a, Lonicera japonica. b, Angelica gigas. c, Epimedium koreanum. d, Leonurus japonicus.

**Litho. With Foil Application**
*Perf. 13½x13¼ Syncopated*
**2021, Nov. 10**

| 2611 | A2197 | Block or horiz. strip of 4 | 3.00 | 1.40 |
|---|---|---|---|---|
| a.-d. | | 430w Any single | .75 | .35 |

A2198

A2199

A2200

Children's Hanboks — A2201

**2021, Nov. 18**    **Litho.**    *Perf. 13¼x13*

| 2612 | | Block or horiz. strip of 4 | 3.00 | 1.40 |
|---|---|---|---|---|
| a. | A2198 | 430w multi | .75 | .35 |
| b. | A2199 | 430w multi | .75 | .35 |
| c. | A2200 | 430w multi | .75 | .35 |
| d. | A2201 | 430w multi | .75 | .35 |

New Year 2022 (Year of the Tiger)
A2202

No. 2613: a, Head of tiger and snowflakes. b, Tiger, paw prints and hearts.

**Litho. & Embossed With Foil Application**
**2021, Dec. 1**    *Perf. 14¼*

| 2613 | A2202 | 430w Pair, #a-b | 1.50 | .70 |
|---|---|---|---|---|
| c. | | Souvenir sheet of 4, 2 each #2613a-2613b | 3.00 | 1.40 |

Portraits of Joseon Kings
A2203

No. 2614: a, King Yeongjo wearing red robe (1694-1776). b, King Taejo wearing blue robe (1335-1408).

**Litho. With Foil Application**
**2022, Feb. 7**    *Perf. 13¼x13*

| 2614 | A2203 | 430w Pair, #a-b | 1.50 | .75 |
|---|---|---|---|---|

Bamboo Investiture Book
A2204

Robe of Prince Yeong
A2205

Seal of Princess Deokon (1822-44)
A2206

White Jade Butterfly Pendants
A2207

**Litho. With Foil Application**
**2022, Feb. 14**    *Perf. 13¼x13½*

| 2615 | | Block or horiz. strip of 4 | 3.00 | 1.40 |
|---|---|---|---|---|
| a. | A2204 | 430w multi | .75 | .35 |
| b. | A2205 | 430w multi | .75 | .35 |
| c. | A2206 | 430w multi | .75 | .35 |
| d. | A2207 | 430w multi | .75 | .35 |

Yun Yong-ha (1922-65), Composer
A2208

*Perf. 13½x13¾*
**2022, Mar. 16**    **Litho.**

| 2616 | A2208 | 430w multi | .70 | .35 |
|---|---|---|---|---|

## SEMI-POSTAL STAMPS

Catalogue values for unused stamps in this section are for Never Hinged items.

Field Hospital — SP1

Nurses Supporting Patient — SP2

*Perf. 13½x14, 14x13½*
**1953, Aug. 1**    **Litho.**    **Wmk. 257**
**Crosses in Red**

| B1 | SP1 | 10h + 5h bl grn | 14.00 | 2.25 |
|---|---|---|---|---|
| B2 | SP2 | 10h + 5h blue | 14.00 | 2.25 |

The surtax was for the Red Cross. Nos. B1-B2 exist imperf.

**Type of Regular Issue, 1956, with Added inscription at Upper Left**
**1957, Sept. 1**    **Wmk. 312**    *Perf. 12½*
**Granite Paper**

| B3 | A111 | 40h + 10h lt bl grn | 8.25 | 2.75 |
|---|---|---|---|---|

**Wmk. 317**

| B4 | A111 | 40h + 10h lt bl grn | 8.25 | 2.75 |
|---|---|---|---|---|

The surtax was for flood relief.

**Rice Farmer Type of Regular Issue, 1961-62**
**1963, July 10**    **Wmk. 317**    *Perf. 12½*

| B5 | A172 | 4w + 1w dk bl | 6.50 | 1.25 |
|---|---|---|---|---|

The surtax was for flood victims in southern Korea.

**1965, Oct. 1**    **Unwmk.**    *Perf. 12½*

| B6 | A172 | 4w + 2w indigo | 3.00 | .75 |
|---|---|---|---|---|

The surtax was for flood relief.

**1965, Oct. 11**

| B7 | A172 | 4w + 2w magenta | 3.00 | .75 |
|---|---|---|---|---|

The surtax was for a scholarship fund.

**Type of Regular Issue 1964-66**
**1966, Nov. 10**    **Litho.**    *Perf. 12½*
**Granite Paper**

| B8 | A186b | 7w + 2w car rose | 4.50 | 1.25 |
|---|---|---|---|---|

The surtax was to help the needy.

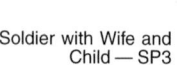

Soldier with Wife and
Child — SP3

**1967, June 20** *Perf. 12½x13*
B9 SP3 7w + 3w rose lil & blk    4.50  .75
The surtax was for veterans of the war in
Viet Nam and their families.

Reservist — SP4

**1968, Aug. 1  Litho.  *Perf. 13x12½***
B10 SP4 7w + 3w grn & blk    7.00 1.25
Issued for the fund-raising drive to arm
reservists.

Flag — SP5

**1968, Nov. 1  Litho.  Unwmk.**
B11 SP5 7w + 3w dk bl & red    27.50 4.00
The surtax was for disaster relief.

**1969, Feb. 15**
B12 SP5 7w + 3w lt grn, dk bl &
red    7.50 1.00
Surtax for military helicopter fund.

**Flag Type of 1968 Redrawn
Zeros Omitted**
**1969, Nov. 1  Litho.  *Perf. 13x12½***
B13 SP5 7w + 3w dk bl & red    27.50 1.00
The surtax was for the searchlight fund.

"Pin of Love" — SP6

**1972, Aug. 1  Photo.  *Perf. 13½x12½***
B14 SP6 10w + 5w blue & car    1.25 .75
Disaster relief.

"Pin of Love" — SP7

**1973, July 1  Photo.  *Perf. 12½x13½***
B15 SP7 10w + 5w multicolored    .65 .50
Disaster relief.

Paddle and Ball — SP8

**1973, Aug. 1  Photo.  *Perf. 13½x12½***
B16 SP8 10w + 5w multicolored    .65 .50
Surtax was for gymnasium to be built to
commemorate the victory of the Korean
women's table tennis team at the 32nd World
Table Tennis Championships.

Lungs — SP9

**1974, Nov. 1  *Perf. 13½x12½***
B17 SP9 10w + 5w green & red    .75 .25
Surtax was for tuberculosis control.

No. 647 Surcharged

*Perf. 13½x12½*
**1977, July 25  Photo.**
B18 A328 20w + 10w green    12.50 12.50
Surtax was for flood relief.

**Seoul 1988 Olympic Games Series**

'88 Seoul
Games
Emblem
SP10

Korean
Tiger,
Mascot
SP11

**1985, Mar. 20  Photo.  *Perf. 13x13½***
B19 SP10 70w + 30w blk & multi    .45 .25
B20 SP11 70w + 30w blk & multi    .45 .25
a.    Souvenir sheet of 2, #B19-20    1.10 1.10

Track and Field — SP12

**1985, June 10**
B21 SP12 70w + 30w shown    .45 .25
B22 SP12 70w + 30w Rowing    .45 .25
a.    Souvenir sheet of 2, #B21-B22    1.10 1.10

**1985, Sept. 16**
B23 SP12 70w + 30w Boxing    .45 .25
B24 SP12 70w + 30w Women's
basketball    .45 .25
a.    Souvenir sheet of 2, #B23-B24    1.10 1.10

**1985, Nov. 1**
B25 SP12 70w + 30w Canoeing    .45 .30
B26 SP12 70w + 30w Cycling    .45 .30
a.    Souvenir sheet of 2, #B25-B26    1.10 1.10
Surtax for the 24th Summer Olympic
Games, Sept. 17-Oct. 2, 1988.

Equestrian — SP18

Designs: No. B28, Fencing. No. B29, Soccer. No. B30, Gymnastic rings.

**1986, Mar. 25  Photo.  *Perf. 13x13½***
B27 SP18 70w + 30w multi    .45 .25
B28 SP18 70w + 30w multi    .45 .25
B29 SP18 70w + 30w multi    .45 .25
B30 SP18 70w + 30w multi    .45 .25

**Souvenir Sheets**
B31    Sheet of 4    9.50 9.50
a.    SP18 370w + 100w like #B27    2.25 2.25
B32    Sheet of 4    9.50 9.50
a.    SP18 400w + 100w like #B28    2.25 2.25
B33    Sheet of 4    9.50 9.50
a.    SP18 440w + 100w like #B29    2.25 2.25
B34    Sheet of 4    9.50 9.50
a.    SP18 470w + 100w like #B30    2.25 2.25

**1986  Photo.  *Perf. 13x13½***
No. B35, Weight lifting. No. B36, Team
handball. No. B37, Judo. No. B38, Field
hockey.

B35 SP18 80w +50w multi    .55 .25
B36 SP18 80w +50w multi    .55 .25
B37 SP18 80w +50w multi    .55 .25
B38 SP18 80w +50w multi    .55 .25

**Souvenir Sheets**
B39    Sheet of 4    8.25 8.25
a.    SP18 370w + 100w like #B35    1.90 1.90
B40    Sheet of 4    8.25 8.25
a.    SP18 400w + 100w like #B36    1.90 1.90

B41    Sheet of 4    9.00 9.00
a.    SP18 440w + 100w like #B37    2.10 2.10
B42    Sheet of 4    9.00 9.00
a.    SP18 470w + 100w like #B38    2.10 2.10
Issue dates: Nos. B35-B36, B39-B40, Oct.
10; others, Nov. 1.

**1987, May 25  Photo.  *Perf. 13x13½***
No. B43, Women's tennis. No. B44, Wrestling. No. B45, Show jumping. No. B46, Diving.

B43 SP18 80w +50w multi    .65 .40
B44 SP18 80w +50w multi    .65 .40
B45 SP18 80w +50w multi    .65 .40
B46 SP18 80w +50w multi    .65 .40

**1987, Oct. 10**
No. B47, Table Tennis. No. B48, Men's
shooting. No. B49, Women's archery. No.
B50, Women's volleyball.

B47 SP18 80w +50w multi    .65 .40
B48 SP18 80w +50w multi    .65 .40
B49 SP18 80w +50w multi    .65 .40
B50 SP18 80w +50w multi    .65 .40

**1988, Mar. 5  Photo.  *Perf. 13x13½***
B51 SP18 80w +20w Sailing    .45 .25
B52 SP18 80w +20w Taekwondo    .45 .25

**1988, May 6  Photo.  *Perf. 13½x13***
No. B53, Torch relay, horiz. No. B54,
Olympic Stadium, horiz.
B53 SP18 80w +20w multi    .45 .25

**Litho. & Engr.**
B54 SP18 80w +20w multi    .45 .25
See Greece No. 1627.

**Souvenir Sheets of 2**
B43a SP18 80w +50w    3.00 3.00
B44a SP18 80w +50w    3.00 3.00
B45a SP18 80w +50w    3.00 3.00
B46a SP18 80w +50w    3.00 3.00
B47a SP18 80w +50w    3.00 3.00
B48a SP18 80w +50w    3.00 3.00
B49a SP18 80w +50w    3.00 3.00
B50a SP18 80w +50w    3.00 3.00
B51a SP18 80w +20w    3.00 3.00
B52a SP18 80w +20w    3.00 3.00
B53a SP18 80w +20w    3.00 3.00
B54a SP18 80w +20w    3.00 3.00

---

**AIR POST STAMPS**

Four-motor
Plane and
Globe — AP1

*Perf. 11½x11*
**1947-50  Litho.  Wmk. 257**
C1 AP1 50wn carmine rose    8.25 2.25
a.    Horiz. pair, imperf. btwn.    165.00
*Perf. 11*
C2 AP1 150wn blue ('49)    1.25 1.25
a.    "KORFA"    12.50 .30
C3 AP1 150wn green ('50)    7.50 4.00
Nos. C1-C3 (3)    17.00
Set, never hinged    30.00
Nos. C2-C3 are redrawn and designs differ
slightly from type AP1.
Issued: 50wn, 10/1.
For surcharge see No. C5.

Plane and Korea
Map — AP2

**1950, Jan. 1**
C4 AP2 60wn light blue    16.00 15.00
Never hinged    27.50

**No. C2 Surcharged with New Value
and Wavy Lines in Black**
**1951, Oct. 10**
C5 AP1 500wn on 150wn bl    3.75 2.25
Never hinged    6.25
a.    "KORFA"    20.00 50.00
Never hinged    30.00
b.    Surcharge inverted    125.00

Douglas C-47 and
Ship — AP3

*Perf. 13x12½*
**1952, Oct. 15  Litho.  Wmk. 257**
C6 AP3 1200wn red brown    .90 .60
C7 AP3 1800wn lt blue    1.50 .60
C8 AP3 4200wn purple    1.90 1.25
Nos. C6-C8 (3)    4.30 2.45
Set, never hinged    7.25
Nos. C6-C8 exist imperf.

**1953, Apr. 5**
C9 AP3 12h dp blue    1.00 .60
C10 AP3 18h purple    1.50 .60
C11 AP3 42h Prus green    2.10 1.25
Nos. C9-C11 (3)    4.60 2.45
Set, never hinged    7.75

Douglas DC-7 over East
Gate, Seoul — AP4

**1954, June 15  *Perf. 12½***
C12 AP4 25h brown    2.00 1.25
C13 AP4 35h deep pink    2.75 1.00
C14 AP4 38h dark green    2.75 1.50
C15 AP4 58h ultra    2.75 1.75
C16 AP4 71h deep blue    6.50 2.00
Nos. C12-C16 (5)    16.75 7.50
Set, never hinged    27.50
Nos. C12-C16 exist imperf.
Counterfeits exist of Nos. C12-C16.

**Type of 1954 Redrawn**
**1956, July 20  Unwmk.**
**Laid Paper**
C17 AP4 70h brt bluish grn    5.00 3.00
C18 AP4 110h brown    3.25 3.00
C19 AP4 205h magenta    9.75 5.00
Nos. C17-C19 (3)    18.00 11.00
Set, never hinged    30.00
Nos. C18-C19 are found on horizontally and
vertically laid paper.

**1957, July  Wmk. 312  *Perf. 12½***
**Granite Paper**
C20 AP4 70h brt bluish grn    4.75 3.00
C21 AP4 110h brown    4.75 3.00
C22 AP4 205h magenta    9.50 5.00
Nos. C20-C22 (3)    19.00 11.00
Set, never hinged    32.50
On the redrawn stamps, Nos. C17-C22, the
lines of the entire design are lighter, and the
colorless character at right end of bottom row
has been redrawn as in illustration above No.
212D.

| Catalogue values for unused
stamps in this section, from this
point to the end of the section, are
for Never Hinged items. |
| --- |

Girl on Palace
Balcony — AP5

Designs: 100h, Suwon Castle. 200h,
Songnyu Gate, Tuksu Palace. 400h,
Kyunghoeru Pavilion.

*Perf. 12½*
**1961, Dec. 1  Unwmk.  Litho.**
C23 AP5 50h lt blue & violet    12.50 5.00
C24 AP5 100h pale grn & se-
pia    22.50 8.00
C25 AP5 200h pale grn & brn    32.50 8.00
C26 AP5 400h grn & pale bl    42.50 10.00
Nos. C23-C26 (4)    110.00 31.00

**Values in Won; Same Designs;
Underlined Zeros Added**
**1962-63**
C27 AP5 5w lt bl & vio
('63)    67.50 20.00
C28 AP5 10w pale grn & sepia    45.00 15.00

| | | | |
|---|---|---|---|
| **C29** | AP5 20w pale grn & brn ('63) | 225.00 | 50.00 |
| **C30** | AP5 40w grn & pale bl ('63) | 60.00 | 25.00 |
| | *Nos. C27-C30 (4)* | 397.50 | 110.00 |

**1964, May 10  Wmk. 317   *Perf. 12½***
**Granite Paper**

| | | | |
|---|---|---|---|
| **C32** | AP5 10w pale grn & sepia | 12.50 | 4.00 |
| **C33** | AP5 20w pale grn & brn | 42.50 | 12.00 |
| **C34** | AP5 40w pale bl & grn | 25.00 | 8.00 |
| | *Nos. C32-C34 (3)* | 80.00 | 24.00 |

**Granite Paper**
**1964, Oct.       Unwmk.      *Perf. 12½***

Designs: 39w, Girl on palace balcony. 64w, Suwon Castle. 78w, Songnyu Gate, Tuksu Palace. 112w, Kyunghoeru Pavilion.

| | | | |
|---|---|---|---|
| **C35** | AP5  39w vio bl & gray olive | 7.50 | 2.50 |
| **C36** | AP5  64w bl & grnsh gray | 10.50 | 2.50 |
| **C37** | AP5  78w grnsh bl & ultra | 19.00 | 5.00 |
| **C38** | AP5 112w blue & green | 8.00 | 2.50 |
| | *Nos. C35-C38 (4)* | 45.00 | 12.50 |

World Map and
Plane — AP6

Designs: 135w, Plane over eastern hemisphere. 145w, Plane over world map. 180w, Plane over world map.

**1973, Dec. 30  Photo.   *Perf. 13x12½***

| | | | |
|---|---|---|---|
| **C39** | AP6 110w pink & multi | 6.75 | 4.00 |
| **C40** | AP6 135w yel grn & red | 7.75 | 4.00 |
| **C41** | AP6 145w lt bl & rose | 9.00 | 4.00 |
| **C42** | AP6 180w lilac & yellow | 27.00 | 8.00 |
| | *Nos. C39-C42 (4)* | 50.50 | 20.00 |

**UPU Type of 1974**
**1974, Oct. 9      Photo.      *Perf. 13***

| | | | |
|---|---|---|---|
| **C43** | A480 110w blue & multi | 2.25 | .75 |
| *a.* | Souvenir sheet of 2 | 11.50 | 11.50 |

**Mt. Fuji, Korean Airlines Jet Type**
**1985, Dec. 18  Photo.   *Perf. 13x13½***
| **C44** | A878 370w brt bl, blk & red | 1.25 | .75 |

**Int'l Year of Peace Type**
**1986, Jan. 15  Photo.   *Perf. 13x13½***
| **C45** | A879 400w multicolored | 1.25 | .75 |

Issued in sheets with two blocks of four.

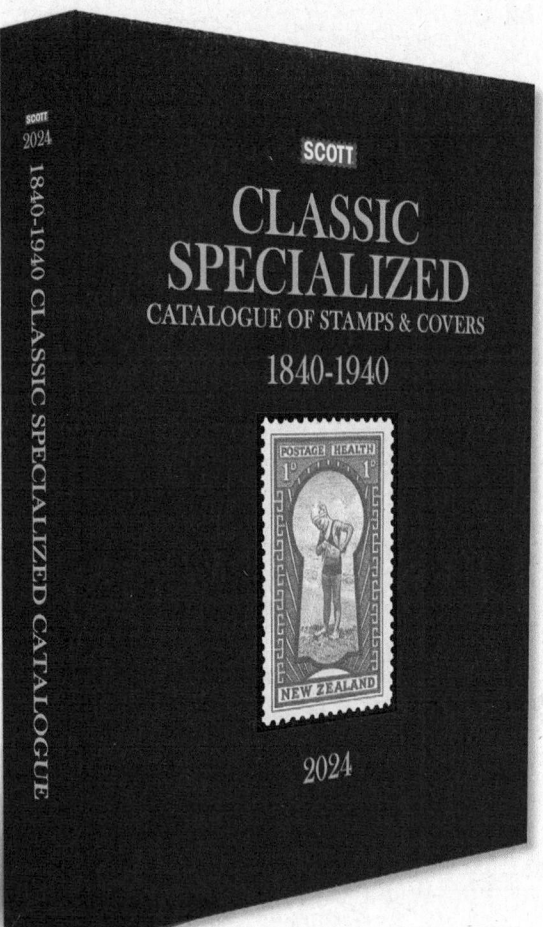

# KOREA, DEMOCRATIC PEOPLE'S REPUBLIC

kə-'rē-ə

LOCATION — Peninsula extending from Manchuria between the Yellow Sea and the Sea of Japan (East Sea)
GOVT. — Republic
AREA — 47,398 sq. mi.
POP. — 24,589,122 (2011 est.)
CAPITAL — Pyongyang

At the end of World War II, American forces occupied South Korea and Russian forces occupied North Korea, with the 38th parallel of latitude as the dividing line. North Korea was administered by a Provisional People's Committee after Feb. 9, 1946. Unoverprinted Japanese stamps continued to be used until the first North Korean issue of March 12, 1946. On Sept. 9, 1948, the Democratic People's Republic of Korea was established, and the last Soviet troops left Korea by the end of the year.

100 Chon = 1 Won (1962)

Catalogue values for unused stamps in this country are for Never Hinged items.

North Korean stamps were issued without gum, unless otherwise noted.
Early issues typically exist in a variety of color shades.
Used values are for cancelled-to-order stamps from 1957-on. Postally used stamps are worth more. Examples on non-philatelic covers are scarce, especially for 1946-1960 issues.

## REPRINTS

During 1955-57 the North Korean Postal Administration created "reprints," actually imitations, of most 1946-56 issues for sale to collectors. These reprints were postally valid, and in some cases may have served real postal needs, but most were created for and sold to overseas collectors.
The reprints are more finely printed than the original stamps and are normally printed on a higher quality white wove paper. They often differ from the original printings in both size and design details. Specific distinguishing characteristics are provided below, with the descriptions of each issue.

## SOVIET OCCUPATION

Rose of Sharon
A1

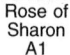

Diamond Mountains (small "50")
A2

Diamond Mountains (large "50") — A3

### Perf 11, Rouletted 12(#3), 11x Imperf or Imperf x11 (#4,5)
**1946, Mar. 12-1955**      **Litho.**

| | | | | |
|---|---|---|---|---|
| 1 | A1 | 20ch red | 85.00 | 300.00 |
| 2 | A2 | 50ch apple grn ('46) | 55.00 | 82.50 |
| a. | | 50ch yel green, buff | 55.00 | 82.50 |
| 3 | A2 | 50ch car rose | 2,000. | 1,650. |
| 4 | A3 | 50ch rose red | 165.00 | 125.00 |
| a. | | Perf 12 ('48) | 165.00 | 125.00 |
| c. | | Perf 10 ('55) | — | — |
| 5 | A3 | 50ch violet | 18.00 | — |
| a. | | Perf 11 ('50) | 300.00 | — |
| b. | | Imperf ('50) | 55.00 | — |
| c. | | Perf 10 ('55) | — | — |

---

| | | | | |
|---|---|---|---|---|
| d. | ImperfxPerf 11, soft paper, vert. lines | | 20.00 | |
| e. | Vert. pair, tete-beche | | 1,250. | |
| f. | 10¾xImperf. | | — | — |
| | Nos. 1-5 (5) | | 2,323. | 2,158. |

No. 4 has lines of colored dots along the horizontal rouletting.
Design sizes: No. 1, 18x21.5-22mm; No. 4, 17.5-18x22-23mm.
Reprints of No. 1 are in yellow green, perf 8½, 8½x9½, 10 or imperf, and measure 18-18.5x23mm. Denomination panel is 4mm high, rather than 3mm. Value $10.
Reprints of No. 4 are perf 10, 10x10½, 11 or imperf, on gummed paper, and measure 17.5-18x22-22.5mm. The double frame lines are clearly separated, and the figures of value are thin and well-formed. Value $10.

Gen. Kim Il Sung (1912-1994) — A4

**1946, Aug. 15**      **Litho.**      **Pin-Perf**

| | | | | |
|---|---|---|---|---|
| 6 | A4 | 50ch brown | 700.00 | 550.00 |

First anniversary of liberation from Japan.
No. 6 has lines of colored dots along the horizontal pin perforations.
No. 6 is inscribed in Korean, Chinese and Russian.
No. 6 in deep violet brown and a 50ch red, similar in design, were printed for presentation to officials and privileged people. Value, $1,900 and $2,250, respectively.

#21c Control overprint

Several varieties of overprints were used to validate various stamps during the chaotic months following the landing of United Nations' forces at Inchon in mid-September 1950, the retreat of North Korean forces to the far north by October, and their renewed advance, after the entry of the Chinese Volunteer Army into the war. Validation overprints are known on Nos. 10, 14, 16, 21, 22, 26, 27, 28, 29, and 31. Other stamps with validation overprints are of dubious origin.

Peasants — A5

### Pin-Perf 12, Imperf (#10)
**1947, Apr. 22-1955**      **Litho.**

| | | | | |
|---|---|---|---|---|
| 7 | A5 | 1w turquoise | 450.00 | 55.00 |
| 8 | A5 | 1w violet ('49) | 800.00 | 175.00 |
| 9 | A5 | 1w dk bl, buff ('50) | 110.00 | 55.00 |
| 10 | A5 | 1w dark blue ('50) | 60.00 | 60.00 |
| a. | | Perf 11ximperf ('50) | 6.00 | 60.00 |
| b. | | Perf 10 ('55) | — | — |

1st anniversary of agrarian reform.
Nos. 7-9 have lines of colored dots along the horizontal pin perforations.
Reprints of type A5 measure 21x24mm, versus the originals' 21-21.5x24-25mm, are finely printed in light blue and are perf 9, 10½, 11 or imperf. Value $10.

Worker and Factory — A6

**1948, June 5**      **Litho.**      **Perf. 11**

| | | | | |
|---|---|---|---|---|
| 11 | A6 | 50ch dark blue | 3,200. | 1,250. |

Second anniversary of the Labor Law.
Design size: 20-20.5x31mm.
Reprints measure 20x30-30.5mm and are perf 9, 10½, 11 or imperf. Value, $10 perf, $10 imperf.

---

Workers and Flag — A7

**1948, Aug. 15**

| | | | | |
|---|---|---|---|---|
| 12 | A7 | 50ch red brown | 4,000. | 1,500. |

Third anniversary of liberation from Japan.

Flag and Map — A8

**1948, Aug. 20**

| | | | | |
|---|---|---|---|---|
| 13 | A8 | 50ch indigo & red | 2,500. | 800.00 |

Adoption of the Constitution of the Democratic People's Republic of Korea, July 10, 1948.

## DEMOCRATIC PEOPLE'S REPUBLIC

North Korean Flag — A9

**1948, Sept. 19**      **Rouletted 12**

| | | | | |
|---|---|---|---|---|
| 14 | A9 | 25ch reddish violet | 15.00 | 100.00 |
| a. | | Perf. 10¼xroulette | | |
| 15 | A9 | 50ch gray blue | 20.00 | 50.00 |
| a. | | Perf 10½ | 40.00 | 75.00 |
| b. | | Perf 10½xroulette | | |

Establishment of the People's Republic, 9/9/48.
Design size: 23x30mm.
Reprints of No. 14 are in blue, on gummed paper, perf 9, 10½ or imperf. Size 20.5x28mm. Value, $10.
No. 15a is perforated over rouletting.

North Korean Flag — A10

**1949, Feb. 9**

| | | | | |
|---|---|---|---|---|
| 16 | A10 | 6w red & blue | 4.00 | 12.00 |
| a. | | Perf 10¼ | 35.00 | 35.00 |

No. 16 exists on both brownish wove and white wove papers.
Design size: 24x32.5-33mm.
Reprints are perf 10¼, 11 or imperf. Size 19x26.5mm. On the originals, the top and bottom panels are blue, with the center field red. On the reprints, these colors are reversed. Value, $10.
For surcharge see No. 42. For overprint see No. 76.

A11        Kim Il Sung University, Pyongyang — A12

**1949**

| | | | | |
|---|---|---|---|---|
| 17 | A11 | 1w violet | 400.00 | 200.00 |
| a. | | Perf. 11 | | |
| 18 | A12 | 1w blue | 1,200. | 125.00 |

Issue dates: No. 17, 8/9; No. 18, Sept.
Design size: 34x21mm.
Reprints of No. 17 are in slate lilac to reddish lilac, perf 8½, 9, 9x9½, 10 or imperf, on gummed paper. Size 31.5-32x20-20.5mm. Value, $10 perf, $10 imperf.

---

North Korean Flags
A13        A14

### Perf 11 or Rouletted 12 (#19)
**1949, Aug. 15**
**With or Without Gum**

| | | | | |
|---|---|---|---|---|
| 19 | A13 | 1w red, grn & blue | 700.00 | 200.00 |
| a. | | Imperfx11 | 700.00 | 200.00 |
| 20 | A14 | 1w red, grn & turq | 1,200. | 200.00 |

4th anniversary of Liberation from Japan.
Design sizes: No. 19, 20.5x31mm; No. 20, 20x29.5mm.

Order of the National Flag — A15

### Rouletted 12, Imperf (#23)
**1950, Apr. 4-1956**      **Litho.**

| | | | | |
|---|---|---|---|---|
| 21 | A15 | 1w pale sage green | 7.00 | 12.00 |
| a. | | 1w olive green | 7.00 | 12.00 |
| b. | | 1w yellow green | 7.00 | 12.00 |
| c. | | With control overprint ('51) | — | 12.00 |
| d. | | 1w emerald green | 7.00 | 12.00 |
| 22 | A15 | 1w red orange | 20.00 | 125.00 |

**Typographed**

| | | | | |
|---|---|---|---|---|
| 23 | A15 | 1w brown orange | 6,000. | 1,250. |
| 24 | A15 | 1w dark green ('51) | 60.00 | 25.00 |
| a. | | Perf 10¼ ('55) | 90.00 | |

**11xImperf.**

| | | | | |
|---|---|---|---|---|
| 25 | A15 | 1w light green | 150.00 | 60.00 |

Design sizes: No. 21, 23-23.5x37mm; No. 22, 20x32mm; No. 23, 22.5-23x36-37mm; No. 24, 22x35.5mm; No. 25, 22.5x36mm.
Reprints of type A15 are in dull blue green on white paper, perf 10¼ or imperf, size 22x35mm, or in red orange on white paper, perf 8½, 9, 10½, 10ximperf or imperf, size 20-20.5x32.5mm. Value (orange), $10 perf.

Flags, Liberation Monument
A16        Flags, Soldier
A17

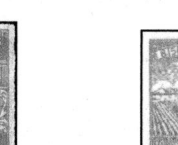

Peasant and Worker
A18        Tractor
A19

**1950, June 20-1956**
**Lithographed, Thin Paper**
**Roul. 12xImperf, Roul. 12 (#28, 29)**

| | | | | |
|---|---|---|---|---|
| 26 | A16 | 1w indigo, lt blue & red | 3.50 | 17.50 |
| a. | | Perf 10¼ ('55) | 12.00 | 24.50 |
| 27 | A16 | 1w brown orange | 9.00 | 60.00 |
| 28 | A17 | 2w red, stl bl & blk | 5.00 | 17.50 |
| a. | | Perf 10¼ ('55) | 12.00 | 24.00 |
| 29 | A18 | 6w green | 6.50 | |
| 30 | A19 | 10w brown | 9.50 | |

**Typographed, Thin Paper, Roul. 12**

| | | | | |
|---|---|---|---|---|
| 31 | A18 | 6w red | 3.50 | 17.50 |
| a. | | Perf 10¼ ('55) | 29.00 | 24.00 |
| b. | | Thick brownish paper, imperf x roul. 12 | 29.00 | 24.00 |

**32** A19 10w brown    3.50    —
  *a.* Thick brownish paper, imperf
     x roul. 12    36.00   32.50
     *Nos. 26-32 (7)*    40.50 112.50

Fifth anniversary of liberation from Japan.
Design sizes: No. 30, 20x27.5mm; No. 31, 22x33mm; No. 32, 22x30mm.
Reprints of No. 26 are on medium white paper, distinguishable by numerous design differences, among which are: characters in top inscription are 1½mm high, rather than 1mm, with 3 short lines at either side, rather than 2; top corner ornaments have a dark center, rather than white; 4 ray beams at left of monument, rather than 3; no dots on right face of spire, while originals have 3 small dots; value numerals within well-formed circles.
Reprints of Nos. 28 and 29 are on medium white paper, perf 10¼, 11 or imperf. No. 28 reprints are in light green, No. 29 in rose red, dull blue and black. Value, $10 each.
Reprints of type A19 are 22x31mm in size, on medium white paper and are perf 10¼ or imperf.

Capitol, Seoul — A20

**1950, July 10**    **Litho.**    *Roul. 12*
**33** A20   1w bl grn, red &
     blue    40.00 *300.00*

Capture of Seoul.

Order of Ri Sun
Sin — A21

**1951, Apr. 5**    **Typo.**    *Imperf*
**34** A21   6w orange    15.00   15.00
  *a.* Perf 10¼    30.00

No. 34 also exists perf 9x10½.
No. 34 is on brownish laid paper. Design size: 21.5-22x29.5-30mm.
Reprints are on white paper, perf 10¼ or imperf. Size 21.5x30mm. On the reprints, the center of the lower left point of the star is open; on the originals, it is hatched. Value, $10 each.
For surcharge see No. 43.

Hero Kim Ki Ok — A22

**1951, Apr. 17**
**35** A22   1w blue    19.50   19.50
  *a.* Perf 10¼    180.00

No. 35 was printed on unbleached and off-white wood-pulp laid papers, with wood chips visible. The laid lines are often difficult or impossible to detect.
Design size: 23-23.5x35.5-36mm.
Reprints are on white wove paper, perf 10¼, 10½ or imperf. Size 22.5x33.5mm. Value, $10 each.

Soviet and North Korean
Flags
A23

Hero Kim Ki U
A24

N. Korean, Chinese &
Russian Soldiers — A25

---

**1951, Aug. 15-1955**    **Litho.**    *Roul. 12*
**36** A23   1w dark blue    75.00   *75.00*
**37** A23   1w red    200.00 *200.00*
**38** A24   1w dark blue    125.00 *125.00*
**39** A24   1w red    125.00 *125.00*
**40** A25   2w dark blue    50.00   *50.00*
**41** A25   2w red    50.00   *50.00*
     *Nos. 36-41 (11)*    1,720.   *1,720.*

**Perf 10¼ Over Roulette (1955)**
**36a** A23   1w dark blue    55.00   *55.00*
**37a** A23   1w red    200.00 *200.00*
**38a** A24   1w dark blue    200.00 *200.00*
**39a** A24   1w red    125.00 *125.00*
**40a** A25   2w dark blue    55.00   *55.00*
**41a** A25   2w red    30.00   *30.00*
     *Nos. 36a-41a (11)*    1,655.   *1,655.*

Nos. 36-41 and 36a-41a exist on both coarse buff and white wove papers. Values are the same. Various perfs and roulettes and roulettes exists; not all combinations are known.
Design sizes: Nos. 36 and 37, 17x23.5mm; Nos. 38 and 39, 16x23mm; Nos. 40 and 41, 23x16.5mm.
Reprints of No. 36 are perf 9, 10½x10 or imperf. Size 15.5-16x22.5mm.
Reprints of No. 38 are perf 9, 10 or imperf. They have no lines of shading between the characters in the top inscription.
Reprints of No. 40 are perf 9, 10 or imperf. Size 22-22.5x16.5mm. The Korean "Won" character at lower right is in 4 parts, rather than 3.
Reprints are all light ultramarine. Value, $10 each.

**Nos. 16, 34 Surcharged**

On No. 16      On No. 34

**1951, Nov. 1**      *Imperf*
**42** A10   5w on 6w red &
     blue (#16)    150.00   60.00
**43** A21   5w on 6w org
     (#34)    1,000.   725.00

Order of Soldier's
Honor — A26

**1951, Nov. 15-1956**
**44** A26   40w scarlet
          (16.5x25mm)    22.50   4.50
  *a.* Perf 10¼ ('55)    22.50   7.75
**45** A26   40w scarlet
          (17x24mm)    12.00   4.50
  *a.* Perf 10¼ ('56)    12.00   7.75

Victory Propaganda — A27

**1951, Nov. 15-1956**
**46** A27   10w dark blue    15.00   7.75
**47** A27   10w dark blue    15.00   7.75
  *a.* Perf 10¼ ('56)    22.50   22.50

No. 47 also exists perf 8½.
Design sizes: No. 46, 17x25.5mm; No. 47, 16.5-17x25mm.
Reprints are in light blue, perf 10¼, 11 or imperf. Size 16.5-17x25mm. Value and inscription at bottom are outlined and clear against cross-hatched background. Value, $10 each.

Ri Su Dok, Guerilla
Hero — A28

**1952, Jan. 10-1955**
**48** A28   70w brown    15.00   3.50
  *a.* Perf 10¼ ('55)    25.00   12.00
  *b.* 70w black brown    120.00
  *c.* As "b," perf 10¼    60.00

---

Dove, Flag &
Globe — A29

**1952, Jan. 20-1957**
**49** A29   20w scar, dp bl & lt bl    24.00   6.00
  *a.* Perf 10¼ ('55)    24.00   12.00

Peace Propaganda.
No. 49 also exists perf 8½, 11 and rouletted 11½.
No. 49 was printed on off-white or buff paper, with broken lines between stamps. Design size: 22x31-31.5mm.
Reprints are perf 10¼ or imperf, in red, slate blue and pale turquoise blue on white paper. Size 22x31mm. They lack the broken lines between stamps. Value, each $50.

Gen. Pang Ho-san — A30

**1952, Apr.**
**50** A30   10w dull purple    60.00   24.00

Honoring North Korean General Bang Ho San.
No. 50 is also known with locally-applied rough perforation.

Labor Day — A31

**1952, Apr. 20-1955**      *Imperf*
**51** A31   10w rose red    300.00 *300.00*
  *a.* Perf 10¼ ('55)    300.00 *300.00*

Enforcement of the Labor
Law, 6th Anniv. — A32

**1952, June 1-1955**
**52** A32   10w light blue    350.00 *350.00*

Design size: 18x26mm. Broken lines between stamps.
Reprints are in dull or slate blue, on thick, gummed paper, with no broken lines between stamps. Size 17.5x25.5-26mm. Value, $10 each.

Day of Anti-U.S.
Imperialist Struggle — A33

**1952, June 4-1956**
**53** A33   10w rose red    180.00 150.00
  *a.* Perf 10¼ ('56)    180.00

Design size: 17.5x25.5-26mm. Broken lines between stamps.
Reprints are in bright rose red, perf 10, 10¼, 11 or imperf. on thick, gummed paper, with no broken lines between stamps. Size 17.5x26mm. Value, $10 each.

North Korean-Chinese
Friendship — A34

**1952, July 25-1956**
**54** A34   20w deep blue    50.00   24.00
  *a.* Perf 10¼ ('56)    50.00   24.00

Design size: 18x21.5mm. Printed on thin white wove paper, with clearly discernible mesh pattern.
Reprints are perf 10¼ or imperf, on thick white wove paper, with no pattern visible. Size 18.5-19x21.5-22mm. Value, $10 each.

---

Flags &      Soldier &
Monument      Monument
A35      A36

**1952-55**
**55** A35   10w carmine    150.00 150.00
  *a.* Perf 10¼ ('55)    200.00
**56** A36   10w scarlet    275.00 275.00
  *a.* Perf 10¼ ('55)    350.00 350.00

Seventh Anniversary of Liberation from Japan.
Issue dates: No. 55, 7/25/52; No. 56, 8/1/52.
Design sizes: No. 55, 20.5-21x27.5-28mm; No. 56, 29.5-30x18.5mm.
Reprints of No. 55 are in vermilion, on thick paper, perf 10¼, 11 or imperf. Size 20.5x27-27.5mm. Value, $10 each.
Reprints of No. 56 are in rose red, perf 10, 10¼, 11 or imperf. Size 30.5-31x18.5-19mm. Value, $10 each.
Note: Original are typographed; reprints are lithographed on thin white paper.

International Youth
Day — A37

**1952, Oct. 20-1955**
**57** A37   10w deep green    72.50   80.00
  *a.* Perf 10¼ ('55)    72.50

No. 57 is on thick paper, with very thin gum. Design size: 20.5-21x28mm.
Reprints are on thin to medium paper, without gum, perf 10¼, 11 or imperf. Size 20x27mm. Value, $10 each.

Soldiers in      Soldier and
Battle      Flag
A38      A39

**1953, Jan. 20-1955**
**58** A38   10w rose carmine    130.00 130.00
  *a.* Perf 10¼ ('55)    130.00
**59** A39   40w red brown    60.00   60.00
  *a.* Perf 10¼ ('55)    75.00

Fifth Anniversary of the Founding of the Korean People's Army.
Design sizes: No. 58, 21.5-22x26-26.5mm; No. 59, 21.5x27mm.
Reprints of No. 58 are on thick, gummed paper, perf 10¼, 11 or imperf. Size: 21.5-22x26.5mm. Value, $10 each.
Reprints of No. 59 are on thick, gummed paper, perf 10, 10½, 11 or imperf. Size: 21.5x26.5mm. Value, $10 each.

Woman with      Women
Flag      and Globe
A40      A41

**1953, Mar. 1-1955**
**60** A40   10w carmine    60.00   60.00
  *a.* Perf 10¼ ('55)    60.00
**61** A41   40w yellow green    72.50   72.50
  *a.* Perf 10¼ ('55)    72.50

International Women's Day.
Design sizes: No. 60, 20x29.5mm; No. 61, 21x29mm.
Reprints of No. 60 are in rose carmine, on thin paper, perf 10¼, 11 or imperf. Size 20.5x30mm.
Reprints of No. 61 may be distinguished from the originals by design differences: the dove's wing consists of many small feathers (3 large feathers on original), the women's mouths are all open (closed on original), and 3 thin connected lines on center woman's shirt (3 thick separate lines on original). Value, $10 each.

Worker
A42

Workers
Marching
A43

**1953, Apr. 15-1955**
62   A42   10w yellow green      60.00  60.00
 *a.*    Perf 10¼ ('55)                72.50   —
63   A43   40w orange brown     60.00  60.00
 *a.*    Perf 10¼ ('55)                72.50   —

May Day
Reprints of No. 62 are in green or emerald green, perf 9½x8½, 10¼, 11 or imperf. Among many design differences, they have 4 horizontal lines between flag and frame line at upper left, many short hatching lines between frame line and top inscription, many horizontal lines between flag and flag pole at upper right, and won letter clear. On originals, there are one or no lines at upper left, no lines between frame line and top inscription, no lines between flag and flag pole, and the won character is not clearly defined. Value, $10 each.
Reprints of No. 63 are perf 10, 10¼ or imperf. On the reprints, the right flag pole touches the frame line, and the left center element of the won character resembles a "T." On the originals, the right flag pole does not touch the frame line, and the center element of the won character resembles an inverted "L." Value, $10 each.

Soldier
A44

Battle
A45

**1953, June 1-1955**
64   A44   10w greenish blue    110.00  110.00
 *a.*    Perf 10¼ ('55)               110.00    —
65   A45   40w scarlet         110.00  130.00
 *a.*    Perf 10¼ ('55)               110.00    —

Day of Anti-U.S. Imperialist Struggle.
Nos. 64 and 65 were issued with gum. Design sizes: 10w, 24x33mm; 40w, 24-24.5x33mm.
Reprints of No. 64 and 65 are on thick paper, perf 10¼, 11 or imperf. Design sizes: 10w, 23.5-24x32mm; 40w, 24x32-32.5mm. No. 64 is in turquoise blue, No. 65 in vermilion or orange vermilion. Value, $10 each.

4th World Festival of
Youth & Students
A46          A47

**1953, June 10-1955**      **With Gum**
66   A46   10w dp dl bl & pale
                     turq bl       72.50  72.50
 *a.*    Perf 10¼ ('55)           85.00    —
67   A47   20w gray grn &pink    60.00  36.00
 *a.*    Perf 10¼ ('55)           72.50    —

Two types of reprints of No. 66 exist. On the reprints, the forelocks of the center and right heads have detailed hairlines, and the right head shows eye and eyebrow. On the originals, both features are solid. Value, $10 each.

Victory Issue — A48

**1953, June 1-1955**      **With Gum**
68   A48   10w brn & yel       360.00  400.00
 *a.*    Perf 10¼ ('55)          325.00  500.00

8th Anniversary of
Liberation from
Japan — A49

**1953, Aug. 5-1955**
69   A49   10w red orange    *4,000.   4,000.*

Design size: 25x35.5mm.
Reprints are perf 10¼ or imperf. Size: 24.5-25x34.5-35mm. Left side of monument is shaded, and windows are fully drawn and shaded. On the originals, the monument is unshaded, and the windows are only partially drawn and half shaded. Value, $10 each.

5th Anniv. Founding of
D.P.R.K. — A50

**1953, Aug. 25-1955**
70   A50   10w dp blue & red   72.50  72.50
 *a.*    Perf 10¼ ('55)           95.00    —

Design size: 21.5-22x29.5-30mm. Inscribed "1948-1953."
Reprints are in blue and vermilion, perf 9x9½ or imperf and are inscribed "1948-1955." Size: 22.5x30mm. Value, each $100.

Liberation
Monument — A51

**1953, Dec. 25-1955**      **With Gum**
71   A51   10w deep slate     72.50  47.50
 *a.*    Perf 10¼ ('55)           72.50    —

Design size: 20x31mm.
Reprints are in deep gray. Size: 19-19.5x30.5-31mm. Value, $10 each.

Worker & Crane — A52

**1954, Jan. 25-1955**      **With Gum**
72   A52   10w light blue     85.00  55.00
 *a.*    Perf 10¼ ('55)          110.00    —

Reconstruction and Economic Development.
Design size: 22x31.5mm.
Reprints are in greenish blue or dull blue, without gum. Size: 21.5x31mm. The horizontal lines defining the sky and clouds are clear and even, and the details of the crane are distinct. Value, $10 each.

Korean People's Army,
6th Anniv. — A53

**1954, Jan. 25-1955**      **With Gum**
73   A53   10w dp car red    350.00    —
 *a.*    Perf 10¼ ('55)          350.00    —
 *b.*    Rouletted             350.00    —

Design size: 23.5-24x38mm.
Reprints are in vermilion or orange vermilion. Size: 23-23.5x37.5-38mm. The design is much clearer than in the originals, with thin distinct characters in top inscription and complete unbroken frame line at right. Value, $10 each.

International Women's
Day — A54

**1954, Feb. 25-1955**      **With Gum**
74   A54   10w carmine       250.00  250.00
 *a.*    Perf 10¼ ('55)          300.00    —

Design size: 19.5-20x29-29.5mm.
Reprints are in vermilion. Size: 20-20.5x29.5-30mm. The USSR and PRC flags at top right are legible, and the shading under the center and right women's chins is represented by several fine lines (solid on originals). Value, $10 each.

Labor Day — A55

**1954, Apr. 15-1955**      **With Gum**
75   A55   10w vermilion      72.50  72.50
 *a.*    Perf 10¼ ('55)           72.50    —

Design size: 20x27-27.5mm.
Reprints are in orange vermilion, perf 8½x9, 9, 10¼ or imperf. Size: 19-19.5x26-26.5. Value, $10 each.

No. 16 overprinted "Fee
Collected" in Korean

**1954, May (?)**
76   A10   6w red & blue    1,750.  1,750.

Day of Anti-U.S.
Imperialist
Struggle — A56

**1954, June 10-1955**      **With Gum**
77   A56   10w red brown     210.00  210.00
 *a.*    Perf 10¼ ('55)          210.00  210.00

National Congress of
Young Activists — A57

**1954, July 20-1955**      **With Gum**
78   A57   10w blue, red &
                     slate     600.00  300.00
 *a.*    Perf 10¼ ('55)          —        —

Design size: 20x30mm.
Reprints are in blue, scarlet vermilion & deep slate. Size: 19.5-20x29-29.5mm. On the originals, the worker's hand is beneath the tassel of the flag and is less than 1mm from the frame line. On the reprints, hand is to the right of the tassel and 2mm from frame line. Value, $10 each.

Liberation from Japan,
9th Anniv. — A58

**1954, Aug. 1-1955**      **With Gum**
79   A58   10w chestnut       50.00  50.00
 *a.*    Perf 10¼ ('55)           50.00    —

Design size: 20-20.5x30mm.
Reprints of No. 79 are perf 10¼, 11 or imperf. Size: 20x29-29.5mm. Soldier's nose line straight and strong, 3 lines of cooling holes in gun barrel (2 on originals). Value, $10 each.

North Korean
Flag — A59

**1954, Aug. 25-1955**      **With Gum**
80   A59   10w blue & dp red  100.00  *100.00*
 *a.*    Perf 10¼ ('55)          120.00    —

Design size: 24x31.5-32mm.
Reprints are in dull blue and bright rose red. Size: 25-25.5x30.5-31mm. Value, $10 each.

Taedong Gate,
Pyongyang — A60

**1954, Sept. 1-1956**      **With Gum**
81   A60   5w reddish brown   15.00  3.75
 *a.*    Perf 10¼ ('56)          22.50    —
82   A60   5w lilac brown     15.00  3.75
 *a.*    Perf 10¼ ('56)          22.50    —

Hwanghae Iron
Works — A61

Hwanghae Iron
Works & Workers —
A61a

No. 84, Hwanghae Iron Works & workers,
horiz.

**1954, Nov. 1-1956**
83   A61   10w light blue     22.50  3.00
 *a.*    Perf 10¼ ('55)          45.00    —
84   A61a  10w chocolate      22.50  3.00
 *a.*    Perf 10¼ ('55)          45.00    —
 *b.*    Roul. 9x8½ ('56)        50.00  50.00

Korean People's Army,
7th Anniversary — A62

**1955, Jan. 25**      **With Gum**
85   A62   10w rose red       36.00  36.00
 *a.*    Perf 10¼                36.00    —

International Women's
Day — A63

**1955, Feb. 25**      **With Gum**
86   A63   10w deep blue      36.00  36.00
 *a.*    Perf 10¼                45.00    —

Reprints are in blue, perf 10¼, imperf and imperf x 10¼. Corners of design are clearly and uniformly indented. Value, $10 each.

A63a          A63b

Labor Day

**1955, Apr. 16**      **With Gum**
86A  A63a  10w green          60.00  30.00
 *a.*    Perf 10¼                —        —
86B  A63b  10w violet brown   60.00  30.00
 *a.*    Perf 10¼                60.00    —

Design sizes: No. 86A, 19.5-20x30mm. No. 86B, 19x30mm.
Reprints of No. 86A measure 19.5x29mm. Reprints of 86B measure 19x29.5mm and are without gum. Value, $10 each.

Admiral Ri Sun-Sin — A64

**1955, May 14-1956**

| | | | | |
|---|---|---|---|---|
| 87 | A64 | 1w blue, *pale green* | 15.00 | 15.00 |
| *a.* | | Perf 10¼ ('56) | 18.00 | |
| 88 | A64 | 2w rose, *buff* | 15.00 | 1.50 |
| *a.* | | Perf 10¼ ('56) | 22.00 | |
| 89 | A64 | 2w rose red ('56) | 30.00 | 2.75 |
| *a.* | | Perf 10¼ ('56) | 30.00 | — |
| | | *Nos. 87-89 (3)* | 60.00 | 19.25 |

No. 89 is redrawn, with a larger "2."
Design sizes: Nos. 87, 88, 20x29-30mm.
Reprints of No. 87 are in dull blue, on pale apple green, perf 10¼, 11½x10½, imperf, or roul. 8½. Size 19x28-28.5mm. Reprints of No. 88 are 19-19.5x28.-28.5mm in size. Value, $10 each.

Labor Law, 9th Anniv. — A65

**1955, May 30**

| | | | | |
|---|---|---|---|---|
| 90 | A65 | 10w rose | 90.00 | 90.00 |
| *a.* | | Perf 10¼ | — | — |

No. 90 was issued with a very thin yellow gum. Design size: 18.5-19x27.5-28mm.
Reprints exist perf 10¼, 11 or imperf. Size 18-18.5x27-27.5mm. Value unused, $10 each.

Korea-U.S.S.R. Friendship Month
A66          A67

**1955, July**                    **Perf. 10**

| | | | | |
|---|---|---|---|---|
| 91 | A66 | 10w rose red | 30.00 | — |
| *a.* | | Imperf | 30.00 | 21.00 |
| 92 | A66 | 10w org red & vio blue | 30.00 | — |
| *a.* | | Imperf | 30.00 | 21.00 |
| 93 | A67 | 20w red & lt blue | 30.00 | — |
| *a.* | | Imperf | 30.00 | 24.00 |
| *b.* | | Inscription below flag in two colors | — | — |
| *c.* | | As "b," imperf | — | — |
| 94 | A67 | 20w ver & lt blue | 24.00 | — |
| *a.* | | Imperf | 24.00 | 21.00 |
| | | *Nos. 91-94 (4)* | 114.00 | |

Issue dates: Nos. 91, 93, 7/16; Nos. 92, 94, 7/20.
Design sizes: No. 91, 22x32.5mm; No. 92, 29.5x43mm; No. 93, 18.5x32mm; No. 94, 24.5-25x42.5x43mm.
Reprints of No. 94 are in light vermilion and light blue, perf 10¼, 11 or imperf, with a very thin gum. Size: 24-24.5x42-43mm. The two blue bands of the flag are solidly colored, with many white spots. On the originals, this area consists of fine lines with few or no white areas. Value, $10 each.

Liberation from Japan, 10th Anniv. — A68

**1955, July 20**                  **Perf. 10¼**

| | | | | |
|---|---|---|---|---|
| 95 | A68 | 10w dull green | 24.00 | — |
| *a.* | | Imperf | 24.00 | 18.00 |
| 96 | A68 | 10w ver, dull blue & chestnut | 24.00 | — |
| *a.* | | Imperf | 24.00 | 18.00 |

Design sizes: No. 95, 21.5-22x31.5-32mm; No. 96, 29-29.5-42-43mm.
Reprints of No. 95 are in dull blue green, perf 10¼, 11 or imperf, on gummed paper. Size: 21-21.5x31mm. Reprints of No. 96 are in rose red, dull to greenish blue and yellow brown, perf 10¼ or imperf. Size: 28-28.5x42.5-43mm. Value, $10 each.

---

Standing Rock in Sea-Kumgang Maritime Park — A69

**1956, Jan. 20**

| | | | | |
|---|---|---|---|---|
| 97 | A69 | 10w blue, *bluish* | 20.00 | — |
| *a.* | | Imperf | 25.00 | 25.00 |

People's Army, 8th Anniv. — A70

**1956, Jan. 20**

| | | | | |
|---|---|---|---|---|
| 98 | A70 | 10w lt brn, *pale yel* | 100.00 | 100.00 |
| | | *grn* | | |
| *a.* | | Imperf | 90.00 | 90.00 |

Design size: 20x27-27.5mm.
Reprints are in chestnut on pale sage green paper, perf 10¼, 11 or imperf. Size: 19.5-20x27mm. Creases in the soldier's shirt are distinct, and nose and eyes are strongly shaded. Value, $10 each.

May Day — A71

**1956, Apr. 29**

| | | | | |
|---|---|---|---|---|
| 99 | A71 | 10w blue | 100.00 | 100.00 |
| *a.* | | Imperf | 100.00 | 100.00 |

Design size: 23.5-24x35-35.5mm.
Reprints are perf 10¼, 11 or imperf, on gummed paper. Size: 23.5x35mm. Clear hatching lines at right of top inscription; many feathers in dove's wing. Value, $10 each.

Ryongwang Pavilion and Taedong Gate, Pyongyang — A72

**1956, May 8**

| | | | | |
|---|---|---|---|---|
| 100 | A72 | 2w light blue | 55.00 | 55.00 |
| *a.* | | Imperf | 55.00 | 55.00 |
| *b.* | | Rouletted | 85.00 | — |

Reprints of No. 100 are on thicker, gummed paper. The tail of the central left element in the "won" inscription at lower right extends beyond the left edge of the L-shaped character beneath it. Value, $6.

Moranbong Theater, Pyongyang — A73

**1956, May 8**

| | | | | |
|---|---|---|---|---|
| 101 | A73 | 40w light green | 30.00 | 12.00 |
| *a.* | | Imperf | 85.00 | 72.50 |

Labor Law, 10th Anniv. — A74

**1956, June 7**

| | | | | |
|---|---|---|---|---|
| 102 | A74 | 10w dark brown | 8.00 | 2.50 |
| *a.* | | Perf 9 | 80.00 | 60.00 |
| *b.* | | Imperf | 180.00 | 120.00 |

---

Korean Children's Union, 10th Anniv. — A75

**1956, June 7**

| | | | | |
|---|---|---|---|---|
| 103 | A75 | 10w dk brown | 15.00 | 6.50 |
| *a.* | | Imperf | 160.00 | 35.00 |

Law on Equality of the Sexes, 10th Anniv. — A76

**1956, July 10**

| | | | | |
|---|---|---|---|---|
| 104 | A76 | 10w dark brown | 10.00 | 3.75 |
| *a.* | | Perf 9 | 25.00 | 15.00 |
| *b.* | | Imperf | 35.00 | 17.50 |

Nationalization of Major Industries, 10th Anniv. — A77

**1956, July 10**

| | | | | |
|---|---|---|---|---|
| 105 | A77 | 10w dark brown | 90.00 | — |
| *a.* | | Imperf | 210.00 | — |

Liberation from Japan, 11th Anniv. — A78

**1956, July 24**

| | | | | |
|---|---|---|---|---|
| 106 | A78 | 10w rose red | 14.00 | 3.25 |
| *a.* | | Imperf | 160.00 | 30.00 |

Machinist — A79

**1956, July 28**

| | | | | |
|---|---|---|---|---|
| 107 | A79 | 1w dark brown | 3.75 | 2.00 |
| *a.* | | Perf 9 | 12.50 | 8.00 |
| *b.* | | Imperf | 32.50 | 14.00 |

Kim Il Sung University, 10th Anniv. — A80

**1956, Sept. 30**

| | | | | |
|---|---|---|---|---|
| 108 | A80 | 10w dark brown | 10.00 | 9.00 |
| *a.* | | Imperf | 32.50 | 14.00 |

4th Congress, Korean Democratic Youth League — A81

**1956, Nov. 3**

| | | | | |
|---|---|---|---|---|
| 109 | A81 | 10w dark brown | 14.00 | 3.25 |
| *a.* | | Imperf | 32.50 | 18.00 |

Model Peasant — A82

---

**1956, Nov. 14**

| | | | | |
|---|---|---|---|---|
| 110 | A82 | 10w rose | 7.50 | 2.25 |
| *a.* | | Imperf | 21.00 | 11.00 |
| *b.* | | Rouletted | — | — |

220th Anniv. Birth of Pak Ji Won (1737-1805) — A83

**1957, Mar. 4**

| | | | | |
|---|---|---|---|---|
| 111 | A83 | 10w blue | 5.00 | 1.25 |
| *a.* | | Imperf | 19.00 | 10.00 |

Tabo Pagoda in Pulguk Temple A84

Ulmil Pavilion, Pyongyang A85

**1957, Mar. 20**

| | | | | |
|---|---|---|---|---|
| 112 | A84 | 5w light blue | 6.00 | 2.50 |
| *a.* | | Rouletted | — | — |
| *b.* | | Perf 11 (with gum) | — | — |
| *c.* | | Imperf | 87.50 | 21.00 |
| 113 | A85 | 40w gray green | 7.50 | 3.25 |
| *a.* | | Perf 11 | — | — |
| *b.* | | Imperf | 22.50 | 11.00 |

No. 113b was issued both with and without gum.

Productivity Campaign — A86

**1957, July 4**      **With or Without Gum**

| | | | | |
|---|---|---|---|---|
| 114 | A86 | 10w ultramarine | 6.75 | 4.50 |
| *a.* | | Perf 11 | — | — |
| *b.* | | Imperf | 32.50 | 15.00 |

Steelworker A87

Voters Marching A88

**1957, Aug.**

| | | | | |
|---|---|---|---|---|
| 115 | A87 | 1w orange | 3.50 | .75 |
| *a.* | | Imperf | 9.50 | 4.25 |
| 116 | A87 | 2w brown | 3.50 | .75 |
| *a.* | | Imperf | 9.50 | 4.25 |
| 117 | A88 | 10w vermilion | 17.50 | 3.25 |
| *a.* | | Imperf | 65.00 | 35.00 |
| | | *Nos. 115-117 (3)* | 24.50 | 4.75 |

Second General Election.
There are two types of the 1w. On type 1, the won character is approx. 2½mm in diameter and is distinct. On type 2, the character is approx. 1½mm in diameter and is virtually illegible.
Issued: 10w, 8/10; 1w, 2w, 8/13.

Founding of Pyongyang, 1530th Anniv. — A89

**1957, Sept. 28**              **Perf. 10**

| | | | | |
|---|---|---|---|---|
| 118 | A89 | 10w blue green | 3.00 | .65 |
| *a.* | | Imperf | 30.00 | 9.00 |

Lenin
A90

Lenin &
Flags
A91

Kim Il Sung
at Pochonbo
A92

Pouring
Steel
A93

**1957**
| | | | | |
|---|---|---|---|---|
| **119** | A90 | 10w gray blue | 2.00 | .95 |
| *a.* | | Imperf | 30.00 | 9.00 |
| **120** | A91 | 10w blue green | 2.00 | .95 |
| *a.* | | Imperf | 30.00 | 9.00 |
| *b.* | | Rouletted 13 | — | — |
| **121** | A92 | 10w red | 2.00 | .95 |
| *a.* | | Imperf | 30.00 | 9.00 |
| *b.* | | Rouletted 13 | — | — |
| **122** | A93 | 10w red orange | 4.50 | .95 |
| *a.* | | Imperf | 120.00 | 13.00 |
| *b.* | | Rouletted 13 | — | — |
| | *Nos. 119-122 (4)* | | *10.50* | *3.80* |

40th Anniversary of the Russian October Revolution.
Issued: Nos. 119, 120, 9/30; No. 121, 10/3; 122, 10/16.
No. 120 exists with gum.

4th Congress World
Federation of Trade
Unions — A94

**1957, Oct. 3**
| | | | | |
|---|---|---|---|---|
| **123** | A94 | 10w ultra & lt grn | 2.50 | 1.10 |
| *a.* | | Imperf | 30.00 | 11.00 |

No. 123a exists with or without gum.

Russian Friendship
Month — A95

**1957, Oct. 16**
| | | | | |
|---|---|---|---|---|
| **124** | A95 | 10w green | 4.50 | 1.10 |
| *a.* | | Imperf | 210.00 | 140.00 |

Doctor
Weighing
Baby — A96

Bandaging
Hand — A97

**1957, Nov. 1**
| | | | | |
|---|---|---|---|---|
| **125** | A96 | 1w red | 9.00 | 1.25 |
| *a.* | | Imperf | 65.00 | 12.00 |
| **126** | A96 | 2w red | 9.00 | 1.25 |
| *a.* | | Imperf | 65.00 | 12.00 |
| *b.* | | Rouletted | — | — |
| **127** | A97 | 10w red | 35.00 | 3.75 |
| *a.* | | Imperf | 130.00 | 35.00 |
| | *Nos. 125-127 (3)* | | *53.00* | *6.25* |

Red Cross.
No. 126 exists without or without gum. No. 126a was issued with gum.

Flying
Dragon
Kettle
A98

Flying
Dragon
Incense
Burner
A99

**1958, Jan. 14**
| | | | | |
|---|---|---|---|---|
| **128** | A98 | 10w blue | 11.00 | 1.40 |
| *a.* | | Imperf | 87.50 | 18.00 |
| **129** | A99 | 10w gray green | 11.00 | 1.40 |
| *a.* | | Imperf | 87.50 | 18.00 |

Nos. 128a and 129a exist with or without gum.

Woljong Temple
Pagoda — A100

**1958, Feb. 21**     *Perf. 10*
| | | | | |
|---|---|---|---|---|
| **130** | A100 | 5w lt green | 1.75 | .65 |
| *a.* | | Imperf | 24.50 | 11.50 |
| *b.* | | Rouletted | — | — |

*Perf. 10½*
| | | | | |
|---|---|---|---|---|
| **131** | A100 | 10w lt blue | 5.00 | 2.25 |
| *a.* | | Imperf | 30.00 | 16.00 |
| *b.* | | Rouletted | — | — |

No. 130 was issued with gum.

Soldier
A101

Soldier, Flag &
Hwanghae Iron
Works
A102

**1958, Feb.**     **Photo**     *Perf. 10*
| | | | | |
|---|---|---|---|---|
| **132** | A101 | 10w blue | 7.25 | 1.00 |
| *a.* | | Imperf | 52.50 | 19.00 |
| *b.* | | Rouletted | — | — |
| *c.* | | Perf 11 | — | — |

*Litho*
| | | | | |
|---|---|---|---|---|
| **133** | A102 | 10w rose | 10.00 | 1.10 |
| *a.* | | Imperf | 52.50 | 19.00 |

10th Anniversary of the Korean People's Army.
No. 133 was issued with or without gum.

Rocket
Launch,
Sputnik
A103

Sputnik in Orbit
A104

Designs: 40w, Sputnik over observatory.

**1958, Mar. 26**     **Photo.**
| | | | | |
|---|---|---|---|---|
| **134** | A103 | 10w dull blue green | 7.75 | 4.50 |
| *a.* | | Imperf | 65.00 | 19.00 |
| **135** | A104 | 20w dull blue green | 7.75 | 4.50 |
| *a.* | | Imperf | 65.00 | 19.00 |
| *b.* | | Rouletted | — | — |
| **136** | A104 | 40w dull blue green | 7.75 | 4.50 |
| *a.* | | Imperf | 65.00 | 19.00 |
| **137** | A103 | 70w dull blue green | 9.00 | 8.00 |
| *a.* | | Imperf | 100.00 | 30.00 |
| | *Nos. 134-137 (4)* | | *32.25* | *21.50* |

International Geophysical Year.
Nos. 134-137 exist with or without gum.

Young Socialist
Constructors
Congress — A105

**1958, May 12**     **Litho.**
| | | | | |
|---|---|---|---|---|
| **138** | A105 | 10w blue | 4.00 | 1.10 |
| *a.* | | Imperf | 27.00 | 10.00 |

Opening of
Hwanghae Iron
Works — A106

**1958, May 22**
| | | | | |
|---|---|---|---|---|
| **139** | A106 | 10w lt blue | 8.50 | 1.25 |
| *a.* | | Imperf | 37.50 | 12.50 |

Commemorative
Badge — A107

**1958, May 27**
| | | | | |
|---|---|---|---|---|
| **140** | A107 | 10w multicolored | 6.25 | 1.35 |
| *a.* | | Imperf | 25.00 | 6.00 |
| *b.* | | Perf 11 | — | — |
| *c.* | | Rouletted | — | — |

Departure of Chinese People's Volunteers.
See No. 150.

4th International
Democratic Women's
Congress — A108

**1958, June 5**
| | | | | |
|---|---|---|---|---|
| **141** | A108 | 10w blue | 2.50 | .95 |
| *a.* | | Imperf | 40.00 | 11.00 |

Congress
Emblem — A109

**1958, July 4**
| | | | | |
|---|---|---|---|---|
| **142** | A109 | 10w grn & red brn | 3.50 | 2.40 |
| *a.* | | Imperf | 27.50 | 6.25 |
| *b.* | | Perf 11 | 11.00 | — |

First Congress of the Young Workers of the World Federation of Trade Unions.

Apartment House,
East
Pyongyang — A110

**1958, July 24**
| | | | | |
|---|---|---|---|---|
| **143** | A110 | 10w lt blue | 5.00 | 1.25 |
| *a.* | | Imperf | 25.00 | 8.75 |
| *b.* | | Perf 11 | — | — |

Workers' Apartment
House,
Pyongyang — A111

**1958, Aug. 21**
| | | | | |
|---|---|---|---|---|
| **144** | A111 | 10w blue green | 5.00 | 1.25 |
| *a.* | | Imperf | 25.00 | 8.75 |

Hungnam
Fertilizer
Plant — A112

Pyongyang
Railway
Station — A113

DPRK Arms
A114

Weaver
A115

Dam,
Pyongyang — A116

**1958**     **Litho.**
| | | | | |
|---|---|---|---|---|
| **145** | A112 | 10w blue green | 6.00 | .95 |
| *a.* | | Imperf | 145.00 | 18.00 |
| *b.* | | Perf 11 | — | — |
| **146** | A113 | 10w dp blue green | 22.00 | 3.50 |
| *a.* | | Imperf | 165.00 | 42.50 |
| *b.* | | Perf 11 | — | — |
| **147** | A114 | 10w red brn & yel grn | 4.50 | 1.00 |
| *a.* | | Imperf | 350.00 | 120.00 |

***Photo***
| | | | | |
|---|---|---|---|---|
| **148** | A115 | 10w sepia | 17.50 | 3.75 |
| *a.* | | Imperf | 225.00 | 62.50 |
| **149** | A116 | 10w sepia | 29.00 | 12.00 |
| *a.* | | Imperf | 165.00 | 35.00 |
| | *Nos. 145-149 (5)* | | *79.00* | *21.20* |

10th Anniversary Korean People's Republic.
Issued: Nos. 145, 146, 8/21; No. 147, 9/7; Nos. 148, 149, 9/10.

Soldier and Troop
Train — A117

**1958, Sept. 10**     **Photo.**     *Perf. 10*
| | | | | |
|---|---|---|---|---|
| **150** | A117 | 10w sepia | 45.00 | 11.50 |
| *a.* | | Imperf | 360.00 | 77.50 |

Departure of Chinese People's Volunteers.

Transplanting Rice
Seedlings — A118

**1958, Sept. 10**     **Litho.**
**With or Without Gum**
| | | | | |
|---|---|---|---|---|
| **151** | A118 | 10w sepia | 2.00 | .65 |
| *a.* | | Imperf | 15.00 | 6.75 |

Winged Horse of
Chollima — A119

**1958, Sept. 16**
| | | | | |
|---|---|---|---|---|
| **152** | A119 | 10w brick red | 3.50 | .65 |
| *a.* | | Imperf | 29.00 | 4.00 |

National Congress of the Innovators in Production.

North Korea-China
Friendship
Month — A120

**1958, Oct. 8**     **With or Without Gum**
| | | | | |
|---|---|---|---|---|
| **153** | A120 | 10w multicolored | 2.25 | .60 |
| *a.* | | Imperf | 17.50 | 4.25 |
| *b.* | | Rouletted | — | — |

National Congress
of Agricultural
Cooperatives
A121

**1959, Jan. 5**     **With or Without Gum**
| | | | | |
|---|---|---|---|---|
| **154** | A121 | 10w dk grnish blue | 3.25 | .80 |
| *a.* | | Imperf | 17.50 | 4.00 |

Gen. Ulchi
Mundok — A122

**1959, Feb. 11**     **With Gum**
| | | | | |
|---|---|---|---|---|
| **155** | A122 | 10w lilac brn & yel | 8.00 | 1.60 |
| *a.* | | Imperf | 30.00 | 14.00 |

See Nos. 157-159 and 209-212.

National Women's
Workers
Congress — A123

**1959, Mar. 29**

**With or Without Gum**

| | | | | |
|---|---|---|---|---|
| 156 | A123 | 10ch brown & red | 4.25 | 1.45 |
| *a.* | | Imperf | 57.50 | |

Jeon
Bong-jun
A124

Kang
Kam
Chan
A125

Ulchi Mundok — A126

**1959, Apr. 1**

| | | | | |
|---|---|---|---|---|
| 157 | A124 | 2ch blue, *lt green* | 2.25 | .40 |
| *a.* | | Imperf | 100.00 | |
| 158 | A125 | 5ch lilac brn, *buff* | 2.50 | .45 |
| *a.* | | Imperf | 100.00 | |
| 159 | A126 | 10ch red brn, *cream* | 5.00 | .60 |
| *a.* | | Imperf | 100.00 | |
| | | Nos. 157-159 (3) | 9.75 | 1.45 |

Nos. 157-159 were issued with gum. Nos. 157a-159a were issued with or without gum.

Soviet Luna 1 Moon
Rocket
Launch — A127

**1959, May 4**    **Perf. 10, 10½**

| | | | | |
|---|---|---|---|---|
| 160 | A127 | 2ch dk vio, *pale buff* | 15.00 | 8.00 |
| *a.* | | Imperf | 260.00 | 57.50 |
| 161 | A127 | 10ch bl, *pale grn* | 30.00 | 11.50 |
| *a.* | | Imperf | 260.00 | 57.50 |

Issued with gum (perf 10) or without gum (perf 10½). Nos. 160a and 161a were issued with gum.

Land Irrigation
Program — A128

**1959, May 27**    **Perf. 10**

| | | | | |
|---|---|---|---|---|
| 162 | A128 | 10ch multicolored | 11.00 | 3.25 |
| *a.* | | Imperf | 40.00 | 11.00 |

Slogan-inscribed Tree,
Chongbong
Bivouac — A129

Statue of Kim Il
Sung — A130    Mt. Paektu — A131

**1959, June 4**    **10, 10¾ (#164)**

| | | | | |
|---|---|---|---|---|
| 163 | A129 | 5ch multicolored | 3.50 | 1.30 |
| *a.* | | Imperf | 95.00 | 17.50 |
| *b.* | | Perf 10¾ | — | — |
| *c.* | | Rouletted | — | — |
| 164 | A130 | 10ch blue & grnsh bl | 3.50 | 1.30 |
| *a.* | | Imperf | 70.00 | 17.50 |

| | | | | |
|---|---|---|---|---|
| 165 | A131 | 10ch violet blue | 5.50 | — |
| *a.* | | Imperf | 70.00 | — |
| | | Nos. 163-165 (3) | 12.50 | 2.60 |

22nd Anniversary of the Battle of Pochondo. No. 164 was issued with gum.

Chollima
Tractor — A132

Jongihwa-58
Electric
Locomotive
A133

Red Star-58
Bulldozer
A134

Chollima
Excavator
A135

SU-50 Universal
Lathe — A136

Sungri-58
Truck — A137

**With or Without gum**

**1959, June 12**    **Perf. 10¾**

| | | | | |
|---|---|---|---|---|
| 166 | A132 | 1ch multicolored | 1.50 | .50 |
| *a.* | | Imperf | 72.50 | 33.00 |
| *b.* | | Rouletted | — | — |
| 167 | A133 | 2ch multicolored | 11.00 | 3.50 |
| *a.* | | Imperf | 145.00 | 62.50 |
| *b.* | | Rouletted | — | — |
| 168 | A134 | 2ch multicolored | 2.50 | .70 |
| *a.* | | Imperf | 97.50 | 18.00 |
| *b.* | | Rouletted | — | — |
| 169 | A135 | 5ch multicolored | 2.50 | 1.25 |
| *a.* | | Imperf | 230.00 | — |
| *b.* | | Rouletted | — | — |
| 170 | A136 | 10ch multicolored | 2.50 | .95 |
| *a.* | | Imperf | 230.00 | — |
| *b.* | | Rouletted | — | — |
| 171 | A137 | 10ch multicolored | 4.50 | .70 |
| *a.* | | Imperf | 230.00 | — |
| | | Nos. 166-171 (6) | 24.50 | 7.60 |

Machine-building Industry.

Armistice
Building,
Panmunjom
A138

Anti-U.S. Protester
A139

Anti-South Korean
Emigration Campaign
A140

Peaceful
Reunification of
Korea
A141

**1959, June 25**    **With Gum**

| | | | | |
|---|---|---|---|---|
| 172 | A138 | 10ch dk blue & blue | 3.50 | .25 |
| *a.* | | Imperf | 175.00 | — |
| *b.* | | Perf 10¼ | — | — |
| 173 | A139 | 20ch dk blue & lt blue | 1.35 | .45 |
| 174 | A140 | 20ch sepia & brn | 9.00 | 2.50 |
| 175 | A141 | 70ch dk brn & lt brn | 40.00 | 11.00 |
| *a.* | | Imperf | 125.00 | — |
| *b.* | | Perf 10¼xRoul | — | — |
| | | Nos. 172-175 (4) | 53.85 | 14.20 |

Day of Struggle for the withdrawal of U.S. troops from South Korea.

Metal
Type — A142

*Samil Wolgan*
Monthly Breaking
Chains — A143

Flag with
Symbols of
Peace and
Literature
A144

Korean Alphabet of
1443 — A145

**1959, Aug. 1**

| | | | | |
|---|---|---|---|---|
| 176 | A142 | 5ch sepia | 25.00 | 9.50 |
| 177 | A143 | 5ch green & red | 7.50 | 3.00 |
| 178 | A144 | 10ch bright blue | 7.50 | 3.00 |
| 179 | A145 | 10ch dp bl & pale brn | 11.00 | 4.75 |
| *a.* | | Souvenir sheet of 4, #176-179 imperf | 105.00 | 52.50 |
| | | Nos. 176-179 (4) | 51.00 | 20.25 |

International Book and Fine Arts Exhibition, Leipzig.

Nos. 176 and 178 were issued with gum. Nos. 177, 179 and 179a were issued without gum.

Milk Cow
Farm — A146

Pig
Farm — A147

**1959, Sept. 20**

| | | | | |
|---|---|---|---|---|
| 180 | A146 | 2ch multicolored | 4.00 | 1.00 |
| 181 | A147 | 5ch multicolored | 5.75 | 1.30 |

No. 180 was issued without gum, No. 181 with gum.

**Economic Development**

Cement
Making — A148

Hydroelectrical
Dam — A149

Salt
Making — A150

Construction — A151

Grain — A152

Sugar — A153

Steel-Making
A154

Fishing — A155

Iron-
Making — A156

Coal
Mining — A157

Textile
Production — A158

Fruit — A159

**Perf. 10½ (#182), 11**

**1959, Sept. 20-1960**

| | | | | |
|---|---|---|---|---|
| 182 | A148 | 1ch multicolored | .70 | .55 |
| *a.* | | Imperf | 175.00 | |
| 183 | A149 | 2ch multicolored | 1.90 | .55 |
| *a.* | | Imperf | 175.00 | |
| 184 | A150 | 5ch multicolored | 3.00 | .70 |
| *a.* | | Imperf | 175.00 | |
| 185 | A151 | 10ch multicolored | 3.25 | 1.00 |
| *a.* | | Imperf | 175.00 | |
| 186 | A152 | 10ch multicolored | 1.50 | .60 |
| *a.* | | Imperf | 175.00 | |
| 187 | A153 | 10ch multicolored | 2.75 | .55 |
| *a.* | | Imperf | 175.00 | |
| 188 | A154 | 10ch multicolored | 2.50 | .60 |
| *a.* | | Imperf | 175.00 | |
| 189 | A155 | 10ch multicolored | 2.25 | .60 |
| *a.* | | Imperf | 175.00 | |

**190** A156 10ch multicolored    1.50   .60
**191** A157 10ch multicolored    2.50   .60
**192** A158 10ch multicolored    1.50   .60
   *a.*    Imperf        175.00   —
**193** A159 10ch multicolored
         ('60)    3.75   .55
   *Nos. 182-193 (12)*    27.10   7.50

No. 193 issued August 1960.
Nos. 183 and 185 were issued with gum, the other values without gum.

Musk Deer — A160

Sable — A161

Marten — A162

Otter — A163

Sika Deer — A164

Pheasant — A165

**1959-62**            *Perf. 11*
**194** A160   5ch multicolored    6.00   .70
**195** A161   5ch multicolored    6.00   .70
**196** A162   5ch multicolored    6.00   .70
**197** A163   5ch multicolored    6.00   .70
**198** A164 10ch multicolored    6.00   .70
**199** A165 10ch multicolored    27.50   2.25
   *Nos. 194-199 (6)*    57.50   5.75

Game Preservation.
Issued: No. 198, 10/24/59; No. 199, 3/25/60; No. 194, 11/11/60; Nos. 195-197, 1/24/62.
Nos. 198 and 199 were issued with gum, Nos. 194-197 without gum.

3rd Korean Trade Unions Congress — A166

**1959, Nov. 4**        **With Gum**
**200** A166   5ch multicolored    1.30   .30

Electric Locomotive A167

Freighter — A168

---

**1959, Nov. 5**
**201** A167   5ch brnsh purple    20.00   3.00
**202** A168 10ch slate green    8.25   2.50

Korean People's Army, 12th Anniv. — A169

**1960, Feb. 8**        **With Gum**
**203** A169   5ch blue    250.00   140.00

Sword Dance A170

Janggo Dance A171

Peasant Dance — A172

**1960, Feb. 25**
**204** A170   5ch multicolored    4.50   .40
**205** A171   5ch multicolored    4.50   .40
**206** A172 10ch multicolored    4.50   .40
   *Nos. 204-206 (3)*    13.50   1.20

Women of 3 Races, Dove A173

Woman Worker A174

**1960, Mar. 8**        **With Gum**
**207** A173   5ch grnish blue & red
         vio    3.00   .25
**208** A174 10ch grn & org    3.00   .50

50th Anniv. of International Women's Day.

Kim Jong Ho, Geographer A175

Kim Hong Do, Painter A176

Pak Yon, Musician A177

Jong Ta San, Scholar A178

**1960**            **With Gum**
**209** A175   1ch gray & pale grn    2.75   .25
**210** A176   2ch dp blue & yel
         buff    3.25   .25
**211** A177   5ch grnish blue &
         grnish yel    12.00   .25
**212** A178 10ch brn & yel    3.25   .25
   *Nos. 209-212 (4)*    21.25   1.00

Issued: 1ch-5ch, 3/16/60; 10ch 6/60.

---

Grapes — A179

Wild fruits: No. 214, Fruit of Actinidia arguta planch. No. 215, Pine-cone. No. 216, Hawthorn berries. No. 217, Chestnuts.

**1960, Apr. 8**        **With Gum**
**213** A179   5ch multicolored    2.75   .90
**214** A179   5ch multicolored    2.75   .90
**215** A179   5ch multicolored    2.75   .90
**216** A179 10ch multicolored    3.00   1.10
**217** A179 10ch multicolored    3.00   1.10
   *Nos. 213-217 (5)*    14.25   4.90

Nos. 214-215 also exist imperf.

Lenin, 90th Birthday — A180

**1960, Apr. 22**        **With Gum**
**218** A180 10ch violet brown    1.60   .25

Koreans and Caricature of U.S. Soldier — A181

**1960, June 20**        **With Gum**
**219** A181 10ch dark blue    7.00   .65

Day of Struggle for Withdrawal of U.S. Troops from South Korea.

Mao Tse-Tung Plaza A182

Taedong River Promenade A183

Youth Street — A184

People's Army Street — A185

Stalin Street — A186

**1960, June 29**        **With Gum**
**220** A182 10ch gray green    1.50   .35
**221** A183 20ch dk bl green    2.75   .40
**222** A184 40ch blackish green    4.00   .75
**223** A185 70ch emerald    7.25   1.75
**224** A186   1w blue    10.00   3.00
   *Nos. 220-224 (5)*    25.50   6.25

Views of rebuilt Pyongyang.

Luna 3 — A187

Luna 2 — A188

---

**1960, July 15**
**225** A187   5ch multicolored    8.00   7.50
**226** A188 10ch multicolored    11.50   3.25

Soviet space flights.
The 5ch was issued with gum, the 10ch without gum.

Mirror Rock — A189

Devil-faced Rock — A190

Dancing Dragon Bridge — A191

Nine Dragon Falls — A192

Mt. Diamond on the Sea — A193

**1960, July 15-1961**
**227** A189   5ch multicolored    1.75   .25
**228** A190   5ch multicolored    1.75   .30
**229** A191 10ch multi ('61)    6.25   .30
**230** A192 10ch multicolored    5.50   .35
**231** A193 10ch multicolored    2.00   .25
   *Nos. 227-231 (5)*    17.25   1.45

Diamond Mountains scenery.
No. 229 issued 2/8/61.
See Nos. 761-764.

Lily A194

Hibiscus A196

Rhododendron A195

Blue Campanula A197

Mauve Campanula — A198

**1960, July 15-1961**      **With Gum**
232 A194   5ch multicolored    1.75   .25
233 A195   5ch multicolored    1.75   .25
234 A196   10ch multicolored   2.50   .45
235 A197   10ch multicolored   2.50   .45
236 A198   10ch multi ('61)    2.50   .45
     *Nos. 232-236 (5)*      11.00   1.85
     No. 236 issued 6/1/61.
     Nos. 232-234 and 236 also exist without gum.

"The Arduous March" — A199

Crossing the Amnok River — A200

Young Communist League Meeting — A201

Showing the Way at Pochonbo A202

Return to Pyongyang A203

**1960, July 26**
237 A199   5ch carmine red    .65   .25
238 A200   10ch deep blue    1.50   .25
239 A201   10ch deep blue    1.50   .25
240 A202   10ch carmine red   1.50   .25
241 A203   10ch carmine red   1.50   .25
     *Nos. 237-242 (5)*      6.65   1.25
     Revolutionary activities of Kim Il Sung.

15th Anniv. Liberation from Japan — A204

**1960, Aug. 6**
242 A204   10ch multicolored   6.00   .25

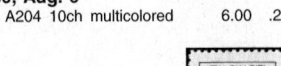

North Korean-Soviet Friendship Month — A205

**1960, Aug. 6**
243 A205   10ch lake, *cream*    19.00   4.00

Okryu Bridge — A206

Grand Theater — A207

Okryu Restaurant A208

**1960, Aug. 11**
244 A206   10ch gray blue    4.00   .35
245 A207   10ch dull violet    3.50   .25
246 A208   10ch turquoise    1.50   .25
     *Nos. 244-246 (3)*      9.00   .85
     Pyongyang buildings.

Tokro River Dam — A209

**1960, Sept. 9**      **With Gum**
247 A209   5ch slate blue    2.75   .25
     Inauguration of Tokro River Hydroelectric Power Station.

World Federation of Trade Unions, 15th Anniv. — A210

**1960, Sept. 16**
248 A210   10ch blue & lt blue   2.10   .25

Repatriation of Korean Nationals from Japan — A211

**1960, Sept. 26**
249 A211   10ch brnish violet   6.50   .30

Korean-Soviet Friendship — A212

**1960, Oct. 5**      **With Gum**
250 A212   10ch brn & org    1.90   .25

Liberation Day Sports Festival, Pyongyang — A213

     Designs: 5ch (No. 251), Runner. 5ch (No. 252), Weight-lifter. 5ch (No. 253), Cyclist. 5ch (No. 254), Gymnast. 5ch (No. 255), Soccer players, horiz. 10ch (No. 256), Swimmer, horiz. 10ch (No. 257), Moranbong Stadium, horiz.

**1960, Oct. 5**
251-257 A213   Set of 7    13.50   2.50

Chinese & North Korean Soldiers A214

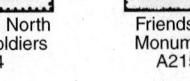

Friendship Monument A215

**1960, Oct. 20**      **With Gum**
258 A214   5ch rose    1.60   .25
259 A215   10ch dp blue    1.60   .25
     10th Anniversary of Chinese People's Volunteers' Entry into Korean War.

World Federation of Democratic Youth, 15th Anniv. — A216

**1960, Nov. 11**
260 A216   10ch multicolored    2.00   .25

Woodpecker A217

Mandarin Ducks A218

Scops Owl — A219

Oriole — A220

**1960-61**
261 A217   2ch yel grn & multi   7.25   .40
262 A218   5ch blue & multi    7.75   .50
263 A219   5ch lt blue & multi   12.50   1.00
264 A220   10ch lt bl grn & multi   7.75   1.00
     *Nos. 261-264 (4)*      35.25   2.90
     Issued: No. 262, 12/15/60; No. 264, 3/15/61; No. 261, 4/22/61; No. 263, 6/1/61.

Wrestling A221

Swinging A222

Archery A223

Seesaw A224

**1960-61**
265 A221   5ch dull grn & multi   1.75   .25
266 A222   5ch yel & multi ('61)   1.75   .25
267 A223   5ch yel gold & multi   8.50   .75
268 A224   10ch lt bl grn & multi   1.75   .25
     *Nos. 265-268 (4)*      13.75   1.50
     Issued: Nos. 265, 267-268, 12/15/60; No. 266 issued 1/6/61.

Agriculture A225

Light Industry A226

Korean Workers' Party Flag — A227

Power Station — A228

Steel-Making A229

**1961, Jan. 1**
269 A225   5ch multicolored   1.75   .25
270 A226   5ch multicolored   3.00   .25
271 A227   10ch multicolored   .85   .25
272 A228   10ch multicolored   1.75   .25
273 A229   10ch multicolored   1.25   .25
     *Nos. 269-273 (5)*      8.60   1.25

Wild Ginseng — A230

     Design: 10ch, cultivated ginseng

**1961**
274 A230   5ch multicolored   4.50   .25
275 A230   10ch multicolored   4.50   .25
     Issued: 10ch, 1/5; 5ch, 3/15.

A231

A232

A233

Factories — A234

**1961, Feb. 8**      **With Gum**
276 A231   5ch red & pale yel   1.25   .25
277 A232   10ch bl grn & pale yel    2.75   .25
278 A233   10ch dp vio blue & pale yel    2.75   .25
279 A234   20ch vio & pale yel   3.25   .50
     *Nos. 276-279 (4)*      10.00   1.25
     Construction of Vinalon Factory.
     See Nos. 350-353.

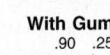

Pyongyang Students' and Children's Palace — A235

**1961, Feb. 8**      **With Gum**
280 A235   2ch red, *yellow*    .90   .25

Korean Revolution Museum — A236

**1961, Feb. 8**      **With Gum**
281 A236   10ch red    .75   .25

Soviet Venus
Rocket — A237

**1961, Feb. 8**
282 A237 10ch turq bl & multi   5.00   .25

Tractor-Plow
A238

Disk-Harrow
A239

Wheat Harvester
A240

Corn Harvester
A241

Tractors — A242

**1961, Feb. 21**            **With Gum**
283 A238  5ch violet            .85   .25
284 A239  5ch blue green        .85   .25
285 A240  5ch dp gray green     .85   .25
286 A241 10ch violet blue      1.25   .25
287 A242 10ch purple           1.25   .25
    *Nos. 283-287 (5)*         5.05  1.25

Opening of Industrial
College — A243

**1961, Mar. 1**            **With Gum**
288 A243 10ch red brn, *buff*   3.00   .25

Agrarian Reform
Law, 15th
Anniv. — A244

**1961, Mar. 1**            **With Gum**
289 A244 10ch dull green, *yel*   3.00   .25

20-Point Political
Program, 20th
Anniv. — A245

**1961, Mar. 15**            **With Gum**
290 A245 10ch dull vio, *pale yel*   2.00   .25

 Mackerel — A246

Dolphin — A247

 Whale — A248

Tunny — A249

Walleye
Pollack — A250

**1961, Apr. 3**
291 A246  5ch yel grn & multi   3.50   .45
292 A247  5ch lt blue & multi   8.00  1.30
293 A248 10ch lt grnish blue &
                multi          8.50   .45
294 A249 10ch gray & multi     8.50   .45
295 A250 10ch dk grn & multi   8.50   .45
    *Nos. 291-295 (5)*         37.00  3.10

Crane-Mounted
Tractor — A251

"Sungri-
1010" Truck
A252

Vertical
Milling
Machine
A253

Victory
April-15
Automobile
A254

8-Meter
Turning
Lathe
A255

Radial
Boring
Lathe
A256

Hydraulic
Press
A257

750-Kg Air
Hammer
A258

200mm
Boring
Lathe
A259

3,000-Ton
Press
A260

3-Ton Air
Hammer
A261

Ssangma-15
Excavator
A262

Jangbaek
Excavator
A263

400-HP
Diesel
Engine
A264

Honing
Lathe
A265

Trolley
A266

8-Meter
Planer
A267

Boring
Lathe
A268

Hobbing
Lathe
A269

Tunnel Drill — A270

**1961-65**
296 A251  1ch red brown      2.50    .25
297 A252  2ch dk brown       2.50    .25
298 A253  2ch dk green        .90    .25
299 A253  2ch grayish brn   50.00  11.00
300 A254  4ch dk blue        6.25    .25
301 A255  5ch dk green       3.50    .25
302 A256  5ch dk bl gray     1.90    .25
 a.       5ch dark gray green 50.00  11.00
303 A257  5ch bl green       1.90    .25
304 A258  5ch red brown      1.60    .25
305 A259  5ch sl violet      2.25    .25
306 A260 10ch gray violet    3.25    .25
 a.      10ch dark blue     50.00    .25
307 A261 10ch blue           3.00    .25
308 A261 10ch brown        200.00  50.00
309 A262 10ch dk vio gray    1.60    .25
310 A263 10ch dk green       3.25    .25
311 A264 10ch dk sl blue     3.25    .25
312 A265 10ch dk blue        3.00    .25
313 A266 40ch dk blue       12.00    .25
314 A267 90ch dk bl green    5.25    .30
315 A268  1w dk vio brown   16.00    .45
316 A269  5w dk brown       32.50   3.25
317 A270 10w vio brown      50.00   6.75
    *Nos. 296-317 (22)*     406.40  75.75

Issued: 1ch, 4/22/61; 2ch, 4/27/61; Nos.
301, 306, 5/20/61; Nos. 307, 308, 3/13/62;
Nos. 302, 317, 7/30/62; 5w, 9/5/62; No. 302a,
9/15/62; No. 308, 12/26/62; Nos. 297, 298,
2/11/63; No. 303, 4/9/63; 90ch, 5/15/63; 4ch,
6/15/63; 40ch, 9/13/63; 1w, 10/16/63; No. 310,
3/20/64; No. 305, 4/28/64; No. 311, 6/25/64;
No. 312, 1/1/65.
    Nos. 296, 297, 301, 303, 306 and 316 are
perf 10¾. Other values are perf 12½.
    Nos. 296-302, 304-307 and 309-315 were
issued with gum. Nos. 303, 308, 316 and 317
were issued without gum.
    Nos. 296-297, 301, 303, 306-308 and 316
are lithographed. Other values are engraved.

Reforestation
Campaign — A271

**1961, Apr. 27**            **With Gum**
318 A271 10ch green             2.25   .30

Peaceful
Reunification of
Korea — A272

**1961, May 9**
319 A272 10ch multicolored     27.00  2.25

Young Pioneers
(Children's
Union) of Korea,
15th
Anniv. — A273

Designs: 5ch, Pioneers swimming. 10ch
(No. 321), Pioneer bugler. 10ch (No. 322) Pioneer visiting battlefield.

**1961, June 1**
320-322 A273  Set of 3          6.00   .90

Labor Law, 15th
Anniv. — A274

**1961, June 21**            **With Gum**
323 A274 10ch dp blue, *pale yel*   1.60   .25

 Plums — A275

 Peaches — A276

 Apples
A277

Persimmons
A278

Pears — A279

**1961, July 11**
324 A275  5ch multicolored      1.40   .25
325 A276  5ch multicolored      1.40   .25
326 A277  5ch multicolored      1.40   .25
327 A278 10ch multicolored      1.40   .25
328 A279 10ch multicolored      1.40   .25
    *Nos. 324-328 (5)*          7.00  1.25

Yuri Gagarin &
Vostok
I — A280

**1961, July 11**
329 A280 10ch dp bl & pale bl   3.00   .70
330 A280 10ch red vio & pale bl 3.00   .70

First manned space flight, April 12.

Nationalization of
Industry, 15th
Anniv. — A281

**1961, July 11**            **With Gum**
331 A281 10ch lt red brown     18.00   .80

Sex Equality Law,
15th
Anniv. — A282

**1961, July 27**            **With Gum**
332 A282 10ch brn red & rose    1.10   .25

Children Planting
Tree — A283

Children: 5ch (No. 334), Reading book.
10ch (No. 335), Playing with ball. 10ch (No.
336), Building a toy house. 10ch (No. 337),
Waving banner.

**1961, Aug. 29**
333-337 A283  Set of 5          5.75   .80

Livestock
Breeding
A284

Fishing Industry
A285

Farming
A286

Textile
Industry
A287

**1961, Aug. 29**

| 338 | A284 | 5ch multicolored | 2.00 | .25 |
|-----|------|------------------|------|-----|
| 339 | A285 | 10ch multicolored | 1.75 | .25 |
| 340 | A286 | 10ch multicolored | 3.00 | .25 |
| 341 | A287 | 10ch multicolored | 2.75 | .30 |
| | | *Nos. 338-341 (4)* | 9.50 | 1.05 |

Improvement of living standards.

Kim Il Sung
Writing Under
Tree — A288

Kim Il Sung at
Desk — A289

Soldiers
Studying — A290

**1961, Sept. 8**     **With Gum**

| 342 | A288 | 10ch violet | 1.35 | .50 |
|-----|------|-------------|------|-----|
| 343 | A289 | 10ch dull violet | 1.35 | .50 |
| 344 | A290 | 10ch dp blue & yel | 2.50 | .50 |
| | | *Nos. 342-344 (3)* | 5.20 | 1.50 |

15th Anniv. of Kim Il Sung's "Ten-Point Program of the Association for the Restoration of the Fatherland."

Kim Il Sung & Party
Banner
A291

Party Emblem,
Workers
A292

Chollima
Statue — A293

**1961, Sept. 8**     **With Gum**

| 345 | A291 | 10ch brown red | .85 | .45 |
|-----|------|----------------|-----|-----|
| 346 | A292 | 10ch green | .85 | .45 |
| 347 | A293 | 10ch violet | .85 | .45 |
| | | *Nos. 345-347 (3)* | 2.55 | 1.35 |

4th Korean Workers' Party Congress.

Miners'
Day — A294

**1961, Sept. 12**     **With Gum**
348   A294   10ch brown     11.50   .65

Pak In Ro (1561-1642),
Poet — A295

**1961, Sept. 12**
349   A295   10ch dk blue & gray
blue     3.25   .25

Aldehyde
Shop — A296

Polymerization &
Saponification
Shops — A297

Glacial Acetic
Acid
Shops — A298

Spinning
Shop — A299

**1961, Oct. 17**     **With Gum**

| 350 | A296 | 5ch red & pale yel | 1.25 | .25 |
|-----|------|--------------------|------|-----|
| 351 | A297 | 10ch dp blue & pale yel | 1.90 | .25 |
| 352 | A298 | 10ch dk brn & pale yel | 1.90 | .25 |
| 353 | A299 | 20ch purple & pale yel | 3.00 | .35 |
| | | *Nos. 350-353 (4)* | 8.05 | 1.10 |

Completion of Vinalon Factory.

Korean &
Soviet
Flags — A300

Korean &
Chinese
Flags — A301

**1961, Oct. 26**

| 354 | A300 | 10ch multicolored | 2.00 | .50 |
|-----|------|-------------------|------|-----|
| 355 | A301 | 10ch multicolored | 2.00 | .50 |

North Korean Friendship Treaties with the Soviet Union and China.

Day of Sports and
Physical Culture — A302

Sports: 2ch, Table tennis. 5ch, Flying model glider. 10ch (No. 358), Basketball. 10ch (No. 359), Rowing. 10ch (No. 360), High jump. 20ch, Emblem.

**1961, Nov. 4**     **With Gum**
356-361   A302   Set of 6     9.00   1.60

No. 209 Surcharged in
Violet

**1961, Nov. 5**
362   5ch on 1ch gray &
pale grn     200.00   150.00
Centenary of publication of "Taedongyojido," map.

Janggun
Rock — A303

Chonbul
Peak — A304

Mansa
Peak — A305

Kiwajip Rock — A306

Mujigae
Rock — A307

**1961, Nov. 29**     **With Gum**

| 363 | A303 | 5ch slate | 1.35 | .25 |
|-----|------|-----------|------|-----|
| 364 | A304 | 5ch brown | 1.35 | .25 |
| 365 | A305 | 10ch br lilac | 2.50 | .25 |
| 366 | A306 | 10ch sl blue | 2.50 | .25 |
| 367 | A307 | 10ch dk blue | 2.50 | .25 |
| | | *Nos. 363-367 (5)* | 10.20 | 1.25 |

Mt. Chilbo scenes.

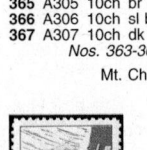

Protection of State
Property — A308

**1961, Nov. 29**     **With Gum**
368   A308   10ch gray green     1.25   .25

WFTU
Emblem — A309

**1961, Nov. 29**     **With Gum**
369   A309   10ch multicolored     1.50   .30

5th Congress of World Federation of Trade Unions.

"Red Banner"
Electric
Locomotive
A310

**1961, Nov. 29**     **With Gum**
370   A310   10ch vio & buff     17.00   1.60

Railway Electrification.

Winter
Sports — A311

Designs (all 10ch): No. 371, Figure skater. No. 372, Speed skater. No. 373, Ice hockey. No. 374, Skiier.

**Figures in Sepia**

**1961, Dec. 12**     **With Gum**
371-374   A311   Set of 4     9.00   .75

**Six Objectives of Production**

Steel — A312

Coal — A313

Grain — A314

Textiles — A315

Sea-Foods
A316

Apartments
A317

**1962, Jan. 1**     **With Gum**

| 375 | A312 | 5ch multicolored | 1.25 | .25 |
|-----|------|------------------|------|-----|
| 376 | A313 | 5ch multicolored | 8.50 | .40 |
| 377 | A314 | 10ch multicolored | 1.25 | .25 |
| 378 | A315 | 10ch multicolored | 3.75 | .25 |
| 379 | A316 | 10ch multicolored | 3.50 | .25 |
| 380 | A317 | 10ch multicolored | 1.25 | .25 |
| | | *Nos. 375-380 (6)* | 19.50 | 1.65 |

See Nos. 442-447.

**Animals**

Korean
Tiger
A318

Racoon Dog
A319

Badger — A320

Bear — A321

**1962, Jan. 24**

| 381 | A318 | 2ch multicolored | 5.00 | .25 |
|-----|------|------------------|------|-----|
| 382 | A319 | 2ch lt grn & brn | 3.50 | .25 |
| 383 | A320 | 5ch lt bl grn & lt red brn | 2.40 | .25 |
| 384 | A321 | 10ch grn & brn | 3.50 | .25 |
| | | *Nos. 381-384 (4)* | 14.40 | 1.00 |

**Traditional Musical Instruments**

Kayagum
A322

Jotae (Flute)
A323

Wolgum
A324

Haegum
A325

Wagonghu — A326

**1962, Feb. 2**
385 A322 10ch multicolored 3.25 .25
386 A323 10ch multicolored 3.25 .25
387 A324 10ch multicolored 3.25 .25
388 A325 10ch multicolored 3.25 .25
389 A326 10ch multicolored 3.25 .25
  Nos. 385-389 (5) 16.25 1.25
  See Nos. 472-476.

**Butterflies**

Luehdorfia
puziloi
A327

Sericinus
telamon
A328

Parnassius
nomion
A329

Inachusio
A330

**1962, Mar. 13**
390 A327 5ch multicolored 4.00 .25
391 A328 10ch multicolored 4.00 .25
392 A329 10ch multicolored 4.00 .25
393 A330 10ch multicolored 4.00 .25
  Nos. 390-393 (4) 16.00 1.00

G. Titov &
Vostok
2 — A331

**1962, Mar. 13**
394 A331 10ch multicolored 3.50 .25
  Second Soviet Manned Space Flight.

Kim Il Sung
Commanding
Troops — A332

Kim Il Sung
Adressing
Workers
A333

***Perf. 10¾ (#397), 12½***
**1962, Apr. 14    Engr.    With Gum**
395 A332 10ch blue 1.20 .25
396 A333 10ch green 1.20 .25
397 A333 10ch rose red 1.20 .25
  Nos. 395-397 (3) 3.60 .75
  Marshall Kim Il Sung's 50th Birthday.

Kim Chaek
A334

Kang Kon
A335

An
Kil — A336

Ryu Kyong
Su — A337

Kim Jong
Suk — A338

Choe Chun
Guk — A339

**1962, Apr. 23    Perf. 12½**
**With Gum**
398 A334 10ch dark brown 6.25 .25
399 A335 10ch dark blue 6.25 .25
400 A336 10ch rose 6.25 .25
401 A337 10ch dark brown 6.25 .25
402 A338 10ch dark blue gray 6.25 .25
403 A338 10ch dark blue green 6.25 .25
404 A339 10ch violet brown 6.25 .25
  Nos. 398-404 (7) 43.75 1.75
  Anti-Japanese Revolutionary Fighters.
  See Nos. 480-484.

National
Mothers'
Meeting,
Pyongyang
A340

**1962, May 23    Litho.    Perf. 10¾**
405 A340 10ch multicolored 2.00 .50

Black-faced
Spoonbill
A341

Brown Hawk
Owl
A342

Eastern
Broad-billed
Roller
A343

Black
Paradise
Flycatcher
A344

Whistling
Swan — A345

**1962, May 23    Perf. 10¾**
406 A341 5ch multicolored 3.00 .35
407 A342 5ch multicolored 11.00 .45
408 A343 10ch multicolored 6.25 .45
409 A344 10ch multicolored 6.25 .45
410 A345 20ch multicolored 7.75 .50
  Nos. 406-410 (5) 34.25 2.20
  Beneficial birds.

Battle of Pochonbo, 25th
Anniv. — A346

**1962, May 23**
411 A346 10ch multicolored 2.00 .25

Croaker — A347

Hairtail — A348

Japanese
Croaker — A349

Japanese Sea
Bass — A350

Gizzard
Shad — A351

**1962, June 28**
412 A347 5ch dp grn & multi 1.75 .25
413 A348 5ch dp blue & multi 1.75 .25
414 A349 10ch apple grn & multi 3.00 .25
415 A350 10ch vio blue & multi 3.00 .25
416 A351 10ch grn & multi 3.00 .25
  Nos. 412-416 (5) 12.50 1.25
  Sea Fish.

Brush Case
A352

Ink Container
A353

Ink Slab
Case — A354

Writing Brush
Stand — A355

Paperweight
A356

Ink Slab — A357

Filing
Cabinet — A358

Kettle — A359

**1962, July 30    Centers in Black**
417 A352 4ch pale blue 1.40 .25
418 A353 5ch ochre 1.40 .25
419 A354 10ch pale green 1.90 .25
420 A355 10ch salmon 1.90 .25
421 A356 10ch violet 1.90 .25
422 A357 10ch orange brown 1.90 .25
423 A358 10ch pale yellow 1.90 .25
424 A359 40ch gray 4.25 .50
  Nos. 417-424 (8) 16.55 2.25
  Antiques of the Koryo and Yi Dynasties.
  Nos. 418 and 420 were issued with gum, the
  other values without gum.

Jong Ta San — A360

**1962, July 30    Engr.    Perf. 12½**
425 A360 10ch dp brnish violet 1.50 .25
  200th Anniv. birth of Jong Ta San,
  philosopher.

National Assembly
Elections
A361           A362

**1962, Oct. 3     Litho.     Perf. 10¾**
426 A361 10ch multicolored     2.50   .45
427 A362 10ch multicolored     2.50   .45

Pyongyang, 1535th Anniv. — A363

**1962, Oct. 15          With Gum**
428 A363 10ch pale blue & blk     1.10   .25

Launch of Soviet
Manned Rockets
Vostok 3 & 4 — A364

**1962, Nov. 12**
429 A364 10ch multicolored     3.50   .70

Spiraea
A365

Echinosophoora
koreensis
A366

Codonopsis
sylvestris
A367

Ginseng
A368

**1962, Nov. 30**
430 A365  5ch multicolored     1.90   .25
431 A366 10ch multicolored     1.90   .25
432 A367 10ch multicolored     1.90   .25
433 A368 10ch multicolored     1.90   .25
        Nos. 430-433 (4)       7.60  1.00

Korean plants.

Uibangryuchui — A369

**1962, Dec. 26**
434 A369 10ch multicolored     5.00   .35

485th anniversary of publication of the medical encyclopedia *Uibangryuchui*, printed with moveable type.

Korean Academy of
Sciences, 10th
Anniv. — A370

**1962, Dec. 26**
435 A370 10ch dull ultra & pale
        turq grn     2.00   .25

Fishing — A371

**1962, Dec. 30**
436 A371 10ch ultra     5.00   .25

European
Mink — A372

Korean Hare
A373

Eurasian Red
Squirrel
A374

Goral
A375

Siberian
Chipmunk
A376

**1962, Dec. 30-1963**
437 A372  4ch app grn & red
        brn     1.50   .40
438 A373  5ch lt grn & gray
        ('63)     1.50   .40
439 A374 10ch yel & gray     2.50   .40
440 A375 10ch pale grn & dk
        brn     2.50   .40
441 A376 20ch lt gray blue &
        red brn     5.00   .40
        Nos. 437-441 (5)     13.00  2.00

Fur-bearing animals.
No. 438 issued 12/30/63.

Coal — A377

Grain — A378

Textiles
A379

Apartment
Construction
A380

Steel — A381

Seafood
A382

**1963, Jan. 1**
442 A377  5ch multicolored     1.50   .25
443 A378 10ch multicolored     1.25   .25
444 A379 10ch multicolored     1.50   .25
445 A380 10ch multicolored     1.25   .25
446 A381 10ch multicolored     1.25   .25
447 A382 40ch multicolored     3.75   .50
        Nos. 442-447 (6)     10.50  1.75

Consolidation of the Achievement of the 6 Objectives. For surcharge, see No. 4539.

Korean People's Army,
15th Anniv. — A383

Designs: 5ch, Airman. 10ch (No. 449), Soldier. 10ch (No. 450), Sailor.

**1963, Feb. 1     Engr.     Perf. 12½**
**With Gum**
448-450 A383  Set of 3     6.00   .65

Peony — A384

Rugosa
Rose — A385

Rhododendron
A386

Campion
A387

Orchid — A388

**1963, Mar. 21     Litho.     Perf. 10¾**
451 A384  5ch gray & multi     1.10   .25
452 A385 10ch grnsh yel & multi     1.50   .25
453 A386 10ch lemon & multi     1.50   .25
454 A387 10ch br yel & multi     1.50   .25
455 A388 40ch green & multi     5.00   .45
        Nos. 451-455 (5)     10.60  1.45

Korean flowers.

Sword Dance
A389

Fan Dance
A390

**1963, Apr. 15**
456 A389 10ch multicolored     7.50   .25
457 A390 10ch multicolored     7.50   .25

International Music and Dance Competition, Pyongyang, April 16-May 17.

South Korea
Uprising of April
19, 3rd
Anniv. — A391

**1963, Apr. 19**
458 A391 10ch multicolored     1.50   .25

Karl Marx — A392

**1963, Apr. 23     Engr.     Perf. 12½**
**With Gum**
459 A392 10ch ultra     2.75   .25

Youth Day — A393

Designs: 2ch, Children in chemistry class. 5ch, Children running. 10ch (No. 462), Girl chasing butterfly. 10ch (No. 463), Boy leading chorus.

**1963, June 15     Litho.     Perf. 10¾**
460-463 A393  Set of 4     12.00  1.00

Armed
Koreans &
Caricature of
American
Soldier
A394

**1963, June 25**
464 A394 10ch multicolored     1.90   .25

Month of Struggle for the Withdrawal of U.S. Troops from South Korea.

Cyrtoclytus
caproides
A395

Cicindela
chinensis
A396

Purpuricenus
lituratus — A397

Agapanthia
pilicornus — A398

**1963, July 24**
465 A395  5ch multicolored     3.00   .25
466 A396 10ch multicolored     4.00   .25
467 A397 10ch multicolored     4.00   .25
468 A398 10ch multicolored     4.00   .25
        Nos. 465-468 (4)     15.00  1.00

Korean beetles.

Victory in Korean War,
10th Anniv. — A399

**1963, July 27**
469 A399 10ch multicolored     1.75   .25

National Emblem
A400

North Korean Flag
A401

**1963, Aug. 15**
470 A400 10ch multicolored    20.00 —
471 A401 10ch multicolored    20.00 —
   No. 471 exists with background in blue. Not issued. Value $750.

Ajaeng (Zither)
A402

Phyongyong (Jade Chimes)
A403

Saenap (Flute)
A404

Rogo (Drums)
A405

Phiri (Pipe) — A406

**1963, Sept. 13**
472 A402 5ch multicolored   1.50 .25
473 A403 5ch multicolored   1.50 .25
474 A404 10ch multicolored   2.50 .25
475 A405 10ch multicolored   2.50 .25
476 A406 10ch multicolored   2.50 .25
   Nos. 472-476 (5)   10.50 1.25
   Korean traditional musical instruments. Nos. 472 and 475 were issued with gum, the other values without gum.

South Gate, Kaesong
A407

Taedong Gate, Pyongyang
A408

Pothong Gate, Pyongyang — A409

**1963, Sept. 13   Engr.   Perf. 12½**
**With Gum**
477 A407 5ch black   .50 .25
478 A408 10ch brown   1.25 .25
479 A409 10ch blue   1.25 .25
   Nos. 477-479 (3)   3.00 .75
   Korean historic buildings. See Nos. 537-538.

Kwon Yong Byok
A410

Ma Tong Hui
A411

Pak Tal — A412

Ri Je Sun — A413

Kim Yong Bom — A414

**1963, Oct. 10   With Gum**
480 A410 5ch brown   6.00 —
481 A411 5ch brown purple   6.00 —
482 A412 10ch grnsh slate   6.00 —
483 A413 10ch carmine rose   6.00 —
484 A414 10ch black brown   70.00 50.00
   Anti-Japanese revolutionary fighters.

Nurse & Children at Playground
A415

Teacher & Children at Fairground
A416

**1963, Nov. 30   Litho.   Perf. 10¾**
485 A415 10ch multicolored   .80 .25
486 A416 10ch multicolored   .80 .25
   Child welfare.

Hwajang Temple
A417

Hyangsan Stream
A418

Kwanum Pavilion & Pagoda — A419

Sangwon Temple — A420

**1963, Nov. 30**
487 A417 5ch multicolored   1.00 .25
488 A418 10ch multicolored   5.25 .25
489 A419 10ch multicolored   2.50 .25
490 A420 10ch multicolored   2.50 .25
   Nos. 487-490 (4)   11.25 1.00
   Mount Myohyang.

Arming the People
A421

Technical Innovation
A422

Mining Industry
A423

Building Homes
A424

**1963, Dec. 5   Engr.   Perf. 12½**
**With Gum**
491 A421 5ch dp rose red   .50 .25
492 A422 10ch red brown   3.25 .25
493 A423 10ch gray violet   1.90 .25
494 A424 10ch gray black   3.50 .25
   Nos. 491-494 (4)   9.15 1.00
   Seven-Year Plan.

Sowing Gourd Seeds — A425

Saving a Swallow
A426

Swallow Carrying Gourd Seed — A427

Sawing Gourd — A428

Treasure Pouring from Gourd — A429

**1963, Dec. 5   Litho.   Perf. 10¾**
495 A425 5ch multicolored   1.25 .25
496 A426 5ch multicolored   2.50 .25
497 A427 10ch multicolored   2.50 .25
498 A428 10ch multicolored   2.00 .25
499 A429 10ch multicolored   2.00 .25
   Nos. 495-499 (5)   10.25 1.25
   Tale of Hung Bu.

Pistol Shooting
A430

Small-Caliber Rifle Shooting
A431

Rifle Shooting
A432

**1963, Dec. 15**
500 A430 5ch multicolored   .90 .25
501 A431 10ch multicolored   1.60 .25
502 A432 10ch multicolored   1.60 .25
   Nos. 500-502 (3)   4.10 .75
   Marksmanship Competition.

Chongjin Mill — A433

Sinuiju Mill — A434

**1964, Jan. 10   Engr.   Perf. 12½**
**With Gum**
503 A433 10ch brn violet   1.10 .25
504 A434 10ch gray   1.10 .25
   Chemical fiber industry.

Wonsan General Strike, 35th Anniv. — A435

**1964, Jan. 14   With Gum**
505 A435 10ch brown   1.50 .25

Korean Alphabet, 520th Anniv. — A436

**1964, Jan. 15   Litho.   Perf. 10¾**
506 A436 10ch multicolored   1.25 .25

Lenin's Death, 40th Anniv. — A437

**1964, Jan. 22   Engr.   Perf. 12½**
**With Gum**
507 A437 10ch rose red   1.50 .25

Whaler — A438

Trawler — A439

Purse-Seine Boat — A440

Dragnet Boat — A441

**1964, Feb. 10   Litho.   Perf. 10¾**
508 A438 5ch multicolored   1.75 .25
509 A439 5ch multicolored   1.75 .25
510 A440 10ch multicolored   3.50 .25
511 A441 10ch multicolored   3.50 .25
   Nos. 508-511 (4)   10.50 1.00
   Korean fishing industry.

March 1 Popular Uprising, 45th Anniv. — A442

**1964, Feb. 10　　Engr.　　Perf. 12½**
**With Gum**
512　A442　10ch dark violet　　1.00　.25

Kabo Peasant War,
70th Anniv. — A443

**1964, Feb. 15　　　　With Gum**
513　A443　10ch violet black　　1.00　.25

Students' and
Children's Palace,
Pyongyang
A444

**1964, Mar. 3　　　　With Gum**
514　A444　10ch grnsh black　　.75　.25

5th Congress,
Democratic
Youth League
of
Korea — A445

**1964, May 12　　Litho.　　Perf. 10¾**
515　A445　10ch multicolored　　1.00　.25

Electric
Train — A446

**1964, May 21**
516　A446　10ch multicolored　　10.50　.45
Electrification of Railway between Pyongyang and Sinuiju.

Popular
Movement in
Chongsan-ri
A447

**1964, June 4　　Engr.　　Perf. 12½**
**With Gum**
517　A447　5ch chestnut　　275.00　125.00

Drum Dance　　　　Dance of
A448　　　　　　　Ecstasy
　　　　　　　　　A449

Small Drum
Dance — A450

**1964, June 15　　Litho.　　Perf. 10¾**
518　A448　2ch multicolored　　1.50　.50
519　A449　5ch multicolored　　2.50　.50
520　A450　10ch multicolored　　4.25　.55
　　　Nos. 518-520 (3)　　8.25　1.55
Korean folk dances.

*For the Sake of
the Fatherland*
A451

**1964, June 15　　Engr.　　Perf. 12½**
**With Gum**
521　A451　5ch carmine red　　2.60　.25
Li Su Bok, soldier.

Nampho
Smelter — A452

Hwanghae Iron
Works — A453

**1964　　　　　　With Gum**
522　A452　5ch bronze green　　6.00　.25
523　A453　10ch gray　　4.00　.25
Issued: 5ch, 6/15. 10ch, 10/15.

Asian Economic
Seminar,
Pyongyang
A454

Design: 10ch, Flags, industrial skyline and cogwheel.

**1964, June 15　　Litho.　　Perf. 10¾**
524　A454　5ch multicolored　　.80　.25
525　A454　10ch multicolored　　1.25　.25

Koreans and
Statue of Kang
Ho Yong, War
Hero — A455

**1964, June 25**
526　A455　10ch multicolored　　1.40　.25
Korean Reunification

Domestic
Poultry
A456

Designs: 2ch, Chickens. 4ch, White chickens. 5ch (No. 529), Black chickens. 5ch (No. 530), Varicolored chickens. 40ch, Helmet guineafowl.

**1964, Aug. 5**
527-531　A456　Set of 5　　7.25　2.00

9th Winter
Olympic Games,
Innsbruck
A457

Designs: 5ch, Skier. 10ch (No. 533), Slalom skier. 10ch (No. 534), Speed skater.

**1964, Aug. 5**
532-534　A457　Set of 3　　4.00　.50

Flags &　　　　Welcoming
"Tobolsk,"　　　Repatriates
Repatriation　　A459
Ship
A458

**1964, Aug. 13**
535　A458　10ch multicolored　　2.25　.25
536　A459　30ch multicolored　　2.25　.25
5th anniversary of agreement for the repatriation of Korean nationals in Japan.

Thonggun　　　Inphung Pavilion,
Pavilion,　　　Kanggye
Uiju — A460　　City — A461

**1964, Aug. 22　　Engr.　　Perf. 12½**
**With Gum**
537　A460　5ch black violet　　.60　.25
538　A461　10ch emerald　　.75　.25
Korean historic sites.

18th Olympic
Games,
Tokyo — A462

Designs: 2ch, Rifleman. 5ch, Cyclists, vert. 10ch (No. 541), Runner. 10ch (No. 542), Wrestlers, vert.. 40ch, Volleyball, vert.

**Photo, Centers Litho**
**1964, Sept. 5　　　　Perf. 10¾**
539-543　A462　Set of 5　　5.00　1.00
Nos. 539-543 exist imperf. Value, $18 unused, $5 canceled.

Sinking of the
*General
Sherman*,
1866 — A463

**1964, Sept. 28　　Engr.　　Perf. 12½**
**With Gum**
544　A463　30ch red brown　　5.50　.50

Kim Il Sung &　　Kim Il Sung
Guerrilla　　　Speaking to
Fighters — A464　Peasants — A465

Battle of
Xiaowangqing
A466

**1964, Sept. 28　　Engr.　　Perf. 12½**
**With Gum**
545　A464　2ch brt violet　　.60　.25
546　A465　5ch blue　　1.15　.25
547　A466　10ch grnsh black　　1.25　.25
　　　Nos. 545-547 (3)　　3.00　.75
Revolutionary paintings.

Kwangju
Students'
Uprising, 35th
Anniv. — A467

**1964, Oct. 15　　　　With Gum**
548　A467　10ch blue violet　　2.40　.25

Weight Lifter　　Runner
A468　　　　A469

Boxers — A470　　Soccer
　　　　　　　Goalie — A471

GANEFO
Emblem — A472

**1964, Oct. 15　　Litho.　　Perf. 10¾**
549　A468　2ch multicolored　　.60　.25
550　A469　5ch multicolored　　.60　.25
551　A470　5ch multicolored　　.60　.25
552　A471　10ch multicolored　　1.25　.25
553　A472　10ch multicolored　　1.00　.25
　　　Nos. 549-553 (5)　　4.05　1.25
1st Games of New Emerging Forces (GANEFO), Djakarta, Indonesia, 1963.
Nos. 549-553 exist imperf. Value, $12 unused, $5 canceled.

Wild
Animals — A473

Animals: 2ch, Lynx. 5ch, Leopard cat. 10ch (No. 556), Yellow-throated marten. 10ch (No. 559), Leopard.

**1964, Nov. 20　　Engr.　　Perf. 12½**
**With Gum**
554-557　A473　Set of 4　　13.00　.90

Fighting South
Vietnam — A474

**1964, Dec. 20　　Litho.　　Perf. 10¾**
558　A474　10ch multicolored　　1.25　.25
Support for North Vietnam.

Prof. Kim Bong
Han — A475

"Bonghan"　　　"Bonghan"
Duct — A476　　Corpuscle — A477

**1964, Dec. 20　　Photo.　　Perf. 10¾**
559　A475　2ch ol grn & brown　　1.30　.25
560　A476　5ch multicolored　　1.60　.25
561　A477　10ch multicolored　　2.10　.25
　　　Nos. 559-561 (3)　　5.00　.75
Kyongrak Biological System.

Technical
Revolution
A478

Ideological
Revolution
A479

Cultural Revolution A480

**1964, Dec. 30**      Litho.
**562** A478 5ch multicolored    .30   .25
**563** A479 10ch multicolored    .55   .25
**564** A480 10ch multicolored    .55   .25
     Nos. 562-564 (3)    1.40   .75
Ideological, Technical and Cultural Revolutions in the Countryside.

"For Arms" — A481

**1964, Dec. 30**   Engr.   *Perf. 12½*
     **With Gum**
**565** A481 4ch brown    1.40   .25
Revolutionary painting.

Consumer Goods A482      Livestock Breeding A483

"All for the Grand Chollima March" — A484

**1964, Dec. 30**   Litho.   *Perf. 10¾*
**566** A482 5ch multicolored    1.50   .25
**567** A483 10ch multicolored    1.50   .25
**568** A484 10ch multicolored    1.10   .25
     Nos. 566-568 (3)    4.10   .75
     Seven-Year Plan.
No. 566 was issued with gum, Nos. 567 and 568 without gum.
Nos. 566-568 also exist imperf. Value, unused $100.

Battle of Luozigou — A485

Battle of Fusong County Seat — A486

Battle of Hongqihe A487

**1965, Jan. 20**   Engr.   *Perf. 12½*
     **With Gum**
**569** A485 10ch dp slate green    1.00   .25
**570** A486 10ch deep violet    1.00   .25
**571** A487 10ch slate violet    1.00   .25
     Nos. 569-571 (3)    3.00   .75
Guerrilla warfare against Japan 1934-1940.

Tuman River — A488      Taedong River — A489

---

Amnok River — A490

**1965, Feb. 27**   Litho.   *Perf. 10¾*
**572** A488 2ch multicolored    .90   .25
**573** A489 5ch multicolored    3.50   .25
**574** A490 10ch multicolored    1.60   .25
     Nos. 572-574 (3)    6.00   .75
     Korean rivers.

1st Congress of the Union of Agricultural Working People of Korea — A491

**1965, Mar. 25**      **With Gum**
**575** A491 10ch multicolored    1.50   .25

Furnacemen, Workers A492

**1965, Mar. 25**      **With Gum**
**576** A492 10ch multicolored    1.00   .25
Ten Major Tasks of Seven-Year Plan.

Sinhung Colliery — A493

Tanchou — A494

**1965, Mar. 31**   Engr.   *Perf. 12½*
     **With Gum**
**577** A493 10ch olive black    1.50   .25
**578** A494 40ch violet    4.50   .25
35th anniversary of workers' uprisings.

Sunhwa River Works — A495

**1965, Mar. 31**   Litho.   *Perf. 10¾*
     **With Gum**
**579** A495 10ch multicolored    .75   .25

A496      South Korean Uprising of April 19, 5th Anniv. — A497

**1965, Apr. 10**      **With Gum**
**580** A496 10ch multicolored    .75   .25
**581** A497 40ch multicolored    1.25   .25
Nos. 580-581 exist imperf. Value, $5 unused.

---

Construction of Pyongyang Thermal Power Station — A498

**1965, Apr. 10**      **With Gum**
**582** A498 5ch dp brn & lt blue    1.90   .25
No. 582 exists imperf. Value, $5 unused.

1st Afro-Asian Conf., Bandung, 10th Anniv. — A499

**1965, Apr. 18**      **With Gum**
**583** A499 10ch multicolored    .85   .25

Crowd Rejoicing A500

Japanese Koreans Demonstrating for Reunification A501

**1965, Apr. 27**   Photo.   **With Gum**
**584** A500 10ch blue & red    1.00   .25
**585** A501 40ch multicolored    1.25   .25
     10th Anniv. of the General Association of Koreans in Japan.
     Nos. 584-585 exist imperf. Value, $25 unused.

Workers Demonstrating A502

**1965, May 10**   Engr.   *Perf. 12½*
     **With Gum**
**586** A502 10ch brown    2.75   .25
     35th Anniv. of General Strike at Pyongyang Rubber Goods Factory.

Workers in Battle — A503      Korean & African Soldiers — A504

**1965, June 20**   Photo.   *Perf. 10¾*
     **With Gum**
**587** A503 10ch multicolored    1.60   .25
**588** A504 40ch multicolored    3.00   .25
     2nd Asian-African Conference, Algiers (subsequently canceled).
     Nos. 587-588 exist imperf. Value, $18 unused.

*Victory-64* 10-Ton Truck — A505

**1965, June 20**   Engr.   *Perf. 12½*
     **With Gum**
**589** A505 10ch grnsh blue    2.25   .25

---

Kim Chang Gol — A506

Jo Kun Sil — A507

An Hak Ryong — A508

**1965, June 20**      **With Gum**
**590** A506 10ch slate    .75   .25
**591** A507 10ch red brown    .75   .25
**592** A508 40ch violet    2.50   .25
     Nos. 590-592 (3)    4.00   .75
     War heroes.
See Nos. 775-777 and 827-830.

Postal Ministers' Conference, Peking — A509

**1965, June 20**   Photo.   *Perf. 10¾*
     **With Gum**
**593** A509 10ch red, yel & blk    2.00   .25

Lake Samil — A510

Jipson Peak — A511

Kwanum Waterfalls A512

**1965, June 20**   Litho.   **With Gum**
**594** A510 2ch multicolored    .85   .25
**595** A511 5ch multicolored    1.40   .25
**596** A512 10ch multicolored    4.00   .25
     Nos. 594-596 (3)    6.25   .75
     Diamond Mountain Scenery.
Nos. 594-596 exist imperf. Value, unused $100.

Kusimuldong A513

Lake Samji — A514

**1965, June 20**   Photo.   **With Gum**
**597** A513 5ch slate blue    .75   .25
**598** A514 10ch grnsh blue    1.00   .25
     Revolutionary battle sites.

Soccer Player
A515

Emblem &
Stadium
A516

**1965, Aug. 1    Litho.    With Gum**
599 A515 10ch multicolored      1.40  .25
600 A516 10ch multicolored      1.40  .25
GANEFO Games, Pyongyang.
Nos. 599-600 exist imperf, with gum. Value,
$15 unused.

Liberation from
Japan, 20th
Anniv. — A517

**1965, Aug. 15    With Gum**
601 A517 10ch multicolored      1.00  .25

Friedrich Engels, 145th
Anniv. Birth — A518

**1965, Sept. 10    Engr.    Perf. 12½**
**With Gum**
602 A518 10ch brown            .50  .25

Sports — A519

Designs: 2ch, Pole vault. 4ch, Javelin. 10ch
(No. 605), Discus. 10ch (No. 606), High jump.
10ch (No. 607), Shot put.

**1965, Sept. 24    Litho.    Perf. 11**
**With Gum**
603-607 A519 Set of 5          4.00  .90
Nos. 603-607 exist imperf, without gum.
Value $18 unused.

Korean Workers' Party, 20th Anniv.
A520

Designs: No. 608a, 10ch, Korean fighters.
No. 608b, 10ch, Party emblem. No. 608c,
10ch, Lenin & Marx. No. 608d, 10ch, Workers
marching. No. 608e, 10ch, Soldiers & armed
workers. No. 608f, 40ch, Workers.

**1965, Oct. 10    Photo.    Perf. 13X13½**
**With Gum**
608 A520 Block of 6, #a.-f.     55.00  22.50
608g      Souvenir sheet of 6,
          #608-613             600.00  400.00

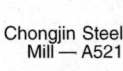

Chongjin Steel
Mill — A521

Kim Chaek Iron
Works — A522

---

**1965, Nov. 25    Engr.    Perf. 12½**
**With Gum**
614 A521 10ch deep violet      5.00  .25
615 A522 10ch sepia            5.00  .25

Rainbow
Trout — A523

Dolly
Trout — A524

Grass
Carp — A525

Carp — A526

Manchurian
Trout — A527

Crucian
Carp — A528

**1965, Dec. 10    Photo.    Perf. 13½**
**With Gum**
616 A523 2ch  multicolored      .75  .25
617 A524 4ch  multicolored     1.00  .25
618 A525 10ch multicolored     2.25  .25
619 A526 10ch multicolored     2.25  .25
620 A527 10ch multicolored     2.25  .25
621 A528 40ch multicolored     3.50  .50
Nos. 616-621 (6)              12.00 1.75
Freshwater fishes.
Nos. 616-621 exist imperf, without gum.
Value $20 unused.

House
Building
A529

Hemp
Weaving
A530

Blacksmith
A531

Wrestling
A532

School
A533

Dance
A534

**1965, Dec. 15    Engr.    Perf. 12½**
**With Gum**
622 A529 2ch  green           .70  .25
623 A530 4ch  maroon         1.35  .25
624 A531 10ch violet         1.75  .25
625 A532 10ch carmine red    1.90  .25
626 A533 10ch blue           1.20  .25
627 A534 10ch brown          1.10  .25
Nos. 622-627 (6)             8.00  1.50
Paintings by Kim Hong Do, 18th century
Korean artist.

---

Students'
Extracurricular
Activities — A535

Designs: 2ch, Children in workshop. 4ch,
Boxing. 10ch (No. 630), Playing violin. 10ch
(No. 631), Chemistry lab.

**1965, Dec. 15    Litho.    Perf. 13¼**
**With Gum**
628-631 A535 Set of 4         2.75  .50
Nos. 628-631 exist imperf. Value, unused
$75.

Whaler — A536

Service
Vessel — A537

**1965, Dec. 15    Engr.    Perf. 12½**
**With Gum**
632 A536 10ch deep blue       1.75  .25
633 A537 10ch slate green     1.75  .25
Korean fishing boats.

Black-capped
Kingfisher
A538

Korean Great Tit
A539

Blue
Magpie — A540

White-faced
Wagtail — A541

Migratory Korean
Grosbeak — A542

**Perf. 11, 13½ (#640)**
**1965, Dec. 30    Litho.    With Gum**
634 A538 4ch  pale yel & multi    2.25  .25
635 A539 10ch pale sal & multi    3.00  .25
636 A540 10ch pale grnsh blue
              & multi             3.00  .25
637 A541 10ch yel & multi         3.00  .25
638 A542 40ch pale yel grn &
              multi               8.50  .75
Nos. 634-638 (5)                 19.75 1.75
Korean birds.
Nos. 634-638 exist imperf, without gum.
Value $29 unused.

Korean
sericulture — A543

Designs: 2ch, Silkworm moth & cocoon. No.
640, 10ch, Ailanthus silk moth. No. 641, 10ch,
Chinese Oak silk moth.

**1965, Dec. 30    Engr.    Perf. 12½**
**With Gum**
639-641 A543 Set of 3        100.00 2.75

---

Hooded
Crane
A544

Japanese
White-
necked
Crane
A545

Manchurian
Crane
A546

Gray
Heron
A547

**1965, Dec. 30    With Gum**
642 A544 2ch  olive brown     3.75  .25
643 A545 10ch dp vio blue     4.00  .45
644 A546 10ch slate purple    4.00  .45
645 A547 40ch slate green     7.00  .80
Nos. 642-645 (4)             18.75 1.95
Wading birds. For surcharge, see No. 4540.

Mollusks — A548

Designs: 5ch, Japanese common squid.
10ch, Giant Pacific octopus.

**1965, Dec. 31    Litho.    Perf. 11**
**With Gum**
646-647 A548 Set of 2         4.00  3.00
Nos. 646-647 exist imperf, without gum.
Value $8 unused.

Korean
Ducks — A549

Designs: 2ch, Spotbill. 4ch, Ruddy
shelduck. 10ch, Mallard. 40ch, Baikal teal.

**1965, Dec. 31    Litho.    Perf. 11**
**With Gum**
648-651 A549 Set of 4        15.00  1.75
Nos. 648-651 exist imperf. Value $30
unused.

Circus, Pyongyang
A550

Trapeze
Performers
A551

Balancing Act
A552

Seesawing
A553

Tightrope
Walker — A554

**1965, Dec. 31**          **Photo.**
652  A550  2ch multicolored      .75  .25
653  A551  10ch multicolored    2.00  .25
654  A552  10ch multicolored    2.00  .25
655  A553  10ch multicolored    2.00  .25
656  A554  10ch multicolored    2.00  .25
    *Nos. 652-656 (5)*          8.75  1.25
           Korean acrobatics.
  Nos. 652-655 were issued with gum, No.
656 without gum.

Korean Flowers — A555

  Designs: No. 657, 4ch, Marvel-of-Peru. No.
658, 10ch, Peony (violet background). No.
659, 10ch, Moss rose (yellow background).
No. 660, 10ch, Magnolia (light blue
background).

**1965, Dec. 31**          **Litho.**
657-660  A555  Set of 4      12.00  .95
  No. 657 was issued without gum, Nos. 658-
60 with gum.
  Nos. 657-660 exist imperf, without gum.
Value $20 unused.

Yachts — A556

  Designs: No. 661, 2ch, Finn Class. No. 662,
10ch, Dragon Class (blue background). No.
663, 10ch, 5.5 Class (violet background). No.
664, 40ch, Star Class.

**1965, Dec. 31  With Gum  Perf. 13½**
661-664  A556  Set of 4       6.00  1.75
  Nos. 661-664 exist imperf, without gum.
Value $10 unused.
  10ch depicting Netherlands class yacht,
with blue background, not issued. Value $750.

1st Congress of the
Org. of Solidarity of
Peoples of Asia, Africa
and Latin
America — A557

**1966, Jan. 3    With Gum    Perf. 11**
665  A557  10ch multicolored     .50  .25

Hosta
A558

Dandelion
A559

Lily of the
Valley
A560

Pink
Convolvulus
A561

Catalpa
Blossom — A562

**1966, Jan. 15**          **With Gum**
666  A558  2ch multicolored    1.25  .25
667  A559  4ch multicolored    1.25  .25
668  A560  10ch multicolored   1.75  .25
669  A561  10ch multicolored   1.75  .25
670  A562  40ch multicolored   5.25  .70
    *Nos. 666-670 (5)*        11.25  1.70
          Korean wildflowers.
  Imperfs exist, without gum. Value, $25
unused.

Primrose
A563

Brillian
Campion
A564

Amur
Pheasant's
Eye — A565

Orange
Lily — A566

Rhododendron — A567

**1966, Feb. 10**          **With Gum**
671  A563  2ch multicolored    1.00  .25
672  A564  4ch multicolored    1.00  .25
673  A565  10ch multicolored   1.40  .25
674  A566  10ch multicolored   1.40  .25
675  A567  90ch multicolored   7.25  .95
    *Nos. 671-675 (5)*        12.05  1.95
          Korean wildflowers.

Land Reform Law, 20th Anniv. — A568

**1966, Mar. 5**          **With Gum**
676  A568  10ch multicolored   1.75  .50

Battle of
Jiansanfen
A569

Battle of
Taehongdan
A570

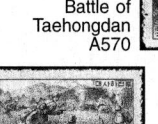

Battle of
Dashahe — A571

**1966, Mar. 25    Engr.    Perf. 12½**
677  A569  10ch  violet brown   .60  .25
678  A570  10ch  dp blue green  .60  .25
679  A571  10ch  brown carmine  .60  .25
    *Nos. 677-679 (3)*         1.80  .75
  Battles of the anti-Japanese revolution.
  No. 678 was issued without gum, the other
values with gum.

Art Treasures of the
Silla Dynasty — A572

  Designs: 2ch, Covered bowl. 5ch, Jar. 10ch,
Censer.

**1966, Apr. 30**          **With Gum**
680-682  A572  Set of 3       4.50  .55

Labor Day, 80th
Anniv. — A573

**1966, May 1    Litho.    Perf. 11**
            **With Gum**
683  A573  10ch multicolored    .75  .25

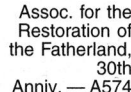

Assoc. for the
Restoration of
the Fatherland,
30th
Anniv. — A574

**1966, May 5    Photo.    With Gum**
684  A574  10ch brn red & yel   .75  .25

Farmer
A575

Worker
A576

**1966, May 30    Litho.    With Gum**
685  A575  5ch multicolored     .50  .25
686  A576  10ch multicolored    .75  .25

Young Pioneers,
20th
Anniv. — A577

**1966, June 6**          **With Gum**
687  A577  10ch multicolored   1.00  .25

Kangson Steel
Works — A578

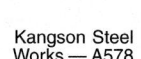

Pongung
Chemical
Works — A579

**1966, June 10    Engr.    Perf. 12½**
            **With Gum**
688  A578  10ch  gray          5.00  .25
689  A579  10ch  deep red      5.00  .25
          Korean Factories.

Fish — A580

  Designs: 2ch, Saury. 5ch, Pacific cod. No.
692, Chum salmon. No. 693, Mackerel. 40ch,
Pink salmon.

**1966, June 10    Photo.    Perf. 11**
690-694  A580  Set of 5      15.00  4.50
  Nos. 690-692 were issued with gum, Nos.
693-694 without gum.
  Nos. 690-694 exist imperf, without gum.
Value, $22, either unused or cancelled.

Prof. Kim Bong Han & Kyongrak
Biological System — A581

**1966, June 30    Photo.    With Gum**
695   A581  Block of 8, #a.-h.   11.00   8.00
695i        Souvenir sheet of 8, #695-
            702                 125.00 100.00

Voshkod
2 — A582

Luna 9 — A583

Luna
10 — A584

**1966, June 30**
703  A582  5ch multicolored     .30  .25
704  A583  10ch multicolored   1.00  .25
705  A584  40ch multicolored   1.75  .35
    *Nos. 703-705 (3)*         3.05  .85
          Space Flight Day.
  Nos. 703-705 exist imperf. Value, $8
unused.

Jules Rimet
Cup — A585

Dribbling
A586

Goal-keeper
A587

**1966, July 11**          **Litho.**
706  A585  10ch multicolored   1.90  .25
707  A586  10ch multicolored   1.90  .25
708  A587  10ch multicolored   1.90  .25
    *Nos. 706-708 (3)*         5.70  .75
        World Cup Championship.
  Nos. 706-708 exist imperf. Value, $20
unused.

Battle of Naphalsan A588

Battle of Seoul A589

Battle of Height 1211 — A590

**1966, July 27    Engr.    Perf. 12½**
**With Gum**
709 A588 10ch red violet       1.10   .25
710 A589 10ch deep green      1.10   .25
711 A590 10ch violet           1.10   .25
    Nos. 709-711 (3)          3.30   .75
       Korean War of 1950-53.

Sex Equality Law, 20th Anniv. — A591

**1966, July 30    Litho.    Perf. 11**
**With Gum**
712 A591 10ch multicolored     1.50   .30

Nationalization of Industry, 20th Anniv. — A592

**1966, Aug. 10          With Gum**
713 A592 10ch multicolored     1.10   .25

Water Jar Dance A593

Bell Dance A594

Dancer in Mural Painting A595

Sword Dance A596

Golden Cymbal Dance — A597

**1966, Aug. 10**
714 A593  5ch multicolored     1.40   .25
715 A594 10ch multicolored     2.50   .25
716 A595 10ch multicolored     2.50   .25
717 A596 15ch multicolored     2.50   .25
718 A597 40ch multicolored     4.50   .30
    Nos. 714-718 (5)          13.40  1.30
       Korean Folk Dances.
5ch and 10ch issued with or without gum.
Other values issued without gum.
Nos. 714-718 exist imperf, without gum.
Value, $20 unused.

Attacking U.S. Soldier A598

Worker with Child A599

Industrialization — A600

**1966, Aug. 15    Engr.    Perf. 12½**
**With Gum**
719 A598 10ch deep green      1.25   .25
720 A599 10ch red violet      1.25   .25
721 A600 10ch violet          5.75   .40
    Nos. 719-721 (3)          8.25   .90
     Korean Reunification Campaign.

Crop-spraying A601

Observing Forest Fire — A602

Geological Survey — A603

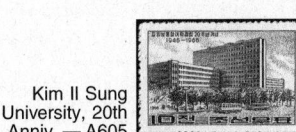

Fish Shoal Detection A604

**1966, Sept. 30    Photo.    Perf. 11**
722 A601  2ch multicolored      .50   .25
723 A602  5ch multicolored     7.00   .25
724 A603 10ch multicolored     1.75   .25
725 A604 40ch multicolored     1.75   .25
    Nos. 722-725 (4)          11.00  1.00
     Industrial uses of aircraft.
2ch, 5ch issued without gum. 10ch, 40ch issued with gum.
Nos. 722-725 exist imperf, without gum. Value, $20 unused.

---

A three-value set honoring revolutionary fighters, with designs similar to types A334-A339, was prepared but not issued. Value $3,500.

---

1st Asian GANEFO Games — A606

Designs: a, 5ch, Judo. b, 10ch, Basketball. c, 10ch, Table tennis.

**1966, Oct. 30    Litho.    Perf. 11**
727 A606  Strip of 3, #a-c     2.00   .55
    Strip of 3, #a-c imperf   50.00   —

Scarlet Finch A607

Hoopoe A608

Korean Crested Lark — A609

Brown Thrush — A610

White-bellied Black Woodpecker — A611

**1966, Oct. 30**
730 A607  2ch multicolored     2.25   .25
731 A608  5ch multicolored     2.50   .25
732 A609 10ch multicolored     2.75   .30
733 A610 10ch multicolored     2.75   .30
734 A611 40ch multicolored     5.75   .80
    Nos. 730-734 (5)          16.00  1.90
    Set of 5, imperf          32.00   —
Korean birds. For surcharge, see No. 4513.

Construction A612

Machine-Tool Production A613

Worker & Graph — A614

Miners A615

**1966, Nov. 20**
735 A612  5ch multicolored      .40   .25
736 A613 10ch multicolored      .75   .25
737 A614 10ch multicolored      .75   .25
738 A615 40ch multicolored     2.10   .45
    Nos. 735-738 (4)           4.00  1.20

Propaganda for increased production.
Nos. 735-737 issued with gum. No. 738 issued without gum.

Parachuting A616

Show Jumping — A617

Motorcycling A618

Telegraphists' Competition A619

**1966, Nov. 30    Engr.    Perf. 12½**
**With Gum**
739 A616  2ch dark brown        .90   .25
740 A617  5ch org vermilion     .65   .25
741 A618 10ch dp violet blue   3.25   .30
742 A619 40ch deep green       2.10   .25
    Nos. 739-742 (4)           6.90  1.05
     National Defense sports.

Samil Wolgan Magazine, 30th Anniv. — A620

**1966, Dec. 1    Photo.    Perf. 11**
743 A620 10ch multicolored      —     —

Korean Deer — A621

Designs: 2ch, Red deer. 5ch, Sika deer. No. 746, 10ch, Reindeer (grazing). No. 747, 10ch, Japanese sambar (erect). 70ch, Fallow deer.

**1966, Dec. 20              Litho.**
744-748 A621 Set of 5         18.00  4.50
    Imperf, #744-748

No. 747 was issued with gum. Other values issued without gum. For surcharge, see No. 4560.

Wild Fruit — A622

Designs: 2ch, Blueberries. 5ch, Pears. 10ch (No. 751), Plums. 10ch (No. 752), Schizandra. 10ch (No. 753), Raspberries. 40ch, Jujube.

**1966, Dec. 30**
749-754 A622 Set of 6         6.00   .65
    Imperf, #749-754         12.50   —

Samson Rocks A623

Ryonju Pond A624

---

**1966, Oct. 1    Engr.    Perf. 12½**
**With Gum**
726 A605 10ch slate violet     1.75   .30

Jinju Pond
A625

The Ten
Thousand
Rocks,
Manmulsang
A626

**1966, Dec. 30　Litho.　Perf. 11**
755　A623　2ch multicolored　　1.00　.25
756　A624　4ch multicolored　　4.00　.25
757　A625　10ch multicolored　　1.00　.25
758　A626　10ch multicolored　　4.00　.25
　　　Nos. 755-758 (4)　　10.00　1.00
　Diamond Mountains scenery.
　Nos. 755-758 are inscribed "1964" but were actually issued in 1966.
　2ch and 4ch issued without gum. 10ch values issued with gum.

Onpo — A627

Myohyang
A628

Songdowon
A629

Hongwon
A630

**1966, Dec. 30　Engr.　Perf. 12½**
**With Gum**
759　A627　2ch blue violet　　1.00　.30
760　A628　4ch turquoise green　　1.15　.30
761　A629　10ch dp blue green　　1.75　.30
762　A630　40ch black　　3.25　.40
　　　Nos. 759-762 (4)　　7.15　1.30
　　Korean rest homes.

Korean People's
Army, 19th
Anniv. — A631

**1967, Feb. 8　Photo.　Perf. 11**
763　A631　10ch multicolored　　.75　.25

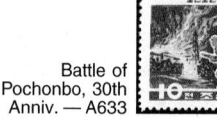

Livestock
Farming — A632

　Designs: 5ch, Sow. 10ch, Goat. 40ch, Bull.

**1967, Feb. 28　　　Litho.**
764-766　A632　Set of 3　　7.50　1.60
　　　Imperf, #764-766　　60.00　—
　5ch, 10ch issued without gum. 40ch issued both with and without gum.

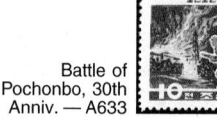

Battle of
Pochonbo, 30th
Anniv. — A633

**1967, Feb. 28　Photo.　With Gum**
767　A633　10ch multicolored　　.75　.25

Universal
Compulsory
Technical
Education — A634

**1967, Apr. 1**
768　A634　10ch multicolored　　.75　.25

29th World Table Tennis
Championships, Pyongyang — A635

　10ch, 40ch designs similar to 5ch.

**1967, Apr. 11　　　Litho.**
769-771　A635　Set of 3　　3.25　.60
　　　Imperf, #769-771　　110.00　—
　5ch issued with or without gum. 10ch, 40ch issued without gum. For surcharge, see No. 4514.

People Helping
Guerrillas,
Wangyugou
A636

Blowing Up
Railway
Bridge — A637

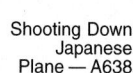

Shooting Down
Japanese
Plane — A638

**1967, Apr. 25　Engr.　With Gum**
772　A636　10ch deep violet　　.50　.25
773　A637　10ch dk vio brown　　4.25　.25
774　A638　10ch slate　　.50　.25
　　　Nos. 772-774 (3)　　5.25　.75
Paintings of the guerrilla war against Japan.

Ri Tae
Hun — A639

Choe Jong
Un — A640

Kim Hwa
Ryong — A641

**1967, Apr. 25　　　With Gum**
775　A639　10ch slate　　1.00　.25
776　A640　10ch reddish violet　　3.00　.25
777　A641　10ch ultramarine　　1.00　.25
　　　Nos. 775-777 (3)　　5.00　.75
　　Heroes of the Republic.

Labor
Day — A642

**1967, May 1　　　Litho.**
778　A642　10ch multicolored　　.75　.25

Pre-School
Education
A643

　Designs of children: 5ch, Learning to count. 10ch, Making model tractor. 40ch, Playing with ball.

**1967, June 1**
779-781　A643　Set of 3　　4.50　.75

Victory
Monument,
Battle of
Pochonbo
A644

**1967, June 4**
782　A644　10ch multicolored　　1.00　.25

Military
Sculpture — A645

　Designs: 2ch, Soldier attacking tank. 5ch, Soldiers with musical instruments. 10ch, Soldier in heroic pose. 40ch, Soldier and child.

**1967, June 25　　　Photo.**
783-786　A645　Set of 4　　3.00　.75
　2ch issued with or without gum. Other values issued without gum.

Medicinal
Plants — A646

　Designs: 2ch, Polygonatum japonicum. 5ch, Abelmoschus manihat. 10ch (No. 789), Rehmannia glutinosa (olive yellow). 10ch (No. 790), Scutellaria baicalensis (turquoise blue background). 10ch (No. 791), Pulsatilla koreana (violet blue). 40ch, Tanacetum boreale.

**1967, July 20　　　Photo.**
787-792　A646　Set of 6　　11.00　1.00
　Nos. 787-789, 791 issued with or without gum. Nos. 790, 792 issued without gum.

Korean
People's
Army — A647

　Designs: 5ch, Aviator, sailor, soldier. 10ch (No. 794), Officer decorating soldier. 10ch (No. 795), Soldier and farmer.

**1967, July 25**
793-795　A647　Set of 3　　2.50　.85
　5ch issued with or without gum. 10ch values issued without gum.

Freighter
"Chollima"
A648

**1967, July 30　Engr.　With Gum**
796　A648　10ch deep green　　2.00　.25

Drilling
Rock — A649

Felling
Trees — A650

Reclaiming
Tideland — A651

**1967, Aug. 5**
797　A649　5ch black brown　　.60　.25
798　A650　10ch blue green　　.80　.25
799　A651　10ch slate　　1.10　.25
　　　Nos. 797-799 (3)　　2.50　.75
　　Revolutionary paintings.
　5ch issued without gum. 10ch values issued with gum.

Crabs — A652

　Designs: 2ch, Erimaculus isenbeckii. 5ch, Neptunus trituberculatus. 10ch, Paralithodes camtschatica. 40ch, Chionoecetes opilio.

**1967, Aug. 10　　　Photo.**
800-803　A652　Set of 4　　8.00　.90

Reunification
of Korea
Propaganda
A653

**1967, Aug. 15　　　Litho.**
804　A653　10ch multicolored　　4.00　.35

　A five-value set, featuring details from famous Korean paintings of the 15th-16th centuries, was prepared for release in August, 1967, but was not issued. Value $2,500.
　A 10ch stamp celebrating the 10th anniversary of the launch of the first USSR space satellite was prepared for release on Sept. 10 but was not issued. Value $1,500.

Waterfalls — A654

Designs: 2ch, Tongrim waterfalls 10ch, Sanju waterfall, Mt. Myohyang. 40ch, Sambang waterfall, Mt. Chonak.

**1967, Oct. 10**
805-807 A654 Set of 3     12.00   .80

2ch issued with or without gum. 10ch, 40ch issued without gum.

"For Fresh Great Revolutionary Upsurge" A655

Designs: 5ch, Ship, train and truck. 10ch (No. 809), Machine industry. 10ch (No. 810), Truck, bulldozer, tractor and farmers. 10ch (No. 811), Construction machinery, buildings. 10ch (No. 812), Chollima flying horse and banners.

**1967, Nov. 1**       **Engr.**
808-812 A655 Set of 5     11.00 1.00

Russian Revolution, 50th Anniv. — A656

**1967, Nov. 7**       **Photo.**
813 A656 10ch multicolored    1.50   .25

Korean Elections A657

Designs: 10ch (No. 814), Voters and flags. 10ch (No. 815), Woman casting ballot (vert.)

**1967, Nov. 23**       **Litho.**
814-815 A657 Set of 2     3.50 1.00

Raptors — A658

Designs: 2ch, Black vulture. 10ch, Rough-legged buzzard. 40ch, White-tailed eagle.

**1967, Dec. 1**       **Photo.**
816-818 A658 Set of 3     14.00 1.75

2ch issued with or without gum. 10ch, 40ch issued without gum. For surcharge, see No. 4512.

Chongjin A659

Hamhung A660

Sinuiju — A661

**1967, Dec. 20**    **Engr.**    **With Gum**
819 A659 5ch bronze green    1.10   .25
820 A660 10ch violet          1.10   .25
821 A661 10ch red violet     1.10   .25
    Nos. 819-821 (3)     3.30   .75
       Korean cities.

Whaler Firing Harpoon — A662

**With or Without Gum**
**1967, Dec. 30**
822 A662 10ch ultramarine    2.50   .25

Soldier with Red Book — A663

Soldier Mounting Bayonet A664

Worker and Bayoneted Rifle — A665

**Litho or Photo (#829)**
**1967, Dec. 30**
823 A663 10ch multicolored    .40   .25
824 A664 10ch multicolored    .40   .25
825 A665 10ch multicolored    .40   .25
    Nos. 823-825 (3)     1.20   .75

Korean People's Army, 20th Anniv. A666

Designs: a, Airman, soldier and sailor. b, Soldier, battle in background. c, Soldier & KDPR arms. d, Soldier & flag. e, Soldier with Red Book. f, Three soldiers, North Korean flag. g, Soldier & worker. h, Soldier saluting. i, Soldier attacking. j, Soldier, sailor & airman beneath flag.

**1968, Feb. 3**       **Litho.**
826 A666 Sheet of 10   80.00 30.00
   a.-j.    10ch, any single    .45   .25

Ri Su Bok (1934-51) A667

Han Kye Ryol (1926-51) A668

**1968, Feb. 10**    **Engr.**    **With Gum**
827 A667 10ch dark rose     550.00
828 A667 10ch light violet    1.00   .25
829 A668 10ch dark green    550.00
830 A668 10ch lt blue violet   1.00   .25
    Nos. 827-830 (4)    1,102.   .50
       War heroes.

Nos. 827 and 829 were prepared but not issued.

Apartment Building, Pyongyang — A669

**1968, Mar. 5**    **Litho.**    **With Gum**
831 A669 10ch bright blue    1.00   .25

Kim Il Sung, 56th Birthday — A670

**1968, Apr. 15**       **With Gum**
832 A670 40ch multicolored   1.10   .35

Printed in sheets of four stamps. Exists in a miniature sheet of one, which is rare (2 examples reported),

Kim Il Sung's Family Home in Mangyongdae — A671

Leaving Home at Age 13 — A672

Mangyong Hill — A673

Kim Il Sung with Father A674

Kim Il Sung with Mother A675

**1968, Apr. 15**
833 A671 10ch multicolored   1.50   .25
834 A672 10ch multicolored   1.50   .25
835 A673 10ch multicolored   1.50   .25
836 A674 10ch multicolored   1.50   .25
837 A675 10ch multicolored   1.50   .25
    Nos. 833-837 (5)    7.50 1.25
   Childhood of Kim Il Sung.
   See Nos. 883-887, 927-930.

Dredger 2 September — A676

**1968, June 5**
838 A676 5ch green       1.40     .25
839 A676 5ch blue      850.00 600.00

Matsutake Mushroom A677

Shiitake Mushroom A678

Meadow Mushroom — A679

**1968, Aug. 10**    **Photo.**    **With Gum**
840 A677 5ch multicolored   20.00   .55
841 A678 10ch multicolored   40.00   .90
842 A679 10ch multicolored   40.00   .90
    Nos. 840-842 (3)   100.00 2.35

Founding of the Korean Democratic People's Republic, 20th Anniv. — A680

Designs: a, Statue of national arms. b, North Korean flag. c, Worker, peasant & flag. d, Soldier & flag. e, Flying Horse of Chollima. f, Soldiers & tanks. g, Battle scene. h, Workers, banner & monument.

**1968, Sept. 2**    **Litho.**    **With Gum**
843 A680 Block of 8, #a.-h.   40.00 35.00
   a.-h.   10ch, any single    1.50   .25

Kaesong Students' and Children's Palace — A681

**1968, Oct. 5**       **With Gum**
844 A681 10ch greenish blue   .50   .25

Domestic Goods — A682

Designs: 2ch, Shopper with domestic items. 5ch, Textile manufacturing. 10ch, Cannery.

**1968, Nov. 5**    **Photo.**    **With Gum**
845-847 A682 Set of 3     2.75   .65

Kim Il Sung's 10-Point Program — A683

Design: 10ch, Two soldiers, Red Book, horiz.

**1968, Dec. 5**       **Litho.**
848-849 A683 Set of 2     1.10   .25

Increasing Agricultural Production A684

Designs: 5ch, Woman carrying eggs. 10ch (No. 851), Woman harvesting wheat. 10ch (No. 852), Woman holding basket of fruit.

**1968, Dec. 10**    **Photo.**    **With Gum**
850-852 A684 Set of 3     1.40   .55

Shellfish
A685

Designs: 5ch (No. 853), Scallop. 5ch (No. 854), Clam. 10ch, Mussel.

**1968, Dec. 20**      **With Gum**
853-855 A685   Set of 3     6.00   .50

Details of Battle of Pochonbo Victory Monument
A686

Designs (all 10ch): No. 856, Kim Il Sung at head of columns, vert. No. 857, shown. No. 858, Figures marching to right, green sky at right (42.75x28mm). No. 859, Figures marching to left (55.5x28mm). No. 860, Figures marching to right (55.5x28mm). No. 861, Figures marching to left, sky at right (42.75x28mm). No. 862, Figures marching to left, sky at left (42.75x28mm).

**1968, Dec. 30**
856-862 A686   Set of 7     3.50   1.35

Grand Theater, Pyongyang
A687

**1968, Dec. 30**
863 A687   10ch dark brown     1.10   .25

Revolutionary Museum, Pochonbo
A688

**1968, Dec. 30**
864 A688   2ch dark green     .55   .25

Rural Technical Development
A689

Designs: 2ch, Irrigation. 5ch, Mechanization of agriculture. 10ch, Electrification. 40ch, Mechanical fertilization and spraying.

**1969, Feb. 25**
865-868 A689   Set of 4     2.50   .80

Rabbits
A690

Designs: 2ch, Gray rabbits. 10ch (No. 870), White rabbits. 10ch (No. 871), Black rabbits. 10ch (No. 872), Brown rabbits. 40ch, White rabbits.

**1969, Mar. 10**
869-873 A690   Set of 5     10.00   1.10
Nos. 869-873 were issued both with and without gum.

Public Health — A691

Designs: 2ch, Old man & girl. 10ch, Nurse with syringe. 40ch, Doctor with woman & child.

**1969, Apr. 1**
874-876 A691   Set of 3     4.25   .60

Farm Machines
A692

Designs: 10ch (No. 877), Rice sower. 10ch (No. 878), Rice harvester. 10ch (No. 879), Herbicide sprayer. 10ch (No. 880), Wheat & barley thresher.

**1969, Apr. 10**      **Engr.**
877-880 A692   Set of 4     3.25   .80

Mangyongdae — A693

Ponghwa
A694

**1969, Apr. 15**      **Litho.**
881 A693   10ch multicolored    1.75   .25
882 A694   10ch multicolored    1.75   .25
Revolutionary historical sites.

Early Revolutionary Years of Kim Il Sung — A695

Designs (all 10ch): No. 883, Kim crossing into Manchuria 1926, aged 13. No. 884, Kim talking to four students around table (blue green frame). No. 885, Kim speaking outdoors to Young Communist League meeting (apple green frame). No. 886, Kim speaking to Young Communist League meeting indoors (lilac frame). No. 887, Kim leading demonstration against teachers (peach frame).

**1969, Apr. 15**
883-887 A695   Set of 5     3.25   1.00
No. 884 was issued with gum. The other values were issued without gum.

Kang Pan Sok (1892-1932), Mother of Kim Il Sung — A696

Designs (all 10ch): No. 888, Birthplace at Chilgol. No. 889, Resisting Japanese police in home. No. 890, Meeting with women's revolutionary association.

**1969, Apr. 21**      **Photo.**
888-890 A696   Set of 3     4.50   .60

Bivouac Sites in War against Japan — A697

Designs: 5ch, Pegaebong. 10ch (No. 892), Mupho, horiz. 10ch (No. 893), Chongbong. 40ch, Konchang, horiz.

**1969, Apr. 21**
891-894 A697   Set of 4     3.00   .80

Chollima Statue — A698

**1969, May 1**
895 A698   10ch blue     .85   .25

Poultry — A699

Designs: 10ch (No. 896), Mangyong chickens. 10ch (No. 897), Kwangpho ducks.

**1969, June 1**      **Engr.**
896-897 A699   Set of 2     5.75   .50

Socialist Education System — A700

Designs: 2ch, Kim Il Sung & children. 10ch, Student & worker with books. 40ch, Male & female students, figure "9."

**1969, June 1**      **Photo.**
898-900 A700   Set of 3     2.25   .60

Pochonbo Battlefield Memorials
A701

Designs: 5ch, Machine gun platform on mountainside. 10ch (No. 902), Statue of Kim Il Sung, vert. 10ch (No. 903), Aspen Tree monument (stele & enclosed tree trunk). 10ch (No. 904), Konjang Hill monument (within forest).

**1969, June 4**
901-904 A701   Set of 4     2.25   .80

Kim Hyong Jik (1894-1926), Father of Kim Il Sung — A702

Designs: 10ch (No. 905), Teaching at Myongsin School. 10ch (No. 906), Outdoor meeting with five other members of Korean National Association.

**1969, July 10**
905-906 A702   Set of 2     1.90   .40

A 10ch stamp honoring the Juvenile Chess Game of Socialist Countries was prepared for release Aug. 5, 1969, but was not issued. Value $1,000.

Sports Day, 20th Anniv. — A703

**1969, Sept. 10**
907 A703   10ch multicolored    1.10   .25

Korean Revolution Museum, Pyongyang — A704

**1969, Sept. 10**      **Litho.**
908 A704   10ch dk blue green    .85   .25

Pres. Nixon Attacked by Pens — A705

**1969, Sept. 18**      **Litho.**
909 A705   10ch multi     3.25   .25
Anti-U.S. Imperialism Journalists' Conference, Pyongyang.

Implementation of the 10-Point Program
A706

Designs: 5ch, Soldiers, battle. 10ch (No. 911), Globe, bayonets attacking dismembered U.S. soldier. 10ch (No. 912), Workers holding Red Books & slogan, vert.

**1969, Oct. 1**      **Photo.**
910-912 A706   Set of 3     10.00   .75

Reunification of Korea — A707

Designs: 10ch (No. 913), Kim Il Sung, marching workers. 10ch (No. 914), Worker & soldier bayoneting U.S. soldier. 50ch, Armed workers in battle, horiz.

**1969, Oct. 1**      **Litho.**
913-915 A707   Set of 3     1.75   .70

Refrigerator-Transport Ship "Taesongsan" — A708

**1969, Dec. 20**      **Engr.**
916 A708   10ch slate purple    1.50   .30

Korean Fish — A709

Designs: 5ch, Yellowtail. 10ch, Dace. 40ch, Mullet.

**1969, Dec. 20**      **Photo.**
917-919 A709   Set of 3     6.50   .65

Guerrilla Conference Sites — A710

Designs: 2ch, Dahuangwai, 1935. 5ch, Yaoyinggou, 1935 (log cabin). 10ch, Xiaohaerbaling, 1940 (tent).

**1970, Feb. 10**
920-922 A710 Set of 3    1.50   .50

Mt. Paektu, Birthplace of the Revolution A711

Views of Mt. Paektu (all 10ch): No. 923, Lake Chon (dull green, tan, black). No. 924, Janggun Peak (pale peach, dull blue, black). No. 925, Piryu Peak (dull yellow, blue green, black). No. 926, Pyongsa Peak (brown orange, blue, red violet).

**1970, Mar. 10**
923-926 A711 Set of 4    3.00   .70
See Nos. 959-961.

Support for North Vietnam — A712

**1970, Mar. 10**
927 A712 10ch multicolored   .75   .25

Revolutionary Activities of Kim Il Sung — A713

Designs (all 10ch): No. 928, Receiving his father's pistols from his mother. No. 929, Receiving smuggled pistols from his mother (other young revolutionaries present). No. 930, Kim speaking with four farmers in field. No. 931, Kim speaking at Kalun meeting.

**1970, Apr. 15**    Litho.
928-931 A713 Set of 4    6.00 1.00

Lenin Birth Centenary — A714

Design: 10ch (No. 933), Lenin with cap, in three-quarter profile.

**1970, Apr. 22**    Photo.
932-933 A714 Set of 2    1.75   .45

Assoc. of Koreans in Japan, 15th Anniv. — A715

Designs (both 10ch): No. 934, Red. No. 935, Maroon.

**1970, Apr. 27**    Engr.
934-935 A715 Set of 2    3.00   .90

Worker-Peasant Red Guard — A716

Design: 10ch (No. 936), Factory worker in uniform, vert.

**1970, May 5**    Photo.
936-937 A716 Set of 2    1.25   .50

Peasant Education A717

Designs: 2ch, Students & newspapers. 5ch, Peasant reading book. 10ch, Students in class.

**1970, June 25**
938-940 A717 Set of 3    1.75   .50

Army Electrical Engineer — A718

**1970, June 25**
941 A718 10ch purple brown   1.00   .25

Month of the Campaign for Withdrawal of U.S. Troops from South Korea — A719

Design: 10ch, Soldier & partisan.

**1970, June 25**
942-943 A719 Set of 2    1.75   .25

Anti-U.S., South Korea Propaganda A720

**1970, June 25**    Engr.
944 A720 10ch deep violet   .75   .25

Campaign for Increased Productivity A721

Designs (all 10ch): No. 945, Quarryman. No. 946, Steelworker. No. 947, Machinist. No. 948, Worker with bag. No. 949, Construction worker. No. 950, Railway flagman.

**1970, Sept. 10**    Photo.
945-950 A721 Set of 6    5.50 1.50

Workers' Party Program — A722

Designs: 5ch, Peasant, farm scene. 10ch, Steelworker. 40ch, Soldiers.

**1970, Oct. 5**    Engr.
951-953 A722 Set of 3    5.50   .70

Korean Workers' Party, 25th Anniv. — A723

**1970, Oct. 10**    Photo.
954 A723 10ch multicolored   1.00   .25

5th Korean Workers' Party Congress A724

Issued in miniature sheet of 10, with one 40ch value (No. 955j) and nine 10ch values. Designs: a, Kim Il Sung, marchers. b, Family & apartment buildings. c, Soldier with Red Book. d, Soldier with binoculars, various weapons. e, Steelworker. f, Workers killing U.S. soldier. g, Farmers. h, Students. i, Schoolgirl with Red

Book, atomic energy symbol. j, Cooperation with South Korean guerillas.

**1970, Nov. 2**    Litho.
955   Sheet of 10, #a.-j.    900.00
   a.-i.   A724 10ch Any single   1.40   .50
   j.   A724 40ch multi   600.00

Soon after release, a design error was discovered on No. 955j, and this stamp was removed from souvenir sheets remaining in stock, usually with the bottom salvage. This is the form in which this set is commonly offered. Value, $25. The full sheet of 10 is scarce.

League of Socialist Working Youth of Korea, 25th Anniv. — A725

**1971, Jan. 17**    Photo.
956 A725 10ch multicolored   .55   .25

Nanhutou Conference, 35th Anniv. — A726

**1971, Feb. 28**
957 A726 10ch multicolored   .55   .25

Land Reform Law, 25th Anniv. — A727

**1971, Mar. 5**
958 A727 2ch multicolored   .55   .25

Mt. Paektu, Second Issue — A728

Designs: 2ch, Mountainscape. 5ch, Paektu Waterfalls, vert. 10ch, Western Peak.

**1971, Mar. 10**
959-961 A728 Set of 3    5.00   .60

Revolutionary Museums A729

Designs (all 10ch): No. 962, Mangyongdae (red orange & ultramarine). No. 963, Phophyong (yellow & brown). No. 964, Junggang (salmon & green).

**1971, Apr. 1**
962-964 A729 Set of 3    2.00   .75

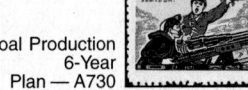

Coal Production 6-Year Plan — A730

**1971, Apr. 1**
965 A730 10ch multicolored   1.50   .25

Revolutionary Activities of Kim Il Sung — A731

Designs (all 10ch): No. 966, Portrait, vert. No. 967, Kim addressing crowd at guerrilla

base camp. No. 968, Kim speaking with children on hillside. No. 969, Kim reviewing Anti-Japanese Guerrilla Army 1932.

**1971, Apr. 15**    Litho.
966-969 A731 Set of 4    3.50   .90

May Day — A732

**1971, May 1**    Photo.
970 A732 1w multicolored   4.00   .45

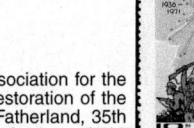

Association for the Restoration of the Fatherland, 35th Anniv. — A733

**1971, May 5**
971 A733 10ch multicolored   1.50   .25

Battles in the Musan Area Command (1939) — A734

Designs: 5ch, Sinsadong Monument. 10ch, Taehongdan Monument, with encased machine guns, horiz. 40ch, Musan headquarters (log cabins in forest), horiz.

**1971, May 23**
972-974 A734 Set of 3    2.50   .70

Koreans in Japan — A735

**1971, May 25**
975 A735 10ch chocolate   .75   .25

A 10ch stamp commemorating the Asia-Africa Invitational Table Tennis Game for Friendship was prepared for release on May 27, 1971, but was not issued. Value $750.

Korean Children's Union, 25th Anniv. — A736

**1971, June 6**
976 A736 10ch multicolored   .75   .25

6th Congress, League of Socialist Working Youth of Korea — A737

Designs: 5ch, Marchers & banners. 10ch, Marchers, banners & globe with map of Korea.

**1971, June 21**
977-978 A737 Set of 2    1.75   .25

Labor Law, 25th
Anniv. — A738

**1971, June 24**
979 A738  5ch multicolored        1.00   .25

Sex Equality Law,
25th
Anniv. — A739

**1971, July 30**
980 A739  5ch multicolored        .75   .25

Universal Compulsory Primary
Education, 15th Anniv. — A740

**1971, Aug. 1**
981 A740  10ch multicolored       .80   .25

South Korean
Revolutionaries
A741

Designs: 5ch, Choe Yong Do (1923-69).
10ch (No. 983), Kim Jong Thae (1926-69),
portrait with rioters killing U.S. soldier. 10ch
(No. 984), Guerrilla fighter with machine gun &
Red Book, battle scene.

**1971, Aug. 1**
982-984 A741  Set of 3           3.50  1.15

Nationalization of
Industry, 25th
Anniv. — A742

**1971, Aug. 10**
985 A742  5ch multicolored       2.75   .25

Anti-Imperialist,
Anti-U.S.
Struggle
A743

Designs: 10ch (No. 986), N. Korean soldier,
U.S. prisoners. 10ch (No. 987), S. Korean
guerrilla fighter. 10ch (No. 988), N.
Vietnamese soldiers, map. 10ch (No. 989),
Cuban soldier, map. 10ch (No. 990), African
guerrilla fighters, map. 40ch, six soldiers of
various nationalities bayoneting dismembered
U.S. soldier.

**1971, Aug. 12**
986-991 A743  Set of 6          *15.00*  3.00

Kim Il Sung
University, 25th
Anniv. — A744

**1971, Oct. 1**
992 A744  10ch multicolored      1.00   .25

Large
Machines — A745

Designs: 2ch, 6,000-ton press. 5ch, Refrig-
erated cargo ship "Ponghwasan." 10ch (No.
995), Sungrisan heavy truck. 10ch (No. 996),
Bulldozer.

**1971, Nov. 2**                   Litho.
993-996 A745  Set of 4          6.50   .50

Tasks of the
6-Year
Plan — A746

Designs (all 10ch): No. 997, Workers & text
on red field. No. 998, Mining. No. 999, Consumer goods. No. 1000, Lathe. No. 1001,
Construction equipment. No. 1002, Consumer
electronic products. No. 1003, Grains, farming. No. 1004, Railway track, transportation.
No. 1005, Freighter. No. 1006, Hand with
wrench, manufacturing scenes. No. 1007,
Crate & export goods on dock.

**1971, Nov. 2**                   Photo.
997-1007 A746  Set of 11        30.00  3.75

Cultural
Revolution
A747

Designs: 2ch, Technical students, university.
5ch, Mechanic. 10ch (No. 1010), Chemist.
10ch (No. 1011), Composer at piano. 10ch
(No. 1012), Schoolchildren.

**1971, Nov. 2**
1008-1012 A747  Set of 5       10.00   .90

Ideological
Revolution
A748

Designs (all 10ch): No. 1013, Workers with
Red Books, banners. No. 1014, Worker with
hydraulic drill. No. 1015, Two workers reading
Red Book. No. 1016, Workers' lecture.

**1971, Nov. 2**
1013-1016 A748  Set of 4        6.00   .50

Improvement
in Living
Standards
A749

**1971, Nov. 2**
1017 A749  10ch multicolored    *2.50*   .25

Solidarity with
International
Revolutionary
Forces — A750

Designs (all 10ch): No. 1018, Revolutionary
placards being driven into U.S. soldier. No.
1019, Japanese militarists being hammered
by mallet. No. 1020, Bayoneted rifles held
aloft. No. 1021, Armed international revolutionaries advancing, horiz.

**1971, Nov. 2**
1018-1021 A750  Set of 4        *5.00*   .80

6-Year
Plan — A751

**1971, Nov. 2**
1022 A751  10ch multicolored    3.50   .25

Three sets were prepared for release
on Nov. 2, 1971, but were not issued:
Butterflies (3 stamps), value $2,500;
Korean Reunification (2 10ch stamps),
value $750; Cultural Revolu-
tion/Improvement of the People's Living
Standards (7 10ch stamps), value
$5,000.

Samil Wolgan Monthly,
35th Anniv. — A752

**1971, Dec. 1**
1023 A752  10ch multicolored    3.50   .25

---

**Domestic Printings**
  Sometime in the early 1970s, the
DPRK post office begin to produce
separate printings of some issues for
domestic use. These stamps were
generally printed on poorer quality
white or brownish unsurfaced papers
and demonstrated poorer overall production values. Serious students of
the period are now working to identify
just which stamps exist in this form
and how to easily distinguish them
from the higher-quality printings
intended for sale to foreign collectors.
At this time, these domestic-use
printings are generally sold for $5-
$20 per stamp.

---

Poultry
Breeding
A753

Designs: 5ch, Chicks. 10ch, Chickens &
automated henhouse. 40ch, Eggs, canned
chicken, dead chickens hanging on hooks.

**1972, Feb. 1**
1024-1026 A753  Set of 3        3.50   .95

War Films
A754

Designs (all 10ch): No. 1027, Man &
woman, from *Vintage Shrine.* No. 1028, Guerrilla bayoneting soldier in back, from *The Fate
of a Self-Defense Corps Member.* No. 1029,
Young woman with a pistol, from *Sea of Blood.*

**1972, Apr. 1**
1027-1029 A754  Set of 3        6.00   .30
  A 10ch value picturing *The Flower Girl* was
prepared but not issued. Value $2,000.

Kim Il
Sung — A755

Kim at Military Conference — A756

Kim by
Lake
Chon
A757

  Various portraits of Kim Il Sung: No. 1030,
shown. No. 1031, In heroic pose. No. 1032,
shown. No. 1033, In wheatfield. No. 1034, In
factory. No. 1035, With foundry workers. No.
1036, Aboard whaling ship. No. 1037, Visiting
hospital. No. 1038, Visiting fruit farm. No.
1039, With railroad surveyors. No. 1040, With
women workers. No. 1041, Sitting with villagers. No. 1042, Touring chicken plant. No.
1043, On park bench with children. No. 1044,
Portrait with marchers.

**1972, Apr. 15**                  Litho.
1030 A755  5ch multicolored      .25   .25
  *a.*   Strip of 3, #1030-1031,
         1044                    2.40
1031 A755  5ch multicolored      .25   .25
1032 A755  5ch multicolored      .25   .25
  *a.*   Pair, #1032, 1043       1.20
1033 A756  10ch multicolored     .55   .25
  *a.*   Block of 10, #1033-1042  10.50
1034 A756  10ch multicolored    2.40   .40
1035 A756  10ch multicolored     .25   .25
1036 A756  10ch multicolored     .70   .25
1037 A756  10ch multicolored    1.05   .25
1038 A756  10ch multicolored     .25   .25
1039 A756  10ch multicolored    2.40   .25
1040 A756  10ch multicolored    1.50   .25
1041 A756  10ch multicolored     .25   .25
1042 A756  10ch multicolored     .50   .25
1043 A756  40ch multicolored     .65   .25
1044 A756  1wn multicolored     1.00   .40
  Nos. 1030-1044 (15)          12.25  4.05

**Souvenir Sheet**
1045 A757  3wn multicolored    10.00  6.00
  60th birthday of Kim Il Sung.
  Nos. 1030-1031 and 1044, 1032 and 1043,
and 1033-1042, respectively, were printed
setenant within their sheets.

---

  A 4-stamp set (2ch, 5ch, 10ch and
15ch values) honoring the 20th Olympic
Games were prepared but not issued.
Value $3,000.

Guerrilla Army,
40th
Anniv. — A758

**1972, Apr. 25**                  Photo.
1046 A758  10ch multicolored    4.00  1.00

Revolutionary Sites — A759

Designs: 2ch, Ryongpho. 5ch, Onjong. 10ch, Kosanjin. 40ch, Jonsung.

**1972, July 27**     Litho.
1047-1050 A759 Set of 4    2.25 .50

Olympic Games, Munich — A760

Designs: 2ch, Volleyball. 5ch, Boxing, horiz. 10ch (No. 1053), Judo. 10ch (No. 1054), Wrestling, horiz. 40ch, Rifle-shooting.

**1972, Oct. 1**
1051-1055 A760 Set of 5    4.00 1.00

Chollima Street, Pyongyang — A761

Designs (street scenes): 5ch, salmon & black. 10ch (No. 1057), dull yellow & black. 10ch (No. 1058), green & black.

**1972, Nov. 1**
1056-1058 A761 Set of 3    5.50 .85

Resource Management A762

Designs: 5ch, Dredging river. 10ch, Forest conservation. 40ch, Tideland reclamation.

**1972, Nov. 1**     Photo.
1059-1061 A762 Set of 3    2.75 .35

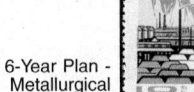

6-Year Plan - Metallurgical A763

Designs (all 10ch): No. 1062, Sheet metal, ingots, smelters. No. 1063, Pipes, foundry.

**1972, Nov. 1**
1062-1063 A763 Set of 2    3.75 .35

6-Year Plan — Mining Industry A764

Designs (all 10ch): No. 1064, Iron ore. No. 1065, Coal.

**1972, Nov. 1**     Litho.
1064-1065 A764 Set of 2    4.50 .45

Three Major Goals of the Technical Revolution A765

Designs (all 10ch): No. 1066, Agricultural mechanization. No. 1067, Industrial automation. No. 1068, Lightening of women's household chores.

**1972, Nov. 2**     Photo.
1066-1068 A765 Set of 3    6.00 .60

6-Year Plan - Machine-Building — A766

Designs (all 10ch): No. 1069, Machine tools. No. 1070, Electronics & automation tools. No. 1071, Single-purpose machines.

**1972, Nov. 2**     Photo.
1069-1071 A766 Set of 3    3.50 .60

6-Year Plan — Chemical Industry A767

Designs (all 10ch): No. 1072, Chemical fertilizers, herbicides, insecticides. No. 1073, Tire, tubing, various chemical products.

**1972, Nov. 2**
1072-1073 A767 Set of 2    2.50 .40

6-Year Plan — Light Industry A768

Designs (all 10ch): No. 1074, Clothing, textiles. No. 1075, Clothing, kitchenware. No. 1076, Household Goods.

**1972, Nov. 2**
1074-1076 A768 Set of 3    3.50 .60

6-Year Plan - Rural Economy A769

Designs (all 10ch): No. 1077, Irrigating field. No. 1078, Bulldozers levelling field. No. 1079, Applying chemical fertilizer.

**1972, Nov. 2**     Litho.
1077-1079 A769 Set of 3    3.50 .65

6-Year Plan - Transportation A770

Designs (all 10ch): No. 1080, Electric train. No. 1081, New railway construction. No. 1082, Coastal & river transport.

**1972, Nov. 2**
1080-1082 A770 Set of 3    8.00 .60

6-Year Plan - Military A771

Designs (all 10ch): No. 1083, Soldier with artillery shell. No. 1084, Navy gunner. No. 1085, Air Force pilot in cockpit.

**1972, Nov. 2**
1083-1085 A771 Set of 3    6.00 .60

6-Year Plan - Food Storage A772

Designs (all 10ch): No. 1086, Food Processing. No. 1087, Packing foodstuffs. No. 1088, Food storage (radishes, fruit, fish).

**1972, Nov. 2**     Photo.
1086-1088 A772 Set of 3    10.00 .55

Struggle for Reunification of Korea — A773

Designs (all 10ch): No. 1089, South Koreans with banners praising Kim Il Sung. No. 1090, S. Korean guerrillas killing U.S. & S. Korean soldiers. No. 1091, March of armed S. Korean workers. No. 1092, S. Koreans rioting, rioters on top of U.S. tank. No. 1093, N. Koreans demonstrating in support of S. Korean revolutionaries. No. 1094, International revolutionaries condemning U.S. soldier. No. 1095, S. Korean marchers carrying banner & Red Book.

**1972, Nov. 2**
1089-1095 A773 Set of 7    13.00 1.20

A 10ch anti-United States propaganda stamp was prepared for release Nov. 2, 1972, but not issued. Value $750.

Machine Tools — A774

Designs: 5ch, Single-axis automatic lathe. 10ch, *Kusong-3* lathe. 40ch, 2,000-ton crank press.

**1972, Dec. 1**     Litho.
1096-1098 A774 Set of 3    6.00 1.00

National Elections — A775

Designs (both 10ch): No. 1099, Voter with registration card. No. 1100, Voter casting ballot.

**1972, Dec. 12**     Photo.
1099-1100 A775 Set of 2    3.00 .50

Korean People's Army, 25th Anniv. A776

Designs: 5ch, Soldier. 10ch, Sailor. 40ch, Pilot.

**1973, Feb. 8**
1101-1103 A776 Set of 3    8.00 1.60

Mangyongdae Historic Sites — A777

Scenes from Kim Il Sung's childhood: 2ch, Wrestling site. 5ch, "Warship" rock. 10ch (No. 1106), Swinging tree, vert. 10ch (No. 1107), Sliding rock. 40ch, Fishing spot on riverside.

**1973, Apr. 15**
1104-1108 A777 Set of 5    4.50 1.00

Mansu Hill Monument — A778

Designs: 10ch (No. 1109), Anti-Japanese revolutionary monument. 10ch (No. 1110), Socialist Revolution & Construction monument. 40ch, Statue of Kim Il Sung. 3w, Korean Revolution Museum, hrz.

**1973, Apr. 15**     Litho.
1109-1112 A778 Set of 4    14.50 2.50

Secret Revolutionary Camps in the 1932 Guerrilla War — A780

Designs: 10ch (No. 1113), Karajibong Camp. 10ch (No. 1114), Soksaegoi Camp.

**1973, Apr. 26**
1113-1114 A780 Set of 2    1.50 .25

Anti-Japanese Propaganda — A781

**1973, June 1**
1115 A781 10ch multicolored    .60 .25

Reunification of Korea — A782

Designs: 2ch, Finger pointing down at destroyed U.S. tanks. 5ch, Electric train, crane lifting tractor. 10ch (No. 1118), Hand holding declaration, map of Korea. 10ch (No. 1119), Leaflets falling on happy crowd. 40ch, Flag & globe.

**1973, June 23**
1116-1120 A782 Set of 5    6.50 .75

Trucks & Tractors — A783

Designs: 10ch (No. 1121), Trucks. 10ch (No. 1122), Bulldozer, tractors.

**1973, July 1**     Photo.
1121-1122 A783 Set of 2    1.60 .30

Socialist Countries' Junior Women's Volleyball Games — A784

**1973, July 27**     Litho.
1123 A784 10ch multicolored    1.10 .25

North Korean Victory in the Korean War — A785

Designs: 10ch (No. 1124), Triumphant N. Koreans & battlefield scene. 10ch (No. 1125), N. Koreans & symbols of military & industrial power.

**1973, July 27**      **Photo.**
1124-1125 A785   Set of 2     3.25   .30

Mansudae Art Troupe A786

Dances: 10ch, *Snow Falls,* dancers with red streamers. 25ch, *Bumper Harvest of Apples.* 40ch, *Azalea of the Fatherland.*

**1973, Aug. 1**      **Litho.**
1126-1128 A786   Set of 3     4.50   .75

Compulsory Secondary Education, 10th Anniv. — A787

**1973, Sept. 1**
1129 A787 10ch multicolored      .85   .25

Writings of Kim Il Sung — A788

Designs (all 10ch): No. 1130, *On Juche in Our Revolution* (claret scene). No. 1131, *Kim Il Sung Selected Works,* crowd holding glowing book aloft. No. 1132, *Let Us Further Strengthen Our Socialist System,* four figures holding open book aloft.

**1973, Sept. 1**
1130-1132 A788   Set of 3     2.50   .40
See Nos. 1180-1181.

DPRK, 25th Anniv. — A789

Designs: 5ch, Foundation of the republic ("1948-1973"). 10ch, Korean War ("1950-1953"). 40ch, Farmer, worker & soldier with scenes of economic development in background ("1948-1973").

**1973, Sept. 9**
1133-1135 A789   Set of 3     3.50   .80

Mt. Myohyang Scenes — A790

Designs: 2ch, Popwang Peak. 5ch, Inhodae Rock. 10ch, Taeha Falls, vert. 40ch, Ryongyon Falls, vert.

**1973, Oct. 1**      **Photo.**
1136-1139 A790   Set of 4     8.25   .75

Party Founding Museum A791

**1973, Oct. 10**
1140 A791   1w multicolored      3.50   .70

People's Athletic Meeting — A792

Designs: 2ch, Soccer player, basketball players. 5ch, High jumper, women sprinters. 10ch (No. 1143), Wrestlers, skier. 10ch (No. 1144), Speed skaters, skier. 40ch, Parachutist, motorcyclists.

**1973, Nov. 1**      **Litho.**
1141-1145 A792   Set of 5     6.50   .75

Socialist Countries' Junior Weightlifting Competition — A793

**1973, Nov. 21**
1146 A793   10ch multicolored      1.40   .25

Moran Hill Scenery — A794

Designs: 2ch, Chongryu Cliff. 5ch, Moran Waterfalls. 10ch, Pubyok Pavilion. 40ch, Ulmil Pavilion.

**1973, Nov. 1**
1147-1150 A794   Set of 4     9.25   1.00

Mt. Kumgang Scenery — A795

Designs: 2ch, Mujigae (Rainbow) Bridge. 5ch, Suspension bridge, Okryu Valley, horiz. 10ch (No. 1153), Chonnyu Peak. 10ch (No. 1154), Chilchung Rock & Sonji Peak, horiz. 40ch, Sujong & Pari Peaks, horiz.

**1973, Nov. 1**
1151-1155 A795   Set of 5     8.25   1.00

Magnolia — A796

**1973, Nov. 1**
1156 A796   10ch multicolored      2.25   .40

South Korean Revolutionary Struggle — A797

Designs (both 10ch): No. 1157, Mob beating U.S. soldier. No. 1158, Armed demonstrators killing U.S. soldier.

**1973, Nov. 2**      **Photo.**
1157-1158 A797   Set of 2     5.25   .30

Scenes from *Butterflies and Cock* Fairy Tale — A798

Designs: 2ch, Cock appearing in the village of butterflies. 5ch, Butterflies discussing how to repel cock. No. 1161, 10ch, Cock chasing butterflies with basket. No. 1162, 10ch, Butterflies luring cock up cliff. 40ch, Cock chasing butterflies off cliff edge. 90ch, Cock drowning.

**1973, Dec. 1**      **Litho.**
1159-1164 A798   Set of 6     17.50   1.20
For surcharge, see No. 4556.

Revolutionary Sites — A799

Designs: 2ch, Buildings, Yonphung. 5ch, Buildings, iron-rail fence, Hyangha. 10ch, Three buildings surrounding courtyard, Changgol. 40ch, Monuments in park-like setting, Paeksong.

**1973, Dec. 1**
1165-1168 A799   Set of 4     3.25   .60

Modern Buildings in Pyongyang A800

Designs: 2ch, Science Library, Kim Il Sung University. 5ch, Building No. 2, Kim Il Sung University, vert. 10ch, War Museum. 40ch, People's Palace of Culture. 90ch, Pyongyang Indoor Stadium.

**1973, Dec. 1**      **Photo.**
1169-1173 A800   Set of 5     4.00   1.00
Nos. 1171-1172 are 60x24mm.

Socialist Constitution of North Korea — A801

Designs (all 10ch): No. 1174, Socialist Constitution, national scenes. No. 1175, Marchers with Red Book & national arms. No. 1176, Marchers with Red Books, national flag, banners.

**1973, Dec. 27**      **Litho.**
1174-1176 A801   Set of 3     2.75   1.00

Korean Songbirds — A802

Designs: 5ch, Great reed warbler. 10ch (No. 1178), Gray starling (green background). 10ch

(No. 1179), Daurian starling (pink background).

**1973, Dec. 28**      **Photo.**
1177-1179 A802   Set of 3     13.00   1.75

Writings of Kim Il Sung — A803

Designs: No. 1180, 10ch, *Let Us Intensify the Anti-Imperialist, Anti-U.S. Struggle,* bayonets threatening U.S. soldier. No. 1181, 10ch, *On the Chollima Movement and the Great Upsurge of Socialist Construction,* Chollima statue.

**1974, Jan. 10**      **Litho.**
1180-1181 A803   Set of 2     1.75   .35

Opening of Pyongyang Metro A804

Designs (all 10ch): No. 1182, Train at platform. No. 1183, Escalators. No. 1184, Underground station hall.

**1974, Jan. 20**
1182-1184 A804   Set of 3     3.00   .50

Socialist Construction A805

Designs (all 10ch): No. 1185, Capital construction. No. 1186, Industry (foundry), vert. No. 1187, Agriculture. No. 1188, Transport. No. 1189, Fishing industry.

**1974, Feb. 20**
1185-1189 A805   Set of 5     10.00   1.15

*Theses on the Socialist Rural Question in Our Country,* 10th Anniv. of Publication — A806

**1974, Feb. 25**
1190 A806   10ch Strip of 3, #a-c   4.00   .75

Farm Machines A807

Designs: 2ch, Compost sprayer. 5ch, *Jonjin* tractor. 10ch, *Taedoksan* tractor (with flat bed).

**1974, Feb. 25**      **Photo.**
1193-1195 A807   Set of 3     3.50   .50

N. Korean Victories at 1973 Sports Contests — A808

Designs: 2ch, Archery (Grenoble). 5ch, Gymnastics (Varna). 10ch, Boxing (Bucharest). 20ch, Volleyball (Pyongyang). 30ch, Rifle-shooting (Sofia). 40ch, Judo (Tbilisi). 60ch, Model aircraft flying (Vienna), horiz. 1.50w, Table tennis (Beijing), horiz.

**Perf. 11, 12 (#1196, 1202-1203)**
**1974, Mar. 10** **Litho.**
1196-1203 A808 Set of 8    11.00  2.00
For surcharges, see Nos. 4562, 4564, 4600.

D.P.R.K.: World's First Tax-Free Country A809

**1974, Apr. 1** *Perf. 11*
1204 A809 10ch multicolored    1.25  .25

Revolutionary Activities of Kim Il Sung — A810

Designs (all 10ch): No. 1205, Kim at Nanhutou Meeting (in log room). No. 1206, Kim writing the 10-Point Program in forest. No. 1207, Kim instructing revolutionary (sitting on bench, outdoor winter scene). No. 1208, Kim at Battle of Laoheishan.

**1974, Apr. 15** *Perf. 12*
1205-1208 A810 Set of 4    3.50  .70

Scenes from the Revolutionary Opera *The Flower Girl* — A811

Designs: 2ch, Kkot Pun's blind younger sister. 5ch, Death of Kkot Pun's mother. 10ch, Kkot Pun resists landlord. 40ch, Kkot Pun setting out on the road of revolution.

**1974, Apr. 30**
1209-1212 A811 Set of 4    12.00  .60

**Souvenir Sheet**
1213 A811 50ch multicolored    16.50  1.50

No. 1213 contains one larger 50ch value, depicting Kroi Pun (The Flower Girl) and the flowers of Revolution, imperf.

Pyongyang Zoo, 15th Anniv. — A812

A813

Designs: 2ch, Wildcat. 5ch, Lynx. No. 1216, 10ch, Fox. No. 1217, 10ch. Wild boar. 20ch, Wolf. 40ch, Bear. 60ch, Leopard. 70ch, Korean tiger. 90ch, Lion.
No. 1223: a, 10ch, Wildcat. b, 30ch, Lynx. c, 50ch, Leopard. d, 60ch, Tiger.

**1974, May 10** *Perf. 11*
1214-1222 A812 Set of 9    14.50  2.50

**Souvenir Sheet**
1223 A813 Sheet of 4, imperf    60.00  —
For surcharges, see Nos. 4541, 4579.

Wild Roses — A814

Designs: 2ch, Prickly wild rose. 5ch, Yellow sweet briar. 10ch (No. 1226), Pink aromatic rose. 10ch (No. 1227), Aronia sweet briar (yellow centers). 40ch, Rosa rugosa.

**1974, May 20**
1224-1228 A814 Set of 5    8.25  1.00

**Souvenir Sheet**

Kim Il Sung with Children A815

**1974, June 1** *Imperf*
1229 A815 1.20w multicolored    8.25  7.50

Wild Flowering Plants — A816

Designs: 2ch, Chinese trumpet vine. 5ch, Day lily. 10ch, Shooting star lily. 20ch, Tiger lily. 40ch, Azalea. 60ch, Yellow day lily.

**1974, May 20** *Perf. 11*
1230-1235 A816 Set of 6    7.50  1.00

Universal Postal Union, Cent. — A817

U.P.U. emblem and: 10ch, Letter carrier and construction site. 25ch, Chollima statue. 40ch, World map & airplanes.

**1974, June 30** *Perf. 12*
1236-1238 A817 Set of 3    6.00  .50

A 60ch souvenir sheet was prepared but not issued. Value $750. For surcharge, see No. 4567.

Amphibians A818

Designs: 2ch, Black spotted frog. 5ch, Oriental fire belly toad. 10ch, North American bull frog. 40ch, Common toad.

**1974, July 10** *Perf. 11*
1239-1242 A818 Set of 4    14.50  1.50
For surcharge, see No. 4542.

Soviet Space Flights A819

Designs: 10ch, Electron 1 & 2. 20ch, Proton 1. 30ch, Venera 3. 40ch, Venera 5 & 6. 50ch, Launch of Chinese satellite Chicomsat 1. 1w, Space flight of dogs "Bjelka" and "Strjelka."

**1974, July 10**
1243-1246 A819 Set of 4    3.00  .50

**Souvenir Sheets**
**Imperf**
1247 A819 50ch multicolored    8.25  1.00
1248 A819 1w multicolored    16.00  2.60
Nos. 1247-1248 each contain one 47x72mm stamp.

Korean Paintings A820

Designs: 2ch, Woman in Namgang Village. 5ch, Old Man on the Raktong River (60x49mm). 10ch, Inner Kumgang in the Morning. 20ch, Mt. Kumgang (60x49mm). 1.50w, Evening Glow Over Kangson.

**1974, July 10**
1249-1252 A820 Set of 4    6.00  .80

**Souvenir Sheet**
**Imperf**
1253 A820 1.50w multicolored    11.00  10.00
For surcharge, see No. 4592.

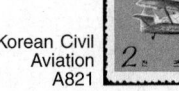

Korean Civil Aviation A821

Designs: 2ch, Antonov AN-2. 5ch, Lisunov LI-2. 10ch, Ilyushin IL-14P. 40ch, Antonov AN-24. 60ch, Ilyushin IL-18. 90ch, Antonov AN-24.

**1974, Aug. 1**
1254-1258 A821 Set of 5    9.25  1.75

**Souvenir Sheet**
**Imperf**
1259 A821 90ch multicolored    13.00  6.50
No. 1264 contains one 49x30mm stamp.

Alpine Plants — A822

Designs: 2ch, Rhododendron. 5ch, White mountain-avens. 10ch, Shrubby cinquefoil. 20ch, Poppies. 40ch, Purple mountain heather. 60ch, Oxytropis anertii.

**1974, Aug. 10** *Perf. 12*
1260-1265 A822 Set of 6    8.00  1.50

Korean Paintings A823

Designs: 10ch, Sobaek Stream in the Morning. 20ch, Combatants of Mt. Laohei (60x40mm).. 30ch, Spring on the Terraced Field. 40ch, Night of Tideland. 60ch, Daughter.

**1974, Aug. 15** *Perf. 11*
1266-1270 A823 Set of 5    12.00  2.00
For surcharge, see No. 4563.

Italian Communist Newspaper L'Unita, 50th Anniv. — A824

**1974, Sept. 1** *Imperf*
1271 A824 1.50w multicolored    24.50  5.00

Revolutionary Sites — A825

Designs: 5ch, Munmyong. 10ch, Unha (log cabin).

**1974, Sept. 9** *Perf. 11*
1272-1273 A825 Set of 2    1.40  .25

Oil-producing Crops — A826

Designs: 2ch, Sesame. 5ch, Perilla-oil plant. 10ch, Sunflower. 40ch, Castor bean.

**1974, Sept. 30**
1274-1277 A826 Set of 4    7.00  1.30
For surcharge, see No. 4543.

Revolutionary Activities of Kim Il Sung — A827

Designs (all 10ch): No. 1278, Portrait in guerrilla uniform, vert. No. 1279, On horseback. No. 1280, Helping a farm family. No. 1281, Negotiating anti-Japanese united front with Chinese commander.

**1974, Oct. 10** *Perf. 12*
1278-1281 A827 Set of 4    6.00  .75

No. 1278 is 42x65mm. Nos. 1279-1281 are 52x34.5mm.

Grand Monument on Mansu Hill — A828

Designs (all 10ch): No. 1282, Soldiers marching right, lead figure holding rifle aloft. No. 1283, Soldiers marching left, lead figure holding rifle aloft. No. 1284, Workers marching right, lead figure holding torch aloft. No. 1285, Workers marching left, lead figure holding torch aloft.

**1974, Oct. 10** *Perf. 11*
1282-1285 A828 Set of 4    3.00  .70

Deep-Sea Fishing — A829

Designs: a, 2ch, Factory ship *Chilbosan*. b, 5ch, Factory ship *Paektusan*. c, 10ch, Cargo ship *Moranbong*. d, 20ch, All-purpose ship. e, 30ch, Trawler. f, 40ch, Stern trawler.

**1974, Nov. 20**
1286 A829  Block of 6          7.00  1.75
a.-f.   Any single             1.10   .30

A830

Kim Il Sung's Crossing of the Amnok
River, 50th Anniv.

**1975, Feb. 3**          **Perf. 12**
1287 A830 10ch multicolored    .65   .25

Pak
Yong
Sun
A831

33rd World Table Tennis
Championships — A832

**1975, Feb. 16**        **Perf. 11x12**
1288 A831 10ch multicolored   3.00   .25

**Souvenir Sheet**
**Imperf**
1289 A832 80ch multicolored   3.25  1.50

Honoring Pak Yong Sun, winner of the 33rd
World Table Tennis Championship, Calcutta.

Pyongyang
Zoo — A833

Designs: 10ch (No. 1290), Zebra. 10ch (No.
1291), African buffalo. 20ch, Giant panda,
horiz. 25ch, Bactrian camel. 30ch, Indian elephant, horiz.

**Perf. 12¼, 10¾ (#1291, 1294)**
**1975, Feb. 20**
1290-1294 A833  Set of 5       7.00  1.15

Koguryo Period Tomb Paintings, 7th
Century — A834

Designs: 10ch, Blue dragon. 15ch, White
tiger. 25ch, Red phoenix, vert. 40ch, Turtle
and snake.

**1975, Mar. 20**          **Perf. 12**
1295-1298 A834  Set of 4       6.00  1.00

The
Guerrilla
Base in
Spring
(1968)
A835

Guerrilla
Army
Landing
at Unggi
(1969)
A836

The
Sewing
Team
Members
(1961)
A837

North Manchuria of China in Spring
(1969) — A838

Comrade Kim Jong Suk Giving
Guidance to the Children's Corps
Members (1970) — A839

**1975, Mar. 30**
1299 A835 10ch multicolored    .55   .25
1300 A836 10ch multicolored    .55   .25
1301 A837 15ch multicolored    .85   .25
1302 A838 20ch multicolored   1.75   .25
1303 A839 30ch multicolored   1.40   .25
     Nos. 1299-1303 (5)       5.10  1.25

Korean Paintings, Anti-Japanese Struggle.
Compare with Nos. 1325-1329, 1330-1335.

Cosmonauts'
Day — A840

Designs:   10ch,  Cosmonaut.  30ch,
Lunokhod-2 on Moon, horiz. 40ch, Soyuz and
Saiyut coupling, horiz.

**1975, Apr. 12**          **Perf. 11¾**
1304-1306 A840  Set of 3       3.00   .50

Revolutionary Activities of Kim Il
Sung — A841

Multicolor portraits of Kim Il Sung: 10ch (No.
1307), Speaking with troops in tent (aqua

frame). 10ch (No. 1308), Greeting peasants
bringing supplies (tan frame). 10ch (No.
1309), Speaking to crowd, arm upraised (light
blue frame). 10ch (No. 1310), With soldiers
around winter campfire (pale tan frame). 10ch
(No. 1311), Lecturing to troops (pink frame).
15ch, At head of troop column in forest. 25ch,
Standing by lake. 30ch, Speaking with peasants, child in lap. 40ch, Presiding over staff
meeting, in tent.

**1975, Apr. 15**          **Perf. 12**
1307-1315 A841  Set of 9       8.25  2.00

**Souvenir Sheet**

Victory Monument — A842

**1975, Apr. 15**          **Imperf**
1316 A842 1w multicolored     16.50  4.00
    Battle of Pochonbo, 38th Anniversary.

Flower Basket &
Kim Il Sung's
Birthplace
A843

Kim Il Sung's Birthplace,
Mangyongdae — A844

**1975, Apr. 15**          **Perf. 12**
1317 A843 10ch multicolored    .35   .25
1318 A844 40ch multicolored   1.60   .25

63rd Birthday of Kim Il Sung.

April 19 South
Korean Popular
Uprising, 15th
Anniv. — A845

**1975, Apr. 19**          **Perf. 11**
1319 A845 10ch multicolored    .65   .25

Ri Dynasty
Paintings — A846

Designs: 5ch, Kingfisher at Lotus Pond.
10ch, Crabs. 15ch, Rose of Sharon. 25ch,
Lotus and Water Bird. 30ch, Tree Peony and
Cock and Hen.

**1975, May 10**
1320-1324 A846  Set of 5      13.00  1.25

On the Road of
Advance
Southward
(1966) — A847

The Assigned
Post
(1968) — A848

For the Sake of the Fatherland
(1965) — A849

Retaliation (1970) — A850

The
Awaited
Ranks
(1970)
A851

**1975, May 10**
1325 A847  5ch multicolored   2.25   .25
1326 A848 10ch multicolored   1.25   .25
1327 A849 15ch multicolored   1.90   .25
1328 A850 25ch multicolored   2.75   .25
1329 A851 30ch multicolored   4.50   .25
     Nos. 1325-1329 (5)      12.65  1.25

Korean Paintings, Anti-Japanese Struggle.
For surcharge, see No. 4606.

Blue Signal
Lamp
(1960) — A852

Pine Tree
(1966) — A853

*Night with Snowfall* (1963) A854

*Smelters* (1968) A855

*Reclamation of Tideland* (1961) — A856

*Mt. Paekgum* (1966) A857

**1975, May 20**

| | | | | |
|---|---|---|---|---|
| 1330 | A852 | 10ch multicolored | 1.10 | .25 |
| 1331 | A853 | 10ch multicolored | 3.75 | .25 |
| 1332 | A854 | 15ch multicolored | 1.10 | .25 |
| 1333 | A855 | 20ch multicolored | 1.25 | .25 |
| 1334 | A856 | 25ch multicolored | 1.25 | .25 |
| 1335 | A857 | 30ch multicolored | 1.25 | .25 |
| | | Nos. 1330-1335 (6) | 9.70 | 1.50 |

Korean Paintings. For surcharge, see No. 4596.

*Chongryon Assoc. of Koreans in Japan, 20th Anniv.* — A858

**1975, May 25**      **Perf. 11¾**

| | | | | |
|---|---|---|---|---|
| 1336 | A858 | 10ch multicolored | 1.10 | — |
| 1337 | A858 | 3w multicolored | 40.00 | — |

*Marathon Race of Socialist Countries* — A859

**1975, June 8**      **Imperf**

| | | | | |
|---|---|---|---|---|
| 1338 | A859 | 1w multicolored | 22.50 | 4.00 |

*Diving* — A860

Divers: 10ch, Man entering water feet-first. 25ch, Man performing somersalt pike. 40ch, Woman entering water head-first.

**1975, June 20**      **Perf. 10¾**

| | | | | |
|---|---|---|---|---|
| 1339-1341 | A860 | Set of 3 | 3.25 | .75 |

---

*Month of Anti-U.S. Joint Struggle* — A861

**1975, June 25**      **Perf. 12¼**

| | | | | |
|---|---|---|---|---|
| 1342 | A861 | 10ch multicolored | 1.40 | .25 |

*Fresh-Water Fish* A862

Fish: 10ch (No. 1343), Memorial fish, swimming to left. 10ch (No. 1344), White fish, swimming to right. 15ch, Notch-jowl. 25ch, Amur catfish. 30ch (No. 1347), Catfish, swimming to right. 30ch (No. 1348), Snakehead, swimming to left.

**1975, June 25**      **Perf. 10¾**

| | | | | |
|---|---|---|---|---|
| 1343-1348 | A862 | Set of 6 | 8.00 | 1.10 |

A863

*10th International Socialist Countries' Junior Friendship Soccer Tournament* — A864

Soccer players, with diff. stadiums in background: 5ch, Green border. 10ch, Tan border. 15ch, Lilac border. 20ch, Pale violet border. 50ch, Dull gold border.

**Perf. 10¾, Imperf (#1354)**

**1975, July 10**

| | | | | |
|---|---|---|---|---|
| 1349-1353 | A863 | Set of 5 | 4.50 | 1.00 |

**Souvenir Sheet**

| | | | | |
|---|---|---|---|---|
| 1354 | A864 | 1w multicolored | 8.25 | 3.25 |

*Parrots* — A865

Parrots: 10ch, Blue & yellow macaw. 15ch, Sulphur-crested cockatoo. 20ch, Blyth's parakeet. 25ch, Rainbow lory. 30ch, Budgerigar.

**1975, July 10**      **Perf. 12**

| | | | | |
|---|---|---|---|---|
| 1355-1359 | A865 | Set of 5 | 17.50 | 1.50 |

For surcharge, see No. 4581.

*Saesallim Street* A866

*Apartment House* A867

---

*Pothonggang Hotel* — A868

**1975, July 20**      **Perf. 11, 12 (#1360)**

| | | | | |
|---|---|---|---|---|
| 1360 | A866 | 90ch multicolored | 20.00 | 20.00 |
| 1361 | A867 | 1w multicolored | 25.00 | 25.00 |
| 1362 | A868 | 2w multicolored | 35.00 | 35.00 |
| | | Nos. 1360-1362 (3) | 80.00 | 80.00 |

New street, buildings in Pyongyang.

*Blossoms* — A869

Blossoms of Flowering Trees: 10ch, White peach. 15ch, Red peach. 20ch, Red plum. 25ch, Apricot. 30ch, Cherry.

**1975, Aug. 20**      **Perf. 10¾**

| | | | | |
|---|---|---|---|---|
| 1363-1367 | A869 | Set of 5 | 7.50 | 1.50 |

*Diamond Mts. Landscapes* — A870

Designs: 5ch, Sejon Peak. 10ch, Chonson Rock. 15ch, Pisa Gate. 25ch, Manmulsang. 30ch, Chaeha Peak.

**1975, Aug. 20**      **Perf. 11¾**

| | | | | |
|---|---|---|---|---|
| 1368-1372 | A870 | Set of 5 | 7.50 | 1.00 |

*Flowers* — A871

Designs: 5ch, Azalea. 10ch, White azalea. 15ch, Mountain rhododendron. 20ch, White rhododendron. 25ch, Rhododendron. 30ch, Yellow rhododendron.

**1975, Aug. 30**      **Perf. 10¾**

| | | | | |
|---|---|---|---|---|
| 1373-1378 | A871 | Set of 6 | 6.50 | 1.50 |

A872

*Aerial Sports for National Defence* — A873

Designs: 5ch (No. 1379), Gliders. 5ch (No. 1380), Remote-controlled model airplane. 10ch (No. 1381), Parachutist in free fall, vert. 10ch (No. 1382), Parachutists landing, vert. 20ch, Parachutist with bouquet of flowers. 50ch, Formation skydiving.

**Perf. 12x11¾, Imperf (#1384)**

**1975, Sept. 9**

| | | | | |
|---|---|---|---|---|
| 1379-1383 | A872 | Set of 5 | 5.00 | .75 |

**Souvenir Sheet**

| | | | | |
|---|---|---|---|---|
| 1384 | A873 | 50ch multicolored | 6.00 | .50 |

---

*Flowers* — A874

Fruit tree blossoms: 10ch, Wild apple. 15ch, Wild pear. 20ch, Hawthorn. 25ch, Chinese quince. 30ch, Flowering quince.

**1975, Sept. 30**      **Perf. 12¼x12**

| | | | | |
|---|---|---|---|---|
| 1385-1389 | A874 | Set of 5 | 5.00 | 1.25 |

*Korean Workers' Party, 30th Anniv.* — A875

Designs: 2ch (No. 1390), Symbolic creation of the Juche Idea. 2ch (No. 1391), Korean soldiers above American graves. 5ch (No. 1392), Hand holding torch with Juche inscription. 5ch (No. 1393), Monument of Chollima, idealized city. 10ch (No. 1394), Chollima winged horse and rider with banner. 10ch (No. 1395), Worker with Red Book. 25ch, South Koreans rioting. 70ch, Map of Korea, Red Book, flowers.

90ch (No. 1398), Kim Il Sung addressing workers, horiz. stamp, vert. souvenir sheet. 90ch (No. 1399), Kim with crowd of workers, city skyline in background, horiz. stamp, horiz. souvenir sheet.

**Perf. 12, Imperf (#1398-1399)**

**1975, Oct. 10**

| | | | | |
|---|---|---|---|---|
| 1390-1397 | A875 | Set of 8 | 7.00 | 2.00 |
| 1398-1399 | A875 | Set of 2 sheets | 8.25 | 4.00 |

*Return of Kim Il Sung to Pyongyang, 30th Anniv.* — A876

**1975, Oct. 14**      **Perf. 12**

| | | | | |
|---|---|---|---|---|
| 1400 | A876 | 20ch multicolored | 1.00 | .25 |

*Redong Sinmun, 30th Anniv.* — A877

**1975, Nov. 1**      **Perf. 11**

| | | | | |
|---|---|---|---|---|
| 1401 | A877 | 10ch multicolored | .85 | .25 |
| a. | | 1w, souvenir sheet, imperf | 5.50 | 5.00 |

*Hyonmu Gate* — A878

*Taedong Gate* — A879

Pothong
Gate — A880

Jongum
Gate — A881

Chilsong
Gate — A882

**Perf. 12x12¼, 12¼x12 (#1406)**
**1975, Nov. 20**

| | | | | |
|---|---|---|---|---|
| 1402 | A878 | 10ch multicolored | 1.40 | .25 |
| 1403 | A879 | 10ch multicolored | 1.40 | .25 |
| 1404 | A880 | 15ch multicolored | 1.90 | .25 |
| 1405 | A881 | 20ch multicolored | 3.50 | .25 |
| 1406 | A882 | 30ch multicolored | 5.00 | .40 |
| | | Nos. 1402-1406 (5) | 13.20 | 1.40 |

Ancient gates of Pyongyang.

Mt. Chilbo
Views
A883

Designs: No. 1407, 10ch, Mae Rock (pale green border). No. 1408, 10ch, Jangsu Peak (pale yellow border). 15ch, Suri Peak. 20ch, Jangsu Peak, diff. 30ch, Rojok Peak.

**1975, Nov. 30**      **Perf. 12x11¾**
1407-1411 A883 Set of 5    10.00 1.25

Wangjaesan Monument — A884

Designs: 10ch, Workers marching. 15ch, Soldiers marching. 25ch, Monument beacon tower, vert. 30ch, Base of tower, statues of Kim Il Sung, workers and soldiers.

**Perf. 11¾, 10¾ (#1413)**
**1975, Dec. 20**
1412-1415 A884 Set of 4    2.75 .75

Banners,
Slogan — A885

Banners,
Workers
A886

**1976, Jan. 17**      **Perf. 12**
| | | | | |
|---|---|---|---|---|
| 1416 | A885 | 2ch multicolored | .35 | .25 |
| 1417 | A886 | 70ch multicolored | .80 | .50 |

League of Socialist Working Youth, 30th Anniv.

Ducks &
Geese — A887

Designs: 10ch, Geese. 20ch, Domesticated ducks. 40ch, Kwangpo ducks.

**Perf. 12, 12x12¼ (#1418)**
**1976, Feb. 5**
1418-1420 A887 Set of 3    7.25 .50
**Perf. 11**
| | | | | |
|---|---|---|---|---|
| 1418a | | 10ch multi | — | — |
| 1419a | | 10ch multi | — | — |

For surcharge, see No. 4519.

Korean People's
Army,
Sculpture — A888

Designs: 5ch, *Oath*. 10ch (No. 1422), *Unity Between Men and Officers*, horiz. 10ch (No. 1423), *This Flag to the Height*.

**Perf. 12, 12¼x12 (#1421)**
**1976, Feb. 8**
1421-1423 A888 Set of 3    2.75 .50

*Rural Road at
Evening*
(1965) — A889

*Passing-on
Technique*
(1970) — A890

*Mother*
(1965) — A891

*Medical Examination in Kindergarten*
(1970) — A892

*Doctress
of the
Village*
(1970)
A893

**1976, Feb. 10**      **Perf. 12**
| | | | | |
|---|---|---|---|---|
| 1424 | A889 | 10ch multicolored | .50 | .25 |
| 1425 | A890 | 15ch multicolored | .55 | .25 |
| 1426 | A891 | 25ch multicolored | .85 | .25 |
| 1427 | A892 | 30ch multicolored | 1.50 | .25 |
| 1428 | A893 | 40ch multicolored | 1.75 | .25 |
| | | Nos. 1424-1428 (5) | 5.15 | 1.25 |

Modern Korean paintings.

Agrarian
Reform
Law, 30th
Anniv.
A894

**1976, Mar. 5**      **Perf. 12**
1429 A894 10ch multicolored    .65 .25

Telephone
Communication
Centenary — A895

Designs: 2ch, Telephones and communication satellite. 5ch, Satellite and antenna. 10ch, Satellite and telecommunications systems. 15ch, Telephone and lineman. 25ch, Satellite and map of receiving stations. 40ch, Satellite and cable-laying barge.
50ch, Satellite and antique telephone.

**Surface Coated Paper**
**1976, Mar. 12**      **Perf. 13¼**
| | | | | |
|---|---|---|---|---|
| 1430-1435 | A895 | Set of 6 | 8.75 | 1.00 |
| 1435a | | Sheet of 8, as #1430-1436 + label, ordinary paper | 10.00 | — |

**Souvenir Sheet**
**Imperf, Without Gum**
1436 A895 50ch multicolored    3.25 .50

Flowers
A896

Designs: 5ch, Cosmos. 10ch, Dahlia. 20ch, Zinnia. 40ch, China aster.

**1976, Mar. 20**      **Perf. 12**
1437-1440 A896 Set of 4    3.00 1.00

Pukchong
Conference, 15th
Anniv. — A897

Designs: 5ch, Fruit processing industry. 10ch, Fruit and orchards.

**1976, Apr. 7**      **Perf. 11½x12**
1441-1442 A897 Set of 2    2.10 .25

Locomotives
A898

Designs: 5ch, Pulgungi electric train. 10ch, Jaju underground electric train. 15ch, Saeppyol diesel locomotive.

**1976, Apr. 10**      **Perf. 11¾**
1443-1445 A898 Set of 3    3.25 .50

For surcharges, see Nos. 4594, 4603.

Many North Korean issues from 1976 on were also issued imperforate. These imperfs were issued for sale for hard currency, mostly to overseas collectors, and were not valid for postage.

Limited quantities of many sets from Scott No. 1446 on were issued without gum.

Day of Space
Flight — A899

Designs: 2ch, Satellite. 5ch, Space station. 10ch, Communications satellite. 15ch, Future space station. 25ch, Satellite. 40ch, Communications satellite.
50ch, Lunar surface vehicle.

**1976, Apr. 12**      **Perf. 13¼**
1446-1451 A899 Set of 6    3.25 1.00
**Souvenir Sheet**
**Imperf**
1452 A899 50ch multicolored    1.60 .50

A900

Kim Il
Sung,
64th
Birthday
A901

**1976, Apr. 15**      **Perf. 12**
1453 A900 10ch multicolored    .85 .25
**Souvenir Sheet**
**Imperf**
1454 A901 40ch multicolored    5.00 .75

A902

3rd Asian Table Tennis
Championships — A903

Designs: 5ch, Paddle and ribbon. 10ch,
Three female players with bouquet. 20ch,
Female player. 25ch, Male player.

**Without Gum**

| 1976, Apr. 25 | | | **Perf. 12** |
|---|---|---|---|
| 1455-1458 A902 | Set of 4 | 3.00 | 1.00 |

**Souvenir Sheet**
*Imperf*

| 1459 A903 50ch multicolored | 3.50 | 1.00 |
|---|---|---|

For surcharges, see Nos. 4582, 4593, 4607.

Association for the Restoration of the
Fatherland, 40th Anniv. — A904

| 1976, May 5 | | | **Perf. 12** |
|---|---|---|---|
| 1460 A904 10ch multicolored | | .75 | .25 |

Pheasants
A905

Designs: 2ch, Golden pheasant. 5ch, Lady
Amherst's pheasant. 10ch, Silver pheasant.
15ch, Reeves' pheasant. 25ch, Copper pheasant. 40ch, Albino ring-necked pheasant.
50ch, Ring-necked pheasant.

**Surface Coated Paper**

| 1976, May 5 | | | **Perf. 11¾** |
|---|---|---|---|
| 1461-1466 A905 | Set of 6 | 5.00 | 1.50 |
| 1466a | Sheet of 8, as #1461-1467 + label, perf 12, ordinary paper | 12.00 | 12.00 |

**Souvenir Sheet**
*Imperf*

| 1467 A905 50ch multicolored | 3.50 | 1.50 |
|---|---|---|

Potong River
Monument — A906

| 1976, May 21 | | | **Perf. 11½** |
|---|---|---|---|
| 1468 A906 10ch multicolored | | 75.00 | — |
| a. | Perf. 10¾ | — | — |

21st
Olympic
Games,
Montreal
A907

Stadium, Olympic rings and: 2ch, Runners.
5ch, Diver. 10ch, Judo. 15ch, Gymnast. 25ch,
Gymnast. 40ch, Fencers.
50ch, Runner with Olympic Torch.

---

**Surface Coated Paper**

| 1976, July 17 | | | **Perf. 13¾** |
|---|---|---|---|
| 1469-1474 A907 | Set of 6 | 6.75 | 1.25 |
| 1474a | Sheet of 8, as #1469-1475 + label, perf 12, ordinary paper | 9.00 | — |

**Souvenir Sheet**
*Imperf*

| 1475 A907 50ch multicolored | 3.50 | 1.50 |
|---|---|---|

For overprints and surcharges, see Nos.
1632-1638, 4568.

Winners, 21st
Olympic Games,
Montreal — A908

Designs: 2ch, Bronze Medal, Hockey —
Pakistan. 5ch, Bronze Medal, Free Pistol —
Rudolf Dollinger (Austria). 10ch, Silver Medal,
Boxing — Li Byong Uk (DPRK). 15ch, Silver
Medal, Cycling — Daniel Morelon (France).
25ch, Gold Medal, Marathon — Waldemar
Cierpinski (DDR). 40ch, Gold Medal, Boxing
— Ku Yong Jo (DPRK).
50ch, Gold, Silver, Bronze Medals.

**Multicolored, with Winners'
Inscriptions in Silver
Surface Coated Paper**

| 1976, Aug. 2 | | | **Perf. 13¼** |
|---|---|---|---|
| 1476-1481 A908 | Set of 6 | 6.00 | 1.00 |
| 1481a | Sheet of 8, as #1476-1482 + label | 9.00 | — |

**Souvenir Sheet**
*Imperf*

| 1482 A908 50ch multicolored | 4.00 | 2.00 |
|---|---|---|

**Same, with Different Winners'
Names**

Designs: 2ch, Swimming — David Wilkie
(UK). 5ch, Running — Lass Viren (Finland).
10ch, Weight Lifting — Vasili Alexeev (USSR).
15ch Swimming — Kornelia Ender (DDR).
25ch, Platform Diving — Klaus Dibiasi (Italy).
40ch, Boxing — Ku Yong Jo (DPRK). No.
1489, 50ch, Gymnastics — Nadia Comaneci
(Romania).
No. 1490, 50ch, Kornelia Ender.

**Ordinary Paper**

| 1976, Aug. 2 | | | **Perf. 13¼** |
|---|---|---|---|
| 1483-1489 A908 | Sheet of 7 + label | 10.00 | 4.00 |

**Souvenir Sheet**
*Imperf*

| 1490 A908 50ch multi | 4.00 | 2.00 |
|---|---|---|

For overprints, see Nos. 1639-1645.

Winners, 21st
Olympic Games,
Montreal — A909

Designs: 2ch, Boxing — Ku Yong Jo
(DPRK). 5ch, Gymnastics — Nadie Comaneci
(Romania). 10ch, Pole Vault — Tadeusz
Slusarski (Poland). 15ch, Hurdling — Guy Drut
(France). 25ch, Cycling — Bernt Johansson
(Sweden). 40ch, Soccer (DDR).
50ch, Boxing — Ko Yong Do (DPRK).

**Surface Coated Paper**

| 1976, Aug. 2 | | | **Perf. 13¼** |
|---|---|---|---|
| 1491-1496 A909 | Set of 6 | 6.00 | 1.25 |
| 1496a | Sheet of 12, as #1491-1497, + 5 labels, ordinary paper | 8.00 | — |

**Souvenir Sheet**
*Imperf*

| 1497 A909 50ch multicolored | 3.00 | .50 |
|---|---|---|

---

International
Activities
A910

Designs: 2ch, UPU Headquarters, Bern.
5ch, World Cup. 10ch, Montreal Olympics Stadium. 15ch, Runner with Olympic Torch. 25ch,
Satellite, junk. 40ch, Satellites.
50ch, World map.

**Surface Coated Paper**

| 1976, Aug. 5 | | | **Perf. 13¼** |
|---|---|---|---|
| 1506-1511 A910 | Set of 6 | 5.00 | 1.50 |
| 1511a | Sheet of 7, #1506-1512 + label, ordinary paper | 7.00 | — |

**Souvenir Sheet**
*Imperf*

| 1512 A910 50ch multicolored | 2.50 | 2.50 |
|---|---|---|

For overprints, see Nos. 1646-1652.

Embroidery
A911

Designs: 2ch, Marsh Magpies. 5ch, Golden
Bird. 10ch, Deer. 15ch, Golden Bird. 25ch,
Fairy. 40ch, Tiger.
50ch, Tiger.

**Surface Coated Paper**

| 1976, Aug. 8 | | | **Perf. 12** |
|---|---|---|---|
| 1513-1518 A911 | Set of 6 | 7.50 | 1.50 |
| 1518a | Sheet of 8, as #1513-1519 + label, perf 13¾, ordinary paper | 18.00 | — |

**Souvenir Sheet**
*Imperf*

| 1519 A911 50ch multicolored | 4.00 | .50 |
|---|---|---|

For surcharges, see Nos. 4598, 4599, 4604.

Model Airplane
Championships
(1975) — A912

Designs: 5ch, Trophy, certificate and medal.
10ch, Trophy and medals. 20ch, Model airplane and emblem. 40ch, Model glider and
medals.

**Without Gum**

| 1976, Aug. 15 | | | **Perf. 12** |
|---|---|---|---|
| 1520-1523 A912 | Set of 4 | 4.75 | 1.00 |

5th Summit
Conference of Non-
Aligned States — A913

| 1976, Aug. 16 | | **Without Gum** | |
|---|---|---|---|
| 1524 A913 10ch multicolored | | .50 | .25 |

Locomotives
A914

Designs: 2ch, "Pulgungi" diesel locomotive.
5ch, "Saeppyol" diesel locomotive. 10ch,

---

"Saeppyol" diesel locomotive (diff.). 15ch,
Electric train. 25ch, "Kumsong" diesel locomotive. 40ch, "Pulgungi" electric locomotive.
50ch, "Kumsong" diesel locomotive.

**Surface Coated Paper**

| 1976, Sept. 14 | | | **Perf. 12x11¾** |
|---|---|---|---|
| 1525-1530 A914 | Set of 6 | 5.50 | 1.00 |
| 1530a | Sheet of 8, as #1525-1531 + label, perf 10½ | 15.00 | — |

**Souvenir Sheet**
*Imperf*

| 1531 A914 50ch multicolored | 6.00 | 3.50 |
|---|---|---|

House of
Culture — A915

**Without Gum**

| 1976, Oct. 7 | | | **Perf. 12** |
|---|---|---|---|
| 1532 A915 10ch black & brown | | 75.00 | — |
| a. | Perf. 10¾ | — | — |

Revolutionary Activities of Kim Il
Sung — A916

Kim Il Sung: 2ch, Visiting the Tosongrang.
5ch, With peasants on hillside. 10ch, With boy
and man at seashore. 15ch, Giving house to
farm-hand. 25ch, On muddy road at front, with
driver and girl. 40ch, Walking in rain with
umbrella.
50ch, Watching boy draw picture by
roadside.

| 1976, Oct. 10 | | | **Perf. 13¼** |
|---|---|---|---|
| 1533-1538 A916 | Set of 6 | 3.00 | .75 |

**Souvenir Sheet**
*Imperf*

| 1539 A916 50ch multicolored | 2.00 | 1.50 |
|---|---|---|

Down-With-Imperialism Union, 50th
Anniv. — A917

**Without Gum**

| 1976, Oct. 17 | | | **Perf. 12** |
|---|---|---|---|
| 1540 A917 20ch multicolored | | 1.00 | .25 |

21st Olympic
Games,
Montreal — A918

Olympic Rings, stadium and: 5ch, Fencer.
10ch, Weightlifter. 15ch, Horse racer. 20ch,
Runner. 25ch, Shot putter. 40ch, Basketball
player.
60ch, Yacht race.

**Simulated 3-D Printing Using Plastic
Overlays**

| 1976, Dec. 21 | | | **Imperf.** |
|---|---|---|---|
| 1541-1546 A918 | Set of 6 | 25.00 | 25.00 |

**Souvenir Sheet**

| 1547 A918 60ch multicolored | 45.00 | 45.00 |
|---|---|---|

**No. 1547 Overprinted with Gold Medal Winners' Names, Events**

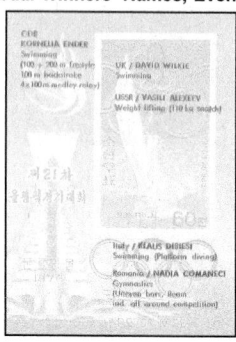

1548　A918　60ch multicolored　　　—　　—

New Year — A919

**Without Gum**

1977, Jan. 1　　　**Perf. 12¼x12**
1549　A919　20ch multicolored　　.50　.25

21st Olympic Games, Montreal (1976) A920

Designs: 5ch, Reverse of Bronze Medal, Montreal skyline. 10ch, Obverse of Bronze Medal, diff. Montreal skyline. 15ch, Obverse of Silver Medal, stadium. 20ch, Reverse of Silver Medal, stadium. 25ch, Reverse of Gold Medal, Olympic Flame. 40ch, Obverse of Gold Medal, Olympic Flame.
60ch, Gold, Silver and Bronze Medals.

**Simulated 3-D Printing Using Plastic Overlays**

1977, Jan. 23　　　**Imperf.**
1550-1555　A920　Set of 6　　25.00　25.00
**Souvenir Sheet**
1556　A920　60ch multicolored　　55.00　55.00

**No. 1556 Overprinted with Gold Medal Winners' Names, Events**

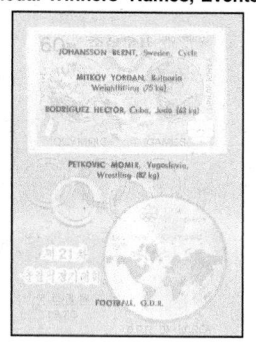

1557　A920　60ch multicolored　　　—　　—

National Costumes of Li Dynasty — A921

---

Seasonal costumes: 10ch, Spring. 15ch, Summer. 20ch, Autumn. 40ch, Winter.

1977, Feb. 10　　　**Perf. 11¾x12**
1558-1561　A921　Set of 4　　4.00　1.00
*1561a*　Sheet of 4, #1558-1561　　5.00　—
No. 1561 is airmail.

Korean Cultural Relics (5th-12th Centuries) — A922

Designs: 2ch, Two Deva kings, Koguryo Dynasty. 5ch, Gold-copper ornament, Koguryo Dynasty. 10ch, Bronze Buddha, Koguryo Dynasty. 15ch, Gold-copper Buddha, Paekje Dynasty. 25ch, Gold crown, Koguryo Dynasty, horiz. 40ch, Gold-copper ornament, Koguryo Dynasty, horiz. 50ch, Gold crown, Silla Dynasty.

1977, Feb. 26　　　**Perf. 13¼**
1562-1568　A922　Set of 7　　5.75　1.60
*1568a*　Sheet of 8, #1562-1568 + label　　6.00　—
No. 1568 is airmail.

Five-Point Program for Land Development A923

**Without Gum**

1977, Mar. 5　　　**Perf. 12**
1569　A923　10ch multicolored　　.50　.25

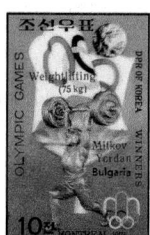

21st Olympic Games, Montreal (1976) — A924

Events, winner's name, nationality, and: 5ch, Cycling. 10ch, Weightlifting. 15ch, Judo. 20ch, Wrestling. 25ch, Football (soccer). 40ch, Boxing.
60ch, Boxing.

**Simulated 3-D Printing Using Plastic Overlays**

1977, Mar. 8　　　**Imperf.**
1570-1575　A924　Set of 6　　45.00　45.00
**Souvenir Sheet**
1576　A924　60ch multicolored　　　—　　—

Korean National Association, 60th Anniv. A925

**Without Gum**

1977, Mar. 23　　　**Perf. 11¾**
1577　A925　10ch multicolored　　.65　.25

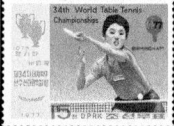

34th World Table-Tennis Championships A926

---

Designs: 10ch, Emblem and trophy. 15ch, Pak Yong Sun. 20ch, Pak Yong Sun with trophy. 40ch, Pak Yong Ok and Yang Ying with trophy.

1977, Apr. 5　　　**Perf. 12**
1578-1581　A926　Set of 4　　4.00　.90
No. 1581 is airmail. For surcharge, see No. 4518.

Kim Il Sung, 65th Birthday A927

Painting of Kim Il Sung: 2ch, Leading Mingyuehkou Meeting. 5ch, Commanding encirclement operation. 10ch, Visiting workers in Kangson. 15ch, Before battle. 25ch, Visiting school. 40ch, Looking over grain fields.
50ch, Kim Il Sung among the artists.

1977, Apr. 15　　　**Perf. 12**
1582-1587　A927　Set of 6　　2.25　.50
**Souvenir Sheet**
1588　A927　50ch multicolored　　1.50　.90

Trolley Buses — A928

Designs: 5ch, "Chollima 72." 10ch, "Chollima 74."

**Without Gum**

1977, Apr. 20　　　**Perf. 12**
1589-1590　A928　Set of 2　　3.00　.25

Korean People's Revolutionary Army, 45th Anniv. — A929

**Without Gum**

1977, Apr. 25　　　**Perf. 12**
1591　A929　40ch multicolored　　1.50　.25

Battle of Pochonbo, 40th Anniv. — A930

**Without Gum**

1977, June 4　　　**Perf. 13¼**
1592　A930　10ch multicolored　　.50　.25

Porcelain — A931

Designs: 10ch, White ceramic teapot, Koryo dynasty. 15ch, White ceramic vase, Ri dynasty. 20ch, Celadon vase, Koryo dynasty. 40ch, Celadon vase, Koryo dynasty, diff.

1977, June 10　　　**Perf. 13¼**
1593-1596　A931　Set of 4　　3.50　.75
*1596a*　Sheet of 4, #1593-1596　　7.00　.95
No. 1596 is airmail.

---

Postal Service — A932

Designs: 2ch, Railway, ship and trucks. 10ch, Postwoman delivering mail. 30ch, Mil Mi-8 helicopter. 40ch, Airliner and world map.

**Without Gum**

1977, June 28　　　**Perf. 13¼**
1597-1600　A932　Set of 4　　5.00　1.25
For surcharges, see Nos. 4515, 4561.

A 3-stamp set and souvenir sheet commemorating the Second Conference of Third World Youth was prepared for release July 1, 1977, but was not issued. Value $3,500.

Butterflies A933

Designs: 2ch, Rapala arata. 5ch, Colias aurora. 10ch, Limenitis populi. 15ch, Anax partherope julius. 25ch, Sympetrum pademontanum elatum.
50ch, Papilio maackii.

1977, July 25　　　**Perf. 12x12¼**
1601-1606　A933　Set of 6　　7.00　1.00
*1606a*　Sheet of 6, #1601-1606　　15.00　—
No. 1606 is airmail.

**Cats and Dogs**

A934　　　　　A935

Cats: 2ch, Gray cat. 10ch, Black and white cat. 25ch, Ginger cat.
Dogs: 5ch, Brindled dog. 15ch, Chow. 50ch, Pungsang.

1977, Aug. 10　　　**Perf. 11¾x12**
1607-1609　A934　Set of 3　　6.00　.50
*1609a*　Sheet of 3, #1607-1609　　8.00　—
1610-1612　A935　Set of 3　　4.00　.50
*1612a*　Sheet of 3, #1610-1612　　6.00　—
No. 1612 is airmail.

Visit of Pres. Tito of Yugoslavia A936

Color of Frame: 10ch, blue green; 15ch, dk gray; 20ch, pale orange; 40ch, light gray.

1977, Aug. 25　　　**Perf. 12**
1613-1616　A936　Set of 4　　40.00　8.00

11-Year Compulsory Education, 5th Anniv. A937

## Without Gum

**1977, Sept. 1**     **Perf. 13¼x13½**
1617  A937  10ch multicolored        .50   .25

Shell-Fish and
Fish — A938

Designs: 2ch, Mactra sulcataria. 5ch, Natica
fortunei. 10ch, Arca inflata. 25ch, Rapana
thomasiana. 50ch, Sphoeroides porphyreus.

**1977, Sept. 5**     **Perf. 11¾x12**
1618-1622  A938  Set of 5         6.00  1.25
1622a     Sheet of 6, #1618-1622 + la-
          bel                      8.00   —

No. 1622 is airmail. For surcharges, see
Nos. 4565, 4578.

Publication of Kim Il
Sung's *Theses on
Socialist
Education* — A939

Designs: 10ch, Students, banners and *Theses.* 20ch, Students, crowd and *Theses.*

**1977, Sept. 5**
1623-1624  A939  Set of 2         1.25   .25

Int'l Seminar on the
Juche Idea — A940

Designs: 2ch, Juche Torch. 5ch, Interracial
crowd holding copies of Kim's Red Book.
10ch, Chollima statue, flags. 15ch, Joined
hands of different races, banner and globe.
25ch, Map of Korea. 40ch, Crowd and slogan.
50ch, Seminar emblem.

**1977, Sept. 14**     **Perf. 11¾x12**
1625-1630  A940  Set of 6         3.50   .60

### Souvenir Sheet
*Imperf*
1631  A940  50ch multicolored     3.00  1.00

### Stamps of 1976 Overprinted

### On Montreal Olympics, #1469-1474

*Methods & Perfs as Before*
**1977, Nov. 8**
1632-1637  A907  Set of 6         9.00   —
1637a     On #1474a, sheet of 8  10.00   —

### Souvenir Sheet
*Imperf*
1638  A907  50ch multicolored     5.00   —

---

On Montreal
Olympics Medal
Winners, #1476-
1482

1639-1644  A908  Set of 6        13.00   —
1644a     On #1481a, sheet of 8  15.00   —

### Souvenir Sheet
*Imperf*
1645  A908  50ch multicolored     5.00   —

### On International Activities, #1506-1512
1646-1651  A910  Set of 6        10.00   —
1651a     On #1511a, sheet of 8  15.00   —

### Souvenir Sheet
*Imperf*
1652  A910  50ch multicolored     5.00   —

Amphilex '77 International Stamp Exhibition,
Amsterdam.

Election of Deputies,
Supreme People's
Assembly — A941

**1977, Nov. 11**     **Perf. 12¼x12**
1653  A941  10ch multicolored     .50   .25

Argentina '78, World Soccer
Championship — A942

Designs: 10ch, Defense. 15ch, Attack. 40ch,
Tackle.
50ch, Shot.

**1977, Dec. 10**     **Perf. 13½**
1654-1656  A942  Set of 3         3.50   .75
1656a     Sheet of 4, as #1654-1657 10.00  —

### Souvenir Sheet
*Imperf*
1657  A942  50ch multicolored     2.50   —

Reelection of Kim Il Sung — A943

**1977, Dec. 15**     **Perf. 12**
1658  A943  10ch multicolored     .60   .25

Org. for
Communication
Cooperation of
Socialist Countries,
20th Anniv. — A944

### Without Gum

**1977, Dec. 16**     **Perf. 11¾x12**
1659  A944  10ch multicolored     .50   .25

---

New
Year — A945

**1978, Jan. 1**     **Perf. 13¼**
1660  A945  10ch multicolored     .60   .25

Winter Olympic
Games, Sapporo-
Innsbruck
A946

Designs: 2ch, 19th century skater. 5ch,
Skier. 10ch, Ice ballet. 15ch, Hunter on skis.
20ch, 18th century woman skier. 25ch, Medieval Scandinavian hunter. 40ch, Skiier.
50ch, Landscape. 60ch, Speed skater.

**1978, Feb. 18**     **Perf. 13¼**
1661-1667  A946  Set of 7         6.00  1.00
1667a     Sheet of 10, as #1661-1669
          + label                 9.00

### Souvenir Sheets
1668  A946  50ch multicolored     5.00   .50
1669  A946  60ch multicolored     4.00   .50

No. 1667 is airmail.
For overprints, see Nos. 1821-1829.

Postal
History — A947

Designs: 2ch, Post rider and horse token.
5ch, Postman on motorcycle. 10ch, Electric
train and postal van. 15ch, Mail steamer and
Mi-8 helicopter. 25ch, Tupolev Tu-154 jetliner
and satellite. 40ch, Dove and UPU
headquarters.
50ch, Dove and UPU emblem. 60ch, Dove
and UPU headquarters.

**1978, Mar. 2**     **Perf. 13¼**
1670-1675  A947  Set of 6         6.00  1.00
1675a     Sheet of 8, as #1670-1677 8.00  —

### Souvenir Sheets
1676-1677  A947  Set of 2         6.00

No. 1675 is airmail.

Rubens, 400th
Anniv. Birth — A948

2ch, 5ch, 40ch, 50ch, Self-portrait, same
design.

**1978, Mar. 20**
1678-1680  A948  Set of 3         3.50   .75
1680a     Sheet of 4, as #1678-1681 6.00

### Souvenir Sheet
1681  A948  50ch multicolored     3.00  1.50

Farm Machines
A949

---

Designs: 10ch (No. 1682), *Chungsong* tractor. 10ch (No. 1683), Sprayer.

**1978, Apr. 1**     **Perf. 11¾x12**
1682-1683  A949  Set of 2         2.50   .25

Pre-Olympics,
Moscow
1980 — A950

Equestrian events: 2ch, Show jumping. 5ch,
Jumping bar. 10ch, Cross Country. 15ch,
Dressage. 25ch, Water splash. 40ch,
Dressage. (diff.).
50ch, 3-Step bar jump.

**1978, Apr. 1**     **Perf. 13¼**
1684-1689  A950  Set of 6         3.50  1.50
1689a     Sheet of 8, as #1684-1690 +
          label                    7.00

### Souvenir Sheet
1690  A950  50ch multicolored     2.50   —

Korean People's
Army Day — A951

Designs: 5ch, Soldier, battle scene. 10ch,
Pilot, soldier, sailor saluting.

**1978, Apr. 1**     **Perf. 11¾x12**
1691-1692  A951  Set of 2         4.00  1.00

Meeting of Kim Il
Sung and Hua
Guo Feng of the
People's
Republic of
China — A951a

Denominations: 15ch, 20ch.

**1978, May**     **Perf. 12**
1692B-1692C  A951a  Set of 2

This set includes a third stamp and a souvenir sheet, which the editors would like to
examine.
Released prior to the meeting between Kim
Il Sung and Hua Guo Feng and withdrawn
when the meeting was canceled.

Ships
A952

Korean ships: 2ch, Cargo ship *Mangy-
ongbong.* 5ch, Freighter *Hyoksin.* 10ch,
Freighter *Chongchongang.* 30ch, Tanker
*Sonbang.* 50ch, Freighter *Taedonggang.*

**1978, May 5**     **Perf. 13¼**
1693-1697  A952  Set of 5         6.00  1.25
1697a     Sheet of 6, as #1693-1697+
          label                    8.00

No. 1697 is airmail.

History of the World
Cup — A953

World Cup Winners (all 20ch, except Nos. 1709, 1710): No. 1698, Uruguay 1930. No. 1699, Italy 1934. No. 1700, France 1938. No. 1701, Brazil 1950. No. 1702, Switzerland 1954. No. 1703, Sweden 1958. No. 1704, Chile 1962. No. 1705, England 1966. No. 1706, Mexico 1970. No. 1707, West Germany 1974. No. 1708, Argentina 1978. 50ch (No. 1709), Soccer players and emblem, horiz.
50ch (No. 1710), World Cup and championship emblem.

**1978, June 1**
| 1698-1709 | A953 | Set of 12 | 10.00 | 3.00 |
| 1709a | | Sheet of 12, as #1698-1708, 1710 | 12.00 | |

**Souvenir Sheet**
| 1710 | A953 | 50ch multicolored | 6.00 | .60 |

No. 1709 is airmail.
For overprints, see Nos. 2051-2063.

World Cup
Winners
A954

Designs: 5ch, Uruguay, 1930, 1950. 10ch, Italy, 1934, 1938. 15ch, West Germany, 1954, 1974. 25ch, Brazil, 1958, 1962, 1970. 40ch, England, 1966. 50ch, World Cup, vert.
50ch, World Cup.

**1978, June 1**
| 1711-1716 | A954 | Set of 6 | 5.00 | 1.25 |
| 1716a | | Sheet of 6, as #1711-15, 1717 | 6.00 | |

**Souvenir Sheet**
| 1717 | A954 | 50ch multicolored | 4.00 | .75 |

No. 1716 is airmail.

Art of the
Revolution
A955

Designs: 10ch, Opera, *Sea of Love.* 15ch, Embroidered kerchief with floral design in the form of map of Korea. 20ch, *Tansimjul* dance. 40ch, *Song of Korea.*

**1978, June 2**
| 1718-1720 | A955 | Set of 3 | 4.50 | .90 |

**Souvenir Sheet**
| 1721 | A955 | 40ch multicolored | 2.50 | .50 |

**Domestic Printings**

Beginning in the 1970s, a number of North Korean stamps have been reprinted for sale and use within the country. Typically, these printings were on unsurfaced paper, with poorer production qualities, and without gum.

Second
Seven-Year
Plan — A956

Designs: 5ch, Electricity and Coal. 10ch, Steel and nonferrous metals. 15ch, Machine products and chemical fertilizers. 30ch, Cement and fishing. 50ch, Grain and tideland reclamation.

---

**1978, June 15**     **Perf. 11½x12**
| 1722-1726 | A956 | Set of 5 | 3.25 | .90 |
| 1722a | 5ch | Unsurfaced white paper, without gum | 8.00 | — |
| 1723a | 10ch | Unsurfaced white paper, without gum | 8.00 | — |
| 1724a | 15ch | Unsurfaced white paper, without gum | 8.00 | — |
| 1725a | 30ch | Unsurfaced white paper, without gum | 5.00 | — |

History of
Olympic
Games &
Winners
A957

Games emblems / medal winners (all 20ch): No. 1727, Athens 1896 / Alfred Flatow. No. 1728, Paris 1900 / Michel Theato. No. 1729, London 1908 / Wyndham Halswelle. No. 1730, Stockholm 1912 / William Kinnear. No. 1731, Antwerp 1920 / Paul Anspach. No. 1732, Paris 1924 / Ugo Frigerio. No. 1733, Amsterdam 1928 / Ahmed El Quafi. No. 1734, Berlin 1936 / Robert Charpentier. No. 1735, London 1948 / Josef Stalder. No. 1736, Helsinki 1952 / Laszlo Papp. No. 1737, Melbourne 1956 / Ronald Delany. No. 1738, Rome 1960 / Jolanda Balas. No. 1739, Tokyo 1964 / Valery Brumel. No. 1740, Mexico 1968 / Vera Caslavska. No. 1741, Munich 1972 / Li Ho Jun.
50ch, Montreal 1976 / Ku Yong Jo.

**1978, June 16**     **Perf. 13¼**
| 1727-1741 | A957 | Set of 15 | 12.00 | 4.50 |
| 1741a | | Sheet of 16, as #1727-1741 | 14.00 | |

**Souvenir Sheet**
| 1742 | A957 | 50ch multicolored | 2.00 | .75 |

Passenger Aircraft — A958

Designs: 2ch, Douglas DC-8-63 jetliner and Comte AC-4 Gentleman. 10ch, Ilyushin Il-62M jetliner and Avia BH-25. 15ch, Douglas DC-8-63 jetliner and Savola Marchetti S-71. 20ch, Tupolev Tu-144 jetliner and Kalinin K-5. 25ch, Tupolev Tu-154 jetliner and Antonov An-2 biplane. 30ch, Ilyushin Il-18 airliner and '30s-era airplane. 40ch, Concorde supersonic jetliner and Wibault 283 trimotor.
50ch, Airbus.

**1978, July 25**
| 1743-1749 | A958 | Set of 7 | 6.00 | 1.00 |
| 1749a | | Sheet of 8, as #1743-1750 | 10.00 | |

**Souvenir Sheet**
| 1750 | A958 | 50ch multicolored | 2.50 | .50 |

For surcharge, see No. 4586.

White-Bellied Black
Woodpecker
Preservation — A959

Designs: 5ch, Dryocopus richardsi, map of habitat, inset map of Korea. 10ch, Woodpecker and eggs. 15ch, Woodpecker feeding young. 25ch, Woodpecker feeding young, diff. 50ch, Woodpecker on tree trunk.

**1978, Aug. 5**     **Perf. 11¾x12**
| 1751-1755 | A959 | Set of 5 | 9.00 | 2.50 |
| 1755a | | Sheet of 6, #1751-1755 + label | 11.00 | |

For surcharge, see No. 4583.

---

Democratic
People's Republic
of Korea, 30th
Anniv. — A960

Designs (all 10ch): No. 1756, Building and flag. No. 1757, Flag with silhouetttes of workers and peasants. No. 1758, Flag with aviator and two soldiers. No. 1759, Chollima statue and city. No. 1760, Workers demonstrating, map of Korea in background. No. 1761, Asian, European and African clasping hands, with torch and "Solidarity" in background.

**Without Gum**

**1978, Sep. 9**     **Perf. 13½x13¼**
| 1756-1761 | A960 | Set of 6 | 4.00 | .75 |
| 1758a | 10ch | Unsurfaced toned paper | 10.00 | — |
| 1759a | 10ch | Unsurfaced toned paper | 15.00 | — |
| 1760a | 10ch | Unsurfaced toned paper | 15.00 | — |

Paintings by Ri Am
(16th
Century) — A961

Designs: 10ch, *Cat and Pup.* 15ch, *Cat on a Tree.* 40ch, *A Pair of Wild Geese.*

**1978, Oct. 16**     **Perf. 13¼**
| 1762-1764 | A961 | Set of 3 | 8.00 | 1.25 |
| 1764a | | Sheet of 4, #1762-1764 + label | 11.00 | — |

World
Cup
Winners,
Argentina
'78
A962

Soccer players: 10ch, Argentina, Champion. 15ch, Holland, Sub-Champion. 25ch, Brazil, Third Place.
50ch, Argentina, Champion.

**1978, Dec. 15**
| 1765-1767 | A962 | Set of 3 | 3.00 | .50 |
| 1767a | | Sheet of 4, as #1765-1768 | 12.00 | |

**Souvenir Sheet**
| 1768 | A962 | 50ch multicolored | 2.50 | 1.50 |

New Year — A963

**Without Gum**

**1979, Jan. 1**     **Perf. 12**
| 1769 | A963 | 10ch multicolored | .50 | .25 |

A964

---

International Year of the Child — A965

Kim Il Sung and children: 5ch, With Children's Corps members in Maanshan. 10ch, Children's Corps members in classroom. 15ch, "The New Year Gathering." 20ch, by roadside, with snowman, kite. 30ch, Looking at children's school work.
Children: 10ch, Tug of war. 15ch, Ballerinas. 20ch, Children of different races holding hands in circle around globe. 25ch, Singing at piano. 30ch, Playing on toy airplane ride.
No. 1780, Kim visiting a kindergarten. No. 1781, as No. 1777.

**1979, Jan. 1**     **Perf. 13¼x13½**
| 1770-1774 | A964 | Set of 5 | 4.00 | 1.00 |
| 1775-1779 | A965 | Set of 5 | 3.00 | 1.00 |

**Souvenir Sheets**

*Imperf*
| 1780 | A964 | 50ch multicolored | 2.50 | 1.75 |
| 1781 | A965 | 50ch multicolored | 2.50 | 1.75 |

Nos. 1770-1779 were issued with setenant labels. Nos. 1780-1781 exist perf. 13¼x13½.

A set of four stamps depicting roses, similar to Type A970, was prepared for release on Jan. 5, 1979, but was not issued.

Story of Two
Generals — A966

Designs: 5ch, Two warriors on horseback. 10ch (No. 1783), Man blowing feather. 10ch (No. 1784), Two generals fighting Japanese invaders. 10ch (No. 1785), Two generals on horseback.

**Without Gum**

**1979, Jan. 10**     **Perf. 11¾x12**
| 1782-1785 | A966 | Set of 4 | 3.00 | .50 |

Worker-Peasant Red
Guards, 20th
Anniv. — A967

**Without Gum**

**1979, Jan. 14**     **Perf. 12x11¾**
| 1786 | A967 | 10ch multicolored | .50 | .25 |

Airships
A968

Designs: 10ch, Clement-Bayard Airship *Fleurus.* 20ch, NI *Norge.* 50ch, *Graf Zeppelin.*

**1979, Feb. 27**     **Perf. 13¼**
| 1787-1788 | A968 | Set of 2 | 2.00 | .40 |
| 1788a | | Sheet of 3, as #1787-1789 | 8.00 | |

**Souvenir Sheet**
| 1789 | A968 | 50ch multicolored | 3.00 | 1.75 |

March 1 Popular
Uprising, 60th
Anniv. — A969

**Without Gum**

**1979, Mar. 1**     **Perf. 11¾x12**
| 1790 | A969 | 10ch multicolored | .60 | .25 |

Roses — A970

Designs: 5ch, Rose. 10ch, Red star rose. 15ch, Flamerose. 20ch, Yellow rose. 30ch, White rose. 50ch, Deep pink rose.

**1979, Apr. 18** **Perf. 13¼**
1791-1796 A970 Set of 6    4.00 1.10
1796a    Sheet of 6, #1791-1796    5.50 —
No. 1796 is airmail.

35th World Table Tennis Championships, Pyongyang — A971

Designs: 5ch, Championship Cup. 10ch, Female doubles. 15ch, Female singles. 20ch, Male doubles. 30ch, Male singles. 50ch, Chollima statue. "Welcome."

**1979, Apr. 25**
1797-1801 A971 Set of 5    3.00 .75
1801a    Sheet of 6, #1797-1802    7.50 —
**Souvenir Sheet**
1802 A971 50ch multicolored    3.00 .45
For surcharges, see Nos. 4516, 4531.

"Let Us Step Up Socialist Construction Under the Banner of the Juche Idea" — A972

Designs: 5ch, Marchers, banner. 10ch (No. 1804), Map of Korea. 10ch (No. 1805), Hand holding torch.

**Without Gum**

**1979, Apr. 28** **Perf. 12**
1803-1805 A972 Set of 3    3.00 .25
1803a    5ch Unsurfaced dull white    15.00 —
     paper
1804a    10ch Unsurfaced dull white    15.00 —
     paper
1805a    10ch Unsurfaced dull white    15.00 —
     paper

Order of Honor of the Three Revolutions — A973

**1979, May 2** **Without Gum**
1806 A973 10ch dp blue & lt    1.50 .25
     blue
a.    Unsurfaced dull white paper    15.00 —

World Telecommunications Day — A974

**1979, May 17** **Without Gum**
1807 A974 10ch multicolored    1.00 .25

Battle in Musan Area, 40th Anniv. — A975

**1979, May 23** **Without Gum**
1808 A975 10ch multicolored    .60 .25

Int'l Friendship Exhibition A976

**1979, May 29** **Without Gum**
1809 A976 10ch multicolored    .60 .25

Albrecht Dürer, 450th Anniv. Death — A977

Details from Dürer paintings: 15ch, Peonies. 20ch, Akeley. 25ch, A Big Tuft of Grass. 30ch, Wing of a Bird. 50ch, Like 30ch.

**1979, June 8** **Perf. 13¼**
1810-1813 A977 Set of 4    5.50 .75
1813a    Souvenir sheet of 4, #1810-    9.00 —
     1813
**Souvenir Sheet**
1814 A977 50ch multicolored    3.50 .60
For surcharge, see No. 4584.

Olympic Games, Moscow 1980 A978

Olympic Torch, Moscow 1980 emblem and: 5ch, Fencers. 10ch, Gymnast. 20ch, Yacht race. 30ch, Runner. 40ch, Weightlifter. 50ch, Horse jump.

**1979, July 1**
1815-1819 A978 Set of 5    3.50 1.25
1819a    Sheet of 6, as #1815-1820    5.00 —
**Souvenir Sheet**
1820 A978 50ch multicolored    3.00 1.50

Nos. 1661-1669 Overprinted

**1979, July 17**
1821-1827 A946 Set of 7    10.00 3.50
1827a    Sheet of 10, as #1821-1829    18.00 —
     + label
**Souvenir Sheets**
1828 A946 50ch multicolored    4.25 1.50
1829 A946 60ch multicolored    8.50 —
No. 1827 is airmail.

Koguryo Dynasty Horsemen A979

Designs: 5ch, Hunting. 10ch, Archery contest. 15ch, Drummer. 20ch, Rider blowing horn. 30ch, Horse and rider in chain mail. 50ch, Hawk hunting.

**1979, Aug. 1**
1830-1835 A979 Set of 6    5.25 .75
1835a    Sheet of 6, as #1830-1835    9.00 —
No. 1835 s airmail.

Olympic Games, Moscow 1980 — A980

Designs: 5ch, Judo. 10ch, Volleyball. 15ch, Cycling. 20ch, Basketball. 25ch, One-oared boat. 30ch, Boxing. 40ch, Shooting. 50ch, Gymnastics.

**1979, Aug. 5** **Perf. 11¾x12**
1836-1842 A980 Set of 7    5.00 1.25
1842a    Sheet of 8, as #1836-1843 +    9.00 —
     label
**Souvenir Sheet**
1843 A980 50ch multicolored    3.00 1.00

Ri Dynasty Knights' Costumes — A981

Designs: 5ch, Knight in armor. 10ch, Knight in ceremonial dress. 15ch, Knight in armor (diff.) 20ch, Soldier in uniform. 30ch, Knight in armor (diff.) 50ch, Knight in armor (diff.)

**1979, Aug. 6** **Perf. 11¾**
1844-1849 A981 Set of 6    4.25 .75
1849a    Sheet of 6, #1844-1849    6.50 —
No. 1849 is airmail.

1980 Summer Olympics, Moscow — A982

Designs: 10ch, Judo. 15ch, Handball. 20ch, Archery. 25ch, Field hockey. 30ch, Boat race. 40ch, Soccer. 50ch, Horse race.

**1979, Sept. 5** **Perf. 11¾x11½**
1850-1855 A982 Set of 6    5.25 1.25
1855a    Sheet of 8, #1850-1856 + la-    8.00 —
     bel
**Souvenir Sheet**
1856 A982 50ch multi    3.00 1.25
For surcharges, see Nos. 4585, 4595.

Chongbong Monument — A983

**Without Gum**

**1979, Sep. 10** **Perf. 12**
1857 A983 10ch multicolored    .60 .25

Sika Deer — A984

Designs: 5ch, Breeder feeding fawn from bottle. 10ch, Doe and suckling fawn. 15ch, Deer drinking from stream. 20ch, Buck walking. 30ch, Deer running. 50ch, Antlers.

**1979, Oct. 5** **Perf. 13½**
1858-1863 A984 Set of 6    4.00 1.25
1863a    Sheet of 6, #1858-1863    6.00 —

Central Zoo, Pyongyang — A985

Designs: 5ch, Moscovy ducks. 10ch, Ostrich. 15ch, Turkey. 20ch, Pelican. 30ch, Guinea fowl. 50ch, Mandarin ducks.

**1979, Oct. 9** **Perf. 12**
1864-1869 A985 Set of 6    6.00 1.75
1869a    Sheet of 6, #1864-1869    8.00 —
No. 1869 is airmail. For surcharge, see No. 4569.

Int'l Year of the Child — A986

Designs: 20ch (No. 1870), Girl with toy sail boat. 20ch (No. 1871), Boy with toy train. 20ch (No. 1872), Boy with model biplane. 20ch (No. 1873), Boy with model spaceman. 30ch (No. 1874), Boy with toy motor boat. 30ch (No. 1875), Boy sitting on toy train. 30ch (No. 1876), Boy with model airplane. 30ch (No. 1877), Boy with model spaceman.
Souvenir Sheets (all 80ch): No. 1878, Boy and model ocean liner. No. 1879, Boy and girl with model train. No. 1880, Boy and Concorde. No. 1881, Girl and satellite.
Miniature sheets of 4: No. 1882, Nos. 1870, 1874, 1878 + label. No. 1883, Nos. 1871, 1875, 1879 + label. No. 1884, Nos. 1872, 1876, 1880 + label. No. 1885, Nos. 1873, 1877, 1881 + label.

**1979, Oct. 13** **Perf. 12x11¾**
1870-1877 A986 Set of 8    13.50 2.75
**Souvenir Sheets**
1878-1881 A986 Set of 4    27.50 2.75
**Miniature Sheets**
1882-1885 A986 Set of 4    27.50 2.75
For surcharges, see Nos. 4520, 4532.

Int'l Year of the Child A987

Children playing soccer: 20ch, Kicking. 30ch, Dribbling. 80ch, Tackling.

**1979, Nov. 15** **Perf. 12x11¾**
1886-1887 A987 Set of 2    5.50 .75
1887a    Sheet of 3, as #1886-1888    11.00 —
**Souvenir Sheet**
1888 A987 80ch multicolored    5.50 .75

Marine Life — A988

Designs: 20ch, Devil stinger fish (*Inimicas japonicus*). 30ch, Black rockfish (*Sebastes schlegeli*). 50ch, Northern sea lion (*Eumetopias jubatus*).

**1979, Dec. 4**
1889-1891 A988  Set of 3          3.75  .75
1891a    Sheet of 3, #1889-1891     5.50   —

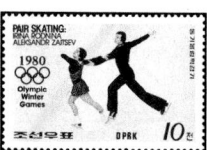

Winter Olympics Games, Lake Placid A989

Designs: 10ch, Figure skating (Irina Rodnina and Aleksandr Zaitsev). 20ch, Ice hockey (Soviet team). 30ch, Ladies' ski relay team. 40ch, Cross-country skiing (Sergei Saveliev, USSR), vert. 50ch, Ladies' speed skating (Tatiana Averina), vert.
60ch, Ice dancing (Ludmila Pakhomova and Aleksandr Gorshkov), stamp vert.

**1979, Dec. 9**
1892-1896 A989  Set of 5          6.00  1.50
1892a    Sheet of 3, #1892-1894     5.00   —
1895a    Sheet of 3, as #1895-1897  10.00   —
**Souvenir Sheet**
1897 A989  60ch multicolored        5.50  4.50

Honey Bees — A990

Designs: 20ch, Bee gathering nectar. 30ch, Bee and blossoms. 50ch, Bee over flower.

**1979, Dec. 22**
1898-1900 A990  Set of 3          6.00  .60
1900a    Sheet of 3, #1898-1900     8.00   —

Kim Il Sung's Birthplace, Hoeryang A991

Sinpha Revolutionary Museum — A992

**1979, Dec. 24**
1901 A991  10ch multicolored        .75  .25
1902 A992  10ch multicolored        .75  .25
Revolutionary historical sites.

New Year — A993

**1980, Jan. 1**
1903 A993  10ch multicolored       1.00  .25

Studying — A994

**1980, Jan. 10**        **Perf. 12x11¾**
1904 A994  10ch multicolored        .50  .25

Unryul Mine Conveyor Belt — A995

**1980, Jan. 20**        **Perf. 11¾x12**
1905 A995  10ch multicolored       1.00  .25

Kim Il Sung, Soldiers and Children A996

Children Playing A997

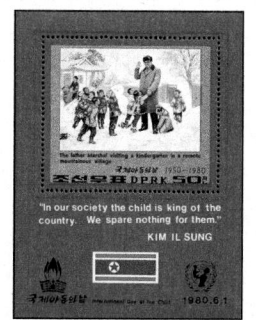

Kim Visiting Kindergarten — A998

**International Day of the Child**
Type A997 (all 10ch): No. 1907, Black, Asian and White children with "6" and "1." No. 1908, Children playing accordion. No. 1909, Children on airplane ride. No. 1910, Children on rocket ride. No. 1911, Children riding tricycles. No. 1912, Children playing with model train.

**1980, Jan. 28**        **Perf. 12x11¾**
1906 A996  10ch multicolored        .35  .25
1907 A997  10ch multicolored       1.60  .35
1908 A997  10ch multicolored        .35  .25
1909 A997  10ch multicolored        .60  .25
1910 A997  10ch multicolored       2.25  .50
1911 A997  10ch multicolored        .50  .25
1912 A997  10ch multicolored        .35  .25
       Nos. 1906-1912 (7)          6.00  2.10
**Souvenir Sheet**
**Perf. 13¼**
1913 A998  50ch multicolored       3.00  1.25

Chongsan-ri Monument — A999

Chongsan-ri Party Headquarters A1000

**1980, Feb. 5**        **Perf. 11¾x12**
1914 A999   10ch multicolored       .50  .25
1915 A1000  10ch multicolored       .50  .25

Monument in Honor of Kim Jong Suk's Return — A1001

**1980, Feb. 16**
1916 A1001  10ch multicolored       .50  .25

Explorers A1002

Designs: 10ch, Vasco Nunez be Balboa (Spain). 20ch, Francisco de Orellana (Spain). 30ch, Haroun Tazieff (France). 40ch, Sir Edmund Hillary (New Zealand) and Shri Tenzing (Nepal).
70ch, Ibn Battuta (Morocco).

**1980, Feb. 18**        **Perf. 13¼**
1917-1920 A1002  Set of 4         5.00  1.10
1920a    Sheet of 6, as #1917-1921
         + label                 10.00   —
**Souvenir Sheet**
1921 A1002  70ch multicolored      4.50  1.50

Ryongpo Revolutionary Museum A1003

**1980, Feb. 23**        **Perf. 11¾**
1922 A1003  10ch lt blue & black   .50  .25

Rowland Hill (1795-1879), Centenary of Death — A1004

Rowland Hill and stamps of: 30ch, Germany, Great Britain (#1), Russia, Switzerland, DPRK and Wurttemberg. 50ch, Great Britain (#1, pair), France, Roman States, Canada, Two Sicilies and India.

**1980, Mar. 1**
1923-1924 A1004  Set of 2         8.50  1.40
1924a    Sheet of 2, #1923-1924   10.00   —

World Red Cross Day — A1005

Designs: No. 1925, 10ch, Emblem of DPRK Red Cross. No. 1926, 10ch, Jean-Henri Dunant. No. 1927, 10ch, Nurse and infant. No. 1928, 10ch, Red Cross ship. No. 1929, 10ch, Red Cross helicopter. No. 1930, 10ch, Nurse with child and doll. No. 1931, 10ch, Map, Red Cross, transports.
50ch, Nurse with syringe.

**1980, Apr. 17**        **Perf. 11¾x11½**
1925-1931 A1005  Set of 7         8.00  1.50
1931a    Sheet of 8, as #1925-1932  15.00   —
**Souvenir Sheet**
1932 A1005  50ch multicolored      5.50  1.75
For overprints and surcharges, see Nos. 2043-2050, 4517, 4570.

Conquerors of the Sea — A1006

Designs: 10ch, Fernando Magellan (Portugal). 20ch, Fridtjof Nansen (Norway). 30ch, Auguste and Jacques Piccard (Sweden). 40ch, Jacques Cousteau (France). 70ch, Capt. James Cook (UK).

**1980, Apr. 30**        **Perf. 13¼**
1933-1936 A1006  Set of 4        10.00  1.90
1936a    Sheet of 6, as #1933-1937
         + label                 16.00   —
**Souvenir Sheet**
1937 A1006  70ch multicolored      6.50  1.50

London 1980 Int'l Philatelic Exhibition A1007

Designs: 10ch, Great Britain #1 and Korean stamps. No. 1939, 20ch, British Guiana One-Cent Magenta and Korean cover. No. 1940, 30ch, Korea #1 (in blue) and modern Korean First Day Cover. 40ch, DPRK Nos. 1 (in green) and 1494. No. 1942, 50ch, DPRK Nos. 470-471.
No. 1943: a, 20ch, Like 10ch. b, 30ch, Like No. 1939. c, 50ch, Like 40ch.

**1980, May 6**
1938-1942 A1007  Set of 5        10.00  1.50
**Souvenir Sheet**
1943 A1007  Sheet of 3, #a-c     15.00  1.50
Nos. 1941, 1943c are airmail.

Conquerors of Sky and Space — A1008

Designs: 10ch, Wright Brothers (USA). 20ch, Louis Bleriot (France). 30ch, Anthony Fokker (USA). 40ch, Secondo Campini (Italy) and Sir Frank Whittle (UK).
70ch, Count Ferdinand von Zeppelin (Germany).

**1980, May 10**
1944-1947 A1008  Set of 4         6.00  1.25
1947a    Sheet of 6, as #1944-1948
         + label                 13.00   —
**Souvenir Sheet**
1948 A1008  70ch multicolored      5.00  1.25

Conquerors of the Universe — A1009

Designs: 10ch, Spaceships. 20ch, Spaceship landing on another planet. 30ch, Spaceships landing on another planet, greeted by dinosaurs. 40ch, Spaceship, dinosaurs.
70ch, Spaceman and dragons.

**1980, May 20**        **Perf. 11¾x12**
1949-1952 A1009  Set of 4         3.50  1.25
1952a    Sheet of 6, as #1949-1953
         + label                 12.00   —
**Souvenir Sheet**
1953 A1009  70ch multicolored      3.50  1.25

**Chongryon, 25th Anniv. — A1010**

**1980, May 25**     *Perf. 12¼x12*
**1954** A1010 10ch multicolored    .50 .25
Chongryon is the General Association of Korean Residents in Japan.

**Pyongyang Maternity Hospital — A1011**

**1980, May 30**     *Perf. 12*
**1955** A1011 10ch multicolored    1.10 .25

**Changgwang Health Complex A1012**

**1980, June 2**     *Perf. 11¾x12*
**1956** A1012 2ch black & lt blue    .60 .25

**Korean Revolutionary Army, 50th Anniv. — A1013**

**1980, July 6**     *Perf. 12*
**1957** A1013 10ch multicolored    .60 .25

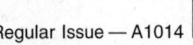

**Regular Issue — A1014**

Designs (all 10ch): No. 1958, Workers' hostel, Samjiyon. No. 1959, *Chongsanri* rice harvester. No. 1960, *Taedonggang* rice transplanter. No. 1961, Corn harvester. No. 1962, Samhwa Democratic Propaganda Hall. No. 1963, Songmun-ri revolutionary historic building (with trees). No. 1964, Sundial. No. 1965, Turtle ship. No. 1966, Phungsan dog. No. 1967, Quail.

**Perf. 11¾, 11½ (#1960, 1965), 12x11¾ (#1964)**
**1980**
**1958-1967** A1014 Set of 10    25.00 3.00
Issued: Nos. 1958-1961, 7/25. Nos. 1962-1967, 8/1.

**6th Congress, Workers' Party of Korea — A1015**

**"Leading the van in the Arduous March" A1016**

**"The great leader inspires and encourages colliers on the spot." — A1017**

Designs (all 10ch): No. 1968, Party emblem, fireworks. No. 1969, Students, Red Book. No. 1970, Workers, banner, Red Book. No. 1971, Young workers, one with accordion. No. 1972, Worker holding wrench aloft. No. 1973, Four young workers, one with streamer, building in background. No. 1974, Map, propaganda slogans. No. 1975, Workers marching with three banners, smoke stacks in background.

**1980, July 30**     *Perf. 12¼x12*
**1968-1975** A1015 Set of 8    6.00 1.25
**Souvenir Sheets**
**1976** A1016 50ch multicolored    3.00 .75
**1977** A1017 50ch multicolored    2.00 .75

**World Cup Soccer Championship 1978-1982 — A1018**

Designs: 20ch, Two soccer players dribbling ball. 30ch, Tackling.
40ch, Tackling (diff.). 60ch, Moving in to tackle.

**1980, Aug. 5**     *Perf. 12*
**1978-1979** A1018 Set of 2    7.50 2.00
*1979a*   Sheet of 4, as #1978-1980   18.00 —
**Souvenir Sheet**
**1980** A1018 Sheet of 2 + label   16.00 2.00
  *a.*   40ch multicolored   3.00 1.00
  *b.*   60ch multicolored   4.00 1.00

**Winter Olympic Games 1980, Gold Medal Winners A1019**

Designs: 20ch, Irina Rodnina and Aleksandr Zaitsev.
1w, Natalia Linitschnuk and Gennadi Karponosov.

**1980, Aug. 10**     *Perf. 13¼*
**1981** A1019 20ch multicolored    6.50 1.60
  *a.* Sheet of 2, as #1981-1982   15.00 —
**Souvenir Sheet**
**1982** A1019 1w multicolored    6.50 2.00

**Albrecht Dürer, 450th Anniv. Death — A1020**

Designs: 20ch, *Soldier with Horse.*
1w, *Horse and Rider.*

**1980, Aug. 18**     *Perf. 11¾x12*
**1983** A1020 20ch multicolored    6.50 1.60
  *a.* Sheet of 2 as #1983-1984   20.00 —
**Souvenir Sheet**
**1984** A1020 1w multicolored    10.00 2.75

**Johannes Kepler, 350th Anniv. Death — A1021**

Designs: 20ch, Kepler, astrolabe and satellites.
1w, Kepler, astrolabe and satellites (diff.).

**1980, Aug. 25**
**1985** A1021 20ch multicolored    2.75 1.25
  *a.*   Sheet of 2, as #1985-1986   12.00 —
**Souvenir Sheet**
**1986** A1021 1w multicolored    6.50 2.25

**3rd Int'l Stamp Fair Essen 1980 A1022**

Designs, Stamps from German and Russian Zeppelin sets, respectively: 10ch, 1m and 30k. 20ch, 2m and 35k. 30ch, 4m and 1r.
50ch, Russian 2r Polar Flight stamp and DPRK No. 1780 stamp.

**1980, Sep. 25**     *Perf. 13¼*
**1987-1989** A1022 Set of 3    6.50 1.25
*1989a*   Sheet of 4, as #1987-1990   30.00 —
**Souvenir Sheet**
**1990** A1022 50ch multicolored    9.00 2.50

**A1023**

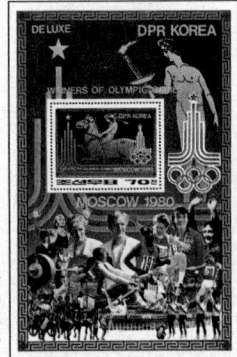

**Moscow Olympic Games Winners A1024**

Designs: 10ch, Free pistol shooting — Aleksandr Melentiev (USSR). 20ch, 4000m Individual pursuit bicycle race — Robert Dill-Bundi (Switzerland). 25ch, Gymnastics — Stoyan Deltchev (Bulgaria). 30ch, Free style wrestling — K). 35ch, Weight-lifting — Ho Bong Choi (DPRK). 40ch, Running — Marita Koch (DDR). 50ch, Modern pentathlon — Anatoly Starostin (USSR).
No. 1998, Boxing — Teofilo Stevenson (Cuba). No. 1999, Ancient Greek rider on horse.

**1980, Oct. 20**     *Perf. 12x11¾*
**1991-1997** A1023 Set of 7    7.00 2.25
*1997a*   Sheet of 8, as #1991-1998   12.00 —
**Souvenir Sheet**
**1998** A1023 70ch multicolored    2.75 2.00
**1999** A1024 70ch multicolored    4.50 2.00

**Josip Broz Tito (1892-1980) A1025**

**1980, Dec. 4**     *Perf. 12¼x12*
**2000** A1025 20ch multicolored    1.00 .25

**First Post-WWII Lufthansa Flight, 25th Anniv. — A1026**

Designs: 20ch, Convair CV 340 airliner.
1w, Airbus A 300.

**1980, Dec. 10**     *Perf. 13¼*
**2001** A1026 20ch multicolored    6.00 2.25
  *a.*   Sheet of 2, as #2001-2002   15.00 —
**Souvenir Sheet**
**2002** A1026 1w multicolored    8.00 3.25

**Liverpool-Manchester Railway, 150th Anniv. — A1027**

Designs: 20ch, *The Rocket.*
1w, Locomotive pulling passenger car and horse car.

**1980, Dec. 16**     *Perf. 11¾*
**2003** A1027 20ch multicolored    6.75 3.00
  *a.*   Sheet of 2, as #2003-2004   20.00 —
**Souvenir Sheet**
**2004** A1027 1w multicolored    8.00 3.00

**Electric Train Centenary A1028**

Designs: 20ch, First E-type electric and steam locomotives.
1w, Electric locomotive exhibited in Berlin, 1879.

**1980, Dec. 24**     *Perf. 13¼*
**2005** A1028 20ch multicolored    6.75 2.50
  *a.*   Sheet of 2, as #2005-2006   22.00 —
**Souvenir Sheet**
**2006** A1028 1w multicolored    13.00 2.75

**Dag Hammarskjold (1905-61), 75th Anniv. of Birth — A1029**

Designs: 20ch, Hammarskjold and UN Building.
1w, Hammarskjold (diff.).

**1980, Dec. 26**     *Perf. 11¾*
**2007** A1029 20ch multicolored    4.00 2.75
  *a.*   Sheet of 2 as #2007-2008   10.00
**Souvenir Sheet**
**2008** A1029 1w multicolored    5.00 2.75

World Chess
Championship,
Merano — A1030

Designs: 20ch, Bobby Fischer-Boris
Spassky chess match.
1w, Viktor Korchnoi-Anatoly Karpov chess
match.

**1980, Dec. 28**        **Perf. 13¼**
2009 A1030 20ch multicolored      7.50 2.25
   *a.*    Sheet of 2, as #2009-2010   18.00 —
**Souvenir Sheet**
2010 A1030 1w multicolored     10.00 2.25

Robert Stolz
(1880-1975),
Composer, Birth
Cent. — A1031

Designs: 20ch, Stoltz with music from *At the
Flower Bed.*
1w, Stoltz working with stamp collection.

**1980, Dec. 30**
2011 A1031 20ch multicolored    4.00 1.25
   *a.*    Sheet of 2, as #2011-2012   12.00 —
**Souvenir Sheet**
2012 A1031 1w multicolored     6.00 1.40

New Year — A1032

**1981, Jan. 1**        **Perf. 12**
2013 A1032 10ch multicolored      1.00 .25

Fairy
Tales — A1033

Designs (all 10ch): No. 2014 Russian fairy
tale. No. 2015 Icelandic. No. 2016, Swedish.
No. 2017, Irish. No. 2018, Italian. No. 2019,
Japanese. No. 2020, German.
70ch (No. 2021): Korean fairy tale, *A Gold
Nugget and Maize Cake.*

**1981, Jan. 30**       **Perf. 13¼**
2014-2020 A1033 Set of 7     12.00 4.00
  *2020a*   Sheet of 8, as #2014-2021   18.00 —
**Souvenir Sheet**
2021 A1033 70ch multicolored    5.75 3.00
    International Year of the Child, 1979.

Changgwang
Street,
Pyongyang
A1034

**1981, Feb. 16**      **Perf. 11¾x12**
2022 A1034 10ch multicolored      .75 .25

World Soccer Cup
Championship
ESPAÑA
'82 — A1035

Designs: 10ch, Tackling. 20ch, Kicking.
30ch, Feinting.
70ch, Three players.

**1981, Feb. 20**       **Perf. 13¼**
2023-2025 A1035 Set of 3    10.00 3.00
  *2025a*   Sheet of 4, as #2023-2026   17.00 —
**Souvenir Sheet**
2026 A1035 70ch multicolored    9.00 3.50
    For overprints, see Nos. 2216.

World Soccer Cup Championship
ESPAÑA '82 (2nd issue) — A1036

Designs: 10ch, Emblem, map and cup.
15ch, Dribbling. 20ch, Heading ball. 25ch,
Tackling. 30ch, Pass.
70ch, Sliding tackle.

**1981, Feb. 28**
2027-2031 A1036 Set of 5    10.00 4.00
  *2031a*   Sheet of 6, as #2027-2032   18.00 —
**Souvenir Sheet**
2032 A1036 70ch multicolored    9.00 3.00

Implementations of
Decisions of 6th
Korean Workers' Party
Congress — A1037

Designs: 2ch, Marchers with book, banners.
10ch (No. 2034), Worker with book. 10ch (No.
2035), Workers and factory. 10ch (No. 2036),
Electricity generation (horiz.). 10ch (No.
2037), Factory, construction scene (horiz.).
10ch (No. 2038), Cement factory, fertilizer
(horiz.). 30ch, Fishing, fabrics (horiz.). 40ch,
Grain, port facilities (horiz.). 1w, Clasped
hands, map of Korea. 1w, Hand holding torch,
"peace" and "solidarity" slogans.

**1981, Mar. 15**       **Perf. 12¼**
2033-2042 A1037 Set of 10    6.00 2.50
 *2033a*    2ch Unsurfaced white pa-
             per, without gum    10.00 —
 *2034a*    10ch Unsurfaced white pa-
             per, without gum    10.00 —
 *2035a*    10ch Unsurfaced white pa-
             per, without gum    10.00 —
 *2039a*    30ch Unsurfaced white pa-
             per, without gum    10.00 —
 *2040a*    40ch Unsurfaced white pa-
             per, without gum    10.00 —
 *2041a*    70ch Unsurfaced white pa-
             per, without gum    10.00 —
 *2042a*    1w Unsurfaced white pa-
             per, without gum    10.00 —

**Nos. 1925-1932 Overprinted
For Nobel Prize Winners in
Medicine**

**1981, Mar. 20**      **Perf. 11¾x11½**
2043-2049 A1005 Set of 7     9.00 3.00
  *2049a*   Sheet of 8, as #2043-2050   12.00 —
**Souvenir Sheet**
2050 A1005 50ch multicolored    9.00

**Nos. 1698-1710 Overprinted History
of the World Cup**

**1981, Mar. 20**       **Perf. 13¼**
2051-2062 A953 Set of 12    24.00 —
  *2062a*   Sheet of 12, #2051-2062   25.00 —
**Souvenir Sheet**
2063 A953 50ch multicolored    12.00 —

Copa de Oro Mini-World Cup
Championships — A1038

Designs: 20ch, Uruguayan and Brazilian
soccer players.
1w, Goalkeeper blocking ball.

**1981, Mar. 27**
2064 A1038 20ch multicolored    4.00 1.25
**Souvenir Sheet**
2065 A1038 1w multicolored    8.00 1.00

España
'82
A1039

Nos. 2066-2068 depict different designs
incorporating bleachers and crowds, with
images of soccer players and trophy that
appear or disappear, depending upon the
angle from which the stamps are viewed. This
effect is created by printing on multiple layers
of thin plastic, with gummed paper backing.

**1981, Apr. 10**        **Imperf.**
2066-2067 A1039 Set of 2,
    20ch, 30ch 25.00   9.00
**Souvenir Sheet**
2068 A1039   1w multicolored 25.00 25.00
    Nos. 2066-2068 are airmail.

Naposta '81
Int'l Stamp
Exhibition,
Stuttgart
A1040

Designs: 10ch, Dornier Do-X flying boat.
20ch, Count von Zeppelin and airship LZ-120.
30ch, Goetz von Berlichingen (1480-1562),
German knight and subject of poem by
Johann von Goethe (1749-1832), also
pictured.
70ch, Mercedes-Benz W 196, 1954
automobile.

**1981, Apr. 28**       **Perf. 12x11¾**
2069-2071 A1040 Set of 3     9.00 1.75
**Souvenir Sheet**
**Perf. 11½x11¾**
2072 A1040 70ch multicolored    6.00 3.00

World
Telecommunications
Day — A1041

**1981, May 17**      **Perf. 11¾x11½**
2073 A1041 10ch multicolored    2.75 .25

Flowers
A1042

Designs: 10ch, Iris pseudodacorus. 20ch,
Iris pallasii. 30ch, Gladiolus gandavensis.

**1981, May 20**       **Perf. 12x11¾**
2074-2076 A1042 Set of 3     3.50 1.60
  *2076a*   Sheet of 3, #2074-2076   4.00 —

WIPA 1981
Stamp
Exhibition,
Vienna
A1043

Designs: 20ch, Austrian WIPA 1981 and
Rudolf Kirchschlager stamps. 30ch, Austrian
Maria Theresa and Franz Josef stamps.
50ch, Kim Il Sung and Korean Children's
Union choir, vert.

**1981, May 22**       **Perf. 13¼**
2077-2078 A1043 Set of 2    6.00 1.60
**Souvenir Sheet**
**Perf. 11½**
2079 A1043 50ch multicolored    6.00 2.75

International
Gymnastc
Federation,
Centen. — A1044

Gymnastic events: 10ch, Rings. 15ch, Pommel horse. 20ch, Long horse. 25ch, Floor.
30ch, Hoop.
70ch, Ribbon, horiz.

**1981, May 25**      **Perf. 11¾x12**
2080-2084 A1044 Set of 5    4.00 1.40
  *2084a*   Sheet of 6, as #2080-2085   15.00 —
**Souvenir Sheet**
**Perf. 11½x11¾**
2085 A1044 70ch multicolored    3.00 1.00
    For overprints, see Nos. 2270-2275.

Mingyuehgou Meeting,
50th Anniv. — A1045

**1981, June 15**      **Perf. 12¼x12**
2086 A1045 10ch multicolored     .50 .25

Taen Work
System, 20th
Anniv. — A1046

**1981, June 25**      **Perf. 12x12¼**
2087 A1046 10ch multicolored     .50 .25

New System of
Agricultural
Guidance, 20th
Anniv. — A1047

**1981, June 25**
2088 A1047 10ch multicolored     .50 .25

Anti-Japanese
Women's Assoc., 55th
Anniv. — A1048

**1981, July 5**       **Perf. 12¼**
2089 A1048   5w multicolored    12.00 1.00

Opera *Sea of Blood*, 10th Anniv. — A1049

**1981, July 17**          *Perf. 12*
2090  A1049  10w multicolored    30.00 10.00

Joan of Arc, 550th Anniv. Death — A1050

Designs: 10ch (No. 2091), Joan of Arc. 10ch (No. 2092a), Archangel Michael. 70ch, Joan of Arc in armor.
No. 2094, as No. 2092b.

**1981, July 20**
2091  A1050  multicolored       3.50  .75
2092  Sheet of 2, #2092a-2092b  9.00  —
  a.  10ch multicolored         —    —
  b.  70ch multicolored         —    —
**Souvenir Sheet**
**Perf. 11½**
2094  A1050  70ch multicolored  7.00 1.90

Down-with-Imperialism Union, 55th Anniv. — A1051

**1981, July 25**          *Perf. 12¼*
2095  A1051  1w multicolored    6.00 2.00

Rembrandt, 375th Birth Anniv. — A1052

Designs: 10ch, *Young Girl by the Window.* 20ch, *Rembrandt's Mother.* 30ch, *Saskia van Uylenburgh.* 40ch, *Pallas Athenae.* 70ch, *Self-portrait.*

**1981, July 25**          *Perf. 13¼*
2096-2099  A1052  Set of 4      7.50 3.00
**Souvenir Sheet**
2100  A1052  70ch multicolored  6.00 3.25

Symposium of the Non-Aligned Countries on Increasing Agricultural Production — A1053

Designs: 10ch, Emblem, banners over Pyongyang. 50ch, Harvesting grain. 90ch, Marchers with banners, tractors, fields, factories.

**1981, Aug. 26**          *Perf. 12*
2101-2103  A1053  Set of 3      2.25 1.10

Royal Wedding — A1054

Designs: 10ch, St. Paul's Cathedral. 20ch, Prince Charles on Great Britain #599. 30ch, Princess Diana. 40ch, Prince Charles in military uniform.
70ch, Prince Charles and Princess Diana.

**1981, Sept. 18**         *Perf. 13¼*
2104-2107  A1054  Set of 4     11.00 3.25
**Souvenir Sheet**
2108  A1054  70ch multicolored 16.50 5.50
For overprints, see Nos. 2205-2209.

Reubens Paintings — A1055

Designs: 10ch, *The Four Philosophers.* 15ch, *Portrait of Helena Fourment.* 20ch, *Portrait of Isabella Brandt.* 25ch, *The Education of Maria de Medici.* 30ch, *Helena Fourment and Her Child.* 40ch, *Helena Fourment in Her Wedding Dress.*
70ch, *Portrait of Nikolaas Rubens.*

**1981, Sept. 20**         *Perf. 11¾x12*
2109-2114  A1055  Set of 6    10.00 3.00
**Souvenir Sheet**
**Perf 11½**
2115  A1055  70ch multicolored 6.00 3.00

Royal Wedding — A1056

Designs: a, 10ch, Prince Charles and Princess Diana wedding portrait. b, 20ch, Charles and Diana with Flower Girl. c, 30ch, Charles and Diana leaving St. Paul's Cathedral. d, 40ch, Wedding portrait (diff.)
70ch, Charles and Diana with Queen Elizabeth on balcony.

**1981, Sept. 29**         *Perf. 13¼*
2116  A1056  Sheet of 4, #a.-d. 17.50 4.50
**Souvenir Sheet**
2120  A1056  70ch multicolored 25.00 6.00
No. 2120 exist imperf.

Philatokyo '81 International Stamp Exhibition, Tokyo — A1057

Design: 10ch, Rowland Hill and first stamps of Great Britain, Japan and DPRK. 20ch, DPRK World Fairy Tale stamps. 30ch, Three Japanese stamps.
70ch, Exhibition Hall.

**1981, Oct. 9**           *Perf. 11¾x11x½*
2121-2123  A1057  Set of 3     9.00 2.50
2123a  Sheet of 4, as #2121-2124, perf 12x11½  27.50 —
**Souvenir Sheet**
2124  A1057  70ch multicolored 7.50 2.10

Philatokyo '81 — A1058

Designs (both 10ch): No. 2125, Two DPRK stamps. No. 2126, DPRK stamp featuring Juche torch.

**1981, Oct. 9**           *Perf. 12x12¼*
2125-2126  A1058  Set of 2     4.00 1.40

League of Socialist Working Youth of Korea, 7th Congress — A1059

**1981, Oct. 20**          *Perf. 12x11¾*
2127  A1059  10ch multicolored  .25  .25
2128  A1059  80ch multicolored 1.00  .35

Bulgarian State, 1300th Anniv. — A1060

**1981, Oct. 20**          *Perf. 12x12¼*
2129  A1060  10ch multicolored  .50  .25

Georgi Dimitrov (1882-1949), Birth Centenary — A1061

**1981, Nov. 5**           *Perf. 12*
2130  A1061  10ch multicolored  .50  .25

Philatelia '81 Int'l Stamp Fair, Frankfurt-am-Main — A1062

**1981, Nov. 14**          *Perf. 13¼*
2131  A1062  20ch multicolored 3.00  .45

A1063          Philexfrance '82 International Stamp Exhibition, Paris — A1064

Designs: 10ch, Count Ferdinand von Zeppelin, *Graf Zeppelin*, Concorde. 20ch, Aircraft — Santos-Dumont 1905, Brequet 1930, Brequet Provence 1950, Concorde 1970. 30ch, Mona Lisa, six French stamps.

No. 2135: 10ch, Hotel des Invalides, Paris. 20ch, Pres. Mitterand of France. 30ch, International Friendship Building. 70ch, Kim Il Sung.
No. 2136: 60ch, Two French stamps picturing Rembrandt portrait and Picasso painting.

**1981, Dec. 1**           *Perf. 13¼*
2132-2134  A1063  Set of 3    10.00 2.50
2135  Sheet of 4, #a.-d.       7.50 2.50
  a.  A1064 10ch multicolored  1.25  .50
  b.  A1064 20ch multicolored  1.25  .50
  c.  A1064 30ch multicolored  1.25  .50
  d.  A1064 70ch multicolored  1.25  .50
**Souvenir Sheet**
2136  A1063  60ch multicolored 7.50 2.25

New Year — A1065

**1982, Jan. 1**           *Perf. 12*
2137  A1065  10ch multicolored  .90  .25

"Korea Prospering Under the Wise Leadership of the Party" — A1066

Party emblem and: 2ch, banners. 10ch (No. 2139), Iron industry. 10ch (No. 2140), Produce, city, countryside. 10ch (No. 2141), Film industry. 10ch (No. 2142), Mining. 10ch (No. 2143), Lighthouse, helicopter. 40ch, Idealized cityscape.

**1982, Feb. 1**
2138-2144  A1066  Set of 7     7.00 1.50

A1067

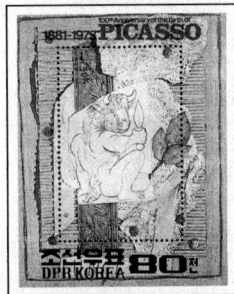

Pablo Picasso (1881-1973), Painter, Birth Centenary — A1068

Designs (Nos. 2145-2148): 10ch, *La Coiffure.* 20ch, *Woman Leaning on Arm.* 25ch, *Child with Pigeon.* 35ch, *Portrait of Gertrude Stein.*
No. 2149: 10ch, *Paulo on a Donkey.* 20ch, *Harlequin.* 25ch, *Reading a Letter.* 35ch, *Harlequin* (diff.) 80ch, *Minotaur.* 90ch, *Mother and Child.*
Nos. 2150-2151: 80ch, *Minotaur.* 90ch, *Mother and Child.*

**1982, Mar. 30**          *Perf. 11¾*
2145-2148  A1067  Set of 4    6.50 1.50
2149  Sheet of 6, #a.-f.      14.00 2.75
  a.  A1067 10ch multicolored  2.25  .45
  b.  A1067 20ch multicolored  2.25  .45
  c.  A1067 25ch multicolored  2.25  .45
  d.  A1067 35ch multicolored  2.25  .45
  e.  A1067 80ch multicolored  2.25  .45

*f.*  A1067  90ch multicolored      2.25    .45

**Souvenir Sheets**

2150-2151  A1068  Set of 2          8.00  4.00

A1069

A1070

Kim Il Sung, 70th Birthday A1071

Type A1069 (both 10ch): No. 2152, Kim Il Sung's Birthplace. No. 2153, Fireworks over Pyongyang.

Type A1070 (10ch), paintings of Kim Il Sung: No. 2154, "The Day Will Dawn." No. 2155, Signaling the start of the Pochonbo battle. No. 2156, Groundbreaking of Potong River Project. No. 2157, Embracing bereaved children. No. 2158, Directing operations at front. No. 2159, "On the Road of Advance." No. 2160, Speaking with workers at Kangson Steel Plant. No. 2161, Talking with peasants. No. 2162, Choosing site for reservoir.

Type A1070 (20ch): No. 2163, Visiting Komdok Valley. No. 2164, With Red Flag Company. No. 2165, With farmers. No. 2166, Opening metallurgical plant. No. 2167, Talking with smelters. No. 2168, At chemical plant. No. 2169, With fishermen.

No. 2170, Kim surrounded by adoring Koreans. No. 2171, Kim as a boy.

**Perf. 11¾x12 (#2151-2152), 12x11¾**
**1982, Apr. 15**
2152-2169      Set of 18           8.00  2.25
**Souvenir Sheets**
**Perf. 13¼**
2170-2171  A1071  60ch Set of 2    5.00  1.75

All type A1070 stamps were issued with setenant labels bearing inscriptions relating to theme of stamp. Values are for stamps with labels attached.

Korean People's Army, 50th Anniv. — A1072

**1982, Apr. 25**                  **Perf. 12**
2172  A1072  10ch multicolored     .50    .25

ESSEN '82 Int'l Stamp Fair — A1073

**1982, Apr. 28**                  **Perf. 11¾x12**
2173  A1073  30ch multicolored     5.00  .50

Four Nature-Remaking Tasks — A1074

**1982, Apr. 30**                  **Perf. 12**
2174  A1074  10ch multicolored     .60    .25

Issued to publicize the program for nature transformation contained in the Second Seven-Year Plan, which included irrigation, land reclamation, terracing, afforestation and water conservation, and reclamation of tidal lands.

Princess Diana, 21st Birthday — A1075

Princess Diana (Nos. 2175-2177): 10ch, As a baby. 20ch, As little girl on swing. 30ch, As little girl wearing red parka.

No. 2178: 50ch, As girl, wearing blue turtleneck sweater. 60ch, With long hair, wearing gray hat. 70ch, Wearing white hat. 80ch, Wearing white blouse and sweater.

Nos. 2179-2180: 40ch, Diana pushing her brother on swing. 80ch, As No. 2178d.

**1982, May 1**                    **Perf. 13¼**
2175-2177  A1075  Set of 3         4.00  1.00
2178      Sheet of 4, #a.-d.      18.00  5.50
  *a.*  A1075  50ch multicolored   3.50  1.25
  *b.*  A1075  60ch multicolored   3.50  1.25
  *c.*  A1075  70ch multicolored   3.50  1.25
  *d.*  A1075  80ch multicolored   3.50  1.25
**Souvenir Sheets**
2179-2180  A1075  Set of 2        10.00  5.00

For overprints, see Nos. 2210-2215.

Tower of the Juche Idea — A1076

**1982, May 21**                   **Perf. 12**
2182  A1076  2w multicolored       7.50  2.00

Arch of Triumph — A1077

**1982, May 22**
2183  A1077  3w multicolored       8.50  2.00

Tigers — A1078

Nos. 2184-2185: 20ch, Tiger cubs. 30ch, Tiger cubs (diff.)

No. 2186 (designs horizontal): 30ch, Tiger cub with mother. 40ch, Two cubs playing. 80ch, Two cubs playing, diff.

Nos. 2187: 80ch, Two cubs, horiz.

**Perf. 11¾x12 (#2185-2186), 12x11¾**
**1982, May 30**
2184-2185  A1078  Set of 2         7.00  1.00
2186      Sheet of 3, #a.-c.      16.00  3.00
  *a.*  A1078  30ch multicolored   3.00   .50
  *b.*  A1078  40ch multicolored   3.00   .50
  *c.*  A1078  80ch multicolored   3.00   .50
**Souvenir Sheet**
2187  A1078  80ch Multicolored     6.00  1.50

ESPANA '82 World Cup Championship — A1079

Flags and players of: 10ch, Group 1 countries — Italy, Peru, Poland, Cameroon. 20ch, Group 2 countries — Germany, Chile, Algeria, Austria. 30ch, Group 3 countries — Argentina, Hungary, Belgium, El Salvador. 40ch, Group 4 countries — Great Britain, Czechoslovakia, France, Kuwait. 50ch, Group 5 countries — Spain, Yugoslavia, Honduras, Northern Ireland. 60ch, Group 6 countries — Brazil, Scotland, USSR, New Zealand.

1w, Soccer players, flags, trophy and ESPANA '82 emblem.

**1982, June 12**                  **Perf. 13¼**
2188-2193  A1079  Set of 6        13.00  4.00
**Souvenir Sheet**
2194  A1079  1w multicolored      11.00  4.00

For overprints, see Nos. 2217-2223.

Space Exploration — A1080

Designs: 10ch, Rocket launch. 20ch, Spaceship over planet.

No. 2197a, Spaceship between planets.

No. 2198, Spaceship exploring desert area of other planet.

**1982, June 20**                  **Perf. 11¾x11½**
2195-2196  A1080  Set of 2         4.00  1.75
2197      Sheet of 3, #2195-2196,
          2197a + label            6.50  2.75
  *a.*  A1080  80ch multicolored   2.25   .75
**Souvenir Sheet**
2198  A1080  80ch multicolored     4.00  1.60

Johann von Goethe (1749-1832), Writer, 150th Death Anniv. — A1081

Silhouettes: 10ch, Charlotte von Stein, 20ch, Goethe's sister. 25ch, Charlotte Buff. 35ch, Lili Schönemann.

No. 2203: 10ch, Goethe's mother. 20ch, Angelika Kauffman. 25ch, Anna Amalia. 35ch, Charlotte von Lengefeld. 80ch, Goethe.

No. 2204: 80ch, Goethe.

**1982, July 25**                  **Perf. 11¾x12**
2199-2202  A1081  Set of 4         4.00  1.60
2203      Sheet of 5, #a.-e. + label  9.00  2.00
  *a.*  A1081  10ch multicolored   1.75   .50
  *b.*  A1081  20ch multicolored   1.75   .50
  *c.*  A1081  25ch multicolored   1.75   .50
  *d.*  A1081  35ch multicolored   1.75   .50
  *e.*  A1081  80ch multicolored   1.75   .50
**Souvenir Sheet**
2204  A1081  80ch multicolored     4.00  1.75

Nos. 2104-2108 Overprinted in Blue

**1982, Aug. 20**
2205-2208  A1054  Set of 4        15.00   —
**Souvenir Sheet**
2209  A1054  70ch multicolored    15.00   —

Nos. 2175-2180 Overprinted in Blue

**1982, Aug. 20**
2210-2212  A1075  Set of 3        15.00   —
2213      Sheet of 4, #a-d        30.00   —
**Souvenir Sheets**
2214-2215  A1075  Set of 2        25.00   —

**Nos. 2025a, 2188-2194 Overprinted in Blue**

**1982, Aug. 25**
2216  A1035  Sheet of 4, #a.-d.   14.00   —
  *a.*       10ch multicolored     1.00   —
  *b.*       20ch multicolored     2.00   —
  *c.*       30ch multicolored     3.00   —
  *d.*       70ch multicolored     6.00   —
2217-2222  A1079  Set of 6        15.00   —
**Souvenir Sheet**
2223  A1079  1w multicolored      12.50   —

ESPANA '82 World Soccer Cup Winners — A1082

Designs: 20ch, Player holding World Cup aloft. 30ch, Three players with World Cup.

No. 2226: 30ch, as No. 2222. 40ch, As No. 2223. 80ch, King Juan Carlos of Spain and two players with World Cup.

No. 2227: 80ch, as No. 2226c.

**1982, Aug. 30**                  **Perf. 13¼**
2224-2225  A1082  Set of 2         4.00  1.00
2226      Sheet of 3, #a.-c. + label  10.00   —
  *a.*  A1082  30ch multicolored    —     —
  *b.*  A1082  40ch multicolored    —     —
  *c.*  A1082  80ch multicolored    —     —
**Souvenir Sheet**
2227  A1082  80ch multicolored     9.00  2.00

A1083

1st
Wedding
Anniv. of
Prince
and
Princess
of Wales
A1084

**1982, Sept. 21**
2228 A1083 30ch multicolored 10.00 4.00

**Souvenir Sheet**
2229 A1084 80ch multicolored 15.00 5.00

No. 2228 was issued in sheets of four stamps and two labels.

Birth of Prince
William of
Wales — A1085

Designs: 10ch, Charles and Diana with Prince William (Charles in suit, Diana in pink hat and dress). 20ch, Couple with William. 30ch, Couple with William (diff.). 40ch, Diana with William. 50ch, Diana with William (diff.).
No. 2235: 10ch, Diana holding bouquet. 20ch, Charles carrying William, with Diana. 30ch, Charles carrying William, with Diana (diff.). 80ch, Couple with William (diff.).
No. 2236 (horiz.): 40ch, Charles and Diana. 50ch, Charles and Diana in evening dress. 80ch, Charles holding William, with Diana.
Nos. 2237-2238 (both 80ch): Diana holding William, with Royal Family; Diana holding William, with godparents.

**1982, Sept. 29**
| | | | | |
|---|---|---|---|---|
| 2230-2234 | A1085 | Set of 5 | 16.00 | 5.00 |
| 2235 | | Sheet of 4, #a.-d. | 16.00 | 6.25 |
| a. | | A1085 10ch multicolored | 3.25 | 1.25 |
| b. | | A1085 20ch multicolored | 3.25 | 1.25 |
| c. | | A1085 30ch multicolored | 3.25 | 1.25 |
| d. | | A1085 80ch multicolored | 3.25 | 1.25 |
| 2236 | | Sheet of 3, #a.-c. | 16.00 | 6.25 |
| a. | | A1085 40ch multicolored | 4.25 | 1.75 |
| b. | | A1085 50ch multicolored | 4.25 | 1.75 |
| c. | | A1085 80ch multicolored | 4.25 | 1.75 |

**Souvenir Sheets**
2237-2238 A1085 Set of 2 24.00 10.00

A1086

Birth of Prince William of
Wales — A1087

Nos. 2239-2244 are composed of layered plastic, on gummed paper, which creates two different images on each stamp, depending on the angle at which it is viewed.
30ch: No. 2239, Charles, Diana and William/Diana holding William. No. 2240, Charles, Diana and William (diff.)/Couple with William (Charles in suit, Diana in pink hat and dress).

No. 2241, Diana and William/Charles and Diana with William (Charles in suit, Diana in blue dress).
80ch: No. 2242, Diana and William, Portrait of Diana/Charles. No. 2243, Diana and William, St. Paul's Church/Wedding portrait of Royal Couple. No. 2244, Charles and Diana with William/Diana holding bouquet.

**1982, Oct. 1** *Imperf.*
2239-2241 A1086 Set of 3 35.00 —

**Souvenir Sheets**
2242-2244 A1087 Set of 3 60.00 —

Nos. 2242-2244 have simulated rouletting.

Bicentenary
of Manned
Flight
A1088

Designs: 10ch, Baldwin's airship *Nulli Secundus II*, 1908. 20ch, Tissandier Brothers' airship, 1883. 30ch, Parseval *PL VIII*, 1912. 40ch, Count Lennox's balloon *Eagle*, 1834.
No. 2249: 10ch, Pauley and Durs Egg's airship, *The Dolphin*, 1818. 20ch, Guyton de Morveau's balloon, 1784. 30ch, Sir George Cayley's airship, 1837. 40ch, Camille Vert's balloon *Poisson Volant*, 1859. 80ch, Dupuy de Lôme's airship, 1872.
No. 2250: Masse's oar-powered balloon, 1784, vert.

**1982, Nov. 21** *Perf. 13¼*
| | | | | |
|---|---|---|---|---|
| 2245-2248 | A1088 | Set of 4 | 7.00 | 2.00 |
| 2249 | | Sheet of 5, #a.-e. + label | 13.00 | 6.00 |
| a. | | A1088 10ch multicolored | 2.25 | 1.00 |
| b. | | A1088 20ch multicolored | 2.25 | 1.00 |
| c. | | A1088 30ch multicolored | 2.25 | 1.00 |
| d. | | A1088 40ch multicolored | 2.25 | 1.00 |
| e. | | A1088 80ch multicolored | 2.25 | 1.00 |

**Souvenir Sheet**
2250 A1088 80ch multicolored 4.50 2.00

Bicentenary of
Manned
Flight — A1089

Designs: 10ch, Balthasar Antoine Dunker's *Utopic Balloon Post*, 1784-90. 20ch, "and they fly into heaven and have no wings." 30ch, Pierre Testu-Brissy's balloon flight with horse, 1796. 40ch, Test flight of Gaston Tissandier's balloon *Zenith*, 1875.
No. 2255: 10ch, Montgolfier balloon at Versailles, 1783. 20ch, Montgolfier Brothers' balloon, 1783. 30ch, Charles' hydrogen balloon landing at Nesle. 40ch, Blanchard and Jeffries' flight over the English Channel, 1785. 80ch, Henri Giffard's balloon *Le Grand Ballon Captif* at World's Fair, 1878.
No. 2256: "Ballons Monte" balloon mail service from besieged Paris, 1870-1871.

**1982, Dec. 10**
| | | | | |
|---|---|---|---|---|
| 2251-2254 | A1089 | Set of 4 | 12.00 | 4.00 |
| 2255 | | Sheet of 5, #a.-e. + label | 25.00 | 6.50 |
| a. | | A1089 10ch multicolored | 4.50 | 1.25 |
| b. | | A1089 20ch multicolored | 4.50 | 1.25 |
| c. | | A1089 30ch multicolored | 4.50 | 1.25 |
| d. | | A1089 40ch multicolored | 4.50 | 1.25 |
| e. | | A1089 80ch multicolored | 4.50 | 1.25 |

**Souvenir Sheet**
2256 A1089 80ch multicolored 5.00 2.00

Tale of the
Hare
A1090

Designs: 10ch, Turtle searching for hare. 20ch, Turtle and hare going to Dragon King Palace. 30ch, Hare swindling Dragon King, demanding her liver. 40ch, Hare cheating turtle.

**1982, Dec. 25** *Perf. 12*
2257-2260 A1090 Set of 4 8.00 1.25

Socialist Constitution,
10th Anniv. — A1091

**1982, Dec. 27**
2261 A1091 10ch multicolored .50 .25

New Year — A1092

**1983, Jan. 1** *Perf. 12¼x12*
2262 A1092 10ch multicolored .50 .25

*Saenal*
Newspaper,
55th Anniv.
A1093

**1983, Jan. 15** *Perf. 11½x11¾*
2263 A1093 10ch multicolored .90 .25

Rembrandt
Paintings — A1094

Designs: 10ch, *Man in Oriental Costume*. 20ch, *The Noble Slav*. 30ch, *Dr. Tulp's Anatomy Lesson* (detail). 40ch, *Two Scholars Disputing*.
No. 2268: 10ch, *Child with Dead Peacocks*. 20ch, *Old Man in Fur Hat*. 30ch, *Portrait of a Fashionable Couple*. 40ch, *Woman with Child*. 80ch, *Woman Holding an Ostrich Feather Fan*.
No. 2269: 80ch, *Self-Portrait*.

**1983, Jan. 25** *Perf. 11¾x11½*
| | | | | |
|---|---|---|---|---|
| 2264-2267 | A1094 | Set of 4 | 8.00 | 1.50 |
| 2268 | | Sheet of 5, #a.-e. + label | 15.00 | 7.50 |
| a. | | A1094 10ch multicolored | 2.00 | 1.00 |
| b. | | A1094 20ch multicolored | 2.00 | 1.00 |
| c. | | A1094 30ch multicolored | 2.00 | 1.00 |
| d. | | A1094 40ch multicolored | 2.00 | 1.00 |
| e. | | A1094 80ch multicolored | 2.00 | 1.00 |

**Souvenir Sheet**
*Perf. 11¾x12*
2269 A1094 80ch multicolored 4.00 1.25

**Nos. 2080-2085 Overprinted "XXIII
Summer Olympic Games 1984" and
Olympic Rings**

**1983, Feb. 10**
2270-2274 A1044 Set of 5 *20.00* —
2274a Sheet of 6, as #2270-2275 75.00 —

**Souvenir Sheet**
2275 A1044 70ch multicolored *25.00* —

Luposta Int'l Air Mail Exhib., Köln
A1095

*Virgin
and
Child*, by
Stephan
Lochner
A1096

**1983, Jan. 25** *Perf. 11¾x11½*
| | | | | |
|---|---|---|---|---|
| 2276 | | 30ch multicolored | 3.00 | 1.00 |
| 2277 | | 40ch multicolored | 3.00 | 1.00 |
| a. | | A1095 Pair, #2276-2277 | 7.00 | 3.00 |

**Souvenir Sheet**
*Perf. 13¼*
2278 A1096 80ch multicolored 3.50 1.75

Wangjaesen
Meeting, 50th
Anniv. — A1097

**1983, Mar. 11** *Perf. 11½x11¾*
2279 A1097 10ch multicolored .50 .25

Karl Marx, Centenary
of Death — A1098

**1983, Mar. 14** *Perf. 11¾x12*
2280 A1098 10ch multicolored 2.25 .25

Thousand-ri
Journey for
Learning, 60th
Anniv. — A1099

**1983, Mar. 16** *Perf. 12*
2281 A1099 10ch multicolored 1.00 .25

A1100

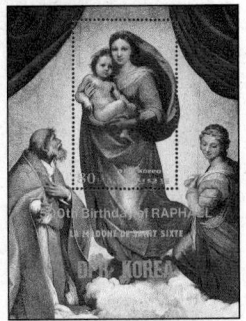

Raphael (1483-1520), 500th Birth
Anniv. — A1101

Designs: 10ch, *Madonna of the Goldfinch.*
30ch, *Madonna of the Grand Duke.* 50ch (No.
2284), *Madonna of the Chair.*
  No. 2285: 20ch, *The School of Athens*
(detail). 50ch (No. 2285b), *Madonna of the
Lamb.* 80ch, *The Beautiful Gardener.*
  No. 2286: 80ch, *Madonna of St. Sixte.*

| 1983, Mar. 20 | | **Perf. 13½** | |
|---|---|---|---|
| 2282-2284 | A1100 Set of 3 | 6.00 | 1.00 |
| 2285 | Sheet of 3, #a.-c. + label | 15.00 | 3.50 |
| *a.* | A1100 20ch multicolored | 4.00 | .75 |
| *b.* | A1100 50ch multicolored | 4.00 | .75 |
| *c.* | A1100 80ch multicolored | 4.00 | .75 |

**Souvenir Sheet**

| 2286 | A1101 80ch multicolored | 4.50 | 1.25 |
|---|---|---|---|

Pyongyang
Buildings
A1102

Designs: 2ch, Chongryu Restaurant. 10ch
(No. 2288), Munsu Street. 10ch (No. 2289),
Ice Rink. 40ch, Department Store No. 1. 70ch,
Grand People's Study House.

| 1983, Apr. 7 | | **Perf. 12¼** | |
|---|---|---|---|
| 2287-2291 | A1102 Set of 5 | 6.00 | .75 |
| 2287a | 2ch Unsurfaced white paper, without gum | 10.00 | — |
| 2288a | 10ch Unsurfaced white paper, without gum | 10.00 | — |
| 2289a | 10ch Unsurfaced white paper, without gum | 10.00 | — |
| 2290a | 40ch Unsurfaced white paper, without gum | 10.00 | — |
| 2291a | 40ch Unsurfaced white paper, without gum | 10.00 | — |

Int'l Institute of the
Juche Idea, 5th
Anniv. — A1103

| 1983, Apr. 9 | | **Perf. 12¼x12** | |
|---|---|---|---|
| 2292 | A1103 10ch multicolored | .50 | .25 |

Pre-Olympic Games, Los Angeles
'84 — A1104

Designs (values in gold): 20ch (No. 2293),
Judo. 30ch (No. 2294), Judo (diff.). 40ch (No.
2295), Boxing. 50ch (No. 2296), Weightlifting.
  No. 2297 (values in black): 20ch, Wrestling.
30ch, Judo (diff.). 40ch, Shooting. 50ch, Wrestling. (diff.) 80ch, Boxing (diff.)
  No. 2298: 80ch, Judo (diff.)

| 1983, Apr. 20 | | **Perf. 11¼** | |
|---|---|---|---|
| 2293-2296 | A1104 Set of 4 | 13.00 | 1.50 |
| 2297 | Sheet of 5, #a.-e. + label | 25.00 | 1.00 |
| *a.* | A1104 20ch multicolored | 4.00 | .25 |
| *b.* | A1104 30ch multicolored | 4.00 | .25 |
| *c.* | A1104 40ch multicolored | 4.00 | .25 |
| *d.* | A1104 50ch multicolored | 4.00 | .25 |
| *e.* | A1104 80ch multicolored | 4.00 | .25 |

**Souvenir Sheet**
**Perf. 13½**

| 2298 | A1104 80ch multicolored | 10.00 | 1.00 |
|---|---|---|---|

World
Communications
Year — A1105

| 1983, Apr. 30 | | **Perf. 11¾x12** | |
|---|---|---|---|
| 2299 | A1105 10ch multicolored | 2.00 | .25 |

TEMBAL '83 Int'l Topical Stamp
Exhib., Basel — A1106

Designs: 20ch, Emblem, giant panda and
stamp. 30ch, Emblem, DPRK flag and "Basel
Dove" stamp (Switzerland No. 3L1).

| 1983, May 21 | | **Perf. 12** | |
|---|---|---|---|
| 2300-2301 | A1106 Set of 2 | 7.50 | .75 |

Old Ships — A1107

Designs: 20ch, *Colourful Cow* (Hamburg,
1402). 35ch, *Great Harry* (England, 1555).
50ch, *Eagle of Lübeck* (Lübeck, 1567).
  No. 2305: 20ch, Turtle Boat (Korea, 1592).
35ch, Admiral Li Sun Sin (1545-98), inventor
of the Turtle Boat. 50ch, *Merkur* (Prussia,
1847). 80ch, *Duchess Elisabeth* (West
Germany).
  No. 2306: 80ch, *Christoforo Colombo* (Italy).

| 1983, May 30 | | **Perf. 11x11¼** | |
|---|---|---|---|
| 2302-2304 | A1107 Set of 3 | 5.00 | 1.50 |
| 2305 | Sheet of 4, #a.-d. + 2 labels | 12.00 | 2.50 |
| *a.* | A1107 20ch multicolored | 3.00 | .50 |
| *b.* | A1107 35ch multicolored | 3.00 | .50 |
| *c.* | A1107 50ch multicolored | 3.00 | .50 |
| *d.* | A1107 80ch multicolored | 3.00 | .50 |

**Souvenir Sheet**
**Perf. 13½x13¼**

| 2306 | A1107 80ch multicolored | 6.00 | 3.00 |
|---|---|---|---|

Steam Locomotives — A1108

Designs: 20ch, *Locomotion* (Great Britain,
1825). 35ch, *De Adler* (Germany, 1835). 50ch,
Austria (1837).
  No. 2310: 20ch, *Drache* (Germany, 1848.
35ch, Korean Train. 50ch, Bristal and Exeter
Railway locomotive (Great Britain, 1853).
80ch, Caledonian Railway locomotive (Great
Britain, 1859).
  No. 2311: 80ch, *Ilmarinen* (Finland, 1860).

| 1983, June 20 | | **Perf. 12x11¾** | |
|---|---|---|---|
| 2307-2309 | A1108 Set of 3 | 13.00 | 2.50 |
| 2310 | Sheet of 4, #a.-d. + 2 labels | 40.00 | 3.50 |
| *a.* | A1108 20ch multicolored | 3.00 | .75 |
| *b.* | A1108 35ch multicolored | 3.00 | .75 |
| *c.* | A1108 50ch multicolored | 3.00 | .75 |
| *d.* | A1108 80ch multicolored | 3.00 | .75 |

**Souvenir Sheet**
**Perf. 12**

| 2311 | A1108 80ch multicolored | 30.00 | 1.50 |
|---|---|---|---|

Publication of the Five-
Point Policy for Korean
Reunification, 10th
Anniv. — A1109

| 1983, June 23 | | **Perf. 12¼** | |
|---|---|---|---|
| 2312 | A1109 10ch multicolored | 1.40 | .25 |

World Conference of Journalists
Against Imperialism and for Friendship
and Peace — A1110

Designs: 10ch, Emblem, Tower of Juche
Idea, fireworks, "Welcome." 40ch, Emblem,
clasped hands, rainbow, "Friendship."
Emblem, map, hand with raised forefinger,
"Korea Is One."

| 1983, July 2 | | **Perf. 12x11¾** | |
|---|---|---|---|
| 2313-2315 | A1110 Set of 3 | 1.75 | .30 |

"Let's Create
the Speed of
the
80s" — A1111

| 1983, July 10 | | **Perf. 12x12¼** | |
|---|---|---|---|
| 2316 | A1111 10ch multicolored | .50 | .25 |

Korean War,
30th
Anniv. — A1112

| 1983, July 27 | | | |
|---|---|---|---|
| 2317 | A1112 10ch multicolored | .50 | .25 |

Bangkok 1983 Int'l Stamp
Exhib. — A1113

Designs: 40ch, *Gorch Foch* and DPRK
#1693. 80ch, Bangkok temple, Great Britain
#1 and DPRK IYC stamp.

| 1983, Aug. 4 | | **Perf. 12x11¾** | |
|---|---|---|---|
| 2318 | A1113 40ch multicolored | 3.50 | 1.00 |

**Souvenir Sheet**
**Perf. 11½x11¾**

| 2319 | A1113 80ch multicolored | 7.00 | 3.50 |
|---|---|---|---|

A1114

Winter
Olympic
Games,
Sarajevo
1984
A1115

Designs: 10ch, Skiier. 30ch, Figure skaters.
50ch, Ski jumper.
  No. 2323 (all vert.): 20ch, Woman figure
skater. 50ch, Hockey player. 80ch, Speed
skater.
  No. 2324, 80ch, Skier shooting rifle
(biathlon).

| 1983, Aug. 20 | | | |
|---|---|---|---|
| 2320-2322 | A1114 Set of 3 | 8.00 | 1.50 |
| 2323 | Sheet of 3, #a.-c., perf 11¾x12 | 17.00 | 2.75 |
| *a.* | A1114 20ch multicolored | 4.00 | .75 |
| *b.* | A1114 50ch multicolored | 4.00 | .75 |
| *c.* | A1114 80ch multicolored | 4.00 | .75 |

**Souvenir Sheet**

| 2324 | A1115 80ch multicolored | 7.50 | 1.25 |
|---|---|---|---|

Democratic
People's
Republic of
Korea, 35th
Anniv. — A1116

| 1983, Sept. 9 | | **Perf. 13¼x13½** | |
|---|---|---|---|
| 2325 | A1116 10ch multicolored | .65 | .25 |

Folk Games — A1117

Designs: 10ch (No. 2326), Archery. 40ch
(No. 2327), Seesaw. No. 2328: 10ch, Flying
kites. 40ch, Swinging.

| 1983, Sept. 20 | | **Perf. 11¾x12** | |
|---|---|---|---|
| 2326-2327 | A1117 Set of 2 | 5.00 | .50 |
| 2328 | Sheet of 2, #a.-b. | 2.50 | .40 |
| *a.* | A1117 10ch multicolored | .75 | .25 |
| *b.* | A1117 40ch multicolored | .75 | .25 |

Korean-Chinese
Friendship — A1118

| 1983, Oct. 25 | | **Perf. 12** | |
|---|---|---|---|
| 2329 | A1118 10ch multicolored | .75 | .25 |

A1119

World Communications Year — A1120

Designs: 30ch (No. 2330), *Redong Sinmun*
and magazine. 40ch (No. 2331), Letters and
forms of postal transport.
  No. 2332: 30ch, Communications satellite,
satellite dish. 40ch, TV camera and relay
tower. 80ch, Telephone and satellite dishes.
  No. 2333, 80ch, Emblem, communications
satellite.

| 1983, Oct. 30 | | **Perf. 13½** | |
|---|---|---|---|
| 2330-2331 | A1119 Set of 2 | 9.00 | 1.75 |
| 2332 | Sheet of 3, #a.-c. | 5.50 | 1.00 |
| *a.* | A1119 30ch multicolored | 1.00 | .25 |
| *b.* | A1119 40ch multicolored | 1.00 | .25 |
| *c.* | A1119 80ch multicolored | 1.00 | .25 |

**Souvenir Sheet**

| 2333 | A1120 80ch multicolored | 6.00 | 1.25 |
|---|---|---|---|

A1121

Paintings by Peter Paul
Rubens — A1122

No. 2334, *Portrait of Helene Fourmet.*
No. 2335 (both horiz.): a, Detail from *Portrait of a Young Lady.* b, *Diana Returning from Hunt.*
No. 2336: *The Bear Hunt.*

**1983, Nov. 10**
| | | | | |
|---|---|---|---|---|
| 2334 | A1121 | 40ch multicolored | 2.00 | .50 |
| 2335 | | Sheet of 2, #a.-b. | 4.50 | 1.25 |
| a. | | A1121 40ch multicolored | 1.75 | .45 |
| b. | | A1121 80ch multicolored | 1.75 | .45 |

**Souvenir Sheet**
| | | | | |
|---|---|---|---|---|
| 2336 | A1122 | 80ch multicolored | 3.25 | .75 |

Olympic
Games, Los
Angeles
1984 — A1123

Designs: 10ch, Sprinter. 30ch, Cyclists. 50ch, Volleyball.
No. 2340: 20ch, Show jumping. 50ch, Fencing. 80ch, Gymnastics.
No. 2341: 80ch, Judo.

**1983, Nov. 30**      *Perf. 11½*
| | | | | |
|---|---|---|---|---|
| 2337-2339 | A1123 | Set of 3 | 10.50 | 1.25 |
| 2340 | | Sheet of 3, #a.-c. | 30.00 | 2.00 |
| a. | | A1123 20ch multicolored | 7.00 | .50 |
| b. | | A1123 50ch multicolored | 7.00 | .50 |
| c. | | A1123 80ch multicolored | 7.00 | .50 |

**Souvenir Sheet**
| | | | | |
|---|---|---|---|---|
| 2341 | A1123 | 80ch multicolored | 3.50 | 1.00 |

Six deluxe souvenir sheets of one, each denominated 1w, exist. Value, set of 6 sheets, $100.

A1124

Antonio Correggio (1489-1534), 450th
Death Anniv. — A1125

---

Designs: 20ch, *St. Catherine.* 35ch, *Madonna.* 50ch, *Madonna with St. John.*
No. 2345: a, *Morning* (detail). b, *Morning* (diff. detail). c, *St. Catherine* (diff.). d, *Madonna and Child.*
No. 2346: *Madonna and Child with Music-Making Angels.*

**1983, Dec. 12**      *Perf. 13¼*
| | | | | |
|---|---|---|---|---|
| 2342-2344 | A1124 | Set of 3 | 5.00 | 1.25 |
| 2345 | | Sheet of 4, #a.-d. | 12.00 | 3.50 |
| a. | | A1124 20ch multicolored | 2.50 | .75 |
| b. | | A1124 35ch multicolored | 2.50 | .75 |
| c. | | A1124 50ch multicolored | 2.50 | .75 |
| d. | | A1124 80ch multicolored | 2.50 | .75 |

**Souvenir Sheet**
| | | | | |
|---|---|---|---|---|
| 2346 | A1125 | 80ch multicolored | 4.50 | 1.25 |

Cats — A1126

Domestic cats, each different, denominated 10ch. Frame color: No. 2347, green. No. 2348, gray. No. 2349, gold. No. 2350, red. No. 2351, blue.

**1983, Dec. 20**
| | | | | |
|---|---|---|---|---|
| 2347-2351 | A1126 | Set of 5 | 12.00 | .50 |

Six souvenir sheets inscribed Sarajevo '84, each containing one 1w stamp, were issued on Dec. 31, 1983. Value $80.

New Year — A1127

**1984, Jan. 1**      *Perf. 12*
| | | | | |
|---|---|---|---|---|
| 2352 | A1127 | 10ch multicolored | 1.00 | .25 |

Korean Workers
Party — A1128

Designs (both 10ch): No. 2353, Komdok General Mining Enterprise, Ore-dressing Plant No. 3, and Party flag. No. 2354, Worker holding books, and Party flag.

**1984, Feb. 16**
| | | | | |
|---|---|---|---|---|
| 2353-2354 | A1128 | Set of 2 | 1.00 | .25 |
| 2353a | | 10ch Unsurfaced white paper, without gum | 20.00 | — |
| 2354a | | 10ch Unsurfaced white paper, without gum | 20.00 | — |

Farm Worker,
Grain — A1129

**1984, Feb. 25**
| | | | | |
|---|---|---|---|---|
| 2355 | A1129 | 10ch multicolored | .60 | .25 |

Publication of the *Theses on the Socialist Rural Question in Our Country*, 20th anniv.

Changdok
School,
Chilgol — A1130

Kim's Birthplace,
Rejoicing
Crowd — A1131

---

**1984, Apr. 15**
| | | | | |
|---|---|---|---|---|
| 2356 | A1130 | 5ch multicolored | .50 | .25 |
| a. | | Unsurfaced white paper, without gum | 15.00 | — |
| 2357 | A1131 | 10ch multicolored | .50 | .25 |
| a. | | Unsurfaced white paper, without gum | 20.00 | — |

Kim Il Sung, 72nd birthday.

A1132

España '84 Int'l Stamp
Exhib. — A1133

Designs: 10ch, *Spanish Riding School of Vienna,* by Julius von Blaas. 20ch, *Ferdinand of Austria,* by Rubens.
No. 2360: 80ch, *Spanish Riding School,* by von Blaas.

**1984, Apr. 27**      *Perf. 13½*
| | | | | |
|---|---|---|---|---|
| 2358-2359 | A1132 | Set of 2 | 3.50 | .75 |

**Souvenir Sheet**
| | | | | |
|---|---|---|---|---|
| 2360 | A1133 | 80ch multicolored | 6.50 | 1.25 |

Kiyang
Irrigation
System, 25th
Anniv.
A1134

**1984, Apr. 30**
| | | | | |
|---|---|---|---|---|
| 2361 | A1134 | 10ch multicolored | .75 | .25 |

Raphael, 500th
Anniv. of Birth (in
1983) — A1135

Designs: 10ch, *Portrait of Angolo Doni.* 20ch, *Portrait of La Donna Velata.* 30ch, *Portrait of Jeanne d'Aragon.* 80ch, *St. Sebastian.*

**1984, Apr. 30**      *Perf. 11¾x12*
| | | | | |
|---|---|---|---|---|
| 2362-2364 | A1135 | Set of 3 | 4.00 | 1.00 |

**Souvenir Sheet**
*Perf. 11¾x11½*
| | | | | |
|---|---|---|---|---|
| 2365 | A1135 | 80ch multicolored | 3.50 | 1.25 |

Socialist
Construction — A1136

**1984, May 20**      *Perf. 12*
| | | | | |
|---|---|---|---|---|
| 2366 | A1136 | 10ch multicolored | .75 | .25 |

---

1984 Winter Olympics Games Medal
Winners — A1137

Designs: 20ch (No. 2367), Speed skating (Karin Enke, DDR). 30ch (No. 2368), Bobsledding (DDR).
No. 2369: 10ch, Ski jumping (Matti Nykaenen, Finland). 20ch (No. 2369b), Slalom (Max Julen, Switzerland). 30ch (No. 2369c), Downhill skiing (Maria Walliser, Switzerland).
No. 2370 (both vert.): 40ch, Cross-country skiing (Thomas Wassberg, Sweden). 80ch, Cross-country skiing (Maria Liisa Hamalainen).
No. 2371 (vert.): 80ch, Biathlon (Peter Angerer, West Germany).

**1984, May 20**      *Perf. 13½*
| | | | | |
|---|---|---|---|---|
| 2367-2368 | A1137 | Set of 2 | 3.50 | .85 |
| 2369 | | Sheet of 3, #a.-c. | 25.00 | 1.25 |
| a. | | A1137 10ch multicolored | 6.00 | .35 |
| b. | | A1137 20ch multicolored | 6.00 | .35 |
| c. | | A1137 30ch multicolored | 6.00 | .35 |
| 2370 | | Sheet of 2, #a.-b. | 5.00 | 1.00 |
| a. | | A1137 40ch multicolored | 2.00 | .40 |
| b. | | A1137 80ch multicolored | 2.00 | .40 |

**Souvenir Sheet**
| | | | | |
|---|---|---|---|---|
| 2371 | A1137 | 80ch multicolored | 3.50 | 1.00 |

Essen '84
Int'l Stamp
Exhib.
A1138

Designs: 20ch, Type "202" express locomotive (1939). 30ch, Type "E" freight locomotive (1919).
No. 2374: 80ch, Type "D" locomotive in Germany.

**1984, May 26**      *Perf. 12x11¾*
| | | | | |
|---|---|---|---|---|
| 2372-2373 | A1138 | Set of 2 | 10.00 | 1.00 |

**Souvenir Sheet**
| | | | | |
|---|---|---|---|---|
| 2374 | A1138 | 80ch multicolored | 9.00 | 1.25 |

Edgar Degas, 150th Birth
Anniv. — A1139

Designs: 10ch, *Mlle. Fiocre in the Ballet 'La Source.'* 20ch, *The Dance Foyer at the Rue le Peletier Opera.* 30ch, *Race Meeting.*
No. 2378: 80ch, *Dancers at the Bars.*

**1984, June 10**      *Perf. 12*
| | | | | |
|---|---|---|---|---|
| 2375-2377 | A1139 | Set of 3 | 8.00 | 1.25 |

**Souvenir Sheet**
*Perf. 11½*
| | | | | |
|---|---|---|---|---|
| 2378 | A1139 | 80ch multicolored | 4.50 | 1.25 |

Irrigation
Experts
Meeting
A1140

**1984, June 16**      *Perf. 11¾x12*
| | | | | |
|---|---|---|---|---|
| 2379 | A1140 | 2ch multicolored | .80 | .25 |

UPU
Congress/Hamburg
1984 Stamp
Exhib. — A1141

No. 2381: 80ch, *Gorch Fock,* DPRK stamp depicting Turtle Boat.

**1984, June 19**
2380 A1141 20ch multicolored 3.50 .35
**Souvenir Sheet**
*Perf. 11¾x11½*
2381 A1141 80ch multicolored 6.00 2.00

Tripartite Talks Proposal — A1142

**1984, June 25** *Perf. 12¼*
2382 A1142 10ch multicolored .75 .25

Alfred Bernhard Nobel, 150th Birth Anniv. (in 1983) — A1143

Designs: 20ch, Nobel in laboratory. 30ch, Nobel portrait.
No. 2385: 80ch, Nobel portrait, diff.

**1984, June 30** *Perf. 13½*
2383-2384 A1143 Set of 2 8.00 .75
**Souvenir Sheet**
2385 A1143 80ch multicolored 7.00 2.00
Nos. 2383 and 2384 were issued se-tenant with labels depicting Nobel's laboratory and home, respectively.

Improvement of Korean Living Standards A1144

**1984, July 10** *Perf. 11¾x12*
2386 A1144 10ch multicolored .70 .25

Kuandian Conf., 65th Anniv. — A1145

**1984, Aug. 17** *Perf. 12x12¼*
2387 A1145 10ch multicolored 1.25 .25

Sunhwa School, Mangyongdae A1146

**1984, Aug. 17** *Perf. 12*
2388 A1146 10ch multicolored 1.10 .25
School of Kim Il Sung's father, Kim Hyong Jik.

A1147

---

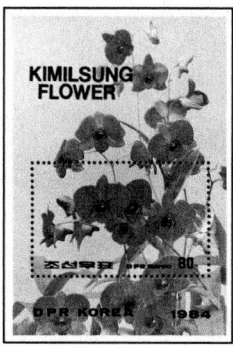

A1148

Flowers: 10ch, *Cattleya loddigesii.* 20ch, *Thunia bracteata.* 30ch, *Phalaenopsis amabilis.*
No. 2392: 80ch, *Kimilsungia.*

**1984, Aug. 20**
2389-2391 A1147 Set of 3 4.00 .60
**Souvenir Sheet**
2392 A1148 80ch multicolored 5.00 1.00

Fishing Industry A1149

Designs: 5ch, Swordfish and trawler. 10ch, Marlin and trawler. 40ch, *Histiophorus orientalis.*

**1984, Aug. 25**
2393-2395 A1149 Set of 3 4.50 1.00

Revolutionary Museum, Chilgol — A1150

**1984, Aug. 29**
2396 A1150 10ch multicolored .90 .25

"Let's All Become the Kim Hyoks and Cha Gwang Sus of the '80s!" — A1151

**1984, Aug. 31**
2397 A1151 10ch multicolored .90 .25

Orient Express, Centenary A1152

Designs: 10ch, Inauguration of a French railway line in 1860. 20ch, Opening of a British railway line in 1821. 30ch, Inauguration of Paris-Rouen line, 1843.
No. 2401: 80ch, Interior views of passenger cars, 1905.

**1984, Sept. 7** *Perf. 13½x13¼*
2398-2400 A1152 Set of 3 8.00 1.25
**Souvenir Sheet**
2401 A1152 80ch multicolored 7.00 1.75

---

Greenwich Meridian Time, Centenary — A1153

Designs: 10ch, Clockface, astronomical observatory.
No. 2403: 80ch, Clock face, buildings, Chollima statue.

**1984, Sept. 15** *Perf. 12*
2402 A1153 10ch multicolored 4.00 —
**Souvenir Sheet**
*Perf. 11¾x11½*
2403 A1153 80ch multicolored 6.00 1.25

Hamhung Grand Theater A1154

**1984, Sept. 21**
2404 A1154 10ch multicolored .90 .25

Automation of Industry — A1155

**1984, Sept. 25** *Perf. 12¼*
2405 A1155 10ch multicolored .90 .25
a. Unsurfaced white paper, without gum 8.00 —

A1156

18th Century Korean Paintings — A1157

Designs: 10ch, *Dragon Angler.* 20ch, *Ox Driver,* horiz. 30ch, *Bamboo,* horiz. 80ch, *Autumn Night.*

**1984, Sept. 30** *Perf. 12 (#2406), 13¼*
2406-2408 A1156 Set of 3 4.00 .60
**Souvenir Sheet**
*Perf. 13¼*
2409 A1157 80ch multicolored 3.50 1.25

K.E. Tsiolkovski (1857-1935), Russian Space Scientist — A1158

Designs: 20ch, Portrait. 30ch, Earth, sputnik.
No. 2412: 80ch, Rocket launch.

**1984, Oct. 5** *Perf. 11¾*
2410-2411 A1158 Set of 2 2.00 .45

---

**Souvenir Sheet**
*Perf. 11¾x11½*
2412 A1158 80ch multicolored 4.00 .75

Container Ships A1159

Designs: 10ch, *Pongdaesan.* 20ch, *Ryongnamsan.* 30ch, *Rungrado.*
No. 2416: 80ch, *Kumgangsan*

**1984, Oct. 6** *Perf. 12x11¾*
2413-2415 A1158 Set of 3 4.00 .85
**Souvenir Sheet**
*Perf. 12*
2416 A1159 80ch multicolored 5.00 1.25

A1160

A1161

Wild Animals: 10ch, Spotted hyenas. 20ch, Caracal. 30ch, Black-backed jackals. 40ch, Foxes.
80ch, Falcon.

**1984, Oct. 13** *Perf. 13¼*
2417-2420 A1160 Set of 4 4.50 1.00
**Souvenir Sheet**
2421 A1161 80ch multicolored 6.50 1.25

Marie Curie (1867-1934), Physicist, 50th Death Anniv. — A1162

No. 2423: 80ch, Portrait of Mme. Curie.

**1984, Oct. 21** *Perf. 12*
2422 A1162 10ch multicolored 4.00 .25
**Souvenir Sheet**
*Perf. 11¾x11½*
2423 A1162 80ch multicolored 6.00 1.25

A1163

Birds: 10ch, Hoopoe. 20ch, South African crowned cranes. 30ch, Saddle-bill stork. 40ch, Chestnut-eared Aracari.
No. 2428: 80ch, Black kite.

## 1984, Nov. 5 — Perf. 11½
2424-2427 A1163 Set of 4    8.50   1.25
**Souvenir Sheet**
2428 A1163 80ch multicolored   8.50   1.25

Space Exploration — A1164

Designs: 10ch, Cosmonaut. 20ch, Cosmonaut on space-walk. 30ch, Cosmonaut (diff.). No. 2432: 80ch, Moon vehicle.

## 1984, Nov. 15 — Perf. 12
2429-2431 A1164 Set of 3    3.00   .60
**Souvenir Sheet**
2432 A1164 80ch multicolored   4.00   1.00

Russian Icebreakers A1165

Designs: 20ch, *Arktika.* 30ch, *Ermak.* No. 2435: 80ch, *Lenin.*

## 1984, Nov. 26 — Perf. 13¼
2433-2434 A1165 Set of 2    3.25   .60
**Souvenir Sheet**
2435 A1165 80ch multicolored   5.00   1.25

A1166

Dmitri Mendeleev (1834-1907), Chemist, 150th Birth Anniv. — A1167

## 1984, Dec. 1 — Perf. 13¼
2436 A1166 10ch multicolored   1.75   .25
**Souvenir Sheet**
2437 A1167 80ch multicolored   4.00   1.25

Historic European Royalty, Scenes — A1168

British Monarchs — A1169

Queen Elizabeth II — A1170

Type A1168: No. 2438 (all 10ch): a, Konrad III, 1149 (Germany). b, Henry VIII (England). c, Henry VI (England). d, King John (England). e, Fleet of Elizabeth I (England). f, Philip II Augustus (France). g, Thames and London Bridge, 1616. h, Elizabeth I (England). i, Charles VII, parade (England).
No. 2439 (all 10ch): a, Prince Eugene, 1706 (Savoy). b, Kaiser Wilhelm II (Germany). c, Philip V (Spain). d, Ludwig II (Bavaria). e, Alfonso XIII (Spain). f, Mary Stuart (Scotland). g, Charles Edward Stuart, 1745 (Scotland). h, Marie-Louise (Austria). i, Charles V, 1547 (Spain).
No. 2440 (Horiz., all 10ch): a, Maria Theresa (Austria). b, Francis I, 1814 (Austria). c, Leopold II, 1844 (Austria). d, Louis XVIII (France). e, Versailles, 1688. f, Louis XIV (France). g, Prince Wilhelm (Germany). h, Franz Joseph I (Austria). i, Ludwig II (Bavaria).
No. 2441 (Horiz., all 10ch): a, Napoleon III (France. b, Rudolph of Habsburg, Basel 1273. c, Henry IV (France). d, Louis XII (France). e, Maximilian I (Holy Roman Empire). f, Peter the Great, Amsterdam Harbor (Russia). g, Louis VIII (France). h, Don Juan/Battle of Lepanto, 1571. i, Neuschwaustein Castle.
Type A1169: No. 2442 (all 10ch): a, William I. b, Richard II. c, Henry V. d, Henry VI. e, Richard III. f, Edward IV. g, Henry VII. h, Henry VIII, full length portrait. i, Henry VIII, ¾-face portrait, as young man.
No. 2443 (all 10ch): a, Henry VIII, ¾-face portrait, as middle-aged man. b, Mary I. c, Elizabeth I, facing left. d, Edward VI. e, Elizabeth I, facing right. f, Lady Jane Grey. g, Mary, Queen of Scots. h, James I. i, Charles I.
No. 2444 (all 10ch): a, Charles I. b, Henrietta Marie. c, Charles II. d, James II. e, George I, seated. f, William IV. g, Queen Anne, full-length portrait. h, George I, in profile. i, Queen Mary II.
No. 2445 (all 10ch): a, Queen Anne, with her son, William, Duke of Gloucester. b, George II, facing forward. c, George II, in profile. d, George IV. e, George III. f, William III. g, William IV. h, Queen Victoria. i, Prince Albert.
No. 2446 (all 10ch): a, Edward VII. b, Queen Alexandra. c, George V and Royal Family. d, George VI. e, George VI and Royal Family. f, Queen Elizabeth II. g, Prince Charles. h, Prince William of Wales, with Prince Charles and Princess Diana. i, Princess Diana.

**Sheets of 9, #a.-i.**

## 1984, Dec. 20 — Perf. 12¼x12
### Types A1168-A1169
2438-2446 Set of 9    125.00   —
**Souvenir Sheet**
**Perf. 11½**
2447 A1170 80ch multicolored   20.00   12.00

Kim Il Sung's Visits to Eastern Europe — A1171

No. 2448 (all 10ch): a, USSR. b, Poland. c, DDR. d, Czechoslovakia.
No. 2249 (all 10ch): a, Hungary. b, Bulgaria. c, Romania.
No. 2450: 10ch, China.

## 1984, Dec. 30 — Perf. 12
2448 A1171 Sheet of 4, #a.-d.   4.50   1.25
2449 A1171 Sheet of 3, #a.-c.   3.50   1.00
**Souvenir Sheet**
**Perf. 11½**
2450 A1171 10ch multicolored   50.00   1.00

New Year — A1172

## 1985, Jan. 1 — Perf. 12
2451 A1172 10ch multicolored   1.90   .25

Kim Il Sung's 1,000-ri Journey, 60th Anniv. A1173

## 1985, Jan. 22 — Perf. 12¼
2452 A1173 Pair, #a.-b.   2.25   .25
a.   5ch multicolored   .75   .25
b.   10ch multicolored   .75   .25

A1174

History of the Motorcar — A1175

Designs: 10ch, Gugnot's Steam Car, 1769. 15ch, Goldsworthy Steam Omnibus, 1825. 20ch, Gottlieb Daimler diesel car, 1885. 25ch, Benx three-wheeled diesel car, 1886. 30ch, Peugot diesel car, 1891. 80ch, Wind-power car.

## 1985, Jan. 25 — Perf. 11½
2453-2457 A1174 Set of 5   7.00   .85
**Souvenir Sheet**
2458 A1175 80ch multicolored   4.50   1.25

Secret Camp, Mt. Paektu — A1176

## 1985, Feb. 16 — Perf. 12
2459 A1176 10ch multicolored   .65   .25
Korean Revolution Headquarters

Lighthouses — A1177

10ch, Taechodo. 20ch, Sodo. 30ch, Pido. 40ch, Suundo.

## 1985, Feb. 23 — Perf. 12¼x11¾
2460-2463 A1177 Set of 4   9.00   1.25
For surcharges, see Nos. 4533-4534.

*The Hedgehog Defeats the Tiger,* Fairy Tale — A1178

Designs: 10ch, Tiger bragging about his strength. 20ch, Tiger going to stamp on rolled-up hedgehog. 30ch, Hedgehog clinging to tiger's nose. 35ch, Fleeing tiger. 40ch, Tiger crawling before hedgehog.

## 1985, Mar. 6 — Perf. 11½
2464-2468 A1178 Set of 5   6.50   1.25

A1179

Mushrooms: 10ch, Pieurotus cornucopiae. 20ch, Pluerotus ostreatus. 30ch, Catathelasma ventricosum.

## 1985, Mar. 16
2469-2471 A1179 Set of 3   6.00   .65
For surcharge, see No. 4521.

A1180

World Cup Soccer 1954-1966 — A1181

Designs: 10ch, W. Germany vs. Hungary, 1954. 20ch, Brazil vs. Sweden, 1958. 30ch, Brazil vs. Czechoslovakia, 1962. 40ch, England vs. W. Germany, 1966. 80ch, DPRK team in quarter final, 1966.

## 1985, Mar. 20 — Perf. 13¼
2472-2475 A1180 Set of 4   4.50   1.00
**Souvenir Sheet**
2476 A1181 80ch multicolored   4.00   1.25

A1182

World Cup Soccer 1970-
1986 — A1183

Designs: 10ch, Brazil vs. Italy, 1970. 20ch,
W. Germany vs. Netherlands, 1974. 30ch,
Argentina vs. Netherlands, 1978. 40ch, Italy
vs. W. Germany, 1982.
80ch, Aztec Stadium, Mexico City.

**1985, Mar. 20**     *Perf. 13¼*
2477-2480 A1182   Set of 4    4.50   1.00

**Souvenir Sheet**
2481 A1183 80ch multicolored    4.00   1.25

Kim Il Sung,
73rd Birthday
A1184

**1985, April 15**     *Perf. 12*
2482 A1184 10ch multicolored    .65   .25

4th Century Musical
Instruments — A1185

Designs: 10ch, Horn player. 20ch, So (panpipes) player.

**1985, May 7**     *Perf. 11½*
2483-2484 A1185   Set of 2    3.50   .25

Chongryon Hall,
Tokyo — A1186

**1985, May 25**
2485 A1186 10ch deep brown    .65   .25

30th anniv. of Chongryon, the General
Association of Korean Residents in Japan.

A1187

Mammals: 5ch, Common marmoset (cal-
lithrix jacchus). 10ch, Ring-tailed lemur (Lemur
catta).

**1985, June 7**
2486-2487 A1187   Set of 2    2.50   .25

---

National Emblem — A1188

**1985, June 20**
2488 A1188 80ch multicolored    3.00   .70

A1189

Argentina '85 Int'l Stamp
Exhib. — A1190

Designs: 10ch, Buenos Aires and Argentina
stamp. 20ch, Iguaçu Falls and Argentine,
DPRK stamps, horiz.
80ch, Gaucho.

**1985, July 5**     *Perf. 11¾*
2489-2490 A1189   Set of 2    3.50   .25

**Souvenir Sheet**
2491 A1190 80ch multicolored    4.00   4.00

12th World Youth and
Students' Festival,
Moscow — A1191

Designs: 10ch, Korean dancer with
streamer, gymnast. 20ch, Spassky Tower,
Festival emblem. 30ch, Youths of different
races.

**1985, July 27**     *Perf. 12¼*
2492-2494 A1191   Set of 3    3.50   .75

Pyongyang
Buildings — A1192

Designs: 2ch, Phyonghwa Pavilion. 40ch,
Skyscraper apartments, Chollima Street.

**1985, Aug. 1**     *Perf. 12*
2495-2496 A1192   Set of 2    1.00   .25
2495a   2ch   Thick toned unsurfaced
      paper, without gum    10.00   —
2496a   40ch   Thick toned unsurfaced
      paper, without gum    5.00   —

---

A1193

Liberation, 40th Anniv. — A1194

Designs: 5ch, Soldiers, battle scene. 10ch
(No. 2498), Korean and Russian soldier with
raised arms. 10ch (No. 2499), Japanese
soldiers surrendering. 10ch (No. 2500), Crowd
with banners, Flame of Juche. 10ch (No.
2501), Student marchers with banners. 10ch
(No. 2502), Liberation monument, vert. 40ch,
Students bearing banners.
80ch, Monument.

**1985, Aug. 15**     *Perf. 11½*
2497-2503 A1193   Set of 7    3.50   1.25
2497a   5ch   Toned unsurfaced pa-
      per, without gum    8.00   —
2498a   10ch   Toned unsurfaced pa-
      per, without gum    8.00   —
2499a   10ch   Toned unsurfaced pa-
      per, without gum    8.00   —
2500a   10ch   Toned unsurfaced pa-
      per, without gum    8.00   —
2501a   10ch   Toned unsurfaced pa-
      per, without gum    8.00   —
2502a   10ch   Toned unsurfaced pa-
      per, without gum    8.00   —
2503a   40ch   Toned unsurfaced pa-
      per, without gum    8.00   —

**Souvenir Sheet**
2504 A1194 80ch multicolored    2.00   2.00

A1195

Halley's Comet — A1196

Designs: 10ch, Halley and Comet. 20ch,
Comet, diagram of course, space probe.
80ch, Comet's trajectory.

**1985, Aug. 25**     *Perf. 13½*
2505-2506 A1195   Set of 2    2.25   .25

**Souvenir Sheet**
2507 A1196 80ch multicolored    4.00   1.25

Flowers — A1197

Designs: 10ch, Hippeastrum hybridum.
20ch, Camellia japonica. 30ch, Cyclamen
persicum.

**1985, Sept. 10**     *Perf. 12*
2508-2510 A1197   Set of 3    7.00   .65

---

A1198

Koguryo Culture, 4th-6th Centuries
A.D. — A1199

Designs: 10ch, Hero. 15ch, Heroine. 20ch,
Flying fairy. 25ch, Hunting.
50ch, Pine tree.

**1985, Sep. 30**     *Perf. 13¼*
2511-2514 A1198   Set of 4    4.00   .65
2514a    Sheet of 4, #2511-2514   4.00   1.00

**Souvenir Sheet**
**Perf. 12**
2515 A1199 50ch multicolored    3.00   .75

Nos. 2511-2514 were issued both in separate sheets and in setenant sheets of four
stamps (No. 2514a).

Korean Worker's Party,
40th Anniv. — A1200

Designs: 5ch, Party Founding Museum.
10ch (No. 2517), Soldier, workers. 10ch (No.
2518), Miner, workers. 40ch, Worker, peasant,
professional worker holding up Party emblem.
No. 2520: 90ch, People holding bouquets of
flowers.

**1985, Oct. 10**     *Perf. 11½*
2516-2519 A1200   Set of 4    1.75   .75
2516a   5ch   Thick toned unsurfaced
      paper, without gum    5.00   —
2517a   10ch   Thick toned unsurfaced
      paper, without gum    10.00   —
2518a   10ch   Thick toned unsurfaced
      paper, without gum    5.00   —
2519a   40ch   Thick toned unsurfaced
      paper, without gum    10.00   —

**Souvenir Sheet**
2520 A1200 90ch multicolored    1.75   .50

Kim Il Sung's Return,
40th Anniv. — A1201

**1985, Oct. 14**     *Perf. 12*
2521 A1201 10ch red brn & lt grn   1.00   .25
  a.   Dull white unsurfaced paper,
      without gum    8.00   —

Italia '85, Int'l
Stamp Exhib.,
Rome — A1202

Designs: 10ch, Colosseum, Rome, and
DPRK stamp. 20ch, *The Holy Family*, by
Raphael. 30ch. Head of Michelangelo's *David*,
vert.
No. 2525: 80ch, Pantheon, Rome.

**1985, Oct. 25**     *Perf. 11½*
2522-2524 A1202   Set of 3    2.75   .65

**Souvenir Sheet**
2525 A1202 80ch multicolored    4.00   1.25

South-West German Stamp Bourse, Sindelfingen A1203

Designs, Mercedes Benz: 10ch, Type 300, 1960. 15ch, Type 770. 20ch, Type W150, 1937. 30ch, Type 600, 1966. No. 2530: 80ch, Mercedes Benz, Type W31, 1938.

**1985, Oct. 25**
2526-2529 A1203 Set of 4    6.50 .65
**Souvenir Sheet**
**Perf. 11¾**
2530 A1203 80ch multicolored    5.25 .75

A1204

13th World Cup Championship, Mexico City — A1205

Designs: 20ch, Dribbling and sliding tackle. 30ch, Jumping kick. 80ch, Goalkeeper and Mexican monuments.

**1985, Nov. 1**    **Perf. 13¼**
2531-2532 A1204 Set of 2    3.25 .50
**Souvenir Sheet**
2533 A1205 80ch multicolored    4.50 1.10

Int'l Youth Year — A1206

Designs: 10ch, Traditional dance. 20ch, Sculpture depicting gymnasts. 30ch, Scientific research. No. 2537: 80ch, Young people of different races.

**1985, Nov. 9**    **Perf. 11½**
2534-2536 A1206 Set of 3    3.25 .50
**Souvenir Sheet**
2537 A1206 80ch multicolored    4.25 1.00

A1207

13th World Cup Championship, Mexico City — A1208

Designs: 20ch, Dribbling. 30ch, Tackling. 80ch, Goalkeeper, bullfighter.

---

**1985, Nov. 20**    **Perf. 12**
2538-2539 A1207 Set of 2    3.25 .50
**Souvenir Sheet**
2540 A1208 80ch multicolored    4.50 1.00

Juche Torch — A1209

New Year

**1986, Jan. 1**    **Perf. 12x12¼**
2541 A1209 10ch multicolored    1.15 .25

History of the Motor Car — A1210

Designs: 10ch, Amédée Bollée and Limousine, 1901. 20ch, Stewart Rolls, Henry Royce and Silver Ghost, 1906. 25ch, Giovanni Agnelli and Fiat car, 1912. 30ch, Ettore Bugatti and Royal coupe, 1928. 40ch, Louis Renault and fiacre, 1906. No. 2547: 80ch, Gottlieb Daimler, Karl Benz and Mercedes S, 1927.

**1986, Jan. 20**    **Perf. 11½**
2542-2546 A1210 Set of 5    8.75 1.15
**Souvenir Sheet**
2547 A1210 80ch multicolored    6.75 .75

World Chess Championship, Moscow — A1211

Designs: 20ch, Gary Kasparov. No. 2549: 80ch, Kasparov-Karpov chess match.

**1986, Feb. 5**    **Perf. 11¾x12**
2548 A1211 20ch multicolored    2.00 .25
**Souvenir Sheet**
**Perf. 12**
2549 A1211 80ch multicolored    4.50 1.15
For surcharges, see Nos. 4522-4523.

Revolutionary Martyrs' Cemetery, Pyongyang A1212

Designs: 5ch, Cemetery Gate. 10ch, Bronze sculpture of draped flag, soldier, workers (detail).

**1986, Feb. 10**    **Perf. 12**
2550-2551 A1212 Set of 2    1.35 .25

Songgan Revolutionary Site, 37th Anniv. of Kim Il Sung's Visit — A1213

**1986, Feb. 16**
2552 A1213 10ch multicolored    .85 .25

Mt. Myohyang Historic Buildings A1214

---

Designs: 10ch, Buddhist Scriptures Museum. 20ch, Taeung Hall of the Pohyon Temple.

**1986, Feb. 20**    **Perf. 12¼**
2553-2554 A1214 Set of 2    1.75 .25

Tropical Fish — A1215

Designs: 10ch, Heniochus acuminatus. 20ch, Amphiprion frenatus.

**1986, Mar. 12**    **Perf. 11½**
2555-2556 A1215 Set of 2    2.25 .30

World Cup Championship, Mexico City — A1216

Designs, soccer players and flags of: 10ch, Italy, Bulgaria, Argentina. 20ch, Mexico, Belgium, Paraguay, Iraq. 25ch, France, Canada, USSR, Hungary. 30ch, Brazil, Spain, Algeria, Northern Ireland. 35ch, W. Germany, Uruguay, Scotland, Denmark. 40ch, Poland, Portugal, Morocco, England. No. 2563: 80ch, Soccer players, World Cup, gold soccer ball, boots.

**1986, Mar. 21**    **Perf. 12**
2557-2562 A1216 Set of 6    9.00 1.45
**Souvenir Sheet**
2563 A1216 80ch multicolored    6.00 .60
For overprints see Nos. 2599-2605.

4th Spring Friendship Art Festival, Pyongyang A1217

**1986, Apr. 5**
2564 A1217 1w multicolored    2.75 .60

Mercedes-Benz, 60th Anniv. — A1218

Designs: 10ch (No. 2565), Daimler No. 1 ("Motorwagen"), 1886. 10ch (No. 2566), Benz-Velo, 1894. 20ch (No. 2567), Mercedes, 1901. 20ch (No. 2568), Benz limousine, 1909. 30ch (No. 2569), Mercedes Tourenwagen, 1914. 30ch (No. 2570), Mercedes Benz 170/6 cylinder, 1931. 40ch (No. 2571), Mercedes Benz 380, 1933. 40ch (No. 2572), Mercedes Benz 540K, 1936. No. 2573: 80ch, Mercedes-Simplex Phaeton, 1904.

**1986, Apr. 8**    **Perf. 11½**
2565-2572 A1218 Set of 8    8.25 1.75
**Souvenir Sheet**
2573 A1218 80ch multicolored    4.50 1.15

Kim Il Sung, 74th Birthday — A1219

**1986, Apr. 15**    **Perf. 12**
2574 A1219 10ch multicolored    .60 .25

Association for the Restoration of the Fatherland, 50th Anniv. — A1220

**1986, May 5**    **Perf. 11¾x12**
2575 A1220 10ch multicolored    .60 .25

---

Intl. Year of Peace — A1221

Designs: 10ch, Dove carrying letter. 20ch, Dove, UN Headquarters. 30ch, Dove, globe, broken missiles. No. 2579: 80ch, Sculpture of children and dove.

**1986, June 18**    **Perf. 11¾x12**
2576-2578 A1221 Set of 3    3.75 1.15
**Souvenir Sheet**
**Perf. 11¾x11½**
2579 A1221 80ch multicolored    4.50 .75

Mona Lisa, by da Vinci — A1222

**1986, July 9**    **Perf. 13½x13¼**
2580 A1222 20ch multicolored    2.75 .25

Irises — A1223

Designs: 20ch, Pink iris. 30ch, Violet iris. No. 2583: 80ch, Magenta iris.

**1986, July 20**    **Perf. 11½**
2581-2582 A1223 Set of 2    4.50 .50
**Souvenir Sheet**
2583 A1223 80ch multicolored    6.00 1.00

Tennis Players — A1224

Designs: 10ch, Kim Un Suk. 20ch, Ivan Lendi. 30ch, Steffi Craf. 50ch, Boris Becker.

**1986, July 30**    **Perf. 13½**
2584 A1224 Block of 4, #a.-d.    6.50 .90
   a.   10ch multicolored    1.35 .25
   b.   20ch multicolored    1.35 .25
   c.   30ch multicolored    1.35 .25
   d.   50ch multicolored    1.35 .25
   e.   10ch Toned unsurfaced paper, without gum    10.00

No. 2584 was printed in sheets containing two setenant blocks. No. 2584d is airmail.

Stampex '86 Stamp Exhib., Adelaide — A1225

Designs: 10ch, Cockatoo; 80ch, Kangaroo, map of Australia, emblems.

**1986, Aug. 4**     *Perf. 11½*
2585 A1225 10ch multicolored   5.00   .25
**Souvenir Sheet**
2586 A1225 80ch multicolored   5.00 1.00

*L'Unita* Festival, Milan — A1227

Designs: 10ch, First issue of *L'Unita*. 20ch, Milan Cathedral. 30ch, Michelangelo's *Pieta*, vert.
No. 2590: 80ch, Enrico Berlinguer, Italian Communist Party leader.

**1986, Aug. 26**
2587-2589 A1227 Set of 3   5.00 2.25
**Souvenir Sheet**
2590 A1227 80ch multicolored   4.25   .75

National Festival of *L'Unita*, the Italian Communist Party newspaper.

A1228

Stockholmia '86 Int'l Stamp Exhib., Stockholm — A1229

Design: 10ch, Icebreaker *Express II* and Swedish stamp.
80ch, UPU emblem, mail coach and Swedish stamps.

**1986, Aug. 28**
2591 A1228 10ch multicolored   1.75   .25
**Souvenir Sheet**
2592 A1229 80ch multicolored   6.50 1.35

DPRK Postage Stamps, 40th Anniv. — A1230

Designs: 10ch, Perf green reprint of Scott No. 1. 15ch, Imperf green reprint of Scott No. 1. 50ch, Scott No. 5.

**1986, Sep. 12**     *Perf. 12¼x12*
2593-2595 A1230 Set of 3   5.50 1.35
No. 2595 is airmail.

DPRK Postage Stamps, 40th Anniv. — A1231

Designs: 10ch, Postal emblems, DPRK #387, 2505. 15ch, Postal emblems, General Post Office, Pyongyang, DPRK #1529, 1749. 50ch, Postal emblems, Kim Il Jung. DPRK #1, #1 reprint in green, vert.

**1986, Oct. 5**     *Perf. 12*
2596-2598 A1231 Set of 3   7.25   .90
No. 2598 is airmail. For surcharge, see No. 4580.

---

**Nos. 2557-2563 Overprinted with World Cup Soccer Championship Results**

**1986, Oct. 14**
2599-2604 A1216 Set of 6   14.50 2.25
**Souvenir Sheet**
2605 A1216 80ch multicolored   9.00 1.30

Down-with-Imperialism Union, 60th Anniv. — A1232

**1986, Oct. 17**     *Perf. 11½*
2606 A1232 10ch multicolored   .65   .25

Gift Animals House, 1st Anniv. A1233

**1986, Oct. 18**     *Perf. 12x11¾*
2607 A1233 2w multicolored   7.75   .85
  *a.*   Toned unsurfaced paper, without gum   10.00   —

United Nations Educational, Scientific and Cultural Organization (UNESCO), 40th anniv. — A1234

Designs: 10ch, Schoolchildren. 50ch, UNESCO emblem, Grand People's Study House, televion, communications satellite and dish, horiz.

**1986, Nov. 4**     *Perf. 12*
2608-2609 A1234 Set of 2   4.25 1.15

Inter-Sputnik, 15th Anniv. — A1235

**1986, Nov. 15**
2610 A1235 5w multicolored   9.00 2.00
  *a.*   Toned unsurfaced paper, without gum   10.00   —

West Sea Barrage A1236

Designs: 10ch, Oil tanker, lock. 40ch, Aerial view of dam. 1.20w, Aerial view of dam (diff.)

**1986, Nov. 20**     *Perf. 12x11¾*
2611-2613 A1236 Set of 3   7.75   .90
  2611a   10ch Toned unsurfaced paper, without gum   5.00   —
  2612a   40ch Toned unsurfaced paper, without gum   8.00   —
  2613a   1.20w Toned unsurfaced paper, without gum   8.00   —

---

Mushrooms and Minerals — A1237

Designs: a, 10ch Lengenbachite. b, 10ch Clitocybe infundibuliformis. c, 15ch Rhodocrosite. d, 15ch Morchella esculenta. e, 50ch Annabergite. f, 50ch Russula.

**1986, Nov. 23**     *Perf. 13¼*
2614 A1237 Block of 6, #a.-f.   15.00 1.15
  *a.*   10ch multicolored   2.25   .25
  *b.*   10ch multicolored   2.25   .25
  *c.*   15ch multicolored   2.25   .25
  *d.*   15ch multicolored   2.25   .25
  *e.*   50ch multicolored   2.25   .25
  *f.*   50ch multicolored   2.25   .25
Printed in setenant blocks within the sheet. Nos. 2614e and 2614f are airmail.

A1238

Exhib. of North Korean 3-D Photos and Stamps, Lima — A1239

Design: 10ch, Machu Picchu and DPRK #1402.
80ch, Korean and Peruvian children.

**1986, Nov. 25**     *Perf. 13¼x13½*
2615 A1238 10ch multicolored   1.75   .25
**Souvenir Sheet**
2616 A1239 80ch multicolored   8.25 1.75

New Year — A1240

Designs: 10ch, Sun, pine tree. 40ch, Hare.

**1987, Jan. 1**     *Perf. 12*
2617-2618 A1240 Set of 2   3.25   .50
  2617a   Perf. 13½

A1241

---

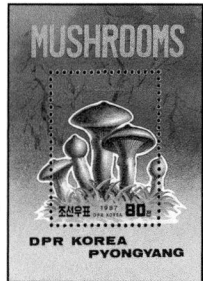

Fungi — A1242

Designs: 10ch, *Pholiota adiposa*. 20ch, *Cantharellus cibarius*. 30ch, *Boletus impolitus*. 80ch, *Gomphidius rutilus*.

**1987, Jan. 5**     *Perf. 11½*
2619-2621 A1241 Set of 3   5.25   .75
**Souvenir Sheet**
2622 A1242 80ch multicolored   6.50 1.35
For surcharge, see No. 4535.

Famous Composers, Death Anniv. — A1243

Designs: 10ch (No. 2623a), Maurice Ravel (1875-1937). 10ch (No. 2623b), Kim Ok Song (1916-65). 20ch, Giovanni Lully (1632-67). 30ch, Franz Liszt (1811-86). 40ch (No.2623e), Stradivarius violins (Antonio Stradivari, 1644-1737). 40ch (No. 2623f), Christoph Gluck (1714-87).

**1987, Jan. 29**     *Perf. 13¼*
2623 A1243 Block of 6, #a.-f.   11.00 1.00
  *a.*   10ch multicolored   1.35   .25
  *b.*   10ch multicolored   1.35   .25
  *c.*   20ch multicolored   1.35   .25
  *d.*   30ch multicolored   1.35   .25
  *e.*   40ch multicolored   1.35   .25
  *f.*   40ch multicolored   1.35   .25
No. 2623 was printed in se-tenant blocks of six within the sheet.

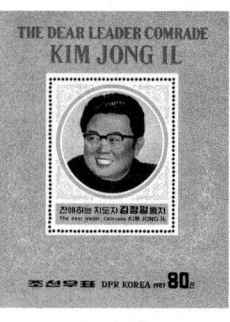

Kim Jong Il, 45th Birthday A1244

**1987, Feb. 16**
2624 A1244 80ch multicolored   2.25   .40

Buildings — A1245

Designs: 5ch, East Pyongyang Grand Theater. 10ch, Pyongyang Koryo Hotel (vert.). 3w, Rungnado Stadium.

**1987, Feb. 23**     *Perf. 12*
2625-2627 A1245 Set of 3   6.75 1.10
  2625a   5ch Stiff brown paper, without gum   9.00   —
  2626a   10ch Stiff brown paper, without gum   4.50   —
  2627a   3w Stiff brown paper, without gum   4.50   —

**Sailing Ships — A1246**

Designs: 20ch, *Gorch Fock.* 30ch, *Tovarisch*, vert.. 50ch (No. 2630), *Belle Poule*, vert. 50ch (No. 2631), *Sagres II*, vert. 1w (No. 2632), Merchantman, Koryo Period (918-1392). 1w (No. 2633), *Dar Mlodziezy*, vert..

| | | **Perf. 13¼** |
|---|---|---|
| **1987, Feb. 25** | | |
| 2628-2633 | A1246 Set of 6 | 10.50 2.50 |

Nos. 2630-2633 are airmail.

**Fire Engines — A1247**

Designs: 10ch, German fire engine. 20ch, Benz fire engine. 30ch, Chemical fire engine. 50ch, Soviet fire engine.

| | | **Perf. 12** |
|---|---|---|
| **1987, Feb. 27** | | |
| 2634-2637 | A1247 Set of 4 | 9.00 1.10 |

No. 2637 is airmail.

**Road Safety — A1248**

Designs (multiple traffic signs): 10ch (No. 2638), Blue sign lower center. 10ch (No. 2639), Red sign lower center. 20ch, Various signs. 50ch, Various signs (diff.)

| | | |
|---|---|---|
| **1987, Feb. 27** | | |
| 2638-2641 | A1248 Set of 4 | 6.75 .85 |

Nos. 2641 is airmail.

**Butterflies and Flowers — A1249**

Designs: No. 2642, Apatura ilia and spiraea. No. 2643, Ypthinia argus and fuchsia. No. 2644, Neptis philyra and aguilegia. No. 2645, Papilio protenor and chrysanthemum. No. 2646, Parantica sita and celosia. No. 2847, Vanessa indica and hibiscus.

| | | |
|---|---|---|
| **1987, Mar. 12** | | |
| 2642-2647 | A1249 Set of 6 | 10.00 1.35 |

For surcharge, see No. 4524.

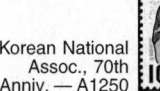

**Korean National Assoc., 70th Anniv. — A1250**

Design: 10ch, Association Monument, Pyongyang.

| | | **Perf. 11½** |
|---|---|---|
| **1987, Mar. 23** | | |
| 2648 | A1250 10ch multicolored | .60 .25 |

A1252

**5th Spring Friendship Art Festival — A1251**

| | | |
|---|---|---|
| **1987, Apr. 6** | | |
| 2649 | A1251 10ch multicolored | .65 .25 |

**Kim Il Sung, 75th Birthday — A1253**

Designs: No. 2650, Mangyong Hill. No. 2651, Kim Il Sung's birthplace, Mangyongdae, horiz. No 2652, Painting, *Profound Affection for the Working Class.* No. 2653, Painting, *A Bumper Crop of Pumpkins.*

| | | **Perf. 12** |
|---|---|---|
| **1987, Apr. 15** | | |
| 2650 | A1252 10ch multicolored | .50 .25 |
| 2651 | A1252 10ch multicolored | .50 .25 |
| 2652 | A1253 10ch multicolored | .50 .25 |
| 2653 | A1253 10ch multicolored | .50 .25 |
| | Nos. 2650-2653 (4) | 2.00 1.00 |

**Horses — A1254**

Designs: No. 2654a, Bay. No. 2654b, Bay, diff. No. 2654c, Gray, rearing. No. 2654d, White horse on beach.

| | | **Perf. 13¼** |
|---|---|---|
| **1987, Apr. 20** | | |
| 2654 | A1254 Block of 4, #a.-d. | 6.50 1.90 |
| *a.* | 10ch multicolored | .50 .25 |
| *b.* | 10ch multicolored | .50 .25 |
| *c.* | 40ch multicolored | 2.25 .65 |
| *d.* | 40ch multicolored | 2.25 .65 |

No. 2654 was printed in se-tenant blocks of four within the sheet.

**Transport — A1255**

Designs: No. 2655, Electric train *Juche.* No. 2656, Electric train *Mangyongdae.* No. 2657, *Sputnik I*, vert. No. 2658, Laika, first animal in space, vert. No. 2659, Tupolev Tu-144 jetliner. No. 2660, Concorde jetliner. No. 2661, Count Ferdinand von Zeppelin and LZ-4. No. 2662, Zeppelin and diagrams of airships.

| | | |
|---|---|---|
| **1987, Apr. 30** | | |
| 2655 | A1255 10ch multicolored | .60 .25 |
| 2656 | A1255 10ch multicolored | .60 .25 |
| *a.* | Pair, #2655-2656 | .75 .40 |
| 2657 | A1255 10ch multicolored | .60 .25 |
| 2658 | A1255 10ch multicolored | 1.00 .25 |
| *a.* | Pair, #2657-2658 | 1.75 .90 |
| 2659 | A1255 20ch multicolored | 1.00 .25 |
| 2660 | A1255 20ch multicolored | 1.00 .25 |
| *a.* | Pair, #2659-2660 | 2.25 .40 |

| | | |
|---|---|---|
| 2661 | A1255 30ch multicolored | 1.35 .25 |
| 2662 | A1255 80ch multicolored | 4.25 .90 |
| *a.* | Pair, #2661-2662 | 6.50 1.15 |
| | Nos. 2655-2662 (8) | 10.40 2.65 |

Nos. 2655/2656, 2657/2658, 2659/2660, 2661/2662 were printed se-tenant within their sheets.

No. 2662 is airmail.

**CAPEX '87 Int'l Stamp Exhibition, Toronto — A1256**

Designs: 10ch, Musk ox. 40ch, Jacques Cartier, *Grand Hermine* and modern ice-breaker, horiz. 60ch, Ice hockey, Calgary '88, horiz.

| | | **Perf. 11** |
|---|---|---|
| **1987, May 30** | | |
| 2663-2665 | A1256 Set of 3 | 5.50 1.15 |

**Int'l Circus Festival, Monaco — A1257**

Designs: No. 2666, Trapeze artists. No. 2667, "Brave Sailors" (N. Korean acrobatic troupe), vert. No. 2668, Korean performers receiving prize. No. 2669, Clown and elephant, vert. 40ch, Performing cat, horses. 50ch, Prince Rainier and family applauding.

| | | **Perf. 12** |
|---|---|---|
| **1987, May 31** | | |
| 2666-2671 | A1257 Set of 6 | 8.75 1.35 |

No. 2871 is airmail.

**Battle of Pochonbo, 50th Anniv. — A1258**

| | | **Perf. 11½** |
|---|---|---|
| **1987, June 4** | | |
| 2672 | A1258 10ch multicolored | .75 .25 |

**Chongchun Street Sports Complex — A1259**

Designs: 5ch, Various sports. 10ch, Indoor swimming pool. 40ch, Weightlifting gymnasium. 70ch, Table-tennis gymnasium. 1w, Angol football stadium. 1.20w, Handball gymnasium.

| | | **Perf. 12** |
|---|---|---|
| **1987, June 18** | | |
| 2673-2678 | A1259 Set of 6 | 9.00 2.00 |
| 2675a | 40ch Toned unsurfaced paper, without gum | 8.00 — |
| 2676a | 70ch Toned unsurfaced paper, without gum | 8.00 — |
| 2677a | 1w Toned unsurfaced paper, without gum | 8.00 — |
| 2678a | 1.20w Toned unsurfaced paper, without gum | 8.00 — |

For surcharge, see No. 4259D.

**Worldwide Fund for Nature (WWF) — A1260**

Aix galericulata: No. 2679, On branch. No. 2680, On shore. No. 2681, In water and on shore. No. 2682, In water.

| | | **Perf. 13¼** |
|---|---|---|
| **1987, Aug. 4** | | |
| 2679-2682 | A1260 Set of 4 | 10.50 1.75 |

For surcharge, see No. 4605.

A1261

**OLYMPHILEX '87 Stamp Exhibition, Rome — A1262**

| | | **Perf. 13¼** |
|---|---|---|
| **1987, Aug. 29** | | |
| 2683 | A1261 10ch multicolored | 1.35 .25 |
| | **Souvenir Sheet** | |
| 2684 | A1262 80ch multicolored | 6.50 1.15 |

**Railway Uniforms — A1263**

No. 2685, Electric train and Metro dispatcher. No. 2686, Underground station and conductress. No. 2687, Train and conductress. No. 2688, Train and railway dispatcher. No. 2689, Orient Express and conductor. No. 2690, Express train and ticket inspector.

| | | |
|---|---|---|
| **1987, Sep. 23** | | |
| 2685-2690 | A1263 Set of 6 | 6.75 1.15 |

**HAFNIA '87 Int'l Stamp Exhibition, Copenhagen — A1264**

Designs: 40ch, White stork. 60ch, The Little Mermaid and sailing ship *Danmark.*

| | | |
|---|---|---|
| **1987, Sep. 26** | | |
| 2691-2692 | A1264 Set of 2 | 4.75 .65 |

A1265

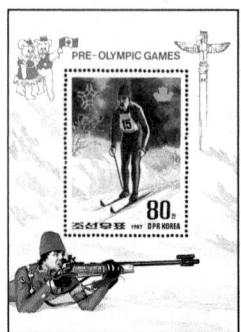

Winter Olympic Games,
Calgary — A1266

40ch: No. 2693, Figure skating. No. 2694,
Ski jump. No. 2695, Downhill skiing. No. 2696,
Cross-country skiing.

**1987, Oct. 16**
2693-2696  A1265  Set of 4        7.25  .90
**Souvenir Sheet**
2697  A1266  80ch multicolored    4.75  .90

PHILATELIA '87 (Koln) and 750th
Anniv. Berlin — A1267

Designs: 10ch, Victory Column. 20ch,
Reichstag, horiz. 30ch, Pfaueninsel Castle.
40ch, Charlottenburg Castle, horiz.
80ch, Olympic Stadium.

**1987, Nov. 5**                    *Perf. 12*
2698-2701  A1267  Set of 4       135.00
**Souvenir Sheet**
*Perf. 11½x12*
2702  A1267  80ch multicolored   90.00

Roland Garros Birth Centenary and
Tennis as an Olympic Sport — A1268

Designs: 20ch (No. 2703), Roland Garros
(1888-1918), aviator; 20ch (No. 2704), Ivan
Lendl and trophy; 40ch, Steffi Graf.
No. 2706: 80ch, Steffi Graf and trophy.

**1987, Nov. 10**                  *Perf. 13¼*
2703-2705  A1268  Set of 3        6.75  .75
**Souvenir Sheet**
*Perf. 11½x12*
2706  A1268  80ch multicolored    9.00 2.75

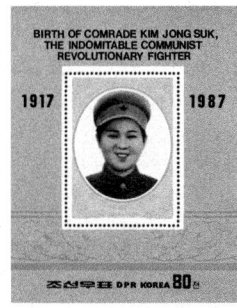

Kim Jong Suk (1917-49),
Revolutionary Hero — A1269

**1987, Dec. 24**
2707  A1269  80ch multicolored    2.25  .50

Pyongyang Buildings — A1270

Dragon — A1271

**1988, Jan. 1**                   *Perf. 12*
2708  A1270  10ch multicolored     .60  .25
2709  A1271  40ch multicolored    1.35  .25
New Year.

*Saenal*
Newspaper, 60th
Anniv. — A1272

**1988, Jan. 15**                  *Perf. 11½*
2710  A1272  10ch multicolored     .85  .25

A1273

Kim Jong Il, 46th Birthday — A1274

Designs: 10ch, Kim Jong Il's birthplace, Mt.
Paektu. 80ch, Kim Jong Il.

**1988, Feb. 16**                  *Perf. 12x11¾*
2711  A1273  10ch multicolored     .50  .25
**Souvenir Sheet**
2712  A1274  80ch multicolored    2.25  .50

Int'l Red Cross, 125th Anniv. — A1275

Designs: a, Henry Dunant. b, N. Korean
Red Cross emblem, map. c, International
Committee Headquarters, Geneva; d, Doctor
examining child, Pyongyang Maternity
Hospital.
80ch, Red Cross and Red Crescent, flags,
globe.

**1988, Feb. 17**                  *Perf. 12*
2713  A1275  Sheet of 4           6.50  .85
  a.      10ch multicolored       1.60  .25
  b.      20ch multicolored       1.60  .25
  c.      20ch multicolored       1.60  .25
  d.      40ch multicolored       1.60  .25
**Souvenir Sheet**
2714  A1275  80ch multicolored    4.25  .75

A1276

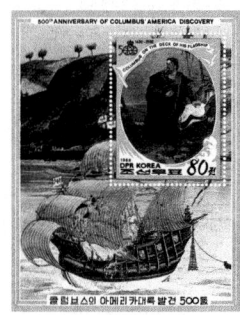

Columbus' Discovery of America,
500th Anniv. — A1277

10ch, *Santa Maria*. 20ch, *Pinta*. 30ch, *Nina*.
80ch, Columbus.

**1988, Mar. 10**                  *Perf. 13¼*
2718  A1276  Strip of 3           4.75  .75
  a.      10ch multicolored       1.15  .25
  b.      20ch multicolored       1.15  .25
  c.      30ch multicolored       1.15  .25
**Souvenir Sheet**
2719  A1277  80ch multicolored    4.75  .75
Nos. 2718a-2718c were printed together in
the sheet in se-tenant strips of three.

JUVALUX
'88 — A1278

Designs: 40ch, Hot air balloons. 60ch,
Steam engine, railroad map of Luxembourg
1900.

**1988, Mar. 29**
2720-2721  A1278  Set of 2        4.75  .75
JUVALUX '88 International Youth Stamp
Exhibition, Luxembourg.

6th Spring Friendship
Art Festival — A1279

Designs: 10ch, Singer. 1.20w, Dancers.

**1988, Apr. 7**                   *Perf. 12*
2722-2723  A1279  Set of 2        4.00 1.15
2722a      10ch, on toned unsurfaced
           paper, without gum      8.00   —

Int'l Institute of the
Juche Idea, 10th
Anniv. — A1280

**1988, Apr. 9**
2724  A1280  10ch multicolored     .50  .25

A1281

Kim Il Sung, 76th Birthday — A1282

Designs: 10ch, Kim Il Sung's Birthplace,
Mangyongdae.
80ch, Kim Il Sung and schoolchildren.

**1988, Apr. 15**
2725  A1281  10ch multicolored     .50  .25
**Souvenir Sheet**
2726  A1282  80ch multicolored    2.25  .40

FINLANDIA '88 Int'l Stamp Exhibition,
Helsinki — A1283

Designs: 40ch, *Urho* ice-breaker. 60ch,
Matti Nykänen, Finnish Olympic ski-jumping
gold and silver medallist.

**1988, May 2**                    *Perf. 13¼*
2727-2728  A1283  Set of 2        4.50  .60

ITALIA '90, 14th World Soccer
Championships — A1284

Designs: 10ch, Soccer match. 20ch, Postcard for 1934 Championship. 30ch, Player
tackling, horiz.
80ch, Italian team, 1982 winners, horiz.

**1988, May 19**
2729-2731  A1284  Set of 3        4.75  .50
**Souvenir Sheet**
2732  A1284  80ch multicolored    4.25  .60

13th World Festival of
Youth and
Students — A1285

Designs: No. 2734, Festival emblem. No. 2735, Woman dancer. No. 2736, Woman, gymnast, Angol Sports Village. No. 2737, Map of Korea, globe and doves. No. 2738, Finger pointing at broken rockets ("Let's build a new world without nuclear weapons"). No. 2739, Three hands of different races releasing dove.

**1988, May 27**      *Perf. 12*
2734-2739 A1285 Set of 6    6.75 1.15
2734a   10ch Thick toned unsurfaced paper, without gum   8.00 —
2735a   10ch Thick toned unsurfaced paper, without gum   8.00 —
2736a   10ch Thick toned unsurfaced paper, without gum   8.00 —
2739a   1.20w Thick toned unsurfaced paper, without gum   8.00 —

Eight Fairies of Mt. Kumgang, Folk-Tale — A1286

Designs: 10ch, Fairy playing the *haegum.* 15ch, Fairies with rainbow. 20ch, Fairy and herdsman husband. 25ch, Couple with infant. 30ch, Couple with son and daughter. 35ch, Family on rainbow, returning to Mt. Kumgang.

**1988, June 20**
2740-2745 A1286 Set of 6    4.50 1.00

PRAGA '88 Int'l Stamp Exhibition, Prague — A1287

Designs: 20ch, Mallard ducks. 40ch, Vladimir Remek, Czechoslovak cosmonaut.

**1988, June 26**      *Perf. 13¼*
2746-2747 A1287 Set of 2    3.75 .45

Birds — A1288

Designs: 10ch, Red crossbill (*Loxia curvirostra japonica*). 15ch, Stonechat (*Saxicola torquata stejnegeri*). 20ch, European nuthatch (*Sitta eoropaea hondoensis*). 25ch, Great spotted woodpecker (*Dendrocopos major japonicus*). 30ch, Common kingfisher (*Alcedo atthis bengalensis*). 35ch, Bohemian waxwing (*Bombycilla garrula centralasiae*).

**1988, July 9**      *Perf. 12*
2748-2753 A1288 Set of 6    9.00 1.60

For surcharge, see No. 4530.

A1289

RICCIONE '88 Int'l Stamp Fair — A1290

**1988, July 25**
2754 A1289 20ch multicolored   .85 .25
**Souvenir Sheet**
2755 A1290 80ch multicolored   3.50 .50

A1291

Australia Bicentenary — A1292

Designs: 10ch, Emu. 15ch, Statin bower birds. 25ch, Kookaberra, vert. 80ch, H.M.S. *Resolution.*

**1988, July 30**      *Perf. 13¼*
2756-2758 A1291 Set of 3    3.75 .60
**Souvenir Sheet**
2759 A1292 80ch multicolored   4.50 .60

Ships — A1293

Designs: 10ch, Floating crane *5-28.* 20ch, Cargo ship *Hwanggumsan.* 30ch, Cargo ship *Jangjasan Chongnyon-ho.* 40ch, Passenger ship *Samjiyon.*

**1988, Aug. 12**      *Perf. 12*
2760-2763 A1293 Set of 4    5.00 .80

A1294

Count Ferdinand von Zeppelin, 150th Birth Anniv. — A1295

Designs: 10ch, LZ 13 *Hansa.* 20ch, LZ 10 *Schwaben.* 30ch, LZ 11 *Viktoria Luise.* 40ch, LZ 3. 1w, Count von Zeppelin.

**1988, Aug. 21**      *Perf. 11¼*
2764-2767 A1294 Set of 4    5.00 .80
**Souvenir Sheet**
**Perf. 13¼**
2768 A1295 1w multicolored   4.50 .90

Kim Il Sung and Jambyn Batmunkh — A1296

**1988, Aug. 30**      *Perf. 12*
2769 A1296 10ch multicolored   .75 .25

Kim Il Sung's visit to Mongolia.

National Heroes Congress — A1297

**1988, Sep. 1**      *Perf. 11¾*
2770 A1297 10ch multicolored   4.25 .25

A1298

Independence, 40th Anniversary — A1299

Designs: 5ch, Tower of Juche Idea. 10ch (No. 2772), Worker, factory. 10ch (No. 2773), Soldier and Mt. Paektu. 10ch (No. 2774), Map, broken U.S. missile. 10ch (No. 2775), Hand holding sign, peace march, globe, doves. 1.20w, Kim Il Sung presiding over design of DPRK flag and emblem.

**1988, Sept. 9**      *Perf. 12*
2771-2775 A1298 Set of 5    1.60 .50
2771a   5ch Toned unsurfaced paper, without gum   20.00 —
**Souvenir Sheet**
**Perf. 11½**
2776 A1299 1.20w multicolored   2.25 .75

FILACEPT '88 Philatelic Exhib., The Hague — A1300

Designs: 40ch, *Sunflowers,* by Vincent Van Gogh. 60ch, *The Chess Game,* by Lucas van Leyden.

**1988, Sept. 18**      *Perf. 13½*
2777-2778 A1300 Set of 2    6.75 1.30

Emblem — A1301

**1988, Sep. 23**      *Perf. 11½*
2779 A1301 10ch multicolored   .60 .25

16th Conference of the Ministers of Communications of Socialist Countries.

Dump Trucks A1302

Designs: 20ch, *Jaju 82* 10-ton truck. 40ch, *Kumsusan* 40-ton truck.

**1988, Sept. 18**      *Perf. 13½*
2780-2781 A1302 Set of 2    1.75 .75

Paintings by O Un Byol — A1303

Designs: 10ch, *Owl.* 15ch, *Dawn.* 20ch, *The Beautiful Rose Received by the Respected Marshall.* 25ch, *The Sun and Bamboo.* 30ch, *Autumn.*

**1988, Oct. 5**      *Perf. 11½*
2782-2786 A1303 Set of 5    5.50 .85

Historic Locomotives — A1304

Designs: 10ch, *Junggi No. 35.* 20ch, *Junggi No. 22.* 30ch, *Jongihwa No. 3.* 40ch, *Junggi No. 307.*

**1988, Oct. 28**      *Perf. 12*
2787-2790 A1304 Set of 4    4.50 .75

A1305

Calgary '88 Winter Olympic Games Winners — A1306

Designs: 10ch, Pirmin Zurbriggen (Switzerland). 20ch, Yvonne Van Gennip (Netherlands). 30ch, Marjo Matikainen (Finland). 40ch, USSR hockey team. 80ch, Katarina Witt (DDR).

**1988, Nov. 1** — **Perf. 13¼**
2791-2794　A1305　Set of 4　3.25　1.15

**Souvenir Sheet**
2795　A1306　80ch multicolored　2.25　.50
　a.　Overprinted with names of
　　　winners in selvage　2.25　.50

First Man and Woman in
Space — A1307

Designs: 20ch, Yuri Gagarin. 40ch, Valentina Tereshkova.

**1988, Nov. 12** — **Perf. 13¼**
2796　A1307　Pair, #a.-b.　1.60　.60
　a.　20ch multicolored　.40　.25
　b.　40ch multicolored　1.00　.45

A1308

INDIA '89 Int'l Philatelic Exhib., New
Delhi — A1309

Design: 20ch, Jawaharlal Nehru (1889-1964), 100th anniversary of birth.
60ch, Fan Dance, Korean Folk Dance.

**1988, Dec. 15** — **Perf. 11¾x12**
2797　A1308　20ch multicolored　1.10　.25

**Souvenir Sheet**
**Perf. 11¾x11½**
2798　A1309　60ch multicolored　3.25　.40

New Year — A1310

Designs: 10ch, Chollima Statue. 20ch, Painting, Dragon Angler. 40ch, Tortoise Serpent, Kangso tomb mural painting, horiz.

**1989, Jan. 1** — **Perf. 13¼**
2799-2801　A1310　Set of 3　3.25　.50

Archery — A1311

Designs: 10ch, Archery. 15ch, Rifle shooting. 20ch, Pistol shooting. 25ch, Parachuting. 30ch, Launching model glider.

**1989, Jan. 10** — **Perf. 12**
2802-2806　A1311　Set of 5　4.25　.75

National defense training.

A1312

Pets Presented to Kim Il
Sung — A1313

Designs: 10ch, Dobermann pinscher. 20ch, Labrador. 25ch, German shepherd. 30ch, Border collies, horiz. 35ch, Serval, horiz.
80ch, Felix libica.

**1989, Jan. 23** — **Perf. 13½**
2807-2811　A1312　Set of 5　4.50　.85

**Souvenir Sheet**
2812　A1313　80ch multicolored　3.75　.60

Kim Jong Il, 47th Birthday — A1314

**1989, Feb. 16** — **Perf. 11¾x12**
2813　A1314　80ch multicolored　1.75　.45

Agriculture — A1315

**1989, Feb. 25** — **Perf. 12**
2814　A1315　10ch multicolored　.65　.25
　a.　Toned unsurfaced paper, without gun　5.00　—

25th anniversary of publication of Kim Il Sung's Theses on the Socialist Rural Question in Our Country.

Mushrooms and
Wild
Fruits — A1316

Designs: 10ch, Rozites caperata and Vitisamurensis. 20ch, Amanita caesarea and Schizandra chinensis. 25ch, Lactarius hygrophoides and Eleagnus crispa. 30ch, Agaricus placomyces and Actinidia arguta. 35ch, Agaricus arvensis and Lycium chinense. 40ch, Suillus grevillei and Juglans cordiformis.
　1w, Gomphidius roseus and Diospyros lotus.

**1989, Feb. 27** — **Perf. 12**
2815-2820　A1316　Set of 6　7.25　1.15

**Souvenir Sheet**
**Perf. 11½x11¾**
2821　A1316　1w multicolored　4.25　.85

13th World Youth and
Students'
Festival — A1317

Designs: 10ch, Girl. 20ch, Children of different races. 30ch, Fairy, rainbow. 40ch, Young people and Tower of Juche Idea.

**1989, Mar. 18** — **Perf. 12¼**
2822-2825　A1317　Set of 4　2.50　.90
2822a　10ch Soft toned unsurfaced
　　　　paper, without gum　15.00　—
2823a　20ch Soft toned unsurfaced
　　　　paper, without gum　8.00　—
2824a　30ch Soft toned unsurfaced
　　　　paper, without gum　8.00　—
2825a　40ch Soft toned unsurfaced
　　　　paper, without gum　8.00　—
2825b　40ch Stiff dull white un-
　　　　surfaced paper, without
　　　　gum　8.00　—

A1318

Butterflies and Insects — A1319

Designs: 10ch, Parnassius eversmanni. 15ch, Colias heos. 20ch, Dilipa fenestra. 25ch, Buthus martensis. 30ch, Trichogramma ostriniae. 40ch, Damaster constricticollis.
　80ch, Parnassius nomion.

**1989, Mar. 23** — **Perf. 12**
2826　A1318　Sheet of 6, #a.-f.　5.50　.90

**Souvenir Sheet**
2827　A1319　80ch multicolored　3.50　.75

Spring Friendship Art
Festival — A1320

**1989, Apr. 6**
2828　A1320　10ch multicolored　.75　.25

Kim Il Sung, 77th
Birthday — A1321

**1989, Apr. 15** — **Perf. 11½**
2829　A1321　10ch multicolored　.50　.25
　a.　Toned unsurfaced paper,
　　　without gum　10.00　—

Battle of the
Musan Area,
50th
Anniv. — A1322

**1989, May 19** — **Perf. 12**
2830　A1322　10ch multicolored　1.00　.25

Jamo System of Dance
Notation — A1323

Designs: 10ch, Mexican dance. 20ch, Ballet duet in Don Quixote. 25ch, Dance of Guinea. 30ch, Cambodian folk dance.
80ch, Korean folk dance.

**1989, May 30**
2831-2834　A1323　Set of 4　3.50　.60

**Souvenir Sheet**
2835　A1323　80ch multicolored　3.00　.50

A1324　　　　　A1325

**1989, June 8** — **Perf. 11½**
2836　A1324　5ch deep blue　.25　.25
　a.　Soft toned unsurfaced paper,
　　　without gum　15.00　—
2837　A1325　10ch red brown　.30　.25

13th World Festival of Youth and Students.

Cartoon, Badger
Measures the
Height — A1326

Designs: 10ch, Badger racing cat and bear to flag pole. 40ch, Cat and bear climbing pole, while badger measures shadow. 50ch, Badger winning the prize.

**1989, June 21**
2838-2840　A1326　Set of 3　3.75　.60

Astronomy — A1327

20ch, Chomosongdae Observatory.
80ch, Saturn (horiz.)

**1989, June 29** — **Perf. 12**
2841　A1327　20ch multicolored　1.30　.25

**Souvenir Sheet**
2842　A1327　80ch multicolored　2.75　.50

Eugène Delacroix's *Liberty Guiding the People* — A1328

**1989, July 7**      **Perf. 12x11½**
2843 A1328 70ch multicolored    2.75 1.75
PHILEXFRANCE '89, Int'l Philatelic Exhib., Paris.

BRASILIANA '89, Int'l Philatelic Exhib., Rio de Janeiro — A1329

**1989, July 28**      **Perf. 12**
2844 A1329 40ch Pele, #1714    1.30 .30

Fire Brigade and Emergency Medical Services — A1330

Designs: 10ch, Nurse and ambulance. 20ch, Surgeon and ambulance. 30ch, Fireman and fire engine. 40ch, Fireman and fire engine (diff.)

**1989, Aug. 12**
2845-2848 A1330 Set of 4    5.50 .60

Plants Presented as Gifts to Kim Il Sung — A1331

Designs: 10ch, Kafir lily (Clivia miniata). 15ch, Tulips (Tulipa gesneriana). 20ch, Flamingo lily (Anthurium andreanum). 25ch, Rhododendron obtusum. 30ch, Daffodils (Narcissus pseudonarcissus). 80ch, (Gerbera hybrida).

**1989, Aug. 19**
2849-2853 A1331 Set of 5    5.00 .90
**Souvenir Sheet**
2854 A1331 80ch multicolored    4.25 .50

150th Anniv. of Postage Stamps / STAMP WORLD LONDON '90 Int'l Philatelic Exhib. — A1332

Designs: 5ch, Letter, ship, plane, map. 10ch, Letters and mail box. 20ch, Stamps, magnifying glass, tongs. 30ch, Fiirst stamps pf DPRK. 40ch, UPU emblem, headquarters, Berne. 50ch, Sir Rowland Hill and Penny Black.

**1989, Aug. 27**
2855-2860 A1332 Set of 6    6.75 1.15

A1333

Alpine Flowers — A1334

Designs: 10ch, Iris setosa. 15ch, Aquilegia japonica. 20ch, Bistorta incana. 25ch, Rhodiola elongata. 30ch, Sanguisorba sitchensis. 80ch, Trollius japonicus.

**1989, Sept. 8**      **Perf. 11½**
2861-2865 A1333 Set of 5    4.75 .90
**Souvenir Sheet**
2866 A1334 80ch multicolored    3.25 .50

Trees bearing Anti-Japanese Patriotic Slogans — A1335

Designs: 10ch, "20 million compatriots, an anti-Japanese heroine of Korea rose on Mt. Paektu," inscribed on tree, Mt. Paektu. 3w, "The future of Korea is bright with the Luminous Star of Mt. Paektu," inscribed on tree, Qun-dong, Pyongyang. 5w, "The General Star of Mt. Paektu shines three thousand-ri expanse of land," inscribed on tree, Mt. Kanbaek.

**1989, Sept. 21**      **Perf. 12¼**
2867-2869 A1335 Set of 3    16.50 10.00
Compare with No. 2885.

Children's Games — A1336

Designs: 10ch, Girl skipping rope. 20ch, Boy with whirligig. 30ch, Boy flying kite. 40ch, Girl spinning top.

**1989, Sept. 30**      **Perf. 12**
2870 A1336 Block of 4, #a.-d.    3.75 .75
   a.   10ch multicolored        .25 .25
   b.   20ch multicolored        1.60 .25
   c.   30ch multicolored        .50 .25
   d.   40ch multicolored        .60 .25

Int'l March for Peace and Reunification of Korea — A1337

**1989, Oct. 1**      **Perf. 11½x12**
2871 A1337 80ch multicolored    2.75 1.60

Locomotives — A1338

Designs: 10ch, Electric train entering station yard. 20ch, Electric train crossing bridge.

25ch, Diesel locomotive. 30ch, Diesel locomotive (diff.). 40ch, Steam locomotive. 50ch, Steam locomotive (diff.).

**1989, Oct. 19**      **Perf. 11¾x12¼**
2872-2877 A1338 Set of 6    5.50 1.15

14th World Soccer Championship, *Italia '90* — A1339

Designs: 10ch, Players and map of Italy. 20ch, Free kick. 30ch, Goal scrimmage. 40ch, Goalkeeper blocking ball.

**1989, Oct. 28**      **Perf. 12x11¾**
2878-2881 A1339 Set of 4    3.75 .60

Magellan A1340

**1989, Nov. 25**      **Perf. 12**
2882 A1340 30ch multicolored    1.15 .25
*Descobrex '89* International Philatelic Exhibition, Portugal.

A1341

A1342

10ch, Mangyong Hill and snow-covered pine branches. 20ch, Koguryo warriors.

**Perf. 11½ (#2883), 12 (#2884)**
**1990, Jan. 1**
2883 A1341 10ch multicolored    .25 .25
   a.   Toned unsurfaced paper, without gum    15.00 —
2884 A1342 20ch multicolored    1.10 .25
   a.   Toned unsurfaced paper, without gum    5.00 —
New Year.

Tree, Mt. Paektu, Bearing Anti-Japanese Patriotic Slogan — A1343

**1990, Jan. 12**      **Perf. 11½**
2885 A1343 5ch multicolored    .50 .25
   a.   Toned unsurfaced paper, without gum    5.00 —

Dogs — A1344

Designs: 20ch, Ryukwoli. 30ch, Phalryuki. 40ch, Komdungi. 50ch, Oluki.

**1990, Jan. 17**
2886 A1344 Sheet of 4    5.00 1.35
   a.   20ch multicolored    .85 .25
   b.   30ch multicolored    .85 .25
   c.   40ch multicolored    .85 .25
   d.   50ch multicolored    .85 .25

Birthplace, Mt. Paektu — A1345

**1990, Feb. 16**
2887 A1345 10ch dp red brn    .50 .25
   a.   Brown unsurfaced paper, without gum    5.00 —
Kim Jong Il's 48th birthday.

Stone Age Man — A1346

Designs: 10ch, Primitive man, stone tools. 20ch, Paleolithic and Neolithic men, camp scene.

**1990, Feb. 21**
2888-2889 A1346 Set of 2    2.75 .30

Bridges — A1347

Designs: 10ch, Rungra Bridge, Pyongyang. 20ch, Pothong Bridge, Pyongyang. 30ch, Suspension bridge between Sinuiju-Ryucho Island. 40ch, Chungsongui Bridge, Pyongyang.

**1990, Feb. 27**      **Perf. 11½**
2890-2893 A1347 Set of 4    4.25 .60
2890a   10ch Thin, coarse brownish paper, without gum    5.00 —

Traditional Warriors' Costumes — A1348

Designs: 20ch, Infantryman (3rd century BC-7th century AD). 30ch, Archer. 50ch, Commander in armor (3rd century BC-7th century AD). 70ch, Koguryo Period officer (10th-14th centuries).

**1990, Mar. 18**
2894-2897 A1348 Set of 4    5.75 1.75
2897a   70ch Dull white unsurfaced paper, without gum    5.00 —

Crabs — A1349

Designs: 20ch, Atergatis subdentatus. 30ch, Platylambrus validus. 50ch, Uca arcuata.

**1990, Mar. 25**
2898-2900 A1349 Set of 3    2.75 .60

Dancers — A1350

**1990, Apr. 7**
2901 A1350 10ch multicolored    .50 .25
Spring Friendship Art Festival, Pyongyang.

A1351

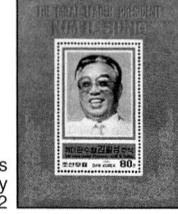

Kim Il Sung's
78th Birthday
A1352

Designs: 10ch, 'Fork in the Road' Monument, Mangyongdae Revolutionary Site. 80ch, Kim Il Sung.

**1990, Apr. 15**    *Perf. 11½x11¾*
2902 A1351 10ch multicolored    .50   .25
**Souvenir Sheet**
2903 A1352 80ch multicolored    2.25   .50

Cacti — A1353

Designs: 10ch, Gynmocalycium sp. 30ch, Phyllocactus hybridus. 50ch, Epiphyllum truncatum.

**1990, Apr. 21**    *Perf. 12¼*
2904-2906 A1353   Set of 3    3.75   .60

A1354

Stamp World London '90 — A1355

Designs: 20ch, Exhibition emblem. 70ch, Sir Rowland Hill.

**1990, May 3**    *Perf. 11½*
2907 A1354 20ch multicolored    .85   .25
**Souvenir Sheet**
2908 A1355 70ch multicolored    2.50   1.10

A1356

Peafowl — A1357

Designs: 10ch, Congo peafowl (Afropavo congensis). 20ch, Common peafowl (Pavo cristatus). 70ch, Common peafowl with tail displayed.

**1990, May 10**    *Perf. 11¾x12*
2909-2910 A1356 Set of 2    2.75   .60
**Souvenir Sheet**
2911 A1357 70ch multicolored    2.75   .60

Bio-engineering — A1358

Designs: 10ch, Dolphin and submarine. 20ch, Bat and sonar dish, satellite. 30ch, Eagle and airplanes. 40ch, Squid and jets.

**1990, May 24**
2912 A1358   Sheet of 4, #a.-d.    6.50 1.15
   *a.*   10ch multicolored    1.15   .25
   *b.*   20ch multicolored    1.15   .25
   *c.*   30ch multicolored    1.15   .25
   *d.*   40ch multicolored    1.15   .25

BELGICA '90 Int'l
Philatelic Exhib.,
Brussels — A1359

Designs: 10ch, Rembrandt, *Self Portrait.* 20ch, Raphael, *Self Portrait.* 30ch, Rubens, *Self Portrait.*

**1990, June 2**    *Perf. 12¼x12*
2913-2915 A1359 Set of 3    2.00   .40

Düsseldorf '90, 10th
Int'l Youth Philatelic
Exhib. — A1360

Designs: 20ch, Steffi Graf, tennis player, with bouquet. 30ch, Exhibition emblem. 70ch, K.H. Rummenigge, German soccer player.

**1990, June 20**
2916-2918 A1360   Set of 3    6.50   .75

A1361

Designs: 10ch, Games mascot, Workers' Stadium, Beijing. 30ch, Chollina Statue and Korean athletes. 40ch, Games emblem, athletes.

**1990, July 14**
2919-2921 A1361 Set of 3    1.75   .60
11th Asian Games, Beijing (Nos. 2919-2920). Third Asian Winter Games, Samjiyon (No. 2921).

14th World Cup
Soccer
Championship
A1362

Designs: 15ch, Emblem of F.I.F.A. (Federation of Football Associations). 20ch, Jules Rimet. 25ch, Soccer ball. 30ch, Olympic Stadium, Rome. 35ch, Goalkeeper. 40ch, Emblem of the German Football Association. 80ch, Emblem of German Football Association and trophy.

**1990, Aug. 8**    *Perf. 13½*
2922-2927 A1362   Set of 6    5.50   .90
**Souvenir Sheet**
2928 A1362 80ch multicolored    2.75 1.35

New Zealand '90
Int'l Philatelic
Exhib., Auckland
A1363

**1990, Aug. 24**    *Perf. 12*
2929 A1363 30ch multicolored    1.60   .40

*Summer at Chipson Peak — A1364*

**1990, Aug. 24**    *Perf. 11½*
2930 A1364 80ch multicolored    2.75   .50
Europa '90 International Stamp Fair, Riccione.

Koguryo
Wedding
Procession
A1365

Designs: 10ch, Man on horse blowing bugle. 30ch, Bridegroom on horse. 50ch, Bride in carriage. 1w, Man on horse beating drum.

**1990, Sept. 3**    *Perf. 12*
2931   Strip of 4, #a.-d.    5.50   .75
   *a.* A1365 10ch multicolored    1.15   .25
   *b.* A1365 30ch multicolored    1.15   .25
   *c.* A1365 50ch multicolored    1.15   .25
   *d.* A1365 1w multicolored    1.15   .25
Printed in setenant strips of four within the sheet.

A1366

Pan-National Rally for Peace and
Reunification of Korea — A1367

Designs: 10ch, Rally emblem, crowd descending Mt. Paektu. 1w, Crowd watching dancers.

**1990, Sept. 15**
2932 A1366 10ch multicolored    .50   .25
**Souvenir Sheet**
2933 A1367 1w multicolored    2.50   .50

Insects — A1368

Designs: 20ch, Praying mantis (Mantis religiosa). 30ch, Lady bug (Coccinella septempunctata). 40ch, Pheropsophus jussoensis. 70ch, Phyllium siccifolium.

**1990, Sept. 20**
2934-2936A A1368   Set of 4    5.50 1.00

Soccer Players — A1369

No. 2938, North and South Korean players entering May Day Stadium.

**1990, Oct. 11**
2937 A1369 Pair, #a.-b.    2.50   .40
   *a.*   10ch multicolored    1.15   .25
   *b.*   20ch multicolored    1.15   .25
**Souvenir Sheet**
2938 A1369 1w multicolored    4.25   .75
North-South Reunification Soccer Games, Pyongyang.

National Reunification
Concert — A1370

**1990, Oct. 17**
2939 A1370 10ch multicolored    .50   .25

Farm Animals — A1371

Designs: 10ch, Ox. 20ch, Pig. 30ch, Goat. 40ch, Sheep. 50ch, Horse.

**1990, Oct. 18**
2940-2944 A1371   Set of 5    5.25   .80
*2944a*    Sheet of 10, 2 ea #2940-2944    12.00 1.60

A1372

A1373

### Chinese Entry Into Korean War, 40th Anniv. — A1374

Designs: 10ch, N. Korean and Communist Chinese soldiers. 20ch, Korean civilians welcoming Chinese soldiers. 30ch, Battle scene, victorious soldiers. 40ch, Postwar reconstruction.
80ch, Friendship Monument.

**1990, Oct. 23**

| | | | | |
|---|---|---|---|---|
| 2945 | A1372 | 10ch multicolored | .25 | .25 |
| 2946 | A1373 | 20ch multicolored | .75 | .25 |
| 2947 | A1373 | 30ch multicolored | .90 | .25 |
| 2948 | A1373 | 40ch multicolored | 1.35 | .25 |
| | Nos. 2945-2948 (4) | | 3.25 | 1.00 |

**Souvenir Sheet**
**Perf. 11¾x11½**

| | | | | |
|---|---|---|---|---|
| 2949 | A1374 | 80ch multicolored | 2.75 | .50 |

For overprint see No. 3282.

### UN Development Program, 40th Anniv. — A1375

**1990, Oct. 24**  **Perf. 13¼**

| | | | | |
|---|---|---|---|---|
| 2950 | A1375 | 1w multicolored | 3.75 | 1.10 |

### Fish — A1376

Designs: 10ch, Sturgeon (Acipenser mikadoi). 20ch, Sea bream (Sparus macrocephalus). 30ch, Flying fish (Cypsilurus agoö). 40ch, Fat greenling (Heragrammos otakii). 50ch, Ray (Myliobatus tobeijei).

**1990, Nov. 20**  **Perf. 12**

| | | | | |
|---|---|---|---|---|
| 2951-2955 | A1376 | Set of 5 | 5.25 | 1.75 |
| 2955a | Sheet of 10, 2 ea #2951-2955 | | 11.00 | 3.75 |

### New Year — A1377

**1990, Dec. 1**

| | | | | |
|---|---|---|---|---|
| 2956 | A1377 | 40ch multicolored | 1.60 | .25 |

### Birds — A1378

Designs: 10ch, Moorhen (Gallinula chloropus). 20ch, Jay (Garrulus glandarius). 30ch, Three-toed woodpecker (Picodes tridactylus). 40ch, Whimbrel (Numenius phaeopus). 50ch, Water rail (Rallus aquaticus)

**1990, Dec. 18**  **Perf. 12**

| | | | | |
|---|---|---|---|---|
| 2957-2961 | A1378 | Set of 5 | 6.00 | 1.75 |
| 2961a | Sheet of 10, 2 ea #2957-2961 | | 12.00 | 4.50 |

A1379

### Pandas — A1380

Designs: 10ch, Giant panda. 20ch, Two giant pandas feeding. 30ch, Giant panda on limb. 40ch, Giant panda on rock. 50ch, Pair of giant pandas. 60ch, Giant panda in tree.

**1991, Jan. 10**  **Perf. 11¾x12**

| | | | | |
|---|---|---|---|---|
| 2962-2967 | A1379 | Set of 6 | 6.50 | 1.60 |
| 2967a | Sheet of 6, #2962-2967 | | 6.50 | 1.60 |

**Souvenir Sheet**
**Perf. 11½**

| | | | | |
|---|---|---|---|---|
| 2968 | A1380 | 1w multicolored | 3.00 | .60 |

For surcharges, see No. 4536-4537.

A1381

### Revolutionary Sites — A1382

**1991, Jan. 10**  **Perf. 12**

| | | | | |
|---|---|---|---|---|
| 2969 | A1381 | 5ch Changsan | .25 | .25 |
| 2970 | A1382 | 10ch Oun | .30 | .25 |

### Endangered Birds — A1383

Designs: 10ch, Black-faced spoonbills (Platalea minor). 20ch, Gray herons (Ardea cinerea). 30ch, Great egrets (Egretta alba). 40ch, Manchurian cranes (Grus japonensis). 50ch, Japanese white-necked cranes (Grus vipio). 70ch, White storks (Ciconia boyciana).

**1991, Feb. 5**

| | | | | |
|---|---|---|---|---|
| 2971-2976 | A1383 | Set of 6 | 5.50 | 1.30 |
| 2976a | Sheet of 6, #2971-2976 | | 6.75 | 1.60 |

### Alpine Butterflies A1384

Designs: 10ch, Clossiana angarensis. 20ch, Erebia embla. 30ch, Nymphalis antiopa. 40ch, Polygonia c-album. 50ch, Colias erate. 60ch, Thecla betulae.

**1991, Feb. 20**  **Perf. 13¼**

| | | | | |
|---|---|---|---|---|
| 2977-2982 | A1384 | Set of 6 | 6.75 | 2.25 |
| 2982a | Sheet of 6, #2977-2982 | | 6.75 | 2.25 |

### Fungi — A1385

Designs: 10ch, Hydnum repandum. 20ch, Phylloporus rhodoxanthus. 30ch, Calvatia craniformis. 40ch, Ramaria botrytis. 50ch, Russula integra.

**1991, Feb. 26**  **Perf. 12x12¼**

| | | | | |
|---|---|---|---|---|
| 2983-2987 | A1385 | Set of 5 | 4.50 | 1.15 |
| 2987a | Sheet of 10, 2 ea #2983-2987 | | 9.00 | 2.25 |

For surcharge, see No. 4546.

A1386

### Revolutionary Sites — A1387

**1991, Mar. 15**  **Perf. 12**

| | | | | |
|---|---|---|---|---|
| 2988 | A1386 | 10ch Kumchon | .30 | .25 |
| 2989 | A1387 | 40ch Samdung | 1.10 | .30 |

A1388

### Silkworm Research — A1389

Designs: 10ch, Dr. Kye Ung (1893-1967), silkworm researcher. 20ch, Chinese oak silk moth, Antheraea pernyi. 30ch, Attacus ricini. 40ch, Antheraea yamamai. 50ch, Bombyx mori. 60ch, Aetias artemis.

**1991, Mar. 27**

| | | | | |
|---|---|---|---|---|
| 2990 | A1388 | 10ch multicolored | .25 | .25 |
| 2991 | A1389 | 20ch multicolored | .60 | .30 |
| 2992 | A1389 | 30ch multicolored | .75 | .40 |
| 2993 | A1389 | 40ch multicolored | 1.10 | .50 |
| 2994 | A1389 | 50ch multicolored | 1.45 | .75 |
| 2995 | A1389 | 60ch multicolored | 1.75 | .75 |
| a. | Sheet of 6, #2990-2995 | | 6.00 | 3.25 |
| | Nos. 2990-2995 (6) | | 5.90 | 2.95 |

### 9th Spring Friendship Art Festival, Pyongyang — A1390

**1991, Apr. 3**

| | | | | |
|---|---|---|---|---|
| 2996 | A1390 | 10ch multicolored | .50 | .25 |

### Antarctic Exploration — A1391

Designs: 10ch, Penguins. 20ch, Research station. 30ch, Elephant seals. 40ch, Research ship. 50ch, Black-backed gulls.
80ch, DPRK flag and map of Antarctica.

**1991, Apr. 20**  **Perf. 11¾x12**

| | | | | |
|---|---|---|---|---|
| 2997-3001 | A1391 | Set of 5 | 5.50 | 1.15 |
| 3001a | Sheet of 6, #2997-3002 | | 8.25 | 1.60 |

**Souvenir Sheet**
**Perf. 11¾**

| | | | | |
|---|---|---|---|---|
| 3002 | A1391 | 80ch multicolored | 2.75 | .50 |

A single stamp like that in No. 3002 is included in No. 3001a.

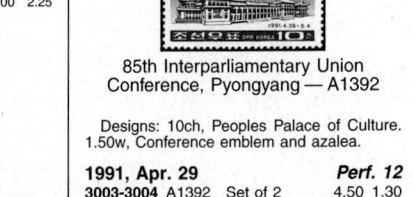

### 85th Interparliamentary Union Conference, Pyongyang — A1392

Designs: 10ch, Peoples Palace of Culture. 1.50w, Conference emblem and azalea.

**1991, Apr. 29**  **Perf. 12**

| | | | | |
|---|---|---|---|---|
| 3003-3004 | A1392 | Set of 2 | 4.50 | 1.30 |

### Map and Kim Jong Ho — A1393

**1991, May 8**  **Perf. 11¾x12**

| | | | | |
|---|---|---|---|---|
| 3005 | A1393 | 90ch multicolored | 2.25 | .75 |

### Dinosaurs A1394

Designs: a, 10ch, Cynognathus. b, 20ch, Brontosaurus. c, 30ch, Stegosaurus and allosaurus. d, 40ch, Pterosauria. e, 50ch, Ichthyosaurus.

**1991, May 21**  **Perf. 12x11¾**

| | | | | |
|---|---|---|---|---|
| 3006 | A1394 | Strip of 5 + label | 6.75 | 1.60 |
| 3006f | Sheet of 5 + label | | 15.50 | 1.75 |

### Barcelona '92 Olympic Games A1395

Designs: No. 3011, 10ch, 100-Meter dash. No. 3012, 10ch, Hurdle race. No. 3013 20ch, Broad jump. No. 3014, 20ch, Throwing discus. No. 3015, 30ch, Shot-put. No. 3016, 30ch, Pole vault. No. 3017, 40ch, High jump. No. 3018, 40ch, Javelin throw.
No. 3019, 80ch, 400-meter race. No. 3020, 80ch, 1500-meter race.

**1991, June 18**

| | | | | |
|---|---|---|---|---|
| 3011-3018 | A1395 | Set of 8 | 3.75 | 1.30 |
| 3018a | Sheet of 10, #3011-3020 | | 11.50 | 2.50 |

**Souvenir Sheets**
**Perf. 11½x11¾**

| | | | | |
|---|---|---|---|---|
| 3019-3020 | A1395 | Set of 2 | 3.25 | 1.15 |

No. 3018a contains single stamps from Nos. 3019-3020 in addition to Nos. 3011-3018.

### Cats A1396

Designs: 10ch, Cats and birds. 20ch, Cat and rat. 30ch, Cat and butterfly. 40ch, Cats and ball. 50ch, Cat and frog.

**1991, July 21**     **Perf. 13¼**
3021-3025 A1396 Set of 5    4.75 2.00

For surcharges, see Nos. 4538, 4547.

Riccione '91 Int'l Stamp Fair — A1397

**1991, Aug. 27**     **Perf. 11¾x12**
3026 A1397 80ch multicolored    2.50 .60

Horses — A1398

Designs: 10ch, Equus caballus. 20ch, Equus asinus and Equus caballus. 30ch, Equus przewalskii. 40ch, Equus asinus. 50ch, Equus caballus, diff.

**1991, Sept. 2**     **Perf. 13½**
3027-3031 A1398 Set of 5    4.50 1.15
3031a   Sheet of 5, #3027-3031   4.50 1.30

A1399

Phila Nippon '91 International Stamp Exhibition — A1400

Fish: 10ch, Pennant coral fish (Heniochus acuminatus). 20ch, Big-spotted trigger fish (Balistoides conspicillum). 30ch, Anemone fish (Amphiprion frenatus). 40ch, Blue surgeon fish (Paracanthurus hepatus). 50ch, Angel fish (Pterophyllum eimekei). 80ch, Tetras (Hyphessobrycon innesi).

**1991, Sept. 20**     **Perf. 12x12¼**
3032-3036 A1399 Set of 5    4.50 1.15
3036a   Sheet of 5, #3032-3036   4.50 1.15
**Souvenir Sheet**
**Perf. 11¾**
3037 A1400 80ch multicolored    4.50 .60

No. 3036 is airmail.

Flowers — A1401

Designs: 10ch, Begonia. 20ch, Gerbera. 30ch, Rhododendrons. 40ch, Phalaenopsis. 50ch, Impatiens sultani. 60ch, Streptocarpus.

**1991, Oct. 16**     **Perf. 12¼x12**
3038-3043 A1401 Set of 6    6.00 1.60
3043a   Sheet of 6, #3038-3043   6.00 1.75

Nos. 3041-3043 commemorate Canada '92 International Youth Stamp Exhibition, Montreal, and include the exhibition emblem.

Panmunjon
A1402

**1991, Oct. 12**     **Perf. 12**
3044 A1402 10ch multicolored    .60 .25

Magnolia — A1403

**1991, Nov. 1**     **Perf. 11½**
3045 A1403 10ch multicolored    .60 .25

DPRK National Flower.

Women's World Soccer Championship, China — A1404

Designs: 10ch, Dribbling. 20ch, Dribbling, diff. 30ch, Heading the ball. 40ch, Overhead kick. 50ch, Tackling. 60ch, Goalkeeper.

**1991, Nov. 3**     **Perf. 12**
3046-3051 A1404 Set of 6    6.00 1.60
3051a   Sheet of 6, #3046-3051   6.00 1.75

A1405

Monkeys — A1406

Designs: 10ch, Squirrel monkeys (Samiri sciureus). 20ch, Pygmy marmosets (Cebuella pygmaea). 30ch, Red-handed tamarins (Saquinas midas). 80ch, Monkey leaping.

**1992, Jan. 1**
3052-3054 A1405 Set of 3    2.00 .65
3054a   Sheet of 3, #3052-3054   2.25 .75
**Souvenir Sheet**
**Perf. 11¾x11½**
3055 A1406 80ch multicolored    2.25 .90

A1407

Birds of Prey — A1408

Designs: 10ch, Bubo bubo. 20ch, Buteo buteo. 30ch, Haliaeetus vocifer. 40ch, Haliaeetus pelagicus. 50ch, Aquila chrysaetos. 80ch, Falco tinnunculus.

**1992, Jan. 5**     **Perf. 13¼**
3056-3060 A1407 Set of 5    4.50 1.60
3060a   Sheet of 12, 2 #3056-3060   9.00 3.25
   + 2 labels
**Souvenir Sheet**
**Perf. 11½**
3061 A1408 80ch multicolored    2.25 .60

No. 3060a, Granada '92 International Stamp Exhibition. For surcharge, see No. 4609.

A1409

50th Birthday of Kim Jong II — A1410

Designs: 10ch, Birthplace, Mt. Paektu. 20ch, Mt. Paektu. 30ch, Lake Chon on top of Mt. Paektu. 40ch, Lake Samji. 80ch, *Snowstorm in Mt. Paektu.*

**1992, Feb. 16**     **Perf. 12x11¾**
3062-3065 A1409 Set of 4    3.00 .75
**Souvenir Sheet**
**Perf. 11¾x11½**
3066 A1410 80ch multicolored    2.75 .60

Transport
A1411

Designs: 10ch, Bus, "Jipsam 88." 20ch, Bus, "Pyongyang 86." 30ch, Trolley bus, "Chollima 84." 40ch, Bus, "Kwangbok Sonyon." 50ch, Tram. 60ch, July 17 Tram.

**1992, Feb. 20**     **Perf. 12¼**
3067-3072 A1411 Set of 6    6.00 1.60
3072a   Sheet of 6, #3067-3072   6.00 1.75

No. 3072a, Essen '92 International Stamp Fair.

Spring Fellowship Art Festival, Pyongyang — A1412

**1992, Apr. 7**
3073 A1412 10ch multicolored    .50 .25

A1413

80th Birthday of Kim II Sung — A1414

Revolutionary Sites: 10ch (No. 3074), Birthplace, Mangyongdao. 10ch (No. 3075), Party emblem, Turubong. 10ch (No. 3076), Map, Ssuksom. 10ch (No. 3077), Statue of soldier, Tongchang. 40ch (No. 3078), Chollima Statue, Kangson. 40ch (No. 3079), Cogwheels, Taean. 1.20w, Monument, West Sea Barrage. 80ch, Kim II Sung among participants in the April Spring Friendship Art Festival.

**1992, Apr. 15**
3074-3080 A1413 Set of 7    6.75 2.00
**Souvenir Sheet**
**Perf. 11½**
3081 A1414 80ch multicolored    2.75 .60

No. 2080 is airmail.

Kang Ban Sok, Mother of Kim II Sung, Birth Centenary — A1415

**1992, Apr. 21**     **Perf. 13¼**
3082 A1415 80ch multicolored    2.00 .60

Korean People's Army, 60th Anniv. — A1416

Designs (all 10ch): No. 3083, Soldier, troops on parade. No. 3084, Pilot, soldiers. No. 3085, Soldier with two civilian women.

**1992, Apr. 25**     **Perf. 12¼**
3083-3085 A1416 Set of 3    1.00 .25
3085a   Sheet of 9, 4 #3085, 2 ea.   2.75 .90
   #3083-3084 + label

25th Olympic Games, Barcelona '92 — A1417

Women's events: 10ch, Hurdle race. 20ch, High jump. 30ch, Shot-put. 40ch, 200-meter race. 50ch, Broad jump. 60ch, Javelin throw. 80ch, 800-meter race.

**1992, May 10**     **Perf. 12x11¾**
3086-3091 A1417 Set of 6    6.00 1.60
3091a   Sheet of 8, #3086-3092 + la-   8.75 2.25
   bel
**Souvenir Sheet**
3092 A1417 80ch multicolored    2.50 .60

Prehistoric Man — A1418

Designs: 10ch, Planting crops. 20ch, Family in shelter, with cooking pot. 30ch, Plowing. 40ch, Indoor life. 50ch, Laying a dolmen.

**1992, June 1**     **Perf. 12x11¾**
3093-3097 A1418 Set of 5    4.50 1.15
3097a   Sheet of 5, #3093-3097 +   5.50 1.30
   label

Birds — A1419

Designs: 10ch, Dryocopus javensis. 20ch, Phasianis colchicus. 30ch, Ciconia boyciana. 40ch, Pitta brachyura. 50ch, Syrrhaptes paradoxus. 60ch, Lyrurus tetrix. 80ch, Sturnus sturnus.

**1992, June 28**      **Perf. 11½**
3098-3103 A1419 Set of 6    6.50 1.60
*3103a*   Sheet of 7, #3098-3104 + label   13.50 —
**Souvenir Sheet**
3104 A1419 80ch multicolored   3.25 1.30
No. 3103a contains a single stamp from No. 3104 in addtion to Nos. 3098-3103.

North-South Joint Statement, 20th Anniv. — A1420

**1992, July 4**
3105 A1420 1.50w multicolored   4.25 1.30
**Souvenir Sheet**
3106 A1420 3w multicolored   8.25 2.50
No. 3106 contains two copies of No. 3105 and label.

Flowers — A1421

Designs: 10ch, Bougainvillea spectabilis. 20ch, Ixora chinensis. 30ch, Dendrobium taysuwie. 40ch, Columnea gloriosa. 50ch, Crinum. 60ch, Ranunculus asiaticus.

**1992, July 15**      **Perf. 12¼**
3107-3112 A1421 Set of 6   6.00 1.60
*3112a*   Sheet of 8, #3107-3112 + 2 labels   6.50 1.75
No. 3112a, Genova '92 International Stamp Exhibition.

The Solar System — A1422

No. 3113: a, Satellite, Venus, Earth, Mars. b, Jupiter. c, Saturn. d, Uranus. e, Neptune, Pluto.
80ch, Earth.

**1992, Aug. 10**      **Perf. 11½**
3113 A1422 50ch Strip of 5, #a-e 7.25 2.25
*3113f*   Sheet of 5, #3113, + 5 labels 8.25 2.50
**Souvenir Sheet**
3114 A1422 80ch multicolored   2.25 1.35

Riccione '92 Int'l Stamp Fair — A1423

Designs: 10ch, C-class yacht. 20ch, Sailboard. 30ch, Rager-class yacht. 40ch, Pin-class yacht. 50ch, 470-class yacht. 60ch, Fair emblem.

**1992, Aug. 27**      **Perf. 12¼**
3119-3124 A1423 Set of 6   6.00 2.00
*3119a*   Sheet of 6 stamps, 2 ea. #3119, 3121, 3123   6.00 2.25
*3120a*   Sheet of 6 stamps, 2 ea. #3120, 3122, 3124   6.00 2.25

A1424

U.C. Sampdoria, Italian Soccer Champion 1991 — A1425

Designs: a, 20ch, Moreno Mannini, defender. b, 30ch, Gianluca Vialli, forward. c, 40ch, Pietro Vierchowod, back. d, 50ch, Fausto Pari, center-half. e, 60ch, Roberto Mancini, forward. f, 1w, club president.
1w, Vialli and Riccardo Garrone, president of club sponsor, ERG.

**1992, Aug. 31**      **Perf. 12**
3125   A1424   Sheet of 6, #a.-f.   8.25 2.75
**Souvenir Sheet**
**Perf. 11½x12**
3131 A1425   1w multicolored   2.75 1.35

A1426

8th World Taekwondo Championship, Pyongyang — A1427

Designs: 10ch, Team pattern. 30ch, Side kick. 50ch, Flying high kick. 70ch, Flying twisting kick. 90ch, Black-belt breaking tiles with fist.
1.20w, Flying twin foot side kick; Choe Hong Hin, president of International Taekwon-Do Federation, in margin.

**1992, Sept. 1**      **Perf. 12**
3132-3136 A1426 Set of 5   7.25 2.25
*3136a*   Sheet of 5, #3132-3136 + label   7.25 2.25
**Souvenir Sheet**
3137 A1427 1.20w multicolored   3.75 1.60
No. 3137 is airmail.

Frogs and Toads — A1428

Designs: No. 3138, 40ch, Rana chosenica. No. 3139, 40ch, Rana arvalis. No. 3140, 40ch, Bufo bufo. No. 3141, 70ch, Rana nigromaculata. No. 3142, 70ch , Hyla japonica. No. 3143, 70ch Rana coreana.

**1992, Sept. 10**      **Perf. 12¼**
3138-3143 A1428 Set of 6   9.00 2.75
*3139a*   Sheet of 8, 4 #3139, 2 ea. #3138, #3140 + label   13.50 4.50
*3142a*   Sheet of 8, 4 #3142, 2 ea. #3141, #3143 + label   13.50 4.50
No. 3143 is airmail.

World Environment Day — A1429

Designs: 10ch, Rhododendron mucronulatum. 30ch, Hirundo rustica. 40ch, Stewartia koreana. 50ch, Dictoptera aurora. 70ch, Metasequoia glyptostroboides. 90ch, Hynobius leechi. 1.20w, Gingko biloba. 1.40w, Cottus poecilopus.

**1992, Oct. 20**      **Perf. 12**
3144-3151 A1429 Set of 8   17.50 4.50
*3151a*   Sheet of 8 stamps, #3144-3151   18.00 4.75
Nos. 3150 and 3151 are airmail.

Whales and Dolphins A1430

Designs: No. 3152, 50ch, Balaenoptera physalus. No. 3153, 50ch, Delphinus delphis. No. 3154, 50ch, Orcinus orca. No. 3155, 50ch, Megaptera nodosa. No. 3156, 50ch, Berardius bairdii. No. 3157, 50ch, Physeter catadon.

**1992, Oct. 20**
3152-3157 A1430 Set of 6   11.00 2.50
*3152a*   Sheet of 3, #3152-3154   5.00 1.15
*3155a*   Sheet of 3, #3155-3157   5.00 1.15
No. 3157 is airmail. For surcharges, see No. 4548, 4588.

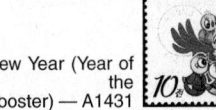

New Year (Year of the Rooster) — A1431

Chickens in various cartoon forms: 10ch, Hen and chicks. 20ch, Young hen. 30ch, Strong cock. 40ch, Prince cock. 50ch, Princess hen. 60ch, King cock.
1.20w, Cock.

**1992, Dec. 7**      **Perf. 11½**
3158-3163 A1431 Set of 6   6.00 1.60
*3163a*   Sheet of 4, #3158-3160, 3163c   3.75 1.35
*3163b*   Sheet of 4, #3161-3163, 3163c   4.50 1.75
**Souvenir Sheet**
3163C A1431 1.20w multicolored 4.50 .90
A single stamp like that in No. 3163C is included in Nos. 3163a and 3163b. For surcharges, see Nos. 4525-4526.

N. Korean Gold Medal Winners at Barcelona Olympics A1432

Designs: 10ch, Choe Chol Su (boxing). 20ch, Pae Kil Su (gymnastics). 50ch, Ri Hak Son (Wrestling). 60ch, Kim Il (wrestling).
No. 3168: a, 30ch, Archer, flame, gold medal, flags of DPRK and Spain. b, 40ch, Emblem, game mascot and Church of the Holy Family, Barcelona.

**1992, Dec. 20**      **Perf. 12**
3164-3167 A1432 Set of 4   4.25 1.10
**Sheet of 6**
3168   #3164-3167, 3168a-3168b 6.50 .60
   *a.*   A1432 30ch multicolored   .35 .25
   *b.*   A1432 40ch multicolored   .50 .30

Fungi — A1433

Designs: 10ch, Golden mushroom (Flammulina velutipes). 20ch, Shaggy caps (Coprinus comatus). 30ch, Ganoderma lucidum. 40ch, Brown mushroom (Lentinus edodes). 50ch, (Volvaria bombycina). 60ch, (Sarcodon aspratus).

1w, Scarlet caterpillar (Cordyceps militaris).

**1993, Jan. 10**      **Perf. 11½**
3169-3174 A1433 Set of 6   6.75 2.25
*3169a*   Sheet of 4, #3169, 3172, 3174, 3175   6.50 2.00
*3170a*   Sheet of 4, #3170, 3171, 3173, 3175   6.50 2.00
**Souvenir Sheet**
3175 A1433   1w multicolored   4.25 .75
A single stamp like that in No. 3175 is included in Nos. 3169a and 3170a.

A1434

Korean Plants — A1435

Designs: 10ch, Keumkangsania asiatica. 20ch, Echinosophora koreensis. 30ch, Abies koreana. 40ch, Benzoin angustifolium. 50ch, Abeliophyllum distichum. 60ch, (Abelia mosanensis).
1w, Pentactina rupicola.

**1993, Jan. 20**      **Perf. 12¼**
3176-3181 A1434 Set of 6   6.50 1.75
*3181a*   Sheet of 6, #3176-3181   6.50 2.00
**Souvenir Sheet**
**Perf. 11½**
3182 A1435   1w multicolored   3.25 1.75

8th Congress of the League of Socialist Working Youth of Korea — A1436

Designs: 10ch, Youths, banner. 20ch, Flame, emblem, motto.

**1993, Jan. 25**      **Perf. 12¼**
3183-3184 A1436 Set of 2   1.35 .40

Phophyong Revolutionary Site Tower & March Corps Emblem — A1437

**1993, Jan. 29**      **Perf. 12x12¼**
3185 A1437 10ch multicolored   .50 .25
70th anniv. of the 250-mile Journey for Learning.

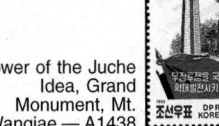

Tower of the Juche Idea, Grand Monument, Mt. Wangjae — A1438

**1993, Feb. 11**
3186 A1438 60ch multicolored   .50 .25
60th anniv. of the Wangjaesan Meeting.

A1439

Kim Jong Il, 51st Birthday — A1440

Designs: 10ch, Kimjongilia (Begonia). 1w, Kim Il Sung writing poem praising Kim Jong Il. Illustration of stamp only. Sheet measures 170mmx95mm, with marginal inscriptions that include reproductions of Kim Il Sung's poem.

**1993, Feb. 16** **Perf. 12**
3187 A1439 10ch multicolored .90 .25
**Souvenir Sheet**
**Perf. 13¼**
3188 A1440 1w multicolored 3.25 .75

Sea Fish — A1441

Designs: 10ch, Pilot fish (Naucrates ductor). 20ch, Japanese stingray (Dasyatis akajei). 30ch, Moonfish (Lampris guttatus). 40ch, Coelacanth (Latimeria chalumnae). 50ch, Grouper (Epinephelus moara). 1.20w, Mako shark (Isurus oxyrhynchus).

**1993, Feb. 25** **Perf. 11½**
3189-3193 A1441 Set of 5 4.50 1.15
3189a Sheet of 2, #3189, #3194 3.00 .45
3190a Sheet of 2, #3190, #3193 3.00 .45
3191a Sheet of 2, #3191, #3192 3.00 .45
**Souvenir Sheet**
3194 A1441 1.20w multicolored 4.25 .75

A single stamp like that in No. 3194 is included in No. 3189a.
No. 3194, Naposta '93.

*Spring on the Hill*, 18th century Korean Painting — A1442

**1993, Mar. 20** **Perf. 12x11½**
3195 A1442 Sheet of 5 6.00 1.60
a.-e. 40ch, any single .90 .30

Spring Friendship Art Festival A1443

**1993, Apr. 5** **Perf. 12x12¼**
3196 A1443 10ch multicolored .75 .25
For surcharge, see No. 4602.

A1444

Kim Il Sung, 80th Birthday, and Publication of *With the Century* — A1445

Designs: 10ch, *With the Century*, Kim Il Sung's Memoir. 1w, Kim Il Sung writing *With the Century*.

**1993, Apr. 15**
3197 A1444 10ch multicolored .50 .25
**Souvenir Sheet**
**Perf. 11½**
3198 A1445 1w multicolored 3.25 .75

A1446

Pyongyang Scenes — A1447

Designs: 10ch, Kwangbok Street. 20ch, Chollima Street. 30ch, Munsu Street. 40ch, Moranbong Street. 50ch, Thongil Street. 1w, Changgwang Street.

**1993, Apr. 20** **Perf. 12x11¾**
3199-3203 A1446 Set of 5 4.25 1.15
**Souvenir Sheet**
**Perf. 11½**
3204 A1447 1w multicolored 3.25 .75

Insects — A1448

Designs: 10ch, Fly (Trichogramma dendrolimi). 20ch, Fly (Brachymeria obscurata). 30ch, Cricket (Metrioptera brachyptera). 50ch, Cricket (Gryllus campestris). 70ch, Beetle (Geocoris pallidipennis). 90ch, Wasp (Cyphononyx dorsalis).

**1993, May 10** **Perf. 12x12¼**
3205-3210 A1448 Set of 6 9.00 2.00
3205a Sheet of 3, #3205, 3207, 3210 4.50 1.15
3206a Sheet of 3, #3206, 3208, 3209 4.50 1.15

Nos. 3205-3210 were issued both in separate sheets and in sheets of 3.

A1449

A1450

**1993, May 19** **Perf. 11½**
3211 A1449 10ch multicolored .50 .25

**Souvenir Sheet**
**Perf. 13¼**
3212 A1450 1.20w multicolored 3.75 .75
Release of Ri In Mo, North Korean war correspondent, from South Korean prison.

World Cup Soccer Championship, U.S.A. — A1451

World Cup and soccer players: 10ch, Tackling. 20ch, Kicking. 30ch, Kicking (diff.). 50ch, Tackling (diff.). 70ch, Blocking. 90ch, Feinting.

**1993, May 25** **Perf. 11½**
3213-3218 A1451 Set of 6 7.75 2.00
3213a Sheet of 3, #3213, 3215, 3218 4.00 1.15
3214a Sheet of 3, #3214, 3216, 3217 4.00 1.15

Birds — A1452

Designs: 10ch, Gray-headed green woodpecker (Picus canus). 20ch, King of paradise (Cicinnurus regius). 30ch, Lesser bird of paradise (Paradisea minor). 40ch, Paradise whydah (Steganura paradisea). 50ch, Magnificent bird of paradise (Diphyllodes magnificus). 60ch, Greater bird of paradise (Paradisea apoda).

**1993, May 29** **Perf. 12**
3219-3224 A1452 Set of 6 6.50 1.60
3219a Sheet of 4, 2 ea. #3219, 3224 3.75 1.00
3220a Sheet of 4, 2 ea. #3220, 3223 3.75 1.00
3221a Sheet of 3, #3221, #3222 3.75 1.00

Nos. 3221, 3221a, 3222, Indopex '93 International Stamp Exhibition, Surabaya, Indonesia.

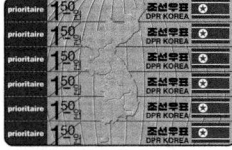

Stampcard — A1453

Design: Map of Korean peninsula.

**1993, May 29** **Rouletted**
**Self-adhesive**
3225 A1453 Card of 6 stamps 20.00 20.00
a.-f. 1.50w, any single 3.00 3.00
For surcharges, see No. 3441.

Korean World Champions — A1454

Designs: 10ch, Kim Myong Nam (weight-lifting, 1990). 20ch, Kim Kwang Suk (gymnastics, 1991). 30ch, Pak Yong Sun (table tennis, 1975, 1977). 50ch, Kim Yong Ok (radio direction-finding, 1990). 70ch, Han Yun Ok (taekwondo, 1987, 1988, 1990). 90ch, Kim Yong Sik (free-style wrestling, 1986, 1989).

**1993, June 15** **Perf. 12x11¾**
3226-3231 A1454 Set of 6 8.25 2.00
3226a Sheet of 6, 2 ea. #3226, 3228, 3231 8.25 2.25
3227a Sheet of 6, 2 ea. #3227, 3229, 3230 8.25 2.25

For surcharge, see No. 4573.

Fruits and Vegetables — A1455

Designs: 10ch, Cabbage and chili peppers. 20ch, Squirrel and horse chestnuts. 30ch, Peach and grapes. 40ch, Birds and persimmons. 50ch, Tomatoes, eggplant and cherries. 60ch, Onion, radishes, garlic bulbs.

**1993, June 25** **Perf. 11¾x12**
3232-3237 A1455 Set of 6 6.00 1.60
3232a Sheet of 3, #3232, 3235, 3237 2.25 .85
3232b As "a," ovptd. "Polska '93" 4.50 1.15
3233c Sheet of 3, #3233, 3234, 3236 2.25 .85

National Emblem — A1456

**1993, July 5** **Perf. 12**
3238 A1456 10ch vermilion .60 .25
For surcharge, see No. 4259A.

Korean War, 40th Anniv. — A1457

A1458

A1459

A1460

Kim Leading Soldiers on the Front — A1461

Kim Surveying Battlefield — A1462

Kim Making 1953 Victory Speech — A1463

Designs: No. 3239, 10ch, Soldiers and civilian women. No. 3240, 10ch, Officer and enlisted man. No. 3241, 10ch, Anti-aircraft missiles on military trucks. No. 3242, 10ch, Guided missiles on carriers. No. 3243, 10ch, Self-propelled missile launchers.

No. 3244, 1w, Kim Il Jong taking salute of paraders.

No. 3245, 10ch, Victory statue (soldier with flag). No. 3246, 10ch, Machine-gunners and refugees. 40ch, Soldiers and flag.

No. 3248a, 10ch, Kim Il Sung conducting planning meeting. b, 20ch, Kim inspecting artillery unit. No. 3249a, 10ch, Kim directing battle for Height 1211. b, 20ch, Kim encouraging machine gun crew. No. 3250a, 10ch, Kim at munitions factory. b, 20ch, Kim directing units of the Second Front. No. 3251a, 10ch, Kim with tank commanders. b, 20ch, Kim directing airmen. No. 3252a, 10ch, Kim with victorious soldiers. b, 20ch, Musicians.

**1993, July 27**
| | | | |
|---|---|---|---|
| 3239-3243 | A1457 | Set of 5 | 2.25 .75 |

**Souvenir Sheet**
***Perf. 13¼***
| | | | |
|---|---|---|---|
| 3244 | A1458 | 1w multicolored | 3.75 .50 |

***Perf. 11¾x12***
| | | | |
|---|---|---|---|
| 3245-3247 | A1459 | Set of 3 | 2.00 .50 |
| 3247a | | Sheet of 3, #3245-3247 | 2.25 .60 |

**Souvenir Sheets of 2, #a-b**
***Perf. 11½***
| | | | |
|---|---|---|---|
| 3248-3252 | A1460 | Set of 5 | 4.50 1.30 |

**Souvenir Sheets**
***Perf. 13¼***
| | | | |
|---|---|---|---|
| 3253 | A1461 | 80ch multicolored | 4.25 .60 |
| 3254 | A1462 | 80ch multicolored | 4.25 .60 |
| 3255 | A1463 | 1w multicolored | 5.50 .60 |

National Reunification Prize Winners — A1464

Designs: 10ch, Choe Yong Do (1923-69). 20ch, Kim Gu (1875-1949). 30ch, Hong Myong Hui (1888-1968). 40ch, Ryo Un Hyong (1886-1947). 50ch, Kim Jong Thae (1926-69). 60ch, Kim Chaek (1903-51).

**1993, Aug. 1** ***Perf. 12***
| | | | |
|---|---|---|---|
| 3256-3261 | A1464 | Set of 6 | 6.00 1.60 |

A1465

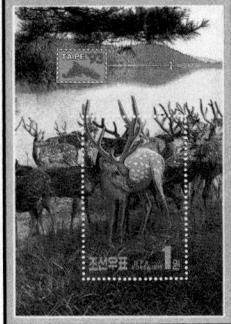

Taipei '93 Int'l Philatelic Exhib. — A1466

Designs: 20ch, *Robina sp.* 30ch, *Hippeastrum cv.*

---

1w, Deer.

**1993, Aug. 14**
| | | | |
|---|---|---|---|
| 3262-3263 | A1465 | Set of 2 | 1.35 .45 |

**Souvenir Sheet**
| | | | |
|---|---|---|---|
| 3264 | A1466 | 1w multicolored | 3.25 1.35 |

350th Anniv. Birth of Sir Isaac Newton, Mathematician and Scientist — A1467

Designs: 10ch, Portrait of Newton. 20ch, Apple tree and formula for Law of Gravitation. 30ch, Reflecting telescope invented by Newton. 50ch, Formula of Binomial Theorem. 70ch, Newton's works, statue.

**1993, Sept. 1** ***Perf. 12¼x12***
| | | | |
|---|---|---|---|
| 3265-3269 | A1467 | Set of 5 | 6.75 1.35 |
| 3265a | | Sheet of 3, #3265, 3266, 3269 | 3.50 3.50 |
| 3265b | | Sheet of 3, #3265, 3267, 3268 | 3.50 3.50 |

For surcharge, see No. 4597.

A1468

Restoration of the Tomb of King Tongmyong, Founder of Koguryo — A1469

Designs: 10ch, King Tongmyong shooting arrow. 20ch, King Tongmyong. 30ch, Restoration monument. 40ch, Jongrung Temple of the Tomb of King Tongmyong. 50ch, Tomb. 80ch, Kim Il Sung visiting restored tomb.

**1993, Sept. 10**
| | | | |
|---|---|---|---|
| 3270-3274 | A1468 | Set of 5 | 4.25 1.15 |

**Souvenir Sheet**
***Perf. 11½***
| | | | |
|---|---|---|---|
| 3275 | A1469 | 80ch multicolored | 2.25 1.35 |

Bangkok '93 Int'l Philatelic Exhib. — A1470

First stamps of North Korea and Thailand.

**1993, Oct. 1**
| | | | |
|---|---|---|---|
| 3276 | A1470 | 1.20w multicolored | 4.50 1.75 |

---

Orchids — A1471

Designs: 10ch, Cyrtopodium andresoni. 20ch, Cattleya. 30ch, Cattleya intermedia "Oculata." 40ch, Potinaria "Maysedo godonsia." 50ch, "Kimilsungia."

**1993, Oct. 15** ***Perf. 12***
| | | | |
|---|---|---|---|
| 3277-3281 | A1471 | Set of 5 | 5.50 1.15 |
| 3281a | | Strip of 5, #3277-3281 | 5.50 5.50 |
| 3277b-3281b | | Set of 5 complete booklets, each containing 5 stamps | 27.00 |

Nos. 3277b-3281b each contain horizontal strips of 5 of one value, taken from sheets. For surcharge, see No. 4549.

**No. 2949 Overprinted**

**1993, Nov. 16**
| | | | |
|---|---|---|---|
| 3282 | A1373 | 80ch multicolored | 2.25 1.35 |

Mao Zedong, Birth Centennial.

A1472

A1473

Mao Zedong, Birth Centennial — A1474

Designs: 10ch, Mao in Yannan (1940). 20ch, Mao in Beijing (1960). 30ch, Mao voting (1953). 40ch, Mao with middle-school students (1959).

No. 3287: Nos. 3283-3286 and: a, Mao proclaiming People's Republic of China (1949). b, Mao and his son, Mao Anying, in Xiangshan, Beijing (1949). c, Mao and Kim Il Sung (1975). No. 3288: As No. 3287c.

**1993, Dec. 26** ***Perf. 11½***
| | | | |
|---|---|---|---|
| 3283-3286 | A1472 | Set of 4 | 3.00 .85 |

**Souvenir Sheets**
| | | | |
|---|---|---|---|
| 3287 | A1473 | Sheet of 7 | 5.50 5.50 |
| a. | | 25ch multicolored | .50 .30 |
| b. | | 25ch multicolored | .50 .30 |
| c. | | 1w multicolored | 1.75 .85 |
| 3288 | A1474 | 1w multicolored | 1.75 1.75 |

---

A1475

A1476

New Year, Year of the Dog — A1477

Designs: 10ch, Phungsan. 20ch, Yorkshire terriers. 30ch, Gordon setter. 40ch, Pomeranian. 50ch, Spaniel with pups. No. 3294, Pointer.

No. 3295, 2 #3289, 1 #3294a; No. 3296, 2 #3290, 1 #3294a; No. 3297, 2 #3291, 1 #3294a; No. 3298, 2 #3292, 1 #3294a; No. 3299, 2 #3293, 1 #3294a.

**1994, Jan. 1** ***Perf. 12***
| | | | |
|---|---|---|---|
| 3289-3293 | A1475 | Set of 5 | 4.50 .90 |
| 3289a-3293a | | Set of 5 complete booklets, each containing 5 stamps | 22.50 |

**Souvenir Sheet**
| | | | |
|---|---|---|---|
| 3294 | A1476 | 1w multicolored | 4.25 1.15 |

**Sheets of 3, #a.-c.**
***Perf. 12***
| | | | |
|---|---|---|---|
| 3295-3299 | A1477 | Set of 5 | 27.00 27.00 |

Nos. 3289a-3293a each contain horizontal strips of 5 of one value, taken from sheets.

A1478

Kim Jong Il, 52nd Birthday — A1479

Designs: 10ch, Purple hyosong flower (Prinula polyantha). 40ch, Yellow hyosong flower (Prinula polyantha).

No. 3302, Kim Il Sung and Kim Jong Il, from embroidery *The Sun of Juche.*

**1994, Feb. 16** ***Perf. 13¼***
| | | | |
|---|---|---|---|
| 3300-3301 | A1478 | Set of 2 | 1.35 .45 |
| a. | | Pair, #3300-3301 | 1.60 1.60 |

**Souvenir Sheet**
| | | | |
|---|---|---|---|
| 3302 | A1479 | 1w multicolored | 3.25 1.15 |

Nos. 3300-3301 exist in a miniature sheet containing 4 of each value, with central label depicting Jong Il Peak and *Kimjongilia.*

Goldfish — A1480

Designs: 10ch, Red and black dragon-eye. 30ch, Red and white bubble-eye. 50ch, Red and white long-finned wenyu. 70ch, Red and white fringetail.

**1994, Feb. 18**       *Perf. 12*

| | | | |
|---|---|---|---|
| 3303 | A1480 | Sheet of 4 | 6.00 1.15 |
| a. | | 10ch multicolored | 1.45 .25 |
| b. | | 30ch multicolored | 1.45 .25 |
| c. | | 50ch multicolored | 1.45 .25 |
| d. | | 70ch multicolored | 1.45 .25 |

A1481

Publication of the *Program of Modeling the Whole Society on the Juche Idea*, 20th Anniv. — A1482

Kim Il Sung proclaiming the *Program*, 1974.

**1994, Feb. 19**

| | | | |
|---|---|---|---|
| 3307 | A1481 | 20ch multicolored | .50 .25 |

**Souvenir Sheet**
**Perf. 11½**

| | | | |
|---|---|---|---|
| 3308 | A1482 | 1.20w multicolored | 4.00 1.15 |

A1483

A1484

Publication of Kim Il Sung's *Theses on the Socialist Rural Question in Our Country*, 30th Anniv. — A1485

Designs: 10ch (No. 3309), Woman propagandist, sound truck. 10ch (No. 3310), Electrical generator, pylon. 10ch (No. 3311), Farm, farm equipment, piles of grain. 40ch (No. 3312), Lab technician with microscope. 40ch (No. 3313), Dancers celebrating bounty harvest.
No. 3314, Kim Il Sung in field. No. 3315, Kim Jong Il walking through field with peasants.

**1994, Feb. 25**       *Perf. 12*

| | | | |
|---|---|---|---|
| 3309-3313 | A1483 | Set of 5 | 3.25 .85 |

**Souvenir Sheets**
**Perf. 11½**

| | | | |
|---|---|---|---|
| 3314 | A1484 | 1w multicolored | 2.25 1.15 |
| 3315 | A1485 | 1w multicolored | 2.25 1.15 |

Ships — A1486

Designs: 20ch, Passenger ship, *Mangyongbong-92*. 30ch, Cargo ship, *Osandok*. 40ch, Processing stern trawler, *Ryongaksan*. 50ch, Stern trawler.
80ch, Passenger ship, *Maekjon No. 1*.

**1994, Mar. 25**       *Perf. 12*

| | | | |
|---|---|---|---|
| 3316-3319 | A1486 | Set of 4 | 4.25 1.15 |
| 3320 | | Sheet of 6, #3316-3319 + 2 #3320a | 9.00 2.25 |
| a. | | A1486 80ch multicolored | 2.25 .75 |

DPRK Flag — A1487

**1994, Mar. 30**       *Perf. 13¼*

| | | | |
|---|---|---|---|
| 3321 | A1487 | 10ch car & dp blue | .50 .25 |
| a. | | Perf. 12 | |

For surcharges, see Nos. 4259B and 4571.

A1488

Kim Il Sung, 82nd Birthday — A1489

Designs: 10ch, Magnolia and Kim's home. 40ch, Kimilsungia and Kim's home.
No. 3324, Five 40ch stamps, together forming design of Lake Chon (crater lake of Mt. Paektu), with *Song of General Kim Il Sung* music within design, lyrics in sheet margin.

**1994, Apr. 15**       *Perf. 12*

| | | | |
|---|---|---|---|
| 3322-3323 | A1488 | Set of 2 | 1.35 .50 |
| 3323a | | 10ch Sheet of 8 | 6.50 2.00 |
| 3323b | | 40ch Sheet of 8 | 6.50 2.00 |

**Souvenir Sheet**

| | | | |
|---|---|---|---|
| 3324 | A1489 | 2w Sheet of 5 | 6.50 6.50 |
| a.-e. | | 40ch any single | 1.15 1.15 |

Alpine Plants of the Mt. Paektu Area — A1490

Designs: 10ch, Chrysoplenium sphaerospermum. 20ch, Campanula cephalotes. 40ch, Trollius macropetalus. 50ch, Sedum kamtschaticum.
1w, Dianthus repens.

**1994, Apr. 25**       *Perf. 13¼*

| | | | |
|---|---|---|---|
| 3325-3329 | A1490 | Set of 5 | 4.25 1.15 |
| 3325a | | Sheet of 3, #3325, 3327, #3330 | 4.00 1.60 |
| 3326a | | Sheet of 3, #3326, 3328, 3329 | 4.00 1.60 |

**Souvenir Sheet**

| | | | |
|---|---|---|---|
| 3330 | A1490 | 1w multicolored | 3.25 1.35 |

A single stamp like that in No. 3330 is included in No. 3325a.

A1491

Int'l Olympic Committee Centenary — A1492

Designs: 10ch, Olympic rings, DPRK flag. 20ch, Pierre de Coubertin, founder. 30ch, Olympic flag, flame. 50ch, IOC Centenary Congress emblem.
No. 3335, Runner with Olympic Torch. No. 3336, Juan Antonio Samaranch, IOC President and new IOC headquarters.

**1994, May 2**       *Perf. 12*

| | | | |
|---|---|---|---|
| 3331-3334 | A1491 | Set of 4 | 3.75 .90 |

**Souvenir Sheets**
**Perf. 13¼**

| | | | |
|---|---|---|---|
| 3335-3336 | A1492 | Set of 2 | 6.00 1.75 |

International Federation of Red Cross and Red Crescent Societies, 75th Anniv. — A1493

Designs: a, 10ch, Train, pedestrians crossing on overpass ("Prevention of traffic accident"). b, 20ch, Medical personnel in Red Cross boat ("Relief on the Sea"). c, 30ch, Man and girl planting tree ("Protection of the environment"). d, 40ch, Dam, sailboat on lake ("Protection of drought damage").

**1994, May 5**

| | | | |
|---|---|---|---|
| 3337 | A1493 | Strip of 4, #a.-d. | 3.25 2.25 |

**No. 3225 Surcharged**

**1994, May 29    Self-adhesive    *Imperf***

| | | | |
|---|---|---|---|
| 3341 | A1452 | 1.60w on 1.50w | |
| | | Card of 6 | 28.00 28.00 |
| a.-f. | | 1.60w on 1.50w, any single | 7.00 7.00 |

A1494

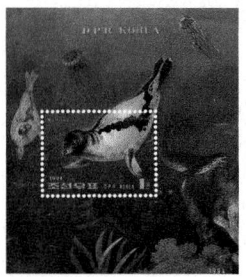

Seals — A1495

Designs: 10ch, Northern fur seal (Callorhinus ursinus). 40ch, Southern elephant seal (Mirounga leonina). 60ch, Southern sea lion (Otaria byronia).
No. 3345: 20ch, California sea lion (Zalophus californianus). 30ch, Ringed seal

(Phoca hispida). 50ch, Walrus (Odobenus rosmarus).
No. 3346, Harp seal (Pagophilus groenlandicus).

**1994, June 10**       *Perf. 11½*

| | | | |
|---|---|---|---|
| 3342-3344 | A1494 | Set of 3 | 3.75 .85 |
| 3345 | A1494 | Sheet of 3 | 4.25 .90 |
| a. | | 20ch multicolored | .75 .25 |
| b. | | 30ch multicolored | 1.15 .25 |
| c. | | 50ch multicolored | 2.00 .50 |

**Souvenir Sheet**

| | | | |
|---|---|---|---|
| 3346 | A1495 | 1w multicolored | 3.25 .90 |

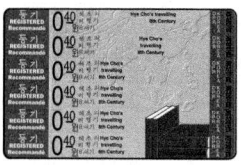

Stampcard — A1496

Map of Asia, books.

**1994, June 17**       *Rouletted*
**Self-adhesive**

| | | | |
|---|---|---|---|
| 3347 | A1496 | Card of 6 stamps | 10.00 10.00 |
| a.-f. | | 40ch, any single | 1.65 1.65 |

Hye Cho's 8th century travels in Central Asia and India.

Stampcard — A1497

Korean Tigers.

**1994, June 18**       *Rouletted*
**Self-adhesive**

| | | | |
|---|---|---|---|
| 3348 | A1497 | Card of 6 stamps | 30.00 30.00 |
| a.-f. | | 1.40w, any single | 5.00 5.00 |

A1498

Kim Il Sung's Leadership of the Korean Workers' Party, 30th Anniv. — A1499

Designs (all 40ch): a, Kim and supporters on cliff ledge, overlooking lake. b, Kim on mountain top, pointing across lake to Mt. Paektu. c, Kim on film set. d, Kim visiting restaurant. e, Kim reviewing tank corps. f, Kim at conference, shaking hands onstage as audience applauds.

**1994, June 19**       *Perf. 12*

| | | | |
|---|---|---|---|
| 3349 | A1498 | Sheet of 6 | 8.00 2.50 |
| 3349g | | Booklet pane of 6, 3 ea. #3349a-3349b | 8.00 — |
| | | Complete booklet. #3349g | 8.50 |
| 3349h | | Booklet pane of 6, 3 ea. #3349c, 3349e | 8.00 — |
| | | Complete booklet. #3349h | 8.50 |
| 3349i | | Booklet pane of 6, 3 ea. #3349d, 3349f | 8.00 — |
| | | Complete booklet. #3349i | 8.50 |

**Souvenir Sheet**
**Perf. 11½**

| | | | |
|---|---|---|---|
| 3350 | A1499 | 1w multicolored | 2.75 .90 |

Stampcard — A1500

Turtle ship.

**1994, June 20**      *Rouletted*
**Self-adhesive**
3356 A1500   Card of 6 stamps   33.00   33.00
a.-f.   1.80w, any single   5.50   5.50

A1501

A1502

Mollusks — A1503

Designs: 30ch, Phalium strigatum. 40ch, Gomphina veneriformis.
No. 3359: a, 10ch, Cardium muticum, No. 3358 and the stamp found in No. 3361.
No. 3360: a, 20ch, Buccinum bayani, No. 3357 and the stamp found in No. 3361.
No. 3361: Neverita didyma

**1994, June 25**      *Perf. 12*
3357-3358 A1501   Set of 2   2.25   .60
**Sheets of 3, #a.-c.**
*Perf. 13¼*
3359-3360 A1502   Set of 2   13.00   9.00
**Souvenir Sheet**
3361 A1503   1.20w multicolored   4.50   1.30
For surcharge, see No. 4608.

Circus Acrobats — A1504

Designs: a, 10ch, Flying trapeze. b, 20ch, Rope dance. c, 30ch, Seesaw. d, 40ch, Unicycle show.

**1994, July 7**      *Perf. 11½*
3362 A1504   Sheet of 4, #a.-d.   3.75   1.15

A1505

Centenary of Birth of Kim Hyong Jik
(1894-1926), Father of Kim Il
Sung — A1506

**1994, July 10**      *Perf. 13¼*
3363 A1505   10ch multicolored   .50   .25
**Souvenir Sheet**
*Perf. 11¾x11½*
3364 A1506   1w multicolored   3.25   1.15

Jeon Bong-jun & Battle
Scene — A1507

**1994, July 15**      *Perf. 12*
3365 A1507   10ch multicolored   .60   .25
Centenary of Kabo Peasant War.

Inoue Shuhachi — A1508

**1994, July 30**      *Perf. 13¼*
3366 A1508   1.20w multicolored   3.75   1.15
Award of the First International Kim Il Sung Prize to Inoue Shuhachi, Director General of the International Institute of the Juche Idea (Japan).

Workers
Marching — A1509

**1994, Aug. 1**      *Perf. 11½*
3367 A1509   10ch multicolored   .50   .25
Workers' Party Economic Strategy.

Fossils — A1510

Designs: 40ch (No. 3368), Onsong fish. 40ch (No. 3369), Metasequoia. 40ch (No. 3370), Mammoth teeth. 80ch, Archaeopteryx.
No. 3372 contains 2 each Nos. 3368, 3371.
No. 3373 contains 2 each Nos. 3369, 3371.
No. 3374 contains 2 each Nos. 3370-3371.

**1994, Aug. 10**      *Perf. 12*
3368-3371 A1510   Set of 4   12.00   1.60
   Complete booklet, 7 #3368   14.50
   Complete booklet, 7 #3369   14.50
   Complete booklet, 7 #3370   14.50
   Complete booklet, 7 #3371   29.00
**Souvenir Sheets**
3372-3374 A1510   Set of 3
     sheets   23.00   18.00

Medicinal
Plants — A1511

Designs: 20ch, Acorus calamus. 30ch, Arctium lappa.
No. 3377 (133x86mm): a, 80ch, Lilium lancifolium. b, 80ch, Codonopsis lanceolata.
No. 3378 (56x83mm): 1w, Ginseng (Panax schinseng), vert.

**1994, Aug. 25**
3375-3376 A1511   Set of 2   1.60   .50
   Complete booklet, 10 #3375   6.50
   Complete booklet, 10 #3376   9.50
**Souvenir Sheets**
*Perf. 13¼*
3377-3378 A1511   Set of 2
     sheets   7.25   1.75

Calisthenics — A1512

Gymnastic routines: a, 10ch, Ribbon twirling. b, 20ch, Ball. c, 30ch, Hoop. d, 40ch, Ribbon twirling (diff.). e, 50ch, Clubs.

**1994, Sept. 7**      *Perf. 12*
3379 A1512   Strip of 5 + label   5.00   1.35
No. 3379 was printed in sheets of 18, containing three No. 3379 in horizontal rows, with a different label in each row.

A1513

A1514

Zhou Enlai (1898-1976), Birth
Centenary — A1515

Portraits of Zhou Enlai: 10ch, As student revolutionary (1919). 20ch, Arrival in Northern Shansi after Long March (1936). 30ch, At Conference of Asian and African Countries, Bandung, Indonesia (1955). 40ch, Speaking with children.
No. 3384: 80ch, Zhou Enlai and Kim Il Sung (1970).
No. 3385: 10ch, as #3380. a, 20ch, Zhou leading Nanchang Uprising (1927). 40ch, as #3383. 80ch, as #3384.
No. 3386: 20ch, as #3381. a, 20ch, Zhou and Mao Tzedong at airport, horiz. 30ch, as #3383. 80ch, as #3385b.

**1994, Oct. 1**      *Perf. 11½*
3380-3383 A1513   Set of 4   3.00   .90
**Souvenir Sheets**
*Perf. 13¼*
3384 A1514   80ch multicolored   2.50   .90
*Perf 11½ (Vert. stamps), 11¾x12¼ (Horiz. stamps)*
3385-3386 A1515   Set of 2   8.75   3.75
Nos. 3380-3383 were issued in sheets of 30 (6x5), with a label beneath each stamp.

World Environment Day — A1516

Each sheetlet contains two 50ch stamps with designs reflecting environmental issues. Themes: No. 3387, Prevention of air pollution. No. 3388, Preventation of water pollution. No. 3389, Protection of animal resources. No. 3390, Protection of forest resources.

**1994, Oct. 5**      *Perf. 12*
**Sheets of 2**
3387-3390 A1516   Set of 4   11.50   11.50

A1517

A1518

Kim Il Sung (1912-94) — A1519

Photos of Kim Il Sung (all 40ch).
No. 3391: a, As young man (1927). b, With Kim Jong Suk, his first wife and mother of Kim Jong Il. c, As captain in Soviet army (1944).
No. 3392: Speaking at lectern upon return to Pyongyang (1945). b, Sitting at desk in office of People's Committee of North Korea. c, Speaking at microphone.

**1994, Oct. 8**
3391 A1517   Sheet of 3, #a.-c.   3.75   1.75
3392 A1518   Sheet of 3, #a.-c.   3.75   1.75
**Souvenir Sheet**
*Perf. 12¼x11¾*
3393 A1519   1w multicolored   3.50   1.15
Compare with Nos. 3401-3403.

A1520

World Cup '94, 15th World Soccer
Championship — A1521

Soccer Players Dribbling: 10ch, Player No.
4. 20ch, Player No. 5. 30ch, Player No. 6.
40ch, Player No. 7. 1w, Player No. 8. 1.50w,
Player No. 9.

| 1994, Oct. 13 | | Perf. 13½ | |
|---|---|---|---|
| 3394-3399 | A1520 Set of 6 | 11.00 | 5.50 |
| 3399a | Sheet of 6, #3394-3399 | 16.50 | 9.00 |

**Souvenir Sheet**

| 3400 | A1521 2.50w multicolored | 6.75 | 3.75 |
|---|---|---|---|

Nos. 3394-3400 were also issued imperf.
Value: set, $24; souvenir sheet, $15.
Nos. 3394-3399 exist in sheetlets on one,
perf and imperf. Value: perf, $24; imperf,
$47.50.

A1522

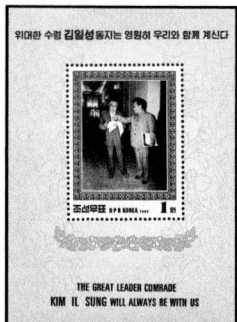

THE GREAT LEADER COMRADE
KIM IL SUNG WILL ALWAYS BE WITH US

Kim Il Sung (1912-94) — A1523

Photos of Kim Il Sung (all 40ch).
No. 3401: a, Making radio broadcast (1950).
b, With soldiers (1951). c, Clapping hands,
crowd of soldiers in background (1953).
No. 3402: a, Talking with workers at
Chongjin Steel Plant (1959). b, Standing in
field, Onchon Plain. c, Talking on telephone.
No. 3403, Kim Il Sung and Kim Jong Il.

| 1994, Oct. 15 | | Perf. 12 | |
|---|---|---|---|
| | **Sheets of 3** | | |
| 3401-3402 | A1522 Set of 2 | 7.25 | 3.75 |
| | **Perf. 12¼x11¾** | | |
| 3403 | A1523 1w multicolored | 3.25 | 1.35 |

Compare with Nos. 3391-3393.

A1524

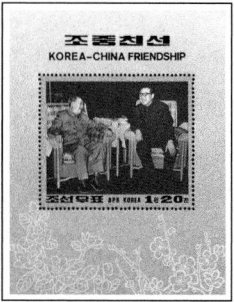

North Korean-Chinese
Friendship — A1525

1w, Kim Il Sung with Mao Zedong.

| 1994, Oct. 25 | | Perf. 11½ | |
|---|---|---|---|
| 3404 | A1524 40ch multicolored | 1.35 | .50 |

**Souvenir Sheet**
**Perf. 13¼**

| 3405 | A1525 1.20w multicolored | 4.00 | 1.75 |
|---|---|---|---|

Composers — A1526

Designs: No. 3406, Ri Myon Sang (1908-
89), score from *It Snows*. No. 3407, Pak Han
Gyu (1919-92), score from *Nobody Knows*.
No. 3408, Ludwig van Beethoven (1770-
1827), score of *Piano Sonata No. 14*. No.
3409, Wolfgang Mozart (1756-91), score of
*Symphony No. 39*.

| 1994, Nov. 25 | | Perf. 11½ | |
|---|---|---|---|
| 3406-3409 | A1526 50ch Set of 4 | 6.00 | 2.00 |

For surcharge, see No. 4550.

National
Emblem — A1527

| 1994, Dec. 10 | | Perf. 12 | |
|---|---|---|---|
| 3410 | A1527 1w dp bl green | 3.75 | .90 |
| 3411 | A1527 3w deep brown | 7.25 | 2.25 |

For surcharge, see No. 4575.

A1528

A1529

Gold Medal Winners, Winter Olympic
Games, Lillehammer — A1530

Designs: 10ch, Pernilla Wiberg (Sweden),
Alpine combined skiing. 20ch, Deborah Com-
pagnoni (Italy), Slalom. 30ch, Oksana Baiul
(Ukraine), Figure skating. 40ch, Dan Jansen
(USA), Speed skating. 1w (No. 3416), Yubow
Jegorowa (Russia), Cross-country skiing. 1w
(No. 3417), Bonnie Blair (USA), Speed
skating.
No. 3418, Bjorn Däehlie and Norwegian ski-
ing team, Alpine combined skiing. No. 3419,
Jekaterina Gordejewa and Serge Grinkow
(Russia), Pairs figure skating. No. 3420, Vreni
Schneider (Switzerland), Alpine combined ski-
ing. No. 3421, Georg Hackl (Germany), Luge.
No. 3422, Jens Weissflog (Germany), Ski
jumping. No. 3423, Masashi Abe, Takanori
Kono, Kenji Ogiwara (Japan), Cross-country
skiing.
No. 3424, Tommy Moe (USA), Downhill
skiing.

| 1994, Dec. 20 | | Perf. 13¼ | |
|---|---|---|---|
| 3412-3417 | A1528 Set of 6 | 10.00 | 2.75 |
| 3417a | Sheet of 6, #3412-3417 | 11.00 | 4.50 |

**Souvenir Sheets**

| 3418-3423 | A1529 1w Set of 6 | 16.50 | 5.50 |
|---|---|---|---|
| 3424 | A1530 2.50w multicolored | 7.25 | 1.35 |

New Year — Year
of the
Pig — A1531

Designs: 20ch, Pigs relaxing. 40ch, Pigs
going to work.
Each 1w: No. 3427, Pigs carrying pumpkin.
No. 3428, Piglets bowing to adult pig.

| 1995, Jan. 1 | | Perf. 11½ | |
|---|---|---|---|
| 3425-3426 | A1531 Set of 2 | 1.40 | .65 |
| 3426a | Sheet of 4, 2 ea #3425-3426 | 3.00 | 3.00 |

**Souvenir Sheets**

| 3427-3428 | A1531 Set of 2 | 5.00 | 4.00 |
|---|---|---|---|

No. 3426a inscribed in margins for Singapore '95 Intl. Stamp Exhibition. Issued, 9/1.

World Tourism Org., 20th
Anniv. — A1532

Designs, each 30ch: a, Tower of the Juche
Idea, Pyongyang. b, Pison Falls on Mt. Myohy-
ang. c, Myogilsang (relief carving of Buddha),
Mt. Kumgang.

| 1995, Jan. 2 | | Perf. 12¼ | |
|---|---|---|---|
| 3429 | A1532 Sheet of 3, #a.-c. +<br>label | 3.00 | .90 |

Mangyondae,
Badasgou,
Emblem — A1533

| 1995, Jan. 22 | | Perf. 11½ | |
|---|---|---|---|
| 3430 | A1533 40ch multicolored | 1.10 | .90 |

70th anniversary of 250-Mile Journey for the
Restoration of the Fatherland.

A1534

A1535

A1536

Kim Jong Il, 53rd Birthday — A1537

Designs: 10ch, Jong Il Peak (Mt. Paekdu)
and 50th Birthday Ode Monument.
No. 3432 (horiz.): a, 20ch Kim Il Sung and
Kim Jong Il; b, 80ch Kim Jong Il inspecting the
West Sea Barrage. No. 3433 (vert.): a, 40ch
Kim Jong Il in business suit; b, Kim Jong Il in
uniform in Taesongsan Martyrs' Cemetary.
No. 3434: 1w, Kim Jong Il inspecting the
Ryongsong Machine Complex.

| 1995, Feb. 16 | | Perf. 12¼ | |
|---|---|---|---|
| 3431 | A1534 10ch multicolored | .25 | .25 |

**Souvenir Sheets**

| 3432 | A1535 Sheet of 2, #a.-b. | 2.10 | 1.50 |
|---|---|---|---|
| 3433 | A1536 Sheet of 2, #a.-b. | 1.90 | 1.25 |
| 3434 | A1537 1w multicolored | 2.10 | 2.10 |

Mausoleum of King
Tangun — A1537a

King Tangun and Mausoleum —
A1537b

Designs: 10ch, Monument. 30ch, Straight
bronze dagger tower. 50ch, Monument
inscribed with King Tangun's exploits. 70ch,
Gate of mausoleum.
50ch, King Tangun and Mausoleum.

| 1995, Feb. 25 | | Perf. 12¼ | |
|---|---|---|---|
| 3434A-3434D | A1537a Set of 4 | 3.25 | 3.25 |

**Souvenir Sheet**
**Perf. 11½**

| 3434E | A1537b 1.40w multi | 3.00 | 3.00 |
|---|---|---|---|

Lighthouses — A1538

Designs: 20ch, Tamaedo Lighthouse. 1.20w, Phido Lighthouse, West Sea Barrage.

**1995, Mar. 10**                      **Perf. 13½**
3435-3436   A1538   Set of 2        4.00  1.75

Mushrooms — A1539

Designs: 20ch, Russula virescens. 30ch, Russula atropurpurea. 1w, Caesar's Mushroom (Amanita caesarea).

**1995, Mar. 25**
3437-3438   A1539   Set of 2        1.75   .60
*3437a*      Booklet pane of 10 #3437   3.50
           Complete booklet, #3437a     4.00
*3438a*      Booklet pane of 10 #3438  17.00    —
           Complete booklet, #3438a    17.50    —
**Souvenir Sheet**
3439   A1539   1w multicolored       4.50  2.50
For surcharges, see Nos. 4527-4528.

Tree Planting Day — A1540

**1995, Apr. 6**                       **Perf. 11½**
3440   A1540   10ch multicolored      .50   .25
*a.*      Sheet of 6                  3.00  3.00

**No. 3225 Surcharged with New Values**

**1995, Apr. 8**                       **Rouletted**
3441   Card of 6 stamps             6.00  6.00
*a.-f.*  30ch on 1.50w, any single   1.00  1.00
Finlandia '95.

Mangyongdae, Birthplace of Kim Il Sung       Tower of Juche Idea and Kimilsungia
A1541                                        A1542

Kim Il Sung and Children A1543

**1995, Apr. 15**                      **Perf. 11½**
3442   A1541   10ch multicolored      .25   .25
*a.*      Sheet of 6                  1.35  1.35
*b.*      Booklet pane of 5            —
         Complete booklet, #3442b     —
3443   A1542   40ch multicolored     1.15   .90
*a.*      Sheet of 6                  6.75  6.75
*b.*      Booklet pane of 5            —

Complete booklet, #3443b             —
**Souvenir Sheet**
**Perf. 13½**
3444   A1543   1w multicolored       3.25  3.25
Kim Il Sung, 82nd birthday. For surcharge, see No. 4610.

A1544

Kim Il Sung's Visit to China, 20th Anniv. A1545

Designs: 10ch, Deng Xiaoping waving. 20ch, Deng sitting in armchair, vert. 50ch, Kim and Deng sitting in armchairs.

**1995, Apr. 17**                      **Perf. 13½**
3445-3446   A1544   Set of 2        1.15  1.15
**Souvenir Sheet**
**Perf. 11½**
3447   A1545   50ch multicolored    1.75  1.75

A1546                               A1547

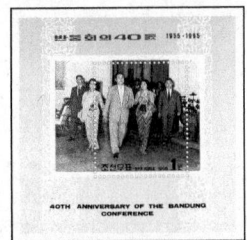

Asian-African Conf., Bandung, 40th Anniv. — A1548

Designs: 10ch, Site of Bendung Conference. 50ch, Kim Il Sung receiving honorary doctorate from Indonesia University. 1w, Kim Il Sung and Kim Jong Il at Conference 40th Anniversary ceremony.

**1995, Apr. 18**                      **Perf. 11½**
3448   A1546   10ch multicolored     .25   .25
3449   A1547   50ch multicolored    1.60   .65
**Souvenir Sheet**
3450   A1548   1w multicolored      3.25  3.25

A1549

Int'l Sports and Cultural Festival for Peace, Pyongyang — A1550

Designs: 20ch, Emblem. 40ch (No. 3452), Dancer. 40ch (No. 3453), Inoki Kanji, leader of Sports Peace Party of Japan. 1w, Nikidozan, wrestling champion.

**1995, Apr. 28**
3451-3453   A1549   Set of 3        2.75  1.75
*3451a*   Sheet of 3, 1 #3451 + 2 #3452   2.75  1.75
*3453a*   Sheet of 3, 2 #3453 + 1 as #3454  6.50  3.75
**Souvenir Sheet**
3454   A1550   1w multicolored      3.25  3.25

Amethyst — A1551

**1995, May 2**
3455   A1551   20ch multicolored     .90   .40
*a.*      Sheet of 6                 6.75  6.75
*b.*      Booklet pane of 10         9.00
         Complete booklet, #3455b   10.00
Finlandia '95. No. 3455a marginal selvage contains a mountain valley scene and is inscribed "Finlandia 95." No. 3455b has selvage around the block of 10 stamps.

White Animals — A1552

Each 40ch: No. 3456, Tree sparrow (Passer montanus). No. 3457, Sea slug (Stichopus japonicus).

**1995, May 12**                      **Perf. 13½**
3456-3457   A1552   Set of 2        2.25  1.35
*3457a*   Sheet of 6, 3 #3456 + 3 #3457   8.25

Fossils — A1553

Designs: a, 50ch, Ostrea. b, 1w, Cladophiebis (fern).

**1995, May 15**                      **Perf. 12**
3458   A1553   Pair, #a.-b.         3.75  1.60
*c.*      Booklet pane of 7, 4 #3458a, 3 #3458b   —
         Complete booklet, #3458c    —

Traditional Games — A1554

Designs: 30ch, Chess. 60ch, Taekwondo. 70ch, Yut.

**1995, May 20**                      **Perf. 11½**
3459-3461   A1554   Set of 3        4.75  1.75
*3459a*   Sheet of 2 #3459 + label   1.60  1.60
*3460a*   Sheet of 2 #3460 + label   3.75  3.75
*3461a*   Sheet of 2 #3461 + label   5.50  5.50
*3461b*   Booklet pane of 6, 2 ea. #3459-3461   9.50
         Complete booklet. #3461b   10.00

General Assoc. of Koreans in Japan, 40th Anniv. — A1555

**1995, May 25**
3462   A1555   1w multicolored      3.25   .85

Atlanta '96 — A1556

Designs, each 50ch: No. 3463, Weight lifter. No. 3464, Boxing. 1w, Marksman shooting clay pigeon.

**1995, June 2**
3463-3464   A1556   Set of 2        3.00  1.15
*3464a*   Sheet of 2 #3463 + 2 #3464   6.75  6.75
**Souvenir Sheet**
3465   A1556   1w multicolored      4.50  4.50

Fungi — A1557

Designs: 40ch, Russula citrina. 60ch, Craterellus cornucopioides. 80ch, Coprinus comatus.

**1995, July 1**                      **Perf. 13¼**
3466-3468   A1557   Set of 3        6.00  1.75
*3466a*   Booklet pane of 10 #3466  13.00
         Complete booklet, #3466a   13.50
*3467a*   Booklet pane of 10 #3467  19.00
         Complete booklet, #3467a   20.00
*3468a*   Booklet pane of 10 #3468  26.00
         Complete booklet, #3468a   27.00
For surcharge, see No. 4553.

A1558

A1559

A1560

Kim Il Sung, 1st Death Anniv. — A1561

No. 3469, 1w, Kim addressing conference for development of agriculture in African countries, 1981.
No. 3470: a, 10ch, Kim greeting Robert Mugabe, President of Zimbabwe. b, 70ch, Kim with King Norodom Sihanouk of Cambodia.
No. 3471: a, 20ch, Kim receiving honorary doctorate, Algeria University, 1975. b, 50ch, Kim with Fidel Castro, 1986.
No. 3472: a, 30ch, Kim talking with Ho Chi Minh, 1958. b, 40ch, Kim greeting Che Guevara, 1960.

**1995, July 8**

| | | | | |
|---|---|---|---|---|
| **3469** | A1558 | 1w multicolored | 2.50 | 2.50 |
| **3470** | A1559 | Sheet of 2, #a.-b. | 2.00 | 2.00 |
| **3471** | A1560 | Sheet of 2, #a.-b. | 2.25 | 2.25 |
| **3472** | A1561 | Sheet of 2, #a.-b. | 1.75 | 1.75 |

Liberation, 50th
Anniv. — A1562

Designs: 10ch, Korean army officer. 30ch, Map of Korea, family. 60ch, Hero of the DPRK medal.

No. 3476, a, 20ch revolutionary soldier, #3414, 2 each.

No. 3477, a, 40ch demonstrators, #3474, 2 each.

**1995, Aug. 15**　　　　**Perf. 11½**

| | | | | |
|---|---|---|---|---|
| **3473-3475** | A1562 | Set of 3 | 2.50 | 1.15 |
| *3475a* | | Booklet pane of 5, #3473-3475, 3476a, 3477a | 4.25 | — |
| | | Complete booklet, #3475a | 4.50 | |

**Souvenir Sheets**

| | | | | |
|---|---|---|---|---|
| **3476** | | Sheet of 4 | 2.25 | 2.25 |
| *a.* | A1562 | 20ch multicolored | .50 | .25 |
| **3477** | | Sheet of 4 | 4.25 | 4.25 |
| *a.* | A1562 | 40ch multicolored | .90 | .45 |

1st Military World
Games — A1564

**1995, Sept. 4**

| | | | | |
|---|---|---|---|---|
| **3479** | A1564 | 40ch multicolored | .90 | .45 |

A1565

A1566

Korea-China Friendship — A1567

Designs: No. 3480, 80ch, Kim Il Sung and Mao Zedong. No. 3481, 80ch, Kim and Zhou Enlai.

No. 3482: a, 50ch, Kim and Zhou Enlai. b, 50ch, Kim receiving gift from Deng Ying-Chao, Premier of the State Council of the People's Republic of China.

**1995, Oct. 1**　　　　**Perf. 12¼**

| | | | | |
|---|---|---|---|---|
| **3480** | A1565 | 80ch multicolored | 1.35 | 1.35 |
| **3481** | A1566 | 80ch multicolored | 1.35 | 1.35 |
| **3482** | A1567 | Sheet of 2, #a.-b. | 2.00 | 2.00 |

A1568

Korean Workers' Party, 50th
Anniv. — A1569

Designs: 10ch, Korean Workers' Party Emblem and Banner. 20ch, Statue of three workers holding party symbols. 40ch, Monument to founding of Party.

No. 3486, Kim Il Sung.

**1995, Oct. 10**　　　　**Perf. 11½**

| | | | | |
|---|---|---|---|---|
| **3483-3485** | A1568 | Set of 3 | 1.45 | .75 |

**Souvenir Sheet**
**Perf. 13½**

| | | | | |
|---|---|---|---|---|
| **3486** | A1569 | 1w multicolored | 2.50 | 2.50 |

Kim Il Sung's
Return to Korea,
50th
Anniv. — A1570

Design: 50ch, Arch of Triumph, Pyongyang.

**1995, Oct. 14**　　　　**Perf. 11½**

| | | | | |
|---|---|---|---|---|
| **3487** | A1570 | 10ch multicolored | .55 | .25 |

Great Tunny — A1571

**Fish**

No. 3488, Great tunny. No. 3489, Pennant coralfish. No. 3490, Needlefish. No. 3491, Bullrout. No. 3492, Imperial butterfly fish.

**1995**　　　　**Perf. 13¼**

| | | | | |
|---|---|---|---|---|
| **3488** | A1571 | 40ch choc & blk | 1.25 | .35 |
| **3489** | A1571 | 50ch choc & blk | 1.50 | .40 |
| **3490** | A1571 | 50ch choc & blk | 1.50 | .40 |
| **3491** | A1571 | 60ch choc & blk | 1.75 | .45 |
| **3492** | A1571 | 5w choc & blk | 15.00 | 3.50 |
| *a.* | | Horiz. strip of 5, #3488-3492 | 22.50 | 5.00 |

**Machines**

10ch, 40-ton truck *Kumsusan*. 20ch, Large bulldozer. 30ch, Hydraulic excavator. 40ch, Wheel loader, vert. 10w, Tractor *Chollima-80*, vert.

| | | | | |
|---|---|---|---|---|
| **3493** | A1571 | 10ch choc & blk | .35 | .25 |
| *a.* | | Perf. 11¼ | — | — |
| **3494** | A1571 | 20ch choc & blk | .75 | .25 |
| **3495** | A1571 | 30ch choc & blk | 1.00 | .25 |
| **3496** | A1571 | 40ch choc & blk | 1.60 | .30 |
| **3497** | A1571 | 10w choc & blk | 27.50 | 7.50 |
| *a.* | | Horiz. strip of 5, #3493-3497 | 32.50 | 10.00 |

**Animals**

30ch, Giraffe, vert. 40ch, Ostrich, vert. 60ch, Bluebuck, vert. 70ch, Bactrian camel. 3w, Indian rhinoceros.

| | | | | |
|---|---|---|---|---|
| **3498** | A1571 | 30ch choc & blk | .85 | .25 |
| **3499** | A1571 | 40ch choc & blk | 1.10 | .35 |
| **3500** | A1571 | 60ch choc & blk | 1.60 | .50 |
| **3501** | A1571 | 70ch choc & blk | 2.00 | .55 |
| **3502** | A1571 | 3w choc & blk | 8.00 | 2.25 |
| *a.* | | Horiz. strip of 5, #3498-3502 | 16.00 | 4.00 |

**Sculptures of Children**

30ch, Boy and pigeon, vert. 40ch, Boy and goose, vert. 60ch, Girl and geese vert. 70ch, Boy and girl comparing heights, vert. 2w, Boy and girl with soccer ball, vert.

| | | | | |
|---|---|---|---|---|
| **3503** | A1571 | 30ch choc & blk | .85 | .25 |
| **3504** | A1571 | 40ch choc & blk | 1.10 | .35 |
| **3505** | A1571 | 60ch choc & blk | 1.60 | .50 |
| **3506** | A1571 | 70ch choc & blk | 2.00 | .50 |
| **3507** | A1571 | 2w choc & blk | 5.75 | 1.60 |
| *a.* | | Vert. strip of 5, #3503-3507 | 13.00 | 4.00 |

**Buildings**

60ch, Pyongyang Circus. 70ch, Country apartment building. 80ch, Pyongyang Hotel. 90ch, Urban apt. towers. 1w, Sosan Hotel.

| | | | | |
|---|---|---|---|---|
| **3508** | A1571 | 60ch choc & blk | 1.75 | .50 |
| **3509** | A1571 | 70ch choc & blk | 2.00 | .55 |
| **3510** | A1571 | 80ch choc & blk | 2.25 | .65 |
| **3511** | A1571 | 90ch choc & blk | 2.50 | .75 |
| **3512** | A1571 | 1w choc & blk | 2.75 | .85 |
| *a.* | | Horiz. strip of 5, #3508-3512 | 13.00 | 4.00 |

Issued: Nos. 3488-3492, 10/20; Nos. 3493-3497, 11/2; Nos. 3498-3502, 11/20; Nos. 3503-3507, 12/5; Nos. 3508-3512, 12/15.

Nos. 3488-3492, 3493-3497, 3498-3502, 3503-3507, and 3508-3512 were printed in vertical (Nos. 3503-3507) or horizontal se-tenant strips within their sheets.

For surcharge, see No. 4259C.

No. 3512B

No. 3512D

**1995, Oct. 20**　　**Rouletted x Imperf**
**Stampcards**
**Self-Adhesive**

| | | | |
|---|---|---|---|
| **3512B** | black, *gold*, card of 8 | 6.00 | 6.00 |
| *a.* | 20ch single stamp | .75 | .75 |
| **3512D** | card of 2 | 50.00 | 50.00 |
| *e.* | 20ch red, *gold* | | |
| *f.* | 17.80w On 20ch, red, *gold* | | |

50th anniversary of the first North Korean stamps.

Kim Hyong Gwon, Kim Il Sung's
Uncle, 90th Birth Anniv. — A1572

**1995, Nov. 4**　　　　**Perf. 12½x12**

| | | | | |
|---|---|---|---|---|
| **3513** | A1572 | 1w multicolored | 2.50 | 1.35 |

New Year — A1573

Rodents: a, 20ch, Guinea pig. b, 20ch, Squirrel. 30ch, White mouse.

**1996, Jan. 1**　　　　**Perf. 11½**

| | | | | |
|---|---|---|---|---|
| **3514** | A1573 | Strip of 3, #a.-c. | 2.75 | .75 |

No. 3514 was issued in sheetlets of eight stamps, two each Nos. 3514a-3514b and four No. 3514c, plus one center label picturing an idyllic landscape, inscribed "1996."

League of Socialist
Working Youth, 50th
Anniv. — A1574

**1996, Jan. 17**

| | | | | |
|---|---|---|---|---|
| **3517** | A1574 | 10ch multicolored | .50 | .25 |

Reconstruction of Tomb
of King Wanggon of
Koryo — A1575

Designs: 30ch, Restoration monument, horiz. 40ch, Entrance gate to royal cemetery. 50ch, King Wanggon's tomb, horiz.

**1996, Jan. 30**

| | | | | |
|---|---|---|---|---|
| **3518-3520** | A1575 | Set of 3 | 3.25 | .90 |

Teng Li-Chuang (Chinese
Singer) — A1576

**1996, Feb. 1**　　　　**Perf. 13¼**

| | | | | |
|---|---|---|---|---|
| **3521** | A1576 | 40ch multicolored | 1.35 | .50 |

3rd Asian Winter Games, Harbin,
China — A1577

Designs, each 30ch: a, Kim Song Sun, Korean speed skater. b, Ye Qiaobo, Chinese sprint skater.

**1996, Feb 4**　　　　**Perf. 11½**

| | | | | |
|---|---|---|---|---|
| **3522** | A1577 | Sheet of 2, #a.-b. | 3.25 | .50 |

See No. 3556.

A1578

Kim Jong Il, 54th Birthday — A1579

10ch, Jong Il Peak and *Kimjongilia*. 80ch, Kim Jong Il and soldiers.

**1996, Feb. 16**

| | | | | |
|---|---|---|---|---|
| **3523** | A1578 | 10ch multicolored | .50 | .25 |

**Souvenir Sheet**
**Perf. 13¼**

| | | | | |
|---|---|---|---|---|
| **3524** | A1579 | 80ch multicolored | 2.50 | .75 |

5th Paektusan Prize International Figure Skating Championship. A1580

Various pairs figure skaters: 10ch, 20ch, 30ch. 50ch, Women's individual skating.

**1996, Feb. 17** — Perf. 11½
3525-3527 A1580 Set of 3 — 1.75 .55
3527a — Booklet pane of 4, #3525-3527, 3528a — 5.00 —
Complete booklet, #3527a — 5.50

**Souvenir Sheet**
3528 — Sheet of 4 — 3.25 .90
a. — A1580 50ch multi — 3.00

Folk Tales — A1581

Screen painting by Ryu Suk: 8 stamps in continuous design, within 206mmx84mm skeetlet.

**1996, Mar. 2**
3529 — Sheet of 8 — 4.50 2.00
a.-h. — A1581 any single — .55 .25

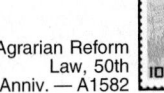

Agrarian Reform Law, 50th Anniv. — A1582

**1996, Mar. 5**
3530 A1582 10ch multicolored — .50 .25
No. 3530 was issued in sheetlets of six, containing 5 No. 3530 and a label depicting a music score, Song of Plowing.

First North Korean Stamps, 50th Anniv. — A1583

**1996, Mar. 12**
3531 A1583 1w multicolored — 3.00 .80

Yangzhou, China — A1584

Taihou Lake, China — A1585

**1996, Mar. 20**
3532 A1584 50ch multicolored — 1.60 .50
3533 A1585 50ch multicolored — 1.60 .50
Chinese Imperial Post, Centennial.

A1586

Kim Il Sung, 83rd Birthday — A1587

Designs: 10ch, Birthplace, Mangyondae. 1w, Portrait of Kim Il Sung.

**1996, Apr. 15**
3534 A1586 10ch multicolored — .50 .25

**Souvenir Sheet**
3535 A1587 1w multicolored — 3.00 .80

China '96 Int'l Stamp Exhib., Beijing — A1588

Designs: No. 3536, Seacoast gateway. No. 3537, Haiyin Pool. 60ch. Pantuo Stone.

**1996, Apr. 22** — Perf. 13½
3536-3537 A1588 10ch Set of 2 — .50 .25

**Souvenir Sheet**
**Perf. 11½**
3538 A1588 60ch multicolored — 1.45 .55

Folk Games — A1589

Designs: 20ch, Kicking stone handmill. 40ch, Shuttlecock. 50ch, Sledding.

**1996, May 2**
3539-3541 A1589 Set of 3 — 3.25 .90
3539a-3541a — Set of 3 sheets of 2 + label — 6.50 6.50

Assoc. for the Restoration of the Fatherland, 60th Anniv. — A1590

**1996, May 5**
3542 A1590 10ch multicolored — .50 .25
a. — Sheet of 5 #3542 + label — 2.25 1.35

Ri Po Ik — A1591

**1996, May 31** — Perf. 13½
3543 A1591 1w multicolored — 2.75 5.00
Ri Po Ik, Kim Il Sung's grandmother, 125th birth anniv.

Polar Animals — A1592

Designs, 50ch: No. 3544a, Arctic fox. No. 3544b, Polar bear. No. 3545a, Emperor penguins. No. 3546b, Leopard seals.

**1996, June 2** — Perf. 11½
3544-3545 A1592 Set of 2 sheets — 6.00 3.75

A1593

Korea Children's Union, 50th Anniv. — A1594

Designs: 10ch, Boy saluting. 1w, Painting of Kim Il Sung with Children's Union members, There's Nothing to Envy in the World.

**1996, June 6**
3546 A1593 10ch multicolored — .50 .25

**Souvenir Sheet**
**Perf. 11½x12**
3547 A1594 1w multicolored — 2.75 .80

Locomotives A1595

Designs, all 50ch: No. 3548, Steam locomotive, facing left. No. 3549, Electric locomotive, facing right. No. 3550, Steam locomotive, facing right. No. 3551, Electric locomotive, facing left.

**1996, June 6** — Perf. 11½
3548-3551 A1595 Set of 4 — 3.25 1.15
Capex '96 World Philatelic Exhibition. For surcharge, see No. 4551.

Kim Chol Ju, Kim Il Sung's Brother, 80th Birth Anniv. — A1596

**1996, June 12** — Perf. 13¼
3552 A1596 1.50w multicolored — 4.00 1.75

Open Book — A1597

**1996, June 15** — Perf. 13½
3553 A1597 40ch multicolored — 1.00 .50
760th anniversary of publication of the Complete Collection of Buddhist Scriptures Printed from 80,000 Wooden Blocks.

Labor Law, 50th Anniv. — A1598

**1996, June 24** — Perf. 11½
3554 A1598 50ch multicolored — .50 .40

Seasonal Birds — A1599

Designs: 10ch, Broad-billed roller. 40ch, Tricolor flycatcher. 50ch, Cuckoo.

**1996, July 5**
3555 A1599 Sheet of 3, #a.-c. — 3.75 1.75
See No. 3569.

3rd Asian Winter Games, Harbin, China (2nd issue) — A1600

Design same as No. 3522, but with a new 30ch value picturing Ye Qiaobo replacing No, 3522b

**1996, July 5**
3556 A1600 Sheet of 2 — 1.60 .90
a. — 30ch multi — .80 .40

Kumsusan Memorial Palace — A1601

Outdoor Crowd, Statue of Kim Il Sung — A1602

Hymn, *The Leader will be with us forever* — A1603

Statue of Kim Il Sung in hall of the Kumsusan Memorial Palace — A1604

**1996, July 8**      **Perf. 12**
3557 A1601 10ch multicolored    .25   .25

**Souvenir Sheets**
**Perf. 13¼, 12 (#3558)**
3558 A1602 1w multicolored   2.75   .90
3559 A1603 1w multicolored   2.75   .90
3560 A1604 1w multicolored   2.75   .90

Kim Il Sung, 2nd Death Anniv.

A1605

Designs, both 10ch: No. 3561, Kim Il Sung meeting Mao Zedong of China, 1954. No. 3562, Kim Il Sung meeting Jiang Zemin of China, 1991.
80ch, Kim shaking hands with Deng Xiaoping of China, horiz.

**1996, July 11**      **Perf. 11½**
3561-3562 A1605 Set of 2   .50   .25

**Souvenir Sheet**
3563 A1605 80ch multicolored   2.00   .90

26th Olympic Games, Atlanta — A1606

Designs, each 50ch: No. 3564, Soccer. No. 3565, Tennis. No. 3566, Hammer throw. No. 3567, Baseball.

**1996, July 19**      **Perf. 12¼**
3564-3567 A1606 Set of 4   5.00 1.75

Sexual Equality Law, 50th Anniv. — A1607

**1996, July 30**      **Perf. 11½**
3568 A1607 10ch multicolored   .25   .25

**Seasonal Bird Type**

Designs: 10ch, Crested shelduck. 40ch, Demoiselle crane. 50ch, White swan.

**1996, Aug. 5**
3569 A1600 Sheet of 3, #a.-c.   2.50 1.15

Industrial Nationalization, 50th Anniv. — A1608

**1996, Aug. 10**      **Perf. 11½**
3570 A1608 50ch multicolored   .85   .40

UNICEF, 50th Anniv. — A1609

Designs: 10ch, Boy with ball, net. 20ch, Boy playing with building blocks. 50ch, Boy eating meal, holding watermelon slice. 60ch, Girl playing accordion.

**1996, Aug. 20**
3571-3574 A1609 Set of 4   2.50 1.00

Nos. 3571-3574 were issued in sheets of four, one containing 2 No. 3571, 1 No. 3573 and a label, the other containing 2 No. 3572, 1 No. 3573 and a different label.

1st Asian Gymnastics Championship, Changsha, China — A1610

No. 3575: a, Pae Kil Su (N. Korea), men's pommel. b, Chen Cui Ting (China), rings. c, Li Jing (China). d, Kim Kwang Suk (N. Korea), asymmetrical bars.

**1996, Sept. 24**
3575 A1610 15ch Sheet of 4, #a-d, + 2 labels   1.35   .55

Kim Il Sung University, 50th Anniv. — A1611

**1996, Oct. 1**
3579 A1611 10ch multicolored   .50   .25

Tiger — A1612

Designs, 50ch: No. 3580, Tiger. No. 3581, Royal spoonbill.
80ch: Stylized dove/hand nurturing sapling, growing out of planet Earth.

**1996, Oct. 13**
3580-3581 A1612 Set of 2   2.75   .65

**Souvenir Sheet**
3582 A1612 80ch multicolored   6.00 1.35

Nos. 3580-3581 were each printed in sheets of four, containing three stamps and a label.

Down-with-Imperialism Union, 70th Anniv. — A1613

**1996, Oct. 17**
3583 A1613 10ch multicolored   .25   .25

A1614

Designs: a, 30ch Huang Ji Gwang. b, 10ch, Score of theme song of film *Red Mountain Ridge*. c, 30ch Huang Ji Gwang heroically dying in battle.

**1996, Oct. 25**
3584 A1614 Sheet of 3, #a.-c.   1.75   .90

Hwang Ji Gwang, Chinese Volunteer, hero of Korean War, 44th death anniv.

History of the Earth — A1615

Each 50ch: a, Earth 7.5 billion years ago. b, 4.5-5 billion years ago. c, 450 million-4.5 billion years ago. d, 100-450 million years ago. e, 100 million years ago to the present.

**1996, Nov. 1**      **Perf. 13½**
3585 A1615 Sheet of 5, #a.-e.   7.25 3.75

Freshwater Fish — A1616

Designs, 20ch: No. 3586, Japanese eel. No. 3587, Menada gray mullet.
80ch, Silver carp.

**1996, Nov. 20**      **Perf. 11½**
3586-3587 A1616 Set of 2   1.35   .35

**Souvenir Sheet**
3588 A1616 80ch multicolored   2.75   .75

Kim Jong Il' Appointment as Supreme Commander of the People's Army, 5th Anniv. — A1617

**1996, Dec. 24**      **Perf. 12**
3589 A1617 20ch multicolored   .55   .25

New Year — Year of the Ox — A1618

Designs, 70ch: No. 3590, *Ox Driver*, by Kim Tu Ryang. No. 3591, Bronze ritual plate decorated with a tiger and two bulls. No. 3592, Cowboy and bull. No. 3593, Cowboy playing flute, sitting on bull.
80ch, *Kosong People's Support to the Front*.

**1997, Jan. 1**      **Perf. 11¾**
3590-3593 A1618 Set of 4   7.25 1.75
3591a, 3593a   Set of 2 sheets   7.25 1.75

**Souvenir Sheet**
3594 A1618 80ch multicolored   2.75   .75

No. 3591a contains Nos. 3590 and 3591, with a central label depicting a bull's head surrounded by zodiacal signs. No. 3593a contains Nos. 3592 and 3593, with the same label.

*Flowers and Butterflies*, by Nam Kye-u (1811-88) — A1619

Designs, each 50ch: a, Three butterflies, flower. b, One small butterfly, flower. c, Large butterfly, leaves.

**1997, Jan. 5**      **Perf. 12¼x11¾**
3595 A1619 Sheetlet of 3, #a.-c.   4.25   .90
   d.   Booklet pane of 6, 2 each
     #3595a-3595b   8.25 —
     Complete booklet, #3595d   8.25

Paintings of Cats and Dogs — A1620

Designs, 50ch: No. 3598, Puppy in basket, touching noses with kitten. No. 3599, Two dogs in basket, kitten.
No. 3600: a, Cat in basket, with dog and skein of yarn alongside. b, Kitten in basket with fruit and flowers, puppy alongside.

**1997, Jan. 25**      **Perf. 11¾x12¼**
3598-3599 A1620 Set of 2   3.00   .90

**Sheets of 4**
3600   Sheet of 4, #3598,
     3600b, 2 #3600a   3.25 1.35
   a.   A1620 50ch multicolored   1.35
   b.   A1620 50ch multicolored   1.35
3601   Sheet of 4, #3599,
     #3600a, 2 #3600b   3.25 1.35

Return of Hong Kong to China — A1621

Hong Kong nightscape, each 20ch: a, Skyscraper with double antennae. b, Skyscraper with single spire. c, Round skyscraper, highrise apartment buildings.

**1997, Feb. 1**      **Perf. 13½**
3602 A1621 Sheet of 3, #a.-c.   2.25   .60

A1622

Kim Jong Il, 55th Birthday — A1623

Designs: 10ch, Birthplace, Mt. Paektu.

No. 3604, Kim Il Sung and Kim Jong Il with farm machine. No. 3605, Kim Jong Il inspecting a Korean People's Army unit.

**1997, Feb. 16**                **Perf. 12**
3603  A1622  10ch multicolored       .50   .25
**Souvenir Sheets**
3604-3605  A1623  1w Set of 2     5.00  1.60

6th Paektusan Prize Int'l Figure Skating Championships, Pyongyang — A1624

Pairs skating, different routines, 50ch: No. 3606, pale reddish brown. No. 3607, blue. No. 3608, green.

**1997, Feb. 17**                **Perf. 11½**
3606-3608  A1624  Set of 3       3.75   .90
3607a      Sheet of 4, 2 ea #3606,
           3607                  5.00  1.35
3608a      Booklet pane of 6, 2 ea.
           #3606-3608            7.25    —
           Complete booklet, #3608a  7.75
3608b      Sheet of 4, 2 ea #3607,
           3608                  5.00  1.35

Kye Sun Hui, Women's Judo Gold Medalist, 1996 Summer Olympic Games, Atlanta — A1625

**1997, Feb. 20**
3611  A1625  80ch multicolored   2.25   .55
3611a        Booklet pane of 5
             #3611                  —     —
             Complete booklet, #3611a  —

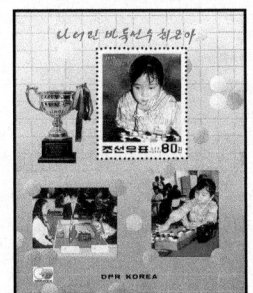

Choe Un A — A1626

**1997, Feb. 25**
3612  A1626  80ch multicolored   2.75   .55
a.           Booklet pane of 5
             Complete booklet, #3612a

Issued to honor Choe Un A, a seven-year-old entrant in the World Go Championships.

Apricots — A1627

Various types of apricots, 50ch: No. 3613, Prunus ansu. No. 3614, Prunus mandshurica. No. 3615, Prunus armeniaca. No. 3616, Prunus sibirica.

**1997, Mar. 4**                 **Perf. 11¼**
3613-3616  A1627  Set of 4       5.50  1.35
3616a      Sheet of 8, 2 ea#3613-3616  11.00  2.75

Foundation of Korean National Assoc., 80th Anniv. — A1628

**1997, Mar. 23**                **Perf. 12¼**
3617  A1628  10ch lt brn & dk grn  .50   .25
a.           Sheet of 8          3.75   .90

A1629

Reforestation Day, 50th Anniv. — A1630

Designs: 10ch, Pine sapling.
No. 3619, Kim Il Sung planting sapling on Munsu Hill.

**1997, Apr. 6**                 **Perf. 11½**
3618  A1629  10ch multicolored    .50   .25
             Complete booklet, 8 #3618
**Souvenir Sheet**
**Perf. 13¼**
3619  A1630  1w multicolored     2.75   .85

A1631

A1632

Kim Il Sung, 85th Birth Anniv. — A1633

Designs: 10ch, Kim's birthplace, Mangyongdae. 20ch, Sliding rock, horiz. 40ch, Warship Rock, horiz.
Each 1w: No. 3623, Painting of Kim among crowd symbolic of the Korean people. No. 3624, Kim in business suit, surrounded by flowers.

**1997, Apr. 15**               **Perf. 12¼**
3620-3622  A1631  Set of 3       1.75   .50
**Souvenir Sheets**
**Perf. 13¼ (#3623), 11¾x12¼ (#3624)**
3623  A1632  1w multicolored     2.50   .85
3624  A1633  1w multicolored     2.50   .85

A1634

Korean People's Army, 65th Anniv. — A1635

Designs: 10ch, KPA cap badge, rockets and jet fighters.
1w, Kim Il Sung and Kim Jong Il at military review.

**1997, Apr. 25**                **Perf. 11½**
3625  A1634  10ch multicolored    .50   .25
**Souvenir Sheet**
**Perf. 12¼x11¾**
3626  A1635  1w multicolored     2.75   .85

A1636

North-South Agreement, 25th Anniv. — A1637

Designs: 10ch, Map of Korea.
1w, Monument to Kim Il Sung's Autograph, Phanmunjom.

**1997, May 4**                  **Perf. 11½**
3627  A1636  10ch multicolored    .90   .25
**Souvenir Sheet**
**Perf. 12x11½**
3628  A1637  1w multicolored     3.75   .85

A1638

Each 10ch: No. 3629, Tower of Juche Idea, flag. No. 3630, Man with flag. No. 3631, Soldier, miner, farmer, scientist.

**1997, May 25**                **Perf. 12¼x12**
3629-3631  A1638  Set of 3        .85   .40

Int'l Friendship Exhib., Myohyang Mountains — A1639

Each 70ch: No. 3632, Exhibition Center. No. 3633, Statue of Kim Il Sung in exhibition entrance hall. No. 3634, Ivory sculpture *Native House in Mangyongdae*. No. 3635, Stuffed crocodile holding wooden cups, with ashtray.

**1997, May 30**                **Perf. 11¾**
3632-3635  A1639  Set of 4
           sheets                6.75  4.50

Battle of Poconbo, 60th Anniv. — A1640

**1997, June 4**                **Perf. 11½**
3636  A1640  40ch multicolored   1.15   .35
a.           Sheet of 6          6.75  6.75
b.           Booklet pane of 6 #3636  6.75
             Complete booklet, #3636b  7.25

No. 3636b contains six stamps in a horizontal strip, within decorative selvage.

Rice Transplantation, Mirin Plain, 50th Anniv. — A1641

Each 1w: No. 3637, Kim Il Sung transplanting rice. No. 3638, Kim Il Sung inspecting a rice-transplanting machine.

**1997, June 7**                **Perf. 13¼**
3637-3638  A1641  Set of 2
           sheets                5.25  1.60

A1642

Return of Hong Kong to China — A1643

No. 3639, each 20ch: a, Signing the Nanjing Treaty, 1842. b, Signing the China-Britain Joint Statement, 1984. c, Deng Xiaoping and Margaret Thatcher. d, Jiang Zenin and Tong Jianhua.
97ch, Deng Xiaoping.

**1997, July 1**    *Perf. 11¾*
3639 A1642 Sheet of 4, #a.-d. 2.75 .75

**Souvenir Sheet**
*Perf. 13¼*
3640 A1643 97ch multicolored 2.75 .90

Fossils — A1644

Designs: 50ch, Redlichia chinensis. 1w, Ptychoparia coreanica.

**1997, July 5**    *Perf. 11½*
3641 A1644 Pair, #a.-b. 4.50 1.15
  c. Booklet pane, 5 #3641a 8.00
    Complete booklet #3641c 8.25
  d. Booklet pane, 5 #3641b 16.00
    Complete booklet #3641d 16.50

Nos. 3641c-3641d each contain horizontal strips of five stamps.

Kim Il Sung, 3rd Death Anniv. — A1645

Each 50ch, Portrait of Kim Il Sung and: No. 3643, Kim speaking at party conference, 1985. No. 3644, Kim inspecting Kim Chaek Ironworks, 1985. No. 3645, Kim at Songsin Cooperative Farm, Sadong District, 1993. No. 3646, Kim being cheered by performing artists, 1986. No. 3647, Kim visiting Jonchon Factory, Jagang Province, 1991. No. 3648, Kim receiving bouquet from soldiers.

**1997, July 8**    *Perf. 11¾x12*
3643-3648 A1645 Set of 6 8.25 2.00
3645a Sheet of 3, #3643-3645 4.25 1.75
3648a Sheet of 3, #3646-3648 4.25 1.75

Folk Games — A1646

Designs: 30ch, Blindman's Bluff. 60ch, Jackstones. 70ch, Arm wrestling.

**1997, July 26**    *Perf. 11½*
3649-3651 A1646 Set of 3 4.25 1.15
3649a-3651a Set of 3 sheets 8.25 3.75
3651b Booklet pane of 6, 2 ea. #3649-3651 8.25
  Complete booklet, #3651b 8.75

Nos. 3649a-3651a each contain 2 stamps + a central label.
No. 3281b contains two each of Nos. 3649-3651, printed in a se-tenant block (3x2), with decorative selvage.

Traditional Korean Women's Clothing — A1647

Designs: 10ch, Spring costume. 40ch, Summer. 50ch, Autumn. 60ch, Winter.

**1997, Aug. 10**
3652-3655 A1647 Set of 4 4.25 1.75
3652a-3654a Set of 3 sheets 16.50 11.00

No. 3652a contains 2 each Nos. 3652-3653; No. 3653a contains 2 each Nos. 3653-3654; No. 3654a contains 2 each Nos. 3654-3655.

Chongryu Bridge — A1648

Both 50ch: No. 3656, Night view of Chongryu Bridge. No. 3657, Panoramic view.

**1997, Aug. 25**
3656-3657 A1648 Set of 2 2.75 .90
3657a Sheet of 2, #3656-3657 3.25 1.35
3657b Booklet pane of 6, 3 ea. #3656-3657 8.25
  Complete booklet, #3657b 8.75

A1649

Juche Era and Sun Day, 85th Anniv. — A1650

10ch, Sun, magnolias, banner, balloons.
Each 1w: No. 3659, Kim Il Sung, slogan, doves. No. 3660, Kim, birthplace Mongyangdae. No. 3661, Kim, Lake Chon, Mt. Paekdu. No. 3662, Kim, Kumsusan Memorial Palace.

**1997, Sept. 3**    *Perf. 13¼*
3658 A1649 10ch multicolored .50 .25

**Souvenir Sheets**
3659-3662 A1650 Set of 4 sheets 10.00 5.50

*Theses on Socialist Education*, 20th Anniv. of Publication A1651

**1997, Sept. 5**    *Perf. 11½*
3663 A1651 10ch multicolored .50 .25
No. 3663 was issued in sheetlets of 6.

Air Koryo — A1652

Sheets of 2 stamps and central label: 20ch, TU-134. 30ch, TU-154. 50ch, IL-62.

**1997, Sept. 14**    *Perf. 13¼*
3664-3666 A1652 Set of 3 sheets 4.50 1.35
3665a Complete booklet, pane of 8, 4 ea. #3664, 3666 6.50
3666a Complete booklet, pane of 8, 4 ea. #3665, 3666 7.25

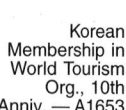

Korean Membership in World Tourism Org., 10th Anniv. — A1653

Views of Mt. Chilbo, each 50ch: No. 3667, Kim Chol Ung. No. 3668, Rojok Beach. No. 3669, Chonbul Peak.

**1997, Sept. 22**    *Perf. 12*
3667-3669 A1653 Set of 3 4.25 1.15
3669a Sheet, #3667-3669 + label 4.50 1.30

Kumgang Mountains — A1654

Each 50ch: No. 3670, Kumgang Gate. No. 3671, Podok Hermitage.

**1997, Oct. 2**
3670-3671 A1654 Set of 2 2.75 .75
3670a Booklet pane of 5 #3670 6.75
  Complete booklet #3670a 7.25
3671a Sheet of 6, 3 each #3670-3671 9.00 3.75
3671b Booklet pane of 5 #3671 6.75
  Complete booklet #3671a 7.25

Mangyongdae Revolutionary School, 50th Anniv. — A1655

**1997, Oct. 12**    *Perf. 11½*
3672 A1655 40ch multicolored 1.15 .30
  a. Booklet pane of 6 6.75
    Complete booklet, #3672a 7.25

Gift Animals — A1656

Animals presented to Kim Il Sung as gifts from foreign governments: 20ch, Lion (from Ethiopia, 1987). 30ch, Jaguar (Japan, 1992). 50ch, Barbary sheep (Czechoslovakia, 1992). 80ch, Scarlet macaw (Austria, 1979).

**1997, Oct. 15**
3673-3676 A1656 Set of 4 5.00 1.15
3673a Sheet of 8, 2 each #3673-3676 10.00 4.50
3673b Booklet pane of 8, 2ea. #3673-3676 10.00
  Complete booklet, #3673b 11.00
For surcharges, see No. 4554-4555.

Qu Shao Yun, Chinese Volunteer Hero — A1657

Designs: a, 30ch, Bust of Qu Shao Yun. b, 10ch, Monument to Qu Shao Yun. c, 30ch, Qu Shao Yun burning to death in battle.

**1997, Oct. 18**
3677 A1657 Sheet of 3, #a.-c. 2.00 .75

Sports — A1658

Designs: No. 3678, 50ch, Bowling. No. 3679, 50ch, Fencing. No. 3680, 50ch Golf.

**1997, Nov. 10**    *Perf. 13¼*
3678-3680 A1658 Set of 3 4.75 1.15
3680a Sheet, 2 each #3678-3680 + 2 labels 10.00 4.50
For surcharge, see No. 4574.

Snails — A1659

Each 50ch: a, Two snails copulating. b, Snail laying eggs. c, Snail.

**1997, Nov. 15**    *Perf. 12¼*
3681 A1659 Strip of 3, #a.-c. 4.50 1.75
  d. Sheet of 6, 2 each #3681a-3681c 8.75 3.75
  e. Booklet pane of 6, 2 ea. #3681a-3681c 8.75
    Complete booklet, #3681e 9.00

Shanghai Int'l Stamp & Coin Exhib. — A1660

**1997, Nov. 19**    *Perf. 11½*
3684 A1660 Sheet of 2, #a.-b. 2.25 .90
  a. 30ch multicolored .90 .30
  b. 50ch multicolored 1.35 .55

New Year — Year of the Tiger
A1661    A1662

Designs: 10ch, "Juche 87," pine boughs, temple. 50ch (No. 3686), Tiger in rocket. 50ch (No. 3687), Tiger in ship.
80ch, Tiger in train.

*Perf. 13¼, 11½ (#3686-3687)*
**1997, Dec. 15**
3685 A1661 10ch multicolored .25 .25
3686 A1662 50ch multicolored .85 .25
3687 A1662 50ch multicolored .85 .25
  a. Sheet of 4, 1 ea #3686-3687, 2 #3688a 4.25 1.75
  Nos. 3685-3687 (3) 1.95 .75

**Souvenir Sheet**
3688 A1662 80ch multicolored 1.75 .75
  a. Perf. 11½
  b. Booklet pane of 8, 2 each #3686-3687, 4 #3688a — —
    Complete booklet, #3688b — —

Complete booklet sold for 5.40w.

Birthplace, Hoeryong A1663

Kim Jong Suk, 80th Birth Anniv. — A1664

**1997, Dec. 24**    *Perf. 13¼*
3689 A1663 10ch multicolored .50 .25
**Souvenir Sheet**
3690 A1664 1w multicolored 2.75 .75

Winter Olympic Games, Nagano, Japan — A1665

Designs: 20ch, Skiing. 40ch, Speed skating.

**1998, Feb. 7**     *Perf. 11½*
3691-3692 A1665 Set of 2   1.15   .60
3692a   Sheet of 4, 2 ea #3691- #3692   2.25   1.15
3692b   Booklet pane of 8, 4 ea. #3691-3692   4.50
    Complete booklet, #3692b   5.00

A1666

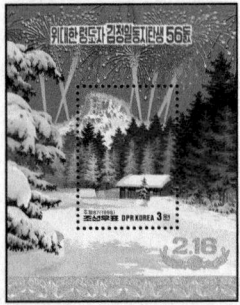
Kim Jong Il, 56th Birthday — A1667

Designs: 10ch, Birth date ("2.16").
3w, Birthplace, log cabin on Mt. Paekdu.

**1998, Feb. 16**
3693 A1666 10ch multicolored   .50   .25
**Souvenir Sheet**
3694 A1667 3w multicolored   4.25   1.75

A1668

Paintings of Mt. Paekdu Wildlife — A1669

Designs: 50ch: No. 3695, Korean tigers. No. 3696, White crane. No. 3697, 50ch: a, Bears. b, Racoons.

**1998, Mar. 6**     *Perf. 11¾x12*
3695-3696 A1668 Set of 2   1.75   .90
3696a   Booklet pane of 8, 2 ea. #3695-3696, 3697a-3697b   7.25
    Complete booklet, #3696a   7.75
**Souvenir Sheet**
3697 A1669   Sheet of 4, #3695-3696, 3697a-3697b   3.75   1.75
a.   A1668 50ch multicolored   .90   .50
b.   A1668 50ch multicolored   .90   .50

Kim Il Sung's 1000-ri Journey, 75th Anniv. — A1670

**1998, Mar. 16**     *Perf. 11½*
3698 A1670 10ch multicolored   .50   .25
a.   Sheet of 10   4.50   1.35

Appt. of Kim Jong Il as Chairman of the Nat'l Defense Commission, 5th Anniv. — A1671

**1998, Apr. 9**
3699 A1671 10ch multicolored   .50   .25

A1672

Kim Il Sung, 86th Birth Anniv. — A1673

Designs: 10ch, Birthplace, flags, flowers. Circular stamps, each 80ch, within 84x155mm sheetlets, depicting portraits of Kim Il Sung at different stages in his life: #3701, As child. #3702, As middle school student. #3703, As young revolutionary. #3704, In suit and tie, ca. 1946. #3705, In military uniform during Korean War. #3706, As middle-aged man, in uniform. #3707, As middle-aged man, in suit and tie. #3708, As old man in suit and tie.

**1998, Apr. 15**
3700 A1672 10ch multicolored   .50   .25
**Souvenir Sheets**
3701-3708 A1673 Set of 8   8.25   3.75

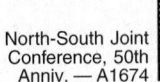
North-South Joint Conference, 50th Anniv. — A1674

**1998, Apr. 21**     *Perf. 13¼*
3709 A1674 10ch multicolored   .50   .25

16th World Cup Soccer Championship, France — A1675

Designs: 30ch, Dribbling. 50ch, Kicking.

**1998, May 5**     *Perf. 11½*
3710-3711 A1675 Set of 2   1.45   5.00
3711a   Sheet of 6, 2 ea #3710-#3711, #3712   5.50   2.75
3711b   Booklet pane of 10, 5 ea. #3710-3711   7.25
    Complete booklet, #3711b   7.75
**Souvenir Sheet**
3712 A1675 80ch multicolored   1.45   5.00
A single stamp like that in No. 3712 is included in No. 3711a.

A1676

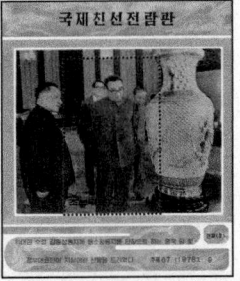
Int'l Friendship Art Exhib., Mt. Myohyang — A1677

Designs: 1w: No. 3713, *Diagram of Automatic Space Station* (USSR). No. 3714, Ceramic flower vase (Egypt). No. 3715, *Crane* (USA). 1w, Kim Il Sung receiving a gift from Deng Xiaoping.

**1998, May 20**     *Perf. 11¾*
3713-3715 A1676 Set of 3   4.25   2.00
3714a   Sheet of 2, #3713 & #3714   2.50   1.30
3715a   Sheet of 2, #3713 & #3715   2.50   1.30
**Souvenir Sheet**     *Perf. 13¼*
3716 A1677 1w multicolored   1.75   .90

A1678

Korean Art Gallery — A1679

Designs: 60ch, *A Countryside in May.* 1.40w, *Dance.* 3w, *Heart-to-heart Talk with a Peasant.*

**1998, May 20**
3717-3718 A1678 Set of 2   2.75   1.35
**Souvenir Sheet**
3719 A1679 3w multicolored   4.25   2.00

Vegetables — A1680

Designs: 10ch, Cabbage. 40ch, Radish. 50ch, Green onion. 60ch, Cucumber. 70ch, Pumpkin. 80ch, Carrot. 90ch, Garlic. 1w, Red pepper.

**1998, May 20**     *Perf. 13¼*
3720 A1680 Sheet of 8, #a.-h.   8.25   4.25

A1681

Int'l Year of the Ocean — A1682

Designs: 10ch, Hydro-Meteorological Headquarters building, ship, oceanographic floating balloons, dolphins, emblem. 80ch, Woman holding child, yachts, emblem. 5w, Vasco da Gama (1460-1524), Portuguese explorer.

**1998, May 22**
3730-3731 A1681 Set of 2   1.75   .85
3731a   Sheet of 4, 2 ea. #3730-3731   1.75   .85
**Souvenir Sheet**
3732 A1682 5w multicolored   6.75   3.50

A1683

Korean Central History Museum, Pyongyang — A1684

Designs: 10ch, Stone Age tool. 2.50w, Fossil monkey skull. 4w, Kim Il Sung visiting the museum.

**1998, June 15**
3733-3734 A1683 Set of 2   3.75   1.75
**Souvenir Sheet**
3735 A1684 4w multicolored   5.50   2.75

A1685

Dr. Ri Sung Gi (1905-96), Inventor of Vinalon — A1686

Designs: 40ch, Dr. Ri Sung Gi and diagram of vinalon nuclear structure. 80ch, Gi working in laboratory.

**1998, June 15**     *Perf. 11½*
3736 A1685 40ch multicolored   .60   .25
a.   Booklet pane of 10   Complete booklet, #3736a
**Souvenir Sheet**
3737 A1686 80ch multicolored   1.25   .85

*Squirrels and Hedgehogs Cartoon — A1687*

Designs: 20ch, Squirrel and Commander of Hedgehog Unit. 30ch, Commander of Hedgehog Unit receiving invitation to banquet celebrating bumper crop. 60ch, Weasel Commander and mouse. 1.20w, Bear falling dead-drunk. 2w, Weasel Commander and mice invading the flower village. 2.50w, Hedgehog scout saving the squirrel.

**1998, June 15**

| | | | |
|---|---|---|---|
| 3738-3743 | A1687 | Set of 6 | 11.00 5.50 |
| 3743a | | Sheet of 6, #3737-3743 | 11.00 5.50 |

A1688

Return of Hong Kong to China, 1st Anniv. — A1689

Designs: 10w: No. 3744, Deng Xiaoping (1904-97), Chinese Prime Minister. No. 3745, Mao Zedong. No. 3746, Kim Il Sung. No. 3747, Deng Xiaoping, Mao Zedong and Kim Il Sung, horiz.

**1998, July 1**
**Embossed with gold foil application**

| | | | |
|---|---|---|---|
| 3744-3746 | A1688 | Set of 3 | 30.00 10.00 |

**Souvenir Sheet**

| | | | |
|---|---|---|---|
| 3747 | A1689 | 10w Gold & multi | 10.00 10.00 |

*Young Wild Mammals A1690*

Designs: 10ch, Tiger cub. 50ch, Donkey foal. 1.60w, Elephant. 2w, Lion cubs.

**1998, July 10**     *Perf. 11½*

| | | | |
|---|---|---|---|
| 3748-3751 | A1690 | Set of 4 | 4.50 2.25 |
| 3751a | | Booklet pane of 8, 2 each #3748-3751 | — — |
| | | Complete booklet, #3751a | — |

Complete booklet sold for 8.60w.

A1691

A1692

Korean War "Victory," 45th Anniv. — A1693

Designs: 45ch, War monument, flag. No. 3753, Kim Il Sung inspecting the front. No. 3754, Gaz-67 jeep and map of Korea, showing Kim's inspection route.

**1998, July 27**     *Perf. 13¼*

| | | | |
|---|---|---|---|
| 3752 | A1691 | 45ch multicolored | .25 .25 |

**Souvenir Sheets**

| | | | |
|---|---|---|---|
| 3753 | A1692 | 2w multicolored | 2.00 1.00 |
| 3754 | A1693 | 2w multicolored | 2.00 1.00 |

Embroidery — A1694

Designs: 10ch, *White Herons in Forest.* 40ch, *Carp.* 1.20w, *Hollyhock.* 1.50w, *Cockscomb.* 4w, *Pine and Cranes.*

**1998, Aug. 10**     *Perf. 11¾x12*

| | | | |
|---|---|---|---|
| 3755-3758 | A1694 | Set of 4 | 2.50 1.25 |
| 3758a | | Booklet pane of 6, #3757, 3758, 2 each #3755-3756 | — — |
| | | Complete booklet, #3758a | — |

Complete booklet sold for 3.90w.

**Perf. 12x12¼**

| | | | |
|---|---|---|---|
| 3759 | | Sheet of 5, #a.-e. + label | 5.75 3.00 |
| a. | | A1694 10ch multicolored | .25 .25 |
| b. | | A1694 40ch multicolored | .40 .25 |
| c. | | A1694 1.20w multicolored | 1.00 .50 |
| d. | | A1694 1.50w multicolored | 1.00 .50 |
| e. | | A1694 4w multicolored | 2.50 1.25 |

**Souvenir Sheet**
**Perf. 11¾x12**

| | | | |
|---|---|---|---|
| 3760 | A1694 | 4w multicolored | 3.00 1.50 |

Traditional Costumes — A1695

Designs: 10ch, Pouch. 50ch, Playthings (dress ornaments). 1.50w, Hairpin. 1.90w, Ornamental silver sword.

**1998, Aug. 20**     *Perf. 11½*

| | | | |
|---|---|---|---|
| 3761-3764 | A1695 | Set of 4 | 3.00 1.50 |
| 3763a | | Sheet of 20, 10 se-tenant pairs #3761 and #3763 | 15.00 7.50 |
| 3764a | | Sheet of 20, 10 se-tenant pairs #3762 and #3764 | 15.00 7.50 |
| 3764b | | Booklet pane of 8, 2 each #3761-3764 | — — |
| | | Complete booklet, #3764b | — |

Complete booklet sold for 8.20w.

Launch of *Kwangmyongsong I,* DPRK's First Earth Satellite — A1696

Designs: 40ch, Rocket, satellite, world map and flag. 1.50w, Rocket, earth and satellite orbit.

**1998, Aug. 31**     *Perf. 13¼*

| | | | |
|---|---|---|---|
| 3765 | A1696 | 40ch multicolored | .35 .25 |

**Souvenir Sheet**

| | | | |
|---|---|---|---|
| 3766 | A1696 | 1.50w multicolored | 1.25 .65 |

A1697

Acclamation of Kim Jong Il as Chairman of the DPRK National Defense Commission — A1698

Designs: 10ch, Proclamation, *Kimjongilia.* 1w, Kim Jong Il.

**1998, Sept. 5**     *Perf. 11½*

| | | | |
|---|---|---|---|
| 3767 | A1697 | 10ch multicolored | .25 .25 |

**Souvenir Sheet**
**Perf. 13¼**

| | | | |
|---|---|---|---|
| 3768 | A1698 | 1w multicolored | .75 .40 |

A1699

Korean DPR, 50th Anniversary — A1700

Designs: 10ch, State Arms, Flag, Tower of Juche Idea.
No. 3770: a, Kim Il Sung saluting crowd from balcony. b, Kim raising cap to crowd in street. c, Kim in suit and white hat, with fruit, stylized and idealized Korean peninsula in background.

**1998, Sept. 9**     *Perf. 13¼*

| | | | |
|---|---|---|---|
| 3769 | A1699 | 10ch multicolored | .25 .25 |
| 3770 | A1700 | 1w Sheet of 6, 2 each a-c | 4.50 2.25 |

Poster: "Let Us Push Ahead with the Forced March for Final Victory" — A1701

**1998, Sept. 15**     *Perf. 11½*

| | | | |
|---|---|---|---|
| 3773 | A1701 | 10ch multicolored | .25 .25 |

A1702

Korean DPR, 50th Anniversary (2nd Issue) — A1703

**1998, Sept. 20**     *Perf. 13¼*

| | | | |
|---|---|---|---|
| 3774 | A1702 | 40ch multicolored | .35 .25 |

**Perf. 11½**

| | | | |
|---|---|---|---|
| 3775 | A1703 | 1w multicolored | 1.00 .50 |

Summer Olympic Games, Sydney — A1704

Designs: 20ch, Cyclist. 50ch, Soccer. 80ch, Show jumping. 1.50w, Javelin throwing. 2.50w, Basketball.

**1998, Sept. 25**

| | | | |
|---|---|---|---|
| 3776-3779 | A1704 | Set of 4 | 2.50 1.25 |
| 3778a | | Sheet of 3, #3777, 3778, as #3780 | 3.00 1.50 |
| 3779a | | Sheet of 3, #3776, 3779, as #3780 | 3.00 1.50 |

**Souvenir Sheet**

| | | | |
|---|---|---|---|
| 3780 | A1704 | 2.50w multi | 2.00 1.00 |

For surcharge, see No. 4529.

Plants Presented as Gifts to Kim Jong Il — A1705

Designs: 20ch, Cyclamen persicum. 2w, Dianthus chinensis.

**1998, Sept. 28**     *Perf. 11½*

| | | | |
|---|---|---|---|
| 3781-3782 | A1705 | Set of 2 | 1.60 .80 |

Nat'l Vaccination Day — A1706

**1998, Oct. 20**     *Perf. 13¼*

| | | | |
|---|---|---|---|
| 3783 | A1706 | 40ch multicolored | .35 .25 |
| a. | | Sheet of 6 | 2.10 1.00 |

**Worldwide Fund for Nature (WWF) — A1707**

Panthera pardus orientalis: No. 3784, 1w, Climbing branch. No. 3785, 1w, Walking in snow. No. 3786, 1w, Looking to left. No. 3787, 1w, Head, full-face.

**1998, Oct. 21**
| | | | | |
|---|---|---|---|---|
| 3784-3787 | A1707 | Set of 4 | 4.00 | 2.00 |
| 3787a | | Sheet of 16, 4 se-tenant blocks of #3784-3787 | 16.00 | 8.00 |

For surcharges, see Nos. 4589-4590.

A1708

**Land and Environment Conservation Day — A1709**

Designs: 10ch, Canal, countryside. 40ch, Modern highway exchange, apartment towers. 1w, Kim Il Sung breaking ground for construction of Pothong River project.

**1998, Oct. 23**     *Perf. 11½*
| | | | | |
|---|---|---|---|---|
| 3788-3789 | A1708 | Set of 2 | .45 | .25 |

**Souvenir Sheet**
*Perf. 12x12¼*
| | | | | |
|---|---|---|---|---|
| 3790 | A1709 | 1w multicolored | .75 | .40 |

**Italia '98 Int'l stamp Exhib., Milan — A1710**

**1998, Oct. 23**     *Perf. 12¼x12*
| | | | | |
|---|---|---|---|---|
| 3791 | A1710 | 2w multicolored | 1.50 | .75 |

A1711

Designs: a, 20ch, Peng Dehuai and Kim Il Sung. b, 20ch, Peng Dehuai, Zhou Enlai, Mao Zedong. c, 30ch, Marshal Peng Dehuai. d, 30ch, Painting, *On the Front.*

**1998, Oct. 24**     *Perf. 11½*
| | | | | |
|---|---|---|---|---|
| 3792 | A1711 | Sheet of 4, #a-d | .75 | .40 |

Birth centenary of Peng Dehuai, Commander of the Chinese People's Volunterrs in the Korean War.

Liu Shaoqi — A1712

Designs: 10ch, Liu Shaoqi. 20ch, Liu sitting with Mao Zedong (1965). 30ch, Liu and his daughter, Xiao Xiao (1964). 40ch, Liu sitting with his wife, Wang Guangmei (1961).

**1998, Nov 24**     *Perf. 13¼*
| | | | | |
|---|---|---|---|---|
| 3796-3799 | A1712 | Set of 4 | .75 | .40 |

**Souvenir Sheet**
*Perf. 11¾x12¼*
| | | | | |
|---|---|---|---|---|
| 3800 | A1712 | 1w multicolored | .75 | .40 |

A1713

**Victory in Korean-Japanese War, 400th Anniv. — A1714**

Designs: 10ch, Victory monument, Yonsang area, Yonan fortress, banners. 30ch, Naval victory monument, Myongryang area, Gen. Ri Sun Sin, turtleship. 1.60w, Monument to Buddhist priest Hyujong, Sosan-Chonghodang, Hyujong, sword, helmet.
No. 3804, *Sea Battle Off Hansan Islet in 1592.*

**1998, Nov 24**     *Perf. 11½*
| | | | | |
|---|---|---|---|---|
| 3801-3803 | A1713 | Set of 3 | 1.50 | .75 |
| 3803a | | Sheet of 15, 5 se-tenant strips of #3801-3803 | 7.50 | 3.75 |

**Souvenir Sheet**
| | | | | |
|---|---|---|---|---|
| 3804 | A1714 | 10w multicolored | 7.50 | 3.00 |

**DPRK Entry into INTERSPUTNIK, 15th Anniv. — A1715**

**1998, Nov. 25**     *Perf. 13¼*
| | | | | |
|---|---|---|---|---|
| 3805 | A1715 | 1w dp grn & lt grn | .75 | .40 |

Korean Goats — A1716

Goat with background color of: 10c, Green. 1w, Purple.

**1998, Nov. 26**
| | | | | |
|---|---|---|---|---|
| 3806-3807 | A1716 | Set of 2 | .80 | .40 |

For surcharge, see No. 4576.

**Sculpture, *A Floral Carriage of Happiness* A1717**

Quotation from Kim Il Sung — A1718

Designs: 10ch, Sculpture, panoramic view of Mangyongdae Schoolchildren's Palace. 1w, Kim Il Sung quotation, "Children are the treasure of our country. Korea of the future is theirs."

**1998, Nov. 26**     *Perf. 11½*
| | | | | |
|---|---|---|---|---|
| 3808 | A1717 | 40ch multicolored | .35 | .25 |
| a. | | Sheet of 4 | 2.00 | 1.00 |

**Souvenir Sheet**
| | | | | |
|---|---|---|---|---|
| 3809 | A1718 | 1w multicolored | .75 | .40 |

**Univeral Declaration of Human Rights, 50th Anniv. — A1719**

**1998, Dec. 10**
| | | | | |
|---|---|---|---|---|
| 3810 | A1719 | 20ch multicolored | .25 | .25 |

**Reptiles — A1720**

Designs: a, 10ch, Reeves turtle. b, 40ch, Skink. c, 60ch, Loggerhead turtle. d, 1.20w, Leatherback turtle.

**1998, Dec. 15**     *Perf. 13¼*
| | | | | |
|---|---|---|---|---|
| 3811 | A1720 | Block of 4, #a-d | 1.75 | .90 |
| e. | | Sheet of 16, 4 #3811 | 17.00 | 3.50 |
| f. | | Complete booklet, 3 ea. #3811 | 13.00 | |

**Mt. Chilbo — A1721**

Designs: 30ch, Thajong Rock. 50ch, Peasant Rock. 1.70w, Couple Rock.

**1998, Dec. 15**     *Perf. 11½*
| | | | | |
|---|---|---|---|---|
| 3815-3817 | A1721 | Set of 3 | 1.75 | .90 |

**Tale of Chung Hyang — A1722**

Designs: 40ch, Marriage of Ri Mong Ryong and Song Chun Hyang. 1.60w, Pyon Hak Do watching Chun Hyang. 2.50w, Ri Mong Ryong and Chun Hyang. 50ch, Chun Hyang in wedding veil.

**1998, Dec. 20**
| | | | | |
|---|---|---|---|---|
| 3818-3820 | A1722 | Set of 3 | 3.50 | 1.75 |
| 3821 | | Sheet of 4, #3818-3820, 3821a | 5.00 | 2.50 |
| a. | | A1722 multicolored | 1.00 | .50 |

Chollima Statue A1723

Arch of Triumph A1724

Tower of Juche Idea — A1725

**1998, Dec. 22**     *Perf. 13¼*
| | | | | |
|---|---|---|---|---|
| 3822 | A1723 | 10ch red | .25 | .25 |
| 3823 | A1724 | 10ch red | .25 | .25 |
| 3824 | A1725 | 10ch red | .25 | .25 |
| 3825 | A1725 | 20ch red org | .25 | .25 |
| 3826 | A1723 | 30ch red org | .35 | .25 |
| 3827 | A1724 | 40ch yel brown | .40 | .25 |
| 3828 | A1724 | 40ch yel brown | .40 | .25 |
| 3829 | A1723 | 70ch yel grn | .65 | .35 |
| 3830 | A1724 | 70ch yel grn | .65 | .35 |
| 3831 | A1724 | 1.20w green | 1.10 | .55 |
| 3832 | A1723 | 1.50w blue green | 1.50 | .75 |
| 3833 | A1724 | 2w blue | 2.00 | 1.00 |
| 3834 | A1724 | 3w blue | 2.75 | 1.40 |
| 3835 | A1725 | 5w dk blue | 5.00 | 2.50 |
| 3836 | A1725 | 10w violet | 9.75 | 5.00 |
| *Nos. 3822-3836 (15)* | | | 25.55 | 13.65 |

For surcharges, see Nos. 4577, 4591, 4611.

**New Year — Year of the Rabbit — A1726**

Designs: 10ch, Rabbit meeting Lion on the road. 1w, Rabbit using mirror to lure lion into pit. 1.50w, Rabbit laughing at Lion in trap. 2.50w, Rabbit.

**1999, Jan. 1**     *Perf. 11½*
| | | | | |
|---|---|---|---|---|
| 3837-3839 | A1726 | Set of 3 | 2.00 | 1.00 |
| 3840 | | Sheet of 4, #3837-3839, 3840a | 4.00 | 2.00 |
| a. | | A1726 2.50w multicolored | 2.00 | 1.00 |
| b. | | Booklet pane of 8, 2 each #3837-3839, 3840a | — | |
| | | Complete booklet, #3840b | — | |

Complete booklet sold for 10.40w.

**Worker-Peasant Red Guards, 40th Anniv. — A1727**

**1999, Jan. 14**     *Perf. 13¼*
| | | | | |
|---|---|---|---|---|
| 3841 | A1727 | 10ch multicolored | .25 | .25 |

Kim Jong Il, 57th Birthday — A1728

40ch, Log cabin (birthplace) on Mt. Paekdu.

**1999, Feb. 16**     *Perf. 11½*
| | | | | |
|---|---|---|---|---|
| 3842 | A1728 | 40ch multicolored | .35 | .25 |

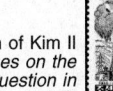

**Publication of Kim Il Sung's *Theses on the Socialist Rural Question in Our Country* — A1729**

**1999, Feb. 25**     *Perf. 13¼*
| | | | | |
|---|---|---|---|---|
| 3843 | A1729 | 10ch multicolored | .25 | .25 |

**March 1 Popular Uprising, 80th Anniv. — A1730**

**1999, Feb. 25**
| | | | | |
|---|---|---|---|---|
| 3844 | A1730 | 10ch olive brn & black | .25 | .25 |

Turtle Ship — A1731

**1999, Mar. 19**
3845 A1731 2w multicolored   1.60   .80
  a.   Booklet pane of 5 #3845   —
     Complete booklet, #3845a   —

Australia '99 World Stamp Expo, Melbourne.
Complete booklet sold for 10.20w.

A1732

Kim Il Sung, 87th Birth
Anniv. — A1733

Designs: 10ch, Childhood Home, Mangyongdae. No. 3847, Kim Il Sung.

**1999, Apr. 15**    **Perf. 11½**
3846 A1732 10ch multicolored   .25   .25
**Souvenir Sheet**
**Perf. 11½x12**
3847 A1733 2w multicolored   1.60   .80

45th World Table
Tennis
Championships,
Belgrade — A1734

**1999, Apr. 26**    **Perf. 11½**
3848 A1734 1.50w multicolored   1.20   .60
For surcharge, see No. 4559.

Ibra '99 Int'l Stamp
Exhib., Nuremberg
— A1735

**1999, Apr. 27**
3849 A1735 1w multicolored   .85   .40
For surcharge, see No. 4557.

Central Zoo,
Pyongyang, 40th
Anniv. — A1736

Designs: 50ch, Chimpanzee, rhinoceros.
60ch, Manchurian crane, deer. 70ch, Zebra,
kangaroo. 2w, Tiger.

**1999, Apr. 30**    **Perf. 13¼**
3850-3852 A1736 Set of 3   1.60   .80
3852a   Booklet pane of 6, 2 each #3850-3852   —
     Complete booklet, #3852a   —
**Souvenir Sheet**
3853 A1736 2w multicolored   1.75   .90
For surcharge, see No. 4552.
Complete booklet of No. 3852a sold for 3.80w.

Central Botanical
Garden, Pyongyang,
40th Anniv. — A1737

Designs: 10ch, Benzoin obtusilobum. 30ch,
Styrax obassia. 70ch, Petunia hybrida. 90ch,
Impatiens hybrida. 2w, Kimsungilia and Kimjongilia.

**1999, Apr. 30**    **Perf. 11½**
3854-3857 A1737 Set of 4   1.60   .80
3857a   Sheet of 4, #3854-3857   1.75   .90
3857b   Booklet pane of 12, 3 each #3854-3857   —
     Complete booklet, #3857b   —
Complete booklet sold for 6.20w.
**Souvenir Sheet**
3858 A1737 2w multicolored   1.75   .90

Three Revolution
Exhibit — A1738

Designs: 60ch, Light Industry Hall. 80ch,
Heavy Industry Hall

**1999, May 2**
3859-3860 A1738 Set of 2   1.20   .60
Three Revolution (ideological, technical, cultural) Exhibition, Ryonmotdong, Sosong District, Pyongyang.

Asia-Pacific Telecommunications
Union, 20th Anniv. — A1739

**1999, May 8**    **Perf. 13¼**
3861 A1739 1w multicolored   .80   .40

Battle of Musan
Area, 60th
Anniv. — A1740

**1999, May 19**    **Perf. 11½**
3862 A1740 10ch multicolored   .25   .25

A1741

Charles
Darwin,
190th
Birth
Anniv.
A1742

No. 3863: a, 30ch, Seagulls. b, 50ch, Bats.
c, 1w, Dolphins. d, 1.20w, Rider on horseback.
e, 1.50w, Korean dancer in traditional dress.

**1999, May 20**    **Sheet of 5 + labels**
3863 A1741 #a-e   3.00   1.50
**Souvenir Sheet**
**Perf. 13¼x12**
3864 A1742 2w multicolored   4.00   2.00

Diego Velazquez
(1599-1660), Artist,
400th Birth
Anniv. — A1743

Designs: No. 3869, 50ch, Princess Margarita in a White Dress. No. 3866, 50ch, Men
Drawing Water from a Well. 3.50w, Self-portrait.

**1999, May 30**    **Perf. 11¾**
3869-3870 A1743 Set of 2   1.00   .50
**Souvenir Sheet**
3871 A1743 3.50w multicolored   3.00   1.50
  a.   Sheet of 3, #3869-3871   4.00   2.00
  b.   Booklet pane of 6, 2 each #3869-3871   —
     Complete booklet, #3871b   —
Complete booklet sold for 9.20w.

Medium and Small
Hydroelectric
Power
Stations — A1744

Designs: 50ch, Rimyongsu Power Station.
1w, Janggasan Power Station.

**1999, May 30**    **Perf. 11½**
3872-3873 A1744 Set of 2   1.20   .60

3rd Women's World Soccer
Championship, USA — A1745

Designs: a, 1w, Dribbling. b, 1.50w, Tackling. c, 1.50w, Goal shot. d, 2w, Knee kick.

**1999, June 8**    **Perf. 13¼**
3874 A1745 Sheet of 4, #a-d   5.00   2.50
  e.   Booklet pane of 4, #3874a-3874d   —
     Complete booklet, #3874e   —
Complete booklet sold for 6.20w.

Mars Exploration — A1746

Designs, each 2w: a, Vostock Rocket. b,
Satellite over Martian crater. c, Mars probe
landing, Martian moons.

**1999, June 10**    **Perf. 11½**
3878 A1746 Sheet of 3, #a.-c.   4.75   2.50

Movie, The Nation and
Destiny — A1747

Scenes from film: a, Man holding candlestick. b, Man in white coat, woman with pistol.
c, Old man in prison cell. d, Man in protective
suit, with goggles on hat.

**1999, June 10**
3879 A1747 1w Sheet of 4, #a-d   3.20   1.60
  e.   Booklet pane of 8, 2 each #3879a-3879d   —
     Complete booklet, #3879e   —
Complete booklet sold for 8.20w.

Tourism — Mt.
Kumgang
A1748

Designs: 20ch, Samil Lagoon. 40ch, Samson Rocks, vert. 60ch, Standing Rock. 80ch,
Kuryong Waterfall. 1w, Kwimyon Rock.

**1999, June 15**    **Perf. 12**
3883-3887 A1748 Set of 5   2.50   1.25

UPU, 125th
Anniv. A1749

**1999, June 20**    **Perf. 11½**
3888 A1749 2w multicolored   1.40   .70

PHILEXFANCE '99 — A1750

2.50w, First stamps of France (1870) and
DPRK (1946).

**1999, July 2**    **Perf. 12**
3889 A1750 2.50w multicolored   2.00   1.00

Kim Il
Sung,
5th
Death
Anniv.
A1751

Designs: a, Kim Il Sung's Mercedes. b,
Kim's railway car.

**1999, July 8**    **Perf. 11½**
3890 A1751 1w Sheet of 2, #a-b   1.60   .80

Kim Hyong Jik (1894-
1926), Revolutionary,
105th Anniv.
Birth — A1752

10ch, Chinese characters for "Jiwon" ("Aim
High"), Kim Hyong Jik's motto, and Mangyong
Hill.

**1999, July 10**
3892 A1752 10ch multicolored   .25   .25

History of
Ceramics
A1753

Designs: 70ch, Engraved-patterned vessel
(5000 B.C.). 80ch, Wit and beauty jar (3rd-4th
Centuries). 1w, Flowered jar. 1.50w, Lotus

decoration celadon kettle (10th-14th Centuries). 2.50w, White china pot with blue flower (15th Century).

**1999, July 15** *Perf. 13¼*
3893-3897 A1753 Set of 5 5.00 2.50

Fish Breeding
A1754

Designs: 50ch, Silver carp. 1w, Common carp. 1.50w, Spotted silver carp.

**1999, July 20**
3898-3900 A1754 Set of 3 2.40 1.20
3900a Booklet pane of 6, 2 each #3898-3900 —
Complete booklet, #3900a —
Complete booklet sold for 6.20w.

Year of Nat'l Independence and Great Solidarity — A1755

**1999, Aug. 5**
3901 A1755 40ch multicolored .35 .25

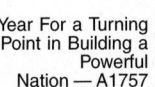
Repatriation of Korean Nationals in Japan, 40th Anniv. — A1756

**1999, Aug. 16** *Perf. 11½*
3902 A1756 1.50w multicolored 1.25 .60

Year For a Turning Point in Building a Powerful Nation — A1757

**1999, Aug. 17**
3903 A1757 40ch multicolored .35 .25

7th World Athletic Championships, Seville — A1758

Designs: 30ch, 100-Meter Race. 40ch, Hurdles. 80ch, Discus.

**1999, Aug. 18**
3904-3906 A1758 Set of 3 1.20 .60

Gift Plants — A1759

No. 3907: a, Acalypha hispida Burm f. b, Allamanda neriifolia Hook. c, Begonia x hiemalis Fotsch. d, Fatsia japonica Decne. e, Streptocarpus hydrida hort. f, Streptocarpus rexii Lindl.

**1999, Aug. 20**
3907 A1759 40ch Sheet of 6, #a-f 2.00 1.00

22nd UPU Congress & China '99 World Philatelic Exhib. — A1760

Paintings by Qiu Ying: a, *Play a Flute to Call Phoenix*. b, *Six Friends in a Pine Forest*. c, *Relics Kept in the Bamboo Field*. d, *Ladies Morning Dressing*.

**1999, Aug. 21**
3913 A1760 40ch Sheet of 4, #a-d 1.50 .75

Mushrooms
A1761

Designs: 40ch, Grifola frondosa. 60ch Lactarius volemus. 1w, Cariolus versicolor.

**1999, Aug. 25**
3917-3919 A1761 Set of 3 2.00 1.00
For surcharge, see No. 4558.

Cacti — A1762

Designs: 40ch, Aporocactus flagelliformis. 50ch Astrophytum ornatum. 60ch, Gymnocalycium michanorichii.

**1999, Sept. 1**
3920-3922 A1762 Set of 3 1.25 .60

Animals of the Zodiac — A1763

No. 3923: a, Rat. b, Ox. c, Tiger. d, Rabbit. e, Dragon. f, Snake.
No. 3924: a, Horse. b, Sheep. c, Monkey. d, Rooster. e, Dog. f, Pig.

**1999, Sept. 10** *Perf. 12½*
**Sheets of 6, #a-f**
3923-3924 A1763 10ch Set of 2 2.00 1.00

Crustaceans — A1764

Designs: 50ch, Pendalus hypsinotus 70ch, Penaeus orientalis. 80ch, Homarus vulgarus.

**1999, Sept. 10** *Perf. 11½*
3935-3937 A1764 Set of 3 2.00 1.00
3937a Booklet pane of 6, 2 each #3935-3937 —
Complete booklet, #3937a —
Complete booklet sold for 4.20w.

Jong Song Ok, Marathon Runner — A1766

**1999, Sept. 20** *Perf. 13¼*
3938 A1765 40ch multicolored .35 .25
a. Booklet pane of 6 #3938 —
Complete booklet, #3938a —
Complete booklet sold for 2.60w.

**Souvenir Sheet**
3939 A1766 2w multicolored 1.60 .80
Victory of Jong Song Ok, Women's Marathon winner at 7th IAAF World Championships, Seville.

DPRK-China Diplomatic Relations, 50th Anniv. — A1767

Designs: 40ch, Mt. Kumgang, Korea. 60ch, Mt. Lushan, China.

**1999, Oct. 5** *Perf. 12¼x11¼*
3940-3941 A1767 Set of 2 1.00 .50
3941a Sheet of 4, #3940-3941 + 2 labels 3.00 1.50
Nos. 3940-3941 were printed both in sheetlets of 6, containing three vertical se-tenant pairs of the two stamps, and in sheetlets of 4, containing a horizontal se-tenant pair and two labels.

A1768

Return of Macao to China — A1769

Type A1768, 1w, Portrait of Pres. Jiang Zemin of China: No. 3942, Gold frame. No. 3943, Green frame.
Type A1769: 20ch (a), Deng Xiaoping sharing toast with Portuguese Prime Minister. 20ch (b), Jiang Zemin shaking hands with Mr Houhua, newly-appointed mayor of Macao special administrative region. 80ch (c), Mao Zedong at National Day Celebration, Tiananmen Square, 1951. Nos. 3944a-3944c, gold background. Nos. 3945a-3945c, green background.

**1999, Nov. 10** *Perf. 13¼*
3942-3943 A1768 Set of 2 sheets 2.00 1.00
3944-3945 A1769 Set of 2 sheets, #a-c 2.50 1.25

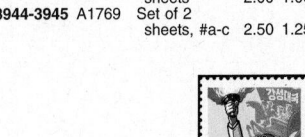
New Year — April 19 Uprising, 40th Anniv. — A1770

**2000, Jan. 1** *Perf. 11½*
3946 A1770 10ch multicolored .25 .25

A1771

Koguryo Era (2nd Century B.C.-7th Century A.D.) — A1772

Designs: 70ch, Yellow dragon. 1.60w, Blue dragon.

**2000, Jan. 1**
3947 A1771 70ch multicolored .70 .35
Complete booklet, 8 #3947 —

**Souvenir Sheet**
*Perf. 11½x11¾*
3948 A1772 1.60w multicolored 1.60 .80
Complete booklet sold for 5.80w.

Painting, *Rural Life* (18th Century) — A1773

No. 3949: a, Peasants weeding. b, Weaving hemp cloth. c, Peasants threshing grain. d, Riverside market.

**2000, Jan. 25** *Perf. 13¼*
3949 A1773 40ch Sheet of 4, #a-d 1.60 .80

Mt. Paekdu Rock Formations A1774

Designs, 20ch: No. 3953, Dinosaur-shaped rock. No. 3954, Eagle-shaped rock. No. 3955, Owl-shaped rock.

**2000, Jan. 30**
3953-3955 A1774 Set of 3 .70 .35

Pongsan Mask Dance — A1775

Folk dances: a, 50ch, Chuibari mask dance. b, 80ch, Ryangban mask dance. c, 1w, Malt-tugi mask dance.

**2000, Feb. 3** — Perf. 11½
3956 A1775 Sheet of 3, #a-c    2.25 1.10

Cats — A1776

Designs: No. 3959, 50ch, Cat on windowsill. No. 3960, 50ch, Kittens playing. No. 3961, 50ch, Mother cat and kittens in basket.

**2000, Feb. 3** — Perf. 13¼
3959-3961 A1776 Set of 3    1.75 .85
3961a  Booklet pane of 8, 2 #3959, 3 each #3960-3961    — —
       Complete booklet, #3961a    —

Complete booklet sold for 4.20w.

Fauna — A1777

No. 3962: Cats: a, Singapura. b, Blue Abyssinian. c, Oriental. d, Scottish fold tabby.
No. 3963: Dogs: a, Shiba inu. b, Yorkshire terrier. c, Japanese chin. d, Afghan hound.
No. 3964: Horses: a, Przewalski's horse. b, Gray cob. c, White horse. d, Donkeys.
No. 3965: Pandas: a, In tree. b, Eating. c, Leaning against tree. d, Mother and cub.
No. 3966: Bears: a, Two polar bears. b, Mother and cub. c, Bear standing. d, Bear reclining.
No. 3967: Snakes: a, Mexican lance-headed rattlesnake (Crotalus polystictus). b, Scarlet king snake (Lampropeltis triangulum elapsoides). c, Green tree python (Chondropython viridis). d, Blood python (Python curtus).
No. 3968: Dinosaurs: a, Corythosaurus. b, Psittacosaurus. c, Megalosaurus. d, Muttaburrasaurus.
No. 3969: Marine Mammals: a, Burmeister's porpoise (Phocoena spinipinnis). b, Finless porpoise (Neophocaena phocaenoides). c, Bottle-nosed dolphin (Tursiops truncatus).d, Curvier's beaked whale (Ziphius cavirostris).
No. 3970: Sharks: a, Port Jackson shark (Heterodontus portusjacksoni). b, Great hammerhead shark (Sphyrna mokarran). c, Zebra shark (Stegostoma fasciatum). d, Ornate Wobbegong carpet shark (Orectolobus cavirostris).
No. 3971: Ducks: a, Ruddy shelduck (Tadorna ferruginea). b, European widgeon (Anas penelope). c, Mandarin drake (Aix galericulata). d, Hottentot teal (Anas hottentota).
No. 3972: Owls: a, Little owl (Athene noctua). b, Ural owl (Strix uralensis). c, Great horned owl (Bubo virginianus). d, Snowy owl (Nyctea scandiaca).
No. 3973: Parrots: a, Slaty-headed parakeet (Psittacula himalayana). b, Male eclectus parrot (Eclectus roratus). c, Major Mitchell's cockatoo (Cacatua leadbeateri). d, Female eclectus parrot (Eclectus roratus).
No. 3974: Butterflies: a, Indian leaf butterfly (Kallima paralekta). b, Spanish festoon (Zerynthia rumina). c, Male and female emerald swallowtails (Papillo palinurus). d, Bhutanitis lidderdalii.
No. 3975: Bees: a, Bumble bee. b, Bumble bee on flower. c, Honey bee (Apis mellifera). d, Honey bee fighting spider.
No. 3976: Spiders: a, Micrommata virescens. b, Araneus quadratus. c, Dolomedes fimbriatus. d, Aculepeira ceropegia.

**2000, Feb. 10** — Sheets of 4, #a-d
3962-3976 A1777 2w Set of 15    150.00 150.00

Kim Jong Il, 59th Birthday — A1778

Design: Birthplace, Mt. Paekdu.

**2000, Feb. 16** — Perf. 11½
4022 A1778 40ch multicolored    .40 .25

Dinosaurs — A1779

Designs: a, Triceratops. b, Saltasaurus. c, Tyrannosaurus.

**2000, Mar. 5** — Perf. 13¼
4023 A1779 1w Sheet of 3, #a-c    3.50 1.75
d.  Sheet of 3, ovptd. with show emblem in margin    3.50 1.75

No. 4023d, Espana 2000 International Stamp Exhibition, Madrid. Issued, 10/6/06.

A1780

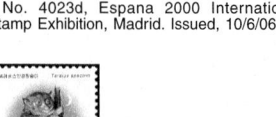
Monkeys — A1781

Designs: No. 4026, 50ch, Western tarsier (Tarsius spectrum). No. 4027, 50ch, Patas monkey (Erythrocebus patas). 2w, Mona monkey (Cercopithecus mona).

**2000, Mar. 25** — Perf. 11½
4026-4027 A1780 Set of 2    1.00 .50
4027a  Sheet of 4, 2 each #4026-4027    2.25 1.10
4027b  Booklet pane of 8, 4 each #4026-4027    —
       Complete booklet, #4027b    —

Complete booklet sold for 4.20w.

**Souvenir Sheet**
4028 A1781 2w multicolored    1.80 .90

Nos. 4026-4027 were issued both separately in panes of 10 and together in sheets of 4.

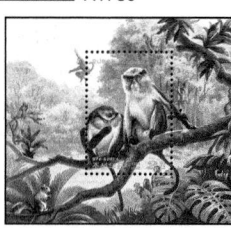
Butterflies — A1782

No. 4029: a, 40ch Peacock (Inachus io). b, 60ch, Swallowtail (Papilio machaon). c, 80ch, Mimic (Hypolimnas misippus Linnaeus). d, 1.20w, (Papilio bianor cramer).

**2000, Mar. 25**
4029 A1782 Sheet of 4, #a-d    3.50 1.75
e.  Booklet pane of 8, 2 each #4029a-4029d    —
    Complete booklet, #4029e    —

Complete booklet sold for 6.20w.

Grand Chollima March — A1783

**2000, Mar. 28**
4033 A1783 10ch multicolored    .25 .25

55th anniversary of the Korean Workers' Party.

April 19 Popular Uprising, 40th Anniv. — A1784

**2000, April 1**
4034 A1784 10ch multicolored    .25 .25

Sun's Day — A1785

**2000, April 15**
4035 A1785 40ch multicolored    .40 .25

88th anniversary of birth of Kim Il Sung. For surcharge, see No. 4587.

Mun Ik Hwan — A1786

**2000, April 25** — Perf. 13¼
4036 A1786 50ch multicolored    .60 .25

Issued in honor of Mun Ik Hwan (1918-94), South Korean political activist, winner of 1990 National Reunification Prize.

Millennium; Korean Workers' Party, 55th Anniv. — A1787

Designs: 40ch, Chollima statue, flag, symbols of national power. 1.20w, Dove with letter, map, "2000."

**2000, May 5**
4037-4038 A1787 Set of 2    1.75 .85

A1788

Orchids — A1789

Designs: 20ch, Cattleya intermedia. 50ch, Dendrobium moschatum. 70ch, Brassolaeliocattleya. 2w, Laeliocattleya.

**2000, May 15**
4039-4041 A1788 Set of 3    1.60 .80
4041a  Booklet pane of 8, 2 each #4039-4040, 4 #4041    — —
       Complete booklet, #4041a    —

Complete booklet sold for 4.40w, and exists imperforate.

**Souvenir Sheet**
4042 A1789 2w multicolored    2.00 1.00

Bridges — A1790

Designs: 20ch, Okryn Bridge. 30ch, Ansan Bridge. 1w, Rungna Bridge.

**2000, May 21**
4043-4045 A1790 Set of 3    2.25 1.10
4045a  Booklet pane of 8, 2 #4043, 3 each #4044-4045    — —
       Complete booklet, #4045a    —

Complete booklet sold for 4.50w.

WIPA 2000 Int'l Stamp Exhib., Vienna — A1791

Traditional Korean musical instruments and folk dances: a, 1w, Okryugum and Jaenggang dance. b, 1.50w, Bungum and Full Moon Viewing dance. c, 1.50w, Janggo drum and "Trio" dance.

**2000, May 30**
4046 A1791 Sheet of 3, #a-c    4.00 2.00

Nos. 4046b-4046c are airmail stamps.

Children's Songs — A1792

Designs: 40ch, Song "Halfmoon," two children in boat. 60ch, Song "Kangram Nostalgia," boy and girl. 1.50w, Song "Spring in Home Village," boy and girl with flowers.

**2000, June 1** — Perf. 11¾x12¼
4049-4050 A1792 Set of 2    1.00 .50

**Souvenir Sheet**
4051 A1792 1.50w multicolored    1.75 .85

Cephalopods — A1793

Designs: 40ch, Nautilus pompilius. 60ch, Octopus vularis. 1.50w, Ommastrephes sloanei pacificus.

**2000, June 15** — Perf. 11½
4052-4053 A1793 Set of 2    1.25 .60

**Souvenir Sheet**
4054 A1793 1.50w multicolored    1.75 .85
a.  Booklet pane of 8, 4 #4052, 2 each #4053-4054    —
    Complete booklet, #4054a    —

No. 4054a exists imperforate. Complete booklet sold for 6w.
For surcharges, see Nos. 4544-4545.

Mandarin Ducks — A1794

Designs: No. 4055, 50ch, Pair of ducks, couple on bridge. No. 4056, 50ch, Pair of ducks, couple in row boat.
1w, Pair of ducks, ducklings.

**2000, June 16**      **Perf. 11¾x12¼**
4055-4056 A1794 Set of 2    1.00   .50
*4056a*   Booklet pane of 7, 3 #4055,    4 #4056     3.75   1.75
   Complete booklet, #4056a    3.75

**Souvenir Sheet**
4057 A1794 1w multicolored    1.00   .50

Nos. 4055-4056 were issued both in separate sheets of 9 (3x3) and in booklet panes of 7, containing 3 No. 4055 and 4 No. 4056, in an alternating arrangement. Complete booklet sold for 3.70w.
For overprints, see Nos. 4071-4073.

Sports A1795

Designs: 80ch, Table tennis. 1w, Basketball. 1.20w, Baseball.

**2000, July 7**      **Perf. 13¼**
4058-4060 A1795 Set of 3    3.50   1.75
*4060a*   Booklet pane of 7, 2 each    #4058-4059, 3 #4060    —
   Complete booklet, #4060a    —

Issed in sheets of 6, 2 each of Nos. 4058-4060. Complete booklet sold for 7.40w.

Trucks — A1796

Designs: 40ch, *Sungri-61 NA.* 70ch, Flatbed truck. 1.50w, *Konsol* 25-50n dump truck.

**2000, July 24**      **Perf. 12**
4061-4063 A1796 Set of 3    2.75   1.50

Korean People's Army — A1797

Portraits of KPA commanders and weapons: 60ch, Ri Tae Hun and 76mm field gun, 80ch, Ko hyon Bink and T-34 tank. 1w, Paek Ki Rah and Yak-9P pursuit plane.

**2000, July 27**
4064-4066 A1797 Set of 3    2.25   1.10

Issed in sheets of 6, 2 each of Nos. 4064-4066.

Minerals A1798

Designs: 30ch, Fluorite. 60ch, Graphite. 1.60w, Magnesite.

**2000, Aug. 15**      **Perf. 13¼**
4067-4069 A1798 Set of 3    1.10   .60
*4069a*   Booklet pane of 8, 3 each    #4067-4068, 2 #4069    —
   Complete booklet, #4069a    —

Complete booklet sold for 6.10w.

**Souvenir Sheet**
4070 A1798 1.60w multicolored    1.60   .80

Nos. 4055-4057
Overprinted

**2000, Aug. 15**      **Perf. 13¼**
4071 A1794 50ch On #4055    .50   .25
4072 A1794 50ch On #4056    .50   .25
*a.*   Booklet pane of 7, 3 #4071, 4    #4072    —
   Complete booklet, #4072a    —

Complete booklet sold for 7.20w.

**Souvenir Sheet**
4073   1w On #4057    1.00   .50

International Stamp Exhibition, Jakarta.

Sydney 2000, Summer Olympic Games — A1799

Designs: a, 80ch, Swimmer. b, 1.20, Cyclist. c, 2w, Runner.

**2000, Sept. 15**      **Perf. 13½**
4074 A1799 Sheet of 3, #a-c    4.25   2.25

Myohyang Mountain A1800

Designs: 40ch (No. 4077), Sanju Falls, wild pig and piglet. 40ch (No. 4078), Inho Rock, Fallow deer, pair. 1.20w, Stag and fawn.

**2000, Sept. 27**      **Perf. 13¼**
4077-4079 A1800 Set of 3    2.00   1.00

A1801

Korean Workers' Party, 55th Anniv. A1802

Designs: 40ch, Party emblem, Party Museum.
No. 4082: a, Kim Il Sung. b, Kim Jong Il. c, Kim Jong Suk.

**2000, Oct. 10**      **Perf. 13¼**
4081 A1801 40ch multicolored    .25   .25

**Souvenir Sheet**
4082 A1802 50ch Sheet of 3, #a-c    1.50   .70

Land Rezoning Project — A1803

10ch, Flags, bulldozer and trucks, urban scene and rice fields.

**2000, Oct. 15**
4083 A1803 10ch multicolored    .25   .25

A1804

Tae Hongdae Potato Farms — A1805

Designs: 40ch, Potatoes, pigs, scientist, collective farm.
2w, painting, *The Great Leader President Kim Il Sung Brought a Bumper Crop of Potato in the Paektu Pleateau.*

**2000, Oct. 20**      **Perf. 11½**
4084 A1804 40ch multicolored    .40   .25

**Souvenir Sheet**
4085 A1805 2w multicolored    1.75   .90

Kim Jong Il & Pres. Jiang Zemin — A1806

**2000, Oct. 21**      **Perf. 11¾x12¼**
4086 A1806 1.20w multicolored    1.75   .85

Visit of Kim Jong Il to China.

Kim Jong Il & Pres. Kim Dae Jung — A1807

**2000, Oct. 23**      **Perf. 11½x12**
4087 A1807 2w multicolored    2.75   1.50

North-South Korean Summit Talks, Pyongyang.

Kim Jong Il & Pres. Putin — A1808

**2000, Oct. 24**      **Perf. 11¾x11½**
4088 A1808 1.50w multicolored    2.25   1.10

Visit of Kim Jong Il to Russia.

Chinese & Korean Soldiers — A1809

Chinese People's Volunteers' Entry Into Korean War, 50th Anniv. — A1810

No. 4090: a, 10ch, Soldiers crossing the Amnok River. b, 10ch, Battle scene. c, 50ch, Kim Il Sung and Chinese officers. d, 50ch, Mao Zedong presiding over meeting to decide upon entry into Korean War. e, 80ch, Chinese soldiers observing battle.

**2000, Oct. 25**      **Perf. 13¼**
4089 A1809 30ch multicolored    .65   .35
4090 A1810 Sheet of 5, #a-e    2.25   1.10

Alpine Flowers — A1811

Designs: 30ch, Aquilegia oxysepala. 50ch, Brilliant campion (Lychnis fulgens). 70ch, Self-heal (Prunela vulgaris).

**2000, Nov. 5**      **Perf. 13½**
4095-4097 A1811 Set of 3    1.50   .60

Nos. 4095-4097 were printed in sheets containing a decorative label.

A1812

Repatriation of Long-Term Prisoners of War — A1813

Designs: 80ch, Returning prisoners receiving bouquets of flowers from women in Pyongyang. 1.20w, Prisoners welcomed by crowd, in front of statue of Kim Il Sung.

**2000, Dec. 20**
4098 A1812 80ch multi    1.00   .50
4099 A1813 1.20w sil & multi    1.25   .60

New Year — A1814

10ch, Flag, trees, factory, missiles, ship, jet planes.

**2001, Jan. 1**      **Perf. 11½**
4100 A1814 10ch multicolored    .25   .25

New Year (2nd Issue) A1815

Tale of the White Snake: 10ch, White Snake meeting Xu Xian. 40ch, Stealing the Immortal Greass. 50ch, White and Green Snakes and Xu Xian. 80ch, Flooding of Jinshan Hill. 1.20w, White Snake and Green Snake.

**2001, Jan. 1**      **Perf. 12½x12**
4101-4104 A1815 Set of 4    3.75   1.75
4104a   Sheet of 4, #4101-4104   3.75   1.75

**Souvenir Sheet**
4105 A1815 1.20w multicolored    2.50   1.10

Nos. 4101-4104 were each issued singly in larger sheets and in combination in sheets of 4 (No. 4104a).

A1816

World Chess Champions — A1817

Designs: 10ch, E. Lasker (1868-1941) and J.R. Capablanca (1888-1942). 20ch, A. Alekhine (1892-1946) and E. Euwe (1901-80). 30ch, M. Botvinnik (1911-95) and V. Smylov (b. 1921). 40ch, T. Petrosian (1929-84) and M. Tal (1936-93). 50ch, B. Spassky (b. 1937) and R. Fisher (b. 1943). 1w, A. Karpov (b. 1954) and G. Kasparov (b. 1963). 2.50w, Wilhelm Steinmetz (1836-1900).

**2001, Jan. 5**      **Perf. 13½**
4106-4111 A1816 Set of 6    5.00   2.50
4111a   Sheet of 6, #4106-4111   5.00   2.50
4111b   Booklet pane of 6, #4106-4111   5.25   —
    Complete booklet, #4111b   5.75   —

**Souvenir Sheet**
4112 A1817 2.50w multicolored    5.00   2.50

No. 4111b contains Nos. 4106-4111 in a se-tenant vertical strip of six, with narrow decorative selvage.
For overprints, see Nos. 4129-4135.

Ri-Dynasty Men's Costumes — A1818

Designs: 10ch, Trousers and jacket. 40ch, Vest. 50ch, Magoja. 70ch, Turumagi 1.50w, Wedding attire.

**2001, Jan. 19**      **Perf. 12x12½**
4113-4116 A1818 Set of 4    3.50   1.75
4116a   Sheet of 5, #4113-4116, 4117a   7.00   3.50

4116b   Booklet pane of 6, #4113-4114, 4116, 4117a, 2 #4115   7.75   —
    Complete booklet, #4116b   8.00   —

**Souvenir Sheet**
4117 A1818 1.50w multicolored    3.50   1.75

Nos. 4113-4116 were each issued both in large sheets and within sheets of 5, in combination with the 1.50w (No. 4117a) value contained in the souvenir sheet, No. 4117. No. 4116b contains the six stamps in a se-tenant horizontal strip with narrow distinctive selvage.

Fire Engines A1819

Fire-fighting vehicles and logos warning against specific fire hazards: 20ch, Small 2-door vehicle (small appliances). 30ch, Large ladder truck (oil can). 40ch, 2-door truck with closed back (match). 60ch, Small truck with ladder and external hose port (gas can). 2w, Old-fashioned fire truck with ladder (cigarette).

**2001, Jan. 20**      **Perf. 12½x12**
4118-4121 A1819 Set of 4    3.50   1.75
4121a   Booklet pane of 12, 3 ea. #4118-4121   10.00
    Complete booklet, #4121a   10.50
4121b   Sheet of 5, #4118-4121, type of #4122 + label   11.00

**Souvenir Sheet**
4122 A1819 2w multicolored    4.50   2.25

No. 4121a contains three attached se-tenant blocks of Nos. 4118-4121, arranged horizontally, with inscribed selvage on left and right sides.

Hong Kong 2001 Stamp Exhibition — A1820

1.40w, Black-naped oriole (Oriolus chinensis).

**2001, Feb. 1**      **Perf. 11½**
4123 A1820 1.40w multicolored    2.75   1.50

Kim Jong Il, 59th Birthday — A1821

10ch, Jong Il Peak in Paekdu Range, *Kimjongilia.*

**2001, Feb. 10**      **Perf. 13½**
4124 A1821 10ch multicolored    .35   .25

New Millenium, Joint Editorial *Rodong Sinmun, Josoninmingun* and *Chongnyonjonwi* Newspapers — A1822

10ch, Flag, symbols of Industry, Agriculture, Transportation

**2001, Mar. 5**
4125 A1822 10ch multicolored    .35   .25

Log Cabin at Revolutionary Headquarters on Mt. Paekdu — A1823

**2001, Mar. 7**      **Perf. 11½**
4126 A1823 40ch multicolored    .70   .30

Kim Il Sung's Birthplace at Mangyongdae A1824

Portraits of Kim Il Sung — A1825

No. 1428 (each 80ch): a, As child. b, As Jilin-Yuwen Middle School student. c, As anti-Japanese revolutionary. d, As leader in early DPRK period. e, As supreme commander of the Korean People's Army. f, As leader during post-Korean War period. g, Portrait in middle age. h, Portrait in old age.

**2001, Apr. 10**      **Perf. 13½**
4127 A1824 10ch multicolored    .45   .25

**Sheet of 8**
4128 A1825   Sheet of 8, #a.-#g   11.00   5.75
    Day of the Sun.

### Nos. 4106-4112 Overprinted in Gold with Biographical Information
**2001, Apr. 20**
4129-4134 A1816 Set of 6    5.75   3.00

**Souvenir Sheet**
4135 A1817 2.50w multicolored    5.75   3.00

Kim Jong Il — A1826

**2001, Apr. 25**      **Perf. 12**
4136 A1826 1w multicolored    1.75   .85

Propaganda issue, with the theme "Long Live the Great Victory of Songun Politics!"

Highways A1827

Designs: 40ch, Pyongyang-Kaesong motorway. 70ch, Pyongyang-Hyangsan tourist expressway. 1.20w, Youth Hero motorway. 1.50w, Pyongyang-Wonsan tourist expressway.

**2001, May 7**      **Perf. 12½x12**
4137-4140 A1827 Set of 4    6.25   3.00

Historical Pavilions A1828

Designs: 40ch, Ryongwang Pavilion in Pyongyang. 80ch, Inphung Pavilion in Kanggye. 1.50w, Paeksang Pavilion in Anju. 2w, Thonggun Pavilion in Uiju.

**2001, May 15**      **Perf. 13¼**
4141-4144 A1828 Set of 4    8.00   4.00
4144a   Booklet pane of 4, #4141-4144   8.00
    Complete booklet, #4144a   8.50

No. 4144a contains Nos. 4141-4144 in a se-tenant block of four, within decorative selvage.

Education in Class Consciousness A1829

**2001, June 5**
4145 A1829 10ch multicolored    .35   .25

Korean Birds — A1830

Designs: 10ch, Luscinia svecica. 40ch, Anser anser. 80ch, Diomedea albatrus. 1w, Charadrius dubius. 1.20w, Uria aalge. 1.50w, Delichon urbica.

**2001, June 9**      **Perf. 11½**
4146 A1830   Sheet of 6, #a.-f.   10.00   5.00
  g.   Booklet pane of 8, #4146c-4146f, 2 ea. #4146a-4146b   11.50
    Complete booklet, #4146g   12.50

BELGICA 2001 Philatelic Exhibition.
No. 4146g contains the eight stamps in a se-tenant horizontal (4x2) block with inscribed selvage on left and right sides.

Chinese Communist Party, 80th Anniv. — A1831

Designs, each 80ch: No. 4147, Mao Zedong. No. 4148, Deng Xiaoping. No. 4149, Jiang Zemin.

**2001, June 15**
4147-4149 A1831 Set of 3    4.25   2.00
    Compare with Nos. 4226-4228.

Mt. Kumol — A1832

Designs: 10ch, Woljong Temple. 40ch, Revolutionary site. 70ch, Potnamu Pavilion. 1.30w, Rock of Tak Peak. 1.50w, Ryongyon Falls.

**2001, July 9**      **Perf. 12x12¼**
4150 A1832   Sheet of 5, #a.-e. + label   6.75   3.50
  f.   Booklet pane of 5, #4150a-4150e + label   7.00
    Complete booklet, #4150f   7.50

No. 4150f contains the stamps and labels of No. 4150 in the same format, but top and bottom marginal selvage is blank, with side selvage containing maple leaf on left and inscriptions on left and right.

Protected Plants — A1833

Designs: 10ch, Rheum Coreanum. 40ch, Forsythia densiflora. 1w, Rhododendron yedoense. 2w, Iris setosa.

**2001, July 20**  **Perf. 13½**
4151-4154 A1833 Set of 4  6.25 3.00
4154a  Booklet pane of 6, #4152,
4154, 2 ea. #4151, 4153  8.00 —
Complete booklet, #4154a  9.00

No. 4154a contains the six stamps in a se-tenant vertical strip of 6, with inscribed selvage on top and bottom margins.

Orchids — A1834

Designs: 10ch, Eria pannea. 40ch, Cymbidium. 90ch, Sophrolaeliocattleya. 1.60w, Cattleya trianae.
No. 4159: 2w, Cypripedium macranthum.

**2001, Aug. 1**
4155-4158 A1834 Set of 4  6.75 3.50
4158a  Booklet pane of 6, #4155-
4156, 4158, #4159a, 2
#4157  13.00
Complete booklet, #4158a  14.00

**Souvenir Sheet**

4159 A1834 2w multicolored  4.50 2.25

No. 4158a contains the six stamps in a se-tenant horizontal strip of 6, with decorative selvage on left and right sides.

Lighthouses — A1835

Designs: 40ch, Pibaldo Lighthouse. 70ch, Soho Lighthouse. 90ch, Komalsan Lighthouse.
No. 4163: 1.50w, Alsom Lighthouse.

**2001, Aug. 18**
4160-4162 A1835 Set of 3  4.50 2.25
4162a  Booklet pane of 6, #4160-
4161, 2 #4162, 2 x #4163a  14.00
Complete booklet, #4162a  14.50
4162b  Sheet of 4, #4160-4162,
4163a  8.00 4.00

**Souvenir Sheet**

4163 A1835 1.50w multicolored  3.50 1.75

Nos. 4160-4162 were issued both separately in large sheets and together, with the 1.50w value from No. 4163, in a sheet of 5 (No.4162b). No. 4162a contains the six stamps in a horizontal strip of 6, with thin plain selvage.

Kim Po Hyon (1871-1955),
Grandfather of Kim Il Sung — A1836

**2001, Aug. 19**
4164 A1836 1w multicolored  1.75 .85

Protected
Animals
A1837

Designs: 10ch, Ciconia nigra. 40ch, Aegypius monachus. 70ch, Hydropotes inermis. 90ch, Nemorhaedus goral.
1.30w, Bubo bubo.

**2001, Sept. 2**
4165-4168 A1837 Set of 4  4.50 2.25
4168a  Sheet of 5, #4165-4168,
4169a + label  8.00 —
4168b  Booklet pane of 6, #4165-
1467, 1469a, 2 x 1468  9.00 —
Complete booklet, #4168b  9.50

**Souvenir Sheet**

4169 A1837 1.30w multicolored  2.75 1.50

Nos. 4165-4168 were issued both separately in large sheets and together, with the 1.30w value from No. No. 4169, in a sheet of 5 (No. 4168a).
No. 4168b contains the six stamps in a se-tenant vertical strip, within narrow decorated selvage.
For surcharge, see No. 4572.

Olympic Games 2008,
Beijing — A1838

Designs, each 56ch: a, Deng Ya Ping, Gold medalist ('96), Women's Singles, Table Tennis. b, Jiang Zemin, PRC president. c, Wang Jun Xia, Chinese athlete. d, Li Ning, Chinese gymnast. e, Fu Ming Xia, Chinese diver.

**2001, Sept. 10**  **Perf. 12½**
4170 A1838 Sheet of 5, #a.-e.  5.75 2.75

Cycle Sports — A1839

Designs: 10ch, Cycle soccer. 40ch, Road racing. 1.50w, Mountainbike racing. 2w, Indoor race.

**2001, Sept. 20**  **Perf. 12**
4171 A1839 Sheet of 4, #a.-d.  8.00 4.00

Space Exploration — A1840

Designs: 10ch, Yuri Gagarin (1934-68), Soviet Cosmonaut. 40ch, Apollo 11 Moon Landing. 1.50w, Kwangmyongsong, North Korean satellite (1998). 2w, Edmund Hailey (1656-1742), Halley's Comet and Giotto satellite.

**2001, Sept. 25**
4172 A1840 Sheet of 4, #a.-d.  7.50 3.50
e.  Booklet pane of 5, #4172a-
4172c, 2 #4172d  12.00 —
Complete booklet, #4172e  13.00

No. 4172e contains five stamps in a se-tenant horizontal strip.

Vladimir Putin and Kim Jong
II — A1841

**2001, Oct. 12**  **Perf. 12½x12**
4173 A1841 1.50w multicolored  2.50 1.25
Visit of Kim Jong II to Russia.

Kim Jong II and Jiang Zemin — A1842

**2001, Oct. 25**  **Perf. 11½x12**
4174 A1842 1.50w multicolored  2.50 1.25

Meeting between Kim Jong II and Jiang Zemin, president of the People's Republic of China.

Kim Jong Suk in Battle — A1843

**2001, Nov. 24**  **Perf. 12½x12**
4175 A1843 1.60w multicolored  3.50 1.75

Kim Jong Suk, anti-Japanese revolutionary hero, 84th birth anniv.

Kim Jong II Inspecting
Troops — A1844

**2001, Dec. 1**  **Perf. 13½**
4176 A1844 1w multicolored  1.75 .85

10th anniv. of appointment of Kim Jong II as Supreme Commander of the Korean People's Army.

Chollima
Statue — A1845

**2002, Jan. 1**
4177 A1845 10ch multicolored  .35 .25
New Year.

A1846

A1847

Horses from painting Ten Horses, by Wang Zhi Cheng (1702-68): 10ch, White horse. 40ch, Bay. 60ch, Pinto. 1.30w, Piebald.
1.60w, Black stallion, from painting Horse Master Jiu Fang Gao, by Xu Bei Hong (1895-1953).

**2002, Jan. 1**
4178-4181 A1846 Set of 4  4.25 2.00
4181a  Sheet of 5, #4178-4181,
4182a  7.25 3.50
4181b  Booklet pane of 6, #4178,
4181, 2 each #4179-4180  10.00 —
Complete booklet, #4181b  10.00

**Souvenir Sheet**

4182 A1847 1.60w multicolored  2.75 1.50

Traditional New Year — Year of the Horse.
Nos. 4178-4181 were issued both separately in large sheets and together, with the 1.60w value from No. 4182, in a sheet of 5 (No. 4181a).
Complete booklet sold for 3.60w.

Flower
Basket — A1848

Kim Jong II with Soldiers — A1849

Kim Jong II — A1850

Kim II Sung, Kim Jong II, Kim Jong
Suk — A1851

**2002, Feb. 1**                    **Perf. 13½**
4183 A1848 10ch multicolored        .35  .25
**Souvenir Sheets**
4184 A1849 1.50w multicolored      2.75 1.50
                                   **Perf. 11½x12**
4185 A1850 2w multicolored         3.50 1.75
                                   **Perf. 12x12½**
4186 A1851 Sheet of 3, #a.-c.      6.75 3.50
    Kim Jong II, 60th Birthday.
    No. 4185 bears a metallic gold application.

Centenary of
First
Zeppelin
Flight
A1852

Designs: 40ch, LZ-1. 80ch, LZ-120. 1.20w,
Zeppelin NT.
2.40w, Zeppelin NT (different view).

**2002, Feb. 5**                    **Perf. 12**
4187-4189 A1852 Set of 3           4.25  2.00
*4189a*    Sheet of 4, #4187-4189,
           4190a                    8.50  4.25
**Souvenir Sheet**
4190 A1852 2.40w multicolored      4.25  2.00
*a.*      Booklet pane of 4, #4187-
          4190                     16.00   —
          Complete booklet, #4190a 16.00
    Nos. 4187-4187 were issued both sepa-
rately in large sheets and together, with the
2.40w value from No. 4190, in a sheet of 4
(No. 4189a). Complete booklet sold for 4.90w.

Banner, Torch,
Soldiers — A1853

**2002, Feb. 25**                   **Perf. 13½**
4191 A1853 10ch multicolored       .35  .25
    Annual joint editorial of the three state
newspapers, *Rodong Sinmun, Josoninm-
ingum* and *Chongnyonjonwi.*

Mushrooms — A1854

Designs: a, 10ch, Collybia confluons. b,
40ch, Sparassis laminosa. c, 80ch, Amanita
vaginata. d, 1.20w, Russia integra. e, 1.50w,
Pholiota squarrosa.

**2002, Feb. 25**                   **Perf. 13½**
4192 A1854  Block of 5, #a-e
            + label                7.50  3.75
*f.*       Booklet pane of 5, #4192a-
           4192e, + label         19.00   —
           Complete booklet, #4192f 19.00
    Complete booklet sold for 4.20w.

A1855

A1856

Kim II Sung (1912-1994) — A1857

Designs: 10ch, Kim II Sung's birthplace,
*Kimsungilia.*
    Nos. 4198-4200 (each 1.50w): No, 4198,
Kim II Sung with Kim Jong Suk (1941). No.
4199, Kim II Sung as student, with black cap
(1927). No. 4200, Kim II Sung and Kim Chaek,
political commissar.
    No. 4201: 2w, Portrait of Kim II Sung.

**2002, Mar. 15**                   **Perf. 13½**
4197 A1855 10ch multicolored       .35  .25
**Souvenir Sheets**
4198-4200 A1856 1.50w Set of 3    6.75 3.50
**With Gold Metallic Application**
                                   **Perf. 11½x12**
4201 A1857 2w multicolored         3.50 1.75

Kang Pan Suk — A1858

**2002, Mar. 21**                   **Perf. 11½x11¾**
4202 A1858 1w multicolored         1.75  .85
    Kang Pan Sok, mother of Kim II Sung, 110th
birth anniv.

20th April Spring
Friendship Art
Festival — A1859

**2002, Mar. 25**                   **Perf. 13¼**
4203 A1859 10ch multicolored       .60  .25

Locomotives
A1860

Designs: 10ch, Kanghaenggun 1.5-01 electric train. 40ch, Samjiyon 1001 electric train.
1.50w, Steam locomotive. 2w, Steam locomotive, diff.
    No. 4208, 2w, Pulgungi 5112 diesel
locomotive.

**2002, Apr. 10**                   **Perf. 11½**
4204-4207 A1860 Set of 4           6.75  3.50
**Souvenir Sheet**
4208 A1860 2w multicolored         3.50  1.75
*a.*      Booklet pane of 5, #4204-
          4208                     27.50   —
          Complete booklet, #4208a 27.50
    For surcharge, see No. 4566. Complete
booklet sold for 6.20w.

He Baozhen, 100th Anniv.
Birth — A1861

Designs: a, 1w, He Baozhen and Liu Shaoqi
in 1923. b, 40ch, He Baozhen's family. c,
30ch, Family home in Dao xian County, Henan
Province. d, 10ch, Letter in Chinese, from Liu
Ying, a wife of Zhang Wentian, Chinese Communist Party official. e, 20ch, Monument at He
Baozhen's birthplace.

**2002, Apr. 20**                   **Perf. 13¼**
4209 A1861  Sheet of 5, #a.-e.     3.50 1.75
    He Baozhen, first wife of Liu Shaoqi, Chair-
man of the People's Republic of China 1959-
68.

Shells — A1862

Designs: 10ch, Cristaria plicata. 40ch,
Lanceolaria cospidata kuroda. 1.50w, Schis-
todesmus lampreyanus. 1.50w, Lamprotula
coreana.

**2002, Apr. 21**
4210-4213 A1862 Set of 4           5.75 2.75
*4213a*    Booklet pane of 6, #4212-
           4213. 2 each #4210-
           4211                    15.00
           Complete booklet, #4213a 15.00
    For surcharge, see No. 4601. Complete
booklet sold for 3.70w.

A1863

Korean People's Army, 70th
Anniv. — A1864

Designs: 10ch, Soldier, sailor, pilot, symbolizing the three branches of the armed forces.
1.60w, Kim II Sung and Kim Jong II walking
with army officers and political functionaries.

**2002, Apr. 25**                   **Perf. 12¼x11¾**
4214 A1863 10ch multicolored       .35  .25
**Souvenir Sheet**
4215 A1864 1.60w multicolored      2.75 1.50

Legend 'Arirang' — A1865

Designs: a, 10ch, Ri Rang and Song Bu as
children. b, 40ch, As young adults. c, 50ch, Ri
Rang killing the landlord. d, 1.50w, Song Bu.

**2002, Apr. 28**                   **Perf. 13¼**
4216 A1865  Sheet of 4, #a.-d.     4.25 2.00

A1866

Mass Gymnastics and Artistic
Performance of 'Arirang' — A1867

Designs: 10ch, Actors. 20ch, Cartoon characters. 30ch, Dancer holding fan. 40ch,
Dancer, gymnasts with hoops.
1w, Dancer with tambourine.

**2002, Apr. 28**                   **Perf. 12¼**
4217-4220 A1866 Set of 4           1.75  .85
**Souvenir Sheet**
4221 A1867 1w multicolored         2.00 1.00
    Nos. 4217-4220 were each issued in sheets
of 6, with pictorial margins and Arirang logo.

Symbols of
Modern Science
& Industry
A1868

**2002, May 2**      **Perf. 13¼**
4222 A1868 10ch multicolored    .35   .25
Science and Technology promotion: "Science and Technology are the Driving Force of Building a Great Prosperous Powerful Nation."

Ryongmun Cavern — A1869

Designs: a, 10ch, Pink stalactite. b, 20ch, Green stalactite. c, 30ch, Golden stalagmite. d, 40ch, Rough-surfaced orange stalagmite.

**2002, May 25**      **Perf. 11½**
4223 A1869   Sheet of 4, #a.-d.   2.75 1.50

Monument — A1870

**2002, May 2**      **Perf. 13¼**
4224 A1870 10ch multicolored    .35   .25
30th Anniv. of the Elucidation of the Three Principles for National Reunification.

Butterflies — A1871

Designs: a, 10ch, Stauropus fagi. b, 40ch, Agrias claudina. c, 1.50w, Catocala nupta. d, 2w, Morpho rhetenor.

**2002, June 30**      **Perf. 11¾**
4225 A1871   Block of 4, #a.-d.   8.50 4.25
  e.    Booklet pane of 5, #4225a,
     4225c-4225d, 2 #4225b   17.50   —
     Complete booklet, #4225e   17.50   —
Complete booklet sold for 4.60w.

**Nos. 4147-4149 with Added Flags in Margins**

A1872

**2002, June 30**      **Perf. 11½**
4226-4228 A1872   Set of 3
        sheets    4.75 2.25
16th National Congress of the Communist Party of China, Beijing, Nov. 8-14. Compare with Nos. 4147-4149.

Elderly Man,
Child, Hospital
A1873

**2002, July 5**      **Perf. 12¼**
4229 A1873 10ch multicolored    .35   .25
50th Anniv. of Universal Free Medical System.

Kim Jong Suk (1917-49) — A1874

Designs: a, 10ch, As child. b, 40ch, As young woman in Children's Corps. c, 1w, In army uniform. d, 1.50w, With long hair, in civilian clothing.

**2002, July 20**      **Perf. 13¼**
4230 A1874   Sheet of 4, #a.-d.   2.50 1.25
Kim Jong Suk, first wife of Kim Il Sung and mother of Kim Jong Il.

Soldier, Worker,
Farmer — A1875

**2002, July 29**      **Perf. 11½**
4231 A1875 10ch multicolored    .35   .25
30th anniv. of the DPRK Constitution.

A1876

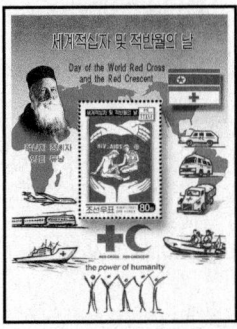

World Red Cross & Red Crescent
Day — A1877

No. 4232: a, 3w, Korean returnees. b, 12w, Red Cross medics administering first aid. c, 150w, North Korean truck delivering aid to South Korean flood victims.
No. 4233: 80w, AIDS victim, family.

**2002, Sept. 20**      **Perf. 13¼**
         **Sheet of 6**
4232 A1876   Sheet, 2 each #a.-
      c.    5.75 2.50
        **Souvenir Sheet**
4233 A1877 80w multicolored    1.75   .85
  a.    Booklet pane of 5, #4232c,
     4233, 2 each #4232a,
     4232b    11.00   —
     Complete booklet, #4233a   11.00   —
Complete booklet sold for 2.75w.

Hong Chang Su, 2000 World Super-
Flyweight Boxing Champion — A1878

**2002, Sept. 25**      **Perf. 11½**
4234 A1878 75w multicolored    1.75   .85

     Souvenir Sheets

Kim Jong Il with Pres. Putin — A1879

Kim Jong Il Shaking Hands with Pres.
Putin — A1880

No. 4235 measures 85x70mm, No. 4236 120x100mm.

**2002, Oct. 15**      **Perf. 13¼**
4235 A1879 70w multicolored    1.75   .85
4236 A1880 120w multicolored   2.25 1.10
Kim Jong Il's Visit to Russia

Siamese Cat — A1881

Cavalier King Charles
Spaniel — A1882

Designs: 12w, Phungsan dog. 100w, White shorthair cat. 150w, Black and white shorthair cat.

**2002, Oct. 20**      **Perf. 12**
4237-4240 A1881   Set of 4    5.75 2.75
  4240a   Booklet pane of 6, #4239-
     4240, 2 each #4237-4238   16.00   —
     Complete booklet, #4240a   16.00   —
        **Souvenir Sheet**
4241 A1882 150w multicolored   3.50 1.75
  a.    Inscr. "World Philatelic Exhi-
     bition Bangkok 2003" and
     emblem in margin    3.50 1.75
No. 4241a issued 10/4/2003. Complete booklet sold for 295w. No. 4240a exists imperforate.

Minerals — A1883

Designs: a, 3w, Pyrite. b, 12w, Magnetite. c, 130w, Calcite. d, 150w, Galena.

**2002, Oct. 25**      **Perf. 13¼**
4242 A1883   Block of 4, #a-d   6.25 3.50
  e.    Booklet pane of 5, #4242am
     4242cm 4242d, 2 each
     #4242b    15.00   —
     Complete booklet, #4242e   15.00   —
Complete booklet sold for 322w.

Kim Jong Il and PM Junichiro Signing
Declaration — A1884

Kim Jong Il with Japanese Prime
Minister Koizumi Junichiro — A1885

Japan-Korea Bilateral Declaration
No. 4246 measures 90x80mm, No. 4247 75x65mm.

**2002, Oct. 25**      **Souvenir Sheets**
4246 A1884 120w multicolored   2.25 1.10
4247 A1885 150w multicolored   3.50 1.75

Kim Il Sung's
Birthplace,
Mangyongdae
A1886

Kim Jong Il's
Birthplace,
Mt. Paektu
A1887

Kim Jong Suk's
Birthplace,
Hoeryong
A1888

Kimilsungia
A1889

Torch,
Tower of
Juche
Idea
A1890

DPRK
Flag
A1891

*Kimjongilia*
A1892

Magnolia
Blossom
A1893

DPRK
Coat of
Arms
A1894

Chollima
Statue
A1895

Victory
Monument
A1896

Party
Founding
Monument
A1897

**Perf. 11½, 13¼x13½ (#4252-4253,
4256-4259)**

**2002, Nov. 20**

| | | | | |
|---|---|---|---|---|
| 4248 | A1886 | 1w violet brn | .25 | .25 |
| 4249 | A1887 | 3w blue green | .25 | .25 |
| 4250 | A1888 | 5w olive brn | .25 | .25 |
| 4251 | A1889 | 10w dk lilac rose | .25 | .25 |
| 4252 | A1890 | 12w dk reddish brn | .25 | .25 |
| 4253 | A1891 | 20w dp blue & red | .40 | .25 |
| 4254 | A1892 | 30w brnsh red | .60 | .25 |
| 4255 | A1893 | 40w dp grnsh blue | .75 | .40 |
| 4256 | A1894 | 50w dk brown | .85 | .50 |
| 4257 | A1895 | 70w dk olive grn | 1.10 | .60 |
| 4258 | A1896 | 100w brown | 1.75 | .85 |
| 4259 | A1897 | 200w dk lilac rose | 3.50 | 1.75 |
| | | *Nos. 4248-4259 (12)* | 10.20 | 5.85 |

See No. 4877. For surcharges, see Nos.
4877A, 4877F.

**Nos. 2675a, 3238, 3321, 3493a
Surcharged**

Surcharge          Surcharge with
without period        period (b)
(a)

**2002     *Method and Perfs as Before***

| | | | |
|---|---|---|---|
| 4259A | A1456(a) | 3w on 10ch | — |
| 4259B | A1487(a) | 3w on 10ch | — |
| 4259C | A1571(b) | 3w on 10ch | — |
| 4259D | A1259(b) | 3w on 40ch | — |

New Year — A1898

**2003, Jan. 1            Perf. 13¼**
4260  A1898  3w multicolored      .35  .25

A1899

Animated Film, *Antelopes Defeat Bald
Eagles* — A1900

Designs: 3w, Mother antelope pleading with
bald eagle stealing her baby. 50w, Antelopes
uniting to defeat bald eagle. 70w, Bald eagle
eating fish poisoned by antelopes. 100w,
Mother antelope reunited with her child.
150w, Antelopes carrying litter full of fruit.

**2003, Jan. 1**

| | | | | |
|---|---|---|---|---|
| 4261-4264 | A1899 | Set of 4 | 3.00 | 1.50 |
| *4264a* | | Booklet pane of 8, 2 each #4261-4264 | *25.00* | — |
| | | Complete booklet, #4264a | *25.00* | |

**Souvenir Sheet**

4265  A1900  150w multicolored    1.75  .85

Complete booklet sold for 461w.

Folk
Festivals — A1901

Designs: 3w, Mother and children greeting
Full Moon (Lunar New Year, Jan. 15). 12w,
Dancers with Full Moon (Lunar New Year).
40w, Two girls on swing (Spring Festival). 70w,
Mother and daughter laying flowers on anti-
Japanese martyrs' monument (Hangawi - Har-
vest Moon Festival). 140w, Peasant dance
(Hangawi - Harvest Moon Festival).
112w, Wresting (Spring Festival).

**2003, Jan. 20            Perf. 11¾**
4266-4270  A1901  Set of 5    3.25  1.50

**Souvenir Sheet**

4271  A1901  112w multicolored    1.75  .75

Soldier — A1902

**2003, Feb. 14            Perf. 13¼**
4272  A1902  12w multicolored    .50  .25

Annual joint editorial of the three state
newspapers, *Rodong Sinmun, Josoninm-
ingum* and *Chongnyonjonwi.*

Weapons,
Proclamation
A1903

**2003, Feb. 15**
4273  A1903  30w multicolored    .60  .25

North Korean withdrawal from the Nuclear
Non-Proliferation Treaty.

Ode Monument — A1904

Sunrise at Mt. Paektu — A1905

**2003, Feb. 16            Perf. 12¼x11¼**
4274  A1904  3w multicolored    .35  .25

**Souvenir Sheet**

4275  A1905  75w multicolored    1.10  .60

Kim Jong II, 61st Birthday.

A1906

Ships — A1907

Designs: 15w, Cargo ship *Paekmagang.*
50w, Dredger *Konsol.* 70w, Passenger ship
*Undok No. 2.* 112w, Cargo ship *Piryugang.*
150w, Excursion ship *Pyongyang No. 1.*

**2003, Feb. 18            Perf. 13½**

| | | | | |
|---|---|---|---|---|
| 4276-4279 | A1906 | Set of 4 | 3.50 | 1.75 |
| *4279a* | | Booklet pane of 6, #4276-4277, 2 each #4278-4279 | *20.00* | — |
| | | Complete booklet, #4279a | *20.00* | |

**Souvenir Sheet**

4280  A1907  150w multicolored    2.00  1.00

Complete booklet sold for 444w.

A1908

Cars Used by Kim II Sung — A1909

Designs: 3w, *Zis.* 14w, *Gaz.* 70w, *Pobeda.*
90w, *Mercedes Benz.*
150w, Painting by Kim San Gon *Delaying
His Urgent Journey.*

**2003, Feb. 20            Perf. 11¾**

| | | | | |
|---|---|---|---|---|
| 4281-4284 | A1908 | Set of 4 | 2.50 | 1.25 |
| *4284a* | | Booklet pane of 6, #4281-4282, 2 each #4283-4284 | *18.50* | — |
| | | Complete booklet, #4284a | *18.50* | |

**Souvenir Sheet**

4285  A1909  150w multicolored    2.25  1.10

Complete booklet sold for 352w.

Book — A1910

**2003, Mar. 15            Souvenir Sheet**
4286  A1910  120w multicolored    2.00  .90

*On the Art of Cinema,* by Kim Jong II, 30th
anniv. of publication.

Army Trumpeter, Map,
Soldiers
Marching — A1911

**2003, Mar. 16**
4287  A1911  15w multicolored    .35  .25

80th anniv. of Kim II Sung's "250-mile Journey for Learning."

Soldier &
Workers — A1912

**2003, Mar. 29**
4288  A1912  3w multicolored    .25  .25

Propaganda issue: "Let us meet the requirements of Songun in ideological viewpoint,
fighting spirit and way of life!"

A1913

Election of Kim Jong II as Chairman of
the DPRK National Defense
Commission, 10th Anniv. — A1914

Designs: 3w, Flags, "10."
No. 4290: a, 12w, Kim Jong II with computer. b, 70w, Kim with military officers, pointing. c, 112w, Kim, with military officers, hand
raised.

**2003, Apr. 9**
4289  A1913  3w multicolored    .25  .25

**Souvenir Sheet**

4290  A1914  Sheet of 3, #a.-c.    4.00  2.00

Kim II Sung's Birthplace,
Mangyongdae, *Kimsungilia* — A1915

**2003, Apr. 15**
4291  A1915  3w multicolored    .25  .25

Day of the Sun—Kim II Sung, 91st birth
anniv.

A1916

**Medals and Orders Presented to Kim Il Sung — A1917**

Designs: 12w, Order of Suhbaatar (Mongolia, 1953). 35w, National Order of Grand Cross (Madagascar, 1985). 70w, Order of Lenin (USSR, 1987). 140w, Order of Playa Giron (Cuba, 1987).
120w, Kim Il Sung being presented with medal by Fidel Castro (1986).

**2003, Apr. 15**     **Perf. 13¼**
4292-4295 A1916 Set of 4   4.00 2.00
**Souvenir Sheet**
**Perf. 13¼**
4296 A1917 120w multicolored   1.75 .75

**Insects — A1918**

Designs: a, 15w, *Pantala flavescens.* b, 70w, *Tibicen japonicus.* c, 220w, Xylotrupes dichotomus. d, 300w, *Lycaena dispar.*

**2003, Apr. 20**     **Perf. 13¼**
4297 A1918 Sheet of 4, #a.-d.   10.00
e.   Booklet pane of 6, #4297c, 4297d, 2 each #4297a-4297b   20.00 —
    Complete booklet, #4297e   20.00

Complete booklet sold for 705w.

**Korean National Dishes A1919**

Designs: 3w, Glutinous rice cake. 30w, Thongkimchi. 70w, Sinsollo.
120w, Pyongyang cold noodles.

**2003, May 1**     **Perf. 11¾**
4298-4300 A1919 Set of 3   1.75 .85
**Souvenir Sheet**
4301 A1919 120w multicolored   1.75 .85

**Victory Monument, Battle in Musan Area — A1920**

**2003, May 19**     **Perf. 12¾**
4302 A1920 90w multicolored   1.50 .75

**Ryangchon Temple A1921**

Designs: 3w, Manse Pavilion. 12w, Buddhist statues. 40w, Painting of Buddha with two saints. 50w, Painting of Buddha with four saints.
120w, Taeung Hall, main shrine of temple.

**2003, May 30**     **Perf. 13¼**
4303-4306 A1921 Set of 4   2.00 1.00
**Souvenir Sheet**
4307 A1921 120w multicolored   2.00 1.00

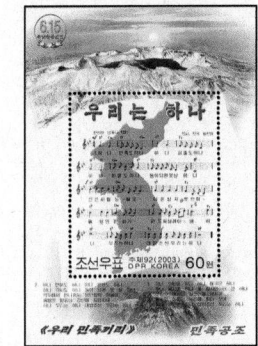

**Map, Song "We Are One" — A1922**

**2003, June 1**
4308 A1922 60w multicolored   1.10 .50

**Wild Animals — A1923**

Designs: a, 3w, Tigers. b, 70w, Bears. c, 150w, Wild boars. d, 230w, Roe deer.

**2003, June 10**
4309 A1923 Sheet of 4, #a.-d.   2.50
e.   Booklet pane of 4, #4309a-4309d   30.00
    Complete booklet, #4309e   30.00 —

Complete booklet sold for 460w.

**Public Bonds of 1950, 2003 — A1924**

**2003, July 25**     **Perf. 13½**
4310 A1924 140w multicolored   2.50 1.25
Campaign to promote purchase of public bonds.

A1925

A1926

**DPRK "Victory" in Korean War, 50th Anniv. — A1927**

Designs: 3w, Distinguished Service Medal.
No. 4312: Kim Il Sung in commander's uniform.
No. 4313: a, 12w, Kim delivering radio address. 35w, Kim talking to soldiers. c, 70w, Kim ratifying armistace agreement. d, 140w, Kim in uniform.
No. 4314: a, 12w, Kim smiling, surrounded by soldiers. 35w, Kim inspecting soldier. c, 70w, Kim Il Sung, Kim Jong Il inspecting army training. d, 140w, Middle-aged Kim Il Sung in suit and tie.
No. 4315: a, 12w, Kim Jong Il receiving bouquet from female soldier. 35w, Kim Jong Il being applauded by soldiers. c, 70w, Kim Jong Il on military inspection. d, 140w, Smiling Kim Jong Il.

**2003, July 27**     **Perf. 13¼**
4311 A1925 3w multicolored   .25 .25
**Souvenir Sheet**
4312 A1926 120w multicolored   2.00 1.00
**Sheets of 4**
**Perf. 11½**
4313-4315 A1927 Set of 3   13.50 6.50

**Orchids — A1928**

Designs: a, 3w, Minicattleya coerulea. b, 100w, Phalanopsis aphrodite. c, 150w, Calanthe discolor. d, 200w, Dendrobium snowflake.

**2003, July 29**     **Perf. 13¼**
4316 A1928 Sheet of 4, #a.-d.   8.25 4.00
e.   Booklet pane of 4, #4316a-4316d   8.25
    Complete booklet, #4316e   8.75

No. 4316e contains Nos. 4316a-4316d in a horizontal strip of four, with selvage similar to that of No. 4316.

A1929

**Birds — A1930**

Designs: 12w, Grus vipio. 70w, Nycticorax nycticorax. 100w, Columba livia var doestricus. 120w, Nymphicus hollandicus. 150w, Strix aluco.
225w, Pseudogyps africanus.

**2003, Aug. 4**     **Perf. 13¼**
4317-4321 A1929 Set of 5   7.00 3.50
4321a   Booklet pane of 6, #4317-4318, 4320-4321, 2 #4319   19.50 —
    Complete booklet, #4321a   19.50
**Souvenir Sheet**
**Perf. 11¾**
4322 A1930 225w multicolored   3.50 2.10
Complete booklet sold for 567w.

**Arctic & Antarctic Animals — A1931**

Designs: a, 15w, Adelie penguins (Pygoscelis adeliae). b, 70w, Walrus (Odobenus rosmarus). c, 140w, Polar bear and cubs (Thalarctos maritimus). d, 150w, Bowhead whale (Balaena mysticetus). e, 220w, Spotted seals (Phoca largha).

**2003, Aug. 20**     **Perf. 11½**
4323 A1931 Sheet of 5, #a.-e. + label   11.00 5.25
a.   Booklet pane of 5 + label
    Complete booklet   15.00

No. 4323a contains one pane, with stamps and label in same arrangement as in No. 4323, surrounded by selvage containing a distinctive arrangement of Polar animals on a primarily yellowish background.

**Mushrooms — A1932**

Designs: a, 3w, Pholiota flammans. b, 12w, Geastrum fimbriatum. c, 70w, Coprinus atramentarius. d, 130w, Pleuotus cornucopiae. 250w, Elfvingia applanata.

**2003, Sept. 5**     **Perf. 13¼**
4324 A1932 Block of 4, #a-d   4.00 2.10
**Souvenir Sheet**
4328 A1932 250w multicolored   4.75 2.40
a.   Booklet pane of 5, #4324a-4324d, 4328   23.00 —
    Complete booklet, #4328a   23.00

Complete booklet sold for 480w. No. 4328a exists imperforate.

**Korean Stamp Exhibition Hall — A1933**

Korean Stamps, Interior of Hall — A1934

**2003, Sept. 5**
4329 A1933 3w multicolored .30 .30
4330 A1934 60w multicolored 1.25 .50

Korean Stamp Exhibition celebrating the 55th anniversary of the DPRK and the inauguration of the Korean Stamp Exhibition Hall.

A1935

A1936

55th Anniv. Founding of DPRK — A1937

Designs: 3w, DPRK Arms, Flag.
No. 4332: Kim Il Sung.

Sheets of 2 with central label: No. 4333: a, 60w, "The Birth of a New Korea" (Kim saluting marchers carrying DPRK flag). b, 60w, "In the Period of Building a New Korea" (Kim Jong Suk and factory workers). No. 4334: a, 60w, "Braving Through a Rain of Bullets Personally" (Kim in jeep in war zone). b, 60w, "Comrade Kim Il Sung, Ever-Victorious Iron-Willed Commander, Personally Commanding the Battle at Height 1211" (Kim on bluff, pointing to battlefield.) No. 4335: a, 60w, "We Trust and Follow Only You, the Leader" (Kim being greeted by villagers). b, 60w, "The Great Leader Kim Il Sung Giving On-the-Spot Guidance to the Pukchang Thermal Power Station" (Kim and factory workers). No. 4336: a, 60w, "The Victory of Korean Revolution Will Be Ensured by the Arms in Our Hand" (Kim speaking to soldiers, Kim Jong Il standing behind). b, 60w, "Keeping Up Songun Politics as All-Powerful Means" (Smiling Kim walking with soldiers symbolizing modern arms).

**2003, Sept. 9**　　**Perf. 11½**
4331 A1935 3w multicolored .30 .30

**Souvenir Sheet**
**Perf. 13¼**
4332 A1936 120w multicolored 2.40 1.25
**Sheets of 2, #a.-b. + label**
**Perf. 12¼x12**
4333-4336 A1937 Set of 4 7.00 3.50

Mao Zedong, 110th Birth Anniv. — A1938

No. 4337: a, 20w, Young Mao speaking at political meeting; b, 30w, Mao walking on shore with woman carrying manuscript. No. 4338: a, 30w, Mao addressing Red partisans; b, 30w, Mao (wearing trenchcoat) leading partisans in field. No. 4339: a, 20w, Mao talking with workers, soldiers; b, 30w, Mao in casual setting, leading discussion with soldiers. No. 4340: a, 30w, Mao addressing crowd in Beijing; b, 30w, Mao with people of various races and nationalities.
No. 4341: Sheet containing Nos. 4337-4338, with attached large label depicting 110 stamps picturing Mao and denominated 140w, the price for which the sheet was sold. No. 4342: Same, but containing Nos. 4339-4340.

**2003, Dec. 26**　　**Perf. 13¼**
**Se-Tenant Pairs with Label Between**
4337-4340 A1938 Set of 4 4.00 2.10
**Souvenir Sheets**
4341-4342 A1938 Set of 2 4.75 2.40

New Year — A1939

Design: 2w, Soldier, workers, tower.

**2004, Jan. 1**　　**Perf. 11½**
4343 A1939 3w multicolored .30 .30
For surcharge, see No. 4877B.

A1940

Monkeys — A1941

Designs: 3w, *Cebus apella*. 60w, *Papio doguera*. 70w, *Cercopithecus aethiops*. 100w, *Saguinus oedipus*. 155w, *Macaca mulatta*.

**2004, Jan. 1**
4344-4347 A1940 Set of 4 4.75 2.40
**Souvenir Sheet**
4348 A1941 155w multicolored 3.00 2.40
　a.　Booklet pane of 5, #4344-4348 23.00 —
　　Complete booklet, #4348a 23.00 —
Complete booklet sold for 403w. See Nos. 4351-4355.

Lunar New Year's Day — A1942

**2004, Jan. 1**
4349 A1942 3w multicolored .30 .30

**Souvenir Sheet**

First Chinese Manned Space Flight — A1943

Designs: a, 91w, Yang Liwei, first Chinese cosmonaut (46mm diameter). b, 98w, Landing capsule, parachute, helicopter (54x45mm).

**Perf. 13¼, Perf. (#4350a)**
**2004, Jan. 30**
4350 A1943 Sheet of 2, #a.-b. 3.00 1.50
　c.　Booklet pane, 2 each #4350a-4350b — —
　　Complete booklet, #4350c — —
　d.　#4350 with Hong Kong 2004 emblem opvt. in sheet margin 3.00 1.50

Booklets containing No. 4350c were issued with and without the Hong Kong 2004 emblem on the cover.

**Nos. 4344-4348 with Hong Kong 2004 Emblem**
**2004, Jan. 30**
4351-4354 A1940 Set of 4 4.75 2.40
**Souvenir Sheet**
4355 A1941 155w multicolored 3.00 1.50

Joint Editorial *Rodong Sinmun, Josoninmingun* and *Chongnyonjonwi* Newspapers A1944

**2004, Feb. 15**　　**Perf. 13¼**
4357 A1944 3w multicolored .30 .30

A1945

**2004, Feb. 16**　　**Perf. 11½**
4358 A1945 3w multicolored .30 .30
**Souvenir Sheet**
**Perf. 13¼**
4359 A1946 Sheet of 4, #a.-d. 2.40 1.25

Kim Jong Il, 62nd Birthday — A1946

No. 4358: 3w, Kim Jong Il's birthplace, Mt. Paektu.
No. 4359 (each 30w): a, "The Thaw of Sobaek Stream" (Spring). b, "The Thunderclap of Jong Il Peak" (Summer). c, "The Secret Camp in Autumn" (Autumn). d, "Hoarfrost in February" (Winter).

Kim Jong Il — A1947

**2004, Feb. 19**　　**Perf. 13¼**
4360 A1947 120w multicolored 2.40 1.25

30th anniv. of publication of the *Program of Modelling the Whole Society on the Juche Idea.*

Rural Village — A1948

Kim Il Sung and Farmers — A1949

**2004, Feb. 25**　　**Perf. 11½**
4361 A1948 3w multicolored .30 .30
**Souvenir Sheet**
**Perf. 12½ x11¾**
4362 A1949 120w multicolored 2.10 2.10

40th anniv. of publication of the "Theses on the Socialist Rural Question in Our Country."

Lighthouses — A1950

Designs: a, 3w, Sokgundo Lighthouse. b, 12w, Yubundo Lighthouse. c, 100w, Jangdokdo Lighthouse. d, 195w, Amryongdan Lighthouse.

**2004, Mar. 20**　　**Perf. 11¾x12½**
4363 A1950 Sheet of 4, #a.-d. 6.00 3.00
　e.　Booklet pane of 4, #4363a-4363d 6.00 —
　　Complete booklet, #4363e 6.50 —

No. 4363e contains Nos. 4363a-4363d in a horizontal strip of 4, surrounded by a seashore selvage.

A1951

Board Games — A1952

Designs: a, 3w, Korean Chess. b, 12w, Goe. c, 90w, Yut. d, 120w, Kknoni (Chinese Checkers).
98w, Playing Korean Chess.

**2004, Mar. 20**     **Perf. 13¼**
4364 A1951 Sheet of 4, #a.-d.   4.75 2.40
e.   Booklet pane of 5, #4364a-
    4364b. 4364d, 2 x 4364c    6.00   —
    Complete booklet, #4363e    6.50

**Souvenir Sheet**
4365 A1952 98w multicolored    2.40 1.25

No. 4364e contains Nos. 4364a-4364d in a horizontal strip of 5, which includes a second copy of the 90w value, with a distinctive printed selvage.

Kim Il Sung's Birthplace, Mangyongdae A1953

Kim Il Sung — A1954

**2004, Apr. 15**     **Perf. 13¼**
4366 A1953 3w multicolored    .30 .30
**Souvenir Sheet**
**Perf. 11¾**
4367 A1954 120w multicolored    2.10 1.10
Kim Il Sung, 92nd birth anniv.

A1955

Tok Islands — A1956

No. 4368: a, 3w, 19th century map of Korea. b, 12w, Western island. c, 106w, Eastern island.
No. 4369: 116w, Both islands, sea gulls.

**2004, Apr. 20**     **Perf. 11½**
4368 A1955 Sheet, #a.-c. + label 3.00 1.50
**Souvenir Sheet**
**Perf.**
4369 A1956 116w multicolored    2.40 1.25
a.   Booklet pane of 4, #4368a-
    4368c, 4369      —
    Complete booklet, #4369a    —

Fossils — A1957

No. 4370: a, 3w, Calcinoplax antiqua. b, 12w, Podozamites lanceolatus. c, 70w, Comptonia naumannii. d, 140w, Clinocardium asagaiense.
No. 4371: 120w, Tingia carbonica.

**2004, May 20**     **Perf. 13¼**
4370 A1957 Sheet of 4, #a.-d.   4.75 2.40
e.   Booklet pane of 5, #4370a-
    4370d, #4371a      6.00   —
    Complete booklet, #4370e    6.50
**Souvenir Sheet**
**Perf. 12½**
4371 A1957 120w multicolored   2.40 1.25
a.   single stamp     2.40 1.25

Cacti — A1958

No. 4372: a, 70w, Notocactus leninghausii. b, 90w, Echinocactus grusonii. c, 100w, Gymnocalycium baldianum. d, 140w, Mammillaria insularis.

**2004, June 2**     **Perf. 11¾x12¼**
4372 A1958 Sheet of 4, #a.-d.   6.00 3.00
e.   Ovptd. "World Stamp Cham-
    pionship 2004" and Singa-
    pore 2004 emblem in
    margin      6.00 3.00
f.   Booklet pane of 4, #4372a-
    4372d      16.00   —
    Complete booklet, #4372f   16.00

Complete booklet sold for 416w. No. 4372e was issued 8/28.

A1959

Unofficial Visit of Kim Jong Il to China — A1960

No. 4373: a, 74w, Kim Jong Il with Hu Jintao, President of the People's Republic of China.
No. 4374: a, 3w, Kim shaking hands with Hu Jintao. b, 12w, Kim with Jiang Zemin, President of China 1997-2003. c, 40w, Kim with Wu Bangguo, Chinese Communist Party leader. d, 60w, Kim clapping hands at outdoor reception.
No. 4375: a, 3w, Kim with Wen Jiabao, Premier of the State Council of the PRC. b, 12w, Kim with Jia Qinglin, Chinese Communist Party leader. c, 40w, Kim with Zeng Qinghong, Vice-President of the PRC. d, 60w, Kim visiting Tianjin.

**2004, June 18**     **Perf. 13¼**
**Souvenir Sheet**
4373 A1959 74w multicolored   1.50 .70
a.   As No. 4373, diff. (horiz.)
    selvage      1.50 .70
**Sheets of 4, #a-d**
4374-4375 A1960 Set of 2   4.00 2.10
4375e   Booklet pane of 9, #4373a,
    4374a-d, 4375a-d    6.00   —
    Complete booklet, #4375e   6.50
No. 4373a is from the booklet No. 4375e.

WPK Flag — A1961

A1962

Kim Jong Il's Appointment to the Central Committee of the Workers' Party of Korea, 40th Anniv. — A1963

No. 4377: a, 12w, Kim reading at desk. b, 100w, Kim standing in front of renderings of proposed Samjiyon Battle Site memorial.
No. 4378: a, 12w, Kim inspecting power station in Jagang Province. b, 100w, Kim with army officers.
No. 4379: a, 12w, Kim visiting the Komdok mine. b, 100w, Kim, outdoor photo portrait.
No. 4380: 130w, Kim Jong Il and Kim Il Sung.

**2004, June 19**
4376 A1961 3w multicolored    .30 .30
**Sheets of 2**
4377-4379 A1962 Set of 3   6.00 3.00
**Souvenir Sheet**
4380 A1963 130w multicolored   1.50 .70

A1964

A1965

Kim Il Sung, 10th Death Anniv. — A1966

No. 4381: 3w, Kimilsungia, monument to Kim Il Sung.
No. 4382: a, 12w, Kim Il Sung and Kim Jong Il visiting State Academy of Sciences. b, 116w, Kim Il Sung and Kim Jong Il on Mt. Paektu.
No. 4383: a, 12w, Kim il Sung with workers b, 116w, Kim directing farmers at Chongan cooperative farm.
No. 4384: a, 12w, Kim with soldiers. b, 116w, Kim with children.
No. 4385: a, 12w, Kim embracing Rev. Mun Ik Hwan. 116w, Kim talking on telephone.
No. 4386: 112w, Kim waving.

**2004, July 8**     **Perf. 11¾**
4381 A1964 3w multicolored    .30 .30
**Sheets of 4, #a-d**
4382-4385 A1965 Set of 4   8.25 4.00
**Souvenir Sheet**
4386 A1966 112w multicolored   1.90 .85

Monument — A1967

**2004, July 10**     **Perf. 11¾**
4387 A1967 112w multicolored   1.90 .85
Kim Hyong Jik, father of Kim Il Sung, 110th birth anniv.

A1968

A1969

Deng Xiaoping, Birth Centennial — A1970

No. 4388: a, 3w, Deng Xiaoping as a student in France. b, 12w, Deng hiking on the Huangshan. c, 35w, Deng saluting at military review. d, 50w, Deng addressing rally celebrating the 35th anniversary of the People's Republic of China.
No. 4389a: Kim Il Sung being greeted by Deng, Chinese crowd during visit to China.
No. 4390: 80w, Deng at seashore.

**2004, July 15**     **Perf. 13¼**
4388 A1968 Strip of 4, #4a-d +
    label      1.90 .85
**Sheet of 5**
4389 A1969 Sheet, #4388,
    4389a, label    3.00 1.50
a.   70w multicolored    .85 .50
**Souvenir Sheet**
4390 A1970 80w multicolored   1.50 .70

Fresh Water Fish — A1971

Designs: a, 3w, Carassius auratus. b, 12w, Tlilapia nilotica. c, 140w, Ophiocephalus argus. d, 165w, Clarias gariepinus.

**2004, Aug. 10**
4391 A1971 Sheet of 4, #a.-d.   5.50 2.75

28th Olympic Games,
Athens — A1972

Designs: a, 3w, Boxing. b, 12w, Soccer. c, 85w, Track and field events. d, 140w, Gymnastics.

**2004, Aug. 10**
4392 A1972　Block or strip of 4,
　　　　　　#a.-d.　　　　　4.00　2.25
　e.　Booklet pane of 4, #4392e　4.00
　　　Complete booklet, #4392e　4.75

No. 4392 was printed in panes of 8 stamps, 2 sets of Nos. 4392a-4392d, with decorative margin depicting athletes, Olympic emblems and Korean inscription. No. 4392e contains Nos. 4392a-4392d in a horizontal strip, with plain marginal selvage.
For overprints, see No. 4409.

Fire Engines — A1973

Designs: a, 3w, Mercedes Benz ladder truck. b, 12w, Fire truck. c, 40w, Jelcz pumper truck. d, 105w, Mercedes Benz fire truck. 97w, ladder truck, diff.

**2004, Aug. 15**
4393 A1973　Sheet of 4, #a.-d.　3.00　1.50
　e.　Booklet pane of 4, #a.-d.　3.00　—
　　　Complete booklet, #4393e　3.50
　f.　A1973 97w Souvenir sheet　1.90　.85

No. 4393e contains Nos. 4393a-4393d in a vertical strip, with marginal selvage similar to that of the sheet.

Airplanes — A1974

Designs: a, 3w, Airbus A340-600. b, 97w, Concorde. c, 104w, Graf Zeppelin DO-X. d, 116w, Junkers JU 52/3m.

**2004, Aug. 20**　　　　　　**Perf. 12**
4394 A1974　Sheet of 4, #a.-d.　6.25　3.25
　e.　Booklet pane of 4, #a.-d.　6.25　—
　　　Complete booklet, #4394e　6.75

No. 4394e contains Nos. 4394a-4394d in a horizontal strip, with pale yellow marginal selvage, with simple ruled lines and inscription.

Visit of Japanese Prime Minister
Koizumi Zunichiro — A1975

**2004, Aug. 25**　　　　　　**Perf. 11¾**
4395 A1975　220w multicolored　3.75　1.90

A1976

**2004, Sept. 21**
4396 A1976　112w multicolored　1.90　.85

An Jung Gun (1879-1910), assassin of Japanese Prime Minister Ito Hirdoumi in 1909, 125th birth anniv.

A1977

Kim Jong Suk (1917-49), Mother of
Kim Jong II — A1978

Designs: 3w, Kim Jong Suk's pistol.
97w, Kim Jong Suk.

**2004, Sept. 22**　　　　　**Perf. 13¼**
4397 A1977　3w multicolored　.30　.30

**Souvenir Sheet**
**Perf. 12**
4398 A1978　97w multicolored　1.90　.85

World Wildlife
Fund — A1979

Swans: 3w, Swan in profile, looking left. 97w, Swan, ¾ profile, head turned to left. 104w, Two swans, one with outstretched wings. 120w, Two swans in water.

**2004, Sept. 30**　　　　　**Perf. 11½**
4399-4402 A1979　Set of 4　5.75　3.00
4402a　Booklet pane of 4, #4399-
　　　4102　　　　　　　5.75　—
　　　Complete booklet, #4402a　6.25

Nos. 4399-4402 were each printed in sheets of 4, with decorative selvage. No. 4402a contains the four stamps in a horizontal se-tenant strip, surrounded by plain selvage.

A1980

Simwon Temple — A1981

Designs: 3w, View of Powkang Hall.
97w, Interior of Powkang Hall, with three golden Buddha statues.

**2004, Oct. 5**　　　　　　**Perf. 11¾**
4403 A1980　3w multicolored　.30　.30

**Souvenir Sheet**
**Perf. 13¼**
4404 A1981　97w multicolored　2.10　1.10

Sidelfingen International Stamp
Fair — A1982

Electric trains: a, 3w, Red and blue train. b, 40w, Yellow train. c, 75w, Green and white train. d, 150w, Red and green train. 120w, Vintage electric train.

**2004, Nov. 5**　　　　　　**Perf. 11½**
4405 A1982　Sheet of 4, #a.-d.　4.50　2.25

**Souvenir Sheet**
4406 A1982　120w multicolored　2.40　1.25
　a.　120w stamp from souvenir
　　　sheet　　　　　　2.40　1.25
　b.　Booklet pane of 5, #4405a-
　　　4405d, #4606a　　　7.50　—
　　　Complete booklet, #4406b　8.25

A1983

Repatriation of Korean Nationals in
Japan, 45th Anniv. — A1984

Designs: 3w, Repatriation ship *Mangyongbong.*
80w, Kim II Sung with repatriated Korean children.

**2004, Dec. 16**　　　　　**Perf. 11½**
4407 A1983　3w multicolored　.30　.30

**Souvenir Sheet**
**Perf. 11¾**
4408 A1984　80w multicolored　1.50　.70

**No. 4392 Overprinted in Silver**

Overprints: a, 3w, Mario Cesar Kindelan Mesa (Boxing, Cuba). b, 12w, Argentine Soccer Team. c, 85w, Yelena Slesarenko (Women's High Jump, Russia). d, 140w, Teng Haibin (Women's Gymnastics, China).

**2004, Dec. 20**　　　　　**Perf. 13¼**
4409 A1972　Block or strip of
　　　　　　4, #a.-d.　　　　4.25　2.25

New Year
2005 — A1985

**2005, Jan. 1**
4410 A1985　3w multicolored　.30　.30

A1986

New Year 2005 — Year of the
Rooster — A1987

Domestic fowl, millet stalk figures: 3w, Rooster. 12w, Hen.
No. 4413: a, 3w, Chick. b, 70w, Rooster, chick. c, 100w, Rooster. d, 140w, Basket of eggs.

**2005, Jan. 1**
4411 A1986　3w multicolored　.30　.30
4412 A1986　12w multicolored　.70　.35
4413 A1987　Sheet of 4, #a.-d.　4.75　.30
　e.　Booklet pane of 6, #4411-
　　　4412, #4413a-d　　　5.50　—
　　　Complete booklet, #4413e　5.70

No. 4413e contains all six values of the set, printed in a se-tenant strip of six, within a plain yellow and green border.

Hen, Classic Chinese
Painting — A1988

**Souvenir Sheet**
**2005, Jan. 10**　　　　　**Perf. 11½**
4414 A1988　97w multicolored　1.90　.85

Kim II Sung's 250-Mile Journey, 80th
Anniv. — A1989

**Souvenir Sheet**
**2005, Jan. 22**　　　　　**Perf. 11¾**
4415 A1989　120w multicolored　1.90　.85

Statue of Kim Il Sung, Chongsan-ri — A1990

**Souvenir Sheet**

**2005, Feb. 8**      **Perf. 13¼**
4416 A1990 120w multicolored   1.80   .85
Creation of the Chongsan-ri Spirit and Chongsan-ri Method.

Songun Scenes — A1991

Designs: a, 3w, Sunrise at Mt. Paektu. b, 12w, Snowscape. c, 40w, Royal azaleas on Chol Pass. d, 50w, Jangja River. e, 60w, Ullim Falls. f, 70w, Handure Plain. g, 70w, Potato blossoms at Taehongdan. h, 100w, Poman-ri.

**2005, Feb. 10**      **Perf. 12¼**
4417 A1991 Sheet of 8, #a.-h.   6.00   3.00

A1992

A1993

Kim Jong Il, 63rd Birthday — A1994

Design: 3w, Kimjongilia, mountains.
No. 4419, 216 Peaks Around Lake Chon on Mt. Paektu, summer scenes, each 50w: a, Mountains, lake on lower right. b, Mountains, lake across foreground. c, Mountains, lake in foreground, shore at lower right.
No. 4420, 216 Peaks Around Lake Chon on Mt. Paektu, winter scenes, each 50w: a, Mountains, frozen lake in foreground. b, Mountains, lake in foreground, sun showing over peaks. c, Mountains, lake in left foreground.

**2005, Feb. 16**      **Perf. 13¼**
4418 A1992 3w multicolored   .30   .30
**Sheets of 3, #a.-c.**
**Perf. 12**
4419 A1993 multicolored   2.40   1.25
4420 A1994 multicolored   2.40   1.25

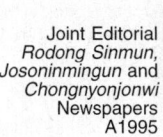

Joint Editorial Rodong Sinmun, Josoninmingun and Chongnyonjonwi Newspapers A1995

**2005, Feb. 16**      **Perf. 13¼**
4421 A1995 3w multicolored   .30   .30

A1996

Naming of the Kimilsungia, 40th Anniv. — A1997

Designs: 3w, Kimilsungia and Kimilsungia-Kimjongilia Exhibition Hall.
120w: Kim Il Sung receiving a Kimilsungia plant from Pres. Sukarno of Indonesia.

**2005, Apr. 13**
4422 A1996 3w multicolored   .30   .30
**Souvenir Sheet**
4423 A1997 120w multicolored   1.90   .85

A1998

Kim Il Sung, 93rd Birth Anniv. — A1999

Designs: 3w, Kimilsungia and Mangyong Hill.
112w: Kim Il Sung standing in front of straw-thatched house at Mangyongdae.

**2005, Apr. 15**
4424 A1998 3w multicolored   .30   .30
**Souvenir Sheet**
**Perf. 11¾**
4425 A1999 112w multicolored   1.90   .85

48th World Table Tennis Championships, Shanghai — A2000

Designs: 3w, Pak Young Sun, Korea. b, 5w, Mao Zedong playing table tennis at the Communist base in Yanan. c, 12w, Wang Liqin, China. d, 20w, J.O. Waldner, Sweden. e, Zhang Yining, China. f, 102w, Werner Schlager, Austria.

**2005, Apr. 23**      **Perf. 11½**
4426 A2000 Sheet of 6, #a.-f.   3.75   1.90
   g.   Booklet pane of 6, #4426a-4426f   3.75   —
     Complete booklet, #4426g   4.25
No. 4426g contains Nos. 4426a-4426f in a se-tenant horizontal strip of six, surrounded by blue selvage depicting the Shanghai 2005

emblem, stylized athletes and Korean inscription.

Pandas — A2001

Designs: 15w, Panda on tree limb. 45w, Panda walking. 70w, Two pandas. 140w, Panda standing
120w, Panda with cub.

**2005, May 3**      **Perf. 13¼**
4427-4430 A2001 Set of 4   4.75   .30
  4430a   Booklet pane of 5, #4427-4430, 4432a   4.75   —
     Complete booklet, #4430a   5.25   —
**Sheet of 5**
4431 A2001 Sheet, #4427-4430, 4432a   7.00   3.00
**Souvenir Sheet**
4432 A2001 120w multicolored   3.50   —
   a.   Single stamp
Nos. 4427-4430 were each issued in separate large panes. No. 4430a contains Nos. 4427-30, 4432a in a se-tenant horizontal strip of 5, with plain white marginal selvage.
For overprints, see Nos. 4451-4455.

Ecosystem of Tok Island — A2002

Designs: a, 3w, Dianthus superbus. b, 3w, Eumetopia jubata. c, 12w, Seagull. d, 50w, Lysimachia mauritania Lam.
e, 97w: Eastern and Western islands, Tok Island.

**Perf. 11¼, Perf. (#4433e)**
**2005, May 5**
4433 A2002 Sheet of 9, #4433e, 2 each #4433a-4433d + 2 labels   14.00   7.00
   f.   Booklet pane, #4433e   —   —
   g.   Booklet pane of 8, 2 each #4433a-4433d, perf. 11¼ on 3 sides   —   —
     Complete booklet, # 4433f, 4433g   —

A2003

General Association of Korean Residents in Japan, 50th Anniv. — A2004

Designs: 3w, Korean family waving flag.
130w: Kim Il Sung shaking hands with man in suit.

**2005, May 25**      **Perf. 13¼**
4434 A2003 3w multicolored   .30   .30
**Souvenir Sheet**
4435 A2004 130w multicolored   1.60   .85

Fauna — A2005

Designs, each 40w: No. 4436, Korean Tiger. No. 4437, Sable.

**2005, June 1**
4436   40w multicolored   .85   .50
4437   40w multicolored   .85   .50
   a.   A2005 Pair, #4436-4437 with label between   2.40   1.25
   b.   Booklet pane, 2 #4437a   2.40   —
     Complete booklet, #4437b   3.00   —
See Russia No. 6911.

A2006

Koguryo Historic Site — A2007

Designs: a, Tomb of a general of Koguryo. b, 70w, Tomb mural depicting hunting scene. c, 100w, Mt. Songsan fortress. d, 130w, Gilded arrowheads.
97w: Monument at Mausoleum of King Kwanggaetho.

**2005, June 14**
4438 A2006 Sheet of 4, #a.-d.   4.75   2.40
   e.   Booklet pane, #4438a-4438d, 4439a   7.00   —
     Complete booklet, #4438e   6.50
**Souvenir Sheet**
4439 A2007 97w multicolored   2.40   1.25
   a.   97w Single from souvenir sheet   2.40   1.25
No. 4438a contains Nos. 4438a-4438d in a horizontal strip of 4, with No. 4439a placed separately, within a 69mmx279mm sheetlet with selvage depicting hunting scene, artifacts and inscription.

Kim Chol Ju (1919-35), Brother of Kim Il Sung. — A2008

**Souvenir Sheet**

**2005, June 14**      **Perf. 11½**
4440 A2008 170w multicolored   1.90   .85

A2009

North-South Joint Declaration, 5th Anniv. — A2010

Designs, all 112w: a, Kim Jong Il and S. Korean President Kim Dae Jung shaking hands. b, Kim Jong Il and Kim Dae Jung standing side-by-side. c, Kim Il Jong and Kim Dae Jung sitting together at table with large flower arrangement. d, Kim Dae Jong and Kim Il Jong at conference table.

167w, Kim Dae Jung and Kim Jong Il smiling, shaking hands, with representatives in background.

**2005, June 15**
4441 A2009 Sheet of 4, #a.-d.  7.00  3.50
**Souvenir Sheet**
4442 A2010 167w multicolored  2.50  1.50

A2011

Amur Tiger — A2012

Designs: a, 3w, Tiger looking left. b, 12w, Tiger growling. c, 130w, Tiger looking forward. d, 200w, Tiger growling, turned to right. 150w: Tiger with cubs.

**2005, July 10**                    *Perf. 11¾*
4443 A2011 Sheet of 4, #a.-d.  4.75  2.40
  e.  Booklet pane, #4443a-
      4443d                     4.75   —
      Complete booklet, #4443e  5.25
**Souvenir Sheet**
*Perf. 11½*
4444 A2012 150w multicolored  2.40  1.25

No. 4443e contains Nos. 4443a-4443d in a horizontal strip of 4, within selvage depicting forest skyline and inscription "Panthera tigris altaika."

Map of Korea — A2013

---

**Souvenir Sheet**
**2005, July 25**              *Perf. 11½*
4445 A2013 130w multicolored  1.90  .90

"June 25-July 27 - Period of Joint Anti-US Struggle" — A2014

Design: 3w, Korean soldier, U.S. POWs, military cemetary, military vehicles.

**2005, July 27**               *Perf. 12*
4446 A2014 3w multicolored  .30  .30

A2015

A2016

A2017

National Liberation, 60th Anniv. — A2018

Design: 3w, Arch of Triumph, magnolia.
No. 4448: a, 60w, Kim Il Sung receiving his father's pistol from his mother. b, 60w, Kim Il Sung founding the Juche-oriented revolutionary armed force. c, 60w, Kim Il Sung commanding the battle at Taehongdan. 60w, Kim Il Sung addressing staff on eve of final offensive against the Japanese. 102w, Kim Il Sung, WWII-era photo.

---

No. 4449: a, Kim Il Sung on ship en route to Wonsan Port landing. b, 60w, Kim Il Sung visiting Kangson Steel Works. c, 60w, Kim Il Sung delivering speech. d, 60w, Kim Il Sung meeting his grandparents, upon his return to Korea. e, 102w, Kim Il Sung with microphone.
No. 4450: 128w, Kim Il Sung.

**2005, Aug. 15**               *Perf. 13¼*
4447 A2015 3w multicolored        .30  .30
**Sheets of 5**
4448 A2016 Sheet, #a.-e.  4.75  2.40
4449 A2017 Sheet, #a.-e.  4.75  2.40
**Souvenir Sheet**
4450 A2018 128w multicolored  1.90  .90

**Nos. 4427-4430, 4432 Overprinted "Taipei 2000" and Emblem in Red and Blue**
**2005, Aug. 19**              *Perf. 13¼*
4451-4454 A2001 Set of 4  4.75  2.50
**Souvenir Sheet**
4455 A2001 120w multicolored  2.50  1.25
18th Asian International Stamp Exhibition, Taipei.

A2019

National Costumes — A2020

Designs: a, 3w, Woman in red dress. b, 80w, Woman in blue dress. c, 100w, Woman in green dress. d, 120w, Woman in white dress with fur collar.
140w, Children.

**2005, Aug. 30**              *Perf. 11½*
4456 A2019 Sheet of 4, #a.-d.  4.00  2.10
4456e  Booklet pane of 4, #4456a-d  4.00  —
       Complete booklet, #4456e     4.50
**Souvenir Sheet**
*Perf. 11¾*
4457 A2020 140w multicolored  2.10  1.10

No. 4456e contains Nos. 4456a-d in a horizontal strip of 4, without the small decorative labels that are printed below the stamps in No. 4456. The stamps are surrounded by a narrow selvage similar to that of the sheet of 4.

Korean Workers' Party, 60th Anniv. — A2021

Design: 3w, Korean soldier and workers, banners, proclamation of Joint Slogan.

**2005, Sept. 8**             *Perf. 13¼*
4458 A2021 3w multicolored  .30  .30

---

A2022

A2023

A2024

A2025

Korean Workers' Party, 60th Anniv. — A2026

Design: 3w, Monument to founding of Party.
No. 4460: a, 12w, Kim Il Sung organizing Down-with-Imperialism Union. b, 30w, Kim Il Sung forming the first Juche-oriented Party organization. c, 60w, Kim Il Sung discussing a draft resolution to Communist Party leaders. d, 90w, Kim Il Sung addressing Central Committee of the Communist Party.
No. 4461: a, 12w, Kim Il Sung at bank of microphones, addressing 6th Congress of the WPK. b, 30w, Kim Il Sung and Kim Jong Il with military officers. c, 60w, Kim Jong Il inspecting Tabaksol Company, a camouflaged army unit. d, 90w, Kim Jong Il addressing crowd in stadium.
No. 4462: 120w, Kim Il Sung. No. 4463: 120w, Kim Jong Il.

**2005, Oct. 10**              *Perf. 13¼*
4459 A2022 3w multicolored        .25  .25
**Sheets of 4**
*Perf. 11¾*
4460 A2023 Sheet, #a.-d.  2.40  1.25
4461 A2024 Sheet, #a.-d.  2.40  1.25
**Souvenir Sheets**
*Perf. 13¼*
4462 A2025 120w multicolored  1.50  .70
4463 A2026 120w multicolored  1.50  .70

Bees — A2027

Designs: a, 3w, Four bees surrounding queen. 12w, Two bees attending to larva. 128w, Bee filling comb cell with honey. 200w, Bee flying.

**2005, Oct. 20**     *Perf. 11½*
4464 A2027 Sheet of 4, #a.-d.    4.75 2.40
    e.   Booklet pane, as #4464a-
        4464d       4.75   —
       Complete booklet, #4443e    5.25

No. 4464e contains four stamps like Nos. 4464a-4464d, but with slightly less yellow in the comb background and a slightly paler blue on the blue design elements. It bears a marginal selvage, with Korean inscription at left and three bees at right.

United Nations, 60th Anniv. — A2028

**2005, Oct. 24**     *Perf. 13¼*
4465 A2028 15w multicolored    .35 .30

A2029

Kaesong Historic Site — A2030

No 4466: a, 35w, Pogwang Hall. b, 35w, Monument to Taegakguksa. c, 35w, Pojo Hall. d, 75w, Ryongthong Temple.
No. 4467: a, 35w, Taesong Shrine. b, 35w, Myongryun Hall. c, 35w, Metal type (round). d, 75w, Sam Gate.

**2005, Oct. 31**     *Perf. 12*
**Sheets of 4, #a.-d.**
4466 A2029 multicolored    2.40 1.25
4467 A2030 multicolored    2.40 1.25

Nos. 4466-4467 each contain three non-denominated labels.

Kim Hyong Gwon Monument — A2031

**Souvenir Sheet**
**2005, Nov. 4**     *Perf. 11½*
4468 A2031 120w multicolored    1.90 .90

Kim Hyong Gwon (1905-36), uncle of Kim Il Sung.

Ulsa Treaty, Centennial A2032

**2005, Nov. 17**     *Perf. 11¾*
4469 A2032 12w multicolored    .35 .30

Ulsa Treaty, under which Korea became a Japanese protectorate.

A2033

A2034

Kaesong Historic Site — A2035

No 4470: a, 35w, Kaesong Namdaemun. b, 35w, Mausoleum of King Kongmin. c, 35w, Sonjuk Bridge. d, 35w, Sungyang Private School. e, 35w, Anhwa Temple (Five Hundred Rahan). f, 35w, Tomb of Pak Ji Won (Yonam).
No. 4471: a, 35w, King Wanggon, founder of Kingdom of Koryo, 935 A.D., round. b, 35w, Front Gate at Mausoleum of King Wanggon. c, 75w, Mausoleum of King Wanggon.
No. 4472: a, 35w, Fortress on Mt. Taehung (North Gate). b, 35w, Marble statue of Kwanumbosal, Kwanum Temple. c, 75w, Pakyon Falls.

**Sheet of 6, #a.-f. + 6 labels**
**2005, Nov. 18**     *Perf. 11½*
4470 A2033 multicolored    1.90 .90
**Sheet of 3, #a.-c. + 2 labels**
      *Perf. 13¼*
4471 A2034 multicolored    1.90 .90
**Sheet of 3, #a.-c. + 4 labels**
    *Perf. 12¼ (a, b); 11½ (c)*
4472 A2035 multicolored    1.90 .90

Visit to DPRK by Hu Jintao, President of the People's Republic of China — A2036

Design: a, 35w, Kim Jong Il meeting with Hu Jintao. b, 35w, Kim Jong Il and Hu Jintao visiting the Taean Friendship Glass Factory. c, 35w, Kim Jong Il and Hu Jintao at state banquet. d, 102w, Kim Jong Il shaking hands with Hu Jintao.

    *Perf. 11½, 13¼ (#4473d)*
**2005, Dec. 15**    **Sheet of 4, #a.-d.**
4473 A2036 multicolored    3.00 1.50

New Year 2006 — A2037

**2006, Jan. 1**    **Litho.**     *Perf. 11½*
4474 A2037 3w multi    .30 .30

New Year 2006 (Year of the Dog) — A2038

Various dogs: 3w, 70w.
No. 4477 — Various dogs: a, 15w. b, 100w. c, 130w.

**2006, Jan. 1**     *Perf. 13¼*
4475-4476 A2038    Set of 2    1.90 .65
4477 A2038    Sheet of 5, #4475-
          4476, 4477a-
          4477c       5.25 2.75
    d.   Souvenir sheet of 1 #4477c   3.00 1.50
       Complete booklet, #4475-
          4476, 4477a-4477c    7.00

Complete booklet sold for 335w.

A2039

League of Socialist Working Youth, 60th Anniv. A2040

No. 4478: a, 3w, Kim Il Sung and microphone. b, 111w, Kim Il Sung and crowd. c, 150w, Kim Jong Il receiving torch.

**2006, Jan. 17**     *Perf. 13¼*
4478 A2039   Sheet of 3, #a-c    6.00 2.40
**Souvenir Sheet**
    *Perf. 11½x12*
4479 A2040 128w multi    3.00 1.50

A2041

New Year 2006 (Year of the Dog) A2042

**Photo. & Engr.**
**2006, Jan. 29**     *Perf. 11x11¼*
4480 A2041 12w multi    .30 .30
**Souvenir Sheet**
    *Perf. 11½x11¼*
4481 A2042 70w multi    1.25 .60

Down With Imperialism Union, 80th Anniv. — A2043

**2006, Feb. 9**    **Litho.**     *Perf. 13½*
4482 A2043 3w multi    .30 .30

**Miniature Sheet**

2006 Winter Olymics, Turin A2044

No. 4483: a, 15w, Ice dancing. b, 85w, Ice hockey. c, 110w, Ski jumping. d, 135w, Speed skating.

**2006, Feb. 10**     *Perf. 13¼*
4483 A2044   Sheet of 4, #a-d    5.75 3.00
   4483e   Booklet pane of 4, #4483a-
          4483d       6.00   —
       Complete booklet, #4483e    6.00

Complete booklet sold for 362w.

A2045

Kim Jong Il, 64th Birthday A2046

No. 4485: a, 12w, Polemonium racemosum. b, 45w, Day lily. c, 100w, Dandelion. d, 140w, Parnassia palustris.

**2006, Feb. 16**     *Perf. 13½*
4484 A2045 3w multi    .30 .30
**Souvenir Sheet**
4485 A2046   Sheet of 4, #a-d    4.75 2.50

A2047

Visit of Kim Jong Il to People's Republic of China A2048

No. 4486 — Kim Jong Il: a, 3w, At Crop Research Institute. b, 12w, At optical fiber factory. c, 35w, At Three Gorges Dam. d, 70w, At Guangzhou Intl. Conference and Exhibition Center. e, 100w, At air conditioner factory. f, 120w, At port of Yandian.
102w, Kim Jong Il and Hu Jintao.

**2006, Mar. 4**      **Perf. 12x12¼**
4486 A2047   Sheet of 6, #a-f   5.50 3.00
**Souvenir Sheet**
**Perf. 11¾**
4487 A2048 102w multi     1.90 .85

A2049

Agrarian Reform Law, 60th Anniv. A2050

**2006, Mar. 5**      **Perf. 11½**
4488 A2049   12w multi + label   .30 .30
**Souvenir Sheet**
4489 A2050 150w multi     1.40 1.25

**Souvenir Sheet**

First North Korean Postage Stamps, 60th Anniv. A2051

**2006, Mar. 12**      **Perf. 11¾**
4490 A2051 158w multi     2.60 1.40

Mt. Kumgang Scenery — A2052

Designs: 3w, Pibong Falls. 12w, Podok Hermitage. 35w, Sokka Peak. 50w, Jipson Peak. 70w, Chongsok Rocks, horiz. 100w, Sejon Peak, horiz. 120w, Chonhwa Rock, horiz. 140w, Piro Peak, horiz.

**2006, Mar. 15**      **Perf. 11¾x12¼**
4491-4498 A2052   Set of 8   8.75 4.50

---

Belgica 2006 World Youth Philatelic Exhibition, Brussels — A2053

Designs: No. 4499, 140w, Jules Verne (1828-1905), writer. No. 4500, 140w, Tyto alba, Volvariella speciosa, Scouting emblem. No. 4501, 140w, Disa grandiflora, Nymphalidae. No. 4502, 140w, Australopithecus afarensis, rocks. No. 4503, 140w, Alaskan malamute, Birman cat, Scouting emblem. No. 4504, 140w, Sunflowers, by Vincent Van Gogh. No. 4505, 140w, Soccer ball, chess knight, table tennis paddle and ball. No. 4506, 140w, Tursiops truncatus, Scouting emblem. No. 4507, 140w, Maglev train, horiz. No. 4508, 140w, 1962 Ernst Grube Type S 4000-1 fire truck, horiz.

**2006, Apr. 13**      **Perf. 11¾**
4499-4508 A2053   Set of 10   23.00 11.50

Kim Il Sung, 94th Anniv. of Birth A2054

**2006, Apr. 15**      **Perf. 11½**
4509 A2054 3w multi + label   .30 .30

Association for the Restoration of the Fatherland, 70th Anniv. — A2055

**2006, May 5**      **Perf. 13½**
4510 A2055 3w multi     .30 .30

Pothong River Improvement Project, 60th Anniv. — A2056

**2006, May 21**      **Perf. 12**
4511 A2056 12w multi     .30 .30

**Various Stamps of 1963-2002 Surcharged in Black and Red**

No. 4563

No. 4565

---

No. 4590

No. 4606

**Methods and Perfs. As Before**
**2006**

| | | | |
|---|---|---|---|---|
| 4512 | A658 | 3w on 2ch #816 | — | — |
| | | (R) | | |
| 4513 | A608 | 3w on 5ch #731 | — | — |
| 4514 | A635 | 3w on 10ch #770 | — | — |
| 4515 | A932 | 3w on 10ch #1598 | — | — |
| 4516 | A971 | 3w on 10ch #1798 | — | — |
| 4517 | A1005 | 3w on 10ch #1929 | — | — |
| 4518 | A926 | 3w on 15ch #1579 | — | — |
| 4519 | A887 | 3w on 20ch #1419 | — | — |
| 4520 | A986 | 3w on 20ch #1873 | — | — |
| | | (R) | | |
| 4521 | A1179 | 3w on 20ch #2470 | — | — |
| 4522 | A1211 | 3w on 20ch #2548 | — | — |
| 4523 | A1211 | 3w on 20ch #2548 | — | — |
| | | (R) | | |
| 4524 | A1249 | 3w on 20ch #2645 | — | — |
| 4525 | A1431 | 3w on 20ch #3159 | — | — |
| 4526 | A1431 | 3w on 20ch #3159 | — | — |
| | | (R) | | |
| 4527 | A1539 | 3w on 20ch #3437 | — | — |
| 4528 | A1539 | 3w on 20ch #3437 | — | — |
| | | (R) | | |
| 4529 | A1704 | 3w on 20ch #3776 | — | — |
| 4530 | A1288 | 3w on 25ch #2751 | — | — |
| 4531 | A971 | 3w on 30ch #1801 | — | — |
| 4532 | A986 | 3w on 30ch #1875 | — | — |
| 4533 | A1177 | 3w on 30ch #2462 | — | — |
| 4534 | A1177 | 3w on 30ch #2462 | — | — |
| | | (R) | | |
| 4535 | A1241 | 3w on 30ch #2621 | — | — |
| 4536 | A1379 | 3w on 30ch #2964 | — | — |
| 4537 | A1379 | 3w on 30ch #2964 | — | — |
| | | (R) | | |
| 4538 | A1396 | 3w on 30ch #3023 | — | — |
| 4539 | A382 | 3w on 40ch #447 | — | — |
| 4540 | A547 | 3w on 40ch #645 | — | — |
| | | (R) | | |
| 4541 | A812 | 3w on 40ch #1219 | — | — |
| 4542 | A818 | 3w on 40ch #1242 | — | — |
| 4543 | A826 | 3w on 40ch #1277 | — | — |
| 4544 | A1793 | 3w on 40ch #4052 | — | — |
| 4545 | A1793 | 3w on 40ch #4052 | — | — |
| | | (R) | | |
| 4546 | A1385 | 3w on 50ch #2987 | — | — |
| 4547 | A1396 | 3w on 50ch #3025 | — | — |
| 4548 | A1430 | 3w on 50ch #3154 | — | — |
| a. | | Double surcharge | | |
| 4549 | A1471 | 3w on 50ch #3281 | — | — |
| 4550 | A1526 | 3w on 50ch #3408 | — | — |
| | | (R) | | |
| 4551 | A1595 | 3w on 50ch #3548 | — | — |
| | | (R) | | |
| 4552 | A1736 | 3w on 60ch #3851 | — | — |
| 4553 | A1557 | 3w on 80ch #3468 | — | — |
| 4554 | A1656 | 3w on 80ch #3676 | — | — |
| 4555 | A1651 | 3w on 80ch #3676 | — | — |
| | | (R) | | |
| 4556 | A798 | 3w on 90ch #1164 | — | — |
| 4557 | A1735 | 3w on 1w #3849 | — | — |
| 4558 | A1761 | 3w on 1w #3919 | — | — |
| 4559 | A1734 | 3w on 1.50w #3848 | — | — |
| 4560 | A621 | 12w on 2ch #744 | — | — |
| 4561 | A932 | 12w on 2ch #1597 | — | — |
| 4562 | A808 | 12w on 20ch #1199 | — | — |
| 4563 | A823 | 12w on 30ch #1268 | — | — |
| | | (R) | | |
| 4564 | A808 | 12w on 40ch #1201 | — | — |
| 4565 | A938 | 12w on 50ch #1622 | — | — |
| 4566 | A1860 | 12w on 2w #4207 | — | — |
| 4567 | A817 | 101w on 10ch #1236 | — | — |
| 4568 | A907 | 101w on 10ch #1471 | — | — |
| 4569 | A985 | 101w on 10ch #1865 | — | — |
| 4570 | A1005 | 101w on 10ch #1926 | — | — |
| 4571 | A1487 | 101w on 10ch #3321 | — | — |
| 4572 | A1837 | 101w on 10ch #4165 | — | — |
| 4573 | A1454 | 101w on 30ch #3228 | — | — |
| 4574 | A1658 | 101w on 50ch #3680 | — | — |
| 4575 | A1527 | 101w on 1w #3410 | — | — |
| 4576 | A1716 | 101w on 1w #3807 | — | — |
| 4577 | A1724 | 101w on 1.20w #3831 | — | — |
| 4578 | A938 | 128w on 5ch #1619 | — | — |
| 4579 | A812 | 128w on 10ch #1216 | — | — |
| 4580 | A1231 | 128w on 15ch #2597 | — | — |
| 4581 | A865 | 128w on 20ch #1357 | — | — |
| 4582 | A903 | 128w on 20ch #1457 | — | — |
| 4583 | A959 | 128w on 25ch #1754 | — | — |
| 4584 | A977 | 128w on 25ch #1812 | — | — |
| 4585 | A982 | 128w on 25ch #1853 | — | — |
| 4586 | A958 | 128w on 40ch #1749 | — | — |
| 4587 | A1785 | 128w on 40ch #4035 | — | — |
| 4588 | A1430 | 128w on 50ch #3157 | — | — |
| 4589 | A1707 | 128w on 1w #3785 | — | — |
| 4590 | A1707 | 128w on 1w #3785 (R) | — | — |

---

| | | | |
|---|---|---|---|---|
| 4591 | A1725 | 128w on 2w #3833 | — | — |
| 4592 | A820 | 134w on 5ch #1250 | — | — |
| 4593 | A903 | 134w on 5ch #1455 | — | — |
| 4594 | A898 | 134w on 10ch #1444 | — | — |
| 4595 | A982 | 134w on 10ch #1850 | — | — |
| 4596 | A855 | 134w on 20ch #1333 | — | — |
| 4597 | A1467 | 134w on 30ch #3267 | — | — |
| 4598 | A911 | 134w on 40ch #1518 | — | — |
| 4599 | A911 | 134w on 40ch #1518 (R) | — | — |
| 4600 | A806 | 134w on 1.50w #1203 | — | — |
| 4601 | A1862 | 134w on 1.50w #4213 | — | — |
| 4602 | A1443 | 158w on 10ch #3196 | — | — |
| 4603 | A898 | 158w on 15ch #1445 | — | — |
| 4604 | A911 | 158w on 15ch #1516 | — | — |
| 4605 | A1260 | 158w on 20ch #2680 | — | — |
| 4606 | A850 | 158w on 25ch #1328 | — | — |
| 4607 | A902 | 158w on 25ch #1458 | — | — |
| 4608 | A1501 | 158w on 30ch #3357 | — | — |
| 4609 | A1407 | 158w on 40ch #3059 | — | — |
| 4610 | A1542 | 158w on 40ch #3443 | — | — |
| 4611 | A1723 | 158w on 5w #3835 | — | — |

Nos. 4562-4564, 4581, 4588, 4598-4599, 4604-4605 are airmail.

Korean Children's Union, 60th Anniv. — A2057

**2006, June 6**     **Litho.**    **Perf. 13½**
4612 A2057 3w multi     .30 .30

2006 World Cup Soccer Championships, Germany — A2058

Various soccer players in action: 3w, 130w, 160w, 210w.

**2006, June 9**      **Perf. 13½**
4613-4616 A2058   Set of 4   8.25 4.00
4616a   Souvenir sheet, #4616 + label   3.50 1.75
4616b   Booklet pane of 4, #4613-4616    8.50
    Complete booklet, #4616b    8.50

Issued: No. 4616a, 10/21/09. Italia 2009 Intl. Philatelic Exhibition (No. 4616a).
Complete booklet sold for 520w.

**Souvenir Sheet**

Kim Chol Ju (1919-35) — A2059

**2006, June 12**      **Perf. 11½x12**
4617 A2059 170w multi     2.75 1.50

**Souvenir Sheet**

Ri Su Bok (1933-51), War Hero and Poet — A2060

**2006, July 27**      **Perf. 11¾**
4618 A2060 120w multi     2.10 1.00

## Miniature Sheet

Circus Performers — A2061

Designs: a, 3w, Trapeze artists (42x35mm). b, 12w, Aerial acrobatic troupe (42x35mm). c, 130w, Seesaw jumper (42x35mm). d, 200w, Juggler (42x64mm).

**Perf. 11½, 11½x12 (200w)**
**2006, Aug. 10**        **Litho.**
4619 A2061 Sheet of 4, #a-d    6.00 3.00

Korean Cuisine A2062

Designs: 3w, Kimchi. 12w, Umegi. 130w, Rice cake dumplings with bean paste. 200w, Sweet rice.

**2006, Aug. 12**        **Perf. 13½**
4620-4623 A2062  Set of 4    6.00 3.00
4623a    Booklet pane of 4, #4620-4623    6.00 —
      Complete booklet, #4623a    6.00

Sea Mammals A2063

Designs: 3w, Megaptera nodosa. 70w, Balaenoptera musculus. 160w, Physeter catodon. 240w, Inia geoffrensis.

**2006, Aug. 20**        **Perf. 11¾**
4624-4627 A2063  Set of 4    7.75 3.75
4627a    Booklet pane of 4, #4624-4627    7.75 —
      Complete booklet, #4627a    7.75

Motorcycles A2064

Various motorcycles.

**2006, Sept. 1**        **Perf. 11½**
4628    Horiz. strip of 4    8.25 4.25
a.   A2064 3w multi    .25 .25
b.   A2064 102w multi    1.60 .85
c.   A2064 150w multi    2.40 1.25
d.   A2064 240w multi    3.75 1.90
e.   Booklet pane of 4, #4628a-4628d    8.25
      Complete booklet, #4628e    8.25

Sinking of the General Sherman, 140th Anniv. — A2065

**2006, Sept. 2**    **Litho.**    **Perf. 13¼**
4629 A2065 130w multi    2.25 1.10

Owls — A2066

Designs: 12w, Tyto alba. 111w, Strix uralensis. 130w, Strix aluco. 160w, Nyctea scandiaca.

**2006, Sept. 10**        **Perf. 11¾**
4630-4633 A2066  Set of 4    6.75 3.50
4633a    Booklet pane of 4, #4630-4633    6.75 —
      Complete booklet, #4633a    6.75
For overprints see Nos. 4648-4651.

## Souvenir Sheet

Kim Il Sung University, 60th Anniv. — A2067

**2006, Oct. 1**        **Perf. 11½x12**
4634 A2067 70w multi    1.25 .60

Famous Koreans — A2068

Designs: 3w, Ulgi Mundok, general. 12w, So Hui (942-998), diplomat and general. 35w, Kim Ung So (1564-1624), general. 70w, Kang Kam Chan (948-1031), general. 102w, Yongae Somun, general. 130w, Ri Kyu Bo (1168-1241), poet. 160w, Mun Ik Jom (1329-98), civil official.

**2006, Oct. 2**        **Perf. 13½**
4635-4641 A2068  Set of 7    8.25 4.50

A2069

**2006, Oct. 17**    **Litho.**    **Perf. 13¼**
4642 A2069 3w multi

Down With Imperialism Union, 80th Anniv. — A2070

No. 4643: a, 70w, Kim Il Sung and followers (50x38mm). b, 102w, Kim Il Sung (46mm diameter). c, 120w, Kim Il Sung and followers on railroad track (50x38mm).

**2006, Oct. 17**    **Litho.**    **Perf. 13¼**
## Souvenir Sheet
**Perf. 11¾ (#4643a, 4643c), Perf.**
4643 A2070    Sheet of 3, #a-c    5.00 2.50

Red Cross Society of North Korea, 60th Anniv. — A2071

**2006, Oct. 18**    **Litho.**    **Perf. 13½**
4644 A2071 30w multi    .55 .30

## Souvenir Sheet

Secondary Education for Koreans in Japan, 60th Anniv. — A2072

**2006, Oct. 21**        **Perf. 13¼**
4645 A2072 110w multi    1.90 .95

## Miniature Sheet

Koguryo Tombs UNESCO World Heritage Site — A2073

No. 4646 — Murals: a, 3w, King (30x42mm). b, 70w, Queen (30x42mm). c, 130w, Subak (52x34mm). d, 135w, Procession (52x34mm). e, 160w, Kitchen (52x34mm).

**Perf. 13¼ (3w, 70w), 12¼x11¾**
**2006, Nov. 4**        **Litho.**
4646 A2073    Sheet of 5, #a-e    —

## Souvenir Sheet

Joson University, 50th Anniv. — A2074

**2006, Nov. 4**        **Perf. 11½**
4647 A2074 110w multi + label    1.90 .95

Nos. 4630-4633 Overprinted in Gold

### Methods and Perfs As Before
**2006, Nov. 16**
4648 A2066  12w on #4630    .30 .30
4649 A2066  111w on #4631    1.75 .90
4650 A2066  130w on #4632    2.10 1.25
4651 A2066  160w on #4633    2.60 1.40
     Nos. 4648-4651 (4)    6.75 3.85

Belgica 2006 World Youth Stamp Exhibition. Location of the overprint varies.

## Souvenir Sheet

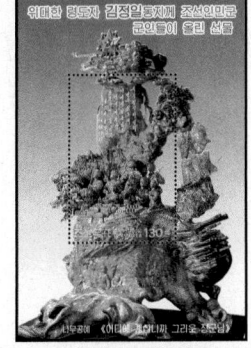

Wooden Sculpture Presented by People's Army Soldiers to Kim Jong Il — A2075

**2006, Dec. 24**    **Litho.**    **Perf. 11½x12**
4652 A2075 130w multi    2.25 1.10

New Year 2007 — A2076

**2007, Jan. 1**    **Litho.**    **Perf. 13½**
4653 A2076 3w multi    .30 .30

New Year 2007 (Year of the Pig) — A2077

Various pigs: 3w, 45w.
No. 4656 — Various pigs: a, 70w. b, 130w.

**2007, Jan. 1**        **Perf. 11½**
4654-4655 A2077  Set of 2    .85 .40
4656 A2077  Sheet, #4654-4655, 4656a, 4656b    4.00 2.10
c.   Booklet pane, #4654-4655, 4656a, 4656b    4.00
      Complete booklet, #4656c    4.00
d.   Souvenir sheet of 1 #4656a    1.20 .60

A2078

Kim Jong Il, 65th Birthday A2079

Designs: 3w, Kimiljonghwa begonia and butterfly.
No. 4658 — Mountain, lake and musical score: a, 12w. b, 70w. c, 100w. d, 140w.

**2007, Feb. 16**        **Perf. 13¼**
4657 A2078 3w multi    .30 .30
4658 A2079 Sheet of 4, #a-d    5.25 2.60

Symbols of Progress — A2080

**2007, Feb. 28**        **Perf. 13¼**
4659 A2080 3w multi    .30 .30
Annual joint editorial of state newspapers.

Butterflies
A2081

Designs: 15w, Callicore selima. 85w, Morpho rhetenor. 110w, Atrophaneura alcinous. 160w, Parnassius bremeri.

**2007, Mar. 5**
| | | | | |
|---|---|---|---|---|
| 4660-4663 | A2081 | Set of 4 | 6.25 | 3.00 |
| 4663a | | Booklet pane of 4, #4660-4663 | 6.25 | — |
| | | Complete booklet, #4663a | 6.25 | |

### Miniature Sheet

Koguryo Tombs UNESCO World Heritage Site — A2082

No. 4664 — Anak Tomb No. 3 paintings: a, 3w, Stable (60x42mm). b, 70w, Well (60x42mm). c, 130w, Milling area (30x42mm). d, 160w, Man blowing horn (30x42mm).

**2007, Mar. 10**
| | | | | |
|---|---|---|---|---|
| 4664 | A2082 | Sheet of 4, #a-d | 6.25 | 3.00 |
| e. | | Booklet pane of 4, #4664a-4664d | 6.25 | — |
| | | Complete booklet, #4664e | 6.25 | |

Korean National Association, 90th Anniv. A2083

**2007, Mar. 23**
| | | | | |
|---|---|---|---|---|
| 4665 | A2083 | 12w multi | .30 | .30 |

Ludwig van Beethoven (1770-1827), Composer A2084

**2007, Mar. 26**
| | | | | |
|---|---|---|---|---|
| 4666 | A2084 | 80w multi | 1.40 | .65 |

Mangyongdae, Birthplace of Kim Il Sung — A2085

Paintings of Kim Il Sung A2086

Kim Il Sung and Family A2087

No. 4668: a, 45w, The Great Leader Kim Il Sung on the 250-Mile Journey for Learning. b, 70w, The Great Leader Kim Il Sung Who Braved Through the Arduous Road of the Anti-Japanese War. c, 100w, Ever Victorious Road. d, 160w, At the Field Predicting the Rich Harvest.

**2007, Apr. 15**     **Perf. 13¼**
| | | | | |
|---|---|---|---|---|
| 4667 | A2085 | 3w multi | .30 | .30 |

**Perf. 11¾**
| | | | | |
|---|---|---|---|---|
| 4668 | A2086 | Sheet of 4, #a-d | 6.25 | 3.00 |

**Souvenir Sheet**
**Perf. 11¾x11½**
| | | | | |
|---|---|---|---|---|
| 4669 | A2087 | 130w multi | 2.25 | 1.10 |

Kim Il Sung (1912-94).

### Miniature Sheet

Rodents A2088

No. 2088: a, 3w, Sciurrus vulgaris. b, 12w, Muscardinus avellanarius. c, 20w, Hypogeomys antimena. d, 30w, Lemniscomys striatus. e, 40w, Pedetes capensis. f, 50w, Rattus norvegicus. g, 80w, Eliomys quercinus. h, 102w, Micromys minutus.

**2007, Apr. 20**     **Perf. 13x13x12¼**
| | | | | |
|---|---|---|---|---|
| 4670 | A2088 | Sheet of 8, #a-h, + 2 labels | 5.50 | 3.75 |

Korean People's Army Soldiers and Mt. Paektu — A2089

Leaders Reviewing Troops — A2090

Kim Il Sung and Kim Jong Il Reviewing Troops — A2091

No. 4672: a, 80w, Kim Il Sung and Kim Jong Il reviewing troops. b, 100w, Kim Jong Il and soldiers.

**2007, Apr. 25**     **Perf. 13¼**
| | | | | |
|---|---|---|---|---|
| 4671 | A2089 | 12w multi | .30 | .30 |

**Perf. 11¾**
| | | | | |
|---|---|---|---|---|
| 4672 | A2090 | Sheet of 2, #a-b | 3.00 | 1.50 |

### Souvenir Sheet
**Perf. 12x11½**
| | | | | |
|---|---|---|---|---|
| 4673 | A2091 | 120w multi | 2.00 | 1.00 |

Korean People's Army, 75th anniv.

Prevention of Bird Flu — A2092

**2007, May 10**     **Perf. 13¼**
| | | | | |
|---|---|---|---|---|
| 4674 | A2092 | 85w multi | 1.60 | .70 |

### Miniature Sheet

First North Korean Currency, 60th Anniv. — A2093

No. 4675 — Banknotes: a, 3w, 10-won note of 1947. b, 12w, 50-chon note of 1947. c, 35w, 100-won note of 1959. d, 50w, 10-won note of 1959. e, 70w, 10-won note of 1978. f, 110w, 1-won note of 1978. g, 130w, 50-won note of 1992. h, 160w, 100-won note of 1992.

**2007, May 20**     **Litho.**
| | | | | |
|---|---|---|---|---|
| 4675 | A2093 | Sheet of 8, #a-h | 9.25 | 4.75 |

### Souvenir Sheet

Battle of Pochonbo, 70th Anniv. — A2094

**2007, June 4**     **Perf. 11½x12**
| | | | | |
|---|---|---|---|---|
| 4676 | A2094 | 120w multi | 2.00 | 1.00 |

Fish — A2095

Designs: 15w, Naso lituratus. 50w, Carassius auratus. 110w, A. citrinellus. 200w, Symphysodon discus.

**2007, July 1**     **Perf. 13¼**
| | | | | |
|---|---|---|---|---|
| 4677-4680 | A2095 | Set of 4 | 6.25 | 3.00 |
| 4680a | | Booklet pane of 4, #4677-4680 | 6.25 | — |
| | | Complete booklet, #4680a | 6.25 | |

Self-disembowelment of Ri Jun at Hague Intl. Peace Conference, Cent. — A2096

**2007, July 14**
| | | | | |
|---|---|---|---|---|
| 4681 | A2096 | 110w brn & grn | 1.90 | .95 |

Fossils A2097

Designs: 15w, Tetracorallia. 70w, Neuropteridium. 130w, Yoldia. 200w, Rhinoceros mandible.

**2007, July 20**
| | | | | |
|---|---|---|---|---|
| 4682-4685 | A2097 | Set of 4 | 7.00 | 3.75 |
| 4685a | | Booklet pane of 4, #4682-4685 | 7.00 | — |
| | | Complete booklet, #4685a | 7.00 | |

### Miniature Sheet

Orchids A2098

No. 4686: a, 3w, Oncidium wyattianum. b, 70w, Cymbidium Red Beauty "Carmen." c, 127w, Dendrobium thyrsifolium. d, 140w, Dendrobium Candy Stripe "Kodama."

**2007, Aug. 3**     **Perf. 12¾**
| | | | | |
|---|---|---|---|---|
| 4686 | A2098 | Sheet of 4, #a-d | 5.50 | 2.75 |
| e. | | Booklet pane of 4, #4686a-4686d | 5.50 | — |
| | | Complete booklet, #4686e | 5.50 | |

Women's Soccer A2099

No. 4687 — Various women soccer players making plays: a, 12w. b, 40w. c, 70w. d, 110w. e, 140w.

**2007, Sept. 10**     **Perf.**
| | | | | |
|---|---|---|---|---|
| 4687 | A2099 | Sheet of 5, #a-e | 6.00 | 3.00 |

**Souvenir Sheet**
| | | | | |
|---|---|---|---|---|
| 4688 | A2099 | 130w shown | 2.25 | 1.10 |

### Miniature Sheet

Flowers A2100

No. 4689: a, Gladiolus gandavensis. b, Iris ensata. c, Rosa hybrida. d, Nelumbo nucifera.

**2007, Sept. 26**     **Perf. 13¼**
| | | | | |
|---|---|---|---|---|
| 4689 | A2100 | 30w Sheet of 4, #a-d | 2.10 | 1.00 |
| e. | | Booklet pane of 4, #4689a-4689d | 2.10 | — |
| | | Complete booklet, #4689e | 2.10 | |

See Russia No. 7045.

### Miniature Sheets

A2101

2008 Summer Olympics,
Beijing — A2102

Nos. 4690 and 4691 — Mascots: a, 3w, Beibei. b, 12w, Jingjing. c, 30w, Huanhuan. d, 70w, Yingying. e, 140w, Nini.
2008 Olympics emblem and: 300w, Hurdler, shooter, group of athletes. 500w, Athletes holding flower bouquets.

**2007, Oct. 15       Litho.       Perf.**
4690  A2101    Sheet of 5, #a-e   —   —
**Litho. With Three-Dimensional Plastic Affixed**
4691  A2101    Sheet of 5, #a-e   —   —
**Printed on Plastic DVD Without Gum**
4692  A2102  300w multi       12.50  12.50
4693  A2102  500w multi       20.00  20.00

No. 4691 sold for 500w, and stamps have other three-dimensional images.

Furniture and Household Furnishings A2103

Designs: 3w, Seal box. 12w, Ornamental chest. 40w, Collapsible dressing table. 70w, Wardrobe. 110w, Chest of drawers. 130w, Chest of drawers, diff.

**2007, Nov. 1       Litho.       Perf. 13¼**
4694-4699  A2103   Set of 6     8.00  6.00
4699a      Booklet pane of 6, #4694-4699    8.00
           Complete booklet, #4699a         8.00

Food — A2104

Designs: 12w, Potato and rice cakes. 50w, Yongchae kimchi. 70w, Fermented flatfish. 110w, Potato cakes.

**2007, Nov. 5**
4700-4703  A2104   Set of 4     5.25  3.75
4703a      Booklet pane of 4, #4700-4703    5.25
           Complete booklet, #4703a         5.25

**Souvenir Sheet**

Summit Meeting of Pres. Kim Jong Il and South Korean Pres. Roh Moo Hyun A2105

**2007, Nov. 10       Perf. 11½x12**
4704  A2105  170w multi         3.75  3.00

---

**Miniature Sheets**

Scenes From Arirang Gymnastics Performance — A2106

No. 4705 — Various scenes: a, 12w. b, 50w.
No. 4706 — Various scenes: a, 120w. b, 155w.

**2007, Nov. 15       Perf. 11½**
**Sheets of 2, #a-b, + Label**
4705-4706  A2106   Set of 2     6.00  4.00

Paintings of Kim Dong Ho — A2107

Designs: 3w, Plowing. 12w, Weaving a Straw Mat. 70w, Thrashing. 130w, Archery.

**2007, Nov. 18       Perf. 13¼**
4707-4710  A2107   Set of 4     4.75  3.00
4710a      Booklet pane of 4, #4707-4710    4.75  —
           Complete booklet, #4710a         4.75

**Souvenir Sheet**

Visit of Viet Nam Communist Party Secretary General Nong Duc Manh — A2108

**2007, Dec. 16       Perf. 12x11½**
4711  A2108  120w multi         2.60  1.75

Home of Kim Jong Suk A2109

Paintings Depicting Kim Jong Suk A2110

No. 4713: a, 30w, Kim Jong Suk and Kim Il Sung (54x45mm). b, 70w, Kim Jong Suk (45mm diameter). c, 110w, Kim Jong Suk in battle (54x45mm).

**2007, Dec. 24       Perf. 12x11½**
4712  A2109  3w multi          .35  .30
**Souvenir Sheet**
**Perf. 13¼, Perf. (#4713b)**
4713  A2110  Sheet of 3, #a-c   4.75  3.50

---

New Year 2008 — A2111

**2008, Jan. 1       Litho.       Perf. 13¼**
4714  A2111  3w multi          .30  .30

Publication of Saenal Sinmun, 80th Anniv. — A2112

**2008, Jan. 15**
4715  A2112  85w multi        1.50  .75

Joint Editorials of State Newspapers A2113

Red flag in upper left corner and: No. 4716, 3w, Arms and flag of North Korea, tower. No. 4717, 3w, Soldiers. No. 4718, 12w, Soldier and flag. No. 4719, 12w, Soldiers, factories and electrical tower, horiz. 30w, Woman and food, horiz. 120w, Musicians, children playing soccer, building. 130w, Men and woman, doves, map of Korea.

**2008, Jan. 30       Perf. 11¾**
4716-4722  A2113   Set of 7     6.75  4.75

Parrots — A2114

Designs: 15w, Melopsittacus undulatus. 85w, Agapornis roseicollis. 155w, Agapornis personata, horiz. 170w, Two Melopsittacus undulatus, horiz.

**2008, Feb. 5       Perf. 13¼**
4723-4726  A2114   Set of 4     9.50  7.00
4726a      Booklet pane of 4, #4723-4726    9.50  —
           Complete booklet, #4726a         9.50

**Souvenir Sheet**

Naming of Kimjongilhwa Begonia, 20th Anniv. — A2115

**2008, Feb. 13       Perf. 11½x12**
4727  A2115  85w multi        2.10  1.50

**Souvenir Sheet**

A2116

---

Flowers A2117

Designs: 3w, Pyrethrum hybridum.
No. 4729: a, 12w, Tulipa gesneriana (30x42mm). b, 70w, Adonis amurensis (30x42mm). c, 120w, Mathiola incana (30x42mm). d, 155w, Kimjongilhwa begonia (44mm diameter)

**2008, Feb. 16       Perf. 13¼**
4728  A2116  3w multi          .50  .30
4729  A2117  Sheet of 4, #a-d  7.50  5.25

Kim Jong Il, 66th birthday.

**Kim Il Sung Birthplace Type of 2002**
**2008, Mar. 15       Litho.       Perf. 11½**
4730  A1886  3w red            .50  .30

For surcharge, see No. 4877C.

**Miniature Sheet**

Publication of "On the Art of Cinema," by Kim Jong Il, 35th Anniv. — A2118

No. 4731 — Various actors and actresses: a, 3w, Musician. b, 85w, Man holding gun. c, 135w, Martial artist. d, 170w, Man, woman and children.

**2008, Mar. 15       Perf. 13¼**
4731  A2118  Sheet of 4, #a-d  6.50  3.25

250-Mile Journey for Learning, 85th Anniv. — A2119

**2008, Mar. 16       Perf. 12**
4732  A2119  15w multi         .50  .30

2008 Summer Olympics, Beijing — A2120

No. 4733: a, 3w, Soccer. b, 12w, Basketball. c, 30w, Tennis. d, 70w, Table tennis.

**2008, Mar. 28**    **Perf. 13¼**
4733 A2120   Block or horiz.
       strip of 4, #a-d   2.60 1.25

Famous
Men — A2121

Designs: 85w, Choe Yong (1316-88), military leader. 160w, Ho Jun (1546-1615), doctor.

**2008, Mar. 29**    **Perf. 12**
4734-4735 A2121  Set of 2   4.00 2.10

Election of Kim Jong Il
as Chairman of
National Defense
Commission, 15th
Anniv. — A2122

**2008, Apr. 9**    **Perf. 13¼**
4736 A2122  12w multi    .50  .30

Souvenir Sheet

Election of Kim Jong Il as Chairman of
National Defense Commission, 15th
Anniv. — A2123

**2008, Apr. 9**    **Perf. 11½x12**
4737 A2123  120w multi

International
Friendship
Exhibition — A2124

Gifts to Kim Il Sung: 3w, Pitcher and oil lamp. 85w, Painting of rooster. 155w, Throne. 135w, Vase with two handles.

**2008, Apr. 15**    **Perf. 11½**
4738-4740 A2124  Set of 3   4.00 2.10
**Souvenir Sheet**
4741 A2124  135w multi    3.50 1.50

North-South
Joint
Conference,
60th
Anniv. — A2125

**2008, Apr. 21**    **Perf. 12**
4742 A2125  12w gray green   .50  .30

---

Mushrooms — A2126

Designs: 12w, Amanita muscaria. 50w, Armillariella mellea. 135w, Macrolepota procera. 155w, Tricholoma terreum.

**2008, May 8**    **Perf. 11½**
4743-4746 A2126  Set of 4   6.50 3.75
*4746a*    Booklet pane of 4, #4743-
       4746        6.50  —
    Complete booklet, #4746a  6.50

Buildings on Mt.
Ryongak — A2127

Designs: 35w, Two buildings. 155w, Building and wall.

**2008, May 25**    **Perf. 13¼**
4747-4748 A2127  Set of 2   3.75 2.10

Musical
Instruments — A2128

Designs: 15w, Hyangbipha (stringed instrument). 50w, Phiri (contrabassoon). 120w, Jangsaenap (oboe). 160w, Kayagum (zither), horiz.

**2008, June 1**    **Perf. 13¼**
4749-4752 A2128  Set of 4   6.50 3.75
*4752a*    Booklet pane of 4, #4749-
       4752        6.50  —
    Complete booklet, #4752a  6.50

Opera
Scenes
and
Scores
A2129

Designs: 3w, Sea of Blood. 12w, The Flower Girl. 85w, The True Daughter of the Party. 120w, Tell Oh Forest. 155w, The Song of Mt. Kumgang.

**2008, June 5**    **Perf. 12x11½**
4753-4757 A2129  Set of 5   6.75 4.75

North Korea
No. 1 and
Romania
No.
1 — A2130

**2008, June 20**    **Perf. 12¼x11¾**
4758 A2130  85w multi   1.90  .95
EFIRO 2008 Intl. Stamp Exhibition, Bucharest, Romania.

---

Capture of
the USS
Pueblo,
40th Anniv.
A2131

**2008, June 25**    **Perf. 12¼x11¾**
4759 A2131  12w multi   .50  .30

Souvenir Sheet

Olympic Torch Relay in
Pyongyang — A2132

**2008, June 26**    **Perf. 11¾x12¼**
4760 A2132  120w multi   2.60 1.40

Minerals —
A2133

Designs: 12w, Serpentine. 75w, Copper pyrite. 135w, Sphalerite. 155w, Molybdenite.

**2008, July 5**    **Perf. 12¼x11¾**
4761-4764 A2133  Set of 4   7.00 4.00
*4764a*    Booklet pane of 4, #4761-
       4764        7.00  —
    Complete booklet, #4764a  7.00

Souvenir Sheets

A2134

A2135

Korean War Ceasefire, 55th
Anniv. — A2136

No. 4765: a, 3w, Kim Il Sung leading troop crossing of Han River. b, 120w, Kim Il Sung with troops.
No. 4766: a, 35w, Kim Il Sung and seated troops. b, 155w, Celebration.
85w, Kim Il Sung at battleground.

---

**2008, July 27**    **Perf. 12x11½**
4765 A2134  Sheet of 2, #a-b  2.40 1.40
4766 A2135  Sheet of 2, #a-b  3.50 2.10
            **Perf. 11½**
4767 A2136  85w multi    1.90 1.00

Souvenir Sheet

Jong Il Peak, 20th Anniv. of
Renaming — A2137

**2008, Aug. 9**    **Perf. 13¼**
4768 A2137  120w multi   2.60 1.50

Food — A2138

Designs: 3w, Rice and wormwood cakes. 70w, Rice cakes. 135w, Pancakes. 155w, Garlic in soy sauce.

**2008, Aug. 20**  **Litho.**  **Perf. 13¼**
4769-4772 A2138  Set of 4   6.25 3.75
*4772a*    Booklet pane of 4, #4769-
       4772        6.25
    Complete booklet, #4772a  6.25

A2139

Songun Revolutionary
Leadership — A2140

**2008, Aug. 25**
4773 A2139  12w multi    .30  .30
**Souvenir Sheet**
4774 A2140  135w multi   2.75 1.50

Miniature Sheet

Koguryo Tombs UNESCO World
Heritage Site — A2141

No. 4775 — Anak Tomb No. 3 paintings: a, 3w, Mask dance (60x42mm). b, 90w, Janghaedok, aide to King Kogukwon (30x42mm). c, 120w, Garage (60x42mm). d, 155w, Stable (60x42mm).

**2008, Sept. 2**  **Litho.**  **Perf. 13¼**
4775 A2141  Sheet of 4, #a-d, +
       label       6.25 3.75
  **e.**    Booklet pane of 4, #4775a-
       4775d      6.25
    Complete booklet, #4775e  6.25

A2142

Flag — A2143

**2008, Sept. 9**      *Perf. 11½*
4776 A2142   3w multi     .50 .30
4777 A2143   155w multi    3.00 1.75
       See No. 4876.

A2144

Creation
of North
Korea,
60th
Anniv.
A2145

Designs: 3w, Chollima Statue, flag of North
Korea, city and flowers. 12w, Torch, flag of the
Supreme Commander, people. 70w, Soldiers.
120w, People on horses. 160w, Handshake.
155w, Creation of National Flag and Arms.

**2008, Sept. 9**      *Perf. 13¼*
4778-4782 A2144   Set of 5   6.25 4.00
     **Souvenir Sheet**
4783 A2145   155w multi   3.00 1.50

Transportation
A2146

Designs: No. 4784, 680w, Niña, ship of
Christopher Columbus. No. 4785, 680w, 1910
Russian steam engine. No. 4786, 680w, Hindenburg over Lake Constance. No. 4787,
680w, Siberian husky dog sled team. No.
4788, 680w, Ivan Basso, cyclist. No. 4789,
680w, Mercedes-Benz-Mets LF 16 fire truck.
No. 4790, 680w, Two Ferrari Enzos. No. 4791,
680w, Eurostar train. No. 4792, 680w, Concorde. No. 4793, 680w, Laika the dog and
Sputnik 2.

**2008, Sept. 15**      *Perf.*
4784-4793 A2146   Set of 10   180.00 150.00

   Nos. 4784-4793 each were printed in sheets
of 2.

     Souvenir Sheet

Salvelinus Malma — A2147

**2008, Oct. 2**    Litho.    *Perf. 13¼*
4794 A2147   135w multi     2.40 1.10

     Miniature Sheet

Moran Hill, Pyongyang — A2148

   No. 4795: a, 3w, Small shelter and bridge.
b, 45w, Large shelter and walkway. c, 100w,
Flora with small shelter, bridges and Pyongyang in distance. d, 135w, Building with steps.

**2008, Oct. 20**
4795 A2148   Sheet of 4, #a-d   5.00 3.00

Introduction of
Compulsory
Secondary
Education, 50th
Anniv. — A2149

**2008, Nov. 1**
4796 A2149   12w multi     .50 .30

Soldier and
Flag — A2150

Woman in
Bean
Field — A2151

**2008, Nov. 17**
4797 A2150   12w multi     .35 .30
4798 A2151   85w multi     1.50 .70

Furniture
A2152

Designs: 50w, Haeju table. 70w, Inkstone
table. 120w, Dressing table with drawer. 170w,
Jewel box.

**2008, Dec. 3**
4799-4802 A2152   Set of 4   6.50 3.50
4802a    Booklet pane of 4, #4799-
       4802        6.50 —
   Complete booklet, #4802a   6.50

     Souvenir Sheet

Ulmil Pavilion, Moran Hill,
Pyongyang — A2153

**Litho. With Three-Dimensional
Plastic Affixed**
**2008, Dec. 15**      *Perf. 13¼*
     **Without Gum**
4803 A2153   85w multi     2.40 1.25

New Year
2009 — A2154

**2009, Jan. 1**    Litho.    *Perf. 11½*
4804 A2154   3w multi     .50 .30
     For surcharge, see No. 4877D.

A2155

Red
Guards,
50th
Anniv.
A2156

**2009, Jan. 14**      *Perf. 11¾*
4805 A2155   12w multi     .50 .30
     **Souvenir Sheet**
4806 A2156   160w multi    3.00 2.00

Traditional
Games
A2157

Designs: 3w, Tug-of-war. 120w, Knee
fighting.

**2009, Jan. 25**      *Perf. 13¼*
4807-4808 A2157   Set of 2   2.40 1.50

Kim Jong Il, 67th
Birthday — A2158

   Unnamed butterfly and flowers: 3w, Crinum
bracteatum. 12w, Begonia. 120w, Callistemon
phoeniceus. 160w, Plumeria rubra.

**2009, Feb. 16**      *Perf. 11¾*
4809-4812 A2158   Set of 4   5.25 3.00

     Souvenir Sheet

Proclamation of Juche Model for
Society, 50th Anniv. — A2159

**2009, Feb. 19**      *Perf. 11½x12*
4813 A2159   170w multi    3.25 1.90

     Souvenir Sheets

A2161

A2162

Joint Editorials of State
Newspapers — A2163

   No. 4814: a, 3w, Torch, Chollima statue. b,
170w, Symbols of industry and transportation.
   No. 4815: a, 12w, Food crops, canned
foods, city. b, 150w, Musical instruments,
sheet music, orchestra, soccer players.
   No. 4816: a, 30w, Soldiers, flag, ships, airplanes and missiles. b, 120w, Soldiers, flags,
city.
   No. 4817: a, 80w, Map of Korea, text. b,
100w, Hands crushing bomb.

**2009, Feb. 22**      *Perf. 11½*
4814 A2160   Sheet of 2, #a-b,
       + 2 labels    3.25 2.10
4815 A2161   Sheet of 2, #a-b,
       + 2 labels    3.00 1.90
4816 A2162   Sheet of 2, #a-b,
       + 2 labels    2.75 1.90
4817 A2163   Sheet of 2, #a-b,
       + 2 labels    3.25 2.10
     Nos. 4814-4817 (4)    12.25 8.00
     For surcharge, see No. 4877E.

     Souvenir Sheets

China 2009 World Stamp Exhibition,
Luoyang — A2164

   No. 4818: a, 3w, Flowers. b, 100w, Flowers,
diff.
   No. 4819: a, 12w, Statue of horse. b, 90w,
Building, steps, sculpture.

**2009, Feb. 25**      *Perf. 11¾*
     **Sheets of 2, #a-b**
4818-4819 A2164   Set of 2   5.25 2.40
4819c    Booklet pane of 4, #4818a-
       4818b, 4819a-4819b   5.25
   Complete booklet, #4819c   5.25

March 1
Uprising
Against
Japan, 90th
Anniv.
A2165

**2009, Mar. 1**      *Perf. 12¼x11¾*
4820 A2165   90w multi    1.90 1.25

Intl. Women's Day, Cent. — A2166

**2009, Mar. 8**                      **Perf. 13¼**
4821  A2166  35w multi                    .60  .35

Gifts to Kim Il Sung A2167

Designs: 3w, Painting of horses. 12w, Fossil fish. 140w, Rifle. 150w, Bear skin.

**2009, Apr. 15**                     **Perf. 13¼**
4822-4825  A2167   Set of 4              5.50  3.50
4825a        Booklet pane of 4, #4822-
                4825                          5.50    —
        Complete booklet, #4825a           5.50
    Complete booklet sold for 322w.

Central Zoo, Pyongyang, 50th Anniv. — A2168

Birds: 12w, Anthropoides paradisea. 70w, Accipiter gentilis. 120w, Larus argentatus. 140w, Balearica pavonina.

**2009, Apr. 30**                     **Perf. 11¾x12¼**
4826-4829  A2168   Set of 4              6.25  3.75
4829a        Booklet pane of 4, #4826-
                4829                          6.25
        Complete booklet, #4829a           6.25

Central Botanical Garden, Pyongyang, 50th Anniv. — A2169

Trees: 3w, Catalpa ovata. 50w, Betula platyphylla. 120w, Juglans cordiformis. 160w, Metasequoia glyptostroboides.

**2009, Apr. 30**                     **Perf. 13¼**
4830-4833  A2169   Set of 4              6.25  3.75
4833a        Booklet pane of 4, #4830-
                4833                          6.25
        Complete booklet, #4833a           6.25

    Complete booklet sold for 350w.

Sports A2170

Designs: 12w, Baseball. 90w, Bowling. 160w, Fencing. 200w, Golf.

**2009, May 2**
4834-4837  A2170   Set of 4              7.75  3.75
4837a        Booklet pane of 4, #4834-
                4837                          7.75    —
        Complete booklet, #4837a           7.75

---

**No. 4189a Surcharged in Gold**

No. 4838: a, 20w on 40ch, LZ1. b, 40w on 80ch, LZ120. c, 1w+109w on 1.20w, Zeppelin NT. d, 2w+168w on 2.40w, Zeppelin NT, diff.

**Method and Perf As Before**
**2009, May 5**
4838  A1852     Sheet of 4, #a-d    6.25  4.00
    Naposta '09 and IBRA '09, Essen, Germany. On Nos. 4838c and 4838d, the obliterator covers the part of the original denomination expressed in chon.

Children's Union Camp — A2171

Children: 3w, Mountaineering. 80w, Collecting butterflies. 120w, At campfire. 170w, At beach.

**2009**            **Litho.**        **Perf. 11½**
4839-4842  A2171    Set of 4             6.25  3.75
4842a        Booklet pane of 4, #4839-
                4842                          6.25    —
        Complete booklet, #4842a           6.25
4842b        Souvenir sheet of 4, #4839-
                4842                          6.25  3.75

    Issued: Nos. 4839-4842, 4842a, 5/6; No. 4842b, 5/14. Hong Kong 2009 Intl. Stamp Exhibition (No. 4842b).

**Souvenir Sheet**

Battle of Musan, 70th Anniv. A2172

**2009, May 22**                      **Perf. 13¼**
4843  A2172  120w multi                 2.90  1.50

**Miniature Sheet**

Kim Jong Il as Member of Central Committee of Workers' Party, 45th Anniv. — A2173

No. 4844 — Kim Jong Il: a, 3w, At desk. b, 12w, At machine shop. c, 120w, Wearing white lab jacket. d, 170w, Looking inside cooking pot.

**2009, June 19**                     **Perf. 11¾**
4844  A2173     Sheet of 4, #a-d    5.75  3.50

Universal Postal Union, 135th Anniv. — A2174

**2009, June 20**                     **Perf. 13¼**
4845  A2174  50w multi                  1.10  .60

---

Insects — A2175

Designs: 50w, Vespa mandarinia, rose. 90w, Cicindela japonica, dandelion. 120w, Locusta migratoria, plant. 140w, Aphaenogaster famelica, mushroom.

**2009, July 1**                      **Perf. 11½**
4846-4849  A2175     Set of 4           7.00  4.75
4849a        Booklet pane of 4, #4846-
                4849                          7.00
        Complete booklet, #4849a           7.00

Okryu Restaurant, Pyongyang A2176

Renovated Pyongyang Buildings — A2177

No. 4851: a, 3w, Kim Chaek University Library (35x28mm). b, 70w, Taedongmun Theater (35x28mm). c, 90w, Chongryu Restaurant (70x28mm). d, 150w, Pyongyang Grand Theater (70x28mm).

**2009, July 2**                      **Perf. 13¼**
4850  A2176  12w multi                   .40  .35
                                      **Perf. 11½**
4851  A2177     Sheet of 4, #a-d    5.25  3.25

**Miniature Sheet**

Eternal Sun of Juche A2178

No. 4852 — Paintings: a, 12w, The Great Leader Kim Il Sung Drawing the Brush Into Our Party's Emblem. b, 50w, First Military Flag. c, 70w, Birth. d, 140w, Every Field With Bumper Harvest.

**2009, July 8**                      **Perf. 13¼**
4852  A2178     Sheet of 4, #a-d    5.25  3.25

Nurse and Child — A2179

Ambulance and Hospital A2180

**2009, July 25**
4853  A2179   12w multi                  .40  .30
4854  A2180  150w multi                 2.60  1.75

**Souvenir Sheet**

Launch of Kwangmyongsong 2 Rocket — A2181

**2009, July 27**                     **Perf. 11½x12**
4855  A2181  120w multi                 2.75  1.50

---

**Souvenir Sheet**

Northern Area Victory Monument, Hamgyong Province — A2182

**2009, Aug. 3**                      **Perf. 13¼**
4856  A2182  120w multi                 2.75  1.50

Musical Instruments — A2183

Designs: 12w, Saenap. 80w, Drum. 140w, Sogoghu. 170w, Flute.

**2009, Aug. 5**                      **Litho.**
4857-4860  A2183    Set of 4            6.50  3.50

150-Day Innovation Campaign A2184

**2009, Aug. 10**
4861  A2184  12w multi                   .40  .30

Fish — A2185

Ships and: 15w, Theragra chalcogramma. 60w, Cyprinus carpio. 140w, Euthynnus pelamis. 160w, Mugil cephalus.

**2009, Sept. 1**
4862-4865  A2185   Set of 4              6.25  3.75
4865a        Booklet pane of 4, #4862-
                4865                          6.25
        Complete booklet, #4865a           6.25

**Miniature Sheets**

Intl. Year of Astronomy — A2186

No. 4866, 95w: a, Chollima Statue, solar eclipse. b, Galileo Galilei, telescope, planets, satellite.
No. 4867, 95w: a, Rabbits, solar eclipse. b, Planets, galaxy.
No. 4868, 95w: a, Dogs, total solar eclipse. b, Chomsongdae Observatory.

**2009, Aug. 29**    **Litho.**    **Perf. 13½**
**Sheets of 2, #a-b, + 2 Labels**
4866-4868  A2186    Set of 3            9.50  7.00
4868c        Souvenir sheet of 1, #4868a     1.40  .95
4868d        Booklet pane of 6, #4866a-
                4866b, 4867a-4867b, 4868a-
                4868b                         9.50
        Complete booklet, #4868d           9.50

**Souvenir Sheets**

A2187

**Year of Friendship With People's Republic of China — A2188**

No. 4869: a, #3287c, 3384, 3716. b, #3563, 4374b, 4473c.
No. 4870: a, Five stamps. b, Six stamps.

**2009, Sept. 2**                    **Perf. 13½**
4869 A2187 60w Sheet of 2, #a-b    2.40 1.25
4870 A2188 60w Sheet of 2, #a-b    2.40 1.25

**Miniature Sheet**

**Birdpex 2010, Antwerp, Belgium A2189**

No. 4871: a, 12w, Coturnicops exquisitus. b, 90w, Porzana pusilla. c, 170w, Porzana fusca.

**2009, Sept. 12**                   **Perf. 11½**
4871 A2189   Sheet of 5,
             #4871c, 2 each
             #4871a-4871b, +
             label                    6.00 3.25
  d.         Booklet pane of 3, #4871a-
             4871c                     4.50  —
             Complete booklet, #4871d  4.50

**Souvenir Sheet**

**Intl. Red Cross and Red Crescent Year A2190**

No. 4872 — Flags of Red Cross, North Korea and: a, 75w, Jean-Henri Dunant, founder of Red Cross. b, 95w, Disaster risk reduction. c, 95w, First aid.

**2009, Sept. 21**                   **Perf. 13½**
4872 A2190   Sheet of 3, #a-c        4.25 2.25

**Souvenir Sheet**

**Kim Jong Suk (1917-49), Mother of Kim Jong Il — A2191**

No. 4873: a, 90w, Portrait (33x45mm). b, 100w, Kim Jong Suk with troops, horiz. (57x36mm).

**2009, Sept. 22**
4873 A2191   Sheet of 2, #a-b        3.25 1.60

**Miniature Sheet**

**People's Republic of China, 60th Anniv. A2192**

No. 4874: a, 10w, Chinese President Hu Jintao. b, 67w, Chinese astronauts. c, 67w, National Stadium, Beijing. d, 84w, National Grand Theater, Beijing.

**2009, Oct. 1**
4874 A2192   Sheet of 4, #a-d        4.00 2.40

**Worldwide Fund for Nature (WWF) — A2193**

No. 4875 — Platalea minor and: a, Snail. b, Fish. c, Crab. d, Shrimp.

**2009, Oct. 5**                     **Perf. 13½**
4875         Horiz. strip of 4       6.25 3.25
  a.         A2193 3w multi           .25  .25
  b.         A2193 12w multi          .25  .25
  c.         A2193 99w multi         1.75  .80
  d.         A2193 266w multi        4.25 2.25
  e.         Sheet of 8, 2 each #4875a-
             4875d, + label          13.00 6.25

**Flag and Torch Types of 2002-08**
**2009, Oct. 15**     **Litho.**     **Perf. 11½**
4876 A2142 10w multi                  .30  .30
                                     **Perf. 13¼**
4877 A1890 30w multi                  .50  .30

Nos. 4249, 4252, 4343, 4730, 4804 and 4814a Surcharged

**Methods and Perfs As Before**
**2009, Oct.**
4877A A1887 10w on 3w #4249   1.10 1.10
4877B A1939 10w on 3w #4343   1.10 1.10
4877C A1886 10w on 3w #4730   1.10 1.10
4877D A2154 10w on 3w #4804   1.10 1.10
4877E A2160 10w on 3w #4814a  1.10 1.10
4877F A1890 30w on 12w #4252  3.50 3.50
      Nos. 4877A-4877F (6)    9.00 9.00

**Reptiles — A2194**

Designs: 15w, Chamaeleo jacksonii. 50w, Naja naja. 110w, Caretta caretta, horiz. 160w, Crocodylus niloticus, horiz.

**2009, Oct. 20**
4878-4881 A2194   Set of 4           5.50 2.75
4881a       Booklet pane of 4, #4878-
            4881                      5.75  —
            Complete booklet, #4881a  5.75

**Miniature Sheets**

**Lighthouses — A2195**

No. 4882: a, Cape Palliser Lighthouse, New Zealand, and Sousa chinensis. b, Tater Du Lighthouse, United Kingdom, and Mary Rose. c, Hornby Lighthouse, Australia, and Passat, Germany. d, Rubjerg Knude Lighthouse, Denmark, and Wappen von Hamburg.
No. 4883: a, Bengtskär Lighthouse, Finland, and Phoebastria albatrus. b, Fanad Lighthouse, Ireland, and Bolma rugosa. c, Cordouan Lighthouse, France, and Sterna fuscata. d, Brandaris Lighthouse, Netherlands, and Pleurotomaria africana.
No. 4884: a, Cape St. Vincent Lighthouse, Portugal, and Sula bassana. b, Europa Point Lighthouse, Gibraltar, and Lambis scorpio. c, Vorontsov Lighthouse, Ukraine, and Grampus griseus. d, Gelendzhik Lighthouse, Russia, and Gibbula magus.

No. 4885: a, Hoy High Lighthouse, Scotland, and Delphinus delphis. b, Lindesnes Lighthouse, Norway, and Stenella coeruleoalba. c, Reykjanesviti Lighthouse, Iceland, and Chlamys varia. d, Seal Point Lighthouse, South Africa, and Chroicocephalus ridibundus.

**2009, Oct. 24   Litho.   Perf. 13x13½**
4882 A2195 760w Sheet of 4,
            #a-d                     50.00 50.00
  e.   Souvenir sheet of 2 #4882a   24.00 24.00
  f.   Souvenir sheet of 2 #4882b   24.00 24.00
  g.   Souvenir sheet of 2 #4882c   24.00 24.00
  h.   Souvenir sheet of 2 #4882d   24.00 24.00
4883 A2195 760w Sheet of 4,
            #a-d                     50.00 50.00
  e.   Souvenir sheet of 2 #4883a   24.00 24.00
  f.   Souvenir sheet of 2 #4883b   24.00 24.00
  g.   Souvenir sheet of 2 #4883c   24.00 24.00
  h.   Souvenir sheet of 2 #4883d   24.00 24.00
4884 A2195 760w Sheet of 4,
            #a-d                     50.00 50.00
  e.   Souvenir sheet of 2 #4884a   24.00 24.00
  f.   Souvenir sheet of 2 #4884b   24.00 24.00
  g.   Souvenir sheet of 2 #4884c   24.00 24.00
  h.   Souvenir sheet of 2 #4884d   24.00 24.00
4885 A2195 760w Sheet of 4,
            #a-d                     50.00 50.00
  e.   Souvenir sheet of 2 #4885a   24.00 24.00
  f.   Souvenir sheet of 2 #4885b   24.00 24.00
  g.   Souvenir sheet of 2 #4885c   24.00 24.00
  h.   Souvenir sheet of 2 #4885d   24.00 24.00

**Souvenir Sheet**

**Repatriation of Korean Nationals in Japan, 50th Anniv. — A2196**

**2009, Dec. 16   Litho.   Perf. 11½x12**
4887 A2196 160w multi                2.60 1.25

**Miniature Sheet**

**End of Juche 98 A2197**

No. 4888: a, 10w, Launch of Kwangmyongsong No. 2 satellite. b, 20w, CNC machine tool industry. c, 20w, Oxygen separator, finished steel products, train and vehicles. d, 30w, Construction vehicles. e, 50w, Namhung Gasification Project, crane with pipe. f, 50w, Apartment buildings on Mansudae Street, Pyongyang. g, 57w, Sturgeons, ostriches, chicken, pig. h, 70w, Apples, farm, Migok-ri model village.i, 80w, Audience, soccer players, singer.

**2009, Dec. 31   Litho.   Perf. 13½**
4888 A2197   Sheet of 9, #a-i        6.25 3.25

**Souvenir Sheet**

**Kim Jong Il and Workers A2198**

**2009, Dec. 31   Litho.   Perf. 13¼**
4889 A2198 100w multi                1.60  .80
             End of Juche 98.

**New Year 2010 — A2199**

**2010, Jan. 1**                     **Perf. 13¼**
4890 A2199 10w multi                  .30  .30

**Tigers — A2200**

Tiger and: 30w, Sun. 67w, Tree. 171w, Tiger and cubs, horiz.

**2010, Jan. 5   Litho.   Perf. 11¾x12¼**
4891-4892 A2200   Set of 2           1.60  .80
4892a       Booklet pane of 4, 2 each
            #4891-4892                3.50  —
            Complete booklet, #4892a  3.50

**Souvenir Sheet**
**Litho. with Three-Dimensional Plastic Affixed**
**Perf. 13¼**
**Without Gum**

4893 A2200 171w multi                2.75 1.50

Complete booklet sold for 213w. No. 4893 contains one 60x42mm stamp.

**Wildlife A2201**

Designs: 35w, Ailuropoda melanoleuca. 60w, Aix galericulata. 80w, Lagenorhynchus obliquidens. 110w, Panthera pardus.

**2010, Jan. 30   Litho.   Perf. 13¼**
4894-4897 A2201   Set of 4           4.75 2.40
4897a       Booklet pane of 4, #4894-
            4897                     11.00  —
            Complete booklet, #4897a 11.00

Complete booklet sold for 304w. No. 4897a exists imperforate.

**Miniature Sheet**

**2010 Winter Olympics, Vancouver — A2202**

No. 4898: a, 10w, Ice hockey. b, 40w, Figure skating. c, 50w, Speed skating. d, 70w, Skiing.

**2010, Feb. 1**                     **Perf. 13**
4898 A2202   Sheet of 8, 2 each
             #a-d                    5.50 5.50
             See No. 4919.

**Kim Jong Il, 68th Birthday A2203**

No. 4899: a, 10w, Impatiens sultanii Royal Rose. b, 50w, Gazania hybrida. c, 70w, Paeonia suffructicosa. d, 110w, Bougainvillea glabra Sanderiana.

# KOREA, DEMOCRATIC PEOPLE'S REPUBLIC

456

**2010, Feb. 16**    *Perf. 11½*
4899 A2203   Vert. strip or block
of 4, #a-d, + 8 labels    4.25 2.10
  e.   Booklet pane of 4, #4899a-
4899d, + 8 labels    4.50 —
   Complete booklet, #4899e   4.50
Complete booklet sold for 259w.

### Miniature Sheet

Joint Editorials of State
Newspapers — A2204

No. 4900: a, 10w, People, soldier, Party Founding Monument, flowers. b, 20w, Woman, city, manufactured items. c, 30w, Woman carrying crops, vegetables. d, 57w, Worker, factory, train, dam. e, 67w, Soldiers. f, 95w, People holding flag showing mpa of unified Korea. g, 125w, Doves, map showing unified Korea.

**2010, Feb. 20**    *Perf. 13¼*
4900 A2204   Sheet of 7, #a-g, +
2 labels    6.50 3.50

A2205

Anti-Imperialism
Posters — A2206

**2010, Mar. 5**
4901 A2205 76w multi    1.40 .65
4902 A2206 95w multi    1.60 .75

Cats — A2207

Designs: 10w, Cat, chicks. 70w, Cats, flower, butterfly. 133w, Cat, mouse. 170w, Cat, kittens, ball of yarn.

**2010, Mar. 25**    *Perf. 11½*
4903-4906 A2207 Set of 4    6.25 3.25
4906a   Booklet pane of 4, #4903-
4906    6.50 —
   Complete booklet, #4906a   6.50
Complete booklet sold for 402w.

### Souvenir Sheet

Birds
A2208

No. 4907: a, 30w, Brachyramphus perdix. b, 125w, Gallinago solitaria. c, 133w, Porzana paykullii.

**2010, Apr. 9**
4907 A2208   Sheet of 3, #a-c, +
3 labels    4.75 2.40
  d.   Booklet pane of 3, #4907a-
4907c    5.00 —
   Complete booklet, #4907d   5.00
Antverpia 2010 International Philatelic Exhibition, Antwerp. Complete booklet sold for 307w.

Gifts to Kim Il
Sung — A2209

Designs: 10w, Eagle figurine. 30w, Crane figurine. 95w, Tiger painting. 152w, Sea turtle figurine, horiz.

**2010, Apr. 15**    *Perf. 13¼*
4908-4911 A2209   Set of 4    4.75 2.40

Orchids and
Insects — A2210

Designs: 30w, Sophronitella brevipendunculata, bee. 80w, Epidendrum radiatum, dragonfly. 120w, Cymbidium Lillian Stewart "Red Carpet," bee. 152w Dendrobium hybrid, butterfly.

**2010, Apr. 20**    *Perf. 11½*
4912-4915 A2210   Set of 4    6.25 3.25
4915a   Booklet pane of 4, #4912-
4915    6.75 —
   Complete booklet, #4915a   6.75
Nos. 4912-4915 each were printed in sheets of 5 + label. Complete booklet sold for 401w.

### Souvenir Sheet

Expo 2010, Shanghai — A2211

No. 4916: a, 10w, Chollima statue, city, flowers. b, 80w, Children watering plant, wind turbines, wildlife.

**2010, May 1**    *Litho.*
4916 A2211   Sheet of 2, #a-b, +
2 labels    1.50 .75

### Miniature Sheet

Table
Tennis
A2212

No. 4917: a, 10w, Man with green shirt. b, 30w, Woman with red shirt. c, 95w, Woman with blue shirt. d, 152w, Man with pink shirt.

**2010, May 10**    *Perf.*
4917 A2212   Sheet of 4, #a-d   4.75 2.50
  e.   Booklet pane of 4, #4917a-
4917d    5.00 —
   Complete booklet, #4917e   5.00
Complete booklet sold for 306w.

Joint Slogans — A2213

**2010, May 12**    *Perf. 11½*
4918 A2213 10w multi    .30 .30

### No. 4898 With Flags of Countries Winning Depicted Events Added at Left of Athlete
### Miniature Sheet

No. 4919: a, 10w, Ice hockey, flag of Canada. b, 40w, Figure skating, flag of People's Republic of China. c, 50w, Speed skating, flag of Netherlands. d, 50w, Speed skating, flag of Czech Republic. e, 70w, Skiing, flag of Italy. f, 70w, Skiing, flag of Germany.

**2010, May 25**    *Perf. 13*
4919 A2202   Sheet of 8,
#4919c-4919f, 2
each #4919a-
4919b    5.25 5.25

### Souvenir Sheet

Dinosaurs — A2214

No. 4920: a, 10w, Brontosaurus. b, 125w, Allosaurus. c, 152w, Pterodactylus.

**2010, June 16**    *Perf. 12¾*
4920 A2214   Sheet of 3, #a-c, +
label    4.75 2.40
  d.   Booklet pane of 3, #4920a-
4920c    5.00 —
   Complete booklet, #4920d   5.00
  e.   As #4920, with Euro-phila
2010 emblem in sheet margin    5.25 2.60
Complete booklet sold for 306w.
Issued: No. 4920e, 10/2.

2010 World Cup Soccer
Championships, South Africa — A2215

No. 4921 — Shirt colors of soccer players: a, 20w, Green, yellow. b, 57w, Yellow, blue. c, 190w, Red, white. 114w, Yellow, white.

**2010, May 31**    *Perf. 13¼*
4921 A2215   Sheet of 3, #a-c, +
3 labels    4.25 2.25
### Souvenir Sheet
4922 A2215 114w multi    1.90 .95
  a.   Booklet pane of 4, #4921a-
4921c, 4922    6.75 —
   Complete booklet, #4922a   6.75
Complete booklet sold for 400w.

### Souvenir Sheet

Intl. Children's Day, 60th
Anniv. — A2216

**2010, June 1**    *Perf. 11¾*
4923 A2216 95w multi    1.60 .85
  a.   As #4923, with Bangkok 2010
emblem in sheet margin   1.60 .85
Issued: No. 4923a, 8/4.

Joint Declaration of
June 15, 2000 on
Reunification of
Korea — A2217

**2010, June 15**    *Perf. 13¼*
4924 A2217 190w multi    3.25 1.60

A2218

A2219

A2220

Visit of
Kim
Jong Il to
People's
Republic
of China
A2221

No. 4925 — Kim Jong Il: a, 20w, And Chinese man pointing. b, 40w Pointing. c, 67w, Walking.
No. 4926 — Kim Jong Il: a, 20w, Standing next to woman. b, 35w, With leg raised. c, 80w, Looking through window.
No. 4927 — Kim Jong Il: a, 20w, Standing next to Chinese Pres. Hu Jintao. b, 40w, Seated at table with Pres. Hu. c, 70w, Shaking hands with Pres. Hu.
60w, Kim Jong Il and Pres. Hu.

**2010, June 20**    *Perf. 13¼*
4925 A2218   Sheet of 3, #a-c, +
6 labels    2.10 1.10
4926 A2219   Sheet of 3, #a-c, +
6 labels    2.25 1.15
4927 A2220   Sheet of 3, #a-c, +
3 labels    2.40 1.25
Nos. 4925-4927 (3)    6.75 3.50
### Souvenir Sheet
### *Perf. 11½x12*
4928 A2221 60w multi    1.00 .45

## Miniature Sheet

Children's Animated Films — A2222

No. 4929 — Scenes from children's animated films: a, 10w, Butterfly and Cock. b, 30w, A Clever Raccoon Dog. c, 95w, A Hedgehog Defeats a Tiger. d, 133w, Regret of Rabbit.

**2010, June 30**     **Perf. 13¼**
4929 A2222   Sheet of 4, #a-d   4.50 2.25

## Souvenir Sheet

Azaleas
A2223

**2010, July 1**     **Litho.**
4930 A2223 85w multi   1.50 .70

## Souvenir Sheet

National
Anthem
A2224

**2010, July 5**     **Perf. 13½**
4931 A2224 50w black   .80 .40

A2225

Liberation of Korea, 65th
Anniv. — A2226

No. 4932 — Paintings: a, 10w, The Great Leader Forming the Korean Revolutionary Army. b, 15w, Bloody and Long Anti-Japanese War. c, 20w, The Azalea in the Fatherland. d, 40w, Pyongyang in New Spring. e, 100w, Historical That Night.
60w, February Festival on the Eve of Korea's Liberation.

**2010, Aug. 15**     **Perf. 13¼**
4932 A2225   Sheet of 5, #a-e, +
    label   3.00 1.60
**Souvenir Sheet**
4933 A2226 60w multi   1.00 .45

A2227

A2228

Start of Songun Revolutionary
Leadership, 50th Anniv. — A2229

No. 4935 — Paintings: a, 15w, General Kim Jong Il Instilling the Traditions of Mt. Paektu in the Soldiers (63x41mm). b, 30w, Military Song of Victory (50x38mm). c, 55w, General to the Frontline, Children to the Camp (50x38mm). d, 80w, Saying He Feels Happiest Among the Soldiers (50x38mm).
70w, Blizzard on Mt. Paektu.

**2010, Aug. 25**     **Perf. 11½**
4934 A2227 10w multi   .30 .30
   **Perf. 12x11½ (#4935a), 11¾**
4935 A2228   Sheet of 4, #a-d   3.00 1.50
    **Souvenir Sheet**
     **Perf. 11¾**
4936 A2229 70w multi   1.25 .60

## Souvenir Sheet

Diplomatic Relations Between North
Korea and Cuba, 50th Anniv. — A2230

**2010, Aug. 29**     **Litho.**     **Perf. 11¾**
4937 A2230 85w multi   1.75 .80

Paintings — A2231

Designs: 15w, Pine Tree and Hawk, by Sin Yun Bok. 35w, Waves of Ongchon, by Jong Son. 70w, Reeds and Wild Geese, by Jo Sok Jin. 100w, After Picking Medicinal Herbs, by Kim Hong Do.

**2010, Sept. 1**     **Litho.**     **Perf. 13¼**
4938-4941 A2231   Set of 4   3.75 1.90
4941a    Booklet pane of 4, #4938-
     4941   3.75 —
   Complete booklet, #4941a   3.75

A2232

A2233

A2234

A2235

A2236

A2237

Pres. Kim Il Sung (1912-94) — A2238

No. 4942: a, 20w, Kim Il Sung being educated by father. b, 55w, Kim Il Sung being educated by mother.
No. 4943: a, 25w, Kim Jong Suk defending Kim Il Sung (64x42mm). b, 30w, Kim Il Sung at secret camp on Mt. Paektu in spring (45x35mm). c, 45w, Kim Il Sung on horseback leading other riders (454x35mm).
No. 4944: a, 10w, Kim Il Sung crossing Amnok River in winter. b, 30w, Kim Il Sung leading protest against Jilin-Hoeryong railway. c, 40w, Kim Il Sung reporting at Youth League meeting. d, 55w, Kang Pan Sok handing over pistols to Kim Il Sung.
No. 4945: a, 20w, Gunshot of Pochonbo. b, 30w, Kim Il Sung burning Minsaengdan documents. c, 40w, Kim Il Sung with members of children's corps. d, 45w, Kim Il Sung leading soldiers.
No. 4946: a, 10w, Kim Il Sung speaking to Anti-Japanese People's Guerilla Army. b, 20w, Kim Il Sung with people after establishing People's Revolutionary Government. c, 35w, Kim Il Sung leading soldiers, diff. d, 90w, Kim Il Sung founding Association for the Restoration of the Fatherland.
50w, Kim Il Sung at podium giving speech.
60w, Kim Il Sung leading solders, diff.

   **Perf. 13¼, 12x11½ (#4943a)**
**2010, Sept. 5**       **Litho.**
4942 A2232   Sheet of 2, #a-b, +
    label   1.25 .60
4943 A2233   Sheet of 3, #a-c, +
    label   1.60 .80
4944 A2234   Sheet of 4, #a-d   2.10 1.10
4945 A2235   Sheet of 4, #a-d   2.10 1.10
4946 A2236   Sheet of 4, #a-d   2.40 1.25
    Nos. 4942-4946 (5)   9.45 4.85

## Souvenir Sheets
    **Perf. 11¾**
4947 A2237 50w multi   .95 .45
4948 A2238 60w multi   1.10 .50

Expo 2010,
Shanghai — A2239

**2010, Sept. 6**     **Litho.**     **Perf. 11½**
4949 A2239 25w multi   .40 .30
   No. 4949 was printed in sheets of 6 + 9 labels.

A2240

Entry of Chinese People's Volunteer
Army Into Korean War, 60th Anniv.
A2241

Designs: 25w, Chinese soldier and Korean woman.
No. 4951: a, 10w, Meeting to decide on the entry of Chinese Volunteer Army into the Korean War, by Gao Quan. (60x42mm). b, 15w, North Korean and Chinese soldiers fighting together (30x42mm). c, For the Peace sculpture (60x42mm). d, Korean children with doves (30x42mm).

**2010, Sept. 10**     **Litho.**     **Perf. 13¼**
4950 A2240 25w multi   .50 .30
4951 A2241   Sheet of 4, #a-d, +
    2 labels   1.25 .65

A2242

A2243

Worker's
Party of
Korea,
65th
Anniv.
A2244

Designs: 10w, Flag of Worker's Party.
No. 4953 — Kim Il Sung: a, 20w, On naval vessel. b, 25w, At rail yard. c, 50w, With farmers. d, 50w, At technology display. e, 60w, With fabric vendor.
70w, Kim Il Sung with party flag.

**2010, Oct. 10**     **Litho.**     **Perf. 11¾**
4952 A2242 10w multi   .30 .30
4953 A2243   Sheet of 6, #4952,
    4953a-4953e   3.75 1.75
    **Souvenir Sheet**
     **Perf. 13½**
4954 A2244 70w multi   1.25 .60

A2245

Visit of Kim Jong II to People's Republic of China A2246

Designs: No. 4955, Kim Jong II shaking hands with Chinese Pres. Hu Jintao.
No. 4956 — Kim Jong II: a, 30w, Signing guestbook at Julin Middle School. b, 42w, Inspecting railway coach. c, 70w, Holding bottle at food processing plant.

**2010, Oct. 28    Litho.    Perf. 11½x12**
4955 A2245 70w multi                1.25   .65
**Perf. 11½**
4956 A2246    Sheet of 3, #a-c, +
          5 labels                  2.75  1.25

Conference of Worker's Party of Korea, Pyongyang — A2247

**2010, Oct. 30                Perf. 13¼**
4957 A2247 30w multi                 .60   .30

New Year 2011 (Juche 100) — A2248

**2011, Jan. 1                    Litho.**
4958 A2248 10w multi                 .30   .30

Souvenir Sheet

Year of the Rabbit A2249

Rabbits — No. 4959: a, 70w, Two rabbits. b, 140w, Two rabbits, diff.

**2011, Jan. 5                Perf. 11½**
4959 A2249    Sheet of 2, #a-b      4.75  1.90
  c.    Booklet pane of 2, #4959a-
         4959b, + 2 labels           5.00   —
       Complete booklet, #4959c      5.00
  d.    Like #4959, with inscriptions
         and emblems added in
         sheet margin                5.25  1.90

Complete booklet sold for 224w.
Issued: No. 4959d, 3/3/12. Added inscriptions on No. 4959d are for Frimung 2012 and Huddex 2012 Stamp Shows, Huddinge, Sweden.

Souvenir Sheet

Indipex 2011 World Philatelic Exhibition, New Delhi — A2250

**2011, Feb. 12                Perf. 13¼**
4960 A2250 70w multi                1.75   .65

Zoo Animals Given to Kim Jong II as Gifts — A2251

Designs: 30w, Capra hircus. 42w, Cercopithecus aethiops. 112w, Cebuella pygmaea. 125w, Hystrix indica, horiz.

**2011, Feb. 16                Perf. 11½**
4961-4964 A2251    Set of 4         7.00  2.75
  4964a    Horiz. strip of 4, #4961-
            4964                     7.25  2.75
  4964b    Booklet pane of 4, #4961-
            4964                     7.25   —
          Complete booklet, #4964b   7.50

Kim Jong II, 69th birthday. Nos. 4961-4964 were printed in sheets of 8, containing 2 of each stamp, + 3 labels. Complete booklet sold for 323w.

Fourth International Martial Arts Games, Tallinn, Estonia — A2252

No. 4965: a, 42w, Emblem. b, 56w, Karate. c, 70w, Pankration. d, 112w, Muaythai.
No. 4966, 70w, Taekwondo.

**2011, Feb. 23                  Litho.**
4965 A2252    Sheet of 4, #a-d, +
            4 labels                 5.25  2.60
**Souvenir Sheet**
4966 A2252 70w multi + label        1.25   .65

Joint Editorials of State Newspapers A2253

Red flag at upper left and: No. 4967, 10w, Two women, three men and pink ribbon. No. 4968, 10w, Man with arm extended, symbols of progress. 30w, Farmer holding sheaf of wheat, train, truck, tractor and food. 70w, Soldiers and flags. 112w, Two men and woman punching missile, map of Korea, vert.

**2011, Feb. 25                Perf. 13¼**
4967-4971 A2253    Set of 5         5.75  2.10

Birds — A2254

Designs: 30w, Paradisaea raggiana. 42w, Cygnus olor. 75w, Pulsatrix perspicillata. 133w, Goura victoria.

**2011, Mar. 2                 Perf. 11½**
4972-4975 A2254    Set of 4         2.00  2.75
  4975a    Booklet pane of 4, #4972-
            4975                     7.25
          Complete booklet, #4975a   7.25

Nos. 4972-4975 were printed in sheets of 8 containing 2 of each stamp + 4 labels. Complete booklet sold for 294w.

Flag of North Korea, Magnolia Flowers, North Korea No. 4 — A2255

**2011, Mar. 12                Perf. 13¼**
4976 A2255 30w multi                 .70   .30

First North Korean postage stamps, 65th anniv.

Miniature Sheets

A2256

Treaty on Friendship Between North Korea and People's Republic of China, 50th Anniv. — A2257

No. 4977: a, Mao Zedong at microphones proclaiming foundation of People's Republic of China, fireworks (30x42mm). b, Mao Zedong and Pres. Kim II Sung shaking hands, 1975 (54x45mm). c, Mao Zedong at microphone holding Chinese coat of arms (30x42mm). d, Mao Zedong at microphone in front of crowd (56x38mm). e, Mao Zedong in front of Chinese flag (28x38mm). f, Mao Zedong and Deng Xiaoping shaking hands (56x38mm).
No. 4978: a, Mao Zedong and Pend Dehuai, wearing cap (45x33mm). b, Mao Zedong and Pres. Kim II Sung shaking hands (36x45mm). c, Mao Zedong and Chen Yi at table with cup and saucer (45x33mm). d, Mao Zedong and Liu Shaoqi, pointing (56x38mm). e, Mao Zedong and Zhou Enlai, teapot and glasses on table (28x38mm). f, Mao Zedong and Zhu De clapping (56x38mm).

**Perf. 13¼ (#4977a-4977c, 4978a-4978c), 11½**
**2011, Mar. 15**
4977 A2256 10w Sheet of 6, #a-f    1.50   .50
4978 A2257 10w Sheet of 6, #a-f    1.50   .45

Souvenir Sheet

Intl. Year of Volunteers — A2258

No. 4979 — Red Cross and: a, 30w, Disaster risk reduction. b, 42w, Promotion activities. c, Emergency relief activities.

**2011, Mar. 31    Litho.    Perf. 13¼**
4979 A2258    Sheet of 3, #a-c, +
            2 labels                 3.50  1.25

Apples on Branch A2259

Kim II Sung at Fruit Orchard A2260

**2011, Apr. 7                  Perf. 12**
4980 A2259 30w multi                 .60   .30
**Souvenir Sheet**
**Perf. 11¾**
4981 A2260 70w multi                1.90   .65

Pukchong Enlarged Meeting of the Presidium of the Central Committee of the Workers' Party of Korea, 50th anniv.

Flowers A2261

No. 4982: a, 30w, Kimilsungia. b, 42w, Callistephus chinensis. c, 70w, Iris ensata var. hortensis. d, 98w, Rosa hybrida. e, 112w, Lilium hybridum cv. Enchantment.

**2011, Apr. 15                Perf. 13**
4982 A2261    Sheet of 5, #a-e      7.00  3.25
  f.    Booklet pane of 5, #4982a-
         4982e                       7.25   —
       Complete booklet, #4982f      7.25

Birthday of Pres. Kim II Sung. No. 4982f sold for 366w.

Sites in Pyongyang A2262

Designs: 30w, Yonggwang Metro Station. 42w, Mangyongdae School Children's Palace. 56w, May Day Stadium. 70w, People's Palace of Culture. 84w, Arch of Triumph. 98w, State Theater. 112w, Party Founding Museum. 140w, Birthpace of Pres. Kim II Sung.

**2011, Apr. 20              Perf. 12¼x11¾**
4983-4990 A2262    Set of 8        12.50  5.50
  4990a    Booklet pane of 8, #4983-
            4990                    12.50
          Complete booklet, #4990a  12.50

No. 4990a sold for 646w.

Magnolia Seiboldii — A2263

Flowers A2264

No. 4992: a, 10w, Kimilsungia. b, 30w, Kimjongilia. c, 42w, Paeonia suffructicosa.

**2011, Apr. 28**            **Perf. 13¼**
4991 A2263 30w multi            .60   .30
**Souvenir Sheet**
**Perf.**
4992 A2264  Sheet of 3, #a-c, +
              3 labels        1.40   .75
  d.   Booklet pane of 4, #4991,
       4992a-4992c            2.40
       Complete booklet, #4992d   2.40
2011 Intl. Horticultural Exposition, Xi'an, People's Republic of China. Complete booklet sold for 126w.

**Miniature Sheet**

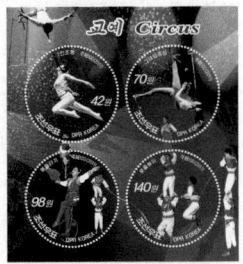

Circus Performers — A2265

No. 4993: a, 42w, Woman suspended by neck. b, 70w, Woman juggling while hanging from trapeze. c, 98w, Unicyclist, members of rope skipping act. d, 140w, Rope skipping act.

**2011, May 5**              **Perf.**
4993 A2265  Sheet of 4, #a-d  8.50  3.25

**Souvenir Sheet**

Chollima Statue, Pyongyang — A2266

**2011, May 20**         **Perf. 11¾x12¼**
4994 A2266 98w multi          2.40   .85

**Souvenir Sheet**

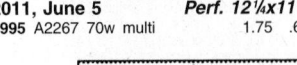

Apples, Taedonggang Combined Fruit Farm — A2267

**2011, June 5**         **Perf. 12¼x11¾**
4995 A2267 70w multi          1.75   .65

Orchids
A2268

No. 4996: a, 10w, Vanda hybrida. b, 30w, Laeliocattleya. c, 70w, Laelia gouldiana. d, 142w, Phalaenopsis.

**2011, June 20**            **Perf. 13¼**
4996 A2268  Block or horiz.
              strip of 4, #a-d  4.75  2.40
  e.   Booklet pane of 4, #4996a-
       4996d                  5.25   —
       Complete booklet, #4996e  5.50
     No. 4996e sold for 266w.

 A2269

 A2270
 A2271
 A2272
 A2273
 A2274
 A2275
 A2276
 A2277
A2278
A2279
 A2280
 A2281

 A2282
 A2283
 A2284
A2285
A2286
A2287
A2288
 A2289
A2290
A2291
 A2292
 A2293

 A2294

Pres. Kim Il Sung (1912-94) — A2295

Various paintings depicting scenes in the life of Kim Il Sung.
No. 5020: a, 25w, October Morning (64x42mm). b, 30w, Kim Il Sung Drawing the Brush Into the Party's Emblem (45x36mm). c, 45w, Kim Il Sung Making Report at Inaugural Conference of the Central Organizational Committee of the Communist Party of North Korea (45x36mm).

**2011, July 5   Litho.   Perf. 13½**
4997 A2269 10w multi + label   .30   .30
4998 A2270 10w multi + label   .30   .30
4999 A2271 10w multi + label   .30   .30
5000 A2272 30w multi + label   .70   .30
5001 A2273 30w multi + label   .70   .30
5002 A2274 30w multi + label   .70   .30
5003 A2275 30w multi + label   .70   .30
5004 A2276 30w multi + label   .70   .30
5005 A2277 30w multi + label   .70   .30
5006 A2278 30w multi + label   .70   .30
5007 A2279 30w multi + label   .70   .30
5008 A2280 30w multi + label   .70   .30
5009 A2281 30w multi + label   .70   .30
5010 A2282 42w multi + label  1.00   .35
5011 A2283 42w multi + label  1.00   .35
5012 A2284 42w multi + label  1.00   .35
5013 A2285 42w multi + label  1.00   .35
5014 A2286 42w multi + label  1.00   .35
5015 A2287 42w multi + label  1.00   .35
5016 A2288 42w multi + label  1.00   .35
5017 A2289 42w multi + label  1.00   .35
5018 A2290 42w multi + label  1.00   .35
5019 A2291 42w multi + label  1.00   .35
   Nos. 4997-5019 (23)       17.90  7.40
**Miniature Sheet**
**Perf. 12x11½ (#5020a), 13½**
5020 A2292  Sheet of 3, #a-c, +
              label           1.75   .85
**Souvenir Sheets**
**Perf. 13½**
5021 A2293 40w multi           .85   .35
**Perf. 11¾**
5022 A2294 50w multi          1.10   .45
5023 A2295 60w multi          1.25   .55
   Nos. 5021-5023 (3)         3.20  1.35

**Souvenir Sheets**

 A2296
 A2297

Visit of Kim Jong Il to People's Republic of China
A2298

**2011, July 15  Litho.  Perf. 12¼x11¾**
5024 A2296 90w multi          2.50   .80

5025　A2297　90w multi　　　　2.50　.80
**Perf. 11¾**
5026　A2298　90w multi + label　　2.00　.80
*Nos. 5024-5026 (3)*　　　　7.00　2.40

Intl. Year of
Chemistry — A2299

**2011, July 29**　　　**Perf. 13½x13¼**
5027　A2299　50w multi　　　　1.25　.55

Camellias
and Birds
A2300

No. 5028: a, Denomination at LL. b, Denomination at UR.

**2011, July 30**　　　**Perf. 11½**
5028　A2300　20w Horiz. pair, #a-b 2.00　.35

**Souvenir Sheet**

Intl. Year
of
Forests
A2301

**2011, July 30**　　　**Perf. 13¼**
5029　A2301　100w multi　　　2.40　.90

**Souvenir Sheet**

Diplomatic Relations Between North
Korea and the European Union, 10th
Anniv. — A2302

**2011, Aug. 1**　　　**Perf. 12x11½**
5030　A2302　140w multi　　　3.50　1.75

**Miniature Sheet**

Cacti
and
Insects
A2303

No. 5031: a, 30w, Gymnocalycium schuetzi-
anum and bee. b, 70w, Rebutia euanthema
and butterfly. c, 98w, Rebutia xanthocarpa and
grasshopper. d, 112w, Notocactus herteri and
beetle.

**2011, Aug. 5**　　　**Perf. 11½**
5031　A2303　Sheet of 4, #a-d　7.25　2.75
*e.*　Booklet pane of 4, #5031a-
　　　5031d　　　　　7.50
　　Complete booklet, #5031e　7.75
Complete booklet sold for 324w.

---

2018 World Cup Soccer
Championships, Russia — A2304

Various soccer players with city names
inscribed at side: No. 5032, 200w, Nizhniy
Novgorod. No. 5033, 200w, Krasnodar. No.
5034, 200w, Kaliningrad. No. 5035, 200w,
Moscow. No. 5036, 200w, Sochi. No. 5037,
200w, Rostov-na-Donu. No. 5038, 200w, St.
Petersburg.

**2011, Aug. 31**　　**Stamps + Labels**
5032-5038　A2304　Set of 7　35.00　11.50
5038a　Sheet of 7, #5032-5038, +
　　　2 labels　　　　35.00　11.50
5038b　Booklet pane of 7, #5032-
　　　5038, without labels　35.00
　　Complete booklet, #5038b　35.00
Complete booklet sold for 1414w.

Dinosaurs
A2305

No. 5039: a, Megalosaurus bucklandi. b,
Staurikosaurus pricei. c, Chasmosaurus belli.

**2011, Sept. 5**　　　**Perf. 12¼x11¾**
5039　Horiz. strip of 3　　5.25　2.60
*a.*　A2305　42w multi　　.75　.35
*b.*　A2305　98w multi　　1.75　.85
*c.*　A2305　140w multi　　2.50　1.25
*d.*　Booklet pane of 3, #5039a-5039c　5.50
　　Complete booklet, #5039d　5.50
Complete booklet sold for 294w.

World Leisure
Expo 2011,
Hangzhou,
People's
Republic of
China — A2306

Emblems and: 10w, Samil Lagoon. 30w,
Xihu.

**2011, Sept. 17**　　　**Perf. 13¼**
5040-5041　A2306　Set of 2　　.90　.35

Fire
Engines
A2307

No. 5042: a, 70w, Mercedes-Benz fire
engine. b, 98w, ZIL ladder truck.
No. 5043: a, 30w, ZIL fire engine. b, 140w,
Mercedes-Benz ladder truck.

**2011, Oct. 5**　　　**Perf. 13¼**
5042　A2307　Sheet of 2, #a-b, +
　　　　2 labels　　　4.00　1.40
5043　A2307　Sheet of 2, #a-b, +
　　　　2 labels　　　4.00　1.40
*c.*　Booklet pane of 4, #5042a-
　　　5042b, 5043a-5043b, + 2 la-
　　　bels　　　　　8.75
　　Complete booklet, #5043c　8.75
Complete booklet sold for 352w.

Famous
People — A2308

---

Designs: 10w, Pak Yon (1378-1458). musician. 30w, Sinsa Im Dang (1504-51), painter.
50w, Jong Yak Yong (1762-1836), philosopher.
70w, Ryu Rin Sok (1842-1915), military
leader.

**2011, Oct. 15**
5044-5047　A2308　Set of 4　3.50　1.40

**Souvenir Sheet**

Kim Jong Il and Chinese State
Councilor Dai Bingguo — A2309

**2011, Oct. 18**
5048　A2309　70w multi　　1.75　1.25

**Souvenir Sheets**

A2310

A2311

Visit of
Kim
Jong Il to
Russia
A2312

**2011, Oct. 18　Litho.　Perf. 11½x12**
5049　A2310　70w multi　　—　—
**Perf. 13¼**
5050　A2311　70w multi　　—　—
5051　A2312　70w multi　　—　—

A2313

A2314

---

A2315

A2316

A2317... 

Friendship Between North Korea and
People's Republic of China — A2317

Design: No. 5052, 10w, Mao Zedong Going
to Anyuan. No. 5053: a, 10w, Mao Zedong. b,
10w, Mao Zedong in army vehicle reviewing
troops. c, 10w, Mao Zedong writing. d, 30w,
Kim Il Sung in suit and tie. e, 30w, Kim Il Sung
and Mao Zedong shaking hands. f, 30w, Kim Il
Sung and Mao Zedong standing at military
parade.
No. 5054: a, 10w, Deng Xiaoping. b, 10w,
Deng Xiaoping in automobile reviewing troops.
c, 10w, Deng Xiaoping saluting. d, 30w, Kim Il
Sung in black shirt. e, 30w, Deng Xiaoping
and Kim Il Sung embracing. f, 30w, Deng Xiaoping
and Kim Il Sung standing.
No. 5055: a, 10w, Jiang Zemin. b, 10w,
Jiang Zemin in automobile reviewing troops. c,
10w, Jiang Zemin at ceremony returning Hong
Kong to China. d, 30w, Kim Jong Il wearing
glasses. e, 30w, Kim Jong Il and Jiang Zemin
shaking hands. f, 30w, Jiang Zemin and Kim
Jong Il shaking hands, cameramen.
No. 5056: a, 10w, Hu Jintao. b, 10w, Hu
Jintao in automobile reviewing troops. c, 10w,
Hu Jintaou holding Olympic torch. d, 30w, Kim
Jong Il without glasses. e, 30w, Hu Jintao
walking with Kim Jong Il. f, 30w, Kim Jong Il
and Hu Jintao shaking hands.

**Perf. 13¼ (#5052), 11¾x12¼**
**2011, Oct. 28**　　　**Litho.**
5052　A2313　10w multi　　.30　.30
**Miniature Sheets**
5053　A2314　Sheet of 6, #a-f　3.00　2.25
5054　A2315　Sheet of 6, #a-f　3.00　2.25
5055　A2316　Sheet of 6, #a-f　3.00　2.25
5056　A2317　Sheet of 6, #a-f　3.00　2.25
*Nos. 5052-5056 (5)*　　12.30　9.30

Publication of
Taedongyojido Map
of Korea by Kim
Jong Ho, 150th
Anniv. — A2318

**2011, Nov. 5**　　　**Perf. 13¼**
5057　A2318　98w multi　　2.40　.90

Minerals
A2319

Designs: 30w, Limonite, crucible with molten metal. 42w, Kotoite, rocket. 58w, Wollastonite, ceramic vases. 98w, Stibnite, tractor and parts.

**2011, Dec. 5**
5058-5061 A2319 Set of 4    5.75 2.10
5061a   Booklet pane of 4, #5057-5060   6.00 —
  Complete booklet, #5060a   6.00 —
Complete booklet sold for 242w.

A2320

Appointment of Kim Jong Il as Supreme Commander of Army, 20th Anniv. — A2321

No. 5062 — Kim Jong Il and: a, 10w, Pilots. b, 30w, Tank soldiers. c, 70w, Sailors. d, 98w, Soldiers carrying packs.
No. 5063, Kim Jong Il and military officer reviewing troops in military vehicle.

**2011, Dec. 24**
5062 A2320   Sheet of 4, #a-d, + central label   3.75 1.90
**Souvenir Sheet**
**Perf. 11¾**
5063 A2321 98w multi   2.40 1.90

Souvenir Sheets

Kim Jong Il (1942-2011) — A2322

Kim Jong Il and Son, Kim Jong Un A2323

**2011, Dec. 29**   **Perf. 12¼x11¾**
5064 A2322 70w multi   1.50 .70
5065 A2323 70w multi   1.50 .70

New Year 2012 — A2324

**2012, Jan. 1**   **Perf. 13¼**
5066 A2324 10w multi   .30 .30

Dragons A2325

No. 5067 — Various dragons: a, 10w. b, 30w. c, 60w.

**2012, Jan. 5**   **Perf. 11½**
5067 A2325   Horiz. strip of 3, #a-c   2.40 1.00
No. 5067 was printed in sheets containing two strips of 3.

Mt. Paektu A2326

Designs: 20w, Lake Samji and Mt. Paektu. 30w, Lake Chon on Mt. Paektu.

**2012, Jan. 17**   **Perf. 12¼x11¾**
5068-5069 A2326 Set of 2   1.20 .50

Butterflies — A2327

No. 5070: a, 30w, Pachliopta coon. b, 70w, Agrias pericles. c, 90w, Buthanitis lidderdalei. d, 120w, Cethosia biblis.

**2012, Jan. 25**   **Perf. 11½**
5070 A2327   Block of 4, #a-d   7.00 3.00
e.   Booklet pane of 4, #5070a-5070d, + 2 labels   7.25 —
  Complete booklet, #5070e   7.25
Complete booklet sold for 324w.

Joint Editorials of State Newspapers A2328

Red flag at upper left and: No. 5071, 10w, Birthplace of Kim Il Sung, torch, soldier, workers. No. 5072, 10w, City buildings, packaged foods, crops and farm animals, horiz. No. 5073, 30w, Torch, symbols of industry, train and truck. No. 5074, 30w, Soldier holding rifle with bayonet, flags, missiles. 40w, Fist squashing people, U.S. Capitol. 50w, Dove, North Korea highlighted on map, rainbow.

**2012, Jan. 27**   **Perf. 13¼**
5071-5076 A2328 Set of 6   3.50 1.40

Calls for Victory by Central Committee and Central Military Commission A2329

**2012, Jan. 30**   **Litho.**
5077 A2329 10w multi   .30 .30

Architecture — A2330

Designs: 60w, Kopernik House, Moscow, Mansudae Street Apartment Buildings, Pyongyang. 100w, Patriarch House, Moscow, East Pyongyang Grand Theater. No. 5080, 140w, Grand People's Study House, Pyongyang, Gnezdikovskiy Palace, Moscow. 190w, Apartement house, Pyongyang, Egg House, Moscow. 210w, Hyangsan Hotel, Pyongyang, Weber Villa, Moscow.
No. 5083, 140w, Patriarch House, Moscow and National Theater, Pyongyang at night.

**2012, Jan. 30**   **Perf. 12**
5078-5082 A2330 Set of 5   16.00 6.25
**Souvenir Sheet**
**Perf. 12x11½**
5083 A2330 140w multi   3.25 1.40
a.   Souvenir sheet of 6, #5078-5083, perf. 12x11½, + 3 labels   16.50 6.75
b.   Booklet pane of 6, #5078-5083, perf. 12x11½   16.50
  Complete booklet, #5083b   16.50
Nos. 5078-5082 were each printed in sheets of 5 + label. Complete booklet sold for 854w.

A2331

A2332

Birthday of Kim Jong Il (1942-2011) — A2333

Designs: 10w, Kimjongilia flower.
No. 5085: a, 40w, Kim Jong Il, soldiers and artillery. 70w, Kim Jong Il, people with flags and sled.
No. 5085, 70w, Kimg Jong Il.

**2012, Feb. 16**   **Perf. 13¼**
5084 A2331 10w multi   .30 .30
5085 A2332   Sheet of 2, #a-b, + 3 labels   2.75 1.00
**Souvenir Sheet**
**Perf. 11½x12**
5086 A2333 70w multi   1.75 .70

Ceramics — A2334

Designs: 30w, Container with lotus flower pattern. 40w, Container with dragon and cloud design.
70w, Pitcher and bowl.

**2012, Mar. 10**   **Perf. 11½**
**Stamps + Labels**
5087-5088 A2334 Set of 2   1.75 .70
**Souvenir Sheet**
5089 A2334 70w multi + label   1.75 .70
a.   Booklet pane of 3, #5087-5089, + 7 labels   5.25 —
  Complete booklet, #5089a   5.25
Complete booklet sold for 154w.

Posthumous Granting of Title of Generalissimo to Kim Jong Il — A2335

**2012, Mar. 20**   **Perf. 13¼**
5090 A2335 10w multi   .30 .30

Birthplace of Kim Jong Il — A2336

**2012, Mar. 20**   **Perf. 13¼**
5091 A2336 10w multi   .30 .30
Designation of Feb. 16 (birthday of Kim Jong Il) as Day of the Shining Star.

Floriade 2012 World Horticultural Expo, Venlo, Netherlands — A2337

**2012, Mar. 22**   **Litho.**
5092 A2337 30w multi   .50 .30

Korean National Association, 95th Anniv. A2338

**2012, Mar. 23**   **Perf. 13¼**
5093 A2338 30w citron   .85 .30

Opening of Korean Stamp Museum, Pyongyang A2339

**2012, Apr. 15**   **Perf. 11½**
5094 A2339 10w multi   .30 .30

A2340

A2341

A2342

A2343

A2344

A2345

A2346

A2347

A2348

A2349

Pres. Kim Il Sung (1912-94) — A2350

No. 5102 — Kim Il Sung: a, With adults and children. b, Wearing hat, addressing men. c, Seated behind microphone. d, With workers at plant.
No. 5103 — Kim Il Sung: a, At trainyard. b, With workers at textile factory. c, Holding ear of corn, with farmers in field. d, Holding ear of corn, with agricultural scientists.
No. 5104 — Kim Il Sung: a, With pilots. b, Seated, talking to soldiers. c, With soldiers inspecting artillery. d, Wearing white jacket, walking with military.

**2012, Apr. 15**                     **Perf. 11½**
| | | | | |
|---|---|---|---|---|
| 5095 | A2340 | 30w multi + label | .90 | .30 |
| 5096 | A2341 | 30w multi + label | .90 | .30 |
| 5097 | A2342 | 30w multi + label | .90 | .30 |
| 5098 | A2343 | 30w multi + label | .90 | .30 |
| 5099 | A2344 | 30w multi + label | .90 | .30 |
| 5100 | A2345 | 30w multi + label | .90 | .30 |
| 5101 | A2346 | 30w multi + label | .90 | .30 |
| | | Nos. 5095-5101 (7) | 6.30 | 2.10 |

**Miniature Sheets**
**Perf. 13¼**
| | | | | |
|---|---|---|---|---|
| 5102 | A2347 | 20w Sheet of 4, #a-d | 2.10 | .70 |
| 5103 | A2348 | 30w Sheet of 4, #a-d | 3.00 | 1.10 |
| 5104 | A2349 | 40w Sheet of 4, #a-d | 3.75 | 1.40 |
| | | Nos. 5102-5104 (3) | 8.85 | 3.20 |

**Souvenir Sheet**
**Perf. 11¾**
| | | | | |
|---|---|---|---|---|
| 5105 | A2350 | 70w multi | 1.75 | 1.00 |

A2351

A2352

Pres. Kim Il Sung (1912-94) — A2353

Designs: 10w, Birthplace of Kim Il Sung, flowers.
No. 5107: a, 70w, Kim Il Sung in field with children. b, 100w, Kim Il Sung seated, holding hand of girl.
No. 5108, 100w, Kim Il Sung at birthplace.

**2012, Apr. 15**                     **Perf. 13¼**
| | | | | |
|---|---|---|---|---|
| 5106 | A2351 | 10w multi | .40 | .30 |

**Miniature Sheet**
**Perf. 11¾**
| | | | | |
|---|---|---|---|---|
| 5107 | A2352 | Sheet of 2, #a-b | 3.75 | 1.40 |

**Souvenir Sheet**
**Perf. 11½x12**
| | | | | |
|---|---|---|---|---|
| 5108 | A2353 | 100w multi | 2.40 | 1.00 |

Souvenir Sheet

Kang Pan Sok (1892-1932), Mother of Kim Il Sung — A2354

**2012, Apr. 21**                     **Perf. 11¾**
| | | | | |
|---|---|---|---|---|
| 5109 | A2354 | 70w multi | 1.75 | .70 |

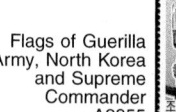

Flags of Guerilla Army, North Korea and Supreme Commander A2355

Kim Il Sung in Military Uniform A2356

**2012, Apr. 25**                     **Perf. 13¼**
| | | | | |
|---|---|---|---|---|
| 5110 | A2355 | 30w multi | .90 | .30 |

**Souvenir Sheet**
**Perf. 11½x12**
| | | | | |
|---|---|---|---|---|
| 5111 | A2356 | 70w multi | 1.75 | .70 |

Korean People's Army, 80th anniv.

Roses — A2357

Color of roses: 30w, Pink and white. 50w, Yellow. 70w, Red.

**2012, Apr. 30**                     **Perf. 12½**
| | | | | |
|---|---|---|---|---|
| 5112-5114 | A2357 | Set of 3 | 3.50 | 1.50 |
| 5114a | | Booklet pane of 3, #5112-5114, + label | 3.75 | — |
| | | Complete booklet, #5114a | 4.00 | |

Values are for stamps with surrounding selvage. Complete booklet sold for 164w.

Principles for National Reunification, 40th Anniv. — A2358

**2012, May 3**                       **Perf. 11½**
| | | | | |
|---|---|---|---|---|
| 5115 | A2358 | 50w red & blue | 1.10 | .50 |

2012 Summer Olympics, London — A2359

Designs: 10w, Track and field. 30w, Judo. 70w, Rhythmic gymnastics. 110w, Swimming and diving.

**2012, May 3**                       **Perf. 13¼**
| | | | | |
|---|---|---|---|---|
| 5116-5119 | A2359 | Set of 4 | 5.00 | 2.10 |
| 5119a | | Booklet pane of 4, #5116-5119 | 5.25 | — |
| | | Complete booklet, #5119a | 5.50 | |

Complete booklet sold for 234w.

Souvenir Sheet

Erection of Statues to Kim Il Sung and Kim Jong Il in Pyongyang — A2360

**2012, May 30**
| | | | | |
|---|---|---|---|---|
| 5120 | A2360 | 50w multi | 1.25 | .50 |

Locomotives A2361

Designs: 50w, Songun Pulgungi 1. 70w, Velaro D407. 90w, Renfe 112.

**2012, May 31**
| | | | | |
|---|---|---|---|---|
| 5121-5123 | A2361 | Set of 3 | 5.00 | 1.90 |
| 5123a | | Booklet pane of 3, #5121-5123 | 5.25 | — |
| | | Complete booklet, #5123a | 5.25 | |

Complete booklet sold for 224w.

Battle of Pochonbo, 75th Anniv. — A2362

**2012, June 4**
| | | | | |
|---|---|---|---|---|
| 5124 | A2362 | 30w multi | .85 | .30 |

Souvenir Sheet

2012 Planete Timbres Stamp Exhibition, Paris — A2363

**2012, June 9**                      **Perf. 12¼x11¾**
| | | | | |
|---|---|---|---|---|
| 5125 | A2363 | 70w multi | 1.75 | .70 |

2012 World Stamp Championships, Jakarta, Indonesia — A2364

**2012, June 18**                     **Perf. 11½**
| | | | | |
|---|---|---|---|---|
| 5126 | A2364 | 30w multi | .75 | .30 |

Birds — A2365

Designs: 50w, Fringilla montifringilla. 70w, Zosterops erythropleura. 90w, Uragus sibiricus.

**2012, June 30**     **Litho.**
5127-5129 A2365   Set of 3   4.75 1.75
5129a    Booklet pane of 3, #5127-
     5129, + label    5.00 —
   Complete booklet, #5129a   5.00 —

Complete booklet sold for 224w.

Free Universal
Medical System,
60th Anniv. — A2366

**2012, July 5**     **Perf. 13¼**
5130 A2366 30w multi    .90 .30

**Souvenir Sheets**

Mao Zedong (1893-1976) and
Poetry — A2367

Kim Il Sung (1912-94) and
Quotes — A2368

No. 5131: a, The Yellow Crane Pavilion, poem by Mao Zedong (character at UL a diagonal line) (34x52mm). b, Mao Zedong writing (54x42mm). c, Huichang, poem by Mao Zedong (complex character with vertical line at UL).

No. 5132: a, 7½ lines of text from reminiscences of Kim Il Sung, and signature (34x52mm). b, Kim Il Sung writing (54x42mm). c, 8 lines of text from reminiscences of Kim Il Sung, and signature (34x52mm).

***Perf. 11¾x12¼, 13¼ (#5131b, 5132b)***
**2012, July 15**
5131 A2367 10w Sheet of 3, #a-c .60 .30
5132 A2368 30w Sheet of 3, #a-c 1.60 .80

**Souvenir Sheet**

Fourth Conference of the Korean
Workers' Party — A2369

No. 5133: a, Kim Jong Il wearing glasses (1941-2011). b, Kim Jong Un.

**2012, July 20**    **Perf. 11¾x12¼**
5133 A2369 30w Sheet of 2, #a-b 1.50 .60

A2370

Korean Children's Union, 66th
Anniv. — A2371

**2012, Aug. 10**     **Perf. 13¼**
5134 A2370 10w multi    .30 .30
**Souvenir Sheet**
5135 A2371 70w multi    1.60 .65

Mother's
Day — A2372

**2012, Sept. 20**    **Perf. 11½**
5136 A2372 10w multi    .30 .30

**Miniature Sheets**

A2373

Poetry of Mao Zedong (1893-
1976) — A2374

No. 5137: a, The People's Liberation Army Captures Nanjing (5½ lines) (34x52mm). b, Swimming (large white areas at UL and LR) (54x42mm). c, Beidaihe (6 full long lines of characters, 2 shorter lines at sides) (34x52mm). d, The Long March (3mm from line at right to frame) (84x21mm). e, Mt. Liupan (6mm from line at right to frame) (84x21mm).

No. 5138: a, Changsha (line at left with 2 characters) (54x42mm). b, Reply to Comrade Guo Moruo (white area in middle of poem (54x42mm). c, Snow (line at right three characters) (63x27mm). d, Loushan Pass (12 lines) (63x27mm). e, In Praise of the Photo Taken by Comrade Lijin of the Fairy Cave at Mt. Lushan (second line from left is single character) (63x27mm). f, The Double Ninth (13 lines with large whtie areas at top and bottom) (63x27mm).

***Perf. 11¾x12¼ (#5137a, 5137c), 13¼***
**2012, Sept. 25**
5137 A2373 10w Sheet of 5, #a-e 1.10 .50
5138 A2374 10w Sheet of 6, #a-f 2.00 .60
Beijing 2012 Intl. Stamp and Coin Exposition.

Giant Pandas — A2375

Designs: 70w, Panda on branch. 90w, Adult and juvenile panda.
120w, Two adult pandas, horiz.

**2012, Dec. 14**    **Litho.**   **Perf. 11½**
5139-5140 A2375 Set of 2   2.75 1.50
**Souvenir Sheet**
    **Perf. 13½**
5141 A2375 120w multi    2.25 1.10
No. 5141 contains one 90x42mm stamp.

Compulsory
Education
A2376

**2012, Dec. 15**    **Litho.**   **Perf. 13¼**
5142 A2376 10w multi    .30 .30

**Souvenir Sheets**

A2377

Kim Jong Il (1942-2011) — A2378

**2012, Dec. 17**   **Litho.**   **Perf. 11½x12**
5143 A2377 50w multi    1.10 .50
    **Perf. 13¼**
5144 A2378 50w multi    1.10 .50

**Souvenir Sheet**

Kim Jong Suk (1917-49) — A2379

**2012, Dec. 24**     **Perf.**
5145 A2379 70w multi    1.75 .65

Constitution, 40th
Anniv. — A2380

**2012, Dec. 27**     **Perf. 13¼**
5146 A2380 30w multi    .70 .30

**Souvenir Sheet**

Launch of Kwangmyongsong 3-2
Satellite — A2381

**2012, Dec. 30**   **Litho.**   **Perf. 13¼**
5147 A2381 50w multi    1.00 .45

New Year
2013
A2382

**2013, Jan. 1**   **Litho.**   **Perf. 11¾**
5148 A2382 10w multi    .25 .25

Stylized
Snake — A2383

**2013, Jan. 5**   **Litho.**   **Perf. 11½**
5149 A2383 10w multi    .25 .25
No. 5149 was printed in sheets of 16 + 4 labels.

Sports — A2384

Designs: 30w, Tennis. 50w, Cricket. 70w, Cycling. 90w, Rugby.

**2013, Jan. 20**   **Litho.**   **Perf. 13¼**
5150-5153 A2384 Set of 4   3.75 1.90
5153a   Booklet pane of 4, #5150-
    5153   4.00 —
   Complete booklet, #5153a   4.00 —
Complete booklet sold of 254w.

A2386

A2387

Kim Jong Il (1942-2011) — A2388

Desings: 5154, Kim Jong Il as child, in oval frame. 5155, shown.

**2013, Feb. 16　Litho.　Perf. 11¾**
5154　A2386　10w multi　.25　.25
5155　A2386　10w multi　.25　.25

**Souvenir Sheets**
5156　A2387　50w multi　.80　.40
5157　A2388　50w multi　.80　.40

New Year's Speech — A2389

Emblem and: No. 5158, 10w, Man with arm extended, rocket, sheaf of wheat, tower for electric lines, train, steel products. No. 5159, 10w, Woman, soldiers, flag, sculptures. No. 5160, 30w, Soccer player, city skyline, silhouettes of musicians and soldiers. No. 5161, 30w, Map of Korean Peninsula, doves.

**2013, Feb. 19　Litho.　Perf. 11½**
5158-5161　A2389　Set of 4　1.25　.60
5161a　Souvenir sheet of 4,
　　　#5158-5161　1.25　.60

**Souvenir Sheet**

Kim Jong Un Making New Year's Speech A2390

**2013, Feb. 19　Litho.　Perf. 11¾**
5162　A2390　50w multi　.80　.40

A2391

A2392

A2393

Military Posters in Korean Art Gallery, Pyongyang A2394

**2013, Feb. 25　Litho.　Perf. 11½**
5163　A2391　10w multi　.25　.25
5164　A2392　10w multi　.25　.25
5165　A2393　30w multi　.45　.25
5166　A2394　30w multi　.45　.25
　　　Nos. 5163-5166 (4)　1.40　1.00

International Red Cross, 150th Anniv. — A2395

**2013, Mar. 6　Litho.　Perf. 13¼**
5167　A2395　30w multi　.45　.25

**Miniature Sheet**

Marine Life A2396

No. 5168: a, 30w, Carcharodon carcharias (44mm diameter). b, 50w, Caretta caretta (38x28mm). c, 90w, Peprilus simillina (28x38mm). d, 110w, Hippocampus histrix (28x38mm).

**2013, Mar. 21　Litho.　Perf. 11½**
5168　A2396　Sheet of 4, #a-d　4.25　2.10
　e.　Booklet pane of 4, #5168a-
　　　5168d　4.50　—
　　　Complete booklet, #5168e　4.50

Complete booklet sold for 294w.

Election of Kim Jong Il as Chairman of National Defense Commission, 20th Anniv. — A2397

**2013, Apr. 9　Litho.　Perf. 13¼**
5169　A2397　30w multi　.45　.25

**Souvenir Sheet**

Monkeys A2398

No. 5170: a, 10w, Monkey. b, 20w, Adult and juvenile monkey.

**Litho. & Engr.**
**2013, Apr. 10　　　　Perf. 12**
5170　A2398　Sheet of 2, #a-b　.45　.25

Flowers — A2399

Designs: 30w, Zinnia elegans cv. Scarlet Flame. 50w, Celosia cristata. 70w, Dahlia x cultorum. 90w, Tropaeolum majus.

**2013, Apr. 15　Litho.　Perf. 13¼**
5171-5174　A2399　Set of 4　3.75　1.90
5174a　Booklet pane of 4, #5171-
　　　5174　4.00　—
　　　Complete booklet, #5174a　4.00

Birthday of Kim Il Sung. Nos. 5171-5174 were printed in sheets of 4 + 2 labels. Complete booklet sold for 254w.

Passage of Kumsusan Palace of the Sun Preservation Law — A2401

**2013, Apr. 25　Litho.　Perf. 13¼**
5176　A2401　30w multi　.45　.25

Values are for stamps with surrounding selvage.

Australia 2013 World Stamp Exhibition, Melbourne — A2402

**2013, May 10　Litho.　Perf. 11½**
5177　A2402　30w multi　.45　.25

**Miniature Sheet**

Owls A2404

No. 5179: a, 40w, Surnia ulula. b, 60w, Nyctea scandiaca. c, 80w, Athene noctua. d, 100w, Tyto alba.

**2013, May 22　Litho.　Perf. 13¼**
5179　A2404　Sheet of 8, 2 each
　　　#5179a-5179d,
　　　+ 4 labels　8.50　4.25
　e.　Booklet pane of 4, #5179a-
　　　5179d, + 2 labels　4.50　—
　　　Complete booklet, #5179e　4.50

Complete booklet sold for 294w.

**Souvenir Sheet**

Meeting of Kim Jong Il and Chinese Leaders A2405

No. 5180 — Meeting with Kim Jong Il at: a, Left. b, Right.

**2013, June 10　Litho.　Perf. 12x11½**
5180　A2405　30w Sheet of 2, #a-
　　　b, + 4 labels　.95　.45

**Souvenir Sheet**

Mt. Paektu A2406

No. 5181: a, Sun over Hyangdo Peak. b, Mountains surrounding Lake Chon. c, Shore of Lake Chon. d, Mt. Paektu, trees in foreground.

**2013, June 10　Litho.　Perf. 12x11½**
5181　A2406　10w Sheet of 4, #a-
　　　d, + 2 labels　.60　.30

Bees — A2407

Various bees and orchids: 30w, 70w, 110w.

**2013, June 12　Litho.　Perf. 13¼**
5182-5184　A2407　Set of 3　3.25　1.60
5184a　Booklet pane of 3, #5182-
　　　5184, + label　3.50　—
　　　Complete booklet, #5184a　3.50

Complete booklet sold for 224w.

A2408

Soldiers — A2409

**2013, June 25　Litho.　Perf. 13¼**
5185　A2408　10w multi　.25　.25
5186　A2409　150w multi　2.25　1.10

Arctic and Antarctic Animals A2410

Designs: 30w, Aptenodytes excelsior. 50w, Rangifer tarandus.

**2013, July 7　Litho.　　　Perf.**
5187-5188　A2410　Set of 2　—　—
5188a　Booklet pane of 2, #5187-
　　　5188, + 2 labels　—　—
　　　Complete booklet, #5188a　—

Nos. 5187-5188 were each printed in sheets of 3 + label.

**Souvenir Sheet**

Pyongyang Folk Park — A2411

No. 5189: a, Tower of the Juche Idea, Arch of Triumph. b, Pagoda at Kumgang Temple, vert.

**2013, July 20　Litho.　Perf. 11½**
5189　A2411　30w Sheet of 2, #a-b　.95　.45

Victory
Sculpture — A2413

Ceasefire in Korean War, 60th
Anniv. — A2514

Kim Il Sung Delivering Radio
Address — A2415

Kim Il
Sung at
Rally
A2416

No. 5195: a, 50w, Kim Il Sung. b, 70w, Kim
Il Sung and soldiers.

**Perf. 13¼, 11½x11¾ (#5195)**

| | | | |
|---|---|---|---|
| **2013, July 27** | | | **Litho.** |
| 5194 | A2413 10w multi | .25 | .25 |
| **Souvenir Sheets** | | | |
| 5195 | A2514 Sheet of 2, #a-b, + 3 labels | 1.90 | .95 |
| 5196 | A2415 70w multi | 1.10 | .55 |
| 5197 | A2416 70w multi | 1.10 | .55 |

Thailand 2013 World
Stamp Exhibition,
Bangkok — A2417

| | | | |
|---|---|---|---|
| **2013, Aug. 2** | | **Litho.** | **Perf. 13¼** |
| 5198 | A2417 10w multi | .25 | .25 |

---

Souvenir Sheet

7th Congress of Korean Children's
Union — A2419

| | | | |
|---|---|---|---|
| **2013, Aug. 10** | | **Litho.** | **Perf. 13¼** |
| 5200 | A2419 70w multi | 1.10 | .55 |

Horses — A2420

Designs: 30w, Shire horses. 50w, Orlov
trotter. 70w, Thoroughbred horses, horiz.

| | | | |
|---|---|---|---|
| **2013, Aug. 28** | | **Litho.** | **Perf. 13¼** |
| 5201-5202 | A2420 Set of 2 | 1.25 | .60 |
| **Souvenir Sheet** | | | |
| 5203 | A2420 70w multi | 1.10 | .55 |
| a. | Booklet pane of 3, #5301-5303 | 2.60 | — |
| | Complete booklet, #5203a | 2.60 | |

Complete booklet sold for 164w.

A2421

Founding of the Democratic People's
Republic of Korea, 65th
Anniv. — A2422

No. 5205: a, Kim Il Sung and flags. b, Kim
Jong Il and mountain.

| | | | |
|---|---|---|---|
| **2013, Sept. 9** | | **Litho.** | **Perf. 11½** |
| 5204 | A2421 30w multi | .50 | .25 |
| **Souvenir Sheet** | | | |
| **Perf. 13¼** | | | |
| 5205 | A2422 50w Sheet of 2, #a-b | 1.60 | .80 |

Mangyongdae in
Spring — A2423

Rungna Island in
Summer
A2424

Moran Hill in
Autumn — A2425

Ryongwang
Pavilion in
Winter — A2426

---

| | | | |
|---|---|---|---|
| **2013, Sept. 25** | **Litho.** | **Perf. 13¼** | |
| 5206 | A2423 30w multi | .50 | .25 |
| 5207 | A2424 50w multi | .80 | .40 |
| 5208 | A2425 70w multi | 1.10 | .55 |
| 5209 | A2426 110w multi | 1.75 | .85 |
| *Nos. 5206-5209 (4)* | | 4.15 | 2.05 |

Ships — A2427

Designs: 30w, Restaurant ship Taedonggang. 50w, Cargo ship Kumrung No. 5. 90w,
Refrigerator cargo ship Rimyongsu No. 7.
110w, Refrigerator cargo ship Turubong No. 3.

| | | | |
|---|---|---|---|
| **2013, Oct. 15** | **Litho.** | **Perf. 11½** | |
| 5210-5213 | A2427 Set of 4 | 4.25 | 2.10 |
| *5213a* | Booklet pane of 4, #5210-5213 | 4.50 | — |
| | Complete booklet, #5213a | 4.50 | |

Complete booklet sold for 294w.

Soldier Commanding
Speedier Construction,
Skiers at Masik Pass
Resort — A2428

| | | | |
|---|---|---|---|
| **2013, Oct. 20** | **Litho.** | **Perf. 13¼x13½** | |
| 5214 | A2428 30w multi | .45 | .25 |

Fossils
A2430

Designs: 30w, Ditomopharangia. 70w,
Dumangia. 110w, Hormotoma.

| | | | |
|---|---|---|---|
| **2013, Nov. 10** | **Litho.** | **Perf. 13** | |
| 5219-5221 | A2430 Set of 3 | 3.25 | 1.60 |
| *5221a* | Booklet pane of 3, #5219-5221 + label | 3.50 | — |
| | Complete booklet, #5221a | 3.50 | |

Complete booklet sold for 224w.

Souvenir Sheets

Kim Jong Il (1942-2011) and
Soldiers — A2435

Kim Jong Il Inspecting
Cotton — A2436

**Perf. 13½x13¼**

| | | | |
|---|---|---|---|
| **2013, Dec. 17** | | **Litho.** | |
| 5226 | A2435 50w multi | .80 | .40 |
| 5227 | A2436 70w multi | 1.10 | .55 |

---

Paintings — A2437

Designs: No. 5228, 30w, Hawk, by Kim Tuk
Sin. No. 5229, 30w, Tiger, by Kim Tuk Sin. No.
5230, 50w, Eagle, by Jang Sung Up. No.
5231, 50w, Carp, by Jo Sok Jin. 70w, Cats, by
Pyon Sang Byok.

| | | | |
|---|---|---|---|
| **Perf. 11¾x12¼** | | | |
| **2013, Dec. 21** | | | **Litho.** |
| 5228-5232 | A2437 Set of 5 | 3.50 | 1.75 |

Intl. Year of Water
Cooperation
A2438

| | | | |
|---|---|---|---|
| **2013, Dec. 26** | **Litho.** | **Perf. 11½** | |
| 5233 | A2438 30w multi | .45 | .25 |

Worker-Peasant Red Guards, 55th
Anniv. — A2440

| | | | |
|---|---|---|---|
| **2014, Jan. 14** | **Litho.** | **Perf. 11½** | |
| 5235 | A2440 30w multi + label | .50 | .25 |

Foods
A2441

Designs: 10w, Peaches and melons. 30w,
Eggplants and grapes. 50w, Pumpkins and
kiwis. 70w, Chestnuts and mushrooms. 90w,
Chinese mustard and persimmons. 110w,
Radish, Chinese cabbage, peppers, garlic and
pears.

| | | | |
|---|---|---|---|
| **2014, Jan. 20** | **Litho.** | **Perf. 12¼x11½** | |
| 5236-5241 | A2441 Set of 6 | 5.50 | 2.25 |
| *5241a* | Booklet pane of 6, #5236-5241 | 5.75 | — |
| | Complete booklet, #5241a | 5.75 | |

Complete booklet sold for 374w.

Ceramics — A2442

Designs: 30w, 12th century Celadon vase.
40w, 19th century porcelain jar.

| | | | |
|---|---|---|---|
| **2014, Jan. 25** | **Litho.** | **Perf. 11½** | |
| **Stamp + label** | | | |
| 5242-5243 | A2442 Set of 2 | 1.10 | .55 |
| *5243a* | Booklet pane of 2, #5242-5243, + 6 labels | 1.40 | — |
| | Complete booklet, #5243a | 1.40 | |

Complete booklet sold for 84w.

A2443

A2444

A2445

A2446

A2447

New Year's Address
of Kim Jong
Un — A2448

**Perf. 13¼x13½, 13½x13¼**
**2014, Feb. 1**     **Litho.**
5244 A2443 10w multi .25 .25
5245 A2444 10w multi .25 .25
5246 A2445 10w multi .25 .25
5247 A2446 30w multi .45 .25
5248 A2447 30w multi .45 .25
5249 A2448 30w multi .45 .25
Nos. 5244-5249 (6) 2.10 1.50

2014 Winter
Olympics,
Sochi, Russia
A2449

Designs: 30w, Skiing. 50w, Speed skating.
70w, Ice hockey. 90w, Bobsledding.

**2014, Feb. 7**   **Litho.**   **Perf. 13¼x13½**
5250-5253 A2449   Set of 4   3.75 1.90
5253a   Booklet pane of 4, #5250-
5253    4.00 —
Complete booklet, #5253a   4.00
Complete booklet sold for 254w.

**Souvenir Sheet**

Kim Jong Il (1942-2011), 72nd
Birthday — A2453

**2014, Feb. 16**   **Litho.**   **Perf. 11½x12**
5257 A2453 50w multi .80 .40

Traditional
Sports
A2458

Designs: 10w, Wrestling. 30w, Archery.
50w, Horse racing.

**Perf. 13½x13¼**
**2014, Mar. 10**    **Litho.**
5262-5264 A2458   Set of 3   1.40 .70

**Souvenir Sheet**

International Years — A2459

No. 5265: a, Intl. Year of Family Farming. b,
Intl. Year of Crystallography.

**2014, Mar. 21**   **Litho.**   **Perf. 11½**
5265 A2459 50w Sheet of 2, #a-
b, + 2 labels   1.60 .80

**Souvenir Sheet**

Munsu Water Park,
Pyongyang — A2461

No. 5267: a, Water slide (32mm diameter).
b, Swimming pools (64x30mm).

**Perf. 11¾x11½ (#5267b)**
**2014, Apr. 3**    **Litho.**
5267 A2461 30w Sheet of 2, #a-b .95 .45

Korean Alphabet,
570th Anniv. — A2462

**2014, Apr. 10**   **Litho.**   **Perf. 13¼**
5268 A2462 30w multi .50 .25
No. 5268 was printed in sheets of 8 + central label.

Plants Presented to
Kim Il Sung — A2463

Designs: 30w, Zygopetalum mackayi. 60w,
Oncidium splendidum. 90w, Paphiopedilum
insigne. 120w, Bletilla striata.

**2014, Apr. 15**   **Litho.**   **Perf. 13¼**
5269-5272 A2463   Set of 4   4.75 2.40
5272a   Booklet pane of 4, #4269-
5272    5.00 —
Complete booklet, #5272a   5.00
Nos. 5269-5272 were each printed in sheets
of 3 + label. Complete booklet sold for 314w.

Astronomy — A2464

No. 5273: a, 30w, Boötes (35x35mm). b,
50w, Ursa Major (35x35mm). c, 70w, Virgo
(35x35mm). d, 90w, Cygnus (35x35mm). e,
Milky Way and maps of constellations
(35x53mm).

**Perf. 11½, 11¾x12¼ (110w)**
**2014, Apr. 20**    **Litho.**
5273 A2464   Sheet of 5, #a-e   5.50 2.75
f.   Booklet pane of 5, #5273a-
5273e    5.75 —
Complete booklet, #5273f   5.75
Complete booklet sold for 364w.

2014 Intl. Horticultural
Exposition, Qingdao,
People's Republic of
China — A2465

**2014, Apr. 25**   **Litho.**   **Perf. 13¼**
5274 A2465 30w multi .50 .25

Fish and
Shellfish — A2467

Designs: 50w, Rhodeus ocellatus ocellatus,
Anodonta calypigos. 70w, Apogon
semilineatus, Glycymeris albolineata. 90w,
Diodon halacanthus, Atrina pectinata japonica. 110w, Cyclopterus lumpus, Pinctata
margarittfera.

**2014, May 11**   **Litho.**   **Perf. 13¼**
5276-5279 A2467   Set of 4   5.00 2.50
5279a   Booklet pane of 4, #5276-
5279    5.25 —
Complete booklet, #5279a   5.25
Complete booklet sold for 334w.
On No. 5278 the scientific name is mispelled "Diodon halacanthus." It should read
"Diodon holocanthus." On No. 5279 the sien-
tific name is mispelled "Pinctata..." It should
read "Pinctada..."

Universal Postal
Union, 140th
Anniv. — A2468

**2014, May 29**   **Litho.**   **Perf. 11½**
5280 A2468 30w multi .50 .25
Admission of North Korea into UPU, 40th
anniv. Printed in sheets of 5 + label.

2014 World Cup
Soccer
Championships,
Brazil — A2469

Player in red shirt: 40w, #12 Dribbling ball.
60w, Tackling opponent, horiz. 80w, #11 Dribbling ball.
100w, Player in yellow shirt.

**2014, June 12**   **Litho.**   **Perf. 13¼**
5281-5283 A2469   Set of 3   2.75 1.40
**Souvenir Sheet**
5284 A2469 110w multi   1.75 .85
a.   Booklet pane of 4, #5281-
5284    4.75 —
Complete booklet, #5284a   4.75
Complete booklet sold for 304w.

International Olympic
Committee, 120th
Anniv. — A2470

**2014, June 16**   **Litho.**   **Perf. 13¼**
5285 A2470 30w multi   .50 .25

A2471

Kim Jong Il's Leadership of Central
Committee of Workers' Party, 50th
Anniv. — A2472

No. 5286 — Paintings of Kim Jong Il: a,
Visiting Mt. Taedok military post. b, With arms
around office workers. c, In barley field. d, Surrounded by people.
50w, Kim Jong Il.

**2014, June 19**   **Litho.**   **Perf. 11¾**
5286 A2471 30w Sheet of 4, #a-d 1.90 .95
**Souvenir Sheet**
**Perf. 11¾x12¼**
5287 A2472 50w multi   .80 .40

Medicinal
Plants — A2476

Designs: 30w, Aronia melanocarpa. 50w,
Lycium chinense. 70w, Ginkgo biloba. 110w,
Crataegus pinnatifida var. major.

**2014, July 17**   **Litho.**   **Perf. 13¼**
5291-5294 A2476   Set of 4   4.00 2.00
5294a   Booklet pane of 4, #5291-
5294    4.25 —
Complete booklet, #5294a   4.25
Complete booklet sold for 275w.

Sports
A2477

Designs: 30w, Table tennis. 50w, Running.
90w, Weight lifting. 110w, Judo.

**2014, July 25**    **Litho.**    *Perf. 13*
5295-5298 A2477   Set of 4    4.25 2.10
5298a    Booklet pane of 4, #5295-
     5298      4.50
   Complete booklet, #5298a    4.50
   Complete booklet sold for 295w.

Worldwide Fund
for Nature
(WWF) — A2478

No. 5299 — Grus japonensis: a, In flight. b, Adult and chick. c, Adults in water. d, Adults and chicks.

**2014, Aug. 5**    **Litho.**    *Perf. 13¼*
5299    Horiz. strip of 4    3.25 1.75
*a.*   A2478 10w multi    .25 .25
*b.*   A2478 30w multi    .45 .25
*c.*   A2478 50w multi    .75 .40
*d.*   A2478 110w multi    1.75 .85
*e.*   Booklet pane of 4, #5299a-5299d   3.50
   Complete booklet, #5299e   3.50

   Complete booklet sold for 215w.

### AIR POST STAMPS

Lisunov Li-2 Airliner
over
Pyongyang — AP1

**1958, Feb. 4**    **Photo.**    *Perf. 10*
C1   AP1 20w blue    11.00 2.00
*a.*   Imperf    22.50 10.00
*b.*   Perf 11    12.00 2.50
*c.*   Rouletted    15.00 10.00
   Korean Civil Aviation.

# REPUBLIC OF KOSOVO

'ko-sˌə-ˌvō

LOCATION — North of Albania and Macedonia
GOVT. — REPUBLIC
AREA — 4,212 sq. mi.
POP. — 2,100,000 (2007 est.)
CAPITAL — Pristina

From 1974 to 1990, Kosovo was an autonomous province of Serbia, a republic within Yugoslavia. In 1990, the autonomy of Kosovo was revoked. A Separatist faction declared Kosovo independence that year, but only Albania recognized it. In 1999, the United Nations Security Council placed Kosovo under a transitional United Nations Administration, and the institutions created by the independent Kosovo were replaced with the United Nations Interim Administration. Starting in 2000, postage stamps were issued by the United Nations Interim Administration, and these can be found as part of the listings for United Nations. The Kosovo Assembly declared independence on Feb. 17, 2008. Kosovo was recognized as independent by numerous countries soon thereafter, and the United Nations Interim Administration ceased issuing stamps. Serbia maintains its claim to the territory.

100 pfennigs = 1 mark
100 cents = (€)1 (2002)

**Catalogue values for all unused stamps in this country are for Never Hinged items.**

Peace in Kosovo — A1

Designs: 20pf, Mosaic depicting Orpheus, c. 5th-6th cent., Podujeve. 30pf, Dardinian idol, Museum of Kosovo. 50pf, Silver coin of Damastion from 4th cent. B.C. 1m, Statue of Mother Teresa, Prizren. 2m, Map of Kosovo.

*Perf. 13½x13, 13½x13¼ (30pf)*

| | | 2000, Mar. 14　Litho. | Unwmk. | |
|---|---|---|---|---|
| 1 | A1 | 20pf multicolored | .65 | .65 |
| 2 | A1 | 30pf multicolored | 1.25 | 1.25 |
| 3 | A1 | 50pf multicolored | 1.60 | 1.60 |
| 4 | A1 | 1m multicolored | 2.00 | 1.80 |
| 5 | A1 | 2m multicolored | 3.75 | 3.50 |
| | | Nos. 1-5 (5) | 9.25 | 8.80 |

Nos. 1-5 were demonetized July 1, 2002.

Beginning with No. 6, Kosovan stamps were not available to collectors through the United Nations Postal Administration.

Peace in Kosovo — A2

Designs: 20pf, Bird. 30pf, Street musician. 50pf, Butterfly and pear. 1m, Children and stars. 2m, Globe and handprints.

| | | 2001, Nov. 12　Litho. | Perf. 14 | |
|---|---|---|---|---|
| 6 | A2 | 20pf multicolored | 1.00 | 1.00 |
| 7 | A2 | 30pf multicolored | 1.25 | 1.25 |
| 8 | A2 | 50pf multicolored | 2.00 | 2.00 |
| 9 | A2 | 1m multicolored | 4.00 | 4.00 |
| 10 | A2 | 2m multicolored | 7.50 | 7.50 |
| | | Nos. 6-10 (5) | 15.75 | 15.75 |

## Peace in Kosovo Type of 2001 With Denominations in Euros Only

| | | 2002, May 2　Litho. | Perf. 14 | |
|---|---|---|---|---|
| 11 | A2 | 10c Like #6 | .75 | .75 |
| 12 | A2 | 15c Like #7 | 1.00 | 1.00 |
| 13 | A2 | 26c Like #8 | 1.50 | 1.50 |
| 14 | A2 | 51c Like #9 | 4.50 | 4.50 |
| 15 | A2 | €1.02 Like #10 | 8.00 | 8.00 |
| | | Nos. 11-15 (5) | 15.75 | 15.75 |

Christmas — A3

Designs: 50c, Candles and garland. €1, Stylized men.

| | | 2003, Dec. 20　Litho. | Perf. 14 | |
|---|---|---|---|---|
| 16 | A3 | 50c multicolored (30,000) | 7.50 | 7.50 |
| 17 | A3 | €1 multicolored (30,000) | 14.50 | 14.50 |

Return of Refugees A4 　 Five Years of Peace A5

| | | 2004, June 29　Litho. | Perf. 13¼x13 | |
|---|---|---|---|---|
| 18 | A4 | €1 multicolored (40,000) | 7.00 | 7.00 |
| 19 | A5 | €2 multicolored (40,000) | 16.00 | 16.00 |

Musical Instruments — A6

| | | 2004, Aug. 31　Litho. | Perf. 13¼x13 | |
|---|---|---|---|---|
| 20 | A6 | 20c Flute (30,000) | 5.00 | 5.00 |
| 21 | A6 | 30c Ocarina (30,000) | 10.00 | 10.00 |

Aprons — A7

Vests — A8

Designs: 20c, Apron from Prizren. 30c, Apron from Rugova. 50c, Three vests. €1, Two vests.

| | | 2004, Oct. 28　Litho. | Perf. 13x13¼ | |
|---|---|---|---|---|
| 22 | A7 | 20c multicolored (30,000) | 5.50 | 5.50 |
| 23 | A7 | 30c multicolored (30,000) | 8.50 | 8.50 |
| 24 | A8 | 50c multicolored (30,000) | 12.00 | 12.00 |
| 25 | A8 | €1 multicolored (30,000) | 26.00 | 26.00 |
| | | Nos. 22-25 (4) | 52.00 | 52.00 |

Mirusha Waterfall — A9

| | | 2004, Nov. 26　Litho. | Perf. 13x13¼ | |
|---|---|---|---|---|
| 26 | A9 | €2 multicolored (40,000) | 7.50 | 7.50 |

House — A10

| | | 2004, Dec. 14　Litho. | Perf. 13x13¼ | |
|---|---|---|---|---|
| 27 | A10 | 50c multicolored (40,000) | 4.50 | 4.50 |

Flowers — A11

| | | 2005, June 29　Litho. | Perf. 13½ | |
|---|---|---|---|---|
| 28 | A11 | 15c Peony (50,000) | 2.25 | 2.25 |
| 29 | A11 | 20c Poppies (50,000) | 3.25 | 3.25 |
| 30 | A11 | 30c Gentian (50,000) | 5.00 | 5.00 |
| | | Nos. 28-30 (3) | 10.50 | 10.50 |

A12

Handicrafts — A13

| | | 2005, July 20　Litho. | Perf. 13¼x13 | |
|---|---|---|---|---|
| 31 | A12 | 20c shown (40,000) | 2.50 | 2.50 |
| 32 | A12 | 30c Cradle (40,000) | 3.00 | 3.00 |
| 33 | A13 | 50c shown (40,000) | 3.25 | 3.25 |
| 34 | A12 | €1 Necklace (40,000) | 4.25 | 4.25 |
| | | Nos. 31-34 (4) | 13.00 | 13.00 |

Village — A14

Town — A15

City — A16

| | | 2005, Sept. 15 | Perf. 13x13½ | |
|---|---|---|---|---|
| 35 | A14 | 20c multicolored (50,000) | 2.00 | 2.00 |
| 36 | A15 | 50c multicolored (110,000) | 3.00 | 3.00 |
| 37 | A16 | €1 multicolored (110,000) | 6.00 | 6.00 |
| | | Nos. 35-37 (3) | 11.00 | 11.00 |

Archaeological Artifacts — A17

| | | 2005, Nov. 2 | Perf. 13½x13 | |
|---|---|---|---|---|
| 38 | A17 | 20c shown (25,000) | 1.25 | 1.25 |
| 39 | A17 | 30c Statue (25,000) | 1.75 | 1.75 |
| 40 | A17 | 50c Sculpture (25,000) | 2.50 | 2.50 |
| 41 | A17 | €1 Helmet (25,000) | 7.50 | 7.50 |
| | | Nos. 38-41 (4) | 13.00 | 13.00 |

Minerals — A18

| | | 2005, Dec. 10 | Perf. 13x13½ | |
|---|---|---|---|---|
| 42 | A18 | €2 multicolored (45,000) | 10.00 | 10.00 |

A19

Europa — A20

| | | 2006, July 20 | Perf. 13¼x13 | |
|---|---|---|---|---|
| 43 | A19 | 50c multicolored (60,000) | 2.25 | 2.25 |
| 44 | A20 | €1 multicolored (60,000) | 4.25 | 4.25 |

Exists Imperf. Value set of two, $75.

Fauna — A21

| | | 2006, May 23　Litho. | Perf. 13 | |
|---|---|---|---|---|
| 45 | A21 | 15c Wolf (190,000) | 1.00 | 1.00 |
| 46 | A21 | 20c Cow (190,000) | 1.25 | 1.25 |
| 47 | A21 | 30c Pigeon (190,000) | 1.40 | 1.40 |
| 48 | A21 | 50c Swan (190,000) | 1.60 | 1.60 |
| 49 | A21 | €1 Dog (190,000) | 2.75 | 2.75 |
| a. | | Souvenir sheet, #45-49, + label (15,000) | 8.75 | 8.75 |
| | | Nos. 45-49 (5) | 8.00 | 8.00 |

Nos. 45-49 are inscribed CPU. Stamps with "Leoprint" imprint are from No. 63a.
No. 49a exists in two shades of green selvage.

Children — A22

Designs: 20c, Children in cradle. 30c, Children reading. 50c, Girls dancing. €1, Child in water.

| | | 2006, June 30　Litho. | Perf. 13 | |
|---|---|---|---|---|
| 50 | A22 | 20c multicolored (40,000) | 1.00 | 1.00 |
| 51 | A22 | 30c multicolored (40,000) | 1.25 | 1.25 |
| 52 | A22 | 50c multicolored (40,000) | 1.75 | 1.75 |
| 53 | A22 | €1 multicolored (40,000) | 3.50 | 3.50 |
| a. | | Souvenir sheet, #50-53 (12,500) | 7.75 | 7.75 |
| | | Nos. 50-53 (4) | 7.50 | 7.50 |

Nos. 50-53 were printed by CPU & Moare.
No. 53a was printed by two printers: 7,500 inscribed "CPU&Moare," and 5,000 inscribed "Leoprint."
Nos. 50-53 from CPO & Moare exists imperforate. Value, set, $75.
No. 53a by CPU & Moare exists imperforate. Value $75.

A23

A24

A25

Tourist Attractions A26

**2006, Sept. 1    Litho.    Perf. 13**

| 54 | A23 | 20c multicolored | | |
|---|---|---|---|---|
| | | (40,000) | 1.00 | 1.00 |
| 55 | A24 | 30c multicolored | | |
| | | (40,000) | 1.25 | 1.25 |
| 56 | A25 | 50c multicolored | | |
| | | (40,000) | 1.75 | 1.75 |
| 57 | A26 | €1 multicolored | | |
| | | (40,000) | 3.25 | 3.25 |
| a. | | Souvenir sheet, #54-57 | | |
| | | (12,500) | 9.50 | 9.50 |
| | | Nos. 54-57 (4) | 7.25 | 7.25 |

Nos. 54-57 were printed by CPU & Moare. No. 57a was printed by two printers: 7,500 inscribed "CPU&Moare," and 5,000 inscribed "Leoprint."

Intl. Peace Day — A27

**2006, Sept. 21    Litho.    Perf. 13**

| 58 | A27 | €2 multicolored | | |
|---|---|---|---|---|
| | | (40,000) | 7.00 | 7.00 |

Ancient Coins — A28

Various coins.

**2006, Nov. 1    Litho.    Perf. 13**

| 59 | A28 | 20c multicolored | | |
|---|---|---|---|---|
| | | (30,000) | 1.00 | 1.00 |
| 60 | A28 | 30c multicolored | | |
| | | (30,000) | 1.50 | 1.50 |
| 61 | A28 | 50c multicolored | | |
| | | (30,000) | 1.75 | 1.75 |
| 62 | A28 | €1 multicolored | | |
| | | (30,000) | 3.25 | 3.25 |
| a. | | Souvenir sheet, #59-62 | | |
| | | (15,000) | 9.50 | 9.50 |
| | | Nos. 59-62 (4) | 7.50 | 7.50 |

Nos. 59-62 are inscribed CPU. Stamps with "Leoprint" imprint are from No. 63a.
No. 62a exists imperforate. Value, $75.

Sculpture — A29

**2006, Dec. 1    Litho.    Perf. 13**

| 63 | A29 | €2 multicolored | | |
|---|---|---|---|---|
| | | (45,000) | 8.00 | 8.00 |
| a. | | Miniature sheet, #45-57, 59-63, + 2 labels (5,000) | 80.00 | 80.00 |

Convention on the Rights of Persons With Disabilities — A30

Emblems of handicaps and: 20c, Children and butterfly. 50c, Handicapped women. 70c, Map of Kosovo. €1, Stylized flower.

**2007, Apr. 23    Litho.    Perf. 14x14¼**

| 64 | A30 | 20c multicolored | | |
|---|---|---|---|---|
| | | (15,000) | 1.25 | 1.25 |
| 65 | A30 | 50c multicolored | | |
| | | (15,000) | 2.50 | 2.50 |
| 66 | A30 | 70c multicolored | | |
| | | (15,000) | 3.00 | 3.00 |
| 67 | A30 | €1 multicolored | | |
| | | (15,000) | 3.75 | 3.75 |
| a. | | Souvenir sheet, #64-67 (20,000) | 12.50 | 12.50 |
| | | Nos. 64-67 (4) | 10.50 | 10.50 |

Color shades vary widely. Printer's waste of this issue exists in the marketplace, including partial prints, missing design elements, and missing colors.
Two varieties of No. 67a, exist differing in text surrounding the stamps. It has not been established if both varieties were officially issued.

Scouting, Cent. — A31

Europa — A32

**2007, May 12    Litho.    Perf. 13¼**

| 68 | A31 | 70c multicolored | | |
|---|---|---|---|---|
| | | (35,000) | 4.25 | 4.25 |
| 69 | A32 | €1 multicolored | | |
| | | (35,000) | 6.25 | 6.25 |
| a. | | Souvenir sheet, #68-69 (15,000) | 90.00 | 90.00 |

A33

A34

A35

International Children's Day — A36

**2007, June 1    Litho.    Perf. 13¼**

| 70 | A33 | 20c multicolored | | |
|---|---|---|---|---|
| | | (38,000) | 1.25 | 1.25 |
| 71 | A34 | 30c multicolored | | |
| | | (38,000) | 1.50 | 1.50 |
| 72 | A35 | 70c multicolored | | |
| | | (38,000) | 2.50 | 2.50 |
| 73 | A36 | €1 multicolored | | |
| | | (38,000) | 4.00 | 4.00 |
| | | Nos. 70-73 (4) | 9.25 | 9.25 |

Nos. 70-73 exist imperf. Value, set $45

Native Costumes — A37

Designs: 20c, Serbian woman. 30c, Prizren Region woman. 50c, Sword dancer. 70c, Drenica Region woman. €1, Shepherd, Rugova.

**2007, July 6    Litho.    Perf. 13½x13¼**

| 74 | A37 | 20c multicolored | | |
|---|---|---|---|---|
| | | (35,000) | 1.25 | 1.25 |
| 75 | A37 | 30c multicolored | | |
| | | (35,000) | 1.75 | 1.75 |
| 76 | A37 | 50c multicolored | | |
| | | (35,000) | 2.00 | 2.00 |
| 77 | A37 | 70c multicolored | | |
| | | (35,000) | 2.50 | 2.50 |
| 78 | A37 | €1 multicolored | | |
| | | (35,000) | 3.25 | 3.25 |
| a. | | Souvenir sheet, #74-78, + label | | |
| | | (15,000) | 12.50 | 12.50 |
| | | Nos. 74-78 (5) | 10.75 | 10.75 |

Masks — A38

Various masks.

**Perf. 13½x13¼**

**2007, Sept. 11    Litho.**

| 79 | A38 | 15c multicolored | | |
|---|---|---|---|---|
| | | (38,000) | .75 | .75 |
| 80 | A38 | 30c multicolored | | |
| | | (38,000) | 1.00 | 1.00 |
| 81 | A38 | 50c multicolored | | |
| | | (38,000) | 2.00 | 2.00 |
| 82 | A38 | €1 multicolored | | |
| | | (38,000) | 3.00 | 3.00 |
| | | Nos. 79-82 (4) | 6.75 | 6.75 |

Sports — A39

Designs: 20c, Soccer ball, basketball, two people standing, person in wheelchair. 50c, Wrestlers. €1, Symbols of 24 sports.

**2007, Oct. 2    Litho.    Perf. 13¼x13½**

| 83 | A39 | 20c multicolored | | |
|---|---|---|---|---|
| | | (38,000) | 1.00 | 1.00 |
| 84 | A39 | 50c multicolored | | |
| | | (38,000) | 2.25 | 2.25 |
| 85 | A39 | €1 multicolored | | |
| | | (38,000) | 4.00 | 4.00 |
| | | Nos. 83-85 (3) | 7.25 | 7.25 |

Nos. 83-85 exist imperf. Value, set $65.

Architecture — A40

Designs: 30c, Stone bridge, Vushtrri. 50c, Hamam, Prizren. 70c, Tower. €1, Tower, diff.

**2007, Nov. 6    Litho.    Perf. 13¼**

| 86 | A40 | 30c multicolored | | |
|---|---|---|---|---|
| | | (38,000) | 1.50 | 1.50 |
| 87 | A40 | 50c multicolored | | |
| | | (38,000) | 2.00 | 2.00 |
| 88 | A40 | 70c multicolored | | |
| | | (38,000) | 2.50 | 2.50 |
| 89 | A40 | €1 multicolored | | |
| | | (38,000) | 3.50 | 3.50 |
| | | Nos. 86-89 (4) | 9.50 | 9.50 |

Nos. 86-89 exist imperf. Value, set $85.

Locomotives — A41

Designs: €1, Diesel locomotive. €2, Steam locomotive

**2007, Dec. 7    Litho.    Perf. 13¼**

| 90 | A41 | €1 multicolored | | |
|---|---|---|---|---|
| | | (50,000) | 4.00 | 4.00 |
| 91 | A41 | €2 multicolored | | |
| | | (50,000) | 8.00 | 8.00 |

Nos. 90-91 exist imperf. Value, set $125.

Skanderbeg (1405-68), Albanian National Hero — A42

**2008, Jan. 17    Litho.    Perf. 13¼**

| 92 | A42 | €2 multicolored | | |
|---|---|---|---|---|
| | | (140,000) | 7.50 | 7.50 |

No. 92 exists imperf. Value, $35.

Kosovo declared its independence from Serbia on Feb. 17, 2008, ending the United Nations Interim Administration. Stamps issued after Feb. 17, 2008, by the Republic of Kosovo will be listed under Kosovo in the *Scott Standard Postage Stamp Catalogue.*

---

### Republic of Kosovo

A42

Teacher's Day — A43

**2008, Mar. 7    Litho.    Perf. 13x13¼**

| 93 | A42 | 70c multi | 2.25 | 2.25 |
|---|---|---|---|---|
| 94 | A43 | €1 multi | 3.25 | 3.25 |

Independence — A44

**2008, Mar. 19    Perf. 13¼x13**
**Stamps With White Frames**

| 95 | | Vert. pair | 5.50 | 5.50 |
|---|---|---|---|---|
| a. | A44 | 20c vio blue & multi | .75 | .50 |
| b. | A44 | 70c red & multi | 3.00 | 2.00 |

**Souvenir Sheet**
**Stamp With Colored Border**

| 96 | A44 | 70c red & multi | 7.00 | 7.00 |
|---|---|---|---|---|

Earth Day — A45

Designs: 30c, Globe, olive branch. 50c, Trees. 70c, Tree, parched land. €1, Man holding tree.

**2008, Apr. 22    Perf. 13x13¼**

| 97-100 | A45 | Set of 4 | 8.00 | 8.00 |
|---|---|---|---|---|

Europa — A46

Designs: Nos. 101, 103a, 70c, Handwritten letter, pen. Nos. 102, 103b, €1, Letter folded into paper airplane.

**2008, May 9    Litho.**
**Stamps With White Frames**

| 101-102 | A46 | Set of 2 | 7.50 | 7.50 |
|---|---|---|---|---|

**Souvenir Sheet**
**Stamps With Colored Frames**

| 103 | A46 | Sheet of 2, #a-b | 20.00 | 20.00 |
|---|---|---|---|---|

Filigree — A47

Designs: 10c, Chest. 15c, Earring. 20c, Figurine of woman. 50c, Necklace. €1, Necklace, diff.

**2008, June 12    Perf. 13¼x13**

| 104-108 | A47 | Set of 5 | 6.75 | 6.75 |
|---|---|---|---|---|

A48 A49

Medicinal Herbs
A50 A51

2008, Sept. 9 Litho. ***Perf. 13¼x13***

109	Horiz. strip of 4	8.00	8.00
a.	A48 30c multi	.75	.75
b.	A49 50c multi	1.00	1.00
c.	A50 70c multi	2.00	2.00
d.	A51 €1 multi	2.75	2.75

Exists Imperf. Value, strip $135.

Breast Cancer Prevention — A52

2008, Oct. 15 Litho. ***Perf. 13¼x13***

110 A52 €1 multi 7.00 7.00

Albanian Alphabet, Cent. — A53

No. 111: a, 70c, Alphabet. b, €1, Notebook page for handwriting practice.

2008, Nov. 14 ***Perf. 13x13¼***

111 A53 Vert. pair, #a-b 4.50 4.50

Adem Jashari (1955-98), Independence Leader — A54

2008, Nov. 28 ***Perf. 13¼x13***

112 A54 €2 multi 6.00 6.00

A55 A56

A57 Visual Arts — A58

2008, Dec. 2 Litho. ***Perf. 13¼***

113	Horiz. strip of 4	8.00	8.00
a.	A55 20c multi	.55	.55
b.	A56 50c multi	1.10	1.10
c.	A57 70c multi	1.75	1.75
d.	A58 €1 multi	2.50	2.50

William G. Walker, Head of Kosovo Verification Mission — A59

Torn Page — A60

2009, Jan. 15

114	A59	50c multi	1.25	1.25
115	A60	70c multi	2.25	2.25

Reçak Massacre, 10th anniv.

Independence, 1st Anniv. — A61

No. 116: a, €1, Hand with pen, independence declaration. b, €2, Flag of Kosovo, date of independence.

Illustration reduced.

2009, Feb. 16 Litho. ***Perf. 13¼***

116 A61 Horiz. pair, #a-b 8.00 8.00

Edith Durham (1863-1944), Writer — A62

2009, Mar. 21

117 A62 €1 multi 3.25 3.25

A63

Decan Monastery — A64

Designs: No. 118, €1, Monastery. No. 119, €2, Monastery, diff.

No. 120: a, €1, Window. b, €2, Painting of Jesus.

2009, Apr. 22

118-119 A63 Set of 2 7.00 7.00

Souvenir Sheet

120 A64 Sheet of 2, #a-b 7.50 7.50

Europa — A65

Designs: €1, Map of Europe, ring of stars, man and girl at telescope. No. 122, €2, Boy and rocket on map of Europe (with white frame around stamp).

No. 123, Like #122, without white frame around stamp.

2009, May 9

121-122 A65 Set of 2 9.50 9.50

Souvenir Sheet

123 A65 €2 multi 10.00 10.00

Intl. Year of Astronomy.

A66 A67

Declaration of the Rights of the Child, 20th Anniv.
A68 A69

2009, June 1

124	A66	20c multi	.75	.75
125	A67	50c multi	1.75	1.75
126	A68	70c multi	2.50	2.50
127	A69	€1 multi	3.50	3.50
		Nos. 124-127 (4)	8.50	8.50

Kosovo's Friendship With United States — A70

2009, Sept. 4

128 A70 €2 multi 7.00 7.00

Lorenc Antoni (1909-91), Composer — A71

2009, Sept. 23

129 A71 €1 multi 4.50 4.50

Germany Weeks in Kosovo — A72

2009, Oct. 3 Litho. ***Perf. 13¼***

130 A72 €1 multi 3.50 3.50

Pjeter Bogdani (c. 1630-89), Writer — A73

2009, Nov. 22

131 A73 €1 multi 3.25 3.25

Art — A74

Works by: 30c, M. Mulliqi. 50c, I. Kodra. 70c, G. Gjokaj. €1, M. Mulliqi, diff.

2009, Dec. 4

132-135 A74 Set of 4 7.00 7.00

A75

Film Personalities — A76

Designs: No. 136, 30c, Faruk Begolli (1944-2007), actor and director. No. 137, 70c, Melihate Qena (1939-2005), actress. €1, Abdurrahman Shala (1922-94), actor and producer.

No. 139: a, 30c, Unnamed person in yellow. b, 70c, Unnamed person in brown, diff.

2010, Jan. 26

136-138 A75 Set of 3 5.50 5.50

Souvenir Sheet

139 A76 Sheet of 2, #a-b 3.25 3.25

Emblems of Kosovo Police, Defense Forces and Security Forces A77

Police and Emblem A78

Security Forces — A79

2010, Feb. 16 **Litho.**

140	A77	30c multi	.85	.85
141	A78	50c multi	1.40	1.40
142	A79	70c multi	1.90	1.90
		Nos. 140-142 (3)	4.15	4.15

A80

Europa A81

Designs: €1, Child reading book under tree. No. 144, €2, Child leaving open book.

No. 145, €2, Boy sitting on book.

2010, May 5 ***Perf. 13¼***

143-144 A80 Set of 2 8.00 8.00

Souvenir Sheet

Perf. 14x14¼

145	A81	€2 multi	5.25	5.25
a.		Perf. 13¼	—	—

2010 World Cup Soccer Championships, South Africa — A82

Designs: €1, Map of Kosovo and emblem of Kosovo Soccer Federation, map of Africa with soccer field. €2, Map of Kosovo and emblem of Kosovo Soccer Federation, map of Africa on soccer ball.
No. 148: a, Soccer ball as pendant on multicolored ribbon. b, Flag of South Africa on soccer ball.

**2010, June 29**    *Perf. 13¼*
146-147 A82   Set of 2    8.00 8.00
**Souvenir Sheet**
*Perf. 14¼x14*
148 A82 50c Sheet of 2, #a-b    3.50 3.50

Azem (1889-1924) and Shota (1895-1927) Galica, Fighters for Albanian Independence — A83

**2010, July 14**    *Perf. 13¼*
149 A83 €2 multi    5.25 5.25

National Parks — A84

Scenery from: 20c, Mirusha National Park. 50c, Rugova National Park. 70c, Gjeravica National Park. €1, Sharri National Park.

**2010, Aug. 2**    *Litho.*
150-153 A84   Set of 4    6.25 6.25

Mother Teresa (1910-97), Humanitarian — A85

**2010, Aug. 26**    *Perf. 13*
154 A85 €1 multi    2.75 2.75
See Albania No. 2889, Macedonia No. 529.

A86

Traffic in the Pathways of Integration — A87

**2010, Sept. 9**    *Litho.*    *Perf. 13¼*
155 A86 70c multi    2.25 2.25
**Souvenir Sheet**
*Perf. 14¼x14*
156 A87   €1 multi    3.50 3.50

A88      A89

A90      A91

Birds A92

No. 161: a, 30c, Brown bird on branch. b, 30c, Blue and red bird on wire. c, 70c, Bird in flight. d, 70c, Blue and red bird on wire, bird in flight.

**2010, Sept. 23**    *Perf. 14x14¼*
157 A88 30c multi    .85 .85
158 A89 50c multi    1.50 1.50
159 A90 70c multi    2.00 2.00
160 A91 €1 multi    3.00 3.00
   *Nos. 157-160 (4)*    7.35 7.35
**Souvenir Sheet**
161 A92   Sheet of 4, #a-d    7.50 7.50

Local Foods — A93

Designs: 70c, Beehive, honeycombs, jar of honey. €1, Plates of food.

**2010, Nov. 8**    *Perf. 14¼x14*
162-163 A93   Set of 2    4.75 4.75

Campaign Against Violence Towards Women — A94

**2010, Nov. 25**
164 A94   €1 multi    3.00 3.00

Historical Photographs of Basare — A95

Various street scenes: 50c, 70c, €1.

**2010, Dec. 6**
165-167 A95   Set of 3    6.50 6.50

A96      Independence, 3rd Anniv. — A97

**2011, Feb. 27**    *Perf. 14¼x14*
168 A96 €1 multi    2.50 2.50
169 A97 €2 multi    5.50 5.50

Elena Gjika (Dore D'Istria, 1828-88), Writer — A98

**2011, Mar. 8**    *Perf. 14x14¼*
170 A98 €1 multi    2.75 2.75

Prizren — A99

Designs: 20c, Houses on hillside. 50c, House and benches. 70c, View of city.

**2011, Mar. 15**
171-173 A99   Set of 3    4.00 4.00

A100      A101

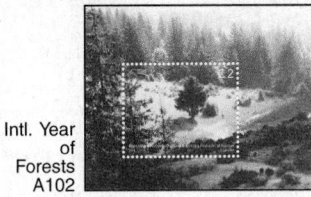

Intl. Year of Forests A102

**2011, May 9**    *Perf. 14¼x14*
174 A100 €1 multi    3.00 3.00
175 A101 €2 multi    5.75 5.75
**Souvenir Sheet**
176 A102 €2 multi    6.00 6.00

Archaeology — A103

Designs: 10c, Building ruins. 15c, Building ruins, diff. €1, Bas-relief head.

**2011, June 7**    *Perf. 14x14¼*
177-179 A103   Set of 3    3.75 3.75
Compare No. 178 with Nos. 243A and 329.

A104

Traditional Costumes of Hasit Region — A105

Designs: 30c, Shoes. 50c, Women's dress. 70c, Pouch. €1, Vest. €2, Kerchief.

**2011, Oct. 19**
180-183 A104   Set of 4    6.75 6.75
**Souvenir Sheet**
184 A105 €2 multi    5.50 5.50

A106

A107

A108

Mills A109

**2011, Nov. 2**
185 A106 50c multi    1.40 1.40
186 A107 70c multi    2.00 2.00
187 A108 €1 multi    2.75 2.75
   *Nos. 185-187 (3)*    6.15 6.15
**Souvenir Sheet**
*Perf. 14¼x14*
188 A109 €2 multi    5.50 5.50

A110

Caves — A111

**2011, Nov. 15**    *Perf. 14x14¼*
189 A110 70c multi    1.90 1.90
190 A111 €1 multi    2.75 2.75

Rooster — A112

Rooster facing: 70c, Right. €1, Left.

**2011, Nov. 21**
191-192 A112   Set of 2    4.75 4.75

Esat Mekuli (1916-93), Poet — A113

**2011, Dec. 17**      *Perf. 14¼x14*
193 A113 €1 multi      2.60 2.60

Enver Zymeri (1979-2011), Police Officer — A114

**2011, Dec. 26**
194 A114 €1 multi      2.60 2.60

Mitrovica — A115

Designs: €1, Monument, workers, street, aerial view of city. €2, Old and new street scenes.

**2012, Jan. 20**      *Perf. 14¼x14*
195-196 A115 Set of 2      8.00 8.00

A116

Freedom Fighters — A117

**2012, Jan. 27**
197 A116 €1 multi      2.60 2.60
198 A117 €1 multi      2.60 2.60

Rexho Mulliqi (1923-82), Composer — A118

**2012, Feb. 23**
199 A118 €1 multi      2.75 2.75

Butterflies A119

Various butterflies: 10c, 70c, €1. €2, Butterflies and orchids.

**2012, Mar. 9**      *Perf. 14x14¼*
200-202 A119 Set of 3      4.75 4.75
**Souvenir Sheet**
203 A119 €2 multi      6.00 6.00

A120

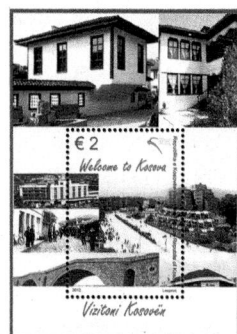

Europa — A121

Designs: €1, Cliff and valley. No. 205, €2, House.
No. 206, €2, Buildings and bridge.

**2012, Apr. 12**      *Perf. 14¼x14*
204-205 A120 Set of 2      8.00 8.00
**Souvenir Sheet**
206 A121 €2 multi      5.75 5.75

Lakes — A122

Designs: 20c, Badovac Lake. 50c, Gazivoda Lake. 70c, Lake Licenat.

**2012, May 3**      *Perf. 14x14¼*
207-209 A122 Set of 3      3.75 3.75
Compare Nos. 208 and 331.

Isa Boletini (1864-1916), Kosovar Freedom Fighter A123

Hasan Prishtina (1873-1933), Prime Minister of Albania A124

**2012, May 21**      *Perf. 14¼x14*
210 A123 70c multi      1.75 1.75
211 A124 €1 multi      2.50 2.50

Bride in Archway — A125

**2012, June 18**
212 A125 €1 multi      2.50 2.50

Mejlinda Kelmendi, Kosovar Judoka Competing for Albania at 2012 Summer Olympics — A126

No. 213: a, 70c, Three images of Kelmendi. b, €1, Two images of Kelmendi.

**2012, July 25**      *Perf. 14x14¼*
213 A126 Pair, #a-b      4.25 4.25
Printed in sheets containing two pairs.

A127

A128

Myths and Legends — A129

**2012, Sept. 5**      *Perf. 14¼x14*
214 A127 70c multi      1.90 1.90
215 A128 €1 multi      2.60 2.60
**Souvenir Sheet**
*Perf. 14¼x14¼*
216 A129 €2 multi      5.25 5.25

Traditional Dances — A130

Various dancers: 50c, 70c, €1.

**2012, Oct. 25**      *Perf. 14¼x14*
217-219 A130 Set of 3      5.75 5.75

Albanian Independence, Cent. — A131

**2012, Nov. 27**
220 A131 €1 multi      2.60 2.60

Marin Barleti (c.1450-c. 1512), Historian — A132

**2012, Dec. 26**
221 A132 €1 multi      2.75 2.75

Independence, 5th Anniv. — A133

**2013, Feb. 17**      *Perf. 14¼x14*
222 A133 €2 multi      5.25 5.25

Pristina — A134

Designs: 50c, Old and modern photographs of Pristina. 70c, Drawing of Pristina buildings. €1, People near building, Pristina skyline.

**2013, Mar. 20**      *Perf. 14¼x14*
223-225 A134 Set of 3      5.75 5.75

A135

A136

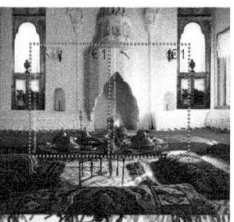

Museum Exhibits A137

No. 228 — Table with window and small wall niche at: a, Left. b, Right.

**2013, Apr. 5**      *Perf. 14x14¼*
226 A135 70c multi      1.90 1.90
227 A136 €1 multi      2.60 2.60
**Souvenir Sheet**
*Perf. 14¼x14*
228 A137 €1 Sheet of 2, #a-b      5.25 5.25

A138

A139

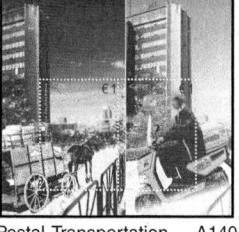

Postal Transportation — A140

No. 231: a, Horse-drawn wagon. b, Postman on scooter.

**2013, May 2**   Litho.   *Perf. 14x14¼*
229 A138 €1 multi      2.60 2.60
230 A139 €2 multi      5.25 5.25
**Souvenir Sheet**
*Perf. 14¼x14*
231 A140 €1 Sheet of 2, #a-b      5.25 5.25

Mountain
Scenery — A141

Designs: 50c, Mt. Gjeravica. 70c Rugova
Canyon (Gryka e Rugoves). €1, Mt. Gjeravica,
diff.

**2013, June 14    Litho.    *Perf. 14¼x14***
232-234 A141    Set of 3              6.00 6.00

Villages — A142

Designs: 50c, Stublla e Eperme. 70c,
Opoja. €1, Lluka e Eperme.

**2013, July 18    Litho.    *Perf. 14x14¼***
235-237 A142    Set of 3              6.00 6.00
235a              Dated "2016"        1.10 1.10

Famous
Women
A143

No. 238: a, 50c, Hyrije Hana (1929-2004),
radio broadcaster. b, 70c, Xheve Lladrovici
(1955-98), freedom fighter. c, €1, Katarina
Josipi (1923-69), actress.

**2013, Aug. 15    Litho.    *Perf. 14¼x14***
238 A143    Horiz. strip of 3, #a-c 5.50 5.50

Bajram Curri
(1862-1925),
Albanian
Politician
A144

**2013, Sept. 9    Litho.    *Perf. 14x14¼***
239 A144    €1 multi              2.75 2.75

Paintings by
Adem Kastrati
(1930-2000)
A145

Various paintings depicting: a, 70c, Buildings on hill. b, €1, Sheep and shepherds. c,
€2, Musicians.

**2013, Sept. 26    Litho.    *Perf. 14x14¼***
240 A145    Vert. strip of 3, #a-c 10.00 10.00

Pristina
University
A146

**2014, Oct. 28    Litho.    *Perf. 14x14¼***
241 A146    €1 multi              2.75 2.75

---

Singers — A147

No. 242: a, 20c, Qamili i Vogel (1923-91). b,
30c, Sali Krasniqi (1919-87). c, 50c, Dervish
Shaqa (1912-85).

**2013, Nov. 15    Litho.    *Perf. 14x14¼***
242 A147    Vert. strip of 3, #a-c 2.75 2.75
   d.      As #242a, dated "2015"    —    —

Bekim Fehmiu (1936-
2010), Actor — A148

**2013, Dec. 5    Litho.    *Perf. 14¼x14***
243 A148    €1 multi              2.75 2.75

Building Ruins —
A148a

**2013    Litho.    *Perf. 14¼x14***
243A A148a 15c multi              —    —
   b.       Dated "2014"          —    —

Compare No. 243A with Nos. 178 and 329.

Paintings by Muslim
Mulliqi (1934-
98) — A149

Various paintings.

**2014, Jan. 13    Litho.    *Perf. 14¼x14***
244         Horiz. strip of 4         7.75 7.75
   a.      A149 30c multi          .80   .80
   b.      A149 60c multi         1.60  1.60
   c.      A149 90c multi         2.50  2.50
   d.      A149 €1 multi          2.75  2.75

Mountain
Climbers — A150

Mountaineering — A151

---

**2014, Feb. 7    Litho.    *Perf. 14¼x14***
245 A150    €1 multi              2.75 2.75
**Souvenir Sheet**
246 A151    €2 multi              5.50 5.50

Pec — A152

Buildings in Pec: €1, Color photograph. €2,
Sepia-toned photograph.

**2014, Mar. 10    Litho.    *Perf. 14x14¼***
247-248 A152    Set of 2          8.25 8.25

World Shotokan
Karate
Championships,
Pristina — A153

No. 249 — Two karateka and: a, 80c,
Colored belts and "5." b, 90c, Map of Kosovo
and world.
   €2, Karateka and map of Kosovo and world.

**2014, Apr. 3    Litho.    *Perf. 14x14¼***
249 A153    Pair, #a-b            4.75 4.75
**Souvenir Sheet**
250 A153    €2 multi              5.50 5.50
No. 249 was printed in sheets containing
two pairs + label.

Ibrahim
Rugova
Highway
A154

No. 251: a, €1, Bridge and interchange. b,
€2, Entrance and exit ramps.

**2014, Apr. 25    Litho.    *Perf. 14x14¼***
251 A154    Pair, #a-b            8.25 8.25

Europa — A155

Musical instruments: €1, Two instruments.
No. 253, €2, Lakuta.
No. 254, €2, Four instruments, horiz.

**2014, May 8    Litho.    *Perf. 14¼x14***
252-253 A155    Set of 2          8.25 8.25
**Souvenir Sheet**
**Perf. 14x14¼**
254 A155    €2 multi              5.50 5.50

Flowers — A156

Designs: 80c, Liliaceae. 90c, Gladiolus
illyricus. €1, Tulipa kosovarica.
   €2, Red flowers.

**2014, June 12    Litho.    *Perf. 14¼x14***
255-257 A156    Set of 3          7.50 7.50
**Souvenir Sheet**
258 A156    €2 multi              5.50 5.50

---

Jeronim de Rada
(1814-1903),
Writer — A157

**2014, July 3    Litho.    *Perf. 14¼x14***
259 A157    €1 multi              2.75 2.75

Woven Items — A158

Various woven items.

**2014, Aug. 8    Litho.    *Perf. 14¼x14***
260         Horiz. strip or block of 4,
            #a-d                     8.75 8.75
   a.      A158 60c multi         1.60  1.60
   b.      A158 80c multi         2.10  2.10
   c.      A158 90c multi         2.40  2.40
   d.      A158 €1 multi          2.60  2.60

Fehmi (1950-98)
and Xheve
(1955-98)
Lladrovci,
Freedom
Fighters — A159

**2014, Sept. 22    Litho.    *Perf. 14x14¼***
261 A159    €2 multi              5.00 5.00

Adrian Krasniqi (1972-
97), Freedom
Fighter — A160

**2014, Oct. 16    Litho.    *Perf. 14¼x14***
262 A160    €1 multi              2.50 2.50

Tringe Smajli (1880-
1917), Freedom
Fighter — A161

**2014, Nov. 2    Litho.    *Perf. 14¼x14***
263 A161    €1 multi              2.50 2.50

Intl. Year of
Crystallography
A162

Various mineral crystals: €1, €2.

**2014, Nov. 20    Litho.    *Perf. 14x14¼***
264-265 A162    Set of 2          7.50 7.50

Granting of Intl.
Olympic Committee
Membership to
Kosovo Olympic
Committee — A163

**2014, Dec. 5    Litho.    *Perf. 14¼x14***
266 A163    €2 multi              5.00 5.00
No. 266 was printed in sheets of 6 + 3
labels.

Gjakova — A164

Various street scenes: €1,€2.

**2015, Jan. 23　Litho.　Perf. 14¼x14**
267-268　A164　Set of 2　　　7.00 7.00

Circular Labyrinth,
Smira — A165

**2015, Feb. 12　Litho.　Perf. 14¼x14**
269　A165　€1 multi　　　2.50 2.50

Lynx — A166

Designs: 80c, Lynx in tree. 90c, Head of lynx. €1, Head of lynx, flag and map of Kosovo.

**2015, Mar. 19　Litho.　Perf. 14x14¼**
270-272　A166　Set of 3　　6.00 6.00

Hashim Hajdini (1949-
99), Patriot — A167

**2015, Mar. 27　Litho.　Perf. 14¼x14**
273　A167　€1 multi　　　2.50 2.50

Waterfall — A168

Designs: 60c, Bridge and rapids. 80c, Rock-strewn river. 90c, Tree near small waterfall.

**2015, Apr. 15　Litho.　Perf. 14¼x14**
274　A168　30c multi　　　　.70　.70
275　A168　60c multi　　　1.40 1.40
276　A168　80c multi　　　1.90 1.90
277　A168　90c multi　　　2.00 2.00
　　Compare Nos. 274 and 330.

Ilaz Kodra (1966-99),
Military
Leader — A169

**2015, Apr. 30　Litho.　Perf. 14¼x14**
278　A169　€2 multi　　　4.75 4.75

A170

A171

Europa
A172

**2015, May 4　Litho.　Perf. 14x14¼**
279　A170　€1 multi　　　2.50 2.50
280　A171　€2 multi　　　4.75 4.75

**Souvenir Sheet**
281　A172　€2 multi　　　4.75 4.75

Ukshin Hoti
(1943-99),
Philosopher
A173

**2015, June 17**
282　A173　€1 multi　　　2.50 2.50

Traditional
Clothing — A174

Designs: 80c, Men's clothing. 90c, Women's clothing. €1, Decorated bag. €2, Vest.

**2015, July 1　　　Perf. 14¼x14**
283-285　A174　Set of 3　　6.00 6.00
**Souvenir Sheet**
286　A174　€2 multi　　　4.75 4.75

Diaspora
A175

**2015, Aug. 2　Litho.　Perf. 14x14¼**
287　A175　€2 multi　　　4.75 4.75

Mark (1926-98), Pren
(1964-99), Kole (1967-
99), and Meme (1973-
99) Lleshi,
Patriots — A176

**2015, Aug. 7　Litho.　Perf. 14¼x14**
288　A176　€1 multi　　　4.75 4.75

Grapes and Wine
Making — A177

Designs: 60c, Embroidered grape design. 80c, Grapes, wine bottle and glass. 90c, Vineyard. €2, Woman harvesting grapes.

**2015, Sept. 18　Litho.　Perf. 14¼x14**
289-291　A177　Set of 3　　5.25 5.25
**Souvenir Sheet**
292　A177　€2 multi　　　4.75 4.75

Anton Ceta (1920-95), Folklorist,
Founder of Reconciliation Committee
A178

**2015, Nov. 3　Litho.　Perf. 14x14¼**
293　A178　€1 multi　　　2.50 2.50

Archaeological
Artifacts — A179

**2015, Dec. 15　Litho.　Perf. 14¼x14**
294　A179　€2 multi　　　4.75 4.75

Street in
Vucitrrn — A180

Vojinovic Tower,
Vucitrn — A181

**2016, Jan. 18　Litho.　Perf. 14x14¼**
295　A180　€1 multi　　　2.50 2.50
296　A181　€2.10 multi　　4.75 4.75

Skender
Rexhepi
(1965-99),
Kosovo
Liberation
Army
Hero — A182

Luan
Haradinaj
(1973-97),
Kosovo
Liberation
Army
Hero — A183

**2016, Feb. 17　Litho.　Perf. 14¼x14**
297　A182　€1 multi　　　2.50 2.50
298　A183　€1 multi　　　2.50 2.50

Art of Rexhep
Ferri — A184

Various paintings.

**2016, Feb. 29　Litho.　Perf. 14¼x14**
299　　　Horiz. strip of 3　　4.75 4.75
　a.　　A184 40c multi　　　　.90　.90
　b.　　A184 80c multi　　　1.75 1.75
　c.　　A184 90c multi　　　2.00 2.00

Souvenir Sheet

Mountain
Tourism
A185

**2016, Mar. 28　Litho.　Perf. 14x14¼**
300　A185　€2.10 multi + label　4.75 4.75
　　See Macedonia No. 704.

Agim
Ramadani
(1963-99),
Kosovo
Liberation
Army
Commander
A186

Sali Cekaj
(1956-99),
Kosovo
Liberation
Army
Commander
A187

**2016, Apr. 9　Litho.　Perf. 14¼x14**
301　A186　€1 multi　　　2.25 2.25
302　A187　€1 multi　　　2.25 2.25

A188

A189

Europa
A190

**2016, May 9　Litho.　Perf. 14x14¼**
303　A188　€1 multi　　　2.50 2.50
304　A189　€2.10 multi　　4.75 4.75
**Souvenir Sheet**
**Perf. 14¼x14**
305　A190　€2 multi　　　4.75 4.75
　　Think Green Issue.

2016 European
Individual Chess
Championships,
Gjakova — A191

**2016, May 23　Litho.　Perf. 14¼x14**
306　A191　€1.80 multi　　4.00 4.00
　　No. 306 was printed in sheets of 2.

Mushrooms — A192

Designs: 60c, Boletus edulis. 80c, Morchella vulgaris. €1.30, Leccinum scabrum. 90c, Amanita muscaria.

**2016, July 4    Litho.    Perf. 14¼x14**
306A-306C  A192  Set of 3          6.00 6.00
307  A192  Sheet of 4, #306A,
           306B, 306C, 307a        8.00 8.00
  a.    90c multi                   2.00 2.00

Nos. 306A, 306B and 306C have misspelled Latin names.

2016 Summer Olympics, Rio de Janeiro — A193

Emblem of the Kosovo Olympic Committee and: €1, Flag of Kosovo. €2.10, Judoka. €2, Stylized sprinter.

**2016, July 29    Litho.    Perf. 14x14¼**
308-309  A193  Set of 2            7.00 7.00
**Souvenir Sheet**
310  A193  €2 multi                4.50 4.50

Canonization of St. Teresa of Calcutta — A194

**2016, Aug. 15    Litho.    Perf. 14x14¼**
311  A194  €2.10 multi             4.75 4.75

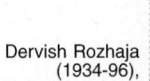

Dervish Rozhaja (1934-96), Biologist — A195

**2016, Aug. 23    Litho.    Perf. 14x14¼**
312  A195  €1.30 multi             3.00 3.00

Kosovo's Affiliation With Soccer Organizations A196

Inscriptions: €1.30, Kosovo in UEFA. €2.10, Kosovo in FIFA.

**2016, Sept. 2    Litho.    Perf. 14x14¼**
313-314  A196  Set of 2            7.75 7.75

Fruits — A197

Designs: 40c, Apples and apple pie. 60c, Pears, juice and cookie. 80c, Blackberries and blackberry jam.

**2016, Sept. 20    Litho.    Perf. 14x14¼**
315-317  A197  Set of 3            4.00 4.00

Traditional Costumes — A198

Designs: 80c, Women's blouse and vest. 90c, Woman wearing costume. €2, Man and woman in costumes.

**2016, Oct. 15    Litho.    Perf. 14¼x14**
318-319  A198  Set of 2            3.75 3.75
**Souvenir Sheet**
320  A198  €2 multi                4.50 4.50

Tetrau Urogallus A199

Bird facing: 90c, Left. €1.30, Right.

**2016, Oct. 28    Litho.    Perf. 14x14¼**
321-322  A199  Set of 2            5.00 5.00

Dodona Puppet Theater — A200

Designs: 80c, Puppet of girl with basket. 90c, Puppets of men on horseback.

**2016, Nov. 12    Litho.    Perf. 14x14¼**
323-324  A200  Set of 2            3.75 3.75

Mountain Tourism — A201

Various photographs of Boge Ski Resort: 60c, 80c, 90c.

**2016, Dec. 19    Litho.    Perf. 14**
325-327  A201  Set of 3            4.75 4.75

80th Birthday of Ismail Kadare, Writer — A202

**2016, Dec. 20    Litho.    Perf. 14x14¼**
328  A202  €1 multi                2.10 2.10

Building Ruins A203

Waterfall A204

Gazivoda Lake — A205

**2016    Litho.    Perf. 14¼x14**
329  A203  15c multi               .35 .35
330  A204  30c multi
**Perf. 14x14¼**
331  A205  50c multi               — —

Compare Nos. 329 with Nos. 178 and 243A. Compare Nos. 330-331 with Nos. 274 and 208.

Buildings in Ferizaj — A206

Designs: €1.30, Buildings at night. €2, Mosque and buildings in daylight.

**2017, Jan. 20    Litho.    Perf. 14¼x14**
332-333  A206  Set of 2           7.25 7.25

Farm Animals — A207

Designs: 20c, Bardoka ewes.
No. 335: a, Red goat. b, Syke ewe and lamb. c, Bardoka ram.

**2017, Feb. 4    Litho.    Perf. 14x14¼**
334  A207  20c multi               .45 .45
335    Horiz. strip of 3          4.00 4.00
  a.  A207 40c multi               .85 .85
  b.  A207 50c multi              1.10 1.10
  c.  A207 90c multi              1.90 1.90

Malush Ahmeti (1951-99), Kosovo Liberation Army Commander A208

Nesimi Dervishdana (1964-81), Independence Demonstrator Shot by Yugoslavian Army — A209

**2017, Feb. 17    Litho.    Perf. 14x14¼**
336  A208  €1.30 multi            2.75 2.75
337  A209  €1.30 multi            2.75 2.75

Flowers — A210

Designs: 80c, Solenanthus krasniqi. 90c, Aster albanicus. €1, Tulipa luanica.

**2017, Mar. 3    Litho.    Perf. 14¼x14**
338-340  A210  Set of 3           5.75 5.75

Xheladin Gashi (1946-2005), General — A211

**2017, Mar. 21    Litho.    Perf. 14x14¼**
341  A211  €1.30 multi            2.75 2.75

Enver Hadri (1941-90), Assassinated Human Rights Activist — A212

**2017, Apr. 2    Litho.    Perf. 14x14¼**
342  A212  €1.30 multi            3.00 3.00

Ulpiana Baptistry — A213

**2017, Apr. 18    Litho.    Perf. 14x14¼**
343  A213  €2 multi               4.50 4.50

Ulpiana Castle — A214

Prizren Fortress — A215

Novo Brdo Fortress A216

**2017, May 9    Litho.    Perf. 14x14¼**
344  A214  €1 multi               2.25 2.25
345  A215  €2 multi               4.50 4.50
**Souvenir Sheet**
346  A216  €2 multi               4.50 4.50

Europa.

A217

A218

A219

Paintings by Engjell Berisha (1926-2010) — A220

**2017, June 6    Litho.    Perf. 14¼x14**
347    Horiz. strip of 4          7.75 7.75
  a.  A217 60c multi             1.40 1.40
  b.  A218 80c multi             1.90 1.90
  c.  A219 90c multi             2.10 2.10
  d.  A220 €1 multi              2.25 2.25

Esat Stavileci (1942-2015), Law Professor A221

**2017, July 11    Litho.    Perf. 14x14¼**
348  A221  €1.30 multi            3.25 3.25

Diving From the Fshetje Bridge — A222

Design: €1.80, Drawing of diver. €2, Photograph of diver, vert.

**2017, July 21    Litho.    Perf. 14x14¼**
349  A222  €1.80 multi            4.25 4.25
**Souvenir Sheet**
**Perf. 14¼x14**
350  A222  €2 multi               4.75 4.75

Tekke of Sheikh Bani, Gjakova — A223

Architecture — A224

No. 352: a, 60c, Tekke of Sheikh Bani (inscription at LR, date at LL). b, 80c, Cathedral of Perpetual Succor, Prizren. c, 90c, Patriarchal Monastery, Pec. d, €1, Hadum Mosque, Gjakova.

**2017, Aug. 4    Litho.    Perf. 14x14¼**
351 A223 60c multi                1.50 1.50
**Miniature Sheet**
352 A224    Sheet of 4, #a-d        8.00 8.00

Traditional Clothing of Medvegja — A225

Designs: €1, Women's kerchief. No. 354, €2, Beaded vest.
No. 355, €2, Women's shoes.

**2017, Sept. 6    Litho.    Perf. 14¼x14**
353-354 A225    Set of 2            7.00 7.00
**Souvenir Sheet**
355 A225    €2 multi                4.75 4.75

Woman Breastfeeding Child — A226

**2017, Oct. 6    Litho.    Perf. 14¼x14**
356 A226    €2 multi                4.75 4.75

Protestant Reformation, 500th Anniv. — A227

**2017, Oct. 21    Litho.    Perf. 14¼x14**
357 A227    €1.80 multi            4.25 4.25

Eliot Engel, U.S. Congressman — A228

**2017, Nov. 20    Litho.    Perf. 14¼x14**
358 A228    €2 multi                4.75 4.75

Kosovo Ballet, 45th Anniv. — A229

Designs: €1, Female dancer. €2, Male and female dancers.

**2017, Dec. 1    Litho.    Perf. 14x14¼**
359-360 A229    Set of 2            7.25 7.25

Famous Men — A230

Designs: No. 361, €1.30, Pajazit Nushi (1933-2015), psychologist. No. 362, €1.30, Mark Krasniqi (1920-2015), writer.

**2017, Dec. 3    Litho.    Perf. 14x14¼**
361-362 A230    Set of 2            6.25 6.25

Skanderbeg (1405-68), Albanian National Hero — A231

**2018, Jan. 17    Litho.    Perf. 14¼x14**
363 A231    €2 multi                5.00 5.00

Birds — A232

Designs: 50c, Falco tinnunculus. €1, Oriolus oriolus.
No. 366: a, Upupa epops. b, Podiceps cristatus. c, Sturnus vulgaris.

**2018, Jan. 31    Litho.    Perf. 14x14¼**
364-365 A232    Set of 2            3.50 3.50
**Miniature Sheet**
366 A232    Sheet of 5, #364, 365,
             366a-366c, + label      8.50 8.50
*a.*    40c multi                    1.00 1.00
*b.*    60c multi                    1.50 1.50
*c.*    80c multi                    2.00 2.00

Republic of Kosovo, 10th Anniv. — A233

**2018, Feb. 17    Litho.    Perf. 14x14¼**
367 A233    €2.10 multi            5.25 5.25

Adem Jashari (1955-98), Kosovo Liberation Army Leader — A234

No. 368: a, €1.80, Adem Jashari Memorial, Prekaz. b, €2, Dove and burning house.

**2018, Mar. 5    Litho.    Perf. 14¼x14**
368 A234    Pair, #a-b              9.50 9.50

Aerial View of Gjilan — A235

Gjilan in 1925 — A236

**2018, Apr. 12    Litho.    Perf. 14x14¼**
369 A235    €1 multi                2.40 2.40
370 A236    €2 multi                4.75 4.75

A237          A238

Bridges A239

**2018, May 9    Litho.    Perf. 14¼x14**
371 A237    €1 multi                2.40 2.40
372 A238    €2 multi                4.75 4.75
**Souvenir Sheet**
**Perf. 14x14¼**
373 A239    €2 multi                4.75 4.75

Europa.

Nazim Gaffuri and Stak Mark Mirdita, Martyrs — A240

**2018, May 25    Litho.    Perf. 14x14¼**
374 A240    €1.30 multi            3.00 3.00

2018 World Cup Soccer Championships, Russia — A241

Designs: €1, Player dribbling ball. €2.10, Goalkeeper and ball.
2, Players and World Cup trophy.

**2018, June 14    Litho.    Perf. 14x14¼**
375-376 A241    Set of 2            7.25 7.25
**Souvenir Sheet**
377 A241    €2 multi                4.75 4.75

Writers — A242

Designs: No. 378, €1.30, Azem Shkreli (1938-97). No. 379, €1.30, Anton Pashku (1937-95).

**2018, June 30    Litho.    Perf. 14¼x14**
378-379 A242    Set of 2            6.00 6.00

A243

A244

Pottery — A245

**2018, July 17    Litho.    Perf. 14x14¼**
380 A243 60c multi                 1.40 1.40
381 A244 80c multi                 1.90 1.90
382 A245 90c multi                 2.10 2.10
    *Nos. 380-382 (3)*              5.40 5.40

Generals — A246

Designs: No. 383, €1.30, Brigadier General Bekim Berisha (1966-98). No. 384, €1.30, General Bedri Shala (1969-98).

**2018, Aug. 10    Litho.    Perf. 14¼x14**
383-384 A246    Set of 2            6.00 6.00

Flowers — A247

Designs: 30c, Achillea clypeolata. 40c, Viola dukadjivica. 60c, Crocus flavus. 80c, Adonis microcarpa. 90c, Leontopodium alpinum.

**2018, Aug. 24    Litho.    Perf. 14¼x14**
385-389 A247    Set of 5            7.00 7.00

A248

Coins and Mosaics From Dresnik Archaeological Site — A249

**2018, Sept. 20    Litho.    Perf. 14x14¼**
390 A248    €2.10 multi            5.00 5.00
**Souvenir Sheet**
391 A249    €2 multi                4.75 4.75

Fehmi Agani (1932-99), Politician A250

Ejup Statovci (1940-97), Law Professor A251

**2018, Oct. 1    Litho.    Perf. 14¼x14**
392 A250    €1.30 multi            3.00 3.00
393 A251    €1.30 multi            3.00 3.00

Fadil Vokrri (1960-2018), Soccer Player — A252

**2018, Oct. 9   Litho.   Perf. 14x14¼**
394 A252 €2.10 multi        4.75 4.75

A253

Shota Ensemble, 70th Anniv. — A254

**2018, Nov. 2   Litho.   Perf. 14x14¼**
395 A253 €1.30 multi        3.00 3.00
396 A254 €1.80 multi        4.25 4.25

Afrim Zhitia (1965-89) and Fahri Fazliu (1963-89), Freedom Fighters — A255

**2018, Nov. 2   Litho.   Perf. 14x14¼**
397 A255 €1.30 multi        3.00 3.00

Xhelal Hajda (1967-98) and Selajdin Mullaabazi (1970-98), Freedom Fighters — A256

**2018, Nov. 16   Litho.   Perf. 14¼x14**
398 A256 €1.30 multi        3.00 3.00

Adem Demaçi (1936-2018), Politician and Writer — A257

**2018, Nov. 28   Litho.   Perf. 14¼x14**
399 A257 €2 multi        4.50 4.50

Martyrs of Gjakova — A258

**2018, Dec. 21   Litho.   Perf. 14¼x14**
400 A258 €1.30 multi        3.00 3.00
No. 400 was printed in sheets of 5 + label.

League of Prizren, 140th Anniv. — A259

**2018, Dec. 28   Litho.   Perf. 14¼x14**
401 A259 €2.10 multi        4.75 4.75
No. 401 was printed in sheets of 5 + label.

A260

Kaçanik — A261

**2019, Jan. 17   Litho.   Perf. 14x14¼**
402 A260 €1 multi        2.40 2.40
403 A261 €2 multi        4.75 4.75

Blinaja National Park — A262

Designs: 40c, Buck. 50c, Deer. 60c, Wildlife near stream.
No. 407: a, Wildlife, hut at left. b, Wildlife, hut at upper right.

**2019, Feb. 20   Litho.   Perf. 14¼x14**
404-406 A262   Set of 3        3.50 3.50
**Souvenir Sheet**
407 A262 €1 Sheet of 2, #a-b        4.50 4.50

**Binaja National Park Type of 2019**
**2019   Litho.   Perf. 14¼x14**
**Stamps With White Frames**
407C A262 40c Like #404        — —
407D A262 50c Like #405        — —

Idriz Seferi (1847-1927), Commander in Uprisings of 1910 and 1912 A263

Shaban Polluzha (1871-1945), Military Leader A264

Marie Shllaku (1922-46), Politician A265

Ismail Imer Thaçi, Teacher and Military Hero A266

**2019, Mar. 25   Litho.   Perf. 14¼x14**
408   Horiz. strip of 4        12.00 12.00
  a. A263 €1.30 multi        3.00 3.00
  b. A264 €1.30 multi        3.00 3.00
  c. A265 €1.30 multi        3.00 3.00
  d. A266 €1.30 multi        3.00 3.00

Paintings by Esat Valla A267

No. 409 — Various unnamed paintings: a, 80c. b, 90c. c, €1.

**2019, Apr. 22   Litho.   Perf. 14¼x14**
409 A267   Horiz. strip of 3, #a-c 6.25 6.25

**Paintings by Esat Valla Type of 2019**
**2019   Litho.   Perf. 14¼x14**
**Stamp With White Frames**
409D A267 €1 Like #409c        — —

Europa — A268

Designs: €1, Buzzard. No. 411, €2, Turtle dove.
No. 412, €2, Great tit, Red-backed shrike, Rock thrush, horiz.

**2019, May 9   Litho.   Perf. 14¼x14**
410-411 A268   Set of 2        6.75 6.75
**Souvenir Sheet**
**Perf. 14x14¼**
412 A268 €2 multi        4.50 4.50

U.S. Pres. Woodrow Wilson (1856-1924) A269

**2019, May 29   Litho.   Perf. 14¼x14**
413 A269 €2 multi        10.00 10.00

Hillary Rodham Clinton, United States Secretary of State From 2009-13 — A270

**2019, June 12   Litho.   Perf. 14x14¼**
414 A270 €2 multi        4.50 4.50

**Miniature Sheet**

Placement of Kosovo Under Transitional United Nations Administration and NATO-led Peacekeeping Force, 20th Anniv. — A271

No. 415: a, U.S. President Bill Clinton. b, Prime Minister of Great Britain Tony Blair. c, U.S. Secretary of State Madeleine Albright. d, U.S. General Wesley Clark.

**2019, June 12   Litho.   Perf. 14¼x14**
415 A271 €2 Sheet of 4, #a-d 18.00 18.00

A272

A273

A274

Modern Art — A275

**2019, July 10   Litho.   Perf. 14¼x14**
416 A272 30c multi        .70 .70
417 A273 40c multi        .90 .90
418 A274 60c multi        1.40 1.40
419 A275 80c multi        1.75 1.75
  Nos. 416-419 (4)        4.75 4.75

Nexhmije Pagarusha (1933-2020), Singer — A276

**2019, Aug. 8   Litho.   Perf. 14¼x14**
420 A276 €2.10 multi        4.75 4.75

**Nexhmije Pagarusha Type of 2019**
**2019   Litho.   Perf. 14¼x14**
**Stamp With White Frames**
420A A276 €2.40 Like #420        — —

A277

A278

2019 Basketball World Championships, People's Republic of China — A279

**2019, Aug. 30   Litho.   Perf. 14x14¼**
421 A277 €1.80 multi        4.00 4.00
422 A278 €2 multi        4.50 4.50
**Souvenir Sheet**
423 A279 €2 multi        4.50 4.50

**Basketball Type of 2019**
**2019   Litho.   Perf. 14x14¼**
**Stamp With White Frames**
423A A277 €1.80 Like #421        — —

Ahmet Gashi (1888-1977), Educator A280

Shtjefen Gjeçovi (1874-1929), Folklorist A281

Mehmet Gjevori
(1910-2007),
Educator — A282

**2019, Sept. 26　Litho.　Perf. 14¼x14**
424　A280　€1.30 multi　　3.00　3.00
425　A281　€1.30 multi　　3.00　3.00
426　A282　€1.30 multi　　3.00　3.00
　　　Nos. 424-426 (3)　　9.00　9.00

Trepca Miners'
Strike, 30th
Anniv. — A283

**2019, Oct. 16　Litho.　Perf. 14x14¼**
427　A283　€1.80 multi　　4.00　4.00

A284

A285

A286

Children's
Day — A287

**2019, Nov. 20　Litho.　Perf. 14x14¼**
428　A284　50c multi　　1.10　1.10
429　A285　60c multi　　1.40　1.40
430　A286　80c multi　　1.75　1.75
431　A287　90c multi　　2.00　2.00
　　　Nos. 428-431 (4)　　6.25　6.25

A288

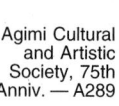

Agimi Cultural
and Artistic
Society, 75th
Anniv. — A289

**2019, Nov. 22　Litho.　Perf. 14x14¼**
432　A288　€1 multi　　2.25　2.25
433　A289　€2 multi　　4.50　4.50

A290

Christmas and
New
Year's — A291

**2019, Dec. 10　Litho.　Perf. 14¼x14**
434　A290　90c multi　　2.00　2.00
435　A291　€1 multi　　2.25　2.25

Podujeva
A292

No. 436: a, €1, Buildings along Llap River.
b, €2, Aerial view of buildings and river.

**2020, Jan. 31　Litho.　Perf. 13**
436　A292　Vert. pair, #a-b　　6.75　6.75

University of
Pristina, 50th
Anniv. — A293

**2020, Feb. 11　Litho.　Perf. 13**
437　A293　€2 multi　　4.50　4.50

Miniature Sheet

Flora
A294

No. 438: a, 30c, Sanguisorba albanica. b,
40c, Taxus baccata. c, 50c, Sempervivum
kosanini. d, 60c, Halacsya sendtneri. e, 90c,
Primula halleri.

**2020, Mar. 10　Litho.　Perf. 14¼x14**
438　A294　Sheet of 10, 2 each　　—　—
　　　#438a-438e, + cen-
　　　tral label

Pristina Half-
Marathon, 20th
Anniv. — A295

**2020, May 20　Litho.　Perf. 14x14¼**
439　A295　€1.80 multi　　4.00　4.00

Postman
Delivering
Mail — A296

Horse-drawn
Mail
Cart — A297

Ship,
Train,
Carrier
Pigeon,
Map of
Europe
A298

**2020, June 1　Litho.　Perf. 14x14¼**
440　A296　€1 multi　　2.25　2.25
441　A297　€2 multi　　4.50　4.50

**Souvenir Sheet**
442　A298　€2 multi　　4.50　4.50
Europa.

Proclamation of
the Republic of
Kosovo, 30th
Anniv. — A299

**2020, July 2　Litho.　Perf. 14x14¼**
443　A299　€2 multi　　4.75　4.75

Campaign
Against Spread
of COVID-19
A300

No. 444 — Stylized COVID-19 viruses and:
a, Globe, protective face masks on hearts. b,
Protective face mask on dove. c, Protective
face mask on map of Kosovo, hands and water
droplets.

**2020, Aug. 14　Litho.　Perf. 14x14¼**
444　　Horiz. strip of 3　　5.50　5.50
　a.　A300 30c multi　　.75　.75
　b.　A300 90c multi　　2.25　2.25
　c.　A300 €1 multi　　2.40　2.40
Printed in sheets of 6 containing two each of
Nos. 444a-444c.

First Albanian
School,
Stubell — A301

**2020, Sept. 1　Litho.　Perf. 14x14¼**
445　A301　€2.10 multi　　5.00　5.00

Paintings by
Tahir
Emra — A302

Various unnamed paintings.

**2020, Sept. 22　Litho.　Perf. 14x14¼**
446　　Horiz. strip of 3　　6.50　6.50
　a.　A302 80c multi　　1.90　1.90
　b.　A302 90c multi　　2.10　2.10
　c.　A302 €1 multi　　2.40　2.40

Heroine of
Kosovo — A303

**2020, Oct. 22　Litho.　Perf. 14¼x14**
447　A303　€2.10 multi　　—　—

Lakes
A304

No. 448 — Various lakes: a, €1.30. b, €2.10

**2020, Nov. 5　Litho.　Perf. 14x14¼**
448　A304　Horiz. pair, #a-b　　8.25　8.25

Children's
Day — A305

No. 449 — Children: a, €1, With kites and
balloons. b, €1.80, Playing with balls.

**2020, Nov. 24　Litho.　Perf. 14x14¼**
449　A305　Vert. pair, #a-b　　6.75　6.75

Holy Archangels
Monastery,
Prizren — A306

**2020. Dec. 10　Litho.　Perf. 14x14¼**
450　A306　€1.80 multi　　4.50　4.50

Pansy — A307

Roses — A308

Flowers — A309

**2020, Dec. 10　Litho.　Perf. 14¼x14**
451　A307　10c multi　　.25　.25
452　A308　15c multi　　.40　.40
453　A309　20c multi　　.50　.50
　　　Nos. 451-453 (3)　　1.15　1.15

Tribute to Medical Personnel Working
During the COVID-19 Pandemic
A310

**2021, Jan. 28　Litho.　Perf. 14**
454　A310　€2.10 multi　　5.25　5.25

A311

Skenderaj
A312

**2021, Feb. 8　Litho.　Perf. 14x14¼**
455　A311　€1 multi　　2.40　2.40
456　A312　€2 multi　　5.00　5.00

Protests for
Republic Status
in Yugoslavia
and Human
Rights, 40th
Anniv. — A313

**2021, Mar. 11　Litho.　Perf. 14x14¼**
457　A313　€1.80 multi　　4.25　4.25

Theater Personalities — A314

No. 458: a, Besim Sahatçiu (1935-2005), director. b, Leze Qena (1935-2020), actress.

**2021, Mar. 25  Litho.  Perf. 14¼x14**
458 A314  €1.30 Pair, #a-b  6.25 6.25

Siqeva Spring — A315

Gorozhupi Spring — A316

King's Spring — A317

**2021, Apr. 7  Litho.  Perf. 14x14¼**
459  Horiz. strip of 3  5.75 5.75
 a. A315 60c multi  1.50 1.50
 b. A316 80c multi  2.00 2.00
 c. A317 90c multi  2.25 2.25

Roe Deer — A317a

**2021, May 7  Litho.  Perf. 14x14¼**
459D A317a  €1 multi  2.50 2.50
 Europa.

Endangered Animals — A318

Designs: €1, Roe deer. No. 461, Brown bear. No. 462, Roe deer, diff.

**2021, May 7  Litho.  Perf. 14x14¼**
460 A318  €1 multi  2.50 2.50
461 A318  €2 multi  5.00 5.00
**Souvenir Sheet**
462 A318  €2 multi  5.00 5.00
 Europa.

Fruits — A319

No. 463: a, Miedra (raspberries). b, Dredheza (wild strawberries). c, Qershiza (wild blueberries).

€2, Wild strawberries, wild blueberries, and raspberries, horiz.

**2021, June 4  Litho.  Perf. 14¼x14**
463  Strip of 3  6.50 6.50
 a. A319 80c multi  1.90 1.90
 b. A319 90c multi  2.10 2.10
 c. A319 €1 multi  2.40 2.40
**Souvenir Sheet**
**Perf. 14x14¼**
464 A319  €2 multi  4.75 4.75

Traditional Games — A320

No. 465: a, €1.30, Stick throwing. b, €1.80, Rock throwing.

**2021, July 2  Litho.  Perf. 14x14¼**
465 A320  Pair, #a-b  7.50 7.50

2020 Summer Olympics, Tokyo — A321

No. 466: a, €1, Judokas, Olympic rings. b, €2.10, Judokas, flag of Kosovo. c, €2, Wrestling.

**2021, July 20  Litho.  Perf. 14x14¼**
466 A321  Pair, #a-b  7.50 7.50
**Souvenir Sheet**
467 A321  €2 multi  4.75 4.75
 The 2020 Summer Olympics were postponed until 2021 because of the COVID-19 pandemic.

Columba Illyrica — A322

**2021, Aug. 17  Litho.  Perf. 14**
468 A322  €2.10 multi  5.00 5.00

Independence Referendum, 30th Anniv. — A323

**2021, Sept. 26  Litho.  Perf. 14**
469 A323  €2.10 multi  5.00 5.00

COVID-19 Vaccination Campaign A324

No. 470 — Hypodermic needle and: a, Man and woman. b, Teacher with books. c, Mother and infant. d, Pregnant woman.

**2021, Oct. 8  Litho.  Perf. 14**
470  Horiz. strip or block of 4  4.25 4.25
 a. A324 30c multi  .70 .70
 b. A324 40c multi  .90 .90
 c. A324 50c multi  1.25 1.25
 d. A324 60c multi  1.40 1.40
**Stamps With White Frames**
471 A324 30c Like #470a  — —
472 A324 40c Like #470b  — —
473 A324 50c Like #470c  — —
474 A324 60c Like #470d  — —

A325

Handcrafted Items — A326

No. 475: a, €1, Hats. b, €2, Horse collars. No. 476, €2, Hands sewing fabric.

**2021, Dec. 10  Litho.  Perf. 14**
475 A325  Pair, #a-b  7.00 7.00
**Souvenir Sheet**
476 A326  €2 multi  4.50 4.50
 No. 475 was printed in sheets of 6 containing 3 each of Nos. 475a-475b.

Art By Simon Shiroka (1927-94) — A327

No. 477 — Various unnamed works of art with denominations of: a, 60c. b, €1. c, €1.30.

**2021, Nov. 4  Litho.  Perf. 14**
477 A327  Horiz. strip of 3, #a-c  6.75 6.75

Carvings by Luan Mulliqi A328

No. 478 — Various unnamed works of art with denominations of: a, 50c. b, 80c. c, €1. d, €1.30.

**2022, Jan. 31  Litho.  Perf. 14**
478 A328  Block of 4, #a-d  8.25 8.25

2022 Winter Olympics, Beijing — A329

Designs: €1, Skier. €2.10, Ski jumper, snowboarder, figure skaters, speed skaters. €2, Skiers.

**2022, Feb. 17  Litho.  Perf. 14**
479-480 A329  Set of 2  7.00 7.00
**Souvenir Sheet**
481 A329  €2 multi  4.50 4.50

Lipjan A330

No. 482: a, €1, Aerial view of Lipjan. b, €2, Church of the Presentation, Lipjan.

**2022, Mar. 9  Litho.  Perf. 14**
482 A330  Pair, #a-b  6.75 6.75

Legend of Rozafa A332

Gogomeli the Scarecrow A333

Legend of the Old Woman's Tears A334

**2022, May 9  Litho.  Perf. 14¼x14**
484 A332  €1 multi  2.25 2.25
485 A333  €2 multi  4.25 4.25
**Souvenir Sheet**
**Perf. 14x14¼**
486 A334  €2 multi  4.25 4.25
 Europa.

Presidential and Parliamentary Elections, 30th Anniv. — A335

**2022, May 24  Litho.  Perf. 14x14¼**
487 A335  €2.10 multi  4.50 4.50

Tahir Zemaj (1952-2003), Commander-in-Chief of Armed Forces of Republic of Kosovo — A336

Mehe Uka (1962-96), Teacher and Hero of Kosovo A337

Tahir Meha (1943-81), Liberation Activist A338

Ismet Rrahmani (1962-98), Teacher and Liberation Activist — A339

**2022, June 12  Litho.  Perf. 14¼x14**
488 A336  €1.30 multi  2.75 2.75
489 A337  €1.30 multi  2.75 2.75
490 A338  €1.30 multi  2.75 2.75
491 A339  €1.30 multi  2.75 2.75
 Nos. 488-491 (4)  11.00 11.00

Global
Peace — A340

**2022, June 20  Litho.   Perf. 14x14¼**
492  A340  €2.10 multi                4.50  4.50

A341

Fish
A342

Designs: Nos. 493, 494a, 40c, Mustaku (one catfish). No. 494b, 50c, Njgala (eels). No. 494c, 80c, Mustaku (two catfish). No. 494d, 90c, Trofta (trout).

**2022, July 29  Litho.   Perf. 14x14¼**
493  A341  40c multi                   .85   .85
494  A342     Block or horiz.
              strip of 4, #a-d         5.50  5.50

Dua Lipa, Singer,
Model and
Philanthropist — A343

**2022, Aug. 7  Litho.   Perf. 14¼x14**
495  A343  €1.80 multi               3.75  3.75

Kosovo Ballet,
50th
Anniv. — A344

No. 496 — "50" and: a, €1.30, Photograph of ballerina. b, €1.80, Drawing of ballerina.

**2022, Sept. 1  Litho.   Perf. 14x14¼**
496  A344     Pair, #a-b              6.25  6.25

School
Classroom
A345

**2022, Sept. 20  Litho.   Perf. 14x14¼**
497  A345  €2 multi                   4.00  4.00

Naim Frasheri Association of Albanian Teachers, 30th anniv.

Doors of
Prizren
A346

No. 498: a, 90c, Door with metal knocker. b, €1, Doors.

**2022, Oct. 10  Litho.   Perf. 14¼x14**
498  A346     Pair, #a-b              3.75  3.75

A347

A348

Mountain
Log
Cabins
A349

**2022, Nov. 15  Litho.   Perf. 14x14¼**
499  A347  90c multi                  1.90  1.90
500  A348  €2 multi                   4.25  4.25

**Souvenir Sheet**
501  A349  €2 multi                   4.25  4.25

# KUWAIT

ku-ʹwāt

LOCATION — Northwestern coast of the Persian Gulf
GOVT. — Sheikdom
AREA — 7,000 sq. mi.
POP. — 1,991,115 (1999 est.)
CAPITAL — Kuwait

Kuwait was under British protection until June 19, 1961, when it became a fully independent state.

16 Annas = 1 Rupee
100 Naye Paise = 1 Rupee (1957)
1000 Fils = 1 Kuwaiti Dinar (1961)

> Catalogue values for unused stamps in this country are for Never Hinged items, beginning with Scott 72 in the regular postage section, Scott C5 in the air post section, and Scott J1 in the postage due section.

There was a first or trial setting of the overprint with the word "Koweit." Twenty-four sets of regular and official stamps were printed with this spelling. Value for set, $55,000.

> Catalogue values for Nos. 1-71 used, are for postally used examples. Stamps with telegraph cancellations are worth less.

### Iraqi Postal Administration
Stamps of India, 1911-23, Overprinted

a

b

**1923-24    Wmk. 39    Perf. 14**
1   A47(a)   ½a green              4.75   15.00
a.     Double overprint            400.00
b.     Vertical pair, one without
       overprint                   2,200.
2   A48(a)   1a dk brn             8.00    5.50
a.     Double overprint            550.00
b.     Vertical pair, one without
       overprint                   2,750.
3   A58(a)   1½a choc              6.75   13.50
4   A49(a)   2a violet             5.75    9.50
a.     2a reddish purple           15.50
5   A57(a)   2a6p ultra            4.25    8.75
6   A51(a)   3a brn org            5.00   26.50
7   A51(a)   3a ultra ('24)        12.50   4.50
8   A52(a)   4a ol green           11.50  27.00
9   A53(a)   6a bister             13.00  16.00

10  A54(a)   8a red vio            12.00  57.50
11  A55(a)   12a claret            16.00  62.50
12  A56(b)   1r grn & red
             brn                   50.00  55.00
a.     1r dp turq grn & org brown  62.00   80.00
13  A56(b)   2r brn & car
             rose                  67.50  120.00
14  A56(b)   5r vio & ultra        140.00 275.00
15  A56(b)   10r car & grn         275.00 600.00
       Nos. 1-15 (15)              632.00 1,296.

Overprint "a" on India No. 102 is generally considered unofficial.
Nos. 1-4, 6-7 exist with inverted overprint. None of these are believed to have been sold at the Kuwait post office.
For overprints see Nos. O1-O13.

1926-35 India Stamps
Overprinted — c

**1929-37                    Wmk. 196**
17  A47    ½a green               6.50   3.00
18  A71    ½a green ('34)         11.00  2.00
19  A48    1a dark brown          7.75   4.00
20  A72    1a dk brown ('34)      16.50  1.25
21  A60    2a dk violet           9.50   2.00
22  A60    2a vermilion           27.50  95.00
23  A49    2a ver ('34)           17.50  6.75
a.     Small die                  8.75   3.00
24  A51    3a ultramarine         6.00   3.50
25  A51    3a car rose ('34)      9.00   4.50
26  A61    4a olive green         40.00 100.00
27  A52    4a ol green ('34)      17.50  14.50
28  A53    6a bister ('37)        27.50  70.00
29  A54    8a red violet          10.00  15.00
30  A55    12a claret             35.00  50.00

Overprinted — d

**31  A56   1r grn & brn          27.50  50.00**
32  A56    2r orange &
           carmine                25.00  75.00
33  A56    5r dk vio & ultra
           ('37)                  145.00 325.00
34  A56    10r car & grn
           ('34)                  325.00 550.00
35  A56    15r ol grn & ultra
           ('37)                  1,000. 1,300.
       Nos. 17-35 (19)            1,764. 2,672.

For overprints see Nos. O15-O25.

**Stamps of India, 1937, Overprinted Type "c" or "d"**

**1939       Wmk. 196       Perf. 13½x14**
45  A80(c)   ½a brown             4.25    3.50
46  A80(c)   1a carmine           4.25    3.50
47  A81(c)   2a scarlet           4.50    5.00
48  A81(c)   3a yel green         6.00    3.25
49  A81(c)   4a dark brown        25.00  30.00
50  A81(c)   6a peacock
             blue                 16.00  20.00
51  A81(c)   8a blue violet       17.50  35.00
52  A81(c)   12a car lake         12.00  85.00
53  A82(d)   1r brown &
             slate                16.00   8.75
a.     Elongated "T"              675.00 725.00
54  A82(d)   2r dk brn &
             dk vio               5.00   27.50
a.     Elongated "T"              700.00 1,200.
55  A82(d)   5r dp ultra &
             dk green             12.00  30.00
a.     Elongated "T"              1,100. 2,100.
56  A82(d)   10r rose car &
             dk violet            50.00  100.00
a.     Double overprint           650.00    —
b.     Elongated "T"              1,600.
57  A82(d)   15r dk grn &
             dk brn               75.00  225.00
a.     Elongated "T"              3,750.
       Nos. 45-57 (13)            247.50 576.50
Set, never hinged                 400.00

The elongated "T" variety was corrected in later printings.

### Indian Postal Administration

From May 24, 1941, until August 1947, the Kuwaiti postal service was administered by India, and during 1941-45 unoverprinted Indian stamps were used in Kuwait.

Kuwait postal services were administered by Pakistan from August 1947 through March 1948. Control was transferred to Great Britain on April 1, 1948.

Stamps of India 1940-43,
Overprinted in Black

**1945      Wmk. 196      Perf. 13½x14**
59  A83    3p slate               2.75  10.00
60  A83    ½a rose violet         1.75   5.50
61  A83    9p lt green            2.75  18.50
62  A83    1a car rose            2.00   2.50
63  A84    1½a dark purple        2.75  11.00
64  A84    2a scarlet             3.00   8.50
65  A84    3a violet              4.00  16.00
66  A84    3½a ultramarine        3.75  17.50
67  A85    4a chocolate           4.00   4.75
68  A85    6a peacock blue        11.00 22.50
69  A85    8a blue violet         5.75  15.00
70  A85    12a car lake           6.00   9.00
71  A81    14a rose violet        11.00  24.00
       Nos. 59-71 (13)            60.50 164.75
Set, never hinged                 110.00

> Catalogue values for unused stamps in this section, from this point to the end of the section, are for Never Hinged items.

### British Postal Administration
See Oman (Muscat) for similar stamps with surcharge of new value only.

Great Britain Nos. 258 to
263, 243 and 248
Surcharged in Black

**1948-49      Wmk. 251      Perf. 14½x14**
72  A101   ½a on ½p grn           6.00   4.25
73  A101   1a on 1p ver           6.00   2.50
74  A101   1½a on 1½p lt
           red brown              6.75   2.50
75  A101   2a on 2p lt org        6.00   2.50
76  A101   2½a on 2½p ul-
           tra                    6.25   1.25
77  A101   3a on 3p violet        6.25   1.10
a.     Pair, one without
       surcharge                  20,000.
78  A102   6a on 6p rose
           lil                    6.25   1.00
79  A103   1r on 1sh brn          13.50  2.50

Great Britain Nos.
249A, 250 and 251A
Surcharged in Black

**              Wmk. 259       Perf. 14**
80  A104   2r on 2sh6p yel
           grn                    14.50  9.00
81  A104   5r on 5sh dull red     19.00  9.00
81A A105   10r on 10sh ultra      95.00  11.50
       Nos. 72-81A (11)           185.50 47.10
Set, hinged                       123.00

Issued: Nos. 72-81, 4/48; 10r, 7/4/49.
Bars of surcharge at bottom on No. 81A.

### Silver Wedding Issue

Great Britain Nos.
267 and 268
Surcharged in
Black

**Perf. 14½x14, 14x14½**
**1948                    Wmk. 251**
82  A109   2½a on 2½p brt ul-
           tra                    4.50   3.00
83  A110   15r on £1 deep
           chalky blue            65.00  42.50

Three bars obliterate the original denomination on No. 83.

## Olympic Games Issue
Great Britain Nos. 271 to 274
Surcharged "KUWAIT" and New Value
in Black

**1948**      *Perf. 14½x14*

| | | | | |
|---|---|---|---|---|
| 84 | A113 | 2½a on 2½p brt ultra | 1.90 | 4.50 |
| 85 | A114 | 3a on 3p dp violet | 2.10 | 4.50 |
| 86 | A115 | 6a on 6p red violet | 2.25 | 4.50 |
| 87 | A116 | 1r on 1sh dk brown | 2.75 | 4.50 |
| | | *Nos. 84-87 (4)* | 9.00 | 18.00 |

A square of dots obliterates the original denomination on No. 87.

## UPU Issue
Great Britain Nos. 276 to 279
Surcharged "KUWAIT", New Value and
Square of Dots in Black

**1949, Oct. 10**

| | | | | |
|---|---|---|---|---|
| 89 | A117 | 2½a on 2½p brt ultra | 1.25 | 2.50 |
| 90 | A118 | 3a on 3p brt vio | 1.50 | 3.00 |
| 91 | A119 | 6a on 6p red vio | 1.60 | 3.00 |
| 92 | A120 | 1r on 1sh brown | 1.75 | 1.75 |
| | | *Nos. 89-92 (4)* | 6.10 | 10.25 |

## Great Britain Nos. 280-285
Surcharged Like Nos. 72-79 in Black

**1950-51**    **Wmk. 251**    *Perf. 14½x14*

| | | | | |
|---|---|---|---|---|
| 93 | A101 | ½a on ½p lt org | 2.75 | 1.50 |
| 94 | A101 | 1a on 1p ultra | 2.75 | 1.60 |
| 95 | A101 | 1½a on 1½p green | 2.75 | 2.25 |
| 96 | A101 | 2a on 2p lt red brown | 2.75 | 1.50 |
| 97 | A101 | 2½a on 2½p ver | 2.75 | 2.75 |
| 98 | A102 | 4a on 4p ultra ('50) | 2.75 | 1.50 |

## Great Britain Nos. 286-288
Surcharged in Black

**Perf. 11x12**
**Wmk. 259**

| | | | | |
|---|---|---|---|---|
| 99 | A121 | 2r on 2sh6p green | 24.00 | 8.75 |
| 100 | A121 | 5r on 5sh dl red | 30.00 | 10.00 |
| 101 | A122 | 10r on 10sh ultra | 50.00 | 11.00 |
| | | *Nos. 93-101 (9)* | 120.50 | 40.85 |

Longer bars, at lower right, on No. 101. Issued: 4a, 10/2/50; others, 5/3/51.

## Stamps of Great Britain, 1952-54
Surcharged "KUWAIT" and New
Value in Black or Dark Blue

**1952-54**    **Wmk. 298**    *Perf. 14½x14*

| | | | | |
|---|---|---|---|---|
| 102 | A126 | ½a on ½p red org ('53) | .30 | 3.00 |
| 103 | A126 | 1a on 1p ultra ('53) | .30 | .25 |
| 104 | A126 | 1½a on 1½p green | .25 | 1.75 |
| 105 | A126 | 2a on 2p red brn ('53) | .35 | .25 |
| 106 | A127 | 2½a on 2½p scarlet | .40 | 1.75 |
| 107 | A127 | 3a on 3p dk pur (Dk Bl) ('54) | .55 | .25 |
| 108 | A128 | 4a on 4p ultra ('53) | 1.60 | 1.00 |
| 109 | A129 | 6a on 6p lilac rose ('54) | 2.25 | .25 |
| 111 | A132 | 12a on 1sh3p dk green ('53) | 6.00 | 2.50 |
| 112 | A131 | 1r on 1sh6p dk blue ('53) | 4.75 | .25 |
| | | *Nos. 102-112 (10)* | 16.75 | 11.25 |

## Coronation Issue
Great Britain Nos. 313-316
Surcharged "KUWAIT" and New Value
in Black

**1953, June 3**

| | | | | |
|---|---|---|---|---|
| 113 | A134 | 2½a on 2½p scarlet | 3.75 | 2.00 |
| 114 | A135 | 4a on 4p brt ultra | 3.25 | 2.00 |
| 115 | A136 | 12a on 1sh3p dk grn | 5.00 | 3.50 |
| 116 | A137 | 1r on 1sh6p dk blue | 4.00 | 1.00 |
| | | *Nos. 113-116 (4)* | 16.00 | 8.50 |

Squares of dots obliterate the original denominations on Nos. 115 and 116.

## Great Britain Stamps of 1955-56
Surcharged "KUWAIT" and New
Value in Black

**1955**    **Wmk. 308**    *Perf. 11x12*

| | | | | |
|---|---|---|---|---|
| 117 | A133 | 2r on 2sh6p dk brown | 9.00 | 3.25 |
| 118 | A133 | 5r on 5sh crimson | 10.00 | 8.00 |
| 119 | A133 | 10r on 10sh dp ultra | 11.00 | 6.00 |
| | | *Nos. 117-119 (3)* | 30.00 | 17.25 |

The surcharge on Nos. 117-119 exists in two types.

---

**1956**      *Perf. 14½x14*

| | | | | |
|---|---|---|---|---|
| 120 | A126 | ½a on ½p red org | .35 | 1.75 |
| 121 | A126 | 1a on 1p ultra | .50 | 3.25 |
| 122 | A126 | 1½a on 1½p green | .40 | .85 |
| 123 | A126 | 2a on 2p red brn | .40 | .50 |
| 124 | A127 | 2½a on 2½p scar | .85 | 4.00 |
| 125 | A128 | 4a on 4p ultra | 4.75 | 3.50 |
| 126 | A129 | 6a on 6p lil rose | 2.25 | .40 |
| 127 | A132 | 12a on 1sh3p dk grn | 10.00 | 8.00 |
| 128 | A131 | 1r on 1sh6p dk bl | 12.00 | .35 |
| | | *Nos. 120-128 (9)* | 31.50 | 22.60 |

## Great Britain Nos. 317-325, 328 and 332 Surcharged "KUWAIT" and New Value in Black

**1957-58**    **Wmk. 308**    *Perf. 14½x14*

| | | | | |
|---|---|---|---|---|
| 129 | A129 | 1np on 5p lt brown | .35 | .70 |
| 130 | A126 | 3np on ½p lt org | .75 | 4.00 |
| 131 | A126 | 6np on 1p ultra | .75 | 1.25 |
| 132 | A126 | 9np on 1½p green | .75 | 3.25 |
| 133 | A126 | 12np on 2p red brn | .75 | 4.25 |
| 134 | A127 | 15np on 2½p scar, type I | .75 | 5.50 |
| a. | | Type II ('58) | 55.00 | 115.00 |
| 135 | A127 | 20np on 3p dk pur | .80 | .45 |
| 136 | A128 | 25np on 4p ultra | 2.75 | 3.25 |
| 137 | A129 | 40np on 6p lilac rose | 1.00 | .30 |
| 138 | A130 | 50np on 9p dp ol grn | 5.75 | 4.00 |
| 139 | A132 | 75np on 1sh3p dk grn | 6.50 | 6.00 |
| | | *Nos. 129-139 (11)* | 20.90 | 32.95 |

The arrangement of the surcharge varies on different values; there are three bars through value on No. 138.

Sheik Abdullah A1

Dhow A2

Oil Derrick — A3

Designs: 50np, Pipe lines. 75np, Main square, Kuwait. 2r, Dhow, derrick and Sheik. 5r, Mosque and Sheik. 10r, Oil plant at Burgan and Sheik.

**Perf. 12½**
**1959, Feb. 1**    **Unwmk.**    **Engr.**

| | | | | |
|---|---|---|---|---|
| 140 | A1 | 5np green | 1.00 | .25 |
| 141 | A1 | 10np rose brown | .70 | .25 |
| 142 | A1 | 15np yellow brown | .60 | .25 |
| 143 | A1 | 20np gray violet | .60 | .25 |
| 144 | A1 | 25np vermilion | 1.00 | .25 |
| 145 | A1 | 40np rose claret | 4.50 | 1.25 |

**Perf. 13½x13**

| | | | | |
|---|---|---|---|---|
| 146 | A2 | 40np dark blue | 1.00 | .25 |
| 147 | A2 | 50np carmine | 1.00 | .25 |
| 148 | A2 | 75np olive green | 1.00 | .45 |

**Perf. 14x13½**

| | | | | |
|---|---|---|---|---|
| 149 | A3 | 1r claret | 1.50 | .55 |
| 150 | A3 | 2r red brn & dp bl | 4.75 | 1.00 |
| 151 | A3 | 5r green | 9.00 | 2.75 |
| 152 | A3 | 10r purple | 27.50 | 6.75 |
| | | *Nos. 140-152 (13)* | 54.15 | 14.50 |

No. 140-141 and 145 were issued in 1958 for local use. They became valid for international mail on Feb. 1, 1959, but No. 145 was withdrawn after two weeks.

Sheik Abdullah and Flag — A4

**1960, Feb. 25**    **Engr.**    *Perf. 14*

| | | | | |
|---|---|---|---|---|
| 153 | A4 | 40np olive grn & red | .65 | .25 |
| 154 | A4 | 60np blue & red | .95 | .30 |

10th anniv. of the accession of Sheik Sir Abdullah As-Salim As-Sabah.

## Types of 1959, Redrawn

Designs: 20f, 3d, Mosque and Sheik. 25f, 100f, Vickers Viscount. 30f, 75f, Dhow, derrick and Sheik. 35f, 90f, Shuwaikh secondary school. 45f, 1d, Wara Hill, Burgan oil field.

---

**1961**      *Perf. 12½*

| | | | | |
|---|---|---|---|---|
| 155 | A1 | 1f green | .45 | .25 |
| 156 | A1 | 2f rose brown | .45 | .25 |
| 157 | A1 | 4f yellow brown | .45 | .25 |
| 158 | A1 | 5f gray violet | .50 | .25 |
| 159 | A1 | 8f yellowish orange | .50 | .25 |
| 160 | A1 | 15f rose claret | .50 | .25 |

*Perf. 14x13½, 13½ (40f, 250f)*

| | | | | |
|---|---|---|---|---|
| 161 | A3 | 20f green | .55 | .25 |
| 162 | A3 | 25f blue | .75 | .25 |
| 163 | A3 | 30f red brn & dp bl | .80 | .25 |
| 164 | A3 | 35f ver & black | .90 | .30 |
| 165 | A2 | 40f dark blue | 1.00 | .30 |
| 166 | A3 | 45f violet brown | 1.20 | .30 |
| 167 | A3 | 75f green & sepia | 1.75 | .75 |
| 168 | A3 | 90f ultra & brown | 1.60 | .65 |
| 169 | A3 | 100f rose red | 2.60 | .30 |
| 170 | A2 | 250f olive green | 10.00 | 1.50 |
| 171 | A3 | 1d orange | 17.50 | 4.00 |
| 172 | A3 | 3d brick red | 47.50 | 25.00 |
| | | *Nos. 155-172 (18)* | 89.00 | 35.35 |

Nos. 165 and 170 are 32x22mm. Issued: 75f, 90f, 4/27; 35f, 5/8; others, 4/1.

Symbols of Telecommunications A5

**Perf. 11½**
**1962, Jan. 11**    **Unwmk.**    **Photo.**
**Granite Paper**

| | | | | |
|---|---|---|---|---|
| 173 | A5 | 8f blue & black | .60 | .25 |
| 174 | A5 | 20f rose & black | 1.40 | .60 |

4th Arab Telecommunications Union Conference.

Mubarakiya School and Sheiks Abdullah and Mubarak A6

**1962, Apr. 15**    **Unwmk.**    *Perf. 11½*

| | | | | |
|---|---|---|---|---|
| 175 | A6 | 8f gldn brn, blk, org & gold | 1.00 | .25 |
| 176 | A6 | 20f lt blue, blk, org & gold | 2.00 | .45 |

50th anniversary of Mubarakiya School.

Arab League Building, Cairo, and Emblem — A7

---

**1962, Apr. 23**      *Perf. 13½x13*

| | | | | |
|---|---|---|---|---|
| 177 | A7 | 20f purple | .50 | .25 |
| 178 | A7 | 45f brown | 1.50 | .65 |

Arab Publicity Week, Mar. 22-28.

Flag of Kuwait — A8

**1962, June 19**      *Perf. 11½*
**Flag in Green, Black & Red**

| | | | | |
|---|---|---|---|---|
| 179 | A8 | 8f black & tan | .60 | .25 |
| 180 | A8 | 20f black & yellow | .90 | .30 |
| 181 | A8 | 45f black & lt blue | 1.75 | .45 |
| 182 | A8 | 90f black & lilac | 2.75 | 1.25 |
| | | *Nos. 179-182 (4)* | 6.00 | 2.25 |

Issued for National Day, June 19.

Malaria Eradication Emblem — A9

**1962, Aug. 1**      *Perf. 13½x13*

| | | | | |
|---|---|---|---|---|
| 183 | A9 | 4f slate green & yel grn | .50 | .25 |
| 184 | A9 | 25f green & gray | 1.50 | .75 |

WHO drive to eradicate malaria. No. 184 has laurel leaves added and inscription rearranged.

Cogwheel, Oil Wells, Camels and Modern Building A10

**Perf. 11x13**
**1962, Dec. 8**    **Unwmk.**    **Litho.**

| | | | | |
|---|---|---|---|---|
| 185 | A10 | 8f multicolored | .55 | .25 |
| 186 | A10 | 20f multicolored | .90 | .35 |
| 187 | A10 | 45f multicolored | 1.50 | .70 |
| 188 | A10 | 75f multicolored | 2.75 | 1.25 |
| | | *Nos. 185-188 (4)* | 5.70 | 2.55 |

Bicentenary of the Sabah dynasty.

Mother and Child — A11

**1963, Mar. 21 Photo. Perf. 14½x14**
189 A11 8f yel, red, blk & green .40 .25
190 A11 20f blue, red, blk & grn .50 .40
191 A11 45f lt ol, red, blk & grn 1.15 .70
192 A11 75f gray, red, blk & grn 1.40 .80
*Nos. 189-192 (4)* 3.45 2.15

Issued for Mother's Day, Mar. 21, 1963.

Wheat Emblem, Date Palm, Cow and Sheep — A12

**1963, Mar. 21 Perf. 14x14½**
193 A12 4f red brn, lt blue & grn .60 .25
194 A12 8f brown, yel & green .75 .40
195 A12 20f red brn, pale vio & green 1.15 .75
196 A12 45f red brn, rose & green 2.00 1.75
*Nos. 193-196 (4)* 4.50 3.15

FAO "Freedom from Hunger" campaign.

Test Tube, Oil Drops and Ship — A13

**1963, Apr. 15 Photo. Perf. 14½x14**
197 A13 4f brown, yel & blue .50 .25
198 A13 20f green, yel & blue .75 .30
199 A13 45f brt mag, yel & blue 1.75 .65
*Nos. 197-199 (3)* 3.00 1.20

Issued for Education Day.

Sheik Abdullah, Flags and Map of Kuwait — A14

**1963, June 19 Perf. 14x13**
**Flags in Black, Bright Green & Red; Denominations in Black**
200 A14 4f ultramarine 1.40 .65
201 A14 5f ocher 1.75 1.10
202 A14 20f bright purple 6.25 4.75
203 A14 50f olive brn 13.00 6.00
*Nos. 200-203 (4)* 22.40 12.50

Second anniversary of National Day.

Lungs and Emblems of World Health Organization and Kuwait Tuberculosis Society — A15

**1963, July 27 Perf. 13x13½**
**Design in Yellow, Black, Emerald & Red**
204 A15 2f ocher .55 .25
205 A15 4f dark green .70 .25
206 A15 8f lt violet blue 1.00 .30
207 A15 20f rose brown 2.25 .80
*Nos. 204-207 (4)* 4.50 1.60

Issued to publicize tuberculosis control.

Sheik Abdullah, Scroll and Scales of Justice — A16

**1963, Oct. 29 Photo. Perf. 11x13**
**Center in Gray**
208 A16 4f dp red & red brn .35 .25
209 A16 8f dk green & red brn .50 .25
210 A16 20f vio brn & red brn .75 .30
211 A16 45f brn org & red brn 1.25 .65
212 A16 75f purple & red brown 1.90 1.25
213 A16 90f ultra & red brown 3.00 3.00
*Nos. 208-213 (6)* 7.75 5.70

Promulgation of the constitution.

Soccer — A17

Sports: 4f, Basketball. 5f, Swimming, horiz. 8f, Track. 15f, Javelin, horiz. 20f, Pole vault, horiz. 35f, Gymnast on rings, horiz. 45f, Gymnast on parallel bars.

**1963, Nov. 8 Unwmk. Perf. 14½x14**
214 A17 1f multicolored .35 .25
215 A17 4f multicolored .35 .25
216 A17 5f multicolored .35 .25
217 A17 8f multicolored .60 .25
218 A17 15f multicolored .80 .35
219 A17 20f multicolored 1.10 .40
220 A17 35f multicolored 2.00 .80
221 A17 45f multicolored 3.50 1.75
*Nos. 214-221 (8)* 9.05 4.30

Arab School Games of 1963.

UNESCO Emblem, Scales and Globe — A18

**1963, Dec. 10 Litho. Perf. 13x12½**
222 A18 8f violet, blk & pale grn .50 .30
223 A18 20f gray, black & yel 1.00 .60
224 A18 25f blue, black & tan 2.25 .90
*Nos. 222-224 (3)* 3.75 1.80

15th anniv. of the Universal Declaration of Human Rights.

Sheik Abdullah — A19

**Perf. 12½x13**
**1964, Feb. 1 Unwmk. Photo.**
**Portrait in Natural Colors**
225 A19 1f gray & silver .25 .25
a. Booklet pane of 6 ('66) 2.25
226 A19 2f brt blue & silver .25 .25
227 A19 4f ocher & silver .30 .25
a. Booklet pane of 6 ('66) 2.25
228 A19 5f fawn & silver .30 .25
229 A19 8f dk brown & sil .30 .25
230 A19 10f citron & sil .40 .25
a. Booklet pane of 6 ('66) 2.25
b. Silver (country name and denomination) omitted 4,600.
231 A19 15f brt green & sil .75 .25
a. Booklet pane of 6 ('66) 6.00
232 A19 20f blue gray & sil .55 .25
a. Booklet pane of 6 ('66) 3.75
b. Silver (country name and denomination) omitted 4,900.
233 A19 25f green & silver .65 .30
234 A19 30f gray grn & sil .75 .30
235 A19 40f brt vio & sil 1.10 .45
236 A19 45f violet & silver 1.20 .55
237 A19 50f olive & silver 1.25 .55
238 A19 70f red lilac & sil 1.50 .65
239 A19 75f rose red & sil 2.00 .80
240 A19 90f ultra & silver 3.00 .80
241 A19 100f pale lilac & sil 3.50 .65

**Perf. 14x14½**
**Size: 25x30mm**
242 A19 250f brown & sil 10.00 2.50
243 A19 1d brown vio & sil 35.00 7.00
*Nos. 225-243 (19)* 63.05 16.55

Ramses II Battling the Hittites (from Abu Simbel) — A20

**Engr. & Litho.**
**1964, Mar. 8 Perf. 13x12½**
244 A20 8f buff, ind & maroon .40 .25
245 A20 20f lt blue, indigo & vio 1.00 .60
246 A20 30f bluish grn, ind & vio 1.60 .70
*Nos. 244-246 (3)* 3.00 1.55

UNESCO world campaign to save historic monuments in Nubia.

Mother and Child — A21

**1964, Mar. 21 Litho. Perf. 14x13**
247 A21 8f green, gray & vio blk .30 .25
248 A21 20f green, red & vio blk .80 .25
249 A21 30f grn, ol bis & vio blk 1.10 .40
250 A21 45f grn, saph & vio blk 1.40 .70
*Nos. 247-250 (4)* 3.60 1.60

Issued for Mother's Day, Mar. 21.

Nurse Giving TB Test, and Thorax — A22

**Perf. 13x13½**
**1964, Apr. 7 Photo. Unwmk.**
251 A22 8f brown & green .60 .25
252 A22 20f green & rose red 1.90 .60

Issued for World Health Day (fight against tuberculosis), Apr. 7, 1964.

Microscope and Dhow — A23

**1964, Apr. 15 Perf. 12½x13**
253 A23 8f multicolored .55 .25
254 A23 15f multicolored .65 .25
255 A23 20f multicolored 1.10 .30
256 A23 30f multicolored 1.75 .70
*Nos. 253-256 (4)* 4.05 1.50

Issued for Education Day.

Doves and State Seal A24

**1964, June 19 Litho. Perf. 13½**
**Seal in Blue, Brown, Black, Red & Green**
257 A24 8f black & bister brn .50 .25
258 A24 20f black & green .80 .30
259 A24 30f black & gray 1.60 .60
260 A24 45f black & blue 1.75 .85
*Nos. 257-260 (4)* 4.65 2.00

Third anniversary of National Day.

Arab Postal Union Emblem — A25

**1964, Nov. 21 Photo. Perf. 11x11½**
261 A25 8f lt blue & brown .50 .25
262 A25 20f yellow & ultra .90 .30
263 A25 45f olive & brown 1.60 .90
*Nos. 261-263 (3)* 3.00 1.45

Permanent Office of the APU, 10th anniv.

Conference Emblem — A26

**1965, Feb. 8 Litho. Perf. 14**
264 A26 8f black, org brn & yel 1.00 .25
265 A26 20f multicolored 1.50 .30

First Arab Journalists' Conference.

Oil Derrick, Dhow, Sun and Doves — A27

**1965, Feb. 25 Perf. 13½**
266 A27 10f lt green & multi .40 .25
267 A27 15f pink & multi .85 .25
268 A27 20f gray & multi 1.50 .50
*Nos. 266-268 (3)* 2.75 1.00

Fourth anniversary of National Day.

Mother and Children — A28

**1965, Mar. 21 Unwmk. Perf. 13½**
269 A28 8f multicolored .50 .25
270 A28 15f multicolored .80 .45
271 A28 20f multicolored 1.25 .70
*Nos. 269-271 (3)* 2.55 1.40

Mother's Day, Mar. 21.

Weather Balloon — A29

**1965, Mar. 23 Photo. Perf. 11½x11**
272 A29 4f deep ultra & yellow .70 .25
273 A29 5f blue & dp orange .80 .25
274 A29 20f dk blue & emerald 1.50 1.25
*Nos. 272-274 (3)* 3.00 1.75

Fifth World Meteorological Day.

Census Chart, Map and Family — A30

**1965, Mar. 28 Litho. Perf. 13½**
275 A30 8f multicolored .35 .25
276 A30 20f multicolored .80 .30
277 A30 50f multicolored 2.10 1.00
*Nos. 275-277 (3)* 3.25 1.55

Issued to publicize the 1965 census.

ICY Emblem — A31

**1965, Mar. 7 Engr.**
278 A31 8f red & black .60 .25
279 A31 20f lt ultra & black 1.25 .30
280 A31 30f emerald & black 2.50 .60
*Nos. 278-280 (3)* 4.35 1.15

International Cooperation Year.

Dagger in Map of
Palestine — A31a

**Perf. 11x11½**

**1965, Apr. 9 Photo. Unwmk.**
281 A31a 4f red & ultra 2.25 .35
282 A31a 45f red & emerald 4.75 1.40

Deir Yassin massacre, Apr. 9, 1948. See
Iraq Nos. 372-373 and Jordan No. 499.

Tower of Shuwaikh
School and Atom
Symbol — A32

**1965, Apr. 15 Litho. Perf. 14x13**
283 A32 4f multicolored .40 .25
284 A32 20f multicolored .90 .45
285 A32 45f multicolored 1.75 1.10
Nos. 283-285 (3) 3.05 1.80

Issued for Education Day.

ITU Emblem, Old
and New
Communication
Equipment — A33

**1965, May 17 Perf. 13½x14**
286 A33 8f dk blue, lt bl & red .40 .30
287 A33 20f green, lt grn & red 1.50 .40
288 A33 45f red, pink & blue 3.00 1.50
Nos. 286-288 (3) 4.90 2.20

ITU, centenary.

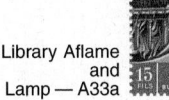

Library Aflame
and
Lamp — A33a

**1965, June 7 Photo. Perf. 11**
289 A33a 8f black, green & red 1.00 .25
290 A33a 15f black, red & green 2.25 .45

Burning of Library of Algiers, June 7, 1962.

Falcon — A34

**1965, Dec. 1 Engr. Perf. 13
Center in Sepia**
291 A34 8f red lilac 2.75 .30
292 A34 15f olive green 2.40 .30
293 A34 20f dark blue 3.50 .60
294 A34 25f orange 3.75 .80
295 A34 30f emerald 4.75 .90
296 A34 40f blue 9.50 1.50
297 A34 50f claret 11.00 1.60
298 A34 90f carmine 19.00 2.75
Nos. 291-298 (8) 56.65 8.75

Book and Wreath
Emblem — A35

**1966, Jan. 10 Photo. Perf. 14x15**
299 A35 8f lt violet & multi .50 .25
300 A35 20f brown red & multi .90 .45
301 A35 30f blue & multi 1.60 .75
Nos. 299-301 (3) 3.00 1.45

Issued for Education Day.

Sheik Sabah al-Salim al-
Sabah — A36

**1966, Feb. 1 Photo. Perf. 14x13**
302 A36 4f lt blue & multi .30 .25
303 A36 5f pale rose & multi .45 .25
304 A36 20f multicolored .75 .25
305 A36 30f lt violet & multi 1.10 .35
306 A36 40f salmon & multi 1.40 .50
307 A36 45f lt gray & multi 1.50 .60
308 A36 70f yellow & multi 3.00 1.25
309 A36 90f pale green & multi 4.50 1.75
Nos. 302-309 (8) 13.00 5.20

Wheat and
Fish — A37

**1966, Feb. 15 Perf. 11x11½**
310 A37 20f multicolored 2.75 1.00
311 A37 45f multicolored 4.00 1.75

"Freedom from Hunger" campaign.

Eagle, Banner,
Scales and
Emblems
A38

**1966, Feb. 25 Litho. Perf. 12½x13**
312 A38 20f tan & multi 1.40 .40
313 A38 25f lt green & multi 1.40 .60
314 A38 45f gray & multi 3.25 1.40
Nos. 312-314 (3) 6.05 2.40

Fifth anniversary of National Day.

Wheel of
Industry and Map
of Arab
Countries — A39

**1966, Mar. 1 Perf. 14x13½**
315 A39 20f brt blue, brt grn &
blk 1.00 .30
316 A39 50f lt red brn, brt grn &
black 1.75 .80

Issued to publicize the conference on industrial development in Arab countries.

Mother and
Children — A40

**1966, Mar. 21 Perf. 11½x11**
317 A40 20f pink & multi 1.00 .30
318 A40 45f multicolored 2.25 .80

Mother's Day, Mar. 21.

Medical Conference
Emblem — A41

**1966, Apr. 1 Photo. Perf. 14½x14**
319 A41 15f blue & red .90 .90
320 A41 30f red & blue 1.60 .90

Fifth Arab Medical Conference, Kuwait.

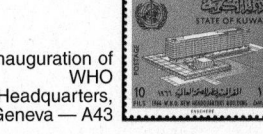

Composite View of a
City — A42

**1966, Apr. 7 Litho. Perf. 12½x13**
321 A42 8f multicolored 1.00 .25
322 A42 10f multicolored 1.75 .30

Issued for World Health Day, Apr. 7.

Inauguration of
WHO
Headquarters,
Geneva — A43

**1966, May 3 Litho. Perf. 11x11½**
323 A43 5f dull sal, ol grn & vio
bl .80 .25
324 A43 10f lt grn, ol grn & vio
blue 1.60 .25

Traffic Signal at
Night — A44

**1966, May 4**
325 A44 10f green, red & black 1.00 .25
326 A44 20f green, red & black 1.25 .45

Issued for Traffic Day.

"Blood
Transfusion" — A45

**1966, May 5 Perf. 13½**
327 A45 4f multicolored .90 .25
328 A45 8f multicolored 1.50 .70

Blood Bank Day, May 5.

Sheik Ahmad and
Ship Carrying First
Crude Oil
Shipment — A46

**1966, June 30 Perf. 13½**
329 A46 20f multicolored 1.00 .55
330 A46 45f multicolored 2.25 1.10

20th anniv. of the first crude oil shipment,
June 30, 1946.

Ministry of
Guidance and
Information
A47

**1966, July 25 Photo. Perf. 11½x11**
331 A47 4f rose & brown .40 .25
332 A47 5f yel brn & brt grn .50 .25
333 A47 8f brt green & purple .70 .25
334 A47 20f salmon & ultra 1.40 .30
Nos. 331-334 (4) 3.00 1.05

Opening of Ministry of Guidance and Information Building.

Fishing Boat,
Lobster, Fish,
Crab and FAO
Emblem — A48

**1966, Oct. 10 Litho. Perf. 13½**
335 A48 4f buff & multi 1.25 .25
336 A48 20f lt lilac & multi 3.00 1.10

Fisheries' Conference of Near East Countries under the sponsorship of the FAO, Oct.
1966.

United Nations
Flag — A49

**1966, Oct. 24 Perf. 13x14**
337 A49 20f blue, dk blue & pink 1.50 .30
338 A49 45f blue, dk bl & pale
grn 2.75 1.40

Issued for United Nations Day.

UNESCO
Emblem — A50

**1966, Nov. 4 Litho. Perf. 12½x13**
339 A50 20f multicolored 1.40 .30
340 A50 45f multicolored 2.75 1.25

20th anniversary of UNESCO.

Kuwait
University
Emblem — A51

**1966, Nov. 27 Photo. Perf. 14½
Emblem in Yellow, Bright Blue,
Green and Gold**
341 A51 8f lt ultra, vio & gold .70 .25
342 A51 10f red, brown & gold .90 .25
343 A51 20f lt yel grn, slate &
gold 2.00 .30
344 A51 45f buff, green & gold 4.00 1.50
Nos. 341-344 (4) 7.60 2.30

Opening of Kuwait University.

Jabir al-Ahmad
al-Jabir and
Sheik
Sabah — A52

**1966, Dec. 11 Perf. 14x13**
345 A52 8f yel green & multi .75 .25
346 A52 20f yellow & multi 1.50 .30
347 A52 45f pink & multi 3.75 1.25
Nos. 345-347 (3) 6.00 1.80

Appointment of the heir apparent, Jabir al-
Ahmad al-Jabir.

Scout Badge and
Square
Knot — A52a

**1966, Dec. 21 Litho. Perf. 14x13**
347A A52a 4f lt ol green &
fawn 1.75 .45
347B A52a 20f yel brn & blue
grn 5.00 1.50

Kuwait Boy Scouts, 30th anniversary.

"Symbols of Science
and Peace" — A53

**1967, Jan. 15 Litho. Perf. 13x14**
348 A53 10f multicolored 1.25 .25
349 A53 45f multicolored 4.75 .65

Issued for Education Day.

Fertilizer
Plant — A54

**1967, Feb. 19    Unwmk.    Perf. 13**
350 A54   8f lt blue & multi    1.00   .25
351 A54 20f cream & multi    2.50   .45
Opening of Chemical Fertilizer Plant.

Sun, Dove and Olive
Branch — A55

**1967, Feb. 25    Litho.    Perf. 13**
352 A55   8f salmon & multi    1.25   .25
353 A55 20f yellow & multi    3.00   .45
Sixth anniversary of National Day.

Map of Arab
States and
Municipal
Building — A56

**1967, Mar. 11    Perf. 14½x13**
354 A56 20f gray & multi    1.50   .60
355 A56 30f lt brown & multi    2.75 1.50
1st conf. of the Arab Cities Org., Kuwait.

Family — A57

**1967, Mar. 21   Litho.   Perf. 13x13½**
356 A57 20f pale rose & multi    1.50   .60
357 A57 45f pale green & multi    3.00 1.50
Issued for Family Day, Mar. 21.

Arab League
Emblem — A58

**1967, Mar. 27    Perf. 13x14**
358 A58   8f gray & dk blue    1.00   .25
359 A58 10f bister & green    2.00   .25
Issued for Arab Publicity Week.

Sabah Hospital and
Physicians at
Work — A59

**1967, Apr. 7    Perf. 14x13**
360 A59   8f dull rose & multi    1.50   .25
361 A59 20f gray & multi    2.50   .65
Issued for World Health Day.

Two Heads of
Ramses II — A60

**1967, Apr. 17    Perf. 13½**
362 A60 15f citron, green & brn    1.50   .30
363 A60 20f chalky blue, grn &
     pur    2.50   .65
Arab Week to Save the Nubian Monuments.

Traffic Policeman
A61

**1967, May 4    Litho.    Perf. 14x13**
364 A61   8f lt green & multi    2.00   .35
365 A61 20f rose lilac & multi    4.25   .85
Issued for Traffic Day.

ITY Emblem — A62

**1967, June 4    Photo.    Perf. 13**
366 A62 20f Prus blue, lt bl & blk    1.25   .30
367 A62 45f rose lilac, lt bl & blk    2.75 1.25
International Tourist Year.

Arab League Emblem
and Hands Reaching
for Knowledge — A63

**1967, Sept. 8    Litho.    Perf. 13x14**
368 A63   8f blue & multi    1.75   .25
369 A63 20f dull rose & multi    3.25   .75
Issued to publicize the literacy campaign.

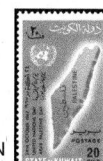

Map of Palestine and UN
Emblem — A64

**1967, Oct. 24    Litho.    Perf. 13**
370 A64 20f blue & pink    2.25   .30
371 A64 45f orange & pink    5.00 1.00
Issued for United Nations Day.

Factory and
Cogwheels
A65

**1967, Nov. 25    Photo.    Perf. 13**
372 A65 20f crimson & yellow    1.50   .30
373 A65 45f gray & yellow    2.75 1.50
3rd Conf. of Arab Labor Ministers, Kuwait.

Flag and Open
Book — A66

**1968, Jan. 15    Litho.    Perf. 14**
374 A66 20f brt blue & multi    1.25   .30
375 A66 45f yel orange & multi    3.50 1.25
Issued for Education Day.

Map of Kuwait and
Oil Derrick — A67

**1968, Feb. 23    Litho.    Perf. 12**
376 A67 10f multicolored    1.25   .35
377 A67 20f multicolored    3.50 1.25
   30th anniv. of the discovery of oil in the
Greater Burgan Field.

Sheik Sabah and
Sun — A68

**1968, Feb. 25    Litho.    Perf. 14x15**
378 A68   8f red lilac & multi    .90   .25
379 A68 10f lt blue & multi    1.00   .25
380 A68 15f violet & multi    1.25   .25
381 A68 20f vermilion & multi    1.60   .35
    Nos. 378-381 (4)    4.75 1.10
Seventh anniversary of National Day.

Open Book and
Emblem — A69

**1968, Mar. 2          Perf. 14**
382 A69   8f yellow & multi    .50   .25
383 A69 20f lilac rose & multi    1.25   .25
384 A69 45f orange & multi    2.25 1.25
    Nos. 382-384 (3)    4.00 1.75
Issued for Teachers' Day.

Family
Picnic — A70

**1968, Mar. 21      Perf. 13½x13**
385 A70   8f blue & multi    .60   .25
386 A70 10f red & multi    .90   .25
387 A70 15f lilac & multi    1.00   .25
388 A70 20f dk brown & multi    1.75   .25
    Nos. 385-388 (4)    4.25 1.00
Issued for Family Day.

Sheik Sabah, Arms of WHO and
Kuwait
A71

**1968, Apr. 7     Photo.    Perf. 12**
389 A71 20f brt lilac & multi    1.75   .65
390 A71 45f multicolored    4.25 1.50
20th anniv. of WHO.

Dagger in
Map of
Palestine
A72

**1968, Apr. 9    Litho.    Perf. 14**
391 A72 20f lt blue & vermilion    3.00   .70
392 A72 45f lilac & vermilion    5.25 1.25
Deir Yassin massacre, 20th anniv.

Street
Crossing — A74

**1968, May 4    Photo.    Perf. 14x14½**
395 A74 10f dk brown & multi    1.10   .50
396 A74 15f brt violet & multi    1.60   .75
397 A74 20f green & multi    2.75 1.00
    Nos. 395-397 (3)    5.45 2.25
Issued for Traffic Day.

Map of Palestine and
Torch — A75

**1968, May 15    Litho.    Perf. 13½x12½**
398 A75 10f lt ultra & multi    1.25   .50
399 A75 20f yellow & multi    3.00   .65
400 A75 45f aqua & multi    5.25 2.10
    Nos. 398-400 (3)    9.50 3.25
Issued for Palestine Day.

Palestinian
Refugees
A76

**1968, June 5    Litho.    Perf. 13x13½**
401 A76 20f pink & multi    .75   .25
402 A76 30f ultra & multi    1.25   .50
403 A76 45f green & multi    2.00   .65
404 A76 90f lilac & multi    4.25 2.00
    Nos. 401-404 (4)    8.25 3.40
International Human Rights Year.

Museum of
Kuwait — A77

**Perf. 12½**
**1968, Aug. 25    Unwmk.    Engr.**
405 A77   1f dk brown & brt grn    .60   .25
406 A77   2f dp claret & grn    .60   .25
407 A77   5f black & orange    .60   .25
408 A77   8f dk brown & grn    .60   .25
409 A77 10f Prus blue & cl    .90   .25
410 A77 20f org brown & blue    1.50   .25
411 A77 25f dk blue & orange    1.75   .25
412 A77 30f Prus blue & yel grn    2.25   .30
413 A77 45f plum & vio black    3.50   .70
414 A77 50f green & carmine    4.00 1.25
    Nos. 405-414 (10)    16.30 4.00

Man Reading
Book, Arab
League, UN and
UNESCO
Emblems — A78

**1968, Sept. 8    Litho.    Perf. 12½x13**
415 A78 15f blue gray & multi    .75   .25
416 A78 20f pink & multi    2.00   .30
Issued for International Literacy Day.

Map of Palestine
on UN Building
and Children with
Tent — A79

**1968, Oct. 25    Litho.    Perf. 13**
417 A79 20f multicolored    .65   .25
418 A79 30f gray & multi    .95   .50
419 A79 45f salmon pink & multi    1.40   .60
    Nos. 417-419 (3)    3.00 1.35
Issued for United Nations Day.

Kuwait Chamber of
Commerce — A80

**1968, Nov. 6    Litho.    Perf. 13½x12½**
420 A80 10f dp orange & dk brn    .80   .25
421 A80 15f rose claret & vio bl    .90   .25
422 A80 20f brown org & dk
     green    1.25   .50
    Nos. 420-422 (3)    2.95 1.00
Opening of the Kuwait Chamber of Commerce Building.

Conference Emblem — A81

**1968, Nov. 10    Litho.    Perf. 13**
**Emblem in Ocher, Blue, Red and Black**
423 A81 10f dk brown & blue    .60  .25
424 A81 15f dk brown & orange    .75  .25
425 A81 20f dk brown & vio blue    .90  .50
426 A81 30f dk brown & org brn   1.25  .60
   *Nos. 423-426 (4)*    3.50 1.60

14th Conference of the Arab Chambers of Commerce, Industry and Agriculture.

Shuaiba Refinery — A82

**1968, Nov. 18    Perf. 13½**
**Emblem in Red, Black and Blue**
427 A82 10f black & lt blue grn    .65  .25
428 A82 20f black & gray    1.20  .40
429 A82 30f black & salmon    1.40  .65
430 A82 45f black & emerald    2.50 1.20
   *Nos. 427-430 (4)*    5.75 2.50

Opening of Shuaiba Refinery.

Koran, Scales and People — A83

**1968, Dec. 19    Photo.    Perf. 14x14½**
431 A83  8f multicolored    .55  .25
432 A83 20f multicolored    1.25  .60
433 A83 30f multicolored    1.90  .85
434 A83 45f multicolored    2.25 1.25
   *Nos. 431-434 (4)*    5.95 2.95

The 1400th anniversary of the Koran.

Boeing 707 — A84

**1969, Jan. 1    Litho.    Perf. 13½x14**
435 A84 10f brt yellow & multi    .80  .25
436 A84 20f green & multi    1.10  .55
437 A84 25f multicolored    1.60  .85
438 A84 45f lilac & multi    3.00 1.10
   *Nos. 435-438 (4)*    6.50 2.75

Introduction of Boeing 707 service by Kuwait Airways.

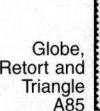

Globe, Retort and Triangle A85

**1969, Jan. 15    Perf. 13**
439 A85 15f gray & multi    1.25  .30
440 A85 20f multicolored    1.25  .70

Issued for Education Day.

Kuwait Hilton Hotel — A86

**1969, Feb. 15    Litho.    Perf. 14x12½**
441 A86 10f brt blue & multi    .90  .25
442 A86 20f pink & multi    1.50  .35

Opening of the Kuwait Hilton Hotel.

Teachers' Society Emblem, Father and Children — A87

**1969, Feb. 15    Perf. 13**
443 A87 10f violet & multi    .75  .25
444 A87 20f rose & multi    1.50  .40

Issued for Education week.

Wreath, Flags and Dove — A88

**1969, Feb. 25    Photo.    Perf. 14½x14**
445 A88 15f lilac & multi    .60  .25
446 A88 20f blue & multi    1.00  .35
447 A88 30f ocher & multi    1.40  .60
   *Nos. 445-447 (3)*    3.00 1.20

Eighth anniversary of National Day.

Emblem, Teacher and Students — A89

**1969, Mar. 8    Litho.    Perf. 13x12½**
448 A89 10f multicolored    .90  .25
449 A89 20f deep red & multi    1.50  .60

Issued for Teachers' Day.

Family — A90

**1969, Mar. 21    Perf. 13½**
450 A90 10f dark blue & multi    .80  .25
451 A90 20f deep car & multi    1.60  .35

Issued for Family Day.

Avicenna, WHO Emblem, Patient and Microscope — A91

**1969, Apr. 7    Litho.    Perf. 13½**
452 A91 15f red brown & multi    1.50  .25
453 A91 20f lt green & multi    3.50  .35

Issued for World Health Day, Apr. 7.

Motorized Traffic Police — A92

**1969, May 4    Litho.    Perf. 12½x13**
454 A92 10f multicolored    2.00  .25
455 A92 20f multicolored    4.00  .65

Issued for Traffic Day.

ILO Emblem — A93

**1969, June 1    Perf. 11½**
456 A93 10f red, black & gold    .60  .25
457 A93 20f lt blue grn, blk & gold    1.40  .35

50th anniv. of the ILO.

S.S. Al Sabahiah — A94

**1969, June 10    Litho.    Perf. 13½**
458 A94 20f multicolored    1.50  .60
459 A94 45f multicolored    3.50 1.60

4th anniversary of Kuwait Shipping Co.

UNESCO Emblem, Woman, Globe and Book — A95

**1969, Sept. 8    Litho.    Perf. 13½**
460 A95 10f blue & multi    .60  .25
461 A95 20f rose red & multi    1.40  .50

International Literacy Day, Sept. 8.

Sheik Sabah — A96

**1969-74    Litho.    Perf. 14**
462 A96  8f lt blue & multi    .40  .25
463 A96 10f pink & multi    .45  .25
464 A96 15f gray & multi    .50  .25
465 A96 20f yellow & multi    .55  .25
466 A96 25f violet & multi    .75  .30
467 A96 30f sal & multi    1.00  .35
468 A96 45f tan & multi    1.50  .50
469 A96 50f yel grn & multi    1.60  .50
470 A96 70f multicolored    1.90  .75
471 A96 75f ultra & multi    2.50  .90
472 A96 90f pale rose & multi    2.50 1.00
  a.    90f brownish rose & multi    2.50 1.00
473 A96 250f lilac & multi    8.00 2.75
473A A96 500f gray green & multi    19.00 7.00
473B A96  1d lilac rose & multi    32.50 11.00
   *Nos. 462-473B (14)*    73.15 26.05

Issued: Nos. 473A-473B, 1/12/74; others 10/5/69.

UN Emblem and Scroll — A97

**1969, Oct. 24    Litho.    Perf. 13**
474 A97 10f emer & multi    .70  .25
475 A97 20f bister & multi    1.35  .30
476 A97 45f rose red & multi    3.50 1.10
   *Nos. 474-476 (3)*    5.55 1.65

Issued for United Nations Day.

Radar, Satellite Earth Station, Kuwait — A98

Design: 45f, Globe and radar, vert.

**1969, Dec. 15    Photo.    Perf. 14½**
477 A98 20f silver & multi    1.75  .30
478 A98 45f silver & multi    3.75 1.10

Inauguration of the Kuwait Earth Station for Satellite Communications.

Globe with Science Symbols, and Education Year Emblem — A99

**1970, Jan. 15    Photo.    Perf. 13½x13**
479 A99 20f brt lilac & multi    1.00  .30
480 A99 45f blue & multi    2.00 1.00

International Education Year.

Shoue — A100

Old Kuwaiti Vessels: 10f, Sambook. 15f, Baghla. 20f, Batteel. 25f, Boom. 45f, Bakkara. 50f, Shipbuilding.

**1970, Feb. 1    Perf. 14½x14**
481 A100  8f multicolored    .60  .30
482 A100 10f multicolored    .65  .40
483 A100 15f multicolored    1.10  .50
484 A100 20f multicolored    1.60  .65
485 A100 25f multicolored    2.00  .75
486 A100 30f multicolored    3.00 1.40
487 A100 50f multicolored    3.75 1.60
   *Nos. 481-487 (7)*    12.70 5.60

Refugee Father and Children — A101

**1970    Photo.    Perf. 14x12½**
488 A101 20f red brown & multi    2.50  .65
489 A101 45f olive & multi    5.00 2.00

Issued for Universal Palestinian Refugees Week, Dec. 16-22, 1969.

Kuwait Flag, Emblem and Sheik Sabah — A102

**1970, Feb. 25    Perf. 13½x13**
490 A102 15f silver & multi    1.00  .30
491 A102 20f gold & multi    1.40  .30

Ninth anniversary of National Day.

Dome of the Rock, Jerusalem, and Boy Commando A103

Designs: 20f, Dome and man commando. 45f, Dome and woman commando.

**1970, Mar. 4    Litho.    Perf. 13**
492 A103 10f pale violet & multi    1.75  .85
493 A103 20f lt blue & multi    3.50 1.75
494 A103 45f multicolored    7.25 3.75
   *Nos. 492-494 (3)*    12.50 6.35

Honoring Palestinian commandos.

Parents and Children A104

**1970, Mar. 21    Perf. 14**
495 A104 20f multicolored    .75  .25
496 A104 30f pink & multi    1.50  .35

Issued for Family Day.

Map of Arab League Countries, Flag and Emblem A104a

**1970, Mar. 22**     *Perf. 11½x11*
497 A104a 20f lt blue, grn & lt brn     .90   .25
498 A104a 45f sal, grn & dk pur   1.60   .60

25th anniversary of the Arab League.

Census Graph and Kuwait Arms — A105

**1970, Apr. 1**    **Litho.**    *Perf. 13½x13*
499 A105 15f dull orange & multi   .60   .25
500 A105 20f yellow & multi    .80   .45
501 A105 30f pink & multi     1.10   .55
    Nos. 499-501 (3)      2.50 1.25

Issued to publicize the 1970 census.

"Fight Cancer," Kuwait Arms, WHO Emblem — A106

**1970, Apr. 7**     *Perf. 13½x13*
502 A106 20f blue, vio bl & rose lil    1.50   .50
503 A106 30f dl yel, vio bl & lil rose   1.75   .70

World Health Organization Day, Apr. 7, and to publicize the fight against cancer.

Traffic Signs — A107

**1970, May 4**    **Photo.**    *Perf. 13½*
504 A107 20f multicolored    2.00   .65
505 A107 30f multicolored    2.75 1.10

Issued for Traffic Day.

Red Crescent — A108

**1970, May 8**   **Litho.**    *Perf. 12½x13½*
506 A108 10f yellow & multi    .60   .25
507 A108 15f emerald & multi   1.40   .45
508 A108 30f tan & multi     3.00   .80
    Nos. 506-508 (3)      5.00 1.50

Intl. Red Crescent and Red Cross Day.

Opening of UPU Headquarters, Bern — A109

**1970, May 25**   **Photo.**    *Perf. 12x11½*
509 A109 20f multicolored    1.25   .30
510 A109 30f multicolored    1.75   .75

Sheik Sabah — A110

**1970, June 15**    **Photo.**    *Perf. 14*
511 A110 20f silver & multi    1.60   .50
512 A110 45f gold & multi     3.25 1.00
  a.   Miniature sheet of 2    8.50 5.00

Nos. 511-512 have circular perforation around vignette set within a white square of paper, perforated on 4 sides. No. 512a contains 2 imperf. stamps similar to Nos. 511-512.

UN Emblem, Symbols of Peace, Progress, Justice — A111

**1970, July 1**   **Litho.**    *Perf. 13½x12½*
513 A111 20f lt green & multi    .75   .25
514 A111 45f multicolored    1.50   .55

25th anniversary of the United Nations.

Tanker Loading Crude Oil from Sea Island — A112

**1970, Aug. 1**     *Perf. 13½x13*
515 A112 20f multicolored    1.75   .50
516 A112 45f multicolored    3.25 1.10

Issued to publicize the artificial "Sea Island" loading facilities in Kuwait.

"Writing," Kuwait and UN Emblems — A113

**1970, Sept. 8**    **Photo.**    *Perf. 13½*
517 A113 10f brt blue & multi    1.25   .25
518 A113 15f brt green & multi   1.50   .55

International Literacy Day, Sept. 8.

National Guard and Emblem — A114

**1970, Oct. 20**    **Photo.**    *Perf. 13x13½*
519 A114 10f gold & multi    1.25   .25
520 A114 20f silver & multi    2.25   .55

First National Guard graduation.

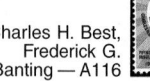

Flag of Kuwait, Symbols of Development A115

**1971, Feb. 25**    **Litho.**    *Perf. 12*
521 A115 20f gray & multi    1.75   .40
522 A115 30f multicolored    2.50   .55

Tenth anniversary of National Day.

Charles H. Best, Frederick G. Banting — A116

**1971, Apr. 7**    **Litho.**    *Perf. 14*
523 A116 20f multicolored    2.00   .40
524 A116 45f multicolored    4.25   .80

World Health Day; discoverers of insulin.

Globe with Map of Palestine — A117

**1971, May 3**   **Litho.**    *Perf. 12½x13*
525 A117 20f yel green & multi   2.00 1.10
526 A117 45f lilac & multi     3.75 2.25

International Palestine Week.

ITU Emblem and Waves — A118

**1971, May 17**    **Photo.**    *Perf. 13x13½*
527 A118 20f silver, dk red & blk   1.25   .30
528 A118 45f gold, dk red & blk    2.75   .85

3rd World Telecommunications Day.

Men of 3 Races — A119

**1971, June 5**   **Litho.**    *Perf. 11½x11*
529 A119 15f red brown & multi   .85   .30
530 A119 30f ultra & multi     1.40   .65

Intl. Year against Racial Discrimination.

Arab Postal Union Emblem — A120

**1971, Aug. 30**     *Perf. 13x12½*
531 A120 20f brown & multi    1.10   .30
532 A120 45f blue & multi     1.90   .80

25th anniv. of the Conf. of Sofar, Lebanon, establishing the Arab Postal Union.

Symbols of Learning, UNESCO and Kuwait Emblems — A121

**1971, Sept. 8**     *Perf. 12*
533 A121 25f dull yellow & multi   1.00   .25
534 A121 60f lt blue & multi     2.25 1.10

International Literacy Day, Sept. 8.

Soccer — A122

Design: 30f, Soccer, different.

**1971, Dec. 10**     *Perf. 13*
535 A122 20f green & multi    2.25   .55
536 A122 30f ultra & multi    3.25 1.00

Regional Sports Tournament, Kuwait, Dec.

UNICEF Emblem and Arms of Kuwait A123

**Litho. & Engr.**
**1971, Dec. 11**     *Perf. 11x11½*
537 A123 25f gold & multi    .90   .35
538 A123 60f silver & multi    2.10   .80

25th anniv. of UNICEF.

Book Year Emblem — A124

**1972, Jan. 2**    **Litho.**    *Perf. 14x13*
539 A124 20f black & buff    1.00   .45
540 A124 45f black & lt blue grn   2.25 1.00

International Book Year.

Kuwait Emblem with 11 Rays, Olive Branch — A125

**1972, Feb. 25**   **Litho.**    *Perf. 13x13½*
541 A125 20f pink, gold & multi   1.25   .30
542 A125 45f lt blue, gold & multi   2.25 1.00

11th anniversary of National Day.

Telecommunications Center — A126

**1972, Feb. 28**     *Perf. 13½*
543 A126 20f lt blue & multi    1.75   .50
544 A126 45f multicolored    4.50 1.50

Opening of Kuwait Telecommunications Center.

"Your Heart is your Health" — A127

**1972, Apr. 7**    **Photo.**    *Perf. 14½x14*
545 A127 20f red & multi    2.25   .60
546 A127 45f red & multi    5.25 1.60

World Health Day.

Nurse and Child — A128

**1972, May 8**   **Litho.**    *Perf. 12½x13*
547 A128 8f vio bl, red & emer   1.25   .30
548 A128 40f pink & multi     5.25 1.40

Red Cross and Red Crescent Day.

Soccer, Olympic Emblems A129

**1972, Sept. 2**    **Litho.**    *Perf. 14½*
549 A129 2f shown      .45   .25
550 A129 4f Running     .45   .25
551 A129 5f Swimming    .55   .25
552 A129 8f Gymnastics   .60   .25
553 A129 10f Discus      .95   .30
554 A129 15f Equestrian   1.35   .35
555 A129 20f Basketball   1.50   .40
556 A129 25f Volleyball    1.60   .55
    Nos. 549-556 (8)      7.45 2.60

20th Olympic Games, Munich, 8/26-9/11.

FAO Emblem, Vegetables, Fish and Ship — A130

1972, Sept. 9 Litho. *Perf. 14x13½*

557	A130	5f blue & multi	.60	.40
558	A130	10f emerald & multi	1.90	1.10
559	A130	20f orange & multi	3.50	2.25
		Nos. 557-559 (3)	6.00	3.75

11th FAO Regional Conference in the Near East, Kuwait, Sept.

National Bank Emblem A131

1972, Nov. 15 Photo. *Perf. 13x14*

560	A131	10f green & multi	.60	.25
561	A131	35f dull red & multi	2.00	.90

20th anniversary of Kuwait National Bank.

Capitals — A132

Relics of Failaka: 5f, View of excavations. 10f, Acanthus leaf capital. 15f, Excavations.

1972, Dec. 4 Litho. *Perf. 12*

562	A132	2f lilac rose & multi	.40	.25
563	A132	5f bister & multi	.55	.25
564	A132	10f lt blue & multi	1.75	.30
565	A132	15f green & multi	2.40	.40
		Nos. 562-565 (4)	5.10	1.20

Flower and Kuwait Emblem — A133

1973, Feb. 25 Litho. *Perf. 13½x13*

566	A133	10f lt olive & multi	.70	.25
567	A133	20f multicolored	1.35	.40
568	A133	30f yellow & multi	2.10	.90
		Nos. 566-568 (3)	4.15	1.55

12th anniversary of National Day.

INTERPOL Emblem — A134

1973, June 3 Litho. *Perf. 12*

569	A134	10f emerald & multi	1.25	.75
570	A134	15f red orange & multi	2.00	1.00
571	A134	20f blue & multi	3.00	1.25
		Nos. 569-571 (3)	6.25	3.00

50th anniv. of Intl. Criminal Police Org. (INTERPOL).

I.C.M.S. Emblem and Flag of Kuwait — A135

1973, June 24 *Perf. 13*

572	A135	30f gray & multi	1.50	.55
573	A135	40f brown & multi	2.50	.80

Intl. Council of Military Sports, 25th anniv.

Kuwait Airways Building — A136

1973, July 1 Litho. *Perf. 12½x14*

574	A136	10f lt green & multi	.75	.25
575	A136	15f lilac & multi	1.00	.30
576	A136	20f lt ultra & multi	1.25	.50
		Nos. 574-576 (3)	3.00	1.05

Opening of Kuwait Airways Corporation Building.

Weather Map of Suez Canal and Persian Gulf Region A137

1973, Sept. 4 Photo. *Perf. 14*

577	A137	5f red & multi	1.00	.25
578	A137	10f green & multi	1.35	.30
579	A137	15f multicolored	1.90	.60
		Nos. 577-579 (3)	4.25	1.15

Intl. meteorological cooperation, cent.

Sheiks Ahmad and Sabah A138

1973, Nov. 12 Photo. *Perf. 14*

580	A138	10f lt green & multi	.75	.25
581	A138	20f yel orange & multi	1.75	.40
582	A138	70f lt blue & multi	5.00	1.50
		Nos. 580-582 (3)	7.50	2.15

Stamps overprinted "Kuwait," 50th anniv.

Mourning Dove, Eurasian Hoopoe, Rock Dove, Stone Curlew A139

Designs: Birds and traps.

1973, Dec. 1 Litho. *Perf. 14*
Size (single stamp): 32x32mm

583	A139	Block of 4	5.50	5.50
a.		5f Mourning dove	.70	.25
b.		5f Eurasian hoopoe	.70	.25
c.		5f Rock dove	.70	.25
d.		5f Stone curlew	.70	.25
584	A139	Block of 4	7.25	7.25
a.		8f Great gray shrike	.90	.35
b.		8f Red-backed shrike	.90	.35
c.		8f Rufous-backed shrike	.90	.35
d.		8f Black-naped oriole	.90	.35
585	A139	Block of 4	8.00	8.00
a.		10f Willow warbler	1.00	.45
b.		10f Great reed warbler	1.00	.45
c.		10f Blackcap	1.00	.45
d.		10f Common (barn) swallow	1.00	.45
586	A139	Block of 4	11.50	11.50
a.		15f Common rock thrush	1.50	1.50
b.		15f European redstart	1.50	1.50
c.		15f Wheatear	1.50	1.50
d.		15f Bluethroat	1.50	1.50
587	A139	Block of 4	13.50	13.50
a.		20f Houbara bustard	1.60	1.60
b.		20f Pin-tailed sandgrouse	1.60	1.60
c.		20f Ypecaha wood rail	1.60	1.60
d.		20f Spotted crake	1.60	1.60

Size (single stamp): 35x35mm

588	A139	Block of 4	17.50	17.50
a.		25f American sparrow hawk	2.00	2.00
b.		25f Great black-backed gull	2.00	2.00
c.		25f Purple heron	2.00	2.00
d.		25f Wryneck	2.00	2.00
589	A139	Block of 4	25.00	25.00
a.		30f European bee-eater	3.00	3.00
b.		30f Goshawk	3.00	3.00
c.		30f Gray wagtail	3.00	3.00
d.		30f Pied wagtail	3.00	3.00
590	A139	Block of 4	32.50	32.50
a.		45f Crossbows	4.25	4.25
b.		45f Tent-shaped net	4.25	4.25
c.		45f Hand net	4.25	4.25
d.		45f Rooftop trap	4.25	4.25
		Nos. 583-590 (8)	120.75	120.75

Human Rights Flame — A141

1973, Dec. 10 Litho. *Perf. 12*

594	A141	10f red & multi	.75	.25
595	A141	40f lt green & multi	2.00	.55
596	A141	75f lilac & multi	3.50	1.50
		Nos. 594-596 (3)	6.25	2.30

25th anniv. of the Universal Declaration of Human Rights.

Promoting Animal Resources — A142

1974, Feb. 16 Litho. *Perf. 12½*

597	A142	30f violet blue & multi	1.50	.40
598	A142	40f rose & multi	1.75	1.00

4th Congress of the Arab Veterinary Union, Kuwait.

Stylized Wheat and Kuwaiti Flag — A143

1974, Feb. 25 *Perf. 13½x13*

599	A143	20f lemon & multi	.60	.25
600	A143	30f bister brn & multi	1.40	.40
601	A143	70f silver & multi	3.00	1.25
		Nos. 599-601 (3)	5.00	1.90

13th anniversary of National Day.

Conference Emblem and Sheik Sabah — A144

1974, Mar. 8 *Perf. 12½*

602	A144	30f multicolored	2.50	.55
603	A144	40f yellow & multi	4.00	1.10

12th Conf. of the Arab Medical Union and 1st Conf. of the Kuwait Medical Soc.

Tournament Emblem — A145

1974, Mar. 15

604	A145	25f multicolored	1.50	.50
605	A145	45f multicolored	2.75	1.10

Third Soccer Tournament for the Arabian Gulf Trophy, Kuwait, Mar. 1974.

Scientific Research Institute A146

1974, Apr. 3 Photo. *Perf. 12½*

606	A146	15f magenta & multi	2.00	.45
607	A146	20f green & multi	2.50	.65

Opening of Kuwait Scientific Research Institute.

Arab Postal Union, Kuwait and UPU Emblems A147

1974, May 1 *Perf. 13x14*

608	A147	20f gold & multi	.75	.25
609	A147	30f gold & multi	1.00	.45
610	A147	60f gold & multi	1.75	.80
		Nos. 608-610 (3)	3.50	1.50

Centenary of Universal Postal Union.

Telephone Dial with Communications Symbols and Globe — A148

1974, May 17 *Perf. 14x13½*

611	A148	10f blue & multi	1.00	.25
612	A148	30f multicolored	2.00	.60
613	A148	40f black & multi	3.00	.80
		Nos. 611-613 (3)	6.00	1.65

World Telecommunications Day, May 17.

Emblem of Unity Council and Flags of Member States — A149

1974, June 25 Litho. *Perf. 13½*

614	A149	20f red, black & green	1.50	.45
615	A149	30f green, black & red	1.50	.65

17th anniversary of the signing of the Arab Economic Unity Agreement.

WPY Emblem, Embryo, "Growth" A150

1974, Aug. 19 Litho. *Perf. 14x14½*

616	A150	30f black & multi	1.50	.40
617	A150	70f violet blue & multi	3.00	1.50

World Population Year.

Development Building and Emblem — A151

1974, Oct. 30 Litho. *Perf. 13x13½*

618	A151	10f pink & multi	.90	.25
619	A151	20f ultra & multi	1.50	.45

Kuwait Fund for Arab Economic Development.

488KUWAIT

Emblem of
Shuaiba
Industrial
Area
A152

**1974, Dec. 17   Litho.   Perf. 12½x12**
620 A152 10f lt blue & multi ......... 1.00 .25
621 A152 20f salmon & multi ......... 2.50 .45
622 A152 30f lt green & multi ........ 3.00 1.00
*Nos. 620-622 (3)* ............ 6.50 1.70

Shuaiba Industrial Area, 10th anniversary.

Arms of Kuwait and
"14" — A153

**1975, Feb. 25   Litho.   Perf. 13x13½**
623 A153 20f multicolored ........... .75 .30
624 A153 70f yel green & multi ...... 2.00 .85
625 A153 75f rose & multi ........... 3.25 1.00
*Nos. 623-625 (3)* ............ 6.00 2.15

14th anniversary of National Day.

Male and
Female
Symbols
A154

**1975, Apr. 14   Photo.   Perf. 11½x12**
626 A154 8f lt green & multi ........ .45 .25
627 A154 20f rose & multi ........... .50 .25
628 A154 30f blue & multi ........... .85 .45
629 A154 70f yellow & multi ........ 2.25 1.10
630 A154 100f black & multi ........ 4.00 1.40
*Nos. 626-630 (5)* ........... 8.05 3.45

Kuwaiti census 1975.

IWY and
Kuwaiti
Women's Union
Emblems
A155

**1975, June 10   Litho.   Perf. 14½**
631 A155 15f brown org & multi ..... 1.10 .25
632 A155 20f olive & multi .......... 1.40 .40
633 A155 30f violet & multi ......... 2.00 .65
*Nos. 631-633 (3)* ........... 4.50 1.30

International Women's Year.

Classroom and
UNESCO
Emblem — A156

**1975, Sept. 8   Litho.   Perf. 12½x12**
634 A156 20f green & multi .......... 1.10 .25
635 A156 30f multicolored .......... 1.90 .65

International Literacy Day.

Symbols of
Measurements — A157

**1975, Oct. 14   Photo.   Perf. 14x13**
636 A157 10f green & multi .......... 1.00 .25
637 A157 20f purple & multi ........ 1.50 .45

World Standards Day.

UN Flag, Rifle and
Olive Branch — A158

**1975, Oct. 24   Litho.   Perf. 12x12½**
638 A158 20f multicolored .......... .90 .25
639 A158 45f orange & multi ........ 2.10 .80

United Nations, 30th anniversary.

Sheik Sabah — A159

**1975, Dec. 22   Litho.   Perf. 12½x12**
640 A159 8f yellow & multi ......... 1.20 .25
641 A159 20f lilac & multi ......... 1.60 .40
642 A159 30f buff & multi .......... 1.90 .50
643 A159 50f salmon & multi ....... 2.75 .75
644 A159 90f lt blue & multi ....... 5.00 1.25
645 A159 100f multicolored ......... 6.25 1.50
*Nos. 640-645 (6)* .......... 18.70 4.65

"Progress"
A160

**1976, Feb. 25   Litho.   Perf. 12**
646 A160 10f multicolored .......... .75 .25
647 A160 20f multicolored ......... 1.50 .35

15th anniversary of National Day.

Medical Equipment,
Emblem and
Surgery — A161

**1976, Mar. 1   Litho.   Perf. 14½**
648 A161 5f dull green & multi ...... .50 .25
649 A161 10f blue & multi .......... 1.50 .45
650 A161 30f gray & multi .......... 4.00 1.50
*Nos. 648-650 (3)* ........... 6.00 2.20

Kuwait Medical Assoc., 2nd annual conference.

Telephones, 1876 and
1976 — A162

**1976, Mar. 10   Litho.   Perf. 12**
651 A162 5f orange & black ......... .80 .25
652 A162 15f lt blue & black ....... 1.90 .35

Centenary of first telephone call by Alexander Graham Bell, Mar. 10, 1876.

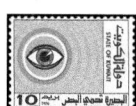

Human Eye — A163

**Photo. & Engr.**
**1976, Apr. 7               Perf. 11½**
653 A163 10f multicolored .......... 1.00 .25
654 A163 20f black & multi ........ 1.60 .30
655 A163 30f multicolored ......... 2.00 .85
*Nos. 653-655 (3)* ........... 4.60 1.40

World Health Day: "Foresight prevents blindness."

Red Crescent
Emblem — A164

**1976, May 8   Litho.   Perf. 12x11½**
656 A164 20f brt green, blk & red .... .65 .30
657 A164 30f vio blue, blk & red ... 1.15 .55
658 A164 45f yellow, blk & red ..... 2.00 .90
659 A164 75f lilac rose, blk & red .. 4.25 2.25
*Nos. 656-659 (4)* ........... 8.05 4.00

Kuwait Red Crescent Society, 10th anniv.

Modern Suburb of
Kuwait — A165

**1976, June 1   Photo.   Perf. 13x13½**
660 A165 10f light green & multi ... 1.00 .25
661 A165 20f salmon & multi ....... 1.75 .35

Habitat, UN Conference on Human Settlements, Vancouver, Canada, May 31-June 11.

Basketball, Kuwait
Olympic
Emblem — A166

Designs: 8f, Running. 10f, Judo. 15f, Fieldball. 20f, Gymnastics. 30f, Water polo. 45f, Soccer. 70f, Swimmers at start.

**1976, July 17   Litho.   Perf. 14½**
662 A166 4f black & multi ......... .40 .25
663 A166 8f red & multi .......... .40 .25
664 A166 10f green & multi ....... .45 .25
665 A166 15f lemon & multi ....... .60 .25
666 A166 20f blue & multi ........ .70 .30
667 A166 30f lilac & multi ....... 1.15 .55
668 A166 45f multicolored ........ 1.60 .75
669 A166 70f brown & multi ....... 2.25 1.10
*Nos. 662-669 (8)* .......... 7.55 3.70

21st Olympic Games, Montreal, Canada, July 17-Aug. 1.

Various Races, Map of
Sri Lanka — A167

**1976, Aug. 16   Photo.   Perf. 14**
670 A167 20f dk blue & multi ...... .65 .25
671 A167 30f purple & multi ...... .90 .55
672 A167 45f green & multi ....... 1.40 .75
*Nos. 670-672 (3)* ........... 2.95 1.55

5th Summit Conf. of Non-aligned Countries, Colombo, Sri Lanka, Aug. 9-19.

"UNESCO,"
Torch and
Kuwait
Arms — A168

**1976, Nov. 4   Litho.   Perf. 12x11½**
673 A168 20f yel green & multi .... .75 .25
674 A168 45f scarlet & multi ..... 2.00 .60

30th anniversary of UNESCO.

Blindman's
Buff — A169

Popular games. 5f, 15f, 30f, vertical.

**Perf. 14½x14, 14x14½**
**1977, Jan. 10               Litho.**
675 A169 5f Pot throwing ......... .35 .25
676 A169 5f Kite flying ......... .35 .25
677 A169 5f Balancing sticks .... .35 .25
678 A169 5f Spinning tops ....... .35 .25
 a. Block of 4, #675-678 .... 2.25 2.25
679 A169 10f shown .............. .65 .30
680 A169 10f Rowing ............. .65 .30
681 A169 10f Hoops .............. .65 .30
682 A169 10f Ropes .............. .65 .30
 a. Block of 4, #679-682 .... 3.25 3.25
683 A169 15f Rope skipping ..... 1.10 .45
684 A169 15f Marbles ........... 1.10 .45
685 A169 15f Cart steering ..... 1.10 .45
686 A169 15f Teetotum .......... 1.10 .45
 a. Block of 4, #683-686 .... 5.50 5.50
687 A169 20f Halma ............. 1.25 .60
688 A169 20f Model boats ....... 1.25 .60
689 A169 20f Pot and candle .... 1.25 .60
690 A169 20f Hide and seek ..... 1.25 .60
 a. Block of 4, #687-690 .... 6.50 6.50
691 A169 30f Throwing bones .... 1.50 .80
692 A169 30f Mystery gifts ..... 1.50 .80
693 A169 30f Hopscotch ......... 1.50 .80
694 A169 30f Catch as catch
              can ............. 1.50 .80
 a. Block of 4, #691-694 .... 7.50 7.50
695 A169 40f Bowls ............. 2.75 1.10
696 A169 40f Sword fighting .... 2.75 1.10
697 A169 40f Mother and child .. 2.75 1.10
698 A169 40f Fivestones ........ 2.75 1.10
 a. Block of 4, #695-698 ... 13.00 13.00
699 A169 60f Hiding a cake ..... 3.50 1.75
700 A169 60f Chess ............. 3.50 1.75
701 A169 60f Dancing .......... 3.50 1.75
702 A169 60f Treasure hunt ..... 3.50 1.75
 a. Block of 4, #699-702 ... 17.00 17.00
703 A169 70f Hobby-horses ...... 4.25 2.00
704 A169 70f Hide and seek ..... 4.25 2.00
705 A169 70f Catch ............. 4.25 2.00
706 A169 70f Storytelling ...... 4.25 2.00
 a. Block of 4, #703-706 ... 20.00 20.00
*Nos. 675-706 (32)* ........ 61.40 29.00

Diseased Knee — A170

**1977, Feb. 15               Perf. 13x13½**
707 A170 20f yellow & multi ...... .75 .25
708 A170 30f multicolored ....... 1.25 .45
709 A170 45f red & multi ........ 1.50 .70
710 A170 75f black & multi ...... 2.50 1.25
*Nos. 707-710 (4)* ........... 6.00 2.65

World Rheumatism Year.

Sheik
Sabah — A171

**1977, Feb. 25   Photo.   Perf. 13½x13**
711 A171 10f multicolored ........ .55 .25
712 A171 15f multicolored ........ .70 .30
713 A171 30f multicolored ....... 1.40 .55
714 A171 80f multicolored ....... 1.75 1.10
*Nos. 711-714 (4)* ........... 4.40 2.20

16th National Day.

Kuwait Tower — A172

**1977, Feb. 26               Perf. 14x13½**
715 A172 30f multicolored ....... 1.00 .25
716 A172 80f multicolored ....... 3.00 1.10

Inauguration of Kuwait Tower.

APU Emblem — A173

**1977, Apr. 12   Litho.   Perf. 13½x14**
| 717 | A173 | 5f yellow & multi | .45 | .25 |
| 718 | A173 | 15f pink & multi | .55 | .25 |
| 719 | A173 | 30f lt blue & multi | 1.10 | .30 |
| 720 | A173 | 80f lilac & multi | 2.60 | 1.10 |
| | | *Nos. 717-720 (4)* | 4.70 | 1.90 |

Arab Postal Union, 25th anniversary.

Electronic Tree — A174

**1977, May 17   Litho.   Perf. 12x12½**
| 721 | A174 | 30f brown & red | 1.75 | .40 |
| 722 | A174 | 80f green & red | 3.75 | 1.50 |

World Telecommunications Day.

Sheik Sabah — A175

**1977, June 1   Photo.   Perf. 11½x12**
| 723 | A175 | 15f blue & multi | 1.25 | 1.10 |
| 724 | A175 | 25f yellow & multi | 2.00 | 1.10 |
| 725 | A175 | 30f red & multi | 2.50 | 1.60 |
| 726 | A175 | 80f violet & multi | 6.75 | 2.75 |
| 727 | A175 | 100f dp org & multi | 8.00 | 3.50 |
| 728 | A175 | 150f ultra & multi | 12.00 | 4.00 |
| 729 | A175 | 200f olive & multi | 16.00 | 6.00 |
| | | *Nos. 723-729 (7)* | 48.50 | 20.05 |

Games Emblem — A176

**1977, Oct. 1   Litho.   Perf. 12**
| 730 | A176 | 30f multicolored | 1.10 | .50 |
| 731 | A176 | 80f multicolored | 2.40 | 1.10 |

4th Asian Basketball Youth Championship, Oct. 1-15.

Dome of the Rock, Bishop Capucci, Fatima Bernawi, Sheik Abu Tair — A177

**1977, Nov. 1   Perf. 14**
| 732 | A177 | 30f multicolored | 3.00 | 1.25 |
| 733 | A177 | 80f multicolored | 7.00 | 3.00 |

Struggle for the liberation of Palestine.

Children and Houses — A178

Children's Paintings: No. 735, Women musicians. No. 736, Boats. No. 737, Women preparing food, vert. No. 738, Women and children, vert. No. 739, Seated woman, vert.

**1977, Nov.   Photo.   Perf. 13½x13**
| 734 | A178 | 15f lt green & multi | .50 | .30 |
| 735 | A178 | 15f yellow & multi | .50 | .30 |
| 736 | A178 | 30f brt yellow & multi | 1.00 | .60 |
| 737 | A178 | 30f lt violet & multi | 1.00 | .60 |
| 738 | A178 | 80f black & multi | 2.50 | 1.60 |
| 739 | A178 | 80f rose & multi | 2.50 | 1.60 |
| | | *Nos. 734-739 (6)* | 8.00 | 5.00 |

Dentist Treating Patient — A179

**1977, Dec. 3**
| 740 | A179 | 30f green & multi | 1.75 | .50 |
| 741 | A179 | 80f violet & multi | 3.25 | 1.40 |

10th Arab Dental Union Congress, Kuwait, Dec. 3-6.

Ships Unloading Water — A180

Kuwait water resources. 30f, 80f, 100f, vert.

**Perf. 14x13½, 13½x14**

**1978, Jan. 25                        Litho.**
| 742 | | Block of 4 | 1.75 | 1.75 |
| | a. | 5f shown | .30 | .25 |
| | b. | 5f Home delivery by camel | .30 | .25 |
| | c. | 5f Man with water bags | .30 | .25 |
| | d. | 5f Man with wheelbarrow | .30 | .25 |
| 743 | | Block of 4 | 2.75 | 2.75 |
| | a. | 10f Well | .50 | .25 |
| | b. | 10f Trough | .50 | .25 |
| | c. | 10f Water hole | .50 | .25 |
| | d. | 10f Irrigation | .50 | .25 |
| 744 | | Block of 4 | 3.50 | 3.50 |
| | a. | 15f Sheep drinking | .65 | .25 |
| | b. | 15f Laundresses | .65 | .25 |
| | c. | 15f Sheep and camels drinking | .65 | .25 |
| | d. | 15f Water stored in skins | .65 | .25 |
| 745 | | Block of 4 | 4.00 | 4.00 |
| | a. | 20f Animals at well | .80 | .25 |
| | b. | 20f Water in home | .80 | .25 |
| | c. | 20f Water pot | .80 | .25 |
| | d. | 20f Communal fountain | .80 | .25 |
| 746 | | Block of 4 | 5.00 | 5.00 |
| | a. | 25f Distillation plant | .95 | .30 |
| | b. | 25f Motorized delivery | .95 | .30 |
| | c. | 25f Water trucks | .95 | .30 |
| | d. | 25f Water towers | .95 | .30 |
| 747 | | Block of 4 | 7.00 | 7.00 |
| | a. | 30f Shower bath | 1.40 | .40 |
| | b. | 30f Water tower | 1.40 | .40 |
| | c. | 30f Gathering rain water | 1.40 | .40 |
| | d. | 30f 2 water towers | 1.40 | .40 |
| 748 | | Block of 4 | 15.50 | 15.50 |
| | a. | 80f Donkey with water bags | 3.00 | 1.10 |
| | b. | 80f Woman with water can | 3.00 | 1.10 |
| | c. | 80f Woman with water skin | 3.00 | 1.10 |
| | d. | 80f Loading tank car | 3.00 | 1.10 |
| 749 | | Block of 4 | 20.00 | 20.00 |
| | a. | 100f Truck delivering water | 4.00 | 1.25 |
| | b. | 100f Barnyard water supply | 4.00 | 1.25 |
| | c. | 100f Children at water basin | 4.00 | 1.25 |
| | d. | 100f Well in courtyard | 4.00 | 1.25 |
| | | *Nos. 742-749 (8)* | 59.50 | 59.50 |

Radar, Torch, Minarets — A181

**1978, Feb. 25   Litho.   Perf. 14x14½**
| 750 | A181 | 30f multicolored | .75 | .25 |
| 751 | A181 | 80f multicolored | 1.75 | .80 |

17th National Day.

Man with Smallpox, Target — A182

**1978, Apr. 17   Litho.   Perf. 12½**
| 752 | A182 | 30f violet & multi | 1.25 | .40 |
| 753 | A182 | 80f green & multi | 3.00 | 1.10 |

Global eradication of smallpox.

Antenna and ITU Emblem — A183

**1978, May 17                        Perf. 14**
| 754 | A183 | 30f silver & multi | .75 | .30 |
| 755 | A183 | 80f silver & multi | 2.00 | .85 |

10th World Telecommunications Day.

Sheik Sabah — A184

**1978, June 28   Litho.   Perf. 13x14**
**Portrait in Brown**
**Size: 21½x27mm**
| 756 | A184 | 15f green & gold | .40 | .25 |
| 757 | A184 | 30f orange & gold | .65 | .45 |
| 758 | A184 | 80f rose lilac & gold | 1.50 | 1.10 |
| 759 | A184 | 100f lt green & gold | 1.75 | 1.25 |
| 760 | A184 | 130f lt brown & gold | 2.00 | 1.75 |
| 761 | A184 | 180f violet & gold | 3.50 | 2.75 |

**Size: 23½x29mm**
| 762 | A184 | 1d red & gold | 15.00 | 9.00 |
| 763 | A184 | 4d blue & gold | 67.50 | 40.00 |
| | | *Nos. 756-763 (8)* | 92.30 | 56.55 |

Mt. Arafat, Pilgrims, Holy Kaaba — A185

**1978, Nov. 9   Photo.   Perf. 11½**
| 764 | A185 | 30f multicolored | 1.25 | .40 |
| 765 | A185 | 80f multicolored | 3.25 | 1.25 |

Pilgrimage to Mecca.

UN and Anti-Apartheid Emblems — A186

**1978, Nov. 27   Litho.   Perf. 12**
| 766 | A186 | 30f multicolored | .75 | .30 |
| 767 | A186 | 80f multicolored | 1.75 | 1.00 |
| 768 | A186 | 180f multicolored | 4.00 | 2.00 |
| | | *Nos. 766-768 (3)* | 6.50 | 3.30 |

Anti-Apartheid Year.

Refugees, Human Rights Emblems — A187

**1978, Dec. 10   Photo.   Perf. 13x13½**
| 769 | A187 | 30f multicolored | 1.00 | .35 |
| 770 | A187 | 80f multicolored | 2.25 | .80 |
| 771 | A187 | 100f multicolored | 3.25 | 1.75 |
| | | *Nos. 769-771 (3)* | 6.50 | 2.90 |

Declaration of Human Rights, 30th anniv.

Information Center — A188

**1978, Dec. 26   Photo.   Perf. 13**
| 772 | A188 | 5f multicolored | .40 | .25 |
| 773 | A188 | 15f multicolored | .55 | .25 |
| 774 | A188 | 30f multicolored | .95 | .35 |
| 775 | A188 | 80f multicolored | 2.10 | 1.00 |
| | | *Nos. 772-775 (4)* | 4.00 | 1.85 |

New Kuwait Information Center.

Kindergarten A189

**1979, Jan. 24   Photo.   Perf. 13½x14**
| 776 | A189 | 30f multicolored | .90 | .50 |
| 777 | A189 | 80f multicolored | 2.10 | 1.10 |

International Year of the Child.

Flag and Peace Doves — A190

**1979, Feb. 25                   Perf. 14½x14**
| 778 | A190 | 30f multicolored | 1.00 | .45 |
| 779 | A190 | 80f multicolored | 2.00 | 1.10 |

18th National Day.

Modern Agriculture in Kuwait — A191

**1979, Mar. 13   Photo.   Perf. 14**
| 780 | A191 | 30f multicolored | .75 | .45 |
| 781 | A191 | 80f multicolored | 2.25 | 1.10 |

4th Congress of Arab Agriculture Ministers of the Gulf and Arabian Peninsula.

World Map, Book, Symbols of Learning — A192

**1979, Mar. 22**
| 782 | A192 | 30f multicolored | 1.00 | .45 |
| 783 | A192 | 80f multicolored | 2.25 | 1.10 |

Cultural achievements of the Arabs.

Children with Balloons — A193

Children's Paintings: No. 785, Boys flying kites. No. 786, Girl and doves. No. 787, Children and houses, horiz. No. 788, Four children, horiz. No. 789, Children sitting in circle, horiz.

**1979, Apr. 18   Photo.   Perf. 14**
| 784 | A193 | 30f yellow & multi | 1.15 | .55 |
| 785 | A193 | 30f buff & multi | 1.15 | .55 |
| 786 | A193 | 30f pale yel & multi | 1.15 | .55 |
| 787 | A193 | 80f lt blue & multi | 2.60 | 1.25 |
| 788 | A193 | 80f yel green & multi | 2.60 | 1.25 |
| 789 | A193 | 80f lilac & multi | 2.60 | 1.25 |
| | | *Nos. 784-789 (6)* | 11.25 | 5.40 |

Cables, ITU Emblem, People — A194

**1979, May 17**
| 790 | A194 | 30f multicolored | .85 | .40 |
| 791 | A194 | 80f multicolored | 2.40 | 1.10 |

World Telecommunications Day.

Military Sports Council Emblem — A195

**1979, June 1   Photo.   Perf. 14**
| 792 | A195 | 30f multicolored | 1.00 | .40 |
| 793 | A195 | 80f multicolored | 2.50 | 1.25 |

29th Intl. Military Soccer Championship.

Child, Industrial Landscape, Environmental Emblems — A196

**1979, June 5**　　Perf. 12x11½
794 A196 30f multicolored　　1.50 .60
795 A196 80f multicolored　　3.50 1.60

World Environment Day, June 5.

Children Holding Globe, UNESCO Emblem — A197

**1979, July 25　Litho.**　Perf. 11½x12
796 A197　30f multicolored　　.75 .40
797 A197　80f multicolored　　1.75 1.00
798 A197 130f multicolored　　3.50 1.50
　　Nos. 796-798 (3)　　6.00 2.90

Intl. Bureau of Education, Geneva, 50th anniv.

Kuwait Kindergartens, 25th Anniversary — A198

Children's Drawings: 80f, Children waving flags.

**1979, Sept. 15　Litho.**　Perf. 12½
799 A198 30f multicolored　　.85 .40
800 A198 80f multicolored　　2.40 1.00

Pilgrims at Holy Ka'aba, Mecca Mosque — A199

**1979, Oct. 29**　　Perf. 14x14½
801 A199 30f multicolored　　1.25 .50
802 A199 80f multicolored　　3.25 1.00

Hegira (Pilgrimage Year).

International Palestinian Solidarity Day — A200

**1979, Nov. 29　Photo.**　Perf. 11½x12
803 A200 30f multicolored　　2.75 .95
804 A200 80f multicolored　　6.75 2.00

Kuwait Airways 25th Anniversary A201

**1979, Dec. 24　Photo.**　Perf. 13x13½
805 A201 30f multicolored　　1.50 .60
806 A201 80f multicolored　　3.50 1.75

19th National Day — A202

**1980, Feb. 25　Litho.**　Perf. 14x14½
807 A202 30f multicolored　　1.00 .40
808 A202 80f multicolored　　2.50 1.00

1980 Population Census — A203

**1980, Mar. 18**　　Perf. 13½x14
809 A203 30f multicolored　　1.10 .35
810 A203 80f multicolored　　2.40 1.00

World Health Day — A204

**1980, Apr. 7**
811 A204 30f multicolored　　2.25 .35
812 A204 80f multicolored　　4.75 1.25

Kuwait Municipality, 50th Anniversary — A205

**1980, May 1　Photo.**　　Perf. 14
813 A205 15f multicolored　　.75 .25
814 A205 30f multicolored　　1.50 .50
815 A205 80f multicolored　　3.75 1.25
　　Nos. 813-815 (3)　　6.00 2.00

Citizens of Kuwait — A206

Future Kuwait (Children's Drawings): 80f, Super highway.

**1980, May 14　Litho.**　Perf. 14x14½
816 A206 30f multicolored　　1.50 .50
817 A206 80f multicolored　　4.50 1.50

World Environment Day — A207

**1980, June 5　Litho.**　Perf. 12x11½
818 A207 30f multicolored　　1.50 .45
819 A207 80f multicolored　　4.50 1.10

Swimming, Moscow '80 and Kuwait Olympic Committee Emblems — A208

**1980, July 19　Litho.**　Perf. 12x12½
820 A208 15f Volleyball　　.55 .25
821 A208 15f Tennis　　.55 .25
　a.　Vert. pair, #820-821　　1.35 1.35
822 A208 30f shown　　.80 .35
823 A208 30f Weight lifting　　.80 .35
824 A208 30f Basketball　　.80 .35
825 A208 30f Judo　　.80 .35
　a.　Block of 4, #822-825　　5.50 5.50
826 A208 80f Gymnast　　2.00 1.00
827 A208 80f Badminton　　2.00 1.00
828 A208 80f Fencing　　2.00 1.00
829 A208 80f Soccer　　2.00 1.00
　a.　Block of 4, #826-829　　11.50 11.50
　　Nos. 820-829 (10)　　12.30 5.90

22nd Summer Olympic Games, Moscow, July 19-Aug. 3.

20th Anniversary of OPEC — A209

**1980, Sept. 16　Litho.**　Perf. 14x14½
830 A209 30f multicolored　　1.75 .50
831 A209 80f multicolored　　3.25 1.10

Hegira (Pilgrimage Year) — A210

**1980, Nov. 9　Photo.**　Perf. 12x11½
832 A210 15f multicolored　　.85 .25
833 A210 30f multicolored　　1.40 .45
834 A210 80f multicolored　　3.25 1.25
　　Nos. 832-834 (3)　　5.50 1.95

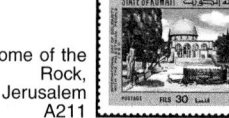

Dome of the Rock, Jerusalem A211

**1980, Nov. 29**　　Perf. 12x11½
835 A211 30f multicolored　　3.00 .90
836 A211 80f multicolored　　8.00 2.50

International Palestinian Solidarity Day.

Avicenna (980-1037), Philosopher and Physician — A212

**1980, Dec. 7**　　Perf. 12x12½
837 A212 30f multicolored　　2.25 .35
838 A212 80f multicolored　　4.25 1.20

Conference Emblem — A213

**1981, Jan. 12　Photo.**　Perf. 13½x13
839 A213 30f multicolored　　1.00 .65
840 A213 80f multicolored　　3.25 1.60

First Islamic Medical Conference.

Girl in Wheelchair A214

International Year of the Disabled: 30f, Man in wheelchair playing billiards, vert.

**Perf. 13½x13, 13x13½**
**1981, Jan. 26**　　Photo.
841 A214 30f multicolored　　1.00 .40
842 A214 80f multicolored　　3.00 1.40

20th National Day — A215

**1981, Feb. 25　Litho.**　Perf. 13x13½
843 A215 30f multicolored　　1.25 .40
844 A215 80f multicolored　　3.00 1.40

First Kuwait Dental Association Conference — A216

**1981, Mar. 14**　　Perf. 11½x12
845 A216 30f multicolored　　2.25 1.00
846 A216 80f multicolored　　6.25 2.25

A217

**1981, May 8　Photo.**　　Perf. 14
847 A217 30f multicolored　　1.75 1.00
848 A217 80f multicolored　　4.75 2.25

Intl. Red Cross day.

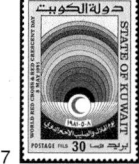

A218

**1981, May 17　Litho.**　Perf. 14½x14
849 A218 30f multicolored　　1.50 .50
850 A218 80f multicolored　　3.25 2.25

13th World Telecommunications day.

World Environment Day — A219

**1981, June 5　Photo.**　　Perf. 12
851 A219 30f multicolored　　1.75 .60
852 A219 80f multicolored　　4.75 1.75

Sief Palace — A220　　A221

**1981, Sept. 16　Litho.**　　Perf. 12
853 A220　　5f multicolored　　.25 .25
854 A220　 10f multicolored　　.25 .25
855 A220　 15f multicolored　　.25 .25
856 A220　 25f multicolored　　.25 .25
857 A220　 30f multicolored　　.25 .25
858 A220　 40f multicolored　　.40 .25
859 A220　 60f multicolored　　.65 .25
860 A220　 80f multicolored　　.85 .45
861 A220 100f multicolored　　1.10 .65
862 A220 115f multicolored　　1.25 .80
863 A220 130f multicolored　　1.40 1.00
864 A220 150f multicolored　　1.75 1.00
865 A220 180f multicolored　　2.10 1.10
866 A220 250f multicolored　　3.00 1.25
867 A220 500f multicolored　　6.00 2.25
868 A221　　1d multicolored　　12.50 3.75
869 A221　　2d multicolored　　27.50 6.00
870 A221　　3d multicolored　　40.00 11.00
871 A221　　4d multicolored　　50.00 15.00
　　Nos. 853-871 (19)　　149.75 46.00

Islamic Pilgrimage A222

**1981, Oct. 7　Photo.**　Perf. 13x13½
872 A222 30f multicolored　　1.00 .60
873 A222 80f multicolored　　3.75 1.50

World Food
Day — A223

**1981, Oct. 16    Litho.    Perf. 13**
874 A223 30f multicolored          1.25   .60
875 A223 80f multicolored          4.00  1.50

A224

**1981, Dec. 30    Photo.    Perf. 14**
876 A224 30f multicolored          1.25   .50
877 A224 80f multicolored          3.50  1.50

20th anniv. of national television.

A225

**1982, Jan. 16    Photo.    Perf. 14**
878 A225 30f multicolored          1.25  1.10
879 A225 80f multicolored          4.50  1.75

First Intl. Pharmacology of Human Blood
Vessels Symposium, Jan. 16-18.

21st Natl. Day — A226

**1982, Feb. 25    Perf. 13½x13**
880 A226 30f multicolored          1.00   .45
881 A226 80f multicolored          3.00  1.25

Scouting
Year — A227

**1982, Mar. 22    Photo.    Perf. 12x11½**
882 A227 30f multicolored          1.25   .60
883 A227 80f multicolored          3.75  1.50

Arab
Pharmacists'
Day — A228

**1982, Apr. 2    Litho.    Perf. 12x11½**
884 A228 30f lt green & multi      1.75   .60
885 A228 80f pink & multi          4.75  1.60

World Health
Day — A229

**1982, Apr. 7    Litho.    Perf. 13½x13**
886 A229 30f multicolored          1.50   .90
887 A229 80f multicolored          4.50  2.75

Arab Postal Union,
30th Anniv. — A230

**1982, Apr. 12    Photo.    Perf. 13½x13**
888 A230 30f multicolored          1.50   .50
889 A230 80f multicolored          5.00  1.50

TB Bacillus
Centenary — A231

**1982, May 24    Litho.    Perf. 11½x12**
890 A231 30f multicolored          2.00   .90
891 A231 80f multicolored          5.50  2.75

1982 World
Cup — A232

**1982, June 17    Photo.    Perf. 14**
892 A232 30f multicolored          1.50   .50
893 A232 80f multicolored          4.50  1.50

10th Anniv. of
Science and Natural
History
Museum — A233

**1982, July 14    Perf. 14**
894 A233 30f multicolored          4.50  2.00
895 A233 80f multicolored         11.00  5.00

6th Anniv. of
United Arab
Shipping
Co. — A234

Designs: Freighters.

**1982, Sept. 1    Perf. 13**
896 A234 30f multicolored          1.50   .45
897 A234 80f multicolored          3.75  1.25

Arab Day of the Palm
Tree — A235

**1982, Sept. 15    Perf. 14**
898 A235 30f multicolored          1.00   .45
899 A235 80f multicolored          2.50  1.25

Islamic
Pilgrimage
A236

**1982, Sept. 26    Litho.**
900 A236 15f multicolored           .75   .30
901 A236 30f multicolored          1.50   .50
902 A236 80f multicolored          4.00  1.50
    *Nos. 900-902 (3)*           6.25  2.30

Desert Flowers &
Plants — A237

Frame colors: No. 903a, green. b, violet. c,
deep salmon. d, rose red. e, pale brown. f,
deep green. g, pale orange. h, brown red. i,
tan. j, violet blue.
    No. 904: a, yellow green. b, pink. c, pale
blue. d, dark blue. e, pale gray green. f, lake.
g, pale orange. h, blue. i, red lilac. j, red
orange.
    No. 905: a, brown. b, pink. c, blue. d, olive
green. e, orange red. f, dark blue. g, green. h,
rose. i, bister. j, pale orange.
    No. 906: a, yellow green. b, dark blue. c,
pale orange. d, rose red. e, green. f, gray violet. g, gray blue. h, violet. i, yellow brown. j,
orange red.
    No. 907: a, lilac. b, blue green. c, pale
orange. d, pale brown. e, violet blue. f, yellow.
g, green blue. h, purple. i, pale brown. j, pale
orange.

**1983, Jan. 25    Litho.    Perf. 12**
903       Strip of 10             4.75  4.75
  a.-j.   A237 10f any single      .40   .30
904       Strip of 10             6.00  6.00
  a.-j.   A237 15f any single      .45   .30
905       Strip of 10            10.00 10.00
  a.-j.   A237 30f any single      .75   .60
906       Strip of 10            12.00 12.00
  a.-j    A237 40f any single, horiz.  .90  .75
907       Strip of 10            27.00 27.00
  a.-j.   A237 80f any single, horiz.  2.00  1.10
    *Nos. 903-907 (5)*          59.75 59.75

22nd Natl.
Day — A238

**1983, Feb. 25    Litho.    Perf. 12½**
908 A238 30f multicolored          1.00   .35
909 A238 80f multicolored          2.75  1.25

25th Anniv. of
Intl. Maritime
Org. — A239

**1983, Mar. 17    Photo.    Perf. 14**
910 A239 30f multicolored           .75   .30
911 A239 80f multicolored          2.25   .90

Map of Middle
East and Africa,
Conference
Emblem — A240

**1983, Mar. 19    Perf. 13**
912 A240 15f multicolored           .50   .25
913 A240 30f multicolored          1.00   .50
914 A240 80f multicolored          2.75  1.50
    *Nos. 912-914 (3)*           4.25  2.25

3rd Intl. Conference on the Impact of Viral
Diseases on the Development of the Middle
East and Africa, Mar. 19-27.

World Health
Day — A241

**1983, Apr. 7    Perf. 12x11½**
915 A241 15f multicolored           .75   .30
916 A241 30f multicolored          1.25   .70
917 A241 80f multicolored          3.50  1.90
    *Nos. 915-917 (3)*           5.50  2.90

World
Communications
Year — A242

**1983, May 17    Photo.    Perf. 13x13½**
918 A242 15f multicolored           .75   .30
919 A242 30f multicolored          1.25   .70
920 A242 80f multicolored          3.25  2.00
    *Nos. 918-920 (3)*           5.25  3.00

World
Environment
Day — A243

**1983, June 5    Litho.    Perf. 12½**
921 A243 15f multicolored           .60   .30
922 A243 30f multicolored          1.40   .70
923 A243 80f multicolored          4.50  2.00
    *Nos. 921-923 (3)*           6.50  3.00

Wall of Old
Jerusalem
A244

**1983, July 25    Litho.    Perf. 12**
924 A244 15f multicolored          1.00   .25
925 A244 30f multicolored          2.00   .55
926 A244 80f multicolored          4.50  1.75
    *Nos. 924-926 (3)*           7.50  2.55

World Heritage Year.

Islamic Pilgrimage
A245

**1983, Sept. 15    Photo.    Perf. 11½**
927 A245 15f multicolored           .60   .25
928 A245 30f multicolored          1.40   .55
929 A245 80f multicolored          3.50  1.75
    *Nos. 927-929 (3)*           5.50  2.55

Intl. Palestinian
Solidarity
Day — A246

**1983, Nov. 29    Photo.    Perf. 14**
930 A246 15f multicolored           .65   .25
931 A246 30f multicolored          1.60   .65
932 A246 80f multicolored          4.25  1.75
    *Nos. 930-932 (3)*           6.50  2.65

21st Pan Arab
Medical
Congress, Jan.
30-Feb.
2 — A247

**1984, Jan. 30    Litho.    Perf. 14½x14**
933 A247 15f purple & multi         .65   .25
934 A247 30f blue grn & multi      1.60   .65
935 A247 80f pink & multi          3.75  1.75
    *Nos. 933-935 (3)*           6.00  2.65

Key, Natl. Emblem,
and Health
Establishments
Emblem — A248

**1984, Feb. 20    Photo.    Perf. 13x13½**
936 A248 15f multicolored           .55   .25
937 A248 30f multicolored           .95   .45
938 A248 80f multicolored          3.00  1.50
    *Nos. 936-938 (3)*           4.50  2.20

Inauguration of Amiri and Al-Razi Hospitals,
Allergy Center and Medical Stores Center.

23rd National
Day — A249

**1984, Feb. 25    Litho.    Perf. 13½**
939 A249 15f multicolored          .75    .25
940 A249 30f multicolored         1.25    .45
941 A249 80f multicolored         3.50   1.50
    Nos. 939-941 (3)              5.50   2.20

2nd Kuwait Intl. Medical
Science Conf., Mar. 4-
8 — A250

**1984, Mar. 4    Photo.**
**Granite Paper**
942 A250 15f multicolored          .75    .25
943 A250 30f multicolored         1.50    .85
944 A250 80f multicolored         3.75   1.70
    Nos. 942-944 (3)              6.00   2.60

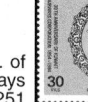

30th Anniv. of
Kuwait Airways
Corp. — A251

**1984, Mar. 15    Perf. 13½**
946 A251 30f multicolored         1.25   1.00
947 A251 80f multicolored         3.75   2.00

Al-Arabi Magazine,
25th Anniv. — A252

**1984, Mar. 20    Perf. 14½x14**
948 A252 15f multicolored          .60    .25
949 A252 30f multicolored         1.15    .50
950 A252 80f multicolored         3.25   1.40
    Nos. 948-950 (3)              5.00   2.15

World Health
Day — A253

**1984, Apr. 7    Perf. 12**
951 A253 15f multicolored          .75    .25
952 A253 30f multicolored         1.25    .45
953 A253 80f multicolored         3.50   1.50
    Nos. 951-953 (3)              5.50   2.20

Hanan Kuwaiti
Orphan Village,
Sudan — A254

**1984, May 15    Litho.    Perf. 12**
954 A254 15f multicolored          .75    .25
955 A254 30f multicolored         1.25    .45
956 A254 80f multicolored         3.50   1.50
    Nos. 954-956 (3)              5.50   2.20

Intl. Civil Aviation
Org., 40th
Anniv. — A255

**1984, June 12**
957 A255 15f multicolored          .75    .35
958 A255 30f multicolored         1.25    .80
959 A255 80f multicolored         3.50   2.00
    Nos. 957-959 (3)              5.50   3.15

Arab Youth
Day — A256

**1984, July 5    Perf. 13½**
960 A256 30f multicolored         1.25    .65
961 A256 80f multicolored         4.00   1.75

1984 Summer
Olympics — A257

**1984, July 28    Perf. 15x14**
962 A257 30f Swimming              .65    .65
963 A257 30f Hurdles               .65    .65
  a.   Pair, #962-963            1.75   1.75
964 A257 80f Judo                 1.90   1.90
965 A257 80f Equestrian           1.90   1.90
  a.   Pair, #964-965            4.75   4.75
    Nos. 962-965 (4)              5.10   5.10

10th Anniv. of
the Science
Club — A258

**1984, Aug. 11    Photo.    Perf. 13½x13**
966 A258 15f multicolored          .50    .35
967 A258 30f multicolored         1.25    .75
968 A258 80f multicolored         2.75   2.00
    Nos. 966-968 (3)              4.50   3.10

Islamic
Pilgrimage
A259

**1984, Sept. 4    Photo.    Perf. 12x11½**
969 A259 30f multicolored         1.50    .75
970 A259 80f multicolored         3.50   2.00

INTELSAT '84,
20th
Anniv. — A260

**1984, Oct. 1    Litho.    Perf. 13½x14**
971 A260 30f multicolored         1.75    .80
972 A260 80f multicolored         4.25   1.90

G.C.C. Supreme
Council, 5th
Session — A261

**1984, Nov. 24    Litho.    Perf. 15x14**
973 A261 30f multicolored         1.25    .65
974 A261 80f multicolored         3.75   1.75

Map of Israel, Fists,
Shattered Star of
David — A262

**1984, Nov. 29    Photo.    Perf. 12**
975 A262 30f multicolored         1.75    .75
976 A262 80f multicolored         4.50   2.00

Intl. Palestinian Solidarity Day.

Globe,
Emblem — A263

**1984, Dec. 24    Perf. 12x11½**
**Granite Paper**
977 A263 30f multicolored         1.25    .75
978 A263 80f multicolored         3.50   2.00

Kuwait Oil Co., 50th anniv.

Intl. Youth
Year — A264

**1985, Jan. 15    Perf. 13½**
979 A264 30f multicolored         1.00    .30
980 A264 80f multicolored         2.75   1.25

24th Natl. Day — A265

**1985, Feb. 25    Litho.    Perf. 14x15**
981 A265 30f multicolored         1.00    .40
982 A265 80f multicolored         4.00   1.25

Intl. Program for the
Development of
Communications
A266

**1985, Mar. 4    Photo.    Perf. 11½**
**Granite Paper**
983 A266 30f multicolored         1.25    .50
984 A266 80f multicolored         3.50   1.60

1st Arab Gulf Week for
Social Work — A267

**1985, Mar. 13    Photo.    Perf. 13½x13**
985 A267 30f multicolored         1.25    .50
986 A267 80f multicolored         3.00   1.60

Kuwait Dental
Assoc. 3rd
Conference
A268

**1985, Mar. 23    Litho.    Perf. 13½**
987 A268 30f multicolored         1.50    .80
988 A268 80f multicolored         3.50   2.00

1985 Census — A269

**1985, Apr. 1    Perf. 14x13½**
989 A269 30f multicolored         1.50    .50
990 A269 80f multicolored         3.50   1.60

World Health
Day — A270

**1985, Apr. 7    Photo.    Perf. 13½x13**
991 A270 30f multicolored         1.50    .55
992 A270 80f multicolored         3.25   1.60

Names
of
Books,
Authors
and
Poets in
Arabic
A271

**1985, May 20    Perf. 12**
**Granite Paper**
993 A271  Block of 4             6.75   4.00
  a.-d.   30f any single         1.40    .75
994 A271  Block of 4            16.50  10.00
  a.-d.   80f any single         3.50   1.40

Central Library, 50th anniv.

World
Environment
Day — A272

**1985, June 5    Perf. 11½**
995 A272 30f multicolored         2.00    .75
996 A272 80f multicolored         4.50   2.00

Org. of Petroleum
Exporting
Countries, 25th
Anniv. — A273

**1985, Sept. 1    Perf. 13x13½**
997 A273 30f multicolored         1.75    .55
998 A273 80f multicolored         4.25   1.60

Inauguration of
Civil Information
System — A274

**1985, Oct. 1    Photo.    Perf. 12x11½**
999 A274 30f multicolored         1.50    .55
1000 A274 80f multicolored        3.75   1.60

Intl. Day of
Solidarity with
Palestinian
People — A275

**1985, Nov. 29    Photo.    Perf. 12**
1001 A275 15f multicolored        1.10    .55
1002 A275 30f multicolored        1.90   1.00
1003 A275 80f multicolored        4.25   2.75
    Nos. 1001-1003 (3)            7.25   4.30

25th Natl.
Day — A276

**1986, Feb. 25    Litho.    Perf. 15x14**
1004 A276 15f multicolored         .75    .30
1005 A276 30f multicolored        1.50    .70
1006 A276 80f multicolored        3.75   2.00
    Nos. 1004-1006 (3)            6.00   3.00

Natl. Red Crescent
Soc., 20th
Anniv. — A277

**1986, Mar. 26    Photo.    Perf. 13½**
1007  A277  20f multicolored         1.10    .40
1008  A277  25f multicolored         1.40    .60
1009  A277  70f multicolored         4.00   1.75
      Nos. 1007-1009 (3)             6.50   2.75

World Health
Day — A278

**1986, Apr. 7         Perf. 13½x13**
1010  A278  20f multicolored         1.00    .65
1011  A278  25f multicolored         1.50    .80
1012  A278  70f multicolored         3.75   2.25
      Nos. 1010-1012 (3)             6.25   3.70

Intl. Peace
Year — A279

**1986, June 5    Litho.    Perf. 13½**
1013  A279  20f multicolored         1.00    .45
1014  A279  25f multicolored         1.75    .70
1015  A279  70f multicolored         3.75   1.75
      Nos. 1013-1015 (3)             6.50   2.90

United Arab
Shipping Co.,
10th
Anniv. — A280

**1986, July 1    Photo.    Perf. 12x11½**
1016  A280  20f Al Mirqab            1.25    .50
1017  A280  70f Al Mubarakiah        5.25   2.00

Gulf Bank, 25th
Anniv. — A281

**1986, Oct. 1    Photo.    Perf. 12½**
1018  A281  20f multicolored         1.00    .55
1019  A281  25f multicolored         1.50    .65
1020  A281  70f multicolored         4.50   1.90
      Nos. 1018-1020 (3)             7.00   3.10

Sadu Art — A282

Various tapestry weavings.

**1986, Nov. 5    Photo.    Perf. 12x11½**
**Granite Paper**
1021  A282  20f multicolored          .85    .40
1022  A282  70f multicolored         2.75   1.50
1023  A282  200f multicolored        6.50   3.75
      Nos. 1021-1023 (3)            10.10   5.65

Intl. Day of
Solidarity with
the Palestinian
People — A283

---

**1986, Nov. 29         Perf. 14**
1024  A283  20f multicolored         1.75    .85
1025  A283  25f multicolored         2.50   1.10
1026  A283  70f multicolored         6.25   3.25
      Nos. 1024-1026 (3)            10.50   5.20

5th Islamic
Summit
Conference
A284

**1987, Jan. 26    Litho.    Perf. 14½**
1027  A284  25f multicolored         1.00    .45
1028  A284  50f multicolored         2.00    .80
1029  A284  150f multicolored        6.00   2.25
      Nos. 1027-1029 (3)             9.00   3.50

26th Natl.
Day — A285

**1987, Feb. 25         Perf. 13½x14**
1030  A285  50f multicolored         1.75    .60
1031  A285  150f multicolored        5.25   2.00

Natl. Health
Sciences
Center — A286

**1987, Mar. 15    Photo.    Perf. 12x11½**
**Granite Paper**
1032  A286  25f multicolored         1.00    .35
1033  A286  150f multicolored        5.00   2.00

3rd Kuwait Intl. Medical Sciences Conference on Infectious Diseases in Developing
Countries.

World Health
Day — A287

**1987, Apr. 7    Photo.    Perf. 13x13½**
1034  A287  25f multicolored          .75    .40
1035  A287  50f multicolored         1.40    .70
1036  A287  150f multicolored        4.75   2.00
      Nos. 1034-1036 (3)             6.90   3.10

Day of Ghods
(Jerusalem)
— A288

**1987, June 7    Photo.    Perf. 12x11½**
1037  A288  25f multicolored          .90    .35
1038  A288  50f multicolored         1.90    .75
1039  A288  150f multicolored        5.25   2.50
      Nos. 1037-1039 (3)             8.05   3.60

Islamic
Pilgrimage to
Miqat Wadi
Mihrim — A289

**1987, Aug.    Photo.    Perf. 13½x14½**
1040  A289  25f multicolored         1.10    .35
1041  A289  50f multicolored         1.90    .80
1042  A289  150f multicolored        5.00   2.50
      Nos. 1040-1042 (3)             8.00   3.65

Arab
Telecommunications
Day — A290

---

**1987, Sept. 9    Litho.    Perf. 14x13½**
1043  A290  25f multicolored          .75    .35
1044  A290  50f multicolored         1.75    .80
1045  A290  150f multicolored        5.00   2.50
      Nos. 1043-1045 (3)             7.50   3.65

World Maritime
Day — A291

**1987, Sept. 24         Perf. 12x11½**
**Granite Paper**
1046  A291  25f multicolored         1.00    .35
1047  A291  50f multicolored         2.00    .75
1048  A291  150f multicolored        5.75   2.00
      Nos. 1046-1048 (3)             8.75   3.10

Al Qurain Housing
Project — A292

**1987, Oct. 5         Perf. 13x13½**
1049  A292  25f multicolored          .70    .35
1050  A292  50f multicolored         1.50    .60
1051  A292  150f multicolored        4.25   1.75
      Nos. 1049-1051 (3)             6.45   2.70

Port Authority,
10th
Anniv. — A293

**1987, Nov. 16    Litho.    Perf. 14½**
1052  A293  25f multicolored         1.00    .35
1053  A293  50f multicolored         1.75    .80
1054  A293  150f multicolored        5.75   2.25
      Nos. 1052-1054 (3)             8.50   3.40

A294

**1987, Nov. 29         Perf. 14x13½**
1055  A294  25f multicolored          .90    .35
1056  A294  50f multicolored         1.60    .70
1057  A294  150f multicolored        5.00   2.25
      Nos. 1055-1057 (3)             7.50   3.30

Intl. Day of Solidarity with the Palestinian
People.

A295

**1988, Feb. 3    Photo.    Perf. 14**
1058  A295  25f multicolored          .75    .30
1059  A295  50f multicolored         1.25    .50
1060  A295  150f multicolored        3.50   1.25
      Nos. 1058-1060 (3)             5.50   2.05

Women's Cultural and Social Soc., 25th
anniv.

A296

---

**1988, Feb. 25**
1061  A296  25f multicolored          .75    .30
1062  A296  50f multicolored         1.25    .50
1063  A296  150f multicolored        3.50   1.25
      Nos. 1061-1063 (3)             5.50   2.05

National Day, 27th anniv.

A297

**1988, Apr. 7    Litho.    Perf. 14x15**
1064  A297  25f multicolored          .80    .30
1065  A297  50f multicolored         1.50    .75
1066  A297  150f multicolored        4.00   1.75
      Nos. 1064-1066 (3)             6.30   2.80

World Health Day, WHO 40th anniv.

A298

**1988, Apr. 24    Photo.    Perf. 12**
**Granite Paper**
1067  A298  35f multicolored         1.00    .35
1068  A298  50f multicolored         1.50    .65
1069  A298  150f multicolored        5.00   2.00
      Nos. 1067-1069 (3)             7.50   3.00

Regional Marine Environment Day. Kuwait
Regional Convention on the Marine Environment, 10th anniv. See Iraq Nos. 1333-1336.

A299

**1988, July 10    Photo.    Perf. 14**
1070  A299  25f multicolored         1.00    .35
1071  A299  50f multicolored         1.50    .60
1072  A299  150f multicolored        5.00   1.75
      Nos. 1070-1072 (3)             7.50   2.60

Kuwait Teachers Soc., 25th anniv.

Pilgrimage to
Mecca — A300

**1988, Sept. 12    Litho.    Perf. 13½x14**
1073  A300  25f multicolored         1.10    .25
1074  A300  50f multicolored         2.00    .55
1075  A300  150f multicolored        6.00   1.75
      Nos. 1073-1075 (3)             9.10   2.55

Palestinian "Children
of Stone" Fighting
Israelis — A301

**1988, Sept. 15    Photo.    Perf. 13x13½**
1076  A301  50f multicolored         1.75    .70
1077  A301  150f multicolored        6.50   2.50

Palestinian Uprising. Dated 1987.

Arab Housing
Day — A302

**1988, Oct. 3**
| | | | | |
|---|---|---|---|---|
| 1078 | A302 | 50f multicolored | 1.25 | .60 |
| 1079 | A302 | 100f multicolored | 2.50 | 1.25 |
| 1080 | A302 | 150f multicolored | 4.25 | 1.75 |
| | | *Nos. 1078-1080 (3)* | 8.00 | 3.60 |

Intl. Day for
Solidarity with the
Palestinian
People — A303

**1988, Nov. 29    Litho.    *Perf. 14x13***
| | | | | |
|---|---|---|---|---|
| 1081 | A303 | 50f multicolored | 1.50 | .60 |
| 1082 | A303 | 100f multicolored | 3.25 | 1.25 |
| 1083 | A303 | 150f multicolored | 5.75 | 1.75 |
| | | *Nos. 1081-1083 (3)* | 10.50 | 3.60 |

A304

**1988, Dec. 5    *Perf. 13x14***
| | | | | |
|---|---|---|---|---|
| 1084 | A304 | 50f multicolored | 1.20 | .50 |
| 1085 | A304 | 100f multicolored | 2.60 | 1.00 |
| 1086 | A304 | 150f multicolored | 4.25 | 1.50 |
| | | *Nos. 1084-1086 (3)* | 8.05 | 3.00 |

Intl. Volunteers Day.

A305

**1989, Feb. 18    Litho.    *Perf. 14x13½***
| | | | | |
|---|---|---|---|---|
| 1087 | A305 | 50f multicolored | 1.00 | .50 |
| 1088 | A305 | 100f multicolored | 2.00 | 1.00 |
| 1089 | A305 | 150f multicolored | 3.50 | 1.50 |
| | | *Nos. 1087-1089 (3)* | 6.50 | 3.00 |

18th Arab Engineering Conference.

28th Natl.
Day — A306

**1989, Feb. 25    *Perf. 13x13½***
| | | | | |
|---|---|---|---|---|
| 1090 | A306 | 50f multicolored | 1.25 | .50 |
| 1091 | A306 | 100f multicolored | 2.25 | 1.00 |
| 1092 | A306 | 150f multicolored | 4.00 | 1.50 |
| | | *Nos. 1090-1092 (3)* | 7.50 | 3.00 |

5th Natl. Dental
Assoc.
Conference — A307

**1989, Mar. 30    Litho.    *Perf. 13½x13***
| | | | | |
|---|---|---|---|---|
| 1093 | A307 | 50f multicolored | 1.00 | .50 |
| 1094 | A307 | 150f multicolored | 3.00 | 1.50 |
| 1095 | A307 | 250f multicolored | 4.50 | 2.00 |
| | | *Nos. 1093-1095 (3)* | 8.50 | 3.75 |

World Health
Day — A308

**1989, Apr. 7    *Perf. 13x13½***
| | | | | |
|---|---|---|---|---|
| 1096 | A308 | 50f multicolored | .70 | .40 |
| 1097 | A308 | 150f multicolored | 2.25 | 1.25 |
| 1098 | A308 | 250f multicolored | 3.75 | 2.00 |
| | | *Nos. 1096-1098 (3)* | 6.70 | 3.65 |

A309

**1989, May 10    *Perf. 13x14***
| | | | | |
|---|---|---|---|---|
| 1099 | A309 | 50f multicolored | .80 | .40 |
| 1100 | A309 | 150f multicolored | 2.50 | 1.25 |
| 1101 | A309 | 250f multicolored | 4.25 | 2.00 |
| | | *Nos. 1099-1101 (3)* | 7.55 | 3.65 |

Arab Board for Medical Specializations, 10th
anniv.

A310

**1989, June 10    Litho.    *Perf. 14x15***
| | | | | |
|---|---|---|---|---|
| 1102 | A310 | 50f multicolored | .90 | .50 |
| 1103 | A310 | 200f multicolored | 3.50 | 2.25 |
| 1104 | A310 | 250f multicolored | 4.50 | 2.75 |
| | | *Nos. 1102-1104 (3)* | 8.90 | 5.50 |

Natl. Journalists Assoc., 25th anniv.

Al-Taneem
Mosque — A311

**1989, July 9    Litho.    *Perf. 13½x14½***
| | | | | |
|---|---|---|---|---|
| 1105 | A311 | 50f multicolored | 1.00 | .50 |
| 1106 | A311 | 150f multicolored | 3.00 | 1.50 |
| 1107 | A311 | 200f multicolored | 4.00 | 2.00 |
| | | *Nos. 1105-1107 (3)* | 8.00 | 4.00 |

Pilgrimage to Mecca.

Arab Housing
Day — A312

**1989, Oct. 2    *Perf. 13½***
| | | | | |
|---|---|---|---|---|
| 1108 | A312 | 25f multicolored | .80 | .25 |
| 1109 | A312 | 50f multicolored | 1.75 | .50 |
| 1110 | A312 | 150f multicolored | 5.75 | 1.75 |
| | | *Nos. 1108-1110 (3)* | 8.30 | 2.50 |

Annual Greenery
Week
Celebration — A313

**1989, Oct. 15    *Perf. 13½x13***
| | | | | |
|---|---|---|---|---|
| 1111 | A313 | 25f multicolored | .75 | .25 |
| 1112 | A313 | 50f multicolored | 1.75 | .50 |
| 1113 | A313 | 150f multicolored | 5.00 | 1.50 |
| | | *Nos. 1111-1113 (3)* | 7.50 | 2.25 |

Dhow — A314

**Numbers in Black, Moon and Dhow
in Gold**

**1989, Nov. 1    *Perf. 14x15***
**Coil Stamps**
| | | | | |
|---|---|---|---|---|
| 1114 | A314 | 50f brt apple grn | 3.00 | 3.00 |
| 1115 | A314 | 100f brt blue | 5.50 | 5.50 |
| 1116 | A314 | 200f vermilion | 10.00 | 10.00 |
| | | *Nos. 1114-1116 (3)* | 18.50 | 18.50 |

Nos. 1114-1116 available only at two post
office locations, where they were dispensed
from machines. Printed in rolls of 3000 con-
secutively numbered stamps. Stamps with
overprinted asterisks but lacking printed numbers are from the ends of coil rolls.

Gulf Investment
Corp., 5th
Anniv. — A315

**1989, Nov. 4    *Perf. 15x14***
| | | | | |
|---|---|---|---|---|
| 1117 | A315 | 25f multicolored | .80 | .25 |
| 1118 | A315 | 50f multicolored | 1.50 | .60 |
| 1119 | A315 | 150f multicolored | 4.50 | 1.60 |
| | | *Nos. 1117-1119 (3)* | 6.80 | 2.45 |

Declaration of
Palestinian State, 1st
Anniv. — A316

**1989, Nov. 15    Litho.    *Perf. 14x15***
| | | | | |
|---|---|---|---|---|
| 1120 | A316 | 50f multicolored | 1.25 | .50 |
| 1121 | A316 | 150f multicolored | 4.00 | 1.75 |
| 1122 | A316 | 200f multicolored | 5.50 | 2.25 |
| | | *Nos. 1120-1122 (3)* | 10.75 | 4.50 |

Zakat House, Orphan
Sponsorship
Program — A317

**1989, Dec. 10    *Perf. 13½x13***
| | | | | |
|---|---|---|---|---|
| 1123 | A317 | 25f multicolored | .55 | .35 |
| 1124 | A317 | 50f multicolored | 1.25 | .85 |
| 1125 | A317 | 150f multicolored | 3.75 | 2.00 |
| | | *Nos. 1123-1125 (3)* | 5.55 | 3.20 |

Kuwait Police, 50th
Anniv. — A318

**1989, Dec. 30    Litho.    *Perf. 15x14***
| | | | | |
|---|---|---|---|---|
| 1126 | A318 | 25f gray & multi | 1.00 | .35 |
| 1127 | A318 | 50f lt ultra & multi | 2.25 | .85 |
| 1128 | A318 | 150f lt violet & multi | 7.00 | 2.00 |
| | | *Nos. 1126-1128 (3)* | 10.25 | 3.20 |

National Day, 29th
Anniv. — A319

**1990, Feb. 25    *Perf. 14x13½***
| | | | | |
|---|---|---|---|---|
| 1129 | A319 | 25f multicolored | 1.25 | .35 |
| 1130 | A319 | 50f multicolored | 2.00 | .85 |
| 1131 | A319 | 150f multicolored | 6.50 | 2.00 |
| | | *Nos. 1129-1131 (3)* | 9.75 | 3.20 |

World
Meteorological
Day — A320

**1990, Mar. 23    Litho.    *Perf. 13½x14***
| | | | | |
|---|---|---|---|---|
| 1132 | A320 | 50f multicolored | 2.50 | .60 |
| 1133 | A320 | 100f multicolored | 5.75 | 1.40 |
| 1134 | A320 | 150f multicolored | 8.25 | 2.00 |
| | | *Nos. 1132-1134 (3)* | 16.50 | 4.00 |

World Health
Day — A321

**1990, Apr. 7    *Perf. 14x15***
| | | | | |
|---|---|---|---|---|
| 1135 | A321 | 50f multicolored | 2.75 | .60 |
| 1136 | A321 | 100f multicolored | 5.75 | 1.40 |
| 1137 | A321 | 150f multicolored | 7.50 | 2.00 |
| | | *Nos. 1135-1137 (3)* | 16.00 | 4.00 |

Hawk — A322

**1990, July 7    Litho.    *Perf. 14½***
| | | | | |
|---|---|---|---|---|
| 1138 | A322 | 50f blue & gold | 6.00 | 10.00 |
| 1139 | A322 | 100f maroon & gold | 8.00 | 11.50 |
| 1140 | A322 | 150f green & gold | 11.00 | 13.50 |
| | | *Nos. 1138-1140 (3)* | 25.00 | 35.00 |

Liberation of
Kuwait — A323

**1991    Litho.    *Perf. 14½***
| | | | | |
|---|---|---|---|---|
| 1141 | A323 | 25f multicolored | 1.25 | .40 |
| 1142 | A323 | 50f multicolored | 2.50 | .80 |
| 1143 | A323 | 150f multicolored | 6.50 | 2.50 |
| | | *Nos. 1141-1143 (3)* | 10.25 | 3.70 |

Peace — A324

**1991, May    *Perf. 13½x14***
| | | | | |
|---|---|---|---|---|
| 1144 | A324 | 50f multicolored | 1.25 | .85 |
| 1145 | A324 | 100f multicolored | 2.50 | 1.60 |
| 1146 | A324 | 150f multicolored | 4.00 | 2.50 |
| | | *Nos. 1144-1146 (3)* | 7.75 | 4.95 |

Reconstruction — A325

**1991, May**
| | | | | |
|---|---|---|---|---|
| 1147 | A325 | 50f multicolored | 1.25 | .85 |
| 1148 | A325 | 150f multicolored | 3.25 | 2.00 |
| 1149 | A325 | 200f multicolored | 4.00 | 2.75 |
| | | *Nos. 1147-1149 (3)* | 8.50 | 5.60 |

Liberation of
Kuwait — A326

Flags of forces joining international coalition
for liberation of Kuwait: a, Sweden. b, USSR.
c, U.S. d, Kuwait. e, Saudi Arabia. f, UN. g,
Singapore. h, France. i, Italy. j, Egypt. k,
Morocco. l, UK. m, Philippines. n, UAE. o,
Syria. p, Poland. q, Australia. r, Japan. s, Hungary. t, Netherlands. u, Denmark. v, New Zealand. w, Czechoslovakia. x, Bahrain. y, Honduras. z, Turkey. aa, Greece. ab, Oman. ac,
Qatar. ad, Belgium. ae, Sierra Leone. af,
Argentina. ag, Norway. ah, Canada. ai, Germany. aj, South Korea. ak, Bangladesh. al,
Bulgaria. am, Senegal. an, Spain. ao, Niger.
ap, Pakistan.
No. 1151, Flags of all forces of coalition.

**1991, July 25    Litho.    *Perf. 14½***
| | | | | |
|---|---|---|---|---|
| 1150 | | 50f Sheet of 42 | 85.00 | 85.00 |
| a.-ap. | A326 | Any single | 1.75 | 1.75 |

**Size: 87x134mm**
***Imperf***
| | | | | |
|---|---|---|---|---|
| 1151 | A326 | 1d multicolored | 37.50 | 37.50 |

Invasion of Kuwait,
1st Anniv. — A327

50f, Human terror. 100f, Invasion of Kuwait. 150f, Environmental terrorism, horiz. 250f, Desert Storm.

**1991, Aug. 2**      **Perf. 14½**
1152 A327 50f multi    2.25   1.00
1153 A327 100f multi   4.25   1.50
1154 A327 150f multi   6.50   2.50

**Size: 90x65mm**
**Imperf**
1155 A327 250f multi     12.50   12.50
    *Nos. 1152-1155 (4)*   25.50   17.50

12th Gulf
Cooperation Council
Summit — A328

Design: 150f, Tree of flags.

**1991, Dec. 23**   **Litho.**   **Perf. 14½**
1156 A328 25f multicolored    .75   .55
   a.   see footnote      .80   .55
1157 A328 150f multicolored   4.25   3.25
   a.   Sheet, 2 ea #1156-1157   11.00   11.00
   b.   Sheet, 2 ea #1156a, 1157   11.00   11.00

No. 1156a has tree with inscriptions (country names in Arabic) in colors of flags shown on No. 1157.

Intl. Literacy
Year — A329

**1992, Feb. 12**   **Litho.**   **Perf. 13½x13**
1158 A329 50f dark blue & buff   1.25   .75
1159 A329 100f dark blue & cit   2.50   1.50
1160 A329 150f dk blue & pale
        lil            3.50   2.00
    *Nos. 1158-1160 (3)*   7.25   4.25

Dated 1990.

OPEC, 30th Anniv. (in
1990) — A330

**1992, Oct. 29**    **Perf. 14½x13½**
1161 A330 25f red & multi    1.00   .50
1162 A330 50f yellow & multi   2.00   1.00
1163 A330 150f green & multi   5.50   3.00
    *Nos. 1161-1163 (3)*   8.50   4.50

31st Natl.
Day — A331

**1992**            **Perf. 14½**
1164 A331 50f Flag, doves   1.25   .50
1165 A331 150f Flags      3.75   1.50
   a.   Min. sheet, 2 ea #1164-1165   10.00   10.00

Liberation Day (No. 1165). Issue dates, 50f, Feb. 25; 150f, Feb. 26.

Don't Forget
Our P.O.W.'s
A332

50f, Flag, chains. 150f, Cell bars, chains.

**1991, Nov. 16**
1166 A332 50f multicolored   1.25   .75
1167 A332 150f multicolored   4.00   2.25
   a.   Min. sheet, 2 each #1166-1167   15.00   15.00

Dated 1991. Issued: 50f, 2/25; 150f, 2/26.

Camels — A333

**1991, Nov. 16**     **Perf. 12½**
1168 A333 25f pink & multi    .90   .90
1169 A333 50f beige & multi   1.50   1.50
1170 A333 150f lt violet & multi   3.75   3.75
1171 A333 200f blue & multi   4.50   4.50
1172 A333 350f orange & multi   9.00   9.00
    *Nos. 1168-1172 (5)*   19.65   19.65

Environmental
Terrorism, by
Jafar
Islah — A334

Designs: No. 1174, Snake, flag, map. No. 1175, Skull, dead fish. No. 1176, Dying camel.

**1992, June**       **Perf. 14½**
1173 A334 150f multicolored   3.25   1.50
1174 A334 150f multicolored   3.25   1.50
1175 A334 150f multicolored   3.25   1.50
1176 A334 150f multicolored   3.25   1.50
   a.   Block of 4, #1173-1176   15.00   15.00
   b.   Miniature sheet of 4, #1173-1176   22.50   22.50
    *Nos. 1173-1176 (4)*   13.00   6.00

Earth Summit, Rio De Janeiro. No. 1176a printed in continuous design.

EXPO '92,
Seville — A335

Designs: No. 1177, Kuwaiti Pavilion, La Giralda Tower, Seville. No. 1178, Dhows. No. 1179, Dhow. No. 1180, Pavilion, dhow.
   Flags of Spain or Kuwait and: No. 1181, Pavilion. No. 1182, La Giralda Tower. No. 1183, La Giralda Tower, dhow. No. 1184, Pavilion, dhow.

**1992, June 19**
1177 A335 50f multicolored   .90   .90
1178 A335 50f multicolored   .90   .90
1179 A335 50f multicolored   .90   .90
1180 A335 50f multicolored   .90   .90
   a.   Block of 4, #1177-1180   4.00   4.00
1181 A335 150f multicolored   2.75   2.75
1182 A335 150f multicolored   2.75   2.75
1183 A335 150f multicolored   2.75   2.75
1184 A335 150f multicolored   2.75   2.75
   a.   Block of 4, #1181-1184   13.50   13.50
   b.   Miniature sheet of 8, #1177-1184   25.00   25.00
    *Nos. 1177-1184 (8)*   14.60   14.60

Nos. 1180a, 1184a have continuous designs.

Palace of
Justice — A336

**1992, July 4**      **Perf. 12½**
1185 A336 25f lilac & multi    .60   .30
1186 A336 50f lil rose & multi   1.25   .50
1187 A336 100f yel grn & multi   2.00   1.00
1188 A336 150f yel org & multi   3.00   1.40
1189 A336 250f blue grn & multi   4.50   2.25
    *Nos. 1185-1189 (5)*   11.35   5.45

1992 Summer
Olympics,
Barcelona — A337

Olympic flag, Fahed Al Ahmed Al Sabah, member of the Intl. Olympic committee and: 50f, Swimmer, soccer player. 100f, Runner, basketball player. 150f, Judo, equestrian.

**1992, July 25**      **Perf. 14½**
1190 A337 50f multicolored   1.50   .65
1191 A337 100f multicolored   3.50   1.25
1192 A337 150f multicolored   5.00   2.00
    *Nos. 1190-1192 (3)*   10.00   3.90

Invasion by
Iraq, 2nd
Anniv. — A338

Children's paintings: No. 1193, Tanks, people holding signs, two people being tortured. No. 1194, Truck, Iraqi soldiers looting. No. 1195, Iraqi soldiers killing civilians, tanks. No. 1196, Houses ablaze. No. 1197, Tanks, civilians, soldiers. No. 1198, Planes bombing in attack on fort. No. 1199, Tank, civilians holding flags, signs. No. 1200, Battlefield.

**1992, Aug. 2**   **Litho.**   **Perf. 14x14½**
1193 A338 50f multicolored   .90   .90
1194 A338 50f multicolored   .90   .90
1195 A338 50f multicolored   .90   .90
1196 A338 50f multicolored   .90   .90
   a.   Block of 4, #1193-1196   4.00   4.00
1197 A338 150f multicolored   2.75   2.75
1198 A338 150f multicolored   2.75   2.75
1199 A338 150f multicolored   2.75   2.75
1200 A338 150f multicolored   2.75   2.75
   a.   Block of 4, #1197-1200   13.50   13.50
   b.   Min. sheet of 8, #1193-1200   25.00   25.00
    *Nos. 1193-1200 (8)*   14.60   14.60

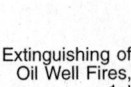

Extinguishing of
Oil Well Fires,
1st
Anniv. — A339

Various scenes showing oil well fire being extinguished.

**1992**      **Litho.**     **Perf. 14½**
1201 A339 25f multi, vert.   .50   .35
1202 A339 50f multi, vert.   1.00   .70
1203 A339 150f multi, vert.   3.00   2.00
1204 A339 250f multicolored   5.25   3.50
    *Nos. 1201-1204 (4)*   9.75   6.55

Kuwait Tower — A340

**1993, Jan. 16**   **Litho.**   **Perf. 14x15**
**Background Color**
1205 A340 25f lilac       .40   .35
1206 A340 100f blue     1.40   1.25
1207 A340 150f salmon   2.25   1.75
    *Nos. 1205-1207 (3)*   4.05   3.35

A341

**1993, Feb. 25**   **Litho.**   **Perf. 13½x14**
1208 A341 25f green & multi   .40   .35
1209 A341 50f blue & multi   .85   .70
1210 A341 150f pink & multi   2.25   1.75
    *Nos. 1208-1210 (3)*   3.50   2.80

National Day, 32nd anniv.

Liberation Day, 2nd
Anniv. — A342

**1993, Feb. 26**     **Perf. 15x14**
1211 A342 25f org yel & multi   .50   .35
1212 A342 50f green & multi   1.25   .75
1213 A342 150f red lilac & multi   3.25   1.75
    *Nos. 1211-1213 (3)*   5.00   2.85

Remembering
Prisoners of
War — A343

Designs: 50f, Prisoner shackled in cell, vert. 150f, Shackled hand pointing to cell window, bird. 200f, Cell, prisoner's face, vert.

**Perf. 13½x14, 14x13½**
**1993, May 15**      **Litho.**
1214 A343 50f multicolored   .85   .85
1215 A343 150f multicolored   2.25   2.25
1216 A343 200f multicolored   2.75   2.75
    *Nos. 1214-1216 (3)*   5.85   5.85

18th Deaf Child
Week — A344

**1993, Apr. 20**   **Litho.**   **Perf. 11½x12**
**Granite Paper**
1217 A344 25f gray & multi   .40   .40
1218 A344 50f green & multi   .85   .85
1219 A344 150f yellow & multi   3.00   2.50
1220 A344 350f blue & multi   5.25   4.75
    *Nos. 1217-1220 (4)*   9.50   8.50

A345

**1993, Aug. 2**   **Litho.**   **Perf. 13½x14**
1221 A345 50f green & multi   .75   .60
1222 A345 150f orange & multi   2.75   1.75

Invasion by Iraq, 3rd anniv.

Kuwait Airforce,
40th
Anniv. — A346

**1993, Dec. 9**   **Litho.**   **Perf. 13x13½**
1223 A346 50f blue & multi   .75   .60
1224 A346 150f green & multi   2.75   1.75

Natl. Day, 33rd
Anniv. — A347

**1994, Feb. 25**   **Litho.**   **Perf. 13½x14**
1225 A347 25f salmon & multi   .65   .40
1226 A347 50f yellow & multi   1.25   .75
1227 A347 150f green & multi   3.25   1.75
    *Nos. 1225-1227 (3)*   5.15   2.90

Liberation Day, 3rd Anniv. — A348

**1994, Feb. 26**
1228 A348 25f yellow & multi .65 .40
1229 A348 50f blue & multi 1.25 .75
1230 A348 150f gray green & multi 3.50 1.90
*Nos. 1228-1230 (3)* 5.40 3.05

Central Bank of Kuwait, 25th Anniv. — A349

**1994, Apr. 20  Litho.  Perf. 13½x13**
1231 A349 25f salmon & multi .65 .40
1232 A349 50f green & multi 1.20 .75
1233 A349 150f blue violet & multi 3.50 2.00
*Nos. 1231-1233 (3)* 5.35 3.15

A350          A351

Intl. Year of the Family — A352

**1994, May 15  Litho.  Perf. 13**
1234 A350 50f multicolored .75 .75
1235 A351 150f multicolored 2.25 2.25
1236 A352 200f multicolored 3.25 3.25
*Nos. 1234-1236 (3)* 6.25 6.00

A353

**1994, June 5  Litho.  Perf. 14**
1237 A353 50f yellow & multi .80 .80
1238 A353 100f blue & multi 1.60 1.60
1239 A353 150f green & multi 2.50 2.50
*Nos. 1237-1239 (3)* 4.90 4.90

Industrial Bank of Kuwait, 20th anniv.

Martyr's Day — A354

**1994, June 15  Litho.  Perf. 13**
1240 A354 50f Whirlpool 1.00 .50
1241 A354 100f Shifting sands 2.00 1.00
1242 A354 150f Finger print 3.00 2.25
1243 A354 250f Clouds 3.50 2.50
 a. Min. sheet of 4, #1240-1243 10.00 10.00
*Nos. 1240-1243 (4)* 9.50 6.25

ILO, 75th Anniv. — A355

**1994, June 25  Litho.  Perf. 14**
1244 A355 50f vio & multi .75 .75
1245 A355 150f pink & multi 2.50 2.50
1246 A355 350f blue & multi 5.75 5.00
*Nos. 1244-1246 (3)* 9.00 8.25

A356

**1994, Aug. 2  Litho.  Perf. 12½x13½**
1247 A356 50f green blue & multi 1.10 .75
1248 A356 150f blue & multi 3.00 2.00
1249 A356 350f lilac & multi 7.00 5.00
*Nos. 1247-1249 (3)* 11.10 7.75

Invasion by Iraq, 4th anniv.

Port Authority — A357

**1994, Aug. 31  Litho.  Perf. 12½x14**
1250 A357 50f pink & multi 1.50 .75
1251 A357 150f blue & multi 4.00 2.00
1252 A357 350f green & multi 9.50 5.00
*Nos. 1250-1252 (3)* 15.00 7.75

Science Club, 20th Anniv. — A358

**1994, Sept. 11  Perf. 14**
1253 A358 50f blue & multi 1.00 .75
1254 A358 100f green & multi 2.10 1.50
1255 A358 150f red & multi 2.75 2.00
*Nos. 1253-1255 (3)* 5.85 4.25

A359

Designs showing emblem and: 50f, Map of Arab countries, building. 100f, Windows, building. 150f, Doors below portico.

**1994, Nov. 12  Perf. 11½**
1256 A359 50f multicolored 1.00 .75
1257 A359 100f multicolored 1.60 1.25
1258 A359 150f multicolored 3.50 2.25
*Nos. 1256-1258 (3)* 6.10 4.25

Arab Towns Organization, opening of headquarters.

ICAO, 50th Anniv. — A360

Designs: 100f, Emblems, sailing ship. 150f, Emblems, co-operation, co-ordination. 350f, Emblem, airplane in flight.

**1994, Dec. 7  Perf. 14½**
1259 A360 100f silver, gold & multi 2.25 2.25
1260 A360 150f silver, gold & multi 3.50 3.50
1261 A360 350f gold & multi 7.50 5.75
*Nos. 1259-1261 (3)* 13.25 11.50

Kuwait Airways, 40th Anniv. — A361

**1994, Dec. 20  Perf. 13x14**
1262 A361 50f lake & multi 1.00 .75
1263 A361 100f green & multi 1.75 1.25
1264 A361 150f slate & multi 3.25 2.25
*Nos. 1262-1264 (3)* 6.00 4.25

1995 Census — A362

**1995, Feb. 6  Litho.  Perf. 14**
1265 A362 50f yellow & multi 1.00 .75
1266 A362 100f green & multi 1.75 1.25
1267 A362 150f brown & multi 3.25 2.25
*Nos. 1265-1267 (3)* 6.00 4.25

National Day, 34th Anniv. — A363

**1995, Feb. 25  Perf. 13**
1268 A363 25f blue & multi .75 .40
1269 A363 50f yellow & multi 1.25 .75
1270 A363 150f lilac & multi 3.50 1.75
*Nos. 1268-1270 (3)* 5.50 2.90

Liberation Day, 4th Anniv. — A364

**1995, Feb. 26**
1271 A364 25f blue & multi .85 .40
1272 A364 50f green & multi 1.60 .75
1273 A364 150f rose lilac & multi 4.75 1.75
*Nos. 1271-1273 (3)* 7.20 2.90

Medical Research A365

50f, Medical building. 100f, Classroom instruction. 150f, Map of Kuwait.

**1995, Mar. 20  Perf. 14**
1274 A365 50f multi 1.00 .75
1275 A365 100f multi 1.50 1.25
1276 A365 150f multi 3.00 2.00
*Nos. 1274-1276 (3)* 5.50 4.00

Arab League, 50th Anniv. — A366

Designs: 50f, Kuwaiti, league flags over emblems, map, vert. 100f, Flags over "50," emblem. 150f, Flags as clasping hands, vert.

**1995, Mar. 22  Perf. 13**
1277 A366 50f multicolored 1.00 .75
1278 A366 100f multicolored 1.50 1.25
1279 A366 150f multicolored 3.00 2.00
*Nos. 1277-1279 (3)* 5.50 4.00

World Health Day — A367

**1995, Apr. 7  Litho.  Perf. 13½x13**
1280 A367 50f blue & multi 1.00 .75
1281 A367 150f pink & multi 3.75 2.00
1282 A367 200f yellow & multi 4.25 2.75
*Nos. 1280-1282 (3)* 9.00 5.50

Volleyball, Cent. — A368

Designs: 50f, One gold ball. 100f, Gold "1," one gold ball. 150f, "1," both balls in gold.

**1995, June 5  Litho.  Perf. 14**
1283 A368 50f shown 1.00 1.00
1284 A368 100f multicolored 2.00 2.00
1285 A368 150f multicolored 3.50 3.00
*Nos. 1283-1285 (3)* 6.50 6.00

Invasion by Iraq, 5th Anniv. — A369

**1995, Aug. 2  Litho.  Perf. 13**
1286 A369 50f purple & multi 1.50 .75
1287 A369 100f red & multi 2.50 1.25
1288 A369 150f green & multi 4.50 2.00
*Nos. 1286-1288 (3)* 8.50 4.00

UN, 50th Anniv. — A370

**1995, Aug. 12  Perf. 13x13½**
1289 A370 25f multi .75 .50
1290 A370 50f orange & multi 1.50 1.00
1291 A370 150f bl grn & multi 2.75 1.75
*Nos. 1289-1291 (3)* 5.00 3.25

FAO, 50th Anniv. — A371

People in traditional dress with: 50f, Cattle, camels, sheep. 100f, Fish, boat. 150f, Poultry, fruits, vegetables.

**1995, Sept. 21  Perf. 13½x13**
1292 A371 50f multicolored 1.00 1.00
1293 A371 100f multicolored 1.50 1.50
1294 A371 150f multicolored 3.00 3.00
 a. Min. sheet of 3, #1292-1294 6.00 6.00
*Nos. 1292-1294 (3)* 5.50 5.50

A372

World Standards Day — A373

**1995, Oct. 14  Perf. 13**
1295 A372 50f multicolored 1.00 .75
1296 A373 100f green & multi 1.50 1.25
1297 A373 150f violet & multi 3.00 2.00
*Nos. 1295-1297 (3)* 5.50 4.00

Flowers — A374

Designs: 5f, Onobrychis ptolemaica. 15f, Convolvulus oxyphyllus. 25f, Papaver rhoeas.

50f, Moltkiopsis ciliata. 150f, Senecio desfontainei.

**1995, Nov. 15    Litho.    Perf. 14½**
| | | | | |
|---|---|---|---|---|
| **1298** | A374 | 5f multicolored | .55 | .30 |
| **1299** | A374 | 15f multicolored | .75 | .40 |
| **1300** | A374 | 25f multicolored | 1.40 | .75 |
| **1301** | A374 | 50f multicolored | 2.40 | 1.25 |
| **1302** | A374 | 150f multicolored | 4.75 | 2.00 |
| | | *Nos. 1298-1302 (5)* | 9.85 | 4.70 |

Natl. Day, 35th Anniv. — A375

**1996, Feb. 25    Perf. 14**
| | | | | |
|---|---|---|---|---|
| **1303** | A375 | 25f lil rose & multi | .75 | .40 |
| **1304** | A375 | 50f blue green & multi | 1.40 | .75 |
| **1305** | A375 | 150f salmon & multi | 4.50 | 2.00 |
| | | *Nos. 1303-1305 (3)* | 6.65 | 3.15 |

Liberation Day, 5th Anniv. — A376

**1996, Feb. 26**
| | | | | |
|---|---|---|---|---|
| **1306** | A376 | 25f violet & multi | .75 | .40 |
| **1307** | A376 | 50f brown & multi | 1.40 | .75 |
| **1308** | A376 | 150f blue green & multi | 4.50 | 2.00 |
| | | *Nos. 1306-1308 (3)* | 6.65 | 3.15 |

Arab City Day — A377

**1996, Mar. 1    Perf. 13½**
| | | | | |
|---|---|---|---|---|
| **1309** | A377 | 50f yel grn & multi | 1.00 | 1.00 |
| **1310** | A377 | 100f pink & multi | 2.00 | 2.00 |
| **1311** | A377 | 150f blue green & multi | 3.00 | 3.00 |
| | | *Nos. 1309-1311 (3)* | 6.00 | 6.00 |

A378

**1996, Jan. 27    Perf. 14**
| | | | | |
|---|---|---|---|---|
| **1312** | A378 | 50f blue & multi | 1.00 | 1.00 |
| **1313** | A378 | 100f gray & multi | 2.00 | 2.00 |
| **1314** | A378 | 150f rose lilac & multi | 3.00 | 3.00 |
| | | *Nos. 1312-1314 (3)* | 6.00 | 6.00 |

Scouting in Kuwait, 60th Anniv. — A379

50f, On top of watchtower. 100f, Drawing water from well. 150f, Planting seedling.

**1996, Jan. 14    Perf. 13½**
| | | | | |
|---|---|---|---|---|
| **1315** | A379 | 50f yellow & multi | 1.25 | 1.25 |
| **1316** | A379 | 100f lilac & multi | 3.00 | 3.00 |
| **1317** | A379 | 150f blue green & multi | 4.75 | 4.75 |
| | | *Nos. 1315-1317 (3)* | 9.00 | 9.00 |

Kuwait Money Show — A380

**1996, Jan. 2    Perf. 14**
| | | | | |
|---|---|---|---|---|
| **1318** | A380 | 25f gold & multi | .75 | .75 |
| **1319** | A380 | 100f blue & multi | 2.50 | 2.50 |
| **1320** | A380 | 150f dk gray & multi | 3.75 | 3.75 |
| | | *Nos. 1318-1320 (3)* | 7.00 | 7.00 |

7th Kuwait Dental Assoc. Conference — A381

**1996, Mar. 27    Litho.    Perf. 14x13½**
| | | | | |
|---|---|---|---|---|
| **1321** | A381 | 25f orange & multi | .65 | .65 |
| **1322** | A381 | 50f violet & multi | 1.10 | 1.10 |
| **1323** | A381 | 150f blue & multi | 3.25 | 3.25 |
| | | *Nos. 1321-1323 (3)* | 5.00 | 5.00 |

UNESCO, 50th Anniv. — A382

**1996, Apr. 10    Perf. 13½x14**
| | | | | |
|---|---|---|---|---|
| **1324** | A382 | 25f violet & multi | .60 | .60 |
| **1325** | A382 | 100f green & multi | 1.90 | 1.90 |
| **1326** | A382 | 150f orange & multi | 3.50 | 3.50 |
| | | *Nos. 1324-1326 (3)* | 6.00 | 6.00 |

1st Oil Exports, 50th Anniv. — A383

**1996, June 30    Litho.    Perf. 13**
| | | | | |
|---|---|---|---|---|
| **1327** | A383 | 25f multicolored | .75 | .75 |
| **1328** | A383 | 100f gray & multi | 2.50 | 2.50 |
| **1329** | A383 | 150f bister & multi | 3.75 | 3.75 |
| | | *Nos. 1327-1329 (3)* | 7.00 | 7.00 |

Rule of Al-Sabah Family, Cent. — A384

**1996, Aug. 12**
| | | | | |
|---|---|---|---|---|
| **1330** | A384 | 25f shown | .65 | .65 |
| **1331** | A384 | 50f Shiek, flags | 1.10 | 1.10 |
| **1332** | A384 | 150f like #1330 | 3.25 | 3.25 |
| | | *Nos. 1330-1332 (3)* | 5.00 | 5.00 |

1996 Summer Olympic Games, Atlanta — A385

**1996, Oct. 5    Perf. 13½**
| | | | | |
|---|---|---|---|---|
| **1333** | A385 | 25f Shooting | .60 | .60 |
| **1334** | A385 | 50f Running | 1.20 | 1.20 |
| **1335** | A385 | 100f Weight lifting | 2.40 | 2.40 |
| **1336** | A385 | 150f Fencing | 4.00 | 4.00 |
| | | *Nos. 1333-1336 (4)* | 8.20 | 8.20 |

A 750f souvenir sheet exists. Value $150.

Kuwait University, 30th Anniv. — A386

**1996, Nov. 27    Litho.    Perf. 13½x14**
| | | | | |
|---|---|---|---|---|
| **1337** | A386 | 25f green & multi | .65 | .65 |
| **1338** | A386 | 100f blue & multi | 2.10 | 2.10 |
| **1339** | A386 | 150f yellow & multi | 3.25 | 3.25 |
| | | *Nos. 1337-1339 (3)* | 6.00 | 6.00 |

1st Children's Cultural Festival — A387

**1996, Nov. 20    Perf. 14x13½**
| | | | | |
|---|---|---|---|---|
| **1340** | A387 | 25f brn gray & multi | .65 | .65 |
| **1341** | A387 | 100f multicolored | 2.10 | 2.10 |
| **1342** | A387 | 150f yel grn & multi | 3.25 | 3.25 |
| | | *Nos. 1340-1342 (3)* | 6.00 | 6.00 |

3rd Al-Qurain Cultrual Festival — A388

**1996, Nov. 20    Perf. 14**
| | | | | |
|---|---|---|---|---|
| **1343** | A388 | 50f orange & multi | 1.25 | 1.25 |
| **1344** | A388 | 100f blue & multi | 2.25 | 2.25 |
| **1345** | A388 | 150f green & multi | 3.50 | 3.50 |
| | | *Nos. 1343-1345 (3)* | 7.00 | 7.00 |

Liberation Tower — A389

**1996, Dec. 10    Perf. 13x13½**
| | | | | |
|---|---|---|---|---|
| **1346** | A389 | 5f red & multi | .25 | .25 |
| **1347** | A389 | 10f yel bis & multi | .25 | .25 |
| **1348** | A389 | 15f brt rose & multi | .40 | .30 |
| **1349** | A389 | 25f pale pink & multi | .50 | .45 |
| *a.* | | Booklet pane of 4 | — | |
| | | Complete booklet, #1349a | — | |
| **1350** | A389 | 50f violet & multi | 1.25 | 1.00 |
| *a.* | | Booklet pane of 4 | — | |
| | | Complete booklet, #1350a | — | |
| **1351** | A389 | 100f brt yel & multi | 2.25 | 1.50 |
| **1352** | A389 | 150f blue & multi | 3.75 | 2.50 |
| *a.* | | Booklet pane of 4 | — | |
| | | Complete booklet, #1352a | — | |
| **1353** | A389 | 200f pink & multi | 3.00 | 3.75 |
| **1354** | A389 | 250f dp bl & multi | 6.00 | 4.50 |
| **1355** | A389 | 350f blue & multi | 8.50 | 6.00 |
| | | *Nos. 1346-1355 (10)* | 26.15 | 20.50 |

Set of 3 booklets, Nos.
1349a-1350a, 1352a    35.00

National Day, 36th Anniv. — A390

**1997, Feb. 25    Litho.    Perf. 14½**
| | | | | |
|---|---|---|---|---|
| **1356** | A390 | 25f blue & multi | .80 | .30 |
| **1357** | A390 | 50f lilac & multi | 1.50 | 1.50 |
| **1358** | A390 | 150f orange & multi | 4.50 | 4.50 |
| | | *Nos. 1356-1358 (3)* | 6.80 | 6.30 |

Liberation Day, 6th Anniv. — A391

**1997, Feb. 26    Perf. 13x13½**
| | | | | |
|---|---|---|---|---|
| **1359** | A391 | 25f tan & multi | .80 | .80 |
| **1360** | A391 | 50f lilac & multi | 1.50 | 1.50 |
| **1361** | A391 | 150f blue & multi | 4.50 | 4.50 |
| | | *Nos. 1359-1361 (3)* | 6.80 | 6.80 |

Marine Life — A392

No. 1368: Various views of a school of shrimp: a, b, c, d, 25f. e, f, g, h, 50f. i, j, k, l, 100f. m, n, o, p, 150f.

**1997, Jan. 15    Perf. 14½**
| | | | | |
|---|---|---|---|---|
| **1362** | A392 | 25f Maid | .40 | .40 |
| **1363** | A392 | 50f Sheim | .75 | .75 |
| **1364** | A392 | 100f Hamoor | 1.50 | 1.50 |
| **1365** | A392 | 150f Sobaity | 2.25 | 2.25 |
| **1366** | A392 | 200f Nagroor | 3.25 | 3.25 |
| **1367** | A392 | 350f Zobaidy | 5.50 | 5.50 |
| | | *Nos. 1362-1367 (6)* | 13.65 | 13.65 |

**Sheet of 16**
| | | | | |
|---|---|---|---|---|
| **1368** | A392 | Sheet of 16, #a.-p. | 24.00 | 24.00 |

Montreal Protocol on Substances that Deplete Ozone Layer, 10th Anniv. — A393

**1997, Sept. 16    Litho.    Perf. 13½x13**
| | | | | |
|---|---|---|---|---|
| **1369** | A393 | 25f blue & multi | .60 | .60 |
| **1370** | A393 | 50f violet & multi | 1.10 | 1.10 |
| **1371** | A393 | 150f bl grn & multi | 3.50 | 3.50 |
| | | *Nos. 1369-1371 (3)* | 5.20 | 5.20 |

Industries Exhibition — A394

**1997, Oct. 1**
| | | | | |
|---|---|---|---|---|
| **1372** | A394 | 25f brt pink & multi | .60 | .60 |
| **1373** | A394 | 50f green & multi | 1.10 | 1.10 |
| **1374** | A394 | 150f blue & multi | 3.50 | 3.50 |
| | | *Nos. 1372-1374 (3)* | 5.20 | 5.20 |

22nd Kuwait Arabic Book Exhibition — A395

**1997, Nov. 19    Litho.    Perf. 13½x13**
**Border Color**
| | | | | |
|---|---|---|---|---|
| **1375** | A395 | 25f pink | .60 | .60 |
| **1376** | A395 | 50f blue | 1.10 | 1.10 |
| **1377** | A395 | 150f blue green | 3.50 | 3.50 |
| | | *Nos. 1375-1377 (3)* | 5.20 | 5.20 |

Cultural History — A396

a, 50f, Qibliya Girls School, 1937. b, 50f, Scissors cutting ribbon, Fine Arts Exhibition, 1959. c, 150f, Folk Theatre Group, 1956. d, 25f, 1st Book Fair, 1975. e, 25f, Kuwait Magazine, 1928. f, 50f, Mubarakiya School, 1912. g, 50f, Kuwait Natl. Museum, 1958. h, 150f, Academy of Music, 1972. i, 25f, A'lam Al-Fikr (periodical), 1970. j, 25f, Al'Bitha Magazine, 1946. k, 50f, Building complex, 1953 (Al-Arabi Magazine). l, 50f, Building, 1959. m, 150f, Al-Sharqiya Cinema, 1955. n, 25f, Al'Lam Al Ma'rifa (periodical), 1978. o, 25f, Dalil Almohtar Fi Alaam al-Bihar (boat), 1923. p, 50f, Alma'had Aldini (arabesques), 1947. q, 50f, Folklore Center, 1956. r, 150f, Theatrical Academy, 1967. s, 25f, Al-Arabi Magazine, 1958. t, 25f, Public Library (book), 1923. u, 50f, Al Ma'Arif Printing Press (Arabic writing), 1947. v, 50f, Literary Club, 1924. w, 150f, Bas Ya Bahar (1st Kuwaitii feature film), 1970. x, 25f, Al Thaqafa Al-Alamiya (periodical), 1981. y, 25f, The World Theatre (periodical), 1969.

**1997, Nov. 30**
| | | | | |
|---|---|---|---|---|
| **1378** | A396 | Sheet of 25, #a.-y. | 30.00 | 30.00 |

Nos. 1378a-1378y each contain year date of event depicted.

Educational Science Museum, 25th Anniv. — A397

Designs: 25f, Whale, quadrant, vert. 50f, Space exploration, whale, dinosaur. No. 1381, Astronaut, dinosaur, satellite dish, airplane, globe, skeleton encircling whale, vert. No. 1382, Coelacanth.

**Perf. 13½x13, 13x13½**
**1997, Nov. 1    Litho.**
| | | | | |
|---|---|---|---|---|
| **1379** | A397 | 25f multicolored | 1.00 | .65 |
| **1380** | A397 | 50f multicolored | 2.00 | 1.00 |
| **1381** | A397 | 150f multicolored | 6.75 | 3.25 |
| | | *Nos. 1379-1381 (3)* | 9.75 | 4.90 |

**Souvenir Sheet**
| | | | | |
|---|---|---|---|---|
| **1382** | A397 | 150f multicolored | 17.00 | 17.00 |

No. 1382 is a continuous design and sold for 1d.

18th Summit of Gulf Cooperation Countries A398

Designs: 25f, Flags of member countries, doves, vert. 50f, Map, birds with flag colors. 150f, Doves perched atop flags, vert.

**1997, Dec. 20**                **Perf. 13½x14**
| | | | | |
|---|---|---|---|---|
| 1383 | A398 | 25f multicolored | .75 | .75 |
| 1384 | A398 | 50f multicolored | 1.50 | 1.50 |
| 1385 | A398 | 150f multicolored | 4.75 | 4.75 |
| a. | | Bklt. pane of 3, #1383-1385 | 22.50 | |
| | | Complete booklet, #1385a | 22.50 | |
| | | Nos. 1383-1385 (3) | 7.00 | 7.00 |

National Day, 37th Anniv. — A399

**1998, Feb. 25    Litho.    Perf. 13x13½**
| | | | | |
|---|---|---|---|---|
| 1386 | A399 | 25f yellow & multi | .80 | .80 |
| 1387 | A399 | 50f pink & multi | 1.40 | 1.40 |
| 1388 | A399 | 150f blue & multi | 4.25 | 4.25 |
| | | Nos. 1386-1388 (3) | 6.45 | 6.45 |

Liberation Day, 7th Anniv. — A400

**1998, Feb. 26**
| | | | | |
|---|---|---|---|---|
| 1389 | A400 | 25f yellow & multi | .80 | .80 |
| 1390 | A400 | 50f orange & multi | 1.40 | 1.40 |
| 1391 | A400 | 150f green & multi | 4.25 | 4.25 |
| | | Nos. 1389-1391 (3) | 6.45 | 6.45 |

Say No to Drugs — A401

**1998, Mar. 16    Litho.    Perf. 13½x13**
| | | | | |
|---|---|---|---|---|
| 1392 | A401 | 25f tan & multi | .80 | .80 |
| 1393 | A401 | 50f blue & multi | 1.40 | 1.40 |
| 1394 | A401 | 150f white & multi | 4.25 | 4.25 |
| | | Nos. 1392-1394 (3) | 6.45 | 6.45 |

Chernobyl disaster, 10th Anniv. — A402

**1997, May 2    Litho.    Perf. 13½x13**
| | | | | |
|---|---|---|---|---|
| 1395 | A402 | 25f orange & multi | .80 | .80 |
| 1396 | A402 | 50f blue & multi | 1.40 | 1.40 |
| 1397 | A402 | 150f red & multi | 4.25 | 4.25 |
| | | Nos. 1395-1397 (3) | 6.45 | 6.45 |

Martyrs — A403

25f, Dates, 1/17, 2/25, 2/26, flowers. 50f, Stylized tree. 150f, Lines, inscriptions.
No. 1401: a, Man with hands in dirt. b, Three boys emptying basket of dirt.

**1998, Mar. 31    Litho.    Perf. 14**
| | | | | |
|---|---|---|---|---|
| 1398 | A403 | 25f multicolored | .75 | .75 |
| 1399 | A403 | 50f multicolored | 1.25 | 1.25 |
| 1400 | A403 | 150f multicolored | 4.00 | 4.00 |
| a. | | Bklt. pane, 2 ea #1398-1400 | 22.50 | |
| | | Complete booklet #1400a | 22.50 | |

---

**Perf. 14½ Between**
**Size: 31x54mm**
| | | | | |
|---|---|---|---|---|
| 1401 | A403 | 500f Pair, a.-b. | 24.00 | 24.00 |
| | | Nos. 1398-1401 (4) | 30.00 | 30.00 |

Ban Land Mines — A405

Stylized amputees using crutches for support: 25f, Two people. 50f, One person. 150f, Two people, nurse.
500f, Three people, nurse.

**1998, Aug. 2    Perf. 14½**
| | | | | |
|---|---|---|---|---|
| 1402 | A405 | 25f multicolored | 1.00 | 1.00 |
| 1403 | A405 | 50f multicolored | 2.00 | 2.00 |
| 1404 | A405 | 150f multicolored | 5.00 | 5.00 |

**Size: 89x82mm**
**Imperf**
| | | | | |
|---|---|---|---|---|
| 1405 | A405 | 500f multicolored | 13.00 | 13.00 |
| | | Nos. 1402-1405 (4) | 21.00 | 21.00 |

Life in Pre-Oil Kuwait — A406

Designs: 25f, Seated at ceremonial meal. 50f, Building boat. 100f, Weaving. 150f, Loading boat. 250f, Pouring water from water skin into bowl. 350f, Man with pigeons.

**1998, Apr. 14    Litho.    Perf. 14**
**Booklet Stamps**
| | | | | |
|---|---|---|---|---|
| 1406 | A406 | 25f multicolored | .50 | .50 |
| 1407 | A406 | 50d multicolored | 1.00 | 1.00 |
| 1408 | A406 | 100f multicolored | 2.00 | 2.00 |
| 1409 | A406 | 150f multicolored | 3.00 | 3.00 |
| 1410 | A406 | 250f multicolored | 5.00 | 5.00 |
| 1411 | A406 | 350f multicolored | 7.00 | 7.00 |
| a. | | Booklet pane, #1406-1411 | 27.50 | |
| | | Complete booklet, #1411a | 27.50 | |

**1998, Sept. 1    Litho.    Perf. 14**

25f, Man shaving another man's head. 50f, Woman using grindstone. 100f, Man pulling thread through cloth. 150f, Man gluing artifacts together. 250f, Potter. 350f, Veiled woman holding rope.

**Booklet Stamps**
| | | | | |
|---|---|---|---|---|
| 1412 | A406 | 25f multicolored | .50 | .50 |
| 1413 | A406 | 50f multicolored | 1.00 | 1.00 |
| 1414 | A406 | 100f multicolored | 2.00 | 2.00 |
| 1415 | A406 | 150f multicolored | 3.00 | 3.00 |
| 1416 | A406 | 250f multicolored | 5.00 | 5.00 |
| 1417 | A406 | 350f multicolored | 7.00 | 7.00 |
| a. | | Booklet pane, #1412-1417 | 27.50 | |
| | | Complete booklet, #1417a | 27.50 | |

Emblem of Kuwait Post — A407

**1998, Oct. 3    Litho.    Perf. 13x13½**
| | | | | |
|---|---|---|---|---|
| 1418 | A407 | 25f green & multi | .50 | .50 |
| 1419 | A407 | 50f blue & multi | 1.00 | 1.00 |
| 1420 | A407 | 100f brt pink & multi | 1.50 | 1.50 |
| 1421 | A407 | 150f orange & multi | 2.75 | 2.75 |
| 1422 | A407 | 250f brick red & multi | 4.25 | 4.25 |
| | | Nos. 1418-1422 (5) | 10.00 | 10.00 |

Intl. Year of the Ocean A408

**1998, June 1    Litho.    Perf. 13½**
| | | | | |
|---|---|---|---|---|
| 1423 | A408 | 25f multi & multi | 1.00 | 1.00 |
| 1424 | A408 | 50f blue & multi | 2.00 | 2.00 |
| 1425 | A408 | 150f lilac & multi | 6.00 | 6.00 |
| | | Nos. 1423-1425 (3) | 9.00 | 9.00 |

No. 1424 is 27x37mm.

---

Union of Consumer Co-operative Societies, 25th Anniv. — A409

**1998, July 1    Litho.    Perf. 13½x13**
| | | | | |
|---|---|---|---|---|
| 1426 | A409 | 25f buff & multi | 1.00 | 1.00 |
| 1427 | A409 | 50f blue & multi | 2.00 | 2.00 |
| 1428 | A409 | 100f multicolored | 6.00 | 6.00 |
| | | Nos. 1426-1428 (3) | 9.00 | 9.00 |

Children's Cultural House — A410

**1998, Nov. 28    Litho.    Perf. 13½x13**
| | | | | |
|---|---|---|---|---|
| 1429 | A410 | 25f yellow & multi | .80 | .80 |
| 1430 | A410 | 50f grn, yel & multi | 1.75 | 1.75 |
| 1431 | A410 | 150f green & multi | 4.50 | 4.50 |
| | | Nos. 1429-1431 (3) | 7.05 | 7.05 |

A411

**1998, Dec. 10    Perf. 14x14½**
| | | | | |
|---|---|---|---|---|
| 1432 | A411 | 25f multicolored | .80 | .80 |
| 1433 | A411 | 50f multicolored | 1.75 | 1.75 |
| 1434 | A411 | 150f multicolored | 4.50 | 4.50 |
| | | Nos. 1432-1434 (3) | 7.05 | 7.05 |

Universal Declaration of Human Rights, 50th anniv.

A412

**1998    Litho.    Perf. 14x14½**
| | | | | |
|---|---|---|---|---|
| 1435 | A412 | 25f orange & multi | .75 | .75 |
| 1436 | A412 | 50f violet & multi | 1.25 | 1.25 |
| 1437 | A412 | 150f green & multi | 4.00 | 4.00 |
| | | Nos. 1435-1437 (3) | 6.00 | 6.00 |

The Public Authority for Applied Education and Training, 25th anniv.

Organ Transplantation in Kuwait, 20th Anniv. — A413

**1999    Litho.    Perf. 13x13½**
| | | | | |
|---|---|---|---|---|
| 1438 | A413 | 50f Liver | 1.50 | 1.50 |
| 1439 | A413 | 150f Heart | 4.50 | 4.50 |

Liberation Day, 8th Anniv. — A414

**1999, Feb. 26**
| | | | | |
|---|---|---|---|---|
| 1440 | A414 | 50f Building | 1.50 | 1.50 |
| 1441 | A414 | 150f Building, diff. | 4.50 | 4.50 |

Sief Palace Complex A415

Various buildings in complex.

---

**1999    Perf. 15x14**
| | | | | |
|---|---|---|---|---|
| 1442 | A415 | 25f multicolored | .40 | .40 |
| 1443 | A415 | 50f multicolored | .70 | .70 |
| 1444 | A415 | 100f multicolored | 1.75 | 1.75 |
| 1445 | A415 | 150f multicolored | 2.75 | 2.75 |
| 1446 | A415 | 250f multicolored | 5.25 | 5.25 |
| 1447 | A415 | 350f multicolored | 7.00 | 7.00 |
| a. | | Booklet pane, #1442-1447 | 22.50 | |
| | | Complete booklet, #1447a | 22.50 | |
| | | Nos. 1442-1447 (6) | 17.85 | 17.85 |

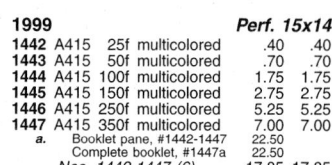

Al Arabi Magazine — A416

**1999    Perf. 13½x13**
| | | | | |
|---|---|---|---|---|
| 1448 | A416 | 50f violet & multi | 1.75 | 1.75 |
| 1449 | A416 | 150f green & multi | 4.75 | 4.75 |

Natl. Day, 38th Anniv. — A417

**1999    Perf. 13x13½**
| | | | | |
|---|---|---|---|---|
| 1450 | A417 | 50f brown & multi | 1.50 | 1.50 |
| 1451 | A417 | 150f blue & multi | 4.50 | 4.50 |

Hawk A418        Sailing Ship A419

50f, Camel. 100f, Traditional Boat.

**1999(?)-2003    Litho.    Perf. 14½x14**
| | | | | |
|---|---|---|---|---|
| 1452 | A418 | 25f multicolored | .90 | .90 |
| 1453 | A418 | 50f multicolored | 1.75 | 1.75 |

**Coil Stamp**
| | | | | |
|---|---|---|---|---|
| 1453A | A419 | 100f multicolored | 2.50 | 2.50 |
| 1454 | A419 | 150f multicolored | 5.50 | 5.50 |
| | | Nos. 1452-1454 (4) | 10.65 | 10.65 |

Issued: 100f, Jan. 2003.

Science Club, 25th Anniv. — A420

Background color: 50f, Blue. 150f, Green. 350f, Red.

**1999, Oct. 20    Litho.    Perf. 13x13¼**
| | | | | |
|---|---|---|---|---|
| 1455-1457 | A420 | Set of 3 | 17.00 | 17.00 |

Intl. Civil Aviation Day — A421

**1999, Dec. 7    Litho.    Perf. 13x13¼**
| | | | | |
|---|---|---|---|---|
| 1458 | A421 | 50f multi | 1.25 | 1.25 |
| 1459 | A421 | 150f multi | 3.25 | 3.25 |
| 1460 | A421 | 250f multi | 5.50 | 5.50 |
| | | Nos. 1458-1460 (3) | 10.00 | 10.00 |

 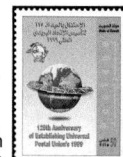

UPU, 125th Anniv. — A421a

Panel colors: 50f, Orange. 150f, Purple. 350f, Green.
1d, Two hemispheres.

**1999 Litho. Perf. 13¼x13**
1460A-1460C A421a Set of 3 11.00 11.00
1460Ce Booklet pane, #1460A-
1460C + label 11.00
Booklet, #1460Ce 11.00
**Size: 100x75mm**
*Imperf*
1460D A421a 1d multi 16.00 16.00

Kuwait Intl. Airport — A422

**2000, Jan. 2 Perf. 13¼x13**
1461 A422 50f multi .85 .85
1462 A422 150f multi 2.00 2.00
1463 A422 250f multi 4.50 4.50
Nos. 1461-1463 (3) 7.35 7.35

National Day, 39th Anniv. — A423

**2000**
1464 A423 25f multi .65 .65
1465 A423 50f multi 1.25 1.25
1466 A423 150f multi 4.25 4.25
Nos. 1464-1466 (3) 6.15 6.15

Liberation Day, 9th Anniv. — A424

**2000**
1467 A424 25f multi 1.25 1.25
1468 A424 50f multi 3.75 3.75
1469 A424 150f multi 5.00 5.00
Nos. 1467-1469 (3) 10.00 10.00

Kuwait Conference for Autism and Communication Deficits — A425

Designs: 25f, Puzzle pieces, three children, Kuwait Tower. 50f, Puzzle pieces, children. 150f, Children, Kuwait Tower, flowers.

**2000 Perf. 13x13¼**
1470 A425 25f multi .65 .65
1471 A425 50f multi 1.25 1.25
1472 A425 150f multi 4.25 4.25
Nos. 1470-1472 (3) 6.15 6.15

Kuwait City — A425a

Background colors: 50f, Blue. 150f, Green. 350f, Red violet.

**2000, Apr. 24 Litho. Perf. 14x14½**
1472A-1472C A425a Set of 3 8.50 8.50

Third Special Education Week — A425b

Background color: 50f, Yellow. 150f, Salmon. 350f, Blue.

**2000, May 10 Perf. 13¼x13**
1472D-1472F A425b Set of 3 8.50 8.50

2000 Summer Olympics, Sydney — A425c

Emblems of 2002 Olympics, Kuwait Olympic Committee and: 25f, Judo. 50f, Shooting. 150f, Swimming. 200f, Weight lifting. 250f, Hurdles. 350f, Soccer.
No. 1472M, Emblems of 2002 Olympics, Kuwait Olympic Committee and judo, swimming, shooting, weight lifting, hurdles and soccer.

**2000 Litho. Perf. 13x13¼**
1472G-1472L A425c Set of 6 20.00 20.00
**Souvenir Sheet**
**Size: 98x69mm**
1472M A425c 1d multi 55.00 55.00

Sixth Gulf Cooperation Council Countries Joint Stamp Exhibition, Kuwait — A425d

Denomination color: 25f, Blue. 50f, Red. 150f, Green.
1d, Emblems of previous exhibitions.

**2000 Litho. Perf. 14¼**
1472N-1472P A425d Set of 3 4.50 4.50
**Size: 146x112mm**
*Imperf*
1472Q A425d 1d multi 17.00 17.00

Intl. Investment Forum — A426

Background colors: 25f, Gray. 50f, White. 150f, Black.

**2000, Mar. 4 Litho. Perf. 13x13¼**
1473-1475 A426 Set of 3 8.00 8.00

National Committee for Missing and Prisoner of War Affairs — A426a

Designs: 25f, Emblem. 50f, Emblem and chains. 150f, Emblem and years.

**2000, Aug. 2 Litho. Perf. 13x13¼**
1475A-1475C A426a Set of 3 3.25 3.25

Kuwaiti Dental Association, 25th Anniv. — A426b

Frame color: 50f, Pink. 150f, Light blue. 350f, Lilac.

**2000, Oct. 15 Perf. 13¼x13**
1475D-1475F A426b Set of 3 6.50 6.50

World Environment Day — A427

Denominations, 50f, 150f, 350f.

**2000 Litho. Perf. 13x13¼**
1476-1478 A427 Set of 3 9.00 9.00

Gulf Investment Corporation, 15th Anniv. — A428

New Gulf Investment Corporation headquarters, emblem, "15" and frame color of: 25f, Green. 50f, Blue. 150f, Red.

**2000, Oct. 31 Litho. Perf. 13¼x13¼**
1479-1481 A428 Set of 3 8.00 8.00

General Administration of Customs, Cent. — A429

Denominations: 50f, 150f, 350f.

**2000 Litho. Perf. 13¼x14**
1482-1484 A429 Set of 3 6.75 6.75
a. Booklet pane, #1482-1484 15.00
Complete booklet, #1484a 15.00
*Imperf*
**Size: 100x75mm**
1485 A429 1d multi 13.50 13.50
No. 1485 contains one 47x28mm perf. 13¼x14 non-denominated label.

Hala Fibrayar — A430

Panel colors: 25f, Purple. 50f, Red violet. 150f, Blue.

**2001 Litho. Perf. 13¼x13**
1486-1488 A430 Set of 3 4.75 4.75

Prisoners of War — A431

Background colors: 25f, White. 50f, Blue & blue green. 150f, Multicolored.

**2001 Perf. 13x13¼**
1489-1491 A431 Set of 3 5.50 5.50

UN High Commissioner for Refugees, 50th Anniv. — A432

Various depictions of anniversary emblem: 25f, 50f, 150f.

**2001**
1492-1494 A432 Set of 3 4.75 4.75

Kuwait, 2001 Arab Cultural Capital — A433

Background colors: 25f, Yellow. 50f, Green. 150f, Blue.

**2001**
1495-1497 A433 Set of 3 4.75 4.75

Liberation Day, 10th Anniv. — A434

Frame color: 25f, Lilac. 50f, Blue. 150f, Yellow.

**2001 Perf. 13¼x13**
1498-1500 A434 Set of 3 4.75 4.75

National Day, 40th Anniv. — A435

Frame color: 25f, Orange. 50f, Yellow. 150f, Blue green.

**2001**
1501-1503 A435 Set of 3 4.75 4.75

Kuwait Diving Team, 10th Anniv. — A436

"10" and: 25f, Fish. 50f, Divers. 150f, Shark, turtle, vert.

**2001 Perf. 13x13¼, 13¼x13**
1504-1506 A436 Set of 3 4.75 4.75

Radio Kuwait, 50th Anniv. — A437

Frame color: 25f, Yellow brown. 50f, Blue, vert. 150f, Red, vert.

**2001 Perf. 13x13¼, 13¼x13**
1507-1509 A437 Set of 3 4.75 4.75

Intifada — A438

Dome of the Rock, Jerusalem: 25f, 50f, 150f.

**2001 Perf. 13¼x13**
1510-1512 A438 Set of 3 5.00 5.00

Year of Dialogue Among Civilizations — A439

Background colors: 25f, Orange & yellow. 50f, Dark & light green. 150f, Rose & pink.

**2001 Perf. 13¼x13**
1513-1515 A439 Set of 3 4.75 4.75

Human Rights — A440

Designs: 25f, Hands covering man's face, vert. 50f, Barbed wire, clock, man's face. 150f, Chains, globe, child, woman.

**2001 Perf. 13¼x13, 13x13¼**
1516-1518 A440 Set of 3 4.75 4.75

A441

A442

AWQAF Foundation — A443

**2001**      **Perf. 14x13**
1519 A441 25f multi .50 .50
1520 A442 50f multi 1.00 1.00
1521 A443 150f multi 3.25 3.25
     *Nos. 1519-1521 (3)* 4.75 4.75

Kuwait Fund for Arab Economic Development, 40th Anniv. — A444

Background colors: 25f, Yellow. 50f, Green & gray.

**2001**      **Perf. 13¼x13**
1522-1523 A444 Set of 2 1.75 1.75

Touristic Enterprises Company, 25th Anniv. — A445

Stylistic flora: 25f, 50f, 100f, 150f. 250f, Combined designs of four stamps.

**2001**      **Perf. 13¼x13**
1524-1527 A445 Set of 4 7.50 7.50
**Size: 60x80mm**
**Imperf**
1528 A445 250f multi 6.00 6.00

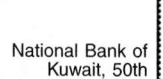
National Bank of Kuwait, 50th Anniv. — A447

Emblem and: 25f, Facade of old building. 50f, Modern building. 150f, Camels.

**2002, Jan. 16**   **Litho.**   **Perf. 13x13¼**
1532-1534 A447 Set of 3 5.50 5.50

Liberation Day, 11th Anniv. — A448

Background color: 25f, Light blue. 50f, Light yellow. 150f, White.

**2002, Feb. 26**      **Perf. 13¼x13**
1535-1537 A448 Set of 3 5.50 5.50

Social Development Office, 10th Anniv. — A449

---

Background color: 25f, Light yellow. 50f, Light blue.

**2002, Apr. 21**
1538-1539 A449 Set of 2 1.75 1.75

41st National Day — A450

Frame color: 25f, Orange. 50f, Green. 150f, Purple.

**2002, Feb. 25**   **Litho.**   **Perf. 13¼x13**
1540-1542 A450 Set of 3 4.50 4.50

Nomadism From the Hejaz to Africa — A451

Top panel color: 25f, Pale orange. 50f, Blue. 150f, Purple.

**2002, Mar. 11**
1543-1545 A451 Set of 3 5.00 5.00

Rehabilitation of Al-Qurain Landfill Site — A452

Panel color: 25f, Blue. 50f, Purple. 150f, Green.

**2002, Apr. 1**
1546-1548 A452 Set of 3 4.50 4.50

Kuwait Scientific Center A453

Designs; Nos. 1549a, 1550e, Lapwing. Nos. 1549b, 1550d, Spur-winged plover. Nos. 1549c, 1550c, Eurasian river otter. Nos. 1549d, 1550b, Saltwater crocodile. Nos. 1549e, 1550i, Fennec fox. Nos. 1549f, 1550h, Caracal. Nos. 1549g, 1550g, Cushion sister starfish. Nos. 1549h, 1550f, Cuttlefish. Nos. 1549i, 1550m, Sand tiger shark. Nos. 1549j, 1550l, Lionfish. Nos. 1549k, 1550k, Kestrel. Nos. 1549l, 1550j, Egyptian fruit bat. Nos. 1549m, 1550a, Science center.

**Perf. 13¼x13¾, 14x13¼ (#1550k)**
**2002, Apr. 17**
1549   Sheet of 13 24.00 24.00
   a.-l.   A453 25f Any single .25 .25
   m.   A453 50f multi .30 .30
1550   Booklet of 13 panes 40.00
   a.-m.   A453 50f Any single pane .30 .30
**Imperf**
**Size: 80x60mm**
1551 A453 250f shown 12.00 12.00

Stamp sizes: Nos. 1549a-1549l, 30x25mm; No. 1549m, 45x27mm. Nos. 1550a-1550j, 1550l-1550m, 50x36mm; No. 1550k, 32x48mm.

Kuwait Foundation for the Advancement of Sciences, 25th Anniv. (in 2001) — A454

Foundation emblem and: 25f, 25th anniversary emblem. 50f, 25th anniversary emblem and building. 150f, Map of Kuwait, vert.

---

**Perf. 13x13¼, 13¼x13**
**2002 ?**      **Litho.**
1552-1554 A454 Set of 3 4.75 4.75

Intl. Volunteers Year (in 2001) — A455

Background colors: 25f, White. 50f, Lilac. 150f, Yellow.

**2002 ?**      **Perf. 13¼x13**
1555-1557 A455 Set of 3 4.50 4.50

National Council for Culture, Arts and Letters, 25th Anniv. — A456

Panel color: 25f, Lilac. 50f, Olive green. 150f, Bright blue. 500f, Lilac.

**2002 ?**      **Perf. 13¼x13**
1558-1560 A456 Set of 3 4.50 4.50
**Souvenir Sheet**
**Imperf**
1561 A456 500f multi 10.00 10.00

No. 1561 contains one 42x58mm stamp.

Kuwait Society of Engineers, 40th Anniv. — A457

Panel color at LR: 25f, Brown. 50f, Bright green. 150f, Yellow green.

**2002**      **Perf. 13x13¼**
1562-1564 A457 Set of 3 4.50 4.50

Public Authority for Applied Education and Training, 20th Anniv. — A458

"20," "1982-2002" and: 25f, Men at work. 50f, Surgeon. 100f, Man with machine. 150f, Building and Kuwait flag. 250f, Ironworkers.

**2002**      **Perf. 13¼x13**
1565-1569 A458 Set of 5 10.00 10.00

42nd National Day — A459

Frame color: 25f, Green. 50f, Red. 150f, Blue.

**2003, Feb. 25**   **Litho.**   **Perf. 13x13¼**
1570-1572 A459 Set of 3 6.75 6.75

Martyr's Bureau — A460

Emblem and: 25f, Ship. 50f, Flag on Qarow Island. 150f, Fingerprint. 350f, Map of Kuwait.

**2003**
1573-1576 A460 Set of 4 14.00 14.00
  1576a   Booklet pane, #1573-1576 14.00 —
   Complete booklet, #1576a 14.00

---

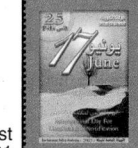
Intl. Day Against Desertification — A461

Designs: 25f, Dead tree. 50f, Log. 150f, Palm trees.

**2003**   **Litho.**   **Perf. 13¼x13**
1577-1579 A461 Set of 3 5.50 5.50

Commercial Bank of Kuwait, 43rd Anniv. — A462

"43" and: 25f, Geometric design. 50f, Old bank building. 150f, New bank building.

**2003**      **Perf. 13**
1580-1582 A462 Set of 3 5.00 5.00

Kuwait Awqaf Public Foundation, 10th Anniv. — A463

Emblem, "10," and: 50f, Building, family. 100f, Fingers. 150f, Man, minaret.

**2004, Jan. 19**
1583-1585 A463 Set of 3 6.00 6.00

A464

A465

Ministry of Information, 50th Anniv. — A466

**2003**
1586 A464 25f multi .65 .65
1587 A465 100f multi 2.25 2.25
1588 A466 150f multi 3.50 3.50
     *Nos. 1586-1588 (3)* 6.40 6.40

43rd National Day — A467

Designs: 25f, Palm tree. 50f, Pearl in shell. 150f, Fortress, flags. 350f, Buildings, dhow.

**2004, Feb. 25**      **Perf. 13¼x13**
1589-1592 A467 Set of 4 12.00 12.00

Kuwait Airways,
50th
Anniv. — A468

Various airplanes: 25f, 50f, 75f, 100f, 125f,
150f.

**2004, Dec. 18 Litho. Perf. 13x13¼**
1593-1598 A468 Set of 6 12.00 12.00

Kuwait
Petroleum
Corporation,
25th
Anniv. — A469

Headquarters: 50f, In daytime. 75f, With sun
on horizon. 125f, At night.

**2005, Jan. 1 Perf. 14½**
1599-1601 A469 Set of 3 8.00 8.00

44th National
Day — A470

Sheikhs, dhow, eagle and: 75f, Towers.
125f, Truck at port.

**2005, Feb. 25 Perf. 14**
1602-1603 A470 Set of 2 4.00 4.00

Liberation Day, 14th
Anniv. — A471

Sheikhs, flag and: 50f, Airplane, satellite
dish. 150f, Tower.

**2005, Feb. 26**
1604-1605 A471 Set of 2 6.00 6.00

Technical Education,
50th Anniv. — A472

Background color: 25f, Purple. 50f, Red.
75f, Orange. 125f, Green.

**2005, Mar. 15**
1606-1609 A472 Set of 4 6.25 6.25

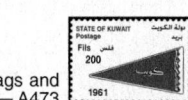

Flags and
Emblems — A473

Designs: No. 1610, Triangular 1961 ship
and harbor flag. No. 1611, 1940 official flag.
No. 1612, 1903 special event flag. No. 1613,
1940-50 ruling family flag. No. 1614, Two 1914
right triangle flags. No. 1615, 1921-40, 1956-
62 and 1962 emblems.
No. 1616, 1962-56 emblem. No. 1617,
1921-40 emblem.
No. 1618, Right triangle flag of 1914 with
Arabic script and emblem in center and script
along short side like that on No. 1613. No.
1619, Right triangle flag of 1914 with Arabic
script in center. No. 1620, Right triangle flag
of 1914 with Arabic script in center and script
along short side.
No. 1621, Triangular 1921 ship and harbor
flag. No. 1622, Like No. 1610. No. 1623, Rectangular 1961 ship and harbor flag. No. 1624,
Rectangular 1921 ship and harbor flag.
No. 1625, 1914-61 official flag. No. 1626,
1871-1914 official flag. No. 1627, 1746-1871
official flag. No. 1628, Like No. 1611. No.
1629, 1921-61 official flag.

No. 1630, 1903 special event flag. No. 1631,
1866 special event flag. No. 1632, 1921 special event flag.
No. 1633, 1921-40 ruling family flag with two
white stripes. No. 1634, Like No. 1613, with
colored background. No. 1635, 1921-40 ruling
family flag with one white stripe.

**2005, Oct. 15 Litho. Perf. 14x13¾**
1610 A473 200f multi 3.00 3.00
1611 A473 250f multi 4.25 4.25

**Perf. 14**
**Size: 40x30mm**
1612 A473 350f multi 5.25 5.25
1613 A473 500f multi 8.50 8.50

**Perf. 14x13¾**
**Size: 60x30mm**
1614 A473 1d multi 14.50 14.50
1615 A473 1d multi 14.50 14.50
Nos. 1610-1615 (6) 50.00 50.00

**Booklet Stamps**
**Self-Adhesive**
**Die Cut Perf. 13**
**Size:40x34mm**
1616 A473 100f multi 2.50 2.50
1617 A473 100f multi 2.50 2.50
a. Booklet pane, #1616-
1617 5.00

**Die Cut Perf. 13x13¼**
**Size: 40x30mm**
1618 A473 175f multi 4.75 4.75
1619 A473 175f multi 4.75 4.75
1620 A473 175f multi 4.75 4.75
a. Booklet pane, #1618-
1620 14.50

**Die Cut Perf. 10x10¾**
**Size: 30x20mm**
1621 A473 200f multi 4.75 4.75
1622 A473 200f multi 4.75 4.75
1623 A473 200f multi 4.75 4.75
1624 A473 200f multi 4.75 4.75
a. Booklet pane, #1621-
1624 19.00
1625 A473 250f multi 4.75 4.75
1626 A473 250f multi 4.75 4.75
1627 A473 250f multi 4.75 4.75
1628 A473 250f multi 4.75 4.75
1629 A473 250f multi 4.75 4.75
a. Booklet pane #1625-1629 24.00

**Die Cut Perf. 13x13¼**
**Size: 40x30mm**
1630 A473 350f multi 7.50 7.50
1631 A473 350f multi 7.50 7.50
1632 A473 350f multi 7.50 7.50
a. Booklet pane, #1630-
1632 22.50
1633 A473 500f multi 12.00 12.00
1634 A473 500f multi 12.00 12.00
1635 A473 500f multi 12.00 12.00
a. Booklet pane, #1633-
1635 36.00
Complete booklet,
#1617a, 1620a, 1624a,
1629a, 1632a, 1635a 125.00
Nos. 1616-1635 (20) 120.50 120.50

Civil
Defense — A474

Designs: 50f, Civil defense workers and
emergency vehicles. 75f, Civil defense workers and children. 125f, Civil defene workers.

**2005, Nov. 15 Litho. Perf. 14½**
1636-1638 A474 Set of 3 5.75 5.75

Al-Arabi Al-Saghir
Children's
Magazine, 20th
Anniv. — A475

Background colors: 100f, Blue. 200f, Yellow.
350f, Red.

**2006, Feb. 1 Litho. Perf. 14¼x13¾**
1639-1641 A475 Set of 3 13.00 13.00

45th National
Day — A476

Frame color: 75f, Purple. 200f, Green. 250f,
Black. 350f, Red.

**2006, Feb. 25 Perf. 13¼**
1642-1645 A476 Set of 4 15.00 15.00

A477

Gulf Cooperation Council, 25th
Anniv. — A478

**Litho. With Foil Application**
**2006, May 25 Perf. 14**
1646 A477 50f multi 5.00 5.00

**Imperf**
**Size: 165x105mm**
1647 A478 500f multi 17.50 17.50

See Bahrain Nos. 628-629, Oman Nos. 477-
478, Qatar Nos. 1007-1008, Saudi Arabia No.
1378, and United Arab Emirates Nos. 831-
832.

Emblem — A479

A480

A481

A482

A483

A484

A485

A486

A487

A488

A489

A490

A491

A492

A493

A494

A495

A496

A497

A498

A499

A500

A501

A502

A503

A504

A505

A506

A507

A508

A509

A510

A511

A512

A513

A514

A515

A516

A517

A518

A519

A520

Coins
A521

**2006, May 30      Litho.      Perf. 13¼**

| 1648 | Sheet of 28, #1648b- | | |
|---|---|---|---|
| | 1648v, 7#1648a | 25.00 | 25.00 |
| a. | A479 50f lt blue & multi | .75 | .75 |
| b. | A480 50f multi | .75 | .75 |
| c. | A481 50f multi | .75 | .75 |
| d. | A482 50f multi | .75 | .75 |
| e. | A483 50f multi | .75 | .75 |
| f. | A484 50f multi | .75 | .75 |
| g. | A485 50f multi | .75 | .75 |
| h. | A486 50f multi | .75 | .75 |
| i. | A487 50f multi | .75 | .75 |
| j. | A488 50f multi | .75 | .75 |
| k. | A489 50f multi | .75 | .75 |
| l. | A490 50f multi | .75 | .75 |
| m. | A491 50f multi | .75 | .75 |
| n. | A492 50f multi | .75 | .75 |
| o. | A493 50f multi | .75 | .75 |
| p. | A494 50f multi | .75 | .75 |
| q. | A495 50f multi | .75 | .75 |
| r. | A496 50f multi | .75 | .75 |
| s. | A497 50f multi | .75 | .75 |
| t. | A498 50f multi | .75 | .75 |
| u. | A499 50f multi | .75 | .75 |
| v. | A500 50f multi | .75 | .75 |
| 1649 | Sheet of 28, #1649b- | | |
| | 1649v, 7#1649a | 70.00 | 70.00 |
| a. | A479 150f pink & multi | 2.25 | 2.25 |
| b. | A501 150f multi | 2.25 | 2.25 |
| c. | A502 150f multi | 2.25 | 2.25 |
| d. | A503 150f multi | 2.25 | 2.25 |
| e. | A504 150f multi | 2.25 | 2.25 |
| f. | A505 150f multi | 2.25 | 2.25 |
| g. | A506 150f multi | 2.25 | 2.25 |
| h. | A507 150f multi | 2.25 | 2.25 |
| i. | A508 150f multi | 2.25 | 2.25 |
| j. | A509 150f multi | 2.25 | 2.25 |
| k. | A510 150f multi | 2.25 | 2.25 |
| l. | A511 150f multi | 2.25 | 2.25 |
| m. | A512 150f multi | 2.25 | 2.25 |
| n. | A513 150f multi | 2.25 | 2.25 |
| o. | A514 150f multi | 2.25 | 2.25 |
| p. | A515 150f multi | 2.25 | 2.25 |
| q. | A516 150f multi | 2.25 | 2.25 |
| r. | A517 150f multi | 2.25 | 2.25 |
| s. | A518 150f multi | 2.25 | 2.25 |
| t. | A519 150f multi | 2.25 | 2.25 |
| u. | A520 150f multi | 2.25 | 2.25 |
| v. | A521 150f multi | 2.25 | 2.25 |

Islamic Development Bank Group annual meeting.

15th Asian
Games, Doha,
Qatar — A522

Designs: 25f, Tennis. 50f, Bowling. 150f, Shooting. 250f, Equestrian. 350f, Fencing.

**2006      Litho.      Perf. 14½**
1650-1654 A522   Set of 5      16.00 16.00

Campaign Against
Hypertension — A523

Frame colors: 50f, Green. 150f, Red. 350f, Brown.

**2007, Jan. 15      Perf. 13¼x13**
1655-1657 A523   Set of 3      9.75 9.75

46th National
Day — A524

Sky color: 25f, Dark blue. 50f, Blue. 150f, Orange brown.

**2007, Feb. 25**
1658-1660 A524   Set of 3      6.50 6.50

Liberation Day,
16th
Anniv. — A525

Frame color: 25f, Red. 50f, Dark blue. 150f, Purple.

**2007, Feb. 26      Litho.      Perf. 13x13¼**
1661-1663 A525   Set of 3      6.75 6.75

Kuwait University,
40th Anniv. (in
2006) — A526

Color behind emblem: 25f, Blue. 50f, Yellow. 150f, Green. 350f, Red.

**2007, Mar. 20**
1664-1667 A526   Set of 4      12.00 12.00

Kuwait Oil Tanker
Company, 50th
Anniv. — A527

Background colors: 25f, Pale blue. 50f, Pale green. 150f, Gray.

**Litho. & Embossed With Foil Application**
**2007, Nov. 25      Perf. 13**
1668-1670 A527   Set of 3      7.50 7.50

Kuwait Philatelic & Numismatic
Society, 1st Anniv. — A528

**2007, Dec. 5      Litho.      Perf. 13¼**
| 1671 | A528 | Horiz. strip of 3 | 7.50 | 7.50 |
|---|---|---|---|---|
| a. | | 25f Coin | 1.00 | 1.00 |
| b. | | 50f Kuwait #146 | 1.60 | 1.60 |
| c. | | 150f Society emblem | 4.25 | 4.25 |

No. 1671c is 60x35mm.

47th National
Day — A529

Designs: 25f, Women voting. 150f, Stylized people, dhows, fish, towers, horiz.

**Perf. 13¼x13, 13x13¼**
**2008, Feb. 25      Litho.**
1672-1673 A529   Set of 2      5.00 5.00

Liberation Day,
17th
Anniv. — A530

Hand holding map of Kuwait with background color of: 25f, Dull rose. 50f, Purple.

**2008, Feb. 26      Litho.      Perf. 13x13¼**
1674-1675 A530   Set of 2      3.75 3.75

First Gulf Cooperation
Council Women's
Sports
Tournament — A531

No. 1676 — Emblem and: a, Gymnastics. b, Running. c, Shooting. d, Basketball. e, Tennis. No. 1677, horiz. — Emblem, five sports with background color of: a, Orange. b, Red. c, Purple. d, Olive green. e, Red violet.

**2008, Mar. 5      Litho.      Perf. 13¼x13**
| 1676 | | Vert. strip of 5 | 5.00 | 5.00 |
|---|---|---|---|---|
| a.-e. | A531 | 25f Any single | .80 | .80 |
| | | **Perf. 13¼x13¼** | | |
| 1677 | | Horiz. strip of 5 | 15.00 | 15.00 |
| a.-e. | A531 | 150f Any single | 2.40 | 2.40 |

Diplomatic Relations Between Kuwait
and Romania, 45th Anniv. — A532

No. 1678: a, Kuwaiti man building ship model. b, Romanian woman weaving.
500f, Flags of Romania and Kuwait, handshake, vert.

**2008, June 21      Perf. 13¼x13**
| 1678 | | Horiz. pair + 2 labels | 13.00 | 13.00 |
|---|---|---|---|---|
| a.-b. | A532 | 150f Either single + label | 6.25 | 6.25 |
| c. | | Miniature sheet, 4 #1678 | 52.50 | — |

**Souvenir Sheet**
**Perf. 13x13¼**
1679   A532 500f multi      26.00 26.00

Labels of Nos. 1678a and 1678b are separated from stamps by a partial row of perforations. The labels, which have different designs, are to the left of No. 1678a and to the right of No. 1678b. The labels are adjacent to each other on half of the pairs on No. 1678c. No. 1678 was also printed in sheets containing 6 pairs, two of which have the labels adjacent. Value, $60.
See Romania Nos. 5053-5054.

Old
Kuwait — A533

Designs: 25f, Drummer and swordsmen. 50f, Drummers and boat painter. 100f, Street with thatched roof. 150f, Fair. 200f, Man and minarets. 250f, Donkey riders at town gate. 350f, Boats in harbor. 500f, People at town gate.

**2008, Aug. 1      Perf. 13**
| 1680 | A533 | 25f multi | .40 | .40 |
|---|---|---|---|---|
| 1681 | A533 | 50f multi | .65 | .65 |
| 1682 | A533 | 100f multi | 1.20 | 1.20 |
| 1683 | A533 | 150f multi | 1.75 | 1.75 |
| 1684 | A533 | 200f multi | 2.40 | 2.40 |
| 1685 | A533 | 250f multi | 3.00 | 3.00 |
| 1686 | A533 | 350f multi | 4.50 | 4.50 |
| 1687 | A533 | 500f multi | 6.00 | 6.00 |
| | Nos. 1680-1687 (8) | | 19.90 | 19.90 |

48th
National
Day
A534

Frame color: 25f, Black. 50f, Green. 150f, Red.
250f, No frame.

**2009, Feb. 25      Litho.      Perf. 13¼**
1688-1690 A534   Set of 3      5.00 5.00
**Size: 100x66mm**
**Imperf**
1691   A534 250f multi      6.00 6.00

Liberation Day, 18th
Anniv. — A535

Denomination color: 25f, Green. 50f, Red. 150f, Black.

**2009, Feb. 26      Perf. 13¾**
1692-1694 A535   Set of 3      4.00 4.00

Kuwait Finance
House — A536

Denomination color: 25f, White. 50f, Silver.
150f, Gold.

**Litho. & Embossed**
2009, June 21          *Perf. 13¾*
1695-1697  A536    Set of 3    4.00  4.00

Kuwait
Chamber of
Commerce and
Industry, 50th
Anniv. — A537

Designs: 25f, Building. 50f, Dhow. 150f,
Cogwheels.

2009       **Granite Paper**       Litho.
1698-1700  A537    Set of 3    4.00  4.00

49th National
Day — A538

Designs: 25f, Buildings and falcon. 50f,
Sheikhs and falcon. 150f, Sheikhs and
buildings.

2010, Feb. 25   Litho.   *Perf. 13¼x13*
1701-1703  A538    Set of 3    5.75  5.75

Liberation Day,
19th
Anniv. — A539

Designs: 25f, Children's drawing of people
waving flags in car and on side of road. 50f,
Child waving flags. 150f, Fabric art of girls
wearing dresses in colors of Kuwait flag.

2010, Feb. 26          *Perf. 13x13¼*
1704-1706  A539    Set of 3    4.50  4.50

Jerusalem, Capital of
Arab Culture — A540

Denomination color: 25f, Green. 50f, Red.

2010, Mar. 26          *Perf. 13¼x13*
1707-1708  A540    Set of 2    6.50  6.50

Kuwait E-
Gate — A541

Frame color: 25f, Pink. 50f, Yellow. 150f,
Light green.

2010, Apr. 20          *Perf. 14x13¼*
1709-1711  A541    Set of 3    5.50  5.50

Organization of the
Petroleum
Exporting
Countries, 50th
Anniv. — A542

Background color: 25f, Gray. 50f, Light blue.
150f, White.

**Litho. & Embossed With Foil
Application**
2010, May 23          *Perf. 13¾*
1712-1714  A542    Set of 3    6.50  6.50

A543          Liberation Day, 20th
              Anniv. and National
              Day, 50th
              Anniv. — A544

No. 1715: a, Flag, shiekh, "20." b, Dove,
sheikhs, flag, "20." c, Flag, sheikh, "50." d,
Flag, sheikh, "50," diff.

**Litho. & Embossed With Foil
Application**
2011, Feb. 25          *Perf. 13¼*
1715       Horiz. strip of 4    4.00  4.00
  a. A543 25f silver & multi       1.00  1.00
  b. A543 25f silver & multi       1.00  1.00
  c. A543 25f gold & multi         1.00  1.00
  d. A544 25f gold & multi         1.00  1.00

A souvenir sheet with a lithographed 250f
stamp was produced in limited quantities.
Value, $50.

A545          A546

A547          A548

Commercial Bank of
Kuwait, 50th Anniv. (in
2010) — A549

2011, Sept.   Litho.   *Perf. 13¼*
1716       Horiz. strip of 5    5.00  5.00
  a. A545 50f multi               1.00  1.00
  b. A546 50f multi               1.00  1.00
  c. A547 50f multi               1.00  1.00
  d. A548 50f multi               1.00  1.00
  e. A549 50f multi               1.00  1.00

15th General
Assembly of
Arab Towns
Organization,
Kuwait (in
2010)
A550

No. 1717 — Stylized tree and man emblem,
Arab Towns Organization emblem, and back-
ground color of: a, Rose brown. b, Yellow. c,
Chocolate. d, Yellow green. e, Blue. f, Gray
green. g, Gray. h, Tan. i, Orange brown. j,
Brown.

2011, Nov. 5          *Perf. 13½*
1717       Block of 10    10.00  10.00
  a.-j. A550 50f Any single        1.00   1.00

---

**Miniature Sheet**

Kuwait Fund for Arab Economic
Development, 50th Anniv. — A551

No. 1718: a, 50th anniversary emblem, red
background. b, Airport terminal with overhanging roof. c, Airport runway. d, Airplane at
Banjul Intl. Airport, Gambia. e, Pipeline. f, Offshore oil rig. g, Workers examining produce. h,
Farm. i, Well. j, Water works. k, Dump truck on
hill. l, Culvert, hill in background. m, Electrical
station. n, Ships in harbor. o, Highway bridge
in populated area. p, Highway interchange. q,
Elevated highway near hill. r, Culvert with
three round holes. s, Elevated highway, diff.

**Sheet of 20**
2011, Dec.          *Perf. 14¼*
1718  A551  150f 2 #1718a, 1
            each
            #1718b-
            1718s         32.50  32.50

Emir                    Emir Sabah
Abdullah III            III (1913-77)
(1895-1965)             A553
A552

Emir Jaber              Emir Saad
III (1926-              (1930-2008)
2006)                   A555
A554

Crown                   Emir Sabah
Prince                  IV
Nawaf                   A557
A556

Sheikh                  Sheikh
Ahmad                   Salim
(1885-1950)             (1864-1921)
A558                    A559

Sheikh                  Sheikh
Jaber II                Mubarak
(1860-1917)             (1840-1915)
A560                    A561

---

Independence, 51st Anniv. — A562

No. 1720 — Flags and scenes of Kuwait
and: a, Sheikh Mubarak (40x30mm). b, Sheikh
Jaber II (40x30mm). c, Emir Abdullah III
(80x30mm). d, Emir Sabah III (40x30mm). e,
Emir Jaber III (40x30mm). f, Sheikh Salim
(40x30mm). g, Sheikh Ahmad (40x30mm). h,
Nine ruling sheikhs and emirs (80x30mm). i,
Emir Saad (40x30mm). j, Emir Sabah IV
(40x30mm).

2012, Feb. 25          *Perf. 13*
1719       Sheet of 10    25.00  25.00
  a. A552 100f multi              2.50   2.50
  b. A553 100f multi              2.50   2.50
  c. A554 100f multi              2.50   2.50
  d. A555 100f multi              2.50   2.50
  e. A556 100f multi              2.50   2.50
  f. A557 100f multi              2.50   2.50
  g. A558 100f multi              2.50   2.50
  h. A559 100f multi              2.50   2.50
  i. A560 100f multi              2.50   2.50
  j. A561 100f multi              2.50   2.50
           *Perf. 13x13¼*
1720  A562   Sheet of 10    25.00  25.00
  a.-j. 150f Any single           2.50   2.50

A563          A564

A565          A566

A567          A568

A569          A570

A571

Liberation Day, 21st
Anniv. — A572

2012, Feb. 26          *Perf. 13¼x13*
1721       Sheet of 10    12.50  12.50
  a. A563 50f multi              1.25   1.25
  b. A564 50f multi              1.25   1.25
  c. A565 50f multi              1.25   1.25
  d. A566 50f multi              1.25   1.25
  e. A567 50f multi              1.25   1.25
  f. A568 50f multi              1.25   1.25
  g. A569 50f multi              1.25   1.25

| | | | |
|---|---|---|---|
| *h.* | A570 50f multi | 1.25 | 1.25 |
| *i.* | A571 50f multi | 1.25 | 1.25 |
| *j.* | A572 50f multi | 1.25 | 1.25 |

### Miniature Sheet

Membership in UNESCO, 50th Anniv.
(in 2010) — A573

No. 1722 — UNESCO membership 50th anniv. emblem and: a, Kuwaiti flag, emblems of Intangible Cultural Heritage, Intl. Festival of Cultural Diversity, Italian National UNESCO Commission, and UNESCO Associated Schools, white background. b, Emblem of Italian National UNESCO Commission, bister and olive background, denomination 3mm tall at UR. c, Intl. Festival of Cultural Diversity emblem, lilac background. d, Stylized "U" and "O", green and red stripes at bottom. e, Stylized figure of man with arms raised, dull orange background. f, Intl. Astronomical Union emblem, orange and green background. g, Man and Biosphere (MaB) emblem, blue and white background. h, Intangible Cultural Heritage emblem, gray and white background. i, Global Geoparks Network emblem, orange background with blue and white concentric circles. j, Multicolored squares below UNESCO emblem, blue and lilac background. k, UNESCO Associated Schools emblem, blue background with brown stripe at bottom. l, Kuwaiti flag, emblems of Global Geoparks Network, Intl. Festival of Cultural Diversity (with French inscription) and Intl. Bureau of Education, white background. m, UNESCO Institute for Lifelong Learning emblem, red, white and blue background. n, Intl. Bureau of Education (IBE) emblem, white background in blue frame. o, World Heritage emblem, orange background with yellow circle. p, Stylized dove, olive and bister background, denomination 2½mm tall at UR. q, Circle and blue stripes, light blue background. r, UNESCO Chair in Sustainable Mountain Development emblem, UHI Millennium Institute emblem, pink and white background with brown stripes at top and bottom. s, Intl. Festival of Cultural Diversity emblem with French inscription, gray background. t, UNESCO spiral emblem, blue and dull orange background.

**2012, June 6**      **Perf. 14**
1722   A573 150f Sheet of 20,
     #a-t     45.00   45.00

A574

A575

A576

A577

A578

A579

A580

A581

A582

A583

A584

A585

A586

A587

A588

A589

A590

A591

A592

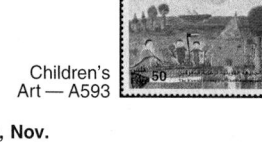

Children's
Art — A593

**2012, Nov.**
| | | | |
|---|---|---|---|
| 1723 | Sheet of 20 | 20.00 | 20.00 |
| *a.* | A574 50f multi | 1.00 | 1.00 |
| *b.* | A575 50f multi | 1.00 | 1.00 |
| *c.* | A576 50f multi | 1.00 | 1.00 |
| *d.* | A577 50f multi | 1.00 | 1.00 |
| *e.* | A578 50f multi | 1.00 | 1.00 |
| *f.* | A579 50f multi | 1.00 | 1.00 |
| *g.* | A580 50f multi | 1.00 | 1.00 |
| *h.* | A581 50f multi | 1.00 | 1.00 |
| *i.* | A582 50f multi | 1.00 | 1.00 |
| *j.* | A583 50f multi | 1.00 | 1.00 |
| *k.* | A584 50f multi | 1.00 | 1.00 |
| *l.* | A585 50f multi | 1.00 | 1.00 |
| *m.* | A586 50f multi | 1.00 | 1.00 |
| *n.* | A587 50f multi | 1.00 | 1.00 |
| *o.* | A588 50f multi | 1.00 | 1.00 |
| *p.* | A589 50f multi | 1.00 | 1.00 |
| *q.* | A590 50f multi | 1.00 | 1.00 |
| *r.* | A591 50f multi | 1.00 | 1.00 |
| *s.* | A592 50f multi | 1.00 | 1.00 |
| *t.* | A593 50f multi | 1.00 | 1.00 |

Kuwait Society for the Handicapped.

### Miniature Sheet

Partnership Between Kuwait and
United Nations, 50th Anniv. — A594

No. 1724 — 50th anniversary emblem and: a, United Nations Headquarters, flags of United Nations and member nations, emblem of Kuwait (60x30mm). b, United Nations House, Kuwait, emblems of various United Nations ororganizations (60x30mm). c, United Nations Secretary General Ban Ki-moon and Sheikh Sabah (30x40mm). d, Emblems of Kuwait and United Nations, national flags (30x40mm). e, Hoisting of Kuwaiti flag at United Nations Headquarters (30x40mm). f, Sheikh Sabah at podium at United Nations (30x40mm). g, United Nations House, and United Nations flag (30x40mm). h, Dhow (30x40mm). i, Kuwait Towers (30x40mm). j, Emblem at United Nations House (30x40mm).

**Perf. 13¼x13¼x14x13¼ (#1724a-
1724b), 14**

**2013, Dec. 1**      **Litho.**
1724   A594 50f Sheet of 10, #a-j   7.50   7.50

A595

A597

A599

A596

A598

A600

A601

A602

A603

53rd National
Day — A604

#### Perf. 13¾x13½
**2014, Feb. 25**      **Litho.**
| | | | |
|---|---|---|---|
| 1725 | Sheet of 10 | 40.00 | 40.00 |
| *a.* | A595 350f multi | 4.00 | 4.00 |
| *b.* | A596 350f multi | 4.00 | 4.00 |
| *c.* | A597 350f multi | 4.00 | 4.00 |
| *d.* | A598 350f multi | 4.00 | 4.00 |
| *e.* | A599 350f multi | 4.00 | 4.00 |
| *f.* | A600 350f multi | 4.00 | 4.00 |
| *g.* | A601 350f multi | 4.00 | 4.00 |
| *h.* | A602 350f multi | 4.00 | 4.00 |
| *i.* | A603 350f multi | 4.00 | 4.00 |
| *j.* | A604 350f multi | 4.00 | 4.00 |

A605

A606

A607

A608

A609

A610

FREE
KUWAIT

A611

A612

A613

Liberation Day,
23rd
Anniv. — A614

#### Perf. 13¾x13½
**2014, Feb. 26**      **Litho.**
| | | | |
|---|---|---|---|
| 1726 | Sheet of 10 | 40.00 | 40.00 |
| *a.* | A605 350f multi | 4.00 | 4.00 |
| *b.* | A606 350f multi | 4.00 | 4.00 |
| *c.* | A607 350f multi | 4.00 | 4.00 |
| *d.* | A608 350f multi | 4.00 | 4.00 |
| *e.* | A609 350f multi | 4.00 | 4.00 |
| *f.* | A610 350f multi | 4.00 | 4.00 |
| *g.* | A611 350f multi | 4.00 | 4.00 |
| *h.* | A612 350f multi | 4.00 | 4.00 |
| *i.* | A613 350f multi | 4.00 | 4.00 |
| *j.* | A614 350f multi | 4.00 | 4.00 |

19th Gulf
Cooperation Council
Stamp Exhibition,
Kuwait — A615

**2014, May 4**    Litho.    *Perf. 13*
1727 A615 25f multi    1.10 1.10

No. 1727 was printed in sheets of 10 with
each stamp in sheet having a different
background.

Modern
Schools
A616

Opening
Schools Abroad
A617

Female
Education
A618

Nutrition and
Health Care
A619

Sheikh
Abdullah Al
Jabir Al Sabah
(1895-1965)
A620

Student
Activities
A621

Girl
Scouts — A622

Heritage
Arts — A623

Boy Scouts — A624

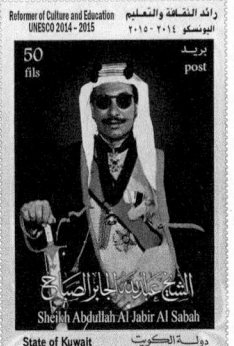

Sheikh
Abdullah
Al Jabir
Al Sabah
A625

---

*Perf. 14, 13¼ (#1728j)*

**2014, Nov. 5**      Litho.
1728    Sheet of 10    8.50 8.50
a. A616 50f multi    .85 .85
b. A617 50f multi    .85 .85
c. A618 50f multi    .85 .85
d. A619 50f multi    .85 .85
e. A620 50f multi    .85 .85
f. A621 50f multi    .85 .85
g. A622 50f multi    .85 .85
h. A623 50f multi    .85 .85
i. A624 50f multi    .85 .85
j. A625 50f multi    .85 .85

**Souvenir Sheets**
*Perf. 13x13½*
1729 A625 250f multi    5.00 5.00

**Litho. With Foil Application**
1730 A625 250f gold & multi    5.00 5.00

Nos. 1729-1730 each contain one
40x60mm stamp.

A626      A627

A628      A629

A630      A631

A632      A633

A634      Kuwait Awqaf
Public
Foundation, 20th
Anniv. — A635

**2014, Nov. 10**    Litho.    *Perf. 13x13¼*
1731    Sheet of 10    11.00 11.00
a. A626 25f multi    1.10 1.10
b. A627 25f multi    1.10 1.10
c. A628 25f multi    1.10 1.10
d. A629 25f multi    1.10 1.10

---

e. A630 25f multi    1.10 1.10
f. A631 25f multi    1.10 1.10
g. A632 25f multi    1.10 1.10
h. A633 25f multi    1.10 1.10
i. A634 25f multi    1.10 1.10
j. A635 25f multi    1.10 1.10

A636

A637

A638

A639

A640

A641

A642

A643

A644

International
Autism
Conference,
Kuwait — A645

---

**2014, Nov. 11**    Litho.    *Perf. 13¾x14*
1732    Sheet of 10    10.00 10.00
a. A636 50f multi    1.00 1.00
b. A637 50f multi    1.00 1.00
c. A638 50f multi    1.00 1.00
d. A639 50f multi    1.00 1.00
e. A640 50f multi    1.00 1.00
f. A641 50f multi    1.00 1.00
g. A642 50f multi    1.00 1.00
h. A643 50f multi    1.00 1.00
i. A644 50f multi    1.00 1.00
j. A645 50f multi    1.00 1.00

Towers
A646

No. 1733: a, Post Tower. b, Liberation
Tower.

**2014, Nov. 23**    Litho.    *Perf. 14¼*
1733 A646 1d Horiz. pair, #a-
b    22.50 22.50

Miniature Sheet

52nd
National
Day (in
2013)
A647

No. 1734: a, Musician and dancers
(60x30mm). b, Children surrounding sheikh
(60x30mm). c, Male dancers wearing waist
sashes (30x45mm). d, Female dancers wearing yellow and black costume (30x45mm). e,
Male dancers wearing black vests (30x45mm).
f, Female dancers wearing purple and yellow
costumes (30x45mm). g, Musician and male
dancers (30x45mm). h, Girls wearing turquoise green dresses (30x45mm). i, Boys
wearing violet and blue costumes, girls in
background (30x45mm). j, Female dancers
with striped skirts (30x45mm).

**2014, Dec. 21**    Litho.    *Perf. 13x13¼*
1734 A647 150f Sheet of 10,
#a-j    17.50 17.50

Miniature Sheet

Liberation Day, 22nd Anniv. (in
2013) — A648

No. 1735: a, Soldiers and black vehicles
with flags (90x30mm). b, Ships (90x30mm). c,
Sheikh meeting troops (45x30mm). d, Soldiers
in personnel carriers in parade (45x30mm). e,
Soldiers carrying guns (45x30mm). f, Helicopter and flag (45x30mm). g, Soldiers with white
boots marching in parade (45x30m). h, Airplanes in flight with colored contrails
(45x30mm). i, Police on motorcycles in parade
(45x30mm). j, Soldiers on small boat
(45x30mm).

**2014, Dec. 21**    Litho.    *Perf. 14¼*
1735 A648 50f Sheet of 10, #a-j    6.00 6.00

Miniature Sheet

Diplomatic Relations Between Kuwait
and European Countries, 50th
Anniv. — A649

No. 1736: a, Netherlands. b, Spain. c, Coat
of arms of Kuwait. d, Germany. e, Hungary. f,
Denmark. g, Greece. h, Turkey. i, Belgium. j,
Italy.

**2014, Dec. 21** **Litho.** **Perf. 13¼**
1736 A649 150f Sheet of 10,
#a-j        18.00 18.00

A650

A651

A652

A653

A654

A655

A656

A657

A658

Constitution, 50th Anniv. — A659

*Perf. 13¾x14, 14x13¾ (#1737j)*
**2014, Dec. 21**        **Litho.**
1737        Sheet of 10     55.00 55.00
a.    A650 500f multi        5.50  5.50
b.    A651 500f multi        5.50  5.50
c.    A652 500f multi        5.50  5.50
d.    A653 500f multi        5.50  5.50

e.    A654 500f multi        5.50  5.50
f.    A655 500f multi        5.50  5.50
g.    A656 500f multi        5.50  5.50
h.    A657 500f multi        5.50  5.50
i.    A658 500f multi        5.50  5.50
j.    A659 500f multi        5.50  5.50

Miniature Sheet

Kuwaiti
Graduate
Society,
50th
Anniv.
A660

No. 1738 — Emblem and: a, Five men at
circular dais (60x40mm). b, Pictures of Kuwaiti
prisoners of war (60x40mm). c, Man in army
uniform, woman with hands over mouth
(30x40mm). d, Men at Kuwaiti Graduate Society Symposium (30x40mm). e, Kuwaitis for
Jerusalem emblem (30x40mm). f, Book cover
with Arabic text and "2007" (30x40mm). g,
Book cover with Arabic text, broken pencil and
"1995-2007" (30x40mm). h, Book cover
depicting stylized head and neck (30x40mm).
i, Page of Arabic text (30x40mm). j, Jigsaw
puzzle with missing pieces (30x40mm).

**2014, Dec. 27** **Litho.** **Perf. 13¼x13**
1738 A660 50f Sheet of 10, #a-j  7.00 7.00

Emir Sabah
IV — A661

Background color: 350f, Blue. 500f, Olive
green. 750f, Light blue. 1d, Light gray.
250f, Brown.

**Litho. With Foil Application**
**2014, Dec. 30**        **Perf. 13¾x13½**
1739-1742 A661  Set of 4    30.00 30.00
**Souvenir Sheet**
*Perf. 13x14x14x14*
1743 A661 250f multi        5.00 5.00
No. 1743 contains one 120x90mm stamp.

Miniature Sheet

54th
National
Day
A662

No. 1744: a, Towers, children wearing red,
white and green caps. b, Male dancers. c,
Female dancers. d, Child with flag of Kuwait
painted on face.

**2015, Feb. 25**        **Litho.**        **Perf. 13¼**
1744 A662 150f Sheet of 4, #a-d  7.50 7.50

Martyrs — A663

No. 1745: a, Ahmad S. Alenezi. b, Ahmad
K. Alenezi. c, Edris B. Alshammari. d, Ebrahim
A. Alsubaie. e, Ebrahim J. Naif. f, Hamed K.
Alshammari. g, Jamal S. Alsalem. h, Jshai'aan
A. Almutairi. i, Jasem N. Alfadhli. j, Ahmad N.
Alenezi. k, Khalaf A. Alenezi. l, Humoud S.
Rashdan. m, Hamad Y. Alsultan. n, Hasan T.
Alfadegh. o, Hasan R. Alshammari. p,
Zakariya A. Bohamad. q, Refa'ie A. Almutairi.
r, Rajaan W. Alazmi. s, Ra'ed M. Sabri. t,
Daham H. Alshammari. u, Diaa A. Alsayegh. v,
Safnan M. Althaferi. w, Sulaiman A. Sulaiman.
x, Salman N. Alazmi. y, Salem M. Alenezi.
No. 1746: a, Abdulrahman N. Abdulrahman.
b, Abduljaleel E. Khaleel. c, Abbas A. Muham-
mad. d, Ayed K. Albraikan. e, Tareq M. Alfad-
hli. f, Faleh S. Althaferi. g, Ghazwan H. Hawas.
h, Obaid S. Alshammari. i, Abdullah E. Saleh.
j, Abdulkareem T. Ali. k, Kulaib S. Farhan. l,
Kamil R. Jabr. m, Fahad A. Alsabah. n, Fraih
B. Alshammari. o, Fayez A. Arashidi. p,
Muhammad Q. Alenezi. q, Muhammad O.
Muhammad. r, Muhammad J. Alaibany. s,
Mohsen A. Alenezi. t, Mut'eb S. Alshammari.
u, Mutlaq M. Almutairi. v, Mus'heb M. Mutlaq.
w, Meshael N. Aladwani. x, Mur'ie N. Alenezi.
y, Muhammad H. Althaydi.

No. 1747: a, Khalid A. Alb'aijan. b, Hamdan
M. Alenezi. c, Jamal S. Allengawi. d, Anwar A.
Alrefai. e, Warid M. Jadran. f, Muhammad M.
Alobaid. g, Majed R. Alkhseli. h, Fahad R.
Althaferi. i, Farhan S. Alruwaili. j, Sahmi M.
Alsubaie. k, Adel A. Alhaie. l, Abdulaziz S.
Kashaan. m, Mufreh K. Alenezi. n, Mansour G.
Alkhseli. o, Matar G. Almajdi. p, Sana A.
Alfudari. q, Rashid K. Althaferi. r, Mussayer F.
Alshammari. s, Abdulrahman M. Abdullah. t,
Muhammad S. Alenezi. u, Ali E. Alraihan. v,
Ibrahim E. Abdullah. w, Ali A. Alsa'baa. x,
Wahid M. Safri. y, Musaed A. Alaskari.
No. 1748: a, Abdullatif A. Alhamdan. b, Bas-
sam M. Sadeq. c, Nawaf M. Alhashan. d,
Abdulhusain A. Albughbish. e, Muhammad J.
Jaber. f, Jafar A. Taqi. g, Habib M. Alsheikh. h,
Abdulrasoul H. Husain. i, Mansour H. Man-
sour. j, Faisal B. Albahar. k, Salem A.
Alkanderi. l, Baqer A. Almousawi. m, Khalid A.
Alsamhan. n, Nasser G. Aladwani. o, Mah-
moud K. Aljasem. p, Mubarak F. Alnout. q,
Bader R. Abdulwahab. r, Ghazi F. Aloutaibi. s,
Sabbar A. Alenezi. t, Saleh H. Saleh. u,
Ahmad A. Kherallah. v, Ibrahim A. Meshael. w,
Muhammad H. Altawash. x, Saad S. Alsham-
mari. y, Hammad S. Alshammari.

**2015, Feb. 26**        **Litho.**        **Perf. 14**
1745        Sheet of 25        7.50 7.50
a.-y.   A663 25f Any single      .30   .30
1746        Sheet of 25        7.50 7.50
a.-y.   A663 25f Any single      .30   .30
1747        Sheet of 25        7.50 7.50
a.-y.   A663 25f Any single      .30   .30
1748        Sheet of 25        7.50 7.50
a.-y.   A663 25f Any single      .30   .30
    Nos. 1745-1748 (4)     30.00 30.00
        Liberation Day, 24th anniv.

Kuwait Institute for Scientific
Research — A664

No. 1749: a, Brid. b, Technician adjusting
scientific equipment. c, Scientists in laboratory. d, Three test tubes. e, Fish. f, Satellite
dishes. g, Building, cars parked at left. h, Bottles. i, Headquarters and reflecting pond. j,
Headquarters, diff.

**2015, Mar.** **Litho.** **Perf. 13x13½**
1749 A664 50f Sheet of 10, #a-j  7.00 7.00

A666

A667

A668

A669

A670

A671

A672

A673

A674

Independence, 55th Anniv. — A675

*Die Cut Perf. 16*
**2016, Feb. 25**                **Litho.**
**Self-Adhesive**
1751        Sheet of 10        — —
a.    A666 50f multi           — —
b.    A667 50f multi           — —
c.    A668 50f multi           — —
d.    A669 50f multi           — —
e.    A670 50f multi           — —
f.    A671 50f multi           — —
g.    A672 50f multi           — —
h.    A673 50f multi           — —
i.    A674 50f multi           — —
j.    A675 50f multi           — —

Souvenir Sheet

First
Post
Office in
Kuwait,
Cent. (in
2015)
A678

Design: 500f, British Residency House,
Safa Post Office, Kishk Shaikh Mubarak, Umm
Mohammed Alsabah House, and General Post
Office.

**2017, Dec.** **Litho.** **Perf. 13¾x13½**
1761 A678 500f multi        — —

Five additional stamps were issued in this
set. The editors would like to examine any
examples.

Miniature Sheet

Abdul Hussain Abdul Rida (1939-
2017), Actor — A679

No. 1762 — Stamp size: a, 86x103mm. b,
40x52mm.

*Perf. 13¾x14 (#1762a), 13 (#1762b)*
**2018, Dec. 16**                **Litho.**
1762 A679 150f Sheet of 10,
        #1762a, 9
        #1762b             — —

## AIR POST STAMPS

### Air Post Stamps of India, 1929-30, Overprinted type "d"

| | | 1933-34 | Wmk. 196 | Perf. 14 | |
|---|---|---|---|---|---|
| C1 | AP1 | 2a dull green | | 24.00 | 27.50 |
| C2 | AP1 | 3a deep blue | | 5.00 | 3.50 |
| C3 | AP1 | 4a gray olive | | 160.00 | 225.00 |
| C4 | AP1 | 6a bister ('34) | | 8.00 | 4.50 |
| | | Nos. C1-C4 (4) | | 197.00 | 260.50 |

Counterfeits of Nos. C1-C4 exist.

> Catalogue values for unused stamps in this section, from this point to the end of the section, are for Never Hinged items.

Dakota and Comet Planes — AP1

**Perf. 11x11½**

| | | 1964, Nov. 29 | Litho. | | Unwmk. |
|---|---|---|---|---|---|
| C5 | AP1 | 20f multicolored | | 2.00 | .30 |
| C6 | AP1 | 25f multicolored | | 2.25 | .40 |
| C7 | AP1 | 30f multicolored | | 2.50 | .65 |
| C8 | AP1 | 45f multicolored | | 4.00 | .90 |
| | | Nos. C5-C8 (4) | | 10.75 | 2.25 |

10th anniversary of Kuwait Airways.

## POSTAGE DUE STAMPS

> Catalogue values for unused stamps in this section are for Never Hinged items.

D1

**Perf. 14x15**

| | | 1963, Oct. 19 | Unwmk. | | Litho. |
|---|---|---|---|---|---|
| | | **Inscriptions in Black** | | | |
| J1 | D1 | 1f ocher | | .60 | .30 |
| J2 | D1 | 2f lilac | | .70 | .45 |
| J3 | D1 | 5f blue | | 1.00 | .30 |
| J4 | D1 | 8f pale green | | 1.60 | .55 |
| J5 | D1 | 10f yellow | | 2.00 | 1.00 |
| J6 | D1 | 25f brick red | | 3.25 | 3.25 |
| | | Nos. J1-J6 (6) | | 9.15 | 5.85 |

D2

| | | 1965, Apr. 1 | | | Perf. 13 |
|---|---|---|---|---|---|
| J7 | D2 | 4f rose & yellow | | .50 | .30 |
| J8 | D2 | 15f dp rose & blue | | 1.75 | .55 |
| J9 | D2 | 40f blue & brt yel grn | | 3.00 | 1.25 |
| J10 | D2 | 50f green & pink | | 3.75 | 1.75 |
| J11 | D2 | 100f dk blue & yel | | 5.50 | 3.25 |
| | | Nos. J7-J11 (5) | | 14.50 | 7.10 |

## OFFICIAL STAMPS

### Stamps of India, 1911-23, Overprinted

Nos. O1-O9

Nos. O10-O14

| | | 1923-24 | Wmk. 39 | Perf. 14 | |
|---|---|---|---|---|---|
| O1 | A47 | ½a green | | 6.50 | 50.00 |
| O2 | A48 | 1a brown | | 5.50 | 27.50 |
| O3 | A58 | 1½a chocolate | | 5.00 | 65.00 |
| O4 | A49 | 2a violet | | 11.00 | 50.00 |

---

| O5 | A57 | 2a6p ultra | | 7.00 | 80.00 |
|---|---|---|---|---|---|
| O6 | A51 | 3a brown org | | 7.50 | 75.00 |
| O7 | A51 | 3a ultra ('24) | | 7.75 | 75.00 |
| O8 | A52 | 4a olive grn | | 6.25 | 75.00 |
| O9 | A54 | 8a red violet | | 9.50 | 110.00 |
| O10 | A56 | 1r grn & brn | | 35.00 | 190.00 |
| O11 | A56 | 2r brn & car rose | | 37.50 | 275.00 |
| O12 | A56 | 5r vio & ultra | | 125.00 | 475.00 |
| O13 | A56 | 10r car & grn | | 250.00 | 440.00 |
| O14 | A56 | 15r ol grn & ultra | | 425.00 | 675.00 |
| | | Nos. O1-O14 (14) | | 938.50 | 2,663. |

### Stamps of India, 1926-30, Overprinted

Nos. O15-O20

Nos. O21-O25

| | | 1929-33 | | Wmk. 196 | |
|---|---|---|---|---|---|
| O15 | A48 | 1a dk brown | | 6.50 | 42.50 |
| O16 | A60 | 2a violet | | 70.00 | 250.00 |
| O17 | A51 | 3a blue | | 6.00 | 55.00 |
| O18 | A61 | 4a ol green | | 6.75 | 90.00 |
| O19 | A54 | 8a red violet | | 9.00 | 130.00 |
| O20 | A55 | 12a claret | | 45.00 | 225.00 |
| O21 | A56 | 1r green & brn | | 14.00 | 275.00 |
| O22 | A56 | 2r buff & car rose | | 18.00 | 400.00 |
| O23 | A56 | 5r dk vio & ultra | | 50.00 | 500.00 |
| O24 | A56 | 10r car & green | | 85.00 | 850.00 |
| O25 | A56 | 15r olive grn & ultra | | 300.00 | 1,450. |
| | | Nos. O15-O25 (11) | | 610.25 | 4,268. |

# KYRGYZSTAN

ˌkir-gi-'stan

## (Kirghizia)

LOCATION — Bounded by Kazakhstan, Uzbekistan, Tadjikistan and China.
GOVT. — Independent republic, member of the Commonwealth of Independent States.
AREA — 77,180 sq. mi.
POP. — 4,546,055 (1999 est.)
CAPITAL — Bishkek

With the breakup of the Soviet Union on Dec. 26, 1991, Kyrgyzstan and ten former Soviet republics established the Commonwealth of Independent States.

In 2013, the Universal Postal Union announced that a second postal organization, Kyrgyz Express Post, was granted permission to provide unrestricted postal services throughout the country. This allowed for competition between the state corporation, Kyrgyz Pochtasy, the original UPU-designated postal operator in Kyrgyzstan having post offices nationwide, and Kyrgyz Express Post for postal business. Listings for stamps issued by Kyrgyz Express Post follow those of the listings for stamps from Kyrgyz Pochtasy.

100 Kopecks = 1 Ruble
100 Tyiyn = 1 Som

> Catalogue values for all unused stamps in this country are for Never Hinged items.

## ISSUES OF KYRGYZ POCHTASY

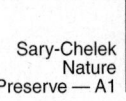

Sary-Chelek Nature Preserve — A1

**Unwmk.**

| | | 1992, Feb. 4 | Litho. | | Perf. 12 |
|---|---|---|---|---|---|
| 1 | A1 | 15k multicolored | | .55 | .55 |

---

Hawk — A2

| | | 1992, Aug. 31 | Litho. | Perf. 12½x12 | |
|---|---|---|---|---|---|
| 2 | A2 | 50k multicolored | | .65 | .65 |

Man with Cattle, by G.A. Aytiev — A3

| | | 1992, Aug. 31 | | | |
|---|---|---|---|---|---|
| 3 | A3 | 1r multicolored | | .40 | .40 |

Handicrafts — A4

| | | 1992, Dec. 1 | Litho. | Perf. 12x11½ | |
|---|---|---|---|---|---|
| 4 | A4 | 1.50r multicolored | | .55 | .55 |

Sites and Landmarks — A5

Designs: 10k, Petroglyphs. 50k, 11th Cent. tower, vert. 1r + 25k, Mausoleum, vert. 2r + 50k, 12th Cent. mausoleum. 3r, Yurt. 5r + 50k, Statue of epic hero Manas, Pishpek. 9r, Commercial complex, Pishpek. 10r, Native jewelry.

| | | 1993, Mar. 21 | Litho. | | Perf. 12 |
|---|---|---|---|---|---|
| 5 | A5 | 10k multicolored | | .25 | .25 |
| 6 | A5 | 50k multicolored | | .25 | .25 |
| 7 | A5 | 1r +25k multi | | .25 | .25 |
| 8 | A5 | 2r +50k multi | | .25 | .25 |
| 9 | A5 | 3r multicolored | | .25 | .25 |
| 10 | A5 | 5r +50k multi | | .30 | .30 |
| 11 | A5 | 9r multi | | .50 | .50 |
| | | Nos. 5-11 (7) | | 2.05 | 2.05 |

**Souvenir Sheet**

| 12 | A5 | 10r multicolored | | 1.00 | 1.00 |
|---|---|---|---|---|---|

Nos. 5-11 exist imperf. Value, set $22.50.

Independence and Admission to UN, 2nd Anniv. — A6

50t, Map. 60t, UN emblem, flag, building, vert.
No. 15a, 120t, like #13. No. 15b, 130t, like #14.

**Perf. 13x12½, 12½x13**

| | | 1993, Aug. 31 | | | Litho. |
|---|---|---|---|---|---|
| 13 | A6 | 50t multicolored | | 1.00 | 1.00 |
| 14 | A6 | 60t multicolored | | 1.25 | 1.25 |

**Souvenir Sheet**
**Imperf**

| 15 | A6 | Sheet of 2, #a.-b. | | 5.25 | 5.25 |
|---|---|---|---|---|---|

Nos. 15a-15b have simulated perforations.

Russia Nos. 4598, 5838, 5984 Surcharged in Violet Blue, Prussian Blue or Black

---

### Methods and Perfs as Before
1993, Apr. 6

| 16 | A2765 | 10r on 1k #5838 (VB) | | .30 | .25 |
|---|---|---|---|---|---|
| 17 | A2765 | 20r on 2k #5984 (PB) | | .35 | .50 |
| 18 | A2139 | 30r on 3k #4598 (Blk) | | .45 | .70 |
| | | Nos. 16-18 (3) | | 1.10 | 1.45 |

Russia Nos. 4599-4600 Surcharged in Blue or Red

### Methods and Perfs as Before
1993, June 29

| 19 | A2138 | 20t on 4k #4599 (Bl) | | .70 | .70 |
|---|---|---|---|---|---|
| 20 | A2139 | 30t on 6k #4600 (R) | | 1.00 | 1.00 |

New Year 1994 (Year of the Dog) — A7

| | | 1994, Feb. 10 | Litho. | Perf. 12x12½ | |
|---|---|---|---|---|---|
| 26 | A7 | 60t multicolored | | .80 | .80 |

No. 26 exists imperf. Value, $1.75.

Musical Instrument A8

| | | 1993, Dec. 30 | Litho. | Perf. 13x12½ | |
|---|---|---|---|---|---|
| 27 | A8 | 30t Komuz | | .40 | .40 |

**Souvenir Sheet**
**Perf. 13**

| 28 | A8 | 140t multi | | 16.00 | 16.00 |
|---|---|---|---|---|---|

No. 28 exists imperf. Value $45.
Issued: No. 27, 12/30; No. 28, 4/4/94.

Panthera Uncia — A9

| | | 1994, Mar. 21 | Litho. | Perf. 12½x12 | |
|---|---|---|---|---|---|
| 29 | A9 | 10t shown | | .35 | .35 |
| 30 | A9 | 20t Lying down | | .40 | .40 |
| 31 | A9 | 30t Seated | | .65 | .65 |
| 32 | A9 | 40t Up close | | .85 | .85 |
| | | Nos. 29-32 (4) | | 2.25 | 2.25 |

World Wildlife Fund.

Flowers — A10

**Perf. 12x12½, 12½x12**

| | | 1994, Aug. 31 | | | Litho. |
|---|---|---|---|---|---|
| | | **Color of Flower** | | | |
| 33 | A10 | 1t violet & white | | .25 | .25 |
| 34 | A10 | 3t white & yellow, horiz. | | .25 | .25 |
| a. | | Miniature sheet of 6 | | 1.60 | 1.60 |
| 35 | A10 | 10t red & yellow | | .40 | .40 |
| 36 | A10 | 16t white & yellow | | .40 | .40 |
| 37 | A10 | 20t pink & yellow | | .50 | .50 |
| 38 | A10 | 30t white & yellow | | .55 | .55 |
| 39 | A10 | 40t yellow & brown | | .65 | .65 |
| a. | | Miniature sheet of 6, #33, #35-39 | | 6.50 | 6.50 |
| b. | | Strip of 7, #33-39 | | 4.00 | 4.00 |
| | | Nos. 33-39 (7) | | 3.00 | 3.00 |

**Souvenir Sheet**

| 40 | A10 | 50t yellow & orange | | 1.60 | 1.60 |
|---|---|---|---|---|---|

Nos. 33-39 exist imperf. Value, set $4.75.
For surcharge see No. 141.

Minerals — A11

**1994, Dec. 1　Litho.　Perf. 13½x13**
| | | | | |
|---|---|---|---|---|
| 41 | A11 | 80t Fluorite-Cinnabar | .65 | .65 |
| 42 | A11 | 90t Calcite | .70 | .70 |
| 43 | A11 | 100t Getchellite | .80 | .80 |
| 44 | A11 | 110t Barite | .85 | .85 |
| 45 | A11 | 120t Orpiment | .90 | .90 |
| 46 | A11 | 140t Stibnite | 1.25 | 1.25 |
| | | Nos. 41-46 (6) | 5.15 | 5.15 |

**Souvenir Sheet**
| | | | | |
|---|---|---|---|---|
| 47 | A11 | 200t Cinnabar | 3.50 | 3.50 |
| a. | | Miniature sheet of 6 | 10.00 | 10.00 |

No. 47a contains Nos. 42-46 and single from No. 47.

Fish — A12

Designs: 110t, Glyptosternum reticulatum. 120t, Leuciscus schmidti. 130t, Piptychus dybowskii. 140t, Nemachilus strauchi. 200t, Cyprinus carpio.

**1994, Dec. 1　　　　Perf. 13x13½**
| | | | | |
|---|---|---|---|---|
| 48 | A12 | 110t multicolored | .55 | .55 |
| 49 | A12 | 120t multicolored | .60 | .60 |
| 50 | A12 | 130t multicolored | .65 | .65 |
| 51 | A12 | 140t multicolored | .80 | .80 |
| a. | | Miniature sheet, #48-51 | 2.75 | 2.75 |
| | | Nos. 48-51 (4) | 2.60 | 2.60 |

**Souvenir Sheet**
| | | | | |
|---|---|---|---|---|
| 52 | A12 | 200t multicolored | 2.25 | 2.25 |

Wild Animals — A13

No. 60: a, 130t, Raptor, diff. b, 170t, Bighorn sheep.

**Perf. 12x12½, 12½x12**
**1995, Apr. 21　　　　　Litho.**
| | | | | |
|---|---|---|---|---|
| 53 | A13 | 110t Bear | .30 | .30 |
| 54 | A13 | 120t Snow leopard, horiz. | .30 | .30 |
| 55 | A13 | 130t Raptor | .35 | .35 |
| 56 | A13 | 140t Woodchuck, horiz. | .40 | .40 |
| 57 | A13 | 150t Raptor, horiz. | .45 | .45 |
| 58 | A13 | 160t Vulture | .50 | .50 |
| 59 | A13 | 190t Fox, horiz. | .65 | .65 |
| | | Nos. 53-59 (7) | 2.95 | 2.95 |

**Souvenir Sheet**
| | | | | |
|---|---|---|---|---|
| 60 | A13 | Sheet of 2, #a.-b. | 1.50 | 1.50 |

Nos. 53-60 exist imperf. Value, set $6.50.

Natl. Costumes — A14

**1995, Mar. 24　　　　Perf. 12x12½**
| | | | | |
|---|---|---|---|---|
| 61 | A14 | 50t shown | .30 | .30 |
| 62 | A14 | 50t Man with mandolin | .30 | .30 |
| 63 | A14 | 100t Man with falcon | .45 | .45 |
| 64 | A14 | 100t Woman seated | .45 | .45 |
| | | Nos. 61-64 (4) | 1.50 | 1.50 |

Nos. 61-64 exist imperf. Value, set $2.50.

---

Traffic Safety — A15

**1995, Mar. 24　　　　　Perf. 12**
| | | | | |
|---|---|---|---|---|
| 65 | A15 | 200t multicolored | .85 | .85 |

**Souvenir Sheet**

End of World War II, 50th Anniv. A16

**1995, May 4　Litho.　Perf. 12x12½**
| | | | | |
|---|---|---|---|---|
| 66 | A16 | 150t multicolored | 1.40 | 1.40 |

UPU Intl. Letter Week — A17

**1995, Oct. 3　Litho.　Perf. 12x12½**
| | | | | |
|---|---|---|---|---|
| 67 | A17 | 200t multicolored | 1.10 | 1.10 |

Natl. Arms — A18

**1995, Oct. 13　　　　　Perf. 12**
| | | | | |
|---|---|---|---|---|
| 68 | A18 | 20t purple | .35 | .35 |
| 69 | A18 | 50t blue | .35 | .35 |
| 70 | A18 | 100t brown | .45 | .45 |
| 71 | A18 | 500t green | 1.50 | 1.50 |
| | | Nos. 68-71 (4) | 2.65 | 2.65 |

Compare with design A37.

Horses — A19

Various adult, juvenile horses.

**1995, Oct. 16　Perf. 12½x12, 12x12½**
**Background Color**
| | | | | |
|---|---|---|---|---|
| 72 | A19 | 10t ocher | .25 | .25 |
| 73 | A19 | 50t light brown, vert. | .25 | .25 |
| 74 | A19 | 100t org brn, vert. | .25 | .25 |
| 75 | A19 | 140t brn ocher, vert. | .40 | .40 |
| 76 | A19 | 150t pink | .60 | .60 |
| 77 | A19 | 200t gray | .60 | .60 |
| 78 | A19 | 300t grnsh yel | .65 | .65 |
| | | Nos. 72-78 (7) | 3.00 | 3.00 |

**Souvenir Sheet**
| | | | | |
|---|---|---|---|---|
| 79 | A19 | 600t Herd of horses, vert. | 2.50 | 2.50 |

Raptors — A20

**1995, Sept. 12　　　Perf. 12x12½**
| | | | | |
|---|---|---|---|---|
| 80 | A20 | 10t Pandion haliaetus | .25 | .25 |
| 81 | A20 | 50t Aquila rapax | .30 | .30 |
| 82 | A20 | 100t Gyps himalayensis | .35 | .35 |
| 83 | A20 | 140t Falco cherrug | .40 | .40 |
| 84 | A20 | 150t Circaetus gallicus | .45 | .45 |
| 85 | A20 | 200t Gypaetus barbatus | .50 | .50 |
| 86 | A20 | 300t Aquila chrysaetos | .70 | .70 |
| | | Nos. 80-86 (7) | 2.95 | 2.95 |

**Souvenir Sheet**
| | | | | |
|---|---|---|---|---|
| 87 | A20 | 600t Halliaeetus albicilla | 2.75 | 2.75 |

"Aquila" spelled wrong on No. 86.
Nos. 80-87 exist imperf. Value: Nos. 80-86, $4.25; No. 87, $3.

---

**Souvenir Sheet**

UN, 50th Anniv. A21

Designs: a, UN headquarters, NYC. b, Mountains, rainbow.

**1995, Oct. 24　Litho.　Perf. 12½x12**
| | | | | |
|---|---|---|---|---|
| 88 | A21 | 100t Sheet of 2, #a.-b. | 1.10 | 1.10 |

Natural Wonders of the World A22

10t, Nile River. 50t, Kilimanjaro. 100t, Sahara Desert. 140t, Amazon River, vert. 150t, Grand Canyon, vert. 200t, Victoria Falls, vert. 350t, Mount Everest. 400t, Niagara Falls. Issyk-Kul Lake, Kyrgyzstan: No. 97, Raptor, row boat, sail boats. No. 98, Water bird, motor boat, row boat.

**1995, Dec. 29　　　　　Perf. 11½**
| | | | | |
|---|---|---|---|---|
| 89 | A22 | 10t multicolored | .30 | .30 |
| 90 | A22 | 50t multicolored | .35 | .35 |
| 91 | A22 | 100t multicolored | .45 | .45 |
| 92 | A22 | 140t multicolored | .50 | .50 |
| 93 | A22 | 150t multicolored | .55 | .55 |
| 94 | A22 | 200t multicolored | .70 | .70 |
| 95 | A22 | 350t multicolored | .90 | .90 |
| 96 | A22 | 400t multicolored | 1.25 | 1.25 |
| | | Nos. 89-96 (8) | 5.00 | 5.00 |

**Souvenir Sheets**
| | | | | |
|---|---|---|---|---|
| 97 | A22 | 600t multicolored | 2.00 | 2.00 |
| 98 | A22 | 600t multicolored | 2.00 | 2.00 |

Reptiles — A23

Designs: 20t, Psammophis lineolatum. No. 100, Natrix tessellata. No. 101, Eublepharis macularius. 100t, Agkistrodon halys. 150t, Eremias arguta. 200t, Elaphe dione. 250t, Asymblepharus. 500t, Lacerta agilis.

**1996, Feb. 2　　　　Perf. 12½x12**
| | | | | |
|---|---|---|---|---|
| 99 | A23 | 20t multicolored | .25 | .25 |
| 100 | A23 | 50t multicolored | .30 | .30 |
| 101 | A23 | 50t multicolored | .30 | .30 |
| 102 | A23 | 100t multicolored | .30 | .30 |
| 103 | A23 | 150t multicolored | .50 | .50 |
| 104 | A23 | 200t multicolored | .60 | .60 |
| 105 | A23 | 250t multicolored | .65 | .65 |
| | | Nos. 99-105 (7) | 2.90 | 2.90 |

**Souvenir Sheet**
| | | | | |
|---|---|---|---|---|
| 106 | A23 | 500t multicolored | 2.25 | 2.25 |

**Souvenir Sheet**

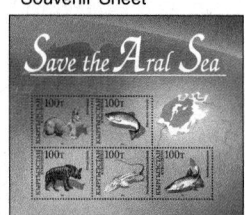

Save the Aral Sea A24

Designs: a, Felis caracal. b, Salmo trutta aralensis. c, Hyaena hyaena. d, Pseudoscaphirhynchus kaufmanni. e, Aspiolucius esocinus.

**1996, Apr. 29　Litho.　Perf. 14**
| | | | | |
|---|---|---|---|---|
| 107 | A24 | 100t Sheet of 5, #a.-e. | 4.00 | 4.00 |

See Kazakhstan No. 145. Tadjikistan No. 91, Turkmenistan No. 52, Uzbekistan No. 113.

---

**Souvenir Sheet**

Fauna A27

a, Aquila chrysaetos. b, Capra falconeri. c, Ovis ammon. d, Gyps himalayensis. e, Equus hemionus. f, Canis lupus. g, Ursus arctor. h, Saiga tatarica.

**1997, Aug. 29　Litho.　Perf. 12x12½**
| | | | | |
|---|---|---|---|---|
| 114 | A27 | 600t Sheet of 8, #a.-h. | 7.00 | 7.00 |

See No. 117.

New Year 1998 (Year of the Tiger) — A28

**1998, June 5　Litho.　Perf. 13½x14**
| | | | | |
|---|---|---|---|---|
| 115 | A28 | 600t multicolored | 1.40 | 1.40 |

Butterflies — A29

Designs: a, Parnasius actius. b, Colias christophi. c, Papilio machaon. d, Colias thisoa. e, Parnassius delphius. f, Panassius tianschanicus.

**1998, June 5**
| | | | | |
|---|---|---|---|---|
| 116 | A29 | 600t Sheet of 6, #a.-f. | 4.50 | 4.50 |

**Fauna Type of 1997**

a, 600t, Capreolus capreolus. b, 1000t, Oriolus oriolus. c, 600t, Pandion haliaetus. d, 1000t, Uncia uncia. e, 600t, Upupa epops. f, 600t, Ciconia ciconia. g, 1000t, Alcedo atthis. h, 1000t, Falco tinnunculus.

**1998, June 5　Litho.　Perf. 12x12½**
| | | | | |
|---|---|---|---|---|
| 117 | A27 | Sheet of 8, #a-h | 10.00 | 10.00 |

Dinosaurs — A31

Designs: a, Saurolophus, vert. b, Euoplocephalus. c, Velociraptor. d, Tyrannosaurus, vert. e, Gallimimus. f, Protoceratops.

**Perf. 14x13½, 13½x14**
**1998, Dec. 4　　　　　Litho.**
| | | | | |
|---|---|---|---|---|
| 118 | A31 | 10s Sheet of 6, #a.-f. | 6.00 | 6.00 |

Universal Declaration of Human Rights, 50th Anniv. — A32

a, Andrei Sakharov (1921-89). b, Crowd of people raising their arms. c, Martin Luther King, Jr. d, Mahatma Gandhi. e, Eleanor Roosevelt.

**1998, Dec. 4　　　　Perf. 14x13½**
| | | | | |
|---|---|---|---|---|
| 119 | A32 | 10s Sheet of 5, #a.-e. + label | 4.75 | 4.75 |

No. 119 exists with 2 different inscriptions on label.

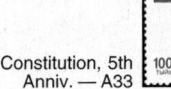

Constitution, 5th
Anniv. — A33

**1998, Dec.**      **Perf. 12**
120   A33   1000t multi      1.60   1.60
*Imperf*
**Size: 120x90mm**
120A A33 10,000t multi      50.00 50.00
No. 120A, issued 2/5/99.

Fauna
A34

Designs: a, 600t, Fish, denomination UR. b,
1000t, Duck standing beside rocks. c, 1000t,
Two birds. d, 1000t, Duck standing beside
water. e, 1000t, Duck swimming. f, 1000t,
Rodent. g, 1000t, Bird. h, 600t, Fish, denomination UL.

**1998, Dec.**   **Litho.**   **Perf. 12**
121   A34   Sheet of 8, #a.-h.    7.50 7.50
No. 121 exists imperf. Value, $9.50.

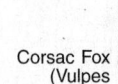

Corsac Fox
(Vulpes
Corsac) — A35

World Wildlife Fund: Nos. 122a, 123a, 10s,
Adult sitting. Nos. 122b, 123b, 10s, Adult
sleeping. Nos. 122c, 123c, 30s, Two standing.
Nos. 122d, 123d, 50s, Adult with young.

**1999, Apr. 27**   **Litho.**   **Perf. 12½x12**
122   A35   Block of 4, #a.-d.    5.50 5.50
**Size: 48x34mm**
**Perf. 13½**
123   A35   Block of 4, #a.-d.    7.50 7.50
Nos. 123a-123d each contain a holographic
image. Soaking in water may affect the
hologram. IBRA '99, World Philatelic Exhibition, Nuremberg (No. 123). No. 123 was
issued in sheets of 8 stamps.
For overprints and surcharges, see Nos.
175, 384.

Aleksandr Pushkin
(1799-1837),
Poet — A36

No. 124: a, 36t, Knight, giant. b, 6s, Man,
woman, fish. c, 10s, Archer, angel. d, 10s,
King in carriage.
20s, Portrait of Pushkin.

**1999, June**   **Litho.**   **Perf. 12x12½**
124   A36   Strip of 4, #a.-d.    3.75 3.75
**Souvenir Sheet**
125   A36   20s multicolored    3.75 3.75
No. 124 printed in sheets of 8 stamps.
Nos. 124-125 exist imperf. Value, set $10.

Natl. Arms — A37

**1999, July**   **Litho.**   **Perf. 11¼x11½**
126   A37   20t dark blue    .80   .80

---

Souvenir Sheet

China 1999 World Philatelic
Exhibition — A38

No. 131: a, 10s, Ailuropoda melanoleuca. b,
15s, Strix leptogrammica.

**1999, Aug. 21**   **Litho.**   **Perf. 13x12½**
131   A38   Sheet of 2, #a.-b.    2.50 2.50
Exists imperf. Value $3.25.

12th World
Kickboxing
Championships,
Bishkek — A39

Emblem, globe and: No. 132, White background. No. 133, Blue panel. c, No. 134,
Green, red, and black panels.
No. 135: a, Black background. b, Yellow and
brown panels.

**1999, Oct. 7**   **Litho.**   **Perf. 13¼**
132   A39   3s multi    .70   .70
133   A39   3s multi    .70   .70
134   A39   3s multi    .70   .70
Nos. 132-134 (3)    2.10 2.10
**Souvenir Sheet**
**Perf. 12½**
135   A39   6s Sheet of 2, #a.-b., +    2.00 2.00
     label
No. 135 contains 37x26mm stamps.

UPU, 125th
Anniv. — A40

6s, Airplane, man on horse.

**1999, Oct.**      **Perf. 14x14¼**
136   A40   3s shown    .55   .55
137   A40   6s multicolored    1.10 1.10

Dogs
A41

No. 138: a, 3s, Taigan. b, 6s, Tasy. c, 6s,
Afghan hound. d, 10s, Saluki. e, 15s, Mid-
Asian shepherd. f, 15s, Akbash dog. g, 20s,
Chow chow. h, 25s, Akita.

**2000, Mar. 18**   **Litho.**   **Perf. 12¼x12**
138   A41   Sheet of 8, #a-h    7.50 7.50
Exists imperf. Value $12.

Kyrgyzstan postal officials have
declared as "not authentic and not
valid" stamps with a face value of 20s
depicting the Beatles, Madonna, Pop
music stars, Tiger Woods, 2000 French
Olympic gold medal winners, Mushrooms, American Political Cartoons
concerning the 2000 Presidential election, The Simpsons, Superman, and
Warner Brothers cartoon characters.

---

Bulat Minzhilkiev(1940-98), Opera
Singer — A42

**2000, Apr. 20**   **Litho.**   **Perf. 14x14¼**
139   A42   5s multi    1.25 1.25

Victory in World
War II, 55th
Anniv. — A43

Heroes: a, Cholponbay Tuleberdiev (1922-
42). b, I. V. Panfilov (1893-1941), vert. c,
Duyshenkul Shopokov (1915-41).

**Perf. 14x14¼ (#140a, 140c), 14¼x14**
**(#140b)**
**2000, May 20**      **Litho.**
140   A43   6s Vert. strip of 3, #a-c   2.75 2.75
Issued in sheets of 2 each Nos. 140a-140c.

No. 33 Surcharged

**2000, Sept. 22**   **Litho.**   **Perf. 12x12½**
141   A10   36t on 1t multi    .50   .90
No. 141 exists with bar obliterators with
smaller numerals and with thinner numerals
and rosette obliterators in magenta. Value:
each, $13.

2000 Summer
Olympics,
Sydney — A44

Designs: 1s, Wrestling. 3s, Hurdles, vert.
6s, Boxing. 10s, Weight lifting, vert.

**Perf. 14x14¼, 14¼x14**
**2000, Sept. 23**
142-145 A44   Set of 4    3.75 3.75

Kyrgyzstan postal officials have
declared as "not authentic and not
valid" a sheet of nine 20s stamps
depicting the History of Golf.

Atay Ogunbaev,
Composer — A45

**2000, Oct. 28**   **Litho.**   **Perf. 14x14¼**
146   A45   6s multi    .85   .85

Butterflies
A46

---

Designs: No. 147, 3s, Aglais urticae. No.
148, 3s, Argynnis aglaja. No. 149, 3s, Colias
thisoa. No. 150, 3s, Inachis io. No. 151, 3s,
Papilio machaon. No. 152, 3s, Parnassius
apollo.

**2000, Nov. 18**      **Perf. 13½**
147-152 A46   Set of 6    4.50 4.50

Kyrgyzstan postal officials have
declared as "not authentic and not
valid" stamps with a face value of 20s
in sheets of 6 depicting Jennifer
Aniston and Tennis, and sheets of 9
depicting Backstreet Boys, Beverly
Hills 90210, Minerals, Penguins, Tom
and Jerry, Prince William, Babylon 5
and the End of Mir.

Intl. Year of
Mountains
(in
2002) — A47

Designs: No. 153, 10s, Khan-Tengri Mountain, 7,010 meters. No. 154, 10s, Victory Peak,
7,439 meters. No. 155, 10s, Lenin Peak, 7,134
meters.

**2000, Dec. 23**   **Litho.**   **Perf. 13½**
153-155 A47   Set of 3    3.25 3.25
  a.   Souvenir sheet, #153-155 +   3.25 3.25
     label

Medals
A48

No. 156: a, 36t, Dank. b, 48t, Baatyr Jene. c,
1s, Manas (third class). d, 2s, Manas (second
class). e, 3s, Manas (first class). f, 6s,
Danaker. g, 10s, Ak Shumkar.

**2001, Jan. 20**   **Litho.**   **Perf. 14¼x14**
156   A48   Sheet of 7, #a-g, + la-   3.25 3.25
     bel

UN High
Commissioner for
Refugees — A49

**2001, Mar. 10**   **Litho.**   **Perf. 14x14¼**
157   A49   10s multi    .95   .95

New Year 2001
(Year of the
Snake) — A50

**2001, Mar. 17**
158   A50   6s multi    .80   .80
Exists imperf. Value $2.25.

Year of Dialogue
Among
Civilizations — A51

**2001, Apr. 14**      **Perf. 13½**
159   A51   10s multi    1.25 1.25

Intl. Year of Mountains — A52

Mountains and: Nos. 160, 163a, 10s, Horses crossing stream. Nos. 161, 163b, 10s, Grazing animals, yurt. Nos. 162, 163c, 10s, Valley.

**2001, July 7** **Perf. 14x14¼**
**With White Frame**
160-162 A52 Set of 3    3.50 3.50

**Souvenir Sheet**
**Without White Frame**
163 A52 10s Sheet of 3, #a-c, + label    4.00 4.00

Bishkek Buildings — A53

Designs: 48t, Communications Building. 1s, Town Hall. 3s, Opera House.

**2001, July 7** **Perf. 14x13¼**
164 A53 48t slate gray    .30 .25
165 A53 1s olive gray    .30 .30
166 A53 3s violet brown    .40 .40
   a. Horiz. strip, #164-166    1.00 1.00

Intl. Year of Ecotourism (in 2002) — A54

Designs: No. 167, 10s, Mountains, lake. No. 168, 10s, Mountains, field of flowers. No. 169, 10s, Sailboat on lake.
No. 170, Mosque, vert.

**2001, July 21** **Perf. 14x14¼**
167-169 A54 Set of 3    4.00 4.00

**Souvenir Sheet**
**Imperf (Simulated Perfs)**
170 A54 10s multi    2.40 2.40

Independence, 10th Anniv. — A55

Designs: 1.50s, Eagle, mountain. 7s, Pres. Askar Akaev, flag.
11.50s, Governmental building.

**2001, Aug. 29** **Perf. 14x14¼**
171-172 A55 Set of 2    4.50 4.50

**Souvenir Sheet**
173 A55 11.50s Sheet of 1 + 8 labels    4.75 4.75

Kurmanbek Baatyr, 500th Anniv. of Birth — A56

**2001, Sept. 8** **Perf. 14¼x14**
174 A56 1.50s multi    .90 .90

**Nos. 123a-123b Surcharged and Nos. 123c-123d Overprinted With Text Only**

No. 175: a, 25s on 10s #123a. b, 25s on 10s, #123b. c, 30s #123c. d, 50s #123d.

---

**Litho. With Hologram**
**2001** **Perf. 13½**
175 A35 Block of 4, #a-d    7.75 7.75

Regional Communications Accord, 10th Anniv. — A57

**2001, Oct. 20 Litho.** **Perf. 14¼x14**
176 A57 7s multi    1.20 1.20

Commonwealth of Independent States, 10th Anniv. — A58

**2001, Dec. 8**
177 A58 6s Prus bl & yel    1.00 1.00

Kyrgyzstan postal officials have declared as "illegal":
Stamps with a face value of 20s in sheets of nine depicting Shrek, Harry Potter, Concorde, Dogs, Tigers, Formula 1 racing, Mother Teresa, and The Beatles;
Stamps with various face values in sheets of nine depicting Defenders of Peace and Freedom, Superman, Green Lantern, Flash, Ironman, Legends of Baseball;
Stamps with various values in sheets of three depicting Princess Diana and Elvis Presley;
Stamps with a face value of 20s in sheets of six depicting Harley Davidson motorcycles;
Souvenir sheets of one 100s stamp depicting Harry Potter and Penguins.

2002 Winter Olympics, Salt Lake City — A59

Designs: 50t, Speed skating. 1.50s, Biathlon. 7s, Ice hockey. 10s, Ski jumping. 50s, Downhill skiing.

**2002, Feb. 23 Litho.** **Perf. 14x14¼**
178-181 A59 Set of 4    2.25 2.25

**Souvenir Sheet**
182 A59 50s multi + label    5.50 5.50

New Year 2002 (Year of the Horse) — A60

**2002, Mar. 23** **Perf. 14x14¼**
183 A60 1s multi    1.10 1.10

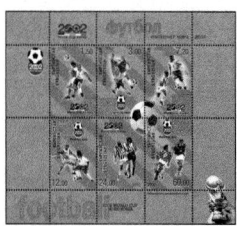

2002 World Cup Soccer Championships, Japan and Korea — A61

---

No. 184: a, 1.50s. b, 3s. c, 7.20s. d, 12s. e, 24s. f, 60s.

**2002, Apr. 13** **Perf. 14¼x14**
184 A61 Sheet of 6, #a-f    11.00 11.00

No. 184 exists with an overprint in silver or gold with scores of the final and third place matches of the tournament. Value: each, $25.

Kyrgyzstan/Pakistan Diplomatic Relations, 10th Anniv. — A62

**2002, Apr. 18** **Perf. 14¼x14**
185 A62 12s multi    1.25 1.25

Kyrgyzstan postal officials have declared as "illegal":
Stamps with a face value of 20s in sheets of nine depicting Pandas, Dinosaurs, Marine Life, Cats and Scouting Emblem, and the Beatles.
Stamps with various face values in sheets of nine depicting Caricatures of World Cup Soccer Players (3 sheets).

Summer Olympics A63

No. 186: a, 1s, Discus, Greece #125 (Athens, 1896). b, 2s, Boxing, France #113 (Paris, 1900). c, 3s, Diving, US #324 (St. Louis, 1904). d, 5s, Weight lifting, Great Britain #127 (London, 1908). e, 7s, Rowing, Sweden #97 (Stockholm, 1912). f, 7s, Hurdles, Belgium #B48 (Antwerp, 1920).
No. 187: a, 1s, Rhythmic gymnastics, France #201 (Paris, 1924). b, 2s, Diving, Netherlands #B25 (Amsterdam, 1928). c, 3s, Table tennis, US #718 (Los Angeles, 1932). d, 5s, Running, Germany #B86 (Berlin, 1936). e, 7s, Fencing, Great Britain #274 (London, 1948). f, 7s, Men's gymnastics (pommel horse), Finland #B112 (Helsinki, 1952).
No. 188: a, 1.50s, Volleyball, Australia #277 (Melbourne, 1956). b, 3s, Tennis, Italy #799 (Rome, 1960). c, 5s, Swimming, Japan #B12 (Tokyo, 1964). d, 5s, Judo, Mexico #990 (Mexico City, 1968). e, 7s, Kayaking, Germany #B490e (Munich, 1972). f, 12s, Yachting, Canada #B11 (Montreal, 1976).
No. 189: a, 1.50s, Men's gymnastics (rings), Russia #B99 (Moscow, 1980). b, 3s, Synchronized swimming, US #2085a (Los Angeles, 1984). c, 5s, Cycling, South Korea #B54 (Seoul, 1988). d, 5s, High jump, Spain #B197 (Barcelona, 1992). e, 7.20s, Sailboarding, US #3068a (Atlanta, 1996). f, 12s, Women's gymnastics, Australia #1779 (Sydney, 2000).

**2002, Aug. 28 Litho.** **Perf. 13x13¼**
**Sheets of 6, #a-f, + 3 labels**
186-189 A63 Set of 4    12.00 12.00

Jalal-Abad A64

Talas A65

Osh — A66

**2002, Dec. 7** **Perf. 13½**
190 A64 20t claret    .30 .30
191 A65 50t claret    .30 .30
192 A66 60t claret    .30 .30
193 A64 1s Prussian bl    .30 .30
194 A65 1.50s Prussian bl    .30 .30
195 A66 2s blue gray    .30 .30
196 A64 3s blue gray    .45 .45
197 A65 7s blue gray    .90 .90
198 A66 10s Prussian bl    1.25 1.25
   Nos. 190-198 (9)    4.40 4.40

---

Kyrgyzstan postal officials have declared as "illegal":
Sheets of 9 with various denominations depicting Looney Tunes Characters (Merry Cristmas! (sic)) (2 different), Harry Potter, 71st Academy Awards, MTV Video Awards.
Sheets of 9 with 20s denominations depicting 20th Century Dreams (5 different), Chess, Teddy bears, MTV Video Awards.
Sheet of 6 with various denominations depicting Dinosaurs.
Sheet of 3 with various denominations depicting Pope John Paul II.

Nos. 33, 35 Surcharged in Red or Black

No. 34 Surcharged

**Methods and Perfs As Before**
**2002, Dec. 28**
199 A10 1.50s on 1t multi (R)    .30 .30
200 A10 3.60s on 3t multi    .40 .40
201 A10 7s on 10t multi    .80 .80
   Nos. 199-201 (3)    1.50 1.50

New denomination is at left on No. 201. Nos. 199-201 exist imperf. Value, set $3.

Olmoskhan Atabekova (1922-87) — A67

**2003, Jan. 11 Litho.** **Perf. 14¼x14**
202 A67 7.20s multi    .75 .75

Intl. Association of Academies of Science, 10th Anniv. — A68

Emblem and: 1.50s, Atom model. 7.20s, Circles.

**2003, Mar. 8** **Perf. 14x14¼**
203-204 A68 Set of 2    1.00 1.00

Gold and Bronze Artifacts From Sakov A69

No. 205: a, 1.50s, Two figurines of people. b, 3s, Coin. c, 3.60s, Lion. d, 5s, Idol with horns. e, 7s, Rooster. f, 10s, Goats. g, 20s, Bird on coin. h, 42s, Animal's head.
No. 206, Mask.

**2003, May 10** **Perf. 14x14¼**
205 A69 Sheet of 8, #a-h    9.75 9.75

**Souvenir Sheet**
**Imperf. (With Simulated Perforations)**
206 A69 42s multi    6.00 6.00

No. 205 exists imperf. with simulated perforations. Value $15.

Bishkek Post Office, 125th Anniv. — A70

Bishkek Post Office, emblem, dove and: 1s, Airplane. 3s, Covered wagon and Jeep. 7s, Covered wagon. 50s, "1878-2003."

**2003, May 31          Perf. 14x14¼**
207-209  A70   Set of 3                1.50  1.50

**Souvenir Sheet**
***Imperf. (With Simulated Perforations)***
210  A70  50s multi                    5.50  5.50

Famous Men A71

Various men: a, 1.50s. b, 3s. c, 3.60s. d, 5s. e, 7.20s. f, 10s. g, 18s. h, 20s. i, 25s. j, 30s.

**2003, June 20          Perf. 14x14¼**
211  A71   Sheet of 10, #a-j   13.00  13.00

Issyk Kul A72

No. 212: a, 1s, Rahat. b, 1.50s, Raduga. c, 2s, Teltoru. d, 3s, Kyrgyzskoe Vzmorije. e, 3.60s, Tamga. f, 5s, Solnyshko. g, 7s, Vityaz. h, 8s, Ak Bermet. i, 12s, Royal Beach. j, 20s, Luchezarnoe Poberejie.

**2003, Aug. 15          Perf. 13½x13¾**
212  A72   Sheet of 10, #a-j, + 10
           labels                        6.50  6.50

Lunar New Year Animals A73

No. 213: a, 1.50s, Rat. b, 3s, Ox. c, 5s, Tiger. d, 7s, Hare. e, 12s, Dragon. f, 12s, Snake. g, 15s, Horse. h, 15s, Sheep. i, 20s, Monkey. j, 20s, Cock. k, 25s, Dog. l, 25s, Pig.

**2003, Aug. 25          Perf. 13x13¼**
213  A73   Sheet of 12, #a-l,
           +4 labels                    14.00  14.00

National Symbols — A74

---

History of Syma Chan A75

Designs: No. 214, 3s, Flag. No. 215, 3s, National anthem. 5s, Coat of arms.

**2003, Oct. 4   Litho.   Perf. 13½**
214-216  A74   Set of 3         1.75  1.75
216a       Souvenir sheet, #214-216  1.75  1.75

**Souvenir Sheet**
217  A75  12s multi               2.00  2.00

New Year 2003 (Year of the Sheep) — A76

**2003, Dec. 30   Litho.   Perf. 14x14¼**
218  A76  1.50s multi               .70  .70

Meerim Fund, 10th Anniv. — A77

Designs: 1.50s, Fund emblem, buildings. 7s, Fund emblem, buildings, diff. 20s, Fund emblem.

**2004, Feb. 17   Litho.   Perf. 14x14¼**
219-220  A77   Set of 2         1.50  1.50

**Souvenir Sheet**
***Perf. 13½***
221  A77  20s multi              3.00  3.00

No. 221 contains one 37x51mm stamp.

New Year 2004 (Year of the Monkey) — A78

**2004, Apr. 3   Litho.   Perf. 14x14¼**
222  A78  3s multi                .80  .80

Automobiles — A79

No. 223: a, 3.60s, 1913 Peugeot. b, 3.60s, 1999 Mercedes-Benz. c, 10s, 1996 Volvo S40. d, 10s, 1908 Ford. e, 15s, 1932 Alfa-Romeo. f, 15s, 1972 VAZ 2101. g, 25s, 1998 Nissan. h, 25s, 1950 ZIS-110.

**2004, May 1   Litho.   Perf. 14x13¼**
223  A79   Sheet of 8, #a-h   9.00  9.00

No. 223 exists imperf. Value $16.

Insects A80

No. 224: a, 3.60s, Insect with red wings. b, 3.60s, Grasshopper. c, 10s, Cricket. d, 10s, Ladybugs. e, 15s, Dragonfly. f, 15s, Praying

---

mantis. g, 25s, Moth with red wings. h, 25s, Bee.

**2004, May 15**
224  A80   Sheet of 8, #a-h   8.50  8.50
2004 Singapore World Stamp Championship. No. 224 exists imperf. Value $15.

FIFA (Fédération Internationale de Football Association), Cent. — A81

No. 225: a, 5s, Soccer ball. b, 6s, FIFA emblem, soccer ball, athletic shoes. c, 7s, Soccer player with red shirt. d, 10s, Soccer player with white shirt.

**2004, May 21   Litho.   Perf. 14x14¼**
225  A81   Block of 4, #a-d   2.75  2.75

**No. 12 Surcharged**

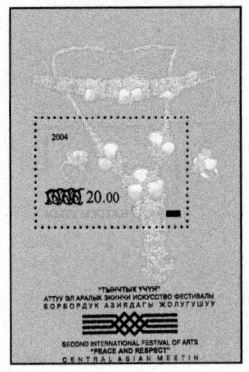

**2004, June 19   Litho.   Perf. 12**
226  A5  20s on 10r #12           2.50  2.50

Peace and Respect Intl. Festival of Arts.

Karakol Region A82

Naryn Region A83

Tokmok Region — A84

**2004, July 6   Litho.   Perf. 13½x13¾**
227  A82  10t indigo             .25  .25
228  A83  20t dark green         .25  .25
229  A84  50t dark brown         .25  .25
230  A82  60t blue               .25  .25
231  A83   1s blue green         .25  .25
232  A84   2s brown              .25  .25
233  A82   3s violet             .50  .50
234  A83   5s green              .75  .75
235  A84   7s light brown      1.00  1.00
       Nos. 227-235 (9)         3.75  3.75

Chynykei Biy (1788-1874) A85

**2004, Sept. 18   Litho.   Perf. 14x14¼**
236  A85  3s multi              .65  .65

National Academy of Sciences, 50th Anniv. — A86

---

Emblem and: 1.50s, Old building. 3.60s, New building.

**2004, Nov. 6**
237-238  A86   Set of 2         .95  .95

Basketball — A87

Basketball player and: 1.50s, Coach Nikolay Zvenchukov. 3.60s, Coach Kubat Karabekov.

**2004, Dec. 4**
239-240  A87   Set of 2        2.00  2.00

Falcon — A88

**2004-05   Litho.   Perf. 13¼x14**
241  A88  10t green             .40  .40
242  A88  50t blue              .40  .40
243  A88   1s brown             .75  .75
       Nos. 241-243 (3)        1.55  1.55

Issued: 1s, 12/28/04. 50t, 2/12/05. 10t, 6/16/05.
Nos. 241-243 exist imperf. Value, set $20.

New Year 2005 (Year of the Rooster) — A89

**2005, Mar. 21   Litho.   Perf. 14**
244  A89  3s multi             1.10  1.10

No. 244 exists imperf. Value, $10.

**Souvenir Sheet**

Salizhan Sharipov, Astronaut — A90

**2005, Apr. 20   Litho.   Perf. 13¾**
245  A90  100s multi          13.50  13.50

Folk Art — A91

Various folk art objects.

**2005, Apr. 23          Perf. 14¼x14**
246        Strip of 6           4.50  4.50
 a.  A91  2s orange panel        .25  .25
 b.  A91  3.60s light blue panel  .25  .25
 c.  A91  7s green panel          .55  .55
 d.  A91  12s green panel         .85  .85
 e.  A91  15s bright pink panel  1.10  1.10
 f.  A91  20s orange panel       1.50  1.50

**Souvenir Sheet**
247  A91  40s multi             4.50  4.50

End of World War II, 60th Anniv. — A92

**2005, May 6          Perf. 14x14¼**
248  A92  5s multi               .85  .85

End of World War II, 60th Anniv. — A93

World War II personalities: No. 249, 5s, Gen. Tito. No. 250, 5s, Cervi Brothers. No. 251, 5s, Ferruccio Parri. No. 252, 10s, Air Marshal Sir Hugh Dowding. No. 253, 10s, Gen. George S. Patton. No. 254, 10s, Gen. Konstantin Rokossovsky. No. 255, 10s, Gen. Harold Alexander. No. 256, 10s, Gen. Omar N. Bradley. No. 257, 10s, Gen. Charles de Gaulle. No. 258, 10s, Gen. Jean Leclerc. No. 259, 10s, Field Marshal Bernard Montgomery. No. 260, 10s, Gen. Ivan Konev. No. 261, 10s, Marshal Georgy Zhukov. No. 262, 10s, Gen. Dwight D. Eisenhower. No. 263, 10s, Marshal Semyon Timoshenko. No. 264, 10s, Gen. Vasily Chuikov. No. 265, 15s, Pres. Franklin D. Roosevelt. No. 266, 15s, Prime Minister Winston Churchill. No. 267, 15s, King George VI. No. 268, 15s, Joseph Stalin.

**Embossed on Metal**
**2005, June 18**    *Die Cut Perf 12½*
**Self-Adhesive**
249-268  A93    Set of 20    60.00  60.00

National Games — A94

**2005, Aug. 6    Litho.    Perf. 14¼x14**
269  A94  3s multi    .60  .60

World Summit on the Information Society, Tunis — A95

**2005, Sept. 10    Perf. 14x14¼**
270  A95  3.60s multi    .75  .75

Falcon — A96

**2005, Sept. 14    Litho.    Perf. 13¼x14**
271  A96  60t violet    .60  .60
No. 271 exists imperf. Value $5.75.

**Souvenir Sheet**

Lakes A97

No. 272: a, 7s, Lake Chatyrkul. b, 20s, Lake Sonkul. c, 25s, Lake Sarychelek. d, 30s, Lake Issyk-Kul.

**2005, Dec. 10    Perf. 14x14¼**
272  A97    Sheet of 4, #a-d    6.25  6.25

Europa Stamps, 50th Anniv. (in 2006) — A98

Designs: 15s, Uzgen Minaret, Kyrgyzstan. 20s, Acropolis, Athens, Greece. 25s, Buran Tower, Kyrgyzstan. 45s, Kolossi Castle, Limassol, Cyprus. 60s, Tash Rabat, Kyrgyzstan. 85s, St. Mark's Basilica, Venice, Italy.

---

**2005, Dec. 29    Perf. 13¼x13**
273-278  A98  Set of 6    17.50  17.50
278a    Souvenir sheet, #273-278    17.50  17.50
Nos. 273-278 and 278a exist imperf. Values: set, $20; sheet, $20.

Tugolbai Sydykbekov (1912-97), Writer — A99

**2006, Jan. 7    Perf. 14x14¼**
279  A99  10s multi    1.00  1.00

New Year 2006 (Year of the Dog) — A100

**2006, Feb. 4**
280  A100  3s multi    .70  .70
No. 280 exists imperf. Value, $10.

2006 Winter Olympics, Turin — A101

**2006, Mar. 11**
281  A101  5s multi    .80  .80
No. 281 exists imperf. Value, $7.50.

Falcon — A102

**2006    Litho.    Perf. 13¼x14**
282  A102  50t Prus blue    .30  .30
283  A102  1s car lake    .40  .40
284  A102  3s black    .50  .50
    Nos. 282-284 (3)    1.20  1.20
Issued: 50t, 4/15; 1s, 5/6; 3s, 8/5. Nos. 282-284 exist imperf. Value, each $6.50.

2006 World Cup Soccer Championships, Germany — A103

**2006, June 9    Litho.    Perf. 14x14¼**
285  A103  15s multi    1.25  1.25

**Miniature Sheet**

Commemorative Coins — A104

No. 286: a, 1.50s, 1995 100-som gold coin. b, 3s, 1995 10-som silver coin. c, 16s, 2000 100-som gold coin. d, 20s, 2001 10-som silver coin. e, 24s, 2002 10-som silver coin depicting flower. f, 28s, 2002 10-som silver coin depicting ram. g, 30s, 2003 10-som silver and gold coin depicting other coins. h, 40s, 2003 10-

---

som silver and gold coin depicting national symbols. i, 45s, 2005 10-som silver coin. j, 50s, 2005 10-som silver and gold coin.

**2006, June 24**
286  A104    Sheet of 10, #a-j    17.50  17.50

Regional Communications Commonwealth, 15th Anniv. — A105

**2006, Sept. 23    Litho.    Perf. 14x14¼**
287  A105  12s multi    1.25  1.25

**Souvenir Sheet**

Public Buildings in Bishkek A106

No. 288: a, Sports arena (two word inscription, large tree at left). b, Theater (three word inscription). c, Philharmonic hall (one word inscription). d, Museum (two word inscription, no tree).

**2006, Sept. 30    Perf. 12¾x13¼**
288  A106  12s Sheet of 4, #a-d    4.00  4.00

Intl. Telecommunications Union Plenipotentiary Conference, Antalya, Turkey — A107

**2006, Oct. 7    Litho.    Perf. 13x13½**
289  A107  25s multi    2.25  2.25

Defense of Moscow in World War II, 65th Anniv. — A108

**2006, Nov. 11    Perf. 14x14¼**
290  A108  7s multi    .70  .70
No. 290 exists imperf. Value, $8.

**Miniature Sheet**

Kyrgyz Cinema, 65th Anniv. A109

No. 291: a, S. Chokmorov (on horse). b, B. Bejshenaliev (man wearing hat). c, T. Tursunbaeva (woman wearing headdress). d, B. Kydykeeva (two women).

**2006, Dec. 9**
291  A109  12s Sheet of 4, #a-d    4.25  4.25

New Year 2007 (Year of the Pig) — A110

**2007, Jan. 27    Litho.    Perf. 14x14¼**
292  A110  3s multi    .50  .50
No. 292 exists imperf. Value, $8.50.

---

**Miniature Sheet**

Paintings A111

No. 293: a, Chingiz Aitmatov (seated man with striped shirt). b, Syimenkul Chokmorov (seated man with clasped hands). c, Kurmangazy Azykbaev (man playing flute). d, Omor Sultanov (seated man wearing light gray suit). e, Zhylkychy Zhakypov (man with dark blue shirt).

**2007, Mar. 3    Litho.    Perf. 14x14¼**
293  A111  12s Sheet of 5, #a-e, + label    5.50  5.50
No. 293 exists imperf. Value, $30.

Kyrgyz National Games — A112

**2007, May 5    Litho.    Perf. 14x14¼**
294  A112  7s multi    .65  .65
No. 294 exists imperf. Value, $8.50.

**Miniature Sheet**

Bishkek-Osh Highway, 50th Anniv. — A113

No. 295: a, Tunnel. b, Road turning to left. c, Road turning to right. d, Straight road.

**2007, May 19    Perf. 13x13¼**
295  A113  25s Sheet of 4, #a-d    6.75  6.75

Aigul — A114

Flower and: 1s, Solid blue background. 100s, Mountains in background.

**2007, June 23    Perf. 13¼x14**
296  A114  1s multi    .50  .50
**Souvenir Sheet**
**Perf. 13¼x13**
297  A114  100s multi    8.00  8.00
No. 296 exists imperf. Value, $7.
No. 297 contains one 30x40mm stamp.

**Miniature Sheet**

Seventh Conference of Shanghai Cooperation Organization — A115

# KYRGYZSTAN

No. 298 — Flags of: a, Kazakhstan. b, Kyrgyzstan. c, People's Republic of China. d, Russia. e, Tajikistan. f, Uzbekistan.

**2007, Aug. 16**  **Perf. 13¾x14½**
298 A115 12s Sheet of 6, #a-f  5.75 5.75

### Miniature Sheet

Birds of Prey A116

No. 299: a, Haliaeetus albicilla. b, Falco rusticolus. c, Aquila chrysaetus. d, Accipiter gentilis. e, Milvus migrans. f, Falco peregrinus.

**2007, Nov. 30**  **Litho.**  **Perf. 14¼**
299 A116 25s Sheet of 6, #a-f  12.00 12.00

Santa Claus — A117

**2007, Dec. 1**  **Perf. 14x14¼**
300 A117 3s multi  .55 .55
No. 300 exists imperf. Value, $7.75.

New Year 2008 (Year of the Rat) — A118

**2008, Jan. 19**  **Perf. 14¼x14**
301 A118 7s multi  .95 .95
No. 301 exists imperf. Value, $8.

Mammals — A119

Designs: Nos. 302, 310a, 7s, Uncia uncia. Nos. 303, 310b, 7s, Ailuropoda melanoleuca. Nos. 304, 310c, 12s, Panthera tigris. Nos. 305, 310d, 12s, Ailurus fulgens. Nos. 306, 310e, 16s, Hystrix cristata. Nos. 307, 310f, 16s, Pygathrix roxellana. Nos. 308, 310g, 25s, Otocolobus manul. Nos. 309, 310h, 25s, Ovis ammon.

**2008, Jan. 19**  **Perf. 14x13½**
**Stamps With White Frames**
302-309 A119  Set of 8  9.50 9.50

### Souvenir Sheet
**Stamps With Colored Frames**
310 A119  Sheet of 8, #a-h  9.25 9.25
Nos. 302-309 exist imperf. Value, set $17.

Kyrgyz National Games — A120

**2008, Mar. 1**  **Perf. 14¼x14**
311 A120 5s multi  .70 .70
No. 311 exists imperf. Value, $6.50.

---

2008 Summer Olympics, Beijing — A121

No. 312: a, Soccer. b, Wrestling. c, Javelin. d, Basketball.

**2008, Mar. 1**  **Perf. 12½x13**
312 A121 20s Block of 4, #a-d  6.25 6.25

### Souvenir Sheet

Mountains — A122

No. 313: a, Khan-Tengri, Kyrgyzstan. b, Sabalan Peak, Iran.

**2008, Mar. 8**  **Perf. 13x13¼**
313 A122 16s Sheet of 2, #a-b, +  4.00 4.00
  central label
See Iran No. 2964.

Outlines of Stamps, Mountain, Kyrgyz Post Emblem — A123

**2008**  **Litho.**  **Perf. 14x13¼**
314 A123 50t multi  .25 .25
315 A123 1s multi  .25 .25
316 A123 3s multi  .25 .25
317 A123 7s multi  .65 .65
  Nos. 314-317 (4)  1.40 1.40
Issued: 1s, 3s, 4/2. 50t, 7s, 5/10.
Nos. 314-317 exist imperf, set $20.

Heroes of the Kyrgyz Republic and Medals — A124

Designs: 10s, Sabira Kumushalieva (1917-2007), actress. 15s, Absamat Masaliev (1933-2004), politician.

**2008, Apr. 5**  **Litho.**  **Perf. 14x14¼**
318-319 A124  Set of 2  2.50 2.50
Nos. 318-319 exist imperf. Value, set $12.50.

### Miniature Sheets

Civil Aircraft A125

No. 320: a, JAK-12. b, MI-2. c, AN-2. d, TU-154. e, IL-14. f, IL-18. g, AN-24. h, MI-4.
No. 321: a, AN-28. b, JAK-40. c, AN-26. d, TU-134. e, IL-76. f, A-320. g, MI-8.
No. 322: a, Sopwith. b, Air-6. c, P5. d, Po-2. e, Ju-52/3. f, ANT-9. g, Mi-1. h, Li-2.

**2008**  **Perf. 14x13¼**
320 A125 20s Sheet of 8, #a-
  h, + central la-
  bel  11.00 11.00
  **Perf. 13x13½**
321 A125 20s Sheet of 7, #a-
  g, + label  10.50 10.50
322 A125 20s Sheet of 8, #a-
  h, + label  10.50 10.50
Issued: No. 320, 5/24; No. 321, 9/20; No. 322, 11/1.

---

Hats — A126

Various hats: 6s, 7s, 12s, 50s.

**2008, June 28**  **Litho.**  **Perf. 14¼x14**
323-326 A126  Set of 4  5.50 5.50
Nos. 323-326 exist imperf. Value, set $22.50.

Yaks A127

No. 325: a, Buka yak (denomination on cloud). b, Mamalak yak (denomination on light blue sky and mountain). c, Inek yak facing right (denomination on purple mountain). d, Inek yak facing left (denomination on dark blue sky and mountain).

**2008, July 26**  **Perf. 13x13¼**
327 A127 25s Block of 4, #a-d  6.50 6.50

Isa Akhunbaev (1908-75), Surgeon — A128

**2008, Aug. 30**  **Perf. 14¼x14**
328 A128 12s multi  .90 .90
No. 328 exists imperf. Value, $7.

### No. 312 Overprinted in Red

No. 329: a, #312a (Soccer) with overprint at bottom. b, #312b (Wrestling) with overprint at bottom. c, #312c (Javelin) with overprint at top. d, #312d (Basketball) with overprint at top. e, #312d with overprint at bottom. f, #312c with overprint at bottom. g, #312b with overprint at top. h, #312a with overprint at top.

**2008, Nov. 22**  **Litho.**  **Perf. 12½x13**
329 A121 20s Sheet of 8, #a-h 21.00 21.00

Campaign Against Drug Abuse — A129

**2008, Dec. 6**  **Perf. 14¼x14**
330 A129 12s multi  1.25 1.25
No. 330 exists imperf. Value, $6.50.

---

New Year 2009 (Year of the Ox) — A130

**2009, Feb. 1**  **Perf. 14x14¼**
331 A130 25s multi  1.60 1.60
No. 331 exists imperf. Value, $6.

Ishembai Abdraimov (1914-2001), Soviet Pilot — A131

**2009, Feb. 26**  **Perf. 14¼x14**
332 A131 10s multi  .85 .85
No. 332 exists imperf. Value, $6.25.

Kok-boru (Buzkashi) A132

**2009, Apr. 25**  **Perf. 14x14¼**
333 A132 25s multi  1.60 1.60
No. 333 exists imperf. Value, $6.

### Miniature Sheet

Horses A133

No. 334 — Various horses: a, 16s. b, 42s. c, 50s. d, 60s.

**2009, May 30**  **Perf. 13x13½**
334 A133  Sheet of 4, #a-d  9.00 9.00

Worldwide Fund for Nature (WWF) — A134

Saker falcon: 10s, Head. 15s, On nest. 25s, In flight. 50s, On nest, with chicks.

**2009, June 20**  **Perf. 13½x14**
335-338 A134  Set of 4  5.50 5.50
338a  Sheet, 4 each #335-338  22.00 22.00
Nos. 335-338 and 338a exist imperf. Values: set of four, $13; sheet of 16, $42.50.

### Miniature Sheet

Scenes From Writings of Chynghyz Aitmatov (1928-2008) — A135

No. 339: a, 7s, Woman, horse, cart and farmer in field. b, 12s, Man and horse. c, 16s, Woman and truck. d, 21s, Women near train. e, 28s, Man carrying boy. f, 30s, Boy with binoculars, buck. g, 45s, Birds flying above horse and rider. h, 60s, Men in canoe.

**2009, Aug. 13**  **Litho.**  **Perf. 13x13¼**
339 A135  Sheet of 8, #a-h, +
  label  11.00 11.00

Barpy Alykulov (1884-1949), Poet — A136

**2009, Aug. 22   Litho.   Perf. 14x13½**
340  A136  16s multi                .95  .95

No. 340 exists imperf. Value, $6.

### Horses Type of 2009

Designs: 16s, Like #334a. 42s, Like #334b. 50s, Like #334c. 60s, Like #334d.

**2009, Sept. 19   Litho.   Perf. 14x14¼**
341-344  A133  Set of 4           9.00  9.00

Nos. 341-344 were each printed in sheets of 6.
Nos. 341-344 exist imperf. Value, set $30.

National Library, 75th Anniv. — A137

**2009, Sept. 30            Perf. 13½x14**
345  A137  12s multi              .90  .90

No. 345 exists imperf. Value, $5.75.

### Miniature Sheet

Glaciers A138

No. 346: a, 12s, Ak-Sai Glacier. b, 16s, Kotur Glacier. c, 21s, Semenovsky Glacier. d, 28s, Zvezdochka Glacier. e, 45s, North Inylchek Glacier. f, 60s, South Inylchek Glacier.

**2009, Dec. 12            Perf. 13x13¼**
346  A138  Sheet of 6, #a-f   10.50 10.50

No. 346 exists imperf. Value, $32.50.

Railways of Kyrgyzstan A139

Designs: 16s, Station. 42s, Train on bridge. 50s, Train leaving tunnel. 60s, Train on bridge over highway.

**2009, Dec. 19            Perf. 14x14¼**
347-350  A139  Set of 4       10.00 10.00

Nos. 347-350 exist imperf. Value, set $32.50.

United Nations Declaration of the Rights of the Child, 50th Anniv. (in 2009) — A140

**2010, Feb. 6**
351  A140  21s multi            1.50  1.50

New Year 2010 (Year of the Tiger) — A141

**2010, Feb. 6**
352  A141  25s multi            1.60  1.60

2010 Winter Olympics, Vancouver — A142

Designs: 21s, Cross-country skiing. 28s, Biathlon. 45s, Giant slalom. 60s, Snowboarding.

**2010, Feb. 12            Perf. 14¼x14**
353-356  A142  Set of 4       10.50 10.50

Peonies A143

No. 357: a, 25s, Flowers. b, 30s, Flower.

**2010, Mar. 30            Perf. 12½**
357  A143  Horiz. pair, #a-b   3.75  3.75
c.      Souvenir sheet, #357b   2.40  2.40

Victory in World War II, 65th Anniv. — A144

**2010, Apr. 10            Perf. 14x14¼**
358  A144  12s multi            .75  .75

### Miniature Sheet

Kyrgyz National Museum of Fine Arts, 75th Anniv. A145

No. 359 — Paintings: a, 12s, Portrait of Y. M. Vengerov, by Ilya E. Repin, 1916. b, 16s, Cabbage Field, by Robert R. Falk, 1910. c, 21s, Dishes on a Red Cloth, by Pyotr P. Konchalovsky, 1916. d, 24s, Seascape in the Crimea, by Ivan K. Ayvazovsky, 1866. e, 28s, Autumn Djailoo, by Semen A. Chuykov, 1945. f, 30s, Evening in the South of Kyrgyzstan, by Gapar A. Aitiev, 1967. g, 42s, Autumn Garden, by A. Ignatev, 1989. h, 45s, By Night, by D. N. Deymant, 1971.

**2010, Apr. 24            Perf. 13x13¼**
359  A145  Sheet of 8, #a-h, +
         central label        13.00 13.00

2010 World Cup Soccer Championships, South Africa — A146

Players and: 24s, Emblem. 30s, World Cup. 42s, Emblem, diff. 60s, World Cup, diff.

**2010, June 26   Litho.   Perf. 14x14¼**
360-363  A146  Set of 4        9.50  9.50

Ancient Silver Jewelry — A147

Designs: 16s, Earrings. 24s, Buttons. 58s, Bangles. 66s, Hair ornaments.

**2010, July 31            Perf. 13½**
364-367  A147  Set of 4       10.00 10.00

### Souvenir Sheet

Kambar-Ata 2 Hydroelectric Station — A148

No. 368: a, 28s, Explosion. b, 42s, Station under construction. c, 60s, Station under construction, diff.

**2010, Aug. 31            Perf. 13x13¼**
368  A148  Sheet of 3, #a-c    7.50  7.50

### Souvenir Sheet

Intl. Telecommunications Union Plenipotentiary Conference, Guadalajara, Mexico — A149

**2010, Sept. 25            Perf. 13**
369  A149  100s multi         6.00  6.00

Famous Men — A150

Designs: 12s, Togolok Moldo (1860-1942), poet. 16s, Murataly Kurenkeev (1860-1949), composer. 21s, Zhenizhok Coco Uulu (1860-1918), poet. 28s, Itzhak Razzakov (1910-79), statesman.

**2010            Perf. 14¼x14**
370-373  A150  Set of 4        4.00  4.00

Issued: 28s, 10/25; others, 10/23.

Turtles — A151

Designs: 16s, Agrionemys horstieldi. 24s, Pseudemys scripta. 48s, Geochelone elegans. 72s, Testudo kleinmanni.

**2010, Dec. 11            Perf. 14x14¼**
374-377  A151  Set of 4        9.00  9.00

New Year 2011 (Year of the Rabbit) — A152

**2011, Jan. 29**
378  A152  24s multi           1.40  1.40

### Miniature Sheet

Animals and National Reserves — A153

No. 379: a, 7s, Eagle, Ala-Archa Reserve. b, 12s, Bear, Chon-Kemin Reserve. c, 16s, Buck, Naryn Reserve. d, 21s, Ram, Sary-Chelek Reserve. e, 24s, Fish, Issyk-Kul Reserve. f, 28s, Duck, Karatal-Zhapryk Reserve. g, 42s, Falcon, Besh-Tash Reserve. h, 45s, Cat, Sarychat-Ertash Reserve. i, 60s, Pheasant, Padysha-Ata Reserve.

**2011, Feb. 25            Perf. 13x13¼**
379  A153  Sheet of 9, #a-i   13.50 13.50

### Souvenir Sheet

First Man in Space, 50th Anniv. A154

No. 380: a, 60s, Vostok 1. b, 90s, Yuri Gagarin (1934-68), first cosmonaut.

**2011, Apr. 2            Perf. 13¼x13**
380  A154  Sheet of 2, #a-b    8.00  8.00

2011 Intl. Ice Hockey Federation Championships, Slovakia — A155

Intl. Ice Hockey Federation emblem and: 28s, Player approaching goalie with puck. 42s, Two players and puck.

**2011, May 14            Perf. 14x14¼**
381-382  A155  Set of 2        4.00  4.00
382a       Miniature sheet of 6, 3
           each #381-382      12.50 12.50

### Miniature Sheet

Bishkek Bus Station, 30th Anniv. A156

No. 383 — Vehicles: a, 12s, PAZ-672 bus, RAF-22038 van. b, 16s, Ikarus-256 bus, GAZ-M24 Volga taxi. c, 21s, LAZ 697R Tourist bus, UAZ-2206 van. d, 24s, Ford E series van, Volvo B12B bus. e, 30s, Volkswagen Transporter T4 van, Setra S 431 dt bus. f, 42s, Mercedes Sprinter 313 van, Mitsubishi Fuso Aero Queen bus.

**2011, July 21            Perf. 13x13¼**
383  A156  Sheet of 6, #a-f +
         central label         8.50  8.50

### No. 123 Overprinted in Gold with Nos. 123c and 123d Surcharged in Metallic Red

No. 384: a, Overprint on #123a. b, Overprint on #123b. c, 60s on 20s #123c. d, 90s on 50s #123d.

**Litho. With Hologram**
**2011, Aug. 5**    *Perf. 13½*
384 A35   Block of 4, #a-d   20.00 20.00

Plum Blossoms A157

No. 385: a, 16s, Denomination at UL. b, 60s, Denomination at UR.

**2011, Aug. 15**   **Litho.**   *Perf. 13*
385 A157   Horiz. pair, #a-b   4.50 4.50

Regional Communications Commonwealth, 20th Anniv. — A158

**2011, Oct. 1**    *Perf. 14x14¼*
386 A158 28s multi   1.75 1.75

Souvenir Sheet

Independence, 20th Anniv. — A159

**2011, Oct. 1**    *Perf. 14*
387 A159 100s multi   6.00 6.00

Commonwealth of Independent States, 20th Anniv. — A160

**2011, Oct. 8**    *Perf. 14x14¼*
388 A160 42s multi   2.75 2.75

Mushrooms — A161

Designs: 16s, Agaricus. 28s, Pleurotus. 42s, Marasmius oreades. 72s, Lycoperdon.

**2011, Nov. 12**   **Litho.**   *Perf. 14¼x14*
389-392 A161   Set of 4   9.00 9.00

Musical Instruments — A162

Designs: 16s, Surnai (wind instrument). 24s, Dobulbas (drum). 48s, Kyl kayak (stringed instrument with bow). 60s, Ooz komuz (mouth harp).

**2011, Nov. 26**
393-396 A162   Set of 4   8.25 8.25

---

Airships — A163

Designs: 12s, Dirigible of Henri Giffard. 28s, LZ-127 Graf Zeppelin. 45s, AU-30 Argus dirigible. 48s, Dirigible of the future.

**2011, Dec. 17**    *Perf. 14x14¼*
397-400 A163   Set of 4   7.75 7.75

New Year 2012 (Year of the Dragon) — A164

**2012, Jan. 14**    *Perf. 13¼*
401 A164 36s multi   2.10 2.10
   Printed in sheets of 4.

Miniature Sheet

Oriental Lunar Calendar Animals A165

No. 402: a, Dog. b, Boar. c, Rat. d, Ox. e, Rooster. f, Tiger. g, Monkey. h, Rabbit. i, Sheep. j, Horse. k, Snake. l, Dragon.

**2012, Jan. 14**    *Perf. 13¾x13½*
402 A165 25s Sheet of 12, #a-l, + central label   18.00 18.00

Women's Headdresses A166

Various headdresses: 16s, 28s, 45s, 60s.

**2012, Feb. 25**    *Perf. 13*
403-406 A166   Set of 4   8.50 8.50

Helianthus — A167

**2012, Mar. 29**    *Perf. 14¼x14*
407 A167 42s multi   2.50 2.50

Bolot Beishenaliev (1937-2002), Actor — A168

Gapar Aitiev (1912-84), Artist — A169

**2012, Apr. 28**    **Litho.**
408 A168 23s multi   1.25 1.25
409 A169 49s multi   2.75 2.75

---

Miniature Sheet

Inventions — A170

No. 410: a, 21s, Writing. b, 23s, Bread. c, 45s, Wheel. d, 49s, Money.

**2012, June 2**    *Perf. 14*
410 A170   Sheet of 4, #a-d   8.25 8.25
   2012 World Stamp Championship, Jakarta, Indonesia.

United Nations Environment Program, 40th Anniv. — A171

**2012, June 5**    *Perf. 14x14¼*
411 A171 45s multi   2.75 2.75

National Games — A172

**2012, Aug. 4**   **Litho.**   *Perf. 14x14¼*
412 A172 28s multi   1.75 1.75

Battle of Borodino, Bicent. A173

No. 413: a, 12s, Battlefield Monument, Borodino. b, 45s, Triumphal Arch, Moscow.

**2012, Aug. 25**    *Perf. 14¼x14*
413 A173   Pair, #a-b   3.50 3.50

Snow Leopard — A174

Designs: 17s, Leopard. 20s, Leopard, diff. 23s, Head of leopard. 30s, Three leopards.

**2012, Sept. 15**    *Perf. 14x14¼*
414-417 A174   Set of 4   5.75 5.75

Man and Woman in Traditional Costumes and Emblem of Regional Communications Commonwealth — A175

**2012, Oct. 20**    *Perf. 14¼x14*
418 A175 30s multi   1.75 1.75

Inscribed Tablets A176

No. 419 — Tablet from: a, 35s, 8th cent. b, 40s, 9th cent.

**2012, Nov. 3**
419 A176   Horiz. pair, #a-b   4.50 4.50

---

Gen. Ysakbek Monuev (1902-49) A177

Ormon Khan (1792-1854), Kyrgyz Tribal Leader A178

**2012, Nov. 24**
420 A177 35s multi   2.25 2.25
421 A178 40s multi   2.50 2.50

Prehistoric Animals — A179

Designs: 23s, Kyrgyzsaurus. 30s, Xenacanthidae. 40s, Longisquama. 52s, Mammoth.

**2012, Dec. 8**    *Perf. 14x14¼*
422-425 A179   Set of 4   9.50 9.50

Souvenir Sheet

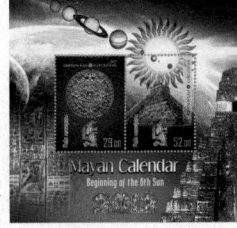

Mayan Calendar A180

No. 426: a, 29s, Mayan calendar. b, 52s, Mayan pyramid.

**2012, Dec. 21**    *Perf. 14*
426 A180   Sheet of 2, #a-b   5.25 5.25

New Year 2013 (Year of the Snake) — A181

**2013, Feb. 16**    *Perf. 14x14¼*
427 A181 30s multi   2.00 2.00

2012 Universal Postal Congress International Stamp Exhibition, Doha, Qatar — A182

No. 428: a, 28s, Gold medal diploma awarded to Kyrgyzstan. b, 43s, Exhibition emblem.

**2013, Feb. 23**
428 A182   Pair, #a-b   4.25 4.25
   No. 428 was printed in sheets containing three pairs.

Miniature Sheet

Walnuts A183

No. 429: a, 17s, Cluster of walnuts on tree branch. b, 20s, Walnuts with opened husks. c, 23s, Walnut in husk, walnuts in shell, opened walnut, jar of product containing walnuts. d,

29s, Walnut in shell, kernels. e, 35s, Basket of walnuts. f, 40s, Walnut grove, mountains.

**2013, Mar. 9**
429　A183　　Sheet of 6, #a-f　　9.50　9.50

National Horse Games — A184

**2013, Mar. 23**
430　A184　35s multi　　　2.25　2.25

Spaceflight of Valentina Tereshkova, First Woman in Space, 50th Anniv. — A185

**2013, Apr. 13**
431　A185　50s multi　　　3.25　3.25

Introduction of Som Currency, 20th Anniv. — A186

**2013, Apr. 27**
432　A186　28s multi　　　1.75　1.75

Marco Polo Argali (Mountain Sheep) — A187

Design: 29s, Head of ram. 35s, Adult and juveniles grazing. 40s, Ram on mountain ledge. 52s, Ram in winter.

**2013, May 18**
433-436　A187　　Set of 4　　11.00　11.00
436a　　　　Souvenir sheet of 4,
　　　　　　　#433-436　　　11.00　11.00

Kozhomkul (1888-1955), Wrestler — A188

**2013, June 8**
437　A188　30s multi　　　1.75　1.75

Sulayman Mountain — A189

**2013, June 22**
438　A189　45s multi　　　3.00　3.00

Miniature Sheet

Worldwide Fund for Nature (WWF) — A190

No. 439 — Snow leopard: a, 29s, Resting on rock. b, 35s, Leaping. c, 43s, Standing on rock. d, 52s, Kittens.

**2013, July 13**
439　A190　Sheet of 4, #a-d　　10.50　10.50

Intl. Forum on Snow Leopard Conservation, Bishkek.

---

Regional Communications Commonwealth Emblem, Train, Airplane, Satellite Dish, Cover and Tablet — A191

**2013, Aug. 17　Litho.　Perf. 14x14¼**
440　A191　36s multi　　　1.90　1.90

Miniature Sheet

13th Shanghai Cooperation Organization Council of Heads of State Session, Bishkek — A192

No. 441 — Emblems or coat of arms of: a, 12s, Kazakhstan. b, 17s, Kyrgyzstan. c, 20s, People's Republic of China. d, 23s, Russia. e, 30s, Tajikistan. f, 35s, Uzbekistan.

**Litho. With Foil Application**
**2013, Sept. 13　　　Perf. 13½x13¼**
441　A192　　Sheet of 6, #a-f　　6.50　6.50

Nasirdin Isanov (1943-91), First Prime Minister of Kyrgyzstan — A193

**2013, Oct. 1　Litho.　Perf. 14x14¼**
442　A193　17s multi　　　1.25　1.25

Kyrgyz Khaganate, 1170th Anniv. — A194

No. 443: a, 20s, Kyrgyz soldier wearing helmet, map of Khaganate. b, 23s, Mounted soldiers. c, 30s, Mounted soildier and petroglyphs.

**2013, Nov. 16　Litho.　Perf. 14¼x14**
443　A194　　Horiz. strip of 3, #a-c 4.25 4.25

Printed in sheets of 6 containing two of each stamp.

Medicinal Plants — A195

Designs: 20s, Capparis spinosa. 30s, Aconitum leucostomum. 35s, Hippophae rhamnoides. 52s, Glycyrrhiza glabra.

**2013, Dec. 14　Litho.　Perf. 14¼x14**
444-447　A195　　Set of 4　　9.25　9.25

New Year 2014 (Year of the Horse) — A196

**2014, Feb. 16　Litho.　Perf. 14x14¼**
448　A196　35s multi　　　2.25　2.25

---

2014 Winter Olympics, Sochi, Russia — A197

Designs: 12s, Speed skating. 21s, Cross-country skiing. 52s, Freestyle skiing. 74s, Bobsledding.

**2014, Feb. 22　Litho.　Perf. 14x14¼**
449-452　A197　　Set of 4　　8.25　8.25

Jousting Horsemen A198

**2014, Mar. 22　Litho.　Perf. 14x14¼**
453　A198　30s multi　　　1.90　1.90

Aykol Manas Monument, Bishkek — A199

**2014, Apr. 15　Litho.　Perf. 13¼x14**
**Background Color**
454　A199　20s green gray　　.95　　.95
455　A199　23s blue gray　　1.10　1.10
456　A199　30s lilac　　　1.40　1.40
457　A199　93s lt green　　4.50　4.50
458　A199　100s lt orange　　4.75　4.75
　　Nos. 454-458 (5)　　　12.70 12.70

Children on Sleds — A200

**2014, May 10　Litho.　Perf. 14x14¼**
459　A200　40s multi　　　2.25　2.25

Medicinal Plants — A201

Designs: 20s, Tussilago farfara. 23s, Ferula foetida. 35s, Ziziphora clinopodioides. 40s, Helichrysum maracandicum.

**2014, May 31　Litho.　Perf. 12¼x12**
460-463　A201　　Set of 4　　6.00　6.00

Worldwide Fund for Nature (WWF) — A202

Aegypius monachus: 29s, Head. 35s, In flight. 62s, Adult and chick in nest. 74s, On ground.

**2014, June 21　Litho.　Perf. 14x14¼**
464-467　A202　　Set of 4　　11.00 11.00
467a　　　　Block of 4, #464-467　　11.00 11.00

Miniature Sheet

Soccer Players A203

---

No. 468: a, 29s, Five players. b, 35s, Three players. c, 40s, Two players. d, 52s, Four players.

**2014, July 1　Litho.　Perf. 12x12¼**
468　A203　　Sheet of 4, #a-d　　8.00 8.00

Dooronbek Sadyrbaev (1939-2008), Film Director, and Medal — A204

**2014, July 26　Litho.　Perf. 14x14¼**
469　A204　35s multi　　　1.90　1.90

Carpets — A205

UNESCO emblem and: 35s, Ala-kiyiz. 45s, Shyrdak.

**2014, Aug. 16　Litho.　Perf. 12x12¼**
470-471　A205　　Set of 2　　4.50　4.50

Nos. 470-471 each were printed in sheets of 5 + label.

Communist Leaders — A206

Designs: 20s, Imanaly Aidarbekov (1884-1938). 29s, Abdykerim Sydykov (1889-1938). 35s, Abdykadyr Orozbekov (1889-1938).

**2014, Aug. 31　Litho.　Perf. 14¼x14**
472-474　A206　　Set of 3　　4.00　4.00

Souvenir Sheet

Kyrgyz State Technical University, 60th Anniv. — A207

No. 475: a, 52s, University building and statue. b, 62s, University building, no statue.

**2014, Sept. 18　Litho.　Perf. 12x12¼**
475　A207　　Sheet of 2, #a-b　　6.00　6.00

Souvenir Sheet

International Telecommunication Union Plenipotentiary Conference, Busan, South Korea — A208

**2014, Oct. 11　Litho.　Perf. 12x12¼**
476　A208　30s multi　　　1.90　1.90

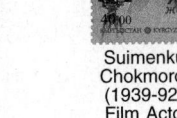

Toktogul
Satylganov
(1864-1933),
Poet
A209

Suimenkul
Chokmorov
(1939-92),
Film Actor
A210

**2014, Nov. 1    Litho.    *Perf. 12¼x12***
477  A209  35s multi                    2.00  2.00
478  A210  40s multi                    2.25  2.25

Kyrgyz Flag
and People
A211

**2014, Dec. 6    Litho.    *Perf. 13x13½***
479  A211  30s multi                    1.90  1.90

**Souvenir Sheet**

Cotton
A212

No. 480: a, 35s, Cotton bolls and leaves. b,
52s, Cotton bolls.

**2014, Dec. 13    Litho.    *Perf. 12x12¼***
480  A212  Sheet of 2, #a-b        4.50  4.50

Endangered
Animals — A213

Designs: 23s, Ursus arctos. 30s,
Otocolobus manul. 40s, Cuon alpinus. 52s,
Lynx lynx linnaeus.

**2014, Dec. 20    Litho.    *Perf. 14x14¼***
481-484  A213  Set of 4                7.75  7.75

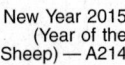

New Year 2015
(Year of the
Sheep) — A214

**2015, Feb. 7    Litho.    *Perf. 12x12¼***
485  A214  40s multi                    2.25  2.25

Sheep
Breeds
A215

No. 486: a, 35s, Aykol. b, 52s, Mountain
merino.

**2015, Feb. 21    Litho.    *Perf. 12x12¼***
486  A215  Pair, #a-b                   4.50  4.50

Famous
People
A216

No. 487: a, 29s, Korgool Dosuev (1890-
1962), singer. b, 35s, Zhumamudin Sheraliev
(1915-94), musician. c, 40s, Myskal Omurka-
nova (1915-76), singer. d, 52s, Alykul
Osmonov (1915-50), poet.

**2015, Mar. 21    Litho.    *Perf. 14¼x14***
487  A216  Horiz. strip of 4, #a-d  7.75  7.75

Dogs and
Cats — A217

Designs: 29s, Ainu. 35s, Persian cat. 62s,
Siamese cat. 74s, Taigan.

**2015, Apr. 4    Litho.    *Perf. 12x12¼***
488-491  A217    Set of 4              9.50  9.50
*491a*    Souvenir sheet of 4, #488-491  9.50  9.50

Victory in World
War II, 70th
Anniv. — A218

70th anniv. emblem and: 30s, Taranchiev
Ismailbek (1923-44), fighter pilot. 40s, War
memorial, soldiers, tanks, map, vert. 52s,
Otorbayev Asanbek (1925-45), soldier.

***Perf. 12x12¼, 12¼x12***
**2015, May 2                            Litho.**
492-494  A218    Set of 3              6.50  6.50
No. 493 was printed in sheets of 2.

**Souvenir Sheet**

Eurasian Economic Union — A219

**2015, May 16    Litho.    *Perf. 13***
495  A219  202s multi                 10.50  10.50

**Miniature Sheet**

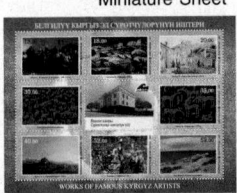

Paintings
A220

No. 496: a, 15s, Poet, by G. Aytiev and D.
Kozhakhmetov. b, 18s, Labyrinth, by D. Nur-
gaziev. c, 20s, Old Street of Osh City, by U.
Akynov. d, 30s, Poppies, by Erbol Dogdurbek.
e, 35s, Mystic Night, by D. Umetov. f, 40s,
Touching Eternity, by S. A. Chuykov. g, 52s,
Holiday, by S. Chokmorov. h, 59s, South
Beach, by S. Torobekov.

**2015, July 18    Litho.    *Perf. 12x12¼***
496  A220    Sheet of 8, #a-h, +
             central label            13.50  13.50

Scenes From the
Epic of
Manas — A221

No. 497 — Various scenes: a, 20s. b, 35s. c,
74s.

**2015, Aug. 1    Litho.    *Perf. 12x12¼***
497  A221    Vert. strip of 3, #a-c    6.75  6.75

Zhusup
Balasagun, 10th
Cent. Poet, and
Kyrgyzstan
National
University — A222

**2015, Aug. 22    Litho.    *Perf. 14x14¼***
498  A222  52s multi                    2.75  2.75

Cars of the 21st
Century — A223

Designs: 33s, Terrafugia TF-X concept flying car. 36s, Mercedes-Benz F015 concept
car. 39s, Tesla Model S. 83s, Toyota Mirai.

**2015, Oct. 10    Litho.    *Perf. 12x12¼***
499-502  A223    Set of 4              8.50  8.50
*502a*    Sheet of 8, 2 each #499-
          502, + label                17.00  17.00
Nos. 499-502 were each printed in sheets of
5 + label.

Worldwide Fund
for Nature
(WWF) — A224

Whooper swans: 36s, Three in flight. 39s,
Adult and chicks in water. 48s, Adult in water.
117s, Adult extending wings.

**2015, Nov. 28    Litho.    *Perf. 12***
503-506  A224    Set of 4             10.00  10.00
*506a*    Souvenir sheet of 8, 2 each
          #503-506                    20.00  20.00

**Souvenir Sheet**

2015 Asian Juniors Chess
Championship, Kyrgyzstan — A225

No. 507 — Various chess pieces on board
with background colors of: a, 48s, Light green
and light blue. b, 55s, Pink and light orange.

**2015, Nov. 28    Litho.    *Perf. 12***
507  A225    Sheet of 2, #a-b          4.25  4.25

New Year 2016
(Year of the
Monkey) — A226

**2016, Feb. 6    Litho.    *Perf. 12x12¼***
508  A226  76s multi                    3.25  3.25

Flowers — A227

Designs: 36s, Tulipa kolpakovskiana. 39s,
Tulip Porto. 48s, Orchid Rio Bamba. 55s, Cattleya Queen Sirikhit Diamond Crown orchid.

**2016, Feb. 13    Litho.    *Perf. 12¼x12***
509-512  A227    Set of 4              7.75  7.75
*512a*    Souvenir sheet of 4, #509-
          512                          7.75  7.75

Regional
Communications
Commonwealth, 25th
Anniv. — A228

**2016, Mar. 12    Litho.    *Perf. 14¼x14***
513  A228  55s multi                    2.25  2.25

Writers — A229

Designs: 48s, Zhakypbek Boogachy (1866-
1935). 83s, Nasirdin Baytemirov (1916-96).

**2016, Mar. 26    Litho.    *Perf. 14¼x14***
514-515  A229    Set of 2              5.75  5.75

Commonwealth of
Independent States,
25th Anniv. — A230

**2016, Apr. 30    Litho.    *Perf. 14¼x14***
516  A230  83s multi                    4.00  4.00

**Souvenir Sheet**

Manned
Space
Flights,
55th
Anniv.
A231

No. 517: a, 22s, Rocket launch. b, 117s,
Docked spacecraft, spacewalker.

**2016, May 14    Litho.    *Perf. 12***
517  A231    Sheet of 2, #a-b          6.25  6.25

**Souvenir Sheet**

Bishkek Trolleybus Management, 65th
Anniv. — A232

No. 518 — Trolleybuses: a, 39s, BMZ-
5298.01 (56x20mm). b, 55s, MTB-82
(40x29mm). c, 83s, MTB-82D (30x27mm).

***Perf. 13 At Bottom (39s), 12 (55s),
13½x13 (83s)***
**2016, June 25                          Litho.**
518  A232    Sheet of 3, #a-c          8.00  8.00

**Souvenir Sheet**

Independence, 25th Anniv. — A233

**2016, July 23    Litho.    *Perf. 12¼x12***
519  A233  100s multi                   4.75  4.75

Taylak (1796-1838),
Warrior — A234

**2016, July 30   Litho.   Perf. 12¼x12**
520 A234 55s multi           2.60 2.60

2016 Summer
Olympics, Rio de
Janeiro — A235

Designs: 22s, Taekwondo. 31s, Soccer.
55s, Golf. 117s, Wrestling.

**2016, Aug. 4   Litho.   Perf. 12x12¼**
521-524 A235   Set of 4      10.50 10.50

Souvenir Sheet

2016 World Nomad Games, Cholpon-
Ata — A236

**2016, Sept. 3   Litho.   Perf. 13**
525 A236 117s multi          5.25 5.25

Traditional
Cuisine — A237

**2016, Sept. 17   Litho.   Perf. 12x12¼**
526 A237 76s multi           3.50 3.50

Arachnids — A238

Designs: 20s, Lycosa singoriensis. 22s,
Eresus collari. 31s, Solifugae. 117s,
Mesobuthus eupeus.

**2016, Oct. 5   Litho.   Perf. 12x12¼**
527-530 A238   Set of 4       8.50 8.50
530a       Souvenir sheet of 4, #527-
           530                8.50 8.50

Paintings by
Vladimir V.
Obraztsov
(1891-1934)
A239

No. 531: a, Return from the Red Army,
1930. b, Conspiracy, 1932.
No. 532: a, Near Globe, 1930. b, On the
Way to China, 1932.
39s, The Guerrillas, 1932.

**2016, Nov. 11   Litho.   Perf. 13x13½**
531 A239   Vert. pair         2.25 2.25
a.     20s multi               .85   .85
b.     31s multi              1.40  1.40
532 A239   Vert. pair         6.25 6.25
a.     22s multi              1.00  1.00
b.     117s multi             5.25  5.25
533 A239 39s multi            1.75  1.75
       Nos. 531-533 (3)      10.25 10.25

Yurts — A240

Designs: 22s, Guest yurt. 117s, Yurt, family
and horse.

**2016, Nov. 26   Litho.   Perf. 12x12¼**
534-535 A240   Set of 2       6.00 6.00

Heroism of
Panfilov Division's
28 Guardsmen,
75th
Anniv. — A241

**2016, Dec. 10   Litho.   Perf. 12x12¼**
536 A241 83s multi           4.00 4.00

No. 536 was printed in sheets of 6 + 2
labels.

New Year 2017
(Year of the
Rooster) — A242

**2017, Jan. 25   Litho.   Perf. 12x12¼**
537 A242 76s multi           3.50 3.50

Worldwide Fund
for Nature
(WWF) — A243

Pelecanus crispus: 22s, One bird in flight.
31s, Two birds in flight. 39s, One bird on water.
117s, Three birds on water.

**2017, Feb. 25   Litho.   Perf. 12x12¼**
538-541 A243   Set of 4       9.75 9.75
541a       Souvenir sheet of 8, 2
           each #538-541      19.50 19.50

Tulipa
Greigii — A244

Ciconia
Nigra — A245

**2017, Mar. 25   Litho.   Perf. 12x12¼**
542 A244 39s multi           1.90 1.90
543 A245 48s multi           2.25 2.25
a.     Souvenir sheet of 4, 2 each
       #542-543              8.50 8.50

National Horse
Games — A246

**2017, Apr. 15   Litho.   Perf. 12x12¼**
544 A246 83s multi           4.00 4.00

Protected Natural
Areas — A247

No. 545 — UNESCO emblem and: a, Sary-
Chelek State Natural Park. b, Besh-Aral State
Natural Park. c, Padysha-Ata State Natural
Park.

**2017, May 6   Litho.   Perf. 12x12¼**
545       Vert. strip of 3    7.25 7.25
a.     A247 39s multi        2.00 2.00
b.     A247 48s multi        2.40 2.40
c.     A247 55s multi        2.75 2.75
Printed in sheets containing two each Nos.
545a-545c.

Famous
People — A248

Designs: 39s, Saira Kiyizbaeva (1917-88),
opera singer. 55s, Sagymbai Orozbakov
(1867-1930), narrator of epic poem, "Manas."

**2017, May 20   Litho.   Perf. 12¼x12**
546-547 A248   Set of 2       4.50 4.50

Souvenir Sheet

Abdylas Maldybaev National Opera
and Ballet Theater, 75th
Anniv. — A249

No. 548: a, 39s, Bulat Minzhikiev (1940-97),
opera singer. b, 48s, Painting of dancers on
theater ceiling. c, 55s, Dmitri Shostakovich
(1906-75), composer.

**2017, June 24   Litho.   Perf. 12¼x12**
548 A249   Sheet of 3, #a-c   7.00 7.00

Baitik Kanaev (1820-
86), Leader of Solto
People — A250

**2017, July 8   Litho.   Perf. 12¼x12**
549 A250 76s multi           4.00 4.00

Year of Morality,
Education and
Culture — A251

**2017, Aug. 12   Litho.   Perf. 12x12¼**
550 A251 76s multi           4.00 4.00

Souvenir Sheet

International Snow Leopard and
Ecosystem Forum, Bishkek — A252

No. 551: a, 39s, Snow leopard in grass. b,
117s, Snow leopard on rocks.

**2017, Aug. 15   Litho.   Perf. 12x12¼**
551 A252   Sheet of 2, #a-b   6.50 6.50

Heroes of the
Kyrgyz
Republic — A253

Medal and: 35s, Ishak Razzakov (1910-79),
politician. 55s, Turdakun Usubaliev (1919-
2015), politician.

**2017, Oct. 14   Litho.   Perf. 12x12¼**
552-553 A253   Set of 2       4.75 4.75

Souvenir Sheet

Emblem of Collective Security Treaty
Organization and Flags of Member
Countries — A254

**2017, Oct. 21   Litho.   Perf. 12x12¼**
554 A254 193s multi          9.75 9.75

Collective Security Treaty, 125th anniv., Collective Security Treaty Organization, 15th
anniv.

Endangered
Animals — A255

Designs: 36s, Lynx lynx. 39s, Marmota
menzbieri. 48s, Cervus elaphus asiaticus.
55s, Martes foina.

**2017, Nov. 4   Litho.   Perf. 12¼x12**
555-558 A255   Set of 4       9.00 9.00
558a       Souvenir sheet of 4, #555-
           558                9.00 9.00

October
Revolution,
Cent. — A256

**2017, Nov. 18   Litho.   Perf. 12x12¼**
559 A256 83s multi           4.50 4.50

Miniature Sheet

Kyrgyz
Epic, Er
Toshtuk
A257

No. 560: a, 22s, Toshtuk. b, 39s, Toshtuk on
horse. c, 48s, Multi-headed monster and
horse's head. d, 55s, Toshtuk, woman and
camel.

**2017, Dec. 2   Litho.   Perf. 12**
560 A257   Sheet of 4, #a-d   8.25 8.25

Rice Varieties — A258

Designs: 22s, Ak Turpak. 83s, Devzira.

**2017, Dec. 29   Litho.   Perf. 12**
561-562 A258   Set of 2       5.50 5.50
562a       Souvenir sheet of 2, #561-
           562                5.50 5.50

Containers and
RCC
Emblem — A259

**2017, Dec. 30   Litho.   Perf. 12**
563 A259 76s multi           3.75 3.75

Miniature Sheet

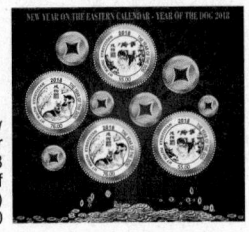

New Year 2018 (Year of the Dog) A260

No. 564: a, 55s, One dog. b, 76s, Two dogs.

**2018, Jan. 22    Litho.    Perf.**
564 A260    Sheet of 4, 2 each
#a-b    13.00 13.00

2018 Winter Olympics, Pyeongchang, South Korea — A261

Designs: 22s, Ski jumping. 31s, Figure skating. 48s, Ice hockey. 117s, Snowboarding.

**2018, Feb. 22    Litho.    Perf. 12**
565-568 A261    Set of 4    11.00 11.00
568a    Souvenir sheet of 4, #565-568    11.00 11.00

Belt Wrestling — A262

**2018, Mar. 17    Litho.    Perf. 12**
569 A262 76s multi    4.00 4.00

Souvenir Sheet

Som and Tyiyn Currencies, 25th Anniv. — A263

**2018, Apr. 5    Litho.    Perf. 13½x13¼**
570 A263 117s multi    6.25 6.25

2018 World Cup Soccer Championships, Russia — A264

Designs: 20s, Two soccer players. 27s, Two soccer players, diff. 48s, Two soccer players, diff. 102s, Three soccer players.

**2018, May 3    Litho.    Perf. 12**
571-574 A264    Set of 4    10.00 10.00
574a    Souvenir sheet of 4, #571-574    10.00 10.00

Jusup Mamay (1918-2014), Narrator of Epic "Manas" — A265

**2018, June 14    Litho.    Perf. 12**
575 A265 76s multi    3.75 3.75

Beetles — A266

Designs: 22s, Scarabaeidae sensu lato. 31s, Lucanus cervus. 83s, Oryctes nasicornis. 117s, Cetonia aurata.

**2018, July 28    Litho.    Perf. 14x14¼**
576-579 A266    Set of 4    13.00 13.00
579a    Souvenir sheet of 4, #576-579    13.00 13.00

Souvenir Sheet

2018 International Telecommunications Union Plenipotentiary Conference, Dubai — A267

**2018, Aug. 25    Litho.    Perf. 13x13¼**
580 A267 117s multi    6.00 6.00

Surma-Tash State Nature Reserve — A268

**2018, Sept. 15    Litho.    Perf. 14x14¼**
581 A268 76s multi    4.25 4.25

Roses — A269

Designs: 20s, Indigoletta climbing hybrid tea roses. 48s, Nicole roses. 55s, Floribunda roses. 83s, Damask roses.

**2018, Oct. 13    Litho.    Perf. 14¼x14**
582-585 A269    Set of 4    10.00 10.00
585a    Souvenir sheet of 4, #582-585    10.00 10.00

Earth Features — A270

Designs: 20s, Arslanbob Waterfall. 26s, Kokomeren River. 76s, Lake Merzbacher. 98s, Ala-Archa Pass.

**2018, Nov. 17    Litho.    Perf. 14x14¼**
586-589 A270    Set of 4    11.00 11.00
589a    Souvenir sheet of 4, #586-589    11.00 11.00

Souvenir Sheet

Kumtor Gold Mine A271

**2018, Dec. 8    Litho.    Perf. 13**
590 A271 259s multi    11.50 11.50

Souvenir Sheet

Rukh Ordo Cultural Center, Cholpon Ata, 90th Anniv. A272

**2018, Dec. 10    Litho.    Perf. 12**
591 A272 130s multi    7.00 7.00

Miniature Sheet

New Year 2019 (Year of the Pig) A273

No. 592: a, 46s, Pig and piglets. b, 98s, Pig.

**2019, Jan. 22    Litho.    Perf.**
592 A273    Sheet of 4, 2 each
#a-b    11.00 11.00

2019 Asian Cup Soccer Tournament, United Arab Emirates — A274

Various soccer players: 20s, 26s, 176s.

**2019, Feb. 18    Litho.    Perf. 14¼x14**
593-595 A274    Set of 3    7.25 7.25
595a    Sheet of 3, #593-595, + 3 labels    7.25 7.25

Dragonflies — A275

Designs: 20s, Libellula quadrimaculata. 36s, Sympycna fusca. 130s, Sonjagaster coronatus.

**2019, Apr. 4    Litho.    Perf. 14¼x14**
596-598 A275    Set of 3    6.00 6.00
598a    Sheet of 3, #596-598    6.00 6.00

Souvenir Sheet

Yuri Gagarin (1934-68), First Man in Space — A276

**2019, May 4    Litho.    Perf. 13x13½**
599 A276 130s multi    4.25 4.25

Royal Philatelic Society, 150th Anniv. A277

Designs: 76s, Agroprom Building, Bishkek. 98s, Tower Bridge, London.

**2019, May 25    Litho.    Perf. 13x12¾**
600-601 A277    Set of 2    5.75 5.75
Nos. 600-601 were each printed in sheets of 5 + label.

China 2019 World Stamp Exhibition, Wuhan, People's Republic of China — A278

No. 602: a, One tiger. b, Two tigers.

**2019, June 11    Litho.    Perf. 14xx14¼**
602    Horiz. pair + central label    5.75 5.75
a.    A278 20s multi    .75 .75
b.    A278 130s multi    5.00 5.00

Shanghai Cooperation Organization Summit, Bishkek — A279

**2019, July 6    Litho.    Perf. 13**
603 A279 76s multi    2.60 2.60
No. 603 was printed in sheets of 5 + label.

Eurasian Economic Union, 5th Anniv. — A280

**2019, Aug. 9    Litho.    Perf. 13**
604 A280 76s multi    2.60 2.60
No. 604 was printed in sheets of 5 + label.

Famous People — A281

Designs: 26s, Darkul Kuyukova (1919-97), actress. 46s, Tattybübü Tursunbayeva (1944-81), actress. 76s, Alymkul Usenbaev (1894-1963), musician.

**2019, Aug. 20    Litho.    Perf. 14¼x14**
605-607 A281    Set of 3    5.25 5.25
Nos. 605-607 were each printed in sheets of 5 + label.

Kurmanjan Datka History and Ethnographic Museum, Gulcha — A282

**2019, Sept. 28    Litho.    Perf. 14x14¼**
608 A282 98s multi    3.50 3.50

Poppies — A283

Designs: 46s, Papaver orientale. 76s, Papaver rhoeas. 98s, Papaver refracta.

**2019, Oct. 12    Litho.    Perf. 12**
609-611 A283    Set of 3    7.25 7.25
611a    Sheet of 3, #609-611    7.25 7.25

Toguz Korgul Game — A284

**2019, Oct. 18    Litho.    Perf. 14x14¼**
612 A284 76s multi    2.75 2.75
No. 612 was printed in sheets of 5 + label.

Portrait of Aleksey I.
Shevtsov, by Ilya E.
Repin (1844-
1930) — A285

**2019, Oct. 26　Litho.　Perf. 14¼x14**
613　A285　98s multi　　　　3.50　3.50
No. 613 was printed in sheets of 5 + label.

Flora — A286

Designs: 36s, Abies semenovii. 76s, Snow lotus. 98s, Tulipa zenaidae.

**2019, Nov. 23　Litho.　Perf. 14¼x14**
614-616　A286　Set of 3　　　7.25　7.25

Ducks — A287

Various ducks: 26s, 98s, 130s.

**2019, Nov. 30　Litho.　Perf. 12**
617-619　A287　Set of 3　　　8.75　8.75
619a　　　Sheet of 3, #617-619　8.75　8.75

Miniature Sheet

International Civil Aviation
Organization, 75th Anniv. — A288

No. 620 — Various airplanes at: a, 20s, Manas Airport. b, 26s, Osh Airport. c, 36s, Issyl-Kul Airport. d, 46s, Karakol Airport. e, 98s, Batken Airport.

**2019, Dec. 13　Litho.　Perf. 14x14¼**
620　A288　Sheet of 5, #a-e, +
　　　　　label　　　　　　7.75　7.75

Mohandas K. Gandhi
(1869-1948), Indian
Nationalist
Leader — A289

**2019, Dec. 14　Litho.　Perf. 14¼x14**
621　A289　98s multi　　　　3.75　3.75
No. 621 was printed in sheets of 5 + label.

Minerals — A290

Designs: 36s, Amethyst. 46s, Zircon. 98s, Tourmaline.

**2019, Dec. 21　Litho.　Perf. 14¼x14**
622-624　A290　Set of 3　　　6.50　6.50

---

Miniature Sheet

New
Year
2020
(Year of
the Rat)
A291

No. 625: a, 46s, Two rats. b, 98s, One rat.

**2020, Feb. 20　Litho.　Perf.**
625　A291　Sheet of 4, 2 each
　　　　　#625a-625b　　　8.25　8.25

Miniature Sheet

Pomegranates — A292

No. 626: a, 20s, Pomegranate flowers. b, 26s, Pomegranates on tree. c, 36s, Pomegranate juice. d, 46s, Two unopened and one split pomegranates. e, 76s, Split pomegranates. f, 98s, Pomegranate shrub.

**2020, Mar. 23　Litho.　Perf. 14x14¼**
626　A292　Sheet of 6, #a-f　7.00　7.00

Melis Ubukeev
(1935-96), Film
Director — A293

**2020, Mar. 28　Litho.　Perf. 14x14¼**
627　A293　98s multi　　　　2.25　2.25

International Year
of Plant
Health — A294

**2020, Apr. 4　Litho.　Perf. 14x14¼**
628　A294　98s multi　　　　2.50　2.50

United Nations,
75th
Anniv. — A295

**2020, Apr. 11　Litho.　Perf. 14x14¼**
629　A295　98s multi　　　　2.25　2.25

Miniature Sheet

Victory in
World
War II,
75th
Anniv.
A296

No. 630 — War heroes: a, 20s, Talgat Yakubekovich Begeldinov (1922-2014). b, 26s, Evdokia Borisovna Pasko (1919-2017). c, 36s, Kalyynur Usenbekovich Usenbekov (1921-2003). d, 46s, Nasyr Baitursynov (1918-95). e, 76s, Kirill Ivanovich Bukhantsev (1919-84).

**2020, July 4　Litho.　Perf. 14x14¼**
630　A296　Sheet of 5, #a-e, +
　　　　　label　　　　　　4.75　4.75

---

Dogs — A297

Designs: 75s, Taigan. 98s, Dobot.

**2020, July 11　Litho.　Perf. 14x14¼**
631-632　A297　Set of 2　　　4.00　4.00
632a　　　Souvenir sheet of 2, #631-
　　　　　632　　　　　　4.00　4.00

Plercotus
Austriacus
A298

Designs. 36s, Bat in flight. 76s, Close-up of head. 98s, Bat in cave.

**2020, Aug. 14　Litho.　Perf. 14x14¼**
633-635　A298　Set of 3　　　4.75　4.75

Kuliypa Konduchalova (1920-2013),
Politician, and Hero of Kyrgyzstan
Medal — A299

**2020, Aug. 21　Litho.　Perf. 14x14¼**
636　A299　76s multi　　　　1.75　1.75

Rescue
Services — A300

Designs. 31s, Fire fighters. 37s, Police. 143s, Emergency medical service.

**2020, Oct. 2　Litho.　Perf. 14x14¼**
637-639　A300　Set of 3　　　4.75　4.75
639a　　　Souvenir sheet of 3, #637-
　　　　　639, + 3 labels　　4.75　4.75
Nos. 637-639 were each printed in sheets of 5 + label.

Man Playing
Ordo — A301

**2020, Oct. 9　Litho.　Perf. 14x14¼**
640　A301　79s multi　　　　1.90　1.90

Medicinal
Plants — A302

Designs. 33s, Rosa. 39s, Crataegus. 143s, Berberis.

**2020, Nov. 27　Litho.　Perf. 14¼x14**
641-643　A302　Set of 3　　　5.00　5.00

Fish — A303

Designs. 56s, Gymnodiptychus dybowskii. 66s, Leuciscus bergi Kaschkarov. 118s, Salmo ischshan.

**2020, Dec. 11　Litho.　Perf. 14x14¼**
644-646　A303　Set of 3　　　5.50　5.50
646a　　　Souvenir sheet of 3, #644-
　　　　　646　　　　　　5.50　5.50

---

Spiders — A304

Designs. 56s, Dictynomorpha strandi. 66s, Zygiella kirgisica bakhvalov. 118s, Clubiona rybini.

**2020, Dec. 18　Litho.　Perf. 14x14¼**
647-649　A304　Set of 3　　　5.50　5.50
649a　　　Souvenir sheet of 3, #647-
　　　　　649　　　　　　5.50　5.50

Miniature Sheet

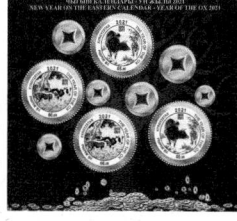

New
Year
2021
(Year of
the Ox)
A305

No. 650: a, 55s, Brown ox and calf. b, 66s, Black-and-white cow and calf.

**2021, Feb. 5　Litho.　Perf.**
650　A305　Sheet of 4, 2 each
　　　　　#650a-650b　　　5.50　5.50

Meles
Leucurus — A306

Various depictions of badger on log. 55s, 66s, 118s.

**2021, Apr. 2　Litho.　Perf. 14x14¼**
651-653　A306　Set of 3　　　5.50　5.50
653a　　　Souvenir sheet of 3, #651-
　　　　　653　　　　　　5.50　5.50

Souvenir Sheet

Mantis
Religiosa
A307

**2021, Apr. 9　Litho.　Perf. 13x13½**
654　A307　140s multi　　　3.25　3.25

Miniature Sheet

Quinces
A308

No. 655: a, 18s, Bee pollinating quince blosssom. b, 22s, Quinces on tree. c, 31s, Whole and cut quinces. d, 37s, Quinces and jar of quince preserves. e, 55s, Quince tree. f, 66s, Quinces in basket.

**2021, Apr. 16　Litho.　Perf. 12x12¼**
655　A308　Sheet of 6, #a-f　5.75　5.75

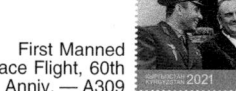

First Manned
Space Flight, 60th
Anniv. — A309

Designs: 31s, Yuri Gagarin (1934-68), first man in space, and Sergei Korolev (1907-66), rocket engineer. 118s, Vostok rocket launch, Valentina Tereshkova, first woman in space.

2021, May 7      Litho.      Perf. 14
656-657  A309   Set of 2                3.75  3.75
657a             Souvenir sheet of 2, #656-
                 657                    3.75  3.75

Regional Communications Commonwealth, 30th Anniv. — A310

2021, June 11   Litho.   Perf. 14x14¼
658  A310  79s multi              1.90  1.90
No. 658 was printed in sheets of 5 + label.

Commonwealth of Independent States, 30th Anniv. — A311

2021, June 25   Litho.   Perf. 14¼x14
659  A311  79s multi              1.90  1.90

2020 Summer Olympics, Tokyo — A312

Designs: 37s, Swimming. 66s, Fencing. 140s, Pole vault.

2021, July 16   Litho.   Perf. 14¼x14
660-662  A312   Set of 3                5.50  5.50
662a             Souvenir sheet of 3, #660-
                 662                    5.50  5.50

The 2020 Summer Olympics were postponed until 2021 because of the COVID-19 pandemic.

Independence, 30th Anniv. — A313

2021, Aug. 30   Litho.   Perf. 14¼x14
663  A313  66s multi              1.50  1.50

Souvenir Sheet

Kyrgyz With a Golden Eagle, Sculpture by Evgeny Lanceray (1848-86) — A314

2021, Sept. 10   Litho.      Perf. 13
664  A314  140s multi             3.25  3.25

Tulipa Sylvestris Var. Turkestanica Regel — A315

Various depictions of tulip with denominations of 31s, 37s, and 140s.

2021, Sept. 17   Litho.   Perf. 14¼x14
665-667  A315   Set of 3                4.75  4.75
667a             Souvenir sheet of 3, #665-
                 667                    4.75  4.75

Suyunbay Eraliev (1921-2016), Poet — A316

2021, Oct. 15   Litho.   Perf. 12x12¼
668  A316  79s multi              1.90  1.90

Merops Apiaster — A317

Various depictions of European bee-eater with denominations of 55s, 66s, and 118s.

2021, Oct. 22   Litho.   Perf. 14¼x14
669-671  A317   Set of 3                5.50  5.50
671a             Souvenir sheet of 3, #669-
                 671                    5.50  5.50

Souvenir Sheet

Horse With Traditional Harness and Saddle — A318

2021, Oct. 29   Litho.      Perf. 13
672  A318  140s multi             3.25  3.25

Eremias Nikolskii — A319

Various depictions of Kyrgyz racerunner with denominations of 37s, 55s, and 140s.

2021, Dec. 3   Litho.      Perf. 12
673-675  A319   Set of 3                5.25  5.25
675a             Souvenir sheet of 3, #673-
                 675                    5.25  5.25

Trollius Lilacinus — A320

Various depictions of Trollius lilacinus with denominations of 31s, 66s, and 118s.

2021, Dec. 10   Litho.      Perf. 12
676-678  A320   Set of 3                5.00  5.00
678a             Souvenir sheet of 3, #676-
                 678                    5.00  5.00

Souvenir Sheet

Satymkul Dzhumanazarov (1951-2007), Bronze Medalist in Marathon at 1980 Summer Olympics — A321

2021, Dec. 17   Litho.   Perf. 13x13½
679  A321  140s multi             3.25  3.25

Diplomatic Relations Between Kyrgyzstan and Poland, 30th Anniv. — A322

Diplomatic Relations Between Kyrgyzstan and Denmark, 30th Anniv. — A323

Diplomatic Relations Between Kyrgyzstan and Sweden, 30th Anniv. — A324

Diplomatic Relations Between Kyrgyzstan and Norway, 30th Anniv. — A325

Diplomatic Relations Between Kyrgyzstan and Vatican City, 30th Anniv. — A326

2022, Apr. 22   Litho.      Perf. 12
680  A322  66s multi              1.50  1.50
681  A323  66s multi              1.50  1.50
682  A324  66s multi              1.50  1.50
683  A325  66s multi              1.50  1.50
684  A326  66s multi              1.50  1.50
           Nos. 680-684 (5)       7.50  7.50

Kyrgyzstan's Admittance Into United Nations, 30th Anniv. — A327

2022, Apr. 29   Litho.      Perf. 12
685  A327  76s multi              1.75  1.75

New Year 2022 (Year of the Tiger) — A328

2022, May 17   Litho.      Perf. 12
686  A328  79s multi              1.90  1.90

2022 Winter Olympics, Beijing — A329

Designs: 58s, Ski jumping. 69s, Figure skating. 118s, Luge.

2022, May 17   Litho.      Perf. 12
687-689  A329   Set of 3                5.75  5.75

Pistachio Nuts — A330

Designs: 58s, Pistachio tree and nuts. 69s, Nuts on tree branch, harvested nut. 118s, Shelled and unshelled nuts.

2022, May 31   Litho.      Perf. 12
690-692  A330   Set of 3                5.75  5.75

Diplomatic Relations Between Kyrgyzstan and Germany, 30th Anniv. — A331

2022, June 10   Litho.      Perf. 12
693  A331  66s multi              1.50  1.50

Abdulmanap Magomedovich Nurmagomedov (1962-2020), Judoka and Combat Sports Coach — A332

2022, Aug. 10   Litho.      Perf. 12
694  A332  65s multi              1.50  1.50

Miniature Sheet

2022 MonacoPhil Philatelic Exhibition — A333

No. 695 — Silhouette of: a, 65s, Napoleon Bonaparte (1769-1821), Emperor of France. b, 75s, Elephants. c, 105s, Soldiers on horseback. d, 159s, Red Fort, Delhi, India.

2022, Aug. 19   Litho.      Perf. 12
695  A333  Sheet of 4, #a-d      10.00 10.00

Eurasian Economic Commission, 10th Anniv. — A334

2022, Aug. 26   Litho.      Perf. 12
696  A334  65s multi              1.60  1.60

Dair A. Asanov (1922-2009), Major General in Army of the Soviet Union — A335

2022, Oct. 21   Litho.      Perf. 12
697  A335  65s multi              1.50  1.50

Goldfish — A336

Inscriptions: 65s, Carassius auratus. 75s, Comet Carassius auratus. 106s, Carassius gibelio forma auratus.

2022, Oct. 28   Litho.      Perf. 12
698-700  A336   Set of 3                5.75  5.75

Traditional Kyrgyz Costumes — A337

Designs: 65s, Woman. 75s, Woman and child. 159s, Man and woman.

2022, Nov. 4   Litho.      Perf. 12
701-703  A337   Set of 3                7.00  7.00

Bayali Isakeev (1897-1938), Chairman of the Council of People's Commissars of the Kyrgyz Soviet Socialist Republic — A338

**2022, Nov. 16    Litho.    Perf. 12**
704  A338  65s multi    1.50  1.50

---

### SEMI-POSTAL STAMPS

Natl. Epic Poem, Manas, Millennium — SP1

SP2

Designs: 10t+5t, Woman with bird in hand. 20t+10t, Bird on man's wrist. No. B3, Women watching as baby held up. No. B4, Woman with spear, leading horse. 40t+15t, Warrior looking at dead dragon. No. B6, Warrior on horse holding axe. No. B7, Man wearing tall hat on horseback. No. B8, Warrior with sword on horseback.
No. B9, Man in red cradling fallen warrior. No. B10, Man in black seated in desert, tornado.

**Perf. 12, Imperf**
**1995, June 16    Litho.**
B1   SP1  10t +5t grnsh bl & ol brn    .40  .40
B2   SP1  20t +10t grnsh bl & ol brn    .40  .40
B3   SP1  30t +10t grnsh bl & ol brn    .40  .40
B4   SP1  30t +10t grnsh bl & ol brn    .40  .40
B5   SP1  40t +15t grnsh bl & ol brn    .40  .40
B6   SP1  50t +15t grnsh bl & ol brn    .40  .40
B7   SP1  50t +15t grnsh bl & ol brn    .40  .40
B8   SP1  50t +15t grnsh bl & ol brn    .40  .40
a.    Sheet of 8, #B1-B8 + label    4.00  4.00
**Souvenir Sheets**
B9   SP2  2s +50t multi    2.00  2.00
B10  SP2  2s +50t multi    2.00  2.00

1996 Summer Olympic Games, Atlanta — SP3

Designs: 100t+20t, Equestrian events. 140t+30t, Boxing. 150t+30t, Archery. 300t+50t, Judo, hot air balloon, sailing, water skiing.

**1996, July 10    Litho.    Perf. 12½x12**
B11  SP3  100t +20t multi    .30  .30
B12  SP3  140t +30t multi    .60  .60
B13  SP3  150t +30t multi    .80  .80
B14  SP3  300t +50t multi    1.25  1.25
     Nos. B11-B14 (4)    2.95  2.95

---

Town of Osh, 3000th Anniv. SP4

No. B15: a, Globe, mountains, mosque, "Osh" and "3000." b, Mosque with three arches, mountains (green panel at UR). c, Solomon's Throne (mosque on mountain). d, Mausoleum of Asaf ibn Burkiya (denomination at LL).
Illustration reduced.

**2000, Feb. 19    Litho.    Perf. 13½**
B15  SP4  6s +25t Sheet of 4, #a-d    3.50  3.50
     Exists imperf. Value $5.

Kurmanzhan Datka, 190th Anniv. of Birth — SP5

**2001, Oct. 13    Litho.    Perf. 14x14¼**
B16  SP5  10s +70t ind & gray    1.60  1.60

## KYRGYZ EXPRESS POST

On May 21, 2013, Kyrgyz Express Post was declared a designated postal operator by the Universal Postal Union, marking the first time the UPU has had two designated postal operators in one country. Kyrgyz Express Post company was created in March 2012 and granted a license from the Kyrgyzstan Ministry of Transport and Communications on Dec. 7, 2012 to offer all types of postal services to customers and to compete with the state corporation Kyrgyz Pochtasy, which has post offices across the country. At the time Kyrgyz Express Post issued its first stamps, it had two post offices and a philatelic bureau in Bishkek.

A1

Methods of Postal Conveyance — A2

Designs: 500s, Jet airplane.
No. 2: a, 25s, Post rider. b, 50s, Locomotive. c, 250s, Mail van.
700s, Dove carrying letter, Universal Postal Union emblem.

**2014, Nov. 18    Litho.    Perf. 14x14½**
1   A1  500s multi    15.00  15.00
2   A1  Sheet of 4, #1, 2a-2c    24.00  24.00
**Souvenir Sheet of 1 + 8 Labels**
**Perf. 13 Syncopated**
3   A2  700s multi    20.00  20.00
     No. 1 was printed in panes of 4.

---

Wild Animals — A3

Designs: 250s, Panthera uncia.
No. 5: a, 15s, Falco cherrug. b, 25s, Bos grunniens. c, 125s, Capra sibirica alaiana.

**2014, Nov. 19    Litho.    Perf. 14x14¾**
4   A3  250s multi    7.50  7.50
5   A3  Sheet of 4, #4 & 5a-5c    15.00  15.00
     No. 4 was printed in sheets of 4.

Falconry A4

Designs: No. 6, 75s, Falcon in flight, denomination at LR. No. 7, 75s, Falcon in flight, denomination at LL. No. 8, 75s, Falcon approaching rabbit.

**Perf. 13 Syncopated**
**2015, May 14    Litho.**
6-8   A4  Set of 3    8.00  8.00
8a    Souvenir sheet of 3, #6-8    8.00  8.00

Souvenir Sheet

First Walks in Space, 50th Anniv. A5

Spacewalker: a, 50s, Alexei Leonov. b, 150s, Edward White.

**2015, July 2    Litho.    Perf.**
9   A5  Sheet of 2, #a-b    6.75  6.75

Souvenir Sheet

Penny Black, 175th Anniv. A6

**2015, July 2    Litho.    Perf. 13¼x13**
10   A6  250s multi    8.25  8.25

Famous Men A7

Designs: 50s, Dante Alighieri (1265-1321), writer. 100s, Pyotr Ilyich Tchaikovsky (1840-93), composer.

**Perf. 13 Syncopated**
**2015, Sept. 2    Litho.**
11-12   A7  Set of 2    5.00  5.00

International Years — A8

Designs: 50s, Intl. Year of Soils. 75s, Intl. Year of Light.

**Perf. 13 Syncopated**
**2015, Sept. 2    Litho.**
13-14   A8  Set of 2    4.25  4.25
14a     Vert. pair, #13-14    4.25  4.25

Nos. 13-14 were each printed in sheets of 8. No. 14a was printed in sheets containing 4 pairs.

---

Souvenir Sheet

Horses A9

No. 15: a, Chestnut horse. b, Chestnut horse with white blaze.

**2015, Dec. 21    Litho.    Perf. 14¾x14**
15   A9  100s Sheet of 2, #a-b    5.50  5.50

Minerals — A10

Designs: No. 16, 50s, Aragonite. No. 17, 50s, Realgar. 75s, Stibnite. 100s, Kyanite.

**2016, Jan. 6    Litho.    Perf. 14x14¾**
16-19   A10  Set of 4    8.00  8.00
19a     Souvenir sheet of 4, #16-19    8.00  8.00

A11

Yeti — A12

**Litho. With Foil Application**
**Serpentine Die Cut 12¾**
**2016, May 19    Self-Adhesive**
**Coil Stamps**
20   A11  (150s) multi    4.50  4.50
21   A12  (250s) multi    7.50  7.50
a.    Booklet pane of 4, 2 each #20-21    24.00  —
     Complete booklet, #21a    24.00

Souvenir Sheets

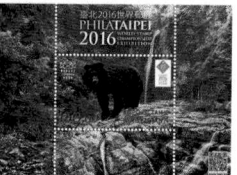

Philataipei 2016 World Stamp Exhibition, Taipei — A13

2016 World Stamp Show, New York A14

**2016, June 3    Litho.    Perf. 14x14½**
22   A13  150s multi    4.50  4.50
23   A14  250s multi    7.50  7.50

Taigan Hunting Dogs A15

Designs: 50s, Black dog. 100s, Mottled dog. 150s, Dog chasing wolf.

**Perf. 13 Syncopated**
**2016, July 28    Litho.**
24-26   A15  Set of 3    9.00  9.00
26a     Souvenir sheet of 3, #24-26    9.00  9.00

Flowers — A16

Designs: No. 27, 50s, Iris orchioides. No. 28, 50s, Leontopodium ochroleucum. No. 29, 100s, Primula turkestanica. No. 30, 100s, Tulipa greigii. 200s, Papaver rhoeas.

**2016, July 29   Litho.   Perf. 14x14½**
27-30  A16  Set of 4                    9.00 9.00
30a       Souvenir sheet of 4, #27-30   9.00 9.00
**Souvenir Sheet**
31  A16  200s multi                     6.00 6.00

2016 Summer Olympics, Rio de Janeiro — A17

Designs: 50s, Cycling. 150s, Tennis.

**2016, Aug. 5   Litho.   Perf. 14x14½**
32-33  A17  Set of 2                    6.00 6.00
Nos. 32-33 each were printed in sheets of 4+2 labels.

2016 World Nomad Games, Cholpon-Ata A18

No. 34: a, Mounted archery. b, Equestrian wrestling. c, Burning horseman.

**2016, Aug. 8   Litho.   Perf. 14x14½**
34   Horiz. strip of 3                  9.00 9.00
a.  A18 50s multi                       1.50 1.50
b.  A18 100s multi                      3.00 3.00
c.  A18 150s multi                      4.50 4.50

**Souvenir Sheet**

Independence of Kyrgyzstan, 25th Anniv. — A19

**Perf. 13 Syncopated**
**2016, Aug. 30                         Litho.**
35  A19  150s multi                     4.50 4.50

42nd Chess Olympiad, Baku, Azerbaijan A20

**2016, Sept. 1   Litho.   Perf. 14x14½**
36  A20  100s multi                     3.00 3.00
No. 36 was printed in sheets of 4 + 2 labels.

Composers and Musicians A21

Designs: No. 37, 50s, Sergei Prokofiev (1891-1953), composer. No. 38, 50s, Yehudi Menuhin (1916-99), violinist. No. 39, 100s, Antonin Dvorák (1841-1904), composer. No. 40, 100s, Wolfgang Amadeus Mozart (1756-1791), composer.

**2016, Sept. 8   Litho.   Perf. 14x14½**
37-40  A21  Set of 4                    9.00 9.00
40a       Souvenir sheet of 4, #37-40   9.00 9.00
Nos. 37-40 each were printed in sheets of 4 + 2 labels.

Schooner Issyk-Kul A22

Ship Progress of Kyrgyzstan A23

President of Kyrgyzstan's Cruiser Moscow — A24

Torpedo Boat — A25

**2016, Nov. 25   Litho.   Perf. 14x14½**
41  A22  50s multi                      1.50 1.50
42  A23  50s multi                      1.50 1.50
43  A24  100s multi                     3.00 3.00
44  A25  100s multi                     3.00 3.00
a.   Souvenir sheet of 4, #41-44        9.00 9.00
     Nos. 41-44 (4)                     9.00 9.00

New Year 2017 — A26

Designs: 50s, Christmas tree and sleigh. 100s, Rooster.

**Perf. 13 Syncopated**
**2017, Feb. 3                          Litho.**
45-46  A26  Set of 2                    4.50 4.50
Nos. 45-46 each were printed in sheets of 5 + label.

Mushrooms — A27

Designs: No. 47, 50s, Pleurotus ostreatus. No. 48, 50s, Leccinum scabrum. No. 49, 100s, Morchella conica. No. 50, 100s, Pleurotus eryngii.

**2017, Apr. 6   Litho.   Perf. 14½x14**
47-50  A27  Set of 4                    9.00 9.00
50a       Souvenir sheet of 4, #47-50   9.00 9.00

Fourth Islamic Solidarity Games, Baku, Azerbaijan A28

Designs: No. 51, 50s, Wrestling. No. 52, 50s, Weight lifting. 75s, Table tennis. 100s, Soccer.

**2017, May 26   Litho.   Perf. 14x14½**
51-54  A28  Set of 4                    8.00 8.00
54a       Souvenir sheet of 4, #51-54, + 2 labels   8.00 8.00

**Souvenir Sheet**

Historic and Cultural Ties With China A29

No. 55: a, 50s, Li Bai (701-62), poet. b, 100s, Illustration for poem "The Ching-Ting Mountain."

**Perf. 13 Syncopated**
**2017, June 29                         Litho.**
55  A29  Sheet of 2, #a-b               4.50 4.50

Horses — A30

No. 56: a, 50s, Trakehner horse. b, 100s, New Kirgiz horse.

**2017, June 30   Litho.   Perf. 14x14½**
56  A30  Pair, #a-b                     4.50 4.50
See Belarus No. 1052.

Flowers — A31

Designs: 50s, Peony. 100s, Chrysanthemum.

**Perf. 13 Syncopated**
**2017, July 7                          Litho.**
57-58  A31  Set of 2                    4.50 4.50
19th International Botanical Congress, Shenzen, People's Republic of China.

Traditional Hunting — A32

Designs: 50s, Archer on horseback. 75s, Hunter on horseback releasing falcon. 100s, Taigan hunting dog chasing fox.

**Perf. 13 Syncopated**
**2017, July 14                         Litho.**
59-61  A32  Set of 3                    6.50 6.50
61a       Souvenir sheet of 3, #59-61   6.50 6.50

Space Exploration, 60th Anniv. — A33

Designs: 50s, Sputnik. 1. 75s, Apollo Lunar Rover. 100s, Tiangong-2 Space Laboratory.

**2017, Nov. 15   Litho.   Perf. 14x14½**
62-64  A33  Set of 3                    6.50 6.50
64a       Souvenir sheet of 3, #62-64   6.50 6.50

**Souvenir Sheet**

National Bank of the Kyrgyz Republic, 25th Anniv. A34

No. 65: a, 50s, 2013 10-som coin depicting Gazella subgutturosa (34x34mm). b, 100s, 2016 500-som banknote and 1-som, 3-som and 10-som coins (34x68mm). c, 100s, 2015 10-som coin depicting Otis tarda (34x34mm).

**Perf. 13 Syncopated**
**2017, Nov. 17       Litho. & Embossed**
65  A34  Sheet of 3, #a-c, + label      7.25 7.25

**Souvenir Sheet**

International Year of Sustainable Tourism for Development — A35

No. 65: a, 50s, Manas Peak. b, 100s, Kel-Suu Lake.

**2017, Nov. 20   Litho.   Perf. 14x14½**
66  A35  Sheet of 2, #a-b               5.75 5.75

Armed Forces of Kyrgyzstan, 25th Anniv. — A36

Designs: No. 67, 50s, Truck-mounted missile launchers. No. 68, 50s, Soldier and armored troop carrier. 75s, Soldiers searching for land mines. 100s, Helicopter and tank.

**2017, Nov. 22   Litho.   Perf. 14x14½**
67-70  A36  Set of 4                    8.00 8.00
70a       Sheet of 4, #67-70, + 2 labels   8.00 8.00

**Souvenir Sheet**

Great Silk Road A37

**Perf. 13 Syncopated**
**2017, Nov. 24       Litho. & Embossed**
71  A37  150s multi                     4.50 4.50

Famous People — A38

Designs: No. 72, 50s, Jonathan Swift (1667-1745), writer. No. 73, 50s, Sir Arthur C. Clarke (1917-2008), science fiction writer. 75s, Marie Sklodowska-Curie (1867-1934), chemist and physicist. No. 75, 100s, Gioachino Rossini (1792-1868), composer. No. 76, 100s, J. R. R. Tolkien (1892-1973), writer.

**2017, Dec. 31   Litho.   Perf. 14x14½**
72-76  A38  Set of 5                    11.00 11.00
76a       Sheet of 5, #72-76, + label   11.00 11.00
Nos. 72-76 were each printed in sheets of 4 + 2 labels.

New Year 2018 (Year of the Dog) — A39

**Litho. With Foil Application**
**2018, Jan. 30   Perf. 13 Syncopated**
77  A39  100s gold & multi              3.00 3.00
No. 77 was printed in sheets of 5 + label.

**Souvenir Sheet**

2018 Winter Olympics, PyeongChang, South Korea — A40

No. 78: a, 50s, Alpine skiing. b, 50s, Biathlon.

**2018, Feb. 23   Litho.   Perf. 14x14½**
78  A40  Sheet of 2, #a-b               6.00 6.00

Karl Marx (1818-83), Political Theorist — A41

**2018, May 5    Litho.    *Perf. 14x14½***
79  A41  100s multi                              3.00  3.00

No. 79 was printed in sheets of 5 + label.

Birds — A42

Designs: 50s, Ibidorhyncha struthersii. 75s, Sitta tephronota. 100s, Anthropoides virgo. 150s, Bubo bubo.

**2018, May 22    Litho.    *Perf. 14x14½***
80-83  A42  Set of 4                            11.00  11.00
83a         Souvenir sheet of 4, #80-            11.00  11.00
            83

Bridges — A43

Designs: 50s, Highway bridge, Kara-Kul. 150s, Railroad bridge, Kuduk.

**2018, June 22    Litho.    *Perf. 14x14½***
84-85  A43  Set of 2                             6.00  6.00
85a         Souvenir sheet of 2, #84-85          6.00  6.00

18th Asian Games, Jakarta, Indonesia — A44

Designs: 100s, Swimming, canoeing, yacht racing. 150s, Taekwondo, volleyball, golf, cycling.

**2018, July 6    Litho.    *Perf. 14x14½***
86-87  A44  Set of 2                             7.50  7.50
87a         Souvenir sheet of 2, #86-87          7.50  7.50

43rd Chess Olympiad, Batumi, Georgia — A45

**2018, Aug. 20    Litho.    *Perf. 14x14½***
88  A45  100s multi                              3.00  3.00

Butterflies A46

Designs: 50s, Parnassius loxias tashkorensis. 100s, Colias regia. 150s, Colias christophi.

**2018, Sept. 7    Litho.    *Perf. 14x14½***
89-91  A46  Set of 3                             8.75  8.75
91a         Souvenir sheet of 3, #89-91          8.75  8.75

Nos. 89-91 were each printed in sheets of 5 + label.

Souvenir Sheet

Diplomatic Relations Between Kyrgyzstan and Latvia, 25th Anniv. — A47

No. 92: a, 50s, Monument to Manas the Great, Bishkek. b, 150s, Lacplesis on Freedom Monument, Riga, Latvia.

---

**2018, Oct. 5    Litho.    *Perf. 14½x14***
92  A47  Sheet of 2, #a-b, + central label      5.75  5.75

See Latvia No. 1003.

Diplomatic Relations Between Kyrgyzstan and Belarus, 25th Anniv. — A48

**2018, Oct. 18    Litho.    *Perf. 14x14½***
93  A48  75s multi                               2.25  2.25

No. 93 was printed in sheets of 6 + 3 central labels. See Belarus No. 1116.

Ivan Turgenev (1818-83), Writer — A49

**2018, Nov. 9    Litho.    *Perf. 14x14½***
94  A49  50s multi                               1.50  1.50

No. 94 was printed in sheets of 5 + label.

Issyk-Kul Lighthouses A50

Ships and: 100s, Lighthouse at left. 150s, Two lighthouses at right.

**2018, Nov. 16    Litho.    *Perf. 14x14½***
95-96  A50  Set of 2                             7.25  7.25
96a         Souvenir sheet of 2, #95-96, + 2 labels    7.25  7.25

Diplomatic Relations Between Kyrgyzstan and Malta, 25th Anniv. — A51

UNESCO World Heritage Sites: 100s, Burana Tower, Kyrgyzstan. 150s, City of Valletta, Malta.

**2018, Nov. 23    Litho.    *Perf. 14x14½***
97-98  A51  Set of 2                             7.25  7.25
98a         Souvenir sheet of 2, #97-98, + 2 labels    7.25  7.25

See Malta No. 1644.

Endangered Species — A52

Designs: 50s, Vormela peregusna. 75s, Otocolobus manul. 100s, Lynx lynx isabellinus. 150s, Ursus arctos isabellinus.

**2018, Dec. 7    Litho.    *Perf. 14x14½***
99-102  A52  Set of 4                           11.00  11.00
102a         Souvenir sheet of 4, #99-102       11.00  11.00

Nos. 99-102 were each printed in sheets of 5 + label.

Chinghiz Aitmatov (1928-2008), Writer — A53

**2018, Dec. 10    Litho.    *Perf. 14x14½***
103  A53  75s multi                             2.25  2.25

No. 103 was printed in sheets of 5 + label.

---

Aleksandr Solzhenitsyn (1918-2008), Writer — A54

**2018, Dec. 11    Litho.    *Perf. 14x14½***
104  A54  100s multi                            3.00  3.00

No. 104 was printed in sheets of 5 + label.

New Year 2019 (Year of the Pig) — A55

**Litho. With Foil Application**
**2019, Jan. 31    *Perf. 13 Syncopated***
105  A55  100s gold & multi                     3.00  3.00

No. 105 was printed in sheet of 5 + label.

Poisonous Mushrooms — A56

Designs: 50s, Clitocybe dealbata. 75s, Agaricus xanthodermus. 100s, Hypholoma fasciculare. 150s, Lepiota brunneoincarnata.

**2019, Mar. 14    Litho.    *Perf. 14¾x14***
106-109  A56  Set of 4                          11.00  11.00
109a          Souvenir sheet of 4, #106-109     11.00  11.00

Nos. 106-109 were each printed in sheets of 5 + label.

Cats — A57

Designs: 50s, Scottish Fold cat. 100s, Siberian cat. 150s, Maine Coon cat.

**2019, Mar. 22    Litho.    *Perf. 14x14¾***
110-112  A57  Set of 3                          8.75  8.75
112a          Souvenir sheet of 3, #110-112     8.75  8.75

Dmitri I. Mendeleev (1834-1907), Creator of Periodic Table of Elements — A58

**2019, Apr. 12    Litho.    *Perf. 14x14¾***
113  A58  100s multi                            3.00  3.00

International Year of the Periodic Table.

Tetrax Tetrax — A59

***Perf. 13 Syncopated***
**2019, May 9                        Litho.**
114  A59  150s multi                            4.25  4.25

---

Souvenir Sheet

Karakol, 150th Anniv. A60

**2019, July 9    Litho.    *Perf. 14x14¾***
115  A60  250s multi                            7.25  7.25

First Man on the Moon, 50th Anniv. A61

**2019, July 20    Litho.    *Perf. 14x14¾***
116  A61  150s multi                            4.50  4.50

Endangered Reptiles and Amphibians — A62

Designs: 50s, Varanus griseus. 75s, Agrionemys horsfieldii. 100s, Rana asiatica Bedriaga. 150s, Vipera renardi.

**2019, Sept. 6    Litho.    *Perf. 14x14¾***
117-120  A62  Set of 4                          11.00  11.00
120a          Souvenir sheet of 4, #117-120     11.00  11.00

Nos. 117-120 were each printed in sheets of 5 + label.

Motorcycles A63

Designs: 50s, Chopper based on 1982 Ural M-67-36. 75s, 2001 Yamaha XV1600. 100s, Custom motorcycle based on 1983 Ural M-67-36. 150s, Café Racer based on 1990 IZH Planeta-5.

**2019, Oct. 16    Litho.    *Perf. 14x14¾***
121-124  A63  Set of 4                          11.00  11.00
124a          Souvenir sheet of 4, #121-124     11.00  11.00

Nos. 121-124 were printed in sheets of 4.

Beekeeping — A64

Designs: 50s, Honeybees at hive entrance. 100s, Honeybees on honeycomb. 150s, Beekeeper tending hive.

***Perf. 13 Syncopated***
**2019, Oct. 28                      Litho.**
125-127  A64  Set of 3                          8.75  8.75
127a          Souvenir sheet of 3, #125-127     8.75  8.75

Nos. 125-127 were printed in sheets of 4.

Turdakun Usubaliev (1919-2015), Politician A65

**2019, Nov. 5    Litho.    *Perf. 14x14¾***
128  A65  100s multi                            3.00  3.00

No. 128 was printed in sheets of 5 + label.

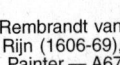

Nikolai Rimsky-Korsakov (1844-1908), Composer — A66

Rembrandt van Rijn (1606-69), Painter — A67

Leonardo da Vinci (1452-1519), Sculptor and Painter — A68

**2019, Nov. 18   Litho.   Perf. 14x14¾**
129  A66  75s multi                  2.25  2.25
130  A67  100s multi                 3.00  3.00
**Souvenir Sheet**
**Perf.  14¾x14**
131  A68  250s multi + label         7.25  7.25
Nos. 129-130 were printed in sheets of 4.

New Year 2020 (Year of the Rat) — A69

**Perf. 13 Syncopated**
**2019, Dec. 2                         Litho.**
132  A69  100s multi                  3.00  3.00
No. 132 was printed in sheet of 5 + label.

Highest Mountain Peaks in Kyrgyzstan — A70

Designs: 50s, Jengish Chokusu. 100s, Lenin Peak. 150s, Khan Tengri.
**2020, Feb. 21   Litho.   Perf. 14x14½**
133-135  A70  Set of 3               8.75  8.75
135a      Souvenir sheet of 3, #133-
          135                        8.75  8.75
Nos. 133-135 were each printed in sheets of 4 + 2 labels.

Jewelry and Women A71

No. 136: a, 100s, Kyrgyz woman and jewelry. b, 150s, Ukrainian woman and jewelry.
**2020, Dec. 9   Litho.   Perf. 14x14½**
136  A71  Horiz. pair, #a-b          6.00  6.00
No. 136 was printed in sheets of 4 pairs with 2 central labels. See Ukraine No. 1280.

A72

Famous Men A73

Designs: 75s, Ivan Bunin (1870-1953), 1933 Nobel laureate in literature. 100s, Federico Fellini (1920-93), film director. 150s, Ludwig van Beethoven (1770-1827), composer. 250s, Raphael (1483-1520), painter.
**2020, Dec. 14   Litho.   Perf. 14x14½**
137-139  A72  Set of 3              8.00  8.00
**Souvenir Sheet**
**Perf. 13½x13 Syncopated**
140  A73  250s multi + label        6.00  6.00
Nos. 137-139 were each printed in sheets of 4 + 2 labels.

Bicyclist — A74

**2020, Dec. 15   Litho.   Perf. 14x14½**
141  A74  150s multi + 3 labels      3.75  3.75
Act Now Climate Action Campaign. No. 141 was printed in sheets of 3 + 9 labels.

Online Chess Olympiad — A75

**2020, Dec. 16   Litho.   Perf. 14½x14**
142  A75  100s multi                 2.50  2.50
  a.    Tete-beche pair              5.00  5.00

Leptopoecile Sophiae — A76

**2020, Dec. 17   Litho.   Perf. 14x14½**
143  A76  150s multi                 3.75  3.75
No. 143 was printed in sheets of 5 + label.

**Souvenir Sheet**

Opening of Central Mosque of Imam Al-Sarakhsi, Bishkek — A77

**Perf. 13x13¼ Syncopated**
**2020, Dec. 21                        Litho.**
144  A77  250s multi                 6.00  6.00
See Turkey No. 3737.

Dogs — A78

Designs: 50s, Dalmatian. 100s, Alaskan malamute. 150s, Akita-inu.
**Perf. 13 Syncopated**
**2020, Dec. 22                        Litho.**
145-147  A78  Set of 3              7.25  7.25
147a      Souvenir sheet of 3, #145-
          147                       7.25  7.25
Nos. 145-147 were each printed in sheets of 5 + label.

New Year 2021 (Year of the Ox) — A79

**Litho. With Foil Application**
**2020, Dec. 31   Perf. 13 Syncopated**
148  A79  100s gold & redsh vio     2.50  2.50
No. 148 was printed in sheets of 5 + label.

Endangered Fish — A80

Designs: 50s, Scizothorax issykkuli. 75s, Capoetobrama kuschakewitschi. 100s, Glyptosternon reticulatum. 150s, Aspiolucius esocinus.
**2021, Mar. 18   Litho.   Perf. 14x14½**
149-152  A80  Set of 4              9.00  9.00
152a      Souvenir sheet of 4, #149-
          152                       9.00  9.00
Nos. 149-152 were each printed in sheets of 5 + label.

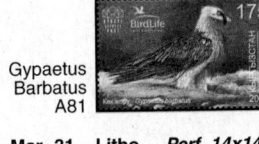

Gypaetus Barbatus A81

**2021, Mar. 31   Litho.   Perf. 14x14½**
153  A81  175s multi                4.25  4.25
No. 153 was printed in sheets of 5 + label.

Yuri Nikulin (1921-97), Circus Clown — A82

**2021, Apr. 17   Litho.   Perf. 14x14½**
154  A82  150s multi                3.50  3.50
No. 154 was printed in sheets of 5 + label.

Saimaluu Tash Petroglyphs A83

Designs: 50s, Animals. 150s, Person with rays around head. 175s, Person and animals.
**2021, May 18   Litho.   Perf. 14x14½**
155-157  A83  Set of 3              9.00  9.00
157a      Souvenir sheet of 3, #155-
          157 + 3 labels            9.00  9.00
Nos. 155-157 were each printed in sheets of 5 + label.

Salyut Space Station, 50th Anniv. — A84

**2021, June 8   Litho.   Perf. 14x14½**
158  A84  175s multi                4.25  4.25
No. 158 was printed in sheets of 5 + label.

International Year of Fruits and Vegetables A85

**2021, June 29   Litho.   Perf. 14x14½**
159  A85  150s multi                3.50  3.50
No. 159 was printed in sheets of 5 + label.

Woodpeckers — A86

Designs: 150s, Dendrocoptes medius. 175s, Dendrocopos leucopterus.
**2021, Dec. 31   Litho.   Perf. 14½x14**
160-161  A86  Set of 2              7.75  7.75
161a      Souvenir sheet of 2, #160-
          161                       7.75  7.75
Nos. 160-161 were each printed in sheets of 5 + label. See Croatia No. 1244.

COVID-19 Pandemic A87

Designs: 150s, Girl with protective mask blowing at dandelions. 175s, Boy with protective mask eating lollipop.
**2021, Dec. 31   Litho.   Perf. 14x14½**
162-163  A87  Set of 2              7.75  7.75
163a      Souvenir sheet of 2, #162-
          163, + 2 labels           7.75  7.75
Nos. 162-163 were each printed in sheets of 5 + label.

Pamir Highway — A88

Designs: 150s, Vehicles on mountainside highway. 175s, Automobile on highway near valley.
**2021, Dec. 31   Litho.   Perf. 14x14½**
164-165  A88  Set of 2              7.75  7.75
165a      Souvenir sheet of 2, #164-
          165, + 2 labels           7.75  7.75
Nos. 164-165 were each printed in sheets of 4 + 2 labels.

Famous Men — A89

Designs: 75s, Walter Scott (1771-1832), writer. 100s, Johannes Kepler (1571-1630), astronomer and mathematician. 150s, Fyodor Dostoevsky (1821-81), writer. 175s, Albrecht Dürer (1471-1528), painter.
**2021, Dec. 31   Litho.   Perf. 14x14½**
166-169  A89  Set of 4            12.00  12.00
Nos. 166-169 were each printed in sheets of 5 + label.

New Year 2022 (Year of the Tiger) — A90

**Perf. 13 Syncopated**
**2021, Dec. 31                        Litho.**
170  A90  150s multi                3.50  3.50
No. 170 was printed in sheets of 5 + label.

## KYRGYZ EXPRESS POST SEMI-POSTALS

Campaign Against COVID-19 Pandemic SP1

**2020, Dec. 30    Litho.    Perf. 14x14½**

| | | | |
|---|---|---|---|
| B1 | SP1 | 150s+50s multi | 5.00  5.00 |

No. B1 was printed in sheets of 5 + label. Surtax for Help the Children Charitable Foundation.

---

# LABUAN

lə-'bü-ən

LOCATION — An island in the East Indies, about six miles off the northwest coast of Borneo

GOVT. — A British possession, administered as a part of the North Borneo Colony

AREA — 35 sq. mi.

POP. — 8,963 (estimated)

CAPITAL — Victoria

The stamps of Labuan were replaced by those of Straits Settlements in 1906.

100 Cents = 1 Dollar

Queen Victoria — A1

On Nos. 1, 2, 3, 4 and 11 the watermark is 32mm high. It is always placed sideways and extends over two stamps.

**1879, May    Engr.    Wmk. 46    Perf. 14**

| | | | |
|---|---|---|---|
| 1 | A1 | 2c green | 1,625. 975.00 |
| 2 | A1 | 6c orange | 240.00 225.00 |
| 3 | A1 | 12c carmine | 1,925. 850.00 |
| 4 | A1 | 16c blue | 77.50 200.00 |
| | | Nos. 1-4 (4) | 3,868. 2,250. |

See Nos. 5-10, 16-24, 33-39, 42-48. For surcharges see Nos. 12-15, 25, 31, 40-41.

**1880-82    Wmk. 1**

| | | | |
|---|---|---|---|
| 5 | A1 | 2c green | 34.00 57.50 |
| 6 | A1 | 6c orange | 145.00 160.00 |
| 7 | A1 | 8c carmine ('82) | 135.00 135.00 |
| 8 | A1 | 10c yel brown | 210.00 100.00 |
| 9 | A1 | 12c carmine | 330.00 400.00 |
| 10 | A1 | 16c blue ('81) | 100.00 130.00 |
| | | Nos. 5-10 (6) | 954.00 982.50 |

A2

A3

A3a

A4

**1880-83    Wmk. 46**

| | | | |
|---|---|---|---|
| 11 | A2 | 6c on 16c blue (with additional "6" across original value) R) | 4,200. 1,325. |

**Wmk. 1**

| | | | |
|---|---|---|---|
| 12 | A2 | 8c on 12c car | 1,825. 1,000. |
| a. | | Original value not obliterated | 3,600. 2,000. |
| b. | | Additional surcharge "8" across original value | 2,300. 1,450. |
| c. | | "8" inverted | 2,100. 1,200. |
| d. | | As "a," "8" inverted | 4,200. |
| 13 | A3 | 8c on 12c car ('81) | 475. 525. |
| 14 | A3a | 8c on 12c car ('81) | 160. 170. |
| a. | | "Eighr" | 22,500. |
| b. | | Inverted surcharge | 16,000. |
| c. | | Double surcharge | 2,900. 2,400. |
| 15 | A4 | $1 on 16c blue (R) ('83) | 4,800. |

On No. 12 the original value is obliterated by a pen mark in either black or red.

---

## Types of 1879 Issue

**1883-86    Wmk. 2**

| | | | |
|---|---|---|---|
| 16 | A1 | 2c green | 30.00 55.00 |
| a. | | Horiz. pair, imperf. btwn. | 18,500. |
| 17 | A1 | 2c rose red ('85) | 4.25 20.00 |
| 18 | A1 | 8c carmine | 325.00 120.00 |
| 19 | A1 | 8c dk violet ('85) | 50.00 9.25 |
| 20 | A1 | 10c yellow brn | 62.50 57.50 |
| 21 | A1 | 10c black brn ('86) | 40.00 72.50 |
| 22 | A1 | 16c blue | 115.00 215.00 |
| 23 | A1 | 16c gray blue ('86) | 125.00 180.00 |
| 24 | A1 | 40c ocher | 37.50 145.00 |
| | | Nos. 16-24 (9) | 789.25 874.25 |

Nos. 1-10, 16-24 are in sheets of 10.
For surcharges see Nos. 26-30, 32.

A5

A6

A7

**1885    Wmk. 1**

| | | | |
|---|---|---|---|
| 25 | A5 | 2c on 16c blue | 1,150. 1,100. |

**Wmk. 2**

| | | | |
|---|---|---|---|
| 26 | A5 | 2c on 8c car | 275.00 550.00 |
| a. | | Double surcharge | |
| 27 | A6 | 2c on 16c blue | 135.00 200.00 |
| a. | | Double surcharge | 7,500. |
| 28 | A7 | 2c on 8c car | 80.00 145.00 |

A8

**1891    Black or Red Surcharge**

| | | | |
|---|---|---|---|
| 29 | A8 | 6c on 8c violet | 16.50 17.00 |
| a. | | 6c on 8c dark violet | 625.00 210.00 |
| b. | | Double surcharge | 390.00 — |
| c. | | As "a," "Cents" omitted | 550.00 550.00 |
| d. | | Inverted surcharge | 90.00 85.00 |
| e. | | Dbl. surch., one inverted | 1,100. — |
| f. | | Dbl. surch., both inverted | 1,100. — |
| g. | | "6" omitted | 625.00 |
| h. | | Pair, one without surcharge | 2,000. 2,000. |
| 30 | A8 | 6c on 8c dk vio (R) | 1,550. 825.00 |
| a. | | Inverted surcharge | 1,850. 925.00 |

**Wmk. 46**

| | | | |
|---|---|---|---|
| 31 | A8 | 6c on 16c blue | 2,800. 2,300. |
| a. | | Inverted surcharge | 15,500. 8,250. |

**Wmk. 2**

| | | | |
|---|---|---|---|
| 32 | A8 | 6c on 40c ocher | 14,000. 5,750. |
| a. | | Inverted surcharge | 12,000. 9,000. |

## Types of 1879 Issue

**1892    Engr.    Unwmk.**

| | | | |
|---|---|---|---|
| 33 | A1 | 2c rose | 7.25 4.25 |
| 34 | A1 | 6c yellow green | 14.50 5.75 |
| 35 | A1 | 8c violet | 13.50 19.50 |
| 36 | A1 | 10c brown | 30.00 9.50 |
| 37 | A1 | 12c deep ultra | 16.00 8.00 |
| 38 | A1 | 16c gray | 30.00 45.00 |
| 39 | A1 | 40c ocher | 27.50 45.00 |
| | | Nos. 33-39 (7) | 138.75 137.00 |

The 2c, 8c and 10c are in sheets of 30; others in sheets of 10.

Nos. 39 and 38 Surcharged

**1893**

| | | | |
|---|---|---|---|
| 40 | A1 | 2c on 40c ocher | 200.00 110.00 |
| a. | | Inverted surcharge | 500.00 675.00 |
| 41 | A1 | 6c on 16c gray | 450.00 180.00 |
| a. | | Inverted surcharge | 675.00 350.00 |
| b. | | Surcharge sideways | 675.00 375.00 |
| c. | | "Six" omitted | — — |
| d. | | "Cents" omitted | — — |
| e. | | Handstamped "Six Cents" | 2,275. |

Surcharges on Nos. 40-41 each exist in 10 types. Counterfeits exist.

No. 41e was handstamped on examples of No. 41 on which the surcharge failed to print or was printed partially or completely albino.

---

From Jan. 1, 1890, to Jan. 1, 1906, Labuan was administered by the British North Borneo Co. Late in that period, unused remainders of Nos. 42-83, 53a, 63a, 64a, 65a, 66a, 68a, 85-86, 96-118, 103a, 107a, J1-J9, J3a and J6a were canceled to order by bars forming an oval. Values for these stamps used are for those with this form of cancellation, unless described as postally used, which are for stamps with dated town cancellations. Nos. 63b, 64b, 65b, 104a, J6a, and possibly others, only exist c.t.o.

For detailed listings of Labuan, see the *Scott Classic Specialized Catalogue*.

## Types of 1879 Issue

**1894, Apr.    Litho.**

| | | | |
|---|---|---|---|
| 42 | A1 | 2c bright rose | 2.00 .65 |
| 43 | A1 | 6c yellow green | 27.50 .65 |
| a. | | Horiz. pair, imperf. btwn. | 11,250. |
| 44 | A1 | 8c bright violet | 29.00 .65 |
| 45 | A1 | 10c brown | 60.00 .65 |
| 46 | A1 | 12c light ultra | 37.50 .80 |
| 47 | A1 | 16c gray | 40.00 .65 |
| 48 | A1 | 40c orange | 60.00 .65 |
| | | Nos. 42-48 (7) | 256.00 4.70 |

Counterfeits exist.

Dyak Chieftain A9

Malayan Sambar A10

Sago Palm A11

Argus Pheasant A12

Arms of North Borneo A13

Dhow A14

Saltwater Crocodile A15

Mt. Kinabalu A16

Arms of North Borneo — A17

**Perf. 12 to 16 and Compound**

**1894    Engr.**

| | | | |
|---|---|---|---|
| 49 | A9 | 1c lilac & black | 2.00 .65 |
| a. | | Vert. pair, imperf. between | 1,300. 575.00 |
| 50 | A10 | 2c blue & black | 3.00 .65 |
| a. | | Imperf., pair | 725.00 |
| 51 | A11 | 3c bister & black | 4.50 .65 |
| 52 | A12 | 5c green & black | 38.50 1.10 |
| a. | | Horiz. pair, imperf. between | 1,800. |
| 53 | A13 | 6c brn red & blk | 3.00 .65 |
| a. | | Imperf., pair | 725.00 350.00 |
| 54 | A14 | 8c rose & black | 13.00 .65 |
| a. | | 8c red & black | 32.50 2.40 |
| 55 | A15 | 12c orange & black | 27.50 .65 |
| 56 | A16 | 18c ol brn & blk | 29.00 .65 |
| b. | | Vert. pair, imperf. between | 2,500. |
| 57 | A17 | 24c lilac & blue | 22.50 1.30 |
| | | Nos. 49-57 (9) | 143.00 6.95 |

**Perf. 13½-14**

| | | | |
|---|---|---|---|
| 49b | A9 | 1c lilac & black | 16.50 |
| 50b | A10 | 2c blue & black | 7.00 |
| 51a | A11 | 3c bister & black | 17.50 |
| 52b | A12 | 5c green & black | 50.00 |
| 53b | A13 | 6c brn red & blk | 3.00 |
| 54b | A14 | 8c rose & black | 45.00 1.00 |

---

| | | | |
|---|---|---|---|
| 54c | A14 | 8c red & black | 45.00 |
| 55a | A15 | 12c orange & black | 77.50 2.75 |
| 56c | A16 | 18c ol brn & blk | 85.00 |
| 56d | A16 | 18c ol bister & blk | 32.50 |
| 57b | A17 | 24c lilac & blue | 20.00 1.25 |
| 57c | A17 | 24c mauve & blue | 40.00 |

**Perf. 13½-14, compound 14½-15**

| | | | |
|---|---|---|---|
| 49c | A9 | 1c lilac & black | 40.00 |
| 50c | A10 | 2c blue & black | 42.50 |
| 51b | A11 | 3c bister & black | — |
| 53c | A13 | 6c brn red & blk | — |

**Perf. 13½-14, compound 12-13**

| | | | |
|---|---|---|---|
| 49d | A9 | 1c lilac & black | 40.00 1.10 |
| 50d | A10 | 2c blue & black | — |
| 51c | A11 | 3c bister & black | 55.00 |
| 52c | A12 | 5c green & black | 65.00 |
| 53d | A13 | 6c brn red & blk | — |
| 55b | A15 | 12c orange & black | — |
| 56e | A16 | 18c ol bister & blk | — |

**Perf. 12-13**

| | | | |
|---|---|---|---|
| 49e | A9 | 1c lilac & black | — |
| 50e | A10 | 2c blue & black | 190.00 |
| 51d | A11 | 3c bister & black | — |
| 52d | A12 | 5c green & black | 210.00 |
| 53e | A13 | 6c brn red & blk | 260.00 |
| 55c | A15 | 12c orange & black | — |

For overprints see Nos. 66-71.

A18

**1895, June    Litho.    Perf. 14**

| | | | |
|---|---|---|---|
| 58 | A18 | 4c on $1 red | 4.25 .50 |
| 59 | A18 | 10c on $1 red | 11.50 .50 |
| 60 | A18 | 20c on $1 red | 52.50 .50 |
| 61 | A18 | 30c on $1 red | 57.50 1.50 |
| 62 | A18 | 40c on $1 red | 57.50 1.50 |
| | | Nos. 58-62 (5) | 183.25 4.50 |

A19

A20

A21

**1896**

| | | | |
|---|---|---|---|
| 63 | A19 | 25c blue green | 45.00 .80 |
| a. | | Imperf, pair | 72.50 |
| b. | | Without overprint | 35.00 2.00 |
| c. | | As "b," imperf, pair | 60.00 |
| 64 | A20 | 50c claret | 42.50 .80 |
| a. | | Imperf, pair | 72.50 |
| b. | | Without overprint | 32.50 2.00 |
| c. | | As "b," imperf, pair | 52.50 |
| 65 | A21 | $1 dark blue | 82.50 1.25 |
| a. | | Imperf, pair | 72.50 |
| b. | | Without overprint | 50.00 3.00 |
| c. | | As "b," imperf, pair | 60.00 |
| | | Nos. 63-65 (3) | 170.00 2.85 |

For surcharges and overprint see Nos. 93-95, 116-118, 120.

Nos. 49-54 Overprinted

**1896    Perf. 12 to 15 and Compound**

| | | | |
|---|---|---|---|
| 66 | A9 | 1c lilac & black | 26.00 1.75 |
| a. | | "JEBILEE" | 1,450. 360.00 |
| b. | | "JUBILE" | 3,000. |
| c. | | Orange overprint | 325.00 24.00 |
| 67 | A10 | 2c blue & black | 52.50 1.75 |
| a. | | Vert. pair, imperf. btwn. | 1,525. |
| b. | | "JEBILEE" | 1,850. |
| c. | | "JUBILE" | 3,500. |
| d. | | Vert. strip of 3, imperf between | 8,000. |
| 68 | A11 | 3c bister & black | 50.00 1.50 |
| a. | | "JEBILEE" | 2,250. 850.00 |
| b. | | "JUBILE" | |
| 69 | A12 | 5c green & black | 72.50 1.50 |
| a. | | Double overprint | 975.00 |
| 70 | A13 | 6c brown red & blk | 47.50 1.00 |
| a. | | Double overprint | 975.00 |
| b. | | "JUBILE" | 3,600. |
| 71 | A14 | 8c rose & black | 57.50 1.00 |
| a. | | Double overprint | 3,000. |
| | | Nos. 66-71 (6) | 306.00 8.50 |

Cession of Labuan to Great Britain, 50th anniv.

**Perf. 13½-14**
66d A9 1c lilac & black 35.00
e. Double overprint 450.00 —
f. Orange overprint 350.00
67e A10 2c blue & black 52.50
68c A11 2c bister & black 57.50 1.50
d. Triple overprint 1,150.
69b A12 5c green & black 72.50 1.50
70c A13 6c brown red & blk 1.00
71b A14 8c rose & black 52.50 1.00

**Perf. 13½-14, compound 14½-15**
67f A10 2c blue & black — 50.00
68e A11 2c bister & black —
70d A13 6c brown red & blk —
71c A14 8c rose & black 60.00 22.50

**Perf. 13½-14, compound 12-13**
66g A9 1c lilac & black 47.50
h. Orange overprint
67g A10 2c blue & black 57.50
68f A11 3c bister & black 450.00 200.00
g. Double overprint 425.00 195.00
h. Triple overprint 775.00
69c A12 5c green & black —

**Perf. 12-13**
69i A9 1c lilac & black —

Cession of Labuan to Great Britain, 50th anniv.

Dyak Chieftain A22

Malayan Sambar A23

Sago Palm A24

Argus Pheasant A25

A26

Dhow — A27

Saltwater Crocodile A28

Mt. Kinabalu "Postal Revenue" A29

Coat of Arms — A30

**Perf. 13½ to 16 and Compound**
**1897-1900** Engr.
72 A22 1c lilac & black 8.00 .60
72A A22 1c red brn & blk 3.75 .80
73 A22 2c blue & black 32.50 .90
a. Vert. pair, imperf between 1,125.
b. Horiz. pair, imperf between 1,550.
75 A24 3c bister & blk 10.00 .60
a. Vert. pair, imperf between 1,325. 675.00
76 A25 5c green & blk 67.50 .85
78 A26 6c brn red & blk 16.00 .60
a. Vert. pair, imperf between 850.00
79 A27 8c red & black 25.00
80 A28 12c red & black 40.00 2.50
82 A30 24c gry lil & bl 14.50 .60
Nos. 72-82 (9) 217.25 7.45

**Perf. 13½-14**
72Ab A22 1c red brn & blk 25.00 .80
73c A23 2c blue & black 26.00 .80
74 A23 2c grn & blk ('00) 4.50 .35
a. Horiz. pair, imperf between 3,100. 1,550.
75b A24 3c bister & blk 10.00 .60
76b A25 5c green & blk 67.50 .90
77 A25 5c lt bl & blk ('00) 27.50 .80
78b A26 6c brn red & blk 8.00 .60
79a A27 8c red & black 60.00 1.00
79b A27 8c vermilion & black 14.50 .80
80a A28 12c red & black 140.00 3.00
81 A29 18c ol bis & blk 125.00 2.40
82a A30 24c gry lil & bl 57.50 2.40

**Perf. 13½-14, compound 14½-15**
72c A22 1c lilac & black —

**Perf. 13½-14, compound 12-13**
73d A23 2c blue & black 62.50
74b A23 2c grn & blk ('00) —
75c A24 3c bister & blk 25.00 2.00
76c A25 5c green & blk —
77a A25 5c lt bl & blk ('00) —
78c A26 6c brn red & blk 8.25
79c A27 8c red & black 52.50 3.25

**Perf. 16**
72Ad A22 1c red brn & blk 25.00
73e A23 2c blue & black 8.50
79d A27 8c red & black 7.50
81a A29 18c ol bis & blk 15.00 .60
a. Vert. pair, imperf between 3,750.

No. 72A used exists only perf. 13½x14.
For surcharges see Nos. 87-89, 110-112.

"Postage & Revenue" A31

"Postage & Revenue" A32

**Perf. 13½ to 16 and Compound**
**1897**
83 A31 18c bister & black 95.00 2.40
84 A32 24c brn lil & bl 50.00 2.40
a. ocher & blue 4.75

**Perf. 13½-14**
83a A31 18c bister & black —
84b A32 24c brn lilac & blue 52.50 2.40

**Perf. 13½-14, compound 12-13**
83c A31 18c bister & black 145.00
84c A32 24c brn lilac & blue
83b A31 18c bister & black 10.00
84d A32 24c brn lilac & blue 57.50

For surcharges see Nos. 92, 115.

"Postage & Revenue" A33
"Postage & Revenue" A34

**1898** Perf. 14½-15
85 A33 12c red & black — 4.00
86 A34 18c bister & black 72.50

**Perf. 13½-14**
85a A33 12c red & black 50.00
86a A34 18c bister & black 42.50 3.75

**Perf. 13½-14, compound 14½-15**
85b A33 12c red & black —

**Perf. 13½-14, compound 12-13**
86b A34 18c bister & black 52.50

**Perf. 12-13**
86c A34 18c bister & black —

**Perf. 16**
85c A33 12c red & black 77.50
86d A34 18c bister & black 57.50

No. 85a cto is always perf. 13½x14.
For surcharges see Nos. 90-91, 113-114.

Regular Issue Surcharged in Black

**1899** Perf. 14½-15
87 A25 4c on 5c grn & blk 62.50 30.00
88 A26 4c on 6c brn red & blk 34.00 22.50
89 A27 4c on 8c red & blk 72.50 52.50
90 A33 4c on 12c red & blk 67.50 42.50
91 A34 4c on 18c bis & blk 40.00 21.50
a. Double surcharge 575.00 675.00
92 A32 4c on 24c lil & bl 40.00 36.00

**Perf. 14**
93 A19 4c on 25c blue grn 7.25 8.00
94 A20 4c on 50c claret 8.75 8.00
95 A21 4c on $1 dk blue 8.75 8.00
Nos. 87-95 (9) 341.25 229.00

**Perf. 13½-14**
88a A26 4c on 6c brn red & blk 45.00 45.00
89a A27 4c on 8c red & blk 52.50 37.50
90a A33 4c on 12c red & blk 62.50 50.00
92a A32 4c on 24c lil & bl 50.00 36.00

**Perf. 13½-14, compound 12-13**
88b A26 4c on 6c brn red & blk 60.00 72.50
89b A27 4c on 8c red & blk 35.00 45.00
90b A33 4c on 12c red & blk 72.50 77.50
92b A32 4c on 24c lil & bl 50.00 35.00

**Perf. 12-13**
89c A27 4c on 8c red & blk —

**Perf. 16**
90c A33 4c on 12c red & blk 62.50 47.50
92c A32 4c on 24c lil & bl 55.00 57.50

Orangutan A35

Sun Bear A36

Railroad Train — A37

**Perf. 12 to 16 and Compound**
**1899-1901**
96 A35 4c yel brn & blk 10.00 .75
a. Vert. pair, imperf. btwn. 1,450.
b. Perf 13½-14, compound 12-13 57.50
97 A35 2c car & blk ('00) 22.50 .90
97a A35 2c car & blk ('00) 6.00 .60
b. Perf 13½-14, compound 12-13 52.50 1.50
c. Perf 16
98 A36 10c gray vio & dk brn, perf. 14½-15 ('02) 60.00 .75
99 A37 16c org brn & grn (G) ('01) 60.00 3.00
a. Perf 14½-15 190.00
b. Perf 13½-14, compound 12-13 100.00
c. Perf 12-13 440.00
Nos. 96-99 (4) 152.50 5.40

Crown — A38

**Perf. 12½ to 16 and Compound**
**1902-03** Engr.
99A A38 1c vio & black 6.75 .60
100 A38 2c grn & blk 5.00 .35
100A A38 3c sepia & blk 4.00 .35
101 A38 4c car & blk 4.00 .35
102 A38 8c org & blk 15.00 .80
103 A38 10c sl blue & brn 4.00 .35
a. Vert. pair, imperf. between 925.00
104 A38 12c yel & black 16.00 .35
a. Vert. strip of 3, imperf. horiz. 4,000.
105 A38 16c org brn & grn 5.75 .35
a. Vert. pair, imperf. between 2,300.
106 A38 18c bis brn & blk 4.00 .35
107 A38 25c grnsh bl & grn 12.00 .60
a. 25c greenish blue & black 625.00
108 A38 50c gray lil & vio 12.00 2.75
109 A38 $1 org & red brn 10.00 2.75
Nos. 99A-109 (12) 98.50 9.95

**Perf. 14½-15**
99Ab A38 1c vio & black 105.00
100b A38 2c green & blk 125.00
101a A38 4c car & black 10.00
102a A38 8c org & black 9.50
103b A38 10c sl blue & brn 9.25 .60
107b A38 25c grnsh bl & grn 18.00 .75
109a A38 $1 org & red brn 12.00 2.40

**Perf. 13½-14, compound 12-13**
99Ac A38 1c vio & black 92.50
101b A38 4c car & black 82.50
108a A38 50c gray lil & vio 19.50

**Perf. 16**
104b A38 12c yel & black 14.50

**Line Through "B" of "LABUAN"**
**Perf. 13½-14**
99Ad A38 1c vio & black 95.00 11.50
100c A38 2c green & blk 85.00 11.50
100Ac A38 3c sepia & blk 82.50 11.25

101c A38 4c car & black 87.50 11.50
102b A38 8c org & black 140.00 12.50
103c A38 10c sl blue & brn 87.50 11.50
104c A38 12c yel & black 160.00 11.50
105b A38 16c org brn & grn 100.00 11.50
106a A38 18c bis brn & blk 95.00 11.25
107c A38 25c grnsh bl & grn 140.00 12.50
108b A38 50c gray lil & vio 210.00 27.50
109b A38 $1 org & red brn 195.00 27.50
Nos. 99Ad-109b (#) * *

There are 3 known examples of No. 104a, all cto. A 16c vertical pair, imperf between has been reported. The editors would like to receive evidence of the existence of this item.

Regular Issue of 1896-97 Surcharged in Black

**1904** Perf. 14½x15
110 A25 4c on 5c grn & blk 57.50 17.00
111 A26 4c on 6c brn red & blk 14.50 17.00
112 A27 4c on 8c red & blk 30.00 17.00
113 A33 4c on 12c red & blk 50.00 17.00
a. Perf 16 52.50
114 A34 4c on 18c bis & blkm perf. 13½-14 30.00 17.00
a. Perf 13½-14, comp. 12-13 42.50
115 A32 4c on 24c brn lil & bl 19.25 17.00
a. Perf 13½-14 42.50
b. Perf 13½-14, comp. 12-13 52.50
c. Perf 16 35.00 17.00
116 A19 4c on 25c blue grn 10.00 17.00
117 A20 4c on 50c clar 10.00 17.00
a. Double surcharge 400.00
118 A21 4c on $1 dark blue 14.00 17.00
Nos. 110-118 (9) 235.25 153.00

**Stamps of North Borneo, 1893, and Labuan No. 65a Overprinted in Black**

a

b

c

**1905**
119 A30(a) 25c slate bl 1,325. 1,100.
120 A21(c) $1 blue 1,050.
121 A33(b) $2 gray grn 4,000.
122 A34(c) $5 red vio 7,250. 1,850.
a. $5 dull purple 7,000. 1,800.
123 A35(c) $10 brown 55,000. 14,500.
Nos. 119, 120 and 123 do not exist postally used. No. 120 exists only cto.

**POSTAGE DUE STAMPS**

Regular Issues Overprinted

**1901** Unwmk. Perf. 14
J1 A23 2c grn & blk 27.50 1.10
a. Double overprint 425.00
J2 A24 3c bis & blk 37.50 1.00
J3b A35 4c car & black 60.00 .60
a. Double overprint 875.00
J4 A25 5c lt blue & blk 57.50 1.50
J5 A26 6c brn red & blk 50.00 1.10
J6 A27 8c red & black 110.00 3.00
a. Center inverted, ovpt. reading down 12,000.
J7 A33 12c red & black 170.00 6.75
a. Overprint reading down 1,125.

| | | | | |
|---|---|---|---|---|
| J8 | A34 | 18c ol bis & blk | 40.00 | 1.75 |
| J9 | A32 | 24c brn lil & bl | 77.50 | 7.75 |
| | | Nos. J1-J9 (9) | 630.00 | 24.55 |

See note after No. 41.

The stamps of Labuan were superseded by those of Straits Settlements in 1906.

---

# LAGOS

'lā-ˌgäs

LOCATION — West Africa, bordering on the former Southern Nigeria Colony
GOVT. — British Crown Colony and Protectorate
AREA — 3,460 sq. mi. (approx.)
POP. — 1,500,000 (1901)
CAPITAL — Lagos

This territory was purchased by the British in 1861 and placed under the Governor of Sierra Leone. In 1874 it was detached and formed part of the Gold Coast Colony until 1886 when the Protectorate of Lagos was established. In 1899 Lagos and the territories of the Royal Niger Company were surrendered to the Crown of Great Britain and formed into the Northern and Southern Nigeria Protectorates. In 1906 Lagos and Southern Nigeria were united to form the Colony and Protectorate of Southern Nigeria.

12 Pence = 1 Shilling

Queen Victoria — A1

**1874-75   Typo.   Wmk. 1   Perf. 12½**

| | | | | |
|---|---|---|---|---|
| 1 | A1 | 1p lilac | 80.00 | 50.00 |
| 2 | A1 | 2p blue | 80.00 | 45.00 |
| 3 | A1 | 3p red brown ('75) | 130.00 | 45.00 |
| 4 | A1 | 4p rose | 150.00 | 50.00 |
| 5 | A1 | 6p blue green | 150.00 | 20.00 |
| 6 | A1 | 1sh orange ('75) | 425.00 | 70.00 |
| a. | | Value 15 ½mm instead of 16 ½mm long | 700.00 | 160.00 |
| | | Nos. 1-6 (6) | 1,015. | 280.00 |

**1876   Perf. 14**

| | | | | |
|---|---|---|---|---|
| 7 | A1 | 1p lilac | 50.00 | 21.00 |
| 8 | A1 | 2p blue | 80.00 | 15.00 |
| 9 | A1 | 3p red brown | 120.00 | 30.00 |
| 10 | A1 | 4p rose | 225.00 | 12.50 |
| 11 | A1 | 6p green | 130.00 | 7.00 |
| 12 | A1 | 1sh orange | 950.00 | 95.00 |
| | | Nos. 7-12 (6) | 1,555. | 180.50 |

The 4p exists with watermark sideways.

**1882-1902   Wmk. 2**

| | | | | |
|---|---|---|---|---|
| 13 | A1 | ½p green ('86) | 2.25 | .95 |
| 14 | A1 | 1p lilac | 42.50 | 27.50 |
| 15 | A1 | 1p car rose | 2.25 | .95 |
| 16 | A1 | 2p blue | 200.00 | 8.50 |
| 17 | A1 | 2p gray | 100.00 | 9.50 |
| 18 | A1 | 2p lil & bl ('87) | 8.50 | 3.25 |
| 19 | A1 | 2½p ultra ('91) | 8.00 | 2.00 |
| a. | | 2½p blue | 90.00 | 57.50 |
| 20 | A1 | 3p orange brn | 30.00 | 8.75 |
| 21 | A1 | 3p lil & brn org ('91) | 3.00 | 3.75 |
| 22 | A1 | 4p rose | 225.00 | 14.00 |
| 23 | A1 | 4p violet | 160.00 | 12.50 |
| 24 | A1 | 4p lil & blk ('87) | 2.50 | 2.00 |
| 25 | A1 | 5p lil & grn ('94) | 3.00 | 12.50 |
| 26 | A1 | 6p olive green | 9.00 | 55.00 |
| 27 | A1 | 6p lil & red vio ('87) | 5.50 | 3.50 |
| 28 | A1 | 6p lilac & car rose ('02) | 5.75 | 13.50 |
| 29 | A1 | 7½p lilac & car rose ('94) | 4.50 | 40.00 |
| 30 | A1 | 10p lil & yel ('94) | 4.50 | 15.00 |
| 31 | A1 | 1sh org ('85) | 21.00 | 25.00 |
| 32 | A1 | 1sh yel grn & blk ('87) | 6.50 | 32.50 |
| 33 | A1 | 2sh6p ol brn ('86) | 375.00 | 325.00 |
| 34 | A1 | 2sh6p green & car rose ('87) | 27.50 | 92.50 |
| 35 | A1 | 5sh blue ('86) | 750.00 | 550.00 |
| 36 | A1 | 5sh grn & ultra ('87) | 50.00 | 175.00 |
| 37 | A1 | 10sh brn vio ('86) | 2,750. | 2,000. |

| | | | | |
|---|---|---|---|---|
| 38 | A1 | 10sh grn & brn ('87) | 120.00 | 275.00 |

Excellent forgeries exist of Nos. 33, 35 and 37 on paper with genuine watermark.

No. 24 Surcharged in Black

**1893**

| | | | | |
|---|---|---|---|---|
| 39 | A1 | ½p on 4p lilac & blk | 11.50 | 4.00 |
| a. | | Double surcharge | 70.00 | 62.50 |
| b. | | Triple surcharge | 175.00 | |
| c. | | ½p on 2p lilac & blue (#18) | — | 27,500. |

Four settings of surcharge.
Only one used example is known of No. 39c. The two unused examples are in museums.

King Edward VII — A3

**1904, Jan. 22**

| | | | | |
|---|---|---|---|---|
| 40 | A3 | ½p grn & bl grn | 3.00 | 6.25 |
| 41 | A3 | 1p vio & blk, red | 1.25 | .25 |
| 42 | A3 | 2p violet & ultra | 6.75 | 7.00 |
| 43 | A3 | 2½p vio & ultra, bl | 1.50 | 1.75 |
| 44 | A3 | 3p vio & org brn | 3.25 | 2.00 |
| 45 | A3 | 6p vio & red vio | 40.00 | 11.50 |
| 46 | A3 | 1sh green & blk | 40.00 | 47.50 |
| 47 | A3 | 2sh6p grn & car rose | 160.00 | 325.00 |
| 48 | A3 | 5sh grn & ultra | 150.00 | 350.00 |
| 49 | A3 | 10sh green & brn | 350.00 | 975.00 |
| | | Nos. 40-49 (10) | 755.75 | 1,726. |

**1904-05   Wmk. 3**
**Ordinary or Chalky Paper**

| | | | | |
|---|---|---|---|---|
| 50 | A3 | ½p grn & bl grn | 14.50 | 3.00 |
| 51a | A3 | 1p vio & blk, red | 1.75 | .25 |
| 52 | A3 | 2p violet & ultra | 5.50 | 3.50 |
| 53a | A3 | 2½p vio & ultra, bl | 2.00 | 18.50 |
| 54 | A3 | 3p vio & org brn | 4.00 | 1.50 |
| 55a | A3 | 6p vio & red vio | 5.00 | 1.75 |
| 56 | A3 | 1sh green & blk | 22.50 | 30.00 |
| 57 | A3 | 2sh6p grn & car rose | 27.50 | 75.00 |
| 58 | A3 | 5sh grn & ultra | 27.50 | 110.00 |
| 59 | A3 | 10sh green & brn | 100.00 | 275.00 |
| | | Nos. 50-59 (10) | 210.25 | 518.50 |

See Scott Classic Specialized Catalogue of Stamps & Covers for detailed listings of ordinary and chalky paper varieties.
The stamps of Lagos were superseded by those of Southern Nigeria.

---

# LAOS

'laus

LOCATION — In northwestern Indo-China
GOVT. — Republic
AREA — 91,400 sq. mi.
POP. — 5,407,453 (1999 est.)
CAPITAL — Vientiane

Before 1949, Laos was part of the French colony of Indo-China and used its stamps until 1951. The kingdom was replaced by the Lao Peoples Democratic Republic Dec. 2, 1975.

100 Cents = 1 Piaster
100 Cents = 1 Kip (1955)

### Imperforates
Most Laos stamps issued during 1951-75 exist as imperforate proofs in issued and trial colors, and also as proofs in small presentation sheets in issued colors. Many post-1975 issues exist imperforate.

### Paper
Most Laos stamps issued before 1976 exist on both white and yellowish papers in approximately equal quantities. Souvenir sheets from this period were printed primarily on yellowish paper. Souvenir sheets printed on white paper are scarce.

| Catalogue values for all unused stamps in this country are for Never Hinged items. |
|---|

Boat on Mekong River
A1

King Sisavang-Vong
A2

Laotian Woman — A3

Designs: 50c, 60c, 70c, Luang Prabang. 1pi, 2pi, 3pi, 5pi, 10pi, Temple at Vientiane.

**1951-52   Unwmk.   Engr.   Perf. 13**

| | | | | |
|---|---|---|---|---|
| 1 | A1 | 10c dk grn & emer | .60 | .25 |
| 2 | A1 | 20c dk car & car | .60 | .25 |
| 3 | A1 | 30c ind & dp ultra | 2.00 | 1.25 |
| 4 | A3 | 30c ind & pur ('52) | 1.00 | .30 |
| 5 | A1 | 50c dark brown | .50 | .50 |
| 6 | A1 | 60c red & red org | .50 | .50 |
| 7 | A1 | 70c ultra & bl grn | 1.25 | .50 |
| 8 | A3 | 80c brt grn & dk bl green ('52) | 1.25 | .60 |
| 9 | A1 | 1pi dk pur & pur | 1.25 | .50 |
| 10 | A3 | 1.10pi dark plum & carmine ('52) | 1.25 | 1.25 |
| 11 | A2 | 1.50pi blk brn & vio brown | 1.60 | 1.25 |
| 12 | A3 | 1.90pi indigo & dp blue ('52) | 1.50 | 1.25 |
| 13 | A1 | 2pi dk grn & gray green | 20.00 | 9.00 |
| 14 | A1 | 3pi dk car & red | 2.50 | 1.50 |
| 15 | A3 | 3pi choc & black brown ('52) | 1.75 | 1.50 |
| 16 | A1 | 5pi ind & dp ultra | 3.25 | 1.75 |
| 17 | A1 | 10pi blk brn & vio brown | 4.25 | 2.00 |
| | | Nos. 1-17 (17) | 45.05 | 24.15 |
| | | Set, hinged | 25.00 | |

A booklet containing 26 souvenir sheets was issued in 1952 on the anniversary of the first issue of Laos stamps. Each sheet contains a single stamp in the center (Nos. 1-17, C2-C4, J1-J6). Value $300.
See No. 223.

UPU Monument and King Sisavang-Vong — A4

**1952, Dec. 7**

| | | | | |
|---|---|---|---|---|
| 18 | A4 | 80c ind, blue & pur | .90 | .80 |
| 19 | A4 | 1pi dk car, car & org brown | .90 | .80 |
| 20 | A4 | 1.20pi dk pur, pur & ultra | 1.00 | .90 |
| 21 | A4 | 1.50pi dk grn, bl grn & dk brn | 1.25 | 1.00 |
| 22 | A4 | 1.90pi blk brn, vio brn & dk Prus grn | 1.50 | 1.25 |
| | | Nos. 18-22,C5-C6 (7) | 16.55 | 14.75 |

Laos' admission to the UPU, May 13, 1952.

Court of Love — A5

**1953, July 14**

| | | | | |
|---|---|---|---|---|
| 23 | A5 | 4.50pi indigo & bl grn | .85 | .55 |
| 24 | A5 | 6pi gray & dark brn | 1.25 | .55 |

Composite of Laotian Temples A6

**1954, Mar. 4**

| | | | | |
|---|---|---|---|---|
| 25 | A6 | 2pi indigo & redsh vio | 27.50 | 20.00 |
| 26 | A6 | 3pi blk brn & scar | 27.50 | 20.00 |
| | | Nos. 25-26,C13 (3) | 175.00 | 135.00 |

Accession of King Sisavang-Vong, 50th anniv.
See No. C13.

Buddha Statue and Monks — A7

**1956, May 24   Engr.   Perf. 13**

| | | | | |
|---|---|---|---|---|
| 27 | A7 | 2k reddish brown | 2.50 | 1.75 |
| 28 | A7 | 3k black | 3.00 | 2.00 |
| 29 | A7 | 5k chocolate | 4.50 | 3.00 |
| | | Nos. 27-29,C20-C21 (5) | 64.00 | 51.75 |

2500th anniversary of birth of Buddha.
See Nos. C20-C21.

UN Emblem — A8

**1956, Dec. 14   Perf. 13½x13**

| | | | | |
|---|---|---|---|---|
| 30 | A8 | 1k black | .65 | .45 |
| 31 | A8 | 2k blue | .90 | .70 |
| 32 | A8 | 4k bright red | 1.25 | .95 |
| 33 | A8 | 6k purple | 1.40 | 1.10 |
| | | Nos. 30-33,C22-C23 (6) | 13.95 | 12.95 |

Admission of Laos to the UN, 1st anniv.

Khouy Player — A9

Khene Player — A10

Musical Instrument: 8k, Ranat.

## 1957, Mar. 25 — Unwmk. — Perf. 13

| | | | | |
|---|---|---|---|---|
| 34 | A9 | 2k multicolored | 1.75 | 1.10 |
| 35 | A10 | 4k multicolored | 2.00 | 1.25 |
| 36 | A9 | 8k org, bl & red brn | 2.50 | 2.00 |
| | | *Nos. 34-36,C24-C26 (6)* | 14.75 | 10.45 |

See Nos. 224, C24-C26.

Harvesting Rice — A11

Drying Rice — A12

## 1957, July 22 — Engr. — Perf. 13

| | | | | |
|---|---|---|---|---|
| 37 | A11 | 3k shown | .90 | .60 |
| 38 | A12 | 5k shown | 1.25 | .75 |
| 39 | A12 | 16k Winnowing rice | 2.00 | 1.50 |
| 40 | A11 | 26k Polishing rice | 4.00 | 2.00 |
| | | *Nos. 37-40 (4)* | 8.15 | 4.85 |

Elephants A13

Various Elephants: 30c, 5k, 10k, 13k, vert.

## 1958, Mar. 17

| | | | | |
|---|---|---|---|---|
| 41 | A13 | 10c multi | 1.00 | .50 |
| 42 | A13 | 20c multi | 1.00 | .50 |
| 43 | A13 | 30c multi | 1.00 | .50 |
| 44 | A13 | 2k multi | 1.50 | .90 |
| 45 | A13 | 5k multi | 2.75 | 1.50 |
| 46 | A13 | 10k multi | 3.00 | 2.00 |
| 47 | A13 | 13k multi | 5.00 | 2.50 |
| | | *Nos. 41-47 (7)* | 15.25 | 8.40 |

For surcharge see No. B5.

Globe and Goddess A14

UNESCO Building and Mother with Children — A15

Designs: 70c, UNESCO building, globe and mother with children. 1k, UNESCO building and Eiffel tower.

## 1958, Nov. 3 — Engr. — Perf. 13

| | | | | |
|---|---|---|---|---|
| 48 | A14 | 50c multicolored | .50 | .25 |
| 49 | A15 | 60c emer, vio & maroon | .65 | .25 |
| 50 | A15 | 70c ultra, rose red & brn | .65 | .25 |
| 51 | A14 | 1k ol bis, cl & grnsh bl | 1.00 | .60 |
| | | *Nos. 48-51 (4)* | 2.80 | 1.35 |

UNESCO Headquarters in Paris opening, Nov. 3.

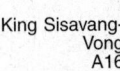

King Sisavang-Vong A16

## 1959, Sept. 16 — Unwmk.

| | | | | |
|---|---|---|---|---|
| 52 | A16 | 4k rose claret | .35 | .35 |
| 53 | A16 | 6.50k orange red | .35 | .35 |
| 54 | A16 | 9k bright pink | .35 | .35 |
| 55 | A16 | 13k green | .75 | .60 |
| | | *Nos. 52-55 (4)* | 1.80 | 1.65 |

For surcharges see Nos. 112-113, B4.

Dancers A17

Student and Torch of Learning A18

Education and Fine Arts: 3k, Globe, key of knowledge and temple. 5k, Dancers and temple.

## 1959, Oct. 1 — Engr. — Perf. 13

| | | | | |
|---|---|---|---|---|
| 56 | A17 | 1k vio blk, ol & bl | .50 | .30 |
| 57 | A18 | 2k maroon & black | .55 | .30 |
| 58 | A17 | 3k slate grn & vio | .85 | .30 |
| 59 | A18 | 5k rose vio, yel & brt grn | 1.10 | .60 |
| | | *Nos. 56-59 (4)* | 3.00 | 1.50 |

Portal of Wat Phou, Pakse — A19

Historic Monuments: 1.50k, That Inghang, Savannakhet, horiz. 2.50k, Phou Temple, Pakse, horiz. 7k, That Luang, Vientiane. 11k, That Luang, Vientiane, horiz. 12.50k, Phousi, Luang Prabang.

## 1959, Nov. 2 — Unwmk. — Perf. 13

| | | | | |
|---|---|---|---|---|
| 60 | A19 | 50c sepia, grn & org | .30 | .25 |
| 61 | A19 | 1.50k multi | .35 | .25 |
| 62 | A19 | 2.50k pur, vio bl & ol | .50 | .40 |
| 63 | A19 | 7k vio, olive & claret | .75 | .50 |
| 64 | A19 | 11k brn, car & grn | .90 | .75 |
| 65 | A19 | 12.50k bl, vio & bister | 1.25 | .80 |
| | | *Nos. 60-65 (6)* | 4.05 | 2.95 |

Due to poor quality control, numerous color varieties exist.

Funeral Urn and Monks A20

King Sisavang-Vong A21

Designs: 6.50k, Urn under canopy. 9k, Catafalque on 7-headed dragon carriage.

## 1961, Apr. 29 — Engr. — Perf. 13

| | | | | |
|---|---|---|---|---|
| 66 | A20 | 4k black, bis & org | .85 | .75 |
| 67 | A20 | 6.50k black & bister | 1.00 | .75 |
| 68 | A20 | 9k black & bister | 1.10 | .85 |
| 69 | A21 | 25k black | 3.00 | 2.25 |
| | | *Nos. 66-69 (4)* | 5.95 | 4.60 |

King Sisavang-Vong's (1885-1959) funeral, Apr. 23-29, 1961.

King Savang Vatthana — A22

## 1962, Apr. 16 — Perf. 13
### Portrait in Brown and Carmine

| | | | | |
|---|---|---|---|---|
| 70 | A22 | 1k ultramarine | .50 | .25 |
| 71 | A22 | 2k lilac rose | .60 | .25 |
| 72 | A22 | 5k greenish blue | .70 | .30 |
| 73 | A22 | 10k olive | .85 | .40 |
| | | *Nos. 70-73 (4)* | 2.65 | 1.20 |

Boy and Malaria Eradication Emblem — A23

9k, Girl. 10k, Malaria eradication emblem.

## 1962, July 19 — Engr.

| | | | | |
|---|---|---|---|---|
| 74 | A23 | 4k bluish grn, blk & buff | .60 | .25 |
| 75 | A23 | 9k lt bl, blk & lt brn | .80 | .40 |
| 76 | A23 | 10k ol, bis & rose red | 1.25 | .45 |
| | | *Nos. 74-76 (3)* | 2.65 | 1.10 |

WHO drive to eradicate malaria. Nos. 74-76 exist imperf.

An imperf. souvenir sheet on white paper with light blue inscription exists. Value, $350. Three other varieties of this sheet also exist: off white paper with light blue inscription, value, $500; white paper with dark blue inscription, value, $350; and off white paper with dark blue inscription, value, $650.

A24

A25

Designs: 50c, Modern mail service (truck, train, plane). 70c, Globe, stamps, dancer. 1k, Ancient mail service (messenger on elephant). 1.50k, Royal Messenger

## 1962, Nov. 15 — Unwmk. — Perf. 13

| | | | | |
|---|---|---|---|---|
| 77 | A24 | 50c multicolored | .60 | .60 |
| 78 | A24 | 70c multicolored | .60 | .60 |
| 79 | A25 | 1k dp clar, grn & blk | 1.25 | 1.25 |
| 80 | A25 | 1.50k multicolored | 1.00 | 1.00 |
| | | *Nos. 77-80 (4)* | 3.45 | 3.45 |

Souvenir sheets exist. One contains the 50c and 70c; the other, the 1k and 1.50k. The sheets exist both perf and imperf in a souvenir booklet of four sheets. Value intact booklet, $350.

Fishermen with Nets — A26

Threshing Rice — A27

Designs: 5k, Plowing and planting in rice paddy. 9k, Woman with infant harvesting rice.

## 1963, Mar. 21 — Perf. 13

| | | | | |
|---|---|---|---|---|
| 81 | A26 | 1k grn, bister & pur | .35 | .30 |
| 82 | A27 | 4k bister, bl & grn | .45 | .35 |
| 83 | A26 | 5k grn, bis & indigo | .65 | .45 |
| 84 | A27 | 9k grn, vio bl & ocher | 1.00 | .50 |
| a. | | Min. sheet of 4, #81-84, imperf. | 5.00 | 5.00 |
| b. | | As "a," left panel of No. 83 green instead of brown | 100.00 | 100.00 |
| | | *Nos. 81-84 (4)* | 2.45 | 1.60 |

FAO "Freedom from Hunger" campaign. No. 84a exists on yellowish and white papers; No. 84b exists only on yellowish paper.

No. 84b exists with gold inscriptions. Value $450.

Queen Khamphouy Handing out Gifts — A28

## 1963, Oct. 10 — Engr.

| | | | | |
|---|---|---|---|---|
| 85 | A28 | 4k brn, dp car & blue | .50 | .40 |
| 86 | A28 | 6k grn, red, yel & bl | .60 | .50 |
| 87 | A28 | 10k bl, dp car & dk brn | .90 | .65 |
| a. | | Miniature sheet of 3, #85-87 | 4.00 | 4.00 |
| | | *Nos. 85-87 (3)* | 2.00 | 1.55 |

Centenary of the International Red Cross.

Man Holding UN Emblem — A29

## 1963, Dec. 10 — Unwmk. — Perf. 13

| | | | | |
|---|---|---|---|---|
| 88 | A29 | 4k dk bl, dp org & vio brn | 1.50 | .80 |

15th anniv. of the Universal Declaration of Human Rights.
No. 88 also was issued imperf. Value, $15.

Temple of That Luang, Map of Nubia and Ramses II — A30

## 1964, Mar. 8 — Engr.

| | | | | |
|---|---|---|---|---|
| 89 | A30 | 4k multicolored | .40 | .40 |
| 90 | A30 | 6k multicolored | .60 | .60 |
| 91 | A30 | 10k multicolored | .75 | .75 |
| a. | | Miniature sheet of 3, #89-91 | 3.00 | 3.00 |
| | | *Nos. 89-91 (3)* | 1.75 | 1.75 |

UNESCO world campaign to save historic monuments in Nubia. No. 91a sold for 25k.

Ceremonial Chalice — A31

Designs: 15k, Buddha. 20k, Soldier leading people through Mekong River Valley. 40k, Royal Palace, Luang Prabang.

## 1964, July 30 — Unwmk. — Perf. 13

| | | | | |
|---|---|---|---|---|
| 92 | A31 | 10k multicolored | .40 | .30 |
| 93 | A31 | 15k multicolored | .60 | .40 |
| 94 | A31 | 20k multicolored | .80 | .60 |
| 95 | A31 | 40k multicolored | 1.25 | .75 |
| a. | | Miniature sheet of 4, #92-95 | 3.50 | 3.50 |
| | | *Nos. 92-95 (4)* | 3.05 | 2.05 |

"Neutral and Constitutional Laos." When the stamps are arranged in a block of four with 40k and 15k in first row and 10k and 20k in second row, the map of Laos appears.
A souvenir booklet containing No. 95a exists. Value, $45.

Prince Vet and Wife Mathie — A32

Scenes from Buddhist Legend of Phra Vet Sandone: 32k, God of the Skies sending his son to earth. 45k, Phaune's daughter with beggar husband. 55k, Beggar cornered by guard and dogs.

**1964, Nov. 17  Photo.  *Perf. 13x12½***

| 96 | A32 | 10k multicolored | .50 | .50 |
|---|---|---|---|---|
| 97 | A32 | 32k multicolored | .75 | .75 |
| 98 | A32 | 45k multicolored | 1.00 | 1.00 |
| 99 | A32 | 55k multicolored | 1.25 | 1.25 |
| a. | | Miniature sheet of 4 | 5.00 | 3.75 |
| | | Nos. 96-99 (4) | 3.50 | 3.50 |

No. 99a contains 4 imperf. stamps similar to Nos. 96-99.

A souvenir booklet containing No. 99a without the sheet number exists. Value, $100.

Lao Women — A33

**1964, Dec. 15  Engr.  *Perf. 13***

| 100 | A33 | 25k blk, org brn & pale ol | .75 | .75 |
|---|---|---|---|---|
| | | Nos. 100,C43-C45 (4) | 3.45 | 2.35 |

Butterflies — A34

10k, Cethosia biblis. 25k, Precis cebrene. 40k, Dysphania militaris.

**1965, Mar. 13  Unwmk.  *Perf. 13***
**Size: 36x36mm**

| 101 | A34 | 10k multi | 2.25 | 1.25 |
|---|---|---|---|---|
| 102 | A34 | 25k multi | 4.25 | 1.75 |

**Size: 48x27mm**

| 103 | A34 | 40k multi | 10.50 | 2.50 |
|---|---|---|---|---|
| | | Nos. 101-103,C46 (4) | 22.50 | 8.00 |

See. No. C46.

Teacher and School, American Aid — A35

Designs: 25k, Woman at Wattay Airport, French aid, horiz. 45k, Woman bathing child and food basket, Japanese aid. 55k, Musicians broadcasting, British aid, horiz.

**1965, Mar. 30  Engr.  *Perf. 13***

| 104 | A35 | 25k bl grn, brn & car rose | .45 | .30 |
|---|---|---|---|---|
| 105 | A35 | 45k ol grn & brn | .95 | .50 |
| 106 | A35 | 55k brt bl & bister | 1.25 | .65 |
| 107 | A35 | 75k multicolored | 1.75 | .80 |
| | | Nos. 104-107 (4) | 4.40 | 2.25 |

Issued to publicize foreign aid to Laos.

Hophabang Temple — A36

**1965, Apr. 23  Unwmk.  *Perf. 13***

| 108 | A36 | 10k multicolored | .75 | .35 |
|---|---|---|---|---|

Telewriter, Map of Laos and Globe — A37

30k, Communication by satellite & map of Laos. 50k, Globe, map of Laos & radio.

**1965, June 15  Engr.  *Perf. 13***

| 109 | A37 | 5k vio bl, brn & red lil | .30 | .25 |
|---|---|---|---|---|
| 110 | A37 | 30k bl, org brn & sl grn | .65 | .50 |
| 111 | A37 | 50k crim, lt bl & bis | 1.25 | .90 |
| a. | | Miniature sheet of 3, #109-111 | 4.75 | 4.75 |
| | | Nos. 109-111 (3) | 2.20 | 1.65 |

ITU, centenary.
A souvenir booklet containing No. 111a exists. Value, $35.

**Nos. 52-53 Surcharged in Dark Blue
with New Value and Bars**

**1965, July 5  Unwmk.  *Perf. 13***

| 112 | A16 | 1k on 4k rose claret | .70 | .25 |
|---|---|---|---|---|
| 113 | A16 | 5k on 6.50k org red | .70 | .25 |

Mother and Child, UNICEF and WHO Emblems — A38

**1965, Sept. 1  Engr.  *Perf. 13***

| 114 | A38 | 35k lt ultra & dk red | .85 | .70 |
|---|---|---|---|---|
| a. | | Miniature sheet | 4.75 | 4.75 |

Mother and Child Protection movement, 6th anniv.

Map of Laos and UN Emblem — A39

**1965, Nov. 3  *Perf. 12½x13***

| 115 | A39 | 5k emer, gray & vio bl | .30 | .25 |
|---|---|---|---|---|
| 116 | A39 | 25k lil rose, gray & vio bl | .45 | .35 |
| 117 | A39 | 40k bl, gray & vio bl | .70 | .50 |
| | | Nos. 115-117 (3) | 1.45 | 1.10 |

UN, 20th anniv. Although first day covers were canceled "Oct. 24," the actual day of issue is reported to have been Nov. 3.

Tikhy (Hockey) — A40

Pastimes: 10k, Two bulls fighting. 25k, Canoe race. 50k, Rocket festival.

**1965, Dec. 23  Engr.  *Perf. 13***

| 118 | A40 | 10k org, brn & gray | .30 | .25 |
|---|---|---|---|---|
| 119 | A40 | 20k grn, ver & dk bl | .40 | .30 |
| 120 | A40 | 25k brt blue & multi | .40 | .35 |
| 121 | A40 | 50k orange & multi | .90 | .50 |
| | | Nos. 118-121 (4) | 2.00 | 1.40 |

Slaty-headed Parakeet — A41

Birds: 15k, White-crested laughing thrush. 20k, Osprey. 45k, Bengal roller.

**1966, Feb. 10  Engr.  *Perf. 13***

| 122 | A41 | 5k car rose, ol & brn | .85 | .50 |
|---|---|---|---|---|
| 123 | A41 | 15k bluish grn, brn & blk | 1.25 | .60 |
| 124 | A41 | 20k dl bl, sep & bister | 2.10 | 1.00 |
| 125 | A41 | 45k vio, Prus bl & sepia | 4.25 | 2.40 |
| | | Nos. 122-125 (4) | 8.45 | 4.50 |

WHO Headquarters, Geneva — A42

**1966, May 3  Engr.  *Perf. 13***

| 126 | A42 | 10k bl grn & indigo | .30 | .25 |
|---|---|---|---|---|
| 127 | A42 | 25k car & dk green | .40 | .30 |
| 128 | A42 | 50k ultra & black | .85 | .70 |
| a. | | Miniature sheet of 3, #126-128 | 19.00 | 19.00 |
| | | Nos. 126-128 (3) | 1.55 | 1.25 |

Inauguration of the WHO Headquarters, Geneva. No. 128a sold for 150k.

Ordination of Buddhist Monk — A43

Folklore: 25k, Women building ceremonial sand hills. 30k, Procession of the Wax Pagoda, vert. 40k, Wrist-tying ceremony (3 men, 3 women), vert.

**1966, May 20  *Perf. 13***

| 129 | A43 | 10k multicolored | .30 | .25 |
|---|---|---|---|---|
| 130 | A43 | 25k multicolored | .45 | .30 |
| 131 | A43 | 30k multicolored | .75 | .50 |
| 132 | A43 | 40k multicolored | 1.00 | .70 |
| | | Nos. 129-132 (4) | 2.50 | 1.75 |

UNESCO Emblem — A44

**1966, July 7  Engr.  *Perf. 13***

| 133 | A44 | 20k ocher & gray | .30 | .25 |
|---|---|---|---|---|
| 134 | A44 | 30k brt blue & gray | .40 | .30 |
| 135 | A44 | 40k brt green & gray | .55 | .50 |
| 136 | A44 | 60k crimson & gray | .80 | .45 |
| a. | | Miniature sheet, #133-136 | 6.00 | 6.00 |
| | | Nos. 133-136 (4) | 2.05 | 1.30 |

UNESCO, 20th anniv. No. 136a sold for 250k.

Addressed Envelope Carrier Pigeon, Globe and Hand with Quill Pen — A45

**1966, Sept. 7  Engr.  *Perf. 13***

| 137 | A45 | 5k red, brn & bl | .30 | .25 |
|---|---|---|---|---|
| 138 | A45 | 20k bl grn, blk & lil | .45 | .30 |
| 139 | A45 | 40k bl, red brn & dk ol bister | .55 | .35 |
| 140 | A45 | 45k brt rose lil, bl grn & black | .75 | .50 |
| a. | | Min. sheet of 4, #137-140 | 6.00 | 6.00 |
| | | Nos. 137-140 (4) | 2.05 | 1.40 |

Intl. Letter Writing Week, Oct. 6-12. No. 140a sold for 250k.

Sculpture from Siprapouthbat Temple — A46

Sculptures: 20k, from Visoun Temple. 50k, from Xiengthong Temple. 70k, from Visoun Temple.

**1967, Feb. 21  Engr.  *Perf. 12½x13***

| 141 | A46 | 5k olive grn & grn | .30 | .25 |
|---|---|---|---|---|
| 142 | A46 | 20k brn ol & gray bl | .70 | .40 |
| 143 | A46 | 50k dk brn & dp claret | 1.25 | .60 |
| 144 | A46 | 70k dk brn & dk magenta | 1.50 | .80 |
| | | Nos. 141-144 (4) | 3.75 | 1.95 |

General Post Office — A47

**1967, Apr. 6  Engr.  *Perf. 13***

| 145 | A47 | 25k brn, grn & vio brn | .35 | .25 |
|---|---|---|---|---|
| 146 | A47 | 50k ind, brt blue & grn | .55 | .40 |
| 147 | A47 | 70k dk red, grn & brn | 1.25 | .75 |
| | | Nos. 145-147 (3) | 2.15 | 1.40 |

Inauguration of the new Post and Telegraph Headquarters.

Snakehead A48

Fish: 35k, Giant catfish. 45k, Spiny eel. 60k, Knifefish.

**1967, June 8  Engr.  *Perf. 13x12½***

| 148 | A48 | 20k dl bl, bis & blk | 1.25 | .50 |
|---|---|---|---|---|
| 149 | A48 | 35k aqua, bis & gray | 1.50 | .60 |
| 150 | A48 | 45k pale grn, bis & ol brn | 2.50 | .70 |
| 151 | A48 | 60k sl grn, bis & blk | 3.75 | .80 |
| | | Nos. 148-151 (4) | 9.00 | 2.60 |

Drumstick Tree Flower — A49

Blossoms: 55k, Turmeric. 75k, Peacock flower. 80k, Pagoda tree.

**1967, Aug. 10  Engr.  *Perf. 12½x13***

| 152 | A49 | 5k red lil, yel & grn | .60 | .35 |
|---|---|---|---|---|
| 153 | A49 | 55k org, mag & lt grn | .90 | .45 |
| 154 | A49 | 75k bl, red & lt grn | 1.25 | .65 |
| 155 | A49 | 80k brt grn, mag & yel | 1.50 | .75 |
| | | Nos. 152-155 (4) | 4.25 | 2.20 |

Banded Krait — A50

Reptiles: 40k, Marsh crocodile. 100k, Malayan moccasin. 200k, Water monitor.

**1967, Dec. 7  Engr.  *Perf. 13***

| 156 | A50 | 5k emer, ind & yel | .85 | .40 |
|---|---|---|---|---|
| 157 | A50 | 40k sep, lt grn & yel | 1.75 | .60 |
| 158 | A50 | 100k lt grn, brn & ocher | 3.50 | 1.75 |
| 159 | A50 | 200k grn, blk & bister | 8.50 | 5.00 |
| | | Nos. 156-159 (4) | 14.60 | 7.75 |

Human Rights Flame A51

**1968, Feb. 8  Engr.  *Perf. 13***

| 160 | A51 | 20k brt grn, red & grn | .30 | .25 |
|---|---|---|---|---|
| 161 | A51 | 30k brn, red & grn | .40 | .30 |
| 162 | A51 | 50k brt bl, red & grn | .80 | .60 |
| a. | | Souv. sheet of 3, #160-162 | 5.00 | 5.00 |
| | | Nos. 160-162 (3) | 1.50 | 1.15 |

Intl. Human Rights Year. No. 162a sold for 250k.

WHO Emblem — A52

**1968, July 5  Engr.  *Perf. 12½x13***

| 163 | A52 | 15k rose vio, ver & ocher | .30 | .25 |
|---|---|---|---|---|
| 164 | A52 | 30k brt bl, brt grn & ocher | .30 | .25 |
| 165 | A52 | 70k ver, plum & ocher | .55 | .40 |
| 166 | A52 | 110k brn, brt rose lil & ocher | .90 | .55 |

**167** A52 250k brt grn, brt bl &
    ocher    2.40  1.50
   *a.*  Souv. sheet of 5, #163-167  6.50  6.50
    *Nos. 163-167 (5)*  4.45  2.95
WHO, 20th anniv. No. 167a sold for 500k.

Parade and
Memorial
Arch — A53

Designs: 20k, Armored Corps with tanks.
60k, Three soldiers with Laotian flag.

**1968, July 15**     *Perf. 13*
**168** A53 15k multicolored  .35  .25
**169** A53 20k multicolored  .45  .35
**170** A53 60k multicolored  .90  .45
    *Nos. 168-170,C52-C53 (5)*  5.95  3.15
Laotian Army. For souvenir sheet see No.
C53a.

Chrysochroa
Mnizechi — A54

Insects: 50k, Aristobia approximator. 90k,
Eutaenia corbetti.

**1968, Aug. 28**   **Engr.**   *Perf. 13*
**171** A54 30k vio bl, grn & yel  .90  .35
**172** A54 50k lil, blk & ocher  1.50  .50
**173** A54 90k bis, blk & org  2.25  1.25
    *Nos. 171-173,C54-C55 (5)*  8.40  4.20
    See. Nos. C54-C55.

Mangoes — A55

Fruits: 50k, Tamarind. 180k, Jackfruit, horiz.
250k, Watermelon, horiz.

**1968, Oct. 3**   **Engr.**   *Perf. 13*
**174** A55 20k ind, lt bl & emer  .40  .25
**175** A55 50k lt bl, emer & brn  1.00  .50
**176** A55 180k sep, org & yel grn  2.00  1.10
**177** A55 250k sep, bis & emer  2.75  1.60
    *Nos. 174-177 (4)*  5.85  3.35

Hurdling
A56

**1968, Nov. 15**   **Engr.**   *Perf. 13*
**178** A56 15k shown  .50  .50
**179** A56 80k Tennis  1.00  .50
**180** A56 100k Soccer  1.00  .50
**181** A56 110k High jump  1.50  1.00
    *Nos. 178-181 (4)*  4.00  2.50
19th Olympic Games, Mexico City, 10/12-27.

Wedding of
Kathanam and
Nang Sida — A57

Design: 200k, Thao Khathanam battling the
serpent Ngou Xouang and the giant bird
Phanga Houng. Design from panels of the
central gate of Ongtu Temple, Vientiane.
Design of 150k is from east gate.

**1969, Feb. 28**   **Photo.**   *Perf. 12x13*
**182** A57 150k blk, gold & red  2.00  1.25
**183** A57 200k blk, gold & red  2.75  1.75

Soukhib Ordered to
Attack — A58

Scenes from Royal Ballet: 15k, Pharak
pleading for Nang Sita. 20k, Thotsakan
reviewing his troops. 30k, Nang Sita awaiting
punishment. 40k, Pharam inspecting troops.
60k, Hanuman preparing to rescue Nang Sita.

**1969**   **Photo.**   *Perf. 14*
**184** A58 10k multicolored  .50  .25
**185** A58 15k blue & multi  .70  .40
**186** A58 20k lt bl & multi  .70  .50
**187** A58 30k salmon & multi  1.00  .55
**188** A58 40k salmon & multi  1.60  .70
**189** A58 60k pink & multi  2.00  1.10
    *Nos. 184-189,C56-C57 (8)*  17.00  8.50
    See Nos. C56-C57. For surcharges see
Nos. B12-B17, CB1-CB2.

ILO Emblem and
Basket Weavers
at Vientiane
Vocational
Center — A59

**1969, May 7**   **Engr.**   *Perf. 13*
**190** A59 30k claret & violet  .50  .40
**191** A59 60k slate grn & vio brn  1.00  .75
    *Nos. 190-191,C58 (3)*  7.00  4.40
    ILO, 50th anniv.

Chinese
Pangolin
A60

**1969, Nov. 6**   **Photo.**   *Perf. 13x12*
**192** A60 15k multicolored  .60  .25
**193** A60 30k multicolored  1.00  .50
    *Nos. 192-193,C59-C61 (5)*  7.85  3.85
    See Nos. C59-C61.

That Luang,
Luang
Prabang — A61

King Sisavang-
Vong
A62

**1969, Nov. 19**   **Engr.**   *Perf. 13*
**194** A61 50k dk brn, bl & bister  .80  .60
**195** A62 70k maroon & buff  1.40  1.00
   *a.*  Pair, #194-195 + label  3.50  3.50
Death of King Sisavang-Vong, 10th anniv.

Carved Capital
from Wat
Xiengthong
A63

**1970, Jan. 10**   **Photo.**   *Perf. 12x13*
**196** A63 70k multicolored  1.75  1.25
    *Nos. 196,C65-C66 (3)*  5.15  2.90

Kongphene
(Midday)
Drum
A64

Designs: 55k, Kongthong (bronze) drum.

**1970, Mar. 30**   **Engr.**   *Perf. 13*
**197** A64 30k bl gray, ol & org  1.00  .60
**198** A64 55k ocher, blk & yel grn  1.75  1.35
    *Nos. 197-198,C67 (3)*  5.75  3.45
    See No. C67.

Lenin Explaining Electrification Plan,
by L. Shmatko — A65

**1970, Apr. 22**   **Litho.**   *Perf. 12½x12*
**199** A65 30k blue & multi  1.10  .55
**200** A65 70k rose red & multi  1.40  .75
    Lenin (1870-1924), Russian communist
leader.

Silk Weaver and
EXPO
Emblem — A66

**1970, July 7**   **Engr.**   *Perf. 13*
**201** A66 30k shown  .70  .30
**202** A66 70k Woman winding
    thread  1.00  .80
    *Nos. 201-202,C69 (3)*  3.45  2.35
Laotian silk industry; EXPO '70 Intl. Exposition, Osaka, Japan, Mar. 15-Sept. 13.
See No. C69.

Wild Boar — A67

**1970, Sept. 7**   **Engr.**   *Perf. 13*
**203** A67 20k green & dp brn  .55  .25
**204** A67 60k dp brn & ol bis  1.00  .45
    *Nos. 203-204,C70-C71 (4)*  9.30  4.45
    See Nos. C70-C71.

Buddha, UN
Headquarters and
Emblem — A68

**1970, Oct. 24**     **Size: 22x36mm**
**205** A68 30k ultra, brn & rose red  .70  .40
**206** A68 70k brt grn, sep & vio  1.40  .60
    *Nos. 205-206,C75 (3)*  4.50  2.10
    UN, 25th anniv.
    See No. C75.

Nakhanet,
Symbol of
Arts and
Culture
A69

85k, Rahu swallowing the moon.

**1971, Feb. 5**
**207** A69 70k shown  1.00  .60
**208** A69 85k multicolored  1.40  .85
    *Nos. 207-208,C76 (3)*  4.80  2.45

Silversmithing
A70

**1971, Apr. 12**   **Engr.**   *Perf. 13*
    **Size: 36x36mm**
**209** A70 30k shown  .35  .25
**210** A70 50k Pottery  .55  .35
    **Size: 47x36mm**
**211** A70 70k Boat building  1.10  .40
    *Nos. 209-211 (3)*  2.00  1.00

Laotian and
African
Children,
UN Emblem
A71

60k, Women musicians, elephants, UN
emblem.

**1971, May 1**   **Engr.**   *Perf. 13*
**212** A71 30k lt grn, brn & blk  .50  .30
**213** A71 60k yel, pur & dull red  1.10  .50
    Intl. year against racial discrimination.

Miss Rotary, Wat Ho
Phrakeo — A72

Design: 30k, Monk on roof of That Luang
and Rotary emblem, horiz.

**1971, June 28**   **Engr.**   *Perf. 13*
**214** A72 30k purple & ocher  .60  .40
**215** A72 70k gray ol, dk bl & rose  1.25  .55
    Rotary International, 50th anniversary.

Dendrobium
Aggregatum — A73

50k, Asocentrum ampullaceum, horiz. 70k,
Trichoglottis fasciata, horiz.

**Perf. 12½x13, 13x12½**
**1971, July 7**     **Photo.**
**Size: 26x36, 36x26mm**
216 A73 30k shown   1.00 .50
217 A73 50k multicolored   1.40 .95
218 A73 70k multicolored   2.00 1.25
Nos. 216-218,C79 (4)   8.90 4.20
See Nos. 230-232, C79, C89.

Palm Civet — A74

Animals: 40k, like 25k. 50k, Lesser mouse deer. 85k, Sika deer.

**1971, Sept. 16**   **Engr.**   **Perf. 13**
219 A74 25k pur, dk bl & blk   .80 .45
220 A74 40k grn, ol bis & blk   1.00 .60
221 A74 50k brt grn & ocher   1.50 .70
222 A74 85k sl grn, grn & brn orange   2.50 1.25
Nos. 219-222,C83 (5)   10.05 5.75
See No. C83.

**Types of 1952-57 with Ornamental Panels and Inscriptions**

Designs: 30k, Laotian woman. 40k, So player (like #C25). 50k, Rama (like #C19).

**1971, Oct. 31**
223 A3 30k brn vio & brn   .50 .30
224 A10 40k sepia, blk & ver   .70 .50
225 AP7 50k ultra, blk & salmon   1.00 .70
Nos. 223-225,C84 (4)   4.20 2.90
**Souvenir Sheet**
225A A3 Sheet of 3   6.00 6.00
  b. 60k   2.00 2.00
  c. 85k   2.00 2.00

20th anniv. of Laotian independent postal service. All stamps inscribed: "Vingtième Anniversaire de la Philatélie Lao," "Postes" and "1971." No. 225A contains No. 223 and 60k and 85k in design of 30k, sold for 250k.

Children Learning to Read — A75

70k, Scribe writing on palm leaves.

**1972, Jan. 30**   **Engr.**   **Perf. 13**
**Size: 36x22mm**
226 A75 30k shown   .35 .30
227 A75 70k multicolored   .70 .50
Nos. 226-227,C87 (3)   2.80 1.80
Intl. Book Year.
See No. C87.

Nam Ngum Hydroelectric Dam, Monument and ECAFE Emblem — A76

**1972, Mar. 28**   **Engr.**   **Perf. 13**
228 A76 40k grn, ultra & lt brn   .35 .25
229 A76 80k grn, brn ol & dk bl   .70 .40
Nos. 228-229,C88 (3)   2.45 1.45

25th anniv. of the Economic Commission for Asia and the Far East (ECAFE), which helped build the Nam Ngum Hydroelectric Dam.
See No. C88.

**Orchid Type of 1971**

Orchids: 40k, Hynchostylis giganterum. 60k, Paphiopedilum exul. 80k, Cattleya, horiz.

**1972, May 5**   **Photo.**   **Perf. 13**
**Size: 26x36mm, 36x26mm**
230 A73 40k lt bl & multi   .95 .35
231 A73 60k multicolored   1.60 .45
232 A73 80k lt bl & multi   2.00 .50
Nos. 230-232,C89 (4)   8.55 2.80

Woman Carrying Water, UNICEF Emblem A77

Children's drawings: 80k, Child learning bamboo-weaving, UNICEF emblem.

**1972, July 20**   **Engr.**   **Perf. 13**
233 A77 50k blue & multi   .70 .50
234 A77 80k brown & multi   1.00 .65
Nos. 233-234,C90 (3)   3.10 2.15
25th anniv. (in 1971) of UNICEF.
See No. C90.

Attopeu Costume, Religious Ceremony — A78

Design: 90k, Phongsaly festival costume.

**1973, Feb. 16**   **Engr.**   **Perf. 13**
235 A78 40k maroon & multi   .50 .30
236 A78 90k multicolored   1.10 .50
Nos. 235-236,C101-C102 (4)   4.90 2.60
See Nos. C101-C102.

Lion from Wat That Luang and Lions Emblem — A79

**1973, Mar. 30**   **Engr.**   **Perf. 13**
237 A79 40k vio bl, rose cl & lil   .70 .25
238 A79 90k pur, org brn & yel   1.10 .40
Nos. 237-238,C103 (3)   3.70 1.40
Lions International of Laos.

Dr. Hansen, Map of Laos, "Dok Hak" Flowers A80

**1973, June 28**   **Engr.**   **Perf. 13**
239 A80 40k multicolored   .60 .30
240 A80 80k multicolored   1.25 .45
Centenary of the discovery by Dr. Armauer G. Hansen of the Hansen bacillus, the cause of leprosy.

Wat Vixun, Monk Blessing Girl Scouts — A81

**1973, Sept. 1**   **Engr.**   **Perf. 13**
241 A81 70k ocher & brown   .90 .40
Nos. 241,C106-C107 (3)   3.25 1.10
25th anniv. of Laotian Scout Movement.

INTERPOL Headquarters A82

**1973, Dec. 22**   **Engr.**   **Perf. 13x12½**
242 A82 40k greenish bl   .45 .25
243 A82 80k brown   .75 .60
Nos. 242-243,C110 (3)   2.60 1.45
Intl. Criminal Police Org., 50th anniv.

Boy Mailing Letter — A83

**1974, Apr. 30**   **Engr.**   **Perf. 13**
244 A83 70k bl, lt grn & ocher   1.00 .25
245 A83 80k lt grn, bl & ocher   1.20 .40
Nos. 244-245,C114-C115 (4)   11.95 3.65
UPU, cent.

Blue Sage — A84

50k, Water lilies, horiz. 80k, Scheffler's kapokier, horiz.

**1974, May 17**
**Size: 26x36mm, 36x26mm**
246 A84 30k grn & vio   .55 .40
247 A84 50k multicolored   .90 .50
248 A84 80k multicolored   1.25 .75
Nos. 246-248,C116 (4)   8.20 4.65
See No. C116.

Mekong River Ferry — A85

90k, Samlo (passenger tricycle), vert.

**1974, July 31**   **Engr.**   **Perf. 13**
249 A85 25k red brn & choc   .40 .40
250 A85 90k brown ol & lt ol   1.25 1.25
Nos. 249-250,C117 (3)   4.15 3.15
See No. C117.

Marconi, Indigenous Transmission Methods, Transistor Radio — A86

**1974, Aug. 28**   **Engr.**   **Perf. 13**
251 A86 60k multicolored   .50 .50
252 A86 90k multicolored   .75 .75
Nos. 251-252,C118 (3)   3.50 2.35
Guglielmo Marconi (1874-1937), Italian electrical engineer and inventor.
See No. C118.

Diastocera Wallichi Tonkinensis A87

90k, Macrochenus isabellunus. 100k, Purpuricenus malaccensis.

**1974, Oct. 23**   **Engr.**   **Perf. 13**
253 A87 50k shown   .90 .60
254 A87 90k multicolored   1.40 .85
255 A87 100k multicolored   1.75 .90
Nos. 253-255,C119 (4)   5.80 3.35
See No. C119.

Temple, Houeisai, and Sapphire — A88

110k, Sapphire panning at Attopeu.

**1975, Feb. 12**   **Engr.**   **Perf. 13x12½**
256 A88 100k bl, brn & grn   1.50 .50
257 A88 110k multicolored   1.75 .75

King Sisavang-Vong, Princes Souvanna Phouma and Souphanou-Vong — A89

**1975, Feb. 21**   **Engr.**   **Perf. 13**
258 A89 80k olive & multi   1.00 .40
259 A89 300k multicolored   1.75 .90
260 A89 420k multicolored   2.00 1.25
Nos. 258-260 (3)   4.75 2.55
1st anniv. of Peace Treaty of Vientiane. A souvenir sheet exists, embossed on paper with a foil application. Value, $10.

Fortuneteller Working on Forecast for New Year (Size of pair: 100x27mm) — A90

New Year Riding Rabbit, and Tiger (Old Year) — A92

Designs: 40k, Chart of New Year symbols. 200k, Fortune teller. 350k, As shown.

**1975, Apr. 14**   **Engr.**   **Perf. 13**
261 40k bister & red brn   .50 .25
262 200k bis, red brn & sl   1.40 .80
  a. A90 Pair, #261-262   2.25 1.75
263 A92 350k blue & multi   2.50 1.60
Nos. 261-263 (3)   4.40 2.65
New Year 1975, Year of the Rabbit.

UN Emblem, "Equality" — A93

200k, IWY emblem, man and woman.

**1975, June 19**   **Engr.**
264 A93 100k dl bl & vio bl   .55 .40
265 A93 200k multi   1.20 .85
  a. Miniature sheet of 2, #264-265   5.50 5.50
International Women's Year.

UPU, Cent. A93a

Designs: 15k, Runner, rocket reaching orbit, vert. 30k, Docked Soyuz capsules, chariot, vert. 40k, Biplane, Concorde. 1000k, Apollo spacecraft in orbit. 1500k, Apollo spacecraft, astronaut, vert. No. 266F, Wagon train, Lunar Rover. No. 266G, Mail truck, Concorde. No. 266H, stagecoach. No. 266I, Zeppelin, locomotive.

**Perf. 13x14, 14x13**
**1975, July 7**   **Litho.**
266 A93a 10k multi   .30 .25
  b. Souvenir sheet of 1   12.50 12.50
266A A93a 15k multi   .50 .25
  b. Souvenir sheet of 1   12.50 12.50

| | | | | |
|---|---|---|---|---|
| 266B | A93a | 30k multi | .70 | .35 |
| a. | | Souvenir sheet of 1 | 12.50 | 12.50 |
| 266C | A93a | 40k multi | .90 | .60 |
| a. | | Souvenir sheet of 1 | 12.50 | 12.50 |
| 266D | A93a | 1000k multi | 2.75 | 2.00 |
| a. | | Souvenir sheet of 1 | 12.50 | 12.50 |
| 266E | A93a | 1500k multi | 4.75 | 3.00 |
| a. | | Souvenir sheet of 1 | 12.50 | 12.50 |
| | | Nos. 266-266E (6) | 9.90 | 6.45 |

### Litho. & Embossed
**Perf. 13½**

| | | | | |
|---|---|---|---|---|
| 266F | A93a | 2500k gold & multi | 11.00 | 11.00 |
| a. | | Souvenir sheet of 1 | 95.00 | 95.00 |
| 266G | A93a | 3000k gold & multi | 11.00 | 11.00 |
| a. | | Souvenir sheet of 1 | 90.00 | 90.00 |

### Souvenir Sheets

| | | | | |
|---|---|---|---|---|
| 266H | A93a | 2500k gold & multi | 35.00 | 35.00 |
| 266I | A93a | 3000k gold & multi | 30.00 | 30.00 |

Nos. 266D-266E, 266G-266I are airmail.
Nos. 266-266E also exist imperf. Value, set of six pairs $150. Nos. 266b, 266Ab and 266Ba-266Ea also exist imperf. Value, set of six sheets $375. Nos. 266Fa, 266Ga and 266H-266I also exist imperf. Value, set of four sheets $550.

Both perforated and imperforate souvenir sheets with blue space images in the selvage exist for 266D and 266E. Value for set of four $35.

No. 266F exists perf and imperf. in sheets of 4.

Apollo-Soyuz Mission — A93b

Designs: 125k, Astronauts, Thomas Stafford, Vance D. Brand, Donald Slayton. 150k, Cosmonauts Alexei Leonov, Valery Koubasov. 200k, Apollo-Soyuz link-up. 300k, Handshake in space. 450k, Preparation for re-entry. 700k, Apollo splashdown.

**1975, July 7    Litho.    Perf. 14x13**

| | | | | |
|---|---|---|---|---|
| 267 | A93b | 125k multicolored | .80 | .75 |
| 267A | A93b | 150k multicolored | .95 | .75 |
| 267B | A93b | 200k multicolored | 1.50 | 1.00 |
| 267C | A93b | 300k multicolored | 2.00 | 1.50 |
| 267D | A93b | 450k multicolored | 3.25 | 1.75 |
| 267E | A93b | 700k multicolored | 3.75 | 1.50 |
| | | Nos. 267-267E (6) | 12.25 | 7.25 |

Nos. 267-267E are airmail.
Nos. 267-267E exist imperf. Value, set $55.00
Nos. 267D-267E exist in souvenir sheets of 1. Value, set perf. $75., set imperf. $150.

Scene from Vet Sandone Legend — A94

Designs: Scenes from Buddhist legend of Prince Vet Sandone.

**1975, July 22    Photo.    Perf. 13**

| | | | | |
|---|---|---|---|---|
| 268 | A94 | 80k multicolored | .65 | .30 |
| 268A | A94 | 110k multicolored | .70 | .40 |
| 268B | A94 | 120k multicolored | .90 | .50 |
| 268C | A94 | 130k multicolored | 1.50 | .60 |
| | | Nos. 268-268C (4) | 3.75 | 1.80 |

American Revolution, Bicent. — A94a

Presidents: 10k, Washington, J. Adams, Jefferson, Madison. 15k, Monroe, J.Q. Adams, Jackson, Van Buren. 40k, Harrison, Tyler, Polk, Taylor. 50k, Filmore, Pierce, Buchanon, Lincoln. 100k, Johnson, Grant, Hayes, Garfield. 123k, Arthur, Cleveland, Harrison. 150k, McKinley, Roosevelt, Taft, Wilson. 200k, Harding, Coolidge, Hoover, Roosevelt. 1000k, Truman, Eisenhower, Kennedy. 1500k, L. Johnson, Nixon, Ford.

**1975, June    Litho.    Perf. 13½**

| | | | | |
|---|---|---|---|---|
| 269 | A94a | 10k multicolored | 5.00 | — |
| 269A | A94a | 15k multicolored | 5.00 | — |
| 269B | A94a | 40k multicolored | 5.00 | — |
| 269C | A94a | 50k multicolored | 5.00 | — |
| 269D | A94a | 100k multicolored | 5.00 | — |
| 269E | A94a | 123k multicolored | 5.00 | — |
| 269F | A94a | 150k multicolored | 5.00 | — |
| 269G | A94a | 200k multicolored | 5.00 | — |
| 269H | A94a | 1000k multicolored | 5.00 | — |
| 269I | A94a | 1500k multicolored | 5.00 | — |
| | | Nos. 269-269I (10) | 50.00 | |

Nos. 269H-269I are airmail. These stamps were not approved by the Laotian government, however they were offered for sale at the Laotian post offices and used as valid postage for a brief period before being withdrawn. There is some question as to whether 269C-269G were sold in the Laotian post offices, however in period covers indicate that they probably were. Also exists imperf., set of 10, $200. Souvenir sheets of one exist both perforated, value $235, and imperforate, value $2,650.

Buddha, Stupas of Borobudur A95

Design: 200k, Borobudur sculptures and UNESCO emblem.

**1975, Aug. 20    Engr.    Perf. 13**

| | | | | |
|---|---|---|---|---|
| 270 | A95 | 100k indigo & multi | .85 | .40 |
| 271 | A95 | 200k multicolored | 1.60 | .85 |
| a. | | Miniature sheet of 2, #270-271 | 2.50 | 2.50 |

UNESCO campaign to save Borobudur Temple, Java.

Coat of Arms of Republic — A96

**1976, Dec. 2    Litho.    Perf. 14**

| | | | | |
|---|---|---|---|---|
| 272 | A96 | 1k blue & multi | .30 | .25 |
| 273 | A96 | 2k rose & multi | .30 | .25 |
| 274 | A96 | 5k brt grn & multi | .30 | .25 |
| 275 | A96 | 10k lilac & multi | .50 | .40 |
| 276 | A96 | 200k orange & multi | 3.50 | 2.25 |
| a. | | Min. sheet of 5, #272-276 | 10.00 | 10.00 |
| | | Nos. 272-276 (5) | 4.90 | 3.40 |

Nos. 272-276 exist imperforate. Value, set $70.
Imperforate miniature sheets of 1 of Nos. 272-276 exist. Value, set $100. In 2021, this set of imperforate miniature sheets of 1 were handstamp overprinted in red to commemorate the 60th anniversary of diplomatic relations between Laos and People's Republic of China.

For overprints and surcharges, see Nos. 426A, 426V, 508C, 676H, 1903.

Thathiang Pagoda, Vientiane — A97

Designs: 2k, 80k, 100k, Phonsi Pagoda, Luang Prabang. 30k, 300k, like 1k.

**1976, Dec. 18    Perf. 13½**

| | | | | |
|---|---|---|---|---|
| 277 | A97 | 1k multicolored | .30 | .25 |
| 278 | A97 | 2k multicolored | .40 | .25 |
| 279 | A97 | 30k multicolored | .85 | .50 |
| 280 | A97 | 80k multicolored | 1.75 | 1.00 |
| 281 | A97 | 100k multicolored | 2.50 | 1.40 |
| a. | | Souv. sheet of 3, #278, 280-281 | 5.25 | |
| b. | | As a, imperf. | 12.00 | |

| | | | | |
|---|---|---|---|---|
| 282 | A97 | 300k multicolored | 4.00 | 2.50 |
| a. | | Souv. sheet of 3, #277, 279, 282 | 5.25 | |
| b. | | As a, imperf. | 12.00 | |
| | | Nos. 277-282 (6) | 9.80 | 5.90 |

Nos. 277-282 exist imperf. Value, set $45.

Silversmith A98

**Perf. 13x12½, 12½x13**

**1977, Apr. 1    Litho.**

| | | | | |
|---|---|---|---|---|
| 283 | A98 | 1k shown | .30 | .25 |
| 284 | A98 | 2k Weaver | .30 | .25 |
| 285 | A98 | 20k Potter | .65 | .25 |
| 286 | A98 | 50k Basket weaver, vert. | 1.25 | .40 |
| | | Nos. 283-286 (4) | 2.50 | 1.15 |

Miniature sheets of 2 exist, perf. and imperf. Values: perf, $13; imperf. $16.
For overprints, see Nos. 426B, 426C, 426D, 426E, 426R, 676B.

Cosmonauts A.A. Gubarev, G.M. Grechko — A99

Government Palace, Vientiane, Kremlin, Moscow A100

20k, 50k, Lenin speaking on Red Square.

**Perf. 12x12½, 12½x12**

**1977, Oct. 25    Litho.**

| | | | | |
|---|---|---|---|---|
| 287 | A99 | 5k multicolored | .30 | .25 |
| 288 | A99 | 20k multicolored | .40 | .25 |
| 289 | A99 | 50k multicolored | .70 | .30 |
| 290 | A99 | 60k multicolored | .90 | .40 |
| 291 | A100 | 100k multicolored | 1.40 | .65 |
| a. | | Souv. sheet of 3, #288, 290-291 | 6.00 | 6.00 |
| 292 | A100 | 250k multicolored | 2.25 | 1.50 |
| a. | | Souv. sheet of 3, #287, 289, 292 | 6.00 | 6.00 |
| | | Nos. 287-292 (6) | 5.95 | 3.35 |

60th anniv. of Russian October Revolution.
Nos. 287-292 exist imperf. Value, set $15.
For overprints, see Nos. 426F, 426N, 676C, 676F, 676I.

Natl. Arms — A101

**1978, May 26    Litho.    Perf. 12½**

| | | | | |
|---|---|---|---|---|
| 293 | A101 | 5k dull org & blk | .30 | .25 |
| 294 | A101 | 10k tan & black | .35 | .25 |
| 295 | A101 | 50k brt pink & blk | .50 | .25 |
| 296 | A101 | 100k yel grn & blk | 1.25 | .45 |
| 297 | A101 | 250k violet & blk | 2.00 | .85 |
| | | Nos. 293-297 (5) | 4.40 | 2.05 |

For overprints, see Nos. 426G, 676J.

A102

Army Day: 20k, Soldiers with flag. 40k, Fighters and burning house, horiz. 300k, Anti-aircraft battery.

**Perf. 12½x12¼, 12½x12¾**

**1978, Sept. 15    Litho.**

| | | | | |
|---|---|---|---|---|
| 298 | A102 | 20k multicolored | .30 | .25 |
| 299 | A102 | 40k multicolored | .55 | .25 |
| 300 | A102 | 300k multicolored | 2.10 | 1.00 |
| | | Nos. 298-300 (3) | 2.95 | 1.50 |

Nos. 298-300 exist imperf. Value, set $55.
For overprints see No. 426O, 426Q, 676A, 676L.

Marchers with Banner — A103

**1978, Dec. 2    Litho.    Perf. 11½**

| | | | | |
|---|---|---|---|---|
| 301 | A103 | 20k shown | .50 | .25 |
| 302 | A103 | 50k Women with flag | .70 | .25 |
| 303 | A103 | 400k Dancer | 2.25 | 1.40 |
| a. | | Sheet of 3, #301-303, imperf. | 4.25 | |
| | | Nos. 301-303 (3) | 3.45 | 1.90 |

National Day. A second printing in slightly different colors and with rough perforation exists; values the same. Stamps in souvenir sheet are in reverse order.

Electronic Tree, Map of Laos, ITU Emblem — A104

Design: 250k, Electronic tree, map of Laos and broadcast tower.

**1979, Jan. 18    Litho.    Perf. 12½**

| | | | | |
|---|---|---|---|---|
| 304 | A104 | 30k multicolored | .30 | .25 |
| 305 | A104 | 250k multicolored | 2.50 | 1.00 |

World Telecommunications Day, 1978.
Nos. 304-305 exist imperf. Value, set $10.
For overprints, see Nos. 426P, 426W, 676K.

Woman Mailing Letter — A105

10k, 80k, Processing mail. 100k, like 5k.

**1979, Jan. 18**

| | | | | |
|---|---|---|---|---|
| 306 | A105 | 5k multicolored | .30 | .25 |
| 307 | A105 | 10k multicolored | .30 | .25 |
| 308 | A105 | 80k multicolored | 1.00 | .30 |
| 309 | A105 | 100k multicolored | 1.40 | .40 |
| | | Nos. 306-309 (4) | 3.00 | 1.20 |

Asian-Oceanic Postal Union, 15th anniv.
Nos. 306-309 exist imperf. Value, set $12.50.
For overprints, see Nos. 426H, 426J, 426K, 426T, 426U, 676E, 676G.

Intl. Year of the Child — A106

No. 310, Playing with ball, vert. No. 311, Studying. No. 312, Playing musical instruments. No. 313, Breast-feeding, vert. No. 314, Map, globe, vert. No. 315, Immunization, vert. No. 316, Girl dancing, vert.

**1979    Litho.    Perf. 11**
**Without Gum**

| | | | | |
|---|---|---|---|---|
| 310 | A106 | 20k multicolored | .30 | .25 |
| 311 | A106 | 50k multicolored | .40 | .25 |
| 312 | A106 | 100k multicolored | 1.00 | .35 |
| 313 | A106 | 200k multicolored | 2.00 | .65 |
| 314 | A106 | 300k multicolored | 1.75 | .65 |
| 315 | A106 | 500k multicolored | 6.00 | 1.50 |
| 316 | A106 | 600k multicolored | 4.00 | 1.50 |
| | | Nos. 310-316 (7) | 15.45 | 5.15 |

Issued: Nos. 310-311, 313, 315, 8/1; others, 12/25.

Imperf sheets of 4 containing Nos. 310-311, 313, 315 and of 3 containing Nos. 312, 314, 316 exist. Value for both sheets $25.

Two varieties of imperf sheet of 3 exist: inscribed "1979" or "1975" on No. 314 vignette. Sheet with "1975" imprint is very scarce.

Nos. 310-316 exist with double perfs, part perfs, and imperf between. Value $35 each.

Traditional Modes of Transportation A107

**1979, Oct. 9**       **Perf. 12½x13**
| | | | | |
|---|---|---|---|---|
| **317** | A107 | 5k Elephants, buffalo, pirogues | .30 | .25 |
| **318** | A107 | 10k Buffalo, carts | .30 | .35 |
| **319** | A107 | 70k like 10k | .65 | 1.50 |
| **320** | A107 | 500k like 5k | 2.50 | 2.00 |
| | | Nos. 317-320 (4) | 3.75 | 4.10 |

Nos. 317-320 exist imperf. Value, set $15.
For overprints, see Nos. 426I, 426L, 426M, 426S, 676D.

5th Anniv. of the Republic A108

30c, Agriculture, vert. 50c, Education, health services. 1k, Three women, vert. 2k, Hydroelectric energy.

**1980, May 30**       **Perf. 11**
| | | | | |
|---|---|---|---|---|
| **321** | A108 | 30c multicolored | .35 | .25 |
| **322** | A108 | 50c multicolored | .60 | .25 |
| **323** | A108 | 1k multicolored | .75 | .40 |
| **324** | A108 | 2k multicolored | 1.75 | 1.10 |
| | | Nos. 321-324 (4) | 3.45 | 2.00 |

Imperf. souvenir sheet of 4 exists in three types. Values: vowel missing above first Lao word at top of sheet, $20; vowel 9mm above first Lao word, $10; vowel 7.5mm above first Lao word, $10.

Lenin, 110th Birth Anniv. — A109

**1980, July 5**    **Perf. 12x12½, 12½x12**
| | | | | |
|---|---|---|---|---|
| **325** | A109 | 1k Lenin reading | .30 | .25 |
| **326** | A109 | 2k Writing | .45 | .25 |
| **327** | A109 | 3k Lenin, red flag, vert. | .65 | .40 |
| **328** | A109 | 4k Orating, vert. | 1.25 | .55 |
| | | Nos. 325-328 (4) | 2.65 | 1.45 |

Nos. 325-328 exist imperf. Value, set $12.50.
Imperf. souvenir sheet of 4 exists. Value $5.

> **From this point to No. 1365, used values are for CTO stamps. For Nos. 426A-426W, 676A-676L, 1318A-1318C, 1359, used values are for postally used stamps.**

5th Anniv. of the Republic A110

50c, Threshing rice. 1.60k, Logging. 4.60k, Veterinary medicine. 5.40k, Rice paddy.

**1980, Dec. 2**       **Perf. 11**
**Without Gum**
| | | | | |
|---|---|---|---|---|
| **329** | A110 | 50c multicolored | .30 | .25 |
| **330** | A110 | 1.60k multicolored | .70 | .30 |
| **331** | A110 | 4.60k multicolored | 1.40 | .50 |
| **332** | A110 | 5.40k multicolored | 1.75 | .80 |
| | | Nos. 329-332 (4) | 4.15 | 1.85 |

Imperf. souvenir sheet of 4 exists. Value $10. Without inscription, value $100.

A111       Globe, Broken Chains — A111a

Grain, Cracked Bomb — A111b

**1981, June 26**       **Perf. 12x12½**
**Without Gum**
| | | | | |
|---|---|---|---|---|
| **333** | A111 | 60c shown | .30 | .25 |
| **334** | A111a | 4.60k multicolored | 1.75 | .80 |
| **335** | A111b | 5.40k multicolored | 2.00 | .85 |
| **a.** | | Souv. sheet of 3, #333-335, imperf. | 7.00 | 7.00 |
| | | Nos. 333-335 (3) | 4.05 | 1.90 |

26th Communist Party (PCUS) Congress. No. 335a sold for 15k.

**Souvenir Sheet**

PHILATOKYO '81 — A112

**1981, Sept. 20**       **Perf. 13**
**Without Gum**
| | | | |
|---|---|---|---|
| **336** | A112 | 10k Pandas | 6.00 4.00 |

1982 World Cup Soccer Championships, Spain — A113

**1981, Oct. 15**       **Perf. 12½**
**Without Gum**
| | | | | |
|---|---|---|---|---|
| **337** | A113 | 1k Heading ball | .30 | .25 |
| **338** | A113 | 2k Dribble | .40 | .25 |
| **339** | A113 | 3k Kick | .55 | .25 |
| **340** | A113 | 4k Goal, horiz. | .75 | .25 |
| **341** | A113 | 5k Dribble, diff. | 1.00 | 1.00 |
| **342** | A113 | 6k Kick, diff. | 1.40 | .80 |
| | | Nos. 337-342 (6) | 4.40 | 2.80 |

Intl. Year of the Disabled — A114

3k, Office worker. 5k, Teacher. 12k, Weaver, fishing net.

**1981**       **Without Gum**       **Perf. 13**
| | | | | |
|---|---|---|---|---|
| **343** | A114 | 3k multicolored | 1.60 | .40 |
| **344** | A114 | 5k multicolored | 2.00 | .80 |
| **345** | A114 | 12k multicolored | 4.00 | 2.00 |
| | | Nos. 343-345 (3) | 7.60 | 3.20 |

Wildcats A115

10c, Felis silvestris ornata. 20c, Felis viverrinus. 30c, Felis caracal. 40c, Neofelis nebulosa. 50c, Felis planiceps. 9k, Felis chaus.

**1981**     **Without Gum**     **Perf. 12½**
| | | | | |
|---|---|---|---|---|
| **346** | A115 | 10c multicolored | .30 | .25 |
| **347** | A115 | 20c multicolored | .30 | .25 |
| **348** | A115 | 30c multicolored | .35 | .25 |
| **349** | A115 | 40c multicolored | .40 | .25 |
| **350** | A115 | 50c multicolored | .45 | .25 |
| **351** | A115 | 9k multicolored | 3.50 | 1.25 |
| | | Nos. 346-351 (6) | 5.30 | 2.50 |

6th Anniv. of the Republic A116

3k, Satellite dish, flag. 4k, Soldier, flag. 5k, Map, flag, women, soldier.

**1981, Dec.**    **Without Gum**    **Perf. 13**
| | | | | |
|---|---|---|---|---|
| **352** | A116 | 3k multicolored | 65.00 | .30 |
| **353** | A116 | 4k multicolored | 80.00 | .40 |
| **354** | A116 | 5k multicolored | 110.00 | .50 |
| | | Nos. 352-354 (3) | 255.00 | 1.20 |

Indian Elephants A117

1k, Head. 2k, Carrying log in trunk. 3k, Transporting people. 4k, In trap. 5k, Adult and young. 5.50k, Herd.

**1982, Jan. 23**       **Perf. 12½x13**
**Without Gum**
| | | | | |
|---|---|---|---|---|
| **355** | A117 | 1k multicolored | .30 | .25 |
| **356** | A117 | 2k multicolored | .60 | .25 |
| **357** | A117 | 3k multicolored | .80 | .30 |
| **358** | A117 | 4k multicolored | 1.10 | .30 |
| **359** | A117 | 5k multicolored | 1.50 | .55 |
| **360** | A117 | 5.50k multicolored | 2.25 | .70 |
| | | Nos. 355-360 (6) | 6.55 | 2.35 |

Laotian Wrestling — A118

Various moves.

**1982, Jan. 30**       **Perf. 13**
**Without Gum**
| | | | | |
|---|---|---|---|---|
| **361** | A118 | 50c multicolored | .30 | .25 |
| **362** | A118 | 1.20k multi, diff. | .30 | .25 |
| **363** | A118 | 2k multi, diff. | .30 | .25 |
| **364** | A118 | 2.50k multi, diff. | .35 | .25 |
| **365** | A118 | 4k multi, diff. | .60 | .35 |
| **366** | A118 | 5k multi, diff. | 1.00 | .55 |
| | | Nos. 361-366 (6) | 2.85 | 1.90 |

Water Lilies — A119

30c, Nymphaea zanzibariensis. 40c, Nelumbo nucifera gaertn rose. 60c, Nymphaea rosea. 3k, Nymphaea nouchali. 4k, Nymphaea white. 7k, Nelumbo nucifera gaertn white.

**1982, Feb. 10**       **Perf. 12½x13**
**Without Gum**
| | | | | |
|---|---|---|---|---|
| **367** | A119 | 30c multicolored | .30 | .25 |
| **368** | A119 | 40c multicolored | .30 | .25 |
| **369** | A119 | 60c multicolored | .30 | .25 |
| **370** | A119 | 3k multicolored | .65 | .25 |
| **371** | A119 | 4k multicolored | 1.00 | .25 |
| **372** | A119 | 7k multicolored | 1.75 | .30 |
| | | Nos. 367-372 (6) | 4.30 | 1.55 |

Birds — A120

50c, Hirundo rustica, vert. 1k, Upupa epops, vert. 2k, Alcedo atthis, vert. 3k, Hypothymis azurea. 4k, Motacilla cinerea. 10k, Orthotomus sutorius.

**1982, Mar. 9**       **Perf. 13**
**Without Gum**
| | | | | |
|---|---|---|---|---|
| **373** | A120 | 50c multicolored | .30 | .25 |
| **374** | A120 | 1k multicolored | .30 | .25 |
| **375** | A120 | 2k multicolored | .50 | .25 |
| **376** | A120 | 3k multicolored | .65 | .25 |
| **377** | A120 | 4k multicolored | 1.25 | .25 |
| **378** | A120 | 10k multicolored | 2.75 | .80 |
| | | Nos. 373-378 (6) | 5.75 | 2.05 |

A121

1982 World Cup Soccer Championships, Spain — A122

Various match scenes.

**1982, Apr. 7**       **Without Gum**
| | | | | |
|---|---|---|---|---|
| **379** | A121 | 1k multicolored | .30 | .25 |
| **380** | A121 | 2k multicolored | .40 | .25 |
| **381** | A121 | 3k multicolored | .55 | .30 |
| **382** | A121 | 4k multicolored | .70 | .40 |
| **383** | A121 | 5k multicolored | 1.00 | .45 |
| **384** | A121 | 6k multicolored | 1.25 | .55 |
| | | Nos. 379-384 (6) | 4.20 | 2.20 |

**Souvenir Sheet**
| | | | |
|---|---|---|---|
| **385** | A122 | 15k multicolored | 4.00 4.00 |

Nos. 379-384 exist imperf.

Butterflies A123

1k, Herona marathus. 2k, Neptis paraka. 3k, Euripus halitherses. 4k, Lebadea martha. 5k, Iton semamora. 6k, Elymnias hypermnestra.

**1982, May 5**       **Perf. 12½x13**
**Without Gum**
| | | | | |
|---|---|---|---|---|
| **386** | A123 | 1k multicolored | .30 | .25 |
| **387** | A123 | 2k multicolored | .60 | .25 |
| **388** | A123 | 3k multicolored | .75 | .30 |
| **389** | A123 | 4k multicolored | 1.25 | .30 |

**Size: 42x26mm**
**Perf. 12½**
| | | | | |
|---|---|---|---|---|
| **390** | A123 | 5k multicolored | 2.00 | .70 |

**Size: 54x36½mm**
**Perf. 13x12½**
| | | | | |
|---|---|---|---|---|
| **391** | A123 | 6k multicolored | 2.50 | .70 |
| | | Nos. 386-391 (6) | 7.40 | 2.50 |

Souvenir Sheet

PHILEXFRANCE '82 — A124

10k, Temple, Vientiane.

**1982, June 9**      **Perf. 13**
**Without Gum**
392 A124 10k multicolored    2.75 2.75

River Vessels
A125

50c, Raft. 60c, River punt. 1k, Houseboat.
2k, Passenger steamer. 3k, Ferry. 8k, Self-propelled barge.

**1982, June 24**      **Without Gum**
393 A125 50c multicolored    .30 .25
394 A125 60c multicolored    .30 .25
395 A125 1k multicolored    .30 .25
396 A125 2k multicolored    .35 .25
397 A125 3k multicolored    .55 .40
398 A125 8k multicolored    1.50 .70
    *Nos. 393-398 (6)*    3.30 2.10

Pagodas
A126

**1982, Aug. 2**      **Without Gum**
399 A126 50c Chanh    .30 .25
400 A126 60c Inpeng    .30 .25
401 A126 1k Dong Mieng    .30 .25
402 A126 2k Ho Tay    .35 .25
403 A126 3k Ho Pha Keo    .60 .30
404 A126 8k Sisaket    1.60 .65
    *Nos. 399-404 (6)*    3.45 1.95

Dogs — A127

**1982, Oct. 13**      **Without Gum**
405 A127 50c Poodle    .30 .25
406 A127 60c Samoyed    .30 .25
407 A127 1k Boston terrier    .30 .25
408 A127 2k Cairn terrier    .40 .25
409 A127 3k Chihuahua    .75 .40
410 A127 8k Bulldog    2.50 .65
    *Nos. 405-410 (6)*    4.55 2.05

World Food
Day — A128

**1982, Oct. 16**      **Without Gum**
411 A128 7k Watering seedlings    1.75 .65
412 A128 8k Planting rice    2.00 .80

Classic
Automobiles
A129

**1982, Nov. 7**      **Without Gum**
413 A129 50c 1925 Fiat    .30 .25
414 A129 60c 1925 Peugeot    .30 .25
415 A129 1k 1925 Berliet    .30 .25
416 A129 2k 1925 Ballot    .40 .25

417 A129 3k 1926 Renault    .75 .40
418 A129 8k 1925 Ford    2.00 .65
    *Nos. 413-418 (6)*    4.05 2.05

7th Anniv. of
the Republic
A130

50c, Kaysone Phomvihan, vert. 1k, Tractors,
field, industry. 2k, Cows, farm. 3k, Truck,
microwave dish. 4k, Nurse, child, vert. 5k,
Education. 6k, Folk dancer, vert.

**1982, Dec. 2**      **Without Gum**
419 A130 50c multicolored    .30 .25
420 A130 1k multicolored    .30 .25
421 A130 2k multicolored    .45 .25
422 A130 3k multicolored    .65 .25
423 A130 4k multicolored    .90 .40
424 A130 5k multicolored    1.10 .40
425 A130 6k multicolored    1.40 .50
    *Nos. 419-425 (7)*    5.10 2.30

Nos. 419-425 exist imperf.

Bulgarian Flag, Coat of Arms and
George Dimitrov (1882-1949),
Bulgarian Statesman
A131

**1982, Dec. 15**      **Perf. 12½**
**Without Gum**
426 A131 10k multicolored    1.90 1.10

Nos. 272, 276, 283,
284, 286-288, 293,
298, 299, 304-309,
317-319 Ovptd. in
Red or Black   

**Methods and Perfs as before**

**1982**
426A A96 1k multi    70.00 70.00
426B A98 1k multi (Bk)    75.00 75.00
426C A98 1k multi    55.00 55.00
426D A98 2k multi    50.00 50.00
426E A98 2k multi (Bk)    65.00 65.00
426F A99 5k multi    85.00 85.00
426G A101 5k dull org &    75.00 75.00
       blk
426H A105 5k multi    55.00 55.00
426I A107 5k multi    35.00 35.00
426J A105 10k multi (Bk)    70.00 70.00
426K A105 10k multi    70.00 70.00
426L A107 10k multi (Bk)    65.00 65.00
426M A107 10k multi    175.00 175.00
426N A99 20k multi    — —
426O A105 20k multi    175.00 175.00
426P A104 30k multi    75.00 75.00
426Q A102 40k multi    85.00 85.00
426R A98 50k multi    85.00 85.00
426S A105 70k multi    115.00 115.00
426T A105 80k multi (Bk)    125.00 125.00
426U A105 100k multi    175.00 175.00
426V A96 200k org &   
       multi
       (Bk)    275.00 275.00
426W A104 250k multi (Bk)    450.00 450.00
    *Nos. 426A-426W (23)*    2,505. 2,505.

Many overprint varieties exist.
Nos. 426A, 426B, 426E, 426H, 426J, 426L,
426Q, 426R, 426S, 426T, 426U, and 426V
exist with inverted "8".
Nos. 426C and 426D exist with "I" instead of
"1".
No. exists 426C with "a" instead of "2".
No. 426F exists with double overprint. Nos.
426J, 426N, and 426V exist with double overprint, one inverted. No. 426J exists with double
overprint, one inverted, with the "1" in the
upright overprint inverted.
No. 426N exists with inverted overprint.
No. 426H exists with "1" inverted.
Nos. 426O and 426P exist with small "2".
Both the "9" and the "2" wore out to the point
where these numbers are almost invisible in
some overprints. These seeming omission
errors appear most prominently with the missing "9" in No. 426E, and the missing "2" in No.
426H.

Constitution of the
USSR, 60th
Anniv. — A132

**1982, Dec. 30**      **Without Gum**
427 A132 3k Kremlin    .65 .40
428 A132 4k Maps    .90 .55
**Souvenir Sheet**
**Perf. 13½x13**
428A    Sheet of 2    3.75 2.00
  b.   A132 5k like 3k    1.25 .65
  c.   A132 10k like 4k    2.50 1.75

Nos. 428Ab-428Ac not inscribed in Laotian
at top; buff and gold decorative margin contains the inscription.

1984 Summer
Olympics, Los
Angeles — A133

**1983, Jan. 25**      **Perf. 13**
**Without Gum**
429 A133 50c Hurdling    .30 .25
430 A133 1k Women's javelin    .30 .25
431 A133 2k Basketball    .35 .25
432 A133 3k Diving    .55 .25
433 A133 4k Gymnastics    .75 .40
434 A133 10k Weight lifting    2.10 .80
    *Nos. 429-434 (6)*    4.35 2.20
**Souvenir Sheet**
435 A133 15k Soccer    3.25 2.00

No. 435 contains one stamp 32x40mm.
Nos. 429-434 exist imperf.

Horses — A134

Various breeds.

**1983, Feb. 1**      **Without Gum**
436 A134 50c multicolored    .30 .25
437 A134 1k multi, diff.    .30 .25
438 A134 2k multi, diff.    .40 .25
439 A134 3k multi, diff.    .65 .25
440 A134 4k multi, diff.    .80 .30
441 A134 10k multi, diff.    2.75 .80
    *Nos. 436-441 (6)*    5.20 2.10

Nos. 436-441 exist imperf.

A135

Raphael, 500th Birth Anniv. — A136

Paintings (details) by Raphael: 50c, St.
Catherine of Alexandra, Natl. Gallery, London.
1k, Adoration of the Kings (spectators), Vatican. 2k, Granduca Madonna, Pitti Gallery, Florence. 3k, St. George and the Dragon, The
Louvre, Paris. 4k, Vision of Ezekiel, Pitti Gallery. No. 447, Adoration of the Kings (Holy
Family), Vatican. No. 448, Coronation of the
Virgin, Vatican.

**1983, Mar. 9**      **Perf. 12½x13**
**Without Gum**
442 A135 50c multicolored    .30 .25
443 A135 1k multicolored    .30 .25
444 A135 2k multicolored    .35 .25
445 A135 3k multicolored    .60 .25
446 A135 4k multicolored    .75 .30
447 A135 10k multicolored    2.50 .80
    *Nos. 442-447 (6)*    4.80 2.10
**Souvenir Sheet**
**Perf. 13x13½**
448 A136 10k multicolored    2.50 1.50

INTERCOSMOS Space
Cooperation
Program — A137

Cosmonaut and flags of USSR and participating nations.

**1983, Apr. 12**      **Perf. 12½**
449 A137 50c Czechoslovakia    .30 .25
450 A137 50c Poland    .30 .25
451 A137 1k East Germany    .30 .25
452 A137 1k Bulgaria    .30 .25
453 A137 2k Hungary    .40 .25
454 A137 3k Mongolia    .65 .25
455 A137 4k Romania    .80 .25
456 A137 6k Cuba    1.25 .40
457 A137 10k France    2.25 .80
    *Nos. 449-457 (9)*    6.55 2.95
**Souvenir Sheet**
**Perf. 13½x13**
458 A137 10k Vietnam    2.75 1.50

No. 458 contains one stamp 32x40mm.
Date of issue: 7/24/83.

A138

First
Manned
Balloon
Flight,
Bicent.
A139

Various balloons.

## 1983, May 4 — Perf. 12½x13

| | | | | |
|---|---|---|---|---|
| 459 | A138 | 50c shown | .30 | .25 |
| 460 | A138 | 1k multi, diff. | .30 | .25 |
| 461 | A138 | 2k multi, diff. | .35 | .25 |
| 462 | A138 | 3k multi, diff. | .50 | .25 |
| 463 | A138 | 4k multi, diff. | .65 | .40 |
| 464 | A138 | 10k multi, diff. | 2.25 | .80 |
| | | Nos. 459-464 (6) | 4.35 | 2.20 |

### Souvenir Sheet
### Perf. 13½x13

| | | | | |
|---|---|---|---|---|
| 465 | A139 | 10k shown | 2.40 | 1.50 |

Nos. 459-464 exist imperf.

### Souvenir Sheet

TEMBAL '83, Basel A140

10k, German Maybach.

## 1983, May 21 — Perf. 13x13½
### Without Gum

| | | | | |
|---|---|---|---|---|
| 466 | A140 | 10k multi | 3.00 | 1.60 |

No. 466 exists imperf.

Flora — A141

1k, Dendrobium sp. 2k, Aerides odoratum. 3k, Dendrobium aggregatum. 4k, Dendrobium. 5k, Moschatum. 6k, Dendrobium sp., diff.

## 1983, June 10 — Perf. 13
### Without Gum

| | | | | |
|---|---|---|---|---|
| 467 | A141 | 1k multicolored | .30 | .25 |
| 468 | A141 | 2k multicolored | .40 | .25 |
| 469 | A141 | 3k multicolored | .60 | .25 |
| 470 | A141 | 4k multicolored | .75 | .25 |
| 471 | A141 | 5k multicolored | 1.10 | .30 |
| 472 | A141 | 6k multicolored | 1.40 | .50 |
| | | Nos. 467-472 (6) | 4.55 | 1.80 |

Nos. 467-472 exist imperf.

1984 Winter Olympics, Sarajevo A142

## 1983, July 2 — Without Gum

| | | | | |
|---|---|---|---|---|
| 473 | A142 | 50c Downhill skiing | .30 | .25 |
| 474 | A142 | 1k Slalom | .30 | .25 |
| 475 | A142 | 2k Ice hockey | .40 | .25 |
| 476 | A142 | 3k Speed skating | .70 | .30 |
| 477 | A142 | 4k Ski jumping | .85 | .30 |
| 478 | A142 | 10k Luge | 2.25 | .80 |
| | | Nos. 473-478 (6) | 4.80 | 2.10 |

### Souvenir Sheet
### Perf. 13x13½

| | | | | |
|---|---|---|---|---|
| 479 | A142 | 15k 2-Man bobsled | 3.50 | 1.50 |

No. 479 contains one 40x32mm stamp. Nos. 473-478 exist imperf.

### Souvenir Sheet

BANGKOK '83 — A143

## 1983, Aug. 4 — Perf. 13½x13

| | | | | |
|---|---|---|---|---|
| 480 | A143 | 10k Boats on river | 2.25 | 1.50 |

No. 480 exists imperf. Value, $60.

Mekong River Fish — A144

1k, Notopterus chitala. 2k, Cyprinus carpio. 3k, Pangasius sp. 4k, Catlocarpio siamensis. 5k, Morulius sp. 6k, Tilapia nilotica.

## 1983, Sept. 5 — Perf. 12½
### Without Gum

| | | | | |
|---|---|---|---|---|
| 481 | A144 | 1k multicolored | .30 | .25 |
| 482 | A144 | 2k multicolored | .40 | .25 |
| 483 | A144 | 3k multicolored | .65 | .25 |
| 484 | A144 | 4k multicolored | .75 | .25 |
| 485 | A144 | 5k multicolored | 1.10 | .30 |
| 486 | A144 | 6k multicolored | 1.50 | .50 |
| | | Nos. 481-486 (6) | 4.70 | 1.80 |

Nos. 481-486 exist imperf.

Explorers and Their Ships A145

1k, Victoria, Magellan. 2k, Grand Hermine, Cartier. 3k, Santa Maria, Columbus. 4k, Cabral and caravel. 5k, Endeavor, Capt. Cook. 6k, Pourquoi-Pas, Charcot.

## 1983, Oct. 8 — Perf. 13x12½
### Without Gum

| | | | | |
|---|---|---|---|---|
| 487 | A145 | 1k multicolored | .30 | .25 |
| 488 | A145 | 2k multicolored | .40 | .25 |
| 489 | A145 | 3k multicolored | .65 | .25 |
| 490 | A145 | 4k multicolored | .75 | .25 |
| 491 | A145 | 5k multicolored | 1.10 | .30 |
| 492 | A145 | 6k multicolored | 1.50 | .50 |
| | | Nos. 487-492 (6) | 4.70 | 1.80 |

No. 492 incorrectly inscribed "CABOT."

Domestic Cats — A146

## 1983, Nov. 9 — Perf. 12½x13
### Without Gum

| | | | | |
|---|---|---|---|---|
| 493 | A146 | 1k Tabby | .30 | .25 |
| 494 | A146 | 2k Long-haired Persian | .60 | .25 |
| 495 | A146 | 3k Siamese | .75 | .25 |
| 496 | A146 | 4k Burmese | .85 | .25 |
| 497 | A146 | 5k Persian | 1.25 | .30 |
| 498 | A146 | 6k Tortoiseshell | 1.75 | .50 |
| | | Nos. 493-498 (6) | 5.50 | 1.80 |

Nos. 493-498 exist imperf.

Karl Marx (1818-1883) A147

4k, Marx, 3 flags, diff., vert. 6k, Marx, flag of Laos.

## 1983, Nov. 30 — Perf. 13
### Without Gum

| | | | | |
|---|---|---|---|---|
| 499 | A147 | 1k shown | .30 | .25 |
| 500 | A147 | 4k multi | 1.00 | .25 |
| 501 | A147 | 6k multi | 1.60 | .55 |
| | | Nos. 499-501 (3) | 2.90 | 1.05 |

8th Anniv. of the Republic A148

1k, Elephant dragging log, vert. 4k, Oxen, pig. 6k, Produce, vert.

## 1983, Dec. 2 — Perf. 12½x13, 13x12½
### Without Gum

| | | | | |
|---|---|---|---|---|
| 502 | A148 | 1k multicolored | .30 | .25 |
| 503 | A148 | 4k multicolored | 1.00 | .25 |
| 504 | A148 | 6k multicolored | 1.60 | .55 |
| | | Nos. 502-504 (3) | 2.90 | 1.05 |

Nos. 502-504 exist imperf.

World Communications Year — A149

50c, Teletype. 1k, Telephone. 4k, Television. 6k, Satellite, dish receiver.

## 1983, Dec. 15 — Perf. 13

| | | | | |
|---|---|---|---|---|
| 505 | A149 | 50c multicolored | .30 | .25 |
| 506 | A149 | 1k multicolored | .30 | .25 |
| 507 | A149 | 4k multicolored | .65 | .30 |
| 508 | A149 | 6k multicolored | 1.00 | .55 |
| | | Nos. 505-508 (4) | 2.25 | 1.35 |

Nos. 275, 306 Overprinted in Red

## 1983 — Method and Perf. As Before

| | | | | |
|---|---|---|---|---|
| 508B | A105 | 5k multi | 450.00 | — |
| 508C | A96 | 10k lilac & multi | 575.00 | — |

1984 Winter Olympics, Sarajevo A150

50c, Women's figure skating. 1k, Speed skating. 2k, Biathlon. 4k, Luge. 5k, Downhill skiing. 6k, Ski jumping. 7k, Slalom. 10k, Ice hockey.

## 1984, Jan. 16

| | | | | |
|---|---|---|---|---|
| 509 | A150 | 50c multicolored | .30 | .25 |
| 510 | A150 | 1k multicolored | .30 | .25 |
| 511 | A150 | 2k multicolored | .40 | .25 |
| 512 | A150 | 4k multicolored | .80 | .30 |
| 513 | A150 | 5k multicolored | 1.00 | .30 |
| 514 | A150 | 6k multicolored | 1.25 | .50 |
| 515 | A150 | 7k multicolored | 1.50 | .55 |
| | | Nos. 509-515 (7) | 5.55 | 2.40 |

### Souvenir Sheet
### Perf. 13½x13

| | | | | |
|---|---|---|---|---|
| 516 | A150 | 10k multicolored | 2.25 | 1.50 |

Nos. 509-511, 514-515 vert. No. 516 contains one stamp 32x40mm.

World Wildlife Fund — A151

Panthera tigris.

## 1984, Feb. 1 — Perf. 13

| | | | | |
|---|---|---|---|---|
| 517 | A151 | 25c Adult, vert. | .50 | .25 |
| 518 | A151 | 25c shown | .50 | .25 |
| 519 | A151 | 3k Nursing cubs | 5.00 | 1.25 |
| 520 | A151 | 4k Two cubs, vert. | 8.00 | 1.75 |
| | | Nos. 517-520 (4) | 14.00 | 3.50 |

1984 Summer Olympics, Los Angeles — A152

Gold medals awarded during previous games, and athletes. 50c, Athens 1896, women's diving. 1k, Paris 1900, women's volleyball. 2k, St. Louis 1904, running. 4k, London 1908, basketball. 5k, Stockholm 1912, judo. 6k, Antwerp 1920, soccer. 7k, Paris 1924, gymnastics. 10k, Moscow 1980, wrestling.

## 1984, Mar 26

| | | | | |
|---|---|---|---|---|
| 521 | A152 | 50c multicolored | .30 | .25 |
| 522 | A152 | 1k multicolored | .30 | .25 |
| 523 | A152 | 2k multicolored | .60 | .25 |
| 524 | A152 | 4k multicolored | 1.10 | .25 |
| 525 | A152 | 5k multicolored | 1.25 | .30 |
| 526 | A152 | 6k multicolored | 1.60 | .40 |
| 527 | A152 | 7k multicolored | 1.90 | .50 |
| | | Nos. 521-527 (7) | 7.05 | 2.20 |

### Souvenir Sheet
### Perf. 12½

| | | | | |
|---|---|---|---|---|
| 528 | A152 | 10k multicolored | 2.75 | 1.50 |

No. 528 contains one stamp 32x40mm.

Musical Instruments A153

## 1984, Mar. 27 — Perf. 13

| | | | | |
|---|---|---|---|---|
| 529 | A153 | 1k Tuned drums | .30 | .25 |
| 530 | A153 | 2k Xylophone | .40 | .25 |
| 531 | A153 | 3k Pair of drums | .65 | .25 |
| 532 | A153 | 4k Hand drum | .90 | .30 |
| 533 | A153 | 5k Barrel drum | 1.10 | .30 |
| 534 | A153 | 6k Pipes, string instrument | 1.25 | .50 |
| | | Nos. 529-534 (6) | 4.60 | 1.85 |

Natl. Day — A154

## 1984, Mar. 30 — Perf. 12½

| | | | | |
|---|---|---|---|---|
| 535 | A154 | 60c Natl. flag | .35 | .25 |
| 536 | A154 | 1k Natl. arms | .50 | .25 |
| 537 | A154 | 2k like 1k | .75 | .25 |
| | | Nos. 535-537 (3) | 1.60 | .75 |

For surcharges, see Nos. 1884-1886, 1899-1901.

Chess — A155

Illustrations of various medieval and Renaissance chess games. 10k, Royal game, human chessmen.

## 1984, Apr. 14 — Perf. 12½x13

| | | | | |
|---|---|---|---|---|
| 538 | A155 | 50c multi | .30 | .25 |
| 539 | A155 | 1k multi, diff. | .30 | .25 |
| 540 | A155 | 2k multi, red brn board, diff. | .50 | .25 |
| 541 | A155 | 2k multi, blk board, diff. | .50 | .25 |
| 542 | A155 | 3k multi, diff. | .70 | .30 |
| 543 | A155 | 4k multi, diff. | 1.25 | .30 |
| 544 | A155 | 8k multi, diff. | 2.25 | .50 |
| a. | | Souv. sheet of 6, #538-540, 542-544, with gutter between | — | — |
| | | Nos. 538-544 (7) | 5.80 | 2.10 |

### Souvenir Sheet
### Perf. 13½x13

| | | | | |
|---|---|---|---|---|
| 545 | A155 | 10k multi | 3.25 | 2.50 |

World Chess Federation, 60th anniv. No. 545 contains one stamp 32x40mm.

ESPANA '84, Madrid — A156

Paintings: 50c, Cardinal Nino de Guevara, by El Greco. 1k, Gaspar de Guzman, Duke of

Olivares, on Horseback, by Velazquez. No. 548, The Annunciation, by Murillo. No. 549, Portrait of a Lady, by Francisco de Zurburan (1598-1664). 3k, The Family of Charles IV, by Goya. 4k, Two Harlequins, by Picasso. 8k, Abstract, by Miro. 10k, Burial of the Count of Orgaz, by El Greco.

**1984, Apr. 27**      *Perf. 12½*
| | | | | |
|---|---|---|---|---|
| 546 | A156 | 50c multicolored | .30 | .25 |
| 547 | A156 | 1k multicolored | .30 | .25 |
| 548 | A156 | 2k multicolored | .45 | .25 |
| 549 | A156 | 2k multicolored | .45 | .25 |
| 550 | A156 | 3k multicolored | .65 | .30 |
| 551 | A156 | 4k multicolored | .90 | .30 |
| 552 | A156 | 8k multicolored | 1.75 | .50 |
| | | *Nos. 546-552 (7)* | 4.80 | 2.10 |

**Souvenir Sheet**
*Perf. 13½x13*
| | | | | |
|---|---|---|---|---|
| 553 | A156 | 10k multicolored | 4.75 | 2.50 |

No. 553 contains one stamp 32x40mm and also exists imperf.

Woodland Flowers — A157

50c, Adonis aestivalis. 1k, Alpinia speciosa. No. 556, 2k, Aeschynanthus speciosus. No. 557, 2k, Cassia lechenaultiana. 3k, Datura meteloides. 4k, Quamoclit pennata. 8k, Commelina benghalensis.

**1984, May 11**      *Perf. 13*
| | | | | |
|---|---|---|---|---|
| 554 | A157 | 50c multicolored | .30 | .25 |
| 555 | A157 | 1k multicolored | .30 | .25 |
| 556 | A157 | 2k multicolored | .45 | .25 |
| 557 | A157 | 2k multicolored | .45 | .25 |
| 558 | A157 | 3k multicolored | .65 | .30 |
| 559 | A157 | 4k multicolored | .90 | .30 |
| 560 | A157 | 8k multicolored | 1.75 | .50 |
| | | *Nos. 554-560 (7)* | 4.80 | 2.10 |

Nos. 554-560 exist imperf.

A158

19th UPU Congress, Hamburg — A159

Classic sport and race cars.

**1984, June 19**
| | | | | |
|---|---|---|---|---|
| 561 | A158 | 50c Nazzaro | .30 | .25 |
| 562 | A158 | 1k Daimler | .30 | .25 |
| 563 | A158 | 2k Delage | .35 | .25 |
| 564 | A158 | 2k Fiat S 57/14B | .35 | .25 |
| 565 | A158 | 3k Bugatti | .50 | .30 |
| 566 | A158 | 4k Itala | .65 | .30 |
| 567 | A158 | 8k Blitzen Benz | 1.40 | .50 |
| | | *Nos. 561-567 (7)* | 3.85 | 2.10 |

**Souvenir Sheet**
*Perf. 12½*
| | | | | |
|---|---|---|---|---|
| 568 | A159 | 10k Winton Bullet | 1.90 | 1.25 |

Paintings by Correggio (1494-1534) — A160

Designs: 50c, Madonna and Child (Holy Family). 1k, Madonna and Child (spectators). No. 571, Madonna and Child (Holy Family, diff.) No. 572, Mystical Marriage of St. Catherine (Catherine, child, two women). 3k, The Four Saints. 4k, Noli Me Tangere. 8k, Christ

Bids Farewell to the Virgin Mary. 10k, Madonna and Child, diff.

**1984, June 26**      *Perf. 13*
| | | | | |
|---|---|---|---|---|
| 569 | A160 | 50c multicolored | .30 | .25 |
| 570 | A160 | 1k multicolored | .30 | .25 |
| 571 | A160 | 2k multicolored | .45 | .25 |
| 572 | A160 | 2k multicolored | .45 | .25 |
| 573 | A160 | 3k multicolored | .65 | .30 |
| 574 | A160 | 4k multicolored | .75 | .30 |
| 575 | A160 | 10k multicolored | 1.40 | .50 |
| | | *Nos. 569-575 (7)* | 4.30 | 2.10 |

**Souvenir Sheet**
*Perf. 13½x13*
| | | | | |
|---|---|---|---|---|
| 576 | A160 | 10k multicolored | 3.25 | 1.75 |

No. 576 contains one stamp 32x40mm, and exists imperforate.

Space Exploration — A161

No. 577, Luna 1. No. 578, Luna 2. No. 579, Luna 3. No. 580, Sputnik 2, Kepler, horiz. No. 581, Lunokhod 2, Newton, horiz. No. 582, Luna 13, Jules Verne, horiz. No. 583, Space station, Copernicus, horiz.

**1984, July 12**      *Perf. 13*
| | | | | |
|---|---|---|---|---|
| 577 | A161 | 50c multicolored | .30 | .25 |
| 578 | A161 | 1k multicolored | .30 | .25 |
| 579 | A161 | 2k multicolored | .35 | .25 |
| 580 | A161 | 2k multicolored | .35 | .25 |
| 581 | A161 | 3k multicolored | .75 | .25 |
| 582 | A161 | 4k multicolored | 1.00 | .40 |
| 583 | A161 | 8k multicolored | 1.75 | .65 |
| | | *Nos. 577-583 (7)* | 4.80 | 2.30 |

Reptiles A162

No. 584, Malaclemys terrapin. No. 585, Bungarus fasciatus. No. 586, Python reticulatus. No. 587, Python molurus, vert. No. 588, Gekko gecko. No. 589, Natrix subminiata. No. 590, Eublepharis macularius.

**1984, Aug. 20**
| | | | | |
|---|---|---|---|---|
| 584 | A162 | 50c multicolored | .30 | .25 |
| 585 | A162 | 1k multicolored | .30 | .25 |
| 586 | A162 | 2k multicolored | .40 | .25 |
| 587 | A162 | 2k multicolored | .40 | .25 |
| 588 | A162 | 3k multicolored | .75 | .25 |
| 589 | A162 | 4k multicolored | 1.00 | .40 |
| 590 | A162 | 8k multicolored | 1.90 | .65 |
| | | *Nos. 584-590 (7)* | 5.05 | 2.30 |

Marsupials A163

No. 591, Schoinobates volans. No. 592, Ornithorhynchus anatinus. No. 593, Sarcophilus harrisii. No. 594, Lasiorhinus latifrons. No. 595, Thylacinus cynocephalus. No. 596, Dasyurops maculatus. No. 597, Wallabia isabelinus.
10k, Macropus rufus.

**1984, Sept. 21**
| | | | | |
|---|---|---|---|---|
| 591 | A163 | 50c multicolored | .30 | .25 |
| 592 | A163 | 1k multicolored | .30 | .25 |
| 593 | A163 | 2k multicolored | .40 | .25 |
| 594 | A163 | 2k multicolored | .40 | .25 |
| 595 | A163 | 3k multicolored | .75 | .25 |
| 596 | A163 | 4k multicolored | 1.00 | .40 |
| 597 | A163 | 8k multicolored | 1.90 | .65 |
| | | *Nos. 591-597 (7)* | 5.05 | 2.30 |

**Souvenir Sheet**
*Perf. 12½*
| | | | | |
|---|---|---|---|---|
| 598 | A163 | 10k multicolored | 2.75 | 1.50 |

AUSIPEX '84, Melbourne. No. 598 contains one stamp 32x40mm and also exists imperf.

Stop Polio Campaign A164

**1984, Sept. 29**      *Perf. 13*
| | | | | |
|---|---|---|---|---|
| 599 | A164 | 5k shown | 1.10 | .55 |
| 600 | A164 | 6k Vaccinating child | 1.20 | .55 |

Art — A165

No. 601, Dragon (hand rail). No. 602, Capital. No. 603, Oval panel. No. 604, Deity. No. 605, Leaves. No. 606, Floral pattern. No. 607, Lotus flower (round panel).

**1984, Oct. 26**
| | | | | |
|---|---|---|---|---|
| 601 | A165 | 50c multicolored | .30 | .25 |
| 602 | A165 | 1k multicolored | .30 | .25 |
| 603 | A165 | 2k multicolored | .40 | .25 |
| 604 | A165 | 2k multicolored | .40 | .25 |
| 605 | A165 | 3k multicolored | .80 | .25 |
| 606 | A165 | 4k multicolored | 1.25 | .40 |
| 607 | A165 | 8k multicolored | 2.50 | .65 |
| | | *Nos. 601-607 (7)* | 5.95 | 2.30 |

Nos. 601-604 and 607 vert.

9th Anniv. of the Republic A166

1k, River boats. 2k, Aircraft. 4k, Bridge building. 10k, Surveying, construction.

**1984, Dec. 17**
| | | | | |
|---|---|---|---|---|
| 608 | A166 | 1k multicolored | .50 | .25 |
| 609 | A166 | 2k multicolored | .70 | .25 |
| 610 | A166 | 4k multicolored | 1.20 | .25 |
| 611 | A166 | 10k multicolored | 2.50 | .95 |
| | | *Nos. 608-611 (4)* | 4.90 | 2.10 |

1986 World Cup Soccer Championships, Mexico — A167

Various match scenes and flag of Mexico.

**1985, Jan. 18**
| | | | | |
|---|---|---|---|---|
| 612 | A167 | 50c multicolored | .30 | .25 |
| 613 | A167 | 1k multi, diff. | .30 | .25 |
| 614 | A167 | 2k multi, diff. | .50 | .25 |
| 615 | A167 | 3k multi, diff. | .65 | .25 |
| 616 | A167 | 4k multi, diff. | .85 | .30 |
| 617 | A167 | 5k multi, diff. | 1.10 | .40 |
| 618 | A167 | 6k multi, diff. | 1.40 | .65 |
| | | *Nos. 612-618 (7)* | 5.10 | 2.35 |

**Souvenir Sheet**
*Perf. 12½*
| | | | | |
|---|---|---|---|---|
| 619 | A167 | 10k multi, diff. | 2.25 | 1.50 |

No. 619 contains one stamp 32x40mm. Nos. 612-618 exist imperf.

Motorcycle, Cent. — A168

1k, 1920 Gnome Rhone. 2k, 1928 F.N. M67C. 3k, 1930 Indian Chief. 4k, 1914 Rudge Multi. 5k, 1953 Honda Benly J. 6k, 1938 CZ.

**1985, Feb. 25**      *Perf. 12½*
| | | | | |
|---|---|---|---|---|
| 620 | A168 | 50c shown | .30 | .25 |
| 621 | A168 | 1k multicolored | .30 | .25 |
| 622 | A168 | 2k multicolored | .40 | .25 |
| 623 | A168 | 3k multicolored | .60 | .25 |
| 624 | A168 | 4k multicolored | .80 | .30 |
| 625 | A168 | 5k multicolored | 1.10 | .40 |
| 626 | A168 | 6k multicolored | 1.25 | .65 |
| | | *Nos. 620-626 (7)* | 4.75 | 2.35 |

Nos. 620-626 exist imperf.

Mushrooms — A169

No. 627, Amanita muscaria. No. 628, Boletus edulis. No. 629, Coprinus comatus. No. 630, Amanita rubescens. No. 631, Xerocomus subtomentosus. No. 632, Lepiota procera. No. 633, Paxillus involutus.

**1985, Apr. 8**      *Perf. 13*
| | | | | |
|---|---|---|---|---|
| 627 | A169 | 50c multicolored | .30 | .25 |
| 628 | A169 | 1k multicolored | .30 | .25 |
| 629 | A169 | 2k multicolored | .50 | .25 |
| 630 | A169 | 2k multicolored | .50 | .25 |
| 631 | A169 | 3k multicolored | .75 | .30 |
| 632 | A169 | 4k multicolored | 1.00 | .40 |
| 633 | A169 | 8k multicolored | 2.00 | .60 |
| | | *Nos. 627-633 (7)* | 5.35 | 2.30 |

Nos. 627-633 exist imperf.

End of World War II, 40th Anniv. — A169a

1k, Battle of Kursk. 2k, Red Army parade, Moscow. 4k, Battle of Stalingrad. 5k, Battle for Berlin. 6k, Victory parade through Brandenburg Gate.

**1985, May**   *Litho.*   *Perf. 12½x12*
| | | | | |
|---|---|---|---|---|
| 633A | A169a | 1k multicolored | 1.40 | .25 |
| 633B | A169a | 2k multicolored | 2.50 | .25 |
| 633C | A169a | 4k multicolored | 4.00 | .40 |
| 633D | A169a | 5k multicolored | 5.00 | .50 |
| 633E | A169a | 6k multicolored | 5.50 | .55 |
| | | *Nos. 633A-633E (5)* | 18.40 | 1.95 |

Lenin, 115th Birth Anniv. — A170

1k, Reading Pravda, horiz. 10k, Addressing revolutionaries.

**1985, June 28**      *Perf. 12½*
| | | | | |
|---|---|---|---|---|
| 634 | A170 | 1k multicolored | .35 | .25 |
| 635 | A170 | 2k shown | 2.00 | .30 |
| 636 | A170 | 10k multicolored | 2.00 | .30 |
| | | *Nos. 634-636 (3)* | 4.35 | .85 |

Orchids — A171

50c, Cattleya percivaliana. 1k, Odontoglossum luteo-purpureum. No. 639, Cattleya lueddemanniana. No. 640, Maxillaria sanderiana. 3k, Miltonia vexillaria. 4k, Oncidium varicosum. 8k, Cattleya dowiana aurea. 10k, Catasetum fimbriatum.

**1985, July 5**      *Perf. 13*
| | | | | |
|---|---|---|---|---|
| 637 | A171 | 50c multicolored | .30 | .25 |
| 638 | A171 | 1k multicolored | .30 | .25 |
| 639 | A171 | 2k multicolored | .45 | .25 |
| 640 | A171 | 2k multicolored | .45 | .25 |
| 641 | A171 | 3k multicolored | .70 | .25 |
| 642 | A171 | 4k multicolored | 1.00 | .40 |
| 643 | A171 | 8k multicolored | 2.25 | .65 |
| | | *Nos. 637-643 (7)* | 5.45 | 2.20 |

**Souvenir Sheet**
*Perf. 13½x13*
| | | | | |
|---|---|---|---|---|
| 644 | A171 | 10k multicolored | 2.75 | 1.50 |

ARGENTINA '85, Buenos Aires. No. 644 contains one stamp 32x40mm.

Fauna — A172

2k, Macaca mulatta. 3k, Bos sauveli. 4k, Hystrix leucura, horiz. 5k, Selenarctos thibotanus, horiz. 10k, Manis pentadactyla.

**1985, Aug. 15**      *Perf. 13*
| | | | | |
|---|---|---|---|---|
| 645 | A172 | 2k multicolored | .35 | .25 |
| 646 | A172 | 3k multicolored | .55 | .25 |
| 647 | A172 | 4k multicolored | .80 | .30 |
| 648 | A172 | 5k multicolored | 1.00 | .30 |
| 649 | A172 | 10k multicolored | 2.00 | .65 |
| | | Nos. 645-649 (5) | 4.70 | 1.75 |

Nos. 645-49 exist imperf.

Apollo-Soyuz Flight, 10th Anniv. — A173

50c, Apollo launch pad, vert. 1k, Soyuz launch pad, vert. No. 652, Apollo approaching Soyuz. No. 653, Soyuz approaching Apollo. 3k, Apollo, astronauts. 4k, Soyuz, cosmonauts. 8k, Docked spacecrafts.

**1985, Sept. 6**
| | | | | |
|---|---|---|---|---|
| 650 | A173 | 50c multicolored | .30 | .25 |
| 651 | A173 | 1k multicolored | .30 | .25 |
| 652 | A173 | 2k multicolored | .40 | .25 |
| 653 | A173 | 2k multicolored | .65 | .25 |
| 654 | A173 | 3k multicolored | .80 | .25 |
| 655 | A173 | 4k multicolored | 1.00 | .30 |
| 656 | A173 | 8k multicolored | 1.60 | .65 |
| | | Nos. 650-656 (7) | 5.05 | 2.20 |

Nos. 650-656 exist imperf.

Aircraft — A174

**1985, Oct. 25**
| | | | | |
|---|---|---|---|---|
| 657 | A174 | 50c Fiat | .30 | .25 |
| 658 | A174 | 1k Cant z.501 | .30 | .25 |
| 659 | A174 | 2k MF-5 | .40 | .25 |
| 660 | A174 | 3k Macchi Castoldi | .65 | .25 |
| 661 | A174 | 4k Anzani | .80 | .25 |
| 662 | A174 | 5k Ambrosini | 1.00 | .30 |
| 663 | A174 | 6k Piaggio | 1.10 | .35 |
| | | Nos. 657-663 (7) | 4.55 | 1.90 |

**Souvenir Sheet**
*Perf. 13x13½*
| | | | | |
|---|---|---|---|---|
| 664 | A174 | 10k MF-4 | 4.50 | 2.40 |

ITALIA '85, Rome. No. 664 contains one stamp 40x32mm and also exists imperf. Nos. 657-663 exist imperf.

Miniature Sheet

Columbus's Fleet — A175

**1985, Oct. 25**      *Perf. 13*
| | | | | |
|---|---|---|---|---|
| 665 | A175 | Sheet of 5 + 4 labels | 15.00 | 7.50 |
| a. | | 1k Pinta | .50 | .25 |
| b. | | 2k Nina | .75 | .25 |
| c. | | 3k Santa Maria | 1.25 | .30 |
| d. | | 4k Columbus | 1.50 | .40 |
| e. | | 5k Map of 1st voyage | 2.00 | 1.50 |

ITALIA '85.

---

UN, 40th Anniv. — A176

**1985, Oct.**
| | | | | |
|---|---|---|---|---|
| 666 | A176 | 2k UN and natl. flag | .55 | .25 |
| 667 | A176 | 3k Coats of arms | .80 | .25 |
| 668 | A176 | 10k Map, globe | 2.50 | 1.00 |
| | | Nos. 666-668 (3) | 3.85 | 1.55 |

Health — A177

1k, Mother feeding child. 3k, Immunization, horiz. 4k, Hospital care, horiz. 10k, Breastfeeding.

**1985, Nov. 15**
| | | | | |
|---|---|---|---|---|
| 669 | A177 | 1k multicolored | .40 | .25 |
| 670 | A177 | 3k multicolored | .80 | .25 |
| 671 | A177 | 4k multicolored | .95 | .30 |
| 672 | A177 | 10k multicolored | 2.00 | .80 |
| | | Nos. 669-672 (4) | 4.15 | 1.60 |

10th Anniv. of the Republic A178

**1985, Dec. 2**
| | | | | |
|---|---|---|---|---|
| 673 | A178 | 3k shown | .65 | .25 |
| 674 | A178 | 10k multi, diff. | 2.50 | 1.00 |

People's Revolutionary Party, 30th Anniv. — A179

**1985, Dec. 30**
| | | | | |
|---|---|---|---|---|
| 675 | A179 | 2k shown | .95 | .25 |
| 676 | A179 | 8k multi, diff. | 2.50 | .65 |

**Nos. 276, 286, 289, 291-292, 297, 299-300, 305, 308-309, 319 Overprinted in Red**

**Methods and Perfs As Before**
**1985**
| | | | | |
|---|---|---|---|---|
| 676A | A102 | 40k multi | 40.00 | 40.00 |
| 676B | A98 | 50k multi | 40.00 | 40.00 |
| 676C | A99 | 50k multi | 100.00 | 100.00 |
| 676D | A107 | 70k multi | 40.00 | 40.00 |
| 676E | A105 | 80k multi | 50.00 | 50.00 |
| 676F | A100 | 100k multi | 120.00 | 120.00 |
| 676G | A105 | 100k multi | 50.00 | 50.00 |
| 676H | A96 | 200k org & multi | 110.00 | 110.00 |
| 676I | A100 | 250k multi | 150.00 | 150.00 |
| 676J | A101 | 250k vio & blk | 170.00 | 170.00 |
| 676K | A104 | 250k multi | 120.00 | 120.00 |
| 676L | A102 | 300k multi | 120.00 | 120.00 |
| | | Nos. 676A-676L (12) | 1,110. | 1,110. |

Overprint varieties exist. An inverted "8" exists in 676A. Inverted overprints exist on 676B and 676K. An overprint reading "1895" instead of "1985" exists both upright and inverted on 676B.

---

1986 World Cup Soccer Championships, Mexico — A180

Various match scenes.

**1986, Jan. 20**
| | | | | |
|---|---|---|---|---|
| 677 | A180 | 50c multicolored | .30 | .25 |
| 678 | A180 | 1k multi, diff. | .30 | .25 |
| 679 | A180 | 2k multi, diff. | .40 | .25 |
| 680 | A180 | 3k multi, diff. | .50 | .25 |
| 681 | A180 | 4k multi, diff. | .70 | .25 |
| 682 | A180 | 5k multi, diff. | .80 | .30 |
| 683 | A180 | 6k multi, diff. | 1.10 | .40 |
| | | Nos. 677-683 (7) | 4.10 | 1.95 |

**Souvenir Sheet**
*Perf. 13x13½*
| | | | | |
|---|---|---|---|---|
| 684 | A180 | 10k multi, diff. | 2.00 | .90 |

No. 684 contains one stamp 40x32mm.

27th Congress of the Communist Party of the Soviet Union — A180a

4k, Cosmonaut, spacecraft. 20k, Lenin.

**1986, Jan.**    *Litho.*    *Perf. 12x12½*
| | | | | |
|---|---|---|---|---|
| 684A | A180a | 4k multicolored | 2.50 | .30 |
| 684B | A180a | 20k multicolored | 7.50 | 1.00 |

Flowering Plants — A181

50c, Pelargonium grandiflorum. 1k, Aquilegia vulgaris. 2k, Fuchsia globosa. 3k, Crocus aureus. 4k, Althaea rosea. 5k, Gladiolus purpureo. 6k, Hyacinthus orientalis.

**1986, Feb. 28**      *Perf. 13*
| | | | | |
|---|---|---|---|---|
| 685 | A181 | 50c multicolored | .30 | .25 |
| 686 | A181 | 1k multicolored | .30 | .25 |
| 687 | A181 | 2k multicolored | .45 | .25 |
| 688 | A181 | 3k multicolored | .65 | .25 |
| 689 | A181 | 4k multicolored | .80 | .30 |
| 690 | A181 | 5k multicolored | 1.00 | .40 |
| 691 | A181 | 6k multicolored | 1.25 | .55 |
| | | Nos. 685-691 (7) | 4.75 | 2.25 |

Butterflies — A182

50c, Aporia hippia. 1k, Euthalia irrubescens. 2k, Japonica lutea. 3k, Pratapa ctesia. 4k, Kallina inachus. 5k, Ixias pyrene. 6k, Parantica sita.

**1986, Mar. 30**
| | | | | |
|---|---|---|---|---|
| 692 | A182 | 50c multicolored | .30 | .25 |
| 693 | A182 | 1k multicolored | .30 | .25 |
| 694 | A182 | 2k multicolored | .45 | .25 |
| 695 | A182 | 3k multicolored | .65 | .25 |
| 696 | A182 | 4k multicolored | .80 | .30 |
| 697 | A182 | 5k multicolored | 1.00 | .40 |
| 698 | A182 | 6k multicolored | 1.25 | .55 |
| | | Nos. 692-698 (7) | 4.75 | 2.25 |

A183

---

First Man in Space, 25th Anniv. A184

Designs: 50c, Launch, Baikonur Space Center, vert. 1k, Interkosmos communications satellite, vert. 2k, Salyut space station. 3k, Yuri Gagarin, Sputnik 1 disengaging stage. 4k, Luna 3, the Moon, vert. 5k, Leonov on first space walk, vert. 6k, Luna 16 lifting off Moon, vert. 10k, Spacecrafts docking.

**1986, Apr. 12**
| | | | | |
|---|---|---|---|---|
| 699 | A183 | 50c multicolored | .30 | .25 |
| 700 | A183 | 1k multicolored | .30 | .25 |
| 701 | A183 | 2k multicolored | .40 | .25 |
| 702 | A183 | 3k multicolored | .65 | .25 |
| 703 | A183 | 4k multicolored | .80 | .25 |
| 704 | A183 | 5k multicolored | 1.00 | .40 |
| 705 | A183 | 6k multicolored | 1.10 | .50 |
| | | Nos. 699-705 (7) | 4.55 | 2.15 |

**Souvenir Sheet**
*Perf. 13x13½*
| | | | | |
|---|---|---|---|---|
| 706 | A184 | 10k multicolored | 2.50 | 1.00 |

No. 706 exists imperf.

Fauna A185

50c, Giraffa camelopardalis. 1k, Panthera leo. 2k, Loxodonta africana africana. 3k, Macropus rufus. 4k, Gymnobelideus leadbeateri. 5k, Phoenicopterus ruber. 6k, Ailuropoda melanoleucus.
10k, Bison, vert.

**1986, May 22**    *Perf. 12½x13, 13x12½*
| | | | | |
|---|---|---|---|---|
| 707 | A185 | 50c multicolored | .30 | .25 |
| 708 | A185 | 1k multicolored | .30 | .25 |
| 709 | A185 | 2k multicolored | .40 | .25 |
| 710 | A185 | 4k multicolored | .70 | .25 |
| 711 | A185 | 4k multicolored | 1.00 | .25 |
| 712 | A185 | 5k multicolored | 1.25 | .30 |
| 713 | A185 | 6k multicolored | 1.50 | .55 |
| | | Nos. 707-713 (7) | 5.45 | 2.10 |

**Souvenir Sheet**
*Perf. 13½x13*
| | | | | |
|---|---|---|---|---|
| 714 | A185 | 10k multicolored | 3.00 | 1.50 |

Nos. 707-712 vert.
No. 714 has the Ameripex '86 stamp exhibition logo in the margin.

Pheasants — A187

50c, Argusianus argus. 1k, Cennaeus nycthemerus. 2k, Phasianus colchicus. 3k, Chrysolophus amherstiae. 4k, Symaticus reevesii. 5k, Chrysolophus pictus. 6k, Syrmaticus soemmerringii.

**1986, June 29**    *Perf. 12½x13*
| | | | | |
|---|---|---|---|---|
| 715 | A187 | 50c multicolored | .30 | .25 |
| 716 | A187 | 1k multicolored | .30 | .25 |
| 717 | A187 | 2k multicolored | .45 | .25 |
| 718 | A187 | 3k multicolored | .60 | .25 |
| 719 | A187 | 4k multicolored | .80 | .25 |
| 720 | A187 | 5k multicolored | 1.00 | .30 |
| 721 | A187 | 6k multicolored | 1.25 | .40 |
| | | Nos. 715-721 (7) | 4.70 | 1.95 |

Snakes A188

No. 722, Elaphe guttata. No. 723, Thalerophis richardi. No. 724, Lampropeltis doliata annulata. No. 725, Diadophis amabilis. No. 726, Boiga dendrophila. No. 727, Python molurus. No. 728, Naja naja.

**1986, July 21    Perf. 12½x13, 13x12½**

| | | | | |
|---|---|---|---|---|
| 722 | A188 | 50c multicolored | .30 | .25 |
| 723 | A188 | 1k multicolored | .30 | .25 |
| 724 | A188 | 1k multicolored | .35 | .25 |
| 725 | A188 | 2k multicolored | .40 | .25 |
| 726 | A188 | 4k multicolored | .70 | .25 |
| 727 | A188 | 5k multicolored | 1.00 | .30 |
| 728 | A188 | 8k multicolored | 1.25 | .40 |
| | | *Nos. 722-728 (7)* | 4.30 | 1.95 |

Nos. 722-723 and 728 vert.

Halley's Comet A189

50c, Acropolis, Athens. #730a, 1k, Bayeux Tapestry. #730b, 2k, Edmond Halley. #731a, 3k, Vega space probe. #731b, 4k, Galileo. #732a, 5k, Comet. #732b, 6k, Giotto probe.

**1986, Aug. 22    Perf. 12½x13**

| | | | | |
|---|---|---|---|---|
| 729 | A189 | 50c multi | .30 | .25 |
| 730 | A189 | Pair, #a.-b. | .75 | .40 |
| 731 | A189 | Pair, #a.-b. | 1.25 | .50 |
| 732 | A189 | Pair, #a.-b. | 2.25 | .70 |
| | | *Nos. 729-732 (4)* | 4.55 | 1.85 |

**Souvenir Sheet**
**Perf. 13x13½**

| | | | | |
|---|---|---|---|---|
| 733 | A189 | 10k Comet, diff. | 2.50 | 1.25 |

Nos. 730-732 printed in continuous designs. Sizes of Nos. 730a, 731a, 732a: 46x25mm; Nos. 730b, 731b, 732b; 23x25mm. No. 733 contains one 40x32mm stamp.

Dogs — A190

50c, Keeshond. 1k, Elkhound. 2k, Bernese. 3k, Pointing griffon. 4k, Sheep dog (border collie). 5k, Irish water spaniel. 6k, Briard. 10k, Brittany spaniels.

**1986, Aug. 28    Perf. 13**

| | | | | |
|---|---|---|---|---|
| 737 | A190 | 50c multicolored | .30 | .25 |
| 738 | A190 | 1k multicolored | .30 | .25 |
| 739 | A190 | 2k multicolored | .45 | .25 |
| 740 | A190 | 3k multicolored | .65 | .25 |
| 741 | A190 | 4k multicolored | .85 | .25 |
| 742 | A190 | 5k multicolored | 1.00 | .30 |
| 743 | A190 | 6k multicolored | 1.25 | .55 |
| | | *Nos. 737-743 (7)* | 4.80 | 2.10 |

**Souvenir Sheet**
**Perf. 13x13½**

| | | | | |
|---|---|---|---|---|
| 744 | A190 | 10k multicolored | 2.10 | 1.10 |

STOCKHOLMIA '86. Nos. 738-743 horiz. No. 744 contains one 40x32mm stamp. Nos. 737-743 exist imprf.

Cacti — A191

Designs: 50c, Mammillaria matudae. 1k, Mammillaria theresae. 2k, Ariocarpus trigonus. 3k, Notocactus crassigibbus. 4k, Astrophytum asterias hybridum. 5k, Melocactus manzanus. 6k, Astrophytum ornatum hybridum.

**1986, Sept. 28    Perf. 13**

| | | | | |
|---|---|---|---|---|
| 745 | A191 | 50c multicolored | .30 | .25 |
| 746 | A191 | 1k multicolored | .30 | .25 |
| 747 | A191 | 2k multicolored | .40 | .25 |
| 748 | A191 | 3k multicolored | .65 | .25 |
| 749 | A191 | 4k multicolored | .80 | .25 |
| 750 | A191 | 5k multicolored | 1.00 | .30 |
| 751 | A191 | 6k multicolored | 1.10 | .40 |
| | | *Nos. 745-751 (7)* | 4.55 | 1.95 |

Nos. 745-751 exist imperf.

Intl. Peace Year — A192

3k, Natl, arms, dove, globe. 5k, Dove, shattered bomb. 10k, Emblem held aloft.

**1986, Oct. 24**

| | | | | |
|---|---|---|---|---|
| 752 | A192 | 3k multicolored | .75 | .25 |
| 753 | A192 | 5k multicolored | 1.10 | .40 |
| 754 | A192 | 10k multicolored | 2.25 | 1.00 |
| | | *Nos. 752-754 (3)* | 4.10 | 1.65 |

UNESCO Programs in Laos — A193

3k, Vat Phu Champasak ruins. 4k, Satellite dish, map, globe. 9k, Laotians learning to read, horiz.

**1986, Nov. 4**

| | | | | |
|---|---|---|---|---|
| 755 | A193 | 3k multicolored | .70 | .25 |
| 756 | A193 | 4k multicolored | 1.00 | .30 |
| 757 | A193 | 9k multicolored | 1.75 | .65 |
| | | *Nos. 755-757 (3)* | 3.45 | 1.20 |

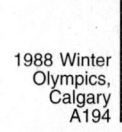

1988 Winter Olympics, Calgary A194

**1987, Jan. 14**

| | | | | |
|---|---|---|---|---|
| 758 | A194 | 50c Speed skating | .30 | .25 |
| 759 | A194 | 1k Biathlon | .30 | .25 |
| 760 | A194 | 2k Pairs figure skating | .40 | .25 |
| 761 | A194 | 3k Luge | .60 | .25 |
| 762 | A194 | 4k 4-Man bobsled | .75 | .25 |
| 763 | A194 | 5k Ice hockey | 1.00 | .30 |
| 764 | A194 | 6k Ski jumping | 1.10 | .40 |
| | | *Nos. 758-764 (7)* | 4.45 | 1.95 |

**Souvenir Sheet**
**Perf. 13½x13**

| | | | | |
|---|---|---|---|---|
| 765 | A194 | 10k Slalom | 2.25 | 1.10 |

Nos. 758-760 vert. No. 765 contains one stamp 32x40mm.

1988 Summer Olympics, Seoul A195

50c, Women's gymnastics. 1k, Women's discus. 2k, Running. 3k, Equestrian. 4k, Women's javelin. 5k, High jump. 6k, Wrestling. 10k, Runners leaving start.

**1987, Feb. 2    Perf. 12½x13, 13x13½**

| | | | | |
|---|---|---|---|---|
| 766 | A195 | 50c multicolored | .30 | .25 |
| 767 | A195 | 1k multicolored | .30 | .25 |
| 768 | A195 | 2k multicolored | .40 | .25 |
| 769 | A195 | 3k multicolored | .65 | .25 |
| 770 | A195 | 4k multicolored | .75 | .25 |
| 771 | A195 | 5k multicolored | 1.00 | .30 |
| 772 | A195 | 6k multicolored | 1.10 | .40 |
| | | *Nos. 766-772 (7)* | 4.50 | 1.95 |

**Souvenir Sheet**
**Perf. 12½**

| | | | | |
|---|---|---|---|---|
| 773 | A195 | 10k multicolored | 2.00 | 1.00 |

Nos. 766, 768, 770 and 772 vert. No. 773 contains one 40x32mm stamp. Nos. 766-772 exist imperf.

Dogs — A196

50c, Great Dane. 1k, Labrador retriever. 2k, St. Bernard. 3k, Schippercke. 4k, Alsatian (German shepherd). 5k, Beagle. 6k, Spaniel.

**1987, Mar. 5    Perf. 12½x13**

| | | | | |
|---|---|---|---|---|
| 774 | A196 | 50c multicolored | .30 | .25 |
| 775 | A196 | 1k multicolored | .30 | .25 |
| 776 | A196 | 2k multicolored | .40 | .25 |
| 777 | A196 | 3k multicolored | .65 | .25 |
| 778 | A196 | 4k multicolored | .75 | .25 |
| 779 | A196 | 5k multicolored | 1.00 | .30 |
| 780 | A196 | 6k multicolored | 1.25 | .55 |
| | | *Nos. 774-780 (7)* | 4.65 | 2.10 |

Space Flight, 30th Anniv. — A197

**1987, Apr. 12    Perf. 13**

| | | | | |
|---|---|---|---|---|
| 781 | A197 | 50c Sputnik 1 | .30 | .25 |
| 782 | A197 | 1k Sputnik 2 | .30 | .25 |
| 783 | A197 | 2k Cosmos 87 | .40 | .25 |
| 784 | A197 | 3k Cosmos | .50 | .25 |
| 785 | A197 | 4k Mars | .65 | .25 |
| 786 | A197 | 5k Luna 1 | .80 | .30 |
| 787 | A197 | 9k Luna 3, vert. | 1.25 | .50 |
| | | *Nos. 781-787 (7)* | 4.20 | 2.05 |

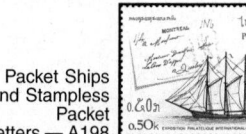

Packet Ships and Stampless Packet Letters — A198

Canada No. 282 A199

50c, "Montreal". 1k, "Paid Montreal". 2k, "Paid" and "Montreal Nov 24". 3k, "Williamsbvrg" and "Forwarded". 4k, "Montreal Fe 18 1844". 5k, "Paid" and "Montreal Jy 10 1848". 6k, "Paid" and "Montreal Paid Ap 16 1861 Canada".

**1987, May 12**

| | | | | |
|---|---|---|---|---|
| 788 | A198 | 50c multicolored | .30 | .25 |
| 789 | A198 | 1k multicolored | .30 | .25 |
| 790 | A198 | 2k multicolored | .35 | .25 |
| 791 | A198 | 3k multicolored | .55 | .25 |
| 792 | A198 | 4k multicolored | .75 | .25 |
| 793 | A198 | 5k multicolored | .85 | .30 |
| 794 | A198 | 6k multicolored | 1.10 | .40 |
| | | *Nos. 788-794 (7)* | 4.20 | 1.95 |

**Souvenir Sheet**
**Perf. 12½**

| | | | | |
|---|---|---|---|---|
| 795 | A199 | 10k multicolored | 2.50 | 1.25 |

CAPEX '87.

Orchids — A200

3k, Vanda teres. 7k, Laeliocattleya. 10k, Paphiopedilum hibrido. 39k, Sobralia. 44k, Paphiopedilum hibrido, diff. 47k, Paphiopedilum hibrido, diff. 50k, Cattleya trianaei. 95k, Vanda tricolor.

**1987, Aug. 10    Litho.    Perf. 13**

| | | | | |
|---|---|---|---|---|
| 796 | A200 | 3k multicolored | .30 | .25 |
| 796A | A200 | 7k multicolored | .30 | .25 |
| 796B | A200 | 10k multicolored | .40 | .25 |
| 796C | A200 | 39k multicolored | .75 | .25 |
| 796D | A200 | 44k multicolored | .80 | .30 |
| 796E | A200 | 47k multicolored | 1.00 | .40 |
| 796F | A200 | 50k multicolored | 1.10 | .40 |
| | | *Nos. 796-796F (7)* | 4.65 | 2.10 |

**Souvenir Sheet**
**Perf. 12½**

| | | | | |
|---|---|---|---|---|
| 796G | A200 | 95k multicolored | 2.25 | 1.10 |

No. 796G contains one 32x40mm stamp. Nos. 796, 796A-796G exist imperf.

Automobiles A201

**1987, July 2    Litho.    Perf. 12½**

| | | | | |
|---|---|---|---|---|
| 797 | A201 | 50c Toyota 480 | .30 | .25 |
| 798 | A201 | 1k Alfa 33 | .30 | .25 |
| 799 | A201 | 2k Ford Fiesta | .65 | .25 |
| 800 | A201 | 3k Datsun | .65 | .25 |
| 801 | A201 | 4k Vauxhall Cavalier | .80 | .25 |
| 802 | A201 | 5k Renault 5 | 1.00 | .30 |
| 803 | A201 | 6k Rover-800 | 1.25 | .55 |
| | | *Nos. 797-803 (7)* | 4.70 | 2.10 |

**Miniature Sheet**
**Perf. 13**

| | | | | |
|---|---|---|---|---|
| 804 | A201 | 10k Talbot | 2.10 | 1.00 |

HAFNIA '87, Denmark A202

Various Indian elephants.

**1987, Sept. 2    Perf. 13**

| | | | | |
|---|---|---|---|---|
| 805 | A202 | 50c Adult, calf | .30 | .25 |
| 806 | A202 | 1k Two adults, calf | .30 | .25 |
| 807 | A202 | 2k Adult eating grass | .40 | .25 |
| 808 | A202 | 3k Adult, diff. | .60 | .25 |
| 809 | A202 | 4k Adult, calf drinking | .75 | .25 |
| 810 | A202 | 5k Adult, diff. | .90 | .30 |
| 811 | A202 | 6k Adult, vert. | 1.10 | .40 |
| | | *Nos. 805-811 (7)* | 4.35 | 1.95 |

**Souvenir Sheet**

| | | | | |
|---|---|---|---|---|
| 812 | A202 | 10k Herd, diff. | 2.25 | 1.10 |

No. 812 contains one stamp 40x32mm.

Horses A203

**Perf. 13x12½, 12½x13**

**1987, June 3    Litho.**

| | | | | |
|---|---|---|---|---|
| 813 | A203 | 50c multicolored | .30 | .25 |
| 814 | A203 | 1k multi, diff. | .30 | .25 |
| 815 | A203 | 2k multi, diff. | .40 | .25 |
| 816 | A203 | 3k multi, diff. | .60 | .25 |
| 817 | A203 | 4k multi, diff. | .75 | .25 |
| 818 | A203 | 5k multi, diff. | 1.00 | .30 |
| 819 | A203 | 6k multi, diff. | 1.10 | .40 |
| | | *Nos. 813-819 (7)* | 4.45 | 1.95 |

Nos. 814-819 vert.

Fish — A204

Designs: 3k, Botia macrancantha. 7k, Oxymocanthus longirostris. 10k, Adioryx caudimaculatus. 39k, Synchiropus splendidus. 44k, Cephalopolis miniatus. 47k, Dendrochirus zebra. 50k, Pomacantus semicirculatus.

**1987, Oct. 14    Litho.    Perf. 13x12½**

| | | | | |
|---|---|---|---|---|
| 820 | A204 | 3k multicolored | .30 | .25 |
| 821 | A204 | 7k multicolored | .30 | .25 |
| 822 | A204 | 10k multicolored | .40 | .25 |
| 823 | A204 | 39k multicolored | .70 | .25 |
| 824 | A204 | 44k multicolored | .80 | .30 |

| | | | |
|---|---|---|---|
| 825 | A204 | 47k multicolored | 1.00 .40 |
| 826 | A204 | 50k multicolored | 1.10 .40 |
| | | *Nos. 820-826 (7)* | 4.60 2.10 |

World Food
Day — A205

1k, Tending crops. 3k, Harvesting corn, vert.
5k, Harvesting wheat. 63k, Youths, fish, vert.
142k, Tending pigs, chickens.

**1987, Oct. 16**      **Perf. 13**

| | | | |
|---|---|---|---|
| 827 | A205 | 1k multicolored | .30 .25 |
| 828 | A205 | 3k multicolored | .30 .25 |
| 829 | A205 | 5k multicolored | .30 .25 |
| 830 | A205 | 63k multicolored | 1.25 .50 |
| 831 | A205 | 142k multicolored | 2.40 1.00 |
| | | *Nos. 827-831 (5)* | 4.55 2.25 |

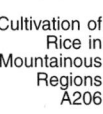

Cultivation of
Rice in
Mountainous
Regions
A206

**1987, Nov. 9**      **Perf. 13**

| | | | |
|---|---|---|---|
| 832 | A206 | 64k Tilling soil | 1.25 .30 |
| 833 | A206 | 100k Rice paddy | 1.90 .80 |

October Revolution,
Russia, 70th
Anniv. — A207

Paintings: 1k, Wounded soldier on battlefield. 2k, Mother and child. 4k, Storming the
Winter Palace. 8k, Lenin and revolutionaries.
10k, Rebuilding Red Square.

**1987, Nov.**      **Perf. 12x12½**

| | | | |
|---|---|---|---|
| 834 | A207 | 1k multicolored | .30 .25 |
| 835 | A207 | 2k multicolored | .40 .25 |
| 836 | A207 | 4k multicolored | .70 .25 |
| 837 | A207 | 8k multicolored | 1.25 .50 |
| 838 | A207 | 10k multicolored | 1.75 .65 |
| | | *Nos. 834-838 (5)* | 4.40 1.90 |

For surcharges, see Nos. 1882-1883.

Women Wearing
Regional
Costumes — A208

**1987, Dec. 2**

| | | | |
|---|---|---|---|
| 839 | A208 | 7k Mountain | .30 .25 |
| 840 | A208 | 38k Urban | .80 .25 |
| 841 | A208 | 144k Mountain, diff. | 2.75 1.10 |
| | | *Nos. 839-841 (3)* | 3.85 1.60 |

Nos. 839-841 exist imperf.

A209

1988 Winter Olympics,
Calgary — A210

**1988, Jan.10**      **Perf. 13x12½**

| | | | |
|---|---|---|---|
| 842 | A209 | 1k Bobsled | .30 .25 |
| 843 | A209 | 4k Biathlon | .30 .25 |
| 844 | A209 | 20k Skiing | .45 .25 |
| 845 | A209 | 42k Ice hockey | .75 .30 |
| 846 | A209 | 63k Speed skating | 1.10 .50 |
| 847 | A209 | 70k Slalom | 1.25 .55 |
| | | *Nos. 842-847 (6)* | 4.15 2.10 |

**Souvenir Sheet**
**Perf. 13**

| | | | |
|---|---|---|---|
| 848 | A210 | 95k Slalom, diff. | 2.25 1.10 |

No. 848 contains one stamp 40x32mm.

ESSEN
'88 — A211

Locomotives: 6k, Sans Pareil, vert. 15k,
Rocket, vert. 20k, Royal George. 25k,
Trevithick. 30k, Novelty. 100k, Tom Thumb.
95k, Locomotion.

**1988**      **Perf. 12½x13, 13x12½**

| | | | |
|---|---|---|---|
| 849 | A211 | 6k multicolored | .30 .25 |
| 850 | A211 | 15k multicolored | .30 .25 |
| 851 | A211 | 20k multicolored | .45 .25 |
| 852 | A211 | 25k multicolored | .55 .25 |
| 853 | A211 | 30k multicolored | .65 .25 |
| 854 | A211 | 100k multicolored | 1.90 .80 |
| | | *Nos. 849-854 (6)* | 4.15 2.05 |

**Souvenir Sheet**
**Perf. 13**

| | | | |
|---|---|---|---|
| 855 | A211 | 95k multicolored | 2.25 1.10 |

No. 855 contains one stamp 40x32mm.
Nos. 849-854 exist imperf.

Intl. Year of
Shelter for the
Homeless
A212

1k, Building frame of house. 27k, Cutting
lumber. 46k, Completed house. 70k,
Community.

**1988**      **Litho.**      **Perf. 13**

| | | | |
|---|---|---|---|
| 856 | A212 | 1k multicolored | .30 .25 |
| 857 | A212 | 27k multicolored | .55 .25 |
| 858 | A212 | 46k multicolored | 1.00 .30 |
| 859 | A212 | 70k multicolored | 1.60 .65 |
| | | *Nos. 856-859 (4)* | 3.45 1.45 |

Dinosaurs
A213

3k, Tyrannosaurus. 7k, Ceratosaurus
nasicornis, vert. 39k, Iguanodon bernissarten-
sis, vert. 44k, Scolosaurus, vert. 47k,
Phororhacus, vert. 50k, Trachodon.
95k, Pteranodon.

**Perf. 13x12½, 12½x13**
**1988, Mar. 3**      **Litho.**

| | | | |
|---|---|---|---|
| 860 | A213 | 3k multicolored | .30 .25 |
| 861 | A213 | 7k multicolored | .30 .25 |
| 862 | A213 | 39k multicolored | .75 .25 |
| 863 | A213 | 44k multicolored | .80 .40 |
| 864 | A213 | 47k multicolored | 1.00 .40 |
| 865 | A213 | 50k multicolored | 1.10 .40 |
| | | *Nos. 860-865 (6)* | 4.25 1.95 |

**Souvenir Sheet**
**Perf. 12½**

| | | | |
|---|---|---|---|
| 866 | A213 | 95k multicolored | 2.25 1.10 |

JUVALUX '88. Nos. 861-864 vert.
Identifications on Nos. 860 and 865 are
switched.
No. 866 contains one 40x32mm stamp.

WHO, 40th
Anniv. — A214

5k, Students, teacher. 27k, Pest control.
164k, Public water supply, vert.

**1988, Apr. 8**      **Perf. 12½**

| | | | |
|---|---|---|---|
| 867 | A214 | 5k multicolored | .30 .25 |
| 868 | A214 | 27k multicolored | .50 .25 |
| 869 | A214 | 164k multicolored | 3.00 1.25 |
| | | *Nos. 867-869 (3)* | 3.80 1.75 |

Flowers — A215

8k, Plumieria rubra. 9k, Althaea rosea. 15k,
Ixora coccinea. 33k, Cassia fistula. 64k, Dahlia
coccinea (pink). 69k, Dahlia coccinea (yellow).
95k, Plumieria, Althaea, Ixora.

**1988**      **Perf. 13x12½**

| | | | |
|---|---|---|---|
| 870 | A215 | 8k multicolored | .30 .25 |
| 871 | A215 | 9k multicolored | .30 .25 |
| 872 | A215 | 15k multicolored | .40 .25 |
| 873 | A215 | 33k multicolored | .75 .25 |
| 874 | A215 | 64k multicolored | 1.25 .50 |
| 875 | A215 | 69k multicolored | 1.50 .55 |
| | | *Nos. 870-875 (6)* | 4.50 2.05 |

**Souvenir Sheet**
**Perf. 13**

| | | | |
|---|---|---|---|
| 876 | A215 | 95k multicolored | 2.50 1.25 |

FINLANDIA '88. No. 876 contains one
32x40mm stamp.

Birds — A216

6k, Pelargopsis capensis. 10k, Coturnix
japonica. 13k, Psittacula roseata. 44k, Treron
bicincta. 63k, Pycnonotus melanicterus. 64k,
Ducula badia.

**1988**      **Perf. 13**

| | | | |
|---|---|---|---|
| 877 | A216 | 6k multicolored | .30 .25 |
| 878 | A216 | 10k multicolored | .30 .25 |
| 879 | A216 | 13k multicolored | .40 .25 |
| 880 | A216 | 44k multicolored | .85 .25 |
| 881 | A216 | 63k multicolored | 1.10 .50 |
| 882 | A216 | 64k multicolored | 1.10 .55 |
| | | *Nos. 877-882 (6)* | 4.05 2.05 |

1988 Summer
Olympics,
Seoul — A217

2k, Javelin. 5k, Long jump. 10k, Horizontal
bar. 12k, Canoeing. 38k, Balance beam. 46k,
Fencing. 100k, Wrestling.
95k, Horizontal bar, diff.

**1988**      **Perf. 12½x12**

| | | | |
|---|---|---|---|
| 883 | A217 | 2k multicolored | .30 .25 |
| 884 | A217 | 5k multicolored | .30 .25 |
| 885 | A217 | 10k multicolored | .40 .25 |
| 886 | A217 | 12k multicolored | .50 .25 |
| 887 | A217 | 38k multicolored | .80 .25 |
| 888 | A217 | 46k multicolored | 1.00 .30 |
| 889 | A217 | 100k multicolored | 2.00 .70 |
| | | *Nos. 883-889 (7)* | 5.30 2.25 |

**Souvenir Sheet**
**Perf. 13**

| | | | |
|---|---|---|---|
| 889A | A217 | 95k multicolored | 2.10 1.00 |

No. 889A contains one 40x32mm stamp.
Nos. 883-889 exist imperf.

Decorative
Stencils — A218

1k, Scarf. 2k, Pagoda entrance, vert. 3k,
Pagoda wall, vert. 25k, Pagoda pillar. 163k,
Skirt.

**1988**      **Perf. 13**

| | | | |
|---|---|---|---|
| 890 | A218 | 1k multicolored | .30 .25 |
| 891 | A218 | 2k multicolored | .30 .25 |
| 892 | A218 | 3k multicolored | .35 .25 |
| 893 | A218 | 25k multicolored | .50 .25 |
| 894 | A218 | 163k multicolored | 3.00 1.50 |
| | | *Nos. 890-894 (5)* | 4.45 2.50 |

Completion of
the 5-Year Plan
(1981-85)
A219

20k, Health care. 40k, Literacy. 50k, Irrigation. 100k, Communication, transport.

**1988**      **Litho.**      **Perf. 13**

| | | | |
|---|---|---|---|
| 895 | A219 | 20k multicolored | .40 .25 |
| 896 | A219 | 40k multicolored | .80 .40 |
| 897 | A219 | 50k multicolored | 1.00 .55 |
| 898 | A219 | 100k multicolored | 1.75 1.00 |
| | | *Nos. 895-898 (4)* | 3.95 2.20 |

Intl. Red Cross
and Red
Crescent
Organizations,
125th
Anniv. — A220

Designs: 4k, Dove, 3 stylized figures representing mankind, vert. 52k, Giving aid to the
handicapped, vert. 144k, Child immunization.

**1988**

| | | | |
|---|---|---|---|
| 899 | A220 | 4k multi | .30 .25 |
| 900 | A220 | 52k multi | 1.10 .55 |
| 901 | A220 | 144k multi | 2.75 1.50 |
| | | *Nos. 899-901 (3)* | 4.15 2.30 |

Chess
Champions
A220a

1k, R. Segura. 2k, Adolph Anderssen. 3k, P.
Morphy. 6k, W. Steinitz. 7k, E. Lasker. 12k,
J.R. Capablanca. 172k, A. Alekhine.

**1988**      **Litho.**      **Perf. 13**

| | | | |
|---|---|---|---|
| 901A | A220a | 1k multicolored | .30 .25 |
| 901B | A220a | 2k multicolored | .30 .25 |
| 901C | A220a | 3k multicolored | .30 .25 |
| 901D | A220a | 6k multicolored | .30 .25 |
| 901E | A220a | 7k multicolored | .30 .25 |
| 901F | A220a | 12k multicolored | .40 .25 |
| 901G | A220a | 172k multicolored | 3.00 1.10 |
| | | *Nos. 901A-901G (7)* | 4.90 2.60 |

Nos. 901C is incorrectly inscribed "Murphy."

1990 World Cup Soccer
Championships, Italy — A221

Various plays.

**1989**      **Perf. 13x12½**

| | | | |
|---|---|---|---|
| 902 | A221 | 10k multi | .30 .25 |
| 903 | A221 | 15k multi | .30 .25 |
| 904 | A221 | 20k multi, diff. | .40 .25 |
| 905 | A221 | 25k multi, diff. | .55 .25 |
| 906 | A221 | 45k multi, diff. | .80 .30 |
| 907 | A221 | 105k multi, diff. | 2.00 .80 |
| | | *Nos. 902-907 (6)* | 4.35 2.10 |

## Souvenir Sheet
### Perf. 13
907A A221 95k multi, diff.   2.10 1.10

No. 907A contains one 40x32mm stamp.

INDIA '89 — A222

Cats.
### 1989, Jan. 7    Perf. 12½
908 A222 5k multi   .30 .25
909 A222 6k multi, diff.   .30 .25
910 A222 10k multi, diff.   .40 .25
911 A222 20k multi, diff.   .60 .25
912 A222 50k multi, diff.   1.10 .40
913 A222 172k multi, diff.   3.25 1.00
   Nos. 908-913 (6)   5.95 2.40

### Souvenir Sheet
### Perf. 13
914 A222 95k multi, diff.   2.10 1.00

No. 914 contains one 32x40mm stamp.

1992 Winter Olympics, Albertville A223

Various figure skaters.
### 1989, May 1    Perf. 13
915 A223 9k multi, vert.   .30 .25
916 A223 10k shown   .30 .25
917 A223 15k multi, diff., vert.   .35 .25
918 A223 24k multi, diff., vert.   .50 .25
919 A223 29k multi, diff., vert.   .65 .25
920 A223 114k multi, diff., vert.   2.00 1.00
   Nos. 915-920 (6)   4.10 2.25

### Souvenir Sheet
### Perf. 12½
921 A223 95k Pairs figure skating   2.10 1.10

No. 921 contains one 32x40mm stamp.

People's Army, 40th Anniv. — A224

2k, Military school, vert. 3k, Health care. 250k, Ready for combat.
### 1989, Jan. 20    Perf. 13
922 A224 1k shown   .30 .25
923 A224 2k multicolored   .30 .25
924 A224 3k multicolored   .30 .25
925 A224 250k multicolored   6.00 1.00
   Nos. 922-925 (4)   6.90 1.75

1992 Summer Olympics, Barcelona A225

5k, Pole vault, vert. 15k, Gymnastic rings, vert. 20k, Cycling. 25k, Boxing. 70k, Archery, vert. 120k, Swimming, vert. 95k, Baseball.
### Perf. 12x12½, 12½x12
### 1989, June 1    Litho.
926 A225 5k multicolored   .30 .25
927 A225 15k multicolored   .30 .25
928 A225 20k multicolored   .30 .25
929 A225 25k multicolored   .40 .30
930 A225 70k multicolored   1.10 .55
931 A225 120k multicolored   1.75 .65
   Nos. 926-931 (6)   4.15 2.25

### Souvenir Sheet
### Perf. 13
932 A225 95k multicolored   2.10 1.10

No. 932 contains one 32x40mm stamp.

PHILEXFRANCE '89 — A226

Paintings by Picasso: 5k, *Beggars by the Edge of the Sea.* 7k, *Maternity.* 8k, *Portrait of Jaime S. Le Bock.* 9k, *Harlequins.* 105k, *Dog with Boy.* 114k, *Girl Balancing on Ball.* 95k *Woman in Hat.*

### 1989, July 17    Perf. 12½x13
933 A226 5k multi   .30 .25
934 A226 7k multi   .30 .25
935 A226 8k multi   .30 .25
936 A226 9k multi   .35 .25
937 A226 105k multi   1.75 .65
938 A226 114k multi   2.00 .80
   Nos. 933-938 (6)   5.00 2.45

### Souvenir Sheet
### Perf. 12½
939 A226 95k multicolored   2.10 1.10

No. 939 contains one 32x40mm stamp.

Cuban Revolution, 30th Anniv. — A227

### 1989, Apr. 20    Litho.    Perf. 13
940 A227 45k shown   1.10 .40
941 A227 50k Flags   1.25 .40

Fight the Destruction of Forests — A228

4k, Planting saplings. 10k, Fight forest fires. 12k, Do not chop down trees. 200k, Map of woodland.

### 1989, Mar. 30    Litho.    Perf. 13
942 A228 4k multicolored   .30 .25
943 A228 10k multicolored   .30 .25
944 A228 12k multicolored   .30 .25
945 A228 200k multicolored   3.25 1.00
   Nos. 942-945 (4)   4.15 1.75

Nos. 944-945 are vert.

Jawaharlal Nehru (1889-1964), Indian Statesman — A229

### 1989, Nov. 9    Litho.    Perf. 12½
946 A229 1k multicolored   .30 .25
947 A229 60k multi, horiz.   1.10 .50
948 A229 200k multi, diff.   3.50 1.10
   Nos. 946-948 (3)   4.90 1.85

Mani Ikara Zapota — A230

No. 950, Psidium guajava. No. 951, Annona sguamosa. No. 952, Durio zibethinus. No. 953, Punica granatum. No. 954, Moridica charautia.

### 1989, Sept. 18    Perf. 12½x13
949 A230 5k shown   .30 .25
950 A230 20k multicolored   .40 .25
951 A230 20k multicolored   .40 .25
952 A230 30k multicolored   .55 .25
953 A230 50k multicolored   .90 .50
954 A230 172k multicolored   3.00 1.00
   Nos. 949-954 (6)   5.55 2.50

A231

Historic Monuments: No. 955, That Sikhotabong, Khammouane. No. 956, That Dam, Vientiane. No. 957, That Ing Hang, Savannakhet. No. 958, Ho Vay Phra Thatluang, Vientiane.

### 1989, Oct. 19    Litho.    Perf. 12½
955 A231 5k multicolored   .30 .25
956 A231 15k multicolored   .30 .25
957 A231 61k multicolored   1.10 .55
958 A231 161k multicolored   2.75 1.25
   Nos. 955-958 (4)   4.45 2.30

1992 Summer Olympics, Barcelona A232

### 1990, Mar. 5    Litho.    Perf. 12½x13
959 A232 10k Basketball   .30 .25
960 A232 30k Hurdles   .45 .25
961 A232 45k High jump   .65 .25
962 A232 50k Cycling   .75 .30
963 A232 60k Javelin   .90 .50
964 A232 90k Tennis   1.40 .80
   Nos. 959-964 (6)   4.45 2.35

### Souvenir Sheet
965 A232 95k Rhythmic gymnastics   2.00 1.00

Nos. 959-964 exist imperf.

1992 Winter Olympics, Albertville A233

10k, Speed skating. 25k, Cross country skiing, vert. 30k, Slalom skiing. 35k, Luge. 80k, Ice dancing, vert. 90k, Biathlon. 95k, Hockey, vert.

### 1990, June 20    Perf. 13
966 A233 10k multicolored   .30 .25
967 A233 25k multicolored   .40 .25
968 A233 30k multicolored   .45 .25
969 A233 35k multicolored   .55 .25
970 A233 80k multicolored   1.25 .55
971 A233 90k multicolored   1.40 .65
   Nos. 966-971 (6)   4.35 2.20

### Souvenir Sheet
972 A233 95k multicolored   2.00 1.00

New Zealand Birds — A234

Designs: 10k, Prosthemadera novaeseelandie. 15k, Alauda arvensis. 20k, Haemotopus unicolor. 50k, Phalacrocorax carbo. 60k, Demigretta sacra. 100k Apteryx australis mantelli. 95k, Phalacrocorax corunculatus.

### 1990, Aug. 24    Perf. 12½
973 A234 10k multicolored   .30 .25
974 A234 15k multicolored   .35 .25
975 A234 20k multicolored   .45 .25
976 A234 50k multicolored   .90 .30
977 A234 60k multicolored   1.10 .50
978 A234 100k multicolored   1.90 .80
   Nos. 973-978 (6)   5.00 2.35

### Souvenir Sheet
979 A234 95k multicolored   2.25 1.10

World Stamp Expo, New Zealand '90. No. 979 contains one 32x40mm stamp and also exists imperf.

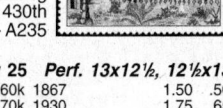

That Luang Temple, 430th Anniv. — A235

### 1990, July 25    Perf. 13x12½, 12½x13
980 A235 60k 1867   1.50 .50
981 A235 70k 1930   1.75 .65
982 A235 130k 1990, vert.   3.25 1.25
   Nos. 980-982 (3)   6.50 2.40

Ho Chi Minh (1890-1969), Vietnamese Leader — A236

40k, Addressing people. 60k, With Laotian President. 160k, Waving, vert.

### 1990, May 11    Perf. 13
983 A236 40k multicolored   .90 .30
984 A236 60k multicolored   1.40 .45
985 A236 160k multicolored   3.75 1.25
   Nos. 983-985 (3)   6.05 2.00

UN Development Program, 40th Anniv. — A237

30k, Surgeons. 45k, Fishermen. 80k, Flight controller, vert. 90k, Power plant.

### 1990, Oct. 24    Litho.    Perf. 13
986 A237 30k multicolored   .75 .25
987 A237 45k multicolored   1.25 .30
988 A237 80k multicolored   2.00 .75
989 A237 90k multicolored   2.25 .90
   Nos. 986-989 (4)   6.25 2.20

15th Anniv. of the Republic A238

Designs: 15k, Placing flowers at monument. 20k, Celebratory parade. 80k, Visiting sick. 120k, Women marching with banner.

### 1990, Dec. 2    Litho.    Perf. 13
990 A238 15k multicolored   .40 .25
991 A238 20k multicolored   .60 .25
992 A238 80k multicolored   2.00 .90
993 A238 120k multicolored   3.00 1.25
   Nos. 990-993 (4)   6.00 2.65

New Year's Day — A239

### 1990, Nov. 20
994 A239 5k shown   .30 .25
995 A239 10k Parade   .30 .25
996 A239 50k Ceremony   .90 .40

### Size: 40x29mm
997 A239 150k Ceremomy, diff.   2.50 1.25
   Nos. 994-997 (4)   4.00 2.15

World Cup Soccer Championships, Italy — A240

Designs: Various soccer players in action.

| 1990 | | Litho. | Perf. 13 | |
|---|---|---|---|---|
| 998 | A240 | 10k multicolored | .30 | .25 |
| 999 | A240 | 15k multicolored | .30 | .25 |
| 1000 | A240 | 20k multicolored | .45 | .25 |
| 1001 | A240 | 25k multicolored | .55 | .25 |
| 1002 | A240 | 45k multicolored | .85 | .30 |
| 1003 | A240 | 105k multicolored | 1.90 | .80 |
| | | Nos. 998-1003 (6) | 4.35 | 2.10 |

**Souvenir Sheets**
*Perf. 12½*

| 1004 | A240 | 95k multi, horiz. | 2.00 | 1.00 |
|---|---|---|---|---|

*Perf. 13*

| 1004A | A240 | 95k multi | 2.00 | 1.00 |
|---|---|---|---|---|

No. 1004 contains one 39x31mm stamp; No. 1004A one 32x40mm stamp.

Intl. Literacy Year — A241

50k, Woman with child, vert. 60k, Monk teaching class. 150k, Two women, man reading.

| 1990, Feb. 27 | | Litho. | Perf. 12½ | |
|---|---|---|---|---|
| 1005 | A241 | 10k shown | .30 | .25 |
| 1006 | A241 | 50k multicolored | 1.00 | .75 |
| 1007 | A241 | 60k multicolored | 1.25 | .90 |
| 1008 | A241 | 150k multicolored | 3.00 | 1.25 |
| | | Nos. 1005-1008 (4) | 5.55 | 3.15 |

Stamp World London '90 — A242

Stamps, modes of mail transport: 15k, Great Britain #1, stagecoach. 20k, US #1, train. 40k, France #3, balloons. 50k, Sardinia #1, post rider. 60k, Indo-China #3, elephant. 95k, Laos #272, jet. 100k, Spain #1, sailing ship.

| 1990, Apr. 26 | | Litho. | Perf. 13x12½ | |
|---|---|---|---|---|
| 1009 | A242 | 15k multicolored | .30 | .25 |
| 1010 | A242 | 20k multicolroed | .40 | .25 |
| 1011 | A242 | 40k multicolored | .70 | .25 |
| 1012 | A242 | 50k multicolored | 1.00 | .30 |
| 1013 | A242 | 60k multicolored | 1.10 | .50 |
| 1014 | A242 | 100k multicolored | 1.90 | .75 |
| | | Nos. 1009-1014 (6) | 5.40 | 2.30 |

**Souvenir Sheet**
*Perf. 13*

| 1015 | A242 | 95k multicolored | 2.00 | 1.00 |
|---|---|---|---|---|

No. 1015 contains one 40x32mm stamp. Nos. 1009-1014 exist imperf.

Endangered Animals A242a

10k, Brow-antlered deer. 20k, Gaur. 40k, Wild water buffalo. 45k, Kouprey. 120k, Javan rhinoceros.

| 1990, Sept. 15 | | Litho. | Perf. 12½ | |
|---|---|---|---|---|
| 1015A | A242a | 10k multicolored | .30 | .25 |
| 1015B | A242a | 20k multicolored | .40 | .25 |
| 1015C | A242a | 40k multicolored | .70 | .25 |
| 1015D | A242a | 45k multicolored | .75 | .30 |
| 1015E | A242a | 120k multicolored | 1.75 | 1.00 |
| | | Nos. 1015A-1015E (5) | 3.90 | 2.05 |

1992 Olympics, Barcelona and Albertville A244

No. 1016, 2-man canoe. No. 1017, 1-man kayak. No. 1018, Bobsled, vert. No. 1019, Cross country skiing. No. 1020, Ski jumping. No. 1021, Biathlon. No. 1022, Diving, vert. No. 1023, Sailing, vert. No. 1024, Speed skating. No. 1025, Swimming.
No. 1026, 2-man kayak. No. 1027, Slalom skiing, vert.

*Perf. 12½x12, 12x12½, 13 (A244)*

| 1991, Jan. 25 | | | | |
|---|---|---|---|---|
| 1016 | A243 | 22k multi | .30 | .25 |
| 1017 | A243 | 32k multi | .30 | .25 |
| 1018 | A244 | 32k multi | .30 | .25 |
| 1019 | A244 | 135k multi | .50 | .25 |
| 1020 | A244 | 250k multi | .85 | .25 |
| 1021 | A244 | 275k multi | 1.00 | .30 |
| 1022 | A243 | 285k multi | 1.00 | .30 |
| 1023 | A243 | 330k multi | 1.20 | .35 |
| 1024 | A244 | 900k multi | 2.75 | 1.00 |
| 1025 | A243 | 1000k multi | 2.50 | 1.00 |
| | | Nos. 1016-1025 (10) | 10.70 | 4.20 |

**Souvenir Sheets**
*Perf. 12½, 13½x13*

| 1026 | A244 | 700k multi | 2.75 | 1.00 |
|---|---|---|---|---|
| 1027 | A244 | 700k multi | 2.75 | 1.00 |

No. 1026 contains one 40x32mm stamp. No. 1027 contains one 32x40mm stamp.

Tourism A245

Designs: 155k, Rapids, Champassak. 220k, Vangvieng. 235k, Waterfalls, Saravane, vert. 1000k Plain of Jars, Xieng Khouang, vert.

| 1991 | | Perf. 13x12½, 12½x13 | | |
|---|---|---|---|---|
| 1028 | A245 | 155k multicolored | .55 | .25 |
| 1029 | A245 | 220k multicolored | .80 | .30 |
| 1030 | A245 | 235k multicolored | 1.00 | .35 |
| 1031 | A245 | 1000k multicolored | 3.25 | 1.10 |
| | | Nos. 1028-1031 (4) | 5.60 | 2.00 |

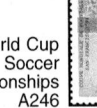

1994 World Cup Soccer Championships A246

Designs: Various players in action.

| 1991 | | Litho. | Perf. 13 | |
|---|---|---|---|---|
| 1032 | A246 | 32k multicolored | .30 | .25 |
| 1033 | A246 | 330k multicolored | .75 | .35 |
| 1034 | A246 | 340k multi, vert. | .85 | .40 |
| 1035 | A246 | 400k multicolored | 1.00 | .45 |
| 1036 | A246 | 500k multicolored | 1.25 | .65 |
| | | Nos. 1032-1036 (5) | 4.15 | 2.10 |

**Souvenir Sheet**
*Perf. 13½x13*

| 1037 | A246 | 700k multi, vert. | 2.00 | 1.00 |
|---|---|---|---|---|

No. 1037 contains one 32x40mm stamp.

Espamer '91, Buenos Aires — A247

25k, Mallard 4-4-2. 32k, Pacific 231 4-6-2. 285k, American style 4-8-4. 650k, Canadian Pacific 4-6-2. 750k, Beyer-Garrant 4-8-2 2-8-4. 700k, Inter-city diesel.

| 1991, June 30 | | Litho. | Perf. 12½x12 | |
|---|---|---|---|---|
| 1038 | A247 | 25k multicolored | .30 | .25 |
| 1039 | A247 | 32k multicolored | .30 | .25 |
| 1040 | A247 | 285k multicolored | .90 | .35 |
| 1041 | A247 | 650k multicolored | 2.00 | .75 |
| 1042 | A247 | 750k multicolored | 2.25 | 1.10 |
| | | Nos. 1038-1042 (5) | 5.75 | 2.70 |

**Souvenir Sheet**
*Perf. 12½*

| 1043 | A247 | 700k multicolored | 2.00 | 1.00 |
|---|---|---|---|---|

Espamer '91, Buenos Aires. No. 1039 does not show denomination or country in Latin characters. Size of Nos. 1038, 1040-1042: 44x28mm.

Musical Celebrations A248

Designs: 220k, Man playing mong, vert. 275k, Man, woman singing Siphandone, vert. 545k, Man, woman singing Khapngum. 690k, People dancing.

| 1991, July 10 | | Litho. | Perf. 13 | |
|---|---|---|---|---|
| 1044 | A248 | 20k multicolored | .30 | .25 |
| 1045 | A248 | 220k multicolored | .55 | .25 |
| 1046 | A248 | 275k multicolored | .75 | .30 |
| 1047 | A248 | 545k multicolored | 1.25 | .65 |
| 1048 | A248 | 690k multicolored | 1.75 | 1.00 |
| | | Nos. 1044-1048 (5) | 4.60 | 2.45 |

Butterflies A248a

55k, Sasakia charonda. 90k, Luendorfia puziloi. 255k, Papilio bianor. 285k, Papilio machaon. 900k, Graphium doson.
700k, Cyrestis thyodamas.

| 1991, Oct. 15 | | Litho. | Perf. 12½x12 | |
|---|---|---|---|---|
| 1048A | A248a | 55k multicolored | .30 | .25 |
| 1048B | A248a | 90k multicolored | .30 | .25 |
| 1048C | A248a | 255k multicolored | .90 | .25 |
| 1048D | A248a | 285k multicolored | 1.00 | .30 |
| 1048E | A248a | 900k multicolored | 2.50 | 1.10 |
| | | Nos. 1048A-1048E (5) | 5.00 | 2.15 |

**Souvenir Sheet**
*Perf. 13*

| 1048F | A248a | 700k multicolored | 3.25 | 1.25 |
|---|---|---|---|---|

No. 1048F contains one 40x32mm stamp. Phila Nippon '91.

Arbor Day — A249

700k, 6 people planting trees. 800k, Nursery.

| 1991, June 1 | | | Perf. 12½ | |
|---|---|---|---|---|
| 1049 | A249 | 250k multicolored | .70 | .35 |
| 1050 | A249 | 700k multicolored | 1.60 | .80 |
| 1051 | A249 | 800k multicolored | 2.00 | 1.10 |
| | | Nos. 1049-1051 (3) | 4.30 | 2.25 |

1992 Winter Olympics, Albertville — A250

*Perf. 12½x12, 12x12½*

| 1992, Jan. 12 | | | Litho. | |
|---|---|---|---|---|
| 1052 | A250 | 200k Bobsled | .50 | .25 |
| 1053 | A250 | 220k Skiing | .60 | .25 |
| 1054 | A250 | 250k Skiing, horiz. | .70 | .25 |
| 1055 | A250 | 500k Luge | 1.25 | .30 |
| 1056 | A250 | 600k Figure skater | 1.50 | .80 |
| | | Nos. 1052-1056 (5) | 4.55 | 1.85 |

**Souvenir Sheet**
*Perf. 12½*

| 1057 | A250 | 700k Speed skater | 2.00 | 1.00 |
|---|---|---|---|---|

No. 1057 contains one 32x40mm stamp.

1992 Summer Olympics, Barcelona — A251

| 1992, Feb. 21 | | Litho. | Perf. 12½ | |
|---|---|---|---|---|
| 1058 | A251 | 32k Women's running | .30 | .25 |
| 1059 | A251 | 245k Baseball | .70 | .25 |
| 1060 | A251 | 275k Tennis | .80 | .25 |
| 1061 | A251 | 285k Basketball | .90 | .30 |
| 1062 | A251 | 900k Boxing, horiz. | 2.25 | 1.00 |
| | | Nos. 1058-1062 (5) | 4.95 | 2.05 |

**Souvenir Sheet**

| 1062A | A251 | 700k Diving | 2.00 | 1.00 |
|---|---|---|---|---|

No. 1062A contains one 40x32mm stamp.

World Health Day — A252

Designs: 200k, Spraying for mosquitoes. 255k, Campaign against smoking. 330k, Receiving blood donation. 1000k, Immunizing child, vert.

| 1992, Apr. 7 | | | | |
|---|---|---|---|---|
| 1063 | A252 | 200k multicolored | .50 | .25 |
| 1064 | A252 | 255k multicolored | .70 | .30 |
| 1065 | A252 | 330k multicolored | .90 | .65 |
| 1066 | A252 | 1000k multicolored | 2.25 | 1.25 |
| | | Nos. 1063-1066 (4) | 4.35 | 2.45 |

A253

Flags, ball and players: 260k, Argentina, Italy. 305k, Germany, Great Britain. 310k, US, World Cup trophy (no players). 350k, Italy, Great Britain. 800k, Germany, Argentina. 700k, Goalie.

| 1992, May 1 | | Litho. | Perf. 13 | |
|---|---|---|---|---|
| 1067 | A253 | 260k multicolored | .60 | .25 |
| 1068 | A253 | 305k multicolored | .65 | .25 |
| 1069 | A253 | 310k multicolored | .70 | .30 |
| 1070 | A253 | 350k multicolored | .80 | .50 |
| 1071 | A253 | 800k multicolored | 1.90 | 1.00 |
| | | Nos. 1067-1071 (5) | 4.65 | 2.30 |

**Souvenir Sheet**
*Perf. 12½*

| 1072 | A253 | 700k multicolored | 3.25 | 1.65 |
|---|---|---|---|---|

1994 World Cup Soccer Championships, US.

A254

Children playing: 220k, Playing drum. 285k, Jumping rope, horiz. 330k, Walking on stilts. 400k, Escape from line, horiz.

| 1992, Nov. 8 | | Litho. | Perf. 13 | |
|---|---|---|---|---|
| 1073 | A254 | 220k multi | .85 | .25 |
| 1074 | A254 | 285k multi | 1.10 | .25 |
| 1075 | A254 | 330k multi | 1.25 | .30 |
| 1076 | A254 | 400k multi | 1.60 | .65 |
| | | Nos. 1073-1076 (4) | 4.80 | 1.45 |

For surcharge, see No. 1902.

Poisonous
Snakes — A255

280k, Naja naja kaouthia. 295k, Naja naja
atra. 420k, Trimeresurus wagleri. 700k, Ophi-
ophagus hannah, vert.

**Perf. 12½x13, 13x12½**

**1992, July 10**      Litho.
1078 A255 280k multicolored   .85   .25
1079 A255 295k multicolored   .85   .25
1080 A255 420k multicolored   1.25   .35
1081 A255 700k multicolored   2.25   1.00
    Nos. 1078-1081 (4)   5.20   1.85

Restoration of Wat
Phou — A256

Different views of Wat Phou.

**Perf. 13x12½, 12½x13**

**1992, Aug. 22**      Litho.
1082 A256 185k multicolored   .50   .30
1083 A256 220k multicolored   .60   .30
1084 A256 1200k multi, horiz.   3.75   1.40
    Nos. 1082-1084 (3)   4.85   2.00

Genoa
'92 — A257

Sailing ships and maps by: 100k, Juan Martinez. 300k, Piri Reis, vert. 350k, Paolo del
Pozo Toscanelli. 400k, Gabriel de Vallseca.
455k, Juan Martinez, diff. 700k, Juan de la
Cosa.

**Perf. 13x12½, 12½x13**

**1992, Sept. 12**
1085 A257 100k multicolored   .30   .25
1086 A257 300k multicolored   .85   .25
1087 A257 350k multicolored   1.10   .25
1088 A257 400k multicolored   1.20   .50
1089 A257 455k multicolored   1.60   .65
    Nos. 1085-1089 (5)   5.05   1.90
      **Souvenir Sheet**
        **Perf. 13**
1090 A257 700k multicolored   2.75   1.00

Traditional Costumes
of the
Montagnards — A258

Various costumes.

**1992, Oct. 2**      Litho.     **Perf. 13**
1091 A258 25k multicolored   .30   .25
1092 A258 55k multicolored   .30   .25
1093 A258 400k multicolored   1.25   .60
1094 A258 1200k multicolored   4.00   1.25
    Nos. 1091-1094 (4)   5.85   2.25

A259

UN, UNESCO emblems, stylized faces and:
330k, Drum. 1000k, Traditional flute.

---

**1991, Nov. 1**    Litho.     **Perf. 13**
1095 A259 285k shown   .85   .35
1096 A259 330k multicolored   1.00   .35
1097 A259 1000k multicolored   3.00   1.35
    Nos. 1095-1097 (3)   4.85   1.95

Cultural Development Decade, 1988-1997.

Apes — A260

**1992, Dec. 22**
1098 A260 10k Black gibbon   .30   .25
1099 A260 100k Douc langur   .30   .25
1100 A260 250k Pileated gibbon   .75   .35
1101 A260 430k Francois langur   1.10   .50
1102 A260 800k Pygmy loris   2.00   .80
    Nos. 1098-1102 (5)   4.45   2.15

Natl.
Customs — A261

Designs: 100k, Woman praying before Buddha, vert. 160k, Procession. 1500k, People
giving food to monks.

**1992, Dec. 2**      **Perf. 12½**
1103 A261 100k multicolored   .30   .25
1104 A261 140k multicolored   .40   .25
1105 A261 160k multicolored   .45   .25
1106 A261 1500k multicolored   4.50   2.25
    Nos. 1103-1106 (4)   5.65   3.00

First Subway
System, 130th
Anniv. — A262

**1993, Jan. 9**     Litho.     **Perf. 13**
1107 A262 15k New York   .30   .25
1108 A262 50k Berlin   .30   .25
1109 A262 100k Paris   .30   .25
1110 A262 200k London   .75   .35
1111 A262 900k Moscow   2.75   1.40
    Nos. 1107-1111 (5)   4.40   2.50
      **Souvenir Sheet**
       **Perf. 13x13½**
1112 A262 700k Antique engine,
       vert.   3.00   1.25

No. 1112 contains one 32x40mm stamp.

Frogs — A263

55k, Kaloula pulchra. 90k, Xenopus muel-
leri. 100k, Centrolenella vireovittata, vert.
185k, Bufo marinus. 1200k, Hyla arborea, vert.

**1993, Feb. 1**     Litho.     **Perf. 12½**
1113 A263 55k multicolored   .30   .25
1114 A263 90k multicolored   .30   .25
1115 A263 100k multicolored   .35   .25
1116 A263 185k multicolored   .70   .35
1117 A263 1200k multicolored   3.50   1.25
    Nos. 1113-1117 (5)   5.15   2.35

Animals — A264

45k, Tupaia glis. 60k, Cynocephalus volans.
120k, Loris grasilis. 500k, Tarsium spectrum.
600k, Symphalangus syndactylus.

---

**1993, Mar. 13**    Litho.     **Perf. 13**
1118 A264 45k multicolored   .30   .25
1119 A264 60k multicolored   .30   .25
1120 A264 120k multicolored   .45   .25
1121 A264 500k multicolored   1.60   .75
1122 A264 600k multicolored   1.90   1.25
    Nos. 1118-1122 (5)   4.55   2.75

Native Houses
A265

Various houses.

**1993, July 12**     Litho.     **Perf. 13**
1123 A265 32k multi, vert.   .50   .40
1124 A265 200k multicolored   1.50   .60
1125 A265 650k multicolored   5.00   1.00
1126 A265 750k multicolored   6.75   1.75
    Nos. 1123-1126 (4)   13.75   3.75

Campaign
Against Illegal
Drugs — A266

Designs: 200k, Drugs, skull smoking cigarette. 430k, Burning confiscated drugs. 900k,
Instructor showing danger of drugs to
audience.

**1993, June 26**      **Perf. 12½**
1127 A266 200k multicolored   .65   .35
1128 A266 430k multicolored   1.50   .75
1129 A266 900k multicolored   3.25   1.40
    Nos. 1127-1129 (3)   5.40   2.50

Shells — A267

20k, Chlamys senatorius nobilis. 30k,
Epitonium prestiosum. 70k, Lambis rugosa.
500k, Conus aulicus. 1000k, Lambis
millepeda.

**1993, May 29**   Litho.   **Perf. 12x12½**
1130 A267 20k multicolored   .30   .25
1131 A267 30k multicolored   .30   .25
1132 A267 70k multicolored   .30   .25
1133 A267 500k multicolored   1.60   .75
1134 A267 1000k multicolored   3.00   1.40
    Nos. 1130-1134 (5)   5.50   2.90

Birds of Prey — A268

10k, Aquila clanga. 100k, Athene brama.
330k, Circus melanoluecos. 1000k, Circaetus
gallicus.

**1993, Aug. 10**    Litho.     **Perf. 13**
1135 A268 10k multicolored   .30   .25
1136 A268 100k multicolored   .50   .25
1137 A268 330k multicolored   1.50   .50
1138 A268 1000k multicolored   4.00   1.40
    Nos. 1135-1138 (4)   6.30   2.40

No. 1137 is horiz.

Environmental
Protection
A269

Designs: 32k, Fighting forest fire. 40k, Animals around clean river. 260k, Rice paddies.
1100k, Water buffalo, people in water.

---

**1993, Sept. 25**    Litho.     **Perf. 13**
1139 A269 32k multicolored   .30   .25
1140 A269 40k multicolored   .30   .25
1141 A269 260k multicolored   1.00   .35
1142 A269 1100k multicolored   4.25   1.40
    Nos. 1139-1142 (4)   5.85   2.25

Bangkok
'93 — A270

Butterflies: 35k, Narathura atosia. 80k,
Parides philoxenus. 150k, Euploea harrisi.
220k, Ixias pyrene. 500k, Elymnias hypermnestra. 700k, Stichopthalma louisa.

**1993, Oct. 1**    Litho.     **Perf. 13**
1143 A270 35k multicolored   .30   .25
1144 A270 80k multicolored   .30   .25
1145 A270 150k multicolored   .45   .25
1146 A270 220k multicolored   .75   .35
1147 A270 500k multicolored   2.00   .85
    Nos. 1143-1147 (5)   3.80   1.95
      **Souvenir Sheet**
1148 A270 700k multicolored   3.00   1.50

No. 1148 contains one 40x32mm stamp.

1994 World Cup
Soccer
Championships,
US — A271

Various soccer players.

**1993, Nov. 3**      **Perf. 13**
1149 A271 10k multicolored   .30   .25
1150 A271 20k multicolored   .30   .25
1151 A271 285k multicolored   1.10   .25
1152 A271 400k multicolored   1.60   .50
1153 A271 800k multicolored   3.25   1.25
    Nos. 1149-1153 (5)   6.55   2.50
      **Souvenir Sheet**
       **Perf. 12½**
1154 A271 700k multicolored   2.75   1.40

Nos. 1154 contains one 32x40mm stamp.

Prehistoric
Birds — A272

10k, Hesperornis. 20k, Dronte. 150k,
Archaeopterix. 600k, Phororhachos. No. 1159,
700k, Dinornis maximus.
No. 1160, 700k, Teratornis, horiz.

**1994, Jan. 20**    Litho.     **Perf. 13**
1155 A272 10k multi   .30   .25
1156 A272 20k multi   .30   .25
1157 A272 150k multi   .60   .25
1158 A272 600k multi   2.00   .60
1159 A272 700k multi   2.25   1.00
    Nos. 1155-1159 (5)   5.45   2.25
      **Souvenir Sheet**
1160 A272 700k multi   2.50   1.25

Intl. Olympic
Committee,
Cent. — A273

100k, Flag, flame. 250k, Ancient Olympians.
1000k, Baron de Coubertin, Olympic runner.

**Perf. 12x12½, 12½x12**

**1994, Mar. 15**      Litho.
1161 A273 100k multi, vert.   .30   .25
1162 A273 250k multi   .75   .25
1163 A273 1000k multi, vert.   3.25   1.50
    Nos. 1161-1163 (3)   4.30   2.00

1994 World Cup Soccer Championships, U.S. — A274

Various soccer plays.

**1994, June 15    Litho.    Perf. 12½**
| | | | | |
|---|---|---|---|---|
| 1164 | A274 | 40k multicolored | .30 | .25 |
| 1165 | A274 | 50k multicolored | .30 | .25 |
| 1166 | A274 | 60k multicolored | .30 | .25 |
| 1167 | A274 | 320k multicolored | 1.10 | .35 |
| 1168 | A274 | 900k multicolored | 3.25 | 1.00 |
| | | Nos. 1164-1168 (5) | 5.25 | 2.10 |

**Souvenir Sheet**
**Perf. 13**
| | | | | |
|---|---|---|---|---|
| 1169 | A274 | 700k multicolored | 3.75 | 1.65 |

No. 1169 contains one 32x40mm stamp and is also known imperf.

Pagodas — A275

Various ornate gables.

**1994, July 1    Litho.    Perf. 12½**
| | | | | |
|---|---|---|---|---|
| 1170 | A275 | 30k multicolored | .30 | .25 |
| 1171 | A275 | 150k multicolored | .55 | .25 |
| 1172 | A275 | 380k multicolored | 1.25 | .40 |
| 1173 | A275 | 1100k multicolored | 3.75 | 1.65 |
| | | Nos. 1170-1173 (4) | 5.85 | 2.55 |

Nos. 1170-1173 exist imperf.

World Wildlife Fund — A276

50k, Ursus Malayanus. 90k, Adult. 200k, Cub, adult. 220k, Adult standing.

**1994, July 23**
| | | | | |
|---|---|---|---|---|
| 1174 | A276 | 50k multi | .75 | .25 |
| 1175 | A276 | 90k multi | 1.00 | .40 |
| 1176 | A276 | 200k multi | 2.25 | 1.00 |
| 1177 | A276 | 220k multi | 3.25 | 1.25 |
| | | Nos. 1174-1177 (4) | 7.25 | 2.90 |

Reptiles — A277

70k, Natrix natrix. 80k, Natrix tessellata. 90k, Salamandra salamandra. 600k, Triturus alpestris. 700k, Triturus cristatus. 800k, Lacerta viridis.

**1994, Aug. 1    Litho.    Perf. 12½**
| | | | | |
|---|---|---|---|---|
| 1178 | A277 | 70k multi, horiz. | .30 | .25 |
| 1179 | A277 | 80k multi, horiz. | .35 | .25 |
| 1180 | A277 | 90k multi, horiz. | .40 | .25 |
| 1181 | A277 | 600k multi, horiz. | 2.50 | .50 |
| 1182 | A277 | 800k multicolored | 3.25 | 1.25 |
| | | Nos. 1178-1182 (5) | 6.80 | 2.50 |

**Souvenir Sheet**
| | | | | |
|---|---|---|---|---|
| 1183 | A277 | 700k multi, horiz. | 3.25 | 1.25 |

No. 1183 contains one 40x32mm stamp.

Intl. Year of the Family — A278

Designs: 500k, Mother taking child to school, horiz. No. 1186, Mother walking with children. No. 1187, Family.

**1994, Sept. 24**
| | | | | |
|---|---|---|---|---|
| 1184 | A278 | 200k multicolored | .85 | .35 |
| 1185 | A278 | 500k multicolored | 2.10 | .75 |
| 1186 | A278 | 700k multicolored | 3.25 | 1.25 |
| | | Nos. 1184-1186 (3) | 6.20 | 2.35 |

**Souvenir Sheet**
| | | | | |
|---|---|---|---|---|
| 1187 | A278 | 700k multicolored | 3.25 | 1.25 |

No. 1187 contains one 32x40mm stamp.

Drums — A279

Designs: 440k, Two people with hanging drum. 450k, Barrel shaped drum. 600k, Hanging drum.

**Perf. 12½, 13x12½ (#1189)**
**1994, Oct. 20    Litho.**
| | | | | |
|---|---|---|---|---|
| 1188 | A279 | 370k multicolored | 1.60 | .40 |
| 1189 | A279 | 440k multicolored | 1.75 | .50 |
| 1190 | A279 | 450k multicolored | 1.75 | .50 |
| 1191 | A279 | 600k multicolored | 2.40 | .75 |
| | | Nos. 1188-1191 (4) | 7.50 | 2.15 |

No. 1189 is 40x29mm.

Elephants A280

400k, Beside railing. 890k, Being ridden, vert.

**1994, Nov. 25**
| | | | | |
|---|---|---|---|---|
| 1192 | A280 | 140k shown | .55 | .25 |
| 1193 | A280 | 400k multi | 1.60 | .80 |
| 1194 | A280 | 890k multi | 3.25 | 1.40 |
| | | Nos. 1192-1194 (3) | 5.40 | 2.45 |

Peace Bridge Between Laos and Thailand — A281

**1994, Apr. 8    Litho.    Perf. 14x14½**
| | | | | |
|---|---|---|---|---|
| 1195 | A281 | 500k multicolored | 2.50 | 1.25 |

Buddha — A282

15k, Phra Xayavoraman 7. 280k, Phra Thong Souk. 390k, Phra Monolom. 800k, Phra Ongtu.

**1994, Aug. 25    Litho.    Perf. 13**
| | | | | |
|---|---|---|---|---|
| 1196 | A282 | 15k multicolored | .30 | .25 |
| 1197 | A282 | 280k multicolored | 1.25 | .35 |
| 1198 | A282 | 390k multicolored | 1.60 | .50 |
| 1199 | A282 | 800k multicolored | 3.50 | 1.40 |
| | | Nos. 1196-1199 (4) | 6.65 | 2.50 |

Dinosaurs — A283

**1994, Dec. 8**
| | | | | |
|---|---|---|---|---|
| 1200 | A283 | 50k Theropod | .30 | .25 |
| 1201 | A283 | 380k Iguanodon | 1.75 | .65 |
| 1202 | A283 | 420k Sauropod | 2.00 | .75 |
| | | Nos. 1200-1202 (3) | 4.05 | 1.65 |

World Tourism Organization, 20th Anniv. — A284

60k, Traditional music. 250k, Traditional dance. 400k, Traditional food. 650k, Waterfalls, vert.

**1995, Jan. 2    Litho.    Perf. 12½**
| | | | | |
|---|---|---|---|---|
| 1203 | A284 | 60k multi | .30 | .25 |
| 1204 | A284 | 250k multi | 1.00 | .25 |
| 1205 | A284 | 400k multi | 1.75 | .50 |
| 1206 | A284 | 650k multi | 2.75 | .90 |
| | | Nos. 1203-1206 (4) | 5.80 | 1.90 |

**Souvenir Sheet**
**Perf. 13**
| | | | | |
|---|---|---|---|---|
| 1207 | A284 | 700k like #1206, vert. | 4.00 | 2.40 |

No. 1207 contains one 32x44mm stamp.

Dinosaurs — A285

**1995, Feb. 20    Perf. 12½**
| | | | | |
|---|---|---|---|---|
| 1208 | A285 | 50k Tracodon | .30 | .25 |
| 1209 | A285 | 70k Protoceratops | .30 | .25 |
| 1210 | A285 | 300k Brontosaurus | 1.25 | .35 |
| 1211 | A285 | 400k Stegosaurus | 1.75 | .50 |
| 1212 | A285 | 600k Tyranosaurus | 2.50 | .75 |
| | | Nos. 1208-1212 (5) | 6.10 | 2.10 |

Birds — A286

50k, Acridotheres javanicus. 150k, Starnus burmannicus. 300k, Acridotheres tristis. 700k, Gracula religiosa.

**1995, Mar. 10**
| | | | | |
|---|---|---|---|---|
| 1213 | A286 | 50k multicolored | .30 | .25 |
| 1214 | A286 | 150k multicolored | .65 | .25 |
| 1215 | A286 | 300k multicolored | 1.25 | .40 |
| 1216 | A286 | 700k multicolored | 3.00 | .90 |
| | | Nos. 1213-1216 (4) | 5.20 | 1.80 |

Nos. 1213-1216 exist imperf.

Francophonie, 25th Anniv. — 1216A

Designs: 50k, People with arms linked. 380k, Temple. 420k, Map of Laos.

**1995, Mar. 20    Litho.    Perf. 13**
| | | | | |
|---|---|---|---|---|
| 1216A | A286a | 50k multi | .30 | .25 |
| 1216B | A286a | 380k multi | 1.50 | .65 |
| 1216C | A286a | 420k multi | 1.75 | .75 |
| | | Nos. 1216A-1216C (3) | 3.55 | 1.65 |

Antique Containers A287

70k, "Hanche" cup, vert. 200k, Resin bowl. 450k, Button design bowl. 600k, Loving cup.

**1995, May 1    Litho.    Perf. 12½**
| | | | | |
|---|---|---|---|---|
| 1217 | A287 | 70k multi | .30 | .25 |
| 1218 | A287 | 200k multi | .85 | .25 |
| 1219 | A287 | 450k multi | 1.90 | .55 |
| 1220 | A287 | 600k multi | 2.50 | .75 |
| | | Nos. 1217-1220 (4) | 5.55 | 1.80 |

1996 Atlanta Pre-Olympics A288

**1995, Apr. 5**
| | | | | |
|---|---|---|---|---|
| 1221 | A288 | 60k Pole vault | .30 | .25 |
| 1222 | A288 | 80k Javelin | .35 | .25 |
| 1223 | A288 | 200k Hammer throw | .85 | .25 |
| 1224 | A288 | 350k Long jump | 1.60 | .40 |
| 1225 | A288 | 700k High jump | 3.25 | .90 |
| | | Nos. 1221-1225 (5) | 6.35 | 2.05 |

**Souvenir Sheet**
| | | | | |
|---|---|---|---|---|
| 1226 | A288 | 700k Baseball | 3.25 | 1.90 |

No. 1226 contains one 40x32mm stamp.

Rocket Festival — A289

Designs: 80k, Launching rocket from scaffolding, vert. 160k, Carrying rocket in procession led by monk. 500k, Man carrying rocket on shoulder. 700k, People looking at rockets on tripods.

**1995, June 1    Litho.    Perf. 13**
| | | | | |
|---|---|---|---|---|
| 1227 | A289 | 80k multicolored | .30 | .25 |
| 1228 | A289 | 160k multicolored | .65 | .25 |
| 1229 | A289 | 500k multicolored | 1.90 | .55 |
| 1230 | A289 | 700k multicolored | 2.50 | .90 |
| | | Nos. 1227-1230 (4) | 5.35 | 1.95 |

Domestic Cats — A290

Designs: 40k, Red tabby longhair. 50k, Siamese seal point. 250k, Red tabby longhair. 400k, Tortoise-shell shorthair. 650k, Tortoise-shell shorthair, vert. 700k, Tortoise-shell shorthair.

**1995, July 25    Litho.    Perf. 12½**
| | | | | |
|---|---|---|---|---|
| 1231 | A290 | 40k multicolored | .30 | .25 |
| 1232 | A290 | 50k multicolored | .30 | .25 |
| 1233 | A290 | 250k multicolored | .80 | .25 |
| 1234 | A290 | 400k multicolored | 1.20 | .30 |
| 1235 | A290 | 650k multicolored | 1.40 | .75 |
| | | Nos. 1231-1235 (5) | 4.00 | 1.80 |

**Souvenir Sheet**
| | | | | |
|---|---|---|---|---|
| 1236 | A290 | 700k multicolored | 2.50 | 1.90 |

No. 1236 contains one 40x32mm stamp.

Insect-Eating Plants — A291

Designs: 90k, Nepenthes villosa. 100k, Dionaea muscipula. 350k, Sarracenia flava. 450k, Sarracenia purpurea. 500k, Nepenthes ampullaria.
1000k, Nepenthes gracilis.

**1995, Aug. 24**
| | | | | |
|---|---|---|---|---|
| 1237 | A291 | 90k multicolored | .30 | .25 |
| 1238 | A291 | 100k multicolored | .40 | .25 |
| 1239 | A291 | 350k multicolored | 1.20 | .35 |
| 1240 | A291 | 450k multicolored | 1.60 | .35 |
| 1241 | A291 | 500k multicolored | 2.00 | .75 |
| | | Nos. 1237-1241 (5) | 5.50 | 1.95 |

**Souvenir Sheet**
| | | | | |
|---|---|---|---|---|
| 1242 | A291 | 1000k multicolored | 4.50 | 2.00 |

No. 1242 contains one 40x32mm stamp.

Insects — A292

Designs: 40k, Lucanus cervus. 50k, Melolontha melolontha. 500k, Xylocopa violacea. 800k, Tettigonia viridissima.

**1995, Sept. 20**
| | | | | |
|---|---|---|---|---|
| 1243 | A292 | 40k multicolored | .30 | .25 |
| 1244 | A292 | 50k multicolored | .30 | .25 |
| 1245 | A292 | 500k multicolored | 2.00 | .50 |
| 1246 | A292 | 800k multicolored | 2.75 | .90 |
| | | Nos. 1243-1246 (4) | 5.35 | 1.90 |

FAO, 50th Anniv. — A293

Designs: 80k, Cattle grazing. 300k, Farmer tilling rice paddy. 1000k, Planting, irrigating rice paddies, stocking pond with fish.

**1995, Oct. 16    Litho.    Perf. 12½**
| | | | | |
|---|---|---|---|---|
| 1247 | A293 | 80k multicolored | .30 | .25 |
| 1248 | A293 | 300k multicolored | 1.00 | .50 |
| 1249 | A293 | 1000k multicolored | 3.50 | 1.70 |
| | | Nos. 1247-1249 (3) | 4.80 | 2.45 |

Traditional Culture — A294

Designs: 50k, Man with musical instrument, two women. 280k, Dance. 380k, Playing game with bamboo poles. 420k, Woman, man with musical instruments.

**1996, Jan. 10**
| | | | | |
|---|---|---|---|---|
| 1250 | A294 | 50k multicolored | .30 | .25 |
| 1251 | A294 | 280k multicolored | 1.40 | .35 |
| 1252 | A294 | 380k multicolored | 2.00 | .50 |
| 1253 | A294 | 420k multicolored | 2.25 | .50 |
| | | Nos. 1250-1253 (4) | 5.95 | 1.60 |

1996 Summer Olympics, Atlanta — A295

30k, Cycling. 150k, Soccer. 200k, Basketball, vert. 300k, Running, vert. 500k, Shooting. 1000k, Pole vault.

**1996, Feb. 20**
| | | | | |
|---|---|---|---|---|
| 1254 | A295 | 30k multi | .30 | .25 |
| 1255 | A295 | 150k multi | .75 | .25 |
| 1256 | A295 | 200k multi | 1.00 | .30 |
| 1257 | A295 | 300k multi | 1.50 | .30 |
| 1258 | A295 | 500k multi | 2.50 | .65 |
| | | Nos. 1254-1258 (5) | 6.05 | 1.70 |

**Souvenir Sheet**
| | | | | |
|---|---|---|---|---|
| 1259 | A295 | 1000k multi | 3.50 | 1.70 |

No. 1259 contains one 38x30mm stamp.

Fauna — A296

Designs: 40k, Helarctos malayanus. 60k, Pelecanus philippensis. 200k, Panthera pardus. 250k, Papilio machaon. 700k, Python molurus.

**1996, Feb. 26    Litho.    Perf. 13**
| | | | | |
|---|---|---|---|---|
| 1260 | A296 | 40k multicolored | .30 | .25 |
| 1261 | A296 | 60k multicolored | .35 | .25 |
| 1262 | A296 | 200k multicolored | 1.10 | .25 |
| 1263 | A296 | 250k multicolored | 1.25 | .30 |
| 1264 | A296 | 700k multicolored | 3.00 | .90 |
| | | Nos. 1260-1264 (5) | 6.00 | 1.95 |

Intl. Women's Day — A297

20k, Weaving textile. 290k, Instructing calisthenics. 1000k, Feeding infant, vert.

**1996, Mar. 8**
| | | | | |
|---|---|---|---|---|
| 1265 | A297 | 20k multicolored | .30 | .25 |
| 1266 | A297 | 290k multicolored | 1.10 | .30 |
| 1267 | A297 | 1000k multicolored | 3.50 | 1.70 |
| | | Nos. 1265-1267 (3) | 4.90 | 2.25 |

A298

Various soccer plays.

**1996, May 3    Litho.    Perf. 13**
| | | | | |
|---|---|---|---|---|
| 1268 | A298 | 20k multicolored | .30 | .25 |
| 1269 | A298 | 50k multicolored | .30 | .25 |
| 1270 | A298 | 300k multicolored | .60 | .30 |
| 1271 | A298 | 400k multicolored | .75 | .50 |
| 1272 | A298 | 500k multicolored | 1.00 | .60 |
| | | Nos. 1268-1272 (5) | 2.95 | 1.90 |

**Souvenir Sheet**
| | | | | |
|---|---|---|---|---|
| 1273 | A298 | 1000k multicolored | 2.50 | 1.50 |

1998 World Soccer Cup Championships, France.
No. 1273 contains one 32x40mm stamp.

Rats — A299

**1996, Apr. 15    Litho.    Perf. 13½x13**
| | | | | |
|---|---|---|---|---|
| 1274 | A299 | 50k purple & multi | .30 | .25 |
| 1275 | A299 | 340k blue & multi | 1.40 | .65 |
| 1276 | A299 | 350k green & multi | 1.40 | .65 |
| 1277 | A299 | 370k red & multi | 1.50 | .75 |
| | | Nos. 1274-1277 (4) | 4.60 | 2.30 |

New Year 1996 (Year of the Rat).

Laos Rural Development Program, 20th Anniv. — A300

50k, Instruction for giving medical care. 280k, Irrigation system. 600k, Bridge over waterway.

**1995, Dec. 2    Perf. 13**
| | | | | |
|---|---|---|---|---|
| 1278 | A300 | 50k multicolored | .30 | .25 |
| 1279 | A300 | 280k multicolored | .55 | .50 |
| 1280 | A300 | 600k multicolored | 1.50 | 1.00 |
| | | Nos. 1278-1280 (3) | 2.35 | 1.75 |

UN, 50th Anniv. — A301

Designs: 290k, Men seated at round table. 310k, Men playing game, checkers. 440k, Boys in swing, playing ball.

**1995, Oct. 24**
| | | | | |
|---|---|---|---|---|
| 1281 | A301 | 290k multicolored | 1.00 | .40 |
| 1282 | A301 | 310k multicolored | 1.10 | .50 |
| 1283 | A301 | 440k multicolored | 1.50 | .75 |
| | | Nos. 1281-1283 (3) | 3.60 | 1.65 |

Antique Aircraft — A302

25k, Morane. 60k, Sopwith Camel. 150k, De Haviland DH-4. 250k, Albatros. 800k, Caudron.

**1996, July 5    Litho.    Perf. 13**
| | | | | |
|---|---|---|---|---|
| 1284 | A302 | 25k multicolored | .30 | .25 |
| 1285 | A302 | 60k multicolored | .30 | .25 |
| 1286 | A302 | 150k multicolored | .65 | .25 |
| 1287 | A302 | 250k multicolored | 1.10 | .35 |
| 1288 | A302 | 800k multicolored | 2.50 | 1.00 |
| | | Nos. 1284-1288 (5) | 4.85 | 2.10 |

Capex '96.

Carts — A303

**1996, Aug. 21**
| | | | | |
|---|---|---|---|---|
| 1289 | A303 | 50k shown | .30 | .25 |
| 1290 | A303 | 100k Cart, diff. | .40 | .25 |
| 1291 | A303 | 440k Pulled by oxen | 1.50 | .65 |
| | | Nos. 1289-1291 (3) | 2.20 | 1.15 |

Flowers — A304

Designs: 50k, Dendrobium secundum. 200k, Ascocentrum miniatum. 500k, Aerides multiflorum. 520k, Dendrobium aggregatum.

**1996, Oct. 25    Litho.    Perf. 13**
| | | | | |
|---|---|---|---|---|
| 1292 | A304 | 50k multicolored | .30 | .25 |
| 1293 | A304 | 200k multicolored | .75 | .25 |
| 1294 | A304 | 500k multicolored | 1.90 | .65 |
| 1295 | A304 | 520k multicolored | 2.00 | .65 |
| | | Nos. 1292-1295 (4) | 4.95 | 1.80 |

Draft Horses — A305

Various breeds.

**1996, Nov. 5    Litho.    Perf. 13**
| | | | | |
|---|---|---|---|---|
| 1296 | A305 | 50k yellow & multi | .30 | .25 |
| 1297 | A305 | 80k green & multi | .30 | .25 |
| 1298 | A305 | 200k pink & multi | .55 | .25 |
| 1299 | A305 | 400k blue & multi | 1.25 | .50 |
| 1300 | A305 | 600k yellow & multi | 1.75 | .75 |
| | | Nos. 1296-1300 (5) | 4.15 | 2.00 |

**Souvenir Sheet**
| | | | | |
|---|---|---|---|---|
| 1301 | A305 | 1000k pink & multi | 3.00 | 1.50 |

No. 1301 contains one 32x40mm stamp.

UNICEF, 50th Anniv. — A306

200k, Children in school. 500k, Child breastfeeding, vert. 600k, Woman pumping water.

**1996, Dec. 11    Litho.**
| | | | | |
|---|---|---|---|---|
| 1302 | A306 | 200k multicolored | .80 | .30 |
| 1303 | A306 | 500k multicolored | 2.00 | .90 |
| 1304 | A306 | 600k multicolored | 2.40 | 1.25 |
| | | Nos. 1302-1304 (3) | 5.20 | 2.45 |

Greenpeace, 25th Anniv. A306a

Turtles: 150k, Dermochelys coriacea on sand. 250k, Dermochelys coriacea in surf. 400k, Erethochelys imbricata. 450k, Chelonia agassizi.

**1996, Dec. 27    Litho.    Perf. 13**
| | | | | |
|---|---|---|---|---|
| 1304A | A306a | 150k multicolored | .80 | .25 |
| 1304B | A306a | 250k multicolored | 1.25 | .50 |
| 1304C | A306a | 400k multicolored | 2.00 | .80 |
| 1304D | A306a | 450k multicolored | 2.25 | .90 |
| e. | | Souvenir sheet, #1304A-1304D | 6.50 | 4.75 |
| | | Nos. 1304A-1304D (4) | 6.30 | 2.45 |

Steam Locomotives A307

Designs: 100k, Kinnaird, 1846. 200k, Pioneer, 1836, portrait of George Stephenson. 300k, Portrait of Robert Stephenson, Long Boiler Express, 1848. 400k, Adler, 1835. 500k, Lord of the Isles, 1851-84. 600k, The Columbine, 1845.
2000k, Best friend of Charleston, 1830.

**Perf. 12½x12, 12x13 (#1306-1309)**
**1997    Litho.**
| | | | | |
|---|---|---|---|---|
| 1305 | A307 | 100k multicolored | .30 | .25 |
| 1306 | A307 | 200k multicolored | .40 | .25 |
| 1307 | A307 | 300k multicolored | .60 | .35 |
| 1308 | A307 | 400k multicolored | .75 | .50 |
| 1309 | A307 | 500k multicolored | 1.00 | .65 |
| 1310 | A307 | 600k multicolored | 1.25 | .75 |
| | | Nos. 1305-1310 (6) | 4.30 | 2.75 |

**Souvenir Sheet**
**Perf. 12½**
| | | | | |
|---|---|---|---|---|
| 1311 | A307 | 2000k multicolored | 3.25 | 3.00 |

Nos. 1305 and 1310 are 43.5x27mm. Nos. 1306-1309 are 42x21mm.
No. 1311 contains one 40x32mm stamp.

Parrots — A308

Designs: 50k, Agapornis personata. 150k, Agapornis cana. 200k, Agapornis lilianae. 400k, Agapornis fischeri. 500k, Agapornis nigregenis. 800k, Agapornis roseicollis.
2000k, Agapornis taranta.

**1997    Perf. 12½**
| | | | | |
|---|---|---|---|---|
| 1312 | A308 | 50k multicolored | .30 | .25 |
| 1313 | A308 | 150k multicolored | .45 | .25 |
| 1314 | A308 | 200k multicolored | .60 | .25 |
| 1315 | A308 | 400k multicolored | 1.00 | .50 |
| 1316 | A308 | 500k multicolored | 1.10 | .65 |
| 1317 | A308 | 800k multicolored | 1.75 | 1.00 |
| | | Nos. 1312-1317 (6) | 5.20 | 2.90 |

**Souvenir Sheet**
| | | | | |
|---|---|---|---|---|
| 1318 | A308 | 2000k multicolored | 5.00 | 4.00 |

No. 1318 contains one 32x40mm stamp.

Year of the Ox — A308a

Designs: 300k, Ox, rider with flag, vert. 440k, Ox, rider with umbrella.

**1997    Litho.    Perf. 13x13½, 13½x13**
| | | | | |
|---|---|---|---|---|
| 1318A | A308a | 50k multi | .30 | .25 |
| 1318B | A308a | 300k multi | 1.60 | 1.40 |
| 1318C | A308a | 440k multi | 2.25 | 1.75 |
| | | Nos. 1318A-1318C (3) | 4.15 | 3.40 |

Cooking
Utensils — A309

50k, Cooking over open fire, vert. 340k, Traditional food containers. 370k, Traditional meal setting.

**1997**
| | | | | |
|---|---|---|---|---|
|1319|A309|50k multicolored|.30|.25|
|1320|A309|340k multicolored|1.00|.55|
|1321|A309|370k multicolored|1.00|.60|
| |Nos. 1319-1321 (3)| |2.30|1.40|

Orchids — A310

Designs: 50k, Roeblingiana. 100k, Findlayanum. 150k, Crepidatum. 250k, Sarcanthus birmanicus. 400k, Cymbidium lowianum. 1000k, Dendrobium gratiossissimum. 2000k, Chamberlainianum.

**1997** Litho. Perf. 12½
| | | | | |
|---|---|---|---|---|
|1322|A310|50k multicolored|.30|.25|
|1323|A310|100k multicolored|.35|.25|
|1324|A310|150k multicolored|.45|.25|
|1325|A310|250k multicolored|.60|.35|
|1326|A310|400k multicolored|.90|.50|
|1327|A310|1000k multicolored|1.75|1.25|
| |Nos. 1322-1327 (6)| |4.35|2.85|

**Souvenir Sheet**
|1328|A310|2000k multicolored|4.25|3.50|

No. 1328 contains one 32x40mm stamp.

Elephants
A311

Elephas maximus: 100k, Adult, vert. 250k, Adult holding log. 300k, Adult, calf.
Loxodonta africana: 350k, Adult. 450k, Adult in water. 550k, Adult, vert. 2000k, Head of adult.

**1997** Litho. Perf. 12½
| | | | | |
|---|---|---|---|---|
|1329|A311|100k multicolored|.30|.25|
|1330|A311|250k multicolored|.60|.35|
|1331|A311|300k multicolored|.65|.35|
|1332|A311|350k multicolored|.70|.40|
|1333|A311|450k multicolored|.85|.55|
|1334|A311|550k multicolored|1.20|.65|
| |Nos. 1329-1334 (6)| |4.30|2.55|

**Souvenir Sheet**
|1335|A311|2000k multicolored|4.25|3.00|

No. 1335 contains one 32x40mm stamp.

Head Pieces
and
Masks — A312

Various designs.

**1997** Litho. Perf. 12½
| | | | | |
|---|---|---|---|---|
|1336|A312|50k multi, vert.|.30|.25|
|1337|A312|100k multi, vert|.30|.25|
|1338|A312|150k multi|.40|.25|
|1339|A312|200k multi, vert.|.55|.25|
|1340|A312|350k multi|1.25|.40|
| |Nos. 1336-1340 (5)| |2.80|1.40|

1998 World Cup
Soccer
Championships,
France — A313

Various soccer plays.

**1997** Litho. Perf. 12½
| | | | | |
|---|---|---|---|---|
|1341|A313|100k multicolored|.30|.25|
|1342|A313|200k multicolored|.50|.25|
|1343|A313|250k multicolored|.55|.30|
|1344|A313|300k multicolored|.55|.30|
|1345|A313|350k multicolored|.65|.40|
|1346|A313|700k multicolored|.95|.80|
| |Nos. 1341-1346 (6)| |3.50|2.30|

**Souvenir Sheet**
|1347|A313|2000k multicolored|3.50|2.50|

Sailing
Ships — A314

50k, Phoenician. 100k, 13th cent. ship. 150k, 15th cent. vessel. 200k, Portuguese caravel, 16th cent. 400k, Dutch, 17th cent. 900k, HMS Victory.
2000k, Grand Henry, 1514.

**1997** Perf. 13
| | | | | |
|---|---|---|---|---|
|1348|A314|50k multicolored|.30|.25|
|1349|A314|100k multicolored|.30|.25|
|1350|A314|150k multicolored|.35|.25|
|1351|A314|200k multicolored|.40|.25|
|1352|A314|400k multicolored|.80|.40|
|1353|A314|900k multicolored|1.40|.80|
| |Nos. 1348-1353 (6)| |3.55|2.20|

**Souvenir Sheet**
|1354|A314|2000k multicolored|3.50|2.50|

No. 1354 contains one 40x28mm stamp.

Canoe
Races — A315

Designs: 50k, Team in red shirts, team in yellow shirts rowing upward. 100k, Crowd cheering on teams. 300k, Teams rowing left. 500k, People standing in canoe cheering on teams.

**1997** Litho. Perf. 12½
| | | | | |
|---|---|---|---|---|
|1355|A315|50k multicolored|.30|.25|
|1356|A315|100k multicolored|.30|.25|
|1357|A315|300k multicolored|.75|.30|
|1358|A315|500k multicolored|1.25|.55|
| |Nos. 1355-1358 (4)| |2.60|1.35|

Admission of Laos to
ASEAN — A316

Central flag: a, Brunei. b, Indonesia. c, Laos. d, Malaysia. e, Taiwan. f, Philippines. g, Singapore. h, Thailand. i, Viet Nam.

**1997, July 23** Litho. Perf. 14x14½
|1359|A316|550k Strip of 9, #a.-i.|9.50|9.50|
|j.| |Sheet of 9, #1359a-1359i + label|15.00|15.00|

Nos. 1359a-1359i also exist in souvenir sheets of 1. No. 1359 was not available in the philatelic market until 8/98.

Vaccination
Day — A317

Design: 50k, Child receiving oral vaccination. 340k, Child receiving shot. 370k, Child in wheelchair.

**1997, Jan. 3** Litho. Perf. 13x13¼
| | | | | |
|---|---|---|---|---|
|1363|A317|50k multi|.30|.25|
|1364|A317|340k multi|1.50|.65|
|1365|A317|370k multi|1.60|.75|
| |Nos. 1363-1365 (3)| |3.40|1.65|

For surcharges, see Nos. 1949-1950.

Beginning with No. 1366, used values are for postally used stamps.

Pseudoryx
Saola — A319

Various views of Pseudoryx saola.

**1997, Feb. 10** Perf. 13x13¼, 13¼x13
| | | | | |
|---|---|---|---|---|
|1366|A319|350k multi|1.60|1.60|
|1367|A319|380k multi, vert.|1.75|1.75|
|1368|A319|420k multi|2.00|2.00|
| |Nos. 1366-1368 (3)| |5.35|5.35|

For surcharges, see Nos. 1951-1952.

ASEAN
(Assoc. of
South East
Asian
Nations),
30th Anniv.
A321

**1997, Aug. 8** Litho. Perf. 13
|1373|A321|150k Headquarters|.90|.65|
|1374|A321|600k Map of Laos|3.50|2.75|

Fishing — A322

Designs: 50k, Holding large net with a pole, vert. 100k, Casting net. 450k, Woman using small net, vert. 600k, Placing fish traps in water.

**1997**
| | | | | |
|---|---|---|---|---|
|1375|A322|50k multicolored|.30|.25|
|1376|A322|100k multicolored|.60|.30|
|1377|A322|450k multicolored|2.00|1.60|
|1378|A322|600k multicolored|2.75|2.00|
| |Nos. 1375-1378 (4)| |5.65|4.15|

New Year 1998
(Year of the
Tiger) — A323

**1998**
| | | | | |
|---|---|---|---|---|
|1379|A323|150k green & multi|.90|.70|
|1380|A323|350k gray & multi|1.75|1.60|
|1381|A323|400k pale lilac & multi|1.90|1.75|
| |Nos. 1379-1381 (3)| |4.55|4.05|

Canoes
A325

Designs: 1100k, Barque. 1200k, Covered pirogue. 2500k, Motorized pirogue.

**1998** Litho. Perf. 14½x14
| | | | | |
|---|---|---|---|---|
|1387|A325|1100k multicolored|2.50|2.50|
|1388|A325|1200k multicolored|2.75|2.75|
|1389|A325|2500k multicolored|6.25|6.25|
| |Nos. 1387-1389 (3)| |11.50|11.50|

A326

Various wind musical instruments.

**1998** Perf. 14x14½
| | | | | |
|---|---|---|---|---|
|1390|A326|900k multicolored|2.25|2.25|
|1391|A326|1200k multicolored|3.25|3.25|
|1392|A326|1500k multicolored|4.00|4.00|
| |Nos. 1390-1392 (3)| |9.50|9.50|

A327

Buddha Luang, Phabang.

**1998**
|1393|A327|3000k multicolored|7.50|7.50|

Orchids
A328

Designs: 900k, Paphiopedilum callosum. 950k, Paphiopedilum concolor. 1000k, Dendrobium thyrsiflorum, vert. 1050k, Dendrobium lindleyi, vert.

**1998** Perf. 14½x14, 14x14½
| | | | | |
|---|---|---|---|---|
|1394|A328|900k multicolored|2.75|2.75|
|1395|A328|950k multicolored|3.00|3.00|
|1396|A328|1000k multicolored|3.00|3.00|
|1397|A328|1050k multicolored|3.25|3.25|
| |Nos. 1394-1397 (4)| |12.00|12.00|

Universal
Declaration of
Human
Rights, 50th
Anniv.
A329

Designs: 170k, Women voting. 300k, Children in classroom.

**1998** Perf. 14½x14
|1398|A329|170k multicolored|2.25|2.25|
|1399|A329|300k multicolored|3.75|3.75|

Historic
Sites — A330

Designs: 10,000k, Hotay Vat Sisaket, vert. 25,000k, Vat Phou. 45,000k, That Luong.

Perf. 14x14¼, 14¼x14
**1998, Sept. 1** Litho.
|1400-1402|A330|Set of 3|120.00|120.00|

People's
Army, 50th
Anniv.
A331

Designs: 1300k, Soldiers, flag, flowers. 1500k, Soldiers, cave, jungle, vert.

**1999, Jan. 20** Litho. Perf. 13¼
|1403|A331|1300k multi|4.00|1.40|
|1404|A331|1500k multi|5.00|1.50|

## Souvenir Sheet

Visit Laos Year (in 2000) A331a

Various temples: b, 2500k. c, 4000k, d, 5500k, e, 8000k.

### 1999, Aug. 1    Typo.    Perf. 13¼
**Gold Stamps**

| | | | |
|---|---|---|---|
| 1404A | A331a | Sheet of 4, #b-e | 25.00 25.00 |
| f. | | As 1404A, with larger margins with Thaipex 99 and China Stamp Exhibition 99 emblems | 30.00 30.00 |
| g. | | As 1404A, with larger margins with China 1999 Philatelic Exhibition emblem | 30.00 30.00 |

No. 1404Af issued 8/2; No. 1404Ag issued 8/4.

Luang Prabang World Heritage Site A332

Designs: 400k, Commemorative marker, vert. 1150k, Building. 1250k, Vat Xiengthong (building with curved roof).

### 1999, Feb. 2
| | | | | |
|---|---|---|---|---|
| 1405 | A332 | 400k multi | 2.50 | .80 |
| 1406 | A332 | 1150k multi | 5.50 | 1.50 |
| 1407 | A332 | 1250k multi | 6.50 | 2.00 |
| | Nos. 1405-1407 (3) | | 14.50 | 4.30 |

Tourism A333

Designs: 200k, Yaos, Muong Sing. 500k, Phadeang, Vangvieng District. 1050k, That Makmo, Luang Prabang. 1300k, Patuxay, Vientiane, vert.

### Perf. 14¾x14, 14x14¾
### 1999, Mar. 2    Litho.
| | | | |
|---|---|---|---|
| 1408 | A333 | 200k multi | 1.00 |
| 1409 | A333 | 500k multi | 1.50 |
| 1410 | A333 | 1050k multi | 2.50 |
| 1411 | A333 | 1300k multi | 3.50 |
| | Nos. 1408-1411 (4) | | 8.50 |

Nocturnal Creatures — A334

Designs: 900k, Glaucidium brodiei. 1600k, Otus lempiji. 2100k, Tyto alba. 2800k, Chironax melanocephalus.

### 1999, July 2    Litho.    Perf. 14x14½
| | | | | |
|---|---|---|---|---|
| 1412 | A334 | 900k multi | 1.50 | 1.00 |
| 1413 | A334 | 1600k multi | 3.00 | 2.00 |
| 1414 | A334 | 2100k multi | 3.50 | 3.00 |
| 1415 | A334 | 2800k multi | 5.00 | 4.00 |
| | Nos. 1412-1415 (4) | | 13.00 | 10.00 |

New Year 1999 (Year of the Rabbit) — A335

1500k, Rabbit, other animals of calendar cycle. 1600k, Rabbit.

---

### 1999, Apr. 15    Litho.    Perf. 14x14¼
| | | | |
|---|---|---|---|
| 1416 | A335 | 1500k multi, vert. | 7.00 5.00 |

### Perf. 14¾x14
| | | | |
|---|---|---|---|
| 1417 | A335 | 1600k multi, horiz. | 8.00 6.00 |

Farming Implements A336

### 1999, May 1    Litho.    Perf. 14¾x14
| | | | | |
|---|---|---|---|---|
| 1418 | A336 | 1500k Plow | 2.50 | 1.50 |
| 1419 | A336 | 2000k Yoke | 3.00 | 2.00 |
| 1420 | A336 | 3200k Plow, diff. | 4.00 | 3.00 |
| | Nos. 1418-1420 (3) | | 9.50 | 6.50 |

UPU, 125th Anniv. A337

### 1999, Oct. 9
| | | | | |
|---|---|---|---|---|
| 1421 | A337 | 2600k shown | 5.00 | 3.00 |
| 1422 | A337 | 3400k Postman | 7.00 | 4.00 |

Wildlife A338

700k, Rhinoceros sondaicus. 900k, Bubalus bubalis. 1700k, Prionodon pardicolor. 1800k, Cervus unicolor. 1900k, Panthera leo.

### Perf. 14¾x14, 14x14¾
### 1999, Nov. 10
| | | | | |
|---|---|---|---|---|
| 1423 | A338 | 700k multi | 1.50 | .60 |
| 1424 | A338 | 900k multi, vert. | 1.75 | .80 |
| 1425 | A338 | 1700k multi | 3.00 | 1.50 |
| 1426 | A338 | 1800k multi | 3.25 | 1.75 |
| 1427 | A338 | 1900k multi, vert. | 3.50 | 1.90 |
| | Nos. 1423-1427 (5) | | 13.00 | 6.55 |

Expo '99, Kunming, China — A339

Designs: 300k, Carved tree stump. 900k, China Hall. 2300k, Science and Technology Hall. 2500k, Laos traditional wooden house.

### 1999, Oct. 15    Perf. 14¾x14
| | | | | |
|---|---|---|---|---|
| 1428 | A339 | 300k multi | .70 | .25 |
| 1429 | A339 | 900k multi | 1.50 | .75 |
| 1430 | A339 | 2300k multi | 3.25 | 1.90 |
| 1431 | A339 | 2500k multi | 4.50 | 2.00 |
| | Nos. 1428-1431 (4) | | 9.95 | 4.90 |

Millennium — A340

No. 1432, 2000k: a, Airport, bus, hospital. b, Temple, tractor, elephant. c, Building, truck. d, River, waterfalls.

### 2000, Jan. 1    Litho.    Perf. 13½
| | | | | |
|---|---|---|---|---|
| 1432 | A340 | Block of 4, #a-d | 10.00 | 5.50 |
| e. | | Souvenir sheet, #1432 | 12.00 | 6.75 |

No. 1432e sold for 10,000k. No. 1432e exists imperf. Value, $30.

New Year 2000 (Year of the Dragon) A341

---

Dragons: 1800k, And other zodiac animals. 2300k, In water.

### 2000, Apr. 1    Perf. 14½x14
| | | | |
|---|---|---|---|
| 1433-1434 | A341 | Set of 2 | 5.50 1.25 |

Wedding Costumes — A342

Designs: 800k, Lao Theung. 2300k, Lao Lum. 3400k, Lao Sung.

### 2000, Oct. 30    Perf. 14x14½
| | | | |
|---|---|---|---|
| 1435-1437 | A342 | Set of 3 | 4.50 3.00 |

Children's Drawings A343

Designs: 300k, Waterfall. 400k, Forest fire. 2300k, Animals at river. 3200k, Animals at river, vert.

### 2000, June 1    Perf. 14½x14, 14x14½
| | | | |
|---|---|---|---|
| 1438-1441 | A343 | Set of 4 | 7.50 3.00 |

Bangkok 2000 Stamp Exhibition — A344

Orchids: 500k, Dendrobium draconis. 900k, Paphiopedilum hirsutissimum. 3000k, Dendrobium sulcatum. 3400k, Rhynchostylis gigantea.

### 2000, Mar. 25    Perf. 14x14½
| | | | | |
|---|---|---|---|---|
| 1442-1445 | A344 | Set of 4 | 10.00 | 3.00 |
| 1445a | | Souv. sheet, #1442-1445, perf. 13½ | 15.00 | 15.00 |

No. 1445a sold for 10,000k. No. 1445a exists imperf. Value, $80.

Peacocks — A345

700k, Male with feathers down, vert., 1000k, Male with feathers up, vert., 1800k, Female. 3500k, Male and female. 10,000k, Male with feathers up, vert.

### 2000, July 10    Perf. 14x14½, 14½x14
| | | | |
|---|---|---|---|
| 1446-1449 | A345 | Set of 4 | 4.50 2.50 |

### Souvenir Sheet
### Perf. 13½
### Litho. With Foil Application
| | | | |
|---|---|---|---|
| 1450 | A345 | 10,000k multi | 7.50 7.50 |

2000 Summer Olympics, Sydney A346

Designs: 500k, Cycling. 900k, Boxing. 2600k, Judo. 3600k, Kayaking.

### 2000, Sept. 15    Litho.    Perf. 14½x14
| | | | | |
|---|---|---|---|---|
| 1451-1454 | A346 | Set of 4 | 6.00 | 3.00 |
| 1454a | | Souvenir sheet, #1451-1454, perf. 13½ | 10.00 | 10.00 |

No. 1454a sold for 10,000k. No. 1454a exists imperf. Value, $40.

---

Laotian postal officials have declared as "illegal" a sheet of stamps for Great People of the 20th Century (Elvis Presley, Roberto Clemente, Marilyn Monroe, Dr. Martin Luther King, Jr., Pope John Paul II, Frank Sinatra, Albert Einstein, Princess Diana and Walt Disney) and stamps depicting Tiger Woods, Payne Stewart, Arnold Palmer, Elvis Presley, Marilyn Monroe, John Lennon and the Beatles.

Women's Costumes — A347

### 2000, Mar. 8    Litho.    Perf. 14¼x14½
| | | | | |
|---|---|---|---|---|
| 1455 | A347 | 100k Kor Loma | .30 | .25 |
| 1456 | A347 | 200k Kor Pchor | .40 | .25 |
| 1457 | A347 | 500k Nhuan Krom | .50 | .25 |
| 1458 | A347 | 900k Taidam | 2.00 | .40 |
| 1459 | A347 | 2300k Yao | 3.00 | 1.00 |
| 1460 | A347 | 2500k Meuy | 3.00 | 1.10 |
| 1461 | A347 | 2600k Sila | 1.50 | 1.10 |
| 1462 | A347 | 2700k Hmong | 3.50 | 1.25 |
| 1463 | A347 | 2800k Yao, diff. | 3.50 | 1.25 |
| 1464 | A347 | 3100k Kor Nukkuy | 3.50 | 1.40 |
| 1465 | A347 | 3200k Kor Pouxang | 3.50 | 1.40 |
| 1466 | A347 | 3300k Yao Lanten | 2.00 | 1.40 |
| 1467 | A347 | 3400k Khir | 2.25 | 1.50 |
| 1468 | A347 | 3500k Kor | 4.00 | 1.50 |
| 1469 | A347 | 3900k Hmong, diff. | 4.00 | 1.75 |
| | Nos. 1455-1469 (15) | | 36.95 | 15.80 |

Laotian-Japanese Bridge Project — A348

Flags, various views of bridge: 900k, 2700k, 3200k.

### 2000, Aug. 2    Perf. 14½x14
| | | | |
|---|---|---|---|
| 1470-1472 | A348 | Set of 3 | 5.00 2.75 |

### Souvenir Sheet

No. 1472A: b, 4000k, Similar to #1470. c, 7500k, Similar to #1471. d, 8500k, Similar to #1472.

### 2000    Typo.    Perf. 13¼x13½
| | | | |
|---|---|---|---|
| 1472A | A348 | Sheet of 3, #b-d | 15.00 15.00 |

No. 1472A contains three 48x33mm stamps in gold. No. 1472A exists imperf. Value, $40.

Tourism — A349

Designs: 300k, Phousy Stupa, Luang Prabang. 600k, Than Chang Cave. 2800k, Inhang Stupa. 3300k, Buddha, Phiawat Temple.

### 2000, Nov. 23    Perf. 14x14½
| | | | |
|---|---|---|---|
| 1473-1476 | A349 | Set of 4 | 6.00 3.00 |

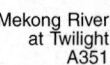

Lao People's Democratic Republic, 25th Anniv. A350

### 2000, Dec. 2    Perf. 13¼
| | | | |
|---|---|---|---|
| 1477 | A350 | 4000k multi | 2.75 1.50 |

Mekong River at Twilight A351

Various views: 900k, 2700k, 3400k.

**2000, June 20** **Perf. 14½x14**
1478-1480 A351 Set of 3 5.00 2.50

Anti-Drug
Campaign
A352

Designs: 100k, Poppy field. 4000k, Burning of seized drugs.

**2000, June 26** **Litho.**
1481-1482 A352 Set of 2 3.50 1.50

Souvenir Sheet

Route 13 Bridge Reconstruction
Project — A353

Bridge in: a, Savannakhet. b, Saravane. c, Pakse.

**2000, Feb. 14** **Perf. 13¼**
1483 A353 4000k Sheet of 3, #a-c 9.00 9.00

Souvenir Sheet

Anti-Polio Campaign — A354

No. 1484: a, 900k, People receiving vaccine. b, 2500k, Family, map of Laos.

**2000, June 1**
1484 A354 Sheet of 2, #a-b 3.50 3.50

Millennium — A355

Designs: 3200k, Satellite, telecommunication dishes, map of Laos, student. 4000k, High tension lines, dam.

**2001, Jan. 1** **Perf. 14x14½**
1485-1486 A355 Set of 2 4.00 2.50

New Year
2001 (Year of
the Snake)
A356

Designs: 900k, Snake coiled around branch. 3500k, Snake, other zodiac animals.

**2001, Apr. 15** **Perf. 14½x14**
1487-1488 A356 Set of 2 4.00 2.00

Cockfighting
A357

Pair of cocks fighting: 500k, 900k, 3300k, 3500k.
10,000k, Single cock, vert.

**2001, Mar. 10** **Perf. 14½x14**
1489-1492 A357 Set of 4 5.50 3.25
**Souvenir Sheet**
**Perf. 13¼**
1493 A357 10,000k multi 7.50 7.50
No. 1493 contains one 36x50mm stamp. No. 1493 exists imperf. Value, $40.

Laos-People's Republic of China
Diplomatic Relations, 40th
Anniv. — A358

**2001, Apr. 25** **Perf. 14¼x14½**
1494 A358 1000k multi 1.25 .40

Phila Nippon
'01 — A359

Birds: Nos. 1495, 1499a, 700k, Egretta intermedia. Nos. 1496, 1499b, 800k, Bubulcus ibis (36x50mm). Nos. 1497, 1499c, 3100k, Ardea cinera (36x50mm). Nos. 1498, 1499d, 3400k, Egretta alba.

**Perf. 14½x14, 13¼ (#1496-1497)**
**2001, Aug. 1** **With White Frames**
1495-1498 A359 Set of 4 6.00 3.00
**Souvenir Sheet**
**Without White Frames**
**Perf. 13¼**
1499 A359 Sheet of 4, #a-d 7.50 7.50
No. 1499 sold for 10,000k. No. 1499 exists imperf. Value, $50.

Mortars and
Pestles
A360

Designs: 900k, Two women using large hand-held pestle, vert. 2600k, Water-driven mortar and pestle. 3500k, Woman operating mechanical mortar and pestle, vert.

**Perf. 14x14½, 14½x14**
**2001, Nov. 15**
1500-1502 A360 Set of 3 4.50 2.25

Ceremonies
A361

Designs: 300k, Pou Nyer and Nya Nyer, vert. 600k, Hae Nang Sangkhan, vert. 1000k, Sand Stupa. 2300k, Hae Prabang, vert. 4000k, Takbat, vert.

**2001, Apr. 13** **Perf. 14x14½, 14½x14**
1503-1507 A361 Set of 5 7.50 3.50

Buddhist
Art — A362

Designs: 200k, Himavanta. 900k, Vanapavesa. 3200k, Kumarakanda. 3600k, Sakkapabba.

**2001, Dec. 5** **Perf. 13¼**
1508-1511 A362 Set of 4 6.00 3.25
1511a Souvenir sheet, #1508-1511 7.00 7.00
No. 1511a exists imperf. Value, $50.

Men's Costumes — A363

Designs: 100k, Yao Mane. 200k, Gnaheun. 500k, Katou. 2300k, Hmong Dam. 2500k, Harlak. 2600k, Kui. 2700k, Krieng. 3100k, Khmu Nhuan. 3200k, Ta Oy. 3300k, Tai Theng. 3400k, Hmong Khao. 3500k, Gnor. 3600k, Phouthai Na Gnom. 4000k, Yao. 5000k, Hmong.

**2001, Feb. 20** **Perf. 14¼x14½**
1512 A363 100k multi .30 .25
1513 A363 200k multi .30 .25
1514 A363 500k multi .30 .25
1515 A363 2300k multi 1.25 .80
1516 A363 2500k multi 1.40 .85
1517 A363 2600k multi 1.40 .85
1518 A363 2700k multi 1.50 .90
1519 A363 3100k multi 1.60 1.00
1520 A363 3200k multi 1.75 1.10
1521 A363 3300k multi 1.75 1.10
1522 A363 3400k multi 1.75 1.25
1523 A363 3500k multi 2.00 1.25
1524 A363 3600k multi 2.00 1.25
1525 A363 4000k multi 2.25 1.50
1526 A363 5000k multi 2.75 1.90
Nos. 1512-1526 (15) 22.30 14.50

Buddhist Temple
Doors — A364

Various doors: 600k, 2300k, 2500k, 2600k.

**2001, Sept. 17** **Litho.** **Perf. 14x14½**
1527-1530 A364 Set of 4 6.00 3.00

Frangipani
Flowers
A365

Designs: 1000k, White flowers. 2500k, Pink flowers, vert. 3500k, Red flowers.

**2001, Oct. 2** **Perf. 14½x14, 14x14½**
1531-1533 A365 Set of 3 4.50 2.50
a. Souvenir sheet, #1531-1533, perf. 13¼ 6.00 4.00

Intl. Volunteers Year — A366

**2001, Dec. 29** **Perf. 13¼**
1534 A366 1000k multi 2.50 .40

Women's
Costumes — A367

Designs: 200k, Meuy. 300k, Leu. 500k, Tai Kouane. 700k, Tai Dam. 1000k, Tai Men. 1500k, Lanten. 2500k, Hmong. 3000k, Phouxang. 3500k, Taitheng. 4000k, Tai O. 5000k, Tai Dam, diff.

**2002, Jan. 10** **Perf. 14x14½**
1535 A367 200k multi .30 .25
1536 A367 300k multi .30 .25
1537 A367 500k multi .30 .25
1538 A367 700k multi .30 .25
1539 A367 1000k multi .50 .30

1540 A367 1500k multi .70 .45
1541 A367 2500k multi 1.25 .75
1542 A367 3000k multi 1.50 .95
1543 A367 3500k multi 1.75 1.10
1544 A367 4000k multi 2.00 1.25
1545 A367 5000k multi 2.25 1.60
Nos. 1535-1545 (11) 11.15 7.40

Intl. Year of
Mountains
A368

Designs: No. 1546, 1500k, Pha Tang. No. 1547, 1500k, Phou Phamane.

**2002, Mar. 30** **Perf. 14½x14**
1546-1547 A368 Set of 2 2.50 1.10
Nos. 1546-1547 are a corrected printing. The first printing, which was erroneously inscribed "LAO PRD" instead of "LAO PDR," was removed from sale after a few panes had been sold. Value, set of 2 $100.

New Year
2002 (Year of
the Horse)
A369

Designs: 1500k, Horse, zodiac animals. 3500k, Galloping horse.

**2002, Apr. 14**
1548-1549 A369 Set of 2 3.00 1.60

Laos - Viet Nam
Cooperation — A370

Designs: 2500k, Musical instruments. 3500k, Laotian leader with Ho Chi Minh, horiz.

**2002, July 18** **Perf. 13**
1550-1551 A370 Set of 2 3.25 1.90

Phila Korea 2002 World
Stamp Exhibition,
Seoul — A371

Insects: Nos. 1552a, 1553a, Sagra femorata. Nos. 1552b, 1552b, Cerambycidae. Nos. 1552c, 1552c, Chrysochroa mniszechii. Nos. 1552d, 1553d, Anoplophora sp. Nos. 1552e, 1553e, Chrysochroa sandersi. Nos. 1552f, 1553f, Mouhotia batesi. Nos. 1552g, 1553g, Megaloxantha assamensis. Nos. 1552h, 1553h, Eupatorus gracillicornis.

**2002, Aug. 1** **Perf. 14½x14**
**Insects and Colored Backgrounds**
1552 Vert. strip of 8 5.00 5.00
a.-h. A371 1000k Any single .50 .30
**Souvenir Sheet**
**Insects On Vegetation**
1553 A371 1000k Sheet of 8, #a-h 5.00 5.00
No. 1553 exists imperf. Value, $45.

Admission to
UPU, 50th
Anniv. — A372

**2002, May 20** **Litho.** **Perf. 13x13¼**
1554 A372 3000k black 2.00 2.00

**Goldfish**
**A373**

No. 1555: a, Pearlscale goldfish. b, Moor. c, Bubble eyes goldfish. d, Red-capped oranda. e, Lionhead goldfish. f, Pom pom. g, Ranchu. h, Fantail goldfish. i, Celestial goldfish. j, Ryukin. k, Brown oranda. l, Veiltail goldfish.

**2002, Oct. 2**       *Perf. 13¼*
1555 A373 1000k Sheet of 12,
    #a-l      6.00 6.00
No. 1555 exists imperf. Value, $25.

**Buffalo**
**Fighting — A374**

Various buffalo: 200k, 300k, 3000k, 4000k.

**2002, Dec. 15**      *Perf. 13x13¼*
1556-1559 A374   Set of 4    4.50 3.00

**Souvenir Sheet**

**National Route 9 Improvement**
**Project — A375**

No. 1560: a, Curve. b, Interchange. c, Curve and building.

**2002, Dec. 18**    **Litho.**    *Perf. 13¼*
1560 A375 1500k Sheet of 3,
    #a-c      6.00 6.00

**Vat Phou**
**World Heritage**
**Site — A376**

Designs: 1500k, Temple, vert. 3000k, Temple, diff. 4000k, Statue of Buddha, vert. 10,000k, Stone carving.

**2003, Feb. 14** *Perf. 14x14½, 14½x14*
1561-1563 A376   Set of 3    4.50 2.60
**Souvenir Sheet**
*Perf. 13¼*
1564 A376 10,000k multi    6.00 6.00
No. 1564 contains one 93x27mm stamp.

**Butterflies — A377**

No. 1565: a, Hasora schoenherr. b, Spindasis lohita. c, Graphium sarpedon. d, Polyura schreiber. e, Castalius rosimon. f, Dalias pasithoe. g, Pachliopta aristolochiae. h, Papilio memnon.
10,000k, Danaus genutia.

**2003, Mar. 8**      *Perf. 14½x14*
1565 A377   Block of 8    6.00 6.00
  **a.-h.**   1000k Any single   .60 .35
**Souvenir Sheet**
*Perf. 13¼*
1566 A377 10,000k multi    6.00 6.00
No. 1566 exists imperf. Value, $30.

**New Year**
**2003 (Year of**
**the**
**Goat) — A378**

Designs: 2500k, Two goats. 5000k, Goat, zodiac animals.

**2003, Apr. 15**      *Perf. 14½x14*
1567-1568 A378   Set of 2    5.00 2.25

**Orchids — A379**

Designs: 200k, Phalaenopsis Paifang's Golden Lion. 300k, Coelogyne lentiginosa. 500k, Phalaenopsis sumatrana. 1000k, Phalaenopsis bellina. 1500k, Paphiopedilum appletonianum. 2000k, Vanda bensonii. 2500k, Dendrobium harveyanum. 3000k, Paphiopedilum glaucophyllum. 3500k, Paphiopedilum gratrixianum. 4000k, Vanda roeblingiana. 5000k, Phalaenopsis Lady Sakhara.

**2003, Apr. 25**     *Perf. 14½x14¼*
1569 A379 200k multi    .30 .25
1570 A379 300k multi    .40 .25
1571 A379 500k multi    .60 .25
1572 A379 1000k multi    .70 .30
1573 A379 1500k multi    .80 .45
1574 A379 2000k multi    1.00 .60
1575 A379 2500k multi    1.25 .75
1576 A379 3000k multi    1.40 .90
1577 A379 3500k multi    1.75 1.00
1578 A379 4000k multi    1.75 1.25
1579 A379 5000k multi    2.25 1.50
   *Nos. 1569-1579 (11)*   12.20 7.50

**Wood**
**Handicrafts**
**A380**

Designs: 500k, Bowl. 1500k, Pitcher and goblets. 2500k, Fluted bowl. 3500k, Bowl, vert.

**2003, May 10**      *Perf. 13*
1580-1583 A380   Set of 4    4.75 2.40

**Traditional**
**Games — A381**

Designs: 1000k, Walking on stringed coconut shells. 3000k, Top spinning. 4000k, Field hockey.

**2003, June 1**
1584-1586 A381   Set of 3    3.50 2.40

**Stop Hunting**
**Campaign**
**A382**

Designs: 1500k, Deer. 2000k, Gun. 4500k, Wild animals.

**2003, July 25**    **Litho.**    *Perf. 13*
1587-1589 A382   Set of 3    3.75 2.50

**Fruit — A383**

Designs: 500k, Mango. 1500k, Watermelon. 2500k, Custard apple. 4000k, Pineapple.

**2003, Aug. 8**      *Perf. 14½x14*
1590-1593 A383   Set of 4    4.50 2.60

**Palm Leaf**
**Manuscripts — A384**

Designs: 500k, Monk writing palm leaf manuscript. 1500k, Palm leaf manuscript. 2500k, Manuscript casket. 3000k, Ho Tai.

**2003, Sept. 12**     *Perf. 14x14½*
1594-1597 A384   Set of 4    4.00 3.00

**Bangkok 2003 Intl.**
**Philatelic**
**Exhibition — A385**

Buddhas of Luang Prabang: 500k, Pha Sene Souk. 1500k, Pha Gnai. 3000k, Pha Ong Luang. 3500k, Pha Ong Sene. 10,000k, Pha Attharatsa.

**2003, Oct. 4**      *Perf. 14x14½*
1598-1601 A385   Set of 4    5.00 3.25
**Souvenir Sheet**
*Perf. 13½*
1602 A385 10,000k multi    6.00 6.00
No. 1602 contains one 30x95mm stamp. No. 1602 exists imperf. Value, $30.

**Textiles — A386**

Various textiles with panel colors of: 500k, Blue. 1000k, Red brown. 3000k, Green. 4000k, Yellow brown.

**2003, Dec. 1**      *Perf. 14x14½*
1603-1606 A386   Set of 4    5.00 3.00

**Installed**
**Emerald**
**Buddha**
**A387**

**2004, Feb. 5**    **Litho.**    *Perf. 14½x14*
1607 A387 5500k multi    3.00 1.90

**Birds — A388**

Designs: 2000k, Buceros bicornis. 2500k, Pycnonotus jocosus. 3000k, Ploceus hypoxanthus. 3500k, Alcedo atthis. 4000k, Magalaima incognita. 4500k, Serilophus lunatus. 5000k, Lacedo pulchella. 5500k, Eurylaimus ochromalus.

**2004, Feb. 20**     *Perf. 14¼x14½*
1608-1615 A388   Set of 8    13.50 11.00

**Dolphins**
**A389**

Two dolphins: 1500k With heads above water. 2500k, Leaping out of water. 3500k, Underwater.

**2004, Mar. 29**     *Perf. 14½x14*
1616-1618 A389   Set of 3    3.50 2.50

**New Year**
**2004 (Year of**
**the Monkey)**
**A390**

Designs: 500k, Two monkeys. 4500k, Monkey, zodiac animals.

**2004, Apr. 15**
1619-1620 A390   Set of 2    2.75 1.75

**FIFA (Fédération Internationale de**
**Football Association), Cent. — A391**

No. 1621 — FIFA emblem and: a, Flags of various countries. b, Soccer players.

**2004, May 21**      *Perf. 13½*
1621 A391 12,000k Pair, #a-b   12.00 10.00
Values are for stamps with surrounding selvage.

**Children's**
**Day — A392**

Designs: 3500k, Four children. 4500k, Children, globe, school.

**2004, June 1**      *Perf. 14½x14*
1622-1623 A392   Set of 2    3.50 2.60

**11th ASEAN Postal**
**Business**
**Meeting — A393**

**2004, July 5**    **Litho.**    *Perf. 14x14½*
1624 A393 5000k multi    3.00 1.75

**Worldwide Fund for Nature**
**(WWF) — A394**

No. 1625 — Cuora amboinensis: a, 5000k, In water. b, 5500k, On rock near water. c, 6000k, Pair. d, 7000k, Head, feet and shell.

**2004, Aug. 16**    **Litho.**    *Perf. 13½x14*
1625 A394   Block of 4, #a-d   6.00 5.00

**Dances — A395**

Designs: 1000k, Tangwai. 1500k, Khabthoume Luangprabang. 2000k, Lao Lamvong. 2500k, Salavan.

**2004, Aug. 23**      *Perf. 14x14¾*
1626-1629 A395    Set of 4    3.25 2.10
*1629a*    Souvenir sheet, #1626-
     1629, perf. 13¼    5.00 5.00

No. 1629a sold for 10,000k. No. 1629a exists imperf. Value, $40.

Marigolds — A396

Designs: 3500k, Yellow, orange marigolds. 5000k, Red and orange marigolds. 5500k, Decorations made with marigolds.

**2004, Sept. 28**      *Perf. 13¼x13*
1630-1632 A396    Set of 3    4.75 4.75

Scenes From Ramakian A397

Various scenes: 3500k, 4500k, 5500k, 6500k.

**2004, Oct. 10**      *Perf. 13¼*
1633-1636 A397    Set of 4    9.00 6.75

Naga Fireball — A398

Designs: 2000k, Figure above river, serpent in river. 3000k, Buildings, serpent, horiz. 3500k, Fireball in serpent's mouth, horiz. 4000k, Fireballs above serpent.

**2004, Oct. 28**      *Perf. 13 Syncopated*
1637-1640 A398    Set of 4    4.25 4.25

Betel Tray — A399

Designs: 2000k, Betel nuts, bowls and containers. 4000k, Betel nut and leaf. 6000k, Betel tray.

**2004, Nov. 11**    **Litho.**    *Perf. 13*
1641-1643 A399    Set of 3    4.00 4.00

Laos — Sweden Diplomatic Relations, 40th Anniv. — A400

**2004, Dec. 12**    **Litho.**    *Perf. 13x13½*
1644 A400 8500k multi    4.00 2.75

Handicrafts A401

Designs: 1000k, Short, round basket. 2000k, Paddle. 2500k, Basket with handle, vert. 5500k, Basket with handle and lid, vert.

*Perf. 14½x14, 14x14½*
**2005, Mar. 10**      **Litho.**
1645-1648 A401    Set of 4    5.25 3.25

New Year 2005 (Year of the Rooster) A402

Rooster and: 2000k, Hen. 7500k, Zodiac animals.

**2005, Apr. 13**      *Perf. 14½x14*
1649-1650 A402    Set of 2    5.00 3.50

Daily Buddhas — A403

Buddha for: 500k, Sunday. 1000k, Monday. 1500k, Tuesday, horiz. 2000k, Wednesday. 2500k, Thursday. 3000k, Friday. 3500k, Saturday.

*Perf. 14x14½, 14½x14*
**2005, May 15**      **Litho.**
1651-1657 A403    Set of 7    6.50 4.50

Rice — A404

Designs: 1500k, Rice plants. 3000k, Cooked rice on plate, horiz. 6500k, Bundles of rice plants, horiz.

*Perf. 13 Syncopated*
**2005, June 1**      **Litho.**
1658-1660 A404    Set of 3    5.25 3.25

Mekong River Giant Catfish A405

Designs: 3500k, Shown. 6500k, Catfish, diff.

**2005, July 13**    **Litho.**    *Perf. 14½x14*
1661-1662 A405    Set of 2    4.75 3.25

Gold Panning — A406

Designs: 2000k, Pan. 7500k, Woman panning for gold, vert.

*Perf. 13 Syncopated*
**2005, Aug. 1**      **Litho.**
1663-1664 A406    Set of 2    4.00 3.00

Folk Songs — A407

Designs: 1000k, Two musicians standing. 3500k, Two musicians seated. 5500k, Four musicians, horiz.

**2005, Sept. 2**
1665-1667 A407    Set of 3    4.50 3.00

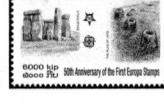

Europa Stamps, 50th Anniv. (in 2006) — A408

Designs: 6000k, Stonehenge, England, and Plain of Jars, Laos. No. 1669, 7000k, Knossos Palace, Greece, and Patuxay, Laos. No. 1670, 7000k, Colosseum, Rome, and Wat Phu,

Laos. No. 1671, 7500k, Stave Church, Lom, Norway, and Wat Xieng Thong, Laos. No. 1672, 7500k, Notre Dame Cathedral, Paris, and That Luang, Laos. 8000k, Trier Cathedral, Germany, and Wat Phra Keo, Laos.

**2005, Oct. 24**    **Litho.**    *Perf. 14¾x14*
1668-1673 A408    Set of 6    15.00 12.50
*1673a*    Souvenir sheet, #1668-
     1673    30.00 30.00

No. 1673a exists imperf. Value, $60.

People's Democratic Republic, 30th Anniv. — A409

Designs: 500k, Flag and building. 1000k, Map, people and flag. 2000k, Flag and coat of arms. 5000k, "30," Coat of arms and people.

**2005, Dec. 2**      *Perf. 13*
1674-1677 A409    Set of 4    4.50 2.50

Diplomatic Relations with Thailand, 55th Anniv. — A410

**2005, Dec. 19**
1678 A410 7500k multi    4.50 2.25

Laos-United Nations Cooperation, 50th Anniv. — A411

Designs: No. 1679, 3000k, Rice harvesters. No. 1679A, 3000k, Children at school gate. No. 1679B, 3000k, Infant health care.

**2005, Oct. 24**    **Litho.**    *Perf. 13x13¼*
1679-1679B A411    Set of 3    4.50 3.50
*1679Bc*    Souvenir sheet,
     #1679-1679B    15.00 15.00

No. 1679Bc sold for 15,000k.

Lao People's Democratic Republic, 30th Anniv. — A411b

**2005, Dec. 16**    **Litho.**    *Perf. 13¼x13*
1679H A411b 15,500k multi    9.00 5.50

**Souvenir Sheet**
1679I A411b 20,000k multi    10.00 7.00

Diplomatic Relations Between Laos and Japan, 50th Anniv. — A411c

Designs: 7000k, Flowers. 20,000k, Temples.

**2005, Dec. 30**      *Perf. 13*
1679J A411c    7000k multi    4.50 2.60
**Size: 170x130mm**
*Imperf*
1679K A411c 20,000k multi    15.00 15.00

Statue of King Phangum Lenglathorany — A412

**2006, Mar. 9**    **Litho.**    *Perf. 14x14½*
1680 A412 8500k multi    3.50 2.60

A souvenir sheet containing one perf. 13½ example of No. 1680 sold for 20,000k.

New Year 2006 (Year of the Dog) — A413

Designs: 2000k, Dog. 6500k, Dog, zodiac animals.

**2006, Apr. 14**      *Perf. 14½x14*
1681-1682 A413    Set of 2    6.50 3.50

AGL Insurance in Laos, 15th Anniv. — A414

AGL Insurance emblem and: 8000k, Car, minivan and motorcycle. 8500k, Map of Laos. 9500k, Family.

**2006, May 1**      *Perf. 13*
1683-1685 A414    Set of 3    11.00 7.75

Friendship Between Vientiane and Moscow — A415

Laotian and Russian: 7500k, Women. 8500k, Sculptures and houses of worship.

**2006, May 1**
1686-1687 A415    Set of 2    8.00 4.75
*1687a*    Souvenir sheet, #1686-
     1687    10.00 10.00

No. 1687a sold for 20,000k.

Diplomatic Relations Between Laos and People's Republic of China, 45th Anniv. — A416

**2006, July 7**      *Perf. 13x12¾*
1688 A416 8500k multi    5.00 5.00

No. 1688 exists imperf. Value, $20.

Shrimp — A417

Various depictions of shrimp: 1000k, 2000k, 4000k, 6000k.

**2006, July 10**      *Perf. 13*
1689-1692 A417    Set of 4    7.00 4.00
*1692a*    Souvenir sheet, #1689-
     1692    8.50 8.50

No. 1692a sold for 15,000k.

Léopold Sédar Senghor (1906-2001), First President of Senegal A418

**2006, Sept. 4**
1693 A418 8500k multi 5.00 3.00

Bronze Drums — A419

Various drums with background colors of: 2000k, Red brown. 3500k, Blue. 7500k, Olive green.

**2006, Oct. 9**
1694-1696 A419 Set of 3 7.00 4.00
1696a Souvenir sheet, #1694-1696 9.00 9.00
No. 1696a sold for 15,000k.

Xieng Khouane Temple — A420

Various views of temple and sculptures: 1000k, 2500k, 3000k, 5000k.

**2006, June 10 Litho. Perf. 13**
1697-1700 A420 Set of 4 6.50 4.00

Bananas — A421

Designs: 1000k, Pisang Masak Hijau. 2000k, Pisang Mas. 4000k, Pisang Ambon. 8000k, Pisang Awak.

**2006, Nov. 1**
1701-1704 A421 Set of 4 7.50 5.00

Opening of Second Thai-Lao Friendship Bridge — A422

Designs: No. 1705, 7500k, Bridge in daylight. No. 1706, 7500k, Bridge at night.

**2006, Dec. 20**
1705-1706 A422 Set of 2 8.00 5.00

Jewelry — A423

Designs: 2000k, Pins. 5000k, Bracelet. 7000k, Earrings. 7500k, Necklace and pendant.

**2007, Jan. 15 Litho. Perf. 13¼x13**
1707-1710 A423 Set of 4 11.00 8.00
1710a Souvenir sheet, #1707-1710 14.00 12.00
No. 1710a sold for 25,000k.

Crabs — A424

Various crabs: 1000k, 2000k, 7000k, 7500k.

**2007, Feb. 20 Perf. 13x13¼**
1711-1714 A424 Set of 4 9.00 6.50
1714a Souvenir sheet, #1711-1714, perf. 13½x13¾ 10.00 9.00
No. 1714a sold for 20,000k.

New Year 2007 (Year of the Pig) — A425

Designs: No. 1715, 7500k, Pig and piglets. No. 1716, 7500k, Pig, zodiac animals.

**2007, Apr. 15 Perf. 13x13¼**
1715-1716 A425 Set of 2 8.00 5.75

Takbat Festival — A425a

Designs: 2000k, Monks standing, women placing items on ground. 5000k, Woman reaching into monk's bowl. 7500k, Women holding bowls.

**2007, July 10 Litho. Perf. 13**
1716A-1716C A425a Set of 3 7.00 5.50

Association of South East Asian Nations (ASEAN), 40th Anniv. — A426

Designs: 7000k, Typical house, Laos. No. 1718: a, Like 7000k. b, Secretariat Building, Bandar Seri Begawan, Brunei. c, National Museum of Cambodia. d, Fatahillah Museum, Jakarta, Indonesia. e, Malayan Railway Headquarters Building, Kuala Lumpur, Malaysia. f, Yangon Post Office, Myanmar. g, Malacañang Palace, Philippines. h, National Museum of Singapore. i, Vimanmek Mansion, Bangkok, Thailand. j, Presidential Palace, Hanoi, Viet Nam.

**2007, Aug. 8 Litho. Perf. 13**
1717 A426 7000k multi 3.00 3.00
1718 Sheet of 10 7.00 7.00
a.-j. A426 700k Any single .50 .40
See Brunei No. 607, Burma No. 370, Cambodia No. 2339, Indonesia Nos. 2120-2121, Malaysia No. 1170, Philippines Nos. 3103-3105, Singapore No. 1265, Thailand No. 2315, and Viet Nam Nos. 3302-3311.

Transportation — A426a

Designs: 2000k, Airplanes. 5000k, Ferry. 7500k, Trucks.

**2007, Sept. 1 Litho. Perf. 13**
1718K-1718M A426a Set of 3 7.00 6.00

That Luang Festival — A426b

Designs: 2000k, Monks leading procession. 5000k, Procession with temple in background. 8000k, Temple at night.

**2007, Nov. 13**
1718N-1718P A426b Set of 3 7.50 5.75

Traditional Foods — A426c

Designs: 2000k, Sticky rice cooked in bamboo tubes. 5500k, Green papaya salad. 7500k, Grilled chicken.

**2007, Dec. 30**
1718Q-1718S A426c Set of 3 7.50 5.75

Worldwide Fund for Nature (WWF) — A427

Hylobates lar: 6000k, Head. 7000k, Adult and juvenile. 8000k, With open mouth. 9000k, Two adults.

**2008 Litho. Perf. 13½x14**
1719-1722 A427 Set of 4 12.00 7.25
1722a Miniature sheet, 4 each #1719-1722 120.00 120.00
Nos. 1719-1722, 1722a exist imperf. Value, Nos. 1719-1722 imperf. block of 4 $40.

2008 Summer Olympics, Beijing — A428

Designs: No. 1723, 5000k, Taekwondo. No. 1724, 5000k, High jump. No. 1725, 5000k, Cycling. No. 1726, 5000k, Soccer.

**2008, Apr. 17 Perf. 12½x13**
1723-1726 A428 Set of 4 8.00 4.75
Nos. 1723-1726 each were printed in sheets of 16. Two sheet varieties exist: English inscriptions in the top and bottom selvage, and a combination of English (right and bottom selvage) and Ukrainian (top and left selvage) inscriptions. Sheets with the English and Ukrainian inscriptions are scarce. Value, set of four singles of Nos. 1723-1726 each with attached Ukrainian selvage $20.

Elephant Festival A429

Designs: 1000k, Tuskless elephant and rider. 2000k, Two elephants and riders. 3000k, Man in crowd holding rope. 5000k, Tusked elephant with rider. 7500k, Woman decorating elephant. 8500k, Elephants moving logs. 20,000k, Elephants, riders and guides.

**2008, Jan. 14 Litho. Perf. 13**
1727-1732 A429 Set of 6 12.00 11.00
**Size: 146x110mm**
*Imperf*
1733 A429 20,000k multi + label 12.50 8.50

Coffee — A430

Designs: Nos. 1734, 1737a, 3000k, Mug and roasted coffee beans. Nos. 1735, 1737b, 5000k, Coffee berries. Nos. 1736, 1737c, 6000k, Roasted coffee beans.

**2008, Feb. 11 Litho. Perf. 13**
**Size: 30x45mm**
1734-1736 A430 Set of 3 8.00 6.25
**Souvenir Sheet**
**Perf. 13¼x13**
1737 A430 Sheet of 3, #a-c 10.00 8.00
No. 1737 contains three 32x43mm stamps and sold for 18,000k.

Cotton — A432

Designs: Nos. 1739, 1742a, 1000k, Woman at cotton gin. Nos. 1740, 1742b, 5000k, Cotton plant. Nos. 1741, 1742c, 5500k, Cotton plant, diff.

**2008, Apr. 10 Perf. 13**
**Size: 45x30mm**
1739-1741 A432 Set of 3 7.50 5.25
**Souvenir Sheet**
**Perf. 13½x13¾**
1742 A432 Sheet of 3, #a-c 8.50 6.75
No. 1742 contains three 42x32mm stamps and sold for 15,000k.

Bees — A434

Designs: 1000k, Bees and honeycomb. 4000k, Bees on flower. 6000k, Beehive. 8500k, Bee in flight.

**2008, June 13 Perf. 13**
1747-1750 A434 Set of 4 11.00 8.75

Waterfalls — A435

Designs: Nos. 1751, 1755a, 500k, Taat Fan Waterfall. Nos. 1752, 1755b, 2000k, Tad Sae Waterfall, horiz. Nos. 1753, 1755c, 5000k, Kuang Si Waterfall. No. 1754, 1755d, 6500k, Khonphapheng Waterfall, horiz.

**2008, July 28 Perf. 13**
**Sizes: 30x45mm, 45x30mm (Horiz. Stamps)**
1751-1754 A435 Set of 4 9.00 6.25
**Souvenir Sheet**
**Perf. 13¾x13½, 13½x13¾**
1755 A435 Sheet of 4, #a-d 9.50 7.25
No. 1755 contains two 32x42mm stamps and two 42x32mm stamps and sold for 16,000k.

Eggplants A436

Designs: Nos. 1756, 1760a, 1000k, White eggplants. Nos. 1757, 1760b, 2000k, Green eggplants. Nos. 1758, 1760c, 4000k, Green, striped eggplants. Nos. 1759, 1760d, 5500k, Purple eggplants.

**2008, Oct. 1 Perf. 13**
**Size: 45x30mm**
1756-1759 A436 Set of 4 8.00 5.75
**Souvenir Sheet**
1760 A436 Sheet of 4, #a-d 9.00 6.75
No. 1760 contains four 42x32mm stamps and sold for 15,000k.

Hmong New Year — A437

Designs: Nos. 1761, 1765a, 1000k, Woman. Nos. 1762, 1765b, 5500k, Two oxen, horiz. Nos. 1763, 1765c, 6000k, Musician. Nos. 1764, 1765d, 7500k, Two women holding umbrellas, horiz.

**2008, Dec. 1**      **Perf. 13**
**Size: 30x45mm, 45x30mm (Horiz. Stamps)**
1761-1764 A437 Set of 4   12.00 9.00
**Souvenir Sheet**
**Perf. 13¾x13½, 13½x13¾**
1765 A437 Sheet of 4, #a-d   12.50 9.00
No. 1765 contains two 32x42mm stamps and two 42x32mm stamps.

Antiquities of Laos — A438

Designs: Nos. 1766, 1770a, 1000k, Haw Phra Kaew. Nos. 1767, 1770b, 2000k, Plain of Jars. Nos. 1768, 1770c, 4000k, Phat That Luang. Nos. 1769, 1770d, 7500k, Temple.

**2009, Jan. 3**      **Perf. 13**
**Stamps With White Frames**
1766-1769 A438 Set of 4   8.50 5.00
**Souvenir Sheet**
**Stamps With Colored Frames**
1770 A438 Sheet of 4, #a-d   8.50 5.25
No. 1770 sold for 15,000k.

A439

A440

A441

Army, 60th Anniv. — A442

**2009, Jan. 20**
1771 A439 2000k multi   2.00 1.25
1772 A440 2000k multi   2.00 1.25
1773 A441 2000k multi   2.00 1.25
1774 A442 2000k multi   2.00 1.25
  a.   Souvenir sheet of 4, #1771-1774   6.00 6.00
     Nos. 1771-1774 (4)   8.00 5.00
No, 1774a sold for 10,000k.

A443

A444

Opening of Laos-Thailand Rail Link — A445

**2009, Mar. 5**
1775 A443 3000k multi   2.00 1.50
1776 A444 3000k multi   2.00 1.50
1777 A445 3000k multi   2.00 1.50
  a.   Souvenir sheet of 3, #1775-1777   12.00 12.00
     Nos. 1775-1777 (3)   6.00 4.50
No. 1777a sold for 15,000k.

China 2009 World Stamp Exhibition — A446

Color of flower: No. 1778, 7500k, White. No. 1779, 7500k, Red.

**2009, Mar. 20**
1778-1779 A446 Set of 2   8.00 6.50
1779a   Souvenir sheet of 2, #1778-1779   12.00 12.00
No. 1779a sold for 20,000k, and exists imperf.

Flowers A447

Designs: 500k, Mari flower. 2000k, Ixora. 4000k, White Vuddish flowers (Calotropis gigantea). 7500k, Lilac Vuddish flowers (Calotropis gigantea).

**2009, May 15**
1780-1783 A447 Set of 4   6.00 5.00
1783a   Souvenir sheet of 4, #1780-1783   8.00 6.00
No. 1783a sold for 15,000k.

Rice Alcohol — A448

Designs: 1000k, Pots with sticks. 2000k, Horn and pot. 5500k, Man and pot.

**2009, Aug. 11**
1784-1786 A448 Set of 3   5.00 5.00
A souvenir sheet containing Nos. 1784-1786 sold for 18,000k.

Postmarks — A449

No. 1787 — Postmark of: a, R. P. Vientiane. b, Centre de Tri. c, Phongsaly. d, Luangnamtha. e, Oudomxay. f, Bokeo. g, Luangpabang. h, Huaphan. i, Sayaboury. j, Xiengkhouang. k, Vientiane. l, Bolikhamxay. m, Khammouane. n, Savannakhet. o, Saravan. p, Sekong. q, Champasack. r, Attapeu.

**2009, Oct. 9**      **Perf. 13½**
1787   Sheet of 18   17.50 17.50
  a.-r.   A449 2000r Any single   .75 .50

25th South East Asian Games, Vientiane A450

Mascots and: 5000k, Red background. 7000k, Flag, blue background.

**2009, Dec. 9**      **Perf. 14½x14**
1788-1789 A450 Set of 2   6.50 6.50
1789a   Souvenir sheet of 2, #1788-1789   9.00 9.00
No. 1789a sold for 15,000k.
Nos. 1788-1789 exist in a souvenir sheet of 4 containing 2 each, along with 4 labels that could be personalized.

Wat Simuong — A451

Designs: 4000k, Statue. 5000k, Stone temple. 6000k, Temple.

**2009, Dec. 7**      **Perf. 13**
1790-1792 A451 Set of 3   9.00 9.00
1792a   Souvenir sheet of 3, #1790-1792   11.00 11.00
No. 1792a sold for 18,000k.

Flora — A452

Designs: 1000k, Litsea cubeba. 3000k, Orthosiphon stamineus, vert. 4000k, Strychnos nux-vomica, vert. 5000k, Zingiber sp. 8000k, Styrax tonkinensis, vert. 9000k, Aquilaria crassna, vert.

**2010, Jun. 30**      **Litho.**
1793-1798 A452 Set of 6   25.00 25.00
1797a   Souvenir sheet of 3   — —
1798a   Souvenir sheet of 3   — —
No. 1797a contains Nos. 1794, 1795, and 1797. No. 1798a contains Nos. 1793, 1796, and 1798.

Rural Life — A453

Designs: 1000k, Huts and people near stream. 6000k, Weavers. 12,000k, Woman and children winnowing rice.

**2010, Feb. 5**
1799-1801 A453 Set of 3   10.00 10.00
1801a   Souvenir sheet of 3, #1799-1801   12.00 12.00
No. 1801a sold for 20,000k.

Laotian Landscapes A454

Designs: 1000k, Cave entrance. 3000k, Lake. 4000k, Boat on river. 10,000k, Canyon.

**2010, Apr. 1**
1802-1805 A454 Set of 4   10.00 10.00
1805a   Souvenir sheet of 4, #1802-1805   12.00 12.00
No. 1805a sold for 20,000k.

Rice Blessing Festival — A455

Designs: 4000k, Boy placing stick in clay pot. 5000k, Offering. 11,000k, People looking at burning candles.

**2010, July 26**
1806-1808 A455 Set of 3   12.00 12.00
1808a   Souvenir sheet of 3, #1806-1808   11.00 11.00
1808b   Souvenir sheet of 1 #1808   11.00 11.00
No. 1808b sold for 15,000k.

Wild Fruit — A456

Color of fruit: 500k, Brown. 1500k, Red. 8000k, Yellow orange. 9000k, Green.

**2010. Sept. 1**
1809-1812 A456 Set of 4   12.00 12.00
1812a   Souvenir sheet of 4, #1809-1812   12.50 12.50
No. 1812a sold for 20,000k.

Vientiane, 450th Anniv. A457

Emblem and Pha That Luang Stupa, Vientiane, in: 1000k, 1889. 3000k, 1910. 5000k, 1935. 6000k, 2010. 20,000k, Golden Stupa and statue, vert.

**2010, Nov. 15**   **Litho.**   **Perf. 14½x14**
1813-1816 A457 Set of 4   8.50 8.50
**Souvenir Sheet**
**Litho. & Embossed With Foil Application**
1817 A457 20,000k gold & multi   12.00 12.00
No. 1817 contains one 48x60mm stamp.

People's Democratic Republic of Laos, 35th Anniv. A458

Designs: 5000k, Army officer pointing. 6000k, Soldiers and large gun, vert. 10,000k, Laotian leaders and soldiers. No. 1821a, Like 10,000k.

**2010, Dec. 2**   **Litho.**   **Perf. 13**
1818-1820 A458 Set of 3   11.00 11.00
1821 A458 Souvenir sheet of 3, #1818, 1819, 1821a   18.00 18.00
  a.   9000k multi   5.00 5.00

Selection of Luang Prabang as UNESCO World Heritage Site, 15th Anniv. — A459

Various views of Luang Prabang festivals: 2000k, 3000k, 5000k, 10,000k.

**2010, Dec. 12**
1822-1825 A459 Set of 4   12.00 12.00
1825a   Souvenir sheet of 4, #1822-1825   12.00 12.00

Traditional Women's Costumes — A460

Various women in traditional costumes: 1000k, 3000k, 4000k, 5000k, 8000k.

**2011, Jan. 31**
1826-1830 A460    Set of 5    12.00 12.00

Potters and Pottery — A461

Designs: 1000k, Potter. 3000k, Clay pot. 5000k, Decorated clay pot. 6000k, Potter, diff.

**2011, Mar. 14**
1831-1834 A461    Set of 4    10.00 10.00

Peonies A462

No. 1835: a, 7000k, Pink peonies. b, 8000k, White peonies.

**2011, Mar. 20**              **Perf. 12½**
1835 A462    Pair, #a-b          10.00 10.00
c.    Souvenir sheet of 1 #1835b    7.00  7.00

Nos. 1835 and 1835a exist imperforate.

Diplomatic Relations Between Laos and Thailand, 60th Anniv. — A463

Designs: No. 1836, 8000k, Laotian woman with black skirt. No. 1837, 8000k, Thai woman with yellow dress. No. 1838, 8000k, White frangipani flowers. No. 1839, 8000k, Yellow Cassia fistula flowers.

**2011, Apr. 22**              **Perf. 13**
1836-1839 A463    Set of 4    20.00 20.00
1839a    Souvenir sheet of 4,
          #1836-1839              25.00 25.00

No. 1839a sold for 35,000k. See Thailand No. 2602.

Dipmomatic Relations Beween Laos and People's Republic of China, 50th Anniv. — A464

**2011, Apr. 25**
1840 A464    9000k multi    5.00 5.00

A souvenir sheet containing one No. 1840 sold for 20,000k.

Orchids A465

Paphiopedilum barbigerum var. sulivongii: 1000k, One flower. 9000k, Three flowers. 11,000k, One flower, with leaves.

**2011, May 22**
1841-1843 A465    Set of 3    20.00 20.00
1843a    Souvenir sheet of 3,
          #1841-1843             30.00 30.00

No. 1843a sold for 25,000k. Imperforate examples of No. 1843a sold for 35,000k.

Forest Products — A466

Products harvested from trees: 3000k, Lac resin. 4000k, Cinnamon. 5000k, Malva nuts. 6000k, Gurjum balsam. 11,000k, Dammar gum. 12,000k, Beeswax, horiz.

**2011, June 15**              **Perf. 13**
1844-1849 A466    Set of 6    25.00 25.00
1848a    Souvenir sheet of 3,
          #1844, 1847, 1848, im-
          perf., on card, without
          gum                       —    —
1849a    Souvenir sheet of 3,
          #1845, 1846, 1849, im-
          perf., on card, without
          gum                       —    —

Nos. 1848a and 1849a each sold for 22,000k.

Wildlife Conservation A467

Designs: 1000k, Asian elephant. 3000k, Tiger. 5000k, Saola. 8000k, Red-shanked douc langur.

**2011, July 13**
1850-1853 A467    Set of 4    12.00 12.00
1853a    Souvenir sheet of 4,
          #1850-1853            15.00 15.00

No. 1853a sold for 20,000k.

Lotus Flowers A468

No. 1854: a, 7000k, Lotus flower. b, 8000k, Lotus flower, diff.

**2011, Aug. 12**
1854 A468    Horiz. pair, #a-b    9.00 9.00

No. 1854 exists as a souvenir sheet of 3 pairs.

A469                    A470

City Pillar, Vientiane A471

**2011, Nov. 10**
1855 A469 9000k multi    6.00  6.00
1856 A470 9000k multi    6.00  6.00
1857 A471 9000k multi    6.00  6.00
a.    Souvenir sheet of 3, #1855-
      1857                20.00 20.00
Nos. 1855-1857 (3)       18.00 18.00

No. 1857a sold for 30,000k.

**Miniature Sheet**

Architecture in Vientiane and Moscow — A472

No. 1858: a, 6000k, Pha That Luang, Vientiane. b, 7000k, St. Basil's Cathedral, Moscow. c, 8000k, Temple, Vientiane. d, 9000k, Egg House, Moscow.

**2011, Dec. 3**              **Perf. 14¼x14**
1858 A472    Sheet of 4, #a-d  25.00 25.00

No. 1858 exists imperforate. For overprint, see No. 1873.

New Year 2012 (Year of the Dragon) — A473

**2012, Jan. 10    Litho.    Perf. 13¼**
1859 A473 8000k multi    4.50 4.50

No. 1859 was printed in sheets of 4.

Laos Pres. Kaysone Phomvihane (1920-92), North Viet Nam Pres. Ho Chi Minh (1890-1969), Flags of Laos and Viet Nam — A474

Buildings in Laos and Viet Nam — A475

**2012, July 18    Litho.    Perf. 13x12¾**
1860 A474 4000k multi    2.50 2.50
1861 A475 12,000k multi  6.50 6.50

See Viet Nam Nos. 3458-3459.

Asia-Europe Summit Meeting, Vientiane A476

Emblems for summit and: 9000k, Laotian temple. 11,000k, Map with Europe and Southeast Asis highlighted.

**2012, Nov. 5    Litho.    Perf. 13x12¾**
1862-1863 A476    Set of 2    9.00 9.00

An imperforate souvenir sheets containing No. 1862 sold for 20,000k. A souvenir sheet containing No. 1863 sold for 20,000k.

Silk Processing A477

Designs: 2000k, Boiling of silk cocoons. 3000k, Spinning of silk. 4000k, Collection of cocoons. 5000k, Mulberries on tree.

**2013, Apr. 22    Litho.    Perf. 13**
1864-1867 A477    Set of 4    7.25 7.25
1867a    Souvenir sheet of 4,
          #1864-1867            13.00 13.00

No. 1867a sold for 25,000k and exists imperforate.

**Miniature Sheet**

Cultural Cooperation Between Laos and Russia — A478

No. 1868: a, 6000k, Patuxai Gate, Vientiane. b, 7000k, Triumphal Arch, Moscow. c, 8000k, Pagoda, Laos. d, 9000k, Tower, Russia.

**2013, July 5    Litho.    Perf. 14¼x14**
1868 A478    Sheet of 4, #a-d  22.00 22.00

No. 1868 exists imperforate.

Fish — A479

Designs: 2000k, Clupisoma sinense. 4000k, Hemibarus filamentus. 6000k, Great white catfish. 9000k, Bagarius yarrelli.

**2013, July 6    Litho.    Perf. 13**
1869-1872 A479    Set of 4    11.00 11.00
1872a    Souvenir sheet of 4,
          #1869-1872            13.00 13.00

No. 1872a sold for 25,000k and exists imperforate.

**No. 1858 Overprinted in Red and Blue**

**Methods and Perfs. As Before**
**2013, July 10**
1873 A472    Sheet of 4, #a-d  57.50 57.50

Nos. 1873a-1873d are Nos. 1858a-1858d with a different part of the overprint covering the sheet. No. 1873 exixts imperforate.

Stupas — A480

Designs: 1000k, Xiengkhoeng Stupa, Huaphanh. 2000k, Wat That Noi Stupa, Luang Prabang. 3000k, Makmo Stupa, Luang Prabang. 4000k, Phonphao Stupa, Luang Prabang. 10,000k, Phousi Stupa, Luang Prabang.

**2013, Nov. 11     Litho.     Perf. 13**
1874-1878  A480   Set of 5              9.75  9.75

Perforate and imperforate souvenir sheets containing one example of No. 1874 exist. Each sheet sold for 25,000k.

Fourth International Mekong Bridge — A481

Designs: No. 1879, 8000k, Border checkpoint and parking lot. No. 1880, 8000k, Bridge.

**2013, Dec. 11     Litho.     Perf. 13**
1879-1880  A481   Set of 2              7.50  7.50
1880a       Souvenir sheet of 2,
                #1879-1880             12.50  12.50

No. 1880a sold for 25,000k and exists imperforate.

First Laos-Thailand Friendship Bridge, 20th Anniv. — A482

No. 1881 — Bridge and: a, Sai Buddha Image Procession Festival, Nong Khai, Thailand, and Wax Candle Procession Festival, Vientiane. b, Pho Chai Temple, Nong Khai, and On Teu Temple, Vientiane.

**2014, Apr. 8     Litho.     Perf. 14½x14**
1881  A482   9000k Horiz. pair, #a-
                b                        8.00  8.00
  c.    Souvenir sheet of 2, #1881a-
        1881b                            9.00  9.00

No. 1881c sold for 20,00k and exists imperforate. See Thailand No. 2807.

Nos. 535-537, 834-835 Handstamp Srchd.

**Methods and Perfs. As Before**
**2014, July 22**
1882  A207   5000k on 1k
                #834
1883  A207   8000k on 2k               3.00  3.00
                #835
1884  A154   10,000k on 60c            4.75  4.75
                #535
1885  A154   11,000k on 1k             6.00  6.00
                #536
1886  A154   12,000k on 2k             6.50  6.50
                #537                    7.00  7.00
        Nos. 1882-1886 (5)            27.25 27.25

A483                    A484

A485

Buddhas — A486

**2014, Oct. 8     Litho.     Perf. 13**
1887  A483   5000k multi               2.40  2.40
1888  A484   5000k multi               2.40  2.40
1889  A485   5000k multi               2.40  2.40
1890  A486   5000k multi               2.40  2.40
  a.    Souvenir sheet of 4, #1887-
        1890                           12.50 12.50

No. 1890a sold for 25,000k and exists imperf.

Tourist Attractions A487

Designs: No. 1891, 5000k, Wat Non-glamchanh, Savannakhet Province. No. 1892, 5000k, Tham Ting Cave, Luang Prabang Province. No. 1893, 5000k. Wat Sisaket Tripitaka Hall, Vientiane. No. 1894, 5000k, Sikhot-tabong Stupa, Khammuan Province. 9000k, Wat Phiawat, Xiengkhuang Province.

**2014, Nov. 11     Litho.     Perf. 13**
1891-1895  A487   Set of 5            14.00 14.00
1895a       Souvenir sheet of 4,
                #1892-1895            16.00 16.00

No. 1895a sold for 25,000k and exists imperf. A souvenir sheet containing No. 1891 sold for 25,000k and exists imperf.

Monuments — A488

Designs: No. 1896, 5000k, King Saya Setthathirath. No. 1897, 5000k, King Chao Anouvong. 11,000k, King Fangoum Maharath.

**2014, Dec. 1     Litho.     Perf. 13**
1896-1898  A488   Set of 3             9.75  9.75
1898a       Souvenir sheet of 3,
                #1896-1898            12.50 12.50

No. 1898a sold for 25,000k and exists imperf.

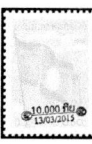

Nos. 276a, 535-537 and 1073 Surcharged

**Methods and Perfs. As Before**
**2015**
1899  A154   10,000k on 60c
                #535                    4.50  4.50
1900  A154   11,000k on 1k
                #536                    5.00  5.00
1901  A154   12,000k on 2k
                #537                    5.50  5.50
1902  A254   13,000k on 220k
                #1073                   6.00  6.00
        Nos. 1899-1902 (4)            21.00 21.00
**Souvenir Sheet**
1903         Sheet of 5, #1903a-
                1903e (#276a)         32.50 32.50
  a.    A96  14,000k on 1k #272        6.50  6.50
  b.    A96  14,000k on 2k #273        6.50  6.50
  c.    A96  14,000k on 5k #274        6.50  6.50
  d.    A96  14,000k on 10k #275       6.50  6.50
  e.    A96  14,000k on 200k #276      6.50  6.50

Issued: 11,000k, 2/19; 10,000k, 12,000k, 13,000k, 2/26; No. 1903, 3/13.

National Posts and Telecommunications Day, 50th Anniv. — A489

Designs: No. 1904, 10,000k, Satellite dish, telegraph key, telephone, people carrying sacks, airplane, letters, mailbox. No. 1905, 10,000k, Communications workers.

**2015, Mar. 13     Litho.     Perf. 13**
1904-1905  A489   Set of 2             9.50  9.50
1905a       Souvenir sheet of 2,
                #1904-1905            12.00 12.00

No. 1905a sold for 25,000k and exists imperf.

 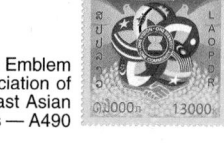

Flags and Emblem of Association of Southeast Asian Nations — A490

**2015, Aug. 8     Litho.     Perf. 13½**
1906  A490   13,000k multi             —     —
  a.    Souvenir sheet of 1            —     —

No. 1906 sold for 25,000k and exists imperforate.
See Brunei No. 656, Burma Nos. 417-418, Cambodia No. 2428, Indonesia No. 2428, Malaysia No. 1562, Philippines No. 3619, Singapore No. 1742, Thailand No. 2875, Viet Nam No. 3529.

Houses of Worship — A491

Designs: No. 1907, 9000k, Pha That Luang, Vientiane. No. 1908, 9000k, Cathedral of the Intercession of the Holy Virgin, Bogolyubovo, Russia.

**2015, Oct. 7     Litho.     Perf. 13½**
1907-1908  A491   Set of 2             8.75  8.75
1908a       Souvenir sheet of 2,
                #1907-1908            —     —

No. 1908a sold for 25,000k and exists imperforate. See Russia No. 7697.

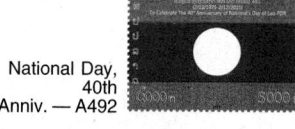

National Day, 40th Anniv. — A492

Designs: No. 1909, 5000k, Flag of Laos. No. 1910, 5000k, People in parade carrying flags, emblem of Laos and photograph of Kaysone Phomvihane. No. 1911, 5000k, Four Laotians. No. 1912, 5000k, Cooling towers and high-speed train.

**2015, Dec. 2     Litho.     Perf. 13**
1909-1912  A492   Set of 4             9.75  9.75
1912a       Souvenir sheet of 4,
                #1909-1912            —     —

No. 1912a sold for 25,000k and exists imperforate.

Selection of Luang Prabang as UNESCO World Heritage Site, 20th Anniv. — A493

Designs: No. 1913, 5000k, Laotian people, spinning wheel. No. 1914, 5000k, Bridge and boats. No. 1915, 5000k, Buddhist monks. No. 1916, 5000k, Building on stilts.

**2015, Dec. 7     Litho.     Perf. 13**
1913-1916  A493   Set of 4             9.75  9.75
1916a       Souvenir sheet of 4,
                #1913-1916            —     —

No. 1916a sold for 22,000k and exists imperforate.

Laotian International Women's Group, 26th Anniv. — A494

**2016, Mar. 8     Litho.     Perf. 13**
1917  A494   13,000k multi             6.00  6.00
  a.    Souvenir sheet of 1            —     —

No. 1917a sold for 25,000k and exists imperforate.

Dhamma Assembly Hall, Wat That Luang — A495

**2016, Nov. 14     Litho.     Perf. 13**
1918  A495   15,000k multi             7.00  7.00
  a.    Souvenir sheet of 1            7.00  7.00
  b.    As "a," imperf.                7.00  7.00

That Luang Stupa Foundation, 450th Anniv. — A496

Designs: No. 1919, 9000k, Shown, gray sky. No. 1920, 9000k, Stupa, blue sky. No. 1921, 9000k: a, Like No. 1919, orange background. b, Like No. 1920, orange background.

**2016, Nov. 16     Litho.     Perf. 13**
1919-1920  A496   Set of 2             9.00  9.00
**Souvenir Sheet**
1921  A496   9000k Sheet of 2, #a-
                b                        9.00  9.00
  c.    As No. 1921, imperf.           9.00  9.00

Launch of Lao Sat-1, 1st Anniv. — A497

Designs: 13,000k, Rocket launch. 15,000k, Lao Sat-1 in space.

**2016, Nov. 21     Litho.     Perf. 13**
1922  A497   13,000k multi             —     —
  a.    Souvenir sheet of 1            —     —
1923  A497   15,000k multi             —     —

No. 1922a sold fro 18,000k and exists imperforate.

A498

A499                    A500

Laotian Traditional Wedding — A501

**2016, Dec. 19    Litho.    Perf. 13**
1924 A498 8000k multi    4.00 4.00
a.    Souvenir sheet of 1
1925 A499 8000k multi    4.00 4.00
1926 A500 8000k multi    4.00 4.00
1927 A501 8000k multi    4.00 4.00
Nos. 1924-1927 (4)    16.00 16.00

No. 1924a sold for 10,000k and exists imperforate.

Flags and National Flowers Association of Southeast Asian Nations — A502

National flower, flag of: No. 1928, 1000k, Sphaerocoryne affinis, Cambodia. No. 1929, 1000k, Dillenia suffruticosa, Brunei. No. 1930, 1000k, Jasminum sambac, Philippines. No. 1931, 1000k, Vanda Miss Joaquim, Singapore. No. 1932, 1000k, Phalaenopsis amabilis, Indonesia. No. 1933, 1000k, Plumeria, Laos. No. 1934, 1000k, Pterocarpus macrocarpus, Myanmar. No. 1935, 1000k, Hibiscus rosa-sinensis, Malaysia. No. 1936, 1000k, Cassia fistula, Thailand. No. 1937, 1000k, Lotus, Viet Nam.

**2016, Dec. 26    Litho.    Perf. 13**
1928-1937 A502    Set of 10    — —
1937a    Souvenir sheet of 10,
    #1928-1937    — —

No. 1937a sold for 18,000k and exists imperforate.

Traditional Women's Clothing — A503

Women wearing various garments: 1000k, 2000k, 3000k, 9000k.
15,000k, Three women in traditional clothing.

**2017, Mar. 8    Litho.    Perf. 13**
1938-1941 A503    Set of 4    8.00 8.00
    **Size: 140x140mm**
    *Imperf*
1942 A503 15,000k multi + perfo-
    rated label    — —

Label on No. 1942 lacks a denomination. No. 1942 exists with the label lacking perforations.

Flower and Emblem of Association of Southeast Asian Nations — A504

**2017, Aug. 8    Litho.    Perf. 13**
1943 A504 9000k multi    — —

Tree House, Bokeo Province — A505

**2017, Dec. 25    Litho.    Perf. 13**
1944 A505 10,000k multi    — —
a.    Souvenir sheet of 1    — —

No. 1944a sold for 15,000k, and exists imperforate.

Ethnic Groups of Laos — A506

Designs: 1000k, Phong woman. 2000k, Thaineua woman. 3000k, Ngouan woman. 8000k, Katu woman.

**2017, Dec. 28    Litho.    Perf. 13**
1945-1948 A506    Set of 4    — —

A souvenir sheet containing No. 1948 sold for 18,000k and exists imperforate.

**Nos. 1364-1365, 1367-1368 Handstamp Surcharged**

**Methods and Perfs. As Before**
**2018, May 1**
1949 A317    8000k on 340k
    #1364    — —
1950 A317    8000k on 370k
    #1365    — —
1951 A319    17,000k on 380k
    #1367    — —
1952 A319    20,000k on 420k
    #1368    — —

Zodiac Animals — A507

Designs: No. 1953, 2000k, Rat. No. 1954, 2000k, Ox. No. 1955, 2000k, Tiger. No. 1956, 2000k, Rabbit. No. 1957, 2000k, Dragon. No. 1958, 2000k, Snake. No. 1959, 2000k, Horse. No. 1960, 2000k, Goat. No. 1961, 2000k, Monkey. No. 1962, 2000k, Rooster. No. 1963, 2000k, Dog. No. 1964, 2000k, Pig.

**2018, Sept. 18    Litho.    Perf. 13½**
1953-1964 A507    Set of 12    — —
1964a    Souvenir sheet of 12,
    #1953-1964    — —

No. 1964a sold for 25,000k and exists imperforate

Laotian Man and Woman and Emblem of Association of Southeast Asian Nations — A508

**2019    Litho.    Perf. 13**
1965 A508 8000k multi    — —

A souvenir sheet of 1 sold for 20,000k and exists imperf..

A509

Victory Gate Monument — A510

**2019    Litho.    Perf. 13**
1966 A509 8000k multi    — —
1967 A510 8000k multi    — —
a.    Souvenir sheet of 2, #1966-1967    — —

No. 1967a sold for 20,000k and exists imperforate.

A511

A512

Antique Mortars A513

**2019    Litho.    Perf. 13**
1968 A511 8000k multi    — —
1969 A512 8000k multi    — —
1970 A513 8000k multi    — —
a.    Souvenir sheet of 3, #1968-1970    — —

No. 1970a sold for 25,000k and exists imperforate.

---

**SEMI-POSTAL STAMPS**

Laotian Children — SP1

**Unwmk.**
**1953, July 14    Engr.    Perf. 13**
B1 SP1 1.50pi + 1pi multi    2.40 2.25
B2 SP1    3pi + 1.50pi multi    2.75 2.25
B3 SP1 3.90pi + 2.50pi multi    3.00 2.50
    Nos. B1-B3 (3)    8.15 7.00

The surtax was for the Red Cross.

**Nos. 52 and 46 Surcharged: "1k ANNEE MONDIALE DU REFUGIE 1959-1960"**

**1960, Apr. 7**
B4 A16    4k + 1k car red    3.50 3.50
B5 A13 10k + 1k multicolored    5.00 5.00

World Refugee Year, July 1, 1959-June 30, 1960. The surcharge was for aid to refugees.

Flooded Village — SP2

40k+10k, Flooded market place and truck. 60k+15k, Flooded airport and plane.

**1967, Jan. 18    Engr.    Perf. 13**
B6 SP2 20k + 5k multi    .45 .25
B7 SP2 40k + 10k multi    .85 .55
B8 SP2 60k + 15k multi    1.40 1.25
a.    Miniature sheet of 3    6.00 6.00
    Nos. B6-B8 (3)    2.70 2.05

The surtax was for victims of the Mekong Delta flood. No. B8a contains one each of Nos. B6-B8. Size: 148x99mm. Sold for 250k.

Women Working in Tobacco Field — SP3

**1967, Oct. 5    Engr.    Perf. 13**
B9 SP3 20k + 5k multi    .75 .40
B10 SP3 50k + 10k multi    1.25 .75
B11 SP3 60k + 15k multi    2.00 1.10
a.    Souv. sheet of 3, #B9-B11    4.50 4.50
    Nos. B9-B11 (3)    4.00 2.25

Laotian Red Cross, 10th anniv. No. B11a sold for 250k+30k.

**Nos. 184-189 Surcharged: "Soutien aux Victimes / de la Guerre / + 5k"**

**1970, May 1    Photo.    Perf. 14**
B12 A58 10k + 5k multi    .50 .30
B13 A58 15k + 5k multi    .60 .30
B14 A58 20k + 5k multi    .65 .30
B15 A58 30k + 5k multi    .85 .30
B16 A58 40k + 5k multi    1.25 .50
B17 A58 60k + 5k multi    1.30 .60
    Nos. B12-B17,CB1-CB2 (8)    11.65 6.05

**AIR POST STAMPS**

Weaving AP1

Design: 3.30pi, Wat Pra Keo.

**Unwmk.**
**1952, Apr. 13    Engr.    Perf. 13**
C1 AP1 3.30pi dk pur & pur    2.25 1.00
C2 AP1 10pi ultra & bl grn    2.00 1.25
C3 AP1 20pi deep cl & red    3.50 2.75
C4 AP1 30pi blk brn & dk
    brn violet    4.50 4.25
    Nos. C1-C4 (4)    12.25 9.25

See note following No. 17.

UPU Monument and King Sisavang-Vong — AP2

**1952, Dec. 7**
C5 AP2 25pi vio bl & indigo    5.00 4.50
C6 AP2 50pi dk brn & vio brn    6.00 5.50

Laos' admission to the UPU, May 13, 1952.

AP3

AP4

Designs: Various Buddha statues.

**1953, Nov. 18**
| | | | | |
|---|---|---|---|---|
| C7 | AP3 | 4pi dark green | 1.25 | .60 |
| C8 | AP4 | 6.50pi dk bl green | 1.25 | .60 |
| C9 | AP4 | 9pi blue green | 1.75 | .90 |
| C10 | AP3 | 11.50pi red, yel & dk vio brn | 2.75 | 1.25 |
| C11 | AP4 | 40pi purple | 4.50 | 1.75 |
| C12 | AP4 | 100pi olive | 8.00 | 4.50 |
| | | Nos. C7-C12 (6) | 19.50 | 9.60 |

Great Oath of Laos ceremony.

### Accession Type of Regular Issue

**1954, Mar. 4**      **Unwmk.**
| | | | | |
|---|---|---|---|---|
| C13 | A6 | 50pi indigo & bl grn | 120.00 | 95.00 |
| | | Hinged | 75.00 | |

Ravana
AP6

Sita and Rama — AP7

Scenes from the Ramayana: 4k, Hanuman, the white monkey. 5k, Ninh Laphath, the black monkey. 20k, Lucy with a friend of Ravana. 30k, Rama.

**1955, Oct. 28**    **Engr.**    *Perf. 13*
| | | | | |
|---|---|---|---|---|
| C14 | AP6 | 2k bl grn, emer & ind | .75 | .45 |
| C15 | AP6 | 4k red brn, dk red brn & ver | 1.20 | .90 |
| C16 | AP6 | 5k scar, sep & olive | 1.90 | 1.40 |
| C17 | AP7 | 10k blk, org & brn | 3.75 | 1.60 |
| C18 | AP7 | 20k vio, dk grn & olive | 5.25 | 2.75 |
| C19 | AP7 | 30k ultra, blk & salmon | 6.75 | 4.00 |
| | | Nos. C14-C19 (6) | 19.60 | 11.10 |

See No. 225.

### Buddha Type of Regular Issue, 1956

**1956, May 24**
| | | | | |
|---|---|---|---|---|
| C20 | A7 | 20k carmine rose | 27.00 | 20.00 |
| C21 | A7 | 30k ol sepia & brn | 27.00 | 25.00 |

2500th anniversary of birth of Buddha.

UN Emblem — AP8

**1956, Dec. 14**
| | | | | |
|---|---|---|---|---|
| C22 | AP8 | 15k light blue | 4.25 | 4.25 |
| C23 | AP8 | 30k deep claret | 5.50 | 5.50 |

Admission of Laos to the UN, 1st anniv.

### Types of Regular Issue, 1957

Musical Instruments: 12k, Khong vong. 14k, So. 20k, Kong.

**1957, Mar. 25**    **Unwmk.**    *Perf. 13*
| | | | | |
|---|---|---|---|---|
| C24 | A9 | 12k multicolored | 2.50 | 1.60 |
| C25 | A10 | 14k multicolored | 2.75 | 1.90 |
| C26 | A10 | 20k bl grn, yel grn & pur | 3.25 | 2.60 |
| | | Nos. C24-C26 (3) | 8.50 | 6.10 |

Monk Receiving Alms — AP9

Monks Meditating in Boat AP10

18k, Smiling Buddha. 24k, Ancient temple painting (horse and mythological figures.)

**1957, Nov. 5**
| | | | | |
|---|---|---|---|---|
| C27 | AP9 | 10k dk pur, pale brn & dk grn | 1.25 | 1.25 |
| C28 | AP10 | 15k dk vio brn, brn org & yel | 1.25 | 1.25 |
| C29 | AP9 | 18k slate grn & ol | 1.50 | 1.50 |
| C30 | AP10 | 24k claret, org yel & blk | 3.25 | 3.25 |
| | | Nos. C27-C30 (4) | 7.25 | 7.25 |

No. C28 measures 48x27mm. No. C30, 48x36mm. See No. C84.

Mother Nursing Infant — AP11

**1958, May 2**      **Cross in Red**
| | | | | |
|---|---|---|---|---|
| C31 | AP11 | 8k lil gray & dk gray | 1.30 | .75 |
| C32 | AP11 | 12k red brn & brn | 1.50 | 1.00 |
| C33 | AP11 | 15k sl grn & bluish green | 1.60 | 1.00 |
| C34 | AP11 | 20k bister & vio | 2.10 | 1.50 |
| | | Nos. C31-C34 (4) | 6.50 | 4.25 |

3rd anniversary of Laotian Red Cross.

Plain of Stones, Xieng Khouang — AP12

Papheng Falls, Champassak — AP13

Natl. Tourism Industry: 15k, Buffalo cart. 19k, Buddhist monk and village.

**1960, July 1**    **Engr.**    *Perf. 13*
| | | | | |
|---|---|---|---|---|
| C35 | AP12 | 9.50k bl, ol & claret | .50 | .50 |
| C36 | AP13 | 12k vio bl, red brn & gray | .50 | .50 |
| C37 | AP13 | 15k yel grn, ol gray & cl | .75 | .75 |
| C38 | AP12 | 19k multicolored | 1.00 | 1.00 |
| | | Nos. C35-C38 (4) | 2.75 | 2.75 |

Pou Gneu Nha Gneu Legend AP14

Garuda AP15

Hanuman, the White Monkey AP16

Nang Teng One Legend AP17

**1962, Feb. 19**    **Unwmk.**    *Perf. 13*
| | | | | |
|---|---|---|---|---|
| C39 | AP14 | 11k grn, car & ocher | .60 | .60 |
| C40 | AP15 | 14k ultra & org | .60 | .60 |
| C41 | AP16 | 20k multicolored | .80 | .80 |
| C42 | AP17 | 25k multicolored | .90 | .90 |
| | | Nos. C39-C42 (4) | 2.90 | 2.90 |

Makha Bousa festival.

Yao Hunter — AP18

**1964, Dec. 15**    **Engr.**    *Perf. 13*
| | | | | |
|---|---|---|---|---|
| C43 | AP18 | 5k shown | .55 | .25 |
| C44 | AP18 | 10k Kha hunter | .55 | .35 |
| C45 | AP18 | 50k Meo woman | 1.60 | 1.00 |
| a. | | Min. sheet of 4, #100, C43-C45 | 7.50 | 6.50 |
| | | Nos. C43-C45 (3) | 2.70 | 1.60 |

No. C45a exists imperf in a booklet. Value, intact booklet $75.

### Butterfly Type of 1965

**1965, Mar. 13**      **Size: 48x27mm**
| | | | | |
|---|---|---|---|---|
| C46 | A34 | 20k Attacus atlas | 5.50 | 2.50 |

Phayre's Flying Squirrel — AP19

Designs: 25k, Leopard cat. 75k, Javan mongoose. 100k, Crestless porcupine. 200k, Binturong.

**1965, Oct. 7**    **Engr.**    *Perf. 13*
| | | | | |
|---|---|---|---|---|
| C47 | AP19 | 25k dk brn, yel grn & ocher | .50 | .25 |
| C48 | AP19 | 55k brown & blue | .75 | .35 |
| C49 | AP19 | 75k brt grn & brn | 1.00 | .50 |
| C50 | AP19 | 100k ocher, brn & blk | 1.75 | 1.10 |
| C51 | AP19 | 200k red & black | 3.50 | 2.50 |
| | | Nos. C47-C51 (5) | 7.50 | 4.70 |

### Army Type of Regular Issue

Design: 200k, 300k, Parading service flags before National Assembly Hall.

**1968, July 15**    **Engr.**    *Perf. 13*
| | | | | |
|---|---|---|---|---|
| C52 | A53 | 200k multicolored | 1.75 | .85 |
| C53 | A53 | 300k multicolored | 2.50 | 1.25 |
| a. | | Souv. sheet of 5, #168-170, C52-C53 | 6.00 | 6.00 |

No. C53a sold for 600k.

### Insect Type of Regular Issue

Insects: 120k, Dorysthenes walkeri, horiz. 160k, Megaloxantha bicolor, horiz.

**1968, Aug. 28**    **Engr.**    *Perf. 13*
| | | | | |
|---|---|---|---|---|
| C54 | A54 | 120k brn, org & blk | 1.50 | .85 |
| C55 | A54 | 160k rose car, Prus bl & yel | 2.25 | 1.25 |

### Ballet Type of Regular Issue

Designs: 110k, Sudagnu battling Thotsakan. 300k, Pharam dancing with Thotsakan.

**1969**      **Photo.**    *Perf. 14*
| | | | | |
|---|---|---|---|---|
| C56 | A58 | 110k multicolored | 3.50 | 1.75 |
| a. | | Souv. sheet of 4, #187-189, C56, imperf. | 24.00 | 24.00 |
| C57 | A58 | 300k multicolored | 7.00 | 3.25 |
| a. | | Souv. sheet of 4, #184-186, C57, imperf. | 24.00 | 24.00 |

No. C56a sold for 480k; No. C57a for 650k.

For surcharges see Nos. CB1-CB2.

Timber Industry, Paksane — AP20

**1969, May 7**    **Engr.**    *Perf. 13*
| | | | | |
|---|---|---|---|---|
| C58 | AP20 | 300k olive bister & blk | 5.50 | 3.25 |

ILO, 50th anniversary.

### Animal Type of Regular Issue

Animals: 70k, Malaysian black bear. 120k, White-handed gibbon, vert. 150k, Indochinese tiger.

**1969, Nov. 6**    **Photo.**    *Perf. 12x13*
| | | | | |
|---|---|---|---|---|
| C59 | A60 | 70k multicolored | 1.10 | .60 |
| C60 | A60 | 120k multicolored | 2.40 | 1.10 |
| C61 | A60 | 150k multicolored | 2.75 | 1.40 |
| | | Nos. C59-C61 (3) | 5.85 | 3.10 |

Hairdressing, by Marc Leguay — AP21

Paintings: No. C63, Village Market, by Marc Leguay, horiz. No. C64, Tree on the Bank of the Mekong, by Marc Leguay, horiz.

**1969-70**    **Photo.**    *Perf. 12x13, 13x12*
| | | | | |
|---|---|---|---|---|
| C62 | AP21 | 120k multicolored | 1.00 | .40 |
| C63 | AP21 | 150k multicolored | 2.00 | .65 |
| C64 | AP21 | 150k multi ('70) | 2.00 | .65 |
| | | Nos. C62-C64 (3) | 5.00 | 1.70 |

See Nos. C72-C74.

Wat Xiengthong, Luang Prabang AP22

**1970, Jan. 10**      *Perf. 12x13, 13x12*
| | | | | |
|---|---|---|---|---|
| C65 | AP22 | 100k Library, Wat Sisaket, vert. | 1.40 | .65 |
| C66 | AP22 | 120k shown | 2.00 | 1.00 |

### Drum Type of 1970

**1970, Mar. 30**    **Engr.**    *Perf. 13*
| | | | | |
|---|---|---|---|---|
| C67 | A64 | 125k Pong wooden drum, vert. | 3.00 | 1.50 |

Franklin D. Roosevelt (1882-1945) AP23

**1970, Apr. 12**
| | | | | |
|---|---|---|---|---|
| C68 | AP23 | 120k olive & slate | 1.60 | 1.10 |

### EXPO '70 Type of Regular Issue

Design: 125k, Woman boiling cocoons in kettle, and spinning silk thread.

**1970, July 7**    **Engr.**    *Perf. 13*
| | | | | |
|---|---|---|---|---|
| C69 | A66 | 125k olive & multi | 1.75 | 1.25 |

See note after No. 202.

### Animal Type of Regular Issue

**1970, Sept. 7**    **Engr.**    *Perf. 13*
| | | | | |
|---|---|---|---|---|
| C70 | A67 | 210k Leopard | 2.75 | 1.25 |
| C71 | A67 | 500k Gaur | 5.00 | 2.50 |

## Painting Type of 1969-70

Paintings by Marc Leguay: 100k, Village Foot Path. 120k, Rice Field in Rainy Season, horiz. 150k, Village Elder.

**Perf. 11½x13, 13x11½**

**1970, Dec. 21**     Photo.

| | | | |
|---|---|---|---|
| C72 | AP21 | 100k multicolored | 1.10 1.10 |
| C73 | AP21 | 120k multicolored | 1.40 1.40 |
| C74 | AP21 | 150k multicolored | 1.60 1.60 |
| | | Nos. C72-C74 (3) | 4.10 4.10 |

## UN Type of Regular Issue

125k, Earth Goddess Nang Thorani wringing her hair; UN Headquarters and emblem.

**1970, Oct. 24**     **Perf. 13**

Size: 26x36mm

C75 A68 125k brt bl, pink & dk grn    2.40 1.10

Hanuman and Nang Matsa AP24

**1971, Feb. 5**     **Perf. 13**

C76 AP24 125k multicolored    2.40 1.00

## Orchid Type of Regular Issue

Design: 125k, Brasilian cattleya.

**1971, July**   Photo.   **Perf. 13x12½**

Size: 48x27mm

C79 A73 125k multi    4.50 1.50

Laotian and French Women, That Luang Pagoda and Arms — AP25

**1971, Aug. 6**   Engr.   **Perf. 13**

| | | | |
|---|---|---|---|
| C80 | AP25 | 30k brn & dull red | .25 .25 |
| C81 | AP25 | 70k vio & lilac | .50 .40 |
| C82 | AP25 | 100k slate grn & grn | .70 .55 |
| | | Nos. C80-C82 (3) | 1.45 1.20 |

Kinship between the cities Keng Kok, Laos, and Saint Astier, France.

## Animal Type of Regular Issue

**1971, Sept. 16**

C83 A74 300k Javan rhinoceros   4.25 2.75

## Type of 1957 with Ornamental Panel and Inscription

Design: Monk receiving alms (like No. C27).

**1971, Oct. 31**   Engr.   **Perf. 13**

C84 AP9 125k dk pur, pale brn & dk grn    2.00 1.40

20th anniv. of Laotian independent postal service. No. C84 inscribed: "Vingtième Anniversaire de la Philatélie Lao," "Poste Aerienne" and "1971."

Sunset Over the Mekong, by Chamnane Prisayane AP26

Design: 150k, "Quiet Morning" (village scene), by Chamnane Prisayane.

**1971, Dec. 20**   Photo.   **Perf. 13x12**

C85 AP26 125k black & multi   1.00 1.00
C86 AP26 150k black & multi   1.25 1.25

## Book Year Type of Regular Issue

Design: 125k, Father teaching children to read palm leaf book.

---

**1972, Jan. 30**   Engr.   **Perf. 13**

Size: 48x27mm

C87 A75 125k bright purple   1.75 1.00

## Dam Type of Regular Issue

Design: 145k, Nam Ngum Hydroelectric Dam and ECAFE emblem.

**1972, Mar. 28**   Engr.   **Perf. 13**

C88 A76 145k brown, bl & grn   1.40 .80

## Orchid Type of Regular Issue

**1972, May 5**   Photo.   **Perf. 13x12½**

Size: 48x27mm

C89 A73 150k Vanda teres, horiz. 4.00 1.50

## UNICEF Type of Regular Issue

Design: 120k, Boy riding buffalo to water hole (child's drawing).

**1972, July**   Engr.   **Perf. 13**

C90 A77 120k multicolored   1.40 1.00

Nakharath, Daughter of the Dragon King — AP27

Wood carvings from Wat Sikhounvieng Dongmieng, Vientiane: 120k, Nang Kinnali, Goddess from Mt. Kailath. 150k, Norasing, Lion King from Himalayas.

**1972, Sept. 15**   Engr.   **Perf. 13**

| | | | |
|---|---|---|---|
| C91 | AP27 | 100k blue green | .70 .70 |
| C92 | AP27 | 120k violet | .80 .80 |
| C93 | AP27 | 150k brn orange | 1.10 1.10 |
| | | Nos. C91-C93 (3) | 2.60 2.60 |

That Luang Religious Festival AP28

**1972, Nov. 18**   Engr.   **Perf. 13**

C94 AP28 110k Presentation of wax castles   .90 .90
C95 AP28 125k Procession   1.10 1.10

Workers in Rice Field, by Leguay — AP29

Paintings by Mark Leguay: No. C97, Women and water buffalo in rice field. Nos. C98, Rainy Season in Village (Water buffalo in water). No. C99, Rainy Season in Village (Water buffalo on land). 120k, Mother and Child.

**1972, Dec. 23**   Photo.   **Perf. 13**

| | | | |
|---|---|---|---|
| C96 | AP29 | 50k multicolored | .45 .45 |
| C97 | AP29 | 50k multicolored | .45 .45 |
| C98 | AP29 | 70k multicolored | .65 .65 |
| C99 | AP29 | 70k multicolored | .65 .65 |
| C100 | AP29 | 120k yel & multi | 1.25 1.25 |
| | | Nos. C96-C100 (5) | 3.45 3.45 |

Nos. C97, C99 have denomination and frame at right.

## Costume Type of Regular Issue

Women's Costumes: 120k, Luang Prabang marriage costume. 150k, Vientiane evening costume.

**1973, Feb. 16**   Engr.   **Perf. 13**

C101 A78 120k multicolored   1.40 .80
C102 A78 150k brown & multi   1.90 1.00

---

Lions Club Emblems, King Sayasettha-Thirath — AP30

**1973, Mar. 30**   Engr.   **Perf. 13**

C103 AP30 150k rose & multi   1.90 .75

Lions Club of Vientiane.

Rahu with Rockets and Sputnik AP31

Space achievements: 150k, Laotian festival rocket and US lunar excursion module.

**1973, May 11**   Engr.   **Perf. 13**

C104 AP31 80k ultra & multi   .55 .35
C105 AP31 150k buff & ultra   1.00 .45

Dancing Around Campfire AP32

Design: 125k, Boy Scouts helping during Vientiane Flood, 1966.

**1973, Sept. 1**   Engr.   **Perf. 13**

C106 AP32 110k vio & orange   1.10 .30
C107 AP32 125k Prus grn & bis   1.25 .40

Laotian Scout Movement, 25th anniv.

Sun Chariot and WMO Emblem AP33

Design: 90k, Nang Mékhala, the weather goddess, and WMO emblem, vert.

**1973, Oct. 24**   Engr.   **Perf. 13**

C108 AP33 90k vio, red & ocher   .75 .35
C109 AP33 150k ocher, red & brn ol   .85 .50

Intl. meteorological cooperation, cent.

Woman in Poppy Field, INTERPOL Emblem AP34

**1973, Dec. 22**   Engr.   **Perf. 13**

C110 AP34 150k vio, yel grn & red   1.40 .60

Intl. Criminal Police Org., 50th anniv.

Phra Sratsvady, Wife of Phra Phrom — AP35

Designs: 110k, Phra Indra on 3-headed elephant Erawan. 150k, Phra Phrom, the Creator, on phoenix. Designs show giant sculptures in park at Thadeua.

**1974, Mar. 23**   Engr.   **Perf. 13**

| | | | |
|---|---|---|---|
| C111 | AP35 | 100k lilac, red & blk | .80 .40 |
| C112 | AP35 | 110k car, vio & brn | 1.00 .50 |
| C113 | AP35 | 150k ocher, vio & sepia | 1.25 .70 |
| | | Nos. C111-C113 (3) | 3.05 1.60 |

---

UPU Emblem, Women Reading Letter AP36

**1974**   Engr.   **Perf. 13**

C114 AP36 200k lt brn & car   3.75 1.00
C115 AP36 500k lilac & red   6.00 2.00
   a.   Souvenir sheet   5.50 5.50

Centenary of Universal Postal Union. Issue dates: 200k, Apr. 30; 500k, Oct. 9.

## Flower Type of 1974

**1974, May 17**   Size: 36x36mm

C116 A84 500k Pitcher plant   5.50 3.00

## Transportation Type of Regular Issue

**1974, July 31**   Engr.   **Perf. 13**

C117 A85 250k Sampan   2.50 1.50

## Marconi Type of 1974

Old & new means of communications.

**1974, Aug. 28**   Engr.   **Perf. 13**

C118 A86 200k vio bl & brn   2.25 1.10

## Insect Type of 1974

110k, Sternocera multipunctata.

**1974, Oct. 23**   Engr.   **Perf. 13**

C119 A87 110k grn, blue & red   1.75 1.00

Boeing 747 — AP37

**1986, June 2**   Litho.   **Perf. 12½**

C120 AP37 20k shown   3.50
C121 AP37 50k IL86   8.00

## AIR POST SEMI-POSTAL STAMPS

**Nos. C56-C57 Surcharged: "Soutien aux Victimes / de la Guerre / + 5k"**

**1970, May 1**   Photo.   **Perf. 13**

CB1 A58 110k + 5k multi   3.00 1.50
CB2 A58 300k + 5k multi   3.50 2.25

The surtax was for war victims.

## POSTAGE DUE STAMPS

Vat-Sisaket Monument D1     Boat and Raft D2

**Perf. 13½x13**

**1952-53**   Unwmk.   Engr.

| | | | |
|---|---|---|---|
| J1 | D1 | 10c dark brown | .40 .25 |
| J2 | D1 | 20c purple | .40 .25 |
| J3 | D1 | 50c carmine | .50 .25 |
| J4 | D1 | 1pi dark green | .60 .25 |
| J5 | D1 | 2pi deep ultra | .70 .25 |
| J6 | D1 | 5pi rose violet | 1.25 1.00 |
| J7 | D2 | 10pi indigo ('53) | 2.00 .80 |
| | | Nos. J1-J7 (7) | 5.85 3.05 |

Serpent — D3

558 | LAOS — LATAKIA — LATVIA

**1973, Oct. 31     Photo.     Perf. 13**

| | | | |
|---|---|---|---|
| J8 | D3 | 10k yellow & multi | .40 .25 |
| J9 | D3 | 15k emerald & multi | .45 .25 |
| J10 | D3 | 20k blue & multi | .60 .25 |
| J11 | D3 | 50k scarlet & multi | .75 .40 |
| | | Nos. J8-J11 (4) | 2.20 1.15 |

## PARCEL POST STAMPS

Wat Ong Theu — PP1

**2000, June 7     Litho.     Die Cut**
**Self-Adhesive**
**Serial Number in Black**

| | | | | |
|---|---|---|---|---|
| Q1 | PP1 | 5000k orange | 5.00 | 5.00 |
| Q2 | PP1 | 40,000k milky blue | 30.00 | 30.00 |
| Q3 | PP1 | 60,000k gray blue | 32.50 | 32.50 |
| Q4 | PP1 | 80,000k cerise | 55.00 | 55.00 |
| Q5 | PP1 | 100,000k carmine | 65.00 | 65.00 |
| Q6 | PP1 | 250,000k ultra | 160.00 | 160.00 |
| | | Nos. Q1-Q6 (6) | 347.50 | 347.50 |

Phra That Luang PP2

**2003, Aug. 14     Die Cut**
**Self-Adhesive**
**Serial Number in Black**

| | | | | |
|---|---|---|---|---|
| Q7 | PP2 | 5000k vio bl & bl | 5.00 | 5.00 |
| Q8 | PP2 | 40,000k claret & red | 30.00 | 30.00 |
| Q9 | PP2 | 60,000k grn & claret | 45.00 | 45.00 |
| Q10 | PP2 | 90,000k red & blue | 70.00 | 70.00 |
| | | Nos. Q7-Q10 (4) | 150.00 | 150.00 |

Pha That Luang, Vientiane PP7

**2013, July 3     Litho.     Imperf.**
**Self-Adhesive**
**Frame Color**

| | | | | |
|---|---|---|---|---|
| Q17 | PP7 | 50,000k blue | 25.00 | 20.00 |
| Q18 | PP7 | 100,000k red | 45.00 | 37.50 |
| Q19 | PP7 | 200,000k green | 85.00 | 67.50 |
| | | Nos. Q17-Q19 (3) | 155.00 | 125.00 |

# LATAKIA

ˌla-tə-ˈkē-ə

LOCATION — A division of Syria in Western Asia
GOVT. — French Mandate
AREA — 2,500 sq. mi.
POP. — 278,000 (approx. 1930)
CAPITAL — Latakia

This territory, included in the Syrian Mandate to France under the Versailles Treaty, was formerly known as Alaouites. The name Latakia was adopted in 1930. See Alaouites and Syria.

100 Centimes = 1 Piaster

**Stamps of Syria Overprinted in Black or Red**

**Perf. 12x12½, 13½**

**1931-33     Unwmk.**

| | | | |
|---|---|---|---|
| 1 | A6 | 10c red violet | 1.25 1.25 |
| 2 | A6 | 10c vio brn ('33) | 1.60 1.60 |
| 3 | A6 | 20c dk blue (R) | 1.25 1.25 |
| 4 | A6 | 20c brn org ('33) | 1.60 1.60 |
| 5 | A6 | 25c gray grn (R) | 1.25 1.25 |
| 6 | A6 | 25c dk bl gray (R) ('33) | 1.60 1.60 |
| 7 | A9 | 50c violet | 2.00 2.00 |
| 8 | A15 | 75c org red ('32) | 3.25 3.25 |
| 9 | A10 | 1p green (R) | 2.40 2.40 |
| 10 | A11 | 1.50p bis brn (R) | 3.25 3.25 |
| 11 | A11 | 1.50p dp grn ('33) | 4.00 4.00 |
| 12 | A12 | 2p dk vio (R) | 4.00 4.00 |
| 13 | A13 | 3p yel grn (R) | 6.00 6.00 |
| 14 | A14 | 4p orange | 5.50 5.50 |
| 15 | A15 | 4.50p rose car | 5.75 5.75 |
| 16 | A16 | 6p grnsh blk (R) | 5.75 5.75 |
| 17 | A17 | 7.50p dl blue (R) | 5.50 5.50 |
| a. | | Inverted overprint | 650.00 |
| 18 | A19 | 10p dp brown (R) | 9.50 9.50 |
| a. | | Inverted overprint | 650.00 |
| 19 | A19 | 15p dp green (R) | 11.00 11.00 |
| 20 | A20 | 25p violet brn | 24.00 24.00 |
| 21 | A21 | 50p dk brown (R) | 22.50 22.50 |
| a. | | Inverted overprint | 650.00 |
| 22 | A22 | 100p red orange | 55.00 55.00 |
| | | Nos. 1-22 (22) | 177.95 177.95 |

## AIR POST STAMPS

Air Post Stamps of Syria, 1931, Overprinted in Black or Red

**1931-33     Unwmk.     Perf. 13½**

| | | | | |
|---|---|---|---|---|
| C1 | AP2 | 50c ocher | 1.25 | 1.25 |
| a. | | Inverted overprint | 1,200. | 1,200. |
| C2 | AP2 | 50c blk brn (R) ('33) | 2.50 | 2.50 |
| C3 | AP2 | 1p ches brn | 2.50 | 2.50 |
| C4 | AP2 | 2p Prus blue (R) | 4.00 | 4.00 |
| C5 | AP2 | 3p blue grn (R) | 5.50 | 5.50 |
| C6 | AP2 | 5p red violet | 7.00 | 7.00 |
| C7 | AP2 | 10p sl grn (R) | 8.75 | 8.75 |
| C8 | AP2 | 15p orange red | 12.50 | 12.50 |
| C9 | AP2 | 25p orange brn | 24.00 | 24.00 |
| C10 | AP2 | 50p black (R) | 40.00 | 40.00 |
| C11 | AP2 | 100p magenta | 42.50 | 42.50 |
| | | Nos. C1-C11 (11) | 150.50 | 150.50 |

## POSTAGE DUE STAMPS

Postage Due Stamps of Syria, 1931, Overprinted

**1931     Unwmk.     Perf. 13½**

| | | | |
|---|---|---|---|
| J1 | D7 | 8p blk, gray bl (R) | 26.00 26.00 |
| J2 | D8 | 15p blk, dl rose (R) | 26.00 26.00 |

Stamps of Latakia were superseded in 1937 by those of Syria.

# LATVIA

ˈlat-vē-ə

(Lettonia, Lettland)

LOCATION — Northern Europe, bordering on the Baltic Sea and the Gulf of Riga
GOVT. — Independent Republic
AREA — 25,395 sq. mi.
POP. — 2,353,874 (1999 est.)
CAPITAL — Riga

Latvia was created a sovereign state following World War I and was admitted to the League of Nations in 1922. In 1940 it became a republic in the Union of Soviet Socialist Republics. Latvian independence was recognized by the Soviet Union on Sept. 6, 1991.

100 Kapeikas = 1 Rublis
100 Santims = 1 Lat (1923, 1993)
100 Kopecks = 1 Ruble (1991)
100 Cents = 1 Euro (2014)

Catalogue values for unused stamps in this country are for Never Hinged items, beginning with Scott 300 in the regular postage section, Scott B150 in the semi-postal section, and Scott 2N45 in the Russian Occupation section.

**Watermarks**

Wmk. 108 Honeycomb

Wmk. 145 — Wavy Lines

Wmk. 181 Wavy Lines

Wmk. 197 — Star and Triangles

Wmk. 212 Multiple Swastikas

Wmk. 265 — Multiple Waves

Wmk. 387 — Squares and Rectangles

Arms — A1

**Printed on the Backs of German Military Maps**
**Unwmk.**

**1918, Dec. 18     Litho.     Imperf.**

| | | | |
|---|---|---|---|
| 1 | A1 | 5k carmine | .75 1.50 |

**Perf. 11½**

| | | | |
|---|---|---|---|
| 2 | A1 | 5k car ver | .75 1.50 |

Values given are for stamps where the map on the back is printed in brown and black. Maps printed only in black are valued at: No. 1 unused $2.00; used $5.75; No. 2 unused $1.20, used $2.50. Stamps with no map at all valued: No. 1 unused $1.50, used $3.25; No. 2 unused $1.20, used $2.25. Stamps with no printing on the back are from the outer rows of some sheets.
See No. 1007.

**Redrawn**
**Paper with Ruled Lines**

**1919     Imperf.**

| | | | |
|---|---|---|---|
| 3 | A1 | 5k carmine | .25 .25 |
| 4 | A1 | 10k dark blue | .25 .25 |
| 5 | A1 | 15k green | .50 .50 |

**Perf. 11½**

| | | | |
|---|---|---|---|
| 6 | A1 | 5k carmine | 2.40 4.00 |
| 7 | A1 | 10k dark blue | 2.40 4.00 |
| 8 | A1 | 15k deep green | 7.25 9.50 |
| | | Nos. 3-8 (6) | 13.05 18.50 |

In the redrawn design the wheat heads are thicker, the ornament at lower left has five points instead of four, and there are minor changes in other parts of the design.
The sheets of this and subsequent issues were usually divided in half by a single line of perforation gauging 10. Thus stamps are found with this perforation on one side.

**1919     Pelure Paper     Imperf.**

| | | | |
|---|---|---|---|
| 9 | A1 | 3k lilac | 4.75 4.50 |
| 10 | A1 | 5k carmine | .25 .25 |
| 11 | A1 | 10k deep blue | .25 .25 |
| 12 | A1 | 15k dark green | .25 .25 |
| 13 | A1 | 20k orange | .25 .25 |
| 13A | A1 | 25k gray | 40.00 47.50 |
| 14 | A1 | 35k dark brown | .25 .25 |
| 15 | A1 | 50k purple | .25 .25 |
| 16 | A1 | 75k emerald | 2.50 2.75 |
| | | Nos. 9-16 (9) | 48.75 56.25 |

**Perf. 11½, 9½**

| | | | |
|---|---|---|---|
| 17 | A1 | 3k lilac | 35.00 30.00 |
| 18 | A1 | 5k carmine | .80 .80 |
| 19 | A1 | 10k deep blue | 4.00 3.50 |
| 20 | A1 | 15k dark green | 2.75 4.00 |
| 21 | A1 | 20k orange | 3.75 4.00 |
| 22 | A1 | 35k dark brown | 4.50 6.50 |
| 23 | A1 | 50k purple | 5.50 8.00 |
| 24 | A1 | 75k emerald | 8.00 11.00 |
| | | Nos. 17-24 (8) | 64.30 68.30 |

Values are for perf 11½. Examples Perf 9½ sell for more.
Nos. 17-24 are said to be unofficially perforated varieties of Nos. 9-16.

**1919     Wmk. 108     Imperf.**

| | | | |
|---|---|---|---|
| 25 | A1 | 3k lilac | .30 .25 |
| 26 | A1 | 5k carmine | .30 .25 |
| 27 | A1 | 10k deep blue | .30 .25 |
| 28 | A1 | 15k dark green | .30 .25 |
| 29 | A1 | 20k orange | .35 .25 |
| 30 | A1 | 25k gray | .40 .35 |
| 31 | A1 | 35k dark brown | .35 .25 |
| 32 | A1 | 50k purple | .35 .25 |
| 33 | A1 | 75k emerald | .35 .25 |
| | | Nos. 25-33 (9) | 3.00 2.35 |

The variety "printed on both sides" exists for 3k, 10k, 15k, 20k and 35k. Value, $20 each.
See Nos. 57-58, 76-82. For surcharges and overprints see Nos. 86, 132-133, 2N1-2N8, 2N12-2N19.

Liberation of Riga — A2

**1919     Wmk. 108**

| | | | |
|---|---|---|---|
| 43 | A2 | 5k carmine | .25 .25 |
| 44 | A2 | 15k deep green | .25 .25 |
| 45 | A2 | 35k brown | .35 .80 |
| | | Nos. 43-45 (3) | .85 1.30 |

**Unwmk.**
**Pelure Paper**

| | | | |
|---|---|---|---|
| 49 | A2 | 5k carmine | 9.50 16.00 |
| 50 | A2 | 15k deep green | 9.50 16.00 |
| 51 | A2 | 35k brown | 21.00 16.00 |
| | | Nos. 49-51 (3) | 40.00 48.00 |

For surcharge and overprints see Nos. 87, 2N9-2N11, 2N20-2N22.

Rising Sun — A4

**1919** *Imperf.*
55 A4 10k gray blue .80 .50
*Perf. 11½*
56 A4 10k gray blue .80 *1.50*

**Type of 1918**
**1919 Laid Paper** *Perf. 11½*
57 A1 3r slate & org 1.00 1.00
58 A1 5r gray brn & org 1.00 1.00
See No. 82.

**Independence Issue**

Allegory of One Year of Independence — A5

**Wove Paper**
**Size: 33x45mm**
**1919, Nov. 18** **Unwmk.**
59 A5 10k brown & rose 1.25 2.00
**Laid Paper**
60 A5 10k brown & rose 1.25 2.00
**Size: 28x38mm**
61 A5 10k brown & rose .30 .40
a. Imperf. 50.00
62 A5 35k indigo & grn .30 .40
a. Vert. pair, imperf. btwn. 50.00 45.00

Back of No. 63 Block

**Wmk. 197**
**Thick Wove Paper**
**Blue Design on Back**
63 A5 1r green & red .45 .45
*Nos. 59-63 (5)* 3.55 5.25

There are two types of Nos. 59 and 60. In type I the trunk of the tree is not outlined. In type II it has a distinct white outline.
No. 63 was printed on the backs of unfinished 5r bank notes of the Workers and Soldiers Council, Riga.
For surcharges see Nos. 83-85, 88, 94.

Warrior Slaying Dragon — A6

**1919-20** **Unwmk.** *Perf. 11½*
**Wove Paper**
64 A6 10k brown & car .50 .50
a. Horiz. pair, imperf. btwn. 55.00 45.00
65 A6 25k ind & yel grn .50 .50
a. Pair, imperf. btwn. 55.00 45.00
66 A6 35k black & bl ('20) .50 .50
a. Horiz. pair, imperf. btwn. 55.00 45.00
67 A6 1r dp gray grn & brn ('20) .50 .50
a. Horiz. pair, imperf. vert. 50.00 40.00
b. Horiz. pair, imperf. btwn. 50.00 40.00
*Nos. 64-67 (4)* 2.00 2.00
Set, never hinged 5.75

Issued in honor of the liberation of Kurzeme (Kurland). The paper sometimes shows impressed quadrille lines.
For surcharges see Nos. 91-93.

**Latgale Relief Issue**

Latvia Welcoming Home Latgale Province — A7

Partial Design of No. 68 Back

**Brown and Green Design on Back**
**1920, Mar.**
68 A7 50k dk green & rose .50 .50
a. Horiz. pair, imperf. vert. 50.00
69 A7 1r slate grn & brn .50 .50
a. Horiz. pair, imperf. vert. 50.00
Set, never hinged 10.00

Nos. 68-69 were printed on the backs of unfinished bank notes of the government of Colonel Bermondt-Avalov and on the so-called German "Ober-Ost" money.
For surcharges see Nos. 95-99.

**First National Assembly Issue**

Latvia Hears Call to Assemble — A8

**1920**
70 A8 50k rose .50 .30
a. Imperf., pair 9.00 11.00
71 A8 1r blue .50 .30
a. Vert. pair, imperf. btwn. 45.00 45.00
b. Imperf., pair 20.00 15.00
72 A8 3r dk brn & grn .50 .80
73 A8 5r slate & vio brn 1.00 .80
*Nos. 70-73 (4)* 2.50 2.20
Set, never hinged 10.00

For surcharges see Nos. 90, 134.

**Type of 1918 Issue**
**Wove Paper**
**1920-21** **Unwmk.** *Perf. 11½*
76 A1 5k carmine .25 .25
78 A1 20k orange .25 .25
79 A1 40k lilac ('21) .30 .25
80 A1 50k violet .35 .25
81 A1 75k emerald .35 .25
82 A1 5r gray brn & org ('21) 1.50 1.00
*Nos. 76-82 (6)* 3.00 2.25
Set, never hinged 6.00

No. 63 Surcharged in Black, Brown or Blue

**1920, Sept. 1**
83 A5 10r on 1r grn & red (Bk) 1.00 *1.60*
84 A5 20r on 1r grn & red (Br) 2.50 *3.25*
85 A5 30r on 1r grn & red (Bl) 3.50 *4.00*
*Nos. 83-85 (3)* 7.00 8.85
Set, never hinged 17.50

Types of 1919 Surcharged

**1920-21** **Wmk. 108** *Perf. 11½*
86 A1 2r on 10k dp blue 1.75 7.25
87 A2 2r on 35k brown .50 5.50
Set, never hinged 5.00

No. 62 Surcharged in Red

**Unwmk.**
88 A5 2r on 35k ind & grn .40 .50
Never hinged .80

No. 70 Surcharged in Blue

**1921**
90 A8 2r on 50k rose .50 .60
Never hinged 1.00

Nos. 64-66 Surcharged in Red or Blue

**1920-21**
91 A6 1r on 35k blk & bl (R) .35 .40
92 A6 2r on 10k brn & rose (Bl) .60 .80
93 A6 2r on 25k brn & grn (R) .35 .40
a. Imperf.
*Nos. 91-93 (3)* 1.30 1.60
Set, never hinged 3.25

On Nos. 92 and 93 the surcharge reads "DIVI 2 RUBLI."

No. 83 with Added Surcharge

**1921** **Wmk. 197**
94 A5 10r on 10r on 1r 1.50 1.00
Never hinged 5.00

Latgale Relief Issue of 1920 Surcharged in Black or Blue

**1921, May 31** **Unwmk.**
95 A7 10r on 50k 1.25 .80
a. Imperf.
96 A7 20r on 50k 3.75 4.00
97 A7 30r on 50k 5.00 4.00
98 A7 50r on 50k 7.50 5.00
99 A7 100r on 50k (Bl) 17.50 16.00
*Nos. 95-99 (5)* 35.00 29.80
Set, never hinged 62.50

Excellent counterfeits exist.

Arms and Stars for Vidzeme, Kurzeme & Latgale — A10

Type I, slanting cipher in value.
Type II, upright cipher in value.

**Perf. 10, 11½ and Compound**
**Wmk. Similar to 181**
**1921-22** **Typo.**
101 A10 50k violet (II) .50 .30
102 A10 1r orange yel .50 .50
103 A10 2r deep green .25 .25
104 A10 3r brt green .65 .45
105 A10 5r rose 1.40 .40
106 A10 6r dp claret 2.00 .80
107 A10 9r orange 1.25 .55

108 A10 10r blue (I) 1.25 .25
109 A10 15r ultra 3.25 .50
a. Printed on both sides 50.00
110 A10 20r dull lilac (II) 20.00 2.00

Coat of Arms — A11

**1922, Aug. 21** *Perf. 11½*
111 A11 50r dk brn & pale brn (I) 30.00 4.50
112 A11 100r dk bl & pale bl (I) 35.00 4.50
*Nos. 101-112 (12)* 96.05 15.00
Set, never hinged 200.00

Nos. 101-131 sometimes show letters and numerals of the paper maker's watermark "PACTIEN LIGAT MILLS 1858." Stamps showing part of the inscription command a 100 percent premium. Pairs with the complete year "1858" command a 300 percent premium.
See Nos. 126-131, 152-154.

A12

**2 SANTIMS**
Type A, tail of "2" ends in an upstroke.
Type B, tail of "2" is nearly horizontal.

**1923-25** *Perf. 10, 11, 11½*
113 A12 1s redsh pur .40 .25
114 A12 2s yel org (A) .60 .35
115 A12 4s dark green .60 .25
a. Horiz. pair, imperf. btwn. 55.00 50.00
116 A12 5s lt green ('25) 2.50 .65
117 A12 6s grn, yel ('25) 3.50 .25
118 A12 10s rose red (I) 1.50 .25
a. Horiz. pair, imperf. btwn. 55.00 50.00
119 A12 12s claret .25 .40
120 A12 15s brn, sal 3.50 .25
a. Horiz. pair, imperf. btwn. 55.00 50.00
121 A12 20s dp blue (II) 1.50 .25
122 A12 25s ultra ('25) .50 .25
123 A12 30s pink (I) ('25) 5.00 .25
124 A12 40s lilac (I) .50 .25
125 A12 50s lil gray (II) 3.75 .35
126 A11 1 l dk brn & pale brn 12.50 1.00
127 A11 2 l dk blue & blue 20.00 1.60
130 A11 5 l dp grn & pale grn 60.00 5.00
131 A11 10 l car rose & pale rose (I) 3.00 6.00
*Nos. 113-131 (17)* 121.10 17.60
Set, never hinged 250.00

Value in "Santims" (1s); "Santimi" (2s-6s) or "Santimu" (others).
See note after No. 112.
See Nos. 135-151, 155-157. For overprints and surcharges see Nos. 164-167, B21-B23.

Nos. 79-80 Surcharged

No. 72 Surcharged

**1927** **Unwmk.** *Perf. 11½*
132 A1 15s on 40k lilac .40 .40
133 A1 15s on 50k violet 1.15 *1.50*
134 A8 1 l on 3r brn & grn 9.00 7.00
*Nos. 132-134 (3)* 10.55 8.90
Set, never hinged 24.00

**Types of 1923-25 Issue**
**1927-33** **Wmk. 212** *Perf. 10, 11½*
135 A12 1s dull violet .25 .25
136 A12 2s org yel (A) .35 .25
137 A12 2s org yel (B) ('33) .30 .25
138 A12 3s org red ('31) .25 .25
139 A12 4s dk green ('29) 3.50 2.25
140 A12 5s lt green ('31) .50 .25
141 A12 6s grn, yel .25 .25
142 A12 7s dk green ('31) .50 .25
143 A12 10s red (I) 2.50 .70
144 A12 10s grn, yel (I) ('32) 10.00 .25
145 A12 15s brn, sal 3.50 .45

| | | |
|---|---|---|
| **146** | A12 | 20s pink (I) | 5.00 | .25 |
| **147** | A12 | 20s pink (II) | 6.00 | .25 |
| **148** | A12 | 30s lt blue (I) | 1.25 | .40 |
| **149** | A12 | 35s dk blue ('31) | 1.50 | .25 |
| **150** | A12 | 40s dl lil (I) ('29) | 2.25 | .25 |
| **151** | A12 | 50s gray (II) | 2.50 | .45 |
| **152** | A11 | 1 l dk brn & pale brn | 8.00 | .30 |
| **153** | A11 | 2 l dk bl & bl ('31) | 30.00 | 2.25 |
| **154** | A11 | 5 l grn & pale grn ('33) | 140.00 | 30.00 |
| | | Nos. 135-154 (20) | 218.40 | 39.80 |
| | | Set, never hinged | 400.00 | |

The paper of Nos. 141, 144 and 145 is colored on the surface only.
See note above No. 113 for types A and B, and note above No. 101 for types I and II.

### Type of 1927-33 Issue
### Paper Colored Through

**1931-33**　　*Perf. 10*

| | | |
|---|---|---|
| **155** | A12 | 6s grn, *yel* | .25 | .25 |
| **156** | A12 | 10s grn, *yel* (I) ('33) | 15.00 | .25 |
| **157** | A12 | 15s brn, *salmon* | 3.00 | .25 |
| | | Nos. 155-157 (3) | 18.25 | .75 |
| | | Set, never hinged | 37.50 | |

View of
Rezekne — A13

Designs (Views of Cities): 15s, Jelgava.
20s, Cesis (Wenden). 30s, Liepaja (Libau).
50s, Riga. 1 l, Riga Theater.

**1928, Nov. 18　Litho.　*Perf. 10, 11½***

| | | |
|---|---|---|
| **158** | A13 | 6s dp green & vio | 1.00 | .40 |
| **159** | A13 | 15s dk brn & ol grn | 1.00 | .40 |
| **160** | A13 | 20s cerise & bl grn | 1.25 | .45 |
| **161** | A13 | 30s ultra & vio brn | 1.50 | .40 |
| **162** | A13 | 50s dk gray & plum | 1.50 | 1.00 |
| **163** | A13 | 1 l blk brn & brn | 3.75 | 1.75 |
| | | Nos. 158-163 (6) | 10.00 | 4.40 |
| | | Set, never hinged | 20.00 | |

10th anniv. of Latvian Independence.

### Riga Exhibition Issue

Stamps of 1927-33
Overprinted

**1932, Aug. 30　　*Perf. 10, 11***

| | | |
|---|---|---|
| **164** | A12 | 3s orange | 1.00 | .50 |
| **165** | A12 | 10s green, *yel* | 1.00 | .50 |
| **166** | A12 | 20s pink (I) | 2.10 | 1.00 |
| **167** | A12 | 35s dark blue | 4.75 | 2.00 |
| | | Nos. 164-167 (4) | 8.85 | 4.00 |
| | | Set, never hinged | 30.00 | |

Riga Castle
A19

Allegory of
Latvia
A21

Arms and
Shield
A20

Ministry of
Foreign
Affairs
A22

**1934, Dec. 15　Litho.　*Perf. 10½, 10***

| | | |
|---|---|---|
| **174** | A19 | 3s red orange | .25 | .25 |
| **175** | A20 | 5s yellow grn | .25 | .25 |
| **176** | A20 | 10s gray grn | 1.00 | .25 |
| **177** | A21 | 20s deep rose | 1.00 | .25 |
| **178** | A22 | 35s dark blue | .35 | .25 |
| **179** | A19 | 40s brown | .35 | .25 |
| | | Nos. 174-179 (6) | 3.20 | 1.50 |
| | | Set, never hinged | 6.00 | |

Atis
Kronvalds
A23

A.
Pumpurs
A24

Juris
Maters
A25

Mikus
Krogzemis
(Auseklis)
A26

**1936, Jan. 4　Wmk. 212　*Perf. 11½***

| | | |
|---|---|---|
| **180** | A23 | 3s vermilion | 3.50 | 4.75 |
| **181** | A24 | 10s green | 3.50 | 4.75 |
| **182** | A25 | 20s rose pink | 3.50 | 6.00 |
| **183** | A26 | 35s dark blue | 3.50 | 6.00 |
| | | Nos. 180-183 (4) | 14.00 | 21.50 |
| | | Set, never hinged | 35.00 | |

President Karlis
Ulmanis — A27

**1937, Sept. 4　Litho.　*Perf. 10, 11½***

| | | |
|---|---|---|
| **184** | A27 | 3s org red & brn org | .25 | .25 |
| **185** | A27 | 5s yellow grn | .25 | .25 |
| **186** | A27 | 10s dk sl grn | .75 | .60 |
| **187** | A27 | 20s rose lake & brn lake | 1.50 | .60 |
| **188** | A27 | 25s black vio | 2.25 | 1.25 |
| **189** | A27 | 30s dark blue | 2.25 | 1.25 |
| **190** | A27 | 35s indigo | 1.00 | 1.00 |
| **191** | A27 | 40s lt brown | 2.00 | 1.25 |
| **192** | A27 | 50s olive blk | 2.25 | 1.50 |
| | | Nos. 184-192 (9) | 12.50 | 7.95 |
| | | Set, never hinged | 25.00 | |

60th birthday of President Ulmanis.

Independence
Monument,
Rauna
(Ronneburg)
A28

Monument
Entrance to
Cemetery at Riga
A29

Independence
Monument,
Jelgava
A30

War Memorial,
Valka
A31

Independence
Monument,
Iecava — A32

Independence
Monument,
Riga — A33

Tomb of Col.
Kalpaks — A34

### Thick Paper

#### Unwmk.

**1937, July 12　Litho.　*Perf. 10***

| | | |
|---|---|---|
| **193** | A28 | 3s vermilion | .65 | .90 |
| **194** | A29 | 5s yellow grn | .65 | .90 |
| **195** | A30 | 10s deep grn | .65 | .50 |
| **196** | A31 | 20s carmine | 1.60 | 1.00 |
| **197** | A32 | 30s lt blue | 2.25 | 2.00 |

#### Wmk. 212

**Engr.　　　*Perf. 11½***
**Thin Paper**

| | | |
|---|---|---|
| **198** | A33 | 35s dark blue | 2.25 | 2.00 |
| **199** | A34 | 40s brown | 3.50 | 3.00 |
| | | Nos. 193-199 (7) | 11.55 | 10.30 |
| | | Set, never hinged | 25.00 | |

View of
Vidzeme
A35

General J. Balodis
A37

President Karlis
Ulmanis — A38

Views: 5s, Latgale. 30s, Riga waterfront.
35s, Kurzeme. 40s, Zemgale.

**1938, Nov. 17　　*Perf. 10, 10½x10***

| | | |
|---|---|---|
| **200** | A35 | 3s brown org | .25 | .25 |
| **a.** | | Booklet pane of 4 | 45.00 | |
| **201** | A35 | 5s yellow grn | .25 | .25 |
| **a.** | | Booklet pane of 4 | 45.00 | |
| **202** | A37 | 10s dk green | .25 | .25 |
| **a.** | | Booklet pane of 2 | 45.00 | |
| **203** | A38 | 20s red lilac | .25 | .25 |
| **a.** | | Booklet pane of 2 | 45.00 | |
| **204** | A35 | 30s deep blue | .90 | .25 |
| **205** | A35 | 35s indigo | .90 | .25 |
| **a.** | | Booklet pane of 2 | 45.00 | |
| **206** | A35 | 40s rose violet | 1.25 | .25 |
| | | Nos. 200-206 (7) | 4.05 | 1.75 |
| | | Set, never hinged | 12.00 | |

The 20th anniversary of the Republic.

School,
Riga — A42

Independence
Monument,
Riga — A45

President Karlis
Ulmanis — A49

Designs: 5s, Castle of Jelgava. 10s, Riga
Castle. 30s, Symbol of Freedom. 35s, Community House Daugavpils. 40s, Powder Tower
and War Museum, Riga.

**1939, May 13　Photo.　　*Perf. 10***

| | | |
|---|---|---|
| **207** | A42 | 3s brown orange | .25 | .80 |
| **208** | A42 | 5s deep green | .50 | .80 |
| **209** | A42 | 10s dk slate grn | .75 | .80 |
| **210** | A45 | 20s dk car rose | 1.50 | 1.60 |
| **211** | A42 | 30s brt ultra | 1.00 | .80 |
| **212** | A42 | 35s dark blue | 1.50 | 1.60 |
| **213** | A45 | 40s brown violet | 2.00 | 1.00 |
| **214** | A49 | 50s grnsh black | .80 | .80 |
| | | Nos. 207-214 (8) | 10.50 | 8.40 |
| | | Set, never hinged | 20.00 | |

5th anniv. of National Unity Day.

Harvesting
Wheat
A50

Apple
A51

**1939, Oct. 8**

| | | |
|---|---|---|
| **215** | A50 | 10s slate green | .90 | .60 |
| **216** | A51 | 20s rose lake | .90 | .65 |
| | | Set, never hinged | 3.00 | |

8th Agricultural Exposition held near Riga.

Arms and Stars for
Vidzeme, Kurzeme and
Latgale — A52

**1940**

| | | |
|---|---|---|
| **217** | A52 | 1s dk vio brn | .30 | .30 |
| **218** | A52 | 2s ocher | .40 | .30 |
| **219** | A52 | 3s red orange | .25 | .25 |
| **220** | A52 | 5s dk olive brn | .25 | .25 |
| **221** | A52 | 7s dk green | .30 | .30 |
| **222** | A52 | 10s dk blue grn | .75 | .25 |
| **224** | A52 | 20s dp car red | .75 | .25 |
| **225** | A52 | 30s dp red brn | 1.25 | .30 |
| **226** | A52 | 35s brt ultra | .25 | .80 |
| **228** | A52 | 50s dk slate grn | 1.75 | .80 |
| **229** | A52 | 1 l olive green | 3.50 | 2.40 |
| | | Nos. 217-229 (11) | 9.75 | 6.20 |
| | | Set, never hinged | 25.00 | |

> Catalogue values for unused
> stamps in this section, from this
> point to the end of the section, are
> for Never Hinged items.

Natl. Arms — A70

**1991, Oct. 19　Litho.　*Perf. 13x12½***

| | | |
|---|---|---|
| **300** | A70 | 5k multicolored | 5.00 | 5.00 |
| **301** | A70 | 10k multicolored | .40 | .40 |
| **302** | A70 | 15k multicolored | .50 | .50 |
| **303** | A70 | 20k multicolored | .65 | .65 |
| **304** | A70 | 40k multicolored | 1.25 | 1.25 |
| **305** | A70 | 50k multicolored | 1.75 | 1.75 |

**Size: 28x32mm**

***Perf. 13½x14***

| | | |
|---|---|---|
| **306** | A70 | 100k silver & multi | 2.75 | 2.75 |
| **307** | A70 | 200k gold & multi | 5.00 | 5.00 |
| | | Nos. 300-307 (8) | 17.30 | 17.30 |

> Most issues, Nos. 300-342, have
> one blocked value that was not
> freely available at Latvian post
> offices.

**Russia Nos. 5984, 5985a Ovptd.
"LATVIJA" and Srchd. in Red Lilac,
Orange, Green, Violet**

**1991, Dec. 23　Photo.　*Perf. 12x11½***

| | | |
|---|---|---|
| **308** | A2765 | 100k on 7k (RL) | .50 | .50 |
| **a.** | | Vert. pair, one without ovpt. | 8.00 | |
| **b.** | | Litho., perf. 12x12½ | .50 | .50 |

***Perf. 12x12½***

**Litho.**

| | | |
|---|---|---|
| **309** | A2765 | 300k on 2k (O) | .85 | .85 |
| **a.** | | Vert. pair, one without ovpt. | 8.00 | |
| **310** | A2765 | 500k on 2k (G) | 1.25 | 1.25 |
| **a.** | | Vert. pair, one without ovpt. | 8.00 | |
| **311** | A2765 | 1000k on 2k (V) | 2.40 | 2.40 |
| **a.** | | Vert. pair, one without ovpt. | 8.00 | |
| | | Nos. 308-311 (4) | 5.00 | 5.00 |

On Nos. 308-311 the sixth row of the sheet
was not surcharged.
Forgeries exist.

Liberty Monument,
Riga — A71

## 1991, Dec. 28 — Perf. 12½x13

| | | | | |
|---|---|---|---|---|
| 312 | A71 | 10k ol brn & multi | .25 | .25 |
| 313 | A71 | 15k violet & multi | 1.00 | 1.00 |
| 314 | A71 | 20k bl grn & multi | .80 | .80 |
| 315 | A71 | 30k ol grn & multi | .90 | .90 |
| 316 | A71 | 50k choc & multi | 1.25 | 1.25 |
| 317 | A71 | 100k dp blue & multi | 1.25 | 1.25 |
| | | *Nos. 312-317 (6)* | 5.45 | 5.45 |

A72    A73

Monuments — A74

## 1992, Feb. 29 — Perf. 14

| | | | | |
|---|---|---|---|---|
| 318 | A72 | 10k black | .25 | .25 |
| 319 | A73 | 20k violet black | .40 | .25 |
| 320 | A73 | 30k brown | .55 | .25 |
| 321 | A72 | 30k purple | .55 | .25 |
| 322 | A74 | 40k violet blue | .75 | .25 |
| 323 | A74 | 50k green | .90 | .25 |
| 324 | A73 | 50k olive green | .90 | .25 |
| 325 | A74 | 100k red brown | 1.75 | .60 |
| 326 | A72 | 200k blue | 2.75 | 1.10 |
| | | *Nos. 318-326 (9)* | 8.80 | 3.45 |

**Russia Nos. 4599, 5984, 5985a Ovptd. "LATVIJA" and Srchd. in Red, Brown, Emerald and Violet**

## 1992, Apr. 4 — Perf. 12x11½

| | | | | |
|---|---|---|---|---|
| 327 | A2765 | 1r on 7k (R) | .25 | .25 |

### Perf. 12x12½
### Litho.

| | | | | |
|---|---|---|---|---|
| 328 | A2765 | 3r on 2k (Br) | .40 | .25 |
| 329 | A2765 | 5r on 2k (E) | .65 | .35 |
| 330 | A2765 | 10r on 2k (V) | 1.10 | .75 |
| 331 | A2138 | 25r on 4k | 2.25 | 1.75 |
| | | *Nos. 327-331 (5)* | 4.65 | 3.35 |

Surcharged denominations expressed in rubles (large numerals) and kopecks (small zeros).

Birds of the Baltic
Shores — A75

### Litho. & Engr.
## 1992, Oct. 3 — Perf. 12½x13
### Booklet Stamps

| | | | | |
|---|---|---|---|---|
| 332 | A75 | 5r Pandion haliaetus | .35 | .35 |
| 333 | A75 | 5r Limosa limosa | .35 | .35 |
| 334 | A75 | 5r Mergus merganser | .35 | .35 |
| 335 | A75 | 5r Tadorna tadorna | .35 | .35 |
| a. | | Booklet pane of 4, #332-335 | 2.25 | |

See Estonia Nos. 231-234a, Lithuania Nos. 427-430a, and Sweden Nos. 1975-1978a.

Christmas — A76

2r, 10r Angels with children around Christmas tree. 3r, Angels with musical instruments, Christmas tree. 15r, Nativity scene.

## 1992, Nov. 21 — Litho. — Perf. 13½x13

| | | | | |
|---|---|---|---|---|
| 336 | A76 | 2r silver & multi | 1.00 | 1.00 |
| 337 | A76 | 3r multicolored | .30 | .25 |
| 338 | A76 | 10r gold & multi | 1.00 | .60 |
| 339 | A76 | 15r multicolored | 1.50 | 1.00 |
| | | *Nos. 336-339 (4)* | 3.80 | 2.85 |

Russia Nos. 4728,
5107, 5109 Surcharged
in Brown or Blue

---

### Perfs. & Printing Methods as Before
## 1993, Feb. 26

| | | | | |
|---|---|---|---|---|
| 340 | A2229 | 50r on 6k #4728 (Br) | .75 | .55 |
| 341 | A2435 | 100r on 6k #5109 | 1.60 | 1.00 |
| 342 | A2435 | 300r on 6k #5107 | 4.25 | 3.00 |
| | | *Nos. 340-342 (3)* | 6.60 | 4.55 |

Traditional
Costumes — A77

## 1993, Apr. 29 — Litho. — Perf. 13x13½

| | | | | |
|---|---|---|---|---|
| 343 | A77 | 5s Kuldiga | .25 | .25 |
| 344 | A77 | 10s Alsunga | .30 | .25 |
| 345 | A77 | 20s Lielvarde | .55 | .30 |
| 346 | A77 | 50s Rucava | 1.50 | .80 |
| 347 | A77 | 100s Zemgale | 3.00 | 1.50 |
| 348 | A77 | 500s Ziemellatgale | 15.00 | 12.00 |
| a. | | Miniature sheet of 6, #343-348 | 25.00 | 25.00 |
| | | *Nos. 343-348 (6)* | 20.60 | 15.10 |

See Nos. 400-401, 415-416, 440-441, 466-467.

21st Natl. Song Festival
A78    A79

## 1993, July 3 — Litho. — Perf. 12½x13

| | | | | |
|---|---|---|---|---|
| 349 | A78 | 3s rose brn, gold & black | 1.00 | .50 |
| 350 | A78 | 5s purple, gold & black | 1.50 | .80 |
| 351 | A79 | 15s multicolored | 2.00 | 1.25 |
| | | *Nos. 349-351 (3)* | 4.50 | 2.55 |

A80

## 1993, Aug. 28 — Litho. — Perf. 14

| | | | | |
|---|---|---|---|---|
| 352 | A80 | 15s Pope John Paul II | 1.10 | .90 |

A81

## 1993, Nov. 11 — Litho. — Perf. 12½x13

| | | | | |
|---|---|---|---|---|
| 353 | A81 | 5s silver, black & red | .70 | .30 |
| 354 | A81 | 15s gold, black & red | 1.30 | .45 |

Independence, 75th anniv.

A82

## 1994, Apr. 2 — Litho. — Perf. 14

| | | | | |
|---|---|---|---|---|
| 355 | A82 | 15s multicolored | 1.00 | .60 |

Evalds Valters, actor, 100th birthday.

A83    LATVIJA 5

---

## 1994, Apr. 20 — Litho. — Perf. 12½x13

| | | | | |
|---|---|---|---|---|
| 356 | A83 | 5s Biathlon | .40 | .40 |
| 357 | A83 | 10s 2-man bobsled | .85 | .40 |
| 358 | A83 | 15s Luge | 1.00 | .65 |
| 359 | A83 | 100s Men's figure skating | 5.75 | 3.25 |
| | | *Nos. 356-359 (4)* | 8.00 | 4.70 |

### Souvenir Sheet

| | | | | |
|---|---|---|---|---|
| 360 | A83 | 200s like #357 | 8.00 | 7.00 |

1994 Winter Olympics, Lillehammer.

Ethnographical
Open Air
Museum — A84

## 1994, Apr. 30 — Litho. — Perf. 13x12½

| | | | | |
|---|---|---|---|---|
| 361 | A84 | 5s multicolored | .80 | .35 |

1994 Basketball Festival,
Riga — A85

## 1994, June 4 — Litho. — Perf. 12½x13

| | | | | |
|---|---|---|---|---|
| 362 | A85 | 15s multicolored | 1.10 | .55 |

Provincial Municipal
Arms — A86

Nos. 363-377A are inscribed with the year date of issue below the design. The year noted in each description is the date that appears on the stamp.

### Perf. 13x12½, 14x14¼ (#373)
**1994-2007**

| | | | | |
|---|---|---|---|---|
| 363 | A86 | 1s Kurzeme, "1994" | .25 | .25 |
| a. | | "1996" | .25 | .25 |
| b. | | "1997" | .75 | .25 |
| c. | | "1998" | .25 | .25 |
| d. | | Perf 14x14¼, "1999" | 1.25 | .50 |
| e. | | As "f," "2002" | .25 | .25 |
| f. | | Perf. 13¼x13¾, "2006" | .25 | .25 |
| g. | | As "f," "2007" | .25 | .25 |
| h. | | As "d," "2011" | .25 | .25 |
| i. | | As "d," "2012" | .25 | .25 |
| 364 | A86 | 2s Auce, "1996" | .40 | .25 |
| a. | | "1997" | .40 | .25 |
| b. | | "1998" | .30 | |
| c. | | Perf 14x14¼, "1999" | 1.25 | 1.25 |
| d. | | As "c," "2000" | .40 | .25 |
| e. | | As "c," "2002" | .25 | .25 |
| f. | | Perf 13¼x13¾, "2005" | .25 | .25 |
| g. | | As "f," "2006" | .25 | .25 |
| h. | | As "f," "2007" | .25 | .25 |
| i. | | As "c," "2011" | .25 | .25 |
| j. | | As "c," "2012" | .25 | .25 |
| k. | | As "c," "2013" | .25 | .25 |
| 365 | A86 | 3s Zemgale, 1994 | .55 | .35 |
| a. | | Perf 14x14¼, "1999" | .55 | .35 |
| b. | | As "a," "2000" | .25 | .35 |
| c. | | As "a," "2002" | .25 | .25 |
| d. | | Perf 13¼x13¾, "2005" | .25 | .25 |
| e. | | As "d," "2006" | .25 | .25 |
| f. | | As "d," "2007" | .25 | .25 |
| g. | | Perf. 14x14¼, "2010" | .25 | .25 |
| h. | | As "g," "2011" | .25 | .25 |
| i. | | As "g," "2012" | .25 | .25 |
| j. | | As "g," "2013" | .25 | .25 |
| 366 | A86 | 5s Vidzeme, "1994" | .55 | .25 |
| a. | | "1996" | .50 | .50 |
| b. | | Perf 14x14¼, "1999" | .50 | .50 |
| c. | | As "b," "2000" | .50 | .50 |
| 367 | A86 | 8s Livani, "1995" | .50 | .40 |
| a. | | "1996" | .50 | .40 |
| 368 | A86 | 10s Latgale, "1994" | .50 | .50 |
| a. | | "1997" | 1.60 | 1.00 |
| b. | | "1998" | .50 | .50 |
| 369 | A86 | 13s Preili, "1996" | .70 | .70 |
| a. | | Perf. 14x14¼, "2010" | .50 | .50 |
| 370 | A86 | 16s Ainazi, "1995" | .80 | .80 |
| a. | | "1996" | 1.00 | 1.00 |
| 371 | A86 | 20s Grobina, "1995" | 1.00 | 1.00 |
| a. | | "1996" | 1.00 | 1.00 |
| 372 | A86 | 24s Tukums, "1995" | 1.10 | 1.10 |
| a. | | "1996" | 1.10 | 1.10 |
| 373 | A86 | 28s Madona, "1996" | 1.75 | 1.50 |
| 374 | A86 | 30s Riga, "1994" | 1.50 | 1.50 |
| 375 | A86 | 36s Priekule, "1996" | 2.25 | 1.50 |
| 376 | A86 | 50s Natl. arms, "1994" | 2.25 | 2.25 |

### Size: 29x24mm
### Perf. 14

| | | | | |
|---|---|---|---|---|
| 377 | A86 | 100s Riga | 4.25 | 2.50 |
| 377A | A86 | 200s Natl. arms | 8.75 | 4.75 |
| | | *Nos. 363-377A (16)* | 27.10 | 19.60 |

Issued: No. 363, 6/21/94; No. 363a, 1/30/96; No. 363b, 2/5/97; No. 363c, 1/12/98; No. 363d, 1/20/99; No. 363e, 2/6/02; No. 363f, 9/9/06; No. 363g, 6/8/97; No. 363h, 6/8/11; No. 363i, 3/15/12. No. 364, 4/12/96; No. 364a, 2/5/97; No. 364b, 2/11/98; No. 364c, 1/20/99;

---

No. 364d, 4/26/00; No. 364e, 2/6/02; No. 364f, 9/10/05; No. 364g, 9/9/06; No. 364h, 6/8/07. No. 364i, 6/8/11; No. 364j, 3/15/12. No. 364k, 3/3/13. No. 365, 6/21/94; No. 365a, 3/16/99; No. 365b, 4/26/00; No. 365c, 2/6/02; No. 365d, 9/10/05; No. 365e, 9/9/06; No. 365f, 6/8/07; No. 365g, 2/15/10; No. 365h, 6/8/11; No. 365i, 3/15/12. No. 365j, 3/3/13. No. 366, 6/21/94; No. 366a, 1/30/96; No. 366b, 1/20/99; No. 366c, 4/26/00. No. 367, 6/1/95; No. 367a, 1/30/96. No. 368, 6/21/94; No. 368a, 8/28/97; No. 368b, 8/4/98. No. 369, 4/12/96; No. 369a, 3/12/10. No. 370, 6/1/95; No. 370a, 4/8/96. No. 371, 6/1/95; No. 371a, 9/6/96. No. 372, 6/1/95; No. 372a, 4/8/96. No. 373, 11/5/96. No. 374, 12/21/94. No. 375, 11/5/96. Nos. 376, 377, 378, 12/21/94.

See Nos. 450-451, 472-473, 482-483, 506-507, 525-526.

A87

## 1994, Sept. 24 — Litho. — Perf. 14

| | | | | |
|---|---|---|---|---|
| 378 | A87 | 5s multicolored | .80 | .30 |

University of Latvia, 75th anniv.

A88

Items balanced on scales (Europa): 10s, Latvian coins. 50s, Locked chest, money card.

## 1994, Oct. 29 — Litho. — Perf. 14x13½

| | | | | |
|---|---|---|---|---|
| 379 | A88 | 10s multicolored | .65 | .25 |
| a. | | Tete-beche pair | 1.75 | 1.75 |
| 380 | A88 | 50s multicolored | 2.75 | 1.50 |
| a. | | Tete-beche pair | 7.00 | 6.00 |

Dormouse — A89

## 1994, Nov. 19 — Litho. — Perf. 13½x13

| | | | | |
|---|---|---|---|---|
| 381 | A89 | 5s shown | .45 | .35 |
| 382 | A89 | 10s Among leaves | .75 | .35 |
| 383 | A89 | 10s Eating berries | .75 | .35 |
| 384 | A89 | 15s Berry, large mouse | 1.50 | .50 |
| | | *Nos. 381-384 (4)* | 3.45 | 1.55 |

World Wildlife Fund.

A90

Christmas: 3s, Angel. 8s, Angels playing flute & violin. 13c, Angels singing. 100s, Candles.

## 1994, Dec. 3 — Perf. 14

| | | | | |
|---|---|---|---|---|
| 385 | A90 | 3s multicolored | .30 | .25 |
| 386 | A90 | 8s multicolored | .55 | .25 |
| 387 | A90 | 13s multicolored | 1.00 | .30 |
| 388 | A90 | 100s multicolored | 5.00 | 2.10 |
| | | *Nos. 385-388 (4)* | 6.85 | 2.90 |

A91

Children's Fairy Tales, by Margarita Staraste: 5s, Elf with candle. No. 390, Small bear in snow. No. 391, Boy on sled.

### Perf. 13x12½ on 3 Sides
## 1994, Dec. 17 — Booklet Stamps

| | | | | |
|---|---|---|---|---|
| 389 | A91 | 5s multicolored | .50 | .50 |
| 390 | A91 | 10s multicolored | .50 | .50 |
| 391 | A91 | 10s multicolored | .50 | .50 |
| a. | | Booklet pane, 2 each #389-391 | 3.00 | |
| | | Complete booklet, #391a + label | 3.25 | |
| | | *Nos. 389-391 (3)* | 1.50 | 1.50 |

A92

**1995, Feb. 18** *Perf. 14*
**392** A92 10s multicolored .80 .50
European safe driving week.

... 

A93

**1995, Mar. 4** **Litho.** *Perf. 14*
**393** A93 15s silver, blue & red .75 .60
UN, 50th anniv.

 A94

Via Baltica Highway Project: Nos. 394, 395b, Castle, Bauska, Latvia. No. 395a, Beach Hotel, Parnu, Estonia. No. 395c, Kaunas, Lithuania.

**1995, Apr. 20** **Litho.** *Perf. 14*
**394** A94 8s multicolored .50 .50
**Souvenir Sheet**
**395** A94 18s Sheet of 3, #a.-c. 2.75 2.75
See Estonia Nos. 288-289, Lithuania Nos. 508-509.

A95

8s, Dendrocopos leucotos. 20s, Crex crex. 24s, Chlidonias leucopterus.

**1995, July 8** **Litho.** *Perf. 12½*
**396** A95 8s multicolored .50 .50
**397** A95 20s multicolored 1.20 1.20
**398** A95 24s multicolored 1.60 1.60
Nos. 396-398 (3) 3.30 3.30
European nature conservation year.

Julian Cardinal Vaivods, Birth Cent. — A96

**1995, Aug. 18** **Litho.** *Perf. 14*
**399** A96 8s multicolored .65 .50

**Traditional Costume Type of 1993**
**1995, Sept. 8** **Litho.** *Perf. 13x13½*
**400** A77 8s Nica .40 .40
**Souvenir Sheet**
**401** A77 100s Like #400 4.50 4.50

Friendly Appeal, by Karlis Ulmanis, 60th Anniv. — A97

**1995, Sept. 8** *Perf. 14*
**402** A97 8s multicolored .50 .50

Riga, 800th Anniv. — A98

**1995, Sept. 23** *Perf. 13½*
**403** A98 8s Natl. Opera .40 .40
**404** A98 16s Natl. Theatre .80 .80
**Size: 45x27mm**
**405** A98 24s Academy of Arts 1.00 1.00
**406** A98 36s State Art Museum 1.50 1.50
Nos. 403-406 (4) 3.70 3.70
See Nos. 508-511, 529-531, 529-531.

Peace and Freedom — A99

Heroes from national epic, Lacplesis, dates of independence: 16s, Spidola with sword and shield, 1918. 50s, Lacplesis with leaves and banner, 1991.

**1995, Nov. 15** **Litho.** *Perf. 13½*
**407** A99 16s multicolored .75 .75
a. Tete beche pair 2.50 2.50
**408** A99 50s multicolored 2.25 2.25
a. Tete beche pair 5.00 5.00
Europa.

 Christmas — A100

Designs: No. 409, Characters surrounding Christmas tree at night. No. 410, Santa gliding through sky holding candle. 15s, Characters outside snow-covered house. 24s, Santa standing between dog and cat.

**1995, Dec. 2**
**409** A100 6s multicolored .55 .25
**410** A100 6s multicolored .55 .25
**411** A100 15s multicolored .30 .60
**412** A100 24s multicolored 2.25 1.00
Nos. 409-412 (4) 3.65 2.10

Pauls Stradins (1896-1958), Physician — A101

**1996, Jan. 17** **Litho.** *Perf. 14*
**413** A101 8s multicolored .40 .25

Zenta Maurina (1897-1978) — A102

**1996, May 10** **Litho.** *Perf. 13½x14*
**414** A102 36s multicolored 1.60 .95
a. Tete beche pair 3.25 3.25
Europa.

**Traditional Costume Type of 1993**
**1996, May 18** **Litho.** *Perf. 13x13½*
**415** A77 8s Barta .50 .25
**Souvenir Sheet**
**416** A77 100s like No. 415 4.00 3.00
**Souvenir Sheet**

Children's Games — A103

**1996, June 8** **Litho.** *Perf. 14x13½*
**417** A103 48s Sheet of 1 2.75 2.25

1996 Summer Olympic Games, Atlanta — A104

*Perf. 14x13½, 13½x14*
**1996, June 19**
**418** A104 8s Cycling,vert. .40 .25
**419** A104 16s Basketball, vert .70 .40
**420** A104 24s Walking, vert. .80 .50
**421** A104 36s Canoeing 1.50 .80
Nos. 418-421 (4) 3.40 1.95
**Souvenir Sheet**
**422** A104 100s Javelin 4.50 3.50

Nature Museum, 150th Anniv. — A105

Butterflies: 8s, Papilio machaon. 24s, Catocala fraxini. 80s, Pericallia matronula.

**1996, Aug. 30** *Perf. 13*
**423** A105 8s multicolored .35 .25
**424** A105 24s multicolored .90 .45
**425** A105 80s multicolored 3.75 1.90
Nos. 423-425 (3) 5.00 2.60

Car Production in Latvia — A106

Designs: 8s, 1912 Russo-Balt fire truck. 24s, 1899 Leutner-Russia. 36s, 1939 Ford-Vairogs.

**1996, Oct. 25** **Litho.** *Perf. 13x12½*
**426** A106 8s multicolored .35 .25
**427** A106 24s multicolored 1.20 .55
**428** A106 36s multicolored 1.50 .85
Nos. 426-428 (3) 3.05 1.65

City of Riga, 800th Anniv. — A107

**1996, Dec. 5** **Litho.** *Perf. 13½*
**429** A107 8s Building front .40 .25
**Size: 30x26mm**
**430** A107 16s Stained glass window .75 .40
**Size: 37x26mm**
**431** A107 24s Buildings 1.25 .55
**432** A107 30s Art figures 1.25 .70
Nos. 429-432 (4) 3.65 1.90

Christmas — A108

Designs: 6s, Santa's elves, presents. 14s, Santa on skis, dog, children in animal costumes. 20s, Child in front of Christmas tree, santa in chair, pets.

**1996, Dec. 7** *Perf. 14*
**433** A108 6s multicolored .30 .25
**434** A108 14s multicolored .70 .35
**435** A108 20s multicolored 1.00 .50
Nos. 433-435 (3) 2.00 1.10
See Nos. 458-460.

Birds — A109

Designs: 10s, Caprimulgus eurpaeus. 20s, Aquila clanga. 30s, Acrocephalus paludicola.

**1997, Feb. 8** *Perf. 13x12½*
**436** A109 10s multicolored .50 .25
**437** A109 20s multicolored .90 .45
**438** A109 30s multicolored 1.40 .70
Nos. 436-438 (3) 2.80 1.40

Turn of the Epochs — A110

**1997, Mar. 25** **Litho.** *Perf. 14*
**439** A110 10s multicolored .70 .35

**Traditional Costume Type of 1993**
**1997, Apr. 3** *Perf. 13x13½*
**440** A77 10s Rietumvidzeme 1.25 .80
**Souvenir Sheet**
**441** A77 100s like #440 4.25 3.50
Stamp Day.

Legend of Rozi Turaidas — A111

**1997, Apr. 26** **Litho.** *Perf. 12½x13*
**442** A111 32s multicolored 1.50 .70
a. Tete beche pair 3.50 3.50
Europa.

Old Baltic Ships — A112

Designs: 10s, Linijkugis, 17th cent. No. 444: a, Linijkugis, 17th cent., diff. b, Kurenas 16th cent. c, Maasilinn ship, 16th cent.

**1997, May 10** *Perf. 14x14½*
**443** A112 10s multicolored .50 .40
**Souvenir Sheet**
**444** A112 20s Sheet of 3, #a.-c. 3.00 2.75
See Estonia Nos. 322-323, Lithuania Nos. 571-572.

Port of Ventspils, Cent. — A113

**1997, May 21** **Litho.** *Perf. 13½x14*
**445** A113 20s Hermes, Poseidon .90 .50

Children's Activities — A114

Designs: 10s, Stamp collecting. 12s, Riding dirt bike, vert. 20s, Boy in hockey uniform, girl in skiwear, vert. 30s, Tennis, soccer, basketball.

**1997, June 7** *Perf. 13½x13*
**446** A114 10s multicolored .45 .25
**447** A114 12s multicolored .60 .30
**448** A114 20s multicolored .90 .45
**449** A114 30s multicolored 1.25 .75
Nos. 446-449 (4) 3.20 1.75

**Municipal Arms Type of 1994**
**1997-2005** **Litho.** *Perf. 13x12½*
**Date imprint below design**
**450** A86 10s Valmiera, "1997" 1.00 .50
a. "1998" 1.00 .50
b. Perf 14x14¼, "1999" 1.00 .50
c. "2000" 1.00 .50

| | | |
|---|---|---|
| *d.* | Perf. 13¼x13¾, "2001" | 1.00 .50 |
| *e.* | "2005" | 1.00 .40 |
| 451 | A86 20s Rezekne, "1997" | 2.25 1.00 |

Issued: No. 450, 9/6/97; No. 450a, 1/12/98; No. 450b, 1/20/99; No. 450c, 4/26/00; No. 450d, 9/12/01; No. 450e, 9/10/05. No. 451, 9/6/97.

Nature Preserves — A115

**1997, Oct. 18    Litho.    Perf. 13x12½**
452 A115 10s Moricsala, 1912    .50 .25
453 A115 30s Slitere, 1921    1.50 .80

See Nos. 464-465.

City of Riga, 800th Anniv. — A116

10s, Woman, house, 12th cent. 20s, Monument to Bishop Albert, seal of the bishop, rosary, writing tool, 13th-16th cent. 30s, Riga castle, weapons used during Middle Ages. 32s, Houses, arms of Riga, statue of St. John.

**1997, Nov. 27    Litho.    Perf. 13x14**
454 A116 10s multicolored    .50 .30
455 A116 20s multicolored    .85 .45
456 A116 30s multicolored    1.25 .70
**Size: 27x26mm**
457 A116 32s multicolored    1.40 .80
    *Nos. 454-457 (4)*    4.00 2.25

See Nos. 468-471, 488-491, 508-511, 529-531.

**Christmas Type of 1996**

People dressed in masks, costumes for mummery: 8s, Santa, bear. 18s, Two goats. 28s, Horse.

**1997, Nov. 29    Perf. 14**
458 A108 8s multicolored    .40 .25
459 A108 18s multicolored    .90 .40
460 A108 28s multicolored    1.40 .60
    *Nos. 458-460 (3)*    2.70 1.25

A117

**1998, Jan. 31    Litho.    Perf. 14x13½**
461 A117 20s multicolored    1.00 .75

1998 Winter Olympic Games, Nagano.

A118

Statue at Spridisi, museum home of Anna Brigadere(1861-1933), writer.

**1998, Feb. 21    Litho.    Perf. 13½**
462 A118 10s multicolored    .65 .35

National Song Festival — A119

**1998, Mar. 28    Litho.    Perf. 13x14**
463 A119 30s multicolored    2.50 1.25
    *a.* Tete beche pair    5.50 5.50

Europa.

**Nature Preserves Type of 1997**
**1998, Apr. 30    Perf. 13x12½**
464 A115 10s Grini, 1936    .45 .25
465 A115 30s Teici, 1982    1.25 1.00

**Traditional Costume Type of 1993**

No. 467, Krustpils, man wearing crown of leaves.

**1998, May 9    Perf. 13x13½**
466 A77 10s Krustpils region    .75 .30
**Souvenir Sheet**
467 A77 100s multicolored    5.00 5.00

**City of Riga, 800th Anniv., Type of 1997**

10s, Dannenstern House, 16th and 17th cent. coins issued by kings of Poland and Sweden, 17th cent. wooden sculpture. 20s, City Library, monument to G. Herder, poet, philosopher, teacher. 30s, 18th cent. arsenal, column celebrating defeat of Napoleon's troops, octant, compass. 40s, Sculpture of Mother Latvia at Warriors' Cemetery, entrance to Cemetery, obv. & rev. of 5 lat coin, 1930.

**1998, May 29    Litho.    Perf. 13x14**
468 A116 10s multicolored    .45 .25
469 A116 20s multicolored    1.00 .45
470 A116 30s multicolored    1.30 .60
471 A116 40s multicolored    1.75 .85
    *Nos. 468-471 (4)*    4.50 2.15

No. 468 is 30x26mm.

**Municipal Arms Type of 1994**
**1998-2004    Litho.    Perf. 13¼x13¾**
**Date imprint below design**
472 A86 15s Bauska, "1998"    .55 .40
473 A86 30s Liepaja, "1998"    1.25 1.00
    *a.* Perf 13½x14, "2004"    1.35 1.10

Issued: No. 472, 473, 9/26/98; No. 473a, 9/7/04.

World Stamp Day — A120

**1998, Oct. 20    Litho.    Perf. 14**
474 A120 30s #2, various stamps    1.25 .75

Dome Church, Riga, 1211 — A121

**1998, Oct. 23**
475 A121 10s multicolored    .70 .40

Pres. Janis Cakste (1859-1927) — A122

**1998, Nov. 11    Perf. 14x13½**
476 A122 10s multicolored    .50 .35

See No. 497, 515, 524.

Independence, 80th Anniv. — A123

**1998, Nov. 14    Perf. 13x12½**
477 A123 10s shown    .45 .30
478 A123 30s Arms, flags    1.40 .90

Christmas — A124

Christmas elves: 10s, Rolling snow balls. 20s, Decorating tree, preparing presents. 30s, Pulling sled over snow.

**1998, Nov. 28    Perf. 13½x14**
479 A124 10s multicolored    .55 .35
480 A124 20s multicolored    1.20 .75
481 A124 30s multicolored    1.50 .95
    *Nos. 479-481 (3)*    3.25 2.05

**Municipal Arms Type of 1994**
**1999-2004    Litho.    Perf. 13¼x13¾**
**Date imprint below design**
482 A86 15s Ogre, "1999"    .80 .45
    *a.* "2000"    .90 .55
483 A86 40s Jelgava, "1999"    2.00 1.10
    *a.* "2004"    1.50 .85

Issued: No. 482, 2/12/99; No. 482a, 2/25/00. No. 483, 4/10/99; No. 483a, 9/7/04.

Nature Parks and Reserves — A125

Europa: 30s, Krustkalnu Nature Reserve. 60s, Gauja Natl. Nature Park.

**1999, Mar. 20    Perf. 13x12½**
484 A125 30s multicolored    1.75 1.00
485 A125 60s multicolored    4.00 2.00

Council of Europe, 50th Anniv. — A126

**1999, Apr. 24**
486 A126 30s multicolored    1.50 1.00

Rudolfs Blaumanis (1863-1908), Writer — A127

**1999, Apr. 24    Perf. 14x13**
487 A127 110s multicolored    4.25 2.00

**City of Riga, 800th Anniv. Type**

10s, Streetcar. 30s, Schooner "Widwud." 40s, Airplane. 70s, TK-type locomotive.

**Perf. 13¼x13¾**
**1999, June 26    Litho.**
488 A116 10s multicolored    .40 .30
489 A116 30s multicolored    1.20 .80
490 A116 40s multicolored    1.60 1.10
491 A116 70s multicolored    2.50 1.75
    *Nos. 488-491 (4)*    5.70 3.95

No. 488 is 30x27mm.

Aglona Basilica — A129

**1999, July 10    Litho.    Perf. 14x14½**
492 A129 15s multicolored    .80 .40
    Complete booklet, 6 #492    12.00

"Baltic Chain," 10th Anniv. — A130

Families and flags: 15s, No. 494a, Latvian. No. 494: b, Lithuanian. c, Estonian.

**1999, Aug. 23    Litho.    Perf. 12½x13**
493 A130 15s multicolored    1.25 .50
**Souvenir Sheet**
494 A130 30s Sheet of 3, #a.-c.    4.25 4.00

See Estonia Nos. 366-367, Lithuania Nos. 639-640.

Rundâle Palace — A131

**1999, Sept. 25    Litho.    Perf. 14**
495 A131 20s multicolored    .90 .65

See Nos. 512, 536, 578.

Landscape, by Julijs Feders (1838-1909) — A132

**1999, Oct. 13    Litho.    Perf. 13½**
496 A132 15s multi    .85 .55

**Presidents Type of 1998**

15s, Pres. Gustavs Zemgals (1871-1939).

**1999, Nov. 16    Litho.    Perf. 14x13½**
497 A122 15s multicolored    .75 .55

A134

**1999, Nov. 25    Perf. 14x14½**
498 A134 40s multi    2.00 1.00

UPU, 125th anniv.

A135

Christmas and Millennium: 12s, Santa, tree, candle. 15s, Santa, tree, children. 40s, Santa, tree with ornaments.

**1999, Nov. 27    Perf. 14¼**
499 A135 12s multi    .65 .30
500 A135 15s multi    .80 .40
501 A135 40s multi    2.00 1.00
    *Nos. 499-501 (3)*    3.45 1.70

Nude, by J. Rozentals — A136

**Perf. 14½x14¼**
**2000, Feb. 26    Litho.**
502 A136 40s multi    2.00 1.50

Aleksandrs Caks (1901-50), Poet — A137

**2000, Apr. 8    Litho.    Perf. 14x13½**
503 A137 40s multi    2.00 .90
    Booklet, 6 #503    12.50

**Europa, 2000**
**Common Design Type**

**2000, May 9**
504 CD17 60s multi    5.00 2.40
    *a.* Tete beche pair    10.00 10.00

Ice
Hockey
A138

**Wmk. 387**

**2000, June 21    Litho.    Perf. 14**
505 A138 70s multi + label          3.25 1.75

Issued in sheets of 8 + 8 labels. Vertical columns of four labels, which depict players Helmut Balderis, Vitalijs Samoilovs, Sandis Ozolinsh and Arturs Irbe, flank a central block of eight stamps. Color photos of the players appear at left or right of the labels.

**Municipal Arms Type of 1994**

**2000-05    Unwmk.    Perf. 13¼x13¾**
**Date imprint below design**
506 A86 15s Daugavpils, "2000"    .75    .50
  a.    "2005"                      .65    .45
507 A86 15s Jūrmala, "2000"        .75    .50
  a.    "2001"                      .75    .50
  b.    "2002"                      .75    .50
  c.    "2005"                      .65    .45

Issued: No. 506, 7/6/00; No. 506a, 8/5/05. No. 507, 7/6/00; No. 507a, 9/12/01; No. 507b, 1/12/02; No. 507c, 8/5/05.

**City of Riga, 800th Anniv. Type of 1995**

Designs: 20s, Central Market. No. 509, Riga Zoo. No. 510, Riga Dome Organ. 70s, Powder Tower.

**2000, July 22    Perf. 13¼x14**
**Size: 40x28mm**
508 A98 20s multi                  1.00    .50
**Size: 47x28mm**
509 A98 40s multi                  1.75 1.00
  Complete booklet, 6 #509      10.50
**Perf. 14x13¼**
**Size: 28x32mm**
510 A98 40s multi                  1.75 1.00
511 A98 70s multi                  3.00 1.25
  Nos. 508-511 (4)            7.50 3.75

**Palace Type of 1999**
**2000, Aug. 12    Perf. 13¼x14**
512 A131 40s Jelgava Palace        1.75 1.00
  Booklet, 6 #512              11.50

2000
Summer
Olympics,
Sydney
A139

**2000, Sept. 15    Perf. 14¼x14**
513 A139 70s multi + label          3.00 2.00
  See No. 518.

Millennium — A140

No. 514: a, 15s, Freedom Monument, Riga. b, House of Blackheads, Riga.

**Perf. 14x13¼**
**2000, Sept. 28    Litho.    Wmk. 387**
514 A140    Pair + label            3.00 2.75
  a.    15s multi              .80    .40
  b.    50s multi             2.00 1.10

**President Type of 1998**
**Perf. 13¾x13¼**
**2000, Nov. 11    Unwmk.**
515 A122 15s Alberts Kveisis
    (1881-1936)              .80    .50

Orthodox
Cathedral — A141

**2000, Nov. 17    Perf. 14**
516 A141 40s multi                  1.75 1.00
  See Nos. 537, 559, 573.

Red Cross — A142

**2000, Nov. 22**
517 A142 15s multi                  .75    .45

**Olympics Type of 2000**
**2000, Nov. 22**
518 A139 40s multi                  1.75 1.00

Issued in sheets of 4 + 2 different labels depicting gold medal winner Igors Vihrovs.

Christmas — A143

Designs: 12s, Watch. No. 520, 15s, Angels. No. 521, 15s, Madonna and child.

**2000, Nov. 25**
519-521 A143    Set of 3            1.90 1.00

International
Recognition of Latvia,
80th Anniv. — A144

**2001, Jan. 13    Litho.    Perf. 14**
522 A144 40s multi                  1.75 1.25

Kad Silavas
Mostas, by
Vilhelmis
Purvitis — A145

**Perf. 14¼x14½**
**2001, Feb. 1    Litho.    Unwmk.**
523 A145 40s multi                  2.75 1.50
  Booklet, 6 #523              16.50

**President Type of 1998**
**2001, Feb. 17    Perf. 13¾x13¼**
524 A122 15s Karlis Ulmanis
    (1877-1942)              .75    .40

**Municipal Arms Type of 1994**
**2001-06    Perf. 13¼x13¾**
**Date imprint below design**
525 A86 5s Smiltene, "2001"        .60    .30
  a.    "2002"                   .60    .30
  b.    "2005"                   .30    .30
  c.    "2006"                   .30    .30
  d.    Perf. 14x14¼, "2011"     .30    .30
  e.    As "d," "2012"           .30    .30
  f.    As "d," "2013"           .30    .30
526 A86 15s Kuldiga, "2001"        .70    .40
  a.    "2002"                   .70    .40

Issued: No. 525, 3/5/01; No. 525a, 9/16/02; No. 525b, 9/10/05; No. 525c, 9/9/06. No. 525d, 6/8/11; No. 525e, 3/15/12; No. 525f, 3/3/13. No. 526, 3/5/01; No. 526a, 9/16/02.

Narrow Gauge
Locomotive — A146

**2001, Mar. 24    Perf. 14**
527 A146 40s multi                  1.75 1.25

Europa — A147

**2001, Apr. 14**
528 A147 60s multi                  3.50 1.75
  a.    Tete beche pair         4.50 4.50

**Riga, 800th Anniv. Type of 1995**
Riga in: No. 529a, 20th cent. No. 529b, 21st cent. 60s, 16th cent. 70s, 17th cent.

**2001, May 24    Litho.    Perf. 13¾x13½**
**Size: 29x33mm (each stamp)**
529    A98 15s Horiz. pair, #a-b    1.50    .75
**Size: 47x28mm**
**Perf. 13½x13¾**
530    A98 60s multi                2.50 1.25
531    A98 70s multi                2.75 1.40
  Nos. 529-531 (3)            6.75 3.40

Kakisa Dzirnavas, by
Karlis Skalbe — A148

**2001, June 9    Perf. 13¾**
532 A148 40s multi                  1.75 1.00
  Booklet, 6 #532              10.50

**Souvenir Sheet**

Mikhail Tal (1936-92), Chess
Champion — A149

**2001, Aug. 18    Litho.    Perf. 14**
533 A149 100s multi                 4.50 3.50

Baltic Coast
Landscapes — A150

Designs: 15s, No. 535a, Vidzeme. No. 535b, Palanga. No. 535c, Lahemaa.

**2001, Sept. 15    Perf. 13½**
534 A150 15s multi                  2.00 1.00
  Booklet, 6 #534              13.00
**Souvenir Sheet**
535    Sheet of 3                   4.25 3.50
  a.-c.    A150 30s Any single  1.25    .75

See Estonia Nos. 423-424, Lithuania Nos. 698-699.

**Palace Type of 1999**
**2001, Oct. 24    Perf. 14½x14**
536 A131 40s Cesvaines Palace      2.00 1.25
  a.    Perf. 13¼x14            2.00 1.25
  b.    Booklet pane, 6 #536a   12.00
  Booklet, #536b               12.00

**House of Worship Type of 2000**
**2001, Nov. 3    Perf. 13¾x14**
537 A141 70s Riga Synagogue        3.00 1.50
  Booklet, 6 #537              24.00

Latvian
Seamen
A151

Designs: 15s, Krisjanis Valdemars (1825-91), founder of Naval College. 70s, Duke Jekabs Ketlers (1610-82), shipbuilder.

**2001, Nov. 14    Perf. 13¼x14**
538-539 A151    Set of 2            3.50 2.25

Christmas — A152

Designs: 12s, Rabbits. No. 541, Dog, rabbit. No. 542, 15s, Lambs.

**2001, Nov. 22    Perf. 13¼**
540-542 A152    Set of 3            2.00 1.25

Town Arms — A153

**2002, Jan. 29    Litho.    Perf. 13¼x13¾**
543 A153    5s Ludza               .40    .35
544 A153   10s Dobele              .60    .50
  a.    Perf. 14x14¼, dated "2012"  .50    .50
  b.    As "a," "2013"          .40    .50
545 A153   15s Sigulda             .80    .60
  Nos. 543-545 (3)            1.80 1.45

See Nos. 565-567, 585-587, 609-611, 638-640, 670-672, 696-698, 726-728, 753-755, 776-777, 798-800, 824-826.
Issued: No. 544a, 3/15/12; No. 544b, 3/3/13.

2002 Winter
Olympics, Salt
Lake
City — A154

**2002, Feb. 8    Perf. 13¼x13¾**
546 A154 40s multi                  2.00 1.25
  a.    Booklet pane of 6, perf.
    13¼x13¾ on 3 sides     17.00    —
  Booklet, #546a               17.00

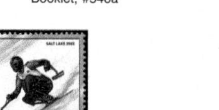

2002 Winter
Paralympics, Salt Lake
City — A155

**2002, Mar. 5    Perf. 14¼x13¾**
547 A155 15s multi                  1.00    .70

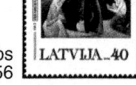

Refugees, by Jekabs
Kazaks — A156

**2002, Apr. 20    Litho.    Perf. 14½x14¼**
548 A156 40s multi                  2.00 1.25

Europa — A157

**2002, May 4    Perf. 14**
549 A157 60s multi                  2.50 1.75
  a.    Tete-beche pair         6.00 6.00

Endangered
Plants — A158

Designs: 15s, Cypripedium calceolus. 40s, Trapa natans.

**2002, May 25    Perf. 13¾**
550-551 A158    Set of 2            2.50 1.50
  See Nos. 568-569, 589-590, 612-613.

Latvian Armed
Forces — A159

**2002, June 15    Perf. 13¾x13¼**
552 A159 40s multi                  1.60 1.10

Janis Jaunsudrabins
(1877-1962),
Writer — A160

**2002, July 6**   *Perf. 13¾x13½*
553 A160 40s multi   1.75 1.10
a.   Booklet pane of 6, perf.
   13¾x13½ on 3 sides   12.00
   Booklet, #553a   12.00

Kristians Johans Dals (1839-1904) and Ship — A161

**2002, July 20**   *Perf. 13¼x13¾*
554 A161 70s multi   2.75 1.75

Fish — A162

Designs: 15s, Gadus morhua callarias. 40s, Siluris glanis.

**2002, Aug. 10   Litho.**   *Perf. 14*
555-556 A162   Set of 2   2.50 1.75
a.   Booklet pane, perf. 14 on 3
   sides   15.00
   Booklet, #556a   15.00

Souvenir Sheet

Venta River Bridge A163

**2002, Aug. 24**   *Perf. 12¾x12½*
557 A163 100s multi   4.25 3.50

Jaunmoku Palace — A164

**2002, Sept. 14**   *Perf. 14¼x13¾*
558 A164 40s multi   1.75 1.25

**House of Worship Type of 2000**
70s, Grebenschikov Old Belief Praying House.

**2002, Oct. 12**   *Perf. 13¾x14*
559 A141 70s multicolored   3.00 1.75
a.   Booklet pane of 6, perf.
   13¾x14 on 3 sides   20.00
   Booklet, #559a   20.00

Mittens — A165

**2002, Nov. 2**   *Perf. 13¼x13¾*
560 A165 15s multi   .85 .50

See Nos. 579, 604, 629.

Christmas — A166

Designs: 12s, Elf on sack, Christmas tree. No. 562, 15s, Angel, Christmas tree. No. 563, 15s, Elves on gift.

**2002, Nov. 23**   *Perf. 13¾x13¼*
561-563 A166   Set of 3   2.00 1.25

A Man Entering a Room, by Niklavs Strunke (1894-1966) — A167

**2003, Jan. 25   Litho.**   *Perf. 13¼x14*
564 A167 40s multi   1.75 1.25

**Town Arms Type of 2002**
**2003, Feb. 15**   *Perf. 13¼x13¾*
565 A153 10s Balvi   .50 .25
566 A153 15s Gulbene   .65 .40
567 A153 20s Ventspils   .90 .60
   Nos. 565-567 (3)   2.05 1.25

**Endangered Plants Type of 2002**
Designs: 15s, Ophrys insectifera. 30s, Taxus baccata.

**2003, Mar. 21**   *Perf. 13¾*
568 A158 15s multi   .75 .50
569 A158 30s multi   1.75 1.00
a.   Perf. 14½x14¼ on 3 sides   2.00 1.00
b.   Booklet pane, 6 #569a   12.00 —
   Complete booklet, #569b   12.00

Straumeni, by Edvarts Virza (1883-1940) — A168

**2003, Apr. 12**   *Perf. 13¾x13¼*
570 A168 40s multi   1.75 1.25

Europa — A169

**2003, May 3   Litho.**   *Perf. 13¼x13¾*
571 A169 60s multi   2.75 1.75
a.   Tete beche pair   6.00 6.00

Kolka Lighthouse — A170

**2003, May 17**   *Perf. 13¾x13¼*
572 A170 60s multi   2.50 1.75

See Nos. 602, 626, 662, 676, 709, 746.

**House of Worship Type of 2000**
**2003, June 6**   *Perf. 13¼x13¾*
573 A141 70s Salvation Temple, horiz.   3.00 1.75

Souvenir Sheet

Gauja River Bridge, Sigulda A171

**2003, July 19**
574 A171 100s multi   4.75 3.75

Fish — A172

Designs: 15s, Thymallus thymallus. 30s, Salmo salar.

**2003, Aug. 2**   *Perf. 14x13¾*
575 A172 15s multi   .75 .50
576 A172 30s multi   1.75 1.25
a.   Booklet pane of 6, perf.
   14x13¾ on 3 sides   13.00 —
   Complete booklet, #576a   13.00

Motacilla Alba — A173

**2003, Aug. 30**   *Perf. 14¾x14*
577 A173 15s multi   1.00 .50

**Palace Type of 1999**
**2003, Sept. 27**   *Perf. 14¼x13¾*
578 A131 40s Birini Palace   1.75 1.25
a.   Booklet pane of 6   11.00
   Complete booklet, #578a   11.00

**Mittens Type of 2002**
**2003, Oct. 11**   *Perf. 14x13¾*
579 A165 15s Libiesi mittens   .80 .45

Motorcycle Racing — A174

**2003, Oct. 31**   *Perf. 13¼x13¾*
580 A174 70s multi   3.00 1.75
a.   Booklet pane of 6   20.00
   Complete booklet, #580a   20.00

Christmas — A175

Designs: 12s, Madonna and Child with two angels. No. 582, 15s, The Annunciation (golden brown frame). No. 583, 15s, Nativity (gray frame).

**2003, Nov. 22**   *Perf. 13¾x14¼*
581-583 A175   Set of 3   2.25 1.25

*Still Life with Triangle*, by Romans Suta — A176

**2004, Jan. 25   Litho.**   *Perf. 13¼x14*
584 A176 40s multi   1.75 1.00

**Town Arms Type of 2002**
**2004, Feb. 14**   *Perf. 13¼x13¾*
585 A153 5s Valka   .30 .30
586 A153 15s Cesis   .60 .60
587 A153 20s Saldus   .80 .80
   Nos. 585-587 (3)   1.70 1.70

Reinis (1839-1920) and Matiss (1848-1926) Kaudzites, Writers — A177

**2004, Mar. 20**   *Perf. 13¾*
588 A177 40s multi   1.60 1.00

**Endangered Plants Type of 2002**
Designs: 15s, Gentiana cruciata. 30s, Onobrychis arenaria.

**2004, Apr. 3**
589-590 A158   Set of 2   2.00 1.25

2006 World Ice Hockey Championships, Riga — A178

**2004, Apr. 17   Litho.**   *Perf. 13¼x13¾*
591 A178 30s multi   1.50 .80
a.   Booklet pane of 4, perf.
   13¼x13¾ on 3 sides   15.00 —
   Complete booklet, #591a   15.00

Admission to European Union — A179

Designs: No. 592, 30s, Stars, map of Europe, flags of newly-added countries. No. 593, 30s, Seven stars.

**2004, May 1**   *Perf. 13x13¼*
592-593 A179   Set of 2   2.50 1.75

Europa — A180

**2004, May 8   Litho.**   *Perf. 13¼x13¾*
594 A180 60s multi   2.50 1.75
a.   Tete beche pair   5.50 5.50

European Soccer Championships, Portugal — A181

**2004, June 3**   *Perf. 14x13½*
595 A181 30s multi   1.40 1.25

Fish — A182

Designs: 15s, Oncorhynchus mykiss. 30s, Psetta maxima.

**2004, June 26**   *Perf. 13¼x14*
596 A182 15s multi   .60 .40
597 A182 30s multi   1.50 .90
a.   Booklet pane of 6, perf.
   13¼x14 on 3 sides   11.00 —
   Complete booklet, #597a   11.00

See Nos. 620-621.

Visit of Pres. Bill Clinton to Latvia, 10th Anniv. — A183

**2004, July 6**   *Perf. 13¾x13¼*
598 A183 40s multi   1.75 1.25

Souvenir Sheet

Dzelzcela Bridge, Riga — A184

**2004, July 24**   *Perf. 13¼x13¾*
599 A184 100s multi   4.25 4.25

2004 Summer Olympics, Athens — A185

**2004, Aug. 14   Litho.**   *Perf. 14*
600 A185 30s multi   1.25 .90

St. Jacob's Cathedral — A186

**Perf. 13¾x13¼**
**2004, Aug. 28** **Litho.**
601 A186 40s multi 1.75 1.25

**Lighthouse Type of 2003**
**2004, Sept. 18**
602 A170 60s Mikelbaka 2.75 1.50
a. Booklet pane of 4, perf.
13¾x13¼ on 3 sides 12.00 —
Complete booklet, #602a 12.00

Jaunpils Palace — A187

**2004, Oct. 15** **Perf. 14¼x13¾**
603 A187 40s multi 1.75 1.25
a. Booklet pane of 6, perf.
14¼x13¾ on 3 sides 11.00 —
Complete booklet, #603a 11.00

See Nos. 628, 678.

**Mittens Type of 2002**
**2004, Nov. 6** **Perf. 13¼x13¾**
604 A165 15s Piebalga mittens .80 .50

Christmas — A188

Designs: 12s, Children, rabbit, bird, heart. No. 606, 15s, Snowman, birds. No. 607, 15s, Angel.

**2004, Dec. 4** **Perf. 13¾x13¼**
605-607 A188 Set of 3 1.75 1.25

1905 Revolution, Cent. — A189

**2005, Jan. 13 Litho. Perf. 13¾x13¼**
608 A189 15s multi 1.10 .65

**Town Arms Type of 2002**
**2005, Feb. 11** **Perf. 13¼x13¾**
609 A153 15s Aluksne .60 .40
610 A153 15s Talsi .60 .40
611 A153 40s Jekabpils 1.50 1.25
Nos. 609-611 (3) 2.70 2.05

**Endangered Plants Type of 2002**
Designs: 20s, Pulsatilla patens. 30s, Allium ursinum.

**2005, Mar. 5** **Perf. 13¼**
612-613 A158 Set of 2 2.00 1.25
613a Booklet pane of 6 #613, perf.
13¼ on 3 sides 12.00 —
Complete booklet, #613a 12.00

Krimuldas Church, 800th Anniv. — A190

**2005, Mar. 19** **Perf. 13¼x13¾**
614 A190 40s multi 1.60 1.00

The Adventures of Baron Munchausen, by Rudolph Erich Raspe — A191

**2005, Apr. 1 Litho. Perf. 13¼x13¾**
615 A191 30s multi 1.25 .90

Europa — A192

**2005, Apr. 23**
616 A192 60s multi 2.50 1.50
a. Tete beche pair 6.00 6.00

Mother and Child, by Janis Rozentals A193

**2005, May 8** **Perf. 14x13¼**
617 A193 40s multi 1.60 1.00
a. Booklet pane of 4, perf. 14x13¼
on 3 sides 7.25 —
Complete booklet, #617a 7.25

Baumanu Karlis (1835-1905), Composer of National Anthem — A194

**2005, May 21** **Perf. 13¾x13¼**
618 A194 20s multi .80 .50

Kaive Oak — A195

**Serpentine Die Cut 14**
**2005, June 11** **Self-Adhesive**
619 A195 15s multi 1.00 .75
Printed in sheets of 8.

**Fish Type of 2004**
Designs: 15s, Lampetra fluviatilis. 40s, Clupea harengus membras.

**2005, Aug. 13 Litho. Perf. 13¼x14**
620-621 A182 Set of 2 2.25 1.50

Pope John Paul II (1920-2005) — A196

**2005, Aug. 14** **Perf. 14¼x13½**
622 A196 15s multi .80 .50

**Souvenir Sheet**

Latvian National Library A197

**2005, Aug. 27** **Perf. 13¼x12¾**
623 A197 100s multi 4.00 3.75

Janis Plieksans (Rainis), (1865-1929), Writer — A198

**2005, Sept. 10** **Perf. 14¼**
624 A198 40s multi 1.60 1.00
a. Booklet pane of 6, perf. 14¼
on 3 sides 11.00 —
Complete booklet, #624a 11.00

**Souvenir Sheet**

Bridge Over Railroad Tracks, Riga A199

**2005, Sept. 24** **Perf. 13¼x13¾**
625 A199 100s multi 5.50 4.00

**Lighthouse Type of 2003**
**2005, Oct. 8** **Perf. 14x13¼**
626 A170 40s Daugavgrivas 1.75 1.00
a. Booklet pane of 4, perf. 14x13¼
on 3 sides 8.50 —
Complete booklet, #626a 8.50

Gunars Astra (1931-88), Human Rights Activist in Soviet Union — A200

**2005, Oct. 22** **Perf. 13½x14¼**
627 A200 15s multi .60 .40

**Palace Type of 2004**
**2005, Nov. 5** **Perf. 13¼x14**
628 A187 40s Durbes Palace,
horiz. 1.60 1.00

**Mittens Type of 2002**
**2005, Nov. 26** **Perf. 13¼x13¾**
629 A165 20s Dienvidlatgale mittens .80 .50

Christmas — A201

Designs: 12s, Goat riding on wolf's back. No. 631, 15s, Woman, dog near tree, vert. No. 632, 15s, Cat, woman carrying rooster, vert.

**2005, Dec. 3 Serpentine Die Cut 15**
**Self-Adhesive**
630-632 A201 Set of 3 1.75 1.25

Europa Stamps, 50th Anniv. — A202

Latvian Europa stamps: Nos. 633, 637a, 10s, #414. Nos. 634, 637b, 15s, #463. Nos. 635, 637c, 15s, #442. Nos. 636, 637d, 20s, #484-485.

**2006, Jan. 7 Litho. Perf. 13¾x13¼**
633-636 A202 Set of 4 2.50 1.50
**Souvenir Sheet**
**Perf. 13½ Syncopated**
637 A202 Sheet of 4, #a-d 2.25 2.25
No. 637 contains four 45x28mm stamps.

**Town Arms Type of 2002**
**2006, Jan. 11** **Perf. 13¼x13¾**
638 A153 7s Aizkraukle .30 .25
639 A153 22s Kraslava .80 .60
640 A153 31s Limbazi 1.25 .90
Nos. 638-640 (3) 2.35 1.75

2006 Winter Olympics, Turin — A203

**2006, Feb. 4** **Perf. 14**
641 A203 45s multi 1.75 1.25

Stamerienas Palace — A204

**2006, Feb. 25** **Perf. 14¼x13¾**
642 A204 95s multi 3.50 2.25

Zvartes Iezis — A205

**Serpentine Die Cut 14**
**2006, Mar. 11** **Self-Adhesive**
643 A205 22s multi .80 .55
Printed in sheets of 8.

**Souvenir Sheet**

Raunu Railroad Bridge A206

**2006, Mar. 25** **Perf. 13½x14**
644 A206 100s multi 3.75 3.25

2006 World Ice Hockey Championships, Riga — A207

**Perf. 13½x14¼**
**2006, Mar. 31** **Litho.**
645 A207 55s multi + label 2.00 1.25
a. Booklet pane of 4, perf.
13½x14¼ on 3 sides, without
labels 10.00 —
Complete booklet, #645a 10.00

Cesis, 800th Anniv. — A208

Various sites in Cesis: 22s, 31s, 45s, 55s. 45s and 55s are horiz.

**Perf. 13¼x13¾, 13¾x13¼**
**2006, Apr. 7**
646-649 A208 Set of 4 6.00 4.00

Traditional Jewelry — A209

No. 650: a, Brooch, Latvia. b, Bracelet, Kazakhstan.

**2006, Apr. 19** **Perf. 14x13¾**
650 A209 22s Horiz. pair, #a-b 1.75 1.00
See Kazakhstan No. 509.

Europa — A210

**2006, May 3**    *Perf. 13½x14¼*
651 A210 85s multi    3.25 2.50
a.   Tete beche pair    7.00 7.00

Ciganiete ar
Tamburinu, by Karlis
Huns — A211

**2006, May 13**    *Perf. 13¼x14*
652 A211 40s multi    1.50 1.00
a.   Booklet pane of 4, perf. 13¼x14
   on 3 sides    7.00
   Complete booklet, #652a   7.00

A212

Personalizable
Stamps — A213

**2006, June 9**    *Perf. 13¾*
653 A212 31s yel bister   1.25 1.00
654 A213 31s yel bister   1.25 1.00

Stamp vignettes could be personalized by customers, presumably for an extra fee.

"Big Christopher"
Statue — A214

**2006, June 16**    *Perf. 14x13½*
655 A214 36s multi    1.40 1.00

Art by Anna
Koshkina — A215

**Booklet Stamp**

*Die Cut Perf. 14½x13 on 3 Sides*
**2006, Aug. 11**    **Self-Adhesive**
656 A215 22s multi    .90 .60
a.   Booklet pane of 8    7.25

Volunteer Army, 15th
Anniv. — A216

**2006, Aug. 23**    *Perf. 13½x14*
657 A216 22s multi    .90 .60

Staburags — A217

**2006, Sept. 9 Litho.**  *Perf. 14¼x13¾*
658 A217 58s multi    2.25 1.50
a.   Tete beche pair    5.00 5.00

---

Wild Animals and Their
Tracks — A218

Designs: 45s, Lynx lynx. 55s, Cervus elaphus.

**2006, Sept. 23**   *Perf. 14¼x13½*
659-660 A218   Set of 2   3.75 2.50
659a   Booklet pane of 4 #659, perf.
   14¼x13½ on 3 sides   7.50
   Complete booklet, #659a   7.50
659b   Tete beche pair   4.00 4.00
660a   Tete beche pair   4.50 4.50

See Nos. 691-692, 719-720, 744-745.

Pansija Pili, Novel by
Anslavs Eglitis (1906-
93) — A219

**2006, Oct. 14 Litho.**  *Perf. 13¼x13½*
661 A219 67s multi    2.50 1.50

**Lighthouse Type of 2003**
**2006, Oct. 27**   *Perf. 14¼x13½*
662 A170 40s Mersraga Lighthouse    1.50 1.00
a.   Booklet pane of 4, perf.
   14¼x13½ on 3 sides   7.00
   Complete booklet, #662a   7.00

NATO Summit,
Riga — A220

**2006, Nov. 17**   *Perf. 13¾x13¼*
663 A220 55s multi    2.25 1.25

Christmas — A221

Cookies in shape of: 18s, Christmas tree. 22s, Star. 31s, Crescent moon. 45s, Bell.

*Serpentine Die Cut 14*
**2006, Nov. 17**    **Self-Adhesive**
664-667 A221   Set of 4   4.50 3.25

Oskars Kalpaks
(1882-1919), First
Commander-in-chief
of Latvian
Army — A222

**2007, Jan. 6**    *Perf. 14¼x14*
668 A222 22s multi    .85 .60

Mobile
Telecommunications
in Latvia, 15th
Anniv. — A223

**2007, Jan. 19**
669 A223 22s multi    .85 .60
a.   Tete beche pair    2.00 2.00

**Town Arms Type of 2002**
**2007, Feb. 3**    *Perf. 13¼x13¾*
670 A153 5s Staicele    .25 .25
   Perf. 14x14¼, "2010"   .25 .25
671 A153 10s Sabile    .35 .25
672 A153 22s Vecumnieki   .80 .65
   *Nos. 670-672 (3)*   1.40 1.15
Issued: No. 670a, 3/12/10.

---

Tilts Tornkalna,
Painting by Ludolfs
Liberts (1895-
1959) — A224

**2007, Feb. 17**    *Perf. 14¼x14*
673 A224 58s multi    2.25 1.50

Pauls Stradins
Museum of the
History of
Medicine, Riga,
50th
Anniv. — A225

**2007, Mar. 9**    *Perf. 14x14¼*
674 A225 22s multi    .85 .60

Baltic Coast — A226

*Serpentine Die Cut 14*
**2007, Mar. 24**    **Self-Adhesive**
675 A226 22s multi    .85 .60

**Lighthouse Type of 2003**
**2007, Apr. 14**   *Perf. 13¾x13½*
676 A170 67s Papes Lighthouse   2.50 1.75
a.   Booklet pane of 4, perf.
   13¾x13½ on 3 sides   12.00
   Complete booklet, #676a   12.00

Europa — A227

**2007, Apr. 28 Litho.**  *Perf. 13½x14¼*
677 A227 85s multi    3.25 2.50
a.   Tete beche pair    7.50 7.50

Scouting, cent.

**Palace Type of 2004**
**2007, June 8 Litho.**  *Perf. 13½x14¼*
678 A187 22s Krustpils, horiz.   .85 .60

UNESCO
World Heritage
Sites — A228

Designs: 36s, Historic Center of Riga. 45s, Historic Centers of Straslund and Wismar, Germany.

**2007, July 12 Litho.**  *Perf. 14x13¾*
679-680 A228   Set of 2   3.50 2.50
See Germany Nos. 2449-2450.

Sigulda, 800th
Anniv. — A229

Designs: 22s, New Sigulda Castle. 31s, Bobsled course. 40s, Sigulda Castle ruins.

*Serpentine Die Cut 15¼*
**2007, Aug. 10**    **Self-Adhesive**
681-683 A229   Set of 3   3.75 2.50

---

Berries and
Mushrooms — A230

Designs: 22s, Vaccinium vitis-idaea. 58s, Cantharellus cibarius.

**2007, Aug. 25**   *Perf. 14x13½*
684 A230 22s multi    .80 .55
a.   Tete beche pair    2.00 2.00
685 A230 58s multi    2.25 1.50
a.   Booklet pane of 4, perf.
   14x13½ on 3 sides   10.00
   Complete booklet, #685a   10.00
b.   Tete beche pair    5.00 5.00

See Nos. 715-716, 742-743, 767-768.

Organized
Soccer in
Latvia,
Cent. — A231

**2007, Sept. 8**    *Perf. 13¾*
686 A231 45s multi    1.75 1.75

Values are for stamps with surrounding selvage.

**Souvenir Sheet**

Aivieksti
Railroad
Bridge
A232

**2007, Oct. 13**    *Perf. 14*
687 A232 100s multi    3.75 3.75

Latvia Post, 375th
Anniv. — A233

Designs: 22s, Postrider. 31s, Postal worker and van.

*Serpentine Die Cut 15*
**2007, Oct. 20**    **Litho.**
   **Self-Adhesive**
688-689 A233   Set of 2   2.10 1.60

13th Century
Decorations
A234

**2007, Nov. 3**    *Perf. 13¼x14*
690 A234 60s multi    2.50 1.75

**Wild Animals and Their Tracks Type
of 2006**

Designs: 45s, Vulpes vulpes. 55s, Alces alces.

**2007, Nov. 16**   *Perf. 14¼x13½*
691 A218 45s multi    1.75 1.25
a.   Tete beche pair    3.50 3.50
692 A218 55s multi    2.25 1.50
a.   Tete beche pair    5.00 5.00

Christmas — A235

Christmas tree and children with: 22s, Musical instruments. 31s, Cookies. 45s, Skis and sled.

### Serpentine Die Cut 15
**2007, Nov. 24**    **Self-Adhesive**
693-695 A235 Set of 3    3.75   3.00

### Town Arms Type of 2002 With Country Name at Top
**2008, Feb. 9**    *Perf. 13¼x13¾*
696 A153 22s Salaspils    .75   .60
697 A153 28s Plavinas    .95   .75
698 A153 45s Saulkrasti    1.60   1.25
   Nos. 696-698 (3)    3.30   2.60

Easter — A236

**2008, Feb. 23**    *Perf. 13¼x13*
699 A236 22s multi    .80   .80

Augli, by Leo Svemps — A237

**2008, Mar. 8**   **Litho.**   *Perf. 13x13¼*
700 A237 63s multi    2.40   2.40

State Awards of the Baltic Countries — A238

Designs: Nos. 701, 702a, Order of Three Stars, Latvia. No. 702b, Order of Vytautas the Great, Lithuania. No. 702c, Order of the National Coat of Arms, Estonia.

**2008, Mar. 15**    *Perf. 13½x13¾*
701 A238 31s multi    1.25   1.25

**Souvenir Sheet**
702 A238 31s Sheet of 3, #a-c    3.50   3.50

On No. 701, the second line of type above the medal is 18mm wide, while it is 15mm wide on No. 702a.
See Estonia Nos. 592-593, Lithuania Nos. 862-863.

Worldwide Fund for Nature (WWF) — A239

Bats: 22s, Barbastella barbastellus. 31s, Myotis dasycneme. 45s, Barbastella barbastellus, vert. 55s, Myotis dasycneme, vert.

### Perf. 13½x14¼, 14¼x13½
**2008, Apr. 12**
703 A239 22s multi    .80   .80
  a.   Tete beche pair    1.75   1.75
704 A239 31s multi    1.15   1.15
  a.   Tete beche pair    2.75   2.75
705 A239 45s multi    1.60   1.60
  a.   Tete beche pair    3.50   3.50
706 A239 55s multi    1.75   1.75
  a.   Tete beche pair    4.50   4.50
   Nos. 703-706 (4)    5.30   5.30

Europa — A240

Designs: 45s, Letters and postcards. 85s, Person writing letter.

**2008, Apr. 22**    *Perf. 13½*
707 A240 45s multi    1.75   1.75
  a.   Tete beche pair    4.00   4.00
708 A240    multi    3.25   3.25
  a.   Tete beche pair    7.50   7.50

### Lighthouse Type of 2003
**2008, May 5**    *Perf. 14¼x13½*
709 A170 63s Akmenraga Lighthouse    2.25   2.25
  a.   Booklet pane of 4, perf.
     14¼x13½ on 3 sides    12.00   —
     Complete booklet, #709a    12.00

European Orienteering Championships, Ventspils — A241

**2008, May 23**   **Litho.**   *Perf. 13x13¼*
710 A241 45s multi    1.60   1.60
  a.   Tete beche pair    4.00   4.00

Nature Protection — A242

### Serpentine Die Cut 12½
**2008, June 7**    **Self-Adhesive**
711 A242 22s multi    .85   .85

Riga Museum Foundations A243

**2008, June 26**    *Perf. 13x13½*
712 A243 22s multi    .85   .85

2008 Summer Olympics, Beijing — A244

**2008, Aug. 8**    *Perf. 13½x13*
713 A244 63s multi    2.25   2.25

Sudraba Fairy Tale — A245

### Perf. 14¼x13½
**2008, Aug. 23**    **Litho.**
714 A245 22s multi    .85   .85
  a.   Tete beche pair    1.90   1.90

### Berries and Mushrooms Type of 2007
Designs: 22s, Vaccinium myrtillus. 58s, Leccinum aurantiacum.

**2008, Sept. 6**    *Perf. 14x13½*
715 A230 22s multi    .80   .80
  a.   Tete beche pair    2.00   2.00
716 A230 58s multi    2.00   2.00
  a.   Perf. 13½x14 on 3 sides    2.25   2.25
  b.   Booklet pane of 4 #716a    9.00   —
     Complete booklet, #716b    9.00
  c.   Tete beche pair    4.50   4.50

Souvenir Sheet

Kandavas Bridge — A246

**2008, Sept. 27**    *Perf. 14*
717 A246 100s multi    3.75   3.75

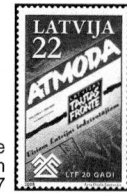

Tautas Fronte Newspaper, 20th Anniv. — A247

**2008, Oct. 8**    *Perf. 13½*
718 A247 22s multi    .85   .85
  a.   Tete beche pair    1.75   1.75

### Wild Animals and Their Tracks Type of 2006
Designs: 45s, Martes martes. 55s, Castor fiber.

**2008, Oct. 10**    *Perf. 14¼x13½*
719 A218 45s multi    1.75   1.75
  a.   Tete beche pair    3.50   3.50
720 A218 55s multi    2.25   2.25
  a.   Tete beche pair    5.00   5.00

Maris Strombergs, 2008 BMX Cycling Olympic Gold Medalist A248

**2008, Oct. 24**    *Perf. 13½*
721 A248 22s multi    .85   .85

Plate, Bow and Tablecloth — A249

**2008, Oct. 25**    *Perf. 13½x13¾*
722 A249 28s multi    1.00   1.00

Latvian Republic, 90th Anniv. — A250

**2008, Nov. 7**    *Perf. 13¼x13*
723 A250 31s multi    1.25   1.25

Mezotnes Palace — A251

**2008, Nov. 8**    *Perf. 13½x14¼*
724 A251 63s multi    2.40   2.40

Christmas — A252

**2008, Nov. 28**    *Perf. 14¼x13¾*
725 A252 25s multi    .90   .90

### Town Arms Type of 2002 With Country Name at Top
**2009, Jan. 10**   **Litho.**   *Perf. 14x14¼*
726 A153 33s Dagda    1.25   1.25
727 A153 35s Balozi    1.40   1.40
728 A153 60s Stende    2.00   2.00
   Nos. 726-728 (3)    4.65   4.65

Brooch, 8th Cent. A.D. — A253

**2009, Jan. 24**    *Perf. 14*
729 A253 98s multi    3.50   3.50
  a.   Tete beche pair    7.50   7.50

Dancing Boy and Animals Folktale — A254

**2009, Feb. 21**    *Perf. 13¼*
730 A254 40s multi    1.50   1.50

Souvenir Sheet

Preservation of Polar Regions and Glaciers — A255

No. 731: a, 35s, Polar bear. b, 55s, Penguins.

**2009, Mar. 18**   **Litho.**   *Perf. 13¼*
731 A255 Sheet of 2, #a-b    3.75   3.75

Europa — A256

Designs: 50s, Janis Ikaunieks, astronomer, and Baldone Observatory telescope. 55s, Map of solar system, asteroid, University of Latvia Institute of Astronomy, radio telescope, five astronomers.

**2009, Apr. 2**    *Perf. 14x13¾*
732 A256 50s multi    2.25   2.25
  a.   Tete beche pair    4.75   4.75
733 A256 55s multi    2.50   2.50
  a.   Tete beche pair    5.25   5.25

Intl. Year of Astronomy.

Natl. Museum of History — A257

**2009, May 14**    *Perf. 13½*
734 A257 35s multi    1.40   1.40

Basketball — A258

Player from opposing team and: 35s, Male Latvian team player, 1935. 40s, Female TTT Riga player. 60s, Male ASK Riga player. 120s, Latvian player in 2009 Women's European Basketball Championships.

**2009, June 6**
735-737 A258 Set of 3    5.25   5.25

**Souvenir Sheet**
738 A258 120s multi    4.50   4.50

Nos. 735-737 each were printed in sheets of 9 + label.

Bauska, 400th Anniv. — A259

**2009, July 10 Litho. Perf. 13½x14**
739 A259 38s multi    1.35 1.35

Steam Locomotive A260

**2009, Aug. 5 Litho. Perf. 13½**
740 A260 35s multi    1.40 1.40

**Souvenir Sheet**

Dienvidu Bridge, Riga A261

**2009, Aug. 22**
741 A261 100s multi    4.00 4.00

**Berries and Mushrooms Type of 2007**

Designs: 55s, Fragaria vesca. 60s, Russula paludosa.

**2009, Sept. 12**
742 A230 55s multi    2.25 2.25
   a.   Tete beche pair    5.00 5.00
743 A230 60s multi    2.50 2.50
   a.   Tete beche pair    5.50 5.50
   b.   Perf. 13½ on 3 sides    2.50 2.50
   c.   Booklet pane of 4 #743b    11.00
     Complete booklet, #743c    11.00

**Wild Animals and Their Tracks Type of 2006**

Designs: 35s, Canis lupus. 98s, Lepus europaeus.

**2009, Oct. 21 Perf. 13½x14¼**
744 A218 35s multi    1.25 1.25
   a.   Tete beche pair    2.75 2.75
745 A218 98s multi    4.00 4.00
   a.   Tete beche pair    8.25 8.25

**Lighthouse Type of 2003**

**2009, Nov. 5 Litho. Perf. 13¼**
746 A170 63s Liepaja Lighthouse    2.60 2.60

Republic of Latvia, 91st Anniv. — A262

Designs: 35s, Formation of Latvian People's Council, Nov. 17, 1918. 40s, Proclamation of Latvian Republic, Nov. 18, 1918. 100s, First meeting of Constitutional Assembly, May 1, 1920.

**2009, Nov. 14 Litho. Perf. 14**
747-749 A262   Set of 3    6.75 6.75

Christmas — A263

Designs: 35s, Horse Christmas ornament, building. 55s, Fish Christmas ornament, building. 60s, Snowflake Christmas ornament.

**2009, Nov. 27 Perf. 13¼**
750-752 A263   Set of 3    5.75 5.75

---

**Town Arms Type of 2002 With Country Name at Top**

**2010, Jan. 16 Litho. Perf. 14x14¼**
753 A153 35s Viesite    1.25 1.25
754 A153 40s Ligatne    1.40 1.40
755 A153 55s Iecava    2.00 2.00
   Nos. 753-755 (3)    4.65 4.65

2010 Winter Olympics, Vancouver A264

**2010, Feb. 5 Perf. 13¼x13¾**
756 A264 55s multi    2.10 2.10

Peonies — A265

**2010, Mar. 26 Perf. 13¼**
757 A265 35s multi    1.25 1.25
   a.   Tete beche pair    2.75 2.75

Europa — A266

Designs: 55s, Girl holding books, characters from children's books. 120s, Boy reading book, ship, castle, mountain.

**2010, Apr. 9 Litho. Perf. 13½x13¼**
758 A266 55s multi    2.00 2.00
   a.   Tete beche pair    4.25 4.25
759 A266 120s multi    4.00 4.00
   a.   Tete beche pair    8.75 8.75

Expo 2010, Shanghai — A267

**2010, Apr. 23 Perf. 13¼**
760 A267 150s multi    5.25 5.25

Declaration of May 4, 1990, 20th Anniv. — A268

**2010, May 4**
761 A268 35s multi    1.40 1.40
   Tete beche pair    3.00 3.00

Fire Fighting Museum — A269

**2010, May 21**
762 A269 98s multi    3.75 3.75
   a.   Tete beche pair    7.75 7.75

Birds — A270

Designs: 35s, Coracias garrulus. 98s, Bubo bubo, vert.

**Perf. 14x13¾, 13¾x14**
**2010, June 18**
763-764 A270   Set of 2    5.00 5.00
   See Nos. 790-791.

---

Talsos Sports Hall — A271

**2010, July 16 Perf. 13¼**
765 A271 150s multi    5.75 5.75

RP Series Locomotive A272

**2010, Aug. 5 Perf. 13¼x13½**
766 A272 40s multi    1.50 1.50

**Berries and Mushrooms Type of 2007**

Designs: 55s, Rubus ideus. 120s, Leccinum scabrum.

**2010, Sept. 10 Perf. 13½x13¼**
767 A230 55s multi    2.00 2.00
   a.   Tete beche pair    4.50 4.50
768 A230 120s multi    4.75 4.75
   a.   Tete beche pair    9.75 9.75

**Lighthouse Type of 2003**

**2010, Oct. 15 Litho. Perf. 13½x13¼**
769 A170 98s Uzavas Lighthouse    3.75 3.75
   a.   Booklet pane of 4, perf. 13½x13¼ on 3 sides    16.00
     Complete booklet, #769a    16.00

Republic of Latvia, 92nd Anniv. — A273

National symbols: 35s, Flag. 38s, Arms. 98s, Anthem.

**2010, Nov. 12 Litho. Perf. 14**
770-772 A273   Set of 3    6.50 6.50

Christmas — A274

Designs: 35s, Girl, cat, Christmas tree. 60s, Boy with gift, bird in tree.

**2010, Dec. 3 Perf. 13½x13¼**
773 A274 35s multi    1.35 1.35
   a.   Tete beche pair    3.00 3.00
774 A274 60s multi    2.40 2.40
   a.   Tete beche pair    5.00 5.00

New Year 2011 (Year of the Rabbit) — A275

**2011, Jan. 14 Litho. Perf. 13½x13¼**
775 A275 35s multi    1.40 1.40

**Town Arms Type of 2002 With Country Name at Top**

**2011, Feb. 25 Litho. Perf. 14x14¼**
776 A153 35s Ikskiles    1.10 1.10
777 A153 98s Carnikavas    4.25 4.25

Rose — A276

---

**2011, Mar. 25 Perf. 13½x13¼**
778 A276 35s multi    1.35 1.35
   a.   Tete beche pair    3.00 3.00

Europa — A277

Animals in forest: 55s, Deer. 120s, Wolf.

**2011, Apr. 8 Perf. 14x13¾**
779 A277 55s multi    1.90 1.90
   a.   Tete beche pair    4.00 4.00
780 A277 120s multi    4.00 4.00
   a.   Tete beche pair    8.50 8.50

Intl. Year of Forests.

**Souvenir Sheet**

Struve Geodetic Arc A278

No. 781: a, 35s, Map of arc and stone. b, 55s, Map and Friedrich Georg Wilhelm von Struve (1793-1864), astronomer.

**2011, May 5 Perf. 13¼x13½**
781 A278   Sheet of 2, #a-b    3.25 3.25

First Coin of Riga, 800th Anniv. — A279

**2011, May 23 Perf. 13½x13¼**
782 A279 98s multi    3.75 3.75
   a.   Tete beche pair    8.00 8.00

Johanna (1904-90) and Zanis Lipke (1900-87), Rescuers of Jews During World War II — A280

**2011, July 4 Perf. 14x13¾**
783 A280 60s multi    2.25 2.25
   a.   Tete beche pair    5.00 5.00

Phoenix III Passenger Coach — A281

**2011, Aug. 5 Perf. 13¼x13½**
784 A281 33s multi    1.25 1.25

A282

A283

Personalized Stamps — A284

**2011, Aug. 22** — *Perf. 13¾*
785 A282 35s yel bis & blk — 1.30 1.30
786 A283 55s yel bis & blk — 2.10 2.10
787 A284 60s yel bis & blk — 2.25 2.25
*Nos. 785-787 (3)* — 5.65 5.65

The generic vignettes shown for Nos. 785-787 could be personalized by customers for an extra fee.

Latvian Cycling Federation, 125th Anniv. — A285

**2011, Aug. 25** — *Perf. 14x13¾*
788 A285 35s multi — 1.40 1.40

Port of Riga — A286

**2011, Sept. 2 Litho.** — *Perf. 13¼x13½*
789 A286 60s multi — 2.25 2.25

**Birds Type of 2010**

Designs: 35s, Hippolais icterina. 98s, Circaetus gallicus, vert.

**2011, Sept. 23 Litho.** — *Perf. 14x13¾*
790 A270 35s multi — 1.25 1.25
a. Perf. 13¾x14 on 3 sides, granite paper — 1.25 1.25
b. Booklet pane of 4 #790a — 8.50
Complete booklet, #790b — 8.50

*Perf. 13¾x14*
791 A270 98s multi — 3.75 3.75
a. Perf. 13¾x14 on 3 sides, granite paper — 3.75 3.75
b. Booklet pane of 4 #791a — 15.00
Complete booklet, #791b — 15.00

Parventa Library, Ventspils — A287

**2011, Oct. 14** — *Perf. 13½x13¼*
792 A287 100s multi — 4.00 4.00

Republic of Latvia, 93rd Anniv. — A288

Designs: 35s, Merchant fleet ships and their captains. 60s, Krisjanis Valdemars, founder of Latvian Naval School, Ainazi. 100s, Admiral Teodors Spade, Navy emblem, ships and sailors.

**2011, Nov. 11** — *Perf. 14*
**Granite Paper**
793-795 A288 Set of 3 — 7.50 7.50

Christmas — A289

Designs: 35s, Reindeer with clothesline between antlers, Santa Claus with ripped bag. 60s, Santa Claus pushing reindeer and bag on dragon's back.

**2011, Dec. 2** — *Perf. 13¼*
**Granite Paper**
796-797 A289 Set of 2 — 3.75 1.90

**Town Arms Type of 2002 With Country Name At Top**
**2012, Jan. 7** — *Perf. 13¼x13¾*
798 A153 33s Piltene — 1.25 .90
799 A153 35s Riga — 1.40 1.00
800 A153 38s Lielvardes Novads — 1.50 1.10
*Nos. 798-800 (3)* — 4.15 3.00

Nos. 798-800 are dated "2011."

Library No. 1 Restaurant, Riga — A290

**2012, Jan. 27** — *Perf. 13¼*
801 A290 35s multi — 1.40 1.40

Lilies — A291

**2012, Feb. 11**
802 A291 35s multi — 1.40 1.40
a. Tete beche pair — 3.00 3.00

Europa — A292

Designs: 55s, Dancers. 120s, National Opera House.

**2012, Mar. 17** — *Perf. 14*
803 A292 55s multi — 2.10 2.10
a. Tete beche pair — 4.50 4.50
804 A292 120s multi — 4.50 4.50
a. Tete beche pair — 9.50 9.50

Riga Zoo, Cent. A293

**2012, Apr. 14** — *Perf. 13¼*
805 A293 Block or horiz. strip of 3 + label — 6.00 6.00
a. 35s Lion — 1.40 1.40
b. 55s Horse — 2.10 2.10
c. 60s Frog — 2.25 2.25
d. Booklet pane of 4 #805c, perf. 13¼ on 3 sides — 9.50
Complete booklet, #805d — 9.50

Janis Misins (1862-1945), Librarian — A294

**2012, Apr. 25** — *Perf. 13¼*
806 A294 98s multi — 3.75 3.75
a. Tete beche pair — 8.00 8.00

Port of Ventspils A295

**2012, May 11** — *Perf. 13¼x13½*
807 A295 35s multi — 1.25 1.25

Birds — A296

Designs: 35s, Hirundo rustica. 98s, Carduelis carduelis.

**2012, June 16 Litho.** — *Perf. 13¾x14*
808-809 A296 Set of 2 — 5.00 5.00

2012 Summer Olympics, London — A297

**2012, July 14** — *Perf. 13¼x13½*
810 A297 60s multi — 2.25 2.25
a. Tete beche pair — 5.00 5.00

Ungurmuiza Manor — A298

**2012, Aug. 18**
811 A298 98s multi — 3.75 3.75

Friedrich Zander (1887-1933), Rocketry Pioneer — A299

**2012, Aug. 23** — *Perf. 13¼*
812 A299 60s multi — 2.25 2.25
a. Tete beche pair — 5.00 5.00

**Souvenir Sheet**

Duchy of Courland and Semigallia, 450th Anniv. — A300

No. 813: a, 35s, Duke Ernsts Johans Birons (1690-1772). b, 55s, Duke Jekabs Kettlers (1610-82).

**Granite Paper**
**2012, Sept. 21** — *Perf. 13¼x13½*
813 A300 Sheet of 2, #a-b — 3.50 3.50

Riga Technical University, 150th Anniv. — A301

**2012, Oct. 8** — *Perf. 13¼*
814 A301 98s multi — 3.75 3.75

Railway Bridges — A302

Train and: Nos. 815, 816a, Carnikava Bridge, Latvia. No. 816b, Lyduvenai Bridge, Lithuania. No. 816c, Narva Bridge, Estonia.

**2012** — *Perf. 13¼*
815 A302 35s multi — 1.40 1.40

**Souvenir Sheet**
816 A302 55s Sheet of 3, #a-c — 6.00 6.00

Issued: No. 815, 10/8; No. 816, 10/25. See Estonia Nos. 713-714, Lithuania Nos. 985-986.

Republic of Latvia, 94th Anniv. — A303

Composers: 35s, Emils Darzins (1875-1910). 60s, Jazeps Vitols (1863-1948). 100s, Talivaldis Kenins (1919-2008).

**2012, Nov. 10 Litho.** — *Perf. 14*
817-819 A303 Set of 3 — 7.25 7.25

Latvian Medalists at 2012 Summer Olympics, London — A304

Designs: No. 820, 35s, Martins Plavins and Janis Smedins, beach volleyball bronze medalists. No. 821, 35s, Maris Strombergs, BMX cycling gold medalist.

**2012, Nov. 23** — *Perf. 13¼*
820 A304 35s multi — 1.30 1.30
a. Tete beche pair — 2.75 2.75
821 A304 35s multi — 1.30 1.30
a. Tete beche pair — 2.75 2.75

Christmas — A305

Designs: 35s, Girl, gifts, Christmas tree. 60s, Snow-covered house.

**2012, Nov. 30** — *Perf. 14x13¾*
822 A305 35s multi — 1.25 1.25
a. Tete beche pair — 2.75 2.75
823 A305 60s multi — 2.50 2.50
a. Tete beche pair — 5.25 5.25

**Town Arms Type of 2002 With Country Name at Top**
**2013, Jan. 13** — *Perf. 14*
824 A153 35s Varaklani — 1.40 1.40
825 A153 60s Strencu Novads — 2.40 2.40
826 A153 98s Varkavas Novads — 3.75 3.75
*Nos. 824-826 (3)* — 7.55 7.55

Janis Uzraugs, Cyclist — A306

**2013, Jan. 30** — *Perf. 13¾x13½*
827 A306 35s multi — 1.40 1.40

Starting with No. 827, 2013 stamps also have euro denominations, in anticipation of a change to the euro currency in 2014.

Dailes Theater, Riga — A307

**2013, Feb. 15** — *Perf. 13¼x13½*
828 A307 100s multi — 3.75 3.75

Irises — A308

**2013, Mar. 8** — *Perf. 13¼*
829 A308 35s multi — 1.40 1.40
a. Tete beche pair — 3.00 3.00

Europa — A309

Postal vehicles: 55s, Horse-drawn carriage, rail car. 120s, Airplane, truck, van, bicycle.

**2013, Apr. 19**     *Perf. 14x13¾*

**Granite Paper**

| | | | | |
|---|---|---|---|---|
| **830** | A309 | 55s multi | 2.10 | 2.10 |
| *a.* | | Tete beche pair | 4.50 | 4.50 |
| *b.* | | Booklet pane of 4, perf. 14x13¼ on 3 sides | 8.50 | — |
| | | Complete booklet, #830b | 8.50 | |
| **831** | A309 | 120s multi | 4.50 | 4.50 |
| *a.* | | Tete beche pair | 9.50 | 9.50 |

**Souvenir Sheet**

Paul Walden (1863-1957),
Chemist — A310

**2013, May 14**     *Perf. 13¼*

**Granite Paper**

| | | | | |
|---|---|---|---|---|
| **832** | A310 | 100s multi | 4.00 | 4.00 |

 Birds — A311

Designs: 35s, Clangula hyemalis. 98s, Merops apiaster, vert.

*Perf. 14x13¾, 13¾x14*

**2013, June 7**     Litho.

| | | | | |
|---|---|---|---|---|
| **833-834** | A311 | Set of 2 | 5.25 | 5.25 |

**Souvenir Sheet**

25th Latvian Song and Dance Festival A312

No. 835: a, Singers. b, Dancers.

**2013, June 28**     Litho.     *Perf. 13¼*

| | | | | |
|---|---|---|---|---|
| **835** | A312 | 35s Sheet of 2, #a-b | 2.60 | 2.60 |

Cover With Russia (Wenden) No.
L2 — A313

**2013, July 12**     Litho.     *Perf. 13¼*

**Granite Paper**

| | | | | |
|---|---|---|---|---|
| **836** | A313 | 100s multi | 3.75 | 3.75 |

First postage stamp issued in Latvia, 150th anniv.

Cats — A314

Designs: 35s, Kittins in basket. 98s, Cats in doorway,vert.

*Perf. 14x13¾, 13¾x14*

**2013, July 29**     Litho.

| | | | | |
|---|---|---|---|---|
| **837-838** | A314 | Set of 2 | 5.00 | 5.00 |

Port of Liepaja — A315

**2013, Aug. 23**     Litho.     *Perf. 13½*

| | | | | |
|---|---|---|---|---|
| **839** | A315 | 98s multi | 3.75 | 3.75 |

---

Latvia University of Agriculture, 150th Anniv. — A316

**2013, Sept. 16**     Litho.     *Perf. 13¼*

| | | | | |
|---|---|---|---|---|
| **840** | A316 | 40s multi | 1.60 | 1.60 |

Mark Rothko (1903-70), Painter — A317

**2013, Sept. 25**     Litho.     *Perf. 13¾x14*

| | | | | |
|---|---|---|---|---|
| **841** | A317 | 60s multi | 2.40 | 2.40 |

Latvian Popular Front, 25th Anniv. — A318

**2013, Oct. 5**     Litho.     *Perf. 13¾x14*

| | | | | |
|---|---|---|---|---|
| **842** | A318 | 35s multi | 1.40 | 1.40 |

Printing in Latvia, 425th Anniv. — A319

**2013, Oct. 22**     Litho.     *Perf. 13¼*

**Granite Paper**

| | | | | |
|---|---|---|---|---|
| **843** | A319 | 60s multi | 2.40 | 2.40 |

No. 843 was printed in sheets of 8 + 4 labels.

Pink Ribbon and Flower — A320

**2013, Oct. 30**     Litho.     *Perf. 14*

| | | | | |
|---|---|---|---|---|
| **844** | A320 | 4s multi | .40 | .40 |

Breast cancer awareness.

Republic of Latvia, 95th Anniv. — A321

Writers: 35s, Rainis (1865-1929). 60s, Rudolfs Blaumanis (1863-1908). 98s, Zenta Maurina (1897-1978).

**2013, Nov. 8**     Litho.     *Perf. 13¾*

| | | | | |
|---|---|---|---|---|
| **845-847** | A321 | Set of 3 | 7.50 | 7.50 |

Christmas — A322

Falling snow and: 35s, Girl on rocking horse, Christmas gifts. 60s, Girl and cats on building's roof.

**2013, Nov. 22**     Litho.     *Perf. 14x13¾*

**Granite Paper**

| | | | | |
|---|---|---|---|---|
| **848-849** | A322 | Set of 2 | 3.75 | 3.75 |

**100 Cents = 1 Euro**

Flowers — A323

---

Designs: 3c, Narcissi. 47c, Crocuses. 57c, Pansies. 78c, Cornflowers. 85c, Poppies. €1.39, Asters.

**2014, Jan. 2**     Litho.     *Perf. 14*

| | | | | |
|---|---|---|---|---|
| **850** | A323 | 3c multi | .30 | .25 |
| *a.* | | Dated "2016" | .30 | .25 |
| *b.* | | Dated "2022" | .30 | .30 |
| **851** | A323 | 47c multi | 1.40 | .30 |
| **852** | A323 | 57c multi | 1.75 | .90 |
| **853** | A323 | 78c multi | 2.25 | 1.25 |
| **854** | A323 | 85c multi | 2.75 | 1.40 |
| **855** | A323 | €1.39 multi | 4.00 | 2.10 |
| *a.* | | Souvenir sheet of 6, #850-855 | 13.00 | 13.00 |
| | | *Nos. 850-855 (6)* | 12.45 | 6.20 |

See Nos. 867-870, 895-899.
Issued: No. 850a, 1/29/16; No. 850b, 6/2/22.

Imants Ziedonis (1933-2013), Poet — A324

**2014, Jan. 6**     Litho.     *Perf. 13¼x13¾*

| | | | | |
|---|---|---|---|---|
| **856** | A324 | 50c multi | 1.40 | 1.10 |

Bildmuseet, Umea, Sweden — A325     National Library, Riga, Latvia — A326

**2014, Jan. 16**     Litho.     *Perf. 13¼*

**Granite Paper**

| | | | | |
|---|---|---|---|---|
| **857** | A325 | 50c multi | 1.30 | 1.30 |
| **858** | A326 | 78c multi | 2.00 | 2.00 |

Selection of Umea and Riga as European Capitals of Culture. See Sweden Nos. 2720-2721.

2014 Winter Olympics, Sochi, Russia — A327

**2014, Feb. 7**     Litho.     *Perf. 13¼x13½*

**Granite Paper**

| | | | | |
|---|---|---|---|---|
| **859** | A327 | 85c multi | 2.00 | 1.75 |

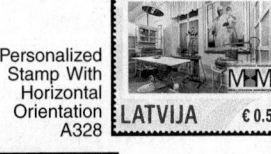

Personalized Stamp With Horizontal Orientation A328

Personalized Stamp With Vertical Orientation — A329

*Perf. 13¼x13½, 13½x13¼*

**2014, Feb. 28**     Litho.

| | | | | |
|---|---|---|---|---|
| **860** | A328 | 50c multi | 1.40 | .70 |
| **861** | A329 | 50c multi | 1.40 | .70 |
| **862** | A328 | 78c multi | 2.25 | 1.10 |
| **863** | A329 | 78c multi | 2.25 | 1.10 |
| **864** | A328 | 85c multi | 2.40 | 1.25 |
| **865** | A329 | 85c multi | 2.40 | 1.25 |
| | | *Nos. 860-865 (6)* | 12.10 | 6.10 |

Stamps with generic images of museums and their displays were made available on Nos. 860, 863 and 865. Stamps with generic images of airplanes were made available on Nos. 861, 862 and 864.

---

Tulips — A330

**2014, Mar. 7**     Litho.     *Perf. 13¼*

| | | | | |
|---|---|---|---|---|
| **866** | A330 | 50c multi | 1.60 | 1.10 |

**Flowers Type of 2014**

Designs: 1c, Daisies. 4c, Hepatica. 7c, Marigolds. 50c, Lily of the valley.

**2014, Mar. 22**     Litho.     *Perf. 14*

| | | | | |
|---|---|---|---|---|
| **867** | A323 | 1c multi | .30 | .30 |
| *a.* | | Dated "2015" | .30 | .30 |
| *b.* | | Dated "2016" | .30 | .30 |
| *c.* | | Dated "2017" | .30 | .30 |
| *d.* | | Dated "2019" | .25 | .25 |
| *f.* | | Dated "2022" | .30 | .30 |
| **868** | A323 | 4c multi | .30 | .30 |
| *a.* | | Dated "2015" | .30 | .30 |
| *b.* | | Dated "2016" | .30 | .30 |
| *c.* | | Dated "2017" | .30 | .30 |
| *d.* | | Dated "2019" | .25 | .25 |
| *e.* | | Dated "2021" | .25 | .25 |
| *f.* | | Dated "2022" | .30 | .30 |
| **869** | A323 | 7c multi | .30 | .30 |
| *a.* | | Dated "2015" | .30 | .30 |
| *c.* | | Dated "2017" | .30 | .30 |
| *d.* | | Dated "2019" | .25 | .25 |
| *e.* | | Dated "2021" | .25 | .25 |
| *f.* | | Dated "2022" | .30 | .30 |

**Granite Paper**

| | | | | |
|---|---|---|---|---|
| **870** | A323 | 50c multi | 1.40 | 1.40 |
| *b.* | | Dated "2016," plain paper | 1.10 | 1.10 |
| | | *Nos. 867-870 (4)* | 2.30 | 2.30 |

Issued: Nos. 867a, 868a, 869a, 5/5/15; Nos. 867b, 870a, 1/29/16; No. 868b, 7/12/16; Nos. 867c, 868c, 869b, 1/13/17; Nos. 867d, 868d, 869d, 1/15/19; Nos. 868e, 869e, 1/15/21; Nos. 867f, 868f, 1/10/22; No. 869f, 6/2/22.

Diplomatic Relations With Georgia, 20th Anniv. — A331

*Perf. 13¼x13½*

**2014, Mar. 28**     Litho.

**Granite Paper**

| | | | | |
|---|---|---|---|---|
| **871** | A331 | 85c multi | 2.00 | 1.25 |

See Georgia No. 491.

Europa — A332

Musical instruments: 78c, Kokle (zither). €1.71, Dudas (bagpipe).

**2014, Apr. 11**     Litho.     *Perf. 14x13¾*

**Granite Paper**

| | | | | |
|---|---|---|---|---|
| **872-873** | A332 | Set of 2 | 7.00 | 3.50 |
| *872a* | | Booklet pane of 4 #872, perf. 14x13¾ on 3 sides | 10.00 | — |
| | | Complete booklet, #872a | 10.00 | |

Emblem of *Te!* Television Show — A333

**2014, Apr. 17**     Litho.     *Perf. 13¼x13¾*

**Granite Paper**

| | | | | |
|---|---|---|---|---|
| **874** | A333 | 50c deep lilac | 1.50 | 1.10 |

Birds — A334

Designs: 50c, Lymnocryptes minimus. €1.39, Upupa epops, vert.

*Perf. 13¾x14, 14x13¾*
2014, May 16      Litho.
875-876 A334   Set of 2     5.25 2.60

Latvian Medalists at 2014 Winter Olympics — A335

Designs: No. 877, 50c, Martin Dukurs, silver medalist in skeleton. No. 878, 50c, Daumants Dreiskens, Oskars Melbardis, Janis Strenga, Arvis Vilkaste, silver medalists in four-man bobsled. No. 879, 50c, Juris Sics, Andris Sics, bronze medalists in men's doubles luge. No. 880, 50c, Juris Sics, Andris Sics, Martins Rubenis, Eliza Tiruma, bronze medalists in Mixed team relay luge.

2014, May 27    Litho.    *Perf. 13¼*
**Granite Paper**
877-880 A335   Set of 4     5.50 2.75
Nos. 877-880 each were printed in sheets of 4.

Janis Cimze (1814-81), Collector and Publisher of Folk Songs — A336

2014, July 3   Litho.   *Perf. 13¼x13½*
**Granite Paper**
881 A336 57c multi     1.60 .80

Turaida Castle, 800th Anniv. — A337

2014, July 11   Litho.   *Perf. 13¼x13½*
882 A337 50c multi     1.40 .70

Baltic Chain Demonstration, 25th Anniv. — A338

Designs: 50c, Three women.
No. 884: a, Five adults and one child. b, Like #883. c, Man and child.

2014, Aug. 23    Litho.    *Perf. 13¼*
883 A338 50c multi     1.40 .70
**Souvenir Sheet**
884 A338 78c Sheet of 3, #a-c     6.25 3.25
See Estonia Nos. 764-765; Lithuania No. 1031.

Gothards Fridrihs Stenders (1714-96), Lexicographer — A339

2014, Aug. 24    Litho.    *Perf. 13¼*
885 A339 €1.39 multi     3.75 1.90
No. 885 was printed in sheets of 8 + 4 labels.

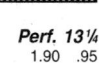
Ainazu Lighthouse — A340

2014, Sept. 12    Litho.    *Perf. 13¼*
886 A340 71c multi     1.90 .95

---

Latvian Academy of Arts — A341

2014, Oct. 17    Litho.    *Perf. 13¼*
887 A341 €1.42 multi     3.50 1.75

Republic of Latvia, 96th Anniv. — A342

Designs: 57c, Painter. 64c, Graphic artist. 78c, Sculptor.

2014, Nov. 7    Litho.    *Perf. 14*
888-890 A342   Set of 3     5.00 2.50

Christmas — A343

Designs: 50c, Forest in winter. 85c, City in winter, horiz.

2014, Nov. 27    Litho.    *Perf. 13½*
891-892 A343   Set of 2     3.50 1.75

Singing Trees — A344

2014, Dec. 4    Litho.    *Perf. 14x13¾*
893 A344 50c multi     1.25 .60

Latvian Presidency of Council of the European Union — A345

2015, Jan. 6    Litho.    *Perf. 13¾x14*
894 A345 64c multi     1.50 .75

**Flowers Type of 2014**
Designs: 10c, Crocuses. 25c, Asters. 70c, Lilies. 78c, Gerbera daisies. €2.13, Pansies.

2015, Jan. 9    Litho.    *Perf. 14*
**Dated "2015"**
895 A323   10c multi     .30 .25
   a.   Dated "2017"     .30 .25
   c.   Dated "2022"     .30 .30
896 A323   25c multi     .65 .30
   a.   Dated "2018"     .60 .30
   b.   Dated "2021"     .60 .30
   c.   Dated "2022"     .60 .30
897 A323   70c multi     1.75 .80
898 A323   78c multi     2.00 .90
899 A323   €2.13 multi     5.00 2.50
   a.   Dated "2018"     5.00 2.50
   Nos. 895-899 (5)     9.70 4.75

Issued: No. 895a, 1/13/17. Nos. 896a, 899a, 6/8/18; No. 896b, 1/15/21; Nos. 895c, 896c, 1/10/22.

Green Week — A346

2015, Jan. 15   Litho.   *Perf. 13¼x13¾*
900 A346 50c multi     1.25 .60

---

Arms of Riga — A347

National Arms — A348

2015, Jan. 30    Litho.    *Perf. 14x13¾*
901 A347 €1 sil & multi     2.25 1.10
   a.   Dated "2019"     2.25 1.10
902 A348 €2 sil & multi     4.50 2.25
   a.   Dated "2019"     4.50 2.25
903 A348 €5 gold & multi     11.50 5.75
   Nos. 901-903 (3)     18.25 9.10
Issued: Nos. 901a, 902a, 3/22/19.

Jelgava, 750th Anniv. — A349

2015, Feb. 5    Litho.    *Perf. 13½*
904 A349 €1.71 multi     3.75 1.90

Asterolepis Ornata and Fossils — A350

2015, Feb. 20    Litho.    *Perf. 13¼*
905 A350 71c multi     1.60 .80

Helianthus — A351

2015, Mar. 6    Litho.    *Perf. 13¼*
906 A351 50c multi     1.10 .55

Europa — A352

Designs: 78c, Dolls. €1.71, Teddy bears.

2015, Apr. 10    Litho.    *Perf. 14x13¾*
907 A352   78c multi     1.75 .90
   a.   Tete-beche pair     3.50 3.50
   b.   Booklet pane of 4, perf. 14x13¾
     on 3 sides     7.00 —
     Complete booklet, #907b     7.00
908 A352   €1.71 multi     4.00 2.00

Kurzemes Literary Society, 200th Anniv. — A353

2015, Apr. 21    Litho.    *Perf. 13¼*
909 A353 85c multi     1.90 .95
No. 909 was printed in sheets of 10 + 2 central labels.

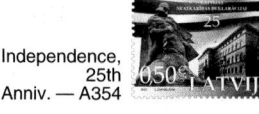
Independence, 25th Anniv. — A354

2015, Apr. 29   Litho.   *Perf. 13¼x13½*
910 A354 50c multi     1.25 .60

---

World Press Freedom Day — A355

2015, May 3   Litho.   *Perf. 13¼x13¾*
911 A355 57c multi     1.40 .70

Latvian Fire Services, 150th Anniv. — A356

2015, May 15    Litho.    *Perf. 13¼*
912 A356 €1.42 multi     3.25 1.60

Birds — A357

Designs: 71c, Oriolus oriolus. €1.42, Pluvialis apricaria, vert.

*Perf. 14x13¾, 13¾x14*
2015, June 26      Litho.
913-914 A357   Set of 2     5.25 2.75

Rundales Palace — A358

2015, July 24    Litho.    *Perf. 13¼*
915 A358 €1.57 multi     3.50 1.75

**Miniature Sheet**

Signs of the Zodiac A359

No. 916: a, Aries. b, Cancer. c, Libra. d, Capricorn. e, Taurus. f, Leo. g, Scorpio. h, Aquarius. i, Gemini. j, Virgo. k, Sagittarius. l, Pisces.

2015, Aug. 7    Litho.    *Perf. 13¼*
916 A359 50c Sheet of 12, #a-l     13.50 6.75

Salacgrivas Lighthouse — A360

*Perf. 13¼x13½*
2015, Aug. 21      Litho.
917 A360 78c multi     1.75 .85

Poets A361

No. 918: a, Rainis (1865-1929). b, Aspazija (1865-1943).

*Perf. 13¼x13½*
2015, Sept. 11      Litho.
918 A361 50c Sheet of 2, #a-b     2.25 1.10

Latvian Riflemen, Cent. — A362

**2015, Oct. 25 Litho. Perf. 13¼x13½**
919 A362 €1.71 multi 3.75 1.90

Republic of Latvia, 97th Anniv. — A363

Architects: 50c, Janis Fridrihs Baumanis (1834-91). 64c, Eizens Laube (1880-1967), Janis Alksnis (1869-1939), Konstantins Peksens (1859-1928). €1.39, Marta Stana (1913-72).

**2015, Nov. 13 Litho. Perf. 14**
920-922 A363 Set of 3 5.50 2.75

Nos. 920-922 were each printed in sheets of 8 + central label.

Christmas — A364

Designs: 50c, Gift box, pine cones and Christmas ornaments. 85c, Christmas ornaments and pine cones.

***Serpentine Die Cut 14¼x15 Syncopated***

**2015, Dec. 3 Litho.**
**Self-Adhesive**
923-924 A364 Set of 2 3.00 1.50

Attack of Soviet Forces Against Latvian Barricades, 25th Anniv. — A365

**2016, Jan. 13 Litho. Perf. 13¼**
925 A365 54c multi 1.25 .60

Coats of Arms of Municipalities — A366

Designs: 50c, Alsunga. 57c, Beverina. €1.39, Smiltene.

***Serpentine Die Cut 20x18 Syncopated***

**2016, Jan. 29 Litho.**
**Self-Adhesive**
926 A366 50c red & multi 1.10 .55
927 A366 57c blue & multi 1.25 .60
928 A366 €1.39 tan & multi 3.00 1.50
Nos. 926-928 (3) 5.35 2.65

See Nos. 956-958, 984-986, 1011-1013, 1040-1044, 1063-1065.

Stuffed Male and Female Tetrao Tetrix from Latvian Natural History Museum — A367

**2016, Feb. 19 Litho. Perf. 13¼**
929 A367 €1.71 multi 3.75 1.90

Nymphaea — A368

**2016, Mar. 4 Litho. Perf. 13¼**
930 A368 50c multi 1.25 .60

**Souvenir Sheet**

Janis Rozentals (1866-1916), Painter — A369

No. 931: a, Kardinasana (Temptation), painting by Rozentals. b, Rozentals.

**2016, Mar. 18 Litho. Perf. 13¼**
931 A369 50c Sheet of 2, #a-b 2.25 1.10

2016 Floorball World Championships, Riga — A370

**2016, Apr. 9 Litho. Perf. 13¼x13½**
932 A370 64c multi 1.50 .75

A371 Europa — A372

**2016, May 9 Litho. Perf. 13¼**
933 A371 78c multi 1.75 .85
934 A372 78c multi 1.75 .85
a. Tete-beche pair 3.50 3.50
b. Booklet pane of 4, perf. 13¼ on 3 sides 7.00 —
Complete booklet, #934b 7.00

Think Green Issue.

Birds — A373

Designs: 71c, Glaucidium passerinum. €1.71, Dendrocopos major.

**2016, May 20 Litho. Perf. 13¾x14**
935-936 A373 Set of 2 5.50 2.75

**Souvenir Sheet**

1941 Deportation of Latvians to Siberia, 75th Anniv. — A374

No. 937 — Photographs of deportees and inscription: a, "14.06.1941." b, "Litene."

**2016, June 14 Litho. Perf. 13¼**
937 A374 50c Sheet of 2, #a-b 2.25 1.10

Cesis Concert Hall — A375

**2016, July 15 Litho. Perf. 13¼x13½**
938 A375 €1.57 multi 3.50 1.75

Gustavs Erenpreiss (1891-1956), Bicycle Manufacturer — A376

**2016, July 23 Litho. Perf. 13¼**
939 A376 50c multi 1.10 .55

Restoration of Latvian Independence, 25th Anniv. — A377

**2016, Aug. 21 Litho. Perf. 13¼**
940 A377 50c multi 1.10 .55

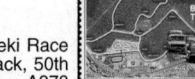

Bikernieki Race Track, 50th Anniv. — A378

**2016, Sept. 9 Litho. Perf. 13¼x13¾**
941 A378 57c multi 1.25 .65

Krustpils Railroad Station — A379

**2016, Sept. 12 Litho. Perf. 13¾**
942 A379 €1.49 multi 3.50 1.75

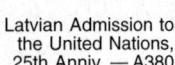

Latvian Admission to the United Nations, 25th Anniv. — A380

**2016, Sept. 18 Litho. Perf. 14x13¾**
943 A380 54c multi 1.25 .60

Andrejs Pumpurs (1841-1902), Poet and Army Officer — A381

***Perf. 13¼x13½***
**2016, Sept. 22 Litho.**
944 A381 €1.41 multi 3.25 1.60

Ovisi Lighthouse — A382

**2016, Oct. 7 Litho. Perf. 13¼**
945 A382 90c multi 2.00 2.00
a. Booklet pane of 4, perf. 13¼ on 3 sides 8.00 —
Complete booklet, #945a 8.00

Archbishop Janis Pommers (1876-1934) — A383

**2016, Oct. 12 Litho. Perf. 13¼**
946 A383 50c multi 1.10 1.10

Barquentine Andreas Weide — A384

**2016, Oct. 28 Litho. Perf. 13¼**
947 A384 61c multi 1.40 1.40

Baltic Assembly, 25th Anniv. — A385

**2016, Nov. 8 Litho. Perf. 13½x13¼**
**Stamp With White Frame**
948 A385 50c multi 1.10 1.10
**Souvenir Sheet**
**Stamp With Multicolored Frame**
949 A385 €1.39 multi 3.00 3.00

See Estonia Nos. 827-828, Lithuania Nos. 1088-1089.

**Souvenir Sheet**

Medalists at 2016 Paralympics, Rio de Janeiro — A386

No. 950: a, Diana Dadzite, javelin gold medalist. b, Aigars Apinis, discus gold medalist. c, Edgars Bergs, shot put bronze medalist.

**2016, Nov. 15 Litho. Perf. 13¼**
950 A386 50c Sheet of 3, #a-c, + label 3.25 3.25

Republic of Latvia, 98th Anniv. — A387

Designs: 50c, Janis Lusis, Dainis Kula and Inese Jaunzeme, Olympic gold medalists in javelin. 57c, Uljana Semjonova and Janis Krumins, Olympic medalists in basketball. €1.42, Sandis Ozolinsh, Sergejs Zoltoks, Arturs Irbe, Helmuts Balderis, Karlis Skrastins, past Latvian National Team and National Hockey League players.

**2016, Nov. 17 Litho. Perf. 14**
951-953 A387 Set of 3 5.50 5.50

A388

Christmas — A389

## Serpentine Die Cut 14¼x15
### Syncopated
**2016, Nov. 25**       Litho.
#### Self-Adhesive
954 A388 50c multi     1.10 1.10
955 A389 78c multi     1.75 1.75

### Coats of Arms of Municipalities
### Type of 2016
Designs: 50c, Olaine. 57c, Rojas. €1.39, Malpils.

## Serpentine Die Cut 20x18
### Syncopated
**2017, Jan. 13**       Litho.
#### Self-Adhesive
956 A366   50c green & multi   1.10 .55
957 A366   57c blue & multi   1.25 .60
958 A366   €1.39 red & multi   3.00 1.50
    Nos. 956-958 (3)     5.35 2.65

Rosa Canina — A390

**2017, Feb. 17**    Litho.    *Perf. 13¼*
959 A390 €1.42 multi     3.00 1.50

Freesia — A391

**2017, Mar. 3**    Litho.    *Perf. 13¼*
960 A391 64c multi     1.40 .70

Europa — A392

Designs: 78c, Cesvaine Palace. €1.71, Bauska Castle.

**2017, Apr. 21**   Litho.   *Perf. 14x13¾*
961 A392   78c multi     1.75 .85
  *a.*   Tete-beche pair    3.50 1.75
  *b.*   Booklet pane of 4, perf. 14x13¾
     on 3 sides    7.00 —
     Complete booklet, #961b   7.00
962 A392 €1.71 multi     3.75 1.90

Schooner
Abraham — A393

**2017, May 9**    Litho.    *Perf. 13¼*
963 A393 61c multi     1.40 .70

Family
Day — A394

**2017, May 15**    Litho.    *Perf. 13¼*
964 A394 50c multi     1.10 .55

### Souvenir Sheet

Janis Tidemanis (1897-1964),
Painter — A395

No. 965: a, Masks, by Tidemanis. b, Tidemanis.

**2017, May 26**    Litho.    *Perf. 13¼*
965 A395 50c Sheet of 2, #a-b   2.25 1.10

1903 Krastin
Automobile
A396

**2017, June 2**   Litho.   *Perf. 13¼x13½*
966 A396 €1.39 multi     3.25 1.60

Meles Meles — A397

**2017, June 16**   Litho.   *Perf. 14x13¾*
967 A397 85c multi     2.00 1.00

Birds — A398

Designs: 50c, Motacilla flava. €1.41, Porzana parva.

**2017, July 14**   Litho.   *Perf. 14x13¾*
968-969 A398   Set of 2     5.00 2.50

Ceramic Sculpture
by Dainis
Pundurs — A399

**2017, Aug. 18**    Litho.    *Perf. 13¼*
970 A399 €1.49 multi     3.75 1.90

Rojas
Lighthouse — A400

**2017, Sept. 8**    Litho.    *Perf. 13¼*
971 A400 90c multi     2.10 1.10
  *a.*   Booklet pane of 4, perf. 13¼ on
     3 sides    8.50 —
     Complete booklet, #971a   8.50

University of Latvia
Natural Sciences
Academic
Center — A401

**2017, Sept. 28**    Litho.    *Perf. 13¼*
972 A401 €1.39 multi     3.25 1.60

Eduards Veidenbaums
(1867-92), Poet — A402

**2017, Oct. 3**    Litho.    *Perf. 13¼*
973 A402 57c multi     1.40 .70

Venta-1, First
Latvian Satellite
A403

**2017, Oct. 6**   Litho.   *Perf. 13¼x13½*
974 A403 85c multi     2.00 1.00

Anti-Corruption
Campaign — A404

**2017, Oct. 10**    Litho.    *Perf. 13¼*
975 A404 50c multi     1.25 .60

Andreas Knopken (c. 1468-1539) and
Martin Luther (1483-1546), Religious
Reformers — A405

**2017, Oct. 27**    Litho.    *Perf. 13¼*
976 A405 85c multi     2.00 1.00

Protestant Reformation, 500th anniv.

Republic of Latvia, 99th
Anniv. — A406

Designs: 50s, Friedrich Zander (1887-1933), rocket designer, Karlis Steins (1911-83), astronomer, Janis Ikaunieks (1912-69), astronomer, and Arturs Balklavs (1933-2005), astronomer. 57s, Surgeons Romans Lacis, Pauls Stradins (1896-1958) and Viktors Kalnberzs. €1.42, Chemists Pauls Valdens (1863-1957), Janis Stradins and Wilhelm Ostwald (1853-1932).

**2017, Nov. 3**    Litho.    *Perf. 14*
977-979 A406   Set of 3     6.00 6.00

### Souvenir Sheet

Alona Ostapenko, 2017 French Open
Tennis Champion — A407

**2017, Nov. 10**    Litho.    *Perf. 13¼*
980 A407 €1.42 multi     3.50 3.50

A408          A409

Christmas — A410

## Serpentine Die Cut 14¼x14½
### Syncopated
**2017, Nov. 24**       Litho.
#### Self-Adhesive
981 A408 50c multi     1.25 1.25
982 A409 78c multi     1.90 1.90
983 A410 85c multi     2.10 2.10
    Nos. 981-983 (3)     5.25 5.25

### Coats of Arms of Municipalities
### Type of 2016
Designs: 50c, Kegums. 57c, Rundale. €1.39, Seja.

## Serpentine Die Cut 20x18
### Syncopated
**2018, Jan. 19**       Litho.
#### Self-Adhesive
984 A366   50c citron & multi   1.25 .60
985 A366   57c car lake & multi   1.40 .70
986 A366   €1.39 dk grn & multi   3.50 1.75
    Nos. 984-986 (3)     6.15 3.05

2018 Winter
Olympics,
PyeongChang, South
Korea — A411

**2018, Feb. 2**    Litho.    *Perf. 14x13¾*
987 A411 61c multi     1.50 .75

Gypsum Rock in Latvia
Museum of Natural
History — A412

**2018, Feb. 16**    Litho.    *Perf. 13¼*
988 A412 €1.42 multi     3.50 1.75

### Souvenir Sheet

Ansis Cirulis (1883-1942),
Painter — A413

No. 989: a, *Shipping*, stained-glass panels by Cirulis. b, Cirulis and stained-glass window.

**2018, Feb. 23**    Litho.    *Perf. 13¼*
989 A413 50c Sheet of 2, #a-b   2.50 1.25

Flag and Map of
Latvia — A414

## Serpentine Die Cut 14 on 3 Sides
**2018, Mar. 9**       Litho.
#### Self-Adhesive
990 A414 50c multi     1.25 .60

Independence, cent.

Europa — A415

Designs: 78c, Jugla Railway Bridge. €1.49, Gauja River Bridge.

**2018, Apr. 20**   Litho.   *Perf. 14x13¾*
991 A415   78c multi     1.90 .95
  *a.*   Booklet pane of 4, perf. 13¾ on
     3 sides    7.75
     Complete booklet, #991a   7.75
992 A415 €1.49 multi     3.75 1.90

No. 991a contains two vertical tete-beche pairs.

Amphitheater,
Garden of
Destiny — A416

**2018, May 18**    Litho.    *Perf. 13¼*
993 A416 61c multi     1.50 .75

Birds — A417

Designs: 50c, Tringa totanus. €1.41, Aegithalos caudatus.

**2018, June 8  Litho.  Perf. 14x13¼**
994-995  A417  Set of 2  4.50  2.25

Republic of Latvia, Cent. — A418

Designs: 54c, Haralds Mednis (1906-2000), conductor. 57c, Dancers. €1.42, People and Ligo Festival banner.

**2018, June 29  Litho.  Perf. 14**
996-998  A418  Set of 3  6.00  3.00

1939 Ford-Vairogs V8 Automobile A419

**2018, July 13  Litho.  Perf. 13¼x13½**
999  A419  €1.39 multi  3.25  1.60

Najas Tenuissima — A420

**2018, Aug. 10  Litho.  Perf. 13¼**
1000  A420  85c multi  2.00  1.00

Curonian Kings — A421

**2018, Sept. 7  Litho.  Perf. 13¼x13½**
1001  A421  €5 multi  11.50  5.75

Visit of Pope Francis to Latvia — A422

**2018, Sept. 24  Litho.  Perf. 13¼**
1002  A422  61c multi  1.40  .70

Souvenir Sheet

Diplomatic Relations Between Latvia and Kyrgyzstan, 25th Anniv. — A423

No. 1003: a, Lacplesis on Freedom Monument, Riga. b, Monument to Manas the Great, Bishkek, Kyrgyzstan.

**2018, Oct. 5  Litho.  Perf. 13½**
1003  A423  €1.10  Sheet of 2, #a-b, + central label  5.00  2.50

See Kyrgyz Express Post No. 92.

Riga Latvian Society, 150th Anniv. — A424

**2018, Oct. 12  Litho.  Perf. 13¼x13½**
1004  A424  54c multi  1.25  .60

Ragaciema Lighthouse — A425

**2018, Oct. 19  Litho.  Perf. 13¼**
1005  A425  64c multi  1.50  .75

Souvenir Sheet

Oskars Melbardis and Janis Strenga, Bronze Medalists in Bobsledding at 2018 Winter Olympics — A426

**2018, Nov. 1  Litho.  Perf. 13¼**
1006  A426  €3.06 multi  7.00  3.50

**Arms Type of 1918 Redrawn With Euro Denominations**
**2018, Nov. 16  Litho.  Perf. 14**
1007  A1  54c carmine  1.25  .60

First Latvian postage stamps, cent.

Christmas — A427

Designs: 50c, Man, woman, dog and cat, holiday feast. 78c, Person in bear costume dancing. 85c, Family welcoming Santa Claus.

***Serpentine Die Cut 14½x15 Syncopated***
**2018, Nov. 23  Litho.**
**Self-Adhesive**
1008-1010  A427  Set of 3  5.00  2.50

**Coats of Arms of Municipalities Type of 2016**
Designs: 50c, Tukums. 54c, Aizpute. 57c, Rucava.

***Serpentine Die Cut 20x18 Syncopated***
**2019, Jan. 18  Litho.**
**Self-Adhesive**
1011  A366  50c green & multi  1.25  .60
1012  A366  54c red & multi  1.25  .60
1013  A366  57c blue & multi  1.40  .70
Nos. 1011-1013 (3)  3.90  1.90

Souvenir Sheet

Johans Valters (1869-1932), Painter — A428

No. 1014: a, Farm Girl, by Valters. b, Valters.

**2019, Feb. 8  Litho.  Perf. 13¼**
1014  A428  50c Sheet of 2, #a-b  2.25  1.10

Gnorimus Nobilis — A429

**2019, Feb. 15  Litho.  Perf. 13¼**
1015  A429  €1.57 multi  3.75  1.90

Sliteres Lighthouse — A430

**2019, Mar. 15  Litho.  Perf. 13¼**
1016  A430  90c multi  2.00  1.00

Matisa Street Water Tower, Riga — A431

**2019, Mar. 29  Litho.  Perf. 13¼**
1017  A431  61c multi  1.40  .70

Europa — A432

Motacilla alba: 78c, Entire bird. €1.71, Head of bird.

**2019, Apr. 26  Litho.  Perf. 14x13¾**
1018  A432  78c multi  1.75  .90
  *a.*  Booklet pane of 4, perf.
       14x13¾ on 3 sides  7.00  —
       Complete booklet, #1018a  7.00
1019  A432  €1.71 multi  4.00  2.00

Mother's Day — A433

**2019, May 10  Litho.  Perf. 13¼**
1020  A433  50c multi  1.10  .55

1938 Ford-Vairogs V8 Fire Truck — A434

**2019, May 24  Litho.  Perf. 13¼x13½**
1021  A434  €1.39 multi  3.25  1.60

Ligo Day Floral Crown — A435

***Serpentine Die Cut 14¾x14¼ Syncopated***
**2019, June 13  Litho.**
**Self-Adhesive**
1022  A435  50c multi  1.10  .55

Rihards Zarins (1869-1939), Graphic Artist and Stamp Designer — A436

**2019, June 27  Litho.  Perf. 13¼**
1023  A436  57c multi  1.40  .70

No. 1023 was printed in sheets of 8 + 4 central labels.

Latvian Army, Cent. — A437

Designs: No. 1024, 50c, Helicopters and crew members. No. 1025, 50c, Tank. No. 1026, 50c, Ships.

**2019, July 10  Litho.  Perf. 13¼x13½**
1024-1026  A437  Set of 3  3.50  1.75

Passerby, Painting by Blind Child Attending Strazsumuiza Boarding School — A438

**2019, July 26  Litho.  Perf. 13¼**
1027  A438  90c multi  2.00  1.00

Clanga Pomarina — A439

**2019, Aug. 16  Litho.  Perf. 14x13¾**
1028  A439  78c multi  1.75  .85

Latvian Academy of Art, Cent. — A440

**2019, Aug. 20  Litho.  Perf. 13½**
1029  A440  85c multi  1.90  .95

Father's Day — A441

**2019, Sept. 8  Litho.  Perf. 13¼**
1030  A441  50c multi  1.10  .55

University of Latvia, Cent. — A442

Designs: 57c, Old building. 85c, Modern building.

**2019, Sept. 27  Litho.  Perf. 14**
1031-1032  A442  Set of 2  3.25  1.60

Nos. 1031-1032 were each printed in sheets of 8 + 4 labels.

Ivan Zavoloko (1897-1984), Educator and Clergyman — A443

**2019, Oct. 3  Litho.  Perf. 14**
1033  A443  90c multi  2.00  1.00

Garlieb Merkelis (1769-1850), Writer — A444

**2019, Nov. 1  Litho.  Perf. 13¼x13½**
1034 A444 €1.42 multi      3.25 1.60

Defeat of the Bermontian Army (West Russian Volunteer Army), Cent. — A445

**2019, Nov. 7  Litho.  Perf. 13¼x13½**
1035 A445 50c multi      1.10 .55

Christmas — A446

Designs: 50c, Mouse on ice skates. 78c, Two snowmen. 85c, Girl wearing stocking cap.

*Serpentine Die Cut 14¾x14¼ Syncopated*
**2019, Nov. 22  Litho.**
**Self-Adhesive**
1036-1038 A446 Set of 3      4.75 2.40

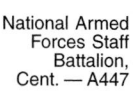

National Armed Forces Staff Battalion, Cent. — A447

*Perf. 13¼x13½*
**2019, Dec. 10  Litho.**
1039 A447 50c multi      1.10 .55

**Coats of Arms of Municipalities Type of 2016**
Designs: €1, Durbe. €1.29, Krimulda. €1.35, Koknese. €1.42, Babite. €1.54, Vilani.

*Serpentine Die Cut 20x18 Syncopated*
**2020, Jan. 3  Litho.**
**Self-Adhesive**
1040 A366 €1 sil & dp blue      2.25 1.10
1041 A366 €1.29 gold & red      3.00 1.50
1042 A366 €1.35 sil, gold & brn pur      3.00 1.50
1043 A366 €1.42 sil & multi      3.25 1.60
1044 A366 €1.54 sil, gold & emer      3.50 1.75
  Nos. 1040-1044 (5)      15.00 7.45

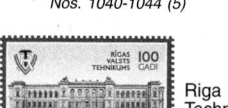

Riga State Technical School, Cent. — A448

**2020, Jan. 10  Litho.  Perf. 13½**
1045 A448 €1 multi      2.25 1.10

Four-masted Ship Eurasia — A449

**2020, Jan. 31  Litho.  Perf. 13¼**
1046 A449 €1.27 multi      1.75 .85

Baltic Amber — A450

**2020, Feb. 14  Litho.  Perf. 13¼**
1047 A450 €2.69 multi      6.00 3.00

Europa — A451

Designs: €1.35, Mail deliverer on bicycle. €1.42, Post rider and coach.

**2020, May 8  Litho.  Perf. 13¼**
1048-1049 A451 Set of 2      6.25 3.25
  Ancient Postal Routes.

Alises Street Water Tower, Riga — A452

**2020, May 15  Litho.  Perf. 13¼**
1050 A452 €1.71 multi      3.75 1.90

International Year of Plant Health — A453

**2020, May 29  Litho.  Perf. 13¾**
1051 A453 €2.25 multi      5.00 2.50

Birds — A454

Designs: €1.27, Tetrastes bonasia. €2.14, Alcedo atthis.

**2020, June 19  Litho.  Perf. 13¾**
1052-1053 A454 Set of 2      7.75 4.00

*Banuta,* Opera by Alfreds Kalnins (1879-1951), Cent. — A455

**2020, July 3  Litho.  Perf. 13¼x13½**
1054 A455 €1 multi      2.40 1.25

Souvenir Sheet

Gustavs Klucis (1895-1938), Photographer and Poster Designer — A456

No. 1055: a, *Construction,* 1921 poster design. b, Klucis.

**2020, July 10  Litho.  Perf. 13¼**
1055 A456 €1 Sheet of 2, #a-b  4.75 2.40

Gospel of Jersika, 750th Anniv. — A457

**2020, Aug. 21  Litho.  Perf. 13¼**
1056 A457 €1 multi      2.40 1.25
No. 1056 was printed in sheets of 8 + 4 labels.

Emilija Gudriniece (1920-2004), Organic Chemist A458

*Perf. 13¼x13½*
**2020, Sept. 18  Litho.**
1057 A458 €1 multi      2.40 1.25

Janis Dalins (1904-78), Race Walker — A459

**2020, Oct. 23  Litho.  Perf. 13¼**
1058 A459 €1 multi      2.40 1.25

Eduard Smilgis (1886-1966), Founder of Dailes Theater and Director — A460

**2020, Nov. 19  Litho.  Perf. 13¼**
1059 A460 €1 multi      2.40 1.25
  Dailes Theater, Riga, cent.

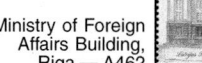

Christmas — A461

Designs: €1, Santa Claus holding lantern. €1.42, Santa Claus and reindeer with gift. €1.54, Santa Claus carrying Christmas tree, boy on sled.

*Serpentine Die Cut 14¾x14¼ Syncopated*
**2020, Nov. 27  Litho.**
**Self-Adhesive**
1060-1062 A461 Set of 3      9.50 4.75

**Coats of Arms of Municipalities Type of 2016**
Designs: 62c, Grobina. 89c, Engure. €1, Ropazi.

*Serpentine Die Cut 20x18 Syncopated*
**2021, Jan. 8  Litho.**
**Self-Adhesive**
1063 A366 62c red & multi      1.50 .75
1064 A366 89c brt blue & multi      2.25 1.10
1065 A366 €1 blue grn & multi      2.40 1.25
  Nos. 1063-1065 (3)      6.15 3.10

Ministry of Foreign Affairs Building, Riga — A462

**2021, Jan. 26  Litho.  Perf. 13¼**
1066 A462 €1 multi      2.40 1.25
International Recognition of Latvian Sovereignty, cent.

Barquentine Mercator — A463

**2021, Feb. 19  Litho.  Perf. 13¼**
1067 A463 €1.27 multi      3.00 1.50

Ernests Birznieks-Upitis (1871-1960), Writer — A464

**2021, Mar. 26  Litho.  Perf. 13¼**
1068 A464 €1.27 multi      3.00 1.50

Endangered Animals — A465

Designs: €1, Margaritifera margaritifera. €1.27, Ciconia nigra.

**2021, Apr. 23  Litho.  Perf. 14**
1069-1070 A465 Set of 2      5.50 2.75
  Europa.

Ciekurkains Water Tower, Riga — A466

**2021, May 14  Litho.  Perf. 13¼**
1071 A466 €1 multi      2.50 1.25

2021 Ice Hockey World Championships, Latvia — A467

**2021, May 21  Litho.  Perf. 13¼x13½**
1072 A467 €1.71 multi      4.25 2.10

Latvian Soccer Federation, Cent. — A468

**2021, May 27  Litho.  Perf. 13¼**
1073 A468 €1 multi      2.50 1.25

Souvenir Sheet

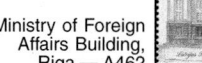

National Symbols A469

No. 1074 — Latvian: a, Flag. b, Coat of arms.

**2021, June 15  Litho.  Perf. 13¼**
1074 A469 €1 Sheet of 2, #a-b  4.75 2.40

Gladiolus Imbricatus — A470

**2021, July 2  Litho.  Perf. 13¼**
1075 A470 €1.27 multi      3.00 1.50

Birds — A471

Designs: €1, Perdix perdix. €1.27, Pyrrhula pyrrhula.

**2021, July 16   Litho.   Perf. 14x13¾**
1076-1077 A471   Set of 2   5.50 2.75

Items in Porcelain Museum, Riga — A472

**2021, Aug. 6   Litho.   Perf. 13¼**
1078 A472   €1 multi   2.40 1.25

Latvian National Guard, 30th Anniv. — A473

**Perf. 13¼x13½**
**2021, Aug. 11   Litho.**
1079 A473   €1 multi   2.40 1.25

Riga State Gymnasium No. 1 — A474

**Perf. 13¼x13½**
**2021, Aug. 27   Litho.**
1080 A474   €1 multi   2.40 1.25

Souvenir Sheet

Janis Pauluks (1906-84), Painter — A475

No. 1081: a, Felicita in a Colored Dress, by Janis Pauluks. b, Pauluks.

**2021, Sept. 2   Litho.   Perf. 13¼**
1081 A475   €1 Sheet of 2, #a-b   4.75 2.40

Irbe Lighthouse — A476

**2021, Sept. 17   Litho.   Perf. 13¼**
1082 A476   €1.27 multi   3.00 1.50

Souvenir Sheet

Janis Lusis (1939-2020), Gold Medalist Javelin Thrower at 1968 Summer Olympics — A477

**2021, Sept. 24   Litho.   Perf. 13¼**
1083 A477   €2.69 multi   6.25 3.25

Illustration by Anita Paegle From The Ghost of Roses — A478

**2021, Oct. 1   Litho.   Perf. 13¼x13½**
1084 A478   €1 multi   2.40 1.25

Janis Poruks (1871-1911), Writer — A479

**2021, Oct. 13   Litho.   Perf. 13¼**
1085 A479   €1 multi   2.40 1.25

Christmas — A480

Designs: €1, Cat, Christmas tree and ornaments. €1.42, Dog and Christmas gifts. €1.54, Mouse and pine cones.

**Serpentine Die Cut 14¼x14¾ Syncopated**
**2021, Nov. 15   Litho.**
**Self-Adhesive**
1086-1088 A480   Set of 3   9.00 4.50

Latvian 3-on-3 Basketball Team, Gold Medalists at 2020 Summer Olympics — A481

**2021, Nov. 29   Litho.   Perf. 13¼**
1089 A481   €1 multi   2.25 1.10

The 2020 Summer Olympics were postponed until 2021 because of the COVID-19 pandemic.

Domesticated Animals — A482

Designs: €1.20, Cat. €1.47, Dog. €1.56, Rooster and hen. €1.75, Goose.

**Serpentine Die Cut 20x18 Syncopated**
**2022, Jan. 14   Litho.**
**Self-Adhesive**
1090 A482   €1.20 multi   2.75 1.40
1091 A482   €1.47 multi   3.25 1.60
1092 A482   €1.56 multi   3.50 1.75
1093 A482   €1.75 multi   4.00 2.00
Nos. 1090-1093 (4)   13.50 6.75

Gaff Schooner Eufrosine, 120th Anniv. — A483

**2022, Jan. 21   Litho.   Perf. 13¼**
1094 A483   €1.44 multi   3.25 1.60

Items in Latvian Sports Museum, Riga — A484

**2022, Jan. 25   Litho.   Perf. 13¼**
1095 A484   €1.44 multi   3.25 1.60

Vilhelms Purvitis (1872-1945), Painter — A485

**2022, Mar. 4   Litho.   Perf. 13¼**
1096 A485   €1.20 multi   2.75 1.40

Svarcmuiza Manor, Riga — A486

**2022, Mar. 11   Litho.   Perf. 13¼**
1097 A486   €2.34 multi   5.25 2.60

Gunars Astra (1931-88), Anti-Soviet Dissident — A487

**2022, Mar. 25   Litho.   Perf. 13¼**
1098 A487   €1.20 multi   2.75 1.40

Heavenly Father Feeding Grass Snakes — A488

Heavenly Father On White Horse — A489

**2022, Apr. 8   Litho.   Perf. 14x13¾**
1099 A488   €1.77 multi   3.75 1.90
1100 A489   €1.98 multi   4.25 2.10
Europa.

Alice's Adventures in Wonderland, by Lewis Carroll — A490

**2022, Apr. 29   Litho.   Perf. 13¼x13½**
1101 A490   €1.20 multi   2.60 1.30

Latvian Constitution, Cent. — A491

**2022, May 6   Litho.   Perf. 13¼**
1102 A491   €1.20 multi   2.60 1.30

Latvian Olympic Committee, Cent. — A492

**2022, May 11   Litho.   Perf. 13¼**
1103 A492   €1.20 multi   2.60 1.30

Renovation of Museum of the Occupation of Latvia, Riga — A493

**2022, May 18   Litho.   Perf. 13¼x13½**
1104 A493   €1.20 multi   2.60 1.30

University of Latvia Botanical Garden, Cent. — A494

**2022, June 2   Litho.   Perf. 13¼**
1105 A494   €1.20 multi   2.60 1.30

Lobelia Dortmanna — A495

**2022, June 17   Litho.   Perf. 13¼**
1106 A495   €1.20 multi   2.50 1.25

Birds — A496

Designs: €1.20, Apus apus. €1.47, Pica pica.

**2022, July 8   Litho.   Perf. 13¾**
1107-1108 A496   Set of 2   5.50 2.75

Diplomatic Relations Between Latvia and the United States, Cent. — A497

**2022, July 28   Litho.   Perf. 13½x13¼**
1109 A497   €1.98 multi   4.00 2.00

Water Tower, Riga — A498

**2022, Aug. 12   Litho.   Perf. 13¼**
1110 A498   €1.20 multi   2.40 1.25

Concordat Between Latvia and Vatican City, Cent. — A500

**2022, Sept. 1   Litho.   Perf. 13¼x13½**
1112 A500   €2.46 multi   4.50 2.25
See Vatican City No. 1803.

Souvenir Sheet

Hilda Vika (1897-1963), Painter — A501

No. 1113: a, In Autumn, by Hilda Vika. b, Vika.

**2022, Sept. 23   Litho.   Perf. 13¼**
1113 A501   €1.20 Sheet of 2, #a-b   4.75 2.40

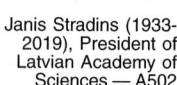

Janis Stradins (1933-2019), President of Latvian Academy of Sciences — A502

**2022, Oct. 7**    **Litho.**    **Perf. 13¼**
1114   A502   €1.20 multi    2.40   1.25

Latvian Parliament, Cent. — A503

**2022, Oct. 20**    **Litho.**    **Perf. 14**
1115   A503   €1.20 multi    2.40   1.25

Zenta Maurina (1897-1978), Writer — A504

**2022, Oct. 28**    **Litho.**    **Perf. 13¼**
1116   A504   €1.20 multi    2.40   1.25

Christmas — A505

Designs: €1.20, Four gnomes. €1.50, Two gnomes. €1.98, Three gnomes.

*Serpentine Die Cut 14¼x14¾ Syncopated*
**2022, Nov. 11**    **Litho.**
**Self-Adhesive**
1117-1119   A505   Set of 3    9.75   5.00

## SEMI-POSTAL STAMPS

"Mercy" Assisting Wounded Soldier — SP1

### Brown and Green Design on Back
**1920**    **Unwmk.**    **Typo.**    **Perf. 11½**
B1   SP1   20(30)k dk brn & red    .50   1.20
B2   SP1   40(55)k dk bl & red    .50   1.20
B3   SP1   50(70)k dk grn & red    .50   1.60
B4   SP1   1(1.30)r dl sl & red    .50   1.60
### Wmk. 197
### Blue Design on Back
B5   SP1   20(30)k dk brn & red    .70   1.20
B6   SP1   40(55)k dk bl & red    .70   1.20
   a.   Vert. pair, imperf. btwn.    40.00
B7   SP1   50(70)k dk grn & red    .70   1.60
B8   SP1   1(1.30)r dk sl & red    .70   2.40
### Wmk. Similar to 145
### Pink Paper    Imperf.
### Brown, Green and Red Design on Back
B9   SP1   20(30)k dk brn & red    1.00   2.50
B10   SP1   40(55)k dk bl & red    1.00   2.50
B11   SP1   50(70)k dk grn & red    1.00   2.50
B12   SP1   1(1.30)r dk sl & red    2.00   4.25
   *Nos. B1-B12 (12)*    9.80   23.75
   Set, never hinged    22.50

These semi-postal stamps were printed on the backs of unfinished bank notes of the Workers and Soldiers Council, Riga, and the Bermondt-Avalov Army. Blocks of stamps showing complete banknotes on reverse are worth approximately three times the catalogue value of the stamps.

Nos. B1-B8 Surcharged

### Brown and Green Design on Back
**1921**    **Unwmk.**    **Perf. 11½**
B13   SP1   20k + 2r dk brn & red    2.50   4.00
B14   SP1   40k + 2r dk bl & red    2.50   4.00
B15   SP1   50k + 2r dk grn & red    2.50   4.00
B16   SP1   1r + 2r dk sl & red    2.50   4.00
### Wmk. 197
### Blue Design on Back
B17   SP1   20k + 2r dk brn & red    10.00   40.00
B18   SP1   40k + 2r dk bl & red    10.00   40.00
B19   SP1   50k + 2r dk grn & red    10.00   40.00
B20   SP1   1r + 2r dk sl & red    10.00   40.00
   *Nos. B13-B20 (8)*    50.00   176.00
   Set, never hinged    150.00

Regular Issue of 1923-25 Surcharged in Dark Blue and Light Blue

**1923**    **Wmk. Similar to 181**    **Perf. 10**
B21   A12   1s + 10s redsh pur    .70   1.75
B22   A12   2s + 10s yel org    .70   1.75
B23   A12   4s + 10s dk green    .70   1.75
   *Nos. B21-B23 (3)*    2.10   5.25
   Set, never hinged    5.00

The surtax benefited the Latvian War Invalids Society.

Lighthouse and Harbor, Liepaja (Libau) SP2

Church at Liepaja SP5

Coat of Arms of Liepaja — SP6

Designs: 15s (25s), City Hall, Liepaja. 25s (35s), Public Bathing Pavilion, Liepaja.

**1925, July 23**    **Perf. 11½**
B24   SP2   6s (12s) red brn & dp blue    3.75   5.50
B25   SP2   15s (25s) dk bl & brn    2.25   4.00
B26   SP2   25s (35s) vio & dk grn    3.75   4.00
B27   SP5   30s (40s) dk blue & lake    6.75   12.00
B28   SP6   50s (60s) dk grn & vio    9.75   16.00
   *Nos. B24-B28 (5)*    26.25   41.50
   Set, never hinged    55.00

Tercentenary of Liepaja (Libau). The surtax benefited that city. Exist imperf. Value, unused set $500.

President Janis Cakste — SP7

**1928, Apr. 18**    **Engr.**
B29   SP7   2s (12s) red orange    2.25   3.25
B30   SP7   6s (16s) deep green    2.25   3.25
B31   SP7   15s (25s) red brown    2.25   3.25
B32   SP7   25s (35s) deep blue    2.25   3.25
B33   SP7   30s (40s) claret    2.25   3.25
   *Nos. B29-B33 (5)*    11.25   16.25
   Set, never hinged    35.00

The surtax helped erect a monument to Janis Cakste, 1st pres. of the Latvian Republic.

Venta River — SP8

View of Jelgava — SP10

View of Cesis (Wenden) SP12

Allegory, "Latvia" — SP9

National Theater, Riga — SP11

Riga Bridge and Trenches SP13

### Perf. 11½, Imperf.
**1928, Nov. 18**    **Wmk. 212**    **Litho.**
B34   SP8   6s (16s) green    2.50   2.75
B35   SP9   10s (20s) scarlet    2.50   2.75
B36   SP10   15s (25s) maroon    2.50   2.75
B37   SP11   30s (40s) ultra    2.50   2.75
B38   SP12   50s (60s) dk gray    2.50   2.75
B39   SP13   1 l (1.10 l) choc    2.50   2.75
   *Nos. B34-B39 (6)*    15.00   16.50
   Set, never hinged    35.00

The surtax was given to a committee for the erection of a Liberty Memorial.

Z. A. Meierovics — SP14

**1929, Aug. 22**    **Perf. 11½, Imperf.**
B46   SP14   2s (4s) orange    3.00   3.00
B47   SP14   6s (12s) dp grn    3.00   3.00
B48   SP14   15s (25s) red brown    3.00   3.00
B49   SP14   25s (35s) deep blue    3.00   3.00
B50   SP14   30s (40s) ultra    3.00   3.00
   *Nos. B46-B50 (5)*    15.00   15.00
   Set, never hinged    42.50

The surtax was used to erect a monument to Z. A. Meierovics, Latvian statesman.

Tuberculosis Cross SP15

Gustavs Zemgals SP17

Allegory of Hope for the Sick SP16

Riga Castle SP18

Daisies and Double-barred Cross SP20

Tuberculosis Sanatorium, near Riga SP22

Cakste, Kviesis and Zemgals SP23

Designs: No. B61, Janis Cakste, 1st pres. of Latvia. No. B63, Pres. Alberts Kviesis.

**1930, Dec. 4**    **Typo.**    **Perf. 10, 11½**
B56   SP15   1s (2s) dk vio & red org    .75   .85
B57   SP15   2s (4s) org & red org    .75   .85
B58   SP16   4s (8s) dk grn & red    .75   .85
B59   SP17   5s (10s) brt grn & dk brn    1.50   1.75
B60   SP18   6s (12s) ol grn & bister    1.50   1.75
B61   SP17   10s (20s) dp red & blk    2.20   2.25
B62   SP20   15s (30s) mar & dl green    2.25   2.25
B63   SP17   20s (40s) rose lake & ind    2.25   2.25
B64   SP22   25s (50s) multi    3.00   3.50
B65   SP23   30s (60s) multi    3.50   4.00
   *Nos. B56-B65 (10)*    18.45   20.30
   Set, never hinged    55.00

Surtax for the Latvian Anti-Tuberculosis Soc. For surcharges see Nos. B72-B81.

J. Rainis and New Buildings, Riga — SP24

Character from Play and Rainis — SP25

Characters from Plays — SP26

Rainis and Lyre — SP27

Flames, Flag and Rainis — SP28

**1930, May 23**    **Wmk. 212**    **Perf. 11½**
B66   SP24   1s (2s) dull violet    .75   3.25
B67   SP25   2s (4s) yellow org    .75   3.25
B68   SP26   4s (8s) dp green    .75   3.25
B69   SP27   6s (12s) yel grn & red brown    .75   3.25
B70   SP28   10s (20s) dark red    22.50   47.50
B71   SP27   15s (30s) red brn & yel grn    22.50   47.50
   *Nos. B66-B71 (6)*    48.00   108.00
   Set, never hinged    95.00

Sold at double face value, surtax going to memorial fund for J. Rainis (Jan Plieksans, 1865-1929), writer and politician.
Exist imperf. Value twice that of perf. stamps.

Nos. B56 to B65 Surcharged in Black With Bars

Nos. B56 to B65
Surcharged in Black
Without Bars

**1931, Aug. 19**     *Perf. 10, 11½*

| | | | |
|---|---|---|---|
| B72 | SP18 | 9s on 6s (12s) | 1.00 | 2.00 |
| B73 | SP15 | 16s on 1s (2s) | 12.50 | 24.00 |
| B74 | SP15 | 17s on 2s (4s) | 1.25 | 2.00 |
| B75 | SP16 | 19s on 4s (8s) | 3.75 | 8.50 |
| B76 | SP17 | 20s on 5s (10s) | 2.50 | 8.50 |
| B77 | SP20 | 23s on 15s (30s) | 1.00 | 1.50 |
| B78 | SP17 | 25s on 10s (20s) | 2.50 | 4.00 |
| B79 | SP17 | 35s on 20s (40s) | 3.75 | 7.00 |
| B80 | SP22 | 45s on 25s (50s) | 10.00 | 20.00 |
| B81 | SP23 | 55s on 30s (60s) | 12.50 | 32.50 |
| | *Nos. B72-B81 (10)* | | 50.75 | 110.50 |
| | Set, never hinged | | 110.00 | |

The surcharge replaces the original total
price, including surtax.
Nos. B73-B81 have no bars in the
surcharge. The surtax aided the Latvian Anti-
Tuberculosis Society.

Lacplesis, the
Deliverer — SP29

Designs: 1s, Kriva telling stories under Holy
Oak. 2s, Enslaved Latvians building Riga
under knight's supervision. 4s, Death of Black
Knight. 5s, Spirit of Lacplesis over freed Riga.

**Inscribed: "AIZSARGI" (Army
Reserve)**

**1932, Feb. 10**    *Perf. 10½, Imperf.*

| | | | | |
|---|---|---|---|---|
| B82 | SP29 | 1s (11s) vio brn & bluish | 2.50 | 2.50 |
| B83 | SP29 | 2s (17s) ocher & ol green | 2.50 | 2.50 |
| B84 | SP29 | 3s (23s) red brn & org brown | 2.50 | 2.50 |
| B85 | SP29 | 4s (34s) dk grn & green | 2.50 | 2.50 |
| B86 | SP29 | 5s (45s) grn & emerald | 2.50 | 2.50 |
| | *Nos. B82-B86 (5)* | | 12.50 | 12.50 |
| | Set, never hinged | | 22.00 | |

Surtax aided the Militia Maintenance Fund.

Marching
Troops — SP30

Infantry in
Action — SP31

Nurse
Binding
Soldier's
Wound
SP32

Army Soup
Kitchen
SP33

Gen. J. Balodis — SP34

**1932, May**     *Perf. 10½, Imperf.*

| | | | | |
|---|---|---|---|---|
| B87 | SP30 | 6s (25s) ol brn & red violet | 4.00 | 6.50 |
| B88 | SP31 | 7s (35s) dk bl grn & dark blue | 4.00 | 6.50 |
| B89 | SP32 | 10s (45s) ol grn & blk brn | 4.00 | 6.50 |
| B90 | SP33 | 12s (55s) lake & ol green | 4.00 | 6.50 |
| B91 | SP34 | 15s (75s) red org & brn vio | 4.00 | 6.50 |
| | *Nos. B87-B91 (5)* | | 20.00 | 32.50 |
| | Set, never hinged | | 45.00 | |

The surtax aided the Latvian Home Guards.

Symbolical
of Unified
Latvia
SP35

Symbolical
of the
Strength of
the Latvian
Union
SP36

Aid to the
Sick
SP37

"Charity"
SP38

**Wmk. 212**
**1936, Dec. 28**    Litho.    *Perf. 11½*

| | | | | |
|---|---|---|---|---|
| B92 | SP35 | 3s orange red | 1.50 | 2.50 |
| B93 | SP36 | 10s green | 1.50 | 2.50 |
| B94 | SP37 | 20s rose pink | 1.50 | 3.00 |
| B95 | SP38 | 35s blue | 1.50 | 3.00 |
| | *Nos. B92-B95 (4)* | | 6.00 | 11.00 |
| | Set, never hinged | | 12.00 | |

**Souvenir Sheets**

SP39

**1938, May 12**    Wmk. 212    *Perf. 11*

| | | | | |
|---|---|---|---|---|
| B96 | SP39 | Sheet of 2 | 12.00 | 50.00 |
| | | Never hinged | 22.50 | |
| a. | | 35s Justice Palace, Riga | 2.00 | 5.00 |
| b. | | 40s Power Station, Kegums | 2.00 | 5.00 |

Sold for 2 l. The surtax of 1.25 l was for the
National Reconstruction Fund.
No. B96 exists imperf.

**Overprinted in Blue with Dates 1934
1939 and "15" over "V"**

**1939**

| | | | | |
|---|---|---|---|---|
| B97 | SP39 | Sheet of 2 | 15.00 | 75.00 |
| | | Never hinged | 40.00 | |

5th anniv. of Natl. Unity Day. Sold for 2 lats.
Surtax for the Natl. Reconstruction Fund.

Natl. Olympic
Committee — SP50

**1992, Feb. 8**    Litho.    *Perf. 13½x13*
**Background Color**

| | | | | |
|---|---|---|---|---|
| B150 | SP50 | 50k +25k gray | .60 | .60 |
| B151 | SP50 | 50k +25k buff | 1.25 | 1.25 |
| B152 | SP50 | 100k +50k bister | .80 | .80 |
| | *Nos. B150-B152 (3)* | | 2.65 | 2.65 |

No. B150 inscribed "Berlin 18.09.91."

Flags of Latvia and
Ukraine — SP51

**2022, Mar. 10**    Litho.    *Perf. 13¼*

| | | | | |
|---|---|---|---|---|
| B153 | SP51 | €1.44 + (€1.50) multi | 6.75 | 6.75 |

No. B153 was printed in sheets of 3 + 1
label. The sheet sold for €9 with half of the
proceeds of the sale of the stamps going to
the Ziedot.lv charity fund for Ukrainian assistance after its invasion by Russia.

---

# AIR POST STAMPS

Blériot XI — AP1

**Wmk. Wavy Lines Similar to 181**
**1921, July 30**    Litho.    *Perf. 11½*

| | | | | |
|---|---|---|---|---|
| C1 | AP1 | 10r emerald | 3.00 | 4.50 |
| a. | | Imperf. | 6.00 | 35.00 |
| C2 | AP1 | 20r dark blue | 3.00 | 4.50 |
| a. | | Imperf. | 6.00 | 35.00 |
| | Set, perf, never hinged | | 12.00 | |
| | Set, imperf, never hinged | | 25.00 | |

**1928, May 1**

| | | | | |
|---|---|---|---|---|
| C3 | AP1 | 10s deep green | 4.50 | 1.60 |
| C4 | AP1 | 15s red | 2.00 | 1.60 |
| C5 | AP1 | 25s ultra | 3.75 | 2.50 |
| a. | | Pair, imperf. btwn. | 35.00 | |
| | *Nos. C3-C5 (3)* | | 10.25 | 5.70 |
| | Set, never hinged | | 16.00 | |

Nos. C1-C5 sometimes show letters of a
paper maker's watermark "PACTIEN LIGAT
MILLS."

**1931-32**    Wmk. 212    *Perf. 11½*

| | | | | |
|---|---|---|---|---|
| C6 | AP1 | 10s deep green | 1.00 | .90 |
| a. | | Perf. 11 | 12.00 | 14.50 |
| C7 | AP1 | 15s red | 1.50 | 1.00 |
| a. | | Perf. 11 | 120.00 | 32.50 |
| C8 | AP1 | 25s deep blue ('32) | 8.50 | 1.25 |
| a. | | Perf. 11 | 28.00 | 14.50 |
| | *Nos. C6-C8 (3)* | | 11.00 | 3.15 |
| | Set, never hinged | | 22.50 | |

**Type of 1921 Overprinted or
Surcharged in Black**

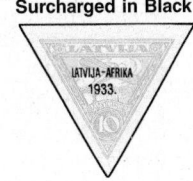

**1933, May 26**    Wmk. 212    *Imperf.*

| | | | | |
|---|---|---|---|---|
| C9 | AP1 | 10s deep green | 40.00 | 80.00 |
| C10 | AP1 | 15s red | 40.00 | 80.00 |
| C11 | AP1 | 25s deep blue | 40.00 | 80.00 |
| C12 | AP1 | 50s on 15s red | 200.00 | 525.00 |
| C13 | AP1 | 100s on 25s dp blue | 200.00 | 525.00 |
| | *Nos. C9-C13 (5)* | | 520.00 | 1,290. |
| | Set, never hinged | | 825.00 | |

Honoring and financing a flight from Riga to
Bathurst, Gambia. The plane crashed at Neus-
tettin, Germany.
Counterfeits exist of Nos. C1-C13.

# AIR POST SEMI-POSTAL STAMPS

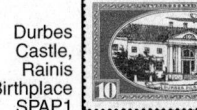

Durbes
Castle,
Rainis
Birthplace
SPAP1

**Wmk. 212**
**1930, May 26**    Litho.    *Perf. 11½*

| | | | | |
|---|---|---|---|---|
| CB1 | SPAP1 | 10s (20s) red & olive green | 6.50 | 14.50 |
| CB2 | SPAP1 | 15s (30s) dk yel grn & cop red | 6.50 | 14.50 |
| | Set, never hinged | | 25.00 | |

Surtax for the Rainis Memorial Fund.

**Imperf.**

| | | | | |
|---|---|---|---|---|
| CB1a | SPAP1 | 10s (20s) | 10.00 | 27.50 |
| CB2a | SPAP1 | 15s (30s) | 10.00 | 27.50 |
| | Set, never hinged | | 40.00 | |

---

**Nos. C6-C8 Surcharged in Magenta,
Blue or Red**

**1931, Dec. 5**

| | | | | |
|---|---|---|---|---|
| CB3 | AP1 | 10s + 50s dp grn (M) | 6.50 | 7.50 |
| CB4 | AP1 | 15s + 1 l red (Bl) | 6.50 | 7.50 |
| CB5 | AP1 | 25s + 1.50 l dp blue | 6.50 | 7.50 |
| | *Nos. CB3-CB5 (3)* | | 19.50 | 22.50 |
| | Set, never hinged | | 40.00 | |

Surtax for the Latvian Home Guards.

**Imperf.**

| | | | | |
|---|---|---|---|---|
| CB3a | AP1 | 10s + 50s | 10.00 | 11.00 |
| CB4a | AP1 | 15s + 1 l | 10.00 | 11.00 |
| CB5a | AP1 | 25s + 1.50 l | 10.00 | 11.00 |
| | *Nos. CB3a-CB5a (3)* | | 30.00 | 33.00 |
| | Set, never hinged | | 55.00 | |

SPAP2

**1932, June 17**     *Perf. 10½*

| | | | | |
|---|---|---|---|---|
| CB6 | SPAP2 | 10s (20s) dk sl grn & grn | 12.50 | 25.00 |
| CB7 | SPAP2 | 15s (30s) brt red & buff | 12.50 | 25.00 |
| CB8 | SPAP2 | 25s (50s) dp bl & gray | 12.50 | 25.00 |
| | *Nos. CB6-CB8 (3)* | | 37.50 | 75.00 |
| | Set, never hinged | | 75.00 | |

Surtax for the Latvian Home Guards.

**Imperf.**

| | | | | |
|---|---|---|---|---|
| CB6a | SPAP2 | 10s (20s) | 12.50 | 25.00 |
| CB7a | SPAP2 | 15s (30s) | 12.50 | 25.00 |
| CB8a | SPAP2 | 25s (50s) | 12.50 | 25.00 |
| | *Nos. CB6a-CB8a (3)* | | 37.50 | 75.00 |
| | Set, never hinged | | 75.00 | |

Icarus
SPAP3

Leonardo da
Vinci
SPAP4

Charles
Balloon
SPAP5

Wright Brothers
Biplane
SPAP6

Bleriot Monoplane
SPAP7

**1932, Dec.**     *Perf. 10, 11½*

| | | | | |
|---|---|---|---|---|
| CB9 | SPAP3 | 5s (25s) ol bis & grn | 17.50 | 20.00 |
| CB10 | SPAP4 | 10s (50s) ol brn & gray grn | 17.50 | 20.00 |
| CB11 | SPAP5 | 15s (75s) red brn & gray grn | 17.50 | 20.00 |
| CB12 | SPAP6 | 20s (1 l) gray grn & lil rose | 17.50 | 20.00 |
| CB13 | SPAP7 | 25s (1.25 l) brn & bl | 17.50 | 20.00 |
| | *Nos. CB9-CB13 (5)* | | 87.50 | 100.00 |
| | Set, never hinged | | 150.00 | |

Issued to honor pioneers of aviation. The
surtax of four times the face value was for
wounded Latvian aviators.

**Imperf.**

| | | | | |
|---|---|---|---|---|
| CB9a | SPAP3 | 5s (25s) | 17.50 | 20.00 |
| CB10a | SPAP4 | 10s (50s) | 17.50 | 20.00 |
| CB11a | SPAP5 | 15s (75s) | 17.50 | 20.00 |
| CB12a | SPAP6 | 20s (1 l) | 17.50 | 20.00 |
| CB13a | SPAP7 | 25s (1.25 l) | 17.50 | 20.00 |

Nos. CB9a-CB13a (5)   87.50   100.00
Set, never hinged   175.00

Icarus
Falling
SPAP8

Monument
to Aviators
SPAP9

Proposed Tombs for
Aviators
SPAP10     SPAP11

**1933, Mar. 15**     **Perf. 11½**

| CB14 | SPAP8 | 2s (52s) blk & ocher | 14.00 | 20.00 |
|---|---|---|---|---|
| CB15 | SPAP9 | 3s (53s) blk & red org | 14.00 | 20.00 |
| CB16 | SPAP10 | 10s (60s) blk & dk yel green | 14.00 | 20.00 |
| CB17 | SPAP11 | 20s (70s) blk & cerise | 14.00 | 20.00 |

Nos. CB14-CB17 (4)   56.00   80.00
Set, never hinged   125.00

50s surtax for wounded Latvian aviators.

**Imperf.**

| CB14a | SPAP8 | 2s (52s) | 15.00 | 21.00 |
|---|---|---|---|---|
| CB15a | SPAP9 | 3s (53s) | 15.00 | 21.00 |
| CB16a | SPAP10 | 10s (60s) | 15.00 | 21.00 |
| CB17a | SPAP11 | 20s (70s) | 15.00 | 21.00 |

Nos. CB14a-CB17a (4)   60.00   84.00
Set, never hinged   135.00

Biplane Taking
Off — SPAP12

Designs: 7s (57s), Biplane under fire at Riga. 35s (1.35 l), Map and planes.

**1933, June 15**   **Wmk. 212**   **Perf. 11½**

| CB18 | SPAP12 | 3s (53s) org & sl blue | 19.00 | 40.00 |
|---|---|---|---|---|
| CB19 | SPAP12 | 7s (57s) sl bl & dk brn | 19.00 | 40.00 |
| CB20 | SPAP12 | 35s (1.35 l) dp ultra & ol blk | 19.00 | 40.00 |

Nos. CB18-CB20 (3)   57.00   120.00
Set, never hinged   135.00

Surtax for wounded Latvian aviators. Counterfeits exist.

**Imperf.**

| CB18a | SPAP12 | 3s (53s) | 22.50 | 42.50 |
|---|---|---|---|---|
| CB19a | SPAP12 | 7s (57s) | 22.50 | 42.50 |
| CB20a | SPAP12 | 35s (1.35 l) | 22.50 | 42.50 |

Nos. CB18a-CB20a (3)   67.50   127.50
Set, never hinged   140.00

American Gee-
Bee
SPAP13

English Seaplane
S6B — SPAP14

Graf Zeppelin
over
Riga — SPAP15

DO-X — SPAP16

**1933, Sept. 5**     **Perf. 11½**

| CB21 | SPAP13 | 8s (68s) brn & gray blk | 40.00 | 85.00 |
|---|---|---|---|---|
| CB22 | SPAP14 | 12s (1.12 l) brn car & ol grn | 40.00 | 85.00 |
| CB23 | SPAP15 | 30s (1.30 l) bl & gray blk | 50.00 | 90.00 |
| CB24 | SPAP16 | 40s (1.90 l) brn vio & indigo | 40.00 | 85.00 |

Nos. CB21-CB24 (4)   170.00   345.00
Set, never hinged   275.00

Surtax for wounded Latvian aviators.

**Imperf.**

| CB21a | SPAP13 | 8s (68s) | 40.00 | 85.00 |
|---|---|---|---|---|
| CB22a | SPAP14 | 12s (1.12 l) | 40.00 | 85.00 |
| CB23a | SPAP15 | 30s (1.30 l) | 50.00 | 95.00 |
| CB24a | SPAP16 | 40s (1.90 l) | 40.00 | 90.00 |

Nos. CB21a-CB24a (4)   170.00   355.00
Set, never hinged   275.00

---

# OCCUPATION STAMPS

## Issued under German Occupation

German Stamps of 1905-
18 Handstamped

### Red Overprint

**1919**    **Wmk. 125**    **Perf. 14, 14½**

| 1N1 | A22 | 2½pf gray | 275.00 | 325.00 |
|---|---|---|---|---|
| 1N2 | A16 | 5pf green | 225.00 | 100.00 |
| 1N3 | A22 | 15pf dk vio | 375.00 | 100.00 |
| 1N4 | A16 | 20pf blue vio | 135.00 | 65.00 |
| 1N5 | A16 | 25pf org & blk, yel | 475.00 | 325.00 |
| 1N6 | A16 | 50pf pur & blk, buff | 475.00 | 325.00 |

### Violet Blue Overprint

| 1N7 | A22 | 2½pf gray | 275.00 | 325.00 |
|---|---|---|---|---|
| 1N8 | A16 | 5pf green | 225.00 | 120.00 |
| 1N9 | A16 | 10pf carmine | 190.00 | 47.50 |
| 1N10 | A22 | 15pf dk vio | 325.00 | 325.00 |
| 1N11 | A16 | 20pf bl vio | 135.00 | 65.00 |
| 1N12 | A16 | 25pf org & blk, yel | 675.00 | 525.00 |
| 1N13 | A16 | 50pf pur & blk, buff | 675.00 | 525.00 |

Nos. 1N1-1N13 (13)   4,460.   3,173.

Inverted and double overprints exist, as well as counterfeit overprints.
Some experts believe that Nos. 1N1-1N7 were not officially issued. All used examples are canceled to order.

Russian Stamps
Overprinted

**1941, July**

| 1N14 | A331 | 5k red (#734) | 1.00 | 4.25 |
|---|---|---|---|---|
| 1N15 | A109 | 10k blue (#616) | 1.00 | 4.25 |
| 1N16 | A332 | 15k dk grn (#735) | 32.50 | 72.50 |
| 1N17 | A97 | 20k dull grn (#617) | 1.00 | 4.25 |
| 1N18 | A333 | 30k dp blue (#736) | 1.00 | 4.25 |
| 1N19 | A111 | 50k dp brn (#619A) | 3.50 | 10.00 |

Nos. 1N14-1N19 (6)   40.00   99.50
Set, never hinged   77.50

Issued: 20k, 30k, 7/17; 5k, 10k, 7/18; 15k, 7/19; 50k, 7.23.
Nos. 1N14-1N19 were replaced by German stamps in mid-October. On Nov. 4, 1941, German stamps overprinted "Ostland" (Russia Nos. N9-N28) were placed into use.
The overprint exists on imperf examples of the 10k and 50k stamps. Value, each $800.
Counterfeit overprints exist.

# KURLAND

German Stamps
Surcharged

**1945, Apr. 20**

| 1N20 | A115 | 6pf on 5pf dp yel grn (#509) | 37.50 | 72.50 |
|---|---|---|---|---|
| | | Never hinged | 72.50 | |
| 1N21 | A115 | 6 pf 10pf dk brn (#511A) | 15.00 | 30.00 |
| | | Never hinged | 27.50 | |
| a. | | Inverted surcharge | 100.00 | 175.00 |
| | | Never hinged | 175.00 | |
| b. | | Double surcharge | 85.00 | 150.00 |
| | | Never hinged | 150.00 | |
| 1N22 | A115 | 6 pf on 20pf blue | 8.50 | 14.50 |
| | | Never hinged | 16.00 | |
| a. | | Inverted surcharge | 100.00 | 175.00 |
| | | Never hinged | 175.00 | |
| b. | | Double surcharge | 85.00 | 150.00 |
| | | Never hinged | 150.00 | |

Germany Nos. MQ1
& MQ1a Surcharged

### Perf 13½

| 1N23 | MPP1 | 12pf on (-) red brn, (#MQ1) | 42.50 | 72.50 |
|---|---|---|---|---|
| | | Never hinged | 82.50 | |
| a. | | Inverted surcharge | 150.00 | 275.00 |
| | | Never hinged | 275.00 | |
| b. | | Double surcharge | 150.00 | 275.00 |
| | | Never hinged | 275.00 | |

### Rouletted

| 1N24 | MPP1 | 12pf on (-) red brn, (#MQ1a) | 6.50 | 16.00 |
|---|---|---|---|---|
| | | Never hinged | 16.00 | |
| a. | | Inverted surcharge | 75.00 | 135.00 |
| | | Never hinged | 135.00 | |
| b. | | Double surcharge | 67.50 | 120.00 |
| | | Never hinged | 120.00 | |

Nos. 1N20-1N24 (5)   110.00   205.50
Set, never hinged   200.00

Nos. 1N20-1N24 were used in the German-held enclave of Kurland (Courland) from April 20-May 8, 1945.
Counterfeit surcharges are plentiful.

---

# ISSUED UNDER RUSSIAN OCCUPATION

Fake overprints/surcharges exist on Nos. 2N1-2N36.

---

The following stamps were issued at Mitau during the occupation of Kurland by the West Russian Army under Colonel Bermondt-Avalov.

Stamps of Latvia
Handstamped

### On Stamps of 1919

**1919**    **Wmk. 108**    **Imperf.**

| 2N1 | A1 | 3k lilac | 40.00 | 52.50 |
|---|---|---|---|---|
| 2N2 | A1 | 5k carmine | 40.00 | 52.50 |
| 2N3 | A1 | 10k dp blue | 140.00 | 240.00 |
| 2N4 | A1 | 20k orange | 40.00 | 52.50 |
| 2N5 | A1 | 25k gray | 40.00 | 52.50 |
| 2N6 | A1 | 35k dk brown | 40.00 | 52.50 |
| 2N7 | A1 | 50k purple | 40.00 | 52.50 |
| 2N8 | A1 | 75k emerald | 40.00 | 80.00 |

### On Riga Liberation Stamps

| 2N9 | A2 | 5k carmine | 40.00 | 52.50 |
|---|---|---|---|---|
| 2N10 | A2 | 15k dp green | 20.00 | 40.00 |
| 2N11 | A2 | 35k brown | 20.00 | 40.00 |

Stamps of Latvia
Overprinted

### On Stamps of 1919

| 2N12 | A1 | 3k lilac | 6.00 | 9.50 |
|---|---|---|---|---|
| 2N13 | A1 | 5k carmine | 6.00 | 9.50 |
| 2N14 | A1 | 10k dp blue | 120.00 | 200.00 |
| 2N15 | A1 | 20k orange | 12.00 | 20.00 |
| 2N16 | A1 | 25k gray | 27.50 | 60.00 |
| 2N17 | A1 | 35k dk brown | 20.00 | 27.50 |
| 2N18 | A1 | 50k purple | 20.00 | 27.50 |

| 2N19 | A1 | 75k emerald | 20.00 | 27.50 |
|---|---|---|---|---|

### On Riga Liberation Stamps

| 2N20 | A2 | 5k carmine | 4.00 | 8.00 |
|---|---|---|---|---|
| 2N21 | A2 | 15k dp green | 4.00 | 8.00 |
| 2N22 | A2 | 35k brown | 4.00 | 8.00 |
| a. | | Inverted overprint | 200.00 | |

Nos. 2N1-2N22 (22)   743.50   1,173.

The letters "Z. A." are the initials of "Zapadnaya Armiya"-i.e. Western Army.

Russian Stamps of 1909-17
Surcharged

### On Stamps of 1909-12

#### Perf. 14, 14½x15
#### Unwmk.

| 2N23 | A14 | 10k on 2k grn | 6.00 | 8.00 |
|---|---|---|---|---|
| a. | | Inverted surcharge | 30.00 | |
| 2N24 | A15 | 30k on 4k car | 8.00 | 8.00 |
| 2N25 | A14 | 40k on 5k cl | 8.00 | 9.50 |
| 2N26 | A15 | 50k pn 10k dk bl | 6.00 | 8.00 |
| 2N27 | A11 | 70k on 15k red brn & bl | 6.00 | 8.00 |
| a. | | Inverted surcharge | 200.00 | |
| 2N28 | A8 | 90k on 20k bl & car | 12.00 | 16.00 |
| 2N29 | A11 | 1r on 25k grn & vio | 6.00 | 8.00 |
| 2N30 | A11 | 1½r on 35k red brn & grn | 47.50 | 65.00 |
| 2N31 | A8 | 2r on 50k vio & grn | 12.00 | 16.00 |
| a. | | Inverted surcharge | 120.00 | |
| 2N32 | A11 | 4r on 70k brn & org | 20.00 | 27.50 |

#### Perf. 13½

| 2N33 | A9 | 6r on 1r pale brn, brn & org | 27.50 | 40.00 |
|---|---|---|---|---|

### On Stamps of 1917
#### Imperf

| 2N34 | A14 | 20k on 3k red | 6.00 | 8.00 |
|---|---|---|---|---|
| 2N35 | A14 | 40k on 5k claret | 95.00 | 100.00 |
| 2N36 | A12 | 10r on 3.50r mar & lt grn | 80.00 | 80.00 |
| a. | | Inverted surcharge | 300.00 | |

Nos. 2N23-2N36 (14)   340.00   402.00

Eight typographed stamps of this design were prepared in 1919, but never placed in use. They exist both perforated and imperforate. Value, set, imperf. $1, perf. $2.
Reprints and counterfeits exist.

> **Catalogue values for unused stamps in this section, from this point to the end of the section, are for Never Hinged items.**

Arms of Soviet
Latvia — OS1

**1940**   **Typo.**   **Wmk. 265**   **Perf. 10**

| 2N45 | OS1 | 1s dk violet | .25 | .25 |
|---|---|---|---|---|
| 2N46 | OS1 | 2s orange yel | .25 | .25 |
| 2N47 | OS1 | 3s orange ver | .25 | .25 |
| 2N48 | OS1 | 5s dk olive grn | .25 | .25 |
| 2N49 | OS1 | 7s turq green | .25 | .80 |
| 2N50 | OS1 | 10s slate green | 2.00 | .40 |
| 2N51 | OS1 | 20s brown lake | 1.20 | .25 |
| 2N52 | OS1 | 30s light blue | 2.40 | .40 |
| 2N53 | OS1 | 35s brt ultra | .25 | .40 |
| 2N54 | OS1 | 40s chocolate | 2.00 | 1.20 |
| 2N55 | OS1 | 50s lt gray | 2.50 | 1.20 |
| 2N56 | OS1 | 1 l lt brown | 3.25 | 1.50 |
| 2N57 | OS1 | 5 l brt green | 24.00 | 13.50 |

Nos. 2N45-2N57 (13)   38.85   20.65

Used values of Nos. 2N45-2N57 are for CTOs. Commercially used examples are worth three times as much.

---

# LEBANON

'le-bə-nən

## (Grand Liban)

LOCATION — Asia Minor, bordering on the Mediterranean Sea
GOVT. — Republic
AREA — 4,036 sq. mi.
POP. — 3,562,699 (1999 est.)
CAPITAL — Beirut

Formerly a part of the Syrian province of Turkey, Lebanon was occupied by French forces after World War I. It was mandated to France after it had been declared a separate state. Limited autonomy was granted in 1927 and full independence achieved in 1941. The French issued two sets of occupation stamps (with T.E.O. overprint) for Lebanon in late 1919. The use of these and later occupation issues (of 1920-24, with overprints "O.M.F." and "Syrie-Grand Liban") was extended to Syria, Cilicia, Alaouites and Alexandretta. By custom, these are all listed under Syria.

100 Centimes = 1 Piaster
100 Piasters = 1 Pound

### Watermark

Wmk. 400

---

Catalogue values for unused stamps in this country are for Never Hinged items, beginning with Scott 177 in the regular postage section, Scott B13 in the semipostal section, Scott C97 in the airpost section, Scott CB5 in the airpost semi-postal section, Scott J37 in the postage due section, and Scott RA11 in the postal tax section.

---

### Issued under French Mandate

Stamps of France 1900-21 Surcharged

| | 1924 | Unwmk. | Perf. 14x13½ | |
|---|---|---|---|---|
| 1 | A16 | 10c on 2c vio brn | 1.60 | 1.60 |
| a. | | Inverted surcharge | 45.00 | 45.00 |
| 2 | A22 | 25c on 5c orange | 1.60 | 1.60 |
| 3 | A22 | 50c on 10c green | 1.60 | 1.60 |
| 4 | A20 | 75c on 15c sl grn | 2.75 | 2.40 |
| 5 | A22 | 1p on 20c red brn | 1.60 | 1.60 |
| a. | | Double surcharge | 45.00 | 45.00 |
| b. | | Inverted surcharge | 45.00 | 45.00 |
| 6 | A22 | 1.25p on 25c blue | 4.50 | 2.40 |
| a. | | Double surcharge | 42.50 | 42.50 |
| 7 | A22 | 1.50p on 30c org | 2.75 | 2.40 |
| 8 | A22 | 1.50p on 30c red | 2.75 | 2.40 |
| 9 | A20 | 2.50p on 50c dl bl | 2.40 | 2.00 |
| a. | | Inverted surcharge | 37.50 | 37.50 |

Surcharged

| | | | | |
|---|---|---|---|---|
| 10 | A18 | 2p on 40c red & pale bl | 5.50 | 3.75 |
| a. | | Inverted surcharge | 27.50 | 27.50 |
| 11 | A18 | 3p on 60c vio & ultra | 8.00 | 6.75 |
| 12 | A18 | 5p on 1fr cl & ol grn | 10.00 | 7.50 |
| 13 | A18 | 10p on 2fr org & pale bl | 15.00 | 12.00 |
| a. | | Inverted surcharge | 50.00 | 50.00 |
| 14 | A18 | 25p on 5fr dk bl & buff | 22.50 | 19.00 |
| a. | | Inverted surcharge | 85.00 | 85.00 |
| | | Nos. 1-14 (14) | 82.55 | 66.60 |

Broken and missing letters and varieties of spacing are numerous in these surcharges.
For overprints see Nos. C1-C4.

---

### Stamps of France, 1923, (Pasteur) Surcharged "GRAND LIBAN" and New Values

| | | | | |
|---|---|---|---|---|
| 15 | A23 | 50c on 10c green | 3.50 | 1.10 |
| a. | | Inverted surcharge | 37.50 | 27.50 |
| 16 | A23 | 1.50p on 30c red | 4.50 | 2.25 |
| 17 | A23 | 2.50p on 50c blue | 3.75 | 1.10 |
| a. | | Inverted surcharge | 32.50 | 30.00 |
| | | Nos. 15-17 (3) | 11.75 | 4.45 |

### Commemorative Stamps of France, 1924, (Olympic Games) Surcharged "GRAND LIBAN" and New Values

| | | | | |
|---|---|---|---|---|
| 18 | A24 | 50c on 10c gray grn & yel grn | 25.00 | 25.00 |
| a. | | Inverted surcharge | 350.00 | |
| 19 | A25 | 1.25p on 25c rose & dk rose | 25.00 | 25.00 |
| a. | | Inverted surcharge | 350.00 | |
| 20 | A26 | 1.50p on 30c brn red & blk | 25.00 | 25.00 |
| a. | | Inverted surcharge | 350.00 | |
| 21 | A27 | 2.50p on 50c ultra & dk bl | 25.00 | 25.00 |
| a. | | Inverted surcharge | 350.00 | |
| | | Nos. 18-21 (4) | 100.00 | 100.00 |

Stamps of France, 1900-24, Surcharged

| | | **1924-25** | | |
|---|---|---|---|---|
| 22 | A16 | 0.10p on 2c vio brn | 1.00 | .50 |
| 23 | A22 | 0.25p on 5c orange | 1.25 | .75 |
| 24 | A22 | 0.50p on 10c green | 2.00 | 1.40 |
| 25 | A20 | 0.75p on 15c gray grn | 1.75 | 1.10 |
| 26 | A22 | 1p on 20c red brn | 1.50 | .95 |
| 27 | A22 | 1.25p on 25c blue | 2.25 | 1.60 |
| 28 | A22 | 1.50p on 30c red | 2.00 | 1.25 |
| 29 | A22 | 1.50p on 30c orange | 62.50 | 57.50 |
| 30 | A22 | 2p on 35c vio ('25) | 2.25 | 1.60 |
| 31 | A20 | 3p on 60c lt vio ('25) | 3.00 | 2.10 |
| 32 | A20 | 4p on 85c ver | 3.50 | 2.50 |

Surcharged

| | | | | |
|---|---|---|---|---|
| 33 | A18 | 2p on 40c red & pale bl | 2.25 | 1.60 |
| a. | | 2nd line of Arabic reads "2 Piastre" (singular) | 2.50 | .50 |
| 34 | A18 | 2p on 45c grn & bl ('25) | 27.50 | 22.50 |
| 35 | A18 | 3p on 60c vio & ultra | 3.50 | 2.50 |
| 36 | A18 | 5p on 1fr cl & ol grn | 4.25 | 3.25 |
| 37 | A18 | 10p on 2fr org & pale bl | 9.75 | 8.50 |
| 38 | A18 | 25p on 5fr dk bl & buff | 15.00 | 13.50 |
| | | Nos. 22-38 (17) | 145.25 | 123.10 |

Last line of surcharge on No. 33 has four characters, with a 9-like character between the third and fourth in illustration. Last line on No. 33a is as illustrated.
The surcharge may be found inverted on most of Nos. 22-38, and double on some values.
For overprints see Nos. C5-C8.

### Stamps of France 1923-24 (Pasteur) Surcharged as Nos. 22-32

| | | | | |
|---|---|---|---|---|
| 39 | A23 | 0.50p on 10c green | 2.00 | .85 |
| a. | | Inverted surcharge | 35.00 | 25.00 |
| b. | | Double surcharge | 40.00 | 21.00 |
| 40 | A23 | 0.75p on 15c green | 2.25 | 1.40 |
| 41 | A23 | 1.50p on 30c red | 2.75 | 1.40 |
| a. | | Inverted surcharge | 35.00 | 25.00 |
| 42 | A23 | 2p on 45c red | 5.00 | 3.50 |
| a. | | Inverted surcharge | 35.00 | 21.00 |
| 43 | A23 | 2.50p on 50c blue | 2.00 | .95 |
| a. | | Inverted surcharge | 35.00 | 21.00 |
| b. | | Double surcharge | 40.00 | 21.00 |
| 44 | A23 | 4p on 75c blue | 5.00 | 3.50 |
| | | Nos. 39-44 (6) | 19.00 | 11.60 |

France Nos. 198 to 201 (Olympics) Surcharged as Nos. 22-32

| | | | | |
|---|---|---|---|---|
| 45 | A24 | 0.50p on 10c | 32.50 | 32.50 |
| 46 | A25 | 1.25p on 25c | 32.50 | 32.50 |
| 47 | A26 | 1.50p on 30c | 32.50 | 32.50 |
| 48 | A27 | 2.50p on 50c | 32.50 | 32.50 |
| | | Nos. 45-48 (4) | 130.00 | 130.00 |

---

France No. 219 (Ronsard) Surcharged

| | | | | |
|---|---|---|---|---|
| 49 | A28 | 4p on 75c bl, *bluish* | 3.50 | 3.50 |
| a. | | Inverted surcharge | 67.50 | 52.50 |

Cedar of Lebanon
A1

Crusader Castle, Tripoli
A3

View of Beirut — A2

Designs: 50c, Crusader Castle, Tripoli. 75c, Beit-ed-Din Palace. 1p, Temple of Jupiter, Baalbek. 1.25p, Mouktara Palace. 1.50p, Harbor of Tyre. 2p, View of Zahle. 2.50p, Ruins at Baalbek. 3p, Square at Deir-el-Kamar. 5p, Castle at Sidon. 25p, Square at Beirut.

| | | **1925** | Litho. | **Perf. 12½, 13½** | |
|---|---|---|---|---|---|
| 50 | A1 | 0.10p dark violet | | .50 | .25 |

| | | | **Photo.** | | |
|---|---|---|---|---|---|
| 51 | A2 | 0.25p olive black | | .95 | .25 |
| 52 | A2 | 0.50p yellow grn | | .75 | .25 |
| 53 | A2 | 0.75p brn orange | | .75 | .25 |
| 54 | A2 | 1p magenta | | 2.00 | .80 |
| 55 | A2 | 1.25p deep green | | 2.25 | 1.40 |
| 56 | A2 | 1.50p rose red | | 2.00 | .25 |
| 57 | A2 | 2p dark brown | | 1.25 | .25 |
| 58 | A2 | 2.50p peacock bl | | 2.00 | .80 |
| 59 | A2 | 3p orange brn | | 2.75 | 1.10 |
| 60 | A2 | 5p violet | | 3.00 | 1.40 |
| 61 | A3 | 10p violet brn | | 7.50 | 2.10 |
| 62 | A2 | 25p ultramarine | | 20.00 | 12.00 |
| | | Nos. 50-62 (13) | | 45.70 | 21.10 |

For surcharges and overprints see Nos. 63-107, B1-B12, C9-C38, CB1-CB4.

Stamps of 1925 with Bars and Surcharged

| | | **1926** | | |
|---|---|---|---|---|
| 63 | A2 | 3.50p on 0.75p brn org | 1.50 | 1.50 |
| 64 | A2 | 4p on 0.25p ol blk | 2.50 | 2.50 |
| 65 | A2 | 6p on 2.50p pck bl | 2.00 | 2.00 |
| 66 | A2 | 12p on 1.25p dp grn | 1.40 | 1.40 |
| 67 | A2 | 20p on 1.25p dp grn | 6.75 | 6.75 |

---

Stamps of 1925 with Bars and Surcharged

| | | | | |
|---|---|---|---|---|
| 68 | A2 | 4.50p on 0.75p brn org | 2.75 | 2.75 |
| 69 | A2 | 7.50p on 2.50p pck bl | 2.75 | 2.75 |
| 70 | A2 | 15p on 25p ultra | 2.75 | 2.75 |
| | | Nos. 63-70 (8) | 22.40 | 22.40 |

No. 51 with Bars and Surcharged

| | | **1927** | | |
|---|---|---|---|---|
| 71 | A2 | 4p on 0.25p ol blk | 2.50 | 2.50 |

### Issues of Republic under French Mandate

Stamps of 1925 Issue Overprinted in Black or Red

| | | **1927** | | |
|---|---|---|---|---|
| 72 | A1 | 0.10p dark vio (R) | .55 | .25 |
| a. | | Black overprint | 37.50 | |
| 73 | A2 | 0.50p yellow grn | .55 | .25 |
| 74 | A2 | 1p magenta | .55 | .25 |
| 75 | A2 | 1.50p rose red | .80 | .60 |
| 76 | A2 | 2p dark brown | 1.10 | .90 |
| 77 | A2 | 3p orange brn | .90 | .25 |
| 78 | A2 | 5p violet | 1.75 | 1.00 |
| 79 | A3 | 10p violet brn | 2.25 | 1.10 |
| 80 | A2 | 25p ultramarine | 19.00 | 8.00 |
| | | Nos. 72-80 (9) | 27.45 | 12.60 |

On Nos. 72 and 79 the overprint is set in two lines. On all stamps the double bar obliterates GRAND LIBAN.

### Same Overprint on Provisional Issues of 1926-27

15 PIASTERS ON 25 PIASTERS
TYPE I — "République Libanaise" at foot of stamp.
TYPE II — "République Libanaise" near top of stamp.

| | | | | |
|---|---|---|---|---|
| 81 | A2 | 4p on 0.25p ol blk | .75 | .25 |
| 82 | A2 | 4.50p on 0.75p brn org | .85 | .25 |
| 83 | A2 | 7.50p on 2.50p pck bl | 1.10 | .25 |
| 84 | A2 | 15p on 25p ultra (I) | 7.50 | 5.25 |
| a. | | Type II | 11.50 | 8.00 |
| | | Nos. 81-84 (4) | 10.20 | 6.00 |

Most of Nos. 72-84 are known with overprint double, inverted or on back as well as face.

## Stamps of 1927 Overprinted in Black or Red

**1928**

| | | | | |
|---|---|---|---|---|
| 86 | A1 | 0.10p dark vio (R) | .80 | .60 |
| | a. | French overprint omitted, on #50 | | |
| 87 | A2 | 0.50p yel grn (Bk) | 2.00 | 1.50 |
| | a. | Arabic overprint inverted | 35.00 | 25.00 |
| 88 | A2 | 1p magenta (Bk) | 1.00 | .70 |
| | a. | Inverted overprint | 35.00 | 25.00 |
| 89 | A2 | 1.50p rose red (Bk) | 2.00 | 1.50 |
| 90 | A2 | 2p dk brn (R) | 2.75 | 2.10 |
| 90A | A2 | 2p dk brn (Bk+R) | 110.00 | 110.00 |
| 91 | A2 | 3p org brn (Bk) | 1.90 | 1.40 |
| 92 | A2 | 5p violet (Bk+R) | 3.50 | 2.75 |
| 93 | A2 | 5p violet (R) | 3.00 | 2.40 |
| | a. | French ovpt. below Arabic | 30.00 | 14.00 |
| 94 | A3 | 10p vio brn (Bk) | 5.00 | 4.25 |
| | a. | Double overprint | 100.00 | 90.00 |
| | b. | Double overprint inverted | | |
| | c. | Inverted overprint | 100.00 | 70.00 |
| 95 | A2 | 25p ultra (Bk+R) | 11.50 | 10.50 |
| 95A | A2 | 25p ultra (R) | 13.00 | 13.00 |
| | | Nos. 86-95A (12) | 156.45 | 150.70 |

On all stamps the double bar with Arabic overprint obliterates Arabic inscription.

**Same Overprint on Nos. 81-84**

| | | | | |
|---|---|---|---|---|
| 96 | A2 | 4p on 0.25p (Bk+R) | 2.00 | 1.50 |
| 97 | A2 | 4.50p on 0.75p (Bk) | 2.00 | 1.50 |
| 98 | A2 | 7.50p on 2.50p (Bk+R) | 4.50 | 3.50 |
| 99 | A2 | 7.50p on 2.50p (R) | 7.00 | 6.00 |
| 100 | A2 | 15p on 25p (II) (Bk+R) | 11.00 | 9.50 |
| | a. | Arabic overprint inverted | | |
| 101 | A2 | 15p on 25p (I) (R) | 14.00 | 12.00 |
| | | Nos. 96-101 (6) | 40.50 | 34.00 |

The new values are surcharged in black. The initials in ( ) refer to the colors of the overprints.

## Stamps of 1925 Srchd. in Red or Black

**1928-29     Perf. 13½**

| | | | | |
|---|---|---|---|---|
| 102 | A2 | 50c on 0.75p brn org (Bk) ('29) | 1.50 | 1.90 |
| 103 | A2 | 2p on 1.25p dp grn | 1.50 | 1.90 |
| 104 | A2 | 4p on 0.25p ol blk | 1.50 | 1.90 |
| | a. | Double surcharge | 35.00 | 25.00 |
| 105 | A2 | 7.50p on 2.50p pck bl | 2.50 | 2.75 |
| | a. | Double surcharge | 40.00 | 25.00 |
| | b. | Inverted surcharge | 55.00 | 25.00 |
| 106 | A2 | 15p on 25p ultra | 22.50 | 10.00 |
| | | Nos. 102-106 (5) | 29.50 | 18.45 |

On Nos. 103, 104 and 105 the surcharged numerals are 3¼mm high, and have thick strokes.

## No. 86 Surcharged in Red

**1928**

| | | | | |
|---|---|---|---|---|
| 107 | A1 | 5c on 0.10p dk vio | 1.75 | .30 |

## Silkworm, Cocoon and Moth — A4

**1930, Feb. 11   Typo.   Perf. 11**

| | | | | |
|---|---|---|---|---|
| 108 | A4 | 4p black brown | 15.00 | 15.00 |
| 109 | A4 | 4½p vermilion | 15.00 | 15.00 |
| 110 | A4 | 7½p dark blue | 15.00 | 15.00 |
| 111 | A4 | 10p dk violet | 15.00 | 15.00 |
| 112 | A4 | 15p dark green | 15.00 | 15.00 |
| 113 | A4 | 25p claret | 15.00 | 15.00 |
| | | Nos. 108-113 (6) | 90.00 | 90.00 |

Sericultural Congress, Beirut. Presentation imperfs exist.

Pigeon Rocks, Ras Beirut — A5

View of Bickfaya — A8

Beit-ed-Din Palace — A10

Crusader Castle, Tripoli — A11

Ruins of Venus Temple, Baalbek — A12

Ancient Bridge, Dog River — A13

Belfort Castle — A14

Afka Falls — A19

20c, Cedars of Lebanon. 25c, Ruins of Bacchus Temple, Baalbek. 1p, Crusader Castle, Sidon Harbor. 5p, Arcade of Beit-ed-Din Palace. 6p, Tyre Harbor. 7.50p, Ruins of Sun Temple, Baalbek. 10p, View of Hasbeya. 25p, Government House, Beirut. 50p, View of Deir-el-Camar. 75c, 100p, Ruins at Baalbek.

**1930-35   Litho.   Perf. 12½, 13½**

| | | | | |
|---|---|---|---|---|
| 114 | A5 | 0.10p brn org | .60 | .25 |
| 115 | A5 | 0.20p yellow brn | .60 | .25 |
| 116 | A5 | 0.25p deep blue | .75 | .45 |

**Photo.**

| | | | | |
|---|---|---|---|---|
| 117 | A8 | 0.50p orange brn | 3.00 | 1.50 |
| 118 | A11 | 0.75p ol brn ('32) | 1.50 | 1.00 |
| 119 | A8 | 1p deep green | 1.75 | 1.25 |
| 120 | A8 | 1p brn vio ('35) | 3.00 | 1.00 |
| 121 | A10 | 1.50p violet brn | 3.25 | 1.90 |
| 122 | A10 | 1.50p dp grn ('32) | 3.50 | 1.50 |
| 123 | A11 | 2p Prussian bl | 4.50 | 1.60 |
| 124 | A12 | 3p black brown | 4.50 | 1.60 |
| 125 | A13 | 4p orange brn | 4.75 | 1.60 |
| 126 | A14 | 4.50p carmine | 5.00 | 1.60 |
| 127 | A13 | 5p greenish blk | 3.00 | 1.50 |
| 128 | A13 | 6p brn violet | 5.25 | 2.75 |
| 129 | A10 | 7.50p deep blue | 5.00 | 1.60 |
| 130 | A10 | 10p dk ol grn | 9.00 | 1.60 |
| 131 | A19 | 15p blk violet | 11.50 | 3.50 |
| 132 | A19 | 25p blue green | 20.00 | 6.00 |
| 133 | A8 | 50p apple grn | 60.00 | 15.00 |
| 134 | A11 | 100p black | 70.00 | 19.00 |
| | | Nos. 114-134 (21) | 220.45 | 66.45 |

See Nos. 135, 144, 152-155. For surcharges see Nos. 147-149, 161, 173-174.

## Pigeon Rocks Type of 1930-35 Redrawn

**1934   Litho.   Perf. 12½x12**

| | | | | |
|---|---|---|---|---|
| 135 | A5 | 0.10p dull orange | 6.75 | 4.00 |

Lines in rocks and water more distinct. Printer's name "Hélio Vaugirard, Paris," in larger letters.

Cedar of Lebanon A23

President Emile Eddé A24

Dog River Panorama — A25

**1937-40   Typo.   Perf. 14x13½**

| | | | | |
|---|---|---|---|---|
| 137 | A23 | 0.10p rose car | .50 | .25 |
| 137A | A23 | 0.20p aqua ('40) | .50 | .25 |
| 137B | A23 | 0.25p pale rose lilac ('40) | .50 | .25 |
| 138 | A23 | 0.50p magenta | .50 | .25 |
| 138A | A23 | 0.75p brown ('40) | .50 | .25 |

**Engr.**
**Perf. 13**

| | | | | |
|---|---|---|---|---|
| 139 | A24 | 3p dk violet | 4.00 | .75 |
| 140 | A24 | 4p black brown | .75 | .25 |
| 141 | A24 | 4.50p carmine | 1.00 | .25 |
| 142 | A25 | 10p brn carmine | 2.25 | .25 |
| 142A | A25 | 12½p dp ultra ('40) | 1.00 | .25 |
| 143 | A25 | 15p dk grn ('38) | 4.00 | .75 |
| 143A | A25 | 20p chestnut ('40) | 1.00 | .25 |
| 143B | A25 | 25p crimson ('40) | 1.50 | .60 |
| 143C | A25 | 50p dk vio (R) | 5.00 | 1.60 |
| 143D | A25 | 100p sepia ('40) | 3.50 | 2.25 |
| | | Nos. 137-143D (15) | 26.50 | 8.45 |

Nos. 137A, 137B, 138A, 142A, 143A, 143B, 143C, and 143D exist imperforate.
For surcharges see Nos. 145-146A, 150-151, 160, 162, 175-176.

View of Bickfaya — A26

## Type A8 Redrawn

**1935 (?)   Photo.   Perf. 13½**

| | | | | |
|---|---|---|---|---|
| 144 | A26 | 0.50p orange brown | 17.50 | 9.75 |

Arabic inscriptions more condensed.

Stamps of 1930-37 Surcharged in Black or Red

**1937-42     Perf. 13, 13½**

| | | | | |
|---|---|---|---|---|
| 145 | A24 | 2p on 3p dk vio | 1.50 | 1.50 |
| 146 | A24 | 2½p on 4p blk brn | 1.50 | 1.50 |
| 146A | A24 | 2½p on 4p black brown (R) ('42) | 1.50 | 1.50 |
| 147 | A10 | 6p on 7.50p dp bl (R) | 4.00 | 4.00 |

## Stamps of 1930-35 and Type of 1937-40 Surcharged in Black or Red

**Perf. 13½, 13**

| | | | | |
|---|---|---|---|---|
| 148 | A8 | 7.50p on 50p ap grn | 2.50 | 2.50 |
| 149 | A11 | 7.50p on 100p blk (R) | 2.50 | 2.50 |
| 150 | A25 | 12.50p on 7.50p dk bl (R) | 5.00 | 5.00 |

Type of 1937-40 Srchd. in Red

**1939   Engr.   Perf. 13**

| | | | | |
|---|---|---|---|---|
| 151 | A25 | 12½p on 7.50p dk bl | 2.00 | 2.00 |
| | | Nos. 145-151 (8) | 20.50 | 20.50 |

## Type of 1930-35 Redrawn Imprint: "Beiteddine-Imp.-Catholique-Beyrouth-Liban."

**1939   Litho.   Perf. 11½**

| | | | | |
|---|---|---|---|---|
| 152 | A10 | 1p dk slate grn | 2.25 | .75 |
| 153 | A10 | 1.50p brn violet | 2.25 | .75 |
| 154 | A10 | 7.50p carmine lake | 2.25 | 1.10 |
| | | Nos. 152-154 (3) | 6.75 | 2.10 |

## Bridge Type of 1930-35 Imprint: "Degorce" instead of "Hélio Vaugirard"

**1940   Engr.   Perf. 13**

| | | | | |
|---|---|---|---|---|
| 155 | A13 | 5p grnsh blue | 1.50 | .25 |

Exists imperforate.

## Independent Republic

Amir Beshir Shehab — A27

**1942, Sept. 18   Litho.   Perf. 11½**

| | | | | |
|---|---|---|---|---|
| 156 | A27 | 0.50p emerald | 3.00 | 3.00 |
| 157 | A27 | 1.50p sepia | 3.00 | 3.00 |
| 158 | A27 | 6p rose pink | 3.00 | 3.00 |
| 159 | A27 | 15p dull blue | 3.00 | 3.00 |
| | | Nos. 156-159 (4) | 12.00 | 12.00 |

1st anniv. of the Proclamation of Independence, Nov. 26, 1941. See Nos. C80-C81.
Nos. 156-159 exist imperforate.

Nos. 140, 154 and 142A Surcharged in Blue, Green or Black

**1943     Perf. 13, 11½**

| | | | | |
|---|---|---|---|---|
| 160 | A24 | 2p on 4p (Bl) | 6.00 | 6.25 |
| 161 | A10 | 6p on 7.50p (G) | 2.60 | .85 |
| 162 | A25 | 10p on 12½p (Bk) | 2.60 | .85 |
| | | Nos. 160-162 (3) | 11.20 | 7.95 |

The surcharge is arranged differently on each value.

Parliament Building — A28

Government House, Beirut — A29

**1943   Litho.   Perf. 11½**

| | | | | |
|---|---|---|---|---|
| 163 | A28 | 25p salmon rose | 12.00 | 5.00 |
| 164 | A29 | 50p bluish green | 12.00 | 5.00 |
| 165 | A28 | 150p light ultra | 12.00 | 5.00 |
| 166 | A29 | 200p dull vio brn | 12.00 | 5.00 |
| | | Nos. 163-166 (4) | 48.00 | 20.00 |
| | | Nos. 163-166,C82-C87 (10) | 137.25 | 93.00 |

2nd anniv. of Proclamation of Independence. Nos. 163-166 exist imperforate. For overprints see Nos. 169-172.

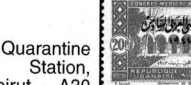
Quarantine Station, Beirut — A30

## Black Overprint

**1943, July 8     Photo.**

| | | | | |
|---|---|---|---|---|
| 167 | A30 | 10p cerise | 5.50 | 3.50 |
| 168 | A30 | 20p light blue | 5.50 | 3.50 |
| | | Nos. 167-168,C88-C90 (5) | 25.00 | 17.75 |

Arab Medical Congress, Beirut.

## Nos. 163 to 166 Overprinted in Blue, Violet, Red or Black

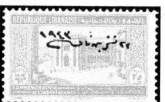

**1944**

| | | | | |
|---|---|---|---|---|
| 169 | A28 | 25p sal rose (Bl) | 15.00 | 15.00 |
| 170 | A29 | 50p bluish grn (V) | 15.00 | 15.00 |
| 171 | A28 | 150p lt ultra (R) | 15.00 | 15.00 |
| 172 | A29 | 200p dull vio brn (Bk) | 17.50 | 15.00 |
| | | Nos. 169-172,C91-C96 (10) | 218.25 | 208.25 |

Return to office of the president and his ministers, Nov. 22, 1943.

## Type of 1930 and No. 142A Surcharged in Violet, Black or Carmine

### 1945    Unwmk.    Engr.    *Perf. 13*

| | | | | |
|---|---|---|---|---|
| 173 | A13 | 2p on 5p dk bl grn (V) | 1.25 | .25 |
| 174 | A13 | 3p on 5p dk bl grn (Bk) | 1.25 | .25 |
| 175 | A25 | 6p on 12½p deep ultra (Bk) | 1.50 | .35 |
| 176 | A25 | 7½p on 12½p deep ultra (C) | 2.50 | .95 |
| | | Nos. 173-176 (4) | 6.50 | 1.80 |

Trees at bottom on Nos. 175 and 176.

> Catalogue values for unused stamps in this section, from this point to the end of the section, are for Never Hinged items.

Citadel of Jubayl (Byblos) — A31

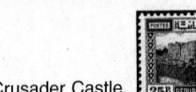

Crusader Castle, Tripoli — A32

### 1945    Litho.    *Perf. 11½*

| | | | | |
|---|---|---|---|---|
| 177 | A31 | 15p violet brown | 4.50 | 3.50 |
| 178 | A31 | 20p deep green | 4.50 | 3.50 |
| 179 | A32 | 25p deep blue | 4.50 | 4.50 |
| 180 | A32 | 50p dp carmine | 7.50 | 4.00 |
| | | Nos. 177-180,C97-C100 (8) | 71.00 | 34.60 |

See Nos. 229-233.

Soldiers and Flag of Lebanon — A33

### 1946    Litho.
### Stripes of Flag in Red Orange

| | | | | |
|---|---|---|---|---|
| 181 | A33 | 7.50p red & pale lil | 1.40 | .25 |
| 182 | A33 | 10p lil & pale lilac | 2.40 | .25 |
| 183 | A33 | 12.50p choc & yel grn | 3.25 | .25 |
| 184 | A33 | 15p sepia & pink | 4.00 | .25 |
| 185 | A33 | 20p ultra & pink | 3.50 | .30 |
| 186 | A33 | 25p dk grn & yel grn | 5.50 | .35 |
| 187 | A33 | 50p dk bl & pale bl | 12.00 | 1.25 |
| 188 | A33 | 100p gray blk & pale bl | 16.00 | 2.50 |
| | | Nos. 181-188 (8) | 48.05 | 5.40 |

Type of 1946 Ovptd. in Red

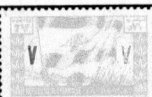

### 1946, May 8
### Stripes of Flag in Red

| | | | | |
|---|---|---|---|---|
| 189 | A33 | 7.50p choc & pink | 1.50 | .25 |
| 190 | A33 | 10p dk vio & pink | 1.75 | .25 |
| 191 | A33 | 12.50p lake & vio gray | 2.00 | .45 |
| 192 | A33 | 15p lt grn & pale grn | 3.25 | .65 |
| 193 | A33 | 20p sl grn & yel grn | 3.00 | .70 |
| 194 | A33 | 25p sl bl & pale bl | 5.00 | .95 |
| 195 | A33 | 50p ultra & vio gray | 7.50 | .90 |
| 196 | A33 | 100p blk & pale bl | 11.00 | 2.25 |
| | | Nos. 189-196 (8) | 35.00 | 6.40 |

See Nos. C101-C106, note after No. C106.

Cedar of Lebanon A34      Night Herons over Mt. Sanin A35

---

### 1946-47    Unwmk.    *Perf. 10½*

| | | | | |
|---|---|---|---|---|
| 197 | A34 | 0.50p red brn ('47) | .80 | .25 |
| 198 | A34 | 1p purple ('47) | 1.20 | .25 |
| 199 | A34 | 2.50p violet | 2.75 | .25 |
| 200 | A34 | 5p red | 3.25 | .25 |
| 201 | A34 | 6p gray ('47) | 4.00 | .25 |

#### *Perf. 11½*

| | | | | |
|---|---|---|---|---|
| 202 | A35 | 12.50p deep car | 24.00 | .25 |
| | | Nos. 197-202,C107-C110 (10) | 98.25 | 9.10 |

For surcharge see No. 246.

A36      Crusader Castle, Tripoli — A37

### 1947    Litho.    *Perf. 14x13½*

| | | | | |
|---|---|---|---|---|
| 203 | A36 | 0.50p dark brown | 1.25 | .25 |
| 204 | A36 | 2.50p bright green | 1.60 | .25 |
| 205 | A36 | 5p car rose | 3.50 | .25 |

#### *Perf. 11½*

| | | | | |
|---|---|---|---|---|
| 206 | A37 | 12.50p rose pink | 9.00 | .45 |
| 207 | A37 | 25p ultramarine | 9.00 | .50 |
| 208 | A37 | 50p turq green | 25.00 | 1.00 |
| 209 | A37 | 100p violet | 34.00 | 5.25 |
| | | Nos. 203-209 (7) | 83.35 | 7.95 |

A38      Zubaida Aqueduct — A39

### 1948    *Perf. 14x13½*

| | | | | |
|---|---|---|---|---|
| 210 | A38 | 0.50p blue | .65 | .25 |
| 211 | A38 | 1p yel brown | .75 | .25 |
| 212 | A38 | 2.50p rose violet | .95 | .25 |
| 213 | A38 | 3p emerald | 2.40 | .25 |
| 214 | A38 | 5p crimson | 2.75 | .25 |

#### *Perf. 11½*

| | | | | |
|---|---|---|---|---|
| 215 | A39 | 7.50p rose red | 6.00 | .25 |
| 216 | A39 | 10p dl violet | 4.25 | .25 |
| 217 | A39 | 12.50p blue | 9.00 | .40 |
| 218 | A39 | 25p blue vio | 15.00 | .90 |
| 219 | A39 | 50p green | 27.50 | 4.75 |
| | | Nos. 210-219 (10) | 69.25 | 7.80 |

See Nos. 227A-228A, 234-237. For surcharge see No. 245.

Europa A40      Avicenna A41

### 1948    Litho.

| | | | | |
|---|---|---|---|---|
| 220 | A40 | 10p dk red & org red | 4.75 | 1.40 |
| 221 | A40 | 12.50p pur & rose | 5.50 | 1.90 |
| 222 | A40 | 25p ol grn & pale green | 6.50 | 1.50 |
| 223 | A41 | 30p org brn & buff | 7.25 | 1.50 |
| 224 | A41 | 40p Prus grn & buff | 10.50 | 1.50 |
| | | Nos. 220-224 (5) | 34.50 | 7.80 |

UNESCO. Nos. 220 to 224 exist imperforate (see note after No. C145).

Camel Post Rider — A42

### 1949, Aug. 16    Unwmk.    *Perf. 11½*

| | | | | |
|---|---|---|---|---|
| 225 | A42 | 5p violet | 1.60 | .40 |
| 226 | A42 | 7.50p red | 2.40 | .40 |
| 227 | A42 | 12.50p blue | 3.25 | 1.00 |
| | | Nos. 225-227,C148-C149 (5) | 24.00 | 9.50 |

UPU, 75th anniv. See note after No. C149.

---

## Cedar Type of 1948 Redrawn and Jubayl Type of 1945

Original

Redrawn

### 1949    Litho.    *Perf. 14x13½*

| | | | | |
|---|---|---|---|---|
| 227A | A38 | 0.50p blue | 2.75 | .25 |
| 228 | A38 | 1p red orange | 2.75 | .25 |
| 228A | A38 | 2.50p rose lilac | 13.00 | .35 |

#### *Perf. 11½*

| | | | | |
|---|---|---|---|---|
| 229 | A31 | 7.50p rose red | 4.00 | .25 |
| 230 | A31 | 10p violet brn | 7.00 | .25 |
| 231 | A31 | 12.50p deep blue | 14.00 | .25 |
| 232 | A31 | 25p violet | 25.00 | .40 |
| 233 | A31 | 50p green | 47.50 | 1.90 |
| | | Nos. 227A-233 (8) | 116.00 | 3.90 |

On No. 227A in left numeral tablet, top of "P" stands higher than flag of the 1¼mm high "5." On No. 210, tops of "P" and the 2mm "5" are on same line.
On No. 228, "1 P." is smaller than on No. 211, and has no line below "P."
On No. 228A, the "O" does not touch tablet frame; on No. 212, it does. No. 228A exists on gray paper.

## Cedar Type of 1948 Redrawn and

Ancient Bridge across Dog River — A43

### 1950    Litho.    *Perf. 14x13½*

| | | | | |
|---|---|---|---|---|
| 234 | A38 | 0.50p rose red | .40 | .25 |
| 235 | A38 | 1p salmon | 1.00 | .25 |
| 236 | A38 | 2.50p violet | 1.50 | .25 |
| 237 | A38 | 5p claret | 3.50 | .25 |

Cedar slightly altered and mountains eliminated.

#### *Perf. 11½*

| | | | | |
|---|---|---|---|---|
| 238 | A43 | 7.50p rose red | 3.50 | .25 |
| 239 | A43 | 10p rose vio | 5.00 | .25 |
| 240 | A43 | 12.50p light blue | 11.00 | .25 |
| 241 | A43 | 25p deep blue | 15.00 | 1.25 |
| 242 | A43 | 50p emerald | 35.00 | 5.00 |
| | | Nos. 234-242 (9) | 75.90 | 8.00 |

See Nos. 251-255, 310-312.

Flags and Building — A44

### 1950, Aug. 8    *Perf. 11½*

| | | | | |
|---|---|---|---|---|
| 243 | A44 | 7.50p gray | 2.00 | .25 |
| 244 | A44 | 12.50p lilac rose | 2.00 | .25 |
| | | Nos. 243-244,C150-C153 (6) | 15.25 | 4.20 |

Conf. of Emigrants, 1950. See note after No. C153.

### Nos. 213 and 201 Surcharged with New Value and Bars in Carmine

### 1950    Unwmk.    *Perf. 14x13½, 10½*

| | | | | |
|---|---|---|---|---|
| 245 | A38 | 1p on 3p emerald | 1.25 | .25 |
| 246 | A34 | 2.50p on 6p gray | 1.25 | .25 |

Cedar — A45

### 1951    Litho.    *Perf. 14x13½*

| | | | | |
|---|---|---|---|---|
| 247 | A45 | 0.50p rose red | .40 | .25 |
| 248 | A45 | 1p light brown | .80 | .25 |
| 249 | A45 | 2.50p slate gray | 3.75 | .25 |
| 250 | A45 | 5p rose lake | 4.50 | .25 |

---

## Bridge Type of 1950, Redrawn

| | | | *Typo.* | *Perf. 11½* |
|---|---|---|---|---|
| 251 | A43 | 7.50p red | 4.50 | .25 |
| 252 | A43 | 10p dl rose vio | 6.00 | .25 |
| 253 | A43 | 12.50p blue | 11.00 | .25 |
| 254 | A43 | 25p dull blue | 20.00 | .25 |
| 255 | A43 | 50p green | 40.00 | 3.75 |
| | | Nos. 247-255 (9) | 90.95 | 6.00 |

Nos. 238-242 are lithographed from a fine-screen halftone; "P" in the denomination has serifs. Nos. 251-255 are typographed and much coarser; "P" without serifs.

Cedar A46      Ruins at Baalbek A47

Design: 50p, 100p, Beaufort Castle.

### 1952    Litho.    *Perf. 14x13½*

| | | | | |
|---|---|---|---|---|
| 256 | A46 | 0.50p emerald | 1.00 | .25 |
| 257 | A46 | 1p orange brn | 1.10 | .25 |
| 258 | A46 | 2.50p grnsh blue | 2.50 | .25 |
| 259 | A46 | 5p car rose | 3.75 | .25 |

#### *Perf. 11½*

| | | | | |
|---|---|---|---|---|
| 260 | A47 | 7.50p red | 4.50 | .25 |
| 261 | A47 | 10p brt violet | 6.25 | .70 |
| 262 | A47 | 12.50p blue | 7.00 | .70 |
| 263 | A47 | 25p violet bl | 7.75 | 1.40 |
| 264 | A47 | 50p dk blue grn | 21.00 | 2.75 |
| 265 | A47 | 100p chocolate | 42.50 | 7.50 |
| | | Nos. 256-265 (10) | 97.35 | 14.30 |

Cedar of Lebanon A48      Postal Administration Building A49

### 1953    *Perf. 14x13½*

| | | | | |
|---|---|---|---|---|
| 266 | A48 | 0.50p blue | .85 | .25 |
| 267 | A48 | 1p rose lake | 1.10 | .25 |
| 268 | A48 | 2.50p lilac | 1.25 | .25 |
| 269 | A48 | 5p emerald | 2.25 | .25 |

#### *Perf. 11½*

| | | | | |
|---|---|---|---|---|
| 270 | A49 | 7.50p car rose | 3.25 | .25 |
| 271 | A49 | 10p dp yel grn | 4.50 | .65 |
| 272 | A49 | 12.50p aquamarine | 6.25 | .75 |
| 273 | A49 | 25p ultra | 8.25 | 1.40 |
| 274 | A49 | 50p violet brn | 16.50 | 3.00 |
| | | Nos. 266-274 (9) | 44.20 | 7.05 |

See No. 306.

A50

Gallery, Beit-ed-Din Palace — A51

### 1954    *Perf. 14x13½*

| | | | | |
|---|---|---|---|---|
| 275 | A50 | 0.50p blue | .30 | .25 |
| 276 | A50 | 1p dp orange | .50 | .25 |
| 277 | A50 | 2.50p purple | .80 | .25 |
| 278 | A50 | 5p blue green | 1.75 | .25 |

#### *Perf. 11½*

| | | | | |
|---|---|---|---|---|
| 279 | A51 | 7.50p dp carmine | 2.75 | .25 |
| 280 | A51 | 10p dl ol grn | 4.00 | .35 |
| 281 | A51 | 12.50p blue | 7.00 | 1.00 |
| 282 | A51 | 25p vio blue | 9.00 | 2.75 |
| 283 | A51 | 50p aqua | 17.00 | 5.00 |
| 284 | A51 | 100p black brn | 37.50 | 9.00 |
| | | Nos. 275-284 (10) | 80.60 | 19.35 |

## Arab Postal Union Issue

Globe — A52

**1955, Jan. 1     Litho.     Perf. 13½x13**
285 A52 12.50p blue green         1.25   .25
286 A52   25p violet              1.75   .25
    Nos. 285-286,C197 (3)         4.25   .75

Founding of the APU, July 1, 1954.

Cedar                    Jeita Cave
A53                      A54

**1955                    Perf. 14x13½**
287 A53 0.50p violet blue         .50   .25
288 A53   1p vermilion            .60   .25
289 A53 2.50p purple              .90   .25
290 A53   5p emerald             1.10   .25

**Perf. 11½**
291 A54 7.50p deep orange        1.75   .25
292 A54  10p yellow grn          2.00   .25
293 A54 12.50p blue              2.50   .25
294 A54  25p dp vio blue         4.50   .25
295 A54  50p dk gray grn         8.50   .45
    Nos. 287-295 (9)            22.35  2.45

See Nos. 308-309, 315-318, 341-343A. For overprint see No. 351.

Cedar of                  Globe and
Lebanon                   Columns
A55                       A56

**1955     Unwmk.     Perf. 13x13½**
296 A55 0.50p dark blue           .25   .25
297 A55   1p deep orange          .50   .25
298 A55 2.50p deep violet         .65   .25
299 A55   5p green               1.25   .25
300 A56 7.50p yel org & cop
                 red             1.50   .25
301 A56  10p emer & sal          1.75   .25
302 A56 12.50p ultra & bl grn    2.00   .25
303 A56  25p dp ultra & brt
                 pink            3.50   .25
304 A56  50p dk grn & lt bl      4.50   .25
305 A56 100p dk brn & sal        7.00   .50
    Nos. 296-305 (10)           22.90  2.75

For surcharge see No. 333.

## Cedar Type of 1953 Redrawn

**1956                    Perf. 13x13½**
306 A48 2.50p violet            10.00  1.75

No. 306 measures 17x20½mm. The "2p.50" is in Roman (upright) type face.

## Cedar Type of 1955 Redrawn & Bridge Type of 1950, Second Redrawing

**1957     Litho.     Perf. 13x13½**
308 A53 0.50p light ultra         .45   .25
309 A53 2.50p claret              .90   .25

**Perf. 11½**
310 A43 7.50p vermilion          2.00   .40
311 A43  10p brn orange          2.40   .50
312 A43 12.50p blue              3.25   .75
    Nos. 308-312 (5)             9.00  2.15

On Nos. 308 and 309 numerals are slanted and clouds slightly changed.
Nos. 310-312 inscribed "Liban" instead of "Republique Libanaise," and different Arabic characters.

---

Runners — A57

**1957, Sept. 12     Litho.     Perf. 13**
313 A57 2.50p shown              1.20   .25
314 A57 12.50p Soccer players    1.75   .30
    Nos. 313-314,C243-C244 (4)   9.20  3.55

Second Pan-Arab Games, Beirut.
A souvenir sheet of 4 contains Nos. 313-314, C243-C244. Value, $130.

## Cedar Type of 1955 Redrawn and

Workers                  Ancient
A58                      Potter
                         A59

**1957     Unwmk.     Perf. 13x13½**
315 A53 0.50p light blue          .25   .25
316 A53   1p light brown          .40   .25
317 A53 2.50p bright vio          .40   .25
318 A53   5p light green          .65   .25

**Perf. 11½, 13½x13 (A59)**
319 A58 7.50p crim rose          1.00   .25
320 A58  10p dull red brn        1.00   .25
321 A58 12.50p bright blue       1.20   .25
322 A59  25p dull blue           4.00   .25
323 A59  50p yellow grn          5.00   .25
324 A59 100p sepia               5.75   .60
    Nos. 315-324 (10)           19.65  2.85

The word "piaster" is omitted on No. 315; on Nos. 316 and 318 there is a line below "P"; on No. 317 there is a period between "2" and "50."
Nos. 315-318 are 16mm wide and have three shading lines above tip of cedar. See No. 343A and footnote.
For surcharges see Nos. 334-335, 339.

Cedar of                  Soldier and
Lebanon                   Flag
A60                       A61

**1958     Litho.     Perf. 13**
325 A60 0.50p blue                .40   .25
326 A60   1p dull orange          .60   .25
327 A60 2.50p violet              .80   .25
328 A60   5p yellow grn          1.20   .25
329 A61 12.50p bright blue       1.75   .25
330 A61  25p dark blue           2.00   .25
331 A61  50p orange brn          2.25   .25
332 A61 100p black brn           3.25   .35
    Nos. 325-332 (8)            12.25  2.10

For surcharges see Nos. 336-338.

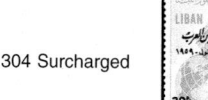

No. 304 Surcharged

**1959, Sept. 1**
333 A56 30p on 50p dk grn & lt
                 bl              1.60   .25

Arab Lawyers Congress. See No. C265.

---

No. 323 Surcharged

**1959                    Perf. 13½x13**
334 A59 30p on 50p yel grn       1.40   .25
335 A59 40p on 50p yel grn       2.00   .30

Convention of the Assoc. of Arab Emigrants in the United States.

## Nos. 329-330 and 323 Surcharged with New Value and Bars

**1959               Perf. 13, 13½x13**
336 A61 7.50p on 12.50p brt bl   1.00   .25
337 A61  10p on 12.50p brt bl    1.20   .25
338 A61  15p on 25p dark blue    1.30   .25
339 A59  40p on 50p yel grn      1.75   .25
    Nos. 336-339,C271 (5)        7.85  1.30

Arab League
Center,
Cairo — A62

**Perf. 13x13½**
**1960, May 23     Unwmk.     Litho.**
340 A62 15p lt blue green         .75   .25

Opening of the Arab League Center and the Arab Postal Museum in Cairo.
For overprint see No. 352.

## Cedar Type of 1955, Second Redrawing

**1960     Litho.     Perf. 13x13½**
341 A53 0.50p light violet       1.00   .25
342 A53   1p rose claret         1.00   .25
343 A53 2.50p ultramarine        1.20   .25
343A A53   5p light green        1.40   .25
    Nos. 341-343A (4)            4.60  1.00

Nos. 341-343A are 16½-17mm wide and have two shading lines above cedar. In other details they resemble the redrawn A53 type of 1957 (Nos. 315-318).

President Fuad
Chehab — A63

**1960     Photo.     Perf. 13½**
344 A63 0.50p bl grn & dp blu-
                 ish grn          .25   .25
345 A63 2.50p olive               .25   .25
346 A63   5p green                .25   .25
347 A63 7.50p rose brown          .35   .25
348 A63  15p bright blue          .75   .25
349 A63  50p lilac               1.60   .25
350 A63 100p brown               3.75   .25
    Nos. 344-350 (7)             7.20  1.75

Nos. 343A and 340
Overprinted in Red

**1960, Nov.     Litho.     Perf. 13x13½**
351 A53  5p light green           .70   .25
352 A62 15p lt blue green        1.40   .25

Arabian Oil Conference, Beirut.

President Fuad
Chehab — A64

**1961, Feb.     Litho.     Perf. 13½x13**
353 A64 2.50p blue & light bl     .50   .25
354 A64 7.50p dark vio & pink    1.00   .25
355 A64  10p red brn & yel       1.50   .25
    Nos. 353-355 (3)             3.00   .75

---

Cedar                    Post Office, Beirut
A65                      A66

**1961     Unwmk.     Litho.     Perf. 13**
356 A65 2.50p green               .75   .25

**Redrawn**
357 A65 2.50p orange             1.25   .25
358 A65   5p maroon              1.25   .25
359 A65  10p black               1.50   .25

Nos. 357-359 have no clouds.

**Perf. 11½**
361 A66 2.50p rose carmine        .75   .25
362 A66   5p bright green        1.40   .25
363 A66  15p dark blue           2.10   .25
    Nos. 356-363 (7)             9.00  1.75

Cedars — A67

10p, 15p, 50p, 100p, View of Zahle.

**1961     Litho.     Perf. 13**
365 A67 0.50p green               .45   .25
366 A67   1p brown                .45   .25
367 A67 2.50p ultramarine         .45   .25
368 A67   5p carmine              .65   .25
369 A67 7.50p violet              .85   .25
370 A67  10p dark brown          2.25   .25
371 A67  15p dark blue           2.50   .25
372 A67  50p dark green          2.75   .25
373 A67 100p black               3.25   .35
    Nos. 365-373 (9)            13.60  2.35

See Nos. 381-384.

Unknown Soldier
Monument — A68

**1961, Dec. 30     Unwmk.     Perf. 12**
374 A68 10p shown                3.00   .25
375 A68 15p Soldier & flag       3.75   .25

Anniv. of Lebanon's independence; evacuation of foreign troops, Dec. 31, 1946.
See Nos. C329-C330.

Bugler — A69          Scout Carrying
                      Flag and Scout
                      Emblem — A70

Designs: 2.50p, First aid. 6p, Lord Baden-Powell. 10p, Scouts building campfire.

**1962, Mar. 1     Litho.     Perf. 12**
376 A69 0.50p yel grn, blk & yel 1.20   .25
377 A70   1p multicolored        1.20   .25
378 A70 2.50p dk red, blk & grn  1.20   .25
379 A70   6p multicolored        1.20   .25
380 A70  10p dp bl, blk & yel    1.20   .25
    Nos. 376-380,C331-C333 (8)   8.65  2.10

50th anniversary of Lebanese Boy Scouts.

Type of 1961
Redrawn

Designs as before.

**1962     Unwmk.     Perf. 13**
381 A67 0.50p yellow green       1.20   .25
382 A67   1p brown               1.20   .25
383 A67 2.50p ultramarine        1.30   .25
384 A67  15p dark blue           3.25   .25
    Nos. 381-384,C341-C342 (6)  14.30  1.65

Temple of Nefertari, Abu Simbel — A71

**1962, Aug. 1    Unwmk.    Perf. 13**
390 A71 5p light ultra            1.00  .25
391 A71 15p brn lake & mar        1.40  .25
Campaign to save the historic monuments in Nubia. See Nos. C351-C352.

Cherries — A72

Designs: 50c, 2.50p, 7.50p, Cherries. 1p, 5p, Figs. 10p, 17.50p, 30p, Grapes. 50p, Oranges. 100p, Pomegranates.

**1962    Vignette Multicolored    Litho.**
392 A72 0.50p violet blue         1.50  .25
393 A72 1p gray blue              1.50  .25
394 A72 2.50p brown               1.50  .25
395 A72 5p bright blue            1.50  .25
396 A72 7.50p lilac rose          1.50  .25
397 A72 10p chocolate             1.75  .25
398 A72 17.50p slate              2.50  .25
399 A72 30p slate grn             2.75  .25
400 A72 50p green                 3.00  .25
401 A72 100p brown blk            5.00  .50
  Nos. 392-401,C359-C366 (18)    31.65 5.05

Elementary Schoolboy — A73

**1962, Oct. 1    Litho.    Perf. 12**
404 A73 30p multicolored          1.20  .25
Students' Day, Oct. 1. See No. C355.

Cedar of Lebanon
A74        A75

**1963-64    Unwmk.    Perf. 13x13½**
405 A74 0.50p green               5.75  .25
406 A75 0.50p gray grn ('64)      1.20  .25
407 A75 2.50p ultra ('64)         1.20  .25
408 A75 5p brt pink ('64)         1.30  .25
409 A75 7.50p orange ('64)        1.40  .25
410 A75 17.50p rose lil ('64)     1.75  .25
  Nos. 405-410 (6)               12.60 1.50

Bicyclist — A76

**1964, Feb. 11    Litho.    Perf. 13**
415 A76 2.50p shown               1.20  .25
416 A76 5p Basketball             1.20  .25
417 A76 10p Track                 1.20  .25
  Nos. 415-417,C385-C387 (6)      5.40 1.50
4th Mediterranean Games, Naples, Sept. 21-29, 1963.

Hyacinth — A77

**1964    Unwmk.    Perf. 13x13½**
**Size: 26x27mm**
418 A77 0.50p shown               1.20  .25
419 A77 1p Hyacinth               1.20  .25
420 A77 2.50p Hyacinth            1.20  .25
421 A77 5p Cyclamen               1.20  .25
422 A77 7.50p Cyclamen            1.20  .25
**Perf. 13**
**Size: 26x37mm**
423 A77 10p Poinsettia            1.20  .25
424 A77 17.50p Anemone            2.00  .25
425 A77 30p Iris                  3.00  .25
426 A77 50p Poppy                 5.75  .40
  Nos. 418-426,C391-C397 (16)    23.75 4.15
See Nos. C391-C397.

Temple of the Sun, Baalbek — A78

**1965, Jan. 11    Litho.    Perf. 13x13½**
429 A78 2.50p blk & red org       1.60  .25
430 A78 7.50p black & blue        2.25  .25
  Nos. 429-430,C420-C423 (6)      7.40 1.70
International Festival at Baalbek.

Swimmer — A79

**1965, Jan. 23    Engr.    Perf. 13**
431 A79 2.50p shown               2.00  .25
432 A79 7.50p Fencer              2.00  .25
433 A79 10p Basketball, vert.     3.25  .25
  Nos. 431-433,C424-C426 (6)      9.00 1.50
18th Olympic Games, Tokyo, Oct. 10-25, 1964.

Birds — A80

5p, Bullfinch. 10p, European goldfinch. 15p, Hoopoe. 17.50p, Rock partridge. 20p, Golden Oriole. 32.50p, European bee-eater.

**1965    Engr.    Perf. 13**
434 A80 5p multicolored           6.50  .25
435 A80 10p multicolored         10.50  .25
436 A80 15p multicolored          8.00  .25
437 A80 17.50p multicolored       9.75  .25
438 A80 20p shown                12.00  .25
439 A80 32.50p multicolored      16.00  .25
  Nos. 434-439 (6)               62.75 1.50
For surcharge see No. 459.

Cow and Calf — A81

**1965    Photo.    Perf. 11x12**
440 A81 0.50p shown               1.60  .25
441 A81 1p Rabbit                 1.75  .25
442 A81 2.50p Ewe & lamb          2.00  .25
  Nos. 440-442 (3)                5.35  .75

Hippodrome, Beirut — A82

1p, Pigeon Rocks. 2.50p, Tabarja. 5p, Ruins, Beit-Méry. 7.50p, Statue and ruins, Anjar.

**1966    Unwmk.    Perf. 12x11½**
443 A82 0.50p gold & multi        1.40  .25
444 A82 1p gold & multi           1.60  .25
445 A82 2.50p gold & multi        1.75  .25
446 A82 5p gold & multi           2.00  .25
447 A82 7.50p gold & multi        2.25  .25
  Nos. 443-447 (5)                9.00 1.25
See Nos. C486-C492. For surcharge see No. 460.

ITY Emblem and Cedars — A83

**1967    Photo.    Perf. 11x12**
448 A83 0.50p lem, blk & brt bl   1.00  .25
449 A83 1p sal, blk & brt bl      1.00  .25
450 A83 2.50p gray, blk & brt bl  1.25  .25
451 A83 5p lt rose lil, blk & brt bl  1.25  .25
452 A83 7.50p yel, blk & brt bl   1.75  .25
  Nos. 448-452 (5)                6.25 1.25
Intl. Tourist Year; used as a regular issue. See Nos. C515-C522. For surcharge see No. 461.

Goat and Kid — A84

**1968, Feb.    Photo.    Perf. 12x11½**
453 A84 0.50p shown               2.40  .25
454 A84 1p Cattle                 3.25  .25
455 A84 2.50p Sheep               4.00  .25
456 A84 5p Camels                 5.00  .25
457 A84 10p Donkey                5.75  .25
458 A84 15p Horses                7.50  .25
  Nos. 453-458 (6)               27.90 1.50
See Nos. C534-C539.

**No. 439 Surcharged in Black**

**1972, Apr.    Engr.    Perf. 13**
459 A80 25p on 32.50p multi      18.00  .25

**Nos. 447 and 452 Surcharged with New Value and Bars**
**Perf. 12x11½, 11x12**
**1972, May    Photo.**
460 A82 5p on 7.50p multi         3.75  .25
461 A83 5p on 7.50p multi         3.75  .25

Cedar — A85

**1974    Litho.    Perf. 11**
462 A85 0.50p orange & olive      .25  .25

Army Badge — A86

**1980, Dec. 28    Litho.    Perf. 11½**
463 A86 25p multicolored          2.00  .25
Army Day. See Nos. C792-C793.

Pres. Elias Sarkis — A87

**1981, Sept. 23    Photo.    Perf. 14x13½**
464 A87 125p multicolored         2.75  .80
465 A87 300p multicolored         2.75 1.60
466 A87 500p multicolored         7.50 2.40
  Nos. 464-466 (3)               13.00 4.80

World Food Day, Oct. 16, 1981 — A88

**1982, Nov. 23    Photo.    Perf. 12x11½**
467 A88 50p Stork carrying food packages  1.75  .30
468 A88 75p Wheat, globe          2.00  .50
469 A88 100p Produce              2.25  .65
  Nos. 467-469 (3)                6.00 1.45

World Communications Year — A89

**1983, Dec. 19    Photo.    Perf. 14**
470 A89 300p multicolored         6.00 1.75

Illustrations from Khalil Gibran's The Prophet — A90

**1983, Dec. 19    Perf. 13½x14**
471 A90 200p The Soul Is Back     2.75 1.00
472 A90 300p The Family           4.25 1.75
473 A90 500p Self-portrait        7.50 2.40
474 A90 1000p The Prophet        15.00 4.75
  a. Souvenir sheet, #471-474    32.50 32.50
  Nos. 471-474 (4)               29.50 9.90
No. 474a sold for £25.

Scouting Year — A91

**1983, Dec. 19    Perf. 14**
475 A91 200p Rowing               2.60  .50
476 A91 300p Signaling            3.00  .60
477 A91 500p Camp                 5.50 1.00
  Nos. 475-477 (3)               11.10 2.10

Cedar of Lebanon — A93

**1984, Dec.    Photo.    Perf. 14½x13½**
481 A93 5p multicolored           1.60  .25

Flowers — A94

**1984, Dec.    Photo.    Perf. 14½x13½**
482 A94 10p Iris of Sofar         1.40  .25
483 A94 25p Periwinkle            2.00  .30
484 A94 50p Flowering thorn       2.60  .40
  Nos. 482-484 (3)                6.00  .95
For surcharges see Nos. 531-532.

Defense — A95

**1984, Dec.   Photo.   Perf. 14½x13½**
485 A95  75p  Dove over city        3.50   .90
486 A95  150p Soldier, cedar        4.75  1.90
487 A95  300p Olive wreath,
              cedar                  6.25  3.50
       Nos. 485-487 (3)            14.50  6.30

Temple
Ruins — A96

**1985   Photo.   Perf. 13½x14½**
488 A96  100p Fakra        3.00   .55
489 A96  200p Bziza        3.50  1.10
490 A96  500p Tyre         6.50  2.75
       Nos. 488-490 (3)   13.00  4.40

Pres. Gemayel, Map
of Lebanon, Dove,
Text — A97

**1988, Feb. 1   Litho.   Perf. 14**
491 A97  £50 multicolored   4.00  1.60

Pres. Gemayel,
Military Academy
Graduate — A98

**1988, Mar. 9**
492 A98  £25 multicolored   4.50  1.35
   Booklets containing Nos. 491-492, were
given to dignitaries. Value for booklet, $110.

Arab Scouts, 75th
Anniv. — A99

**1988, Mar. 9   Perf. 13½x14½**
493 A99  £20 multicolored   4.50  1.10

UN Child Survival
Campaign — A100

**1988, Mar. 9   Perf. 14½x13½**
494 A100  £15 multicolored   2.75  .60

Prime Minister
Rashid Karame
(1921-1987),
Satellite, Flags,
Earth — A101

**1988, Mar. 9   Perf. 13½x14½**
495 A101  £10 multicolored   2.00  .50

1st World Festival
for Youths of
Lebanese Descent
in
Uruguay — A102

**1988, Mar. 9**
496 A102  £5 multicolored   2.00  .50

Cedar — A103

**1989   Photo.   Perf. 13x13½**
497 A103  £50 dk grn & vio      2.40   .30
498 A103  £70 dk grn & brn      2.75   .40
499 A103  £100 dk grn & brt
               yel             3.25   .40
500 A103  £200 dk grn & bluish
               grn             4.75  1.00
501 A103  £500 dk grn & brt
               yel grn         8.75  2.40
       Nos. 497-501 (5)       21.90  4.50

Independence, 50th Anniv. — A104

   Designs: £200, Al Muntazah Restaurant,
Zahle, 1883. £300, Sea Castle, Sidon, vert.
£500, Presidential Palace, Baabda. £1000,
Army graduation ceremony, vert. £3000, Bei-
rut 2000, architectural plan. £5000, Pres. Elias
Harawi, Lebanese flag, vert.

**1993   Litho.   Perf. 14**
502 A104  £200 multi     1.60   .25
503 A104  £300 multi     2.10   .50
504 A104  £500 multi     3.25   .75
505 A104  £1000 multi    4.75  1.60
506 A104  £3000 multi    8.50  2.75
507 A104  £5000 multi   16.50  7.50
       Nos. 502-507 (6) 36.70 13.35

For overprints, see Nos. 533B, 533C, 533G.

**Size: 126x150mm**
***Imperf***
508 A104  £10,000 multi     52.50 52.50

A105

   Environmental Protection: £100, Stop polluting atmosphere. £200, Stop fires. £500, Trees,
building. £1000, Birds, trees in city. £2000,
Mosaic of trees. £5000, Green tree in middle
of polluted city.

**1994, May 7   Litho.   Perf. 13½x13**
509 A105  £100 multicolored    1.90   .25
510 A105  £200 multicolored    2.25   .50
511 A105  £500 multicolored    3.75  1.00
512 A105  £1000 multicolored   6.00  1.75
513 A105  £2000 multicolored   9.75  3.00
514 A105  £5000 multicolored  22.00  7.00
       Nos. 509-514 (6)       45.65 13.50

For overprints see Nos. 533D, 533H, 537.

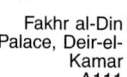

A106

**1995, May 6   Litho.   Perf. 13½x13**
515 A106  £1500 Martyr's Day   7.00  3.00
   For overprint see No. 534.

Anniversaries and
Events — A107

   £500, UNICEF, 50th anniv., horiz. £1000,
Intl. Year of the Family (1994), horiz. £2000,
ILO, 75th anniv. (in 1994), horiz. £3000, Bar
Association (Berytus Nutrix Legum), 75th
anniv.

**1996, Feb. 21   Litho.   Perf. 14**
516 A107  £500 multi, horiz.    3.50   .90
517 A107  £1000 multi, horiz.   5.50  1.90
518 A107  £2000 multi, horiz.   9.50  3.50
519 A107  £3000 multicolored  14.00  5.50
       Nos. 516-519 (4)       32.50 11.80

For overprints, see Nos. 533E, 534A, 535A.

Anniversaries and
Events of
1995 — A108

   £100, Opening of Museum of Arab Postage
Stamps. £500, FAO, 50th anniv. £1000, UN,
50th anniv. £2000, Arab League, 50th anniv.
£3000, Former Pres. René Moawad (1925-
89).

**1996, Feb. 21   Perf. 13½x13**
520 A108  £100 multicolored    2.10   .25
521 A108  £500 multicolored    3.50   .90
522 A108  £1000 multicolored   5.50  1.75
523 A108  £2000 multicolored   9.00  3.25
524 A108  £3000 multicolored  14.00  5.25
       Nos. 520-524 (5)       34.10 11.40

For overprints see Nos. 533A, 533F, 533I,
535-536.

Massacre at
Cana — A109

**1997, Oct. 13   Litho.   Perf. 14**
525 A109  £1100 multicolored  20.00 10.00
   For overprint see No. 533J.

1997 Visit of
Pope John Paul II
to
Lebanon — A110

**1998, May 11   Litho.   Perf. 13½x13**
526 A110  £10,000 multi      120.00 100.00
   For overprint see Nos. 533O, 538.

Fakhr al-Din
Palace, Deir-el-
Kamar
A111

   £100, Chehab Palace, Hasbaya, vert. £300,
ESCWA Building, Beirut, vert. £1100, Grand
Seraglio, Beirut.

**1999   Litho.   Perf. 12**
527 A111  £100 multicolored   1.50   .25
528 A111  £300 multicolored   2.50   .45
529 A111  £500 shown          3.00   .80
530 A111  £1100 multicolored  6.00  1.75
       Nos. 527-530 (4)      13.00  3.25

Nos. 484, 485 and
C775 Surcharged in
Silver and Black

**Methods and Perfs. as before**
**1999**
531 A94   £100 on 50p
               (#484)       1.75   .25
532 A95   £300 on 75p
               (#485)       2.50   .45
533 AP154 £1100 on 70p
               (#C775)      6.00  1.75
       Nos. 531-533 (3)    10.25  2.45

Nos. 502, 504-505,
511-512, 516, 518-
522, 525 Overprinted
in Gold

Similar to Nos. 534-538 but with
Symbol Oriented as a Cross

**Methods and Perfs As Before**
**1999**
533A A108 £100 multi        20.00
533B A104 £200 multi        20.00
533C A104 £500 multi
               (#504)       32.50   —
533D A105 £500 multi
               (#501)       35.00   —
533E A107 £500 multi        35.00
533F A108 £500 multi
               (#521)       35.00
533G A104 £1000 multi
               (#505)       70.00
533H A105 £1000 multi       60.00
533I A108 £1000 multi
               (#522)       40.00
533J A109 £1100 multi
               (#525)      425.00   —
533K A106 £1500 multi       50.00
533L A107 £2000 multi       95.00
533M A107 £3000 multi
               (#519)      140.00   —
533N A105 £5000 multi      275.00
533O A110 £10,000 multi
               (#526)      550.00   —
       Nos. 533A-533O (15) 1,883.

Nos. 514, 515, 523,
524 and 526
Overprinted in Gold or
Silver

**Methods and Perfs As Before**
**1999**
534 A106 £1500 multi        16.00   5.00
535 A108 £2000 multi        24.00   9.00
536 A108 £3000 multi (S)    31.00  12.50
537 A105 £5000 multi        42.50  17.50
538 A110 £10,000 multi      85.00  40.00
       Nos. 534-538 (5)    198.50  84.00

Cedar of Lebanon — A112

**Perf. 13x13¼, 11x11¼ (£500, £1000,
£1100)**
**1999-2000   Litho.   Unwmk.**
539 A112 £100 dark red       .50   .25
540 A112 £300 Prus blue     1.00   .35

**Wmk. 400**
541 A112 £500 green         1.50   .65
 a.   Perf. 13x13¼           1.50   .65
 b.   Booklet pane, 10 #541a 15.00
      Booklet, #541b        15.00
542 A112 £1000 blue         3.50  1.25
543 A112 £1100 olive brn    3.75  1.40
 a.   Perf. 13x13¼           3.75  1.40
 b.   Booklet pane, 10 #543a 37.50
      Booklet, #543b        37.50
544 A112 £1500 vio blue     4.50  1.90
 a.   Booklet pane, 10 #544 45.00
      Booklet, #544a        45.00
 b.   Perf. 11x11¼           4.50  1.90
       Nos. 539-544 (6)     14.75  5.80

## Cedar of Lebanon Type of 2000 Redrawn
**Perf. 11x11¼, 13x13¼ (£1000)**
**2001-02     Litho.     Unwmk.**
**Numerals 1½mm Tall**

| | | | | |
|---|---|---|---|---|
| 544C | A112 | £500 olive grn | | |
| | | ('02) | 1.60 | 1.25 |
| 544D | A112 | £1000 blue | 3.25 | 2.50 |
| 544E | A112 | £1500 brown | 3.75 | 2.75 |
| 544F | A112 | £1500 purple | 5.25 | 3.75 |
| g. | | Perf. 13x13¼ | 27.50 | 27.50 |
| | | Nos. 544C-544F (4) | 13.85 | 10.25 |

On Nos. 539-544, numerals are 2mm tall.

A113

**2001     Litho.     Perf. 11¼x11**
545 A113  £1100 multi         4.50  2.00

Geneva Conventions, 50th Anniv. (in 1999) — A114

Red Cross/Red Crescent — A115

**2001     Litho.     Perf. 11x11½**
546 A114  £500 shown       2.50  1.00
547 A114  £1100 "50," fist  5.00  2.00
548 A115  £1500 shown       6.25  3.00
   Nos. 546-548 (3)        13.75  6.00

SOS Children's Villages — A116

**2001**
549 A116  £300 multi         2.25  1.00

Prisoners in Israel — A117

**2001**
550 A117  £500 multi         4.00  2.00

Ibrahim Abd el Al (1908-59), Hydrologist A118

**2001**
551 A118  £1000 multi        4.25  2.00

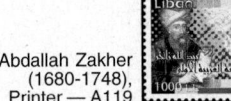

Abdallah Zakher (1680-1748), Printer — A119

**2001**
552 A119  £1000 multi        6.50  3.00

Elias Abu Chabke (1904-49), Poet — A120

**2001     Perf. 11½x11**
553 A120  £1500 multi       13.50  6.50

Saint Joseph University, 125th Anniv. (in 2000) — A121

**2001     Perf. 11x11½**
554 A121  £5000 multi       17.50  8.50

Economic & Social Commission for Western Asia, 25th Anniv. (in 1999) — A122

**2001     Perf. 11½x11**
555 A122  £10,000 multi     32.50 20.00

Arab Woman's Day — A123

**2002, Feb. 1     Litho.     Perf. 13¼x13½**
556 A123  £1000 multi        3.50  2.75

Arab League Summit Conference, Beirut — A124

Arab League member flags and: £2000, Emblem. £3000, Cedar tree, Lebanese Pres. Emile Lahoud.

**2002, Mar. 27**
557-558 A124  Set of 2     18.50 11.00

### Souvenir Sheet

Israeli Withdrawal From Southern Lebanon, 2nd Anniv. — A125

No. 559: a, Pres. Emile Lahoud, flag. b, Pres. Lahoud holding book. c, Pres. Lahoud and map. d, Pres. Lahoud receiving sword.

**2002, Mar. 27     Perf. 13¼**
559 A125  £1100 Sheet of 4,
          #a-d            11.00  9.50

### Souvenir Sheet

Martyrs of Justice A126

**2002, June 14     Perf. 13¼x13½**
560 A126  £3000 multi        7.00  5.75

UPU, 125th Anniv. (in 1999) — A127

**2002, Oct. 11     Litho.     Perf. 13½x13¼**
561 A127  £2000 multi        7.00  3.25

City Views A128

Ruins A129

Paleontonlogy A130

Designs: £100 Old souk, Zouk Mikael. £300, Old souk, Sidon. £500, Byblos. £1000, Souk, Tripoli. £1100, Bzira. £1500, Arqa. £2000, Niha. £3000, Mousailah Citadel. £5000, Libanobythus milkii in amber. £10,000, Nematonotus longispinus fossil.

**Perf. 13¼x13½, 13½x13¼**
**2002-03                          Litho.**

| | | | | |
|---|---|---|---|---|
| 562 | A128 | £100 multi | .50 | .25 |
| 563 | A128 | £300 multi | .90 | .50 |
| 564 | A128 | £500 multi | 1.75 | .90 |
| 565 | A128 | £1000 multi | 2.50 | 1.75 |
| 566 | A129 | £1100 multi | 3.00 | 2.00 |
| 567 | A129 | £1500 multi | 3.50 | 2.75 |
| 568 | A129 | £2000 multi | 4.50 | 3.75 |
| 569 | A129 | £3000 multi | 7.25 | 5.75 |
| 570 | A130 | £5000 multi | 24.00 | 9.25 |
| 571 | A130 | £10,000 multi | 37.50 | 18.00 |
| | | Nos. 562-571 (10) | 85.40 | 44.90 |

Issued: £100, £300, 10/11; £1000, £1500, £2000, £3000, £10,000, 11/20; £500, £1100, 12/20; £5000, 1/8/03.

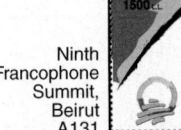

Ninth Francophone Summit, Beirut A131

Summit emblem and: No. 572, £1500. Mountains. No. 573, £1500, Pres. Emile Lahoud.

**2002, Oct. 23     Perf. 13¼x13½**
572-573 A131  Set of 2       7.00  5.50

Beirut, 1999 Arab Cultural Capital — A132

**2002, Nov. 13**
574 A132  £2000 multi        5.00  4.00

Independence, 60th Anniv. (in 2001) — A133

Stylized flag and: No. 575, £1250, Crowd viewing horse and rider. No. 576, £1250, Men and flag on staff. No. 577, £1750, Arabic text. No. 578, £1750, Soldier saluting group of men. £6000, Vignettes of Nos. 575-578.

**2003, Dec. 5     Litho.     Perf. 12¾x13**
575-578 A133  Set of 4     20.00 20.00
           *Imperf*
        **Size: 160x110mm**
579 A133  £6000 multi       22.50 22.50

Faqra Ski Resort — A134

**2004     Litho.     Perf. 11x11¼**
580 A134  £500 multi         2.50  2.50

General Post Office, Beirut — A135

Post office in: £100, 1953. £300, 2002.

**2004                     Perf. 11¼x11**
581-582 A135  Set of 2      2.50  2.50

Al Bustan Festival — A136

**2004     Litho.     Perf. 11x11¼**
583 A136  £1000 multi        4.00  4.00

St. George's Hospital, Beirut, 125th Anniv. (in 2003) A137

**2004, Oct. 28     Litho.     Perf. 11x11¼**
584 A137  £3000 multi        5.50  5.50

Ski Resorts — A138

**2004     Litho.     Perf. 11x11¼, 11¼x11**

| | | | | |
|---|---|---|---|---|
| 585 | A138 | £100 Kamouaa | .70 | .70 |
| 586 | A138 | £100 Aayoun Siman | .70 | .70 |
| 587 | A138 | £250 Laklouk, vert. | 1.35 | 1.35 |
| 588 | A138 | £300 Zaarour | 1.75 | 1.75 |
| 589 | A138 | £300 Kanat Bakish | 1.75 | 1.75 |
| 590 | A138 | £1000 Cedres | 3.75 | 3.75 |
| | | Nos. 585-590 (5) | 8.25 | 8.25 |

Issued: No. 585, 10/28; £250, 11/26; No. 588, 10/28; Nos. 586, 589, £1000, 12/10.

Baalbeck Intl. Festival A139

Tyre Festival A140

Beiteddine Festival A141

Byblos Intl. Festival A142

**Perf. 11x11¼, 11¼x11**

**2004, Nov. 26**      **Litho.**
591 A139   £500 multi    .80 .80
592 A140   £1250 multi   2.00 2.00
593 A141   £1400 multi   2.25 2.25
594 A142   £1750 multi   2.75 2.75
    Nos. 591-594 (4)   7.80 7.80

Rotary International, Cent. — A143

**2005, Feb. 23**      **Perf. 11¼x11**
595 A143   £3000 multi    6.25 6.25

Beirut Buildings — A144

Designs: £100, Rafiq Hariri Intl. Airport. £250, Parliament. £300, Camille Chamoun Sports Center. £500, National Museum. £1000, Governmental Palace. £1250, Bank of Lebanon. £1400, St. Paul's Cathedral. £1750, Bahaeddine Hariri Mosque. £2000, Presidential Palace.

**2005**    **Litho.**    **Perf. 13x13½**
596-604 A144   Set of 9    25.00 25.00
   Issued: £100, £300, £500, £1000, 10/11; others, 11/11.

Pres. Rafiq Hariri (1944-2005) A145

Designs: No. 605, £1250, Pres. Hariri, flag. No. 606, £1250, Pres. Hariri, mosque, church and statues. No. 607, £1750, Pres. Hariri, mosque. No. 608, £1750, Child kissing picture of Pres. Hariri.

**2006, Feb. 13**      **Perf. 13¼x13**
605-608 A145   Set of 4    15.00 15.00
608a    Souvenir sheet, #605-608, imperf.    10.50 10.50
   No. 608a has embossed margin and simulated perforations between stamps.

Arabic Book Exhibition — A146

**2007, Apr. 18**   **Litho.**   **Perf. 13x13¼**
609 A146   £1000 multi    2.25 2.25

Basil Fuleihan (1963-2005), Economy Minister A147

Fuleihan: £500, Wearing cap and gown, suit and tie. £1500, With flags of Lebanon and European Union. £2000, With flag of Lebanon. £4000, Vignettes of Nos. 610-612, map and flag of Lebanon.

**2007, Apr. 18**      **Perf. 13¼x13**
610-612 A147   Set of 3    10.00 10.00

**Size: 160x100mm**
**Imperf**
613 A147   £4000 multi    6.00 6.00

Pres. Fouad Chehab (1902-73) A148

**2007, June 4**      **Perf. 13¼x13**
614 A148   £1400 multi    2.40 2.40

World Summit on the Information Society, Tunis (in 2005) — A149

**2007, July 2**      **Perf. 13x13¼**
615 A149   £100 multi    .50 .50

Léopold Sédar Senghor (1906-2001), First President of Senegal A150

**2007, July 2**      **Perf. 13¼x13**
616 A150   £300 multi    .75 .75

Intl. Year of Sports and Physical Education (in 2005) — A151

**2007, July 2**      **Perf. 13x13¼**
617 A151   £500 multi    1.25 1.25

OPEC Development Fund, 30th Anniv. — A152

**2007, July 2**
618 A152   £1400 multi    2.25 2.25

Baalbeck Intl. Festival, 50th Anniv. A153

50th anniv. emblem and: £1000, Names of performers. £5000, Female performers.

**2007, July 2**      **Perf. 13¼x13**
619-620 A153   Set of 2    12.00 12.00

Islamic Makassed Association of Sidon, 125th Anniv. (in 2004) A154

Emblem and: £1400, Pres. Rafiq Hariri. £1750, Prime Minister Riad El Solh.

**2007, July 2**
621-622 A154   Set of 2    9.00 9.00

Islamic Makassed Association of Beirut, 125th Anniv. (in 2003) A155

Emblem and: £250, "125" in Arabian script. £500, Prime Minister Saeb Salam. £1400, Pres. Rafiq Hariri. £1750, Omar El Daouk.

**2007, July 2**
623-626 A155   Set of 4    9.00 9.00

Souvenir Sheet

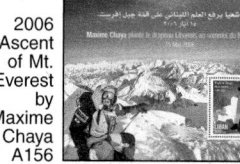

2006 Ascent of Mt. Everest by Maxime Chaya A156

**2007, July 2**
627 A156   £3000 multi    9.00 9.00

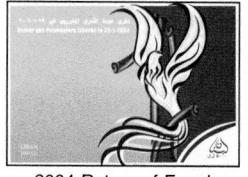

2004 Return of Freed Prisoners — A157

**2007, July 2**      **Imperf.**
628 A157   £5000 multi    10.00 10.00

Souvenir Sheet

Hills, by Nizar Daher A158

**2007, July 2**   **Litho.**   **Perf. 13¼x13**
629 A158   £5000 multi    10.00 10.00

Rotary International District 2450 Conference, Beirut A159

**2008, Apr. 30**   **Litho.**   **Perf. 13¼x13**
630 A159   £2000 multi    3.00 3.00

Kahlil Gibran (1883-1931), Writer and Artist — A160

Designs: £100, Mother and Her Child. £500, Sultana. £1400, Gibran Museum, Bsharri. £2000, Gibran.
£4000, Gibran and vignettes of Nos. 631-634, horiz.

**2008, Apr. 30**      **Perf. 13x13¼**
631-634 A160   Set of 4    11.00 11.00
**Imperf**
**Size: 160x110mm**
635 A160   £4000 multi    5.75 5.75

Army Day — A161

Emblem and: £500, Soldier and flag of Lebanon. £1000, Stylized flag of Lebanon. £1250, Soldier holding wheat stalks. £1750, Eye.
£4500, Soldiers and vignettes of Nos. 636-639.

**2008**    **Litho.**    **Perf. 13¼x13**
636-639 A161   Set of 4    8.00 8.00
**Size: 160x110mm**
**Imperf**
640 A161   £4500 multi    8.00 8.00

Souvenir Sheet

Arab Postal Day A162

No. 641 — Emblem and: a, World map and pigeon. b, Camel caravan.

**Perf. 13¼ Vert. Through Center**
**2008**
641 A162   £5000 Sheet of 2,
      #a-b    20.00 20.00
   Stamps have simulated perforations on three sides.

Lebanon Post, 10th Anniv. A163

Simulated postmarks, Lebanon Post emblem, streamers, airplane and: £1250, "10" in Arabian script. £1750, Open envelope and "10th anniversary."

£3000, Simulated postmarks, Lebanon Post emblem, streamers, airplane and vignettes of Nos. 642-643.

**2008**  **Perf. 13¼x13**
642-643 A163  Set of 2  5.50 5.50
**Size: 160x110mm**
*Imperf*
644 A163  £3000 multi  6.75 6.75

Trees and Map of Mediterranean Area — A164

**2008, Nov. 20**  **Perf. 13**
645 A164  £1750 multi  2.40 2.40

See France No. 3569.

Gen. François El Hajj (1953-2007) A165

**2009, Jan. 8**  **Perf. 13x13¼**
646 A165  £1750 multi  2.60 2.60

Universal Declaration of Human Rights, 60th Anniv. A166

**2009, Jan. 8**  **Perf. 13¼x13**
647 A166  £2000 multi  4.00 4.00

Dated 2008.

Beirut, World Book Capital — A167

**2009, Sept. 17**  **Litho.**  **Perf. 13x13¼**
648 A167  £750 multi  2.50 2.50

Jerusalem, Capital of Arab Culture A168

**2009, Sept. 17**  **Perf. 13¼x13**
649 A168  £1000 multi  3.00 3.00

Pierre Deschamps (1873-1958), Founder of French Lay Mission A169

**2009, Sept. 17**
650 A169  £500 blue & black  .85 .85

Sixth Francophone Games, Beirut A170

**2009, Sept. 28**
651 A170  £1000 multi  2.40 2.40

Fire Fighters — A171

Fire fighters with panel color of: £100, Green. £250, Red.

**2010, Aug. 2**  **Litho.**  **Perf. 13x13¼**
652-653 A171  Set of 2  .50 .50

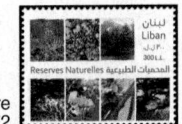

Nature Reserves — A172

**2010, Aug. 2**
654 A172  £300 multi  .45 .45

Architecture — A173

Various buildings with frame color of: £500, Red. £1000, Blue. £1200, Red.

**2010, Aug. 2**  **Perf. 13¼x13**
655-657 A173  Set of 3  3.75 3.75

Soap Production A174

**2010, Aug. 2**  **Perf. 13¼x13**
658 A174  £1400 multi  1.90 1.90

Soldier, Map of Lebanon — A175

**2010, Aug. 2**
659 A175  £1750 multi  2.40 2.40

Lungs and Cigarette Butts — A176

**2010, Aug. 2**
660 A176  £2000 multi  2.75 2.75

Syringe and Arrows — A177

**2010, Aug. 2**  **Perf. 13¼x13**
661 A177  £5000 black & red  7.00 7.00

Imam Al Ouzaai (707-74) A178

**2010, Oct. 9**
662 A178  £1000 multi  1.40 1.40

Grand Mufti Hassan Khaled (1921-89) A179

Musa as-Sadr (1929-78), Religious Leader — A180

**2010, Oct. 9**  **Perf. 13¼x13**
663 A179  £1400 multi  2.00 2.00
**Perf. 13x13¼**
664 A180  £1400 multi  2.00 2.00

Assassinated Political Leaders — A181

Designs: No. 665, £1400, Kamal Jumblatt (1917-77). No. 666, £1400, Prime Minister Rashid Karami (1921-87). No. 667, £1400, President René Moawad (1925-89). No. 668, £1400, President Bachir Gemayel (1947-82), horiz.

**2010, Oct. 9**  **Perf. 13x13¼, 13¼x13**
665-668 A181  Set of 4  8.00 8.00

World Tourism Day — A182

**2010, Oct. 9**  **Perf. 13x13¼**
669 A182  £2000 multi  3.00 3.00

Dove and Flowers — A183

**2010, Oct. 9**
670 A183  £3000 multi  6.00 6.00

Source of the Alphabet — A184

Arab Permanent Postal Commission A185

Famous People — A186

Designs: £1750, Sabah, singer and actress. £2250, Nabih Abou El-Hossn, actor. £2750, Hassan Alaa Eddine (1939-75), comedian. £3000, Caracalla Dance Ensemble. £5000, Alfred (1924-2006), Michel (1921-1981) and Youssef (1926-2001) Basbous, sculptors. £10,000, Said Akl, poet.

**2011, May 23**  **Litho.**  **Perf. 13x13¼**
671 A184  £250 multi  .35 .35
672 A185  £500 multi  .70 .70
673 A186  £1750 multi  2.50 2.50
674 A186  £2250 multi  3.25 3.25
675 A186  £2750 multi  4.00 4.00
676 A186  £3000 multi  4.25 4.25
677 A186  £5000 multi  7.50 7.50
678 A186  £10,000 multi  15.00 15.00
Nos. 671-678 (8)  37.55 37.55

**Famous People Type of 2011 and**

Ehden Reserve A187    Pres. Suleiman Franjieh (1910-92) A188

Designs: £1500, Fayrouz, singer. £2000, Wadih El-Safi, singer.

**Perf. 13x13¼, 13¼x13 (£1000)**
**2011, June 27**
679 A187  £750 multi  1.10 1.10
680 A188  £1000 multi  1.40 1.40
681 A186  £1500 multi  2.10 2.10
682 A186  £2000 multi  3.00 3.00
Nos. 679-682 (4)  7.60 7.60

Pres. Michel Suleiman A189

Pres. Suleiman and: £750, Cedar trees. £1750, People at President's Summer Residence, Beiteddine. £2500, Dove with flags of Syria and Lebanon on wings. £2750, United Nations emblem.

**2011, Nov. 5**  **Perf. 13¼x13**
683-686 A189  Set of 4  12.00 12.00

Mother's Day — A190

**2012, Mar. 12**  **Perf. 13x13¼**
687 A190  £2000 multi  72.50 72.50

590                                    LEBANON

Lions International in Lebanon, 60th Anniv. — A191

**2012, Apr. 2**
688 A191  £750 multi                    1.60 1.60

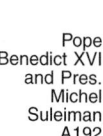

Pope Benedict XVI and Pres. Michel Suleiman A192

**2012, Sept. 15**        *Perf. 13¼x13*
689 A192  £1250 multi                   2.10 2.10
Visit of Pope Benedict XVI to Lebanon.

Beirut Marathon, 10th Anniv. — A193

**2012, Nov. 12**
690 A193  £750 multi                    1.25 1.25

Christmas A194

**2012, Nov. 13**        *Perf. 13x13¼*
691 A194  £2000 multi                   3.25 3.25

World Map and Statue of Lebanese Man — A195

**2012, Nov. 21  Litho.  *Perf. 13x13¼***
692 A195  £500 multi                    5.00 5.00

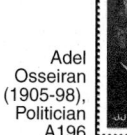

Adel Osseiran (1905-98), Politician A196

**2012, Nov. 21  Litho.  *Perf. 13¼x13***
693 A196  £1000 multi                   1.60 1.60

National Scientific Research Council, 50th Anniv. A197

**2012, Dec. 10**
694 A197  £250 multi                    .45 .45

Pres. Michel Suleiman — A198

**2012, Dec. 13**        *Perf. 13x13¼*
695 A198  £250 multi                    10.00 10.00

Ghassan Tueni (1926-2012), Journalist and Politician — A199

**2012, Dec. 14**
696 A199  £750 multi                    1.25 1.25

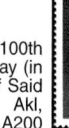

100th Birthday (in 2011) of Said Akl, Poet — A200

**2012, Dec. 26**        *Perf. 13¼x13*
697 A200  £500 multi                    .80 .80

Mother's Day — A201

**2013, Mar. 20**        *Perf. 13x13¼*
698 A201  £2000 multi                   3.00 3.00

Lebanon Post, 15th Anniv. — A202

**2013, Nov. 11  Litho.  *Perf. 13x13¼***
699 A202  £3000 multi                   3.00 3.00

Amin Maalouf, Member of French Academy A203

**2013, Nov. 19  Litho.  *Perf. 13¼x13***
700 A203  £100 multi                    1.00 1.00

Independence, 70th Anniv. — A204

**2013, Nov. 27  Litho.  *Perf. 13x13¼***
701 A204  £1000 multi                   1.75 1.75

Christmas — A205

**2013, Dec. 16  Litho.  *Perf. 13¼x13***
702 A205  £2000 multi                   3.00 3.00

Armenian Genocide Monument, Bikfaya — A206

**2014, Apr. 15  Litho.  *Perf. 13¼x13***
703 A206  £2000 multi                   2.50 2.50

Medicine, Law and Engineering Faculties of St. Joseph University, Cent. — A207

**2014, Apr. 29  Litho.  *Perf. 13x13¼***
704 A207  £500 multi                    .85 .85

Famous Women — A208

Designs: No. 705, £2000, Laure Moughha-izel (1929-97), women's rights advocate. No. 706, £2000, Mounira el Solh (1911-2010), advocate for women's rights and the disabled. No. 707, £2000, Alexandra Issa el Khoury, President of Lebanese Red Cross. No. 708, £2000, Anissa Najjar, founder of Al Ahlia Magazine.

**2014, May 22  Litho.  *Perf. 13¼x13***
705-708 A208  Set of 4                  14.00 14.00

Bank of Lebanon, 50th Anniv. — A209

**2014, June 2  Litho.  *Perf. 13x13¼***
709 A209  £1750 multi                   1.50 1.50

Father's Day — A210

**2014, June 17  Litho.  *Perf. 13¼x13***
710 A210  £1750 multi                   1.50 1.50

Euromed Postal Emblem and Mediterranean Sea — A211

**2014, July 9  Litho.  *Perf. 13x13¼***
711 A211  £1000 multi                   1.00 1.00

2014 World Cup Soccer Championships, Brazil — A212

Designs: £1750, Mascot. £2000, Emblem.

**2014, July 12  Litho.  *Perf. 13¼x13***
712-713 A212  Set of 2                  7.25 7.25

Monsignor Germanos Mouakkad (1853-1912), Missionary — A213

**2014, Sept. 5  Litho.  *Perf. 13¼x13***
714 A213  £250 multi                    .60 .60

Youssef Bey Karam (1823-89), Leader of 1866-67 Rebellion Against Ottoman Rule — A214

**2014, Nov. 10  Litho.  *Perf. 13¼x13***
715 A214  £1750 multi                   1.50 1.50

Writers — A215

Designs: No. 716, £1750, Kamal Youssef El-Hage (1917-76). No. 717, £1750, Ounsi El-Hage (1937-2014). No. 718, £1750, Joseph Harb (1941-2014).

**2014, Nov. 10  Litho.  *Perf. 13¼x13***
716-718 A215  Set of 3                  8.75 8.75

Independence, 71st Anniv. — A216

**2014, Nov. 22  Litho.  *Perf. 13¼x13***
719 A216  £2750 multi                   2.75 2.75

Christmas and New Year's Day — A217

**2014, Dec. 16  Litho.  *Perf. 13¼x13***
720 A217  £5000 multi                   6.00 6.00

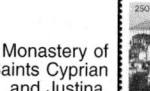

Monastery of Saints Cyprian and Justina, Kfifane — A218

Monastery of Saint Saviour, Joun — A219    Monastery of St. John Castle, Beit Mery — A220

**2015, Jan. 15  Litho.  *Perf. 13x13¼***
721 A218  £250 multi                    1.75 1.75
722 A219  £250 multi                    .50 .50

       *Perf. 13¼x13*
723 A220  £250 multi                    .50 .50
       Nos. 721-723 (3)                 2.75 2.75

Said Freiha (1912-78), Founder and Publisher of Dar Assayad News Magazine — A221

**2015, Jan. 20    Litho.    Perf. 13x13¼**
724 A221  £1750 multi                        3.25 3.25

Emblem of General Security Forces A222

Emblem of Internal Security Forces A223

**2015, Mar. 17    Litho.    Perf. 13¼x13**
725 A222  £1750 multi                        1.75 1.75
726 A223  £1750 multi                        1.75 1.75

Mother's Day — A224

**2015, Mar. 20    Litho.    Perf. 13¼x13**
727 A224  £2000 multi                        2.00 2.00

Pierre Sadek (1938-2013), Political Cartoonist A225

**2015, May 26    Litho.    Perf. 13x13¼**
728 A225  £2250 multi                        2.25 2.25

Famous People — A226

Designs: No. 729, £1750, Amin al-Hafez (1926-2009), prime minister. No. 730, £1750, Leila Osseiran (1934-2007), writer and wife of Amin al-Hafez.

**2015, July 7    Litho.    Perf. 13¼x13**
729-730 A226    Set of 2                     6.50 6.50

Euromed Postal Emblem, Boats of the Mediterranean Sea — A227

**2015, July 9    Litho.    Perf. 13x13¼**
731 A227  £5000 multi                        5.00 5.00

Politicians A228

Designs: No. 732, £1750, Riad El Solh (1894-1951), first prime minister. No. 733, £1750, Bechara El Khoury (1890-1964), prime minister and president.

**2015, July 14    Litho.    Perf. 13x13¼**
732-733 A228    Set of 2                     6.50 6.50

The Red Sunset, by Saliba Douaihy (1915-94) A229

**2015, Aug. 11    Litho.    Perf. 13¼x13**
734 A229  £2000 multi                        2.00 2.00

Flag Day — A230

**2015, Nov. 21    Litho.    Perf. 13x13¼**
735 A230  £2000 multi                        2.00 2.00

End of 2015 — A231

**2015, Dec. 30    Litho.    Perf. 13¼x13**
736 A231  £2000 multi                        2.00 2.00

Jawad Boulos (1900-82), Historian A232

Hani Fahs (1946-2014), Shiite Cleric A233

**2016, Feb. 17    Litho.    Perf. 13¼x13**
737 A232  £2000 multi                        2.00 2.00
738 A233  £2000 multi                        2.00 2.00

Flags and Church of Saidet et Tallé, Deir al-Qamar — A234

**2016, Apr. 2    Litho.    Perf. 13¼x13**
739 A234  £250 multi                         .50  .50

Labor Day — A235

**2016, Apr. 30    Litho.    Perf. 13x13¼**
740 A235  £2000 multi                        2.00 2.00

Martyr's Day — A236

**2016, May 5    Litho.    Perf. 13x13¼**
741 A236  £2000 multi                        2.00 2.00

Fish of the Mediterranean Sea — A237

**2016, July 9    Litho.    Perf. 13x13¼**
742 A237  £2250 multi                        2.25 2.25

Baalbek International Festival, 60th Anniv. — A238

**2016, July 26    Litho.    Perf. 13x13¼**
743 A238  £2000 multi                        2.00 2.00

Lebanese Olympic Committee — A239

**2016, Aug. 5    Litho.    Perf. 13¼x13**
744 A239  £250 multi                         .50  .50

Elie Snaifer (1935-2005), Comedian — A240

**2016, Sept. 6    Litho.    Perf. 13¼x13**
745 A240  £250 multi                         .50  .50

Admittance to Universal Postal Union, 70th Anniv. — A241

**2016, Oct. 8    Litho.    Perf. 13x13¼**
746 A241  £2000 multi                        2.00 2.00

Université la Sagesse, 140th Anniv. (in 2015) A242

**2016, Oct. 22    Litho.    Perf. 13¼x13**
747 A242  £2000 multi                        2.00 2.00

Arab Postal Day — A243

Globe at: No. 748, £10,000, Right (blue background). No. 749, £10,000, Left (blue green background).

**2016, Nov. 4    Litho.    Perf. 13¼x13**
748-749 A243    Set of 2                     37.50 37.50

Famous Men — A244

Contributors to Lebanese independence: No. 750, £250, Habib Abou Chahla, Speaker of Parliament. No. 751, £250, Adnan Al Hakim, member of Parliament. No. 752, £250, Saadi Al Mounla (1890-1975), Prime minister. No. 753, £250, Majid Arslan (1908-83), governmental minister. No. 754, £250, Rashid Baydoun (1889-1971), governmental minister. No. 755, £250, Camille Chamoun (1900-87), President. No. 756, £250, Mohamad El Fadi, member of Parliament. No. 757, £250, Hamid Frangieh (1907-81), member of Parliament. No. 758, £250, Pierre Gemayel (1905-84), member of Parliament. No. 759, £250, Sabri Hamadeh (1902-76), Speaker of Parliament. No. 760, £250, Maroun Kanaan (1890-1981), deputy of Jezzine. No. 761, £250, Abdul Hamid Karami (1890-1950), Prime minister. No. 762, £250, Henri Pharaon (1901-93), foreign minister. No. 763, £250, Saeb Salam (1905-2000), Prime minister. No. 764, £250, Selim Takla (1895-1945), foreign minister.

**2016, Nov. 18    Litho.    Perf. 13x13¼**
750-764 A244    Set of 15                    7.25 7.25

Independence Day.

American University of Beirut, 150th Anniv. — A245

**2016, Dec. 3    Litho.    Perf. 13x13¼**
765 A245  £2000 multi                        2.00 2.00

Zaki Nassif (1918-2004), Composer — A246

**2016, Dec. 15    Litho.    Perf. 13¼x13**
766 A246  £2000 multi                        2.00 2.00

New Year 2017 — A247

**2016, Dec. 29    Litho.    Perf. 13¼x13**
767 A247  £5000 multi                        5.00 5.00

Anti-Polio Campaign, 30th Anniv. A248

**2017, Jan. 20    Litho.    Perf. 13¼x13**
768 A248  £2000 multi                        2.00 2.00

International Women's Day — A249

**2017, Mar. 29   Litho.   Perf. 13¼x13**
769 A249 £10,000 multi     10.00 10.00

Museums — A250

Designs: No. 770, £2000, Sursock Museum. No. 771, £2000, Minerals from Mineral Museum, Beirut. No. 772, £2000, Sculptures from National Museum, Beirut.

**2017, May 16   Litho.   Perf. 13x13¼**
770-772 A250   Set of 3    12.00 12.00
National Museum, 75th anniv. (No. 772).

Dar Al Aytam Al Islamiya Orphanage A251

**2017, June 13   Litho.   Perf. 13x13¼**
773 A251 £2000 multi     2.00 2.00

World Music Day — A252

**2017, June 21   Litho.   Perf. 13¼x13**
774 A252 £250 multi     .65 .65

Cedar of Lebanon — A253

**2017, July 8   Litho.   Perf. 13¼x13**
775 A253 £2250 multi     2.25 2.25

Mikhail Naimy (1889-1998), Writer — A254

**2017, July 22   Litho.   Perf. 13x13¼**
776 A254 £250 multi     .65 .65

Army Day — A255

**2017, July 31   Litho.   Perf. 13¼x13**
777 A255 £2000 multi     2.00 2.00

Carlos Ghosn, Automobile Industry Executive — A256

**2017, Aug. 28   Litho.   Perf. 13¼x13**
778 A256 £2000 multi     2.00 2.00

Zalfa Chamoun (1910-71), Wife of Pres. Camille Chamoun — A257

**2017, Oct. 6   Litho.   Perf. 13x13¼**
779 A257 £2000 multi     2.00 2.00

Nasri Chamessedine (1927-83), Singer — A258

**2017, Oct. 19   Litho.   Perf. 13x13¼**
780 A258 £250 multi     .65 .65

Caritas Lebanon Charity — A259

**2017, Nov. 3   Litho.   Perf. 13¼x13**
781 A259 £2000 multi     2.00 2.00

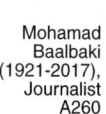

Mohamad Baalbaki (1921-2017), Journalist A260

**2017, Nov. 9   Litho.   Perf. 13¼x13**
782 A260 £2000 multi     2.00 2.00

Pres. Michel Aoun — A261

Pres. Aoun and Crowd A262

People Carrying Large Flag of Lebanon A263

**2017, Dec. 6   Litho.   Perf. 13x13¼**
783 A261 £5000 multi     5.00 5.00
**Perf. 13¼x13**
784 A262 £5000 multi     5.00 5.00
785 A263 £5000 multi     5.00 5.00
Nos. 783-785 (3)     15.00 15.00

St. Valentine's Day — A264

**2018, Feb. 7   Litho.   Perf. 13x13¼**
786 A264 £2000 multi     2.00 2.00
No. 786 has a heart-shaped hole.

Mohamad Chatah (1951-2013), Assassinated Diplomat — A265

**2018, Feb. 22   Litho.   Perf. 13x13¼**
787 A265 £250 multi     .50 .50

Mahmoud Kahil (1936-2013), Editorial Cartoonist — A266

**2018, Mar. 7   Litho.   Perf. 13¼x13**
788 A266 £2000 multi     2.00 2.00

Rachid Solh (1926-2014), Prime Minister — A267

**2018, Mar. 16   Litho.   Perf. 13¼x13**
789 A267 £250 multi     .50 .50

Elie Saab, Fashion Designer — A268

**Litho. With Foil Application**
**2018, Mar. 29   Perf. 13¼x13**
790 A268 £2000 gold & multi     2.00 2.00

Sunset, Painting by Nizar Daher — A269

**2018, Apr. 19   Litho.   Perf. 13x13¼**
791 A269 £2000 multi     2.00 2.00

Our Lady of Mantara Shrine, Maghdouché A270

**2018, Apr. 30   Litho.   Perf. 13x13¼**
792 A270 £1750 multi     1.75 1.75

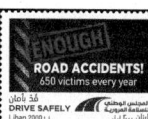

Traffic Safety Campaign A271

**2018, May 2   Litho.   Perf. 13x13¼**
793 A271 £2000 multi     2.00 2.00

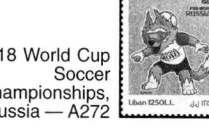

2018 World Cup Soccer Championships, Russia — A272

2018 World Cup emblem and: £1250, Mascot Zabivaka. £2250, Soccer ball and Russian buildings.

**2018, June 13   Litho.   Perf. 13¼x13**
794-795 A272   Set of 2    6.75 6.75

A273

**Litho. With Foil Application**
**2018, June 25   Perf. 13¼x13**
796 A273 £5000 multi     5.00 5.00
Riad Salamé, 25th Anniv. as Governor of the Central Bank of Lebanon.

Nasrallah Sfeir, Cardinal Patriarch Emeritus of Antioch and the Levant — A274

**2018, July 3   Litho.   Perf. 13¼x13**
797 A274 £2000 multi     2.00 2.00

Beiteddine Palace, Beiteddine A275

**2018, July 9   Litho.   Perf. 13x13¼**
798 A275 £2250 multi     2.25 2.25

Dr. Ghaleb Chahine, Politician, 50th Anniv. of Death — A276

**2018, Aug. 8   Litho.   Perf. 13¼x13**
799 A276 £500 multi     1.00 1.00

Emily Nasrallah (1931-2018), Writer — A277

**2018, Sept. 5   Litho.   Perf. 13x13¼**
800 A277 £1250 multi     1.25 1.25

Independence, 75th
Anniv. — A278

**2018, Nov. 19 Litho.** *Perf. 13¼x13*
801 A278 £10,000 multi 10.00 10.00

Sami Solh (1887-
1968), Prime
Minister — A279

**2018, Dec. 27 Litho.** *Perf. 13x13¼*
802 A279 £1250 multi 1.25 1.25

**Miniature Sheet**

Mother's
Day
A280

No. 803 — Flower with petals in: a, Dark
blue. b, Blue. c, Bright blue. d, Light blue. e,
Pale blue. f, Dark purple. g, Red violet. h, Purple. i, Lilac. j, Pale lilac. k, Dark magenta. l,
Magenta. m, Lilac rose. n, Pink. o, Pale pink.
p, Bright vermilion. q, Orange red. r, Orange.
s, Yellow. t, White.

**2019, Mar. 20 Litho.** *Perf. 13¼x13*
803 A280 Sheet of 20 150.00 150.00
a.-t. £1250 Any single 7.50 7.50

Waste Sorting — A281

Recycling emblem and: No. 804, £500,
Organic waste (green background). No. 805,
£500, Recyclable material (red background).
No. 806, £500, Non-recyclable material (gray
background).

**2019, Apr. 9 Litho.** *Perf. 13¼x13*
804-806 A281 Set of 3 3.00 3.00

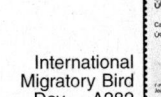

International
Migratory Bird
Day — A282

Designs: No. 807, £2250, Carduelis carduelis. No. 808, £2250, Cyanistes caeruleus. No.
809, £2250, Ciconia ciconia.

**2019, May 13 Litho.** *Perf. 13x13¼*
807-809 A282 Set of 3 13.50 13.50

Court of
Cassation,
Cent.
A283

**2019, June 12 Litho.** *Perf. 13¼x13*
810 A283 £2250 multi 2.25 2.25

Traditional
Costumes — A284

Designs: No. 811, £2000, 19th century Emir
wearing tarboush. No. 812, £2000, 19th century Emira wearing tantour.

**2019, July 8 Litho.** *Perf. 13x13¼*
811-812 A284 Set of 2 8.00 8.00

Express Mail
Service, 20th
Anniv.
A285

**2019, Sept. 10 Litho.** *Perf. 13¼x13*
813 A285 £2000 multi 2.00 2.00

Mohandas K.
Gandhi (1869-
1948), Indian
Nationalist
Leader — A286

**2019, Sept. 30 Litho.** *Perf. 13x13¼*
814 A286 £1000 multi 2.00 2.00

Flag of Palestinian
Authority, Doves,
Dome of the
Rock, Jerusalem
A287

**2019, Oct. 9 Litho.** *Perf. 13¼x13*
815 A287 £2250 multi 2.25 2.25
Jerusalem, capital of Palestinian Authority.

Sacred Heart
College,
Beirut, 125th
Anniv.
A288

**2019, Oct. 26 Litho.** *Perf. 13¼x13*
816 A288 £1000 multi 1.00 1.00

Evangelical
Church, Beirut,
150th
Anniv. — A289

**2019, Nov. 28 Litho.** *Perf. 13¼x13*
817 A289 £1000 multi 1.00 1.00

**Miniature Sheet**

Piano Fantasia in G Minor (Op. 77), by
Ludwig Van Beethoven (1770-
1827) — A290

No. 818 — Score in Beethoven's handwrit-
ing truncated at right: a, Clefs and key signa-
tures, "BTHVN" in white. b, Barred notes in top
staff, "BTHVN" in white. c, Note and rest on
top staff, "BTHVN" in color. d, Rest on top
staff, "BTHVN" in white. e, Start of slur (rising
arc above staff), "BTHVN" in white. f, White
rectangle and "BTHVN" in color over score. g,
Notation above staff, first two notes in series of
barred notes, "BTHVN" in white. h, Barred
notes in staff, continuation of barred noted
from lower staff from above, "BTHVN" in white.
i, Two staffs, rest on bottom staff, "BTHVN" in
color. j, "Poco" to left of denomination,
"BTHVN" in white. k, Four barred notes on
lower staff near denomination, "BTHVN" in
white. l, Eyes and nose of Beethoven. m, Face
and collar of Beethoven. n, Two sets of three
barred notes near denomination "BTHVN" in
white. o, Two sets of three barred notes,
"BTHVN" in color. p, Vertical measure line in
center, running through top staff, "BTHVN" in
white. q, Lower staff with change of key (four
flats), "BTHVN" in white. r, Rest under denomination, "BTHVN" in color. s, Vertical measure
line at left, notes similiar to those shown on "r,"
"BTHVN" in white. t, No measure line at left,
notes similar to those on "s," "BTHVN" in
white.

**2020, Mar. 4 Litho.** *Perf. 13x13¼*
818 A290 £250 Sheet of 20,
#a-t 52.50 52.50

"Thank You to
Our Hero
Caregivers"
A291

**2020, July 1 Litho.** *Perf. 13¼x13*
819 A291 £1000 multi 1.00 1.00
Tribute to coronavirus pandemic caregivers.

Lebanes Red
Cross, 75th
Anniv. — A292

**2020, July 9 Litho.** *Perf. 13¼x13*
820 A292 £1000 multi 1.00 1.00

Traditional
Foods — A293

No. 821: a, Hummus. b, Kibbeh. c, Tab-
bouleh. d, Manousheh.

**2020, July 17 Litho.** *Perf. 13x13¼*
821 Horiz. strip of 4 5.75 5.75
a.-d. A293 £1000 Any single 1.40 1.40

Georges Schehadé
(1905-89),
Writer — A294

**2020, Aug. 12 Litho.** *Perf. 13¼x13*
822 A294 £500 multi .80 .80

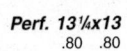

Ameen Rihani (1876-
1940), Writer — A295

**2020, Aug. 31 Litho.** *Perf. 13¼x13*
823 A295 £500 multi .80 .80

State of
Greater
Lebanon,
Cent.
A296

**2020, Sept. 1 Litho.** *Perf. 13¼x13*
824 A296 £1000 met gray brn 1.60 1.60

Michel Eddé (1928-
2019),
Politician — A297

**2020, Sept. 17 Litho.** *Perf. 13¼x13*
825 A297 £500 multi .80 .80

Elias Hoayek
(1843-1931),
Patriarch of
Antioch — A298

**2020, Sept. 28 Litho.** *Perf. 13x13¼*
826 A298 £2000 multi 2.00 2.00

Diplomatic Relations Between
Lebanon and Mexico, 75th
Anniv. — A299

No. 827: a, Templo Mayor Archaeological
Site and Metropolitan Cathedral, Mexico City
(text in Spanish). b, Temple of Bacchus, Baalbek, Lebanon (text in Arabic).

**2020, Sept. 30 Litho.** *Perf. 13¼x13*
827 A299 £5000 Horiz. pair,
#a-b 13.50 13.50
See Mexico Nos. 3178-3179.

Beirut Ammonium Nitrate Explosion of
Aug. 4, 2020 — A300

**2020, Oct. 12 Litho.** *Imperf.*
828 A300 £10,000 multi 10.00 10.00
No. 828 has simulated perforations. Proceeds of the sale of No. 828 go to the Lebanese Civil Defense for the rebuilding of Beirut.

United Nations, 75th Anniv. — A301

**2020, Oct. 24    Litho.    Perf. 13¼x13**
829   A301   £2250 multi         2.40   2.40

Arab League, 75th Anniv. — A302

**2020, Nov. 13    Litho.    Perf. 13x13¼**
830   A302   £500 multi         .80   .80

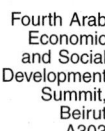

Fourth Arab Economic and Social Development Summit, Beirut A303

**2020, Nov. 25    Litho.    Perf. 13¼x13**
831   A303   £2000 multi        2.00   2.00

Brummana High School, Brummana — A304

**2020, Dec. 18    Litho.    Perf. 13½x13**
832   A304   £1000 multi        1.40   1.40

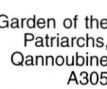

Garden of the Patriarchs, Qannoubine A305

**2021, Mar. 25    Litho.    Perf. 13x13¼**
833   A305   £10,000 multi      13.50   13.50

ESA Business School, Beirut, 25th Anniv. — A306

**2021, Apr. 15    Litho.    Perf. 13x13¼**
834   A306   £2000 multi        2.75   2.75

Earth Day — A307

No. 835: a, Jabal Moussa Reserve. b, Chouf Biosphere Reserve. c, Côtière de Tyr Nature Reserve. d, Aammiq Wetland.

**2021, Apr. 21    Litho.    Perf. 13x13¼**
835     Horiz. strip of 4      11.00   11.00
a.-d.   A307 £2000 Any single    2.75   2.75

---

Rhythmical Composition in Red, Painting by Saloua Raouda Choucair (1916-2017) — A308

**2021, June 2    Litho.    Perf. 13x13¼**
836   A308   £5000 multi        6.25   6.25

Miniature Sheet

A309

No. 837: a, Sheet music of the Rahbani Brothers, inscriptions in white frame at left and top. b, Sheet music of the Rahbani Brothers, inscriptions in white frame at top and right. c, Sheet music of the Rahbani Brothers, inscriptions in white frame at left and bottom. d, Sheet music of Rahbani Brothers, stringed instrument, inscriptions in white frame at bottom and right. e, Assi (1923-86) and Mansour Rahbani (1925-2009), musicians and composers.

**2021, June 21    Litho.    Perf. 13x13¼**
837   A309   Sheet of 20, #837a-
          837d, 16 #837e   13.50   13.50
a.-e.   A309 £500 Any single     .65    .65

Traditional Handcrafted Jewelry — A310

**2021, Aug. 24    Litho.    Perf. 13¼x13**
838   A310   £2250 multi        3.00   3.00

Rachid Nakhlé (1873-1939), Lyricist of Lebanese National Anthem A311

Wadia Sabra (1876-1952), Composer of Lebanese National Anthem A312

**2021, Nov.    Litho.    Perf. 13¼x13**
839   A311   £1750 multi        2.40   2.40
840   A312   £1750 multi        2.40   2.40

Salwa and Adib Haddad, Television Actors — A313

**2021, Dec. 10    Litho.    Perf. 13x13¼**
841   A313   £1000 multi        1.40   1.40

---

## SEMI-POSTAL STAMPS

Stamps of 1925 Srchd. in Red or Black

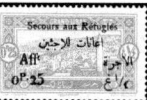

---

**1926      Unwmk.      Perf. 14x13½**
B1   A2   0.25p + 0.25p ol blk     4.25   4.25
B2   A2   0.25p + 0.50p yel grn
         (B)                4.25   4.25
B3   A2   0.25p + 0.75p brn org
         (B)                4.25   4.25
B4   A2   0.50p + 1p mag       4.75   4.75
B5   A2   0.50p 1.25p         5.00   5.00
B6   A2   0.50p + 1.50p rose red
         (B)                5.00   5.00
   a.   Double surcharge       40.00   30.00
B7   A2   0.75p + 2p dk brn     5.00   5.00
B8   A2   0.75p + 2.50p pck bl   5.50   5.50
B9   A2   1p + 3p org brn       5.50   5.50
B10   A2   1p + 5p vio (B)       5.50   5.50
B11   A3   2p + 10p vio brn
         (B)                5.50   5.50
B12   A2   5p + 25p ultra       5.50   5.50
      Nos. B1-B12 (12)     60.00   60.00

On No. B11 the surcharge is set in six lines to fit the shape of the stamp. All values of this series exist with inverted surcharge. Value each, $17.50.
See Nos. CB1-CB4.

> Catalogue values for unused stamps in this section, from this point to the end of the section, are for Never Hinged items.

Boxing SP1

**1961, Jan. 12    Litho.    Perf. 13**
B13   SP1   2.50p + 2.50p shown   .40   .25
B14   SP1   5p + 5p Wrestling    .40   .25
B15   SP1   7.50p + 7.50p Shot
          put              .40   .25
  Nos. B13-B15,CB12-CB14 (6)   10.95   4.50

17th Olympic Games, Rome, Aug. 25-Sept. 11, 1960.

Nos. B13-B15 with Arabic and French Overprint in Black, Blue or Green and two Bars through Olympic Inscription: "CHAMPIONNAT D'EUROPE DE TIR, 2 JUIN 1962"

**1962, June 2**
B16   SP1   2.50p + 2.50p blue &
          brn (Bk)         .40   .25
B17   SP1   5p + 5p org & brn
          (G)              .70   .25
B18   SP1   7.50p + 7.50p vio & brn
          (Bl)            .80   .35
  Nos. B16-B18,CB15-CB17 (6)   7.55   3.60

European Marksmanship Championships held in Lebanon.

Red Cross — SP2

No. B20, Stylized profile. No. B21, Globe, emblems, dove.

**1988, June 8    Litho.    Perf. 14**
B19   SP2   £10 + £1 shown       1.75
B20   SP2   £20 + £2 multi        2.75
B21   SP2   £30 + £3 multi        3.75
      Nos. B19-B21 (3)        8.25

---

## AIR POST STAMPS

Nos. 10-13 with Additional Overprint

**1924      Unwmk.      Perf. 14x13½**
C1   A18   2p on 40c         13.00   13.00
   a.   Double surcharge       52.50   52.50
C2   A18   3p on 60c         13.00   13.00
   a.   Invtd. surch. and ovpt.   87.50   87.50

---

C3   A18   5p on 1fr         13.00   13.00
   a.   Dbl. surch. and ovpt.    72.50   72.50
   b.   "5" omitted         300.00
C4   A18   10p on 2fr        13.00   13.00
   a.   Invtd. surch. and ovpt.   110.00   110.00
   b.   Dbl. surch. and ovpt.    60.00   60.00
      Nos. C1-C4 (4)       52.00   52.00

Nos. 33, 35-37 Overprinted

C5   A18   2p on 40c        13.00   13.00
   a.   Overprint reversed     45.00
C6   A18   3p on 60c        13.00   13.00
   a.   Overprint reversed     45.00
C7   A18   5p on 1fr        13.00   13.00
   a.   Overprint reversed     45.00
C8   A18   10p on 2fr       13.50   13.50
   a.   Overprint reversed     45.00
   b.   Double surcharge      45.00
      Nos. C5-C8 (4)      52.50   52.50

Nos. 57, 59-61 Overprinted in Green

**1925**
C9   A2   2p dark brown      4.00   4.00
C10   A2   3p orange brown    4.00   4.00
C11   A2   5p violet         4.00   4.00
   a.   Inverted overprint
C12   A3   10p violet brown    4.00   4.00
      Nos. C9-C12 (4)    16.00   16.00

Nos. 57, 59-61 Ovptd. in Red — c

**1926**
C13   A2   2p dark brown      5.25   5.25
C14   A2   3p orange brown    5.25   5.25
C15   A2   5p violet         5.25   5.25
C16   A3   10p violet brown    5.25   5.25
      Nos. C13-C16 (4)    21.00   21.00

Airplane pointed down on No. C16. Exist with inverted overprint. Value, each $45.

**Issues of Republic under French Mandate**

Nos. C13-C16 Overprinted — d

**1927**
C17   A2   2p dark brown      4.75   4.75
C18   A2   3p orange brown    4.75   4.75
C19   A2   5p violet         4.75   4.75
C20   A3   10p violet brown    4.75   4.75
      Nos. C17-C20 (4)    19.00   19.00

On No. C19 "Republique Libanaise" is above the bars. Overprint set in two lines on No. C20.

Nos. C17-C20 with Additional Ovpt. — e

**1928             Black Overprint**
C21   A2   2p brown        12.50   10.00
   a.   Double overprint     65.00   65.00
   b.   Inverted overprint    65.00   65.00
C22   A2   3p orange brown   12.50   10.00
   a.   Double overprint     65.00   65.00
C23   A2   5p violet        12.50   10.00
   a.   Double overprint     65.00   65.00
C24   A3   10p violet brown   12.50   10.00
   a.   Double overprint     65.00   65.00
      Nos. C21-C24 (4)    50.00   40.00

On Nos. C21-C24 the airplane is always in red.

Nos. 52, 54, 57, 59-62 Ovptd. in Red or Black — f

**1928**

| | | | | |
|---|---|---|---|---|
| C25 | A2 | 2p dark brown | 4.50 | 4.50 |
| C26 | A2 | 3p orange brown | 3.00 | 3.00 |
| C27 | A2 | 5p violet | 4.50 | 4.50 |
| C28 | A3 | 10p violet brown | 4.50 | 4.50 |

**1929**

| | | | | |
|---|---|---|---|---|
| C33 | A2 | 0.50p yellow green | 1.25 | 1.25 |
| a. | | Inverted overprint | 45.00 | 45.00 |
| C34 | A2 | 1p magenta (Bk) | 1.00 | 1.00 |
| a. | | Inverted overprint | 45.00 | 45.00 |
| C35 | A2 | 25p ultra | 190.00 | 160.00 |
| a. | | Inverted overprint | 525.00 | 525.00 |
| | | Nos. C25-C34 (6) | 18.75 | 18.75 |
| | | Nos. C25-C35 (7) | 208.75 | 178.75 |

On Nos. C25-C28 the airplane is always in red.

On No. C28 the overprinted orientation is horizontal. The bars covering the old country names are at the left.

The red overprint of a silhouetted plane and "Republique Libanaise," as on Nos. C25-C27, was also applied to Nos. C9-C12. These are believed to have been essays, and were not regularly issued.

No. 62 with Surcharge Added in Red

Two types of surcharge:

I — The "5" of "15 P." is italic. The "15" is 4mm high. Arabic characters for "Lebanese Republic" and for "15 P." are on same line in that order.

II — The "5" is in Roman type (upright) and smaller; "15" is 3½mm high. Arabic for "Lebanese Republic" is centered on line by itself, with Arabic for "15 P." below right end of line.

| | | | | |
|---|---|---|---|---|
| C36 | A2 | 15p on 25p ultra (I) | 225.00 | 175.00 |
| a. | | Type II (#106) | 800.00 | 800.00 |

**Nos. 102 Overprinted Type "c" in Blue**

| | | | | |
|---|---|---|---|---|
| C37 | A2 | 0.50p on 0.75p | 1.00 | 1.00 |
| a. | | Airplane inverted | 45.00 | |
| b. | | French and Arabic surch. invtd. | | |
| c. | | "P" omitted | | |
| d. | | Airplane double | 50.00 | |

**No. 55 Surcharged in Red**

**1930**

| | | | | |
|---|---|---|---|---|
| C38 | A2 | 2p on 1.25p dp green | 1.75 | 1.25 |
| a. | | Inverted surcharge | 72.50 | 45.00 |

Airplane over Racheya — AP2

Designs: 1p, Plane over Broumana. 2p, Baalbek. 3p, Hasroun. 5p, Byblos. 10p, Kadicha River. 15p, Beirut. 25p, Tripoli. 50p, Kabeljas. 100p, Zahle.

**1930-31          Photo.          Perf. 13½**

| | | | | |
|---|---|---|---|---|
| C39 | AP2 | 0.50p dk violet ('31) | .50 | .50 |
| C40 | AP2 | 1p yellow grn ('31) | .80 | .80 |
| C41 | AP2 | 2p dp orange ('31) | 2.50 | 2.50 |
| C42 | AP2 | 3p magenta ('31) | 2.50 | 2.50 |
| C43 | AP2 | 5p indigo | 2.50 | 2.50 |
| C44 | AP2 | 10p orange red | 3.25 | 3.25 |
| C45 | AP2 | 15p orange brn | 3.25 | 3.25 |
| C46 | AP2 | 25p gray vio ('31) | 4.75 | 4.75 |
| C47 | AP2 | 50p dp claret | 9.00 | 9.00 |
| C48 | AP2 | 100p olive brown | 12.00 | 12.00 |
| | | Nos. C39-C48 (10) | 41.05 | 41.05 |

Nos. C39-C48 exist imperforate. Value, set $200.

**Tourist Publicity Issue**

Skiing in Lebanon — AP12

Bay of Jounie — AP13

**1936, Oct. 12**

| | | | | |
|---|---|---|---|---|
| C49 | AP12 | 0.50p slate grn | 3.00 | 3.00 |
| C50 | AP13 | 1p red orange | 3.75 | 3.75 |
| C51 | AP12 | 2p black violet | 3.75 | 3.75 |
| C52 | AP13 | 3p yellow grn | 4.00 | 4.00 |
| C53 | AP12 | 5p brown car | 4.00 | 4.00 |
| C54 | AP13 | 10p orange brn | 4.00 | 4.00 |
| C55 | AP13 | 15p dk carmine | 37.50 | 37.50 |
| C56 | AP12 | 25p green | 125.00 | 125.00 |
| | | Nos. C49-C56 (8) | 185.00 | 185.00 |

Nos. C49-C56 exist imperforate. Value, set $650.

Lebanese Pavilion at Exposition AP14

**1937, July 1          Perf. 13½**

| | | | | |
|---|---|---|---|---|
| C57 | AP14 | 0.50p olive black | 1.50 | 1.50 |
| C58 | AP14 | 1p yellow green | 1.50 | 1.50 |
| C59 | AP14 | 2p dk red orange | 1.50 | 1.50 |
| C60 | AP14 | 3p dk olive grn | 1.50 | 1.50 |
| C61 | AP14 | 5p deep green | 2.00 | 2.00 |
| C62 | AP14 | 10p carmine lake | 9.00 | 9.00 |
| C63 | AP14 | 15p rose lake | 10.00 | 10.00 |
| C64 | AP14 | 25p orange brn | 17.50 | 17.50 |
| | | Nos. C57-C64 (8) | 44.50 | 44.50 |

Paris International Exposition.

Arcade of Beit-ed-Din Palace — AP15

Ruins of Baalbek — AP16

**1937-40          Engr.          Perf. 13**

| | | | | |
|---|---|---|---|---|
| C65 | AP15 | 0.50p ultra ('38) | .35 | .25 |
| C66 | AP15 | 1p hen brn ('40) | .35 | .25 |
| C67 | AP15 | 2p sepia ('40) | .35 | .25 |
| C68 | AP15 | 3p rose ('40) | 3.25 | 1.25 |
| C69 | AP15 | 5p lt green ('40) | .35 | .25 |
| C70 | AP16 | 10p dull violet | .35 | .25 |
| C71 | AP16 | 15p turq bl ('40) | 2.75 | 1.75 |
| C72 | AP16 | 25p violet ('40) | 6.00 | 5.00 |
| C73 | AP16 | 50p yel grn ('40) | 11.00 | 7.00 |
| C74 | AP16 | 100p brown ('40) | 6.00 | 3.50 |
| | | Nos. C65-C74 (10) | 30.75 | 19.75 |

Nos. C65-C74 exist imperforate.

Medical College of Beirut — AP17

**1938, May 9          Photo.          Perf. 13**

| | | | | |
|---|---|---|---|---|
| C75 | AP17 | 2p green | 2.40 | 2.75 |
| C76 | AP17 | 3p orange | 2.40 | 2.75 |
| | | Never hinged | 4.75 | |
| C77 | AP17 | 5p lilac gray | 4.50 | 5.25 |
| C78 | AP17 | 10p lake | 8.50 | 9.75 |
| | | Nos. C75-C78 (4) | 17.80 | 20.50 |

Medical Congress.

Maurice Noguès and View of Beirut AP18

**1938, July 15          Perf. 11**

| | | | | |
|---|---|---|---|---|
| C79 | AP18 | 10p brown carmine | 4.00 | 1.50 |
| a. | | Souv. sheet of 4, perf. 13½ | 35.00 | 20.00 |
| b. | | Perf. 13½ | 9.00 | 4.50 |

10th anniversary of first Marseille-Beirut flight, by Maurice Noguès.

No. C79a has marginal inscriptions in French and Arabic. Exists imperf.; value $250.

**Independent Republic**

Plane Over Mt. Lebanon — AP19

**1942, Sept. 18          Litho.          Perf. 11½**

| | | | | |
|---|---|---|---|---|
| C80 | AP19 | 10p dk brown vio | 5.75 | 6.50 |
| C81 | AP19 | 50p dk gray grn | 5.75 | 6.50 |

1st anniv. of the Proclamation of Independence, Nov. 26, 1941.

Nos. C80 and C81 exist imperforate.

Bechamoun AP20

Rachaya Citadel — AP21

Air View of Beirut — AP22

**1943, May 1          Perf. 11½**

| | | | | |
|---|---|---|---|---|
| C82 | AP20 | 25p yellow grn | 4.75 | 4.75 |
| C83 | AP20 | 50p orange | 6.50 | 5.50 |
| C84 | AP21 | 100p buff | 6.50 | 5.50 |
| C85 | AP21 | 200p blue vio | 8.00 | 7.25 |
| C86 | AP22 | 300p sage green | 21.00 | 17.50 |
| C87 | AP22 | 500p sepia | 42.50 | 32.50 |
| | | Nos. C82-C87 (6) | 89.25 | 73.00 |

2nd anniv. of the Proclamation of Independence. Nos. C82-C87 exist imperforate.

See Nos. 163-166. For overprints see Nos. C91-C96.

Bhannes Sanatorium AP23

**1943, July 8          Photo.**
**Black Overprint**

| | | | | |
|---|---|---|---|---|
| C88 | AP23 | 20p orange | 3.75 | 2.75 |
| C89 | AP23 | 50p steel blue | 4.25 | 3.50 |
| C90 | AP23 | 100p rose violet | 6.00 | 4.50 |
| | | Nos. C88-C90 (3) | 14.00 | 10.75 |

Arab Medical Congress, Beirut.

Nos. C82 to C87 Overprinted in Red, Blue or Violet

**1944, Nov. 23**

| | | | | |
|---|---|---|---|---|
| C91 | AP20 | 25p yel grn (R) | 7.25 | 7.25 |
| C92 | AP20 | 50p orange (Bl) | 12.00 | 12.00 |
| C93 | AP21 | 100p buff (V) | 14.00 | 14.00 |
| C94 | AP21 | 200p blue vio (R) | 25.00 | 25.00 |
| C95 | AP22 | 300p sage grn (R) | 32.50 | 30.00 |
| C96 | AP22 | 500p sepia (Bl) | 65.00 | 60.00 |
| | | Nos. C91-C96 (6) | 155.75 | 148.25 |

Return to office of the President and his ministers, Nov. 22, 1943.

Catalogue values for unused stamps in this section, from this point to the end of the section, are for Never Hinged items.

Falls of Litani AP24

The Cedars AP25

**1945, July          Unwmk.          Litho.**

| | | | | |
|---|---|---|---|---|
| C97 | AP24 | 25p gray brown | 3.50 | 2.10 |
| C98 | AP24 | 50p rose violet | 5.00 | 2.75 |
| C99 | AP25 | 200p violet | 15.00 | 5.25 |
| C100 | AP25 | 300p brown black | 26.50 | 10.00 |
| | | Nos. C97-C100 (4) | 50.00 | 20.10 |

Lebanese Soldiers at Bir Hacheim — AP26

**1946, May 8**

| | | | | |
|---|---|---|---|---|
| C101 | AP26 | 15p bl blk, org & red org | 1.00 | .25 |
| C102 | AP26 | 20p red, lil & bl | 1.00 | .60 |
| C103 | AP26 | 25p brt bl, org & red | 1.25 | .25 |
| C104 | AP26 | 50p gray blk, bl & red | 1.75 | .50 |
| C105 | AP26 | 100p pur, pink & red | 5.00 | 1.25 |
| C106 | AP26 | 150p brn, pink & red | 6.00 | 3.75 |
| | | Nos. C101-C106 (6) | 16.00 | 6.60 |

Victory of the Allied Nations in WWII, 1st anniv.

Three imperf. souvenir sheets of 14 exist. They contain one each of Nos. C101-C106 and 189-196 in changed colors. One has sepia inscriptions, and one on thin white card has blue inscriptions. Value $30 each. The third, with blue inscriptions, is on thick honey-combed chamois card. Value $110.

**Night Herons Type**

**1946, Sept. 11**

| | | | | |
|---|---|---|---|---|
| C107 | A35 | 10p orange | 5.75 | .80 |
| C108 | A35 | 25p ultra | 6.50 | .25 |
| C109 | A35 | 50p blue green | 20.00 | 1.30 |
| C110 | A35 | 100p dk vio brn | 30.00 | 5.25 |
| | | Nos. C107-C110 (4) | 62.25 | 7.60 |

Symbols of Communications AP28

**1946, Nov. 22**

| | | | | |
|---|---|---|---|---|
| C111 | AP28 | 25p deep blue | 1.75 | .70 |
| C112 | AP28 | 50p green | 2.50 | .80 |
| C113 | AP28 | 75p orange red | 4.25 | 1.75 |
| C114 | AP28 | 150p brown black | 6.00 | 2.75 |
| | | Nos. C111-C114 (4) | 14.50 | 6.00 |

Arab Postal Congress, Sofar, 1946.

Stone Tablet, Dog River and Pres. Bechara el-Khoury AP29

**1947, Feb. 11**

| | | | | |
|---|---|---|---|---|
| C115 | AP29 | 25p ultra | 7.00 | .35 |
| C116 | AP29 | 50p dull rose | 9.00 | .60 |
| C117 | AP29 | 75p gray black | 11.00 | .65 |
| C118 | AP29 | 150p orange blue | 17.50 | 1.40 |
| | | Nos. C115-C118 (4) | 44.50 | 3.00 |

Evacuation of foreign troops from Lebanon, Dec. 31, 1946.

Bay of Jounie — AP30

Government House, Beirut — AP31

**1947, Feb. 11          Grayish Paper**

| | | | | |
|---|---|---|---|---|
| C119 | AP30 | 5p dp blue grn | .50 | .25 |
| C120 | AP30 | 10p rose vio | .75 | .25 |
| C121 | AP30 | 15p vermilion | 1.75 | .25 |
| C122 | AP30 | 20p orange | 2.00 | .25 |
| a. | | 20p red orange, white paper | 1.75 | .25 |
| C123 | AP30 | 25p deep blue | 2.40 | .25 |
| C124 | AP30 | 50p henna brn | 4.00 | .25 |
| C125 | AP30 | 100p chocolate | 8.50 | .25 |
| C126 | AP30 | 150p dk vio brn | 14.00 | .40 |
| C127 | AP31 | 200p slate | 22.00 | 1.90 |
| C128 | AP31 | 300p black | 35.00 | 5.00 |
| | | Nos. C119-C128 (10) | 91.40 | 9.05 |

See Nos. C145A-C147B.

Post Horn
and Letter
AP32

Phoenician Galley
AP33

**1947, June 17**     **Litho.**
| | | | | |
|---|---|---|---|---|
| C129 | AP32 | 10p brt ultra | 1.40 | .40 |
| C130 | AP32 | 15p rose car | 1.60 | .40 |
| C131 | AP32 | 25p bright blue | 2.00 | .65 |
| C132 | AP33 | 50p dk slate grn | 4.75 | .75 |
| C133 | AP33 | 75p purple | 5.75 | 1.55 |
| C134 | AP33 | 100p dark brown | 7.25 | 2.00 |
| | | Nos. C129-C134 (6) | 22.75 | 5.75 |

Lebanon's participation in the 12th UPU congress, Paris.

Lebanese
Village — AP34

**1948, Sept. 1**     **Perf. 11½**
| | | | | |
|---|---|---|---|---|
| C135 | AP34 | 5p dp orange | .60 | .25 |
| C136 | AP34 | 10p rose lilac | 1.40 | .25 |
| C137 | AP34 | 15p orange brn | 3.00 | .25 |
| C138 | AP34 | 20p slate | 3.75 | .25 |
| C139 | AP34 | 25p Prus blue | 8.50 | .80 |
| C140 | AP34 | 50p gray black | 14.00 | 1.15 |
| | | Nos. C135-C140 (6) | 31.25 | 2.95 |

Apollo
AP35

Minerva
AP36

**1948, Nov. 23**     **Unwmk.**
| | | | | |
|---|---|---|---|---|
| C141 | AP35 | 7.50p blue & lt blue | 3.25 | .80 |
| C142 | AP35 | 15p black & gray | 4.00 | 1.00 |
| C143 | AP35 | 20p rose brn & rose | 4.25 | 1.55 |
| C144 | AP36 | 35p car rose & rose | 6.50 | 2.00 |
| C145 | AP36 | 75p bl grn & lt green | 12.00 | 4.00 |
| | | Nos. C141-C145 (5) | 30.00 | 9.35 |

UNESCO. Nos. C141-C145 exist imperforate, and combined with Nos. 220-224 in an imperforate souvenir sheet on thin buff cardboard, with black inscriptions in top margin in Arabic and at bottom in French. Value $250.

**Bay Type of 1947 Redrawn**

**1949**     **White Paper**
| | | | | |
|---|---|---|---|---|
| C145A | AP30 | 10p rose lilac | 9.00 | 1.00 |
| C146 | AP30 | 15p dark green | 11.00 | 1.25 |
| C147 | AP30 | 20p orange | 25.00 | 9.00 |
| C147A | AP30 | 25p dark blue | 65.00 | 3.25 |
| C147B | AP30 | 50p brick red | 275.00 | 35.00 |
| | | Nos. C145A-C147B (5) | 385.00 | 49.50 |

In the redrawn designs, Nos. C145A, C147 and C147B have zeros with broader centers than in the 1947 issue (Nos. C120, C122 and C124).

Helicopter Mail
Delivery — AP37

**1949, Aug. 16**     **Unwmk.**     **Perf. 11½**
| | | | | |
|---|---|---|---|---|
| C148 | AP37 | 25p deep blue | 6.75 | 3.50 |
| C149 | AP37 | 50p green | 10.00 | 4.00 |
| a. | | Souvenir sheet of 5, #225-227, C148-C149 | 65.00 | 30.00 |

UPU, 75th anniv. No. 149a exists on thin cardboard. Value $250.

Homing
Birds — AP38

Pres. Bechara el-
Khoury
AP39

**1950, Aug. 8**     **Litho.**
| | | | | |
|---|---|---|---|---|
| C150 | AP38 | 5p violet blue | 2.75 | .65 |
| C151 | AP38 | 15p rose vio | 3.00 | .70 |
| C152 | AP39 | 25p chocolate | 2.25 | .95 |
| C153 | AP39 | 35p gray green | 3.25 | 1.40 |
| a. | | Souvenir sheet of 6, #243-244, C150-C153, chamois paper | 70.00 | 55.00 |
| | | Nos. C150-C153 (4) | 11.25 | 3.70 |

Conference of Emigrants, 1950.

Crusader Castle,
Sidon
Harbor — AP40

**1950, Sept. 7**
| | | | | |
|---|---|---|---|---|
| C154 | AP40 | 10p chocolate | 1.00 | .25 |
| C155 | AP40 | 15p dark green | 2.00 | .25 |
| C156 | AP40 | 20p crimson | 4.00 | .25 |
| C157 | AP40 | 25p ultra | 7.00 | .80 |
| C158 | AP40 | 50p gray black | 10.00 | 2.25 |
| | | Nos. C154-C158 (5) | 24.00 | 3.80 |

**1951, June 9**     **Redrawn**     **Typo.**
| | | | | |
|---|---|---|---|---|
| C159 | AP40 | 10p grnsh black | 1.60 | .25 |
| C160 | AP40 | 15p black brown | 2.40 | .25 |
| C161 | AP40 | 20p vermilion | 2.40 | .25 |
| C162 | AP40 | 25p deep blue | 3.25 | .25 |
| C163 | AP40 | 35p lilac rose | 6.50 | 1.90 |
| C164 | AP40 | 50p indigo | 9.00 | 1.90 |
| | | Nos. C159-C164 (6) | 25.15 | 4.80 |

Nos. C154-C158 are lithographed from a fine-screen halftone; Nos. C159-C164 are typographed and much coarser, with larger plane and many other differences.

Khaldé
International
Airport,
Beirut — AP41

Design: 50p to 300p, Amphitheater, Byblos.

**1952**     **Litho.**     **Perf. 11½**
| | | | | |
|---|---|---|---|---|
| C165 | AP41 | 5p crimson | 1.50 | .25 |
| C166 | AP41 | 10p dark gray | 1.50 | .25 |
| C167 | AP41 | 15p rose vio | 1.75 | .25 |
| C168 | AP41 | 20p brown org | 2.00 | .25 |
| C169 | AP41 | 25p grnsh blue | 2.00 | .25 |
| C170 | AP41 | 35p violet bl | 2.75 | .25 |
| C171 | AP41 | 50p blue green | 14.00 | .60 |
| C172 | AP41 | 100p deep blue | 55.00 | 2.40 |
| C173 | AP41 | 200p dk blue grn | 35.00 | 3.50 |
| C174 | AP41 | 300p black brn | 52.50 | 7.50 |
| | | Nos. C165-C174 (10) | 168.00 | 15.50 |

Lockheed
Constellation — AP42

**1953, Oct. 1**
| | | | | |
|---|---|---|---|---|
| C175 | AP42 | 5p yellow green | .75 | .25 |
| C176 | AP42 | 10p deep plum | 1.00 | .25 |
| C177 | AP42 | 15p scarlet | 1.40 | .25 |
| C178 | AP42 | 20p aqua | 1.75 | .25 |
| C179 | AP42 | 25p blue | 3.25 | .25 |
| C180 | AP42 | 35p orange brn | 4.75 | .25 |
| C181 | AP42 | 50p violet blue | 9.00 | .25 |
| C182 | AP42 | 100p black brown | 13.00 | 1.90 |
| | | Nos. C175-C182 (8) | 34.90 | 3.65 |

Ruins at
Baalbek — AP43

Irrigation Canal,
Litani — AP44

**1954, Mar.**
| | | | | |
|---|---|---|---|---|
| C183 | AP43 | 5p yel green | .60 | .25 |
| C184 | AP43 | 10p dull purple | .75 | .25 |
| C185 | AP43 | 15p carmine | 1.20 | .25 |
| C186 | AP43 | 20p brown | 1.60 | .25 |
| C187 | AP43 | 25p dull blue | 2.00 | .25 |
| C188 | AP43 | 35p black brn | 2.40 | .25 |
| C189 | AP44 | 50p dk olive grn | 8.00 | .25 |
| C190 | AP44 | 100p dp car | 15.50 | .30 |
| C191 | AP44 | 200p dark brown | 22.00 | 1.00 |
| C192 | AP44 | 300p dk gray blue | 42.50 | 1.25 |
| | | Nos. C183-C192 (10) | 96.55 | 3.90 |

See Nos. C229-C232.

Khaldé
International
Airport,
Beirut — AP45

**1954, Apr. 23**     **Perf. 11½**
| | | | | |
|---|---|---|---|---|
| C193 | AP45 | 10p pink & rose red | 1.00 | .25 |
| C194 | AP45 | 25p dp bl & gray bl | 2.25 | .40 |
| C195 | AP45 | 35p dl brn & yel brn | 3.50 | .75 |
| C196 | AP45 | 65p dp grn & grn | 5.00 | 1.30 |
| | | Nos. C193-C196 (4) | 11.75 | 2.70 |

Opening of Beirut's Intl. Airport. Exist imperf.

**Arab Postal Union Type of Regular Issue, 1955**

**1955, Jan. 1**     **Perf. 13½x13**
| | | | | |
|---|---|---|---|---|
| C197 | A52 | 2.50p yellow brn | 1.25 | .25 |

Rotary
Emblem — AP47

**1955, Feb. 23**     **Perf. 11½**
| | | | | |
|---|---|---|---|---|
| C198 | AP47 | 35p dull green | 1.25 | .35 |
| C199 | AP47 | 65p dull blue | 2.00 | .45 |

Rotary International, 50th anniversary.

Skiing Among the
Cedars — AP48

**1955, Feb. 24**     **Litho.**
| | | | | |
|---|---|---|---|---|
| C200 | AP48 | 5p blue green | 1.60 | .25 |
| C201 | AP48 | 15p crimson | 1.75 | .25 |
| C202 | AP48 | 20p lilac | 2.25 | .25 |
| C203 | AP48 | 25p blue | 4.00 | .25 |
| C204 | AP48 | 35p olive brn | 5.25 | .25 |
| C205 | AP48 | 50p chocolate | 9.00 | .60 |
| C206 | AP48 | 65p deep blue | 14.00 | 1.75 |
| | | Nos. C200-C206 (7) | 37.85 | 3.60 |

See Nos. C233-C235. For surcharge see No. C271.

Tourist — AP49

**1955, Sept. 10**     **Unwmk.**     **Perf. 13**
| | | | | |
|---|---|---|---|---|
| C207 | AP49 | 2.50p brn vio & lt bl | .40 | .25 |
| C208 | AP49 | 12.50p ultra & lt bl | .55 | .25 |
| C209 | AP49 | 25p indigo & lt bl | 1.20 | .25 |
| C210 | AP49 | 35p ol grn & lt bl | 1.40 | .25 |
| a. | | Sheet of 4, #C207-C210, imperf. | 18.00 | 6.25 |
| | | Nos. C207-C210 (4) | 3.55 | 1.00 |

Tourist Year. No. C210a is printed on cardboard.

Oranges — AP50

Designs: 25p, 35p, 50p, Grapes, vert. 65p, 100p, 200p, Apples.

**1955, Oct. 15**
| | | | | |
|---|---|---|---|---|
| C211 | AP50 | 5p yel grn & yel | 1.00 | .25 |
| C212 | AP50 | 10p dk grn & dp orange | 1.10 | .25 |
| C213 | AP50 | 15p yel grn & red orange | 1.25 | .25 |
| C214 | AP50 | 20p olive & yel org | 1.90 | .25 |
| C215 | AP50 | 25p blue & vio bl | 2.60 | .25 |
| C216 | AP50 | 35p green & cl | 3.25 | .25 |
| C217 | AP50 | 50p blk brn & dl yel | 3.25 | .25 |
| C218 | AP50 | 65p green & lemon | 6.25 | .25 |
| C219 | AP50 | 100p yel grn & dp orange | 8.00 | .70 |
| C220 | AP50 | 200p green & car | 14.00 | 3.50 |
| | | Nos. C211-C220 (10) | 42.60 | 6.20 |

For surcharge see No. C265.

United Nations
Emblem — AP52

**1956, Jan. 23**     **Perf. 11½**
| | | | | |
|---|---|---|---|---|
| C221 | AP52 | 35p violet blue | 4.25 | 1.50 |
| C222 | AP52 | 65p green | 5.25 | 1.75 |

UN, 10th anniv. (in 1955).
An imperf. souvenir sheet contains one each of Nos. C221 and C222. Value $72.50.

Temple of the
Sun
Colonnade,
Masks and
Lion's
Head — AP53

Temple of
Bacchus,
Baalbek — AP54

Design: 35p, 65p, Temple of the Sun colonnade, masks and violincello.

**1956, Dec. 10**     **Litho.**     **Perf. 13**
| | | | | |
|---|---|---|---|---|
| C223 | AP53 | 2.50p dark brown | .85 | .25 |
| C224 | AP53 | 10p green | 1.10 | .25 |
| C225 | AP54 | 12.50p light blue | 1.10 | .25 |
| C226 | AP54 | 25p brt vio bl | 1.60 | .35 |
| C227 | AP53 | 35p red lilac | 3.00 | .45 |
| C228 | AP53 | 65p slate blue | 4.25 | .90 |
| | | Nos. C223-C228 (6) | 11.90 | 2.45 |

International Festival at Baalbek.

**Skiing Type of 1955 Redrawn and**

Irrigation Canal,
Litani — AP55

**1957**     **Litho.**     **Perf. 11½**
| | | | | |
|---|---|---|---|---|
| C229 | AP55 | 10p brt violet | .65 | .25 |
| C230 | AP55 | 15p orange | .90 | .25 |
| C231 | AP55 | 20p yel green | 1.00 | .25 |
| C232 | AP55 | 25p slate blue | 1.10 | .25 |
| C233 | AP48 | 35p gray green | 2.50 | .25 |
| C234 | AP48 | 65p dp claret | 4.00 | .25 |
| C235 | AP48 | 100p brown | 6.00 | .65 |
| | | Nos. C229-C235 (7) | 16.15 | 2.15 |

Different Arabic characters used for the country name; letters in "Liban" larger.
For surcharge see No. C271.

Pres. Camille
Chamoun and
King
Saud — AP56

King Saud,
Pres.
Chamoun,
King
Hussein,
Pres.
Kouatly, King
Faisal, Pres.
Nasser
AP57

LEBANON

597

Pres. Chamoun and: No. C237, King Hussein. No. C238, Pres. Kouatly. No. C239, King Faisal. No. C240, Pres. Nasser. 25p, Map of Lebanon.

**1957, July 15   Litho.   Perf. 13**
| C236 | AP56 | 15p green | .60 | .25 |
| C237 | AP56 | 15p blue | .60 | .25 |
| C238 | AP56 | 15p red lilac | .60 | .25 |
| C239 | AP56 | 15p red orange | .60 | .25 |
| C240 | AP56 | 15p claret | .60 | .25 |
| C241 | AP56 | 25p blue | .60 | .25 |
| C242 | AP57 | 100p dl red brn | 5.00 | 1.20 |
| | | *Nos. C236-C242 (7)* | 8.60 | 2.70 |

Congr. of Arab Leaders, Beirut, 11/12-15/56.

Fencing — AP58

50p, Pres. Chamoun and stadium with flags.

**1957, Sept. 12   Unwmk.   Perf. 13**
| C243 | AP58 | 35p claret | 2.75 | 1.25 |
| C244 | AP58 | 50p lt green | 3.50 | 1.75 |

2nd Pan-Arab Games, Beirut. See note on souvenir sheet below No. 314.

Symbols of Communications AP59

Power Plant, Chamoun AP60

**1957   Perf. 13x13½, 11½ (AP60)**
| C245 | AP59 | 5p brt green | .55 | .25 |
| C246 | AP59 | 10p yel orange | .60 | .25 |
| C247 | AP59 | 15p brown | .60 | .25 |
| C248 | AP59 | 20p maroon | .80 | .25 |
| C249 | AP59 | 25p violet blue | 1.10 | .25 |
| C250 | AP60 | 35p violet brn | 1.40 | .25 |
| C251 | AP60 | 50p green | 1.60 | .25 |
| C252 | AP60 | 65p sepia | 2.25 | .25 |
| C253 | AP60 | 100p dark gray | 3.00 | .55 |
| | | *Nos. C245-C253 (9)* | 11.90 | 2.55 |

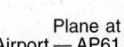

Plane at Airport — AP61

Cogwheel AP62

**1958-59   Unwmk.   Perf. 13**
| C254 | AP61 | 5p green | .50 | .25 |
| C255 | AP61 | 10p magenta | .65 | .25 |
| C256 | AP61 | 15p dull violet | .80 | .25 |
| C257 | AP61 | 20p orange ver | .95 | .25 |
| C258 | AP61 | 25p dk vio bl | 1.20 | .25 |
| C259 | AP62 | 35p grnsh gray | 1.40 | .25 |
| C260 | AP62 | 50p aquamarine | 1.90 | .25 |
| C261 | AP62 | 65p pale brown | 3.25 | .25 |
| C262 | AP62 | 100p brt ultra | 3.75 | .25 |
| | | *Nos. C254-C262 (9)* | 14.40 | 2.25 |

Nos. C259 and C261 Srchd. in Black or Dark Blue

**1959   Unwmk.   Litho.   Perf. 13**
| C263 | AP62 | 30p on 35p grnsh gray | .80 | .25 |
| C264 | AP62 | 40p on 65p pale brn (Bl) | 1.25 | .40 |

Arab Engineers Congress.

No. C217 Surcharged

**1959, Sept. 1**
| C265 | AP50 | 40p on 50p blk brn & dull yel | 1.25 | .40 |

Arab Lawyers Congress.

Myron's Discobolus AP63

Wreath and Hand Holding Torch AP64

**1959, Oct. 11   Litho.   Perf. 11½**
| C266 | AP63 | 15p shown | .80 | .25 |
| C267 | AP63 | 30p Weight lifter | 1.00 | .25 |
| C268 | AP64 | 40p shown | 1.55 | .35 |
| | | *Nos. C266-C268 (3)* | 3.35 | .85 |

3rd Mediterranean Games, Beirut.
A souvenir sheet on white cardboard contains one each of Nos. C266-C268, imperf. Sold for 100p. Value *$55*

Soldiers and Flag — AP65

**1959, Nov. 25   Perf. 13½x13**
| C269 | AP65 | 40p sep, brick red & sl | 1.50 | .30 |
| C270 | AP65 | 60p sep, dk grn & brick red | 2.00 | .35 |

Lebanon's independence, 1941-1959.

**No. C234 Surcharged with New Value and Bars**
**1959, Dec. 15   Perf. 11½**
| C271 | AP48 | 40p on 65p dp claret | 2.60 | .30 |

Hands Planting Tree — AP66

**1960, Jan. 18   Litho.   Perf. 11½**
| C272 | AP66 | 20p rose vio & grn | .90 | .25 |
| C273 | AP66 | 40p dk brn & green | 1.10 | .35 |

Friends of the Tree Society, 25th anniv.

Postal Administration Building — AP67

**1960, Feb.   Unwmk.   Perf. 13**
| C274 | AP67 | 20p green | .80 | .25 |

President Fuad Chehab — AP68

**1960, Mar. 12   Photo.   Perf. 13½**
| C275 | AP68 | 5p green | .40 | .25 |
| C276 | AP68 | 10p Prus blue | .40 | .25 |
| C277 | AP68 | 15p orange brn | .40 | .25 |
| C278 | AP68 | 20p brown | .45 | .25 |
| C279 | AP68 | 30p olive | .65 | .25 |
| C280 | AP68 | 40p dull red | .75 | .25 |
| C281 | AP68 | 50p blue | .80 | .25 |
| C282 | AP68 | 70p red lilac | .90 | .25 |
| C283 | AP68 | 100p dark green | 1.60 | .35 |
| | | *Nos. C275-C283 (9)* | 6.35 | 2.35 |

Uprooted Oak Emblem — AP69

**1960, Apr. 7   Litho.   Perf. 13½x13**
**Size: 20½x36½mm**
| C284 | AP69 | 25p yellow brn | .95 | .25 |
| C285 | AP69 | 40p green | 1.10 | .30 |
| a. | | Souv. sheet of 2, #C284-C285, imperf. | 35.00 | 15.50 |

**Size: 20x36mm**
| C284b | AP69 | 25p yellow brown | 1.00 | .40 |
| C285b | AP69 | 40p green | 1.75 | .65 |

World Refugee Year, 7/1/59-6/30/60.
No. C285a sold for 150p.
Nos. C284b-C285b appear fuzzy and pale when compared to the bolder, clear-cut printing of Nos. C284-C285. Issue date: July 18.
Nos. C284b-C285b exist with carmine surcharges of "30P.+15P." (on C284b) and "20P.+10P." (on C285b), repeated in Arabic, with ornaments covering original denominations. Value, $17.

Martyrs' Monument — AP70

Martyrs of May 6th: 70p, Statues from Martyrs' monument, horiz.

**1960, May 6   Perf. 13x13½, 13½x13**
| C286 | AP70 | 20p rose lilac & grn | .65 | .25 |
| C287 | AP70 | 40p Prus grn & dk grn | .80 | .25 |
| C288 | AP70 | 70p gray olive & blk | 1.60 | .40 |
| | | *Nos. C286-C288 (3)* | 3.05 | .90 |

Pres. Chehab and King of Morocco — AP71

**1960, June 1   Perf. 13x13½**
| C289 | AP71 | 30p choc & dk brn | .90 | .30 |
| C290 | AP71 | 70p blk, dk brn & buff | 1.75 | .35 |

Visit of King Mohammed V of Morocco.
A souvenir sheet of 2 on white cardboard contains Nos. C289-C290, imperf. Value $72.50.

Child Learning to Walk — AP72

**1960, Aug. 16   Litho.   Perf. 13½x13**
| C291 | AP72 | 20p shown | .80 | .25 |
| C292 | AP72 | 60p Mother & child | 1.60 | .35 |
| | | *Nos. C291-C292,CB10-CB11 (4)* | 5.55 | 1.40 |

Day of Mother and Child, Mar. 21-22.

Bird, Ribbon of Flags and Map of Beirut — AP73

40p, Cedar & birds. 70p, Globes & cedar, horiz.

**Perf. 13½x13, 13x13½**
**1960, Sept. 20   Unwmk.**
| C293 | AP73 | 20p multicolored | .50 | .25 |
| C294 | AP73 | 40p vio, bl & grn | .75 | .25 |
| C295 | AP73 | 70p multicolored | 1.00 | .25 |
| | | *Nos. C293-C295 (3)* | 2.25 | .75 |

Union of Lebanese Emigrants in the World. A souvenir sheet of 3 contains Nos. C293-C295, imperf., printed on cardboard. Sold for 150p. Value $22.50.

Pres. Chehab and Map of Lebanon — AP74

**1961, Feb.   Litho.   Perf. 13½x13**
| C296 | AP74 | 5p bl grn & yel grn | .40 | .25 |
| C297 | AP74 | 10p brown & bister | .40 | .25 |
| C298 | AP74 | 70p vio & rose lilac | 1.00 | .30 |

Casino, Maameltein Lebanon — AP75

**1961   Perf. 13x13½**
| C299 | AP75 | 15p rose claret | .55 | .25 |
| C300 | AP75 | 30p greenish blue | .90 | .25 |
| C301 | AP75 | 40p brown | 1.10 | .25 |
| C302 | AP75 | 200p bis brn & dl bl | 4.25 | 1.15 |
| | | *Nos. C296-C302 (7)* | 8.60 | 2.70 |

On Nos. C299-C301, the denomination, inscription and trees differ from No. C302.

UN, 15th Anniv. (in 1960) — AP76

20p, UN Emblem & map of Lebanon, vert. 30p, UN Emblem & symbolic building, vert. 50p, UN Headquarters, New York.

**1961, May 5   Perf. 13½x13, 13x13½**
| C306 | AP76 | 20p lake & lt blue | .65 | .25 |
| C307 | AP76 | 30p green & beige | .70 | .25 |
| C308 | AP76 | 50p vio bl & grnsh bl | 1.30 | .25 |
| a. | | Souvenir sheet of 3 | 9.00 | 9.00 |
| | | *Nos. C306-C308 (3)* | 2.65 | .75 |

No. C308a contains one each of Nos. C306-C308, imperf., against a light blue background showing UN emblem. Sold for 125p.

Pottery Workers — AP77

**1961, July 11   Litho.   Perf. 13x13½**
| C309 | AP77 | 30p shown | 2.50 | .25 |
| C310 | AP77 | 70p Weaver | 1.40 | .25 |

Issued for Labor Day, 1961.

Fireworks AP78

Water Skiing AP79

70p, Tourists on boat ride through cave.

**1961, Aug. 8   Perf. 13½x13, 13x13½**
| C311 | AP78 | 15p lt pur & dk bl | 1.40 | .90 |
| C312 | AP79 | 40p blue & pink | 2.00 | 1.10 |
| C313 | AP79 | 70p dull brn & pink | .85 | .45 |
| | | *Nos. C311-C313 (3)* | 4.25 | 2.45 |

Issued to publicize tourist month.

Highway Circle at
Dora, Beirut
Suburb — AP80

**1961, Aug.**     **Perf. 11½**
C314 AP80 35p yellow green .95 .25
C315 AP80 50p orange brown 1.15 .40
C316 AP80 100p gray 1.15 .50
*Nos. C314-C316 (3)* 3.25 1.15

Beach at
Tyre — AP81

Afka
Falls — AP82

**1961, Sept.**    **Litho.**    **Perf. 13**
C317 AP81 5p carmine rose .50 .25
C318 AP81 10p brt violet .75 .25
C319 AP81 15p bright blue .80 .25
C320 AP81 20p orange 1.00 .25
C321 AP81 30p brt green 1.25 .25
C322 AP82 40p dp claret 1.00 .25
C323 AP82 50p ultramarine 1.10 .25
C324 AP82 70p yellow green 1.50 .25
C325 AP82 100p dark brown 2.00 .35
*Nos. C317-C325 (9)* 9.90 2.35

See Nos. C341-C342.

Entrance to
UNESCO Building
AP83

"UNESCO"
and Cedar
AP84

Design: 50p, UNESCO headquarters, Paris.

**1961, Nov. 20**    **Unwmk.**    **Perf. 12**
C326 AP83 20p bl, buff & blk .60 .25
C327 AP84 30p lt grn, blk & mag .70 .25
C328 AP83 50p multicolored 1.10 .25
*Nos. C326-C328 (3)* 2.40 .75

UNESCO, 15th anniv.

Emir Bechir and
Fakhr-el-Din El
Maani — AP85

**1961, Dec. 30**     **Litho.**
C329 AP85 25p Cedar emblem .60 .25
C330 AP85 50p shown .90 .25

See note after No. 375.

**Scout Types of Regular Issue, 1962**

15p, Trefoil & cedar emblem. 20p, Hand making Scout sign. 25p, Lebanese Scout emblem.

**1962, Mar. 1**    **Unwmk.**    **Perf. 12**
C331 A70 15p grn, blk & red .65 .25
C332 A69 20p lil, blk & yel .75 .25
C333 A70 25p multicolored 1.25 .35
*Nos. C331-C333 (3)* 2.65 .85

Arab League Building,
Cairo — AP86

**1962, Mar. 20**     **Perf. 13**
C334 AP86 20p ultra & lt bl .55 .25
C335 AP86 30p red brn & pink .70 .25
C336 AP86 50p grn & grnsh bl .90 .25
*Nos. C334-C336 (3)* 2.15 .75

Arab League Week, Mar. 22-28. See Nos. C372-C375.
Nos. C334-C336 exist perforated 10½. Only 50 sets known. Value, $180.

Blacksmith
AP87

Farm Tractor
AP88

**Perf. 13½x13, 13x13½**

**1962, May 1**     **Litho.**
C337 AP87 5p green & lt blue .45 .25
C338 AP87 10p blue & pink .45 .25
C339 AP88 25p brt vio & pink .70 .25
C340 AP88 35p car rose & blue .90 .25
*Nos. C337-C340 (4)* 2.50 1.00

Issued for Labor Day.

**Types of 1961 Redrawn with Large
Numerals Similar to Redrawn
Regular Issue of 1962**

**1962**     **Perf. 13**
C341 AP81 5p carmine rose 1.10 .25
C342 AP82 40p deep claret 6.25 .40

Hand Reaching for
Malaria Eradication
Emblem — AP89

Design: 70p, Malaria eradication emblem.

**1962, July 2**    **Litho.**    **Perf. 13½x13**
C349 AP89 30p tan & brown .80 .25
C350 AP89 70p bluish lil & vio 1.00 .40

WHO drive to eradicate malaria.

Bas-relief of Isis,
Kalabsha Temple,
Nubia — AP90

**1962, Aug. 1**    **Unwmk.**    **Perf. 13**
C351 AP90 30p yellow green 1.60 .25
C352 AP90 50p slate 3.25 .50

Campaign to save historic monuments in Nubia.

Spade, Heart,
Diamond,
Club — AP91

**1962, Sept.**
C353 AP91 25p car rose, blk & red 3.25 1.25
C354 AP91 40p multicolored 4.50 1.25

European Bridge Championship Tournament.

College
Student — AP92

**1962, Oct. 1**     **Perf. 12**
C355 AP92 45p multicolored .75 .25

Issued for Students' Day, Oct. 1.

Sword Severing
Chain — AP93

**1962, Nov. 22**    **Litho.**    **Perf. 13**
C356 AP93 25p vio, lt bl & red .90 .25
C357 AP93 25p bl, lt bl & red .90 .25
C358 AP93 25p grn, lt bl & red .90 .25
*Nos. C356-C358 (3)* 2.70 .75

19th anniversary of independence.

**Fruit Type of Regular Issue, 1962**

5p, Apricots. 10p, 30p, Plums. 20p, 40p, Apples. 50p, Pears. 70p, Medlar. 100p, Lemons.

**1962**     **Vignette Multicolored**
C359 A72 5p orange brown .50 .25
C360 A72 10p black .55 .25
C361 A72 20p brown .60 .25
C362 A72 30p gray .75 .25
C363 A72 40p dark gray 1.00 .25
C364 A72 50p light brown 1.25 .25
C365 A72 70p gray olive 1.50 .30
C366 A72 100p blue 3.00 .50
*Nos. C359-C366 (8)* 9.15 2.30

Harvest — AP94

Design: 15p, 20p, UN Emblem and hand holding Wheat Emblem, horiz.

**1963, Mar. 21**    **Litho.**    **Perf. 13**
C367 AP94 2.50p ultra & yel .40 .25
C368 AP94 5p gray grn & yel .40 .25
C369 AP94 7.50p rose lil & yel .40 .25
C370 AP94 15p rose brn & pale grn .65 .25
C371 AP94 20p rose & pale grn .80 .25
*Nos. C367-C371 (5)* 2.65 1.25

FAO "Freedom from Hunger" campaign.

**Redrawn Type of 1962, Dated
"1963"**

Design: Arab League Building, Cairo.

**1963, Mar.**    **Unwmk.**    **Perf. 12**
C372 AP86 5p violet & lt blue .40 .25
C373 AP86 10p green & lt blue .40 .25
C374 AP86 15p claret & lt blue .45 .25
C375 AP86 20p gray & lt blue .60 .25
*Nos. C372-C375 (4)* 1.85 1.00

Issued for Arab League Week.

Blood Transfusion
AP95

Design: 35p, 40p, Nurse and infant, vert.

**1963, Oct. 5**    **Unwmk.**    **Perf. 13**
C376 AP95 5p green & red .40 .25
C377 AP95 20p grnsh bl & red .45 .25
C378 AP95 35p org, red & blk .60 .25
C379 AP95 40p purple & red .80 .25
*Nos. C376-C379 (4)* 2.25 1.00

Centenary of International Red Cross.

Lyre Player and
Columns — AP96

**1963, Nov. 7**    **Unwmk.**    **Perf. 13**
C380 AP96 35p lt bl, org & blk 1.25 .25

International Festival at Baalbek.

Lebanon Flag, Rising
Sun — AP97

**1964, Jan. 8**      **Litho.**
C381 AP97 5p bluish grn, ver & yel .40 .25
C382 AP97 10p yel grn, ver & yel .45 .25
C383 AP97 25p ultra, ver & yel .60 .25
C384 AP97 40p gray, ver & yel .90 .30
*Nos. C381-C384 (4)* 2.35 1.05

20th anniversary of Independence.

**Sports Type of Regular Issue, 1964**

**1964, Feb. 11**    **Unwmk.**    **Perf. 13**
C385 A76 15p Tennis .45 .25
C386 A76 17.50p Swimming, horiz. .55 .25
C387 A76 30p Skiing, horiz. .80 .25
   *a.*   Souvenir sheet of 3 13.00 10.00
*Nos. C385-C387 (3)* 1.80 .75

No. C387a contains three imperf. stamps similar to Nos. C385-C387 with simulated orange brown perforations and green marginal inscription. Sold for 100p.

Anemone — AP98

**1964, June 9**    **Unwmk.**    **Perf. 13**
C391 AP98 5p Lily .40 .25
C392 AP98 10p Ranunculus .50 .25
C393 AP98 20p shown .60 .25
C394 AP98 40p Tuberose .80 .25
C395 AP98 45p Rhododendron .90 .25
C396 AP98 50p Jasmine 1.00 .25
C397 AP98 70p Yellow broom 1.60 .25
*Nos. C391-C397 (7)* 5.80 1.75

Girls Jumping
Rope — AP99

Children's Day: 20p, 40p, Boy on hobby-horse, vert.

**1964, Apr. 8**
C398 AP99 5p emer, org & red .40 .25
C399 AP99 10p yel brn, org & red .45 .25
C400 AP99 20p dp ultra, lt bl & org .50 .25
C401 AP99 40p lil, lt bl & yel .80 .25
*Nos. C398-C401 (4)* 2.15 1.00

Flame and UN
Emblem — AP100

40p, Flame, UN emblem and broken chain.

**1964, May 15**    **Litho.**    **Unwmk.**
C402 AP100 20p sal, org & brn .40 .25
C403 AP100 40p lt bl, gray bl & org .60 .25

15th anniv. (in 1963) of the Universal Declaration of Human Rights.

Arab League Conference — AP101

**1964, Apr. 20**     **Perf. 13x13½**
| | | | | |
|---|---|---|---|---|
| C404 | AP101 | 5p blk & pale sal | .75 | .25 |
| C405 | AP101 | 10p black | .90 | .30 |
| C406 | AP101 | 15p green | 1.25 | .25 |
| C407 | AP101 | 20p dk brn & pink | 1.60 | .50 |
| | | Nos. C404-C407 (4) | 4.50 | 1.45 |

Arab League meeting.

Child in Crib — AP102

Beit-ed-Din Palace and Children — AP103

**1964, July 20**     **Perf. 13½x13, 13½**
| | | | | |
|---|---|---|---|---|
| C408 | AP102 | 2.50p multicolored | .40 | .25 |
| C409 | AP102 | 5p multicolored | .40 | .25 |
| C410 | AP102 | 15p multicolored | .50 | .25 |
| C411 | AP103 | 17.50p multicolored | .65 | .25 |
| C412 | AP103 | 20p multicolored | .75 | .25 |
| C413 | AP103 | 40p multicolored | .80 | .25 |
| | | Nos. C408-C413 (6) | 3.50 | 1.50 |

Ball of the Little White Beds, Beirut, for the benefit of children's hospital beds.

Clasped Hands and Map of Lebanon — AP104

**1964, Oct. 16**     **Litho.**     **Perf. 13½x13**
| | | | | |
|---|---|---|---|---|
| C414 | AP104 | 20p yel grn, yel & gray | .65 | .25 |
| C415 | AP104 | 40p slate, yel & gray | 1.10 | .40 |

Congress of the Intl. Lebanese Union.

Rocket Leaving Earth — AP105

Battle Scene AP106

**1964, Nov. 24**     **Unwmk.**     **Perf. 13½**
| | | | | |
|---|---|---|---|---|
| C416 | AP105 | 5p multicolored | .40 | .25 |
| C417 | AP105 | 10p multicolored | .40 | .25 |
| C418 | AP106 | 40p sl blue & blk | .80 | .25 |
| C419 | AP106 | 70p dp claret & blk | 1.60 | .40 |
| | | Nos. C416-C419 (4) | 3.20 | 1.15 |

21st anniversary of independence.

Woman in Costume — AP107

---

Design: 10p, 15p, Man in costume.

**1965, Jan. 11**     **Litho.**     **Perf. 13½**
| | | | | |
|---|---|---|---|---|
| C420 | AP107 | 10p multicolored | .60 | .25 |
| C421 | AP107 | 15p multicolored | .75 | .25 |
| C422 | AP107 | 25p green & multi | 1.00 | .30 |
| C423 | AP107 | 40p brown & multi | 1.20 | .40 |
| | | Nos. C420-C423 (4) | 3.55 | 1.20 |

International Festival at Baalbek.

Equestrian AP108

25p, Target shooting, vert. 40p, Gymnast on rings.

**1965, Jan. 23**     **Engr.**     **Perf. 13**
| | | | | |
|---|---|---|---|---|
| C424 | AP108 | 15p shown | .40 | .25 |
| C425 | AP108 | 25p mutlicolored | .50 | .25 |
| C426 | AP108 | 40p multicolored | .60 | .25 |
| a. | | Souvenir sheet of 3, #C424-C426, imperf. | 14.50 | 7.50 |
| | | Nos. C424-C426 (3) | 1.50 | .75 |

18th Olympic Games, Tokyo, Oct. 10-25, 1964. No. 426a sold for 100p.

Heliconius Cybria — AP109

30p, Pericallia matronula. 40p, Red admiral. 45p, Satyrus semele. 70p, Machaon. 85p, Aurore. 100p, Morpho cypris. 200p, Erasmia sanguiflua. 300p, Papilio crassus. 500p, Charaxes ameliae.

**1965**     **Unwmk.**     **Perf. 13**
**Size: 36x22mm**
| | | | | |
|---|---|---|---|---|
| C427 | AP109 | 30p multi | 3.00 | .25 |
| C428 | AP109 | 35p multi | 4.25 | .35 |
| C429 | AP109 | 40p multi | 5.25 | .35 |
| C430 | AP109 | 45p multi | 6.00 | .50 |
| C431 | AP109 | 70p multi | 7.25 | .75 |
| C432 | AP109 | 85p multi | 8.00 | .90 |
| C433 | AP109 | 100p multi | 12.00 | 1.00 |
| C434 | AP109 | 200p multi | 19.00 | 1.25 |
| C435 | AP109 | 300p multi | 26.00 | 3.50 |

**Engr. and Litho.**
**Perf. 12**
**Size: 35x25mm**
| | | | | |
|---|---|---|---|---|
| C436 | AP109 | 500p lt ultra & blk | 52.50 | 7.00 |
| | | Nos. C427-C436 (10) | 143.25 | 15.85 |

For surcharges see Nos. C654-C656.

Pope Paul VI and Pres. Charles Helou AP110

**1965, June 28**     **Photo.**     **Perf. 12**
| | | | | |
|---|---|---|---|---|
| C437 | AP110 | 45p gold & brt vio | 4.50 | .90 |
| a. | | Souv. sheet of 1, imperf. | 45.00 | 29.00 |

Visit of Pope Paul VI to Lebanon. No. C437a sold for 50p.

Cedars of Friendship AP111

**1965, Oct. 16**     **Photo.**     **Perf. 13x12½**
| | | | | |
|---|---|---|---|---|
| C438 | AP111 | 40p multicolored | 1.50 | .25 |

Cocoon, Spindle and Silk — AP112

15p, 30p, 40p, 50p, Silk weaver at loom.

---

**1965, Oct. 16**     **Perf. 12½x13**
**Design in Buff and Bright Green**
| | | | | |
|---|---|---|---|---|
| C439 | AP112 | 2.50p brown | 1.25 | .25 |
| C440 | AP112 | 5p dk olive grn | 1.25 | .25 |
| C441 | AP112 | 7.50p Prus blue | 1.25 | .25 |
| C442 | AP112 | 15p deep ultra | 1.25 | .25 |
| C443 | AP112 | 30p deep claret | 1.50 | .25 |
| C444 | AP112 | 40p brown | 2.40 | .25 |
| C445 | AP112 | 50p rose brown | 3.50 | .60 |
| | | Nos. C439-C445 (7) | 12.40 | 2.10 |

Parliament Building — AP113

**1965, Oct. 26**     **Perf. 13x12½**
| | | | | |
|---|---|---|---|---|
| C446 | AP113 | 35p red, buff & brn | .65 | .25 |
| C447 | AP113 | 40p emer, buff & brn | .80 | .25 |

Centenary of the Lebanese parliament.

UN Headquarters, NYC, UN Emblem and Lebanese Flags — AP114

**1965, Nov. 10**     **Engr.**     **Perf. 12**
| | | | | |
|---|---|---|---|---|
| C448 | AP114 | 2.50p dull blue | .40 | .25 |
| C449 | AP114 | 10p magenta | .40 | .25 |
| C450 | AP114 | 17.50p dull violet | .40 | .25 |
| C451 | AP114 | 30p green | .50 | .25 |
| C452 | AP114 | 40p brown | .70 | .25 |
| | | Nos. C448-C452 (5) | 2.40 | 1.25 |

UN, 20th anniv. A souvenir sheet contains one 40p imperf. stamp in bright rose lilac. Sold for 50p. Value $15.

Playing Card King, Laurel and Cedar — AP115

**1965, Nov. 15**     **Photo.**     **Perf. 12½x13**
| | | | | |
|---|---|---|---|---|
| C453 | AP115 | 2.50p multicolored | .60 | .25 |
| C454 | AP115 | 15p multicolored | .90 | .25 |
| C455 | AP115 | 17.50p multicolored | 1.00 | .25 |
| C456 | AP115 | 40p multicolored | 1.15 | .25 |
| | | Nos. C453-C456 (4) | 3.65 | 1.00 |

Intl. Bridge Championships. A souvenir sheet contains two imperf. stamps similar to Nos. C454 and C456. Sold for 75p. Value $22.50.

Dagger in Map of Palestine — AP116

**1965, Dec. 12**     **Perf. 12½x11**
| | | | | |
|---|---|---|---|---|
| C457 | AP116 | 50p multicolored | 4.50 | .50 |

Deir Yassin massacre, Apr. 9, 1948.

ITU Emblem, Old and New Communication Equipment and Early Bird Satellite — AP117

**1966, Apr. 15**     **Perf. 13x12½**
| | | | | |
|---|---|---|---|---|
| C458 | AP117 | 2.50p multi | .45 | .25 |
| C459 | AP117 | 15p multi | .50 | .25 |
| C460 | AP117 | 17.50p multi | .55 | .25 |
| C461 | AP117 | 25p multi | .90 | .25 |
| C462 | AP117 | 40p multi | 1.20 | .25 |
| | | Nos. C458-C462 (5) | 3.60 | 1.25 |

ITU, centenary (in 1965).

---

Folk Dancers Before Temple of Bacchus AP118

Designs: 7.50p, 15p, Dancers before Temple of Jupiter, vert. 30p, 40p, Orchestra before Temple of Bacchus.

**1966, July 20**     **Unwmk.**     **Perf. 12**
**Gold Frame**
| | | | | |
|---|---|---|---|---|
| C463 | AP118 | 2.50p brn vio, bl & orange | .50 | .25 |
| C464 | AP118 | 5p mag, bl & org | .50 | .25 |
| C465 | AP118 | 7.50p vio bl, bl & pink | .50 | .25 |
| C466 | AP118 | 15p pur, bl & pink | .55 | .25 |
| C467 | AP118 | 30p dk grn, org & blue | .60 | .25 |
| C468 | AP118 | 50p vio, org & bl | 1.00 | .25 |
| | | Nos. C463-C468 (6) | 3.65 | 1.50 |

11th International Festival at Baalbek.

Opening of WHO Headquarters, Geneva — AP119

**1966, Aug. 25**     **Engr.**     **Perf. 12**
| | | | | |
|---|---|---|---|---|
| C469 | AP119 | 7.50p dp yel grn | .35 | .25 |
| C470 | AP119 | 17.50p car rose | .45 | .25 |
| C471 | AP119 | 25p blue | .70 | .25 |
| | | Nos. C469-C471 (3) | 1.50 | .75 |

Skier — AP120

Designs: 5p, Children on toboggan. 17.50p, Cedar in snow. 25p, Ski lift.

**1966, Sept. 15**     **Photo.**     **Perf. 12x11½**
| | | | | |
|---|---|---|---|---|
| C472 | AP120 | 2.50p multi | .40 | .25 |
| C473 | AP120 | 10p multi | .40 | .25 |
| C474 | AP120 | 17.50p multi | .60 | .25 |
| C475 | AP120 | 25p multi | .80 | .25 |
| | | Nos. C472-C475 (4) | 2.20 | 1.00 |

International Festival of Cedars.

Sarcophagus of King Ahiram with Early Alphabet — AP121

15p, Phoenician ship. 20p, Map of the Mediterranean Sea showing Phoenician travel routes, and ship. 30p, Phoenician with alphabet tablet.

**Litho. & Engr.**
**1966, Sept. 25**     **Perf. 12**
| | | | | |
|---|---|---|---|---|
| C476 | AP121 | 10p dl grn, blk & lt brn | .40 | .25 |
| C477 | AP121 | 15p rose lil, brn & ocher | .40 | .25 |
| C478 | AP121 | 20p tan, dk brn & bl | .50 | .25 |
| C479 | AP121 | 30p org, dk brn & yel | .80 | .25 |
| | | Nos. C476-C479 (4) | 2.10 | 1.00 |

Invention of alphabet by Phoenicians.

Child in Bathtub and UNICEF Emblem — AP122

5p, Boy in rowboat. 7.50p, Girl skier. 15p, Girl feeding bird. 20p, Boy doing homework. 50p, Children of various races, horiz.

**1966, Oct. 10　Photo.　Perf. 11½x12**

| | | | | |
|---|---|---|---|---|
| C480 | AP122 | 2.50p multi | .40 | .25 |
| C481 | AP122 | 5p multi | .40 | .25 |
| C482 | AP122 | 7.50p multi | .50 | .25 |
| C483 | AP122 | 15p multi | .60 | .25 |
| C484 | AP122 | 20p multi | .80 | .25 |
| | *Nos. C480-C484 (5)* | | 2.70 | 1.25 |

**Miniature Sheet**

*Imperf*

| | | | | |
|---|---|---|---|---|
| C485 | AP122 | 50p dl yellow & multi | 6.00 | 3.00 |

UNICEF; World Children's Day. No. C485 contains one horizontal stamp 43x33mm.

**Scenic Type of Regular Issue, 1966**

Designs: 10p, Waterfall, Djezzine. 15p, Castle of the Sea, Saida. 20p, Amphitheater, Jubayl (Byblos). 30p, Temple of the Sun, Baalbek. 50p, Beit-ed-Din Palace. 60p, Church of Christ the King, Nahr-el-Kalb. 75p, Abu Bakr Mosque, Tripoli.

**1966, Oct. 12　　　　Perf. 12x11½**

| | | | | |
|---|---|---|---|---|
| C486 | A82 | 10p gold & multi | .40 | .25 |
| C487 | A82 | 15p gold & multi | .50 | .25 |
| C488 | A82 | 20p gold & multi | .60 | .25 |
| C489 | A82 | 30p gold & multi | .80 | .25 |
| C490 | A82 | 50p gold & multi | 1.40 | .25 |
| C491 | A82 | 60p gold & multi | 1.60 | .25 |
| C492 | A82 | 75p gold & multi | 2.40 | .25 |
| | *Nos. C486-C492 (7)* | | 7.70 | 1.75 |

Symbolic Water Cycle — AP123

15p, 20p, Different wave pattern without sun.

**1966, Nov. 15　Photo.　Perf. 12½**

| | | | | |
|---|---|---|---|---|
| C493 | AP123 | 5p red, bl & vio bl | .40 | .25 |
| C494 | AP123 | 10p org, bl & brn | .40 | .25 |
| C495 | AP123 | 15p org, emer & dk brn | .50 | .25 |
| C496 | AP123 | 20p org, emer & grnsh blue | .60 | .25 |
| | *Nos. C493-C496 (4)* | | 1.90 | 1.00 |

Hydrological Decade (UNESCO), 1965-74.

Daniel Bliss — AP124

Designs: 30p, Chapel, American University, Beirut. 50p, Daniel Bliss, D.D., and American University, horiz.

**1966, Dec. 3**

| | | | | |
|---|---|---|---|---|
| C497 | AP124 | 20p grn, yel & brn | .50 | .25 |
| C498 | AP124 | 30p red brn, grn & blue | .60 | .25 |

**Souvenir Sheet**

*Imperf*

| | | | | |
|---|---|---|---|---|
| C499 | AP124 | 50p grn, brn & org brown | 3.00 | 1.50 |

Cent. of American University, Beirut, founded by the Rev. Daniel Bliss (1823-1916). Nos. C497-C498 are printed each with alternating labels showing University emblem. No. C499 contains one stamp 59x37mm.

Flags of Arab League Members, Hand Signing Scroll AP125

**1967, Aug. 2　Photo.　Perf. 12x11½**

| | | | | |
|---|---|---|---|---|
| C500 | AP125 | 5p brown & multi | .40 | .25 |
| C501 | AP125 | 10p multicolored | .40 | .25 |
| C502 | AP125 | 15p black & multi | .45 | .25 |
| C503 | AP125 | 20p multicolored | .55 | .25 |
| | *Nos. C500-C503 (4)* | | 1.80 | 1.00 |

Signing of Arab League Pact in 1945.

Veteran's War Memorial Building, San Francisco AP126

10p, 20p, 30p, Scroll, flags of Lebanon & UN.

**1967, Sept. 1　Photo.　Perf. 12x11½**

| | | | | |
|---|---|---|---|---|
| C504 | AP126 | 2.50p blue & multi | .50 | .25 |
| C505 | AP126 | 5p multicolored | .50 | .25 |
| C506 | AP126 | 7.50p multicolored | .50 | .25 |
| C507 | AP126 | 10p blue & multi | .50 | .25 |
| C508 | AP126 | 20p multicolored | .60 | .25 |
| C509 | AP126 | 30p multicolored | .75 | .25 |
| | *Nos. C504-C509 (6)* | | 3.35 | 1.50 |

San Francisco Pact (UN Charter), 22nd anniv.

Ruins at Baalbek AP127

Intl. Tourist Year: 10p, Ruins at Anjar. 15p, Bridge over Ibrahim River and ruins. 20p, Boat on underground lake, Jaita cave. 50p, St. George's Bay, Beirut.

**1967, Sept. 25　　　　Perf. 12½**

| | | | | |
|---|---|---|---|---|
| C510 | AP127 | 5p multicolored | .50 | .25 |
| C511 | AP127 | 10p multicolored | .60 | .25 |
| C512 | AP127 | 15p violet & multi | .80 | .25 |
| C513 | AP127 | 20p brn & multi | .95 | .25 |
| | *Nos. C510-C513 (4)* | | 2.85 | 1.00 |

**Souvenir Sheet**

*Imperf*

| | | | | |
|---|---|---|---|---|
| C514 | AP127 | 50p multicolored | 22.00 | 16.00 |

View of Tabarja AP128

Views: 15p, Pigeon Rock and shore, Beirut. 17.50p, Beit-ed-Din Palace. 20p, Ship at Sidon. 25p, Tripoli. 30p, Beach at Byblos. 35p, Ruins, Tyre. 40p, Temple of Bacchus, Baalbek.

**1967, Oct.　　　　　Perf. 12x11½**

| | | | | |
|---|---|---|---|---|
| C515 | AP128 | 10p multi | .60 | .25 |
| C516 | AP128 | 15p multi | 1.15 | .25 |
| C517 | AP128 | 17.50p multi | 1.60 | .25 |
| C518 | AP128 | 20p multi | 1.60 | .25 |
| C519 | AP128 | 25p multi | 1.60 | .25 |
| C520 | AP128 | 30p multi | 2.25 | .25 |
| C521 | AP128 | 35p multi | 3.00 | .25 |
| C522 | AP128 | 40p multi | 3.00 | .25 |
| | *Nos. C515-C522 (8)* | | 15.80 | 2.00 |

Intl. Tourist Year; used as a regular airmail issue.

India Day AP129

**1967, Oct. 30　Engr.　Perf. 12**

| | | | | |
|---|---|---|---|---|
| C523 | AP129 | 2.50p orange | .40 | .25 |
| C524 | AP129 | 5p magenta | .40 | .25 |
| C525 | AP129 | 7.50p brown | .40 | .25 |
| C526 | AP129 | 10p blue | .45 | .25 |
| C527 | AP129 | 15p green | .50 | .25 |
| | *Nos. C523-C527 (5)* | | 2.15 | 1.25 |

Globe and Arabic Inscription AP130

Design: 10p, 20p, 30p, UN emblem.

**1967, Nov. 25　Engr.　　Perf. 12**

| | | | | |
|---|---|---|---|---|
| C528 | AP130 | 2.50p rose | .40 | .25 |
| C529 | AP130 | 5p gray blue | .40 | .25 |
| C530 | AP130 | 7.50p green | .40 | .25 |
| C531 | AP130 | 10p brt carmine | .40 | .25 |
| C532 | AP130 | 20p violet blue | .40 | .25 |
| C533 | AP130 | 30p dark green | .65 | .25 |
| | *Nos. C528-C533 (6)* | | 2.75 | 1.50 |

Lebanon's admission to the UN. A 100p rose red souvenir sheet in the globe design exists. Value, $5.50.

Basking Shark — AP131

Fish: 30p, Needlefish. 40p, Pollack. 50p, Cuckoo wrasse. 70p, Red mullet. 100p, Rainbow trout.

**1968, Feb.　Photo.　Perf. 12x11½**

| | | | | |
|---|---|---|---|---|
| C534 | AP131 | 20p multi | 1.40 | .25 |
| C535 | AP131 | 30p multi | 1.40 | .25 |
| C536 | AP131 | 40p multi | 2.10 | .25 |
| C537 | AP131 | 50p multi | 3.00 | .25 |
| C538 | AP131 | 70p multi | 5.25 | .25 |
| C539 | AP131 | 100p multi | 6.50 | .25 |
| | *Nos. C534-C539 (6)* | | 19.65 | 1.50 |

Ski Jump AP132

5p, 7.50p, 10p, Downhill skiers (various). 25p, Congress emblem (skis and cedar).

**1968　　　　Perf. 12½x11½**

| | | | | |
|---|---|---|---|---|
| C540 | AP132 | 2.50p multicolored | .40 | .25 |
| C541 | AP132 | 5p multicolored | .40 | .25 |
| C542 | AP132 | 7.50p multicolored | .40 | .25 |
| C543 | AP132 | 10p multicolored | .40 | .25 |
| C544 | AP132 | 25p multicolored | .60 | .25 |
| | *Nos. C540-C544 (5)* | | 2.20 | 1.25 |

26th Intl. Ski Congress, Beirut. A 50p imperf. souvenir sheet exists in design of the 25p. Value, $6.50.

Emir Fakhr al-Din II — AP133

2.50p, Emira Khaskiah. 10p, Citadel of Sidon, horiz. 15p, Citadel of Chekif & grazing sheep, horiz. 17.50p, Citadel of Beirut & harbor, horiz.

**Perf. 11½x12, 12x11½**

**1968, Feb. 20　　　　Litho.**

| | | | | |
|---|---|---|---|---|
| C546 | AP133 | 2.50p multicolored | .40 | .25 |
| C547 | AP133 | 5p multicolored | .40 | .25 |
| C548 | AP133 | 10p multicolored | .40 | .25 |
| C549 | AP133 | 15p multicolored | .60 | .25 |
| C550 | AP133 | 17.50p multicolored | .60 | .25 |
| | *Nos. C546-C550 (5)* | | 2.40 | 1.25 |

In memory of the Emir Fakhr al-Din II. A 50p imperf. souvenir sheet exists showing the Battle of Anjar. Value $11.50.

Roman Bust — AP134

Ruins of Tyre: 5p, Colonnade, horiz. 7.50p, Arch, horiz. 10p, Banquet, bas-relief.

**Litho. & Engr.**

**1968, Mar. 20　　　　Perf. 12**

| | | | | |
|---|---|---|---|---|
| C552 | AP134 | 2.50p pink, brn & buff | .40 | .25 |
| C553 | AP134 | 5p yel, brn & lt bl | .50 | .25 |
| C554 | AP134 | 7.50p lt grnsh bl, brn & yel | .65 | .25 |
| C555 | AP134 | 10p sal, brn & lt bl | .80 | .25 |
| a. | | Souvenir sheet | 18.00 | 14.00 |
| | *Nos. C552-C555 (4)* | | 2.35 | 1.00 |

No. C555a contains one dark brown and light blue stamp, perf. 10½x11½. Sold for 50p. Exists imperf. Value $22.50.
For surcharge see No. C657.

Emperor Justinian — AP135

Design: 15p, 20p, Justinian and map of the Mediterranean, horiz.

**Perf. 11½x12, 12x11½**

**1968, May 10　　　　Photo.**

| | | | | |
|---|---|---|---|---|
| C556 | AP135 | 5p blue & multi | .45 | .25 |
| C557 | AP135 | 10p blue & multi | .45 | .25 |
| C558 | AP135 | 15p red & multi | .50 | .25 |
| C559 | AP135 | 20p blue & multi | .55 | .25 |
| | *Nos. C556-C559 (4)* | | 1.95 | 1.00 |

Beirut, site of one of the greatest law schools in antiquity; Emperor Justinian (483-565), who compiled and preserved the Roman law.

Arab League Emblem — AP136

**1968, June 6　Photo.　Perf. 12x11½**

| | | | | |
|---|---|---|---|---|
| C560 | AP136 | 5p orange & multi | .40 | .25 |
| C561 | AP136 | 10p multicolored | .40 | .25 |
| C562 | AP136 | 15p pink & multi | .50 | .25 |
| C563 | AP136 | 20p multicolored | .65 | .25 |
| | *Nos. C560-C563 (4)* | | 1.95 | 1.00 |

Issued for Arab League Week.

Cedar and Globe Emblem AP137

**1968, July 10**

| | | | | |
|---|---|---|---|---|
| C564 | AP137 | 2.50p sal pink, brn & green | .40 | .25 |
| C565 | AP137 | 5p gray, brn & grn | .45 | .25 |
| C566 | AP137 | 7.50p brt bl, brn & grn | .50 | .25 |
| C567 | AP137 | 10p yel grn, brn & grn | .60 | .25 |
| | *Nos. C564-C567 (4)* | | 1.95 | 1.00 |

3rd Congress of Lebanese World Union.

Temple of Jupiter, Baalbek AP138

Designs: 10p, Fluted pilasters, cella of Bacchus Temple. 15p, Corniche, south peristyle of Jupiter Temple, horiz. 20p, Gate, Bacchus Temple. 25p, Ceiling detail, south peristyle of Bacchus Temple.

**1968, Sept. 25    Photo.    Perf. 12½**
| | | | |
|---|---|---|---|
| C568 | AP138 | 5p gold & multi | .40 .25 |
| C569 | AP138 | 10p gold & multi | .40 .25 |
| C570 | AP138 | 15p gold & multi | .50 .25 |
| C571 | AP138 | 20p gold & multi | .60 .25 |
| C572 | AP138 | 25p gold & multi | .80 .25 |
| | Nos. C568-C572 (5) | | 2.70 1.25 |

13th Baalbek International Festival.

Broad Jump and Phoenician Statue AP139

Designs: 10p, High jump and votive stele, Phoenician, 6th century B.C. 15p, Fencing and Olmec jade head, 500-400 B.C. 20p, Weight lifting and axe in shape of human head, Vera Cruz region. 25p, Aztec stone calendar and Phoenician ship.

**1968, Oct. 19    Photo.    Perf. 12x11½**
| | | | |
|---|---|---|---|
| C573 | AP139 | 5p lt ultra, yel & gray | .45 .25 |
| C574 | AP139 | 10p mag, lt ultra & blk | .45 .25 |
| C575 | AP139 | 15p cit, ocher & brn | .45 .25 |
| C576 | AP139 | 20p dp org, brn & ocher | .55 .25 |
| C577 | AP139 | 25p light brown | .90 .25 |
| | Nos. C573-C577 (5) | | 2.80 1.25 |

19th Olympic Games, Mexico City, 10/12-27.

Human Rights Flame and Tractor — AP140

Human Rights Flame and: 15p, People. 25p, Boys of 3 races placing hands on globe.

**1968, Dec. 10    Litho.    Perf. 11½**
| | | | |
|---|---|---|---|
| C578 | AP140 | 10p multicolored | .45 .25 |
| C579 | AP140 | 15p yellow & multi | .55 .25 |
| C580 | AP140 | 25p lilac & multi | .90 .25 |
| | Nos. C578-C580 (3) | | 1.90 .75 |

International Human Rights Year.

Minshiya Stairs, Deir El-Kamar — AP141

Views in Deir El-Kamar: 15p, The Seraglio Kiosk. 25p, Old paved city road.

**1968, Dec. 26**
| | | | |
|---|---|---|---|
| C581 | AP141 | 10p multicolored | .40 .25 |
| C582 | AP141 | 15p multicolored | .50 .25 |
| C583 | AP141 | 25p multicolored | .65 .25 |
| | Nos. C581-C583 (3) | | 1.55 .75 |

1st Municipal Council in Lebanon, established in Deir El-Kamar by Daoud Pasha, cent.

Nurse Treating Child, and UN Emblem AP142

Designs: 10p, Grain, fish, grapes and jug. 15p, Mother and children. 20p, Reading girl and Phoenician alphabet. 25p, Playing children.

**1969, Jan. 20    Litho.    Perf. 12**
| | | | |
|---|---|---|---|
| C584 | AP142 | 5p blk, lt bl & sepia | .45 .25 |
| C585 | AP142 | 10p blk, brt yel & grn | .45 .25 |
| C586 | AP142 | 15p blk, red lil & ver | .45 .25 |
| C587 | AP142 | 20p blk, citron & bl | .45 .25 |
| C588 | AP142 | 25p blk, pink & bis brn | .65 .25 |
| | Nos. C584-C588 (5) | | 2.45 1.25 |

UNICEF, 22nd anniversary.

Silver Coin from Byblos, 5th Century B.C. AP143

National Museum, Beirut: 5p, Gold dagger, Byblos, 18th cent. B.C. 7.50p, King Dining in the Land of the Dead, sarcophagus of Ahiram, 13-12th cent. B.C. 30p, Breastplate with cartouche of Amenemhat III (1849-1801 B.C.). 40p, Phoenician bird vase from Khalde, 8th cent. B.C.

**Photogravure; Gold Impressed**
**1969, Feb. 20    Perf. 12**
| | | | |
|---|---|---|---|
| C589 | AP143 | 2.50p grn, yel & lt bl | .45 .25 |
| C590 | AP143 | 5p vio, brn & yel | .55 .25 |
| C591 | AP143 | 7.50p dl yel, brn & pink | .70 .25 |
| C592 | AP143 | 30p blue & multi | .90 .25 |
| C593 | AP143 | 40p multicolored | 1.00 .25 |
| | Nos. C589-C593 (5) | | 3.60 1.25 |

Intl. Congress of Museum Councils; 20th anniv. of the Intl. Council of Museums.

Water Skier — AP144

Designs: 5p, Water ballet. 7.50p, Parachutist, vert. 30p, Yachting, vert. 40p, Regatta.

**1969, Mar. 3    Litho.    Perf. 11½**
| | | | |
|---|---|---|---|
| C594 | AP144 | 2.50p multicolored | .40 .25 |
| C595 | AP144 | 5p multicolored | .40 .25 |
| C596 | AP144 | 7.50p multicolored | .40 .25 |
| C597 | AP144 | 30p multicolored | .80 .25 |
| C598 | AP144 | 40p multicolored | 1.00 .25 |
| | Nos. C594-C598 (5) | | 3.00 1.25 |

Tomb of Unknown Soldier at Military School AP145

2.50p, Frontier guard. 7.50p, Soldiers doing forestry work. 15p, Army engineers building road. 30p, Ambulance and helicopter. 40p, Ski patrol.

**1969, Aug. 1    Litho.    Perf. 12x11½**
| | | | |
|---|---|---|---|
| C599 | AP145 | 2.50p multicolored | .40 .25 |
| C600 | AP145 | 5p multicolored | .40 .25 |
| C601 | AP145 | 7.50p multicolored | .40 .25 |
| C602 | AP145 | 15p multicolored | .40 .25 |
| C603 | AP145 | 30p multicolored | .50 .25 |
| C604 | AP145 | 40p multicolored | .50 .25 |
| | Nos. C599-C604 (6) | | 2.70 1.50 |

25th anniversary of independence.

Crosses and Circles — AP146

**1971, Jan. 6    Photo.    Perf. 11½x12**
| | | | |
|---|---|---|---|
| C605 | AP146 | 15p shown | .45 .25 |
| C606 | AP146 | 85p Crosses, cedar | 1.50 .40 |

Lebanese Red Cross, 25th anniversary.

Foil Fencing AP147

10p, Flags of participating Arab countries. 15p, Flags of participating non-Arab countries. 40p, Sword fencing. 50p, Saber fencing.

**1971, Jan. 15    Litho.    Perf. 12**
| | | | |
|---|---|---|---|
| C607 | AP147 | 10p yellow & multi | .40 .25 |
| C608 | AP147 | 15p yellow & multi | .40 .25 |
| C609 | AP147 | 35p yellow & multi | .50 .25 |
| C610 | AP147 | 40p yellow & multi | .65 .25 |
| C611 | AP147 | 50p yellow & multi | .80 .25 |
| | Nos. C607-C611 (5) | | 2.75 1.25 |

10th World Fencing Championships, held in Lebanon.

Agricultural Workers, Arab Painting, 12th Century AP148

**1971, Feb. 1**
| | | | |
|---|---|---|---|
| C612 | AP148 | 10p silver & multi | .80 .25 |
| C613 | AP148 | 40p gold & multi | 1.40 .25 |

International Labor Organization.

UPU Building and Monument, Bern — AP149

**1971, Feb. 15    Litho.    Perf. 12**
| | | | |
|---|---|---|---|
| C614 | AP149 | 15p yel, blk & dp org | .80 .25 |
| C615 | AP149 | 35p dp org, yel & blk | 1.40 .30 |

Opening of new UPU Headquarters in Bern, Switzerland.

Ravens Burning Owls — AP150

Children's Day: 85p, Jackal and lion. Designs of the 15p and 85p are after 13th-14th century paintings, illustrations for the "Kalila wa Dumna."

**1971, Mar. 1    Photo.    Perf. 11**
**Size: 30x30mm**
| | | | |
|---|---|---|---|
| C616 | AP150 | 15p gold & multi | .25 .25 |

**Perf. 12x11½**
**Size: 38½x29mm**
| | | | |
|---|---|---|---|
| C617 | AP150 | 85p gold & multi | 2.40 .65 |

Map and Flag of Arab League AP151

**1971, Mar. 20    Perf. 12x11½**
| | | | |
|---|---|---|---|
| C618 | AP151 | 30p orange & multi | .50 .25 |
| C619 | AP151 | 70p yellow & multi | 1.10 .30 |

Arab League, 25th anniv.

Bechara el Khoury AP152

Famous Lebanese Men: No. C620, Symbolic design for Imam al Ouzai. No. C622, Hassan Kamel al Sabbah. No. C623, Kahlil Gibran.

**1971, Apr. 10**
| | | | |
|---|---|---|---|
| C620 | AP152 | 25p lt grn, gold & brn | .25 .25 |
| C621 | AP152 | 25p yel, gold & brn | .35 .25 |
| C622 | AP152 | 25p yel, gold & brn | .35 .25 |
| C623 | AP152 | 25p lt grn, gold & brn | .35 .25 |
| | Nos. C620-C623 (4) | | 1.30 1.00 |

Education Year Emblem, Computer Card — AP153

**1971, Apr. 30    Photo.    Perf. 11½x12**
| | | | |
|---|---|---|---|
| C624 | AP153 | 10p blk, vio & bl | .35 .25 |
| C625 | AP153 | 40p blk, org & yel | .70 .25 |

Intl. Education Year.

Maameltein Bridge AP154

5p, Jamhour Substation. 15p, Hotel Management School. 20p, Litani Dam. 25p, Television set wiring. 35p, Temple of Bziza. 40p, Jounieh Port. 45p, Airport radar. 50p, Flower. 70p, New School of Sciences. 85p, Oranges. 100p, Arbanieh earth satellite station.

**1971, May    Litho.    Perf. 12**
| | | | |
|---|---|---|---|
| C626 | AP154 | 5p multicolored | .25 .25 |
| C627 | AP154 | 10p multicolored | .25 .25 |
| C628 | AP154 | 15p multicolored | .40 .25 |
| C629 | AP154 | 20p multicolored | .70 .25 |
| C630 | AP154 | 25p multicolored | 1.00 .25 |
| C631 | AP154 | 35p multicolored | 1.30 .25 |
| C632 | AP154 | 40p multicolored | 1.30 .25 |
| C633 | AP154 | 45p multicolored | 1.40 .25 |
| C634 | AP154 | 50p multicolored | 2.25 .25 |
| C635 | AP154 | 70p multicolored | 3.25 .25 |
| C636 | AP154 | 85p multicolored | 4.50 .25 |
| C637 | AP154 | 100p multicolored | 5.75 .35 |
| | Nos. C626-C637 (12) | | 22.35 3.10 |

For overprints and surcharges see Nos. C771, C775, C779, 533.

Dahr-el-Bacheq Sanatorium — AP155

**1971, June 1**
| | | | |
|---|---|---|---|
| C638 | AP155 | 50p shown | 1.15 .25 |
| C639 | AP155 | 100p multi, diff. | 1.60 .55 |

Campaign against tuberculosis.

Solar Wheel (Festival Emblem) — AP156

**1971, July 1    Photo.    Perf. 11**
| | | | |
|---|---|---|---|
| C640 | AP156 | 15p ultra & org | .25 .25 |
| C641 | AP156 | 85p Corinthian capital | 1.00 .30 |

16th Baalbek International Festival.

Mirage Fighters Flying Over Baalbek Ruins — AP157

Army Day: 15p, 155mm Cannon. 40p, Army Headquarters. 70p, Naval patrol boat.

**1971, Aug. 1**     *Perf. 12x11½*
| | | | | |
|---|---|---|---|---|
| **C642** | AP157 | 15p gold & multi | 3.00 | .25 |
| **C643** | AP157 | 25p gold & multi | 5.25 | .25 |
| **C644** | AP157 | 40p gold & multi | 7.25 | .25 |
| **C645** | AP157 | 70p gold & multi | 12.00 | .25 |
| | *Nos. C642-C645 (4)* | | 27.50 | 1.00 |

Wooden Console, Al Aqsa Mosque — AP158

**1971, Aug. 21**     *Perf. 12*
| | | | | |
|---|---|---|---|---|
| **C646** | AP158 | 15p dk brn & ocher | .75 | .25 |
| **C647** | AP158 | 35p dk brn & ocher | 1.25 | .25 |

2nd anniversary of the burning of Al Aqsa Mosque in Jerusalem.

Lenin (1870-1924) AP159

**1971, Oct. 1**     *Perf. 12x11½*
| | | | | |
|---|---|---|---|---|
| **C648** | AP159 | 30p gold & multi | .60 | .25 |
| **C649** | AP159 | 70p multicolored | 1.40 | .30 |

UN Emblem, World Map — AP160

**1971, Oct. 24**     *Perf. 13x12½*
| | | | | |
|---|---|---|---|---|
| **C650** | AP160 | 15p multicolored | .35 | .25 |
| **C651** | AP160 | 85p multicolored | 1.15 | .35 |

UN, 25th anniv. (in 1970).

The Rape of Europa, Mosaic from Byblos AP161

**1971, Nov 20**     *Litho.*     *Perf. 12*
| | | | | |
|---|---|---|---|---|
| **C652** | AP161 | 10p slate & multi | .40 | .25 |
| **C653** | AP161 | 40p gold & multi | 2.00 | .25 |

Publicity for World Lebanese Union (ULM).

**Nos. C435-C436 Surcharged**

**Engr.; Engr. & Litho.**
**1972, May**     *Perf. 13, 12*
| | | | | |
|---|---|---|---|---|
| **C654** | AP109 | 100p on 300p | 16.00 | .35 |
| **C655** | AP109 | 100p on 500p | 16.00 | .35 |
| **C656** | AP109 | 200p on 300p | 28.00 | .65 |
| | *Nos. C654-C656 (3)* | | 60.00 | 1.35 |

The numerals on No. C655 are taller (5mm) and bars spaced 1½mm apart.

**No. C554 Surcharged**

**1972, June**    **Litho. & Engr.**    *Perf. 12*
| | | | | |
|---|---|---|---|---|
| **C657** | AP134 | 5p on 7.50p multi | 2.40 | .25 |

Hibiscus — AP162

**1973**     *Litho.*     *Perf. 12*
| | | | | |
|---|---|---|---|---|
| **C658** | AP162 | 2.50p shown | .25 | .25 |
| **C659** | AP162 | 5p Roses | .25 | .25 |
| **C660** | AP162 | 15p Tulips | .35 | .25 |
| **C661** | AP162 | 25p Lilies | .95 | .25 |
| **C662** | AP162 | 40p Carnations | 1.05 | .25 |
| **C663** | AP162 | 50p Iris | 1.50 | .25 |
| **C664** | AP162 | 70p Apples | 1.15 | .25 |
| **C665** | AP162 | 75p Grapes | 1.30 | .25 |
| **C666** | AP162 | 100p Peaches | 1.75 | .35 |
| **C667** | AP162 | 200p Pears | 6.25 | .25 |
| **C668** | AP162 | 300p Cherries | 6.75 | .55 |
| **C669** | AP162 | 500p Oranges | 11.00 | .90 |
| | *Nos. C658-C669 (12)* | | 32.55 | 4.05 |

For overprints see Nos. C758-C759, C763, C766, C769, C772, C776, C778, C782, C785-C787.

Lebanese House — AP163

Designs: Old Lebanese houses.

**1973**     *Perf. 14*
| | | | | |
|---|---|---|---|---|
| **C670** | AP163 | 35p yel & multi | 2.00 | .25 |
| **C671** | AP163 | 50p lt bl & multi | 3.00 | .25 |
| **C672** | AP163 | 85p buff & multi | 4.75 | .25 |
| **C673** | AP163 | 100p multicolored | 6.25 | .35 |
| | *Nos. C670-C673 (4)* | | 16.00 | 1.10 |

For overprints see Nos. C768, C773, C780, C783.

Woman with Rose — AP164

Lebanese Costumes: 10p, Man. 20p, Man on horseback. 25p, Woman playing mandolin.

**1973, Sept. 1**     *Litho.*     *Perf. 14*
| | | | | |
|---|---|---|---|---|
| **C674** | AP164 | 5p yellow & multi | .70 | .25 |
| **C675** | AP164 | 10p yellow & multi | 2.00 | .25 |
| **C676** | AP164 | 20p yellow & multi | 3.25 | .25 |
| **C677** | AP164 | 25p yellow & multi | 4.50 | .25 |
| | *Nos. C674-C677 (4)* | | 10.45 | 1.00 |

For overprints see Nos. C760-C761, C764, C767.

Swimming, Temple at Baalbek AP165

Designs: 10p, Running and portal. 15p, Woman athlete and castle. 20p, Women's volleyball and columns. 25p, Basketball and aqueduct. 50p, Women's table tennis and buildings. 75p, Handball and building. 100p, Soccer and cedar.

**1973, Sept. 25**    **Photo.**    *Perf. 11½x12*
| | | | | |
|---|---|---|---|---|
| **C678** | AP165 | 5p multicolored | .25 | .25 |
| **C679** | AP165 | 10p multicolored | .25 | .25 |
| **C680** | AP165 | 15p grn & multi | .30 | .25 |
| **C681** | AP165 | 20p multicolored | .30 | .25 |
| **C682** | AP165 | 25p ultra & multi | .40 | .25 |
| **C683** | AP165 | 50p org & multi | 1.00 | .25 |
| **C684** | AP165 | 75p vio & multi | 1.20 | .35 |
| **C685** | AP165 | 100p multicolored | 2.25 | .65 |
| **a.** | | Souvenir sheet | 3.00 | 1.40 |
| | *Nos. C678-C685 (8)* | | 5.95 | 2.50 |

5th Pan-Arabic Scholastic Games, Beirut. No. C685a contains one stamp with simulated perforations similar to No. C685; gold inscription and denomination.

View of Brasilia AP166

20p, Old Salvador (Bahia). 25p, Lebanese sailing ship enroute from the Old World to South America. 50p, Dom Pedro I & Emir Fakhr al-Din II.

**1973, Nov. 15**    **Litho.**    *Perf. 12*
| | | | | |
|---|---|---|---|---|
| **C686** | AP166 | 5p gold & multi | .35 | .25 |
| **C687** | AP166 | 20p gold & multi | 1.75 | .30 |
| **C688** | AP166 | 25p gold & multi | 1.75 | .30 |
| **C689** | AP166 | 50p gold & multi | 4.00 | .55 |
| | *Nos. C686-C689 (4)* | | 7.85 | 1.40 |

Sesquicentennial of Brazil's independence.

Inlay Worker — AP167

**1973, Dec. 1**
| | | | | |
|---|---|---|---|---|
| **C690** | AP167 | 10p shown | .65 | .25 |
| **C691** | AP167 | 20p Weaver | 1.00 | .25 |
| **C692** | AP167 | 35p Glass blower | 1.60 | .30 |
| **C693** | AP167 | 40p Potter | 2.25 | .40 |
| **C694** | AP167 | 50p Metal worker | 2.40 | .40 |
| **C695** | AP167 | 70p Cutlery maker | 4.00 | .55 |
| **C696** | AP167 | 85p Lace maker | 5.75 | .80 |
| **C697** | AP167 | 100p Handicraft Museum | 6.50 | 1.15 |
| | *Nos. C690-C697 (8)* | | 24.15 | 4.10 |

Lebanese handicrafts.
For overprints see Nos. C762, C765, C770, C774, C777, C781, C784.

Camp Site, Log Fire and Scout Emblem AP168

Designs: 5p, Lebanese Scout emblem and map. 7½p, Lebanese Scout emblem and map of Middle East. 10p, Lord Baden-Powell, ruins of Baalbek. 15p, Girl Guide, camp and emblem. 20p, Lebanese Girl Guide and Scout emblems. 25p, Scouts around camp fire. 30p, Symbolic globe with Lebanese flag and Scout emblem. 35p, Flags of participating nations. 50p, Old man, and Scout chopping wood.

**1974, Aug. 24**    **Litho.**    *Perf. 12*
| | | | | |
|---|---|---|---|---|
| **C698** | AP168 | 2.50p multi | .60 | .25 |
| **C699** | AP168 | 5p multi | .60 | .25 |
| **C700** | AP168 | 7.50p multi | 1.15 | .25 |
| **C701** | AP168 | 10p multi | 1.15 | .25 |
| **C702** | AP168 | 15p multi | 1.40 | .45 |
| **a.** | | Vert. strip of 5, #C698-C702 | 5.75 | |
| **C703** | AP168 | 20p multi | 2.00 | .55 |
| **C704** | AP168 | 25p multi | 3.00 | .55 |
| **C705** | AP168 | 30p multi | 4.00 | .55 |
| **C706** | AP168 | 35p multi | 4.75 | .75 |
| **C707** | AP168 | 50p multi | 5.75 | 1.15 |
| **a.** | | Vert. strip of 5, #C703-C707 | 20.00 | |
| | *Nos. C698-C707 (10)* | | 24.40 | 5.00 |

11th Arab Boy Scout Jamboree, Smar-Jubeil, Aug. 1974. Nos. C702-C703 are for the 5th Girl Guide Jamboree, Deir-el-Kamar.

Mail Train and Postman Loading Mail, UPU Emblem AP169

UPU Emblem and: 20p, Postal container hoisted onto ship. 25p, Postal Union Congress Building, Lausanne, and UPU Headquarters, Bern. 50p, Fork-lift truck loading mail on plane.

**1974, Nov. 4**    **Photo.**    *Perf. 11½x12*
| | | | | |
|---|---|---|---|---|
| **C708** | AP169 | 5p multicolored | .40 | .25 |
| **C709** | AP169 | 20p multicolored | 1.60 | .25 |
| **C710** | AP169 | 25p multicolored | 2.40 | .25 |
| **C711** | AP169 | 50p ultra & multi | 5.00 | .60 |
| | *Nos. C708-C711 (4)* | | 9.40 | 1.35 |

Centenary of Universal Postal Union.

Congress Building, Sofar — AP170

Arab Postal Union Emblem and: 20p, View of Sofar. 25p, APU Headquarters, Cairo. 50p, Ministry of Post, Beirut.

**1974, Dec. 4**    **Litho.**    *Perf. 13x12½*
| | | | | |
|---|---|---|---|---|
| **C712** | AP170 | 5p orange & multi | .30 | .25 |
| **C713** | AP170 | 20p yellow & multi | .50 | .25 |
| **C714** | AP170 | 25p blue & multi | .75 | .25 |
| **C715** | AP170 | 50p multicolored | 3.50 | .80 |
| | *Nos. C712-C715 (4)* | | 5.05 | 1.55 |

Arab Postal Union, 25th anniversary.

Mountain Road, by Omar Onsi — AP171

Paintings by Lebanese artists: No. C717, Clouds, by Moustapha Farroukh. No. C718, Woman, by Gebran Kahlil Gebran. No. C719, Embrace, by Cesar Gemayel. No. C720, Self-portrait, by Habib Serour. No. C721, Portrait of a Man, by Daoud Corm.

**1974, Dec. 6**    **Litho.**    *Perf. 13x12½*
| | | | | |
|---|---|---|---|---|
| **C716** | AP171 | 50p lilac & multi | 1.60 | .40 |
| **C717** | AP171 | 50p blue & multi | 1.60 | .40 |
| **C718** | AP171 | 50p green & multi | 1.60 | .40 |
| **C719** | AP171 | 50p lt vio & multi | 1.60 | .40 |
| **C720** | AP171 | 50p brown & multi | 1.60 | .40 |
| **C721** | AP171 | 50p gray brn & multi | 1.60 | .40 |
| | *Nos. C716-C721 (6)* | | 9.60 | 2.40 |

Hunter Spearing Lion — AP172

Excavations at Hermel: 10p, Statue of Astarte. 25p, Dogs hunting boar, tiled panel. 35p, Greco-Roman tomb.

**1974, Dec. 13**
| | | | | |
|---|---|---|---|---|
| **C722** | AP172 | 5p blue & multi | .35 | .25 |
| **C723** | AP172 | 10p lilac & multi | .80 | .25 |
| **C724** | AP172 | 25p multicolored | 1.90 | .25 |
| **C725** | AP172 | 35p multicolored | 2.40 | .35 |
| | *Nos. C722-C725 (4)* | | 5.45 | 1.10 |

UNESCO Emblems and Globe — AP173

**1974, Dec. 16**     *Perf. 12½x13*
| | | | | |
|---|---|---|---|---|
| **C726** | AP173 | 5p violet & multi | .35 | .25 |
| **C727** | AP173 | 10p bister & multi | .75 | .25 |
| **C728** | AP173 | 25p blue & multi | 1.75 | .25 |
| **C729** | AP173 | 35p multicolored | 2.25 | .35 |
| | *Nos. C726-C729 (4)* | | 5.10 | 1.10 |

International Book Year.

Symbolic Stamp under Magnifying Glass — AP174

Designs (Symbolic): 10p, Post horns. 15p, Stamp printing. 20p, Mounted stamp.

**1974, Dec. 20**     *Perf. 13x12½*
| | | | | |
|---|---|---|---|---|
| **C730** | AP174 | 5p blue & multi | .25 | .25 |
| **C731** | AP174 | 10p olive & multi | .35 | .25 |
| **C732** | AP174 | 15p brown & multi | .75 | .25 |
| **C733** | AP174 | 20p lilac & multi | .90 | .25 |
| | *Nos. C730-C733 (4)* | | 2.25 | 1.00 |

Georgina Rizk — AP175

5p, 25p, Georgina Rizk in Lebanese costume.

**1974, Dec. 21**
| | | | | |
|---|---|---|---|---|
| C734 | AP175 | 5p multicolored | .25 | .25 |
| C735 | AP175 | 20p violet & multi | .50 | .25 |
| C736 | AP175 | 25p yellow & multi | .70 | .25 |
| C737 | AP175 | 50p blue & multi | 1.35 | .25 |
| a. | | Souvenir sheet of 4 | 7.25 | 4.00 |
| | | Nos. C734-C737 (4) | 2.80 | 1.00 |

Georgina Rizk, Miss Universe 1971. No. C737a contains 4 stamps similar to Nos. C734-C737 with simulated perforations.

UNICEF Emblem, Helicopter, Camel, Supplies AP176

UNICEF Emblem and: 25p, Child welfare clinic. 35p, Kindergarten class. 70p, Girls in chemistry laboratory.

**1974, Dec. 28 Litho. Perf. 12½x13**
| | | | | |
|---|---|---|---|---|
| C738 | AP176 | 20p multicolored | .25 | .25 |
| C739 | AP176 | 25p multicolored | .25 | .25 |
| C740 | AP176 | 35p blue & multi | .70 | .25 |
| C741 | AP176 | 70p blue & multi | 1.60 | .25 |
| a. | | Souvenir sheet of 4 | 5.50 | 2.90 |
| | | Nos. C738-C741 (4) | 2.80 | 1.00 |

UNICEF, 25th anniv. No. C741a contains 4 stamps similar to Nos. C738-C741 with simulated perforations. Sold for 200p.

Discus and Olympic Rings — AP177

**1974, Dec. 30 Perf. 13x12½**
| | | | | |
|---|---|---|---|---|
| C742 | AP177 | 5p shown | .25 | .25 |
| C743 | AP177 | 10p Shot put | .30 | .25 |
| C744 | AP177 | 15p Weight lifting | .40 | .25 |
| C745 | AP177 | 35p Running | .80 | .25 |
| C746 | AP177 | 70p Wrestling | 1.15 | .25 |
| C747 | AP177 | 85p Javelin | 1.90 | .35 |
| a. | | Souvenir sheet of 6 | 7.50 | 5.00 |
| | | Nos. C742-C747 (6) | 4.80 | 1.60 |

20th Olympic Games, Munich, Aug. 26-Sept. 11, 1972. No. C747a contains 6 stamps similar to Nos. C742-C747 with simulated perforations.

Clouds and Environment Emblem — AP178

**1975**
| | | | | |
|---|---|---|---|---|
| C748 | AP178 | 5p shown | .25 | .25 |
| C749 | AP178 | 25p Landscape | .50 | .25 |
| C750 | AP178 | 30p Flowers and tree | .50 | .25 |
| C751 | AP178 | 40p Waves | .75 | .25 |
| a. | | Souvenir sheet of 4 | 6.50 | 4.50 |
| | | Nos. C748-C751 (4) | 2.00 | 1.00 |

UN Conf. on Human Environment, Stockholm, June 5-16, 1972. No. C751a contains four stamps similar to Nos. C748-C751 with simulated perforations. Sold for 150p.

Archaeology AP179

Symbols of: 25p, Science & medicine. 35p, Justice & commerce. 70p, Industry & commerce.

**1975, Aug. Litho. Perf. 12½x13**
| | | | | |
|---|---|---|---|---|
| C752 | AP179 | 20p multicolored | .80 | .25 |
| C753 | AP179 | 25p multicolored | 1.15 | .25 |
| C754 | AP179 | 35p blue & multi | 1.60 | .40 |
| C755 | AP179 | 70p buff & multi | 3.50 | .70 |
| | | Nos. C752-C755 (4) | 7.05 | 1.60 |

Beirut, University City.

Stamps of 1971-73 Ovptd. with Various Overall Patterns Including Cedars in Blue, Red, Orange, Lilac, Brown or Green

**1978 Litho. Perf. 12, 14**
| | | | | |
|---|---|---|---|---|
| C758 | AP162 | 2.50p (#C658;B) | .30 | .25 |
| C759 | AP162 | 5p (#C659;R) | .30 | .25 |
| C760 | AP164 | 5p (#C674;B) | .30 | .25 |
| C761 | AP164 | 10p (#C675;B) | .30 | .25 |
| C762 | AP167 | 10p (#C690;O) | .30 | .25 |
| C763 | AP162 | 15p (#C660;R) | 1.10 | .25 |
| C764 | AP164 | 20p (#C676;B) | .75 | .25 |
| C765 | AP167 | 20p (#C691;B) | .75 | .25 |
| C766 | AP162 | 25p (#C661;R) | .75 | .25 |
| C767 | AP164 | 25p (#C677;B) | 1.50 | .25 |
| C768 | AP163 | 35p (#C670;Br) | 1.75 | .25 |
| C769 | AP162 | 40p (#C662;L) | 1.75 | .25 |
| C770 | AP167 | 40p (#C693;G) | 1.75 | .25 |
| C771 | AP154 | 45p (#C633;L) | 1.75 | .25 |
| C772 | AP162 | 50p (#C663;L) | 2.60 | .25 |
| C773 | AP163 | 50p (#C671;L) | 2.60 | .25 |
| C774 | AP167 | 50p (#C694;Br) | 2.60 | .25 |
| C775 | AP154 | 70p (#C635;L) | 3.00 | .55 |
| C776 | AP162 | 70p (#C664;L) | 3.00 | .55 |
| C777 | AP167 | 70p (#C695;Br) | 3.00 | .55 |
| C778 | AP167 | 75p (#C665;Br) | 4.75 | .55 |
| C779 | AP154 | 85p (#C636;R) | 3.50 | .60 |
| C780 | AP163 | 85p (#C672;R) | 3.50 | .60 |
| C781 | AP167 | 85p (#C696;G) | 3.50 | .60 |
| C782 | AP162 | 100p (#C666;O) | 5.50 | .80 |
| C783 | AP163 | 100p (#C673;R) | 5.50 | .80 |
| C784 | AP167 | 100p (#C697;L) | 5.50 | .80 |
| C785 | AP162 | 200p (#C667;O) | 11.00 | 2.75 |
| C786 | AP162 | 300p (#C668;O) | 15.50 | 5.25 |
| C787 | AP162 | 500p (#C669;O) | 22.00 | 7.50 |
| | | Nos. C758-C787 (30) | 110.40 | 26.15 |

Heart and Arrow — AP180

**1978, Apr. 7 Litho. Perf. 12**
| | | | | |
|---|---|---|---|---|
| C788 | AP180 | 50p blue, blk & red | 1.10 | .80 |

World Health Day; drive against hypertension.

Poet Mikhail Naimy and Sannine Mountains — AP181

Designs: 50p, Naimy and view of Al Chakhroub Baskinta. 75p, Naimy portrait in sunburst, vert.

**1978, May 17**
| | | | | |
|---|---|---|---|---|
| C789 | AP181 | 25p gold & multi | .75 | .25 |
| C790 | AP181 | 50p gold & multi | 1.30 | .45 |
| C791 | AP181 | 75p gold & multi | 2.00 | .65 |
| | | Nos. C789-C791 (3) | 4.05 | 1.35 |

Mikhail Naimy Festival.

**Army Day Type of 1980**

Designs: 50p, Emir Fakhr al-Din statue, vert. 75p, Soldiers and flag.

**1980, Dec. 28 Litho. Perf. 11½**
| | | | | |
|---|---|---|---|---|
| C792 | A86 | 50p multicolored | 1.20 | .25 |
| C793 | A86 | 75p multicolored | 1.60 | .35 |

28th UPU Congress, Rio de Janeiro, 1979 — AP182

**1981, Feb. 17 Photo. Perf. 12x11½**
| | | | | |
|---|---|---|---|---|
| C794 | AP182 | 25p multicolored | .95 | .25 |
| C795 | AP182 | 50p multicolored | 2.10 | .65 |
| C796 | AP182 | 75p multicolored | 3.00 | .90 |
| | | Nos. C794-C796 (3) | 6.05 | 1.80 |

Intl. Year of the Child (1979) — AP183

**1981, Mar. 25 Litho. Perf. 12x11½**
| | | | | |
|---|---|---|---|---|
| C797 | AP183 | 100p multicolored | 4.00 | 1.25 |

1974 Chess Championships AP184

Various chess pieces. Nos. C799-C802 vert.

**Perf. 12x11½, 11½x12**
**1980-81 Photo.**
| | | | | |
|---|---|---|---|---|
| C798 | AP184 | 50p multicolored | 1.90 | .65 |
| C799 | AP184 | 75p multicolored | 2.25 | .85 |
| C800 | AP184 | 100p multicolored | 2.75 | 1.25 |
| C801 | AP184 | 150p multicolored | 4.50 | 2.40 |
| C802 | AP184 | 200p multicolored | 5.75 | 3.25 |
| | | Nos. C798-C802 (5) | 17.15 | 8.40 |

Makassed Islamic Institute Centenary (1978) — AP185

**1981 Photo. Perf. 13½x14**
| | | | | |
|---|---|---|---|---|
| C803 | AP185 | 50p Children | .80 | .25 |
| C804 | AP185 | 75p Institute | 1.20 | .25 |
| C805 | AP185 | 100p Makassed | 1.40 | .35 |
| | | Nos. C803-C805 (3) | 3.40 | .85 |

## AIR POST SEMI-POSTAL STAMPS

**Nos. C13-C16 Surcharged Like Nos. B1-B12**

**1926 Perf. 13½**
| | | | | |
|---|---|---|---|---|
| CB1 | A2 | 1p + 2p dk brn | 15.00 | 8.00 |
| CB2 | A2 | 2p + 3p org brn | 15.00 | 8.00 |
| CB3 | A2 | 3p + 5p violet | 15.00 | 8.00 |
| CB4 | A3 | 5p + 10p vio brn | 15.00 | 8.00 |
| | | Nos. CB1-CB4 (4) | 60.00 | 32.00 |

These stamps were sold for their combined values, original and surcharged. The latter represented their postal franking value and the former was a contribution to the relief of refugees from the Djebel Druze War.

Catalogue values for unused stamps in this section, from this point to the end of the section, are for Never Hinged items.

**Independent Republic**

Natural Bridge, Faraya — SPAP1

Bay of Jounie — SPAP2

**Perf. 11½**
**1947, June 27 Unwmk. Litho.**
**Cross in Carmine**
| | | | | |
|---|---|---|---|---|
| CB5 | SPAP1 | 12.50 + 25p brt bl grn | 13.50 | 3.75 |
| CB6 | SPAP1 | 25 + 50pi blue | 17.00 | 4.50 |
| CB7 | SPAP2 | 50 + 100pi choc | 20.00 | 5.25 |
| CB8 | SPAP2 | 75 + 150pi brt pur | 40.00 | 10.00 |
| CB9 | SPAP2 | 100 + 200pi sl | 75.00 | 14.00 |
| | | Nos. CB5-CB9 (5) | 165.50 | 37.50 |

The surtax was for the Red Cross.

**Mother & Child Type of Air Post Stamps, 1960**

**1960, Aug. 16 Perf. 13½x13**
| | | | | |
|---|---|---|---|---|
| CB10 | AP72 | 20p + 10p dk red & buff | .90 | .25 |
| CB11 | AP72 | 60p + 15p bl & lt bl | 2.25 | .55 |

**Olympic Games Type of Semi-Postal Issue, 1961**

**1961, Jan. 12 Unwmk. Perf. 13**
| | | | | |
|---|---|---|---|---|
| CB12 | SP1 | 15p + 15p Fencing | 3.25 | 1.25 |
| CB13 | SP1 | 25p + 25p Bicycling | 3.25 | 1.25 |
| CB14 | SP1 | 35p + 35p Swimming | 3.25 | 1.25 |
| | | Nos. CB12-CB14 (3) | 9.75 | 3.75 |

An imperf. souvenir sheet exists, containing one each of Nos. CB12-CB14. Value $32.50.

**Nos. CB12-CB14 with Arabic and French Overprint in Green, Red or Maroon**

**1962, June 2**
| | | | | |
|---|---|---|---|---|
| CB15 | SP1 | 15p + 15p (G) | 1.25 | .50 |
| CB16 | SP1 | 25p + 25p (M) | 2.00 | 1.00 |
| CB17 | SP1 | 35p + 35p (R) | 2.40 | 1.25 |
| | | Nos. CB15-CB17 (3) | 5.65 | 2.75 |

European Marksmanship Championships held in Lebanon.

## POSTAGE DUE STAMPS

**Postage Due Stamps of France, 1893-1920, Surcharged like Regular Issue**

**1924 Unwmk. Perf. 14x13½**
| | | | | |
|---|---|---|---|---|
| J1 | D2 | 50c on 10c choc | 6.75 | 4.25 |
| J2 | D2 | 1p on 20c ol grn | 6.75 | 4.25 |
| J3 | D2 | 2p on 30c red | 6.75 | 4.25 |
| J4 | D2 | 3p on 50c vio brn | 6.75 | 4.25 |
| J5 | D2 | 5p on 1fr red brn, straw | 6.75 | 4.25 |
| | | Nos. J1-J5 (5) | 33.75 | 21.25 |

Postage Due Stamps of France, 1893-1920, Surcharged

**1924**
| | | | | |
|---|---|---|---|---|
| J6 | D2 | 0.50p on 10c choc | 7.25 | 4.00 |
| J7 | D2 | 1p on 20c ol grn | 7.25 | 4.00 |
| J8 | D2 | 2p on 30c red | 7.25 | 4.00 |
| J9 | D2 | 3p on 50c vio brn | 7.25 | 4.00 |
| J10 | D2 | 5p on 1fr red brn, straw | 7.25 | 4.00 |
| | | Nos. J6-J10 (5) | 36.25 | 20.00 |

Ancient Bridge across Dog River — D3

Designs: 1p, Village scene. 2p, Pigeon Rocks, near Beirut. 3p, Belfort Castle. 5p, Venus Temple at Baalbek.

**1925 Photo. Perf. 13½**
| | | | | |
|---|---|---|---|---|
| J11 | D3 | 0.50p brown, yellow | .95 | .45 |
| J12 | D3 | 1p violet, rose | 1.35 | .65 |
| J13 | D3 | 2p black, blue | 2.25 | .90 |
| J14 | D3 | 3p black, red org | 3.50 | 2.00 |
| J15 | D3 | 5p black, bl grn | 5.75 | 3.75 |
| | | Nos. J11-J15 (5) | 13.80 | 7.75 |
| | | Set, never hinged | 42.50 | |

Nos. J11 to J15 Overprinted

## 1927

| | | | | | |
|---|---|---|---|---|---|
| J16 | D3 | 0.50p brown, *yellow* | 1.50 | .40 |
| J17 | D3 | 1p violet, *rose* | 2.50 | .85 |
| J18 | D3 | 2p black, *blue* | 3.50 | 1.25 |
| J19 | D3 | 3p black, *red org* | 7.25 | 3.00 |
| J20 | D3 | 5p black, *bl grn* | 9.50 | 4.50 |
| | | *Nos. J16-J20 (5)* | 24.25 | 10.00 |
| | | Set, never hinged | 35.00 | |

Nos. J16-J20 with
Additional Ovpt.

## 1928

| | | | | |
|---|---|---|---|---|
| J21 | D3 | 0.50p brn, *yel* (Bk+R) | 1.75 | 1.25 |
| J22 | D3 | 1p vio, *rose* (Bk) | 1.75 | 1.25 |
| J23 | D3 | 2p blk, *bl* (Bk+R) | 3.00 | 2.00 |
| J24 | D3 | 3p blk, *red org* (Bk) | 6.00 | 3.50 |
| J25 | D3 | 5p blk, *bl grn* (Bk+R) | 6.75 | 4.25 |
| | | *Nos. J21-J25 (5)* | 19.25 | 12.25 |
| | | Set, never hinged | 65.00 | |

No. J23 has not the short bars in the upper corners.

### Postage Due Stamps of 1925 Overprinted in Red like Nos. J21-J25

## 1928

| | | | | |
|---|---|---|---|---|
| J26 | D3 | 0.50p brn, *yel* (R) | 1.00 | .50 |
| J27 | D3 | 2p blk, *bl* (R) | 4.25 | 3.50 |
| J28 | D3 | 5p blk, *bl grn* (R) | 11.50 | 7.50 |
| | | *Nos. J26-J28 (3)* | 16.75 | 11.50 |
| | | Set, never hinged | 32.50 | |

No. J28 has not the short bars in the upper corners.

Bas-relief of a
Ship — D5

D6

D7

D8

Bas-relief from
Sarcophagus of
King
Ahiram — D9

D10

## 1930-40    Photo.; Engr. (No. J35)

| | | | | |
|---|---|---|---|---|
| J29 | D4 | 0.50p black, *brt rose* | .75 | .50 |
| J30 | D5 | 1p blk, *gray bl* | 1.25 | 1.00 |
| J31 | D6 | 2p blk, *yellow* | 1.75 | 1.25 |
| J32 | D7 | 3p blk, *bl grn* | 1.75 | 1.25 |
| J33 | D8 | 5p blk, *orange* | 7.25 | 5.50 |
| J34 | D9 | 8p blk, *lt rose* | 5.00 | 3.50 |
| J35 | D8 | 10p dk green ('40) | 7.75 | 4.50 |
| J36 | D10 | 15p black | 6.75 | 2.75 |
| | | *Nos. J29-J36 (8)* | 32.25 | 20.25 |
| | | Set, never hinged | 65.00 | |

Nos. J29-J36 exist imperf.

> **Catalogue values for unused stamps in this section, from this point to the end of the section, are for Never Hinged items.**

---

### Independent Republic

National Museum,
Beirut — D11

## 1945    Unwmk.    Litho.    *Perf. 11½*

| | | | | |
|---|---|---|---|---|
| J37 | D11 | 2p brn black, *yel* | 8.25 | 2.00 |
| J38 | D11 | 5p ultra, *rose* | 10.00 | 2.50 |
| J39 | D11 | 25p blue, *bl green* | 14.00 | 4.00 |
| J40 | D11 | 50p dark bl, *blue* | 17.50 | 6.00 |
| | | *Nos. J37-J40 (4)* | 49.75 | 14.50 |

D12

## 1947

| | | | | |
|---|---|---|---|---|
| J41 | D12 | 5p black, *green* | 6.00 | 1.25 |
| J42 | D12 | 25p blk, *yellow* | 62.50 | 3.50 |
| J43 | D12 | 50p black, *blue* | 30.00 | 6.00 |
| | | *Nos. J41-J43 (3)* | 98.50 | 10.75 |

Hermel
Monument — D13

## 1948

| | | | | |
|---|---|---|---|---|
| J44 | D13 | 2p blk, *yellow* | 4.75 | 3.75 |
| J45 | D13 | 3p black, *brt rose* | 9.00 | 3.00 |
| J46 | D13 | 10p black, *blue* | 22.50 | 5.50 |
| | | *Nos. J44-J46 (3)* | 36.25 | 12.25 |

D14

## 1950

| | | | | |
|---|---|---|---|---|
| J47 | D14 | 1p brt carmine | 3.50 | .30 |
| J48 | D14 | 5p violet blue | 13.00 | .60 |
| J49 | D14 | 10p gray green | 27.50 | 1.50 |
| | | *Nos. J47-J49 (3)* | 44.00 | 2.40 |

D15

## 1952

| | | | | |
|---|---|---|---|---|
| J50 | D15 | 1p carmine | .75 | .30 |
| J51 | D15 | 2p bright violet | .75 | .30 |
| J52 | D15 | 3p dk blue green | 1.50 | .30 |
| J53 | D15 | 5p blue | 2.00 | .35 |
| J54 | D15 | 10p chocolate | 2.75 | .55 |
| J55 | D15 | 25p black | 20.00 | 1.25 |
| | | *Nos. J50-J55 (6)* | 27.75 | 3.05 |

D16

## 1953

| | | | | |
|---|---|---|---|---|
| J56 | D16 | 1p carmine red | .35 | .30 |
| J57 | D16 | 2p blue green | .35 | .30 |
| J58 | D16 | 3p orange | .35 | .30 |
| J59 | D16 | 5p lilac rose | .60 | .30 |
| J60 | D16 | 10p brown | .95 | .35 |
| J61 | D16 | 15p deep blue | 2.00 | .75 |
| | | *Nos. J56-J61 (6)* | 4.60 | 2.30 |

D17

## 1955    Unwmk.    *Perf. 13*

| | | | | |
|---|---|---|---|---|
| J62 | D17 | 1p orange brown | .40 | .25 |
| J63 | D17 | 2p yellow green | .40 | .25 |
| J64 | D17 | 3p blue green | .40 | .25 |
| J65 | D17 | 5p carmine lake | .40 | .25 |
| J66 | D17 | 10p gray green | .60 | .25 |
| J67 | D17 | 15p ultramarine | .70 | .30 |
| J68 | D17 | 25p red lilac | 1.50 | .80 |
| | | *Nos. J62-J68 (7)* | 4.40 | 2.35 |

---

Cedar of Lebanon — D18

## 1966    Photo.    *Perf. 11½*

| | | | | |
|---|---|---|---|---|
| J69 | D18 | 1p bright green | .60 | .25 |
| J70 | D18 | 5p rose lilac | .60 | .25 |
| J71 | D18 | 15p ultramarine | .75 | .55 |
| | | *Nos. J69-J71 (3)* | 1.95 | 1.05 |

Emir Fakhr al-Din II — D19

## 1968    Litho.    *Perf. 11*

| | | | | |
|---|---|---|---|---|
| J72 | D19 | 1p dk & lt gray | .50 | .25 |
| J73 | D19 | 2p dk & lt blue grn | .50 | .25 |
| J74 | D19 | 3p deep org & yel | .50 | .25 |
| J75 | D19 | 5p brt rose lil & pink | .50 | .25 |
| J76 | D19 | 10p olive & lemon | .50 | .25 |
| J77 | D19 | 15p vio & pale violet | .75 | .40 |
| J78 | D19 | 25p brt & lt blue | 1.25 | 1.00 |
| | | *Nos. J72-J78 (7)* | 4.50 | 2.65 |

---

## POSTAL TAX STAMPS

Fiscal Stamp
Surcharged in Violet

### Wmk. A T 39 Multiple

## 1945            *Perf. 13½*

| | | | | |
|---|---|---|---|---|
| RA1 | R1 | 5pi on 30c red brn | 475.00 | 3.00 |

The tax was for the Lebanese Army.

No. RA1 Overprinted in
Black

## 1948

| | | | | |
|---|---|---|---|---|
| RA2 | R1 | 5pi on 30c red brn | 20.00 | 2.50 |

Fiscal Stamps
Surcharged in Various
Colors

| | | | | |
|---|---|---|---|---|
| RA3 | R1 | 5pi on 15p dk vio bl (R) | 22.50 | 1.60 |
| a. | | Brown surcharge | 52.50 | 4.50 |
| RA4 | R1 | 5pi on 25c dk blue green (R) | 22.50 | 2.00 |
| RA5 | R1 | 5pi on 30c red brn (Bl) | 29.00 | 4.00 |
| RA6 | R1 | 5pi on 60c lt ultra (Br) | 47.50 | 3.00 |
| RA7 | R1 | 5pi on 3pi salmon rose (Ult) | 22.50 | 3.75 |

No RA4 exists with watermarks "AT37" or "AT38."

Same With Additional
Overprint

| | | | | |
|---|---|---|---|---|
| RA8 | R1 | 5pi on 10pi red | 95.00 | 6.50 |

---

Fiscal Stamp
Surcharged Like Nos.
RA3-RA7 with Top
Arabic Characters
Replaced by

| | | | | |
|---|---|---|---|---|
| RA9 | R1 | 5pi on 3pi rose (Bk+V) | 20.00 | 2.10 |

Fiscal Stamp
Surcharged in Black
and Violet

| | | | | |
|---|---|---|---|---|
| RA10 | R1 | 5pi on 3pi sal rose | *360.00* | 25.00 |

The tax was to aid the war in Palestine.

> **Catalogue values for unused stamps in this section, from this point to the end of the section, are for Never Hinged items.**

Family among Ruins — R2

## 1956    Unwmk.    Litho.    *Perf. 13*

| | | | |
|---|---|---|---|
| RA11 | R2 | 2.50pi brown | 5.00 | .25 |

The tax was for earthquake victims. These stamps were obligatory on all inland mail and all mail going to Arab countries.

Building a House — R3

## 1957-58         *Perf. 13½x13*

| | | | | |
|---|---|---|---|---|
| RA12 | R3 | 2.50p dk brown | 4.25 | .25 |
| RA13 | R3 | 2.50p dk blue grn ('58) | 2.50 | .25 |

### Type of 1957 Redrawn

## 1959

| | | | | |
|---|---|---|---|---|
| RA14 | R3 | 2.50p light brown | 2.75 | .25 |

On No. RA14 the denomination is on top and the Arabic lines are at the bottom of design.

R4

## 1961    Unwmk.      *Perf. 13½x13*

| | | | | |
|---|---|---|---|---|
| RA15 | R4 | 2.50p yellow brown | 2.50 | .25 |

Building a House — R5

## 1962         *Perf. 13½x14*

| | | | | |
|---|---|---|---|---|
| RA16 | R5 | 2.50p blue green | 2.50 | .25 |

The tax was for the relief of earthquake victims.

# LEEWARD ISLANDS

'lē-wərd 'ī-ləndz

LOCATION — A group of islands in the West Indies, southeast of Puerto Rico
GOVT. — British Colony
AREA — 423 sq. mi.
POP. — 108,847 (1946)
CAPITAL — St. John

While stamps inscribed "Leeward Islands" were in use, 1890-1956, the colony consisted of the presidencies (now colonies) of Antigua, Montserrat, St. Christopher (St. Kitts) with Nevis and Anguilla, the British Virgin Islands and Dominica (which became a separate colony in 1940).

Each presidency issued its own stamps, using them along with the Leeward Islands general issues. The Leeward Islands federation was abolished in 1956.

12 Pence = 1 Shilling
20 Shillings = 1 Pound
100 Cents = 1 Dollar

**Catalogue values for unused stamps in this country are for Never Hinged items, beginning with Scott 116.**

Queen Victoria — A1

| 1890 | | Typo. | Wmk. 2 | Perf. 14 | |
|---|---|---|---|---|---|
| 1 | A1 | ½p lilac & green | | 3.75 | 1.40 |
| 2 | A1 | 1p lilac & car | | 8.75 | .25 |
| 3 | A1 | 2½p lilac & ultra | | 9.50 | .30 |
| 4 | A1 | 4p lilac & org | | 12.00 | 9.50 |
| 5 | A1 | 6p lilac & brown | | 13.50 | 15.50 |
| 6 | A1 | 7p lilac & slate | | 12.00 | 21.00 |
| 7 | A1 | 1sh green & car | | 24.00 | 62.50 |
| 8 | A1 | 5sh green & ultra | | 145.00 | 330.00 |
| | | Nos. 1-8 (8) | | 228.50 | 440.45 |

Denomination of Nos. 7-8 are in color on plain tablet: "ONE SHILLING" or "FIVE SHILLINGS."
For overprints and surcharges see Nos. 9-19.

## Jubilee Issue

Regular Issue of 1890 Handstamp Overprinted

| 1897, July 22 | | | | |
|---|---|---|---|---|
| 9 | A1 | ½p lilac & green | 8.25 | 26.00 |
| 10 | A1 | 1p lilac & car | 9.25 | 26.00 |
| 11 | A1 | 2½p lilac & ultra | 9.75 | 26.00 |
| 12 | A1 | 4p lilac & org | 57.50 | 80.00 |
| 13 | A1 | 6p lilac & brown | 62.50 | 130.00 |
| 14 | A1 | 7p lilac & slate | 62.50 | 130.00 |
| 15 | A1 | 1sh green & car | 130.00 | 275.00 |
| 16 | A1 | 5sh green & ultra | 525.00 | 850.00 |
| | | Nos. 9-16 (8) | 864.75 | 1,543. |

### Double Overprints

| 9a | A1 | ½p | 1,400. | |
|---|---|---|---|---|
| b. | | Triple overprint | 9,000. | |
| 10a | A1 | 1p | 1,150. | |
| b. | | Triple overprint | 6,250. | |
| 11a | A1 | 2½p | 1,350. | |
| 12a | A1 | 4p | 1,350. | |
| 13a | A1 | 6p | 1,700. | 4,500. |
| 14a | A1 | 7p | 1,700. | 2,100. |
| 15a | A1 | 1sh | 2,250. | |
| 16a | A1 | 5sh | 6,000. | |

60th year of Queen Victoria's reign.
Excellent counterfeits of Nos. 9-16 exist.

## Stamps of 1890 Surcharged in Black or Red

b

c

---

| 1902, Aug. | | | |
|---|---|---|---|
| 17 | A1(b) | 1p on 4p lilac & org | 7.00 | 12.00 |
| a. | | Tall narrow "O" in "One" | 47.50 | 87.50 |
| b. | | Double surcharge | 6,000. | |
| 18 | A1(b) | 1p on 6p lilac & brn | 8.00 | 19.00 |
| a. | | Tall narrow "O" in "One" | 67.50 | 150.00 |
| 19 | A1(c) | 1p on 7p lilac & sl | 7.00 | 15.00 |
| | | Nos. 17-19 (3) | 22.00 | 46.00 |

King Edward VII — A4

Numerals of ¼p, 2p, 3p and 2sh6p of type A4 are in color on plain tablet. The 1sh and 5sh denominations are expressed as "ONE SHILLING" and "FIVE SHILLINGS" on plain tablet.

### 1902

| 20 | A4 | ½p violet & green | 6.00 | 1.10 |
|---|---|---|---|---|
| 21 | A4 | 1p vio & car rose | 11.00 | .25 |
| 22 | A4 | 2p violet & bister | 3.00 | 4.50 |
| 23 | A4 | 2½p violet & ultra | 6.75 | 2.50 |
| 24 | A4 | 3p violet & black | 11.50 | 8.00 |
| 25 | A4 | 6p violet & brown | 3.00 | 9.00 |
| 26 | A4 | 1sh grn & car rose | 11.50 | 30.00 |
| 27 | A4 | 2sh6p green & blk | 32.50 | 80.00 |
| 28 | A4 | 5sh green & ultra | 65.00 | 95.00 |
| | | Nos. 20-28 (9) | 150.25 | 230.35 |

| 1905-11 | | Wmk. 3 | |
|---|---|---|---|

**Chalky Paper (Ordinary Paper #29, 33)**

| 29 | A4 | ½p vio & grn ('06) | 5.25 | 2.75 |
|---|---|---|---|---|
| a. | | Chalky paper ('08) | 32.50 | 23.00 |
| 30 | A4 | 1p vio & car rose | 11.50 | .90 |
| 31 | A4 | 2p vio & bis ('08) | 14.00 | 27.00 |
| 32 | A4 | 2½p vio & ultra | 80.00 | 50.00 |
| 33 | A4 | 3p violet & black | 25.00 | 62.50 |
| a. | | Chalky paper ('08) | 60.00 | 100.00 |
| 34 | A4 | 3p violet, yel ('10) | 3.75 | 8.00 |
| 35 | A4 | 6p vio & brn ('08) | 55.00 | 100.00 |
| 36 | A4 | 6p violet & red violet ('11) | 10.00 | 11.00 |
| 37 | A4 | 1sh grn & car rose ('08) | 55.00 | 140.00 |
| 38 | A4 | 1sh blk & grn, grn ('11) | 12.00 | 22.50 |
| 39 | A4 | 2sh6p blk & red, blue ('11) | 45.00 | 55.00 |
| 40 | A4 | 5sh grn & red, yel ('11) | 50.00 | 70.00 |
| | | Nos. 29-40 (12) | 366.50 | 549.65 |

| 1907-11 | | Ordinary Paper | |
|---|---|---|---|
| 41 | A4 | ¼p brown ('09) | 3.00 | 1.90 |
| 42 | A4 | ½p green | 6.25 | 1.90 |
| 43 | A4 | 1p scarlet | 16.50 | .85 |
| a. | | 1p rose carmine | 50.00 | 3.75 |
| 44 | A4 | 2p gray ('11) | 5.50 | 14.50 |
| 45 | A4 | 2½p ultramarine | 9.00 | 4.50 |
| | | Nos. 41-45 (5) | 40.25 | 23.65 |

King George V — A5

For description of dies I and II, see "Dies of British Colonial Stamps" in Table of Contents.
The ½p, 1p, 2½p and 6p denominations of type A5 show the numeral on horizontally-lined tablet. The 1sh and 5sh denominations are expressed as "ONE SHILLING" and "FIVE SHILLINGS" on plain tablet.

Die I

| 1912 | | Ordinary Paper | |
|---|---|---|---|
| 46 | A5 | ¼p brown | 1.90 | 1.10 |
| 47 | A5 | ½p green | 5.50 | 2.00 |
| 48 | A5 | 1p carmine | 5.25 | 1.10 |
| a. | | 1p scarlet | 15.00 | 1.10 |
| 49 | A5 | 2p gray grn | 4.25 | 5.75 |
| 50 | A5 | 2½p ultramarine | 3.50 | 7.25 |

| 1912-22 | | Chalky Paper | |
|---|---|---|---|
| 51 | A5 | 3p red brn & vio, yel | 4.00 | 26.00 |
| 52 | A5 | 4p ol & red, yel (Die II) ('22) | 8.00 | 24.00 |
| 53 | A5 | 6p vio & red vio | 4.75 | 9.25 |
| 54 | A5 | 1sh blk, bl grn, ol back | 17.50 | 8.50 |
| a. | | 1sh black, green | 3.75 | 8.50 |
| 55 | A5 | 2sh vio & ultra, bl (Die II) ('22) | 18.00 | 65.00 |
| 56 | A5 | 2sh6p black & red, blue ('14) | 24.00 | 57.50 |
| 57 | A5 | 5sh grn & red, yel ('14) | 65.00 | 120.00 |
| a. | | 5sh green & red, lemon ('15) | 50.00 | 85.00 |
| | | Nos. 46-57 (12) | 161.65 | 327.45 |

---

| 1913, Nov. | | Surface-colored Paper | |
|---|---|---|---|
| 58 | A5 | 3p dk vio, yel | 95.00 | 180.00 |
| 59 | A5 | 1sh black, green | 90.00 | 40.00 |
| 60 | A5 | 5sh green & red, yel | 55.00 | 90.00 |
| | | Nos. 58-60 (3) | 240.00 | 310.00 |

King George V — A6

Die II

| 1921-32 | | Wmk. 4 | Ordinary Paper | |
|---|---|---|---|---|
| 61 | A5 | ¼p dk brn ('22) | 2.50 | 1.10 |
| a. | | ¼p dark brown ('32) | 16.50 | 21.00 |
| 62 | A5 | ½p green | 1.25 | .80 |
| a. | | ½p green (I) ('32) | 27.50 | 65.00 |
| 63 | A5 | 1p carmine | 2.50 | .60 |
| a. | | 1p rose red (I) ('32) | 45.00 | 1.00 |
| b. | | 1p bright scarlet (II) ('29) | 15.00 | 2.50 |
| 64 | A5 | 1p dp violet ('22) | 2.50 | 1.10 |
| 65 | A5 | 1½p rose red ('26) | 9.25 | 1.50 |
| 66 | A5 | 1½p org brn ('29) | 2.25 | .25 |
| a. | | 1½p red brown (I) ('32) | 4.50 | 3.00 |
| 68 | A5 | 2p gray ('22) | 3.25 | .85 |
| 69 | A5 | 2½p orange ('23) | 14.00 | 67.50 |
| 70 | A5 | 2½p ultra ('27) | 3.75 | 1.40 |
| a. | | Die I ('32) | 7.50 | 3.75 |
| 71 | A5 | 3p ultra ('23) | 17.50 | 42.50 |
| a. | | 3p deep ultramarine ('25) | 65.00 | 65.00 |

**Chalky Paper**

| 72 | A5 | 3p violet, yel | 8.50 | 6.75 |
|---|---|---|---|---|
| 73 | A5 | 4p blk & red, yel ('23) | 4.00 | 24.00 |
| 74 | A5 | 5p vio & yel ol ('22) | 2.75 | 4.50 |
| 75 | A5 | 6p vio & red vio ('23) | 19.00 | 50.00 |
| a. | | Die I ('32) | 32.50 | 100.00 |
| 76 | A5 | 1sh blk, emer ('23) | 11.00 | 8.50 |
| a. | | 1sh black, green (I) ('32) | 60.00 | 85.00 |
| 77 | A5 | 2sh vio & ultra, bl ('22) | 25.00 | 45.00 |
| a. | | 2sh red purple & blue, blue ('26) | 14.00 | 52.50 |
| 78 | A5 | 2sh6p blk & red, bl ('23) | 13.00 | 27.00 |
| 79 | A5 | 3sh green & vio | 12.50 | 42.50 |
| 80 | A5 | 4sh black & scar | 21.00 | 42.50 |
| 81 | A5 | 5sh grn & red, yel | 50.00 | 85.00 |
| 82 | A6 | 10sh red & grn, emer ('28) | 80.00 | 140.00 |

**Wmk. 3**

| 83 | A6 | £1 black & vio, red ('28) | 240.00 | 325.00 |
|---|---|---|---|---|
| | | Nos. 61-66,68-83 (22) | 545.50 | 918.35 |

Common Design Types pictured following the introduction.

## Silver Jubilee Issue
Common Design Type
*Perf. 11x12*

| 1935, May 6 | | Engr. | Wmk. 4 | |
|---|---|---|---|---|
| 96 | CD301 | 1p car & dk blue | 1.75 | 3.25 |
| 97 | CD301 | 1½p blk & ultra | 2.75 | 1.60 |
| 98 | CD301 | 2½p ultra & brn | 4.75 | 4.75 |
| 99 | CD301 | 1sh brn vio & ind | 26.50 | 40.00 |
| | | Nos. 96-99 (4) | 35.75 | 49.60 |
| | | Set, never hinged | 45.00 | |

## Coronation Issue
Common Design Type

| 1937, May 12 | | | Perf. 13½x14 | |
|---|---|---|---|---|
| 100 | CD302 | 1p carmine | .50 | 1.00 |
| 101 | CD302 | 1½p org brn | .50 | 1.50 |
| 102 | CD302 | 2½p bright ultra | .55 | 1.50 |
| | | Nos. 100-102 (3) | 1.55 | 4.00 |
| | | Set, never hinged | 3.00 | |

A7

King George VI — A8

| 1938-51 | | Typo. | Perf. 14 | |
|---|---|---|---|---|
| 103 | A7 | ¼p brown | .40 | 1.50 |
| a. | | ¼p deep brown, chalky paper ('49) | .25 | 1.75 |
| 104 | A7 | ½p green | .75 | .75 |
| 105 | A7 | 1p carmine | 1.25 | 1.75 |
| a. | | 1p scarlet ('42) | 1.40 | 12.50 |
| b. | | 1p red ('48) | 3.75 | 6.75 |
| 106 | A7 | 1½p red brown | .80 | .50 |
| 107 | A7 | 2p gray | 2.00 | 2.25 |
| a. | | 2p slate gray ('42) | 4.00 | 3.75 |
| 108 | A7 | 2½p ultramarine | .60 | 4.00 |
| a. | | 2½p bright blue | 18.00 | 1.20 |

---

| 109 | A7 | 3p dl org ('42) | .40 | .90 |
|---|---|---|---|---|
| a. | | 3p brown orange | 22.50 | 2.75 |
| 110 | A7 | 6p vio & red vio | 6.00 | 3.50 |
| a. | | 6p deep dull purple & bright purple | 16.00 | 7.00 |
| b. | | 6p purple & deep magenta | 9.00 | 5.50 |
| 111 | A7 | 1sh blk & grn, emer ('42) | 3.50 | 1.50 |
| a. | | 1sh black, emerald, chalky paper | 10.00 | 5.50 |
| 112 | A7 | 2sh vio & ultra, bl | 7.75 | 2.25 |
| a. | | 2sh reddish purple & blue, blue, chalky paper | 17.00 | 3.00 |
| 113 | A7 | 5sh grn & red, yel | 21.00 | 18.00 |
| a. | | 5sh green & red, yel, chalky paper | 30.00 | 22.50 |
| 114 | A8 | 10sh dp ver & dp grn, emer, ordinary paper ('47) | 82.50 | 100.00 |
| a. | | 10sh dp red & bluish grn, green, chalky paper | 125.00 | 140.00 |
| b. | | 10sh dull red & pale grn, green, ordinary paper ('44) | 475.00 | 375.00 |
| c. | | 10sh red & green, green, ordinary paper ('45) | 100.00 | 90.00 |

Two dies were used for the 1p, differing in thickness of shading line at base of "1."

| | | Wmk. 3 | Perf. 13 | |
|---|---|---|---|---|
| 115 | A8 | £1 blk & vio, scar ('51) | 22.50 | 37.50 |
| a. | | £1 black & brown purple, red, perf. 14 | 225.00 | 375.00 |
| | | Never hinged | 375.00 | |
| b. | | £1 black & purple, carmine, perf. 14 ('41) | 55.00 | 55.00 |
| | | Never hinged | 90.00 | |
| c. | | £1 black & brown purple, salmon, perf. 14 ('43) | 27.50 | 29.00 |
| | | Never hinged | 45.00 | |
| d. | | Wmkd. sideways (as #115, perf. 13) | 4,000. | |
| | | Never hinged | 7,000. | |
| | | Nos. 103-115 (13) | 149.45 | 174.40 |
| | | Set, never hinged | 210.00 | |

The 3p-£1 were issued on chalky paper in 1938 and on ordinary paper in 1942. Values are for the most common varieties.
Issued: #115, 12/13/51; others, 11/25/38.
See Nos. 120-125.

**Catalogue values for unused stamps in this section, from this point to the end of the section, are for Never Hinged items.**

## Peace Issue
Common Design Type
*Perf. 13½x14*

| 1946, Nov. 1 | | Wmk. 4 | Engr. | |
|---|---|---|---|---|
| 116 | CD303 | 1½p brown | .25 | .75 |
| 117 | CD303 | 3p deep orange | .25 | .75 |

## Silver Wedding Issue
Common Design Types

| 1949, Jan. 2 | | Photo. | Perf. 14x14½ | |
|---|---|---|---|---|
| 118 | CD304 | 2½p bright ultra | .25 | .25 |

*Perf. 11½x11*

**Engr.; Name Typographed**

| 119 | CD305 | 5sh green | 6.75 | 8.00 |
|---|---|---|---|---|

## George VI Type of 1938

| 1949, July 1 | | Typo. | Perf. 13½x14 | |
|---|---|---|---|---|
| 120 | A7 | ½p gray | 2.00 | 1.50 |
| 121 | A7 | 1p green | .55 | .25 |
| 122 | A7 | 1½p orange & black | 1.75 | .40 |
| 123 | A7 | 2p crimson rose | 1.40 | 1.25 |
| 124 | A7 | 2½p black & plum | 1.00 | .25 |
| 125 | A7 | 3p ultramarine | 1.00 | .25 |
| | | Nos. 120-125 (6) | 7.70 | 3.90 |

## UPU Issue
Common Design Types

**Engr.; Name Typo. on 3p and 6p**

| 1949, Oct. 10 | | Perf. 13½, 11x11½ | | |
|---|---|---|---|---|
| 126 | CD306 | 2½p slate | .25 | 2.40 |
| 127 | CD307 | 3p indigo | 2.00 | 2.40 |
| 128 | CD308 | 6p red lilac | .40 | 2.40 |
| 129 | CD309 | 1sh blue green | .40 | 2.40 |
| | | Nos. 126-129 (4) | 3.05 | 9.60 |

## University Issue
Common Design Types
*Perf. 14x14½*

| 1951, Feb. 16 | | Engr. | Wmk. 4 | |
|---|---|---|---|---|
| 130 | CD310 | 3c gray black & org | .35 | 2.00 |
| 131 | CD311 | 12c lilac & rose car | 1.00 | 2.00 |

## Coronation Issue
Common Design Type

| 1953, June 2 | | | Perf. 13½x13 | |
|---|---|---|---|---|
| 132 | CD312 | 3c dk green & black | 1.00 | 2.25 |

A9       Queen Elizabeth II — A10

**1954, Feb. 22**    **Typo.**    **Perf. 14**

| | | | | |
|---|---|---|---|---|
| 133 | A9 | ½c brown | .25 | .60 |
| 134 | A9 | 1c gray | 1.25 | 1.50 |
| 135 | A9 | 2c green | 1.75 | .25 |
| 136 | A9 | 3c orange & blk | 2.50 | 1.50 |
| 137 | A9 | 4c rose red | 1.75 | .25 |
| 138 | A9 | 5c blk & claret | 2.25 | 1.50 |
| 139 | A9 | 6c orange | 2.25 | .65 |
| 140 | A9 | 8c deep ultra | 2.75 | .25 |
| 141 | A9 | 12c rose vio & mag | 2.00 | .25 |
| 142 | A9 | 24c black & green | 2.00 | .30 |
| 143 | A9 | 48c rose vio & ultra | 8.00 | 4.00 |
| 144 | A9 | 60c brown & green | 6.00 | 3.25 |
| 145 | A9 | $1.20 yel grn & rose red | 7.00 | 4.50 |

**Perf. 13**

| | | | | |
|---|---|---|---|---|
| 146 | A10 | $2.40 red & blue grn | 12.00 | 7.75 |
| 147 | A10 | $4.80 black & claret | 16.00 | 11.00 |
| | | Nos. 133-147 (15) | 67.75 | 37.55 |

---

# Trust Scott to protect your collection
## with our full line of Scott Binders and Album Accessories

### 3-RING BINDER & SLIPCASE

With this three ring binder, pages lay flat while the locking mechanism ensures that the rings won't pop open, even when the binder is full.

| Item | | Retail | AA |
|---|---|---|---|
| ACBR01D | Small Metal-Hinged Binder | $46.99 | **$37.59** |
| ACBR01SET | 3-Ring Binder and Slipcase – small | $85.49 | **$70.32** |
| ACSR01 | Small Slipcase | $38.50 | **$32.73** |
| ACBR03D | Large Metal-Hinged Binder | $46.99 | **$37.59** |
| ACBR03SET | 3-Ring Binder and Slipcase | $85.49 | **$70.32** |
| ACSR03 | Large Slipcase | $38.50 | **$32.73** |

### 2-POST BINDER & SLIPCASE

For the traditional Scott collector, the standard hinge post binder is the perfect fit. Scott album pages are punched with rectangular holes that fit on rectangular posts. The posts and pages are held by a rod that slides down from the top. With the post binder pages do not lie flat.

| Item | | Retail | AA |
|---|---|---|---|
| ACBS03 | Large 2-Post Binder | $59.99 | **$47.99** |
| ACBS03SET | 2-Square Post Binder and Slipcase | $98.49 | **$80.72** |
| ACSS03 | Large 2-Post Slipcase | $38.50 | **$32.73** |
| ACBU | Universal 2-Post Binder | $42.99 | **$36.54** |
| ACBUSET | Universal Binder and Slipcase | $81.49 | **$69.27** |
| ACSU | Universal 2-Post Slipcase | $38.50 | **$32.73** |

### BINDER LABELS

Labels are available for just about every National and Specialty Album produced by Amos Media Co. These elegantly styled, self-adhesive labels add just the right touch to your album. For a complete listing of the labels available visit our web site or call our toll free number.

| Item | Retail | AA |
|---|---|---|
| National or Specialty Series Labels | $5.99 | **$4.99** |
| Custom Labels | $16.99 | **$10.99** |

### SPECIALTY BINDER ACCESSORIES

Protect your investment with these great flysheets and glassine interleaving. The first and last pages in your album will stay free from wrinkles and tears.

| Item | | Retail | AA |
|---|---|---|---|
| ACC101 | Green Protector Fly Sheets for 2-Post Binders (2 Pack) | $6.99 | **$5.82** |
| ACC102 | Black Protector Fly Sheets for 3-Ring Binders (2 Pack) | $6.99 | **$5.82** |
| ACC107 | Glassine Interleaving 100 Sheets per pack | $14.99 | **$12.85** |
| ACC145 | Page Dividers for 3-Ring & 2-Post Binders (10 Pack) | $6.99 | **$5.82** |

### PAGE PROTECTORS

Protect your stamps and album pages with a clear archival quality plastic sleeve. Sleeves fit over the entire page and protects pages from creases, fingerprints and tears. Sold in packages of 25.

| Item | | Retail | AA |
|---|---|---|---|
| ACC166 | Fits National/Specialty Series Pages (2-Post & 3-Ring) | $14.99 | **$12.59** |

### SCOTT FILLER STRIPS

Use strips every 15 to 20 pages in 2-post albums to balance overstuffed binders.

| Item | | Retail | AA |
|---|---|---|---|
| ACC105 | 24 Strips Included | $13.99 | **$10.76** |

**FREE SHIPPING!**
on orders $75+

Prices are subject to change. See **AmosAdvantage.com** for current pricing.

# AmosAdvantage.com
## 1-800-572-6885

# LESOTHO

lə-'sō-ˌtō

LOCATION — An enclave within the Republic of South Africa
GOVT. — Independent state in British Commonwealth
AREA — 11,720 sq. mi.
POP. — 2,128,950 (1999 est.)
CAPITAL — Maseru

Basutoland, the British Crown Colony, became independent, October 4, 1966, taking the name Lesotho.

100 Cents = 1 Rand
100 Lisente (s) = 1 Maloti (1979)

**Catalogue values for all unused stamps in this country are for Never Hinged items.**

### Watermark

Wmk. 362 — Basotho Hat Multiple

Moshoeshoe I and II — A1

#### Perf. 12½x13

| 1966, Oct. 4 | | | Photo. | Unwmk. | |
|---|---|---|---|---|---|
| 1 | A1 | 2½c red brn, blk & red | | .25 | .25 |
| 2 | A1 | 5c red brn, blk & brt bl | | .25 | .25 |
| 3 | A1 | 10c red brn, blk & brt green | | .25 | .25 |
| 4 | A1 | 20c red brn, blk & red lilac | | .30 | .30 |
| | | Nos. 1-4 (4) | | 1.05 | 1.05 |

Lesotho's independence, Oct. 4, 1966.

Basutoland Nos. 72-74, 76-82 Overprinted

#### Perf. 13½

| 1966, Nov. 1 | | | Wmk. 4 | Engr. | |
|---|---|---|---|---|---|
| 5 | A7 | ½c dk brown & gray | | .25 | .25 |
| 6 | A7 | 1c dp grn & gray blk | | .25 | .25 |
| 7 | A7 | 2c orange & dp blue | | .90 | .25 |
| 8 | A7 | 3½c dp blue & indigo | | .50 | .25 |
| 9 | A7 | 5c dk grn & org brn | | .30 | .25 |
| 10 | A7 | 10c rose vio & dk ol | | .35 | .25 |
| 11 | A7 | 12½c aqua & brown | | 6.00 | .35 |
| 12 | A7 | 25c lil rose & dp ultra | | .70 | .25 |
| 13 | A7 | 50c dp car & black | | 1.60 | .75 |

#### Perf. 11½

| 14 | A8 | 1r dp claret & blk | | 2.25 | 3.50 |
|---|---|---|---|---|---|
| a. | | "Lseotho" | | 85.00 | |
| | | Nos. 5-14 (10) | | 13.10 | 6.35 |

**Same Overprint on Nos. 87-91 and Type of 1954**

| | | | Wmk. 314 | Perf. 13½ | |
|---|---|---|---|---|---|
| 15 | A7 | 1c green & gray blk | | .25 | .25 |
| 16 | A7 | 2½c car & ol green | | .65 | .25 |
| 17 | A7 | 5c dk grn & org brn | | .30 | .25 |
| 18 | A7 | 12½c aqua & brown | | .50 | .25 |
| 19 | A7 | 50c dp car & black | | .95 | .45 |

#### Perf. 11½

| 20 | A8 | 1r dp claret & blk | | .95 | .90 |
|---|---|---|---|---|---|
| a. | | "Lseotho" | | 50.00 | 70.00 |
| | | Nos. 15-20 (6) | | 3.60 | 2.35 |

UNESCO Emblem, Microscope, Book, Violin and Retort — A2

## Unwmk.

| 1966, Dec. 1 | | | Litho. | Perf. 14 | |
|---|---|---|---|---|---|
| 21 | A2 | 2½c green & ocher | | .25 | .25 |
| 22 | A2 | 5c olive & brt green | | .25 | .25 |
| 23 | A2 | 12½c ver & lt blue | | .30 | .25 |
| 24 | A2 | 25c dull blue & orange | | .50 | .60 |
| | | Nos. 21-24 (4) | | 1.30 | 1.35 |

20th anniv. of UNESCO.

King Moshoeshoe II and Corn — A3

King Moshoeshoe II — A4

Designs: 1c, Bull. 2c, Aloes. 2½c, Basotho hat. 3½c, Merino sheep. 5c, Basotho pony. 10c, Wheat. 12½c, Angora goat. 25c, Maletsunyane Falls. 50c, Diamonds. 1r, Coat of Arms.

#### Perf. 13½x14½

| 1967, Apr. 1 | | | Photo. | Unwmk. | |
|---|---|---|---|---|---|
| 25 | A3 | ½c violet & green | | .25 | .25 |
| 26 | A3 | 1c dk red & brown | | .25 | .25 |
| 27 | A3 | 2c green & yellow | | .25 | .80 |
| 28 | A3 | 2½c yel bister & blk | | .25 | .25 |
| 29 | A3 | 3½c yellow & black | | .25 | .25 |
| 30 | A3 | 5c brt blue & yel bis | | .25 | .25 |
| 31 | A3 | 10c gray & ocher | | .35 | .25 |
| 32 | A3 | 12½c orange & blk | | .30 | .30 |
| 33 | A3 | 25c ultra & blk | | .60 | .50 |
| 34 | A3 | 50c Prus green & blk | | 5.00 | 2.00 |
| 35 | A3 | 1r gray & multi | | 1.00 | 1.00 |

#### Perf. 14½x13½

| 36 | A4 | 2r mag, blk & gold | | 1.25 | 1.75 |
|---|---|---|---|---|---|
| | | Nos. 25-36 (12) | | 10.00 | 7.85 |

See Nos. 47-59.

University Buildings and Graduates A4a

| 1967, Apr. 7 | | | Perf. 14x14½ | | |
|---|---|---|---|---|---|
| 37 | A4a | 1c yel, sep & dp blue | | .25 | .25 |
| 38 | A4a | 2½c blue, sep & dp bl | | .25 | .25 |
| 39 | A4a | 12½c dl rose, sep & dp bl | | .25 | .25 |
| 40 | A4a | 25c lt vio, sep & dp bl | | .25 | .25 |
| | | Nos. 37-40 (4) | | 1.00 | 1.00 |

1st conferment of degrees by the Univ. of Botswana, Lesotho and Swaziland at Roma, Lesotho.

Statue of Moshoeshoe I — A5

1st Anniv. of Independence: 12½c, Flag of Lesotho. 25c, Crocodile.

| 1967, Oct. 4 | | | Photo. | Perf. 14 | |
|---|---|---|---|---|---|
| 41 | A5 | 2½c apple green & black | | .25 | .25 |
| 42 | A5 | 12½c multicolored | | .45 | .45 |
| 43 | A5 | 25c tan, blk & dp green | | .80 | .80 |
| | | Nos. 41-43 (3) | | 1.50 | 1.50 |

Boy Scout and Lord Baden-Powell A6

| 1967, Nov. 1 | | | Unwmk. | Perf. 14x14½ | |
|---|---|---|---|---|---|
| 44 | A6 | 15c lt ol grn, dk grn & brn | | .35 | .25 |

60th anniversary of the Boy Scouts.

World Map and WHO Emblem — A7

20th anniv. of WHO: 25c, Nurse and child, arms of Lesotho and WHO emblem.

| 1968, Apr. 8 | | | Photo. | Perf. 14x14½ | |
|---|---|---|---|---|---|
| 45 | A7 | 2½c dp bl, car rose & gold | | .25 | .25 |
| 46 | A7 | 25c gold, gray grn & redsh brown | | .45 | .40 |

### Types of 1967

Design: 3c, Sorghum. Others as before.

#### Perf. 13½x14½

| 1968-69 | | | Photo. | Wmk. 362 | |
|---|---|---|---|---|---|
| 47 | A3 | ½c violet & green | | .25 | .25 |
| 48 | A3 | 1c dk red & brown | | .25 | .25 |
| 49 | A3 | 2c green & yellow | | .25 | .25 |
| 50 | A3 | 2½c yel bister & blk | | .25 | .25 |
| 51 | A3 | 3c lt brn, dk brn & green | | .25 | .25 |
| 52 | A3 | 3½c yellow & black | | .25 | .25 |
| 53 | A3 | 5c brt bl & yel bis | | .50 | .25 |
| 54 | A3 | 10c gray & ocher | | .30 | .60 |
| 55 | A3 | 12½c org & blk ('69) | | .80 | .90 |
| 56 | A3 | 25c ultra & blk ('69) | | 1.75 | 1.15 |
| 57 | A3 | 50c Prussian grn & black ('69) | | 12.50 | 3.00 |
| 58 | A3 | 1r gray & multi | | 2.25 | 2.25 |

#### Perf. 14½x13½

| 59 | A4 | 2r magenta, blk & gold ('69) | | 9.00 | 11.50 |
|---|---|---|---|---|---|
| | | Nos. 47-59 (13) | | 28.60 | 21.15 |

Hunters, Rock Painting — A8

Rock Paintings: 3½c, Baboons. 5c, Javelin thrower, vert. 10c, Archers. 15c, Cranes, vert. 20c, Eland. 25c, Hunting scene.

#### Perf. 14½x14, 14x14½

| 1968, Nov. 1 | | | | Wmk. 362 | |
|---|---|---|---|---|---|
| 60 | A8 | 3c dk & lt green & brn | | .35 | .25 |
| 61 | A8 | 3½c dk brown & yel | | .45 | .25 |
| 62 | A8 | 5c sepia, yel & red brn | | .50 | .25 |
| 63 | A8 | 10c black, brt rose & org | | .60 | .30 |
| 64 | A8 | 15c olive brn & buff | | .85 | .45 |
| 65 | A8 | 20c black, yel & lt grn | | 1.00 | .60 |
| 66 | A8 | 25c dk brown, yel & org | | 1.10 | .90 |
| | | Nos. 60-66 (7) | | 4.85 | 3.00 |

Protection for Lesotho's rock paintings.

Queen Elizabeth II Hospital — A9

Designs: 10c, Radio Lesotho. 12½c, Leabua Jonathan Airport. 25c, Royal Palace.

| 1969, Mar. 11 | | | Litho. | Perf. 14x13½ | |
|---|---|---|---|---|---|
| 67 | A9 | 2½c multicolored | | .25 | .25 |
| 68 | A9 | 10c multicolored | | .25 | .25 |
| 69 | A9 | 12½c multicolored | | .25 | .25 |
| 70 | A9 | 25c multicolored | | .25 | .25 |
| | | Nos. 67-70 (4) | | 1.00 | 1.00 |

Centenary of Maseru, capital of Lesotho.

Mosotho Horseman and Car — A10

Designs: 12½c, Car on mountain pass. 15c, View from Sani Pass and signal flags. 20c, Map of Lesotho and Independence Trophy.

| 1969, Sept. 26 | | | Photo. | Perf. 14½x14 | |
|---|---|---|---|---|---|
| 71 | A10 | 2½c brown & multi | | .25 | .25 |
| 72 | A10 | 12½c multicolored | | .25 | .25 |
| 73 | A10 | 15c multicolored | | .30 | .30 |
| 74 | A10 | 20c yellow & multi | | .30 | .30 |
| | | Nos. 71-74 (4) | | 1.10 | 1.10 |

Roof of Africa Auto Rally, Sept. 19-20.

Gryponyx — A11

Prehistoric Reptile Footprints, Moyeni: 3c, Dinosaur. 10c, Plateosauravus and Footprints. 15c, Tritylodon. 25c, Massospondylus.

#### Perf. 14½x14

| 1970, Jan. 5 | | | | Wmk. 362 | |
|---|---|---|---|---|---|
| | | Size: 60x23mm | | | |
| 75 | A11 | 3c brown, yel & black | | 1.00 | .75 |
| | | Perf. 15x14 | | | |
| | | Size: 40x23mm | | | |
| 76 | A11 | 5c maroon, blk & pink | | 1.40 | .40 |
| 77 | A11 | 10c sepia, blk & yel | | 1.50 | .45 |
| 78 | A11 | 15c slate grn, blk & yel | | 2.00 | 2.50 |
| 79 | A11 | 25c gray blue, blk & bl | | 3.00 | 2.50 |
| | | Nos. 75-79 (5) | | 8.90 | 6.60 |

Moshoeshoe I — A12

Design: 25c, Moshoeshoe I with top hat.

| 1970, Mar. 11 | | | Litho. | Wmk. 362 | |
|---|---|---|---|---|---|
| 80 | A12 | 2½c brt grn & car rose | | .25 | .25 |
| 81 | A12 | 25c lt blue & org brn | | .25 | .25 |

Cent. of the death of Moshoeshoe I, chief of the Bakoena clan of the Basothos.

UN Headquarters, New York — A13

2½c, UN emblem. 12½c, UN emblem, people. 25c, UN emblem, peace dove.

| 1970, June 26 | | | Litho. | Perf. 14½x14 | |
|---|---|---|---|---|---|
| 82 | A13 | 2½c pink, red brn & bl | | .25 | .25 |
| 83 | A13 | 10c blue & multi | | .25 | .25 |
| 84 | A13 | 12½c olive, ver & lt blue | | .25 | .25 |
| 85 | A13 | 25c tan & multi | | .25 | .25 |
| | | Nos. 82-85 (4) | | 1.00 | 1.00 |

25th anniversary of the United Nations.

Basotho Hat Gift Shop, Maseru — A14

Tourism: 5c, Trout fishing. 10c, Horseback riding. 12½c, Skiing, Maluti Mountains. 20c, Holiday Inn, Maseru.

| 1970, Oct. 27 | | | | Perf. 14x14½ | |
|---|---|---|---|---|---|
| 86 | A14 | 2½c multicolored | | .25 | .25 |
| 87 | A14 | 5c multicolored | | .25 | .25 |
| 88 | A14 | 10c multicolored | | .30 | .30 |
| 89 | A14 | 12½c multicolored | | .30 | .30 |
| 90 | A14 | 20c multicolored | | .35 | .35 |
| | | Nos. 86-90 (5) | | 1.45 | 1.45 |

Corn — A15

Designs: 1c, Bull. 2c, Aloes. 2½c, Basotho hat. 3c, Sorghum. 3½c, Merino sheep. 4c, National flag. 5c, Basotho pony. 10c, Wheat. 12½c, Angora goat. 25c, Maletsunyane Falls. 50c, Diamonds. 1r, Coat of Arms. 2r, Statue of King Moshoeshoe I in Maseru, vert.

| 1971 | | | Litho. Wmk. 362 | Perf. 14 | |
|---|---|---|---|---|---|
| 91 | A15 | ½c lilac & green | | .25 | .25 |
| 92 | A15 | 1c brn red & brn | | .25 | .25 |
| 93 | A15 | 2c yel brn & yel | | .25 | .25 |
| 94 | A15 | 2½c dull yel & blk | | .25 | .25 |
| 95 | A15 | 3c bis, brn & grn | | .25 | .25 |
| 96 | A15 | 3½c yellow & black | | .25 | .25 |
| 97 | A15 | 4c ver & multi | | .25 | .25 |
| 98 | A15 | 5c blue & brown | | .25 | .25 |
| 99 | A15 | 10c gray & ocher | | .35 | .30 |
| 100 | A15 | 12½c orange & brn | | .45 | .35 |
| 101 | A15 | 25c ultra & blk | | .75 | .60 |
| 102 | A15 | 50c lt bl grn & blk | | 6.50 | 4.00 |
| 103 | A15 | 1r gray & multi | | 1.90 | 1.75 |
| 104 | A15 | 2r ultra & brown | | 1.40 | 2.25 |
| a. | | Unwmkd. ('80) | | .25 | 3.50 |
| | | Nos. 91-104 (14) | | 13.35 | 11.25 |

Issue dates: 4c, Apr. 1; others, Jan. 4.
For overprints and surcharges see Nos. 132-135, 245, 312.

Lammergeier — A16

Birds: 5c, Bald ibis. 10c, Rufous rock jumper. 12½c, Blue korhaan (bustard). 15c, Painted snipe. 20c, Golden-breasted bunting. 25c, Ground woodpecker.

**1971, Mar. 1**      **Perf. 14**
| | | | | |
|---|---|---|---|---|
| 105 | A16 | 2½c multicolored | 2.75 | .25 |
| 106 | A16 | 5c multicolored | 3.75 | 2.10 |
| 107 | A16 | 10c multicolored | 4.00 | 1.60 |
| 108 | A16 | 12½c multicolored | 4.25 | 3.25 |
| 109 | A16 | 15c multicolored | 4.75 | 4.25 |
| 110 | A16 | 20c multicolored | 4.75 | 4.25 |
| 111 | A16 | 25c multicolored | 5.25 | 4.25 |
| | | *Nos. 105-111 (7)* | 29.50 | 19.95 |

Lionel Collett Dam — A17

Designs: 10c, Contour farming. 15c, Earth dams. 25c, Beaver dams.

**1971, July 15**     **Litho.**     **Wmk. 362**
| | | | | |
|---|---|---|---|---|
| 112 | A17 | 4c multicolored | .25 | .25 |
| 113 | A17 | 10c multicolored | .25 | .25 |
| 114 | A17 | 15c multicolored | .25 | .25 |
| 115 | A17 | 25c multicolored | .25 | .25 |
| | | *Nos. 112-115 (4)* | 1.00 | 1.00 |

Soil conservation and erosion control.

Diamond Mining — A18

10c, Potter. 15c, Woman weaver at loom. 20c, Construction worker and new buildings.

**1971, Oct. 4**
| | | | | |
|---|---|---|---|---|
| 116 | A18 | 4c olive & multi | 1.40 | .40 |
| 117 | A18 | 10c ocher & multi | .55 | .25 |
| 118 | A18 | 15c red & multi | .85 | .60 |
| 119 | A18 | 20c dk brown & multi | 1.10 | 1.40 |
| | | *Nos. 116-119 (4)* | 3.90 | 2.65 |

Mail Cart, 19th Century — A19

Designs: 10c, Postal bus. 15c, Cape of Good Hope No. 17, vert. 20c, Maseru Post Office.

**1972, Jan. 3**
| | | | | |
|---|---|---|---|---|
| 120 | A19 | 5c pink & black | .25 | .25 |
| 121 | A19 | 10c lt blue & multi | .25 | .25 |
| 122 | A19 | 15c gray, black & blue | .25 | .25 |
| 123 | A19 | 20c yellow & multi | .35 | .60 |
| | | *Nos. 120-123 (4)* | 1.10 | 1.35 |

Centenary of mail service between Maseru and Aliwal North in Cape Colony.

Runner and Olympic Rings — A20

**1972, Sept. 1**
| | | | | |
|---|---|---|---|---|
| 124 | A20 | 4c shown | .25 | .25 |
| 125 | A20 | 10c Shot put | .25 | .25 |
| 126 | A20 | 15c Hurdles | .40 | .35 |
| 127 | A20 | 25c Broad jump | .60 | .60 |
| | | *Nos. 124-127 (4)* | 1.50 | 1.45 |

20th Olympic Games, Munich, 8/26-9/11.

Adoration of the Shepherds, by Matthias Stomer — A21

**1972, Dec. 1**     **Litho.**     **Perf. 14**
| | | | | |
|---|---|---|---|---|
| 128 | A21 | 4c blue & multi | .25 | .25 |
| 129 | A21 | 10c red & multi | .25 | .25 |
| 130 | A21 | 25c emerald & multi | .25 | .25 |
| | | *Nos. 128-130 (3)* | .75 | .75 |

Christmas.

WHO Emblem — A22

**1973, Apr. 7**     **Litho.**     **Perf. 13½**
| | | | | |
|---|---|---|---|---|
| 131 | A22 | 20c blue & yellow | .60 | .60 |

WHO, 25th anniversary.

**Nos. 94, 97-99 ovptd. "O.A.U. / 10th Anniversary / Freedom in Unity"**

**1973, May 25**     **Wmk. 362**     **Perf. 14**
| | | | | |
|---|---|---|---|---|
| 132 | A15 | 2½c dull yellow & black | .25 | .25 |
| 133 | A15 | 4c vermilion & multi | .25 | .25 |
| 134 | A15 | 5c blue & brown | .25 | .25 |
| 135 | A15 | 10c gray & ocher | .25 | .25 |
| | | *Nos. 132-135 (4)* | 1.00 | 1.00 |

Basotho Hat, WFP/FAO Emblem A23

Designs: 15c, School lunch. 20c, Child drinking milk and cow. 25c, Map of mountain roads and farm workers.

**1973, June 1**     **Perf. 13½**
| | | | | |
|---|---|---|---|---|
| 136 | A23 | 4c ultra & multi | .25 | .25 |
| 137 | A23 | 15c buff & multi | .25 | .25 |
| 138 | A23 | 20c yellow & multi | .25 | .25 |
| 139 | A23 | 25c violet & multi | .25 | .25 |
| | | *Nos. 136-139 (4)* | 1.00 | 1.00 |

World Food Program, 10th anniversary.

Christmas Butterfly — A24

Designs: Butterflies of Lesotho.

**1973, Sept. 3**     **Perf. 14x14½**
| | | | | |
|---|---|---|---|---|
| 140 | A24 | 4c Mountain Beauty | 1.10 | .25 |
| 141 | A24 | 5c shown | 1.25 | .60 |
| 142 | A24 | 10c Painted lady | 2.00 | .60 |
| 143 | A24 | 15c Yellow pansy | 3.25 | 2.00 |
| 144 | A24 | 20c Blue pansy | 3.25 | 2.10 |
| 145 | A24 | 25c African monarch | 3.50 | 2.75 |
| 146 | A24 | 30c Orange tip | 3.50 | 3.75 |
| | | *Nos. 140-146 (7)* | 17.85 | 12.05 |

Map of Northern Lesotho and Location of Diamond Mines — A25

Designs: 15c, Kimberlite (diamond-bearing) rocks. 20c, Diagram of Kimberlite volcano, vert. 30c, Diamond prospector, vert.

**Perf. 13½x14, 14x13½**
**1973, Oct. 1**     **Litho.**     **Wmk. 362**
| | | | | |
|---|---|---|---|---|
| 147 | A25 | 10c gray & multi | 2.25 | .50 |
| 148 | A25 | 15c multicolored | 2.50 | 2.25 |
| 149 | A25 | 20c multicolored | 2.50 | 2.50 |
| 150 | A25 | 30c multicolored | 3.75 | 7.00 |
| | | *Nos. 147-150 (4)* | 11.00 | 12.25 |

International Kimberlite Conference.

Nurses' Training and Medical Care — A26

Designs: 10c, Classroom, student with microscope. 20c, Farmers with tractor and bullock team and crop instruction. 25c, Potter and engineers with lathe. 30c, Boy scouts and young bricklayers.

**1974, Feb. 18**     **Litho.**     **Perf. 13½x14**
| | | | | |
|---|---|---|---|---|
| 151 | A26 | 4c lt blue & multi | .25 | .25 |
| 152 | A26 | 10c ocher & multi | .25 | .25 |
| 153 | A26 | 20c multicolored | .25 | .25 |
| 154 | A26 | 25c bister & multi | .25 | .25 |
| 155 | A26 | 30c yellow & multi | .25 | .25 |
| | | *Nos. 151-155 (5)* | 1.25 | 1.25 |

Youth and development.

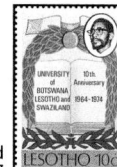

Open Book and Wreath — A27

Designs: 15c, Flags of Botswana, Lesotho and Swaziland; cap and diploma. 20c, Map of Africa and location of Botswana, Lesotho and Swaziland. 25c, King Moshoeshoe II, Chancellor of UBLS, capping graduate.

**1974, Apr. 7**     **Litho.**     **Perf. 14**
| | | | | |
|---|---|---|---|---|
| 156 | A27 | 10c multicolored | .25 | .25 |
| 157 | A27 | 15c multicolored | .25 | .25 |
| 158 | A27 | 20c multicolored | .25 | .25 |
| 159 | A27 | 25c multicolored | .25 | .50 |
| | | *Nos. 156-159 (4)* | 1.00 | 1.25 |

10th anniversary of the University of Botswana, Lesotho and Swaziland.

Senqunyane River Bridge, Marakabei A28

5c, Tsoelike River Bridge. 10c, Makhaleng River Bridge. 15c, Seaka Bridge, Orange/Senqu River. 20c, Masianokeng Bridge, Phuthiatsana River. 25c, Mahobong Bridge, Hlotse River.

**1974, June 26**     **Wmk. 362**     **Perf. 14**
| | | | | |
|---|---|---|---|---|
| 160 | A28 | 4c multicolored | .25 | .25 |
| 161 | A28 | 5c multicolored | .25 | .25 |
| 162 | A28 | 10c multicolored | .25 | .25 |
| 163 | A28 | 15c multicolored | .50 | .40 |
| 164 | A28 | 20c multicolored | .55 | .55 |
| 165 | A28 | 25c multicolored | .60 | .60 |
| | | *Nos. 160-165 (6)* | 2.40 | 2.30 |

Bridges and rivers of Lesotho.

UPU Emblem — A29

**1974, Sept. 6**     **Litho.**     **Perf. 14x13**
| | | | | |
|---|---|---|---|---|
| 166 | A29 | 4c shown | .25 | .25 |
| 167 | A29 | 10c Map of Lesotho | .25 | .25 |
| 168 | A29 | 15c GPO, Maseru | .25 | .40 |
| 169 | A29 | 20c Rural mail delivery | .80 | 1.00 |
| | | *Nos. 166-169 (4)* | 1.55 | 1.90 |

Centenary of Universal Postal Union.

Siege of Thaba-Bosiu A30

King Moshoeshoe I A31

5c, King Moshoeshoe II laying wreath at grave of Moshoeshoe I. 20c, Makoanyane, warrior hero.

**Perf. 12½x12, 12x12½**
**1974, Nov. 25**
| | | | | |
|---|---|---|---|---|
| 170 | A30 | 4c multicolored | .25 | .25 |
| 171 | A30 | 5c multicolored | .25 | .25 |
| 172 | A31 | 10c multicolored | .25 | .25 |
| 173 | A31 | 20c multicolored | .60 | .40 |
| | | *Nos. 170-173 (4)* | 1.35 | 1.15 |

Sesquicentennial of Thaba-Bosiu becoming the capital of Basutoland and Lesotho.

Mamokhorong A32

Musical Instruments of the Basotho: 10c, Lesiba. 15c, Setolotolo. 20c, Meropa (drums).

**Perf. 14x14½**
**1975, Jan. 25**     **Wmk. 362**
| | | | | |
|---|---|---|---|---|
| 174 | A32 | 4c multicolored | .25 | .25 |
| 175 | A32 | 10c multicolored | .25 | .25 |
| 176 | A32 | 15c multicolored | .30 | .30 |
| 177 | A32 | 20c multicolored | .50 | .50 |
| a. | | Souvenir sheet of 4, #174-177 | 1.75 | 2.00 |
| | | *Nos. 174-177 (4)* | 1.30 | 1.30 |

View, Sehlabathebe National Park — A33

5c, Natural arch. 15c, Mountain stream. 20c, Lake and mountains. 25c, Waterfall.

**1975, Apr. 8**     **Litho.**     **Perf. 14**
| | | | | |
|---|---|---|---|---|
| 178 | A33 | 4c multicolored | .35 | .25 |
| 179 | A33 | 5c multicolored | .35 | .25 |
| 180 | A33 | 20c multicolored | .70 | .70 |
| 181 | A33 | 20c multicolored | .70 | .70 |
| 182 | A33 | 25c multicolored | .90 | .90 |
| | | *Nos. 178-182 (5)* | 3.00 | 2.80 |

Sehlabathebe National Park.

Moshoeshoe I (1824-1870) A34

Mofumahali Mantsebo Seeiso (1940-1960) A35

Leaders of Lesotho: 4c, Moshoeshoe II. 5c, Letsie I (1870-1891). 6c, Lerotholi (1891-1905). 10c, Letsie II (1905-1913). 15c, Griffith (1913-1939). 20c, Seeiso Griffith Lerotholi (1939-1940).

**1975, Sept. 10**     **Litho.**     **Wmk. 362**
| | | | | |
|---|---|---|---|---|
| 183 | A34 | 3c dull blue & black | .25 | .25 |
| 184 | A34 | 4c lilac rose & black | .25 | .25 |
| 185 | A34 | 5c pink & black | .25 | .25 |
| 186 | A34 | 6c brown & black | .25 | .25 |
| 187 | A34 | 10c rose car & black | .25 | .25 |
| 188 | A34 | 15c orange & black | .25 | .25 |
| 189 | A34 | 20c olive & black | .25 | .30 |
| 190 | A35 | 25c lt blue & black | .25 | .40 |
| | | *Nos. 183-190 (8)* | 2.00 | 2.20 |

No. 190 issued for Intl. Women's Year.

Mokhibo, Women's Dance — A36

Traditional Dances: 10c, Ndlamo, men's dance. 15c, Raleseli, men and women. 20c, Mohobelo, men's dance.

**1975, Dec. 17**     **Perf. 14x14½**
| | | | | |
|---|---|---|---|---|
| 191 | A36 | 4c blue & multi | .25 | .25 |
| 192 | A36 | 10c black & multi | .25 | .25 |
| 193 | A36 | 15c black & multi | .30 | .40 |

**194** A36 20c blue & multi .40 .70
  *a.*  Souvenir sheet of 4, #191-194   5.00 5.00
    *Nos. 191-194 (4)*   1.20 1.60

Enrollment in
Junior Red
Cross — A37

Designs: 10c, First aid team and truck. 15c,
Red Cross nurse on horseback in rural area.
25c, Supplies arriving by plane.

**1976, Feb. 20**   **Litho.**   *Perf. 14*
**195** A37   4c red & multi   .55 .40
**196** A37 10c red & multi   .80 .60
**197** A37 15c red & multi   1.05 1.00
**198** A37 25c red & multi   1.60 2.00
    *Nos. 195-198 (4)*   4.00 4.00

Lesotho Red Cross, 25th anniversary.

Mosotho Horseman
A38

King
Moshoeshoe II
A39

2c, Tapestry (weavers and citation). 4c, Map
of Lesotho. 5c, Hand holding Lesotho brown
diamond. 10c, Lesotho Bank. 15c, Flags of
Lesotho and Organization of African Unity.
25c, Sehlabathebe National Park. 40c, Pottery. 50c, Pre-historic rock painting.

**1976, June 2**      *Perf. 14*
**199** A38   2c multicolored   .25 .35
**200** A38   3c multicolored   .25 .30
**201** A38   4c multicolored   1.40 .25
**202** A38   5c multicolored   .50 .90
**203** A38 10c multicolored   .30 .30
**204** A38 15c multicolored   1.60 .80
**205** A38 25c multicolored   .50 .60
  *a.*  Unwmkd. ('80)   1.60 4.00
**206** A38 40c multicolored   .70 1.25
  *a.*  Unwmkd. ('80)   4.25 11.00
**207** A38 50c multicolored   2.25 2.00
  *a.*  Unwmkd. ('80)   6.00 10.00
**208** A39   1r multicolored   1.00 *1.75*
    *Nos. 199-208 (10)*   8.75 8.50

For surcharges see Nos. 302-311.

Soccer — A40

Olympic Rings and: 10c, Weight lifting. 15c,
Boxing. 25c, Discus.

**1976, Aug. 9**   **Litho.**   **Wmk. 362**
**209** A40   4c citron & multi   .25 .25
**210** A40 10c lilac & multi   .25 .25
**211** A40 15c salmon & multi   .30 .30
**212** A40 25c blue & multi   .65 .65
    *Nos. 209-212 (4)*   1.45 1.45

21st Olympic Games, Montreal, Canada,
July 17-Aug. 1.

Rising Sun of
Independence — A41

Designs: 10c, Opening gates. 15c, Broken
chain. 25c, Plane over Molimo Restaurant.

**1976, Oct. 4**      *Perf. 14*
**213** A41   4c yellow & multi   .25 .25
**214** A41 10c pink & multi   .25 .25
**215** A41 15c blue & multi   .50 .25
**216** A41 25c dull blue & multi   .60 .50
    *Nos. 213-216 (4)*   1.60 1.25

Lesotho's independence, 10th anniversary.

---

Telephones,
1876 and
1976 — A42

Designs: 10c, Woman using telephone, and
1895 telephone. 15c, Telephone operators
and wall telephone. 25c, A.G. Bell and 1905
telephone.

      *Perf. 13x13½*
**1976, Dec. 6**      **Wmk. 362**
**217** A42   4c multicolored   .25 .25
**218** A42 10c multicolored   .25 .25
**219** A42 15c multicolored   .35 .35
**220** A42 25c multicolored   .50 .50
    *Nos. 217-220 (4)*   1.35 1.35

Centenary of first telephone call by Alexander Graham Bell, Mar. 10, 1876.

Aloe Striatula — A43

Aloes and Succulents: 4c, Aloe aristata. 5c,
Kniphofia caulescens. 10c, Euphorbia
pulvinata. 15c, Aloe saponaria. 20c, Caralluma lutea. 25c, Aloe polyphylla.

**1977, Feb. 14**   **Litho.**   *Perf. 14*
**221** A43   3c multicolored   .30 .25
**222** A43   4c multicolored   .35 .25
**223** A43   5c multicolored   .40 .25
**224** A43 10c multicolored   .55 .25
**225** A43 15c multicolored   1.50 .60
**226** A43 20c multicolored   1.50 .60
**227** A43 25c multicolored   1.75 .80
    *Nos. 221-227 (7)*   6.35 2.80

Rock
Rabbits — A44

      *Perf. 14x14½*
**1977, Apr. 25**      **Wmk. 362**
**228** A44   4c shown   6.00 .55
**229** A44   5c Porcupine   6.00 .75
**230** A44 10c Polecat   6.00 .60
**231** A44 15c Klipspringers   18.50 2.75
**232** A44 25c Baboons   20.00 3.00
    *Nos. 228-232 (5)*   56.50 7.65

Man with Cane,
Concentric
Circles — A45

Man with Cane: 10c, Surrounded by flames
of pain. 15c, Surrounded by chain. 25c, Man
and globe.

**1977, July 4**   **Litho.**   *Perf. 14*
**233** A45   4c red & yellow   .25 .25
**234** A45 10c dk blue & lt blue   .25 .25
**235** A45 15c blue green & yellow   .40 .25
**236** A45 25c black & orange   .50 .60
    *Nos. 233-236 (4)*   1.40 1.35

World Rheumatism Year.

Small-mouthed
Yellow-fish — A46

Fresh-water Fish: 10c, Orange River mud
fish. 15c, Rainbow trout. 25c, Oreodaimon
quathlambae.

**1977, Sept. 28**   **Wmk. 362**   *Perf. 14*
**237** A46   4c multicolored   .40 .25
**238** A46 10c multicolored   .75 .25
**239** A46 15c multicolored   1.50 .60
**240** A46 25c multicolored   1.60 1.25
    *Nos. 237-240 (4)*   4.25 2.35

---

White and Black
Equal — A47

Designs: 10c, Black and white jigsaw puzzle. 15c, White and black cogwheels. 25c,
Black and white handshake.

**1977, Dec. 12**   **Litho.**   *Perf. 14*
**241** A47   4c lilac rose & black   .25 .25
**242** A47 10c brt blue & black   .25 .25
**243** A47 15c orange & black   .25 .25
**244** A47 15c lt green & black   .30 .30
    *Nos. 241-244 (4)*   1.05 1.05

Action to Combat Racism Decade.

No. 99 Surcharged

**1977, Dec. 7**
**245** A15 3c on 10c gray & ocher   1.75 1.50

Poppies — A48

Flowers of Lesotho: 3c, Diascia integerrima.
4c, Helichrysum trilineatum. 5c, Zaluzianskya
maritima. 10c, Gladioli. 15c, Chironia krebsii.
25c, Wahlenbergia undulata. 40c, Brunsvigia
radulosa.

**1978, Feb. 13**   **Litho.**   **Wmk. 362**
**246** A48   2c multicolored   .25 .30
**247** A48   3c multicolored   .25 .30
**248** A48   4c multicolored   .25 .25
**249** A48   5c multicolored   .25 .30
**250** A48 10c multicolored   .25 .30
**251** A48 15c multicolored   .25 .45
**252** A48 25c multicolored   .80 1.00
**253** A48 40c multicolored   1.40 2.00
    *Nos. 246-253 (8)*   3.70 4.85

Edward Jenner
Vaccinating
Child — A49

Global Eradication of Smallpox: 25c, Child's
head and WHO emblem.

**1978, May 8**   **Litho.**   *Perf. 13½x13*
**254** A49   5c multicolored   .40 .25
**255** A49 25c multicolored   1.40 1.50

Tsoloane Falls — A50

Lesotho Waterfalls: 10c, Qiloane Falls. 15c,
Tsoelikana Falls. 25c, Maletsunyane Falls.

**1978, July 28**   **Litho.**   *Perf. 14*
**256** A50   4c multicolored   .25 .25
**257** A50 10c multicolored   .30 .30
**258** A50 15c multicolored   .55 .55
**259** A50 25c multicolored   .85 .85
    *Nos. 256-259 (4)*   1.95 1.95

---

Flyer 1 — A51

25c, Orville and Wilbur Wright, Flyer 1.

**1978, Oct. 9**   **Wmk. 362**   *Perf. 14½*
**260** A51   5c multicolored   .25 .25
**261** A51 25c multicolored   1.00 1.00

75th anniversary of 1st powered flight.

Dragonflies — A52

Insects: 10c, Winged grasshopper. 15c,
Wasps. 25c, Praying mantis.

**1978, Dec. 18**   **Litho.**   *Perf. 14*
**262** A52   4c multicolored   .25 .25
**263** A52 10c multicolored   .30 .30
**264** A52 15c multicolored   .45 .45
**265** A52 25c multicolored   .75 .75
    *Nos. 262-265 (4)*   1.75 1.75

Trees — A53

**1979, Mar. 26**   **Litho.**   *Perf. 14*
**266** A53   4c Leucosidea Sericea   .25 .25
**267** A53 10c Wild olive   .25 .25
**268** A53 15c Blinkblaar   .40 .40
**269** A53 25c Cape holly   .55 .55
    *Nos. 266-269 (4)*   1.45 1.45

Reptiles — A54

**1979, June 4**   **Wmk. 362**   *Perf. 14*
**270** A54   4s Agama Lizard   .35 .35
**271** A54 10s Berg adder   .45 .40
**272** A54 15s Rock lizard   .65 .55
**273** A54 25s Spitting snake   1.15 1.00
    *Nos. 270-273 (4)*   2.60 2.30

A55

**1979, Oct. 22**   **Litho.**   *Perf. 14½*
**274** A55   4s Basutoland No. 2   .25 .25
**275** A55 15s Basutoland No. 72   .30 .30
**276** A55 25s Penny Black   .45 .45
    *Nos. 274-276 (3)*   1.00 1.00

     **Souvenir Sheet**
**277** A55 50s Lesotho No. 122   .90 .90

Sir Rowland Hill (1795-1879), originator of
penny postage.

Intl. Year of the
Child — A56

Children's Games, by Brueghel the Elder,
and IYC emblem: 4s, Children Climbing Tree.
10s, Follow the leader. 15s, Three cup montie.
25s, Entire painting.

**1979, Dec. 10   Wmk. 362   *Perf. 14½***
| | | | | |
|---|---|---|---|---|
| 278 | A56 | 4s multicolored | .25 | .25 |
| 279 | A56 | 10s multicolored | .25 | .25 |
| 280 | A56 | 15s multicolored | .25 | .25 |
| | | *Nos. 278-280 (3)* | .75 | .75 |

**Souvenir Sheet**
| | | | | |
|---|---|---|---|---|
| 281 | A56 | 25s multicolored | .75 | .75 |

Beer Strainer, Brooms and Mat — A57

**1980, Feb. 18   Litho.   *Perf. 14½***
| | | | | |
|---|---|---|---|---|
| 282 | A57 | 4s shown | .25 | .25 |
| 283 | A57 | 10s Winnowing basket | .25 | .25 |
| 284 | A57 | 15s Basotho hat | .30 | .30 |
| 285 | A57 | 25s Grain storage pots | .50 | .50 |
| | | *Nos. 282-285 (4)* | 1.30 | 1.30 |

Qalabane Ambush — A58

Gun War Centenary: 4s, Praise poet, text. 5s, Basotho army commander Lerotholi. 15s, Snider and Martini-Henry rifles. 25s, Map of Basutoland showing battle sites.

**1980, May 6   Litho.   *Perf. 14***
| | | | | |
|---|---|---|---|---|
| 286 | A58 | 4s multicolored | .25 | .25 |
| 287 | A58 | 5s multicolored | .25 | .25 |
| 288 | A58 | 10s multicolored | .30 | .30 |
| 289 | A58 | 15s multicolored | .65 | .40 |
| 290 | A58 | 25s multicolored | .80 | .65 |
| | | *Nos. 286-290 (5)* | 2.25 | 1.85 |

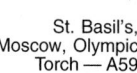

St. Basil's, Moscow, Olympic Torch — A59

No. 292, Torch and flags. No. 293, Soccer. No. 294, Running. No. 295, Misha and stadium. No. 296,

**1980, Sept. 20   Litho.   *Perf. 14½***
| | | | | |
|---|---|---|---|---|
| 291 | A59 | 25s shown | .35 | .35 |
| 292 | A59 | 25s multicolored | .35 | .35 |
| 293 | A59 | 25s multicolored | .35 | .35 |
| 294 | A59 | 25s multicolored | .35 | .35 |
| 295 | A59 | 25s multicolored | .35 | .35 |
| a. | | Strip of 5, #291-295 | 2.25 | 2.25 |

**Souvenir Sheet**
| | | | | |
|---|---|---|---|---|
| 296 | A59 | 1.40m multicolored | 2.00 | 2.00 |

22nd Summer Olympic Games, Moscow, July 19-Aug. 3.

Beer Mug and Man Drinking A60     Prince Philip A61

**Wmk. 362**

**1980, Oct. 1   Litho.   *Perf. 14***
| | | | | |
|---|---|---|---|---|
| 297 | A60 | 4s shown | .25 | .25 |
| 298 | A60 | 10s Beer brewing pot | .25 | .25 |
| 299 | A60 | 15s Water pot | .25 | .25 |
| 300 | A60 | 25s Pots and jugs | .30 | .30 |
| | | *Nos. 297-300 (4)* | 1.05 | 1.00 |

**Souvenir Sheet**
***Perf. 14x14½***
| | | | | |
|---|---|---|---|---|
| 301 | | Sheet of 4 | 1.25 | 1.25 |
| a. | A61 | 40s shown | .30 | .30 |
| b. | A61 | 40s Queen Elizabeth | .30 | .30 |
| c. | A61 | 40s Prince Charles | .30 | .30 |
| d. | A61 | 40s Princess Anne | .30 | .30 |

Traditional pottery; 250th birth anniversary of Josiah Wedgewood, potter.

---

**Nos. 104, 199-208 Surcharged**

Nos. 302-303, 304, 306-308, 310

No. 304a

No. 305

No. 309     Nos. 311-312

**Wmk. 362**

**1980, Oct. 20   Litho.   *Perf. 14***
| | | | | |
|---|---|---|---|---|
| 302 | A38 | 2s on 2c multi | .25 | .25 |
| 303 | A38 | 3s on 3c multi | .25 | .25 |
| 304 | A38 | 5s on 5c multi | .25 | .25 |
| a. | | 6s on 5s on 5c multi | .25 | .25 |
| 305 | A38 | 6s on 4c multi | .25 | .25 |
| 306 | A38 | 10s on 10c multi | .25 | .25 |
| 307 | A38 | 25s on 25c multi | .35 | .35 |
| 308 | A38 | 40s on 40c multi | .55 | .55 |
| 309 | A38 | 50s on 50c multi | .80 | .80 |
| 310 | A38 | 75s on 15c multi | 2.00 | 2.00 |
| 311 | A39 | 1m on 1r multi | 2.40 | 2.40 |
| 312 | A15 | 2m on 2r multi | 4.50 | 4.50 |
| | | *Nos. 302-312 (11)* | 11.85 | 11.85 |

Numerous surcharge errors exist (double triple, inverted, etc.).

Queen Mother Elizabeth and Prince Charles — A62

Basutoland No. 36, Flags of Lesotho and Britain — A63

**1980, Dec. 1   Unwmk.   *Perf. 14½***
| | | | | |
|---|---|---|---|---|
| 313 | | Sheet of 9 | 3.75 | 3.75 |
| a. | A62 | 5s shown | .25 | .25 |
| b. | A62 | 10s Portrait | .25 | .25 |
| c. | A63 | 1m shown | 1.10 | 1.10 |

Queen Mother Elizabeth, 80th birthday. No. 313 contains 3 each Nos. 313a-313c.

St. Agnes' Anglican Church, Teyateyaneng A63a

---

Nativity A64

4s, Lesotho Evangelical Church, Morija. 25s, Our Lady's Victory Cathedral, Maseru. 75s, University Chapel, Roma.

**1980, Dec. 8   *Perf. 14x14½***
| | | | | |
|---|---|---|---|---|
| 314 | A63a | 4s multicolored | .25 | .25 |
| 315 | A63a | 15s shown | .25 | .25 |
| 316 | A63a | 25s multicolored | .25 | .25 |
| 317 | A63a | 75s multicolored | .25 | .25 |
| | | *Nos. 314-317 (4)* | 1.00 | 1.00 |

**Souvenir Sheet**
| | | | | |
|---|---|---|---|---|
| 318 | A64 | 1.50m shown | .90 | .90 |

Christmas.

Voyager Satellite and Saturn — A65

**1981, Mar. 15   Litho.   *Perf. 14***
| | | | | |
|---|---|---|---|---|
| 319 | | Strip of 5 | 2.50 | 2.50 |
| a. | A65 | 25s Voyager, planet | .40 | .40 |
| b. | A65 | 25s shown | .40 | .40 |
| c. | A65 | 25s Voyager, Saturn's rings | .40 | .40 |
| d. | A65 | 25s Columbia space shuttle | .40 | .40 |
| e. | A65 | 25s Columbia, diff. | .40 | .40 |

**Souvenir Sheet**
| | | | | |
|---|---|---|---|---|
| 320 | A65 | 1.40m Saturn | 2.50 | 2.50 |

Voyager expedition to Saturn and flight of Columbia space shuttle.

Rock Pigeons A66

1s, Greater kestrel, vert. 3s, Crowned cranes, vert. 5s, Bokmakierie, vert. 6s, Cape robins, vert. 7s, Yellow canary, vert. 10s, Red-billed teal. 25s, Malachite kingfisher, vert. 40s, Malachite sunbirds. 60s, Orange-throated longclaw. 75s, African hoopoe. 1m, Red bishops. 2m, Egyptian goose. 5m, Lilac-breasted rollers.

**1981, Apr. 20   Unwmk.   *Perf. 14½***
| | | | | |
|---|---|---|---|---|
| 321 | A66 | 1s mutlicolored | .25 | .25 |
| 322 | A66 | 2s shown | .25 | .25 |
| 323 | A66 | 3s multicolored | .25 | .25 |
| 324 | A66 | 5s multicolored | .25 | .25 |
| 325 | A66 | 6s multicolored | .40 | .25 |
| 326 | A66 | 7s multicolored | .40 | .25 |
| 327 | A66 | 10s multicolored | .40 | .25 |
| 328 | A66 | 25s multicolored | 1.00 | .60 |
| 329 | A66 | 40s multicolored | 1.25 | 1.00 |
| 330 | A66 | 60s multicolored | 1.60 | 1.50 |
| 331 | A66 | 75s multicolored | 2.00 | 1.75 |
| 332 | A66 | 1m multicolored | 2.50 | 2.50 |
| 333 | A66 | 2m multicolored | 4.75 | 4.75 |
| 334 | A66 | 5m multicolored | 9.00 | 9.00 |
| | | *Nos. 321-334 (14)* | 24.30 | 22.85 |

For surcharges see Nos. 558A, 561-563, 598A, 599, 600B, 600C.

**1981   *Perf. 13***
| | | | | |
|---|---|---|---|---|
| 321a | A66 | 1s | 1.40 | .70 |
| 322a | A66 | 2s | 1.60 | .70 |
| 324a | A66 | 5s | 2.00 | .70 |
| 327a | A66 | 10s | 2.00 | .70 |
| | | *Nos. 321a-327a (4)* | 7.00 | 2.80 |

**1982, June 14   Wmk. 373   *Perf. 14½***
| | | | | |
|---|---|---|---|---|
| 321b | A66 | 1s | .25 | .40 |
| 322b | A66 | 2s | .25 | .40 |
| 323a | A66 | 3s | .35 | .40 |
| 324b | A66 | 5s | .35 | .45 |
| 325a | A66 | 6s | .35 | .25 |
| 326a | A66 | 7s | .35 | .25 |
| 327b | A66 | 10s | .35 | .25 |
| 328a | A66 | 25s | 1.00 | .45 |
| 329a | A66 | 40s | 1.10 | .50 |
| 330a | A66 | 60s | 1.50 | .90 |
| 331a | A66 | 75s | 2.00 | .90 |
| 332a | A66 | 1m | 2.40 | *2.75* |
| 333a | A66 | 2m | 3.00 | *4.00* |
| 334a | A66 | 5m | 6.00 | *10.00* |
| | | *Nos. 321b-334a (14)* | 19.25 | 21.90 |

**Common Design Types pictured following the introduction.**

---

**Royal Wedding Issue**
Common Design Type and

Royal Wedding A66a

**Unwmk.**

**1981, July 22   Litho.   *Perf. 14***
| | | | | |
|---|---|---|---|---|
| 335 | CD331 | 25s Bouquet | .25 | .25 |
| a. | | Booklet pane of 3 + label | .80 | |
| 336 | CD331 | 50s Charles | .25 | .25 |
| a. | | Booklet pane of 3 + label | 1.40 | |
| 337 | CD331 | 75s Couple | .40 | .40 |
| b. | | Booklet pane of 3 + label | 1.60 | |
| c. | | Bklt. pane of 3, #335-337 + label | 1.25 | |
| | | *Nos. 335-337 (3)* | .90 | .90 |

**1981   Litho.   *Perf. 14½***
**Souvenir Sheet**
| | | | | |
|---|---|---|---|---|
| 337A | A66a | 1.50m Couple | 1.75 | 1.75 |

Nos. 335-337A exist imperf. Value, set $8.

Tree Planting — A67

6s, Duke of Edinburgh and flags. 25s, Digging. 40s, Mountain climbing. 75s, Emblem. 1.40m, Duke of Edinburgh.

**1981, Oct. 30   Litho.   *Perf. 14½***
| | | | | |
|---|---|---|---|---|
| 338 | A67 | 6s multicolored | .25 | .25 |
| 339 | A67 | 7s shown | .25 | .25 |
| 340 | A67 | 25s multicolored | .25 | .25 |
| 341 | A67 | 40s multicolored | .40 | .40 |
| 342 | A67 | 75s multicolored | .65 | .65 |
| | | *Nos. 338-342 (5)* | 1.80 | 1.80 |

**Souvenir Sheet**
| | | | | |
|---|---|---|---|---|
| 343 | A67 | 1.40m multi | 1.75 | 1.75 |

Duke of Edinburgh's Awards, 25th anniv. No. 343 contains 1 45x29mm stamp, perf. 13½.

Santa Claus at Globe, by Norman Rockwell — A68

The Mystic Nativity, by Botticelli A69

Christmas: Saturday Evening Post covers by Norman Rockwell.

**1981, Oct. 5   *Perf. 13½x14***
| | | | | |
|---|---|---|---|---|
| 344 | A68 | 6s multicolored | .25 | .25 |
| 345 | A68 | 10s multicolored | .25 | .25 |
| 346 | A68 | 15s multicolored | .25 | .25 |
| 347 | A68 | 20s multicolored | .30 | .30 |
| 348 | A68 | 25s multicolored | .35 | .35 |
| 349 | A68 | 60s multicolored | .65 | .65 |
| | | *Nos. 344-349 (6)* | 2.05 | 2.05 |

**Souvenir Sheet**
| | | | | |
|---|---|---|---|---|
| 350 | A69 | 1.25m multicolored | 2.00 | 2.00 |

Chacma Baboons — A70

## Perf. 14x13½, 14½ (20s, 40s, 50s)

**1982, Jan. 15**     Litho.
| | | | | |
|---|---|---|---|---|
| 351 | A70 | 6s African wild cat | 3.75 | .50 |
| 352 | A70 | 20s shown | 4.75 | 1.25 |
| 353 | A70 | 25s Cape eland | 5.75 | 1.90 |
| 354 | A70 | 40s Porcupine | 6.75 | 2.50 |
| 355 | A70 | 50s Oribi | 7.00 | 3.25 |
| | | Nos. 351-355 (5) | 28.00 | 9.40 |

### Souvenir Sheet
#### Perf. 14
| | | | | |
|---|---|---|---|---|
| 356 | A70 | 1.50m Black-backed jackal | 10.50 | 8.50 |

6s, 25s; 50x37mm. No. 356 contains one stamp 48x31mm.

Scouting Year — A71

**1982, Mar. 5**     Litho.     Perf. 14x13½
| | | | | |
|---|---|---|---|---|
| 357 | A71 | 6s Bugle call | .25 | .25 |
| 358 | A71 | 30s Hiking | .50 | .50 |
| 359 | A71 | 40s Drawing | .70 | .70 |
| 360 | A71 | 50s Holding flag | .90 | .90 |
| 361 | A71 | 75s Salute | 1.30 | 1.30 |
| a. | | Booklet pane of 10 + sheet | 11.00 | |
| | | Nos. 357-361 (5) | 3.65 | 3.65 |

### Souvenir Sheet
| | | | | |
|---|---|---|---|---|
| 362 | A71 | 1.50m Baden-Powell | 2.40 | 2.40 |

No. 361a contains 2 each Nos. 357-361 with gutter and No. 362.
Nos. 357-361 issued in sheets of 8 with gutter.

1982 World Cup Soccer — A72

Championships, 1930-1978: a, Uruguay, 1930. b, Italy, 1934. c, France, 1938. d, Brazil, 1950. e, Switzerland, 1954. f, Sweden, 1958. g, Chile, 1962. h, England, 1966. i, Mexico, 1970. j, Germany, 1974. k, Argentina, 1978. l, World Cup.

**1982, Apr. 14**     Perf. 14½
| | | | | |
|---|---|---|---|---|
| 363 | | Sheet of 12 | 4.00 | 4.00 |
| a.-l. | | A72 15s any single | .25 | .25 |

### Souvenir Sheet
| | | | | |
|---|---|---|---|---|
| 364 | A72 | 1.25m Stadium | 2.00 | 2.00 |

Nos. 363b, 363c, 363f, 363g, 363j, 363k exist se-tenant in sheets of 72.

George Washington's Birth Bicentenary — A73

Paintings: 6s, Portrait. 7s, With children. 10s, Indian Chief's Prophecy. 25s, With troops. 40s, Arriving at New York. 1m, Entry into New York. 1.25m, Crossing Delaware.

**1982, June 7**
| | | | | |
|---|---|---|---|---|
| 365 | A73 | 6s multicolored | .25 | .25 |
| 366 | A73 | 7s multicolored | .25 | .25 |
| 367 | A73 | 10s multicolored | .25 | .25 |
| 368 | A73 | 25s multicolored | .35 | .35 |
| 369 | A73 | 40s multicolored | .45 | .45 |
| 370 | A73 | 1m multicolored | .90 | .90 |
| | | Nos. 365-370 (6) | 2.45 | 2.45 |

### Souvenir Sheet
| | | | | |
|---|---|---|---|---|
| 371 | A73 | 1.25m multicolored | 1.75 | 1.75 |

### Princess Diana Issue
### Common Design Type
### Wmk. 373
**1982, July 1**     Litho.     Perf. 14
| | | | | |
|---|---|---|---|---|
| 372 | CD333 | 30s Arms | .75 | .75 |
| 373 | CD333 | 50s Diana | .75 | .75 |
| 374 | CD333 | 75s Wedding | 1.00 | 1.00 |
| 375 | CD333 | 1m Portrait | 1.50 | 1.50 |
| | | Nos. 372-375 (4) | 4.00 | 4.00 |

Sesotho Bible Centenary — A74

6s, Man reading bible. 15s, Angels, bible. 1m, Bible, Maseru Cathedral.

**1982, Aug. 20**     Litho.     Perf. 14½
| | | | | |
|---|---|---|---|---|
| 376 | A74 | 6s multi | .25 | .25 |
| 377 | A74 | 15s multi | .25 | .25 |

#### Size: 59½x40½mm
| | | | | |
|---|---|---|---|---|
| 378 | A74 | 1m multi | .40 | .40 |
| | | Nos. 376-378 (3) | .90 | .90 |

Issued in sheets of 9 (3 each Nos. 376-378).

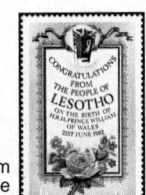

Birth of Prince William of Wales, June 21 — A75

**1982, Sept. 30**
| | | | | |
|---|---|---|---|---|
| 379 | A75 | 6s Congratulation | 3.25 | 3.25 |
| 380 | A75 | 60s Diana, William | 1.75 | 1.75 |

Issued in sheets of 6 (No. 379, 5 No. 380).

Christmas A76

Designs: Scenes from Walt Disney's The Twelve Days of Christmas. Stamps of same denomination se-tenant.

**1982, Dec. 1**     Litho.     Perf. 11
| | | | | |
|---|---|---|---|---|
| 381 | A76 | 2s multicolored | .25 | .25 |
| 382 | A76 | 2s multicolored | .25 | .25 |
| 383 | A76 | 3s multicolored | .25 | .25 |
| 384 | A76 | 3s multicolored | .25 | .25 |
| 385 | A76 | 4s multicolored | .25 | .25 |
| 386 | A76 | 4s multicolored | .25 | .25 |
| 387 | A76 | 75s multicolored | 1.40 | 2.00 |
| 388 | A76 | 75s multicolored | 1.40 | 2.00 |
| | | Nos. 381-388 (8) | 4.30 | 5.50 |

### Souvenir Sheet
#### Perf. 14x13½
| | | | | |
|---|---|---|---|---|
| 389 | A76 | 1.50m multicolored | 4.00 | 4.00 |

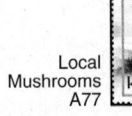

Local Mushrooms A77

10s, Lepista caffrorum. 30s, Broomexia congregate. 50s, Afroboletus luteolus. 75s, Lentinus tuberregium.

**1983, Jan. 11**     Perf. 14½
| | | | | |
|---|---|---|---|---|
| 390 | A77 | 10s multicolored | .25 | .25 |
| 391 | A77 | 30s multicolored | .50 | .40 |
| a. | | Booklet pane of 2, #390, 391 | 1.05 | |
| 392 | A77 | 50s multicolored | .90 | .80 |
| 393 | A77 | 75s multicolored | 1.25 | 1.10 |
| a. | | Booklet pane of 4, #390-393 | 4.00 | |
| | | Nos. 390-393 (4) | 2.90 | 2.55 |

Commonwealth Day — A78

**1983, Mar. 14**     Litho.     Perf. 14½
| | | | | |
|---|---|---|---|---|
| 394 | A78 | 5s Ba-Leseli dance | .25 | .25 |
| 395 | A78 | 30s Tapestry weaving | .25 | .25 |
| 396 | A78 | 60s Elizabeth II | .35 | .35 |
| 397 | A78 | 75s Moshoeshoe II | .40 | .40 |
| | | Nos. 394-397 (4) | 1.25 | 1.25 |

Trance Dancers — A79

Hunters — A79a

Rock Paintings: 25s, Baboons, Sehonghong Thaba Tseka. 60s, Hunter attacking mountain reedbuck, Makhetha Berera. 75s, Eland, Leribe.

**1983, May 20**     Litho.     Perf. 14½
| | | | | |
|---|---|---|---|---|
| 398 | A79 | 6s multicolored | .35 | .35 |
| 399 | A79 | 25s multicolored | .70 | .70 |
| 400 | A79 | 60s multicolored | .80 | .80 |
| 401 | A79 | 75s multicolored | .90 | .90 |
| | | Nos. 398-401 (4) | 2.75 | 2.75 |

### Souvenir Sheet
| | | | | |
|---|---|---|---|---|
| 402 | | Sheet of 5, #398-401, 402a | 3.00 | 3.00 |
| a. | | A79a 10s multicolored | .30 | .25 |

Manned Flight Bicentenary A80

**1983, July 11**     Litho.     Perf. 14½
| | | | | |
|---|---|---|---|---|
| 403 | A80 | 7s Montgolfier, 1783 | .25 | .25 |
| 404 | A80 | 30s Wright brothers | .45 | .35 |
| 405 | A80 | 60s 1st airmail plane | .85 | .75 |
| 406 | A80 | 1m Concorde | 2.50 | 2.50 |
| | | Nos. 403-406 (4) | 4.05 | 3.85 |

### Souvenir Sheet
| | | | | |
|---|---|---|---|---|
| 407 | | Sheet of 5 | 3.00 | 3.00 |
| a. | | A80 6s Dornier 228 | .30 | .30 |

No. 407 contains Nos. 403-406, 407a (60x60mm).

Sesquicentennial of French Missionaries' Arrival — A81

6s, Rev. Eugene Casalis, flags. 25s, Morija, 1833. 40s, Baptism of Libe. 75s, Map of Basutoland, 1834.

**1983, Sept. 5**     Litho.     Perf. 13½x14
| | | | | |
|---|---|---|---|---|
| 408 | A81 | 6s multicolored | .30 | .30 |
| 409 | A81 | 25s multicolored | .30 | .30 |
| 410 | A81 | 40s multicolored | .30 | .30 |
| 411 | A81 | 75s multicolored | .65 | .65 |
| | | Nos. 408-411 (4) | 1.55 | 1.55 |

Christmas A82

Scenes from Disney's Old Christmas, from Washington Irving's Sketch Book: 2s, Christmas Eve, diff. 3s, Christmas Day. 4s, Christmas Day, diff. 5s, Christmas dinner. 6s, Christmas dinner, diff. 75s, Christmas games. 1m, Christmas dancers. 1.75m, Christmas Eve.

**1983, Dec.**     Litho.     Perf. 14
| | | | | |
|---|---|---|---|---|
| 412 | A82 | 1s shown | .25 | .25 |
| 413 | A82 | 2s multicolored | .25 | .25 |
| 414 | A82 | 3s multicolored | .25 | .25 |
| 415 | A82 | 4s multicolored | .25 | .25 |
| 416 | A82 | 5s multicolored | .25 | .25 |
| 417 | A82 | 6s multicolored | .25 | .25 |
| 418 | A82 | 75s multicolored | 2.25 | 2.25 |
| 419 | A82 | 1m multicolored | 2.50 | 2.50 |
| | | Nos. 412-419 (8) | 6.25 | 6.25 |

### Souvenir Sheet
| | | | | |
|---|---|---|---|---|
| 420 | A82 | 1.75m multicolored | 5.00 | 5.00 |

African Monarch — A83

Butterflies: 2s, Mountain Beauty. 3s, Orange Tip. 4s, Blue Pansy. 5s, Yellow Pansy. 6s, African Migrant. 7s, African Leopard. 10s, Suffused Acraea. 15s, Painted Lady. 20s, Lemon Traveller. 30s, Foxy Charaxes. 50s, Broad-Bordered Grass Yellow. 60s, Meadow White. 75s, Queen Purple Tip. 1m, Diadem. 5m, Christmas Butterfly.

**1984, Jan. 20**     Litho.
| | | | | |
|---|---|---|---|---|
| 421 | A83 | 1s shown | .50 | .35 |
| 422 | A83 | 2s multicolored | .50 | .35 |
| 423 | A83 | 3s multicolored | .60 | .40 |
| 424 | A83 | 4s multicolored | .60 | .40 |
| 425 | A83 | 5s multicolored | .60 | .40 |
| 426 | A83 | 6s multicolored | .60 | .40 |
| 427 | A83 | 7s multicolored | .60 | .40 |
| 428 | A83 | 10s multicolored | .70 | .50 |
| 429 | A83 | 15s multicolored | 1.10 | 1.10 |
| 430 | A83 | 20s multicolored | 1.50 | 1.25 |
| 431 | A83 | 30s multicolored | 1.75 | 1.75 |
| 432 | A83 | 50s multicolored | 1.75 | 1.75 |
| 433 | A83 | 60s multicolored | 1.75 | 1.75 |
| 434 | A83 | 75s multicolored | 1.90 | 2.00 |
| 435 | A83 | 1m multicolored | 1.90 | 1.90 |
| 436 | A83 | 5m multicolored | 3.00 | 4.50 |
| | | Nos. 421-436 (16) | 19.35 | 19.30 |

For surcharges see Nos. 559-560, 561A, 564-566, 600, 600A, 600D, 617A-617B.

Easter — A84

Designs: Nos. 437a-437j, The Ten Commandments. 1.50m, Moses holding tablets.

**1984, Mar. 30**     Litho.     Perf. 14
| | | | | |
|---|---|---|---|---|
| 437 | | Sheet of 10 + 2 labels | 6.50 | 6.50 |
| a.-j. | | A84 20s any single | .30 | .30 |

### Souvenir Sheet
| | | | | |
|---|---|---|---|---|
| 438 | A84 | 1.50m multicolored | 1.75 | 1.75 |

No. 438 contains one stamp 45x29mm.

1984 Summer Olympics A85

10s, Torch bearer. 30s, Equestrian. 50s, Swimming. 75s, Basketball. 1m, Running. 1.50m, Flags, flame, stadium.

**1984, May 5**     Litho.     Perf. 13½
| | | | | |
|---|---|---|---|---|
| 439 | A85 | 10s multicolored | .25 | .25 |
| 440 | A85 | 30s multicolored | .25 | .25 |
| 441 | A85 | 50s multicolored | .25 | .25 |
| 442 | A85 | 75s multicolored | .35 | .35 |
| 443 | A85 | 1m multicolored | .45 | .45 |
| | | Nos. 439-443 (5) | 1.55 | 1.55 |

### Souvenir Sheet
| | | | | |
|---|---|---|---|---|
| 444 | A85 | 1.50m multicolored | 1.60 | 1.60 |

Prehistoric Footprints A86

10s, Sauropodomorph. 30s, Lesothosaurus. 50s, Carnivorous dinosaur.

**1984, July 2**     Litho.     Perf. 13½
| | | | | |
|---|---|---|---|---|
| 445 | A86 | 10s multicolored | .25 | .25 |
| 446 | A86 | 30s multicolored | .80 | .80 |
| 447 | A86 | 50s multicolored | 1.45 | 1.45 |
| | | Nos. 445-447 (3) | 2.50 | 2.50 |

Mail Coach Bicentenary and Ausipex '84 — A87

6s, Wells Fargo, 1852. 7s, Basotho mail cart, 1900. 10s, Bath mail coach, 1784. 30s, Cobb coach, 1853. 50s, Exhibition buildings. 1.75m, Penny Black, Basutoland #O4, Western Australia #3.

| 1984, Sept. 5 | Litho. | Perf. 14 | |
|---|---|---|---|
| 448 | A87 | 6s multicolored | .25 | .25 |
| a. | | Sheet of 4 #448, 1 #451A | 1.00 | 1.00 |
| 449 | A87 | 7s multicolored | .25 | .25 |
| a. | | Sheet of 4 #449, 1 #451A | 1.00 | 1.00 |
| 450 | A87 | 10s multicolored | .25 | .25 |
| a. | | Sheet of 4 #450, 1 #451A | 1.00 | 1.00 |
| 451 | A87 | 30s multicolored | .25 | .25 |
| b. | | Sheet of 4 #451, 1 #451A | 1.00 | 1.00 |

**Size: 82x26mm**

| 451A | A87 | 50s multicolored | .45 | .45 |
|---|---|---|---|---|
| | Nos. 448-451A (5) | | 1.45 | 1.45 |

**Souvenir Sheet**

| 452 | A87 | 1.75m multicolored | 3.25 | 3.25 |
|---|---|---|---|---|

No. 452 contains one stamp 82x26mm.

Trains — A88

6s, Orient Express, 1900. 15s, 05.001, Class 5, 1935. 30s, Cardean, Caledonian, 1906. 60s, Santa Fe, Super Chief, 1940. 1m, Flying Scotsman, 1934.
2m, The Blue Train, 1972.

| 1984, Nov. 5 | Litho. | Perf. 13½ | |
|---|---|---|---|
| 453 | A88 | 6s multicolored | .25 | .25 |
| 454 | A88 | 15s multicolored | .30 | .30 |
| 455 | A88 | 30s multicolored | .40 | .40 |
| 456 | A88 | 60s multicolored | .80 | 1.25 |
| 457 | A88 | 1m multicolored | 1.60 | 2.00 |
| | Nos. 453-457 (5) | | 3.35 | 4.20 |

**Souvenir Sheet**
**Perf. 14x13½**

| 458 | A88 | 2m multicolored | 2.10 | 2.10 |
|---|---|---|---|---|

Indigenous Young Animals — A89

15s, Cape Eland calf. 20s, Chacma baboons. 30s, Oribo calf. 75s, Red rock hares. 1m, Black-backed jackals.

| 1984, Dec. 20 | | Perf. 14½ | |
|---|---|---|---|
| 459 | A89 | 15s multicolored | .25 | .25 |
| 460 | A89 | 20s multicolored | .30 | .30 |
| 461 | A89 | 30s multicolored | .45 | .45 |
| 462 | A89 | 75s multicolored | .90 | 1.25 |

**Size: 47x28mm**
**Perf. 13½**

| 463 | A89 | 1m multicolored | 1.25 | 1.75 |
|---|---|---|---|---|
| | Nos. 459-463 (5) | | 3.15 | 4.00 |

King Moshoeshoe II — A90

6s, Royal crown, 1974. 30s, Moshoeshoe II, 1966. 75s, In Basotho dress. 1m, In military uniform.

| 1985, Jan. 30 | Litho. | Perf. 15 | |
|---|---|---|---|
| 464 | A90 | 6s multicolored | .25 | .25 |
| 465 | A90 | 30s multicolored | .25 | .25 |
| 466 | A90 | 75s multicolored | .45 | .45 |
| 467 | A90 | 1m multicolored | .65 | .65 |
| | Nos. 464-467 (4) | | 1.60 | 1.60 |

25th anniversary of reign.

Miniature Sheet

Easter — A91

Stations of the Cross: a, Condemned to death. b, Bearing cross. c, Falls the first time. d, Meets his mother. e, Cyrenean helps carry cross. f, Veronica wipes His face. g, Second fall. h, Consoles women of Jerusalem. i, Third fall. j, Stripped. k, Nailed to cross. l, Dies on cross. m, Taken down from cross. n, Laid in sepulchre.
No. 469, The Crucifixion, detail, by Mathias Grunewald (c. 1460-1528).

| 1985, Mar. 8 | | Perf. 11 | |
|---|---|---|---|
| 468 | A91 | Sheet of 14 + label | 6.50 | 6.50 |
| a.-n. | | 20s any single | .25 | .25 |

**Souvenir Sheet**
**Perf. 14**

| 469 | A91 | 2m multicolored | 2.25 | 2.25 |
|---|---|---|---|---|

Queen Mother, 85th Birthday A92

Photographs: 10s, Queen Mother, Princess Elizabeth, 1931. 30s, 75th birthday portrait. 60s With Queen Elizabeth II and Princess Margaret, 80th birthday. No. 473, With Queen Elizabeth II, Princess Diana, Princes Henry and Charles, christening of Prince Henry.
No. 474, like No. 473, with Prince William.

| 1985, May 30 | | Perf. 13½x14 | |
|---|---|---|---|
| 470 | A92 | 10s multicolored | .25 | .25 |
| 471 | A92 | 30s multicolored | .90 | .90 |
| 472 | A92 | 60s multicolored | 1.00 | 1.00 |
| 473 | A92 | 2m multicolored | 1.75 | 1.75 |
| | Nos. 470-473 (4) | | 3.90 | 3.90 |

**Souvenir Sheet**

| 474 | A92 | 2m multicolored | 2.00 | 2.00 |
|---|---|---|---|---|

No. 474 contains one stamp 38x51mm.

Automobile Centenary A93

Luxury cars: 6s, BMW 732i. 10s, Ford LTD Crown Victoria. 30s, Mercedes-Benz 500SE. 90s, Cadillac Eldorado Biarritz. No. 479, Rolls Royce Silver Spirit.
No. 480, 1907 Rolls Royce Silver Ghost Tourer, vert.

| 1985, June 10 | | Perf. 14 | |
|---|---|---|---|
| 475 | A93 | 6s multicolored | .35 | .25 |
| 476 | A93 | 10s multicolored | .50 | .25 |
| 477 | A93 | 30s multicolored | .80 | .60 |
| 478 | A93 | 90s multicolored | 1.50 | 1.50 |
| 479 | A93 | 2m multicolored | 3.00 | 3.00 |
| | Nos. 475-479 (5) | | 6.15 | 5.60 |

**Souvenir Sheet**

| 480 | A93 | 2m multicolored | 5.50 | 5.50 |
|---|---|---|---|---|

No. 480 contains one stamp 38x51mm.

Audubon Birth Bicentenary A94

Illustrations of North American bird species by artist and naturalist John J. Audubon: 5s, Cliff swallow, vert. 6s, Great crested grebe. 10s, Vesper sparrow. 30s, Greenshank. 60s, Stilt sandpiper. 2m, Glossy ibis.

| 1985, Aug. 5 | | Perf. 14½ | |
|---|---|---|---|
| 481 | A94 | 5s multicolored | .55 | .45 |
| 482 | A94 | 6s multicolored | .70 | .45 |
| 483 | A94 | 10s multicolored | 1.25 | .60 |
| 484 | A94 | 30s multicolored | 1.75 | 1.75 |
| 485 | A94 | 60s multicolored | 2.25 | 2.25 |
| 486 | A94 | 2m multicolored | 3.50 | 3.50 |
| | Nos. 481-486 (6) | | 10.00 | 9.00 |

Nos. 481-486 printed in sheets of 5 with labels picturing various birds.

Intl. Youth Year, Girl Guides 75th Anniv. — A95

10s, Mountain climbing. 30s, Medical research. 75s, Guides on parade. No. 490, 2m, Guide saluting.
No. 491, Lady Baden-Powell, World Chief Guide.

| 1985, Sept. 26 | | Perf. 15 | |
|---|---|---|---|
| 487 | A95 | 10s multicolored | .25 | .25 |
| 488 | A95 | 30s multicolored | .60 | .60 |
| 489 | A95 | 75s multicolored | 1.25 | 1.25 |
| 490 | A95 | 2m multicolored | 2.50 | 2.50 |
| | Nos. 487-490 (4) | | 4.60 | 4.60 |

**Souvenir Sheet**

| 491 | A95 | 2m multicolored | 3.50 | 3.50 |
|---|---|---|---|---|

UN, 40th Anniv. — A96

Designs: 10s, UN No. 1, flag, horiz. 30s, Dish satellite, Ha Sofonia Earth Satellite Station, ITU emblem. 50s, Aircraft, Maseru Airport, ICAO emblem, horiz. 2m, Maimonides (1135-1204), medieval Jewish scholar, WHO emblem.

| 1985, Oct. 15 | Litho. | Perf. 15 | |
|---|---|---|---|
| 492 | A96 | 10s multicolored | .30 | .30 |
| 493 | A96 | 30s multicolored | .50 | .50 |
| 494 | A96 | 50s multicolored | .90 | .90 |
| 495 | A96 | 2m multicolored | 4.50 | 4.50 |
| | Nos. 492-495 (4) | | 6.20 | 6.20 |

Wildflowers — A97

6s, Cosmos. 10s, Small agapanthus. 30s, Pink witchweed. 60s, Small iris. 90s, Wild geranium. 1m, Large spotted orchid.

| 1985, Nov. 11 | | Perf. 11 | |
|---|---|---|---|
| 496 | A97 | 6s multicolored | .45 | .25 |
| 497 | A97 | 10s multicolored | .60 | .25 |
| 498 | A97 | 30s multicolored | 1.10 | .75 |
| 499 | A97 | 60s multicolored | 1.75 | 1.75 |
| 500 | A97 | 90s multicolored | 2.25 | 2.25 |
| 501 | A97 | 1m multicolored | 3.00 | 3.00 |
| | Nos. 496-501 (6) | | 9.15 | 8.25 |

Mark Twain, Author, Jacob and Wilhelm Grimm, Fabulists — A98

Disney characters acting out Mark Twain quotes or portraying characters from The Wishing Table, by the Grimm Brothers.

| 1985, Dec. 2 | | Perf. 11 | |
|---|---|---|---|
| 502 | A98 | 6s multicolored | .25 | .25 |
| 503 | A98 | 10s multicolored | .25 | .25 |
| 504 | A98 | 50s multicolored | 1.40 | 1.40 |
| 505 | A98 | 60s multicolored | 1.90 | 1.90 |
| 506 | A98 | 75s multicolored | 2.25 | 2.25 |
| 507 | A98 | 90s multicolored | 2.75 | 2.75 |
| 508 | A98 | 1m multicolored | 3.00 | 3.00 |
| 509 | A98 | 1.50m multicolored | 5.00 | 5.00 |
| | Nos. 502-509 (8) | | 16.80 | 16.80 |

**Souvenir Sheets**
**Perf. 14**

| 510 | A98 | 1.25m multicolored | 6.00 | 6.00 |
|---|---|---|---|---|
| 511 | A98 | 1.50m multicolored | 6.00 | 6.00 |

Christmas. Nos. 505, 507 printed in sheets of 8.

World Wildlife Fund — A99

Lammergeier vulture.

| 1986, Jan. 20 | | Perf. 15 | |
|---|---|---|---|
| 512 | A99 | 7s Male | 2.00 | .75 |
| 513 | A99 | 15s Male, female | 3.75 | 1.00 |
| 514 | A99 | 50s Male in flight | 5.50 | 2.00 |
| 515 | A99 | 1m Adult, young | 7.00 | 3.50 |
| | Nos. 512-515 (4) | | 18.25 | 7.25 |

Flora and Fauna — A100

9s, Prickly pear. 12s, Stapelia. 35s, Pig's ears. No. 519, 2m, Columnar cereus.
No. 520, 2m, Black eagle.

| 1986, Jan. 20 | | | |
|---|---|---|---|
| 516 | A100 | 9s multicolored | .50 | .25 |
| 517 | A100 | 12s multicolored | .50 | .25 |
| 518 | A100 | 35s multicolored | .75 | .50 |
| 519 | A100 | 2m multicolored | 2.75 | 2.50 |
| | Nos. 516-519 (4) | | 4.50 | 3.50 |

**Souvenir Sheet**

| 520 | A100 | 2m multicolored | 9.75 | 9.75 |
|---|---|---|---|---|

1986 World Cup Soccer Championships, Mexico — A101

Various soccer plays.

| 1986, Mar. 17 | | Perf. 14 | |
|---|---|---|---|
| 521 | A101 | 35s multicolored | 1.25 | 1.25 |
| 522 | A101 | 50s multicolored | 1.75 | 1.75 |
| 523 | A101 | 1m multicolored | 3.50 | 3.50 |
| 524 | A101 | 2m multicolored | 7.00 | 7.00 |
| | Nos. 521-524 (4) | | 13.50 | 13.50 |

**Souvenir Sheet**

| 525 | A101 | 3m multicolored | 10.00 | 10.00 |
|---|---|---|---|---|

New Currency, 1st Anniv. (in 1980) A101a

No. 525A — Both sides of: b, 1979 Intl. Year of the Child gold coin. c, Five-maloti banknote. d, 1979 50-lisente coin. e, Ten-maloti banknote. f, 1979 1-sente coin.

**1986, Apr. 1    Litho.    Perf. 13¾x14**
525A        Horiz. strip of 5        30.00 32.50
  b.-f.  A101a 30s Any single        6.00  6.50

A102

Halley's Comet — A103

Designs: 9s, Hale Telescope, Mt. Palomar, Galileo. 15s, Pioneer Venus 2 probe, 1985 sighting. 70s, 684 sighting illustration, Nuremberg Chronicles. 3m, 1066 sighting, Norman conquest of England. 4m, Comet over Lesotho.

**1986, Apr. 5**
526 A102  9s multicolored    .65   .25
527 A102 15s multicolored    .90   .25
528 A102 70s multicolored   2.00   .75
529 A102  3m multicolored   5.50  6.00
  Nos. 526-529 (4)           9.05  7.25

**Souvenir Sheet**
530 A103  4m multicolored   8.50  8.50

**Queen Elizabeth II, 60th Birthday**
**Common Design Type**
Designs: 90s, In pantomime during youth. 1m, At Windsor Horse Show, 1971. 2m, At Royal Festival Hall, 1971. 4m, Age 8.

**1986, Apr. 21**
531 CD339 90s lt yel bis & black  .55  .55
532 CD339 1m pale grn & multi     .65  .65
533 CD339 2m dull vio & multi    1.30 1.30
  Nos. 531-533 (3)               2.50 2.50

**Souvenir Sheet**
534 CD339 4m tan & black    2.75 2.75
  For overprints see Nos. 636-639.

Statue of Liberty, Cent. — A104

Statue and famous emigrants: 15s, Bela Bartok (1881-1945), composer. 35s, Felix Adler (1857-1933), philosopher. 1m, Victor Herbert (1859-1924), composer. No. 538, David Niven (1910-1983), actor. No. 539, Statue, vert.

**1986, May 1**
535 A104 15s multicolored    .90  .25
536 A104 35s multicolored    .90  .35
537 A104  1m multicolored   3.25 1.75
538 A104  3m multicolored   5.00 3.00
  Nos. 535-538 (4)          10.05 5.35

**Souvenir Sheet**
539 A104  3m multicolored   6.50 6.50

AMERIPEX '86 — A105

Walt Disney characters: 15s, Goofy, Mickey. 35s, Mickey, Pluto. 1m, Goofy. 2m, Donald, Pete. 4m, Goofy, Chip'n'Dale.

**1986, May 22    Perf. 11**
540 A105 15s multicolored   1.10  .25
541 A105 35s multicolored   1.40  .45
542 A105  1m multicolored   3.00 1.90
543 A105  2m multicolored   3.50 2.50
  Nos. 540-543 (4)          9.00 5.10

**Souvenir Sheet**
**Perf. 14**
544 A105  4m multicolored  11.00 11.00

**Royal Wedding Issue, 1986**
**Common Design Type**
Designs: 50s, Prince Andrew and Sarah Ferguson. 1m, Andrew. 3m, Andrew at helicopter controls. 4m, Couple, diff.

**1986, July 23    Perf. 14**
545 CD340 50s multicolored   .50   .50
546 CD340  1m multicolored   .95   .95
547 CD340  3m multicolored  2.25  2.25
  Nos. 545-547 (3)          3.70  3.70

**Souvenir Sheet**
548 CD340  4m multicolored  3.75  3.75

Natl. Independence, 20th Anniv. — A106

9s, Basotho pony, rider. 15s, Mohair spinning. 35s, River crossing. 4m, Moshoeshoe I.

**1986, Oct. 20    Litho.    Perf. 15**
549 A106  9s multicolored    .25   .25
550 A106 15s multicolored    .25   .25
551 A106 35s multicolored    .35   .35
552 A106  3m Thaba Tseka P.O. 2.25 2.25
  Nos. 549-552 (4)          3.10  3.10

**Souvenir Sheet**
553 A106  4m multicolored   7.00  7.00

Christmas — A107

Walt Disney characters: 15s, Chip'n'Dale. 35s, Mickey, Minnie. 1m, Pluto. 2m, Aunt Matilda. 5m, Huey and Dewey.

**1986, Nov. 4    Litho.    Perf. 11**
554 A107 15s multicolored    .85   .25
555 A107 35s multicolored   1.25   .40
556 A107  1m multicolored   1.75  1.60
557 A107  2m multicolored   2.50  2.50
  Nos. 554-557 (4)          6.35  4.75

**Souvenir Sheet**
**Perf. 14**
558 A107  5m multicolored  10.00 10.00

**Butterfly and Bird Type of 1981-84**
**Surcharged**
**1986    Litho.    Perf. 14, 14½**
558A A66   9s on 10s #327b   6.00  1.75
  b.        9s on 10s #327   4.00  4.00
559  A83   9s on 30s No. 431      .25   .25
  a.        9s on 30s #431 (surcharge smaller & sans serif)  7.50  5.00
560  A83   9s on 60s No. 433      .25   .25
561  A66  15s on 1s No. 321      85.00
  b.       15s on 1s #321a       7.00  8.50
  c.       15s on 1s #321b      10.00  4.50
561A A83  15s on 1s No. 421      2.50  2.50
562  A66  15s on 2s No. 322       .30   .25
563  A66  15s on 60s No. 330      .30   .25
  a.       15s on 60s #330a      4.50  5.00
564  A83  15s on 2s No. 422       .30   .25
565  A83  15s on 3s No. 423       .30   .25
566  A83  35s on 75s No. 434     24.00 17.50
  a.       35s on 75s #434, small "s"  50.00 52.50
  Nos. 558A-566 (10)          119.20 23.25
Issued: Nos. 559-560, July 1. Nos. 561-563, Aug. 22. Nos. 561A, 564-566, June 25. See Nos. 617A-617B.

Roof of Africa Rally — A108

**1987, Apr. 28    Litho.    Perf. 14**
567 A108  9s White car      .45   .25
568 A108 15s Motorcycle #26 .55   .25
569 A108 35s Motorcycle #25 .75   .35
570 A108  4m Red car       3.25  3.25
  Nos. 567-570 (4)         5.00  4.10

1988 Summer Olympics, Seoul — A109

**1987, May 29    Perf. 14**
571 A109  9s Tennis         .80   .25
572 A109 15s Judo           .80   .25
573 A109 20s Running        .90   .25
574 A109 35s Boxing        1.00   .45
575 A109  1m Diving        1.25  1.10
576 A109  3m Bowling       3.00  3.00
  Nos. 571-576 (6)         7.75  5.30

**Souvenir Sheet**
577  A109  2m Tennis, diff. 2.75  2.75
577A A109  4m Soccer        5.25  5.25
  See Nos. 606-611.
No. 577A shows green at lower left diagonal half of the flag.

Inventors and Innovators A110

Designs: 5s, Sir Isaac Newton, reflecting telescope. 9s, Alexander Graham Bell, telephone. 75s, Robert H. Goddard, liquid fuel rocket. 4m, Chuck Yeager (b. 1923), test pilot. No. 582, Mariner 10 spacecraft.

**1987, June 30    Perf. 15**
578 A110  5s multicolored   .45   .25
579 A110  9s multicolored   .45   .25
580 A110 75s multicolored  1.00   .75
581 A110  4m multicolored  3.50  3.50
  Nos. 578-581 (4)         5.40  4.75

**Souvenir Sheet**
582  A110  4m multicolored  4.75  4.70

Fauna and Flora — A111

5s, Gray rhebuck. 9s, Cape clawless otter. 15s, Cape gray mongoose. 20s, Free state daisy. 35s, River bells. 1m, Turkey flower. 2m, Sweet briar. 3m, Mountain reedbuck.
No. 591, Pig-lily. No. 592, Cape wildebeest.

**1987, Aug. 14**
583 A111  5s multicolored    .50   .25
584 A111  9s multicolored    .50   .25
585 A111 15s multicolored    .70   .25
586 A111 20s multicolored    .80   .25
587 A111 35s multicolored    .90   .35
588 A111  1m multicolored   2.00  1.00
589 A111  2m multicolored   2.50  2.00
590 A111  3m multicolored   3.00  3.00
  Nos. 583-590 (8)         10.90  7.35

**Souvenir Sheet**
591  A111  2m multicolored  3.00  3.00
592  A111  4m multicolored  5.25  5.25
  Nos. 586-589 and 591 vert.

16th World Scout Jamboree, Australia, 1987-88 — A112

**1987, Sept. 10    Litho.    Perf. 14**
593 A112  9s Orienteering   .25   .25
594 A112 15s Playing soccer .25   .25
595 A112 35s Kangaroos      .65   .65
596 A112 75s Salute, flag  1.25  1.25
597 A112  4m Windsurfing   6.25  6.25
  Nos. 593-597 (5)         8.65  8.65

**Souvenir Sheet**
598 A112  4m Map, flag of Australia  5.25  5.25

Nos. 324, 425, 424, 328 and 427 Surcharged

**1987    Litho.    Perf. 14½, 14**
598A A66   9s on 5s No. 324    .75   .25
599  A66  15s on 5s No. 324   2.00   .25
600  A83  15s on 5s No. 425    .25   .25
600A A83  20s on 4s No. 424    .25   .25
600B A66  35s on 25s No. 328  1.50   .60
  e.       35s on 25s #328, small "s"
  f.       35s on 25s #328a
  g.       35s on 25s #328a, small "s"
600C A66  35s on 75s #331
  h.       35s on 75s #331, small "s"
600D A83  40s on 7s No. 427    .40   .40
Issued: Nos. 599-600, 11/16; No. 600B, 12/15; Nos. 598A, 600A, 600D, 12/30.

A113

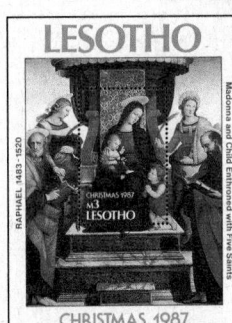

A114

Religious paintings (details) by Raphael: 9s, Madonna and Child. 15s, Marriage of the Virgin. 35s, Coronation of the Virgin. 90s, Madonna of the Chair. 3m, Madonna and Child Enthroned with Five Saints.

**1987, Dec. 21    Perf. 14**
601 A113  9s multicolored    .25   .25
602 A113 15s multicolored    .25   .25
603 A113 35s multicolored   1.25  1.25
604 A113 90s multicolored   3.00  3.00
  Nos. 601-604 (4)          4.75  4.75

**Souvenir Sheet**
605 A114  3m multicolored   4.50  4.50
  Christmas.

**Summer Olympics Type of 1987**
**1987, Nov. 30    Litho.    Perf. 14**
606 A109  5s like 9s        .25   .25
607 A109 10s like 15s       .25   .25
608 A109 25s like 20s       .25   .25
609 A109 40s like 35s       .35   .35
610 A109 50s like 1m        .50   .50
611 A109 3.50m like 3m     3.25  3.25
  Nos. 606-611 (6)          4.85  4.85

**Souvenir Sheet**
612 A109  4m Soccer        4.00  4.00
No. 612 shows green at lower right diagonal half of the flag.

Discovery of America, 500th Anniv. (in 1992) — A115

Columbus's fleet and marine life: 9s, Spotted trunkfish. 15s, Green sea turtle. 35s, Common dolphin. 5m, White-tailed tropicbird. 4m, Ship.

**1987, Dec. 14**    **Litho.**    *Perf. 14*

| | | | | |
|---|---|---|---|---|
| 613 | A115 | 9s multicolored | .25 | .25 |
| 614 | A115 | 15s multicolored | .25 | .25 |
| 615 | A115 | 35s multicolored | .60 | .60 |
| 616 | A115 | 5m multicolored | 8.00 | 8.00 |
| | | *Nos. 613-616 (4)* | 9.10 | 9.10 |

**Souvenir Sheet**

| | | | | |
|---|---|---|---|---|
| 617 | A115 | 4m multicolored | 6.50 | 6.50 |

Nos. 328, 559
Surcharged

**1988**

**Methods and Perfs as Before**

| | | | | |
|---|---|---|---|---|
| 617A | A83 | 3s on 9s on 30s | | |
| 617B | A83 | 7s on 9s on 30s | | |
| 617C | A66 | 16s on 25s No. 328 | — | — |

Issued: Nos. 617A, 617B, 2/2/88; No. 617C, 3/88.

Birds — A116

2s, Pied kingfisher. 3s, Three-banded plover. 5s, Spurwing goose. 10s, Clapper lark. 12s, Red-eyed bulbul. 16s, Cape weaver. 20s, Red-headed finch. 30s, Mountain chat. 40s, Stone chat. 55s, Pied barbet. 60s, Cape glossy starling. 75s, Cape sparrow. 1m, Cattle egret. 3m, Giant kingfisher. 10m, Crowned guinea fowl.

**1988, Apr. 5**    **Litho.**    *Perf. 15*

| | | | | |
|---|---|---|---|---|
| 618 | A116 | 2s multicolored | .25 | .25 |
| 619 | A116 | 3s multicolored | .25 | .25 |
| 620 | A116 | 5s multicolored | .25 | .25 |
| 621 | A116 | 10s multicolored | .25 | .25 |
| 622 | A116 | 12s multicolored | .25 | .25 |
| 623 | A116 | 16s multicolored | .25 | .25 |
| 624 | A116 | 20s multicolored | .25 | .25 |
| 625 | A116 | 30s multicolored | .30 | .30 |
| 626 | A116 | 40s multicolored | .40 | .40 |
| 627 | A116 | 55s multicolored | .55 | .55 |
| 628 | A116 | 60s multicolored | .60 | .60 |
| 629 | A116 | 75s multicolored | .75 | .75 |
| 630 | A116 | 1m multicolored | .85 | .85 |
| 631 | A116 | 3m multicolored | 2.50 | 2.50 |
| 632 | A116 | 10m multicolored | 9.00 | 9.00 |
| | | *Nos. 618-632 (15)* | 16.70 | 16.70 |

For surcharges see Nos. 755, 805-806.

**1989, Sept. 18**      *Perf. 14*

| | | | | |
|---|---|---|---|---|
| 620a | A116 | 5s multicolored | .25 | .25 |
| 622a | A116 | 12s multicolored | .25 | .25 |
| 623a | A116 | 16s multicolored | .25 | .25 |
| 624a | A116 | 20s multicolored | .25 | .25 |
| 630a | A116 | 1m multicolored | .80 | .80 |
| 631a | A116 | 3m multicolored | 2.40 | 2.40 |
| 632a | A116 | 10m multicolored | 8.00 | 8.00 |
| | | *Nos. 620a-632a (7)* | 12.20 | 12.20 |

Dated 1989.

**1990**      *Perf. 12½x12*

| | | | | |
|---|---|---|---|---|
| 620b | A116 | 5s multicolored | .25 | .25 |
| 622b | A116 | 12s multicolored | .25 | .25 |
| 623b | A116 | 16s multicolored | .25 | .25 |
| 624b | A116 | 20s multicolored | .25 | .25 |
| 630b | A116 | 1m multicolored | .80 | .80 |
| 631b | A116 | 3m multicolored | 2.40 | 2.40 |
| 632b | A116 | 10m multicolored | 8.00 | 8.00 |
| | | *Nos. 620b-632b (7)* | 12.20 | 12.20 |

Dated 1989.

**1991 (?)**      *Perf. 11½x13*

| | | | | |
|---|---|---|---|---|
| 620c | A116 | 5s multicolored | .25 | .25 |
| 622c | A116 | 12s multicolored | .25 | .25 |
| 623c | A116 | 16s multicolored | .25 | .25 |
| 624c | A116 | 20s multicolored | .25 | .25 |
| 630c | A116 | 1m multicolored | .80 | .80 |
| 631c | A116 | 3m multicolored | 2.40 | 2.40 |
| 632c | A116 | 10m multicolored | 8.00 | 8.00 |
| | | *Nos. 620c-632c (7)* | 12.20 | 12.20 |

Dated 1989.

**Nos. 531-534 Ovptd. "40th WEDDING ANNIVERSARY / H.M. QUEEN ELIZABETH II / H.R.H. THE DUKE OF EDINBURGH" in Silver**

**1988, May 3**      *Perf. 14*

| | | | | |
|---|---|---|---|---|
| 636 | CD339 | 90s lt yel bis & blk | .90 | .90 |
| 637 | CD339 | 1m pale grn & multi | 1.00 | 1.00 |
| 638 | CD339 | 2m dull vio & multi | 2.00 | 2.00 |
| | | *Nos. 636-638 (3)* | 3.90 | 3.90 |

**Souvenir Sheet**

| | | | | |
|---|---|---|---|---|
| 639 | CD339 | 4m tan & black | 4.00 | 4.00 |

FINLANDIA '88, Helsinki, June 1-12 — A117

Disney animated characters and Helsinki sights: 1s, Touring President's Palace. 2s, Sauna. 3s, Lake Country fishing. 4s, Finlandia Hall. 5s, Photographing Sibelius Monument. 10s, Pony trek, youth hostel. 3m, Olympic Stadium. 5m, Santa Claus, Arctic Circle. No. 648, Market Square. No. 649, Lapp encampment, vert.

**1988, June 2**    **Litho.**    *Perf. 14x13½*

| | | | | |
|---|---|---|---|---|
| 640 | A117 | 1s multicolored | .25 | .25 |
| 641 | A117 | 2s multicolored | .25 | .25 |
| 642 | A117 | 3s multicolored | .25 | .25 |
| 643 | A117 | 4s multicolored | .25 | .25 |
| 644 | A117 | 5s multicolored | .25 | .25 |
| 645 | A117 | 10s multicolored | .30 | .30 |
| 646 | A117 | 3m multicolored | 4.25 | 3.50 |
| 647 | A117 | 5m multicolored | 5.25 | 4.75 |
| | | *Nos. 640-647 (8)* | 11.05 | 9.80 |

**Souvenir Sheets**
*Perf. 14x13½, 13½x14*

| | | | | |
|---|---|---|---|---|
| 648 | A117 | 4m multicolored | 4.50 | 4.50 |
| 649 | A117 | 4m multicolored | 4.50 | 4.50 |

Mickey Mouse, 60th anniv.

A118

55s, Pope giving communion. 2m, Leading procession. 3m, Walking in garden. 4m, Wearing scullcap. 5m, Pope, Archbishop Morapeli of Lesotho, horiz.

**1988, Sept. 1**    **Litho.**    *Perf. 14*

| | | | | |
|---|---|---|---|---|
| 650 | A118 | 55s multicolored | .50 | .50 |
| 651 | A118 | 2m multicolored | 1.60 | 1.60 |
| 652 | A118 | 3m multicolored | 2.50 | 2.50 |
| 653 | A118 | 4m multicolored | 3.50 | 3.50 |
| | | *Nos. 650-653 (4)* | 8.10 | 8.10 |

**Souvenir Sheet**

| | | | | |
|---|---|---|---|---|
| 654 | A118 | 5m multicolored | 8.00 | 8.00 |

Visit of Pope John Paul II, Sept. 14-16.

A119

Small indigenous mammals: 16s, Rock hyrax. 40s, Honey badger. 75s, Genet. 3m, Yellow mongoose. 4m, Meerkat.

**1988, Oct. 13**    **Litho.**    *Perf. 14*

| | | | | |
|---|---|---|---|---|
| 655 | A119 | 16s multicolored | .25 | .25 |
| 656 | A119 | 40s multicolored | .85 | .85 |
| 657 | A119 | 75s multicolored | 1.50 | 1.50 |
| 658 | A119 | 3m multicolored | 5.75 | 5.75 |
| | | *Nos. 655-658 (4)* | 8.35 | 8.35 |

**Souvenir Sheet**

| | | | | |
|---|---|---|---|---|
| 659 | A119 | 4m multicolored | 5.25 | 5.25 |

Birth of Venus, 1480, by Botticelli — A120

Paintings: 25s, View of Toledo, 1608, by El Greco. 40s, Maids of Honor, 1656, by Diego Velazquez. 50s, The Fifer, 1866, by Manet. 55s, The Starry Night, 1889, by Van Gogh. 75s, Prima Ballerina, 1876, by Degas. 2m, Bridge over Water Lilies, 1899, by Monet. 3m, Guernica, 1937, by Picasso. No. 668, The Presentation of the Virgin in the Temple, c. 1534, by Titian. No. 669, The Miracle of the Newborn Infant, 1511, by Titian.

**1988, Oct. 17**    **Litho.**    *Perf. 13½x14*

| | | | | |
|---|---|---|---|---|
| 660 | A120 | 15s multicolored | .40 | .25 |
| 661 | A120 | 25s multicolored | .55 | .25 |
| 662 | A120 | 40s multicolored | .65 | .40 |
| 663 | A120 | 50s multicolored | .75 | .50 |
| 664 | A120 | 55s multicolored | .80 | .55 |
| 665 | A120 | 75s multicolored | .90 | .90 |
| 666 | A120 | 2m multicolored | 2.00 | 2.00 |
| 667 | A120 | 3m multicolored | 2.50 | 2.50 |
| | | *Nos. 660-667 (8)* | 8.55 | 7.35 |

**Souvenir Sheets**

| | | | | |
|---|---|---|---|---|
| 668 | A120 | 4m multicolored | 3.50 | 3.50 |
| 669 | A120 | 4m multicolored | 3.50 | 3.50 |

1988 Summer Olympics, Seoul — A121

12s, Wrestling, horiz. 16s, Equestrian. 55s, Shooting, horiz. 4m, Olympic flame.

**1988, Nov. 11**    **Litho.**    *Perf. 14*

| | | | | |
|---|---|---|---|---|
| 670 | A121 | 12s multicolored | .25 | .25 |
| 671 | A121 | 16s multicolored | .25 | .25 |
| 672 | A121 | 55s multicolored | .40 | .40 |
| 673 | A121 | 3.50m like 16s | 2.10 | 2.10 |
| | | *Nos. 670-673 (4)* | 3.00 | 3.00 |

**Souvenir Sheet**

| | | | | |
|---|---|---|---|---|
| 674 | A121 | 4m multicolored | 4.75 | 4.75 |

Intl. Tennis Federation, 75th Anniv. — A122

Tennis champions, views of cities or landmarks: 12s, Yannick Noah, Eiffel Tower, horiz. 20s, Rod Laver, Sydney Opera House and Harbor Bridge, horiz. 30s, Ivan Lendl, Prague, horiz. 65s, Jimmy Connors, Tokyo. 1m, Arthur Ashe, Barcelona. 1.55m, Althea Gibson, NYC. 2m, Chris Evert, Vienna. 2.40m, Boris Becker, London. 3m, Martina Navratilova, Golden Gate Bridge, horiz. 4m, Steffi Graf, Berlin, West Germany.

**1988, Nov. 18**

| | | | | |
|---|---|---|---|---|
| 675 | A122 | 12s multi | .70 | .25 |
| 676 | A122 | 20s multi | .90 | .25 |
| 677 | A122 | 30s multi | .80 | .35 |
| 678 | A122 | 65s multi | .95 | .80 |
| 679 | A122 | 1m multi | 1.25 | 1.25 |
| 680 | A122 | 1.55m multi | 1.50 | 1.50 |
| 681 | A122 | 2m multi | 2.25 | 2.25 |
| 682 | A122 | 2.40m multi | 2.50 | 2.50 |
| 683 | A122 | 3m multi | 3.00 | 3.00 |
| | | *Nos. 675-683 (9)* | 13.85 | 12.15 |

**Souvenir Sheet**

| | | | | |
|---|---|---|---|---|
| 684 | A122 | 4m multi | 4.50 | 4.50 |

No. 676 has "Sidney" instead of "Sydney."
No. 679 has "Ash" instead of Ashe."

Paintings by Titian — A123

Designs: 12s, The Averoldi Polyptych. 20s, Christ and the Adulteress (Christ). 35s, Christ and the Adulteress (adultress). 45s, Angel of the Annunciation. 65s, Saint Dominic. 1m, The Vendramin Family. 2m, Mary Magdalen. 3m, The Tribute Money. No. 693, Christ and the Woman Taken in Adultery. No. 694, The Mater Dolorosa.

**1988, Dec. 1**      *Perf. 14x13½*

| | | | | |
|---|---|---|---|---|
| 685 | A123 | 12s multicolored | .40 | .25 |
| 686 | A123 | 20s multicolored | .50 | .25 |
| 687 | A123 | 35s multicolored | .60 | .35 |
| 688 | A123 | 45s multicolored | .70 | .45 |
| 689 | A123 | 65s multicolored | .70 | .65 |
| 690 | A123 | 1m multicolored | .90 | .90 |
| 691 | A123 | 2m multicolored | 1.75 | 1.75 |
| 692 | A123 | 3m multicolored | 2.50 | 2.50 |
| | | *Nos. 685-692 (8)* | 8.05 | 7.10 |

**Souvenir Sheets**

| | | | | |
|---|---|---|---|---|
| 693 | A123 | 5m multicolored | 4.50 | 4.50 |
| 694 | A123 | 5m multicolored | 4.50 | 4.50 |

Birth of Titian, 500th anniv. Nos. 685-693 inscribed "Christmas 1988."

Intl. Red Cross, 125th Anniv. — A124

Anniv. emblem, supply and ambulance planes: 12s, Pilatus PC-6 Turbo Porter. 20s, Cessna Caravan. 55s, De Havilland DHC-6 Otter. 3m, Douglas DC-3 in thunderstorm. 4m, Douglas DC-3, diff.

**1989, Jan. 30**    **Litho.**    *Perf. 14*

| | | | | |
|---|---|---|---|---|
| 695 | A124 | 12s multicolored | .25 | .25 |
| 696 | A124 | 20s multicolored | .25 | .25 |
| 697 | A124 | 55s multicolored | 1.25 | 1.25 |
| 698 | A124 | 3m multicolored | 5.25 | 5.25 |
| | | *Nos. 695-698 (4)* | 7.00 | 7.00 |

**Souvenir Sheet**

| | | | | |
|---|---|---|---|---|
| 699 | A124 | 4m multi, vert. | 9.00 | 9.00 |

Landscapes by Hiroshige A125

Designs: 12s, Dawn Mist at Mishima. 16s, Night Snow at Kambara. 20s, Wayside Inn at Mariko Station. 35s, Shower at Shono. 55s, Snowfall on the Kisokaido Near Oi. 1m, Autumn Moon at Seba. 3.20m, Evening Moon at Ryogaku Bridge. 5m, Cherry Blossoms, Arashiyama. No. 708, Listening to the Singing Insects at Dokanyama. No. 709, Moonlight, Nagakubo.

**1989, June 19**    **Litho.**    *Perf. 14x13½*

| | | | | |
|---|---|---|---|---|
| 700 | A125 | 12s multi | .40 | .25 |
| 701 | A125 | 16s multi | .45 | .25 |
| 702 | A125 | 20s multi | .45 | .25 |
| 703 | A125 | 35s multi | .45 | .30 |
| 704 | A125 | 55s multi | .70 | .45 |
| 705 | A125 | 1m multi | 1.00 | .80 |
| 706 | A125 | 3.20m multi | 2.25 | 2.25 |
| 707 | A125 | 5m multi | 3.75 | 3.75 |
| | | *Nos. 700-707 (8)* | 9.45 | 8.30 |

**Souvenir Sheets**

| | | | | |
|---|---|---|---|---|
| 708 | A125 | 4m multi | 4.25 | 4.25 |
| 709 | A125 | 4m multi | 4.25 | 4.25 |

Hirohito (1901-1989) and enthronement of Akihito as emperor of Japan.

PHILEXFRANCE '89, French Revolution Bicent. — A126

Disney characters wearing insurgent uniforms: 1s, General. 2s, Infantry. 3s, Grenadier. 4s, Cavalry. 5s, Hussar. 10s, Marine. 3m, Natl. guard. 5m, Admiral.

No. 718, Natl. guard, royal family, horiz. No. 719, La Marseillaise.

**1989, July 10** *Perf. 13½x14, 14x13½*
| | | | | |
|---|---|---|---|---|
| 710 | A126 | 1s multicolored | .25 | .25 |
| 711 | A126 | 2s multicolored | .25 | .25 |
| 712 | A126 | 3s multicolored | .25 | .25 |
| 713 | A126 | 4s multicolored | .25 | .25 |
| 714 | A126 | 5s multicolored | .25 | .25 |
| 715 | A126 | 10s multicolored | .25 | .25 |
| 716 | A126 | 3m multicolored | 3.00 | 3.00 |
| 717 | A126 | 5m multicolored | 4.75 | 4.75 |
| | | Nos. 710-717 (8) | 9.25 | 9.25 |

**Souvenir Sheets**
| | | | | |
|---|---|---|---|---|
| 718 | A126 | 4m multicolored | 5.00 | 5.00 |
| 719 | A126 | 4m multicolored | 5.00 | 5.00 |

Maloti Mountains — A127

No. 720: a, Sotho thatched dwellings. b, Two trees, cliff edge. c, Waterfall. d, Tribesman.

**1989, Sept.** **Litho.** *Perf. 14*
| | | | | |
|---|---|---|---|---|
| 720 | | Strip of 4 | 4.00 | 4.00 |
| a.-d. | | A127 1m any single | .75 | .75 |

**Souvenir Sheet**
| | | | | |
|---|---|---|---|---|
| 721 | A127 | 4m Flora | 4.25 | 4.25 |

Mushrooms — A128

12s, Paxillus involutus. 16s, Ganoderma applanatum. 55s, Suillus granulatus. 5m, Stereum hirsutum.
4m, Scleroderma flavidum.

**1989, Sept. 8** **Litho.** *Perf. 14*
| | | | | |
|---|---|---|---|---|
| 722 | A128 | 12s multicolored | .35 | .25 |
| 723 | A128 | 16s multicolored | .35 | .25 |
| 723A | A128 | 55s multicolored | .65 | .55 |
| 724 | A128 | 5m multicolored | 4.50 | 4.50 |
| | | Nos. 722-724 (4) | 5.85 | 5.55 |

**Souvenir Sheet**
| | | | | |
|---|---|---|---|---|
| 725 | A128 | 4m multicolored | 6.25 | 6.25 |

Birds — A129

12s, Marsh sandpipers. 65s, Little stints. 1m, Ringed plovers. 4m, Curlew sandpipers. 5m, Ruff, vert.

**1989, Oct. 23** **Litho.** *Perf. 14*
| | | | | |
|---|---|---|---|---|
| 726 | A129 | 12s multicolored | .25 | .25 |
| 727 | A129 | 65s multicolored | 1.10 | 1.10 |
| 728 | A129 | 1m multicolored | 1.75 | 1.75 |
| 729 | A129 | 4m multicolored | 6.25 | 6.25 |
| | | Nos. 726-729 (4) | 9.35 | 9.35 |

**Souvenir Sheet**
| | | | | |
|---|---|---|---|---|
| 730 | A129 | 5m multicolored | 11.00 | 11.00 |

1st Moon Landing, 20th Anniv. — A130

Highlights of the Apollo 11 mission: 12s, Liftoff. 16s, Eagle landing. 40s, Astronaut on ladder. 55s, Buzz Aldrin. 1m, Solar wind experiment. 2m, Eagle lifting off. 3m, Columbia in orbit. 4m, Splashdown.
5m, Astronaut, Eagle.

**1989, Nov. 6** *Perf. 14*
| | | | | |
|---|---|---|---|---|
| 731 | A130 | 12s multicolored | .25 | .25 |
| 732 | A130 | 16s multicolored | .25 | .25 |
| 733 | A130 | 40s multicolored | .40 | .40 |
| 734 | A130 | 55s multicolored | .60 | .60 |
| 735 | A130 | 1m multicolored | .90 | .90 |
| 736 | A130 | 2m multicolored | 1.75 | 1.75 |
| 737 | A130 | 3m multicolored | 2.40 | 2.40 |
| 738 | A130 | 5m multicolored | 3.50 | 3.50 |
| | | Nos. 731-738 (8) | 10.05 | 10.05 |

**Souvenir Sheet**
| | | | | |
|---|---|---|---|---|
| 739 | A130 | 5m multicolored | 6.75 | 6.75 |

Nos. 731, 733, 738-739 vert.

World Stamp Expo '89 — A131

Cathedral Church of Sts. Peter and Paul, Washington, DC — A132

No. 740: a, Postal marking, England, 1680. b, Wax seal and feather, Germany, 1807. c, Crete #1. d, Perot postmaster's provisional, Bermuda, 1848. e, Pony Express handstamp, US, 1860. f, Finland #1. g, Fiji #1. h, Swedish newspaper handstamp, 1823. i, Bhor #1.

**1989, Nov. 17** **Litho.** *Perf. 14*
| | | | | |
|---|---|---|---|---|
| 740 | A131 | Sheet of 9 | 8.25 | 8.25 |
| a.-i. | | 75s any single | .35 | .35 |

**Souvenir Sheet**
| | | | | |
|---|---|---|---|---|
| 741 | A132 | 4m shown | 4.00 | 4.00 |

Christmas — A133

Religious paintings by Velazquez: 12s, The Immaculate Conception. 20s, St. Anthony Abbot and St. Paul the Hermit. 35s, St. Thomas the Apostle. 55s, Christ in the House of Martha and Mary. 1m, St. John Writing the Apocalypse on Patmos. 3m, The Virgin Presenting the Chasuble to St. Ildephonsus. 4m, The Adoration of the Magi. 5m, The Coronation of the Virgin.

**1989, Dec. 18**
| | | | | |
|---|---|---|---|---|
| 742 | A133 | 12s multicolored | .25 | .25 |
| 743 | A133 | 20s multicolored | .25 | .25 |
| 744 | A133 | 35s multicolored | .35 | .35 |
| 745 | A133 | 55s multicolored | .55 | .55 |
| 746 | A133 | 1m multicolored | .80 | .80 |
| 747 | A133 | 3m multicolored | 2.25 | 2.25 |
| 748 | A133 | 4m multicolored | 3.00 | 3.00 |
| | | Nos. 742-748 (7) | 7.45 | 7.45 |

**Souvenir Sheet**
| | | | | |
|---|---|---|---|---|
| 749 | A133 | 5m multicolored | 9.00 | 9.00 |

1990 World Cup Soccer Championships, Italy — A134

Various athletes, emblem and name of previous championship host nations: 12s, England, 1966. 16s, Mexico, 1970. 55s, West Germany, 1974. 5m, Spain, 1982.
4m, Diego Maradona, Argentina.

**1989, Dec. 27**
| | | | | |
|---|---|---|---|---|
| 750 | A134 | 12s multicolored | .25 | .25 |
| 751 | A134 | 16s multicolored | .25 | .25 |
| 752 | A134 | 55s multicolored | 1.00 | 1.00 |
| 753 | A134 | 5m multicolored | 6.50 | 6.50 |
| | | Nos. 750-753 (4) | 8.00 | 8.00 |

**Souvenir Sheet**
| | | | | |
|---|---|---|---|---|
| 754 | A134 | 4m multicolored | 7.50 | 7.50 |

**No. 622a Surcharged**

**1990** **Litho.** *Perf. 14*
| | | | | |
|---|---|---|---|---|
| 755 | A116 | 16s on 12s multi | — | — |

Orchids — A135

Designs: 12s, Satyrium princeps. 16s, Huttonaea pulchra. 55s, Herschelia graminifolia. 1m, Ansellia gigantea. 1.55m, Polystachya pubescens. 2.40m, Penthea filicornis. 3m, Disperis capensis. 4m, Disa uniflora.
5m, Stenoglottis longifolia.

**1990, Mar. 12** **Litho.** *Perf. 14*
| | | | | |
|---|---|---|---|---|
| 756 | A135 | 12s multicolored | .25 | .25 |
| 757 | A135 | 16s multicolored | .25 | .25 |
| 758 | A135 | 55s multicolored | .90 | .90 |
| 759 | A135 | 1m multicolored | 1.60 | 1.60 |
| 760 | A135 | 1.55m multicolored | 2.25 | 2.25 |
| 761 | A135 | 2.40m multicolored | 3.50 | 3.50 |
| 762 | A135 | 3m multicolored | 4.25 | 4.25 |
| 763 | A135 | 4m multicolored | 6.00 | 6.00 |
| | | Nos. 756-763 (8) | 19.00 | 19.00 |

**Souvenir Sheet**
| | | | | |
|---|---|---|---|---|
| 764 | A135 | 5m multicolored | 10.00 | 10.00 |

Expo '90.

Butterflies — A136

12s, Pseudo ergolid. 16s, Painted lady. 55s, Ringed pansy. 65s, False acraea. 1m, Eyed pansy. 2m, Golden pansy. 3m, African monarch. 4m, African giant swallowtail.
5m, Citrus swallowtail.

**1990, Feb. 26** **Litho.** *Perf. 14*
| | | | | |
|---|---|---|---|---|
| 765 | A136 | 12s multicolored | .95 | .25 |
| 766 | A136 | 16s multicolored | 1.10 | .25 |
| 767 | A136 | 55s multicolored | 1.60 | .55 |
| 768 | A136 | 65s multicolored | 1.75 | .65 |
| 769 | A136 | 1m multicolored | 2.40 | 1.10 |
| 770 | A136 | 2m multicolored | 3.75 | 2.25 |
| 771 | A136 | 3m multicolored | 5.25 | 3.25 |
| 772 | A136 | 4m multicolored | 6.50 | 5.50 |
| | | Nos. 765-772 (8) | 23.30 | 13.80 |

**Souvenir Sheet**
| | | | | |
|---|---|---|---|---|
| 773 | A136 | 5m multicolored | 11.00 | 11.00 |

Queen Mother, 90th Birthday A137

**1990, July 5** **Litho.** *Perf. 14*
| | | | | |
|---|---|---|---|---|
| 774 | | 1.50m In hat | 1.25 | 1.25 |
| 775 | | 1.50m Two children | 1.25 | 1.25 |
| 776 | | 1.50m Young woman | 1.25 | 1.25 |
| a. | | A137 Strip of 3, #774-776 | 4.50 | 4.50 |
| | | Nos. 774-776 (3) | 3.75 | 3.75 |

**Souvenir Sheet**
| | | | | |
|---|---|---|---|---|
| 777 | A137 | 5m Child | 5.50 | 5.50 |

A139

Designs: 12s, King Moshoeshoe II, Prince Mohato wearing blankets. 16s, Prince Mohato in Seana-Marena blanket. 1m, Pope John Paul II in Seana-Marena blanket. 3m, Basotho men on horses.
5m, Pope with blanket and hat.

**1990, Aug. 17** **Litho.** *Perf. 14*
| | | | | |
|---|---|---|---|---|
| 778 | A139 | 12s multicolored | .25 | .25 |
| 779 | A139 | 16s multicolored | .25 | .25 |
| 780 | A139 | 1m multicolored | 1.40 | 1.40 |
| 781 | A139 | 3m multicolored | 3.50 | 3.50 |
| | | Nos. 778-781 (4) | 5.40 | 5.40 |

**Souvenir Sheet**
| | | | | |
|---|---|---|---|---|
| 782 | A139 | 5m multi, horiz. | 7.50 | 7.50 |

Highland Water Project — A140

16s, Moving gravel. 20s, Fuel truck. 55s, Piers for bridge construction. 2m, Road construction.
5m, Drilling blasting holes.

**1990, Aug. 24**
| | | | | |
|---|---|---|---|---|
| 783 | A140 | 16s multicolored | .25 | .25 |
| 784 | A140 | 20s multicolored | .25 | .25 |
| 785 | A140 | 55s multicolored | .90 | .90 |
| 786 | A140 | 2m multicolored | 2.75 | 2.75 |
| | | Nos. 783-786 (4) | 4.15 | 4.15 |

**Souvenir Sheet**
| | | | | |
|---|---|---|---|---|
| 787 | A140 | 5m multicolored | 7.25 | 7.25 |

UNICEF Save the Children Campaign — A141

12s, Breastfeeding. 55s, Oral rehydration. 1m, Baby being weighed.

**1990, Sept. 26** **Litho.** *Perf. 14*
| | | | | |
|---|---|---|---|---|
| 788 | A141 | 12s multicolored | .25 | .25 |
| 789 | A141 | 55s multicolored | 1.75 | 1.75 |
| 790 | A141 | 1m multicolored | 2.50 | 2.50 |
| | | Nos. 788-790 (3) | 4.50 | 4.50 |

1992 Summer Olympics, Barcelona — A142

16s, Triple jump. 55s, 200-meter race. 1m, 5000-meter race. 4m, Equestrian show jumping.
5m, Lighting Olympic flame.

**1990, Oct. 5**
| | | | | |
|---|---|---|---|---|
| 791 | A142 | 16s multicolored | .25 | .25 |
| 792 | A142 | 55s multicolored | 1.00 | 1.00 |
| 793 | A142 | 1m multicolored | 1.50 | 1.50 |
| 794 | A142 | 4m multicolored | 5.50 | 5.50 |
| | | Nos. 791-794 (4) | 8.25 | 8.25 |

**Souvenir Sheet**
| | | | | |
|---|---|---|---|---|
| 795 | A142 | 5m multicolored | 8.50 | 8.50 |

Christmas — A143

Different details from paintings by Rubens: 12s, 1m, 3m, Virgin and Child. 16s, 80s, 2m, 4m, Adoration of the Magi. 55s, Head of One of the Three Kings, diff. 5m, Assumption of the Virgin.

**1990, Dec. 5    Litho.        Perf. 13½x14**
| | | | | |
|---|---|---|---|---|
| 796 | A143 | 12s multicolored | .25 | .25 |
| 797 | A143 | 16s multicolored | .25 | .25 |
| 798 | A143 | 55s multicolored | .55 | .55 |
| 799 | A143 | 80s multicolored | .85 | .85 |
| 800 | A143 | 1m multicolored | 1.00 | 1.00 |
| 801 | A143 | 2m multicolored | 2.10 | 2.10 |
| 802 | A143 | 3m multicolored | 2.75 | 2.75 |
| 803 | A143 | 4m multicolored | 3.75 | 3.75 |
| | | Nos. 796-803 (8) | 11.50 | 11.50 |

**Souvenir Sheet**
| | | | | |
|---|---|---|---|---|
| 804 | A143 | 5m multicolored | 7.25 | 7.25 |

**Nos. 625-626 Surcharged**

**1991, Jan. 18    Litho.        Perf. 15**
| | | | | |
|---|---|---|---|---|
| 805 | A116 | 16s on 30s #625 | — | — |
| 806 | A116 | 16s on 40s #626 | — | — |

Phila Nippon '91 — A144

Walt Disney characters visit Japan: 20s, Mickey at Nagasaki Peace Park. 30s, Mickey at Kamakura Beach. 40s, Mickey, Donald entertain at Bunraku Puppet Theater. 50s, Mickey, Donald eat soba at noodle shop. 75s, Minnie, Mickey at tea house. 1m, Mickey, Bullet Train. 3m, Mickey, deer at Todaiji Temple. 4m, Mickey, Minnie before Imperial Palace. No. 815, Mickey skiing at Happo-One, Nagano. No. 816, Mickey, Minnie at Suizenji Park.

**1991, June 10   Litho.   Perf. 14x13½**
| | | | | |
|---|---|---|---|---|
| 807 | A144 | 20s multicolored | .25 | .25 |
| 808 | A144 | 30s multicolored | .25 | .25 |
| 809 | A144 | 40s multicolored | .50 | .50 |
| 810 | A144 | 50s multicolored | .70 | .70 |
| 811 | A144 | 75s multicolored | 1.40 | 1.40 |
| 812 | A144 | 1m multicolored | 1.40 | 1.40 |
| 813 | A144 | 3m multicolored | 3.75 | 3.75 |
| 814 | A144 | 4m multicolored | 5.00 | 5.00 |
| | | Nos. 807-814 (8) | 13.25 | 13.25 |

**Souvenir Sheets**
| | | | | |
|---|---|---|---|---|
| 815 | A144 | 5m multicolored | 5.50 | 5.50 |
| 816 | A144 | 6m multicolored | 5.50 | 5.50 |

Entertainers in Films About Africa — A145

Designs: 12s, Stewart Granger, King Solomon's Mines. 16s, Johnny Weissmuller, Tarzan, the Ape Man. 30s, Clark Gable, Grace Kelly, Mogambo. 55s, Sigourney Weaver, Gorillas in the Mist. 70s, Humphrey Bogart, Katharine Hepburn, The African Queen. 1m, John Wayne, Hatari. 2m, Meryl Streep, Out of Africa. 4m, Eddie Murphy, Arsenio Hall, Coming to America. 5m, Elsa, Born Free.

**1991, June 20        Litho.      Perf. 14**
| | | | | |
|---|---|---|---|---|
| 817 | A145 | 12s multicolored | .65 | .25 |
| 818 | A145 | 16s multicolored | .65 | .25 |
| 819 | A145 | 30s multicolored | .80 | .25 |
| 820 | A145 | 55s multicolored | .95 | .70 |
| 821 | A145 | 70s multicolored | 1.25 | .90 |

| | | | | |
|---|---|---|---|---|
| 822 | A145 | 1m multicolored | 1.60 | 1.25 |
| 823 | A145 | 2m multicolored | 2.50 | 2.50 |
| 824 | A145 | 4m multicolored | 4.25 | 4.25 |
| | | Nos. 817-824 (8) | 12.65 | 10.35 |

**Souvenir Sheet**
| | | | | |
|---|---|---|---|---|
| 825 | A145 | 5m multicolored | 6.75 | 6.75 |

Butterflies A146

2s, Satyrus aello. 3s, Erebia medusa. 5s, Melanargia galathea. 10s, Erebia aethiops. 20s, Coenonympha pamphilus. 25s, Pyrameis atalanta. 30s, Charaxes jasius. 40s, Colias palaeno. 50s, Colias cliopatra. 60s, Colias philodice. 70s, Rhumni gonepterix. 1m, Colias caesonia. 2m, Pyrameis cardui. 3m, Danaus chrysippus. 10m, Apatura iris.

**No date inscription below design**

**1991, Aug. 1        Litho.        Perf. 13½**
| | | | | |
|---|---|---|---|---|
| 827 | A146 | 2s multicolored | .25 | .25 |
| 828 | A146 | 3s multicolored | .25 | .25 |
| 829 | A146 | 5s multicolored | .25 | .25 |
| 830 | A146 | 10s multicolored | .25 | .25 |
| 831 | A146 | 20s multicolored | .30 | .25 |
| 832 | A146 | 25s multicolored | .30 | .25 |
| 833 | A146 | 30s multicolored | .45 | .30 |
| 834 | A146 | 40s multicolored | .45 | .35 |
| 835 | A146 | 50s multicolored | .50 | .45 |
| 836 | A146 | 60s multicolored | .60 | .55 |
| 837 | A146 | 70s multicolored | .60 | .60 |
| 838 | A146 | 1m multicolored | .90 | .90 |
| 839 | A146 | 2m multicolored | 1.75 | 1.75 |
| 840 | A146 | 3m multicolored | 2.50 | 2.50 |
| 840A | A146 | 10m multicolored | 8.75 | 8.75 |
| | | Nos. 827-840A (15) | 18.10 | 17.65 |

For surcharge see No. 1062.

**1992, Apr.              Inscribed "1992"**
| | | | | |
|---|---|---|---|---|
| 827a | A146 | 2s multicolored | .25 | .25 |
| 828a | A146 | 3s multicolored | .25 | .25 |
| 829a | A146 | 5s multicolored | .25 | .25 |
| 830a | A146 | 10s multicolored | .25 | .25 |
| 831a | A146 | 20s multicolored | .30 | .25 |
| 832a | A146 | 25s multicolored | .30 | .25 |
| 833a | A146 | 30s multicolored | .45 | .30 |
| 834a | A146 | 40s multicolored | .50 | .35 |
| 835a | A146 | 50s multicolored | .65 | .45 |
| 836a | A146 | 60s multicolored | .70 | .70 |
| 837a | A146 | 70s multicolored | 1.00 | 1.00 |
| 838a | A146 | 1m multicolored | 1.25 | 1.25 |
| 839a | A146 | 2m multicolored | 2.75 | 2.75 |
| 840a | A146 | 3m multicolored | 4.00 | 4.00 |
| 840Aa | A146 | 10m multicolored | 8.75 | 8.75 |
| | | Nos. 827a-840Aa (15) | 21.65 | 21.05 |

SADCC, 10th Anniv. — A147

Tourism: 12s, Wattled cranes. 16s, Butterfly, flowers in national parks. 25s, Tourist bus and Mukurub, the Finger of God. 3m, People in traditional dress.

**1991, Oct. 10   Litho.   Perf. 14x13½**
| | | | | |
|---|---|---|---|---|
| 841 | A147 | 12s multicolored | 1.75 | 1.75 |
| 842 | A147 | 16s multicolored | 1.75 | 1.75 |
| 843 | A147 | 25s multicolored | 1.75 | 1.75 |
| | | Nos. 841-843 (3) | 5.25 | 5.25 |

**Souvenir Sheet**
| | | | | |
|---|---|---|---|---|
| 844 | A147 | 3m multicolored | 5.50 | 5.50 |

Say No to Drugs — A148

**1991, Oct. 10**
| | | | | |
|---|---|---|---|---|
| 845 | A148 | 16s multicolored | 2.25 | 2.25 |

Charles de Gaulle, Birth Cent. — A149

DeGaulle: 40s, Wearing brigadier general's kepi. 50s, Facing left. 60s, Facing right. 4m, In later years.

**1991, Dec. 6        Litho.        Perf. 14**
| | | | | |
|---|---|---|---|---|
| 846 | A149 | 20s black & brown | .25 | .25 |
| 847 | A149 | 40s black & violet | .65 | .65 |
| 848 | A149 | 50s black & olilve | .85 | .85 |
| 849 | A149 | 60s black & dk blue | 1.00 | 1.00 |
| 850 | A149 | 4m black & brn org | 6.75 | 6.75 |
| | | Nos. 846-850 (5) | 9.50 | 9.50 |

Christmas — A150

Engravings by Albrecht Durer: 20s, St. Anne with Mary and the Child Jesus. 30s, Mary on the Grass Bench. 50s, Mary with the Crown of Stars. 60s, Mary with Child beside a Tree. 70s, Mary with Child beside the Wall. 1m, Mary in a Halo on the Crescent Moon. 2m, Mary Breastfeeding Her Child. 4m, Mary with the Infant in Swaddling Clothes. No. 859, Holy Family with the Dragonfly. No. 860, The Birth of Christ.

**1991, Dec. 13       Litho.      Perf. 12**
| | | | | |
|---|---|---|---|---|
| 851 | A150 | 20s rose & black | .25 | .25 |
| 852 | A150 | 30s blue & black | .50 | .50 |
| 853 | A150 | 50s green & black | .80 | .80 |
| 854 | A150 | 60s red & black | 1.00 | 1.00 |
| 855 | A150 | 70s yellow & black | 1.10 | 1.10 |
| 856 | A150 | 1m yel org & black | 1.60 | 1.60 |
| 857 | A150 | 2m violet & black | 2.75 | 2.75 |
| 858 | A150 | 4m dk blue & black | 5.75 | 5.75 |
| | | Nos. 851-858 (8) | 13.75 | 13.75 |

**Souvenir Sheets**
**Perf. 14½**
| | | | | |
|---|---|---|---|---|
| 859 | A150 | 5m blue & black | 5.00 | 5.00 |
| 860 | A150 | 5m pink & black | 5.00 | 5.00 |

Games — A151

Walt Disney characters playing games: 20s, Mickey, Pluto playing pin the tail on the donkey. 30s, Mickey enjoying board game, Mancala. 40s, Mickey hoop rolling. 50s, Minnie with hula hoops. 70s, Mickey throwing Frisbee to Pluto. 1m, Donald trying to play Diabolo. 2m, Huey, Dewey and Louie playing marbles. 3m, Donald frustrated by Rubik's cube. No. 869, Donald and Mickey's nephews in tug-of-war. No. 870, Mickey, Donald stick fighting.

**1991, Dec. 16        Perf. 13½x14**
| | | | | |
|---|---|---|---|---|
| 861 | A151 | 20s multicolored | .25 | .25 |
| 862 | A151 | 30s multicolored | .55 | .55 |
| 863 | A151 | 40s multicolored | .65 | .65 |
| 864 | A151 | 50s multicolored | .90 | .90 |
| 865 | A151 | 70s multicolored | 1.25 | 1.25 |
| 866 | A151 | 1m multicolored | 1.75 | 1.75 |
| 867 | A151 | 2m multicolored | 3.25 | 3.25 |
| 868 | A151 | 3m multicolored | 5.00 | 5.00 |
| | | Nos. 861-868 (8) | 13.60 | 13.60 |

**Souvenir Sheets**
| | | | | |
|---|---|---|---|---|
| 869 | A151 | 5m multicolored | 6.00 | 6.00 |
| 870 | A151 | 5m multicolored | 6.00 | 6.00 |

**Royal Family Birthday, Anniversary**
Common Design Type

**1991, Dec. 9        Litho.        Perf. 14**
| | | | | |
|---|---|---|---|---|
| 871 | CD347 | 50s multicolored | .70 | .70 |
| 872 | CD347 | 70s multicolored | .95 | .95 |
| 873 | CD347 | 1m multicolored | 1.40 | 1.40 |
| 874 | CD347 | 3m multicolored | 4.25 | 4.25 |
| | | Nos. 871-874 (4) | 7.30 | 7.30 |

**Souvenir Sheet**
| | | | | |
|---|---|---|---|---|
| 875 | CD347 | 4m Charles, Diana, sons | 6.25 | 6.25 |

Charles and Diana, 10th wedding anniversary.

**Queen Elizabeth II's Accession to the Throne, 40th Anniv.**
Common Design Type

**1992, Feb. 6        Litho.        Perf. 14**
| | | | | |
|---|---|---|---|---|
| 881 | CD348 | 20s multicolored | .25 | .25 |
| 882 | CD348 | 30s multicolored | .40 | .40 |
| 883 | CD348 | 1m multicolored | 1.25 | 1.25 |
| 884 | CD348 | 4m multicolored | 4.00 | 4.00 |
| | | Nos. 881-884 (4) | 5.90 | 5.90 |

**Souvenir Sheet**
| | | | | |
|---|---|---|---|---|
| 885 | CD348 | 5m multicolored | 6.00 | 6.00 |

Birds — A152

Designs: a, Lanner falcon. b, Bataleur. c, Red-headed finch. d, Lesser-striped swallow. e, Alpine swift. f, Diederik cuckoo. g, Malachite sunbird. h, Crimson-breasted shrike. i, Pintailed whydah. j, Lilac-breasted roller. k, Black korhaan. l, Black-collared barbet. m, Secretary bird. n, Red-billed quelea. o, Red bishop. p, Ring-necked dove. q, Yellow canary. r, Orange-throated longclaw. s, Blue waxbill. t, Golden bishop.

**1992, Feb. 10              Perf. 14½**
| | | | | |
|---|---|---|---|---|
| 886 | A152 | 30s Sheet of 20, #a.-t. | 17.50 | 17.50 |

World Columbian Stamp Expo '92, Chicago — A153

Walt Disney characters depicting native Americans: 30s, Donald Duck making arrowheads. 40s, Goofy playing lacrosse. 1m, Mickey, Donald planting corn. 3m, Minnie Mouse mastering art of beading. No. 891, Mickey as "Blackhawk" hunting for moose.

**1992, Apr.    Litho.    Perf. 13½x14**
| | | | | |
|---|---|---|---|---|
| 887 | A153 | 30s multicolored | .55 | .55 |
| 888 | A153 | 40s multicolored | .65 | .65 |
| 889 | A153 | 1m multicolored | 1.75 | 1.75 |
| 890 | A153 | 3m multicolored | 4.50 | 4.50 |
| | | Nos. 887-890 (4) | 7.45 | 7.45 |

**Souvenir Sheet**
| | | | | |
|---|---|---|---|---|
| 891 | A153 | 5m multicolored | 7.75 | 7.75 |

Granada '92 — A154

Walt Disney characters in Spanish costumes: 20s, Minnie Mouse as Lady of Rank, 1540-1660. 50s, Mickey as conqueror of Lepanto, 1571. 70s, Donald Duck from Galicia, 1880. 2m, Daisy Duck from Aragon, 1880. No. 901, Goofy as bullfighter.

**1992, Apr. 13    Litho.    Perf. 13½x14**
| | | | | |
|---|---|---|---|---|
| 897 | A154 | 20s multicolored | .25 | .25 |
| 898 | A154 | 50s multicolored | 1.25 | 1.25 |
| 899 | A154 | 70s multicolored | 1.60 | 1.60 |
| 900 | A154 | 2m multicolored | 4.00 | 4.00 |
| | | Nos. 897-900 (4) | 7.10 | 7.10 |

**Souvenir Sheet**
| | | | | |
|---|---|---|---|---|
| 901 | A154 | 5m multicolored | 7.75 | 7.75 |

Dinosaurs A155

20s, Stegosaurus. 30s, Ceratosaurus. 40s, Procompsognathus. 50s, Lesothosaurus. 70s, Plateosaurus. 1m, Gasosaurus. 2m, Massospondylus. 3m, Archaeopteryx.

No. 915, Archaeopteryx, diff. No. 916, Lesothosaurus, diff.

**1992, June 9**      **Perf. 14**
| | | | |
|---|---|---|---|
| 907 | A155 | multicolored | .25 .25 |
| 908 | A155 | 30s multicolored | .65 .65 |
| 909 | A155 | 40s multicolored | .75 .75 |
| 910 | A155 | 50s multicolored | 1.00 1.00 |
| 911 | A155 | 70s multicolored | 1.40 1.40 |
| 912 | A155 | 1m multicolored | 2.00 2.00 |
| 913 | A155 | 2m multicolored | 3.50 3.50 |
| 914 | A155 | 3m multicolored | 5.25 5.25 |
| | | Nos. 907-914 (8) | 14.80 14.80 |

**Souvenir Sheet**
| | | | |
|---|---|---|---|
| 915 | A155 | 5m multicolored | 7.75 7.75 |
| 916 | A155 | 5m multicolored | 7.75 7.75 |

No. 915 printed in continuous design.

1992 Olympics, Barcelona and Albertville — A156

Designs: 20s, Discus. 30s, Long jump. 40s, Women's 4x100-meter relay. 70s, Women's 100-meter dash. 1m, Parallel bars. 2m, Two-man luge, horiz. 3m, Women's cross-country skiing, horiz. 4m, Biathlon.
No. 925, Ice hockey, horiz. No. 926, Women's figure skating.

**1992, Aug. 5**    **Litho.**    **Perf. 14**
| | | | |
|---|---|---|---|
| 917 | A156 | 20s multicolored | .25 .25 |
| 918 | A156 | 30s multicolored | .25 .25 |
| 919 | A156 | 40s multicolored | .30 .30 |
| 920 | A156 | 70s multicolored | .65 .65 |
| 921 | A156 | 1m multicolored | .95 .95 |
| 922 | A156 | 2m multicolored | 1.75 1.75 |
| 923 | A156 | 3m multicolored | 2.50 2.50 |
| 924 | A156 | 4m multicolored | 3.50 3.50 |
| | | Nos. 917-924 (8) | 10.15 10.15 |

**Souvenir Sheet**
| | | | |
|---|---|---|---|
| 925 | A156 | 5m multicolored | 5.25 5.25 |
| 926 | A156 | 5m multicolored | 5.25 5.25 |

Christmas — A158

Details or entire paintings: 20s, Virgin and Child, by Sassetta. 30s, Coronation of the Virgin, by Master of Bonastre. 40s, Virgin and Child, by Master of Saints Cosmas and Damian. 70s, The Virgin of Great Panagia, by Russian School, 12th cent. 1m, Madonna and Child, by Vincenzo Foppa. 2m, Madonna and Child, by School of Lippo Memmi. 3m, Virgin and Child, by Barnaba da Modena. 4m, Virgin and Child, by Simone Dei Crocifissi.
No. 935, Virgin & Child Enthroned & Surrounded by Angels, by Cimabue. No. 936, Virgin and Child with Saints (entire triptych), by Dei Crocifissi.

**1992, Nov. 2**    **Litho.**    **Perf. 13½x14**
| | | | |
|---|---|---|---|
| 927 | A158 | 20s multicolored | .25 .25 |
| 928 | A158 | 30s multicolored | .45 .45 |
| 929 | A158 | 40s multicolored | .55 .55 |
| 930 | A158 | 70s multicolored | 1.10 1.10 |
| 931 | A158 | 1m multicolored | 1.50 1.50 |
| 932 | A158 | 2m multicolored | 2.75 2.75 |
| 933 | A158 | 3m multicolored | 4.25 4.25 |
| 934 | A158 | 4m multicolored | 5.75 5.75 |
| | | Nos. 927-934 (8) | 16.60 16.60 |

**Souvenir Sheets**
| | | | |
|---|---|---|---|
| 935 | A158 | 5m multicolored | 6.50 6.50 |
| 936 | A158 | 5m multicolored | 6.50 6.50 |

**Souvenir Sheet**

World Trade Center, New York City A159

**1992, Oct. 28**    **Litho.**    **Perf. 14**
| | | | |
|---|---|---|---|
| 937 | A159 | 5m multicolored | 10.00 10.00 |

Postage Stamp Mega Event '92, NYC.

---

Anniversaries and Events — A160

Designs: 20s, Baby harp seal. 30s, Giant panda. 40s, Graf Zeppelin, globe. 70s, Woman grinding corn. 4m, Zeppelin shot down over Cuffley, UK by Lt. Leefe Robinson flying BE 2c, WWI. No. 943, Valentina Tereshkova, first woman in space. No. 944, West African crowned cranes. No. 945, Dr. Ronald McNair.

**1993, Jan.**    **Litho.**    **Perf. 14**
| | | | |
|---|---|---|---|
| 938 | A160 | 20s multicolored | .25 .25 |
| 939 | A160 | 30s multicolored | .40 .40 |
| 940 | A160 | 40s multicolored | .50 .50 |
| 941 | A160 | 70s multicolored | .90 .90 |
| 942 | A160 | 4m multicolored | 4.75 4.75 |
| 943 | A160 | 5m multicolored | 5.75 5.75 |
| | | Nos. 938-943 (6) | 12.55 12.55 |

**Souvenir Sheets**
| | | | |
|---|---|---|---|
| 944 | A160 | 5m multicolored | 6.50 6.50 |
| 945 | A160 | 5m multicolored | 6.50 6.50 |

Earth Summit, Rio de Janeiro (Nos. 938-939, 944). Count Zeppelin, 75th death anniv. (Nos. 940, 942). Intl. Conference on Nutrition, Rome (No. 941). Intl. Space Year (Nos. 943, 945).

Louvre Museum, Bicent. — A161

No. 947 — Details or entire paintings, by Nicolas Poussin: a, Orpheus and Eurydice. b-c, Rape of the Sabine Women (left, right). d-e, The Death of Sapphira (left, right). f-g, Echo and Narcissus (left, right). h, Self-portrait.
No. 948, The Moneychanger and His Wife, by Quentin Metsys.

**1993, Mar. 19**    **Litho.**    **Perf. 12**
| | | | |
|---|---|---|---|
| 947 | A161 | 70s Sheet of 8, #a.-h. + label | 8.75 8.75 |

**Souvenir Sheet**
**Perf. 14½**
| | | | |
|---|---|---|---|
| 948 | A161 | 5m multicolored | 7.25 7.25 |

No. 948 contains one 55x88mm stamp.

Flowers — A162

**1993, June**    **Litho.**    **Perf. 14**
| | | | |
|---|---|---|---|
| 949 | A162 | 20s Healing plant | .25 .25 |
| 950 | A162 | 30s Calla lily | .25 .25 |
| 951 | A162 | 40s Bird of Paradise | .30 .30 |
| 952 | A162 | 70s Belladonna | .75 .75 |
| 953 | A162 | 1m African lily | 1.00 1.00 |
| 954 | A162 | 2m Veldt lily | 2.00 2.00 |
| 955 | A162 | 4m Watsonia | 3.75 3.75 |
| 956 | A162 | 5m Gazania | 4.50 4.50 |
| | | Nos. 949-956 (8) | 12.80 12.80 |

**Souvenir Sheets**
| | | | |
|---|---|---|---|
| 957 | A162 | 7m Leadwort | 5.75 5.75 |
| 958 | A162 | 7m Desert rose | 5.75 5.75 |

**Miniature Sheet**

The 40th Anniversary of the Coronation of HM Queen Elizabeth II

Coronation of Queen Elizabeth II, 40th Anniv. — A163

No. 959: a, 20s, Official coronation photograph. b, 40s, St. Edward's Crown, Scepter with the Cross. c, 1m, Queen Mother. d, 5m, Queen, family.
7m, Conversation Piece at Royal Lodge, Windsor, by Sir James Gunn, 1950.

---

**1993, June 2**    **Litho.**    **Perf. 13½x14**
| | | | |
|---|---|---|---|
| 959 | A163 | Sheet, 2 each, #a.-d. | 8.00 8.00 |

**Souvenir Sheet**
**Perf. 14**
| | | | |
|---|---|---|---|
| 960 | A163 | 7m multicolored | 15.00 15.00 |

Butterflies A164

20s, Bi-colored pansy. 40s, Golden pansy. 70s, Yellow pansy. 1m, Pseudo ergolid. 2m, African giant swallowtail. 5m, False acraea.
No. 967, 7m, Seasonal pansy. No. 968, 7m, Ringed pansy.

**1993, June 30**    **Litho.**    **Perf. 14**
| | | | |
|---|---|---|---|
| 961 | A164 | 20s multicolored | .25 .25 |
| 962 | A164 | 40s multicolored | .35 .35 |
| 963 | A164 | 70s multicolored | .55 .55 |
| 964 | A164 | 1m multicolored | .90 .90 |
| 965 | A164 | 2m multicolored | 1.75 1.75 |
| 966 | A164 | 5m multicolored | 3.75 3.75 |
| | | Nos. 961-966 (6) | 7.55 7.55 |

**Souvenir Sheets**
| | | | |
|---|---|---|---|
| 967 | A164 | 7m multicolored | 5.50 5.50 |
| 968 | A164 | 7m multicolored | 5.50 5.50 |

African Trains — A165

Designs: 20s, East African Railways Vulcan 2-8-2, 1929. 30s, Zimbabwe Railways Class 15A, 1952. 40s, South African Railways Class 25 4-8-4, 1953. 70s, East African Railways A58 Class Garratt. 1m, South Africa Class 9E Electric. 2m, East African Railways Class 87, 1971. 3m, East African Railways Class 92, 1971. 5m, South Africa Class 26 2-D-2, 1982.
No. 977, Algeria 231-132BT Class, 1937. No. 978, South African Railway Class 6E Bo-Bo, 1969.

**1993, Sept. 24**    **Litho.**    **Perf. 14**
| | | | |
|---|---|---|---|
| 969 | A165 | 20s multicolored | .25 .25 |
| 970 | A165 | 30s multicolored | .40 .40 |
| 971 | A165 | 40s multicolored | .45 .45 |
| 972 | A165 | 70s multicolored | .90 .90 |
| 973 | A165 | 1m multicolored | 1.25 1.25 |
| 974 | A165 | 2m multicolored | 2.40 2.40 |
| 975 | A165 | 3m multicolored | 3.25 3.25 |
| 976 | A165 | 5m multicolored | 5.25 5.25 |
| | | Nos. 969-976 (8) | 14.15 14.15 |

**Souvenir Sheets**
| | | | |
|---|---|---|---|
| 977 | A165 | 7m multicolored | 6.75 6.75 |
| 978 | A165 | 7m multicolored | 6.75 6.75 |

Taipei '93 — A166

Disney characters in Taiwan: 20s, Chung Cheng Park, Keelung. 30s, Chiao-Tienkung Temple Festival. 40s, Procession. 70s, Temple Festival. 1m, Queen's Head Rock Formation, Yehliu, vert. 1.20m, Natl. Concert Hall, Taiwan, vert. 2m, C.K.S. Memorial Hall, Taiwan, vert. 2.50m, Grand Hotel, Taipei.
No. 987, 6m, Natl. Palace Museum, Taipei. No. 988, 6m, Presidential Palace Museum, Taipei, vert.

**1993**    **Litho.**    **Perf. 14x13½, 13½x14**
| | | | |
|---|---|---|---|
| 979-986 | A166 | Set of 8 | 13.00 13.00 |

**Souvenir Sheets**
| | | | |
|---|---|---|---|
| 987-988 | A166 | Set of 2 | 11.00 11.00 |

Domestic Cats — A167

Various cats: 20s, 30s, 70s, 5m.
No. 992A, Brown cat eating mouse, vert.

---

**1993, Oct. 29**    **Litho.**    **Perf. 14**
| | | | |
|---|---|---|---|
| 989-992 | A167 | Set of 4 | 6.50 6.50 |

**Souvenir Sheet**
| | | | |
|---|---|---|---|
| 992A | A167 | 5m multicolored | 5.50 5.50 |

Traditional Houses — A168

Designs: 20s, Khoaling, Khotla. 30s, Lelapa le seotloana morao ho, 1833. 70s, Thakaneng, Baroetsana. 4m, Mohlongoafatse pele ho, 1833.
No. 996A, Lelapa litema le mekhabiso.

**1993, Sept. 24**
| | | | |
|---|---|---|---|
| 993-996 | A168 | Set of 4 | 7.25 7.25 |

**Souvenir Sheet**
| | | | |
|---|---|---|---|
| 996A | A168 | 4m multicolored | 5.50 5.50 |

A169

Players, country: 20s, Khomari, Lesotho. 30s, Mohale, Lesotho. 40s, Davor, Yugoslavia; Rincon, Colombia. 50s, Lekhotla, Lesotho. 70s, Khali, Lesotho. 1m, Milla, Cameroun. 1.20m, Platt, England. 2m, Rummenigge, Germany; Lerby, Denmark.
No. 1005, Stejskal & Hasek, Czechoslovakia; Baresi, Italy, horiz. No. 1006, Lindenberger, Czechoslovakia; Schillaci, Italy.

**1993**    **Litho.**    **Perf. 13½x14**
| | | | |
|---|---|---|---|
| 997-1004 | A169 | Set of 8 | 9.50 9.50 |

**Souvenir Sheets**
**Perf. 13**
| | | | |
|---|---|---|---|
| 1005-1006 | A169 | 6m Set of 2 | 11.00 11.00 |

1994 World Cup Soccer Championships, US.

A170

New Democratic Government: 20s, King Letsie III signs oath of office under new constitution. 30s, Parliament building. 50s, Dr. Ntsu Mokhehle sworn in as prime minister. 70s, Transfer of power from Major Gen. P. Ramaema to Dr. Mokhehle.
30s, 50s, 70s are horizontal.

**1994, Apr. 2**    **Litho.**    **Perf. 14**
| | | | |
|---|---|---|---|
| 1007 | A170 | 20s multicolored | .25 .25 |
| 1008 | A170 | 30s multicolored | .45 .45 |
| 1009 | A170 | 50s multicolored | .65 .65 |
| 1010 | A170 | 70s multicolored | .90 .90 |
| | | Nos. 1007-1010 (4) | 2.25 2.25 |

A171

PHILAKOREA '94 — A172

Frogs: 35s, Aquatic river. 50s, Bubbling kassina. 1m, Guttural toad. 1.50m, Common river. No. 1015, 5m, Green frog statue. No. 1016, 5m, Black spotted frog, oriental white-eye bird, vert.

**1994, Aug. 16    Litho.    Perf. 14**
1011-1014 A171   Set of 4        3.25  3.25
**Souvenir Sheets**
1015-1016 A172   Set of 2       11.00 11.00

ICAO, 50th
Anniv. — A173

Designs: 35s, Airplane, passengers on ground. 50s, Airplane, control tower. 1m, Airplane banking, terminal, control tower. 1.50m, Airplane ascending.

**1994            Litho.        Perf. 14**
1017 A173   35s multicolored     .25  .25
1018 A173   50s multicolored     .65  .65
1019 A173    1m multicolored    1.25 1.25
1020 A173   1.50m multicolored  2.00 2.00
        Nos. 1017-1020 (4)      4.15 4.15

Medicinal
Plants — A174

Designs: 35s, Tagetes minuta. 50s, Plantago lanceolata. 1m, Amaranthus spinosus. 1.50m, Taraxacum officinale. 5m, Datura stramonium.

**1995, May 22    Litho.    Perf. 14**
1021-1024 A174   Set of 4        2.25  2.25
**Souvenir Sheet**
1025 A174   5m multicolored      2.75  2.75

Pius XII Natl.
University, 50th
Anniv. — A175

Designs: 35s, Pius XII College, 1962. 50s, Univ. of Basutoland, Bechuanaland Protectorate & Swaziland, 1965. 70s, Univ. of Botswana, Lesotho & Swaziland, 1970. 1m, Univ. of Bostswana, Lesotho & Swaziland, 1975. 1.50m, Natl. Univ. of Lesotho, 1988. 2m, Natl. Univ. of Lesotho, procession of vice-chancellors at celebration.

**1995, July 26    Litho.    Perf. 14**
1026-1031 A175   Set of 6        4.25  4.25

World Tourism
Organization, 20th
Anniv. — A176

Designs: 35s, Qiloane Pinnacle, Thaba-Bosiu, horiz. 50s, Rock Formation, Ha Mohalenyane, horiz. 1m, Botsoela Falls, Malealea. 1.50m, Backpacking, Makhaleng River Gorge, horiz.
4m, Red hot pokers.

**1995, Aug. 28    Litho.    Perf. 14**
1032-1035 A176   Set of 4        2.75  2.75
**Souvenir Sheet**
1036 A176   4m multicolored      2.50  2.50

No. 1036 contains one 38x58mm stamp.
No. 1036 withdrawn 9/15 because "Pokers" was misspelled "Porkers."

UN, 50th
Anniv. — A177

UN emblem and: 35s, Peace dove. 50s, Scales of justice. 1.50m, Handshake of reconciliation, horiz.

**1995, Sept. 26**
1037-1039 A177   Set of 3        2.25  2.25

---

Christmas — A178

Roses: 35s, Sutter's Gold. 50s, Michele Meilland. 1m, J. Otto Thilow. 2m, Papa Meilland.

**1995, Nov. 1    Litho.    Perf. 14**
1040-1043 A178   Set of 4        2.75  2.75

A179

UNICEF, 50th Anniv.: 35s, Using iodized salt. 50s, Taking care of livestock, horiz. 70s, Children in classroom. horiz. 1.50m, Children learning traditional dance, singing, horiz.

**1996, July 30    Litho.    Perf. 14**
1044-1047 A179   Set of 4        2.50  2.50

A180

1996 Summer Olympic Games, Atlanta: 1m, US Basketball team, 1936, horiz. 1.50m, Olympic Stadium, Brandenburg Gate, Berlin, horiz. 2m, Jesse Owens, 1936. 3m, Motor boating, horiz.
Past Olympic medalists: No. 1052a, Glen Morris, long jump, decathlon, 1936. b, Said Aouita, 5000-meters, 1984. c, Arnie Robinson, long jump, 1976. d, Hans Woellke, shot put, 1936. e, Renate Stecher, 100-meters, 1972. f, Evelyn Ashford, 100-meters, 1984. g, Willie Davenport, 110-meter hurdles, 1968. h, Bob Beamon, long jump, 1968. i, Heidi Rosendhal, long jump, 1972.
No. 1053, 8m, Michael Gross, swimming, 1984. No. 1054, 8m, Kornelia Ender, swimming, 1976.

**1996, Aug. 1**
1048-1051 A180   Set of 4       4.00  4.00
1052 A180   1.50m Sheet of 9,
            #a.-i.            10.50 10.50
**Souvenir Sheets**
1053-1054 A180   Set of 2      11.50 11.50

Maps of
Lesotho
A181

No. 1055 — 1911 map: a, Lephaqlioa. b, Maqaleng. c, Molapo. d, Nkeu. e, No area specified. f, Rafanyane. g, No area specified (7800). h, Madibomatso River. i, Konyani. j, Semena River.
No. 1056 — 1978 map: a, No area specified. b, Lepaqoa. c, Mamoha (name). d, Ha Nkisi. e, Ha Rafanyan, Ha Thoora. f, Ha Mikia, Ha Ntseli. g, Ha Kosetabole, Ha Mpeli. h, Ha Selebeli, Ha Theko. i, Ha Rapooane, Ha Ramabotsa. j, Ha Ramani, Khohlontso (Kolberg).
No. 1057 — Locations on 1994 Map: a, Mafika-Lisiu Pass. b, Rampai's Pass, Ha Lesaoana. c, Ha Masaballa. d, Ha Nkisi, Ha Molotanyan. e, Ha Rafanyane, Kobong. f, Laitsoka Pass. g, Katse Reservoir. h, Seshote. i, Ha Rapoeea, Ha Kennan. j, Katse (i, name), Ha Mense.

**1996            Sheets of 10, #a-j**
1055-1057 A181 35s Set of 3    15.00 15.00

---

Trains — A182

No. 1058, 1.50m: a, ETR 450, Italy. b, TGV, France. c, XPT, Australia. d, Blue Train, South Africa. e, IC 255, Great Britain. f, Bullet Train, Japan.
No. 1059, 1.50m: a, WP Streamlined 4-6-2, India. b, Canadian Pacific 2471, Canada. c, The Caledonian 4-2-2, Scotland. d, William Mason 4-4-0, US. e, Trans-Siberian Express, Russia. f, Swiss Federal 4-6-0, Switzerland.
No. 1060, 8m, 52 Class, Germany. No. 1061, 8m, ICE, Germany.

**1996, Sept. 1    Litho.    Perf. 14**
            Sheets of 6, #a-f
1058-1059 A182   Set of 2      11.50 11.50
**Souvenir Sheets**
1060-1061 A182   Set of 2       9.50  9.50

Nos. 1060-1061 each contain one 56x42mm stamp.

**No. 833 Surcharged**

**1996            Litho.    Perf. 13½**
1062 A146   20s on 30s multi    2.00  1.00

Christmas — A183

Women from Mother's Unions: 35s, Methodist Church. 50s, Roman Catholic Church. 1m, Lesotho Evangelical Church. 1.50m, Anglican Church.

**1996, Dec. 10    Litho.    Perf. 14**
1063-1066 A183   Set of 4       2.75  2.75

Highlands Water
Project — A184

Designs: 35s, "Cooperation for Development." 50s, "Nature and Heritage." 1m, "An Engineering Feat." 1.50m, "LHDA 10th Anniv., 1986-1996."

**1997, Apr. 21    Litho.    Perf. 14**
1067-1070 A184   Set of 4       3.25  3.25

No. 1070 is 72x25mm.

Environmental
Protection — A184a

Emblem of National Environment Secretariat and: 35s, Animals grazing on reclaimed land. 50s, Person throwing trash in can. 1m, Hands holding globe with tree. 1.20m, Trash and recycling emblem. 1.50m, Collection of rainwater.

**1997, June 30**
1070A-1070E  A184a   Set of 5    3.00  3.00

---

1998 World Cup
Soccer
Championships,
France — A185

Players: 1m, Schmeichel, Denmark. 1.50m, Bergkamp, Holland. 2m, Southgate, England. 2.50m, Asprilla, Colombia. 3m, Gascoigne, England. 4m, Giggs, Wales.
No. 1077: Various action scenes of Argentina vs. Holland, 1978.
No. 1078, 8m, Littbarski, W. Germany, horiz. No. 1079, 8m, Shearer, England.

**1997, Oct. 31            Perf. 13½**
1071-1076 A185   Set of 6       6.50  6.50
1077 A185   1.50m Sheet of 6,
            #a.-f.             11.00 11.00
**Souvenir Sheets**
1078-1079 A185   Set of 2       9.00  9.00

Butterflies
A186

No. 1080: a, Spialia spio. b, Cyclyrius pirithous. c, Acraea satis. d, Belenois aurota. e, Spindasis natalensis. f, Torynesis orangica. g, Lepidochrysops variabilis. h, Pinacopteryx eriphea. i, Anthene butleri.
No. 1081, 8m, Bematistes aganice. No. 1082, 8m, Papilio demodocus.

**1997, Nov. 28            Perf. 14**
1080 A186   1.50m Sheet of 9,
            #a.-i.             7.75  7.75
**Souvenir Sheets**
1081-1082 A186   Set of 2      11.00 11.00

Morija Museum
and Archives, 40th
Anniv. — A187

Designs: 35s, Rock paintings, child, vert. 45s, Lower jaw of hippopotamus, hippo walking in water. 50s, Traditional attire, vert. 1m, Traditional musical instruments, vert. 1.50m, Award, Man with ceremonial garb, vert. 2m, Boy riding bull.

**Perf. 14½ Syncopated Type A**
**1998, Jan. 30            Litho.**
1083-1088 A187   Set of 6      3.25  3.25

Diana, Princess of
Wales (1961-
97) — A188

Designs: No. 1089, Various portaits. No. 1090, Taking flowers from child.

**1998, Mar. 16    Litho.    Perf. 13½**
1089 A188   3m Sheet of 6, #a.-f.  9.00  9.00
**Souvenir Sheet**
1090 A188   9m multicolored        9.00  9.00

A189

A190

Wildlife
A191

No. 1091 — Cape vulture: a, Head. b, Perched on rock with head down. c, Looking left. d, Looking right.
No. 1092: a, Atitlan grebe. b, Cabot's tragopan. c, Spider monkey. d, Dibatag. e, Right whale. f, Imperial parrot. g, Cheetah. h, Brown-eared pheasant. i, Leatherback turtle. j, Imperial woodpecker. k, Andean condor. l, Barbary deer. m, Grey gentle lemur. n, Cuban parrot. o, Numbat. p, Short-tailed albatross. q, Green turtle. r, White rhinoceros. s, Diademed sifaka. t, Galapagos penguin.
No. 1093: a, Impala. b, Black bear. c, Buffalo. d, Elephant. e, Kangaroo. f, Lion. g, Panda. h, Tiger. i, Zebra.
No. 1094, 8m, Nectarinia talatala. No. 1095, 8m, Psephotus chrysopterygius. No. 1096, 8m, Percina tanasi.
No. 1097, 8m, Monkey.

**1998, Apr. 27      Litho.      Perf. 14**
1091  A189   1m Strip of 4,
                   #a.-d.              4.50   4.50
1092  A190   1m Sheet of 20,
                   #a.-t.             11.00  11.00
1093  A191   1.50m Sheet of 9,
                   #a.-i.              7.00   7.00
        **Souvenir Sheets**
1094-1096 A190   Set of 3    12.00  12.00
1097  A191   8m multicolored   4.00   4.00
No. 1091 was issued in sheets of 12 stamps. World Wildlife Fund (No. 1091).

Cats — A192

Designs: 70s, Siamese. 1m, Chartreux. 2m, Korat. 3m, Egyptian mau. 4m, Bombay. 5m, Burmese.
No. 1104, 2m: a, Japanese bobtail. b, British white. c, Bengal. d, Abyssinian. e, Snowshoe. f, Scottish fold.
No. 1105, 2m: a, Maine coon. b, Balinese. c, Persian. d, Javanese. e, Turkish angora. f, Tiffany.
No. 1106, 8m, Singapura. No. 1107, 8m, Tonkinese.

**1998, May 18**
1098-1103 A192   Set of 6    7.75   7.75
        **Sheets of 6, #a-f**
1104-1105 A192   Set of 2    16.00  16.00
        **Souvenir Sheets**
1106-1107 A192   Set of 2    10.00  10.00

Mushrooms
A193

Designs: 70s, Laccaria laccata. 1m, Mutinus caninus. 1.50m, Tricholoma lascivum. 2m, Clitocybe geotrapa. 3m, Amanita excelsa. 4m, Red-capped bolete.
No. 1114: a, Parrot wax cap. b, Cortinarius obtusus. c, Volvariella bombycina. d, Cortinarius caerylescens. e, Laccaria amethystea. f, Tricholoma aurantium. g, Amanita excelsa. h, Clavaria helvola. i, Cortinarius caerylescens. j, Russula queletii. k, Amanita phalloides. l, Lactarius delicious.
No. 1115, 8m, Amanita pantherina. No. 1116, 8m, Boletus satanus.

**1998, June 15      Litho.      Perf. 14**
1108-1113 A193   Set of 6    6.50   6.50
1114  A193   1m Sheet of 12,
                   #a.-l.              6.50   6.50
        **Souvenir Sheets**
1115-1116 A193   Set of 2    9.00   9.00

Japanese Film
Stars — A194

No. 1117: a, Takamine Hideko. b, James Shigeta. c, Miyoshi Umeki. d, May Ishimara. e, Sessue Hayakawa. f, Miiko Taka. g, Mori Masayuki. h, Hara Setsuko. i, Kyo Machiko.
10m, Toshiro Mifune.

**1998, July 14      Litho.      Perf. 14**
1117  A194   2m Sheet of 9, #a.-i.  7.50   7.50
        **Souvenir Sheet**
1118  A194   10m multicolored   4.00   4.00

Prehistoric
Animals — A195

No. 1119, 2m: a, Nyctosaurus (b). b, Volcanoes, wings of nyctosaurus, eudimorphadon. c, Eudimorphodon (b). d, Apatosaurus (g). e, Peteinosaurus (d, f, i). f, Tropeognathus. g, Pteranodon ingens (d). h, Ornithodesmus (g, i). i, Wuerhosaurus.
No. 1120, 2m: a, Ceresiosaurus (b, c, d). b, Rhomaleosaurus (a). c, Anomalocaris (b, f). d, Mixosaurus (e, g, h). e, Stethacanthus. f, Dunklosteus (c, e, i). g, Tommotia. h, Sanctacaris. i, Ammonites (a, f, h).
No. 1121, 2m: a, Rhamphorhynchus (b, d). b, Brachiosaurus (c, f). c, Mamenchisaurus hochuanensis (a, d, e, f). d, Ceratosaurus nasicornis (e, g, h). e, Archaeopteryx (b). f, Leaellynasaura amicargraphica (e, h, i). g, Chasmosaurus belli (h). h, Deinonychus, Pachyrhinosaurus (g). i, Deinonychus (h).
No. 1122, 10m, Woolly rhinoceros. No. 1123, 10m, Tyrannosaurus. No. 1124, 10m, Coelophysis.

**1998, Aug. 10      Sheets of 9, #a-i**
1119-1121 A195   Set of 3    24.00  24.00
        **Souvenir Sheets**
1122-1124 A195   Set of 3    14.00  14.00

Intl. Year of the
Ocean — A196

Fish: No. 1125, 1m, Treefish. No. 1126, 1m, Tiger barb. No. 1127, 1m, Bandtail puffer. No. 1128, 1m, Cod. No. 1129, 1.50m, Filefish. No. 1130, 1.50m, Clown loach. No. 1131, 1.50m, Sicklefin killie. No. 1132, 1.50m, Christy's lyretail. No. 1133, 2m, Brook trout. No. 1134, 2m, Pacific electric ray. No. 1135, 2m, Bighead searobin. No. 1136, 2m, Emerald betta. 3m, Harlequin tuskfish. 4m, Half-moon angelfish. 5m, Spotted trunkfish. 6m, Wolf-eel. 7m, Cherubfish.
No. 1142, 2m: a, Platy variatus. b, Archerfish. c, Clown knifefish. d, Angelicous. e, Black arowana. f, Spotted scat. g, Kribensis. h, Golden pheasant.
No. 1143, 2m: a, Bluegill. b, Grayling. c, Walleye. d, Brown trout. e, Atlantic salmon. f, Northern pike. g, Large mouth bass. h, Rainbow trout.
No. 1144, 2m: a, Purple firefish. b, Halequin sweetlips. c, Clown wrasse. d, Bicolor angelfish. e, False cleanerfish. f, Mandarinfish. g, Regal tang. h, Clownfish.
No. 1145, 2m: a, Weakfish. b, Red drum. c, Blue marlin. d, Yellowfin tuna. e, Barracuda. f, Striped bass. g, White shark. h, Permit.
No. 1146, 12m, Cyprinus carpio. No. 1147, 12m, Oncorhynchus. No. 1148, 12m, Pseudopleuronectes americanus. No. 1149, 12m, Heterodontus francisci.

**1998, Oct. 15      Litho.      Perf. 14**
1125-1141 A196   Set of 17   17.50  17.50
        **Sheets of 8, #a-h**
1142-1145 A196   Set of 4    26.00  26.00
        **Souvenir Sheets**
1146-1149 A196   Set of 4    19.00  19.00

Africa in
Films — A197

No. 1150: a, "Simba." b, "Call to Freedom." c, "Cry the Beloved Country." d, "King Solomon's Mines." e, "Flame and the Fire." f, "Cry Freedom." g, "Bophal" h, "Zulu."
10m "Born Free," horiz.

**1998, July 14      Litho.      Perf. 14**
1150  A197   2m Sheet of 8, #a.-
                   h.                  7.50   7.50
        **Souvenir Sheet**
1151  A197   10m multicolored   4.00   4.00

Flowers — A198

Designs: 10s, Pelargonium sidoides. 15s, Aponogeton ranunculiflorus. 20s, Sebaea leiostyla. 40s, Sebaea grandis. 50s, Satyrium neglectum. 60s, Massonia jasminiflora. 70s, Ajuga ophrydis. 80s, Nemesia fruticans. 1m, Aloe broomii. 2m, Wahlenbergia androsacea. 2.50m, Phygelius capensis. 3m, Dianthus basuticus. 4.50m, Rhodohypoxis baurii. 5m, Turbina oblongata. 6m, Hibiscus microcarpus. 10m, Lobelia erinus, moraea stricta.

**1998      Litho.      Perf. 14**
1152  A198   10s multicolored    .25    .25
1153  A198   15s multicolored    .25    .25
1154  A198   20s multicolored    .25    .25
1155  A198   40s multicolored    .25    .25
1156  A198   50s multicolored    .25    .25
1157  A198   60s multicolored    .25    .25
1158  A198   70s multicolored    .25    .25
1159  A198   80s multicolored    .40    .40
1160  A198   1m multicolored     .50    .50
1161  A198   2m multicolored    1.00   1.00
1162  A198   2.50m multicolored 1.25   1.25
1163  A198   3m multicolored    1.50   1.50
1164  A198   4.50m multicolored 2.25   2.25
1165  A198   5m multicolored    2.40   2.40
1166  A198   6m multicolored    3.00   3.00
1167  A198   10m multicolored   4.50   4.50
        Nos. 1152-1167 (16)     18.55  18.55
Nos. 1152-1167 are dated 1997.

Coronation of King Letsie III, 1st
Anniv. — A199

No. 1168: a, Receiving crown. b, Waving. c, Facing left.

**1998, Oct. 31**
1168  A199   1m Strip of 3, #a.-c.   2.25   2.25

Dogs — A200

Designs: 70s, Akita. 1m, Canaan. 2m, Eskimo. 4.50m, Norwegian elkhound.
No. 1173, 2m: a, Cirneco dell'etna. b, Afghan hound. c, Finnish spitz. d, Dalmatian. e, Basset hound. f, Shar-pei.
No. 1174, 2m: a, Boxer. b, Catalan sheepdog. c, English toy spaniel. d, Greyhound. e, Keeshond. f, Bearded collie.
No. 1175, 8m, Rough collie. No. 1176, 8m, Borzoi.

**1999, May 18      Litho.      Perf. 14**
1169-1172 A200   Set of 4    4.00   4.00
        **Sheets of 6, #a-f**
1173-1174 A200   Set of 2    11.00  11.00
        **Souvenir Sheets**
1175-1176 A200   Set of 2    10.00  10.00

Birds — A201

Designs: 70s, Belted kingfisher. 1.50m, Palm cockatoo, vert. 2m, Red-tailed hawk. 3m, Tufted puffin. 4m, Reddish egret. 5m, Hoatzin, vert.
No. 1183, 2m: a, Evening grosbeak. b, Lesser blue-winged pitta. c, Altamira oriole. d, Rose-breasted grosbeak. e, Yellow warbler. f, American goldfinch. g, Northern flicker. i, Western tanager.
No. 1184, 2m, vert: a, Blue jay. b, Northern cardinal. c, Yellow-headed blackbird. d, Red crossbill. e, Cedar waxwing. f, Vermilion flycatcher. g, Pileated woodpecker. h, Western meadowlark. i, Kingfisher.
No. 1185, 8m, Great egret. No. 1186, 8m, Zosterops erythropleura.

**1999, June 28      Litho.      Perf. 14**
1177-1182 A201   Set of 6    8.00   8.00
        **Sheets of 9, #a-i**
1183-1184 A201   Set of 2    19.00  19.00
        **Souvenir Sheets**
1185-1186 A201   Set of 2    10.00  10.00
No. 1183c is incorrectly inscribed "Atlamira."

Orchids — A202

Designs: 1.50m, Cattleya dowiana. 3m, Diurus behri. 4m, Ancistrochilus rothchildianus. 5m, Aerangis curnowiana. 7m, Arachnis flos-aeris. 8m, Aspasia principissa.
No. 1193, 2m: a, Dendrobium bellaudum. b, Dendrobium trigonopus. c, Dimerandra emarginata. d, Dressleria eburnea. e, Dracula tubeana. f, Disa kirstenbosch. g, Encyclia alata. h, Epidendrum pseudepidendrum. i, Eriopsis biloba.
No. 1194, 2m: a, Apasia epidendroides. b, Barkaria lindleyana. c, Bifrenaria tetragona. d, Bulbophyllum graveolens. e, Brassavola flagellaris. f, Bollea lawrenceana. g, Caladenia carnea. h, Catasetum macrocarpum. i, Cattleya aurantiaca.
No. 1195, 2m: a, Cochleanthes discolor. b, Cischweinfia dasyandra. c, Ceratostylis retisquama. d, Comparettia speciosa. e, Cryptostylis subulata. f, Cycnoches ventricsum. g, Dactylorhiza maculata. h, Cypripedium calceolus. i, Cymbidium finlaysonianum.
No. 1196, 10m, Paphiopedilum tonsum. No. 1197, 10m, Laelia rubescens. No. 1198, 10m, Ansellium africana. No. 1199, 10m, Ophrys apifera.

**1999, July 30      Litho.      Perf. 14**
1187-1192 A202   Set of 6    13.00  13.00
        **Sheets of 9, #a-i**
1193-1195 A202   Set of 3    22.50  22.50
        **Souvenir Sheets**
1196-1199 A202   Set of 4    15.00  15.00

Chinese Art — A203

No. 1200 — Paintings by Pan Tianshou (1897-1971): a, Water Lily at Night. b, Hen and Chicks. c, Plum Blossom and Orchid. d, Plum Blossom and Banana Tree. e, Crane and Pine. f, Swallows. g, Eagle on the Pine (black eagle). h, Palm Tree. i, Eagle on the Pine (gray eagle). j, Orchids.
No. 1201: a, Sponge Gourd. b, Dragonfly.

**1999, Aug. 16**          *Perf. 13x13¼*
1200 A203 1.50m Sheet of 10,
#a.-j.                          8.50 8.50
**Souvenir Sheet**
1201 A203     6m Sheet of 2,
#a.-b.                    6.50 6.50
China 1999 World Philatelic Exhibition.
No. 1201 contains two 51x40mm stamps.

**Souvenir Sheet**

UN Rights of the Child Convention,
10th Anniv. — A204

No. 1202: a, Black boy. b, Asian girl. c, Cau-
casian boy.

**1999, Aug. 16**                 *Perf. 14*
1202 A204 2m Sheet of 3, #a.-c.  3.00 3.00

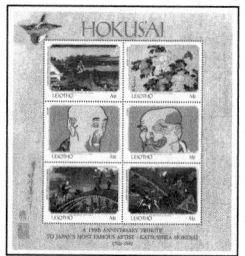

Paintings by Hokusai (1760-
1849) — A205

No. 1203, 3m: a, Nakamaro Watching the
Moon from a Hill. b, Peonies and Butterfly. c,
The Blind (bald man, both eyes open). d, The
Blind (bald man, one eye shut). e, People
Crossing an Arched Bridge (two at crest). f,
People Crossing an Arched Bridge (river).
No. 1204, 3m: a, A View of Sumida River in
Snow. b, Two Carp. c, The Blind (man with
hair, both eyes shut). d, The Blind (man with
hair, one eye open). e, Fishing by Torchlight. f,
Whaling off the Goto Islands.
No. 1205, 10m, The Moon Above Yodo
River and Osaka Castle, vert. No. 1206, 10m,
Bellflower and Dragonfly, vert.

**1999, Aug. 16**                 *Perf. 13¾*
**Sheet of 6, #a-f**
1203-1204 A205   Set of 2      14.00 14.00
**Souvenir Sheets**
1205-1206 A205   Set of 2       8.00 8.00

Queen Mother (b.
1900) — A206

No. 1207: a, Wearing hat, 1938. b, With
King George VI, 1948. c, Wearing tiara, 1963.
d, Wearing hat, 1989.
15m, Waving at Clarence House.

**1999, Aug. 16**                 *Perf. 14*
1207 A206   5m Sheet of 4, #a.-
d., + label               7.50 7.50
**Souvenir Sheet**
*Perf. 13¾*
1208 A206 15m multicolored       6.25 6.25
No. 1208 contains one 38x51mm stamp.

Johann
Wolfgang von
Goethe (1749-
1832)
A207

No. 1209: a, Mephistopheles appears as a
dog in Faust's study. b, Portraits of Goethe
and Friedrich von Schiller. c, Mephistopheles
disguised as dog scorching the earth.

---

12m, Mephistopheles.

**1999, Aug. 16**                 *Perf. 14*
1209 A207   6m Sheet of 3, #a.-
c.                        6.25 6.25
**Souvenir Sheet**
1210 A207 12m multicolored       4.50 4.50

IBRA '99, Nuremberg,
Germany — A208

Designs: 7m, Austerity 2-10-10 locomotive,
building in Frankfurt am Main. 8m, Adler locomotive, Brandenburg Gate.

**1999, Aug. 16**             *Perf. 14x14½*
1211 A208   7m multicolored      2.75 2.75
1212 A208   8m multicolored      3.25 3.25

Ships — A209

No. 1213, 4m: a, James Watt. b, Savannah.
c, Amistad. d, Brick. e, Great Briain. f, Sirius.
No. 1214, 4m: a, France. b, Queen Eliza-
beth II. c, United States. d, Queen Elizabeth I.
e, Michelangelo. f, Mauretania.
No. 1215, 4m: a, New Jersey. b, Aquila. c,
De Zeven Provincien. d, Formidable. e, Vittorio
Veneto. f, Hampshire.
No. 1216, 4m: a, Shearwater. b, British sub-
marine. c, Hovercraft SRN 130. d, Italian sub-
marine. e, Sr. N/3. f, Soucoupe Plongeante.
No. 1217, 15m, E. W. Morrison. No. 1218,
15m, Titanic. No. 1219, 15m, German U-boat.
No. 1220, 15m, Enterprise.

**1999, Dec. 31**      *Litho.*     *Perf. 14*
**Sheets of 6, #a.-f.**
1213-1216 A209   Set of 4     30.00 30.00
**Souvenir Sheets**
1217-1220 A209   Set of 4     21.00 21.00
Names of ships are only found on sheet
margins.

Millennium — A210

No. 1221 — Highlights of the 12th century:
a, Chinese make first rocket. b, Burmese temple guardian. c, Troubador. d, Abbé Suger. e,
Pope Adrian IV. f, King Henry II of England. g,
Holy Roman Emperor Barbarossa. h, Yoritomo
establishes shogunate in Japan. i, Crusader
monument. j, Ibn Rushd translates Aristotle. k,
Archbishop Thomas Becket. l, Leaning Tower
of Pisa. m, Pivot windmill. n, Saladin. o, Richard the Lion-Hearted. p, Easter Island statues
(60x40mm) q, Third Crusade begins.

**1999, Dec. 31**            *Perf. 12¾x12½*
1221 A210 1.50m Sheet of 17,
#a.-q.                  11.00 11.00

Wedding of King Letsie
III to Karabo Anne
Motsoeneng — A211

No. 1222: a, King, bride in Western attire. b,
Bride. c, King. d, King, bride in native attire.

**2000, Feb. 18**     *Litho.*     *Perf. 14*
1222 A211 1m Sheet of 4, #a.-d.,
+ label                  3.75 3.75

---

Prince
William,
18th
Birthday
A212

No. 1223: a, Wearing bow tie. b, Wearing
scarf. c, Wearing striped shirt. d, Wearing
sweater, holding car door.
15m, Wearing sweater, diff.

**2000, June 21**     *Litho.*     *Perf. 14*
1223 A212   4m Sheet of 4, #a-d  6.50 6.50
**Souvenir Sheet**
*Perf. 13¾*
1224 A212 15m multi              6.50 6.50
No. 1223 contains four 28x42mm stamps.

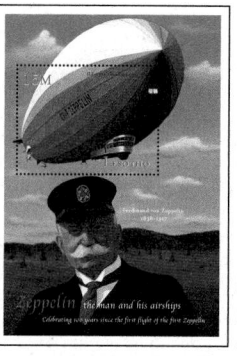

First
Zeppelin
Flight,
Cent.
A213

No. 1225 — Ferdinand von Zeppelin and: a,
LZ- 127. b, LZ-130. c, LZ-10.
15m, LZ-130, diff.

**2000, July 6**                  *Perf. 14*
1225 A213   8m Sheet of 3, #a-c  8.50 8.50
**Souvenir Sheet**
1226 A213 15m multi              6.50 6.50
No. 1225 contains three 42x28mm stamps.

Berlin
Film
Festival,
50th
Anniv.
A214

No. 1227: a, Gena Rowlands. b, Vlastimil
Brodsky. c, Carlos Saura. d, La Collection-
euse. e, Le Depart. f, Le Diable Probablement.
15m, Stammheim.

**2000, July 6**
1227 A214   6m Sheet of 6,
#a-f                  12.00 12.00
**Souvenir Sheet**
1228 A214 15m multi              6.50 6.50

**Souvenir Sheets**

2000 Summer Olympics,
Sydney — A215

---

No. 1229: a, Nedo Nadi. b, Swimming. c,
Aztec Stadium, Mexico City and Mexican flag.
d, Ancient Greek boxers.

**2000, July 6**
1229 A215   6m Sheet of 4, #a-d   8.50 8.50

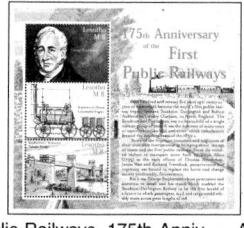

Public Railways, 175th Anniv. — A216

No. 1230: a, George Stephenson. b, Stephenson's patent locomotive engine. c, Stephenson's Britannia Tubular Bridge.

**2000, July 6**
1230 A216   8m Sheet of 3, #a-c   8.50 8.50

Johann Sebastian Bach (1685-
1750) — A217

**2000, July 6**
1231 A217 15m multi              6.50 6.50

Flowers — A218

Designs: 4m, Moore's crinum. 5m, Flame
lily. 6m, Cape clivia. 8m, True sugarbush.
No. 1236, 3m: a, Spotted leaved arum. b,
Christmas bells. c, Lady Monson. d, Wild
pomegranate. e, Blushing bride. f, Bot River
protea.
No. 1237, 3m: a, Starry gardenia. b, Pink
hibiscus. c, Dwarf poker. d, Coast kaffirboom.
e, Rose cockade. f, Pride of Table Mountain.
No. 1238, 3m: a, Drooping agpanthus. b,
Yellow marsh afrikander. c, Weak stemmed
painted lady. d, Impala lily. e, Beatrice wat-
sonia. f, Pink arum.
No. 1239, 15m, Green arum. No. 1240,
15m, Red hairy erica, horiz.

**2000, July 12**
1232-1235 A218   Set of 4        9.00 9.00
**Sheets of 6, #a-f**
1236-1238 A218   Set of 3      21.00 21.00
**Souvenir Sheets**
1239-1240 A218   Set of 2      15.00 15.00

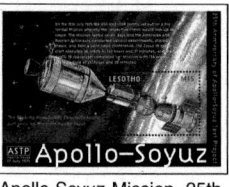

Apollo-Soyuz Mission, 25th
Anniv. — A219

No. 1241: a, Apollo 18 and Soyuz 19
docked. b, Apollo 18. c, Soyuz 19.

**2000, July 6**     *Litho.*     *Perf. 14*
1241 A219   8m Sheet of 3,
#a-c                   9.00 9.00
**Souvenir Sheet**
1242 A219 15m shown              6.50 6.50

## Souvenir Sheet

Albert Einstein (1879-1955) — A220

**2000, July 6**   **Perf. 14¼**
1243 A220 15m multi         6.50 6.50

Endangered Wildlife — A221

No. 1244, 4m, horiz.: a, Alethe. b, Temminck's pangolin. c, Cheetah. d, African elephant. e, Chimpanzee. f, Northern white rhinoceros.
No. 1245, 4m, horiz.: a, African black rhinoceros. b, Leopard. c, Roseate tern. d, Mountain gorilla. e, Mountain zebra. f, Zanzibar red colobus monkey.
No. 1246, horiz: a, Wildebeest. b, Tree hyrax. c, Red lechwe. d, Eland.
No. 1247, 15m, Dugong. No. 1248, 15m, West African manatee.

**2000, Aug. 10   Litho.   Perf. 14**
**Sheets of 6, #a-f**
1244-1245 A221   Set of 2    18.00 18.00
1246 A221  5m Sheet of 4, #a-
     d                          7.75  7.75
**Souvenir Sheets**
1247-1248 A221   Set of 2    16.00 16.00
The Stamp Show 2000, London.

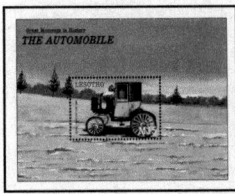

Automobiles — A222

No. 1249, 3m: a, 1960 Cadillac El Dorado Seville. b, 1955-75 Citroen DS. c, 1961 Ford Zephyr Zodiac Mk II. d, 1945-55 MG TF. e, 1949-65 Porsche 356. f, 1955 Ford Thunderbird.
No. 1250, 3m: a, 1948-52 Cisitalia 202 Coupe. b, 1990s Dodge Viper. c, 1968-69, TVR Vixen SI. d, 1957-70 Lotus 7. e, 1964-68 Ferrari 275 GTB/4. f, 1951 Pegasus Touring Spider.
No. 1251, 4m: a, 1913 Fiat Type O. b, 1914 Stutz Bearcat. c, 1924 French Levat. d, 1888 Benz Motorwagen. e, 1925 Isota Fraschini Type 8A. f, 1887 Markus Motor Carriage.
No. 1252, 4m: a, 1951 Morris Minor. b, 1935 Hispano-Suiza Type 68. c, 1949 MG TC. d, 1955 Morgan 4/4. e, 1950 Jaguar XK120. f, 1946-49 Triumph 1800/2000 Roadster.
No. 1253, 15m, 1896 Bersey Electric Car. No. 1254, 15m, 1948-71 Morris Minor 1000. No. 1255, 15m, 1953-63 AC Ace. No. 1256, 15m, Ferrari F40, vert.
Illustration reduced.

**2000, Sept. 1      Sheets of 6, #a-f**
1249-1252 A222   Set of 4    30.00 30.00
**Souvenir Sheets**
1253-1256 A222   Set of 4    25.00 25.00

Fight Against
AIDS — A223

Designs: 70s, "Fight AIDS, not people living with it." 1m, "Speed kills, so does AIDS. Go Slow!" 1.50m, "People with AIDS need friends, not rejection," vert. 2.10m, "Even when you're off duty, protect the nation."

**2001, Jan. 22      Litho.      Perf. 14**
1257-1260 A223   Set of 4     5.00 5.00

Butterflies
A224

Designs: 70s, Great orange tip. 1m, Red-banded pereute. 1.50m, Sword grass brown. No. 1264, 2m, Striped blue crow. No. 1265, 3m, Alfalfa. 4m, Doris.
No. 1267, 2m: a, African migrant. b, Large oak blue. c, Wanderer. d, Tiger swallowtail. e, Union jack. f, Saturn. g, Broad-bordered grass yellow. h, Hewitson's uraneis.
No. 1268, 2m: a, Orange-banded sulfur. b, Large wood nymph. c, Postman. d, Palmfly. e, Gulf fritillary. f, Cairns birdwing. g, Common morpho. h, Common dotted border.
No. 1269, 3m: a, Bertoni's antwren (bird). b, Clorinde. c, Iolas blue. d, Mocker swallowtail. e, Common Indian crow. f, Grecian shoemaker. g, Small flambeau. h, Orchid swallowtail.
No. 1270, 15m, Crimson tip. No. 1271, 15m, Forest queen.

**2001, Mar. 1   Litho.   Perf. 13¼x13¾**
1261-1266 A224   Set of 6     7.00 7.00
**Sheets of 8, #a-h**
1267-1269 A224   Set of 3    24.00 24.00
**Souvenir Sheets**
1270-1271 A224   Set of 2    22.00 22.00

Phila Nippon '01,
Japan — A225

Designs: 1.50m, Man in carriage from The Battle of Lepanto and the Map of the World, by unknown artist. 2m, Battle scene from The Battle of Lepanto and the Map of the World. 3m, Crane from Birds and Flowers of the Four Seasons, by Eitoku Kano. 4m, The Four Elegant Pastimes. 7m, Maple Viewing at Mount Takao, by unknown artist. 8m, The Four Accomplishments, by Yusho Kaiho.
No. 1278, 5m: a, Portrait of a Lady, by unknown artist. b, Portrait of Tadakatsu Honda, by unknown artist. c, Portrait of the Wife of Tokujo Goto, by unknown aritst. d, Portrait of Emperor Go-yosei, by Takanobu Kano. e, Portrait of Tenzuiin, Hideyoshi's Mother, by Sochin Hoshuku.
No. 1279, 6m: a, Portrait of Yusai Hosokawa, by Suden Ishin. b, Portrait of Sen No Rikyu, attributed to Tohaku Hasegawa. c, Portrait of Oichi No Kata, by unknown artist. d, Portrait of Ittetsu Inaba, attributed to Hasegawa. e, Portrait of Nobunaga Oda, by Sochin Kokei.
No. 1280, 15m, Portrait of Ieyasu Tokugawa, by unknown artist. No. 1281, 15m, Portrait of Hideyoshi Toyotomi, by unknown artist.

**Perf. 13¾, 14 (#1278-1279)**
**2001, May 31                      Litho.**
1272-1277 A225   Set of 6     6.00 6.00
**Sheets of 5, #a-e**
1278-1279 A225   Set of 2    30.00 30.00
**Souvenir Sheets**
1280-1281 A225   Set of 2    14.50 14.50
Size of stamps on Nos. 1278-1279: 85x28mm.
Nos. 1274-1275 are incorrectly inscribed. No. 1274 actually depicts "Landscape with Flowers and Birds." No. 1275 shows a detail from"The Four Elegant Pastimes," by Eitoku Kano.

Mushrooms — A226

Designs: No. 1282, 5m, Bell-shaped panaeolus. No. 1283, 5m, Golden false pholiota. No. 1284, 5m, Shiny cap. No. 1285, 5m, Sooty brown waxy cap.
No. 1286, 3m: a, Violet cortinarius. b, Angel's wings. c, Collybia velutibes. d, Lentinellus. e, Anthurus aseroiformis. f, Caesar's mushroom.
No. 1287, 4m: a, Pungent cortinarius. b, Peziza sarcosphaera. c, Emetic russula. d, Questionable stropharia. e, Apricot jelly mushroom. f, Anise-scented clitocybe.
No. 1288, 15m, Cone-shaped waxy cap, horiz. No. 1289, 15m, Boletus, horiz.

**2001, June 29                      Perf. 14**
1282-1285 A226   Set of 4     9.00 9.00
**Sheets of 6, #a-f**
1286-1287 A226   Set of 2    19.00 19.00
**Souvenir Sheets**
1288-1289 A226   Set of 2    14.00 14.00
Belgica 2001 Intl. Stamp Exhibition, Brussels (Nos. 1286-1289).

UN High
Commissioner for
Refugees, 50th
Anniv. — A227

Designs: 70s, Silhouette of woman and child. 1m, Child and animal. 1.50m, Woman, vert. 2.10m, Information technology, vert.

**2001, Aug. 20                      Perf. 14**
1290-1293 A227   Set of 4     4.75 4.75

Birds of Prey — A228

Designs: 70s, Black kite. 1m, Martial eagle. 1.50m, Bateleur. 2.10m, African goshawk. 2.50m, Bearded vulture. 3m, Jackal buzzard.

**2001, Oct. 1      Litho.      Perf. 14**
1294-1299 A228   Set of 6     6.00 6.00

Southern African
Wildlife — A229

Designs: 1m, Grass owl. 2.10m, Klipspringer. 3m, Saddlebacked jackal. 5m, Black wildebeest.
No. 1304, 4m: a, Damara zebra. b, Bontebok. c, Eland. d, Lion. e, Saddlebacked jackal, diff. f, Yellow-billed kite.
No. 1305, 4m: a, Aardvark. b, Rock kestrel. c, Black-footed cat. d, Springhare. e, Aardwolf. f, Rock hyrax.
No. 1306, 15m, black-shouldered kite. No. 1307, 15m, Caracal, vert.

**2001, Oct. 15      Litho.      Perf. 14**
1300-1303 A229   Set of 4     6.00  6.00
**Sheets of 6, #a-f**
1304-1305 A229   Set of 2    21.00 21.00
**Souvenir Sheets**
1306-1307 A229   Set of 2    15.00 15.00

Reign of
Queen
Elizabeth
II, 50th
Anniv.
A230

No. 1308: a, Queen seated. b, Queen with Prince Philip and British flag. c, Queen with man. c, Prince Philip.
20m, Queen wearing black suit.

**2002, Feb. 6      Litho.      Perf. 14¼**
1308 A230   8m Sheet of 4,
     #a-d                    13.00 13.00
**Souvenir Sheet**
1309 A230 20m multi          10.00 10.00

United We
Stand — A231

**2002, Aug. 13                      Perf. 14**
1310 A231 7m multi            4.00 4.00
Printed in sheets of 4.

SOS Children's
Village,
Lithabaneng
A232

**2002, Aug. 13**
1311 A232 10m multi           4.50 4.50

Rotary International in
Lesotho, 25th
Anniv. — A233

Designs: 8m, Horner Wood. 10m, Paul Harris.
No. 1314, 25m, Stylized globe and clasped hands. No. 1315, 25m, Golden Gate Bridge, horiz.

**2002, Aug. 13**
1312-1313 A233   Set of 2     7.00 7.00
**Souvenir Sheets**
1314-1315 A233   Set of 2    18.00 18.00

20th World Scout Jamboree,
Thailand — A234

No. 1316: a, Sheet bend knots. b, Pup and forester tents. c, Canoeing. d, Water rescue. 25m, A night under the stars.

**2002, Aug. 13**
1316 A234   9m Sheet of 4,
     #a-d                    11.50 11.50
**Souvenir Sheet**
1317 A234 25m multi          11.00 11.00

Intl. Year of Mountains — A235

No. 1318, horiz.: a, Mt. Machache. b, Mt. Thabana Li-Mèle. c, Mt. Qiloane. d, Mt. Thaba Bosiu.
25m, Mt. Rainier, US.

**2002, Aug. 13**
1318 A235   8m Sheet of 4,
#a-d                                11.50 11.50
**Souvenir Sheet**
1319 A235  25m multi                11.50 11.50

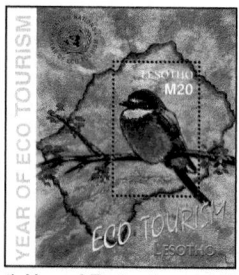

Intl. Year of Ecotourism — A236

No. 1320, horiz.: a, Plant. b, Flowers. c, Man and horses. d, Lion. e, Frog. f, House.
20m, Bird.

**2002, Aug. 13**
1320 A236   6m Sheet of 6,
#a-f                                13.00 13.00
**Souvenir Sheet**
1321 A236  20m multi                 8.50  8.50

Flowers, Insects and Spiders A237

No. 1322, 6m — Flowers: a, Angel's fishing rod. b, Marigold. c, Joan's blood. d, Mule pink. e, Tiger lily. f, Comtesse de Bouchaud.
No. 1323, 6m — Orchids: a, Phragmipedium besseae. b, Cypripedium calceolus. c, Cattleya Louise Georgiana. d, Brassocattleya binosa. e, Laelia gouldiana. f, Paphiopedilum maudiae.
No. 1324, 6m, horiz. — Insects: a, Leaf grasshopper. b, Golden-ringed dragonfly. c, Weevil-hunting wasp. d, European grasshopper. e, Thread-waisted wasp. f, Mantid.
No. 1325, 20m, Bleeding heart. No. 1326, 20m, Brassavola tuberculata. No. 1327, 20m, Orb web spider.

**2002, Aug. 30            Perf. 14**
**Sheets of 6, #a-f**
1322-1324 A237   Set of 3     35.00 35.00
**Souvenir Sheets**
1325-1327 A237   Set of 3     25.00 25.00

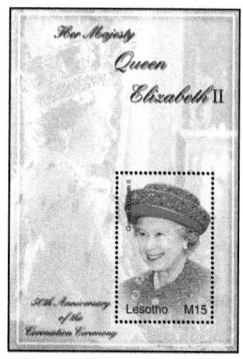

Coronation of Queen Elizabeth II, 50th Anniv. (in 2003) — A238

No. 1328: a, Wearing blue hat. b, Wearing white hat. c, Wearing black hat.
15m, Wearing red hat.

**2004, May 17      Litho.      Perf. 14**
1328 A238   8m Sheet of 3, #a-c   7.00  7.00
**Souvenir Sheet**
1329 A238  15m multi               4.50  4.50

Prince William, 21st Birthday (in 2003) A239

No. 1330: a, Wearing sunglasses. b, Wearing suit and tie c, Wearing sports shirt.
15m, As young boy.

**2004, May 17**
1330 A239   8m Sheet of 3, #a-c   8.00  8.00
**Souvenir Sheet**
1331 A239  15m multi               4.75  4.75

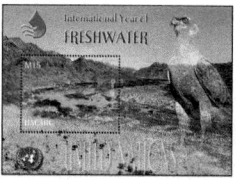

Intl. Year of Fresh Water (in 2003) A240

No. 1332: a, Top of Qiloane Falls (gray water at top). b, Middle portion of Qiloane Falls (narrow at top). c, Bottom portion of Qiloane Falls.
15m, Orange River.

**2004, May 17            Perf. 14¼**
1332 A240   8m Sheet of 3,
#a-c                           12.00 12.00
**Souvenir Sheet**
1333 A240  15m multi            7.50  7.50

Powered Flight, Cent. (in 2003) A241

No. 1334: a, Louis Blériot's Canard at Bagatelle, 1906. b, Blériot's Double-winged Libellule, 1907. c, Cross-country flight of Blériot VIII, Toury to Artenay, 1908. d, Blériot XII test flight, 1909.
15m, Blériot XI.

**2004, May 17**
1334 A241   6m Sheet of 4, #a-d   9.00  9.00
**Souvenir Sheet**
1335 A241  15m multi               6.75  6.75

Worldwide Fund for Nature (WWF) — A242

No. 1336 — Southern bald ibis: a, On nest, country name in white at LR. b, Flying to right, black denomination. c, Standing on rock, black denomination. d, Facing left.
No. 1337 — Southern bald ibis: a, Standing on rock, red denomination. b, Flying to left, red denomination. c, On nest, country name in black at UR.

**2004, May 17                Perf. 14**
1336        Horiz. strip of 4      4.00  4.00
a.-d.  A242 3m Any single           .80   .80
1337        Horiz. strip of 4
#1336d, 1337a-1337c   4.00  4.00
a.-c.  A242 3m Any single           .80   .80
No. 1336 printed in sheets of 4 strips. No. 1337 printed in sheets of 2 strips.

Mammals A243

Designs: 1m, Cape porcupine. 1.50m, Brown rat. 2.10m, Springhare, vert. No. 1341, 5m, South African galago, vert.
No. 1342, 5m: a, Striped grass mouse. b, Greater galago. c, Ground pangolin. d, Banded mongoose.
15m, Egyptian rousette, vert.

**2004, May 17**
1338-1341 A243   Set of 4     7.00  7.00
1342 A243   5m Sheet of 4, #a-d   9.50  9.50
**Souvenir Sheet**
1343 A243  15m multi               8.00  8.00

Birds — A244

Designs: 1.50m, Secretary bird. 2.10m, Gray-crowned crane. 3m, Pied avocet. 5m, Common kestrel.
No. 1348: a, European roller. b, Common cuckoo. c, Great spotted cuckoo. d, Pel's fishing owl.
15m, Kori bustard.

**2004, May 17**
1344-1347 A244   Set of 4     8.00  8.00
1348 A244   6m Sheet of 4,
#a-d                           12.00 12.00
**Souvenir Sheet**
1349 A244  15m multi               9.50  9.50

Butterflies A245

Designs: 1.50m, Acraea rabbaiae. 2.10m, Alaena margaritacea. 4m, Bematistes aganice. No. 1353, 6m, Acraea quirina.
No. 1354, 6m: a, Bematistes excisa male. b, Bematistes excisa female. c, Bematistes epiprotea. d, Bematistes poggei.
15m, Acraea satis.

**2004, May 17**
1350-1353 A245   Set of 4     8.00  8.00
1354 A245   6m Sheet of 4,
#a-d                           11.00 11.00
**Souvenir Sheet**
1355 A245  15m multi               7.50  7.50

Flowers — A246

Designs: 1.50m, Sparaxis grandiflora. 2.10m, Agapanthus africanus. 3m, Protea linearis. No. 1359, 5m, Nerine cultivars.
No. 1360, 5m: a, Kniphofia uvaria. b, Amaryllis belladonna. c, Cazania splendens. d, Erica coronata.
15m, Saintpaulia cultivars.

**2004, May 17**
1356-1359 A246   Set of 4     6.75  6.75
1360 A246   5m Sheet of 4, #a-d   9.00  9.00
**Souvenir Sheet**
1361 A246  15m multi               6.00  6.00

Houses — A247

Designs: 70s, Mokhoro. 1m, Heisi. 1.50m, Lesotho. 2.10m, Mohlongoa-Fat'se.

**2005, Feb. 21      Litho.      Perf. 14**
1362-1365 A247   Set of 4     4.00  4.00

Girl Guides — A248

Girl Guides: 70s, Dancing. 1m, Marching in parade. 1.50m, Collecting cans, vert. 2.10m, Standing near building.
10m, Leader holding microphone, vert.

**2005, May 20      Litho.      Perf. 14**
1366-1369 A248   Set of 4     4.75  4.75
**Souvenir Sheet**
1370 A248  10m multi               6.25  6.25

Pope John Paul II (1920-2005) — A249

**2005, Aug. 22            Perf. 12¾**
1371 A249  10m multi               6.25  6.25
Printed in sheets of 4.

**Souvenir Sheet**

Rotary International, Cent. — A250

No. 1372: a, Alleviating poverty. b, Advancement of literacy. c, Helping at-risk children.

**2005, Aug. 22**
1372 A250   8m Sheet of 3, #a-c   7.75  7.75

World Cup Soccer Championships, 75th Anniv. — A251

No. 1373, horiz. — Players from final match from: a, 1930. b, 1938. c, 1990.
15m, Bodo Illgner, 1990 goalie for Germany.

**2005, Aug. 22                Perf. 12**
1373 A251   8m Sheet of 3, #a-c   9.50  9.50
**Souvenir Sheet**
1374 A251  15m multi               6.50  6.50

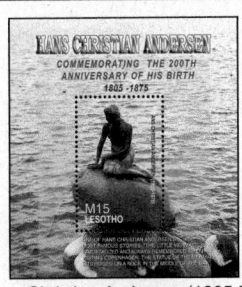

Hans Christian Andersen (1805-75), Author — A252

No. 1375: a, Statue of Andersen, Copenhagen. b, Childhood home of Andersen, Odense, Denmark. c, Scene from "The Steadfast Tin Soldier".
15m, Little Mermaid statue, Copenhagen.

**2005, Aug. 22**     *Perf. 12¾*
1375 A252   8m Sheet of 3, #a-c   9.75 9.75
**Souvenir Sheet**
1376 A252 15m multi   6.50 6.50

Jules Verne (1828-1905), Writer — A253

No. 1377, horiz.: a, Journey to the Center of the Earth. b, Verne, without hat. c, 20,000 Leagues Under the Sea.
15m, Verne wearing hat.

**2005, Aug. 22**
1377 A253   8m Sheet of 3, #a-c   10.00 10.00
**Souvenir Sheet**
1378 A253 15m multi   6.50 6.50

Albert Einstein (1879-1955), Physicist — A254

No. 1379, horiz. — Einstein and: a, Country name in black. b, Nikola Tesla, Charles Steinmetz. c, Country name in red violet.
15m, Time Magazine "Person of the Century" cover.

**2005, Aug. 22**
1379 A254   8m Sheet of 3, #a-c   10.00 10.00
**Souvenir Sheet**
1380 A254 15m multi   6.50 6.50

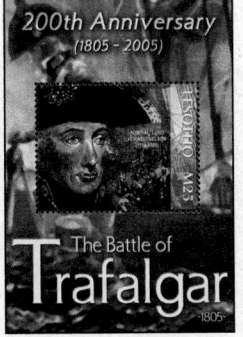

Battle of Trafalgar, Bicent. A255

No. 1381: a, HMS Victory. b, Admiral Horatio Nelson facing left. c, Nelson wounded in battle. d, Ships in battle.
25m, Nelson facing right.

**2005, Aug. 22**     *Perf. 12¾*
1381 A255   8m Sheet of 4, #a-d   19.00 19.00
**Souvenir Sheet**    *Perf. 12*
1382 A255 25m multi   19.00 19.00
No. 1381 contains four 42x28mm stamps.

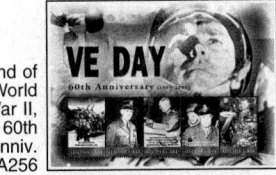

End of World War II, 60th Anniv. A256

No. 1383, 4m — V-E Day: a, U.S. troops land on Omaha Beach, 1944. b, Gen. George C. Marshall. c, German Field Marshal Wilhelm Keitel signing surrender. d, Generals Dwight D. Eisenhower and George S. Patton. e, Soldiers sifting through war damage.
No. 1384, 4m — V-J Day: a, USS Arizona. b, Bunker, Chula Beach, Tinian Island. c, Bockscar flight crew. d, Newspaper announcing Japanese surrender. e, Historic marker commemorating loading of second atomic bomb on Tinian Island.

**2005, Aug. 22**     *Perf. 12¾*
**Sheets of 5, #a-e**
1383-1384 A256   Set of 2   13.00 13.00

A257

People and Livestock A258

Designs: 70 l, Boy riding calf. 1m, Man feeding cattle. 1.50m, Cattle tenders playing game. 2.10m, Shepherd carrying lamb.
10m, Dancers.

**2006, Mar. 13**   Litho.   *Perf. 14*
1385-1388 A257   Set of 4   4.00 4.00
**Souvenir Sheet**
1389 A258 10m multi   6.50 6.50

A259

Women Balancing Items on Heads — A260

Women carrying: 70 l, Sticks. 1m, Cooking pot. 1.50m, Water jar. 2.10m, Bowl of fruit.
10m, Bowl of grain.

**2006, June 19**
1390-1393 A259   Set of 4   4.00 4.00
**Souvenir Sheet**
1394 A260 10m multi   5.75 5.75

A261

Handicrafts — A262

Designs: 70 l, Baskets. 1m, Artist and drawing, vert. 1.50m, Painted pottery. 2.10m, Figurines of stork and fish, decorated bull's horn.
10m, Boy, native costume.

**2006, Oct. 9**   Litho.   *Perf. 14¼*
1395-1398 A261   Set of 4   4.00 4.00
**Souvenir Sheet**
1399 A262 10m multi   6.50 6.50

Birds — A263

Designs: 1m, Crested caracara. 1.50m, Wood storks. 2.10m, Tawny-shouldered blackbird. No. 1403, 15m, Jabiru.
No. 1404: a, Great blue heron. b, Anna's hummingbird. c, Gray silky flycatcher. d, Limpkin.
No. 1405, 15m, Western reef heron. No. 1406, 15m, Monk parakeet.

**2007, Aug. 20**   Litho.   *Perf. 14*
1400-1403 A263   Set of 4   24.00 24.00
1404 A263   6m Sheet of 4, #a-d   8.00 8.00
**Souvenir Sheets**
1405-1406 A263   Set of 2   10.00 10.00

Butterflies — A264

Designs: 1m, Mylothris erlangeri. 1.50m, Papilio nireus. 2.10m, Acraea terpiscore. 10m, Salamis temora.
No. 1411: a, Danaus chrysippus. b, Myrina silenus. c, Chrysiridia madagascariensis. d, Hypolimnas dexithea.
No. 1412, 15m, P. demodocus. No. 1413, 15m, Amphicallia tigris.

**2007, Aug. 20**
1407-1410 A264   Set of 4   9.00 9.00
1411 A264   6m Sheet of 4, #a-d   7.00 7.00
**Souvenir Sheets**
1412-1413 A264   Set of 2   9.00 9.00

Orchids — A265

Designs: 1.50m, Spiranthes laciniata. 2.10m, Triphora craigheadii. 3m, Arethusa bulbosa. 10m, Calypso bulbosa.
No. 1418: a, Encyclia tampensis. b, Prosthechea cochleata. c, Vanilla pompona. d, Cypripedium acaule.
No. 1419, 15m, Vanilla barbellata. No. 1420, 15m, Epidendrum radicans.

**2007, Aug. 20**
1414-1417 A265   Set of 4   22.50 22.50
1418 A265   6m Sheet of 4, #a-d   7.50 7.50
**Souvenir Sheets**
1419-1420 A265   Set of 2   10.00 10.00

A266

A267

Mushrooms — A268

Designs: 1m, Amanita pantherina. 1.50m, Agaricus xanthodermus. 2.10m, Amanita rubescens. No. 1424, 15m, Amanita phalloides.
No. 1425: a, Amanita phalloides, diff. b, Amanita pantherina, diff. c, Panaeolus papilionaceus. d, Amanita rubescens, diff.
No. 1426, 15m, Amanite panther. No. 1427, 15m, Podaxis pistillaris.

**2007, Aug. 20**
1421-1424 A266   Set of 4   12.00 12.00
1425 A267   6m Sheet of 4, #a-d   12.00 12.00
**Souvenir Sheets**
1426 A267 15m multi   9.00 9.00
1427 A268 15m multi   9.00 9.00

**Miniature Sheet**

2008 Summer Olympics, Beijing — A269

No. 1428: a, Rowing. b, Softball. c, Wrestling. d, Volleyball.

**2008, Aug. 18**   Litho.   *Perf. 12*
1428 A269   3.50m Sheet of 4, #a-d   6.50 6.50

In 2015 Lesotho postal officials declared as "illegal" a number of souvenir sheets of 1 depicting subjects such as wild mammals, wild cats, dogs, frogs, turtles, insects, penguins, Marie Curie and Brigitte Bardot.

Independence, 50th Anniv. — A270

Designs: 10m, Thaba Bosiu National Monument. 15m, National flags of Lesotho mounted on the Basotho hat. 20m, Lesotho National Parliament Houses.

**2016, Oct. 4**   Litho.   *Perf. 13¼*
1429 A270 10m multi   — —
1430 A270 15m multi   — —
1431 A270 20m multi   — —

World Post
Day — A271

Inscriptions: 2m, Mail sorting and packaging. 5m, Mail delivery. 10m, Lesotho Central Post Office. 15m, Morija Post Office. 20m, Maseru Main Post Office. 25m, Maseru Central Post Office.

**2016, Oct. 9**   **Litho.**   *Perf. 13¼*
1432-1437 A271   Set of 6   —   —

## POSTAGE DUE STAMPS

Basutoland Nos. J9-J10
Overprinted

**Wmk. 314**
**1966, Nov. 1**   **Typo.**   *Perf. 14*
J1   D2   1c carmine   .30   .75
  a.   "Lseotho"   35.00
J2   D2   5c dark purple   .30   .90
  a.   "Lseotho"   55.00

D1

*Perf. 13½*
**1967, Apr. 1**   **Unwmk.**   **Litho.**
J3   D1   1c dark blue   .25   3.00
J4   D1   2c dull rose   .25   3.50
J5   D1   5c emerald   .40   3.50
  Nos. J3-J5 (3)   .90   10.00

**1976, Nov. 30**   **Wmk. 362**
J7   D1   2c dull rose   3.00   3.00
J8   D1   5c emerald   3.00   3.00

D2

**1986**   **Litho.**   *Perf. 13x13½*
J9   D2   2s green   .55   .55
J10   D2   5s blue   .55   .55
J11   D2   25s purple   .55   .55
  Nos. J9-J11 (3)   1.65   1.65

# LIBERIA

lī-'bir-ē-ə

LOCATION — West coast of Africa, between Ivory Coast and Sierra Leone
GOVT. — Republic
AREA — 43,000 sq. mi.
POP. — 2,602,100 (1997 est.)
CAPITAL — Monrovia

100 Cents = 1 Dollar

Catalogue values for unused stamps in this country are for Never Hinged items, beginning with Scott 330 in the regular postage section, Scott B19 in the semi-postal section, Scott C67 in the airpost section, and Scott CB4 in the airpost semi-postal section.

Values for unused stamps are for examples with original gum as defined in the catalogue introduction. Any exceptions will be noted. Very fine examples of Nos. 1-3, 13-21 and 157-159 will have perforations just clear of the design due to the narrow spacing of the stamps on the plates and/or imperfect perforating methods.

## Watermarks

Wmk. 116 —
Crosses and
Circles

Wmk. 143

For watermarks 373 and 384 see British Watermark page.

"Liberia" — A1

A1a

**Thick Paper**
**1860**   **Unwmk.**   **Litho.**   *Perf. 12*
1   A1   6c red   400.00   300.00
  a.   Imperf, pair   500.00
2   A1   12c deep blue   25.00   50.00
  a.   Imperf, pair   250.00
3   A1a   24c green   50.00   50.00
  a.   Imperf, pair   300.00
  Nos. 1-3 (3)   475.00   400.00

Stamps set very close together. Examples of the 12c occasionally show traces of a frame line around the design.

**Medium to Thin Paper**
**With a single-line frame around each stamp, about 1mm from the border**
**1864**   *Perf. 11, 12*
7   A1   6c red   62.50   85.00
  a.   Imperf, pair   225.00
8   A1   12c blue   80.00   95.00
  a.   Imperf, pair   225.00
9   A1a   24c lt green   87.50   100.00
  a.   Imperf, pair   225.00
  Nos. 7-9 (3)   230.00   280.00

Stamps set about 5mm apart. Margins large and perforation usually outside the frame line.

**1866-69**   **Without Frame Line**
13   A1   6c lt red   25.00   40.00
14   A1   12c lt blue   25.00   40.00
15   A1a   24c lt yellow grn   25.00   40.00
  Nos. 13-15 (3)   75.00   120.00

Stamps set 2-2½mm apart with small margins. Stamps are usually without frame line but those from one transfer show broken and irregular parts of a frame.

**1880**   **With Frame Line**   *Perf. 10½*
16   A1   1c ultra   5.00   8.00
17   A1   2c rose   5.00   5.25
  a.   Imperf, pair   175.00
18   A1   6c violet   5.00   5.25
19   A1   12c yellow   5.00   5.25
20   A1a   24c rose red   6.00   5.50
  Nos. 16-20 (5)   26.00   29.25

Unused values for Nos. 16-20 are for stamps without gum.
For surcharges see Nos. 157-159.

**Counterfeits**
Counterfeits exist of Nos. 1-28, 32 and 64.

From Arms of
Liberia — A2

**1881**
21   A2   3c black   15.00   10.00
Unused value is for a stamp without gum.

A3

A4

Slanting Lines

Network Lines

On No. 22 the openings in the figure "8" enclose a pattern of slanting lines. Compare with No. 32.

**1882**   *Perf. 11½, 12, 14*
22   A3   8c blue   50.00   10.00
23   A4   16c red   8.00   5.00

**Canceled to Order**
Beginning with the issue of 1885, values in the used column are for "canceled to order" stamps. Postally used examples sell for much more.

A5

A6

From Arms of
Liberia — A7

*Perf. 10½, 11, 12, 11½x10½, 14, 14½*
**1885**
24   A5   1c carmine   2.00   2.00
  a.   1c rose   2.00   2.00
25   A5   2c green   2.00   2.00
26   A5   3c violet   2.00   2.00
27   A5   4c brown   2.00   2.00
28   A5   6c olive gray   2.00   2.00
29   A6   8c bluish gray   4.00   4.00
  a.   8c lilac   7.00   7.00
30   A6   16c yellow   15.00   12.00
31   A7   32c deep blue   35.00   29.00
  Nos. 24-31 (8)   64.00   55.00

In the 1885 printing, the stamps are spaced 2mm apart and the paper is medium. In the 1892 printing, the stamps are 4½mm apart. For surcharges see Nos. J1-J2.

**Imperf., Pair**
24b   A5   1c   3.00
25a   A5   2c   4.75
26a   A5   3c   5.00
27a   A5   4c   5.00
28a   A5   6c   4.25   4.25
29b   A6   8c   12.50
30a   A6   16c   30.00
31a   A7   32c   50.00

Imperf. pairs with 2mm spacing sell for higher prices.

A8

The openings in the figure "8" are filled with network lines.

**1889**   *Perf. 12, 14*
32   A8   8c blue   4.25   4.25
  a.   Imperf., pair   20.00
See No. 22.

A9

Elephant
A10

Oil Palm
A11

Pres. Hilary
R. W.
Johnson
A12

Vai Woman
in Full Dress
A13

Coat of
Arms — A14

Liberian
Star — A15

Coat of
Arms
A16

Hippopotamus
A17

Liberian Star
A18

President
Johnson
A19

**1892-96**   **Wmk. 143**   **Engr.**   *Perf. 15*
33   A9   1c vermilion   .50   .40
  a.   1c blue (error)   40.00
34   A9   2c blue   .50   .40
  a.   2c vermilion (error)   40.00
35   A10   4c green & blk   2.00   1.25
  a.   Center inverted   225.00
36   A11   6c blue green   .70   .50
37   A12   8c brown & blk   .95   .95
  a.   Center inverted   500.00   500.00
  b.   Center sideways   750.00
38   A12   10c chrome yel & indigo ('96)   .95   .65
39   A13   12c rose red   .95   .65
40   A13   15c slate ('96)   .95   .65
41   A14   16c lilac   3.50   1.75
  a.   16c deep greenish blue (error)   110.00
42   A14   20c vermilion ('96)   3.50   1.75
43   A15   24c ol grn ('96)   2.00   1.10
44   A15   25c yel grn ('96)   2.00   1.40
45   A16   30c steel bl ('96)   6.25   4.50
46   A16   32c grnsh blue   3.50   2.75
  a.   32c lilac (error)   110.00
47   A17   $1 ultra & blk   12.00   9.00
  a.   $1 blue & black   13.50   11.00

| 48 | A18 | $2 brown, *yel* | 9.00 | 8.00 |
|---|---|---|---|---|
| 49 | A19 | $5 carmine & blk | 10.00 | 10.00 |
| a. | | Center inverted | 400.00 | 400.00 |
| | | Nos. 33-49 (17) | 59.25 | 45.70 |

Many imperforates, part-perforated and mis-perforated varieties exist.

The 1c, 2c and 4c were issued in sheets of 60; 6c, sheet of 40; 8c, 10c, sheets of 30; 12c, 15c, 24c, 25c, sheets of 20; 16c, 20c, 30c, sheets of 15; $1, $2, $5, sheets of 10.

For overprints & surcharges see Nos. 50, 64B-64F, 66, 71-77, 79-81, 85-93, 95-100, 160, O1-O13, O15-O25, O37-O41, O44-O45.

### No. 36 Surcharged

a

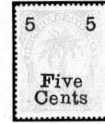
b

| 1893 | | | | |
|---|---|---|---|---|
| 50 | A11 (a) 5c on 6c blue grn | | 1.75 | 1.10 |
| a. | "5" with short flag | | 6.00 | 6.00 |
| b. | Both 5's with short flags | | 5.00 | 5.00 |
| c. | "i" dot omitted | | 19.00 | 19.00 |
| d. | Surcharge "b" | | 30.00 | 30.00 |

"Commerce," Globe and Krumen — A22

| 1894 | Unwmk. | Engr. | Imperf. |
|---|---|---|---|
| 52 | A22 5c carmine & blk | | 5.00 5.00 |

**Rouletted**

| 53 | A22 5c carmine & blk | | 10.00 7.50 |
|---|---|---|---|

For overprints see Nos. 69, O26-O27.

Oil Palm
A23

Hippopotamus
A24

Elephant
A25

Liberty
A26

| 1897-1905 | Wmk. 143 | Perf. 14 to 16 |
|---|---|---|
| 54 | A23 | 1c lilac rose | 1.00 | .65 |
| a. | | 1c violet | | .65 |
| 55 | A23 | 1c dp grn ('00) | 1.25 | .95 |
| 56 | A23 | 1c lt green ('05) | 3.00 | 1.60 |
| 57 | A24 | 2c bister & blk | 3.00 | 1.60 |
| 58 | A24 | 2c org red & blk ('00) | 6.00 | 2.10 |
| 59 | A24 | 2c rose & blk ('05) | 3.00 | 1.60 |
| 60 | A25 | 5c lake & black | 3.00 | 1.60 |
| a. | | 5c lilac rose & black | 3.00 | 1.60 |
| 61 | A25 | 5c gray bl & blk ('00) | 6.00 | 5.00 |
| 62 | A25 | 5c ultra & blk ('05) | 4.25 | 2.75 |
| a. | | Center inverted | 1,600. | |
| 63 | A26 | 50c red brn & blk | 4.00 | 3.50 |
| | | Nos. 54-63 (10) | 34.50 | 21.35 |

For overprints & surcharges see Nos. 65, 66A-68. 70, 78, 82-84, M1, O28-O36, O42, O92.

A27

Two types:
I — 13 pearls above "Republic Liberia."
II — 10 pearls.

---

| 1897 | Unwmk. | Litho. | Perf. 14 |
|---|---|---|---|
| 64 | A27 3c red & green (I) | | .25 | .60 |
| a. | Type II | | 20.00 | .25 |

No. 64a is considered a reprint, unissued. "Used" examples are CTO.
For surcharge see No. 128.

Official Stamps
Handstamped in Black

| 1901-02 | | | Wmk. 143 |
|---|---|---|---|
| | **On Nos. O7-O8, O10-O12** | | |
| 64B | A14 16c lilac | | 525.00 | 525.00 |
| 64C | A15 24c ol grn, *yel* | | 575.00 | 400.00 |
| 64D | A17 $1 blue & blk | | 3,000. | 2,000. |
| 64E | A18 $2 brown, *yel* | | — | — |
| 64F | A19 $5 car & blk | | — | — |

**On Stamps with "O S" Printed**

| 65 | A23 | 1c green | 37.50 | 40.00 |
|---|---|---|---|---|
| 66 | A9 | 2c blue | 100.00 | 100.00 |
| 66A | A24 | 2c bister & blk | — | 150.00 |
| 67 | A24 | 2c org red & blk | 45.00 | 40.00 |
| 68 | A25 | 5c gray bl & blk | 37.50 | 35.00 |
| 69 | A22 | 5c vio & grn (No. O26) | 300.00 | 300.00 |
| 70 | A25 | 5c lake & blk | 275.00 | 225.00 |
| 71 | A12 | 10c yel & blue blk | 37.50 | 60.00 |
| a. | | "O S" omitted | — | |
| 72 | A13 | 15c slate | 40.00 | 60.00 |
| 73 | A14 | 16c lilac | 550.00 | 350.00 |
| 74 | A14 | 20c vermilion | 42.50 | 50.00 |
| 75 | A15 | 24c ol grn, *yel* | 52.50 | 50.00 |
| 76 | A15 | 25c yellow grn | 42.50 | 50.00 |
| a. | | "O S" omitted | 750.00 | |
| 77 | A16 | 30c steel blue | 42.50 | 40.00 |
| 78 | A26 | 50c red brn & blk | 100.00 | 52.50 |
| 79 | A17 | $1 ultra & blk | 325.00 | 275.00 |
| a. | | "O S" omitted | — | |
| 80 | A18 | $2 brn, *yel* | 2,000. | 1,800. |
| 81 | A19 | $5 car & blk | 2,500. | 2,000. |
| a. | | "O S" omitted | 3,000. | 2,750. |

**On Stamps with "O S" Handstamped**

| 82 | A23 | 1c deep green | 62.50 | — |
|---|---|---|---|---|
| 83 | A24 | 2c org red & blk | 75.00 | — |
| 84 | A25 | 5c lake & blk | 200.00 | — |
| 85 | A12 | 10c yel & bl blk | 125.00 | — |
| 86 | A14 | 20c vermilion | 140.00 | — |
| 87 | A15 | 24c ol grn, *yel* | 140.00 | — |
| 88 | A15 | 25c yel grn | 160.00 | — |
| 89 | A16 | 30c steel blue | 525.00 | — |
| 90 | A16 | 32c grnsh blue | 210.00 | — |

Varieties of Nos. 65-90 include double and inverted overprints.

Nos. 47, O10, O23a Surcharged in Carmine

75c.

| 1902 | | | |
|---|---|---|---|
| 91 | A17 75c on $1 #47 | | 15.00 | 13.00 |
| a. | Thin "C" and comma | | 25.00 | 25.00 |
| b. | Inverted surcharge | | 62.50 | 62.50 |
| c. | As "a," inverted | | | |
| 92 | A17 75c on $1 #O10 | | 2,750. | |
| a. | Thin "C" and comma | | 4,250. | |
| 93 | A17 75c on $1 #O23a | | 4,000. | |
| a. | Thin "C" and comma | | 5,250. | |

Liberty — A29

| 1903 | Unwmk. | Engr. | Perf. 14 |
|---|---|---|---|
| 94 | A29 3c black | | .30 | .25 |
| a. | Printed on both sides | | 50.00 | |
| b. | Perf. 12 | | 20.00 | 6.00 |

For overprint see No. O43.

**Stamps of 1892 Surcharged in Blue**

a

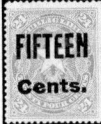
b

TEN Cents.

FIFTEEN Cents.

---

| 1903 | | | Wmk. 143 |
|---|---|---|---|
| 95 | A14 (a) 10c on 16c lilac | | 3.00 | 5.00 |
| 96 | A15 (b) 15c on 24c ol grn, *yel* | | 4.50 | 6.00 |
| 97 | A16 (b) 20c on 32c grnsh bl | | 6.25 | 8.50 |
| | Nos. 95-97 (3) | | 13.75 | 19.50 |

### Nos. 50, O3 and 45 Surcharged in Black or Red

| 1904 | | | |
|---|---|---|---|
| 98 | A11 1c on 5c on 6c bl grn | | .70 | .55 |
| a. | "5" with short flag | | 4.25 | 4.25 |
| b. | Both 5's with short flags | | 8.75 | 8.75 |
| c. | "i" dot omitted | | 10.00 | 10.00 |
| d. | Surcharge on #50d | | 15.00 | 15.00 |
| e. | Inverted surcharge | | 7.50 | 7.50 |
| 99 | A10 2c on 4c grn & blk | | 2.75 | 4.00 |
| a. | Pair, one without surcharge | | 35.00 | |
| b. | Double surcharge | | 50.00 | |
| c. | Double surcharge, red and blk | | 62.50 | |
| d. | Surcharged on back also | | 25.00 | |
| e. | "Official" overprint missing | | 35.00 | |
| 100 | A16 2c on 30c stl bl (R) | | 9.50 | 15.00 |
| | Nos. 98-100 (3) | | 12.95 | 19.55 |

African Elephant
A33

Mercury
A34

Chimpanzee
A35

Great Blue Touraco
A36

Agama — A37

Head of Liberty From Coin — A39

Egret — A38

A40

Liberian Flag
A41

Pygmy Hippopotamus
A42

---

Liberty with Star of Liberia on Cap
A43

Mandingos
A44

Executive Mansion and Pres. Arthur Barclay — A45

| 1906 | Unwmk. | Engr. | Perf. 14 |
|---|---|---|---|
| 101 | A33 | 1c green & blk | 1.75 | .50 |
| 102 | A34 | 2c carmine & blk | .35 | .25 |
| 103 | A35 | 5c ultra & blk | 3.00 | .85 |
| 104 | A36 | 10c red brn & blk | 14.00 | .85 |
| 105 | A37 | 15c pur & dp grn | 10.00 | 3.00 |
| 106 | A38 | 20c orange & blk | 9.00 | 2.50 |
| 107 | A39 | 25c dull blue & gray | 1.00 | .25 |
| 108 | A40 | 30c deep violet | 1.00 | .25 |
| 109 | A41 | 50c dp grn & blk | 1.25 | .25 |
| 110 | A42 | 75c brown & blk | 13.00 | 2.50 |
| 111 | A43 | $1 rose & gray | 3.50 | .25 |
| 112 | A44 | $2 dp grn & blk | 5.00 | .35 |
| 113 | A45 | $5 red brn & blk | 10.00 | .50 |
| | | Nos. 101-113 (13) | 72.85 | 12.30 |

For surcharges see Nos. 114, 129, 130, 141, 145-149, 161, M2, M5, O72-O73, O82-O85, O96. For overprints see Nos. O46-O58.

### Center Inverted

| 101a | A33 | 1c | 110.00 | 55.00 |
|---|---|---|---|---|
| 102a | A34 | 2c | 120.00 | 35.00 |
| 103a | A35 | 5c | 175.00 | 175.00 |
| 104a | A36 | 10c | 80.00 | 80.00 |
| 105a | A37 | 15c | 175.00 | 175.00 |
| 106b | A38 | 20c | 175.00 | 175.00 |
| 107a | A39 | 25c | 75.00 | 75.00 |
| 109b | A41 | 50c | 75.00 | 75.00 |
| 110b | A42 | 75c | 125.00 | 125.00 |
| 111a | A43 | $1 | 100.00 | 100.00 |
| 112a | A44 | $2 | 95.00 | 95.00 |

## Imperf., Pairs

| 101b | A33 | 1c | 13.50 | |
| 102b | A34 | 2c | 5.50 | |
| 106a | A38 | 20c | 20.00 | |
| 107b | A39 | 25c | 55.00 | 45.00 |
| 109a | A41 | 50c | 20.00 | |
| 110a | A42 | 75c | 20.00 | |
| 113a | A45 | $5 | 27.00 | |

### No. 104 Surcharged in Black

**1909**

| 114 | A36 | 3c on 10c red brn & blk | 6.00 | 6.00 |

Coffee Plantation A46     Pres. Barclay A47

S. S. Pres. Daniel E. Howard, former Gunboat Lark — A48

Commerce with Caduceus — A49

Vai Woman Spinning Cotton A50     Blossom and Fruit of Pepper Plants A51

Circular House A52     President Barclay A53

Men in Canoe — A54     Liberian Village — A55

**1909-12**     **Perf. 14**

| 115 | A46 | 1c yel grn & blk | .70 | .55 |
| 116 | A47 | 2c lake & blk | .70 | .55 |
| 117 | A48 | 5c ultra & blk | .70 | .55 |
| 118 | A49 | 10c plum & blk, perf. 12½ ('12) | .70 | .55 |
| a. | | Imperf., pair | 19.00 | |
| b. | | Perf 14 ('12) | 2.25 | 2.25 |
| c. | | As "b," pair, imperf between | 27.50 | |
| d. | | Perf 12½x14 | 2.75 | 2.25 |
| 119 | A50 | 15c indigo & blk | 3.50 | .60 |
| 120 | A51 | 20c rose & grn | 4.50 | .60 |
| b. | | Imperf. | | |
| 121 | A52 | 25c dk brn & blk | 1.40 | .60 |
| a. | | Imperf. | | |
| 122 | A53 | 30c dark brown | 4.50 | .60 |
| 123 | A54 | 50c green & blk | 4.50 | .60 |
| 124 | A55 | 75c red brn & blk | 4.50 | .60 |
| | | Nos. 115-124 (10) | 25.70 | 5.80 |

**Rouletted**

| 125 | A49 | 10c plum & blk | .75 | .45 |

For surcharges see Nos. 126-127E, 131-133, 136-140, 142-144, 151-156, 162, B1-B2, M3-M4, M6-M7, O70-O71, O74-O81, O86-O91, O97.
For overprints see Nos. O59-O69.

## Center Inverted

| 116a | A47 | 2c | 70.00 | 60.00 |
| 117a | A48 | 5c | 62.50 | 55.00 |
| 119a | A50 | 15c | 100.00 | 60.00 |
| 120a | A51 | 20c | 70.00 | 60.00 |
| 121b | A52 | 25c | 47.50 | 42.50 |
| 123a | A54 | 50c | 95.00 | 80.00 |

## Stamps and Types of 1909-12 Surcharged in Blue or Red

3 CENTS INLAND POSTAGE

**1910-12**     **Rouletted**

| 126 | A49 | 3c on 10c plum & blk (Bl) | .40 | .25 |
| a. | | "3" inverted | | |
| 126B | A49 | 3c on 10c blk & ultra (R) | 30.00 | 5.00 |

No. 126B is roulette 7. It also exists in roulette 13.

**Perf. 12½, 14, 12½x14**

| 127 | A49 | 3c on 10c plum & blk (Bl) ('12) | .40 | .25 |
| a. | | Imperf., pair | 22.50 | |
| b. | | Double surcharge, one invtd. | 22.50 | |
| c. | | Double vertical surcharge | | |
| 127E | A49 | 3c on 10c blk & ultra (R) ('12) | 17.00 | .55 |
| | | Nos. 126-127E (4) | 47.80 | 6.05 |

Nos. 64, 64a Surcharged in Dark Green

**1913**

| 128 | A27 | 8c on 3c red & grn (I) | .30 | .25 |
| a. | | Surcharge on No. 64a | 3.00 | .25 |
| b. | | Double surcharge | 6.25 | |
| c. | | Imperf., pair | 20.00 | |
| d. | | Inverted surcharge | 25.00 | |

## Stamps of Preceding Issues Surcharged

a     b

**1914**     **On Issue of 1906**

| 129 | A39 (a) | 2c on 25c dl bl & gray | 11.50 | 3.25 |
| 130 | A40 (b) | 5c on 30c dp vio | 11.50 | 3.25 |

**On Issue of 1909**

| 131 | A52 (a) | 2c on 25c brn & blk | 11.50 | 3.25 |
| 132 | A53 (b) | 5c on 30c dk brown | 11.50 | 3.25 |
| 133 | A54 (a) | 10c on 50c grn & blk | 11.50 | 3.25 |
| | | Nos. 129-133 (5) | 57.50 | 16.25 |

Liberian House — A57

Providence Island, Monrovia Harbor — A58

**1915**   **Engr.**   **Wmk. 116**   **Perf. 14**

| 134 | A57 | 2c red | .25 | .25 |
| 135 | A58 | 3c dull violet | .25 | .25 |

For overprints see Nos. 196-197, O113-O114, O128-O129.

## Nos. 109, 111-113, 119-124 Surcharged in Dark Blue, Black or Red

c     d

e

f     g

**1915-16**     **Unwmk.**

| 136 | A50 (c) | 2c on 15c (R) | .90 | .90 |
| 137 | A52 (d) | 2c on 25c (R) | 8.50 | 8.50 |
| 138 | A51 (e) | 5c on 20c (Bk) | 1.10 | 6.25 |
| 139 | A53 (f) | 5c on 30c (R) | 4.50 | 4.50 |
| a. | | Double surcharge | 15.00 | 15.00 |
| 140 | A53 (g) | 5c on 30c (R) | 40.00 | 40.00 |

h     i

| 141 | A41 (h) | 10c on 50c (R) | 8.00 | 8.00 |
| a. | | Double surch., one invtd. | | |
| 142 | A54 (i) | 10c on 50c (R) | 15.00 | 15.00 |
| a. | | Double surcharge red & blk | 50.00 | 50.00 |
| b. | | Blue surcharge | 35.00 | 35.00 |
| 143 | A54 (i) | 10c on 50c (Bk) | 20.00 | 15.00 |

j     k

| 144 | A55 (j) | 20c on 75c (Bk) | 4.00 | 7.50 |
| 145 | A43 (k) | 25c on $1 (Bk) | 42.50 | 42.50 |

l     m

| 146 | A44 (l) | 50c on $2 (R) | 12.00 | 12.00 |
| a. | | "Ceuts" | 30.00 | 22.50 |
| 147 | A44 (m) | 50c on $2 (R) | 800.00 | 800.00 |

n

| 148 | A45 | $1 on $5 (Bk) | 65.00 | 65.00 |
| a. | | Double surcharge | 90.00 | 90.00 |

o

| 149 | A45 | $1 on $5 (R) | 52.50 | 52.50 |

The color of the red surcharge varies from light dull red to almost brown.

**Handstamped Surcharge, Type "i"**

| 150 | A54 | 10c on 50c (Dk Bl) | 14.00 | 14.00 |

### No. 119 Surcharged in Black

| 151 | A50 | 2c on 15c | 650.00 | 650.00 |

### No. 119 Surcharged in Red

| 152 | A50 | 2c on 15c | 45.00 | 40.00 |
| a. | | Double surcharge | 92.50 | |

## Nos. 116-117 Surcharged in Black or Red

a     b

c     d

e     f

g     h

i     j

k     l

m     n

o     p

q

r

s

t

Types A-J are for No. 153. Types K-T are for No. 154.

| | | | | |
|---|---|---|---|---|
| **153** | A47 | 1c on 2c lake & blk | 2.50 | 2.50 |
| a. | | Strip of 10 types | 35.00 | |
| **154** | A48 | 2c on 5c ultra & blk (R) | 3.50 | 2.50 |
| a. | | Black surcharge | 14.00 | 14.00 |
| b. | | Strip of 10 types (R) | 35.00 | |
| c. | | Strip of 10 types (Bk) | 175.00 | |

The 10 types of surcharge are repeated in illustrated sequence on 1c on 2c in each horiz. row and on 2c on 5c in each vert. row of sheets of 100 (10x10).

**No. 116 and Type of 1909 Surcharged**

| | | | | |
|---|---|---|---|---|
| **155** | A47 | 1c on 2c lake & blk | 190.00 | 190.00 |

**No. 117 Surcharged**

| | | | | |
|---|---|---|---|---|
| **156** | A48 | 2c on 5c turq & blk | 140.00 | 140.00 |

**Nos. 18-20 Surcharged**

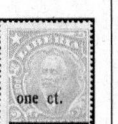

**1916**

| | | | | |
|---|---|---|---|---|
| **157** | A1 | 3c on 6c violet | 45.00 | 45.00 |
| a. | | Inverted surcharge | 100.00 | 75.00 |
| **158** | A1 | 5c on 12c yellow | 3.00 | 3.00 |
| a. | | Inverted surcharge | 17.50 | 17.50 |
| b. | | Surcharge sideways | 17.50 | |
| **159** | A1 | 10c on 24c rose red | 2.75 | 3.00 |
| a. | | Inverted surcharge | 15.00 | 15.00 |
| b. | | Surcharge sideways | 20.00 | |
| | | Nos. 157-159 (3) | 50.75 | 51.00 |

Unused values for Nos. 157-159 are for examples without gum.

**Nos. 44 and 108 Surcharged**

p                           r

**1917**                          **Wmk. 143**

| | | | | |
|---|---|---|---|---|
| **160** | A15 (p) | 4c on 25c yel grn | 12.00 | 12.00 |
| a. | | "OUR" | 27.50 | 27.50 |
| b. | | "FCUR" | 27.50 | 27.50 |

**Unwmk.**

| | | | | |
|---|---|---|---|---|
| **161** | A40 (r) | 5c on 30c dp vio | 90.00 | 90.00 |

**No. 118 Surcharged in Red**

**1918**

| | | | | |
|---|---|---|---|---|
| **162** | A49 | 3c on 10c plum & blk | 2.75 | 4.25 |
| a. | | "3" inverted | 9.25 | 9.25 |

Bongo Antelope A59

Symbols of Liberia A61

Two-spot Palm Civet — A60

A62

Palm-nut Vulture A66

Oil Palm A63

Mercury — A64

Traveler's Tree A65

"Mudskipper" or Bommi Fish — A67

Mandingos A68

"Liberia" A71

Coast Scene — A69

Liberia College — A70

**1918          Engr.          Perf. 12½, 14**

| | | | |
|---|---|---|---|
| **163** | A59 | 1c dp grn & blk | .75 | .25 |
| **164** | A60 | 2c rose & blk | .90 | .25 |
| **165** | A61 | 5c gray bl & blk | .25 | .25 |
| **166** | A62 | 10c dark green | .30 | .25 |
| **167** | A63 | 15c blk & dk grn | 3.50 | .25 |
| **168** | A64 | 20c claret & blk | .40 | .25 |
| **169** | A65 | 25c dk grn & grn | 3.75 | .25 |
| **170** | A66 | 30c red vio & blk | 17.00 | .80 |
| **171** | A67 | 50c ultra & blk | 30.00 | 3.50 |
| **172** | A68 | 75c ol bis & blk | 3.00 | .25 |
| **173** | A69 | $1 yel brn & bl | 7.50 | .25 |
| **174** | A70 | $2 lt vio & blk | 8.00 | .25 |
| **175** | A71 | $5 dark brown | 8.50 | .40 |
| | | Nos. 163-175 (13) | 83.85 | 7.20 |

For surcharges see Nos. 176-177, 228-229, 248-270, B3-B15, O111-O112, O155-O157.

For overprints see Nos. O98-O110.

**Nos. 163-164, F10-F14 Surcharged**

**1920**

| | | | | |
|---|---|---|---|---|
| **176** | A59 | 3c on 1c grn & blk | 1.10 | 1.10 |
| a. | | "CEETS" | 17.00 | 17.00 |
| b. | | Double surcharge | 10.00 | 10.00 |
| c. | | Triple surcharge | 15.00 | 15.00 |
| **177** | A60 | 4c on 2c rose & blk | 1.10 | 1.10 |
| a. | | Inverted surcharge | 20.00 | 20.00 |
| b. | | Double surcharge | 10.00 | 10.00 |
| c. | | Double surcharge, one invtd. | 18.00 | |
| d. | | Triple surcharge, one inverted | 25.00 | 25.00 |
| e. | | Quadruple surcharge | 30.00 | 30.00 |
| f. | | Typewritten surcharge | | |
| g. | | Same as "f" but inverted | | |
| h. | | Printed and typewritten surcharges, both inverted | | |
| **178** | R6 | 5c on 10c bl & blk | 2.50 | 2.75 |
| a. | | Inverted surcharge | 10.00 | 10.00 |
| b. | | Double surcharge | 10.00 | 10.00 |
| c. | | Double surcharge, one invtd. | 15.00 | 15.00 |
| d. | | Typewritten surcharge ("five") | | 100.00 |
| e. | | Printed and typewritten surcharges | 100.00 | |
| **179** | R6 | 5c on 10c org red & blk | 2.50 | 2.75 |
| a. | | 5c on 10c orange & black | 4.00 | 2.75 |
| b. | | Inverted surcharge | 15.00 | |
| c. | | Double surcharge | 15.00 | |
| d. | | Double surcharge, one invtd. | 18.00 | 15.00 |
| e. | | Typewritten surch. in violet | 100.00 | 100.00 |
| f. | | Typewritten surch. in black | | |
| g. | | Printed and typewritten surcharges | 100.00 | |
| **180** | R6 | 5c on 10c grn & blk | 2.50 | 2.75 |
| a. | | Double surcharge | 10.00 | 10.00 |
| b. | | Double surcharge, one invtd. | 18.00 | 18.00 |
| c. | | Inverted surcharge | | 18.00 |
| d. | | Quadruple surcharge | 25.00 | 25.00 |
| e. | | Typewritten surcharge | | 100.00 |
| f. | | Printed and typewritten surcharges | | |
| **181** | R6 | 5c on 10c vio & blk (Monrovia) | 4.00 | 5.00 |
| a. | | Double surcharge, one invtd. | 25.00 | 25.00 |
| **182** | R6 | 5c on 10c mag & blk (Robertsport) | 2.25 | 2.40 |
| a. | | Double surcharge | 15.00 | 15.00 |
| b. | | Double surcharge, one invtd. | 15.00 | 15.00 |
| c. | | Double surcharge, both invtd. | 25.00 | |
| | | Nos. 176-182 (7) | 15.95 | 17.85 |

Cape Mesurado A75

Pres. Daniel E. Howard A76

Arms of Liberia A77

Crocodile A78

Pepper Plant — A79          Leopard — A80

Village Scene — A81

Krumen in Dugout — A82

Rapids in St. Paul's River — A83

Bongo Antelope — A84

Hornbill — A85

Elephant — A86

**1921          Wmk. 116          Perf. 14**

| | | | | |
|---|---|---|---|---|
| **183** | A75 | 1c green | .25 | .25 |
| **184** | A76 | 5c dp bl & blk | .25 | .25 |
| **185** | A77 | 10c red & dl bl | .25 | .25 |
| **186** | A78 | 15c dl vio & grn | 6.50 | .55 |
| **187** | A79 | 20c rose red & grn | 2.75 | .25 |
| **188** | A80 | 25c org & blk | 7.50 | .55 |
| **189** | A81 | 30c grn & dl vio | .40 | .25 |
| **190** | A82 | 50c org & ultra | .45 | .25 |
| **191** | A83 | 75c red & blk brn | .80 | .25 |
| a. | | Center inverted | | 70.00 |
| **192** | A84 | $1 red & blk | 20.00 | 1.75 |
| **193** | A85 | $2 yel & ultra | 16.00 | 1.25 |
| **194** | A86 | $5 car rose & vio | 32.50 | 1.50 |
| | | Nos. 183-194 (12) | 87.65 | 7.35 |

For overprints see Nos. 195, 198-208, O115-O127, O130-O140.

**Nos. 134-135, 183-194 Ovptd.**

| | | | | |
|---|---|---|---|---|
| **195** | A75 | 1c green | 22.50 | .40 |
| **196** | A57 | 2c red | 22.50 | .40 |
| **197** | A58 | 3c dull violet | 32.50 | .40 |
| **198** | A76 | 5c dp bl & blk | 3.50 | .30 |
| **199** | A77 | 10c red & dull bl | 50.00 | .40 |
| **200** | A78 | 15c dull vio & grn | 22.50 | 1.40 |
| **201** | A79 | 20c rose red & grn, ovpt. invtd. | 7.25 | .75 |
| **202** | A80 | 25c orange & blk | 22.50 | 1.40 |
| **203** | A81 | 30c grn & dull vio | 2.50 | .30 |
| **204** | A82 | 50c orange & ultra | 3.50 | .30 |
| **205** | A83 | 75c red & blk brn | 4.75 | .30 |
| **206** | A84 | $1 red & blk | 62.50 | 2.10 |
| **207** | A85 | $2 yellow & ultra | 22.50 | 2.10 |
| **208** | A86 | $5 car rose & vio | 60.00 | 2.75 |
| | | Nos. 195-208 (14) | 339.00 | 13.30 |

Overprint exists inverted in Nos. 195-208 and normal on No. 201.

First Settlers Landing at Cape Mesurado from U. S. S. Alligator — A87

**1923          Litho.**

| | | | | |
|---|---|---|---|---|
| **209** | A87 | 1c lt blue & blk | 18.00 | .45 |
| **210** | A87 | 2c claret & ol gray | 26.00 | .45 |
| **211** | A87 | 5c ol grn & ind | 26.00 | .45 |
| **212** | A87 | 10c bl grn & vio | 1.00 | .45 |
| **213** | A87 | $1 rose & brn | 3.25 | .45 |
| | | Nos. 209-213 (5) | 74.25 | 2.25 |

Centenary of founding of Liberia.

Memorial to J. J. Roberts, 1st Pres. — A88

Hall of Representatives, Monrovia — A89

Liberian Star — A90

A91

Pres. Charles Dunbar Burgess King — A92

Hippopotamus A93

Antelope — A94

West African Buffalo — A95

Grebos Making Dumboy A96

Pineapple A97

Carrying Ivory Tusk — A98

Rubber Planter's House A99

Stockton Lagoon A100

Grebo Houses A101

## 1923    *Perf. 13½x14½, 14½x13½* — White Paper

| | | | | |
|---|---|---|---|---|
| 214 | A88 | 1c yel grn & dp grn | 7.50 | 1.25 |
| 215 | A89 | 2c claret & brn | 7.50 | .25 |
| 216 | A90 | 3c lilac & blk | .35 | .25 |
| 217 | A91 | 5c bl vio & blk | 115.00 | .25 |
| 218 | A92 | 10c slate & brn | .35 | .25 |
| 219 | A93 | 15c bister & bl | 35.00 | .50 |
| 220 | A94 | 20c bl grn & vio | 2.50 | .25 |
| 221 | A95 | 25c org red & brn | 160.00 | .60 |
| 222 | A96 | 30c dk brn & vio | .60 | .25 |
| 223a | A97 | 50c dull vio & brn, *brnsh* | 1.00 | .25 |
| 224 | A98 | 75c gray & bl | 1.90 | .40 |
| 225a | A99 | $1 dp red & dk vio, *brnsh* | 4.50 | .60 |
| 226 | A100 | $2 orange & blue | 7.50 | .80 |
| 227a | A101 | $5 dp grn & brn, *brnsh* | 8.00 | .90 |
| | | Nos. 214-227a (14) | 351.70 | 6.90 |

No. 163 Surcharged in Black

## 1926    Unwmk.    *Perf. 14*

| | | | | |
|---|---|---|---|---|
| 228 | A59 | 2c on 1c dp grn & blk | 3.50 | 3.50 |
| a. | | Surcharge with ornamental design as on #O155 | 17.00 | |

No. 163 Surcharged in Red

## 1927

| | | | | |
|---|---|---|---|---|
| 229 | A59 | 2c on 1c dp grn & blk | 9.50 | 9.50 |
| a. | | "Ceuts" | 14.00 | |
| b. | | "Vwo" | 14.00 | |
| c. | | "Twc" | 14.00 | |
| d. | | Double surcharge | 27.50 | |
| e. | | Wavy lines omitted | 17.50 | |

Palms A102

Map of Africa A103

President Burgess King — A104

## 1928    Engr.    *Perf. 12*

| | | | | |
|---|---|---|---|---|
| 230 | A102 | 1c green | .75 | .50 |
| 231 | A102 | 2c violet | .50 | .35 |
| 232 | A102 | 3c bister brn | .50 | .35 |
| a. | | Horiz. pair, imperf vert. | | |
| 233 | A103 | 5c ultra | 1.00 | .55 |
| 234 | A104 | 10c olive gray | 1.40 | .55 |
| 235 | A103 | 15c dull violet | 6.25 | 2.25 |
| 236 | A103 | $1 red brown | 77.50 | 26.50 |
| | | Nos. 230-236 (7) | 87.90 | 31.05 |

For surcharges & overprints see Nos. 288A, 289A, 290A-291, 292A, C1-C3, O158-O165.

### Nos. 164-168, 170-175 Surcharged in Various Colors and Styles

No. 248

No. 250

## 1936    *Perf. 12½, 14*

| | | | | |
|---|---|---|---|---|
| 248 | A60 | 1c on 2c (Bl) | .50 | 3.50 |
| 249 | A61 | 3c on 5c (Bl) | .45 | 2.00 |
| 250 | A62 | 4c on 10c (Br) | .45 | 2.00 |
| 251 | A63 | 6c on 15c (Bl) | .50 | 3.50 |
| 252 | A64 | 8c on 20c (V) | .45 | 2.00 |

| | | | | |
|---|---|---|---|---|
| 253 | A66 | 12c on 30c (V) | 1.25 | 9.75 |
| 254 | A67 | 14c on 50c (Bl) | 1.40 | 11.00 |
| 255 | A68 | 16c on 75c (Br) | .70 | 5.50 |
| 256 | A69 | 18c on $1 (Bk) | .70 | 5.50 |
| a. | | 22c on $1 yellow brown & blue | 8.00 | |
| 257 | A70 | 22c on $2 (V) | .85 | 7.75 |
| 258 | A71 | 24c on $5 (Bk) | 1.50 | 9.75 |
| | | Nos. 248-258 (11) | 8.75 | 62.25 |

### Official Stamps, Nos. O99-O110, Srchd. or Ovptd. in Various Colors & Styles

## 1936

| | | | | |
|---|---|---|---|---|
| 259 | A60 | 1c on 2c (Bl) | .45 | 4.00 |
| 260 | A61 | 3c on 5c (Bl) | .45 | 4.00 |
| 261 | A62 | 4c on 10c (Bl) | .45 | 4.00 |
| 262 | A63 | 6c on 15c (Bl) | .45 | 4.00 |
| 263 | A64 | 8c on 20c (V) | .45 | 4.00 |
| 264 | A66 | 12c on 30c (V) | 1.65 | 20.00 |
| a. | | "193" instead of "1936" | 20.00 | |
| 265 | A67 | 14c on 50c (Bk) | 2.25 | 21.00 |
| 266 | A68 | 16c on 75c (Bk) | 1.10 | 12.00 |
| 267 | A69 | 18c on $1 (Bk) | 1.10 | 12.00 |
| 268 | A70 | 22c on $2 (Bl) | 1.40 | 15.00 |
| 269 | A71 | 24c on $5 (Bk) | 1.75 | 17.00 |
| 270 | A65 | 25c (Bk) | 2.25 | 21.00 |
| | | Nos. 259-270 (12) | 13.75 | 138.00 |

Hornbill A106

Designs: 2c, Bushbuck. 3c, West African dwarf buffalo. 4c, Pygmy hippopotamus. 5c, Lesser egret. 6c, Pres. E. J. Barclay.

## *Perf. Compound of 11½, 12, 12½, 14* — 1937, Apr. 10    Engr.    Unwmk.

| | | | | |
|---|---|---|---|---|
| 271 | A106 | 1c yel grn & blk | 1.50 | .45 |
| 272 | A106 | 2c carmine & blk | 1.50 | .45 |
| 273 | A106 | 3c violet & blk | 1.50 | .45 |
| 274 | A106 | 4c orange & blk | 2.25 | .70 |
| 275 | A106 | 5c blue & blk | 2.25 | .65 |
| 276 | A106 | 6c green & blk | .80 | .25 |
| | | Nos. 271-276 (6) | 9.80 | 2.95 |

Coast Line of Liberia, 1839 — A107

Seal of Liberia, Map and Farming Scenes A108

Thomas Buchanan and Residence at Bassa Cove — A109

## 1940, July 29    Engr.    *Perf. 12*

| | | | | |
|---|---|---|---|---|
| 277 | A107 | 3c dark blue | .35 | .35 |
| 278 | A108 | 5c dull red brn | .35 | .35 |
| 279 | A109 | 10c dark green | .35 | .35 |
| | | Nos. 277-279 (3) | 1.05 | 1.05 |

100th anniv. of the founding of the Commonwealth of Liberia.

For overprints & surcharges see Nos. 280-282, B16-B18, C14-C16, CB1-CB3, CE1, CF1, E1, F35.

### Imperforates

Many stamps of Liberia exist imperforate or with various perforation errors, in issued and trial colors, and also in small presentation sheets in issued colors.

### Nos. 277-279 Overprinted in Red or Blue

## 1941, Feb. 21

| | | | | |
|---|---|---|---|---|
| 280 | A107 | 3c dk blue (R) | 2.50 | 2.50 |
| 281 | A108 | 5c dull red brn (Bl) | 2.50 | 2.50 |
| 282 | A109 | 10c dark green (R) | 2.50 | 2.50 |
| | | Nos. 280-282,C14-C16 (6) | 15.75 | 15.75 |

Royal Antelope A110

Bay-thighed Diana Monkey A115

2c, Water chevrotain. 3c, White-shouldered duiker. 4c, Bushbuck. 5c, Zebra antelope.

## 1942    Engr.

| | | | | |
|---|---|---|---|---|
| 283 | A110 | 1c violet & fawn | 1.10 | .25 |
| 284 | A110 | 2c brt ultra & yel brn | 1.40 | .25 |
| 285 | A110 | 3c brt grn & yel brn | 1.90 | .90 |
| 286 | A110 | 4c blk & red org | 2.40 | 1.90 |
| 287 | A110 | 5c olive & fawn | 3.00 | 1.90 |
| 288 | A115 | 10c red & black | 5.25 | 2.40 |
| | | Nos. 283-288 (6) | 15.05 | 7.60 |

### Nos. 231, 233-234, 271-276 Srchd. with New Values and Bars or X's in Violet, Black, Red Brown or Blue

No. 288A

No. 289A

No. 292A      No. 295

## *Perf. 12, 12x12½, 14* — 1944-46    Unwmk.

| | | | | |
|---|---|---|---|---|
| 288A | A102 | 1c on 2c (Bk) | 9.25 | 6.50 |
| 289 | A106 | 1c on 4c (Bk) | 60.00 | 47.50 |
| 289A | A104 | 1c on 10c (R Br) | 12.50 | 9.50 |
| b. | | Double surcharge, one red brown, one violet | 25.00 | 19.00 |
| 290 | A106 | 2c on 3c | 70.00 | 50.00 |
| 290A | A103 | 2c on 5c (Bk) | 2.75 | 2.75 |
| 290B | A103 | 2c on 5c (Bl) | 21.00 | 21.00 |
| 291 | A102 | 3c on 2c | 30.00 | 35.00 |
| 292 | A106 | 4c on 5c | 11.00 | 7.25 |
| 292A | A104 | 4c on 10c (Bk) | 3.25 | 3.25 |
| b. | | Double surch., one inverted | | |
| 293 | A106 | 5c on 1c (Bk) | 100.00 | 50.00 |
| 294 | A106 | 6c on 2c (Bk) | 11.00 | 9.50 |
| 295 | A106 | 10c on 6c | 11.00 | 9.50 |
| | | Nos. 288A-295 (12) | 341.75 | 240.00 |

Surcharges on Nos. 289, 290, 293, 294 are found double or inverted. Such varieties command a small premium.

Pres. Franklin D. Roosevelt Reviewing Troops — A116

## 1945, Nov. 26    Engr.    *Perf. 12½* — Grayish Paper

| | | | | |
|---|---|---|---|---|
| 296 | A116 | 3c brt violet & blk | .25 | .25 |
| 297 | A116 | 5c dk blue & blk | .45 | .45 |
| | | Nos. 296-297,C51 (3) | 2.95 | 2.10 |

In memory of Pres. Franklin D. Roosevelt (1882-1945).

Monrovia
Harbor — A117

**1947, Jan. 2**
**298** A117 5c deep blue          .25   .25
  Opening of the Monrovia Harbor Project,
Feb. 16, 1946. See No. C52.

**Without Inscription at Top**
**1947, May 16**
**299** A117 5c violet              .25   .25
       See No. C53.

1st US
Postage
Stamps and
Arms of
Liberia
A118

**1947, June 6**
**300** A118 5c carmine rose        .25   .25
  *Nos. 300,C54-C56 (4)*     1.20  1.00
  Cent. of US postage stamps and the 87th
anniv. of Liberian postal issues.

Matilda Newport
Firing
Cannon — A119

**1947, Dec. 1        Engr. & Photo.**
**Center in Gray Black**
**301** A119 1c brt blue green      .25   .25
**302** A119 3c brt red violet      .25   .25
**303** A119 5c brt ultra           .60   .25
**304** A119 10c yellow            3.25   .80
  *Nos. 301-304,C57 (5)*     5.60  1.85
  125th anniv. of Matilda Newport's defense
of Monrovia, Dec. 1, 1822.

Liberian Star — A120

  Cent. of Independence: 2c, Liberty. 3c,
Liberian Arms. 5c, Map of Liberia.

**1947, Dec. 22               Engr.**
**305** A120 1c dark green          .55   .25
**306** A120 2c brt red vio         .55   .25
**307** A120 3c brt purple          .55   .25
**308** A120 5c dark blue           .55   .25
  *Nos. 305-308,C58-C60 (7)*  3.80  1.95
       Centenary of independence

Natives
Approaching
Village — A124

Rubber Tapping
and
Planting — A125

Landing of First
Colonists
A126

Jehudi Ashmun
and Defenders
A127

**1949, Apr. 4      Litho.    Perf. 11½**
**309** A124 1c multicolored        .45   .75
**310** A125 2c multicolored        .45   .75
**311** A126 3c multicolored        .45   .75
**312** A127 5c multicolored        .45   .75
  *Nos. 309-312,C63-C64 (6)*  2.50  4.30
  Nos. 309-312 exist perf. 12½ and sell at a
much lower price. The status of the perf. 12½
set is indefinite.

Stephen
Benson — A128

  Liberian Presidents: 1c, Pres. Joseph J.
Roberts. 3c, Daniel B. Warner. 4c, James S.
Payne. 5c, Executive mansion. 6c, Edward J.
Roye. 7c, A. W. Gardner and A. F. Russell. 8c,
Hilary R. W. Johnson. 9c, Joseph J. Cheese-
man. 10c, William D. Coleman. 15c, Garretson
W. Gibson. 20c, Arthur Barclay. 25c, Daniel E.
Howard. 50c, Charles D. B. King. $1, Edwin J.
Barclay.

**1948-50  Unwmk.  Engr.   Perf. 12½**
**Caption and Portrait in Black**
**313** A128 1c green ('48)        2.75  7.00
**314** A128 2c salmon pink         .40   .65
**315** A128 3c rose violet         .40   .65
  **a.**   "1876-1878" added      16.00 40.00
**316** A128 4c lt olive grn        .90   .90
**317** A128 5c ultra               .50   .90
**318** A128 6c red orange          .90  1.75
**319** A128 7c lt blue ('50)      1.10  2.10
**320** A128 8c carmine            1.10  2.40
**321** A128 9c red violet         1.25  2.10
**322** A128 10c yellow ('50)       .85   .55
**323** A128 15c yellow orange     1.00   .70
**324** A128 20c blue gray         1.40  1.40
**325** A128 25c cerise            2.00  2.10
**326** A128 50c aqua              3.75  1.40
**327** A128 $1 rose lilac         6.25  1.40
  *Nos. 313-327,C65 (16)*    25.15 26.65
  Issued: 1c, 11/18; 7c, 10c, 1950; others,
7/21/49.
  See Nos. 328, 371-378, C65, C118.

Pres. Joseph J.
Roberts
A129

**1950**
**328** A129 1c green & blk         .25   .25

Hand Holding
Book — A130

**1950, Feb. 14**
**329** A130 5c deep blue           .45   .25
  National Literacy Campaign. See No. C66.

┌─────────────────────────────────┐
│ **Catalogue values for unused** │
│ **stamps in this section, from this** │
│ **point to the end of the section, are** │
│ **for Never Hinged items.**     │
└─────────────────────────────────┘

UPU Monument
A131

First UPU
Building,
Bern — A132

**1950, Apr. 21   Engr.    Unwmk.**
**330** A131 5c green & blk         .25   .25
**331** A132 10c red vio & blk      .25   .25
  *Nos. 330-331,C67 (3)*     3.25  3.25
  UPU, 75th anniv. (in 1949).
  Exist imperf. Value, $6.50.

Jehudi
Ashmun and
Seal of Liberia
A133

John Marshall,
Ashmun and Map of
Town of Marshall
A134

  Designs (Map or View and Two Portraits):
2c, Careysburg, Gov. Lott Carey (1780-1828),
freed American slave, and Jehudi Ashmun
(1794-1828), American missionary credited as
founder of Liberia. 3c, Town of Harper, Robert
Goodloe Harper (1765-1825), American
statesman, and Ashmun. 5c, Upper
Buchanan, Gov. Thomas Buchanan and
Ashmun. 10c, Robertsport, Pres. Joseph J.
Roberts and Ashmun.

**1952, Apr. 10              Perf. 10½**
**332** A133 1c deep green          .25   .25
**333** A133 2c scarlet & ind       .30   .25
**334** A133 3c purple & grn        .30   .25
**335** A134 4c brown & grn         .30   .25
**336** A133 5c ultra & org red     .30   .25
**337** A134 10c org red & dk bl    .30   .25
  *Nos. 332-337,C69 (8)*     2.70  2.45
  Nos. 332-337 exist imperf. Value about two
and one-half times that of the perf. set.
  No. 334 exists with center inverted. Value
$50.
  See No. C69a.

UN
Headquarters
Building
A135

Scroll and Flags
A136

  10c, Liberia arms, letters "UN" and
emblem.

**1952, Dec. 20    Unwmk.    Perf. 12½**
**338** A135 1c ultra               .30   .30
**339** A136 4c car & ultra         .30   .30
**340** A136 10c red brn & yel      .30   .30
  **a.**  Souvenir sheet of 3, #338-340  2.00  2.00
  *Nos. 338-340,C70 (4)*     1.80  1.55
  Nos. 338-340 and 340a exist imperforate.
Values: set $5; souvenir sheet $3.50.

Pepper Bird
A137

Roller — A138

Hornbill
— A138a

Kingfisher
— A138b

Jacana —
A138c

Weaver —
A138d

**1953, Nov. 18              Perf. 10½**
**341** A137 1c shown              1.00   .25
**342** A138 3c shown              1.00   .25
**343** A138a 4c yellow & brown    1.60   .25
**344** A138b 5c mauve & bl grn    1.75   .25
**345** A138c 10c grn & dp mag     1.90   .25
**346** A138d 12c brn & org        2.50   .25
  *Nos. 341-346 (6)*         9.75  1.50
  Exist imperf. Value, set unused $12.

Tennis — A139

**1955, Jan. 26   Litho.    Perf. 12½**
**347** A139 3c shown               .25   .25
**348** A139 5c Soccer              .25   .25
**349** A139 25c Boxing             .40   .25
  *Nos. 347-349,C88-C90 (6)*  1.80  1.65

Callichilia
Stenosepala — A140

  Various Native Flowers: 7c, Gomphia sub-
cordata. 8c, Listrostachys caudata. 9c,
Musaenda isertiana.

**1955, Sept. 28              Unwmk.**
**350** A140 6c yel grn, org & yel  .30   .25
**351** A140 7c emer, yel & car     .30   .25
**352** A140 8c yel grn, buff & bl  .30   .25
**353** A140 9c orange & green      .40   .25
  *Nos. 350-353,C91-C92 (6)*  2.10  1.50

Rubber
Tapping — A141

**1955, Dec. 5              Perf. 12½**
**354** A141 5c emerald & yellow    .25   .25
  *Nos. 354,C97-C98 (3)*     1.20   .75
  50th anniv. of Rotary Intl. No. 354 exists
printed entirely in emerald.

Statue of
Liberty — A142

Coliseum, New
York
City — A143

Design: 6c, Globe inscribed FIPEX.

**1956, Apr. 28**     *Perf. 12*
355 A142 3c brt grn & dk red brn   .25   .25
356 A143 4c Prus grn & bis brn   .25   .25
357 A143 6c gray & red lilac   .25   .25
   *Nos. 355-357,C100-C102 (6)*   2.15 1.50

Fifth International Philatelic Exhibition
(FIPEX), NYC, Apr. 28-May 6, 1956.

Kangaroo and
Emu — A144

Discus
Thrower — A145

Designs: 8c, Goddess of Victory and
Olympic symbols. 10c, Classic chariot race.

**1956, Nov. 15**    Litho.    Unwmk.
358 A144 4c lt ol grn & gldn brn   .25   .25
359 A145 6c emerald & gray   .25   .25
360 A144 8c lt ultra & redsh brn   .25   .25
361 A144 10c rose red & blk   .40   .25
   *Nos. 358-361,C104-C105 (6)*   2.15 2.00

16th Olympic Games at Melbourne, Nov.
22-Dec. 8, 1956.
Nos. 358-361 exist imperf.

Idlewild Airport,
New
York — A146

Roberts Field,
Liberia, plane &
Pres. Tubman —
A146a

**Lithographed and Engraved**
**1957, May 4**     *Perf. 12*
362 A146 3c orange & dk blue   .25   .25
363 A146a 5c red lilac & blk   .25   .25
   *Nos. 362-363,C107-C110 (6)*   3.15 1.50

1st anniv. of direct air service between Roberts Field, Liberia, and Idlewild (Kennedy), NY.
See Nos. C107-C110.

Orphanage
Playground
A147

Orphanage and: 5c, Teacher and pupil. 6c,
Singing boys and natl. anthem. 10c, Children
and flag.

---

**1957, Nov. 25**    Litho.    *Perf. 12*
364 A147 4c green & red   .25   .25
365 A147 5c bl grn & red brn   .25   .25
366 A147 6c brt vio & bis   .25   .25
367 A147 10c ultra & rose car   .25   .25
   *Nos. 364-367,C111-C112 (6)*   2.25 1.50

Founding of the Antoinette Tubman Child
Welfare Foundation.

Windmill and
Dutch
Flag — A148

Designs: No. 369, German flag and Brandenburg Gate. No. 370, Swedish flag, palace
and crowns.

**Engraved and Lithographed**
**1958, Jan. 10**    Unwmk.    *Perf. 10½*
**Flags in Original Colors**
368 A148 5c reddish brn   .25   .25
369 A148 5c blue   .25   .25
370 A148 5c lilac rose   .25   .25
   *Nos. 368-370,C114-C117 (7)*   2.55 2.55

European tour of Pres. Tubman in 1956.
Exist imperf.

**Presidential Types of 1948-50**
Designs as before.

**1958-60**    Engr.    *Perf. 12*
**Caption and Portrait in Black**
371 A129 1c salmon pink   .45   .25
372 A128 2c brt yellow   .45   .25
373 A128 10c blue gray   .55   .55
374 A128 15c brt bl & blk ('59)   .25   .25
375 A128 20c dark red   .65   .65
376 A128 25c blue   .65   .65
377 A128 50c red lil & blk ('59)   .75   .65
378 A128 $1 bister brn ('60)   5.75   .75
   *Nos. 371-378,C118 (9)*   10.75 4.90

Many shades of 1c.

Open Globe
Projection
A149

Designs: 5c, UN Emblem and building. 10c,
UN Emblem. 12c, UN Emblem and initials of
agencies.

**1958, Dec. 10**    Litho.    *Perf. 12*
379 A149 3c gray, bl & blk   .30   .25
380 A149 5c blue & choc   .25   .25
381 A149 10c black & org   .40   .25
382 A149 12c black & car   1.10 1.10
   *Nos. 379-382 (4)*   2.05 1.85

10th anniv. of the Universal Declaration of
Human Rights. See No. C119.

People of Africa on the
March — A150

**1959, Apr. 15**
383 A150 20c orange & brown   .45   .45
African Freedom Day, Apr. 15. Exists imperf.
See No. C120.

Symbols of
UNESCO — A151

**1959, May 11**     Unwmk.
384 A151 25c dp plum & emer   .55   .55

Opening of UNESCO Headquarters in
Paris, Nov. 3, 1958. Exists imperf.
See Nos. C121, C121a.

---

Abraham
Lincoln — A152

**1959, Nov. 20**    Engr.    *Perf. 12*
385 A152 10c ultra & blk   .40   .40
386 A152 15c orange & blk   .40   .40
   **a.**   Souv. sheet of 3, Nos. 385-386,
      C122, imperf.   2.50 4.00
   *Nos. 385-386,C122 (3)*   1.70 1.70

150th anniv. of the birth of Abraham Lincoln.

Touré, Tubman
and
Nkrumah — A153

**1960, Jan. 27**    Litho.    Unwmk.
387 A153 25c crimson & blk   .55   .55

1959 "Big Three" conference of Pres. Sékou
Touré of Guinea, Pres. William V. S. Tubman
of Liberia and Prime Minister Kwame
Nkrumah of Ghana at Saniquellie, Liberia. See
No. C123.

World Refugee Year
Emblem — A154

**1960, Apr. 7**     *Perf. 11½*
388 A154 25c emerald & blk   .70 1.00

World Refuge Year, July 1, 1959-June 30,
1960. See No. C124, C124a. Exist imperf.

Map of Africa — A155

**1960, May 11**    Litho.    *Perf. 11½*
389 A155 25c green & black   .60   .60

10th anniv. of the Commission for Technical
Cooperation in Africa South of the Sahara
(C.C.T.A.). See No. C125.

Weight Lifter and
Porter — A156

Designs: 10c, Rower and canoeists, horiz.
15c, Walker and porter.

**1960, Sept. 6**     Unwmk.
390 A156 5c dk brn & emer   .25   .25
391 A156 10c brown & red lil   .25   .25
392 A156 15c brown & org   .70   .70
   *Nos. 390-392,C126 (4)*   2.10 1.95

17th Olympic Games, Rome, 8/25-9/11.
Exist imperf.

Liberian Stamps of
1860 — A157

**1960, Dec. 1**    Litho.    *Perf. 11½*
393 A157 5c multicolored   .25   .25
394 A157 20c multicolored   .70   .70
   *Nos. 393-394,C128 (3)*   1.95 1.95

Liberian postage stamps, cent.

---

Laurel Wreath — A158

**1961, May 19**    Unwmk.    *Perf. 11½*
395 A158 25c red & dk blue   .60   .60

Liberia's membership in the UN Security
Council. Exists imperf. Value, Nos. 395, C130
$6.
See Nos. C130-C131 and note after No.
C131.

Anatomy
Class — A159

**1961, Sept. 8**     *Perf. 11½*
396 A159 25c green & brown   .60   .60

15th anniv. of UNESCO. Nos. 396 and
C132 exist imperf. Value, $3.
See Nos. C132-C133.

Joseph J. Roberts
Monument,
Monrovia — A160

Design: 10c, Pres. Roberts and old and new
presidential mansions, horiz.

**1961, Oct. 25**     Litho.
397 A160 5c orange & sepia   .25   .25
398 A160 10c ultra & sepia   .45   .25
   *Nos. 397-398,C134 (3)*   1.40 1.20

150th anniv. of the birth of Joseph J. Roberts, 1st pres. of Liberia. Exist imperf.

Boy Scout — A161

Design: Insignia and Scouts camping.

**1961, Dec. 4**    Unwmk.    *Perf. 11½*
399 A161 5c lilac & sepia   .25   .25
400 A161 10c ultra & bister   .50   .50
   *Nos. 399-400,C135 (3)*   2.15 2.15

Boy Scouts of Liberia. Exist imperf. Value,
$5.50.

Dag
Hammarskjold and
UN
Emblem — A162

**1962, Feb. 1**     *Perf. 12*
401 A162 20c black & ultra   .45   .45

Dag Hammarskjold, Secretary General of
the UN, 1953-61. See Nos. C137-C138.

Malaria Eradication
Emblem — A163

**1962, Apr. 7**    Litho.    *Perf. 12½*
402 A163 25c dk green & red   .55   .45

WHO drive to eradicate malaria. Nos. 402,
C137 exist imperf. Value, $5.
See Nos. C139-C140.

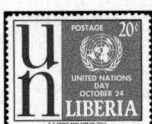

United Nations Emblem — A164

**1962, Oct. 22**    *Perf. 12x12½*
403 A164 20c green & yel bister   .35 .35

Issued to mark the observance of United Nations Day, Oct. 24, as a national holiday. See Nos. C144-C145.

Executive Mansion, Monrovia — A165

1c, 80c, Executive Mansion, Monrovia. 5c, Treasury Department Building, Monrovia. 10c, Information Service. 15c, Capitol.

**1962-64**
403A A165   1c vio bl & dp org ('64)   .25 .25
404 A165   5c lt blue & pur   .25 .25
405 A165   10c bister & brn   .25 .25
406 A165   15c salmon & dk bl   .40 .30
406A A165   80c brn & yel ('64)   1.75 1.20
   Nos. 403A-406A,C146-C148 (9)   8.35 6.30

    See Nos. C146-C148.

"FAO" Emblem and Food Bowl — A166

**1963, Mar. 21**    *Perf. 12½*
407 A166 5c aqua & dk car   .40 .25

FAO "Freedom from Hunger" campaign. See Nos. C149-C150.

Rocket in Space — A167

Design: 15c, Space capsule and globe.

**1963, May 27**   Litho.   *Perf. 12½*
408 A167 10c dp vio bl & yel   .25 .25
409 A167 15c blue & red brn   .60 .60
   Nos. 408-409,C151 (3)   1.40 1.25

Achievements in space exploration for peaceful purposes. Exist imperf. Value, $8.

Red Cross — A168

10c, Centenary emblem and torch, vert.

**1963, Aug. 26**   Unwmk.   *Perf. 11½*
410 A168 5c blue grn & red   .25 .25
411 A168 10c gray & red   .25 .25
   Nos. 410-411,C153-C154 (4)   1.60 1.60

Intl. Red Cross, cent. See Nos. C153-C154.

Palm Tree and Scroll — A169

**1963, Oct. 28**    *Perf. 12½*
412 A169 20c brown & green   .40 .40

Conference of African heads of state for African Unity, Addis Ababa, May, 1963. See No. C156.

Ski Jump — A170

**1963, Dec. 11**   Unwmk.   *Perf. 12½*
413 A170 5c rose red & dk vio bl   .25 .25
   Nos. 413,C157-C158 (3)   1.30 1.30

9th Winter Olympic Games, Innsbruck, Austria, Jan. 29-Feb. 9, 1964. Exist imperf. Value, $6.

John F. Kennedy — A171

**1964, Apr. 6**    Litho.
414 A171 20c blk & brt blue   .35 .35

John F. Kennedy (1917-63). Nos. 414, C160 exist imperf. Value, set $5. See Nos. C160-C161.

Syncom Satellite — A172

Satellites: 15c, Relay I, vert. 25c, Mariner II.

**1964, June 22**   Unwmk.   *Perf. 12½*
415 A172 10c orange & emer   .30 .25
416 A172 15c brt car rose & vio   .40 .25
417 A172 25c blue, org & blk   .40 .70
   Nos. 415-417 (3)   1.10 1.20

Progress in space communications and the peaceful uses of outer space. See No. C162. Exist imperf. Value, set $9.

Mt. Fuji — A173

Designs: 15c, Torii and Olympic flame. 25c, Cherry blossoms and stadium.

**1964, Sept. 15**    Litho.
418 A173 10c orange yel & emer   .25 .25
419 A173 15c lt red & purple   .25 .25
420 A173 25c ocher & red   .95 .95
   Nos. 418-420 (3)   1.45 1.45

Issued for the 18th Olympic Games, Tokyo, Oct. 10-25, 1964. See No. C163. Exist imperf. Value, set $9.

Boy Scout Emblem and Scout Sign — A174

10c, Bugle and Liberian Scout emblem, horiz.

**1965, Mar. 8**   Litho.   *Perf. 12½*
421 A174 5c lt blue & brown   .30 .25
422 A174 10c dk green & ocher   .40 .25
   Nos. 421-422,C164 (3)   1.50 1.30

Liberian Boy Scouts. Exist imperf. Value, set $8.

"Emancipation" by Thomas Ball — A175

Designs: 20c, Abraham Lincoln and John F. Kennedy, horiz. 25c, Lincoln by Augustus St. Gaudens, Lincoln Park, Chicago.

**1965, May 3**   Unwmk.   *Perf. 12½*
423 A175 5c dk gray & brn org   .25 .25
424 A175 20c emer & lt gray   .50 .50
425 A175 25c maroon & blue   .65 .65
   Nos. 423-425 (3)   1.40 1.40

Centenary of the death of Abraham Lincoln. Exist imperf. Value, set $9. See No. C166.

ICY Emblem — A176

**1965, June 21**   Litho.   *Perf. 12½*
426 A176 12c orange & brn   .40 .40
427 A176 25c vio blue & brn   .75 .40
428 A176 50c emerald & brn   1.50 .85
   Nos. 426-428 (3)   2.65 1.50

Intl. Cooperation Year. See No. C167.

ITU Emblem, Old and New Communication Equipment — A177

**1965, Sept. 21**   Unwmk.   *Perf. 12½*
429 A177 25c brt grn & red brn   .40 .40
430 A177 35c black & car rose   .50 .50
   Nos. 429-430,C168 (3)   1.70 1.60

Cent. of the ITU.

Pres. Tubman and Liberian Flag — A178

**1965, Nov. 29**    Litho.
431 A178 25c red, ultra & brn   .60 .60

Pres. William V. S. Tubman's 70th birthday. See No. C169, C169a.

Churchill in Admiral's Uniform — A179

Designs: 15c, Churchill giving "V" sign, vert.

**1966, Jan. 18**   Litho.   *Perf. 12½*
432 A179 15c orange & blk   .40 .25
433 A179 20c black & brt grn   .90 .90
   Nos. 432-433,C170 (3)   2.00 1.70

Issued in memory of Sir Winston Spencer Churchill (1874-1965), statesman and World War II leader. Exist imperf. Value, set $6.

Pres. Joseph J. Roberts — A180

Presidents: 2c, Stephen Benson. 3c, Daniel Bashiel Warner. 4c, James S. Payne. 5c, Edward James Roye. 10c, William D. Coleman. 25c, Daniel Edward Howard. 50c, Charles Dunbar Burgess King. 80c, Hilary R. W. Johnson. $1, Edwin J. Barclay. $2, Joseph James Cheeseman ("Cheesman" on stamp).

**1966-69**   Litho.   *Perf. 12½*
434 A180 1c black & brick red   .25 .25
435 A180 2c black & yellow   .25 .25
436 A180 3c black & lilac   .25 .25
437 A180 4c ap grn & blk ('67)   .25 .25
438 A180 5c black & dull org   .25 .25
439 A180 10c pale grn & blk ('67)   .25 .25
440 A180 25c black & lt blue   .60 .25
441 A180 50c blk & brt lil rose   1.25 .90
442 A180 80c dp rose & blk ('67)   1.90 1.10
443 A180 $1 black & ocher   2.25 .25
   *Perf. 11½x11*
443A A180 $2 blk & dp red lil ('69)   4.50 3.00
   Nos. 434-443A,C182 (12)   12.60 7.30

Soccer Players and Globe — A181

Designs: 25c, World Championships Cup, ball and shoes, vert. 35c, Soccer player dribbling, vert.

**1966, May 3**   Litho.   *Perf. 12½*
444 A181 10c brt green & dk brn   .40 .25
445 A181 25c brt pink & brn   .60 .30
446 A181 35c brown & orange   .80 .45
   Nos. 444-446 (3)   1.80 1.00

World Cup Soccer Championships, Wembley, England, July 11-30. Exist imperf. Value, $14. See No. C172.

Pres. Kennedy Taking Oath of Office — A182

20c, 1964 Kennedy stamps, #414, C160.

**1966, Aug. 16**   Litho.   *Perf. 12½*
447 A182 15c red & blk   .25 .25
448 A182 20c brt bl & red lil   .30 .30
   Nos. 447-448,C173-C174 (4)   1.45 1.05

3rd anniv. of Pres. Kennedy's death (Nov. 22). Exist imperf. Value, set $12.

Children on Seesaw and UNICEF Emblem — A183

Design: 80c, Boy playing doctor.

**1966, Oct. 25**   Unwmk.   *Perf. 12½*
449 A183 5c brt blue & red   .35 .25
450 A183 80c org brn & yel grn   .90 .90

20th anniv. of UNICEF.

Giraffe — A184

Designs: 3c, Lion. 5c, Slender-nosed crocodile, horiz. 10c, Baby chimpanzees. 15c, Leopard, horiz. 20c, Black rhinoceros, horiz. 25c, Elephant.

**1966, Dec. 20**
451 A184 2c multicolored   1.00 .25
452 A184 3c multicolored   1.00 .25
453 A184 5c multicolored   1.00 .25
   a.   Black omitted ("5c LIBERIA" and imprint)   50.00
454 A184 10c multicolored   1.00 .25
455 A184 15c multicolored   1.10 .30
456 A184 20c multicolored   1.75 .55
457 A184 25c multicolored   2.40 .65
   Nos. 451-457 (7)   9.25 2.50

Jamboree Badge — A185

Designs: 25c, Boy Scout emblem and various sports, horiz. 40c, Scout at campfire and vision of moon landing, horiz.

**1967, Mar. 23**   Litho.   *Perf. 12½*
458 A185 10c brt lil rose & grn   .25 .25
459 A185 25c brt red & blue   .55 .55
460 A185 40c brt grn & brn org   1.00 .85
   Nos. 458-460 (3)   1.80 1.65

12th Boy Scout World Jamboree, Farragut State Park, Idaho, Aug. 1-9. Exist imperf. Value, set $9. See No. C176.

A186

Pre-Hispanic Sculpture of Mexico: 25c, Aztec Calendar and Olympic rings. 40c, Mexican pottery, sombrero and guitar, horiz.

**1967, June 20    Litho.    *Perf. 12½***
| | | | | |
|---|---|---|---|---|
| 461 | A186 | 10c ocher & violet | .25 | .25 |
| 462 | A186 | 25c lt bl, org & blk | .50 | .25 |
| 463 | A186 | 40c yel grn & car | .75 | .50 |
| | | Nos. 461-463 (3) | 1.50 | 1.00 |

Issued to publicize the 19th Olympic Games, Mexico City. Exist imperf. Value, set $8.

See No. C177.

A187

Designs: 5c, WHO Office for Africa, horiz. 80c, WHO Office for Africa.

**1967, Aug. 28    Litho.    *Perf. 12½***
| | | | | |
|---|---|---|---|---|
| 464 | A187 | 5c blue & ol bister | .25 | .25 |
| 465 | A187 | 80c emer & ol bister | 1.50 | 1.50 |

Inauguration of the WHO Regional Office for Africa in Brazzaville, Congo.

Boy Playing African Rattle — A188

Africans Playing Native Instruments: 3c, Tom-tom and soko violin, horiz. 5c, Mang harp, horiz. 10c, Alimilim. 15c, Xylophone drums. 25c, Large tom-toms. 35c, Large harp.

**1967, Oct. 16    Litho.    *Perf. 14***
| | | | | |
|---|---|---|---|---|
| 466 | A188 | 2c violet & multi | .25 | .25 |
| 467 | A188 | 3c blue & multi | .25 | .25 |
| 468 | A188 | 5c lilac rose & multi | .25 | .25 |
| 469 | A188 | 10c yel grn & multi | .25 | .25 |
| 470 | A188 | 15c violet & multi | .40 | .25 |
| 471 | A188 | 25c ocher & multi | .80 | .40 |
| 472 | A188 | 35c dp rose & multi | 1.25 | .65 |
| | | Nos. 466-472 (7) | 3.45 | 2.30 |

Ice Hockey — A189

Designs: 25c, Ski jump. 40c, Bobsledding.

**1967, Nov. 20    Litho.    *Perf. 12½***
| | | | | |
|---|---|---|---|---|
| 473 | A189 | 10c emer & vio bl | .25 | .25 |
| 474 | A189 | 25c grnsh bl & dp plum | .35 | .25 |
| 475 | A189 | 40c ocher & org brn | .60 | .50 |
| | | Nos. 473-475 (3) | 1.20 | 1.00 |

10th Winter Olympic Games, Grenoble, France, Feb. 6-18, 1968. See No. C178.

Pres. William Tubman — A190

**1967, Dec. 22    Litho.    *Perf. 12½***
| | | | | |
|---|---|---|---|---|
| 476 | A190 | 25c ultra & brown | .75 | .30 |

## Souvenir Sheet
### *Imperf*
| | | | | |
|---|---|---|---|---|
| 477 | A190 | 50c ultra & brown | 2.00 | 2.00 |

Inauguration of President Tubman, Jan. 1, 1968. No. 476 exists imperf. No. 477 contains one stamp with simulated perforations and picture frame.

Human Rights Flame — A191

**1968, Apr. 26    Litho.    *Perf. 12½***
| | | | | |
|---|---|---|---|---|
| 478 | A191 | 3c ver & dp bl | .25 | .25 |
| 479 | A191 | 80c brown & emer | 1.25 | 1.25 |

Intl. Human Rights Year. See No. C179. Exist imperf.

Martin Luther King, Jr. — A192

Designs: 15c, Mule-drawn hearse and Dr. King. 35c, Dr. King and Lincoln monument by Daniel Chester French, horiz.

**1968, July 11    Unwmk.    *Perf. 12½***
| | | | | |
|---|---|---|---|---|
| 480 | A192 | 15c brt bl & brn | .25 | .25 |
| 481 | A192 | 25c indigo & brn | .40 | .25 |
| 482 | A192 | 35c olive & blk | .65 | .40 |
| | | Nos. 480-482 (3) | 1.30 | .90 |

Rev. Dr. Martin Luther King, Jr. (1929-1968), American civil rights leader. Value, set $8.

See No. C180. Exist imperf.

Javelin and Diana Statue, Mexico City — A193

Designs: 25c, Discus, pyramid and serpent god Quetzalcoatl. 35c, Woman diver and Xochicalco from ruins near Cuernavaca.

**1968, Aug. 22    Litho.    *Perf. 12½***
| | | | | |
|---|---|---|---|---|
| 483 | A193 | 15c dp vio & org brn | .30 | .25 |
| 484 | A193 | 25c red & brt blue | .50 | .25 |
| 485 | A193 | 35c brown & emer | .85 | .45 |
| | | Nos. 483-485 (3) | 1.65 | .95 |

19th Olympic Games, Mexico City, Oct. 12-27. Exist imperf. Value, set $7.
See No. C181.

Pres. Wm. V. S. Tubman — A194

Unification Monument, Voinjama-Lofa County — A195

**1968, Dec. 30    Unwmk.    *Perf. 12½***
| | | | | |
|---|---|---|---|---|
| 486 | A194 | 25c silver, blk & brn | 1.25 | .55 |

## Souvenir Sheet
### *Imperf*
| | | | | |
|---|---|---|---|---|
| 487 | A195 | 80c silver, ultra & red | 2.00 | 2.00 |

25th anniv. of Pres. Tubman's administration.

"ILO" with Cogwheel and Wreath — A196

**1969, Apr. 16    Litho.    *Perf. 12½***
| | | | | |
|---|---|---|---|---|
| 488 | A196 | 25c lt blue & gold | .55 | .40 |

50th anniv. of the ILO. Exists imperf. See No. C183.

Red Roofs, by Camille Pissarro A197

Paintings: 3c, Prince Balthasar Carlos on Horseback, by Velazquez, vert. 10c, David and Goliath, by Caravaggio. 12c, Still Life, by Jean Baptiste Chardin. 15c, The Last Supper, by Leonardo da Vinci. 20c, Regatta at Argenteuil, by Claude Monet. 25c, Judgment of Solomon, by Giorgione, vert. 35c, Sistine Madonna, by Raphael.

**1969, June 26    Litho.    *Perf. 11***
| | | | | |
|---|---|---|---|---|
| 489 | A197 | 3c gray & multi | .25 | .25 |
| 490 | A197 | 5c gray & multi | .25 | .25 |
| 491 | A197 | 10c lt blue & multi | .25 | .25 |
| 492 | A197 | 12c gray & multi | .40 | .25 |
| 493 | A197 | 15c gray & multi | .40 | .25 |
| 494 | A197 | 20c gray & multi | .55 | .25 |
| 495 | A197 | 25c gray & multi | .75 | .25 |
| 496 | A197 | 35c gray & multi | 1.10 | .35 |
| | | Nos. 489-496 (8) | 3.95 | 2.10 |

See Nos. 502-509.

African Development Bank Emblem — A198

**1969, Aug. 12    Litho.    *Perf. 12½***
| | | | | |
|---|---|---|---|---|
| 497 | A198 | 25c blue & brown | .55 | .35 |
| 498 | A198 | 80c yel grn & red | 1.40 | .65 |

5th anniversary of the African Development Bank. Exist imperf.

Moon Landing and Liberia No. C174 — A199

15c, Memorial tablet left on moon, rocket, earth & moon, horiz. 35c, Take-off from moon.

**1969, Oct. 15    Litho.    *Perf. 12½***
| | | | | |
|---|---|---|---|---|
| 499 | A199 | 15c blue & blue | .55 | .25 |
| 500 | A199 | 25c dk vio bl & org | .80 | .25 |
| 501 | A199 | 35c gray & red | 1.25 | .25 |
| | | Nos. 499-501 (3) | 2.60 | .75 |

Man's 1st landing on the moon, July 20, 1969. US astronauts Neil A. Armstrong and Col. Edwin E. Aldrin, Jr., with Lieut. Col. Michael Collins piloting Apollo 11. Exist imperf. Value, set $10.
See No. C184.

### Painting Type of 1969

Paintings: 3c, The Gleaners, by Francois Millet. 5c, View of Toledo, by El Greco, vert. 10c, Heads of Negroes, by Rubens. 12c, The Last Supper, by El Greco. 15c, Dancing Peasants, by Brueghel. 20c, Hunters in the Snow, by Brueghel. 25c, Detail from Descent from the Cross, by Rogier van der Weyden, vert. 35c, The Ascension, by Murillo (inscribed "The Conception"), vert.

**1969, Nov. 18    Litho.    *Perf. 11***
| | | | | |
|---|---|---|---|---|
| 502 | A197 | 3c lt blue & multi | .25 | .25 |
| 503 | A197 | 5c lt blue & multi | .25 | .25 |
| 504 | A197 | 10c lt blue & multi | .25 | .25 |
| 505 | A197 | 12c gray & multi | .40 | .25 |
| 506 | A197 | 15c gray & multi | .45 | .25 |
| 507 | A197 | 20c gray & multi | .55 | .25 |
| 508 | A197 | 25c gray & multi | .80 | .30 |
| 509 | A197 | 35c lt blue & multi | 1.00 | .30 |
| | | Nos. 502-509 (8) | 3.95 | 2.10 |

Peace Dove, UN Emblem and Atom — A200

**1970, Apr. 16    Litho.    *Perf. 12½***
| | | | | |
|---|---|---|---|---|
| 510 | A200 | 5c green & silver | .25 | .25 |

25th anniv. of the UN. Exists imperf. See No. C185.

Official Emblem A201

Designs: 10c, Statue of rain god Tlaloc, vert. 25c, Jules Rimet cup and sculptured wall, vert. 35c, Sombrero and soccer ball. 55c, Two soccer players.

**1970, June 10    Litho.    *Perf. 12½***
| | | | | |
|---|---|---|---|---|
| 511 | A201 | 5c pale blue & brn | .25 | .25 |
| 512 | A201 | 10c emerald & ocher | .30 | .25 |
| 513 | A201 | 25c dp rose lil & gold | .55 | .25 |
| 514 | A201 | 35c ver & ultra | .80 | .35 |
| | | Nos. 511-514 (4) | 1.90 | 1.10 |

### Souvenir Sheet
### *Perf. 11½*
| | | | | |
|---|---|---|---|---|
| 515 | A201 | 55c brt bl, yel & grn | 1.60 | 1.25 |

9th World Soccer Championships for the Jules Rimet Cup, Mexico City, May 30-June 21, 1970. Exist imperf.

EXPO '70 Emblem, Japanese Singer and Festival Plaza — A202

Designs (EXPO '70 Emblem and): 3c, Male Japanese singer, EXPO Hall and floating stage. 5c, Tower of the Sun and view of exhibition. 7c, Tanabata Festival. 8c, Awa Dance Festival. 25c, Sado-Okesa Dance Festival. 50c, Ricoh Pavilion with "eye," and Mt. Fuji, vert.

**1970, July    Litho.    *Perf. 11***
| | | | | |
|---|---|---|---|---|
| 516 | A202 | 2c multicolored | .25 | .25 |
| 517 | A202 | 3c multicolored | .25 | .25 |
| 518 | A202 | 5c multicolored | .30 | .25 |
| 519 | A202 | 7c multicolored | .45 | .25 |
| 520 | A202 | 8c multicolored | .55 | .25 |
| 521 | A202 | 25c multicolored | 1.40 | .30 |
| | | Nos. 516-521 (6) | 3.20 | 1.55 |

### Souvenir Sheet
| | | | | |
|---|---|---|---|---|
| 522 | A202 | 50c multicolored | 2.50 | .75 |

Issued to publicize EXPO '70 International Exhibition, Osaka, Japan, Mar. 15-Sept. 13.

UPU Headquarters and Monument, Bern — A203

Design: 80c, Like 25c, vert.

**1970, Aug. 25     *Perf. 12½***
| | | | | |
|---|---|---|---|---|
| 523 | A203 | 25c blue & multi | 1.00 | .35 |
| 524 | A203 | 80c multicolored | 1.60 | .90 |

Inauguration of the new UPU Headquarters in Bern. Exist imperf.

Napoleon as Consul, by Joseph Marie Vien, Sr. — A204

Paintings of Napoleon: 5c, Visit to a School, by unknown painter. 10c, Napoleon Bonaparte, by François Pascal Gerard. 12c, The French Campaign, by Ernest Meissonier. 20c, Napoleon Signing Abdication at Fontainebleau, by François Bouchot. 25c, Napoleon Meets Pope Pius VII, by Jean-Louis Demarne. 50c, Napoleon's Coronation, by Jacques Louis David.

**1970, Oct. 20     Litho.     Perf. 11**

| | | | | |
|---|---|---|---|---|
| 525 | A204 | 3c blue & multi | .25 | .25 |
| 526 | A204 | 5c blue & multi | .25 | .25 |
| 527 | A204 | 10c blue & multi | .45 | .25 |
| 528 | A204 | 12c blue & multi | .65 | .25 |
| 529 | A204 | 20c blue & multi | .95 | .25 |
| 530 | A204 | 25c blue & multi | 1.75 | .25 |
| | | Nos. 525-530 (6) | 4.30 | 1.50 |

**Souvenir Sheet**
*Imperf*

| | | | | |
|---|---|---|---|---|
| 531 | A204 | 50c blue & multi | 2.50 | .50 |

200th anniv. of the birth of Napoleon Bonaparte (1769-1821). No. 531 contains one stamp with simulated perforations.

Pres. Tubman — A205

**1970, Nov. 20     Litho.     Perf. 13½**

| | | | | |
|---|---|---|---|---|
| 532 | A205 | 25c multicolored | 1.00 | .35 |

**Souvenir Sheet**
*Imperf*

| | | | | |
|---|---|---|---|---|
| 533 | A205 | 50c multicolored | 1.60 | 1.10 |

Pres. Tubman's 75th birthday. No. 533 contains one imperf. stamp with simulated perforations.

Adoration of the Kings, by Rogier van der Weyden A206

Paintings (Adoration of the Kings, by): 5c, Hans Memling. 10c, Stefan Lochner. 12c, Albrecht Altdorfer, vert. 20c, Hugo van der Goes, Adoration of the Shepherds. 25c, Hieronymus Bosch, vert. 50c, Andrea Mantegna (triptych).

**Perf. 13½x14, 14x13½**

**1970, Dec. 21                          Litho.**

| | | | | |
|---|---|---|---|---|
| 534 | A206 | 3c multicolored | .25 | .25 |
| 535 | A206 | 5c multicolored | .25 | .25 |
| 536 | A206 | 10c multicolored | .30 | .25 |
| 537 | A206 | 12c multicolored | .40 | .25 |
| 538 | A206 | 20c multicolored | .40 | .25 |
| 539 | A206 | 25c multicolored | .70 | .25 |
| | | Nos. 534-539 (6) | 2.30 | 1.50 |

**Souvenir Sheet**
*Imperf*

| | | | | |
|---|---|---|---|---|
| 540 | A206 | 50c multicolored | 2.50 | .60 |

Christmas 1970.
No. 540 contains one 60x40mm stamp.

Dogon Tribal Mask — A207

African Tribal Ceremonial Masks: 2c, Bapendé. 5c, Baoulé. 6c, Dédougou. 9c, Dan. 15c, Bamiléké. 20c, Bapendé mask and costume. 25c, Bamiléké mask and costume.

**1971, Feb. 24     Litho.     Perf. 11**

| | | | | |
|---|---|---|---|---|
| 541 | A207 | 2c lt green & multi | .25 | .25 |
| 542 | A207 | 3c pink & multi | .25 | .25 |
| 543 | A207 | 5c lt blue & multi | .25 | .25 |
| 544 | A207 | 6c lt green & multi | .25 | .25 |
| 545 | A207 | 9c lt blue & multi | .25 | .25 |
| 546 | A207 | 15c pink & multi | .45 | .25 |
| 547 | A207 | 20c lt green & multi | .55 | .35 |
| 548 | A207 | 25c pink & multi | .75 | .35 |
| | | Nos. 541-548 (8) | 3.00 | 2.20 |

Astronauts on Moon A208

Designs: 5c, Astronaut and lunar transport vehicle. 10c, Astronaut with US flag on moon. 12c, Space capsule in Pacific Ocean. 20c, Astronaut leaving capsule. 25c, Astronauts Alan B. Shepard, Stuart A. Roosa and Edgar D. Mitchell.

**1971, May 20     Litho.     Perf. 13½**

| | | | | |
|---|---|---|---|---|
| 549 | A208 | 3c dk blue & multi | .25 | .25 |
| 550 | A208 | 5c dk blue & multi | .25 | .25 |
| 551 | A208 | 10c dk blue & multi | .35 | .25 |
| 552 | A208 | 12c dk blue & multi | .50 | .25 |
| 553 | A208 | 20c dk blue & multi | .75 | .25 |
| 554 | A208 | 25c dk blue & multi | .90 | .35 |
| | | Nos. 549-554 (6) | 3.00 | 1.60 |

Apollo 14 moon landing, Jan. 31-Feb. 9. Exist imperf.
See No. C186.

Map, Liberian Women and Pres. Tubman — A209

3c, Pres. Tubman & women at ballot box, vert.

**1971, May 27                          Perf. 12½**

| | | | | |
|---|---|---|---|---|
| 555 | A209 | 3c ultra & brn | .25 | .25 |
| 556 | A209 | 80c green & brn | 1.75 | 1.75 |

25th anniversary of women's suffrage.

Hall of Honor, Munich, and Olympic Flag A210

Munich Views and Olympic Flag: 5c, General view. 10c, National Museum. 12c, Max Joseph's Square. 20c, Propylaeum on King's Square. 25c, Liesel-Karlstadt Fountain.

**1971, June 28     Litho.     Perf. 11**

| | | | | |
|---|---|---|---|---|
| 557 | A210 | 3c multicolored | .25 | .25 |
| 558 | A210 | 5c multicolored | .25 | .25 |
| 559 | A210 | 10c multicolored | .25 | .25 |
| 560 | A210 | 12c multicolored | .30 | .25 |
| 561 | A210 | 20c multicolored | .55 | .25 |
| 562 | A210 | 25c multicolored | .80 | .35 |
| | | Nos. 557-562 (6) | 2.40 | 1.60 |

Publicity for the 20th Summer Olympic Games, Munich, Germany, 1972. Exist imperf. Value, set $7.50.
See No. C187.

Boy Scout, Emblem and US Flag — A211

Boy Scout, Natl. Flag & Boy Scout Emblem of: 5c, German Federal Republic. 10c, Australia. 12c, Great Britain. 20c, Japan. 25c, Liberia.

**1971, Aug. 6     Litho.     Perf. 13½**

| | | | | |
|---|---|---|---|---|
| 563 | A211 | 3c multicolored | .25 | .25 |
| 564 | A211 | 5c multicolored | .25 | .25 |
| 565 | A211 | 10c multicolored | .25 | .25 |
| 566 | A211 | 12c multicolored | .30 | .25 |
| 567 | A211 | 20c multicolored | .50 | .25 |
| 568 | A211 | 25c multicolored | .75 | .25 |
| | | Nos. 563-568 (6) | 2.30 | 1.50 |

13th Boy Scout World Jamboree, Asagiri Plain, Japan, Aug. 2-10. Exist imperf.
See No. C188.

Pres. Tubman (1895-1971) — A212

**1971, Aug. 23                          Perf. 12½**

| | | | | |
|---|---|---|---|---|
| 569 | A212 | 3c black, ultra & brn | .25 | .25 |
| 570 | A212 | 25c blk, brt rose lil & brn | .80 | .80 |

Zebra and UNICEF Emblem A213

Animals (UNICEF Emblem and Animals with their Young): 7c, Koala. 8c, Llama. 10c, Red fox. 20c, Monkey. 25c, Brown bear.

**1971, Oct. 1                          Perf. 11**

| | | | | |
|---|---|---|---|---|
| 571 | A213 | 5c multicolored | .25 | .25 |
| 572 | A213 | 7c multicolored | .40 | .25 |
| 573 | A213 | 8c multicolored | .40 | .25 |
| 574 | A213 | 10c multicolored | .55 | .25 |
| 575 | A213 | 20c multicolored | 1.00 | .35 |
| 576 | A213 | 25c multicolored | 1.25 | .45 |
| | | Nos. 571-576 (6) | 3.85 | 1.80 |

25th anniv. of UNICEF. See No. C189.

Sapporo 72 Emblem, Long-distance Skiing, Sika Deer — A214

3c, Sledding & black woodpecker. 5c, Ski Jump & brown bear. 10c, Bobsledding & murres. 15c, Figure skating & pikas. 25c, Downhill skiing & Japanese cranes.

**1971, Nov. 4                          Perf. 13x13½**

| | | | | |
|---|---|---|---|---|
| 577 | A214 | 2c multicolored | .25 | .25 |
| 578 | A214 | 3c multicolored | .25 | .25 |
| 579 | A214 | 5c multicolored | .25 | .25 |
| 580 | A214 | 10c multicolored | .30 | .25 |
| 581 | A214 | 15c multicolored | .50 | .25 |
| 582 | A214 | 25c multicolored | 2.10 | .25 |
| | | Nos. 577-582 (6) | 3.65 | 1.50 |

11th Winter Olympic Games, Sapporo, Japan, Feb. 3-13, 1972. Exist imperf. Value, set $10.
See No. C190.

Dove Carrying Letter, APU Emblem — A215

**1971, Dec. 9                          Perf. 12½**

| | | | | |
|---|---|---|---|---|
| 583 | A215 | 25c ultra & dp org | .60 | .55 |
| 584 | A215 | 80c gray & dp brn | 1.60 | 1.25 |

10th anniversary of African Postal Union.

Pioneer Fathers' Monument, Monrovia — A216

Designs: 3c, 25c, Sailing ship "Elizabeth," Providence Island, horiz. 35c, as 20c.

**1972, Jan. 1**

| | | | | |
|---|---|---|---|---|
| 585 | A216 | 3c lt. blue & yel grn | .25 | .25 |
| 586 | A216 | 20c orange & blue | .80 | .60 |
| 587 | A216 | 25c orange & purple | .80 | .65 |
| 588 | A216 | 35c lil rose & brt grn | 1.40 | 1.00 |
| | | Nos. 585-588 (4) | 3.25 | 2.50 |

Founding of Liberia, sesqui. See No. C191.

Pres. Tolbert and Map of Liberia — A217          Pres. William R. Tolbert, Jr. — A217a

**1972, Jan. 1**

| | | | | |
|---|---|---|---|---|
| 589 | A217 | 25c brt grn & brown | .65 | .40 |
| 590 | A217a | 80c blue & brown | 1.75 | .70 |

Inauguration of William R. Tolbert, Jr. as 19th president of Liberia.

Soccer and Swedish Flag A218

Olympic Rings, "Motion" Symbol and: 5c, Swimmers at start, Italian flag. 10c, Equestrian, British flag. 12c, Bicycling, French flag. 20c, Long jump, US flag. 25c, Running and Liberian flag.

**1972, May 19     Litho.     Perf. 11**

| | | | | |
|---|---|---|---|---|
| 591 | A218 | 3c lemon & multi | .25 | .25 |
| 592 | A218 | 5c lt lilac & multi | .25 | .25 |
| 593 | A218 | 10c multicolored | .55 | .25 |
| 594 | A218 | 12c gray & multi | .75 | .25 |
| 595 | A218 | 20c lt blue & multi | 1.00 | .30 |
| 596 | A218 | 25c pink & multi | 1.20 | .35 |
| | | Nos. 591-596 (6) | 4.00 | 1.65 |

20th Olympic Games, Munich, Aug. 26-Sept. 10. Exist imperf. Value, set $10.
See No. C192.

Y's Men's Club Emblem, Map — A219

Design: 90c, Y's Men's Club emblem and globe; inscribed "fifty and forward."

**1972, June 12                          Perf. 13½**

| | | | | |
|---|---|---|---|---|
| 597 | A219 | 15c purple & gold | .40 | .25 |
| 598 | A219 | 90c vio bl & emer | 2.10 | 1.50 |

Intl. Y's Men's Club, 50th anniv.

Astronaut and Lunar Rover A220

5c, Moon scene reflected in astronaut's helmet. 10c, Astronauts with cameras. 12c, Astronauts placing scientific equipment on moon. 20c, Apollo 16 badge. 25c, Astronauts riding lunar rover.

**1972, June 26**
| | | | | |
|---|---|---|---|---|
| 599 | A220 | 3c lt blue & multi | .25 | .25 |
| 600 | A220 | 5c red org & multi | .25 | .25 |
| 601 | A220 | 10c pink & multi | .35 | .25 |
| 602 | A220 | 12c yellow & multi | .65 | .25 |
| 603 | A220 | 20c lt vio & multi | .80 | .25 |
| 604 | A220 | 25c emerald & multi | 1.40 | .25 |
| | | *Nos. 599-604 (6)* | 3.70 | 1.50 |

Apollo 16 US moon mission, Apr. 15-27, 1972. Exist imperf. Value, set $10. See No. C193.

Emperor Haile Selassie — A221

**1972, July 21**          **Perf. 14x14½**
| | | | | |
|---|---|---|---|---|
| 605 | A221 | 20c olive grn & yel | .55 | .55 |
| 606 | A221 | 25c maroon & yel | .75 | .75 |
| 607 | A221 | 35c brown & yel | .80 | .80 |
| | | *Nos. 605-607 (3)* | 2.10 | 2.10 |

80th birthday of Emperor Haile Selassie of Ethiopia.

Ajax, 1809, and Figurehead — A222

Famous sailing ships and their figureheads: 5c, Hogue, 1811. 7c, Ariadne, 1816. 15c, Royal Adelaide, 1828. 20c, Rinaldo, 1860. 25c, Nymphe, 1888.

**1972, Sept. 6**          **Perf. 11**
| | | | | |
|---|---|---|---|---|
| 608 | A222 | 3c shown | .25 | .25 |
| 609 | A222 | 5c multicolored | .35 | .25 |
| 610 | A222 | 7c multicolored | .55 | .25 |
| 611 | A222 | 15c multicolored | .75 | .25 |
| 612 | A222 | 20c multicolored | .95 | .25 |
| 613 | A222 | 25c multicolored | 1.25 | .45 |
| | | *Nos. 608-613 (6)* | 4.10 | 1.70 |

See No. C194.

Pres. Tolbert Taking Oath, Richard A. Henries A223

**1972, Oct. 23          Litho.          Perf. 13½**
| | | | | |
|---|---|---|---|---|
| 614 | A223 | 15c green & multi | .65 | .65 |
| 615 | A223 | 25c vio blue & multi | .95 | .95 |

Pres. William R. Tolbert, Jr. sworn in as 19th President of Liberia, July 23, 1971. See No. C195.

Klaus Dibiasi, Italy, Diving A224

8c, Valery Borzov, USSR, running. 10c, Hideaki Yanagida, Japan, wrestling. 12c, Mark Spitz, US, swimming. 15c, Kipchoge Keino, Kenya, 3000-meter steeplechase. 25c, Richard Meade, Great Britain, equestrian. 55c, Hans Winkler, Germany, grand prix jumping.

**1973, Jan. 5          Litho.          Perf. 11**
| | | | | |
|---|---|---|---|---|
| 616 | A224 | 5c lt blue & multi | .25 | .25 |
| 617 | A224 | 8c violet & multi | .30 | .25 |
| 618 | A224 | 10c multicolored | .40 | .25 |
| 619 | A224 | 12c green & multi | .50 | .25 |
| 620 | A224 | 15c orange & multi | .60 | .25 |
| 621 | A224 | 25c pale salmon & multi | 1.00 | .30 |
| | | *Nos. 616-621 (6)* | 3.05 | 1.55 |

**Souvenir Sheet**
| | | | | |
|---|---|---|---|---|
| 622 | A224 | 55c multicolored | 3.25 | 1.50 |

Gold medal winners in 20th Olympic Games. Exist imperf. Values: set $10; souvenir sheet $8.

Astronaut on Moon and Apollo 17 Badge — A225

Designs (Apollo 17 Badge and): 3c, Astronauts on earth in lunar rover. 10c, Astronauts collecting yellow lunar dust. 15c, Astronauts in lunar rover exploring moon crater. 20c, Capt. Eugene A. Cernan, Dr. Harrison H. Schmitt and Comdr. Ronald E. Evans on launching pad. 25c, Astronauts on moon with scientific equipment.

**1973, Mar. 28          Litho.          Perf. 11**
| | | | | |
|---|---|---|---|---|
| 623 | A225 | 2c blue & multi | .30 | .25 |
| 624 | A225 | 3c blue & multi | .30 | .25 |
| 625 | A225 | 10c blue & multi | .30 | .25 |
| 626 | A225 | 15c blue & multi | .50 | .25 |
| 627 | A225 | 20c blue & multi | .90 | .30 |
| 628 | A225 | 25c blue & multi | .90 | .40 |
| | | *Nos. 623-628 (6)* | 3.20 | 1.70 |

Apollo 17 US moon mission, Dec. 7-19, 1972. Exist imperf. Value, set $10. See No. C196.

Locomotive, England — A226

Designs: Locomotives, 1895-1905.

**1973, May 4**
| | | | | |
|---|---|---|---|---|
| 629 | A226 | 2c shown | .25 | .25 |
| 630 | A226 | 3c Netherlands | .35 | .25 |
| 631 | A226 | 10c France | .65 | .25 |
| 632 | A226 | 15c United States | .85 | .25 |
| 633 | A226 | 20c Japan | 1.75 | .25 |
| 634 | A226 | 25c Germany | 2.50 | .35 |
| | | *Nos. 629-634 (6)* | 6.35 | 1.60 |

See No. C197.

OAU Emblem and Flags A227

**1973, May 24          Litho.          Perf. 13½**
| | | | | |
|---|---|---|---|---|
| 635 | A227 | 3c multicolored | .25 | .25 |
| 636 | A227 | 5c multicolored | .25 | .25 |
| 637 | A227 | 10c multicolored | .25 | .25 |
| 638 | A227 | 15c multicolored | .30 | .25 |
| 639 | A227 | 25c multicolored | .55 | .45 |
| 640 | A227 | 50c multicolored | 1.25 | .95 |
| | | *Nos. 635-640 (6)* | 2.85 | 2.40 |

10th anniv. of the Organization for African Unity.

WHO Emblem, Edward Jenner and Roses A228

Designs (WHO Emblem and): 4c, Sigmund Freud and pansies. 10c, Jonas E. Salk and chrysanthemums. 15c, Louis Pasteur and scabiosa caucasica. 20c, Emil von Behring and rhododendron. 25c, Alexander Fleming and tree mallows.

**1973, June 26          Litho.          Perf. 11**
| | | | | |
|---|---|---|---|---|
| 641 | A228 | 1c gray & multi | .25 | .25 |
| 642 | A228 | 4c orange & multi | .25 | .25 |
| 643 | A228 | 10c lt blue & multi | .25 | .25 |
| 644 | A228 | 15c rose & multi | .35 | .25 |
| 645 | A228 | 20c blue & multi | .50 | .25 |
| 646 | A228 | 25c yel grn & multi | .75 | .40 |
| | | *Nos. 641-646 (6)* | 2.35 | 1.65 |

25th anniv. of WHO. See No. C198.

Stanley Steamer, 1910 — A229

Classic automobiles: 3c, Cadillac, 1903. 10c, Clement-Bayard, 1904. 15c, Rolls Royce, 1907. 20c, Maxwell, 1905. 25c, Chadwick, 1907.

**1973, Sept. 11          Litho.          Perf. 11**
| | | | | |
|---|---|---|---|---|
| 647 | A229 | 2c shown | .25 | .25 |
| 648 | A229 | 3c multicolored | .25 | .25 |
| 649 | A229 | 10c multicolored | .30 | .25 |
| 650 | A229 | 15c multicolored | .40 | .25 |
| 651 | A229 | 20c multicolored | .55 | .25 |
| 652 | A229 | 25c multicolored | .65 | .35 |
| | | *Nos. 647-652 (6)* | 2.40 | 1.60 |

See No. C199.

Copernicus, Armillary Sphere, Satellite Communication — A230

Portraits of Copernicus and: 4c, Eudoxus solar system. 10c, Aristotle, Ptolemy, Copernicus and satellites. 15c, Saturn and Apollo spacecraft. 20c, Orbiting astronomical observatory. 25c, Satellite tracking station.

**1973, Dec. 14          Litho.          Perf. 13½**
| | | | | |
|---|---|---|---|---|
| 653 | A230 | 1c yellow & multi | .25 | .25 |
| 654 | A230 | 4c lt violet & multi | .25 | .25 |
| 655 | A230 | 10c lt blue & multi | .25 | .25 |
| 656 | A230 | 15c yel grn & multi | .40 | .25 |
| 657 | A230 | 20c buff & multi | .55 | .25 |
| 658 | A230 | 25c pink & multi | .60 | .30 |
| | | *Nos. 653-658 (6)* | 2.30 | 1.55 |

Nicolaus Copernicus (1473-1543), Polish astronomer. Exist imperf. See No. C200.

Radio Tower, Map of Africa — A231

15c, 25c, Map of Liberia, Radio tower and man listening to broadcast. 17c, like 13c.

**1974, Jan. 16          Litho.          Perf. 13½**
| | | | | |
|---|---|---|---|---|
| 659 | A231 | 13c mag & multi | .45 | .45 |
| 660 | A231 | 15c yellow & multi | .45 | .45 |
| 661 | A231 | 17c lt gray & multi | .60 | .50 |
| 662 | A231 | 25c brt green & multi | .75 | .50 |
| | | *Nos. 659-662 (4)* | 2.25 | 1.90 |

20th anniv. of Radio ELWA, Monrovia.

Thomas Coutts, 1817; Aureal, 1974; UPU Emblem A232

Designs (UPU Emblem and): 3c, Jet, satellite, Post Office, Monrovia, ship. 10c, US and USSR telecommunication satellites. 15c, Mail runner and jet. 20c, Futuristic mail train and mail truck. 25c, American Pony Express rider.

**1974, Mar. 4          Litho.          Perf. 13½**
| | | | | |
|---|---|---|---|---|
| 663 | A232 | 2c ocher & multi | .25 | .25 |
| 664 | A232 | 3c lt green & multi | .25 | .25 |
| 665 | A232 | 10c lt blue & multi | .25 | .25 |
| 666 | A232 | 15c pink & multi | .35 | .25 |
| 667 | A232 | 20c gray & multi | .80 | .25 |
| 668 | A232 | 25c lt lilac & multi | .75 | .40 |
| | | *Nos. 663-668 (6)* | 2.65 | 1.65 |

Cent. of UPU. Exist imperf. Value, set $15. See No. C201.

Fox Terrier A233

**1974, Apr. 16          Litho.          Perf. 13½**
| | | | | |
|---|---|---|---|---|
| 669 | A233 | 5c shown | .25 | .25 |
| 670 | A233 | 10c Boxer | .25 | .25 |
| 671 | A233 | 16c Chihuahua | .45 | .25 |
| 672 | A233 | 19c Beagle | .55 | .25 |
| 673 | A233 | 25c Golden retriever | .60 | .25 |
| 674 | A233 | 50c Collie | 1.40 | .25 |
| | | *Nos. 669-674 (6)* | 3.50 | 1.50 |

Exist imperf. See No. C202.

1974 World Cup Soccer Championships, Munich. — A234

Flags and scenes from games played by: 1c, West Germany and Chile. 2c, Australia and East Germany. 5c, Brazil and Yugoslavia. 10c, Zaire and Scotland. 12c, Netherlands and Uruguay. 15c, Sweden and Bulgaria. 20c, Italy and Haiti. 25c, Poland and Argentina.

**1974, June 4          Litho.          Perf. 11**
| | | | | |
|---|---|---|---|---|
| 675 | A234 | 1c shown | .25 | .25 |
| 676 | A234 | 2c multicolored | .25 | .25 |
| 677 | A234 | 5c multicolored | .25 | .25 |
| 678 | A234 | 10c multicolored | .25 | .25 |
| 679 | A234 | 12c multicolored | .30 | .25 |
| 680 | A234 | 15c multicolored | .45 | .25 |
| 681 | A234 | 20c multicolored | .60 | .25 |
| 682 | A234 | 25c multicolored | .50 | .45 |
| | | *Nos. 675-682 (8)* | 2.85 | 2.20 |

Exist imperf. Value, set $20. See No. C203.

Chrysiridia Madagascariensis — A235

Tropical Butterflies: 2c, Catagramma sorana. 5c, Erasmia pulchella. 17c, Morpho cypris. 25c, Agrias amydon. 40c, Vanessa cardui.

**1974, Sept. 11          Litho.          Perf. 13½**
| | | | | |
|---|---|---|---|---|
| 683 | A235 | 1c gray & multi | .25 | .25 |
| 684 | A235 | 2c gray & multi | .25 | .25 |
| 685 | A235 | 5c gray & multi | .25 | .25 |
| 686 | A235 | 17c gray & multi | .75 | .25 |
| 687 | A235 | 25c gray & multi | 1.00 | .30 |
| 688 | A235 | 40c gray & multi | 1.90 | .45 |
| | | *Nos. 683-688 (6)* | 4.40 | 1.75 |

See No. C204.

Pres. Tolbert and Medal A236

$1, Pres. Tolbert, medal & Liberian flag.

**1974, Dec. 10          Litho.          Perf. 13½**
| | | | | |
|---|---|---|---|---|
| 689 | A236 | 3c multi | .25 | .25 |
| 690 | A236 | $1 multi, vert. | 1.75 | 1.50 |

Pres. William R. Tolbert, Jr., recipient of 1974 Family of Man Award.

Winston Churchill, 1940 — A237

Churchill and: 10c, RAF planes in dog fight. 15c, In naval launch on way to Normandy. 17c, In staff car reviewing troops in desert. 20c, Aboard landing craft crossing Rhine. 25c, In conference with Pres. Roosevelt.

| | | | |
|---|---|---|---|
| **1975, Jan. 17** | **Litho.** | | **Perf. 13½** |
| 691 | A237 | 3c multicolored | .25 .25 |
| 692 | A237 | 10c multicolored | .25 .25 |
| 693 | A237 | 15c multicolored | .25 .25 |
| 694 | A237 | 17c multicolored | .40 .25 |
| 695 | A237 | 20c multicolored | .50 .25 |
| 696 | A237 | 25c multicolored | .75 .30 |
| | *Nos. 691-696 (6)* | | 2.40 1.55 |

Sir Winston Churchill (1874-1965), birth centenary. Exist imperf. Value, set $10.
See No. C205.

Women's Year Emblem and Marie Curie — A238

3c, Mahalia Jackson with microphone. 5c, Joan of Arc. 10c, Eleanor Roosevelt and children. 20c, Matilda Newport firing cannon. 50c, Valentina Tereshkova in space suit.

| | | | |
|---|---|---|---|
| **1975, Mar. 14** | **Litho.** | | **Perf. 14½** |
| 697 | A238 | 2c citron & multi | .25 .25 |
| 698 | A238 | 3c dull orange & multi | .25 .25 |
| 699 | A238 | 5c lilac rose & multi | .25 .25 |
| 700 | A238 | 10c yellow & multi | .25 .25 |
| 701 | A238 | 25c yellow grn & multi | .55 .25 |
| 702 | A238 | 50c lilac & multi | .90 .65 |
| | *Nos. 697-702 (6)* | | 2.45 1.90 |

Intl. Women's Year 1975. Exist imperf. Value, set $10.
See No. C206.

Old State House, Boston, US No. 627 A239

10c, George Washington, US #645. 15c, Town Hall & Court House, Philadelphia, US #798. 20c, Benjamin Franklin, US #835. 25c, Paul Revere's Ride, US #618. 50c, Santa Maria, US #231.

| | | | |
|---|---|---|---|
| **1975, Apr. 25** | **Litho.** | | **Perf. 13½** |
| 703 | A239 | 5c multicolored | .25 .25 |
| 704 | A239 | 10c multicolored | .35 .25 |
| 705 | A239 | 15c multicolored | .55 .25 |
| 706 | A239 | 20c multicolored | .60 .25 |
| 707 | A239 | 25c multicolored | .90 .25 |
| 708 | A239 | 50c multicolored | 2.00 .50 |
| | *Nos. 703-708 (6)* | | 4.65 1.75 |

American Revolution Bicentennial. Exist imperf. Value, set $10.
See No. C207.

Dr. Schweitzer, Hospital and Baboon Mother A240

Designs (Dr. Schweitzer and): 3c, Elephant, and tribesmen poling boat. 5c, Water buffalo, egret, man and woman paddling canoe. 6c, Antelope and dancer. 25c, Lioness, woman cooking outdoors. 50c, Zebra and colt, doctor's examination at clinic.

| | | | |
|---|---|---|---|
| **1975, June 26** | **Litho.** | | **Perf. 13½** |
| 709 | A240 | 1c multicolored | .25 .25 |
| 710 | A240 | 3c multicolored | .25 .25 |
| 711 | A240 | 5c multicolored | .25 .25 |
| 712 | A240 | 6c multicolored | .25 .25 |
| 713 | A240 | 25c multicolored | .55 .25 |
| 714 | A240 | 50c multicolored | 1.25 .65 |
| | *Nos. 709-714 (6)* | | 2.80 1.90 |

Dr. Albert Schweitzer (1875-1965), medical missionary, birth centenary. Exist imperf. Value, set $10.
See No. C208.

American-Russian Handshake in Space — A241

Designs (Apollo-Soyuz Emblem and): 5c, Apollo. 10c, Soyuz. 20c, Flags and maps of US and USSR. 25c, A. A. Leonov, and V. N. Kubasov. 50c, D. K. Slayton, V. D. Brand, T. P. Stafford.

| | | | |
|---|---|---|---|
| **1975, Sept. 18** | **Litho.** | | **Perf. 13½** |
| 715 | A241 | 5c multicolored | .25 .25 |
| 716 | A241 | 10c multicolored | .25 .25 |
| 717 | A241 | 15c multicolored | .30 .25 |
| 718 | A241 | 20c multicolored | .45 .25 |
| 719 | A241 | 25c multicolored | .50 .25 |
| 720 | A241 | 50c multicolored | 1.10 .45 |
| | *Nos. 715-720 (6)* | | 2.85 1.70 |

Apollo Soyuz space test project (Russo-American cooperation), launching July 15; link-up, July 17. Exist imperf. Value, set $10.
See No. C209.

Presidents Tolbert, Siaka Stevens; Treaty Signing; Liberia and Sierra Leone Maps A242

| | | | |
|---|---|---|---|
| **1975, Oct. 3** | **Litho.** | | **Perf. 13½** |
| 721 | A242 | 2c gray & multi | .25 .25 |
| 722 | A242 | 3c gray & multi | .25 .25 |
| 723 | A242 | 5c gray & multi | .25 .25 |
| 724 | A242 | 10c gray & multi | .25 .25 |
| 725 | A242 | 25c gray & multi | .50 .30 |
| 726 | A242 | 50c gray & multi | .90 .55 |
| | *Nos. 721-726 (6)* | | 2.40 1.85 |

Mano River Union Agreement between Liberia and Sierra Leone, signed Oct. 3, 1973.

Figure Skating A243

Designs (Winter Olympic Games Emblem and): 4c, Ski jump. 10c, Slalom. 25c, Ice hockey. 35c, Speed skating. 50c, Two-man bobsled.

| | | | |
|---|---|---|---|
| **1976, Jan. 23** | **Litho.** | | **Perf. 13½** |
| 727 | A243 | 1c lt blue & multi | .25 .25 |
| 728 | A243 | 4c lt blue & multi | .25 .25 |
| 729 | A243 | 10c lt blue & multi | .35 .25 |
| 730 | A243 | 25c lt blue & multi | .75 .25 |
| 731 | A243 | 35c lt blue & multi | .90 .25 |
| 732 | A243 | 50c lt blue & multi | 1.10 .75 |
| | *Nos. 727-732 (6)* | | 3.60 2.00 |

12th Winter Olympic Games, Innsbruck, Austria, Feb. 4-15. Exist imperf. Value, set $11.
See No. C210.

Pres. Tolbert Taking Oath of Office A244

25c, Pres. Tolbert at his desk, vert. $1, Seal & flag of Liberia, $400 commemorative gold coin.

| | | | |
|---|---|---|---|
| **1976, Apr. 5** | **Litho.** | | **Perf. 13½** |
| 733 | A244 | 3c multicolored | .25 .25 |
| 734 | A244 | 25c multicolored | .50 .50 |
| 735 | A244 | $1 multicolored | 2.00 1.75 |
| | *Nos. 733-735 (3)* | | 2.75 2.50 |

Inauguration of President William R. Tolbert, Jr., Jan. 5, 1976.

Weight Lifting and Olympic Rings A245

Designs (Olympic Rings and): 3c, Pole vault. 10c, Hammer and shot put. 25c, Yachting. 35c, Women's gymnastics. 50c, Hurdles.

| | | | |
|---|---|---|---|
| **1976, May 4** | **Litho.** | | **Perf. 13½** |
| 736 | A245 | 2c gray & multi | .25 .25 |
| 737 | A245 | 3c orange & multi | .25 .25 |
| 738 | A245 | 10c lt violet & multi | .30 .25 |
| 739 | A245 | 25c lt green & multi | .60 .25 |
| 740 | A245 | 35c yellow & multi | .75 .60 |
| 741 | A245 | 50c pink & multi | 1.00 .60 |
| | *Nos. 736-741 (6)* | | 3.15 2.20 |

21st Olympic Games, Montreal, Canada, July 17-Aug. 1. Exist imperf. Value, set $11.
See No. C211.

A. G. Bell, Telephone and Receiver, 1876, UPU Emblem A246

UPU Emblem and: 4c, Horsedrawn mail coach and ITU emblem. 5c, Intelsat IV satellite, radar and ITU emblem. 25c, A. G. Bell, ship laying underwater cable, 1976 telephone. 40c, A. G. Bell, futuristic train, telegraph and telephone wires. 50c, Wright brothers' plane, Zeppelin and Concorde.

| | | | |
|---|---|---|---|
| **1976, June 4** | **Litho.** | | **Perf. 13½** |
| 742 | A246 | 1c green & multi | .25 .25 |
| 743 | A246 | 4c ocher & multi | .25 .25 |
| 744 | A246 | 5c orange & multi | .25 .25 |
| 745 | A246 | 25c green & multi | .90 .25 |
| 746 | A246 | 40c lilac & multi | 1.10 .55 |
| 747 | A246 | 50c blue & multi | 1.25 .70 |
| | *Nos. 742-747 (6)* | | 4.00 1.95 |

Cent. of 1st telephone call by Alexander Graham Bell, Mar. 10, 1876. Exist imperf. Value, set $25.
See No. C212.

Gold Nugget on Chain, Gold Panner A247

1c, Mano River Bridge. 5c, "V" ring. 10c, Rubber tire, tree. 15c, Harvesting. 20c, Hydroelectric plant. 25c, Mesurado shrimp. 27c, Woman tie-dying cloth. 55c, Lake Piso, barracuda. $1, Train hauling iron ore.

| | | | |
|---|---|---|---|
| **1976-81** | **Litho.** | | **Perf. 14½** |
| 749 | A247 | 1c multicolored | .25 .25 |
| 750 | A247 | 3c shown | .25 .25 |
| 751 | A247 | 5c multicolored | .25 .25 |
| 752 | A247 | 7c like 5c ('81) | .75 .25 |
| 753 | A247 | 10c multicolored | .30 .25 |
| 754 | A247 | 15c multicolored | .55 .45 |
| 755 | A247 | 17c like 55c ('81) | 1.75 .60 |
| 756 | A247 | 20c multicolored | .65 .45 |
| 757 | A247 | 25c multicolored | .85 .25 |
| 758 | A247 | 27c multicolored | .90 .65 |
| 759 | A247 | 55c multicolored | 2.75 .75 |
| 760 | A247 | $1 multicolored | 3.25 2.50 |
| | *Nos. 749-760 (12)* | | 12.50 6.90 |

See Nos. 945-953.

Rhinoceros A249

African Animals: 3c, Zebra antelope. 5c, Chimpanzee, vert. 15c, Pigmy hippopotamus. 25c, Leopard. $1, Gorilla, vert.

| | | | |
|---|---|---|---|
| **1976, Sept. 1** | **Litho.** | | **Perf. 13½** |
| 763 | A249 | 2c orange & multi | .25 .25 |
| 764 | A249 | 3c gray & multi | .25 .25 |
| 765 | A249 | 5c blue & multi | .25 .25 |
| 766 | A249 | 15c brt blue & multi | .45 .25 |
| 767 | A249 | 25c ultra & multi | 1.00 .45 |
| 768 | A249 | $1 multicolored | 3.50 1.10 |
| | *Nos. 763-768 (6)* | | 5.70 2.55 |

See No. C213.

Maps of US and Liberia; Statue of Liberty, Unification Monument, Voinjama and Liberty Bell — A250

$1, George Washington, Gerald R. Ford, Joseph J. Roberts (1st Pres. of Liberia), William R. Tolbert, Jr., Bicentennial emblem, US & Liberian flags.

| | | | |
|---|---|---|---|
| **1976, Sept. 21** | **Litho.** | | **Perf. 13½** |
| 769 | A250 | 25c multicolored | .50 .30 |
| 770 | A250 | $1 multicolored | 1.50 .75 |

American Bicentennial and visit of Pres. William R. Tolbert, Jr. to the US, Sept. 21-30. See No. C214.

Baluba Masks and Festival Emblem — A251

Tribal Masks: 10c, Bateke. 15c, Basshilele. 20c, Igungun. 25c, Masai. 50c, Kifwebe.

| | | | |
|---|---|---|---|
| **1977, Jan. 20** | **Litho.** | | **Perf. 13½** |
| 771 | A251 | 5c yellow & multi | .25 .25 |
| 772 | A251 | 10c green & multi | .30 .25 |
| 773 | A251 | 15c salmon & multi | .45 .25 |
| 774 | A251 | 20c lt blue & multi | .45 .25 |
| 775 | A251 | 25c violet & multi | .60 .25 |
| 776 | A251 | 50c lemon & multi | 1.20 .30 |
| | *Nos. 771-776 (6)* | | 3.25 1.55 |

FESTAC '77, 2nd World Black and African Festival, Lagos, Nigeria, Jan. 15-Feb. 12. See No. C215.

Latham's Francolin A252

Birds of Liberia: 10c, Narina trogon. 15c, Rufous-crowned roller. 20c, Brown-cheeked hornbill. 25c, Common bulbul. 50c, Fish eagle. 80c, Gold Coast touraco.

| | | | |
|---|---|---|---|
| **1977, Feb. 18** | **Litho.** | | **Perf. 14** |
| 777 | A252 | 5c multicolored | .30 .25 |
| 778 | A252 | 10c multicolored | .45 .25 |
| 779 | A252 | 15c multicolored | .65 .25 |
| 780 | A252 | 20c multicolored | .95 .25 |
| 781 | A252 | 25c multicolored | 1.20 .25 |
| 782 | A252 | 50c multicolored | 2.40 .65 |
| | *Nos. 777-782 (6)* | | 5.95 1.90 |

**Souvenir Sheet**

| | | | |
|---|---|---|---|
| 783 | A252 | 80c multicolored | 3.50 1.75 |

Edmund Coffin, Combined Training, US — A253

Designs: 15c, Alwin Schockemohle, single jump. Germany, vert. 20c, Christine Stuckelberger, Switzerland, individual dressage. 25c, Prix de Nations (team), France.

| | | | |
|---|---|---|---|
| **1977, Apr. 22** | **Litho.** | | **Perf. 13½** |
| 784 | A253 | 5c ocher & multi | .35 .25 |
| 785 | A253 | 15c ocher & multi | .70 .25 |
| 786 | A253 | 20c ocher & multi | .85 .25 |
| 787 | A253 | 25c ocher & multi | 1.10 .35 |
| | *Nos. 784-787,C216 (5)* | | 5.40 1.70 |

Equestrian gold medal winners in Montreal Olympic Games. Exist imperf. Value, set $10.

See No. C217.

Elizabeth II Wearing Crown A254

Designs: 25c, Elizabeth II Prince Philip, Pres. and Mrs. Tubman. 80c, Elizabeth II, Prince Philip, royal coat of arms.

**1977, May 23   Litho.     Perf. 13½**
788  A254  15c silver & multi     .35  .25
789  A254  25c silver & multi     .55  .25
790  A254  80c silver & multi    1.75  .55
     Nos. 788-790 (3)            2.65 1.05

25th anniversary of the reign of Queen Elizabeth II. Nos. 788-790 exist imperf. Value, set $8.
See No. C218.

Jesus Blessing Children — A255

Christmas: 25c, The Good Shepherd. $1, Jesus and the Samaritan Woman. Designs after stained-glass windows, Providence Baptist Church, Monrovia.

**1977, Nov. 3   Litho.     Perf. 13½**
791  A255  20c lt blue & multi     .30  .25
792  A255  25c lt blue & multi     .45  .35
793  A255  $1 lt blue & multi     1.40  .75
     Nos. 791-793 (3)            2.15 1.35

Dornier DOX, 1928 — A256

Progress of Aviation: 3c, Piggyback space shuttle, 1977. 5c, Eddie Rickenbacker and Douglas DC 3. 25c, Charles A. Lindbergh and Spirit of St. Louis. 35c, Louis Bleriot and Bleriot XI. 50c, Orville and Wilbur Wright and flying machine, 1903. 80c, Concorde landing at night at Dulles Airport, Washington, DC.

**1978, Jan. 6   Litho.     Perf. 13½**
794  A256  2c multicolored     .25  .25
795  A256  3c multicolored     .25  .25
796  A256  5c multicolored     .25  .25
797  A256  25c multicolored    .55  .25
798  A256  35c multicolored    .90  .55
799  A256  50c multicolored   1.25  .50
     Nos. 794-799 (6)         3.45 2.05
**Souvenir Sheet**
800  A256  80c multicolored   2.75 1.00

Exist imperf. Values, set $10, souvenir sheet $15.

Baladeuse by Santos-Dumont, 1903 — A257

Airships: 3c, Baldwin's, 1908, and US flag. 5c, Tissandier brothers', 1883. 25c, Parseval PL VII, 1912. 40c, Nulli Secundus II, 1908. 50c, R34 rigid airship, 1919.

**1978, Mar. 9   Litho.     Perf. 13½**
801  A257  2c multicolored     .25  .25
802  A257  3c multicolored     .25  .25
803  A257  5c multicolored     .25  .25
804  A257  25c multicolored    .50  .25

805  A257  40c multicolored     .70  .25
806  A257  50c multicolored    1.10  .25
     Nos. 801-806 (6)          3.05 1.50

75th anniv. of the Zeppelin. Exist imperf. Value, set $12.
See No. C219.

Soccer, East Germany and Brazil A258

Soccer Games: 2c, Poland and Argentina, vert. 10c, West Germany and Netherlands. 25c, Yugoslavia and Brazil. 35c, Poland and Italy, vert. 50c, Netherlands and Uruguay.

**1978, May 16   Litho.     Perf. 13½**
807  A258  2c multicolored     .25  .25
808  A258  5c multicolored     .25  .25
809  A258  10c multicolored    .25  .25
810  A258  25c multicolored    .70  .25
811  A258  35c multicolored    .90  .45
812  A258  50c multicolored   1.40  .60
     Nos. 807-812 (6)          3.75 2.05

11th World Cup Soccer Championships, Argentina, June 1-25. Exist imperf. Value, set $15.
See No. C220.

Coronation Chair — A259

Designs: 25c, Imperial state crown. $1, Buckingham Palace, horiz.

**1978, June 12**
813  A259  5c multicolored     .25  .25
814  A259  25c multicolored    .55  .25
815  A259  $1 multicolored    2.10  .75
     Nos. 813-815 (3)          2.90 1.25

25th anniversary of coronation of Queen Elizabeth II. Exist imperf. Value, set $9.
See No. C221.

Jinnah, Liberian and Pakistani Flags A260

**1978, June   Litho.     Perf. 13**
816  A260  30c multicolored   37.50 8.25

Mohammed Ali Jinnah (1876-1948), first Governor General of Pakistan.

Carter and Tolbert Families A261

Designs: 25c, Pres. Tolbert, Rosalynn Carter and Pres. Carter at microphone, Robertsfield Airport. $1, Jimmy Carter and William R. Tolbert, Jr. in motorcade from airport.

**1978, Oct. 26   Litho.     Perf. 13½**
817  A261  5c multicolored     .25  .25
818  A261  25c multicolored    .65  .65
819  A261  $1 multicolored    2.50 2.50
     Nos. 817-819 (3)          3.40 3.40

Pres. Carter's visit to Liberia, Apr. 1978.

Soccer Game: Italy-France A262

Soccer Games: 1c, Brazil-Spain, horiz. 10c, Poland-West Germany, horiz. 27c, Peru-Scotland. 35c, Austria-West Germany. 50c, Argentina the victor.

**1978, Dec. 8   Litho.     Perf. 13½**
820  A262  1c multicolored     .25  .25
821  A262  2c multicolored     .25  .25
822  A262  10c multicolored    .30  .25
823  A262  27c multicolored    .70  .50
824  A262  35c multicolored    .90  .60
825  A262  50c multicolored   1.25  .90
     Nos. 820-825 (6)          3.65 2.75

1978 World Cup Soccer winners. Exist imperf. Value, set $10.
See No. C222.

Liberian Lumbermen A263

Designs: 10c, Hauling timber by truck, vert. 25c, Felling trees with chain saw. 50c, Moving logs.

**1978, Dec. 15   Litho.     Perf. 13½x14**
826  A263  5c multicolored     .25  .25
827  A263  10c multicolored    .30  .25
828  A263  25c multicolored    .65  .40
829  A263  50c multicolored   1.40  .90
     Nos. 826-829 (4)          2.60 1.80

8th World Forestry Congress, Djakarta, Indonesia.

"25" and Waves — A264

Design: $1, Radio tower and waves.

**1979, Apr. 6   Litho.     Perf. 14x13½**
830  A264  35c multicolored    .65  .65
831  A264  $1 multicolored    1.75 1.75

25th anniversary of Radio ELWA.

Emblems of IYC, African Child's Decade and SOS Village A265

Designs: 25c, $1, like 5c, with UNICEF emblem replacing SOS emblem. 35c, like 5c.

**1979, Apr. 6           Perf. 13½x14**
832  A265  5c multicolored     .25  .25
833  A265  25c multicolored    .25  .25
834  A265  35c multicolored    .60  .60
835  A265  $1 multicolored    1.40 1.40
     Nos. 832-835 (4)          2.50 2.50

IYC and Decade of the African Child.

Presidents Gardner and Tolbert, and Post Office, Monrovia A266

Design: 35c, Anthony W. Gardner, William R. Tolbert, Jr. and UPU emblem.

**1979, Apr. 2   Litho.     Perf. 13½x14**
836  A266  5c multicolored     .25  .25
837  A266  35c multicolored    .95  .95

Cent. of Liberia's joining UPU.

Unity Problem, Map of Africa, Torches A267

Designs: 27c, Masks. 35c, Elephant, giraffe, lion, antelope, cheetah and map of Africa. 50c, Huts, pepper birds and map of Africa.

**1979, July 6   Litho.     Perf. 14x13½**
838  A267  5c multicolored     .30  .25
839  A267  27c multicolored    .50  .35
840  A267  35c multicolored    .75  .45
841  A267  50c multicolored   1.10 1.10
     Nos. 838-841 (4)          2.65 2.15

Organization for African Unity, 16th anniversary, and OAU Summit Conference.

Liberia No. 666, Rowland Hill — A268

10c, Pony Express rider, 1860. 15c, British mail coach, 1800. 25c, Mail steamship John Penn, 1860. 27c, Stanier Pacific train, 1939. 50c, Concorde. $1, Curtiss Jenny, 1916.

**1979, July 20**
842  A268  3c multicolored     .25  .25
843  A268  10c multicolored    .25  .25
844  A268  15c multicolored    .35  .35
845  A268  25c multicolored    .60  .50
846  A268  27c multicolored    .65  .50
847  A268  50c multicolored   1.10 1.00
     Nos. 842-847 (6)          3.20 2.85
**Souvenir Sheet**
848  A268  $1 multicolored    2.25 1.60

Sir Rowland Hill (1795-1879), originator of penny postage. Exist imperf. Value, set $20.

Red Cross, Pres. Tolbert Donating Blood A269

Design: 50c, Red Cross, Pres. Tolbert.

**1979, Aug. 15   Litho.     Perf. 13½**
849  A269  30c multicolored    .50  .50
850  A269  50c multicolored   1.25 1.25

National Red Cross, 30th anniversary and blood donation campaign.

M.S. World Peace A270

Design: $1, M.S. World Peace, diff.

**1979, Aug. 15**
851  A270  5c multicolored     .25  .25
852  A270  $1 multicolored    2.40 2.40

2nd World Maritime Day, March 16; Liberia Maritime Program, 30th anniversary.

A Good Turn, by Norman Rockwell — A271

Paintings — Scouting through the eyes of Norman Rockwell (1925-76): No. 853: a, Stories. b, 3 branches of Scouts. c, camping. d, Church. e, Animal care. f, advancements. g, Scout, Lincoln. h, First aid on puppy. i, Reading with elderly and dog. j, Scout teaching cubs.

No. 854: a, "1910." b, Feeding dog. c, Man, dog, Scout on top of rock. d, Merit badges. e, Hiking in mountains. f, With explorer and eagle. g, Wearing new uniform. h, Indian lore. i, First camping. j, Group saluting.

No. 855: a, Eagle ceremony. b, Hiking with compass. c, The Scouting Trail. d, Phyical fitness. e, Prayer. f, Tales of the sea. g, Foreign and US scouts dancing. h, Building a birdhouse. i, In front of flag. j, Rescuing girl and kitten.

No. 856: a, Painting outdoors. b, Scout saluting in front of flag. c, Scout, Lincoln, Washington, eagle. d, Starting on hike. e, Knot tying. f, Reading instructions. g, Scouts of 6 nations. h, Boy, Girl Scouts and leaders. i, "On my honor..." j, Cooking outdoors.

No. 857: a, Portaging. b, "Spirit of '76." c, Saluting flag with astronaut. d, 5 branches of scouting. e, Planting trees. f, Washington praying. g, First aid on dog. h, Saying grace in mess tent. i, First time in Scout uniform. j, Rock climbing.

**1979, Sept. 1    Litho.    Perf. 11**

| | | | | |
|---|---|---|---|---|
| 853 | A271 | 5c #a.-j, any single | .40 | .25 |
| 854 | A271 | 10c #a.-j, any single | .40 | .25 |
| 855 | A271 | 15c #a.-j, any single | .65 | .35 |
| 856 | A271 | 25c #a.-j, any single | 1.20 | .40 |
| 857 | A271 | 35c #a.-j, any single | 1.75 | .70 |
| | | Nos. 853-857, Set of 50 in 5 strips of 10 | 50.00 | 20.00 |

Exist imperf. Value, set of 5 strips $55.

Mrs. Tolbert, Children, Children's Village Emblem A272

40c, Mrs. Tolbert, children, emblem, vert.

**1979, Nov. 14    Litho.    Perf. 14**

| | | | | |
|---|---|---|---|---|
| 858 | A272 | 25c multicolored | .60 | .60 |
| 859 | A272 | 40c multicolored | 1.25 | 1.00 |

SOS Children's Village in Monrovia, Liberia.

Rotary International Headquarters, Evanston, Ill., Emblem — A273

Rotary Emblem and: 5c, Vocational services. 17c, Man in wheelchair, nurse, vert. 27c, Flags of several nations. 35c, People of various races holding hands around globe. 50c, Pres. Tolbert, map of Africa, vert. $1, "Gift of Life."

**1979, Dec. 28    Perf. 11**

| | | | | |
|---|---|---|---|---|
| 860 | A273 | 1c multicolored | .25 | .25 |
| 861 | A273 | 5c multicolored | .25 | .25 |
| 862 | A273 | 17c multicolored | .40 | .40 |
| 863 | A273 | 27c multicolored | .70 | .70 |
| 864 | A273 | 35c multicolored | .75 | .75 |
| 865 | A273 | 50c multicolored | 1.40 | 1.40 |
| | | Nos. 860-865 (6) | 3.75 | 3.75 |

**Souvenir Sheet**

| | | | | |
|---|---|---|---|---|
| 866 | A273 | $1 multicolored | 2.75 | 2.75 |

Rotary International, 75th anniversary. Exist imperf. Values: set $14; souvenir sheet $11.

Ski Jump, Lake Placid '80 Emblem A274

Lake Placid '80 Emblem and: 5c, Figure skating. 17c, Bobsledding. 27c, Cross-country skiing. 35c, Women's speed skating. 50c, Ice hockey. $1, Slalom.

**1980, Jan. 21**

| | | | | |
|---|---|---|---|---|
| 867 | A274 | 1c multicolored | .30 | .25 |
| 868 | A274 | 5c multicolored | .30 | .25 |
| 869 | A274 | 17c multicolored | .75 | .45 |

| | | | | |
|---|---|---|---|---|
| 870 | A274 | 27c multicolored | 1.50 | .90 |
| 871 | A274 | 35c multicolored | 1.50 | .90 |
| 872 | A274 | 50c multicolored | 2.10 | 1.25 |
| | | Nos. 867-872 (6) | 6.45 | 4.00 |

**Souvenir Sheet**

| | | | | |
|---|---|---|---|---|
| 873 | A274 | $1 multicolored | 2.75 | 2.00 |

13th Winter Olympic Games, Lake Placid, NY, Feb. 12-24. Exist imperf. Values: set $12.50; souvenir sheet $25.

Pres. Tolbert, Pres. Stevens, Maps of Liberia and Sierra Leone, Mano River A275

**1980, Mar. 6    Litho.    Perf. 14x13½**

| | | | | |
|---|---|---|---|---|
| 874 | A275 | 8c multicolored | .25 | .25 |
| 875 | A275 | 27c multicolored | .65 | .65 |
| 876 | A275 | 35c multicolored | .75 | .75 |
| 877 | A275 | 80c multicolored | 1.90 | 1.90 |
| | | Nos. 874-877 (4) | 3.55 | 3.55 |

Mano River Agreement, 5th anniversary; Mano River Postal Union, 1st anniversary.

Redemption Horn — A276

10c, Sgt. Doe and Soldiers, Clenched Hands Angel, horiz. 14c, Citizens, map, Flag, horiz. $2, Sgt. Samuel Doe.

**1981, Feb. 6    Litho.    Perf. 14**

| | | | | |
|---|---|---|---|---|
| 878 | A276 | 1c multicolored | .25 | .25 |
| 879 | A276 | 6c like 1c | .25 | .25 |
| 880 | A276 | 10c multicolored | .25 | .25 |
| 881 | A276 | 14c multicolored | .30 | .25 |
| 882 | A276 | 23c like 10c | .35 | .35 |
| 883 | A276 | 31c like 14c | .60 | .60 |
| 884 | A276 | 41c like $2 | .75 | .75 |
| 885 | A276 | $2 multicolored | 4.00 | 4.00 |
| | | Nos. 878-885 (8) | 6.75 | 6.70 |

Establishment of new government under the People's Redemption Council, Apr. 12, 1980.

Soccer Players, World Cup, Flags of 1930 and 1934 Finalists A277

Soccer Players, Cup, Flags of Finalists from: 5c, 1938, 1950. 20c, 1954, 1958. 27c, 1962, 1966. 40c, 1970, 1974. 55c. 1978. $1, Spanish team.

**1981, Mar. 4    Litho.    Perf. 14**

| | | | | |
|---|---|---|---|---|
| 886 | A277 | 3c multicolored | .25 | .25 |
| 887 | A277 | 5c multicolored | .25 | .25 |
| 888 | A277 | 20c multicolored | .45 | .45 |
| 889 | A277 | 27c multicolored | .65 | .65 |
| 890 | A277 | 40c multicolored | .90 | .90 |
| 891 | A277 | 55c multicolored | 1.25 | 1.25 |
| | | Nos. 886-891 (6) | 3.75 | 3.75 |

**Souvenir Sheet**

| | | | | |
|---|---|---|---|---|
| 892 | A277 | $1 multicolored | 2.50 | 1.75 |

ESPANA '82 World Cup Soccer Championship.
Exists imperf. Values: set, $12; souvenir sheet, $10.

Sgt. Samuel Doe and Citizens A278

27c, Doe, Liberian flag. 30c, Clasped arms. $1, Doe, soldiers, Justice.

**1981, Apr. 7    Litho.    Perf. 14**

| | | | | |
|---|---|---|---|---|
| 893 | A278 | 22c shown | .50 | .50 |
| 894 | A278 | 27c multicolored | .65 | .65 |
| 895 | A278 | 30c multicolored | .90 | .90 |
| 896 | A278 | $1 multicolored | 2.50 | 2.50 |
| | | Nos. 893-896 (4) | 4.55 | 4.55 |

People's Redemption Council government, first anniversary.

Royal Wedding — A279

31c, Couple. 41c, Initials, roses. 62c, St. Paul's Cathedral.
$1, Couple, horiz.

**1981, Aug. 12    Litho.    Perf. 14x13½**

| | | | | |
|---|---|---|---|---|
| 897 | A279 | 31c multicolored | .65 | .65 |
| 898 | A279 | 41c multicolored | .85 | .85 |
| 899 | A279 | 62c multicolored | 1.50 | 1.50 |
| | | Nos. 897-899 (3) | 3.00 | 3.00 |

**Souvenir Sheet**

| | | | | |
|---|---|---|---|---|
| 900 | A279 | $1 multicolored | 2.50 | 2.50 |

Nos. 897-899 exist imperf. Value, set $7.

John Adams, US President, 1797-1801 — A280

Washington Crossing the Delaware — A281

5c, Wm. H. Harrison. 10c, Martin Van Buren. 17c, James Monroe. 20c, John Q. Adams. 22c, James Madison. 27c, Thomas Jefferson. 30c, Andrew Jackson. 40c, John Tyler. 80c, George Washington.

**1981, July 4    Perf. 11**

| | | | | |
|---|---|---|---|---|
| 901 | A280 | 4c shown | .25 | .25 |
| 902 | A280 | 5c multicolored | .25 | .25 |
| 903 | A280 | 10c multicolored | .25 | .25 |
| 904 | A280 | 17c multicolored | .40 | .30 |
| 905 | A280 | 20c multicolored | .45 | .35 |
| 906 | A280 | 22c multicolored | .55 | .45 |
| 907 | A280 | 27c multicolored | .60 | .55 |
| 908 | A280 | 30c multicolored | .70 | .60 |
| 909 | A280 | 40c multicolored | .90 | .85 |
| 910 | A280 | 80c multicolored | 1.90 | 1.60 |
| | | Nos. 901-910 (10) | 6.25 | 5.45 |

**Souvenir Sheet**

| | | | | |
|---|---|---|---|---|
| 911 | A281 | $1 multicolored | 2.75 | 2.75 |

**1981, Nov. 26    Litho.    Perf. 11**

6c, Rutherford B. Hayes. 12c, Ulysses S. Grant. 14c, Millard Fillmore. 15c, Zachary Taylor. 20c, Abraham Lincoln. 27c, Andrew Johnson. 31c, James Buchanan. 41c, James A. Garfield. 50c, James K. Polk. 55c, Franklin Pierce.
$1, Washington at Valley Forge.

| | | | | |
|---|---|---|---|---|
| 912 | A280 | 6c multicolored | .25 | .25 |
| 913 | A280 | 12c multicolored | .25 | .25 |
| 914 | A280 | 14c multicolored | .25 | .25 |
| 915 | A280 | 15c multicolored | .30 | .25 |
| 916 | A280 | 20c multicolored | .45 | .30 |
| 917 | A280 | 27c multicolored | .50 | .45 |
| 918 | A280 | 31c multicolored | .60 | .45 |
| 919 | A280 | 41c multicolored | .90 | .75 |
| 920 | A280 | 50c multicolored | 1.10 | .85 |
| 921 | A280 | 55c multicolored | 1.20 | .90 |
| | | Nos. 912-921 (10) | 5.80 | 4.70 |

**Souvenir Sheet**

| | | | | |
|---|---|---|---|---|
| 922 | A281 | $1 multicolored | 4.25 | 4.25 |

**1982, Apr. 7    Litho.    Perf. 11**

4c, William H. Taft. 5c, Calvin Coolidge. 6c, Benjamin Harrison. 10c, Warren G. Harding. 22c, Grover Cleveland. 27c, Chester Arthur. 31c, Woodrow Wilson. 41c, William McKinley. 80c, Theodore Roosevelt.
$1, Signing Constitution, horiz.

| | | | | |
|---|---|---|---|---|
| 923 | A280 | 4c multicolored | .25 | .25 |
| 924 | A280 | 5c multicolored | .25 | .25 |
| 925 | A280 | 6c multicolored | .25 | .25 |
| 926 | A280 | 10c multicolored | .25 | .25 |
| 927 | A280 | 22c multicolored | .60 | .50 |
| 928 | A280 | 27c multicolored | .75 | .75 |
| 929 | A280 | 31c multicolored | .85 | .85 |
| 930 | A280 | 41c multicolored | 1.00 | 1.00 |
| 931 | A280 | 80c multicolored | 1.60 | 1.60 |
| | | Nos. 923-931 (9) | 5.80 | 5.70 |

**Souvenir Sheet**

| | | | | |
|---|---|---|---|---|
| 932 | A281 | $1 multicolored | 2.75 | 2.75 |

**1982, July 15    Litho.    Perf. 11**

4c, Jimmy Carter. 6c, Gerald Ford. 14c, Harry Truman. 17c, F. D. Roosevelt. 23c, L. B. Johnson. 27c, Richard Nixon. 31c, John F. Kennedy. 35c, Ronald Reagan. 50c, Herbert Hoover. 55c, Dwight D. Eisenhower.
$1, Battle of Yorktown.

| | | | | |
|---|---|---|---|---|
| 933 | A280 | 4c multicolored | .25 | .25 |
| 934 | A280 | 6c multicolored | .25 | .25 |
| 935 | A280 | 14c multicolored | .30 | .30 |
| 936 | A280 | 17c multicolored | .40 | .40 |
| 937 | A280 | 23c multicolored | .45 | .45 |
| 938 | A280 | 27c multicolored | .50 | .50 |
| 939 | A280 | 31c multicolored | .60 | .60 |
| 940 | A280 | 35c multicolored | .75 | .75 |
| 941 | A280 | 50c multicolored | 1.00 | 1.00 |
| 942 | A280 | 55c multicolored | 1.20 | 1.20 |
| | | Nos. 933-942 (10) | 5.70 | 5.70 |

**Souvenir Sheet**
**Perf. 14x13½**

| | | | | |
|---|---|---|---|---|
| 943 | A281 | $1 multicolored | 2.75 | 2.75 |
| | | See No. 1113. | | |

**Type of 1976**

**1981-83    Litho.    Perf. 14½x13½**
**Size: 34x20mm**

| | | | | |
|---|---|---|---|---|
| 945 | A247 | 1c like #749 | .25 | .25 |
| 946 | A247 | 3c like #750 | .25 | .25 |
| 947 | A247 | 6c like #753 | .25 | .25 |
| 948 | A247 | 15c like #754 | .60 | .60 |
| 949 | A247 | 25c like #757 | 1.00 | 1.00 |
| 950 | A247 | 31c like #756 | 1.25 | 1.25 |
| 951 | A247 | 41c like #758 | 1.75 | 1.75 |
| 952 | A247 | 80c like #759 | 3.50 | 3.50 |
| 953 | A247 | $1 like #760 | 5.00 | 5.00 |
| | | Nos. 945-953 (9) | 13.85 | 13.85 |

Issued: Nos. 946-947, 949, 950, 11/27/81; Nos. 945, 953, 10/12/82; Nos. 948, 951, 12/10/82; No. 952, 11/3/83.

Intl. Year of the Disabled (1981) A282

Designs: Various disabled people.

**1982, Mar. 24    Litho.    Perf. 14**

| | | | | |
|---|---|---|---|---|
| 954 | A282 | 23c multi, vert. | .50 | .45 |
| 955 | A282 | 62c multicolored | 1.10 | 1.00 |

30th Anniv. of West African Examinations Council A283

**1982, Mar. 24**

| | | | | |
|---|---|---|---|---|
| 956 | A283 | 6c multicolored | .25 | .25 |
| 957 | A283 | 31c multicolored | 1.10 | 1.00 |

21st Birthday of Princess Diana — A284

31c, 41c, 62c, Diana portraits. $1, Wedding.

**1982, July 1**     *Perf. 14x13½*
958 A284 31c multicolored .65 .65
959 A284 41c multicolored .90 .90
960 A284 62c multicolored 1.50 1.50
    *Nos. 958-960 (3)* 3.05 3.05
**Souvenir Sheet**
961 A284 $1 multicolored 2.50 2.50

Nos. 958-961
Overprinted in Silver

**1982, Aug. 30   Litho.**    *Perf. 14x13½*
962 A284 31c multicolored .65 .65
963 A284 41c multicolored .90 .90
964 A284 62c multicolored 1.50 1.50
    *Nos. 962-964 (3)* 3.05 3.05
**Souvenir Sheet**
965 A284 $1 multicolored 2.50 2.50

Birth of Prince William of Wales, June 21.

3rd Natl.
Redemption
Day — A285

3c, Fallah Varney. 6c, Samuel Doe. 10c, Jlatoh N. Podier, Jr. 15c, Jeffry S. Gbatu. 31c, Thomas G. Quiwonkpa. 41c, Abraham D. Kollie.

**1983, Apr. 5   Litho.**    *Perf. 13½*
966 A285 3c multicolored .25 .25
967 A285 6c multicolored .25 .25
968 A285 10c multicolored .25 .25
969 A285 15c multicolored .30 .30
970 A285 31c multicolored .85 .85
971 A285 41c multicolored 1.40 1.40
    *Nos. 966-971 (6)* 3.30 3.30
**Souvenir Sheet**
972 A285 $1 like 6c 2.60 2.60

Natl.
Archives
Opening
A286

Building views.

**1983, Apr. 5**
973 A286 6c multicolored *1.25 1.25*
974 A286 31c multicolored *2.25 2.25*

Christmas
1983 — A287

Raphael Paintings: 6c, Circumcision of Christ. 15c, Adoration of the Magi. 25c, Announcement to Mary. 31c, Madonna with Baldachin. 41c, Holy Family. 62c, Detail of Madonna with Child Surrounded by Five Saints. $1.25 Madonna of Foligno.

**1983, Dec. 14   Litho.**    *Perf. 13½*
975 A287 6c multicolored .25 .25
976 A287 15c multicolored .25 .25
977 A287 25c multicolored .45 .35
978 A287 31c multicolored .60 .50
979 A287 41c multicolored .75 .65
980 A287 62c multicolored 1.00 1.00
    *Nos. 975-980 (6)* 3.30 3.00
**Souvenir Sheet**
981 A287 $1.25 multicolored 2.60 1.90
Sheets of 1 showing entire painting exist.

Mano River
Union, 10th
Anniv. (1983)
A288

6c, Training school graduates. 25c, Emblem. 31c, Maps, leaders. 41c, Guinea's accession. 75c, Guinea's accession, diff.

**1984, Apr. 6   Litho.**    *Perf. 14x13½*
982 A288 6c multicolored .25 .25
983 A288 25c multicolored .70 .70
984 A288 31c multicolored .90 .90
985 A288 41c multicolored 1.25 1.25
    *Nos. 982-985 (4)* 3.10 3.10
**Souvenir Sheet**
986 A288 75c multicolored 2.60 2.60

4th Natl.
Redemption
Day — A289

3c, Hospital, New Kru Town. 10c, Ganta-Harper Highway construction. 20c, Constitution Assembly opening. 31c, Doe at highway construction. 41c, Draft Constitution presentation.

**1984, Apr. 12**     *Perf. 14½*
987 A289 3c multicolored .25 .25
988 A289 10c multicolored .25 .25
989 A289 20c multicolored .45 .45
990 A289 31c multicolored 1.00 1.00
991 A289 41c multicolored 1.40 1.40
    *Nos. 987-991 (5)* 3.35 3.35

Adoration of the
Wise Men, by
Rubens (1577-
1640)
A290

15c, Crowning of Katharina. 25c, Mother and Child Adored by Wise Men. 31c, Madonna and Child with Halo. 41c, Adoration of the Shepherds. 62c, Madonna and Child with Saints. $1.25, Madonna Adored by Saints.

**1984, June 1   Litho.**    *Perf. 13½*
992 A290 6c shown .25 .25
993 A290 15c multicolored .30 .30
994 A290 25c multicolored .45 .45
995 A290 31c multicolored .60 .60
996 A290 41c multicolored .75 .75
997 A290 62c multicolored 1.20 1.20
    *Nos. 992-997 (6)* 3.55 3.55
**Souvenir Sheet**
998 A290 $1.25 multicolored 4.25 4.25
Sheets of 1 showing entire painting exist.

1984 Summer
Olympics — A291

3c, Jesse Owens, 1936. 4c, Rafer Johnson, 1960. 25c, Miruts Yifter, 1980. 41c, Kipchoge Keino, 1968, 1972. 62c, Muhammad Ali, 1960. $1.25, Wilma Rudolph, 1960, horiz.

**1984, July 2**     *Perf. 13½x14*
999 A291 3c multicolored .25 .25
1000 A291 4c multicolored .25 .25
1001 A291 25c multicolored .75 .75
1002 A291 41c multicolored 1.20 1.20
1003 A291 62c multicolored 2.00 2.00
    *Nos. 999-1003 (5)* 4.45 4.45
**Souvenir Sheet**
*Perf. 14x13½*
1004 A291 $1.25 multicolored 4.25 4.25

1984
Louisiana
Expo — A292

6c, Water birds. 31c, Ship, Buchanan Harbor. 41c, Fish. 62c, Train carrying iron ore.

**1984, July 24**     *Perf. 14½*
1005 A292 6c multicolored .25 .25
1006 A292 31c multicolored 1.00 1.00
1007 A292 41c multicolored 1.25 1.25
1008 A292 62c multicolored 2.00 2.00
    *Nos. 1005-1008 (4)* 4.50 4.50

Pygmy
Hippopotamus,
World Wildlife
Fund Emblem
A293

Various pygmy hippopotomi.

**1984, Nov. 22   Litho.**    *Perf. 14½*
1009 A293 6c multicolored .75 .75
1010 A293 10c multicolored 1.00 1.00
1011 A293 20c multicolored 2.75 2.75
1012 A293 31c multicolored 4.00 4.00
    *Nos. 1009-1012 (4)* 8.50 8.50
Exist imperf.

Indigent
Children
Home,
Bensonville
A294

First Lady Mrs. Nancy Doe and various children.

**1984, Dec. 14**
1013 A294 6c multicolored .25 .25
1014 A294 31c multicolored 1.00 1.00

Natl.
Redemption
Day, Apr.
12 — A295

6c, Army barracks, Monrovia. 31c, Pan-African Plaza, Monrovia.

**1985, Apr. 5   Litho.**    *Perf. 14½*
1015 A295 6c multicolored .25 .25
1016 A295 31c multicolored 1.00 1.00
Liberian Revolution, fifth anniv.

Audubon Birth
Bicentenary
A296

Illustrations by artist/naturalist J. J. Audubon: 1c, Bohemian waxwing. 3c, Bay-breasted warbler. 6c, White-winged crossbill. 31c, Red phalarope. 41c, Eastern bluebird. 62c, Northern cardinal.

**1985, Apr. 5**
1017 A296 1c multicolored .25 .25
1018 A296 3c multicolored .25 .25
1019 A296 6c multicolored .30 .25
1020 A296 31c multicolored 1.10 1.00
1021 A296 41c multicolored 1.60 .75
1022 A296 62c multicolored 2.25 2.00
    *Nos. 1017-1022 (6)* 5.75 4.50

Venus and
Mirror — A297

Paintings (details) by Rubens: 15c, Adam & Eve in Paradise. 25c, Andromeda. 31c, The Three Graces. 41c, Venus & Adonis. 62c, The

Daughters of Leucippus. $1.25, The Judgement of Paris.

**1985, Nov. 14   Litho.**    *Perf. 14*
1023 A297 6c multicolored .25 .25
1024 A297 15c multicolored .55 .55
1025 A297 25c multicolored .85 .85
1026 A297 31c multicolored 1.00 1.00
1027 A297 41c multicolored 1.40 1.40
1028 A297 62c multicolored 2.40 2.40
    *Nos. 1023-1028 (6)* 6.45 6.45
**Souvenir Sheet**
1029 A297 $1.25 multicolored 3.25 3.25
Sheets of 1 showing entire painting exist.

1986 World Cup Soccer
Championships, Mexico — A298

6c, Germany-Morocco, 1970. 15c, Zaire-Brazil, 1974. 25c, Tunisia-Germany, 1978. 31c, Cameroun-Peru, 1982, vert. 41c, Algeria-Germany, 1982. 62c, 1986 Senegal team. $1.25, Liberia-Nigeria.

**1985, Nov. 14**
1030 A298 6c multicolored .25 .25
1031 A298 15c multicolored .35 .35
1032 A298 25c multicolored .60 .60
1033 A298 31c multicolored .85 .85
1034 A298 41c multicolored 1.10 1.10
1035 A298 62c multicolored 1.60 1.60
    *Nos. 1030-1035 (6)* 4.75 4.75
**Souvenir Sheet**
1036 A298 $1.25 multicolored 3.25 3.25

Queen Mother, 85th
Birthday — A299

31c, Elizabeth in garter robes. 41c, At the races. 62c, In garden, waving. $1.25, Wearing diadem.

**1985, Dec. 12   Litho.**    *Perf. 14½*
1037 A299 31c mutlicolored .60 .60
1038 A299 41c multicolored .85 .85
1039 A299 62c multicolored 1.20 1.20
    *Nos. 1037-1039 (3)* 2.65 2.65
**Souvenir Sheet**
1040 A299 $1.25 multicolored 2.25 2.25

World Food
Day — A300

**1985, Dec. 12**
1041 A300 25c multicolored .75 .70
1042 A300 31c multicolored 1.25 1.00

AMERIPEX
'86 — A301

25c, The Alamo. 31c, Liberty Bell. 80c, #344, 802, C102.

**1986, June 10   Litho.**    *Perf. 14½*
1043 A301 25c multicolored 1.00 .65
1044 A301 31c multicolored 1.10 .85
1045 A301 80c multicolored 2.90 2.10
    *Nos. 1043-1045 (3)* 5.00 3.60

Statue of Liberty, Cent. — A302

20c, Unveiling, 1886. 31c, Frederic A. Bartholdi. $1, Statue close-up.

**1986, June 10**
| 1046 | A302 | 20c multicolored | .50 | .50 |
| 1047 | A302 | 31c multicolored | .90 | .90 |
| 1048 | A302 | $1 multicolored | 2.75 | 2.75 |
| | | Nos. 1046-1048 (3) | 4.15 | 4.15 |

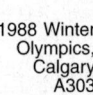

1988 Winter Olympics, Calgary A303

1984 Gold medalists: 3c, Max Julen, Switzerland, men's giant slalom. 6c, Debbie Armstrong, U.S., women's giant slalom. 31c, Peter Angerer, West Germany, biathlon. 60c, Bill Johnson, U.S., men's downhill. 80c, East Germany, 4-man bobsled. $1.25, H. Stangassinger, F. Wembacher, West Germany, 2-man luge.

**1987, Aug. 21     Litho.     Perf. 14**
| 1049 | A303 | 3c multicolored | .25 | .25 |
| 1050 | A303 | 6c multicolored | .25 | .25 |
| 1051 | A303 | 31c multicolored | .70 | .70 |
| 1052 | A303 | 60c multicolored | 1.40 | 1.40 |
| 1053 | A303 | 80c multicolored | 1.60 | 1.60 |
| | | Nos. 1049-1053 (5) | 4.20 | 4.20 |

**Souvenir Sheet**
| 1054 | A303 | $1.25 multicolored | 2.25 | 2.25 |

City of Berlin, 750th Anniv. — A304

6c, State (Royal) Theater in the Gendarmenmarkt, c. 1820, architect Schinkel. 31c, Kaiser Friedrich Museum, Museum Is. on River Spree. 60c, Charlottenburg Castle, 17th cent. 80c, Modern church bell tower & Kaiser Wilhelm Gedachtniskirche. $1.50, MIRAK rocket development, Spaceship Society Airfield, Reinickendorf, 1930.

**1987, Sept. 4**
| 1055 | A304 | 6c multicolored | .25 | .25 |
| 1056 | A304 | 31c multicolored | .70 | .70 |
| 1057 | A304 | 60c multicolored | 1.40 | 1.40 |
| 1058 | A304 | 80c multicolored | 1.60 | 1.60 |
| | | Nos. 1055-1058 (4) | 3.95 | 3.95 |

**Souvenir sheet**
**Perf. 11½**
| 1059 | A304 | $1.50 buff & dk brown | 3.50 | 3.50 |

No. 1059 contains one 25x61mm stamp.

Shakespearean Plays — A305

**1987, Nov. 6     Litho.     Perf. 14**
| 1060 | A305 | Sheet of 8 | 6.50 | 6.50 |
| a. | | 3c Othello | .25 | .25 |
| b. | | 6c Romeo & Juliet | .25 | .25 |
| c. | | 10c The Merry Wives of Windsor | .25 | .25 |
| d. | | 15c Henry IV | .25 | .25 |
| e. | | 31c Hamlet | .45 | .45 |
| f. | | 60c Macbeth | .90 | .90 |
| g. | | 80c King Lear | 1.10 | 1.10 |
| h. | | $2 Shakespeare and the Globe Theater, 1598 | 2.75 | 2.75 |

Amateur Radio Association, 25th Anniv. — A306

No. 1061, Emblem. No. 1062, Village. No. 1063, On-the-Air certificate. No. 1064, Globe, flags.

**1987, Nov. 23     Litho.     Perf. 14**
| 1061 | A306 | 10c multicolored | .35 | .35 |
| 1062 | A306 | 10c multicolored | .35 | .35 |
| 1063 | A306 | 35c multicolored | 1.20 | 1.20 |
| 1064 | A306 | 35c multicolored | 1.20 | 1.20 |
| | | Nos. 1061-1064 (4) | 3.10 | 3.10 |

**Miniature Sheets**

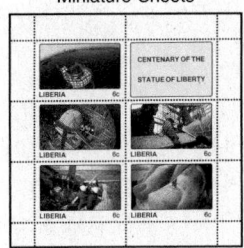

Statue of Liberty, Cent. (in 1986) — A307

No. 1065: a, Torch, southern view of NYC. b, Overhead view of crown and scaffold. c, 4 workmen repairing crown. d, 5 workmen, crown. e, Statue's right foot.
No. 1066: a, Tall ship, statue. b, Bay Queen ferry. c, Statue on poster at a construction site, NYC. d, Tug boat, tall ship. e, Building frieze.
No. 1067: a, Statue flanked by fireworks. b, Lighting of the statue. c, Crown observatory illuminated. d, Statue surrounded by fireworks. e, Crown and torch observatories illuminated.
No. 1068: a, Liberty "Happy Birthday" poster at a construction site. b, Ships in NY Harbor. c, Woman renovating statue nose. d, Man & woman renovating nose. e, Man, nose. #1068a-1068e vert.

**1987, Dec. 10               Perf. 13½**
| 1065 | A307 | Sheet of 5 + label | 1.10 | 1.10 |
| a.-e. | | 6c any single | .25 | .25 |
| 1066 | A307 | Sheet of 5 + label | 2.25 | 2.25 |
| a.-e. | | 15c any single | .40 | .40 |
| 1067 | A307 | Sheet of 5 + label | 4.25 | 4.25 |
| a.-e. | | 31c any single | .80 | .80 |
| 1068 | A307 | Sheet of 5 + label | 7.50 | 7.50 |
| a.-e. | | 60c any single | 1.40 | 1.40 |
| | | Nos. 1065-1068 (4) | 15.10 | |

Nos. 1065-1068 contain label inscribed "CENTENARY OF THE STATUE OF LIBERTY" in two or five lines.

Second Republic, 2nd Anniv. — A308

Design: Natl. flag, coat of arms, hand grip, Pres. Doe and Vice Pres. Moniba.

**1988, Jan. 6               Perf. 14½**
| 1069 | A308 | 10c multicolored | .45 | .45 |
| 1070 | A308 | 35c multicolored | .90 | .90 |

UN Child Survival Campaign A309

3c, Breast-feeding. 6c, Oral rehydration therapy, vert. 31c, Immunization. $1, Growth monitoring, vert.

Inauguration of the Second Republic — A310

Design: Pres. Doe greeting Chief Justice Emmanuel N. Gbalazeh.

**1988, Jan. 15     Perf. 13x13½, 13½x13**
| 1071 | A309 | 3c multicolored | .25 | .25 |
| 1072 | A309 | 6c multicolored | .25 | .25 |
| 1073 | A309 | 31c multicolored | 1.60 | 1.60 |
| 1074 | A309 | $1 multicolored | 4.50 | 2.90 |
| | | Nos. 1071-1074 (4) | 6.60 | 5.00 |

**1988, Jan. 15     Perf. 13x13½**
| 1075 | A310 | 6c multicolored | .30 | .30 |

Samuel Kanyon Doe Sports Complex, Opened Apr. 12, 1986 — A311

**1988, Jan. 15**
| 1076 | A311 | 31c multicolored | .90 | .90 |

Green (Agricultural) Revolution A312

**1988, Apr. 4               Perf. 15**
| 1077 | A312 | 10c multicolored | .35 | .35 |
| 1078 | A312 | 35c multicolored | 1.20 | 1.20 |

US Peace Corps in Liberia, 25th Anniv. — A313

**1988, Apr. 4**
| 1079 | A313 | 10c multicolored | .35 | .35 |
| 1080 | A313 | 35c multicolored | 1.20 | 1.20 |

**Souvenir Sheet**

1988 Summer Olympics, Seoul — A314

**1988, Apr. 14               Perf. 14**
| 1081 | A314 | $3 multicolored | 7.50 | 7.50 |

Organization of African Unity, 25th Anniv. — A315

**1988, May 25**
| 1082 | A315 | 10c multicolored | .35 | .35 |
| 1083 | A315 | 35c multicolored | 1.10 | 1.10 |
| 1084 | A315 | $1 multicolored | 3.50 | 3.50 |
| | | Nos. 1082-1084 (3) | 4.95 | 4.95 |

Rail Transport — A316

10c, GP10 at Nimba. 35c, Triple-headed iron ore train.
No. 1087, King Edward II, 1930. No. 1088, GWR 57 No. 3697, 1941. No. 1089, GWR 0-4-2T No. 1408, 1932. No. 1090, GWR No. 7034 Ince Castle, 1950.

**1988, July 30     Litho.     Perf. 14½**
| 1085 | A316 | 10c multicolored | .50 | .50 |
| 1086 | A316 | 35c multicolored | 1.40 | 1.40 |

**Souvenir Sheets**
**Perf. 11**
| 1087 | A316 | $2 multicolored | 4.25 | 4.25 |
| 1088 | A316 | $2 multicolored | 4.25 | 4.25 |
| 1089 | A316 | $2 multicolored | 4.25 | 4.25 |
| 1090 | A316 | $2 multicolored | 4.25 | 4.25 |

Nos. 1087-1090 contain one 64x44mm stamp each.

**Nos. 1087-1090 with Added Text**

**1993, Aug. 3     Souvenir Sheets**
| 1087a | | With added text in margin | 6.00 | 6.00 |
| 1088a | | With added text in margin | 6.00 | 6.00 |
| 1089a | | With added text in margin | 6.00 | 6.00 |
| 1090a | | With added text in margin | 6.00 | 6.00 |

Added text on Nos. 1087a-1090a reads: "25th ANNIVERSARY OF THE LAST STEAM TRAIN TO / RUN ON BRITISH RAIL 1968-1993."

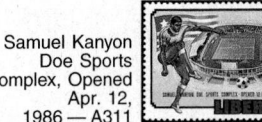

1988 Summer Olympics, Seoul — A317

10c, Baseball. 35c, Hurdles. 45c, Fencing. 80c, Synchronized swimming. $1, Yachting. $1.50, Tennis.

**1988, Sept. 13               Litho.**
| 1091 | A317 | 10c multicolored | .25 | .25 |
| 1092 | A317 | 35c multicolored | .65 | .65 |
| 1093 | A317 | 45c multicolored | .90 | .90 |
| 1094 | A317 | 80c multicolored | 1.50 | 1.50 |
| 1095 | A317 | $1 multicolored | 2.00 | 2.00 |
| | | Nos. 1091-1095 (5) | 5.30 | 5.30 |

**Souvenir Sheet**
| 1096 | A317 | $1.50 multicolored | 2.25 | 2.25 |

Intl. Tennis Federation, 75th anniv. ($1.50).

St. Joseph's Catholic Hospital, 25th Anniv. — A318

No. 1098, Hospital, 4 staff members. No. 1099, St. John of God. No. 1100, Doctor, nurse, map.

**1988, Aug. 26     Litho.     Perf. 14½**
| 1097 | A318 | 10c shown | .25 | .25 |
| 1098 | A318 | 10c multicolored | .25 | .25 |
| 1099 | A318 | 35c multicolored | .70 | .70 |
| 1100 | A318 | $1 multicolored | 2.00 | 2.00 |
| | | Nos. 1097-1100 (4) | 3.20 | 3.20 |

Common Design Types pictured following the introduction.

**Lloyds of London, 300th Anniv.**
Common Design Type

CD341

Designs: 10c, Royal Exchange destroyed by fire, 1838, vert. 35c, Air Liberia BN2A aircraft. 45c, Supertanker Chevron Antwerp. $1, Lakonia on fire off Madeira, 1963, vert.

**1988, Oct. 31     Litho.     Perf. 14**
| 1101 | CD341 | 10c multicolored | .25 | .25 |
| 1102 | CD341 | 35c multicolored | .75 | .75 |
| 1103 | CD341 | 45c multicolored | 1.00 | 1.00 |
| 1104 | CD341 | $1 multicolored | 2.25 | 2.25 |
| | | Nos. 1101-1104 (4) | 4.25 | 4.25 |

Sasa Players — A319

10c, Monkey bridge, vert. 45c, Snake dancers, vert.

### Perf. 14x14½, 14½x14
**1988, Sept. 30**      **Litho.**
| | | | | |
|---|---|---|---|---|
| 1105 | A319 | 10c multicolored | .35 | .35 |
| 1106 | A319 | 35c shown | 1.00 | 1.00 |
| 1107 | A319 | 45c multicolored | 1.40 | 1.40 |
| | | *Nos. 1105-1107 (3)* | 2.75 | 2.75 |

Intl. Fund for Agricultural Development, 10th Anniv. — A320

10c, Crops. 35c, Spraying crops, livestock.

**1988, Oct. 7**   **Litho.**   **Perf. 14x14½**
| | | | | |
|---|---|---|---|---|
| 1108 | A320 | 10c multicolored | .40 | .40 |
| 1109 | A320 | 35c multicolored | 1.50 | 1.50 |

3rd Anniv. of the 2nd Republic A321

10c, Pres. Doe, officials. 50c, Pres. Doe, doctor.

**1989, Jan. 6**    **Litho.**    **Perf. 14**
| | | | | |
|---|---|---|---|---|
| 1110 | A321 | 10c multicolored | .35 | .35 |
| 1111 | A321 | 35c like 10c | 1.10 | 1.10 |
| 1112 | A321 | 50c multicolored | 1.75 | 1.75 |
| | | *Nos. 1110-1112 (3)* | 3.20 | 3.20 |

### US Presidents Type of 1981-82
**1989, Jan. 20**     **Perf. 13½x14**
| | | | | |
|---|---|---|---|---|
| 1113 | A280 | $1 George Bush | 2.60 | 2.60 |

Rissho Kosei-Kai Buddhist Assoc., Tokyo, 50th Anniv. — A322

Natl. flags and: No. 1114, "Harmony" in Japanese. No. 1115, Organization headquarters, Tokyo. No. 1116, Nikkyo Niwano, founder. 50c, Statue of Buddha in the Great Sacred Hall.

**1989, Feb. 28**   **Litho.**   **Perf. 14x14½**
| | | | | |
|---|---|---|---|---|
| 1114 | A322 | 10c multicolored | .45 | .45 |
| 1115 | A322 | 10c multicolored | .45 | .45 |
| 1116 | A322 | 10c multicolored | .45 | .45 |
| 1117 | A322 | 50c multicolored | 2.00 | 2.00 |
| | | *Nos. 1114-1117 (4)* | 3.35 | 3.35 |

Liberian-Japanese friendship.

#### Souvenir Sheet

Emperor Hirohito of Japan (1901-1989) — A323

Commemorative coins: a, Silver. b, Gold.

**1989, Feb. 28**   **Unwmk.**   **Perf. 14½**
| | | | | |
|---|---|---|---|---|
| 1118 | A323 | Sheet of 2 | 6.00 | 6.00 |
| a.-b. | | 75c any single | 2.50 | 2.50 |

For overprint see No. 1147.

Mano River Union, 15th Anniv. — A324

Natl. flag, crest and: 10c, Union Glass Factory, Gardnersville, Monrovia. 35c, Pres. Doe, Momoh of Sierra Leone and Conte of Guinea. 45c, Monrovia-Freetown Highway. 50c, Sierra

---

Leone-Guinea land postal services. $1, Communique, 1988 summit.

#### Unwmk.
**1989, May 8**    **Litho.**    **Perf. 14**
| | | | | |
|---|---|---|---|---|
| 1119 | A324 | 10c multicolored | .30 | .30 |
| 1120 | A324 | 35c multicolored | 1.00 | 1.00 |
| 1121 | A324 | 45c multicolored | 1.25 | 1.25 |
| 1122 | A324 | 50c multicolored | 1.40 | 1.40 |
| 1123 | A324 | $1 multicolored | 2.75 | 2.75 |
| | | *Nos. 1119-1123 (5)* | 6.70 | 6.70 |

World Telecommunications Day — A325

**1989, May 17**   **Litho.**   **Perf. 12½**
| | | | | |
|---|---|---|---|---|
| 1124 | A325 | 50c multicolored | 1.25 | 1.25 |

#### Common Design Type

Moon Landing, 20th Anniv. — CD342

Apollo 11: 10c, Recovery ship USS Okinawa. 35c, Buzz Aldrin, Neil Armstrong and Michael Collins. 45c, Mission emblem. $1, Aldrin steps on the Moon. $2, Aldrin preparing to conduct experiments on the Moon's surface.

### Perf. 14x13½, 14 (35c, 45c)
**1989, July 20**   **Wmk. 384**
**Size of Nos. 1126-1127: 29x29mm**
| | | | | |
|---|---|---|---|---|
| 1125 | CD342 | 10c multicolored | .25 | .25 |
| 1126 | CD342 | 35c multicolored | .75 | .75 |
| 1127 | CD342 | 45c multicolored | 1.00 | 1.00 |
| 1128 | CD342 | $1 multicolored | 2.25 | 2.25 |
| | | *Nos. 1125-1128 (4)* | 4.25 | 4.25 |

#### Souvenir Sheet
| | | | | |
|---|---|---|---|---|
| 1129 | CD342 | $2 multicolored | 4.25 | 4.25 |

#### Souvenir Sheet

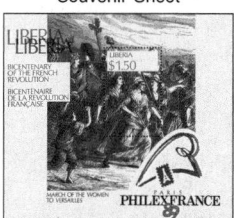

The Women's March on Versailles — A326

**1989, July 7**   **Wmk. 384**   **Perf. 14**
| | | | | |
|---|---|---|---|---|
| 1130 | A326 | $1.50 multicolored | 3.00 | 3.00 |

French revolution, bicent., PHILEXFRANCE '89.

#### Souvenir Sheet

Renovation and Re-dedication of the Statue of Liberty, 1986 — A327

Photographs: a, Workman. b, French dignitary, US flag. c, Dignitaries at ceremony, statue.

### Perf. 14x13½
**1989, Oct. 2**   **Litho.**   **Wmk. 373**
| | | | | |
|---|---|---|---|---|
| 1131 | A327 | Sheet of 3 | 1.75 | 1.75 |
| a.-c. | | 25c any single | .55 | .55 |

World Stamp Expo '89 and PHILEX-FRANCE '89.

---

#### Souvenir Sheet

A328

**1989, Nov. 17**   **Unwmk.**   **Perf. 14½**
| | | | | |
|---|---|---|---|---|
| 1132 | A328 | $2 black | 4.50 | 4.50 |

World Stamp Expo '89, Washington, DC.

Jawaharlal Nehru, 1st Prime Minister of Independent India — A329

45c, Nehru, signature, flag. 50c, Nehru, signature.

**1989, Dec. 22**   **Unwmk.**   **Perf. 14**
| | | | | |
|---|---|---|---|---|
| 1133 | A329 | 45c multicolored | .75 | .75 |
| 1134 | A329 | 50c multicolored | 1.90 | 1.90 |

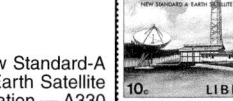

New Standard-A Earth Satellite Station — A330

**1990, Jan. 5**
| | | | | |
|---|---|---|---|---|
| 1135 | A330 | 10c shown | .25 | .25 |
| 1136 | A330 | 35c multi, diff. | 1.00 | 1.00 |

US Educational & Cultural Foundation in Liberia, 25th Anniv. (in 1989) — A331

**1990, Jan. 5**
| | | | | |
|---|---|---|---|---|
| 1137 | A331 | 10c multicolored | .25 | .25 |
| 1138 | A331 | 45c multicolored | 1.10 | 1.10 |

Pan-African Postal Union, 10th Anniv. — A332

**1990, Jan. 18**     **Perf. 13x12½**
| | | | | |
|---|---|---|---|---|
| 1139 | A332 | 35c multicolored | .80 | .80 |

Flags of Liberian Counties — A333

Designs: a, Bomi. b, Bong. c, Grand Bassa. d, Grand Cape Mount. e, Grand Gedeh. f, Grand Kru. g, Lofa. h, Margibi. i, Maryland. j, Montserrado. k, Nimba. l, Rivercess. m, Sinoe.

### Perf. 14x13½
**1990, Mar. 2**   **Litho.**   **Unwmk.**
| | | | | |
|---|---|---|---|---|
| 1140 | | Strip of 13 | 5.00 | 5.00 |
| a.-m. | A333 | 10c any single | .30 | .30 |
| 1141 | | Strip of 13 | 13.00 | 13.00 |
| a.-m. | A333 | 35c any single | 1.00 | 1.00 |
| 1142 | | Strip of 13 | 15.00 | 15.00 |
| a.-m. | A333 | 45c any single | 1.10 | 1.10 |
| 1143 | | Strip of 13 | 20.00 | 20.00 |
| a.-m. | A333 | 50c any single | 1.40 | 1.40 |
| 1144 | | Strip of 13 | 37.50 | 37.50 |
| a.-m. | A333 | $1 any single | 2.75 | 2.75 |
| | | *Nos. 1140-1144 (5)* | 90.50 | 90.50 |

---

### Queen Mother, 90th Birthday
Common Design Types

Designs: 10c, At age 6. $2, At age 22.

#### Perf. 14x15
**1991, Oct. 28**     **Wmk. 384**
| | | | | |
|---|---|---|---|---|
| 1145 | CD343 | 10c multicolored | .25 | .25 |

#### Perf. 14½
| | | | | |
|---|---|---|---|---|
| 1146 | CD344 | $2 brn & blk | 3.00 | 3.00 |

For overprints see Nos. 1162-1163.

#### No. 1118 Overprinted

#### Perf. 14½
**1991, Nov. 16**   **Litho.**   **Unwmk.**
| | | | | |
|---|---|---|---|---|
| 1147 | A323 | Sheet of 2 | 3.50 | 3.50 |
| a.-b. | | 75c any single | 1.50 | 1.50 |

National Unity A334

Designs: 35c, Hands clasp over map of Liberia. 45c, Liberian flag, hands, African map. 50c, All Liberia conference, March 1991, conferees, flag, map.

**1991, Dec. 30**     **Perf. 13½**
| | | | | |
|---|---|---|---|---|
| 1148 | A334 | 35c multicolored | 1.00 | 1.00 |
| 1149 | A334 | 45c multicolored | 1.25 | 1.25 |
| 1150 | A334 | 50c multicolored | 1.40 | 1.40 |
| | | *Nos. 1148-1150 (3)* | 3.65 | 3.65 |

1992 Summer Olympics, Barcelona A335

**1992, Aug. 7**    **Litho.**    **Perf. 14**
| | | | | |
|---|---|---|---|---|
| 1151 | A335 | 45c Boxing | 1.50 | 1.50 |
| 1152 | A335 | 50c Soccer | 1.60 | 1.40 |
| 1153 | A335 | $1 Weight lifting | 3.25 | 2.75 |
| 1154 | A335 | $2 Water polo | 6.00 | 5.50 |
| | | *Nos. 1151-1154 (4)* | 12.35 | 10.90 |

#### Souvenir Sheet
| | | | | |
|---|---|---|---|---|
| 1155 | A335 | $1.50 Running | 6.00 | 6.00 |

Disarmament A336

Designs: 50c, Disarm today. $1, Join your parents & build Liberia. $2, Peace must prevail in Liberia.

**1993, Feb. 10**   **Litho.**   **Perf. 13½x14**
| | | | | |
|---|---|---|---|---|
| 1156 | A336 | 50c multicolored | 1.50 | 1.50 |
| 1157 | A336 | $1 multicolored | 2.90 | 2.90 |
| 1158 | A336 | $2 multicolored | 5.50 | 5.50 |
| | | *Nos. 1156-1158 (3)* | 9.90 | 9.90 |

See Nos. 1237-1239.

## Miniature Sheets

Flora and Fauna — A337

No. 1159 — Flora: a, Papaya. b, Sausage tree. c, Angraecum eichlerianum. d, Arachnis flos-aeris. e, Screw pine. f, African tulip tree. g, Coffee tree. h, Bolusiella talbotii. i, Bulbophyllum lepidum. j, Oeceoclades maculata. k, Plectrelminthus caudatus. l, Diaphananthe rutila.

No. 1160 — Fauna: a, Diana monkey. b, Flying squirrel. c, Egyptian rousette. d, Serval. e, Potto. f, Chimpanzee. g, African horned chameleon. h, Royal python. i, Golden cat. j, Banded duiker. k, Pygmy hippopotamus. l, Water chevrotain.

No. 1161 — Birds: a, Grey heron. b, Bat hawk. c, Martial eagle. d, Little sparrow hawk. e, Hoopoe. f, Red bishop. g, Purple-throated sunbird. h, African fish eagle. i, African grey parrot. j, Black-crowned night heron. k, Swallow. l, Great white egret.

| | 1993-94 | Litho. | Perf. 14 | |
|---|---|---|---|---|
| 1159 | A337 | 70c Sheet of 12, | | |
| | | #a.-l. | 25.00 | 25.00 |
| 1160 | A337 | 90c Sheet of 12, | | |
| | | #a.-l. | 27.50 | 27.50 |
| 1161 | A337 | $1 Sheet of 12, | | |
| | | #a.-l. | 24.00 | 24.00 |
| | | Nos. 1159-1161 (3) | 76.50 | 76.50 |

Issued: 70c, 10/14; 90c, 11/18; $1, 1/14/94.

Nos. 1145-1146 Ovptd. with Hong Kong '94 Emblem

| | Perf. 14x15 | | | |
|---|---|---|---|---|
| 1994, Feb. 18 | Litho. | | Wmk. 384 | |
| 1162 | CD343 | 10c multicolored | .35 | .35 |
| | Perf. 14½ | | | |
| 1163 | CD344 | $2 multicolored | 5.25 | 5.25 |

## Miniature Sheet

Roberts Field, Monrovia, 50th Anniv. — A338

No. 1164: a, Vickers Supermarine Spitfire Mk IX. b, Boeing B-17G. c, Douglas A-20 Boston. d, North American B-25J Mitchell. e, Beech C-45 Expeditor. f, Douglas C-54. g, Piper L4 Cub. h, Martin PBM-3C.

| 1994, July 11 | Litho. | Perf. 13½x13 |
|---|---|---|
| 1164 A338 | 35c Sheet of 8, | |
| | #a.-h. + label | 10.00 10.00 |

## Souvenir Sheets

Locomotives — A339

Designs: No. 1165, $1, Class A3 #60044 Melton, Class A4 #60017 Silver Fox. No. 1166, $1, GWR 2-6-2 Prairie Tank #4561. No. 1167, $1, GWR 2-6-2 Small Prairie. No. 1168, $1, GWR Castle Class 4-6-0 No. Kingswear Castle. No. 1169, $1, GWR 0-6-0 Pannier Tank. No. 1170, $1, Bong Mining Company diesel hauling iron ore.

| 1994, Aug. 16 | Litho. | Perf. 14 |
|---|---|---|
| 1165-1170 A339 | Set of 6 | 14.00 14.00 |

See Nos. 1194-1199, 1205.

Liberian Natl. Red Cross, 75th Anniv. — A340

Designs: 70c, No. 1172, Globe. No. 1173, $2, Jean-Henri Dunant.

| 1994, Oct. 3 | Litho. | Perf. 14½x14 | |
|---|---|---|---|
| 1171 | A340 | 70c multicolored | 1.90 1.90 |
| 1172 | A340 | $1 multicolored | 2.50 2.50 |
| 1173 | A340 | $1 multicolored | 2.50 2.50 |
| 1174 | A340 | $2 multicolored | 5.50 5.50 |
| | | Nos. 1171-1174 (4) | 12.40 12.40 |

### End of World War II, 50th Anniv.
#### Common Design Types

Designs: 70c, Sunderland on U-boat patrol. 90c, US Army Engineer Task Force. $1, MV Abosso sunk off Liberia, 1942. No. 1178, MV Adda sunk off Liberia, 1941.

No. 1179, Obverse of U.S. Victory Medal depicting Liberty.

| 1995, May 8 | Litho. | Perf. 13½ | |
|---|---|---|---|
| 1175 | CD351 | 70c multicolored | 1.75 1.00 |
| 1176 | CD351 | 90c multicolored | 2.00 1.40 |
| 1177 | CD351 | $1 multicolored | 2.50 1.50 |
| 1178 | CD351 | $2 multicolored | 4.50 2.75 |
| | | Nos. 1175-1178 (4) | 10.75 6.65 |

#### Souvenir Sheet
#### Perf. 14

| 1179 | CD352 | $2 multicolored | 4.50 4.50 |
|---|---|---|---|

Wild Animals — A341

| 1995, June 1 | | | Perf. 14 | |
|---|---|---|---|---|
| 1180 | A341 | 70c Cheetah | 2.00 | 2.00 |
| 1181 | A341 | 70c Giraffe | 2.00 | 2.00 |
| 1182 | A341 | 90c Rhinoceros | 2.00 | 2.00 |
| 1183 | A341 | $1 Elephant | 3.00 | 3.00 |
| 1184 | A341 | $2 Lion | 6.00 | 6.00 |
| | | Nos. 1180-1184 (5) | 15.00 | 15.00 |

#### Souvenir Sheet

1995 IAAF World Track & Field Championships, Gothenburg — A342

No. 1185: a, Merlene Ottey. b, Heike Drechsler.

| 1995, Aug. 4 | Litho. | Perf. 14 | |
|---|---|---|---|
| 1185 A342 | $1 Sheet of 2, #a.-b. | 8.50 8.50 | |

### Miniature Sheet

Orchids — A343

No. 1186: a, Ancistrochilus rothschildianus. b, Disa uniflora. c, Polystachya ottoniana. d, Aerangis brachycarpa. e, Plectrelminthus caudatus. f, Polystachya bella. g, Ansellia africana. h, Bulbophyllum cochleatum.

| 1995, Sept. 1 | | Perf. 13 | |
|---|---|---|---|
| 1186 A343 | 70c Sheet of 8, #a.-h. + label | 17.00 17.00 | |

Singapore '95.

### UN, 50th Anniv.
#### Common Design Type

Designs: 25c, UN Land Rovers. 50c, Delivering food supplies. $1, Ilyushin IL-76 freighter airlifting supplies. $2, MIL MI-8 helicopter.

| 1995, Oct. 24 | Litho. | Perf. 14 | |
|---|---|---|---|
| 1187 | CD353 | 25c multicolored | .90 .90 |
| 1188 | CD353 | 50c multicolored | 1.50 1.50 |
| 1189 | CD353 | $1 multicolored | 3.00 3.00 |
| 1190 | CD353 | $2 multicolored | 5.50 5.50 |
| | | Nos. 1187-1190 (4) | 10.90 10.90 |

Economic Community of West African States, 20th Anniv. — A344

Designs: 25c, Map, Liberian flag, soldiers, civilians. 50c, Soldier carrying child, vert. $1, Logo, vert.

| | Perf. 13½x13, 13½x13 | | |
|---|---|---|---|
| 1995, Nov. 10 | | Litho. | |
| 1191 | A344 | 25c multicolored | .75 .75 |
| 1192 | A344 | 50c multicolored | 1.50 1.50 |
| 1193 | A344 | $1 multicolored | 3.00 3.00 |
| | | Nos. 1191-1193 (3) | 5.25 5.25 |

### Train Type of 1994
#### Souvenir Sheets

Designs: No. 1194, $1, 4-4-0 locomotive 11 "The Reno," galloping horses. No. 1195, $1, Halwill station, Southern Region T9 class locomotive #30719. No. 1196, $1, GWR 0-4-2T "1400" class locomotive #1408, cricket match. No. 1197, $1, LMS Jubilee class 4-6-0, #45684 "Jutland," Kettering station. No. 1198, $1, GWR 2-6-2 "Prairie" locomotive #4547, Lustleigh station. No. 1199, $1, Wainwright "H" class 0-4-4T locomotive, winter countryside.

| 1996, Feb. 29 | Litho. | Perf. 14x15 |
|---|---|---|
| 1194-1199 A339 | Set of 6 | 15.00 15.00 |

Modern Olympic Games, Cent. — A345

| 1996, Apr. 22 | | | Perf. 13 | |
|---|---|---|---|---|
| 1200 | A345 | 20c Runners | .60 | .60 |
| 1201 | A345 | 35c Boxing | 1.00 | 1.00 |
| 1202 | A345 | 50c Javelin | 1.40 | 1.40 |
| 1203 | A345 | $1 Hurdles | 2.75 | 2.75 |
| | | Nos. 1200-1203 (4) | 5.75 | 5.75 |

Butterflies — A346

No. 1204: a, Papilio zalmoxis. b, Papilio dardanus. c, Charaxes varanes. d, Acraea natalica. e, Euphaedra neophron. f, Craphium antheus. g, Salamis anacardii. h, Kallima cymodoce. i, Precis hierta.

| 1996, May 22 | Litho. | Perf. 13½ |
|---|---|---|
| 1204 A346 | 70c Sheet of 9, #a.-i. | 14.00 14.00 |

#### Train Type of 1994
#### Souvenir Sheet

Design: Class Pacific locomotive, Canadian Pacific Railroad.

| 1996, June 8 | Litho. | Perf. 14x15 |
|---|---|---|
| 1205 A339 | $1 multi | 2.25 2.25 |

CAPEX '96.

Fish — A347

No. 1206: a, Atlantic Sailfish. b, Guinean flyingfish. c, Blue marlin. d, Little tunny (e). e, Common dolphinfish (f). f, Guachanche barracuda. g, Guinean parrotfish. h, Cadenat's chromis (g). i, Dusky grouper (h). j, Hoefler's butterflyfish (k). k, African hind (l). l, West African Angelfish.

| 1996, July 15 | Litho. | Perf. 14 |
|---|---|---|
| 1206 A347 | 90c Sheet of 12, #a.-l. | 20.00 20.00 |

Butterflies — A348

No. 1207: a, Euphaedra judith. b, Euphaedra eleus. c, Acraea encedon. d, Euphaedra neophron. e, Liptena praestans. f, Neptis exalenca. g, Palla decius. h, Salamis cytora. i, Pseudacraea dolomena. j, Anaphaeis eriphia. k, Euphaedra themis. l, Hadrodontes varanes.

No. 1208: a, Papilio mnestheus. b, Papilio nobilis. c, Graphium antheus. d, Asterope benguelae. e, Graphium illyris. f, Emphaedra eupalus. g, Charaxes protoclea. h, Cymothoe beckeri. i, Euphaedra cyparissa. j, Coliades chalybe. k, Mimacraea neokoton. l, Charaxes ethalion.

$2, Charaxes pelias.

| 1996 | | Litho. | Perf. 14 | |
|---|---|---|---|---|
| 1207 | A348 | 20c Sheet of 12, #a.-l. | 7.50 | 7.50 |
| 1208 | A348 | 25c Sheet of 12, #a.-l. | 8.00 | 8.00 |
| | | **Souvenir Sheet** | | |
| 1209 | A348 | $2 multicolored | 4.50 | 4.50 |

Birds
A349

Designs, horiz: 35c, African jacana. 50c, Pel's fishing owl. $1, Paradise whydah.

No. 1213: a, Turtle dove. b, Bee-eater. c, Golden oriole. d, Pied flycatcher. e, Sardinian warbler. f, Goliath heron. g, Rock thrush. h, Kestrel. i, Cattle egret. j, Woodchat shrike. k, Hoopoe. l, Great egret.

No. 1214, horiz: a, Red faced crimsonwing. b, Egyptian goose. c, African pitta. d, Paradise flycatcher. e, Garganey. f, Southern carmine bee-eater. g, Fulvous whistling duck. h, Village weaver. i, Martial eagle.

$2, Pintail duck, horiz.

**1996**
| | | | | |
|---|---|---|---|---|
| 1210-1212 | A349 | Set of 3 | 4.50 | 4.50 |
| 1213 | A349 | 25c Sheet of 12, #a.-l. | 7.25 | 7.25 |
| 1214 | A349 | 35c Sheet of 9, #a.-i. | 8.00 | 8.00 |

**Souvenir Sheet**
| | | | | |
|---|---|---|---|---|
| 1215 | A349 | $2 multicolored | 4.75 | 4.75 |

Marilyn Monroe (1926-62) — A350

**1996**
| | | | | |
|---|---|---|---|---|
| 1216 | A350 | 20c multicolored | .70 | .70 |

No. 1216 was issued in sheets of 16.

UNICEF, 50th Anniv. — A351

Designs: 35c, Education for all. 70c, Health care. $1, Children first.

**1996, Sept. 16**      *Perf. 13½x13*
| | | | |
|---|---|---|---|
| 1217-1219 | A351 | 35c Set of 3 | 5.50 5.50 |

1996 Summer Olympic Games, Atlanta — A352

Designs: No. 1220, 20c, Cricket (discontinued sport), vert. No. 1221, 20c, Babe Didrikson, vert. No. 1222, 20c, Vitaly Scherbo, winner of 6 gold medals, 1992, vert. No. 1223, 35c, Betty Robinson, vert. No. 1224, 50c, Cuban baseball team, gold medal, 1992. No. 1225, 50c, Ancient Greek wall painting of boxers, vert. No. 1226, $1, Stadium, Barcelona, 1992. No. 1227, $1, Stadium, Amsterdam, 1928, vert.

No. 1228, 35c, vert. — Olympic events: a, Men's athletics. b, Men's gymnastics. c, Weight lifting. d, Women's volleyball. e, Women's diving. f, Women's gymnastics. g, Women's track. h, Women's tennis. i, Discus.

No. 1229, 35c, vert. — Boxing gold medalists, boxing: a, Tyrell Biggs, U.S. b, Isan Gura, Tanzania (no medal). c, Mark Breland, U.S. d, Teofilo Stevenson, Cuba. e, Ray Leonard, U.S. f, Michael Spinks, U.S. g, Joe Frazier, U.S. h, Floyd Patterson, US. i, George Foreman, US.

$2, Evelyn Ashford.

**1996**      **Litho.**      *Perf. 14*
| | | | |
|---|---|---|---|
| 1220-1227 | A352 | Set of 8 | 14.00 |

**Sheets of 9, #a-i**
| | | | |
|---|---|---|---|
| 1228-1229 | A352 | Set of 2 | 22.50 |

**Souvenir Sheet**
| | | | |
|---|---|---|---|
| 1230 | A352 | $2 multicolored | 7.00 |

---

Flowers and Flowering Trees — A353

No. 1231: a, Olive tree. b, Olive flower. c, Fig tree. d, Almond tree. e, Almug tree. f, Cedar. g, Pomegranate (b). h, Citron. i, Date palm (d, e, j). j, Date palm (fruit). k, Cedar of Lebanon. l, Rock rose. m, Narcissus. n, Oleander (i). o, Date palm (flower). p, Shittah tree. q, Hyacinth. r, Barley, flax (s). s, Grape vine. t, Lily of the field. u, Mandrake. v, Caper desire. w, Madonna lily. x, Aloe (s). y, Date palm tree.

**1996**
| | | | |
|---|---|---|---|
| 1231 | A353 | 25c Sheet of 25, #a.-y. | 25.00 25.00 |

History of Rock and Roll A354

No. 1232: a, Wilson Pickett. b, Bill Haley. c, Otis Redding. d, Fats Domino. e, Buddy Holly. f, Chubby Checker. g, Marvin Gaye. h, Jimi Hendrix.

**1996**      *Perf. 13½x14*
| | | | |
|---|---|---|---|
| 1232 | A354 | 35c Sheet of 8, #a.-h. + label | 8.00 8.00 |

Kingfisher — A355

No. 1233 — Kingfishers: a, Striped. b, Greyheaded. c, Pied. d, Giant. e, Shining-blue.

**1996, Oct. 7**      **Litho.**      *Perf. 13½*
| | | | |
|---|---|---|---|
| 1233 | A355 | 75c Strip of 5, #a.-e. | 7.50 7.50 |

See No. 1236.

Mao Zedong, 20th Anniv. of Death — A356

**1996, Nov. 1**      **Litho.**      *Perf. 14½x14*
| | | | |
|---|---|---|---|
| 1234 | A356 | $1 shown | 2.50 2.50 |
| 1235 | A356 | $1 As older man | 2.50 2.50 |

**Kingfisher Type of 1996**
**Souvenir Sheet**

**1997, Feb. 3**      **Litho.**      *Perf. 14*
| | | | |
|---|---|---|---|
| 1236 | A355 | $1 Like #1233b | 2.00 2.00 |

Hong Kong '97. No. 1236 contains one 29x43mm stamp.

---

**Disarmament Type of 1993**
Inscribed "PEACE TODAY"

**1997**      **Litho.**      **13½x14**
| | | | | |
|---|---|---|---|---|
| 1237 | A336 | $1 Like #1157 | 3.00 | 3.00 |
| 1238 | A336 | $2 Like #1158 | 5.00 | 5.00 |
| 1239 | A336 | $3 Like #1156 | 9.00 | 9.00 |
| | | *Nos. 1237-1239 (3)* | | 17.00 |

Nos. 1237-1239 are dated 1996.

Wildlife — A357

No. 1240: a, Olive baboon. b, Leopard. c, African tree pangolin. d, Vervet. e, Aardvark. f, Spotted hyena. g, Hunting dog. h, Thomson's gazelle. i, Warthog. j, African civet. k, Nile crocodile. l, African polecat.

**1997, Apr. 2**      **Litho.**      *Perf. 14*
| | | | |
|---|---|---|---|
| 1240 | A357 | 50c Sheet of 12, #a.-l. | 15.00 15.00 |

Deng Xiaoping (1904-97), British Transfer of Hong Kong — A358

Different portraits of Deng Xiaoping, "July 1, 1997," Hong Kong: 70c, In daylight, vert. $1, At night.

No. 1243: a, 50c. b, 70c. c, $1.20.

**1997**      **Litho.**      *Perf. 14*
| | | | |
|---|---|---|---|
| 1241 | A358 | 70c multicolored | 2.00 |
| 1242 | A358 | $1 multicolored | 3.25 |
| 1243 | A358 | Sheet of 3, #a.-c. | 7.75 |

No. 1241 is 28x44mm, and was issued in sheets of 4. No. 1242 was issued in sheets of 3.

UNESCO, 50th Anniv. A359

No. 1244, 50c, vert.: a, Canals, Venice, Italy. b, Mosque of Badshahi, Gardens of Shalamar, Lahore, Pakistan. c, Palace of Orando, Spain. d, Grounds of Temple of Hera, Greece. e, Church and Monastery of Daphni, Greece. f, Fraser Island, Australia. g, Canadian Rocky Mountains Park, Canada. h, Church of Santo Domingo Puebla, Mexico.

No. 1245, 50c, vert.: a, City of Ohrid and lake, Macedonia. b, Thracian Tomb of Sveshtari, Bulgaria. c, Monastery of Hossios Luckas, Greece. d, Church of Santa Cristina of Lena, Spain. e, Church of Santa Maria Della Salute, Venice, Italy. f, Center of Puebla, Mexico. g, Bagrati Cathedral, Georgia. h, Quebec City, Canada.

No. 1246: a, Ngorongoro Conservation Area, Tanzania. b, Garamba Natl. Park, Zaire. c, Canaima Natl. Park, Venezuela. d, Simien Natl. Park, Ethiopia. e, Mana Pools Natl. Park, Zimbabwe.

No. 1247, $2, Palace of Diocletian, Split, Croatia. No., 1248, $2, Monument of Nubia at Abu Simbel, Egypt. No. 1249, $2, Quedlinberg, Germany.

*Perf. 13½x14, 14x13½*
**1997, June 17**      **Litho.**
**Sheets of 8, #a-h + Label**
| | | | |
|---|---|---|---|
| 1244-1245 | A359 | Set of 2 | 27.50 |
| 1246 | A359 | 70c Sheet of 5, #a-e, + label | 12.50 |

**Souvenir Sheets**
| | | | |
|---|---|---|---|
| 1247-1249 | A359 | Set of 3 | 21.00 |

Queen Elizabeth II, Prince Philip, 50th Wedding Anniv. — A360

---

No. 1250: a, Queen holding umbrella. b, Royal arms. c, Prince in white uniform, Queen. d, Queen waving, Prince. e, Windsor Castle. f, Prince Philip.

No. 1251, $2, Queen seated on sofa. No. 1252, $2, Queen, Prince wearnig robes of Order of the Garter.

**1997, June 17**      *Perf. 14*
| | | | |
|---|---|---|---|
| 1250 | A360 | 50c Sheet of 6, #a.-f. | 11.00 |

**Souvenir Sheet**
| | | | |
|---|---|---|---|
| 1251-1252 | A360 | $2 Set of 2 | 14.00 |

Grimm's Fairy Tales — A361

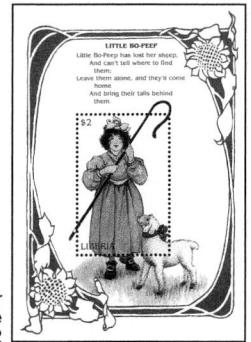

Mother Goose A362

No. 1253 — Scenes from Rapunzel: a, Girl. b, Wicked person, raven. c, Prince.

No. 1254, Prince rescuing girl.

No. 1255, Little Bo Peep, sheep.

**1997, June 17**      *Perf. 13½x14*
| | | | |
|---|---|---|---|
| 1253 | A361 | $1 Sheet of 3, #a.-c. | 10.00 |

**Souvenir Sheets**
| | | | |
|---|---|---|---|
| 1254 | A361 | $2 multicolored | 7.00 |

             *Perf. 14*
| | | | |
|---|---|---|---|
| 1255 | A362 | $2 multicolored | 7.00 |

1998 Winter Olympics, Nagano — A363

Designs: 50c, Olympic Stadium, Lillehammer, 1994. 70c, Johann Koss, speed skating. $1, Katarina Witt, figure skating. $1.50, Sonia Henie, figure skating.

No. 1260: a, K. Seizinger, Alpine downhill skiing. b, J. Weissflog, 120-m ski jump. c, T. Kono, Nordic combined. d, G. Hackl, luge.

No. 1261: a, E. Bredesen, 90-m ski jump. b, L. Kjus, downhill skiing. c, B. Daehlie, cross-country skiing. d, P. Wiberg, combined Alpine skiing. e, S.L. Hattestad, freestyle skiing. f, G. Weder, D. Acklin, 2-man bobsled. g, Swedish hockey player. h, T. Alsgaard, cross-country skiing.

No. 1262, $2, German biathlete, 1994. No. 1263, $2, M. Wasmeier, giant slalom. No. 1264, $2, J. Koss, speed skating, diff. No. 1265, $2, V. Schneider, slalom.

**1997, June 23**      *Perf. 14*
| | | | |
|---|---|---|---|
| 1256-1259 | A363 | Set of 4 | 13.00 |
| 1260 | A363 | 50c Strip or block of 4, #a.-d. | 7.00 |
| 1261 | A363 | 50c Sheet of 8, #a.-h. | 14.00 |

**Souvenir Sheets**
| | | | |
|---|---|---|---|
| 1262-1265 | A363 | Set of 4 | 27.50 |

No. 1260 was issued in sheets of 8 stamps.

Flowers — A364

No. 1266, 50c: a, Sugar cane dahlia. b, Windsor tall phlox. c, Creative art daylily. d, Columbine. e, Infinite Grace bearded iris. f, Fairy lilies mini amaryllis.
No. 1267, 50c: a, White coneflower. b, Peggy Lee hybrid tea rose. c, Daffodil. d, Bowl of Beauty peony. e, Hardy lily. f, Windflower.
No. 1268, $2, Lily-flowered tulip. No. 1269, $2, Chrysanthemum Potomac.

**1997, July 1    Litho.    Perf. 14**
**Sheets of 6, #a-f**
1266-1267  A364  Set of 2    20.00 20.00
**Souvenir Sheets**
1268-1269  A364  Set of 2    16.00 16.00

Flora and Fauna — A365

No. 1270: a, Lovebirds. b, Genet. c, Leopard, crowned night heron. d, Gorilla. e, Giant wild boar. f, Elephant. g, Sterculia flower, skink. h, Ladybugs, bush baby. i, Cape primroses, ground hornbill.
No. 1271, $2, Rufus-crowned roller. No. 1272, $2, Gray heron.

**1997, July 1**
1270  A365  50c Sheet of 9, #a.-i.    13.00 13.00
**Souvenir Sheets**
1271-1272  A365  Set of 2    12.00 12.00

Chernobyl Disaster, 10th Anniv. — A366

**1997, June 17  Litho.    Perf. 13½x14**
1273  A366  $1 UNESCO    3.25 3.25

Marcello Mastroianni (1923-96), Actor — A367

No. 1274 — Scenes from motion pictures: a, Casanova, 1970. b, Divorce Italian Style. c, 8 ½. d, La Dolce Vita.

**1997, Sept. 3**
1274  A367  75c Sheet of 4, #a.-d.    10.00 10.00

Contemporary Artists and Paintings — A368

No. 1275, 50c: a, Andy Warhol (1927-87). b, "Multicolored Retropective," by Warhol, 1979. c, "The Three Muscians," by Picasso, 1921. d, Pablo Picasso (1881-1973). e, Henri Matisse (1869-1954). f, "The Dance," by Matisse, 1910. g, "Lavender Mist," by Pollock, 1950. h, Jackson Pollock (1912-56).
No. 1276, 50c: a, Piet Mondrian (1872-1944). b, "Broadway Boogie Woogie," by Mondrian, 1942-43. c, "Persistence of Memory," by

Dali, 1931. d, Salvador Dali (1904-89). e, Roy Lichtenstein (1923-97). f, "Artist's Studio: The Dance," by Lichtenstein, 1974. g, "Europe After the Rain," by Ernst, 1940-42. h, Max Ernst (1891-1976).

**1997, Sept. 3    Perf. 14**
**Sheets of 8, #a-h**
1275-1276  A368  Set of 2    27.50 27.50
Nos. 1275b-1275c, 1275f-1275g, 1276b-1276c, 1276f-1276g are 53x38mm.

Owls A369

No. 1277: a, Akun eagle owl. b, Shelley's eagle owl. c, African wood owl. d, Rufous fishing owl. e, Maned owl. f, Sandy scops owl.

**1997**
1277  A369  50c Sheet of 6, #a.-f.    9.00 9.00

Birds — A370

Designs: 1c, Black bee-eater. 2c, Yellow-billed barbet. 3c, Carmine bee-eater. 4c, Malachite kingfisher. 5c, Emerald cuckoo. 10c, Blue-throated roller. 15c, Blue-headed bee-eater. 20c, Black-collared lovebird. 25c, Broad-billed roller. 50c, Blue-breasted kingfisher. 70c, Little bee-eater. 75c, Yellow spotted barbet. 90c, White-throated bee-eater. $1, Double-toothed barbet. $2, Blue-cheeked bee-eater. $3, Narina's trogon.

**1997**
1278  A370  1c multicolored    .25 .25
1279  A370  2c multicolored    .25 .25
1280  A370  3c multicolored    .25 .25
1281  A370  4c multicolored    .25 .25
1282  A370  5c multicolored    .25 .25
1283  A370  10c multicolored    .25 .25
1284  A370  15c multicolored    .40 .40
1285  A370  20c multicolored    .50 .50
1286  A370  25c multicolored    .65 .65
1287  A370  50c multicolored    1.25 1.25
1288  A370  70c multicolored    1.90 1.90
1289  A370  75c multicolored    2.00 2.00
1290  A370  90c multicolored    2.40 2.40
1291  A370  $1 multicolored    2.75 2.75
1292  A370  $2 multicolored    5.25 5.25
1293  A370  $3 multicolored    7.75 7.75
Nos. 1278-1293 (16)    26.35 26.35

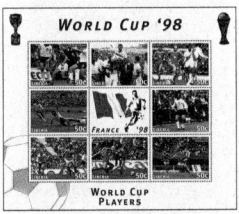

1998 World Cup Soccer A371

Players, country, vert: 50c, Salenko, Russia. 70c, Schillaci, Italy. $1, Lineker, England. $1.50, Pele, Brazil. $2, Fontaine, France. $2, Rahn, W. Germany.
No. 1300, 50c, vert: a, Ardiles, Argentina. b, Romario, Brazil. c, Rummenigge, Germany. d, Charlton, England. e, Villa, Argentina. f, Matthäus, Germany. g, Maradona, Argentina. h, Lineker, England.
No. 1301, 50c: a, Paulo Rossi, Italy. b, Ademir, Brazil. c, Grzegorz Lato, Poland. d, Gary Lineker, England. e, Gerd Muller, W. Germany. f, Johan Cruyff, Holland. g, Karl-Heinz Rummenigge, Germany. h, Mario Kempes, Argentina.
No. 1302, $6, Beckenbauer, W. Germany, vert. No. 1303, $6, Maier, W. Germany, vert.

**Perf. 13½x14, 14x13½**
**1997, Oct. 1    Litho.**
1294-1299  A371  Set of 6    18.00 18.00
**Sheets of 8, #a-h, + Label**
1300-1301  A371  Set of 2    27.50 27.50
**Souvenir Sheets**
1302-1303  A371  Set of 2    40.00 40.00

Marine Life — A372

No. 1304: a, Flamingoes (beach, palm trees). b, Six flamingoes. c, Sailfish (d). d, Egret. e, Yellow-tail snapper. f, Manatee. g, Clown coris. h, White-collar butterflyfish. i, Royal angelfish. j, Titan triggerfish. k, Three-striped wrasse. l, Pacific blue-eye. m, Wobbegono. n, Jellyfish. o, Sea urchin, red sea triggerfish. p, Harlequin fish.
No. 1305, $2, Seahorses, vert. No. 1306, $2, Anemone fish.

**1998, Mar. 9    Litho.    Perf. 14**
1304  A372  20c Sheet of 16, #a.-p.    9.50 9.50
**Souvenir Sheets**
**Perf. 13½x14, 14x13½**
1305-1306  A372  Set of 2    12.00 12.00
No. 1305 contains one 38x51mm stamp, No. 1306 contains one 51x38mm stamp.

Butterflies A373

Designs: No. 1307, 50c, Orange tip. No. 1308, 50c, Saturn. No. 1309, 50c, Queen of Spain fritillary. No. 1310, 50c, Plain tiger. No. 1311, 50c, Doris. No. 1312, 50c, Forest queen. No. 1313, 50c, Figure-of-eight. No. 1314, 50c, Orange-barred sulphur.
No. 1315, 50c: a, Alfalfa. b, Orange-barred sulphur, diff. c, Union jack. d, Mocker swallowtail. e, Large green-banded blue. f, Common dotted border.
No. 1316, 50c: a, Cairns birdwing. b, Leafwing. c, Banded kin shoemaker. d, Tiger swallowtail. e, Adonis blue. f, Palmfly.
No. 1317, $2, Great orange tip. No. 1318, $2, Japanese emperor.

**1998, Apr. 6    Litho.    Perf. 14**
1307-1314  A373  Set of 8    12.00 12.00
**Sheets of 6, #a-f**
1315-1316  A373  Set of 2    18.00 18.00
**Souvenir Sheets**
1317-1318  A373  Set of 2    12.00 12.00

Noah's Ark — A374

No. 1319: a, Condors. b, Giraffes, skunks. c, Mallard ducks. d, Snowy owl. e, Snowy owl (face forward). f, Noah. g, Noah's wife. h, Polar bears. i, Elephants. j, Zebras. k, Rhinoceros. l, Sheep. m, Ruby-throated hummingbird. n, Wives of Noah's sons. o, Bats. p, Ring-necked pheasant. q, Tiger. r, Deer. s, Kangaroos. t, Camels. u, Red-eyed frogs. v, Raccoons. w, Rooster, hen. x, Marmosets. y, Lions.
$2, Black-legged kittiwake gull, ark on top of mountain, horiz.

**1998, May 4    Litho.    Perf. 14**
1319  A374  15c Sheet of 25, #a.-y.    11.00 11.00
**Souvenir Sheet**
1320  A374  $2 multicolored    6.00 6.00

World Wildlife Fund — A375

No. 1321 — Liberian Mongoose: a, Looking straight ahead. b, Holding object between front paws. c, With front legs on branch. d, With mouth wide open.

**1998, June 16    Litho.    Perf. 14**
1321  A375  32c Block or strip of 4, #a.-d.    5.50 5.50
Issued in sheets of 12 stamps.

Mushrooms — A376

Designs: 10c, Lepiota cristata. 15c, Russula emetica. 20c, Coprinus comatus. 30c, Russula cyanoxantha. 50c, Cortinarius violaceus. 75c, Amanita cothurnata. $1, Stropharia cyanea. $1.20, Panaeolus semiovatus.
No. 1330, 40c: a, Collybia butryacea. b, Asterophora parasitica. c, Tricholomopsis rutilans. d, Marasmius alliaceus. e, Mycena crocata. f, Mycena polygramma. g, Oudemansiella mucida. h, Entoloma conferendum. i, Entoloma serrulatum.
No. 1331, 40c: a, Cordyceps militaris. b, Xylaria hypoxlon. c, Sarcoscypha austriaca. d, Auriscalpium. e, Fomitopsis pinicola. f, Pleurotus ostreatus. g, Lepista flaccida. h, Clitocybe metachroa. i, Hygrocybe conica.
No. 1332, $2, Gomphidus roseus. No. 1333, $2, Paxillus atrotomentosus. No. 1334, $2, Russula occidentalis. No. 1335, $2, Cantharellus cibarius.

**1998, July 1**
1322-1329  A376  Set of 8    14.00 14.00
**Sheets of 9, #a-i**
1330-1331  A376  Set of 2    24.00 24.00
**Souvenir Sheets**
1332-1335  A376  Set of 4    27.50 27.50

Monarchs — A377

No. 1336, 50c: a, Kaiser Wilhelm II, Germany. b, Qabus Bin Said, Oman. c, King Albert, Belgium. d, Haile Selassie, Ethiopia. e, King Hussein, Jordan. f, Sheik Jaber Al-Ahmad Al-Sabah, Kuwait.
No. 1337, 50c: a, Alexander the Great, Greece. b, Charlemagne, France. c, Cleopatra, Egypt. d, Henry VIII, England. e, Peter the Great, Russia. f, Frederick the Great, Prussia.
No. 1338, 50c: a, Queen Beatrix, Netherlands. b, King Juan Carlos, Spain. c, Queen Elizabeth II, England. d, Franz Joseph I, Austria-Hungary. e, Princess Grace, Monaco. f, King Carl XVI Gustaf, Sweden.
No. 1339, $2, Empress Michiko, Japan. No. 1340, $2, Emperor Akihito, Japan. No. 1341, $2, Kublai Khan, China.

**1998, July 27    Litho.    Perf. 14**
**Sheets of 6, #a-f**
1336-1338  A377  Set of 3    24.00 24.00
**Souvenir Sheets**
1339-1341  A377  Set of 3    21.00 21.00

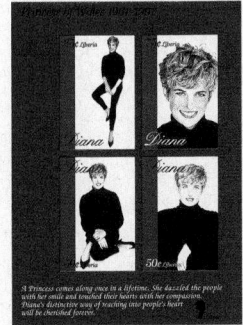

Diana, Princess of Wales (1961-97) — A378

Various portraits of Diana in black outfit.

**1998    Imperf.**
1342  A378  50c Sheet of 4, #a.-d.  4.00 4.00

Birds — A379

No. 1343, 32c, Great green macaw. No. 1344, 32c, Crowned pigeon, vert. No. 1345, 32c, Blue-gray tanager. No. 1346, 32c, Roseate spoonbill, vert. No. 1347, 32c, Red-capped manakin. No. 1348, 32c, Groove-billed ani. No. 1349, 32c, South African crowned crane, vert.

No. 1350, vert: a, African sunbird. b, Seven-colored tanager. c, Red-throated bee-eater. d, Blue-crowned motmot. e, Duvaucel's trogon. f, Green bulbul. g, Grass-green tanager. h, Turaco. i, Hammer-head. j, Sarus crane. k, Limpkin. l, Ground hornbill.

No. 1351, $2, Red-crested touraco. No. 1352, $2, Flamingo, vert.

**1998, Aug. 31**    **Litho.**    **Perf. 14**
1343-1349 A379   Set of 7    7.00   7.00
1350 A379 32c Sheet of 12,
     #a.-l.           12.00 12.00

**Souvenir Sheets**
1351-1352 A379   Set of 2    12.00 12.00

Children's Stories — A380

No. 1354: a, Tom Sawyer, by Mark Twain. b, Peter Rabbit, by Beatrix Potter. c, The Nutcracker, by E.T.A. Hoffman. d, Hansel & Gretel, by The Brothers Grimm. e, The Princess and the Pea, by Hans Christian Andersen. f, Oliver Twist, by Charles Dickens. g, Little Red Riding Hood, by The Brothers Grimm. h, Rumpelstiltskin, by The Brothers Grimm. i, The Wind & the Willows, by Kenneth Grahame.

$2, Rapunzel, by Brothers Grimm.

**1998, Sept. 16**   **Litho.**   **Perf. 14½**
1354 A380 40c Sheet of 9,
     #a.-i.           12.00 12.00

**Souvenir Sheet**
**Perf. 13½**
1355 A380   $2 multicolored    7.00   7.00
No. 1355 contains one 38x51mm stamp.

Island, Marine Life — A381

No. 1356: a, Litoria peronii. b, Volcano, denomination UL. c, Volcano, denomination UR. d, Egretta alba. e, Graphium antiphates itamputi. f, Rhododendron zoelleri. g, Boat. h, Lava flow. i, Cormorants. j, Vaccinium. k, Caranx latus. l, Dugongs. m, Underwater lava flow. n, Cetocarus bicolor. o, Chilomycterus spilostylus. p, Lienardella fasliatus. q, Aerobatus. r, Gray reef shark. s, Acanthurus leucosternon, denomination UR. t, Hippocampus kuda. u, Coral, denomination UR. v, Chelonia. w, Myripristis hexogona. x, Coral, denomination, UL. y, Acanthurus leucosternon, denonination UL.

No. 1357: a, Sperm whale (b, c). b, Lollipop tang. c, Bottlenose dolphin (b, f). d, Jackass penguin (h). e, Harlequin tuskfish. f, Manta ray (a, b, e, j). g, Sealion. h, Grouper (g, l). i, Hammerhead shark (m). j, Butterfly fish. k, Garibaldi (g). l, Marine iguana (p). m, Loggerhead turtle (n). n, Seahorse. o, Horseshow crab (n, p). p, Moray eel.

No. 1358, 32c: a, Walrus. b, Pockfish-harlequin. c, Striped marlin. d, Whale shark. e, Spiny boxfish. f, Porcupine fish. g, Octopus. h, Dragonfish. i, Sea krait.

No. 1359, 32c: a, Snapping turtle. b, Atlantic spadefish. c, Bottlenose dolphin. d, Humpback whale. e, Whitetip shark. f, Twilight and deep seafish. g, Moorish idol. h, American lobster. i, Stingrays.

---

No. 1360, $2, Great white shark. No. 1361, $2, Banner fish. No. 1362, $2, Killer whale. No. 1363, $2, Surgeon fish.

**1998, Oct. 15**        **Perf. 14**
1356 A381 15c Sheet of 25,
     #a.-y.           12.00 12.00
1357 A381 20c Sheet of 16,
     #a.-p.           10.00 10.00

**Sheets of 9, #a-i**
1358-1359 A381   Set of 2    18.00 18.00

**Souvenir Sheets**
1360-1363 A381   Set of 4    22.50 22.50
International Year of the Ocean.

Diana, Princess of Wales (1961-97) — A382

No. 1364: a, Inscription panel at left. b, Panel at right.

**1998, Oct. 26**   **Litho.**   **Perf. 14½x14**
1364 A382 50c Horiz. pair, #a-b   3.00 3.00
No. 1364 was issued in sheets of 3 pairs.

Pablo Picasso (1881-1973) A383

Entire paintings or details: 50c, Woman Throwing a Stone, 1931. 70c, Man with Sword and Flower, 1969, vert. $1, Large Bather with a Book, 1937, vert.
$2, French Cancan, 1901.

**1998, Oct. 26**        **Perf. 14½**
1365-1367 A383   Set of 3    7.50 7.50

**Souvenir Sheet**
1368 A383   $2 multicolored    7.00 7.00

1998 World Scout Jamboree, Chile — A385

No. 1371: a, Daniel Carter Beard, Ernest Thompson Seton, award scouts, 1912. b, Robert Baden-Powell in Matabeleland, 1896. c, Scout repairing small girl's wagon.

**1998, Oct. 26**
1371 A385 $1 Sheet of 3, #a.-
        c.          10.00 10.00

Enzo Ferrari (1898-1988), Automobile Manufacturer A386

No. 1372: a, King Leopold Cabriolet. b, 195 S. c, 250 GTO 64.
$2, 250MM Cabriolet.

---

**1998, Oct. 26**   **Litho.**   **Perf. 14**
1372 A386 $1 Sheet of 3, #a.-c.   9.00 9.00
**Souvenir Sheet**
1373 A386   $2 multicolored    8.50 8.50
No. 1373 contains one 91x35mm stamp.

Royal Air Force, 80th Anniv. — A387

No. 1374: a, Hawker Hurricane XII. b, Avro Lancaster in flight. c, Avro Lancaster B2. d, Supermarine Spitfire HG Mk 1XB.
No. 1375, $2, Bristol F2B fighter, Eurofighter. No. 1376, $2, Hawk, biplane.

**1998, Oct. 26**
1374 A387 70c Sheet of 4,
     #a.-d.         9.50   9.50
**Souvenir Sheet**
1375-1376 A387   Set of 2    14.00 14.00

Famous People and Events of the Twentieth Cent. — A388

No. 1380, 40c: a, Mao Tse-tung. b, Cultural Revolution begins. c, Promoting Third World unity. d, Zhou Enlai. e, Deng Xiaoping. f, Hong Kong returns to China, 1997. g, Shanghai, an Asian metropolis. h, Jiang Zemin.

No. 1381, 40c: a, Robert E. Peary. b, Expedition to the North Pole. c, Climbing Mt. Everest. d, Sir Edmund Hillary. e, Neil Armstrong. f, Walking on the moon. g, Expedition to the South Pole. h, Roald Amundsen.
$2, Matthew Henson.

**1998, Dec. 1**    **Litho.**    **Perf. 14**
**Sheets of 8, #a-h**
1380-1381 A388   Set of 2    22.50 22.50
**Souvenir Sheet**
1382 A388   $2 multicolored    6.50 6.50
Nos. 1380b-1380c, 1380f-1380g, 1381b-1381c, 1380f-1381g are each 53x38mm.

Classic Cars — A389

Designs: No. 1383, 32c, 1966-72 Lamborghini Miura. No. 1384, 32c, 1966-93 Alfa Romeo Spider. No. 1385, 32c, 1948-61 Jaguar XK140. No. 1386, 32c, 1959-63 Lotus Elite.

No. 1387, 50c: a, 1949-53 Bristol 401. b, 1952-55 Bentley Continental R. c, 1973-75 Lancia stratos. d, 1963-67 Chevrolet Corvette Stingray. e, 1948-52 Austin A90 Atlantic. f, 1969-90 Aston Martin V8.

No. 1388, 50c: a, 1961-75 Jaguar E-Type. b, 1955-57 Ford Thunderbird. c, 1964-73, Ford Mustang GT350. d, 1957-77 Fiat 500. e, 1955-59 BMW 507. f, 1963-65 Buick Riviera.

No. 1389, $2, 1945-55 MG TD. No. 1390, $2, 1959-65 Rolls Royce Silver Cloud.

**1998, Dec. 24**
1383-1386 A389   Set of 4    4.00   4.00
**Sheets of 6, #a-f**
1387-1388 A389   Set of 2    20.00 20.00
**Souvenir Sheets**
1389-1390 A389   Set of 2    13.00 13.00

New Year 1999 (Year of the Rabbit) A390

Paintings, by Liu Jiyou (1918-83): No. 1391, Two rabbits. No. 1392, Three rabbits. No. 1393, Two rabbits, flowers, vert.

---

**1999, Jan. 5**
1391 A390 50c multicolored    1.75 1.75
1392 A390 50c multicolored    1.75 1.75
**Souvenir Sheet**
1393 A390   $2 multicolored    6.50 6.50
Nos. 1391-1392 were issued in sheets of 2 each. No. 1393 contains one 43x52mm stamp.

US Presidents — A391

No. 1394, 75c, Various portraits of Abraham Lincoln. No. 1395, 75c, Various portraits of Bill Clinton.

**1998, Dec. 1**   **Litho.**   **Perf. 14**
**Sheets of 4, #a-d**
1394-1395 A391   Set of 2    20.00 20.00

Zhou Enlai (1898-1976), Chinese Premier — A392

Various portraits.

**1999**      **Litho.**      **Perf. 14**
1396 A392 50c Sheet of 6,
     #a.-f.           10.00 10.00
**Souvenir Sheet**
1397 A392   $2 multicolored    7.00 7.00

Raptors — A393

Designs: 50c, Snowy owl. 70c, Barn owl. $1, American kestrel. $1.50, Golden eagle.
No. 1402, 50c: a, Eurasian eagle owl. b, Osprey. c, Egyptian vulture. d, Lizard buzzard. e, Pale chanting goshawk. f, Bald eagle.

No. 1403, 50c: a, Goshawk. b, Laughing falcon. c, Oriental bay-owl. d, Swallow-tailed kite. e, Secretary bird. f, Brown falcon.

No. 1404, $2, Northern harrier. No. 1405, $2, Peregrine falcon.

**1999, Jan. 4**
1398-1401 A393   Set of 4    11.00 11.00
**Sheets of 6, #a-f**
1402-1403 A393   Set of 2    20.00 20.00
**Souvenir Sheets**
1404-1405 A393   Set of 2    13.00 13.00

Dinosaurs A395

No. 1406, 50c, Pachyrinosaur. No. 1407, 50c, Centrosaurus, vert. No. 1408, 70c, Pentaceratops, vert. No. 1409, 70c, Oviraptor, vert. $1, Corythosaur. $1.50, Stegosaurus, vert.

No. 1412, 40c: a, Baryonyx (e). b, Pachycephalosaur (a, c). c, Homalocephale. d, Pterodustro (f). e, Pycnosteroides. f, Giant nautiloid. g, Kronosaur (e, f). h, Giant cephalopod (g).

No. 1413, 40c: a, Camarasaur. b, Albertosaur (c, f, g). c, Eudimorhodon (b, d). d, Dimorphodon (c). e, Compsognathus. f, Torosaurus. g, Nodosaurid (h). h, Probactrosaurus.

No. 1414, $2, Tarbosaurus, vert. No. 1415, $2, Shunosaurus, vert.

**1999, Jan. 18**
1406-1411 A395 Set of 6 12.00 12.00
**Sheets of 8, #a-h**
1412-1413 A395 Set of 2 22.50 22.50
**Souvenir Sheets**
1414-1415 A395 Set of 2 13.00 13.00

Dinosaurs — A396

Designs: 50c, Brachiosaurus, vert. 70c, Tyrannosaurus, vert. $1, Mosasaurus. $1.50, Triceratops.
No. 1420: a, Albertosaurus. b, Parasaurolophus. c, Styracosaurus. d, Struthiomimus. e, Ankylosaurus. f, Chasmosaurus.
No. 1421, $2, Deinonychus. No. 1422, $2, Stegosaurus.

**1999**
1416-1419 A396 Set of 4 9.00 9.00
1420 A396 50c Sheet of 6, 10.00 10.00
  #a.-f.
**Souvenir Sheets**
1421-1422 A396 Set of 2 13.00 13.00

Flowers — A397

Designs: No. 1423, 50c, Tecophilaea cyanocrocus. 70c, Nymphoides peltata. $1, Angraecum scottianum. $1.50, Grevillea dielsiana.
No. 1427, 50c: a, Cyrtopodium parvilforum. b, Catharanthus roseus. c, Acacia acuminata. d, Herbertia lahue. e, Protea venusta. f, Clianthus formosus.
No. 1428, 50c: a, Dendrobium rarum. b, Cyrtorchis arcuata. c, Zygopetalum intermedium. d, Cassia fistula. e, Saintpaulia ionantha. f, Heliconia collinsiana.
No. 1429, $2, Hibiscus tilliaceus. No. 1430, $2, Rhododendron thomsonii.

**1999, Feb. 8**
1423-1426 A397 Set of 4 11.00 11.00
**Sheets of 6, #a-f**
1427-1428 A397 Set of 2 20.00 20.00
**Souvenir Sheets**
1429-1430 A397 Set of 2 13.00 13.00

Orchids — A398

Designs: No. 1431, 50c, Tridactyle bicaudata. No. 1432, 50c, Angraecum infundibulare. No. 1433, 70c, Oeceoclades maculata. No. 1434, 70c, Ophyrs fusca. No. 1435, $1, Sobennikoffia robusta. No. 1436, $1, Stenoglottis fimbriata. No. 1437, $1.50, Plectrelminthus caudatus. No. 1438, $1.50, Satyrium erectum.
No. 1439, 50c: a, Angraecrum eichlerianum. b, Ansellia africana. c, Cymbidiella pardalina. d, Angraecum eburnium. e, Ancistrochilus rothchildianus. f, Aerangis luteoalba.
No. 1440, 50c: a, Dis cardinalis. b, Cytorchus arcuata. c, Cynorkis compacta. d, Disa kewensis. e, Eulophia guineensis. f, Eulophia speciosa.
No. 1441, $2, Angraecum compactum. No. 1442, $2, Calanthe vestita.

**1999, Mar. 13**
1431-1438 A398 Set of 8 22.50 22.50
**Sheets of 6, #a-f**
1439-1440 A398 Set of 2 19.00 19.00
**Souvenir Sheets**
1441-1442 A398 Set of 2 13.00 13.00

Orchids — A399

Designs: No. 1443, 50c, Calypso bulbosa. No. 1444, 50c, Maclellanara pagan lovesong. No. 1445, 70c, Masdevallia chimaera. No. 1446, 70c, Yamadara midnight. $1, Cleistes divaricata. $1.50, Oncidium golden sunset.
No. 1449: a, Trichopilia tortilis. b, Stenoglottis longifolia. c, Telipogon pulcher. d, Esmeralda clarkei. e, Papilionanthe teres. f, Mormodes rolfeanum. g, Cypripedium acaule. h, Serapias lingua.

**1999, Mar. 13**
1443-1448 A399 Set of 6 15.00 15.00
1449 A399 30c Sheet of 8, 9.00 9.00
  #a.-h.

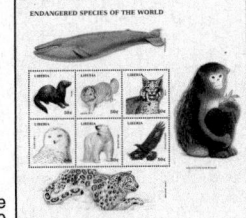

Wildlife — A400

No. 1450: a, Mink. b, Arctic fox. c, Lynx. d, Snowy owl. e, Polar bear. f, Golden eagle. $2, Big horn sheep.

**1999, Feb. 24** **Litho.** **Perf. 14**
1450 A400 50c Sheet of 6, #a.-f. 7.00 7.00
**Souvenir Sheet**
1451 A400 $2 multicolored 5.00 5.00

Flora and Fauna A401

No. 1452: a, Madgascan red fody. b, Indri (e). c, Coral-billed nuthatch. d, Sifaka (g, j). e, Golden piper. f, Aye aye (i). g, Broad-bordered grass yellow butterfly. h, Ring-tailed lemur (g, j, k). i, Parson's chameleon. j, Madagascar day gecko. k, Leaf-tailed gecko. l, Orchid.
No. 1453, $2, Wattled false sunbird. No. 1454, $2, Parson's chameleon. No. 1455, $2, Ring-tailed lemur.

**1999, Apr. 1**
1452 A401 20c Sheet of 12, 7.00 7.00
  #a.-l.
**Souvenir Sheets**
1453-1455 A401 Set of 3 15.00 15.00

Seabirds — A402

Designs: No. 1456, 50c, Harlequin duck. No. 1457, 50c, Eleonor's falcon, vert. No. 1458, 70c, Wilson's plover. No. 1459, 70c, Common eider. No. 1460, $1, Little tern. No. 1461, $1, American oystercatcher. No. 1462, $1.50, Herring gull, vert. No. 1463, $1.50, Brown pelican, vert.
No. 1464, 30c, vert.: a, Great cormorant. b, Crested cormorant. c, Red faced cormorant. d, Whimbrel. e, Tufted puffin. f, Ivory gull. g, Common murre. h, Shelduck. i, Razorbill.
No. 1465, 30c: a, Common tern. b, Black-legged kittiwake. c, Barnacle goose. d, Black-headed gull. e, Semipalmated plover. f, Northern gannet. g, King eider. h, Iceland gull. i, Ring-billed gull.
No. 1466, $2, Arctic loon. No. 1467, $2, Atlantic puffin. No. 1468, $2, California gull, vert.

**1999, Apr. 1** **Litho.** **Perf. 14**
1456-1463 A402 Set of 8 17.00 17.00
**Sheets of 9, #a-i**
1464-1465 A402 Set of 2 13.00 13.00
**Souvenir Sheets**
1466-1468 A402 Set of 3 15.00 15.00

Queen Mother (b. 1900) — A404

No. 1475: a, With King George VI at wedding, 1923. b, In Nairobi, 1959. c, Wearing tiara, 1953. d, Wearing hat, 1990. $2, Wearing hat, 1990, diff.

**1999, Aug. 4** **Perf. 14**
1475 A404 $1 Sheet of 4, #a.-d., 9.00 9.00
  + label
**Souvenir Sheet**
**Perf. 13¾**
1476 A404 $2 multicolored 5.00 5.00
No. 1476 contains one 38x51mm stamp.

Trains — A405

Designs: 32c, Nozomi Train, Japan. 40c, 401 Intercity Express, Germany. 50c, C53, Japan Railways. 70c, Beuth 2-2-2, Germany.
No. 1481, 40c: a, "Adler," Germany. b, Suburban EMU, Japan. c, Class 01, 4-6-2, Germany. d, Class 120 Bo-Bo, Germany. e, Class P8, 4-6-0, Germany. f, Fujikawa Express, Japan. g, Class 081, Germany. h, Kodama 8-car train, Japan. i, Class C62, 4-6-4, Japan.
No. 1482, 40c: a, KF Type, 4-8-4, China. b, Minobu Line train, Japan. c, Class S34-40, Germany. d, Class EF81, Bo-Bo, Japan. e, V200, B-B, Germany. f, SVT 877 "Flying Hamburger," Japan. g, C51, 4-6-2 Japan Railways. h, AEO Single rail car, Germany. i, Class D51, Japan.
No. 1483, $2, Yamonote Line train, Japan. No. 1484, $2, Class B8, Germany.

**1999, Aug. 25** **Litho.** **Perf. 14**
1477-1480 A405 Set of 4 4.50 4.50
**Sheets of 9, #a-i**
1481-1482 A405 Set of 2 17.00 17.00
**Souvenir Sheets**
1483-1484 A405 Set of 2 10.00 10.00

Dogs — A406

No. 1485, Lhasa apso. 70c, Samoyed. No. 1487, vert.: a, Dalmatian. b, Pyrennean Mountain dog. c, Golden retriever. d, Bearded collie. e, Basset hound. f, Bernese Mountain dog.
No. 1488, Beagle, vert.

**1999, Aug. 30** **Perf. 14**
1485 A406 50c multicolored 1.25 1.25
1486 A406 70c multicolored 1.75 1.75
1487 A406 Sheet of 6, #a.-f. 7.50 7.50
**Souvenir Sheet**
1488 A406 $2 multicolored 5.00 5.00

During 1999-2004 Liberia was torn by a brutal and chaotic civil war that reduced the nation to a state of anarchy. Government services, including postal operations, functioned erratically, if at all, for months at a time. During this period, overseas stamp agents continued to produce stamps under pre-war contracts, and a large number of issues appeared to be marketed to overseas collectors. It appears that some of these stamps have been released in Liberia since the end of hostilities. These will be listed when their sale and postal use has been confirmed.

Paintings by Norman Rockwell — A580

Paintings: $15, Playing Party Games. $30, Saturday Night Out. $35, The Portrait. No. 2328, $50, Grandpa's Little Ballerina.
No. 2329, $50: a, The Cave of the Winds. b, Redhead Loves Hatty. c, The Rivals. d, Three's Company.
No. 2330, $50: a, Distortion. b, Summer Vacation. c, Runaway Pants. d, Tumble.
No. 2331, $50: a, Daydreams. b, A Patient Friend. c, Lands of Enchantment. d, The Little Spooners.
No. 2332, $50: a, The Skating Lesson. b, The Fortune Teller. c, God Bless You. d, Knowledge is Power.

**2005, Jan. 10** **Litho.** **Perf. 14¼**
2325-2328 A580 Set of 4 7.00 7.00
**Sheets of 4, #a-d**
2329-2332 A580 Set of 4 40.00 40.00

Jules Verne (1828-1905), Writer — A581

No. 2333, $30: a, The Adventures of Captain Hatteras. b, The Mysterious Island (deflated balloon). c, The Mysterious Island (Men looking at ape). d, 20,000 Leagues Under the Sea (spotlights on ship).
No. 2334, $30: a, Around the World in Eighty Days. b, From the Earth to the Moon (people watching man on space capsule ladder). c, Paris in the Twentieth Century. d, Master of the World (ship captain at wheel).
No. 2335, $30: a, The Chase of the Golden Meteor. b, Master of the World (flying machine, country name in white). c, Five Weeks in a Balloon. d, From the Earth to the Moon (rocket in space).
No. 2336, $30: a, The Mysterious Island (People in balloon basket). b, Robur the Conqueror. c, Round the Moon. d, Master of the World (flying machine, country name in black).
No. 2337, $30: Scenes from 20,000 Leagues Under the Sea: a, Ships on water. b, Shark and octopus attacking ship. c, Shark attacking diver. d, Squid attacking ship.
No. 2338, $100, Deep sea divers. No. 2339, $100, Admiral Richard E. Byrd. No. 2340, $100, Radio satellite communication. No. 2341, $100, Long range ballistic missile. No. 2342, $100, Extravehicular satellite repair.

**2005, Jan. 11** **Perf. 13¼x13½**
**Sheets of 4, #a-d**
2333-2337 A581 Set of 5 32.50 32.50
**Souvenir Sheets**
2338-2342 A581 Set of 5 27.50 27.50

Marilyn Monroe (1926-62), Actress — A582

**2005, Jan. 26** **Perf. 14**
2343 A582 $12 multi .95 .95

Prehistoric Animals — A583

No. 2344, $50: a, Torosaurus. b, Tyrannosaurus. c, Polacanthus. d, Stegosaurus.

No. 2345, $50: a, Smilodon. b, Brontothere. c, Doedicurus. d, Moeritherium.
No. 2346, $50: a, Cymbospondylus. b, Archelon. c, Xiphactinus. d, Dunkleosteus.
No. 2347, $120, Stegosaurus, diff. No. 2348, $120, Woolly rhinoceros. No. 2349, $120, Odobenocetops.

**2005, Jan. 26**      *Perf. 13¼x13½*
**Sheets of 4, #a-d**
2344-2346 A583   Set of 3    32.50 32.50
**Souvenir Sheet**
2347-2349 A583   Set of 3    18.00 18.00

Battle of Trafalgar, Bicent. A584

Various ships: $10, $20, $40, $50. $100, Death of Admiral Horatio Nelson.

**2005, May 4**      *Perf. 14¼*
2350-2353 A584   Set of 4    6.00 6.00
**Souvenir Sheet**
2354 A584 $100 multi    5.50 5.50

Hans Christian Andersen (1805-75), Author — A585

No. 2355: a, Medal. b, Open book. c, Andersen.
$100, Sketch of Little Mermaid.

**2005, May 4**      *Perf. 14¼*
2355 A585 $50 Sheet of 3, #a-c 7.50 7.50
**Souvenir Sheet**
2356 A585 $100 multi    5.50 5.50

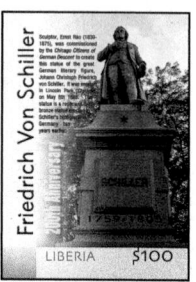

Friedrich von Schiller (1759-1805), Writer — A586

No. 2357: a, Bust of Schiller on round pedestal. b, Bust and foliage. c, Bust on monument.
$100, Statue of Schiller, Chicago.

**2005, May 4**      *Perf. 14¼*
2357 A586 $50 Sheet of 3, #a-c 7.50 7.50
**Size: 48x67mm**
**Imperf**
2358 A586 $100 multi    5.50 7.50
No. 2357 contains three 28x42mm stamps.

**Miniature Sheets**

Elvis Presley (1935-77) — A587

No. 2359, $35 — Presley in: a, 1956. b, 1969. c, 1969 (country name in yellow). d, 1969 (country name in pink). e, 1970.
No. 2360, $35 — Presley wearing: a, Red suit and white shirt. b, Yellow sweater. c, Red shirt. d, Brown suit. e, Gray suit.

---

**2005, May 19**      *Perf. 13½x13¼*
**Sheets of 5, #a-e**
2359-2360 A587   Set of 2    19.00 19.00

Pope John Paul II (1920-2005) — A588

**2005, Aug. 22**      *Perf. 12¾*
2361 A588 $50 multi    2.50 2.50
Printed in sheets of 4.

World Cup Soccer Championships, 75th Anniv. — A589

No. 2362: a, Norbert Eder. b, Paul Breitner. c, Thomas Helmer.
$100, Manfred Kaltz.

**2005, Aug. 22**      *Perf. 13¼*
2362 A589   $60 Sheet of 3, #a-c 10.00 10.00
**Souvenir Sheet**
**Perf. 12**
2363 A589 $100 multi    5.50 5.50

Albert Einstein (1879-1955), Physicist — A590

No. 2364 — Einstein and: a, Charlie Chaplin. b, Max Planck. c, William Allen White.
$100, J. Robert Oppenheimer.

**2005, Aug. 22**      *Perf. 12¾*
2364 A590 $60 Sheet of 3, #a-c 9.00 9.00
**Souvenir Sheet**
2365 A590 $100 multi    5.00 5.00

End of World War II, 60th Anniv. A591

No. 2366, $40 — V-E Day: a, Gen. Dwight D. Eisenhower. b, Prime Minister Winston Churchill. c, Gen. George Patton. d, Field Marshal Bernard Montgomery.
No. 2367, $40 — V-E Day: a, Air Marshal Sir Arthur "Bomber" Harris. b, Gen. Douglas MacArthur. c, Field Marshal Alan Brooke. d, Pres. Franklin D. Roosevelt.
No. 2368, $40 — V-J Day: a, RAF Wellington bomber. b, Mitsubishi A6M Zero. c, RAF Hudson bomber. d, B-17 bomber.
No. 2369, $40 — V-J Day: a, P-51 Mustang. b, RAF Hamilcar glider. c, P-38 Lightning. d, RAF Supermarine Spitfire.

**2005, Aug. 22**      *Perf. 13¼x13½*
**Sheets of 4, #a-d**
2366-2369 A591   Set of 4    26.00 26.00

---

Worldwide Fund for Nature (WWF) — A592

No. 2370: a, Jentink's duiker. b, Head of Ogilby's duiker. c, Ogilby's duiker. d, Head of Jentink's duiker.

**2005, Aug. 31**      *Perf. 14*
2370 A592 $20 Block or vert. strip of 4, #a-d   4.00 4.00
e.   Miniature sheet, 2 each #2370a-2370d   6.50 6.50

Rotary International, Cent. — A593

Emblem: $10, $25, $35, $50.
$100, Mother Teresa.

**2005, Sept. 22**      *Perf. 14*
2371-2374 A593   Set of 4    6.00 6.00
**Souvenir Sheet**
2375 A593 $100 multi    5.00 5.00
No. 2371-2374 exist imperf. Value, $20.

Christmas — A594

Paintings: $20, Glory to God, by Kim Ki-chang. $25, Flight Into Egypt, by Fra Angelico. $30, Christmas Mom, by Will Hickock Low. $50, The Nativity, by Bernardino Luini.
$100, Adoration of the Magi, by Nicolas Poussin.

**2005, Dec. 1**
2376-2379 A594   Set of 4    6.00 6.00
**Souvenir Sheet**
2380 A594 $100 multi    5.00 5.00

Elvis Presley (1935-77) — A595

***Variable Serpentine Die Cut***
**2006, Jan. 17**   Litho. & Embossed
**Without Gum**
2381 A595 $350 gold & multi   20.00 20.00

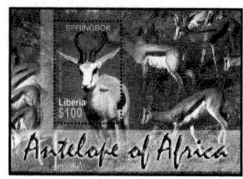

African Antelopes — A596

No. 2382: a, Gemsbok. b, Kudu. c, Sable antelope. d, Impala.
$100, Springbok.

**2006, Jan. 17**   Litho.    *Perf. 13½*
2382 A596   $45 Sheet of 4, #a-d 9.00 9.00
**Souvenir Sheet**
2383 A596 $100 multi    5.00 5.00

---

Mammals — A597

No. 2384: a, Jackal. b, Fox. c, Wolf. d, Coyote.
$100, Hyena.

**2006, Jan. 17**
2384 A597 $45 Sheet of 4, #a-d 9.00 9.00
**Souvenir Sheet**
2385 A597 $100 multi    5.00 5.00

Wild Cats A598

No. 2386: a, Jaguar. b, Lion. c, Puma. d, Cheetah.
$100, Siberian tiger.

**2006, Jan. 17**
2386 A598 $45 Sheet of 4, #a-d 9.00 9.00
**Souvenir Sheet**
2387 A598 $100 multi    5.00 5.00

Animals of the Bible A599

No. 2388, $45: a, Lions. b, Camels. c, Doves. d, Donkey.
No. 2389, $45: a, Foxes. b, Vultures. c, Turtles. d, Ducks.
No. 2390, $45: a, Goat. b, Bear. c, Ravens. d, Sheep.
No. 2391, $120, Pig. No. 2392, $120, Whale. No. 2393, $120, Snake.

**2006, Jan. 17**      **Sheets of 4, #a-d**
2388-2390 A599   Set of 3    25.00 25.00
**Souvenir Sheets**
2391-2393 A599   Set of 3    20.00 20.00

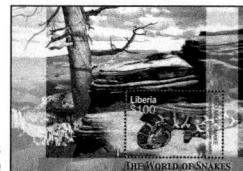

Snakes A600

No. 2394: a, Rough green snake. b, Speckled king snake. c, Garter snake. d, Brown snake.
$100, Red milk snake.

**2006, Jan. 27**
2394 A600 $45 Sheet of 4, #a-d 9.00 9.00
**Souvenir Sheet**
2395 A600 $100 multi    5.00 5.00

2006 Winter Olympics, Turin — A601

Designs: $20, Austria #B337. $25, Poster for 1976 Innsbruck Winter Olympics, vert. $35, Austria #B338. $50, Austria #B335. $70, US #3555. $100, Poster for 2002 Salt Lake City Winter Olympics, vert.

| 2006, Apr. 6 | | Perf. 13½ | |
|---|---|---|---|
| 2396-2399 | A601 | Set of 4 | 8.00 8.00 |
| 2399A | A601 | $70 multi | 4.00 4.00 |
| 2399B | A601 | $100 multi | 6.00 6.00 |

Nos. 2399A-2399B were not made available until 2007.

### Souvenir Sheet

Benjamin Franklin (1706-90), Statesman — A602

| 2006, May 27 | | | Perf. 13½ | |
|---|---|---|---|---|
| 2400 | A602 | $120 multi | | 7.50 7.50 |

Washington 2006 World Philatelic Exhibition.

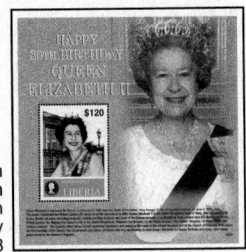

Queen Elizabeth II, 80th Birthday A603

No. 2401 — Hat color: a, Green. b, Blue. c, Beige. d, Black.
$120, Queen wearing tiara.

| 2006, June 13 | | | Perf. 14¼ | |
|---|---|---|---|---|
| 2401 | A603 | $40 Sheet of 4, #a-d | 9.00 9.00 |

### Souvenir Sheet

| 2402 | A603 | $120 multi | 7.00 7.00 |
|---|---|---|---|

Rembrandt (1606-69), Painter — A604

Artwork: $15, Young Man in a Turban. $30, Man Leaning on a Windowsill. $40, Officer with a Gold Chain. $45, The Art Dealer Clement de Jonghe.
No. 2407, $60: a, Self-portrait, 1633. b, Self-portrait, 1634. c, Self-portrait, 1639. d, Self-portrait, 1640.
No. 2408, $60: a, Christ and the Canaanite Woman. b, The Mocking of Christ. c, Head of an Old Man (Three-quarters view). d, Head of an Old Man (profile).
No. 2409, $60: a, David and Jonathan. b, Nude Woman with a Snake. c, The Abduction of Europa. d, Daniel and Cyrus Before the Idol Bel.
No. 2410, $60: a, Shah Jahan and Dara Shikoh. b, Farm Building Surrounded by Trees. c, Two Thatched Cottages with Figures at Window. d, A Sailing Boat on Wide Expanse of Water.
No. 2411, $120, Bearded Old Man with a Gold Chain. No. 2412, $120, A Scholar in His Study. No. 2413, $120, Rembrandt's Mother. No. 2414, $120, Portrait of Jan Six.

| 2006, June 13 | | | Litho. | |
|---|---|---|---|---|
| 2403-2406 | A604 | Set of 4 | 7.00 7.00 |

### Sheets of 4, #a-d

| 2407-2410 | A604 | Set of 4 | 50.00 50.00 |
|---|---|---|---|

### Imperf
### Size: 76x103mm

| 2411-2414 | A604 | Set of 4 | 30.00 30.00 |
|---|---|---|---|

### Souvenir Sheet

Wolfgang Amadeus Mozart (1756-91), Composer — A605

| 2006, July 25 | | | Perf. 12¾ | |
|---|---|---|---|---|
| 2415 | A605 | $120 multi | 7.50 7.50 |

### Miniature Sheet

Chinese Ceramics A606

No. 2416: a, Bowl with red, black and white exterior, brown interior. b, Bowl with blue and white exterior, blue, red and white interior. c, Bowl with green on white exterior, square opening. d, Bowl with red, white and blue exterior, brown interior. e, Bowl with green on white exterior, circular opening. f, Bowl with red, white and green exterior, square opening.

| 2006, Aug. 16 | | | Perf. 12x12¼ | |
|---|---|---|---|---|
| 2416 | A606 | $35 Sheet of 6, #a-f | 12.00 12.00 |

Inauguration of Pres. Ellen Johnson-Sirleaf A607

Designs: $10, Pres. Johnson-Sirleaf and flag. $25, Certification by National Election Commission, horiz. $30, Casting of ballots. $40, Pres. Johnson-Sirleaf holding child, horiz.
$100, Pres. Johnson-Sirleaf at microphone.

| 2006, Aug. 22 | | | Perf. 13¼ | |
|---|---|---|---|---|
| 2417-2420 | A607 | Set of 4 | 6.00 6.00 |

### Souvenir Sheet

| 2421 | A607 | $100 multi | 6.00 6.00 |
|---|---|---|---|

Millennium Development Goals A608

Goals: No. 2422, $10, Achieve universal primary education (graduates). No. 2423, $10, Promote gender equality and empower women. No. 2424, $25, Eradicate extreme hunger and poverty. No. 2425, $25, Reduce child mortality. No. 2426, $30, Develop a global partnership for development (map). No. 2427, $30, Develop a global partnership for development (ships and airplane). No. 2428, $40, Improve maternal health. $50, Achieve universal primary education (classroom). No. 2430, $100, Ensure environmental sustainability. No. 2431, $100, Combat HIV/AIDS, malaria and other diseases.
No. 2432, Achieve universal primary education (classroom), vert.

| 2006, Sept. 22 | | | | |
|---|---|---|---|---|
| 2422-2431 | A608 | Set of 10 | 25.00 25.00 |

### Souvenir Sheet

| 2432 | A608 | $100 multi | 6.00 6.00 |
|---|---|---|---|

Space Achievements — A609

No. 2433, $40 — Intl. Space Station: a, Country name and denomination in black, at top. b, Country name in black, denomination in white. c, Country name and denomination in white, at top. d, Country name and denomination in black, at bottom. e, Space shuttle (country name and denomination in white, at bottom). f, Astronaut (country name and denomination in white, at bottom.
No. 2434, $40, vert. — Apollo 11: a, Lunar module. b, Rocket on launch pad. c, Nose cone of rocket. d, Astronaut on moon. e, Command module. f, Astronauts and rocket.
No. 2435, $55, vert. — First Flight of Space Shuttle Columbia: a, Astronaut Bob Crippen. b, Front of space shuttle. c, Astronaut John Young. d, Tail of space shuttle.
No. 2436, $55 — Space Shuttle returns to space: a, Wing. b, Fuselage, reflection of sunlight. c, Wing inscribed "Discovery." d, Fuselage and Earth.
No. 2437, $120, Apollo-Soyuz. No. 2438, $120, Mars Reconnaissance Orbiter. No. 2439, $120, Venus Express. No. 2440, $120, Deep Impact Probe.

| 2006, Oct. 3 | | Litho. | Perf. 12¾ | |
|---|---|---|---|---|
| **Sheets of 6, #a-f** | | | | |
| 2433-2434 | A609 | Set of 2 | 30.00 30.00 |
| **Sheets of 4, #a-d** | | | | |
| 2435-2436 | A609 | Set of 2 | 25.00 25.00 |
| **Souvenir Sheets** | | | | |
| 2437-2440 | A609 | Set of 4 | 25.00 25.00 |

Christopher Columbus (1451-1506), Explorer — A610

Designs: $25, Columbus, drawings of ships. $50, Columbus, ships, horiz. $70, Columbus and Santa Maria, horiz. $100, Ship, crew encountering natives, horiz.
$120, Men on shore.

| 2006, Nov. 15 | | | | |
|---|---|---|---|---|
| 2441-2444 | A610 | Set of 4 | 12.50 12.50 |

### Souvenir Sheet

| 2445 | A610 | $120 multi | 7.00 7.00 |
|---|---|---|---|

### Souvenir Sheet

Christmas — A611

No. 2446 — Details from The Adoration of the Magi, by Peter Paul Rubens: a, Man and boy. b, Mary. c, Man with headcovering. d, Infant Jesus.

| 2006, Dec. 21 | | Litho. | Perf. 14 | |
|---|---|---|---|---|
| 2446 | A611 | $40 Sheet of 4, #a-d | 9.00 9.00 |

A612

Concorde — A613

No. 2447, $30 — Concorde: a, G-BOAF. b, G-BOAB.

No. 2448, $35 — Concorde: a, F-BVFA on runway. b, G-BOAA taking off.

| 2007, Mar. 1 | | Litho. | Perf. 13½ | |
|---|---|---|---|---|
| **Horiz. Pairs, #a-b** | | | | |
| 2447-2448 | A612 | Set of 2 | 7.50 7.50 |
| **Litho. & Embossed** | | | | |
| **Without Gum** | | | | |
| *Irregular Serpentine Die Cut* | | | | |
| 2449 | A613 | $350 gold & multi | 20.00 20.00 |

### Souvenir Sheet

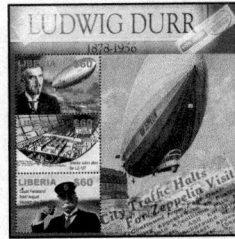

Ludwig Durr (1878-1956), Engineer — A614

No. 2450: a, Durr and Zeppelin. b, Interior cabin plan for LZ-127. c, Count Ferdinand von Zeppelin.

| 2007, Mar. 1 | | Litho. | Perf. 13¼ | |
|---|---|---|---|---|
| 2450 | A614 | $60 Sheet of 3, #a-c | 10.00 10.00 |

### Souvenir Sheet

Marilyn Monroe (1926-62), Actress — A615

Various portraits.

| 2007, Mar. 1 | | | | |
|---|---|---|---|---|
| 2451 | A615 | $50 Sheet of 4, #a-d | 12.00 12.00 |

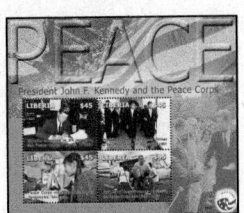

Pres. John F. Kennedy (1917-62) — A616

No. 2452, $45: a, Signing executive order establishing the Peace Corps. b, With Sargent Shriver. c, Peace Corps volunteers in Tanganyika. d, Jack Hood Vaughn, second director of Peace Corps.
No. 2453, $45 — Kennedy: a, And Eleanor Roosevelt. b, Delivering Alliance for Progress speech. c, With Mrs. Kennedy in Venezuela. d, And Secretary of State Dean Rusk.

| 2007, Mar. 1 | | | Litho. | |
|---|---|---|---|---|
| **Sheets of 4, #a-d** | | | | |
| 2452-2453 | A616 | Set of 2 | 20.00 20.00 |

Mushrooms — A617

Designs: $25, Boletus edulis. $35, Begriipt russula. No. 2456, $45, Lactarius helvus. $50, Amanita pantherina.
No. 2458, $45: a, Russula cyanoxantha. b, Cantharellus subalbidus. c, Leccinum oxydalile. d, Boletus badius.
No. 2459, $45: a, Amanita bingensis. b, Chlorophyllum molybdites. c, Calvatia utriformis. d, Amanita loosii.

No. 2460, $100, Amanita muscaria. No. 2461, $100, Chlorophyllum molybdites, diff. No. 2462, $100, Agaricus silvaticus.

**2007, Mar. 1**
2454-2457 A617 Set of 4    9.00   9.00
**Sheets of 4, #a-d**
2458-2459 A617 Set of 2   20.00 20.00
**Souvenir Sheets**
2460-2462 A617 Set of 3   18.00 18.00

Scouting, Cent. — A618

Designs: $50, Scouts and 2006 World Jamboree emblem. $150, Scouts, horiz.

**2007, Mar. 15**
2463 A618 $50 multi    3.00 3.00
**Souvenir Sheet**
2464 A618 $150 multi    9.00 9.00
No. 2463 was printed in sheets of 4.

Pope Benedict XVI — A619

**2007, Nov. 30 Litho. Perf. 13¼**
2465 A619 $30 multi    1.75 1.75

**Miniature Sheet**

New Year 2007 (Year of the Boar) A620

No. 2466 — Wild Boar, by Liu Jiyou with text "Year of the Boar" in: a, Red. b, Green. c, Brown. d, Blue.

**2007, Nov. 30**
2466 A620 $30 Sheet of 4, #a-d   7.00 7.00

**Miniature Sheet**

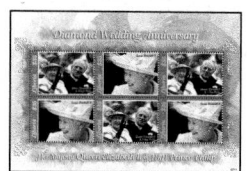

Wedding of Queen Elizabeth II and Prince Philip, 60th Anniv. A621

No. 2467: a, Couple, denomination in white. b, Queen, denomination in yellow. c, Couple, denomination in lilac. d, Queen, denomination in white. e, Couple, denomination in yellow. f, Queen, denomination in lilac.

**2007, Nov. 30**
2467 A621 $35 Sheet of 6, #a-f    12.00 12.00

Princess Diana (1961-97) — A622

No. 2468 — Various depictions of Diana with denomination in: a, Red violet. b, Blue. c, Green. d, Red.
$125, Red denomination.

**2007, Nov. 30**
2468 A622 $45 Sheet of 4, #a-d    10.00 10.00
**Souvenir Sheet**
2469 A622 $125 multi    7.50 7.50

Souvenir Sheets

Pres. Ellen Johnson-Sirleaf and Foreign Dignitaries — A623

Pres. Johnson-Sirleaf meeting with: No. 2470, $100, Chinese Pres. Hu Jintao. No. 2471, $100, U.S. Pres. George W. Bush.

**2007, Nov. 30**
2470-2471 A623 Set of 2   12.00 12.00

**Miniature Sheet**

Elvis Presley (1935-77) — A624

No. 2472 — Presley: a, Wearing red and white sweater, country name in white. b, Holding guitar, country name in blue. c, Wearing cap, country name in white. d, Holding guitar, country name in red violet. e, Wearing cap, country name in red violet. f, Wearing red and white sweater, country name in yellow.

**2007, Nov. 30**
2472 A624 $35 Sheet of 6, #a-f    12.00 12.00

Souvenir Sheet

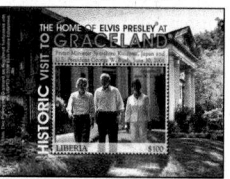

Japanese Prime Minister Junchiro Koizumi, U.S. Pres. George W. Bush and Wife at Graceland — A625

**2007, Nov. 30**
2473 A625 $100 multi    6.00 6.00

New Year 2008 (Year of the Rat) — A626

**2007, Dec. 26 Litho. Perf. 11½x12**
2474 A626 $25 multi    1.50 1.50
Printed in sheets of 4.

Birds — A627

Designs: $20, Pin-tailed whydahs. $30, Lesser honeyguides. $40, African jacanas. $50, Malachite sunbirds.
No. 2479, $45, horiz.: a, White-brown sparrow weavers. b, Parasitic weavers. c, Black-winged orioles. d, Crested guineafowl.
No. 2480, $45, horiz.: a, Red-billed francolins. b, Rufous-crowned rollers. c, African golden orioles. d, Black-crowned tchagras.
No. 2481, $100, Kori bustard. No. 2482, $100, Ostrich. No. 2483, $100, Great white pelican, horiz.

**2007, Dec. 26 Perf. 14**
2475-2478 A627 Set of 4    8.00 8.00
**Sheets of 4, #a-d**
2479-2480 A627 Set of 2   20.00 20.00
**Souvenir Sheets**
2481-2483 A627 Set of 3   18.00 18.00

Butterflies — A628

Designs: $20, Appias epaphia. $30, Papilio bromius. $40, Charaxes jasius. $50, Mimacraea marshalli dohertyi.
No. 2488, $45: a, Belenois thysa. b, Papilio pelodorus. c, Cymothoe sangaris. d, Colotis aurigineus.
No. 2489, $45: a, Junonia hierta. b, Myrina silenus. c, Byblia ilithyia. d, Argyrogrammana attsonii.
No. 2490, $100, Iolaus menas. No. 2491, $100, Leptomyrina hirundo. No. 2492, $100, Pinacopteryx eriphia.

**2007, Dec. 26**
2484-2487 A628 Set of 4    8.00 8.00
**Sheets of 4, #a-d**
2488-2489 A628 Set of 2   20.00 20.00
**Souvenir Sheets**
2490-2492 A628 Set of 3   18.00 18.00

Orchids — A629

Designs: $20, Neobenthamia gracilis. $30, Eulophia guineensis. $40, Aerangis curnowiana. $50, Cymbidiella pardalina.
No. 2497, $45: a, Ophrys lutea. b, Ophrys holoserica. c, Ophrys fusca. d, Ophrys scolopax.
No. 2498, $45: a, Disa veitchii. b, Disa racemosa. c, Disa kewensis. d, Disa diores.
No. 2499, $100, Disa crassicornis. No. 2500, $100, Aerangis citrata. No. 2501, $100, Angraecum sororium.

**2007, Dec. 26**
2493-2496 A629 Set of 4    8.00 8.00
**Sheets of 4, #a-d**
2497-2498 A629 Set of 2   20.00 20.00
**Souvenir Sheets**
2499-2501 A629 Set of 3   18.00 18.00

Christmas — A630

Designs: $30, Madonna and Child. $40, Holy Family. $45, Flight into Egypt. $50, The Three Magi, horiz.

**2007, Dec. 26 Perf. 14x14¾, 14¾x14**
2502-2505 A630 Set of 4   10.00 10.00

**Miniature Sheet**

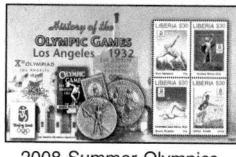

2008 Summer Olympics, Beijing — A631

No. 2506: a, Babe Didrikson. b, 1932 Summer Olympics poster. c, Helene Madison. d, Chuhei Nambu.

**2008, Apr. 8 Perf. 12¾**
2506 A631 $30 Sheet of 4, #a-d   7.00 7.00

National Basketball Association Players — A632

No. 2507 — NBA and Boston Celtics emblems and Kevin Garnett: a, Wearing white uniform, not holding basketball. b, Wearing green uniform. c, Wearing white uniform, holding basketball.
No. 2508 — NBA and Boston Celtics emblems and Paul Pierce: a, Wearing white uniform, hands at side. b, Wearing green uniform. c, Wearing white uniform, pointing.
No. 2509 — NBA and Washington Wizards emblems and Gilbert Arenas: a, Wearing white uniform, hands on hips. b, Wearing blue uniform. c, Wearing white uniform, with basketball.
No. 2510 — NBA and Milwaukee Bucks emblems and Yi Jianlian: a, Wearing white uniform, basketball at left. b, Wearing blue green uniform. c, Wearing white uniform, basketball at right.

**2008, Apr. 30 Perf. 13½x13¼**
2507   Vert. strip of 3    7.00 7.00
a.-c.   A632 $40 Any single   1.25 1.25
2508   Vert. strip of 3    7.00 7.00
a.-c.   A632 $40 Any single   1.25 1.25
2509   Vert. strip of 3    7.00 7.00
a.-c.   A632 $40 Any single   1.25 1.25
2510   Vert. strip of 3    7.00 7.00
a.-c.   A632 $40 Any single   1.25 1.25
  Nos. 2507-2510 (4)   28.00 28.00
Nos. 2507-2510 each printed in sheets of 6 containing 2 of each stamp in strip.

**Souvenir Sheet**

Meeting of Liberian Pres. Ellen Johnson-Sirleaf and US Pres. George W. Bush. — A633

No. 2511: a, Pres. Bush. b, Pres. Johnson-Sirleaf.

**2008, June 12 Perf. 13¼**
2511 A633 $125 Sheet of 2, #a-b   12.00 12.00

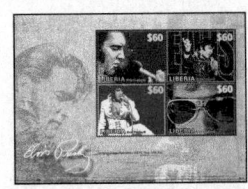
Elvis Presley (1935-77) — A634

No. 2512 — Presley: a, Holding microphone, red background. b, Holding microphone, "Elvis" in lights. c, Holding microphone, blue background. d, Wearing glasses.

**2008, June 12**     *Perf. 13¼*
2512 A634 $60 Sheet of 4, #a-d    12.00 12.00

Space Achievements — A635

No. 2513, $40 — International Space Station with denomination at: a, UR. b, UL. c, LR.
No. 2514, $40 — Chandra X-ray Observatory: a, Observatory below nebula. b, Interior of Observatory. c, Observatory above nebula.
No. 2515: a, Callisto, Europa, Voyager I, Jupiter and Io. b, Lift-off of Voyager I. c, Voyager I record cover. d, Voyager I, Titan and Saturn.
No. 2516, $150, International Space Station, horiz. No. 2517, $150, Chandra X-ray Observatory, horiz. No. 2518, $150, Voyager I and rings of Saturn, horiz.
Illustration reduced.

**2008, June 12**     *Perf. 13¼*
**Horiz. Strips of 3, #a-c**
2513-2514 A635 Set of 2    18.00 18.00
**Miniature Sheet**
2515 A635 $60 Sheet of 4, #a-d    18.00 18.00
**Souvenir Sheets**
2516-2518 A635 Set of 3    24.00 24.00

Nos. 2513-2514 were each printed in sheets of 6 containing 2 of each stamp in strip.

Pope Benedict XVI — A636

**2008, June 30**     *Litho.*
2519 A636 $45 multi    2.00 2.00
Printed in sheets of 4.

County Flags — A637

Flag of: No. 2520, $10, Maryland County. No. 2521, $10, Montserrado County. No. 2522, $25, Gbarpolu County. No. 2523, $25, Grand Bassa County. No. 2524, $30, Grand Cape Mount County. No. 2525, $30, Nimba County. No. 2526, $40, Lofa County. No. 2527, $40, Sinoe County. No. 2528, $50, Bong County. No. 2529, $50, Margibi County. No. 2530, $100, Bomi County. No. 2531, $100, Grand Gedeh County. No. 2532, $100, Grand Kru County. No. 2533, $100, River Cess County. No. 2534, $100, River Gee County.

**2008, June 30**
2520-2534 A637 Set of 15    26.00 26.00

---

Miniature Sheet

Ferrari F2008 A638

No. 2535: a, "F" under "E" of "Liberia." b, "F" under "B" of Liberia. c, Side view of car. d, Car straddling yellow line on track.

**2008, Sept. 5**   *Litho.*   *Perf. 13½*
2535 A638 $60 Sheet of 4, #a-d    12.00 12.00

A639

Election of Barack Obama as US President — A640

Inscriptions: No. 2537, Joseph Biden. No. 2539a, Joseph Robinette Biden, Jr. No. 2539B: c, Barack Obama. d, Joseph Biden.

*Perf. 14¼x14¾, 12¼x11¾ (#2538)*
**2008, Nov. 5**
2536 A639 $45 shown    1.50 1.50
2537 A639 $45 multi    1.50 1.50
2538 A640 $65 shown    2.10 2.10
   Nos. 2536-2538 (3)    5.10 5.10
**Souvenir Sheet**
2539    Sheet of 2, #2536, 2539a    3.00 3.00
  a. A639 $45 multi    1.50 1.50
2539B    Sheet of 2    17.00 17.00
  c.-d. A639 $160 Either single    8.50 8.50

No. 2536 was printed in sheets of 9 and in No. 2539. No. 2537 was printed in sheets of 9. No. 2538 was printed in sheets of 4.

A641

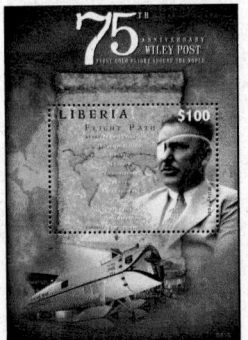
Solo Aerial Circumnavigation of the World by Wiley Post, 75th Anniv. — A642

No. 2540: a, Post arriving in Cleveland. b, Harold Gatty, navigator. c, Post wearing pressure suit. d, Post atop plane. e, Post and wife Mae. f, The Winnie Mae. $100, Post and map of flight.

---

**2008, Nov. 24**     *Perf. 13¼*
2540 A641 $40 Sheet of 6, #a-f    12.00 12.00
**Souvenir Sheet**
2541 A642 $100 multi    6.00 6.00

Christmas — A643

Paintings: $10, The Nativity, by Martin Schongauer. $25, Birth of Christ, by Robert Campin. $30, Adoration of the Magi, by Geertgen tot Sint Jans. $40, The Birth of Christ, by Sandro Botticelli.

**2008, Dec. 1**   *Litho.*   *Perf. 14¼x14¾*
2542-2545 A643 Set of 4    3.50 3.50

New Year 2009 (Year of the Ox) — A644

**2009, Jan. 2**     *Perf. 12*
2546 A644 $60 multi    1.90 1.90
Printed in sheets of 4.

Blindness — A645

Designs: $10, Blind student reading Braille. $30, Blind man in crosswalk. $45, Blind man, map of Liberia. $100, Sighted man leading blind man.

**2009, Jan. 4**     *Perf. 14¾x14¼*
2547-2550 A645 Set of 4    5.75 5.75

Miniature Sheets

Star Trek A646

No. 2551: a, Captain Kirk. b, USS Enterprise. c, Scotty. d, Uhura. e, Spock. f, Spock, Rand and Kirk.
No. 2552: a, Scotty. b, Spock and Kirk. c, Dr. McCoy. d, Sulu.

**2009, Jan. 14**     *Perf. 11½*
2551 A646 $35 Sheet of 6, #a-f    6.75 6.75
    *Perf. 13½x13¼*
2552 A646 $60 Sheet of 4, #a-d    7.50 7.50
No. 2552 contains four 38x51mm stamps.

---

Miniature Sheet

Abraham Lincoln (1809-65), US President — A647

No. 2553: a, US #1282. b, US #555. c, US #367. d, US #222.

**2009, Feb. 2**     *Perf. 13¼x13½*
2553 A647 $60 Sheet of 4, #a-d    7.50 7.50

Miniature Sheet

John F. Kennedy (1917-63), US President — A648

No. 2554 — Kennedy: a, Greeting Cuban-exile Bay of Pigs invasion force, with wife Jackie, shaking hand. b, Standing with Jackie. c, In White House. d, With Jackie at stadium.

**2009, Feb. 25**     *Perf. 11¼x11½*
2554 A648 $50 Sheet of 4, #a-d    6.25 6.25

A649

Peonies A650

No. 2556: a, White peony, tan background. b, Pink peony, white background.

**2009, Apr. 10**     *Perf. 13¼*
2555 A649 $32 multi    1.00 1.00
**Souvenir Sheet**
2556 A650 $65 Sheet of 2, #a-b    4.00 4.00
No. 2555 was printed in sheets of 6.

Miniature Sheets

A651

China 2009 World Stamp Exhibition, Luoyang — A653

No. 2557: a, Panda, Chengdu. b, West Lake, Hangzhou. c, Bonsai Garden, Suzhou. d, Fuzi Miao and Qinhuai River, Nanjing.

No. 2558: a, Ornamental plaque (770-476 B.C.). b, Vessel (206 B.C.-A.D. 8). c, Covered jar (1279-1368). d, Head of a Bodhisattva (618-907).

No. 2559: a, Wheel of mountain bike. b, Hand holding tennis racquet. c, Hand holding water polo ball. d, Hand holding handball.

**2009, Apr. 10**     **Perf. 12½**
| | | | |
|---|---|---|---|
| 2557 | A651 $35 Sheet of 4, #a-d | 4.50 | 4.50 |

**Perf. 12**
| | | | |
|---|---|---|---|
| 2558 | A652 $35 Sheet of 4, #a-d | 4.50 | 4.50 |
| 2559 | A653 $35 Sheet of 4, #a-d | 4.50 | 4.50 |
| | Nos. 2557-2559 (3) | 13.50 | 13.50 |

Pope Benedict XVI — A654

**2009, May 4**     **Perf. 11¼x11½**
| | | | |
|---|---|---|---|
| 2560 | A654 $60 multi | 1.75 | 1.75 |

Printed in sheets of 4.

### Miniature Sheet

Felix Mendelssohn (1809-47), Composer — A655

No. 2561: a, Portrait of young Mendelssohn, by Carl Begas. b, Fanny Mendelssohn, sister of Felix. c, Mendelssohn's sketch of Thomasschule, Leipzig. d, Leipzig Conservatory. e, Portrait of Mendelssohn, by James Warren Childe. f, Mendelssohn drawing made during visit to Scotland.

**2009, May 4**     **Perf. 11¼x11½**
| | | | |
|---|---|---|---|
| 2561 | A655 $50 Sheet of 6, #a-f | 8.75 | 8.75 |

A656

A657

A658

A659

Elvis Presley (1935-77) — A660

No. 2562 — Background color: a, Red brown. b, Tan. c, Gray green. d, Black.

**2009, May 4**     **Perf. 13¼**
| | | | |
|---|---|---|---|
| 2562 | A656 $65 Sheet of 4, #a-d | 7.50 | 7.50 |

**Souvenir Sheets**
**Perf. 14¼**
| | | | |
|---|---|---|---|
| 2563 | A657 $160 multi | 4.75 | 4.75 |
| 2564 | A658 $160 multi | 4.75 | 4.75 |
| 2565 | A659 $160 multi | 4.75 | 4.75 |
| 2566 | A660 $160 multi | 4.75 | 4.75 |
| | Nos. 2563-2566 (4) | 19.00 | 19.00 |

US Presidents — A661

No. 2567, $20, vert.: a, George Washington. b, John Adams. c, Thomas Jefferson. d, James Madison. e, James Monroe. f, John Quincy Adams. g, Andrew Jackson. h, Martin Van Buren. i, William Henry Harrison. j, John Tyler. k, James K. Polk. l, Zachary Taylor. m, Millard Fillmore. n, Franklin Pierce. o, James Buchanan.

No. 2568, $20, vert.: a, Abraham Lincoln. b, Andrew Johnson. c, Ulysses S. Grant. d, Rutherford B. Hayes. e, James A. Garfield. f, Chester A. Arthur. g, Grover Cleveland (1885-89). h, Benjamin Harrison. i, Grover Cleveland (1893-97). j, William McKinley. k, Theodore Roosevelt. l, William Howard Taft. m, Woodrow Wilson. n, Warren G. Harding. o, Calvin Coolidge.

No. 2569, $20, vert.: a, Herbert Hoover. b, Franklin D. Roosevelt. c, Harry S Truman. d, Dwight D. Eisenhower. e, John F. Kennedy. f, Lyndon B. Johnson. g, Richard M. Nixon. h, Gerald R. Ford. i, Jimmy Carter. j, Ronald Reagan. k, George H. W. Bush (1989-93). l, William J. Clinton. m, George W. Bush (2001-09). n, Barack H. Obama. o, Presidential seal. $320, Barack Obama.

**2009, May 4**     **Perf. 13¼**
**Sheets of 15, #a-o**
| | | | | |
|---|---|---|---|---|
| 2567-2569 | A661 | Set of 3 | 26.00 | 26.00 |
| 2568p | Sheet of 9 #2568a | | 5.25 | 5.25 |
| 2569p | Miniature sheet, #2569o, 14 #2569n | | 8.50 | 8.50 |

**Souvenir Sheet**
**Perf. 14¼**
| | | | |
|---|---|---|---|
| 2570 | A661 $320 multi | 9.25 | 9.25 |

Nos. 2567-2569 each contain fifteen 28x42mm stamps. Issued: No. 2568p, 3/23/10. 2569p, 9/4. See Nos. 3179-3181.

Famous People — A662

Designs: No. 2571, $50, Madame Suakoko (1816-1927), first female paramount chief. No. 2572, $50, Chief Flomo Doughba Barwulor.

**2009, Aug. 2**  **Litho.**   **Perf. 11¼x11½**
| | | | |
|---|---|---|---|
| 2571-2572 | A662 | Set of 2 | 2.75 2.75 |

Masks — A663

Designs: $10, Korkpor mask. $25, Landa mask. $35, Borwhoo mask. $45, Zoba mask. $100, Kote mask.

**2009, Aug. 2**     **Perf. 13¼**
| | | | |
|---|---|---|---|
| 2573-2577 | A663 | Set of 5 | 6.00 6.00 |

Dance — A664

Designs: $30, Traditional dancers. $40, Traditional dancers, diff. $45, Poro dancers.

**2009, Aug. 2**
| | | | |
|---|---|---|---|
| 2578-2580 | A664 | Set of 3 | 3.25 3.25 |

**Souvenir Sheet**

Monkey Bridge A665

**2009, Aug. 2**
| | | | |
|---|---|---|---|
| 2581 | A665 $100 multi | 2.75 | 2.75 |

### Miniature Sheets

Players in 2009 National Basketball Association All-Star Game — A666

No. 2582, $30 — Eastern All-stars: a, Ray Allen. b, Kevin Garnett. c, Danny Granger. d, Devin Harris. e, Dwight Howard. f, Allen Iverson. g, LeBron James. h, Joe Johnson. i, Rashard Lewis. j, Paul Pierce. k, Dwayne Wade. l, Mo Williams.

No. 2583, $30 — Western All-stars: a, Chauncey Billups. b, Kobe Bryant. c, Tim Duncan. d, Pau Gasol. e, Yao Ming. f, Dirk Nowitzki. g, Shaquille O'Neal. h, Tony Parker. i, Chris Paul. j, Brandon Roy. k, Amar'e Stoudemire. l, David West.

**2009, Aug. 2**     **Perf. 11¼x11½**
**Sheets of 12, #a-l**
| | | | | |
|---|---|---|---|---|
| 2582-2583 | A666 | Set of 2 | 20.00 | 20.00 |

Liberian Presidents A667

Designs: $10, Ellen Johnson-Sirleaf. $25, Moses Z. Blah. $35, Charles M.G. Taylor. $45, Samuel K. Doe. $50, William Richard Tolbert. $70, William V.S. Tubman.

Nos. 2590, 2611, Joseph Jenkins Roberts. Nos. 2591, 2612, Stepehen Allen Benson. Nos. 2592, 2613, Daniel Bashiel Warner. Nos. 2593, 2614, James Spriggs Payne. Nos. 2594, 2615, Edward James Roye. Nos. 2595, 2616, Anthony Williams Gardiner. Nos. 2596, 2617, Alfred Francis Russell. Nos. 2597, 2618, Hilary R.W. Johnson. Nos. 2598, 2619, Joseph James Cheeseman. Nos. 2599, 2620, William David Coleman. Nos. 2600, 2621, Garretson W. Gibson. Nos. 2601, 2622, Arthur Barclay. Nos. 2602, 2623, Daniel E. Howard. Nos. 2603, 2624, Charles D.B. King. Nos. 2604, 2625, Edwin James Barclay. No. 2605, Tubman. No. 2606, Tolbert. No. 2607, Doe. No. 2608, Taylor. No. 2609, Blah. No. 2610, Johnson-Sirleaf.

**2009, Aug. 22**     **Perf. 12¾**
| | | | | |
|---|---|---|---|---|
| 2584 | A667 | $10 multi | .30 | .30 |
| 2585 | A667 | $25 multi | .70 | .70 |
| 2586 | A667 | $35 multi | 1.00 | 1.00 |
| 2587 | A667 | $45 multi | 1.25 | 1.25 |
| 2588 | A667 | $50 multi | 1.40 | 1.40 |
| 2589 | A667 | $70 multi | 2.00 | 2.00 |
| 2590 | A667 | $100 multi | 2.75 | 2.75 |
| 2591 | A667 | $100 multi | 2.75 | 2.75 |
| 2592 | A667 | $100 multi | 2.75 | 2.75 |
| 2593 | A667 | $100 multi | 2.75 | 2.75 |
| 2594 | A667 | $100 multi | 2.75 | 2.75 |
| 2595 | A667 | $100 multi | 2.75 | 2.75 |
| 2596 | A667 | $100 multi | 2.75 | 2.75 |
| 2597 | A667 | $100 multi | 2.75 | 2.75 |
| 2598 | A667 | $100 multi | 2.75 | 2.75 |
| 2599 | A667 | $100 multi | 2.75 | 2.75 |
| 2600 | A667 | $100 multi | 2.75 | 2.75 |
| 2601 | A667 | $100 multi | 2.75 | 2.75 |
| 2602 | A667 | $100 multi | 2.75 | 2.75 |
| 2603 | A667 | $100 multi | 2.75 | 2.75 |
| 2604 | A667 | $100 multi | 2.75 | 2.75 |
| 2605 | A667 | $100 multi | 2.75 | 2.75 |
| 2606 | A667 | $100 multi | 2.75 | 2.75 |
| 2607 | A667 | $100 multi | 2.75 | 2.75 |
| 2608 | A667 | $100 multi | 2.75 | 2.75 |
| 2609 | A667 | $100 multi | 2.75 | 2.75 |
| 2610 | A667 | $100 multi | 2.75 | 2.75 |
| 2611 | A667 | $500 multi | 14.00 | 14.00 |
| 2612 | A667 | $500 multi | 14.00 | 14.00 |
| 2613 | A667 | $500 multi | 14.00 | 14.00 |
| 2614 | A667 | $500 multi | 14.00 | 14.00 |
| 2615 | A667 | $500 multi | 14.00 | 14.00 |
| 2616 | A667 | $500 multi | 14.00 | 14.00 |
| 2617 | A667 | $500 multi | 14.00 | 14.00 |
| 2618 | A667 | $500 multi | 14.00 | 14.00 |
| 2619 | A667 | $500 multi | 14.00 | 14.00 |
| 2620 | A667 | $500 multi | 14.00 | 14.00 |
| 2621 | A667 | $500 multi | 14.00 | 14.00 |
| 2622 | A667 | $500 multi | 14.00 | 14.00 |
| 2623 | A667 | $500 multi | 14.00 | 14.00 |

| | | | |
|---|---|---|---|
| 2624 | A667 | $500 multi | 14.00 14.00 |
| 2625 | A667 | $500 multi | 14.00 14.00 |
| | Nos. 2584-2625 (42) | | 274.40 274.40 |

Chinese Aviation, Cent. A668

No. 2626: a, H-2 missiles. b, H-2B missiles. c, H-12 missiles on trucks. d, H-12 missiles on truck. $150, H-9 missiles.

**2009, Nov. 12**     *Perf. 14*
2626 A668 $50 Sheet of 4, #a-d   6.00 6.00

**Souvenir Sheet**
*Perf. 14¼*
2627 A668 $150 multi     4.50 4.50

No. 2626 contains four 42x32mm stamps.

**Miniature Sheet**

Charles Darwin (1809-82), Naturalist — A669

No. 2628: a, Rhea darwinii. b, Proctotretus fitzingerii. c, Vespertilio chiloensis. d, Geospiza fortis.

**2009, Dec. 10**     *Perf. 12x11½*
2628 A669 $60 Sheet of 4, #a-d   7.50 7.50

**Miniature Sheet**

The Three Stooges A670

No. 2629: a, Stooges with open book. b, Moe sticking drill into Curly's mouth. c, Stooges at table looking at book. d, Curly pointing stick at man.

**2009, Dec. 10**     *Perf. 11½x12*
2629 A670 $60 Sheet of 4, #a-d   7.50 7.50

**Miniature Sheet**

Pres. John F. Kennedy and Wife, Jacqueline — A671

No. 2630: a, Pres. Kennedy with Jacqueline, wearing cape. b, Pres. Kennedy. c, Pres. Kennedy with Jacqueline in limousine. d, Jacqueline Kennedy and crowd. e, Pres. Kennedy and wife (Jacqueline holding arm of husband). f, Jacqueline Kennedy.

**2009, Dec. 10**     *Perf. 11¼x11½*
2630 A671 $60 Sheet of 6, #a-
    f     11.00 11.00

Intl. Year of Astronomy — A672

No. 2631, horiz.: a, Sergei Korolev and Luna 9. b, Luna 9 horizontal on transporter. c, Lift-off of Luna 9. d, Luna 9 over Moon. e, Luna 9 open, with antennae erect. f, Luna 9 open, antennae not erect.
$160, Lift-off of Apollo 11.

**2009, Dec. 10**     *Perf. 13½*
2631 A672 $40 Sheet of 6, #a-f   7.50 7.50

**Souvenir Sheet**
2632 A672 $160 multi     5.00 5.00

Nos. 2631a, 2631b and 2631d have country name misspelled as "Libeira."

Christmas — A673

Paintings: $25, Nativity (Holy Night), by Correggio. $40, Adoration of the Magi, by Bartolomé Esteban Murillo. $50, Adoration of the Magi, by Vicente Gil. $100, Adoration of the Magi, by Peter Paul Rubens.

**2009, Dec. 10**     *Perf. 13¼x13*
2633-2636 A673   Set of 4    6.50 6.50

**Miniature Sheet**

Awarding of Nobel Peace Prize to US Pres. Barack Obama A674

No. 2637 — Pres. Obama wearing: a, Red tie, facing right. b, Red tie, facing forward. c, Blue tie, facing forward. d, Blue tie, facing left.

**2009, Dec. 30**   *Litho.*   *Perf. 12x11½*
2637 A674 $60 Sheet of 4, #a-d   7.00 7.00

**Miniature Sheet**

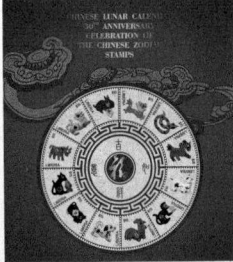

Chinese Zodiac Animals A675

No. 2638: a, Dragon. b, Snake. c, Horse. d, Goat. e, Monkey. f, Rooster. g, Dog. h, Pig. i, Rat. j, Ox. k, Tiger. l, Rabbit.

**2010, Jan. 4**     *Perf. 12½*
2638 A675 $15 Sheet of 12, #a-l   6.00 6.00

**Souvenir Sheet**

New Year 2010 (Year of the Tiger) A676

No. 2639: a, Tiger. b, Tiger and Chinese characters.

**2010, Jan. 4**     *Perf. 14¾x14¼*
2639 A676 $130 Sheet of 2, #a-b 7.50 7.50

**Miniature Sheets**

Dogs A677

No. 2640, $65 — German shorthaired pointer: a, At duckpond. b, With trees and building in background. c, On rocks. d, Sniffing flowers.
No. 2641, $65 — Chihuahua: a, On pink dog bed. b, Standing. c, At pond. d, In small pot.

**2010, Jan. 19**     *Perf. 11½x12*
**Sheets of 4, #a-d**
2640-2641 A677   Set of 2    15.00 15.00

**Miniature Sheets**

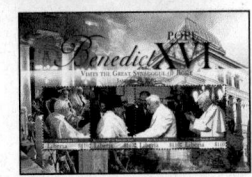

Visit of Pope Benedict XVI to Great Synagogue of Rome — A679

No. 2642: a, Great Synagogue. b, Pope Benedict XVI and Rome's Chief Rabbi Riccardo Di Segni. c, Pope Benedict XVI and Cardinal. d, Rabbi Di Segni and man wearing white yarmulke.
No. 2643: a, Pope Benedict XVI and Rabbi Di Segni seated. b, Rome's former Chief Rabbi Elio Toaff. c, Pope Benedixt XVI, standing and reaching for Toaff. d, Pope Benedict XVI with hands clasped.

**2010, Mar. 23**     *Perf. 12x11½*
2642 A678 $110 Sheet of 4,
    #a-d     12.50 12.50

*Perf. 11½*
2643 A679 $110 Sheet of 4,
    #a-d     12.50 12.50

**Miniature Sheets**

Boy Scouts of America, Cent. A680

No. 2644, $55 — Merit badges: a, Swimming, First Aid. b, Environmental Science, Family Life. c, Citizenship in the Community, Personal Management. d, Camping, Lifesaving. e, Citizenship in the Nation, Communications. f, Personal Fitness, Citizenship in the World.
No. 2645, $55 — Merit badges: a, Aviation, Fishing. b, Engineering, Electronics. c, Medicine, Music. d, Graphic Arts, Soil and Water Conservation. e, Cinematography, Oceanography. f, Animal Science, Art.

**2010, Mar. 23**     *Perf. 13¼*
**Sheets of 6, #a-f**
2644-2645 A680   Set of 2    19.00 19.00

Whales and Dolphins A681

No. 2646: a, Harbor porpoise. b, Killer whale. c, Sowerby's beaked whale. d, Atlantic spotted dolphin. e, Atlantic hump-backed dolphin. f, Clymene dolphin.
$180, Gervais beaked whale.

**2010, Apr. 26**     *Perf. 14¾x14¼*
2646 A681 $60 Sheet of 6,
    #a-f     10.50 10.50

**Souvenir Sheet**
2647 A681 $180 multi     5.25 5.25

US Pres. Barack Obama and Wife, Michelle A682

No. 2648: a, Pres. Obama. b, Pres Obama with arm around wife's waist. c, Pres. Obama and wife dancing. d, Michelle Obama.
No. 2649, Head of Michelle Obama. No. 2650, Michelle Obama (30x81mm).

**2010, Apr. 26**     *Perf. 14¼x14¾*
2648 A682 $60 Sheet of 4, #a-d 7.00 7.00

**Souvenir Sheets**
2649 A682 $100 multi     3.00 3.00
2650 A682 $100 multi     3.00 3.00

**Miniature Sheets**

A683

Pres. Abraham Lincoln (1809-65) — A684

No. 2651, $80 — Lincoln: a, Facing right, hand visible at LR. b, Facing left. c, Facing right, no hand visible. d, Facing right, hand visible at center bottom.

No. 2652, $80 — Lincoln: a, Photograph without hat. b, Photograph with hat. c, Lincoln Memorial sculpture. d, Mount Rushmore sculpture.

**2010, June 25**                    **Perf. 12x11½**
2651  A683  $80 Sheet of 4, #a-d    9.00  9.00
2652  A684  $80 Sheet of 4, #a-d    9.00  9.00

Girl Guides, Cent. A685

No. 2653, horiz.: a, Three Girl Guides, one wearing cap. b, Three Girl Guides wearing neckerchiefs. c, Three Girl Guides. d, Five Girl Guides in uniform.

$160, Girl Guide wearing cap.

**2010, June 25**                    **Perf. 13x13¼**
2653  A685  $65 Sheet of 4, #a-d    7.25  7.25

**Souvenir Sheet**
**Perf. 13¼x13**
2654  A685  $160 multi             4.50  4.50

Lech Kaczynski (1949-2010), President of Poland — A686

**2010, Aug. 27**                    **Perf. 11½**
2655  A686  $75 multi              2.10  2.10
       Printed in sheets of 4.

Paintings by Michelangelo Merisi da Caravaggio (1573-1610) — A687

No. 2656, horiz.: a, The Beheading of St. John the Baptist. b, Judith Beheading Holofernes. c, Abraham's Sacrifice. d, Medusa.

$180, The Penitent Mary Magdalene.

**2010, Aug. 27**        **Perf. 11½x11¼**
2656  A687  $80 Sheet of 4, #a-d    9.00  9.00

**Souvenir Sheet**
**Perf. 11¼x11½**
2657  A687  $180 multi             5.25  5.25

Henri Dunant (1828-1910), Founder of the Red Cross — A688

No. 2658 — Red Cross, Florence Nightingale, depictions of war casualties and nurses, and portrait of Dunant in: a, Gray green. b, Brown. c, Purple. d, Gray blue.

$180, Red Cross, Nightingale, war casualties at Red Cross station, Dunant in purple.

**2010, Aug. 27**                    **Perf. 11½x12**
2658  A688  $80 Sheet of 4, #a-d    9.00  9.00

**Souvenir Sheet**
**Perf. 11½x11¼**
2659  A688  $180 multi             5.25  5.25

**Miniature Sheets**

A689

A690

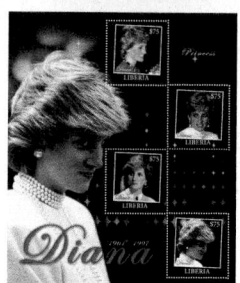

A691

Princess Diana (1961-97) — A691

No. 2660 — Princess Diana with: a, Bare shoulders and single-stand pearl necklace. b, Pink and white hat. c, White dress, earrings, no hat. d, White hat, dark blue and white dress.

No. 2661 — Princess Diana with: a, Tiara. b, Pink hat and dress. c, Green sweater, white blouse. d, Red and white jacket, white blouse.

No. 2662 — Princess Diana with: a, Red dress and flower bouquet. b, White dress, pendant earrings, no hat. c, Bare shoulders and multi-strand pearl necklace. d, White dress, pearl necklace, no hat.

**2010, Aug. 27**                    **Perf. 13¼**
2660  A689  $75 Sheet of 4, #a-d    8.50  8.50
2661  A690  $75 Sheet of 4, #a-d    8.50  8.50
2662  A691  $75 Sheet of 4, #a-d    8.50  8.50
       Nos. 2660-2662 (3)          25.50 25.50

**Miniature Sheets**

A692

A693

Elvis Presley (1935-77) — A694

No. 2663 — Presley: a, With hands pointing left. b, Holding microphone. c, With guitar, holding microphone.

No. 2664 — Paintings of Presley with backgrounds of: a, Green and black. b, Orange and bister. c, Black and red.

No. 2665: a, Presley's face in orange and yellow. b, Presley's face in light blue and white. c, Presley's face in blue and gray. d, Silhouette of Presley.

**2010, Aug. 27**                    **Perf. 11½x11¼**
2663  A692  $90 Sheet of 3, #a-c    7.75  7.75
                    **Perf. 11¼x11½**
2664  A693  $90 Sheet of 3, #a-c    7.75  7.75
                    **Perf. 13**
2665  A694  $90 Sheet of 4, #a-d   10.00 10.00
       Nos. 2663-2665 (3)          25.50 25.50

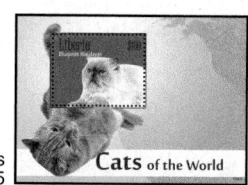

Cats A695

No. 2666, vert.: a, Siberian. b, Turkish Angora. c, British shorthair. d, Maine coon. e, Abyssinian. f, Scottish fold.

$180, Bluepoint Himalayan.

**2010, Oct. 27**                    **Perf. 11¼x11½**
2666  A695  $60 Sheet of 6, #a-f   10.50 10.50

**Souvenir Sheet**
**Perf. 11½x11¼**
2667  A695  $180 multi             5.25  5.25
Nos. 2666-2667 exist imperf. Value, set $25.

**Miniature Sheets**

Pres. John F. Kennedy (1917-63) — A696

No. 2668, $80 — Olive bister frames with Kennedy: a, Walking with Vice-president Lyndon B. Johnson. b, On telephone. c, At lectern. d, Looking upwards.

No. 2669, $80 — Blue frames with Kennedy: a, At lectern. b, Walking with McGeorge Bundy. c, Campaigning in New York City. d, With hands clasped.

No. 2670, $80 — Red frames with Kennedy: a, With Dr. Wernher von Braun. b, With wife, Jacqueline, watching space flight on television. c, At lectern. d, Viewing Friendship 7 space capsule.

**2010, Oct. 27**          **Perf. 12x11½**
**Sheets of 4, #a-d**
2668-2670  A696  Set of 3          28.00 28.00

Christmas — A697

Paintings: $25, The Annunciation, by Fra Angelico. $40, The Angelic Announcement to the Shepherds, by Taddeo Gaddi. $50, Adoration of the Shepherds, by Guido Reni. $100, Virgin and Child with Angels and Saints, by Felice Torelli.

**2010, Oct. 27**   **Litho.**   **Perf. 11½**
2671-2674  A697  Set of 4          6.25  6.25

Liberian Politicians — A698

Designs: $25, Pres. Ellen Johnson-Sirleaf receiving gift. $45, Pres. Johnson Sirleaf standing with Chinese Pres. Hu Jintao, vert. No. 2677, $50, Pres. Johnson-Sirleaf reading. No. 2678, $50, Vice-president Joseph N. Boakai. No. 2679, $100, Pres. Johnson-Sirleaf sitting with Pres. Hu. No. 2680, $100, Pres. Johnson-Sirleaf shaking hands with Vice-president Boakai. No. 2681, $100, Pres. Johnson-Sirleaf wearing sash of office, vert. No. 2682, $500, Pres. Johnson-Sirleaf meeting with international investors. No. 2683, $500, Pres. Johnson-Sirleaf with Vice-president Boakai and cabinet.

**2010, Dec. 16**                    **Perf. 12**
2675-2683  A698  Set of 9           5.00  5.00

Nos. 2675-2683 were sold to the philatelic trade at prices well below that indicated by currency exchange rates at the date of issue.

Mother Teresa (1910-97), Humanitarian — A699

Various photos with frame color of: No. 2684, $80, Olive bister. No. 2685, $80, Blue.

**2010, Dec. 16**
2684-2685  A699  Set of 2          4.50  4.50

Nos. 2684-2685 each were printed in sheets of 4.

Pope John Paul II (1920-2005) A700

No. 2686 — Red background: a, Without crucifix. b, With crucifix.

No. 2687 — Purple background: a, With crucifix. b, Without crucifix.

**2010, Dec. 16**
2686  A700  $80 Pair, #a-b         4.50  4.50
2687  A700  $80 Horiz. pair, #a-b  4.50  4.50

Nos. 2686-2687 each were printed in sheets containing two pairs.

Paintings of Sandro Botticelli (1455-1510) — A701

No. 2688 — Details from The Birth of Venus: a, Head of Venus. b, Reversed image of torso of winged zephyrs. c, Reversed image of heads of winged zephyrs. d, Nymph. $160, Portrait of St. Augustine, vert.

**2010, Dec. 16**       *Perf. 12*
2688 A701   $80 Sheet of 4, #a-d 9.00 9.00

**Souvenir Sheet**
*Perf. 12½x12¾*
2689 A701   $160 multi      4.50 4.50
No. 2689 contains one 38x50mm stamp.

Michael Jackson (1958-2009), Singer — A703

No. 2690 — Jackson: a, With arched back, holding microphone. b, Moving hat to cover face. c, Wearing white glove and hat. d, With arched back, arms stretched outward.
No. 2691 — Jackson: a, Wearing red shirt. b, Holding microphone. c, With arm outstretched. d, With spotlights in background, holding microphone.
$180, Jackson singing.

**2010, Dec. 16**       *Perf. 12*
2690 A702   $80 Sheet of 4, #a-d 9.00 9.00
2691 A703   $80 Sheet of 4, #a-d 9.00 9.00

**Souvenir Sheet**
2692 A703   $180 multi     5.00 5.00

Miniature Sheets

Mao Zedong (1893-1976), Chairman of People's Republic of China — A704

Hu Jintao, President of People's Republic of China — A705

No. 2693 — Mao: a, Without cap, no pockets shown on jacket. b, Wearing cap, pockets shown on jacket. c, Without cap, pockets shown on jacket. d, With cap, no pockets shown on jacket.
No. 2694 — Pres. Hu: a, Ear at left visible, tie over jacket. b, Both ears visible. c, Ear at right visible. d, Ear at left visible, tie under jacket.

**2010, Nov. 7**    *Litho.*    *Perf. 12*
2693 A704   $90 Sheet of 4, #a-d 10.50 10.50
2694 A705   $90 Sheet of 4, #a-d 10.50 10.50
Beijing 2010 Intl. Philatelic Exhibition.

Miniature Sheet

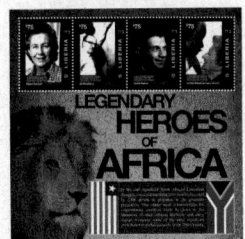

Anti-Apartheid Activists of South Africa — A706

No. 2695: a, Helen Suzman (1917-2009). b, Eli Weinberg (1908-81). c, Hymie Barsel (1920-87). d, Esther Barsel (1924-2008), and South African Pres. Nelson Mandela.

**2011, Mar. 1**
2695 A706   $75 Sheet of 4, #a-d 8.50 8.50

Chinese Zodiac Animals A707

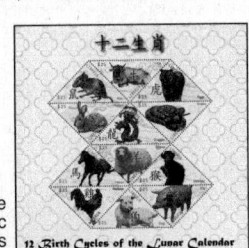

New Year 2011 (Year of the Rabbit) A708

No. 2696: a, Rat. b, Ox. c, Tiger. d, Rabbit. e, Dragon. f, Snake. g, Horse. h, Sheep. i, Monkey. j, Rooster. k, Dog. l, Pig.

**2011, Mar. 28**
2696 A707   $25 Sheet of 12, #a-l 8.50 8.50

**Souvenir Sheet**
2697 A708    Sheet of 2 #2697a 5.75 5.75
   *a.*    $100 Single stamp    2.75 2.75

British Monarchs — A709

Designs: No. 2698, $80, King George V (1865-1936). No. 2699, $80, King Edward VIII (1894-1972). No. 2700, $80, King George VI (1895-1952). No. 2701, $80, Queen Elizabeth II.

*Perf. 13 Syncopated, 12 (#2700)*
**2011, Mar. 28**
2698-2701 A709   Set of 4    9.00 9.00
Nos. 2698-2701 each were printed in sheets of 4.

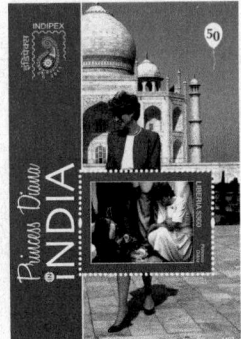

Princess Diana (1961-97) in India — A710

No. 2702, vert. — Princess Diana: a, Greeting girl with hands together, red background. b, Touching woman on cot, red background. c, Talking with Mother Teresa, red background. d, Shaking hands with seated man, purple background. e, With woman and small boy, purple background. f, At Taj Mahal, purple background.
$360, Princess Diana talking with seated people.

**2011, Mar. 28**    *Perf. 13 Syncopated*
2702 A710   $60 Sheet of 6, #a-f 10.00 10.00

**Souvenir Sheet**
2703 A710   $360 multi    10.00 10.00
Indipex 2011 Intl. Philatelic Exhibition, New Delhi.

Engagement of Prince William and Catherine Middleton — A711

Deisgns: No. 2704, $65, Couple, dull green background. No. 2705, $65, Couple, gray background.
No. 2706, $100: a, Catherine Middleton. b, Prince William.
No. 2707, $100, horiz.: a, Couple, Middleton touching hat. b, Couple, Middleton not touching hat.

*Perf. 12, 13 Syncopated (#2707)*
**2011, Mar. 28**
2704-2705 A711   Set of 2    3.75 3.75
**Sheets of 2, #a-b**
2706-2707 A711   Set of 2    11.50 11.50

Pres. John F. Kennedy (1917-63) — A712

No. 2708 — Kennedy: a, Oval portrait. b, Close-up of head. c, Wearing patterned tie. d, Wearing pinstripe suit and solid tie.
$180, Kennedy, diff.

**2011, Mar. 28**       *Perf. 12*
2708 A712   $80 Sheet of 4, #a-d 9.00 9.00

**Souvenir Sheet**
2709 A712   $180 multi    5.00 5.00

Miniature Sheets

U.S. Civil War, 150th Anniv. A713

No. 2710, $80 — Lieutenant Colonel John B. Baylor, Major Isaac Lynde and Battle of Mesilla image: a, Town and valley of Mesilla. b, Fort Fillmore. c, Confederates near the Organ Mountains. d, Union soldiers firing at long range.
No. 2711, $80 — Colonel Martin E. Green, Colonel David Moore and Battle of Athens image: a, Confederates near the Fabius River. b, Col. Moore leads Union troops. c, Cavalries clash at Athens encounter. d, Col. Green's Missouri State Guard.
No. 2712, $80 — Major General Sterling Price, Captain Nathaniel Lyon and Battle of Wilson's Creek image: a, Missouri State Guardsmen on Bloody Hill. b, Confederate battery in action. c, Lt. Omar Weaver is wounded. d, 2nd Kansas Infantry on Bloody Hill.
No. 2713, $80 — Brigadier General John B. Floyd, Colonel Erastus Tyler and Battle of Kessler's Cross Lanes image: a, Confederate forces in the Kanawha Valley. b, 7th Ohio Regiment at Kessler's Cross Lanes. c, The Union forces surprised and routed. d, Confederate forces near the Gauley River.
No. 2714, $80 — Captain Samuel Barron, Major General Benjamin F. Butler and Battle of Hatteras Inlet image: a, Capture of Fort Hatteras. b, Union Atlantic blockading squadron. c, USS Harriet Lane. d, USS Cumberland.

**2011, Mar. 28**    *Perf. 13 Syncopated*
**Sheets of 4, #a-d**
2710-2714 A713   Set of 5    45.00 45.00

Mushrooms — A714

No. 2715: a, Penny bun. b, Ola'h. c, The miller. d, False ink cap. e, The blusher. f, Glistening ink cap.
No. 2716: a, Death cap. b, Panther cap.

**2011, Mar. 28**       *Perf. 12*
2715 A714   $65 Sheet of 6, #a-f 11.00 11.00

**Souvenir Sheet**
2716 A714   $65 Sheet of 2, #a-b 3.75 3.75

Birds A715

No. 2717: a, Red-faced cisticola. b, Orange-cheeked waxbill. c, Zebra waxbill. d, African firefinch.
No. 2718, $180, Guinea turaco. No. 2719, $180, Lavender waxbill, vert.

**Perf. 12, 13 Syncopated (#2718)**
**2011, Mar. 28**
2717 A715 $80 Sheet of 4,
#a-d                    9.00   9.00
**Souvenir Sheets**
2718-2719 A715   Set of 2   10.00  10.00

Miniature Sheets

Zodiac Constellations — A716

No. 2720, $100: a, Aries. b, Leo. c, Sagittarius.
No. 2721, $100: a, Gemini. b, Libra. c, Aquarius.
No. 2722, $100: a, Cancer. b, Scorpio. c, Pisces.
No. 2723, $100: a, Virgo. b, Taurus. c, Capricorn.

**2011, Mar. 28**                  **Perf. 12**
**Sheets of 3, #a-c**
2720-2723 A716   Set of 4   34.00  34.00

Souvenir Sheets

Pres. Ellen Johnson-Sirleaf — A717

Designs: $45, Pres. Johnson-Sirleaf and Chinese President Hu Jintao. No. 2725, $100, Pres. Johnson-Sirleaf. No. 2726, $100, Pres. Johnson-Sirleaf and Pres. Hu, horiz.

**2011, Mar. 28   Perf. 13¼x13, 13x13¼**
2724-2726 A717   Set of 3   7.00  7.00

Souvenir Sheets

Popes and Their Arms A718

No. 2727, $250: a, Pope Pius XII (1876-1958). b, Arms of Pope Pius XII.
No. 2728, $250: a, Pope John XXIII (1881-1963). b, Arms of Pope John XXIII.

**2011, Mar. 28**                  **Imperf.**
**Sheets of 2, #a-b**
**Without Gum**
2727-2728 A718   Set of 2   28.00  28.00

Visit of Chinese President Hu Jintao to Washington, D.C. — A719

---

No. 2729 — Presidents Hu Jintao and Barack Obama: a, Shaking hands. b, Standing near lectern. c, Greeting crowd. d, Walking outside of White House.
$180, Reviewing troops.

**2011, Mar. 28       Litho.       Perf. 12**
2729 A719 $75 Sheet of 4, #a-d  8.50  8.50
**Souvenir Sheet**
2730 A719 $180 multi              5.25  5.25

Back to the Soil — A720

Inscriptions: $25, Invest in the Soil Rubber Farm. $45, Women scratching rice, horiz. $50, Rice nursery in Bong County. $70, The soil is a bank. $100, President Ellen Johnson-Sirleaf harvesting rice, horiz. No. 2736, $500, Fresh fruits and vegetables. No. 2737, $500, Harvesting rice, horiz.

**Perf. 12¾x12½, 12½x12¾**
**2011, Mar. 28**
2731-2737 A720   Set of 7   37.50  37.50

Worldwide Fund for Nature (WWF) — A721

No. 2738 — Water chevrotain: a, Standing in foliage. b, In water. c, Eating. d, Pair in foliage.

**2011, June 30**                  **Perf. 13¼**
2738      Strip of 4           5.75  5.75
a.-d.   A721 $50 Any single     1.40  1.40
   e.   Souvenir sheet of 8, 2 each
        #2738a-2738d            11.50  11.50

Miniature Sheet

A.C. Milan Soccer Team A722

No. 2739 — Team emblem and photographs of: a, 2003 UEFA Champions League match. b, Centennial emblem, 1999. c, 2001 6-0 A.C. Milan- Milan Inter match. d, Carlo Ancelloti. e, 2010-11 team. f, Paolo Maldini. g, 2007 UEFA Champions League match. h, Team members with 2007 FIFA Club World Cup. i, Team owner Italian Prime Minister Silvio Berlusconi.

**2011, June 30**                  **Perf. 13½**
2739 A722 $35 Sheet of 9, #a-i   8.75  8.75

Miniature Sheets

Chocolate Candy — A724

No. 2740: a, Cacao pods. b, Sun. c, Ship. d, Fires. e, Mound of cocoa powder. f, Milk and butter. g, Chocolate bar and wrapped candy. h, Cash register and chocolate bar. i, Mouth and chocolate bar.
No. 2741 — Piece of candy with: a, Chocolate coating with white chocolate swirls. b, Dark chocolate coating with walnut. c, White chocolate coating with dark chocolate swirls.

---

d, White chocolate coating with chocolate swirls. e, Chocolate coating with dark chocolate ribbons. f, Dark chocolate coating with chocolate sprinkles. g, Chocolate coating with chocolate rosette. h, Dark chocolate coating with almond. i, White chocolate coating with candy heart.

**2011, June 30   Perf. 13 Syncopated**
2740 A723 $30 Sheet of 9, #a-i   7.50  7.50
2741 A724 $30 Sheet of 9, #a-i   7.50  7.50
   Nos. 2740-2741 each are impregnated with a chocolate aroma.

A725

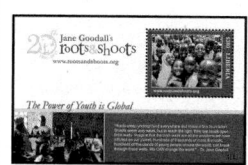

U.S. Civil War, 150th Anniv. A726

No. 2742: a, Union General Ulysses S. Grant. b, Drum, rifles, Union and Confederate flags. c, Confederate General Robert E. Lee. d, Pres. Abraham Lincoln. e, Cannons.
No. 2743 — Paintings depicting Lincoln: a, Abraham Lincoln, by William F. Cogswell. b, The Peacemakers, by George Healy. c, President Lincoln Writing the Proclamation of Freedom, by David Gilmour Blythe.

**2011, June 30**                  **Perf. 12¾x13**
2742 A725 $70 Sheet of 5, #a-e  9.75  9.75
                  **Perf. 13¼x13**
2743 A726 $100 Sheet of 3, #a-c  8.25  8.25

Jane Goodall's Roots and Shoots, 25th Anniv. A727

No. 2744: a, Adult showing group of children how to plant seedlings. b, Two children planting seedlings. c, Children holding sign. d, Children and teachers in classroom.
$180, Children.

**2011, June 30**                  **Perf. 13x13¼**
2744 A727 $90 Sheet of 4,
                  #a-d            10.00  10.00
**Souvenir Sheet**
2745 A727 $180 multi              5.00  5.00

A728

---

A729

A730

A731

A732

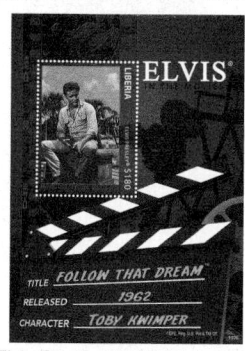

A733

Elvis Presley (1935-77) — A734

No. 2746: a, Face in color. b, Face in black and white, microphone cord above "E." c, As "b," microphone between "I" and "S." d, As "b," microphone cord above "L." e, As "b," microphone cord above "S." f, As "b," microphone cord between "V" and "I."
No. 2747: a, Head of microphone above shoulder. b, Head of microphone even with edge of guitar. c, Head of microphone at right. d, Head of microphone even with tip of chin.
No. 2748 — Presley: a, On motorcycle. b, Wearing white tie. c, Wearing white shirt open at neck. d, Playing guitar.

**2011, June 30**      *Perf. 12¾x13*
2746 A728   $60 Sheet of 6,
      #a-f       10.00   10.00
*Perf. 13¼x13*
2747 A729   $80 Sheet of 4,
      #a-d       8.75   8.75
*Perf. 13 Syncopated*
2748 A730   $90 Sheet of 4,
      #a-d       10.00   10.00
    Nos. 2746-2748 (3)     28.75   28.75
**Souvenir Sheets**
*Perf. 12¾*
2749 A731   $180 multi    5.00   5.00
2750 A732   $180 multi    5.00   5.00
2751 A733   $180 multi    5.00   5.00
2752 A734   $180 multi    5.00   5.00
    Nos. 2749-2752 (4)    20.00   20.00

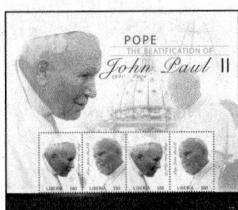

Beatification of Pope John Paul
II — A735

No. 2753 — Pope John Paul II facing: a,
Right, gray area at LR. b, Left, gray area at
top. c, Right, no gray area at LR. d, Left, no
gray area at top.
$180, Pope John Paul II wearing miter and
green stole.

**2011, Aug. 5**    Litho.    *Perf. 12*
2753 A735   $80 Sheet of 4, #a-d   9.00   9.00
**Souvenir Sheet**
2754 A735   $180 multi    5.00   5.00

Statue of
Liberty,
125th
Anniv.
A736

No. 2755 — Inscription at right: a, National
Monument. b, Lighting the Night Sky. c, Liberty Island, New York Harbor. d, Designed by
Frédéric Auguste Bartholdi. e, Enlightening
the World, 1886, by Edward Moran. f, Under
Construction in Paris, France.
$180, Statue of Liberty and Manhattan
buildings, horiz.

**2011, Aug. 5**        *Perf. 12*
2755 A736   $60 Sheet of 6,
      #a-f       10.00   10.00
**Souvenir Sheet**
*Perf. 12½*
2756 A736   $180 multi    5.00   5.00
  No. 2756 contains one 51x38mm stamp.

Butterflies — A737

No. 2757: a, Gaudy commodore. b, Yellow
pansy. c, White lady swallowtail. d, Broad-bordered grass yellow. e, Blue pansy. f, Citrus
swallowtail.
No. 2758: a, Mimic female. b, Wandering
donkey acaea.

**2011, Aug. 5**        *Perf. 12*
2757 A737   $65 Sheet of 6,
      #a-f       11.00   11.00
**Souvenir Sheet**
2758 A737   $100 Sheet of 2,
      #a-b       5.50   5.50

---

Miniature Sheets

A738

Princess Diana (1961-97) — A739

No. 2759: a, Wearing hat with veil. b, Wearing dark hat and winter jacket. c, Without hat.
d, Wearing dark hat and white dress.
No. 2760: a, Wearing blue dress and necklace. b, Wearing blue hat. c, Wearing blue
jacket, no necklace. d, Wearing white hat.

**2011, Aug. 5**    *Perf. 13 Syncopated*
2759 A738   $75 Sheet of 4, #a-d   8.25   8.25
2760 A739   $75 Sheet of 4, #a-d   8.25   8.25

First
Man in
Space,
50th
Anniv.
A740

No. 2761, $80: a, Statue of Yuri Gagarin. b,
American astronaut John Glenn. c, Gagarin on
medal. d, Vostok spacecraft in orbit.
No. 2762, $80, horiz.: a, Gagarin souvenir
medal. b, Mosaic of Gagarin. c, Vostok rocket
on train. d, American astronauts Virgil Grissom and John Young.
No. 2763, $180, Gagarin. No. 2764, $180,
Vostok spacecraft, horiz.

**2011, Aug. 5**    *Perf. 13 Syncopated*
**Sheets of 4, #a-d**
2761-2762 A740   Set of 2   18.00   18.00
**Souvenir Sheets**
2763-2764 A740   Set of 2   10.00   10.00

Orchids
A741

No. 2765: a, Polystachya longiscapa. b,
Vanilla polylepis. c, Ansellia africana. d,
Bolusiella maudiae.
No. 2766, $180, Polystachya zambesiaca.
No. 2767, $180, Polystachya bella.

**2011, Aug. 5**        *Perf. 12*
2765 A741   $80 Sheet of 4, #a-
      d       9.00   9.00
**Souvenir Sheets**
2766-2767 A741   Set of 2   10.00   10.00

Sept. 11,
2001
Terrorist
Attacks,
10th
Anniv.
A742

No. 2768: a, World Trade Center. b, Sep-
tember 11 Memorial, New York. c, Tribute in
Light. d, The Pentagon.
$200, World Trade Center and Brooklyn
Bridge, vert.

---

**2011, Sept. 11**    *Perf. 13 Syncopated*
2768 A742   $75 Sheet of 4, #a-d   8.25   8.25
**Souvenir Sheet**
2769 A742   $200 multi    5.50   5.50

Chinese Civil
Engineering
A743

Designs: $40, Qingdao Cross-sea Bridge.
No. 2771 — Qingdao Jiaozhouwan Under-
sea Tunnel: a, Entrance. b, Cross-sectional
diagram.

**2011, Oct. 11**       Litho.
2770 A743   $40 multi    1.10   1.10
2771 A743   $25 Sheet of 6, 3
      each #2771a-
      2771b      4.25   4.25
  No. 2770 was printed in sheets of 4.

A744

Wedding of Prince William and
Catherine Middleton — A745

No. 2772 — Red frames: a, Bride facing
right. b, Couple kissing. c, Couple holding
hands. d, Groom. e, Bride facing left. f, Couple
in coach.
No. 2773 — Blue frames: a, Couple holding
hands. b, Groom waving. c, Bride facing left. d,
Couple in coach, groom waving. e, Couple
standing, bride waving. f, Groom facing right.
$180, Couple in coach, bride waving.

**2011, Oct. 11**       *Perf. 12*
2772 A744   $80 Sheet of 6,
      #a-f       13.50   13.50
2773 A745   $80 Sheet of 6,
      #a-f       13.50   13.50
**Souvenir Sheet**
2774 A745   $180 multi    5.00   5.00

Christmas — A746

Paintings: $25, Madonna with Members of
the Pesaro Family, by Titian. $40, The Nativity,
by Prero della Francesca. $50, The Virgin of

---

the Rocks, by Leonardo da Vinci. $100,
Madonna with Child, by Fra Filippo Lippi.

**2011, Oct. 11**    *Perf. 13 Syncopated*
2775-2778 A746   Set of 4   6.00   6.00

Chinese
Zodiac
Animals
A747

New
Year
2012
(Year of
the
Dragon)
A748

No. 2779: a, Rat. b, Ox. c, Tiger. d, Rabbit.
e, Dragon. f, Snake. g, Horse. h, Sheep. i,
Monkey. j, Rooster. k, Dog. l, Boar.

**Litho. With Foil Application**
**2011, Oct. 11**    *Perf. 13 Syncopated*
2779 A747   $18 Sheet of 12, #a-
      l       6.00   6.00
**Souvenir Sheet**
*Litho.*
*Perf. 13¼*
2780 A748   $200 multi    5.75   5.75
  China 2011 World Philatelic Exhibition, Wuxi
(No. 2780).

Binhai
New
Area,
People's
Republic
of China
A749

No. 2781: a, Dove, city. b, Highway cloverleaf interchange. c, City at nightfall. d, Ship at
dock.
$160, City, ship, airplanes, rocket.

*Perf. 13 Syncopated*
**2011, Oct. 26**       Litho.
2781 A749   $40 Sheet of 4, #a-d   4.50   4.50
**Souvenir Sheet**
2782 A749   $160 multi    4.50   4.50
  No. 2782 contains one 119x40mm stamp.

Peking
Opera
A750

No. 2783 — Character with: a, Two sharp
teeth, (gray, red and pink face). b, Beard
(black and red face). c, Heart-shaped nose
(pink, red and black face). d, Ten teeth (red,
black and gray face). $180, Character with red,
dark red and black face.

**2011, Oct. 26**       *Perf. 13¼*
2783 A750   $50 Sheet of 4, #a-d   5.75   5.75
**Souvenir Sheet**
2784 A750   $180 multi    5.00   5.00
  China 2011 Intl. Philatelic Exhibition, Wuxi.
No. 2784 contains one 44x44mm stamp.

Pres. Ronald Reagan
(1911-2004) — A751

Flags and Pres. Reagan wearing suit: No. 2785, $100, Without handkerchief in suit pocket. No. 2786, $100, With handkerchief in suit pocket.

**2011, Dec. 16    Perf. 13 Syncopated**
2785-2786  A751  Set of 2          5.50 5.50
　Nos. 2785-2786 each were printed in sheets of 3.

Awarding of Nobel
Peace Prize to Pres.
Ellen Johnson-Sirleaf
A752

Designs: $75, Shown. $250, Pres. Johnson-Sirleaf, horiz.

**2011, Dec. 5                           Perf. 12**
2787  A752  $75 multi             2.10 2.10
**Souvenir Sheet**
2788  A752  $250 multi            7.00 7.00
　No. 2787 was printed in sheets of 6. No. 2788 contains one 50x30mm stamp.

Reptiles
A753

No. 2789: a, Natal green snake. b, African tree snake. c, African python.
　No. 2790: a, African spiny-tailed lizard. b, Western Cape crag lizard. c, Eastern Cape crag lizard. d, Armadillo lizard.
　No. 2791: a, African tent tortoise. b, Serrated tortoise.
　No. 2792: a, Underside of Nile crocodile. b, Top of Nile crocodile.

**2011, Dec. 16                         Perf. 12**
2789  A753  $90 Sheet of 3,
　　　　　　#a-c                      7.50 7.50
2790  A753  $90 Sheet of 4,
　　　　　　#a-d                     10.00 10.00
**Souvenir Sheets**
2791  A753  $180 Sheet of 2,
　　　　　　#a-b                    10.00 10.00
2792  A753  $180 Sheet of 2,
　　　　　　#a-b                    10.00 10.00
　No. 2790 contains four 50x30mm stamps. No. 2792 contains two 80x30mm stamps.

Completion of St. Paul's Cathedral,
London, 300th Anniv. — A754

---

No. 2793: a, Plan of Cathedral. b, Building St. Paul's by J. Seymour Lucas. c, Architect Sir Christopher Wren. d, Pope Clement XI. e, St. Paul's Cathedral. f, Pope Benedict XVI.
　No. 2794: a, Pope Clement XI, diff. b, Pope Benedict XVI, diff.

**2011, Dec. 16    Perf. 13 Syncopated**
2793  A754  $50 Sheet of 6, #a-f  8.25 8.25
**Souvenir Sheet**
2794  A754  $150 Sheet of 2, #a-b 8.25 8.25
　St. Paul's Cathedral is an Anglican cathedral and was not visited by Pope Benedict XVI in his travels to the United Kingdom.

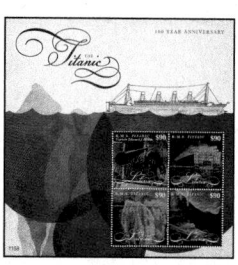

Sinking
of the
Titanic,
Cent.
A755

No. 2795: a, Titanic Captain Edward J. Smith. b, Cross-section of the Titanic. c, Iceberg. d, Titanic sinking.
　$250, Titanic sinking, vert.

**2012, Jan. 1                           Perf. 13¼**
2795  A755  $90 Sheet of 4,
　　　　　　#a-d                     10.00 10.00
**Souvenir Sheet**
**Perf. 12**
2796  A755  $250 multi            7.00 7.00
　No. 2796 contains one 38x50mm stamp.

Souvenir Sheet

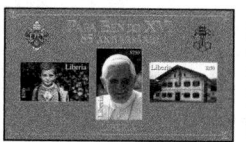

Pope
Benedict
XVI, 85th
Birthday
A756

No. 2797: a, Joseph Ratzinger as young boy (44x25mm). b, Pope Benedict XVI, vert. (30x44mm). c, Birthplace of Pope Benedict XVI (44x25mm).

**2012, Feb. 22                         Imperf.**
2797  A756  $250 Sheet of 3,
　　　　　　#a-c                     21.00 21.00

Mao Zedong (1893-
1976), Chairman of
People's Republic of
China — A757

Photograph of Mao Zedong: No. 2798, $25, No. 2802a, $90, With blue background. No. 2799, $25, No. 2802b, $90, Reading in library. No. 2800, $25, No. 2802c, $90, Waving. No. 2801, $25, No. 2802d, $90, Seated.

**2012, Feb. 22    Litho.    Perf. 14**
2798-2801  A757  Set of 4         2.75 2.75
2802  A757  $90 Sheet of 4, #a-d  9.75 9.75

Premiere
of The
Three
Stooges
Movie
A758

No. 2803: a, Chris Diamantopolous as Moe, denomination in yellow. b, Diamantopolous as Moe, denomination in orange. c, Sean Hayes as Larry, denomination in yellow. d, Hayes as Larry, denomination in orange. e, Will Sasso as Curly, denomination in yellow. f, Sasso as Curly, denomination in orange.

---

No. 2804: a, Stooges, denomination in blue. b, Stooges, denomination in red violet.

**2012, Mar. 13    Perf. 13 Syncopated**
2803  A758  $75 Sheet of 6,
　　　　　　#a-c                    12.50 12.50
**Souvenir Sheet**
2804  A758  $125 Sheet of 2,
　　　　　　#a-b                     7.00 7.00

Meeting of U.S. Pres. Barack Obama
and Xi Jinping, Vice-President of
People's Republic of China — A759

No. 2805: a, Xi Jinping. b, Temple, Beijing. c, Pres. Obama. d, Washington Monument.
　No. 2806: a, Xi Jinping, diff. b, Pres. Obama, diff.

**2012, Apr. 4                            Perf. 12**
2805  A759  $90 Sheet of 4,
　　　　　　#a-d                     10.00 10.00
**Souvenir Sheet**
2806  A759  $125 Sheet of 2,
　　　　　　#a-b                     7.00 7.00

African
Wildlife
A760

No. 2807: a, West African giraffe (30x80mm). b, Dorcas gazelle (30x40mm). c, Blue duiker (30x40mm). d, Red river hog (30x40mm). e, Hartebeest (30x40mm).
　No. 2808, horiz.: a, Spotted hyena. b, Side-striped jackal. c, Serval.
　No. 2809, African bush elephant. No. 2810, Patas monkey.

**2012, May 3                             Perf. 14**
2807  A760  $75 Sheet of 5,
　　　　　　#a-e                    10.50 10.50
**Perf. 12**
2808  A760  $100 Sheet of 3,
　　　　　　#a-c                     8.25 8.25
**Souvenir Sheets**
2809  A760  $250 multi            7.00 7.00
2810  A760  $250 multi            7.00 7.00

Miniature Sheet

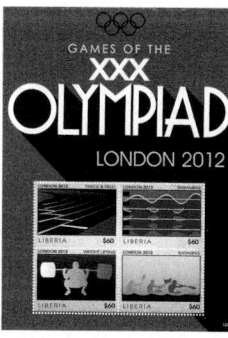

2012 Summer Olympics,
London — A761

No. 2811: a, Track and field. b, Swimming. c, Weight lifting. d, Kayaking.

**2012, May 30                           Perf. 14**
2811  A761  $60 Sheet of 4, #a-d  6.50 6.50

Dinosaurs — A762

---

No. 2812, horiz.: a, Albertaceratops. b, Zuniceratops. c, Prestosaurus. d, Saurolophus. e, Ampelosaurus. f, Euoplocephalus.
　No. 2813: a, Pachyrhinosaurus. b, Hypsilophodon.

**2012, June 27    Perf. 13 Syncopated**
2812  A762  $75 Sheet of 6,
　　　　　　#a-f                    12.50 12.50
**Souvenir Sheet**
2813  A762  $125 Sheet of 2,
　　　　　　#a-b                     7.00 7.00

Dogs
A763

No. 2814, $120: a, Afghan hound. b, Dalmatian. c, Greyhound.
　No. 2815, $120: a, English bulldog. b, Bichon Frise. c, Dachshund.
　No. 2816, $250, Scottish terrier. No. 2817, $250, Poodle.

**2012, June 27    Perf. 14, 12 (#2816)**
**Sheets of 3, #a-c**
2814-2815  A763  Set of 2        20.00 20.00
**Souvenir Sheets**
2816-2817  A763  Set of 2        14.00 14.00

SOS Children's
Village, Liberia,
30th Anniv. (in
2011) — A764

SOS Children's Village emblem, map of Liberia and: $45, Inscription and slogan. $55, Inscription and palm tree.

**2012, Feb. 14                           Perf. 14**
2818-2819  A764  Set of 2         2.75 2.75

Miniature Sheet

Apes
A765

No. 2820: a, Barbary macaque. b, Bonobo. c, Silverback gorilla. d, Chacma baboon.

**2012, Aug. 9                            Perf. 12**
2820  A765  $90 Sheet of 4, #a-d  9.75 9.75

Souvenir Sheets

Elvis Presley (1935-77) — A766

Designs: No. 2821, $250, Presley with guitar, light blue frame. No. 2822, $250, Presley behind microphone, light blue frame. No. 2823, $250, Two black-and-white photographs of Presley, dull red frame. No. 2824, $250, Color and black-and-white photographs of Presley, red frame. No. 2825, $250, Presley in army uniform, red frame.

**2012, Aug. 9                            Perf. 12½**
2821-2825  A766  Set of 5        35.00 35.00

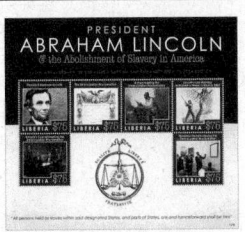

First Draft of the Emancipation
Proclamation, 150th Anniv. — A767

No. 2826: a, Pres. Abraham Lincoln. b,
Printed copy of Emancipation Proclamation. c,
Man reading Emancipation Proclamation. d,
Lincoln's Last Warning, political cartoon from
Harper's Weekly, 1862. e, First Reading of the
Emancipation Proclamation of President Lin-
coln, by Francis Bicknell Carpenter. f, Pres.
Barack Obama viewing Emancipation
Proclamation.
  $250, President Lincoln Writing the Procla-
mation of Freedom, by David Gilmour Blythe,
horiz.

**2012, Sept. 21**       **Perf. 13¾**
2826 A767 $75 Sheet of 6,
      #a-f       12.50 12.50
**Souvenir Sheet**
**Perf. 12½**
2827 A767 $250 multi     7.00 7.00
  No. 2827 contains one 51x38mm stamp.

Chinese Zodiac
Animals — A768

Designs: No. 2828, $15, Monkeys. No.
2829, $15, Cock.

**2012, Sept. 27**     **Perf. 13¼x13**
2828-2829 A768   Set of 2    .85 .85

Christmas — A769

Paintings: $25, Adoration of the Shepherds,
by Guido Reni. $35, Adoration of the Shep-
herds, by Correggio. $40, Holy Family with St.
John the Baptist, by Michelangelo. $45, Tempi
Madonna (detail), by Raphael. $50, The
Annunciation, by Francisco Goya. $100, Virgin
and Child Before an Archway, by Albrecht
Dürer.

**2012, Oct. 1**      **Perf. 12½**
2830-2835 A769  Set of 6    8.25 8.25

Giant
Pandas
A770

No. 2836 — Giant Panda: a, On tree, facing
left. b, Eating. c, Walking, foliage at right. d,
With log at right.
  $220, Panda on tree, vert.

**2012, Nov. 15**   **Perf. 13 Syncopated**
2836 A770 $85 Sheet of 4, #a-d 7.00 7.00
**Souvenir Sheet**
2837 A770 $220 multi    6.00 6.00
  Beijing 2012 Intl. Stamp Exhibition.

---

Aircraft
Carriers
A771

No. 2838: a, Admiral Gorshkov, Russia. b,
Dédalo, Spain. c, Foch (R99), France. d, USS
Philippine Sea. e, USS Intrepid. f, HTMS
Chakri Naruebet, Thailand.
  $250, USS Ticonderoga, horiz.

**2012, Nov. 28**      **Perf. 13¾**
2838 A771 $75 Sheet of 6,
     #a-f     12.50 12.50
**Souvenir Sheet**
**Perf. 12½**
2839 A771 $250 multi   6.75 6.75
  No. 2839 contains one 51x38mm stamp.

Flowers
A772

No. 2840: a, Nymphaea lotus. b, Papaver
somniferum. c, Protea repens. d, Liparia
splendens. e, Tulipa florenskyi. f, Gladiolus
carmineus.
  $280, Zantedeschia aethiopica, vert.

**2013, Jan. 8**      **Perf. 13¾**
2840 A772 $70 Sheet of 6,
     #a-f     11.50 11.50
**Souvenir Sheet**
**Perf. 12½**
2841 A772 $280 multi   7.75 7.75
  No. 2841 contains one 38x51mm stamp.

World
Radio
Day
A773

No. 2842: a, Hindenburg disaster reporting,
1937. b, Winston Churchill's "We Shall Fight
on the Beaches" broadcast, 1940. c, Pres.
John F. Kennedy's Cuban Missile Crisis
address, 1962. d, Dr. Martin Luther King, Jr.'s
"I Have a Dream" speech, 1963.
  $250, Orson Welles' "War of the Worlds"
broadcast, 1938.

**2013, Jan. 8**      **Perf. 12½**
2842 A773 $90 Sheet of 4, #a-d 9.75 9.75
**Souvenir Sheet**
**Perf.**
2843 A773 $250 multi   6.75 6.75
  No. 2843 contains one 38mm diameter
stamp.

Gems
and
Rocks
A774

No. 2844, $100: a, Aquamarine. b, Euclase.
c, Rainbow garnet.
No. 2845, $100: a, Rhodochrosite. b, Opal.
c, Tanzanite.
Mo. 2846: a, Agate with red inner rings,
small hole. b, Agate with white inner rings,
large hole.

---

**2013, Jan. 8**      **Perf. 13¾**
**Sheets of 3, #a-c**
2844-2845 A774  Set of 2  16.50 16.50
**Souvenir Sheet**
**Perf. 12½**
2846 A774 $140 Sheet of 2,
     #a-b     7.75 7.75
  Nos. 2844-2845 each contain three
35x35mm stamps.

American Civil Rights Leaders — A775

No. 2847, $85: a, Harriet Tubman (c. 1820-
1913), abolitionist (without head covering). b,
Frederick Douglass (1818-95), abolitionist. c,
John Brown (1800-59), abolitionist. d, Martha
Coffin Wright (1806-75), abolitionist.
No. 2848, $85: a, Union Major General
David Hunter (1802-86). b, Pres. Abraham
Lincoln (1809-65). c, Susan B. Anthony (1820-
1906), suffragist. d, Tubman (with head
covering).
No. 2849, $280, Tubman and slave capture
reward notice. No. 2850, $280, Tubman,
daughter Gertie and husband Nelson Davis,
horiz.

**2013, Mar. 20**      **Perf. 12½**
**Sheets of 4, #a-d**
2847-2848 A775  Set of 2  18.50 18.50
**Souvenir Sheets**
**Perf. 12**
2849-2850 A775  Set of 2  15.50 15.50
  No. 2849 contains on 30x40mm stamp. No.
2850 contains one 40x30mm stamp.

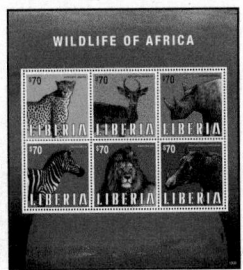

African
Wildlife
A776

No. 2851: a, Acionyx jubatus. b, Aepyceros
melampus. c, Diceros bicornis. d, Equus
grevyi. e, Panthera leo. f, Phacochoerus
africanus.
No. 2852, vert.: a, Giraffa camelopardalis. b,
Loxodonta africana. c, Connochaetes
taurinus.
  $280, Panthera pardus pardus, horiz.

**2013, Apr. 3**      **Perf. 13¾**
2851 A776 $70 Sheet of 6,
     #a-f     11.50 11.50
**Perf. 12**
2852 A776 $100 Sheet of 3,
     #a-c     8.25 8.25
**Souvenir Sheet**
**Perf. 12½**
2853 A776 $280 multi   7.75 7.75
  No. 2852 contains three 30x50mm stamps.
No. 2853 contains one 51x38mm stamp.

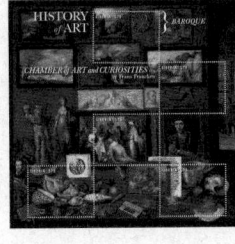

History
of Art
A777

---

No. 2854 — Chamber of Art and Curiosities,
by Frans Francken (details) with: a, Fish at UR.
b, Seahorse at L. c, Religious painting and
tasselled cord. d, Shells, book at LL. e, Shells,
bowl at top.
No. 2855, $100, vert.: a, Girl with a Pearl
Earring, by Johannes Vermeer. b, A Com-
mander Being Armed for Battle, by Peter Paul
Rubens. c, David with the Head of Goliath, by
Caravaggio.
No. 2856, $100, vert.: a, Still-life with Flow-
ers, by Rachel Ruysch. b, Maddalena
Penitente, by Artemisia Gentileschi. c, The
Fruit and Vegetable Costermonger, by Louise
Moillon.
  $280, La Gamme d'Amour, by Jean-Antoine
Watteau.

**2013, Apr. 4**   **Litho.**   **Perf. 12½**
2854 A777 $75 Sheet of 5,
     #a-e     10.50 10.50
**Sheets of 3, #a-c**
2855-2856 A777  Set of 2  16.50 16.50
**Souvenir Sheet**
2857 A777 $280 multi   7.75 7.75

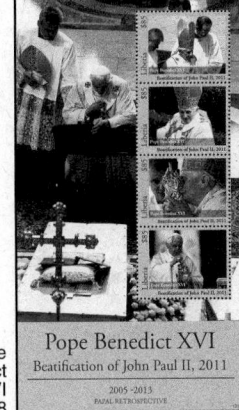

Pope
Benedict
XVI
A778

No. 2858, $85 — Pope Benedict XVI at
Beatification Ceremony for Pope John Paul II:
a, Wearing miter, with two assistants. b, Wear-
ing miter, waving. c, Kissing glass object. d,
Holding censer.
No. 2859, $85 — Pope Benedict XVI visiting
Germany: a, Meeting Chancellor Angela Mer-
kel. b, Waving. c, With German President
Christian Wulff and wife. d, Facing left.
No. 2860, $280, Pope Benedict XVI seated
at beatification ceremony. No. 2861, $280,
Pope Benedict XVI with Wulff and Merkel.

**2013, Apr. 29**      **Perf. 12**
**Sheets of 4, #a-d**
2858-2859 A778  Set of 2  18.50 18.50
**Souvenir Sheets**
2860-2861 A778  Set of 2  15.50 15.50

Lady Margaret Thatcher (1925-2013),
British Prime Minister — A779

No. 2862 — Thatcher: a, At microphone. b,
Wearing black dress, facing left. c, With Pres.
Ronald Reagan. d, With hand on chin.
  $280, Thatcher, vert.

**2013, June 1**      **Perf. 12**
2862 A779 $85 Sheet of 4, #a-d 9.25 9.25
**Souvenir Sheet**
**Perf. 12½**
2863 A779 $280 multi   7.50 7.50
  No. 2863 contains one 38x51mm stamp.

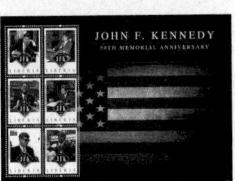

Pres. John F. Kennedy (1917-
63) — A780

No. 2864 — Pres Kennedy: a, On telephone. b, Sitting in rocking chair. c, Standing behind microphone. d, Signing document. e, Wearing sunglasses. f, Standing in crowd.
$280, Pres. Kennedy on yacht.

**Perf. 13 Syncopated**
**2013, June 25** Litho.
2864 A780 $70 Sheet of 6, #a-f 11.00 11.00
**Souvenir Sheet**
2865 A780 $280 multi 7.50 7.50

Medicinal Plants — A781

No. 2866: a, Acacia. b, Rooibos. c, Buchu. d, Caralluma. e, Common myrrh. f, Shea tree.
$280, Aloe, vert.

**2013, June 25** Litho. **Perf. 13¾**
2866 A781 $70 Sheet of 6, #a-f 11.00 11.00
**Souvenir Sheet**
**Perf. 12¾**
2867 A781 $280 multi 7.50 7.50
No. 2867 contains one 38x51mm stamp.

Birds A782

No. 2868, $85: a, Barnacle geese. b, Brown pelican. c, Long-billed curlew. d, Eurasian griffon.
No. 2869, $85: a, Eastern great egret. b, Red and green macaw. c, Roseate spoonbill. d, Mute swan.
No. 2870, $280, Blue peafowl. No. 2871, $280, Crowned crane, vert.

**Perf. 14, 12 (#2871)**
**2013, July 30** Litho.
**Sheets of 4, #a-d**
2868-2869 A782 Set of 2 17.50 17.50
**Souvenir Sheets**
2870-2871 A782 Set of 2 14.50 14.50

Birth of Prince George of Cambridge — A783

No. 2872: a, Duchess of Cambridge handing Prince George to Duke of Cambridge. b, Duke of Cambridge holding Prince George. c, Duchess of Cambridge holding Prince George. d, Duke and Duchess of Cambridge, Prince George.
$280, Duke and Duchess of Cambridge, Prince George.

**2013, Sept. 17 Litho. Perf. 12x12½**
2872 A783 $85 Sheet of 4, #a-d 8.50 8.50
**Souvenir Sheet**
**Perf. 13¼**
2873 A783 $280 multi 7.00 7.00
No. 2873 contains one 38x51mm stamp.

Coronation of Queen Elizabeth II, 60th Anniv. — A784

No. 2874 — Queen Elizabeth II wearing: a, Pink jacket and hat. b, Pink jacket, pink and white hat, fur coat. c, Gray hat and dress. d, Black hat and coat.
$280, Queen Elizabeth II wearing black feathered hat.

**2013, Oct. 7 Litho. Perf. 13¾**
2874 A784 $85 Sheet of 4, #a-d 8.50 8.50
**Souvenir Sheet**
2875 A784 $280 multi 7.00 7.00

Miniature Sheet

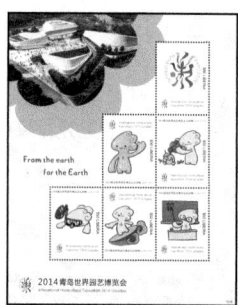

2014 Intl. Horiticultural Exposition, Qingdao, People's Republic of China — A785

No. 2876: a, Exposition emblem. b, Mascot waving. c, Mascot with watering can. d, Mascot snorkeling. e, Mascot surfing. f, Mascot teaching.

**2013, Jan. 1 Litho. Perf. 14**
2876 A785 $50 Sheet of 6, #a-f 8.25 8.25

Miniature Sheet

Famous Stamp Errors A786

No. 2877: a, Sweden #1a. b, India #6c. c, Canal Zone #157a. d, Belgium #139a. e, Western Australia #3a. f, United States #C3a. g, Canada #387a. h, Philippines #357. i, United States #1204.

**2013, Jan. 1 Litho. Perf. 14**
2877 A786 $70 Sheet of 9, #a-i 17.50 17.50

New Year 2014 (Year of the Horse) A787

No. 2878 — Six steeds of Zhaoling from the Mausoleum of Tang Emperor Taizong: a, Horse and attendant. b, Horse facing left, galloping. c, Horse facing left, walking. d, Horse facing right, galloping, diagonal crack running from denomination to horse's head. e, Horse facing right, walking. f, Horse facing right, galloping, vertical crack behind horse's head running to bottom.
$280, Horse's head.

**2013, Nov. 25 Litho. Perf. 14**
2878 A787 $70 Sheet of 6, #a-f 10.50 10.50
**Souvenir Sheet**
**Perf. 12**
2879 A787 $280 multi 7.00 7.00

Intl. Red Cross, 150th Anniv. A788

No. 2880: a, Horse-drawn ambulances at Red Cross site. b, Red Cross equipment bag. c, Red Cross volunteer tending to prisoners near train. d, Red Cross stenciled on wall.
$280, Jean-Henri Dunant, Red Cross founder.

**2013, Dec. 2 Litho. Perf. 14**
2880 A788 $85 Sheet of 4, #a-d 8.50 8.50
**Souvenir Sheet**
2881 A788 $280 multi 7.00 7.00

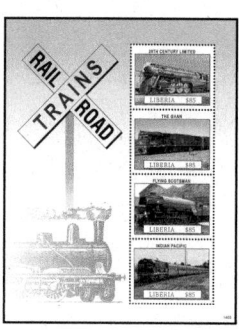

Trains A789

No. 2882: a, 20th Century Limited, United States. b, Ghan, Australia. c, Flying Scotsman, Great Britain. d, Indian Pacific, Australia.
$280, Super Chief, United States, vert.

**2013, Dec. 2 Litho. Perf. 14**
2882 A789 $85 Sheet of 4, #a-d 8.50 8.50
**Souvenir Sheet**
2883 A789 $280 multi 7.00 7.00

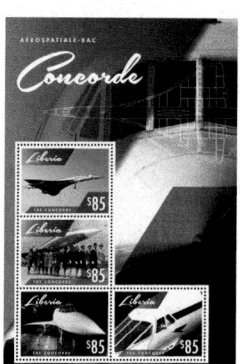

Concorde — A790

No. 2884: a, Concorde in flight. b, Concorde and flight attendants. c, Nose of Concorde. d, Pilot in cockpit window of Concorde.
$280, Concorde in flight in front of clouds.

**2013, Dec. 2 Litho. Perf. 14**
2884 A790 $85 Sheet of 4, #a-d 8.50 8.50
**Souvenir Sheet**
**Perf. 12**
2885 A790 $280 multi 7.00 7.00
No. 2885 contains one 50x30mm stamp.

Miniature Sheets

Zodiac Constellations — A791

No. 2886, $70: a, Aries. b, Leo. c, Virgo. d, Cancer. e, Taurus. f, Pisces.
No. 2887, $70: a, Gemini. b, Libra. c, Sagittarius. d, Scorpio. e, Aquarius. f, Capricorn.

**2013, Dec. 2 Litho. Perf. 12**
**Sheets of 6, #a-f**
2886-2887 A791 Set of 2 21.00 21.00

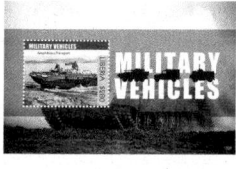

Military Vehicles A792

No. 2888: a, Light utility vehicle. b, Armored personnel carrier. c, Half-track armored personnel carrier. d, Amphibious vehicle.
$280, Amphibious transport.

**2013, Dec. 23 Litho. Perf. 14**
2888 A792 $85 Sheet of 4, #a-d 8.50 8.50
**Souvenir Sheet**
**Perf. 12**
2889 A792 $280 multi 7.00 7.00

Christmas — A793

Paintings: $25, Madonna and Child, by Taddeo di Bartolo. $40, Madonna and Saints, by Giovanni Bellini. $50, Nativity, by Lorenzo Lotto. $175, San Marco Altarpiece, by Fra Angelico.

**2013, Dec. 2 Litho. Perf. 12½**
2890-2893 A793 Set of 4 7.25 7.25

A794

A795

Nelson Mandela (1918-2013), President of South Africa — A796

No. 2894 — Mandela: a, Wearing green and red shirt, denomination in black. b, Close-up of head. c, With clenched fist, two people in background. d, Wearing flowered shirt, brick wall in background. e, With fist raised, crowd in background. f, Sitting in chair, flag in background.
No. 2895 — Mandela: a, Wearing gray blue shirt, pen in breast pocket. b, Wearing suit and tie, curtains in background. c, Wearing shirt with gray squares, black background. d, Wearing blue and white shirt with red AIDS ribbon under collar button. e, Wearing brown and red shirt. f, Wearing suit and tie, with fist raised.

$280, Mandela in suit and tie, diff. $765, Mandela waving.

**2013, Dec. 15    Litho.    Perf. 14**
2894  A794  $70  Sheet of 6,
                    #a-f                    10.50  10.50
2895  A795  $70  Sheet of 6,
                    #a-f                    10.50  10.50

**Souvenir Sheets**
**Perf. 12**
2896  A795  $280  multi            7.00  7.00

**Litho., Margin Embossed With Foil Application**
**Without Gum**
**Imperf**
2897  A796  $765  multi          19.00  19.00

Christening of Prince George of Cambridge — A797

No. 2898: a, Prince George. b, Duchess of Cambridge holding Prince George. c, Duke of Cambridge holding Prince George. d, Duke and Duchess of Cambridge, Prince George. $280, Prince George, diff.

**2013, Dec. 31    Litho.    Perf. 14**
2898  A797  $85  Sheet of 4, #a-d  8.50  8.50

**Souvenir Sheet**
**Perf. 12**
2899  A797  $280  multi            7.00  7.00

Poems by Mao Zedong — A798

A799

Mao Zedong (1893-1976), Chinese Communist Leader — A800

No. 2900 — Poem with: a, 13 vertical columns of characters. b, 12 vertical columns of characters. c, 11 vertical columns of characters.
No. 2901 — Mao Zedong: a, With other people, building's roof visible. b, With Jawaharlal Nehru. c, With Kwame Nkrumah at dinner table. d, Surrounded by people from different countries.
No. 2902: a, Painting of Mao Zedong carrying scroll. b, Black-and-white photograph of Mao Zedong without hat. c, Painting of Mao Zedong with cap. d, Black-and-white photograph of Mao Zedong with cap. e, Painting of Mao Zedong without cap. f, Great Wall of China.

**2013, Mar. 7    Litho.    Perf. 14**
2900          Horiz. strip of 3     1.25  1.25
a.-c.  A798  $15  Any single          .40   .40
2901  A799  $15  Sheet of 4, #a-d   1.60  1.60
2902  A800  $15  Sheet of 6, #a-f   2.50  2.50

No, 2900 was printed in sheets of 6, containing two of each stamp.

---

World Leaders — A800a

Designs: No. 2902A, $100, Liberian Pres. Ellen Johnson Sirleaf, People's Republic of China Premier Xi Jinping, U.S. Pres. Barack Obama. No. 2902B, $100, Former leaders of People' Republic of China Hu Jintao and Mao Zedong. $125, Mao Zedong and first Liberian Pres. Joseph Jenkins Roberts. $150, Xi Jinping and Ellen Johnson Sirleaf.

**2013, Dec. 6    Litho.    Perf. 12**
2902A-2902D  A800a  Set of 4  12.00  12.00

**Souvenir Sheet**

Elvis Presley (1935-77) — A801

**Litho., Sheet Margin Embossed**
**2014, Jan. 1    Imperf.**
2903  A801  $740  multi          18.50  18.50

Yosemite National Park A802

No. 2904: a, Cathedral Rocks. b, Yosemite Falls. c, Giant sequoias. d, Tenaya Lake. e, Hetch Hetchy Reservoir. f, Half Dome. $280, El Capitan.

**2014, Jan. 2    Litho.    Perf. 14**
2904  A802  $70  Sheet of 6,
                    #a-f                    10.50  10.50

**Souvenir Sheet**
**Perf. 12¾**
2905  A802  $280  multi            7.00  7.00

Yosemite Grant, 150th anniv. No. 2905 contains one 51x38mm stamp.

**Miniature Sheets**

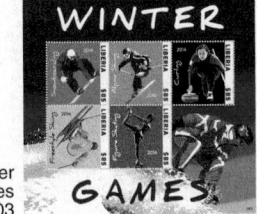

Winter Games A803

No. 2906, $85: a, Snowboarding. b, Alpine skiing. c, Curling. d, Freestyle skiing. e, Figure skating.
No. 2907, $85: a, Ski jumping. b, Ice hockey. c, Bobsled. d, Cross-country skiing. e, Speed skating.

**2014, Mar. 5    Litho.    Perf. 13¾**
**Sheets of 5, #a-e**
2906-2907  A803  Set of 2  20.00  20.00

Paintings A804

No. 2908: a, $125: a, Portrait of a Man Aged 32, by Frans Pourbus the Younger. b, Apricot

---

Branch, by Georg Flegel. c, Meu Taporo, by Paul Gauguin.
No. 2909, $125: a, Portrait of a Woman, by Antonio del Pollaiuolo. b, A World, by Maximilian Lenz. c, Woman Carrying a Pitcher on Her Head, by Camille Pissarro.
No. 2910, $350, The Piano Lesson, by Pierre-Auguste Renoir. No. 2911, $350, The Japanese Bridge, by Claude Monet.

**2014, Mar. 10    Litho.    Perf. 12¾**
**Sheets of 3, #a-c**
2908-2909  A804  Set of 2  17.50  17.50

**Size: 100x100mm**
**Imperf**
2910-2911  A804  Set of 2  16.50  16.50

A805

A806

A807

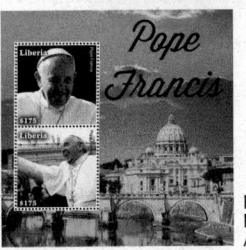

Pope Francis A808

No. 2912 — Pope Francis: a, Waving. b, Looking up. c, Hugging boy. d, Smiling.
No. 2913 — Pope Francis: a, Looking left. b, Waving, diff. c, Waving, with other hand over heart. d, Waving in front of building.
No. 2914 — Pope Francis, denominations with large numerals: a, Looking right. b, Talking to young girl.
No. 2915 — Pope Francis, denominations with small numerals: a, Smiling, diff. b, With arm extended.

**2014, Mar. 24    Litho.    Perf. 13¾**
2912  A805  $100  Sheet of 4, #a-
                    d              9.50  9.50
2913  A806  $100  Sheet of 4, #a-
                    d              9.50  9.50

**Souvenir Sheets**
2914  A807  $175  Sheet of 2, #a-
                    b              8.25  8.25
2915  A808  $175  Sheet of 2, #a-
                    b              8.25  8.25

Mythical Creatures — A809

No. 2916, $100: a, Dragon. b, Minotaur. c, Centaur. d, Phoenix.
No. 2917, $100, vert.: a, Vampire. b, Leprechaun. c, Mermaid. d, Angel.

---

No. 2918, $175, vert.: a, Werewolf. b, Unicorn.
No. 2919, $175, vert.: a, Mermaid, with arms above head. b, Mermaid, swimming.

**Perf. 14 (#2916), 12¾**
**2014, Apr. 2    Litho.**
**Sheets of 4, #a-d**
2916-2917  A809  Set of 2  19.00  19.00

**Souvenir Sheets of 2, #a-b**
2918-2919  A809  Set of 2  16.50  16.50

No. 2917 contains four 38x51mm stamps. Nos. 2918-2919 each contain two 38x51mm stamps.

A810

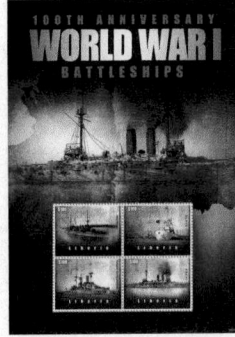

World War I, Cent. A811

No. 2920: a, Battle of Vimy Ridge, 1915. b, Battle of Gallipoli, 1915. c, Battle of the Somme, 1916. d, Battle of St. Mihiel, 1918.
No. 2921 — Battleships: a, Voltaire. b, Slava. c, Kaiser Barbarossa. d, Asahi.
No. 2922: a, Battle of Verdun, 1916. b, Third Battle of Ypres, 1917.
No. 2923 — Battleships: a, USS Alabama. b, SMS Helgoland.

**2014, May 19    Litho.    Perf. 12**
2920  A810  $100  Sheet of 4, #a-d  9.50  9.50
2921  A811  $100  Sheet of 4, #a-d  9.50  9.50

**Souvenir Sheets**
2922  A810  $175  Sheet of 2, #a-b  8.25  8.25

**Perf. 14**
2923  A811  $175  Sheet of 2, #a-b  8.25  8.25

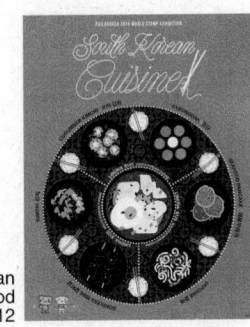

Korean Food A812

No. 2924: a, Boneless ribs and Kimchi. b, Cucumber kimchi and Gyeongdan. c, Seafood pancake and Japchae. $350, Soft tofu stew.

**2014, June 17    Litho.    Perf. 13**
2924  A812  $125  Sheet of 3, #a-
                    c, + central la-
                    bel            8.25  8.25

**Souvenir Sheet**
**Perf.**
2925  A812  $350  multi            7.75  7.75

Philakorea 2014 World Stamp Exhibition, Seoul

2014 World Cup Soccer Championships, Brazil — A813

Team photographs: No. 2926, $30, Algeria. No. 2927, $30, Argentina. No. 2928, $30, Australia. No. 2929, $30, Belgium. No. 2930, $30, Bosnia & Herzegovina. No. 2931, $30, Brazil. No. 2932, $30, Cameroun. No. 2933, $30, Chile. No. 2934, $30, Colombia. No. 2935, $30, Costa Rica. No. 2936, $30, Cote d'Ivoire (Ivory Coast). No. 2937, $30, Croatia. No. 2938, $30, Ecuador. No. 2939, $30, England. No. 2940, $30, France. No. 2941, $30, Germany. No. 2942, $30, Ghana. No. 2943, $30, Greece. No. 2944, $30, Honduras. No. 2945, $30, Iran. No. 2946, $30, Italy. No. 2947, $30, Japan. No. 2948, $30, South Korea. No. 2949, $30, Mexico. No. 2950, $30, Netherlands. No. 2951, $30, Nigeria. No. 2952, $30, Portugal. No. 2953, $30, Russia. No. 2954, $30, Spain. No. 2955, $30, Switzerland. No. 2956, $30, United States. No. 2957, $30, Uruguay.

**2014, June 17　　Litho.　　Perf. 14**
2926-2957 A813　Set of 32　　21.50 21.50

Nos. 2926-2957 each were printed in sheets of 6. See No. 2980.

Orchids A814

No. 2958, $100: a, Disa racemosa. b, Eulophia nutans. c, Eulophia hians. d, Eulophia ensata.
No. 2959, $100: a, Satyrium erectum. b, Satyrium coriifolium. c, Eulophia buchanani. d, Disa gladioflora.
No. 2960, $175: a, Habenaria bonatea. b, Polystachya pubescens.
No. 2961, $175: a, Eulophia reichenbachiana. b, Disa uniflora.

**2014, June 23　　Litho.　　Perf. 14**
**Sheets of 4, #a-d**
2958-2959 A814　Set of 2　　18.00 18.00
**Souvenir Sheets of 2, #a-b**
2960-2961 A814　Set of 2　　15.50 15.50

Bats A815

No. 2962, $100: a, Lissonycteris angolensis. b, Epomophorus gambianus. c, Nanonycteris veldkampii. d, Epomops buettikoferi.
No. 2963, $100: a, Coleura afrea. b, Epomophorus wahlbergi. c, Miniopterus africanus. d, Rhinolophus ferrumequinum.
No. 2964, $175: a, Miniopterus inflatus. b, Taphozous mauritianus.
No. 2965, $175: a, Micropteropus pusillus. b, Rousettus aegyptiacus.

**2014, Aug. 14　Litho.　Perf. 12x12½**
**Sheets of 4, #a-d**
2962-2963 A815　Set of 2　　17.50 17.50
**Souvenir Sheets of 2, #a-b**
2964-2965 A815　Set of 2　　15.50 15.50

Mongooses — A816

No. 2966, $100: a, Dwarf mongoose. b, Selous's mongoose. c, Kusimanse. d, Long-nosed mongoose.
No. 2967, $100: a, Angolan slender mongoose. b, Yellow mongoose. c, Ethiopian dwarf mongoose. d, Banded mongoose.
No. 2968, $175: a, Meerkat. b, Alexander's kusimanse.
No. 2969, $175: a, Slender mongoose. b, Somalian slender mongoose.

**2014, Aug. 27　　Litho.　　Perf. 14**
**Sheets of 4, #a-d**
2966-2967 A816　Set of 2　　17.50 17.50
**Souvenir Sheets of 2, #a-b**
2968-2969 A816　Set of 2　　15.50 15.50

Paintings by Henri de Toulouse-Lautrec (1864-1901) — A817

No. 2970, $100: a, Party in the Moulin Rouge. b, Count Alphonse de Toulouse-Lautrec Driving a Four-Horse Hitch. c, Equestrienne. d, Two Girls in Bed.
No. 2971, $100, vert.: a, Moulin Rouge La Goulue. b, Babylone d'Allemagne. c, Portrait of Madame la Comtesse de Toulouse-Lautrec. d, Portait of Vincent van Gogh.
No. 2972, $200, vert.: a, La Clownesse Assise. b, La Clownesse.
No. 2973, $200, vert.: a, The Stage Manager Behind the Scenes. b, Portrait of Louis Pascal.

**2014, Aug. 27　　Litho.　　Perf. 14**
**Sheets of 4, #a-d**
2970-2971 A817　Set of 2　　17.50 17.50
**Souvenir Sheets of 2, #a-b**
2972-2973 A817　Set of 2　　17.50 17.50

National Parks of Africa A818

No. 2974: a, Serengeti National Park, Tanzania (single tree). b, Victoria Falls, Zambia. c, Mt. Kilimanjaro, Kenya (view from mountain). d, Drakensberg Mountains, South Africa. e, Matopos National Park, Zimbabwe. f, Serengeti National Park (trees and vehicle path). g, Mt. Kilimanjaro (view of mountain). h, Sapo National Park, Liberia. i, Golden Gate Highlands National Park, South Africa. $350, Namib-Naukluft National Park, Namibia.

**2014, Sept. 3　　Litho.　　Perf. 13¾**
2974 A818　$85 Sheet of 9, #a-i　　16.50 16.50
**Souvenir Sheet**
2975 A818　$350 multi　　7.50 7.50

Race Horses A819

No. 2976, $100: a, Flying Childers. b, Highflyer. c, Regulus. d, Sceptre.
No. 2977, $100: a, Cherimoya. b, American Eclipse. c, Bay Middleton. d, Crucifix.
No. 2978, $175: a, Kincsem. b, Eclipse. $350, Goldfinder.

**2014, Sept. 3　　Litho.　　Perf. 14**
**Sheets of 4, #a-d**
2976-2977 A819　Set of 2　　17.50 17.50
**Perf. 12½**
2978 A819　$175 Sheet of 2, #a-b　7.50 7.50
**Souvenir Sheet**
2979 A819　$350 multi　　7.50 7.50

No. 2978 contains two 51x38mm stamps; No. 2979 contains one 51x38 stamp.

**No. 2941 With Inscription Added in Yellow**

**and**

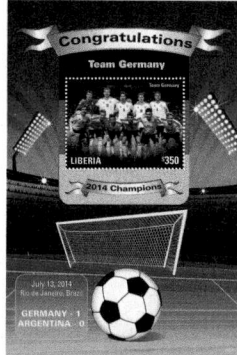

German Soccer Team, 2014 World Cup Champions — A820

**2014, Sept. 4　　Litho.　　Perf. 14**
2980 A813　$30 multi　　.65　.65
**Souvenir Sheet**
**Perf. 12½**
2981 A820　$350 multi　　7.50 7.50

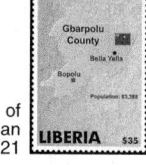

Maps and Flags of Liberian Counties — A821

County: $35, Gbarpolu. $45, Lofa. $55, Grand Cape Mount. $70, Bomi. $90, Montserrado. No. 2987, Bong. No. 2988, Margibi. $150, Grand Bassa. $175, Rivercess. $250, Nimba. $350, Sinoe. No. 2993, Grand Gedeh. No. 2994, Grand Kru. No. 2995, Maryland. No. 2996, Rivergee.

**2014, July 1　　Litho.　　Perf. 14**
2982 A821　$35 multi　　.80　.80
2983 A821　$45 multi　　1.00 1.00
2984 A821　$55 multi　　1.25 1.25
2985 A821　$70 multi　　1.60 1.60
2986 A821　$90 multi　　2.00 2.00
2987 A821　$100 multi　　2.25 2.25
2988 A821　$100 multi　　2.25 2.25
2989 A821　$150 multi　　3.50 3.50
2990 A821　$175 multi　　4.00 4.00
2991 A821　$250 multi　　5.50 5.50
2992 A821　$350 multi　　7.75 7.75
2993 A821　$500 multi　　11.00 11.00
2994 A821　$500 multi　　11.00 11.00
2995 A821　$500 multi　　11.00 11.00
2996 A821　$500 multi　　11.00 11.00
　Nos. 2982-2996 (15)　　75.90 75.90

Mei Lanfang (1894-1961), Peking Opera Performer — A822

No. 2997 — Mei Lanfang in various costumes, as shown.
$350, Mei Lanfang, diff.

**2014, Sept. 4　　Litho.　　Perf. 12**
2997 A822　$100 Sheet of 4, #a-d 8.75 8.75
**Souvenir Sheet**
2998 A822　$350 multi　　7.75 7.75

Gold Medalists at 2014 Winter Olympics, Sochi, Russia — A823

No. 2999: a, Vic Wild, snowboarding, Russia (40x30mm). b, Canadian ice hockey player (40x30mm). c, Jorgen Graabak, Nordic combined skiing, Norway (40x60mm).
No. 3000: a, Kamil Stoch, ski jumping, Poland (30x40mm). b, Anton Kushnir, freestyle skiing, Belarus (30x40mm).

**2014, Sept. 15　　Litho.　　Perf. 14**
2999 A823　$125 Sheet of 3, #a-c 8.25 8.25
**Souvenir Sheet**
3000 A823　$175 Sheet of 2, #a-b 7.75 7.75

Endangered African Animals — A824

No. 3001, $100: a, Okapi. b, Barbary macaque. c, African wild dog. d, Abbott's duiker.
No. 3002, $100: a, Aldabra flying fox. b, Black and rufous elephant shrew. c, Mandrill. d, Sun-tailed monkey.
No. 3003, $350, Alaotran gentle lemur. No. 3004, $350, Mountain gorilla.

**2014, Oct. 20　　Litho.　　Perf. 14**
**Sheets of 4, #a-d**
3001-3002 A824　Set of 2　　17.50 17.50
**Souvenir Sheets**
**Perf. 12½**
3003-3004 A824　Set of 2　　15.00 15.00

Nos. 3003-3004 each contain one 38x51mm stamp.

Garden Flowers A825

No. 3005, $125: a, Coneflowers. b, Calendulas. c, Purple asters.
No. 3006, $125: a, French marigolds. b, Tickseeds. c, Cosmos.
No. 3007, $350, Black-eyed Susans. No. 3008, $350, Forget-me-nots.

**2014, Oct. 20** Litho. *Perf. 12*
**Sheets of 3, #a-c**
3005-3006 A825 Set of 2   16.50 16.50
**Souvenir Sheets**
3007-3008 A825 Set of 2   15.00 15.00

A826

New Year 2015 (Year of the Ram) A827

No. 3010 — Ram facing: a, Forward. b, Left.

**2014, Nov. 3** Litho. *Perf. 14*
3009 A826 $100 multi   2.25 2.25
*Perf. 12½*
3010 A827 $100 Horiz. pair, #a-b 4.50 4.50

No. 3009 was printed in sheets of 6. No. 3010 was printed in sheets containing two pairs.

Campaign Against Ebola Virus — A828

No. 3011: a, Medical worker wearing protective gear. b, Child. b, Mother holding child. c, Woman and medical device.

**2014, Nov. 11** Litho. *Perf. 14*
3011 A828 $50 Block or horiz. strip of 4, #a-d 4.50 4.50

Printed in sheets of 16, containing 3 #3011c, 4 each #3011a, 3011b, 3011d, + label.

Christmas — A829

Paintings by Peter Paul Rubens (1577-1640): $100, The Education of the Virgin. $125, Saint Francis Receiving the Infant Jesus from the Hands of the Virgin. No. 3014, $175, Teresa of Avila's Vision of the Dove. No. 3015, $175, The Assumption of the Virgin Mary.

**2014, Nov. 24** Litho. *Perf. 12½*
3012-3015 A829 Set of 4   12.50 12.50

Domestic Cats A830

Domestic Cats A831

No. 3016 — British shorthair cat with background color of: a, Gray. b, Pink. c, Blue. d, Green blue.
No. 3017 — Various photographs of Maine Coon cats, as shown.
No. 3018, $350, Siberian cat. No. 3019, $350, Ragdoll cat.

**2014, Dec. 16** Litho. *Perf. 14*
3016 A830 $100 Sheet of 4, #a-d   8.75 8.75
3017 A831 $100 Sheet of 6, #a-f   13.00 13.00
**Souvenir Sheets**
3018 A831 $350 multi   7.50 7.50
*Perf. 13¼*
3019 A831 $350 multi   7.50 7.50

No. 3019 contains one 35x35mm stamp.

Wild Cats A833

Wild Cats A833

No. 3020 — Various photographs of lions, as shown.
No. 3021 — Various photographs of cheetahs, as shown.
No. 3022, $350, Serval. No. 3023, $350, Caracal.

*Perf. 13 Syncopated*
**2014, Dec. 16** Litho.
3020 A832 $100 Sheet of 4, #a-d 8.75 8.75
3021 A833 $100 Sheet of 4, #a-d 8.75 8.75
**Souvenir Sheets**
3022 A833 $350 multi   7.50 7.50
3023 A833 $350 multi   7.50 7.50

Economic Community of West African States, 40th Anniv. — A834

**2015** Litho. *Perf. 13x13¼*
3024 A834 $50 multi   — —

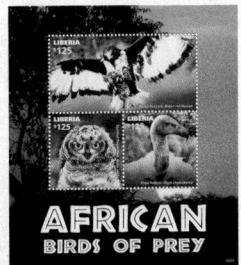

Birds of Prey A835

No. 3025, $125: a, Jackal buzzard (64x32mm). b, Spotted eagle owl (32x32mm). c, Cape vulture (32x32mm).
No. 3026, $125: a, African goshawk (32x64mm). b, Bateleur (32x32mm). c, Eurasian eagle owl (32x32mm).
No. 3027, $350, Golden eagle, vert. No. 3028, $350, Martial eagle, vert.

**2015, Jan. 5** Litho. *Perf. 12½*
**Sheets of 3, #a-c**
3025-3026 A835 Set of 2   16.50 16.50
**Souvenir Sheets**
*Perf. 13¼*
3027-3028 A835 Set of 2   15.00 15.00
Nos. 3027-3028 each contain one 38x51mm stamp.

Photographs of Earth Taken from Space — A836

No. 3029: a, Kizimen Volcano, Russia. b, Issaouane Erg, Algeria. c, Fringing Coral Reef, Red Sea. d, Ice on Lake Michigan, United States. e, Paris, France. f, Zambezi River Delta, Mozambique.
$350, Mr. Everest and nearby Himalayan peaks.

**2015, Jan. 21** Litho. *Perf. 11½x12*
3029 A836 $100 Sheet of 6, #a-f   13.00 13.00
**Souvenir Sheet**
3030 A836 $350 multi   7.75 7.75

A837

Spheniscus Demersus — A838

No. 3031: a, One penguin in water. b, Three penguins under water. c, Penguin out of water. d, Three penguins with heads above water.
No. 3032: a, One penguin facing right on beach, yellow sky. b, One penguin facing left on beach, light blue sky. c, One penguin facing right on beach, pale green water in background. d, One penguin, foliage in foreground. e, Two penguins. f, Three penguins.
No. 3033, $350, One penguin, diff. No. 3034, $350, Two penguins, diff.

**2015, Feb. 2** Litho. *Perf. 14*
3031 A837 $100 Sheet of 4, #a-d   8.75 8.75
3032 A838 $100 Sheet of 6, #a-f   13.00 13.00
**Souvenir Sheets**
3033-3034 A838 Set of 2   15.00 15.00

Fennec Fox A839

No. 3035: a, Fox facing left. b, Fox facing forward. c, Fox asleep.
$350, Fox facing forward, diff.

**2015, Feb. 2** Litho. *Perf. 12½*
3035 A839 $125 Sheet of 3, #a-c 8.25 8.25
**Souvenir Sheet**
3036 A839 $350 multi   7.75 7.75

World War I Alpine Troops of Italy A840

No. 3037: a, Regiment members carrying bicycle. b, Regiment members on mountaintop. c, Regiment members climbing mountain. d, Soldier with camera on tripod.
$350, Regiment members near mountain barracks.

**2015, Feb. 2** Litho. *Perf. 14*
3037 A840 $100 Sheet of 4, #a-d 8.75 8.75
**Souvenir Sheet**
*Perf. 12*
3038 A840 $350 multi   7.75 7.75

World War I, cent.

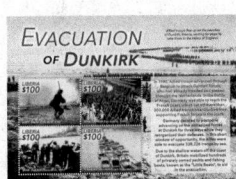

Evacuation of Dunkirk, 75th Anniv. — A841

No. 3039: a, Soldier on beach. b, Troops gathered for evacuation. c, Troops on ship. d, Little boats returning from evacuation.
$350, Troops on little boats.

**2015, Mar. 2** Litho. *Perf. 14*
3039 A841 $100 Sheet of 4, #a-d 8.75 8.75
**Souvenir Sheet**
*Perf. 12½*
3040 A841 $350 multi   7.75 7.75

No. 3040 contains one 51x38mm stamp.

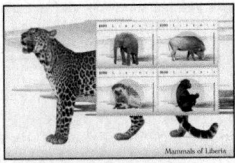

Mammals — A842

No. 3041, $100: a, African bush elephant. b, Common warthog. c, Four-toed hedgehog. d, Common chimpanzee.
No. 3042, $100: a, Gambian epauletted fruit bat. b, Bushbuck. c, Leopard. d, Hippopotamus.
No. 3043, $350, Campbell's mona monkey, vert. No. 3044, $350, Giant pangolin, vert.

**2015, Mar. 2**    **Litho.**    *Perf. 14¾x14*
**Sheets of 4, #a-d**
3041-3042 A842    Set of 2    17.50 17.50
**Souvenir Sheets**
*Perf. 14x14¾*
3043-3044 A842    Set of 2    15.00 15.00

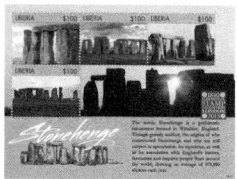

Stonehenge — A843

No. 3045: Various photographs of stone pillars at Stonehenge, as shown.
$350, Stonehenge, diff.

**2015, Mar. 3**    **Litho.**    *Perf. 11½x12*
3045 A843 $100 Sheet of 4, #a-d   8.75 8.75
**Souvenir Sheet**
*Perf. 13½x13¼*
3046 A843 $350 multi    7.75 7.75
2015 Europhilex Stamp Exhibition, London. No. 3046 contains one 50x30mm stamp.

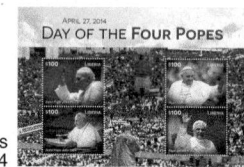

Popes
A844

No. 3047: a, St. John Paul II. b, Pope Francis. c, St. John XXIII. d, Pope Benedict XVI.
$350, Pope Benedict XVI, diff.

**2015, Mar. 24**    **Litho.**    *Perf. 14*
3047 A844 $100 Sheet of 4, #a-d   8.75 8.75
**Souvenir Sheet**
*Perf. 12*
3048 A844 $350 multi    7.75 7.75
Canonization of St. John Paul II and St. John XXIII.

Western
Bongo
A845

No. 3049 — Western bongo: a, Blue green background, four legs visible. b, Red background, adult and juvenile. c, Red background, bongo facing right. d, Blue green background, no legs visible. e, Blue green background, head of bongo. f, Red background, bongo facing left.
$350, Head of bongo, vert.

**2015, Mar. 24**    **Litho.**    *Perf. 14*
3049 A845 $100 Sheet of 6,
   #a-f    13.00 13.00
**Souvenir Sheet**
*Perf. 12*
3050 A845 $350 multi    7.75 7.75

Visit of
Prince
William
to Japan
A846

No. 3051 — Prince William and: a, Tokyo Governor Yoichi Masuzoe holding umbrellas. b, Crown Prince Naruhito shaking hands. c, Japanese Prime Minister Shinzo Abe with children at Koriyama park. d, Masuzoe at tea ceremony. e, Abe, Prince William waving. f, Dinner guests at Ryokan, Koriyama.
$350, Prince William visiting British Commonwealth war graves, Yokohama.

**2015, May 4**    **Litho.**    *Perf. 13x13¼*
3051 A846 $100 Sheet of 6,
   #a-f    13.00 13.00
**Souvenir Sheet**
*Perf. 12x12½*
3052 A846 $350 multi    7.75 7.75

Queen Elizabeth II, Longest-Reigning British Monarch — A847

No. 3051 — Photographs of Queen Elizabeth II with dogs taken in: a, 1974. b, 1972. c, 1936. d, 1976. e, 1971.
$350, Queen Elizabeth II and dog, 1971, diff.

**2015, May 25**    **Litho.**    *Perf. 14*
3053 A847 $100 Sheet of 5,
   #a-e    11.00 11.00
**Souvenir Sheet**
*Perf. 12*
3054 A847 $350 multi    7.75 7.75

Lee Kuan Yew (1923-2015), Prime Minister of Singapore — A848

No. 3055 — Lee with: a, Queen Elizabeth II, 1989. b, Pres. Barack Obama, 2009. c, Pres. George H. W. Bush, 1989. d, Chinese General Secretary Xi Jinping, 2010.
No. 3056: a, Lee Kuan Yew, 2009. b, Pres. Obama, 2009.

**2015, May 25**    **Litho.**    *Perf. 14*
3055 A848 $100 Sheet of 4, #a-d   8.75 8.75
**Souvenir Sheet**
3056 A848 $175 Sheet of 2, #a-b   7.75 7.75

Birth of Princess Charlotte of Cambridge — A849

No. 3057: a, Duke and Duchess of Cambridge holding Princess Charlotte, window behind Duke. b, As "a," window behind Duchess. c, Duchess of Cambridge holding Princess Charlotte. d, As "a," steps in background.
$350, Princess Charlotte.

**2015, July 13**    **Litho.**    *Perf. 14*
3057 A849 $100 Sheet of 4, #a-d   8.75 8.75
**Souvenir Sheet**
3058 A849 $350 multi    7.75 7.75

African
Wildlife
A850

No. 3059: a, African buffalo. b, Side-striped jackal. c, African bush elephant. d, Patas monkey. e, Common kusimanse. f, African pygmy hedgehog.
$350, African leopard.

**2015, July 13**    **Litho.**    *Perf. 14*
3059 A850 $100 Sheet of 6,
   #a-f    13.00 13.00
**Souvenir Sheet**
*Perf. 12*
3060 A850 $350 multi    7.75 7.75

Sir Rowland Hill (1795-1879), Postal Reformer — A851

No. 3061: a, Hill as older man. b, Hill as younger man, hand on neck.
$3.50, Hill and Great Britain #1.

**2015, July 13**    **Litho.**    *Perf. 12*
3061 A851 $100 Pair, #a-b    4.50 4.50
**Souvenir Sheet**
*Perf. 13¾*
3062 A851 $350 multi    7.75 7.75
No. 3061 is printed in sheets containing two pairs. No. 3062 contains one 35x70mm stamp.

Miniature Sheets

Stamps of United Nations Member Countries — A852

No. 3063, $100: a, Lesotho #1. b, Liberia #1. c, Libya #1. d, Liechtenstein #1. e, Lithuania #1. f, Luxembourg #1.
No. 3064, $100: a, Macedonia #1. b, Malagasy Republic (Madagascar) #8. c, Malawi #1. d, Malaysia #1. e, Maldive Islands #1. f, Mali #1.
No. 3065, $100: a, Malta #1. b, Marshall Islands #1. c, Mauritania #1. d, Mauritius #1. e, Mexico #1. f, Micronesia #1.
No. 3066, $100: a, Moldova #1. b, Monaco #1. c, Mongolia #1. d, Montenegro #123. e, Morocco #A1. f, Mozambique #1.
No. 3067, $100: a, Switzerland #41. b, Syria #11. c, Tajikistan #1. d, Tanzania #5. e, Thailand #1. f, Timor #1.
No. 3068, $100: a, Togo #1. b, Tonga #1. c, Trinidad & Tobago #1. d, Tunisia #1. e, Turkey #1. f, Turkmenistan #1.
No. 3069, $100: a, Tuvalu #1. b, Uganda #1. c, Ukraine #100. d, United Arab Emirates #1. e, Uruguay #1. f, Uzbekistan #1.
No. 3070, $100: a, Vanuatu #280a. b, Venezuela #4. c, Viet Nam #1. d, Yemen #2. e, Zambia #1. f, Zimbabwe #414.

**2015, July 13 Litho.**   *Perf. 12¾x12½*
**Sheets of 6, #a-f**
3063-3070 A852    Set of 8    105.00 105.00

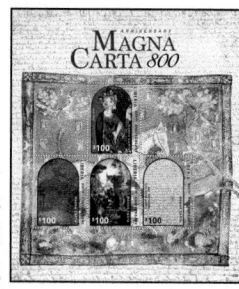

Magna
Carta,
800th
Anniv.
A853

No. 3071: a, King John. b, Dark brown image of riginal Magna Carta manuscript, 1215. c, King John on throne. d, As "b," beige image.
$350, Signing of the Magna Carta.

**2015, Aug. 3**    **Litho.**    *Perf. 14*
3071 A853 $100 Sheet of 4, #a-d   8.75 8.75
**Souvenir Sheet**
3072 A853 $350 multi    7.75 7.75

Muhammad Ali (1942-2016), Boxer — A854

No. 3073: Various photographs of Ali, as shown.
$350, Ali, diff.

**2015, Aug. 10**    **Litho.**    *Perf. 12½x12*
3073 A854 $100 Sheet of 4, #a-d   8.75 8.75
**Souvenir Sheet**
3074 A854 $350 multi    7.75 7.75

Pres. Abraham Lincoln (1809-65) — A855

No. 3073: Various photographs of Lincoln, as shown.
$350, Lincoln, diff.

**2015, Sept. 2**    **Litho.**    *Perf. 12*
3075 A855 $100 Sheet of 4, #a-d   8.75 8.75
**Souvenir Sheet**
*Perf. 12¾*
3076 A855 $350 multi    7.75 7.75
No. 3076 contains one 38x51mm stamp.

Sir Winston Churchill (1874-1965), Prime Minister of Great Britain — A856

No. 3077 — Churchill: a, Sitting with dog. b, Sitting with wife, Clementine. c, Aiming gun. d, Shielding his eyes. e, Painting. f, With kangaroo.
$350, Churchill with wife on ship.

**2015, Sept. 30**    **Litho.**    *Perf. 13¾*
3077 A856 $100 Sheet of 6,
   #a-f    13.00 13.00
**Souvenir Sheet**
3078 A856 $350 multi    7.75 7.75

Details of Paintings of Flowers by
Vincent van Gogh (1853-90) — A857

No. 3078: a, Three Sunflowers in a Vase,
1888. b, Still Life: Japanese Vase with Roses
and Anemones, 1890. c, Vase with Red Poppies, 1886. d, Vase with Oleanders and
Books, 1888. e, Vase with Red Gladioli, 1886.
f, Blossoming Almond Branch in a Glass with a
Book, 1888.
$350, Still Life: Vase with Pink Roses, 1890,
horiz.

2015, Nov. 2   Litho.   Perf. 13¼x12½
3079 A857 $100 Sheet of 6,
             #a-f                13.00 13.00
        Souvenir Sheet
           Perf. 12
3080 A857 $350 multi           7.75  7.75
No. 3080 contains one 50x30mm stamp.

Christmas — A858

Paintings by Filippo Lippi (c. 1406-69):
$100, Martelli Annunciation. $150, Adoration
in the Forest. $175, Annunciation. $200,
Madonna and Child.

2015, Nov. 2   Litho.   Perf. 12½
3081-3084 A858  Set of 4   13.50 13.50

Pres. Dwight D. Eisenhower (1890-
1969) — A859

No. 3085 — Eisenhower: a, With arms
raised. b, Sitting on desk. c, Standing behind
microphones, flag in background. d, At ros-
trum with microphones and water glasses. e,
Looking through blinker glasses. f, Smiling,
window in background.
$350, Eisenhower and Richard M. Nixon,
horiz.

2015, Nov. 25   Litho.   Perf. 13¾
3085 A859 $100 Sheet of 6,
             #a-f                13.00 13.00
        Souvenir Sheet
           Perf. 14
3086 A859 $350 multi           7.75  7.75
No. 3086 contains one 80x30mm stamp.

New Year 2016
(Year of the
Monkey) — A860

Nos. 3087 and 3088: a, Monkey holding fruit
near mouth. b, Moneky standing in tree above
fruit.

2015, Nov. 25   Litho.   Perf. 13¾
3087 A860 $32 Vert. pair, #a-b   1.40  1.40
        Souvenir Sheet
        Perf. 13¾x13½
3088 A860 $90 Sheet of 2, #a-b   4.00  4.00
No. 3087 was printed in sheets containing
four pairs.

Pope
Francis
in New
York City
A861

No. 3089 — Various photographs of Pope
Francis at World Trade Center, as shown.
$350, Pope Francis waving, New York City
skyline in background.

2015, Nov. 25   Litho.   Perf. 14
3089 A861 $100 Sheet of 6,
             #a-f                13.00 13.00
        Souvenir Sheet
           Perf. 12
3090 A861 $350 multi           7.75  7.75

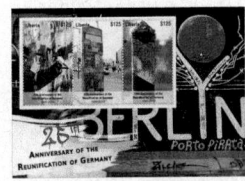

Reunification of Germany, 25th
Anniv. — A862

No. 3091: a, Person hammering at Berlin
Wall. b, Piece of Berlin Wall on street corner.
c, Border marker with emblem of German
Democratic Republic.
$350, Wall with graffiti, horiz.

2015, Dec. 7   Litho.   Perf. 12
3091 A862 $125 Sheet of 3, #a-c  9.00  9.00
        Souvenir Sheet
3092 A862 $350 multi           8.25  8.25
No. 3092 contains one 80x30mm stamp.

Miniature Sheets

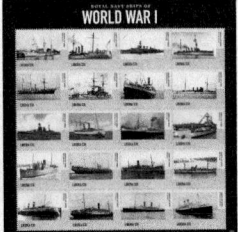

Ships of
World
War
I — A863

No. 3093, $30: a, HMS Algerine. b, HMS
Amethyst. c, HMS Cardiff. d, HMS Dartmouth.
e, HMS Fantome. f, HMS Goliath. g, HMS Hil-
debrand. h, HMS Laburnum. i, HMS Malaya. j,
SS Kinsfauns Castle. k, SS Orcoma. l, HMS
Renown. m, HMS Adventuress. n, SS Hima-
laya. o, SS Patuca. p, RFA Bacchus. q, SS
Alsatian. r, SS Arlanza. s, SS Caronia. t, SS
Empress of Britain.

No. 3094, $30: a, HMS Amazon. b, HMS
Antrim. c, HMS Astraea. d, HMS Birmingham.
e, HMS Bristol. f, HMS Cicala. g, HMS Eurya-
lus. h, HMS Galatea. i, HMS Hampshire. j, SS
City of London. k, SS Laconia. l, HMS Hum-
ber. m, HMS Kent. n, SS Orvieto. o, SS Won-
ganella. p, HMS Nighthawk. q, HMS Rinaldo.
r, HMS Valerian. s, MS Jupiter. t, SS
Armadale.

2015, Dec. 7   Litho.   Perf. 14
        Sheets of 20, #a-t
3093-3094 A863  Set of 2   28.50 28.50

Aliens in Star Trek: Enterprise
Television Series — A864

No. 3095: a, Silik, a Suliban. b, Shran, a
Andorian. c, Antaak, a Klingon. d, T'Pol, a Vul-
can. e, Soval, a Vulcan. f, Dr. Phlox, a
Denobulan.
$350, Dr. Phlox, diff.

Perf. 13¼x12½
2015, Dec. 21   Litho.
3095 A864 $100 Sheet of 6,
             #a-f                14.50 13.00
        Souvenir Sheet
           Perf. 13¼
3096 A864 $350 multi           8.25  8.25
No. 3096 contains one 38x51mm stamp.

Miniature Sheets

A865

Declaration of the Roman Catholic
Church With Non-Christian Religions,
50th Anniv. — A866

No. 3097: a, Pope John Paul II at Western
Wall, Jerusalem. b, Pope Benedict XVI at
Western Wall. c, Pope Francis at Western
Wall. d, Pope John Paul II, Chief Rabbis of
Israel Yisrael Meir Lau and Eliyahu Bakshi-
Doron. e, Pope Benedict XVI, Chief Rabbis of
Israel Yona Metzger and Shlomo Amar. f,
Pope Francis, Chief Rabbis David Lau and
Shlomo Amar.
No. 3098: a, Pope John Paul II, Bernard-
Henri Lévy. b, Pope Benedict XVI, Rabbi Ric-
cardo DiSegni. c, Pope Benedict XVI, Rabbi
David Rosen, Chief Rabbi Amar. d, Pope Ben-
edict XVI, Chief Rabbi Lord Jonathan Sacks.
e, Pope Francis, Martin Budd, Chair of Interna-
tional Jewish Committee for Interreligious
Consultations. f, Pope Francis, Chief Rabbi
David Lau, Vatican Secretary of State Pietro
Parolin. g, Pope Francis at Yad Vashem, Israel.

2015, Dec. 21   Litho.   Perf. 14
3097 A865 $100 Sheet of 6,
             #a-f                14.50 14.50
3098 A866 $100 Sheet of 7,
             #a-g                16.50 16.50

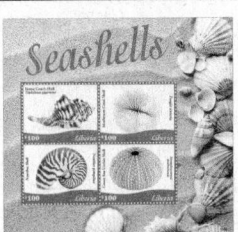

Seashells and Marine Life — A867

No. 3099: a, Horse conch. b, Mushroom
coral. c, Nautilus. d, Green sea urchin.
No. 3100: a, Sea snail shell. b, Triton's trumpet. c, Tiger cowrie. d, Giant African snail
shell. e, Pearlized nautilus shell. f, Banded
bonnet.
$350, Scallops.

Perf. 12, 14 (#3100)
2015, Dec. 31                   Litho.
3099 A867 $100 Sheet of 4,
             #a-d                 9.50  9.50
3100 A867 $100 Sheet of 6,
             #a-f                14.50 14.50
        Souvenir Sheet
3101 A867 $350 multi           8.25  8.25

Souvenir Sheets

Elvis Presley (1935-77) — A868

Inscriptions: No. 3102, $350, Joining the
fight against cancer. No. 3103, $350, Donates
wallaby to Memphis Zoo. No. 3104, $350, First
Las Vegas concert. No. 3105, $350, Promot-
ing polio awareness.

Perf. 12, 14 (#3104-3105)
2016, Jan. 28                   Litho.
3102-3105 A868  Set of 4   34.00 34.00

Reptiles
A869

No. 3106: a, Leopard tortoise. b, Eyelash
bush viper. c, Gaboon viper. d, Mossy leaf-
tailed gecko.
No. 3107: a, Madagascar day gecko. b,
Radiated turtle. c, Red-headed rock agama. d,
Nile crocodile. e, Pancake tortoise. f, Nile
monitor.
$350, Parson's chameleon.

2016, Jan. 28   Litho.   Perf. 12
3106 A869 $100 Sheet of 4,
             #a-d                 9.75  9.75
3107 A869 $100 Sheet of 6,
             #a-f                14.50 14.50
        Souvenir Sheet
3108 A869 $350 multi           8.50  8.50

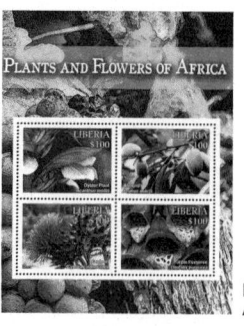

PLANTS AND FLOWERS OF AFRICA

Flora
A870

No. 3109: a, Oyster plant. b, Almond. c, Cardoon. d, Purple foxglove.
No. 3110: a, Burning bush. b, Bay laurel. c, African oil palm. d, Poppy. e, Bird cherry. f, Blessed Mary's thistle.
$350, Maidenhair ferns, vert.

**2016, Feb. 20    Litho.    Perf. 14**
3109  A870  $100  Sheet of 4,
        #a-d                    9.50    9.50
3110  A870  $100  Sheet of 6,
        #a-f                   14.50   14.50

**Souvenir Sheet**
3111  A870  $350  multi        8.25    8.25

Birds of West Africa

Birds
A871

No. 3112: a, African broadbill. b, Buff-spotted woodpecker. c, Rufous-naped lark. d, Eurasian wryneck.
No. 3113: a, African pied hornbill. b, Black-and-white-casqued hornbill. c, Black-casqued hornbill. d, African gray hornbill. e, White-crested hornbill. f, Yellow-casqued hornbill.
$350, Flamingos.

**2016, Feb. 20    Litho.    Perf. 14**
3112  A871  $100  Sheet of 4,
        #a-d                    9.50    9.50
3113  A871  $100  Sheet of 6,
        #a-f                   14.50   14.50

**Souvenir Sheet**
**Perf. 12**
3114  A871  $350  multi        8.25    8.25

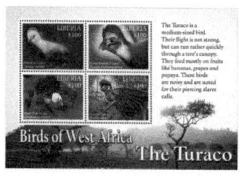

Turacos
A872

No. 3115: a, Fischer's turaco. b, Purple-crested turaco. c, Great blue turaco. d, Guinea turaco.
No. 3116, vert.: a, Green turaco. b, Turaco unicolor. c, Violet turaco. d, White-cheeked turaco. e, Livingstone's turaco. f, White-crested turaco.
$350, Red-crested turaco.

**2016, Feb. 20    Litho.    Perf. 14**
3115  A872  $100  Sheet of 4,
        #a-d                    9.50    9.50
3116  A872  $100  Sheet of 6,
        #a-f                   14.50   14.50

**Souvenir Sheet**
**Perf. 12**
3117  A872  $350  multi        8.25    8.25

Jimi Hendrix (1942-70), Rock Musician — A873

No. 3118 — Various photographs of Hendrix, as shown.
$350, Hendrix, horiz.

**2016, Mar. 8    Litho.    Perf. 14**
3118  A873  $100  Sheet of 6,
        #a-f                   13.50   13.50

**Souvenir Sheet**
**Perf. 12½**
3119  A873  $350  multi        7.75    7.75
No. 3119 contains one 51x38mm stamp.

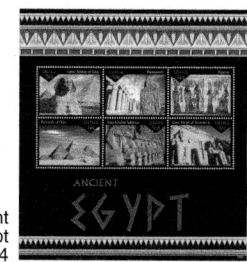

Ancient Egypt
A874

No. 3120: a, Great Sphinx of Giza. b, Ramesseum. c, Papyrus. d, Pyramids of Giza. e, Ram-headed Sphinxes. f, Giant Temple of Ramesses II.
$350, Wall painting.

**2016, Mar. 18    Litho.    Perf. 14**
3120  A874  $100  Sheet of 6,
        #a-f                   13.50   13.50

**Souvenir Sheet**
**Perf. 12**
3121  A874  $350  multi        7.75    7.75

90th Birthday of Queen Elizabeth II
A875

No. 3122 — Queen Elizabeth II: a, In 1927. b, In 1953, wearing George IV State diamond diadem. c, In 1953, wearing Imperial State Crown. d, In 1928.
$415, Queen Elizabeth II wearing diadem, 1953, diff.

**2016, Apr. 1    Litho.    Perf. 13¾**
3122  A875  $100  Sheet of 4, #a-d  9.00  9.00

**Souvenir Sheet**
3123  A875  $415  multi        9.25    9.25

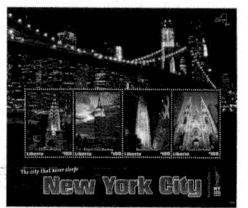

New York City Landmarks — A876

No. 3124: a, Chrysler Building. b, Empire State Building. c, Rockefeller Center. d, St. Patrick's Cathedral.
$415, Brooklyn Bridge, horiz.

**2016, Apr. 1    Litho.    Perf. 12½**
3124  A876  $100  Sheet of 4, #a-d  9.00  9.00

**Souvenir Sheet**
**Perf. 14**
3125  A876  $415  multi        9.25    9.25
2016 World Stamp Show, New York City. No. 3125 contains one 80x30mm stamp.

William Shakespeare (1564-1616), Writer — A877

No. 3126 — Various scenes from *Julius Caesar*, as shown.
$500, Shakespeare, vert.

**2016, May 30    Litho.    Perf. 12½**
3126  A877  $100  Sheet of 4,
        #a-d                    9.00    9.00

**Souvenir Sheet**
**Perf. 12**
3127  A877  $500  multi       11.00   11.00
No. 3127 contains one 50x60mm stamp.

**Souvenir Sheet**

2016 World Stamp Show, New York City
A878

**2016, May 30    Litho.    Perf. 12½x12**
3128  A878  $925  multi       20.50   20.50

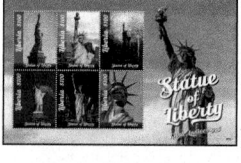

Statue of Liberty, 130th Anniv.
A879

No. 3129 — Various photographs of Statue of Liberty, as shown.
No. 3130: a, Statue of Liberty, diff. b, Statue of Liberty and Manhattan buildings.
$415, Statue of Liberty, diff.

**2016, June 30    Litho.    Perf. 14**
3129  A879  $100  Sheet of 6,
        #a-f                   13.00   13.00

**Souvenir Sheets**
**Perf. 12**
3130  A879  $200  Sheet of 2,
        #a-b                    8.75    8.75
**Perf. 12½**
3131  A879  $415  multi        9.00    9.00
No. 3131 contains one 38x51mm stamp.

**Souvenir Sheets**

Elvis Presley (1935-77) — A880

Inscriptions: No. 3132, $415, Visits memorial he helped build. No. 3133, $415, Plays Cotton Pickin' Jamboree. No. 3134, $415, Tupelo Youth Center fundraiser. No. 3135, $415, Sponsors football team, horiz.

**Perf. 13¼x13, 13x13¼**
**2016, June 30    Litho.**
3132-3135  A880  Set of 4    36.50   36.50

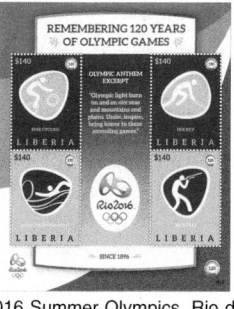

REMEMBERING 120 YEARS OF OLYMPIC GAMES

2016 Summer Olympics, Rio de Janeiro — A881

No. 3136, $140: a, BMX cycling. b, Field hockey. c, Marathon swimming. d, Shooting.
No. 3137, $140: a, Judo. b, Canoe slalom. c, Triathlon. d, Equestrian jumping.
No. 3138, $200: a, Running. b, Karoline Radke (1903-83), 1928 gold medalist in 800-meter race.

**2016, July 7    Litho.    Perf. 14**
**Sheets of 4, #a-d**
3136-3137  A881  Set of 2    24.50   24.50
**Souvenir Sheet**
**Perf. 12½**
3138  A881  $200  Sheet of 2,
        #a-b                    8.75    8.75
No. 3138 contains two 38x51mm stamps.

Sept. 11, 2001 Terrorist Attacks, 15th Anniv.
A882

No. 3139: a, Tribute in Light. b, Firefighters with caps removed. c, World Trade Center during day. d, Firefigher and flowers. e, World Trade Center at night. f, Firefighters with flags.
$400, Tribute in Light, diff.

**2016, July 19    Litho.    Perf. 14**
3139  A882  $100  Sheet of 6,
        #a-f                   13.50   13.50

**Souvenir Sheet**
**Perf. 12½**
3140  A882  $400  multi        8.75    8.75
No. 3140 contains one 38x51mm stamp.

A883

A884

A886

Hillary Clinton, 2016 Democratic Candidate for U.S. President — A885

A887

Donald Trump, 2016 Republican Candidate for U.S. President — A888

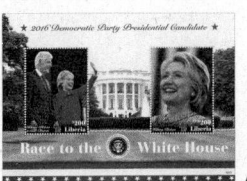

*2016 Democratic Party Presidential Candidate*

Race to the White House — A889

*2016 Presidential Candidates*

Race to the White House — A890

*2016 Republican Party Presidential Candidate*

Race to the White House — A891

No. 3157: a, Hillary Clinton and her husband, Pres. Bill Clinton. b, Hillary Clinton.
No. 3158: a, Hillary Clinton, diff. b, Donald Trump, diff.
No. 3159: a, Trump and his wife, Melania. b, Donald Trump, diff.

**2016, July 19    Litho.    Perf. 12½**

| | | | |
|---|---|---|---|
| 3141 | A883 | $20.16 multi | .45 .45 |
| 3142 | A884 | $20.16 multi | .45 .45 |
| 3143 | A885 | $20.16 multi | .45 .45 |
| 3144 | A886 | $20.16 multi | .45 .45 |
| 3145 | A887 | $20.16 multi | .45 .45 |
| 3146 | A888 | $20.16 multi | .45 .45 |

**Size: 35x35mm**
**Perf. 13¾**

| | | | |
|---|---|---|---|
| 3147 | A883 | $100 multi | 2.25 2.25 |
| 3148 | A884 | $100 multi | 2.25 2.25 |
| 3149 | A885 | $100 multi | 2.25 2.25 |
| 3150 | A886 | $100 multi | 2.25 2.25 |
| 3151 | A887 | $100 multi | 2.25 2.25 |
| 3152 | A888 | $100 multi | 2.25 2.25 |
| 3153 | | Horiz. pair | 6.50 6.50 |
| a. | A883 | $140 multi | 3.25 3.25 |
| b. | A884 | $140 multi | 3.25 3.25 |
| 3154 | A885 | $140 multi | 3.25 3.25 |
| 3155 | A886 | $100 multi | 3.25 3.25 |
| 3156 | | Horiz. pair | 6.50 6.50 |
| a. | A887 | $140 multi | 3.25 3.25 |
| b. | A888 | $140 multi | 3.25 3.25 |
| | Nos. 3141-3156 (16) | | 35.70 35.70 |

**Souvenir Sheets**
**Perf. 13¼**

| | | | |
|---|---|---|---|
| 3157 | A889 | $200 Sheet of 2, #a-b | 8.75 8.75 |
| 3158 | A890 | $200 Sheet of 2, #a-b | 8.75 8.75 |
| 3159 | A891 | $200 Sheet of 2, #a-b | 8.75 8.75 |
| | Nos. 3157-3159 (3) | | 26.25 26.25 |

Nos. 3141 and 3142 were printed in sheets of 20 containing ten of each stamp. Nos. 3143 and 3144 were printed in sheets of 20 containing ten of each stamp. Nos. 3145 and 3146 were printed in sheets of 20 containing ten of each stamp. Nos. 3147 and 3148 were printed in sheets of six containing three of each stamp. Nos. 3149 and 3150 were printed in sheets of six containing three of each stamp. Nos. 3151 and 3152 were printed in sheets of six containing three of each stamp. Nos. 3153 and 3156 were each printed in sheets containing two pairs. Nos. 3154 and 3155 were printed in sheets of four containing two of each stamp.

Captains From *Star Trek* Television Series — A892

No. 3160: a, Capt. Jonathan Archer. b, Capt. Jean-Luc Picard. c, Capt. James T. Kirk. d, Capt. Benjamin Sisko. e, Capt. Kathryn Janeway.
$400, Captains Archer, Picard, Kirk, Sisko and Janeway, horiz.

**2016, Aug. 29    Litho.    Perf. 12**

| | | | |
|---|---|---|---|
| 3160 | A892 | $150 Sheet of 5, #a-e | 17.00 17.00 |

**Souvenir Sheet**

| | | | |
|---|---|---|---|
| 3161 | A892 | $400 multi | 9.00 9.00 |

No. 3161 contains one 90x50mm stamp.

European Space Agency, 50th Anniv. — A893

No. 3162: a, European Space Agency Headquarters, Paris. b, French Guyana Space Center. c, Giotto Probe and Halley's Comet. d, Ariane N'Koltang Tracking Station, Gabon. $400, Ariane 1 rocket, vert.

**2016, Sept. 9    Litho.    Perf. 14**

| | | | |
|---|---|---|---|
| 3162 | A893 | $150 Sheet of 4, #a-d | 13.50 13.50 |

**Souvenir Sheet**
**Perf. 12**

| | | | |
|---|---|---|---|
| 3163 | A893 | $400 multi | 9.00 9.00 |

Visit to Argentina of Pres. Barack Obama — A894

No. 3164: a, Pres. Obama and Argentina Pres. Mauricio Macri, denomination at LR (60x40mm). b, Pres. Obama (30x40mm). c, Presidents Obama and Macri, denomination at LL (60x40mm). d, Pres. Macri (30x40mm). $400, Presidents Obama and Macri shaking hands, horiz.

**2016, Sept. 26    Litho.    Perf. 14**

| | | | |
|---|---|---|---|
| 3164 | A894 | $150 Sheet of 4, #a-d | 13.50 13.50 |

**Souvenir Sheet**
**Perf. 12½**

| | | | |
|---|---|---|---|
| 3165 | A894 | $400 multi | 9.00 9.00 |

No. 3165 contains one 51x38mm stamp.

A895

A896

Diplomatic Relations Between Liberia and People's Republic of China, 40th Anniv. — A897

**2016, Nov. 3    Litho.    Perf. 12**

| | | | |
|---|---|---|---|
| 3166 | | Sheet of 25, #3166c, 12 each #3166a-3166b | 58.50 58.50 |
| a. | A895 | $100 multi | 2.25 2.25 |
| b. | A896 | $100 multi | 2.25 2.25 |
| c. | A897 | $200 multi | 4.50 4.50 |

A898

A899

A900

Worldwide Fund for Nature (WWF) — A901

**2016, Nov. 3    Litho.    Perf. 14**

| | | | |
|---|---|---|---|
| 3167 | | Horiz. strip of 4 | 9.00 9.00 |
| a. | A898 | $100 multi | 2.25 2.25 |
| b. | A899 | $100 multi | 2.25 2.25 |
| c. | A900 | $100 multi | 2.25 2.25 |
| d. | A901 | $100 multi | 2.25 2.25 |
| e. | | Souvenir sheet of 8, 2 each #3167a-3167d | 18.00 18.00 |

Paintings by Hieronymus Bosch (c. 1450-1516) — A902

No. 3168 — Details fom *The Haywain Triptych*: a, Adam and Eve. b, Lute player, woman and angels. c, Creatures with tails. d, Creatures with animal's heads.
No. 3169 — Details from *The Last Judgment* with denomination at: a, LL. b, LR.

**2016, Nov. 14    Litho.    Perf. 14**

| | | | |
|---|---|---|---|
| 3168 | A902 | $180 Sheet of 4, #a-d | 16.00 16.00 |

**Souvenir Sheet**
**Perf. 12**

| | | | |
|---|---|---|---|
| 3169 | A902 | $250 Sheet of 2, #a-b | 11.00 11.00 |

No. 3169 contains two 30x50mm stamps.

New Year 2017 (Year of the Rooster) A903

No. 3170 — Rooster facing: a, Right. b, Left.

**2016, Nov. 17    Litho.    Perf. 13¾**

| | | | |
|---|---|---|---|
| 3170 | A903 | $180 Horiz. pair, #a-b | 8.00 8.00 |

No. 3170 was printed in sheets containing two pairs.

A904

Christmas — A905

**2016, Dec. 1    Litho.    Perf. 12½**
**Ribbon Color**

| | | | |
|---|---|---|---|
| 3171 | A904 | $180 red | 4.00 4.00 |
| 3172 | A905 | $180 red | 4.00 4.00 |
| 3173 | A904 | $360 green | 8.00 8.00 |
| 3174 | A905 | $360 green | 8.00 8.00 |
| | Nos. 3171-3174 (4) | | 24.00 24.00 |

A906

A907

The Monkey King
A908

No. 3175 — Scenes from *The Monkey King*, as shown.

**2016, Dec. 1    Litho.    Perf. 12½**

| | | | |
|---|---|---|---|
| 3175 | A906 | $180 Sheet of 4, #a-d | 16.00 16.00 |

**Souvenir Sheets**
**Perf. 12**

| | | | |
|---|---|---|---|
| 3176 | A907 | $360 multi | 8.00 8.00 |
| 3177 | A908 | $360 multi | 8.00 8.00 |

**Miniature Sheet**

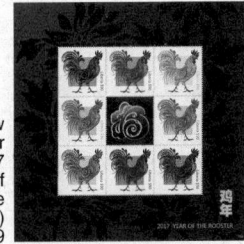

New Year 2017 (Year of the Rooster) A909

No. 3178 — Color of square behind rooster: a, Pink. b, Peach. c, Pale yellow. d, Dull blue green. e, Light green. f, Light blue. g, Gray blue. h, Reddish lilac.

**2016, Dec. 15    Litho.    Perf. 13¾**

| | | | |
|---|---|---|---|
| 3178 | A909 | $90 Sheet of 8, #a-h, + central label | 16.00 16.00 |

**U.S. Presidents Type of 2009**

No. 3179, vert: a, Herbert Hoover. b, Franklin D. Roosevelt. c, Harry S. Truman. d, Dwight D. Eisenhower. e, John F. Kennedy. f, Lyndon B. Johnson. g, Richard M. Nixon. h, Gerald R.

Ford. i, Jimmy Carter. j, Ronald Reagan. k, George H.W. Bush. l, William J. Clinton. m, George W. Bush. n, Barack H. Obama. o, Donald J. Trump.
No. 3180: a, Presidential seal. $450, Donald J. Trump.

| | | | | Perf. 13¼ |
|---|---|---|---|---|
| **2016-17** | | **Litho.** | | |
| **3179** | A669 | $45 Sheet of 15, | | |
| | | #a-o | 14.50 | 14.50 |
| **3180** | A661 | $45 Sheet of 15, | | |
| | | #3180a, 14 | | |
| | | #3179o | 14.50 | 14.50 |

**Souvenir Sheet**
**Perf. 12½**

| **3181** | A661 | $450 multi | 10.00 | 10.00 |
|---|---|---|---|---|

Issued: No. 3179, 2/28/17; No. 3180, 4/28/17; No. 3181, 12/26/16. Nos. 3179 and 3180 each contain fifteen 28x42mm stamps. A souvenir sheet similar to No. 3181 depicting Hillary Clinton exists.

A910

Wolverine Frogs — A911

No. 3182: a, Top of frog's leg under "1." b, Head of frog at bottom. c, Top of frog's leg under "A." d, White background.
No. 3183: a, Head of frog. b, Head of frog and body of other frog.

| **2017, Feb. 28** | | **Litho.** | | **Perf. 12** |
|---|---|---|---|---|
| **3182** | A910 | $180 Sheet of 4, | | |
| | | #a-d | 15.50 | 15.50 |

**Souvenir Sheet**
**Perf. 12x12½**

| **3183** | A911 | $250 Sheet of 2, | | |
|---|---|---|---|---|
| | | #a-b | 11.00 | 11.00 |

Chinese People's Liberation Army, 90th Anniv. — A912

Designs: No. 3184, $30, Soldiers, flag, Great Wall of China. No. 3185, $30, Soldiers, flag, tank, ship and airplanes.

**Perf. 13¼x13¾**

| **2017, Mar. 14** | | **Litho.** | | |
|---|---|---|---|---|
| **3184-3185** | A912 | Set of 2 | 1.40 | 1.40 |

Return of Hong Kong to People's Republic of China, 20th Anniv. — A913

Golden Bauhinia sculpture, Hong Kong, and No. 3186, $20, Aerial view of Hong Kong. No. 3187, $20, Lion sculpture, Hong Kong skyline.

**Perf. 13¼x13¾**

| **2017, Mar. 14** | | **Litho.** | | |
|---|---|---|---|---|
| **3186-3187** | A913 | Set of 2 | .85 | .85 |

Wildlife — A914

Designs: $4000, Nile crocodile. $6000, Red river hog. $10,000, Leopard.

**Perf. 12½x13¼**

| **2017, Mar. 14** | | **Litho.** | | |
|---|---|---|---|---|
| **3188** | A914 | $4000 multi | 85.00 | 85.00 |
| **3189** | A914 | $6000 multi | 130.00 | 130.00 |
| **3190** | A914 | $10,000 multi | 215.00 | 215.00 |
| | | Nos. 3188-3190 (3) | 430.00 | 430.00 |

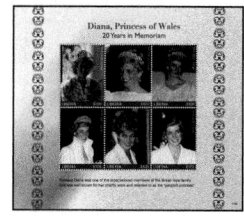

Princess Diana (1961-97) — A915

No. 3191 — Princess Diana wearing: a, Blue and white tunic. b, White dress and tiara. c, Pale blue dress and tiara. d, White jacket with high collar and tiara. e, White jacket, man in background. f, White jacket and pearl earrings.
No. 3192 — Princess Diana wearing: a, White jacket and cap. b, Blue green dress and white hat.

| **2017, Mar. 31** | | **Litho.** | | **Perf. 14** |
|---|---|---|---|---|
| **3191** | A915 | $120 Sheet of 6, | | |
| | | #a-f | 15.50 | 15.50 |

**Souvenir Sheet**

| **3192** | A915 | $180 Sheet of 2, | | |
|---|---|---|---|---|
| | | #a-b | 7.75 | 7.75 |

Miniature Sheets

Pres. John F. Kennedy (1917-63) — A916

No. 3193, $180 — Pres. Kennedy: a, In official presidential portrait (30x80mm). b, Looking at Friendship 7 space capsule (30x40mm). c, Pointing at announcement of creation of Committee on Equal Opportunity in Housing (30x80mm). d, Signing document during Cuban Missile Crisis (30x40mm).
No. 3194, $180 — Pres. Kennedy: a, With photographer in background (40x30mm). b, In car shaking hands (40x30mm). c, Standing behind microphone (40x30mm). d, On campaign poster (80x30mm).
No. 3195, $180 — Pres. Kennedy with: a, Brothers, Robert and Edward (35x35mm). b, Son, John, Jr. (35x35mm). c, Daughter, Caroline (35x35mm). d, Wife, Jacqueline (35x35mm)

**Perf. 14, 13¾ (#3195)**

| **2017, Mar. 31** | | **Litho.** | | |
|---|---|---|---|---|
| **Sheets of 4, #a-d** | | | | |
| **3193-3195** | A916 | Set of 3 | 46.00 | 46.00 |

Animals of the World A917

No. 3196: a, Malaysian golden gliding frog. b, Honeybee. c, African wild dog. d, Monarch butterflies.
$360, Matschie's tree kangaroo, vert.

| **2017, Apr. 14** | | **Litho.** | | **Perf. 12½** |
|---|---|---|---|---|
| **3196** | A917 | $180 Sheet of 4, | | |
| | | #a-d | 15.50 | 15.50 |

**Souvenir Sheet**

| **3197** | A917 | $360 multi | 7.75 | 7.75 |
|---|---|---|---|---|

Flag of People's Republic of China, Golden Bauhinia Statue, Hong Kong and Deng Xiaoping (1904-97), Leader of People's Republic of China — A918

| **2017, Apr. 14** | | **Litho.** | | **Perf. 13½** |
|---|---|---|---|---|
| **3198** | A918 | $20 multi | .45 | .45 |

Hong Kong Special Administrative Region, 20th anniv.

Hong Kong Special Administrative Region, 20th Anniv. — A919

Scenes of Hong Kong and years: No. 3199, $20, "1997-1998." No. 3200, $20, "1999." No. 3201, $20, "2000." No. 3202, $20, "2001." No. 3203, $20, "2002." No. 3204, $20, "2003." No. 3205, $20, "2004." No. 3206, $20, "2005." No. 3207, $20, "2006." No. 3208, $20, "2007." No. 3209, $20, "2008." No. 3210, $20, "2009." No. 3211, $20, "2010." No. 3212, $20, "2011." No. 3213, $20, "2012." No. 3214, $20, "2013." No. 3215, $20, "2014." No. 3216, $20, "2015." No. 3217, $20, "2016." No. 3218, $20, "2017."

| **2017, Apr. 14** | | **Litho.** | | **Perf. 14½x14** |
|---|---|---|---|---|
| **3199-3218** | A919 | Set of 20 | 8.75 | 8.75 |

Fennec Foxes A920

No. 3219: a, Head of fox facing forward. b, Head of fox facing right. c, Fox sleeping. d, Fox standing on rock.
No. 3220; a, Fox sitting. b, Fox standing.

| **2017, July 24** | | **Litho.** | | **Perf. 14** |
|---|---|---|---|---|
| **3219** | A920 | $180 Sheet of 4, | | |
| | | #a-d | 16.00 | 16.00 |

**Souvenir Sheet**

| **3220** | A920 | $250 Sheet of 2, | | |
|---|---|---|---|---|
| | | #a-b | 11.00 | 11.00 |

Diana Monkeys A921

No. 3221: a, Monkey holding food in paw. b, Monkey, front tooth visible. c, Monkey, diff.
No. 3222, horiz.: a, Monkey and wooden pole. b, Monkey and tree leaves.

| **2017, July 24** | | **Litho.** | | **Perf. 14** |
|---|---|---|---|---|
| **3221** | A921 | $200 Sheet of 3, | | |
| | | #a-c | 13.50 | 13.50 |

**Souvenir Sheet**

| **3222** | A921 | $200 Sheet of 2, | | |
|---|---|---|---|---|
| | | #a-b | 9.00 | 9.00 |

A922

Elephants — A923

No. 3223: a, Two adults and one juvenile elephants. b, One adult elephant in jungle. b, Four elephants. c, Elephant in grassland.
No. 3224 — Adult and juvenile elephants: a, Adult facing left. b, Adult's trunk touching juvenile. c, Juvenile's trunk touching adult's trunk.

| **2017, July 24** | | **Litho.** | | **Perf. 14** |
|---|---|---|---|---|
| **3223** | A922 | $180 Sheet of 4, | | |
| | | #a-d | 16.00 | 16.00 |

**Souvenir Sheet**

| **3224** | A923 | $180 Sheet of 3, | | |
|---|---|---|---|---|
| | | #a-c | 12.00 | 12.00 |

A924

African Penguins A925

No. 3225: a, Two penguins on beach. b, One penguin, feet not visible. c, Two penguins grooming. d, One penguin, feet visible.
No. 3226 — Various photographs of penguins, as shown.

| **2017, July 24** | | **Litho.** | | **Perf. 14** |
|---|---|---|---|---|
| **3225** | A924 | $180 Sheet of 4, | | |
| | | #a-d | 16.00 | 16.00 |

**Souvenir Sheet**

| **3226** | A925 | $180 Sheet of 3, | | |
|---|---|---|---|---|
| | | #a-c | 12.00 | 12.00 |

New Year 2018 (Year of the Dog) A926

No. 3227: a, Laika, first dog to orbit Earth. b, Morris Frank and Buddy, first seeing-eye dog in the U.S. c, Hachiko, dog that waited for dead owner for nine years. d, Balto, lead sled dog in 1925 Nome serum run.
$360, Owney, the mail dog.

| **2017, July 24** | | **Litho.** | | **Perf. 14** |
|---|---|---|---|---|
| **3227** | A926 | $180 Sheet of 4, | | |
| | | #a-d | 16.00 | 16.00 |

**Souvenir Sheet**
**Perf. 12¾**

| **3228** | A926 | $360 multi | 8.00 | 8.00 |
|---|---|---|---|---|

No. 3228 contains one 38x51mm stamp.

Souvenir Sheets

Elvis Presley (1935-77) — A927

Inscription: No. 3229, $360, First National #1 Best Seller. No. 3230, $360, Elvis' First RCA Recording Session. No. 3231, $360,

Appears in First Movie. No. 3232, $360, Elvis Decides to Record "Hound Dog."

**2017, Oct. 26     Litho.     Perf. 12¾**
3229-3232  A927     Set of 4          24.00 24.00

A928

Lions Clubs International, Cent. — A929

No. 3233: a, Helen Keller. b, Lions Club Youth with earphones. c, Lions Club Youth near tents. d, 1918 emblem. e, 1920 emblem. f, Current emblem.
No. 3234 — Centenary emblem and: a, Members and statue of lion. b, Confetti. c, Slogan. d, Melvin Jones (1879-1961), founder.

**2017, Oct. 26     Litho.     Perf. 14**
3233  A928  $100 Sheet of 6,
                   #a-f          10.00 10.00
**Souvenir Sheet**
**Perf. 12¾**
3234  A929  $100 Sheet of 4,
                   #a-d          6.75  6.75
**Miniature Sheet**

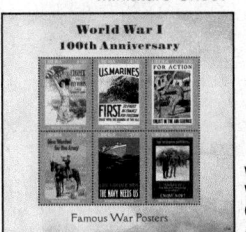

World War I, Cent. A930

No. 3235 — Poster inscribed: a, "Fight or Buy Bonds." b, "U.S. Marines First to Fight in France For Freedom." c, "For Action Enlist in the Air Service." d, "Men Wanted for the Army." e, "Pull Together Men the Navy Needs Us." f, "The Veteran's Farewell."

**2017, Nov. 17     Litho.     Perf. 14**
3235  A930  $120 Sheet of 6,
                   #a-f          11.50 11.50

A931

2018 World Cup Soccer Championships, Russia — A932

**2018, Jan. 1     Litho.     Perf. 14**
3236  A931  $150 multi          2.40  2.40
3237  A932  $150 multi          2.40  2.40
  a.    Sheet of 8, 4 each #3236-
        3237                     19.50 19.50

---

**Miniature Sheet**

Visit of Pres. Donald Trump to Asia-Pacific Economic Cooperation Economic Leaders Meeting, Viet Nam — A933

No. 3238: a, Vietnamese Prime Minister Nguyen Xuân Phúc wearing blue tie. b, Pres. Trump wearing red tie. c, Prime Minister Nguyen wearing red tie. d, Pres. Trump wearing blue striped tie.

**2018, Jan. 24     Litho.     Perf. 13x12½**
3238  A933  $180 Sheet of 4,
                   #a-d          12.00 12.00

Hyenas A934

No. 3239: a, $90, Two Spotted hyenas. b, $90, Brown hyena. c, $100, Striped hyena. d, $100, Spotted hyena. e, $150, Spotted hyena, diff. f, $150, Aardwolf.
No. 3240 — Various photographs of Spotted hyenas: a, $175. b, $185. c, $195.

**2018, Jan. 24     Litho.     Perf. 14**
3239  A934     Sheet of 6, #a-f    11.00 11.00
**Souvenir Sheet**
**Perf. 12**
3240  A934     Sheet of 3, #a-c    9.00  9.00

Presidents and Vice-Presidents of the United States — A935

No. 3241, $100: a, George Washington, John Adams and flag. b, Adams. c, Washington, Adams and their signatures. d, Adams, Thomas Jefferson and flag. e, Jefferson. f, Adams, Jefferson and their signatures.
No. 3242, $100: a, Jefferson, Aaron Burr and flag. b, Burr. c, Jefferson, Burr and their signatures. d, Jefferson, George Clinton and flag. e, Clinton. f, Jefferson, Clinton and their signatures.
No. 3243, $100: a, James Madison, Elbridge Gerry and flag. b, Gerry. c, Madison, Gerry and their signatures. d, James Monroe, Daniel D. Tompkins and flag. e, Tompkins. f, Monroe, Tompkins and their signatures.

**2018, Feb. 1     Litho.     Perf. 14**
**Blocks of 6, #a-f**
3241-3243  A935     Set of 3      30.00 30.00

Monkeys A936

No. 3244: a, Collared mangabey. b, Mona monkey. c, Green monkey. d, Patas monkey.
No. 3245, horiz.: a, Diana monkey. b, Sooty mangabey,

**2018, Feb. 8     Litho.     Perf. 13¾**
3244  A936  $180 Sheet of 4,
                   #a-d          11.00 11.00
**Souvenir Sheet**
**Perf. 14**
3245  A936  $250 Sheet of 2,
                   #a-b          7.75  7.75
No. 3245 contains two 40x30mm stamps.

---

A937

Wild Horses A938

No. 3246: a, $150, Brown horse on beach. b, $200, Two horses in field. c, $250, Herd of horses. d, $300, Gray horse in water.
No. 3247: a, $200, Horse and colt. b, $250, Two horses, diff. c, $300, Black horse with white blaze.

**2018, Feb. 8     Litho.     Perf. 14**
3246  A937     Sheet of 4, #a-d    14.00 14.00
**Souvenir Sheet**
3247  A938     Sheet of 3, #a-c    11.50 11.50

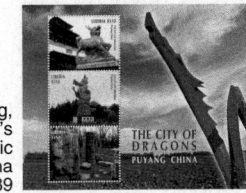

Puyang, People's Republic of China A939

No. 3248: a, $150, Qicheng Ruins. b, $350, Dragon statue. c, $550, Dragon statue and building.
$850, Red Dragon statue, vert.

**2018, Mar. 14     Litho.     Perf. 14**
3248  A939     Sheet of 3, #a-c    16.00 16.00
**Souvenir Sheet**
3249  A939  $850 multi            13.00 13.00
No. 3249 contains one 40x60mm stamp.

Planets A940

No. 3250: a, Mercury, Venus, Earth, Mars and Jupiter. b, Jupiter, Saturn, Uranus and Neptune.
$550, Sun and the planets.

**2018, Apr. 23     Litho.     Perf. 14**
3250  A940  $390 Sheet of 2,
                   #a-b          12.00 12.00
**Souvenir Sheet**
3251  A940  $550 multi            8.50  8.50
No. 3251 contains one 80x30mm stamp.

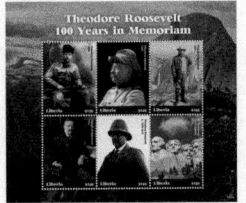

Pres. Theodore Roosevelt (1858-1919) — A941

No. 3252 — Roosevelt: a, In 1885. b, In 1898. c, In 1903. d, In 1904. e, Circa 1909-10. f, On Mount Rushmore.
$360, Official White House portrait of Roosevelt, by John Singer Sargent.

**2018, Apr. 23     Litho.     Perf. 14**
3252  A941  $120 Sheet of 6,
                   #a-f          11.00 11.00

---

**Souvenir Sheet**
**Perf. 12**
3253  A941  $360 multi            5.50  5.50
**Miniature Sheet**

Billy Graham (1918-2018), Evangelist — A942

No. 3254 — Graham with: a, His wife, Ruth, Queen Elizabeth II, Queen Mother and Prince Philip (80x30mm). b, Pres. Barack Obama (40x30mm). c, Pres. John F. Kennedy (40x30mm). d, Pres. George W. Bush (40x30mm). e, Pres. Richard Nixon (40x30mm).

**2018, Apr. 26     Litho.     Perf. 14**
3254  A942  $200 Sheet of 5,
                   #a-e          15.00 15.00

**Souvenir Sheet**

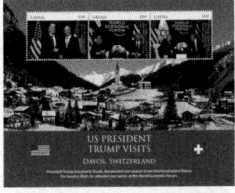

Pres. Donald Trump at World Economic Forum — A943

No. 3255 — Pres. Trump and: a, Swiss Pres. Alain Berset. b, British Prime Minister Theresa May. c, Israeli Prime Minister Benjamin Netanyahu.

**2018, Apr. 26     Litho.     Perf. 14**
3255  A943  $260 Sheet of 3,
                   #a-c          12.00 12.00

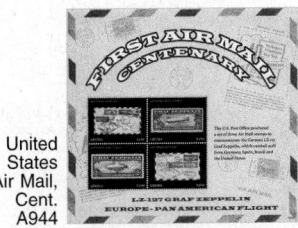

United States Air Mail, Cent. A944

No. 3256: a, 1930 Graf Zeppelin cover with handwritten address. b, United States #C14. c, United States #C15. d, 1930 Graf Zeppelin cover with typewritten address.
$500, United States #C13.

**2018, Apr. 26     Litho.     Perf. 14**
3256  A944  $250 Sheet of 4,
                   #a-d          15.00 15.00
**Souvenir Sheet**
**Perf. 12¾**
3257  A944  $500 multi            7.50  7.50
No. 3257 contains one 51x38mm stamp.

Miniature Sheets

2018 Winter Olympics, Pyeongchang, South Korea — A945

No. 3258, $175: a, Speed skiing. b, Bobsledding. c, Figure skating. d, Ice hockey. e, Nordic combined skiing.
No. 3259, $175: a, Short track speed skating. b, Ski jumping. c, Skeleton. d, Snowboarding. e, Speed skating.
No. 3260, $175: a, Biathlon. b, Cross-country skiing. c, Curling. d, Freestyle skiing. e, Luge.

**2018, Apr. 26    Litho.    Perf. 13¾**
**Sheets of 5, #a-e**
3258-3260 A945    Set of 3    40.00 40.00

Liberian President George Weah — A946

Various photographs of Weah and Liberian flag: $100, $200, $250.
No. 3264, $500, Weah wearing suit and tie. No. 3265, $500, Weah wearing green presidential sash.

**2018    Litho.    Perf. 13¼x12½**
3261-3263 A946    Set of 3    8.00 8.00
**Souvenir Sheets**
**Perf. 13¾**
3264-3265 A946    Set of 2    13.50 13.50
Issued: Nos. 3261-3263, 5/12; Nos. 3264-3265, 6/30. Nos. 3264-3265 each contain one 70x70mm stamp.

Miniature Sheet

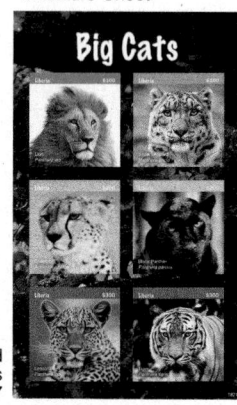

Wild Cats A947

No. 3266: a, $100, Lion. b, $100, Snow leopard. c, $200, Cheetah. d, $200, Black panther. e, $300, Leopard. f, $300, Tiger.

**Die Cut Perf. 13**
**2018, May 22    Litho.**
**Self-Adhesive**
3266 A947    Sheet of 6, #a-f    17.50 17.50

Miniature Sheet

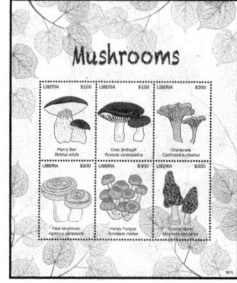

Mushrooms — A948

No. 3267: a, $100, Penny buns. b, $100, Crab brittlegills. c, $200, Chanterelles. d, $200, Field mushrooms. e, $300, Honey fungus. f, $300, Sponge morels.

**2018, May 22    Litho.    Perf. 14**
3267 A948    Sheet of 6, #a-f    17.50 17.50

Duikers A949

No. 3268: a, $200, Common duiker. b, $250, Red forest duiker. c, $300, Two Red forest duikers. d, $350, Common duiker, diff. $500, Common duiker, diff.

**2018, May 22    Litho.    Perf. 14**
3268 A949    Sheet of 4, #a-d    16.00 16.00
**Souvenir Sheet**
**Perf. 12¾**
3269 A949    $500 multi    7.25 7.25
No. 3269 contains one 51x38mm stamp.

Coronation of Queen Elizabeth II, 65th Anniv. — A950

No. 3270 — Queen Elizabeth II: a, $250, Waving (30x40mm). b, $250, Sitting in coach (30x40mm). c, $390, Wearing coronation robes (30x80mm). $500, Queen Elizabeth II holding orb and scepter.

**2018, May 22    Litho.    Perf. 14**
3270 A950    Sheet of 3, #a-c    13.00 13.00
**Souvenir Sheet**
**Perf. 12¾**
3271 A950    $500 multi    7.25 7.25
No. 3271 contains one 38x51mm stamp.

Miniature Sheet

Birth of Prince Louis of Cambridge — A951

No. 3272 — Duke and Duchess of Cambridge: a, At their wedding. b, With Prince George. c, With Princess Charlotte. d, With Prince Louis.

**2018, July 13    Litho.    Perf. 13¾**
3272 A951    $250 Sheet of 4, #a-d    13.00 13.00

Miniature Sheet

Engagement of Prince Harry and Meghan Markle — A952

No. 3273: a, Prince Harry, arms not visible. b, Markle, crowd in background. c, Prince Harry, arms visible. d, Markle, and woman standing behind her.

**2018, July 13    Litho.    Perf. 14**
3273 A952    $250 Sheet of 4, #a-d    13.00 13.00

Wedding of Prince Harry and Meghan Markle A953

No. 3274: a, Couple holding hands. b, Arms of the Duchess of Sussex. c, Arms of the Duke of Sussex. d, Couple kissing. $500, Couple holding hands, diff.

**2018, July 13    Litho.    Perf. 13¾**
3274 A953    $250 Sheet of 4, #a-d    13.00 13.00
**Souvenir Sheet**
3275 A953    $500 multi    6.50 6.50

Souvenir Sheets

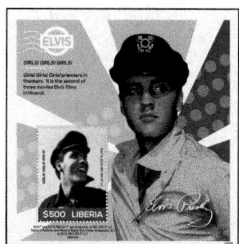

Elvis Presley (1935-77) — A954

Inscriptions: No. 3276, $500, *Girls! Girls! Girls!* No. 3277, $500, Mexico City bans Elvis's movie *G.I. Blues.* No. 3278, $500, Public karate demonstration. No. 3279, $500, Documentary *That's the Way It Is,* horiz.

**2018, July 13    Litho.    Perf. 14**
3276-3279 A954    Set of 4    26.00 26.00

Souvenir Sheets

Praga 2018 World Stamp Exhibition, Prague — A955

Illustrations by Alfons Mucha (1860-1939): No. 3280, $500, Epopea Slava. No. 3281, $500, 8th Sokol Festival, Prague.

**2018, July 15    Litho.    Perf. 12**
3280-3281 A955    Set of 2    13.00 13.00

Souvenir Sheet

Nelson Mandela (1918-2013), President of South Africa — A956

**2018, July 18    Litho.    Perf. 13¾**
3282 A956    $550 multi    7.25 7.25

African Guineafowl — A957

No. 3283: a, $170, Helmeted Guineafowl. b, $170, Crested Guineafowl. c, $170, Vulturine Guineafowl. d, $180, Helmeted Guineafowl, diff. e, $180, Crested Guineafowl, diff. f, $180m Vulturine Guineafowl, diff. $500, White-breasted Guineafowl.

**2018, Aug. 8    Litho.    Perf. 14**
3283 A957    Sheet of 6, #a-f    14.00 14.00
**Souvenir Sheet**
**Perf. 13¾**
3284 A957    $500 multi    6.50 6.50
No. 3284 contains one 35x35mm stamp.

Souvenir Sheets

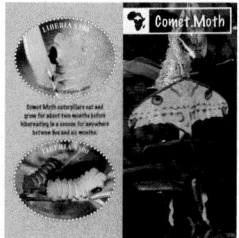

Comet Moth Caterpillars — A958

Comet Moths A959

No. 3285: a, One caterpillar. b, Two caterpillars. No. 3286: a, Moth above green foliage. b, Moth on tree.

**2018, Aug. 8    Litho.    Perf.**
3285 A958    $390 Sheet of 2, #a-b    10.00 10.00
3286 A959    $390 Sheet of 2, #a-b    10.00 10.00

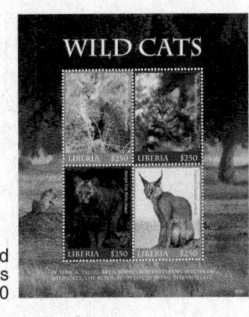

Wild Cats A960

No. 3287: a, African wildcat. b, Black-footed cat. c, Jungle cat. d, Caracal. $500, Sand cat, horiz.

**2018, Sept. 14     Litho.     Perf. 14**
3287 A960 $250 Sheet of 4, #a-d     13.00 13.00

**Souvenir Sheet**
**Perf. 12¾**
3288 A960 $500 multi     6.50 6.50
No. 3288 contains one 51x38mm stamp.

A961

New Year 2019 (Year of the Pig) A962

No. 3289: a, Red pig facing right. b, Yellow pig facing left and flowers. c, Red pig facing left.

**2018, Sept. 14     Litho.     Perf. 14**
3289 A961 $210 Sheet of 3, #a-c     8.25 8.25

**Souvenir Sheet**
**Perf. 13¾**
3290 A962 $300 multi     4.00 4.00

**Souvenir Sheet**

Butterflies — A963

No. 3291: a, $100, Giant blue swallowtail. b, $200, Blue mother-of-pearl. c, $300, Blue diadem.

**2018, Oct. 25     Litho.     Perf.**
3291 A963 Sheet of 3, #a-c     7.75 7.75

**Souvenir Sheet**

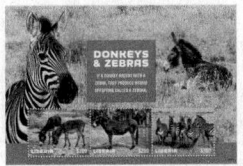

Donkeys and Zebras A964

No. 3292: a, $200, Two donkeys. b, $250, Zedonk. c, $300, Five zebras.

**2018, Oct. 25     Litho.     Perf. 12**
3292 A964 Sheet of 3, #a-c     9.75 9.75

---

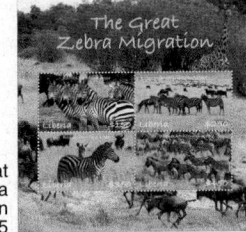

Great Zebra Migration A965

No. 3293 — Various photographs of Burchell's zebras: a, $150. b, $250. c, $350. d, $450.
$600, Burchell's zebras, diff.

**2018, Oct. 25     Litho.     Perf. 12**
3293 A965 Sheet of 4, #a-d     15.50 15.50

**Souvenir Sheet**
3294 A965 $600 multi     7.25 7.25
No. 3294 contains one 40x30mm stamp.

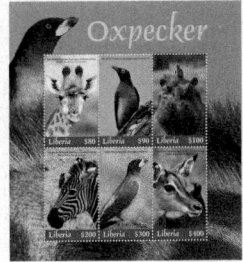

Oxpeckers — A966

No. 3295: a, $80, Red-billed oxpecker on giraffe. b, $90, Red-billed oxpecker. c, $100, Yellow-billed oxpecker on hippopotamus. d, $200, Red-billed oxpecker on Plains zebra. e, $300, Yellow-billed oxpecker. f, $400, Red-billed oxpecker on impala.
$600, Five Red-billed oxpeckers on African buffalo, horiz.

**2018, Oct. 25     Litho.     Perf. 12**
3295 A966 Sheet of 6, #a-f     15.00 15.00

**Souvenir Sheet**
**Perf. 12¾**
3296 A966 $600 multi     7.75 7.75
No. 3296 contains one 51x38mm stamp.

Flight of Apollo 11, 50th Anniv. (in 2019) A967

No. 3297: a, $150, Crew members Edwin "Buzz" Aldrin, Neil Armstrong and Michael Collins in suits and ties. b, $250, Crew members in space suits. c, $350, Pres. Nixon addressing quarantined crew members after flight.
$500, Crew members in space capsule.

**2018, Oct. 25     Litho.     Perf. 12**
3297 A967 Sheet of 3, #a-c     9.75 9.75

**Souvenir Sheet**
**Perf. 12¾**
3298 A967 $500 multi     6.50 6.50
No. 3298 contains one 51x38mm stamp.

---

**Souvenir Sheet**

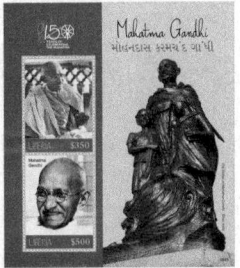

Mohandas K. Gandhi (1869-1948), Indian Nationalist Leader — A968

No. 3299 — Various photographs of Gandhi: a, $350. b, $500.

**2018, Dec. 5     Litho.     Perf. 14**
3299 A968 Sheet of 2, #a-b     11.00 11.00

African Waterfalls — A969

No. 3300: a, $160, Boti Falls. b, $260, Boti Falls, diff. c, $360, Kintampo Waterfalls.
No. 3301: a, $160, Wli Waterfalls. b, $260, Ouzoud Falls. c, $360, Murchison Falls.
$500, Kpatawee Waterfall, horiz.

**2018, Dec. 17     Litho.     Perf. 12**
**Sheets of 3, #a-c**
3300-3301 A969 Set of 2     20.00 20.00

**Souvenir Sheet**
**Perf. 12¾x12½**
3302 A969 $500 multi     6.50 6.50
No. 3302 contains one 51x38mm stamp.

New Year 2019 (Year of the Pig) A970

No. 3303 — Stamps with red frames and heads of various pigs: a, $150. b, $200. c, $250. d, $300.
No. 3304, $300: a, Panda. b, Pig (green panels).

**2018, Dec. 17     Litho.     Perf. 12**
3303 A970 Sheet of 4, #a-d     11.50 11.50

**Souvenir Sheet**
3304 A970 $300 Sheet of 2, #a-b     7.75 7.75

Lizards A971

No. 3305: a, $170, Red-headed rock agama. b, $170, Mwanza flat-headed rock agama. c, $170, Ground agama. d, $180, Mwanza flat-headed rock agama, diff. e, $180, Ground agama, diff. f, $180, Red-headed rock agama, diff.

**2018, Dec. 25     Litho.     Perf. 14**
3305 A971 Sheet of 6, #a-f     13.50 13.50

---

Meleguetta Peppers — A972

No. 3306: a, $100, Seeds. b, $200, Flower bud. c, $300, Flower. d, $400, Fruits.
$500, Flower, vert.

**2018, Dec. 31     Litho.     Perf. 12½**
3306 A972 Sheet of 4, #a-d     13.00 13.00

**Souvenir Sheet**
**Perf. 12**
3307 A972 $500 multi     6.50 6.50
No. 3307 contains one 30x50mm stamp.

**Miniature Sheet**

Garden Bulbul, National Bird of Liberia A973

No. 3308 — Arms of Liberia and: a, $100, Bird on perch. b, $200, Head of bird. c, $300, Bird on branch. d, $400, Two birds.

**2018, Dec. 31     Litho.     Perf. 14**
3308 A973 Sheet of 4, #a-d     13.00 13.00

White Rhinoceros — A974

No. 3309: a, $100, Adult and juvenile rhinoceros. b, $300, Adult rhinoceros. c, $500, Rhinoceros and lion.
$800, Head of rhinoceros

**2019, Feb. 25     Litho.     Perf. 12**
3309 A974 Sheet of 3, #a-c     11.00 11.00

**Souvenir Sheet**
**Perf.**
3310 A974 $800 multi     10.00 10.00
No. 3310 contains one 38mm diameter stamp.

**Miniature Sheet**

Marabou Stork A975

No. 3311 — Various photographs of stork: a, $250. b, $300. c, $350. d, $400.

**2019, Mar. 11     Litho.     Perf. 12**
3311 A975 Sheet of 4, #a-d     16.00 16.00

**Souvenir Sheet**

African Openbill Stork A976

No. 3312 — Various photographs of stork: a, $200. b, $300. c, $400.

**2019, Mar. 11**    **Litho.**    **Perf. 14**
3312 A976   Sheet of 3, #a-c   11.00 11.00

Souvenir Sheet

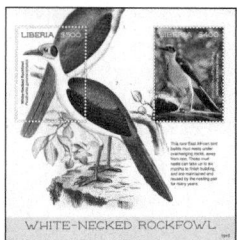

White-necked Rockfowl — A977

No. 3313: a, $400, Photograph. b, $500, Drawing.

**2019, Mar. 11**    **Litho.**    **Perf. 14**
3313 A977   Sheet of 2, #a-b   11.00 11.00

Miniature Sheet

Cuckooshrikes — A978

No. 3314: a, Blue cuckooshrike. b, Ghana cuckooshrike. c, Female red-shouldered cuckooshrike. d, Male red-shouldered cuckooshrike.

**2019, Mar. 13**    **Litho.**    **Perf. 14**
3314 A978 $300 Sheet of 4, #a-d   15.00 15.00

Souvenir Sheets

Spiders A979

Insects A980

No. 3315 — Various photographs of Wasp spider: a, $100. b, $300. c, $500.
No. 3316 — Various photographs of Dung beetle, as shown.
No. 3317 — Various photographs of Giant African mantis: a, $200. b, $300. c, $400.
No. 3318: a, $250, Rainbow bush locust. b, $300, Migratory locust. c, $350, Milkweed grasshopper.
No. 3319, $300: a, African fruit beetle. b, Derby's flower beetle. c, Goliath beetle.

**2019, Mar. 29**    **Litho.**    **Perf. 12**
| | | | | |
|---|---|---|---|---|
| 3315 | A979 | | Sheet of 3, #a-c | 11.00 11.00 |
| 3316 | A980 | $300 | Sheet of 3, #a-c | 11.00 11.00 |
| 3317 | A979 | | Sheet of 3, #a-c | 11.00 11.00 |
| 3318 | A980 | | Sheet of 3, #a-c | 11.00 11.00 |

3319 A980 $300 Sheet of 3, #a-c   11.00 11.00
   Nos. 3315-3319 (5)   55.00 55.00

Long-beaked Common Dolphin — A981

No. 3320: a, $100, Dolphin and fish. b, $100, Two dolphins. c, $200, Dolphin at water's surface. d, $200, Dolphin and fish, diff. e, $300, Dolphin and tail fin of other dolphin. f, $300, Dolphin, diff.
$800, Dolphin and Pomarine jaeger, horiz.

**2019, Apr. 8**    **Litho.**    **Perf. 14**
3320 A981   Sheet of 6, #a-f   14.00 14.00
**Souvenir Sheet**
3321 A981 $800 multi   9.50 9.50
No. 3321 contains one 80x30mm stamp.

Piapiacs A982

No. 3322: a, $250, Piapiac on branch. b, $300, Two piapiacs. c, $350, Piapiac on ground.
$800, Piapiac on animal's back.

**2019, Apr. 18**    **Litho.**    **Perf. 12**
3322 A982   Sheet of 3, #a-c   10.50 10.50
**Souvenir Sheet**
     **Perf.**
3323 A982 $800 multi   9.50 9.50
No. 3323 contains one 33x43mm stamp.

African Buffalo A983

No. 3324: a, $150, Head of buffalo. b, $250, Buffalo and cattle egrets. c, $350, Herd. d, $450, Buffalo, diff.
$800, Buffalo, diff.

**2019, Apr. 19**    **Litho.**    **Perf. 12**
3324 A983   Sheet of 4, #a-d   14.00 14.00
**Souvenir Sheet**
     **Perf. 12½**
3325 A983 $800 multi   9.50 9.50
No. 3325 contains one 51x38mm stamp.

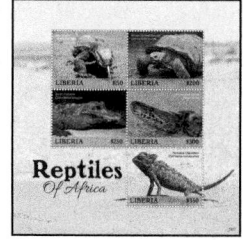

Reptiles A984

No. 3326: a, $150, Nile monitor. b, $200, African spurred tortoise. c, $250, Dwarf crocodile. d, $300, African rock python. e, $350, Namaqua chameleon.
$800, Nile crocodile.

**2019, Apr. 24**    **Litho.**    **Perf. 14**
3326 A984   Sheet of 5, #a-e   15.00 15.00
**Souvenir Sheet**
3327 A984 $800 multi   9.50 9.50
No. 3327 contains one 80x30mm stamp.

Chimpanzees — A985

No. 3328: a, $150, Head of Common chimpanzee. b, $250, Adult and juvenile Eastern chimpanzees. c, $350, Three Common chimpanzees. d, $450, Head of Eastern chimpanzee.
No. 3329, $500: a, Common chimpanzee. b, Head of Eastern chimpanzee, diff.

**2019, May 1**    **Litho.**    **Perf. 12**
3228 A985   Sheet of 4, #a-d   14.00 14.00
**Souvenir Sheet**
     **Perf. 14**
3329 A985 $500 Sheet of 2, #a-b   12.00 12.00

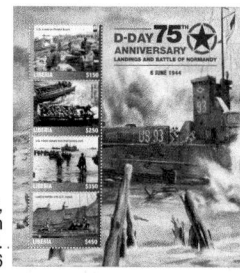

D-Day, 75th Anniv. A986

No. 3330: a, $150, U.S. troops on Omaha Beach. b, $250, U.S. troops in landing craft. c, $350, U.S. troops debark from their landing craft. d, $450, Loading bombs onto U.S. vessel.
$750, The Tough Beach, by Dwight Shepler.

**2019, May 29**    **Litho.**    **Perf. 12**
3330 A986   Sheet of 4, #a-d   12.50 12.50
**Souvenir Sheet**
     **Perf. 14**
3331 A986 $750 multi   8.00 8.00

Guinea Turaco A987

No. 3332: a, $200, One Guinea turaco. b, $300, Two Guinea turacos. c, $400, One Guinea turaco, diff.
$800, Head of Gunea turaco, vert.

**2019, June 8**    **Litho.**    **Perf. 12**
3332 A987   Sheet of 3, #a-c   9.25 9.25
**Souvenir Sheet**
     **Perf.**
3333 A987 $800 multi   8.25 8.25
No. 3333 contains one 33x43mm oval stamp.

Slender Mongoose — A988

No. 3334 — Various photographs of mongooses: a, $150. b, $250. c, $350. d, $450.
No. 3335 — Mongoose: a, To left of dirt mound. b, To right of dirt mound.

**2019, June 8**    **Litho.**    **Perf. 14**
3334 A988   Sheet of 4, #a-d   12.50 12.50
**Souvenir Sheet**
     **Perf. 12**
3335 A988 $500 Sheet of 2, #a-b   10.50 10.50

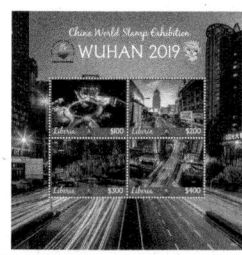

China 2019 World Stamp Exhibition, Wuhan — A989

No. 3336 — Various photographs of Wuhan: a, $100. b, $200. c, $300. d, $400.
$500, Pagoda, vert.

**2019, June 10**    **Litho.**    **Perf. 14**
3336 A989   Sheet of 4, #a-d   10.50 10.50
**Souvenir Sheet**
     **Perf. 12½**
3337 A989 $500 multi   5.25 5.25
No. 3337 contains one 38x51mm stamp.

Miniature Sheet

Birth of Archie Mountbatten-Windsor — A990

No. 3338: a, $200, King George VI, Queen Mary and infant Princess Elizabeth. b, $200, Prince Charles, Princess Diana and infant Prince Harry. c, $400, Duke and Duchess of Cambridge with infant Prince George. d, $400, Duke and Duchess of Sussex with infant Archie Mountbatten-Windsor.

**2019, June 29**    **Litho.**    **Perf. 14**
3338 A990   Sheet of 4, #a-d   12.50 12.50

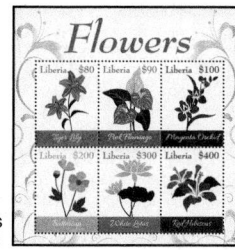

Flowers A991

No. 3339: a, $80, Tiger lily. b, $90, Pink flamingo. c, $100, Magenta orchid. d, $200, Buttercup. e, $300, White lotus. f, $400, Red hibiscus.
No. 3340: a, $100, Pink daisy. b, $200, White tulip. c, $300, Morning glory. d, $400, Orange rose.

**2019, Sept. 29 Litho. Perf. 12**
3339 A991 Sheet of 6, #a-f 11.50 11.50
**Souvenir Sheet**
**Perf. 14**
3340 A991 Sheet of 4, #a-d 9.75 9.75

Hornbills
A992

No. 3341: a, $200, Black-casqued hornbill. b, $300, Grey-checkered hornbill. c, $400, White-crested hornbill.
No. 3342: $800, African grey hornbill, vert.

**2019, Sept. 29 Litho. Perf. 14**
3341 A992 Sheet of 3, #a-c 8.75 8.75
**Souvenir Sheet**
**Perf. 14**
3342 A992 $800 multi 7.75 7.75
No. 3342 contains one 38x51mm stamp.

A993

No. 3343, $200 — Minerals: a, Galena ore. b, Ruby. c, Quarts on pyrite. d, Petalite. e, Malachite. f, Sapphire.
No. 3344, $200 — Monkeys: a, Mandrillus sphinx. b, Nasalis larvatus. c, Macac silenus. d, Macaca fuscata. e, Saguinus oedipus. f, Saimiri sciureus.
No. 3345, $200 — Birds of Liberia: a, Coracias cyanogaster. b, Corythornis cristatus. c, Otus sengalensis. d, Numida meleagris. e, Corythaeola cristata. f, Psittacula krameri.
No. 3346, $200 — Cats: a, Persian. b, American shorthair. c, Sphynx. d, Turkish angora. e, Bengal. f, Somali.
No. 3347, $200 — Mushrooms and Owls: a, Boletus edulis and Strix varia. b, Athene cunicularia and Cantharellus cibarius. c, Lentinula edodes and Tyto alba. d, Amanita virosa and Asio otus. e, Strix aluco and Hypsizygus tessellatus. f, Morchella esculenta and Asio flammeus.
No. 3348, $200 — Orchids: a, Dendrobium speciosum. b, Cymbidium Enzan Knuckle "Pink Puma". c, Calypso bulbosa. d, Serapias lingua. e, Rhyncholaeliocattleya Vasin "Yen Jitt". f, Platanthera chlorantha.
No. 3349, $1200, Fluorite. No. 3350, $1200, Macaca mulatta. No. 3351, $1200, Haliaeetus vocifer. No. 3352, $1200, Selkirk Rex. No. 3353, $1200, Lactarius deliciosus and Strix varia. No. 3354, $1200, Cypripedium calceolus.

**2020, Jan. 6 Litho. Perf. 13x13¼**
**Sheets of 6 # a-f**
3343-3348 A993 Set of 6 75.00 75.00
**Souvenir Sheets**
3349-3354 A993 Set of 6 75.00 75.00

A994

No. 3355, $200 — Dogs: a, Bernese mountain dog. b, Pug. c, Weimaraner. d, Rhodesian ridgeback. e, English bulldog. f, Beagle.
No. 3356, $200 — Marine life of Liberia: a, Aetobatus narinari. b, Orcinus orca. c, Megaptera novaeangliae. d, Physeter macrocephalus. e, Stenella longirostris. f, Chelonia mydas.

No. 3357, $200 — Crocodiles: a, Crocodylus siamensis. b, Melanosuchus niger. c, Gavialis gangeticus; d, Crocodylus niloticus. e, Crocodylus palustris. f, Crocodylus acutus.
No. 3358, $200 — Leopards: a, Panthera pardus in tree. b, Adult with cub. c, Standing to left. d, Standing to right. e, Facing forward. f, Laying down.
No. 3359, $200 — Elephants: a, Loxodonta Africana adult and baby. b, Spraying water. c, Facing right. d, Facing left. e, Facing forward. f, Two adults.
No. 3360, $200 — Dinosaurs: a, Einiosaurus procurvicornis. b, Parasaurolophus walker. c, Apatosaurus ajax. d, Stegosaurus stenops. e, Coelurus bauri. f, Pachycephalosaurus wyomingensis.
No. 3361, $200 — Butterflies: a, Gonepteryx rhamni. b, Nymphalis antiopa. c, Polyommatus bellargus. d, Melanargia galathea. e, Pieris napi. f, Anthocharis cardamines.
No. 3362, $1200, Golden retriever. No. 3363, $1200, Makaira nigricans. No. 3364, $1200, Crocodylus niloticus. No. 3365, $1200, Panthera pardus. No. 3366, $1200, Loxodonta Africana. No. 3367, $1200, Tyrannosaurus rex. No. 3368, $1200, Apatura iris.

**2020, Jan. 6 Litho. Perf. 13x13¼**
**Sheets of 6 # a-f**
3355-3361 A994 Set of 7 90.00 90.00
**Souvenir Sheets**
3362-3368 A994 Set of 7 90.00 90.00

A995

No. 3369: Year of the Rat with rat in 50 different poses.

**2020, Jan. 6 Litho. Perf. 13x13½**
3369 A995 $100 Sheet of 50, 55.00 55.00
#a-ax

A996

A997

A998

Personalized Stamps — A999

**2020, Jan. 6 Litho. Perf. 13x13¼**
**Liberian Flag**
3370 A996 $210 red & dk bl 2.25 2.25
**"Republique of Liberia"**
3371 A997 $210 red & dk bl 2.25 2.25
**Green Panel with White Star**
3372 A998 $210 grn 2.25 2.25
**"Liberia" with Red Star**
3373 A999 $210 dk bl & red 2.25 2.25
Nos. 3370-3373 were each printed in sheets of 24 that could be personalized. A generic image showing Pope John Paul II was made available. Values are for stamps with or without printed vignette.

Penny Black, 180th Anniv. — A1000

**Litho. With Foil Application**

**2020, Mar 26 Perf. 13½x13**
3374 A1000 $250 gold & multi 2.50 2.50
**Souvenir Sheet**
**Perf. 13x13½**
3375 A1000 $1300 gold & mul- 13.00 13.00
ti
No. 3374 was printed in sheets of 6.

A1001

A1002

No. 3376, $300 — Elvis Presley (1935-77): a, With Frank Sinatra. b, With pink 1955 Cadillac. c, With American flag. d, Under spotlight.
No. 3377, $300 — Queen (musical group), 50th anniv.: a, Freddie Mercury. b, Brian May. c, John Deacon. d, Roger Taylor.
No. 3378, $300 — Nelson Mandela's release from prison, 30th anniv.: a, Facing left. b, At Nobel prize ceremony. c, Waving flag. d, Facing right.
No. 3379, $300 — Rabindranath Tagore (1861-1941), writer: a, With Mahatma Gandhi. b, And Nobel Prize in Literature. c, Holding book. d, With Albert Einstein.
No. 3380, $300 — Albert Einstein (1878-1955), physicist: a, Smoking pipe. b, Equation on paper. c, With medal for Nobel Prize in Physics. d, With signature.
No. 3381, $300 — Jules Verne (1828-1905), writer of: a, In Search of the Castaways. b, Around the Moon. c, The Archipelago on Fire. d, Twenty Thousand Leagues Under the Sea.
No. 3382, $300 — Boris Pasternak (1890-1960), writer: a, Portrait with pen nib. b, With medal for Nobel Prize in Literature, holding book. c, With Nobel medal, notepad and pen. d, As young man.
No. 3383, $300 — High-speed trains: a, E6 Series Shinkansen. b, British Rail Class 801. c, ICE 4. d, RENFE Class 490.
No. 3384, $300 — African trains: a, Locomotive CDD3B1. b, South African Class 5 4-6-2. c, Class 15A (4-6-4+4-6-4). d, EMD G22C series.
No. 3385, $300 — Concorde: a, Concorde Air France. b, Beatrice Vialle, the first French female pilot on a supersonic airliner. c, Mike Bannister, the chief pilot of British Airways Concorde fleet. d, Barbara Harmer, the first qualified female Concorde pilot.
No. 3386, $300 — Airbus A380: a, A380 over Dubai. b, British Airways A380. c, A380 plus. d, Gray livery A380 (no markings on airplane).
No. 3387, $300 — Fire engines: a, Yankee-Walter PLF 6000. b, IFA G5 TLF 15 fire truck. c, Scania R480 CB. d, Mercedes-Benz L 1113.
No. 3388, $300 — Special transport: a, HMMWV M997. b, Renault Midlum security and public order vehicle. c, Ford F150 Raptor police vehicle. d, Ford E-450 ambulance.
No. 3389, $300 — Extinct species: a, Purgatorius unio. b, Equus scotti. c, Entelodon magnus. d, Deinotherium giganteum.
No. 3390, $600 — Presley: a, With American flag, diff. b, At microphone.
No. 3391, $600 — Queen: a, Entire band. b, Mercury, diff.
No. 3392, $600 — Mandela: a, Like #3378a. b, Africa map and child.
No. 3393, $600 — Tagore: a, With medal for Nobel Prize in Literature, diff. b, Like #3379a.
No. 3394, $600 — Einstein: a, In front of chalkboard. b, And Relativity equation.
No. 3395, $600 — Verne: a, Portrait and signature. b, The Chase of the Golden Meteor.
No. 3396, $600 — Pasternak: a, With Nobel medal and books. b, Like #3382a.
No. 3397, $600 — High-speed trains: a, ED250. b, H5 Series Shinkansen.
No. 3398, $600 — African trains: a, South African Class 25NC 4-8-4. b, South African Class B 0-6-4T.
No. 3399, $600 — Concorde: a, Like #3385d. b, British Airways Concorde.
No. 3400, $600 — Airbus A380: a, Lufthansa A380. b, A380, diff.
No. 3401, $600 — Fire engines: a, Ford C Tanker. b, KAMAZ 43502 Fire Truck.

No. 3402, $600 — Special transport: a, Eurocopter AS 365 N2 Dauphin. b, KATMERCILER riot control vehicle.
No. 3403, $600 — Extinct species: a, Kaprosuchus saharicus. b, Carcharocles megalodon.

**2020, Mar. 26 Litho. Perf. 13x13½**
**Sheets of 4 # a-d, + Central Label**
3376-3389 A1001 Set of 14 170.00 170.00
**Souvenir Sheets**
3390-3403 A1002 Set of 14 170.00 170.00

A1003

No. 3404, $300 — Carassius auratus goldfish: a, With blue in background. b, Swimming up. c, White and orange fish. d, Swimming down.
No. 3405, $300 — Tulips and Windmill at: a, Zaanse Schans, Netherlands. b, Bremen, Germany. c, Valensole, France. d, Sanok, Poland.
No. 3406, $300 — Critically endangered species: a, Panthera pardus orientalis. b, Eretmochelys imbricata. c, Elephas maximus sumatranus. d, Propithecus diadema.
No. 3407, $300 — Dolphins: a, Lagenorhynchus obscurus. b, Cephalorhynchus commersonii. c, Grampus griseus. d, Stenella longirostris.
No. 3408, $300 — Lighthouses: a, Lindesnes Lighthouse, Norway. b, Brockton Point Lighthouse, Canada. c, Chroicocephalus ridibundus and Cape Horn Lighthouse, Chile. d, Alnes Lighthouse, Norway.
No. 3409, $300 — Turtles: a, Chelonoidis carbonaria. b, Chelonia mydas. c, Centrochelys sulcate. d, Stigmochelys pardalis.
No. 3410, $300 — Snakes: a, Protobothrops jerdonii. b, Vipera seoanei. c, Vipera berus. d, Eryx johni.
No. 3411, $300 — Parrots: a, Ara macao. b, Ara militaris. c, Aratinga solstitialis. d, Myiopsitta monachus.
No. 3412, $300 — Rare birds: a, Amazilia luciae and Neophema chrysogaster. b, Leucopsar Rothschildi. c, Mergus squamatus. d, Strigops habroptilus.
No. 3413, $300 — Rare birds: a, Pharomachrus mocinno. b, Crax rubra. c, Batrachostomus moniliger. d, Aix galericulata.
No. 3414, $300 — Bees: a, Apis mellifera. b, Bombus affinis. c, Bombus terrestris. d, Xylocopa virginica.
No. 3415, $300 — Beetles: a, Leptinotarsa decemlineata. b, Lygistopterus sanguineus. c, Anoplotrupes stercorosus. d, Cetonia aurata.
No. 3416, $300 — Big cats: a, Panthera uncia. b, Panthera onca. c, Panthera tigris. d, Panthera pardus.
No. 3417, $300 — Giraffes: a, Giraffa camelopardalis giraffa. b, Giraffa camelopardalis peralta. c, Giraffa camelopardalis camelopardalis. d, Giraffa camelopardalis tippelskirchi.
No. 3418, $300 — Arctic Ocean animals: a, Sterna paradisaea. b, Pusa hispida. c, Vulpes lagopus. d, Monodon monoceros.
No. 3419, $600 — Goldfish: a, Orange and white fish, diff. b, Orange, white and black fish.
No. 3420, $600 — Tulips and Windmill at: a, Keukenhof, Lisse, South Holland. b, Sibiu, Transylvania, Romania.
No. 3421, $600 — Critically Endangered Species: a, Diceros bicornis. b, Alcedo euryzona.
No. 3422, $600 — Dolphins: a, Stenella frontalis. b, Tursiops truncatus.
No. 3423, $600 — Lighthouses: a, Sterna paradisaea and Tranoy Lighthouse, Norway. b, Stercorarius parasiticus and Kermorvan Lighthouse, France.
No. 3424, $600 — Turtles: a, Chelonia mydas, diff. b, Testudo horsfieldii.
No. 3425, $600 — Snakes: a, Boa constrictor. b, Python bivittatus.
No. 3426, $600 — Parrots: a, Melopsittacus undulatus. b, Eolophus roseicapilla.
No. 3427, $600 — Rare birds: a, Geronticus eremita. b, Porphyrio hochstetteri.
No. 3428, $600 — Rare birds: a, Rupicola peruvianus peruvianus. b, Eumomota superciliosa.
No. 3429, $600 — Bees: a, Thyreus nitidulus. b, Andrena cineraria.
No. 3430, $600 — Beetles: a, Eupatorus gracilicornis. b, Coccinella septempunctata.
No. 3431, $600 — Big cats: a, Panthera leo. b, Panthera tigris altaica.
No. 3432, $600 — Giraffes: a, Giraffa camelopardalis reticulata. b, Giraffa camelopardalis angolensis.
No. 3433, $600 — Arctic Ocean animals: a, Fratercula arctica. b, Odobenus rosmarus.

**2020, Mar. 26 Litho. *Perf. 13x13½***
**Sheets of 4 # a-d, + Central Label**
3404-3418 A1003 Set of 15 180.00 180.00
**Souvenir Sheets**
3419-3433 A1003 Set of 15 180.00 180.00

Ludwig van Beethoven (1770-1827),
Composer — A1004

**2020, June 28 Litho. *Perf. 13½x13½***
3434 A1004 $300 multi + label 2.50 2.50

H.H. Dorje Chang
Buddha III,
Religious
Leader — A1005

**2020, June 28 Litho. *Perf. 13x13½***
3435 A1005 $100 multi 1.00 1.00
No. 3435 was printed in sheets of 6.

Fighting the Coronavirus
Pandemic — A1006

No. 3436 — Various healthcare workers,
patients and family members, as shown.

**2020, June 28 Litho. *Perf. 13x13½***
3436 A1006 $120 Sheet of 16,
    #a-p 19.50 19.50

The Penny Black Against COVID-
19 — A1007

No. 3437 — Penny Black stamp with various
protective face masks, as shown.

**2020, June 28 Litho. *Perf. 13½x13***
3437 A1007 $200 Sheet of 6,
    #a-f 12.00 12.00

Stop COVID-19 Novel
Coronavirus — A1008

No. 3438 — Various depictions of
coronavirus, as shown.
  $1200, Coronavirus, diff.

**2020, June 28 Litho. *Perf.***
3438 A1008 $300 Sheet of 4,
    #a-d 12.00 12.00
**Souvenir Sheet**
3439 A1008 $1200 multi 12.00 12.00

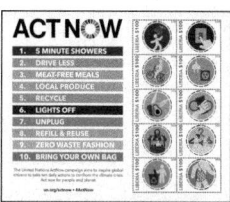

United Nations Act Now
Campaign — A1009

No. 3440: a, Five-minute showers. b, Lights
off. c, Drive less. d, Unplug. e, Meat-free
meals. f, Refill and reuse. g, Local produce. h,
Zero-waste fashion. i, Recycle. j, Bring your
own bag.

***Perf. 13¼x13½***
**2020, June 28 Litho.**
3440 A1009 $100 Sheet of 10,
    #a-j 10.00 10.00

Great Britain's
Withdrawal From the
European
Union — A1010

Nos. 3441a-3441-bx: Great Britain Penny
Black with different letters. Nos. 3441by-
3441cv, Great Britain Penny Red with different
letters.

**2020, June 28 Litho. *Perf. 13½x13***
3441      Sheet of 100, #a-cv 1.20 1.20
  *a.-cv.* A1010 $1.20 Any single .25 .25

Marilyn Monroe
A1012

No. 3442, $200 — Towards the Year of the
Ox: a-f, Ox in various poses, as shown.
No. 3443, $200 — Butterflies: a, Nymphalis
antiopa. b, Aglais io. c, Eurema nicippe. d,
Argynnis pandora. e, Parnassius apollo. f,
Castalius rosimon.
No. 3444, $200 — Paintings by Peter Paul
Rubens (1577-1640): a, Old Woman and Boy
with Candles. b, The Battle of the Amazons. c,
Self-portrait. d, The Tiger Hunt. e, Portrait of
Alatheia Talbot, Countess of Arundel. f, Daniel
in the Lion's Den.
No. 3445, $200 — Mushrooms: a, Flammu-
lina velutipes. b, Morchella esculenta. c,
Melolontha melolontha and Fistulina hepatica.
d, Arion vulgaris and Cerioporus squamosus.
e, Flammulina velutipes. f, Omocestus viridu-
lus and Lentinula edodes.
No. 3446, $1200, Ox, diff. No. 3447, $1200,
Siproeta stelenes. No. 3448, $1200, The Vir-
gin and Child in a Painting Surrounded by Fruit
and Flowers, by Rubens. No. 3449, $1200,
Coccinella septempunctata and Boletus
edulis.

**2020, June 28 Litho. *Perf. 13x13½***
**Sheets of 6 # a-f**
3442-3445 A1011 Set of 4 48.00 48.00
**Souvenir Sheets**
3446-3449 A1011 Set of 4 48.00 48.00

No. 3450, $300 — Marilyn Monroe (1926-
62), actress: a, With spotlight in background.
b, Photos looking forward and to left. c, With

bedroom in background. d, With camera, clap-
board and stage.
No. 3451, $300 — Neil Armstrong (1930-
2012), first man on Moon: a, Apollo 11 Com-
mand and Service Module. b, Armstrong and
Apollo 11 patch. c, Armstrong in space suits.
d, Gemini 8 spacecraft and patch.
No. 3452, $300 — St. John Paul II (1920-
2005): a, Holding crucifix, wearing miter. b,
With Pope Francis. c, With Mother Teresa. d,
Wearing miter, giving blessing.
No. 3453, $300 — Fire engines: a, Isuzu
FTR 900. b, Scania P320 4x2 Pumper. c,
Scania 94D 260. d, Hino 500.
No. 3454, $300 — Steam trains: a, Ja 1271.
b, VSM 50 3654-6. c, C17 Class No. 974. d,
E&P 4.
No. 3455, $300 — The Launch of SpaceX
Demo-2: a, Dragon 2. b, Astronauts Robert L.
Behnken and Douglas G. Hurley and Falcon 9
rocket, May 30, 2020. c, Elon Musk and Falcon
9 over Scripps Pier at La Jolla shores. d, Fal-
con 9 rocket with SpaceX Demo-2.
No. 3456, $300 — Princess Diana: a, With
crowd in background. b, Wearing glasses. c,
Wearing bridal veil. d, Holding Prince William.
No. 3457, $1200, Monroe, clapboard and
film reel. No. 3458, $1200, Armstrong and
footprint on Moon. No. 3459, $1200, St. John
Paul II, diff. No. 3460, $1200, Isuzu FVZ. No.
3461, $1200, LNER Class A3 4472 Flying
Scotsman. No. 3462, $1200, Falcon 9 rocket.
No. 3463, $1200, Princess Diana wearing hat.

**2020, June 28 Litho. *Perf. 13½***
**Sheets of 4 # a-d**
3450-3456 A1012 Set of 7 42.00 42.00
**Souvenir Sheets**
3457-3463 A1012 Set of 7 42.00 42.00

A1013

Worldwide Fund for Nature Stamps
From Countries Beginning With
"R" — A1014

No. 3464 — Stamp from: a, Romania, from
1984. b, Rwanda, from 1985. c, Russia, from
1993. d, Romania, from 1994. e, Russia, from
2004. f, Romania, from 2006.
No. 3465, $330, Romania, from 2006. No.
3466, $330, Romania, from 1994. No. 3467,
$330, Russia, from 1993. No. 3468, $330,
Rwanda, from 1985. No. 3469, $330, Russia,
from 2004, vert. No. 3470, $330, Romania,
from 1984, vert.

***Perf. 13¼x13½***
**2020, June 28 Litho.**
3464 A1013 $225 Sheet of 6,
    # a-f 13.50 13.50
**Souvenir Sheets**
***Perf. 13x13½, 13½x13 (#3469, 3470)***
3465-3470 A1014 Set of 6 19.50 19.50

A1015

A1016

A1017

A1018

Oxen From "Five
Oxen," Painting
by Han Huang
(723-87) — A1019

Entire "Five Oxen" Painting
A1020

No. 3476: a, Three oxen. b, Two oxen.

**2020, Oct. 26 Litho. *Perf. 13x13¼***
3471 A1015 $3 multi .25 .25
3472 A1016 $3 multi .25 .25
3473 A1017 $3 multi .25 .25
3474 A1018 $3 multi .25 .25
3475 A1019 $3 multi .25 .25
  *a.* Horiz. strip of 5, #3471-3475 .25 .25
3476 A1020 $3 Horiz. pair, #a-b .25 .25
No. 3475a was printed in a sheet containing
four strips. Nos. 3471-3476 were printed in a
sheet containing four each of Nos. 3471-3475
and two No. 3476.

Liquid
Natural
Gas
Tanker
Ship
Maria
Energy
A1021

**2020, Oct. 26 Litho. *Perf. 13x13¼***
3477 A1021 $500 multi 5.50 5.50

International Day
of Family
Remittances
A1022

**2020, Oct. 26 Litho. *Perf. 13x13¼***
3478 A1022 $300 multi 3.25 3.25
**Souvenir Sheet**
3479 A1022 $1200 multi 13.00 13.00
No. 3478 was printed in sheets of 8 + central label.

Souvenir Sheet

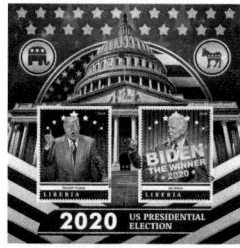

2020 United States Presidential
Candidates — A1023

No. 3480: a, Donald J. Trump. b, Joseph R.
Biden Jr.

**2020, Oct. 26 Litho. *Perf. 13¼x13***
3480 A1023 $600 Sheet of 2,
    #a-b 13.00 13.00

A1024

A1025

Liberian National COVID-19
Response — A1026

No. 3481 — Map of Liberia and: a, Stylized
people around globe. b, Ministry of Health
emblem. c, Ebola virus.
No. 3482: a, Ministry of Health emblem
(39x39mm). b, Ebola virus (39x39mm). c, Stylized people around globe (39x50mm).
$2000, Stylized people around globe, diff.

*Perf. 13x13¼ (#3481), 13¼ (#3482a-
3482b), 13¼x13 (#3482c, 3483)*
**2020, Oct. 26**      Litho.
3481 A1024   $300 Vert. strip
       of 3, #a-c    10.00 10.00
**Souvenir Sheets**
3482 A1025 $1200 Sheet of 3,
       #a-c    40.00 40.00
3483 A1026 $2000 multi    22.00 22.00

COVID-19
Virus and
Soccer Field
A1027

**2020, Oct. 26**   Litho.   *Perf. 13x13¼*
3484 A1027 $2000 multi    22.00 22.00
   *a.*    Souvenir sheet of 1    22.00 22.00
Suspension of sporting events due to
COVID-19 pandemic.

Tropical Forest
Animal
Conservation
A1028

Monitoring of Illegal Logging During
COVID-19 Pandemic — A1029

Designs: No. 3485, $400, Chimpanzee. No.
3486, $400, Timneh parrot. No. 3487, $400,

Slender-snouted crocodile. No. 3488, $400,
Diana monkey. No. 3489, $400, White-bellied
pangolin. No. 3490, $400, Pygmy
hippopotamus.

**2020, Oct. 26**   Litho.   *Perf. 13x13¼*
3485-3490 A1028   Set of 6    26.50 26.50
  *3490a*   Souvenir sheet of 6,
     #3485-3490    26.50 26.50
**Souvenir Sheet**
*Perf. 13¼*
3491 A1029 $2500 multi    27.50 27.50
Nos. 3485-3490 were each printed in sheets
of 8 + central label.

A1030

No. 3492, $300 — Panthera leo: a, Lioness
facing right. b, Lioness and cubs. c, Lion and
tree. d, Male lion facing left.
No. 3493, $300 — Cats: a, American
shorthair cat. b, Maine coon cat. c, Ragdoll
cat. d, British shorthair cat.
No. 3494, $300 — Owls: a, Tyto alba. b,
Strix varia and Amanita muscaria. c, Bubo
scandiacus and Morchella esculenta. d,
Athene cunicularia.
No. 3495, $300 — Bee-eaters: a, Merops
pusillus. b, Merops albicollis. c, Merops viridis.
d, Merops apiaster.
No. 3496, $300 — Bees: a, Andrena fulva.
b, Apis dorsata. c, Andrena cineraria. d,
Xylocopa virginica.
No. 3497, $300 — Shells: a, Spondylus
gaederopus. b, Cypraecassis rufa. c, Turbo
petholatus. d, Phyllonotus pomum.
No. 3498, $300 — Orchids: a, Paphi-
opedilum lawrenceanum. b, Cymbidium
aloifolium. c, Dendrobium kingianum. d, Cat-
tleya labiata.
No. 3499, $300 — Prehistoric humans: a,
Neanderthals hunting a bison. b, Skulls of
Neanderthal and modern human. c, Tools
used by prehistoric humans. d, Homo
neanderthalensis.
No. 3500, $300 — Egyptian monuments: a,
Temple of Edfu. b, Pyramid of Djoser. c, Bent
Pyramid. d, Great Temple of Abu Simbel.
No. 3501, $300 — Fight against malaria: a,
Hand holding blood vial testing positive for
malaria, mosquito. b, Mosquito on arm, blood
cells. c, Man spraying field with insecticide. d,
Red Cross worker carrying sick person,
mosquito.
No. 3502, $300 — Paintings by Vincent van
Gogh (1853-90) (detail): a, Ward in the Hospi-
tal in Arles, 1889. b, The Sower, 1888. c,
Memory of the Garden at Etten, 1888. d, The
Red Vineyard, 1888.
No. 3503, $300 — Art by Alphonse Mucha
(1860-1939) (detail): a, Lefevre Utile, 1903. b,
The Slav Epic No. 4: Tsar Simeon I of Bulga-
ria, 1923. c, The Slav Epic No. 19: The Aboli-
tion of Serfdom in Russia, 1914. d, Flirt
Lefevre Utile, 1899.
No. 3504, $300 — Chess in paintings: a,
The Chess Game, by Ludwig Deutsch (1855-
1935) (detail). b, A Game of Chess, by Henry
Siddons Mowbray (1858-1928). c, The Chess
Players, by Honoré Daumier (1808-79)
(detail). d, Faust and Mephistopheles Playing
Chess, by Friedrich August Moritz Retzsch
(1779-1857).
No. 3505, $300 — Lighthouses: a, Lindes-
nes Lighthouse, Norway. b, Grótta Lighthouse,
Iceland. c, Portofino Lighthouse, Italy. d, Lista
Lighthouse, Norway.
No. 3506, $1200, Panthera leo with its kill.
No. 3507, $1200, Russian blue cat. No. 3508,
$1200, Bubo virginianus. No. 3509, $1200,
Merops apiaster, diff. No. 3510, $1200, Osmia
bicornis. No. 3511, $1200, Nautilus pompilius.
No. 3512, $1200, Rhynchostylis gigantea. No.
3513, $1200, Homo neanderthalensis making
fire. No. 3514, $1200, Karnak Temple Com-
plex. No. 3515, $1200, Doctor treating child
with malaria. No. 3516, $1200, The Night
Café, by van Gogh, 1888. No. 3517, $1200,
Reverie, by Mucha, 1897. No. 3518, $1200,
The Chess Players, by Jacques-Clément Bernard Wagrez (1850-1908). No. 3519, $1200,
Cape Blanco Lighthouse, Oregon.

**2020, Oct. 26**   Litho.   *Perf. 13¼*
**Sheets of 4, #a-d**
3492-3505 A1030 Set of 14 185.00 185.00

**Souvenir Sheets**
*Perf. 13¼x13*
3506-3519 A1030 Set of 14 185.00 185.00
Nos. 3506-3519 each contain one
39x60mm stamp.

A1031

No. 3520, $300 — Princess Diana (1961-
97): a, With roses and Kensington Palace in
background. b, Holding Prince William. c, With
children, holding flowers. d, With Launceston
Place, London in background.
No. 3521, $300 — Meghan, Duchess of
Sussex: a, Standing with Prince Harry, and
scene from television movie *When Sparks Fly.*
b, Wearing hat. c, Walking with Prince Harry,
scene from movie *Horrible Bosses.* d, With
Prince Harry at their wedding, scene from tele-
vision movie *Dater's Handbook.*
No. 3522, $300 — Battle of France, 80th
anniv.: a, French soldiers in World War II, coin
and battle map. b, Soldiers, Arc de Triomphe,
German Sd. Kfz 231 armored car. c, French
SOMUA S35 tank, soldier and battle map. d,
German Panzer IV tank ans soldiers.
No. 3523, $1200, Princess Diana wearing
gown. No. 3524, $1200, Duke and Duchess of
Sussex. No. 3625, $1200, French SOMUA
S35 tank, Gen. Charles de Gaulle 1890-1970),
Eiffel Tower and flag of France.

**2020, Oct. 26**   Litho.   *Perf. 13¼x13*
**Sheets of 4, #a-d**
3520-3522 A1031 Set of 3    40.00 40.00
**Souvenir Sheets**
3523-3525 A1031 Set of 3    40.00 40.00

A1032

No. 3526, $300 — 80th birthday of Pelé: a,
Pelé and soccer player Ivan Vutsov (1939-
2019). b, Pelé dribbling soccer ball, and holding soccer ball. c, Pelé holding soccer ball. d,
Pelé and soccer player Gustavo Peña (1955-
2004).
No. 3527, $300 — Battle of Okinawa, 75th
anniv.: a, Lieutenant General Simon Bolivar
Buckner, Jr. (1886-1945), flag of the United
States, Stinson L-5 Sentinel. b, Map of Oki-
nawa, flag of Japan and Mitsuru Ushijima
(1887-1945), Japanese general. c, Marines on
beach and USS Idaho. d, Mitsubishi Ki-67.
No. 3528, $300 — Flying dinosaurs: a,
Anhanguera blittersdorffi. b, Anurognathus
ammoni. c, Pteranodon longiceps. d,
Microraptor zhaoianus.
No. 3529, $300 — Tall ships: a, Christian
Radich, Norway. b, Juan Sebastián de Elcano,
Spain. c, Royal Clipper, Sweden. d, Amerigo
Vespucci, Italy.
No. 3530, $300 — Steam locomotives: a,
London and South Western Railway N15
Class "King Arthur." b, Metropolitan Railway E
Class O-4-4T No. 1. c, London, Brighton and
South Coast Railway B1 Class 0-4-2. d,
London, Brighton and South Coast Railway
Terrier Class No. 672 "Fenchurch."
No. 3531, $300 — Trains of Norway: a, NSB
Di 4. b, NSB Class 69. c, NSB Class 73. d,
CargoNet CD 312.
No. 3532, $300 — Audi automobiles, 110th
anniv.: a, DKW Junior. b, Audi Quattro B2. c,
Audi 100 LS. d, Auto Union 1000.
No. 3533, $300 — Fire engines: a, 1994
Mercedes-Benz Unimog U1550 L. b, 1995
Montauk, New York Fire Department 9-3-1
Pierce Lance. c, 2013 Ferrara Intruder II. d,
1989 Mercedes-Benz 1222 AF.
No. 3534, $1200, Pelé, soccer stadium flag
of Brazil. No. 3535, $1200, Japanese battle-
ship Yamato. No. 3536, $1200, Pteranodon
longiceps, diff. No. 3537, $1200, Statsraad
Lehmkuhl, Norway. No. 3538, $1200, Fairburn

Class 4 2-6-4T locomotive. No. 3539, $1200,
NSB Class 72. No. 3540, $1200, Auto Union
1000 Sp. No. 3541, $1200, 2005 American
LaFrance1500/750/F fire truck.

**2020, Oct. 26**   Litho.   *Perf. 13x13¼*
**Sheets of 4, #a-d**
3526-3533 A1032   Set of 8    105.00 105.00
**Souvenir Sheets**
3534-3541 A1032   Set of 8    105.00 105.00

Joseph R. Biden Jr., 2020 President-
Elect of the Untied States — A1033

No. 3542 — Background color: a, Blue. b,
Org brown. c, Purple. d, Green.
$1200, President-elect Biden and Pres.
Donald J. Trump.

**2020, Nov. 30**   Litho.   *Perf. 13x13¼*
3542 A1033   $300 Sheet of 4,
     #a-d    15.50 15.50
**Souvenir Sheet**
3543 A1033 $1200 multi    15.50 15.50
No. 3543 contains one 50x39mm stamp.

A1034

No. 3544, $300 — Bruce Lee (1940-1973),
movie actor: a, With leg raised at right. b,
Wearing suit and tie at right. c, Wearing white
t-shirt at left. d, With dragon at left.
No. 3545, $300 — James Dean (1931-55),
movie actor: a, Standing and wearing cowboy
hat at right. b, Sitting on steps at left. c, Wearing blue shirt at left and cowboy hat at right. d,
On motorcycle at right.
No. 3546, $300 — Freemasons: a, Sugar
Ray Robinson (1921-89), boxer. b, Henry Ford
(1863-1947), automobile manufacturer. c,
Alexander Fleming (1881-1955), discoverer of
penicillin. d, Wolfgang Amadeus Mozart
(1756-91), composer.
No. 3547, $300 — Salvation Army, 155th
anniv.: a, Musicians. b, Bell ringer. c, People
at food pantry. d, Salvation Army hat and
cornet.
No. 3548, $300 — Discovery of Lascaux,
France cave paintings, 80th anniv.: a, Cave
painting and discoverers Marcel Ravidat
(1922-95), Georges Agniel (1924-2012), Jacques Marsal (1926-89), and Simon Coencas
(1927-2020). b, Cave painting and Ravidat
holding lantern. c, Cave painting and iron
oxide rock. d, People viewing cave painting.
No. 3549, $300 — Sinking of the RMS
Titanic: a, Titanic under construction. b,
Titanic and its captain, Edward Smith (1850-
1912). c, Titanic sinking. d, Titanic and front
pages of newspapers reporting on the sinking.
No. 3550, $300 — Submarines: a, Jin-class
submarine. b, Seawolf-class submarine. c,
Song-class submarine. d, Collins-class
submarine.
No. 3551, $300 — First Zeppelin flight,
120th anniv.: a, Ferdinand von Zeppelin
(1838-1917), manufacture, Graf Zeppelin in
flight, map of world. b, Signature of Zeppelin,
medal depicting Zeppelin, Zeppelin in flight. c,
LZ127 Graf Zeppelinand airplanes in flight,
medal depicting Zeppelin, ferry boat. d,
Zeppelin, Graf Zeppelin at mooring site,
automobile.
No. 3552, $300 — Max Immelmann (1890-
1916), German World War I flying ace: a,
Immelman, flag and German airplane. b, Airplane and diagram showing Immelmann turn.
c, MG 08 machine gun and Iron Cross. d,
Immelman, medal depicting him, and Fokker
E.III airplane.
No. 3553, $300 — Launch of Lunokhod I
lunar probe, 50th anniv.: a, Lunokhod 1 on
Moon, mission pin. b, Lunokhod 1 control
panel, Russia #3834. c, Lunokhod 1 control
panel, sectional view of wheel hub, Luna 17. d,

Luna, 17, Lunokhod 1 and Lunokhod 1 wristwatch.

No. 3554, $300 — Neil Armstrong (1930-2012), first man on Moon: a, Armstrong in space suit, medals. b, Apollo 11 spacecraft and mission patch. c, Gemini 8 spacecraft and mission patch. d, Armstrong and jet plane.

No. 3555, $300 — 1980 Summer Olympics, Moscow, 40th anniv.: a, Russia #6576I and memorabilia. b, Russia #B104 and shotputter. c, Russia #B66 and weight lifter. d, Romania #2868 and Olympic torch.

No. 3556, $300 — Dinosaurs: a, Ankylosaurus magniventris. b, Spinosaurus aegyptiacus. c, Triceratops prorsus. d, Heterodontosaurus tucki.

No. 3557, $1200, Lee, dragon and film reel. No. 3558, $1200, Dean and his signature. No. 3559, $1200, George Washington (1732-99), first president of United States, and Masonic square and compass. No. 3560, $1200, Salvation Army member and child. No. 3561, $1200, Ravidat and Lascaux cave painting. No. 3562, $1200, Titanic, newspaper front page reporting on the sinking, paperboy selling newspapers. No. 3563, $1200, Vanguard-class submarine. No. 3564, $1200, Map of Europe, North and South America showing path of Zeppelin flight, Zeppelin wearing hat, Zeppelin in flight. No. 3565, $1200, Immelmann, Fokker E.III, Prussian Order of Merit. No. 3566, $1200, Lunokhod 1 crew training, and Lunokhod 1 mission pin. No. 3567, $1200, Armstrong, Apollo 11 crewmembers Edwin "Buzz" Aldrin, Jr. and Michael Collins and flag of the United States. No. 3568, $1200, Russia #B99, hurdler. No. 3569, $1200, Tarbosaurus bataar, Stegosaurus stenops.

**2020, Nov. 30    Litho.    Perf. 13¼**
**Sheets of 4, #a-d**

3544-3556  A1034  Set of 13  200.00  200.00

**Souvenir Sheets**

3557-3569  A1034  Set of 13  200.00  200.00

A1035

No. 3570, $300 — Pandas: a, Ailurus fulgens with head at left. b, Ailuropoda melanoleuca with arm wrapped around tree. c, Ailuropoda melanoleuca facing left. d, Ailurus fulgens with head at right.

No. 3571, $300 — Tigers: a, Panthera tigris tigris, head at right. b, Panthera tigris tigris drinking at water hole. c, Panthera tigris sondaica. d, Panthera tigris tigris in water.

No. 3572, $300 — Sled dogs: a, Four Siberian huskies. b, Two Kugsha dogs. c, Two Siberian huskies leading dog team, musher in background. d, Alaskan huskies.

No. 3573, $300 — Service dogs: a, Newfoundland. b, St. Bernard. c, Golden retriever. d, Labrador retriever.

No. 3574, $300 — Dugong dugon: a, With four striped fish. b, With fish's tail at right. c, With two striped fish. d, With one striped fish.

No. 3575, $300 — Dolphins: a, Stenella longirostris jumping out of water. b, Stenella longirostris above water and arcing toward water. c, Three Tursiops truncatus. d, Two Tursiops truncatus and fish.

No. 3576, $300 — Hummingbirds: a, Calypte costae. b, Calypte anna. c, Archilochus colubris. d, Colibri thalassinus.

No. 3577, $300 — Water birds: a, Gavia arctica. b, Platalea leucorodia. c, Calidris pusilla. d, Fratercula cirrhata.

No. 3578, $300 — Butterflies: a, Pontia protodice. b, Colias philodice. c, Dryas iulia. d, Phyciodes tharos.

No. 3579, $300 — Mushrooms: a, Pholiota flammans and Calliphora vomitoria. b, Entoloma hochstetteri. c, Clitocybe nuda and Apantesis phalerata. d, Gyromitra esculenta.

No. 3580, $300 — Fossils: a, Asteroceras obtusum. b, Carcharocles megalodon tooth. c, Seirocrinus subangularis. d, Athleta spinosa.

No. 3581, $300 — Johann Sebastian Bach (1685-1750), composer: a, Drawing depicting Bach and his signature. b, Statue of Bach, Leipzig, Germany. c, Bach playing organ. d, Bust of Bach.

No. 3582, $300 — Gustav Mahler (1860-1911), composer: a, Mahler looking right, orchestra in background. b, Mahler seated, piano in background. c, Mahler standing, choir in background. d, Mahler looking right, orchestra in background.

No. 3583, $300 — Detail of paintings by Ilya Repin (1844-1930): a, Leo Tolstoy in the Forest, 1891. b, Ivan the Terrible and His Son Ivan on November 16, 1581. c, Sadko, 1876. d, What a Freedom!, 1903.

No. 3584, $300 — Detail of paintings by Claude Monet (1840-1926): a, The Studio Boat, 1874. b, Madame Monet in a Japanese Kimono, 1876. c, Woman with a Parasol — Madame Monet and Her Son, 1875. d, Garden at Sainte-Adresse, 1867.

No. 3585, $300 — Campaign against COVID-19: a, Health worker holding vial. b, Sign for personal distancing. c, People touching glass partition. d, Workers spraying disinfectant.

No. 3586, $300 — International Year of Plant Health: a, Hand watering sprout in test tube. b, Hand touching grain stalk. c, Sprouting plant in ground. d, Hypodermic needle in tomato.

No. 3587, $300 — Lighthouses decorated with Christmas decorations: a, Fort Gratiot Lighthouse, Michigan. b, Nobska Lighthouse, Massachusetts. c, Kleiner Preusse, Germany. d, Sanibel Island light, Florida.

No. 3588, $1200, Ailurus fulgens, horiz. No. 3589, $1200, Ailuropoda melanoleuca, horiz. No. 3590, $1200, Panthera tigris leaping, horiz. No. 3591, $1200, Panthera tigris sondaica, horiz. No. 3592, $1200, Team of Siberian huskies pulling sled, horiz. No. 3593, $1200, Alaskan huskies pulling sled, horiz. No. 3594, $1200, Labrador retriever guide dog, horiz. No. 3595, $1200, German shepherd police dog, horiz. No. 3596, $1200, Dugong dugon an striped fish, horiz. No. 3597, $1200, Dugong dugon alone, horiz. No. 3598, $1200, Delphinus capensis, horiz. No. 3599, $1200, Two Tursiops truncatus, horiz. No. 3600, $1200, Anthracotharax prevostii, horiz. No. 3601, $1200, Calliphlox amethystina, horiz. No. 3602, $1200, Pelecanus erythrorhynchos, horiz. No. 3603, $1200, Actophilornis africanus, horiz. No. 3604, $1200, Plebejus argyrognomon, horiz. No. 3605, $1200, Lycaena hyllus, horiz. No. 3606, $1200, Mycena crocata, horiz. No. 3607, $1200, Laccaria amethystina, horiz. No. 3608, $1200, Latimeria chalumnae fossil, horiz. No. 3609, $1200, Eusthenopteron foordi, horiz. No. 3610, Sculpture of Bach, horiz. No. 3611, $1200, Drawing of Bach, musicians, horiz. No. 3612, $1200, Mahler, silhouettes of musicians, horiz. No. 3613, $1200, Mahler, person writing musical notes, horiz. No. 3614, $1200, Demonstration On October 17, 1905, painting by Repin, 1906-10, horiz. No. 3615, $1200, Self-portrait with Natalia Nordman, painting by Repin, 1903, horiz. No. 3616, $1200, Grand Canal, Venice, painting by Monet, 1908, horiz. No. 3617, $1200, Springtime, painting by Monet, 1872, horiz. No. 3618, $1200, Doctor with stethoscope holding housing symbol, horiz. No. 3619, $1200, Health workers in laboratory, horiz. No. 3620, $1200, Seedling in earth, symbols, horiz. No. 3621, $1200, Technician holding seedling in Petri dish, horiz. No. 3622, $1200, Nubble Lighthouse, Maine, with Christmas lights. No. 3623, $1200, Roanoke Marshes Lighthouse, North Carolina, and boats with Christmas lights, horiz.

**2020, Nov. 30    Litho.    Perf. 13¼**
**Sheets of 4, #a-d**

3570-3587  A1035  Set of 18  275.00  275.00

**Souvenir Sheets**

3588-3623  A1035  Set of 36  550.00  550.00

Nos. 3588-3623 each contain one 48x33mm stamp.

New Year 2021 (Year of the Ox) — A1036

Designs: $300, Two cows. $600, Two oxen.

**2020, Nov. 30    Litho.    Perf. 13¼**
3624-3625  A1036    Set of 2    11.50  11.50

A1037

No. 3626, $300 — Alexander Alekhine (1892-1946), chess player: a, With chess table, clock and king. b, With arms folded, two chess boards. c, With hand touching his head. d, With arms folded behind chess board.

No. 3627, $300 — Wolfgang Amadeus Mozart (1756-91), composer and: a, His signature. b, 2008 Austrian 1-euro coin, 1998 Austrian 5000-schilling banknote. c, Musical score. d, Medal depicting him.

No. 3628, $300 — Antonio Vivaldi (1678-1741), composer: a, Violin and San Giovanni Church, Bragora, Italy, site of Vivaldi's baptism. b, Vivaldi and title page of his oratorio, Juditha Triumphans Devicta Holofernis Barbarie. c, Musical score, piano, violin and medal depicting Vivaldi. d, Musical score and monument to Vivaldi, Vienna.

No. 3629, $300 — First smallpox vaccination by Edward Jenner (1749-1823), 225th anniv.: a, Vial of smallpox vaccine, vaccinated and unvaccinated boys. b, Jenner and smallpox virus. c, Edward Jenner Vaccinating a Boy, painting by Eugène-Ernest Hillemacher (1818-87). d, Child with smallpox, smallpox viuses.

No. 3630, $300 — Heinrich Barth (1821-65), explorer of Africa, and: a, Map of his 1850-55 journeys, Barth's arrival in Timbuktu. b, His signature, map of Africa, people outside of walled town. c, Map of Africa, map of Lac region of Chad, compass. d, His signature, compass, map of his 1850-55 journeys.

No. 3631, $300 — Richard Francis Burton (1821-90), explorer of Africa, and: a, Map of Africa and Lake Tanganyika. b, His signature and map of Africa. c, Map of his journey in central Africa, canoe. d, Map of Africa and Masonic square and compass.

No. 3632, $300 — Fridtjof Nansen (1861-1930), 1922 Nobel peace laureate and explorer, and: a, Nobel medal, map of his 1888 Greenland expedition. b, His whaling ship, the Jason. c, His invention, the Nansen bottle. d, Ship.

No. 3633, $300 — Fire engines: a, E-One Custom Pumper. b, Scania 113H. c, HME 4x4 Custom Pumper. d, HME Custom Rescue Pumper.

No. 3634, $300 — Boeing airplanes: a, Boeing-Stearman Model 75 over Boeing Plant 1. b, Boeing Model 40C and William E. Boeing (1881-1956), airplane manufacturer. c, Boeing 247D and Boeing. d, Boeing P-26 Peashooter over manufacturing plant.

No. 3635, $300 — Commercial air service of the Concorde: a, British Airways Concorde, flag of Great Britain at UL. b, Air France Concorde, Eiffel Tower, flag of France at top. c, British Airways Concorde, Big Ben, flag of Great Britain at UR. d, Air France Concorde, flag of France at bottom.

No. 3636, $300 — Sergei P. Korolev (1907-66), spacecraft designer, and: a, R-7 Semyorka rocket and medal depicting Korolev. b, Yuri Gagarin (1934-68), first man in space. c, Sputnik 2. d, Sputnik 1.

No. 3637, $300 — Launch of Shenzhou 2, 20th anniv: a, Shenzhou 2, flag of People's Republic of China on flagpole, lower star on flag partially visible. b, Shenzhou 2, Jiuquan Satellite Launch Center, flag of People's Republic of China. c, Shenzhou 2, flag of People's Republic of China on flagpole, all stars on flag complete. d, Shenzhou 2, flag of People's Republic of China, no flagpole.

No. 3638, $1200, Alekhine and chess pieces. No. 3639, $1200, Mozart playing harpsichord and musical score. No. 3640, $1200, Vivaldi and musical score. No. 3641, $1200, Edward Jenner Vaccinating His Own Son Against Smallpox, sculpture by Giulio Monteverde (1837-1917). No. 3642, $1200, Barth, his signature, compass, map of Africa, and expedition members and animals. No. 3643, $1200, Burton, maps of Africa and the African Great Lakes region. No. 3644, $1200, Nansen and his wife, Eva (1858-1907), opera singer. No. 3645, $1200, Isuzu FTR fire truck. No. 3646, $1200, Boeing B-1, Frederick Rentschler (1887-1956), aircraft engine designer, and Boeing. No. 3647, $1200, British Airways Concorde and flag of Great Britain made into paper airplane. No. 3648, $1200, Korolev and medal. No. 3649, $1200, Shenzhou 2, flag of People's Republic of China on flagpole, diff.

**2021, Feb. 1    Litho.    Perf. 13¼**
**Sheets of 4, #a-d**

3626-3637  A1037    Set of 12  170.00  170.00

**Souvenir Sheets**

3638-3649  A1037    Set of 12  170.00  170.00

Garnets
A1038

No. 3650 — Garnet from: a, Little Three Mine, California. b, Outokumpu, Finland. c, Vesper Peak, Washington. d, Merelani Hills, Tanzania. e, Asbestos, Quebec, Canada.

No. 3651 — Garnet from: a, Val Malenco, Italy. b, Wrangell Island, Alaska.

**2021, Feb. 1    Litho.    Perf. 13x13¼**
3650  A1038  $200  Sheet of 5,
#a-e, + label    12.00  12.00

**Souvenir Sheet**

3651  A1038  $600  Sheet of 2,
#a-b    14.00  14.00

A1039

No. 3652, $300 — John le Carré (1931-2020), writer of spy novels: a, Le Carré holding umbrella and handwriting manuscript. b, Scene from 1990 film, The Russia House. c, Rover P6 3500 S RHD automobile. d, Le Carré and Brandenburg Gate Quadriga.

No. 3653, $300 — Princess Diana (1961-97): a, Wearing yellow dress. b, Wearing red jacket. c, Wearing white hat. d, Wearing purple blouse.

No. 3654, $300 — Marilyn Monroe (1926-62), actress: a, At seashore. b, Looking out of window. c, With Hollywood sign. d, Sitting on chair with leg raised.

No. 3655, $300 — Clark Gable (1901-60), actor, Masonic square and compass, and movie poster for: a, The Misfits. b, Gone With the Wind. c, Honky Tonk. d, Boom Town.

No. 3656, $300 — African trains: a, South African Class Afro 4000. b, TER Dakar-AIBD. c, South African Class 37-076. d, AML ES44AC.

No. 3657, $300 — Chinese high-speed trains: a, CRH380A. b, China Star DJJ2. c, CRH3. d, CRH2B.

No. 3658, $1200, Le Carré, buildings and palm trees. No. 3659, $1200, Princess Diana wearing blue hat and jacket. No. 3660, $1200, Monroe and Tom Ewell (1909-94), actor. No. 3661, $1200, Gable, movie projector reel, Masonic square and compass. No. 3662, $1200, Lamco 79094 train. No. 3663, $1200, CRH2A-2260.

**2021, Feb. 1    Litho.    Perf. 13x13¼**
**Sheets of 4, #a-d**

3652-3657  A1039    Set of 6    85.00  85.00

**Souvenir Sheets**

3658-3663  A1039    Set of 6    85.00  85.00

A1040

No. 3664, $300 — Cats: a, Scottish Fold cat. b, Don Sphynx cat. c, Abyssinian cat. d, American Shorthair cat.

No. 3665, $300 — Cuckoos: a, Cacomantis pallidus. b, Carpococcyx renauldi. c, Guira guira. d, Cuculus saturatus.

No. 3666, $300 — Warblers: a, Setophaga ruticilla. b, Protonotaria citrea. c, Cardellina pusilla. d, Setophaga pensylvanica.

No. 3667, $300 — Butterflies: a, Tirumala septentrionis. b, Pararge aegeria. c, Phengaris arion. d, Gonepteryx rhamni.

No. 3668, $300 — Fish: a, Balistoides conspicillum. b, Cheilinus fasciatus. c, Haplochromis ahli. d, Zebrasoma flavescens.

No. 3669, $300 — Turtles: a, Trachemys scripta elegans. b, Chelonia mydas. c, Pelodiscus sinensis. d, Chrysemys picta.

No. 3670, $300 — Prehistoric water animals: a, Eurhinosaurus longirostris. b, Ceresiosaurus lanzi. c, Tylosaurus proriger. d, Ichthyosaurus communis.

No. 3671, $300 — Extinct species: a, Thylacinus cynocephalus. b, Gomphotherium angustidens. c, Coelodonta antiquitatis. d, Thylacoleo carnifex.

No. 3672, $300 — Orchids: a, Epidendrum radicans. b, Calena major. c, Habenaria medusa. d, Habenaria rhodocheila.

No. 3673, $300 — Lighthouses: a, Cape Neddick Light, Maine. b, Rokkozaki Lighthouse, Japan. c, Tokarev Lighthouse, Russia. d, Race Point Lighthouse, Massachusetts.

No. 3674, $1200, Scottish Straight cat. No. 3675, $1200, Clamator jacobinus. No. 3676, $1200, Phylloscopus sibilatrix. No. 3677, $1200, Papilio machaon. No. 3678, $1200, Arothron nigropunctatus. No. 3679, $1200, Chelonia mydas, diff. No. 3680, $1200, Hybodus hauffianus. No. 3681, $1200, Smilodon fatalis. No. 3682, $1200, Pecteilis radiata. No. 3683, $1200, Highland Lighthouse, Massachusetts.

## 2021, Feb. 1 — Litho. — Perf. 13x13¼
### Sheets of 4, #a-d
3664-3673 A1040 Set of 10 140.00 140.00
### Souvenir Sheets
3674-3683 A1040 Set of 10 140.00 140.00

New England Wildflowers — A1041

No. 3684, $200: a, Bittersweet nightshade. b, Creeping buttercup. c, Swamp azalea. d, Orange jewelweed. e, Japanese rose. f, American white waterlily.

No. 3685, $200, vert.: a, Black-eyed Susan. b, English plantain. c, Spotted St. John's wort. d, Indian pipe. e, Spotted knapweed. f, Common soapwort.

No. 3686, $1200, Bittersweet nightshade, diff. No. 3687, $1200, Wood sorrel.

## 2021, Feb. 1 — Litho. — Perf. 13¼
### Sheets of 4, #a-d
3684-3685 A1041 Set of 2 28.00 28.00
### Souvenir Sheets
3686-3687 A1041 Set of 2 28.00 28.00

No. 3686 contains one 75x51mm stamp. No. 3687 contains one 51x51mm stamp.

Paintings A1042

No. 3688, $300 — Paintings by Pierre-Auguste Renoir (1841-1919): a, Dance at Le Moulin de la Galette, 1876. b, The Large Bathers, 1884-87. c, The Bathers, 1918-19. d, Luncheon of the Boating Party, 1880-81.

No. 3689, $300 — Paintings by Rembrandt van Rijn (1606-69): a, The Anatomy Lesson of Dr. Nicolaes Tulp, 1632. b, Danae, 1636-43. c, The Blinding of Samson, 1636. d, The Night Watch (detail), 1642.

No. 3690, $1200, Dance in the City, by Renoir, 1883, vert. No. 3691, $1200, The Prodigal Son in the Tavern, by Rembrandt, c. 1637, vert.

## 2021, Feb. 1 — Litho. — Perf. 13x13¼
### Sheets of 4, #a-d
3688-3689 A1042 Set of 2 28.00 28.00
### Souvenir Sheets
### Perf. 13¼x13
3690-3691 A1042 Set of 2 28.00 28.00

COVID-19 Pandemic A1043

COVID-19 virus, world leaders infected with virus, flags and Red Cross emblems: No. 3692, $125, Valery Giscard d'Estaing (1926-2020), ex-President of France, flag of France, French Red Cross emblem. No. 3693, $125, Donald Trump, United States President, flag of United States, American Red Cross emblem. No. 3694, $125, Jair Bolsonaro, President of Brazil, flag of Brazil, Brazilian Red Cross emblem. No. 3695, $125, Silvio Berlusconi, Prime Minister of Italy, flag of Italy, Italian Red Cross emblem. No. 3696, $125, Emmanuel Macron, President of France, flag of France, French Red Cross emblem. No. 3697, $125, Prince Albert II of Monaco, flag of Monaco, Monegasque Red Cross emblem. No. 3698, $125, Boris Johnson, Prime Minister of Great

Britain, flag of Great Britain, British Red Cross emblem. No. 3699, $125, Michel Barnier, European Union Brexit negotiator, Baron David Frost, British Brexit negotiator, flags of Great Britain and European Union, emblem of the European Union Red Cross office. No. 3700, $125, Mikhail Mishustin, Prime Minister of Russia, flag of Russia, Russian Red Cross emblem.

## 2021, Feb. 1 — Litho. — Perf. 12¾x13¼
3692-3700 A1043 Set of 9 13.50 13.50
3700a Souvenir sheet of 9, #3692-3700 13.50 13.50

Nos. 3692-3700 were each printed in sheets of 8 + central label.

---

## SEMI-POSTAL STAMPS

### No. 127 Surcharged in Red

## 1915 — Unwmk. — Perf. 14
B1 A49 2c + 3c on 10c 2.00 3.50
a. Double red surcharge
b. Double blue surcharge
c. Both surcharges double
d. Pair, one without "2c"

### Same Surcharge
### On Official Stamp of 1912
B2 A49 2c + 3c on 10c blk & ultra 2.00 3.50
a. Double surcharge

### Regular Issue of 1918 Surcharged in Black and Red

## 1918 — Perf. 12½, 14
B3 A59 1c + 2c dp grn & blk 1.40 10.50
B4 A60 2c + 2c rose & blk 1.40 10.50
a. Double surch., one inverted
b. Invtd. surch., cross double
c. Invtd. surch., cross omitted 17.00
B5 A61 5c + 2c gray bl & blk .65 3.00
a. Imperf., pair 19.00
B6 A62 10c + 2c dk green 1.25 3.00
a. Inverted surcharge 5.75 27.50
B7 A63 15c + 2c blk & dk grn 5.25 10.50
B8 A64 20c + 2c claret & blk 2.10 8.50
B9 A65 25c + 2c dk grn & grn 4.25 15.00
B10 A66 30c + 2c red vio & blk 10.00 10.50
B11 A67 50c + 2c ultra & blk 8.50 16.00
B12 A68 75c + 2c ol bis & blk 3.75 30.00
B13 A69 $1 + 2c yel brn & bl 6.25 57.50
B14 A70 $2 + 2c lt vio & blk 8.50 80.00
B15 A71 $5 + 2c dk brown 20.00 200.00
Nos. B3-B15 (13) 73.30 455.00

Used values are for postally canceled stamps.

### Nos. 277-279 Surcharged in Red or Blue

## 1941 — Unwmk. — Perf. 12
B16 A107 3c + 2c dk blue (R) 2.25 2.25
B17 A108 5c + 2c dull red brn 2.25 2.25
B18 A109 10c + 2c dk grn (R) 2.25 2.25
Nos. B16-B18 (3) 6.75 6.75

**Catalogue values for unused stamps in this section, from this point to the end of the section, are for Never Hinged items.**

Research SP1

## Lithographed and Engraved
## 1954 — Unwmk. — Perf. 12½
B19 SP1 5c + 5c rose lilac & blk .25 .25
Nos. B19,CB4-CB6 (4) 1.40 1.00

The surtax was for the Liberian Government Hospital. No. B19 exists imperforate.

Remember the African Child — SP2

Designs: 25c + 10c, Village life. 70c + 20c, Mr. Sean feeding children. 75c + 15c, Fleeing conflict. 80c + 20c, Nuns teaching children. No. B24, Nuns killed in Oct. 1992, vert. No. B25, Sean Devereux (1964-93), vert.

## Perf. 13½x14
## 1994, Jan. 6 — Unwmk. — Litho.
B20 SP2 25c +10c multi 1.00 1.00
B21 SP2 70c +20c multi 2.75 2.75
B22 SP2 75c +15c multi 2.75 2.75
B23 SP2 80c +20c multi 3.00 3.00
Nos. B20-B23 (4) 9.50 9.50

### Souvenir Sheets
B24 SP2 $1.50 +50c multi 6.00 6.00
B25 SP2 $1.50 +50c multi 6.00 6.00

Surtax for Sean Devereux Liberian Children's Fund.

Charities SP3

Designs: 25c+10c, No. B30, Natl. map in flag colors, blind man with cane. No. B27, Logo depicting children. No. B28, Blind man crossing street. No. B29, Dr. Herman Gmeiner, children.

## 1995 — Litho. — Perf. 14
B26 SP3 25c +10c multi .80 .80
B27 SP3 80c +20c multi 2.40 2.40
B28 SP3 80c +20c multi 2.40 2.40
B29 SP3 $1.50 +50c multi 5.50 5.50
B30 SP3 $1.50 +50c multi 5.50 5.50
Nos. B26-B30 (5) 16.60 16.60

Christian Assoc. of the Blind, 10th anniv. (Nos. B26, B28, B30). SOS Children's Village (Nos. B27, B29).
Issued: Nos. B27, B29, 4/26; others, 4/28.

George Weah, Soccer Player — SP4

Designs: 50c+20c, In AC Milan strip. 75c+25c, In Liberia Natl. strip. 80c+20c, With 1989 Golden Ball Award. $1.50+50c, Two-time Golden Ball Winner.

## 1995, Oct. 6 — Litho. — Perf. 13x13½
B31 SP4 50c +20c multi 2.00 2.00
B32 SP4 75c +25c multi 2.75 2.75
B33 SP4 80c +20c multi 2.75 2.75
B34 SP4 $1.50 +50c multi 5.25 5.25
a. Souvenir sheet of 1, perf. 13 5.25 5.25
Nos. B31-B34 (4) 12.75 12.75

Issued: No. B34a, 6/24/96. Surcharge for Liberian charities supported by George Weah.

## AIR POST STAMPS

Regular Issue of 1928 Srchd. in Black

## 1936, Feb. 28 — Unwmk. — Perf. 12
C1 A102 6c on 2c violet 250.00 275.00
C2 A102 6c on 3c bis brn 250.00 275.00

### Same Srch. on Official Stamp of 1928

C3 A102 6c on 1c green 250.00 275.00
m. On No. 230 (error) 750.00
Nos. C1-C3 (3) 750.00 825.00

Values are for stamps with disturbed gum. Many counterfeits exist.

Waco Plane AP1

## 1936, Sept. 30 — Engr. — Perf. 14
C3A AP1 1c yellow grn & blk .30 .30
C3B AP1 2c carmine & blk .30 .30
C3C AP1 3c purple & blk .30 .30
C3D AP1 4c orange & blk .30 .30
C3E AP1 5c blue & blk .30 .30
C3F AP1 6c green & blk .30 .30
Nos. C3A-C3F (6) 1.80 1.80

Liberia's 1st air mail service of Feb. 28, 1936.
Nos. C3A-C3F exist in pairs imperf. between (value, $50 each) and in pairs imperf. (value $15 each).

Eagle in Flight — AP2

Trimotor Plane — AP3

Egrets — AP4

Sikorsky Amphibian — AP5

Designs: 3c, 30c, Albatross.

## 1938, Sept. 12 — Photo. — Perf. 12½
C4 AP2 1c green .25 .25
C5 AP3 2c red orange .40 .25
C6 AP3 3c olive green .50 .25
C7 AP4 4c orange .60 .25
C8 AP4 5c brt blue grn 1.00 .25
C9 AP3 10c violet 1.00 .25
C10 AP3 20c magenta 1.25 .25
C11 AP3 30c gray black 2.25 .25
C12 AP2 50c brown 3.00 .25
C13 AP5 $1 blue 5.25 2.50
Nos. C4-C13 (10) 15.50 2.50

For surcharges see Nos. C17-C36, C45-C46, C47-C48, C49-C50.

## Nos. 280-282 Overprinted in Red or Dark Blue

**1941, Feb. 25** — *Perf. 12*
| | | | | |
|---|---|---|---|---|
| **C14** | A107 | 3c dark blue (R) | 2.75 | 2.75 |
| **C15** | A108 | 5c dull red brn (DB) | 2.75 | 2.75 |
| **C16** | A109 | 10c dark green (R) | 2.75 | 2.75 |
| | | *Nos. C14-C16 (3)* | 8.25 | 8.25 |

## Nos. C4-C13 Surcharged in Black

**1941** — *Perf. 12½*
| | | | | |
|---|---|---|---|---|
| **C17** | AP2 | 50c on 1c green | 3,250. | 325.00 |
| **C18** | AP3 | 50c on 2c red org | | 200.00 105.00 |
| **C19** | AP3 | 50c on 3c ol grn | 200.00 | 105.00 |
| **C20** | AP4 | 50c on 4c org | 90.00 | 60.00 |
| **C21** | AP4 | 50c on 5c brt bl grn | 90.00 | 60.00 |
| **C22** | AP3 | 50c on 10c vio | 90.00 | 50.00 |
| **C23** | AP5 | 50c on 20c mag | 2,750. | 70.00 |
| **C24** | AP3 | 50c on 30c gray blk | 75.00 | 40.00 |
| **C25** | AP2 | 50c brown | 75.00 | 40.00 |
| **C26** | AP5 | $1 blue | 90.00 | 40.00 |

Nos. C18, C19, C22, C24, and C26 exist with inverted overprints. Values C18 and C19, $225 each; others, $100 each.

## Nos. C17 to C26 with Additional Overprint

**1942**
| | | | | |
|---|---|---|---|---|
| **C27** | AP2 | 50c on 1c green | 6.75 | 6.75 |
| **C28** | AP3 | 50c on 2c red org | 6.75 | 5.75 |
| **C29** | AP3 | 50c on 3c ol grn | 6.00 | 5.75 |
| **C30** | AP4 | 50c on 4c orange | 4.75 | 6.00 |
| **C31** | AP4 | 50c on 5c brt bl grn | 3.00 | 3.00 |
| **C32** | AP3 | 50c on 10c violet | 4.25 | 4.25 |
| **C33** | AP5 | 50c on 20c mag | 4.25 | 4.25 |
| **C34** | AP3 | 50c on 30c gray blk | 4.75 | 4.75 |
| **C35** | AP2 | 50c brown | 4.75 | 4.75 |
| **C36** | AP5 | $1 blue | 4.25 | 4.25 |
| | | *Nos. C27-C36 (10)* | 49.50 | 49.50 |

Plane and Air Route from United States to South America and Africa — AP6

Plane over House — AP7

**1942-44** — *Engr.* — *Perf. 12*
| | | | | |
|---|---|---|---|---|
| **C37** | AP6 | 10c rose | .25 | .25 |
| **C38** | AP7 | 12c brt ultra ('44) | .25 | .25 |
| **C39** | AP7 | 24c turq grn ('44) | .25 | .25 |
| **C40** | AP6 | 30c brt green | .25 | .25 |
| **C41** | AP6 | 35c red lilac ('44) | .25 | .25 |
| **C42** | AP6 | 50c violet | .25 | .25 |
| **C43** | AP6 | 70c olive gray ('44) | .35 | .25 |
| **C44** | AP6 | $1.40 scarlet ('44) | 1.00 | .45 |
| | | *Nos. C37-C44 (8)* | 2.85 | 2.20 |

## No. C3A-C3C, C5-C8, C12 Srchd. with New Values and Large Dot, Bar or Diagonal Line in Violet, Blue, Black or Violet and Black

No. C45

No. C46

No. C46A

No. C48

No. C48B

No. C49

No. C50

**1944-45** — *Perf. 12½*
| | | | | |
|---|---|---|---|---|
| **C45** | AP3 | 10c on 2c (V+Bk) | 40.00 | 25.00 |
| **C46** | AP4 | 10c on 5c (V+Bk) ('45) | 14.00 | 12.00 |
| **C46A** | AP1 | 30c on 1c (Bk) | 150.00 | 70.00 |
| **C47** | AP3 | 30c on 3c (V) | 165.00 | 65.00 |
| **C48** | AP4 | 30c on 4c (V+Bk) | 14.00 | 12.00 |
| **C48A** | AP1 | 50c on 3c (Bk) | 37.50 | 32.50 |
| **C48B** | AP1 | 70c on 2c (Bk) | 70.00 | 60.00 |
| **C49** | AP3 | $1 on 3c (Bl) | 27.50 | 22.50 |
| **C50** | AP2 | $1 on 50c (V) | 42.50 | 26.50 |
| | | *Nos. C45-C50 (9)* | 560.50 | 325.50 |

These surcharges were handstamped with the possible exception of the large "10 CTS." of No. C46 and the "30 CTS." of No. C48. On No. C47, the new value was created by hand-stamping a small, violet, broken "O" beside the large "3" of the basic stamp.

Surcharges on Nos. C46A, C48A, C48B are found inverted. Values same as normal.

## Roosevelt Type of Regular Issue

**1945, Nov. 26** — *Engr.*
| | | | | |
|---|---|---|---|---|
| **C51** | A116 | 70c brn & blk, *grysh* | 2.25 | 1.40 |

Examples on thick white paper appeared later on the stamp market. Value, $1 unused or used.

## Monrovia Harbor Type

**1947, Jan. 2**
| | | | | |
|---|---|---|---|---|
| **C52** | A117 | 24c brt bluish grn | 1.50 | 1.25 |

## Without Inscription at Top

**1947, May 16**
| | | | | |
|---|---|---|---|---|
| **C53** | A117 | 25c dark carmine | .90 | .45 |

## 1st US Postage Stamps Type

**1947, June 6**
| | | | | |
|---|---|---|---|---|
| **C54** | A118 | 12c green | .25 | .25 |
| **C55** | A118 | 25c brt red violet | .30 | .25 |
| **C56** | A118 | 50c brt blue | .40 | .25 |
| *a.* | | Souv. sheet of 4, #300, C54-C56 | 50.00 | |
| | | Never hinged | 100.00 | |
| | | *Nos. C54-C56 (3)* | .60 | .60 |
| | | Set, never hinged | 2.10 | |

No. C56a exists imperf. Values: hinged $65; never hinged $160.

Matilda Newport Firing Cannon AP11

**1947, Dec. 1** — *Engr. & Photo.*
| | | | | |
|---|---|---|---|---|
| **C57** | AP11 | 25c scar & gray blk | 1.25 | .30 |

See note after No. 304.

Monument to Joseph J. Roberts AP12

Centenary Monument AP14

Design: 25c, Flag of Liberia.

**1947, Dec. 22** — *Engr.*
| | | | | |
|---|---|---|---|---|
| **C58** | AP12 | 12c brick red | .30 | .25 |
| **C59** | AP12 | 25c carmine | .50 | .25 |
| **C60** | AP14 | 50c red brown | .80 | .45 |
| | | *Nos. C58-C60 (3)* | 1.60 | .85 |
| | | Set, never hinged | 6.00 | |

Centenary of independence.

L. I. A. Plane in Flight — AP15

**1948, Aug. 17** — *Perf. 11½*
| | | | | |
|---|---|---|---|---|
| **C61** | AP15 | 25c red | 1.50 | 1.50 |
| **C62** | AP15 | 50c deep blue | 1.00 | 1.00 |
| | | Set, never hinged | 5.00 | |

1st flight of Liberian Intl. Airways, Aug. 17, 1948. Exist imperf.

Map and Citizens AP16

Farm Couple, Arms and Agricultural Products AP17

**1949, Apr. 12** — *Litho.* — *Perf. 11½*
| | | | | |
|---|---|---|---|---|
| **C63** | AP16 | 25c multicolored | .35 | .65 |
| **C64** | AP17 | 25c multicolored | .35 | .65 |
| | | Set, never hinged | 2.00 | |

Nos. C63-C64 exist perf. 12½. Definite information concerning the status of the perf. 12½ set has not reached the editors. The set also exists imperf.

## Type of Regular Issue of 1948-50

Design: William V. S. Tubman.

**1949, July 21** — *Engr.* — *Perf. 12½*
| | | | | |
|---|---|---|---|---|
| **C65** | A128 | 25c blue & black | .60 | .65 |
| | | Never hinged | 1.60 | |

See No. C118.

Sun and Open Book — AP18

**1950, Feb. 14** — *Engr.* — *Perf. 12½*
| | | | | |
|---|---|---|---|---|
| **C66** | AP18 | 25c rose carmine | 1.00 | .50 |
| | | Never hinged | 2.75 | |
| *a.* | | Souv. sheet of 2, #329, C66, imperf. | 1.75 | 1.75 |
| | | Never hinged | 4.75 | |

Campaign for National Literacy.

> Catalogue values for unused stamps in this section, from this point to the end of the section, are for Never Hinged items.

UPU Monument — AP19

**1950, Apr. 21**
| | | | | |
|---|---|---|---|---|
| **C67** | AP19 | 25c orange & vio | 2.75 | 2.75 |
| *a.* | | Souv. sheet of 3, #330-331, C67, imperf. | 24.00 | 24.00 |

UPU, 75th anniv. (in 1949). No. C67 exists imperf.

Map of Monrovia, James Monroe and Ashmun AP20

50c, Jehudi Ashmun, President Tubman & map.

**1952, Apr. 1** — *Perf. 10½*
| | | | | |
|---|---|---|---|---|
| **C68** | AP20 | 25c lilac rose & blk | .25 | .25 |
| **C69** | AP20 | 50c dk blue & car | .70 | .70 |
| *a.* | | Souvenir sheet of 8 | 24.00 | |

Nos. C68-C69 exist imperf. Value about two and one half times that of the perf. set.

Nos. C68-C69 exist with center inverted. Value $50 each.

No. C69a contains one each of Nos. 332 and C68, and types of Nos. 333-337 and C69 with centers in black; imperf.

The 25c exists in colors of the 50c and vice versa. Value, each $8.

Flags of Five Nations AP21

**1952, Dec. 10** — *Perf. 12½*
| | | | | |
|---|---|---|---|---|
| **C70** | AP21 | 25c ultra & carmine | .90 | .65 |
| *a.* | | Souvenir sheet | 2.25 | 2.25 |

Nos. C70 and C70a exist imperforate. Value, No. C70a, imperf., $4.50.

Road Building AP22

Designs: 25c, Ships in Monrovia harbor. 35c, Diesel locomotive. 50c, Free port, Monrovia. 70c, Roberts Field. $1, Wm. V. S. Tubman bridge.

**1953, Aug. 3** — *Litho.*
| | | | | |
|---|---|---|---|---|
| **C71** | AP22 | 12c orange brown | .25 | .25 |
| **C72** | AP22 | 25c lilac rose | .25 | .25 |
| **C73** | AP22 | 35c purple | 1.00 | .25 |
| **C74** | AP22 | 50c orange | 1.00 | .25 |
| **C75** | AP22 | 70c dull green | 1.75 | .25 |
| **C76** | AP22 | $1 blue | 2.25 | 1.00 |
| | | *Nos. C71-C76 (6)* | 6.50 | 2.25 |

Exist imperf. See Nos. C82-C87.

Flags, Emblem and Children AP23

**1954, Sept. 27**    **Size: 51x39mm**
C77 AP23 $5 bl, red, vio bl & blk    40.00 40.00

A reproduction of No. C77, size 63x49mm, was prepared for presentation purposes. Value $35.
Half the proceeds from the sale of No. C77 was given to the UNICEF.

UN Technical Assistance Agencies AP24

Designs: 15c, Printing instruction. 20c, Sawmill maintenance. 25c, Geography class.

**1954, Oct. 25**
C78 AP24 12c black & blue    .25 .25
C79 AP24 15c dk brown & yel    .25 .25
C80 AP24 20c black & yel grn    .25 .25
C81 AP24 25c vio blue & red    .80 .25
     Nos. C78-C81 (4)    1.55 1.00

UN Technical Assistance program.
Nos. C78-C81 exist imperf.

**Type of 1953 Inscribed:**
**"Commemorating Presidential Visit**
**U. S. A.-1954"**

Designs as before.

**1954, Nov. 19**
C82 AP22 12c vermilion    .25 .25
C83 AP22 25c blue    .80 .25
C84 AP22 35c carmine rose    3.50 2.00
C85 AP22 50c rose violet    .95 .30
C86 AP22 70c orange brown    1.25 .55
C87 AP22 $1 dull green    1.90 .80
     Nos. C82-C87 (6)    8.65 4.15

Visit of Pres. William V.S. Tubman to the US. Exist imperforate.

Baseball — AP25

**1955, Jan. 26**    **Litho.**    **Perf. 12½**
C88 AP25 10c shown    .30 .30
C89 AP25 12c Swimming    .30 .30
C90 AP25 25c Running    .30 .30
   a.    Souvenir sheet    18.00 18.00
     Nos. C88-C90 (3)    .90 .90

No. C90a contains 1 each of Nos. 349, C90 with colors transposed. Exists imperf.; same value.

Costus — AP26

Design: 25c, Barteria nigritiana.

**1955, Sept. 28**    **Unwmk.**    **Perf. 12½**
C91 AP26 20c violet, grn & yel    .40 .25
C92 AP26 25c green, red & yel    .40 .25

UN Emblem AP27      UN Charter AP28

15c, General Assembly. 25c, Gabriel L. Dennis signing UN Charter for Liberia.

**1955, Oct. 24**    **Unwmk.**    **Perf. 12**
C93 AP27 10c ultra & red    .25 .25
C94 AP27 15c violet & blk    .25 .25
C95 AP27 25c green & red brn    .60 .25
C96 AP28 50c brick red & grn    1.50 .25
     Nos. C93-C96 (4)    2.60 1.00

10th anniv. of the UN, Oct. 24, 1955.

Rotary International Headquarters, Evanston, Ill. — AP29

Design: 15c, View of Monrovia.

**1955, Dec. 5**    **Litho.**    **Perf. 12½**
C97 AP29 10c deep ultra & red    .25 .25
C98 AP29 15c redsh brn, red & bis    .70 .25

**Souvenir Sheet**
C99 AP29 50c deep ultra & red    1.75 1.75
     Nos. C97-C99 (3)    2.70 2.25

No. C99 design as No. C97, but redrawn and with leaves omitted.
50th anniversary of Rotary International.
Nos. C97-C99 exist without Rotary emblem; No. C97 printed entirely in deep ultramarine; No. C98 with bister impression omitted.

**FIPEX Type of Regular Issue**

10c, New York Coliseum. 12c, Globe inscribed FIPEX. 15c, 50c, Statue of Liberty.

**1956, Apr. 28**    **Unwmk.**    **Perf. 12**
C100 A143 10c rose red & ultra    .25 .25
C101 A143 12c orange & purple    .25 .25
C102 A142 15c aqua & red lilac    .90 .25
     Nos. C100-C102 (3)    1.40 .75

**Souvenir Sheet**
C103 A142 50c lt green & brn    1.75 1.75

Olympic Park, Melbourne AP32

20c, 40c, Map of Australia & Olympic torch.

**1956, Nov. 15**    **Unwmk.**    **Perf. 12**
C104 AP32 12c emerald & vio    .50 .50
C105 AP32 20c multicolored    .50 .50

**Souvenir Sheet**
C106 AP32 40c multicolored    7.50 7.50
     Nos. C104-C106 (3)    8.50 8.50

16th Olympic Games, Melbourne, 11/22-12/8.
Nos. C104-C105 exist imperf.

**Type of Regular Issue, 1957**

12c, 25c, Idlewild airport, NYC. 15c, 50c, Roberts Field, Liberia, plane & Pres. Tubman.

**Lithographed and Engraved**
**1957, May 4**    **Perf. 12**
C107 A146 12c brt grn & dk bl    .25 .25
C108 A146 15c red brn & blk    .25 .25
C109 A146 25c carmine & dk bl    .75 .25
C110 A146 50c lt ultra & blk    1.40 .25
     Nos. C107-C110 (4)    2.65 1.00

**Type of Regular Issue, 1957**

Orphanage and: 15c, Nurse inoculating boy. 35c, The Kamara triplets. 70c, Children and flag.

**1957, Nov. 25**    **Litho.**    **Perf. 12**
C111 A147 15c lt blue & brn    .25 .25
C112 A147 35c maroon & lt gray    1.00 .25

**Souvenir Sheet**
C113 A147 70c ultra & rose car    1.50 1.25
     Nos. C111-C113 (3)    2.75 1.75

**Type of Regular Issue, 1958**

10c, Italian flag & Colosseum. #C115, French flag & Arc de Triomphe. #C116, Swiss flag & chalet. #C117, Vatican flag & St. Peter's.

**Engr. and Litho.**
**1958, Jan. 10**    **Perf. 10½**
**Flags in Original Colors**
C114 A148 10c dark gray    .45 .45
C115 A148 15c dp yellow grn    .45 .45
C116 A148 15c ultra    .45 .45
C117 A148 15c purple    .45 .45
     Nos. C114-C117 (4)    1.80 1.80

**Type of Regular Issue, 1948-50**
Design: William V. S. Tubman.

**1958**    **Engr.**    **Perf. 12**
C118 A128 25c lt green & blk    1.25 .90

**Souvenir Sheet**

*Declaration of Human Rights*

Preamble to Declaration of Human Rights — AP33

**1958, Dec. 17**    **Litho.**    **Perf. 12**
C119 AP33 20c blue & red    2.75 2.75

10th anniv. of the signing of the Universal Declaration of Human Rights. Exists imperf.

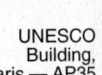

Liberians Reading Proclamation — AP34

**1959, Apr. 15**        **Unwmk.**
C120 AP34 25c blue & brown    .60 .60

African Freedom Day, Apr. 15.

UNESCO Building, Paris — AP35

**1959, May 1**
C121 AP35 25c ultra & red    .60 .50
   a.    Souvenir sheet    1.75 1.75

Opening of UNESCO Headquarters in Paris, Nov. 3, 1958.

**Lincoln Type of Regular Issue**
**1959, Nov. 20**    **Engr.**    **Perf. 12**
C122 A152 25c emerald & black    .90 .90

For souvenir sheet see No. 386a.

Touré, Tubman and Nkrumah — AP36

**1960, Jan. 27**    **Litho.**    **Unwmk.**
C123 AP36 25c beige, vio bl & blk    .60 .80

See note after No. 387.

**WRY Type of Regular Issue, 1960**
**1960, Apr. 7**      **Perf. 11½**
C124 A154 25c ultra & black    .80 .70
   a.    Souv. sheet of 2, #388, C124, imperf.    3.50 2.75

Map of Africa — AP37

**1960, May 11**      **Perf. 11½**
C125 AP37 25c ultra & brown    .80 .80

See note after No. 389.

**Olympic Games Type of 1960**

Designs: 25c, Javelin thrower and hunter, horiz. 50c, Runner and stadium, horiz.

**1960, Sept. 6**      **Perf. 11½**
C126 A156 25c brown & brt ultra    .90 .70

**Souvenir Sheet**
*Imperf*
C127 A156 50c lilac & brown    3.50 3.50

**Stamp Centenary Type of 1960**
**1960, Dec. 1**    **Litho.**    **Perf. 11½**
C128 A157 25c multicolored    1.00 1.00

**Souvenir Sheet**
C129 A157 50c multicolored    1.75 1.75

No. C129 exists imperf.

Globe, Dove and UN Emblem — AP38

Design: 50c, Globe and dove.

**1961, May 19**    **Unwmk.**    **Perf. 11½**
C130 AP38 25c indigo & red    .50 .50

**Souvenir Sheet**
C131 AP38 50c red brn & emerald    2.25 2.25

Liberia's membership in the UN Security Council.
A second souvenir sheet contains one each of Nos. 395, C130 and the 50c from No. C131, imperf. Size: 133x83mm. Value $8.
No. C130 exists imperf.

Science Class — AP39

Design: 50c, Science class, different design.

**1961, Sept. 8**      **Litho.**
C132 AP39 25c purple & brown    .50 .25

**Souvenir Sheet**
C133 AP39 50c blue & brown    1.75 1.75

15th anniv. of UNESCO.

Joseph J. Roberts and Providence Island — AP40

**1961, Oct. 25**    **Litho.**    **Perf. 11½**
C134 AP40 25c emerald & sepia    .70 .70
   a.    Souvenir sheet of 3    1.75 1.75

150th anniv. of the birth of Joseph J. Roberts, 1st pres. of Liberia.
No. C134a contains three imperf. stamps similar to Nos. 397-398 and C134, but printed in different colors; 5c, emerald & sepia. 10c, orange & sepia. 25c, ultramarine & sepia.

## Scout Type of Regular Issue and

Boy Scout — AP41

**1961, Dec. 4  Unwmk.  Perf. 11½**
C135 AP41 25c emerald & sepia  1.40 1.40

**Souvenir Sheet**

Design: Like No. 399.
C136 A161 35c dull blue & sepia  3.50 3.50
No. C136 exists imperf. Value, $10.

## Dag Hammarskjold Type of 1962
**1962, Feb. 1  Unwmk.  Perf. 12**
C137 A162 25c black & red lilac  .60  .60
**Souvenir Sheet**
*Imperf*
C138 A162 50c black & ultra  1.75 1.75

Malaria
Eradication
Emblem — AP42

**1962, Apr. 7  Perf. 12½**
C139 AP42 25c purple & orange  .60  .50
**Souvenir Sheet**
*Imperf*
C140 AP42 50c dark red & ultra  2.00 1.50

AP43

Design: 12c, 25c, 50c, Pres. Tubman, Statue of Liberty, New York Skyline and Flags of US and Liberia.

**1962, Sept. 17  Litho.  Perf. 11½x12**
C141 AP43 12c multicolored  .25  .25
C142 AP43 25c multicolored  .60  .50
C143 AP43 50c multicolored  1.25  .85
Nos. C141-C143 (3)  2.10 1.60
Pres. Tubman's visit to the US in 1961.

United Nations
Emblem and
Flags — AP44

Design: 50c, UN emblem.

**1962, Oct. 22  Perf. 12x12½**
C144 AP44 25c lt ultra & dk bl  .50  .50
**Souvenir Sheet**
*Imperf*
C145 AP44 50c brt grnsh bl & blk  2.00 1.25
Observance of UN Day, Oct. 24, as a national holiday.

## Building Type of Regular Issue
12c, 70c, Capitol. 50c, Information Service. $1, Treasury Department Building, Monrovia.

**1962-63  Perf. 12x12½, 12 (70c)**
C146 A165 12c brt yel grn & mar  .25  .25
C147 A165 50c orange & ultra  1.20 1.20
C147A A165 70c brt pink & dk bl ('63)  1.60 1.20
C148 A165 $1 sal & blk ('63)  2.40 1.40
Nos. C146-C148 (4)  5.45 4.05

---

"FAO" Emblem and
Globe — AP45

Design: 50c, "FAO" and UN Emblems.

**1963, Mar. 21  Unwmk.  Perf. 12½**
C149 AP45 25c dk green & yel  .65  .50
**Souvenir Sheet**
*Perf. 12*
C150 AP45 50c emerald & ultra  2.00 1.75
FAO "Freedom from Hunger" campaign.

## Type of Regular Issue, 1963
Designs: 25c, Telstar satellite, vert. 50c, Telstar and rocket, vert.

**1963, May 27  Litho.  Perf. 12½**
C151 A167 25c Prus blue & org  .55  .40
**Souvenir Sheet**
*Perf. 12*
C152 A167 50c dp violet & yel  2.50 1.50
No. C152 exists imperf. Value $12.50.

Red Cross —
AP45a

Design: 25c, Red Cross and globe. 50c, Centenary emblem and globe.

**1963, Aug. 26  Unwmk.  Perf. 12**
C153 AP45a 25c purple & red  .40  .40
C154 AP45a 50c deep ultra & red  .70  .70

Map of Africa — AP46

**1963, Oct. 28  Perf. 12½**
C156 AP46 25c red orange & grn  .30  .30
See note after No. 412.

## Olympic Type of Regular Issue
10c, Torch and mountains. 25c, Mountains, horiz. 50c, Torch, background like No. 413.

**1963, Dec. 11  Litho.  Perf. 12½**
C157 A170 10c vio blue & red  .25  .25
C158 A170 25c green & orange  .80  .80
**Souvenir Sheet**
*Perf. 12*
C159 A170 50c gray & red  1.75 1.75
No. C159 exists imperf. Value $12.

## Kennedy Type of Regular Issue, 1964
Designs: 25c, John F. Kennedy, vert. 50c, John F. Kennedy (like No. 414).

**1964, Apr. 6  Unwmk.  Perf. 12½**
C160 A171 25c blk & red lil  .60  .50
**Souvenir Sheet**
*Perf. 12*
C161 A171 50c blk & red lil  1.75 1.40
An imperf. miniature sheet containing one of No. C160 exists. No marginal inscription. Value $10.

## Satellite Type of Regular Issue
**Souvenir Sheet**
Design: Launching rocket separating from booster in space, vert.

**1964, June 22  Litho.**
C162 A172 50c vio bl & red  3.00 3.00
Exists imperf. Value $9.

---

## Olympic Type of Regular Issue
**Souvenir Sheet**
Design: 50c, Runner and Olympic rings.

**1964, Sept. 15  Unwmk.  Perf. 12**
C163 A173 50c grnsh bl & red  3.00 1.25
Exists imperf. Value $6.

## Scout Type of Regular Issue, 1965
Designs: 25c, Liberian flag and fleur-delis. 50c, Globe and Scout emblem.

**1965, Mar. 8  Litho.  Perf. 12½**
C164 A174 25c crimson & ultra  .80  .80
**Souvenir Sheet**
*Perf. 12*
C165 A174 50c yellow & lilac  3.00 3.00
No. C165 exists imperf. Value $7.

## Lincoln Type of Regular Issue
**Souvenir Sheet**
50c, Lincoln and John F. Kennedy, horiz.

**1965, May 3  Unwmk.  Perf. 12**
C166 A175 50c dp plum & lt gray  1.75 1.75
Exists imperf. Value $5.50.

## ICY Type of Regular Issue, 1965
**Souvenir Sheet**

**1965, June 21  Litho.**
C167 A176 50c car rose & brn  1.75 1.75

## ITU Type of Regular Issue, 1965
**1965, Sept. 21  Unwmk.  Perf. 12½**
C168 A177 50c red org & vio bl  .80  .70

## Tubman Type of Regular Issue
25c, Pres. Tubman and coat of arms.

**1965, Nov. 29  Litho.  Perf. 12½**
C169 A178 25c ultra, red & brn  .70  .70
a.   Souv. sheet of 2, #431, C169, imperf.  1.75 1.75

## Churchill Type of Regular Issue
25c, "Angry Lion" portrait by Karsh & Parliament, London. 50c, "Williamsburg Award Dinner" portrait by Karsh & map of Europe.

**1966, Jan. 18  Litho.  Perf. 12½**
C170 A179 25c blk & vio bl  .70  .55
**Souvenir Sheet**
*Perf. 12*
C171 A179 50c blk & red lil  1.75 1.75
No. C171 exists imperf.

## Soccer Type of Regular Issue
**Souvenir Sheet**
Design: 50c, Soccer match in stadium.

**1966, May 3  Litho.  Perf. 11½**
C172 A181 50c ultra & red brn  2.50 2.50
Exists imperf. Value $15.

## Kennedy Type of Regular Issue
25c, UN General Assembly & Pres. Kennedy. 35c, Pres. Kennedy & rocket on launching pad, Cape Kennedy. 40c, Flame on grave at Arlington.

**1966, Aug. 16  Litho.  Perf. 12½**
C173 A182 25c ultra, blk & ocher  .40  .25
C174 A182 35c dk vio bl & pink  .50  .25
**Souvenir Sheet**
*Perf. 11½*
C175 A182 40c dk vio bl & multi  2.00 2.00
No. C175 exists imperf. Value $20.

## Boy Scout Type of Regular Issue
**Souvenir Sheet**
50c, Scout at campfire & vision of moon landing.

**1967, Mar. 23  Litho.  Perf. 12½**
C176 A185 50c brt red lil & scar  4.00 4.00
Exists imperf. Value $8.

## Olympic Type of Regular Issue
**Souvenir Sheet**
Design: 50c, Pre-Hispanic sculpture, serape and Olympic rings, horiz.

**1967, June 20  Litho.  Perf. 12½**
C177 A186 50c vio & car  3.75 1.60
Exists imperf. Value $15.

---

## Winter Olympic Games Type of Regular Issue
**Souvenir Sheet**
Design: 50c, Woman skater.

**1967, Nov. 20  Litho.  Perf. 11½**
C178 A189 50c ver & blk  2.25  .70
Exists imperf. Value $15.

## Human Rights Type of Regular Issue
**Souvenir Sheet**

**1968, Apr. 26  Litho.  Perf. 11½**
C179 A191 80c bl & red  2.50 1.10
No. C179 exists imperf.

## M. L. King Type of Regular Issue
**Souvenir Sheet**
55c, Pres. Kennedy congratulating Dr. King.

**1968, July 11  Litho.  Perf. 11½**
C180 A192 55c brn & blk  3.00 1.00
Exist imperf. Value, $9.

## Olympic Type of Regular Issue
**Souvenir Sheet**
Design: 50c, Steeplechase and ancient sculpture.

**1968, Aug. 22  Litho.  Perf. 11½**
C181 A193 50c brt bl & org brn  2.25 1.10
Exists imperf. Value $15.

## President Type of Regular Issue 1966-69
Design: 25c, Pres. William V. S. Tubman.

**1969, Feb. 18  Litho.  Perf. 11½x11**
C182 A180 25c blk & emer  .60  .30

## ILO Type of Regular Issue
Design: 80c, "ILO" surrounded by cogwheel and wreath, vert.

**1969, Apr. 16  Litho.  Perf. 12½**
C183 A196 80c emer & gold  2.00 1.10
No. C183 exists imperf.

## Apollo 11 Type of Regular Issue
**Souvenir Sheet**
65c, Astronauts Neil A. Armstrong, Col. Edwin E. Aldrin, Jr., & Lieut. Col. Michael Collins, horiz.

**1969, Oct. 15  Litho.  Perf. 11½**
C184 A199 65c dk vio bl & brt red  2.00 1.10
Exists imperf. Value $20.

## UN Type of 1970
Design: $1, UN emblem, olive branch and plane as symbols of peace and progress, vert.

**1970, Apr. 16  Litho.  Perf. 12½**
C185 A200 $1 ultra & sil  2.00 1.00
Exists imperf.

## Apollo 14 Type of Regular Issue
**Souvenir Sheet**
Design: 50c, Moon, earth and star.

**1971, May 20  Litho.  Imperf.**
C186 A208 50c multi  2.75 2.75

**Souvenir Sheet**

Olympic
Yachting
Village,
Kiel, and
Yachting
AP47

**1971, June 28  Litho.  Perf. 14½x14**
C187 AP47  Sheet of 2  2.75 2.75
a.   25c multi  .65  .65
b.   30c multi  .80  .80
Publicity for the 20th Summer Olympic Games, and the yachting races in Kiel, Germany, 1972. Exists imperf. Value, $9.

### Boy Scout Type of Regular Issue
#### Souvenir Sheet
Boy Scouts of various nations cooking, horiz.

**1971, Aug. 6    Litho.    Perf. 15**
C188 A211 50c multi                    3.50 3.50
Exists imperf.

### UNICEF Type of Regular Issue
#### Souvenir Sheet
UNICEF emblem & Bengal tigress with cubs.

**1971, Oct. 1    Imperf.**
C189 A213 50c multi                    3.00 3.00

#### Souvenir Sheet

Japanese Royal Family — AP48

**1971, Nov. 4    Perf. 15**
C190 AP48 50c multi                    3.25 3.25
11th Winter Olympic Games, Sapporo, Japan, Feb. 3-13, 1972. Exists imperf. Value $15.

### Sesquicentennial Type of Regular Issue
#### Souvenir Sheet
Design: 50c, Sailing ship "Elizabeth" between maps of America and Africa, horiz.

**1972, Jan. 1    Litho.    Imperf.**
C191 A216 50c car & vio bl             2.40 2.40

### Olympic Type of Regular Issue
#### Souvenir Sheet
Design: 55c, View of Olympic Stadium and symbol of "Motion."

**1972, May 19    Litho.    Perf. 15**
C192 A218 55c multi                    4.00 4.00
Exists imperf. Value, $8.

### Apollo 16 Type of Regular Issue
#### Souvenir Sheet
Lt. Comdr. Thomas K. Mattingly, 2nd, Capt. John W. Young & Lt. Col. Charles M. Duke, Jr.

**1972, June 26    Litho.    Perf. 15**
C193 A220 55c pink & multi             2.00 2.00
Exists imperf. Value $10.

### Ship Type of 1972
#### Souvenir Sheet
Design: Lord Nelson's flagship Victory, and her figurehead (1765).

**1972, Sept. 6    Litho.    Perf. 15**
C194 A222 50c multi                    2.50 2.50

### Pres. Tolbert Type of 1972.
#### Souvenir Sheet

**1972, Oct. 23    Litho.    Perf. 15**
C195 A223 55c multi                    1.60 1.60

### Apollo 17 Type of Regular Issue
#### Souvenir Sheet
55c, Apollo 17 badge, moon and earth.

**1973, Mar. 28    Litho.    Perf. 11**
C196 A225 55c bl & multi               1.90 1.90
Exists imperf. Value $10.

### Locomotive Type of Regular Issue
#### Souvenir Sheet
Design: 55c, Swiss locomotive.

**1973, May 4    Litho.    Perf. 11**
C197 A226 55c multi                    2.75 2.75

### WHO Type of Regular Issue 1973
#### Souvenir Sheet
Design: 55c, WHO emblem, Paul Ehrlich and poppy anemones.

**1973, June 26    Litho.    Perf. 11**
C198 A228 55c lt vio & multi           2.00 2.00

### Automobile Type of Regular Issue
#### Souvenir Sheet
Franklin 10 HP cross-engined 1904-05 models.

**1973, Sept. 11    Litho.    Perf. 11**
C199 A229 55c multi                    2.00 2.00

### Copernicus Type of Regular Issue
#### Souvenir Sheet
Design: 55c, Copernicus and concept of orbiting station around Mars.

**1973, Dec. 14    Litho.    Perf. 13½**
C200 A230 55c gray & multi             2.00 2.00
Exists imperf. Value $15.

### UPU Type of Regular Issue
#### Souvenir Sheet
55c, UPU emblem and English coach, 1784.

**1974, Mar. 4    Litho.    Perf. 13½**
C201 A232 55c multi                    2.50 2.25
Exists imperf. Value $15.

### Dog Type of Regular Issue
#### Souvenir Sheet
Design: Hungarian sheepdog (kuvasz).

**1974, Apr. 16    Litho.    Perf. 13½**
C202 A233 75c multi                    3.25 2.25
Exists imperf.

### Soccer Type of Regular Issue
#### Souvenir Sheet
Design: 60c, World Soccer Championship Cup and Munich Stadium.

**1974, June 4    Litho.    Perf. 11**
C203 A234 60c multi                    2.00 2.00
Exists imperf. Value $12.

### Butterfly Type of Regular Issue
#### Souvenir Sheet
Tropical butterfly: 60c, Pierella nereis.

**1974, Sept. 11    Litho.    Perf. 13½**
C204 A235 60c gray & multi             3.50 2.50

### Churchill Type of 1974
#### Souvenir Sheet
60c, Churchill at easel painting landscape.

**1975, Jan. 17    Litho.    Perf. 13½**
C205 A237 60c multi                    1.50 1.50
Exists imperf. Value $10.

### Women's Year Type of 1975
#### Souvenir Sheet
Design: 75c, Vijaya Lakshmi Pandit, Women's Year emblem and dais of UN General Assembly.

**1975, Mar. 14    Litho.    Perf. 13**
C206 A238 75c gray & multi             1.25 1.25
Exists imperf. Value $10.

### American Bicentennial Type
#### Souvenir Sheet
Design: 75c, Mayflower and US No. 548.

**1975, Apr. 25    Litho.    Perf. 13½**
C207 A239 75c multi                    2.50 2.50
Exists imperf. Value $11.

### Dr. Schweitzer Type, 1975
#### Souvenir Sheet
Schweitzer as surgeon in Lambarene Hospital.

**1975, June 26    Litho.    Perf. 13½**
C208 A240 60c multi                    2.25 2.25
Exists imperf. Value $11.

### Apollo-Soyuz Type, 1975
#### Souvenir Sheet
75c, Apollo-Soyuz link-up and emblem.

**1975, Sept. 18    Litho.    Perf. 13½**
C209 A241 75c multi                    2.00 1.90

### Winter Olympic Games Type, 1976
#### Souvenir Sheet
Downhill skiing & Olympic Games emblem.

**1976, Jan. 23    Litho.    Perf. 13½**
C210 A243 75c multi                    1.60 1.50
Exists imperf. Value $9.

### Olympic Games Type, 1976
#### Souvenir Sheet
Design: 75c, Dressage and jumping.

**1976, May 4    Litho.    Perf. 13½**
C211 A245 75c multi                    1.90 1.90
Exists imperf. Value $9.

### Bell Type
#### Souvenir Sheet
Design: 75c, A. G. Bell making telephone call, UPU and ITU emblems.

**1976, June 4    Litho.    Perf. 13½**
C212 A246 75c ocher & multi            2.50 2.25
Exists imperf. Value $11.

### Animal Type of 1976
#### Souvenir Sheet
Design: 50c, Elephant, vert.

**1976, Sept. 1    Litho.    Perf. 13½**
C213 A249 50c org & multi              3.25 2.00

### Bicentennial Type of 1976
#### Souvenir Sheet
Design: 75c, Like No. 770.

**1976, Sept. 21    Litho.    Perf. 13½**
C214 A250 75c multi                    2.40 2.40
Exist imperf. Value, $12.

### Mask Type of 1977
#### Souvenir Sheet
75c, Ibo mask and Festival emblem.

**1977, Jan. 20    Litho.    Perf. 13½**
C215 A251 75c lil & multi              1.75 1.75

### Equestrian Type of 1977
Designs: 55c, Military dressage (team), US. 80c, Winners receiving medals, vert.

**1977, Apr. 22    Litho.    Perf. 13½**
C216 A253 55c ocher & multi            2.40 .60
#### Souvenir Sheet
C217 A253 80c ocher & multi            2.10 2.10
No. C217 exists imperf. Value $9.

### Elizabeth II Type of 1977
#### Souvenir Sheet
75c, Elizabeth II, laurel and crowns.

**1977, May 23    Litho.    Perf. 13½**
C218 A254 75c sil & multi              1.25 1.25
Exists imperf. Value $9.

### Zeppelin Type of 1978
#### Souvenir Sheet
75c, Futuristic Goodyear aerospace airship.

**1978, Mar. 9    Litho.    Perf. 13½**
C219 A257 75c multi                    1.75 1.40
Exists imperf. Value $10.

### Soccer Type of 1978
#### Souvenir Sheet
Soccer game Netherlands & Uruguay, vert.

**1978, May 16    Litho.    Perf. 13½**
C220 A258 75c multi                    2.00 1.25
Exists imperf. Value $20.

### Coronation Type of 1978
#### Souvenir Sheet
Design: 75c, Coronation coach, horiz.

**1978, June 12**
C221 A259 75c multi                    2.25 1.75
Exists imperf. Value $14.

### Soccer Winners' Type of 1978
#### Souvenir Sheet
Design: 75c, Argentine team, horiz.

**1978, Dec. 8    Litho.    Perf. 13½**
C222 A262 75c multi                    2.50 1.20
Exists imperf. Value $12.50.

---

## AIR POST SEMI-POSTAL STAMPS

### Nos. C14-C16 Overprinted in Red or Blue Like Nos. B16-B18

**1941    Unwmk.    Perf. 12**
CB1 A107 3c +2c dk bl (R)              4.00 4.00
CB2 A108 5c +2c dl red brn
          (Bl)                         4.00 4.00
CB3 A109 10c +2c dk grn (R)            4.00 4.00
    Nos. CB1-CB3 (3)                  12.00 12.00

> Catalogue values for unused stamps in this section, from this point to the end of the section, are for Never Hinged items.

Nurses Taking Oath
SPAP1

Designs: 20c+5c, Liberian Government Hospital. 25c+5c, Medical examination.

**1954, June 21    Litho. & Engr.**
      Size: 39½x28½mm
CB4 SPAP1 10c +5c car & blk            .30 .25
CB5 SPAP1 20c +5c emer & blk           .40 .25
      Size: 45x34mm
CB6 SPAP1 25c +5c ultra, car &
          blk                          .45 .25
    Nos. CB4-CB6 (3)                  1.15 .75
Surtax for the Liberian Government Hospital. Nos. CB4-CB6 exist imperf. No. CB6 exists with carmine omitted.

---

## AIR POST SPECIAL DELIVERY STAMP

### No. C15 Overprinted in Dark Blue Like No. E1

**1941    Unwmk.    Perf. 12**
CE1 A108 10c on 5c dl red brn          2.00 2.00

---

## AIR POST REGISTRATION STAMP

### No. 278 Overprinted in Dark Blue

**1941    Unwmk.    Perf. 12**
CF1 A108 10c on 5c dl red brn          2.00 2.00

## SPECIAL DELIVERY STAMP

### No. 278 Surcharged in Dark Blue

| | | | | |
|---|---|---|---|---|
| **1941** | | **Unwmk.** | **Perf. 12** | |
| E1 | A108 | 10c on 5c dl red brn | 2.00 | 2.00 |

## REGISTRATION STAMPS

R1

| | | | | |
|---|---|---|---|---|
| **1893** | **Unwmk.** | **Litho.** | **Perf. 14, 15** | |
| *Without Value Surcharged* | | | | |
| F1 | R1 | (10c) blk (Buchanan) | 250. | 250. |
| F2 | R1 | (10c) blk (Greenville) | 2,500. | — |
| F3 | R1 | (10c) blk (Harper) | 2,500. | — |
| F4 | R1 | (10c) blk (Monrovia) | 30. | 30. |
| F5 | R1 | (10c) blk (Robertsport) | 1,000. | 1,000. |

### Types of 1893 Surcharged in Black

| | | | | |
|---|---|---|---|---|
| **1894** | | | **Perf. 14** | |
| F6 | R1 | 10c bl, *pink* (Buchanan) | 5.50 | 5.50 |
| F7 | R1 | 10c grn, *buff* (Harper) | 5.50 | 5.50 |
| F8 | R1 | 10c red, *yel* (Monrovia) | 5.50 | 5.50 |
| F9 | R1 | 10c rose, *blue* (Robertsport) | 5.50 | 5.50 |
| | | Nos. F6-F9 (4) | 22.00 | 22.00 |

Exist imperf or missing one 10. Value, each $10.

President Garretson W. Gibson — R6

| | | | | |
|---|---|---|---|---|
| **1903** | | **Engr.** | **Perf. 14** | |
| F10 | R6 | 10c bl & blk (Buchanan) | 1.75 | .25 |
| *a.* | | Center inverted | 100.00 | |
| F11 | R6 | 10c org red & blk ("Grenville") | 1.75 | |
| *a.* | | Center inverted | 100.00 | |
| *b.* | | 10c orange & black | 1.90 | .25 |
| F12 | R6 | 10c grn & blk (Harper) | 1.75 | .25 |
| *a.* | | Center inverted | 100.00 | |
| F13 | R6 | 10c vio & blk (Monrovia) | 1.75 | .25 |
| *a.* | | Center inverted | 100.00 | |
| *b.* | | 10c lilac & black | 1.90 | |
| F14 | R6 | 10c magenta & blk (Robertsport) | 1.75 | .25 |
| *a.* | | Center inverted | 100.00 | |
| | | Nos. F10-F14 (5) | 8.75 | |
| | | Nos. F10, F11b, F12-F14 | | .75 |

For surcharges see Nos. 178-182.

S.S. Quail on Patrol
R7

| | | | | |
|---|---|---|---|---|
| **1919** | **Litho.** | **Serrate Roulette 12** | | |
| F15 | R7 | 10c blk & bl (Buchanan) | 1.40 | 2.75 |
| | | **Serrate Roulette 12, Perf. 14** | | |
| F16 | R7 | 10c ocher & blk ("Grenville") | 1.40 | 2.75 |
| F17 | R7 | 10c grn & blk (Harper) | 1.40 | 2.75 |
| F18 | R7 | 10c vio & bl (Monrovia) | 1.40 | 2.75 |

---

| | | | | |
|---|---|---|---|---|
| F19 | R7 | 10c rose & blk (Robertsport) | 1.40 | 2.75 |
| | | Nos. F15-F19 (5) | 7.00 | 13.75 |

Gabon Viper
R8

### Wmk. Crosses and Circles (116)

| | | | | |
|---|---|---|---|---|
| **1921** | | **Engr.** | **Perf. 13x14** | |
| F20 | R8 | 10c cl & blk (Buchanan) | 80.00 | 3.50 |
| F21 | R8 | 10c red & blk (Greenville) | 30.00 | 3.50 |
| F22 | R8 | 10c ultra & blk (Harper) | 40.00 | 3.50 |
| F23 | R8 | 10c org & blk (Monrovia) | 30.00 | 3.50 |
| *a.* | | Imperf., pair | 225.00 | |
| F24 | R8 | 10c grn & blk (Robertsport) | 30.00 | 3.50 |
| *a.* | | Imperf., pair | 225.00 | |
| | | Nos. F20-F24 (5) | 210.00 | 17.50 |

### Nos. F-20-F24 Overprinted in Black

| | | | | |
|---|---|---|---|---|
| F25 | R8 | 10c (Buchanan) | 37.50 | 6.25 |
| F26 | R8 | 10c (Greenville) | 37.50 | 6.25 |
| F27 | R8 | 10c (Harper) | 37.50 | 6.25 |
| F28 | R8 | 10c (Monrovia) | 37.50 | 6.25 |
| F29 | R8 | 10c (Robertsport) | 37.50 | 6.25 |
| | | Nos. F25-F29 (5) | 187.50 | 31.25 |

Nos. F20-F24 are printed tete-beche. Thus, the "1921" overprint appears upright on half the stamps in a sheet and inverted on the other half. Values are the same for either variety.

Passengers Going Ashore from Ship — R9

Designs: No. F31, Transporting merchandise, shore to ship (Greenville). No. F32, Sailing ship (Harper). No. F33, Ocean liner (Monrovia). No. F34, Canoe in surf (Robertsport).

| | | | | |
|---|---|---|---|---|
| **1924** | | **Litho.** | **Perf. 14** | |
| F30 | R9 | 10c gray & carmine | 7.00 | .60 |
| F31 | R9 | 10c gray & blue grn | 7.00 | .60 |
| F32 | R9 | 10c gray & orange | 7.00 | .60 |
| F33 | R9 | 10c gray & blue | 7.00 | .60 |
| F34 | R9 | 10c gray & violet | 7.00 | .60 |
| | | Nos. F30-F34 (5) | 35.00 | 3.00 |

### No. 278 Surcharged in Dark Blue

| | | | | |
|---|---|---|---|---|
| **1941** | | **Unwmk.** | **Perf. 12** | |
| F35 | A108 | 10c on 5c dull red brn | 2.00 | 2.00 |

---

## POSTAGE DUE STAMPS

### Nos. 26, 28 Surcharged

| | | | | |
|---|---|---|---|---|
| **1892** | | **Unwmk.** | **Perf. 11** | |
| J1 | A5 | 3c on 3c violet | 6.50 | 4.25 |
| *a.* | | Imperf., pair | 30.00 | |
| *b.* | | Inverted surcharge | 45.00 | 45.00 |

---

| | | | | |
|---|---|---|---|---|
| *c.* | | As "a," inverted surcharge | 110.00 | |
| | | **Perf. 12** | | |
| J2 | A5 | 6c on 6c olive gray | 15.00 | 13.50 |
| *a.* | | Imperf., pair | 40.00 | |
| *b.* | | Inverted surcharge | 52.50 | 35.00 |

D2

### Engr.; Figures of Value Typographed in Black

| | | | | |
|---|---|---|---|---|
| **1893** | | **Wmk. 143** | **Perf. 14, 15** | |
| J3 | D2 | 2c org, *yel* | 2.00 | 1.00 |
| J4 | D2 | 4c rose, *rose* | 2.00 | 1.00 |
| J5 | D2 | 6c brown, *buff* | 2.00 | 1.25 |
| J6 | D2 | 8c blue, *blue* | 2.00 | 1.25 |
| J7 | D2 | 10c grn, *lil rose* | 2.25 | 1.50 |
| J8 | D2 | 20c vio, *gray* | 2.25 | 1.50 |
| *a.* | | Center inverted | 110.00 | 110.00 |
| J9 | D2 | 40c ol brn, *grnsh* | 4.50 | 3.00 |
| | | Nos. J3-J9 (7) | 17.00 | 10.50 |

All values of the above set exist imperforate. Each value also exists with center inverted.

## MILITARY STAMPS

"LFF" are the initials of "Liberian Frontier Force." Nos. M1-M7 were issued for the use of troops sent to guard the frontier.

### Issues of 1905, 1906 and 1909 Surcharged

| | | | | |
|---|---|---|---|---|
| **1916** | | | **Wmk. 143** | |
| M1 | A23 | 1c on 1c lt grn | 190.00 | 190.00 |
| *a.* | | 2nd "F" inverted | 250.00 | 250.00 |
| *b.* | | "FLF" | 250.00 | 250.00 |
| *c.* | | Inverted surcharge | 250.00 | 250.00 |
| | | **Unwmk.** | | |
| M2 | A33 | 1c on 1c grn & blk | 600.00 | 550.00 |
| *a.* | | 2nd "F" inverted | 700.00 | 600.00 |
| *b.* | | "FLF" | 700.00 | 600.00 |
| M3 | A46 | 1c on 1c yel grn & blk | 4.00 | 4.75 |
| *a.* | | 2nd "F" inverted | 7.50 | 7.50 |
| *b.* | | "FLF" | 7.50 | 7.50 |
| M4 | A47 | 1c on 2c lake & blk | 4.00 | 4.75 |
| *a.* | | 2nd "F" inverted | 7.50 | 7.50 |
| *b.* | | "FLF" | 7.50 | 7.50 |

Surcharge exists sideways on Nos. M2, M5; double on Nos. M1-M4; inverted on Nos. M2-M4.

### Nos. O46, O59-O60 Surcharged

| | | | | |
|---|---|---|---|---|
| M5 | A33 | 1c on 1c | 500.00 | 475.00 |
| *a.* | | 2nd "F" inverted | 700.00 | 650.00 |
| *b.* | | "FLF" | 700.00 | 650.00 |
| M6 | A46 | 1c on 1c | 4.75 | 5.50 |
| *a.* | | 2nd "F" inverted | 9.00 | 9.00 |
| *b.* | | "FLF" | 9.00 | 9.00 |
| *c.* | | "LFF 1c" inverted | 12.50 | 12.50 |
| *d.* | | As "a" and "1c" inverted | | 15.00 |
| *e.* | | "FLF 1c" inverted | | 15.00 |
| M7 | A47 | 1c on 2c | 3.25 | 4.00 |
| *a.* | | 2nd "F" inverted | 6.50 | 6.50 |
| *b.* | | "FLF" | 6.50 | 6.50 |
| *c.* | | Pair, one without "LFF 1c" | | |

## OFFICIAL STAMPS

### Types of Regular Issues Overprinted in Various Colors

| | | | | |
|---|---|---|---|---|
| | | **Perf. 12½ to 15 and Compound** | | |
| **1892** | | | **Wmk. 143** | |
| O1 | A9 | 1c vermilion | .80 | .80 |
| O2 | A9 | 2c blue | .80 | .80 |
| O3 | A10 | 4c grn & blk | .80 | .80 |
| O4 | A11 | 6c bl grn | .80 | .80 |

---

| | | | | |
|---|---|---|---|---|
| O5 | A12 | 8c brn & blk | .80 | .80 |
| O6 | A13 | 12c rose red | 2.00 | 2.00 |
| O7 | A14 | 16c red lilac | 2.00 | 2.00 |
| O8 | A15 | 24c ol grn, *yel* | 2.00 | 2.00 |
| O9 | A16 | 32c grnsh bl | 2.00 | 2.00 |
| O10 | A17 | $1 bl & blk | 40.00 | 16.00 |
| O11 | A18 | $2 brn, *yel* | 16.00 | 11.50 |
| O12 | A19 | $5 car & blk | 24.00 | 9.00 |
| | | Nos. O1-O12 (12) | 92.00 | 48.50 |

a

"5" With Short Flag

| | | | | |
|---|---|---|---|---|
| **1893** | | | | |
| O13 | A11 | 5c on 6c bl grn (a) (No. 50) | 1.20 | 1.20 |
| *a.* | | "5" with short flag | 6.00 | 6.00 |
| *b.* | | Both 5's with short flags | 6.00 | 6.00 |
| *c.* | | "i" dot omitted | 20.00 | 20.00 |
| *d.* | | Overprinted on #50d | 45.00 | 45.00 |

Overprinted in Various Colors

| | | | | |
|---|---|---|---|---|
| **1894** | | | | |
| O15 | A9 | 1c vermilion | .70 | .35 |
| O16 | A9 | 2c blue | .85 | .40 |
| *a.* | | Imperf. | | |
| O17 | A10 | 4c grn & blk | 1.00 | .55 |
| O18 | A12 | 8c brn & blk | 1.00 | .55 |
| O19 | A13 | 12c rose red | 1.40 | .60 |
| O20 | A14 | 16c red lilac | 1.40 | .60 |
| O21 | A15 | 24c ol grn, *yel* | 1.40 | .70 |
| O22 | A16 | 32c grnsh bl | 2.75 | .80 |
| O23 | A17 | $1 bl & blk | 27.50 | 21.00 |
| *a.* | | $1 ultra & black | 27.50 | 21.00 |
| O24 | A18 | $2 brn, *yel* | 27.50 | 21.00 |
| O25 | A19 | $5 car & blk | 125.00 | 87.50 |
| | | Nos. O15-O25 (11) | 190.50 | 134.05 |
| | | **Unwmk.** | | |
| | | **Imperf** | | |
| O26 | A22 | 5c vio & grn | 3.50 | 2.25 |
| | | **Rouletted** | | |
| O27 | A22 | 5c vio & grn | 3.50 | 2.25 |

### Regular Issue of 1896-1905 Overprinted in Black or Red

| | | | | |
|---|---|---|---|---|
| **1898-1905** | | **Wmk. 143** | **Perf. 14, 15** | |
| O28 | A23 | 1c lil rose | 1.10 | .90 |
| O29 | A23 | 1c dp grn ('00) | 1.10 | .90 |
| O30 | A23 | 1c lt grn (R) ('05) | 1.10 | .90 |
| O31 | A24 | 2c bis & blk | 2.25 | .60 |
| *a.* | | Pair, one without overprint | 900.00 | |
| O32 | A24 | 2c org red & blk ('00) | 3.25 | 1.50 |
| O33 | A24 | 2c rose & blk ('05) | 5.50 | 2.75 |
| O34 | A25 | 5c lake & blk | 3.75 | 1.50 |
| O35 | A25 | 5c gray bl & blk ('00) | 4.25 | 1.50 |
| O36 | A25 | 5c ultra & blk (R) ('05) | 7.25 | 3.75 |
| O37 | A12 | 10c chr yel & ind | 2.25 | 1.75 |
| O38 | A13 | 15c slate | 2.25 | 1.75 |
| O39 | A14 | 20c vermilion | 3.75 | 2.10 |
| O40 | A15 | 25c yel grn | 2.25 | 1.75 |
| O41 | A16 | 30c steel blue | 5.50 | 2.75 |
| O42 | A26 | 50c red brn & blk | 5.50 | 2.75 |
| | | Nos. O28-O42 (15) | 51.05 | 27.15 |

For surcharge see No. O92.

Official stamps overprinted "ORDINARY" or with a bar with an additional surcharge are listed as Nos. 64B-90, 92-93, 99.

Red Overprint

**1903**    **Unwmk.**    *Perf. 14*
O43 A29 3c green   .25 .25
  a. Overprint omitted   5.00
  b. Inverted overprint

Two overprint types: I — Thin, sharp, dark red. II — Thick, heavier, orange red. Same value.

No. 50 Surcharged in Black

No. 45 Surcharged in Red

**1904**    **Wmk. 143**
O44 A11 1c on 5c on 6c bl grn   1.60 2.00
  a. "5" with short flag   4.25
  b. Both "5s" with straight flag   8.00 8.00
O45 A16 2c on 30c steel blue   9.50 9.50
  a. Double surcharge, red and black
  b. Surcharge also on back

Types of Regular Issue Overprinted in Various Colors   a

**1906**    **Unwmk.**
O46 A33 1c grn & blk (R)   .65 .40
O47 A34 2c car & blk (Bl)   .25 .25
  a. Center and overprint inverted   30.00 3.00
  b. Inverted overprint   6.00
O48 A35 5c ultra & blk (Bk)   .65 .40
  a. Inverted overprint   15.00 15.00
  b. Center and overprint invtd.   50.00
O49 A36 10c dl vio & blk (R)   .75 .55
  a. Inverted overprint   10.00 10.00
  b. Center and overprint invtd.   50.00
O50 A37 15c brn & blk (Bk)   3.00 .55
  a. Inverted overprint   4.50
  b. Overprint omitted   12.00 6.00
  c. Center and overprint invtd.   60.00
O51 A38 20c dp grn & blk (R)   .75 .55
  a. Overprint omitted   15.00
O52 A39 25c plum & gray (Bl)   .50 .25
  a. With 2nd ovpt. in blue, invtd.   15.00
O53 A40 30c dk brn (Bk)   .55 .25
O54 A41 50c org brn & dp grn (G)   .75 .25
  a. Inverted overprint   5.00 4.00
O55 A42 75c ultra & blk (Bk)   1.40 .95
  a. Inverted overprint   9.50 5.75
  b. Overprint omitted   22.50
O56 A43 $1 dp grn & gray (R)   .90 .25
  a. Inverted overprint
O57 A44 $2 plum & blk (Bl)   2.75 .25
  a. Overprint omitted   22.50 15.00
O58 A45 $5 org & blk (Bk)   5.50 .25
  a. Overprint omitted   11.00
  b. Inverted overprint   12.00 8.00
  Nos. O46-O58 (13)   18.40 5.15

Nos. O52, O54, O55, O56 and O58 are known with center inverted.
For surcharges see Nos. O72, O82-O85, O96.

  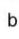 b

**1909-12**
O59 A46 1c emer & blk (R)   .40 .25
O60 A47 2c car rose & brn (Bl)   .40 .25
  a. Overprint omitted
O61 A48 5c turq & blk (Bk)   .45 .25
  a. Double overprint, one inverted   7.50
O62 A49 10c blk & ultra (R)   .60 .25
  ('12)   .60 .25
O63 A50 15c cl & blk (Bl)   .60 .45
O64 A51 20c bis & grn (Bk)   1.10 .55
O65 A52 25c ultra & grn (Bk)   1.10 .55
  a. Double overprint   4.75 4.75
O66 A53 30c dk bl (R)   .85 .25
O67 A54 50c brn & grn (Bk)   1.40 .40
  a. Center inverted   27.50
  b. Inverted overprint   4.00 2.75
O68 A55 75c pur & blk (R)   1.50 .25
  Nos. O59-O68 (10)   8.40 3.45

Nos. O63, O64, O67 and O68 are known without overprint and with center inverted.
For surcharges see Nos. O74-O81, O86-O90, O97.

*Rouletted*
O69 A49 10c blk & ultra (R)   1.00 .95

**Nos. 126B and 127E Overprinted type "a" ("OS") in Red**
**1910-12**    *Rouletted*
O70 A49 3c on 10c blk & ultra   .70 1.25
*Perf. 12½, 14, 12½x14*
O71 A49 3c on 10c blk & ultra ('12)   .70 .40
  a. Pair, one without srch., the other with dbl. srch., one invtd.
  b. Double surcharge, one inverted   4.00

Stamps of Preceding Issues Srchd. with New Values like Regular Issue and — c

**1914**    **On Nos. O52 and 110**
O72 A39 (a) 2c on 25c plum & gray   30.00 10.50
O73 A42 (c) 20c on 75c brn & blk   8.75 5.25
  **On Nos. O66 and O68**
O74 A53 (b) 5c on 30c dk bl   8.75 5.25
O75 A55 (c) 20c on 75c pur & blk (R)   13.00 5.25
  Nos. O72-O75 (4)   60.50 26.25

**Official Stamps of 1906-09 Surcharged Like Regular Issues of Same Date**
**1915-16**
O76 A50 (c) 2c on 15c (Bk)   .95 .50
O77 A52 (d) 2c on 25c (Bk)   5.25 5.25
O78 A51 (e) 5c on 20c (Bk)   .95 .65
O79 A53 (g) 5c on 30c (R)   10.00 8.50
O80 A54 (i) 10c on 50c (Bk)   5.50 3.25
O81 A55 (j) 20c on 75c (R)   2.75 2.75
O82 A43 (k) 25c on $1 (R)   20.00 20.00
  a. "25" double   25.00
  b. "OS" inverted   25.00
O83 A44 (l) 50c on $2 (Bk)   50.00 50.00
  a. "Ceuts"   70.00 70.00
O84 A44 (m) 50c on $2 (Br)   22.50 22.50
O85 A45 (n) $1 on $5 (Bk)   21.00 21.00

**Handstamped Surcharge**
O86 A54 (i) 10c on 50c (Bk)   11.00 11.00

**Nos. O60-O61 Surcharged like Nos. 153-154 in Black or Red**

a1, b1

c1, d1

e1, f1

g1, h1

i1, j1

O87 A47 1c on 2c   2.75 2.75
  Strip of 10 types   30.00
O88 A48 2c on 5c (R)   2.75 2.75
  Strip of 10 types (R)   30.00
  a. Black surcharge   10.00 10.00
  Strip of 10 types (Bk)   140.00

See note following Nos. 153-154.

Nos. O60-O61 Surcharged
O90 A47 1c on 2c   125.00 125.00
O91 A48 2c on 5c   100.00 100.00

No. O42 Surcharged
O92 A26 10c on 50c (Bk)   11.00 11.00

No. O53 Surcharged
**1917**
O96 A40 5c on 30c dk brn   21.00 21.00
  a. "FIV"   35.00 35.00
The editors consider the 1915-17 issues unnecessary and speculative.

**No. O62 Surcharged in Red like No. 162**
**1918**
O97 A49 3c on 10c blk & ultra   2.40 2.40

Types of Regular Issue of 1918 Ovptd. Type "a" in Black, Blue or Red

**1918**    **Unwmk.**    *Perf. 12½, 14*
O98 A59 1c dp grn & red brn (Bk)   .60 .25
O99 A60 2c red & blk (Bl)   .60 .25
O100 A61 5c ultra & blk (R)   1.10 .25
O101 A62 10c ultra (R)   .60 .25
O102 A63 15c choc & dk grn (Bl)   2.75 .60
O103 A64 20c gray lil & blk (R)   .85 .25
O104 A65 25c choc & grn (Bk)   5.25 .65
O105 A66 30c brt vio & blk (R)   6.50 .65
O106 A67 50c mar & blk (Bl)   7.75 .65
  a. Overprint omitted   11.00
O107 A68 75c car brn & blk (Bl)   3.00 .25
O108 A69 $1 ol bis & turq bl (Bk)   6.00 .25
O109 A70 $2 ol bis & blk (R)   9.25 .25
O110 A71 $5 yel grn (Bk)   12.00 .40
  Nos. O98-O110 (13)   56.25 4.95

For surcharges see Nos. 259-269, O111-O112, O155-O157. For overprint see No. 270.

**Official Stamps of 1918 Surcharged like Regular Issue**

**1920**
O111 A59 3c on 1c grn & red brn   1.10 .70
  a. "CEETS"   15.00 15.00
  b. Double surcharge   8.00 8.00
  c. Double srch., one invtd.   15.00 15.00
  d. Triple surcharge   20.00 20.00
O112 A60 4c on 2c red & blk   .70 .70
  a. Inverted surcharge   12.00 12.00
  b. Double surcharge   12.00 12.00
  c. Double srch., one invtd.   10.00 10.00
  d. Triple surcharge   15.00 15.00

Types of Regular Issues of 1915-21 Overprinted

**1921**    **Wmk. 116**    *Perf. 14*
O113 A57 2c rose red   8.25 .25
O114 A58 3c brown   1.75 .25
O115 A79 20c brn & ultra   2.25 .40

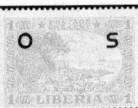

Regular Issues of 1921 Overprinted
O116 A75 1c dp grn   1.75 .25
O117 A76 5c dp bl & brn   1.75 .25
O118 A77 10c red vio & blk   .85 .25
O119 A78 15c blk & grn   4.75 .60
  a. Double overprint
O120 A80 25c org & blk   6.50 .60
O121 A81 30c brn & red   1.75 .25
O122 A82 50c grn & blk   1.75 .25
  a. Overprinted "S" only
O123 A83 75c bl & vio   3.25 .25
O124 A84 $1 bl & blk   22.50 .65
O125 A85 $2 grn & org   12.00 .95
O126 A86 $5 grn & bl   13.50 2.10
  Nos. O113-O126 (14)   82.60 7.30

Preceding Issues Overprinted

**1921**
O127 A75 1c dp grn   7.50 .25
O128 A57 2c rose red   7.50 .25
O129 A58 3c brown   7.50 .25
O130 A76 5c dp bl & brn   4.50 .25
O131 A77 10c red vio & blk   7.50 .25
O132 A78 15c blk & grn   8.50 .25
O133 A79 20c brn & ultra   8.50 .40
O134 A80 25c org & grn   8.25 .80
O135 A81 30c brn & red   7.50 .25
O136 A82 50c grn & blk   8.75 .25
O137 A83 75c bl & vio   5.50 .25
O138 A84 $1 bl & blk   15.00 2.00
O139 A85 $2 org & grn   19.00 2.25
O140 A86 $5 grn & bl   15.00 3.25
  Nos. O127-O140 (14)   130.50 10.95

Types of Regular Issue of 1923 Ovptd.

**1923**    *Perf. 13½x14½, 14½x13½*
**White Paper**
O141 A88 1c bl grn & blk   8.75 .25
O142 A89 2c dl red & yel brn   8.75 .25
O143 A90 3c gray bl & blk   8.75 .25
O144 A91 5c org & dk grn   8.75 .25
O145 A92 10c ol bis & dk vio   8.75 .25
O146 A93 15c yel grn & bl   1.10 .40
O147 A94 20c vio & ind   1.10 .40
O148 A95 25c brn & red brn   32.50 .40
**White, Buff or Brownish Paper**
O149a A96 30c dp ultra & brn   1.10 .30
  b. Overprint omitted   2.00
O150a A97 50c dl bis & red brn   2.25 .45
O151 A98 75c gray & grn   2.25 .25
O152a A99 $1 red org & grn   2.25 .65
  b. Overprint omitted   11.00
O153 A100 $2 red lil & red   4.50
O154a A101 $5 bl & brn vio   4.50 2.25
  Nos. O141-O154a (14)   96.80 6.25

No. O98 Surcharged in Red Brown

No. O98 Surcharged in Black

**1926**    **Unwmk.**    *Perf. 14*
O155 A59 2c on 1c   2.25 2.25
  a. "Gents"   15.00
  b. Surcharged in black   5.75
  c. As "b," "Gents"   15.00

## 1926
**O156** A59 2c on 1c    1.00   1.00
   *a.*   Inverted surcharge    20.00
   *b.*   "Gents"    10.00

No. O98 Surcharged in Red

## 1927
**O157** A59 2c on 1c    35.00   35.00
   *a.*   "Ceuts"    55.00
   *b.*   "Vwo"    55.00
   *c.*   "Twc"    55.00

Regular Issue of 1928 Overprinted in Red or Black

## 1928          *Perf. 12*
**O158** A102 1c grn (R)    1.10   .55
**O159** A102 2c gray vio (R)    3.50   2.10
**O160** A102 3c bis brn (Bk)    3.75   4.25
**O161** A103 5c ultra (R)    1.10   .55
**O162** A104 10c ol gray (R)    3.50   1.75
**O163** A103 15c dl vio (R)    3.50   1.00
**O164** A103 $1 red brn (Bk)    77.50   22.50
   *Nos. O158-O164 (7)*    93.95   32.70

For surcharges see Nos. C3, O165.

### No. O162 Surcharged with New Value and Bar in Black
## 1945    Unwmk.    *Perf. 12*
**O165** A104 4c on 10c (Bk)    12.00   12.00

---

# LIBYA

'li-bē-ə

(Libia)

LOCATION — North Africa, bordering on the Mediterranean Sea
GOVT. — Republic
AREA — 679,358 sq. mi.
POP. — 4,992,838 (1999 est.)
CAPITAL — Tripoli

In 1939, the four northern provinces of Libya, a former Italian colony, were incorporated in the Italian national territory. Included in the territory is the former Turkish Vilayet of Tripoli, annexed in 1912. Libya became a kingdom on Dec. 24, 1951. The Libyan Arab Republic was established Sept. 1, 1969. "People's Socialist . . ." was added to its name in 1977. See Cyrenaica and Tripolitania.

100 Centesimi = 1 Lira
Military Authority Lira (1951)
Franc (1951)
1,000 Milliemes = 1 Pound (1952)
1,000 Dirhams = 1 Dinar (1972)

## Watermarks

Wmk. 140 — Crown

Wmk. 195 — Multiple Crown and Arabic F

---

Wmk. 310 — Multiple Crescent and Star

---

**Catalogue values for unused stamps in this country are for Never Hinged items, beginning with Scott 102 in the regular postage section, Scott C51 in the airpost section, Scott E13 in the special delivery section, Scott J25 in the postage due section, Scott O1 in the official section, Scott N1 in the Fezzan-Ghadames section, Scott 2N1 in the Fezzan section, Scott 2NB1 in the Fezzan semipostal section, Scott 2NC1 in the Fezzan airpost section, Scott 2NJ1 in the Fezzan postage due section, Scott 3N1 in the Ghadames section, and Scott 3NC1 in the Ghadames airpost section.**

---

**Used values in italics are for postally used stamps. CTO's sell for about the same as unused, hinged stamps.**

Stamps of Italy Overprinted in Black

## 1912-22    Wmk. 140    *Perf. 14*
**1** A42 1c brown ('15)    1.40   .85
   *a.*   Double overprint    250.00   250.00
**2** A43 2c orange brn    1.40   .50
**3** A48 5c green    1.50   .35
   *a.*   Double overprint    90.00   90.00
   *b.*   Imperf., pair    300.00
   *c.*   Inverted overprint    —
   *d.*   Pair, one without overprint    450.00   450.00
**4** A48 10c claret    14.00   .35
   *a.*   Pair, one without overprint    475.00   475.00
   *b.*   Double overprint    160.00   160.00
**5** A48 15c slate ('22)    5.50   8.50
**6** A45 20c orange ('15)    5.50   .35
   *a.*   Double overprint    175.00   175.00
   *b.*   Pair, one without overprint    800.00   800.00
**7** A50 20c brn org ('18)    4.25   5.50
   *a.*   Double overprint    175.00
**8** A49 25c blue    5.50   .35
   *b.*   Double overprint    175.00
**9** A49 40c brown    14.00   1.00
**10** A45 45c ol grn ('17)    37.50   30.00
   *a.*   Inverted overprint    675.00
**11** A49 50c violet    35.00   1.40
**12** A49 60c brn car ('18)    19.00   25.00
**13** A46 1 l brn & grn    ('15)    62.50   1.75
**14** A46 5 l bl & rose ('15)    425.00   500.00
**15** A51 10 l gray grn & red    ('15)    35.00   190.00
   *Nos. 1-15 (15)*    667.05   765.90

Two types of overprint were applied to this issue. Type I has bold letters, with dots close within "i"; type II has thinner letters, with dots further away within "i." All values, along with Nos. E1 and E2, received the type I overprint, and values shown are for this type. Nos. 1, 3-4, 6, 8, 11, 13-15 and E1-E2 also received the type II overprint. For detailed listings, see the *Scott Classic Specialized Catalogue of Stamps and Covers.*
For surcharges see Nos. 37-38.

Overprinted in Violet

## 1912            Unwmk.
**16** A58 15c slate    275.00   3.00
   *a.*   Blue black overprint    *21,000.*   *42.50*

---

No. 16 Surcharged

## 1916, Mar.    Unwmk.
**19** A58 20c on 15c slate    60.00   12.50

Roman Legionary A1

Diana of Ephesus A2

Ancient Galley Leaving Tripoli A3

"Victory" A4

## 1921    Engr.    Wmk. 140    *Perf. 14*
**20** A1 1c blk & gray brn    2.75   7.00
**21** A1 2c blk & red brn    2.75   7.00
**22** A1 5c blk & grn    3.50   .70
   *a.*   5c black & red brown (error)    1,900.
   *b.*   Center inverted    60.00   90.00
   *c.*   Imperf., pair    550.00   550.00
**23** A2 10c blk & rose    3.50   .70
   *a.*   Center inverted    60.00   90.00
**24** A2 15c blk brn & brn org    85.00   2.75
   *a.*   Center inverted    150.00   275.00
**25** A2 25c dk bl & bl    3.50   .25
   *a.*   Center inverted    20.00   30.00
   *b.*   Imperf., pair    775.00   775.00
**26** A3 30c blk & blk brn    35.00   .70
   *a.*   Center inverted    2,750.   3,000.
**27** A3 50c blk & ol grn    16.00   .25
   *a.*   50c black & brown (error)    625.00
   *b.*   Center inverted    4,750.
**28** A3 55c black & vio    16.00   24.00
**29** A4 1 l dk brn & brn    47.50   .25
**30** A4 5 l blk & dk blue    27.50   21.00
**31** A4 10 l dk bl & ol grn    300.00   160.00
   *Nos. 20-31 (12)*    543.00   224.60

See No. 47-61. For surcharges see No. 102-121.

### Perf. 14x13¼
**20d** A1 1c blk & gray brn    5.50   11.00
**21d** A1 2c blk & red brn    5.50   11.00
**22d** A1 5c blk & red green    7.00   1.40
**23d** A2 10c blk & rose    7.00   1.40
**24d** A2 15c blk & brn org    160.00   5.50
**25d** A2 25c dk bl & bl    7.00   .35
**26d** A3 30c blk & blk brn    70.00   1.40
**27d** A3 50c blk & ol grn    32.50   .35
**28d** A3 55c blk & vio    32.50   55.00
**29d** A4 1 l dk brn & brn    95.00   .35
**30d** A4 5 l blk & dk blue    55.00   30.00
**31d** A4 10 l blk & ol grn    625.00   190.00

Italy Nos. 136-139 Overprinted

## 1922, Apr.
**33** A64 5c olive green    1.75   6.25
   *a.*   Double overprint    475.00   475.00
**34** A64 10c red    1.75   6.25
   *a.*   Double overprint    475.00   475.00
   *b.*   Inverted overprint    950.00   950.00
**35** A64 15c slate green    2.00   11.00
**36** A64 25c ultramarine    2.00   11.00
   *Nos. 33-36 (4)*    7.50   34.50

3rd anniv. of the victory of the Piave.

Nos. 11, 8 Surcharged

## 1922, June 1
**37** A49 40c on 50c violet    3.50   2.10
**38** A49 80c on 25c blue    3.50   8.50

---

Libyan Sibyl — A6

## 1924-31    Unwmk.    *Perf. 14½x14*
**39** A6 20c deep green    .70   .25
   *c.*   Vert. pair, imperf between and top    1,400.
   *d.*   Horiz. pair, imperf between and at right    1,400.
   *e.*   Horiz. pair, imperf between and at left    1,400.
**40** A6 40c brown    2.10   .70
   *b.*   Imperf single    275.00   *425.00*
**41** A6 60c deep blue    .70   .25
   *b.*   Imperf single    275.00
**42** A6 1.75 l orange ('31)    1.40   .25
**43** A6 2 l carmine    4.25   1.00
   *b.*   Imperf single    275.00   *425.00*
**44** A6 2.55 l violet ('31)    8.50   17.50
   *Nos. 39-44 (6)*    17.65   19.95
## 1926-29           *Perf. 11*
**39a** A6 20c    45.00   .30
**40a** A6 40c    32.50   2.40
**41a** A6 60c    32.50   .45
**43a** A6 2 l ('29)    15.00   5.00
   *Nos. 39a-43a (4)*    125.00   8.15

### Type of 1921
## 1924-40    Unwmk.    *Perf. 13½ to 14*
**47** A1 1c blk & gray brown    2.75   5.50
**48** A1 2c blk & red brn    2.75   5.50
**49** A1 5c blk & green    3.50   .70
**50** A1 7½c blk & brn ('31)    1.40   14.00
**51** A2 10c blk & dl red    2.75   .30
   *b.*   10c blk & carmine    2.75   .30
   *c.*   As "b," center inverted    175.00
**52** A2 15c blk brn & org    8.50   1.00
   *b.*   Center inverted, perf. 11    4,500.   6,500.
**53** A2 25c dk bl & bl    42.50   .50
   *a.*   Center inverted    240.00   350.00
**54** A3 30c blk & blk brn    2.75   .50
**55** A3 50c blk & ol grn    2.75   .30
   *b.*   Center inverted    4,500.
**56** A3 55c black & vio    625.00   825.00
**57** A4 75c vio & red ('31)    6.50   .25
**58** A4 1 l dk brn & brn    10.00   .35
**59** A3 1.25 l indigo & ultra ('31)    1.40   .25
**60** A4 5 l blk & dk bl ('40)    150.00   *175.00*
   *Nos. 47-60 (14)*    862.55   1,029.

### Perf. 11
**47a** A1 1c    375.00
**48a** A1 2c    375.00
**49a** A1 5c    70.00   17.50
**51a** A2 10c    35.00   7.00
**52a** A2 15c    475.00   45.00
**54a** A3 30c    140.00   2.10
**55a** A3 50c    775.00   .25
**58a** A4 1 l    350.00   .35
**60a** A4 5 l ('37)    *2,400.*   450.00
**61** A4 10 l blk & ol grn ('37)    625.00   500.00

Nos. 47a and 48a were not sent to the colony. A few philatelically inspired covers exist.

### Italy Nos. 197 and 88 Overprinted Like Nos. 1-15
## 1929    Wmk. 140    *Perf. 14*
**62** A86 7½c light brown    10.00   55.00
   *a.*   Double overprint
**63** A46 1.25 l blue & ultra    60.00   21.00
   *a.*   Inverted overprint    3,750.

### Italy No. 193 Overprinted Like Nos. 33-36
## 1929    Unwmk.    *Perf. 11*
**64** A85 1.75 l deep brown    75.00   2.10
   *h.*   Perf 13¾    12,000.

Water Carriers — A7

Man of Tripoli — A8

Designs: 25c, Minaret. 30c, 1.25 l, Tomb of Holy Man near Tagiura. 50c, Statue of Emperor Claudius at Leptis. 75c, Ruins of gardens.

## 1934, Feb. 17    Photo.    *Perf. 14*
**64A** A7 10c brown    4.25   17.50
**64B** A8 20c car rose    4.25   15.00
**64C** A8 25c green    4.25   15.00

| | | | | |
|---|---|---|---|---|
| 64D | A7 | 30c dark brown | 4.25 | 15.00 |
| 64E | A8 | 50c purple | 4.25 | 15.00 |
| 64F | A7 | 75c rose | 4.25 | 27.50 |
| 64G | A7 | 1.25 l blue | 55.00 | 95.00 |

Nos. 64A-64G (7)  80.50  200.00
Nos. 64A-64G,C14-C18 (12)  508.50  980.00

8th Sample Fair, Tripoli.

Bedouin Woman — A15

**1936, May 11  Wmk. 140  Perf. 14**

| 65 | A15 | 50c violet | 1.75 | 2.75 |
|---|---|---|---|---|
| 66 | A15 | 1.25 l deep blue | 1.75 | 7.75 |

10th Sample Fair, Tripoli.

Highway Memorial Arch — A16

**1937, Mar. 15**

| 67 | A16 | 50c copper red | 2.75 | 5.50 |
|---|---|---|---|---|
| 68 | A16 | 1.25 l sapphire | 2.75 | 12.50 |

Nos. 67-68,C28-C29 (4)  11.00  36.00

Coastal road to the Egyptian frontier, opening.

Nos. 67-68 Overprinted in Black

**1937, Apr. 24**

| 69 | A16 | 50c copper red | 14.00 | 35.00 |
|---|---|---|---|---|
| 70 | A16 | 1.25 l sapphire | 14.00 | 35.00 |

Nos. 69-70,C30-C31 (4)  56.00  140.00

11th Sample Fair, Tripoli.

Roman Wolf and Lion of St. Mark — A17

View of Fair Buildings — A18

**1938, Feb. 20**

| 71 | A17 | 5c brown | .30 | 1.00 |
|---|---|---|---|---|
| 72 | A18 | 10c olive brown | .30 | .70 |
| 73 | A17 | 25c green | .55 | 1.25 |
| 74 | A18 | 50c purple | .55 | .55 |
| 75 | A17 | 75c rose red | 1.40 | 2.75 |
| 76 | A18 | 1.25 l dark blue | 1.40 | 7.00 |

Nos. 71-76,C32-C33 (8)  7.30  21.50

12th Sample Fair, Tripoli.

Augustus Caesar (Octavianus) A19

Goddess Abundantia A20

**1938, Apr. 25**

| 77 | A19 | 5c olive brown | .25 | 1.40 |
|---|---|---|---|---|
| 78 | A20 | 10c brown red | .25 | 1.40 |
| 79 | A19 | 25c dk yel green | .50 | .70 |
| 80 | A20 | 50c dk violet | .50 | .45 |
| 81 | A19 | 75c green | 1.40 | 1.75 |
| 82 | A20 | 1.25 l dull blue | 1.40 | 2.75 |

Nos. 77-82,C34-C35 (8)  5.65  13.95

Birth bimillenary of Augustus Caesar (Octavianus), first Roman emperor.

Desert City — A21

View of Ghadames — A22

**1939, Apr. 12  Photo.**

| 83 | A21 | 5c olive brown | .70 | 1.00 |
|---|---|---|---|---|
| 84 | A22 | 20c red brown | .70 | 1.00 |
| 85 | A21 | 50c rose violet | .70 | 1.00 |
| 86 | A22 | 75c scarlet | .70 | 3.50 |
| 87 | A21 | 1.25 l gray blue | 1.40 | 4.25 |

Nos. 83-87,C36-C38 (8)  6.60  17.70

13th Sample Fair, Tripoli.

Modern City — A23

Oxen and Plow A24

Mosque A25

**1940, June 3  Wmk. 140  Perf. 14**

| 88 | A23 | 5c brown | .70 | 1.00 |
|---|---|---|---|---|
| 89 | A24 | 10c red orange | .70 | .70 |
| 90 | A25 | 25c dull green | .70 | 1.00 |
| 91 | A24 | 50c dark violet | .70 | .70 |
| 92 | A24 | 75c crimson | .70 | 3.50 |
| 93 | A25 | 1.25 l ultramarine | 1.40 | 5.50 |
| 94 | A24 | 2 l + 75c rose lake | 1.40 | 16.00 |

Nos. 88-94,C39-C42 (11)  9.70  50.50

Triennial Overseas Exposition, Naples.

"Two Peoples, One War," Hitler and Mussolini — A26

**1941, May 16**

| 95 | A26 | 5c orange | 2.10 | 8.00 |
|---|---|---|---|---|
| 96 | A26 | 10c brown | 2.10 | 8.00 |
| 97 | A26 | 20c dull violet | 3.50 | 8.00 |
| 98 | A26 | 25c green | 3.50 | 8.00 |
| 99 | A26 | 50c purple | 3.50 | 8.00 |
| 100 | A26 | 75c scarlet | 3.50 | 21.00 |
| 101 | A26 | 1.25 l sapphire | 3.50 | 21.00 |

Nos. 95-101,C43 (8)  24.45  124.00
Set, never hinged  42.50

The Rome-Berlin Axis.

> **Catalogue values for unused stamps in this section, from this point to the end of the section, are for Never Hinged items.**

### United Kingdom of Libya

Stamps of Cyrenaica 1950 Surcharged in Black

### For Use in Tripolitania

**1951, Dec. 24  Unwmk.  Perf. 12½**

| 102 | A2 | 1mal on 2m rose car | .30 | .30 |
|---|---|---|---|---|
| 103 | A2 | 2mal on 4m dk grn | .30 | .30 |
| 104 | A2 | 4mal on 8m red org | .30 | .30 |
| 105 | A2 | 10mal on 10m pur | .50 | .50 |
| 106 | A2 | 6mal on 12m red | .50 | .50 |
| a. | | Inverted surcharge | 30.00 | 30.00 |
| 107 | A2 | 10mal on 20m dp bl | .90 | .90 |
| a. | | Arabic "20" for "10" | 25.00 | 25.00 |
| 108 | A3 | 24mal on 50m choc & ultra | 3.50 | 3.50 |
| 109 | A3 | 48mal on 100m bl blk & car rose | 14.00 | 14.00 |

| 110 | A3 | 96mal on 200m vio & pur | 30.00 | 30.00 |
|---|---|---|---|---|
| 111 | A3 | 240mal on 500m dk grn & org | 75.00 | 75.00 |

Nos. 102-111 (10)  125.30  125.30

The surcharge is larger on Nos. 108 to 111.

### For Use in Fezzan
Same Surcharge in Francs

| 112 | A2 | 2fr on 2m rose car | .30 | .70 |
|---|---|---|---|---|
| 113 | A2 | 4fr on 4m dk grn | .30 | .70 |
| 114 | A2 | 8fr on 8m red org | .40 | .90 |
| 115 | A2 | 10fr on 10m pur | .55 | 1.40 |
| 116 | A2 | 12fr on 12m red | 1.00 | 2.25 |
| 117 | A2 | 20fr on 20m dp bl | 2.00 | 5.00 |
| 118 | A3 | 48fr on 50m choc & ultra | 42.50 | 47.50 |
| 119 | A3 | 96fr on 100m bl blk & car rose | 42.50 | 260.00 |
| 120 | A3 | 192fr on 200m vio & pur | 120.00 | 275.00 |
| 121 | A3 | 480fr on 500m dk grn & org | 225.00 | 300.00 |

Nos. 112-121 (10)  434.55  893.45

The surcharge is larger on Nos. 118-121. A second printing of Nos. 118-121 has an elongated first character in second line of Arabic surcharge.

Cyrenaica Nos. 65-77 Overprinted in Black

### For Use in Cyrenaica

| 122 | A2 | 1m dark brown | .25 | .45 |
|---|---|---|---|---|
| 123 | A2 | 2m rose carmine | .30 | .45 |
| 124 | A2 | 3m orange | .30 | .55 |
| 125 | A2 | 4m dark green | 35.00 | 55.00 |
| 126 | A2 | 5m gray | .30 | .55 |
| 127 | A2 | 8m red orange | .75 | 1.50 |
| 128 | A2 | 10m purple | 1.25 | 2.15 |
| 129 | A2 | 12m red | 1.40 | 2.50 |
| 130 | A2 | 20m deep blue | 2.00 | 4.00 |
| 131 | A3 | 50m choc & ultra | 9.50 | 19.00 |
| 132 | A3 | 100m bl blk & car rose | 17.50 | 24.00 |
| 133 | A3 | 200m violet & pur | 55.00 | 70.00 |
| 134 | A3 | 500m dk grn & org | 180.00 | 190.00 |

Nos. 122-134 (13)  303.55  370.15

Wider spacing between the two lines on Nos. 131-134.

King Idris
A27        A28

**1952, Apr. 15  Engr.  Perf. 11½**

| 135 | A27 | 2m yellow brown | .30 | .25 |
|---|---|---|---|---|
| 136 | A27 | 4m gray | .30 | .25 |
| 137 | A27 | 5m blue green | 20.00 | .65 |
| 138 | A27 | 8m vermilion | .90 | .55 |
| 139 | A27 | 10m purple | 20.00 | .40 |
| 140 | A27 | 12m lilac rose | 1.75 | .40 |
| 141 | A27 | 20m deep blue | 22.50 | .90 |
| 142 | A27 | 25m chocolate | 22.50 | .90 |
| 143 | A28 | 50m brown & blue | 3.00 | 1.40 |
| 144 | A28 | 100m gray blk & car rose | 5.25 | 3.00 |
| 145 | A28 | 200m dk blue & pur | 11.00 | 6.00 |
| 146 | A28 | 500m dk grn & brn orange | 37.50 | 21.00 |

Nos. 135-146 (12)  145.00  35.70

For surcharge and overprints see Nos. 168, O1-O8.

Globe — A29

**1955, Jan. 1  Photo.  Wmk. 195**

| 147 | A29 | 5m yellow brown | 2.00 | 1.30 |
|---|---|---|---|---|
| 148 | A29 | 10m green | 3.00 | 2.00 |
| 149 | A29 | 30m violet | 5.50 | 3.50 |

Nos. 147-149 (3)  10.50  6.80

Arab Postal Union founding, July 1, 1954.

Nos. 147-149 Overprinted

**1955, Aug. 1**

| 150 | A29 | 5m yellow brn | 1.00 | .65 |
|---|---|---|---|---|
| 151 | A29 | 10m green | 2.00 | 1.10 |
| 152 | A29 | 30m violet | 3.75 | 2.00 |

Nos. 150-152 (3)  6.75  3.75

Arab Postal Congress, Cairo, Mar. 15.

Emblems of Tripolitania, Cyrenaica and Fezzan with Royal Crown — A30

**1955  Engr.  Wmk. 310  Perf. 11½**

| 153 | A30 | 2m lemon | 2.00 | .70 |
|---|---|---|---|---|
| 154 | A30 | 3m slate blue | .25 | .25 |
| 155 | A30 | 4m gray green | 2.75 | 1.25 |
| 156 | A30 | 5m light blue grn | .85 | .25 |
| 157 | A30 | 10m violet | 1.50 | .25 |
| 158 | A30 | 18m crimson | .25 | .25 |
| 159 | A30 | 20m orange | .50 | .25 |
| 160 | A30 | 30m blue | .85 | .25 |
| 161 | A30 | 35m brown | 1.25 | .25 |
| 162 | A30 | 40m rose carmine | 2.00 | .60 |
| 163 | A30 | 50m olive | 1.25 | .60 |

Size: 27½x32½mm

| 164 | A30 | 100m dk green & pur | 2.75 | 1.20 |
|---|---|---|---|---|
| 165 | A30 | 200m ultra & rose car | 10.00 | 2.50 |
| 166 | A30 | 500m grn & orange | 20.00 | 12.00 |

Size: 26½x32mm

| 167 | A30 | £1 ocher, brn & yel | 30.00 | 18.00 |
|---|---|---|---|---|

Nos. 153-167 (15)  79.20  38.60

See Nos. 177-179, 192-206A.

No. 136 Surcharged

**1955, Aug. 25  Unwmk.**

| 168 | A27 | 5m on 4m gray | 2.00 | .90 |
|---|---|---|---|---|

Tomb of El Senussi, Jagbub — A31

**Perf. 13x13½**

**1956, Sept. 14  Photo.  Wmk. 195**

| 169 | A31 | 5m green | .50 | .50 |
|---|---|---|---|---|
| 170 | A31 | 10m bright violet | .60 | .50 |
| 171 | A31 | 15m rose carmine | 1.40 | 1.25 |
| 172 | A31 | 30m sapphire | 2.25 | 1.40 |

Nos. 169-172 (4)  4.75  3.65

Death centenary of the Imam Seyyid Mohammed Aly El Senussi (in 1859).

Map, Flags and UN Headquarters — A32

**1956, Dec. 14  Litho.  Perf. 13½x13**

| 173 | A32 | 15m bl, ocher & ol bis | .75 | .35 |
|---|---|---|---|---|
| 174 | A32 | 35m bl, ocher & vio brn | 1.60 | .75 |

Libya's admission to the UN, 1st anniv.

Globe and Postal Emblems — A33

## 1957 Wmk. 195 Perf. 13½x13
175 A33 15m blue 1.50 1.50
176 A33 500m yellow brown 22.00 12.00

Arab Postal Congress, Tripoli, Feb. 9.

### Emblems Type of 1955
## 1957 Wmk. 310 Engr. Perf. 11½
177 A30 1m black, yellow .25 .25
178 A30 2m bister brown .25 .25
179 A30 4m brown carmine .35 .35
Nos. 177-179 (3) .85 .85

UN Emblem and Broken Chain — A34

## Unwmk.
## 1958, Dec. 10 Photo. Perf. 14
180 A34 10m bluish violet .35 .25
181 A34 15m green .60 .35
182 A34 30m ultramarine 1.50 .85
Nos. 180-182 (3) 2.45 1.45

Universal Declaration of Human Rights, 10th anniv.

Date Palms and FAO Emblem — A35

## 1959, Dec. 5 Unwmk. Perf. 14
183 A35 10m pale vio & black .40 .25
184 A35 15m bluish grn & blk .60 .45
185 A35 45m light blue & blk 1.50 1.20
Nos. 183-185 (3) 2.50 1.90

1st Intl. Dates Conf., Tripoli, Dec. 5-11.

Arab League Center, Cairo, and Arms of Libya — A36

## Perf. 13x13½
## 1960, Mar. 22 Wmk. 328
186 A36 10m dull grn & blk .60 .35

Opening of the Arab League Center and the Arab Postal Museum in Cairo.

Emblems of WRY and UN, Arms of Libya — A37

## 1960, Apr. 7 Unwmk. Perf. 14
187 A37 10m violet & black .60 .35
188 A37 45m blue & black 1.75 1.25

World Refugee Year, 7/1/59-6/30/60.

Palm Tree and Radio Mast — A38

## 1960, Aug. 4 Engr. Perf. 13x13½
189 A38 10m violet .35 .25
190 A38 15m blue green .50 .25
191 A38 45m dk carmine rose 1.80 1.45
Nos. 189-191 (3) 2.65 1.75

3rd Arab Telecommunications Conf., Tripoli, Aug. 4.

### Emblems Type of 1955
## 1960 Wmk. 310 Engr. Perf. 11½
### Size: 18x21½mm
192 A30 1m black, gray .25 .25
193 A30 2m bis brn, buff .25 .25
194 A30 3m blue, bluish .25 .25
195 A30 4m brn car, rose .25 .25

196 A30 5m grn, greenish .25 .25
197 A30 10m vio, pale vio .25 .25
198 A30 15m brown, buff .25 .25
199 A30 20m orange, buff .50 .25
200 A30 30m red, pink .50 .25
201 A30 40m rose car, rose .75 .25
202 A30 45m blue, bluish .85 .25
203 A30 50m olive, buff .85 .25
### Size: 27½x32½mm
204 A30 100m dk grn & pur, gray 1.50 .70
205 A30 200m bl & rose car, bluish 4.25 1.40
206 A30 500m green & org, greenish 30.00 9.00
### Size: 26½x32mm
206A A30 £1 ocher, brn & grn, brn 35.00 18.00
Nos. 192-206A (16) 75.95 32.10

Watchtower and Broken Chain — A39

## 1961, Aug. 9 Photo. Unwmk.
207 A39 5m lt yel grn & brn .50 .25
208 A39 15m light blue & brn .85 .35

Issued for Army Day, Aug. 9, 1961.

Map of Zelten Oil Field and Tanker at Marsa Brega — A40

## 1961, Oct. 25 Perf. 11½
209 A40 15m ol grn & buff .50 .25
210 A40 50m red brn & pale vio 1.50 1.00
211 A40 100m ultra & blue 3.50 1.25
Nos. 209-211 (3) 5.50 2.50

Opening of first oil pipe line in Libya.

Hands Breaking Chain, Tractor and Cows — A41

Designs: 50m, Modern highways and buildings. 100m, Machinery.

## 1961, Dec. 24 Perf. 11½
### Granite Paper
212 A41 15m pale grn, grn & brown .25 .25
213 A41 50m buff & brown .90 .60
214 A41 100m sal, vio & brn 3.25 1.25
Nos. 212-214 (3) 4.40 2.10

10th anniversary of independence.

Camel Riders A42

15m, Well. 50m, Oil installations in desert.

## 1962, Feb. 20 Photo. Perf. 12
215 A42 10m choc & org brn .85 .25
216 A42 15m plum & yel grn 1.00 .60
217 A42 50m emer & ultra 2.75 2.10
a. Souv. sheet of 3, #215-217, imperf. 65.00 30.00
Nos. 215-217 (3) 4.60 2.95

Intl. Fair, Tripoli, Feb. 20-Mar. 20. Nos. 215-217 exist imperf. Value about twice that of perf.

Malaria Eradication Emblem and Palm — A43

## 1962, Apr. 7 Unwmk. Perf. 11½
218 A43 15m multicolored .60 .50
219 A43 50m grn, yel & brn 1.50 1.20

WHO drive to eradicate malaria.

Exist imperf. Value $10.

Two imperf. souvenir sheets exist, one containing the 15m, the other the 50m. Sold for 20m and 70m respectively. Value for both, $34.

Ahmed Rafik El Mehdawi (1898-1961), Poet — A44

## 1962, July 6 Engr. Perf. 13x14
220 A44 15m green .40 .25
221 A44 20m brown .85 .50

El Mehdawi, 1st death anniv.

Clasped Hands and Scout Emblem — A45

Designs: 10m, 30m, Boy Scouts. 15m, 50m, Scout emblem and tents.

## 1962, July 13 Photo. Perf. 12
222 A45 5m yel, blk & red .25 .25
223 A45 10m bl, blk & yel .50 .25
224 A45 15m multicolored .60 .50
Nos. 222-224 (3) 1.35 1.00

### Souvenir Sheet
### Imperf
225 Sheet of 3 20.00 20.00
a. A45 20m yellow, black & red 5.00 5.00
b. A45 30m blue, black & yellow 5.00 5.00
c. A45 50m blue gray, yel, blk & grn 5.00 5.00

Third Libyan Scout meeting (Philia). Nos. 222-224 exist imperf. Value for set, $3.

Drop of Oil with New City, Desert, Oil Wells and Map of Coast Line — A46

## 1962, Nov. 25 Perf. 11x11½
226 A46 15m grn & vio blk .50 .25
227 A46 50m brn org & ol 1.40 .75

Opening of the Essider Terminal Sidrah pipeline system.

Centenary Emblem — A47

## Litho. & Photo.
## 1963, Jan. 1 Perf. 11½
228 A47 10m rose, blk, red & bl .75 .40
229 A47 15m citron, blk, red & bl .85 .60
230 A47 20m gray, blk, red & bl 1.60 .85
Nos. 228-230 (3) 3.20 1.85

Centenary of the International Red Cross.

Rainbow and Arches over Map of Africa and Libya A48

## 1963, Feb. 28 Litho. Perf. 13½
231 A48 15m multicolored .50 .35
232 A48 30m multicolored .85 .35
233 A48 50m multicolored 1.80 1.00
Nos. 231-233 (3) 3.15 1.70

Tripoli Intl. Fair "Gateway of Africa," Feb. 28-Mar. 28. Every other horizontal row inverted in

sheet of 50 (25 tête bêche pairs). Value, set of tête bêche pairs, $6.50.

Date Palm and Well — A49

Designs: 15m, Camel and flock of sheep. 45m, Sower and tractor.

## 1963, Mar. 21 Photo. Perf. 11½
234 A49 10m green, lt bl & bis .50 .25
235 A49 15m pur, lt grn & bis .60 .25
236 A49 45m dk bl, sal & sep 1.60 1.00
Nos. 234-236 (3) 2.70 1.75

FAO "Freedom from Hunger" campaign.

Man with Whip and Slave Reaching for UN Emblem — A50

## 1963, Dec. 10 Unwmk. Perf. 11½
237 A50 5m red brown & bl .25 .25
238 A50 15m deep claret & bl .50 .25
239 A50 50m green & blue 1.25 .75
Nos. 237-239 (3) 2.00 1.25

Universal Declaration of Human Rights, 15th anniv.

Exhibition Hall and Finger Pointing to Libya — A51

## 1964, Feb. 28 Photo. Perf. 11½
240 A51 10m red brn, gray grn & brn 1.00 .25
241 A51 15m pur, gray grn & brn 1.40 .60
242 A51 30m dk bl, gray grn & brn 2.00 1.40
Nos. 240-242 (3) 4.40 2.25

3rd Intl. Fair, Tripoli, Feb. 28-Mar. 20.

Child Playing with Blocks — A52

Design: 15m, Child in bird's nest.

## 1964, Mar. 22 Perf. 11½
243 A52 5m multicolored .25 .25
244 A52 15m multicolored .60 .25
245 A52 45m multicolored 1.75 .85
a. Souvenir sheet of 3, #243-245, imperf. 5.00 5.00
Nos. 243-245 (3) 2.60 1.35

Children's Day. Exist imperf. Value about 1½ times that of perf. No. 245a sold for 100m.

Lungs and Stethoscope — A53

## 1964, Apr. 7 Photo. Perf. 13½x14
246 A53 20m deep purple 1.25 .60

Campaign against tuberculosis.

Map of Libya — A54

**1964, Apr. 27   Unwmk.   Perf. 11½**
247  A54  5m emerald & org  .25  .25
248  A54  50m blue & yellow  1.50  .60
First anniversary of Libyan union.

Moth Emerging from Cocoon, Veiled and Modern Women — A55

**1964, June 15   Litho. & Engraved**
249  A55  10m vio bl & lt grn  .35  .25
250  A55  20m vio blue & yel  .75  .60
251  A55  35m vio bl & pink  1.25  1.10
  a.  Souv. sheet of 3, #249-251  5.50  5.50
    Nos. 249-251 (3)  2.35  1.95
To honor Libyan women in a new epoch. No. 251a sold for 100m.

Hand Giving Scout Sign, Scout and Libyan Flags — A56

Design: 20m, Libyan Scout emblem and hands.

**1964, July 24   Photo.   Perf. 12x11½**
252  A56  10m lt bl & multi  .85  .35
253  A56  20m multicolored  1.75  .85
  a.  Souvenir sheet of 2, #252-253, imperf.  11.50  11.50
Opening of new Boy Scout headquarters; installation of Crown Prince Hassan al-Rida el Senussi as Chief Scout. No. 253a sold for 50m.
Nos. 252-253 exist imperf. Value about 1½ times that of perf.

Bayonet, Wreath and Map — A57

**1964, Aug. 9   Litho.   Perf. 14x13½**
254  A57  10m yel grn & brn  .25  .25
255  A57  20m org & blk  .75  .35
Founding of the Senussi Army.

Ahmed Bahloul el-Sharef — A58

**1964, Aug. 11   Engr.   Perf. 11½**
256  A58  15m lilac  .50  .25
257  A58  20m greenish blue  .85  .50
Poet Ahmed Bahloul el-Sharef, died 1953.

Soccer — A59

**1964, Oct. 1   Litho.   Perf. 14**
**Black Inscriptions and Gold Olympic Rings**
258  A59  5m shown  .75  .50
259  A59  10m Bicycling  .75  .50
260  A59  20m Boxing  .75  .50
261  A59  30m Sprinter  .75  .60
262  A59  35m Woman diver  .75  .60
263  A59  50m Hurdling  .75  .60
  a.  Block of 6, #258-263  5.00  5.00
18th Olympic Games, Tokyo, Oct. 10-25. No. 263a printed in sheet of 48. The two blocks in each double row are inverted in relation to the two blocks in the next row, providing various tete beche and se-tenant arrangements.
Nos. 258-263 exist imperf. Value for set, $27.50.

Perf. and imperf. souvenir sheets exist containing six 15m stamps in the designs and colors of Nos. 258-263. Sheets sold for 100m. Value for both, $32.50.

Arab Postal Union Emblem — A59a

**1964, Dec. 1   Photo.   Perf. 11x11½**
264  A59a  10m yellow & blue  .25  .25
265  A59a  15m pale vio & org brn  .50  .25
266  A59a  30m lt yel grn & brn  1.40  .85
    Nos. 264-266 (3)  2.15  1.35
Permanent Office of the APU, 10th anniv.

International Cooperation Year Emblem — A60

**1965, Jan. 1   Litho.   Perf. 14½x14**
267  A60  5m vio bl & gold  .50  .25
268  A60  15m rose car & gold  1.50  .70
Imperfs. exist. Value about twice that of perfs.
See Nos. C51-C51a.

European Bee Eater — A61

Birds: 5m, Long-legged buzzard, vert. 15m, Chestnut-bellied sandgrouse. 20m, Houbara bustard. 30m, Spotted sandgrouse. 40m, Libyan Barbary partridge, vert.

**1965, Feb. 10   Photo.   Perf. 11½**
**Granite Paper**
**Birds in Natural Colors**
269  A61  5m gray & black  1.25  .50
270  A61  10m lt bl & org brn  2.00  .55
271  A61  15m lt green & blk  2.25  .60
272  A61  20m pale lil & blk  3.75  .85
273  A61  30m tan & dark brn  4.75  1.50
274  A61  40m dull yel & blk  5.50  1.90
    Nos. 269-274 (6)  19.50  5.90

Map of Africa with Libya — A62

**1965, Feb. 28   Photo.   Perf. 11½**
**Granite Paper**
275  A62  50m multicolored  1.00  .55
4th Intl. Tripoli Fair, Feb. 28-Mar. 20.

Compass Rose, Rockets, Balloons and Stars — A63

**1965, Mar. 23   Litho.**
276  A63  10m multicolored  .25  .25
277  A63  15m multicolored  .50  .35
278  A63  50m multicolored  1.50  1.00
    Nos. 276-278 (3)  2.25  1.60
Fifth World Meteorological Day.

ITU Emblem, Old and New Communication Equipment — A64

**1965, May 17   Unwmk.**
279  A64  10m sepia  .25  .25
280  A64  20m red lilac  .35  .25
281  A64  50m lilac rose  1.25  .90
    Nos. 279-281 (3)  1.85  1.40
ITU, centenary.

Library Aflame and Lamp — A65

**1965, June   Litho.   Perf. 11½**
282  A65  15m multicolored  .50  .25
283  A65  50m multicolored  1.25  .55
Burning of the Library of Algiers, June 7, 1962.

Rose — A66

**1965, Aug.   Litho.   Perf. 14**
284  A66  1m shown  .25  .25
285  A66  2m Iris  .25  .25
286  A66  3m Opuntia  .35  .25
287  A66  4m Sunflower  .75  .25
    Nos. 284-287 (4)  1.60  1.00

Jet Plane and Globe — A67

**1965, Oct.   Photo.   Perf. 11½**
288  A67  5m multicolored  .25  .25
289  A67  10m multicolored  .50  .25
290  A67  15m multicolored  1.00  .25
    Nos. 288-290 (3)  1.75  .75
Issued to publicize Libyan Airlines.

Forum, Cyrene — A68

Designs: 100m, Arch of Trajan. 200m, Temple of Apollo, Cyrene. 500m, Antonine Temple of Jupiter, Sabratha, horiz. £1, Theater, Sabratha.

**Perf. 12x11½, 11½x12**
**1965, Dec. 24   Engr.   Wmk. 310**
291  A68  50m vio blue & olive  2.00  .60
292  A68  100m Prus bl & dp org  2.75  .85
293  A68  200m pur & Prus bl  6.50  1.50
294  A68  500m car rose & grn  15.00  4.00
295  A68  £1 grn & dp org  32.50  10.00
    Nos. 291-295 (5)  58.75  16.95
Nos. 293-295 with "Kingdom of Libia" in both Arabic and English blocked out with a blue felt-tipped pen were issued June 21, 1970, by the Republic.

Mausoleum at Germa — A69

**Perf. 11½**
**1966, Feb. 10   Unwmk.   Litho.**
296  A69  70m purple & salmon  3.00  1.00
"POLIGRAFICA & CARTEVALORI-NAPLES" and Libyan Coat of Arms printed on back in yellow green. See No. E13.
Booklet pane containing 4 No. 296 and 4 No. E13 exists. Value $30.

Globe in Space, Satellites A70

**1966, Feb. 28   Perf. 12**
297  A70  15m multi & gold  .50  .25
298  A70  45m multi & gold  1.00  .45
299  A70  55m multi & gold  1.25  .65
    Nos. 297-299 (3)  2.75  1.35
5th Intl. Fair at Tripoli, Feb. 28-Mar. 20.

Arab League Center, Cairo, and Emblem — A71

**Litho. & Photo.**
**1966, Mar. 22   Perf. 11**
300  A71  20m car, emer & blk  .35  .35
301  A71  55m brt bl, ver & blk  1.50  .65
Issued to publicize the Arab League.

**Souvenir Sheet**

WHO Headquarters, Geneva, and Emblem — A72

**1966, May 3   Litho.   Imperf.**
302  A72  50m multicolored  9.50  15.00
Inauguration of the WHO headquarters. See Nos. C55-C57.

Tuareg and Camel — A73

A74

Three Tuareg Riders A75

Design: 20m, like 10m, facing left.

**1966, June 20   Unwmk.   Perf. 10**
303  A73  10m bright red  1.25  .80
304  A73  20m ultramarine  2.75  1.50
305  A74  50m multicolored  6.00  4.00
  a.  Strip of 3, Nos. 303-305  11.00  8.50

**Imperf**
306  A75  100m multicolored  16.00  16.00

Gazelle
A76

Emblem
A77

**Perf. 13x11, 11x13**

**1966, Aug. 12**       **Litho.**
307 A76 5m lt grn, blk & red   .50   .25
308 A77 25m multicolored   .90   .35
309 A77 65m multicolored   2.50   .65
     Nos. 307-309 (3)   3.90   1.25

1st Arab Girl Scout Camp (5m); 7th Arab Boy Scout Camp, Good Daim, Libya, Aug. 12 (25m, 60m).

UNESCO
Emblem — A78

**1967, Jan.**    **Litho.**    **Perf. 10x10½**
310 A78 15m multicolored   .50   .25
311 A78 25m multicolored   1.10   .45

UNESCO, 20th anniv. (in 1966).

Castle of Columns,
Tolemaide — A79

Design: 55m, Sebha Fort, horiz.

**Perf. 13x13½, 13½x13**

**1966, Dec. 24**       **Engr.**
312 A79 25m lil, red brn & blk   .65   .35
313 A79 55m blk, lil & red brn   1.25   .65

Fair Emblem — A80

**1967, Feb. 28**    **Photo.**    **Perf. 11½**
314 A80 15m multicolored   .65   .25
315 A80 55m multicolored   1.00   .55

6th Intl. Fair, Tripoli, Feb. 28-Mar. 20.

Oil Tanker,
Marsa Al
Hariga
Terminal
A81

**1967, Feb. 14**    **Litho.**    **Perf. 10**
316 A81 60m multicolored   2.25   .75

Opening of Marsa Al Hariga oil terminal.

Tourist Year
Emblem — A82

**1967, May 1**    **Litho.**    **Perf. 10½x10**
317 A82 5m gray, blk & brt bl   .25   .25
318 A82 10m lt bl, blk & brt bl   .25   .25
319 A82 45m pink, blk & brt bl   .75   .35
     Nos. 317-319 (3)   1.25   .85

International Tourist Year.

---

Map of
Mediterranean and
Runners — A83

**1967, Sept. 8**    **Litho.**    **Perf. 10½**
320 A83 5m shown   .25   .25
321 A83 10m Javelin   .25   .25
322 A83 15m Bicyling   .25   .25
323 A83 45m Soccer   .75   .55
324 A83 75m Boxing   1.10   .75
     Nos. 320-324 (5)   2.60   2.05

5th Mediterranean Games, Tunis, Sept. 8-17.

A84

Arab League emblem and hands reaching for knowledge.

**1967, Oct. 1**    **Litho.**    **Perf. 12½x13**
325 A84 5m orange & dk pur   .25   .25
326 A84 10m brt grn & dk pur   .25   .25
327 A84 15m lilac & dk pur   .25   .25
328 A84 25m blue & dk pur   .50   .25
     Nos. 325-328 (4)   1.25   1.00

Literacy campaign.

Human Rights
Flame — A85

**1968, Jan. 15**    **Litho.**    **Perf. 13½x14**
329 A85 15m grn & vermilion   .35   .25
330 A85 60m org & vio bl   .90   .55

International Human Rights Year.

Map, Derrick, Plane
and Camel
Riders — A86

**1968, Feb. 28**    **Photo.**    **Perf. 11½**
331 A86 55m car rose, brn & yel   1.25   .75

7th Intl. Fair, Tripoli, Feb. 28-Mar. 20.

Arab League
Emblem — A87

**1968, Mar. 22**    **Engr.**    **Perf. 13½**
332 A87 10m blue gray & car   .25   .25
333 A87 45m fawn & green   .90   .65

Issued for Arab League Week.

Children, Statuary
Group — A88

Children's Day: 55m, Mother and children.

**1968, Mar. 21**    **Litho.**    **Perf. 11**
334 A88 25m gray, blk & mag   .65   .35
335 A88 55m gray & multi   1.25   .65

---

Hands Reaching for
WHO Emblem — A89

**1968, Apr. 7**    **Photo.**    **Perf. 13½x14½**
336 A89 25m rose cl, dk bl &
        gray bl   .60   .25
337 A89 55m bl, blk & gray   .90   .55

WHO, 20th anniversary.

From Oil Field to
Tanker — A90

**1968, Apr. 23**    **Litho.**    **Perf. 11**
338 A90 10m multicolored   .50   .25
339 A90 60m multicolored   1.50   .80

Opening of the Zueitina oil terminal.

Teacher and
Crowd — A91

**1968, Sept. 8**    **Litho.**    **Perf. 13½**
340 A91 5m bright pink   .25   .25
341 A91 10m orange   .25   .25
342 A91 15m blue   .25   .25
343 A91 20m emerald   .50   .50
     Nos. 340-343 (4)   1.25   1.25

Literacy campaign.

Arab Labor
Emblem — A92

**1968, Nov. 3**    **Photo.**    **Perf. 14x13½**
344 A92 10m multicolored   .25   .25
345 A92 15m multicolored   .50   .25

4th session of the Arab Labor Ministers' Conf., Tripoli, Nov. 3-10.

Wadi el Kuf
Bridge and Road
Sign — A93

**1968, Dec. 25**    **Litho.**    **Perf. 11x11½**
346 A93 25m ultra & multi   .40   .35
347 A93 60m emer & multi   1.00   .90

Opening of the Wadi el Kuf Bridge.

Television Screen
and Chart — A94

**1968, Dec. 25**    **Photo.**    **Perf. 14x13½**
348 A94 10m yellow & multi   .25   .25
349 A94 30m lilac & multi   .90   .45

Inauguration of television service, Dec. 24.

Melons — A95

---

**1969, Jan.**    **Photo.**    **Perf. 11½**
**Granite Paper**
350 A95 5m shown   .25   .25
351 A95 10m Peanuts   .25   .25
352 A95 15m Lemons   .25   .25
353 A95 20m Oranges   .40   .25
354 A95 25m Peaches   .65   .35
355 A95 35m Pears   1.25   .55
     Nos. 350-355 (6)   3.05   1.90

Nos. 350-355 with "Kingdom of Libya" in both English and Arabic blocked out with a blue felt-tipped pen were issued in December, 1971, by the Republic.

Tripoli Fair
Emblem — A96

**1969, Apr. 8**    **Granite Paper**
356 A96 25m silver & multi   .40   .25
357 A96 35m bronze & multi   .65   .35
358 A96 40m gold & multi   .75   .45
     Nos. 356-358 (3)   1.80   1.05

8th Intl. Fair, Tripoli, Mar. 6-26.

Weather Balloon
and
Observer — A97

**1969, Mar. 23**    **Photo.**    **Perf. 14x13**
359 A97 60m gray & multi   1.50   .80

World Meteorological Day, Mar. 23.

Cogwheel and
Workers — A98

**1969, Mar. 29**    **Litho.**    **Perf. 13½**
360 A98 15m blue & multi   .25   .25
361 A98 55m salmon & multi   .75   .55

10th anniversary of Social Insurance.

ILO Emblem — A99

**1969, June 1**    **Photo.**    **Perf. 14**
362 A99 10m bl grn, blk & lt ol   .25   .25
363 A99 60m car rose, blk & lt ol   .90   .65

ILO, 50th anniversary.

African Tourist
Year Emblem
A100

**1969, July**       **Perf. 11½**
**Emblem in Emerald, Light Blue &
Red**
364 A100 15m emer & silver   .45   .25
365 A100 30m blk & gold   .90   .65

Issued to publicize African Tourist Year.

**Libyan Arab Republic**

Soldiers, Tanks and
Planes — A101

**1969, Dec. 7**    **Photo.**    **Perf. 12x12½**
366 A101 5m org & multi   .45   .25
367 A101 10m ultra & multi   .70   .40
368 A101 15m multicolored   1.00   .50
369 A101 25m multicolored   1.50   .70

370 A101 45m brt bl & multi 1.75 1.10
371 A101 60m multicolored 3.00 1.50
Nos. 366-371 (6) 8.40 4.45

Establishment of the Libyan Arab Republic, Sept. 1, 1969. See Nos. 379-384.

Dish Antenna, Flags and Carrier Pigeon — A102

**1970, Mar. 1 Photo. Perf. 11½**
**Granite Paper**
372 A102 15m multicolored .70 .25
373 A102 20m multicolored 1.10 .40
374 A102 25m multicolored 1.50 .50
375 A102 40m multicolored 2.10 1.10
Nos. 372-375 (4) 5.40 2.25

Map of Arab League Countries, Flag and Emblem A102a

**1970, Mar. 22**
376 A102a 10m lt bl, brn & grn .35 .25
377 A102a 15m org, brn & grn .60 .25
378 A102a 20m ol, brn & grn 1.00 .45
Nos. 376-378 (3) 1.95 .95

25th anniversary of the Arab League.

Type A101 Redrawn — A103

**1970, May 2 Photo. Perf. 12x12½**
379 A103 5m org & multi .40 .25
380 A103 10m ultra & multi .70 .60
381 A103 15m multicolored 1.00 .50
382 A103 25m multicolored 1.50 1.40
383 A103 45m brt bl & multi 1.75 1.10
384 A103 60m multicolored 3.00 1.50
Nos. 379-384 (6) 8.35 5.35

On Nos. 379-384 the numerals are in black, the bottom inscription is in 2 lines and several other changes.

Inauguration of UPU Headquarters, Bern — A104

**1970, May 20 Photo. Perf. 11½x11**
385 A104 10m multicolored .25 .25
386 A104 25m multicolored .60 .25
387 A104 60m multicolored 1.25 .65
Nos. 385-387 (3) 2.10 1.15

Arms of Libyan Arab Republic — A105

**1970, June 20 Photo. Perf. 11**
388 A105 15m black & brt rose .25 .25
389 A105 25m vio bl, yel & brt rose .50 .25
390 A105 45m emer, yel & brt rose 1.75 .45
Nos. 388-390 (3) 2.50 .95

Evacuation of US military base in Libya.

Flags, Soldiers and Tank — A106

**1970, Sept. 1 Photo. Perf. 11x11½**
391 A106 20m multicolored .75 .25
392 A106 25m multicolored 1.00 .55
393 A106 30m blue & multi 1.60 .75
Nos. 391-393 (3) 3.35 1.55

Libyan Arab Republic, 1st anniv.

UN Emblem, Dove and Scales — A107

**1970, Oct. 24 Photo. Perf. 11x11½**
394 A107 5m org & multi .60 .35
395 A107 10m olive & multi .90 .45
396 A107 60m multicolored 2.50 .90
Nos. 394-396 (3) 4.00 1.70

25th anniversary of the United Nations.

Map and Flags of UAR, Libya, Sudan — A107a

**1970, Dec. 27 Photo. Perf. 11½**
397 A107a 15m lt grn, car & blk 7.00 2.25

Signing of the Charter of Tripoli affirming the unity of UAR, Libya and the Sudan, Dec. 27, 1970.

UN Emblem, Dove and Globe — A108

**1971, Jan. 10 Litho. Perf. 12x11½**
398 A108 15m multicolored .60 .25
399 A108 20m multicolored .90 .45
400 A108 60m lt vio & multi 2.50 .90
Nos. 398-400 (3) 4.00 1.60

UN declaration on granting of independence to colonial countries and peoples, 10th anniv.

Education Year Emblem — A109

**1971, Jan. 16**
401 A109 5m red, blk & ocher .25 .25
402 A109 10m red, blk & emer .60 .55
403 A109 20m red, blk & vio bl 1.60 .80
Nos. 401-403 (3) 2.45 1.60

International Education Year.

Al Fatah Fighter — A110

**1971, Mar. 14 Photo. Perf. 11**
404 A110 5m ol & multi .50 .25
405 A110 10m yel & multi .80 .25
406 A110 100m multicolored 1.90 .25
Nos. 404-406 (3) 3.20 .75

Fight for the liberation of Palestine.

Tripoli Fair Emblem — A111

**1971, Mar. 18 Litho. Perf. 14**
407 A111 15m multicolored .35 .25
408 A111 30m org & multi .90 .45

9th International Fair at Tripoli.

10th Anniv. of OPEC — A112

**1971, May 29 Litho. Perf. 12**
409 A112 10m yellow & brown .25 .25
410 A112 70m pink & vio bl 1.60 .65

Globe and Waves — A113

**1971, June 10 Perf. 14½x13½**
411 A113 25m brt grn, blk & vio bl .50 .25
412 A113 35m gray & multi 1.25 1.00

3rd World Telecommunications Day, May 17, 1971.

Map of Africa and Telecommunications Network — A114

**1971, June 10**
413 A114 5m yel, blk & grn .25 .25
414 A114 15m dl bl, blk & grn .40 .25

Pan-African telecommunications system.

Torchbearer and Banner — A115

**1971, June 15 Photo. Perf. 11½x12**
415 A115 5m yel & multi .25 .25
416 A115 10m org & multi .35 .35
417 A115 15m multicolored .50 .45
Nos. 415-417 (3) 1.10 1.05

Evacuation of US military base, 1st anniv.

Ramadan Suehli — A116

**1971, Aug. 24 Perf. 14x14½**
418 A116 15m multicolored .25 .25
419 A116 55m bl & multi 1.00 .55

Ramadan Suehli (1879-1920), freedom fighter.
See Nos. 422-423, 426-427, 439-440, 479-480.

Date Palm — A117

**1971, Sept. 1**
420 A117 5m multicolored .25 .25
421 A117 15m multicolored 1.25 1.25

Sept. 1, 1969 Revolution, 2nd anniv.

**Portrait Type of 1971**
Portrait: Omar el Mukhtar (1858-1931), leader of the Martyrs.

**1971, Sept. 16 Perf. 14x14½**
422 A116 5m lt grn & multi .25 .25
423 A116 100m multicolored 2.50 1.50

Gamal Abdel Nasser (1918-1970), President of Egypt — A118

**1971, Sept. 28 Photo. Perf. 11x11½**
424 A118 5m lil, grn & blk .35 .25
425 A118 15m grn, lil & blk 1.25 .25

**Portrait Type of 1971**
Ibrahim Usta Omar (1908-50), patriotic poet.

**1971, Oct. 8 Litho. Perf. 14x14½**
426 A116 25m vio bl & multi .60 .60
427 A116 30m multicolored 1.10 .45

Racial Equality Emblem — A119

**1971, Oct. 24 Perf. 13½x14½**
428 A119 25m multicolored .60 .25
429 A119 35m multicolored 1.10 .45

Intl. Year Against Racial Discrimination.

Arab Postal Union Emblem — A120

**1971, Nov. 6 Litho. Perf. 14½**
**Emblem in Black, Yellow and Blue**
430 A120 5m red .25 .25
431 A120 10m violet .40 .25
432 A120 15m bright rose lilac .40 .25
Nos. 430-432 (3) 1.05 .75

Conference of Sofar, Lebanon, establishing Arab Postal Union, 25th anniv.

Postal Union Emblem and Letter — A121

25m, 55m, APU emblem, letter and dove.

**1971, Dec. Photo. Perf. 11½x11**
433 A121 10m org brn, bl & blk .35 .25
434 A121 15m org, lt bl & blk .50 .35
435 A121 25m lt grn, org & blk .75 .55
436 A121 55m lt brn, yel & blk 1.60 .70
Nos. 433-436 (4) 3.20 1.85

10th anniversary of African Postal Union. Issued: 25m, 55m, 12/2; 10m, 15m, 12/12.

**Despite the change from milliemes to dirhams in 1972, both currencies appear on stamps until August.**

Book Year Emblem — A122

**1972, Jan. 1    Litho.    Perf. 12½x13**
437 A122 15m ultra, brn, gold &
       blk                        .35   .35
438 A122 20m gold, brn, ultra &
       blk                        .60   .60
International Book Year.

**Portrait Type of 1971**
Ahmed Gnaba (1898-1968), poet of unity.

**1972, Jan. 12        Perf. 14x14½**
439 A116 20m red & multi         .60   .25
440 A116 35m olive & multi       .85   .45

Coat of Arms — A123

**1972, Feb. 10   Photo.   Perf. 14½**
**Size: 19x23mm**
441 A123  5m gray & multi        .25   .25
442 A123 10m lt ol & multi       .25   .25
443 A123 15d lilac & multi       .25   .25
445 A123 25m lt bl & multi       .25   .25
446 A123 30m rose & multi        .35   .25
447 A123 35m lt ol & multi       .45   .25
448 A123 40m dl yel & multi      .60   .25
449 A123 45m lt grn & multi      .75   .35
451 A123 55m multicolored       1.00   .50
452 A123 60m bister & multi     1.90   .65
453 A123 65d multicolored        .75   .55
454 A123 70d lt vio & multi     1.00   .65
455 A123 80d ocher & multi      1.50   .80
456 A123 90m bl & multi         1.90   .90
**Size: 27x32mm**
**Perf. 14x14½**
457 A123 100d multicolored      2.25  1.20
458 A123 200d multicolored      3.75  2.25
459 A123 500d multicolored      9.50  6.50
460 A123 £1 multicolored       17.50 11.00
       Nos. 441-460 (18)       44.20 27.10
During the transition from millimemes and pounds to dirhams and dinars, stamps were issued in both currencies.

A124

A124a

A124b

**Coil Stamps**

**1972, July 27  Photo.  Perf. 14½x14**
461 A124  5m sl bl, ocher &
       black                    2.75  2.25
462 A124a 20m bl, lil & blk    12.00  2.25
463 A124b 50m bl, ol & blk     27.50  5.50
       Nos. 461-463 (3)        42.25 10.00
See Nos. 496-498, 575-577.

Tombs at Ghirza — A125

Designs: 10m, Kufic inscription, Agedabia, horiz. 15m, Marcus Aurelius Arch, Tripoli. 25m, Exchange of weapons, mural from Wan Amil Cave. 55m, Garamanthian (Berber) chariot, petroglyph, Wadi Zigza. 70m, Nymph Cyrene strangling a lion, bas-relief, Cyrene.

**1972, Feb. 15    Litho.    Perf. 14**
464 A125  5m lilac & multi       .50   .50
465 A125 10m multicolored        .50   .50
466 A125 25m dp org & multi     1.00   .90
467 A125 25m emer & multi       1.50   .90
468 A125 55m scar & multi       3.50   .90
469 A125 70m ultra & multi      7.00  1.25
       Nos. 464-469 (6)        14.00  4.40

Fair Emblem — A126

**1972, Mar. 1**
470 A126 25d gray & multi        .60   .25
471 A126 35d multicolored        .65   .25
472 A126 50d multicolored       1.40   .35
473 A126 70d multicolored       1.60   .60
       Nos. 470-473 (4)         4.25  1.45
10th International Fair at Tripoli.

Dissected Arm, and Heart — A127

**1972, Apr. 7            Perf. 14½**
474 A127 15d multicolored       1.50   .45
475 A127 25d multicolored       3.25  1.00
"Your heart is your health," World Health Day.

"Arab Unity" — A128

**Litho. & Engr.**
**1972, Apr. 17         Perf. 13½x13**
476 A128 15d bl, yel & blk       .25   .25
477 A128 20d lt grn, yel & blk   .60   .25
478 A128 25d lt ver, yel & blk  1.25   .80
       Nos. 476-478 (3)         2.10  1.30
Fed. of Arab Republics Foundation, 1st anniv.

**Portrait Type of 1971**
Suleiman el Baruni (1870-1940), patriotic writer.

**1972, May 1    Litho.    Perf. 14x14½**
479 A116 10m yellow & multi     1.25   .80
480 A116 70m dp org & multi     2.00  1.00

Environment Emblem — A129

**1972, Aug. 15     Litho.     Perf. 14½**
481 A129 15m red & multi         .60   .25
482 A129 55m green & multi      1.40   .40
UN Conference on Human Environment, Stockholm, June 5-16.

Olympic Emblems — A130

**1972, Aug. 26**
483 A130 25d brt bl & multi     2.00   .60
484 A130 35d red & multi        3.00  1.25
20th Olympic Games, Munich, 8/26-9/11.

Emblem and Broken Chain — A131

**1972, Oct. 1     Litho.     Perf. 14x13½**
485 A131 15d blue & multi        .40   .25
486 A131 25d yellow & multi      .90   .35
Libyan Arab Republic, 3rd anniv.

Dome of the Rock, Jerusalem — A132

**1972            Perf. 12½x13**
487 A132 10d multicolored        .40   .25
488 A132 25d multicolored        .60   .25

Nicolaus Copernicus (1473-1543), Polish Astronomer — A133

Design: 25d, Copernicus in Observatory, by Jan Matejko, horiz.

**Perf. 14½x13½, 13½x14½**
**1973, Feb. 26**
489 A133 15d yellow & multi      .40   .25
490 A133 25d blue & multi        .60   .35

Eagle and Fair Buildings — A134

**1973, Mar. 1        Perf. 13½x14½**
491 A134  5d dull red & multi    .40   .25
492 A134 10d blue grn & multi    .60   .25
493 A134 15d vio blue & multi   1.25   .25
       Nos. 491-493 (3)         2.25   .75
11th International Fair at Tripoli.

Blind Person, Books, Loom and Basket — A135

**1973, Apr. 18   Photo.   Perf. 12x11½**
494 A135 20d gray & multi       8.25  1.60
495 A135 25d dull yel & multi  12.00  5.25
Role of the blind in society.

**Numeral Type of 1972**
**Denominations in Dirhams**

A135a

A135b

A135c

**Coil Stamps**

**1973, Apr. 26  Photo.  Perf. 14½x14**
496 A135a  5d sl bl, ocher & blk 1.00  1.00
497 A135b 20d blue, lilac & blk 1.50  1.50
498 A135c 50d blue, olive & blk 5.50  5.50
       Nos. 496-498 (3)         8.00  8.00

Map of Africa — A136

**1973, May 25  Photo.  Perf. 11x11½**
499 A136 15d yel, green & brown  .50   .25
500 A136 25d lt yel grn, grn &
       blk                      1.00   .50
"Freedom in Unity" (Org. for African Unity).

INTERPOL Emblem and General Secretariat, Paris — A138

**Perf. 13½x14½**
**1973, June 30            Litho.**
501 A138 10d lilac & multi       .25   .25
502 A138 15d ocher & multi       .50   .25
503 A138 25d lt grn & multi      .75   .25
       Nos. 501-503 (3)         1.50   .75
50th anniv. of Intl. Criminal Police Org.

Map of Libya, Houses, People, Factories, Tractor — A139

**1973, July 15      Photo.      Perf. 11½**
504 A139 10d rose red, black &
       ultra                    4.25   .85
505 A139 25d ultra, blk & grn   6.00  1.90
506 A139 35d grn, blk & org    11.50  3.75
       Nos. 504-506 (3)        21.75  6.50
General census.

World Meteorological Organization Emblem — A140

**1973, Aug. 1         Perf. 12½x11**
507 A140  5d ver, blk & bl       .25   .25
508 A140 10d yel grn, blk & bl   .50   .50
Intl. meteorological cooperation, cent.

Soccer A141

**1973, Aug. 10     Photo.     Perf. 11½**
509 A141  5d yel grn & dk brn    .50   .25
510 A141 25d orange & dk brn    1.10   .70
2nd Palestinian Cup Soccer Tournament.

Torch and Grain — A142

**1973, Sept. 1      Litho.      Perf. 14**
511 A142 15d brown & multi       .50   .25
512 A142 25d emer & multi       1.40   .25
4th anniv. of Sept. 1 Revolution.

Writing Hand, Lamp and Globe — A143

**1973, Sept. 8**
513 A143 25d multicolored        .60   .60
Literacy campaign.

Gate of First City Hall — A144

**1973, Sept. 18**     *Perf. 13*
514 A144 10d shown .50 .50
515 A144 25d Khondok fountain .60 .60
516 A144 35d Clock tower .90 .35
Nos. 514-516 (3) 2.00 1.45
Centenary of Tripoli as a municipality.

Militia, Flag and
Factories — A145

**1973, Oct. 7**   Photo.   *Perf. 11½x11*
517 A145 15d yel, blk & red .50 .25
518 A145 25d green & multi .75 .35
Libyan Militia.

Revolutionary Proclamation by
Khadafy — A146

70d, as 25d, with English inscription.

**1973, Oct. 15**   Litho.   *Perf. 12½*
519 A146 25d orange & multi .50 .50
520 A146 70d green & multi 1.50 .75
Proclamation of People's Revolution by
Pres. Muammar Khadafy.

FAO Emblem,
Camel Pulling
Plow — A147

**1973, Nov. 1**   Photo.   *Perf. 11*
521 A147 10d ocher & multi .25 .25
522 A147 25d dk brn & multi .50 .50
523 A147 35d black & multi .75 .35
Nos. 521-523 (3) 1.50 1.10
World Food Org., 10th anniv.

Human Rights
Flame — A148

**1973, Dec. 20**   Photo.   *Perf. 11x11½*
524 A148 25d pur, car & dk bl .35 .35
525 A148 70d lt grn, car & dk bl 1.50 .65
Universal Declaration of Human Rights,
25th anniv.

Fish — A149

Designs: Various fish from Libyan waters.

**1973, Dec. 31**   Photo.   *Perf. 14x13½*
526 A149 5d light blue & multi .65 .50
527 A149 10d light blue & multi 1.25 .45
528 A149 15d light blue & multi 1.90 .55
529 A149 20d light blue & multi 2.75 .60
530 A149 25d light blue & multi 5.25 1.50
Nos. 526-530 (5) 11.80 3.60

**1975, Jan. 5**
526a A149 5d greenish blue & multi 2.25 1.50
527a A149 10d greenish blue & multi 4.50 1.50
528a A149 15d greenish blue & multi 4.50 1.50
529a A149 20d greenish blue & multi 6.50 .90
530a A149 25d greenish blue & multi 8.50 2.75
Nos. 526a-530a (5) 26.25 8.00

Scout, Sun and Scout
Signs — A150

**1974, Feb. 1**   Litho.   *Perf. 11½*
531 A150 5d lt blue & multi 1.25 .40
532 A150 20d rose lil & multi 3.50 .65
533 A150 25d turq grn & multi 5.75 2.60
Nos. 531-533 (3) 10.50 3.65
Libyan Boy Scouts.

Fair Emblem, Flags of
Participants — A151

**1974, Mar. 1**   Litho.   *Perf. 12x11½*
534 A151 10d lt ultra & multi .65 .40
535 A151 25d tan & multi 1.00 .55
536 A151 35d lt green & multi 1.90 .25
Nos. 534-536 (3) 3.55 1.20
12th Tripoli International Fair.

Protected Family,
WHO Emblem — A152

**1974, Apr. 7**   Litho.   *Perf. 12½*
537 A152 5d lt green & multi .35 .25
538 A152 25d red & multi .60 .60
World Health Day.

Minaret and
Star — A153

**1974, Apr. 16**    *Perf. 11½x11*
539 A153 10d pink & multi .50 .50
540 A153 25d yellow & multi 1.00 .60
541 A153 35d orange & multi 1.40 .50
Nos. 539-541 (3) 2.90 1.60
City University of Bengazi, inauguration.

UPU Emblem and
Star — A154

**1974, May 22**   Litho.   *Perf. 13½x14½*
542 A154 25d multicolored 7.50 1.10
543 A154 70d multicolored 14.00 2.25
Centenary of Universal Postal Union.

Traffic Signs — A156

**1974, June 8**   Photo.   *Perf. 11*
547 A156 5d gold & multi .25 .25
548 A156 10d gold & multi .40 .25
549 A156 25d gold & multi .50 .25
Nos. 547-549 (3) 1.15 .75
Automobile and Touring Club of Libya.

Tank, Oil Refinery,
Book — A157

Symbolic
"5"
A158

**1974, Sept. 1**   Litho.   *Perf. 14*
550 A157 5d red & multi .25 .25
551 A157 20d violet & multi .40 .40
552 A157 25d vio bl & multi .40 .40
553 A157 35d green & multi .50 .50
Nos. 550-553 (4) 1.55 1.55

**Souvenir Sheet**
*Perf. 13*
554 A158 55d yel & maroon 9.50 9.50
Revolution of Sept. 1, 5th anniv. English
inscription on No. 554.

WPY Emblem and
Crowd — A159

**1974, Oct. 19**    *Perf. 14*
555 A159 25d multicolored .35 .25
556 A159 35d lt brn & multi .75 .60
World Population Year.

Libyan Woman — A160

Libyan Costumes: 10d, 15d, Women. 20d,
Old man. 25d, Man riding camel. 50d, Man on
horseback.

**1975, Mar. 1**   Litho.   *Perf. 13x12½*
557 A160 5d org yel & multi .25 .25
558 A160 10d org yel & multi .25 .25
559 A160 15d org yel & multi .50 .25
560 A160 20d org yel & multi .75 .25
561 A160 25d org yel & multi 1.50 .75
562 A160 50d org yel & multi 2.75 .75
Nos. 557-562 (6) 6.00 2.50

Congress
Emblem — A161

**1975, Mar. 4**   Litho.   *Perf. 12x12½*
563 A161 10d brown & multi .25 .25
564 A161 25d vio & multi .40 .40
565 A161 35d gray & multi .75 .25
Nos. 563-565 (3) 1.40 .90
Arab Labor Congress.

Teacher Pointing
to Blackboard
A162

**1975, Mar. 10**    *Perf. 11½*
566 A162 10d gold & multi .25 .25
567 A162 25d gold & multi .50 .25
Teacher's Day.

Bodies, Globe,
Proclamation — A163

**1975, Apr. 7**   Litho.   *Perf. 12½*
568 A163 20d lilac & multi .40 .40
569 A163 25d emer & multi .50 .25
World Health Day.

Woman and Man in
Library — A164

**1975, May 25**   Litho.   *Perf. 12½*
570 A164 10d bl grn & multi .25 .25
571 A164 25d olive & multi .50 .50
572 A164 35d lt vio & multi .60 .60
Nos. 570-572 (3) 1.35 1.35
Libyan Arab Book Exhibition.

Festival
Emblem — A165

**1975, July 5**   Litho.   *Perf. 13x12½*
573 A165 20d lt bl & multi .40 .40
574 A165 25d orange & multi .50 .50
2nd Arab Youth Festival.

**Redrawn Type of 1973 Without
"LAR"**
**Coil Stamps**
**1975, Aug. 15**   Photo.   *Perf. 14½x14*
575 A124 5d blue, org & blk .50 .50
576 A124 20d blue, yel & blk 1.00 1.00
577 A124 50d blue, grn & blk 2.00 2.00
Nos. 575-577 (3) 3.50 3.50

Games Emblem and
Arms — A166

**1975, Aug. 23**    *Perf. 13x12½*
578 A166 10d salmon & multi .25 .25
579 A166 25d lilac & multi .50 .50
580 A166 50d yellow & multi 1.40 .40
Nos. 578-580 (3) 2.15 1.15
7th Mediterranean Games, Algiers, 8/23-9/6.

Peace Dove, Symbols
of Agriculture and
Industry — A167

Khadafy's Head Over Desert — A168

690      LIBYA

Design: 70d, Peace dove, diff.

**1975, Sept.   Litho.   Perf. 13x12½**
581 A167   25d multicolored   .40   .25
582 A167   70d multicolored   1.40   .50

**Souvenir Sheet**
*Imperf*
**Litho. & Embossed**
583 A168 100d multicolored   6.00 6.00

6th anniversary of Sept. 1 revolution. No. 583 contains one stamp with simulated perforations.

Khalil Basha
Mosque
A169

Al Kharruba
Mosque
A170

Mosques: 10d, Sidi Abdulla El Shaab. 15d, Sidi Ali El Fergani. 25d, Katikhtha. 30d, Murad Agha. 35d, Maulai Mohammed.

**1975, Dec. 13   Litho.   Perf. 12½**
584 A169   5d gray & multi   .25   .25
585 A169   10d purple & multi   .25   .25
586 A169   15d green & multi   .25   .25
587 A170   20d ocher & multi   .40   .25
588 A170   25d multicolored   .40   .25
589 A170   30d multicolored   .50   .25
590 A170   35d lilac & multi   .75   .60
    *Nos. 584-590 (7)*   2.80 2.10

Mohammed's 1405th birthday.

Arms of Libya and
People — A171

**1976, Jan. 15   Photo.   Perf. 13**
591 A171   35d blue & multi   .50   .25
592 A171   40d multicolored   .60   .25

General National (People's) Congress.

Islamic - Christian
Dialogue
Emblem — A172

**1976, Feb. 5   Litho.   Perf. 13x12½**
593 A172   40d gold & multi   .60   .25
594 A172 115d gold & multi   1.90   .90

Seminar of Islamic-Christian Dialogue, Tripoli, Feb. 1-5.

Woman Blowing
Horn — A173

National Costumes: 20d, Lancer. 30d, Drummer. 40d, Bagpiper. 100d, Woman carrying jug on head.

**1976, Mar. 1   Litho.   Perf. 13x12½**
595 A173   10d multicolored   .25   .25
596 A173   20d multicolored   .50   .40
597 A173   30d pink & multi   1.00   .25
598 A173   40d multicolored   1.25   .25
599 A173 100d yel & multi   3.00   .50
    *Nos. 595-599 (5)*   6.00 1.65

14th Tripoli International Fair.

Telephones, 1876
and 1976, ITU
and UPU
Emblems — A174

70d, Alexander Graham Bell, telephone, satellites, radar, ITU & UPU emblems.

**1976, Mar. 10   Photo.   Perf. 13**
600 A174   40d multicolored   2.50   .80
  a.   Souvenir sheet of 4   10.00 10.00
601 A174   70d multicolored   4.00   .80
  a.   Souvenir sheet of 4   16.50 16.50

Centenary of first telephone call by Alexander Graham Bell, Mar. 10, 1876.
Nos. 600a and 601a exist imperf. Value, both sheets $100.

Mother and
Child — A175

**1976, Mar. 21   Perf. 12**
602 A175   85d gray & multi   1.50 1.25
603 A175 110d pink & multi   1.60 1.50

International Children's Day.

Hands, Eye and
Head — A176

**1976, Apr. 7   Photo.   Perf. 13½x13**
604 A176   30d multicolored   .35   .35
605 A176   35d multicolored   .50   .50
606 A176   40d multicolored   .60   .60
    *Nos. 604-606 (3)*   1.45 1.45

"Foresight prevents blindness;" World Health Day.

Little
Bittern — A177

Birds of Libya: 10d, Great gray shrike. 15d, Songbird. 20d, European bee-eater, vert. 25d, Hoopoe.

**Perf. 13x13½, 13½x13**
**1976, May 1   Litho.**
607 A177   5d orange & multi   .65   .50
608 A177   10d ultra & multi   1.40 1.10
609 A177   15d rose & multi   2.75 1.40
610 A177   20d yellow & multi   4.75 1.50
611 A177   25d blue & multi   9.50 2.75
    *Nos. 607-611 (5)*   19.05 7.25

Al Barambekh — A178

Designs: 15d, Whale, horiz. 30d, Lizard (alwaral), horiz. 40d, Mastodon skull, horiz. 70d, Hawk. 115d, Wild mountain sheep.

**1976, June 20   Litho.   Perf. 12½**
612 A178   10d multicolored   1.40 1.10
613 A178   15d multicolored   2.50 1.90
614 A178   30d multicolored   3.00 2.40
615 A178   40d multicolored   5.00 4.25
616 A178   70d multicolored   8.75 7.25
617 A178 115d multicolored   14.50 12.25
    *Nos. 612-617 (6)*   35.15 29.15

Museum of Natural History.

Bicycling — A179

**1976, July 17   Litho.   Perf. 12x11½**
**Granite Paper**
618 A179   15d shown   .25   .25
619 A179   25d Boxing   .50   .50
620 A179   70d Soccer   1.50 1.50
    *Nos. 618-620 (3)*   2.25 2.25

**Souvenir Sheet**
621 A179 150d Symbolic of
    various sports 16.00 16.00

21st Olympic Games, Montreal, Canada, July 17-Aug. 1.

Tree Growing from
Globe — A180

**1976, Aug. 9   Perf. 13**
622 A180 115d multicolored   1.25   .90

5th Conference of Non-Aligned Countries, Colombo, Sri Lanka, Aug. 9-19.

Beginning with No. 622 numerous issues are printed with multiple coats of arms in pale green on back of stamps.

Symbols of Agriculture
and Industry — A181

Drummer
and
Pipeline
A182

**1976, Sept. 1   Perf. 14½x14**
623 A181   30d yel & multi   .40   .25
624 A181   40d multicolored   .50   .25
625 A181 100d multicolored   1.25   .90
    *Nos. 623-625 (3)*   2.15 1.40

**Souvenir Sheet**
**Perf. 13**
626 A182 200d multicolored   6.00 6.00

Sept. 1 Revolution, 7th anniv.

Sports, Torch and
Emblems — A183

145d, Symbolic wrestlers and various emblems.

**1976, Oct. 6   Litho.   Perf. 13**
627 A183   15d multicolored   .25   .25
628 A183   30d multicolored   .35   .35
629 A183 100d multicolored   1.60   .90
    *Nos. 627-629 (3)*   2.20 1.50

**Souvenir Sheet**
630 A183 145d multi, horiz.   4.50 4.50

5th Arab Games, Damascus, Syria.

Chess Board, Rook,
Knight, Emblem — A184

**1976, Oct. 24   Photo.   Perf. 11½**
631 A184   15d pink & multi   2.10   .45
632 A184   30d buff & multi   3.50 1.00
633 A184 100d multicolored   10.50 2.00
    *Nos. 631-633 (3)*   16.10 3.45

The "Against" (protest) Chess Olympiad, Tripoli, Oct. 24-Nov. 15.

A185

Designs: Various local flowers.

**1976, Nov. 1   Photo.   Perf. 11½**
**Granite Paper**
634 A185   15d lilac & multi   .35   .35
635 A185   20d multicolored   .35   .35
636 A185   35d yellow & multi   .80   .25
637 A185   40d salmon & multi   1.25   .35
638 A185   70d multicolored   3.00   .50
    *Nos. 634-638 (5)*   5.75 1.80

International Archives Council Emblem
and Document — A186

**1976, Nov. 10   Litho.   Perf. 13x13½**
639 A186   15d brown, org & buff   .25   .25
640 A186   35d brn, brt grn & buff   .35   .35
641 A186   70d brown, blue & buff   .75   .75
    *Nos. 639-641 (3)*   1.35 1.35

Arab Regional Branch of International Council on Archives, Baghdad.

Holy Ka'aba and
Pilgrims — A187

**1976, Dec. 12   Litho.   Perf. 14**
642 A187   15d multicolored   .25   .25
643 A187   30d multicolored   .25   .25
644 A187   70d multicolored   .80   .80
645 A187 100d multicolored   1.00 1.00
    *Nos. 642-645 (4)*   2.30 2.30

Pilgrimage to Mecca.

Numeral — A188

**Coil Stamps**
**1977, Jan. 15   Photo.   Perf. 14½x14**
646 A188   5d multicolored   .25   .25
647 A188   20d multicolored   .35   .35
648 A188   50d multicolored   .90   .90
    *Nos. 646-648 (3)*   1.50 1.50

Covered
Basket — A189

Designs: 20d, Leather bag. 30d, Vase. 40d, Embroidered slippers. 50d, Ornate saddle. 100d, Horse with saddle and harness.

**1977, Mar. 1    Litho.    Perf. 12½x12**
| | | | | |
|---|---|---|---|---|
| 649 | A189 | 10d multicolored | .25 | .25 |
| 650 | A189 | 20d multicolored | .25 | .25 |
| 651 | A189 | 30d multicolored | .35 | .25 |
| 652 | A189 | 40d multicolored | .60 | .35 |
| 653 | A189 | 50d multicolored | 1.00 | .35 |
| | | Nos. 649-653 (5) | 2.45 | 1.45 |

**Souvenir Sheet**
*Imperf*

654 A189 100d multicolored    4.50 4.50

15th Tripoli International Fair. No. 654 contains one stamp 49x53mm with simulated perforations.

Girl and Flowers, UNICEF Emblem — A190

Children's drawings, UNICEF Emblem and: 30d, Clothing store. 40d, Farm yard.

**1977, Mar. 28    Litho.    Perf. 13x13½**
| | | | | |
|---|---|---|---|---|
| 655 | A190 | 10d multicolored | .35 | .25 |
| 656 | A190 | 30d multicolored | .60 | .35 |
| 657 | A190 | 40d multicolored | .75 | .35 |
| | | Nos. 655-657 (3) | 1.70 | 1.10 |

Children's Day.

Gun, Fighters, UN Headquarters A191

**1977, Mar. 13    Perf. 13½**
| | | | | |
|---|---|---|---|---|
| 658 | A191 | 15d multicolored | .25 | .25 |
| 659 | A191 | 25d multicolored | .25 | .25 |
| 660 | A191 | 70d multicolored | 1.25 | 1.25 |
| | | Nos. 658-660 (3) | 1.75 | 1.75 |

Battle of Al-Karamah, 9th anniversary.

Child, Raindrop, WHO Emblem — A192

**1977, Apr. 7    Litho.    Perf. 13x12½**
| | | | | |
|---|---|---|---|---|
| 661 | A192 | 15d multicolored | .25 | .25 |
| 662 | A192 | 30d multicolored | .50 | .50 |

World Health Day.

Arab Postal Union, 25th Anniv. — A193

**1977, Apr. 12    Perf. 13½**
| | | | | |
|---|---|---|---|---|
| 663 | A193 | 15d multicolored | .25 | .25 |
| 664 | A193 | 30d multicolored | .35 | .35 |
| 665 | A193 | 40d multicolored | .50 | .50 |
| | | Nos. 663-665 (3) | 1.10 | 1.10 |

Maps of Africa and Libya — A194

**1977, May 8    Litho.    Perf. 14x13½**
| | | | | |
|---|---|---|---|---|
| 666 | A194 | 40d multicolored | 1.50 | 1.25 |
| 667 | A194 | 70d multicolored | 2.25 | 1.90 |

African Labor Day.

Map of Libya and Heart — A195

**1977, May 10    Perf. 14½x14**
| | | | | |
|---|---|---|---|---|
| 668 | A195 | 5d multicolored | .35 | .25 |
| 669 | A195 | 10d multicolored | .50 | .35 |
| 670 | A195 | 30d multicolored | 1.40 | .60 |
| | | Nos. 668-670 (3) | 2.25 | 1.20 |

Libyan Red Crescent Society.

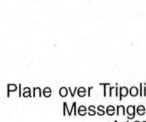

Electronic Tree, ITU Emblem, Satellite and Radar — A196

Electronic Tree, ITU Emblem and: 115d, Communications satellite, Montreal Olympics emblem, boxer on TV screen. 200d, Spacecraft over earth. 300d, Solar system.

**1977, May 17    Litho.    Perf. 13½x13**
| | | | | |
|---|---|---|---|---|
| 671 | A196 | 60d multicolored | .80 | .80 |
| 672 | A196 | 115d multicolored | 2.00 | 2.00 |
| 673 | A196 | 200d multicolored | 3.75 | 3.75 |
| | | Nos. 671-673 (3) | 6.55 | 6.55 |

**Souvenir Sheet**

674 A196 300d multicolored    8.50 6.50

9th World Telecommunications Day. No. 674 contains one stamp 52x35mm.
Nos. 671-673 exist imperf. Value, set $45. They also exist in miniature sheets of 4, perf and imperf. Values: set perf, $100; set imperf, $135.

Plane over Tripoli, Messenger — A197

UPU Emblem and: 25d, Concorde, messenger on horseback. 150d, Loading transport plane and messenger riding camel. 300d, Graf Zeppelin LZ127 over Tripoli.

**1977, May 17    Litho.    Perf. 13½**
| | | | | |
|---|---|---|---|---|
| 675 | A197 | 20d multicolored | .80 | .80 |
| 676 | A197 | 25d multicolored | 1.75 | 1.75 |
| 677 | A197 | 150d multicolored | 3.50 | 3.50 |
| | | Nos. 675-677 (3) | 6.05 | 6.05 |

**Souvenir Sheet**

678 A197 300d multicolored    8.50 6.50

UPU centenary (in 1974). No. 678 contains one stamp 52x35mm.
Nos. 675-678 exist imperf. Values: set $45; souvenir sheet, $50. Nos. 675-677 also exist in miniature sheets of 4, perf and imperf. Values: set perf, $60; set imperf, $125.

Mosque — A198

Various Mosques. 50d, 100d, vertical.

**1977, June 1    Photo.    Perf. 14**
| | | | | |
|---|---|---|---|---|
| 679 | A198 | 40d multicolored | .55 | .55 |
| 680 | A198 | 50d multicolored | .80 | .80 |
| 681 | A198 | 70d multicolored | 1.10 | 1.10 |
| 682 | A198 | 90d multicolored | 1.40 | 1.40 |
| 683 | A198 | 100d multicolored | 1.60 | 1.60 |
| 684 | A198 | 115d multicolored | 2.10 | 2.10 |
| | | Nos. 679-684 (6) | 7.55 | 7.55 |

Palestinian Archbishop Hilarion Capucci, Jailed by Israel in 1974, Map of Palestine — A199

**1977, Aug. 18    Litho.    Perf. 13½**
| | | | | |
|---|---|---|---|---|
| 687 | A199 | 30d multicolored | .40 | .40 |
| 688 | A199 | 40d multicolored | .55 | .55 |
| 689 | A199 | 115d multicolored | 2.10 | 1.00 |
| | | Nos. 687-689 (3) | 3.05 | 1.95 |

Raised Hands, Pylons, Wheel, Buildings — A200

Star and Ornament — A201

**1977, Sept. 1    Litho.    Perf. 13½x12½**
| | | | | |
|---|---|---|---|---|
| 690 | A200 | 15d multicolored | .25 | .25 |
| 691 | A200 | 30d multicolored | .35 | .35 |
| 692 | A200 | 85d multicolored | 1.25 | .60 |
| | | Nos. 690-692 (3) | 1.85 | 1.20 |

**Souvenir Sheet**
**Perf. 12½**

693 A201 100d gold & multi    5.00 3.50

8th anniversary of Sept. 1 Revolution.

Team Handball A202

**1977, Oct. 8    Perf. 13½**
| | | | | |
|---|---|---|---|---|
| 694 | A202 | 5d Swimmers, vert. | .25 | .25 |
| 695 | A202 | 10d shown | .25 | .25 |
| 696 | A202 | 15d Soccer, vert. | .25 | .25 |
| 697 | A202 | 25d Table tennis | .75 | .75 |
| 698 | A202 | 40d Basketball, vert. | 1.60 | .90 |
| | | Nos. 694-698 (5) | 3.10 | 2.40 |

7th Arab School Games.

Steeplechase A203

Show Emblem and: 10d, Bedouin on horseback. 15d, Show emblem (Horse and "7"), vert. 45d, Steeplechase. 100d, Hurdles. 115d, Bedouins on horseback.

**1977, Oct. 10    Perf. 14½**
| | | | | |
|---|---|---|---|---|
| 699 | A203 | 5d multicolored | .25 | .25 |
| 700 | A203 | 10d multicolored | .25 | .25 |
| 701 | A203 | 15d multicolored | .35 | .35 |
| 702 | A203 | 45d multicolored | .90 | .90 |
| 703 | A203 | 115d multicolored | 2.00 | 2.00 |
| | | Nos. 699-703 (5) | 3.75 | 3.75 |

**Souvenir Sheet**

704 A203 100d multicolored    4.50 4.50

7th Intl. Turf Championships, Tripoli, Oct. 1977.

Dome of the Rock, Jerusalem — A204

**1977, Oct. 14    Perf. 14½x14**
| | | | | |
|---|---|---|---|---|
| 705 | A204 | 5d multicolored | .30 | .25 |
| 706 | A204 | 10d multicolored | .45 | .25 |

Palestinian fighters and their families.

"The Green Book" A205

35d, Hands with broken chain holding hook over citadel. 40d, Hands above chaos. 115d, Dove and Green Book rising from Africa, world map.

**1977    Litho.    Perf. 14**
| | | | | |
|---|---|---|---|---|
| 707 | A205 | Strip of 3 | 2.75 | 2.75 |
| a. | | 35d multicolored | .35 | .35 |
| b. | | 40d multicolored | .50 | .50 |
| c. | | 115d multicolored | 1.75 | 1.75 |

The Green Book, by Khadafy outlines Libyan democracy. Green descriptive inscription on back beneath gum, in English on 35d, French on 40d, Arabic on 115d.

Emblems A206

**1977    Perf. 12½x13**
| | | | | |
|---|---|---|---|---|
| 708 | A206 | 5d multicolored | .60 | .25 |
| 709 | A206 | 15d multicolored | .80 | .25 |
| 710 | A206 | 30d multicolored | 1.10 | .35 |
| | | Nos. 708-710 (3) | 2.50 | .85 |

Standardization Day.

Elephant hunt. — A207

Rock Carvings, Wadi Mathendous, c. 8000 B.C.: 10d, Crocodile and Young. 20d, Giraffe, vert. 30d, Antelope. 40d, Trumpeting elephant.

**1978, Jan. 1    Perf. 12½x13, 13x12½**
| | | | | |
|---|---|---|---|---|
| 711 | A207 | 10d multicolored | .25 | .25 |
| 712 | A207 | 15d multicolored | .25 | .25 |
| 713 | A207 | 20d multicolored | .35 | .35 |
| 714 | A207 | 30d multicolored | .60 | .60 |
| 715 | A207 | 40d multicolored | 1.00 | 1.00 |
| | | Nos. 711-715 (5) | 2.45 | 2.45 |

Silver Pendant — A208

Silver Jewelry: 10d, Ornamental plate. 20d, Necklace with pendants. 25d, Crescent-shaped brooch. 115d, Armband.

**1978, Mar. 1    Litho.    Perf. 13x12½**
| | | | | |
|---|---|---|---|---|
| 716 | A208 | 5d multicolored | .25 | .25 |
| 717 | A208 | 10d multicolored | .25 | .25 |
| 718 | A208 | 20d multicolored | .25 | .25 |
| 719 | A208 | 25d multicolored | .25 | .25 |
| 720 | A208 | 115d multicolored | 1.50 | 1.50 |
| | | Nos. 716-720 (5) | 2.50 | 2.50 |

Tripoli International Fair.

Emblem, Compass and Lightning — A209

**1978, Mar. 10    Perf. 13½**
| | | | | |
|---|---|---|---|---|
| 721 | A209 | 30d multicolored | .50 | .50 |
| 722 | A209 | 115d multicolored | 2.00 | 2.00 |

Arab Cultural Education Organization.

Children's Drawings and UNICEF Emblem — A210

a, Dancing. b, Children with posters. c, Shopping street. d, Playground. e, Bride and attendants.

**1978, Mar. 21**
723 A210 40d Strip of 5, #a.-e.  7.25 7.25
Children's Day.

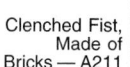

Clenched Fist, Made of Bricks — A211

**1978, Mar. 22**
728 A211 30d multicolored  .65 .40
729 A211 115d multicolored  1.50 .70
Determination of Arab people.

Blood Pressure Gauge, WHO Emblem — A212

**1978, Apr. 7**  Perf. 13x12½
730 A212 30d multicolored  .35 .35
731 A212 115d multicolored  1.75 .90
World Health Day, drive against hypertension.

Antenna and ITU Emblem — A213

**1978, May 17  Photo.  Perf. 13½**
732 A213 30d silver & multi  .35 .25
733 A213 115d gold & multi  1.50 .65
10th World Telecommunications Day.

Games Emblem — A214

**1978, July 13  Litho.  Perf. 12½**
734 A214 15d multicolored  .25 .25
735 A214 30d multicolored  .35 .35
736 A214 115d multicolored  1.50 1.50
Nos. 734-736 (3)  2.10 2.10
3rd African Games, Algiers, 1978.

Inauguration of Tripoli International Airport — A215

**1978, Aug. 10  Litho.  Perf. 13½**
737 A215 40d shown  .50 .50
738 A215 115d Terminal  2.00 .90

View of Ankara — A216

**1978, Aug. 17**
739 A216 30d multicolored  .50 .25
740 A216 35d multicolored  .60 .35
741 A216 115d multicolored  1.60 1.60
Nos. 739-741 (3)  2.70 2.20
Turkish-Libyan friendship.

Soldiers, Jet, Ship — A217

35d, Tower, Green Book, oil derrick. 100d, View of Tripoli with mosque and modern buildings. 115d, View of Tripoli within cogwheel.

**1978, Sept. 1  Perf. 14½**
742 A217 30d multicolored  .50 .50
743 A217 35d org & multi  .35 .35
744 A217 115d blue & multi  1.50 1.25
Nos. 742-744 (3)  2.35 2.10
**Souvenir Sheet**
745 A217 100d multicolored  2.75 2.75
9th anniversary of Sept. 1 Revolution. No. 745 contains one 50x41mm stamp.

Quarry and Symposium Emblem — A218

Designs: 40d, Oasis lake. 115d, Crater.

**1978, Sept. 16  Perf. 13½**
746 A218 30d multicolored  .50 .50
747 A218 40d multicolored  .60 .60
748 A218 115d multicolored  2.00 2.00
Nos. 746-748 (3)  3.10 3.10
2nd Symposium on Libyan Geology.

Green Book and Three Races — A219

**1978, Oct. 18  Perf. 12½**
749 A219 30d multicolored  .25 .25
750 A219 40d multicolored  .50 .50
751 A219 115d multicolored  1.25 1.25
Nos. 749-751 (3)  2.00 2.00
International Anti-Apartheid Year.

Pilgrims, Minarets, Holy Kaaba — A220

**1978, Nov. 9  Photo.  Perf. 12**
752 A220 5d multicolored  .25 .25
753 A220 10d multicolored  .25 .25
754 A220 15d multicolored  .25 .25
755 A220 20d multicolored  .25 .25
Nos. 752-755 (4)  1.00 1.00
Pilgrimage to Mecca.

Handclasp over Globe — A221

**1978, Nov. 10  Litho.  Perf. 13½**
756 A221 30d multicolored  .40 .30
757 A221 40d multicolored  .50 .40
758 A221 115d multicolored  1.50 1.25
Nos. 756-758 (3)  2.40 1.95
Technical Cooperation Among Developing Countries Conf., Buenos Aires, Argentina, Sept. 1978.

Fists, Guns, Map of Israel — A222

40d, 115d, Map of Arab countries and Israel, eagle and crowd. 145d, like 30d.

**1978, Dec. 5  Litho.  Perf. 13½**
759 A222 30d multi  .35 .35
760 A222 40d multi, horiz.  .50 .50
761 A222 115d multi, horiz.  1.25 1.25
762 A222 145d multi  1.50 .90
Nos. 759-762 (4)  3.60 3.00
Anti-Israel Summit Conf., Baghdad, Dec. 2-8.

Scales, Globe and Human Rights Flame — A223

**1978, Dec. 10**
763 A223 15d multicolored  .25 .25
764 A223 30d multicolored  .50 .50
765 A223 115d multicolored  1.25 1.25
Nos. 763-765 (3)  2.00 2.00
Universal Declaration of Human Rights, 30th anniv.

Libyan Fort and Horse Racing — A224

**1978, Dec. 11**
766 A224 20d multicolored  .40 .25
767 A224 40d multicolored  .50 .50
768 A224 115d multicolored  1.50 1.50
Nos. 766-768 (3)  2.40 2.25
Libyan Study Center.

Lilienthal's Glider, 1896 — A225

25d, Spirit of St. Louis, 1927. 30d, Adm. Byrd's Polar flight, 1929. 50d, Graf Zeppelin, 1934, hydroplane and storks. 115d, Wilbur and Orville Wright and Flyer A. No. 774, Icarus falling. No. 775, Eagle and Boeing 727.

**1978, Dec. 26  Litho.  Perf. 14**
769 A225 20d multicolored  .25 .25
770 A225 25d multicolored  .45 .45
771 A225 30d multicolored  1.40 1.40
772 A225 50d multicolored  1.60 1.60
773 A225 115d multicolored  1.40 1.40
Nos. 769-773 (5)  5.10 5.10
**Souvenir Sheets**
774 A225 100d multicolored  3.00 3.00
775 A225 100d multicolored  3.00 3.00
75th anniversary of 1st powered flight. Nos. 769-773 issued also in sheets of 4. Value, set perf. $45. Also exists imperf. Nos. 774-775 exist imperf. Value, pair $50.

Mounted Stag's Head — A226

**Coil Stamps**
**1979, Jan. 15  Photo.  Perf. 14½x14**
776 A226 5d multicolored  .35 .35
777 A226 20d multicolored  .75 .75
778 A226 50d multicolored  1.50 1.50
Nos. 776-778 (3)  2.60 2.60

Carpobrotus Acinaciformis A227

Flora of Libya: 15d, Caralluma europaea. 20d, Arum cirenaicum. 35d, Lavatera arborea. 40d, Capparis spinosa. 50d, Ranunculus asiaticus.

**1979, May 15  Litho.  Perf. 14**
779 A227 10d multicolored  .25 .25
780 A227 15d multicolored  .25 .25
781 A227 20d multicolored  .25 .25
782 A227 35d multicolored  .60 .60
783 A227 40d multicolored  .60 .60
784 A227 50d multicolored  .75 .75
Nos. 779-784 (6)  2.70 2.70

People, Torch, Olive Branches — A228

**1979  Litho.  Perf. 13x12½**
**Size: 18x23mm**
785 A228 5d multi  .25 .25
786 A228 10d multi  .25 .25
787 A228 15d multi  .25 .25
788 A228 30d multi  .35 .25
789 A228 50d multi  .50 .25
790 A228 60d multi  .60 .35
791 A228 70d multi  .75 .35
792 A228 100d multi  1.25 .60
793 A228 115d multi  1.25 .60
**Perf. 13½**
**Size: 26½x32mm**
794 A228 200d multi  1.90 1.25
795 A228 500d multi  4.75 2.50
796 A228 1000d multi  10.00 6.25
Nos. 785-796 (12)  22.10 13.15
See Nos. 1053-1055.

Tortoise — A229

Animals: 10d, Antelope. 15d, Hedgehog. 20d, Porcupine. 30d, Arabian camel. 35d, African wildcat. 45d, Gazelle. 115d, Cheetah. 10d, 30d, 35d, 45d, vert.

**1979, Feb. 1  Litho.  Perf. 14½**
797 A229 5d multicolored  .25 .25
798 A229 10d multicolored  .25 .25
799 A229 15d multicolored  .65 .65
800 A229 20d multicolored  .65 .65
801 A229 30d multicolored  1.10 .65
802 A229 35d multicolored  1.50 .65
803 A229 45d multicolored  1.75 .80
804 A229 115d multicolored  3.50 1.25
Nos. 797-804 (8)  9.65 5.15

Rug and Tripoli Fair Emblem A230

Tripoli Fair emblem and various rugs.

**1979, Mar. 1  Litho.  Perf. 11**
805 A230 10d multicolored  .25 .25
806 A230 15d multicolored  .25 .25
807 A230 30d multicolored  .35 .35
808 A230 45d multicolored  .50 .50
809 A230 115d multicolored  1.25 1.25
Nos. 805-809 (5)  2.60 2.60
17th Tripoli Fair.
Exist imperf. Value, set $30.

Children's Drawings and IYC Emblem — A231

a, Families and planes. b, Shepherd, sheep and dog. c, Beach umbrellas. d, Boat in storm. e, Traffic policeman.

**1979, Mar. 20**     **Perf. 13½**
810 A231 20d Strip of 5, #a.-e.    5.00 3.50

Intl. Year of the Child.
Exists imperf. Value $30.

Book, World Map, Arab Achievements A232

**1979, Mar. 22**     **Perf. 13**
815 A232 45d multicolored    .50 .50
816 A232 70d multicolored    .75 .75

WMO Emblem, Weather Map and Tower — A233

**1979, Mar. 23**
817 A233 15d multicolored    .25 .25
818 A233 30d multicolored    .35 .35
819 A233 50d multicolored    .60 .60
   Nos. 817-819 (3)    1.20 1.20

World Meteorological Day.

Medical Services, WHO Emblem A234

**1979, Apr. 7**
820 A234 40d multicolored    .60 .60

Farmer Plowing and Sheep A235

**1979, Sept. 1**    **Litho.**    **Perf. 14½**
821 A235   Block of 4    1.00 1.00
  a.   15d Harvester, sheep    .25 .25
  b.   15d Men holding Green Book    .25 .25
  c.   15d Oil field    .25 .25
  d.   15d Oil refinery    .25 .25
822 A235   Block of 4    2.00 2.00
  a.   30d Dish antenna    .40 .40
  b.   30d Hospital    .40 .40
  c.   30d Doctor examining patient    .40 .40
  d.   30d Surgery    .40 .40
823 A235   Block of 4    3.00 3.00
  a.   40d Street, Tripoli    .50 .50
  b.   40d Steel mill    .50 .50
  c.   40d Tanks    .50 .50
  d.   40d Tuareg horsemen    .50 .50
824 A235   Block of 4    4.00 4.00
  a.   70d Revolutionaries, Green Book    .90 .90
  b.   70d Crowd, map of Libya    .90 .90
  c.   70d Mullah    .90 .90
  d.   70d Student    .90 .90
   Nos. 821-824 (4)    10.00 10.00

**Souvenir Sheets**
*Imperf*
825 A235 50d Revolution symbols, Green Book    2.50 2.50
826 A235 50d Monument    2.50 2.50

Sept. 1st revolution, 10th anniversary.

Volleyball — A236

**1979, Sept. 10**
827 A236 45d shown    .50 .50
828 A236 115d Soccer    1.25 1.25

Universiade '79 World University Games, Mexico City, Sept.
Exists imperf. Value, set $17.50.

Mediterranean Games, Split, Yugoslavia A237

**1979, Sept. 15**   **Litho.**   **Perf. 12x11½**
829 A237 15d multicolored    .50 .50
830 A237 30d multicolored    1.40 1.00
831 A237 70d multicolored    3.50 1.00
   Nos. 829-831 (3)    5.40 2.00

Exhibition Emblem — A238

**1979, Sept. 25**   **Photo.**   **Perf. 11½x11**
832 A238 45d multicolored    .50 .50
833 A238 115d multicolored    1.50 1.50

TELECOM '79, 3rd World Telecommunications Exhibition, Geneva, Sept. 20-26.

A239

No. 834: a, 10d, Seminar emblem, Green Book, crowd. b, 35d, Meeting hall (Size: 67x43½mm). c, 100d, Col. Khadafy. No. 835, Central portion of #834c.

**1979, Oct. 1**
834 A239   Strip of 3, #a.-c.    2.50 2.50
**Size: 87x114mm**
*Imperf*
835 A239 100d multicolored    3.50 3.50

Intl. Seminar of the Green Book, Benghazi, Oct. 1-3. No. 834 has continuous design.

Evacuation of Foreign Forces A240

**1979, Oct. 7**
837 A240 30d shown    .60 .40
838 A240 40d Tuareg horsemen    .90 .50

**Souvenir Sheet**
*Imperf*
839 A240 100d Vignettes    3.00 3.00

Cyclist, Championship Emblem A241

15d, Cyclist, emblem on left side. 30d, Two cyclists, emblem on right side.

**1979, Nov. 21**
840 A241 15d shown    .25 .25
841 A241 30d multicolored    .50 .50

Junior Cycling Championships, Tripoli, Nov. 21-23. Issued in sheetlets of 4.

Hurdles, Olympic Rings, Moscow '80 Emblem A242

**1979, Nov. 21**
842 A242   45d Equestrian    .50 .50
843 A242   60d Javelin    .75 .75
844 A242   115d Hurdles    1.50 1.50
845 A242   160d Soccer    1.75 1.75
   Nos. 842-845 (4)    4.50 4.50

**Souvenir Sheets**
846 A242 150d shown    3.75 3.75
847 A242 150d like #845    3.75 3.75

Pre-Olympics (Moscow '80 Olympic Games). Nos. 842-845 issued in sheetlets of 4 and sheets of 20 (4x5) with silver Moscow '80 Emblem covering background of every 20 stamps. Value, set of sheetlets of 4, $45.
Nos. 842-847 exist imperf. Values: set $55; souvenir sheets, $90.

Intl. Day of Cooperation with Palestinian People — A242a

**1979, Nov. 29**   **Photo.**   **Perf. 12**
847A A242a 30d multicolored    .25 .25
847B A242a 115d multicolored    1.75 1.75

Tug of War, Jumping A243

National Games: No. 848, Polo, leap frog. No. 849, Racing, ball game, No. 850, Wrestling, log rolling. No. 852, Horsemen.

**1980, Feb. 15**    **Perf. 14½**
848 A243   Block of 4, #a.-d.    1.00 1.00
849 A243   Block of 4, #a.-d.    1.00 1.00
850 A243   Block of 4, #a.-d.    1.00 1.00
851 A243   Block of 4, #a.-d.    2.00 2.00
852 A243   Block of 4, #a.-d.    3.50 3.50
   Nos. 848-852 (5)    8.50 8.50

Battles A244

No. 853: a, 20d, Gardabia, 1915. b, 35d, same. No. 854: a, 20d, Shoghab, 1913. b, 35d, same. No. 855: a, 20d, Fundugh Al-Shibani, 1922. b, 35d, same. No. 856: a, 20d, Ghira. b, 35d, same.

Pairs have continuous design.

**1980**    **Litho.**    **Perf. 14½**
853 A244   Pair, #a.-b.    1.25 1.25
854 A244   Pair, #a.-b.    1.25 1.25
855 A244   Pair, #a.-b.    1.25 1.25
856 A244   Pair, #a.-b.    1.25 1.25
   Nos. 853-856 (4)    5.00 5.00

Issued: No. 853, 4/28; No. 854, 5/25; No. 855, 6/1; No. 856, 8/15.
See Nos. 893-896, 921-932, 980-991, 1059-1070.

Girl Guides Examining Plant — A245

30d, Guides cooking. 50d, Scouts at campfire. 115d, Scouts reading map.

**1980, Aug. 22**    **Perf. 13½**
861 A245   15d shown    .25 .25
862 A245   30d multicolored    .35 .35
863 A245   50d multicolored    .60 .60
864 A245   115d multicolored    1.50 1.50
   Nos. 861-864 (4)    2.70 2.70

**Souvenir Sheets**
865 A245 100d like #861    2.25 2.25
866 A245 100d like #863    2.25 2.25

8th Pan Arab Girl Guide and 14th Pan Arab Scout Jamborees, Aug.

Men Holding OPEC Emblem — A246

**1980, Sept. 15**    **Perf. 14½**
867 A246 45d Emblem, globe    .50 .50
868 A246 115d shown    1.50 1.50

20th anniversary of OPEC.

Martyrdom of Omar Muktar, 1931 — A247

**1980, Sept. 16**
869 A247 20d multicolored    .25 .25
870 A247 35d multicolored    .50 .50

**Souvenir Sheet**
870A A247 100d multicolored    2.50 2.50

UNESCO Emblem and Avicenna — A248

**1980, Sept. 20**
871 A248 45d Scientific symbols    .50 .50
872 A248 115d shown    1.50 1.50

School Scientific Exhibition, Sept. 20-24 and birth millenium of Arab physician Avicenna (115d).

18th Tripoli Fair — A249

Various musical instruments. 15d vert.

## 1980     Litho.     Perf. 13½
| | | | | |
|---|---|---|---|---|
| 873 | A249 | 5d multicolored | .25 | .25 |
| 874 | A249 | 10d multicolored | .25 | .25 |
| 875 | A249 | 15d multicolored | .25 | .25 |
| 876 | A249 | 20d multicolored | .25 | .25 |
| 877 | A249 | 25d multicolored | .40 | .40 |
| | | Nos. 873-877 (5) | 1.40 | 1.40 |

**Souvenir Sheet**
| | | | | |
|---|---|---|---|---|
| 878 | A249 | 100d Musicians | 2.50 | 2.50 |

World Olive Oil
Year — A250

## 1980, Jan. 15    Litho.    Perf. 13½
| | | | | |
|---|---|---|---|---|
| 879 | A250 | 15d multicolored | .25 | .25 |
| 880 | A250 | 30d multicolored | .35 | .35 |
| 881 | A250 | 45d multicolored | .50 | .50 |
| | | Nos. 879-881 (3) | 1.10 | 1.10 |

Intl. Year of the Child (1979) — A251

Children's drawings: a, Riding horses. b, water sports. c, Fish. d, Gift sale. e, Preparing feast.

## 1980, Mar. 21
| | | | | |
|---|---|---|---|---|
| 882 | | Strip of 5 | 5.00 | 5.00 |
| a.-e. | A251 20d any single | | .50 | .40 |

The Hegira,
1500th
Anniv. — A252

## 1980, Apr. 1
| | | | | |
|---|---|---|---|---|
| 883 | A252 | 50d multicolored | .60 | .60 |
| 884 | A252 | 115d multicolored | 1.50 | 1.50 |

Operating
Room,
Hospital
A253

## 1980, Apr. 7    Litho.    Perf. 13½
| | | | | |
|---|---|---|---|---|
| 885 | A253 | 20d multicolored | .40 | .40 |
| 886 | A253 | 50d multicolored | .75 | .75 |

World Health Day.

Sheik Zarruq Festival,
Misurata, June 16-
20 — A254

## 1980, June 16
| | | | | |
|---|---|---|---|---|
| 887 | A254 | 40d multicolored | .50 | .50 |
| 888 | A254 | 115d multicolored | 1.50 | 1.50 |

**Souvenir Sheet**
| | | | | |
|---|---|---|---|---|
| 889 | A254 | 100d multicolored | 2.75 | 2.75 |

Arabian Towns
Organization — A255

## 1980, July 1     Perf. 11½x12
| | | | | |
|---|---|---|---|---|
| 890 | A255 | 15d Ghadames | .25 | .25 |
| 891 | A255 | 30d Derna | .35 | .35 |
| 892 | A255 | 50d Tripoli | .60 | .60 |
| | | Nos. 890-892 (3) | 1.20 | 1.20 |

### Battles Type of 1980
No. 893: a, 20d, Yefren, 1915, b, 35d, same.
No. 894: a, 20d, El Hani, 1911, b, 35d, same.
No. 895: a, 20d, Sebha, 1914, b, 35d, same.
No. 896: a, 20d, Sirt, 1912, b, 35d, same.
Pairs have continuous design.

## 1980        Perf. 13½
| | | | | |
|---|---|---|---|---|
| 893 | A244 | Pair, #a.-b. | 1.25 | 1.25 |
| 894 | A244 | Pair, #a.-b. | 1.25 | 1.25 |
| 895 | A244 | Pair, #a.-b. | 1.25 | 1.25 |
| 896 | A244 | Pair, #a.-b. | 1.25 | 1.25 |
| | | Nos. 893-896 (4) | 5.00 | 5.00 |

Issued: No. 893, 7/16; No. 894, 10/23; No. 895, 11/27; No. 896, 12/31.

Sept. 1
Revolution, 11th
Anniv. — A256

Achievements of the Revolution: 5d, Oil industry. 10d, Youth festival. 15d, Agriculture. 25d, Transportation. 40d, Education. 115d, Housing.

100d, Montage of achievements.

## 1980, Sept. 1
| | | | | |
|---|---|---|---|---|
| 901 | A256 | 5d multicolored | .25 | .25 |
| 902 | A256 | 10d multicolored | .25 | .25 |
| 903 | A256 | 15d multicolored | .50 | .50 |
| 904 | A256 | 25d multicolored | 1.25 | .50 |
| 905 | A256 | 40d multicolored | 1.25 | .50 |
| 906 | A256 | 115d multicolored | 3.00 | 1.25 |
| | | Nos. 901-906 (6) | 6.50 | 3.25 |

**Souvenir Sheet**
| | | | | |
|---|---|---|---|---|
| 907 | A256 | 100d multicolored | 2.75 | 2.75 |

No. 907 contains one stamp 30x50mm.

World Tourism
Conference — A257

## 1980, Sept. 10
| | | | | |
|---|---|---|---|---|
| 908 | A257 | 45d multicolored | .50 | .50 |
| 909 | A257 | 115d multicolored | 1.50 | 1.50 |

Intl. Year of the
Disabled — A258

Intl. Year of the Disabled emblem and: 20d, Eye, man on crutches. 45d, Stylized globe. 115d, Eye, man on crutch, hands.

## 1981, Jan. 1        Perf. 15
| | | | | |
|---|---|---|---|---|
| 910 | A258 | 20d lt. green, blue & blk | .25 | .25 |
| 911 | A258 | 45d blue, blk & grn | .35 | .25 |
| 912 | A258 | 115d lt. grn, blue & grn | 1.50 | .50 |
| | | Nos. 910-912 (3) | 2.10 | 1.00 |

### Nos. 911-912 Redrawn with Arabic Writing and "Arab League" Above Emblem

## 1981, Nov. 21    Litho.    Perf. 15
| | | | | |
|---|---|---|---|---|
| 913 | A258 | 45d blue & multi | .35 | .25 |
| 914 | A258 | 115d rose & multi | 1.10 | 1.10 |

UPA Disabled Persons Campaign. Design redrawn to include Arab League Emblem.

Mosaics
A259

## 1981, Jan. 15      Perf. 13½
| | | | | |
|---|---|---|---|---|
| 915 | A259 | 10d Horse | 1.00 | .25 |
| 916 | A259 | 20d Sailing ship | 1.00 | .50 |
| 917 | A259 | 30d Peacocks | 2.00 | .50 |
| 918 | A259 | 40d Panther | 2.00 | .50 |
| 919 | A259 | 50d Musician | 2.50 | .50 |
| 920 | A259 | 115d Fish | 6.50 | 1.00 |
| | | Nos. 915-920 (6) | 15.00 | 3.25 |

### Battles Type of 1980
No. 921: a, 20d, Dernah, 1912, b, 35d, same. No. 922: a, 20d, Tawargha, 1923. b, 35d, same. No. 923: a, 20d, Bir Tagreft, 1928. b, 35d, same. No. 924: a, 20d, .Funduk El-Jamel Misurata, 1915 b, 35d, same. No. 925: a, 20d, Zuara, 1912. b, 35d, same. No. 926: a, 20d, Sidi El-Khemri, 1915. b, 35d, same. No. 927: a, 20d, El-Khoms, 1913. b, 35d, same. No. 928: a, 20d, Roghdalin, 1912. b, 35d, same. No. 929: a, 20d, Rughbat El-Naga, 1925. b, 35d, same. No. 930: a, 20d, Tobruk. 1911. 1922. b, 35d, same. No. 931: a, 20d, Bir Ikshadia, 1924. b, 35d, same. No. 932: a, 20d, Ain Zara, 1924. b, 35d, same.
Pairs have continuous design.

## 1981     Perf. 13½, 14½ (#926, 932)
| | | | | |
|---|---|---|---|---|
| 921 | A244 | Pair, #a.-b. | 1.25 | 1.25 |
| 922 | A244 | Pair, #a.-b. | 1.25 | 1.25 |
| 923 | A244 | Pair, #a.-b. | 1.25 | 1.25 |
| 924 | A244 | Pair, #a.-b. | 1.25 | 1.25 |
| 925 | A244 | Pair, #a.-b. | 1.25 | 1.25 |
| 926 | A244 | Pair, #a.-b. | 1.25 | 1.25 |
| 927 | A244 | Pair, #a.-b. | 1.25 | 1.25 |
| 928 | A244 | Pair, #a.-b. | 1.25 | 1.25 |
| 929 | A244 | Pair, #a.-b. | 1.25 | 1.25 |
| 930 | A244 | Pair, #a.-b. | 1.25 | 1.25 |
| 931 | A244 | Pair, #a.-b. | 1.25 | 1.25 |
| 932 | A244 | Pair, #a.-b. | 1.25 | 1.25 |
| | | Nos. 921-932 (12) | 15.00 | 15.00 |

Issued: No. 921, 1/17; No. 922, 2/25; No. 923, 3/20; No. 924, 4/13; No. 925, 5/26; No. 926, 6/4; No. 927, 7/27; No. 928, 8/15; No. 929, 9/16; No. 930, 10/27; No. 931, 11/19; No. 932, 12/4.

Tripoli Intl.
Fair — A260

Ceramicware.

## 1981, Mar. 1      Perf. 13½
| | | | | |
|---|---|---|---|---|
| 945 | A260 | 5d Bowls, horiz. | .25 | .25 |
| 946 | A260 | 10d Lamp | .25 | .25 |
| 947 | A260 | 15d Vase | .25 | .25 |
| 948 | A260 | 45d Water jar, horiz. | .60 | .25 |
| 949 | A260 | 115d Spouted water jar, horiz. | 1.75 | .60 |
| | | Nos. 945-949 (5) | 3.10 | 1.60 |

No. 707b,
Crowd — A261

## 1981, Mar. 2      Perf. 15
| | | | | |
|---|---|---|---|---|
| 950 | A261 | 50d multicolored | .35 | .35 |
| 951 | A261 | 115d multicolored | 1.50 | .50 |

People's Authority Declaration, The Green Book.

Children's Day,
IYC — A262

Children's illustrations: a, Desert camp. b, Women doing chores. c, Village scene. d, Airplane over playground. e, Minaret, camel, man.

## 1981, Mar. 21    Litho.    Perf. 13½
| | | | | |
|---|---|---|---|---|
| 952 | | Strip of 5 | 5.00 | 5.00 |
| a.-e. | A262 20d any single | | .50 | .40 |

Bank of Libya, 25th
Anniv. — A263

## 1981, Apr. 1    Litho.    Perf. 13½
| | | | | |
|---|---|---|---|---|
| 953 | A263 | 45d multicolored | .50 | .35 |
| 954 | A263 | 115d multicolored | 1.75 | 1.10 |

**Souvenir Sheet**
| | | | | |
|---|---|---|---|---|
| 955 | A263 | 50d multicolored | 1.50 | 1.50 |

World Health
Day — A264

## 1981, Apr. 7      Perf. 14
| | | | | |
|---|---|---|---|---|
| 956 | A264 | 45d multicolored | .50 | .50 |
| 957 | A264 | 115d multicolored | 1.50 | .75 |

Intl. Year for Combating
Racial
Discrimination — A265

## 1981, July 1      Perf. 15
| | | | | |
|---|---|---|---|---|
| 958 | A265 | 45d multicolored | 1.10 | .65 |
| 959 | A265 | 50d multicolored | 1.50 | .75 |

September 1 Revolution, 12th
Anniv. — A266

No. 960: a-b, Helicopter and jets; c-d, Paratroopers. No. 961: a-b, Tanks; c-d, Frogman parade. No. 962: a-b, Twelve-barrel rocket launchers; c-d, Trucks with rockets. No. 963: a-b, Sailor parade; c-d, Jeep and trucks with twelve-barrel rocket launchers. No. 964: a-b, Wheeled tanks and jeeps; c-d, Tank parade. Nos. 960-962 vert. Pairs have continuous designs.

## 1981, Sept. 1      Perf. 14½
| | | | | |
|---|---|---|---|---|
| 960 | A266 | 5d Block of 4, #a.-d. | 1.40 | 1.40 |
| 961 | A266 | 10d Block of 4, #a.-d. | 1.40 | 1.40 |
| 962 | A266 | 15d Block of 4, #a.-d. | 1.40 | 1.40 |
| 963 | A266 | 20d Block of 4, #a.-d. | 1.40 | 1.40 |
| 964 | A266 | 25d Block of 4, #a.-d. | 2.75 | 2.75 |
| | | Nos. 960-964 (5) | 8.35 | 8.35 |

**Souvenir Sheet**
**Perf. 11**
| | | | | |
|---|---|---|---|---|
| 965 | A266 | 50d Naval troop marching | 7.00 | 7.00 |

No. 965 contains one 63x38mm stamp.

### Miniature Sheet

Butterflies — A267

**1981, Oct. 1**  **Perf. 14½**
966  A267  Sheet of 16  11.00
  a.-d.  5d, any single  .25  .25
  e.-h.  10d, any single  .45  .45
  i.-l.  15d, any single  .50  .40
  m.-p.  25d, any single  1.00  .60

No. 966 printed in a continuous design, stamps of same denomination in blocks of 4. Sheetlets exist containing blocks of 4 for each denomination. Value, set of 4 sheets, $20.

World Food Day — A268

**1981, Oct. 16**  **Perf. 15**
967  A268  45d multicolored  .50  .50
968  A268  200d multicolored  2.50  2.50

Fruit — A269

**1981, Nov. 17**  **Perf. 13½**
969  A269  5d Grapes  .25  .25
970  A269  10d Dates  .25  .25
971  A269  15d Lemons  .25  .25
972  A269  20d Oranges  .40  .25
973  A269  35d Cactus fruit  .80  .35
974  A269  55d Pomegranates  1.50  .60
  Nos. 969-974 (6)  3.45  1.95

Miniature Sheet

A270

Mosaics: a, Animals facing right. b, Orpheus playing music. c, Animals facing left. d, Fish. e, Fishermen. f, Fish in basket. g, Farm yard. h, Birds eating fruit. i, Milking a goat.

**1982, Jan. 1**  **Perf. 13½**
975  A270  Sheet of 9  9.00  9.00
  a.-i.  45d any single  .75  .75

Nos. 975a-975c, shown in illustration, printed in continuous design.

3rd Intl. Koran Reading Contest — A271

Designs: 10d, Stone tablets, Holy Ka'aba, Mecca. 35d, Open Koran, creation of the world. 115d, Scholar, students.

**1982, Jan. 7**
976  A271  10d multicolored  .25  .25
977  A271  35d multicolored  .50  .25
978  A271  115d multicolored  1.50  .75
  Nos. 976-978 (3)  2.25  1.25

**Souvenir Sheet**
979  A271  100d like 115d  3.50  3.50

**Battles Type of 1980**

No. 980: a, 20d, Hun Gioffra, 1915; b, 35d, same. No. 981: a, 20d, Gedabia, 1914; b, 35d, same. No. 982: a, 20d, El-Asaba, 1913; b, 35d, same. No. 983: a, 20d, El-Habela, 1917; b, 35d, same. No. 984: a, 20d, Suk El-Ahad, 1915; b, 35d, same. No. 985: a, 20d, El-Tangi, 1913; b, 35d, same. No. 986: a, 20d, Sokna, 1913; b, 35d, same. No. 987: a, 20d, Wadi Smalus, 1925; b, 35d, same. No. 988: a, 20d, Sidi Abuagela, 1917; b, 35d, same. No. 989: a, 20d, Sidi Surur, 1914; b, 35d, same. No. 990:

a, 20d, Kuefia, 1911; b, 35d, same. No. 991: a, 20d, Abunjeim, 1940; b, 35d, same.
Pairs have continuous design.

**1982**  **Perf. 13½, 14½ (#985-988)**
980  A244  Pair, #a.-b.  1.25  1.25
981  A244  Pair, #a.-b.  1.25  1.25
982  A244  Pair, #a.-b.  1.25  1.25
983  A244  Pair, #a.-b.  1.25  1.25
984  A244  Pair, #a.-b.  1.25  1.25
985  A244  Pair, #a.-b.  1.25  1.25
986  A244  Pair, #a.-b.  1.25  1.25
987  A244  Pair, #a.-b.  1.25  1.25
988  A244  Pair, #a.-b.  1.25  1.25
989  A244  Pair, #a.-b.  1.25  1.25
990  A244  Pair, #a.-b.  1.25  1.25
991  A244  Pair, #a.-b.  1.25  1.25
  Nos. 980-991 (12)  15.00  15.00

Issued: No. 980, 1/26; No. 981, 3/8; No. 982, 3/23; No. 983, 4/24; No. 984, 5/15; No. 985, 6/19; No. 986, 7/23; No. 987, 8/11; No. 988, 9/4; No. 989, 10/14; No. 990, 11/28; No. 991, 12/13.

Tripoli Intl. Fair — A272

5d, Grinding stone. 10d, Ox-drawn plow. 25d, Pitching hay. 35d, Tapestry weaving. 45d, Traditional cooking. 100d, Grain harvest.

**1982, Mar. 1**  **Perf. 13x12½**
1004  A272  5d multicolored  .25  .25
1005  A272  10d multicolored  .25  .25
1006  A272  25d multicolored  .25  .25
1007  A272  35d multicolored  .50  .25
1008  A272  45d multicolored  .75  .35
1009  A272  100d multicolored  1.50  .75
  Nos. 1004-1009 (6)  3.50  2.10

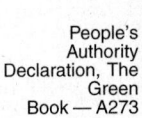

People's Authority Declaration, The Green Book — A273

**1982, Mar. 2**  **Perf. 13½**
1010  Strip of 3  8.00  8.00
  a.  A273  100d Harvester combine  1.25  .60
  b.  A273  200d Khadafy, scholar, rifles  2.50  2.25
  c.  A273  300d Govt. building, citizens  3.25  2.25

Scouting Movement, 75th Anniv. — A274

**1982, Mar. 2**
1011  Strip of 4  22.50  22.50
  a.  A274  100d Cub scout, blimp  1.75  .80
  b.  A274  200d Scouts, dog  3.25  1.45
  c.  A274  300d Scholar, scout  4.75  2.00
  d.  A274  400d Boy scout, rocket  7.25  3.75

**Souvenir Sheets**
1012  A274  500d Green Book  8.00  8.00
1013  A274  500d Khadafy, scouts  8.00  8.00

Nos. 1012-1013 each contain one stamp 39x42mm.
Nos. 1011-1013 exist imperf.

13th African Soccer Cup Championships A275

**1982, Mar. 5**
1014  A275  100d multi  1.50  .75
1015  A275  200d multi  3.00  1.50

1982 World Cup Soccer Championships, Spain — A276

World Cup trophy and various soccer plays.

**1982, Mar. 15**  **Perf. 14½**
1016  A276  45d multi  .60  .60
1017  A276  100d multi  1.50  1.50
1018  A276  200d multi  2.75  2.75
1019  A276  300d multi  3.25  3.25
  Nos. 1016-1019 (4)  8.10  8.10

**Souvenir Sheets**
1020  A276  500d like 45d  7.50  7.50
1021  A276  500d like 100d  7.50  7.50

Nos. 1016-1019 issued in sheets of 8 overprinted in silver with soccer ball in motion. Value $75. Sheetlets of 4 in each denomination exist without overprint.
Nos. 1020-1021 have Arabic text in green on reverse. Value $35.
Nos. 1016-1019 exist imperf. Value $15.
Nos. 1020-1021 also exist imperf.

Palestinian Children's Day — A277

Designs: a, Two children. b, Girl with bowl. c, Girl with kaffiyeh. d, Girl hiding. e, Boy.

**1982, Mar. 7**  **Perf. 13½**
1022  Strip of 5  2.75  2.75
  a.-e.  A277  20d, any single  .40  .40

Miniature Sheet

Birds A278

**1982, Apr. 1**  **Perf. 14½**
1023  A278  Sheet of 16  20.00  20.00
  a.-d.  15d, any single  .50  .45
  e.-h.  25d, any single  .75  .60
  i.-l.  45d, any single  1.10  1.00
  m.-p.  95d, any single  2.40  1.80

No. 1023a-1023p printed se-tenant in a continuous design; stamps of same denomination in blocks of 4.
Each denomination was also printed in a sheet of 16, each sheet containing four se-tenant blocks of the same denomination. Value, set of four sheets, $75.

Teaching Hospitals Anniv. — A279

**1982, Apr. 7**  **Perf. 13x12½**
1024  A279  95d multi  1.25  1.25
1025  A279  100d multi  1.25  1.25
1026  A279  205d multi  2.75  2.75
  Nos. 1024-1026 (3)  5.25  5.25

Arab Postal Union, 30th — A280

**1982, Apr. 12**  **Perf. 13½**
1027  A280  100d multi  1.50  .75
1028  A280  200d multi  2.75  1.50

1982 World Chess Championships — A281

Board positions and chessmen: a, Chinese piece. b, African piece. c, Modern piece. d, European piece.
500d, Overhead view of chessboard.

**1982, May 1**
1029  A281  Block of 4  10.00  10.00
  a.-d.  100d, any single  2.25  1.10

**Souvenir Sheet**
1030  A281  500d multicolored  10.00  10.00

No. 1030 contains one stamp 39x42mm.
Nos. 1029 and 1030 exist imperf.

World Telecommunications Day — A282

**1982, May 17**
1031  A282  100d multi  1.25  1.25
1032  A282  200d multi  2.50  2.50

Map of Libya, Green Book — A283

**1982, June 11**
1033  A283  200d multi  2.50  1.50

**Souvenir Sheet**
1034  A283  300d multi  5.00  5.00

Post Day, FIP 51st anniv.

Organization of African Unity, 19th Summit — A284

50d, OAU flag, Arab family. 100d, Map of Africa, emblem. 200d, Khadafy, Green Book. 300d, Fist, map.

**1982, Aug. 5**  **Perf. 14**
1035  A284  50d multicolored  .75  .75
1036  A284  100d multicolored  1.25  1.25
  **Size: 69x40mm**
1037  A284  200d mutlicolored  2.50  2.50
  Nos. 1035-1037 (3)  4.50  4.50

**Souvenir Sheet**
  **Perf. 13x13½**
1038  A284  300d multicolored  5.00  5.00

No. 1038 contains one stamp 29x42mm.

September 1 Revolution, 13th Anniv. — A285

Khadafy in uniforms and various armed forces' exercises.

**1982, Sept. 1** **Perf. 11½**
| | | | | |
|---|---|---|---|---|
| 1039 | A285 | 15d multi | .25 | .25 |
| 1040 | A285 | 20d multi | .25 | .25 |
| 1041 | A285 | 30d multi | 1.00 | 1.00 |
| 1042 | A285 | 45d multi | .60 | .60 |
| 1043 | A285 | 70d multi | 1.00 | 1.00 |
| 1044 | A285 | 100d multi | 1.50 | 1.50 |
| | | Nos. 1039-1044 (6) | 4.60 | 4.60 |

**Souvenir Sheet**
**Imperf**
| | | | |
|---|---|---|---|
| 1045 | A285 | 200d multi | 4.00 4.00 |

Libyan Red Crescent, 25th Anniv. — A286

**1982, Oct. 5** **Perf. 13½**
| | | | | |
|---|---|---|---|---|
| 1046 | A286 | 100d Palm tree | 1.75 | 1.25 |
| 1047 | A286 | 200d "25," crescents | 3.50 | 2.50 |

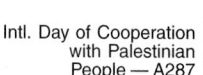

Intl. Day of Cooperation with Palestinian People — A287

**1982, Nov. 29**
| | | | | |
|---|---|---|---|---|
| 1048 | A287 | 100d gray grn & blk | 1.50 | .75 |
| 1049 | A287 | 200d brt bl, gray grn & blk | 2.75 | 1.50 |

Al-Fateh University Symposium on Khadafy's Green Book — A288

100d, Khadafy in uniform. 200d, Khadafy, map, Green Book.

**1982, Dec. 1** **Perf. 12**
| | | | | |
|---|---|---|---|---|
| 1050 | A288 | 100d multicolored | 1.25 | 1.10 |
| 1051 | A288 | 200d multicolored | 2.50 | 2.50 |

**Miniature Sheet**

Flowers — A289

Designs: a, Philadelphus. b, Hypericum. c, Antinhinum. d, Lily. e, Capparis. f, Tropaeolum. g, Rose. h, Chrysanthemum. i, Nigella damascena. j, Gaillardia lanceolata. k, Dahlia. l, Dianthus carophyllus. m, Notobasis syriaca.

n, Nerium oleander. o, Iris histriodes. p, Scolymus hispanicus.

**1983, Jan. 1** **Perf. 14½**
| | | | |
|---|---|---|---|
| 1052 | A289 | Sheet of 16 | 10.00 10.00 |
| *a.-p.* | | 25d, any single | .50 .40 |

**Torch Type of 1979**

**1983, Jan. 2** **Perf. 13½**
Size: 26½x32mm
| | | | | |
|---|---|---|---|---|
| 1053 | A228 | 250d multi | 3.25 | 2.00 |
| 1054 | A228 | 1500d multi | 20.00 | 12.50 |
| 1055 | A228 | 2500d multi | 37.50 | 25.00 |
| | | Nos. 1053-1055 (3) | 60.75 | 39.50 |

Customs Cooperation Council, 30th Anniv. — A290

**1983, Jan. 15** **Perf. 14½x14**
| | | | | |
|---|---|---|---|---|
| 1056 | A290 | 25d Arab riding horse | .25 | .25 |
| 1057 | A290 | 50d Riding camel | .60 | .60 |
| 1058 | A290 | 100d Drawing sword | 1.50 | 1.50 |
| | | Nos. 1056-1058 (3) | 2.35 | 2.35 |

**Battles Type of 1980**

No. 1059, Ghaser Ahmed, 1922. No. 1060, Sidi Abuarghub, 1923. No. 1061, Ghar Yunes, 1913. No. 1062, Bir Otman, 1926. No. 1063, Sidi Sajeh, 1922. No. 1064, Ras El-Hamam, 1915. No. 1065, Zawiet Ishghefa, 1913. No. 1066, Wadi Essania, 1930. No. 1067, El-Meshiashta, 1917. No. 1068, Gharara, 1925. No. 1069, Abughelan, 1922. No. 1070, Mahruka, 1913.
Pairs have continuous design.

**1983** **Perf. 13½**
| | | | | |
|---|---|---|---|---|
| 1059 | A244 | 50d Pair, #a.-b. | 2.00 | 2.00 |
| 1060 | A244 | 50d Pair, #a.-b. | 2.00 | 2.00 |
| 1061 | A244 | 50d Pair, #a.-b. | 2.00 | 2.00 |
| 1062 | A244 | 50d Pair, #a.-b. | 2.00 | 2.00 |
| 1063 | A244 | 50d Pair, #a.-b. | 2.00 | 2.00 |
| 1064 | A244 | 250d Pair, #a.-b. | 2.00 | 2.00 |
| 1065 | A244 | 50d Pair, #a.-b. | 2.00 | 2.00 |
| 1066 | A244 | 50d Pair, #a.-b. | 2.00 | 2.00 |
| 1067 | A244 | 50d Pair, #a.-b. | 2.00 | 2.00 |
| 1068 | A244 | 50d Pair, #a.-b. | 2.00 | 2.00 |
| 1069 | A244 | 50d Pair, #a.-b. | 2.00 | 2.00 |
| 1070 | A244 | 50d Pair, #a.-b. | 2.00 | 2.00 |
| | | Nos. 1059-1070 (12) | 24.00 | 24.00 |

Issued: No. 1059, 1/26; No. 1060, 2/2; No. 1061, 3/26; No. 1062, 4/9; No. 1063, 5/2; No. 1064, 6/24; No. 1065, 7/13; No. 1066, 8/8; No. 1067, 9/9; No. 1068, 10/22; No. 1069, 11/17; No. 1070, 12/24.

**Miniature Sheet**

Farm Animals — A291

Designs: a, Camel. b, Cow. c, Horse. d, Bull. e, Goat. f, Dog. g, Sheep. h, Ram. i, Goose. j, Turkey hen. k, Rabbit. l, Pigeon. m, Turkey. n, Rooster. o, Hen. p, Duck.

**1983, Feb. 15** **Perf. 14½**
| | | | |
|---|---|---|---|
| 1083 | A291 | Sheet of 16 | 10.00 10.00 |
| *a.-p.* | | 25d any single | .50 .40 |

Tripoli Intl. Fair — A292

Libyans playing traditional instruments.

**1983, Mar. 5** **Perf. 14½x14, 14x14½**
| | | | | |
|---|---|---|---|---|
| 1084 | A292 | 40d multi, vert. | .60 | .40 |
| 1085 | A292 | 45d multicolored | .75 | .50 |
| 1086 | A292 | 50d multi, vert. | .75 | .50 |
| 1087 | A292 | 55d multicolored | 1.00 | .60 |
| 1088 | A292 | 75d multi, vert. | 1.25 | .90 |
| 1089 | A292 | 100d multi, vert. | 1.60 | 1.10 |
| | | Nos. 1084-1089 (6) | 5.95 | 4.00 |

Intl. Maritime Organization, 25th Anniv. — A293

Early sailing ships.

**1983, Mar. 17** **Perf. 14½**
| | | | | |
|---|---|---|---|---|
| 1090 | A293 | 100d Phoenician | 2.00 | .75 |
| 1091 | A293 | 100d Viking | 2.00 | .75 |
| 1092 | A293 | 100d Greek | 2.00 | .75 |
| 1093 | A293 | 100d Roman | 2.00 | .75 |
| 1094 | A293 | 100d Libyan | 2.00 | .75 |
| 1095 | A293 | 100d Pharoah's ship | 2.00 | .75 |
| | | Nos. 1090-1095 (6) | 12.00 | 4.50 |

Children's Day (1983) — A294

Children's illustrations: a, Car. b, Tractor towing trailer. c, Children, dove. d, Boy Scouts. e, Dinosaur.

**1983, Mar. 21** **Perf. 14x14½**
| | | | |
|---|---|---|---|
| 1096 | | Strip of 5 | 2.75 2.75 |
| *a.-e.* | A294 | 20d, any single | .40 .30 |

1st Intl. Symposium on Khadafy's Green Book — A295

50d, Khadafy, Green Book, map. 70d, Lecture hall, emblem. 80d, Khadafy, Green Book, emblem.
100d, Khadafy, Green Books.

**1983, Apr. 1** **Perf. 13½**
| | | | | |
|---|---|---|---|---|
| 1097 | A295 | 50d multicolored | .60 | .40 |
| 1098 | A295 | 70d multicolored | 1.00 | .50 |
| 1099 | A295 | 80d multicolored | 1.10 | .75 |
| | | Nos. 1097-1099 (3) | 2.70 | 1.65 |

**Souvenir Sheet**
**Perf. 12½**
| | | | |
|---|---|---|---|
| 1100 | A295 | 100d multicolored | 3.00 3.00 |

No. 1100 contains one stamp 57x48mm.

World Health Day — A296

25d, Healthy children, vert. 50d, Man in wheelchair, vert. 100d, Girl in hospital bed.

**1983, Apr. 7** **Perf. 12½**
| | | | | |
|---|---|---|---|---|
| 1101 | A296 | 25d multicolored | .25 | .25 |
| 1102 | A296 | 50d multicolored | .60 | .40 |
| 1103 | A296 | 100d multicolored | 1.25 | .75 |
| | | Nos. 1101-1103 (3) | 2.10 | 1.40 |

Pan-African Economic Committee, 25th Anniv. — A297

**1983, Apr. 20** **Perf. 13½**
| | | | | |
|---|---|---|---|---|
| 1104 | A297 | 50d multi | .60 | .40 |
| 1105 | A297 | 100d multi | 1.25 | .75 |
| 1106 | A297 | 250d multi | 3.00 | 2.00 |
| | | Nos. 1104-1106 (3) | 4.85 | 3.15 |

**Miniature Sheet**

Fish — A298

Designs: a, Labrus bimaculatus. b, Trigloporus lastoviza. c, Thalassoma pavo. d, Apogon imberbis. e, Scomber scombrus. f, Spondyliosoma cantharus. g, Trachinus draco. h, Blennius pavo. i, Scorpaena notata. j, Serranus scriba. k, Lophius piscatorius. l, Uranoscopus scaber. m, Auxis thazard. n, Zeus faber. o, Dactylopterus volitans. p, Umbrina cirrosa.

**1983, May 15** **Perf. 14½**
| | | | |
|---|---|---|---|
| 1107 | A298 | Sheet of 16 | 10.00 10.00 |
| *a.-p.* | | 25d any single | .40 .30 |

Still-life by Gauguin (1848-1903) — A299

Paintings: No. 1108b, Abstract, unattributed. c, The Conquest of Tunis by Charles V, by Rubens. d, Arab Musicians in a Carriage, unattributed.
No. 1109a, Khadafy Glorified on Horseback, unattributed, vert. b, Triumph of David over the Syrians, by Raphael, vert. c, Laborers, unattributed, vert. d, Flower Vase, by van Gogh, vert.

**1983, June 1** **Perf. 11**
| | | | |
|---|---|---|---|
| 1108 | | Strip of 4 | 3.00 3.00 |
| *a.-d.* | A299 | 50d, any single | .50 .35 |
| 1109 | | Strip of 4 | 3.00 3.00 |
| *a.-d.* | A299 | 50d, any single | .50 .35 |

**Souvenir Sheet**

Ali Siala A300

Scientists: No. 1110b, Ali El-Najar.

**1983, June 1**
| | | | |
|---|---|---|---|
| 1110 | A300 | Sheet of 2 | 3.50 3.50 |
| *a.-b.* | | 100d, any single | 1.50 1.50 |

1984 Summer Olympic Games, Los Angeles — A301

**1983, June 15** **Perf. 13½**
| | | | | |
|---|---|---|---|---|
| 1111 | A301 | 10d Basketball | .25 | .25 |
| 1112 | A301 | 15d High jump | .25 | .25 |
| 1113 | A301 | 25d Running | .25 | .25 |
| 1114 | A301 | 50d Gymnastics | .50 | .40 |
| 1115 | A301 | 100d Wind surfing | 1.25 | .75 |
| 1116 | A301 | 200d Shot put | 2.50 | 1.60 |
| | | Nos. 1111-1116 (6) | 5.00 | 3.50 |

**Souvenir Sheets**
| | | | | |
|---|---|---|---|---|
| 1117 | A301 | 100d Equestrian | *3.00* | *3.00* |
| 1118 | A301 | 100d Soccer | *3.00* | *3.00* |

Nos. 1111-1116 exist imperf. Value, set $22.50. Nos. 1117-1118 also exist imperf.
Nos. 1111-1116 exist printed together in a miniature sheet of 6. Values: perf $35; imperf $50. Each value was also printed in a miniature sheet of 4. Value, set of 6 sheets, $45.

World
Communications
Year — A302

**1983, July 1**      *Perf. 13*
1119 A302   10d multicolored    .40 .30
1120 A302   50d multicolored    .90 .60
1121 A302   100d multicolored   2.00 1.25
    *Nos. 1119-1121 (3)*    3.30 2.15

The Green Book,
by
Khadafy — A303

Ideologies: 10d, The House is to be served
by its residents. 15d, Power, wealth and arms
are in the hands of the people. 20d, Masters in
their own castles, vert. 35d, No democracy
without popular congress. 100d, The authority
of the people, vert. 140d, The Green Book is
the guide of humanity for final release.
200d, Khadafy in uniform.

**1983, Aug. 1**      *Perf. 13½*
1122 A303   10d multi     .25 .25
1123 A303   15d multi     .25 .25
1124 A303   20d multi     .25 .25
1125 A303   35d multi     .40 .25
1126 A303   100d multi    1.25 .75
1127 A303   140d multi    1.75 1.25
    *Nos. 1122-1127 (6)*    4.15 3.00

**Souvenir Sheet**
**Litho. & Embossed**
1128 A303   200d multi    4.50 4.50

No. 1128 contains one gold embossed
stamp 36x51mm.

2nd African Youth
Sports Festival — A304

Designs: a, Team Handball. b, Basketball. c,
Javelin. d, Running. e, Soccer.

**1983, Aug. 22**      *Litho.*
1129    Strip of 5     7.50 4.00
  a.-e.   A304 100d, any single   1.25 .75

September 1 Revolution, 14th
Anniv. — A305

Women in the Armed Forces.

**1983, Sept. 1**      *Perf. 11½*
1130 A305   65d multi     .75 .75
1131 A305   75d multi     .90 .90
1132 A305   90d multi    1.00 1.00
1133 A305   100d multi    1.25 1.25
1134 A305   150d multi    1.75 1.75
1135 A305   250d multi    3.25 3.25
    *Nos. 1130-1135 (6)*    8.90 8.90

**Souvenir Sheet**
*Perf. 11*
1136 A305   200d multi    4.50 4.50

No. 1136 contains one stamp 63x38mm.

2nd Islamic
Scout
Jamboree
A306

**1983, Sept. 2**      *Perf. 12½*
1137 A306   50d Saluting    .75 .75
1138 A306   100d Camping   2.00 2.00

**Souvenir Sheet**
1139    Sheet of 2     4.50 4.50
  a.    A306 100d like 50d   2.00 2.00

No. 1139 contains Nos. 1138 and 1139a.

Traffic Day — A307

30d, Youth traffic monitors. 70d, Traffic
officer. 200d, Motorcycle police.

**1983, Oct. 1**      *Perf. 14½x14*
1140 A307   30d multicolored   1.25 .75
1141 A307   70d multicolored   2.50 1.00
1142 A307   200d multicolored   8.00 3.50
    *Nos. 1140-1142 (3)*    11.75 5.25

Saadun (1893-
1923) — A308

**1983, Oct. 11**      *Perf. 13½*
1143 A308   100d multicolored   1.50 .75

1st Manned
Flight,
Bicent.
A309

Early aircraft and historic flights: a, Americana, 1910. b, Nulli Secundus, 1907. c, J. B.
Meusnier, 1785. d, Blanchard and Jeffries,
1785, vert. e, Pilatre de Rozier, 1784, vert. f,
Montgolfiere, Oct. 19, 1783, vert.

**1983, Nov. 1**
1144    Strip of 6     11.00 11.00
  a.-f.   A309 100d, any single   1.60 .85

Intl. Day of
Cooperation with
Palestinian
People — A310

**1983, Nov. 29**      *Perf. 14½x14*
1145 A310   30d pale vio & lt bl
            grn      .50 .30
1146 A310   70d lil & lt yel grn   1.40 .55
1147 A310   200d lt ultra & grn   3.75 2.00
    *Nos. 1145-1147 (3)*    5.65 2.85

**Miniature Sheet**

Roman
Mosaic
A311

Designs: Nos. 1148a-1148c, Gladiators.
Nos. 1148d-1148f, Musicians, Nos. 1148g-
1148i, Hunters.

**1983, Dec. 1**      *Perf. 12*
1148 A311   Sheet of 9    7.00 7.00
  a.-i.   50d, any single     .75 .35

Nos. 1148a-1148c, 1148d-1148f and
1148g-1148i se-tenant in a continuous design.

Achievements of
the Sept. 1
Revolution
A312

**1983, Dec. 15**      *Perf. 13½*
1149 A312   10d Mosque    .25 .25
1150 A312   15d Agriculture   .25 .25
1151 A312   20d Industry    .40 .25
1152 A312   35d Office building   .50 .25
1153 A312   100d Health care   1.50 .60
1154 A312   200d Airport    2.25 1.10
    *Nos. 1149-1154 (6)*    5.15 2.70

**Souvenir Sheet**
**Litho. & Embossed**
1155 A312   200d Khadafy   4.50 4.50

No. 1155 contains one gold embossed
stamp 36x51mm.

Khadafy,
Irrigation Project
Survey
Map — A313

**1983, Dec. 15**
1156 A313   150d multicolored   2.25 1.25

A314            A315

Famous men: No. 1157a, Mahmud Burkis.
No. 1157b, Ahmed El-Bakbak. No. 1157c,
Mohamed El-Misurati. No. 1157d, Mahmud
Ben Musa. No. 1157e, Abdulhamid Ben
Ashiur. No. 1158a, Hosni Fauzi El-Amir. No.
1158b, Ali Haidar El-Saati. No. 1159, Mahmud
Mustafa Dreza. No. 1160, Mehdi El-Sherif. No.
1161a, Ali El-Gariani. No. 1161b, Muktar
Shakshuki. No. 1161c, Abdurrahman El-
Busayri. No. 1161d, Ibbrahim Bakir. No.
1161e, Mahmud El-Janzuri. No. 1162a,
Ahmed El-Feghi Hasan. No. 1162b, Bashir El
Jawab.

**1984**     *Litho.*     *Perf. 13½*
1157    Strip of 5     6.00 6.00
  a.-e.   A314 100d any single   1.10 1.10
1158    Pair      3.50 1.50
  a.-b.   A314 100d any single   1.50 .60
1159 A314   100d multi    1.75 .60
1160 A315   100d multi    1.75 .60
1161    Strip of 5    15.00 15.00
  a.-e.   A314 100d any single   2.50 2.50
1162    Pair      6.00 6.00
  a.-b.   A315 200d any single   2.50 2.50
    *Nos. 1157-1162 (6)*    34.00 29.70

Issued: Nos. 1157, 1161-1162, 1/1; No.
1158-1160, 2/20.

**Miniature Sheet**

Water Sports — A316

Designs: a, Two windsurfers. b, Two-man
craft. c, Two-man craft, birds. d, Wind sailing,
skis. e, Water skier facing front. f, Fisherman
in boat. g, Power boating. h, Water skier facing
right. i, Fisherman in surf. j, Kayaking. k, Surfing. l, Water skier wearing life jacket. m, Scuba

diver sketching underwater. n, Diver. o,
Snorkel diver removing fish from harpoon. p,
Scuba diver surfacing.

**1984, Jan. 10**      *Perf. 14½*
1164 A316   Sheet of 16   8.50 8.50
  a.-p.   25d any single    .50 .50

African Children's Day — A317

Designs: a, Khadafy, girl scouts. b, Khadafy,
children. c, Map, Khadafy, children (size:
63x44mm).

**1984, Jan. 15**     *Litho.*    *Perf. 14½*
1165 A317   Strip of 3    3.50 3.50
  a.-b.   50d, any single    .80 .80
  c.    100d multi    2.00 2.00

Women's
Emancipation
A318

70d, Women, diff., vert. 100d, Soldiers,
Khadafy.

**1984, Jan. 20**      *Perf. 12*
1166 A318   55d multicolored   .75 .40
1167 A318   70d multicolored   1.25 .45
1168 A318   100d multicolored   1.50 .75
    *Nos. 1166-1168 (3)*    3.50 1.60

Irrigation — A319

No. 1169: a, Desert, water. b, Produce,
sheep grazing. c, Khadafy, irrigation of desert
(size: 63x44mm). Nos. 1170-1171, Khadafy,
map.

**1984, Feb. 1**      *Perf. 14½*
1169 A319   Strip of 3    2.50 2.50
  a.-b.   50d any single    .50 .25
  c.    100d multicolored   1.50 .60

**Size: 72x36mm**
*Perf. 13½*
1170 A319   100d multicolored   1.50 .60

**Souvenir Sheet**
1171 A319   300d multicolored   *7.00 7.00*

World
Heritage
A320

Architectural ruins: 50d, Theater, Sabratha.
60d, Temple, Cyrene. 70d, Monument,
Sabratha, vert. 100d, Arena, Leptis Magna.
150d, Temple, Cyrene, diff. 200d, Basilica,
Leptis Magna.

**1984, Feb. 10**      *Perf. 12*
1172 A320   50d multicolored   .60 .25
1173 A320   60d multicolored   .75 .30
1174 A320   70d multicolored   .90 .35
1175 A320   100d multicolored   1.50 .60
1176 A320   150d multicolored   2.00 .90
1177 A320   200d multicolored   2.75 1.40
    *Nos. 1172-1177 (6)*    8.50 3.80

Silver Dirhams Minted
A.D. 671-757 — A321

Designs: a, Hegira 115. b, Hegira 93. c,
Hegira 121. d, Hegira 49. e, Hegira 135.

**Litho. & Embossed**
**1984, Feb. 15**      *Perf. 13½*
1178    Strip of 5    15.00 15.00
  a.-e.   A321 200d, any single   2.75 1.25

Tripoli Intl. Fair — A322

Tea served in various settings.

| **1984, Mar. 5** | | **Litho.** | **Perf. 12½** | |
|---|---|---|---|---|
| 1179 | A322 | 25d multicolored | .25 | .25 |
| 1180 | A322 | 35d multicolored | .40 | .25 |
| 1181 | A322 | 45d multicolored | .75 | .25 |
| 1182 | A322 | 55d multicolored | .90 | .40 |
| 1183 | A322 | 75d multicolored | 1.10 | .40 |
| 1184 | A322 | 100d multicolored | 1.75 | .95 |
| | | *Nos. 1179-1184 (6)* | 5.15 | 2.50 |

Musicians — A323

Designs: a, Muktar Shiaker Murabet. b, El-Aref El-Jamal. c, Ali Shiaalia. d, Bashir Fehmi.

| **1984, Mar. 15** | | | **Perf. 14½** | |
|---|---|---|---|---|
| 1185 | | Strip of 4 + label | 9.00 | 9.00 |
| a.-d. | A323 | 100d, any single | 1.90 | 1.00 |

Children's Day, IYC — A324

Children's drawings: a, Recreation. b, Rainy day. c, Military strength. d, Playground. e, Porch swing, children, motorcycle.

| **1984, Mar. 21** | | | **Perf. 14** | |
|---|---|---|---|---|
| 1186 | | Strip of 5 | 2.75 | 2.75 |
| a.-e. | A324 | 20d, any single | .45 | .25 |

Arab League Constitution, 39th Anniv. — A325

| **1984, Mar. 22** | | | **Perf. 13½** | |
|---|---|---|---|---|
| 1187 | A325 | 30d multicolored | .60 | .60 |
| 1188 | A325 | 40d multicolored | .70 | .70 |
| 1189 | A325 | 50d multicolored | 1.00 | 1.00 |
| | | *Nos. 1187-1189 (3)* | 2.30 | 2.30 |

**Miniature Sheet**

Automobiles, Locomotives — A326

| **1984, Apr. 1** | | | | |
|---|---|---|---|---|
| 1190 | A326 | Sheet of 16 | 30.00 | 30.00 |
| a.-h. | | 100d, Car, any single | 1.75 | .90 |
| i.-p. | | 100d, Locomotive, any single | 1.75 | .90 |

No. 1190 pictures outline of two camels in gold. Size: 214x135mm.

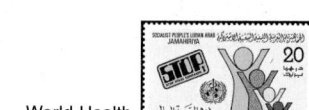

World Health Day — A327

| **1984, Apr. 7** | | | **Perf. 14½** | |
|---|---|---|---|---|
| 1191 | A327 | 20d Stop Polio | .25 | .25 |
| 1192 | A327 | 30d No. 910 | .40 | .25 |
| 1193 | A327 | 40d Arabic text | .90 | .40 |
| | | *Nos. 1191-1193 (3)* | 1.55 | .90 |

Crafts — A328

Designs: a, Shoemaker. b, Saddler. c, Women, wool. d, Spinner. e, Weaver. f, Tapestry weavers.

| **1984, May 1** | | | **Perf. 12½** | |
|---|---|---|---|---|
| 1194 | | Strip of 6 | 15.00 | 15.00 |
| a.-f. | A328 | 150d, any single | 2.25 | 1.25 |

Postal and Telecommunications Union Congress — A329

Designs: a, Telephones, mail. b, Computer operators. c, Emblem.

| **1984, May 15** | | | **Perf. 14½** | |
|---|---|---|---|---|
| 1195 | A329 | Strip of 3 | 3.50 | 3.50 |
| a.-b. | | 50d, any single | .75 | .40 |
| c. | | 100d multicolored | 1.50 | .75 |

Armed Crowd — A330

A331

No. 1197a, Map, Fire, Military. No. 1197b, Soldiers. No. 1197c, Khadafy. No. 1198, Khadafy giving speech.

| **1984, May 17** | | **Perf. 12, 14½ (#1197)** | | |
|---|---|---|---|---|
| 1196 | A330 | 50d multi | .90 | .40 |
| 1197 | A331 | Strip of 3 | 3.00 | 3.00 |
| a.-b. | | 50d, any single | .75 | .25 |
| c. | | 100d multi | 1.75 | .90 |
| 1198 | A330 | 100d multi | 1.50 | .75 |
| | | *Nos. 1196-1198 (3)* | 5.40 | 4.15 |

Abrogation of the May 17 Treaty. Size of No. 1197c: 63x45mm.

Youth War Casualties A332

70d, Damaged flag. 100d, Children imprisoned.

| **1984, June 4** | | | **Perf. 10** | |
|---|---|---|---|---|
| 1199 | A332 | 70d multi | 1.00 | .40 |
| 1200 | A332 | 100d multi | 1.50 | .75 |

**Miniature Sheet**

Green Book Quotations — A333

Designs: a, The Party System Aborts Democracy. b, Khadafy. c, Partners Not Wage-Workers. d, No Representation in Lieu of the People . . . e, Green Book. f, Committees Everywhere. g, Forming Parties Splits Societies. h, Party building, text on track. i, No Democracy without Popular Congresses.

| **1984, June 20** | | | **Perf. 14** | |
|---|---|---|---|---|
| 1201 | A333 | Sheet of 9 | 14.00 | 14.00 |
| a.-i. | | 100d, any single | 1.50 | .75 |

See No. 1270.

Folk Costumes — A334

Background colors: a, Green. b, Beige. c, Violet. d, Pale greenish blue. e, Salmon rose. f, Blue.

| **1984, July 1** | | | **Perf. 14½x14** | |
|---|---|---|---|---|
| 1202 | | Strip of 6 | 12.50 | 12.50 |
| a.-f. | A334 | 100d, any single | 1.75 | 1.00 |

**Miniature Sheet**

Natl. Soccer Championships — A335

Stadium, star, world cup and various action scenes.

| **1984, July 15** | | | **Perf. 13½** | |
|---|---|---|---|---|
| 1203 | A335 | Sheet of 16 | 20.00 | 20.00 |
| a.-p. | | 70d, any single | 1.10 | .60 |

1984 Los Angeles Olympics — A336

| **1984, July 28** | | | | |
|---|---|---|---|---|
| 1204 | A336 | 100d Soccer | 2.00 | 1.10 |
| 1205 | A336 | 100d Basketball | 2.00 | 1.10 |
| 1206 | A336 | 100d Swimming | 2.00 | 1.10 |
| 1207 | A336 | 100d Sprinting | 2.00 | 1.10 |
| 1208 | A336 | 100d Windsurfing | 2.00 | 1.10 |
| 1209 | A336 | 100d Discus | 2.00 | 1.10 |
| | | *Nos. 1204-1209 (6)* | 12.00 | 6.60 |

**Souvenir Sheets**

| 1210 | A336 | 250d Equestrian | 6.25 | 6.25 |
|---|---|---|---|---|
| 1211 | A336 | 250d Arab equestrian | 6.25 | 6.25 |

World Food Day — A337

1212, Forest scenes. 1213, Men riding camels, oasis.

| **1984, Aug. 1** | | | **Perf. 12** | |
|---|---|---|---|---|
| 1212 | A337 | 100d multicolored | 1.75 | .75 |
| 1213 | A337 | 200d multicolored | 3.50 | 1.25 |

**Miniature Sheet**

Sept. 1 Revolution, 15th Anniv. — A338

Designs: a, Green books, building at right angle. b, Green book, building, minaret. c, Minaret, party building and grounds. d, Revolution leader. e, Eight-story building. f, Construction, dome. g, Highway, bridge. h, Green book, building at left angle. i, Shepherd, sheep. j, Harvester. k, Tractors. l, Industry. m, Khadafy. n, Irrigation pipe, man drinking. o, Silos, factory. p, Shipping.

| **1984, Sept. 15** | | | **Perf. 14½** | |
|---|---|---|---|---|
| 1214 | A338 | Sheet of 16 | 9.00 | 9.00 |
| a.-p. | | 25d single | .50 | .25 |

A339

Evacuation Day — A340

No. 1215: b, Warrior facing left; c, Khadafy leading battle (size: 63x45mm). No. 1216, Female rider. No. 1217, Battle scene. No. 1218, Italian whipping Libyan.

| **1984, Oct. 7** | | | | |
|---|---|---|---|---|
| 1215 | A339 | Strip of 3 | 3.50 | 3.50 |
| a.-b. | | 50d, any single | .75 | .40 |
| c. | | 100d multi | 1.50 | .60 |
| | | **Perf. 11½** | | |
| 1216 | A340 | 100d multicolored | 1.50 | .60 |
| 1217 | A340 | 100d multicolored | 1.50 | .60 |
| 1218 | A340 | 100d multicolored | 1.50 | .60 |
| | | *Nos. 1215-1218 (4)* | 8.00 | 5.30 |

**Miniature Sheet**

Equestrians — A341

Various jumping, racing and dressage exercises printed in a continuous design.

| **1984, Oct. 15** | | | **Perf. 13½** | |
|---|---|---|---|---|
| 1219 | A341 | Sheet of 16 | 9.00 | 9.00 |
| a.-p. | | 25d any single | .50 | .50 |

PHILAKOREA '84.

Agricultural Traditions — A342

Designs: a, Farmer. b, Well, man, ox. c, Basket weaver. d, Shepherd, ram. e, Tanning hide. f, Coconut picker.

**1984, Nov. 1**      **Perf. 13½**
**1220**    Strip of 6      12.50   12.50
   a.-f.   A342 100d, any single    1.75   1.00

Union of Arab Pharmacists, 9th Congress — A343

**1984, Nov. 6**      **Perf. 12**
**1221**   A343 100d multicolored    1.75   1.75
**1222**   A343 200d multicolored    3.50   3.50

Arab-African Union — A344

No. 1223, Map, banner, crowd. No. 1224, Men, flags.

**1984, Nov. 15**      **Perf. 12**
**1223**   A344 100d multicolored    1.75   1.75
**1224**   A344 100d multicolored    1.75   1.75

Nos. 1046, 1147 — A345

**1984, Nov. 29**      **Perf. 12½**
**1225**   A345 100d pink & multi    3.75   3.75
**1226**   A345 150d brt yel grn & multi    4.75   4.75
Intl. Day of Cooperation with the Palestinian People.

Miniature Sheet

Intl. Civil Aviation Organization, 40th Anniv. — A346

Aircraft: a, Boeing 747 SP, 1975. b, Concorde, 1969. c, Lockheed L1011-500 Tristar, 1978. d, Airbus A310, 1982. e, Tupolev TU-134A, 1962. f, Shorts 360, 1981. g, Boeing 727, 1963. h, Caravelle 10, 1965. i, Fokker F27, 1955. j, Lockheed 749A Constellation, 1946. k, Martin 130, 1955. l, Douglas DC-3, 1936. m, Junkers JU-52, 1932. n, Lindbergh's Spirit of St. Louis, 1927 Ryan. o, De Havilland Moth, 1925. p, Wright Flyer, 1903.

**1984, Dec. 7**      **Perf. 13½**
**1227**   A346   Sheet of 16    27.50   27.50
   a.-p.   70d any single    1.50   .75

African Development Bank, 20th Anniv. — A347

"20" in different configurations and: 70d, Map, symbols of industry, education and agriculture. 100d, Symbols of research and development.

**1984, Dec. 15**
**1228**   A347 50d multicolored    .90   .90
**1229**   A347 70d multicolored    1.25   1.25
**1230**   A347 100d multicolored    1.75   1.75
Nos. 1228-1230 (3)    3.90   3.90

UN Child Survival Campaign — A348

No. 1231, Mother, child. No. 1232, Children. No. 1233, Boys at military school. No. 1234, Khadafy, children.

**1985, Jan. 1**      **Perf. 12**
**1231**   A348 70d multicolored    1.50   .75
**1232**   A348 70d multicolored    1.50   .75
**1233**   A348 70d multicolored    1.50   .75
**1234**   A348 70d multicolored    1.50   .75
Nos. 1231-1234 (4)    6.00   3.00

Irrigation — A349

**1985, Jan. 15**      **Perf. 14½x14**
**1235**   A349 100d shown    2.00   1.00
**1236**   A349 100d Flowers    2.00   1.00
**1237**   A349 100d Map, water    2.00   1.00
Nos. 1235-1237 (3)    6.00   3.00

Drop of Water, Map A350

**Souvenir Sheet**
**Perf. 14x14½**
**1238**   A350 200d shown    4.00   4.00

Musicians A351

No 1239: a, Kamel El-Ghadi; b, Lute. No. 1240: a, Ahmed El-Khogia; b, Violin. No. 1241: a, Mustafa El-Fallah; b, Zither. No. 1242: a, Mohamed Hamdi; b, Mask.

**1985, Feb. 1**      **Perf. 14½**
**1239**   A351 Pair    5.00   3.75
   a.-b.   100d, any single    2.25   1.75
**1240**   A351 Pair    5.00   3.75
   a.-b.   100d, any single    2.25   1.75
**1241**   A351 Pair    5.00   3.75
   a.-b.   100d, any single    2.25   1.75
**1242**   A351 Pair    5.00   3.75
   a.-b.   100d, any single    2.25   1.75
Nos. 1239-1242 (4)    20.00   15.00

Nos. 1239-1242 printed in sheets of 20, four strips of 5 consisting of two pairs each musician flanking center stamps picturing instruments.

Gold Dinars Minted A.D. 699-727 A352

No. 1243: a, Hegira 105. b, Hegira 91. c, Hegira 77. No. 1244, Dinar from Zuela.

**Litho. and Embossed**
**1985, Feb. 15**      **Perf. 13½**
**1243**    Strip of 3    12.50   12.50
   a.-c.   A352 200d, any single    4.00   2.50
**Souvenir Sheet**
**1244**   A352 300d multi    7.50   7.50

Fossils — A353

**1985, Mar. 1**      **Litho.**      **Perf. 13½**
**1245**   A353 150d Frog    6.00   3.00
**1246**   A353 150d Fish    6.00   3.00
**1247**   A353 150d Mammal    6.00   3.00
Nos. 1245-1247 (3)    18.00   9.00

People's Authority Declaration — A354

Khadafy wearing: a, Folk costume. b, Academic robe. c, Khaki uniform. d, Black uniform. e, White uniform.

**1985, Mar. 2**      **Litho.**      **Perf. 14½**
**1248**    Strip of 5    10.00   10.00
   a.-e.   A354 100d, any single    2.00   1.50

Tripoli Intl. Fair — A355

Musicians playing: a, Cymbals. b, Double flute, bongo. c, Wind instrument, drum. d, Drum. e, Tambourine.

**1985, Mar. 5**      **Perf. 14**
**1249**    Strip of 5    10.00   10.00
   a.-e.   A355 100d, any single    1.90   1.75

Children's Day, IYC — A356

Children's drawings, various soccer plays: a, Goalie and player. b, Four players. c, Players as letters of the alphabet. d, Goalie save. e, Player heading the ball.

**1985, Mar. 21**      **Perf. 12**
**1250**    Strip of 5    7.50   7.50
   a.-e.   A356 20d, any single    .40   .25

Intl. Program for Development of Telecommunications — A357

**1985, Apr. 1**
**1251**   A357 30d multicolored    .40   .40
**1252**   A357 70d multicolored    1.00   1.00
**1253**   A357 100d multicolored    2.00   2.00
Nos. 1251-1253 (3)    3.40   3.40

World Health Day — A358

**1985, Apr. 7**
**1254**   A358 40d Invalid, nurses    1.00   .60
**1255**   A358 60d Nurse, surgery    1.50   1.00
**1256**   A358 100d Nurse, child    2.50   1.60
Nos. 1254-1256 (3)    5.00   3.20

Miniature Sheet

Sea Shells — A359

Designs: a, Mytilidae. b, Muricidae (white). c, Cardiidae. d, Corallophilidae. e, Muricidae. f, Muricacea. g, Turridae. h, Argonautidae. i, Tonnidae. j, Aporrhaidae. k, Trochidae. l, Cancellariidae. m, Epitoniidae. n, Turbnidae. o, Mitridae. p, Pectinidae.

**1985, Apr. 20**
**1257**   A359   Sheet of 16    13.00   13.00
   a.-p.   25d, any single    .60   .25

Tripoli Intl. Book Fair — A360

**1985, Apr. 28**      **Perf. 13½**
**1258**   A360 100d multi    2.00   1.50
**1259**   A360 200d multi    4.00   3.00

Intl. Youth Year — A361

Games: No. 1260a, Jump rope. No. 1260b, Board game. No. 1260c, Hopscotch. No. 1260d, Stickgame. No. 1260e, Tops. No. 1261a, Soccer. No. 1261b, Basketball.

**1985, May 1**
**1260**    Strip of 5    6.00   6.00
   a.-e.   A361 20d, any single    .40   .25
**Souvenir Sheet**
**1261**    Sheet of 2    9.00   9.00
   a.-b.   A361 100d, any single    3.00   1.00

No. 1261 contains 2 stamps 30x42mm.

Miniature Sheet

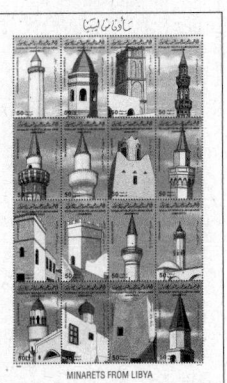

Mosque Minarets and Towers — A362

Mosques: a, Abdussalam Lasmar. b, Zaoviat Kadria. c, Zaoviat Amura. d, Gurgi. e, Mizran. f, Salem. g, Ghat. h, Ahmed Karamanli. i, Atya. j, El Kettani. k, Benghazi. l, Derna. m, El Derug. n, Ben Moussa. o, Ghadames. p, Abdulwahab.

**1985, May 15**                                **Perf. 12**
1262  A362  Sheet of 16                    15.00  15.00
*a.-p.*      50d, any single                    .75    .60

Hamida El-
Anezi — A363

**1985, June 1     Litho.        Perf. 13½**
1263  A363  100d multicolored             2.00  1.50
1264  A363  100d Jamila Zemerli           2.00  1.50

Teachers' Day.

A364

Battle of the Philadelphia: a, Ship sinking. b,
Militia. c, Hand-to-hand combat.

**1985 June 12**
1265  A364      Strip of 3                 4.00  4.00
*a.-b.*      50d, any single               1.00  1.00
*c.*         100d multicolored             1.75  1.75

Size of No. 1265c: 60x48mm. Continuous
design with No. 1265c in middle.

A365

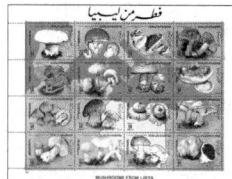

Khadafy's Islamic Pilgrimage — A366

"The Holy Koran is the Law of Society" and
Khadafy: a, Writing. b, Kneeling. c, With Holy
Kaaba. d, Looking in window. e, Praying at
pilgrimage ceremony.

**1985, June 16**
1266          Strip of 5                   22.50 22.50
*a.-e.*      A365 200d, any single          4.00  2.50

**Souvenir Sheet**
1267  A366  300d multicolored              6.50  6.50

**Miniature Sheet**

Mushrooms — A367

Designs: a, Leucopaxillus lepistoides. b,
Amanita caesarea. c, Coriolus hirsutus. d,
Cortinarius subfulgens. e, Dermocybe pratensis. f, Macrolepiota excoriata. g, Amanita cur-
tipes. h, Trametes ljubarskyi. i, Pholiota
aurivella. j, Boletus edulis. k, Geastrum ses-
sile. l, Russula sanguinea. m, Cortinarius
herculeus. n, Pholiota lenta. o, Amanita ruben-
scens. p, Scleroderma polyrhizum.

**1985, July 15**
1268  A367  Sheet of 16                    17.50 17.50
*a.-p.*      50d, any single               1.00   .40

No. 1268 exists imperf. Value $50.

---

Women's Folk
Costumes — A368

Designs: a, Woman in violet. b, In white. c,
In brown and blue. d, In blue. e, In red.

**1985, Aug. 1             Perf. 14½x14**
1269        Strip of 5                     10.00 10.00
*a.-e.*     A368 100d, any single          1.75  1.50

**Green Book Quotations Type of
1984**
**Miniature Sheet**

Designs: a, In Need Freedom Is Latent. b,
Khadafy reading. c, To Make A Party You Split
Society. d, Public Sport Is for All the Masses.
e, Green Books, doves. f, Wage-Workers Are
a Type of Slave . . . g, People Are Only Harmo-
nious with Their Own Arts and Heritages. h,
Khadafy orating. i, Democracy Means Popular
Rule Not Popular Expression.

**1985, Aug. 15               Perf. 14**
1270        Sheet of 9                     17.50 17.50
*a.-i.*     A333 100d, any single          1.75  1.50

A369

September 1 Revolution, 16th
Anniv. — A370

Designs: a, Food. b, Oil pipeline, refinery. c,
Capital, olive branch. d, Mosque, modern
buildings. e, Flag, mountains. f, Telecommunications apparatus.

**1985, Sept. 1             Perf. 12½**
1271        Strip of 6                     12.50 12.50
*a.-f.*     A369 100d, any single          2.00  1.50

**Souvenir Sheet**
1272  A370  200d multi                     4.50  4.50

Mosque
Entrances — A371

Designs: a, Zauiet Amoura, Janzour. b,
Shiaieb El-ain, Tripoli. c, Zauiet Abdussalam
El-asmar, Zliten. d, Karamanli, Tripoli. e,
Gurgi, Tripoli.

**1985, Sept. 15            Perf. 14**
1273        Strip of 5                     10.00 10.00
*a.-e.*     A371 100d, any single          2.00  1.50

**Miniature Sheet**

Basketball — A372

Various players in action.

---

**1985, Oct. 1     Litho.     Perf. 13x12½**
1274        Sheet of 16                    9.00  9.00
*a.-p.*     A372 25d any single             .50   .40

Evacuation — A373

Designs: a, Man on crutches, web, tree. b,
Man caught in web held by disembodied
hands. c, Three men basking in light.

**1985, Oct. 7                Perf. 15**
1275  A373  Strip of 3                     7.00  7.00
*a.-c.*     100d any single                1.75  1.50

Stamp Day — A374

Italia 85: a, Man sitting at desk, Type A228,
Earth. b, Magnifying glass, open stock book,
Type A228. c, Stamps escaping envelope.

**1985, Oct. 25              Perf. 12**
1276  A374  Strip of 3                     4.00  4.00
*a.-c.*     50d, any single                1.00   .60

1986 World Cup
Soccer
Championships
A375

No. 1277, Block, heading the ball. No. 1278,
Kick, goalie catching ball. No. 1279, Goalie,
block, dribble. No. 1280, Goalie, dribble, slid-
ing block. No. 1281, Goalie catching the ball.
No. 1282, Block.
No. 1283, Four players.

**1985, Nov. 1              Perf. 13½**
1277  A375  100d multicolored             2.00  1.50
1278  A375  100d multicolored             2.00  1.50
1279  A375  100d multicolored             2.00  1.50
1280  A375  100d multicolored             2.00  1.50
1281  A375  100d multicolored             2.00  1.50
1282  A375  100d multicolored             2.00  1.50
      Nos. 1277-1282 (6)                  12.00  9.00

**Souvenir Sheet**
1283  A375  200d multicolored             8.50  8.50

Intl. Day of
Cooperation with
the Palestinian
People — A376

**1985, Nov. 29    Litho.    Perf. 12½**
1284  A376  100d multi                     1.75  1.50
1285  A376  150d multi                     3.25  2.25

**Khadafy**

A377                         A377a

**Perf. 12½x13,  13¼x13**
**1986, Jan. 1                        Engr.**
1286  A377   50d vermilion       40.00  70.00
1287  A377   60d blue            40.00  70.00
1288  A377   70d carmine         40.00  70.00
1289  A377   80d violet          40.00  70.00
1290  A377   90d brown           40.00  70.00
1291  A377  100d dk grn          50.00  80.00
1292  A377  200d dk rose         50.00  80.00
1293  A377  250d brt grn         50.00  80.00
1294  A377a 300d grysh
                 blue            50.00  80.00
1295  A377a 500d redsh
                 brn             50.00  80.00

---

1296  A377a 1500d grysh
                  grn            55.00  85.00
1297  A377a 2500d purple         65.00  95.00
      Nos. 1286-1297 (12)       570.00 930.00

Supposedly Nos. 1286-1297 were on sale
for two hours. Value on first day cover, $400.

---

**Importation Prohibited**
Importation of the stamps of Libya
was prohibited as of Jan. 7, 1986.

General Post and Telecommunications
Co. — A378

**1986, Jan. 15                Perf. 12**
1298  A378  100d yel & multi          2.25  1.50
1299  A378  150d yel grn & multi      2.75  2.00

Peoples Authority Declaration — A379

Designs: b, Hand holding globe and paper.
c, Dove, Khadafy's Green Book (size:
53x37mm).

**1986, Mar. 2            Perf. 12½x13**
1300  A379  Strip of 3                 4.50  4.50
*a.-b.*     50d, any single            1.00   .60
*c.*        100d multicolored          2.00  1.25

Musical
Instruments
A380

Designs: a, Flute. b, Drums. c, Horn. d,
Cymbals. e, Hand drum.

**1986, Mar. 5**
1301        Strip of 5                 10.00 10.00
*a.-e.*     A380 100d any single        2.00  1.50

Tripoli International Fair.

Intl. Children's
Day — A381

Designs: a, Boy Scout fishing. b, Riding
camel. c, Chasing butterflies. d, Beating drum.
e, Soccer game.

**1986, Mar. 21              Perf. 13½**
1302        Strip of 5                 8.50  8.50
*a.-e.*     A381 50d any single        1.25   .75

World Health
Day — A382

**1986, Apr. 7**
1303  A382  250d sil & multi          5.00  3.00
1304  A382  250d gold & multi         5.00  3.00

Government Programs — A383

Designs: a, Medical examinations. b, Education. c, Farming (size: 63x42mm).

**1986, May 1**     *Perf. 14½*
| | | | |
|---|---|---|---|
| 1305 | A383 | Strip of 3 | 3.75 3.75 |
| a.-b. | | 50d any single | .85 .60 |
| c. | | 100d multicolored | 1.75 1.25 |

### Miniature Sheet

**World Cup Soccer Championships, Mexico — A384**

Designs: No. 1306a, 2 players. No. 1306b, 3 players in red and white shirts, one in green. No. 1306c, 2 players, referee. No. 1306d, Shot at goal. No. 1306e, 2 players with striped shirts. No. 1306f, 2 players with blue shirts, one with red.

No. 1307, 7 players. No. 1308, 1st Libyan team, 1931.

**1986, May 31**     *Perf. 13½*
| | | | |
|---|---|---|---|
| 1306 | A384 | Sheet of 6 | 7.50 7.50 |
| a.-f. | | 50d any single | 1.10 .75 |

**Souvenir Sheets**
| | | | |
|---|---|---|---|
| 1307 | A384 | 200d multicolored | 6.50 6.50 |
| 1308 | A384 | 200d multicolored | 6.50 6.50 |

Nos. 1307-1308 each contain one 52x37mm stamp.

### Miniature Sheet

**Vegetables — A385**

Designs: a, Peas. b, Zucchini. c, Beans. d, Eggplant. e, Corn. f, Tomato. g, Red pepper. h, Cucumbers. i, Garlic. j, Cabbage. k, Cauliflower. l, Celery. m, Onions. n, Carrots. o, Potato. p, Radishes.

**1986, June 1**     *Perf. 13x12½*
| | | | |
|---|---|---|---|
| 1309 | | Sheet of 16 | 15.00 15.00 |
| a.-p. | A385 | 50d any single | .85 .75 |

No. 1309 has a continuous design.

### Miniature Sheet

**Khadafy and Irrigation Project — A386**

Khadafy and: a, Engineer reviewing plans, drill rig. b, Map. c, Well. d, Drought conditions. e, Water pipe. f, Pipes, pulleys, equipment. g, Lowering water pipe. h, Construction workers, trailer. i, Hands holding water. j, Opening water valve. k, Laying pipeline. l, Trucks hauling pipes. m, Khadafy holding green book, city. n, Giving vegetables to people. o, Boy drinking, man cultivating field. p, Men in prayer, irrigation. (Khadafy not shown on Nos. 1310h, 1310i, 1310k, 1310 l, 1310o.)

**1986, July 1**     *Perf. 13½*
| | | | |
|---|---|---|---|
| 1310 | | Sheet of 16 | 35.00 35.00 |
| a.-p. | A386 | 100d any single | 2.00 1.40 |

A387

A388

---

**American Attack on Libya, Apr. 15 — A389**

Designs: Nos. 1311a-1311p, Various scenes in Tripoli during and after air raid. No. 1312a. F14 aircraft. No. 1312b, Aircraft carrier, people. No. 1312c, Sinking of USS *Philadelphia*, 1801.

**1986, July 13**
| | | | |
|---|---|---|---|
| 1311 | A387 | Sheet of 16, #a.-p. | 26.00 26.00 |
| 1312 | A388 | Strip of 3 | 3.50 3.50 |
| a.-b. | | 50d multicolored | .85 .65 |
| c. | | 100d multicolored | 1.75 1.25 |
| 1313 | A389 | 100d multicolored | 2.10 1.50 |

No. 1312 has a continuous design. Size of No. 1312b: 60x38mm.

**Khadafy's Peace Methods — A390**

Khadafy: b, Reading Green Book. c, With old woman. d, Praying with children. e, Visiting sick. f, Driving tractor.

**1986, July 13**
| | | | |
|---|---|---|---|
| 1314 | | Sheet of 6 | 12.50 12.50 |
| a.-f. | A390 | 100d any single | 2.00 1.40 |

### Miniature Sheet

**Green Book Quotations A391**

Designs: a, The House Must be Served by its Own Tenant. b, Khadafy. c, The Child is Raised by His Mother. d, Democracy is the Supervision of the People by the People. e, Green Books. f, Representation is a Falsification of Democracy. g, The Recognition of Profit is an Acknowledgement of Exploitation. h, Flowers. i, Knowledge is a Natural Right of Every Human Being...

**1986, Aug. 1**     *Perf. 14*
| | | | |
|---|---|---|---|
| 1315 | | Sheet of 9 | 19.00 19.00 |
| a.-i. | A391 | 100d any single | 2.00 1.40 |

**Sept. 1st Revolution, 17th Anniv. — A392**

a, Public health. b, Agriculture. c, Sunflowers by Vincent Van Gogh. d, Defense. e, Oil industry.

**1986, Sept. 1**
| | | | |
|---|---|---|---|
| 1316 | | Strip of 5 | 22.50 22.50 |
| a.-e. | A392 | 200d any single | 4.00 2.75 |

A393

**Arab-African Union, 1st Anniv. — A394**

No. 1317, Libyan, Arab horsemen. No. 1318, Women in native dress.

---

**1986, Sept. 15**     *Perf. 12*
| | | | |
|---|---|---|---|
| 1317 | A393 | 250d multicolored | 5.00 4.00 |
| 1318 | A394 | 250d multicolored | 5.00 4.00 |

**Evacuation Day — A395**

Designs: a, Mounted warrior. b, Two horsemen, infantry. c, Cavalry charge.

**1986, Oct. 7**     *Perf. 13½*
| | | | |
|---|---|---|---|
| 1319 | A395 | Strip of 3 | 6.00 6.00 |
| a. | | 50d multicolored | 1.00 .60 |
| b. | | 100d multicolored | 2.00 1.10 |
| c. | | 150d multicolored | 2.75 2.40 |

**Intl. Peace Year — A396**

**1986, Oct. 24**     *Perf. 14½*
| | | | |
|---|---|---|---|
| 1320 | A396 | 200d bl & multi | 4.00 3.00 |
| 1321 | A396 | 200d grn & multi | 4.00 3.00 |

**Solidarity with the Palestinians A397**

**1986, Nov. 29**     *Perf. 12½*
| | | | |
|---|---|---|---|
| 1322 | A397 | 250d pink & multi | 5.00 4.00 |
| 1323 | A397 | 250d blue & multi | 5.00 4.00 |

**Music and Dance — A398**

Designs: a, Man beating drum. b, Masked dancer. c, Woman dancing with jugs on her head. d, Man playing bagpipe. e, Man beating hand drum.

**1986, Dec. 1**     *Perf. 12*
| | | | |
|---|---|---|---|
| 1324 | | Strip of 5 | 8.00 8.00 |
| a.-e. | A398 | 70d any single | 1.50 1.25 |

**Gazella Leptoceros A399**

**1987, Mar. 2**     *Perf. 13½*
| | | | |
|---|---|---|---|
| 1325 | A399 | 100d Two adults | 3.00 2.00 |
| 1326 | A399 | 100d Fawn nursing | 3.00 2.00 |
| 1327 | A399 | 100d Adult sleeping | 3.00 2.00 |
| 1328 | A399 | 100d Adult drinking | 3.00 2.00 |
| | | *Nos. 1325-1328 (4)* | 12.00 8.00 |

World Wildlife Fund.
Nos. 1325-1328 exist imperf. Value, set $27.50.

A400

Crowd of People and: a, Oilfields. b, Buildings. c, Khadafy, buildings, globe.

**1987, Mar. 2**     *Perf. 13½*
| | | | |
|---|---|---|---|
| 1329 | A400 | Strip of 3 | 40.00 40.00 |
| a.-b. | | 500d multicolored | 10.00 8.00 |
| c. | | 1000d multicolored | 20.00 15.00 |

People's Authority declaration.
No. 1329 has a continuous design. Size of No. 1329c: 42x37mm.

---

### Miniature Sheet

A401

Sept. 1st Revolution, 18th Anniv.: a, Shepherd, sheep. b, Khadafy. c, Mosque. d, Irrigation pipeline. e, Combine in field. f, Khadafy at microphones. g, Harvesting grain. h, Irrigation. i, Soldier. j, Militiaman. k, Fountain. l, Skyscrapers. m, House, women. n, Children. o, Assembly hall. p, Two girls.

**1987, Sept. 1**     *Perf. 13½*
| | | | |
|---|---|---|---|
| 1330 | | Sheet of 16 | 70.00 70.00 |
| a.-p. | A401 | 150d any single | 3.00 2.25 |

No. 1330 has a continuous design.

**Libyan Freedom Fighters — A402**

No. 1331: a, Omer Abed Anabi Al Mansuri. b, Ahmed Ali Al Emrayd. c, Khalifa Said Ben Asker. d, Mohamed Ben Farhat Azawi. e, Mohamed Souf Al Lafi Al Marmori.

**1988, Feb. 15**
| | | | |
|---|---|---|---|
| 1331 | | Strip of 5 | 29.00 29.00 |
| a. | A402 | 100d multicolored | 2.00 1.25 |
| b. | A402 | 200d multicolored | 5.75 4.25 |
| c. | A402 | 300d multicolored | 8.00 4.50 |
| d. | A402 | 400d multicolored | |
| e. | A402 | 500d multicolored | 9.00 6.50 |

**Freedom Festival Day — A403**

**1988, June 1**
| | | | |
|---|---|---|---|
| 1332 | A403 | 100d yel & multi | 1.75 1.25 |
| 1333 | A403 | 150d grn & multi | 3.00 2.00 |
| 1334 | A403 | 250d brn org & multi | 5.00 3.50 |
| | | *Nos. 1332-1334 (3)* | 9.75 6.75 |

### Miniature Sheet

**American Attack on Libya, 2nd Anniv. — A404**

Khadafy: a, With woman and children. b, Playing chess. c, Fleeing from bombing with children. d, Praying in desert. e, Praying with children. f, Visiting wounded child. g, With infants and children, horiz. h, Delivering speech, horiz. i, With family, horiz.

No. 1336, In desert, vert. No. 1337, Making speech.

**1988, July 13**
| | | | |
|---|---|---|---|
| 1335 | A404 | Sheet of 9 | 25.00 25.00 |
| a.-i. | | 150d any single | 2.75 2.00 |

## Souvenir Sheets
### Litho. & Embossed

| | | | | |
|---|---|---|---|---|
| **1336** | A404 | 500d gold & multi | 10.00 | 10.00 |
| **1337** | A404 | 500d gold & multi | 10.00 | 10.00 |

No. 1335 exists imperf.

September 1st Revolution, 19th Anniv. — A405

### 1988, Sept. 19                         Litho.

| | | | | |
|---|---|---|---|---|
| **1338** | A405 | 100d brt bl & multi | 1.75 | 1.25 |
| **1339** | A405 | 250d gray & multi | 4.50 | 3.00 |
| **1340** | A405 | 300d cit & multi | 5.00 | 4.25 |
| **1341** | A405 | 500d bl grn & multi | 10.00 | 7.00 |
| | *Nos. 1338-1341 (4)* | | 21.25 | 15.50 |

1988 Summer Olympics, Seoul — A406

### 1988, Sept. 17

| | | | | |
|---|---|---|---|---|
| **1342** | A406 | 150d Tennis | 2.75 | 2.00 |
| **1343** | A406 | 150d Equestrian | 2.75 | 2.00 |
| **1344** | A406 | 150d Relay race | 2.75 | 2.00 |
| **1345** | A406 | 150d Soccer | 2.75 | 2.00 |
| **1346** | A406 | 150d Distance race | 2.75 | 2.00 |
| **1347** | A406 | 150d Cycling | 2.75 | 2.00 |
| | *Nos. 1342-1347 (6)* | | 16.50 | 12.00 |

### Souvenir Sheet

| | | | | |
|---|---|---|---|---|
| **1348** | A406 | 750d Soccer, diff. | 13.00 | 13.00 |

No. 1348 contains one 30x42mm stamp. Exists imperf. Nos. 1342-1347 exist in miniature sheets of 1. Value, set $37.50.

### Miniature Sheet

1988 Summer Olympics, Seoul — A407

### 1988, Sept 17

| | | | | |
|---|---|---|---|---|
| **1350** | A407 | Sheet of 3 | 8.50 | 8.50 |
| *a.* | | 100d Bedouin rider | 2.00 | 2.00 |
| *b.* | | 200d shown | 3.00 | 3.00 |
| *c.* | | 200d Show jumping, diff. | 3.00 | 3.00 |

Olymphilex '88, Seoul.

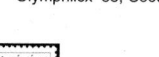
A408

Design: Libyan Palm Tree.

### 1988, Nov. 1

| | | | | |
|---|---|---|---|---|
| **1351** | A408 | 500d Fruit | 10.00 | 6.50 |
| **1352** | A408 | 1000d Palm tree | 18.00 | 12.00 |

A409

### 1988

| | | | | |
|---|---|---|---|---|
| **1353** | A409 | Strip of 3 | 11.50 | 11.50 |
| *a.* | | 100d shown | 2.00 | 1.40 |
| *b.* | | 200d Boy with rocks | 3.50 | 2.75 |
| *c.* | | 300d Flag, map | 5.75 | 4.25 |

Palestinian uprising. No. 1353b, size: 45x39mm.

---

People's Authority Declaration A410

### 1989

| | | | | |
|---|---|---|---|---|
| **1354** | A410 | 260d dk grn & multi | 5.00 | 3.00 |
| **1355** | A410 | 500d gold & multi | 10.00 | 6.00 |

### Miniature Sheet

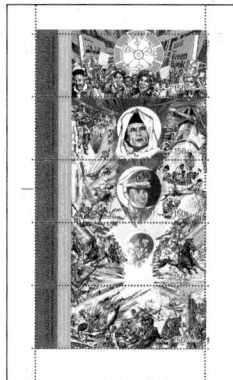

September 1 Revolution, 20th Anniv. — A411

Designs: a, Crowd, Green Books, emblem. b, Soldiers, Khadafy, irrigation pipeline. c, Military equipment, Khadafy, communication and transportation. d, Mounted warriors. e, Battle scenes.

### 1989                                  Perf. 13½

| | | | | |
|---|---|---|---|---|
| **1356** | A411 | Sheet of 5 | 14.00 | 14.00 |
| *a.-e.* | | 150d any single | 2.75 | 2.00 |
| *f.* | | Bkt. pane of 5, perf. 13½ horiz. | 14.00 | 14.00 |

### Souvenir Sheet

| | | | | |
|---|---|---|---|---|
| **1357** | A411 | 250d Khadafy | 4.00 | 4.00 |

No. 1357 contains one 36x51mm stamp. Stamps from No. 1356f have gold border at right.

Libyans Deported to Italy A412

No. 1359, Libyans in boats. No. 1360, Khadafy, crescent moon. No. 1361, Khadafy at left, in desert. No.1362, Khadafy at right, soldiers. No. 1363, Khadafy in center, Libyans.

### 1989

| | | | | |
|---|---|---|---|---|
| **1358** | A412 | 100d shown | 1.75 | 1.25 |
| **1359** | A412 | 100d multicolored | 1.75 | 1.25 |
| **1360** | A412 | 100d multicolored | 1.75 | 1.25 |
| **1361** | A412 | 100d multicolored | 1.75 | 1.25 |
| **1362** | A412 | 100d multicolored | 1.75 | 1.25 |
| | *Nos. 1358-1362 (5)* | | 8.75 | 6.25 |

### Souvenir Sheet

| | | | | |
|---|---|---|---|---|
| **1363** | A412 | 150d multicolored | 3.00 | 3.00 |

No. 1363 contains one 72x38mm stamp.

A413

### 1989                                  Perf. 12

| | | | | |
|---|---|---|---|---|
| **1364** | A413 | 150d multicolored | 2.75 | 2.75 |
| **1365** | A413 | 200d multicolored | 4.25 | 4.25 |

Demolition of Libyan-Tunisian border fortifications.

---

Solidarity with the Palestinians — A414

300d, Man, flag, crowd. 500d, Emblem.

### 1989                              Perf. 12x11½

| | | | | |
|---|---|---|---|---|
| **1366** | A414 | 100d shown | 2.25 | 2.25 |
| **1367** | A414 | 300d multicolored | 6.50 | 6.50 |
| **1368** | A414 | 500d multicolored | 10.00 | 10.00 |
| | *Nos. 1366-1368 (3)* | | 18.75 | 18.75 |

Ibn Annafis, Physician — A415

### 1989                                  Perf. 12

| | | | | |
|---|---|---|---|---|
| **1369** | A415 | 100d multicolored | 2.75 | 2.75 |
| **1370** | A415 | 150d multicolored | 4.00 | 4.00 |

Intl. Literacy Year — A416

### 1990, Oct. 18        Litho.    Perf. 14
### Granite Paper

| | | | | |
|---|---|---|---|---|
| **1371** | A416 | 100d multicolored | 1.75 | 1.75 |
| **1372** | A416 | 300d multicolored | 8.00 | 8.00 |

A417

### 1990, Oct. 18              Granite Paper

| | | | | |
|---|---|---|---|---|
| **1373** | A417 | 100d multicolored | 1.75 | 1.75 |
| **1374** | A417 | 400d multicolored | 5.25 | 5.25 |

Organization of Petroleum Exporting Countries (OPEC), 30th anniv.

A418

### 1990, June 28                 Perf. 11½x12

| | | | | |
|---|---|---|---|---|
| **1375** | A418 | 100d brt org & multi | 1.75 | 1.75 |
| **1376** | A418 | 400d grn & multi | 8.00 | 8.00 |

Evacuation of US military base, 20th anniv.

People's Authority Declaration — A419

### 1990, Apr. 24

| | | | | |
|---|---|---|---|---|
| **1377** | A419 | 300d bl & multi | 5.00 | 5.00 |
| **1378** | A419 | 500d vio & multi | 10.00 | 10.00 |

---

A420

Plowing Season in Libya: 2000d, Man on tractor plowing field.

### 1990, Dec. 4                          Perf. 14
### Granite Paper

| | | | | |
|---|---|---|---|---|
| **1379** | A420 | 500d multicolored | 11.00 | 11.00 |
| **1380** | A420 | 2000d multicolored | 37.50 | 37.50 |

A421

### 1990, Nov. 5                          Perf. 14
### Granite Paper

| | | | | |
|---|---|---|---|---|
| **1381** | A421 | 100d grn & multi | 1.75 | 1.75 |
| **1382** | A421 | 400d vio & multi | 8.00 | 8.00 |
| **1383** | A421 | 500d bl & multi | 9.25 | 9.25 |
| | *Nos. 1381-1383 (3)* | | 19.00 | 19.00 |

### Souvenir Sheet
### Perf. 11½

| | | | | |
|---|---|---|---|---|
| **1384** | A421 | 500d Trophy, map, horiz. | 11.00 | 11.00 |

World Cup Soccer Championships, Italy. No. 1384 contains one 38x33mm stamp.

Sept. 1st Revolution, 21st Anniv. — A422

### 1990, Sept. 3                          Perf. 14
### Granite Paper

| | | | | |
|---|---|---|---|---|
| **1385** | A422 | 100d multicolored | 2.00 | 2.00 |
| **1386** | A422 | 400d multicolored | 8.50 | 8.50 |
| **1387** | A422 | 1000d multicolored | 21.00 | 21.00 |
| | *Nos. 1385-1387 (3)* | | 31.50 | 31.50 |

### Imperf
### Size: 120x90mm

| | | | | |
|---|---|---|---|---|
| **1388** | A422 | 200d multi, diff. | 8.50 | 8.50 |

Maghreb Arab Union, 2nd Anniv. — A423

### 1991, Mar. 10       Litho.    Perf. 13½

| | | | | |
|---|---|---|---|---|
| **1389** | A423 | 100d multicolored | 2.00 | 2.00 |
| **1390** | A423 | 300d gold & multi | 5.75 | 5.75 |

People's Authority Declaration A424

### 1991, Mar. 10

| | | | | |
|---|---|---|---|---|
| **1391** | A424 | 300d multicolored | 5.00 | 5.00 |
| **1392** | A424 | 400d silver & multi | 10.00 | 10.00 |

Children's Day — A425

100d, Butterflies, girl. 400d, Bird, boy.

**1991, Mar. 22**
1393 A425 100d multicolored 2.75 2.75
1394 A425 400d multicolored 10.00 10.00

World Health
Day — A426

**1991, Apr. 7**
1395 A426 100d blue & multi 1.75 1.75
1396 A426 200d green & multi 3.50 3.50

Scenes from
Libya — A427

100d, Wadi el Hayat, vert. 250d, Mourzuk.
500d, Ghadames.

**1991, June 20**
1397 A427 100d multicolored 1.75 1.75
1398 A427 250d multicolored 5.00 5.00
1399 A427 500d multicolored 10.00 10.00
    Nos. 1397-1399 (3) 16.75 16.75

Irrigation Project — A428

a, Laborers, heavy equipment. b, Khadafy,
heavy equipment. c, Livestock, fruit &
vegetables.

**1991, Aug. 28** *Perf. 12*
1400 A428 50d Strip of 3, #a.-
       c. 3.50 3.50

No. 1400 has a continuous design. Size of
No. 1400b: 60x36mm.

Sept. 1st
Revolution, 22nd
Anniv. — A429

300d, Chains, roses & "22". 400d, Chains,
"22".

**1991, Sept. 1** *Perf. 13½*
1401 A429 300d multicolored 5.75 5.75
1402 A429 400d multicolored 7.25 7.25
    a.    Souv. sheet of 2, #1401-
          1402 16.00 16.00

Telecom
'91 — A430

100d, Emblems, vert. 500d, Buildings, satellite dish.

**1991, Oct. 7** *Litho.* *Perf. 13½*
1403 A430 100d multicolored 1.75 1.75
1404 A430 500d multicolored 9.25 9.25

Libyans Deported
to Italy — A431

100d, Monument, soldier. 400d, Ship, refugees, soldiers.

**1991, Oct. 26** *Litho.* *Perf. 13½*
1405 A431 100d multicolored 1.75 1.75
1406 A431 400d multicolored 7.25 7.25
    a.    Souv. sheet of 2, #1405-
          1406 10.00 10.00

Arab
Unity — A432

**1991, Nov. 15** *Perf. 12*
1407 A432 50d tan & multi 1.00 1.00
1408 A432 100d blue & multi 2.00 2.00

**Miniature Sheet**

Trucks, Automobiles
and
Motorcycles — A433

Designs: a-d, Various trucks. e-h, Various
off-road race cars. i-p, Various motorcycles.

**1991, Dec. 28** *Perf. 14*
1409 A433 50d Sheet of 16,
       #a.-p. 17.50 17.50

Eagle          Col. Khadafy
A434           A434a

**1992** *Perf. 11½*
**Granite Paper (#1412-1419)**
**Background Colors**
1412 A434 100d yellow 1.40 .85
1413 A434 150d blue gray 2.25 1.25
1414 A434 200d brt blue 2.75 1.75
1415 A434 250d orange 3.75 2.00
1416 A434 300d purple 4.25 2.50
1417 A434 400d brt pink 5.75 3.50
1418 A434 450d brt grn 7.25 3.75
                    *Perf. 13½*
1420 A434a 500d yel grn 6.50 3.50
1421 A434a 1000d rose 13.00 7.00
1422 A434a 2000d blue 26.00 14.00
1423 A434a 5000d violet 65.00 37.50
1424 A434a 6000d yel brn 80.00 45.00
    Nos. 1412-1424 (12) 217.90 122.60

Issued: No 1412-1416, 1418-1419, 1/1;
Nos. 1420-1424, 9/1.

People's Authority
Declaration — A435

**1992, Mar.** *Litho.* *Perf. 12*
1425 A435 100d yellow & multi 1.50 1.50
1426 A435 150d blue & multi 2.25 2.25

African Tourism
Year (in
1991) — A436

**1992, Apr. 5** *Perf. 14½*
**Granite Paper**
1427 A436 50d purple & multi .75 .75
1428 A436 100d pink & multi 1.40 1.40

1992 Summer
Olympics,
Barcelona — A437

**1992, June 15** *Perf. 12*
1429 A437 50d Tennis .75 .75
1430 A437 50d Long jump .75 .75
1431 A437 50d Discus .75 .75
    Nos. 1429-1431 (3) 2.25 2.25
       **Size: 106x82mm**
          *Imperf*
1432 A437 100d Olympic torch,
          rings 1.50 1.50

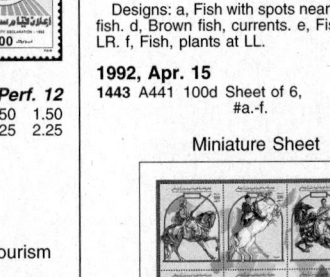

Revolutionary
Achievements
A438

Designs: 100d, Palm trees. 150d, Steel mill.
250d, Cargo ship. 300d, Libyan Airlines. 400d,
Natl. Assembly, Green Books. 500d, Irrigation
pipeline, Khadafy.

**1992, June 30** *Perf. 14*
**Granite Paper**
1433 A438 100d multicolored 1.40 1.40
1434 A438 150d multicolored 2.25 2.25
1435 A438 250d multicolored 3.75 3.75
1436 A438 300d multicolored 4.25 4.25
1437 A438 400d multicolored 5.75 5.75
1438 A438 500d multicolored 7.25 7.25
    Nos. 1433-1438 (6) 24.65 24.65

Tripoli Intl.
Fair — A439

50d, Horse & buggy. 100d, Horse & sulky.

**1992, Mar.** *Perf. 12*
1439 A439 50d multicolored
1440 A439 100d multicolored

Maghreb Arab
Union
Philatelic
Exhibition
A440

**1992, Feb. 17** *Perf. 14½*
1441 A440 75d blue green &
          multi 2.50 1.75
1442 A440 80d blue & multi 2.50 1.75

**Miniature Sheet**

Fish — A441

Designs: a, Fish with spots near eye. b, Thin
fish. d, Brown fish, currents. e, Fish, plants at
LR. f, Fish, plants at LL.

**1992, Apr. 15** *Perf. 14*
1443 A441 100d Sheet of 6,
          #a.-f. 14.00 14.00

**Miniature Sheet**

Horsemanship — A442

Designs: a, Woman rider with gun. b, Man
on white horse. c, Mongol rider. d, Roman
officer. e, Cossack rider. f, Arab rider. 250d,
Two Arab riders.

**1992, Apr. 25** *Perf. 13½x14*
1444 A442 100d Sheet of 6,
          #a.-f. 9.50 9.50
       **Souvenir Sheet**
1445 A442 250d multicolored 5.00 5.00

Khadafy
A443

Designs: No. 1450a, like No. 1446. b, like
No. 1447. c, like No. 1448. d, like No. 1449.

**1992, Jan. 1** *Perf. 14x13½*
1446 A443 100d blue grn &
          multi 2.00 2.00
1447 A443 100d gray & multi 2.00 2.00
1448 A443 100d rose lake &
          multi 2.00 2.00
1449 A443 100d yellow & multi 2.00 2.00
    Nos. 1446-1449 (4) 8.00 8.00
       **Souvenir Sheet**
1450 A443 150d Sheet of 4,
          #a.-d. 11.00 11.00

Evacuation of Foreign
Forces — A444

75d, Horse, broken chain. 80d, Flag, broken
chain.

**1992, Oct. 7** *Litho.* *Perf. 14*
1451 A444 75d multicolored 1.00 1.00
1452 A444 80d multicolored 1.00 1.00

Costumes — A445

Women wearing various traditional
costumes.
Denomination color: a, green. b, black. c,
violet blue. d, sky blue. e, yellow brown.

**1992, Dec. 15** *Litho.* *Perf. 12*
1453 A445 50d Strip of 5, #a.-
          e. 4.00 4.00

Sept. 1st Revolution,
23rd Anniv. — A446

50d, Torch, "23". 100d, Flag, "23".
250d, Eagle, "23".

**1992, Sept. 1**
1454 A446 50d multicolored .75 .75
1455 A446 100d multicolored 1.40 1.40
       **Souvenir Sheet**
1456 A446 250d multicolored 3.50 3.50

No. 1456 contains one 50x40mm stamp.

Libyans
Deported to
Italy — A447

**1992, Oct. 26**
1457 A447 100d tan & multi 1.40 1.40
1458 A447 250d blue & multi 3.00 3.00

Oasis — A448

Designs: 100d, Gazelle drinking. 200d,
Camels, palm trees, vert. 300d, Palm trees,
camel and rider.

**1992, Oct. 1**     **Perf. 14**
**1459** A448 100d multicolored   1.50   1.50
**1460** A448 200d multicolored   3.00   3.00
**1461** A448 300d multicolored   5.00   5.00
    *Nos. 1459-1461 (3)*    9.50   9.50

Palestinian Intifada A449

Designs: 100d, Palestinian holding rock and flag. 300d, Map of Israel and Palestine, Dome of the Rock, Palestinian flag, olives, hand holding rock, vert.

**1992, Nov. 26**   **Litho.**   **Perf. 12**
**1462-1463** A449   Set of 2    4.50   4.50

Doctors — A450

Designs: 40d, Dr. Mohamed Ali Imsek (1883-1945). 60d, Dr. Aref Adhani Arif (1884-1935).

**1993, Feb. 1**
**1464-1465** A450   Set of 2    1.25   1.25

Intl. Conference on Nutrition, Rome — A451

Background colors: 70d, Blue. 80d, Green.

**1993, Feb. 15**
**1466-1467** A451   Set of 2    1.75   1.75

People's Authority Declaration A452

Col. Khadafy, map of Libya, crowd, eagle, oil rig, pipeline and tanker: 60d, 65d, 75d.

**1993, Mar. 2**     **Perf. 14¾**
**1468-1470** A452   Set of 3    2.25   2.25

Tripoli Intl. Fair — A453

Various Fair participants, Fair emblem and panel color of: No. 1471, 60d, Pink. No. 1472, 60d, Yellow green. No. 1473, 60d, Blue, vert. No. 1474, 60d, Orange, vert.
100d, People on horses.

**1993, Mar. 15**     **Perf. 14**
**1471-1474** A453   Set of 4    2.50   2.50
    **Souvenir Sheet**
    **Perf. 11¾**
**1475** A453 100d multi     1.50   1.50
   No. 1475 contains one 38x32mm stamp.

World Health Day — A454

---

Designs: 75d, Doctor and three nurses examining child. 85d, Doctor and two nurses examining woman.

**1993, Apr. 7**     **Perf. 13¼**
**1476-1477** A454   Set of 2    1.60   1.60

Children's Day — A455

No. 1478 — Various girls with background of: a, Gray green (red headdress). b, Red curtains. c, Gray. d, Home furnishings. e, Beige.

**1993, May 1**     **Perf. 13¾**
**1478**    Horiz. strip of 5   4.25   4.25
   **a.-e.** A455 75d Any single   .80   .80

    **Miniature Sheet**

Watercraft — A456

No. 1479: a, Ship with swan's head figurehead. b, Ship with triangular sail and oars. c, Ship with one large white sail. d, Ship with rectangular sail and oars. e, Ship with three triangular sails. f, Sailboat, map of Western Mediterranean area. g, Sailboat, map of Eastern Mediterranean area. h, Ship with two red triangular sails. i, Ship with four sails, red flag. j, Sailboat, map of Western Libya. k, Sailboat, map of Eastern Libya. l, Ship with three sails on main mast. m, Ocean liner with black hull. n, Ship with six tan sails. o, Ship with furled sails. p, Ocean liner with white hull.

**1993, July 15**     **Perf. 13¼**
**1479** A456 50d Sheet of 16,
     #a-p    10.00   10.00

    **Miniature Sheet**

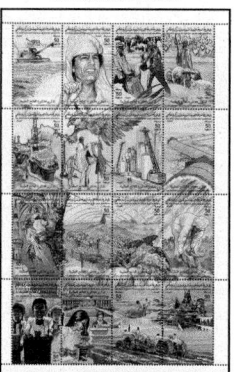

Sept. 1 Revolution, 24th Anniv. — A457

No. 1480: a, Grain combine. b, Col. Khadafy. c, Cows, man with feed bucket. d, Shepherd and sheep. e, Oil platform, map of Western Libya. f, Eagle, man on camel, map of Eastern Libya. g, Cranes lifting large tanks. h, Water pipeline. i, Man picking dates. j, Man in field, crates of vegetables. k, Crates of vegetables. l, Man picking vegetables. m, Three children. n, Building, women at typewriter and microscope. o, Man in field, tractor. p, Tractors in field.

**1993, Dec. 10**     **Perf. 14**
**1480** A457 50d Sheet of 16,
     #a-p    12.00   12.00

---

    **Miniature Sheet**

Libyans Deported to Italy A458

No. 1481: a, Guard tower, soldier with gun, woman tending to sick man. b, Soldier with gun and bayonet guarding Libyans. c, Col. Khadafy with headdress. d, Man holding box and walking stick. e, Soldiers whipping man. f, Man on horse. g, Four men. h, Soldier guarding people looking at hanged man. i, Soldier standing near wooden post, soldier guarding Libyans. j, Woman on camel, soldiers. k, Soldiers on horses among Libyans. l, Boat with deportees. m, Col. Khadafy without headdress. n, Libyan with arm raised, hand of Col. Khadafy. o, Soldier pointing gun at horseman with sword. p, Horseman carrying gun.

**1993, Dec. 15**     **Perf. 14½**
**1481** A458 50d Sheet of 16,
     #a-p    12.00   12.00

    **Miniature Sheet**

Items Made of Silver A459

No. 1482: a, Medallion with five-pointed star and tassels. b, Wristband. c, Medallion with star with ten rays and tassels. d, Rod with tassels. e, Necklace. f, Slippers.

   **Litho. & Embossed With Foil**
     **Application**
**1994, Aug. 10**     **Perf. 13¼**
**1482** A459 55d Sheet of 6, #a-f   4.25   4.25

A460

Sept. 1 Revolution, 25th Anniv. — A461

No. 1483: a, Jet, Col. Khadafy in robe (40x40mm). b, Warriors on horseback, mother and child, Col. Khadafy in military uniform (60x60mm). c, Ship, shepherd, man and woman, man on camel (40x40mm).

**1994, Sept. 1**   **Litho.**   **Perf. 12**
**1483** A460 100d Horiz. strip
     of 3, #a-c    4.25   4.25
    **Souvenir Sheet**
**1484** A461 1000d multi    13.50   13.50

1994 World Cup Soccer Championships, United States — A462

World Cup, and various soccer players with horizontal stripes in: No. 1485, 100d, Red and

---

brown. No. 1486, 100d, Red violet, purple, and green. No. 1487, 100d, Green and purple. No. 1488, 100d, Green, black and yellow. No. 1489, 100d, Orange, brown and red. No. 1490, 100d, Yellow orange, brown and orange.
   No. 1491, 500d, Soccer players, World Cup, red violet background. No. 1492, 500d, Soccer player, ball, "1990," horiz.

**1994, Oct. 15**     **Perf. 13¼**
**1485-1490** A462   Set of 6    8.50   8.50
    **Souvenir Sheets**
**1491-1492** A462   Set of 2    14.00   14.00
   No. 1491 contains one 42x51mm stamp;
No. 1492 contains one 51x42mm stamp.

    **Miniature Sheet**

Libyans Deported to Italy A463

No. 1493: a, Col. Khadafy. b, Airplane, man with rifle. c, Two men, one with rifle, nose of airplane. d, Tail of airplane, man with rifle. e, Soldier with bayoneted rifle, Libyans looking at dead animal. f, Libyans with rifles, camel. g, Nose of camel, horsemen and soldiers. h, Man carrrying child, drawn swords, horsemen. i, Soldier with whip. j, Man with open mouth. k, Tank and soldiers. l, Soldiers on horseback, women. m, Woman tending to injured man, man with bound hands, rifles. n, Soldier bayoneting man. o, Building, women, soldiers on horseback. p, Deportees in boats.

**1994, Oct. 26**     **Perf. 12**
**1493** A463 95d Sheet of 16,
     #a-p    22.50   22.50

Mosques — A464

No. 1494 — Mosques in: a, Darghut. b, Benghazi. c, Kabao. d, Gouzgu. e, Siala. f, El Kettani.

**1994, Nov. 15**     **Litho.**
**1494**    Horiz. strip of 6   11.50   11.50
    **a.-f.** A464 70d Any single   1.50   1.50

    **Miniature Sheet**

People's Authority Declaration — A465

No. 1495: a, Navy ship, jet, women soldiers. b, Wheat, hand holding Green Book, tractor trailer cab. c, Family, water pipeline, tractor trailers. d, Fruit, vegetables, people holding Green Book. e, Col. Khadafy, butterfly, flowers. f, Young men, fruit and vegetables.

**1994, Dec. 1**     **Perf. 14¾**
**1495** A465 80d Sheet of 6, #a-
     f    12.00   12.00

Evacuation of Foreign Forces — A466

Denomination in: 65d, Blue. 95f, Green.

**1994, Dec. 15**      ***Perf. 14***
1496-1497 A466   Set of 2     2.75 2.75

### Miniature Sheet

Khadafy
Prize for
Human
Rights
A467

No. 1498: a, Helmeted soldiers, men with
sticks, South African flag. b, Men with sticks,
South African flag. c, South African Pres. Nelson Mandela. d, Col. Khadafy. e, Indian at fire,
crescent moon. f, Armed Indians on horses. g,
Indian chief. h, Indian dancer. i, Men with
rifles, jets. j, Women, jet, open book. k, Open
book. l, Surgeons. m, Palestinians with flag,
denomination at left. n, Palestinians with flag,
denomination at right. o, Palestinians throwing
rocks. p, Palestinians, soldiers.

**1994, Dec. 31**      ***Perf. 13¼***
1498 A467 95d Sheet of 16,
    #a-p     20.00 40.00

No. 1498 was first issued with marginal
inscription with incorrect spelling of "Prize" as
"Price." Value is for sheet with corrected spelling. Value, sheet with incorrect spelling $300.

People's Authority
Declaration — A468

Background color: No. 1499, 100d, Green.
No. 1500, 100d, Blue. No. 1501, 100d, Yellow.

**1995, July 1**      ***Perf. 12***
1499-1501 A468   Set of 3    2.25 2.25

Arab League, 50th
Anniv. — A469

Background color: No. 1502, 200d, Green.
No. 1503, 200d, Blue.
No. 1504: a, Emblem in silver. b, Emblem in
gold.

**1995, July 20**   **Litho.**   ***Perf. 13¼***
1502-1503 A469   Set of 2    7.50 7.50
**Litho. & Embossed With Foil
Application**
1504 A469 1000d Sheet of 2,
    #a-b     13.00 13.00

### Miniature Sheet

Libyan
Soccer
Players
A470

No. 1505: a, Messaud Zentuti. b, Salem
Shermit. c, Ottoman Marfua. d, Ghaleb Siala.
e, 1935 Libyan Team. f, Senussi Mresila.

**1995, Aug. 1**      **Litho.**
1505 A470 100d Sheet of 6, #a-f 9.50 9.50

---

### Miniature Sheet

Zoo
Animals
A471

No. 1506: a, Camel. b, Secretary bird. c,
African wild dog. d, Oryx. e, Baboon. f, Golden
jackal. g, Crowned eagle. h, Eagle owl. i,
Desert hedgehog. j, Sand gerbil. k, Addax. l,
Fennec. m, Lanner falcon. n, Desert wheatear.
o, Pintailed sandgrouse. p, Jerboa.

**1995, Aug. 15**      ***Perf. 13¾x14***
1506 A471 100d Sheet of 16,
    #a-p     25.00 25.00

### Miniature Sheet

Fruit
A472

No. 1507: a, Grapefruit. b, Wild cherries. c,
Mulberries. d, Strawberry tree fruit (arbutus).
e, Plums. f, Pears. g, Apricots. h, Almonds. i,
Prickly pears. j, Lemons. k, Peaches. l, Dates.
m, Olives. n, Oranges. o, Figs. p, Grapes.

**1995, Aug. 20**
1507 A472 100d Sheet of 16,
    #a-p     24.00 24.00

### Miniature Sheet

Sept. 1 Revolution, 26th
Anniv. — A473

No. 1508: a, Students and chemist. b, Minaret, fist of Col. Khadafy, men. c, Col. Khadafy.
d, Scientists and buildings. e, Nurses, doctor
and patients. f, Surgeons. g, Woman at keyboard, shoemakers. h, Audio technicians,
musician. i, Crane, bulldozer and buildings. j,
Grain elevator. k, Offshore oil rig, nose of airplane. l, Tail of airplane, ship. m, Goats and
sheep. n, Water pipeline. o, Camels, vegetables, water. p, Fruit, grain combine.

**1995, Sept. 1**
1508 A473 100d Sheet of 16,
    #a-p     22.50 22.50

---

Scouts
A474

No. 1509 — Scouting emblem and: a, Antelope, Scout and butterflies (40x40mm). b,
Scouts, butterflies, antelope and cat
(60x40mm). c, Scouts, wheat, butterfly, flower.

**1995, Sept. 10**      ***Perf. 12***
1509 A474 250d Horiz. strip of
    3, #a-c     17.00 17.00

American Attack on Libya, 9th
Anniv. — A475

No. 1510: a, Ships and people (40x50mm).
b, Airplanes, helicopters and people, hand
holding Green Book (60x50mm). c, Airplane,
mother and child (40x50mm).

**1995, Sept. 15**
1510 A475 100d Horiz. strip of 3,
    #a-c     4.50 4.50

Tripoli Intl.
Fair — A476

Horsemen with background colors of: No.
1511, 100d, Light blue. No. 1512, 100d, Blue.
No. 1513, 100d, Violet. No. 1514, 100d, Blue
green, vert. No. 1515, 100d, Blue green with
black stripes, vert. No. 1516, 100d, Orange,
vert.
    1000d, Col. Khadafy on horse.

**1995, Sept. 20**
1511-1516 A476   Set of 6    9.00 9.00
**Souvenir Sheet**
1517 A476 1000d multi    14.00 14.00

No. 1517 contains one 80x50mm stamp.

### Miniature Sheet

City of Ghadames — A477

No. 1518: a, Camel, woman with water jugs.
b, Woman with bread on wooden board. c,
Seated woman with vase. d, Woman feeding
chickens. e, Woman at spinning wheel. f,
Woman standing. g, Woman cooking. h,
Woman milking goat. i, Shoemaker. j, Man at
loom. k, Metalworker with hammer. l, Date
picker. m, Men at religious school. n, Potter. o,
Tanner. p, Man picking tomatoes.

***Perf. 14½x14¼***
**1995, Sept. 30**      **Litho.**
1518 A477 100d Sheet of 16,
    #a-p     21.00 21.00

Evacuation of Foreign
Forces — A478

Panel color: 50d, Pink. 100d, Green. 200d,
Lilac.

**1995, Oct. 7**   **Litho.**   ***Perf. 14¾x14¼***
1519-1521 A478   Set of 3    5.00 5.00

---

Bees and
Flowers — A479

Panel color: No. 1522, 100d, Green. No.
1523, 100d, Pink. No. 1524, 100d, Purple.

**1995, Oct. 10**      ***Perf. 14¼x14¾***
1522-1524 A479   Set of 3    4.50 4.50

Dr. Mohamed
Feituri — A480

**1995, Oct. 20**      ***Perf. 14¾x14¼***
1525 A480 200d multi    2.75 2.75

Campaign Against
Smoking — A481

Color of central stripe: No. 1526, 100d,
Orange. No. 1527, 100d, Yellow.

**1995, Oct. 20**
1526-1527 A481   Set of 2    3.25 3.25

### Miniature Sheet

Libyans
Deported
to Italy
A482

No. 1528: a, Col. Khadafy. b, Horsemen. c,
Battle scene with blue sky, denomination at
LR. d, Battle scene with blue sky, airplane,
denomination at LL. e, Battle scene, arch. f,
Battle scene, red building at UR. g, Battle
scene with red sky, soldier holding pistol. h,
Battle scene with red sky, building at UR. i,
Three Libyans in foreground. j, Battle scene
with running soldiers. k, Battle scene of horsemen and riflemen facing right. l, Soldiers, Libyan man in foreground at LR. m, Two
horsemen with arms raised. n, Man in foreground shooting at horsemen. o, Children. p,
Child, deportees in boats.

**1995, Oct. 26**      ***Perf. 12***
1528 A482 100d Sheet of 16,
    #a-p     22.00 22.00

### Miniature Sheet

Musical Instruments — A483

No. 1529: a, Rababa. b, Nouba (drum). c,
Clarinet. d, Drums. e, Magruna. f, Zukra. g, Zil

(cymbals). h, Kaman (violin). i, Guitar. j, Trumpet. k, Tapla (drum). l, Gonga (drum). m, Saxophone. n, Piano. o, Gandon (zither). p, Ood.

**1995, Nov. 1**      *Perf. 13¾x14*
1529 A483 100d Sheet of 16,
     #a-p      21.00 21.00

Doors of
Mizda — A484

No. 1530: a, Blue door. b, Door with arched design in rectangular doorway. c, Log door. d, Door with rounded top in archway. e, Door of planks in rectangular doorway.

**1995, Nov. 10**      *Perf. 13¼*
1530    Horiz. strip of 5    3.50 3.50
   *a.-e.* A484 100d Any single    .65   .65

Intl. Olympic
Committee,
Cent. — A485

Denomination color: No. 1531, 100d, Red. No. 1532, 100d, Black.

**1995, Nov. 15**      *Perf. 13½*
1531-1532 A485   Set of 2    1.40 1.40

Prehistoric Animals — A486

No. 1533: a, Baryonyx. b, Oviraptor. c, Stenonychosaurus. d, Tenontosaurus. e, Yangchuanosaurus. f, Stegotetrabelodon, denomination at LR. g, Stegotetrabelodon, denomination at LL. h, Psittacosaurus. i, Heterodontosaurus. j, Loxodonta atlantica. k, Mammuthus. l, Erlikosaurus. m, Cynognathus. n, Plateosaurus. o, Staurikosaurus. p, Lystrosaurus.

500d, Stegotetrabelodon, horiz.

**1995, Nov. 20**      *Perf. 13½*
1533 A486   Miniature sheet
     of 16    12.50 12.50
   *a.-p.*   100d Any single    .75   .70
     **Souvenir Sheet**
     *Perf. 13¼*
1534 A486 500d multi      4.25 4.25
No. 1534 contains one 53x49mm stamp.

Children's
Day — A487

No. 1535: a, Boy, dinosaur with cane. b, Boy on elephant. c, Boy, Scout emblem, turtle and mushroom. d, Dinosaur and soccer ball. e, Boy with gun, pteranodon.

**1995, Nov. 25**      *Perf. 13½*
1535    Horiz. strip of 5    15.00 15.00
   *a.-e.* A487 100d Any single    2.75 2.75

Palestinian Intifada — A488

No. 1536: a, Boy throwing object at helicopter. b, Dome of the Rock, Palestinian with flag. c, People, Palestinian flag.

**1995, Nov. 29**      *Perf. 14*
1536 A488 100d Horiz. strip of 3,
     #a-c      4.50 4.50

Intl. Civil
Aviation
Organization,
50th
Anniv. — A489

Denomination color: No. 1537, 100d, Black. No. 1538, 100d, Blue.

**1995, Dec. 7**      *Perf. 13½x13¼*
1537-1538 A489   Set of 2    1.40 1.40

United Nations, 50th
Anniv. — A490

Background color: No. 1539, 100d, Dark red lilac. No. 1540, 100d, Light red lilac.

**1995, Dec. 20**      *Perf. 13½*
1539-1540 A490   Set of 2    1.40 1.40

     **Miniature Sheet**

Flowers
A491

No. 1541: a, Iris germanica. b, Canna edulis. c, Nerium oleander. d, Papaver rhoeas. e, Strelitzia reginae. f, Amygdalus communis.

**1995, Dec. 31**      *Perf. 14¾*
1541 A491 200d Sheet of 6,
     #a-f      11.00 11.00

People's Authority
Declaration — A492

Panel color: 100d, Pink. 150d, Light blue. 200d, Light green.

**1996, Mar. 2**      *Perf. 13¼*
1542-1544 A492   Set of 3    5.00 5.00

1996 Summer Olympics,
Atlanta — A493

No. 1545: a, Soccer. b, Long jump. c, Tennis. d, Cycling. e, Boxing. f, Equestrian.
No. 1546, 500d, Runner. No. 1547, 500d, Equestrian, diff.

**1996, Aug. 15**      *Perf. 14½*
1545 A493 100d Sheet of 6,
     #a-f      6.75   6.75
     **Souvenir Sheets**
1546-1547 A493   Set of 2    11.00 11.00

     **Miniature Sheet**

Sept. 1 Revolution, 27th
Anniv. — A494

No. 1548: a, Camel, man, fruits, water. b, Water pipeline, fruit. c, Tractor, water, women. d, Oil worker. e, Tailor. f, Seamstress, Col. Khadafy's fist. g, Col. Khadafy. h, Building, women with microscope. i, Nurses at anatomy lesson, man with microscope. j, School child. k, Woman with open book. l, Man playing zither. m, Airplanes. n, Dish antenna, ship, man on camel. o, Ship, television camera. p, Television actress, woman at microphone.

**1996, Sept. 1**      *Perf. 13¾x14*
1548 A494 100d Sheet of 16,
     #a-p      20.00 20.00

     **Miniature Sheet**

American Attack on Libya, 10th
Anniv. — A495

No. 1549: a, Left side of missile, explosion. b, Right side of missile, man with raised arms. c, Casualties, airplanes. d, Airplane at left, man on ground. e, Firefighter spraying burning car. f, Damaged vehicles. g, Col. Khadafy. h, Casualties, airplane at top. i, Rescuers assisting casualties. j, Man with extended hand. k, Woman with hands to face. l, Stretcher bearers. m, Three men and casualty. n, Man with bloody hand. o, Woman and child casualties. p, Burning car, rescuers attending to bleeding casualty.

**1996, Sept. 15**      *Perf. 13¾*
1549 A495 100d Sheet of 16,
     #a-p      20.00 20.00

     **Miniature Sheet**

Crustaceans — A496

No. 1550: a, Necora puber. b, Lissa chiragra. c, Palinurus elephas. d, Scyllarus arctus. e, Carcinus maenas. f, Calappa granulata. g, Parapenaeus longirostris. h, Nephrops norvegicus. i, Eriphia verrucosa. j, Cancer pagurus. k, Penaeus kerathurus. l, Squilla mantis. m, Maja squinado. n, Pilumnus hirtellus. o, Pagurus alatus. p, Macropodia tenuirostris.

**1996, Oct. 1**      *Perf. 14x13¾*
1550 A496 100d Sheet of 16,
     #a-p      20.00 20.00

     **Miniature Sheet**

Intl. Day of Maghreb
Handicrafts — A497

Various handicrafts.

**1996, Oct. 15**      *Perf. 13¾x14*
1551 A497 100d Sheet of 16,
     #a-p      20.00 20.00

     **Miniature Sheet**

Libyans
Deported
to Italy
A498

No. 1552: a, Guard tower, soldier with gun, woman tending to sick man. b, Soldier with gun and bayonet, soldier on horseback. c, Col. Khadaf with headdress. d, Man holding box and walking stick. e, Soldiers whipping man. f, Man on horse. g, Four men. h, Soldier guarding people looking at hanged man. i, Soldier standing near wooden post, soldier guarding Libyans. j, Woman on camel, soldiers. k, Soldiers on horses among Libyans. l, Boat with deportees. m, Col. Khadafy without headdress. n, Libyan with arm raised, hand of Col. Khadafy. o, Soldier pointing gun at horseman with sword. p, Horseman carrying gun.

**1996, Oct. 26**      *Litho.*
1552 A498 100d Sheet of 16,
     #a-p      20.00 20.00

     **Miniature Sheet**

Horses
A499

No. 1553: a, Brown horse, lake at right. b, Brown horse in front of lake, tree at right. c, Brown horse in front of lake, tree at right. d, Dark brown horse, trees in background. e, Dark brown horse with raised leg. f, Horse at base of tree. g, Gray horse galloping. h, Piebald horse. i, Gray horse, palm tree at left. j, Head of black horse and tail of brown horse. k, Brown horse, palm fronds at upper right. l, Brown horse with gray mane, palm tree at right. m, Head of black horse, body of gray horse, tail of brown horse. n, Head of brown horse, body of black horse, hindquarters of two brown horses. o, Head of brown horse, parts of three other brown horses. p, Head of brown horse, chest of another brown horse, palm tree at right.

**1996, Oct. 30**      *Perf. 14x13¾*
1553 A499 100d Sheet of 16,
     #a-p      20.00 20.00

## Miniature Sheet

Camels
A500

No. 1554: a, Camelus dromedarius with head at right. b, Head of Camelus dromedarius. c, Camelus dromedarius with head at left. d, Camelus ferus bactrianus with head at right. e, Camelus ferus ferus. f, Camelus ferus bactrianus with head at left.

**1996, Nov. 15** *Perf. 12*
1554 A500 200d Sheet of 6,
#a-f 13.50 13.50

Press and
Information — A501

Designs: 100d, Photographer, newspapers, computer. 200d, Musicians, video technician, computer, dish antenna.

**1996, Nov. 20**
1555-1556 A501 Set of 2 3.25 3.25

## Miniature Sheet

Fossils and Prehistoric
Animals — A502

No. 1557: a, Mene rhombea fossil. b, Mesodon macrocephalus fossil. c, Eyron arctiformis fossil. d, Stegosaurus. e, Pteranodon. f, Allosaurus.

**1996, Nov. 25**
1557 A502 200d Sheet of 6,
#a-f 16.00 16.00

Palestinian
Intifada — A503

Frame color: 100d, Yellow. 150d, Green. 200d, Blue.

**1996, Nov. 29**
1558-1560 A503 Set of 3 5.00 5.00

African Children's
Day — A504

Designs: 50d, Child, beige frame. 150d, Child, blue frame. 200d, Mother, child, dove.

**1996, Dec. 5** *Perf. 13¼*
1561-1563 A504 Set of 3 2.50 2.50

Children's
Day — A505

No. 1564 — Various cats with background colors of: a, Rose. b, Blue green. c, Blue. d, Yellow green. e, Gray green.

**1996, Dec. 5**
1564 Horiz. strip of 5 5.50 5.50
a.-e. A505 100d Any single 1.00 1.00

Intl.
Family
Day
A506

No. 1565 — Family and: a, 150d, Building (21x27mm). b, 150d, Automobile (21x27mm). c, 200d, Stylized globe (46x27mm).

**1996, Dec. 10** *Perf. 13x13¼*
1565 A506 Horiz. strip of 3, #a-c 3.00 3.00

## Miniature Sheet

Teachers
A507

No. 1566: a, Mohamed Kamel El-Hammali. b, Mustafa Abdulla Ben-Amer. c, Mohamed Messaud Fesheka. d, Kairi Mustafa Serraj. e, Muftah El-Majri. f, Mohamed Hadi Arafa.

**1996, Dec. 15** *Perf. 13¼*
1566 A507 100d Sheet of 6, #a-f 3.75 3.75

## Miniature Sheet

Singers
A508

No. 1567: a, Mohamed Salim and zither. b, Mohamed M. Sayed Bumedyen and flute. c, Otman Najim and ood. d, Mahmud Sherif and tapla. e, Mohamed Ferjani Marghani and piano. f, Mohamed Kabazi and violin.

**1996, Dec. 15**
1567 A508 100d Sheet of 6, #a-f 3.75 3.75

## Miniature Sheet

Reptiles
A509

No. 1568: a, Snake, leaves and building at top. b, Snake, building at top. c, Turtle, water and part of snake. d, Snake on tree branch. e, Brown lizard on rock. f, Cobra with head at left. g, Cobra and water. h, Turtle, water, tail of cobra. i, Green lizard on rock. j, Snake, foliage at bottom. k, Snake, foliage at bottom and right. l, Lizard with curled tail. m, Turtle on rock. n, Cobra with head at right. o, Turtle on grass. p, Gray lizard on rock.

**1996, Dec. 20** *Perf. 13¾x14*
1568 A509 100d Sheet of 16,
#a-p 18.50 18.50

## Miniature Sheet

Tripoli
Intl. Fair
A510

No. 1569: a, Mirror and brush. b, Container and plate. c, Two containers with rounded bases. d, Two containers on pedestals. e, Oval ornament. f, Brushes.

### Litho. & Embossed with Foil Application
**1996, Dec. 30** *Perf. 13¾*
1569 A510 100d Sheet of 6, #a-f 6.75 6.75

A511

People's Authority Declaration, 20th
Anniv. — A512

Frame color: 100d, Yellow. 200d, Blue. 300d, Green.

**1997, Mar. 2** *Litho.* *Perf. 12*
1570-1572 A511 Set of 3 7.75 7.75

### Souvenir Sheet
*Imperf*
1573 A512 10,000d multi 90.00 90.00
No. 1573 has a perforated label that bears the denomination but lacks the country name.

Scouts
and
Philately
A513

No. 1574: a, 50d, Group of scouts, open album, wheat, flag. b, 50d, Two scouts, two albums, wheat. c, 100d, Butterflies, books, scouts and flags.

**1997, Mar. 15** *Perf. 14*
1574 A513 Horiz. strip of 3, #a-c 2.75 2.75

Health
Care
A514

No. 1575: a, 50d, Doctor looking at test tube. b, 50d, Doctor, microscope. c, 100d, Doctor and nurse examining baby.

**1997, Apr. 7**
1575 A514 Horiz. strip of 3, #a-c 2.25 2.25

Buildings — A515

Designs: 50d, Shown. 100d, Building with attached tower, vert. 200d, Tower, vert.

*Perf. 14¼x14¾, 14¾x14¼*
**1997, Apr. 15**
1576-1578 A515 Set of 3 5.00 5.00

Campaign Against
Smoking — A516

Frame color: 100d, Blue. 150d, Green. 200d, Pink.

**1997, Apr. 30** *Perf. 14¾x14¼*
1579-1581 A516 Set of 3 2.75 2.75

Arab National Central
Library — A517

Building, map, open book, and olive branches with background in: 100d, Blue. 200d, Green.
1000d, Building, map, books, computer and Col. Khadafy, horiz.

**1997, Aug. 10** *Perf. 13¼*
1582-1583 A517 Set of 2 1.75 1.75

### Souvenir Sheet
1584 A517 1000d multi 6.00 6.00
No. 1584 contains one 116x49mm stamp.

Arab Tourism Year — A518

*Perf. 13¼x13½*
**1997, Aug. 20** *Litho.*
1585 A518 Horiz. strip of 3 10.50 10.50
a. 100d Black denomination 2.00 2.00
b. 200d Red denomination 3.75 3.75
c. 250d Blue denomination 4.75 4.75

## Miniature Sheet

A519

Sept. 1 Revolution, 28th
Anniv. — A520

No. 1586: a, 100d, Mother and child. b, 100d, Col. Khadafy as student. c, 100d, Khadafy at microphone. d, 100d, People on tank. e, 100d, Khadafy and man in suit. f, 100d, Khadafy with fist raised. g, 100d, Woman, child, corner of Green Book. h, 100d, Three people, corner of Green Book. i, 100d, Khadafy with pen. j, 100d, Man and child. k, 100d, Government buildings, helicopters. l, 100d, Khadafy in military uniform. m, 500d, Khadafy on horse. Size of Nos. 1586a-1586l: 28x43mm. Size of No. 1586m: 56x86mm.

## Litho., Litho with Foil Application
### (#1586m)
**1997, Sept. 1**      *Perf. 14*
1586 A519   Sheet of 13, #a-m    17.50 17.50

### Souvenir Sheet
*Perf. 13¾*
1587 A520 500d multi    6.00 6.00

### Miniature Sheet

Intl. Day of Maghreb
Handicrafts — A521

No. 1588 — Various shoes with toes pointing to: a, LR corner. b, Bottom. c, LL corner. d, UR corner. e, Top. f, UL corner.

### Litho. With Foil Application
**1997, Sept. 20**      *Perf. 13¾*
1588 A521 300d Sheet of 6,
   #a-f    18.00 18.00

### Miniature Sheet

Tripoli
Intl. Fair
A522

No. 1589 — Items made of silver: a, Medallion with tassels. b, Round medallion. c, Diamond-shaped medallion with tassels. d, Curved medallion. e, Necklace. f, Ring.

### Litho. & Embossed With Foil Application
**1997, Sept. 20**
1589 A522 500d Sheet of 6,
   #a-f    19.00 19.00

Evacuation of Foreign
Forces — A523

Denominations: 100d, 150d, 250d.

**1997, Oct. 7   Litho.   Perf. 14¾x14¼**
1590-1592 A523   Set of 3    2.75 2.75

### Miniature Sheet

Libyans
Deported
to Italy
A524

No. 1593: a, Person carrying water jug. b, Col. Khadafy with headdress. c, Man, soldier on horse. d, Soldier and Libyans. e, Soldier whipping man. f, Soldier, man on horse. g, Libyan man and man in uniform. h, People at hanging. i, Man with purple fez, woman with red headdress. j, People, horse and camel. k,

Col. Khadafy without headdress. l, Deportees on boats. m, Hand of Khadafy above pillars. n, Horsemen and pillars. o, Horsemen. p, Horsemen and hand of Khadafy.

**1997, Oct. 26**      *Perf. 14*
1593 A524 200d Sheet of 16,
   #a-p    32.50 32.50

Worldwide Fund for
Nature
(WWF) — A525

No. 1594 — Felis lybica: a, With prey at water. b, Adult and kittens. c, Under tree. d, Two adults.

**1997, Nov. 1**      *Perf. 13¼*
1594   Horiz. strip of 4    7.50 7.50
   a.-d.   A525 200d Any single    1.75 1.75
Printed in sheets containing two strips.

### Souvenir Sheet

Natl. Society for Wildlife
Conservation — A526

No. 1595: a, Antelope facing forward. b, Ram. c, Antelope facing left.

**1997, Nov. 1**      *Perf. 13¼*
1595 A526 100d Sheet of 3,
   #a-c    14.00 14.00

### Miniature Sheet

American Attack on Libya, 11th
Anniv. — A527

No. 1596: a, Explosion. b, Green Book, Libyan airplanes. c, Minarets, hand of Col. Khadafy. d, Col. Khadafy without headdress. e, Wing of American airplane. f, Nose of American airplane. g, Libyan airplanes. h, People looking at tail of American airplane. i, Rockets hitting American airplane. j, Arm of Col. Khadafy. k, Col. Khadafy with headdress. l, Man, fist of Col. Khadafy. m, Rockets and people. n, Col. Khadafy visiting injured person. o, Col. Khadafy kissing girl's hand. p, People with fists raised.

**1997, Nov. 15**      *Perf. 14*
1596 A527 200d Sheet of 16,
   #a-p    34.00 34.00

### Miniature Sheet

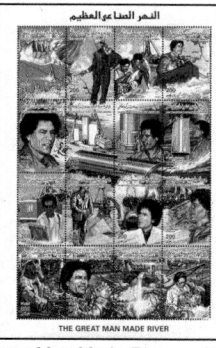

Great Man-Made River — A528

No. 1597: a, Fist, outline map of Libya. b, Col. Khadafy pointing to pipeline. c, Technicians reading paper, equipment. d, Col. Khadafy pointing to map. e, Col. Khadafy. f, Pipe, crane lifting cylinders. g, Col. Khadafy, pipe, vertical cylinder. h, Col. Khadafy, vertical cylinder. i, Col. Khadafy, construction trailer. j, Technician and equipment. k, Col. Khadafy, pipes lifted by crane. l, Col. Khadafy, line of trucks carrying pipe. m, Man with hand on spigot. n, Col. Khadafy with clasped hands. o, Hands under faucet, crops. p, Woman, child, flowers and fruit.

**1997, Dec. 1**      *Perf. 14*
1597 A528 200d Sheet of 16,
   #a-p    34.00 34.00

People's
Authority
Declaration
A529

Panel color: 150d, Blue green. 250d, Purple. 300d, Blue.

**1998, Mar. 2**      *Perf. 13¼*
1598-1600 A529   Set of 3    10.50 10.50

### Miniature Sheet

Tripoli
Intl. Fair
A530

No. 1601 — Items made of silver: a, Container with two spouts. b, Bowl on pedestal. c, Amphora. d, Container on tray. e, Lidded bowl. f, Three-legged container.

### Litho. & Embossed With Foil Application
**1998, Mar. 5**      *Perf. 13¾*
1601 A530 400d Sheet of 6,
   #a-f    24.00 24.00

Children's
Day — A531

No. 1602 — Various girls in native dress with background colors of: a, Light blue. b, Yellow green. c, Red orange. d, Lilac. e, Yellow brown.

**1998, Mar. 21   Litho.   Perf. 13¼**
1602   Horiz. strip of 5    5.50 5.50
   a.-e.   A531 100d Any single    1.00 1.00

World Health
Day — A532

Panel color: 150d, Buff. 250d, Light blue. 300d, Lilac.

**1998, Apr. 7**
1603-1605 A532   Set of 3    7.75 7.75

American Attack on Libya, 12th
Anniv. — A533

No. 1606 — Airplanes, ships and: a, Helicopters, people with raised fists (28x48mm). b, Mother and child, Col. Khadafy (60x48mm). c, Man, boy and birds (28x48mm).

**1998, Apr. 15**
1606 A533 100d Horiz. strip of 3,
   #a-c    3.50 3.50

Libyan Blind
Association, 35th
Anniv. — A534

Designs: 150d, Eye, hand with cane, raised hand. 250d, Blind people, stringed instrument, books.

**1998, May 1**      *Perf. 12*
1607-1608 A534   Set of 2    4.75 4.75

Arab Bee
Union — A535

Frame color: 250d, Blue. 300d, Yellow. 400d, Light green.

**1998, June 1**
1609-1611 A535   Set of 3    13.50 13.50

1998 World Cup Soccer
Championships, France — A536

No. 1612 — Soccer player with: a, Ball at LR, orange and white lines at bottom. b, Top of World Cup. c, Ball at left, orange and white lines at bottom. d, No visible uniform number, left part of stadium at bottom. e, Bottom of World Cup, stadium. f, Uniform No. 5, right part of stadium at bottom.
No. 1613, 1000d, Player, World Cup, denomination at LL. No. 1614, 1000d, Player, World Cup, denomination at LR.

**1998, June 10**      *Perf. 13¼*
1612 A536 200d Sheet of 6,
   #a-f    15.00 15.00

### Souvenir Sheets
1613-1614 A536   Set of 2    *24.00 24.00*
Nos. 1613-1614 each contain one 42x51mm stamp.

## Miniature Sheet

World Book Day A537

No. 1615: a, Man, boy, mosque. b, Gymnasts. c, Science teacher at blackboard, student, ear. d, Men picking vegetables. e, Men at blackboard, man with machinery. f, Man with headset microphone, world map. g, Teacher with compass, student. h, Scientists with microscope. i, Girl writing, horseman. j, Teacher, student, map of Libya, globe. k, Music teacher at blackboard, student. l, Woman at sewing machine. m, Chemistry teacher and student. n, Teacher and women at typewriters. o, Cooks. p, Woman at computer keyboard, computer technician.

**1998, June 23**
1615  A537  100d Sheet of 16,
    #a-p        17.50 17.50

Map of the Great Man-Made River — A538

Denomination color: 300d, Green. 400d, Blue.
2000d, Bister.

**Litho. & Embossed With Foil Application**
**1998, July 1**
1616-1617  A538  Set of 2    8.50  8.50
**Souvenir Sheet**
1618  A538  2000d gold & multi  22.00 22.00

## Miniature Sheet

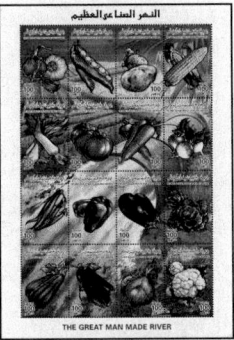

Great Man-Made River and Vegetables — A539

No. 1619: a, Garlic. b, Peas. c, Potatoes. d, Corn. e, Leeks. f, Tomatoes. g, Carrots. h, Radishes. i, Beans. j, Peppers. k, Eggplant. l, Lettuce. m, Squash. n, Cucumbers. o, Onions, p, Cauliflower.

**1998, Sept. 1**    **Litho.**    **Perf. 14**
1619  A539  100d Sheet of 16,
    #a-p        21.00 21.00

## Miniature Sheet

Children's Day — A540

---

No. 1620 — Scouting trefoil and: a, Scouts, dog. b, Scouts saluting, birds. c, Scouts saluting, flags, tents. d, Scouts, sheep. e, Scouts playing musical instruments, tying down tent. f, Scouts at campfire, bird, boat.

**1998, Aug. 1**    **Perf. 14¼**
1620  A540  400d Sheet of 6,
    #a-f        55.00 55.00

A541

Sept. 1 Revolution, 29th Anniv. — A542

No. 1621: a, Col. Khadafy. b, Horseman, pipeline, vegetables. c, Fruit, pipeline, head of eagle. d, Tail of eagle, minaret. e, Surgeons, students. f, Book, map of Northwestern Africa. g, Book, men, map of Northeastern Africa and Arabian Peninsula. h, Mosque. i, People with flags, grain combine. j, Ship. k, Apartment buildings, l, Boy. m, People, irrigation rig, building. n, Building with flagpole at right. o, Building with flagpole at right, irrigation rig. p, Building, irrigation rig.

**1998, Sept. 1**    **Litho.**    **Perf. 14¼**
1621  A541  200d Sheet of 16,
    #a-p        37.50 37.50
**Souvenir Sheet**
**Litho. & Embossed**
**Perf. 13½x13¾**
1622  A542  200d shown    2.50  2.50

Evacuation of Foreign Forces — A543

Panel color: 100d, Pink. 150d, Light green. 200d, Light blue.

**1998, Oct. 7**    **Litho.**    **Perf. 13¼**
1623-1625  A543  Set of 3    5.00  5.00

Stamp Day — A544

Panel color: 300d, Buff. 400d, Blue.

**1998, Oct. 9**    **Perf. 12**
1626-1627  A544  Set of 2  10.00 10.00

---

## Miniature Sheet

Libyans Deported to Italy A545

No. 1628: a, Ship, trucks. b, Bound woman, barbed wire. c, Man, barbed wire. d, Soldiers marching Libyans at gunpoint. e, Airplane, battle scene. f, Barbed wire, line of Libyans. g, Barbed wire, soldier and Libyan. h, Soldiers aiming rifles at Libyans, man with camel. i, Horseman, man ladling water. j, Soldier in boat. k, Boats with deportees. l, Boats with deportees, ships. m, Horsemen, man carrying woman. n, Horsemen raising rifles. o, Horseman and flag. p, Mother and child.

**1998, Oct. 26**    **Perf. 13¼**
1628  A545  150d Sheet of 16,
    #a-p        26.00 26.00

## Miniature Sheet

Leadership of Islam — A546

No. 1629: a, 100d, White mosque, minaret at left. b, 100d, White mosque, minaret at right. c, 100d, Modern mosque. d, 100d, Mosque seen through arch. e, 100d, Mosque and palm tree, minaret at left. f, 100d, Mosque with blue dome. g, 100d, Mosque with brown dome, six minarets. h, 100d, Mosque, five minarets. i, 500d, Koran, Holy Kaaba. j, 500d, Col. Khadafy on horse. Sizes: 100d stamps, 28x42mm; 500d stamps, 56x84mm.

**Litho., Litho. With Foil Application (#1629j)**
**1998, Nov. 1**    **Perf. 14**
1629  A546  Sheet of 10, #a-j  22.00 22.00

## Miniature Sheet

Scouts and the Handicapped — A547

No. 1630: a, Scout reading to boy in wheelchair, butterfly. b, Scout leader instructing group of Scouts. c, Scout photographing bird, boy in wheelchair. d, Scout raising flag, boy in wheelchair. e, Scout sawing log, boy in wheelchair. f, Scout near campfire, boy in wheelchair. g, Scouts with pots in fire, crutches. h, Scouts with pad of paper and pencil. i, Wheelchair basketball player in purple uniform. j, Wheelchair basketball player making shot. k,

---

Handicapped runners. l, Man in wheelchair playing table tennis. m, Man in wheelchair playing hockey. n, Man in wheelchair throwing shot put. o, Handicapped cyclist. p, Handicapped javelin thrower.

**1998, Nov. 15**    **Litho.**    **Perf. 13¼**
1630  A547  100d Sheet of 16,
    #a-p        27.50 27.50

## Miniature Sheet

A548

Sept. 1 Revolution, 30th Anniv. — A549

No. 1631: a, 100d, Antelopes and "30." b, 100d, Mosque. c, 100d, Woman playing stringed instrument. d, 100d, Horsemen in desert. e, 100d, Grain combine. f, 100d, Ship. g, 100d, Ship, horsemen, flag. h, 100d, Horsemen, flag. i, 100d, Water pipeline, fruit. j, 100d, Butterflies, shepherd and sheep. k, 100d, Building, ship, horse's legs. l, 100d, Dates. m, 200d, Col. Khadafy on horse. Sizes: 100d stamps; 28x42mm, 56x84mm.

**Litho., Litho. With Foil Application (#1631m, 1632)**
**1999, Sept. 1**    **Perf. 14**
1631  A548  Sheet of 13, #a-
    m        12.00 12.00
**Souvenir Sheet**
**Perf. 13¾**
1632  A549  200d shown    2.00  2.00

A550

Organization of African Unity Assembly of Heads of State and Government, Tripoli — A551

No. 1633: a, Pipeline worker, musicians, minarets. b, Surgeons, woman carrying jug. c, Artisan, camel rider, satellite. d, Col. Khadafy, butterflies. e, Pipeline worker, fruit picker. f, Fruit picker, grain combine.

**1999, Sept. 8**  **Litho.**  **Perf. 14¼x14½**
1633  A550  300d Sheet of 6,
    #a-f        13.50 13.50
**Souvenir Sheet**
**Perf. 13¾x14**
1634  A551  500d shown    4.00  4.00

Evacuation of Foreign Forces — A552

Frame color: 150d, Pink. 250d, Beige. 300d, Light blue.

**1999, Oct. 7** **Perf. 12**
1635-1637 A552 Set of 3 8.25 8.25

A553

People's Authority Declaration — A554

No. 1638: a, Col. Khadafy with fist raised, man on camel. b, People looking at book. c, Airplane, building, dish antenna. d, Antelope, weaver, tractor. e, Open faucet, pipeline. f, Pipeline, fruit pickers.
No. 1639, 300d, Map of Libya, Col. Khadafy with raised fist, building. No. 1640, 300d, Dove, people, Col. Khadafy.

**2000, Mar. 2 Litho. Perf. 14½x14¼**
1638 A553 100d Sheet of 6, #a-f 4.75 4.75
**Souvenir Sheets**
**Perf. 13¾**
**Litho. & Embossed with Foil Application**
1639-1640 A554 Set of 2 5.00 5.00

A555

Sept. 1 Revolution, 31st Anniv. — A556

No. 1641: a, Man walking, camel rider. b, Tea drinkers, camels. c, Col. Khadafy. d, Men with raised fists. e, Machinist with torch. f, Boy reading. g, Classroom. h, Scientist. i, Mother and child. j, People attending speech. k, Man and palm tree. l, Patient in X-ray machine. m, Mosque. n, Bulldozer, crane and building. o, Oil workers. p, Bulldozer.
No. 1642, 300d, Col. Khadafy, minaret. No. 1643, 300d, Col. Khadafy, boy and palm tree.

**2000, Sept. 1 Litho. Perf. 14**
1641 A555 100d Sheet of 16, #a-p 12.50 12.50

---

**Souvenir Sheets**
**Litho. With Foil Application**
**Perf. 13¾**
1642-1643 A556 Set of 2 5.00 5.00

El-Mujahed Mohamed Abdussalam Ahmeda Abouminiar El-Gaddafi — A557

No. 1644: a, Man holding box. b, Palm tree and horsemen. c, Horsemen and soldiers on horseback. d, Soldiers and armed horsemen. e, Horseman raising rifle above head. f, Men raising rifles, Col. Khadafy.
300d, Man reading book.

**2000, Sept. 9 Litho. Perf. 13¼**
1644 A557 200d Sheet of 6, #a-f 9.50 9.50
**Souvenir Sheet**
**Litho. & Embossed With Foil Application**
1645 A557 300d multi 2.50 2.50

**Souvenir Sheet**

España 2000 Intl. Philatelic Exhibition — A558

No. 1646: a, A. Castellano (1926-97). b, M. B. Karamanli (1922-95).

**2000, Oct. 6 Litho. Imperf.**
1646 A558 250d Sheet of 2, #a-b 4.00 4.00

People's Authority Declaration — A559

Denomination color: 150d, Pink. 200d, Blue.

**2001, Mar. 2 Perf. 14**
1647-1648 A559 Set of 2 2.75 2.75

**Miniature Sheet**

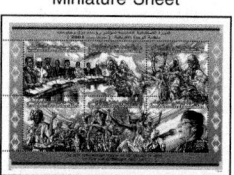

Organization of African Unity Assemby of Heads of State and Government — A560

No. 1649: a, Heads of various states. b, Heads of state, horsemen. c, Men on camels. d, People with hands raised. e, Man holding picture of Col. Khadafy. f, Col. Khadafy at microphone.

**2001, Mar. 2 Litho. Perf. 13½x13¼**
1649 A560 200d Sheet of 6, #a-f 9.50 9.50

---

**Souvenir Sheets**

Organization of African Unity Assembly of Heads of State and Government — A561

Background colors: No. 1650, 500d, Gold. No. 1651, 500d, Silver.

**Litho. & Embossed With Foil Application**
**2001, Mar. 2 Perf. 13¼**
1650-1651 A561 Set of 2 8.50 8.50

**Miniature Sheet**

Tripoli Intl. Fair A562

No. 1652: a, Rear view of saddle. b, Side view of saddle. c, Front view of saddle. d, Stirrup. e, Four pieces of tack. f, Two pieces of tack.

**Litho. & Embossed with Foil Application**
**2001, Apr. 2 Perf. 13¾**
1652 A562 300d Sheet of 6, #a-f 22.00 22.00

**Miniature Sheet**

Fight Against American Aggression — A563

No. 1653: a, Exploding jet. b, American jet. c, Pilot. d, American plane shooting missile. e, Parachute. f, Airplanes. g, Child crying. h, Palm tree, explosion. i, Missiles. j, Broken egg. k, Teddy bear. l, Clock. m, Explosion in city. n, Man rescuing casualty. o, Man holding child casualty. p, Family fleeing.

**2001, Apr. 15 Litho. Perf. 13¼**
1653 A563 100d Sheet of 16, #a-p 13.00 13.00

Desertification Project — A564

No. 1654: a, Man with hoe (30x39mm). b, Men near stream (60x39mm). c, Camels (30x39mm).

**2001, June 26 Litho. Perf. 13¼**
1654 A564 250d Horiz. strip of 3, #a-c 12.00 12.00

---

**Miniature Sheet**

Great Man-Made River — A565

No. 1655: a, Smokestack. b, Pipeline and flags. c, Palm tree, fruit. d, Grapes. e, Clothed boy, rainbow. f, Bathing boy, rainbow. g, Woman carrying fruit. h, Woman holding jug. i, Woman with red and black headdress. j, Woman with green striped headdress. k, Duck, rainbow. l, Boy running. m, Drummer hitting drum with hand. n, Horn player. o, Drummer hitting drum with stick. p, Tractors in field.

**2001, Sept. 15 Litho. Perf. 11¾**
1655 A565 200d Sheet of 16, #a-p 29.00 29.00

A566

Sept. 1 Revolution, 32nd Anniv. — A567

No. 1656: a, Col. Khadafy in headdress. b, Buildings, water pipeline, helicopters, tank, horsemen. c, Ship, airplane, camel rider. d, Tea drinkers, explosion. e, Children. f, Pillars, antelopes, woman. g, Man walking, camel rider. h, Camels, birds. i, Woman with container. j, Sword fight. k, Man and camel rider. l, Camels, pipeline worker, fruit. m, Potter. n, Musicians and weaver. o, Artisan. p, Col. Khadafy with clasped hands.
No. 1657, 300d, Col. Khadafy, pipeline and fruit (gold background). No. 1658, 300d, Col. Khadafy, pipeline and fruit (silver background).

**Litho. and Hologram**
**2001, Sept. 1 Perf. 13¼**
1656 A566 100d Sheet of 16, #a-p 27.50 27.50
q. Booklet pane, #a-p, litho. 27.50 —
Complete booklet, #1656q 27.50
**Souvenir Sheets**
**Litho. & Embossed With Foil Application**
1657-1658 A567 Set of 2 5.50 5.50

Intl. Day of the Orphan — A568

Panel color: 100d, Blue. 200d, Red violet. 300d, Olive green.

**2001, Oct. 1   Litho.   Perf. 14¾x14½**
1659-1661  A568   Set of 3        9.00 9.00

Health Care — A569

Arabic inscription color: 200d, Green. 300d, Yellow orange.

**2001, Dec. 1   Litho.   Perf. 14**
1662-1663  A569   Set of 2        6.50 6.50

**Miniature Sheet**

Tourism
A570

Various tourist attractions.

**2002, May 1                       Perf. 11¾**
1664  A570  200d Sheet of 16,
       #a-p                        52.50 52.50

Intl. Customs Day — A571

Designs: 200d, 400d.

**2002, July 1                      Perf. 14**
1665-1666  A571   Set of 2        8.25 8.25

A572

Sept. 1 Revolution, 33rd Anniv. — A573

No. 1667: a, Col. Khadafy. b, Airplanes. c, Camel rider, woman pouring tea. d, Artisans. e, Bulldozer, building. f, Chemist, oil rig. g, Ships. h, Doctors and patients. i, Technician at industrial plant. j, Man at computer, k, Man, spigot, water pipeline, crane. l, Chemist, man at microscope. m, Television camera and technician. n, Fruit, vegetables, grain combine. o, Spear carriers, musician. p, Map of Africa, musicians.
No. 1668, 300d, Col. Khadafy, map of Africa (gold background). No. 1669, 300d, Col. Khadafy, map of Africa (silver background).

**Litho. & Hologram**
**2002, Sept. 1          Perf. 13¼**
1667  A572  100d Sheet of 16,
       #a-p                        22.50 22.50
  q.   Booklet pane, #a-p, litho.  40.00
       Complete booklet, #1667q    50.00
**Souvenir Sheets**
**Litho. & Embossed With Foil Application**
1668-1669  A573  Set of 2         8.00 8.00

Universal Declaration of Human Rights, 50th Anniv. — A576

Panel color: 250d, Red orange. 500d, Blue green.

**2002, Nov. 1          Litho.   Perf. 14**
1672-1673  A576   Set of 2        9.50 9.50

Universal Postal Union, 125th Anniv. — A577

Panel color: 200d, Blue. 250d, Red violet.

**2002, Dec. 1**
1674-1675  A577   Set of 2        5.50 5.50

A580

September 1 Revolution, 34th Anniv. — A581

No. 1679: a, 300d, Doctors and microscope (30x40mm). b, 300d, Nurses studying anatomy (30x40mm). c, 300d, Mother and child (30x40mm). d, 300d, Soldiers, white flag (30x40mm). e, 500d, Teachers, students, building (60x40mm). f, 500d, Helicopter, pilot, women, nurse and patients (60x40mm). g, 500d, Marching band, soldiers in vehicle (60x40mm). h, 1000d, Col. Khadafy, airplane, satellite dish.

**2003, May 20   Litho.   Perf. 12**
1679  A580  Sheet of 8, #a-h     22.50 22.50
**Souvenir Sheet**
**Litho. & Embossed With Foil Application**
1680  A581  2000d multi         17.00 17.00

September 1 Revolution, 35th Anniv. — A582

Background color: 750d, Gray green. 1000d, Yellow green.

**2004   Litho.   Perf. 13**
1681-1682  A582   Set of 2        4.50 4.50

Khairi Khaled Nuri (1943-2004), Philatelist — A583

**2004   Litho. & Hologram   Perf. 13¼**
1683  A583  500d multi           2.00 2.00

People's Authority Declaration, 27th Anniv. — A584

Color of rays: 400d, Yellow brown. 1000d, Blue green.

**2004   Litho.   Perf. 13**
1684-1685  A584   Set of 2       12.00 12.00

1st Communication and Information Technology Exhibition — A585

**2005, July 29          Perf. 13**
1686  A585  750d multi           5.00 5.00
**Souvenir Sheet**
**Imperf**
1687  A585  1000d multi          6.00 6.00

People's Authority Declaration, 28th Anniv. A586

Delegates: 300d, Seated. 1000d, Voting.

**2005                          Perf. 13**
1688-1689  A586   Set of 2       12.00 12.00

September 1 Revolution, 36th Anniv. — A587

Background color: 750d, Yellow orange. 1000d, Blue.

**2005**
1690-1691  A587   Set of 2       15.00 15.00

**Miniature Sheet**

Total Solar Eclipse of March 29, 2006 A588

No. 1692 — Eclipse and: a, Band of totality over map of Libya. b, Buildings, map of Libya. c, Altitude and duration figures. d, Stylized fish, camel, cactus, palm tree and Libyan. e, Saddled camel. f, Camels and riders.

**2006, Mar. 29**
1692  A588  250d Sheet of 6,
       #a-f                      12.50 12.50

People's Authority Declaration, 29th Anniv. — A589

Wheat ear, flag, fist and torch with background color of: 400d, Yellow. 1000d, Blue.

**2006, Nov. 1**
1693-1694  A589   Set of 2       11.00 11.00

September 1 Revolution, 37th Anniv. A590

**2006**
1695  A590  1000d multi          8.00 8.00

Famous African Leaders — A591

Map of Africa and: No. 1696, 500d, Gamal Abdel Nasser (1918-70), Egyptian President. No. 1697, 500d, Kwame Nkrumah (1909-72), President of Ghana. No. 1698, 500d, Ahmed Ben Bella, President of Algeria. No. 1699, 500d, Patrice Lumumba (1925-61), Congolese Prime Minister. No. 1700, 500d, Kenneth Kaunda, President of Zambia. No. 1701, 500d, Julius Nyerere (1922-99), President of Tanzania. No. 1702, 500d, Modibo Keita (1915-77), President of Mali.
1000d, Map of Africa, Nasser, Nkrumah, Ben Bella, Lumumba, Kaunda, Nyerere and Keita, horiz.

**2007, Mar. 6                   Perf. 12¾**
1696-1702  A591   Set of 7       32.50 32.50
1702a   Miniature sheet of 7,
        #1696-1702               32.50 32.50
        **Size: 98x75mm**
        **Imperf**
1703  A591  1000d multi          8.00 8.00

Third Communication and Information Technology Exhibition — A592

**2007, May 27          Perf. 13**
1704  A592  750d multi           6.50 6.50

712

LIBYA

Tripoli, Capital of Islamic Culture — A593

**2007, June 16** Litho.
1705 A593 500d multi 4.50 4.50

Intl. Day Against Drug Abuse and Illicit Trafficking — A594

**2007, June 26**
1706 A594 750d multi 6.50 6.50

People's Authority Declaration, 30th Anniv. — A595

**2007, July 4**
1707 A595 750d multi 6.50 6.50

36th Tripoli Intl. Fair A596

No. 1708: a, Ring (orange background). b, Pendant (green background). c, Ring (purple background). Illustration reduced.

**2007, July 4** Perf. 13x13x13¼
1708 Strip of 3 16.00 16.00
a.-c. A596 500d Any single 3.50 3.00

Printed in sheets containing 2 strips + 2 labels. Value, $32.50.

Mosque — A597

**2007, Aug. 24** Litho. Perf. 13
1709 A597 500d multi 5.00 5.00
a. Souvenir sheet of 1 5.00 5.00

African Soccer Federation, 50th Anniv. — A598

**2007, Aug. 25**
1710 A598 750d multi 6.50 6.50

Values are for stamps with surrounding selvage.

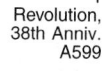

September 1 Revolution, 38th Anniv. A599

**2007, Sept. 1** Litho. Perf. 13
1711 A599 1000d multi 8.00 8.00
a. Souvenir sheet of 1 8.00 8.00

Khadafy Project for African Women, Children and Youth — A600

**2007, Sept. 9**
1712 A600 500d multi 4.25 4.25

Libyan Red Crescent Society, 50th Anniv. — A601

Red Crescent emblem and: 500d, Red Crescent volunteers. 1000d, 50th anniversary emblem.

**2007** Perf. 13
1713-1714 A601 Set of 2 12.50 12.50

People's Authority Declaration, 31st Anniv. A602

Type I — Two dots and vertical line in Arabic inscription directly above second "A" in "Jamahiriya."
Type II — No dots or vertical line in Arabic inscription directly above second "A" in "Jamahiriya."

**2008, Mar. 2** Litho. Perf. 13
1715 A602 500d multi, type I 50.00 50.00
a. Type II 4.50 4.50

37th Tripoli International Fair — A603

No. 1716: a, Emblems, colored rectangles. b, Emblems. c, Emblems, buildings, displays. Illustration reduced.

**2008, Apr. 2** Perf. 13x12¾
1716 A603 500d Horiz. strip of 3, #a-c 13.00 13.00

Printed in sheets of 6 containing two of each stamp.

Worldwide Fund for Nature (WWF) — A604

Rueppell's fox: No. 1717, Head. No. 1718, Walking. No. 1719, Curled up. No. 1720, Sitting.

**2008, May 1** Perf. 12
1717 A604 750f multi 1.50 1.50
a. Imperf. 6.00 6.00

| | | | |
|---|---|---|---|
| 1718 A604 750f multi | 1.50 | 1.50 |
| a. Imperf. | 6.00 | 6.00 |
| 1719 A604 750f multi | 1.50 | 1.50 |
| a. Imperf. | 6.00 | 6.00 |
| 1720 A604 750f multi | 1.50 | 1.50 |
| a. Imperf. | 6.00 | 6.00 |
| b. Horiz. strip of 4, #1717-1720 | 8.00 | 8.00 |
| c. Horiz. strip of 4, #1717a-1720a | 35.00 | 35.00 |

Fourth Telecommunications and Information Technology Exhibition — A605

**2008, May 25** Perf. 13
1721 A605 1000d multi 6.75 6.75

Gamal Abdel Nasser (1918-70), Egyptian President — A606

**2008, July 23**
1722 A606 500d multi 5.00 5.00

Egyptian Revolution, 56th anniv.

Khadafy 6+6 Mediterranean Project — A607

**2008, July 27**
1723 A607 750d multi 5.00 5.00

Tenth Meeting of Leaders and Heads of State of Community of Sahel-Sahara Countries — A608

**2008, Aug. 3**
1724 A608 1000d multi 6.00 6.00

Libyan Participation in 2008 Summer Olympics, Beijing — A609

**2008, Aug. 18**
1725 A609 1000d multi 8.00 8.00

September 1 Revolution, 39th Anniv. — A610

Col. Khadafy with denomination in: No. 1726, White. No. 1727, Green.

**2008, Sept. 1** Perf. 13x12¾
1726 A610 1000d multi 8.00 8.00
**Souvenir Sheet**
1727 A610 1000d multi 8.00 8.00

Total Mobile Phone Penetration in Libya — A611

**2008, Sept. 11** Perf. 13
1728 A611 750d multi 6.00 6.00

Fourth Intl. Waatasemu Women's Competition for Koran Memorization A612

**2008, Sept. 23**
1729 A612 750d multi 5.00 5.00

Koran Exhibition — A613

**2008, Sept. 26**
1730 A613 500d multi 3.50 3.50

People's Authority Declaration, 32nd Anniv. A614

**2009, Mar. 9**
1731 A614 500d multi 3.00 3.00

Support for Gaza Palestinians A615

**2009, May 7**
1732 A615 1000d multi 5.00 5.00

American Aggression Against Libya A616

**2009, May 14**    Litho.    *Perf. 13*
1733   A616 500d multi      4.00 4.00

Fifth Telecommunications and Information Technology Exhibition — A617

**2009, May 30**
1734   A617 500d multi      3.00 3.00

Omar Bongo (1935-2009), President of Gabon — A618

**2009, June 20**    Litho.    *Perf. 13*
1735   A618 750d multi      3.00 3.00

16th Mediterranean Games, Pescara, Italy — A619

**2009, June 26**
1736   A619 500d multi      3.00 3.00

Jerusalem, Capital of Arab Culture A620

**2009, Aug. 3**
1737   A620 1000d multi      4.50 4.50

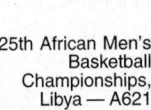

25th African Men's Basketball Championships, Libya — A621

**2009**
1738   A621 500d multi      3.00 3.00

---

Souvenir Sheet

September 1 Revolution, 40th Anniv. — A622

No. 1739 — Col. Khadafy and background color of: a, 400d, Yellow. b, 600d, White. c, 750d, Green.

**2009**
1739   A622    Sheet of 3, #a-c    7.50 7.50

Col. Khadafy, Map of Africa and African Union Emblem A623

**Litho. & Embossed With Foil Application**
**2009**    *Serpentine Die Cut 11*
**Self-Adhesive**
1740   A623 1000d multi      4.50 4.50
**Souvenir Sheet**
1741   A623 2000d multi      9.00 9.00

First Al Fateh Futsal (Indoor Soccer) Contintental Cup Tournament A624

**2009, Oct. 12**    Litho.    *Perf. 13*
1742   A624 500d multi      1.50 1.50

Another 500d stamp depicting the camel mascot of the tournament, the emblem of the tournament (pictured on No. 1742) and flags of Libya, Guatemala, Solomon Islands, Iran, Uruguay and Spain, was printed se-tenant with No. 1742, but this additional stamp was not issued.

Pan-African Postal Union, 30th Anniv. A625

**2010, Jan. 18**
1743   A625 500d multi      1.50 1.50

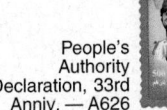

People's Authority Declaration, 33rd Anniv. — A626

---

**Litho. With Foil Application**
**2010, Mar. 2**    *Serpentine Die Cut 10*
**Self-Adhesive**
1744   A626 500d multi      1.50 1.50

22nd Session of the Council of the League of Arab States, Sirt — A627

**Serpentine Die Cut 10**
**2010, Mar. 27**    **Self-Adhesive**
1745   A627 500d multi      1.50 1.50

Organization of Petroleum Exporting Countries, 50th Anniv. — A628

**2010, June 1**    Litho.    *Perf. 13*
1746   A628 1000d multi      2.75 2.75

Evacuation of US Forces From Bases in Libya, 40th Anniv. — A629

**2010, June 9**
1747   A629 1000d multi      3.00 3.00

Libyan Revolution After 40 Years — A630

No. 1748: a, Nationalization of banks and insurance companies. b, Nationalization of the oil sector. c, Declaration of the People's Revolution, 1973 d, Arab Republics Union. e, Italian evacuation from Libyan soil. f, Evacuation of American troops from Libyan soil. g, Evacuation of British troops from Libyan soil. h, Dawn of Great A-Fatah, 1969. i, Al-Fatah, an industrial revolution. j, Huge residential projects. k, Al-Fatah, an agricultural revolution. l, Establishment of the largest electricity networks. m, Establishment of roads network in Great Jamahiriya. n, Al-Fatah scientific revolution. o, Comprehensive health welfare. p, Al-Fatah, an Islamic revolution. q, Defining death line. r, The great Man-made River builder. s, Wajda City Agreement, 1984. t, Producer's revolution, 1978. u, The Green Book. v, The birth of first Jamahiriya in history, 1977. w, Student's revolution, 1976. x, Tunisia-Libya Jerba Unity Agreement. y, The African Arab Union, Sept. 9, 1999. z, By the Community of Sahel and Saharan States. aa, Break of the injustice embargo against Great Jamahiriya. ab, Demolition of borders. ac, The Arab Magreb Union, 1989. ad, Great Green Charter for Human Rights. ae, Demolition of jails. af, Courageous response to the failed NATO aggression. ag, The 40th anniversary of the 1st September Revolution. ah, Moammar Khadafy, heart of the world. ai, The return of the political hostage A. B. Almagrahi. aj, Italian apology to Libya about the Colonial period. ak, Moammar Khadafy, the king of Africa kings. al, Revolution of telecommunication and technology. am, The establishment of huge fleet maritime transports. an, Emancipation of women lost by the Great Al-Fatah Revolution.

---

**Litho. With Foil Application**
**Serpentine Die Cut 10**
**2010, Aug. 23**    **Self-Adhesive**
1748    Sheet of 40      57.50
a.-an.   A630 400d Any single    1.40 1.40

Great Green Document of Human Rights, 22nd Anniv. — A631

Dr. Martin Luther King, Jr., civil rights marchers, and scroll with: 1500d, Arabic text. 2000d, English text.

**2010, Aug. 28**    Litho.    *Perf. 13*
1749-1750 A631   Set of 2    15.00 15.00

Miniature Sheets

Sept. 23, 2009 Speech of Col. Khadafy to United Nations Security Council, 1st Anniv. A633

No. 1753, 1000d — Map of world, Col. Khadafy, U.N. emblem, text of speech in Arabic with: a, First line of text 53mm, second line of text 47mm. b, First line of text 68mm. c, First line of text 53mm, second line of text 52mm. d, First line of text 44mm, second line of text 42mm. e, First line of text 61mm, First line of text 45mm, second line of text 58mm.
No. 1754, 1000d — Map of world, Col. Khadafy, U.N. emblem, text of speech in English starting with: a, "Brothers, you can in our political life . . ." b, "In order that colonization is not repeated . . ." c, "The solution to achieve democracy . . ." d, "The International Court of Justice . . ." e, "Africa as of now . . ." f, "The International Atomic Energy Agency . . ."
No. 1755, 1000d — Map of world, Col. Khadafy, U.N. emblem, text of speech in French starting with: a, "Vous voyez, mes frères . . ." b, "Pour eviter une nouvelle colonisation . . ." c, "Donc la solution . . ." d, "La Cour Internationale de Justice . . ." e, "L'Afrique a besoin . . ." f, "L'Agence Internationale de l'Energie . . ."

**2010, Sept. 23**    Litho.    *Perf. 13*
**Sheets of 6, #a-f**
1753-1755 A633   Set of 3    60.00 60.00

February 17, 2011 Revolution — A635

Denominations: 250d, 500d, 750d, 1000d, 5000d.

**2011**    Litho.    *Perf. 13¼*
1757-1761 A635   Set of 5    22.50 22.50

February 17 Revolution, 1st Anniv. — A636

No. 1762: a, Woman in burqa, man waving flag. b, Crowd with flag. c, Flowers and emblem. No. 1763, Map of Libya, flag in circle.

**2012, Feb. 17**      *Perf. 13*
1762    Horiz. strip of 3    6.00 6.00
a.-b.   A636 500d Either single    1.50 1.50
c.   A636 1000d multi    3.00 3.00
**Souvenir Sheet**
1763   A636 1000d multi    3.00 3.00

Children's Drawings — A637

No. 1764: a, Tree with colors of Libyan flag, flowers. b, Flowers and trees. c, People and various animals. d, Child with flag, house. e, Boat with flag, palm tree.

**2012, Sept. 12**     **Perf. 12¾**
| | | | |
|---|---|---|---|
| 1764 | Horiz. strip of 5 | 8.25 | 8.25 |
| a. | A637 100d multi | .40 | .40 |
| b. | A637 200d multi | .80 | .80 |
| c. | A637 .80 multi | 1.00 | 1.00 |
| d. | A637 500d multi | 2.00 | 2.00 |
| e. | A637 1000d multi | 4.00 | 4.00 |

Independence, 61st Anniv. — A638

National colors, "61," and: 500d, Crescent and star. 1000d, Olive branch, crescent and star.

**2012, Dec. 24**     **Perf. 13¼**
| | | | |
|---|---|---|---|
| 1765-1766 | A638 | Set of 2 | 16.50 16.50 |

Monument to the Foundation of the Libyan Army — A639

**2013, Feb. 17**
| | | | |
|---|---|---|---|
| 1767 | A639 | 500d multi | 6.50 6.50 |

A640

A641

February 17 Revolution, 2nd Anniv. — A642

**2013, Feb. 17**     **Perf. 13**
| | | | |
|---|---|---|---|
| 1768 | Horiz. strip of 3 | 19.50 | 19.50 |
| a. | A640 250d multi | 2.75 | 2.75 |
| b. | A641 500d multi | 5.50 | 5.50 |
| c. | A642 1000d multi | 11.00 | 11.00 |

**Miniature Sheet**

Tripoli International Fair — A643

No. 1769: a, Necklace and pendants. b, Fair emblem. c, Triangular pendant. d, Semi-circular pendant. e, Pin. f, Earrings.

**2013, Apr. 2**
| | | | |
|---|---|---|---|
| 1769 | A643 | 500d Sheet of 6, #a-f | 19.50 19.50 |

Intl. Letter Writing Competition for Young People — A644

**2013, May 4**     **Litho.**     **Perf. 13**
| | | | |
|---|---|---|---|
| 1770 | A644 1000d multi | 6.75 6.75 |

February 17 Revolution, 2nd Anniv. — A645

Libyan flag with background color of: 5000d, Light blue. 10,000d, Light orange.

**Litho. & Embossed With Foil Application**
**2013, May 27**     **Serpentine Die Cut 10**
**Self-Adhesive**
| | | | |
|---|---|---|---|
| 1771 | A645 5000d multi | 24.00 24.00 |
| 1772 | A645 10,000d multi | 47.50 47.50 |

Campaign Against Desertification A646

**2013, June 17**     **Litho.**     **Perf. 13¼**
| | | | |
|---|---|---|---|
| 1773 | A646 500d multi | 10.00 10.00 |

Libyan Parliament Building, Al Bayda, 50th Anniv. (in 2014) — A647

**2013, Aug. 20**     **Litho.**     **Perf. 13¼**
| | | | |
|---|---|---|---|
| 1774 | A647 500d multi | 4.25 4.25 |

Benghazi Lighthouse — A648

**2013, Aug. 20**     **Litho.**     **Perf. 13**
| | | | |
|---|---|---|---|
| 1775 | A648 1000d multi | 11.00 11.00 |

**Miniature Sheet**

Dinosaurs — A651

No. 1779: a, Triceratops. b, Head of dinosaur, building ruins. c, Tyrannosaurus, sky in background. d, Tyrannosaurus, head upright, building ruins in background, no sky. e, Dinosaurs and flowers. f, Tyrannosaurus, head lowered, building ruins in background, no sky.

**2013, Dec. 11**     **Litho.**     **Perf. 12¾**
| | | | |
|---|---|---|---|
| 1779 | A651 250d Sheet of 6, #a-f | 19.00 19.00 |

Independence, 62nd Anniv. — A652

No. 1780: a, King Idris, Libyan flag. b, Emblem. c, Horseman carrying flag, King Idris, Omar Mukhtar, map of Libya.

**2013, Dec. 24**     **Litho.**     **Perf. 13**
| | | | |
|---|---|---|---|
| 1780 | Horiz. strip of 3 | 13.00 | 13.00 |
| a. | A652 250d multi | 1.75 | 1.75 |
| b. | A652 750d multi | 5.00 | 5.00 |
| c. | A652 1000d multi | 6.50 | 6.50 |

National Post Day — A653

**2013, Dec. 24**     **Litho.**     **Perf. 13¼**
| | | | |
|---|---|---|---|
| 1781 | A653 100d multi | 7.75 7.75 |

2013 National Stamp Exhibition — A654

**2013, Dec. 25**     **Litho.**     **Perf. 13**
| | | | |
|---|---|---|---|
| 1782 | A654 100d multi | 4.25 4.25 |

February 17th Revolution, 3rd Anniv. — A655

No. 1783: a, Stylized people and emblem. b, Libyan people and flags. c, Torch and map of Libya.

**2014, Feb. 17**     **Litho.**     **Perf. 13**
| | | | |
|---|---|---|---|
| 1783 | Horiz. strip of 3 | 16.50 | 16.50 |
| a. | A655 500d multi | 3.75 | 3.75 |
| b. | A655 750d multi | 5.50 | 5.50 |
| c. | A655 1000d multi | 7.25 | 7.25 |

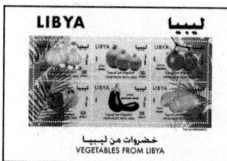

Libya, Champions of 2014 African Nations Soccer Championships — A656

No. 1784: a, 500d, Libyan team, trophy. b, 750d, Trophy, Libyan Soccer Federation emblem, map of Libya.

**2014, Feb. 17**     **Litho.**     **Perf. 13**
| | | | |
|---|---|---|---|
| 1784 | A656 Horiz. pair, #a-b | 7.75 7.75 |

**Miniature Sheet**

Vegetables — A657

No. 1786: a, Garlic. b, Onions. c, Tomatoes. d, Peppers. e, Eggplants. f, Potatoes.

**2014, Feb. 24**     **Litho.**     **Perf. 12¾**
| | | | |
|---|---|---|---|
| 1786 | A657 500d Sheet of 6, #a-f | 19.00 19.00 |

Scouting in Libya, 60th Anniv. A658

No. 1787: a, 500d, Scouts. b, 1000d, Ali Khalefa Zaidi (1909-66), scouting leader.

**2014, Feb. 27**     **Litho.**     **Perf. 13**
| | | | |
|---|---|---|---|
| 1787 | A658 Horiz. pair, #a-b | 19.00 19.00 |

**Miniature Sheet**

2014 Tripoli International Fair — A659

No. 1788: a, Bazin with meat. b, Fair emblem, map of Libya. c, Couscous with meat. d, Bazin with fish. e, Fair emblems. f, Couscous with fish.

**2014, Apr. 2**     **Litho.**     **Perf. 13**
| | | | |
|---|---|---|---|
| 1788 | A659 500d Sheet of 6, #a-f | 19.00 19.00 |

Castles A660

Designs: 100d, Sebha Castle. 1000d, Murzuq Castle.

**2014, June 26**     **Litho.**     **Perf. 13**
| | | | |
|---|---|---|---|
| 1789-1790 | A660 Set of 2 | 9.00 9.00 |

A661

A662

Mosques — A663

**2014, July 20**     **Litho.**     **Perf. 13**
| | | | |
|---|---|---|---|
| 1791 | Horiz. strip of 3 | 11.50 | 11.50 |
| a. | A661 500d multi | 3.75 | 3.75 |
| b. | A662 500d multi | 3.75 | 3.75 |
| c. | A663 500d multi | 3.75 | 3.75 |

Euromed Postal Emblem and Mediterranean Sea — A664

**2014, July 28**     **Litho.**     **Perf. 13**
| | | | |
|---|---|---|---|
| 1792 | A664 500d multi | 9.00 9.00 |

Libyan Army, 63rd Anniv. — A665

**2014, Aug. 9 Litho. Perf. 13**
1793 A665 500d multi 7.75 7.75

Liberation of Tripoli, 3rd Anniv. A666

**2014, Aug. 20 Litho. Perf. 13**
1794 A666 500d multi 10.00 10.00

Martyr's Day — A667

**2014, Sept. 16 Litho. Perf. 13**
1795 A667 500d multi 7.75 7.75

Libya Insurance Company, 50th Anniv. — A668

**2014, Dec. 24 Litho. Perf. 13**
1796 A668 1000d multi 10.00 10.00

Independence, 63rd Anniv. — A669

**2014, Dec. 24 Litho. Perf. 13**
1797 A669 1000d multi 7.75 7.75

Intl. Children's Day — A670

No. 1798 — UNICEF emblem and: a, Scout, tent, butterflies, Libyan flag. b, Hands. c, Scout, butterflies, mushrooms.

**2014 Litho. Perf. 13**
1798 Horiz. strip of 3 14.00 14.00
a. A670 250d multi 1.75 1.75
b. A670 750d multi 5.25 5.25
c. A670 1000d multi 7.00 7.00

A671

A672

February 17 Revolution, 4th Anniv. — A673

**2015, Feb. 17 Litho. Perf. 13**
1799 Horiz. strip of 3 15.00 15.00
a. A671 1000d multi 5.00 5.00
b. A672 1000d multi 5.00 5.00
c. A673 1000d multi 5.00 5.00

Boats in Harbor — A674

**2015, July 9 Litho. Perf. 13**
1800 A674 750d multi 7.75 7.75

**Miniature Sheet**

2015 Tripoli International Fair — A675

No. 1801: a, Pot with handles, rope and wide bottom. b, Map of Libya. c, Pot with narrow bottom and two handles connected by rope. d, Mortar and pestle. e, Pot with three handles. f, Pot suspended from rope.

**2015, Apr. 2 Litho. Perf. 13**
1801 A675 500d Sheet of 6, #a-f 15.50 15.50

Martyr's Day A676

Omar Mukhtar (1858-1931), resistance leader, and: 500d, Horsemen, eagle, flowers. 1000d, Libyan flag.

**2015, Sept. 16 Litho. Perf. 13**
1802 A676 500d multi 6.50 6.50
**Size: 120x80mm**
**Imperf**
1803 A676 1000d multi 9.00 9.00

**Miniature Sheet**

Flowers A677

No. 1804: a, Narcissi. b, Ophrys fuciflora. c, Calla lily. d, Cestrum nocturnum. e, Bird of paradise. f, Jasmine.

**2015, Nov. 1 Litho. Perf. 13**
1804 A677 500d Sheet of 6, #a-f 17.00 17.00

UNESCO, 70th Anniv. A678

**2015, Nov. 16 Litho. Perf. 13**
1805 A678 500d multi 6.50 6.50

International Children's Day — A679

**2015, Nov. 20 Litho. Perf. 13**
1806 A679 500d multi 6.50 6.50

Architecture A680

Designs: No. 1807, 750d, Nalut Archaeological Site. No. 1808, 750d, Building in Ghadames.

**2015, Dec. 10 Litho. Perf. 13**
1807-1808 A680 Set of 2 12.00 12.00

Independence Day — A681

**2015, Dec. 24 Litho. Perf. 13**
1809 A681 500d multi 6.50 6.50

Stamp Day — A682

**2015, Dec. 24 Litho. Perf. 13**
1810 A682 500d multi 6.50 6.50

Dates — A683

**2015, Dec. 31 Litho. Perf. 13½**
**Background Color**
1811 A683 500d yel grn 2.00 2.00
1812 A683 1000d lilac 4.00 4.00
1813 A683 2000d bistre yellow 8.00 8.00
1814 A683 5000d turq blue 20.00 20.00
1815 A683 10,000d brt green 40.00 40.00
Nos. 1811-1815 (5) 74.00 74.00

Second National Stamp Exhibition — A684

**2016, Jan. 30 Litho. Perf. 13**
1816 A684 1000d multi 9.00 9.00

February 17 Revolution, 5th Anniv. — A685

No. 1817 — Laurel branches and: a, Flag and map of Libya. b, Handshake. c, Map of Libya.

**2016, Feb. 17 Litho. Perf. 13**
1817 Horiz. strip of 3 12.00 12.00
a.-c. A685 500d Any single 4.00 4.00

Martyr's Day — A686

Omar Mukhtar (1858-1931), resistance leader, and: 500d, Building. 1000d, Map of Libya, building, Mukhtar on horse.

**2016, Sept. 16 Litho. Perf. 13**
1818 A686 500d multi 7.75 7.75
**Size: 110x76mm**
**Imperf**
1819 A686 1000d multi 13.00 13.00

International Children's Day — A687

No. 1820 — UNICEF emblem and: a, Two children with sign. b, Three children holding pictures. c, Child reading book.

**2016, Nov. 20 Litho. Perf. 13**
1820 Horiz. strip of 3 10.50 10.50
a.-c. A687 500d Any single 3.50 3.50

Independence Day — A688

**2016, Dec. 24 Litho. Perf. 13**
1821 A688 1000d multi 7.75 7.75

February 17 Revolution, 6th Anniv. — A689

No. 1822: a, 500d, Map and flag of Libya. b, 1000d, Map of Libya in circle.

**2017, Feb. 17 Litho. Perf. 13**
1822 A689 Horiz. pair, #a-b 10.00 10.00

Children's Day — A690

No. 1823: a, Map of Libya, children, flag, butterflies, flowers. b, Map of Libya, flowers, children with balloons. c, Boy with kites and camel.

**2017, Mar. 21  Litho.    Perf. 13¼x13**
1823 A690 500d Horiz. strip of
3, #a-c        11.50 11.50

Miniature Sheet

2017 Tripoli International Fair — A691

No. 1824: a, Bowl with lid. b, Emblem. c, Lidded bowl with handles. d, Stirrups. e, Coffee pot. f, Candleholder.

**2017, Apr. 2  Litho.    Perf. 13**
1824 A691 500d Sheet of 6,
#a-f         14.50 14.50

Month of Ramadan — A692

**2017, June 23  Litho.    Perf. 13¼x13**
1825 A692 1000d multi        — —

Olives and Olive Tree — A693

**2017, Aug. 6  Litho.    Perf. 13**
1826 A693  5000d yel & multi  14.50 14.50
1827 A693 10,000d rose lil &
multi        29.00 29.00

Souvenir Sheet

Omar Mukhtar (1858-1931), National Hero — A694

**2017, Nov. 1  Litho.    Perf. 13**
1828 A694 1000d multi        10.00 10.00

Martyr's Day.

International Children's Day — A695

**2017, Nov. 20  Litho.    Perf. 13**
1829 A695 1000d multi        10.00 10.00

International Day of Solidarity With the Palestinian People — A696

**2017, Nov. 29  Litho.    Perf. 13**
1830 A696 2000d multi        16.00 16.00

Libyan postal officials have declared as "illegal" miniature sheets and souvenir sheets depicting high-speed trains and Renaissance paintings of Jacopo Pontormo that are inscribed "State of Libya."

Independence, 66th Anniv. — A697

**2017, Dec. 24  Litho.    Perf. 13**
1831 A697 500d multi        7.25 7.25

Amazigh Year (Year of the Berber People) — A698

**2018, Jan. 13  Litho.    Perf. 13**
1832 A698 2000d multi        8.75 8.75

February 17th Revolution, 7th Anniv. — A699

**2018, Feb. 23  Litho.    Perf. 13**
1833 A699 1000d multi        5.75 5.75

Miniature Sheet

Tripoli International Fair — A700

No. 1834: a, Picture with circle in square frame depicting two men in boat. b, Fair emblem. c, Mosaic depicting woman. d, Hexagonal picture depicting man. e, Main gate of fair. f, Mosaic depicting ship.

**2018, Apr. 2  Litho.    Perf. 13**
1834 A700 500d Sheet of 6, #a-f  8.75 8.75

A701

A702

A703

A704

Koran Competition A705

**2018, May 10  Litho.    Perf. 13½**
1835      Horiz. strip of 5   1.75 1.75
  a. A701 50d multi           .35  .35
  b. A702 50d multi           .35  .35
  c. A703 50d multi           .35  .35
  d. A704 50d multi           .35  .35
  e. A705 50d multi           .35  .35

Souvenir Sheet

Nelson Mandela (1918-2013), President of South Africa — A706

**2018, July 18  Litho.    Perf. 13½**
1836 A706 1000d multi        4.50 4.50

Miniature Sheet

International Migrants Day — A707

No. 1837: a, Migrants and truck convoy. b, Migrants in truck. c, Migrant man and baby near truck. d, Woman carrying infant, man carrying suitcase, child. e, Boat and map of Mediterranean area. f, Women carrying two children. g, Migrant in water wearing life vest, head at top center. h, Migrant in water wearing life vest, head at upper right. i, Woman holding a child with pacifier in mouth. j, Migrants in water wearing life vest near life boat. k, Migrants in life boat. l, Migrants in water near sinking ship.

**2018, Dec. 18  Litho.    Perf. 13¼**
1837 A707 100d Sheet of 12,
#a-l         10.00 10.00

Independence, 67th Anniv. — A708

**2018, Dec. 24  Litho.    Perf. 13¼x13**
1838 A708 1000d multi        5.75 5.75

Third National Stamp Exhibition — A709

**2018, Dec. 25  Litho.    Perf. 13**
1839 A709 1000d multi        5.75 5.75

Berber (Amazigh) New Year — A710

**2019, Jan. 13  Litho.    Perf. 13**
1840 A710 500d multi        — —

February 17 Revolution, 8th Anniv. — A711

**2019, Feb. 17  Litho.    Perf. 13**
1841 A711 500d multi        — —

A712

A713

A714

A715

A716

Textiles — A717

**2019, Apr. 2     Litho.     Perf. 13**

| 1842 | Sheet of 6 | 10.00 | 10.00 |
|---|---|---|---|
| a. | A712 500d multi | 1.60 | 1.60 |
| b. | A713 500d multi | 1.60 | 1.60 |
| c. | A714 500d multi | 1.60 | 1.60 |
| d. | A715 500d multi | 1.60 | 1.60 |
| e. | A716 500d multi | 1.60 | 1.60 |
| f. | A717 500d multi | 1.60 | 1.60 |

2019 Tripoli International Fair.

February 17 Revolution,
9th Anniv. — A718

**2020, Feb. 17     Litho.     Perf. 14¼x14**

| 1843 | A718 500d multi | — | — |

## SEMI-POSTAL STAMPS

Many issues of Italy and Italian Colonies include one or more semipostal denominations. To avoid splitting sets, these issues are generally listed as regular postage, semipostals or airmails, etc.

Semi-Postal Stamps of
Italy Overprinted

**1915-16     Wmk. 140     Perf. 14**

| B1 | SP1 | 10c + 5c rose | 3.50 | 14.00 |
|---|---|---|---|---|
| a. | | Double overprint | 825.00 | |
| B2 | SP2 | 15c + 5c slate | 30.00 | 24.00 |
| B3 | SP2 | 20c + 5c org ('16) | 4.25 | 30.00 |
| | | Nos. B1-B3 (3) | 37.75 | 68.00 |

No. B2 with Additional
Surcharge

**1916, Mar.**

| B4 | SP2 | 20c on 15c + 5c slate | 30.00 | 30.00 |
|---|---|---|---|---|
| a. | | Double surcharge | 850.00 | |

View of Port,
Tripoli — SP1

Designs: B5, B6, View of port, Tripoli. B7, B8, Arch of Marcus Aurelius. B9, B10, View of Tripoli.

**1927, Feb. 15     Litho.**

| B5 | SP1 | 20c + 5c brn vio & black | 3.50 | 15.00 |
|---|---|---|---|---|
| B6 | SP1 | 25c + 5c bl grn & black | 3.50 | 15.00 |
| B7 | SP1 | 40c + 10c blk brn & black | 3.50 | 15.00 |
| B8 | SP1 | 60c + 10c org brn & black | 3.50 | 15.00 |
| B9 | SP1 | 75c + 20c red & black | 3.50 | 15.00 |

| B10 | SP1 | 1.25 l + 20c bl & blk | 24.00 | 42.50 |
|---|---|---|---|---|
| | | Nos. B5-B10 (6) | 41.50 | 117.50 |

First Sample Fair, Tripoli. Surtax aided fair. See Nos. EB1-EB2.

View of
Tripoli
SP2

Knights of Malta
Castle
SP3

Designs: 50c+20c, Date palm. 1.25 l+20c, Camel riders. 2.55 l+50c, View of Tripoli. 5 l+1 l, Traction well.

**1928, Feb. 20     Wmk. 140     Perf. 14**

| B11 | SP2 | 30c + 20c mar & blk | 3.50 | 15.00 |
|---|---|---|---|---|
| B12 | SP2 | 50c + 20c bl grn & blk | 3.50 | 15.00 |
| B13 | SP2 | 1.25 l + 20c red & blk | 3.50 | 15.00 |
| B14 | SP3 | 1.75 l + 20c bl & blk | 3.50 | 15.00 |
| B15 | SP3 | 2.55 l + 50c brn & blk | 7.00 | 22.50 |
| B16 | SP3 | 5 l + 1 l pur & blk | 9.50 | 35.00 |
| | | Nos. B11-B16 (6) | 30.50 | 117.50 |

2nd Sample Fair, Tripoli, 1928. The surtax was for the aid of the Fair.

Olive
Tree — SP4

Herding — SP5

Designs: 50c+20c, Dorcas gazelle. 1.25 l+20c, Peach blossoms. 2.55 l+50c, Camel caravan. 5 l+1 l, Oasis with date palms.

**1929, Apr. 7**

| B17 | SP4 | 30c + 20c mar & blk | 14.00 | 27.50 |
|---|---|---|---|---|
| B18 | SP4 | 50c + 20c bl grn & blk | 14.00 | 27.50 |
| B19 | SP4 | 1.25 l + 20c scar & blk | 14.00 | 27.50 |
| B20 | SP5 | 1.75 l + 20c bl & blk | 14.00 | 27.50 |
| B21 | SP5 | 2.55 l + 50c yel brn & blk | 14.00 | 27.50 |
| B22 | SP5 | 5 l + 1 l pur & blk | 125.00 | 300.00 |
| | | Nos. B17-B22 (6) | 195.00 | 437.50 |

3rd Sample Fair, Tripoli, 1929. The surtax was for the aid of the Fair.

Harvesting
Bananas
SP6

Water Carriers
SP7

Designs: 50c, Tobacco plant. 1.25 l, Venus of Cyrene. 2.55 l+45c, Black bucks. 5 l+1 l, Motor and camel transportation. 10 l+2 l, Rome pavilion.

**1930, Feb. 20     Photo.**

| B23 | SP6 | 30c dark brown | 4.25 | 17.50 |
|---|---|---|---|---|
| B24 | SP6 | 50c violet | 4.25 | 17.50 |
| B25 | SP6 | 1.25 l deep blue | 4.25 | 17.50 |
| B26 | SP7 | 1.75 l + 20c scar | 7.00 | 26.00 |
| B27 | SP7 | 2.55 l + 45c dp grn | 16.00 | 37.50 |
| B28 | SP7 | 5 l + 1 l dp org | 16.00 | 50.00 |
| B29 | SP7 | 10 l + 2 l dk vio | 16.00 | 62.50 |
| | | Nos. B23-B29 (7) | 67.75 | 228.50 |

4th Sample Fair at Tripoli, 1930. The surtax was for the aid of the Fair.

Statue of
Ephebus
SP8

Exhibition Pavilion
SP9

Designs: 25c, Arab musician. 50c, View of Zeughet. 1.25 l, Snake charmer. 1.75 l+25c, Windmill. 2.75 l+45c, "Zaptie." 5 l+1 l, Mounted Arab.

**1931, Mar. 8**

| B30 | SP8 | 10c black brown | 5.50 | 9.75 |
|---|---|---|---|---|
| B31 | SP8 | 25c green | 5.50 | 9.75 |
| B32 | SP8 | 50c purple | 5.50 | 9.75 |
| B33 | SP8 | 1.25 l blue | 5.50 | 14.00 |
| B34 | SP8 | 1.75 l + 25c car rose | 5.50 | 16.00 |
| B35 | SP8 | 2.75 l + 45c org | 5.50 | 24.00 |
| B36 | SP8 | 5 l + 1 l dl vio | 15.00 | 35.00 |
| B37 | SP9 | 10 l + 2 l brn | 50.00 | 70.00 |
| | | Nos. B30-B37 (8) | 98.00 | 188.25 |
| | | Nos. B30-B37,C3,EB3 (10) | 104.90 | 229.75 |

Fifth Sample Fair, Tripoli. Surtax aided fair.

Papaya
Tree
SP10

Dorcas
Gazelle
SP12

Ar Tower,
Mogadiscio
SP11

Designs: 10c, 50c, Papaya tree. 20c, 30c, Euphorbia abyssinica. 25c, Fig cactus. 75c, Mausoleum, Ghirza. 1.75 l+25c, Lioness. 5 l+1 l, Bedouin with camel.

**1932, Mar. 8**

| B38 | SP10 | 10c olive brn | 7.00 | 16.00 |
|---|---|---|---|---|
| B39 | SP10 | 20c brown red | 7.00 | 16.00 |
| B40 | SP10 | 25c green | 7.00 | 16.00 |
| B41 | SP10 | 30c olive blk | 7.00 | 16.00 |
| B42 | SP10 | 50c dk violet | 7.00 | 16.00 |
| B43 | SP10 | 75c carmine | 8.50 | 16.00 |
| B44 | SP11 | 1.25 l dk blue | 8.50 | 24.00 |
| B45 | SP11 | 1.75 l + 25c ol brn | 27.50 | 77.50 |
| B46 | SP11 | 5 l + 1 l dp bl | 27.50 | 190.00 |
| B47 | SP12 | 10 l + 2 l brn violet | 125.00 | 350.00 |
| | | Nos. B38-B47 (10) | 232.00 | 737.50 |
| | | Nos. B38-B47,C4-C7 (14) | 416.00 | 1,168. |

Sixth Sample Fair, Tripoli. Surtax aided fair.

Ostrich
SP13

Arab Musician
SP14

Designs: 25c, Incense plant. 30c, Arab musician. 50c, Arch of Marcus Aurelius. 1.25 l, African eagle. 5 l+1 l, Leopard. 10 l+2.50 l, Tripoli skyline and fasces.

**1933, Mar. 2     Photo.     Wmk. 140**

| B48 | SP13 | 10c dp violet | 37.50 | 42.50 |
|---|---|---|---|---|
| B49 | SP13 | 25c dp green | 21.00 | 42.50 |
| B50 | SP14 | 30c org brn | 21.00 | 42.50 |
| B51 | SP13 | 50c purple | 21.00 | 42.50 |
| B52 | SP13 | 1.25 l dk blue | 50.00 | 77.50 |
| B53 | SP14 | 5 l + 1 l ol brn | 110.00 | 175.00 |
| B54 | SP13 | 10 l + 2.50 l car | 110.00 | 300.00 |
| | | Nos. B48-B54 (7) | 370.50 | 722.50 |
| | | Nos. B48-B54,C8-C13 (13) | 481.50 | 1,103. |

Seventh Sample Fair, Tripoli. Surtax aided fair.

Pomegranate
Tree — SP15

Designs: 50c+10c, 2 l+50c, Musician. 75c+15c, 1.25 l+25c, Tribesman.

**1935, Feb. 16**

| B55 | SP15 | 10c + 10c brn | 1.75 | 5.00 |
|---|---|---|---|---|
| B56 | SP15 | 20c + 10c rose red | 1.75 | 5.00 |
| B57 | SP15 | 50c + 10c pur | 1.75 | 5.00 |
| B58 | SP15 | 75c + 15c car | 1.75 | 5.00 |
| B59 | SP15 | 1.25 l + 25c dl blue | 1.75 | 5.00 |
| B60 | SP15 | 2 l + 50c ol grn | 1.75 | 12.50 |
| | | Nos. B55-B60 (6) | 10.50 | 37.50 |
| | | Nos. B55-B60,C19-C24 (12) | 27.00 | 108.00 |

Ninth Sample Fair, Tripoli. Surtax aided fair.

## AIR POST STAMPS

Italy Nos. C3 and
C5 Overprinted

**1928-29     Wmk. 140     Perf. 14**

| C1 | AP2 | 50c rose red | 14.00 | 27.50 |
|---|---|---|---|---|
| C2 | AP2 | 80c brn vio & brn ('29) | 55.00 | 77.50 |

Airplane — AP1

**1931, Mar. 8     Photo.     Wmk. 140**

| C3 | AP1 | 50c blue | 1.40 | 14.00 |

See note after No. B37.

Seaplane over
Bedouin
Camp — AP2

Designs: 50c, 1 l, Seaplane over Bedouin camp. 2 l+1 l, 5 l+2 l, Seaplane over Tripoli.

**1932, Mar. 1     Perf. 14**

| C4 | AP2 | 50c dark blue | 15.00 | 42.50 |
|---|---|---|---|---|
| C5 | AP2 | 1 l org brown | 15.00 | 42.50 |
| C6 | AP2 | 2 l + 1 l dk gray | 29.00 | 120.00 |
| C7 | AP2 | 5 l + 2 l car | 125.00 | 225.00 |
| | | Nos. C4-C7 (4) | 207.50 | 495.00 |

See note after No. B47.

Seaplane Arriving
at Tripoli — AP3

Designs: 50c, 2 l+50c, Seaplane arriving at Tripoli. 75c, 10 l+2.50 l, Plane over Tagiura. 1 l, 5 l+1 l, Seaplane leaving Tripoli.

**1933, Mar. 1**

| C8 | AP3 | 50c dp green | 11.00 | 22.50 |
|---|---|---|---|---|
| C9 | AP3 | 75c carmine | 11.00 | 22.50 |
| C10 | AP3 | 1 l dk blue | 11.00 | 22.50 |
| C11 | AP3 | 2 l + 50c pur | 18.00 | 52.50 |
| C12 | AP3 | 5 l + 1 l org brn | 30.00 | 85.00 |
| C13 | AP3 | 10 l + 2.50 l gray blk | 30.00 | 175.00 |
| | | Nos. C8-C13 (6) | 125.00 | 390.00 |

See note after No. B54.

Seaplane over
Tripoli Harbor
AP4

Airplane
and Camel
AP5

Designs: 50c, 5 l+1 l, Seaplane over Tripoli harbor. 75c, 10 l+2 l, Plane and minaret.

**1934, Feb. 17     Photo.     Wmk. 140**

| C14 | AP4 | 50c slate bl | 14.00 | 30.00 |
|---|---|---|---|---|
| C15 | AP4 | 75c red org | 14.00 | 30.00 |
| C16 | AP4 | 5 l + 1 l dp grn | 125.00 | 210.00 |

| | | | | |
|---|---|---|---|---|
| **C17** | AP4 | 10 l + 2 l dl vio | 125.00 | *210.00* |
| **C18** | AP5 | 25 l + 3 l org brn | 150.00 | *300.00* |
| | *Nos. C14-C18 (5)* | | 487.00 | *900.00* |

Eighth Sample Fair, Tripoli. Surtax aided fair. See Nos. CE1-CE2.

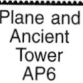

Plane and Ancient Tower
AP6

Camel Train
AP7

Designs: 25c+10c, 3 l+1.50 l, Plane and ancient tower. 50c+10c, 2 l+30c, Camel train. 1 l+25c, 10 l+5 l, Arab watching plane.

**1935, Apr. 12**

| | | | | |
|---|---|---|---|---|
| **C19** | AP6 | 25c + 10c green | 1.40 | *5.50* |
| **C20** | AP7 | 50c + 10c slate bl | 1.40 | *5.50* |
| **C21** | AP7 | 1 l + 25c blue | 1.40 | *5.50* |
| **C22** | AP7 | 2 l + 30c rose red | 1.40 | *9.50* |
| **C23** | AP6 | 3 l + 1.50 l brn | 1.40 | *9.50* |
| **C24** | AP7 | 10 l + 5 l dl vio | 9.50 | *35.00* |
| | *Nos. C19-C24 (6)* | | 19.00 | *81.50* |

See note after No. B60.

Cyrenaica No. C6
Overprinted in Black

**1936, Oct.**

| | | | | |
|---|---|---|---|---|
| **C25** | AP2 | 50c purple | 24.00 | .35 |

**Same on Tripolitania Nos. C8 and C12**

**1937**

| | | | | |
|---|---|---|---|---|
| **C26** | AP1 | 50c rose carmine | .70 | .25 |
| **C27** | AP2 | 1 l deep blue | 2.10 | .85 |
| | Set, never hinged | | 7.00 | |

See Nos. C45-C50.

Ruins of Odeon Theater, Sabrata — AP8

**1937, Mar. 15**      Photo.

| | | | | |
|---|---|---|---|---|
| **C28** | AP8 | 50c dark violet | 2.75 | *7.00* |
| **C29** | AP8 | 1 l vio black | 2.75 | *11.00* |
| | Set, never hinged | | 13.50 | |

Opening of a coastal road to the Egyptian frontier.

**Nos. C28-C29 Overprinted "XI FIERA DI TRIPOLI"**

**1937, Mar. 15**

| | | | | |
|---|---|---|---|---|
| **C30** | AP8 | 50c dark violet | 14.00 | *35.00* |
| **C31** | AP8 | 1 l violet blk | 14.00 | *35.00* |
| | Set, never hinged | | 70.00 | |

11th Sample Fair, Tripoli.

View of Tripoli — AP9

**1938, Mar. 12**      Perf. 14

| | | | | |
|---|---|---|---|---|
| **C32** | AP9 | 50c dk olive grn | 1.40 | *2.75* |
| **C33** | AP9 | 1 l slate blue | 1.40 | *5.50* |
| | Set, never hinged | | 7.00 | |

12th Sample Fair, Tripoli.

Eagle Attacking Serpent — AP10

**1938, Apr. 25**      Wmk. 140

| | | | | |
|---|---|---|---|---|
| **C34** | AP10 | 50c olive brown | .35 | *1.75* |
| **C35** | AP10 | 1 l brn violet | 1.00 | *3.75* |
| | Set, never hinged | | 3.25 | |

Birth bimillenary Augustus Caesar (Octavianus), first Roman emperor.

Arab and Camel — AP11

Design: 50c, Fair entrance.

**1939, Apr. 12**      Photo.

| | | | | |
|---|---|---|---|---|
| **C36** | AP11 | 25c green | .70 | *2.10* |
| **C37** | AP11 | 50c olive brown | .70 | *2.10* |
| **C38** | AP11 | 1 l rose violet | 1.00 | *2.75* |
| | *Nos. C36-C38 (3)* | | 1.90 | *6.70* |
| | Set, never hinged | | 6.00 | |

13th Sample Fair, Tripoli.

Plane Over Modern City — AP12

Design: 1 l, 5 l+2.50 l, Plane over oasis.

**1940, June 3**

| | | | | |
|---|---|---|---|---|
| **C39** | AP12 | 50c brn blk | .70 | *.85* |
| **C40** | AP12 | 1 l brn vio | .70 | *1.75* |
| **C41** | AP12 | 2 l + 75c indigo | 1.00 | *7.00* |
| **C42** | AP12 | 5 l + 2.50 l copper brn | 1.00 | *12.50* |
| | *Nos. C39-C42 (4)* | | 4.10 | *25.50* |
| | Set, never hinged | | 8.50 | |

Triennial Overseas Exposition, Naples.

AP13

Design: 50c, Hitler, Mussolini and Inscription "Two Peoples, One War".

**1941, Apr. 24**

| | | | | |
|---|---|---|---|---|
| **C43** | AP13 | 50c slate green | 2.75 | *42.50* |
| | Never hinged | | 7.00 | |

Rome-Berlin Axis.

**Cyrenaica No. C9 Overprinted in Black Like No. C25**

**1941**

| | | | | |
|---|---|---|---|---|
| **C44** | AP3 | 1 l black | 12.50 | *70.00* |
| | Never hinged | | 30.00 | |

**Same Overprint on Tripolitania Nos. C9-C11, C13-C15**

| | | | | |
|---|---|---|---|---|
| **C45** | AP1 | 60c red orange | .75 | |
| **C46** | AP1 | 75c deep blue | .75 | *47.50* |
| **C47** | AP1 | 80c dull violet | .75 | *100.00* |
| **C48** | AP2 | 1.20 l dark brown | .75 | *140.00* |
| **C49** | AP2 | 1.50 l orange red | .75 | *175.00* |
| **C50** | AP2 | 5 l green | .75 | |
| | *Nos. C45-C50 (6)* | | 4.50 | |
| | *Set, never hinged* | | 10.00 | |

> **Catalogue values for unused stamps in this section, from this point to the end of the section, are for Never Hinged items.**

**United Kingdom of Libya**
ICY Type of Regular Issue

**Perf. 14½x14**

**1965, Jan. 1**     Litho.     Unwmk.

| | | | | |
|---|---|---|---|---|
| **C51** | A60 | 50m reddish lil & gold | 1.90 | .90 |
| *a.* | Souvenir sheet | | 5.00 | 5.00 |

No. C51a exists with simulated perfs.; same value.

Hands Holding Facade of Abu Simbel
AP14

**1966, Jan. 1**     Photo.     Perf. 11½
**Granite Paper**

| | | | | |
|---|---|---|---|---|
| **C52** | AP14 | 10m bis & dk brn | .40 | .25 |
| *a.* | Souvenir sheet of 4 | | 2.00 | 3.75 |
| **C53** | AP14 | 15m gray grn & dk grn | .50 | .25 |
| *a.* | Souvenir sheet of 4 | | 2.50 | 5.00 |
| **C54** | AP14 | 40m dl sal & dk brn | 1.60 | .65 |
| *a.* | Souvenir sheet of 4 | | 6.50 | 13.00 |
| | *Nos. C52-C54 (3)* | | 2.50 | 1.15 |

UNESCO world campaign to save historic monuments in Nubia.

Inauguration of WHO Headquarters, Geneva — AP15

**Perf. 10x10½**

**1966, May 3**     Litho.     Unwmk.

| | | | | |
|---|---|---|---|---|
| **C55** | AP15 | 20m blk, yel & bl | .25 | .25 |
| **C56** | AP15 | 50m blk, yel grn & red | .90 | .65 |
| **C57** | AP15 | 65m blk, sal & brn red | 1.40 | 1.40 |
| | *Nos. C55-C57 (3)* | | 2.55 | 2.30 |

Flag and Globe — AP16

**1966, Oct. 1**     Photo.     Perf. 11½
**Granite Paper**

| | | | | |
|---|---|---|---|---|
| **C58** | AP16 | 25m multicolored | .50 | .40 |
| **C59** | AP16 | 60m multicolored | 1.40 | 1.00 |
| **C60** | AP16 | 85m gray & multi | 1.90 | 1.40 |
| | *Nos. C58-C60 (3)* | | 3.80 | 2.80 |

Inauguration of Kingdom of Libya Airlines, 1st anniv.

---

**AIR POST SPECIAL DELIVERY STAMPS**

APSD1

**Wmk. 140**

**1934, Feb. 17**     Photo.     Perf. 14

| | | | | |
|---|---|---|---|---|
| **CE1** | APSD1 | 2.25 l olive blk | 55.00 | *70.00* |
| **CE2** | APSD1 | 4.50 l + 1 l gray blk | 55.00 | *70.00* |
| | Set, never hinged | | 280.00 | |

8th Sample Fair at Tripoli. The surtax was for the aid of the Fair.

---

**SPECIAL DELIVERY STAMPS**

Special Delivery Stamps of Italy Overprinted

Two types of overprint. See note preceding No. 1 for descriptions.

**1915-16.**     Wmk. 140     Perf. 14

| | | | | |
|---|---|---|---|---|
| **E1** | SD1 | 25c rose red, ovpt. type I | 80.00 | 32.50 |
| **E2** | SD2 | 30c blue & rose, ovpt. type I | 8.00 | 32.50 |
| | Set, never hinged | | 217.50 | |

Issued: Nos. E1, E2, Nov. 1915.
For surcharges see Nos. E7-E8.

"Italia" — SD3

No. E3

No. E4

No. E5

No. E6

Nos. E5-E6 bottom-corner denominations and words are reversed from Nos. E3-E4.

**1921-23**     Engr.     Perf. 13½

| | | | | |
|---|---|---|---|---|
| **E3** | SD3 | 30c blue & rose | 2.25 | *8.00* |
| **E4** | SD3 | 50c rose red & brn | 4.75 | *11.00* |
| **E5** | SD3 | 60c dk red & brn ('23) | 8.00 | *17.00* |
| **E6** | SD3 | 2 l dk bl & red ('23) | 15.00 | *30.00* |
| | *Nos. E3-E6 (4)* | | 30.00 | *66.00* |
| | Set, never hinged | | 65.00 | |

30c, 2 l inscribed "EXPRES."
For surcharges see Nos. E9-E12.

**Nos. E1-E2 Surcharged**

**1922, June 1**

| | | | | |
|---|---|---|---|---|
| **E7** | SD1 | 60c on 25c rose red | 12.50 | *17.50* |
| **E8** | SD2 | 1.60 l on 30c bl & rose | 15.00 | *35.00* |
| | Set, never hinged | | 67.50 | |

**Nos. E5-E6 Surcharged in Blue or Red**

No. E9

Nos. E10, E12

No. E11

**1926-36**

| | | | | |
|---|---|---|---|---|
| **E9** | SD3 | 70c on 60c | 7.50 | *15.00* |
| **E10** | SD3 | 2.50 l on 2 l (R) | 14.00 | *27.50* |

Map of Fezzan-Ghadames, Soldier
and Camel — OS3

### 1946   Unwmk.   Engr.   *Perf. 13*

| | | | | |
|---|---|---|---|---|
| 1N1 | OS1 | 10c black | .35 | .35 |
| 1N2 | OS1 | 50c rose | .35 | .35 |
| 1N3 | OS1 | 1fr brown | .45 | .45 |
| 1N4 | OS1 | 1.50fr green | .55 | .55 |
| 1N5 | OS1 | 2fr ultramarine | .70 | .70 |
| 1N6 | OS2 | 2.50fr violet | .90 | .90 |
| 1N7 | OS2 | 3fr rose carmine | 1.20 | 1.20 |
| 1N8 | OS2 | 5fr chocolate | 1.20 | 1.20 |
| 1N9 | OS2 | 6fr dark green | 1.10 | 1.10 |
| 1N10 | OS3 | 10fr blue | 1.20 | 1.20 |
| 1N11 | OS3 | 15fr violet | 1.50 | 1.50 |
| 1N12 | OS3 | 20fr red | 1.75 | 1.75 |
| 1N13 | OS3 | 25fr sepia | 1.75 | 1.75 |
| 1N14 | OS3 | 40fr dark green | 2.25 | 2.25 |
| 1N15 | OS3 | 50fr deep blue | 2.50 | 2.50 |
| | | *Nos. 1N1-1N15 (15)* | 17.75 | 17.75 |

## FEZZAN

> Catalogue values for unused stamps in this section are for Never Hinged items.

Monument, Djerma Oasis OS1

Tombs of the Beni-Khettab OS2

Well at Gorda — OS3

Col. Colonna d'Ornano and Fort at Murzuch — OS4

Philippe F. M. de Hautecloque (Gen. Jacques Leclerc) — OS5

### 1949   Unwmk.   Engr.   *Perf. 13*

| | | | | |
|---|---|---|---|---|
| 2N1 | OS1 | 1fr black | 1.20 | 1.20 |
| 2N2 | OS1 | 2fr lil pink | 1.25 | 1.25 |
| 2N3 | OS2 | 4fr red brn | 2.10 | 2.10 |
| 2N4 | OS2 | 5fr emerald | 2.10 | 2.10 |
| 2N5 | OS3 | 8fr blue | 2.75 | 2.75 |
| 2N6 | OS3 | 10fr brown | 4.50 | 4.50 |
| 2N7 | OS3 | 12fr dk grn | 7.00 | 7.00 |
| 2N8 | OS4 | 15fr sal red | 10.00 | 10.00 |
| 2N9 | OS4 | 20fr brn blk | 5.00 | 5.00 |
| 2N10 | OS5 | 25fr dk bl | 5.50 | 5.50 |
| 2N11 | OS5 | 50fr cop red | 10.00 | 10.00 |
| | | *Nos. 2N1-2N11 (11)* | 51.40 | 51.40 |

Camel Raising — OS6

Agriculture OS7

Well Drilling OS8

---

Ahmed Bey — OS9

### 1951

| | | | | |
|---|---|---|---|---|
| 2N12 | OS6 | 30c brown | 1.40 | 1.40 |
| 2N13 | OS6 | 1fr dp bl | 1.40 | 1.40 |
| 2N14 | OS6 | 2fr rose car | 1.40 | 1.40 |
| 2N15 | OS7 | 4fr red | 2.10 | 2.10 |
| 2N16 | OS7 | 5fr green | 2.10 | 2.10 |
| 2N17 | OS7 | 8fr dp bl | 2.10 | 2.10 |
| 2N18 | OS8 | 10fr sepia | 5.50 | 5.50 |
| 2N19 | OS8 | 12fr dp grn | 6.25 | 6.25 |
| 2N20 | OS8 | 15fr brt red | 7.00 | 7.00 |
| 2N21 | OS9 | 20fr blk brn & vio brn | 7.00 | 7.00 |
| 2N22 | OS9 | 25fr dk bl & bl | 7.75 | 7.75 |
| 2N23 | OS9 | 50fr ind & brn org | 8.50 | 8.50 |
| | | *Nos. 2N12-2N23 (12)* | 52.50 | 52.50 |

## OCCUPATION SEMI-POSTAL STAMPS

> Catalogue values for unused stamps in this section are for Never Hinged items.

"The Unhappy Ones" OSP1     OSP2

### 1950   Unwmk.   Engr.   *Perf. 13*

| | | | | |
|---|---|---|---|---|
| 2NB1 | OSP1 | 15fr + 5fr red brn | 3.25 | 3.25 |
| 2NB2 | OSP2 | 25fr + 5fr blue | 3.25 | 3.25 |

The surtax was for charitable works.

---

## OCCUPATION AIR POST STAMPS

> Catalogue values for unused stamps in this section are for Never Hinged items.

Airport in Fezzan OAP1     Plane over Fezzan OAP2

### 1948   Unwmk.   Engr.   *Perf. 13*

| | | | | |
|---|---|---|---|---|
| 2NC1 | OAP1 | 100fr red | 7.00 | 7.00 |
| 2NC2 | OAP2 | 200fr indigo | 10.00 | 10.00 |

Oasis — OAP3     Murzuch — OAP4

### 1951

| | | | | |
|---|---|---|---|---|
| 2NC3 | OAP3 | 100fr dark blue | 9.75 | 9.75 |
| 2NC4 | OAP4 | 200fr vermilion | 14.00 | 14.00 |

## OCCUPATION POSTAGE DUE STAMPS

> Catalogue values for unused stamps in this section are for Never Hinged items.

---

Oasis of Brak — D1

### 1950   Unwmk.   Engr.   *Perf. 13*

| | | | | |
|---|---|---|---|---|
| 2NJ1 | D1 | 1fr brown black | 1.40 | 1.40 |
| 2NJ2 | D1 | 2fr deep green | 1.40 | 1.40 |
| 2NJ3 | D1 | 3fr red brown | 2.10 | 2.10 |
| 2NJ4 | D1 | 5fr purple | 2.10 | 2.10 |
| 2NJ5 | D1 | 10fr red | 4.25 | 4.25 |
| 2NJ6 | D1 | 20fr deep blue | 6.25 | 6.25 |
| | | *Nos. 2NJ1-2NJ6 (6)* | 17.50 | 17.50 |

## GHADAMES

> Catalogue values for unused stamps in this section are for Never Hinged items.

Cross of Agadem — OS1

### 1949   Unwmk.   Engr.   *Perf. 13*

| | | | | |
|---|---|---|---|---|
| 3N1 | OS1 | 4fr sep & red brn | 1.75 | 1.75 |
| 3N2 | OS1 | 5fr pck bl & dk grn | 1.75 | 1.75 |
| 3N3 | OS1 | 8fr sep & org brn | 4.50 | 4.50 |
| 3N4 | OS1 | 10fr blk & dk ultra | 4.50 | 4.50 |
| 3N5 | OS1 | 12fr vio & red vio | 12.00 | 12.00 |
| 3N6 | OS1 | 15fr brn & red brn | 8.50 | 8.50 |
| 3N7 | OS1 | 20fr sep & emer | 10.00 | 10.00 |
| 3N8 | OS1 | 25fr sepia & blue | 12.50 | 12.50 |
| | | *Nos. 3N1-3N8 (8)* | 55.50 | 55.50 |

## OCCUPATION AIR POST STAMPS

> Catalogue values for unused stamps in this section are for Never Hinged items.

Cross of Agadem — OAP1

### 1949   Unwmk.   Engr.   *Perf. 13*

| | | | | |
|---|---|---|---|---|
| 3NC1 | OAP1 | 50fr pur & rose | 16.00 | 16.00 |
| 3NC2 | OAP1 | 100fr sep & pur brn | 19.00 | 19.00 |

---

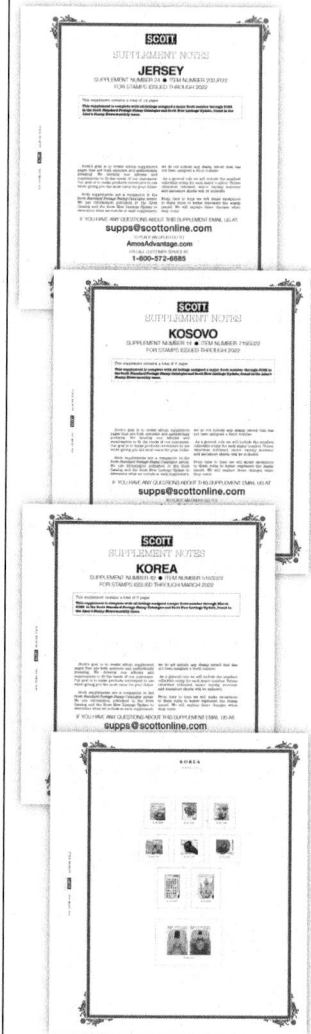

# LIECHTENSTEIN

'lik-tən-ˌshtin

LOCATION — Central Europe southeast of Lake Constance, between Austria and Switzerland
GOVT. — Principality
AREA — 61.8 sq. mi.
POP. — 31,320 (1997)
CAPITAL — Vaduz

The Principality of Liechtenstein is a sovereign state consisting of the two counties of Schellenberg and Vaduz. Since 1921 the post office has been administered by Switzerland.

100 Heller = 1 Krone
100 Rappen = 1 Franc (1921)

Catalogue values for unused stamps in this country are for Never Hinged items, beginning with Scott 368 in the regular postage section, Scott B22 in the semipostal section, Scott C24 in the air post section, and Scott O30 in the offical section.

## Watermarks

Greek Cross — Wmk. 183

Crown and Initials — Wmk. 296

## Austrian Administration of the Post Office

Prince Johann II — A1

### Perf. 12½x13
### 1912, Feb. 1    Unwmk.    Typo.
#### Thick Chalky Paper

| | | | | |
|---|---|---|---|---|
| 1 | A1 | 5h yellow green | 42.50 | 17.50 |
| 2 | A1 | 10h rose | 85.00 | 17.50 |
| 3 | A1 | 25h dark blue | 85.00 | 55.00 |
| | | Nos. 1-3 (3) | 212.50 | 90.00 |
| | | Set, never hinged | 900.00 | |

### 1915    Thin Unsurfaced Paper

| | | | | |
|---|---|---|---|---|
| 1a | A1 | 5h yellow green | 14.00 | 21.00 |
| 2a | A1 | 10h rose | 85.00 | 32.50 |
| 3a | A1 | 25h dark blue | 600.00 | 200.00 |
| b. | | 25h ultramarine | 350.00 | 425.00 |
| | | Never hinged | 1,550. | |
| | | #1a-3a, never hinged | 2,500. | |

Coat of Arms — A2     Prince Johann II — A3

### 1917-18

| | | | | |
|---|---|---|---|---|
| 4 | A2 | 3h violet | 2.00 | 2.00 |
| 5 | A2 | 5h yellow green | 2.00 | 2.00 |
| 6 | A3 | 10h claret | 2.00 | 2.00 |
| 7 | A3 | 15h dull red | 2.00 | 2.00 |
| 8 | A3 | 20h dark green | 2.00 | 2.00 |
| 9 | A3 | 25h deep blue | 2.00 | 2.00 |
| | | Nos. 4-9 (6) | 12.00 | 12.00 |
| | | Set, never hinged | 51.00 | |

Exist imperf. Value set unused original gum, $525; never hinged, $1,150.

---

For surcharges see Nos. 11-16.

Prince Johann II — A4

### Dates in Upper Corners
### 1918, Nov. 12

| | | | | |
|---|---|---|---|---|
| 10 | A4 | 20h dark green | .70 | 2.75 |
| | | Never hinged | 5.50 | |

Accession of Prince Johann II, 60th anniv.
Exists imperf. Value, unused original gum, $225; never hinged, $560.

## National Administration of the Post Office
### Stamps of 1917-18 Overprinted or Surcharged

a       b

c

### 1920

| | | | | |
|---|---|---|---|---|
| 11 | A2(a) | 5h yellow green | 2.75 | 8.75 |
| a. | | Inverted overprint | 70.00 | 175.00 |
| | | Never hinged | 140.00 | |
| b. | | Double overprint | 14.00 | 85.00 |
| | | Never hinged | 35.00 | |
| 12 | A3(a) | 10h claret | 2.75 | 9.50 |
| a. | | Inverted overprint | 70.00 | 175.00 |
| | | Never hinged | 140.00 | |
| b. | | Double overprint | 14.00 | 105.00 |
| | | Never hinged | 35.00 | |
| c. | | Overprint type "c" | 14.00 | 105.00 |
| | | Never hinged | 27.50 | |
| 13 | A3(a) | 25h deep blue | 2.75 | 9.50 |
| a. | | Inverted overprint | 70.00 | 105.00 |
| | | Never hinged | 140.00 | |
| b. | | Double overprint | 14.00 | 105.00 |
| | | Never hinged | 27.50 | |
| 14 | A2(b) | 40h on 3h violet | 2.75 | 9.50 |
| a. | | Inverted surcharge | 70.00 | 175.00 |
| | | Never hinged | 140.00 | |
| 15 | A3(c) | 1k on 15h dull red | 2.75 | 9.50 |
| a. | | Inverted surcharge | 70.00 | 175.00 |
| b. | | Overprint type "a" | 87.50 | 350.00 |
| | | Never hinged | 315.00 | |
| 16 | A3(c) | 2½k on 20h dk grn | 2.75 | 9.50 |
| a. | | Inverted overprint | 70.00 | 105.00 |
| | | Nos. 11-16 (6) | 16.50 | 56.25 |
| | | Set, never hinged | 71.00 | |

Coat of Arms A5     Chapel of St. Mamertus A6

Coat of Arms with Supporters — A15

Designs: 40h, Gutenberg Castle. 50h, Courtyard, Vaduz Castle. 60h, Red Tower, Vaduz. 80h, Old Roman Tower, Schaan. 1k, Castle at Vaduz. 2k, View of Bendern. 5k, Prince Johann I. 7½k, Prince Johann II.

### 1920     Engr.     Imperf.

| | | | | |
|---|---|---|---|---|
| 18 | A5 | 5h olive bister | .35 | 5.75 |
| 19 | A5 | 10h deep orange | .35 | 5.75 |
| 20 | A5 | 15h dark blue | .35 | 5.75 |
| 21 | A5 | 20h deep brown | .35 | 5.75 |
| 22 | A5 | 25h dark green | .35 | 5.75 |
| 23 | A5 | 30h gray black | .35 | 5.75 |
| 24 | A5 | 40h dark red | .35 | 5.75 |

---

| | | | | |
|---|---|---|---|---|
| 25 | A6 | 1k blue | .35 | 5.75 |

#### Perf. 12½

| | | | | |
|---|---|---|---|---|
| 32 | A5 | 5h olive bister | .35 | .70 |
| 33 | A5 | 10h deep orange | .35 | .70 |
| 34 | A5 | 15h deep blue | .35 | .70 |
| 35 | A5 | 20h red brown | .35 | .70 |
| 36 | A5 | 25h olive green | .35 | .70 |
| 37 | A5 | 30h dark gray | .35 | .70 |
| 38 | A5 | 40h claret | .35 | .70 |
| 39 | A6 | 50h yellow green | .35 | .70 |
| 40 | A6 | 60h red brown | .35 | .70 |
| 41 | A6 | 80h rose | .35 | .70 |
| 42 | A6 | 1k dull violet | .70 | 1.00 |
| 43 | A6 | 2k light blue | .70 | 1.25 |
| 44 | A6 | 5k black | .70 | 1.50 |
| 45 | A6 | 7½k slate | .70 | 1.75 |
| 46 | A15 | 10k ocher | .70 | 3.00 |
| | | Nos. 18-46 (23) | 9.80 | 61.50 |
| | | Set, never hinged | 41.00 | |

No. 25 perf. 12½ was not officially issued. It is known mint, used and on cover.
Used values for Nos. 18-46 are for canceled to order stamps. Value with postal cancels approximately $95.
Many denominations of Nos. 32-46 are found imperforate, imperforate vertically and imperforate horizontally.
For surcharges see Nos. 51-52.

Madonna and Child — A16

### 1920, Oct. 5

| | | | | |
|---|---|---|---|---|
| 47 | A16 | 50h olive green | 1.00 | 2.10 |
| 48 | A16 | 80h brown red | 1.00 | 2.10 |
| 49 | A16 | 2k dark blue | 1.00 | 2.75 |
| | | Nos. 47-49 (3) | 3.00 | 6.95 |
| | | Set, never hinged | 10.50 | |

80th birthday of Prince Johann II.

#### Imperf., Singles

| | | | | |
|---|---|---|---|---|
| 47a | A16 | 50h | 7.00 | 1,400. |
| 48a | A16 | 80h | 7.00 | 1,400. |
| 49a | A16 | 2k | 7.00 | 1,400. |
| | | Set, never hinged | 63.00 | |

On 1/31/21 the Swiss took over the Post Office administration. Previous issues were demonetized and remainders of Nos. 4-49 were sold.

## Swiss Administration of the Post Office
### No. 19 Surcharged

No. 51      No. 52

### 1921    Unwmk.   Engr.   Imperf.

| | | | | |
|---|---|---|---|---|
| 51 | A5 | 2rp on 10h dp org | 1.40 | 50.00 |
| a. | | Double surcharge | 105.00 | 140.00 |
| b. | | Inverted surcharge | 105.00 | 160.00 |
| c. | | Double surch., one inverted | 105.00 | 175.00 |
| 52 | A5 | 2rp on 10h dp org | .70 | 50.00 |
| | | First day cover (2/27/21) | | 875.00 |
| a. | | Double surcharge | 72.50 | 160.00 |
| b. | | Inverted surcharge | 72.50 | 160.00 |
| c. | | Double surch., one inverted | 87.50 | 190.00 |

Arms with Supporters A19    Chapel of St. Mamertus A20

View of Vaduz — A21

Designs: 25rp, Castle at Vaduz. 30rp, View of Bendern. 35rp, Prince Johann II. 40rp, Old Roman Tower at Schaan. 50rp, Gutenberg Castle. 80rp, Red Tower at Vaduz.

---

### 1921    Perf. 12½, 9½ (2rp, 10rp, 15rp)
#### Surface Tinted Paper (#54-61)

| | | | | |
|---|---|---|---|---|
| 54 | A19 | 2rp lemon | 1.40 | 14.00 |
| 55 | A19 | 2½rp black | 2.10 | 17.50 |
| a. | | Perf. 9½ | 1.40 | 70.00 |
| 56 | A19 | 3rp orange | 2.10 | 17.50 |
| a. | | Perf. 9½ | 140.00 | 5,000. |
| 57 | A19 | 5rp olive green | 14.00 | 2.10 |
| a. | | Perf. 9½ | 70.00 | 27.50 |
| | | Never hinged | 225.00 | |
| 58 | A19 | 7½rp dark blue | 7.00 | 42.50 |
| a. | | Perf. 9½ | 275.00 | 1,050. |
| 59 | A19 | 10rp yellow green | 27.50 | 17.50 |
| a. | | Perf. 12½ | 27.50 | 14.00 |
| 60 | A19 | 13rp brown | 10.50 | 90.00 |
| a. | | Perf. 9½ | 100.00 | 2,450. |
| b. | | Perf. 12½x9½ | 210.00 | — |
| | | Never hinged | 425.00 | |
| 61 | A19 | 15rp dark violet | 25.00 | 70.00 |
| a. | | Perf. 12½ | 27.50 | 27.50 |
| | | Never hinged | 50.00 | |
| 62 | A20 | 20rp dull vio & blk | 70.00 | 2.10 |
| 63 | A20 | 25rp rose red & blk | 3.50 | 5.00 |
| 64 | A20 | 30rp dp grn & blk | 85.00 | 21.00 |
| 65 | A20 | 35rp brn & blk, straw | 7.00 | 17.50 |
| 66 | A20 | 40rp dk blue & blk | 10.50 | 7.00 |
| 67 | A20 | 50rp dk grn & blk | 17.50 | 10.50 |
| 68 | A20 | 80rp gray & blk | 32.00 | 85.00 |
| 69 | A21 | 1fr dk claret & blk | 55.00 | 55.00 |
| | | Nos. 54-69 (16) | 370.10 | 474.20 |
| | | Set, never hinged | 1,039. | |

Nos. 54-69 exist imperforate; Nos. 54-61, partly perforated. See Nos. 73, 81. For surcharges see Nos. 70-71.

Nos. 58, 60a Surcharged in Red

### 1924     Perf. 12½, 9½

| | | | | |
|---|---|---|---|---|
| 70 | A19 | 5rp on 7½rp | 1.40 | 3.50 |
| a. | | Perf. 9½ | 19.00 | 17.50 |
| | | Never hinged | 50.00 | |
| 71 | A19 | 10rp on 13rp | 1.75 | 3.50 |
| | | Never hinged | 5.25 | |
| a. | | Perf. 12½ | 20.00 | 52.50 |

---

## Type of 1921
### Granite Paper

| 1924 | | Wmk. 183 | Perf. 11½ | |
|---|---|---|---|---|
| 73 | A19 | 10rp green | 21.00 | 3.50 |

Peasant
A28

Government Palace and Church at Vaduz
A30

10rp, 20rp, Courtyard, Vaduz Castle.

| 1924-28 | | Typo. | Perf. 11½ | |
|---|---|---|---|---|
| 74 | A28 | 2½rp ol grn & red vio ('28) | 1.40 | 5.50 |
| 75 | A28 | 5rp brown & blue | 2.75 | .75 |
| 76 | A28 | 7½rp bl grn & brn ('28) | 2.10 | 5.50 |
| 77 | A28 | 15rp red brn & bl grn ('28) | 10.50 | 35.00 |

**Engr.**

| 78 | A28 | 10rp yellow grn | 11.25 | .70 |
|---|---|---|---|---|
| 79 | A28 | 20rp deep red | 42.50 | .70 |
| 80 | A30 | 1½fr blue | 85.00 | 110.00 |
| | | Nos. 74-80 (7) | 155.50 | 158.15 |
| | | Set, never hinged | 503.00 | |

### Bendern Type of 1921

| 1925 | | | | |
|---|---|---|---|---|
| 81 | A20 | 30rp blue & blk | 17.50 | 3.50 |

Prince Johann II — A31

Prince Johann II as Boy and Man — A32

| 1928, Nov. 12 | | Typo. | Wmk. 183 | |
|---|---|---|---|---|
| 82 | A31 | 10rp lt brn & ol grn | 7.00 | 7.00 |
| 83 | A31 | 20rp org red & ol grn | 10.50 | 14.00 |
| 84 | A31 | 30rp sl bl & ol grn | 35.00 | 25.00 |
| 85 | A31 | 60rp red vio & ol grn | 70.00 | 70.00 |

**Engr.**
**Unwmk.**

| 86 | A32 | 1.20fr ultra | 50.00 | 87.50 |
|---|---|---|---|---|
| 87 | A32 | 1.50fr blk brn | 87.50 | 210.00 |
| 88 | A32 | 2fr deep car | 87.50 | 210.00 |
| 89 | A32 | 5fr dark green | 87.50 | 245.00 |
| | | Nos. 82-89 (8) | 435.00 | 868.50 |
| | | Set, never hinged | 1,040. | |

70th year of the reign of Prince Johann II.

Prince Francis I, as a Child — A33

Prince Francis I as a Man — A34

Princess Elsa — A35

Prince Francis and Princess Elsa — A36

| 1929, Dec. 2 | | | Photo. | |
|---|---|---|---|---|
| 90 | A33 | 10rp olive green | .55 | 4.25 |
| 91 | A34 | 20rp carmine | .85 | 7.00 |
| 92 | A35 | 30rp ultra | 1.40 | 17.50 |
| 93 | A36 | 70rp brown | 25.00 | 110.00 |
| | | Nos. 90-93 (4) | 27.80 | 138.75 |
| | | Set, never hinged | 77.00 | |

Accession of Prince Francis I, Feb. 11, 1929.

Grape Girl — A37

Mountain Cattle — A39

Mt. Naafkopf A41

Rofenberg Chapel A43

Alpine Hotel, Malbun A45

Schellenberg Monastery A47

Mountain Cottage A49

Chamois Hunter — A38

Courtyard, Vaduz Castle — A40

Chapel at Steg A42

Chapel of St. Mamertus A44

Gutenberg Castle A46

Castle at Vaduz A48

Prince Francis and Princess Elsa A50

| 1930 | | Perf. 10½, 11½, 11½x10½ | | |
|---|---|---|---|---|
| 94 | A37 | 3rp brown lake | 1.10 | 2.80 |
| 95 | A38 | 5rp deep green | 2.80 | 7.00 |
| 96 | A39 | 10rp dark violet | 2.50 | 7.00 |
| a. | | Perf. 11½x10½ | 11.00 | 120.00 |
| | | Never hinged | 28.00 | |
| 97 | A40 | 20rp dp rose red | 42.50 | 7.00 |
| 98 | A41 | 25rp black | 8.50 | 45.00 |
| a. | | Perf. 11½ | 105.00 | 350.00 |
| | | Never hinged | 350.00 | |
| 99 | A42 | 30rp dp ultra | 8.50 | 10.50 |
| a. | | Perf. 11½x10½ | 1,050. | 2,500. |
| | | Never hinged | 2,175. | |
| 100 | A43 | 35rp dark green | 11.00 | 21.00 |
| a. | | Perf. 11½ | 8,750. | 14,000. |
| | | Never hinged | 13,500. | |
| 101 | A44 | 40rp lt brown | 11.00 | 11.00 |
| 102 | A45 | 50rp blk brn | 105.00 | 21.00 |
| a. | | Perf. 11½ | 165.00 | 245.00 |
| | | Never hinged | 600.00 | |
| 103 | A46 | 60rp olive blk | 105.00 | 42.50 |
| 104 | A47 | 90rp violet brn | 105.00 | 350.00 |
| 105 | A48 | 1.20fr olive brn | 125.00 | 375.00 |
| a. | | Perf. 11½x10½ | 8,750. | 14,000. |
| | | Never hinged | 13,500. | |

Mt. Naafkopf A51

Vaduz Castle — A53

Gutenberg Castle A52

| 106 | A49 | 1.50fr black violet | 70.00 | 77.50 |
|---|---|---|---|---|
| 107 | A50 | 2fr gray grn & red brn | 85.00 | 140.00 |
| a. | | Perf. 11½x10½ | 3,850. | 7,750. |
| | | Never hinged | 6,750. | |
| | | Nos. 94-107 (14) | 681.90 | 1,117. |
| | | Set, never hinged | 1,600. | |

For overprints see Nos. O1-O8.

| 1933, Jan. 23 | | | Perf. 14½ | |
|---|---|---|---|---|
| 108 | A51 | 25rp red orange | 200.00 | 87.50 |
| 109 | A52 | 90rp dark green | 10.50 | 105.00 |
| 110 | A53 | 1.20fr red brown | 85.00 | 300.00 |
| | | Nos. 108-110 (3) | 295.50 | 492.50 |
| | | Set, never hinged | 840.00 | |

For overprints see Nos. O9-O10.

80th Birthday of Prince Francis I — A54

| 1933, Aug. 28 | | | Perf. 11 | |
|---|---|---|---|---|
| 111 | A54 | 10rp purple | 21.00 | 42.50 |
| 112 | A54 | 20rp brn car | 21.00 | 42.50 |
| 113 | A54 | 30rp dark blue | 21.00 | 42.50 |
| | | Nos. 111-113 (3) | 63.00 | 127.50 |
| | | Set, never hinged | 180.00 | |

Prince Francis I — A55

| 1933, Dec. 15 | | Engr. | Perf. 12½ | |
|---|---|---|---|---|
| 114 | A55 | 3fr violet blue | 125.00 | 250.00 |
| | | Never hinged | 250.00 | |

See No. 152.

### Agricultural Exhibition Issue
#### Souvenir Sheet

Arms of Liechtenstein — A56

| 1934, Sept. 29 | | | Perf. 12 | |
|---|---|---|---|---|
| | | **Granite Paper** | | |
| 115 | A56 | 5fr brown | 1,400. | 2,500. |
| | | Never hinged | 2,250. | |
| | | Single stamp | 1,000. | 1,750. |
| | | Never hinged | 1,400. | |

See No. 131.

Coat of Arms A57

"Three Sisters" (Landmark) A58

Church of Schaan A59

Rathaus, Vaduz A61

Bendern A60

Samina Valley A62

Samina Valley in Winter — A63

Ruin at Schellenberg A64

Government Palace — A65

Vaduz Castle — A66

Gutenberg Castle — A68

Alpine Hut — A69

Princess Elsa — A70

Coat of Arms — A71

60rp, Vaduz castle, diff. 1.50fr, Valuna.

| 1934-35 | | Photo. | Perf. 11½ | |
|---|---|---|---|---|
| 116 | A57 | 3rp copper red | .35 | .70 |
| 117 | A58 | 5rp emerald | 5.50 | 2.10 |
| 118 | A59 | 10rp deep violet | 2.75 | 1.40 |
| 119 | A60 | 15rp red org | .35 | 1.40 |
| 120 | A61 | 20rp red | .70 | 1.40 |
| 121 | A62 | 25rp brown | 28.00 | 65.00 |
| 122 | A63 | 30rp dk blue | 5.50 | 2.10 |
| 123 | A64 | 35rp gray grn | 2.75 | 8.50 |
| 124 | A65 | 40rp brown | 1.75 | 7.00 |
| 125 | A66 | 50rp lt brown | 25.00 | 21.00 |
| 126 | A66 | 60rp claret | 2.10 | 9.00 |
| 127 | A68 | 90rp deep green | 8.50 | 32.00 |
| 128 | A69 | 1.20fr deep blue | 3.50 | 32.00 |
| 129 | A69 | 1.50fr brn car | 4.25 | 35.00 |
| | | Nos. 116-129 (14) | 91.00 | 218.60 |
| | | Set, never hinged | 275.00 | |

**Engr.**
**Perf. 12½**

| 130 | A70 | 2fr hen brn ('35) | 85.00 | 250.00 |
|---|---|---|---|---|
| 131 | A71 | 5fr dk vio ('35) | 425.00 | 1,050. |
| | | Never hinged | 700.00 | |

No. 131 has the same design as the 5fr in the souvenir sheet, No. 115. See No. 226, B14. For overprints see Nos. O11-O20.

# Easy Online Bidding

Bridge at Malbun — A72

Labor: 20rp, Constructing Road to Triesenberg. 30rp, Binnen Canal. 50rp, Bridge near Planken.

**1937, June 30**     **Photo.**
| | | | | |
|---|---|---|---|---|
| **132** | A72 | 10rp brt violet | 1.75 | 2.10 |
| **133** | A72 | 20rp red | 1.75 | 2.75 |
| **134** | A72 | 30rp brt blue | 1.75 | 3.50 |
| **135** | A72 | 50rp yellow brown | 1.75 | 4.25 |
| | | Nos. 132-135 (4) | 7.00 | 12.60 |
| | | Set, never hinged | 21.00 | |

Ruin at Schalun A76

Peasant in Rhine Valley A77

Ruin at Schellenberg A78

Knight and Gutenberg Castle — A79

Baron von Brandis and Vaduz Castle — A80

Designs: 5rp, Chapel at Masescha. 10rp, Knight and Vaduz Castle. 15rp, Upper Valüna Valley. 20rp, Wooden Bridge over Rhine, Bendern. 25rp, Chapel at Steg. 90rp, "The Three Sisters". 1fr, Frontier stone. 1.20fr, Gutenberg Castle and Harpist. 1.50fr, Alpine View of Lawena and Schwartzhorn.

**1937-38**
| | | | | |
|---|---|---|---|---|
| **136** | A76 | 3rp yellow brown | .35 | .70 |

**Pale Buff Shading**
| | | | | |
|---|---|---|---|---|
| **137** | A76 | 5rp emerald | .35 | .35 |
| **138** | A76 | 10rp violet | .35 | .35 |
| **139** | A76 | 15rp dk slate grn | .35 | .70 |
| **140** | A76 | 20rp brn org | .35 | .70 |
| **141** | A76 | 25rp chestnut | .70 | 3.50 |
| **142** | A77 | 30rp blue & gray | 3.50 | 1.40 |
| **143** | A78 | 40rp dark green | 2.10 | 2.75 |
| **144** | A79 | 50rp dark brown | 1.40 | 7.00 |
| **145** | A80 | 60rp dp claret ('38) | 2.75 | 3.50 |
| **146** | A80 | 90rp gray vio ('38) | 7.00 | 42.50 |
| **147** | A80 | 1fr red brown | 2.10 | 17.50 |
| **148** | A80 | 1.20fr dp brn ('38) | 7.00 | 32.00 |
| **149** | A80 | 1.50fr slate bl ('38) | 4.25 | 32.50 |
| | | Nos. 136-150 (14) | 32.55 | 145.45 |
| | | Set, never hinged | 97.00 | |

For overprints see Nos. O21-O29.

**Souvenir Sheet**

Josef Rheinberger — A91

**1938, July 30**    **Engr.**    **Perf. 12**
| | | | | |
|---|---|---|---|---|
| **151** | A91 | Sheet of 4 | 27.50 | 27.50 |
| | | Never hinged | 70.00 | |
| *a.* | | 50rp slate gray | 3.50 | 5.25 |
| | | Never hinged | 7.00 | |

Third Philatelic Exhibition of Liechtenstein. Sheet size: 99¾x135mm.
See No. 153.

**Francis Type of 1933**
**Thick Wove Paper**

**1938, Aug. 15**     **Perf. 12½**
| | | | | |
|---|---|---|---|---|
| **152** | A55 | 3fr black, *buff* | 10.50 | 100.00 |

Issued in memory of Prince Francis I, who died July 25, 1938. Sheets of 20.

Josef Gabriel Rheinberger (1839-1901), German Composer and Organist — A92

**1939, Mar. 31**
| | | | | |
|---|---|---|---|---|
| **153** | A92 | 50rp slate green | 1.10 | 6.25 |
| | | Never hinged | 2.40 | |

Issued in sheets of 20. See No. 151.

Scene of Homage, 1718 — A93

**1939, May 29**
| | | | | |
|---|---|---|---|---|
| **154** | A93 | 20rp brown lake | 1.40 | 2.75 |
| **155** | A93 | 30rp slate blue | 1.40 | 2.75 |
| **156** | A93 | 50rp gray green | 1.40 | 2.75 |
| | | Nos. 154-156 (3) | 4.20 | 8.25 |
| | | Set, never hinged | 14.00 | |

Honoring Prince Franz Joseph II. Sheets of 20.

Cantonal Coats of Arms — A94

Prince Franz Joseph II — A96

Design: 3fr, Arms of Principality.

**1939**
| | | | | |
|---|---|---|---|---|
| **157** | A94 | 2fr dk green, *buff* | 7.00 | 42.50 |
| **158** | A94 | 3fr indigo, *buff* | 4.50 | 42.50 |
| **159** | A96 | 5fr brown, *buff* | 14.00 | 27.50 |
| *a.* | | Sheet of 4 | 90.00 | 140.00 |
| | | Never hinged | 175.00 | |
| | | Nos. 157-159 (3) | 25.50 | 112.50 |
| | | Set, never hinged | 63.00 | |

2fr, 3fr issued in sheets of 12; 5fr in sheets of 4.

Prince Johann as a Child — A100

Memorial Tablet — A101

Prince Johann II — A102

30rp, Prince Johann and Tower at Vaduz. 50rp, Prince Johann and Gutenberg Castle. 1fr, Prince Johann in 1920 and Vaduz Castle.

**1940**    **Photo.**    **Perf. 11½.**
| | | | | |
|---|---|---|---|---|
| **160** | A100 | 20rp henna brown | .60 | 2.25 |
| **161** | A100 | 30rp indigo | .60 | 3.25 |
| **162** | A100 | 50rp dk slate grn | 1.10 | 10.50 |
| **163** | A100 | 1fr brown vio | 8.25 | 70.00 |

| | | | | |
|---|---|---|---|---|
| **164** | A101 | 1.50fr violet blk | 10.50 | 67.50 |
| **165** | A102 | 3fr brown | 4.25 | 22.50 |
| | | Nos. 160-165 (6) | 25.30 | 176.00 |
| | | Set, never hinged | 52.50 | |

Birth centenary of Prince Johann II.
Nos. 160-164 issued in sheets of 25; No. 165 in sheets of 12.
Issue dates: 3fr, Oct. 5; others Aug. 10.

Gathering Corn — A103

Wine Press — A104

Sharpening Scythe — A105

Milkmaid and Cow — A106

Native Costume — A107

**1941, Apr. 7**
| | | | | |
|---|---|---|---|---|
| **166** | A103 | 10rp dull red brown | .75 | .45 |
| **167** | A104 | 20rp lake | .75 | 1.10 |
| **168** | A105 | 30rp royal blue | .75 | 2.50 |
| **169** | A106 | 50rp myrtle green | 2.40 | 14.00 |
| **170** | A107 | 90rp deep claret | 2.40 | 14.00 |
| | | Nos. 166-170 (5) | 7.05 | 32.05 |
| | | Set, never hinged | 16.00 | |

Madonna and Child — A108

**1941, July 7**     **Engr.**
| | | | | |
|---|---|---|---|---|
| **171** | A108 | 10fr brown car | 37.50 | 97.50 |
| | | Never hinged | 75.00 | |

Issued in sheets of 4.

Johann Adam Andreas — A109

Designs: 30rp, Wenzel. 100rp, Anton Florian. 150rp, Joseph Adam.

**1941, Dec. 18**     **Photo.**
| | | | | |
|---|---|---|---|---|
| **172** | A109 | 20rp brown car | .50 | 1.25 |
| **173** | A109 | 30rp royal blue | .70 | 2.50 |
| **174** | A109 | 100rp violet blk | 1.90 | 13.00 |
| **175** | A109 | 150rp slate green | 1.90 | 13.00 |
| | | Nos. 172-175 (4) | 5.00 | 29.75 |
| | | Set, never hinged | 11.00 | |

Saint Lucius A113

Designs: 30rp, Reconstruction of Vaduz Castle. 50rp, Signing the Treaty of May 3, 1342. 1fr, Battle of Gutenberg. 2fr, Scene of Homage, 1718.

**1942, Apr. 22**    **Engr.**    **Perf. 11½**
| | | | | |
|---|---|---|---|---|
| **176** | A113 | 20rp brn org, *buff* | 1.40 | .95 |
| **177** | A113 | 30rp steel bl, *buff* | 1.40 | 1.40 |
| **178** | A113 | 50rp dk ol grn, *buff* | 1.90 | 5.50 |

| | | | | |
|---|---|---|---|---|
| **179** | A113 | 1fr dull brn, *buff* | 2.50 | 13.50 |
| **180** | A113 | 2fr vio blk, *buff* | 2.75 | 14.00 |
| | | Nos. 176-180 (5) | 9.95 | 35.35 |
| | | Set, never hinged | 20.00 | |

600th anniversary of the separation of Liechtenstein from the House of Monfort.

Johann Karl — A118

30rp, Franz Joseph I. 1fr, Alois I. 1.50fr, Johann I.

**1942, Oct. 5**     **Photo.**
| | | | | |
|---|---|---|---|---|
| **181** | A118 | 20rp rose | .50 | 1.25 |
| **182** | A118 | 30rp brt blue | .50 | 3.00 |
| **183** | A118 | 1fr rose lilac | 1.75 | 16.00 |
| **184** | A118 | 1.50fr deep brown | 2.00 | 16.00 |
| | | Nos. 181-184 (4) | 4.75 | 36.25 |
| | | Set, never hinged | 11.00 | |

Prince Franz Joseph II A122

Countess Georgina von Wilczek A123

Prince and Princess A124

**1943, Mar. 5**
| | | | | |
|---|---|---|---|---|
| **185** | A122 | 10rp dp rose violet | .55 | 1.10 |
| **186** | A123 | 20rp henna brown | .55 | 1.10 |
| **187** | A124 | 30rp slate blue | .55 | 1.10 |
| | | Nos. 185-187 (3) | 1.65 | 3.30 |
| | | Set, never hinged | 3.50 | |

Marriage of Prince Franz Joseph II and Countess Georgina von Wilczek.

Prince Johann II — A126

Princes: 20rp, Alois II. 100rp, Franz Joseph I. 150rp, Franz Joseph II.

**Perf. 11½**

**1943, July 5**   **Unwmk.**   **Photo.**
| | | | | |
|---|---|---|---|---|
| **188** | A126 | 20rp copper brown | .35 | .60 |
| **189** | A126 | 30rp deep ultra | .60 | 1.10 |
| **190** | A126 | 100rp olive gray | 1.10 | 7.00 |
| **191** | A126 | 150rp slate green | 1.25 | 7.00 |
| | | Nos. 188-191 (4) | 3.30 | 15.70 |
| | | Set, never hinged | 8.00 | |

Sheets of 20.

Terrain before Reclaiming — A129

30rp, Draining the Canal. 50rp, Plowing Reclaimed Land. 2fr, Harvesting Crops.

**1943, Sept. 6**
| | | | | |
|---|---|---|---|---|
| **192** | A129 | 10rp violet black | .30 | .55 |
| **193** | A129 | 30rp deep blue | .85 | 2.00 |
| **194** | A129 | 50rp slate green | 1.10 | 8.50 |
| **195** | A129 | 2fr olive brown | 2.00 | 12.50 |
| | | Nos. 192-195 (4) | 4.25 | 23.55 |
| | | Set, never hinged | 8.75 | |

Vaduz A133

Gutenberg A134

**1943, Dec. 27**
| | | | |
|---|---|---|---|
| 196 | A133 10rp dark gray | .45 | .45 |
| 197 | A134 20rp chestnut brown | .50 | 1.00 |
| | Set, never hinged | 2.40 | |

Planken        Bendern
A135           A136

Designs: 10rp, Triesen. 15rp, Ruggell. 20rp, Vaduz. 25rp, Triesenberg. 30rp, Schaan. 40rp, Balzers. 50rp, Mauren. 60rp, Schellenberg. 90rp, Eschen. 1fr, Vaduz Castle. 120rp, Valuna Valley. 150rp, Lawena.

**1944-45**
| | | | |
|---|---|---|---|
| 198 | A135 3rp dk brn & buff | .25 | .25 |
| 199 | A136 5rp sl grn & buff | .25 | .25 |
| 200 | A136 10rp gray & buff | .25 | .25 |
| 201 | A136 15rp bl gray & buff | .30 | .60 |
| 202 | A136 20rp org red & buff | .30 | .40 |
| 203 | A136 25rp dk rose vio & buff | .30 | .80 |
| 204 | A136 30rp blue & buff | .35 | .40 |
| 205 | A136 40rp brown & buff | .55 | 1.00 |
| 206 | A136 50rp bluish blk & pale gray | .70 | 1.60 |
| 207 | A136 60rp green & buff | 3.75 | 5.00 |
| 208 | A136 90rp ol grn & buff | 3.75 | 5.00 |
| 209 | A136 1fr dp cl & buff | 2.25 | 5.00 |
| 210 | A136 120rp red brown | 2.25 | 5.75 |
| 211 | A136 150rp royal blue | 2.25 | 5.75 |
| | Nos. 198-211 (14) | 17.50 | 32.05 |
| | Set, never hinged | 40.00 | |

Issue years: 10rp, 15rp, 40rp-1fr, 1945; others, 1944. See No. 239. For surcharge and overprints see No. 236, O30-O36.

Crown and Rose — A149

**1945, Apr. 9**
| | | | |
|---|---|---|---|
| 212 | A149 20rp multicolored | .85 | .55 |
| 213 | A149 30rp multicolored | .85 | 1.40 |
| 214 | A149 1fr multicolored | 1.00 | 4.50 |
| | Nos. 212-214 (3) | 2.70 | 6.45 |
| | Set, never hinged | 4.50 | |

Birth of Prince Johann Adam Pius, Feb. 14, 1945. Sheets of 20.

Prince Franz        Arms of
Joseph             Liechtenstein
II — A150          and Vaduz
                   Castle — A152

Design: 3fr, Princess Georgina.

**1944-45**                    **Photo.**
| | | | |
|---|---|---|---|
| 215 | A150 2fr brown, buff | 6.00 | 16.00 |
| 216 | A150 3fr dark green | 3.50 | 11.50 |

**Engr.**
| | | | |
|---|---|---|---|
| 217 | A152 5fr bl gray, cr ('45) | 10.50 | 32.50 |
| | Nos. 215-217 (3) | 20.00 | 60.00 |
| | Set, never hinged | 40.00 | |

Nos. 215-217 were issued in sheets of 8. See Nos. 222, 259-260.

Saint Lucius — A153

**1946, Mar. 14   Unwmk.   Perf. 11½**
| | | | |
|---|---|---|---|
| 218 | A153 10fr gray blk, cr | 16.00 | 30.00 |
| | Never hinged | 45.00 | |
| | Sheet of 4 | 150.00 | 200.00 |
| | Never hinged | 190.00 | |

Issued in sheets measuring 105x130mm.

Red            Varying
Deer — A154    Hare — A155

Capercaillie — A156

**1946, Dec. 10                  Photo.**
| | | | |
|---|---|---|---|
| 219 | A154 20rp henna brown | 1.50 | 2.50 |
| 220 | A155 30rp grnsh blue | 1.50 | 3.25 |
| 221 | A156 150rp olive brown | 3.00 | 11.50 |
| | Nos. 219-221 (3) | 6.00 | 17.25 |
| | Set, never hinged | 12.00 | |

**Arms Type of 1945**

**1947, Mar. 20                  Engr.**
| | | | |
|---|---|---|---|
| 222 | A152 5fr henna brn, cream | 11.00 | 37.50 |
| | Never hinged | 25.00 | |

Issued in sheets of 8.

Chamois        Alpine Marmot
A157           A158

Golden Eagle — A159

**1947, Oct. 15   Photo.   Unwmk.**
| | | | |
|---|---|---|---|
| 223 | A157 20rp henna brown | 1.60 | 1.90 |
| 224 | A158 30rp grnsh blue | 2.25 | 3.25 |
| 225 | A159 150rp dark brown | 4.25 | 19.00 |
| | Nos. 223-225 (3) | 8.10 | 24.15 |
| | Set, never hinged | 17.00 | |

**Elsa Type of 1935**

**1947, Dec. 10   Engr.   Perf. 14½**
| | | | |
|---|---|---|---|
| 226 | A70 2fr black, yelsh | 2.25 | 12.50 |
| | Never hinged | 5.00 | |

Issued in memory of Princess Elsa, who died Sept. 28, 1947. Sheets of 20.

Portrait of Ginevra dei
Benci by Leonardo da
Vinci — A160

Designs: 20rp, Girl, Rubens. 30rp, Self-portrait, Rembrandt. 40rp, Canon, Massys. 50rp, Madonna, Memling. 60rp, French Painter, 1456, Fouquet. 80rp, Lute Player, Gentileschi. 90rp, Man, Strigel. 120rp, Man, Raphael.

**1949, Mar. 15   Photo.   Perf. 11½**
| | | | |
|---|---|---|---|
| 227 | A160 10rp dark green | .25 | .35 |
| 228 | A160 20rp henna brown | .60 | .80 |
| 229 | A160 30rp sepia | 1.25 | .90 |
| 230 | A160 40rp blue | 3.00 | .90 |
| 231 | A160 50rp violet | 2.50 | 6.75 |
| 232 | A160 60rp grnsh gray | 5.50 | 6.25 |
| 233 | A160 80rp brown orange | 1.25 | 4.25 |
| 234 | A160 90rp olive bister | 5.50 | 5.75 |
| 235 | A160 120rp claret | 1.25 | 5.25 |
| | Nos. 227-235 (9) | 21.10 | 31.20 |
| | Set, never hinged | 47.50 | |

Issued in sheets of 12.
See No. 238.

**No. 198 Surcharged with New Value
and Bars in Dark Brown**

**1949, Apr. 14**
| | | | |
|---|---|---|---|
| 236 | A135 5rp on 3rp dk brn & buff | .35 | .55 |
| | Never hinged | .85 | |

Map, Post Horn
and
Crown — A161

**1949, May 23**
| | | | |
|---|---|---|---|
| 237 | A161 40rp blue & indigo | 2.00 | 4.00 |
| | Never hinged | 3.75 | |

75th anniversary of the UPU.
For surcharge see No. 246.

**Portrait Type of 1949**
**Souvenir Sheet**
**Unwmk.**

**1949, Aug. 6   Photo.   Imperf.**
| | | | |
|---|---|---|---|
| 238 | Sheet of 3 | 55.00 | 95.00 |
| | Never hinged | 110.00 | |
| a. | A160 10rp dull green | 4.75 | 10.00 |
| b. | A160 20rp lilac rose | 30.00 | 60.00 |
| c. | A160 40rp blue | 4.75 | 10.00 |

5th Philatelic Exhibition.
Sheet size: 121½x69½mm. Sold for 3fr.

**Scenic Type of 1944**

**1949, Dec. 1                  Perf. 11½**
| | | | |
|---|---|---|---|
| 239 | A136 5rp dk brown & buff | 12.00 | 1.20 |
| | Never hinged | 26.00 | |

Rossauer Castle,    Church at
Vienna — A163       Bendern — A164

Prince Johann Adam
Andreas — A165

**1949, Nov. 15   Engr.   Perf. 14½**
| | | | |
|---|---|---|---|
| 240 | A163 20rp dark violet | .90 | 2.00 |
| 241 | A164 40rp blue | 2.25 | 6.25 |
| 242 | A165 150rp brown red | 5.00 | 9.25 |
| | Nos. 240-242 (3) | 8.15 | 17.50 |
| | Set, never hinged | 20.00 | |

250th anniv. of the purchase of the former dukedom of Schellenberg. Sheets of 20.
For surcharge see No. 265.

Roe Deer        Black Grouse
A166            A167

Badger — A168

**1950, Mar. 7   Photo.   Perf. 11½**
| | | | |
|---|---|---|---|
| 243 | A166 20rp red brown | 6.00 | 6.00 |
| 244 | A167 30rp Prus green | 6.25 | 9.00 |
| 245 | A168 80rp dark brown | 13.50 | 45.00 |
| | Nos. 243-245 (3) | 25.75 | 60.00 |
| | Set, never hinged | 50.00 | |

Issued in sheets of 20.

**No. 237 Surcharged with New Value
and Bars Obliterating
Commemorative Inscriptions**

**1950, Nov. 7**
| | | | |
|---|---|---|---|
| 246 | A161 1fr on 40rp bl & ind | 10.00 | 45.00 |

Boy Cutting
Bread — A169

Designs: 10rp, Laborer. 15rp, Cutting hay. 20rp, Harvesting corn. 25rp, Load of hay. 30rp, Wine grower. 40rp, Farmer and scythe. 50rp, Cattle raising. 60rp, Plowing. 80rp, Woman with potatoes. 90rp, Potato cultivation. 1fr, Tractor with potatoes.

**Perf. 11½**

**1951, May 3   Unwmk.   Photo.**
| | | | |
|---|---|---|---|
| 247 | A169 5rp claret | .25 | .25 |
| 248 | A169 10rp green | .25 | .45 |
| 249 | A169 15rp yellow brown | 1.75 | 5.00 |
| 250 | A169 20rp olive brown | .50 | .65 |
| 251 | A169 25rp rose brown | 2.25 | 5.00 |
| 252 | A169 30rp grnsh gray | 1.25 | .55 |
| 253 | A169 40rp deep blue | 3.75 | 6.50 |
| 254 | A169 50rp violet brown | 3.00 | 4.00 |
| 255 | A169 60rp brown | 3.00 | 4.00 |
| 256 | A169 80rp henna brown | 3.75 | 6.75 |
| 257 | A169 90rp olive green | 7.00 | 7.50 |
| 258 | A169 1fr indigo | 18.00 | 10.00 |
| | Nos. 247-258 (12) | 44.75 | 49.65 |
| | Set, never hinged | 110.00 | |

**Types of 1944, Redrawn**
**Perf. 12½x12**

**1951, Nov. 20   Engr.   Wmk. 296**
| | | | |
|---|---|---|---|
| 259 | A150 2fr dark blue | 9.00 | 37.50 |
| a. | Perf. 14½ | 450.00 | 160.00 |
| 260 | A150 3fr dk red brown | 80.00 | 110.00 |
| a. | Perf. 14½ | 50.00 | 210.00 |
| | Set, never hinged | 175.00 | |
| | Set, perf. 14½, never hinged | 900.00 | |

Issued in sheets of 20.

Portrait, Savolodo A170

Madonna, Botticelli A171

Design: 40rp St. John, Del Sarto.

### Perf. 11½
**1952, Mar. 27  Unwmk.  Photo.**
261 A170 20rp violet brown 15.00 2.75
262 A171 30rp brown olive 10.50 7.00
263 A170 40rp violet blue 5.25 5.75
*Nos. 261-263 (3)* 30.75 15.50
Set, never hinged 80.00

Issued in sheets of 12.

Vaduz Castle — A172

### Wmk. 296
**1952, Sept. 25  Engr.  Perf. 14½**
264 A172 5fr deep green 85.00 150.00
Never hinged 140.00

Issued in sheets of 9.

### No. 241 Surcharged with New Value and Wavy Lines in Red
**1952, Sept. 25  Unwmk.**
265 A164 1.20fr on 40rp blue 12.00 *50.00*
Never hinged 24.00

Portrait of a Young Man A173

St. Nicholas by Zeitblom A174

Designs: 30rp, St. Christopher by Cranach. 40rp, Leonhard, Duke of Hag, by Kulmbach.

### Perf. 11½
**1953, Feb. 5  Unwmk.  Photo.**
266 A173 10rp dk olive green 1.25 1.25
267 A174 20rp olive brown 5.25 3.00
268 A173 30rp violet brown 13.00 10.00
269 A173 40rp slate blue 18.00 *40.00*
*Nos. 266-269 (4)* 37.50 54.25
Set, never hinged 75.00

Issued in sheets of 12.

Lord Baden-Powell A175

**1953, Aug. 4  Engr.  Perf. 13x13½**
270 A175 10rp deep green .70 .90
271 A175 20rp dark brown 6.75 2.25
272 A175 25rp red 5.75 18.00
273 A175 40rp deep blue 5.50 6.00
*Nos. 270-273 (4)* 18.70 27.15
Set, never hinged 37.50

Intl. Scout Conf. Sheets of 20.

Alemannic Disc, 600 A. D. — A176

Prehistoric Settlement of Borscht — A177

Design: 1.20fr, Rössen jug.

**1953, Nov. 26  Perf. 11½**
274 A176 10rp orange brown 4.00 *11.50*
275 A177 20rp deep gray green 4.75 *11.50*
276 A176 1.20fr dark blue gray 17.50 *32.50*
*Nos. 274-276 (3)* 26.25 55.50
Set, never hinged 65.00

Opening of National Museum, Vaduz.

Soccer Players — A178

Designs: 20rp, Player kicking ball. 25rp, Goalkeeper. 40rp, Two opposing players.

**1954, May 18  Photo.**
277 A178 10rp dull rose & brn 1.25 .90
278 A178 20rp olive green 3.75 1.40
279 A178 25rp orange brown 7.50 30.00
280 A178 40rp lilac gray 7.50 9.00
*Nos. 277-280 (4)* 20.00 *41.30*
Set, never hinged 42.50

See Nos. 289-292, 297-300, 308-311, 320-323.

### Nos. B19-B21 Surcharged with New Value and Bars in Color of Stamp
**1954, Sept. 28  Unwmk.  Perf. 11½**
281 SP15 35rp on 10rp+10rp 2.50 2.25
282 SP16 60rp on 20rp+10rp 11.00 10.50
283 SP15 65rp on 40rp+10rp 3.50 7.25
*Nos. 281-283 (3)* 17.00 20.00
Set, never hinged 30.00

Madonna in Wood, 14th Century — A179

**1954, Dec. 16  Engr.**
284 A179 20rp henna brown 1.50 1.90
285 A179 40rp gray 8.50 17.50
286 A179 1fr dark brown 8.50 17.00
*Nos. 284-286 (3)* 18.50 36.40
Set, never hinged 37.50

Prince Franz Joseph II A180

Princess Georgina A181

**1955, Apr. 5  Perf. 14½  Cream Paper**
287 A180 2fr dark brown 32.50 37.50
288 A181 3fr dark green 32.50 37.50
Set, never hinged 140.00

Issued in sheets of 9.

### Sports Type of 1954
Designs: 10rp, Slalom. 20rp, Mountain climbing. 25rp, Skiing. 40rp, Resting on summit.

**1955, June 14  Photo.  Perf. 11½**
289 A178 10rp aqua & brn vio .45 .80
290 A178 20rp green & ol bis 2.50 .80
291 A178 25rp lt ultra & sep 7.50 16.00
292 A178 40rp olive & pink 7.50 6.00
*Nos. 289-292 (4)* 17.95 23.60
Set, never hinged 37.50

Prince Johann Adam — A183

Portraits: 20rp, Prince Philipp. 40rp, Prince Nikolaus. 60rp, Princess Nora.

**Granite Paper**

**1955, Dec. 14  Cross in Red**
293 A183 10rp dull violet .75 .70
294 A183 20rp slate green 3.00 1.60
295 A183 40rp olive brown 3.00 7.25
296 A183 60rp rose brown 3.25 4.00
*Nos. 293-296 (4)* 10.00 13.55
Set, never hinged 20.00

Liechtenstein Red Cross, 10th anniversary.

### Sports Type of 1954
Designs: 10rp, Javelin thrower. 20rp, Hurdling. 40rp, Pole vaulting. 1fr, Sprinters.

### Perf. 11½
**1956, June 21  Unwmk.  Photo.  Granite Paper**
297 A178 10rp lt red brn & ol grn .45 .60
298 A178 20rp lt ol grn & pur 1.90 .60
299 A178 40rp pale & vio brn 2.75 3.25
300 A178 1fr org ver & ol brn 6.50 12.00
*Nos. 297-300 (4)* 11.60 16.45
Set, never hinged 22.50

Eagle, Crown and Oak Leaves — A184

**1956, Aug. 21  Granite Paper**
301 A184 10rp dk brown & gold 1.10 1.00
302 A184 120rp slate blk & gold 4.25 4.25
Set, never hinged 12.50

150th anniversary of independence.

Prince Franz Joseph II — A185

**1956, Aug. 21**
303 A185 10rp dark green .95 .45
304 A185 15rp bright ultra 1.40 2.75
305 A185 25rp purple 1.40 2.75
306 A185 60rp dark brown 4.75 2.25
*Nos. 303-306 (4)* 8.50 8.20
Set, never hinged 17.50

50th birthday of Prince Franz Joseph II.

Prince Johann Adam — A186

**1956, Aug. 21  Granite Paper**
307 A186 20rp olive green 1.75 .70
Never hinged 3.50

Issued to publicize the 6th Philatelic Exhibition, Vaduz, Aug. 25-Sept. 2. Sheets of 9.

### Sports Type of 1954
Designs: 10rp, Somersault on bar. 15rp, Exercise on pommel horse. 25rp, Exercise on rings. 1.50fr, Somersault on parallel bars.

**1957, May 14  Photo.  Perf. 11½**
308 A178 10rp pale rose & ol grn .95 .95
309 A178 15rp pale grn & dl pur 2.75 *7.00*
310 A178 25rp ol bis & Prus grn 3.75 *8.25*
311 A178 1.50fr lemon & sepia 11.00 *19.00*
*Nos. 308-311 (4)* 18.45 35.20
Set, never hinged 32.50

**1957, Sept. 10  Perf. 11½  Granite Paper**
312 A187 10rp dark violet 1.90 2.25
313 A187 20rp brown carmine 1.90 .95
314 A187 1fr green 3.25 8.00
*Nos. 312-314 (3)* 7.05 11.20
Set, never hinged 16.00

See Nos. 326-328, 332-334, 353-355.

Lord Baden-Powell — A188

Design: 10rp, Symbolical torchlight parade.

**1957, Sept. 10  Unwmk.**
315 A188 10rp blue black .75 1.50
316 A188 20rp dark brown .75 1.50
a. Sheet, 6 each #315-316 12.00 21.00
Never hinged 21.00
Set, never hinged 3.00

Cent. of the birth of Lord Baden-Powell and the 60th anniv. of the Boy Scout movement.

Chapel of St. Mamertus — A189

40rp, Madonna and saints. 1.50fr, Pieta.

**1957, Dec. 16  Perf. 11½**
317 A189 10rp dark brown .35 .35
318 A189 40rp dark blue 1.10 *5.50*
319 A189 1.50fr brown lake 6.50 9.50
*Nos. 317-319 (3)* 7.95 15.35
Set, never hinged 15.00

Issued in sheets of 20. Sheet inscribed: "Furstentum Liechtenstein" and "Weihnacht 1957" (Christmas 1957).

### Sports Type of 1954
Designs: 15rp, Girl swimmer. 30rp, Fencers. 40rp, Tennis. 90rp, Bicyclists.

**1958, Mar. 18  Photo.  Granite Paper**
320 A178 15rp lt blue & pur .65 1.00
321 A178 30rp pale rose lil & ol gray 1.50 6.00
322 A178 40rp sal pink & sl bl 2.50 6.00
323 A178 90rp lt ol grn & vio brn .80 4.00
*Nos. 320-323 (4)* 5.45 17.00
Set, never hinged 21.00

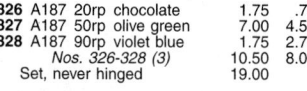

Relief Map of Liechtenstein A190

**1958, Mar. 18**
324 A190 25rp bister, vio & red .35 .75
325 A190 40rp blue, vio & red .75 .75
Set, never hinged 2.25

World's Fair, Brussels, Apr. 17-Oct. 19. Sheets of 25. For surcharges see Nos. B22-B23.

### Tree-Bush Type of 1957
Designs: 20rp, Maples at Lawena. 50rp, Holly at Schellenberg. 90rp, Yew at Maurerberg.

**1958, Aug. 12  Perf. 11½  Granite Paper**
326 A187 20rp chocolate 1.75 .75
327 A187 50rp olive green 7.00 4.50
328 A187 90rp violet blue 1.75 2.75
*Nos. 326-328 (3)* 10.50 8.00
Set, never hinged 19.00

Sts. Moritz and Agatha — A191

 note: Pine — A187, Prince Johann Adam — A183

Christmas: 35rp, St. Peter. 80rp, Chapel of St. Peter, Mals-Balzers.

**1958, Dec. 4    Photo.    Unwmk.**
**Granite Paper**
329 A191 20rp dk slate green    1.90  2.50
330 A191 35rp dk blue violet    1.90  2.50
331 A191 80rp dark brown    1.90  2.50
  Nos. 329-331 (3)    5.70  7.50
  Set, never hinged    9.50

  Issued in sheets of 20.

**Tree-Bush Type of 1957**

Designs: 20rp, Larch in Lawena. 50rp, Holly on Alpila. 90rp, Linden in Schaan.

**1959, Apr. 15    Perf. 11½**
332 A187 20rp dark violet    2.50  2.40
333 A187 50rp henna brown    2.50  2.40
334 A187 90rp dark green    2.50  2.40
  Nos. 332-334 (3)    7.50  7.20
  Set, never hinged    14.00

"The Good Shepherd" — A192

**1959, Apr. 15    Unwmk.**
335 A192 30rp rose violet & gold    .50  .85
  Never hinged    .90

Issued in memory of Pope Pius XII.

Flags and Rhine Valley — A193

Man Carrying Hay — A194

Apple Harvest — A195

Designs: 5rp, Church at Bendern and sheaves. 20rp, Rhine embankment. 30rp, Gutenberg Castle. 40rp, View from Schellenberg. 50rp, Vaduz Castle. 60rp, Naafkopf, Falknis Range. 75rp, Woman gathering sheaves. 90rp, Woman in vineyard. 1fr, Woman in kitchen. 1.30fr, Return from the field. 1.50fr, Family saying grace.

**1959-64    Granite Paper**
336 A193  5rp gray olive
       ('61)    .25  .25
337 A193 10rp dull violet    .25  .25
338 A193 20rp lilac rose    .25  .25
339 A193 30rp dark red    .25  .25
340 A193 40rp olive grn ('61)    1.10  .55
341 A193 50rp deep blue    .30  .35
342 A193 60rp brt grnsh bl    .45  .55
343 A194 75rp deep ocher
       ('60)    1.10  1.00
344 A194 80rp olive grn ('61)    .90  .90
345 A194 90rp red lilac ('61)    .90  .90
346 A194  1fr chestnut ('61)    .90  .90
347 A195 1.20fr orange ver
       ('60)    1.40  1.10
348 A195 1.30fr brt green ('64)    1.10  .90
349 A195 1.50fr brt blue ('60)    1.40  1.40
  Nos. 336-349 (14)    10.55  9.55
  Set, never hinged    12.50

Belfry, Bendern Church — A196

Christmas: 60rp, Sculpture, bell, St. Theodul's church. 1fr, Sculpture, tower of St. Lucius' church.

**1959, Dec. 2    Unwmk.    Perf. 11½**
350 A196  5rp dk slate green    .55  .25
351 A196 60rp olive    3.50  4.25
352 A196  1fr deep claret    2.75  2.50
  Nos. 350-352 (3)    6.80  7.00
  Set, never hinged    11.00

  Issued in sheets of 20.

**Tree-Bush Type of 1957**

Designs: 20rp, Beech tree on Gafadura. 30rp, Juniper on Alpila. 50rp, Pine on Sass.

**1960, Sept. 19**
353 A187 20rp brown    3.75  5.25
354 A187 30rp deep plum    3.75  5.25
355 A187 50rp Prus green    12.00  15.00
  Nos. 353-355 (3)    19.50  25.50
  Set, never hinged    32.50

**Europa Issue**

Honeycomb A197

**1960, Sept. 19    Perf. 14**
356 A197 50rp multicolored    30.00  30.00
     Never hinged    55.00

Issued to promote the idea of a united Europe. Sheets of 20.

Princess Gina — A198

Portraits: 1.70fr, Prince Johann Adam Pius. 3fr, Prince Franz Joseph II.

**1960-64    Engr.    Perf. 14**
356A A198 1.70fr violet ('64)    1.00  1.50
  b.    Imperf., pair    1,750.  1,750.
357  A198  2fr dark blue    2.25  2.00
  a.    Imperf., pair    1,750.  1,750.
358  A198  3fr deep brown    2.25  2.00
  Nos. 356A-358 (3)    5.50  5.50
  Set, never hinged    7.00

  Issued in sheets of 16.

Heinrich von Frauenberg — A199

Minnesingers: 20rp, King Konradin. 25rp, Ulrich von Liechtenstein. 30rp, Kraft von Toggenburg. 35rp, Ulrich von Gutenberg. 40rp, Heinrich von Veldig. 1fr, Konrad von Alstetten. 1.50fr, Walther von der Vogelweide. 2fr, Tannhäuser. (Designs from 14th century Manesse manuscript.)

**1961-62    Photo.    Perf. 11½**
359 A199 15rp multi    .60  .75
360 A199 20rp multi ('62)    .30  .30
361 A199 25rp multi    1.25  1.65
362 A199 30rp multi ('62)    .40  .40
363 A199 35rp multi    1.50  2.00
364 A199 40rp multi ('62)    .65  .65
365 A199  1fr multi    2.50  2.00
366 A199 1.50fr multi    9.25  15.00
367 A199  2fr multi ('62)    1.65  1.65
  Nos. 359-367 (9)    18.10  24.40
  Set, never hinged    22.50

Issued in sheets of 20. See Nos. 381-384, 471.

┌─────────────────────────────────────┐
│ **Catalogue values for unused**      │
│ **stamps in this section, from this**│
│ **point to the end of the section, are**│
│ **for Never Hinged items.**          │
└─────────────────────────────────────┘

**Europa Issue, 1961**

Cogwheels — A200

**1961, Oct. 3    Unwmk.    Perf. 13½**
368 A200 50rp multicolored    .35  .25

Printed in sheets of 20.

**Souvenir Sheet**

Prince Johann II — A201

Portraits: 10rp, Francis I. 25rp, Franz Joseph II.

**1962, Aug. 2    Photo.    Perf. 11½**
369 A201  Sheet of 3    7.00  5.00
  a.    5rp gray green    2.00  1.25
  b.   10rp deep rose    2.00  1.25
  c.   25rp blue    2.00  1.25

50th anniv. of Liechtenstein's postage stamps and in connection with the Anniv. Stamp Exhib., Vaduz, Aug. 4-12. No. 369 sold for 3fr.

Hands — A202

**1962, Aug. 2**
370 A202 50rp indigo & red    .45  .45

Europa. Issued in sheets of 20.

Malaria Eradication Emblem — A203

**1962, Aug. 2    Engr.**
371 A203 50rp turquoise blue    .60  .45

WHO drive to eradicate malaria. Sheets of 20.

Pietà — A204

Designs: 50rp, Angel with harp, fresco. 1.20fr, View of Mauren.

**1962, Dec. 6    Photo.**
372 A204 30rp magenta    .60  .60
373 A204 50rp deep orange    .85  .85
374 A204 1.20fr deep blue    1.10  1.10
  Nos. 372-374 (3)    2.55  2.55

Issued in sheets of 20.

Prince Franz Joseph II — A205

**1963, Apr. 3    Engr.    Perf. 13½x14**
375 A205 5fr dull green    4.00  3.00

Accession of Prince Franz Joseph II, 25th anniv.
Sheets of 8. Exists imperf. Value $1,500.

Angel of the Annunciation — A206

**Perf. 11½**
**1963, Aug. 26    Unwmk.    Photo.**
376 A206 20rp shown    .60  .40
377 A206 80rp Three Kings    .60  .40
378 A206  1fr Family    1.00  .80
  Nos. 376-378 (3)    2.20  1.60

Centenary of the International Red Cross.

**Europa Issue**

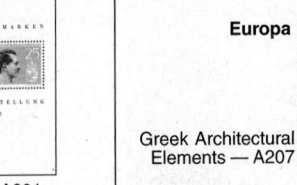

Greek Architectural Elements — A207

**1963, Aug. 26**
379 A207 50rp multicolored    1.00  1.00

Bread and Milk — A208

**1963, Aug. 26**
380 A208 50rp dk red pur & brn    .70  .50

FAO "Freedom from Hunger" campaign.

**Minnesinger Type of 1961-62**

Minnesingers: 25rp, Heinrich von Sax. 30rp, Kristan von Hamle. 75rp, Werner von Teufen. 1.70fr, Hartmann von Aue.

**Perf. 11½**
**1963, Dec. 5    Unwmk.    Photo.**
381 A199 25rp multicolored    .45  .45
382 A199 30rp multicolored    .45  .45
383 A199 75rp multicolored    .75  .75
384 A199 1.70fr multicolored    1.50  1.50
  Nos. 381-384 (4)    3.15  3.15

  Issued in sheets of 20.

Olympic Rings, Flags of Austria and Japan — A209

**1964, Apr. 15    Perf. 11½**
385 A209 50rp Prus bl, red & blk    .60  .60

Olympic Games 1964. Sheets of 20.

Arms of Counts of Werdenberg-Vaduz A210

Coats of Arms: 30rp, Barons of Brandis. 80rp, Counts of Sulz. 1.50fr, Counts of Hohenems.

**1964, Sept. 1    Photo.**
386 A210 20rp multicolored    .40  .40
387 A210 30rp multicolored    .40  .40
388 A210 80rp multicolored    .40  .40
389 A210 1.50fr multicolored    .80  .80
  Nos. 386-389 (4)    2.00  2.00

  See Nos. 396-399.

**Europa Issue**

Roman Castle, Schaan — A211

**1964, Sept. 1    Perf. 13x14**
390 A211 50rp multicolored    .75  .75

Masescha Chapel — A212

40rp, Mary Magdalene, altarpiece. 1.30fr, Madonna with Sts. Sebastian & Roch, altarpiece.

**1964, Dec. 9      Photo.      Perf. 11½**
| | | | | |
|---|---|---|---|---|
| 391 | A212 | 10rp violet black | .40 | .40 |
| 392 | A212 | 40rp dark blue | .40 | .40 |
| 393 | A212 | 1.30rp deep claret | 1.00 | 1.00 |
| | | *Nos. 391-393 (3)* | 1.80 | 1.80 |

Issued in sheets of 20.

Peter Kaiser — A213

**1964, Dec. 9      Engr.**
| | | | | |
|---|---|---|---|---|
| 394 | A213 | 1fr dk grn, *buff* | .95 | .95 |

Kaiser (1793-1864), historian. Sheets of 20.

Madonna, Wood Sculpture, 18th Century — A214

**Perf. 11½**
**1965, Apr. 22      Unwmk.      Engr.**
| | | | | |
|---|---|---|---|---|
| 395 | A214 | 10fr orange red | 7.00 | 4.00 |

Issued in sheets of 4.

**Arms Type of 1965**

Lords of: 20rp, Schellenberg. 30rp, Gutenberg. 80rp, Frauenberg. 1fr, Ramschwag.

**Perf. 11½**
**1965, Aug. 31      Unwmk.      Photo.**
| | | | | |
|---|---|---|---|---|
| 396 | A210 | 20rp multicolored | .45 | .45 |
| 397 | A210 | 30rp multicolored | .45 | .45 |
| 398 | A210 | 80rp multicolored | .65 | .65 |
| 399 | A210 | 1fr multicolored | .65 | .65 |
| | | *Nos. 396-399 (4)* | 2.20 | 2.20 |

Alemannic Ornament — A215

Europa: The design is from a belt buckle, about 600 A.D., found in a man's tomb near Eschen.

**1965, Aug. 31**
| | | | | |
|---|---|---|---|---|
| 400 | A215 | 50rp vio bl, gray & brn | *.45* | *.35* |

The Annunciation by Ferdinand Nigg — A216

Paintings by Nigg: 30rp, The Three Kings. 1.20fr, Jesus in the Temple, horiz.

**1965, Dec. 7      Photo.      Perf. 11½**
| | | | | |
|---|---|---|---|---|
| 401 | A216 | 10rp yel grn & dk grn | .40 | .40 |
| 402 | A216 | 30rp orange & red brn | .40 | .40 |
| 403 | A216 | 1.20fr ultra & grnsh bl | .60 | .60 |
| | | *Nos. 401-403 (3)* | 1.40 | 1.40 |

Ferdinand Nigg (1865-1949), painter.

Princess Gina and Prince Franz Josef Wenzel — A217

**1965, Dec. 7**
| | | | | |
|---|---|---|---|---|
| 404 | A217 | 75rp gray, buff & gold | .60 | .50 |

Communication Symbols — A218

**1965, Dec. 7**
| | | | | |
|---|---|---|---|---|
| 405 | A218 | 25rp multicolored | .60 | .45 |

Centenary of the ITU.

Soil Conservation, Tree — A219

20rp, Clean air, bird. 30rp, Unpolluted water, fish. 1.50fr, Nature preservation, sun.

**1966, Apr. 26      Photo.      Perf. 11½**
| | | | | |
|---|---|---|---|---|
| 406 | A219 | 10rp brt yellow & grn | .40 | .40 |
| 407 | A219 | 20rp blue & dk blue | .40 | .40 |
| 408 | A219 | 30rp brt green & ultra | .40 | .40 |
| 409 | A219 | 1.50fr yellow & red | .70 | .70 |
| | | *Nos. 406-409 (4)* | 1.90 | 1.90 |

Issued to publicize nature conservation.

Prince Franz Joseph II — A220

**1966, Apr. 26**
| | | | | |
|---|---|---|---|---|
| 410 | A220 | 1fr gray, gold, buff & dk brn | .75 | .75 |

60th birthday of Prince Franz Joseph II.

Arms of Barons of Richenstein — A221

Coats of Arms: 30rp, Vaistli knights. 60rp, Lords of Trisun. 1.20fr, von Schiel.

**Light Gray Background**

**1966, Sept. 6      Photo.      Perf. 11½**
| | | | | |
|---|---|---|---|---|
| 411 | A221 | 20rp multicolored | .30 | .30 |
| 412 | A221 | 30rp multicolored | .30 | .30 |
| 413 | A221 | 60rp multicolored | .30 | .30 |
| 414 | A221 | 1.20fr multicolored | .60 | .60 |
| | | *Nos. 411-414 (4)* | 1.50 | 1.50 |

Common Design Types pictured following the introduction.

**Europa Issue, 1966**
Common Design Type
**1966, Sept. 6      Photo.      Perf. 14x13**
Size: 25x32mm
| | | | | |
|---|---|---|---|---|
| 415 | CD9 | 50rp ultra, dp org & lt grn | *.40* | *.35* |

Vaduz Parish Church A222        St. Florin A223

30rp, Madonna. 1.70fr, God the Father.

**1966, Dec. 6      Photo.      Perf. 11½**
| | | | | |
|---|---|---|---|---|
| 416 | A222 | 5rp orange red & cit | .30 | .25 |
| 417 | A223 | 20rp lemon & magenta | .30 | .25 |
| 418 | A223 | 30rp dull rose & dp bl | .30 | .25 |
| 419 | A223 | 1.70fr gray & red brown | .85 | .65 |
| | | *Nos. 416-419 (4)* | 1.75 | 1.40 |

Restoration of the Vaduz Parish Church.

**Europa Issue, 1967**
Common Design Type
**1967, Apr. 20      Photo.      Perf. 11½**
| | | | | |
|---|---|---|---|---|
| 420 | CD10 | 50rp multicolored | .45 | .40 |

The Man from Malans and his White Horse — A225

Fairy Tales of Liechtenstein: 30rp, The Treasure of Gutenberg. 1.20fr, The Giant of Guflina slaying the Dragon.

**1967, Apr. 20**
| | | | | |
|---|---|---|---|---|
| 421 | A225 | 20rp multicolored | .30 | .25 |
| 422 | A225 | 30rp multicolored | .30 | .25 |
| 423 | A225 | 1.20fr green & multi | .85 | .65 |
| | | *Nos. 421-423 (3)* | 1.45 | 1.15 |

See Nos. 443-445, 458-460.

Souvenir Sheet

Prince Hans Adam and Countess Kinsky — A226

**1967, June 26      Engr.      Perf. 14x13½**
| | | | | |
|---|---|---|---|---|
| 424 | A226 | Sheet of 2 | 2.40 | 2.00 |
| *a.* | | 1.50fr slate blue (Prince) | 1.00 | 1.00 |
| *b.* | | 1.50fr red brown (Countess) | 1.00 | 1.00 |

Wedding of Prince Hans Adam of Liechtenstein and Marie Aglae Countess Kinsky of Wichnitz and Tettau, July 30, 1967.

EFTA Emblem — A227

**1967, Sept. 28      Photo.      Perf. 11½**
| | | | | |
|---|---|---|---|---|
| 425 | A227 | 50rp multicolored | .55 | .45 |

European Free Trade Association. See note after Norway No. 501.

A228

Christian Symbols: 20rp, Alpha and Omega. 30rp, Trophaeum (The Victorious Cross). 70rp, Chrismon.

**1967, Sept. 28**
| | | | | |
|---|---|---|---|---|
| 426 | A228 | 20rp rose cl, blk, & gold | .25 | .25 |
| 427 | A228 | 30rp multicolored | .25 | .25 |
| 428 | A228 | 70rp dp ultra, blk & gold | .60 | .45 |
| | | *Nos. 426-428 (3)* | 1.10 | .95 |

A229

**1967, Sept. 28      Engr. & Litho.**
| | | | | |
|---|---|---|---|---|
| 429 | A229 | 1fr rose claret & pale grn | .75 | .55 |

Johann Baptist Büchel (1853-1927), priest, educator, historian and poet. Printed on fluorescent paper.

Peter and Paul, Patron Saints of Mauren — A230

Patron Saints: 5rp, St. Joseph, Planken. 10rp, St. Laurentius, Schaan. 30rp, St. Nicholas, Balzers. 40rp, St. Sebastian, Nendeln. 50rp, St. George, Schellenberg Chapel. 60rp, St. Martin, Eschen. 70rp, St. Fridolin, Ruggell. 80rp, St. Gallus, Triesen. 1fr, St. Theodul, Triesenberg. 1.20fr, St. Ann, Vaduz Castle. 1.50fr, St. Mary, Bendern-Gamprin. 2fr, St. Lucius, patron saint of the Principality.

**1967-71      Photo.      Perf. 11½**
| | | | | |
|---|---|---|---|---|
| 430 | A230 | 5rp multi ('68) | .25 | .25 |
| 431 | A230 | 10rp multi ('68) | .25 | .25 |
| 432 | A230 | 20rp blue & multi | .25 | .25 |
| 433 | A230 | 30rp dark red & multi | .25 | .25 |
| 433A | A230 | 40rp multi ('71) | .45 | .35 |
| 434 | A230 | 50rp multi ('68) | .40 | .30 |
| 435 | A230 | 60rp multi ('68) | .45 | .35 |
| 436 | A230 | 70rp multi | .50 | .40 |
| 437 | A230 | 80rp multi ('68) | .55 | .50 |
| 438 | A230 | 1fr multi ('68) | .75 | .55 |
| 439 | A230 | 1.20fr violet bl & multi | .80 | .90 |
| 440 | A230 | 1.50fr multi ('68) | 1.10 | .95 |
| 441 | A230 | 2fr multi ('68) | 1.25 | 1.25 |
| | | *Nos. 430-441 (13)* | 7.25 | 6.55 |

Issued: 20rp, 30rp, 70rp, 1.20fr, 12/7/67; 5rp, 1.50fr, 8/29/68; 40rp, 6/11/71; 2fr, 12/5/68; others 4/25/68.

**Europa Issue, 1968**
Common Design Type
**1968, Apr. 25**
Size: 32½x23mm
| | | | | |
|---|---|---|---|---|
| 442 | CD11 | 50rp crimson, gold & ultra | .45 | .40 |

**Fairy Tale Type of 1967**

30rp, The Treasure of St. Mamerten. 50rp, The Goblin from the Bergerwald. 80rp, The Three Sisters. (Denominations at right.)

**1968, Aug. 29**
| | | | | |
|---|---|---|---|---|
| 443 | A225 | 30rp Prus blue, yel & red | .25 | .25 |
| 444 | A225 | 50rp green, yel & bl | .40 | .30 |
| 445 | A225 | 80rp brt bl, yel & lt bl | .65 | .55 |
| | | *Nos. 443-445 (3)* | 1.30 | 1.10 |

Arms of Liechtenstein and Wilczek — A231

**1968, Aug. 29**
| | | | | |
|---|---|---|---|---|
| 446 | A231 | 75rp multicolored | .65 | .65 |

Silver wedding anniversary of Prince Franz Joseph II and Princess Gina.

Sir Rowland Hill — A232

Portraits: 30rp, Count Philippe de Ferrari. 80rp, Carl Lindenberg. 1fr, Maurice Burrus. 1.20fr, Théodore Champion.

## 1968-69   Engr.   Perf. 14x13½
| | | | | |
|---|---|---|---|---|
| 447 | A232 | 20rp green | .25 | .25 |
| 448 | A232 | 30rp red brown | .25 | .25 |
| 449 | A232 | 80rp dark brown | .55 | .45 |
| 450 | A232 | 1fr black | .70 | .65 |
| 451 | A232 | 1.20fr dark blue | .90 | .70 |

Nos. 447-451 (5)    2.65 2.30

Issued to honor "Pioneers of Philately."
Issued: 80rp, 1.20fr, 8/28/69; others, 12/5/68.
See Nos. 509-511.

Coat of Arms — A233

### 1969, Apr. 24   Engr.   Perf. 14x13½
452 A233 3.50fr dark brown    2.50 1.60

Sheets of 16.

### Europa Issue, 1969
Common Design Type

**1969, Apr. 24   Photo.   Perf. 14**
**Size: 33x23mm**
453 CD12 50rp brn red, yel & grn    .45 .45

"Biology" (Man and DNA Molecule) — A234

30rp, "Physics" (man and magnetic field). 50rp, "Astronomy" (man and planets). 80rp, "Art" (artist and Prince Franz Joseph II and Princess Gina).

**1969, Aug. 28   Photo.   Perf. 11½**
| | | | | |
|---|---|---|---|---|
| 454 | A234 | 10rp grn, dk bl & dp cl | .25 | .25 |
| 455 | A234 | 30rp brown & multi | .25 | .25 |
| 456 | A234 | 50rp ultra & green | .50 | .30 |
| 457 | A234 | 80rp brn, dk brn & yel | .75 | .50 |

Nos. 454-457 (4)    1.75 1.30

250th anniv. of the Duchy of Liechtenstein.

### Fairy Tale Type of 1967
20rp, The Cheated Devil. 50rp, The Fiery Red Goat. 60rp, The Grafenberg Treasure (toad). (Denominations at right.)

**1969, Dec. 4   Photo.   Perf. 11½**
| | | | | |
|---|---|---|---|---|
| 458 | A225 | 20rp multicolored | .25 | .25 |
| 459 | A225 | 50rp yellow & multi | .40 | .35 |
| 460 | A225 | 60rp red & multi | .55 | .45 |

Nos. 458-460 (3)    1.20 1.05

"T" and Arms of Austria-Hungary, Liechtenstein and Switzerland — A235

**1969, Dec. 4   Perf. 13½**
461 A235 30rp gold & multi    .45 .30

Cent. of the Liechtenstein telegraph system.

Arms of St. Lucius Monastery, Chur — A236

Arms of Ecclesiastic Patrons: 50rp, Pfäfers Abbey (dove). 1.50fr, Chur Bishopric (stag).

**1969, Dec. 4   Perf. 11½**
| | | | | |
|---|---|---|---|---|
| 462 | A236 | 30rp multicolored | .45 | .25 |
| 463 | A236 | 50rp multicolored | .45 | .35 |
| 464 | A236 | 1.50fr multicolored | 1.25 | 1.00 |

Nos. 462-464 (3)    2.15 1.60

See Nos. 475-477, 486-488.

Prince Wenzel — A237

**1970, Apr. 30   Photo.   Perf. 11½**
465 A237 1fr sepia & multi    .80 .80

25th anniv. of the Liechtenstein Red Cross.

Orange Lily — A238

Native Flowers: 30rp, Bumblebee orchid. 50rp, Glacier crowfoot. 1.20fr, Buck bean.

**1970, Apr. 30**
| | | | | |
|---|---|---|---|---|
| 466 | A238 | 20rp multicolored | .25 | .25 |
| 467 | A238 | 30rp green & multi | .25 | .25 |
| 468 | A238 | 50rp olive & multi | .55 | .55 |
| 469 | A238 | 1.20fr multicolored | 1.10 | .75 |

Nos. 466-469 (4)    2.15 1.80

Issued to publicize the European Conservation Year 1970. See Nos. 481-484, 500-503.

### Europa Issue, 1970
Common Design Type

**1970, Apr. 30   Litho.   Perf. 14**
**Size: 31½x20½mm**
470 CD13 50rp emerald, dk bl & yel    .45 .45

### Minnesinger Type of 1961-62
Souvenir Sheet

Minnesingers: 30rp, Wolfram von Eschenbach. 50rp, Reinmar der Fiedler. 80rp, Hartmann von Starkenberg. 1.20fr, Friedrich von Hausen.

**1970, Aug. 27   Photo.   Perf. 11½**
| | | | | |
|---|---|---|---|---|
| 471 | | Sheet of 4 | 2.50 | 2.25 |
| a. | A199 | 30rp multicolored | .25 | .25 |
| b. | A199 | 50rp multicolored | .30 | .30 |
| c. | A199 | 80rp multicolored | .50 | .50 |
| d. | A199 | 1.20fr multicolored | .65 | .65 |

Wolfram von Eschenbach (1170-1220), German minnesinger (poet). Sold for 3fr.

Prince Franz Joseph II — A239

Portrait: 2.50fr, Princess Gina.

**1970-71   Engr.   Perf. 14x13½**
| | | | | |
|---|---|---|---|---|
| 472 | A239 | 2.50fr violet blue ('71) | 1.90 | 1.40 |
| 473 | A239 | 3fr black | 2.25 | 1.25 |

Issued: 2.50fr, 6/11; 3fr, 12/3. Sheets of 16.

Mother & Child, Sculpture by Rudolf Schädler — A240

**1970, Dec. 3   Photo.   Perf. 11½**
474 A240 30rp dark red & multi    .45 .35

Christmas.

### Ecclesiastic Arms Type of 1969
Arms of Ecclesiastic Patrons: 20rp, Abbey of St. John in Thur Valley (Lamb of God). 30rp, Ladies' Abbey, Schänis (crown). 75rp, Abbey of St. Gallen (bear rampant).

**1970, Dec. 3**
| | | | | |
|---|---|---|---|---|
| 475 | A236 | 20rp lt blue & multi | .25 | .25 |
| 476 | A236 | 30rp gray, red & gold | .25 | .25 |
| 477 | A236 | 75rp multicolored | .60 | .50 |

Nos. 475-477 (3)    1.10 1.00

Bronze Boar, La Tène Period — A241

30rp, Peacock, Roman, 2nd cent. 75rp, Decorated copper bowl, 13th cent.

**1971, Mar. 11   Photo.   Perf. 11½**
| | | | | |
|---|---|---|---|---|
| 478 | A241 | 25rp dp ultra & bluish blk | .25 | .25 |
| 479 | A241 | 30rp dk brown & green | .25 | .25 |
| 480 | A241 | 75rp green, yel & brn | .60 | .45 |

Nos. 478-480 (3)    1.10 .95

Opening of the National Museum, Vaduz.

### Flower Type of 1970
Flowers: 10rp, Cyclamen. 20rp, Moonwort. 50rp, Superb pink. 1.50fr, Alpine columbine.

**1971, Mar. 11**
| | | | | |
|---|---|---|---|---|
| 481 | A238 | 10rp multicolored | .25 | .25 |
| 482 | A238 | 20rp multicolored | .25 | .25 |
| 483 | A238 | 50rp multicolored | .45 | .35 |
| 484 | A238 | 1.50fr multicolored | 1.25 | .85 |

Nos. 481-484 (4)    2.20 1.70

### Europa Issue, 1971
Common Design Type

**1971, June 11   Photo.   Perf. 13½**
**Size: 31x21mm**
485 CD14 50rp grnsh bl, yel & blk    .45 .45

### Ecclesiastic Arms Type of 1969
Arms of Ecclesiastic Patrons: 30rp, Knights of St. John, Feldkirch (Latin and moline crosses). 50rp, Weingarten Abbey (grapes). 1.20fr, Ottobeuren Abbey (eagle and cross).

**1971, Sept. 2   Photo.   Perf. 11½**
| | | | | |
|---|---|---|---|---|
| 486 | A236 | 30rp bister & multi | .25 | .25 |
| 487 | A236 | 50rp multicolored | .40 | .30 |
| 488 | A236 | 1.20fr gray & multi | 1.00 | .75 |

Nos. 486-488 (3)    1.65 1.30

Princely Crown — A242

Design: 70rp, Page from constitution.

**1971, Sept. 2   Photo.   Perf. 11½**
| | | | | |
|---|---|---|---|---|
| 489 | A242 | 70rp grn, gold, blk & cop | .55 | .55 |
| 490 | A242 | 80rp dk bl, gold, red & plum | .65 | .65 |

50th anniversary of the constitution.

Madonna, by Andrea della Robbia — A243

**1971, Dec. 9**
491 A243 30rp multicolored    .45 .35

Christmas 1971.

Long-distance Skiing — A244

Olympic Rings and: 40rp, Ice hockey. 65rp, Downhill skiing, women's. 1.50fr, Figure skating, women's.

**1971, Dec. 9**
| | | | | |
|---|---|---|---|---|
| 492 | A244 | 15rp lemon & dk brn | .25 | .25 |
| 493 | A244 | 40rp multicolored | .35 | .30 |
| 494 | A244 | 65rp multicolored | .55 | .45 |
| 495 | A244 | 1.50fr multicolored | 1.25 | .90 |

Nos. 492-495 (4)    2.40 1.90

11th Winter Olympic Games, Sapporo, Japan, Feb. 3-13, 1972.

**1972, Mar. 16   Photo.   Perf. 11**
10rp, Gymnast. 20rp, High jump. 40rp, Running, women's. 60rp, Discus. All horiz.
| | | | | |
|---|---|---|---|---|
| 496 | A244 | 10rp claret, brn & gray | .25 | .25 |
| 497 | A244 | 20rp olive, brn & yel | .25 | .25 |
| 498 | A244 | 40rp red, brn & gray | .30 | .30 |
| 499 | A244 | 60rp brn, dk brn & bl | .65 | .50 |

Nos. 496-499 (4)    1.45 1.30

20th Olympic Games, Munich, Aug. 26-Sept. 10.

### Flower Type of 1970
Flowers: 20rp, Anemone. 30rp, Turk's cap. 60rp, Alpine centaury. 1.20fr, Reed mace.

**1972, Mar. 16**
| | | | | |
|---|---|---|---|---|
| 500 | A238 | 20rp dk blue & multi | .25 | .25 |
| 501 | A238 | 30rp olive & multi | .25 | .25 |
| 502 | A238 | 60rp multicolored | .45 | .40 |
| 503 | A238 | 1.20fr multicolored | .85 | .75 |

Nos. 500-503 (4)    1.80 1.65

### Europa Issue, 1972
Common Design Type

**1972, Mar. 16**
504 CD15 40rp dk ol, bl grn & rose red    .45 .45

### Souvenir Sheet

Bendern and Vaduz Castle A246

**1972, June 8   Engr.   Perf. 13½**
| | | | | |
|---|---|---|---|---|
| 505 | A246 | Sheet of 2 | 2.40 | 1.75 |
| a. | | 1fr violet blue | .75 | .65 |
| b. | | 2fr carmine | 1.50 | 1.10 |

8th Liechtenstein Philatelic Exhibition, LIBA 1972, Vaduz, Aug. 18-27.

Faun, by Rudolf Schädler — A247

**1972, Sept. 7   Photo.   Perf. 11½**
| | | | | |
|---|---|---|---|---|
| 506 | A247 | 20rp shown | .25 | .25 |
| 507 | A247 | 30rp Dancer | .25 | .25 |
| 508 | A247 | 1.10fr Owl | .85 | .60 |

Nos. 506-508 (3)    1.35 1.10

Sculptures made of roots and branches by Rudolf Schädler.

### Portrait Type of 1968-69
Portraits: 30rp, Emilio Diena. 40rp, André de Cock. 1.30fr, Theodore E. Steinway.

**1972, Sept. 7   Engr.   Perf. 14x13½**
| | | | | |
|---|---|---|---|---|
| 509 | A232 | 30rp Prus green | .25 | .25 |
| 510 | A232 | 40rp dk violet brn | .30 | .25 |
| 511 | A232 | 1.30fr violet blue | 1.00 | .80 |

Nos. 509-511 (3)    1.55 1.30

Pioneers of Philately.

Madonna with Angels, by Ferdinand Nigg — A248

**1972, Dec. 7   Photo.   Perf. 11½**
512 A248 30rp black & multi    .50 .40

Christmas 1972.

Silum — A249

Landscapes: 10rp, Lawena Springs. 15rp, Ruggell Marsh. 25rp, Steg, Kirchlispitz. 30rp, Fields, Schellenberg. 40rp, Rennhof, Mauren. 50rp, Tidrüfe Vaduz. 60rp, Eschner Riet. 70rp,

Mittagspitz. 80rp, Three Sisters, Schaan Forest. 1fr, St. Peter's and Tower House, Mäls. 1.30fr, Road, Frommenhaus. 1.50fr, Ox Head Mountain. 1.80fr, Hehlawangspitz. 2fr, Saminaschlucht.

**1972-73    Engr. & Litho.    Perf. 11½**

| | | | | |
|---|---|---|---|---|
| 513 | A249 | 5rp brn, yel & mag | .25 | .25 |
| 514 | A249 | 10rp slate grn & cit | .25 | .25 |
| 515 | A249 | 15rp red brn & cit | .25 | .25 |
| 516 | A249 | 25rp dk vio & pale grn | .25 | .25 |
| 517 | A249 | 30rp purple & buff | .25 | .25 |
| 518 | A249 | 40rp vio & pale salmon | .30 | .25 |
| 519 | A249 | 50rp vio bl & rose | .40 | .35 |
| 520 | A249 | 60rp grn & yel | .50 | .45 |
| 521 | A249 | 70rp dk & lt blue | .60 | .50 |
| 522 | A249 | 80rp Prus grn & cit | .65 | .55 |
| 523 | A249 | 1fr red brn & lt grn | .85 | .65 |
| 524 | A249 | 1.30fr ultra & lt grn | 1.10 | 1.00 |
| 525 | A249 | 1.50fr brn & lt blue | 1.25 | 1.00 |
| 526 | A249 | 1.80fr brown & buff | 1.50 | 1.25 |
| 527 | A249 | 2fr sepia & pale grn | 1.65 | 1.40 |
| | *Nos. 513-527 (15)* | | 10.05 | 8.65 |

Issued: 10rp, 15rp, 80rp, 1fr, 1.50fr, 12/7; 30rp, 1.30fr, 1.80fr, 3/8/73; 50rp, 60rp, 70rp, 6/7/73; 5rp, 25rp, 40rp, 2fr, 12/6/73.

**Europa Issue, 1973**
**Common Design Type**

**1973, Mar. 8    Photo.    Perf. 11½**
**Size: 33x23mm**

| | | | | |
|---|---|---|---|---|
| 528 | CD16 | 30rp purple & multi | .25 | .25 |
| 529 | CD16 | 40rp blue & multi | .35 | .35 |

Nautilus Cup — A250

70rp, Ivory tankard. 1.10fr, Silver goblet.

**1973, June 7    Photo.    Perf. 11½**

| | | | | |
|---|---|---|---|---|
| 530 | A250 | 30rp gray & multi | .25 | .25 |
| 531 | A250 | 70rp multicolored | .50 | .40 |
| 532 | A250 | 1.10fr dk blue & multi | .90 | .60 |
| | *Nos. 530-532 (3)* | | 1.65 | 1.25 |

Drinking vessels from the Princely Treasury.

Arms of Liechtenstein and Municipalities A251

**Engraved & Photogravure**
**1973, Sept. 6    Perf. 14x13½**

| | | | |
|---|---|---|---|
| 533 | A251 | 5fr black & multi | 4.00 2.50 |

Coenonympha Oedippus — A252

Designs: 15rp, Alpine newt. 25rp, European viper (adder). 40rp, Common curlew. 60rp, Edible frog. 70rp, Dappled butterfly. 80rp, Grass snake. 1.10fr, Three-toed woodpecker.

**1973-74    Photo.    Perf. 11½**

| | | | | |
|---|---|---|---|---|
| 534 | A252 | 15rp bl grn & multi | .25 | .25 |
| 535 | A252 | 25rp yellow & multi | .30 | .25 |
| 536 | A252 | 30rp orange & multi | .25 | .25 |
| 537 | A252 | 40rp brown & multi | .35 | .35 |
| 538 | A252 | 60rp bl grn & multi | .60 | .60 |
| 539 | A252 | 70rp brt blue & multi | .65 | .60 |
| 540 | A252 | 80rp blue & multi | .70 | .70 |
| 541 | A252 | 1.10fr org red & multi | 1.00 | 1.00 |
| | *Nos. 534-541 (8)* | | 4.10 | 4.00 |

Issue dates: 30rp, 40rp, 60rp, 80rp, Dec. 6. 15rp, 25rp, 70rp, 1.10fr, June 6, 1974.

Virgin and Child, by Bartolomeo di Tommaso — A253

**Engraved & Lithographed**
**1973, Dec. 6    Perf. 13½**

| | | | |
|---|---|---|---|
| 542 | A253 | 30rp gold & multi | .50 .30 |

Christmas 1973.

The Vociferant Horseman, by Andrea Riccio — A254

Europa: 40rp, Kneeling Venus, by Antonio Susini.

**1974, Mar. 21    Photo.    Perf. 11½**

| | | | | |
|---|---|---|---|---|
| 543 | A254 | 30rp tan & multi | .35 | .30 |
| 544 | A254 | 40rp ultra & multi | .50 | .45 |

Chinese Vase, 19th Century — A255

Chinese vases from Princely Treasury.

**1974, Mar. 21**

| | | | | |
|---|---|---|---|---|
| 545 | A255 | 30rp shown | .30 | .25 |
| 546 | A255 | 50rp from 1740 | .45 | .35 |
| 547 | A255 | 60rp from 1830 | .55 | .40 |
| 548 | A255 | 1fr circa 1700 | .95 | .60 |
| | *Nos. 545-548 (4)* | | 2.25 | 1.60 |

Soccer — A256

**1974, Mar. 21**

| | | | |
|---|---|---|---|
| 549 | A256 | 80rp lemon & multi | .80 .75 |

World Soccer Championships, Munich June 13-July 7.

Post Horn and UPU Emblem — A257

**1974, June 6    Perf. 13½**

| | | | | |
|---|---|---|---|---|
| 550 | A257 | 40rp gold, green & blk | .35 | .30 |
| 551 | A257 | 60rp gold, red & blk | .55 | .40 |

Centenary of Universal Postal Union.

Bishop F. A. Marxer — A258

**Photogravure and Engraved**
**1974, June 6    Perf. 14x13½**

| | | | |
|---|---|---|---|
| 552 | A258 | 1fr multicolored | .95 .75 |

Bicentenary of the death of Bishop Franz Anton Marxer (1703-1775).

Prince Constantin — A259

Prince Hans Adam — A260

Princess Gina and Prince Franz Joseph II — A261

80rp, Prince Maximilian. 1.20fr, Prince Alois.

**1974-75    Photo.    Perf. 11½**

| | | | | |
|---|---|---|---|---|
| 553 | A259 | 70rp dk green & gold | .70 | .55 |
| 554 | A259 | 80rp dp claret & gold | .75 | .65 |
| 555 | A259 | 1.20fr bluish blk & gold | 1.10 | 1.00 |

**Engr.**
**Perf. 14x13½**

| | | | |
|---|---|---|---|
| 556 | A260 | 1.70fr slate green | 1.40 1.00 |

**Photogravure and Engraved**
**Perf. 13½x14**

| | | | | |
|---|---|---|---|---|
| 557 | A261 | 10fr gold & choc | 6.50 | 4.50 |
| | *Nos. 553-557 (5)* | | 10.45 | 7.70 |

No. 557 printed in sheets of 4.
Issued: 1.70fr, 12/5; 10fr, 9/5/74; others, 3/13/75.

St. Florian — A262

50rp, St. Wendelin. 60rp, Virgin Mary with Sts. Anna and Joachim. 70rp, Nativity.

**1974, Dec. 5    Photo.    Perf. 12**

| | | | | |
|---|---|---|---|---|
| 560 | A262 | 30rp multicolored | .30 | .25 |
| 561 | A262 | 50rp multicolored | .40 | .35 |
| 562 | A262 | 60rp multicolored | .50 | .40 |
| 563 | A262 | 70rp multicolored | .65 | .50 |
| | *Nos. 560-563 (4)* | | 1.85 | 1.50 |

Designs are from 19th century devotional glass paintings. Christmas 1974.

"Cold Sun," by Martin Frommelt — A263

Europa: 60rp, "Village," by Louis Jaeger.

**1975, Mar. 13    Perf. 11½**

| | | | | |
|---|---|---|---|---|
| 564 | A263 | 30rp multicolored | .25 | .25 |
| 565 | A263 | 60rp multicolored | .50 | .45 |

Red Cross Activities — A264

**1975, June 5    Photo.    Perf. 11½**

| | | | |
|---|---|---|---|
| 566 | A264 | 60rp dk blue & multi | .55 .55 |

30th anniv. of the Liechtenstein Red Cross.

Coronation Robe A265

Imperial Crown — A266

**1975    Engr. & Photo.    Perf. 14**

| | | | | |
|---|---|---|---|---|
| 567 | A266 | 30rp Imperial cross | .30 | .25 |
| 568 | A266 | 60rp Imperial sword | .45 | .40 |
| 569 | A266 | 1fr Orb | .90 | .75 |
| 570 | A265 | 1.30fr shown | 1.75 | 1.60 |
| 571 | A266 | 2fr shown | 3.50 | 2.75 |
| | *Nos. 567-571 (5)* | | 6.90 | 5.75 |

Treasures of the Holy Roman Empire from the Treasury of the Hofburg in Vienna, Austria. Issue dates: 1.30fr, Sept. 4; others, June 5. See Nos. 617-620.

St. Mamerten, Triesen — A267

Designs: 50rp, Red House, Vaduz, 14th century. 70rp, Prebendary House, Eschen, 14th century. 1fr, Gutenberg Castle.

**1975, Sept. 4    Photo.    Perf. 11½**

| | | | | |
|---|---|---|---|---|
| 572 | A267 | 40rp multicolored | .40 | .30 |
| 573 | A267 | 50rp multicolored | .45 | .30 |
| 574 | A267 | 70rp plum & multi | .85 | .60 |
| 575 | A267 | 1fr dk blue & multi | 1.10 | .75 |
| | *Nos. 572-575 (4)* | | 2.80 | 1.95 |

European Architectural Heritage Year 1975.

Speed Skating — A268

Designs (Olympic Rings and): 25rp, Ice hockey. 70rp, Downhill skiing. 1.20fr, Slalom.

**1975, Dec. 4    Photo.    Perf. 11½**

| | | | | |
|---|---|---|---|---|
| 576 | A268 | 20rp multicolored | .25 | .25 |
| 577 | A268 | 25rp multicolored | .25 | .25 |
| 578 | A268 | 70rp multicolored | .65 | .50 |
| 579 | A268 | 1.20fr yellow & multi | 1.25 | .95 |
| | *Nos. 576-579 (4)* | | 2.40 | 1.95 |

12th Winter Olympic Games, Innsbruck, Austria, Feb. 4-15, 1976.

Daniel in the Lions' Den — A269

Designs: 60rp, Virgin and Child. 90rp, St. Peter. All designs are after Romanesque sculptured capitals in Chur Cathedral, c. 1208.

**Photogravure and Engraved**
**1975, Dec. 4    Perf. 14**

| | | | | |
|---|---|---|---|---|
| 580 | A269 | 30rp gold & purple | .25 | .25 |
| 581 | A269 | 60rp gold & green | .45 | .40 |
| 582 | A269 | 90rp gold & claret | .80 | .75 |
| | *Nos. 580-582 (3)* | | 1.50 | 1.40 |

Christmas and Holy Year 1975.

River Crayfish — A270

World Wildlife Fund: 40rp, European pond turtle. 70rp, Old-world otter. 80rp, Lapwing.

**1976, Mar. 11    Photo.    Perf. 11½**

| | | | | |
|---|---|---|---|---|
| 583 | A270 | 25rp multicolored | .50 | .25 |
| 584 | A270 | 40rp multicolored | .75 | .35 |
| 585 | A270 | 70rp multicolored | 1.10 | .55 |
| 586 | A270 | 80rp multicolored | 1.75 | 1.00 |
| | *Nos. 583-586 (4)* | | 4.10 | 2.15 |

Mouflon — A271

Europa: 80rp, Pheasant family. Ceramics by Prince Hans von Liechtenstein.

**1976, Mar. 11**
587 A271 40rp multicolored .40 .35
588 A271 80rp violet & multi .80 .75

Roman Fibula, 3rd Century — A272

**1976, Mar. 11**
589 A272 90rp vio bl, grn & gold 1.00 .80

Historical Association of Liechtenstein, 75th anniversary.

**Souvenir Sheet**

Franz Josef II 50fr-Memorial Coin — A273

**1976, June 10  Photo.  Imperf.**
590 A273 Sheet of 2 1.75 1.75
  a. 1fr blue & multi .85 .85
  b. 1fr red & multi .85 .85

70th birthday of Prince Franz Joseph II of Liechtenstein.

Judo and Olympic Rings — A274

Designs (Olympic Rings and): 50rp, volleyball. 80rp, Relay race. 1.10fr, Long jump, women's.

**1976, June 10  Perf. 11½**
591 A274 35rp multicolored .25 .25
592 A274 50rp multicolored .45 .40
593 A274 80rp multicolored .65 .60
594 A274 1.10fr multicolored 1.00 .75
  Nos. 591-594 (4) 2.35 2.00

21st Olympic Games, Montreal, Canada, July 17-Aug. 1.

Rubens' Sons, Albrecht and Nikolas — A275

Rubens Paintings: 50rp, Singing Angels. 1fr, The Daughters of Cecrops, horiz. (from Collection of Prince of Liechtenstein).

**Size: 24x38mm**

**1976, Sept. 9  Engr.  Perf. 13½x14**
595 A275 50rp gold & multi .70 .70
596 A275 70rp gold & multi 1.00 1.00

**Size: 48x38mm**

597 A275 1fr gold & multi 2.75 2.75
  Nos. 595-597 (3) 4.45 4.45

400th anniversary of the birth of Peter Paul Rubens (1577-1640), Flemish painter. Sheets of 8 (2x4).

Zodiac Signs — A276

**1976-78  Photo.  Perf. 11½**
598 A276 20rp Pisces .25 .25
599 A276 40rp Aries .35 .35
600 A276 40rp Cancer ('77) .40 .35
601 A276 40rp Scorpio ('78) .45 .45
602 A276 50rp Sagittarius ('78) .50 .45
603 A276 70rp Leo ('77) .65 .65
604 A276 75rp Taurus .75 .70
605 A276 80rp Virgo ('77) .75 .75
606 A276 80rp Capricorn ('78) .75 .70
607 A276 90rp Gemini 1.00 .95
608 A276 1.10fr Libra ('77) 1.10 1.10
609 A276 1.50fr Aquarius ('78) 1.25 1.25
  Nos. 598-609 (12) 8.20 7.75

Flight into Egypt — A277

Monastic Wax Works: 20rp, Holy Infant of Prague, horiz. 80rp, Holy Family and Trinity. 1.50fr, Holy Family, horiz.

**1976, Dec. 9  Photo.  Perf. 11½**
610 A277 20rp multicolored .25 .25
611 A277 50rp multicolored .45 .35
612 A277 80rp multicolored .60 .50
613 A277 1.50fr multicolored 1.40 1.10
  Nos. 610-613 (4) 2.70 2.20

Christmas 1976.

Ortlieb von Brandis, Sarcophagus — A278

**Photogravure and Engraved**
**1976, Dec. 9  Perf. 13½x14**
614 A278 1.10fr gold & dk brown 1.00 .70

Ortlieb von Brandis, Bishop of Chur (1458-1491).

Map of Liechtenstein, by J. J. Heber, 1721 — A279

Europa: 80rp, View of Vaduz, by Ferdinand Bachmann, 1815.

**1977, Mar. 10  Photo.  Perf. 12½**
615 A279 40rp multicolored .40 .40
616 A279 80rp multicolored .80 .80

**Treasure Type of 1975**

40rp, Holy Lance and Particle of the Cross. 50rp, Imperial Evangel of St. Matthew. 80rp, St. Stephen's Purse. 90rp, Tabard of Imperial Herald.

**Engraved and Photogravure**
**1977, June 8  Perf. 14**
617 A266 40rp gold & multi .40 .25
618 A266 50rp gold & multi .50 .40
619 A266 80rp gold & multi .70 .55
620 A266 90rp gold & multi 1.00 .80
  Nos. 617-620 (4) 2.60 2.00

Treasures of the Holy Roman Empire from the Treasury of the Hofburg in Vienna.

Emperor Constantius II Coin — A280

Coins: 70rp, Lindau bracteate, c. 1300. 80rp, Ortlieb von Brandis, 1458-1491.

**1977, June 8  Photo.  Perf. 11½**
**Granite Paper**
621 A280 35rp gold & multi .35 .25
622 A280 70rp silver & multi .60 .50
623 A280 80rp silver & multi .80 .55
  Nos. 621-623 (3) 1.75 1.30

Frauenthal Castle — A281

Castles: 50rp, Gross Ullersdorf. 80rp, Liechtenstein Castle near Mödling, Austria. 90rp, Liechtenstein Palace, Vienna.

**Engraved and Photogravure**
**1977, Sept. 8  Perf. 13½x14**
624 A281 20rp slate grn & gold .25 .25
625 A281 50rp magenta & gold .50 .40
626 A281 80rp dk violet & gold .80 .65
627 A281 90rp dk blue & gold .90 .75
  Nos. 624-627 (4) 2.45 2.05

Children — A282

Traditional Costumes: 70rp, Two girls. 1fr, Woman in festival dress.

**1977, Sept. 8  Photo.  Perf. 11½**
**Granite Paper**
628 A282 40rp multicolored .50 .35
629 A282 70rp multicolored .75 .60
630 A282 1fr multicolored 1.25 .75
  Nos. 628-630 (3) 2.50 1.70

Princess Tatjana — A283

**1977, Dec. 7  Photo.  Perf. 11½**
631 A283 1.10fr brown & gold 1.20 .75

Angel — A284

Sculptures by Erasmus Kern: 50rp, St. Rochus. 80rp, Virgin and Child. 1.50fr, God the Father.

**1977, Dec. 7**
632 A284 20rp multicolored .25 .25
633 A284 50rp multicolored .45 .35
634 A284 80rp multicolored .75 .50
635 A284 1.50fr multicolored 1.50 1.00
  Nos. 632-635 (4) 2.95 2.10

Christmas 1977.

Liechtenstein Palace, Vienna — A285

Europa: 80rp, Feldsberg Castle.

**Photogravure and Engraved**
**1978, Mar. 2  Perf. 14**
636 A285 40rp gold & slate blue .35 .30
637 A285 80rp gold & claret .75 .70

Farmhouse, Triesen — A286

Designs: 20rp, Houses, Upper Village, Triesen. 35rp, Barns, Balzers. 40rp, Monastery, Bendern. 50rp, Residential Tower, Balzers-Mäls. 70rp, Parish house. 80rp, Farmhouse, Schellenberg. 90rp, Parish house, Balzers. 1fr, Rheinberger House, Music School, Vaduz. 1.10fr, Street, Mitteldorf, Vaduz. 1.50fr, Town Hall, Triesenberg. 2fr, National Museum and Administrator's Residence, Vaduz.

**1978  Photo.  Perf. 11½**
638 A286 10rp multicolored .25 .25
639 A286 20rp multicolored .25 .25
640 A286 35rp multicolored .30 .25
641 A286 40rp multicolored .30 .25
642 A286 50rp multicolored .45 .30
643 A286 70rp multicolored .60 .40
644 A286 80rp multicolored .65 .45
645 A286 90rp multicolored .80 .50
646 A286 1fr multicolored .85 .55
647 A286 1.10fr multicolored 1.00 .65
648 A286 1.50fr multicolored 1.20 .80
649 A286 2fr multicolored 1.75 1.10
  Nos. 638-649 (12) 8.40 5.75

Vaduz Castle — A287

Vaduz Castle: 50rp, Courtyard. 70rp, Staircase. 80rp, Triptych from High Altar, Castle Chapel.

**Engraved and Photogravure**
**1978, June 1  Perf. 13½x14**
650 A287 40rp gold & multi .40 .30
651 A287 50rp gold & multi .50 .40
652 A287 70rp gold & multi .70 .60
653 A287 80rp gold & multi .95 .70
  Nos. 650-653 (4) 2.55 2.00

40th anniversary of reign of Prince Franz Joseph II. Sheet of 8.

Prince Karl I, Coin, 1614 — A288

Designs: 50rp, Prince Johann Adam, medal, 1694. 80rp, Prince Josef Wenzel, medal, 1773.

**1978, Sept. 7  Photo.  Perf. 11½**
654 A288 40rp multicolored .35 .30
655 A288 50rp multicolored .50 .40
656 A288 80rp multicolored .95 .70
  Nos. 654-656 (3) 1.80 1.40

Adoration of the Shepherds — A289

Stained-glass Windows, Triesenberg: 50rp, Holy Family. 80rp, Adoration of the Kings.

**1978, Dec. 7  Photo.  Perf. 11½**
657 A289 20rp multicolored .25 .25
658 A289 50rp multicolored .50 .40
659 A289 80rp multicolored .80 .70
  Nos. 657-659 (3) 1.55 1.35

Christmas 1978.

Piebald, by Hamilton and Faistenberger
A290

Golden Carriage of Prince Joseph Wenzel, by Martin von Meytens
A291

Design: 80rp, Black stallion, by Johann Georg von Hamilton.

**Photo. & Engr.**

| | | | | |
|---|---|---|---|---|
| **1978, Dec. 7** | | **Perf. 13½x14** | | |
| 660 | A290 | 70rp multicolored | .60 | .50 |
| 661 | A290 | 80rp multicolored | .70 | .60 |
| | | **Perf. 12** | | |
| 662 | A291 | 1.10fr multicolored | .95 | .70 |
| | *Nos. 660-662 (3)* | | 2.25 | 1.80 |

Sheets of 8.

Mail Plane over Schaan — A292

Europa: 80rp, Zeppelin over Vaduz Castle.

| | | | | |
|---|---|---|---|---|
| **1979, Mar. 8** | **Photo.** | | **Perf. 11½** | |
| 663 | A292 | 40rp multicolored | .50 | .45 |
| 664 | A292 | 80rp multicolored | .65 | .60 |

First airmail service, St. Gallen to Schaan, Aug. 31, 1930, and first Zeppelin flight to Liechtenstein, June 10, 1931.

Child Drinking — A293

90rp, Child eating. 1.10fr, Child reading.

| | | | | |
|---|---|---|---|---|
| **1979, Mar. 8** | | | | |
| 665 | A293 | 80rp silver & multi | .75 | .70 |
| 666 | A293 | 90rp silver & multi | .85 | .85 |
| 667 | A293 | 1.10fr silver & multi | .95 | .95 |
| | *Nos. 665-667 (3)* | | 2.55 | 2.50 |

International Year of the Child.

Ordered Wave Fields
A294

Sun over Continents
A296

Council of Europe — A295

| | | | | |
|---|---|---|---|---|
| **1979, June 7** | **Litho.** | | **Perf. 11½** | |
| 668 | A294 | 50rp multicolored | .50 | .40 |
| | | **Photo.** | | |
| 669 | A295 | 80rp multicolored | .65 | .55 |
| 670 | A296 | 100rp multicolored | .80 | .65 |
| | *Nos. 668-670 (3)* | | 1.95 | 1.60 |

Intl. Radio Consultative Committee (CCIR) of the Intl. Telecommunications Union, 50th anniv. (50rp); Entry into Council of Europe (80rp); aid to developing countries (100rp).

Heraldic Panel of Carl Ludwig von Sulz — A297

Heraldic Panels of: 70rp, Barbara von Sulz, née zu Staufen. 1.10fr, Ulrich von Ramschwag and Barbara von Hallwil.

**Photogravure and Engraved**

| | | | | |
|---|---|---|---|---|
| **1979, June 1** | | | **Perf. 13½** | |
| 671 | A297 | 40rp multicolored | .55 | .30 |
| 672 | A297 | 70rp multicolored | .65 | .50 |
| 673 | A297 | 1.10fr multicolored | 1.10 | .95 |
| | *Nos. 671-673 (3)* | | 2.30 | 1.75 |

Sts. Lucius and Florin, Fresco in Waltensburg-Vuorz Church — A298

**Photogravure and Engraved**

| | | | | |
|---|---|---|---|---|
| **1979, Sept. 6** | | | **Perf. 13½** | |
| 674 | A298 | 20fr multicolored | 14.00 | 7.50 |

Patron saints of Liechtenstein. Printed in sheets of 4.

Annunciation, Embroidery A299

Christmas (Ferdinand Nigg Embroideries): 50rp, Christmas. 80rp, Blessed Are the Peacemakers.

| | | | | |
|---|---|---|---|---|
| **1979, Dec. 6** | **Engr.** | | **Perf. 13½** | |
| 675 | A299 | 20rp multicolored | .50 | .25 |
| 676 | A299 | 50rp multicolored | .50 | .35 |
| 677 | A299 | 80rp multicolored | .80 | .50 |
| | *Nos. 675-677 (3)* | | 1.80 | 1.10 |

Cross-Country Skiing — A300

Olympic Rings and: 70rp, Oxhead Mountain. 1.50fr, Ski lift.

| | | | | |
|---|---|---|---|---|
| **1979, Dec. 6** | **Photo.** | | **Perf. 12** | |
| 678 | A300 | 40rp multicolored | .45 | .25 |
| 679 | A300 | 70rp multicolored | .65 | .45 |
| 680 | A300 | 1.50fr multicolored | 1.25 | 1.00 |
| | *Nos. 678-680 (3)* | | 2.35 | 1.70 |

13th Winter Olympic Games, Lake Placid, NY, Feb. 12-24, 1980.

Arms of Bailiff Andreas Buchel, 1690 — A301

Various arms: 70rp, Georg Marxer, 1745. 80rp, Luzius Frick, 1503. 1.10rp, Adam Oehri, 1634.

| | | | | |
|---|---|---|---|---|
| **1980, Mar. 10** | **Photo.** | | **Perf. 11½** | |
| | | **Granite Paper** | | |
| 681 | A301 | 40rp shown | .30 | .30 |
| 682 | A301 | 70rp multicolored | .50 | .45 |
| 683 | A301 | 80rp multicolored | .85 | .70 |
| 684 | A301 | 1.10fr multicolored | .75 | .70 |
| | *Nos. 681-684 (4)* | | 2.40 | 2.15 |

See Nos. 704-707, 729-732.

Princess Maria Leopoldine Esterhazy, by Antonio Canova — A302

Europa: 80rp, Maria Theresa, Duchess of Savoy, by Martin van Meytens.

| | | | | |
|---|---|---|---|---|
| **1980, Mar. 10** | | | | |
| 685 | A302 | 40rp multicolored | .40 | .35 |
| 686 | A302 | 80rp multicolored | .60 | .50 |

Milking Pail — A303

Old Alpine Farm Tools: 50rp, Wooden heart, ceremonial cattle decoration. 80rp, Butter churn.

| | | | | |
|---|---|---|---|---|
| **1980, Sept. 8** | | | | |
| 687 | A303 | 20rp multicolored | .25 | .25 |
| 688 | A303 | 50rp multicolored | .45 | .35 |
| 689 | A303 | 80rp multicolored | .75 | .55 |
| | *Nos. 687-689 (3)* | | 1.45 | 1.15 |

Liechtenstein No. 94 — A304

| | | | | |
|---|---|---|---|---|
| **1980, Sept 8** | | | | |
| 690 | A304 | 80rp multicolored | .80 | .60 |

Postal Museum, 50th anniversary.

Crossbow with Spanning Device — A305

90rp, Spear, knife. 1.10fr, Rifle, powderhorn.

| | | | | |
|---|---|---|---|---|
| **1980, Sept. 8** | **Engr.** | | **Perf. 13½x14** | |
| 691 | A305 | 80rp shown | .60 | .55 |
| 692 | A305 | 90rp multicolored | .75 | .60 |
| 693 | A305 | 1.10fr multicolored | .90 | .65 |
| | *Nos. 691-693 (3)* | | 2.25 | 1.80 |

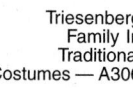

Triesenberg Family In Traditional Costumes — A306

70rp, Folk dancers, Schellenberg. 80rp, Brass band, Mauren.

| | | | | |
|---|---|---|---|---|
| **1980, Sept. 8** | **Photo.** | | **Perf. 12** | |
| | | **Granite Paper** | | |
| 694 | A306 | 40rp shown | .45 | .25 |
| 695 | A306 | 70rp multicolored | .70 | .50 |
| 696 | A306 | 80rp multicolored | .75 | .60 |
| | *Nos. 694-696 (3)* | | 1.90 | 1.35 |

Green Beeches, Matrula Forest — A307

50rp, White firs, Valorsch Valley. 80rp, Beech forest, Schaan. 1.50fr, Forest, Oberplanken.

**Photogravure and Engraved**

| | | | | |
|---|---|---|---|---|
| **1980, Dec. 9** | | | **Perf. 14** | |
| 697 | A307 | 40rp shown | .35 | .25 |
| 698 | A307 | 50rp multicolored | .45 | .40 |
| 699 | A307 | 80rp multicolored | .75 | .55 |
| 700 | A307 | 1.50fr multicolored | 1.40 | 1.00 |
| | *Nos. 697-700 (4)* | | 2.95 | 2.20 |

Glad Tidings — A308

| | | | | |
|---|---|---|---|---|
| **1980, Dec. 9** | **Photo.** | | **Perf. 11½** | |
| | | **Granite Paper** | | |
| 701 | A308 | 20rp shown | .25 | .25 |
| 702 | A308 | 50rp Creche | .45 | .35 |
| 703 | A308 | 80rp Epiphany | .70 | .60 |
| | *Nos. 701-703 (3)* | | 1.40 | 1.20 |

Christmas 1980.

**Bailiff Arms Type of 1980**

40rp, Anton Meier, 1748. 70rp, Kaspar Kindle, 1534. 80rp, Hans Adam Negele, 1600. 1.10fr, Peter Matt, 1693.

| | | | | |
|---|---|---|---|---|
| **1981, Mar. 9** | **Photo.** | | **Perf. 11½** | |
| | | **Granite Paper** | | |
| 704 | A301 | 40rp multicolored | .45 | .30 |
| 705 | A301 | 70rp multicolored | .75 | .50 |
| 706 | A301 | 80rp multicolored | .80 | .60 |
| 707 | A301 | 1.10fr multicolored | 1.10 | .90 |
| | *Nos. 704-707 (4)* | | 3.10 | 2.30 |

Fireworks at Vaduz Castle — A309

Europa: 80rp, National Day procession.

| | | | | |
|---|---|---|---|---|
| **1981, Mar. 9** | | | **Perf. 12½** | |
| | | **Granite Paper** | | |
| 708 | A309 | 40rp multicolored | .35 | .30 |
| 709 | A309 | 80rp multicolored | .65 | .60 |

Souvenir Sheet

Prince Alois, Princess Elisabeth and Prince Franz Joseph II A310

| | | | | |
|---|---|---|---|---|
| **1981, June 9** | **Photo.** | | **Perf. 13** | |
| | | **Granite Paper** | | |
| 710 | A310 | Sheet of 3 | 2.75 | 2.50 |
| a. | | 70rp shown | .50 | .50 |
| b. | | 80rp Princes Alois and Franz Joseph II | .55 | .55 |
| c. | | 150rp Prince Franz Joseph II | 1.00 | 1.00 |

75th birthday of Prince Franz Joseph II.

Scout Emblems — A311

| | | | | |
|---|---|---|---|---|
| **1981, June 9** | | | | |
| 711 | A311 | 20rp multicolored | .50 | .40 |

50th anniversary of Boy Scouts and Girl Guides.

Man in
Wheelchair — A312

**1981, June 9**
712 A312 40rp multicolored .50 .40
International Year of the Disabled.

St. Theodul, 1600th
Birth Anniv. — A313

**1981, June 9**
713 A313 80rp multicolored .80 .55

Mosses and
Lichens — A314

40rp, Xanthoria parietina. 50rp, Parmelia
physodes. 70rp, Sphagnum palustre. 80rp,
Amblystegium.

**Photogravure and Engraved**
**1981, Sept. 7** *Perf. 13½*
714 A314 40rp multicolored .45 .30
715 A314 50rp multicolored .45 .35
716 A314 70rp multicolored .60 .50
717 A314 80rp multicolored .70 .60
Nos. 714-717 (4) 2.20 1.75

Gutenberg
Castle — A315

**1981, Sept. 7**
718 A315 20rp shown .45 .25
719 A315 40rp Castle yard .45 .30
720 A315 50rp Parlor .45 .35
721 A315 1.10fr Great Hall .95 .85
Nos. 718-721 (4) 2.30 1.75

St. Charles Borromeo
(1538-1584) — A316

Famous Visitors to Liechtenstein (Paintings): 70rp, Goethe (1749-1832), by Angelica
Kauffmann. 80rp, Alexander Dumas (1824-
1895). 1fr, Hermann Hesse (1877-1962), by
Cuno Amiet.

**Lithographed and Engraved**
**1981, Dec. 7** *Perf. 14*
722 A316 40rp multicolored .35 .30
723 A316 70rp multicolored .60 .50
724 A316 80rp multicolored .70 .60
725 A316 1fr multicolored .80 .70
Nos. 722-725 (4) 2.45 2.10
See Nos. 747-750.

St. Nicholas — A317

50rp, Adoration of the Kings. 80rp, Holy
Family.

**1981, Dec. 7** *Photo.* *Perf. 11½*
**Granite Paper**
726 A317 20rp shown .25 .25
727 A317 50rp multicolored .45 .40
728 A317 80rp multicolored .70 .60
Nos. 726-728 (3) 1.40 1.25
Christmas 1981.

**Bailiff Arms Type of 1980**
40rp, Johann Kaiser, 1664. 70rp, Joseph
Anton Kaufmann, 1748. 80rp, Christoph Walser, 1690. 1.10fr, Stephan Banzer, 1658.

**1982, Mar. 8** *Photo.*
**Granite Paper**
729 A301 40rp multicolored .35 .35
730 A301 70rp multicolored .55 .50
731 A301 80rp multicolored .70 .60
732 A301 1.10fr multicolored 1.00 .80
Nos. 729-732 (4) 2.60 2.25

Europa
1982 — A318

40rp, Peasants' Uprising, 1525. 80rp, Imperial Direct Rule, 1396.

**1982, Mar. 8** **Granite Paper**
733 A318 40rp multicolored .35 .30
734 A318 80rp multicolored .65 .60

Hereditary Prince Hans
Adam — A319

No. 736, Princess Marie Aglae.

**1982, June 7** **Granite Paper**
735 A319 1fr shown .75 .75
736 A319 1fr multicolored .75 .75
LIBA '82, 10th Liechtenstein Philatelic Exhibition, Vaduz, July 31-Aug. 8.

1982 World
Cup — A320

Designs: Sports arenas.

**1982, June 7** **Granite Paper**
737 A320 15rp Triesenberg .40 .25
738 A320 25rp Mauren .40 .25
739 A320 1.80fr Balzers 1.40 1.25
Nos. 737-739 (3) 2.20 1.75

Farming — A321

**1982, Sept. 20** *Photo.* *Perf. 11½*
**Granite Paper**
740 A321 30rp shown .40 .25
741 A321 50rp Horticulture .40 .40
742 A321 70rp Forestry .60 .50
743 A321 150rp Dairy farming 1.25 1.10
Nos. 740-743 (4) 2.65 2.25

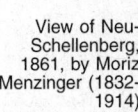

View of Neu-
Schellenberg,
1861, by Moriz
Menzinger (1832-
1914)
A322

**Photogravure and Engraved**
**1982, Sept. 20** *Perf. 13½x14*
744 A322 40rp shown .50 .30
745 A322 50rp Vaduz, 1860 .60 .35
746 A322 100rp Bendern, 1868 1.00 .85
Nos. 744-746 (3) 2.10 1.50

**Visitor Type of 1981**
Paintings: 40rp, Emperor Maximilian I
(1459-1519), by Bernhard Strigel. 70rp, Georg

Jenatsch (1596-1639). 80rp, Angelika Kaufmann (1741-1807), self portrait. 1fr, Fidelis
von Sigmaringen (1577-1622).

**1982, Dec. 6** *Perf. 14*
747 A316 40rp multicolored .45 .30
748 A316 70rp multicolored .70 .45
749 A316 80rp multicolored .80 .45
750 A316 1fr multicolored 1.00 .65
Nos. 747-750 (4) 2.95 1.85

Christmas 1982 — A323

Chur Cathedral sculptures: 20rp, Angel
playing lute. 50rp, Virgin and Child. 80rp,
Angel playing organ.

**1982, Dec. 6** *Photo.* *Perf. 11½*
**Granite Paper**
751 A323 20rp multicolored .25 .25
752 A323 50rp multicolored .50 .35
753 A323 80rp multicolored .75 .55
Nos. 751-753 (3) 1.50 1.15

Europa 1983 — A324

Designs: 40rp, Notker Balbulus of St. Gall
(840-912), Benedictine monk, poet and liturgi-
cal composer. 80rp, St. Hildegard of Bingen
(1098-1179).

**1983, Mar. 7** *Photo.*
754 A324 40rp multicolored .40 .30
755 A324 80rp multicolored .65 .55

A325

Shrovetide and Lenten customs: 40rp, Last
Thursday before Lent. 70rp, Begging for eggs
on Shrove Tuesday. 180fr, Bonfire, first Sunday in Lent.

**Photogravure and Engraved**
**1983, Mar. 7** *Perf. 14*
756 A325 40rp multicolored .35 .30
757 A325 70rp multicolored .60 .45
758 A325 1.80fr multicolored 1.50 1.25
Nos. 756-758 (3) 2.45 2.00
See Nos. 844-846, 915-917, 952-954.

A326

Landscapes by Anton Ender (b. 1898):
40rp, Schaan, on the Zollstrasse. 50rp,
Balzers with Gutenberg Castle. 2fr, Stag by
the Reservoir.

**1983, June 6** *Photo.* *Perf. 12*
759 A326 40rp multicolored .35 .30
760 A326 50rp multicolored .50 .35
761 A326 2fr multicolored 2.00 1.50
Nos. 759-761 (3) 2.85 2.15

Protection of Shores
and Coasts — A327

40rp, Manned flight bicentenary. 50rp,
World communications year. 80rp, Humanitarian aid.

**1983, June 6**
762 A327 20rp shown .25 .25
763 A327 40rp multicolored .35 .35
764 A327 50rp multicolored .45 .45
765 A327 80rp multicolored .70 .70
Nos. 762-765 (4) 1.75 1.75

Pope John
Paul II — A328

**1983, Sept. 5** *Photo.*
766 A328 80rp multicolored .90 .75

Princess Gina — A329

3fr, Prince Franz Joseph II.

**1983, Sept. 5** *Perf. 12x11½*
767 A329 2.50fr shown 2.25 1.25
768 A329 3fr multicolored 2.75 1.75

Christmas
1983 — A330

**1983, Dec. 5** *Photo.* *Perf. 12*
**Granite Paper**
769 A330 20rp Seeking shelter .25 .25
770 A330 50rp Child Jesus .40 .30
771 A330 80rp The Three Magi .70 .55
Nos. 769-771 (3) 1.35 1.10

1984 Winter Olympics,
Sarajevo — A331

Snowflakes.

**1983, Dec. 5** *Photo.* *Perf. 11½x12*
**Granite Paper**
772 A331 40rp multicolored .40 .30
773 A331 80rp multicolored .80 .60
774 A331 1.80fr multicolored 1.65 1.10
Nos. 772-774 (3) 2.85 2.00

Famous Visitors to
Liechtenstein — A332

Paintings: 40rp, Count Alexander Was-
siljewitsch Suworow-Rimnikski (1730-1800),
Austro-Russian Army general. 70rp, Karl
Rudolf Count von Buol-Schauenstein (1760-
1833). 80rp, Carl Zuckmayer (1896-1977),
playwright. 1fr, Curt Goetz (1888-1960), actor
and playwright.

**Photogravure and Engraved**
**1984, Mar. 12** *Perf. 14*
775 A332 40rp multicolored .40 .30
776 A332 70rp multicolored .70 .55
777 A332 80rp multicolored .80 .60
778 A332 1fr multicolored 1.00 .75
Nos. 775-778 (4) 2.90 2.20

Europa (1959-
1984) — A333

**1984, Mar. 12** *Photo.* *Perf. 12*
**Granite Paper**
779 A333 50rp multicolored .45 .40
780 A333 80rp multicolored .65 .60

A334

The Destruction of Trisona Fairy Tale Illustrations: Root Carvings by Beni Gassner — 35rp, Warning messenger. 50rp, Buried town. 80rp, Spared family.

### Photogravure and Engraved

| 1984, June 12 | | | Perf. 14 | |
|---|---|---|---|---|
| 781 | A334 | 35rp multicolored | .35 | .30 |
| 782 | A334 | 50rp multicolored | .50 | .40 |
| 783 | A334 | 80rp multicolored | .80 | .70 |
| | Nos. 781-783 (3) | | 1.65 | 1.40 |

1984 Summer Olympics — A335

| 1984, June 12 | Photo. | Perf. 11½ | | |
|---|---|---|---|---|
| Granite Paper | | | | |
| 784 | A335 | 70rp Pole vault | .65 | .50 |
| 785 | A335 | 80rp Discus | .75 | .55 |
| 786 | A335 | 1fr Shot put | 1.00 | .75 |
| | Nos. 784-786 (3) | | 2.40 | 1.80 |

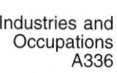

Industries and Occupations A336

5rp, Banking & trading. 10rp, Construction, plumbing. 20rp, Production, factory worker. 35rp, Contracting, draftswoman. 45rp, Manufacturing, sales rep. 50rp, Catering. 60rp, Carpentry. 70rp, Public health. 80rp, Industrial research. 1fr, Masonry. 1.20fr, Industrial management. 1.50fr, Post & communications.

| 1984, Sept. 10 | | Photo. | Perf. 11½ | |
|---|---|---|---|---|
| 787 | A336 | 5rp multicolored | .25 | .25 |
| 788 | A336 | 10rp multicolored | .25 | .25 |
| 789 | A336 | 20rp multicolored | .25 | .25 |
| 790 | A336 | 35rp multicolored | .35 | .30 |
| 791 | A336 | 45rp multicolored | .45 | .35 |
| 792 | A336 | 50rp multicolored | .50 | .40 |
| 793 | A336 | 60rp multicolored | .60 | .50 |
| 794 | A336 | 70rp multicolored | .70 | .55 |
| 795 | A336 | 80rp multicolored | .80 | .65 |
| 796 | A336 | 1fr multicolored | 1.00 | .80 |
| 797 | A336 | 1.20fr multicolored | 1.25 | 1.00 |
| 798 | A336 | 1.50fr multicolored | 1.50 | 1.20 |
| | Nos. 787-798 (12) | | 7.90 | 6.50 |

Princess Marie Aglae — A337

2fr, Prince Hans Adam.

### Photogravure and Engraved

| 1984, Dec. 10 | | | Perf. 14x13½ | |
|---|---|---|---|---|
| 799 | A337 | 1.70fr shown | 1.50 | 1.25 |
| 800 | A337 | 2fr multicolored | 1.90 | 1.40 |

Christmas 1984 — A338

| 1984, Dec. 10 | | Photo. | Perf. 11 | |
|---|---|---|---|---|
| 801 | A338 | 35rp Annunciation | .35 | .30 |
| 802 | A338 | 50rp Holy Family | .55 | .40 |
| 803 | A338 | 80rp Three Kings | .80 | .70 |
| | Nos. 801-803 (3) | | 1.70 | 1.40 |

Europa 1985 — A339

| 1985, Mar. 11 | | Photo. | Perf. 11½ | |
|---|---|---|---|---|
| 804 | A339 | 50rp Three Muses | .45 | .40 |
| 805 | A339 | 80rp Pan and Muses | .70 | .65 |

Orders and Monestaries A340

50rp, St. Elisabeth. 1fr, Schellenberg Convent. 1.70fr, Gutenberg Mission.

### Photogravure and Engraved

| 1985, Mar. 11 | | | Perf. 13½x14 | |
|---|---|---|---|---|
| 806 | A340 | 50rp multicolored | .55 | .45 |
| 807 | A340 | 1fr multicolored | 1.10 | .90 |
| 808 | A340 | 1.70fr multicolored | 1.90 | 1.60 |
| | Nos. 806-808 (3) | | 3.55 | 2.95 |

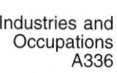

Cardinal Virtues — A341

| 1985, June 10 | | Photo. | Perf. 11½x12 | |
|---|---|---|---|---|
| 809 | A341 | 35rp Justice | .35 | .30 |
| 810 | A341 | 50rp Temperance | .50 | .40 |
| 811 | A341 | 70rp Prudence | .70 | .55 |
| 812 | A341 | 1fr Fortitude | 1.00 | .80 |
| | Nos. 809-812 (4) | | 2.55 | 2.05 |

Princess Gina, President of Natl. Red Cross, 40th Anniv. — A342

Portrait and: 20rp, Helping refugees, 1945. 50rp, Rescue service. 1.20fr, Child refugees, 1979.

| 1985, June 10 | | | Perf. 12x11½ | |
|---|---|---|---|---|
| 813 | A342 | 20rp multicolored | .25 | .25 |
| 814 | A342 | 50rp multicolored | .65 | .40 |
| 815 | A342 | 1.20fr multicolored | 1.50 | 1.10 |
| | Nos. 813-815 (3) | | 2.40 | 1.75 |

#### Souvenir Sheet

State Visit of Pope John Paul II A343

Designs: 50rp, Papal coat of arms. 80rp, Chapel of St. Maria zum Trost, Dux, Schaan. 1.70fr, Our Lady of Liechtenstein, St. Mary the Comforter.

| 1985, Feb. 2 | | | Perf. 11½ | |
|---|---|---|---|---|
| 816 | A343 | Sheet of 3 | 3.25 | 2.75 |
| a. | | 50rp multi | 1.00 | .90 |
| b. | | 80rp multi | 1.00 | .90 |
| c. | | 1.70fr multi | 1.00 | .90 |

Paintings from the Princely Collections — A344

50rp, Portrait of a Canon, by Quintin Massys (1466-1530). 1fr, Portrait of Clara Serena Rubens, by Peter Paul Rubens (1577-1640). 1.20fr, Portrait of the Duke of Urbino, by Raphael (1483-1520).

### Photogravure and Engraved

| 1985, Sept. 2 | | | Perf. 14 | |
|---|---|---|---|---|
| 817 | A344 | 50rp multicolored | .55 | .50 |
| 818 | A344 | 1fr multicolored | 1.25 | 1.10 |
| 819 | A344 | 1.20fr multicolored | 1.50 | 1.40 |
| | Nos. 817-819 (3) | | 3.30 | 3.00 |

Christmas 1985 — A345

| 1985, Dec. 9 | | Photo. | Perf. 11½x12 | |
|---|---|---|---|---|
| 820 | A345 | 35rp Frankincense | .45 | .35 |
| 821 | A345 | 50rp Gold | .65 | .50 |
| 822 | A345 | 80rp Myrrh | 1.10 | .85 |
| | Nos. 820-822 (3) | | 2.20 | 1.70 |

Kirchplatz Theater, 15th Anniv. — A346

50rp, Tragedy. 80rp, Commedia dell'arte. 1.50rp, Opera buffa.

### Photogravure and Engraved

| 1985, Dec. 9 | | | Perf. 14 | |
|---|---|---|---|---|
| 823 | A346 | 50rp multicolored | .40 | .35 |
| 824 | A346 | 80rp multicolored | .55 | .45 |
| 825 | A346 | 1.50rp multicolored | 1.75 | 1.40 |
| | Nos. 823-825 (3) | | 2.70 | 2.20 |

Weapons from the Prince's Armory — A347

Designs: 35rp, Halberd, bodyguard of Prince Charles I. 50rp, German morion, 16th cent. 80rp, Halberd, bodyguard of Prince Carl Eusebius.

| 1985, Dec. 9 | | | Perf. 13½x14½ | |
|---|---|---|---|---|
| 826 | A347 | 35rp multicolored | .35 | .35 |
| 827 | A347 | 50rp multicolored | .45 | .40 |
| 828 | A347 | 80rp multicolored | .75 | .65 |
| | Nos. 826-828 (3) | | 1.55 | 1.40 |

Europa 1986 — A348

| 1986, Mar. 10 | | Photo. | Perf. 12 | |
|---|---|---|---|---|
| 829 | A348 | 50rp Swallows | .45 | .40 |
| 830 | A348 | 90rp Robin | .95 | .90 |

A349

Views of Vaduz Castle: 20rp, Outer courtyard. 25rp, View from the south ('89). 50rp, Castle, mountains. 90rp, Inner gate ('87). 1.10fr, Back view. 1.40fr, Inner courtyard ('87).

#### Granite Paper

| 1986-89 | | Photo. | Perf. 11½x12 | |
|---|---|---|---|---|
| 832 | A349 | 20rp multicolored | .25 | .25 |
| 833 | A349 | 25rp multicolored | .35 | .35 |
| 835 | A349 | 50rp multicolored | .40 | .35 |
| 838 | A349 | 90rp multicolored | 1.10 | .70 |
| 840 | A349 | 1.10fr multicolored | .90 | .75 |
| 841 | A349 | 1.40fr multicolored | 1.75 | 1.20 |
| | Nos. 832-841 (6) | | 4.75 | 3.60 |

Fasting Sacrifice — A350

| 1986, Mar. 10 | | Photo. | Perf. 12 | |
|---|---|---|---|---|
| 843 | A350 | 1.40fr multicolored | 1.50 | 1.25 |

### Customs Type of 1983

35rp, Palm Sunday procession. 50rp, Wedding. 70rp, Rogation Day procession.

#### Photogravure and Engraved

| 1986, June 9 | | | Perf. 13½ | |
|---|---|---|---|---|
| 844 | A325 | 35rp multicolored | .40 | .35 |
| 845 | A325 | 50rp multicolored | .60 | .40 |
| 846 | A325 | 70rp multicolored | .80 | .60 |
| | Nos. 844-846 (3) | | 1.80 | 1.35 |

A352

Karl Freiherr Haus von Hausen (1823-89), founder.

| 1986, June 9 | | Photo. | Perf. 11½ | |
|---|---|---|---|---|
| 847 | A352 | 50rp multicolored | .65 | .50 |

Natl. Savings Bank, Vaduz, 125th anniv.

A353

#### Photogravure and Engraved

| 1986, June 9 | | | Perf. 13½ | |
|---|---|---|---|---|
| 848 | A353 | 3.50fr multicolored | 3.50 | 2.50 |

Prince Franz Joseph II, 80th birthday.

Hunting — A354

35rp, Roebuck, Ruggeller Riet. 50rp, Chamois in winter, Rappenstein. 1.70fr, Rutting stag, Lawena.

| 1986, Sept. 9 | | | Perf. 13x13½ | |
|---|---|---|---|---|
| 849 | A354 | 35rp multicolored | .35 | .25 |
| 850 | A354 | 50rp multicolored | .50 | .40 |
| 851 | A354 | 1.70fr multicolored | 1.90 | 1.50 |
| | Nos. 849-851 (3) | | 2.75 | 2.15 |

Crops — A355

50rp, White cabbage, beets. 80rp, Red cabbage. 90rp, Potatoes, onions, garlic.

| 1986, Sept. 9 | | Photo. | Perf. 12x11½ | |
|---|---|---|---|---|
| 852 | A355 | 50rp multicolored | .55 | .45 |
| 853 | A355 | 80rp multicolored | .90 | .70 |
| 854 | A355 | 90rp multicolored | 1.00 | .80 |
| | Nos. 852-854 (3) | | 2.45 | 1.95 |

Christmas — A356

Archangels.

| 1986, Dec. 9 | | | Perf. 11½ | |
|---|---|---|---|---|
| 855 | A356 | 35rp Michael | .45 | .30 |
| 856 | A356 | 50rp Gabriel | .65 | .50 |
| 857 | A356 | 90rp Raphael | 1.25 | 1.00 |
| | Nos. 855-857 (3) | | 2.35 | 1.80 |

Trees — A357

**1986, Dec. 9**
| | | | | |
|---|---|---|---|---|
| 858 | A357 | 25rp Silver fir | .30 | .25 |
| 859 | A357 | 90rp Spruce | 1.10 | .85 |
| 860 | A357 | 1.40fr Oak | 1.65 | 1.25 |
| | | *Nos. 858-860 (3)* | 3.05 | 2.35 |

Europa 1987 — A358

Modern architecture: 50rp, Primary school, 1980, Gamprin. 90rp, Parish church, c. 1960, Schellenburg.

**1987, Mar. 9  Photo.  Perf. 11½x12**
**Granite Paper**
| | | | | |
|---|---|---|---|---|
| 861 | A358 | 50rp multicolored | .60 | .55 |
| 862 | A358 | 90rp multicolored | 1.25 | 1.00 |

Nicholas Among the Thorns — A359

**1987, Mar. 9  Perf. 11½**
**Granite Paper**
| | | | | |
|---|---|---|---|---|
| 863 | A359 | 1.10fr multicolored | 1.40 | 1.00 |

Nicholas von der Flue (1417-1487), canonized in 1947.

Hereditary Prince Alois — A360

**Photo. & Engr.**
**1987, June 9  Perf. 14**
| | | | | |
|---|---|---|---|---|
| 864 | A360 | 2fr multicolored | 2.50 | 2.00 |

No. 864 printed in sheets of 8.

Fish — A361

50rp, Cottus gobio. 90rp, Salmo trutta fario. 1.10fr, Thymallus thymallus.

**1987, June 9  Photo.  Perf. 11½**
| | | | | |
|---|---|---|---|---|
| 865 | A361 | 50rp multicolored | .60 | .50 |
| 866 | A361 | 90rp multicolored | 1.10 | .85 |
| 867 | A361 | 1.10fr multicolored | 1.40 | 1.10 |
| | | *Nos. 865-867 (3)* | 3.10 | 2.45 |

A362

Liechtenstein City Palace, Vienna.

**1987, Sept. 7  Photo.  Perf. 11½**
**Granite Paper**
| | | | | |
|---|---|---|---|---|
| 868 | A362 | 35rp Arch | .45 | .35 |
| 869 | A362 | 50rp Entrance | .60 | .50 |
| 870 | A362 | 90rp Staircase | 1.10 | .90 |
| | | *Nos. 868-870 (3)* | 2.15 | 1.75 |

House of Liechtenstein Coat of Arms — A363

**1987, Sept. 7  Perf. 11½**
| | | | | |
|---|---|---|---|---|
| 871 | A363 | 1.40fr multicolored | 1.60 | 1.25 |

Purchase of County of Vaduz, 275th anniv.

Diet, 125th Anniv. — A364

**1987, Sept. 7  Perf. 11½**
| | | | | |
|---|---|---|---|---|
| 872 | A364 | 1.70fr Constitution of 1862 | 2.00 | 1.50 |

Christmas — A365

The Evangelists, illuminated codices from the Golden Book, c. 1100, Abbey of Pfafers, purportedly made under the direction of monks from Reichenau Is.

**Photo. & Engr.**
**1987, Dec. 7  Perf. 14**
| | | | | |
|---|---|---|---|---|
| 873 | A365 | 35rp St. Matthew | .50 | .30 |
| 874 | A365 | 50rp St. Mark | .65 | .40 |
| 875 | A365 | 60rp St. Luke | .80 | .50 |
| 876 | A365 | 90rp St. John | 1.25 | .75 |
| | | *Nos. 873-876 (4)* | 3.20 | 1.95 |

1988 Winter Olympics, Calgary — A366

Humorous drawings by illustrator Paul Flora of Austria: 25rp, The Toil of the Cross-country Skier. 90rp, Courageous Pioneer of Skiing. 1.10fr, As Grandfather Used to Ride on a Bobsled.

**1987, Dec. 7  Perf. 14x13½**
| | | | | |
|---|---|---|---|---|
| 877 | A366 | 25rp multicolored | .30 | .30 |
| 878 | A366 | 90rp multicolored | 1.10 | 1.00 |
| 879 | A366 | 1.10fr multicolored | 1.40 | 1.25 |
| | | *Nos. 877-879 (3)* | 2.80 | 2.55 |

See Nos. 888-891.

Europa 1988 — A367

Modern communication & transportation: 50rp, Satellite dish. 90rp, High-speed monorail.

**1988, Mar. 7  Photo.  Perf. 11½x12**
**Granite Paper**
| | | | | |
|---|---|---|---|---|
| 880 | A367 | 50rp multicolored | .60 | .55 |
| 881 | A367 | 90rp multicolored | 1.00 | .90 |

European Campaign to Protect Undeveloped and Developing Lands — A368

80rp, Forest preservation. 90rp, Layout for village development. 1.70rp, Traffic planning.

**1988, Mar. 7  Perf. 12**
**Granite Paper**
| | | | | |
|---|---|---|---|---|
| 882 | A368 | 80rp multicolored | .85 | .75 |
| 883 | A368 | 90rp multicolored | .90 | .85 |
| 884 | A368 | 1.70rp multicolored | 1.75 | 1.50 |
| | | *Nos. 882-884 (3)* | 3.50 | 3.10 |

Balancing nature conservation with natl. development.

**Souvenir Sheet**

Succession to the Throne — A369

Portraits: a, Crown Prince Hans Adam. b, Prince Alois, successor to the crown prince. c, Prince Franz Josef II, ruler.

**Photo. & Engr.**
**1988, June 6  Perf. 14½x13½**
| | | | | |
|---|---|---|---|---|
| 885 | A369 | Sheet of 3 | 4.50 | 3.50 |
| a. | | 50rp black, gold & bright blue | .70 | .55 |
| b. | | 50rp black, gold & sage green | .70 | .55 |
| c. | | 2fr black, gold & deep rose | 3.00 | 2.25 |

North and South Campaign — A370

**1988, June 6  Photo.  Perf. 12x11½**
| | | | | |
|---|---|---|---|---|
| 886 | A370 | 50rp Public radio | .85 | .55 |
| 887 | A370 | 1.40fr Adult education | 2.40 | 1.50 |

Cultural cooperation with Costa Rica. See Costa Rica Nos. 401-402.

**Olympics Type of 1988**

Humorous drawings by illustrator Paul Flora of Austria: 50rp, Cycling. 80rp, Gymnastics. 90rp, Running. 1.40fr, Equestrian.

**Photo. & Engr.**
**1988, Sept. 5  Perf. 14x13½**
| | | | | |
|---|---|---|---|---|
| 888 | A366 | 50rp multicolored | .70 | .50 |
| 889 | A366 | 80rp multicolored | 1.10 | .75 |
| 890 | A366 | 90rp multicolored | 1.20 | .80 |
| 891 | A366 | 1.40fr multicolored | 1.90 | 1.40 |
| | | *Nos. 888-891 (4)* | 4.90 | 3.45 |

Roadside Shrines — A371

25rp, Kaltweh Chapel, Balzers. 35rp, Oberdorf, Vaduz, c. 1870. 50rp, Bangstrasse, Ruggell.

**1988, Sept. 5  Photo.  Perf. 11½x12**
**Granite Paper**
| | | | | |
|---|---|---|---|---|
| 892 | A371 | 25rp multicolored | .35 | .30 |
| 893 | A371 | 35rp multicolored | .45 | .40 |
| 894 | A371 | 50rp multicolored | .65 | .55 |
| | | *Nos. 892-894 (3)* | 1.45 | 1.25 |

Christmas — A372

35rp, Joseph, Mary. 50rp, Christ child. 90rp, Adoration of the Magi.

**1988, Dec. 5  Photo.  Perf. 11½x12**
**Granite Paper**
| | | | | |
|---|---|---|---|---|
| 895 | A372 | 35rp multicolored | .40 | .30 |
| 896 | A372 | 50rp multicolored | .55 | .40 |
| 897 | A372 | 90rp multicolored | 1.00 | .70 |
| | | *Nos. 895-897 (3)* | 1.95 | 1.40 |

The Letter — A373

Details of Portrait of Marie-Therese de Lamballe (The Letter), by Anton Hickel (1745-1798): 90rp, Handkerchief and writing materials in open desk. 2fr, Entire painting.

**Photo. & Engr.**
**1988, Dec. 5  Perf. 13x13½**
| | | | | |
|---|---|---|---|---|
| 898 | A373 | 50rp shown | .65 | .50 |
| 899 | A373 | 90rp multicolored | 1.10 | .80 |
| 900 | A373 | 2fr multicolored | 2.50 | 1.90 |
| | | *Nos. 898-900 (3)* | 4.25 | 3.20 |

Europa 1989 — A374

Traditional children's games: 50rp, Cat and Mouse. 90rp,

**Granite Paper**
**1989, Mar. 6  Photo.  Perf. 11½x12**
| | | | | |
|---|---|---|---|---|
| 901 | A374 | 50rp multicolored | .70 | .65 |
| 902 | A374 | 90rp multicolored | 1.40 | 1.25 |

Josef Gabriel Rheinberger (1839-1901), Composer, and Score — A375

**Photo. & Engr.**
**1989, Mar. 6  Perf. 14x13½**
| | | | | |
|---|---|---|---|---|
| 903 | A375 | 2.90fr multicolored | 3.25 | 2.50 |

Fish — A376

50rp, Esox lucius. 1.10fr, Salmo trutta lacustris. 1.40fr, Noemacheilus barbatulus.

**1989, June 5  Photo.  Perf. 12x11½**
**Granite Paper**
| | | | | |
|---|---|---|---|---|
| 904 | A376 | 50rp multicolored | .65 | .50 |
| 905 | A376 | 1.10fr multicolored | 1.40 | 1.00 |
| 906 | A376 | 1.40fr multicolored | 1.75 | 1.25 |
| | | *Nos. 904-906 (3)* | 3.80 | 2.75 |

World Wildlife Fund — A377

25rp, Charadrius dubuis. 35rp, Hyla arborea. 50rp, Libelloides coccajus. 90rp, Putorius putorius.

**1989, June 5  Perf. 12**
**Granite Paper**
| | | | | |
|---|---|---|---|---|
| 907 | A377 | 25rp multicolored | .55 | .35 |
| 908 | A377 | 35rp multicolored | .90 | .55 |
| 909 | A377 | 50rp multicolored | 1.20 | .75 |
| 910 | A377 | 90rp multicolored | 2.25 | 1.40 |
| | | *Nos. 907-910 (4)* | 4.90 | 3.05 |

Mountains — A378

**1989, Sept. 4**    **Photo.**    *Perf. 11½*
**Granite Paper**

| | | | | |
|---|---|---|---|---|
| 911 | A378 | 50rp Falknis | .50 | .45 |
| 912 | A378 | 75rp Plassteikopf | .75 | .65 |
| 913 | A378 | 80rp Naafkopf | .80 | .70 |
| 914 | A378 | 1.50fr Garselliturm | 1.50 | 1.25 |
| | | *Nos. 911-914 (4)* | 3.55 | 3.05 |

See Nos. 930-939.

### Customs Type of 1983

Autumn activities: 35rp, Alpine herdsman and flock return from pasture. 50rp, Shucking corn. 80rp, Cattle market.

**Photo. & Engr.**

**1989, Sept. 4**    *Perf. 14*

| | | | | |
|---|---|---|---|---|
| 915 | A325 | 35rp multicolored | .40 | .30 |
| 916 | A325 | 50rp multicolored | .60 | .45 |
| 917 | A325 | 80rp multicolored | .95 | .75 |
| | | *Nos. 915-917 (3)* | 1.95 | 1.50 |

Christmas — A379

Details of the triptych *Adoration of the Magi,* by Hugo van der Goes (50rp) and student (35rp, 90rp), late 15th cent.: 35rp, Melchior and Balthazar. 50rp, Caspar and holy family. 90rp, Donor with St. Stephen.

**1989, Dec. 4**    *Perf. 13½*
**Size of 35rp and 90rp: 23x41mm**

| | | | | |
|---|---|---|---|---|
| 918 | A379 | 35rp multicolored | .45 | .35 |
| 919 | A379 | 50rp shown | .60 | .45 |
| 920 | A379 | 90rp multicolored | 1.10 | .80 |
| | | *Nos. 918-920 (3)* | 2.15 | 1.60 |

Minerals — A380

**1989, Dec. 4**    *Perf. 13½x13*

| | | | | |
|---|---|---|---|---|
| 921 | A380 | 50rp Scepter quartz | .60 | .50 |
| 922 | A380 | 1.10fr Pyrite ball | 1.40 | 1.00 |
| 923 | A380 | 1.50fr Calcite | 1.75 | 1.25 |
| | | *Nos. 921-923 (3)* | 3.75 | 2.75 |

Europa 1990 — A381

Post offices.

**1990, Mar. 5**    **Photo.**    *Perf. 11½x12*
**Granite Paper**

| | | | | |
|---|---|---|---|---|
| 924 | A381 | 50rp shown | .70 | .60 |
| 925 | A381 | 90rp Modern p.o. | 1.25 | 1.10 |

Postage Stamps, 150th Anniv. — A382

**1990, Mar. 5**    *Perf. 11½*
**Granite Paper**

| | | | | |
|---|---|---|---|---|
| 926 | A382 | 1.50fr Penny Black | 2.25 | 1.65 |

1990 World Cup Soccer Championships, Italy — A383

**1990, Mar. 5**    **Granite Paper**    *Perf. 12*

| | | | | |
|---|---|---|---|---|
| 927 | A383 | 2fr multicolored | 2.75 | 1.75 |

1st Anniv. of Death — A384

2fr, Princess Gina, (1921-1989). 3fr, Prince Franz Joseph II, (1906-1989).

**1990, June 5**    **Litho.**    *Perf. 11½*
**Granite Paper**

| | | | | |
|---|---|---|---|---|
| 928 | A384 | 2fr shown | 2.25 | 1.40 |
| 929 | A384 | 3fr multi | 3.25 | 2.25 |

### Mountains Type of 1989

5rp, Augstenberg. 10rp, Hahnenspiel. 35rp, Nospitz. 40rp, Ochsenkopf. 45rp, Drei Schwestern. 60rp, Kuhgrat. 70rp, Galinakopf. 1fr, Schonberg. 1.20fr, Bleikaturm. 1.60fr, Schwarzhorn. 2fr, Scheienkopf.

**1990-93**      **Granite Paper**

| | | | | |
|---|---|---|---|---|
| 930 | A378 | 5rp multicolored | .25 | .25 |
| 931 | A378 | 10rp multicolored | .25 | .25 |
| 933 | A378 | 35rp multicolored | .45 | .30 |
| 933A | A378 | 40rp multicolored | .50 | .45 |
| 934 | A378 | 45rp multicolored | .45 | .35 |
| 935 | A378 | 60rp multicolored | .70 | .55 |
| 936 | A378 | 70rp multicolored | .75 | .60 |
| 938 | A378 | 1fr multicolored | .95 | .75 |
| 939 | A378 | 1.20fr multicolored | 1.40 | 1.10 |
| 940 | A378 | 1.60fr multicolored | 2.00 | 1.40 |
| 941 | A378 | 2.50fr multicolored | 2.50 | 1.75 |
| | | *Nos. 930-941 (11)* | 10.20 | 7.75 |

Issued: 5, 45, 70rp, 1fr, 6/5; 10, 35, 60rp, 1.20fr, 9/3; 40rp, 6/3/91; 1.60fr, 3/2/92; 2fr, 3/1/93.

A385

Paintings by Benjamin Steck (1902-1981): 80rp, Fruit, dish. 1.50fr, Basket, fruit, stein.

**Photo. & Engr.**

**1990, June 5**    *Perf. 14*

| | | | | |
|---|---|---|---|---|
| 942 | A385 | 50rp shown | .70 | .55 |
| 943 | A385 | 80rp multicolored | 1.10 | .80 |
| 944 | A385 | 1.50fr multicolored | 2.25 | 1.60 |
| | | *Nos. 942-944 (3)* | 4.05 | 2.95 |

A386

Game birds.

**Photo. & Engr.**

**1990, Sept. 3**    *Perf. 13x13½*

| | | | | |
|---|---|---|---|---|
| 945 | A386 | 25rp Pheasant | .35 | .25 |
| 946 | A386 | 50rp Blackcock | .70 | .45 |
| 947 | A386 | 2fr Mallard duck | 2.75 | 1.90 |
| | | *Nos. 945-947 (3)* | 3.80 | 2.60 |

European Postal Communications, 500th Anniv. — A387

**1990, Dec. 3**    *Perf. 13½x14*

| | | | | |
|---|---|---|---|---|
| 948 | A387 | 90rp multicolored | 1.50 | 1.00 |

A388

Christmas (Lenten Cloth of Bendern): 35rp, The Annunciation. 50rp, Birth of Christ. 90rp, Adoration of the Magi.

**1990, Dec. 3**    **Photo.**    *Perf. 12*
**Granite Paper**

| | | | | |
|---|---|---|---|---|
| 949 | A388 | 35rp multicolored | .50 | .35 |
| 950 | A388 | 50rp multicolored | .70 | .50 |
| 951 | A388 | 90rp multicolored | 1.25 | .90 |
| | | *Nos. 949-951 (3)* | 2.45 | 1.75 |

A389

Holiday Customs: 35rp, St. Nicholas Visiting Children on Feast of St. Nicholas. 50rp, Waking "sleepyheads" on New Year's Day. 1.50fr, Good wishes on New Year's Day.

**Photo. & Engr.**

**1990, Dec. 3**    *Perf. 14*

| | | | | |
|---|---|---|---|---|
| 952 | A389 | 35rp multicolored | .45 | .30 |
| 953 | A389 | 50rp multicolored | .65 | .45 |
| 954 | A389 | 1.50fr multicolored | 2.00 | 1.40 |
| | | *Nos. 952-954 (3)* | 3.10 | 2.15 |

Europa — A390

Designs: 50rp, Telecommunications satellite, Olympus I. 90rp, Weather satellite, Meteosat.

**1991, Mar. 4**    **Photo.**    *Perf. 11½*
**Granite Paper**

| | | | | |
|---|---|---|---|---|
| 955 | A390 | 50rp multicolored | .80 | .60 |
| 956 | A390 | 90rp multicolored | 1.25 | 1.10 |

St. Ignatius of Loyola (1491-1556), Founder of Jesuit Order — A391

90rp, Wolfgang Amadeus Mozart.

**1991, Mar. 4**    *Perf. 11½*
**Granite Paper**

| | | | | |
|---|---|---|---|---|
| 957 | A391 | 80rp multicolored | 1.10 | .80 |
| 958 | A391 | 90rp multicolored | 1.25 | .90 |

UN Membership, 1990 — A392

**1991, Mar. 4**    *Perf. 11½*
**Granite Paper**

| | | | | |
|---|---|---|---|---|
| 959 | A392 | 2.50fr multicolored | 3.00 | 2.00 |

A393

Paintings: 50rp, Maloja, by Giovanni Giacometti. 80rp, Rheintal, by Ferdinand Gehr. 90rp, Bergell, by Augusto Giacometti. 1.10fr, Hoher Kasten, by Hedwig Scherrer.

**Granite Paper**

**1991, June 3**    **Photo.**    *Perf. 11½*

| | | | | |
|---|---|---|---|---|
| 960 | A393 | 50rp multicolored | .60 | .40 |
| 961 | A393 | 80rp multicolored | .95 | .65 |
| 962 | A393 | 90rp multicolored | 1.00 | .65 |
| 963 | A393 | 1.10fr multicolored | 1.40 | .95 |
| | | *Nos. 960-963 (4)* | 3.95 | 2.65 |

Swiss Confederation, 700th anniv.

Military Uniforms — A394

Designs: 50rp, Non-commissioned officer, private. 70rp, Uniform tunic, trunk. 1fr, Sharpshooters, officer and private.

**Photo. & Engr.**

**1991, June 3**    *Perf. 13½x14*

| | | | | |
|---|---|---|---|---|
| 964 | A394 | 50rp multicolored | .75 | .55 |
| 965 | A394 | 70rp multicolored | 1.10 | .75 |
| 966 | A394 | 1fr multicolored | 1.20 | .85 |
| | | *Nos. 964-966 (3)* | 3.05 | 2.15 |

Last action of Liechtenstein's military, 1866 (70rp).

Princess Marie — A395

3.40fr, Prince Hans Adam II.

**Photo. & Engr.**

**1991, Sept. 2**    *Perf. 13x13½*

| | | | | |
|---|---|---|---|---|
| 967 | A395 | 3fr shown | 2.90 | 2.25 |
| 968 | A395 | 3.40fr multicolored | 3.25 | 2.60 |

LIBA 92, Natl. Philatelic Exhibition — A396

**1991, Sept. 2**    **Photo.**    *Perf. 11½*
**Granite Paper**

| | | | | |
|---|---|---|---|---|
| 969 | A396 | 90rp multicolored | 1.10 | .95 |

A397

Christmas (Altar of St. Mamertus Chapel, Triesen): 50rp, Mary. 80rp, Madonna and Child. 90rp, Angel Gabriel.

**Photo. & Engr.**

**1991, Dec. 2**    *Perf. 13½x14*

| | | | | |
|---|---|---|---|---|
| 970 | A397 | 50rp multicolored | .70 | .50 |
| 971 | A397 | 80rp multicolored | 1.10 | .80 |
| 972 | A397 | 90rp multicolored | 1.25 | .90 |
| | | *Nos. 970-972 (3)* | 3.05 | 2.20 |

A398

1992 Winter Olympics, Albertville: 70rp, Cross-country skiers, doping check. 80rp, Hockey players, good sportsmanship. 1.60fr, Downhill skier, safety precautions.

**Granite Paper**

**1991, Dec. 2**    **Photo.**    *Perf. 11½x12*

| | | | | |
|---|---|---|---|---|
| 973 | A398 | 70rp multicolored | .95 | .70 |
| 974 | A398 | 80rp multicolored | 1.10 | .85 |
| 975 | A398 | 1.60fr multicolored | 2.25 | 1.75 |
| | | *Nos. 973-975 (3)* | 4.30 | 3.30 |

**1992, Mar. 2**    **Photo.**    *Perf. 11½*

1992 Summer Olympics, Barcelona: 50rp, Women's relay, drugs, broken medal. 70rp, Cycling, safety precautions. 2.50fr, Judo, good sportsmanship.

**Granite Paper**

| | | | | |
|---|---|---|---|---|
| 976 | A398 | 50rp multicolored | .65 | .50 |
| 977 | A398 | 70rp multicolored | .90 | .70 |
| 978 | A398 | 2.50fr multicolored | 3.25 | 2.50 |
| | | *Nos. 976-978 (3)* | 4.80 | 3.70 |

Discovery of America, 500th Anniv. — A400

**1992, Mar. 2**       **Granite Paper**
979 A400 80rp shown     1.10 1.00
980 A400 90rp New York skyline   1.40 1.25
         Europa.

Postillion Blowing     Clown in
Horn             Envelope
A401            A402

Designs: No. 982, Postillion delivering valentine. No. 984, Wedding violinist.

**Photo. & Engr.**
**1992, June 1**     **Perf. 14x13½**
981 A401 50rp multicolored    .65 .55
982 A401 50rp multicolored    .65 .55
**Photo.**
**Perf. 12½**
**Granite Paper**
983 A402 50rp multicolored    .65 .55
984 A402 50rp multicolored    .65 .55
    Nos. 981-984 (4)    2.60 2.20

Souvenir Sheet

Prince Hans-Adam and Princess
Marie, 25th Wedding Anniv. — A403

Designs: a, 2fr, Coat of Arms of Liechtenstein-Kinsky Alliance. b, 2.50fr, Prince Hans-Adam and Princess Marie.

**1992, June 1**     **Perf. 11½**
**Granite Paper**
985 A403 Sheet of 2, #a.-b.    5.75 4.00

Ferns — A404

40rp, Blechnum spicant. 50rp, Asplenium trichomanes. 70rp, Phyllitis scolopendrium. 2.50fr, Asplenium ruta-muraria.

**Photo. & Engr.**
**1992, Sept. 7**     **Perf. 14**
986 A404 40rp multicolored    .50 .35
987 A404 50rp multicolored    .55 .40
988 A404 70rp multicolored    .85 .60
989 A404 2.50fr multicolored   3.00 2.25
    Nos. 986-989 (4)    4.90 3.60

Creation of Vaduz
County, 650th
Anniv. — A405

**1992, Sept. 7**     **Perf. 13½x14**
990 A405 1.60fr multicolored   2.50 1.60

Christmas — A406

Scenes in Triesen: 50rp, Chapel, St. Mamertus. 90rp, Nativity scene, St. Gallus Church. 1.60rp, St. Mary's Chapel.

**1992, Dec. 7**     **Photo.**
**Perf. 11½**
**Granite Paper**
991 A406 50rp multicolored    .60 .45
992 A406 90rp multicolored    1.10 .80
993 A406 1.60fr multicolored   2.00 1.40
    Nos. 991-993 (3)    3.70 2.65

Hereditary Prince
Alois — A407

**Photo. & Engr.**
**1992, Dec. 7**     **Perf. 13x13½**
994 A407 2.50fr multicolored   3.50 3.50

A408

Europa (Contemporary paintings): 80rp, 910805, by Bruno Kaufmann. 1fr, The Little Blue, by Evi Kliemand.

**1993, Mar. 1**     **Photo.**    **Perf. 11½x12**
**Granite Paper**
995 A408 80rp multicolored    .90 .75
996 A408 1fr multicolored    1.10 .90

A409

Paintings by Hans Gantner (1853-1914): 50rp, Chalets in Steg and Naafkopf. 60rp, Sass Mountain with Hunting Lodge. 1.80fr, Red House in Vaduz.

**1993, Mar. 1**     **Perf. 11½**
**Granite Paper**
997 A409 50rp multicolored    .65 .45
998 A409 60rp multicolored    .75 .50
999 A409 1.80fr multicolored   2.25 1.50
    Nos. 997-999 (3)    3.65 2.45

Tibetan Art — A410

60rp, Detail from Thangka painting, Tale of the Ferryman. 80rp, Religious dance mask. 1fr, Detail from Thangka painting, The Tale of the Fish.

**1993, June 7**     **Photo.**    **Perf. 11½**
**Granite Paper**
1000 A410 60rp multicolored    .75 .55
1001 A410 80rp multicolored    1.00 .75
1002 A410 1fr multicolored    1.25 .95
    Nos. 1000-1002 (3)    3.00 2.25

Church Missionary
Work — A411

**1993, June 7**     **Perf. 11½x12**
**Granite Paper**
1003 A411 1.80fr Tree of life   2.10 1.60

A412

Contemporary painting: Black Hatter, by Friedensreich Hundertwasser.

**Photo. & Engr.**
**1993, June 7**     **Perf. 14x13½**
1004 A412 2.80fr multicolored   4.00 2.40

Souvenir Sheet

Marriage of Hereditary Prince Alois and Duchess Sophie of Bavaria, July 3 — A413

**1993, June 7**     **Photo.**    **Perf. 11½**
**Granite Paper**
1005 A413 4fr multicolored    5.25 3.50

Wild Animals — A414

**Photo. & Engr.**
**1993, Sept. 6**     **Perf. 13x13½**
1006 A414 60rp Badger    .85 .60
1007 A414 80rp Marten    1.10 .75
1008 A414 1fr Fox    1.40 .95
    Nos. 1006-1008 (3)    3.35 2.30

Meadow Plants — A415

50rp, Origanum vulgare. 60rp, Salvia pratensis. 1fr, Seseli annuum. 2.50fr, Prunella grandiflora.

**1993, Sept. 6**
1009 A415 50rp multicolored    .65 .45
1010 A415 60rp multicolored    .80 .55
1011 A415 1fr multicolored    1.25 .85
1012 A415 2.50fr multicolored   3.25 2.25
    Nos. 1009-1012 (4)    5.95 4.10
    See Nos. 1056-1059.

Christmas — A416

Calligraphic Christmas texts by: 60rp, Rainer Maria Rilke. 80rp, Th. Friedrich. 1fr, Rudolph Alexander Schroder.

**1993, Dec. 6**     **Photo.**    **Perf. 11½x12**
**Granite Paper**
1013 A416 60rp multicolored    .80 .55
1014 A416 80rp multicolored    1.00 .70
1015 A416 1fr multicolored    1.25 .90
    Nos. 1013-1015 (3)    3.05 2.15

A417

**1993, Dec. 6**     **Granite Paper**
1016 A417 60rp Ski jump    .80 .65
1017 A417 80rp Slalom skiing   1.00 .80
1018 A417 2.40fr Bobsled    3.00 2.40
    Nos. 1016-1018 (3)    4.80 3.85
    1994 Winter Olympics, Lillehammer.

Anniversaries
and
Events — A418       A419

A420

**1994, Mar. 7**     **Photo.**
**Perf. 11½**
**Granite Paper**
1019 A418 60rp multicolored    .70 .70
1020 A419 1.80fr multicolored   2.00 2.00
1021 A420 2.80fr multicolored   3.00 3.00
    Nos. 1019-1021 (3)    5.70 5.70

Principality of Liechtenstein, 275th anniv. (No. 1019). Intl. Olympic Committee, cent. (No. 1020). 1994 World Cup Soccer Championships, US (No. 1021).

Alexander von Humboldt
(1769-1859) — A421

Europa: 80rp, Vultur gryphus. 1fr, Rhexia cardinalis.

**Photo. & Engr.**
**1994, Mar. 7**     **Perf. 13x13½**
1022 A421 80rp multicolored   1.10 .90
1023 A421 1fr multicolored    1.40 1.00

Mobile, by Jean
Tinguely (1925-
91) — A422

**Photo. & Engr.**
**1994, June 6**     **Perf. 13½x14**
1024 A422 4fr multicolored    4.50 4.50

Letter
Writing — A423

**1994, June 6**     **Photo.**    **Perf. 12½**
**Granite Paper**
1025 A423 60rp Elephant    .90 .80
1026 A423 60rp Cherub    .90 .80
1027 A423 60rp Pig    .90 .80
1028 A423 60rp Dog    .90 .80
    Nos. 1025-1028 (4)    3.60 3.20

Life Cycle of
Grape
Vine — A424

Designs: No. 1029, Spring, vine beginning to flower. No. 1030, Summer, green grapes on vine. No. 1031, Autumn, ripe grapes ready for harvest. No. 1032, Winter, bare vine in snow.

**1994, Sept 5**     **Photo.**    **Perf. 11½**
**Granite Paper**
1029 A424 60rp multicolored    .90 .80
1030 A424 60rp multicolored    .90 .80
1031 A424 60rp multicolored    .90 .80
1032 A424 60rp multicolored    .90 .80
  a    Block of 4, #1029-1032   4.00 4.00

    No. 1032a is continuous design.

Minerals — A425

60rp, Strontianite. 80rp, Faden quartz. 3.50fr, Ferrous dolomite.

**Photo. & Engr.**

**1994, Sept. 5**     *Perf. 13½x12½*

| | | | | |
|---|---|---|---|---|
| 1033 | A425 | 60rp multicolored | .80 | .80 |
| 1034 | A425 | 80rp multicolored | 1.10 | 1.10 |
| 1035 | A425 | 3.50fr multicolored | 4.75 | 4.75 |
| | | Nos. 1033-1035 (3) | 6.65 | 6.65 |

A426

Christmas contemporary art, by Anne Frommelt: 60rp, The True Light. 80rp, Peace on Earth. 1fr, See the House of God.

**1994, Dec. 5**    **Photo.**    *Perf. 11½*
**Granite Paper**

| | | | | |
|---|---|---|---|---|
| 1036 | A426 | 60rp multicolored | .80 | .60 |
| 1037 | A426 | 80rp multicolored | 1.10 | .80 |
| 1038 | A426 | 1fr multicolored | 1.40 | .90 |
| | | Nos. 1036-1038 (3) | 3.30 | 2.30 |

A427

The Four Elements, by Ernst Steiner.

**Photo. & Engr.**

**1994, Dec. 5**     *Perf. 14*

| | | | | |
|---|---|---|---|---|
| 1039 | A427 | 60rp Earth | .75 | .60 |
| 1040 | A427 | 80rp Water | 1.10 | .80 |
| 1041 | A427 | 1fr Fire | 1.25 | .90 |
| 1042 | A427 | 2.50fr Air | 3.50 | 2.60 |
| | | Nos. 1039-1042 (4) | 6.60 | 4.90 |

Peace and Freedom — A428

Europa: 80rp, 1fr, Excerpts from speeches of Prince Franz Josef II.

**1995, Mar. 6**    **Photo.**    *Perf. 11½*
**Granite Paper**

| | | | | |
|---|---|---|---|---|
| 1043 | A428 | 80rp multicolored | 1.10 | .90 |
| 1044 | A428 | 1fr multicolored | 1.40 | 1.10 |

A429

Anniversaries and Events
A430      A431

60rp, Princess Marie, Bosnian children.

**1995, Mar. 6**     **Granite Paper**

| | | | | |
|---|---|---|---|---|
| 1045 | A429 | 60rp multicolored | .80 | .60 |
| 1046 | A430 | 1.80fr multicolored | 2.50 | 2.00 |
| 1047 | A431 | 3.50fr multicolored | 4.75 | 3.50 |
| | | Nos. 1045-1047 (3) | 8.05 | 6.10 |

Liechtenstein Red Cross, 50th anniv. (No. 1045). UN, 50th anniv. (No. 1046). The Alps, European Landscape of the Year 1995-96 (No. 1047).

Falknis Group, by Anton Frommelt (1895-1975) — A432

Paintings: 80rp, Three Oaks. 4.10fr, Rhine below Triesen.

**1995, June 6**    **Photo.**    *Perf. 12*
**Granite Paper**

| | | | | |
|---|---|---|---|---|
| 1048 | A432 | 60rp multicolored | .85 | .65 |
| 1049 | A432 | 80rp multicolored | 1.20 | .90 |
| 1050 | A432 | 4.10fr multicolored | 6.00 | 4.75 |
| | | Nos. 1048-1050 (3) | 8.05 | 6.30 |

Letter Writing — A433

No. 1051, Girl, boy building heart with bricks. No. 1052, Boy, girl bandaging sunflower. No. 1053, Girl, boy & rainbow. No. 1054, Boy in hot air balloon delivering letter to girl.

**1995, June 6**     *Perf. 12½*
**Granite Paper**

| | | | | |
|---|---|---|---|---|
| 1051 | A433 | 60rp multicolored | .85 | .65 |
| 1052 | A433 | 60rp multicolored | .85 | .65 |
| 1053 | A433 | 60rp multicolored | .85 | .65 |
| 1054 | A433 | 60rp multicolored | .85 | .65 |
| a. | | Vert. strip of 4, #1051-1054 + label | 3.50 | 3.50 |

Liechtenstein-Switzerland Postal Relationship — A434

**Litho. & Engr.**

**1995, Sept. 5**     *Perf. 13½*

| | | | | |
|---|---|---|---|---|
| 1055 | A434 | 60rp multicolored | 1.00 | .65 |

See Switzerland No. 960.
No. 1055 and Switzerland No. 960 are identical. This issue was valid for postage in both countries.

**Plant Type of 1993**

60rp, Arnica montana. 80rp, Urtica dioica. 1.80fr, Valeriana officinalis. 3.50rp, Ranunculus ficaria.

**Photo. & Engr.**

**1995, Sept. 5**     *Perf. 13x13½*

| | | | | |
|---|---|---|---|---|
| 1056 | A415 | 60rp multicolored | .75 | .65 |
| 1057 | A415 | 80rp multicolored | 1.00 | .80 |
| 1058 | A415 | 1.80fr multicolored | 2.25 | 2.00 |
| 1059 | A415 | 3.50fr multicolored | 4.50 | 4.00 |
| | | Nos. 1056-1059 (4) | 8.50 | 7.55 |

Christmas — A435

Paintings by Lorenzo Monaco: 60rp, Angel kneeling, facing right. 80rp, Madonna and Child, two angels at her feet. 1fr, Angel kneeling, facing left.

**Photo. & Engr.**

**1995, Dec. 4**     *Perf. 14½x13½*

| | | | | |
|---|---|---|---|---|
| 1060 | A435 | 60rp multicolored | .80 | .65 |
| 1061 | A435 | 80rp multicolored | 1.10 | .90 |
| 1062 | A435 | 1fr multicolored | 1.40 | 1.10 |
| | | Nos. 1060-1062 (3) | 3.30 | 2.65 |

A436

Painting: 4fr, Lady with Lap Dog, by Paul Wunderlich.

**1995, Dec. 4**

| | | | | |
|---|---|---|---|---|
| 1063 | A436 | 4fr multicolored | 5.50 | 4.50 |

Bronze Age in Europe — A437

**1996, Mar. 4**    **Photo.**    *Perf. 11½*
**Granite Paper**

| | | | | |
|---|---|---|---|---|
| 1064 | A437 | 90rp Crucible, pin | 1.50 | 1.25 |

Countess Nora Kinsky (1888-1923), Nurse, Mother of Princess Gina — A438

Profile and: 90rp, Mar. 7, 1917 diary entry. 1.10fr, Feb. 28, 1917 diary entry.

**1996, Mar. 4**     **Granite Paper**

| | | | | |
|---|---|---|---|---|
| 1065 | A438 | 90rp multicolored | 1.75 | 1.00 |
| 1066 | A438 | 1.10fr multicolored | 2.25 | 1.25 |

Paintings of Village Views, by Marianne Siegl, Based on Sketches by Otto Zeiller — A439

10rp, Eschen. 20rp, Farmhouse, St. Joseph's Chapel, Planken. 80rp, Farmhouse, Ruggell. 1fr, Postal auxiliary office, Nendeln. 1.20fr, Buildings, Triesen. 1.30fr, Upper Village, Triesen. 1.70fr, St. Theresa's Church, Schaanwald. 2fr, Rural houses, barns, Gamprin. 4fr, Parish Church, center of village, Triesenberg. 5fr, Vaduz Castle.

**1996-99**    **Photo.**    *Perf. 12*
**Granite Paper**

| | | | | |
|---|---|---|---|---|
| 1068 | A439 | 10rp multicolored | .25 | .25 |
| 1069 | A439 | 20rp multicolored | .35 | .25 |
| 1070 | A439 | 80rp multicolored | 1.25 | .90 |
| 1071 | A439 | 1fr multicolored | 1.75 | .90 |
| 1072 | A439 | 1.20fr multicolored | 2.00 | 1.10 |
| 1073 | A439 | 1.30fr multicolored | 2.25 | 1.10 |
| 1074 | A439 | 1.70fr multicolored | 2.75 | 1.50 |
| 1075 | A439 | 2fr multicolored | 2.75 | 1.75 |
| 1076 | A439 | 4fr multicolored | 6.75 | 3.50 |
| 1077 | A439 | 5fr multicolored | 8.50 | 5.50 |
| | | Nos. 1068-1077 (10) | 28.60 | 16.75 |

Issued: 10rp, 5fr, 3/4/96; 20rp, 1.30fr, 1.70fr, 3/3/97; 2fr, 4fr, 6/2/98; 80rp, 1fr, 1.20fr, 3/1/99.
See Nos. 1167-1175A.

Modern Olympic Games, Cent. — A440

**1996, June 3**    **Photo.**    *Perf. 11½*
**Granite Paper**

| | | | | |
|---|---|---|---|---|
| 1079 | A440 | 70rp Gymnastics | 1.10 | .90 |
| 1080 | A440 | 90rp Hurdles | 1.40 | 1.00 |
| 1081 | A440 | 1.10fr Cycling | 2.00 | 1.10 |
| | | Nos. 1079-1081 (3) | 4.50 | 3.00 |

Ferdinand Gehr, 100th Birthday — A441

Various paintings of flowers.

**1996, June 3**     **Granite Paper**

| | | | | |
|---|---|---|---|---|
| 1083 | A441 | 70rp multicolored | 1.10 | .90 |
| 1084 | A441 | 90rp multicolored | 1.40 | 1.00 |
| 1085 | A441 | 1.10fr multicolored | 2.00 | 1.10 |

**Size: 33x23mm**

| | | | | |
|---|---|---|---|---|
| 1086 | A441 | 1.80fr multicolored | 2.75 | 2.00 |
| | | Nos. 1083-1086 (4) | 7.25 | 5.00 |

Austria, Millennium A442

**Photo. & Engr.**

**1996, Sept. 2**     *Perf. 13½*

| | | | | |
|---|---|---|---|---|
| 1087 | A442 | 90rp multicolored | 1.50 | 1.10 |

New Constitution, 75th Anniv. A443

**Litho., Engr. & Embossed**

**1996, Sept. 2**     *Perf. 14*

| | | | | |
|---|---|---|---|---|
| 1088 | A443 | 10fr Natl. arms | 14.00 | 13.00 |

A444

Paintings by Russian Artist, Eugen Zotow (1881-1953): 70rp, "Country Estate in Poltava." 1.10fr, "Three Bathers in a Park in Berlin." 1.40fr, "View of Vaduz."

**Photo. & Engr.**

**1996, Dec. 2**     *Perf. 14*

| | | | | |
|---|---|---|---|---|
| 1089 | A444 | 70rp multicolored | 1.10 | .75 |
| 1090 | A444 | 1.10fr multicolored | 2.00 | 1.10 |
| 1091 | A444 | 1.40fr multicolored | 2.25 | 1.50 |
| | | Nos. 1089-1091 (3) | 5.35 | 3.35 |

A445

Christmas: Illuminated manuscripts, symbols of the Evangelists.

**1996, Dec. 2**

| | | | | |
|---|---|---|---|---|
| 1092 | A445 | 70rp Matthew | 1.10 | .75 |
| 1093 | A445 | 90rp Mark | 1.40 | .90 |
| 1094 | A445 | 1.10fr Luke | 1.75 | 1.10 |
| 1095 | A445 | 1.80fr John | 2.75 | 2.00 |
| | | Nos. 1092-1095 (4) | 7.00 | 4.75 |

A446

**Photo. & Engr.**

**1997, Mar. 3**     *Perf. 13½*

| | | | | |
|---|---|---|---|---|
| 1096 | A446 | 70rp multicolored | 1.10 | .65 |

Franz Schubert (1797-1828), composer.

A447

Europa, Liechtenstein Myths: 90rp, Wild Gnomes. 1.10fr, Foal of Planken.

**1997, Mar. 3**    **Photo.**    *Perf. 12*
**Granite Paper**

| | | | | |
|---|---|---|---|---|
| 1097 | A447 | 90rp multicolored | 1.75 | 1.00 |
| 1098 | A447 | 1.10fr multicolored | 2.25 | 1.10 |

St. Lucius, Virgin Mary Holding Infant Jesus, St. Florin, by Gabriel Dreher — A448

**Photo. & Engr.**
**1997, June 2**     **Perf. 13½x13**
1099 A448 20fr multicolored   24.00 17.00

A449

Painting, "Jeune Fille en Fleur," by Enrico Baj.

**1997, Aug. 22**   **Photo.**   **Perf. 11½**
**Granite Paper**
1100 A449 70rp multicolored    1.40 1.00

Mushrooms — A450

70rp, Phaeolepiota aurea. 90rp, Helvella silvicola. 1.10fr, Aleuria aurantia.

**Photo. & Engr.**
**1997, Aug. 22**     **Perf. 14**
1101 A450 70rp multicolored   1.20 .60
1102 A450 90rp multicolored   1.50 .80
1103 A450 1.10fr multicolored   1.90 1.00
    Nos. 1101-1103 (3)   4.60 2.40

Railway in Liechtenstein, 125th Anniv. — A451

Train stations: 70rp, Schaanwald. 90rp, Nendeln. 1.80fr, Schaan-Vaduz.

**1997, Aug. 22**   **Photo.**   **Perf. 11½**
**Granite Paper**
1104 A451 70rp multicolored   1.20 .60
1105 A451 90rp multicolored   1.50 .80
1106 A451 1.80fr multicolored   2.90 1.60
    Nos. 1104-1106 (3)   5.60 3.00

Christmas Tree Decorations — A452

90rp, Bell. 1.10fr, Oval with pointed ends.

**Photo. & Engr.**
**1997, Dec. 1**     **Perf. 14**
1107 A452 70rp shown   1.20 .60
1108 A452 90rp multicolored   1.50 .80
1109 A452 1.10fr multicolored   1.90 1.60
    Nos. 1107-1109 (3)   4.60 3.00

A453

Skiing, 1998 Winter Olympic Games, Nagano.

**1997, Dec. 1**   **Photo.**   **Perf. 12½**
**Granite Paper**
1110 A453 70rp Cross-country   1.40 1.00
1111 A453 90rp Slalom   1.75 1.25
1112 A453 1.80fr Downhill   3.50 2.50
    Nos. 1110-1112 (3)   6.65 4.75

A454

Contemporary Art, Paintings by Heinz Mack: No. 1113, Verano (Der Sommer). No. 1114, Hommage An Liechtenstein. No. 1115, Zwischen Tag Und Traum. No. 1116, Salute Chirico!.

**1998, Mar. 2**     **Perf. 12**
**Granite Paper**
1113 A454 70rp multicolored   1.20 .85
1114 A454 70rp multicolored   1.20 .85
1115 A454 70rp multicolored   1.20 .85
1116 A454 70rp multicolored   1.20 .85
   a.   Block or strip of 4, #1113-1116   5.00 3.50

Festivals — A455

Europa: 90rp, National holiday. 1.10fr, Festival of the Musical Societies.

**1998, Mar. 2**     **Granite Paper**
1117 A455 90rp multicolored   *1.75 1.00*
1118 A455 1.10fr multicolored   *2.25 1.10*

Customs Treaty with Switzerland, 75th Anniv. — A456

**1998, Mar. 2**     **Granite Paper**
1119 A456 1.70fr multicolored   2.75 2.00

1998 World Cup Soccer Championships, France — A457

**1998, Mar. 2**     **Granite Paper**
1120 A457 1.80fr multicolored   2.75 2.00

Letter Writing — A458

Clown: No. 1121, With woman. No. 1122, Holding four leaf clovers. No. 1123, Tipping hat. No. 1124, Holding paper with heart.

**Photo. & Engr.**
**1998, June 2**     **Perf. 14**
1121 A458 70rp multicolored   1.20 .60
1122 A458 70rp multicolored   1.20 .60
1123 A458 70rp multicolored   1.20 .60
1124 A458 70rp multicolored   1.20 .60
   a.   Strip of 4, #1121-1124   5.00 3.50

1848 Protest March — A459

**1998, Sept. 7**   **Photo.**   **Perf. 12**
**Granite Paper**
1125 A459 1.80fr multicolored   3.00 1.75

A460

Traditional Crafts: 90rp, Cooper's tools, tub. 2.20fr, Wooden shoemaker's tools, clog. 3.50fr, Cartwright's tools, wheel.

**1998, Sept. 7**     **Granite Paper**
1126 A460 90rp multicolored   1.40 1.00
1127 A460 2.20fr multicolored   3.50 2.40
1128 A460 3.50fr multicolored   5.50 3.75
    Nos. 1126-1128 (3)   10.40 7.15
    See Nos. 1215-1217.

A461

Christmas (Nativity Scene in high relief): 70rp, Soldier, Virgin Mary. 90rp, Entire nativity scene. 1.10fr, Joseph, donkey.

**Photo. & Engr.**
**1998, Dec. 7**     **Perf. 14**
1129 A461 70rp multicolored   1.20 .75
1130 A461 90rp multicolored   1.40 1.00
1131 A461 1.10fr multicolored   1.75 1.25
    Nos. 1129-1131 (3)   4.35 3.00

    No. 1130 is 34x26mm.

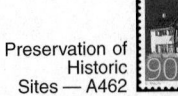

Preservation of Historic Sites — A462

Older buildings, Hinterschellenberg: 90rp, Guest house. 1.70fr, St. George's Chapel, vert. 1.80fr, Farmhouse.

**1998, Dec. 7**   **Photo.**   **Perf. 11½**
**Granite Paper**
1132 A462 90rp multicolored   1.40 1.00
1133 A462 1.70fr multicolored   2.75 2.00
1134 A462 1.80fr multicolored   2.75 2.00
    Nos. 1132-1134 (3)   6.90 5.00

Telephone in Liechtenstein, Cent. — A463

**1998, Dec. 7**     **Granite Paper**
1135 A463 2.80fr multicolored   5.00 3.25

A464

Europa (Conservation Areas): 90rp, Snake, Schwabbrünnen-Aescher marshland. 1.10fr, Bird, Ruggell marsh.

**Granite Paper**
**1999, Mar. 1**   **Photo.**   **Perf. 11½x12**
1136 A464 90rp multicolored   *1.75 1.00*
1137 A464 1.10fr multicolored   *2.25 1.25*

Unterland, 300th Anniv. — A465

Continuous scene of villages: a, Schellenberg, buildings, fortress. b, Mauren, domed steeple on church. c, Eschen,, church, houses. d, Ruggell, road leading into village. e, Gamprin, gray-roofed buildings, church.

**1999, Mar. 1**     **Perf. 12**
**Granite Paper**
1138 A465   Sheet of 5 + label   9.00 6.25
   a.-e.   90rp any single   1.75 1.25

Anniversaries — A466

Stylized designs: No. 1139, Council of Europe 50th anniv. emblem. No. 1140, Bird holding letter. No. 1141, Hand holding heart.

**1999, May 25**   **Photo.**   **Perf. 11½x12**
**Granite Paper**
1139 A466 70rp multicolored   .90 .60
1140 A466 70rp multicolored   .90 .60
1141 A466 70rp multicolored   .90 .60
    Nos. 1139-1141 (3)   2.70 1.80

    No. 1140, UPU, 125th anniv. No. 1141, Caritas Liechtenstein, 75th anniv.

8th Games of the Small European States — A467

**1999, May 25**     **Granite Paper**
1142 A467 70rp Judo   .90 .60
1143 A467 70rp Swimming   .90 .60
1144 A467 70rp Javelin   .90 .60
1145 A467 90rp Volleyball   1.25 .75
1146 A467 90rp Squash   1.25 .75
1147 A467 90rp Tennis   1.25 .75
1148 A467 90rp Table tennis   1.25 .75
1149 A467 90rp Cycling   1.25 .75
1150 A467 90rp Shooting   1.25 .75
    Nos. 1142-1150 (9)   10.20 6.30

Johann Wolfgang von Goethe (1749-1832), Poet — A468

Quotations and scenes from Faust: 1.40fr, "Grey, dear friend, is all theory and green the golden tree of life." 1.70fr, "I'll take the wager!...Done! And again, and again!"

**Photo. & Engr.**
**1999, Sept. 9**     **Perf. 14**
1151 A468 1.40fr multicolored   1.50 1.10
1152 A468 1.70fr multicolored   2.50 1.50

Paintings by Eugen Verling (1891-1968) — A469

Designs: 70rp, Herrengasse. 2fr, Old Vaduz with Castle. 4fr, House in Fürst-Franz-Josef-Strasse, Vaduz.

**1999, Sept. 9**
1153 A469 70rp multicolored   .90 .60
1154 A469 2fr multicolored   2.60 1.50
1155 A469 4fr multicolored   5.25 3.25
    Nos. 1153-1155 (3)   8.75 5.35

A470

Walser house identification marks.

**1999, Dec. 6**   **Photo.**   **Perf. 11¾**
**Granite Paper**
1156 A470 70rp Door mark   .90 .60
1157 A470 90rp Picture mark   1.10 .75
1158 A470 1.80fr Axe mark   2.10 1.75
    Nos. 1156-1158 (3)   4.10 3.10

A471

3.60fr, Johann Gutenberg, inventer of letter-press printing.

**Photo. & Engr.**

**1999, Dec. 6** — *Perf. 13½*
1159　A471　3.60fr multicolored　　4.50　3.25

Christmas Paintings by Joseph Walser — A472

70rp, The Annunciation. 90rp, Nativity. 1.10fr, Presentation of Jesus.

**1999, Dec. 6** — *Perf. 13½x14¼*
1160　A472　70rp multicolored　　　.90　.60
1161　A472　90rp multicolored　　　1.10　.75
1162　A472　1.10fr multicolored　　1.40　.95
　　　Nos. 1160-1162 (3)　　　　3.40　2.30

**Souvenir Sheet**

Millennium — A473

Designs: 70rp, The Adoration of the Shepherds, by Matthias Stomer. 1.10fr, The Magi, by Ferdinand Gehr.

**2000, Jan. 1　Photo.** — *Perf. 12*
**Granite Paper**
1163　A473　Sheet of 2　　　　4.00　2.25
　a.　70rp multi　　　　　　　1.40　.85
　b.　1.10fr multi　　　　　　2.25　1.40
　　　Christianity, 2000th anniv.

Creation of Liechtenstein Post, Ltd. — A474

**2000, Jan. 1** — *Perf. 11¾*
**Granite Paper**
1164　A474　90rp multi　　　　　2.00　1.10

**Village Views Type of 1996**

Designs: 50rp, Church and vicarage, Ruggell. 60rp, Chapel of St. Peter, Balzers. 70rp, Parish church, Schellenberg. 1.10fr, Holy Cross Chapel, Eschen. 1.40fr, Farmhouse, parish church, Mauren. 1.80fr, Chapel of Peace, Malbun. 1.90fr, Tower of Church of St. Lawrence, Schaan. 2.20fr, Höfle District, Balzers. 4.50fr, Church mound, Bendern.

**2000-01　Photo.** — *Perf. 11¾*
**Granite Paper**
1167　A439　50rp multi　　　　　.75　.45
1168　A439　60rp multi　　　　　.95　.50
1169　A439　70rp multi　　　　　1.10　.65
1171　A439　1.10fr multi　　　　1.75　1.10
1172　A439　1.40fr multi　　　　2.10　1.40
1173　A439　1.80fr multi　　　　2.75　1.75
1174　A439　1.90fr multi　　　　2.75　1.75
1175　A439　2.20fr multi　　　　3.50　2.00
1175A　A439　4.50fr multi　　　　7.00　4.25
　　　Nos. 1167-1175A (9)　　22.65　13.85

Issued: 70rp, 1.80fr, 2.20fr, 4.50fr, 6/5/01.

"Gods Once Walked" Exhibition at Vaduz Museum of Art — A475

Designs: 70rp, Mars and Rhea Silvia, by Peter Paul Rubens. 1.80fr, Cupid With Soap Bubble, by Rembrandt.

**Photo. & Engr.**
**2000, Mar. 6** — *Perf. 13½x12¾*
1176　A475　70rp multi　　　　　1.10　.65
1177　A475　1.80fr multi　　　　2.60　1.75

---

**Europa, 2000**
Common Design Type
**2000, May 9　Photo.** — *Perf. 11½x11¾*
**Granite Paper**
1178　CD17　1.10fr multi　　　　2.25　1.75

Expo 2000, Hanover — A476

Art by Friedensreich Hundertwasser: 70rp, Fragrance of Humus. 90rp, Do Not Wait Houses — Move. 1.10fr, The Car: A Drive Towards Nature and Creation.

**Photo. & Engr.**
**2000, May 9** — *Perf. 14¼x13½*
1179　A476　70rp multi　　　　　1.40　.80
1180　A476　90rp multi　　　　　1.75　1.00
1181　A476　1.10fr multi　　　　2.25　1.25
　　　Nos. 1179-1181 (3)　　　5.40　3.05

Images of Peace — A477

Art by mouth and foot painters: 1.40fr, Dove of Peace, by Antonio Martini. 1.70fr, Universal Peace, by Alberto Alvarez. 2.20fr, Rainbow, by Eiichi Minami.

**2000, May 9　Photo.** — *Perf. 11¾x11½*
1182　A477　1.40fr multi　　　　2.25　1.25
1183　A477　1.70fr multi　　　　2.60　1.50
1184　A477　2.20fr multi　　　　3.50　2.00
　　　Nos. 1182-1184 (3)　　　8.35　4.75

2000 Summer Olympics, Sydney — A478

Designs: 80rp, Koalas on rings. 1fr, High jump by kangaroo joey. 1.30fr, Emus racing. 1.80fr, Platypuses swimming.

**2000, Sept. 4　Photo.** — *Perf. 11¾*
**Granite Paper**
1185　A478　80rp multi　　　　　1.10　.65
1186　A478　1fr multi　　　　　1.25　.75
1187　A478　1.30fr multi　　　　1.60　1.00
1188　A478　1.80fr multi　　　　2.25　1.40
　　　Nos. 1185-1188 (4)　　　6.20　3.80

Organization for Security and Co-operation In Europe, 25th Anniv. — A479

**2000, Sept. 4** — **Granite Paper**
1189　A479　1.30fr multi　　　　2.50　1.50

Issued in sheets of 20 stamps and 5 labels.

Opening Of Liechtenstein Art Museum — A480

Designs: 80rp, The Dreaming Bee, by Joan Miró. 1.20fr, Cube by Sol LeWitt. 2fr, A Bouquet of Flowers, by Roelant Savery.

**2000, Sept. 4　Photo.** — *Perf. 11¾*
**Granite Paper (#1190-1191)**
1190　A480　80rp multi　　　　　1.60　.95
1191　A480　1.20fr multi　　　　2.40　1.40

**Size: 31x46mm**
**Photo. & Engr.**
*Perf. 13¾*
1192　A480　2fr multi　　　　　4.00　2.40
　　　Nos. 1190-1192 (3)　　　8.00　4.75

---

Mushrooms — A481

90rp, Mycena adonis. 1.10fr, Chalciporus amarellus. 2fr, Hygrocybe caylptriformis.

**Photo. & Engr.**
**2000, Dec. 4** — *Perf. 14¼*
1193-1195　A481　Set of 3　　　8.00　4.50

Christmas — A482

Various creches: 80rp, 1.30fr, 1.80fr.

**2000, Dec. 4** — *Perf. 13¾x14*
1196-1198　A482　Set of 3　　　6.50　4.00

Europa — A483

**2001, Mar. 5　Photo.** — *Perf. 11½x11¾*
**Granite Paper**
1199　A483　1.30fr multi　　　　2.25　1.50

Liechtenstein's Presidency of Council of Europe — A484

**2001, Mar. 5** — *Perf. 11¾*
**Granite Paper**
1200　A484　1.80fr multi　　　　2.90　1.75

Scratch-off Greetings — A485

Postman in: No. 1201, 70rp, Red uniform (hidden flower bouquet). No. 1202, 70rp, Blue uniform (hidden envelope).

**2001, Mar. 5** — **Granite Paper**
1201-1202　A485　Set of 2 un-scratched　　2.50　1.25
　　　Set, scratched　　　　　　　　1.50

Easter Eggs of the Russian Czars — A486

Designs: 1.20fr, Silver egg. 1.80fr, Cloisonné egg. 2fr, Porcelain egg.

**Photo. & Engr.**
**2001, Mar. 5** — *Perf. 13¾*
1203-1205　A486　Set of 3　　　10.00　6.00

Liechtenstein Historical Association, Cent. — A487

Designs: No. 1206, 70rp, Mars of Gutenberg. No. 1207, Carolignian cruciform fibula.

---

**2001, June 5　Photo.** — *Perf. 11¾*
**Granite Paper**
1206-1207　A487　Set of 2　　　2.75　1.75

Josef Gabriel Rheinberger (1839-1901), Musician — A488

**Photo. & Engr.**
**2001, Sept. 3** — *Perf. 14*
1208　A488　3.50fr multi　　　　5.75　3.50

Votive Pictures — A489

Designs: 70rp, 1733 picture, Chapel of Our Lady, Dux. 1.20fr, 1802 picture, St. George's Chapel, Schellenberg. 1.30fr, 1718 picture, Chapel of Our Lady, Dux.

**2001, Sept. 3** — *Perf. 13½*
1209-1211　A489　Set of 3　　　6.50　4.00

Building Preservation — A490

Designs: 70rp, St. Theresa's Chapel, Schaanwald. 90rp, St. Johann's winery, Mauren. 1.10fr, Pirsch transformer station, Schaanwald.

**2001, Sept. 3　Photo.** — *Perf. 11¾*
**Granite Paper**
1212-1214　A490　Set of 3　　　5.25　3.25

See Nos. 1232-1233, 1251-1252, 1295-1296, 1323-1324, 1361-1362, 1394-1395, 1424.

**Traditional Crafts Type of 1998**

Designs: 70rp, Blacksmith's tools, horseshoe, yoke bars. 90rp, Rakemaker's tools, rake. 1.20fr, Saddler's tools, horse collar.

**2001, Dec. 3　Photo.** — *Perf. 11¾*
**Granite Paper**
1215-1217　A460　Set of 3　　　4.50　3.00

Abstract Art by Gottfried Honegger — A491

Untitled works: 1.80fr, 2.20fr.

**2001, Dec. 3** — *Perf. 11½*
**Granite Paper**
1218-1219　A491　Set of 2　　　6.50　4.00

Christmas — A492

Medallions: 70rp, Annunciation. 90rp, Nativity. 1.30fr, The Presentation of the Lord.

**2001, Dec. 3** — *Perf. 12x11¾*
**Granite Paper**
1220-1222　A492　Set of 3　　　4.00　3.50

Liechtenstein Students' Spice Bees Experiment on Space Shuttle — A493

**2002, Mar. 4  Photo.  Perf. 13½x14¼**
1223  A493  90rp multi  1.75 1.10

LIBA.02 Stamp Exhibition, Vaduz — A494

**2002, Mar. 4  Perf. 13¾**
1224  A494  1.20fr multi  2.10 1.10

Europa — A495

Designs: 90rp, Tightrope walker. 1.30fr, Juggler.

**Photo. & Engr.**
**2002, Mar. 4  Perf. 14¼x14**
1225-1226  A495  Set of 2  4.25 3.75

Intl. Year of Mountains A496

Intl. Commision for Protection of the Alps A497

**2002, Mar. 4  Photo.  Perf. 13¾x13½**
1227  A496  70rp multi  1.40 .85
1228  A497  1.20fr multi  2.40 1.40

Paintings by Friedrich Kaufmann (1892-1972) A498

Views of: 70rp, Schellenberg. 1.30fr, Schaan. 1.80fr, Steg.

**2002, Mar. 4  Perf. 13½x13¾**
1229-1231  A498  Set of 3  6.50 4.00

**Building Preservation Type of 2001**
Designs: 70rp, House, Popers, horiz. 1.20fr, House, Weiherring, horiz.

**Perf. 13¾x13½**
**2002, June 3  Photo.**
1232-1233  A490  Set of 2  3.25 2.00

2002 World Cup Soccer Championships, Japan and Korea — A499

**2002, June 3  Perf. 13½x14¼**
1234  A499  1.80fr multi  3.25 2.00

Royalty — A500

Designs: 3fr, Princess Marie. 3.50fr, Prince Hans Adam II.

**2002, June 3  Perf. 13¾x13½**
1235-1236  A500  Set of 2  10.00 7.00

Liba.02 Stamp Exhibition, Vaduz — A501

Liechtenstein stamps depicting: 90rp, Various topics. 1.30fr, Royalty.

**2002, Aug. 8  Photo.  Perf. 13½**
1237-1238  A501  Set of 2  3.50 2.50

**Royalty Type of 2002**
Designs: 2fr, Hereditary Princess Sophie. 2.50fr, Hereditary Prince Alois.

**2002, Aug. 8  Perf. 13¾x13½**
1239-1240  A500  Set of 2  7.00 4.00

Orchids — A502

Designs: 70rp, Epipogium aphyllum. 1.20fr, Ophrys insectifera. 1.30fr, Nigritella nigra.

**2002, Aug. 8  Perf. 13½x13¾**
1241-1243  A502  Set of 3  5.25 3.75
See Nos. 1288-1290.

Inn Sign Art — A503

Designs: 1.20fr, Eagle, Vaduz. 1.80fr, Angel, Balzers. 3fr, Eagle, Bendern.

**Photo. & Engr.**
**2002, Nov. 25  Perf. 13½x14¼**
1244-1246  A503  Set of 3  10.00 5.25

Christmas — A504

Batik art by Sister Regina Hassler: 70rp, Search for Shelter. 1.20fr, Nativity. 1.80fr, Flight to Egypt.

**Perf. 14¼x13½**
**2002, Nov. 25  Photo.**
1247-1249  A504  Set of 3  6.25 4.50

Europa — A505

**2003, Mar. 3  Photo.  Perf. 13½x12¾**
1250  A505  1.20fr multi  2.25 2.00

**Building Preservation Type of 2001**
Designs: 70rp, St. Fridolin Church, Ruggell. 2.50fr, House, Spidach, horiz..

**Perf. 13½x13¾, 13¾x3½**
**2003, Mar. 3**
1251-1252  A490  Set of 2  5.50 4.25

Viticulture Throughout the Year — A506

Designs: 1.30fr, Pruning (February). 1.80fr, Tying vines to arbor (March). 2.20fr, Hoeing soil (April).

**2003  Perf. 14¼**
1253-1255  A506  Set of 3  9.00 6.50

Designs: 1.20fr, Looping vines (May). 1.80fr, Leaf work (June). 3.50fr, Removing high growth (July).

1256-1258  A506  Set of 3  11.00 8.25

Designs: 70rp, Thinning out of vines (August). 90rp, Harvesting grapes (September). 1.10fr, Pressing grapes (October).

1259-1261  A506  Set of 3  5.00 3.75

Designs: 70rp, First tasting of wine (November). 90rp, Harvest of frozen grapes (December). 1.20fr, Bottling wine (January).

1262-1264  A506  Set of 3  5.00 3.75

Issued: Nos. 1253-1255, 3/3; Nos. 1256-1258, 6/2; Nos. 1259-1261, 9/1; Nos. 1262-1264, 11/24.

Liechtenstein Association for the Disabled, 50th Anniv. — A507

**2003, June 2  Photo.  Perf. 14¼**
1265  A507  70rp multi  1.40 1.10

Reopening of National Museum — A508

Museum building and: 1.20fr, Ammonite fossil. 1.30fr, Shield of bailiff of Vaduz.

**2003, June 2  Perf. 14**
1266-1267  A508  Set of 2  5.00 3.75

White Storks and Nest — A509

**Photo. & Engr.**
**2003, Sept. 1  Perf. 12¾x13½**
1268  A509  2.20fr multi  3.75 2.75

Saints — A510

Designs: No. 1269, 1.20fr, St. Blasius. No. 1270, 1.20fr, St. George. No. 1271, 1.30fr, St. Erasmus. No. 1272, 1.30fr, St. Vitus.

**2003, Sept. 1  Perf. 13½**
1269-1272  A510  Set of 4  8.00 6.00

Stamps of the same denomination were printed in sheets of 20 arranged in blocks of 10 of each stamp separated by a horizontal gutter.
See Nos. 1280-1285, 1308-1311.

Children's Drawings — A511

Designs: 70rp, Cow, by Laura Beck. No. 1274, 1.80fr, Apple Tree, by Patrick Marxer, vert. No. 1275, 1.80fr, Bee, by Laura Lingg.

**Perf. 13½x14¼, 14¼x13½**
**2003, Nov. 24  Photo.**
1273-1275  A511  Set of 3  7.00 5.00

Christmas — A512

Reverse glass paintings: 70rp, Archangel Gabriel. 90rp, Nativity. 1.30fr, Three Magi.

**2003, Nov. 24  Perf. 14¼x13½**
1276-1278  A512  Set of 3  5.75 4.25

AHV Old Age and Survivor's Insurance, 50th Anniv. — A513

**2004, Jan. 3  Photo.  Perf. 14**
1279  A513  85rp multi  1.40 1.00

**Saints Type of 2003**
Designs: No. 1280, 1fr, St. Achatius. No. 1281, 1fr, St. Margareta. No. 1282, 1.20fr, St. Christophorus. No. 1283, 1.20fr, St. Pantaleon. No. 1284, 2.50fr, St. Aegidius. No. 1285, 2.50fr, St. Cyriakus.

**Photo. & Engr.**
**2004, Mar. 1  Perf. 13½**
1280-1285  A510  Set of 6  15.00 13.00

Stamps of the same denomination were printed in sheets of 20 arranged in blocks of 10 of each stamp separated by a horizontal gutter.

Europa — A514

**2004, Mar. 1  Photo.  Perf. 13¾x13½**
1286  A514  1.30fr multi  2.50 2.25

2004 Summer Olympics, Athens — A515

**2004, June 1  Photo.  Perf. 14¼**
1287  A515  85rp multi  1.50 1.25

**Orchid Type of 2002**
Designs: 85rp, Ophrys apifera. 1fr, Orchis ustulata. 1.20fr, Epipactis purpurata.

**2004, June 1  Perf. 13½x13¾**
1288-1290  A502  Set of 3  6.00 4.75

Aerial Views — A516

**2004, June 1  Perf. 13½**
1291  A516  15rp Bendern  .30 .25
1292  A516  85rp Gross-Steg  1.50 1.20
1293  A516  1fr Tuass  1.75 1.40
1294  A516  6fr Gutenberg  10.00 7.75
  Nos. 1291-1294 (4)  13.55 10.60
See No. 1312, 1331-1333, 1340-1341, 1375-1377.

**Building Preservation Type of 2001**
Designs: 2.20fr, House on Unterdorfstrasse, horiz. 2.50fr, Row of houses, Dorfstrasse, horiz.

**Perf. 13¾x13½**
**2004, Sept. 6  Photo.**
1295-1296  A490  Set of 2  7.50 6.00

## Miniature Sheet

Classical
Music
A537

No. 1360: a, The Magic Flute, by Wolfgang
Amadeus Mozart. b, Radetzky March, by
Johann Strauss. c, Rhapsody in Blue, by
George Gershwin. d, Water Music, by George
Frideric Handel. e, Pastoral Symphony, by
Ludwig van Beethoven. f, Waltz of the Flowers,
by Peter Ilich Tchaikovsky. g, The Swan, by
Camille Saint-Saens. h, A Midsummer Night's
Dream, by Felix Mendelssohn.

**2006, Sept. 4          Perf. 13½x14¼**
1360   A537     Sheet of 8      14.00  14.00
a.-h.      1fr Any single              1.75   1.50

**Building Preservation Type of 2001**
Designs: 1.80fr, Governor's residence and
Liechtenstein Institute, Bendern. 3.50fr, Bühl
House, Gamprin, horiz.

**Perf. 13½x13¾, 13¾x13½**
**2006, Nov. 20                    Photo.**
1361-1362  A490   Set of 2          8.00  6.50

Inventions — A538

Designs: 1.30fr, Curta calculator. 1.40fr,
Carena film camera. 2.40fr, PAV sliding
caliper.

**2006, Nov. 20          Perf. 14¼x14**
1363-1365  A538   Set of 3          8.00  6.50

Christmas — A539

Frescos from Chapel of St. Mary, Dux: 85rp,
The Annunciation. 1fr, Nativity. 1.30fr, Presentation at the Temple.

**Photo. & Engr.**
**2006, Nov. 20          Perf. 13½**
1366-1368  A539   Set of 3          6.25  5.00

Scouting,
Cent. — A540

**2007, Mar. 5     Photo.    Perf. 14¼**
1369   A540   1.30fr multi          2.00  1.75

Portrait of a Lady,
by Bernardino
Zaganelli da
Cotignola — A541

**Litho. & Engr.**
**2007, Mar. 5                   Perf. 13¾**
1370   A541   2.40fr multi          4.00  3.50
See Austria No. 2086.

Musical
Terms — A542

Designs: 85rp, Allegro. 1.80fr, Capriccio.
2fr, Crescendo. 3.50fr, Con fuoco.

**2007, Mar. 5     Photo.    Perf. 13½**
1371-1374  A542   Set of 4       14.00  12.00

**Aerial Views Type of 2004**
**2007, June 4     Photo.    Perf. 13½**
1375   A516   1.10fr Nendeln        1.75  1.40
1376   A516   1.80fr Malbun         2.75  2.10
1377   A516   2.60fr Ackerland      4.00  3.00
     Nos. 1375-1377 (3)             8.50  6.50

Greeting Card
Art — A543

Designs: 85rp, Boy delivering flower and letter to girl. 1fr, Two children carrying litter with
cake, flowers and letter. 1.30fr, Bird carrying
letter.

**2007, June 4            Rouletted 6¾**
1378-1380  A543   Set of 3          6.00  6.00
Punched holes are in stamp frames to give
stamps a lacelike appearance.

Paintings of Rhine
Landscapes by
Johann Ludwig
Bleuler (1792-
1850)
A544

Designs: 1fr, Castle and Village of Vaduz.
1.30fr, Rätikon Mountain. 2.40fr, Confluence
of the Ill and Rhine.

**Perf. 13½x14¼**
**2007, June 4          Photo. & Engr**
1381-1383  A544   Set of 3          7.00  7.00

**Pastures Type of 2005**
Designs: 1fr, Hintervalorsch. 1.40fr, Sücka.
2.20fr, Guschgfiel.

**Perf. 13½x14¼**
**2007, Sept. 3                    Photo.**
1384-1386  A527   Set of 3          7.00  7.00

Technical Innovations
From
Liechtenstein — A545

Designs: 1.30fr, Hilti hammer and drill.
1.80fr, Kaiser mobile walking excavator.
2.40fr, Hoval AluFer composite heating tube.

**2007, Sept. 3            Perf. 14¼**
1387-1389  A545   Set of 3          8.00  6.00
See Nos. 1425-1427.

Beetles — A546

Designs: 85rp, Trichodes apiarius. 100rp,
Cetania aurata. 130rp, Dytiscus marginalis.

**2007, Sept. 3     Litho.    Perf. 13¾x14**
1390-1392  A546   Set of 3          5.75  4.00

Panoramic View of
Liechtenstein — A547

**2007, Oct. 1     Litho.    Perf. 14**
1393   A547   130rp multi           2.50  2.00

**Building Preservation Type of 2001**
Designs: 2fr, St. Martin's Church, Eschen.
2.70fr, Mill, Eschen. horiz.

**Perf. 13½x13¾, 13¾x13½**
**2007, Nov. 19                    Photo.**
1394-1395  A490   Set of 2          7.00  5.00

New Parliament
Building — A548

**2007, Nov. 19                Perf. 13¾**
1396   A548   130rp multi           2.00  1.50

Natural
Phenomena — A549

Designs: 85rp, Rainbow above Three Sisters Massif. 100rp, Lightning over Bendern.
180rp, Ice crystal halo around Moon over
Malbun.

**2007, Nov. 19     Litho.    Perf. 14¼**
1397-1399  A549   Set of 3          5.00  4.00

Christmas — A550

Designs: 85rp, Chapel of St. Mary, Gam-
prin-Oberbühl. 1fr, Büel Chapel, Eschen.
1.30fr, Chapel of St. Wolfgang, Triesen.

**Perf. 13½x14¼**
**2007, Nov. 19                    Photo.**
1400-1402  A550   Set of 3          5.25  4.00

**Pastures Type of 2005**
Designs: 2.60fr, Guschg. 3fr, Güschgle.

**2008, Mar. 3  Photo.  Perf. 13½x14¼**
1403-1404  A527   Set of 2          9.50  7.50

Europa — A551

**2008, Mar. 3  Litho.  Perf. 13½x13¾**
1405   A551   130rp multi           2.00  1.50

Volunteer Fire
Fighters — A552

**2008, Mar. 3                  Perf. 13½**
1406   A552   1fr multi             2.00  1.50

Sleeping Princess
Marie Franziska, by
Friedrich von
Amerling — A553

**2008, Mar. 3          Photo. & Engr.**
1407   A553   2.40fr multi          4.00  3.50
See Austria No. 2144.

Spoerry-Areal,
Vaduz — A554

Chapel of St.
Mamertus,
Triesen — A555

Vaduz Castle — A556

**2008, Mar. 3     Litho.    Perf. 14**
1408   A554   85rp multi            1.50  1.10
1409   A555   1fr multi             1.75  1.25
1410   A556   1.30fr multi          2.25  1.60
     Nos. 1408-1410 (3)             5.50  3.95

Mother and Queen of the
Precious Blood with
Child, by Unknown
Artist — A557

**2008, June 2  Litho.  Perf. 12¾x13½**
1411   A557   220rp multi           4.25  3.50
Schellenberg Convent, 150th anniv.

2008 Summer
Olympics,
Beijing — A558

Mascots involved in: 85rp, Martial arts.
100rp, Soccer.

**2008, June 2          Perf. 14¼x13½**
1412-1413  A558   Set of 2          3.50  2.75

2008 Paralympics,
Beijing — A559

Designs: 130rp, Marathon. 180rp, Table
tennis.

**2008, June 2          Perf. 13½x14¼**
1414-1415  A559   Set of 2          5.00  4.00

2008 European
Soccer
Championships,
Austria and
Switzerland — A560

Designs: No. 1416, 130rp, St. Stephen's
Cathedral, Vienna, soccer player waltzing, vio-
linist. No. 1417, 130rp, Soccer fans holding
Liechtenstein flag, wearing Swiss hat, and

Austrian scarf. No. 1418, 130rp, Alphorn player, Matterhorn, soccer player.

**2008, June 2**                    **Perf. 14**
1416-1418  A560  Set of 3        7.50  6.50
Nos. 1416-1418 printed in sheets containing 4 No. 1417 and 6 each Nos. 1416 and 1418.

Hymenopterans A561

Designs: 85rp, Osmia brevicornis. 1fr, Epeoloides coecutiens. 1.30fr, Odynerus spinipes.

**2008, June 2**                    **Perf. 14¼**
1419-1421  A561  Set of 3        6.00  5.00

**Souvenir Sheet**

Prince Karl I (1569-1627) — A562

**Photo. & Engr.**
**2008, Sept. 1**               **Perf. 13¾x13½**
1422  A562  5fr multi            9.00  9.00
Princely house of Liechtenstein, 400th anniv.

**Miniature Sheet**

Drawings by Wilhelm Busch (1832-1908) — A563

No. 1423: a, Schoolmaster Lampel. b, Hans Huckebein. c, Max and Moritz. d, Widow Bolte. e, Pious Helene. f, Fipps the Monkey. g, Tailor Böck. h, Balduin Bählamm.

**2008, Sept. 1  Photo.  Perf. 14x13¾**
1423  A563  Sheet of 8          20.00  20.00
a.-h.    1.30fr Any single        2.50   2.00

**Building Preservation Type of 2001**
Design: Schädler Ceramics Building, Nendeln, horiz.

**Perf. 13¾x13½**
**2008, Nov. 17**                **Photo.**
1424  A490  3.80fr multi         7.50  6.50

**Technical Innovations Type of 2007**
Designs: 1.20fr, Neutrik NC3MX audio cable connectors. 1.40fr, Ivoclar Vivadent bluephase polymerization unit. 2.20fr, Presta DeltaValveControl variable valve-lift system.

**2008, Nov. 17**                **Perf. 14¼**
1425-1427  A545  Set of 3        7.50  6.50

Christmas — A564

Designs: 85rp, Candles, flowers and evergreen branches. 100rp, Children carrying holly, horiz. 130rp, Christmas tree and gifts.

**Perf. 14¼x14½, 14½x14¼**
**2008, Nov. 17**                **Litho.**
1428-1430  A564  Set of 3        6.00  5.00

Civil Protection Volunteers A565

**2009, Mar. 2  Litho.  Perf. 13¾x13½**
1431  A565  1fr multi            1.75  1.40
See Nos. 1471-1472, 1566-1567.

Europa — A566

**Litho. With Hologram Affixed**
**2009, Mar. 2**                 **Perf. 14¼**
1432  A566  1.30fr multi         2.50  2.00

Land Registry, 200th Anniv. — A567

**2009, Mar. 2**  **Litho.**     **Perf. 13¾**
1433  A567  330rp multi          6.25  5.00

Liechtenstein Post AG, 10th Anniv. — A568

Designs: 85rp, Counter clerk handling package. 100rp, Mail deliverer. 130rp, Mail sorter.

**2009, Mar. 2**                 **Perf. 13¾x13½**
1434-1436  A568  Set of 3        6.00  5.00

Linoleum Prints by Stephan Sude — A569

Designs: 1fr, Unfolding. 1.30fr, Awareness. 2.70fr, Fulfillment.

**2009, Mar. 2**                 **Perf. 14x13¼**
1437-1439  A569  Set of 3        9.50  7.50

Alpine Association, Cent. — A570

Crosses on summits of: 100rp, Kuegrat. 130rp, Langspitz, vert. 220rp, Rappastein, vert. 240rp, Jahn-Turm and Wolan.

**Perf. 13¾x13½, 13½x13¾**
**2009, June 8**                 **Litho.**
1440-1443  A570  Set of 4       12.00  8.00

Forests — A571

Designs: 85rp, Ants in forest. 1fr, Path in forest. 1.40fr, Boulder against tree on hillside. 1.60fr, Cut timber.

**2009, June 8**                 **Perf. 13½**
1444-1447  A571  Set of 4        9.00  7.00

Vaduz Castle — A572

Castle in: 130rp, Spring. 180rp, Summer.

**2009, June 8    Photo.    Perf. 13¾**
1448-1449  A572  Set of 2        5.50  4.50
See Nos. 1488-1489.

Liechtenstein Philatelic Society, 75th Anniv. — A573

**2009, Sept. 7  Litho.  Perf. 13x13¼**
1450  A573  130rp multi          2.25  1.50
Holes are drilled along the map border.

Badminton Cabinet Ornamentation A574

Panels with bird and flower designs: 1.30fr, Bird with blue head. 2fr, Three birds, vert. (35x50mm). 4fr, Bird with red head.

**Perf. 14, 13¾ (2fr)**
**2009, Sept. 7**               **Photo. & Engr.**
1451-1453  A574  Set of 3       12.50  9.00

Butterflies — A575

Designs: 85rp, Pieris rapae. 100rp, Parnassius apollo. 130rp, Melanargia galathea. 200rp, Vanessa atalanta.

**2009, Sept. 7  Litho.  Perf. 12x12½**
**Self-Adhesive**
1454-1457  A575  Set of 4        9.00  7.00
See Nos. 1480-1482, 1515-1516.

Chapel of St. Mamerta, Triesen — A576

**2009, Sept. 16**               **Perf. 14**
1458  A576  130rp multi          2.25  1.50

Contemporary Architecture A577

Designs: 85rp, University of Applied Sciences, Vaduz. 260rp, Art Museum, Vaduz. 350rp, Border crossing, Rugell.

**Perf. 13½x13¾**
**2009, Nov. 16**                **Litho.**
1459-1461  A577  Set of 3       12.50  9.00
See Nos. 1473-1474.

Lifestyle Museum, Schellenberg A578  Former Customs House, Vaduz A579

Parish House, Bendern — A580

**2009, Nov. 16**                **Perf. 12¼**
**Self-Adhesive**
1462  A578  20rp multi           .35   .25
1463  A579  50rp multi           .85   .65
1464  A580  60rp multi          1.10   .75
    Nos. 1462-1464 (3)          2.30  1.65

Christmas — A581

Advent windows by children: 85rp, Annunciation. 100rp, Journey to Bethlehem. 130rp, Nativity. 180rp, Magi and Star of Bethlehem.

**2009, Nov. 16**                **Perf. 13½x13¾**
1465-1468  A581  Set of 4        8.00  6.00

2010 Winter Olympics, Vancouver — A582

Designs: 1fr, Downhill skier. 1.80fr, Cross-country skier, horiz.

**2010, Feb. 12  Litho.  Perf. 13¾**
1469-1470  A582  Set of 2        4.50  3.50

**Civil Protection Volunteers Type of 2009**
Designs: 85rp, Mountain rescuers. 1.30rp, Water rescuers.

**2010, Mar. 1**                 **Perf. 13¾x13½**
1471-1472  A565  Set of 2        3.50  2.75

**Contemporary Architecture Type of 2009**
Designs: 260rp, Natural gas filling station, Vaduz. 360rp, Liechtenstein Electric Power Authority transformer station, Schaan.

**2010, Mar. 1**                 **Perf. 13½x13¾**
1473-1474  A577  Set of 2        9.50  7.00

Agriculture — A583

Designs: 85rp, Fields. 1fr, Flowers, hillside farmers. 1.10fr, Combine in field. 1.30fr, Cattle.

**2010, Mar. 1  Photo.  Perf. 13½x13¼**
1475-1478  A583  Set of 4        7.00  5.00

## Souvenir Sheet

Expo 2010, Shanghai — A584

No. 1479: a, Atmospheric View of Vaduz, by Johann Jakob Schmidt (40x36mm). b, Tidal Bore on the Qiantang River, by Xu Gu (32x60mm).

**Photo. & Engr.**
| | | **Perf. 14** | |
|---|---|---|---|
| 2010, May 1 | | | |
| 1479 A584 | Sheet of 2 | 6.50 | 6.50 |
| a. | 1.60fr multi | 3.00 | 3.00 |
| b. | 1.90fr multi | 3.50 | 3.50 |
| c. | As #1479, imperf. | 6.50 | 6.50 |
| d. | As "a," imperf. | 3.00 | 3.00 |
| e. | As "b," imperf. | 3.50 | 3.50 |

### Butterflies Type of 2009

Designs: 140rp, Coenonympha oedippus. 160rp, Gonepteryx rhamni. 260rp, Papilio machaon.

**2010, June 7  Litho.  Perf. 12x12½**
**Self-Adhesive**
1480-1482 A575  Set of 3  9.75 8.00

Liechtenstein Disability Insurance, 50th Anniv. — A585

**2010, June 7  Perf. 14x13¼**
1483 A585 1fr multi  1.75 1.40

European Free Trade Association, 50th Anniv. — A586

**2010, June 7  Perf. 12x12½**
1484 A586 140rp multi  2.50 2.00

Interpol Vaduz, 50th Anniv. — A587

**2010, June 7  Perf. 12¼**
1485 A587 1.90fr multi  3.50 2.75

Ceiling Frescoes in Liechtenstein Museum, Vienna — A588

Frescoes by Johann Michael Rottmayr: 1fr, Ariadne Giving Theseus the Thread. 1.40fr, Surrender of the Golden Fleece to Jason.

**Photo. & Engr.**
**2010, June 7  Perf. 14**
1486-1487 A588  Set of 2  4.25 3.50

Values are for stamps with surrounding selvage.

### Vaduz Castle Type of 2009

Castle in: 140rp, Autumn, vert. 190rp, Winter, vert.

**2010, Sept. 6  Photo.  Perf. 13¾**
1488-1489 A572  Set of 2  6.50 5.00

Europa — A589

**2010, Sept. 6  Litho.  Perf. 14**
1490 A589 140rp multi  2.75 2.25

Renewable Energy — A590

Designs: 100rp, Water. 140rp, Wood. 280rp, Geothermal.

**Litho. & Photo.**
**2010, Sept. 6  Perf. 14x13¾**
1491-1493 A590  Set of 3  10.50 8.00

Parts of the designs of Nos. 1491-1493 were printed with thermochromic ink that changes color when warmed. See Nos. 1509-1511.

Rhine Valley Landscape — A591

No. 1494: a, Eschnerberg and Dreischwestern Mountains, cart path, denomination at LL. b, Alvier Mountains, denomination at LR.

**2010, Sept. 6  Litho.  Perf. 14x13¼**
1494  Horiz. pair  4.00 4.00
a.-b. A591 1fr Either single  2.00 1.75

Schaan-Vaduz Railroad Station — A592

Red House, Vaduz — A593

St. Joseph Church, Triesenberg — A594

**2010, Nov. 15  Litho.  Perf. 12¼**
**Self-Adhesive**
1495 A592 1.10fr multi  1.90 1.50
1496 A593 1.80fr multi  3.25 2.50
1497 A594 1.90fr multi  3.50 2.75
Nos. 1495-1497 (3)  8.65 6.75

Works From Liechtenstein Museum of Art — A595

Designs: 100rp, Normale e Anormale, embroidery by Alighiero Boetti. 220rp, Testa, sculpture by Marisa Merz. 360rp, Untitled sculpture by Jannis Kounellis.

**2010, Nov. 15  Perf. 13¾x13½**
1498-1500 A595  Set of 3  12.00 9.00

Christmas — A596

Ceiling frescoes from Maria-Hilf Chapel, Mäls: 85rp, Annunciation. 1fr, Visitation of Mary. 1.40fr, Presentation of Jesus in the Temple.

**2010, Nov. 15  Photo.  Perf. 14**
1501-1503 A596  Set of 3  6.25 5.00

National Library, 50th Anniv — A597

**Litho. With Foil Application**
**2011, Mar. 14  Perf. 12½x12**
**Self-Adhesive**
1504 A597 1fr black & gold  2.25 2.25

Liechtensteinische Landesbank, 150th Anniv. — A598

**2011, Mar. 14  Litho.  Perf. 12¼**
**Self-Adhesive**
1505 A598 1fr multi  2.25 2.25

2011 Games of the Small States, Liechtenstein — A599

Designs: 85rp, Track, volleyball, cycling. 1fr, Judo, shooting, squash. 1.40fr, Table tennis, tennis, swimming.

**2011, Mar. 14  Litho.  Perf. 13½**
1506-1508 A599  Set of 3  6.25 4.50

### Renewable Energy Type of 2010

Designs: 100rp, Photovoltaics. 110rp, Solar energy. 290rp, Wind energy.

**Litho. & Photo.**
**2011, Mar. 14  Perf. 14x13¾**
1509-1511 A590  Set of 3  9.50 7.50

Parts of the designs of Nos. 1509-1511 were printed with thermochromic ink that changes color when warmed.

Decorative Eggs Collected by Adulf Peter Goop — A600

Designs: 1fr, Moscow Workshop Easter egg. 1.40fr, Apple Blossom Egg, by Karl Fabergé, horiz. (47x33mm). 2.60fr, Easter egg, by Pavel Akimovich Ovchinnikov.

**Litho. & Engr.**
**2011, Mar. 14  Perf. 13¾**
1512-1514 A600  Set of 3  9.50 7.50

### Butterflies Type of 2009

Designs: 220rp, Inachis io. 500rp, Anthocharis cardamines.

**2011, June 6  Litho.  Perf. 12x12½**
**Self-Adhesive**
1515-1516 A575  Set of 2  15.00 15.00

For surcharges, see Nos. 1556, 1856.

Europa — A601

**2011, June 6  Perf. 12½x12**
1517 A601 1.40fr multi  3.00 2.50
Intl. Year of Forests.

Children of Hereditary Prince Alois and Duchess Sophie — A602

Designs: 1fr, Prince Nikolaus. 1.80fr, Prince Georg. 2fr, Princess Marie Caroline. 2.60fr, Prince Joseph Wenzel.

**Photo. & Engr.**
**2011, June 6  Perf. 13½**
1518-1521 A602  Set of 4  15.00 12.00
1521a  Souvenir sheet of 4, #1518-1521  15.00 15.00

Fruit, by Shirana Shahbazi — A603

**2011, Sept. 9  Litho.  Perf. 13¼x13½**
1522 A603 100rp multi  2.00 1.50
See Switzerland No. 1423.

Photographs of Liechtenstein by Xiao Hui Wang — A604

Designs: 1.30fr, Alpine Rhine. 3.70fr, Water Reflections.

**2011, Sept. 9  Perf. 13¼x14**
1523-1524 A604  Set of 2  9.50 7.50

### Miniature Sheet

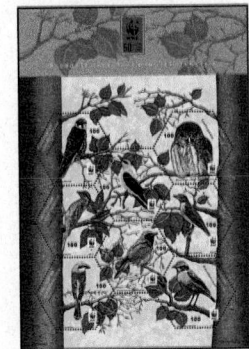

Worldwide Fund for Nature (WWF), 50th Anniv. — A605

No. 1525 — Endangered birds in Liechtenstein: a, Falco subbuteo. b, Glaucidium passerinum. c, Oriolus oriolus. d, Jynx torquilla. e, Luscinia megarhynchos. f, Phoenicurus phoenicurus. g, Lanius collurio. h, Saxicola rubetra.

**2011, Sept. 9  Perf. 12½**
**Self-Adhesive**
1525 A605  Sheet of 8  16.00 16.00
a.-h.  100rp Any single  2.00 2.00

Ruggell Marsh A606

**2011, Sept. 28**                    *Perf. 14*
1526  A606  140rp multi                2.75  2.25

Castles — A607

Designs: 100rp, Gutenberg Castle. 140rp, Schellenberg Castle. 200rp, Schalun Castle. 260rp, Vaduz Castle.

**Photo. & Engr.**
**2011, Nov. 14**                *Perf. 13½x14¼*
1527-1530  A607  Set of 4        13.00  10.00

Christmas — A608

Creche figures from: 85rp, St. Gallus Church, Triesen. 100rp, St. Florin Church, Vaduz (38x32mm). 140rp, Church of the Assumption, Bendern (32x38mm).

*Perf. 12¼, 12x12½ (100rp), 12½x12 (140rp)*
**2011, Nov. 14**                    Litho.
**Self-Adhesive**
1531-1533  A608  Set of 3        6.00  4.50

New Year 2012 (Year of the Dragon) A609

**Litho. With Foil Application**
**2011, Nov. 14**                    *Perf. 12½*
1534  A609  190rp red & gold        4.25  4.25
    The dragon vignette was laser cut. Printed in sheets of 4.

Liechtenstein Postage Stamps, Cent. — A610

Princes of Liechtenstein: 1fr, Johann II. 1.40fr, Franz I. 2.20fr, Franz Josef II. 2.80fr, Hans Adam II.

**2012, Feb. 1  Litho.  Perf. 13½x13¾**
1535-1538  A610  Set of 4       14.00  11.00
1538a          Souvenir sheet of 4,
             #1535-1538, imperf.      14.00  14.00
    A booklet containing four panes each containing eight examples of each stamp, No. 1538a, a designer-signed and numbered example of No. 1538a in changed colors, examples of Nos. 1535-1538 and their imperforates with first day cancels, and reproductions of Nos. 1-3 was printed in limited quantities and sold for 100fr.

Cattle Moving Past Parliament Building — A611

**2012, Mar. 5**                    *Perf. 13¾*
1539  A611  140rp multi            2.75  2.25
                Europa.

Liechtenstein Parilament and Constitution, 150th Anniv. — A612

Designs: 1fr, Reverse of 1862 Vereinsthaler, excerpt from first page of Constitutional Charter. 1.40fr, Obverse of 1862 Vereinsthaler, letter authorizing the opening of Parliament.

**Litho. & Embossed**
**2012, Mar. 5**                *Perf. 13½x13¾*
1540-1541  A612  Set of 2        4.50  3.50

Pfälzer Hutte Mountain Lodge — A613

**2012, June 14  Litho.  Perf. 13¾**
1542  A613  140rp multi            3.00  3.00
            See Germany No. 2677.

2012 Summer Olympics, London — A614

Designs: 100rp, Swimming. 140rp, Tennis.

**2012, June 14**                    *Perf. 13¼*
1543-1544  A614  Set of 2        4.50  3.50

Flowers — A615

Designs: 85rp, Dahlie (dahlia). 140pr, Pfingstrose (peony). 500rp, Zinnie (zinnia).

**2012, June 14**                *Perf. 12½x12*
**Self-Adhesive**
1545-1547  A615  Set of 3       15.00  15.00
    See Nos. 1573-1575, 1643-1645.

Mountain Valleys A616

No. 1548: a, Lawenatal Valley (denomination at LL). b, Valünatal Valley (denomination at LR).

**2012, June 14**                *Perf. 14x13¼*
1548          Horiz. pair            4.25  4.25
a.-b.    A616 1fr Either single      2.10  2.10

**Souvenir Sheet**

Liechtenstein Oberland, 300th Anniv. — A617

No. 1549 — Stylized flags of: a, Planken and Schaan. b, Vaduz and Tresenberg. c, Triesen and Balzers.

**Perf. 14 Vert. on 1 or 2 Sides**
**2012, June 14**
1549  A617    Sheet of 3          9.50  9.50
a.          1fr multi              1.75  1.75
b.          1.40fr multi           2.50  2.50
c.          2.60fr multi           4.50  4.50

**Souvenir Sheet**

Winning Art in Stamp Design Contest A618

No. 1550 — Art by: a, N. Schwarz. b, R. Graf. c, G. Rodrigues-Margreiter.

**2012, Aug. 16**                *Perf. 13¾x13½*
1550  A618    Sheet of 3        13.00  13.00
a.          100rp multi            2.25  2.25
b.          140rp multi            3.00  3.00
c.          360rp multi            7.75  7.75
    LIBA 2012 Stamp Exhibition, Schaan.

Antique Automobiles A619

Designs: 85rp, 1908 Brasier. 100rp, 1911 Stanley Steamer. 140rp, 1915 Ford Model T Speedster. 190rp, 1920 Hinstin.

**Litho. with Foil Application**
**2012, Sept. 3**
1551-1554  A619  Set of 4       11.00  11.00

**Miniature Sheet**

Characters From Literature — A620

No. 1555: a, Till Eulenspiegel. b, Sherlock Holmes. c, Don Quixote. d, Hamlet. e, Robin Hood. f, Robinson Crusoe. g, Baron Münchhausen. h, Quasimodo.

**2012, Sept. 3**    Litho.    *Perf. 13¾*
1555  A620    Sheet of 8       18.00  18.00
a.-h.    1fr Any single          2.25  2.25

No. 1516 Surcharged in Purple

**Self-Adhesive**
**2012, Oct. 4**                *Perf. 12x12½*
1556  A575  600rp on 500rp
                #1516             13.00  13.00

Reliefs by Massimiliano Soldani-Benzi (1656-1740) — A621

Designs: 1fr, Christ's Descent from the Cross. 1.40fr, Christ on the Mount of Olives.

**Litho. & Engr.**
**2012, Nov. 12**                *Perf. 13¾x14*
1557-1558  A621  Set of 2        5.25  5.25

Art by Hanna Roeckle — A622

Designs: 100rp, Crystal B. 140rp, Crystal G.

**2012, Nov. 12**    Litho.    *Perf. 13¾*
1559-1560  A622  Set of 2        5.25  5.25

Christmas — A623

Archangels: 85rp, Raphael. 100rp, Michael. 140rp, Gabriel. 190rp, Uriel.

**Self-Adhesive**
**Litho. With Foil Application**
**2012, Nov. 12**                *Perf. 12¼x12½*
1561-1564  A623  Set of 4       11.00  11.00

New Year 2013 (Year of the Snake) — A624

**Self-Adhesive**
**Litho. With Foil Application**
**2012, Nov. 12**                    *Perf. 12½*
1565  A624  190rp red & gold        4.25  4.25
    The snake vignette was laser cut. Printed in sheets of 4.

**Civil Protection Volunteers Type of 2009**

Designs: 1fr, Avalanche rescue squad. 1.40fr, Civil protection and emergency management workers.

**2013, Mar. 4  Litho.  Perf. 13¾x13½**
1566-1567  A565  Set of 2        5.25  5.25

Europa — A625

**2013, Mar. 4**                *Perf. 14¼x14¼*
1568  A625  1.40fr multi            3.00  3.00

Mathematics and Nature — A626

Various leaves and: 100rp, Fibonacci sequence. 260rp, Sum of adjacent Fibonacci numbers. 400rp, Golden ratio.

**Litho. With Foil Application**
**2013, Mar. 4**                *Perf. 13¼x13½*
1569-1571  A626  Set of 3       16.50  16.50

Switzerland-Liechtenstein Customs Treaty, 90th Anniv. — A627

No. 1572: a, Rhine Valley, Gonzen, Swiss flag, denomination at UL. b, Liechtenstein Valley, Ellhorn and Liechtenstein flag, denomination at UR.

**2013, Mar. 4 Litho. Perf. 13¼**
1572 Horiz. pair    8.75 8.75
*a.-b.* A627 2fr Either single    4.25 4.25

**Flowers Type of 2012**

Designs: 100rp, Gentiana rhaetica. 190rp, Myosotis alpestris. 400rp, Rhododendron hirsutum.

**2013, June 3 Perf. 12½x12**
**Self-Adhesive**
1573-1575 A615   Set of 3    15.00 15.00

Landscapes by Hans Kliemand (1922-76) A628

Designs: 100rp, View of Vaduz. 190rp, View Into the Rhine Valley.

**Litho. & Engr.**
**2013, June 3 Perf. 12¾x13**
1576-1577 A628   Set of 2    6.50 6.50

Baby Animals — A629

Designs: 85rp, Ibex. 100rp, Chamois.140rp, Marmot. 190rp, Alpine hare.

**2013, June 3 Litho. Perf. 12x12½**
**Self-Adhesive**
1578-1581 A629   Set of 4    11.50 11.50

Bridges A630

No. 1582: a, End of Vaduz-Sevelen Bridge over Rhine River (27x27mm). b, Entire Vaduz-Sevelen Bridge (57x27mm).
No. 1583: a, End of Schaan-Buchs Railway Bridge (27x27mm). b, Entire Schaan-Buchs Bridge (57x27mm).

**2013, June 3 Perf. 14x13¼**
1582 A630   Horiz. pair    4.25 4.25
*a.* 85rp multi    1.90 1.90
*b.* 100rp multi    2.25 2.25
1583 A630   Horiz. pair    7.25 7.25
*a.* 140rp multi    3.00 3.00
*b.* 190rp multi    4.25 4.25

See Nos. 1600-1601.

Performing Arts — A631

Designs: 100rp, Ballet dancer. 140rp, Actors in theater production. 200rp, Actors in musical theater production. 400rp, Magician.

**2013, Sept. 2 Perf. 12x12½**
**Self-Adhesive**
1584-1587 A631   Set of 4    18.00 18.00

Automobiles A632

Designs: 85rp, 1954 Aston Martin DB 2/4. 100rp, 1958 Ferrari 250 GT PF. 140rp, 1955 Jaguar XK 140. 190rp, 1956 Mercedes-Benz 300 SL.

**Litho. & Embossed With Foil Application**
**2013, Sept. 2 Perf. 13¼x13**
1588-1591 A632   Set of 4    11.00 11.00

Paintings by Ivan Myasoyedov (Eugen Zotow) (1881-1953) A633

No. 1592: a, Voyage of the Argonauts, 1909. b, Silum, 1945.

**2013, Sept. 2 Litho. Perf. 14**
1592   Pair    8.75 8.75
*a.* A633 140rp multi    3.00 3.00
*b.* A633 260rp multi    5.75 5.75

Printed in sheets of 10 containing 5 each #1592a-1592b, + 2 labels. See Russia No. 7473.

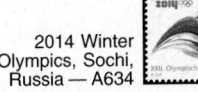

2014 Winter Olympics, Sochi, Russia — A634

**Litho. & Thermographed With Foil Application**
**2013, Nov. 11 Perf. 13¼x13½**
1593 A634 2.60fr multi    5.75 5.75

Portions of the design contain grit from a stone from Sochi.

**Souvenir Sheet**

Floral-Patterned Silk Wall Covering in Small Courbaril Room of Liechtenstein Palace, Vienna — A635

**Litho. & Embossed With Foil Application**
**2013, Nov. 11 Perf. 14¼x14½**
**Silk-Faced Paper**
1594 A635   Sheet of 3    13.00 13.00
*a.* 1fr multi    2.25 2.25
*b.* 1.40fr multi    3.00 3.00
*c.* 3.60fr multi    7.75 7.75

Christmas — A636

Designs: 85rp, Annunciation. 1fr, Nativity. 1.40fr, Angel announcing birth of Christ to shepherds and sheep. 1.90fr, Three Kings.

**Litho. With Foil Application**
**2013, Nov. 11 Perf. 12½x12**
**Self-Adhesive**
1595-1598 A636   Set of 4    11.50 11.50

New Year 2013 (Year of the Horse) — A637

**Litho. With Foil Application**
**2013, Nov. 11 Perf. 12½**
**Self-Adhesive**
1599 A637 190rp red & gold    4.25 4.25

The horse vignette was laser cut. Printed in sheets of 4.

In 2014, Liechtenstein began issuing personalizable stamps bearing the inscription "Liechtensteinsche Post AG." Stamps in three different orientations (square, landscape and portrait) could be created for two different frame types, each of which were made available initially in denominations of 55c, 85c, €1, €1.40, €1.90, and €2. These were sold in sheets of 20 stamps. Sheets containing 10 stamps with various non-personalizable images were to be produced and sold for special events.

**Bridges Type of 2013**

No. 1582: a, End of Buchs-Schaan Footbridge (27x27mm). b, Entire Buchs-Schaan Bridge (57x27mm).
No. 1583: a, End of Bendern-Haag Bridge over the Rhine River (27x27mm). b, Entire Bendern-Haag Bridge (57x27mm).

**2014, Mar. 10 Litho. Perf. 14x13¼**
1600 A630   Horiz. pair    4.25 4.25
*a.* 85rp multi    1.90 1.90
*b.* 100rp multi    2.25 2.25
1601 A630   Horiz. pair    7.50 7.50
*a.* 140rp multi    3.25 3.25
*b.* 190rp multi    4.25 4.25

Josef Gabriel Rheinberger (1839-1901), Composer — A638

**Perf. 13¾x13¼**
**2014, Mar. 10 Litho.**
1602 A638 1.40fr multi    3.25 3.25

Europa — A639

**2014, Mar. 10 Litho. Perf. 12½x12**
1603 A639 140rp multi    3.25 3.25

**Souvenir Sheet**

Winged Altarpiece Bequeathed to National Museum — A640

No. 1604 — Details of altarpiece: a, St. Christopher Carrying the Christ Child (33x45mm). b, St. Sebastian (33x45mm). c, St. Anne and St. Mary with the Christ Child (84x44mm).

**Perf. 14x13¾, 13½ (600rp)**
**2014, Mar. 10 Litho.**
1604 A640   Sheet of 3    20.50 20.50
*a.* 100rp multi    2.25 2.25
*b.* 200rp multi    4.50 4.50
*c.* 600rp multi    13.50 13.50

No. 1640 is sold folded in half, with stamps appearing through the die cut holes in the sheet margin. The top part of the sheet margin, with the holes, is printed on both sides.

**Souvenir Sheet**

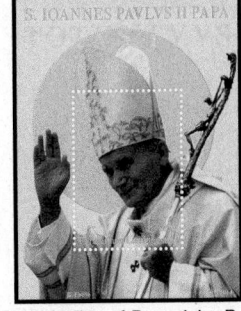

Canonization of Pope John Paul II — A641

**Litho. With Foil Application**
**2014, Apr. 28 Perf. 14¼x14**
1605 A641 1.40fr multi    3.25 3.25

Ancient Coins Found in Liechtenstein A642

Map of Liechtenstein and: 85rp, Roman silver denarius of Julius Caesar, c. 49-48 B.C. 100rp, Florentine golden florin, c. 1360. 130rp, Silver penny, c. 1360.

**Litho. & Embossed With Foil Application**
**2014, June 2 Perf. 13½x13¾**
1606-1608 A642   Set of 3    7.00 7.00

Amphibians — A643

Designs: 85rp, Yellow-bellied toad. 2.90fr, Great crested newt. 3.70fr, Alpine salamander.

**2014, June 2 Litho. Perf. 12¼**
**Self-Adhesive**
1609-1611 A643   Set of 3    17.00 17.00

Flowers — A644

Designs: 100rp, Iris sibirica. 280rp, Parnassia palustris. 360rp, Menyanthes trifoliata.

**2014, June 2 Litho. Perf. 12½x12**
**Self-Adhesive**
1612-1614 A644   Set of 3    16.50 16.50

Lindau Messenger Courier Service — A645

**2014, Sept. 1 Litho. Perf. 14x13¼**
1615 A645 140rp multi    3.00 3.00

No. 1615 was printed in sheets of 8 + 4 labels.

Etchings by Brigitte Hasler — A646

Designs: 100rp, Dust Image A. 140rp, Dust Image B.

Litho. With Foil Application

2014, Sept. 1 ***Perf. 13¼***

1616-1617 A646 Set of 2 5.25 5.25

Intl. Year of Crystallography — A647

Designs: 100rp, Initial crystal metamorphosis sequence. 200rp, Final crystal metamorphosis sequence.

Litho. & Embossed

2014, Sept. 1 ***Perf. 13½x13¼***

1618-1619 A647 Set of 2 6.50 6.50

Sedans — A648

Designs: 85rp, 1933 Rolls-Royce Phantom II. 100rp, 1929 Pierce-Arrow Type 133. 140rp, 1935 Studebaker Big Six. 190rp, 1948 Jaguar Mark IV.

Litho. With Foil Application

2014, Sept. 1 ***Perf. 13¼x13***

1620-1623 A648 Set of 4 11.50 11.50

1620a Inscribed "Rolls-Royce" (with hyphen) 1.75 1.75

Issued: No. 1620a, 11/10. No. 1620 is inscribed "Rolls Royce" (without hyphen).

Reign of Prince Hans Adam II, 25th Anniv. — A649

Perf. 13¼x13¾

2014, Nov. 10 **Litho. & Engr.**

1624 A649 2fr multi 4.25 4.25

Painting by Jens W. Beyrich — A650

Painting by Hong Sek-Chern A651

2014, Nov. 10 **Litho.** ***Perf. 13x13¼***

1625 A650 190rp multi 4.00 4.00

1626 A651 190rp multi 4.00 4.00

See Singapore Nos. 1706-1707.

Chinese Porcelain in Princely Collection — A652

Designs: 1fr, Famille Rose plate, c. 1722-35. 1.90fr, Kraak kendi, c. 1572-1620 (27x43mm). 2.80fr, Imari baluster vase with lid, c. 1736-95 (27x43mm). 3.60fr, Imari plate with lotus blossoms, c. 1736-95.

Perf. 13¾x13¼, 12x11¼ (#1628-1629)

Litho. & Engr. With Foil Application

2014, Nov. 10

1627-1630 A652 Set of 4 19.00 19.00

Christmas — A653

Chapels: 85rp, Freedom Chapel, Malbun. 100rp, St. Wendelin's Chapel, Steg. 140rp, St. Theodul's Chapel, Masescha.

Litho. With Foil Application

2014, Nov. 10 ***Perf. 12¼x12½***

Self-Adhesive

1631-1633 A653 Set of 3 6.75 6.75

New Year 2015 (Year of the Ram) — A654

Litho. With Foil Application

2014, Nov. 10 ***Perf. 12½***

Self-Adhesive

1634 A654 190rp red & gold 4.00 4.00

The ram vignette was laser cut. Printed in sheets of 4.

Prince Hans Adam II, 70th Birthday — A655

Perf. 13¼x13¾

2015, Feb. 14 **Litho. & Engr.**

1635 Pair 6.50 6.50

a. A655 1fr green & multi 2.10 2.10

b. A655 2fr red & multi 4.25 4.25

No. 1635 was printed in sheets containing two pairs.

Liechtenstein Traditional Costume Association, 50th Anniv. — A656

2015, Mar. 2 **Litho.** ***Perf. 12x12½***

Self-Adhesive

1636 A656 85rp multi 1.75 1.75

Liechtenstein Development Service, 50th Anniv. — A657

2015, Mar. 2 **Litho.** ***Perf. 12x12½***

Self-Adhesive

1637 A657 100rp multi 2.10 2.10

Postage Stamps, 175th Anniv. — A658

2015, Mar. 2 **Litho.** ***Perf. 12½x12***

Self-Adhesive

1638 A658 1.40fr multi 3.00 3.00

Liechtenstein's Admission to United Nations, 25th Anniv. — A659

2015, Mar. 2 **Litho.** ***Perf. 13½x13***

1639 A659 190rp multi 4.00 4.00

International Year of Light — A660

2015, Mar. 2 **Litho.** ***Perf. 13¾x13¼***

1640 A660 1.90fr multi 4.00 4.00

Microperforations are incorporated in the vignette.

Europa — A661

Toys: No. 1641, 1.40fr, Polar bear in freezer. No. 1642, 1.40fr, Goat on lemon.

2015, Mar. 2 **Litho.** ***Perf. 13½x13¼***

1641-1642 A661 Set of 2 6.00 6.00

Flowers Type of 2012

Designs: 85rp, Succisa pratensis. 100rp, Astrantia major. 130rp, Leucanthemum vulgare.

2015, June 1 **Litho.** ***Perf. 12½x12***

Self-Adhesive

1643-1645 A615 Set of 3 6.75 6.75

Reptiles — A662

Designs: 1.80fr, Zauneidechse (sand lizard). 2fr, Schlingnatter (smooth snake). 5fr, Bergeidechse (common lizard).

2015, June 1 **Litho.** ***Perf. 12¼***

Self-Adhesive

1646-1648 A662 Set of 3 19.00 19.00

Keystone Decorations From Cathedral of St. Florin, Vaduz — A663

Designs: 100rp, Pelican. 140rp, Lamb of God. 190rp, Eagle. 200rp, Lion.

2015, June 1 **Litho.** ***Perf. 13***

1649-1652 A663 Set of 4 13.50 13.50

Schwabbrünnen Nature Reserve — A664

No. 1653: a, Pond, denomination at UL. b, Pond, denomination at UR. c, Meadow, denomination at UL. d, Meadow, denomination at UR.

2015, June 1 **Litho.** ***Perf. 13¼***

1653 A664 Block of 4 8.50 8.50

a.-d. 100rp Any single 2.10 2.10

Alpine Landscapes — A665

No. 1654: a, Malbuntal, Liechtenstein. b, Herder's dwellings, Velika Planina, Slovenia.

2015, Sept. 7 **Litho.** ***Perf. 14x13½***

1654 A665 Pair 6.00 6.00

a.-b. 140rp Either single 3.00 3.00

See Slovenia No. 1141.

Commercial Vehicles — A666

Designs: 85rp, 1945 Kaiser Auto tractor. 100rp, 1967 Raimündle tractor. 140rp, Unimog. 190rp, 1921 Fordson tractor.

Litho. With Foil Application

2015, Sept. 7 ***Perf. 13¼x13***

1655-1658 A666 Set of 4 10.50 10.50

Miniature Sheet

Apple Varieties A667

No. 1659: a, Treisenberger Weinapfel. b, Damason Reinette. c, Leuser. d, Grosser Rheinischer Bohnapfel. e, Freiherr von Berlepsch. f, Rollapfel. g, Goldparmäne. h, Rösli Marie.

2015, Sept. 7 **Litho.** ***Perf. 12½***

Self-Adhesive

1659 A667 Sheet of 8 24.00 24.00

a.-h. 140rp Any single 3.00 3.00

Jewelry Found at Archaeological Sites — A668

Map of Liechtenstein and: 85rp, Red jasper brooch, 1st-2nd cent. 100rp, Gold ring with chalcedony cameo, 3rd cent. 130rp, Glass cameo, 1st cent.

Litho. & Embossed With Foil Application

2015, Nov. 16 ***Perf. 13¼x13½***

1660-1662 A668 Set of 3 6.25 6.25

Paintings by Jacques Jordaens (1593-1678) A669

Designs: 100rp, Adoration of the Shepherds. 140rp, As the Old Sing, So the Young Ones Pipe (47x38mm). 190rp, Meleager and Atalante (44x38mm).

2015, Nov. 16 **Litho.** ***Perf. 13¼***

1663-1665 A669 Set of 3 8.50 8.50

Christmas — A670

Designs (from Christmas carols): 85p, Rose (Lo, How a Rose E'er Blooming). 100rp, Nativity (Silent Night). 140rp, Angels (Oh, How Joyfully). 190rp, Shepherds and Star of Bethlehem (Come, All Ye Shepherds).

**Perf. 12¼x12½**
**2015, Nov. 16          Litho.**
**Self-Adhesive**
1666-1669  A670   Set of 4      10.00 10.00

New Year 2016 (Year of the Monkey) A671

**Litho. With Foil Application**
**2015, Nov. 16          Perf. 12½**
**Self-Adhesive**
1670  A671  190rp red & gold      3.75 3.75
The monkey vignette was laser cut. Printed in sheets of 4.

Four Seasons A672

**2016, Mar. 7   Litho.   Perf. 13¼x14**
1671  A672  150rp multi      3.00 3.00

A673              Europa — A674

**2016, Mar. 7   Litho.   Perf. 14x13½**
1672  A673  150rp multi      3.00 3.00
**Self-Adhesive**
**Perf. 12x12½**
1673  A674  150rp multi      3.00 3.00

Paintings by Alois Ritter (1910-86) A675

Designs: 100rp, Ruggeller Riet, 1951. 200rp, Im Bofel, 1986.
**2016, Mar. 7   Litho.   Perf. 13½x13¾**
1674-1675  A675  Set of 2      6.00 6.00

Tools Found at Archaeological Sites — A676

Map of Liechtenstein and: 100rp, Flint dagger, 4th cent. B.C. 150rp, Razor, 12th cent. B.C. 200rp, Winged axe, 5th cent. B.C.

**Litho. & Embossed With Foil Application**
**2016, Mar. 7          Perf. 13¼x13½**
1676-1678  A676  Set of 3      9.00 9.00

Trees — A677

**2016, Mar. 7   Litho.   Perf. 13x13¼**
**Self-Adhesive**
1679  A677  85rp Oak      1.75 1.75
1680  A677  100rp Weeping willow      2.00 2.00
1681  A677  150rp Walnut      3.00 3.00
1682  A677  170rp Aspen      3.50 3.50
1683  A677  200rp Birch      4.00 4.00
Nos. 1679-1683 (5)      14.25 14.25

2016 Summer Olympics, Rio de Janeiro — A678

Designs: 100rp, Archery. 200rp, Judo.
**Litho. With Foil Application**
**2016, June 6          Perf. 12½x12**
**Self-Adhesive**
1684-1685  A678  Set of 2      6.25 6.25

17th Century Gold and Silver Items — A679

Designs: 1fr, Sailing boat drinking vessel. 1.50fr, Diana on a stag drinking vessel. 2fr, Turbo shell cup.
**Litho. With Foil Application**
**2016, June 6          Perf. 13¾x13½**
1686-1688  A679  Set of 3      9.25 9.25

Ruggeller Riet Nature Reserve — A680

No. 1689: a, Pond, denomination at UL. b, Pond, denomination at UR. c, Meadow in fog, denomination at UL. d, Meadow in fog, denomination at UR.
**2016, June 6   Litho.   Perf. 13¼**
1689  A680   Block of 4      8.50 8.50
a.-d.   100rp Any single      2.10 2.10

**Miniature Sheet**

Pear Varieties A681

No. 1690: a, Herbstlängler. b, Kugeläugstler. c, Hermannsbirne. d, Rote Holzbirne. e, Sulse Längler. f, Sülibirne. g, Wolfsbirne. h, Tollbirne.
**2016, June 6   Litho.   Perf. 12½**
**Self-Adhesive**
1690  A681   Sheet of 8      17.00 17.00
a.-h.   100rp Any single      2.10 2.10

Young Woman on a Balcony, by Gerrit Dou — A682

**2016, Sept. 5   Engr.   Perf. 11¾**
1691  A682  150rp multi      3.25 3.25
See Czech Republic No. 3680.

Religious Fraternities A683

Map of Liechtenstein and religious art: 100rp, Maria Hilf Fraternity (Madonna and Child altarpeice, Maria Hilf Chapel, Balzers). 150rp, St. Anne Fraternity (statue of St. Anne, Vaduz Castle) (42x35mm). 200rp, St. Sebastian Fraternity (St. Sebastian and angels, St. Sebastain Chapel, Nendeln).

**2016, Sept. 5   Litho.   Perf. 14½**
1692-1694  A683   Set of 3      9.25 9.25

Photographs of Tree Bark, by Erich Allgäuer — A684

Designs: 100rp, Woman. 150rp, Man. 200rp, Woman with Hat.
**2016, Sept. 5   Litho.   Perf. 13½**
1695-1697  A684   Set of 3      9.25 9.25

Motorcycles A685

Designs: 85rp, 1928 M. Thun. 100rp, 1920 Harley-Davidson. 150rp, 1948 Norton with Type Stolz sidecar. 200rp, 1933 Rudge.
**Litho. With Foil Application**
**2016, Sept. 5          Perf. 13¼**
1698-1701  A685   Set of 4      11.00 11.00

**Souvenir Sheet**

Liechtenstein Without People — A686

No. 1702: a, Border marker, rusted sign, badger (20 years after people). b, Eagle (100

years after people). c, Parrots and rainbow (500 years after people).

**Litho. With Foil Application**
**2016, Nov. 14          Perf. 14x13½**
1702  A686   Sheet of 3      12.00 12.00
a.-c.   200rp Any single      4.00 4.00
No. 1702 was sold folded into thirds.

Christmas — A687

Christmas card illustrations: 85rp, Child with lantern. 100rp, Family exchanges Christmas presents, vert. 150rp, City scene with snow, vert. 200rp, Children walking in forest.

**Litho. With Foil Application**
**Perf. 12x12½, 12½x12**
**2016, Nov. 14**
**Self-Adhesive**
1703-1706  A687   Set of 4      11.00 11.00

New Year 2017 (Year of the Rooster) A688

**Litho. With Foil Application**
**2016, Nov. 14          Perf. 12½**
**Self-Adhesive**
1707  A688  200rp red & gold      4.00 4.00
The rooster vignette was laser cut. Printed in sheets of 4.

Europa A689

Designs: No. 1708, 150rp, Vaduz Castle. No. 1709, 150rp, Gutenberg Castle, Balzers.
**2017, Mar. 6   Litho.   Perf. 14¼**
1708-1709  A689   Set of 2      6.00 6.00

Outdoor Sports — A690

Winning photographs in youth photography contest: 85rp, Smooth Powder Turn, by Julius Tiefenthaler. 100rp, Winter Storm Windsurfing, by Yannick Oberhofer. 200rp, Sunset Backflip, by Tiefenthaler.
**2017, Mar. 6   Litho.   Perf. 13½**
1710-1712  A690   Set of 3      7.75 7.75

Tools of Tradesmen — A691

Hand and tools of: 130rp, Mason. 180rp, Tailor. 200rp, Goldsmith.
**2017, Mar. 6   Litho.   Perf. 12½x12¼**
**Dated "2017"**
1713-1715  A691   Set of 3      10.00 10.00
See Nos. 1741-1743.

Grain Crops — A692

Designs: 85rp, Oats. 100rp, Barley. 150rp, Corn. 200rp, Millet.

**2017, Mar. 6    Litho.    Perf. 12¼**
**Self-Adhesive**
1716-1719 A692    Set of 4    10.50 10.50

HPZ Remedial Education Center, Schaan, 50th Anniv. — A693

**2017, June 6    Litho.    Perf. 12x12½**
**Self-Adhesive**
1720 A693 1fr multi    2.10 2.10

Paintings by Peter Fendi (1796-1842) — A694

Designs: 85rp, Request for Admission. 1fr, Sneaking a Peek. 1.50fr, A Child's Prayer.

**Litho. With Foil Application**
**2017, June 6    Perf. 13½x13¼**
1721-1723 A694    Set of 3    7.00 7.00

Gampriner Seelein Nature Reserve — A695

No. 1724 — Lake Gampriner Seelein in: a, Autumn, denomination at UL. b, Autumn, denomination at UR. c, Winter, denomination at UL. d, Winter, denomination at UR.

**2017, June 6    Litho.    Perf. 13¼**
1724 A695    Block of 4    8.50 8.50
a.-d.    100rp Any single    2.10 2.10

**Souvenir Sheet**

50th Wedding Anniversary of Prince Hans-Adam II and Princess Marie — A696

No. 1725: a, Vaduz Castle and flower (18x60mm). b, Prince and Princess (46x60mm). c, Crown and joined wedding rings (41x60mm).

**Litho. With Foil Application, Litho. & Embossed With Foil Application (2.80fr)**
**2017, June 6    Perf. 14¼x14½**
1725 A696    Sheet of 3    13.00 13.00
a.    1.30fr multi    2.75 2.75
b.    2.20fr multi    4.50 4.50
c.    2.80fr multi    5.75 5.75

Settlement Area of Liechtenstein A697

**2017, Sept. 4    Litho.    Perf. 14x13¼**
1726 A697 150rp multi    3.25 3.25

Rappastein, Painting by Helmut Ditsch — A698

**2017, Sept. 4    Litho.    Perf. 14x13½**
1727 A698 380rp multi    8.00 8.00

**Souvenir Sheet**

Balzers Mail Collection Station, 200th Anniv. — A699

No. 1728: a, Postman and girl. b, Posthorn. c, Horse-drawn mail coach.

**Litho. & Engr. With Foil Application**
**2017, Sept. 4    Perf. 13¾x14¼**
1728 A699    Sheet of 3    13.50 13.50
a.    1.30fr multi    2.75 2.75
b.    2.20fr multi    4.75 4.75
c.    2.80fr multi    6.00 6.00

**Miniature Sheet**

Stone Fruit Varieties A700

No. 1729: a, Mombacher Frühaprikose apricots. b, Kirkespflaume plums. c, Grüne Reineclaude plums. d, Hauszwetschge plums. e, Ungarische Beste apricots. f, Schauenburger cherries. g, Mirabelle von Nancy plums. h, Gelbe Denise cherries.

**2017, Sept. 4    Litho.    Perf. 12½**
**Self-Adhesive**
1729 A700    Sheet of 8    17.00 17.00
a.-h.    100rp Any single    2.10 2.10

2018 Winter Olympics, Pyeongchang, South Korea — A701

Designs: 170rp, Nordic skiing. 200rp, Alpine skiing.

**2017, Nov. 13    Litho.    Perf. 12x12½**
1730-1731 A701    Set of 2    7.75 7.75

Worldwide Fund for Nature (WWF) — A702

Designs: 85rp, Castor fiber. 100rp, Lynx lynx. 130rp, Canis lupus. 150rp, Ciconia ciconia.

**2017, Nov. 13    Litho.    Perf. 12x12½**
**Self-Adhesive**
1732-1735 A702    Set of 4    9.50 9.50

Christmas — A703

Designs: 85rp, Star of Bethlehem, trees and house. 100rp, Star, forest and house. 150rp, Moon, forest and house. 200rp, Moon over church.

**2017, Nov. 13    Litho.    Perf. 12½x12**
**Self-Adhesive**
1736-1739 A703    Set of 4    11.00 11.00

New Year 2018 (Year of the Dog) — A704

**Litho. With Foil Application**
**2017, Nov. 13    Perf. 12½**
**Self-Adhesive**
1740 A704 200rp red & gold    4.25 4.25

The dog vignette was laser cut. Printed in sheets of 4.

**Tools of Tradesmen Type of 2017**
Hand and tools of: 100rp, Bookbinder. 130rp, Instrument maker. 180rp, Shoemaker.

**2018, Mar. 5    Litho.    Perf. 12½x12¼**
**Dated "2018"**
1741-1743 A691    Set of 3    8.75 8.75

Balzers Footbridge — A705

Old Rhine Bridge, Vaduz A706

**Litho. With Foil Application**
**2018, Mar. 5    Perf. 14x13¼**
1744 A705 150rp sil & multi    3.25 3.25
1745 A706 150rp sil & multi    3.25 3.25
Europa.

Vegetables — A708

Designs: 85rp, Eggplant. 100rp, Radishes. 150rp, Zucchinis. 200rp, Peperoni peppers.

**2018, Mar. 5    Litho.    Perf. 12¼**
**Self-Adhesive**
1748-1751 A708    Set of 4    11.50 11.50

Direct Suffrage, Cent. — A709

**2018, June 4    Litho.    Perf. 13¾x13¼**
1752 A709 100rp multi    2.00 2.00

Mountain Summit Crosses — A710

Cross on: 100rp, Kelchle. 150rp, Kläusli. 200rp, Mittlerspitz. 260rp, Hubel.

**2018, June 4    Litho.    Perf. 13x13¼**
1753-1756 A710    Set of 4    14.50 14.50

Hälos Nature Reserve A711

No. 1757 — Reserve in: a, Spring (blue skies, denomination at UL). b, Spring (blue skies, denomination at UR). c, Summer (cloudy skies, denomination at UL). d, Summer (cloudy skies, denomination at UR).

**2018, June 4    Litho.    Perf. 13¼**
1757 A711    Block of 4    8.00 8.00
a.-d.    100rp Any single    2.00 2.00

**Souvenir Sheet**

50th Birthday of Hereditary Prince Alois — A712

No. 1758: a, Green princely hat (30x30mm). b, Hereditary Prince Alois (30x36mm). c, Red princely hat (30x30mm).

**Litho. & Engr.**
**2018, June 11    Perf. 14x13¼**
1758 A712    Sheet of 3    6.75 6.75
a.    1.30fr multi    1.40 1.40
b.    2.20fr multi    2.25 2.25
c.    2.80fr multi    3.00 3.00

Biedermann House, Schellenberg, 500th Anniv. — A713

**Litho. & Embossed**
**2018, Sept. 3    Perf. 13¼x14**
1759 A713 2fr multi    4.25 4.25

Bird's Eyes — A714

Paintings by Gustav Klimt (1862-1918) — A707

Designs: 2.60fr, The Kiss. 3.70fr, Death and Life.

**Litho. With Foil Application**
**2018, Mar. 5    Perf. 14½**
1746-1747 A707    Set of 2    13.50 13.50

Eye of: 100rp, Gray heron. 130rp, Great crested grebe. 150rp, Cormorant.

**Litho. & Embossed**
**2018, Sept. 3** Perf. 14
1760-1762 A714 Set of 3 7.75 7.75

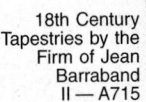

18th Century Tapestries by the Firm of Jean Barraband II — A715

Designs: 100rp, The Tea Ceremony. 150rp, Audience with the Emperor of China (60x42mm). 180rp, The Scholar Before the Great Mogul (33x36mm).

**2018, Sept. 3** Litho. Perf. 13¼
1763-1765 A715 Set of 3 9.00 9.00

**Miniature Sheet**

Music for Dancing — A716

No. 1766: a, Saxophone player. b, Dancer with castanets. c, Roller skater with boom box. d, Keytar player. e, Concertina player. f, Banjo player. g, Dancer with maracas. h, Cello player.

**2018, Sept. 3** Litho. Perf. 14
1766 A716 Sheet of 8 17.00 17.00
a.-h. 100rp Any single 2.10 2.10

Immigrants — A717

Map of Liechtenstein and: 85rp, Arab man. 100rp, African man. 130rp, Asian woman.

**2018, Nov. 12** Litho. Perf. 14x13¾
1767-1769 A717 Set of 3 6.50 6.50

Christmas — A718

Star of Bethlehem and: 85rp, Three Magi. 100rp, Magi and shepherds. 150rp, People and dog. 200rp, Nativity.

**2018, Nov. 12** Litho. Perf. 12x12½
**Self-Adhesive**
1770-1773 A718 Set of 4 11.00 11.00

New Year 2019 (Year of the Boar) — A719

**Litho. With Foil Application**
**2018, Nov. 12** Perf. 12½
**Self-Adhesive**
1774 A719 200rp red & gold 4.00 4.00

The boar vignette was laser cut. Printed in sheets of 4.

Principality of Liechtenstein, 300th Anniv. — A720

**2019, Jan. 23 Embroidered** Imperf.
**Self-Adhesive**
1775 A720 630rp gold & red 13.00 13.00

An item similar to No. 1775 with gold threads and eight Swarovski crystals was produced in limited quantities and sold for 300fr.

Emil Beck (1888-1973), Envoy to Switzerland and Prince Eduard (1872-1951), Envoy to Austria — A721

**2019, Mar. 4** Litho. Perf. 13¼x13
1776 A721 220rp multi 4.50 4.50

Representation of Liechtenstein in foreign countries, cent.

A722  Golden Eagle (National Bird) — A723

**2019, Mar. 4** Litho. Perf. 13¾x14
1777 Vert. pair 6.00 6.00
a. A722 1.50fr multi 3.00 3.00
b. A723 1.50fr multi 3.00 3.00

Europa.

Dragonflies — A724

Designs: 85rp, Calopteryx virgo. 100rp, Anax imperator. 180rp, Phyrrhosoma nymphula. 260rp, Calopteryx splendens.

**2019, Mar. 4** Litho. Perf. 12x12½
**Self-Adhesive**
1778-1781 A724 Set of 4 12.50 12.50

See Nos. 1804-1807.

First Man on the Moon, 50th Anniv. — A725

Designs: 180rp, Astronaut on Moon. 200rp, Lunar Module on Moon.

**Litho. With Foil Application**
**2019, June 3** Perf. 12
1782-1783 A725 Set of 2 7.75 7.75

Mountains — A726

No. 1784: a, Falkniskette, denomination at UL. b, Falkniskette, denomination at UR. c, Schönberg, denomination at UL. d, Schönberg, denomination at UR.

**2019, June 3** Litho. Perf. 13¼
1784 A726 Block of 4 8.00 8.00
a.-d. 100rp Any single 2.00 2.00

**Souvenir Sheet**

Leonardo da Vinci (1452-1519), Sculptor and Painter — A727

No. 1785: a, Sketch of flying machine. b, Self-portrait. c, Anatomical sketches.

**2019, June 3** Litho. Perf. 13½x13¼
1785 A727 Sheet of 3 13.00 13.00
a. 1.30fr multi 2.60 2.60
b. 2.20fr multi 4.50 4.50
c. 2.60fr multi 5.75 5.75

**Souvenir Sheet**

Coat of Arms of Liechtenstein — A728

**Litho. & Embossed With Foil Application**
**2019, June 3** Perf. 14x13¾
1786 A728 630rp multi 13.00 13.00

Principality of Liechtenstein, 300th Anniv.

Red House, Vaduz — A729

**Litho. & Engr. With Foil Application**
**2019, Sept. 2** Perf. 13
1787 A729 150rp gold & multi 3.00 3.00

Triesen — A730

Designs: 130rp, Lady Chapel. 200rp, Old Village Center.

**Litho. & Embossed**
**2019, Sept. 2** Perf. 13½x13¾
1788-1789 A730 Set of 2 6.75 6.75

Sculptures by Pier Jacopo Alari-Bonacolsi (c. 1455-1528) — A731

Designs: 1.40fr, Bust of a Young Man. 1.70fr, Hercules with a Lion's Skin. 2.20fr, Equestrian Statue of Marcus Aurelius.

**Litho. With Foil Application**
**2019, Sept. 2** Perf. 12x11¼
1790-1792 A731 Set of 3 10.00 10.00

**Souvenir Sheet**

Circumnavigation by Crew of Ferdinand Magellan, 500th Anniv. — A732

No. 1793: a, Magellan's ship, Victoria. b, Death of Magellan in the Philippines. c, Magellan (c. 1480-1521).

**Litho. Sheet Margin Litho. With Foil Application**
Perf. 12 on 3 or 4 Sides
**2019, Sept. 2**
1793 A732 Sheet of 3 13.00 13.00
a. 130rp multi 2.75 2.75
b. 220rp multi 4.50 4.50
c. 280rp multi 5.75 5.75

Photographs of Ice, by Sepp Köppel — A733

Designs: 100rp, Ice Flow. 110rp, Stone Islands. 130rp, Streamlines.

**Litho. & Embossed With Thermography**
**2019, Nov. 11** Perf. 13¼x13½
1794-1796 A733 Set of 3 7.00 7.00

Grit is embedded in the thermographic ink used on parts of the vignette.

Christmas — A734

Designs: 85rp, Snowman. 100rp, Nutcracker. 150rp, Rocking horse. 200rp, Angel.

**Litho. With Foil Application**
**2019, Nov. 11** Perf. 12½
**Self-Adhesive**
1797-1800 A734 Set of 4 11.00 11.00

New Year 2020 (Year of the Rat) — A735

**Litho. With Foil Application**
**2019, Nov. 11** Perf. 12½
**Self-Adhesive**
1801 A735 200rp red & gold 4.00 4.00

The rat vignette was laser cut. Printed in sheets of 4.

A736

Diversity — A737

Perf. 13¼x13½
**2019, Nov. 14** Litho.
1802 A736 85rp multi 1.75 1.75
1803 A737 100rp multi 2.00 2.00

See Switzerland Nos. 1743-1744.

## Dragonflies Type of 2019

Designs: 85rp, Platycnemis latipes. 130rp, Sympetrum fonscolombii. 180rp, Crocothemis erythraea. 200rp, Sympetrum depressiusculum.

**2020, Mar. 2    Litho.    Perf. 12x12½**
**Self-Adhesive**
1804-1807  A724   Set of 4        12.50 12.50

Liechtenstein's Membership in European Economic Area, 25th Anniv. — A738

**2020, Mar. 2    Litho.    Perf. 13¼x13**
1808  A738  220rp multi              4.75 4.75

Europa
A739

No. 1809 — Lindau Messenger Courier Service: a, Mounted postrider. b, Stagecoach.

**2020, Mar. 2    Litho.    Perf. 14**
1809  A739   Pair                    6.50 6.50
a.-b.     150rp Either single         3.25 3.25
Printed in sheets containing 2 each Nos. 1809a-1809b.

### Souvenir Sheet

Royal Birthdays
A740

No. 1810: a, Princess Marie, 80th birthday. b, Prince Hans-Adam II, 75th birthday.

### Litho. With Foil Application
**2020, Mar. 2          Perf. 13¼x13**
1810  A740   Sheet of 2       13.50 13.50
a.     2fr gold & multi            4.25 4.25
b.     4.30fr gold & multi         9.00 9.00

Untitled (Indian Banner: World), Printed Banner by Matt Mullican — A741

**2020, June 2    Litho.    Perf. 12**
1811  A741  150rp black & red      3.25 3.25

2020 Summer Olympics, Tokyo — A742

Designs: 170rp, Synchronized swimming. 280rp, Judo.

### Litho. With Foil Application
**2020, June 2          Perf. 12**
1812-1813  A742  Set of 2        9.50 9.50
The 2020 Summer Olympics were postponed until 2021 because of the coronavirus pandemic.

Waters of Liechtenstein — A743

---

No. 1814: a, Valunerbach, denomination at UL. b, Valunerbach, denomination at UR. c, Schwabbrünnen, denomination at UL. d, Schwabbrünnen, denomination at UR.

**2020, June 2    Litho.    Perf. 13¼**
1814  A743   Block of 4           8.50 8.50
a.-d.     100rp Any single          2.10 2.10

### Souvenir Sheet

Egon Rheinberger (1870-1936), Artist and Architect — A744

No. 1815: a, Sketch of the Maultasch Ruins Near Appiano. b, Wall painting of unicorn in Gutenberg Castle. c, Rheinberger.

### Litho., Sheet Margin Litho. With Foil Application
**2020, June 2          Perf. 12**
1815  A744   Sheet of 3      13.50 13.50
a.     130rp multi               2.75 2.75
b.     220rp multi               4.75 4.75
c.     280rp multi               6.00 6.00

Recycling
A745

**2020, Sept. 7  Embroidered  Imperf.**
**Self-Adhesive**
1816  A745  630rp green & blue  14.00 14.00

Balzers
A746

Designs: 100rp, Mill buildings. 180rp, Mäls District buildings.

### Litho. & Embossed
**2020, Sept. 7          Perf. 13¼**
1817-1818  A746  Set of 2        6.25 6.25

Paintings by Peter Paul Rubens (1577-1640) — A747

Designs: 1.50fr, The Hunt of Diana. 2.20fr, The Hunt of Meleager and Atalanta.

### Litho. With Foil Application
**2020, Sept. 7          Perf. 12**
1819-1820  A747  Set of 2        8.00 8.00

### Souvenir Sheet

Self-portrait, by Raphael (1483-1520) — A748

### Litho. With Foil Application
**2020, Sept. 7          Perf. 12**
1821  A748  630rp multi          14.00 14.00

---

### Souvenir Sheet

Ludwig van Beethoven (1770-1827), Composer — A749

### Litho. & Engr.
**2020, Nov. 16          Perf. 13¼**
1822  A749  6.30fr multi          14.00 14.00

Christmas — A750

Numerals in denominations hanging like Christmas ornaments: 85rp, 100rp, 150rp, 200rp.

### Litho. With Holographic Foil
**2020, Nov. 16          Perf. 12½x12**
**Self-Adhesive**
1823-1826  A750   Set of 4       12.00 12.00

New Year 2021 (Year of the Ox) — A751

### Litho. With Foil Application
**2020, Nov. 16          Perf. 12½**
**Self-Adhesive**
1827  A751  200rp red & gold       4.50 4.50
The ox vignette was laser cut. Printed in sheets of 4.

Operette Balzers, 75th Anniv. — A752

### Litho. With Foil Application
**2021, Mar. 1          Perf. 12**
1828  A752  85rp gold & multi      1.90 1.90

First Session of United Nations General Assembly, 75th Anniv. A753

**2021, Mar. 1   Litho.   Perf. 11¼x11½**
1829  A753  5.20fr multi          11.50 11.50

Songbirds — A754

Designs: 85rp, Fichtenkreuzschnabel (crossbill). 100rp, Zitronenzeisig (lemon siskin). 150rp, Mauerläufer (wall creeper). 200rp, Neuntöter (red-backed shrike).

---

**2021, Mar. 1    Litho.    Perf. 12½x12**
**Self-Adhesive**
1830-1833  A754   Set of 4       12.00 12.00
For surcharge, see No. 1855.

Europa
A755

No. 1834 — Endangered species: a, Astacus astacus. b, Mustela nivalis.

**2021, Mar. 1    Litho.    Perf. 14¼x14**
1834  A755   Pair                  6.50 6.50
a.-b.     150rp Either single        3.25 3.25

1620 Map of Upper Rhine Valley by Hans Conrad Gyger (1599-1674) — A756

### Litho. & Embossed
**2021, June 7          Perf. 13¾x13½**
1835  A756  150rp multi            3.25 3.25

Art by Prince Hans (1910-75) A757

Designs: 260rp, Elephant. 430rp, Zebra Herd.

### Litho. & Embossed
**2021, June 7          Perf. 13½**
1836-1837  A757   Set of 2       15.00 15.00

Trails
A758

No. 1838: a, Upper Silum Trail, denomination at UL. b, Upper Silum Trail, denomination at UR. c, Trail to Gapfahl, denomination at UL. d, Trail to Gapfahl, denomination at UR.

**2021, June 7    Litho.    Perf. 13¼**
1838  A758   Block of 4           9.00 9.00
a.-d.     100rp Any single          2.25 2.25

### Souvenir Sheet

PEN International, Cent. — A759

No. 1839 — Quotations (in German) with words covered by scratch-off panel from: a, Friedrich Schiller (1759-1805). b, Emily Dickinson (1830-86). c, Johann Wolfgang von Goethe (1749-1832).

### Litho. With Scratch-off Coating
**2021, June 7          Perf. 13x13¼**
1839  A759   Sheet of 3      14.00 14.00
a.     100rp multi               2.25 2.25
b.     150rp multi               3.25 3.25
c.     380rp multi               8.25 8.25

Values are for unscrached stamps.

First E-Mail Message, 50th Anniv. — A760

**2021, Sept. 6** **Litho.** *Perf. 12*
1840 A760 100rp multi 2.25 2.25

Constitution of the Principality of Liechtenstein, Cent. — A761

Designs: 85rp, Freedom. 100rp, Peace. 150rp, Democracy.

**2021, Sept. 6** **Litho.** *Perf. 14x13½*
1841-1843 A761 Set of 3 7.25 7.25

Souvenir Sheet

Paintings by Eugen Zotow (1881-1953) — A762

No. 1844: a, View of Vaduz Castle (47x32mm). b, Self-portrait (32x32mm).

**2021, Sept. 6** **Litho.** *Perf. 12*
1844 A762 Sheet of 2 7.75 7.75
a. 140rp multi 3.00 3.00
b. 220rp multi 4.75 4.75

See Ukraine No. 1314.

Souvenir Sheet

Dante Alighieri (c. 1265-1321), Writer — A763

No. 1845: a, Portrait of Alighieri. b, Writing hand with quill.

**Litho. & Engr.**
**2021, Sept. 6** *Perf. 13¾x14*
1845 A763 Sheet of 2 17.00 17.00
a. 3.70fr gray & black 8.00 8.00
b. 4fr gray & black 8.75 8.75

Souvenir Sheet

Blockchain Technology — A764

**2021, Sept. 6** **Litho.** *Perf. 12½x12¼*
1846 A764 520rp multi 11.50 11.50

Doctors Without Borders, 50th Anniv. — A765

**2021, Nov. 15** **Litho.** *Perf. 13½*
1847 A765 370rp multi 8.00 8.00

Liechtenstein Chess Federation, 50th Anniv. — A766

Chess board and pieces: 85rp, Knight. 180rp, King.

**Litho. & Embossed With Foil Application**
**2021, Nov. 15** *Perf. 13½*
1848-1849 A766 Set of 2 5.75 5.75

Christmas — A767

Designs: 85rp, Star of Bethlehem. 100rp, Sheep and flowers. 150rp, Dove with olive branch. 200rp, Candle.

**Litho. With Foil Application**
**2021, Nov. 15** *Perf. 12¼*
**Self-Adhesive**
1850-1853 A767 Set of 4 12.00 12.00

New Year 2022 (Year of the Tiger) — A768

**Litho. With Foil Application**
**2021, Nov. 15** *Perf. 12½*
**Self-Adhesive**
1854 A768 200rp red & gold 4.50 4.50

The tiger vignette was laser cut. Printed in sheets of 4.

No. 1831 Surcharged / No. 1515 Surcharged

**Methods and Perfs As Before**
**2022, Jan. 3**
**Self-Adhesive**
1855 A754 90rp on 100rp #1831 2.00 2.00
1856 A575 110rp on 220rp #1515 2.40 2.40

Wild Bees — A769

Designs: 90rp, Large scabious mining bee. 1.10fr, Carpenter bee. 1.80fr, Mountain bumblebee. 2.30fr, Cuckoo bee.

**2022, Jan. 3** **Litho.** *Perf. 12¼*
**Self-Adhesive**
1857-1860 A769 Set of 4 13.50 13.50

2022 Winter Olympics, Beijing — A770

Designs: 1.10fr, Skiing. 2.10fr, Two-man bobsledding.

**Litho. & Embossed With Foil Application**
**2022, Feb. 4** *Perf. 13½*
1861-1862 A770 Set of 2 7.00 7.00

Chimney Sweeps and Good Luck Symbols — A771

Designs: 90rp, Male chimney sweep and horseshoes. 110rp, Female chimney sweep and four-leaf clovers.

**Litho. With Foil Application**
**2022, Mar. 7** *Perf. 13½*
1863-1864 A771 Set of 2 4.50 4.50

Europa A772

No. 1865: a, Legend of the Tälibudel. b, Legend of the White Woman.

**2022, Mar. 7** **Litho.** *Perf. 12¼x12*
1865 A772 Pair 8.00 8.00
a.-b. 1.80fr Either single 4.00 4.00

Souvenir Sheet

Molière (1622-73), Playwright and Actor — A773

No. 1866: a. Molière's acting group, Troupe du Roi. b, L'Ecole des Femmes, play by Molière. c, Portrait of Molière, by Pierre Mignard.

**2022, Mar. 7** **Litho.** *Perf. 12*
1866 A773 Sheet of 3 11.50 11.50
a.-b. 110rp Either single 2.00 2.00
c. 410rp multi 7.25 7.25

Glass of Water — A774

**2022, June 7** **Litho.** *Perf. 12*
1867 A774 180rp multi 3.75 3.75

Mountains — A775

No. 1868: a, Alpspitz, denomination at UL. b, Alpspitz, denomination at UR. c, Drei Kapuziner, denomination at UL. d, Drei Kapuziner, denomination at UR.

**2022, June 7** **Litho.** *Perf. 13¼*
1868 A775 Block of 4 9.00 9.00
a.-d. 110rp Any single 2.25 2.25

Souvenir Sheet

Princess Marie of Liechtenstein (1940-2021) — A776

**2022, June 7** **Litho.** *Perf. 12*
1869 A776 6.30fr multi 13.50 13.50

Souvenir Sheet

Oskar Werner (1922-84), Actor — A777

No. 1870 — Werner: a, Looking left, as young man. b, Wearing sunglasses. c, Looking right, holding drink.

**Litho. With Foil Application**
**2022, June 7** *Perf. 12*
1870 A777 Sheet of 3 6.25 6.25
a.-b. 90rp Either single 1.90 1.90
c. 110rp multi 2.25 2.25

Planken A778

Designs: 90rp, Village center. 110rp, Schuhmacher-Nägele House.

**Litho. & Embossed** *Perf. 13¼*
**2022, Sept. 9**
1871-1872 A778 Set of 2 4.00 4.00

Paintings by Ferdinand Runk (1764-1834) A779

Paintings: 90rp, Eisgrub Castle Park. 1.10fr, Lundenburg Castle. 1.80fr, Schlössen am Schüttel in the Prater.

**Litho. With Foil Application**
**2022, Sept. 9** *Perf. 12*
1873-1875 A779 Set of 3 7.75 7.75

Souvenir Sheet

Austrian Federal Railways Reihe 4024 Railcar A780

**2022, Sept. 9** **Litho.** *Perf. 12*
1876 A780 180rp multi 3.75 3.75
a. Souvenir sheet of 3, Austria #3010, Liechtenstein #1876, Switzerland #1891 9.50 —

Feldkirch-Schaan-Buchs railway line, 150th anniv. No. 1876a sold for 4.65fr. See Austria No. 3010, Switzerland No. 1891.

## Souvenir Sheet

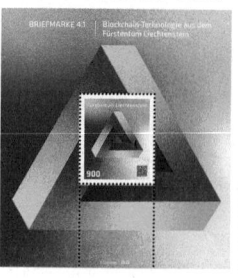

Optical
Illusion
and QR
Code
A781

**2022, Sept. 9  Litho.  Perf. 12½x12¼**
1877 A781 900rp multi        18.50 18.50

Blockchain technology.

---

## SEMI-POSTAL STAMPS

Prince Johann II — SP1

**Wmk. 183**
**1925, Oct. 5   Engr.      Perf. 11½**
B1  SP1 10rp yellow green     42.50 22.50
B2  SP1 20rp deep red         21.00 22.50
B3  SP1 30rp deep blue         7.00  7.00
    Nos. B1-B3 (3)            70.50 52.00
    Set, never hinged        210.00

85th birthday of the Prince Regent. Sold at a premium of 5rp each, the excess being devoted to charities.

Coat of Arms — SP2

**1927, Oct. 5          Typo.**
B4  SP2 10rp multicolored     10.50 25.00
B5  SP2 20rp multicolored     10.50 25.00
B6  SP2 30rp multicolored      5.00 21.00
    Nos. B4-B6 (3)            26.00 71.00
    Set, never hinged         62.00

87th birthday of Prince Johann II. These stamps were sold at premiums of 5, 10 and 20rp respectively. The money thus obtained was devoted to charity.

Railroad Bridge Demolished by Flood — SP3

Designs: 10rp+10rp, Inundated Village of Ruggel. 20rp+10rp, Austrian soldiers rescuing refugees. 30rp+10rp, Swiss soldiers salvaging personal effects.

**1928, Feb. 6   Litho.    Unwmk.**
B7  SP3  5rp + 5rp brn vio
         & brn              17.50 26.00
B8  SP3 10rp + 10rp bl grn
         & brn              25.00 26.00
B9  SP3 20rp + 10rp dl red
         & brn              25.00 26.00
B10 SP3 30rp + 10rp dp bl
         & brn              21.00 26.00
    Nos. B7-B10 (4)         88.50 104.00
    Set, never hinged       30.00

The surtax on these stamps was used to aid the sufferers from the Rhine floods.

Coat of Arms — SP7    Princess Elsa — SP8

Design: 30rp, Prince Francis I.

---

**1932, Dec. 21            Photo.**
B11 SP7 10rp (+ 5rp) olive
         grn               17.50 25.00
B12 SP8 20rp (+ 5rp) rose
         red               17.50 22.50
B13 SP8 30rp (+ 10rp) ultra 22.50 32.50
    Nos. B11-B13 (3)        57.50 80.00
    Set, never hinged      160.00

The surtax was for the Child Welfare Fund.

## Postal Museum Issue
### Souvenir Sheet

SP10

**1936, Oct. 24   Litho.   Imperf.**
B14 SP10 Sheet of 4        15.00 35.00
    Never hinged           60.00

Sheet contains 2 each, Nos. 120, 122. Sold for 2fr.

"Protect the Child" — SP11

Designs: No. B16, "Take Care of the Sick." No. B17, "Help the Aged."

**Perf. 11½**
**1945, Nov. 27   Photo.   Unwmk.**
B15 SP11 10rp + 10rp multi   .65  1.75
B16 SP11 20rp + 20rp multi   .65  2.25
B17 SP11  1fr + 1.40fr multi 4.75 20.00
    Nos. B15-B17 (3)        6.05 24.00
    Set, never hinged      11.00

### Souvenir Sheet

Post Coach SP14

**1946, Aug. 10**
B18 SP14 Sheet of 2        21.00 32.50
    Never hinged           35.00
a.    10rp dark violet brown & buff
                            5.00 15.00
    Never hinged           12.50

25th anniv. of the Swiss-Liechtenstein Postal Agreement. Sheet, size: 82x60½mm, sold for 3fr.

Canal by Albert Cuyp SP15    Willem van Huythuysen by Frans Hals SP16

40rp+10rp, Landscape by Jacob van Ruysdael.

**1951, July 24            Perf. 11½**
B19 SP15 10rp + 10rp ol grn  5.00  7.00
B20 SP16 20rp + 10rp dk vio
         brn                 5.00  7.00
B21 SP15 40rp + 10rp blue    5.00  7.00
    Nos. B19-B21 (3)        15.00 21.00
    Set, never hinged      30.00

Issued in sheets of 12. For surcharges see Nos. 281-283.

Catalogue values for unused stamps in this section, from this point to the end of the section, are for Never Hinged items.

---

### Nos. 324-325 Surcharged with New Value and Uprooted Oak Emblem
**1960, Apr. 7**
B22 A190 30rp + 10rp on 40rp   .55  1.00
B23 A190 50rp + 10rp on 25rp   .90  2.00

World Refugee Year, July 1, 1959-June 30, 1960. The surtax was for aid to refugees.

Growth Symbol — SP17

**1967, Dec. 7   Photo.   Perf. 11½**
B24 SP17 50rp + 20rp multi    .50  .60

Surtax was for development assistance.

---

## AIR POST STAMPS

Airplane over Snow-capped Mountain Peaks — AP1    Airplane above Vaduz Castle — AP2

Airplane over Rhine Valley — AP3

**Perf. 10½, 10½x11½**
**1930, Aug. 12   Photo.   Unwmk.**
### Gray Wavy Lines in Background
C1  AP1 15rp dark brown     10.50 17.50
C2  AP1 20rp slate          25.00 25.00
C3  AP2 25rp olive brown    14.00 45.00
C4  AP2 35rp slate blue     21.00 42.50
C5  AP3 45rp olive green    50.00 87.50
C6  AP3  1fr lake           55.00 62.50
    Nos. C1-C6 (6)         175.50 280.00
    Set, never hinged      518.00

For surcharge see No. C14.

Zeppelin over Naafkopf, Falknis Range — AP4

Design: 2fr, Zeppelin over Valüna Valley.

**1931, June 1            Perf. 11½**
C7  AP4 1fr olive black    70.00 125.00
C8  AP4 2fr blue black    140.00 400.00
    Set, never hinged     565.00

Golden Eagle — AP6

15rp, Golden Eagle in flight, diff. 20rp, Golden Eagle in flight, diff. 30rp, Osprey. 50rp, Eagle.

**1934-35**
C9  AP6 10rp brt vio ('35)   9.00 32.50
C10 AP6 15rp red org ('35)  22.50 30.00
C11 AP6 20rp red ('35)      82.50 30.00
C12 AP6 30rp brt bl ('35)   22.50 30.00
C13 AP6 50rp emerald        15.00 35.00
    Nos. C9-C13 (5)        151.50 157.50
    Set, never hinged     300.00

No. C6 Surcharged

---

**1935, June 24      Perf. 10½x11½**
C14 AP3 60rp on 1fr lake   40.00 42.50
    Never hinged          130.00

Airship "Hindenburg" AP11

Design: 2fr, Airship "Graf Zeppelin."

**1936, May 1            Perf. 11½**
C15 AP11 1fr rose carmine  40.00 75.00
C16 AP11 2fr violet        30.00 75.00
    Set, never hinged     160.00

AP13

10rp, Barn swallows. 15rp, Black-headed Gulls. 20rp, Gulls. 30rp, Eagle. 50rp, Northern Goshawk. 1fr, Lammergeier. 2fr, Lammergeier.

**1939, Apr. 3            Photo.**
C17 AP13 10rp violet         .60  .70
C18 AP13 15rp red orange     .60 2.00
C19 AP13 20rp dark red      2.75  .80
C20 AP13 30rp dull blue     1.20 1.50
C21 AP13 50rp brt green     3.00 3.25
C22 AP13  1fr rose car      2.25 12.00
C23 AP13  2fr violet        2.25 12.00
    Nos. C17-C23 (7)       12.65 32.25
    Set, never hinged      40.00

Catalogue values for unused stamps in this section, from this point to the end of the section, are for Never Hinged items.

AP20

Designs: 10rp, Leonardo da Vinci. 15rp, Joseph Montgolfier. 20rp, Jacob Degen. 25rp, Wilhelm Kress. 30rp, E. G. Robertson. 50rp, W. S. Henson. 1fr, Otto Lilienthal. 2fr, S. A. Andrée. 5fr, Wilbur Wright. 10fr, Icarus.

**1948**
C24 AP20 10rp dark green     .75  .25
C25 AP20 15rp dark violet    .75  .80
C26 AP20 20rp brown         1.00  .25
a.    20rp reddish brown    95.00 3.25
C27 AP20 25rp dark red      1.50 1.25
C28 AP20 40rp violet blue   1.75 1.25
C29 AP20 50rp Prus blue     2.00 1.25
C30 AP20  1fr chocolate     3.50 2.75
C31 AP20  2fr rose lake     5.25 3.50
C32 AP20  5fr olive green   6.50 4.75
C33 AP20 10fr slate black  42.50 14.00
    Nos. C24-C33 (10)      65.50 30.05

Issued in sheets of 9. Exist imperf. Value, set $6,500.

Helicopter, Bell 47-J — AP21

Planes: 40rp, Boeing 707 jet. 50rp, Convair 600 jet. 75rp, Douglas DC-8.

**1960, Apr. 7   Unwmk.   Perf. 11½**
C34 AP21 30rp red orange    2.25 2.25
C35 AP21 40rp blue black    3.75 2.25
C36 AP21 50rp deep claret   9.50 4.00
C37 AP21 75rp olive green   2.00 2.25
    Nos. C34-C37 (4)       17.50 10.75

30th anniv. of Liechtenstein's air post stamps.

## POSTAGE DUE STAMPS

### National Administration of the Post Office

D1

| | | | | | |
|---|---|---|---|---|---|
| **1920** | | **Unwmk.** | **Engr.** | **Perf. 12½** | |
| J1 | D1 | 5h rose red | | .35 | .40 |
| J2 | D1 | 10h rose red | | .35 | .40 |
| J3 | D1 | 15h rose red | | .35 | .40 |
| J4 | D1 | 20h rose red | | .35 | .55 |
| J5 | D1 | 25h rose red | | .35 | .55 |
| J6 | D1 | 30h rose red | | .35 | .55 |
| J7 | D1 | 40h rose red | | .35 | .55 |
| J8 | D1 | 50h rose red | | .35 | .55 |
| J9 | D1 | 80h rose red | | .35 | .55 |
| J10 | D1 | 1k dull blue | | .40 | 1.40 |
| J11 | D1 | 2k dull blue | | .40 | 1.40 |
| J12 | D1 | 5k dull blue | | .40 | 1.75 |
| | | *Nos. J1-J12 (12)* | | 4.35 | 9.05 |
| | | Set, never hinged | | 12.50 | |

Nos. J1-J12 exist imperf. (value, unused, set $260) and part perf. (value, each: unused $2; never hinged $7; used $7).
J3 lacks the outside frame lines.

### Swiss Administration of the Post Office

D2

| | | | | | |
|---|---|---|---|---|---|
| **1928** | | **Litho.** | **Wmk. 183** | **Perf. 11½** | |
| | | **Granite Paper** | | | |
| J13 | D2 | 5rp pur & org | | 1.20 | 3.00 |
| J14 | D2 | 10rp pur & org | | 1.20 | 3.00 |
| J15 | D2 | 15rp pur & org | | 1.75 | 13.50 |
| J16 | D2 | 20rp pur & org | | 1.75 | 3.00 |
| J17 | D2 | 25rp pur & org | | 1.75 | 9.00 |
| J18 | D2 | 30rp pur & org | | 6.00 | 13.50 |
| J19 | D2 | 40rp pur & org | | 7.00 | 14.00 |
| J20 | D2 | 50rp pur & org | | 9.00 | 17.50 |
| | | *Nos. J13-J20 (8)* | | 29.65 | 76.50 |
| | | Set, never hinged | | 65.00 | |

Post Horn — D3

### Engraved; Value Typographed in Dark Red

| | | | | | |
|---|---|---|---|---|---|
| **1940** | | **Unwmk.** | | **Perf. 11½** | |
| J21 | D3 | 5rp gray blue | | 1.25 | 2.75 |
| J22 | D3 | 10rp gray blue | | .60 | 1.40 |
| J23 | D3 | 15rp gray blue | | 1.25 | 5.00 |
| J24 | D3 | 20rp gray blue | | .60 | 2.00 |
| J25 | D3 | 25rp gray blue | | 1.25 | 3.50 |
| J26 | D3 | 30rp gray blue | | 2.00 | 5.50 |
| J27 | D3 | 40rp gray blue | | 2.00 | 5.50 |
| J28 | D3 | 50rp gray blue | | 3.00 | 5.50 |
| | | *Nos. J21-J28 (8)* | | 11.95 | 31.15 |
| | | Set, never hinged | | 35.00 | |

## OFFICIAL STAMPS

### Regular Issue of 1930 Overprinted in Various Colors

**Perf. 10½, 11½, 11½x10½**

| | | | | |
|---|---|---|---|---|
| **1932** | | | **Unwmk.** | |
| O1 | A38 | 5rp dk grn (Bk) | 10.50 | 15.50 |
| O2 | A39 | 10rp dark vio (R) | 75.00 | 15.50 |
| O3 | A40 | 20rp dp rose red (Bl) | 90.00 | 15.50 |
| O4 | A42 | 30rp ultra (R) | 17.50 | 21.00 |
| O5 | A43 | 35rp dp grn (Bk) | 14.00 | 35.00 |
| O6 | A45 | 50rp blk brn (Bl) | 77.50 | 21.00 |
| O7 | A46 | 60rp olive blk (R) | 14.00 | 50.00 |
| O8 | A48 | 1.20fr olive brn (G) | 150.00 | 425.00 |
| | | *Nos. O1-O8 (8)* | 448.50 | 598.50 |
| | | Set, never hinged | 1,763. | |

Values are for the most common perf. variety. See Scott Classic Specialized catalogue for detailed listings.

---

Nos. 108, 110 Overprinted in Black

| | | |
|---|---|---|
| **1933** | | **Perf. 14½** |
| O9 | A51 25rp red orange | 42.50 45.00 |
| O10 | A53 1.20fr red brown | 85.00 275.00 |
| | Set, never hinged | 360.00 |

### Regular Issue of 1934-35 Ovptd. in Various Colors

| | | | | |
|---|---|---|---|---|
| **1934-36** | | | **Perf. 11½** | |
| O11 | A58 | 5rp emerald (R) | 2.10 | 3.50 |
| O12 | A59 | 10rp dp vio (Bk) | 4.25 | 3.50 |
| O13 | A60 | 15rp red org (V) | .90 | 3.50 |
| O14 | A61 | 20rp red (Bk) | .70 | 3.50 |
| O15 | A62 | 25rp brown (R) | 35.00 | 115.00 |
| O16 | A62 | 25rp brown (Bk) | 3.50 | 15.00 |
| O17 | A63 | 30rp dark bl (R) | 5.00 | 10.50 |
| O18 | A66 | 50rp lt brown (V) | 1.40 | 17.50 |
| O19 | A68 | 90rp dp grn (Bk) | 7.50 | 10.50 |
| O20 | A69 | 1.50fr brn car (Bl) | 42.50 | 280.00 |
| | | *Nos. O11-O20 (10)* | 102.85 | 462.50 |
| | | Set, never hinged | 358.00 | |

### Regular Issue of 1937-38 Overprinted in Black, Red or Blue

| | | | | |
|---|---|---|---|---|
| **1937-41** | | | | |
| O21 | A76 | 5rp emerald (Bk) | .40 | .75 |
| O22 | A76 | 10rp vio & buff (R) | .80 | 2.00 |
| O23 | A76 | 20rp brn org (Bl) | 1.60 | 2.00 |
| O24 | A76 | 20rp brn org (Bk) ('41) | 1.60 | 2.75 |
| O25 | A76 | 25rp chestnut (Bk) | .80 | 2.75 |
| O26 | A77 | 30rp blue & gray (Bk) | 2.75 | 2.75 |
| O27 | A79 | 50rp dk brn & buff (R) | 1.25 | 2.10 |
| O28 | A80 | 1fr red brown (Bk) | 1.25 | 12.00 |
| O29 | A80 | 1.50fr slate bl (Bk) ('38) | 5.00 | 17.50 |
| | | *Nos. O21-O29 (9)* | 15.45 | 44.60 |
| | | Set, never hinged | 49.50 | |

Catalogue values for unused stamps in this section, from this point to the end of the section, are for Never Hinged items.

Stamps of 1944-45 Overprinted in Black

| | | | | |
|---|---|---|---|---|
| **1947** | | | | |
| O30 | A136 | 5rp slate grn & buff | 1.60 | 1.10 |
| O31 | A136 | 10rp gray & buff | 1.60 | 1.10 |
| O32 | A136 | 20rp org red & buff | 2.10 | 1.10 |
| O33 | A136 | 30rp blue & buff | 2.75 | 1.75 |
| O34 | A136 | 50rp bluish blk & pale gray | 2.75 | 3.50 |
| O35 | A136 | 1fr dp cl & buff | 11.00 | 11.00 |
| O36 | A136 | 150rp royal blue | 11.00 | 14.00 |
| | | *Nos. O30-O36 (7)* | 32.80 | 33.55 |

Crown — O1

### Engr.; Value Typo.

| | | | | |
|---|---|---|---|---|
| **1950-68** | | **Unwmk.** | **Perf. 11½** | |
| | | **Buff Granite Paper** | | |
| | | **Narrow Gothic Numerals** | | |
| O37 | O1 | 5rp red vio & gray | .25 | .25 |
| O38 | O1 | 10rp ol grn & mag | .25 | .25 |
| O39 | O1 | 20rp org brn & bl | .25 | .25 |
| O40 | O1 | 30rp dk red brn & org red | .25 | .25 |
| O41 | O1 | 40rp blue & hn brn | .35 | .35 |
| O42 | O1 | 55rp dk gray grn & red | .70 | 1.10 |
| a. | | White paper ('68) | 45.00 | 125.00 |
| O43 | O1 | 60rp slate & mag | .70 | 1.10 |
| a. | | White paper ('68) | 6.00 | 22.50 |

---

| | | | | |
|---|---|---|---|---|
| O44 | O1 | 80rp red org & gray | .70 | .90 |
| O45 | O1 | 90rp choc & blue | .90 | 1.25 |
| O46 | O1 | 1.20fr grnsh bl & org | 1.10 | 1.25 |
| | | *Nos. O37-O46 (10)* | 5.45 | 6.95 |

| | | | | |
|---|---|---|---|---|
| **1968-69** | | | **Perf. 11½** | |
| | | **White Granite Paper** | | |
| | | **Broad Numerals, Varying Thickness** | | |
| O47 | O1 | 5rp olive brn & org | .25 | .25 |
| O48 | O1 | 10rp violet & car | .25 | .25 |
| O49 | O1 | 20rp ver & emer | .25 | .25 |
| O50 | O1 | 30rp green & red | .25 | .25 |
| O51 | O1 | 50rp ultra & red | .35 | .35 |
| O52 | O1 | 60rp orange & ultra | .40 | .40 |
| O53 | O1 | 70rp maroon & emer | .50 | .50 |
| O54 | O1 | 80rp bl grn & car | .55 | .55 |
| O55 | O1 | 95rp slate & red ('69) | .65 | .65 |
| O56 | O1 | 1fr rose cl & grn | .70 | .70 |
| O57 | O1 | 1.20fr lt red brn & grn | .80 | .80 |
| O58 | O1 | 2fr brn & org ('69) | 1.25 | 1.25 |
| | | *Nos. O47-O58 (12)* | 6.20 | 6.20 |

Government Building, Vaduz — O2

### Engr., Value Typo.

| | | | | |
|---|---|---|---|---|
| **1976-89** | | | **Perf. 14** | |
| O59 | O2 | 10rp yel brn & vio | .25 | .25 |
| O60 | O2 | 20rp car lake & bl | .25 | .25 |
| O61 | O2 | 35rp blue & red | .25 | .25 |
| O62 | O2 | 40rp dull pur & grn | .30 | .30 |
| O63 | O2 | 50rp slate & mag | .40 | .40 |
| O64 | O2 | 70rp vio brn & bl grn | .55 | .55 |
| O65 | O2 | 80rp green & mag | .60 | .60 |
| O66 | O2 | 90rp vio & bl grn | .70 | .70 |
| O67 | O2 | 1fr olive & mag | .80 | .80 |
| O68 | O2 | 1.10fr brown & ultra | .85 | .85 |
| O69 | O2 | 1.50fr dull & red | 1.25 | 1.25 |
| O70 | O2 | 2fr orange & blue | 1.60 | 1.60 |
| O75 | O2 | 5fr rose vio & brn org | 5.75 | 5.75 |
| | | *Nos. O59-O75 (13)* | 13.55 | 13.55 |

Issued: 5fr, 9/4/89; others, 12/9/76.

---

# LITHUANIA

ˌli-thə-ˈwā-nē-ə

### (Lietuva)

LOCATION — Northern Europe bordering on the Baltic Sea
GOVT. — Independent republic
AREA — 25,170 sq. mi.
POP. — 3,584,966 (1999 est.)
CAPITAL — Vilnius

Lithuania was under Russian rule when it declared its independence in 1918. The League of Nations recognized it in 1922. In 1940 it became a republic in the Union of Soviet Socialist Republics.

---

Lithuania declared its independence on March 11, 1990. Lithuanian independence was recognized by the Soviet Union on Sept. 6, 1991.

100 Skatiku = 1 Auksinas
100 Centai = 1 Litas (1922, 1993)
100 Kopecks = 1 Ruble (1991)
100 Cents = 1 Euro (2015)

Catalogue values for unused stamps in this country are for Never Hinged items, beginning with Scott 371 in the regular postage section and Scott B55 in the semi-postal section.

Nos. 1-26 were printed in sheets of 20 (5x4) which were imperf. at the outer sides, so that only 6 stamps in each sheet were fully perforated. Values are for the stamps partly imperf. The stamps fully perforated sell for at least double these values. There was also a printing of Nos. 19-26 in a sheet of 160, composed of blocks of 20 of each stamp. Pairs or blocks with different values se-tenant sell for considerably more than the values for the stamps singly.
Nos. 1-26 are without gum.

### Watermarks

Wmk. 109 — Webbing

Wmk. 144 — Network

Wmk. 145 — Wavy Lines

Wmk. 146 — Zigzag Lines Forming Rectangles

Wmk. 147 — Parquetry

Wmk. 198 — Intersecting Diamonds

Wmk. 209 — Multiple Ovals

Wmk. 238 — Multiple Letters

### First Vilnius Printing

A1

### Thin Figures

**Perf. 11½**

| | | | | |
|---|---|---|---|---|
| **1918, Dec. 27** | | **Unwmk.** | | **Typeset** |
| 1 | A1 | 10sk black | 150.00 | 125.00 |
| 2 | A1 | 15sk black | 150.00 | 100.00 |

Second Vilnius Printing

1918, Dec. 31 **Thick Figures**

No.	Type	Description	Unused	Used
3	A1	10sk black	70.00	55.00
4	A1	15sk black	70.00	55.00
5	A1	20sk black	30.00	16.00
6	A1	30sk black	35.00	17.50
7	A1	40sk black	50.00	25.00
8	A1	50sk black	40.00	17.50
		Nos. 3-8 (6)	295.00	186.00

First Kaunas Issue

A2

1919, Jan. 29

No.	Type	Description	Unused	Used
9	A2	10sk black	7.50	3.75
10	A2	15sk black	7.50	3.75
a.		"5" for "15"	95.00	72.50
11	A2	20sk black	7.50	3.75
12	A2	30sk black	7.50	3.75
		Nos. 9-12 (4)	30.00	15.00

Second Kaunas Issue

A3

1919, Feb. 18

No.	Type	Description	Unused	Used
13	A3	10sk black	4.25	2.50
14	A3	15sk black	4.25	2.50
15	A3	20sk black	4.25	2.50
a.		"astas" for "pastas"	80.00	75.00
16	A3	30sk black	4.25	2.50
17	A3	40sk black	4.25	2.50
18	A3	50sk black	4.25	2.50
19	A3	60sk black	4.25	2.50
		Nos. 13-19 (7)	29.75	17.50

Third Kaunas Issue

A4

1919, Mar. 1

No.	Type	Description	Unused	Used
20	A4	10sk black	4.25	1.75
21	A4	15sk black	4.25	1.75
22	A4	20sk black	4.25	1.75
23	A4	30sk black	4.25	1.75
24	A4	40sk black	4.25	1.75
25	A4	50sk black	4.25	1.75
26	A4	60sk black	4.25	1.75
		Nos. 20-26 (7)	29.75	12.25

The White Knight "Vytis"

A5 A6

A7

Perf. 10½ to 14 & Compound

1919 **Litho.** **Wmk. 144**

Gray Granite Paper

No.	Type	Description	Unused	Used
30	A5	10sk deep rose	1.25	.40
a.		Wmk. vert.	17.50	15.00
31	A5	15sk violet	1.25	.40
a.		Wmk. vert.	17.50	15.00
32	A5	20sk dark blue	1.60	.40
33	A5	30sk deep orange	1.60	.40
a.		Wmk. vert.	17.50	15.00
34	A5	40sk dark brown	1.60	.40
35	A6	50sk blue green	1.60	.50
36	A6	75sk org & dp rose	1.60	.50
37	A7	1auk gray & rose	3.25	.50
38	A7	3auk bis brn & rose	3.25	.50
39	A7	5auk blue grn & rose	3.25	.80
		Nos. 30-39 (10)	20.25	4.80

Nos. 30a, 31a and 33a are from the first printing with watermark vertical showing points to left; various perforations.

Nos. 30-39 exist imperf. Value in pairs, $100.

Issued: Nos. 30a, 31a, 33a, 2/17/19; Nos. 30-36, 3/20/19.

Thick White Paper

1919 **Wmk. 145**

No.	Type	Description	Unused	Used
40	A5	10sk dull rose	.35	.25
41	A5	15sk violet	.35	.25
42	A5	20sk dark blue	.35	.25
43	A5	30sk orange	.35	.25
44	A5	40sk red brown	.35	.25
45	A6	50sk pale grayish green	.35	.25
46	A6	75sk yel & dp rose	.35	.25
47	A7	1auk gray & rose	.95	.35
48	A7	3auk yel brn & rose, perf. 12½	.60	.40
49	A7	5auk bl grn & rose	1.00	.40
		Nos. 40-49 (10)	5.00	2.90

Nos. 40-49 exist imperf. Value in pairs, $90.

A8

Perf. 10½ to 14 & Compound

1919, May 8 **Thin White Paper**

No.	Type	Description	Unused	Used
50	A5	10sk red	.45	.25
51	A5	15sk lilac	.45	.25
52	A5	20sk dull blue	.45	.25
53	A5	30sk buff	.45	.25
54	A5	40sk gray brn	.45	.25
55	A6	50sk lt green	.45	.25
56	A6	60sk violet & red	.45	.25
57	A6	75sk bister & red	.45	.25
58	A8	1auk gray & red	.45	.25
59	A8	3auk lt brown & red	.45	.30
60	A8	5auk blue grn & red	.45	.45
		Nos. 50-60 (11)	4.95	3.00

Nos. 50-60 exist imperf. Value, pairs $150.

See Nos. 93-96. For surcharges see Nos. 114-115, 120-139, 149-150.

"Lithuania" Receiving Benediction
A9

The Spirit of Lithuania Rises
A10

"Lithuania" with Chains Broken
A11

White Knight
A12

1920, Feb. 16 **Wmk. 146** ***Perf. 11½***

No.	Type	Description	Unused	Used
70	A9	10sk dp rose	3.75	*5.25*
71	A9	15sk lt violet	3.75	*5.25*
72	A9	20sk gray blue	3.75	*5.25*
73	A10	30sk yellow brn	3.75	*5.25*
74	A11	40sk brown & grn	3.75	*5.25*
75	A10	50sk deep rose	3.75	*5.25*
76	A10	60sk lt violet	3.75	*5.25*
77	A11	80sk purple & red	3.75	*5.25*
78	A11	1auk green & red	3.75	*5.25*
79	A12	3auk brown & red	3.75	*5.25*
80	A12	5auk green & red	3.75	*5.25*
a.		Right "5" dbl., grn and red	90.00	90.00
		Nos. 70-80 (11)	41.25	*57.75*

Anniv. of natl. independence. The stamps were on sale only 3 days in Kaunas. The stamps were available in other cities after that. Only a limited number of stamps was sold at post offices but 40,000 sets were delivered to the bank of Kaunas.

All values exist imperforate.

White Knight
A13

Grand Duke Vytautas
A14

Grand Duke Gediminas
A15

Sacred Oak and Altar
A16

1920, Aug. 25

No.	Type	Description	Unused	Used
81	A13	10sk rose	.80	1.60
a.		Imperf., pair	40.00	
82	A13	15sk dark violet	.80	1.60
83	A14	20sk grn & lt grn	.80	1.60
84	A13	30sk brown	.80	1.60
a.		Pair, #82, 84	40.00	
85	A15	40sk gray grn & vio	.80	1.60
86	A14	50sk brn & brn org	2.00	2.00
87	A14	60sk red & org	.80	1.60
88	A15	80sk blk, db & red	.80	1.60
89	A16	1auk orange & blk	1.25	1.60
90	A16	3auk green & blk	1.25	1.60
91	A16	5auk gray vio & blk	3.25	2.40
		Nos. 81-91 (11)	13.35	18.80

Opening of Lithuanian National Assembly. On sale for three days.

1920

No.	Type	Description	Unused
92	A14	20sk green & lilac	125.00
92A	A15	40sk gray grn, buff & vio	125.00
92B	A14	50sk brown & gray lil	125.00
92C	A14	60sk red & green	125.00
92D	A15	80sk black, grn & red	125.00
		Nos. 92-92D (5)	625.00

Nos. 92 to 92D were trial printings. By order of the Ministry of Posts, 2,000 examples of each were placed on sale at post offices.

Type of 1919 Issue

1920 **Unwmk.** ***Perf. 11½***

No.	Type	Description	Unused	Used
93	A5	15sk lilac	6.00	4.50
94	A5	20sk deep blue	6.00	4.50
		Wmk. 109		
95	A5	20sk deep blue	5.00	5.00
96	A5	40sk gray brown	9.75	8.50
		Nos. 93-96 (4)	26.75	22.50
		Set, never hinged	40.00	

Watermark vertical or horizontal on Nos. 95-96.

No. 96 exists perf. 10½x11½.

Imperf., Pairs

No.	Type	Description	Unused	Used
93a	A5	15sk	32.00	32.00
94a	A5	20sk	32.00	32.00
95a	A5	20sk	17.00	17.00
96a	A5	40sk	48.00	48.00

Sower
A17

Peasant Sharpening Scythe
A18

Prince Kestutis
A19

Black Horseman
A20

Perf. 11, 11½ and Compound

1921-22

No.	Type	Description	Unused	Used
97	A17	10sk brt rose	.85	.55
98	A17	15sk violet	.35	*.70*
99	A17	20sk ultra	.25	.25
100	A18	30sk brown	2.50	*1.10*
101	A19	40sk red	.25	.25
102	A18	50sk olive	.35	.25
103	A18	60sk grn & vio	2.50	*1.65*
104	A19	80sk brn org & car	.35	.25
105	A19	1auk brown & grn	.35	.25
106	A19	2auk gray bl & red	.35	.25
107	A20	3auk yel brn & dk bl	1.00	.40
108	A17	4auk yel & dk bl ('22)	.45	.25
109	A20	5auk gray blk & rose	1.00	*1.50*
110	A17	8auk grn & blk ('22)	.45	.25
111	A20	10auk rose & vio	1.00	.55
112	A20	25auk bis brn & grn	1.25	*2.75*
113	A20	100auk dl red & gray blk	12.50	8.00
		Nos. 97-113 (17)	25.75	19.20
		Set, never hinged	85.00	

Imperf., Pairs

No.	Type	Description	Unused	Used
97a	A17	10sk	—	
98a	A17	15sk	—	
99a	A17	20sk	—	
100a	A18	30sk	—	
101a	A19	40sk	25.00	
102a	A18	50sk	25.00	
103a	A18	60sk	—	
104a	A19	80sk	—	
105a	A19	1auk	—	
106a	A19	2auk	120.00	
107a	A20	3auk	120.00	
109a	A20	5auk	120.00	
110a	A17	8auk	10.00	10.00
111a	A20	10auk	50.00	
112a	A20	25auk	50.00	
113a	A20	100auk	50.00	

For surcharges see Nos. 140-148, 151-160.

No. 57 Surcharged

Perf. 12½x11½

1922, May **Wmk. 145**

No.	Type	Description	Unused	Used
114	A6	4auk on 75sk bis & red	.90	.25
a.		Inverted surcharge	35.00	35.00

Same with Bars over Original Value

No.	Type	Description	Unused	Used
115	A6	4auk on 75sk bis & red	4.00	*8.00*
a.		Double surcharge	30.00	30.00

Povilas Luksis — A20a

Justinas Staugaitis, Antanas Smetona, Stasys Silingas — A20b

Portraits: 40s, Lt. Juozapavicius. 50s, Dr. Basanavicius. 60s, Mrs. Petkeviciute. 1auk, Prof. Voldemaras. 2auk, Pranas Dovidaitis. 3auk, Dr. Slezevicius. 4auk, Dr. Galvanauskas. 5auk, Kazys Grinius. 6auk, Dr. Stulginskis. 8auk, Pres. Smetona.

1922 **Litho.** **Unwmk.**

No.	Type	Description	Unused	Used
116	A20a	20s blk & car rose	1.25	*2.10*
116A	A20a	40s bl grn & vio	1.25	*2.10*
116B	A20a	50s plum & grnsh bl	1.25	*2.10*
117	A20a	60s pur & org	1.25	*2.10*
117A	A20a	1auk car & lt bl	1.25	*2.10*
117B	A20a	2auk dp bl & yel brn	1.25	*2.10*
c.		Center inverted	100.00	100.00
118	A20a	3auk mar & ultra	1.25	*2.10*
118A	A20a	4auk dk grn & red vio	1.25	*2.10*
118B	A20a	5auk blk brn & dp rose	1.25	*2.10*
119	A20a	6auk dk bl & grnsh bl	1.25	*2.10*
a.		Cliché of 8auk in sheet of 6auk	175.00	*175.00*
119B	A20a	8auk ultra & bis	1.25	*2.10*
119C	A20b	10auk dk vio & bl grn	1.25	*2.10*
		Nos. 116-119C (12)	15.00	25.20
		Set, never hinged	45.00	

League of Nations' recognition of Lithuania. Sold only on Oct. 1, 1922.

Forty sheets of the 6auk each included eight examples of the 8auk.

Stamps of 1919-22 Surcharged in Black, Carmine or Green On Nos. 37-39

1922 **Wmk. 144** ***Perf. 11½x12***

Gray Granite Paper

No.	Type	Description	Unused	Used
120	A7	3c on 1auk	100.00	*100.00*
121	A7	3c on 3auk	100.00	*100.00*
122	A7	3c on 5auk	150.00	*150.00*
		Nos. 120-122 (3)	350.00	350.00
		Set, never hinged	750.00	

White Paper

Perf. 14, 11½, 12½x11½

Wmk. 145

No.	Type	Description	Unused	Used
123	A5	1c on 10sk red	.55	1.50
124	A5	1c on 15sk lilac	.80	1.50
125	A5	1c on 20sk dull bl	.50	1.50
126	A5	1c on 30sk org	*250.00*	*110.00*
127	A5	1c on 30sk buff	.25	.40
128	A5	1c on 40sk gray brn	1.60	1.50

| | | | |
|---|---|---|---|
| 129 | A6 | 2c on 50sk green | .70 | 1.50 |
| 130 | A6 | 2c on 60sk vio & red | .25 | 1.50 |
| 131 | A6 | 2c on 75sk bis & red | .40 | 1.50 |
| 132 | A8 | 3c on 1auk gray & red | .25 | .25 |
| 133 | A8 | 3c on 3auk brn & red | .25 | .25 |
| 134 | A8 | 3c on 5auk bl grn & red | .25 | .25 |

*Nos. 123-125,127-134 (11)* 5.80 10.40
Set, never hinged, *Nos. 123-125, 127-134)* 24.00

## On Stamps of 1920

**1922      Unwmk.      Perf. 11**

| 136 | A5 | 1c on 20sk dp bl (C) | 3.75 | 2.00 |

**Wmk. Webbing (109)
Perf. 11, 11½**

| 138 | A5 | 1c on 20sk dp bl (C) | 3.50 | 2.00 |
| 139 | A5 | 1c on 40sk gray brn (C) | 7.50 | 1.25 |

Stamps of 1921-22
Surcharged

| 140 | A18 | 1c on 50sk ol (C) | .25 | .25 |
| a. | | Imperf., pair | 45.00 | |
| b. | | Inverted surcharge | 40.00 | |
| c. | | Double surch., one invtd. | | |
| 141 | A17 | 3c on 10sk | 11.00 | 8.00 |
| 142 | A17 | 3c on 15sk | .25 | .25 |
| 143 | A17 | 3c on 20sk | .40 | 1.50 |
| 144 | A18 | 3c on 30sk | 18.50 | 12.00 |
| 145 | A19 | 3c on 40sk | .40 | .40 |
| a. | | Imperf., pair | | |
| 146 | A18 | 5c on 50sk | .25 | .25 |
| 147 | A18 | 5c on 60sk | 18.50 | 18.50 |
| 148 | A19 | 5c on 80sk | .55 | .55 |
| a. | | Imperf., pair | 15.00 | 15.00 |

**Wmk. Wavy Lines (145)
Perf. 12½x11½**

| 149 | A6 | 5c on 4auk on 75sk (No. 114) (G) | 1.60 | 10.00 |
| 150 | A6 | 5c on 4auk on 75sk (No. 115) (G) | 16.00 | 17.50 |

**Wmk. Webbing (109)
Perf. 11, 11½**

| 151 | A19 | 10c on 1auk | .80 | .25 |
| a. | | Inverted surcharge | 55.00 | |
| 152 | A19 | 10c on 2auk | .25 | .25 |
| a. | | Inverted surcharge | 50.00 | |
| b. | | Imperf., pair | 45.00 | |
| 153 | A17 | 15c on 4auk | .25 | .25 |
| a. | | Inverted surcharge | 45.00 | |
| 154 | A20 | 25c on 3auk | 18.50 | 18.50 |
| 155 | A20 | 25c on 5auk | 11.00 | 5.00 |
| 156 | A20 | 25c on 10auk | 2.25 | 1.50 |
| a. | | Imperf., pair | 45.00 | |
| 157 | A17 | 30c on 8auk (C) | 1.15 | .35 |
| a. | | Inverted surcharge | 45.00 | 25.00 |
| 158 | A20 | 50c on 25auk | 3.75 | 2.50 |
| 160 | A20 | 1 l on 100auk | 4.00 | 2.50 |

*Nos. 136-160 (23)* 124.40 105.55
Set, never hinged 140.00

A21

Ruin — A22

Seminary Church,
Kaunas — A23

**1923      Litho.      Wmk. 109      Perf. 11**

| 165 | A21 | 10c violet | 7.00 | .25 |
| 166 | A21 | 15c scarlet | 2.50 | .25 |
| 167 | A21 | 20c olive brown | 2.50 | .25 |
| 168 | A21 | 25c dark blue | 2.50 | .25 |
| 169 | A22 | 50c yellow green | 2.50 | .25 |
| 170 | A22 | 60c red | 2.50 | .25 |
| 171 | A23 | 1 l orange & grn | 10.50 | .25 |

---

| 172 | A23 | 3 l red & gray | 15.00 | .45 |
| 173 | A23 | 5 l brown & blue | 21.00 | 1.00 |

*Nos. 165-173 (9)* 66.00 3.20
Set, never hinged 125.00

See Nos. 189-209, 281-282. For surcharges see Nos. B1-B42.

Memel Coat of
Arms — A24

Lithuanian Coat of
Arms — A25

Biruta Chapel
A26

Kaunas, War
Memorial
A27

Trakai
Ruins — A28

Memel
Lighthouse
A29

Memel
Harbor — A30

**Perf. 11, 11½, 12**

**1923, Aug.      Unwmk.**

| 176 | A24 | 1c rose, grn & blk | 1.25 | 1.60 |
| 177 | A25 | 2c dull vio & blk | 1.25 | 1.60 |
| 178 | A26 | 3c yellow & blk | 1.25 | 1.60 |
| 179 | A24 | 5c bl, buff & blk | 2.50 | 4.50 |
| 180 | A27 | 10c orange & blk | 1.90 | 3.00 |
| 181 | A27 | 15c green & blk | 1.90 | 3.00 |
| 182 | A28 | 25c brt vio & blk | 1.90 | 3.00 |
| 183 | A25 | 30c red vio & blk | 4.00 | 7.50 |
| 184 | A29 | 60c ol grn & blk | 2.25 | 3.00 |
| 185 | A30 | 1 l bl grn & blk | 2.25 | 3.00 |
| 186 | A26 | 2 l red & black | 8.25 | 15.00 |
| 187 | A28 | 3 l blue & black | 8.25 | 15.00 |
| 188 | A29 | 5 l ultra & black | 8.25 | 15.00 |

*Nos. 176-188 (13)* 45.20 76.80
Set, never hinged 100.00

This series was issued ostensibly to commemorate the incorporation of Memel with Lithuania.

**Type of 1923**

**1923      Unwmk.      Perf. 11**

| 189 | A21 | 5c pale green | 3.75 | .75 |
| 190 | A21 | 10c violet | 5.00 | .75 |
| a. | | Imperf., pair | 50.00 | |
| 191 | A21 | 15c scarlet | 6.00 | .75 |
| a. | | Imperf., pair | 50.00 | |
| 193 | A21 | 25c blue | 10.00 | .75 |

*Nos. 189-193 (4)* 24.75 3.00
Set, never hinged 60.00

**1923      Wmk. 147**

| 196 | A21 | 2c pale brown | 1.50 | .45 |
| 197 | A21 | 3c olive bister | 2.25 | .45 |
| 198 | A21 | 5c pale green | 2.25 | .45 |
| 199 | A21 | 10c violet | 4.50 | .45 |
| 202 | A21 | 25c deep blue | 11.00 | .45 |
| a. | | Imperf., pair | 40.00 | |
| 204 | A21 | 36c orange brown | 17.50 | 1.50 |

*Nos. 196-204 (6)* 39.00 3.75
Set, never hinged 70.00

---

**Perf. 11½, 14½, 11½x14½**

**1923-25      Wmk. 198**

| 207 | A21 | 25c deep blue | 750.00 | 450.00 |
| 208 | A22 | 50c deep green ('25) | 25.00 | 1.00 |
| 209 | A22 | 60c carmine ('25) | 25.00 | .50 |

Double-barred
Cross — A31

**1927, Jan.      Perf. 11½, 14½**

| 210 | A31 | 2c orange | 1.50 | .35 |
| 211 | A31 | 3c deep brown | 1.50 | .35 |
| 212 | A31 | 5c green | 2.25 | .35 |
| a. | | Imperf., pair | 25.00 | |
| 213 | A31 | 10c violet | 3.25 | .35 |
| 214 | A31 | 15c red | 3.25 | .35 |
| a. | | Imperf., pair | 25.00 | |
| 215 | A31 | 25c blue | 3.25 | .30 |

*Nos. 210-215 (6)* 15.00 2.05
Set, never hinged 45.00

**1926-30      Wmk. 147      Perf. 14½**

| 216 | A31 | 5c green | 35.00 | 150.00 |
| 217 | A31 | 30c blue ('30) | 30.00 | 10.00 |

See Nos. 233-240, 278-280.

Dr. Jonas
Basanavicius — A32

**1927      Unwmk.      Perf. 11½, 14½x11½**

| 219 | A32 | 15c claret & blk | 3.00 | 1.50 |
| 220 | A32 | 25c dull blue & blk | 3.00 | 1.50 |
| 221 | A32 | 50c dk green & blk | 3.00 | 1.50 |
| 222 | A32 | 60c dk violet & blk | 9.00 | 3.00 |

*Nos. 219-222 (4)* 18.00 7.50
Set, never hinged 35.00

Dr. Jonas Basanavicius (1851-1927), patriot and folklorist.

National Arms — A33

**1927, Dec. 23      Wmk. 109      Perf. 14½**

| 223 | A33 | 1 l blue grn & gray | 6.50 | .80 |
| 224 | A33 | 3 l vio & pale grn | 5.00 | .80 |
| 225 | A33 | 5 l brown & gray | 6.00 | 1.40 |

*Nos. 223-225 (3)* 17.50 3.00
Set, never hinged 25.00

Pres. Antanas
Smetona
A34

Decade of
Independence
A35

Dawn of
Peace — A36

**1928, Feb.      Wmk. 109**

| 226 | A34 | 5c org brn & grn | 1.00 | .75 |
| 227 | A34 | 10c violet & blk | 1.25 | .75 |
| 228 | A34 | 15c orange & brn | 1.25 | .75 |
| 229 | A34 | 25c blue & indigo | 1.25 | .75 |
| 230 | A35 | 50c ultra & dl vio | 1.50 | .75 |
| 231 | A35 | 60c carmine & blk | 1.75 | .75 |
| 232 | A36 | 1 l blk brn & drab | 2.00 | 2.25 |

*Nos. 226-232 (7)* 10.00 6.75
Set, never hinged 15.00

10th anniv. of Lithuanian independence.

**Type of 1926**

**1929-31**

| 233 | A31 | 2c orange ('31) | 12.00 | 1.60 |
| 234 | A31 | 5c green | 4.00 | .35 |
| 235 | A31 | 10c violet ('31) | 10.00 | 2.00 |
| 237 | A31 | 15c red | 4.50 | .45 |
| a. | | Tête bêche pair | 45.00 | 35.00 |
| 239 | A31 | 30c dark blue | 6.00 | .45 |

---

**Unwmk.**

| 240 | A31 | 15c red ('30) | 10.00 | .75 |

*Nos. 233-240 (6)* 46.50 5.60
Set, never hinged 85.00

Grand
Duke
Vytautas
A37

Grand Duke,
Mounted
A38

**1930, Feb. 16      Perf. 14**

| 242 | A37 | 2c yel brn & dk brn | .30 | .25 |
| 243 | A37 | 3c dk brn & vio | .30 | .25 |
| 244 | A37 | 5c yel grn & dp org | .30 | .25 |
| 245 | A37 | 10c vio & emer | .30 | .25 |
| 246 | A37 | 15c dp rose & vio | .30 | .25 |
| 247 | A37 | 30c dk bl & brn vio | .50 | .25 |
| 248 | A37 | 36c brn vio & ol blk | .75 | .30 |
| 249 | A37 | 50c dull grn & ultra | .50 | .35 |
| 250 | A37 | 60c dk blue & rose | .50 | .40 |
| 251 | A38 | 1 l bl grn, db & red brn | 2.10 | 1.00 |
| 252 | A38 | 3 l dk brn, sal & dk vio | 3.25 | 1.75 |
| 253 | A38 | 5 l ol brn, gray & red | 7.50 | 2.75 |
| 254 | A38 | 10 l multicolored | 20.00 | 16.00 |
| 255 | A38 | 25 l multicolored | 42.50 | 55.00 |

*Nos. 242-255 (14)* 79.10 79.05
Set, never hinged 200.00

5th cent. of the death of the Grand Duke Vytautas.

Kaunas, Railroad
Station — A39

Cathedral at
Vilnius —
A39a

Designs: 15c, 25c, Landscape on the Neman River. 50c, Main Post Office, Kaunas.

**1932, July 21      Wmk. 238      Perf. 14**

| 256 | A39 | 10c dk red brn & ocher | .40 | .40 |
| 257 | A39 | 15c dk brown & ol | .40 | .40 |
| 258 | A39 | 25c dk blue & ol | 1.25 | 1.25 |
| 259 | A39 | 50c gray blk & ol | 2.50 | 2.50 |
| 260 | A39a | 1 l blue & gray | 6.50 | 6.50 |
| 261 | A39a | 3 l red brn & gray grn | 6.50 | 6.50 |

**Wmk. 198**

| 262 | A39 | 5c vio bl & ocher | .40 | .40 |
| 263 | A39a | 60c grnsh blk & lil | 6.50 | 6.50 |

*Nos. 256-263 (8)* 24.45 24.45
Set, never hinged 60.00

**Imperf.**

| 256a | A39 | 10c dk red brn & ocher | .35 | .35 |
| 257a | A39 | 15c dk brown & ol | .65 | .65 |
| 258a | A39 | 25c dk blue & ol | 1.00 | 1.00 |
| 259a | A39 | 50c gray blk & ol | 2.00 | 2.00 |
| 260a | A39a | 1 l blue & gray | 5.25 | 5.25 |
| 261a | A39a | 3 l red brn & gray grn | 5.25 | 5.25 |
| 262a | A39 | 5c violet bl & ocher | .35 | .35 |
| 263a | A39a | 60c grnsh blk & lil | 5.25 | 5.25 |

Set, never hinged 35.00

Issued for the benefit of Lithuanian orphans.
In September, 1935, a red overprint was applied to No. 259: "ORO PASTAS / LITUANICA II / 1935 / NEW YORK-KAUNAS." Value, $400.

Vytautas
Fleeing from
Prison,
1382 — A40

Designs: 15c, 25c, Conversion of Ladislas II Jagello and Vytautas (1386). 50c, 60c, Battle at Tannenberg (1410). 1 l, 3 l, Meeting of the Nobles (1429).

**1932      Wmk. 209      Perf. 14**

| 264 | A40 | 5c red & rose lake | .35 | .35 |
| 265 | A40 | 10c ol bis & org brn | .35 | .35 |
| 266 | A40 | 15c rose lil & ol grn | .35 | .35 |
| 267 | A40 | 25c dk vio brn & ocher | 1.00 | 1.00 |

| | | | | | |
|---|---|---|---|---|---|
| **268** | A40 | 50c dp grn & bis brn | 1.00 | 1.00 |
| **269** | A40 | 60c ol grn & brn car | 2.40 | 2.40 |
| **270** | A40 | 1 l ultra & ol grn | 2.40 | 2.40 |
| **271** | A40 | 3 l dk brn & dk grn | 2.40 | 2.40 |
| | | Nos. 264-271 (8) | 10.25 | 10.25 |
| | | Set, never hinged | 25.00 | |

#### Imperf.

| | | | | |
|---|---|---|---|---|
| 264a | A40 | 5c red & rose lake | .65 | .65 |
| 265a | A40 | 10c ol bis & org brn | .65 | .65 |
| 266a | A40 | 15c rose lil & ol grn | .65 | .65 |
| 267a | A40 | 25c dk vio brn & ocher | 2.00 | 2.00 |
| 268a | A40 | 50c dp grn & bis brn | 4.50 | 4.50 |
| 269a | A40 | 60c ol grn & brn car | 4.50 | 4.50 |
| 270a | A40 | 1 l ultra & ol grn | 4.50 | 4.50 |
| 271a | A40 | 3 l dk brn & dk grn | 4.50 | 4.50 |
| | | Set, never hinged | 35.00 | |

15th anniversary of independence.

A. Visteliauskas — A41

Designs: 15c, 25c, Petras Vileisis. 50c, 60c, Dr. John Sliupas. 1 l, 3 l, Jonas Basanavicius.

| **1933** | | | **Perf. 14** | |
|---|---|---|---|---|
| **272** | A41 | 5c yel grn & car | .40 | .40 |
| **273** | A41 | 10c ultra & car | .40 | .40 |
| **274** | A41 | 15c orange & red | .40 | .40 |
| **275** | A41 | 25c dk bl & blk brn | 1.25 | 1.25 |
| **276** | A41 | 50c ol gray & dk bl | 1.25 | 1.25 |
| **277** | A41 | 60c org brn & chnt | 5.50 | 5.50 |
| **277A** | A41 | 1 l red & vio brn | 5.50 | 5.50 |
| **277B** | A41 | 3 l turq grn & vio brn | 5.50 | 5.50 |
| | | Nos. 272-277B (8) | 20.20 | 20.20 |
| | | Set, never hinged | 35.00 | |

#### Imperf.

| | | | | |
|---|---|---|---|---|
| 272a | A41 | 5c yel grn & car | .40 | .40 |
| 273a | A41 | 10c ultra & car | .40 | .40 |
| 274a | A41 | 15c orange & red | .40 | .40 |
| 275a | A41 | 25c dk bl & blk brn | 1.25 | 1.25 |
| 276a | A41 | 50c ol gray & dk bl | 1.25 | 1.25 |
| 277a | A41 | 60c org brn & chnt | 5.50 | 5.50 |
| 277Aa | A41 | 1 l red & vio brn | 5.50 | 5.50 |
| 277Ba | A41 | 3 l turq grn & vio brn | 5.50 | 5.50 |
| | | Set, never hinged | 35.00 | |

50th anniv. of the 1st newspaper, "Ausra," in lithuanian language.

Mother and Child — A42

Boy Reading — A42a

Boy Playing With Blocks A42b

Woman and Boy at the Spinning Wheel — A42c

Designs: 25c, Boy reading. 60c, Boy playing with blocks. 3 l, Woman and boy at the spinning wheel.

| **1933, Sept.** | | | **Perf. 14** | |
|---|---|---|---|---|
| **277C** | A42 | 5c dp yel grn & org brn | .35 | .35 |
| **277D** | A42 | 10c rose brn & ultra | .35 | .35 |
| **277E** | A42a | 15c ol grn & plum | .35 | .35 |
| **277F** | A42a | 25c org & gray blk | 1.40 | 1.40 |
| **277G** | A42b | 50c ol grn & car | 1.40 | 1.40 |
| **277H** | A42b | 60c blk & yel org | 5.75 | 5.75 |
| **277I** | A42c | 1 l dk brn & ultra | 5.75 | 5.75 |
| **277K** | A42c | 3 l rose lil & ol grn | 5.75 | 5.75 |
| | | Nos. 277C-277K (8) | 21.10 | 21.10 |
| | | Set, never hinged | 35.00 | |

#### Imperf.

| | | | | |
|---|---|---|---|---|
| 277Ca | A42 | 5c dp yel grn & org brn | .25 | .25 |
| 277Da | A42 | 10c rose brn & ultra | .25 | .25 |
| 277Ea | A42a | 15c ol grn & plum | .25 | .25 |

| | | | | |
|---|---|---|---|---|
| 277Fa | A42a | 25c org & gray blk | 1.00 | 1.00 |
| 277Ga | A42b | 50c ol gray & dk bl | 1.00 | 1.00 |
| 277Ha | A42b | 60c org brn & chnt | 4.25 | 4.25 |
| 277Ia | A42c | 1 l dk brn & ultra | 4.25 | 4.25 |
| 277Ka | A42c | 3 l rose lil & ol grn | 4.25 | 4.25 |
| | | Set, never hinged | 25.00 | |

Issued for the benefit of Lithuanian orphans.

### Types of 1923-26

| **1933-34** | | **Wmk. 238** | **Perf. 14** | |
|---|---|---|---|---|
| **278** | A31 | 2c orange | 42.50 | 6.50 |
| **279** | A31 | 10c dark violet | 60.00 | 9.50 |
| **280** | A31 | 15c red | 42.50 | 4.50 |
| **281** | A22 | 50c green | 42.50 | 9.50 |
| **282** | A22 | 60c red | 42.50 | 9.50 |
| | | Nos. 278-282 (5) | 230.00 | 39.50 |
| | | Set, never hinged | 400.00 | |

Pres. Antanas Smetona, 60th Birthday — A43

| **1934** | | **Engr. Unwmk.** | **Perf. 11½** | |
|---|---|---|---|---|
| **283** | A43 | 15c red | 6.50 | 1.50 |
| **284** | A43 | 30c green | 8.25 | 1.50 |
| **285** | A43 | 60c blue | 10.00 | 2.00 |
| | | Nos. 283-285 (3) | 24.75 | 5.00 |
| | | Set, never hinged | 42.50 | |

A44

Arms A45

Girl with Wheat A46

A47

Knight — A48

### Wmk. 198; Wmk. 209 (35c, 10 l)

| **1934-35** | | **Litho.** | **Perf. 14** | |
|---|---|---|---|---|
| **286** | A44 | 2c rose & dull org | 1.50 | .25 |
| **287** | A44 | 5c bl grn & grn | 1.50 | .25 |
| **288** | A45 | 10c chocolate | 3.50 | .25 |
| **289** | A46 | 25c dk brn & emer | 5.50 | .25 |
| **290** | A46 | 35c carmine | 5.50 | .25 |
| **291** | A46 | 50c dk blue & blue | 10.00 | .25 |
| **292** | A47 | 1 l salmon & mar | 92.50 | .25 |
| **293** | A47 | 3 l grn & gray grn | .45 | .25 |
| **294** | A48 | 5 l maroon & gray bl | .65 | .45 |
| **295** | A48 | 10 l choc & yel | 4.50 | 3.75 |
| | | Nos. 286-295 (10) | 125.60 | 6.20 |
| | | Set, never hinged | 275.00 | |

No. 290 exists imperf. Value, pair $65.
For overprint see No. 2N9.

| **1936-37** | | **Wmk. 238** | **Perf. 14** | |
|---|---|---|---|---|
| | | Size: 17½x23mm | | |
| **296** | A44 | 2c orange ('37) | .40 | .30 |
| **297** | A44 | 5c green | .40 | .30 |

Pres. Smetona — A49

| **1936-37** | | | **Unwmk.** | |
|---|---|---|---|---|
| **298** | A49 | 15c carmine | 5.50 | .35 |
| **299** | A49 | 30c green ('37) | 9.00 | .35 |
| **300** | A49 | 60c ultra ('37) | 10.00 | .35 |
| | | Nos. 298-300 (3) | 24.50 | 1.05 |
| | | Set, never hinged | 40.00 | |

Arms — A50

No. 304 exists in two types:
I — "50" is fat and broad, with "0" leaning to right.
II — "50" is thinner and narrower, with "0" straight.

### Paper with Gray Network

| **1937-39** | | **Wmk. 238** | **Perf. 14** | |
|---|---|---|---|---|
| **301** | A50 | 10c green | .85 | .25 |
| **302** | A50 | 25c magenta | .25 | .25 |
| **303** | A50 | 35c red | .50 | .25 |
| **304** | A50 | 50c brown | .30 | .25 |
| **305** | A50 | 1 l dp vio bl ('39) | .35 | .45 |
| | | Nos. 301-305 (5) | 2.25 | 1.45 |
| | | Set, never hinged | 10.00 | |

For overprint see No. 2N10.

Jonas Basanavicius Reading Act of Independence A51

President Antanas Smetona A52

### Perf. 13x13½

| **1939, Jan. 15** | | **Engr.** | **Unwmk.** | |
|---|---|---|---|---|
| **306** | A51 | 15c dark red | .25 | .30 |
| **307** | A52 | 30c deep green | .50 | .30 |
| **308** | A52 | 35c red lilac | .60 | .45 |
| **309** | A52 | 60c dark blue | .75 | .60 |
| *a.* | | Souvenir sheet of 2, #308-309 | 5.00 | 10.00 |
| *b.* | | As "a," imperf. | 35.00 | 45.00 |
| | | Nos. 306-309 (4) | 2.10 | 1.65 |
| | | Set, never hinged | 5.00 | |

20th anniv. of Independence.
Nos. 309a, 309b sold for 2 l.

### Same Overprinted in Blue

VILNIUS 1939-X-10

| **1939** | | | | |
|---|---|---|---|---|
| **310** | A51 | 15c dark red | .50 | .90 |
| **311** | A52 | 30c deep green | .50 | .90 |
| **312** | A51 | 35c red lilac | 1.25 | 1.00 |
| **313** | A52 | 60c dark blue | 1.25 | 1.00 |
| | | Nos. 310-313 (4) | 3.50 | 3.80 |
| | | Set, never hinged | 7.00 | |

Recovery of Vilnius.

View of Vilnius A53

Gediminas A54

Trakai Ruins — A55

### Unwmk.

| **1940, May 6** | | **Photo.** | **Perf. 14** | |
|---|---|---|---|---|
| **314** | A53 | 15c brn & pale brn | .40 | .25 |
| **315** | A54 | 30c dk grn & lt grn | .90 | .50 |
| **316** | A55 | 60c dk bl & lt bl | 2.00 | .70 |
| *a.* | | Souv. sheet of 3, #314-316, imperf. | 8.00 | 16.00 |
| | | Nos. 314-316 (3) | 3.30 | 1.45 |
| | | Set, never hinged | 5.00 | |

Return of Vilnius to Lithuania, Oct. 10, 1939.
Exist imperf.
No. 316a has simulated perforations in gold. Sold for 2 l.

White Knight A56

Angel A57

Woman Releasing Dove A58

Mother and Children A59

Liberty Bell A60

Mythical Animal A61

| **1940** | | | | |
|---|---|---|---|---|
| **317** | A56 | 5c brown carmine | .40 | .30 |
| **318** | A57 | 10c green | .40 | .45 |
| **319** | A58 | 15c dull orange | .40 | .30 |
| **320** | A59 | 25c light brown | .40 | .40 |
| **321** | A60 | 30c Prussian green | .40 | .30 |
| **322** | A61 | 35c red orange | .40 | .35 |
| | | Nos. 317-322 (6) | 2.40 | 2.10 |
| | | Set, never hinged | 4.50 | |

Nos. 317-322 exist imperf.
For overprints see Nos. 2N11-2N16.

> **Catalogue values for unused stamps in this section, from this point to the end of the section, are for Never Hinged items.**

Nos. 371-399 were issued before the Soviet Union recognized the independence of Lithuania on Sept. 6, 1991, but were available and valid for use after that date.

Angel and Map — A66

Colors: 5k, Green. 10k, Brown violet. 20k, Blue. 50k, Red.

| **1990, Oct. 7** | | **Litho.** | **Imperf.** | |
|---|---|---|---|---|
| | | Without Gum | | |
| **371-374** | A66 | Set of 4 | 1.75 | 1.75 |

### Simulated Perforations and Denomination in Brownish Gray

Colors as before.

| **1990, Dec. 22** | | | **Without Gum** | |
|---|---|---|---|---|
| **375-378** | A66 | Set of 4 | 1.60 | 1.60 |

White Knight "Vytis" A67

Hill With Crosses, Siauliai A68

Design: 200k, Liberty Bell.

| **1991** | | **Photo.** | **Perf. 14** | |
|---|---|---|---|---|
| **379** | A67 | 10k multi | .30 | .25 |
| **380** | A67 | 15k multi | .30 | .25 |
| **381** | A67 | 20k multi | .30 | .25 |
| **382** | A67 | 30k multi | .30 | .25 |
| **383** | A68 | 50k multi | .30 | .25 |
| **384** | A68 | 200k multi | .40 | .25 |

## Litho.
### Imperf
### Without Gum

| | | | | |
|---|---|---|---|---|
| 385 | A67 | 15k dl grn & blk | .30 | .25 |
| 386 | A67 | 25k brn & blk | .30 | .25 |
| 387 | A67 | 30k plum & blk | .30 | .25 |
| | | Nos. 379-387 (9) | 2.80 | 2.25 |

Issued: 10k, 20k, No. 382, 50k, 200k, 1/10; No. 380, 3/15; No. 385, 3/13; 25k, No 387, 7/23.

No. 385 has a simulated outline of a perforated stamp.

See Nos. 411-418.

Liberty Statue — A69

**1991, Feb. 16    Photo.    Perf. 13¾x14**

| | | | | |
|---|---|---|---|---|
| 388 | A69 | 20k multi | .50 | .25 |

Declaration of Independence from Soviet Union, 1st Anniv. — A70

**1991, Mar. 11    Litho.    Perf. 13¼x13**

| | | | | |
|---|---|---|---|---|
| 389 | A70 | 20k multi | .50 | .25 |

Religious Symbols — A71

Designs: 40k, Crosses. 70k, Madonna. 100k, Spires, St. Anne's Church, Vilnius.

**1991, Mar. 15    Photo.    Perf. 13¾x14**

| | | | | |
|---|---|---|---|---|
| 390-392 | A71 | Set of 3 | 1.25 | .75 |

Resistance to Soviet and German Occupation, 50th Anniv. — A72

Designs: 20k, Candle, barbed wire. 50k, Heart, daggers. 70k, Sword, wreath.

**1991, June 14    Litho.    Perf. 13¼**

| | | | | |
|---|---|---|---|---|
| 393-395 | A72 | Set of 3 | 1.25 | .75 |

Fourth World Lithuanian Games — A73

Emblem and: 20k, Map. 50k+25k, Head.

**1991, July 27    Photo.    Perf. 13¼x13**

| | | | | |
|---|---|---|---|---|
| 396-397 | A73 | Set of 2 | 1.00 | .50 |

Expedition to Mt. Everest — A74

Denominations: 20k, 70k.

**1991, Aug. 20    Litho.    Perf. 12½x13**

| | | | | |
|---|---|---|---|---|
| 398-399 | A74 | Set of 2 | 1.00 | .75 |

A75

**1991, Sept. 28    Litho.    Perf. 13x13½**

| | | | | |
|---|---|---|---|---|
| 400 | A75 | 30k Castle | .50 | .30 |
| 401 | A75 | 50k Grand Duke | .50 | .50 |
| 402 | A75 | 70k Early view of Vilnius | 1.00 | 1.00 |
| | | Nos. 400-402 (3) | 2.00 | 1.80 |

Grand Duke Gediminas, 650th death anniv.

Ciconia Nigra — A76

Design: 50k, Grus grus.

**1991, Nov. 21    Litho.    Perf. 14**

| | | | | |
|---|---|---|---|---|
| 403 | A76 | 30k +15k multi | .90 | .55 |
| 404 | A76 | 50k multicolored | 1.00 | .65 |

### White Knight Type of 1991

**1991, Dec. 20    Photo.    Perf. 14**
### Background Colors

| | | | | |
|---|---|---|---|---|
| 411 | A67 | 40k black | .25 | .25 |
| 412 | A67 | 50k purple | .25 | .25 |
| 415 | A67 | 100k dark green | .25 | .25 |
| 418 | A67 | 500k blue | 1.25 | .55 |
| | | Nos. 411-418 (4) | 2.00 | 1.30 |

For surcharges see Nos. 450-452.

Lithuanian Admission to UN — A78

**1992, Mar. 15    Litho.    Perf. 13x13½**

| | | | | |
|---|---|---|---|---|
| 421 | A78 | 100k multicolored | .50 | .30 |

Lithuanian Olympic Participation — A79

Emblems: No. 422, Olympic Committee. No. 423, Albertville. No. 424, Barcelona.

**1992, Mar. 22**

| | | | | |
|---|---|---|---|---|
| 422 | A79 | 50k +25k multi | .30 | .30 |
| 423 | A79 | 130k multi | .45 | .45 |
| 424 | A79 | 280k multi | 1.25 | 1.25 |
| | | Nos. 422-424 (3) | 2.00 | 2.00 |

Surtax for Lithuanian Olympic Committee.

A80

200k, Cypripedium. 300k, Eringium maritimum.

**1992, July 11    Perf. 12½x13**

| | | | | |
|---|---|---|---|---|
| 425 | A80 | 200k multicolored | .40 | .30 |
| 426 | A80 | 300k multicolored | .60 | .50 |

A81

Birds of the Baltic Shores: No. 427, Pandion haliaetus. No. 428, Limosa limosa. No. 429, Mergus merganser. No. 430, Tadorna tadorna.

### Litho. & Engr.
**1992, Oct. 3    Perf. 12½x13**
### Booklet Stamps

| | | | | |
|---|---|---|---|---|
| 427 | A81 | B grn & grnsh blk | .70 | .50 |
| 428 | A81 | B grn & red brn | .70 | .50 |
| 429 | A81 | B grn, red brn & brn | .70 | .50 |
| 430 | A81 | B grn & red brn | .70 | .50 |
| a. | | Booklet pane of 4, #427-430 | 3.50 | |

Sold for 15r on day of issue.
See Estonia Nos. 231-234a, Latvia Nos. 332-335a and Sweden Nos. 1975-1978a.

Coats of Arms — A82

**1992, Oct. 11    Litho.    Perf. 14**

| | | | | |
|---|---|---|---|---|
| 431 | A82 | 2r Kedainiai | .25 | .25 |
| 432 | A82 | 3r Vilnius | .25 | .25 |
| 433 | A82 | 10r National | .55 | .55 |
| | | Nos. 431-433 (3) | 1.05 | 1.05 |

See Nos. 454-456, 497-499, 521-522, 554-556, 586-588, 607-609, 642-644, 677-679, 704-706, 716-718, 736-740, 762-764, 788-789, 813-815, 833-835, 879-881, 887-889, 910-912, 945-947, 958-960.

19th Cent. Costumes — A83

Couples in different traditional costumes of the Suwalki region.

**1992, Oct. 18    Perf. 13x13½**

| | | | | |
|---|---|---|---|---|
| 434 | A83 | 2r multicolored | .25 | .25 |
| 435 | A83 | 5r multicolored | .25 | .25 |
| 436 | A83 | 7r multicolored | .50 | .35 |
| | | Nos. 434-436 (3) | 1.00 | .85 |

See Nos. 465-467, 493-495, 511-513, 539-541.

Churches — A84

300k, Zapishkis Church, 16th cent. 1000k, Saints Peter & Paul Church, Vilnius, 17th cent. 1500k, Christ Church of the Resurrection, Kaunas, 1934.

**1993, Jan. 15    Litho.    Perf. 12**

| | | | | |
|---|---|---|---|---|
| 437 | A84 | 300k bister & blk | .30 | .25 |
| 438 | A84 | 1000k blue green & blk | .70 | .25 |
| 439 | A84 | 1500k gray & blk | 1.00 | .30 |
| | | Nos. 437-439 (3) | 2.00 | .80 |

See Nos. 502-504

Independence A85

Designs: A, Jonas Basanavicius (1851-1927), journalist and politician. B, Jonas Vileisis (1872-1942), lawyer and politician.

**1993, Feb. 16**

| | | | | |
|---|---|---|---|---|
| 440 | A85 | (A) red & multi | .25 | .25 |
| 441 | A85 | (B) green & multi | .95 | .65 |

No. 440 sold for 3r and No. 441 sold for 15r on day of issue.

See Nos. 479-480, 506-507, 536-537, 563-564, 592-593, 622-623, 660-661, 686-687, 711-712.

A86    Grand Duke Vytautas, 600th Birth Anniv. — A87

Designs: 500k, Royal Seal. 1000k, 5000k, Portrait. 1500k, Vytautas in Battle of Grunwald, by Jan Matejko.

**1993, Feb. 27**

| | | | | |
|---|---|---|---|---|
| 442 | A86 | 500k bister, red & blk | .30 | .25 |
| 443 | A87 | 1000k citron, blk & red | .70 | .30 |
| 444 | A87 | 1500k lem, blk & red | 1.00 | .50 |
| | | Nos. 442-444 (3) | 2.00 | 1.05 |

### Souvenir Sheet

| | | | |
|---|---|---|---|
| 445 | A87 | 5000k citron, black & red | 2.00  2.00 |

Famous Lithuanians — A88

Designs: 1000k, Simonas Daukantas (1793-1864), educator and historian. 2000k, Vydunas (1868-1953), preserver of Lithuanian traditional culture. 4500k, Vincas Mykolaitis Putinas (1893-1967), philosopher and psychologist.

**1993, Mar. 13**

| | | | | |
|---|---|---|---|---|
| 446 | A88 | 1000k multicolored | .25 | .25 |
| 447 | A88 | 2000k multicolored | .50 | .50 |
| 448 | A88 | 4500k multicolored | 1.25 | .90 |
| | | Nos. 446-448 (3) | 2.00 | 1.65 |

See Nos. 475-477, 514-516, 533-535, 560-562, 599-601, 624-626.

No. 382, 387 and 411 Surcharged

**1993    Photo, Litho. (#451)    Perf. 14**

| | | | | |
|---|---|---|---|---|
| 450 | A67 | 100k on 30k magenta | .25 | .25 |
| 451 | A67 | 100k on 30k magenta, imperf, without gum | .50 | .25 |
| 452 | A67 | 300k on 40k #411 | .25 | .25 |
| | | Nos. 450-452 (3) | 1.00 | .75 |

Issued: 300k, 1/19; No. 450, 1/26; No. 451, 3/10.

### Coat of Arms Type of 1992
### Size: 24x31mm

**1993, July 3    Litho.    Perf. 11**

| | | | | |
|---|---|---|---|---|
| 454 | A82 | 5c Skuodas | .25 | .25 |
| a. | | Tete-beche pair | .40 | .40 |
| 455 | A82 | 30c Telsiai | .35 | .30 |
| a. | | Tete-beche pair | 1.20 | .60 |
| 456 | A82 | 50c Klaipeda | .55 | .45 |
| a. | | Tete-beche pair | 1.70 | .90 |
| | | Nos. 454-456 (3) | 1.15 | 1.00 |

World Lithuanian Unity Day — A89

5c, The Spring, by M. K. Ciurlionis. 80c, Capts. Steponas Darius and Stasys Girenas.

**1993, July 17    Perf. 13**

| | | | | |
|---|---|---|---|---|
| 457 | A89 | 5c multicolored | .25 | .25 |
| a. | | Tete-beche pair | .30 | |
| 458 | A89 | 80c multicolored | .75 | .75 |
| a. | | Tete-beche pair | 2.40 | |

Deaths of Darius and Girenas, 60th anniv. (No. 458).

Natl. Arms — A90

**1993, July 21    Litho.    *Perf. 13x12½***
459 A90  (A) bister & multi    .30  .25
460 A90  (B) green & multi    .80  .25
No. 459 sold for 5c, No. 460 for 80c on day of issue.
Dated 1992.

Visit of Pope John Paul II — A91

**1993, Sept. 3    Litho.    *Perf. 13½x13***
461 A91  60c Kryziu Kalnas    .50  .30
462 A91  60c Siluva    .50  .30
463 A91  80c Vilnius    .70  .35
464 A91  80c Kaunas    .70  .35
    Nos. 461-464 (4)    2.40 1.30

**Natl. Costumes Type of 1992**
Couples in different traditional costumes of the Dzukai.

**1993, Oct. 30    Litho.    *Perf. 12***
Size: 23x36mm
465 A83  60c multicolored    .40  .25
466 A83  80c multicolored    .60  .35
467 A83  1 l multicolored    1.00  .45
    Nos. 465-467 (3)    2.00 1.05

Lithuanian Postal System, 75th Anniv. — A92

Post offices: No. 468, Klaipeda. No. 469, Kaunas. 80c, Vilnius. 1 l, No. 1.

**1993, Nov. 16**
468 A92  60c multicolored    .40  .25
469 A92  60c multicolored    .40  .25
470 A92  80c multicolored    .60  .30
471 A92  1 l multicolored    .90  .40
    Nos. 468-471 (4)    2.30 1.20

Europa — A93

80c, The Old Master, by A. Gudaitis, 1939.

**1993, Dec. 24    Litho.    *Perf. 12***
472 A93  80c multicolored    2.00 1.40
    a.  Tete-beche pair    4.00 4.00

Endangered Species — A94

**1993, Dec. 30    Litho.    *Perf. 12***
473 A94  80c Emys orbicularis    .60  .30
474 A94  1 l Bufo calamita    1.00  .40
See Nos. 500-501, 519-520.

**Famous Lithuanians Type of 1993**
Designs: 60c, Kristijonas Donelaitis (1714-80), poet. 80c, Vincas Kudirka (1858-99), physician, writer. 1 l, Maironis (1862-1932), poet.

**1994, Mar. 26    Litho.    *Perf. 12***
475 A88  60c multicolored    .40  .25
476 A88  80c multicolored    .65  .30
477 A88  1 l multicolored    1.00  .40
    Nos. 475-477 (3)    2.05  .95

1994 Winter Olympics, Lillehammer — A95

**1994, Feb. 11**
478 A95  1.10 l multicolored    1.00  .40

**Independence Type of 1993**
No. 479, Pres. Antanas Smetona (1874-1944). No. 480, Aleksandras Stulginskis.

**1994, Feb. 16**
479 A85  1 l red brown & multi    .80  .35
480 A85  1 l brown & multi    .80  .35

A96

Natl. Arms — A96a

***Perf. 12, 13½ (40c), 13½x13 (50c)***
**1994-97    Litho.**
481 A96    5c dark brown    .25  .25
482 A96    10c deep violet    .25  .25
483 A96    20c dark green    .25  .25
484 A96    40c deep rose mag    .25  .25
485 A96    50c green blue    .30  .25
486 A96a    1 l gray & multi    .50  .25
    a.  Souvenir sheet of 4    3.00 3.00
487 A96a    2 l buff & multi    1.90  .50
488 A96a    3 l green & multi    2.50  .75
    Nos. 481-488 (8)    6.20 2.75
Independence, 5th anniv. (No. 486a).
Issued: 5c, 10c, 4/9/94; 20c, 11/19/94; 2 l, 3 l, 7/23/94; 1 l, 3/11/95; 40c, 5/4/96; 50c, 4/5/97.

Europa — A97

80c, Artillery rockets, 17th cent.

**1994, May 7    Litho.    *Perf. 12***
491 A97  80c multicolored    .50  .40

Souvenir Sheet

100th Postage Stamp A98

**1994, May 21    Litho.    *Perf. 12***
492 A98  10 l multicolored    10.00 10.00
No. 492 sold for 12 l.

**Natl. Costumes Type of 1992**
Couples in different traditional costumes of Samogitia.

**1994, June 25    Litho.    *Perf. 12***
493 A83    5c multicolored    .30  .25
494 A83    80c multicolored    .60  .25
495 A83    1 l multicolored    .70  .30
    Nos. 493-495 (3)    1.60  .80

Lithuanian World Song Festival — A99

**1994, July 6**
496 A99  10c multicolored    .50  .25

**Coat of Arms Type of 1992**
**1994, Sept. 10    Litho.    *Perf. 12***
Size: 25x32mm
497 A82  10c Punia    .25  .25
498 A82  60c Alytus    .45  .25
499 A82  80c Perloja    .60  .30
    Nos. 497-499 (3)    1.30  .80

**Endangered Species Type of 1993**
**1994, Oct. 22    Litho.    *Perf. 12***
500 A94  20c Nyctalus noctula    .35  .25
501 A94  20c Glis glis    .35  .25

**Church Type of 1993**
**1994, Nov. 12**
502 A84  10c Kaunus, 16th cent.    .25  .25
503 A84  60c Kedainiu, 17th cent.    .45  .25
504 A84  80c Vilnius, 18th cent.    .60  .35
    Nos. 502-504 (3)    1.30  .85

Christmas A101

**1994, Dec. 3    Litho.    *Perf. 12***
505 A101  20c multicolored    .25  .25

**Independence Type of 1993**
No. 506, Pranas Dovydaitis. No. 507, Steponas Kairys.

**1995, Feb. 16    Litho.    *Perf. 12***
506 A85  20c multicolored    .25  .25
507 A85  20c multicolored    .25  .25

A102

Via Baltica Highway Project: Nos. 508, 509c, Kaunas, Lithuania: No. 509a, Beach Hotel, Parnu, Estonia. No. 509b, Castle, Bauska, Latvia.

**1995, Apr. 20    Litho.    *Perf. 14***
508 A102  20c multicolored    .25  .25

**Souvenir Sheet**
509 A102  1 l Sheet of 3, #a.-c.    2.50 2.50
See Estonia Nos. 288-289, Latvia Nos. 394-395.

Sculpture, Mother's School — A103

**1995, Apr. 29    Litho.    *Perf. 12***
510 A103  1 l multicolored    1.00 1.00
Europa.

**Natl. Costumes Type of 1992**
Couples in traditional costumes of Aukstaiciai.

**1995, May 20    Litho.    *Perf. 12***
511 A83  20c multicolored    .25  .25
512 A83  70c multicolored    .60  .25
513 A83  1 l multicolored    .75  .30
    Nos. 511-513 (3)    1.60  .80

**Famous People Type of 1993**
Writers: 30c, Motiejus Valancius (1801-75). 40c, Zemaite (1845-1921). 70c, Kipras Petrauskas (1885-1968).

**1995, May 27    Litho.    *Perf. 12***
514 A88  30c multicolored    .25  .25
515 A88  40c multicolored    .40  .25
516 A88  70c multicolored    .60  .25
    Nos. 514-516 (3)    1.25  .75

Day of Mourning & Hope — A104

**1995, June 14    Litho.    *Perf. 12***
517 A104  20c multicolored    .25  .25

5th World Sports Games — A105

**1995, July 30    Litho.    *Perf. 12***
518 A105  30c multicolored    .25  .25

**Endangered Species Type of 1993**
**1995, Aug. 26    Litho.    *Perf. 12***
519 A94  30c Arctia villica    .40  .25
520 A94  30c Baptria tibiale    .40  .25

**Coat of Arms Type of 1992**
Size: 25x32mm
Arms of villages in Suvalkija: 40c, Virbalis. 1 l, Kudirkos Naumiestis, horiz.

**1995, Sept. 16    Litho.    *Perf. 12***
521 A82  40c multicolored    .30  .25
522 A82  1 l multicolored    .75  .30

Valerie Mesalina, by Pranciskus Smuglevicius A106

**1995, Oct. 6    Litho.    *Perf. 12½***
523 A106  40c multicolored    .50  .25

Castles A107

**1995, Nov. 18    *Perf. 11½x12***
524 A107  40c Vilnius    .30  .25
525 A107  70c Trakai    .60  .30
526 A107  1 l Birzai    .90  .45
    Nos. 524-526 (3)    1.80 1.00

Christmas — A108

Designs: 40c, People celebrating Christmas in outdoor snow scene. 1 l, People with lanterns walking toward church.

**1995, Dec. 2    Litho.    *Perf. 13***
527 A108  40c multicolored    .30  .25
528 A108  1 l multicolored    .75  .45

Bison Bonasus — A109

**1996, Jan. 20    *Perf. 13x13½***
529 A109  30c shown    .25  .25
530 A109  40c Two adults    .40  .25
531 A109  70c Adult, calf    .60  .40
532 A109  1 l Two adults, calf    .80  .80
    a.  Miniature sheet, 2 each #529-532    4.50 4.50
    Nos. 529-532 (4)    2.05 1.70
World Wildlife Fund.

## Famous Lithuanians Type of 1993
Designs: 40c, Kazys Grinius (1866-1950). No. 534, Antanas Zmudzinavicius (1876-1966). No. 535, Balys Sruoga (1896-1947).

**1996, Feb. 2　Litho.　Perf. 13x13½**
| | | | |
|---|---|---|---|
|533|A88|40c multicolored|.30 .25|
|534|A88|1 l multicolored|.60 .40|
|535|A88|1 l multicolored|.60 .40|
| | |Nos. 533-535 (3)|1.50 1.05|

## Independence Type of 1993
No. 536, Vladas Mironas. No. 537, Jurgis Saulys.

**1996, Feb. 16　Litho.　Perf. 13½x13**
|536|A85|40c gray, blk & buff|.30 .25|
|---|---|---|---|
|537|A85|40c olive, blk & buff|.30 .25|

Barbora Radvilaite (1520-51) — A110

**1996, Apr. 27　Litho.　Perf. 13½x13**
|538|A110|1 l multicolored|1.00 1.00|
|---|---|---|---|

Europa.

## 19th Cent. Costumes Type of 1992
Couples in different traditional costumes of the Klaipeda region: No. 540, Man in blue coat. No. 541, Man wearing wooden shoes.

**1996, May 25　Litho.　Perf. 13½**
|539|A83|40c multicolored|.35 .25|
|---|---|---|---|
|540|A83|1 l multicolored|.75 .35|
|541|A83|1 l multicolored|.75 .35|
| | |Nos. 539-541 (3)|1.85 .95|

Day of Mourning and Hope — A116

**1996, June 14　Litho.　Perf. 13½**
|547|A116|40c Christ|.40 .25|
|---|---|---|---|
|548|A116|40c Angel|.40 .25|

A117

Designs: No. 549, Greek discus thrower. No. 550, Basketball players.

**1996, July 19　Perf. 13½x13**
|549|A117|1 l multicolored|1.00 .50|
|---|---|---|---|
|550|A117|1 l multicolored|1.00 .50|

1996 Summer Olympic Games, Atlanta.

Paintings, by M.K. Ciurlionis — A118

No. 551, Kapines, 1909. No. 552, Auka, 1909. No. 553: a, Andante, 1908. b, Allegro, 1908.

**1996, Sept. 21　Litho.　Perf. 13½x13**
|551|A118|40c multicolored|.35 .25|
|---|---|---|---|
|552|A118|40c multicolored|.35 .25|

**Souvenir Sheet**
**Perf. 12½x11½**
|553|A118|3 l Sheet of 2, #a.-b.|5.00 5.00|
|---|---|---|---|

No. 553 contains 26x53mm stamps.

## Coat of Arms Type of 1992
Size: 25x33mm

**1996, Oct. 19　Litho.　Perf. 13½x13**
|554|A82|50c Seduva|.45 .25|
|---|---|---|---|
|555|A82|90c Panevezys|.65 .35|
|556|A82|1.20 l Zarasai|.90 .50|
| | |Nos. 554-556 (3)|2.00 1.10|

Souvenir Sheet

Lithuanian Basketball Team, Bronze Medalists, 1996 Summer Olympic Games, Atlanta A119

**1996, Nov. 16　Perf. 12½**
|557|A119|4.20 l multicolored|3.50 3.50|
|---|---|---|---|

Christmas — A120

**1996, Nov. 30　Perf. 13½x13½**
|558|A120|50c Angels|.35 .25|
|---|---|---|---|
|559|A120|1.20 l Santa on horse|1.00 .50|

## Famous Lithuanians Type of 1993
Designs: 50c, Ieva Simonaityte (1897-1978). 90c, Jonas Sliupas (1861-1944). 1.20 l, Vladas Jurgutis (1885-1966).

**1997, Jan. 23　Litho.　Perf. 13x13½**
|560|A88|50c brown & greem|.40 .25|
|---|---|---|---|
|561|A88|90c gray & yellow|.70 .35|
|562|A88|1.20 l blue green & orange|.90 .45|
| | |Nos. 560-562 (3)|2.00 1.05|

## Independence Type of 1993
No. 563, Mykolas Birziska. No. 564, Kazimieras Saulys.

**1997, Feb. 16　Litho.　Perf. 13½x13**
|563|A85|50c multicolored|.35 .25|
|---|---|---|---|
|564|A85|50c multicolored|.35 .25|

First Lithuanian Book, 450th Anniv. — A121

**1997, Feb. 15　Litho.　Perf. 13½x13**
|565|A121|50c gray & red|.45 .25|
|---|---|---|---|

**Souvenir Sheet**
|566|A121|4.80 l like #565|3.50 3.50|
|---|---|---|---|

No. 566 contains one 29x38mm stamp.

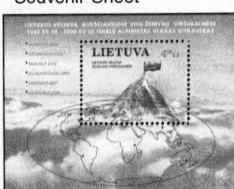
Souvenir Sheet

Flag on Mountain Top A122

**1997, Feb. 25　Perf. 11½x12½**
|567|A122|4.80 l multicolored|4.00 4.00|
|---|---|---|---|

Expeditions to highest peaks on each continent.

Stories and Legends — A123

Children's drawings: No. 568, Girl, horse. No. 569, King, moon, stars, bird, vert.

**1997, Apr. 12　Litho.　Perf. 13**
|568|A123|1.20 l multicolored|1.00 1.00|
|---|---|---|---|
|569|A123|1.20 l multicolored|1.00 1.00|

Europa.

A124

**1997, May 9　Litho.　Perf. 13**
|570|A124|50c multicolored|.45 .25|
|---|---|---|---|

First Lithuanian School, 600th Anniv.

A125

Old Ships of the Baltic Sea: 50c, Kurenas, 16th cent. No. 572: a, Kurenas, 16th cent., diff. b, Maasilinn ship, 16th cent. c, Linijkugis, 17th cent.

**1997, May 10　Perf. 14x14½**
|571|A125|50c multicolored|.45 .25|
|---|---|---|---|
|572|A125|1.20 l Sheet of 3, #a.-c.|3.00 3.00|

See Estonia Nos. 322-323, Latvia Nos. 443-444.

Palanga Botanical Park, Cent. — A126

**1997, June 1　Litho.　Perf. 13½x13½**
|573|A126|50c multicolored|.45 .25|
|---|---|---|---|
|a.| |Tete-beche pair|.90 .90|

Numbers 574-577 are unassigned.

2nd Baltic Sea Games — A127

**1997, June 25　Litho.　Perf. 13½**
|578|A127|90c multicolored|.75 .35|
|---|---|---|---|

Museum Art — A128

Designs: 90c, Animal face carved on ritual staff. 1.20 l, Coins, 15th cent.

**1997, July 12　Perf. 13½x13**
|579|A128|90c multicolored|.75 .35|
|---|---|---|---|
|580|A128|1.20 l multicolored|1.00 .50|

Double Barred Crosses — A129

**1997, Aug. 2　Litho.　Perf. 13½**
|581|A129|20c olive|.30 .25|
|---|---|---|---|
|582|A129|50c brown|.50 .25|
|a.| |Inscribed "1998"|.50 .25|

Nos. 581 and 582 are inscribed "1997." See Nos. 602, 604, 617-619.

Mushrooms — A130

Designs: No. 583, Morchella elata. No. 584, Boletus aereus.

**1997, Sept. 20　Litho.　Perf. 13½x13**
|583|A130|1.20 l multicolored|1.00 .50|
|---|---|---|---|
|a.| |Tete-beche pair|2.00 2.00|
|584|A130|1.20 l multicolored|1.00 .50|
|a.| |Tete-beche pair|2.00 2.00|

Letters of Grand Duke Gediminas — A131

**1997, Oct. 4　Perf. 14**
|585|A131|50c multicolored|.50 .25|
|---|---|---|---|

## Coat of Arms Type of 1992
Size: 25x33mm

**1997, Oct. 18　Litho.　Perf. 13½x13**
|586|A82|50c Neringa|.45 .25|
|---|---|---|---|
|587|A82|90c Vilkaviskis|.80 .35|
|588|A82|1.20 l Pasvalys|1.00 .45|
| | |Nos. 586-588 (3)|2.25 1.05|

Christmas and New Year — A132

**1997, Nov. 22　Litho.　Perf. 13**
|589|A132|50c shown|.40 .25|
|---|---|---|---|
|590|A132|1.20 l Snow on trees|1.00 .50|

1998 Winter Olympic Games, Nagano — A133

**1998, Jan. 17　Litho.　Perf. 14**
|591|A133|1.20 l multicolored|1.00 .45|
|---|---|---|---|
|a.| |Tete-beche pair|2.00 2.00|

## Independence Type of 1993 and

Declaration of Independence — A134

Designs: 50c, Alfonsas Petrulis. 90c, Jokubas Sernas.

**Perf. 13½x12½**
**1998, Feb. 16　Litho.**
|592|A85|50c olive and black|.35 .25|
|---|---|---|---|
|593|A85|90c brown and black|.65 .40|

**Souvenir Sheet**
**Perf. 12½x11½**
|594|A134|6.60 l multicolored|5.00 5.00|
|---|---|---|---|

Independence, 80th anniv.

**Souvenir Sheet**

National Anthem, Cent. A135

**1998, Feb. 16　Perf. 12½**
|595|A135|5.20 l multicolored|4.00 4.00|
|---|---|---|---|

Antanas Gustaitis, Aviator, Birth Cent. — A136

Designs: 2 l, Portrait of Gustaitis, ANBO 41. 3 l, Design drawings, ANBO-VIII.

**1998, Mar. 27    Litho.    Perf. 14**
596  A136  2 l  multicolored          1.50  .85
597  A136  3 l  multicolored          2.50  1.10

Natl. Song Festival — A137

**1998, Apr. 18                 Perf. 13½**
598  A137  1.20 l  multicolored       1.25  1.25
a.    Tete-beche pair                 3.25  3.25

Europa.

**Famous Lithuanians Type of 1993**

50c, Tadas Ivanauskas (1882-1971), scientist. No. 600, Jurgis Baltrusaitis (1873-1944), writer, Jurgis Baltrusaitis (1903-88), historian. No. 601, Stasys Lozoraitis (1898-1983), Stasys Lozoraitis (1924-94), politicians.

**1998, Apr. 25                 Perf. 13x13½**
599  A88  50c  multicolored                .40  .25
**Size: 45x26mm**
600  A88  90c  multicolored                .70  .35
601  A88  90c  multicolored                .70  .35
     Nos. 599-601 (3)                      1.80  .95

**Double-Barred Crosses Type of 1997**

**1998, June 1    Litho.    Perf. 13½**
602  A129  70c  yellow bister              .65  .30
a.    Inscribed "1999"                     .90  .30

No. 602 is inscribed "1998."

2nd Lithuanian Olympic Games, 6th World Lithuanian Games — A138

**1998, June 23                 Perf. 14**
603  A138  1.35 l  multicolored           1.00  .55
a.    Tete beche pair                      2.00  2.00

**Double-Barred Crosses Type of 1997**

**1998, July 4    Litho.    Perf. 13½**
604  A129  35c  plum & pink                .30  .25

Red Book of Lithuania — A139

Fish: No. 605, Coregonus lavaretus holsatus. No. 606, Salmo salar.

**1998, July 11                 Perf. 13x13½**
605  A139  1.40 l  multicolored           1.10  .55
606  A139  1.40 l  multicolored           1.10  .55

**Coat of Arms Type of 1992**
**Size: 25x33mm**

**1998, Sept. 12    Litho.    Perf. 13**
607  A82  70c  Kernave                     .50  .25
608  A82  70c  Trakai                      .50  .25
609  A82  1.35 l  Kaunas                   1.00  .55
     Nos. 607-609 (3)                      2.00  1.05

Vilnius-Cracow Post Route Established, 1562 — A141

**1998, Oct. 9    Litho.    Perf. 14**
611  A141  70c  multicolored               .60  .30

---

Souvenir Sheet

Lithuanian Post, 80th Anniv. A142

**1998, Oct. 9    Litho.    Perf. 12**
612  A142  13 l  multicolored          10.00  10.00

No. 612 contains a holographic image. Soaking in water may affect the hologram.

Museum Paintings A143

70c, "Through the Night," by Antanas Zmuidzinavicius (1876-1966). 1.35 l, "The Garden of Bernardines, Vilnius," by Juozapas Marsevskis (1825-83).

**1998, Oct. 17    Litho.    Perf. 13½x13**
613  A143  70c  multicolored               .60  .30
614  A143  1.35 l  multicolored           1.00  .50

New Year — A144

Christmas: 1.35 l, Winter scene, people walking through giant tree, village.

**1998, Nov. 14    Litho.    Perf. 12½**
615  A144  70c  multicolored               .50  .25
616  A144  1.35 l  multicolored           1.10  .55

**Double-Barred Crosses Type of 1997**

**1998, Nov. 14    Litho.    Perf. 13½**
617  A129  5c  lt & dk citron              .25  .25
a.    Inscribed "1999"                     .25  .25
618  A129  10c  tan & brown                .25  .25
a.    Inscribed "1999"                     .25  .25
619  A129  20c  lt & dk olive green        .25  .25
a.    Inscribed "1999"                     .25  .25
     Nos. 617-619 (3)                      .75  .75

Nos. 617-619 inscribed "1998."

Adam Mickiewicz (1798-1855), Poet — A145

**1998, Dec. 24                 Perf. 14**
620  A145  70c  multicolored               .60  .30
a.    Tete beche pair                      1.25  1.25

---

Souvenir Sheet

Publication of "Postile," by M. Dauksa (1527-1613), 400th Anniv. — A146

**1999, Jan. 23    Litho.    Perf. 12½**
621  A146  5.90 l  brown & gray           5.00  5.00

**Independence Type of 1993**

Designs: No. 622, Petras Klimas. No. 623, Donatas Malinauskas.

**Perf. 13½x12½**
**1999, Feb. 16                 Litho.**
622  A85  70c  red & black                 .50  .30
623  A85  70c  blue & black                .50  .30

**Famous Lithuanians Type of 1993**

Designs: No. 624, Juozas Matulis (1899-1993). No. 625, Augustinas Gricius (1899-1972). 1.35 l, Pranas Skardzius (1899-1975).

**1999, Mar. 19    Litho.    Perf. 13**
624  A88  70c  multicolored                .50  .30
625  A88  70c  multicolored                .50  .30
626  A88  1.35 l  multicolored            1.00  .55
     Nos. 624-626 (3)                      2.00  1.15

NATO, 50th Anniv. — A147

**1999, Mar. 27    Litho.    Perf. 13¾x14**
627  A147  70c  multicolored               .60  .30

National Parks — A148

Europa: No. 628, Traditional homes, lake, islands, Aukotaitija Natl. Park. No. 629, Sand dunes, amber, Curonian Spit Natl. Park.

**1999, Apr. 10    Litho.    Perf. 13x13¼**
628  A148  1.35 l  multicolored           1.25  1.25
629  A148  1.35 l  multicolored           1.25  1.25

Council of Europe, 50th Anniv. — A149

**1999, May 1    Litho.    Perf. 14**
630  A149  70c  multicolored               .60  .30

Melniai Windmill — A150

**1999, May 8    Litho.    Perf. 14**
631  A150  70c  shown                     1.00  .35
632  A150  70c  Pumpenai Windmill  1.00  .35

---

Bees — A151

Designs: 70c, Dasypoda argentata. 2 l, Bombus pomorum.

**1999, June 12                 Perf. 13¼x13**
633  A151  70c  multicolored               .70  .35
634  A151  2 l  multicolored              1.60  .80

UPU, 125th Anniv. — A152

**1999, July 3    Litho.    Perf. 14**
635  A152  70c  multicolored               .60  .30

Lithuanian Philatelic Society Emblems, No. 1, Pre-independence Stamp — A153

**1999, July 31    Litho.    Perf. 14**
636  A153  1 l  multicolored              1.00  .50
     Complete booklet, 10 #636           11.00

Lithuanian Philatelic Society, 75th Anniv.

Souvenir Sheet

Centenary of First Performance of Play, "America in the Baths" — A154

Designs: a, Producers. b, Theater poster.

**1999, Aug. 20    Litho.    Perf. 12½**
637  A154  4 l  Sheet of 2, #a.-b.   5.00  5.00

A155

Baltic Chain, 10th Anniv. — Family and flags: 1 l, No. 640a, Lithuanian. No. 640: b, Estonian. c, Latvian.

**1999, Aug. 23    Litho.    Perf. 12¾**
639  A155  1 l  multicolored               .85  .40
**Souvenir Sheet**
640  A155  2 l  Sheet of 3, #a.-c.   5.00  5.00

See Estonia Nos. 366-367, Latvia Nos. 493-494.

A156

**1999, Aug. 28    Litho.    Perf. 14**
641  A156  70c  multicolored               .60  .25

Freedom fight movement, 50th anniv.

**Coat of Arms Type of 1992**
**Size: 25x33mm**

**1999, Sept. 18                 Perf. 13½x13**
642  A82  70c  Marijampole                 .50  .25
643  A82  1 l  Siauliai                    1.00  .35
644  A82  1.40 l  Rokiskis                 1.25  .45
     Nos. 642-644 (3)                      2.75  1.05

Museum Pieces — A157

Designs: 70c, Sword of Gen. S. Zukauskas. 3 l, Hussar armor.

**1999, Oct. 9**     **Perf. 13¼x13½**
| | | | |
|---|---|---|---|
| 645 | A157 | 70c multicolored | .40 .25 |
| 646 | A157 | 3 l multicolored | 1.00 1.00 |

A158

**1999, Oct. 23**   **Litho.**   **Perf. 14**
| | | | |
|---|---|---|---|
| 647 | A158 | 70c multicolored | .60 .25 |

Simonas Stanevicius (1799-1848), writer.

A159

Christmas and New Year's Day: 1.35 l, Buildings, candles.

**Perf. 12½x13½**
**1999, Nov. 13**     **Litho.**
| | | | |
|---|---|---|---|
| 648 | A159 | 70c shown | .40 .25 |
| 649 | A159 | 1.35 l multicolored | .75 .50 |

Forged Monument Tops — A160

Designs: 10c, Rietavas. 20c, Andriunal. 1 l, Veivirzenai. 1.30 l, Vaizgakiemis. 1.70 l, Baukai.

**2000-06**   **Litho.**   **Perf. 13½x13¼**
**Vignettes in Blue**
**Designs 22mm High**
| | | | |
|---|---|---|---|
| 650 | A160 | 10c tan | .30 .25 |
| a. | | Perf. 11¼, inscr. "2002" | .30 .25 |
| b. | | As "a," inscr. "2003" | .30 .25 |
| c. | | As "a," inscr. "2004" | .30 .25 |
| 651 | A160 | 20c yellow | .35 .25 |
| a. | | Perf. 11¼, inscr. "2002" | .35 .25 |
| b. | | As "a," inscr. "2003" | .35 .25 |
| c. | | As "a," inscr. "2004" | .35 .25 |
| 652 | A160 | 1 l pale rose | .90 .45 |
| a. | | Perf. 11¼, inscr. "2002" | 1.00 .50 |
| 653 | A160 | 1.30 l lt green | 1.10 .55 |
| 654 | A160 | 1.70 l lt blue | 1.40 .70 |
| | | Nos. 651-654 (4) | 3.75 1.95 |

**Perf. 13x12½**
**Designs 20mm High**
| | | | |
|---|---|---|---|
| 655 | A160 | 10c tan | .25 .25 |
| a. | | Inscr. "2006" | .25 .25 |
| 656 | A160 | 20c yellow | .25 .25 |
| a. | | Inscr. "2006" | .25 .25 |

**Designs 21mm High**
| | | | |
|---|---|---|---|
| 657 | A160 | 1 l pale rose | .75 .35 |
| 658 | A160 | 1.30 l lt green | 1.00 .50 |
| | | Nos. 655-658 (4) | 2.25 1.35 |

Issued: Nos. 650-654, 1/3/00; Nos. 650a, 651a, 652a, 5/4/02; Nos. 655-656, 10/8/05; Nos. 657-658, 5/27/06.

**Independence Type of 1993**
Designs: 1.30 l, Jonas Vailokaitis (1886-1994), banker. 1.70 l, Jonas Smilgevicius (1870-1942), banker.

**Perf. 13¼x12¾**
**2000, Feb. 16**     **Litho.**
| | | | |
|---|---|---|---|
| 660 | A85 | 1.30 l multi | .75 .50 |
| 661 | A85 | 1.70 l multi | 1.25 .75 |

---

Souvenir Sheet

Declaration of Independence From Soviet Union, 10th Anniv. — A161

**Perf. 12¼x11½**
**2000, Mar. 11**     **Litho.**
| | | | |
|---|---|---|---|
| 662 | A161 | 7.40 l multi | 5.00 5.00 |

Famous Lithuanians — A162

Designs: 1 l, Vincas Pietaris (1850-1902), writer. 1.30 l, Kanutas Ruseckas (1800-60), artist. 1.70 l, Povilas Visinskis (1875-1906), writer.

**2000, Mar. 25**     **Perf. 13x13¼**
| | | | |
|---|---|---|---|
| 663 | A162 | 1 l multi | .80 .40 |
| 664 | A162 | 1.30 l multi | .90 .50 |
| 665 | A162 | 1.70 l multi | 1.25 .70 |
| | | Nos. 663-665 (3) | 2.95 1.60 |

See Nos. 688-690.

Items From Klaipeda Clock Museum — A163

1 l, Sundial. 2 l, Renaissance-style clock.

**2000, Apr. 15**     **Perf. 12**
| | | | |
|---|---|---|---|
| 666 | A163 | 1 l multi | 1.00 .50 |
| 667 | A163 | 2 l multi | 1.25 .75 |

**Europa, 2000**
**Common Design Type**
**2000, May 9**     **Perf. 13¼x13**
| | | | |
|---|---|---|---|
| 668 | CD17 | 1.70 l multi | 1.50 1.50 |

Birds of Prey From Red Book of Lithuania — A164

1 l, Pandion haliaetus. 2 l, Milvus migrans.

**2000, June 2**     **Perf. 13¼x13**
| | | | |
|---|---|---|---|
| 669 | A164 | 1 l multi | .75 .45 |
| 670 | A164 | 2 l multi | 1.60 .80 |

Sea Museum of Lithuania — A165

No. 671, Spheniscus magellanicus. No. 672, Halichoerus grypus.

**2000, Aug. 26**   **Litho.**   **Perf. 12**
| | | | |
|---|---|---|---|
| 671-672 | A165 | 1 l Set of 2 | 1.50 1.00 |
| 671a | | Tete beche pair | 2.25 2.25 |
| 672a | | Tete beche pair | 2.25 2.25 |

---

2000 Summer Olympics, Sydney — A166

Designs: 1 l, Cycling. 3 l, Swimming.

**2000, Sept. 2**
| | | | |
|---|---|---|---|
| 673-674 | A166 | Set of 2 | 3.00 1.75 |

Souvenir Sheet

Mikalojus Konstantinas Ciurlionis (1875-1911), Artist — A167

**2000, Sept. 22**   **Litho.**   **Perf. 12**
| | | | |
|---|---|---|---|
| 675 | A167 | 4 l multi | 3.00 3.00 |

Reappearance of Lithuanian Postage Stamps, 10th Anniv. — A168

**2000, Oct. 7**   **Litho.**   **Perf. 12**
| | | | |
|---|---|---|---|
| 676 | A168 | 1 l multi | .80 .40 |

**Arms Type of 1992**
Designs: No. 677, 1 l, Raseiniai. No. 678, 1 l, Taurage. 1.30 l, Utena.

**2000, Oct. 21**   **Litho.**   **Perf. 12**
**Size: 25x33mm**
| | | | |
|---|---|---|---|
| 677-679 | A82 | Set of 3 | 2.50 1.40 |

Christmas and New Year's Day — A169

Roadside shrines: 1 l, 1.70 l.

**2000, Nov. 11**
| | | | |
|---|---|---|---|
| 680-681 | A169 | Set of 2 | 2.00 1.00 |

Souvenir Sheet

Holy Year 2000 A170

No. 682: a, Nativity. b, Jesus and disciples. c, Crucifixion. d, Resurrection.

**2000, Nov. 25**
| | | | |
|---|---|---|---|
| 682 | A170 | 2 l Sheet of 4, #a-d | 6.25 6.25 |

---

Advent of New Millennium — A171

**2000, Dec. 2**
| | | | |
|---|---|---|---|
| 683 | A171 | 1 l multi | .80 .40 |

Souvenir Sheet

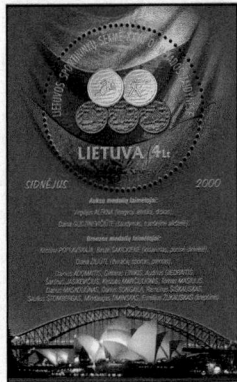

Medals Won at 2000 Summer Olympics, Sydney — A172

**2000, Dec. 9**   **Litho.**   **Perf.**
| | | | |
|---|---|---|---|
| 684 | A172 | 4 l multi | 3.25 3.25 |

Storming of TV Station by Soviet Troops, 10th Anniv. A173

**2001, Jan. 13**     **Perf. 12**
| | | | |
|---|---|---|---|
| 685 | A173 | 1 l multi + label | .85 .40 |

**Independence Type of 1993**
Designs: 1 l, Saliamonas Banaitis (1866-1933), newspaper publisher and politician. 2 l, Justinas Staugaitis (1863-1943), bishop and politician.

**2001, Feb. 16**   **Litho.**   **Perf. 12**
| | | | |
|---|---|---|---|
| 686-687 | A85 | Set of 2 | 2.50 1.25 |

**Famous Lithuanians Type of 2000**
Designs: No. 688, 1 l, Juozas Mikenas (1901-64), artist. No. 689, 1 l, Pranas Vaicaitis (1876-1901), poet. 1.70 l, Petras Vileisis (1851-1926), civil engineer.

**2001, Mar. 24**   **Litho.**   **Perf. 12**
| | | | |
|---|---|---|---|
| 688-690 | A162 | Set of 3 | 3.00 1.50 |

Europa — A174

Designs: No. 691, 1.70 l, Neman River. No. 692, 1.70 l, Lake Galve.

**2001, Apr. 14**     **Perf. 13x13¼**
| | | | |
|---|---|---|---|
| 691-692 | A174 | Set of 2 | 3.00 3.00 |

Flowers From Red Book of Lithuania — A175

Designs: 2 l, Nymphoide peltata. 3 l, Erica tetralix.

**2001, May 12**     **Perf. 13¼x13**
| | | | |
|---|---|---|---|
| 693-694 | A175 | Set of 2 | 4.00 2.00 |

Bridges — A176

Designs: 1 l, Papalauja Bridge. 1.30 l, Pakurojis Dam Bridge.

**2001, June 9**      *Perf. 12*
695-696   A176    Set of 2      1.80   .95

### Souvenir Sheet

Lithuania, 1000th Anniv. (in 2009) — A177

Designs: a, Flag. b, Arms. c, Map of country. d, Map of Europe.

**2001, June 23**      *Perf. 11*
697   A177   2 l   Sheet of 4, #a-d +
       2 labels      6.25   6.25

Baltic Coast Landscapes — A178

Designs: 1 l, No. 699a, Palanga. No. 699b, Lahemaa. No. 699c, Vidzeme.

**2001, Sept. 15**   **Litho.**   *Perf. 13½*
698   A178   1 l   multi      .85   .40

**Souvenir Sheet**
699      Sheet of 3      4.75   4.75
*a.-c.*   A178   2 l   Any single    1.40   1.10

See Estonia Nos. 423-424, Latvia Nos. 534-535.

Ethnographic Open Air Museum Exhibits — A179

19th cent. dwellings from: 1 l, Kirdeikiai. 2 l, Darbenai.

**2001, Sept. 22**      *Perf. 12*
700-701   A179    Set of 2      2.40   1.25

Sculpture by Juozas Zikaras (1881-1944) — A180

**2001, Oct. 4**
702   A180   3 l   multi      2.40   1.25

Postal Regulations Enacted by Stefan Bathory, 1583 — A181

**2001, Oct. 6**
703   A181   1 l   multi      .85   .40

### Coat of Arms Type of 1992
Size: 25x33mm

Designs: 1 l, Lazdijai. 1.30 l, Birzai. 1.70 l, Veliuona.

**2001, Oct. 27**   **Litho.**   *Perf. 12*
704-706   A82    Set of 3      3.00   1.60

Christmas and New Year — A182

Birds on: 1 l, Covered tree. 1.70 l, Christ's cradle.

**2001, Nov. 10**   **Litho.**   *Perf. 12*
707-708   A182    Set of 2      2.00   1.00

### Souvenir Sheet

Dr. Jonas Basanavicius (1851-1927), Patriot, Folklorist — A183

**2001, Nov. 17**      *Perf. 12x11½*
709   A183   5 l   multi      4.00   4.00

2002 Winter Olympics, Salt Lake City — A184

**2002, Jan. 26**   **Litho.**   *Perf. 12*
710   A184   1.70 l   multi     1.40   .70

### Independence Type of 1993
Designs: No. 711, 1 l, Kazys Bizauskas (1892-1941), statesman. No. 712, 1 l, Stanislovas Narutavicius (1862-1932), politician.

**2002, Feb. 16**
711-712   A85    Set of 2      1.50   .80

Famous Lithuanians — A185

Designs: 1 l, Antanas Salys (1902-72), linguist. 1.30 l, Satrijos Ragana (1877-1930), writer. 1.70 l, Oskaras Milasius (1877-1939), poet.

**2002, Mar. 2**   **Litho.**   *Perf. 12*
713-715   A185    Set of 3      3.00   1.50
See Nos. 734-735, 759-761, 782-784, 805-807, 830-832, 858-860, 884-886, 906-908, 934-936, 967-969.

### Coat of Arms Type of 1992
Size: 25x33mm

Designs: No. 716, 1 l, Anyksciai. No. 717, 1 l, Birstonas. 1.70 l, Prienai.

**2002, Mar. 23**
716-718   A82    Set of 3      3.00   1.50

State Historical Archives, 150th Anniv. — A186

**2002, Apr. 6**
719   A186   1 l   multi      .85   .40

Mammals From Red Book of Lithuania — A187

Designs: 1 l, Mustela erminea. 3 l, Lynx lynx.

**2002, Apr. 13**      *Perf. 13x13¼*
720-721   A187    Set of 2      3.00   1.60

Europa — A188

**2002, May 4**   **Litho.**   *Perf. 13¼x13*
722   A188   1.70 l   multi     1.50   1.50

Vilnius Fire and Rescue Brigade, Bicent. — A189

**2002, May 25**      *Perf. 12*
723   A189   1 l   multi      .85   .40

Narrow-gauge Railways — A190

Designs: 1.30 l, TU2 diesel locomotive. 2 l, PT4 steam engine.

**2002, June 8**
724-725   A190    Set of 2      2.75   1.40

### Souvenir Sheet

Lithuania, 1000th Anniv. (in 2009) — A191

Designs: a, Artifact of first people in Lithuania, 10,000 B.C. b, Roman historian Tacitus mentions Aestii people, 98. c, Vikings attack Apuole Castle, 853. d, First mention of Lithuania in Quedlinburg Annals, 1009.

**2002, June 22**      *Perf. 11*
726   A191   2 l   Sheet of 4, #a-d, +
       2 labels      6.25   6.25

### Souvenir Sheet

Klaipeda, 750th Anniv. A192

**2002, Aug. 1**      *Perf. 11½x12¼*
727   A192   5 l   multi      4.00   4.00

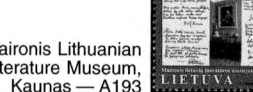

Maironis Lithuanian Literature Museum, Kaunas — A193

Designs: 1 l, Exhibits. 3 l, Museum exterior.

**2002, Sept. 7**      *Perf. 12*
728-729   A193    Set of 2      3.00   1.50

Establishment of Postal Service by King Sigismund III Vasa, 1620 — A194

**2002, Oct. 5**
730   A194   1 l   multi      .85   .40

Christmas and New Year's Day — A195

Cross and: 1 l, Clock, candles and holly. 1.70 l, Christmas tree and angels.

**2002, Nov. 9**
731-732   A195    Set of 2      2.10   1.00

European Children's Day — A196

**2002, Nov. 16**
733   A196   1 l   multi      .85   .40

### Famous Lithuanians Type of 2002
Designs: 1 l, Laurynas Stuoka-Gucevicius (1753-98), architect. 1.30 l, Juozas Eretas (1896-1984), author and politician.

**2003, Jan. 25**      *Perf. 12*
734-735   A185    Set of 2      1.80   .85

### Coat of Arms Type of 1992
Designs: No. 736, 1 l, Gargzdai. No. 737, 1 l, Kretinga. No. 738, 1 l, Palanga. No. 739, 1 l, Papile. No. 740, 1 l, Rietavas.

**2003, Feb. 15**   **Litho.**   *Perf. 12*
Size: 25x33mm
736-740   A82    Set of 5      4.00   2.00

Lighthouses — A198

Designs: 1 l, Pervalka. 3 l, Uostodvaris.

**2003, Mar. 15**
741-742   A198    Set of 2      3.25   1.50

Europa — A199

**2003, Apr. 19**   **Litho.**   *Perf. 13½x13*
743   A199   1.70 l   multi     1.50   1.50
*a.*    Tete beche pair     3.25   3.25

Rebuilding of Palace of Lithuania's Rulers — A200

**2003, Apr. 26**      *Perf. 12*
744   A200   1 l   multi      .85   .40

Vilnius University Astronomical Observatory, 250th Anniv. — A201

**2003, May 10** *Perf. 12*
745 A201 1 l multi .85 .40

 Insects From Red Book of Lithuania — A202

Designs: No. 746, 3 l, Lucanus cervus. No. 747, 3 l, Cerambyx cerdo.

**2003, May 24** *Perf. 13x13½*
746-747 A202 Set of 2 5.00 2.50

**Souvenir Sheet**

 Lithuania, 1000th Anniv. (in 2009) — A203

No. 748: a, Rise of Lithuania, 1183. b, Battle of Siauliai, 1236. c, Coronation of Mindaugas, 1253. d, Selection of Vilnius as capital of Lithuania, 1323.

**2003, June 21** *Perf. 11*
748 A203 2 l Sheet of 4, #a-d, + 2 labels 6.25 3.25

**Souvenir Sheet**

 Coronation of Mindaugas, 750th Anniv. — A204

**2003, July 5** *Perf. 11½x12¼*
749 A204 5 l multi 4.00 2.00

 13th European Hot Air Balloon Championships A205

**2003, Aug. 8** *Perf. 12*
750 A205 1.30 l multi 1.00 .55

 Vincentas Cardinal Sladkevicius (1920-2000) — A206

**2003, Aug. 20**
751 A206 1 l multi .85 .40

Panevezys, 500th Anniv. — A207

**2003, Sept. 7**
752 A207 1 l multi .85 .40

---

 Map of Kaunas-Vilnius-Grodno Postal Route, 1664 — A208

**2003, Oct. 4**
753 A208 1 l multi .85 .40

 Christmas and New Year's Day — A209

Villages at: 1 l, Christmas. 1.70 l, New Year's Eve.

**2003, Nov. 8**
754-755 A209 Set of 2 2.10 1.00

**Souvenir Sheet**

 Lithuania, 2003 European Men's Basketball Champions — A210

**2003, Dec. 6** *Litho. Perf. 12x11½*
756 A210 5 l multi 4.00 2.00

 Gliders in Lithuanian Aviation Museum — A211

Designs: No. 757, 1 l, BK-7. No. 758, 1 l, BRO-12.

**2003, Dec. 17** *Perf. 12*
757-758 A211 Set of 2 1.75 .80

**Famous Lithuanians Type of 2002**

Designs: No. 759, 1 l, Jonas Aistis (1904-73), poet. No. 760, 1 l, Kazimieras Buga (1879-1924), philologist. No. 761, 1 l, Adolfas Jucys (1904-74), physicist.

**2004, Jan. 24** *Litho. Perf. 12*
759-761 A185 Set of 3 2.25 1.25

**Coat of Arms Type of 1992**

Designs: 1 l, Mazeikiai. 1.30 l, Radviliskis. 1.40 l, Ukmerge.

**2004, Feb. 14** *Size: 25x33mm*
762-764 A82 Set of 3 2.75 1.50

 Vilnius University, 425th Anniv. — A213

**2004, Mar. 20**
765 A213 1 l multi .85 .40

---

 Europa — A214

Designs: No. 766, 1.70 l, Sailboat. No. 767, 1.70 l, Beach umbrella.

**2004, Apr. 10** *Litho. Perf. 12*
766-767 A214 Set of 2 3.00 3.00

 Return to Printing Lithuanian in Latin Letters, Cent. — A215

**2004, May 1** *Litho. Perf. 12*
768 A215 1.30 l multi 1.00 .50

 Admission to European Union — A216

No. 769: a, Stars, flags of newly-added countries, map of Europe. b, Stars and Lithuanian flag, map and arms.

**2004, May 1**
769 A216 1.70 l Horiz. pair, #a-b 2.75 1.25

 FIFA (Fédération Internationale de Football Association), Cent. — A217

**2004, May 15**
770 A217 3 l multi 2.25 1.10

 Chiune Sugihara (1900-86), Japanese Diplomat Who Issued Transit Visas to Jews in World War II — A218

**2004, June 19** *Litho. Perf. 12*
771 A218 1 l multi .85 .40

**Souvenir Sheet**

 Lithuania, 1000th Anniv. — A219

No. 772: a, Defense of Pilenai Castle, 1336. b, Battle at the Blue Waters, 1362. c, Christening of Lithuania, 1387. d, Battle of Zalgiris, 1410.

**2004, July 3** *Perf. 11*
772 A219 2 l Sheet of 4, #a-d, + 2 labels 6.00 4.00

 Exhibits in Tadas Ivanauskas Zoology Museum, Kaunas — A220

No. 773: a, Aquila chrysaetos. b, Iguana iguana.

**2004, July 10** *Perf. 12*
773 A220 1 l Horiz. pair, #a-b 1.50 .80

---

 2004 Summer Olympics, Athens — A221

2004 Olympic emblem and: 2 l, Pentathlon equestrian event. 3 l, Canoeing.

**2004, July 31**
774-775 A221 Set of 2 4.00 2.00

 Owls From Red Book of Lithuania — A222

Designs: 1.30 l, Bubo bubo. 3 l, Asio flammeus.

**2004, Oct. 2** *Litho. Perf. 12*
776-777 A222 Set of 2 3.25 1.75

 Kaunas Funiculars — A223

Designs: 1 l, Aleksotas Funicular. 1.30 l, Zaliakalnis Funicular.

**2004, Oct. 16**
778-779 A223 Set of 2 1.75 .95

 Christmas A224

Stars and: 1 l, Christmas tree. 1.70 l, Bird.

**2004, Nov. 6**
780-781 A224 Set of 2 2.00 1.50

**Famous Lithuanians Type of 2002**

Designs: No. 782, 1 l, Kazys Boruta (1905-65), writer. No. 783, 1 l, Petras Kalpokas (1880-1945), painter. No. 784, 1 l, Jonas Puzinas (1905-78), archaeologist.

**2005, Jan. 8** *Litho. Perf. 12*
782-784 A185 Set of 3 2.00 1.50

 Congratulations A225

Designs: No. 785, 1 l, Gerbera daisies, freesias and scroll. No. 786, 1 l, Lilies, freesias and box.

*Serpentine Die Cut 6¾*
**2005, Jan. 29** *Litho.*
**Booklet Stamps**
**Self-Adhesive**
785-786 A225 Set of 2 1.40 1.10
786a Booklet pane, 4 each #785-786 5.50

 Sartai Horse Race, Cent. — A226

**2005, Feb. 5** *Perf. 12*
787 A226 1 l multi .65 .40

**Coat of Arms Type of 1992**

Designs: No. 788, 1 l, Druskininkai. No. 789, 1 l, Vabalninkas.

**2005, Mar. 5** *Size: 25x33mm*
788-789 A82 Set of 2 1.40 1.10

Europa — A227

Designs: No. 790, 1.70 l, Cow, cheese. No. 791, 1.70 l, Loaf of black bread.

**2005, Apr. 9** **Litho.** **Perf. 12**
790-791 A227 Set of 2 3.00 3.00

National Museum, 150th Anniv. A228

No. 792: a, Brass jewelry, 1st-2nd cent. b, Illustration of first exhibition in Aula Hall, Vilnius University.

**2005, May 7**
792 A228 1 l Pair, #a-b 1.40 1.40

Train and Kaunas Railway Tunnel — A229

**2005, June 11**
793 A229 3 l multi 2.00 1.50

Souvenir Sheet

Lithuania, 1000th Anniv. — A230

No. 794: a, Battle of Pabaiskas, 1435. b, Valakai Reform, 1557. c, First Lithuanian statute, 1529. d, Union of Lublin, 1569.

**2005, July 2** **Perf. 11**
794 A230 2 l Sheet of 4, #a-d, + 2 labels 5.50 5.50

90th World Esperanto Congress, Vilnius — A231

**2005, July 23** **Litho.** **Perf. 12**
795 A231 1 l multi .70 .50

Churches — A232

Designs: 1 l, Vilnius Evangelical Lutheran Church. 1.30 l, St. Casimir Church, Vilnius.

**2005, Sept. 3** **Perf. 13½**
796-797 A232 Set of 2 1.50 1.00

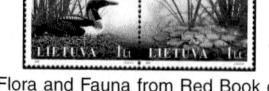

Flora and Fauna from Red Book of Lithuania A233

No. 798: a, Gavia arctica. b, Trapa natans.

**2005, Sept. 10**
798 A233 1 l Horiz. pair, #a-b 1.40 1.40

Souvenir Sheet

Mikolajus Konstantinas Ciurlionis (1875-1911), Painter and Composer — A234

No. 799 — Details from Sonata of the Sea triptych: a, Allegro. b, Andante. c, Finale.

**2005, Sept. 24** **Perf. 14**
799 A234 2 l Sheet of 3, #a-c, + label 4.00 4.00

Map of St. Petersburg-Warsaw Post Road, 1830-36 — A235

**2005, Oct. 8** **Litho.** **Perf. 14¼x14**
800 A235 1 l multi .65 .45

Christmas A236

Designs: 1 l, Candle and snow-covered evergreen branch. 1.70 l, Santa Claus in sleigh.

**2005, Nov. 5** **Perf. 12¾x13**
801-802 A236 Set of 2 1.75 1.25

Dr. Jonas Basanavicius, Vilnius City Hall and Commemorative Medal — A237

**2005, Dec. 3** **Perf. 14¼x14**
803 A237 1 l multi .65 .45
Congress of Lithuanians, cent.

2006 Winter Olympics, Turin — A238

**2006, Jan. 28** **Litho.** **Perf. 14x14¼**
804 A238 1.70 l multi 1.25 .75

**Famous Lithuanians Type of 2002**
Designs: No. 805, 1 l, Adolfas Sapoka (1906-61), historian. No. 806, 1 l, Petras Rimsa (1881-1961), sculptor. No. 807, 1 l, Antanas Vaiciulaitis (1906-92), writer.

**2006, Feb. 11** **Perf. 13½**
805-807 A185 Set of 3 2.00 1.50

Vilnius Album, by Jonas K. Vilcinskis, 160th Anniv. of Publication — A239

**2006, Feb. 25** **Perf. 13x12¾**
808 A239 1 l multi .65 .45

Social Insurance System, 80th Anniv. — A240

**2006, Mar. 18** **Perf. 14¼x14**
809 A240 1 l multi .65 .45

Lithuanian Theater, Music and Cinema Museum, 80th Anniv. — A241

No. 810: a, Parvo camera, 1930s. b, Music box, 1900.

**2006, Mar. 18** **Perf. 13½**
810 A241 1 l Pair, #a-b 1.25 1.25
Printed in sheets containing 10 of each stamp + 5 labels. Each sheet contains se-tenant pairs of the same stamp.

Europa — A242

Designs: No. 811, 1.70 l, Woman dancing with man in wheelchair. No. 812, 1.70 l, People in wheelchairs being pushed around track.

**2006, Apr. 15**
811-812 A242 Set of 2 3.00 3.00

**Coat of Arms Type of 1992**
Designs: No. 813, 1 l, Kupiskis. No. 814, 1 l, Sakiai. No. 815, 1 l, Silute.

**2006, May 13** **Perf. 14x14¼**
**Size: 25x33mm**
813-815 A82 Set of 3 2.00 1.50

Souvenir Sheet

Lithuania, 1000th Anniv. — A243

No. 816: a, Establishment of Vilnius University, 1579. b, Truce of Andrusov, 1667. c, Four-year Sejm, 1788. d, Uprising of 1794.

**2006, July 1** **Perf. 11**
816 A243 2 l Sheet of 4, #a-d, + 2 labels 5.25 5.25

Basilicas — A244

Designs: 1 l, Vilnius Basilica. 1.70 l, Kaunas Basilica.

**2006, Aug. 5** **Perf. 12¾x13**
817-818 A244 Set of 2 1.75 1.25

Birds and Fish From Red Book of Lithuania — A245

No. 819: a, Polysticta stelleri. b, Acipenser sturio.

**2006, Sept. 16** **Perf. 13½**
819 A245 1 l Vert. pair, #a-b 1.40 1.40

Establishment of Lithuania Post and First Postage Stamps, 1918 — A246

**2006, Oct. 7** **Perf. 14¼x14**
820 A246 1 l multi .65 .45

Premiere of Opera "Birute," Cent. — A247

**2006, Nov. 4** **Litho.** **Perf. 13¼x12¾**
821 A247 2 l multi 1.25 .85

Christmas A248

Designs: 1 l, Birds, triangular window. 1.70 l, Trees, star, berries, straw.

**2006, Nov. 18** **Perf. 12¾x13¼**
822-823 A248 Set of 2 1.75 1.40

18th Century Wooden Church Belfries — A249

Belfries from churches in: 10c, Pasvalys. 20c, Rozalimas. 50c, Tryskiai. 1 l, Saukenai. 1.30 l, Vaiguva. 1.70 l, Vajasiskis.

**Die Cut Perf. 12½**
**2007, Jan. 1** **Litho.**
**Self-Adhesive**
824 A249 10c blue & blk .25 .25
825 A249 20c org & blk .25 .25
826 A249 50c bl grn & blk .40 .40
  a. Dated 2009 .40 .40
  b. Dated 2011 .40 .40
827 A249 1 l brn & blk .80 .80
  a. Dated 2009 .80 .80
  b. Dated 2011 .80 .80
828 A249 1.30 l lil & blk 1.00 1.00
829 A249 1.70 l ol brn & blk 1.40 1.40
  Nos. 824-829 (6) 4.10 4.10

Issued: Nos. 826a, 827a, 2/21/09. Nos. 826b, 827b, 1/8/11.
See Nos. 842-846, 1034.

**Famous Lithuanians Type of 2002**
Designs: No. 830, 1 l, Bernardas Brazdzionis (1907-2002), writer. No. 831, 1 l, Vytautas Kazimieras Jonynas (1907-97), artist. 3 l, Leonas Sapiega (1557-1633), state chancellor of the Grand Duchy of Lithuania.

**2007, Jan. 27** **Perf. 13½**
830-832 A185 Set of 3 3.75 3.00

**Coat of Arms Type of 1992**
Designs: 1 l, Svencionys. 1.30 l, Kelme. 2 l, Moletai.

**2007, Mar. 3** **Perf. 14x14¼**
**Size: 25x33mm**
833-835 A82 Set of 3 3.25 2.50

Europa — A250

Designs: No. 836, 1.70 l, Scouting flag, musical score. No. 837, 1.70 l, Symbols of Lithuanian Scouts.

**2007, Apr. 14    Litho.    Perf. 13½**
836-837  A250   Set of 2            2.25  1.60
Scouting, cent.

Churches
A251

Designs: 1 l, St. Anne's and Bernardine Churches, Vilnius. 1.30 l, Church buildings, Pazaislis.

**2007, May 12    Perf. 12¾x13**
838-839  A251   Set of 2            2.00  1.50

Souvenir Sheet

Lithuania, 1000th Anniv. — A252

No. 840: a, Publication of first Lithuanian newspaper, "Ausra," 1883. b, Abolition of the prohibition on printing in Latin characters, 1904. c, Great Seimas of Vilnius, 1905. d, Lithuanian Declaration of Independence, 1918.

**2007, June 23    Litho.    Perf. 11**
840  A252  3 l  Sheet of 4, #a-d,
+ 2 labels                          9.00  9.00

Trakai History Museum A253

No. 841: a, Map of New Trakai in 1600, by J. Kamarauskas. b, Chess pieces, 15th cent.

**2007, July 28    Litho.    Perf. 13½**
841  A253  2 l  Pair, #a-b           3.00  3.00
Printed in sheets containing 10 of each stamp + 5 labels.

**Wooden Church Belfries Type of 2007**

Belfries from churches in: 5c, Vabalininkas, 19th cent. 35c, Varputenai, 18th cent. 1.35 l, Deguciai, 19th cent. 1.55 l, Geidziai, 19th cent. 2.15 l, Pavandenes, 17th cent.

**Die Cut Perf. 12½**
**2007, Sept. 1    Litho.**
**Self-Adhesive**
842  A249   5c yel grn & blk        .25   .25
843  A249   35c gray & blk          .30   .30
844  A249   1.35 l yel & blk       1.00  .70
845  A249   1.55 l brn org & blk   1.10  .80
846  A249   2.15 l rose lake & blk 1.25  1.75
Nos. 842-846 (5)                    3.90  3.85

Juozas Miltinis (1907-94), Actor and Theater Founder — A254

**2007, Sept. 1    Litho.    Perf. 12¾x13**
847  A254  2.45 l multi             1.75  1.25

Birds — A255

No. 848 — Birds of the Cepkeliai Nature Reserve, Lithuania and Katra Sanctuary, Belarus: a, Gallinago media. b, Crex crex.

---

**2007, Oct. 3    Perf. 14**
848     Horiz. pair + central la-
        bel                         5.00  5.00
a.-b.  A255 2.90 l Either single    2.25  2.25
See Belarus No. 625.

Stamps and Covers From Establishment of Lithuania Post in 1992 — A256

**2007, Oct. 6**
849  A256  1.35 l multi             1.25  1.25

Christmas — A257

Conifer sprigs and: 1.35 l, Snowflake, Christmas ornaments. 2.45 l, Stars, globe.

**2007, Nov. 10    Perf. 13x12¾**
850-851  A257   Set of 2            3.25  3.25

Wooden Churches — A258

Churches in: 5c, Antazave, 1794. 10c, Deguciai, 1757. 20c, Inturke, 1855. 35c, Prienai, 1750. 1.35 l, Siaudine, 1775. 1.55 l, Uzventis, 1703.

**Die Cut Perf. 12½**
**2008, Jan. 5    Litho.**
**Self-Adhesive**
852  A258   5c multi               .25   .25
a.     Dated 2011                   .25   .25
853  A258   10c multi              .25   .25
a.     Dated 2009                   .25   .25
b.     Dated 2011                   .25   .25
854  A258   20c multi              .25   .25
a.     Dated 2009                   .25   .25
b.     Dated 2011                   .25   .25
855  A258   35c multi              .30   .30
a.     Dated 2011                   .30   .30
856  A258   1.35 l multi          1.00  1.00
a.     Dated 2009                  1.00  1.00
b.     Dated 2011                  1.10  1.10
857  A258   1.55 l multi          1.10  1.10
Nos. 852-857 (6)                   3.15  3.15
Issued: Nos. 853a, 854a, 856a, 2/21/09; Nos. 853b, 856b, 1/8/11. Nos. 852a, 854b, 855a, 10/8/11.

**Famous Lithuanians Type of 2002**

Designs: 2 l, Martynas Jankus (1858-1946), publisher. 2.15 l, Zenonas Ivinskis (1908-71), historian. 2.90 l, Antanas Maceina (1908-87), philosopher.

**2008, Jan. 19    Litho.    Perf. 13½**
858-860  A185   Set of 3            5.25  4.00

Restoration of Independence, 90th Anniv. — A259

**2008, Feb. 16**
861  A259  1.35 l multi             1.10  .80

State Awards of the Baltic Countries — A260

Designs: Nos. 862, 863a, Order of Vytautas the Great, Lithuania. No. 863b, Order of the National Coat of Arms, Estonia. No. 863c, Order of Three Stars, Latvia.

---

**Perf. 13½x13¾**
**2008, Mar. 15    Litho.**
862  A260  7 l  multi               5.00  3.50
**Souvenir Sheet**
863  A260  5 l  Sheet of 3, #a-c,
+ label                            13.00  13.00
See Estonia Nos. 592-593, Latvia Nos. 701-702.

Items From Rokiskis Regional Museum A261

No. 864: a, Wood carving, by Lionginas Sepka. b, 19th cent. women's clothing.

**2008, Apr. 19    Litho.    Perf. 14**
864  A261  1.55 l  Horiz. pair, #a-b  2.25  2.25

Europa — A262

Designs: No. 865, 2.45 l, Grand Duke Gediminas and his letters of 1323. No. 866, 2.45 l, Vilnius, 2009 European Cultural Capital.

**2008, May 3**
865-866  A262   Set of 2            3.50  2.75

Sajudis Party, 20th Anniv. — A263

**2008, May 31**
867  A263  1.35 l multi             1.00  .75

Expo Zaragoza 2008 — A264

**2008, June 7    Die Cut Perf. 12½**
**Self-Adhesive**
868  A264  2.45 l multi             1.75  1.25

**Miniature Sheet**

Lithuania, 1000th Anniv. — A265

No. 869: a, First Lithuanian Cabinet of Ministers, 1918. b, Consitituent Assembly, 1920. c, Opening of Kaunas University, 1922. d, Occupation of Memel (Klaipeda) by Lithuania, 1923. e, Opening of Zemaiciai Road (man signing document, 1939). f, Return of Vilnius to Lithuania from Poland, 1939.

**2008, June 28    Perf. 14**
869  A265  3 l  Sheet of 6, #a-f   13.00  13.00

Crashed Transatlantic Flight of Captains Steponas Darius and Stasys Girenas, 75th Anniv. — A266

**2008, July 12**
870  A266  2.90 l multi            2.25  1.60

---

2008 Summer Olympics, Beijing — A267

Designs: 2.15 l, Women's marathon. 2.45 l, Yachting.

**2008, July 26**
871-872  A267   Set of 2            3.50  2.75

Apparitions of the Virgin Mary at Siluva, 400th Anniv. — A268

**2008, Aug. 30    Litho.    Perf. 14**
873  A268  1.55 l multi             1.25  1.00

Worldwide Fund for Nature (WWF) — A269

Coracias garrulus: Nos. 874, 878a, 1.35 l, On branch with beak closed, denomination at LR. Nos. 875, 878b, 1.35 l, In flight. Nos. 876, 878c, 1.35 l, On branch with beak open, denomination at LL. Nos. 877, 878d, 1.35 l, On branch with beak closed, denomination at LL.

**2008, Sept. 6    Perf. 14**
**Stamps With White Frames**
874-877  A269   Set of 4            4.00  3.00
**Souvenir Sheet**
**Stamps Without White Frames**
878  A269  1.35 l Sheet of 4, #a-d 4.00  4.00

**Arms Type of 1992**

Designs: No. 879, 1.35 l, Jurbarkas. No. 880, 1.35 l, Joniskis. 3 l, Sirvintos.

**2008, Oct. 4    Litho.**
**Size: 26x31mm**
879-881  A82   Set of 3             4.25  3.50

Christmas and New Year's Day — A270

Designs: 1.35 l, Holiday lights. 2.45 l, Snow-covered evergreen branch.

**2008, Nov. 8    Perf. 14**
882-883  A270   Set of 2            2.75  2.10

**Famous Lithuanians Type of 2002**

Designs: 1.35 l, Jonas Zemaitis (1909-54), military officer. 2 l, Vaclovas Birziska (1884-1956), educator and library founder. 2.15 l, Mecislovas Reinys (1884-1953), archbishop.

**2009, Jan. 17    Litho.    Perf. 14**
884-886  A185   Set of 3            4.00  3.00

**Arms Type of 1992**

Designs: No. 887, 1.35 l, Krekenava. No. 888, 1.35 l, Pakruojis. 3 l, Salcininkai.

**2009, Feb. 21    Litho.    Perf. 14**
**Size: 26x31mm**
887-889  A82   Set of 3             4.50  3.25

## Souvenir Sheet

Protection of Polar Regions and Glaciers — A271

No. 890 — Glacier with sky in: a, Dark blue. b, Light blue.

**2009, Mar. 27**
890 A271 2.90 l Sheet of 2, #a-b 4.50 4.50

Vilnius, 2009 European Cultural Capital — A272

**2009, Apr. 11**
891 A272 2.15 l multi 1.75 1.25

Europa — A273

Telescope and: No. 892, Galileo Galilei, Moon. No. 893, Vilnius University Observatory, Sun.

**2009, Apr. 25** Litho. *Perf. 14*
892 A273 2.45 l multi 2.00 1.50
893 A273 2.45 l multi 2.00 1.50

Intl. Year of Astronomy.

Great Synagogue of Vilnius — A274

**2009, May 23**
894 A274 1.35 l multi 1.00 .75

Palanga Amber Museum A275

No. 895: a, "Sun Stone" (large piece of amber). b, Museum building.

**2009, June 13**
895 A275 1.55 l Pair, #a-b 2.50 2.50

Spindle — A276

**2009, June 27** Litho. *Perf. 14*
896 A276 3.35 l multi 2.75 1.75

Millennium Song Festival, Vilnius.

## Miniature Sheet

Lithuania, 1000th Anniv. — A277

---

No. 897: a, Acceptance of declaration of the Council of the Movement for the Freedom of Lithuania, 1949. b, Illegal production of "Chronicle of the Catholic Church in Lithuania," 1972. c, Lithuanian Reform Movement, 1988. d, Signing of declaration of Lithuanian independence, 1990. e, Entry into European Union, 2004. f, Acceptance into Schengen Area, 2007.

**2009, July 4** Litho. *Perf. 14*
897 A277 3 l Sheet of 6, #a-f 14.00 14.00

Tall Ships Regatta A278

*Perf. 13½x13¾*
**2009, Sept. 25** Litho.
898 A278 3 l multi + label 2.50 1.75

Railways in Lithuania, 150th Anniv. — A279

**2009, Aug. 8** Litho. *Perf. 14*
899 A279 2.90 l multi 2.40 1.75

Order of the Cross of Vytis — A280

**2009, Sept. 19** *Perf. 13½x13¾*
900 A280 7 l multi 6.00 4.50

Flora and Fauna From Red Book of Lithuania A281

No. 901: a, Papilio machaon. b, Gentiana pneumonanthe.

**2009, Oct. 10** *Perf. 14*
901 A281 1.55 l Horiz. pair, #a-b 2.75 2.75

Struve Geodetic Arc UNESCO World Heritage Site — A282

Designs: No. 902, 2 l, Friedrich Georg Wilhelm von Struve and map of Europe. No. 903, 2 l, Arc post in Meskonys, map of triangulation points.

**2009, Oct. 24**
902-903 A282 Set of 2 3.50 2.75

Christmas and New Year's Day — A283

Designs: 1.35 l, Village church. 2.45 l, Houses.

**2009, Nov. 7**
904-905 A283 Set of 2 3.25 2.50

## Famous Lithuanians Type of 2002

Designs: No. 906, 1.35 l, Jonas Karolis Chodkevicius (Jan Karol Chodkiewicz, 1560-1621), hetman and military leader. No. 907, 1.35 l, Jonas Jablonskis (1860-1930), linguist.

---

3 l, Mykolas Krupavicius (1885-1970), Minister of Agriculture.

**2010, Jan. 16** Litho. *Perf. 14*
906-908 A185 Set of 3 4.50 3.25

2010 Winter Olympics, Vancouver — A284

**2010, Jan. 30**
909 A284 2.45 l multi 2.00 1.50

## Arms Type of 1992

Designs: 1.35 l, Silale. 2 l, Jonava. 2.15 l, Varena.

**2010, Feb. 20** *Perf. 14*
**Size: 26x31mm**
910-912 A82 Set of 3 4.25 3.25

Independence, 20th Anniv. — A285

**2010, Mar. 6** Litho.
913 A285 1.35 l multi 1.00 .75

Easter — A286

**2010, Mar. 20** *Perf. 14*
914 A286 1.35 l multi 1.00 .75

Expo 2010, Shanghai — A287

**2010, Apr. 10**
915 A287 2.90 l multi 2.25 1.60

Vladas Mikenas (1910-92), Chess Grand Master — A288

**2010, Apr. 17**
916 A288 2 l multi 1.60 1.25

Europa — A289

Half of book and: No. 917, 2.45 l, Rabbit, girl, numerals. No. 918, 2.45 l, Letters, bird, boy.

**2010, May 8**
917-918 A289 Set of 2 3.50 3.50

---

## Souvenir Sheet

Oak of Stelmuze A290

**2010, June 5**
919 A290 8 l multi 5.75 5.75

Battle of Grunwald, 600th Anniv. — A291

**2010, July 3**
920 A291 2.45 l multi 1.90 1.50

Kretinga Museum, 75th Anniv. A292

No. 921 — Items in Kretinga Museum: a, Fastener fron 2nd-3rd cent., monument b, St. George slaying the dragon, musuem.

**2010, July 10** Litho.
921 A292 1.35 l Pair, #a-b 2.10 1.60

Printed in sheets containing 10 pairs and 5 labels.

2010 Youth Olympics, Singapore — A293

**2010, July 31** *Perf. 14*
922 A293 2.90 l multi 2.25 1.60

Kernave Archaeological UNESCO World Heritage Site — A294

Designs: No. 923, 3 l, View of town and burial mounds. No. 924, 3 l, Road and burial mound.

**2010, Aug. 7**
923-924 A294 Set of 2 4.50 3.50

Flora and Fauna from Red Book of Lithuania A295

No. 925: a, Columba oenas. b, Anax parthenope and flowers.

**2010, Sept. 11**
925 A295 1.35 l Horiz. pair, #a-b 2.00 1.50

Cathedrals — A296

Designs: No. 926, 1.35 l, Transfiguration Cathedral, Kaisiadorys. No. 927, 1.35 l, St. Anthony of Padua Cathedral, Telsiai.

**2010, Oct. 16** *Perf. 14*
926-927 A296 Set of 2 2.00 1.50
See Nos. 949-950.

Christmas
A297

New Year
2011 — A298

**2010, Nov. 6** *Litho.*
928 A297 1.35 l multi 1.00 .75
929 A298 2.45 l multi 2.00 1.50

Grand Cross of the Order of the Lithuanian Grand Duke Gediminas — A299

**2010, Nov. 20** *Perf. 13½x13¾*
930 A299 7 l multi 5.25 3.75

Defenders of Freedom Day — A300

**2011, Jan. 8** *Litho.* *Perf. 14*
931 A300 1.35 l multi 1.10 .80

37th European Basketball Championships, Lithuania — A301

**2011, Jan. 22** *Perf. 14¼x14*
932 A301 2.45 l multi 1.90 1.50

2011 Census — A302

**2011, Feb. 26** *Perf. 14*
933 A302 1.35 l multi 1.10 .80

**Famous Lithuanians Type of 2002**
Designs: 1.35 l, Gabriele Petkevicaite-Bite (1861-1943), writer. 2.15 l, Justinas Vienozinskis (1886-1960), artist. 2.90 l, Stasys Salkauskis (1886-1941), philosopher.

**2011, Mar. 5**
934-936 A185 Set of 3 5.00 3.75

**Souvenir Sheet**

Kaunas, 650th Anniv. A303

No. 937 — Buildings in Kaunas: a, Kauno Rotuse (City Hall). b, Kauno Centrinis Pastas

---

(Main Post Office). c, Perkuno Namas Kaune (Perkunas House).

**2011, Mar. 19**
937 A303 3 l Sheet of 3, #a-c 7.00 7.00

Europa — A304

Tree in foreground, forest and: No. 938, 2.45 l, Field (denomination at LR). No. 939, 2.45 l, River (denomination at LL).

**2011, Apr. 23**
938-939 A304 Set of 2 3.50 2.75
Intl. Year of Forests.

Pilgrim Route of Pope John Paul II — A305

**2011, May 7**
940 A305 2.15 l multi 1.75 1.25

**Miniature Sheet**

Zoo Animals A306

No. 941: a, Giraffa camelopardalis. b, Pelecanus. c, Cichlasoma octofasciatum. d, Ursus maritimus.

**2011, May 21** *Perf. 14¼x13½*
941 A306 4 l Sheet of 4, #a-d 12.50 12.50

Items in Alytus Ethnographic Museum — A307

No. 942: a, Pot and pitchers. b, Blacksmith's bellows.

**2011, June 4** *Perf. 14*
942 A307 2 l Pair, #a-b 3.00 3.00

Czeslaw Milosz (1911-2004), 1980 Nobel Laureate in Literature — A308

**2011, June 18** *Litho.*
943 A308 3.35 l multi 2.75 1.75

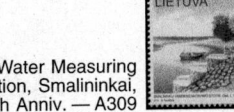

Water Measuring Station, Smalininkai, 200th Anniv. — A309

**2011, July 16**
944 A309 1.35 l multi 1.10 .80
Printed in sheets of 4.

**Arms Type of 1992**
Designs: 1.35 l, Plunge. 2.15 l, Kasiadorys. 2.90 l, Ignalina.

**2011, July 30** *Perf. 14*
945-947 A82 Set of 3 5.00 3.75

---

**Souvenir Sheet**

Stone of Puntukas A310

**2011, Aug. 20**
948 A310 8 l multi 6.25 6.25

Churches — A311

Designs: No. 949, 1.55 l, Church, Trakai. No. 950, 1.55 l, Cathedral, Siaulai.

**2011, Sept. 3**
949-950 A311 Set of 2 2.50 1.75

Battle of Saule, 775th Anniv. — A312

**2011, Sept. 17**
951 A312 2.45 l multi 2.00 1.50

Vilnius Historic Center UNESCO World Heritage Site — A313

Designs: No. 952, 3 l, Gate of Dawn (Ausros Vartai). No. 953, 3 l, St. John's Church.

**2011, Sept. 29** *Litho.*
952-953 A313 Set of 2 4.50 3.75

Haliaeetus Albicilla — A314

**2011, Oct. 8** *Perf. 13½*
954 A314 2.15 l multi 1.75 1.25
Endangered fauna from Red Book of Lithuania.

Christmas — A315

Designs: 1.35 l, Snowman. 2.45 l, Snowflake.

**2011, Nov. 5** *Perf. 14*
955-956 A315 Set of 2 3.00 2.25

---

Grand Cross of the Order for Merits to Lithuania — A316

**2011, Nov. 26** *Perf. 13½x13¾*
957 A316 7 l multi 5.50 3.75

**Arms Type of 1992**
Designs: No. 958, 1.35 l, Kalvarija. No. 959, 1.35 l, Kavarskas. 2.45 l, Naujoji Akmene.

**2012, Jan. 7** *Perf. 14*
**Size: 26x31mm**
958-960 A82 Set of 3 4.00 2.75

Traditional Musical Instruments — A317

Designs: 10c, Wooden panpipes. 20c, Clay pipes. 35c, Bladderbow bass. 1 l, Alder bark trumpet. 1.35 l, Zither. 2.15 l, Cowhorn reed pipes.

**2012, Jan. 7** *Die Cut Perf. 12½*
**Self-Adhesive**
961 A317 10c multi .25 .25
  *a.* Dated "2013" .25 .25
962 A317 20c multi .25 .25
  *a.* Dated "2013" .25 .25
963 A317 35c multi .25 .25
  *a.* Dated "2013" .25 .25
964 A317 1 l multi .75 .75
  *a.* Dated "2013" .80 .80
965 A317 1.35 l multi 1.00 1.00
  *a.* Dated "2013" 1.10 1.10
966 A317 2.15 l multi 1.75 1.75
  Nos. 961-966 (6) 4.25 4.25
Issued: Nos. 964a, 965a, 5/11/13.

**Famous Lithuanians Type of 2002**
Designs: 1.55 l, Mikalojus Radvila Rudasis (Mikolaj Radziwill) (1512-84), Grand Chancellor of Lithuania. 2 l, Domicele Tarabildiene (1912-85), artist. 2.90 l, Stasys Simkus (1887-1943), composer.

**2012, Feb. 4** *Perf. 14*
967-969 A185 Set of 3 4.75 3.50

Maironis (1862-1932), Poet — A318

**2012, Feb. 25**
970 A318 3.35 l multi 2.60 1.75

Spiders From Red Book of Lithuania A319

No. 971: a, Dolomedes plantarius. b, Eresus cinnaberinus.

**2012, Mar. 17**
971 A319 2.90 l Horiz. pair, #a-b 4.25 4.25

Christianization of Lithuania, 625th Anniv. — A320

**2012, Mar. 24** *Perf. 14*
972 A320 1.35 l multi 1.00 1.00

Europa — A321

Designs: No. 973, Hills, trees and river. No. 974, Buildings.

**2012, Apr. 28**
973 A321 2.45 l multi 1.75 1.75
974 A321 2.45 l multi 1.75 1.75

Souvenir Sheet

Year of Museums — A322

**2012, May 12**
975 A322 7 l multi 5.25 5.25

Curonian Spit UNESCO World Heritage Site — A323

Designs: No. 976, 3 l, Fisherman's boat and house. No. 977, 3 l, Sand dunes.

**2012, May 26**
976-977 A323 Set of 2 4.50 4.50

2012 Summer Olympics, London — A324

**2012, June 9**
978 A324 3.35 l Boxing 2.40 2.40
979 A324 3.55 l Rowing 2.60 2.60

Klaipeda, 760th Anniv. — A325

**2012, July 14**
980 A325 2 l multi 1.50 1.50

Battle of Blue Waters, 650th Anniv. — A326

**2012, Aug. 25**
981 A326 2.45 l multi 1.90 1.90

Pres. Algirdas Brazauskas (1932-2010) A327

**2012, Sept. 22**
982 A327 1.35 l multi 1.00 1.00

Establishment of Provisional Lithuanian Currency, 20th Anniv. — A328

**2012, Sept. 29**
983 A328 2 l multi 1.50 1.50

Oskar Minkowski (1858-1931), Diabetes Researcher — A329

**2012, Oct. 20**
984 A329 1.35 l multi 1.00 1.00

Railway Bridges — A330

Train and: Nos. 985, 986a, Lyduvenai Bridge, Lithuania. No. 986b, Narva Bridge, Estonia. No. 986c, Carnikava Bridge, Latvia.

**2012, Oct. 25**
985 A330 8 l multi 6.00 6.00

Souvenir Sheet
**Perf. 13½**
986 A330 4 l Sheet of 3, #a-c 9.00 9.00
See Estonia Nos. 713-714, Latvia Nos. 815-816.

Christmas — A331

Designs: 1.35 l, Body of water. 2.45 l, Snow-covered house.

**2012, Nov. 10**
**Perf. 14**
987-988 A331 Set of 2 2.75 2.75

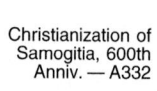

Christianization of Samogitia, 600th Anniv. — A332

**2013, Jan. 5**
**Perf. 13x13¼**
989 A332 2.45 l multi 2.00 2.00

Souvenir Sheet

Flora and Fauna of Zuvintas Biosphere Reserve — A333

No. 990: a, Vulpes vulpes. b, Panurus biarmicus. c, Dactylorhiza maculata.

**2013, Jan. 19**
**Perf. 14¼x14½**
990 A333 3 l Sheet of 3, #a-c 7.25 7.25

New Year 2013 (Year of the Snake) — A334

**2013, Feb. 9**
**Perf. 13x13¼**
991 A334 2.90 l multi 2.25 2.25

Lithuanian Laser Industry — A335

**2013, Feb. 23**
**Perf. 13¼x13**
992 A335 1.35 l multi 1.00 1.00

Famous Lithuanians — A336

Designs: 1.35 l, Antanas Strazdas (1763-1833), poet. 2 l, Pranas Masiotas (1863-1940), writer.

**2013, Mar. 9**
**Perf. 13¼x13**
993-994 A336 Set of 2 2.50 2.50

Uprising of 1863, 150th Anniv. — A337

**2013, Mar. 23**
**Perf. 13x13¼**
995 A337 1.35 l multi 1.00 1.00

Ciconia Ciconia — A338

**2013, Apr. 6**
**Perf. 11**
996 A338 7 l multi 5.50 5.50
No. 996 was printed in sheets of 2.

Europa — A339

Postal vehicles: No. 997, 2.45 l, Tazzari Zero (yellow vehicle). No. 998, 2.45 l, Moskvitch 401 (blue vehicle).

**2013, Apr. 27**
**Perf. 13x13¼**
997-998 A339 Set of 2 3.75 3.75

Mother's Day — A340

**2013, May 4**
**Perf. 13¼x13**
999 A340 1.35 l multi 1.10 1.10

International Red Cross, 150th Anniv. — A341

**2013, May 11**
1000 A341 2.15 l multi 1.75 1.75

Father's Day — A342

**2013, June 1**
1001 A342 1.35 l multi 1.10 1.10

Kaunas Cathedral Basilica, 600th Anniv. — A343

**2013, June 8**
**Perf. 13x13¼**
1002 A343 1.35 l multi 1.10 1.10

Lithuanian Presidency of the European Union — A344

**2013, June 15**
**Perf. 14½x14**
1003 A344 2.45 l multi 1.90 1.90

Souvenir Sheet

Transfer of Klaipeda (Memel) to Lithuanian Control, 90th Anniv. — A345

**2013, June 29**
**Perf. 14¼x14½**
1004 A345 7 l multi 5.25 5.25

First Lithuanian National Olympics, 75th Anniv. — A346

**2013, July 13**
**Perf. 13x13¼**
1005 A346 1.35 l multi 1.10 1.10

A347

2.90 l, Death of Captains Steponas Darius and Stasys Girenas on New York-Kaunas Transatlantic Flight, 80th Anniv.

**2013, July 20**
1006 A347 2.90 l multi 2.25 2.25

Lighthouses — A348

Designs: No. 1007, 2.45 l, Cape Vente Lighthouse. No. 1008, 2.45 l, Kaunas Lighthouse.

**2013, July 27**
**Perf. 13¼x13**
1007-1008 A348 Set of 2 3.75 3.75

Military Uniforms — A349

**2013, Aug. 24 Litho. Perf. 13¼x13**
1009 A349 1.35 l multi 1.10 1.10

Birds From Red Book of Lithuania — A350

Designs: 2.15 l, Acrocephalus paludicola. 2.90 l, Anthus campsetris.

**2013, Sept. 7   Litho.      Perf. 13¼x13**
1010  A350  2.15 l  multi                1.75  1.75
1011  A350  2.90 l  multi                2.25  2.25

Postcrossing Post Cards — A351

**2013, Oct. 5   Litho.      Perf. 13¼x13**
1012  A351  2.45 l  multi                2.00  2.00

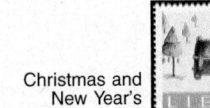

Christmas and New Year's Day — A352

Bear and fox: 1.35 l, Exchanging gifts. 2.45 l, Watching fireworks display.

**2013, Nov. 9   Litho.      Perf. 13x13¼**
1013-1014  A352   Set of 2              3.00  3.00

Kristijonas Donelaitis (1714-80), Poet — A353

**2014, Jan. 4   Litho.      Perf. 13x13¼**
1015  A353  1.55 l  multi                1.25  1.25

2014 Winter Olympics, Sochi, Russia — A354

Designs: 2.15 l, Two-man bobsled. 2.90 l, Ice hockey.

**2014, Jan. 18**
1016-1017  A354   Set of 2              4.00  4.00

Souvenir Sheet

New Year 2014 (Year of the Horse) A355

**2014, Feb. 1   Litho.      Perf. 14¼x14½**
1018  A355  7 l  multi                   5.50  5.50

Shrove Tuesday Masks — A356

**2014. Feb. 15   Litho.      Perf. 13x13¼**
1019  A356  2 l  multi                   1.60  1.60

Re-establishment of Vytautas Magnus University, 25th Anniv. — A357

**2014, Mar. 8   Litho.      Perf. 13¼x13**
1020  A357  1.55 l  multi                1.25  1.25

Admission to NATO, 10th Anniv. — A358

**2014, Mar. 29   Litho.      Perf. 13x13¼**
1021  A358  2.15 l  multi                1.75  1.75

Owls From Red Book of Lithuania — A359

Designs: 2 l, Tyto alba. 3 l, Glaucidium passerinum.

**2014, Apr. 5   Litho.      Perf. 13¼x13**
1022-1023  A359   Set of 2             4.00  4.00
  1023a       Booklet pane of 6, 3 each
               #1022-1023              12.00   —
            Complete booklet, #1023a   12.00

Admission to the European Union, 10th Anniv. — A360

**2014, Apr. 26   Litho.      Perf. 13c13¼**
1024  A360  2.15 l  multi                1.75  1.75

Europa — A361

Designs: No. 1025, 2.45 l, Goat horn (ozragis), wooden bells (skrabalai). No. 1026, 2.45 l, Reed pipe (birbyne), zither (kankles).

**2014, May 3   Litho.      Perf. 13x13¼**
1025-1026  A361   Set of 2              4.00  4.00

Protection of the Baltic Sea — A362

**2014, May 24   Litho.      Perf. 13¼x13**
1027  A362  2.90 l  multi                2.40  2.40
  a.      Tête-bêche pair               4.80  4.80
  b.      Souvenir sheet of 3 #1027a   14.50

No. 1027 was printed in sheets of 9, with the central stamp inverted in relation to the others. No. 1027b was sold with, but not attached to, a booklet cover.

Karaite Judaism A363

No. 1028: a, Seraya Szapszal (1873-1961), leader of Lithuanian Karaite community. b, Kenesa (synagogue), Vilnius.

**2014, June 7   Litho.      Perf. 13x13¼**
1028  A363  2.15 l  Pair, #a-b          3.50  3.50

Lithuanian Song Festival, 90th Anniv. — A364

**2014, June 28   Litho.      Perf. 13¼x13**
1029  A364  1.35 l  multi                1.10  1.10

Lithuanian Term as Non-Permanent Member of United Nations Security Council — A365

**2014, July 12   Litho.      Perf. 13¼x13**
1030  A365  1.35 l  multi                1.10  1.10

In anticipation of Lithuania's official change to Euro currency in January 2015, No. 1030 and stamps issued through the end of 2014 are denominated in litas and the equivalent value in the not-yet-accepted euro currency.

Souvenir Sheet

Baltic Chain Demonstration, 25th Anniv. — A366

No. 1031: a, Five adults and one child. b, Three women. c, Man and child.

**2014, Aug. 23   Litho.      Perf. 13¼**
1031  A366  7 l  Sheet of 3, #a-c  16.00  16.00

See Estonia Nos. 764-765, Latvia Nos. 883-884.

Battle of Orsha, 500th Anniv. — A367

**2014, Sept. 6   Litho.      Perf. 13¼**
1032  A367  2.60 l  multi                1.90  1.90

Earth, LituanicaSAT-1 and Litsat-1 — A368

**2014, Sept. 20   Litho.      Perf. 13x13¼**
1033  A368  2.90 l  multi              2.25  2.25
  a.      Tete-beche pair               4.50  4.50
  b.      Miniature sheet of 6 + 2 la-
           bels                        13.50

No. 1033 was printed in sheets of 16 + 4 labels. No. 1033b was sold with, but unattached to, a booklet cover.

**Wooden Church Belfries Type of 2007 With Added Euro Denomination**

Design: 5c, Belfry from church in Vabalininkas, 19th cent.

***Die Cut Perf. 12½***
**2014, Oct. 11                    Litho.**
             **Self-Adhesive**
1034  A249  5c  multi                    .25   .25

Open Heart Surgery, 50th Anniv. — A369

**2014, Oct. 11   Litho.      Perf. 13¼x13**
1035  A369  2.80 l  multi                2.10  2.10

Christmas — A370

Designs: 1.35 l, Man holding letter and umbrella. 2.80 l, Santa Claus in balloon.

**2014, Nov. 8   Litho.      Perf. 13¼x13**
1036-1037  A370   Set of 2              3.00  3.00

**100 Cents = 1 Euro**

Introduction of Euro Currency — A371

**2015, Jan. 2   Litho.      Perf. 13x13¼**
1038  A371  75c  multi                   1.90  1.90

Coins Depicting White Knight "Vytis" — A372

Coin from: 1c, 1388-90. 3c, 1440-92. 10c, 1562. 29c, 1660. 39c, 1754. 62c, 1925.

***Die Cut Perf. 12½***
**2015, Jan. 2                    Litho.**
             **Self-Adhesive**
1039  A372  1c  ol bis & blk            .25   .25
1040  A372  3c  ol bis & blk            .25   .25
1041  A372  10c  ol bis & blk           .25   .25
1042  A372  29c  ol bis & blk           .70   .70
1043  A372  39c  ol bis & blk           .95   .95
1044  A372  62c  ol bis & blk          1.50  1.50
      Nos. 1039-1044 (6)               3.90  3.90

Endangered Animals — A373

Designs: 71c, Lutra lutra. 87c, Mustela lutreola.

**2015, Jan. 17   Litho.      Perf. 13¼x13**
1045-1046  A373   Set of 2             3.75  3.75

Mikolaj Radziwill (the Black) (1515-65), Grand Hetman — A374

**2015, Feb. 7   Litho.      Perf. 13x13¼**
1047  A374  45c  multi                   1.00  1.00

Declaration of Independence from Soviet Union, 25th Anniv. — A375

**2015, Mar. 7   Litho.      Perf. 13x13¼**
1048  A375  84c  multi                   1.90  1.90

Kaunas Fortress — A376

**2015, Apr. 11 Litho. Perf. 13x13¼**
1049 A376 €2.03 multi 4.75 4.75

A377 — Wooden Toys — A378

**2015, May 9 Litho. Perf. 13¼x13**
1050 A377 71c multi 1.60 1.60
1051 A378 71c multi 1.60 1.60

Europa.

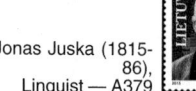

Jonas Juska (1815-86), Linguist — A379

**2015, June 6 Litho. Perf. 13x13¼**
1052 A379 58c multi 1.25 1.25

Pervalka Nature Preserve — A380

**2015, June 20 Litho. Perf. 13x13¼**
1053 A380 97c multi 2.25 2.25

Kretinga Railway Bridge — A381

**2015, July 4 Litho. Perf. 13x13¼**
1054 A381 87c multi 1.90 1.90

Miniature Sheet

Embroidery Designs — A382

No. 1055 — Embroidery designs of various ethnographic groups: a, Mazoji Lietuva. b, Zemaitija. c, Aukstaitija. d, Suvalkija. e, Dzukija.

**2015, July 18 Litho. Perf. 13x13½**
1055 A382 75c Sheet of 5, #a-e 8.25 8.25

Year of Ethnography.

Gown Designed by Juozas Statkevicius A383

**2015, Aug. 8 Litho. Perf. 13½x13¾**
1056 A383 €2.03 multi 4.75 4.75
 a. Sheet of 4 34.00 34.00

No. 1056 was printed in sheets of 2. No. 1056a was sold for €15 with a booklet cover, but unattached to it.

Education and Knowledge Day — A384

**2015, Aug. 29 Litho. Perf. 13¼x13**
1057 A384 45c multi 1.00 1.00

Michal Kleofas Oginski (1765-1833), Composer and Politician — A385

**2015, Sept. 26 Litho. Perf. 13x13¼**
1058 A385 81c multi 1.90 1.90

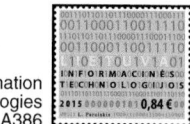

Information Technologies A386

**2015, Oct. 24 Litho. Perf. 13x13¼**
1059 A386 84c multi 1.90 1.90

Traditional Handicrafts — A387

**2015, Nov. 7 Litho. Perf. 13x13¼**
1060 A387 75c multi 1.60 1.60

Christmas and New Year's Day — A388

Christmas tree, people and: 39c, House. 81c, Snowman.

**2015, Nov. 14 Litho. Perf. 13x13¼**
1061-1062 A388 Set of 2 2.60 2.60

White Knight "Vytis" and Flag — A389

Various depictions of Vytis on horseback and flags from: 1c, 1410. 3c, 1553. 10c, 1863. 29c, 1929. 39c, 1989. 62c, 1993.

*Die Cut Perf. 12½*
**2016, Jan. 2 Litho.**
**Self-Adhesive**
1063 A389 1c red & black .25 .25
1064 A389 3c red & black .25 .25
1065 A389 10c red & black .25 .25
1066 A389 29c red & black .65 .65
1067 A389 39c red & black .85 .85
1068 A389 62c red & black 1.40 1.40
 Nos. 1063-1068 (6) 3.65 3.65

Soviet Military Actions Against Lithuania, 25th Anniv. — A390

**2016, Jan. 12 Litho. Perf. 13¼x13**
1069 A390 45c multi 1.00 1.00

Mushrooms — A391

Designs: No. 1070, 84c, Boletus radicans. No. 1071, 84c, Gomphus clavatus.

**2016, Feb. 13 Litho. Perf. 13¼x13**
1070-1071 A391 Set of 2 3.75 3.75
 1071a Booklet pane of 6, 3 each
  #1070-1071 11.50 —
  Complete booklet, #1071a 11.50

No. 1071a contains one example of No. 1070 that is tete-beche in relation to the three adjacent stamps.

Julius Juzeliunas (1916-2001), Composer — A392

**2016, Feb. 20 Litho. Perf. 13x13¼**
1072 A392 39c multi .85 .85

New Verkiai Paper Factory, Vilnius — A393

**2016, Mar. 5 Litho. Perf. 13x13¼**
1073 A393 58c multi 1.40 1.40

Oak Trees, Azuolynas Park, Kaunas — A395

**2016, Apr. 2 Litho. Perf. 13x13¼**
1075 A395 87c multi 2.00 2.00
 a. Booklet pane of 4 8.00 —
  Complete booklet, #1075a 8.00

No. 1075a contains two tete-beche pairs.

Diplomatic Relations Between Lithuania and Japan, 25th Anniv. — A396

**2016, Apr. 16 Litho. Perf. 13x13¼**
1076 A396 €1 multi 2.40 2.40

George Maciunas (1931-78), Co-Founder of Fluxus Art Community — A397

**2016, Apr. 16 Litho. Perf. 13¼x13**
1077 A397 75c multi 1.75 1.75

A398 — Europa — A399

**2016, May 7 Litho. Perf. 13x13¼**
1078 A398 71c multi 1.60 1.60
1079 A399 71c multi 1.60 1.60
 a. Tete-beche pair 3.20 3.20
 b. Booklet pane of 6 #1079 9.75 9.75
  Complete booklet, #1079b 9.75

Think Green Issue.
No. 1079a is found only in No. 1079b.

Cucumbers and Honey — A400

**2016, July 9 Litho. Perf. 13x13¼**
1080 A400 39c multi .90 .90

Souvenir Sheet

Zemaitukas Horses — A401

**2016, July 9 Litho. Perf. 13x13½**
1081 A401 €1.56 multi 3.50 3.50

2016 Summer Olympics, Rio de Janeiro — A402

Christ the Redeemer Statue, Rio de Janeiro, and: 81c, Swimming. 84c, Equestrian.

**2016, Aug. 6 Litho. Perf. 13x13¼**
1082-1083 A402 Set of 2 3.75 3.75

Lithuanian Admission to United Nations, 25th Anniv. — A403

**2016, Sept. 17 Litho. Perf. 13¼x13**
1084 A403 75c multi 1.75 1.75

Seated, by Petras Repsys — A404

**2016, Oct. 9 Litho. Perf. 13¾**
1085 A404 48c multi 1.10 1.10

Pres. Kazys Grinius (1866-1950) — A405

**2016, Oct. 29 Litho. Perf. 13¼x13**
1086 A405 45c multi 1.00 1.00

Souvenir Sheet

Revival of the Lithuanian State, Cent. — A406

No. 1087: a, Auszra Newspaper. b, Dr. Jonas Basanavicius (1851-1927), founder of Auszra. c, Varpas Newspaper.

**2016, Nov. 5 Litho. Perf. 14**
1087 A406 €1.16 Sheet of 3, #a-c 7.50 7.50

Baltic Assembly, 25th Anniv. — A407

**2016, Nov. 8** **Litho.** **Perf. 13½x13¼**
**Stamp With White Frame**
1088 A407 45c multi .95 .95
**Souvenir Sheet**
**Stamp With Multicolored Frame**
1089 A407 97c multi 2.10 2.10

See Estonia Nos. 827-828, Latvia Nos. 948-949.

Christmas and New Year's Day — A408

Designs: 39c, Adult and child with sled, snow-covered houses. 81c, People on city street in winter.

**2016, Nov. 12** **Litho.** **Perf. 13x12¾**
1090-1091 A408 Set of 2 2.60 2.60

Protestant Reformation, 500th Anniv. — A409

**2017, Jan. 7** **Litho.** **Perf. 14**
1092 A409 39c multi .85 .85

Diplomatic Relations Between Lithuania and Israel, 25th Anniv. — A410

**2017, Jan. 7** **Litho.** **Perf. 14**
1093 A410 97c multi 2.10 2.10

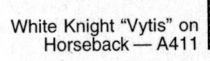

White Knight "Vytis" on Horseback — A411

Depiction of Vytis from: 3c, 14th-15th cent. 10c, 15th cent. 39c, 15th cent., diff. 42c, 16th cent. 94c, 17th-18th cent. €1, 20th cent.

**Die Cut Perf. 12½**
**2017, Jan. 14** **Litho.**
**Self-Adhesive**
1094 A411 3c black .25 .25
1095 A411 10c black .25 .25
1096 A411 39c black .85 .85
1097 A411 42c black .90 .90
1098 A411 94c black 2.00 2.00
1099 A411 €1 black 2.25 2.25
Nos. 1094-1099 (6) 6.50 6.50

Establishment of Samogitian Diocese, 600th Anniv. — A412

**2017, Feb. 10** **Litho.** **Perf. 14**
1100 A412 €1 multi 2.10 2.10

See Vatican City No. 1641.

Kazys Bradunas (1917-2009), Writer — A413

**2017, Feb. 11** **Litho.** **Perf. 14**
1101 A413 39c multi .85 .85

**Souvenir Sheet**

Revival of the Lithuanian State, Cent. — A414

No. 1102: a, Return of Lithuanian press, 1904. b, Great Seimas of Vilnius, 1905. c, Vilnius Conference, 1917.

**2017, Feb. 11** **Litho.** **Perf. 14**
1102 A414 €1.16 Sheet of 3,
#a-c 7.50 7.50

Algirdas Julien Greimas (1917-92), Semiotician A415

**2017, Mar. 4** **Litho.** **Perf. 14**
1103 A415 39c multi .85 .85

Mammals From Red Book of Lithuania — A416

Designs: No. 1104, 42c, Sicista betulina. No. 1105, 42c, Eliomys quercinus.

**2017, Apr. 8** **Litho.** **Perf. 14**
1104-1105 A416 Set of 2 1.90 1.90

Klaipeda Castle — A417 | Birzai Castle — A418

**2017, Apr. 29** **Litho.** **Perf. 14**
1106 A417 81c multi 1.75 1.75
1107 A418 81c multi 1.75 1.75

Europa.

Caraway Seed Cheese — A419

**2017, May 20** **Litho.** **Perf. 14**
1108 A419 52c multi 1.25 1.25

King Wilhelm's Canal Lock — A420

**2017, June 10** **Litho.** **Perf. 14**
1109 A420 94c multi 2.25 2.25

Seimyniskiai Hillfort — A421

**2017, July 8** **Litho.** **Perf. 14**
1110 A421 39c multi .95 .95

Lazarus Arise, by Stanislovas Kuzma — A422

**2017, Aug. 26** **Litho.** **Perf. 14**
1111 A422 94c multi 2.25 2.25

**Souvenir Sheet**

Animals A423

No. 1112: a, Lepus europaeus (European hare). b, Meles meles (European badger). c, Cervus elaphus (red deer).

**2017, Sept. 7** **Litho.** **Perf. 14**
1112 A423 84c Sheet of 3, #a-c 6.00 6.00

Menorah — A424

**2017, Sept. 23** **Litho.** **Perf. 14**
1113 A424 94c multi 2.25 2.25

Jewish minority in Lithuania.

**Souvenir Sheet**

Lithuanian Constitutions — A425

No. 1114 — Scroll and year: a, 1791. b, 1922. c, 1992.

**2017, Oct. 28** **Litho.** **Perf. 14**
1114 A425 84c Sheet of 3, #a-c 6.00 6.00

Constitution of the Republic of Lithuania, 25th anniv.

Christmas A426 | New Year 2018 A427

**2017, Nov. 25** **Litho.** **Perf. 12½x12**
1115 A426 39c blue & red org .95 .95
1116 A427 81c blue & red org 2.00 2.00

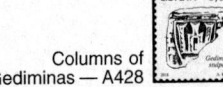

Columns of Gediminas — A428

Columns of Gediminas depictions from: 3c, 15th cent. 10c, 16th cent. 39c, 20th cent. 42c, 19th cent.

**Die Cut Perf. 12½**
**2018, Jan. 5** **Litho.**
**Self-Adhesive**
1117 A428 3c black .25 .25
1118 A428 10c black .25 .25
1119 A428 39c black 1.00 1.00
1120 A428 42c black 1.10 1.10
Nos. 1117-1120 (4) 2.60 2.60

2018 Winter Olympics, PyeongChang, South Korea — A429

Designs: 84c, Curling. 94c, Speed skating.

**2018, Jan. 26** **Litho.** **Perf. 14**
1121-1122 A429 Set of 2 4.50 4.50

**Souvenir Sheet**

Restoration of the State of Lithuania, Cent. — A430

No. 1123: a, House of the Signatories, Vilnius. b, Act of Independence.

**2018, Feb. 9** **Litho.** **Perf. 13¾**
1123 A430 €1.16 Sheet of 2, #a-b 5.75 5.75

Illustration From The Eternal Flame, by Vydunas — A431

**2018, Mar. 16** **Litho.** **Perf. 13¾**
1124 A431 94c multi 2.40 2.40

Vydunas (1863-1953), writer.

Scouting in Lithuania, Cent. — A432

**2018, Mar. 30** **Litho.** **Perf. 14**
1125 A432 52c multi 1.40 1.40

Bridge, Klaipeda — A433 | Bridge, Trakai — A434

**2018, Apr. 20** **Litho.** **Perf. 14**
1126 A433 75c multi 1.90 1.90
1127 A434 75c multi 1.90 1.90

Europa.

Jedrzej Sniadecki (1768-1838), Chemist — A435

**2018, May 18    Litho.    Perf. 13¾**
1128 A435 97c multi                2.25 2.25

Tatars — A436

**2018, June 8    Litho.    Perf. 14**
1129 A436 €1 multi                2.40 2.40

**Miniature Sheet**

Lithuanians Abroad — A437

No. 1130 — Faces of Lithuanians on stylized maps of continents: a, 24 people on North America (58x36mm). b, 18 people on Europe (45x31mm). c, 21 people on East Asia (35x48mm). d. 14 people on South America (37x46mm). e, 13 people on Africa (35x47mm). f, 10 people on Australia (45x29mm).

*Serpentine Die Cut 9¾x9½ (#1130a), 10¼x10 (#1130b, 1130f), 10x9¾ (#1130c), 9½ (#1130d), 10 (#1130e)*
**2018, June 29    Litho.**
**Self-Adhesive**
1130 A437 Sheet of 6            14.00
a.-f.    €1 Any single            2.25 2.25

Coronation of Mother of God of Trakai, 300th Anniv. — A438

**2018, July 27    Litho.    Perf. 13¾**
1131 A438 €1.56 multi            3.75 3.75
No. 1131 was printed in sheets of 4 + 2 labels.

Vanellus Vanellus A439

No. 1132: a, Two lapwings flying to right. b, Two lapwings flying to left. c, Two lapwings, one with worm in beak. d, Lapwing and chick at nest.

**2018, Aug. 17    Litho.    Perf. 14**
1132 A439 49c Block of 4, #a-d    4.50 4.50

**Souvenir Sheet**

Painting for the Millennium of Lithuania, by Sarunas Sauka — A440

**2018, Sept. 14    Litho.    Perf. 14**
1133 A440 99c multi                2.40 2.40

Visit to Lithuania of Pope Francis A441

**2018, Sept. 22    Litho.    Perf. 14**
1134 A441 69c multi                1.60 1.60

**Souvenir Sheet**

Lithuanian Authorities, Cent. — A442

No. 1135: a, Army (tank). b, Jurgis Saulys (1879-1948), diplomat. c, Elena Jackevicaite (1891-1977), first female judge. d, Augustinas Voldemaras (1883-1942), first Prime Minister, and members of his Cabinet.

**2018, Oct. 12    Litho.    Perf. 14**
1135 A442 85c Sheet of 4, #a-d    7.75 7.75

Woman Suffrage in Lithuania, Cent. — A443

**2018, Oct. 26    Litho.    Perf. 14**
1136 A443 55c multi                1.25 1.25

Christmas and New Year's Day — A444

Christmas tree branch and: 10c, Star-shaped cookie ornament. 40c, Orange slice ornament.

**2018, Nov. 23    Litho.    Perf. 14**
1137-1138 A444 Set of 2            1.25 1.25

Lithuania Nos. 1 and 2 — A445

**2018, Nov. 30    Litho.    Perf. 14**
1139 A445 84c multi                1.90 1.90
First Lithuanian postage stamps, cent.

Presidential Flag A446

Historical State Flag A447

National Flag — A448

*Die Cut Perf. 12½*
**2019, Jan. 4    Litho.**
**Self-Adhesive**
1140 A446 3c multi                .25 .25
1141 A447 10c multi                .25 .25
1142 A448 49c multi                1.10 1.10
a.    Die cut perf. 9¼, dated "2021"    1.10 1.10
    Nos. 1140-1142 (3)            1.60 1.60
    Issued: No. 1142a, 9/2/21.

**Souvenir Sheet**

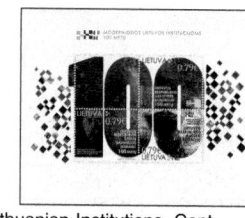

Lithuanian Institutions, Cent. — A449

No. 1143: a, State control (valstybes kontrolei). b, Rifleman's Union (sauliu sajungos ikurimui). c, Customs office (muitinei).

**2019, Jan. 11    Litho.    Perf. 14**
1143 A449 79c Sheet of 3, #a-c,
        + label                5.50 5.50

First Mention of Samogitia in Historical Documents, 800th Anniv. — A450

**2019, Jan. 18    Litho.    Perf. 14**
1144 A450 €1.05 multi            2.40 2.40

Medal for 1919 Battle of Kedainiai — A451

**2019, Feb. 1    Litho.    Perf. 14**
1145 A451 81c multi                1.90 1.90

**Souvenir Sheet**

Lithuanian Partisans — A452

No. 1146: a, Partisan's bunker. b, Council of the Union of Lithuanian Freedom Fighters declaration of 1949.

**2019, Feb. 15    Litho.    Perf. 14**
1146 A452 99c Sheet of 2, #a-b    4.50 4.50

Europa — A453

Ciconia ciconia: No. 1147, 75c, Two adult birds in tree. No. 1148, 75c, Two adults, nest and three chicks.

**2019, Apr. 5    Litho.    Perf. 14**
1147-1148 A453 Set of 2            3.50 3.50

Allium Ursinum — A454

**2019, Apr. 26    Litho.    Perf. 14**
1149 A454 84c multi                1.90 1.90

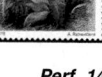

Lithuanian Red Cross, Cent. — A455

**2019, May 3    Litho.    Perf. 14**
1150 A455 84c multi                1.90 1.90

Family Day A456

**2019, May 10    Litho.    Perf. 14**
1151 A456 84c multi + label        1.90 1.90

Stanislaw Moniuszko (1819-72), Composer — A457

**2019, Aug. 9    Litho.    Perf. 14**
1152 A457 49c multi                1.10 1.10

Juozas Tumas (Vaizgantas) (1869-1933), Priest and Writer, and His Dog — A458

**2019, Sept. 20    Litho.    Perf. 14**
1153 A458 49c multi                1.10 1.10

Scene From *Boris Godunov,* Play Directed by Eimuntas Nekrosius (1952-2018) A459

**2019, Oct. 25    Litho.    Perf. 13¾**
1154 A459 49c multi                1.10 1.10

Poppy Milk A460    Sheep A461

**2019, Nov. 22    Litho.    Perf. 14**
1155 A460 49c multi                1.10 1.10
1156 A461 81c multi                1.75 1.75
Christmas.

Banknotes — A462

Designs: 10c, September 1922 1-litas banknote. 49c, November 1922 1-litas banknote. 59c, 1928 100-litas banknote.

**Die Cut Perf. 9¼**
**2020, Jan. 17**       **Litho.**
**Self-Adhesive**
1157 A462 10c multi      .25 .25
1158 A462 49c multi      1.10 1.10
1159 A462 59c multi      1.40 1.40
    Nos. 1157-1159 (3)    2.75 2.75

Aegolius Funereus — A463

**2020, Jan. 31**   **Litho.**   **Perf. 13¼**
1160 A463 75c multi     1.75 1.75

**Souvenir Sheet**

Partisans
A464

No. 1161: a, Jonas Zemaitis-Vytautas (1909-54), Juozas Sibaila-Merainis (1905-53). b, Vytautas Guzas-Kardas (1920-49), Aleksandras Grybinas-Faustas (1920-49).

**2020, Feb. 15**   **Litho.**   **Perf. 13¼**
1161 A464   Sheet of 2    3.75 3.75
   a.   81c multi      1.75 1.75
   b.   84c multi      1.90 1.90

**Souvenir Sheet**

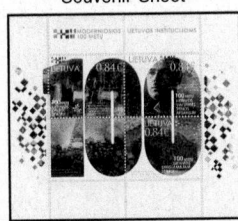

Lithuanian Institutions, Cent. — A465

No. 1162: a, Lithuanian Opera House (operos teatrui). b, Lithuanian border guards (valstybes sienos apsaugai). c, Constituent Seimas (steigiamajam seimui).

**2020, Mar. 6**   **Litho.**   **Perf. 13¼**
1162 A465 84c Sheet of 3, #a-c,
        + label      5.50 5.50

Restoration of Independence, 30th Anniv. — A466

**2020, Mar. 6**   **Litho.**   **Perf. 13¼**
1163 A466 49c multi     1.10 1.10

Elijah of Vilnius (1720-97), Talmudic Scholar — A467

**2020, June 5**   **Litho.**   **Perf. 13¼**
1164 A467 81c multi     1.90 1.90

1841 Letter From    Taurage Post
Svencionys to      Office — A469
Moscow — A468

**2020, June 12**   **Litho.**   **Perf. 13¼**
1165 A468 75c multi     1.75 1.75
1166 A469 75c multi     1.75 1.75
       Europa.

Cold Borscht — A470

**2020, June 19**   **Litho.**   **Perf. 13¼**
1167 A470 49c multi     1.10 1.10

Sigismund II Augustus and Barbara at the Radziwill Court in Vilnius, by Jan Matejko
A471

**2020, Aug. 1**   **Litho.**   **Perf. 13¾x14**
1168 A471 81c gold & multi   1.90 1.90
   Sigismund II Augustus (1520-72), King of Poland and Grand Duke of Lithuania. See Poland No. 4493.

Medal for 1920 Battle of Sirvintos-Giedraiciai — A472

**2020, Sept. 11**   **Litho.**   **Perf. 13¼**
1169 A472 81c multi     1.90 1.90
   Wars of Independence, Cent.

Photograph by Vitas Luckus (1943-87) — A473

**2020, Sept. 25**   **Litho.**   **Perf. 13¼**
1170 A473 84c multi     2.00 2.00

Autumn Wind, by    Lithuanian
Ferdinand Ruscic   Peasants, by
(1870-1936)      Pranciskus
A474           Smuglevicius
             (1745-1807)
             A475

**2020, Oct. 2**   **Litho.**   **Perf. 13¼**
1171 A474 €1.98 multi    4.75 4.75
1172 A475 €2.09 multi    5.00 5.00

St. John Paul II (1920-2005) — A476

**2020, Oct. 16**   **Litho.**   **Perf. 13¼**
1173 A476 75c multi     1.75 1.75

Belarussian Woman in Traditional Clothing — A477

**2020, Oct. 30**   **Litho.**   **Perf. 13¼**
1174 A477 55c multi     1.30 1.30

Christmas — A478

Designs: 49c, Boy and girl decorating Christmas tree. 81c, Girl decorating Christmas tree.

**2020, Nov. 27**   **Litho.**   **Perf. 13¼**
1175-1176 A478   Set of 2    3.25 3.25

National Archives, Cent. — A479

**2021, Jan. 8**   **Litho.**   **Perf. 13¼**
1177 A479 49c multi     1.25 1.25

Birute Marija Alseikaite-Gimbutiene (1921-94), Archaeologist, and Artifacts — A480

**2021, Jan. 22**   **Litho.**   **Perf. 13¼**
1178 A480 49c multi     1.25 1.25

**Souvenir Sheet**

Partisans
A481

No. 1179: a, 81c, Petras Bartkus-Zadgaila (1925-49), Adolfas Ramanauskas-Vanagas (1918-57). b, 84c, Bronius Liesys-Naktis (1922-49), Leonardas Vilhelmas Grigonis-Uzpalis (1905-50).

**2021, Feb. 17**   **Litho.**   **Perf. 13¼**
1179 A481   Sheet of 2, #a-b   4.00 4.00

Grand Dukes of Lithuania — A482

Designs: 10c, Gediminas (c. 1275-1341). 49c, Mindaugas (c. 1203-63).

**Die Cut Perf. 9¼**
**2021, Mar. 12**      **Litho.**
**Self-Adhesive**
1180 A482 10c multi      .25 .25
1181 A482 49c multi      1.25 1.25
    See Nos. 1193-1194.

Pier, Palanga — A483

**2021, Mar. 26**   **Litho.**   **Perf. 13¼**
1182 A483 81c multi     1.90 1.90

Europa — A484

Endangered animals: No. 1183, 75c, Halichoerus grypus. No. 1184, 75c, Lynx lynx.

**2021, Apr. 23**   **Litho.**   **Perf. 13¼**
1183-1184 A484   Set of 2   3.75 3.75

Vincas Cepinskis (1871-1940), Physicist and Politician — A485

**2021, Apr. 30**   **Litho.**   **Perf. 13¼**
1185 A485 84c multi     2.10 2.10

Assumption Cathedral, Vilnius — A486

**2021, June 11**   **Litho.**   **Perf. 13¼**
1186 A486 81c multi     2.00 2.00

Sailboat Jurate — A487

**2021, June 25**   **Litho.**   **Perf. 13¼**
1187 A487 84c multi     2.00 2.00

Jonas Kubilius (1921-2011), Mathematician A488

**2021, July 9**   **Litho.**   **Perf. 13¼**
1188 A488 55c multi     1.30 1.30

2020 Summer Olympics, Tokyo — A489

**2021, July 23**   **Litho.**   **Perf. 13¼**
1189 A489 84c multi     2.00 2.00
   The 2020 Summer Olympics were postponed until 2021 because of the COVID-19 pandemic.

Battle of Chocim, by Józef Brandt (1841-1915) — A490

*Perf. 11x11½ Syncopated*
**2021, Sept. 2**        **Litho.**
**1190** A490 €1.29 multi      3.00 3.00

Battle of Chocim, 400th anniv. See Poland No. 4567; Ukraine No. 1313.

Christmas — A491

Designs: 49c, Reindeer. 81c, Gift box with ribbon.

**2021, Nov. 27**    **Litho.**    *Perf. 13¼*
**1191-1192** A491 Set of 2    3.00 3.00

**Grand Dukes of Lithuania Type of 2021**

Designs: 10c, Jogaila (c. 1352-1434). 55c, Vytautas Didysis (Vytautas the Great) (c. 1350-1430).

*Die Cut Perf. 9¼*
**2022, Jan. 14**          **Litho.**
**Self-Adhesive**
**1193** A482 10c multi      .30 .30
**1194** A482 55c multi      1.25 1.25

Miniature Sheet

Events of 1922, Cent. A492

No. 1195: a, Vladas Jurgutis (1885-1966), chairman of Bank of Lithuania, and 1922 litas banknote. b, Enactment of Lithuanian Constitution by Constituent Seimas. c, First Lithuanian men's and women's basketball teams. d, Mykolas Krupavicius (1885-1970), Minister of Agriculture and land reformer.

**2022, Jan. 28**    **Litho.**    *Perf. 13¼*
**1195** A492 60c Sheet of 4, #a-d   5.50 5.50

Vytautas Magnus University, Kaunas, Cent. — A493

**2022, Feb. 11**    **Litho.**    *Perf. 13¼*
**1196** A493 95c multi      2.25 2.25

Resistance to Soviet Rule — A494

No. 1197: a, Romas Kalanta (1953-72), student who set himself on fire in protest of Soviet rule. b, Chronicles of the Lithuanian Catholic Church, 50th anniv.

**2022, Mar. 18**    **Litho.**    *Perf. 13¼*
**1197** A494 70c Horiz. pair, #a-b   3.25 3.25

Kazimieras Vasiliauskas (1922-2001), Priest Exiled to Siberia by Soviets — A495

**2022, Apr. 8**    **Litho.**    *Perf. 13¼*
**1198** A495 75c multi      1.60 1.60

Egle, the Queen of Serpents A496      Fern Flower A497

**2022, Apr. 29**    **Litho.**    *Perf. 13¼*
**1199** A496 95c multi      2.00 2.00
**1200** A497 95c multi      2.00 2.00

Europa. Lithuanian myths and legends.

Souvenir Sheet

Selection of Esch-sur-Alzette, Luxembourg and Kaunas, Lithuania as 2022 European Capitals of Culture — A498

No. 1598: a, The Bath, by Stasys Usinskas (1905-74). b, Nemrod, by Foni Thyssen (1909-75).

**2022, May 13**    **Litho.**    *Perf. 11½*
**1201** A498   Sheet of 2    5.25 5.25
**a.-b.**   (€1.20) Either single   2.60 2.60

Joint issue between Lithuania and Luxembourg. See Luxembourg No. 1598.

Publication of Little Travel Book, by Franciscus Skorina, First Book Published in Lithuania, 500th Anniv. — A499

**2022, May 20**    **Litho.**    *Perf. 13¼*
**1202** A499 60c multi      1.30 1.30

World Environment Day — A500

**2022, June 3**    **Litho.**    *Perf. 13¼*
**1203** A500 70c multi      1.50 1.50

Minesweeper Suduvis — A501

**2022, July 22**    **Litho.**    *Perf. 13¼*
**1204** A501 65c multi      1.40 1.40

Tree Cake — A502

**2022, Aug. 13**    **Litho.**    *Perf. 13¼*
**1205** A502 55c multi      1.10 1.10

Lithuanian Membership in the Universal Postal Union, Cent. — A504

**2022, Oct. 7**    **Litho.**    *Perf. 13¼*
**1207** A504 60c multi      1.25 1.25

A505

Christmas — A506

**2022, Nov. 25**    **Litho.**    *Perf. 13¼*
**1208** A505 55c multi      1.25 1.25
**1209** A506 95c multi      2.00 2.00

Jonas Mekas (1922-2019), Film Director — A507

**2022, Dec. 21**    **Litho.**    *Perf. 13¼*
**1210** A507 70c multi      1.50 1.50

## SEMI-POSTAL STAMPS

**Regular Issue of 1923-24 Surcharged in Blue, Violet or Black**

On A21             On A22

On A23

| | | **1924, Feb.** | **Wmk. 147** | **Perf. 11** | |
|---|---|---|---|---|---|
| **B1** | A21 | 2c + 2c pale brn (Bl) | | .90 | 2.25 |
| **B2** | A21 | 3c + 3c ol bis (Bl) | | .90 | 2.25 |
| **B3** | A21 | 5c + 5c pale grn (V) | | .90 | 2.25 |
| **B4** | A21 | 10c + 10c vio (Bk) | | 2.25 | 3.25 |
| **B5** | A21 | 36c + 34c org brn (V) | | 4.75 | 12.00 |

**Wmk. Webbing (109)**

| | | | | | |
|---|---|---|---|---|---|
| **B6** | A21 | 10c + 10c vio (Bk) | | 7.50 | 20.00 |
| **B7** | A21 | 15c + 15c scar (V) | | 1.10 | 2.50 |
| **B8** | A21 | 20c + 20c ol brn (Bl) | | 2.25 | 4.00 |
| **B9** | A21 | 25c + 25c bl (Bk) | | 21.00 | 55.00 |
| **B10** | A22 | 50c + 50c yel grn (V) | | 5.25 | 12.00 |
| **B11** | A22 | 60c + 60c red (V) | | 5.25 | 12.00 |
| **B12** | A23 | 1 l + 1 l org & grn (V) | | 6.00 | 16.00 |
| **B13** | A23 | 3 l + 2 l red & gray (V) | | 9.00 | 32.50 |
| **B14** | A23 | 5 l + 3 l brn & bl (V) | | 15.00 | 40.00 |

**Unwmk.**

| | | | | | |
|---|---|---|---|---|---|
| **B15** | A21 | 25c + 25c dp bl (Bk) | | 4.75 | 12.00 |
| | | Nos. B1-B15 (15) | | 86.80 | 228.00 |
| | | Set, never hinged | | 225.00 | |

**For War Invalids**

Semi-Postal Stamps of 1924 Surcharged in Gold or Copper

| | | **1926, Dec. 3** | | **Wmk. 147** | |
|---|---|---|---|---|---|
| **B16** | A21 | 1 + 1c on #B1 | | 1.00 | 1.25 |
| **a.** | | Inverted surcharge | | 40.00 | |
| **B17** | A21 | 2 + 2c on #B2 (C) | | 1.00 | 1.25 |
| **B19** | A21 | 2 + 2c on #B3 | | 1.00 | 1.25 |
| **a.** | | Double surch., one inverted | | 40.00 | |
| **B20** | A21 | 5 + 5c on #B4 | | 2.00 | 2.00 |
| **B21** | A21 | 14 + 14c on #B5 | | 6.00 | 7.00 |

**Wmk. Webbing (109)**

| | | | | | |
|---|---|---|---|---|---|
| **B22** | A21 | 5 + 5c on #B6 | | 10.00 | 10.00 |
| **B23** | A21 | 5 + 5c on #B7 | | 2.00 | 2.00 |
| **B24** | A21 | 10 + 10c on #B8 | | 2.00 | 2.00 |
| **B25** | A21 | 10 + 10c on #B9 | | 65.00 | 65.00 |

**Unwmk.**

| | | | | | |
|---|---|---|---|---|---|
| **B26** | A21 | 10 + 10c on #B15 | | 4.00 | 5.00 |

**Surcharged in Copper or Silver**

On A22          On A23

**Wmk. Webbing (109)**

| | | | | | |
|---|---|---|---|---|---|
| **B27** | A22 | 20 + 20c on #B10 | | 4.00 | 5.00 |
| **B28** | A22 | 25 + 25c on #B11 (S) | | 6.00 | 7.00 |
| **B29** | A23 | 30 + 30c on #B12 (S) | | 9.00 | 11.00 |
| | | Nos. B16-B29 (13) | | 113.00 | 119.75 |
| | | Set, never hinged | | 225.00 | |

**For War Orphans**

Surcharged in Gold

| | | **1926, Dec. 3** | | **Wmk. 147** | |
|---|---|---|---|---|---|
| **B30** | A21 | 1 + 1c on #B1 | | .90 | .90 |
| **B31** | A21 | 2 + 2c on #B2 | | .90 | .90 |
| **a.** | | Inverted surcharge | | 260.00 | |
| **B32** | A21 | 2 + 2c on #B3 | | .90 | .90 |
| **a.** | | Inverted surcharge | | 30.00 | |
| **B33** | A21 | 5 + 5c on #B4 | | 2.00 | 2.25 |
| **B34** | A21 | 19 + 19c on #B5 | | 4.00 | 5.00 |

**Wmk. Webbing (109)**

| | | | | | |
|---|---|---|---|---|---|
| **B35** | A21 | 5 + 5c on #B6 | | 10.00 | 10.00 |
| **B36** | A21 | 10 + 10c on #B7 | | 1.75 | 2.00 |
| **B37** | A21 | 15 + 15c on #B8 | | 2.00 | 2.25 |
| **B38** | A21 | 15 + 15c on #B9 | | 65.00 | 65.00 |

**Unwmk.**

| | | | | | |
|---|---|---|---|---|---|
| **B39** | A21 | 15 + 15c on #B15 | | 3.00 | 3.00 |

**Surcharged in Gold**

On A22          On A23

**Wmk. 109**

| | | | | | |
|---|---|---|---|---|---|
| **B40** | A22 | 25c on #B10 | | 5.00 | 6.00 |
| **B41** | A22 | 30c on #B11 | | 8.00 | 7.00 |
| **B42** | A23 | 50c on #B12 | | 10.00 | 11.00 |
| | | Nos. B30-B42 (13) | | 113.45 | 116.20 |
| | | Set, never hinged | | 225.00 | |

Javelin throwing — SP1

Natl. Olympiad, July 15-20: 5c+5c, Archery. 30c+10c, Diving. 60c+15c, Running.

**Unwmk.**

| | | **1938, July 13** | **Photo.** | **Perf. 14** | |
|---|---|---|---|---|---|
| **B43** | SP1 | 5c + 5c grn & dk grn | | 2.50 | 2.50 |
| **B44** | SP1 | 15c + 5c org & red org | | 2.50 | 2.50 |

| | | | |
|---|---|---|---|
| B45 | SP1 | 30c + 10c bl & dk bl | 4.50 4.50 |
| B46 | SP1 | 60c + 15c tan & brn | 5.75 5.75 |
| | | Nos. B43-B46 (4) | 15.25 15.25 |
| | | Set, never hinged | 45.00 |

### Same Overprinted in Red, Blue or Black

Nos. B47, B50

Nos. B48-B49

**1938, July 13**

| | | | |
|---|---|---|---|
| B47 | SP1 | 5c + 5c (R) | 5.00 5.00 |
| B48 | SP1 | 15c + 5c (Bl) | 5.00 5.00 |
| B49 | SP1 | 30c + 10c (R) | 5.00 5.00 |
| B50 | SP1 | 60c + 15c (Bk) | 10.00 10.00 |
| | | Nos. B47-B50 (4) | 25.00 25.00 |
| | | Set, never hinged | 50.00 |

National Scout Jamboree, July 12-14. Forged cancellations exist.

Basketball Players SP6 SP7

Flags of Competing Nations and Basketball SP8

**1939 Photo. Perf. 14**

| | | | |
|---|---|---|---|
| B52 | SP6 | 15c + 10c copper brn & brn | 3.25 6.50 |
| B53 | SP7 | 30c + 15c myrtle grn & grn | 3.25 6.50 |
| B54 | SP8 | 60c + 40c blue vio & gray vio | 6.00 12.00 |
| | | Nos. B52-B54 (3) | 12.50 25.00 |
| | | Set, never hinged | 25.00 |

3rd European Basketball Championships held at Kaunas. The surtax was used for athletic equipment. Nos. B52-B54 exist imperf. Value, set pairs, $500.

> **Catalogue values for unused stamps in this section, from this point to the end of the section, are for Never Hinged items.**

People Hugging — SP9

**2022, May 6 Litho. Perf. 13¼**

| | | | |
|---|---|---|---|
| B55 | SP9 | €1+€1 multi | 4.25 4.25 |

No. B55 was printed in sheets of 4 + 2 labels. Surtax for Blue/Yellow, an organization supporting the defense of Ukraine against its Russian invaders.

Bayraktar Drone for Ukraine Purchased With Donations From Lithuanians SP10

### Die Cut Perf. 8¾ Syncopated
**2022, June 9 Self-Adhesive Litho.**

| | | | |
|---|---|---|---|
| B56 | SP10 | €1+€1 multi | 4.25 4.25 |

Surtax for Blue/Yellow, an organization supporting the defense of Ukraine against its Russian invaders.

### AIR POST STAMPS

Winged Posthorn AP1

Airplane over Neman River AP2

Air Squadron AP3

Plane over Gediminas Castle AP4

**1921 Litho. Wmk. 109 Perf. 11½**

| | | | |
|---|---|---|---|
| C1 | AP1 | 20sk ultra | 1.25 .75 |
| C2 | AP1 | 40sk red orange | 1.00 .75 |
| C3 | AP1 | 60sk green | 1.10 .75 |
| a. | | Imperf., pair | 45.00 |
| C4 | AP1 | 80sk lt rose | 1.50 .75 |
| a. | | Horiz. pair, imperf. vert. | 50.00 40.00 |
| C5 | AP2 | 1auk green & red | 1.50 .75 |
| a. | | Imperf., pair | 90.00 175.00 |
| C6 | AP3 | 2auk brown & blue | 1.60 .75 |
| C7 | AP4 | 5auk dl blk & red | 2.00 1.75 |
| | | Nos. C1-C7 (7) | 9.95 6.25 |
| | | Set, never hinged | 30.00 |

For surcharges see Nos. C21-C26, C29.

Allegory of Flight — AP5

**1921, Nov. 6**

| | | | |
|---|---|---|---|
| C8 | AP5 | 20sk org & gray bl | 1.40 2.00 |
| C9 | AP5 | 40sk dl bl & lake | 1.40 2.00 |
| C10 | AP5 | 60sk vio bl & ol grn | 1.40 2.00 |
| C11 | AP5 | 80sk ocher & dp grn | 1.40 2.00 |
| a. | | Vert. pair, imperf. btwn. | 35.00 35.00 |
| C12 | AP5 | 1auk bl grn & bl | 1.40 2.00 |
| C13 | AP5 | 2auk gray & brn org | 1.40 2.00 |
| C14 | AP5 | 5auk dl lil & Prus bl | 1.40 2.00 |
| | | Nos. C8-C14 (7) | 9.80 14.00 |
| | | Set, never hinged | 17.50 |

Opening of airmail service.

Plane over Kaunas AP6

### Black Overprint
**1922, July 16 Perf. 11, 11½**

| | | | |
|---|---|---|---|
| C15 | AP6 | 1auk ol brn & red | 1.00 2.75 |
| a. | | Imperf., pair | 60.00 |
| C16 | AP6 | 3auk violet & grn | 1.00 2.75 |
| C17 | AP6 | 5auk dp blue & yel | 1.00 4.00 |
| | | Nos. C15-C17 (3) | 3.00 9.50 |
| | | Set, never hinged | 9.75 |

Nos. C15-C17, without overprint, were to be for the founding of the Air Post service but they were not put in use at that time. Subsequently the word "ZENKLAS" (stamp) was overprinted over "ISTEIGIMAS" (founding) and the date "1921, VI, 25" was obliterated by short vertical lines.
For surcharge see No. C31.

Plane over Gediminas Castle — AP7

**1922, July 22**

| | | | |
|---|---|---|---|
| C18 | AP7 | 2auk blue & rose | 1.10 .85 |
| C19 | AP7 | 4auk brown & rose | 1.10 .85 |
| C20 | AP7 | 10auk black & gray bl | 1.25 1.40 |
| | | Nos. C18-C20 (3) | 3.45 3.10 |
| | | Set, never hinged | 11.00 |

For surcharges see Nos. C27-C28, C30.

### Nos. C1-C7, C17-C20 Surcharged like Regular Issues in Black or Carmine

**1922**

| | | | |
|---|---|---|---|
| C21 | AP1 | 10c on 20sk | 3.25 2.50 |
| C22 | AP1 | 10c on 40sk | 1.75 1.50 |
| C23 | AP1 | 10c on 60sk | 1.75 1.50 |
| a. | | Inverted surcharge | 45.00 |
| C24 | AP1 | 10c on 80sk | 1.75 1.50 |
| C25 | AP2 | 20c on 1auk | 11.00 6.00 |
| C26 | AP3 | 20c on 2auk | 11.00 7.50 |
| a. | | Without "CENT" | 200.00 140.00 |
| C27 | AP7 | 25c on 2auk | 1.00 1.00 |
| a. | | Inverted surcharge | 45.00 40.00 |
| C28 | AP7 | 30c on 4auk (C) | 1.00 1.00 |
| a. | | Double surcharge | 50.00 45.00 |
| C29 | AP4 | 50c on 5auk | 2.00 1.50 |
| C30 | AP7 | 50c on 10auk | 1.00 1.00 |
| a. | | Inverted surcharge | 50.00 45.00 |
| C31 | AP6 | 1 l on 5auk | 16.00 15.00 |
| a. | | Double surcharge | 50.00 45.00 |
| | | Nos. C21-C31 (11) | 51.50 40.00 |
| | | Set, never hinged | 92.50 |

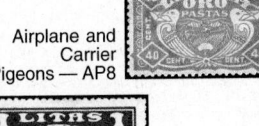

Airplane and Carrier Pigeons — AP8

"Flight" — AP9

**1924, Jan. 28 Wmk. 147 Perf. 11**

| | | | |
|---|---|---|---|
| C32 | AP8 | 20c yellow | 1.15 .75 |
| C33 | AP8 | 40c emerald | 1.15 .75 |
| a. | | Horiz. or vert. pair, imperf. between | 60.00 |
| C34 | AP8 | 60c rose | 1.15 .75 |
| a. | | Imperf., pair | 75.00 |
| C35 | AP9 | 1 l dk brown | 2.50 .75 |
| | | Nos. C32-C35 (4) | 5.95 3.00 |
| | | Set, never hinged | 25.00 |

Most stamps, if not all, of the "unwatermarked" varieties show faint traces of watermark, according to experts.
For surcharges see Nos. CB1-CB4.

Swallow — AP10

**1926, June 17 Wmk. 198 Perf. 14½**

| | | | |
|---|---|---|---|
| C37 | AP10 | 20c carmine rose | 1.10 .50 |
| a. | | Horiz. or vert. pair, imperf. between | 55.00 |
| C38 | AP10 | 40c violet & red org | 1.10 .50 |
| a. | | Horiz. or vert. pair, imperf. between | 55.00 |
| C39 | AP10 | 60c blue & black | 2.25 .50 |
| a. | | Horiz. or vert. pair, imperf. between | 55.00 |
| c. | | Center inverted | 250.00 160.00 |
| | | Nos. C37-C39 (3) | 4.45 1.50 |
| | | Set, never hinged | 6.00 |

Juozas Tubelis AP11

Vytautas and Airplane over Kaunas AP12

Vytautas and Antanas Smetona — AP13

**1930, Feb. 16 Wmk. 109 Perf. 14**

| | | | |
|---|---|---|---|
| C40 | AP11 | 5c blk, bis & brn | 1.50 .35 |
| C41 | AP11 | 10c dk bl, db & blk | 1.50 .35 |
| C42 | AP11 | 15c mar, gray & bl | 1.50 .35 |
| C43 | AP12 | 20c dk brn, org & dl red | 1.50 .80 |
| C44 | AP12 | 40c dk bl, lt bl & vio | 4.00 .80 |
| C45 | AP13 | 60c bl grn, lil & blk | 5.00 .85 |
| C46 | AP13 | 1 l dl red, lil & blk | 9.00 1.60 |
| | | Nos. C40-C46 (7) | 24.00 5.10 |
| | | Set, never hinged | 100.00 |

5th cent. of the death of the Grand Duke Vytautas.

Map of Lithuania, Klaipeda and Vilnius — AP14

15c, 20c, Airplane over Neman. 40c, 60c, City Hall, Kaunas. 1 l, 2 l, Church of Vytautas, Kaunas.

### Wmk. Multiple Letters (238)
**1932, July 21 Perf. 14**

| | | | |
|---|---|---|---|
| C47 | AP14 | 5c ver & ol grn | .35 .70 |
| C48 | AP14 | 10c dk red brn & ocher | .35 .70 |
| C49 | AP14 | 15c dk bl & org yel | .35 .70 |
| C50 | AP14 | 20c sl blk & org | 1.75 5.50 |
| C51 | AP14 | 60c ultra & ocher | 2.50 7.00 |
| C52 | AP14 | 2 l dk bl & yel | 2.75 7.00 |

**Wmk. 198**

| | | | |
|---|---|---|---|
| C53 | AP14 | 40c vio brn & yel | 2.00 5.50 |
| C54 | AP14 | 1 l vio brn & grn | 3.00 7.00 |
| | | Nos. C47-C54 (8) | 13.05 34.10 |
| | | Set, never hinged | 50.00 |

**Imperf.**

| | | | |
|---|---|---|---|
| C47a | AP14 | 5c ver & ol grn | .35 .70 |
| C48a | AP14 | 10c dk red brn & ocher | .35 .70 |
| C49a | AP14 | 15c dk bl & org yel | .35 .70 |
| C50a | AP14 | 20c sl blk & org | 1.75 5.50 |
| C51a | AP14 | 60c ultra & ocher | 2.50 5.50 |
| C52a | AP14 | 2 l dk bl & yel | 2.75 7.00 |
| C53a | AP14 | 40c vio brn & yel | 2.00 7.00 |
| C54a | AP14 | 1 l vio brn & grn | 3.00 7.00 |
| | | Set, never hinged | 50.00 |

Issued for the benefit of Lithuanian orphans.

Mindaugas in the Battle of Shauyai, 1236 — AP15

15c, 20c, Coronation of Mindaugas (1253). 40c, Grand Duke Gediminas and his followers. 60c, Founding of Vilnius by Gediminas (1332). 1 l, Gediminas capturing the Russian Fortifications. 2 l, Grand Duke Algirdas before Moscow (1368).

**1932, Nov. 28 Wmk. 209 Perf. 14**

| | | | |
|---|---|---|---|
| C55 | AP15 | 5c grn & red lil | .45 .70 |
| C56 | AP15 | 10c emer & rose | .45 .70 |
| C57 | AP15 | 15c rose vio & bis brn | .45 .70 |
| C58 | AP15 | 20c rose red & blk brn | 2.25 3.50 |
| C59 | AP15 | 40c choc & dk gray | 3.25 4.75 |
| C60 | AP15 | 60c org & gray blk | 4.50 7.00 |
| C61 | AP15 | 1 l rose vio & grn | 4.50 7.00 |
| C62 | AP15 | 2 l dp bl & brn | 4.50 7.00 |
| | | Nos. C55-C62 (8) | 20.35 31.35 |
| | | Set, never hinged | 45.00 |

**Imperf.**

| | | | |
|---|---|---|---|
| C55a | AP15 | 5c grn & red lil | .45 .70 |
| C56a | AP15 | 10c emer & rose | .45 .70 |
| C57a | AP15 | 15c rose vio & bis brn | .45 .70 |
| C58a | AP15 | 20c rose red & blk brn | 2.25 3.50 |
| C59a | AP15 | 40c choc & dk gray | 3.25 4.75 |
| C60a | AP15 | 60c org & gray blk | 4.50 7.00 |
| C61a | AP15 | 1 l rose vio & grn | 4.50 7.00 |
| C62a | AP15 | 2 l dp bl & brn | 4.50 7.00 |
| | | Set, never hinged | 45.00 |

Anniv. of independence.
Nos. C58-C62 exist with overprint "DARIUS-GIRENAS / NEW YORK-1933- KAUNAS" below small plane. The overprint was applied in New York with the approval of the Lithuanian consul general. Lithuanian postal authorities seem not to have been involved in the creation or release of these overprints.

Trakai Castle, Home of the Grand
Duke Kestutis
AP16

Designs: 15c, 20c, Meeting of Kestutís and
the Hermit Birute. 40c, 60c, Hermit Birute. 1 l,
2 l, Kestutis and his Brother Algirdas.

**1933, May 6**     *Perf. 14, 11*

| | | | | |
|---|---|---|---|---|
| **C63** | AP16 | 5c ol gray & dp bl | .40 | .70 |
| *b.* | | Perf. 11 | .40 | .70 |
| **C64** | AP16 | 10c gray vio & org | | |
| | | brn | .40 | .70 |
| **C65** | AP16 | 15c dp blue & lilac | .40 | .70 |
| **C66** | AP16 | 20c org brn & lilac | 2.00 | 4.00 |
| **C67** | AP16 | 40c lt ultra & lilac | 2.00 | 4.00 |
| **C68** | AP16 | 60c brown & lt ultra | 5.25 | 9.75 |
| **C69** | AP16 | 1 l ol gray & dp bl | 5.25 | 9.75 |
| **C70** | AP16 | 2 l vio gray & yel | | |
| | | grn | 5.25 | 9.75 |
| | | *Nos. C63-C70 (8)* | 20.95 | 39.35 |
| | | Set, never hinged | 35.00 | |

**Imperf.**

| | | | | |
|---|---|---|---|---|
| C63a | AP16 | 5c ol gray & dp bl | .40 | .70 |
| C64a | AP16 | 10c gray vio & org | | |
| | | brn | .40 | .70 |
| C65a | AP16 | 15c dp blue & lilac | .70 | .70 |
| C66a | AP16 | 20c org brn & lilac | 2.00 | 4.00 |
| C67a | AP16 | 40c lt ultra & lilac | 2.00 | 4.00 |
| C68a | AP16 | 60c brown & lt ultra | 5.25 | 9.75 |
| C69a | AP16 | 1 l ol gray & dp bl | 5.25 | 9.75 |
| C70a | AP16 | 2 l vio gray & yel grn | 5.25 | 9.75 |
| | | Set, never hinged | 35.00 | |

Reopening of air service to Berlin-Kaunas-
Moscow, and 550th anniv. of the death of
Kestutis.

Joseph
Maironis
AP17

Joseph Tumas-Vaizgantas — AP17a

Designs: 40c, 60c, Vincas Kudirka. 1 l, 2 l,
Julia A. Zemaite.

**1933, Sept. 15**     *Perf. 14*

| | | | | |
|---|---|---|---|---|
| **C71** | AP17 | 5c crim & dp bl | .25 | .30 |
| **C72** | AP17 | 10c bl vio & grn | .25 | .30 |
| **C73** | AP17a | 15c dk grn & choc | .25 | .30 |
| **C74** | AP17a | 20c brn car & ultra | .50 | .60 |
| **C75** | AP17 | 40c red brn & ol | | |
| | | grn | 1.50 | 2.50 |
| **C76** | AP17 | 60c dk bl & choc | 1.50 | 6.00 |
| **C77** | AP17 | 1 l citron & indigo | 2.50 | 6.25 |
| **C78** | AP17 | 2 l dp grn & red | | |
| | | brn | 3.50 | 10.00 |
| | | *Nos. C71-C78 (8)* | 10.25 | 26.25 |
| | | Set, never hinged | 25.00 | |

**Imperf.**

| | | | | |
|---|---|---|---|---|
| C71a | AP17 | 5c crim & dp bl | .25 | .30 |
| C72a | AP17 | 10c bl vio & grn | .25 | .30 |
| C73a | AP17a | 15c dk grn & choc | .25 | .30 |
| C74a | AP17a | 20c brn car & ol grn | .50 | .60 |
| C75a | AP17 | 40c red brn & ol grn | 1.50 | 2.50 |
| C76a | AP17 | 60c dk bl & choc | 1.50 | 6.00 |
| C77a | AP17 | 1 l citron & indigo | 2.50 | 6.25 |
| C78a | AP17 | 2 l dp grn & red | | |
| | | brn | 3.50 | 10.00 |
| | | Set, never hinged | 25.00 | |

Issued for the benefit of Lithuanian orphans.

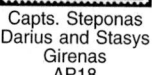

Capts. Steponas
Darius and Stasys
Girenas
AP18

Ill-Fated Plane
"Lituanica"
AP19

The Dark
Angel of
Death
AP20

"Lituanica"
over Globe
AP21

"Lituanica" and White
Knight — AP22

*Perf. 11½*

**1934, May 18**    **Unwmk.**    **Engr.**

| | | | | |
|---|---|---|---|---|
| **C79** | AP18 | 20c scarlet & blk | .25 | .25 |
| **C80** | AP19 | 40c dp rose & bl | .25 | .25 |
| **C81** | AP18 | 60c dk vio & blk | .25 | .25 |
| **C82** | AP20 | 1 l black & rose | .35 | .25 |
| **C83** | AP21 | 3 l gray grn & org | .45 | .50 |
| **C84** | AP22 | 5 l dk brn & bl | 1.75 | 3.25 |
| | | *Nos. C79-C84 (6)* | 3.30 | 4.75 |
| | | Set, never hinged | 5.50 | |

Death of Capts. Steponas Darius and
Stasys Girenas on their New York-Kaunas
flight of 1933.

No. C80 exists with diagonal overprint: "F.
VAITKUS / nugalejo Atlanta / 21-22-IX-1935."
Value $400.

Felix Waitkus and
Map of Transatlantic
Flight — AP23

**Wmk. 238**

**1936, Mar. 24**    **Litho.**    *Perf. 14*

| | | | | |
|---|---|---|---|---|
| **C85** | AP23 | 15c brown lake | 2.25 | .85 |
| **C86** | AP23 | 30c dark green | 3.25 | .85 |
| **C87** | AP23 | 60c blue | 4.50 | 2.50 |
| | | *Nos. C85-C87 (3)* | 10.00 | 4.20 |
| | | Set, never hinged | 13.75 | |

Transatlantic Flight of the Lituanica II, Sept.
21-22, 1935.

---

## AIR POST SEMI-POSTAL STAMPS

**Nos. C32-C35 Surcharged like Nos.
B1-B9 (No. CB1), Nos. B10-B11
(Nos. CB2-CB3), and Nos. B12-B14
(No. CB4) in Red, Violet or Black**

**1924**    **Wmk. 147**    *Perf. 11*

| | | | | |
|---|---|---|---|---|
| **CB1** | AP8 | 20c + 20c yellow (R) | 12.00 | 12.00 |
| **CB2** | AP8 | 40c + 40c emerald | | |
| | | (V) | 12.00 | 12.00 |
| **CB3** | AP8 | 60c + 60c rose (V) | 12.00 | 12.00 |
| **CB4** | AP9 | 1 l + 1 l dk brown | 12.00 | 12.00 |
| | | *Nos. CB1-CB4 (4)* | 48.00 | 48.00 |
| | | Set, never hinged | 80.00 | |

Surtax for the Red Cross. See note following
No. C35.

---

## SOUTH LITHUANIA

## GRODNO DISTRICT

Russian Stamps of 1909-12
Surcharged in Black or Red

**1919**    **Unwmk.**    *Perf. 14, 14½x15*

| | | | | |
|---|---|---|---|---|
| **L1** | A14 | 50sk on 3k red | 60.00 | 57.50 |
| *a.* | | Double surcharge | 250.00 | 250.00 |
| **L2** | A14 | 50sk on 5k claret | 60.00 | 57.50 |
| *a.* | | Imperf., pair | 550.00 | 475.00 |
| **L3** | A15 | 50sk on 10k dk bl | | |
| | | (R) | | 57.50 |
| **L4** | A11 | 50sk on 15k red | | |
| | | brn & bl | 60.00 | 57.50 |
| *a.* | | Imperf., pair | 650.00 | 550.00 |
| **L5** | A11 | 50sk on 25k grn & | | |
| | | gray vio (R) | 60.00 | 57.50 |
| **L6** | A11 | 50sk on 35k red | | |
| | | brn & grn | 60.00 | 57.50 |
| **L7** | A8 | 50sk on 50k vio & | | |
| | | grn | 60.00 | 57.50 |

| | | | | |
|---|---|---|---|---|
| **L8** | A11 | 50sk on 70k brn & | | |
| | | org | 60.00 | 57.50 |
| | | *Nos. L1-L8 (8)* | 480.00 | 460.00 |

Excellent counterfeits are plentiful.
This surcharge exists on Russia No. 119,
the imperf. 1k orange of 1917. Value, unused
$90, used $60.

---

## OCCUPATION STAMPS

The issue formerly listed as Lithuania
1N1-1N12 is now listed as Russia N1-
N12.

### Issued under Russian Occupation

Lithuanian Stamps of
1937-40 Overprinted in
Red or Blue

**1940**    **Wmk. 238**    *Perf. 14*

| | | | | |
|---|---|---|---|---|
| **2N9** | A44 | 2c orange (Bl) | .25 | .25 |
| | | Never hinged | .30 | |
| **2N10** | A50 | 50c brown (Bl) | .25 | .25 |
| | | Never hinged | .75 | |

**Unwmk.**

| | | | | |
|---|---|---|---|---|
| **2N11** | A56 | 5c brown car (Bl) | .25 | .40 |
| | | Never hinged | .30 | |
| **2N12** | A57 | 10c green (R) | 3.75 | 8.00 |
| | | Never hinged | 10.00 | |
| **2N13** | A58 | 15c dull orange (Bl) | .25 | .35 |
| | | Never hinged | .30 | |
| **2N14** | A59 | 25c lt brown (R) | .25 | .35 |
| | | Never hinged | .65 | |
| **2N15** | A60 | 30c Prus green (R) | .25 | .50 |
| | | Never hinged | .65 | |
| **2N16** | A61 | 35c red orange (Bl) | .35 | .50 |
| | | Never hinged | .90 | |
| | | *Nos. 2N9-2N16 (8)* | 5.60 | 10.60 |
| | | Set, never hinged | 10.00 | |

Values for used stamps are for CTOs. Postally used examples are worth considerably
more.
The Lithuanian Soviet Socialist Republic
was proclaimed July 21, 1940.

---

# LOURENCO MARQUES

lə-'ren₍t₎-₍s₎ō-₍₎mär-'kes

LOCATION — In the southern part of
Mozambique in Southeast Africa
GOVT. — Part of Portuguese East
Africa Colony
AREA — 28,800 sq. mi. (approx.)
POP. — 474,000 (approx.)
CAPITAL — Lourenço Marques

Stamps of Mozambique replaced
those of Lourenço Marques in 1920.
See Mozambique No. 360.

    1000 Reis = 1 Milreis
    100 Centavos = 1 Escudo (1913)

King Carlos — A1

*Perf. 11½, 12½, 13½*

**1895**    **Typo.**    **Unwmk.**

| | | | | |
|---|---|---|---|---|
| **1** | A1 | 5r yellow | .80 | .50 |
| **2** | A1 | 10r redsh violet | .80 | .55 |
| **3** | A1 | 15r chocolate | 1.50 | 1.00 |
| **4** | A1 | 20r lavender | 1.50 | 1.00 |
| **5** | A1 | 25r blue green | 1.50 | .50 |
| *a.* | | Perf. 11½ | 4.75 | 1.50 |
| **6** | A1 | 50r light blue | 2.90 | 2.00 |
| *a.* | | Perf. 13½ | 22.50 | 11.00 |
| *b.* | | Perf. 11½ | 4.75 | 1.50 |
| **7** | A1 | 75r rose | 2.25 | 1.80 |
| **8** | A1 | 80r yellow grn | 6.75 | 4.50 |
| **9** | A1 | 100r brn, *yel* | 4.00 | 1.60 |
| *a.* | | Perf. 12½ | 7.25 | 4.75 |
| **10** | A1 | 150r car, *rose* | 6.50 | 4.25 |
| **11** | A1 | 200r dk bl, *bl* | 6.50 | 4.00 |
| **12** | A1 | 300r dk bl, *sal* | 7.25 | 4.75 |
| | | *Nos. 1-12 (12)* | 42.25 | 26.45 |

For surcharges and overprints see Nos. 29,
58-69, 132-137, 140-143, 156-157, 160.

---

## Saint Anthony of Padua Issue

Regular Issues of
Mozambique, 1886 and
1894, Overprinted in
Black

### On 1886 Issue

**1895**    **Without Gum**    *Perf. 12½*

| | | | | |
|---|---|---|---|---|
| **13** | A2 | 5r black | 26.00 | 17.50 |
| **14** | A2 | 10r green | 32.00 | 17.50 |
| **15** | A2 | 20r rose | 35.00 | 19.00 |
| **16** | A2 | 25r lilac | 40.00 | 20.00 |
| **17** | A2 | 40r chocolate | 37.50 | 19.00 |
| **18** | A2 | 50r bl, perf. 13½ | 30.00 | 22.00 |
| *a.* | | Perf. 12½ | 67.50 | 50.00 |
| **19** | A2 | 100r yellow brn | 115.00 | 100.00 |
| **20** | A2 | 200r gray vio | 62.50 | 43.00 |
| **21** | A2 | 300r orange | 70.00 | 57.50 |

### On 1894 Issue

*Perf. 11½*

| | | | | |
|---|---|---|---|---|
| **22** | A3 | 5r yellow | 29.00 | 17.00 |
| **23** | A3 | 10r redsh vio | 42.00 | 22.00 |
| **24** | A3 | 50r light blue | 67.50 | 45.00 |
| *a.* | | Perf. 12½ | 325.00 | 325.00 |
| **25** | A3 | 75r rose, perf. | | |
| | | 12½ | 77.50 | 57.50 |
| **26** | A3 | 80r yellow grn | 97.50 | 77.50 |
| **27** | A3 | 100r brown, *buff* | 240.00 | 190.00 |
| **28** | A3 | 150r car, *rose,* | | |
| | | perf. 12½ | 67.50 | 45.00 |
| | | *Nos. 13-28 (16)* | 1,069. | 769.50 |

No. 12 Surcharged in
Black

**1897, Jan. 2**

| | | | | |
|---|---|---|---|---|
| **29** | A1 | 50r on 300r | 275.00 | 220.00 |

Most examples of No. 29 were issued without gum.

King Carlos — A2

### Name, Value in Black except 500r

**1898-1903**    *Perf. 11½*

| | | | | |
|---|---|---|---|---|
| **30** | A2 | 2½r gray | .50 | .45 |
| **31** | A2 | 5r orange | .50 | .45 |
| **32** | A2 | 10r lt green | .50 | .45 |
| **33** | A2 | 15r brown | 1.70 | 1.20 |
| **34** | A2 | 15r gray green | | |
| | | ('03) | 1.10 | .85 |
| *a.* | | Imperf. | | |
| **35** | A2 | 20r gray violet | 1.00 | .60 |
| *a.* | | Imperf. | | |
| **36** | A2 | 25r sea green | 1.10 | .60 |
| *a.* | | Perf. 13½ | 50.00 | 12.00 |
| *b.* | | 25r light green (error) | 30.00 | 30.00 |
| *c.* | | Perf. 12½ | 160.00 | 140.00 |
| **37** | A2 | 25r car ('03) | .75 | .50 |
| *a.* | | Imperf. | | |
| **38** | A2 | 50r blue | 2.25 | 1.20 |
| **39** | A2 | 50r brown ('03) | 1.40 | 1.10 |
| **40** | A2 | 65r dull bl ('03) | 9.00 | 6.75 |
| **41** | A2 | 75r rose | 2.90 | 2.00 |
| **42** | A2 | 75r lilac ('03) | 2.00 | 1.60 |
| *a.* | | Imperf. | | |
| **43** | A2 | 80r violet | 3.50 | 1.90 |
| **44** | A2 | 100r dk blue, *blue* | 2.50 | 1.00 |
| *a.* | | Perf. 13½ | 25.00 | 7.50 |
| **45** | A2 | 115r org brn, *pink* | | |
| | | ('03) | 7.75 | 7.00 |
| **46** | A2 | 130r brn, *straw* ('03) | 7.75 | 7.00 |
| **47** | A2 | 150r brn, *straw* | 3.75 | 1.90 |
| **48** | A2 | 200r red lil, *pnksh* | 4.75 | 2.50 |
| **49** | A2 | 300r dk bl, *rose* | 4.25 | 2.50 |
| **50** | A2 | 400r dl bl, *straw* | | |
| | | ('03) | 10.00 | 7.50 |
| **51** | A2 | 500r blk & red, *bl* | | |
| | | ('01) | 9.00 | 4.75 |
| **52** | A2 | 700r vio, *yelsh* ('01) | 30.00 | 12.50 |
| | | *Nos. 30-52 (23)* | 107.95 | 66.30 |

For surcharges and overprints see Nos. 57,
71-74, 76-91, 138, 144-155.

Coat of Arms — A3

## Surcharged On Upper and Lower Halves of Stamp

**1899**    *Imperf.*
| | | | | |
|---|---|---|---|---|
| 53 | A3 | 5r on 10r grn & brn | 20.00 | 7.00 |
| 54 | A3 | 25r on 10r grn & brn | 20.00 | 7.00 |
| 55 | A3 | 50r on 10r grn & brn | 30.00 | 11.00 |
| *a.* | | Inverted surcharge | 42.50 | 50.00 |
| 56 | A3 | 50r on 800r grn & brn | 40.00 | 20.00 |
| | | *Nos. 53-56 (4)* | 110.00 | 45.00 |

The lower half of No. 55 can be distinguished from that of No. 56 by the background of the label containing the word "REIS." The former is plain, while the latter is formed of white intersecting curved horizontal lines over vertical shading of violet brown.

Values are for undivided stamps. Halves sell for ¼ as much.

Most examples of Nos. 53-56 were issued without gum. Values are for stamps without gum. Values for stamps with gum are two times the values shown.

### No. 41 Surcharged in Black

**1899**    *Perf. 11½*
| | | | | |
|---|---|---|---|---|
| 57 | A2 | 50r on 75r rose | 7.75 | 4.50 |

Most examples of No. 57 were issued without gum. Values are for stamp without gum.

### Surcharged in Black

### On Issue of 1895

**1902**    *Perf. 11½, 12½*
| | | | | |
|---|---|---|---|---|
| 58 | A1 | 65r on 5r yellow | 4.25 | 3.50 |
| 59 | A1 | 65r on 15r choc | 4.25 | 3.50 |
| 60 | A1 | 65r on 20r lav | 4.25 | 3.50 |
| *a.* | | Perf. 12½ | 75.00 | 62.50 |
| 61 | A1 | 115r on 10r red vio | 4.75 | 4.00 |
| 62 | A1 | 115r on 200r bl, *bl* | 4.75 | 3.75 |
| 63 | A1 | 115r on 300r bl, *sal* | 4.75 | 3.75 |
| 64 | A1 | 130r on 25r grn, perf. 12½ | 4.00 | 3.25 |
| *a.* | | Perf. 11½ | 40.00 | 30.00 |
| 65 | A1 | 130r on 80r yel grn | 4.75 | 4.00 |
| 66 | A1 | 130r on 150r car, *rose* | 5.00 | 4.00 |
| 67 | A1 | 400r on 50r lt bl | 11.75 | 6.50 |
| 68 | A1 | 400r on 75r rose | 11.75 | 6.50 |
| 69 | A1 | 400r on 100r brn, *buff* | 7.75 | 6.00 |

### On Newspaper Stamp of 1893
| | | | | |
|---|---|---|---|---|
| 70 | N1 | 65r on 2½r brn | 4.25 | 3.00 |
| | | *Nos. 58-70 (13)* | 75.50 | 55.25 |

Surcharge exists inverted on Nos. 61, 70.
Nos. 64, 67 and 68 have been reprinted on thin white paper with shiny white gum and clean-cut perforation 13½. Value $6 each.
For overprints see Nos. 132-137, 140-143, 156-157, 160.

### Issue of 1898-1903 Overprinted in Black

**1903**    *Perf. 11½*
| | | | | |
|---|---|---|---|---|
| 71 | A2 | 15r brown | 3.00 | 1.60 |
| 72 | A2 | 25r sea green | 2.25 | 1.40 |
| 73 | A2 | 50r blue | 3.75 | 1.75 |
| 74 | A2 | 75r rose | 4.75 | 2.75 |
| *a.* | | Inverted overprint | 50.00 | 50.00 |
| | | *Nos. 71-74 (4)* | 13.75 | 7.50 |

### Surcharged in Black

**1905**
| | | | | |
|---|---|---|---|---|
| 76 | A2 | 50r on 65r dull blue | 4.75 | 3.50 |

### Regular Issues Overprinted in Carmine or Green

---

**1911**
| | | | | |
|---|---|---|---|---|
| 77 | A2 | 2½r gray | .50 | .45 |
| 78 | A2 | 5r orange | .50 | .45 |
| *a.* | | Double overprint | 10.00 | 10.00 |
| *b.* | | Inverted overprint | 10.00 | 10.00 |
| 79 | A2 | 10r lt grn | .70 | .60 |
| 80 | A2 | 15r gray grn | .70 | .60 |
| *a.* | | Inverted overprint | 10.00 | 10.00 |
| 81 | A2 | 20r dl vio | .70 | .60 |
| 82 | A2 | 25r car (G) | 1.40 | .75 |
| 83 | A2 | 50r brown | 1.20 | .90 |
| 84 | A2 | 75r lilac | 1.90 | .90 |
| 85 | A2 | 100r dk bl, *bl* | 1.90 | .90 |
| 86 | A2 | 115r org brn, *pink* | 15.00 | 6.00 |
| 87 | A2 | 130r brn, *straw* | 1.40 | .90 |
| 88 | A2 | 200r red lil, *pnksh* | 1.50 | .90 |
| 89 | A2 | 400r dl bl, *straw* | 2.75 | 1.75 |
| 90 | A2 | 500r blk & red, *bl* | 3.00 | 1.75 |
| 91 | A2 | 700r vio, *yelsh* | 4.00 | 1.90 |
| | | *Nos. 77-91 (15)* | 36.45 | 19.35 |

### Vasco da Gama Issue of Various Portuguese Colonies Common Design Types Surcharged

### On Stamps of Macao

**1913**    *Perf. 12½-16*
| | | | | |
|---|---|---|---|---|
| 92 | CD20 | ¼c on ½a bl grn | 2.50 | 2.25 |
| 93 | CD21 | ½c on 1a red | 2.50 | 2.25 |
| 94 | CD22 | 1c on 2a red vio | 2.50 | 2.25 |
| 95 | CD23 | 2½c on 4a yel grn | 2.50 | 2.25 |
| 96 | CD24 | 5c on 8a dk bl | 2.50 | 2.25 |
| 97 | CD25 | 7½c on 12a vio brn | 4.75 | 3.50 |
| 98 | CD26 | 10c on 16a bis brn | 4.75 | 3.50 |
| *a.* | | Inverted surcharge | 40.00 | 32.50 |
| 99 | CD27 | 15c on 24a bister | 3.75 | 2.50 |
| | | *Nos. 92-99 (8)* | 24.50 | 19.75 |

### On Stamps of Portuguese Africa

**1913**
| | | | | |
|---|---|---|---|---|
| 100 | CD20 | ¼c on 2½r bl grn | 2.40 | 2.20 |
| 101 | CD21 | ½c on 5r red | 2.40 | 2.20 |
| 102 | CD22 | 1c on 10r red vio | 2.40 | 2.20 |
| 103 | CD23 | 2½c on 25r yel grn | 2.40 | 2.20 |
| 104 | CD24 | 5c on 50r dk bl | 2.40 | 2.20 |
| 105 | CD25 | 7½c on 75r vio brn | 5.75 | 4.75 |
| 106 | CD26 | 10c on 100r bis brn | 3.75 | 2.75 |
| 107 | CD27 | 15c on 150r bis | 3.75 | 2.75 |
| | | *Nos. 100-107 (8)* | 25.25 | 21.25 |

### On Stamps of Timor

| | | | | |
|---|---|---|---|---|
| 108 | CD20 | ¼c on ½a bl grn | 2.40 | 1.90 |
| 109 | CD21 | ½c on 1a red | 2.40 | 1.90 |
| 110 | CD22 | 1c on 2a red vio | 2.40 | 1.90 |
| 111 | CD23 | 2½c on 4a yel grn | 2.40 | 1.90 |
| 112 | CD24 | 5c on 8a dk bl | 2.50 | 2.30 |
| 113 | CD25 | 7½c on 12a vio brn | 4.75 | 3.50 |
| 114 | CD26 | 10c on 16a bis brn | 3.25 | 2.50 |
| 115 | CD27 | 15c on 24a bister | 3.25 | 2.50 |
| | | *Nos. 108-115 (8)* | 23.35 | 18.40 |
| | | *Nos. 92-115 (24)* | 73.10 | 59.40 |

Ceres — A4

### Chalky Paper
### Name and Value in Black

**1914**    Typo.    *Perf. 15x14*
| | | | | |
|---|---|---|---|---|
| 116 | A4 | ¼c olive brn | .70 | .55 |
| 117 | A4 | ½c black | .70 | .55 |
| 118 | A4 | 1c blue grn | .65 | .50 |
| 119 | A4 | 1½c lilac brn | 1.15 | 1.00 |
| 120 | A4 | 2c carmine | 1.90 | 1.00 |
| 121 | A4 | 2½c lt vio | 1.90 | 1.00 |
| 122 | A4 | 5c dp blue | 1.50 | 1.00 |
| 123 | A4 | 7½c yellow brn | 1.90 | 1.50 |
| 124 | A4 | 8c slate | 1.90 | 1.50 |
| 125 | A4 | 10c orange brn | 2.20 | 1.40 |
| 126 | A4 | 15c plum | 2.00 | 1.50 |
| 127 | A4 | 20c yellow grn | 2.90 | 1.90 |
| 128 | A4 | 30c brown, *green* | 3.50 | 1.80 |
| 129 | A4 | 40c brown, *pink* | 10.00 | 6.00 |
| 130 | A4 | 50c orange, *sal* | 6.50 | 4.00 |
| 131 | A4 | 1e green, *blue* | 8.50 | 4.00 |
| | | *Nos. 116-131 (16)* | 39.25 | 16.00 |

### Glazed Paper

| | | | | |
|---|---|---|---|---|
| 131A | A4 | 1c blue grn | 1.75 | 1.45 |
| 131B | A4 | 2½c lt vio | 1.75 | 1.45 |

**1918**    *Ordinary Paper*
| | | | | |
|---|---|---|---|---|
| 131C | A4 | ¼c olive brn | .45 | .40 |
| 131D | A4 | ½c black | .45 | .40 |
| *a.* | | Value omitted | 20.00 | |
| 131E | A4 | 1c blue grn | .45 | .40 |
| 131F | A4 | 1½c lilac brn | .45 | .40 |
| *a.* | | Imperf. | | |
| 131G | A4 | 2c carmine | .45 | .40 |
| 131H | A4 | 2½c lt vio | .45 | .40 |
| 131I | A4 | 5c dp blue | 1.20 | 1.00 |
| 131J | A4 | 7½c yellow brn | 1.40 | 1.00 |
| 131K | A4 | 8c slate | 1.40 | 1.00 |
| 131L | A4 | 10c orange brn | 32.50 | 24.00 |
| 131M | A4 | 15c plum | 2.00 | 1.75 |
| | | *Nos. 131C-131M (11)* | 41.20 | 31.15 |

For surcharges see Nos. 139, 159, 161-162, B1-B12.

---

In 1921 Nos. 131D and 131F were surcharged 10c and 30c respectively, for use in Mozambique as Nos. 230 and 231. These same values, surcharged 5c and 10c respectively, with the addition of the word "PORTEADO," were used in Mozambique as postage dues, Nos. J44 and J45.

### Provisional Issue of 1902 Overprinted Locally in Carmine

**1914**    *Perf. 11½, 12½*
| | | | | |
|---|---|---|---|---|
| 132 | A1 | 115r on 10r red vio | 1.70 | 1.70 |
| *a.* | | "Republica" inverted | 20.00 | |
| 133 | A1 | 115r on 200r bl, *bl* | 1.70 | 1.40 |
| 134 | A1 | 115r on 300r bl, *sal* | 1.70 | 1.70 |
| *a.* | | Double overprint | 40.00 | 40.00 |
| 135 | A1 | 130r on 25r grn | 2.00 | 1.70 |
| *a.* | | Perf. 12½ | 2.90 | 1.70 |
| 136 | A1 | 130r on 80r yel grn | 2.00 | 1.70 |
| 137 | A1 | 130r on 150r car, *rose* | 2.00 | 1.70 |
| | | *Nos. 132-137 (6)* | 11.10 | 9.90 |

No. 135a was issued without gum.

### Nos. 78 and 117 Perforated Diagonally and Surcharged in Carmine

**1915**    *Perf. 11½*
| | | | | |
|---|---|---|---|---|
| 138 | A2 | ¼c on half of 5r org, pair | 6.00 | 5.50 |
| *a.* | | Pair without dividing perfs. | 20.00 | 20.00 |

*Perf. 15x14*
| | | | | |
|---|---|---|---|---|
| 139 | A4 | ¼c on half of ½c blk, pair | 8.50 | 8.00 |

The added perforation on Nos. 138-139 runs from lower left to upper right corners, dividing the stamp in two. Values are for pairs, both halves of the stamp.

### Provisional Issue of 1902 Overprinted in Carmine

**1915**    *Perf. 11½, 12½*
| | | | | |
|---|---|---|---|---|
| 140 | A1 | 115r on 10r red vio | 1.00 | .80 |
| 141 | A1 | 115r on 200r bl, *bl* | 1.10 | .80 |
| 142 | A1 | 115r on 300r bl, *sal* | 1.10 | .80 |
| 143 | A1 | 130r on 150r car, *rose* | 1.20 | .80 |
| | | *Nos. 140-143 (4)* | 4.40 | 3.20 |

### Nos. 34 and 80 Surcharged

**1915**    On Issue of 1903
| | | | | |
|---|---|---|---|---|
| 144 | A2 | 2c on 15r gray grn | 1.70 | 1.20 |

### On Issue of 1911
| | | | | |
|---|---|---|---|---|
| 145 | A2 | 2c on 15r gray grn | 1.70 | 1.20 |
| *a.* | | New value inverted | 22.50 | |

### Regular Issues of 1898-1903 Overprinted Locally in Carmine

**1916**
| | | | | |
|---|---|---|---|---|
| 146 | A2 | 15r gray grn | 2.00 | 1.50 |
| 147 | A2 | 50r brown | 4.00 | 2.60 |
| *a.* | | Inverted overprint | | |
| 148 | A2 | 75r lilac | 4.00 | 2.75 |
| 149 | A2 | 100r blue, *bl* | 3.50 | 1.90 |
| 150 | A2 | 115r org brn, *pink* | 3.50 | 1.90 |
| 151 | A2 | 130r brown, *straw* | 12.50 | 8.75 |
| 152 | A2 | 200r red lil, *pnksh* | 5.25 | 2.75 |
| 153 | A2 | 400r dull bl, *straw* | 8.00 | 5.50 |
| 154 | A2 | 500r blk & red, *bl* | 5.25 | 4.00 |
| 155 | A2 | 700r vio, *yelsh* | 8.50 | 6.00 |
| | | *Nos. 146-155 (10)* | 56.50 | 37.65 |

### Same Overprint on Nos. 67-68

**1917**
| | | | | |
|---|---|---|---|---|
| 156 | A1 | 400r on 50r lt blue | 2.00 | 1.70 |
| *a.* | | Perf. 13½ | 11.50 | 9.00 |
| 157 | A1 | 400r on 75r rose | 3.50 | 2.50 |

No. 69 exists with this overprint. It was not officially issued.

---

### Type of 1914 Surcharged in Red

**1920**    *Perf. 15x14*
| | | | | |
|---|---|---|---|---|
| 159 | A4 | 4c on 2½c violet | 1.40 | .60 |

### Stamps of 1914 Surcharged in Green or Black

a    b

**1921**
| | | | | |
|---|---|---|---|---|
| 160 | A1(a) | ¼c on 115r on 10r red vio (G) | 1.40 | 1.20 |
| 161 | A4(b) | 1c on 2½c vio (Bk) | 1.00 | .70 |
| *a.* | | Inverted surcharge | 40.00 | |
| 162 | A4(b) | 1½c on 2½c vio (Bk) | 1.20 | .80 |
| | | *Nos. 160-162 (3)* | 3.60 | 2.70 |

Nos. 159-162 were postally valid throughout Mozambique. No. 162 exists on glazed paper. Value the same as No. 162.

---

### SEMI-POSTAL STAMPS

### Regular Issue of 1914 Overprinted or Surcharged

a    b

c

**1918**    *Perf. 15x14½*
| | | | | |
|---|---|---|---|---|
| B1 | A4(a) | ¼c olive brn | 3.75 | 4.00 |
| B2 | A4(a) | ½c black | 3.75 | 4.00 |
| B3 | A4(a) | 1c bl grn | 3.75 | 4.00 |
| B4 | A4(a) | 2½c violet | 4.00 | 4.00 |
| B5 | A4(a) | 5c blue | 4.00 | 4.75 |

### Chalky Paper

| | | | | |
|---|---|---|---|---|
| B5A | A4(a) | 5c blue | 4.00 | 4.75 |
| B6 | A4(a) | 10c org brn | 5.00 | 5.25 |
| B7 | A4(b) | 20c on 1½c lil brn | 5.00 | 6.00 |
| B8 | A4(b) | 30c brn, *grn* | 6.00 | 6.50 |
| B9 | A4(b) | 40c on 2c car, ord. paper | 6.00 | 7.50 |
| B10 | A4(b) | 50c on 7½c bis | 8.00 | 8.00 |
| B11 | A4(b) | 70c on 8c slate | 10.00 | 10.00 |
| B12 | A4(c) | $1 on 15c mag | 10.00 | 10.00 |
| | | *Nos. B1-B12 (13)* | 73.25 | 78.75 |

Nos. B1-B12 were used in place of ordinary postage stamps on Mar. 9, 1918. Nos. B3 and B4 also exist on glazed paper. The unsurfaced paper on which Nos. B1-B5 were printed show a diamond pattern when held to the light. This pattern is used to determine genuine stamps.

---

### NEWSPAPER STAMPS

### Numeral of Value — N1

*Perf. 11½*
**1893, July 28**    Typo.    Unwmk.
| | | | | |
|---|---|---|---|---|
| P1 | N1 | 2½r brown | .60 | .65 |
| *a.* | | Perf. 12½ | 30.00 | 27.50 |

For surcharge see No. 70.

## Saint Anthony of Padua Issue

Mozambique No. P6
Overprinted

**1895, July 1**     **Perf. 11½, 13½**
| | | | | |
|---|---|---|---|---|
| P2 | N3 | 2½r brown | 12.50 | 8.50 |
| | a. | Inverted overprint | 30.00 | 30.00 |

# LUXEMBOURG

ˈlək-səm-ˌbərg

LOCATION — Western Europe between southern Belgium, Germany and France
GOVT. — Grand Duchy
AREA — 999 sq. mi.
POP. — 476,200 (2007)
CAPITAL — Luxembourg

12½ Centimes = 1 Silbergroschen
100 Centimes = 1 Franc
100 Cents = 1 Euro (2002)

> Catalogue values for unused stamps in this country are for Never Hinged items, beginning with Scott 321 in the regular postage section, Scott B216 in the semi-postal section.

### Watermarks

Wmk. 110 — Octagons

Wmk. 149 — W

Wmk. 213 — Double Wavy Lines

Wmk. 216 — Multiple Airplanes

Wmk. 246 — Multiple Cross Enclosed in Octagons

Wmk. 247 — Multiple Letters

---

Unused values of Nos. 1-47 are for stamps without gum. Though these stamps were issued with gum, most examples offered are without gum. Stamps with original gum sell for more.

---

Grand Duke William III — A1

### Luxembourg Print
#### Wmk. 149

**1852, Sept. 15**    **Engr.**    **Imperf.**
| | | | | |
|---|---|---|---|---|
| 1 | A1 | 10c gray black | 2,100. | 55.00 |
| | a. | 10c greenish black ('53) | 2,250. | 55.00 |
| | b. | 10c intense black ('54) | 2,400. | 120.00 |
| 2 | A1 | 1sg brown red ('53) | 1,500. | 75.00 |
| | a. | 1sg brick red | 1,500. | 80.00 |
| | b. | 1sg orange red ('54) | 1,300. | 87.50 |
| | c. | 1sg blood red | 2,750. | 475.00 |
| 3 | A1 | 1sg rose ('55) | 1,350. | 87.50 |
| | a. | 1sg carmine rose ('56) | 1,250. | 80.00 |
| | b. | 1sg dark carmine rose, thin paper ('59) | 1,400. | 240.00 |
| | | Nos. 1-3 (3) | | 217.50 |

*Reprints of both values exist on watermarked paper. Some of the reprints show traces of lines cancelling the plates, but others can be distinguished only by an expert. See Nos. 278-279, 603.*

Coat of Arms
A2     A3
### Frankfurt Print

**1859-64**    **Typo.**    **Unwmk.**
| | | | | |
|---|---|---|---|---|
| 4 | A2 | 1c buff ('63) | 130.00 | 450.00 |
| 5 | A2 | 2c black ('60) | 95.00 | 550.00 |
| 6 | A2 | 4c yellow ('64) | 175.00 | 175.00 |
| | a. | 4c orange ('64) | 190.00 | 190.00 |
| 7 | A3 | 10c blue | 175.00 | 20.00 |
| 8 | A3 | 12½c rose | 275.00 | 160.00 |
| 9 | A3 | 25c brown | 350.00 | 275.00 |
| 10 | A3 | 30c rose lilac | 290.00 | 225.00 |
| 11 | A3 | 37½c green | 325.00 | 200.00 |
| 12 | A3 | 40c red orange | 875.00 | 240.00 |

Counterfeits of Nos. 1-12 exist.
See Nos. 13-25, 27-38, 40-47. For surcharges and overprints see Nos. 26, 39, O1-O51.

**1865-71**            **Rouletted**
| | | | | |
|---|---|---|---|---|
| 13 | A2 | 1c red brown | 200.00 | 240.00 |
| 14 | A2 | 2c black ('67) | 20.00 | 13.50 |
| 15 | A2 | 4c yellow ('67) | 600.00 | 175.00 |
| 16 | A2 | 4c green ('71) | 40.00 | 24.00 |
| | | Nos. 13-16 (4) | 860.00 | 452.50 |

**1865-74**      **Rouletted in Color**
| | | | | |
|---|---|---|---|---|
| 17 | A2 | 1c red brn ('72) | 35.00 | 8.00 |
| 18 | A2 | 1c orange ('69) | 40.00 | 8.00 |
| | a. | 1c brown orange ('67) | 120.00 | 35.00 |
| | b. | 1c red orange ('69) | 1,350. | 325.00 |
| 19 | A3 | 10c rose lilac | 120.00 | 4.00 |
| | a. | 10c lilac | 100.00 | 4.00 |
| | b. | 10c gray lilac | 100.00 | 4.00 |
| 20 | A3 | 12½c car ('71) | 175.00 | 8.00 |
| | a. | 12½c rose | 175.00 | 8.00 |
| 21 | A3 | 20c gray brn ('72) | 120.00 | 8.00 |
| | a. | 20c yellow brown ('69) | 125.00 | 8.00 |
| 22 | A3 | 25c blue ('72) | 1,100. | 11.00 |
| 22A | A3 | 25c ultra ('65) | 1,100. | 11.00 |
| 23 | A3 | 30c lilac rose | 1,200. | 80.00 |
| 24 | A3 | 37½c green ('66) | 750.00 | 240.00 |
| 25 | A3 | 40c pale org ('74) | 40.00 | 80.00 |
| | a. | 40c orange red ('66) | 1,050. | 60.00 |

### No. 24 Surcharged in Black

UN FRANC.

**1873**
| | | | | |
|---|---|---|---|---|
| 26 | A3 | 1fr on 37½c bis | 875.00 | 80.00 |
| | a. | Surcharge inverted | | 3,600. |

### Luxembourg Print

**1874**    **Typo.**      **Imperf.**
| | | | | |
|---|---|---|---|---|
| 27 | A2 | 4c green | 110.00 | 110.00 |

A5

**1875-79**    **Narrow Margins**    **Perf. 13**
| | | | | |
|---|---|---|---|---|
| 29 | A2 | 1c red brn ('78) | 35.00 | 8.00 |
| 30 | A2 | 2c black | 125.00 | 27.50 |
| 31 | A2 | 4c green | 2.40 | 9.50 |

---

| | | | | |
|---|---|---|---|---|
| 32 | A2 | 5c yellow ('76) | 175.00 | 24.00 |
| | a. | 5c orange yellow | 600.00 | 125.00 |
| | b. | Imperf. | 925.00 | 1,100. |
| 33 | A3 | 10c gray lilac | 475.00 | 2.40 |
| | b. | 10c lilac | 1,350. | 29.00 |
| | c. | Imperf. | 2,700. | 3,250. |
| 34 | A3 | 12½c lil rose ('77) | 600.00 | 20.00 |
| 35 | A3 | 12½c car rose ('76) | 400.00 | 27.50 |
| 36 | A3 | 25c blue ('77) | 800.00 | 14.00 |
| 37 | A3 | 30c dull rose ('78) | 750.00 | 450.00 |
| 38 | A3 | 40c orange ('79) | 1.60 | 9.50 |
| 39 | A5 | 1fr on 37½c bis ('79) | 8.00 | 27.50 |
| | a. | "Pranc" | 5,250. | 6,400. |
| | b. | Without surcharge | 475.00 | |
| | c. | As "b," imperf. | 700.00 | |
| | | As "c," pair | 1,400. | |

In the Luxembourg print the perforation is close to the border of the stamp. Excellent forgeries of No. 39a are plentiful, as well as faked cancellations on Nos. 31, 38 and 39.
Nos. 32b and 33c are said to be essays; Nos. 39b and 39c printer's waste.

### Haarlem Print
#### Perf. 11½x12, 12½x12, 13½
**1880-81**        **Wide Margins**
| | | | | |
|---|---|---|---|---|
| 40 | A2 | 1c yel brn ('81) | 8.75 | 6.00 |
| 41 | A2 | 2c black | 7.25 | 1.60 |
| 42 | A2 | 5c yellow ('81) | 200.00 | 95.00 |
| 43 | A3 | 10c gray lilac | 160.00 | 1.60 |
| 44 | A3 | 12½c rose ('81) | 190.00 | 190.00 |
| 45 | A3 | 20c gray brn ('81) | 45.00 | 20.00 |
| 46 | A3 | 25c blue | 240.00 | 4.75 |
| 47 | A3 | 30c dull rose ('81) | 8.00 | 24.00 |

#### Gray Yellowish Paper
##### Perf. 12½
| | | | | |
|---|---|---|---|---|
| 42a | A2 | 5c | | 7.25 |
| 43a | A3 | 10c | | 4.00 |
| 44a | A3 | 12½c | | 9.50 |
| 46a | A3 | 25c | | 5.50 |
| | | Nos. 42a-46a (4) | | 26.25 |

Nos. 42a-46a were not regularly issued.

"Industry" and "Commerce" — A6

#### Perf. 11½x12, 12½x12, 12½, 13½
**1882, Dec. 1**        **Typo.**
| | | | | |
|---|---|---|---|---|
| 48 | A6 | 1c gray lilac | .25 | .40 |
| 49 | A6 | 2c olive gray | .25 | .40 |
| 50 | A6 | 4c olive bister | .25 | 2.00 |
| 51 | A6 | 5c lt green | .80 | .40 |
| 52 | A6 | 10c rose | 8.00 | .40 |
| 53 | A6 | 12½c slate | 1.25 | 24.00 |
| 54 | A6 | 20c orange | 3.25 | 1.60 |
| 55 | A6 | 25c ultra | 175.00 | 1.60 |
| 56 | A6 | 30c gray green | 24.00 | 12.00 |
| 57 | A6 | 50c bister brown | 1.20 | 12.00 |
| 58 | A6 | 1fr pale violet | 1.60 | 24.00 |
| 59 | A6 | 5fr brown orange | 37.50 | 160.00 |
| | | Nos. 48-59 (12) | 253.55 | 238.80 |

For overprints see Nos. O52-O64.

Grand Duke Adolphe — A7

#### Perf. 11, 11½, 11½x11, 12½
**1891-93**            **Engr.**
| | | | | |
|---|---|---|---|---|
| 60 | A7 | 10c carmine | .35 | .30 |
| | a. | Sheet of 25, perf. 11½ | 125.00 | |
| 61 | A7 | 12½c slate grn ('93) | 1.00 | .70 |
| 62 | A7 | 20c orange ('93) | 13.00 | 1.00 |
| | a. | 20c brown, perf. 11½ | 160.00 | 240.00 |
| 63 | A7 | 25c blue | 1.00 | 1.00 |
| | a. | Sheet of 25, perf. 11½ | 1,000. | |
| 64 | A7 | 30c olive grn ('93) | 1.00 | 1.00 |
| 65 | A7 | 37½c green ('93) | 2.60 | 3.00 |
| 66 | A7 | 50c brown ('93) | 10.50 | 4.00 |
| 67 | A7 | 1fr dp violet ('93) | 16.00 | 9.00 |
| 68 | A7 | 2½fr black ('93) | 1.60 | 10.00 |
| 69 | A7 | 5fr lake ('93) | 35.00 | 70.00 |
| | | Nos. 60-69 (10) | 82.05 | 100.00 |

No. 62a was never on sale at any post office, but exists postally used.
Perf. 11½ stamps are from the sheets of 25.
For overprints see Nos. O65-O74.

Grand Duke Adolphe — A8

**1895, May 4**    **Typo.**     **Perf. 12½**
| | | | | |
|---|---|---|---|---|
| 70 | A8 | 1c pearl gray | 3.25 | .40 |
| 71 | A8 | 2c gray brown | .30 | .25 |
| 72 | A8 | 4c olive bister | .30 | .75 |

---

| | | | | |
|---|---|---|---|---|
| 73 | A8 | 5c green | 4.25 | .25 |
| 74 | A8 | 10c carmine | 11.00 | .25 |
| | | Nos. 70-74 (5) | 19.10 | 1.90 |

For overprints see Nos. O75-O79.

Coat of Arms
A9

Grand Duke William IV
A10

**1906-26**    **Typo.**     **Perf. 12½**
| | | | | |
|---|---|---|---|---|
| 75 | A9 | 1c gray ('07) | .25 | .25 |
| 76 | A9 | 2c ol brn ('07) | .25 | .25 |
| 77 | A9 | 4c bister ('07) | .25 | .25 |
| 78 | A9 | 5c green ('07) | .25 | .25 |
| 79 | A9 | 5c lilac ('26) | .25 | .25 |
| 80 | A9 | 6c violet ('07) | .25 | .25 |
| 81 | A9 | 7½c orange ('19) | .25 | 1.50 |

#### Engr.
##### Perf. 11, 11½x11
| | | | | |
|---|---|---|---|---|
| 82 | A10 | 10c scarlet | 2.00 | .25 |
| | a. | Souvenir sheet of 10 | 450.00 | 1,200. |
| 83 | A10 | 12½c sl grn ('07) | 2.00 | .45 |
| 84 | A10 | 15c org brn ('07) | 2.60 | .75 |
| 85 | A10 | 20c orange ('07) | 3.25 | .75 |
| 86 | A10 | 25c ultra ('07) | 65.00 | .45 |
| 87 | A10 | 30c ol grn ('08) | .65 | .75 |
| 88 | A10 | 37½c green ('07) | .65 | 1.00 |
| | a. | Perf. 12½ | 16.00 | 12.00 |
| 89 | A10 | 50c brown ('07) | 5.25 | 1.25 |
| 90 | A10 | 87½c dk blue ('08) | 2.00 | 12.50 |
| 91 | A10 | 1fr violet ('08) | 8.00 | 2.00 |
| 92 | A10 | 2½fr red ('08) | 52.50 | 95.00 |
| 93 | A10 | 5fr claret ('08) | 6.50 | 45.00 |
| | | Nos. 75-93 (19) | 152.15 | 163.15 |

No. 82a for accession of Grand Duke William IV to the throne.
For surcharges and overprints see Nos. 94-96, 112-117, O80-O98.

### Nos. 90, 92-93 Surcharged in Red or Black

62½ cts.

**1912-15**
| | | | | |
|---|---|---|---|---|
| 94 | A10 | 62½c on 87½c (R) | 2.75 | 2.50 |
| 95 | A10 | 62½c on 2½fr (Bk) ('15) | 2.75 | 4.50 |
| 96 | A10 | 62½c on 5fr (Bk) ('15) | 2.00 | 3.00 |
| | | Nos. 94-96 (3) | 7.50 | 10.00 |

Grand Duchess Marie Adelaide — A11

**1914-17**   **Engr.**   **Perf. 11½, 11½x11**
| | | | | |
|---|---|---|---|---|
| 97 | A11 | 10c lake | .25 | .25 |
| 98 | A11 | 12½c dull green | .25 | .25 |
| 99 | A11 | 15c sepia | .25 | .25 |
| 100 | A11 | 17½c dp brown ('17) | .25 | .40 |
| 101 | A11 | 25c ultra | .25 | .25 |
| 102 | A11 | 30c bister | .25 | .50 |
| 103 | A11 | 35c dark blue | .25 | .30 |
| 104 | A11 | 37½c black brn | .25 | .30 |
| 105 | A11 | 40c orange | .25 | .30 |
| 106 | A11 | 50c dark gray | .25 | .60 |
| 107 | A11 | 62½c blue green | .40 | 2.00 |
| 108 | A11 | 87½c orange ('17) | .40 | 2.00 |
| 109 | A11 | 1fr orange brown | 2.00 | 1.50 |
| 110 | A11 | 2½fr red | .40 | 1.50 |
| 111 | A11 | 5fr dark violet | 9.50 | 35.00 |
| | | Nos. 97-111 (15) | 15.20 | 45.40 |
| | | Set, never hinged | 65.00 | |

For surcharges and overprints see Nos. 118-124, B7-B10, O99-O113. Nos. 97, 98, 101, 107, 109 and 111 overprinted "Droits de statistique" are revenue stamps.

### Stamps of 1906-19 Surcharged with New Value and Bars in Black or Red

**1916-24**
| | | | | |
|---|---|---|---|---|
| 112 | A9 | 2½c on 5c ('18) | .25 | .25 |
| | a. | Double surcharge | 75.00 | |
| 113 | A9 | 3c on 2c ('21) | .25 | .25 |
| 114 | A9 | 5c on 1c ('23) | .25 | .25 |
| 115 | A9 | 5c on 4c ('23) | .25 | .40 |
| 116 | A9 | 5c on 7½c ('24) | .25 | .25 |
| 117 | A9 | 6c on 2c (R) ('22) | .25 | .25 |
| 118 | A11 | 7½c on 10c ('18) | .25 | .40 |
| 119 | A11 | 17½c on 30c | .25 | .40 |
| 120 | A11 | 20c on 17½c ('21) | .25 | .25 |
| 121 | A11 | 25c on 37½c ('23) | .25 | .25 |
| | a. | Double surcharge | 90.00 | |
| 122 | A11 | 75c on 62½c (R) ('22) | .25 | .25 |

| | | | |
|---|---|---|---|
| 123 | A11 | 80c on 87½c ('22) | .25 .25 |
| 124 | A11 | 87½c on 1fr | .55 5.50 |
| | | Nos. 112-124 (13) | 3.55 8.80 |

Grand Duchess
Charlotte — A12

**1921, Jan. 6    Engr.    Perf. 11½**

| | | | | |
|---|---|---|---|---|
| 125 | A12 | 15c rose | .25 | .25 |
| a. | | Sheet of 5, perf 11 | 400.00 | 250.00 |
| | | Never hinged | 925.00 | |
| b. | | Sheet of 25, perf. 11½,
11x11½, 12x11½ | 8.00 | 17.00 |

Birth of Prince Jean, first son of Grand Duchess Charlotte, Jan. 5 (No. 125a). No. 125 was printed in sheets of 100.
    See Nos. 131-150. For surcharges and overprints see Nos. 154-158, O114-O131, O136.

Vianden
Castle — A13

Foundries at
Esch — A14

Adolphe
Bridge — A15

**1921-34    Perf. 11, 11½, 11x11½**

| | | | |
|---|---|---|---|
| 126 | A13 | 1fr carmine | .25 .40 |
| 127 | A13 | 1fr dk blue ('26) | .25 .45 |
| | | **Perf. 11½x11; 11½ (#129, 130)** | |
| 128 | A14 | 2fr indigo | .30 .80 |
| 129 | A14 | 2fr dk brown ('26) | 7.00 2.00 |
| 130 | A15 | 5fr dk violet | 20.00 9.50 |
| | | Nos. 126-130 (5) | 27.80 13.15 |

For overprints see Nos. O132-O135, O137-138, O140.
See No. B85.

## Charlotte Type of 1921

**1921-26    Perf. 11½**

| | | | | |
|---|---|---|---|---|
| 131 | A12 | 2c brown | .25 | .25 |
| 132 | A12 | 3c olive green | .25 | .25 |
| a. | | Sheet of 25 | 10.00 | 25.00 |
| 133 | A12 | 6c violet | .25 | .25 |
| a. | | Sheet of 25 | 10.00 | 25.00 |
| 134 | A12 | 10c yellow grn | .25 | .25 |
| 135 | A12 | 10c olive brn ('24) | .25 | .25 |
| 136 | A12 | 15c brown olive | .25 | .25 |
| 137 | A12 | 15c pale grn ('24) | .25 | .25 |
| 138 | A12 | 15c dp orange ('26) | .25 | .25 |
| 139 | A12 | 20c dp orange | .25 | .25 |
| a. | | Sheet of 25 | 60.00 | 110.00 |
| 140 | A12 | 20c yellow grn ('26) | .25 | .25 |
| 141 | A12 | 25c dk green | .25 | .25 |
| 142 | A12 | 30c carmine rose | .25 | .25 |
| 143 | A12 | 40c brown orange | .25 | .25 |
| 144 | A12 | 50c deep blue | .25 | .25 |
| 145 | A12 | 50c red ('24) | .25 | .25 |
| 146 | A12 | 75c red | .25 | 1.00 |
| a. | | Sheet of 25 | 325.00 | |
| 147 | A12 | 75c deep blue ('24) | .25 | .25 |
| 148 | A12 | 80c black | .25 | .70 |
| a. | | Sheet of 25 | 325.00 | |
| | | Nos. 131-148 (18) | 4.50 | 5.70 |

For surcharges and overprints see Nos. 154-158, O114-O131, O136.

## Philatelic Exhibition Issue

**1922, Aug. 27    Imperf.
Laid Paper**

| | | | |
|---|---|---|---|
| 149 | A12 | 25c dark green | 1.75 6.00 |
| 150 | A12 | 30c carmine rose | 1.75 6.00 |

Nos. 149 and 150 were sold exclusively at the Luxembourg Phil. Exhib., Aug. 1922.

### Souvenir Sheet

View of Luxembourg — A16

---

**1923, Jan. 3    Perf. 11**

| | | | |
|---|---|---|---|
| 151 | A16 | 10fr dp grn, sheet | 1,500. 2,400. |
| | | Never hinged | 3,000. |

Birth of Princess Elisabeth. See No. 1606.

**1923, Mar.    Perf. 11½**

| | | | |
|---|---|---|---|
| 152 | A16 | 10fr black | 4.50 12.00 |
| a. | | Perf. 12½ ('34) | 4.50 12.00 |

For overprint see No. O141.

The Wolfsschlucht near
Echternach — A17

**1923-34    Perf. 11½**

| | | | |
|---|---|---|---|
| 153 | A17 | 3fr dk blue & blue | 1.50 .80 |
| a. | | Perf. 12½ ('34) | 1.50 .80 |

For overprint see No. O139.

## Stamps of 1921-26 Surcharged with New Values and Bars

**1925-28**

| | | | | |
|---|---|---|---|---|
| 154 | A12 | 5c on 10c yel grn | .25 | .30 |
| 155 | A12 | 15c on 20c yel grn ('28) | .25 | .25 |
| a. | | Bars omitted | | |
| 156 | A12 | 35c on 40c brn org ('27) | .25 | .25 |
| 157 | A12 | 60c on 75c dp bl ('27) | .25 | .25 |
| 158 | A12 | 60c on 80c blk ('28) | .40 | .35 |
| | | Nos. 154-158 (5) | 1.40 | 1.40 |

Grand Duchess
Charlotte — A18

**1926-35    Engr.    Perf. 12**

| | | | | |
|---|---|---|---|---|
| 159 | A18 | 5c dk violet | .25 | .25 |
| 160 | A18 | 10c olive grn | .25 | .25 |
| 161 | A18 | 15c black ('30) | .25 | .25 |
| 162 | A18 | 20c orange | .25 | .30 |
| 163 | A18 | 25c yellow grn | .25 | .30 |
| 164 | A18 | 25c vio brn ('27) | .25 | .30 |
| 165 | A18 | 30c yel grn ('27) | .25 | .25 |
| 166 | A18 | 30c gray vio ('30) | .55 | .25 |
| 167 | A18 | 35c gray vio ('28) | 3.25 | .25 |
| 168 | A18 | 35c yel grn ('30) | .25 | .25 |
| 169 | A18 | 40c olive gray | .25 | .25 |
| 170 | A18 | 50c red brown | .25 | .25 |
| 171 | A18 | 60c blue grn ('28) | 3.25 | .25 |
| 172 | A18 | 65c black brn | .25 | .90 |
| 173 | A18 | 70c blue vio ('35) | .25 | .25 |
| 174 | A18 | 75c rose | .25 | .30 |
| 175 | A18 | 75c bis brn ('27) | .25 | .25 |
| 176 | A18 | 80c bister brn | .25 | 1.25 |
| 177 | A18 | 90c rose ('27) | 1.25 | 1.40 |
| 178 | A18 | 1fr black | 1.25 | .30 |
| 179 | A18 | 1fr rose ('30) | .55 | .25 |
| 180 | A18 | 1¼fr dk blue | .25 | .55 |
| 181 | A18 | 1¼fr yellow ('30) | 9.50 | 1.75 |
| 182 | A18 | 1¼fr blue grn ('31) | .45 | .45 |
| 183 | A18 | 1¼fr rose car ('34) | 15.00 | 2.00 |
| 184 | A18 | 1½fr dp blue ('27) | 1.75 | 1.50 |
| 185 | A18 | 1¾fr dk blue ('30) | .90 | .40 |
| | | Nos. 159-185 (27) | 41.70 | 15.00 |
| | | Set, never hinged | 135.00 | |

For surcharges and overprints see Nos. 186-193, N17-N29, O142-O178.

## Stamps of 1926-35, Surcharged with New Values and Bars

**1928-39**

| | | | | |
|---|---|---|---|---|
| 186 | A18 | 10(c) on 30c yel grn ('29) | .40 | .40 |
| 187 | A18 | 15c on 25c yel grn | .30 | .65 |
| 187A | A18 | 30c on 60c bl grn ('39) | .25 | 1.40 |
| 188 | A18 | 60c on 65c blk brn | .25 | .30 |
| 189 | A18 | 60c on 75c rose | .25 | .30 |
| 190 | A18 | 60c on 80c bis brn | .30 | .60 |
| 191 | A18 | 70(c) on 75c bis brn ('35) | 6.00 | .40 |
| 192 | A18 | 75(c) on 90c rose ('29) | 2.00 | .40 |
| 193 | A18 | 1¾(fr) on 1½fr dp bl ('29) | 4.50 | 1.60 |
| | | Nos. 186-193 (9) | 14.25 | 6.05 |
| | | Set, never hinged | 45.00 | |

The surcharge on No. 187A has no bars.

View of
Clervaux — A19

---

**1928-34    Perf. 12½**

| | | | |
|---|---|---|---|
| 194 | A19 | 2fr black ('34) | 1.50 .80 |
| | | Never hinged | 4.00 |
| a. | | Perf. 11½ ('28) | 2.75 .80 |
| | | Never hinged | 6.00 — |

See No. B66. For overprint see No. O179.

Coat of Arms — A20

**1930, Dec. 20    Typo.    Perf. 12½**

| | | | |
|---|---|---|---|
| 195 | A20 | 5c claret | .85 .40 |
| 196 | A20 | 10c olive green | 1.10 .25 |
| | | Set, hinged | 5.50 |

View of the Lower City
of Luxembourg — A21

**1931, June 20    Engr.**

| | | | |
|---|---|---|---|
| 197 | A21 | 20fr deep green | 3.50 12.00 |
| | | Never hinged | 8.00 |

For overprint see No. O180.

Gate of "Three
Towers" — A22

**1934, Aug. 30    Perf. 14x13½**

| | | | |
|---|---|---|---|
| 198 | A22 | 5fr blue green | 2.50 10.00 |
| | | Never hinged | 7.50 |

For surcharge and overprint see Nos. N31, O181.

Castle From Our
Valley — A23

**1935, Nov. 15    Perf. 12½x12**

| | | | |
|---|---|---|---|
| 199 | A23 | 10fr green | 3.00 12.00 |
| | | Never hinged | 6.50 |

For surcharge and overprint see Nos. N32, O182.

Municipal Palace — A24

**1936, Aug. 26    Photo.    Perf. 11½
Granite Paper**

| | | | |
|---|---|---|---|
| 200 | A24 | 10c brown | .25 .30 |
| 201 | A24 | 35c green | .30 .30 |
| 202 | A24 | 70c red orange | .40 .75 |
| 203 | A24 | 1fr carmine rose | 1.10 1.50 |
| 204 | A24 | 1.25fr violet | 2.00 9.00 |
| 205 | A24 | 1.75fr brt ultra | 1.25 6.00 |
| | | Nos. 200-205 (6) | 5.30 17.85 |
| | | Set, never hinged | 16.00 |

11th Cong. of Intl. Federation of Philately. See No. 859.

Arms of
Luxembourg
A25

William I
A26

---

Designs: 70c, William II. 75c, William III. 1fr, Prince Henry. 1.25fr, Grand Duke Adolphe. 1.75fr, William IV. 3fr, Regent Marie Anne. 5fr, Grand Duchess Marie Adelaide. 10fr, Grand Duchess Charlotte.

**1939, May 27    Engr.    Perf. 12½x12**

| | | | | |
|---|---|---|---|---|
| 206 | A25 | 35c brt green | .25 | .25 |
| 207 | A26 | 50c orange | .25 | .25 |
| 208 | A26 | 70c slate green | .25 | .25 |
| 209 | A26 | 75c sepia | .65 | 1.25 |
| 210 | A26 | 1fr red | 1.75 | 2.50 |
| 211 | A26 | 1.25fr brown violet | .25 | .25 |
| 212 | A26 | 1.75fr dark blue | .25 | .25 |
| 213 | A26 | 3fr lt brown | .25 | .70 |
| 214 | A26 | 5fr gray black | .50 | 3.00 |
| 215 | A26 | 10fr copper red | 1.00 | 6.50 |
| | | Nos. 206-215 (10) | 5.40 | 15.20 |
| | | Set, never hinged | 11.00 | |

Centenary of Independence.

Allegory of Medicinal
Baths — A35

**1939, Sept. 18    Photo.    Perf. 11½**

| | | | |
|---|---|---|---|
| 216 | A35 | 2fr brown rose | .50 2.50 |
| | | Never hinged | 1.25 |

Elevation of Mondorf-les-Bains to town status.
See No. B104. For surcharge see No. N30.

### Souvenir Sheet

A36

**1939, Dec. 20    Engr.    Perf. 14x13**

| | | | | |
|---|---|---|---|---|
| 217 | A36 | Sheet of 3 | 45.00 | 100.00 |
| | | Sheet, never hinged | 100.00 | |
| a. | | 2fr vermilion, buff | 12.00 | 22.50 |
| b. | | 3fr dark green, buff | 12.00 | 22.50 |
| c. | | 5fr blue, buff | 12.00 | 22.50 |

20th anniv. of the reign of Grand Duchess Charlotte (Jan. 15, 1919) and her marriage to Prince Felix (Nov. 6, 1919).
See Nos. B98-B103.

Grand Duchess
Charlotte — A37

**1944-46    Unwmk.    Perf. 12**

| | | | | |
|---|---|---|---|---|
| 218 | A37 | 5c brown red | .25 | .25 |
| 219 | A37 | 10c black | .25 | .25 |
| 219A | A37 | 20c orange ('46) | .25 | .25 |
| 220 | A37 | 25c sepia | .25 | .25 |
| 220A | A37 | 30c carmine ('46) | .25 | .40 |
| 221 | A37 | 35c green | .25 | .40 |
| 221A | A37 | 40c dk blue ('46) | .25 | .40 |
| 222 | A37 | 50c dk violet | .25 | .25 |
| 222A | A37 | 60c orange ('46) | .80 | .25 |
| 223 | A37 | 70c rose pink | .25 | .25 |
| 223A | A37 | 70c dp green ('46) | .35 | .65 |
| 223B | A37 | 75c sepia ('46) | .25 | .25 |
| 224 | A37 | 1fr olive | .25 | .25 |
| 225 | A37 | 1¼fr red orange | .25 | .25 |
| 226 | A37 | 1½fr red orange ('46) | .25 | .25 |
| 227 | A37 | 1¾fr blue | .25 | .25 |
| 228 | A37 | 2fr rose car ('46) | 1.40 | .25 |
| 229 | A37 | 2½fr dp violet ('46) | 2.50 | 4.50 |
| 230 | A37 | 3fr dp yel grn ('46) | .35 | .50 |
| 231 | A37 | 3½fr brt blue ('46) | .35 | .75 |
| 232 | A37 | 5fr dk blue grn | .25 | .25 |
| 233 | A37 | 10fr carmine | .25 | 1.20 |
| 234 | A37 | 20fr deep blue | .45 | 8.00 |
| | | Nos. 218-234 (23) | 10.20 | 20.30 |
| | | Set, never hinged | 16.00 | |

Lion from Duchy
Arms — A38

**1945　　　Engr.　　　Perf. 14x13**
| 235 | A38 | 20c black | .25 | .25 |
|---|---|---|---|---|
| 236 | A38 | 30c brt green | .25 | .40 |
| 237 | A38 | 60c deep violet | .25 | .25 |
| 238 | A38 | 75c brown red | .25 | .25 |
| 239 | A38 | 1.20fr red | .25 | .25 |
| 240 | A38 | 1.50fr rose lilac | .25 | .25 |
| 241 | A38 | 2.50fr lt blue | .25 | .40 |
| | | Set, never hinged | 1.60 | |

Issued: 1.20fr, 5/15/45; 30c, 1.50fr, 2.50fr, 7/19; 20c, 75c, 10/1; 60c, 12/13.

Patton's Grave,
US Military
Cemetery,
Hamm — A39

Gen. Patton,
Broken Chain
and Advancing
Tanks — A40

**1947, Oct. 24　Photo.　Perf. 11½**
| 242 | A39 | 1.50fr dk carmine | .25 | .25 |
|---|---|---|---|---|
| 243 | A40 | 3.50fr dull blue | 1.00 | 2.00 |
| 244 | A39 | 5fr dk slate grn | 1.00 | 2.90 |
| 245 | A40 | 10fr chocolate | 5.25 | 40.00 |
| | | Nos. 242-245 (4) | 7.50 | 45.15 |
| | | Set, never hinged | 15.00 | |

George S. Patton, Jr. (1885-1945), American general.

Esch-sur-
Sûre
Fortifications
A41

Luxembourg
A44

Moselle
River — A42

Steel Mills — A43

**Perf. 11½x11, 11x11½**
**1948, Aug. 5　Engr.　Unwmk.**
| 246 | A41 | 7fr dark brown | 6.00 | .80 |
|---|---|---|---|---|
| 247 | A42 | 10fr dark green | 1.00 | .25 |
| 248 | A43 | 15fr carmine | 1.00 | .80 |
| 249 | A44 | 20fr dark blue | 1.00 | .80 |
| | | Nos. 246-249 (4) | 9.00 | 2.65 |
| | | Set, never hinged | 29.00 | |

Grand Duchess
Charlotte — A45

**1948-49　　　　　　Perf. 11½**
| 250 | A45 | 15c olive brn ('49) | .25 | .25 |
|---|---|---|---|---|
| 251 | A45 | 25c slate | .25 | .25 |
| 252 | A45 | 60c brown ('49) | .25 | .25 |
| 253 | A45 | 80c green ('49) | .25 | .25 |
| 254 | A45 | 1fr red lilac | .70 | .25 |
| 255 | A45 | 1.50fr grnsh bl | .70 | .25 |
| 256 | A45 | 1.60fr slate gray ('49) | .70 | 1.40 |
| 257 | A45 | 2fr dk vio brn | .70 | .25 |
| 258 | A45 | 4fr violet blue | 1.40 | .40 |
| 259 | A45 | 6fr brt red vio ('49) | 2.25 | .40 |
| 260 | A45 | 8fr dull green ('49) | 2.25 | 1.20 |
| | | Nos. 250-260 (11) | 9.70 | 5.15 |
| | | Set, never hinged | 26.00 | |

See Nos. 265-271, 292, 337-340, B151.

Self-Inking
Canceller — A46

**1949, Oct. 6　　　　　Photo.**
| 261 | A46 | 80c blk, Prus grn & pale grn | .25 | .55 |
|---|---|---|---|---|
| 262 | A46 | 2.50fr dk brn, brn red & sal rose | 1.00 | 2.00 |
| 263 | A46 | 4fr blk, bl & pale bl | 2.75 | 6.00 |
| 264 | A46 | 8fr dk brn, brn & buff | 9.00 | 20.00 |
| | | Nos. 261-264 (4) | 13.00 | 28.55 |
| | | Set, never hinged | 25.00 | |

UPU, 75th anniv.

**Charlotte Type of 1948-49**
**1951, Mar. 15　Engr.　　Unwmk.**
| 265 | A45 | 5c red orange | .25 | .25 |
|---|---|---|---|---|
| 266 | A45 | 10c ultra | .25 | .25 |
| 267 | A45 | 40c crimson | .25 | .25 |
| 268 | A45 | 1.25fr dk brown | .70 | .35 |
| 269 | A45 | 2.50fr red | .70 | .25 |
| 270 | A45 | 3fr blue | 4.50 | .35 |
| 271 | A45 | 3.50fr rose lake | 1.90 | .40 |
| | | Nos. 265-271 (7) | 8.55 | 2.10 |
| | | Set, never hinged | 22.50 | |

Agriculture and
Industry — A47

Globe and
Scales — A48

1fr, 3fr, People of Europe & Charter of Freedom.

**1951, Oct. 25　Photo.　Perf. 11½**
| 272 | A47 | 80c deep green | 4.00 | 9.50 |
|---|---|---|---|---|
| 273 | A47 | 1fr purple | 1.75 | .55 |
| 274 | A48 | 2fr black brown | 12.00 | .55 |
| 275 | A47 | 2.50fr dk carmine | 12.00 | 20.00 |
| 276 | A47 | 3fr orange brn | 22.50 | 30.00 |
| 277 | A48 | 4fr blue | 32.50 | 40.00 |
| | | Nos. 272-277 (6) | 84.75 | 100.60 |
| | | Set, never hinged | 175.00 | |

Issued to promote a united Europe.

Grand Duke
William
III — A49

**Perf. 13½x13**
**1952, May 24　Engr.　　Unwmk.**
**Dates, Ornaments in Olive Green**
| 278 | A49 | 2fr black | 21.00 | 30.00 |
|---|---|---|---|---|
| | | Never hinged | 30.00 | |
| 279 | A49 | 4fr red brown | 21.00 | 30.00 |
| | | Never hinged | 30.00 | |
| a. | | Se-tenant pair, #278-279 | 47.50 | 75.00 |
| | | Never hinged | 75.00 | |

Printed in sheets containing two panes of eight stamps each, alternating the two denominations. Centenary of Luxembourg's postage stamps. Price per set, 26fr, which included admission to the CENTILUX exhibition. See Nos. C16-C20.

Hurdle Race — A50

Designs: 2fr, Football. 2.50fr, Boxing. 3fr, Water polo. 4fr, Bicycle racing. 8fr, Fencing.

**1952, Aug. 20　Photo.　Perf. 11½**
**Designs in Black**
| 280 | A50 | 1fr pale green | .25 | .25 |
|---|---|---|---|---|
| 281 | A50 | 2fr brown buff | 1.00 | .25 |
| 282 | A50 | 2.50fr salmon pink | 1.50 | .35 |

| 283 | A50 | 3fr buff | 1.75 | .80 |
|---|---|---|---|---|
| 284 | A50 | 4fr lt blue | 10.50 | 6.00 |
| 285 | A50 | 8fr lilac | 6.00 | 3.50 |
| | | Nos. 280-285 (6) | 21.00 | 11.15 |
| | | Set, never hinged | 50.00 | |

15th Olympic Games, Helsinki; World Bicycling Championships of 1952.

Wedding of Princess Josephine-
Charlotte of Belgium and Hereditary
Grand Duke Jean — A51

**1953, Apr. 1**
| 286 | A51 | 80c dull violet | .25 | .25 |
|---|---|---|---|---|
| 287 | A51 | 1.20fr lt brown | .25 | .25 |
| 288 | A51 | 2fr green | .25 | .25 |
| 289 | A51 | 3fr red lilac | .25 | .30 |
| 290 | A51 | 4fr brt blue | 2.50 | 1.00 |
| 291 | A51 | 9fr brown red | 3.50 | 1.00 |
| | | Nos. 286-291 (6) | 7.00 | 3.05 |
| | | Set, never hinged | 17.50 | |

**Charlotte Type of 1948-49**
**1953, May 18　　　　　Engr.**
| 292 | A45 | 1.20fr gray | .40 | .25 |
|---|---|---|---|---|
| | | Never hinged | .90 | |

Radio
Luxembourg
A52

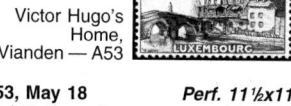

Victor Hugo's
Home,
Vianden — A53

**1953, May 18　　　Perf. 11½x11**
| 293 | A52 | 3fr purple | 2.75 | 1.50 |
|---|---|---|---|---|
| 294 | A53 | 4fr Prussian blue | 1.75 | 1.50 |
| | | Set, never hinged | 9.50 | |

150th birth anniv. of Victor Hugo (No. 294).

St. Willibrord Basilica
Restored — A54

Design: 2.50fr, Interior view.

**1953, Sept. 18　　　Perf. 13x13½**
| 295 | A54 | 2fr red | 1.60 | .40 |
|---|---|---|---|---|
| 296 | A54 | 2.50fr dk gray grn | 2.75 | 5.60 |
| | | Set, never hinged | 8.50 | |

Consecration of St. Willibrord Basilica at Echternach.

Pierre d'Aspelt — A55

**1953, Sept. 25**
| 297 | A55 | 4fr black | 4.00 | 4.00 |
|---|---|---|---|---|
| | | Never hinged | 7.00 | |

Pierre d'Aspelt (1250-1320), chancellor of the Holy Roman Empire and Archbishop of Mainz.

Fencing Swords, Mask
and Glove — A56

**1954, May 6　　　　Perf. 13½x13**
| 298 | A56 | 2fr red brn & blk brn, gray | 1.75 | .75 |
|---|---|---|---|---|
| | | Never hinged | 3.75 | |

World Fencing Championship Matches, Luxembourg, June 10-22.

Winged "L" Over
Map — A57

**1954, May 6　Photo.　Perf. 11½**
| 299 | A57 | 4fr dp bl, yel & red | 6.00 | 3.50 |
|---|---|---|---|---|
| | | Never hinged | 9.00 | |

6th Intl. Fair, Luxembourg, July 10-25.

Flowers — A58

Designs: 80c, Tulips. 2fr, Daffodils. 3fr, Hyacinths. 4fr, Parrot tulips.

**1955, Apr. 1**
| 300 | A58 | 80c multi | .25 | .25 |
|---|---|---|---|---|
| 301 | A58 | 2fr multi | .25 | .25 |
| 302 | A58 | 3fr multi | 1.75 | 3.25 |
| 303 | A58 | 4fr multi | 2.25 | 5.00 |
| | | Nos. 300-303 (4) | 4.50 | 8.75 |
| | | Set, never hinged | 8.50 | |

Flower festival at Mondorf-les-Bains. See Nos. 351-353.

Artisan, Wheel and
Tools — A59

**1955, Sept. 1　Engr.　　Perf. 13**
| 304 | A59 | 2fr dk gray & blk brn | .70 | .35 |
|---|---|---|---|---|
| | | Never hinged | 1.25 | |

Natl. Handicraft Exposition at Luxembourg — Limpertsburg, Sept. 3-12.

Dudelange
Television
Station — A60

**1955, Sept. 1　　　　Unwmk.**
| 305 | A60 | 2.50fr dk brn & redsh brn | .65 | .55 |
|---|---|---|---|---|
| | | Never hinged | 1.75 | |

Installation of the Tele-Luxembourg station at Dudelange.

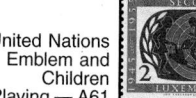

United Nations
Emblem and
Children
Playing — A61

UN, 10th anniv.: 80c, "Charter." 4fr, "Justice" (Sword and Scales). 9fr, "Assistance" (Workers).

**1955, Oct. 24　　　　Perf. 11x11½**
| 306 | A61 | 80c black & dk bl | .25 | .30 |
|---|---|---|---|---|
| 307 | A61 | 2fr red & brown | 1.75 | .25 |
| 308 | A61 | 4fr dk blue & red | 2.00 | 3.25 |
| 309 | A61 | 9fr dk brn & sl grn | .65 | .80 |
| | | Nos. 306-309 (4) | 4.65 | 4.60 |
| | | Set, never hinged | 11.00 | |

A62

# LUXEMBOURG

783

2fr, Anemones. 2.50fr, 4fr, Roses. 3fr, Crocuses.

**1956      Photo.      Perf. 11½**
**Flowers in Natural Colors**

| 310 | A62 | 2fr gray violet | .25 | .25 |
| 311 | A62 | 2.50fr brt blue | 2.50 | 3.75 |
| 312 | A62 | 3fr red brown | 1.00 | 2.00 |
| 313 | A62 | 4fr purple | 1.25 | 1.60 |
| | | Nos. 310-313 (4) | 5.00 | 7.60 |
| | | Set, never hinged | 10.00 | |

Flower Festival at Mondorf-les-Bains (Nos. 310, 312). Nos. 311 and 313 are inscribed: "Luxembourg-Ville des Roses."
Issued: Nos. 310, 312, 4/27; Nos. 311, 313, 5/30.

A63

Steel beam and city emblem.

**1956, May 30**

| 314 | A63 | 2fr grnsh bl, red & blk | .95 | .50 |
| | | Never hinged | 2.25 | |

50th anniversary of Esch-sur-Alzette.

Bessemer Converter and Blast Furnaces A64

Steel Beam and Model of City of Luxembourg A65

Design: 4fr, 6-link chain, miner's lamp.

**Perf. 11x11½, 11½x11**
**1956, Aug. 10      Engr.**

| 315 | A64 | 2fr dull red | 11.00 | .30 |
| 316 | A65 | 3fr dark blue | 11.00 | 17.00 |
| 317 | A64 | 4fr green | 2.00 | 2.75 |
| | | Nos. 315-317 (3) | 24.00 | 20.05 |
| | | Set, never hinged | 45.00 | |

4th anniv. of the establishment in Luxembourg of the headquarters of the European Coal and Steel Community.

"Rebuilding Europe" — A66

**1956, Sept. 15      Perf. 13**

| 318 | A66 | 2fr brown & black | 37.50 | .50 |
| 319 | A66 | 3fr brick red & car | 25.00 | 37.50 |
| 320 | A66 | 4fr brt bl & dp bl | 3.00 | 4.00 |
| | | Nos. 318-320 (3) | 65.50 | 42.00 |
| | | Set, never hinged | 155.00 | |

Cooperation among the six countries comprising the Coal and Steel Community.

---
**Catalogue values for unused stamps in this section, from this point to the end of the section, are for Never Hinged items.**
---

Central Station from Train Window — A67

**1956, Sept. 29      Perf. 13x12½**

| 321 | A67 | 2fr black & sepia | 2.50 | .55 |

Electrification of Luxembourg railways.

---

Ignace de la Fontaine — A68

Design: 7fr, Grand Duchess Charlotte.

**1956, Nov. 7      Perf. 11½**

| 322 | A68 | 2fr gray brown | 1.00 | .25 |
| 323 | A68 | 7fr dull purple | 2.75 | .90 |

Centenary of the Council of State.

Lord Baden-Powell and Luxembourg Scout Emblems — A69

Designs: 2.50fr, Lord Baden-Powell and Luxembourg Girl Scout emblems.

**1957, June 17      Perf. 11½x11**

| 324 | A69 | 2fr ol grn & red brn | 1.00 | .50 |
| 325 | A69 | 2.50fr dk vio & claret | 2.50 | 2.50 |

Birth centenary of Robert Baden-Powell and 50th anniv. of the founding of the Scout movement.

Prince Henry — A70

Children's Clinic — A71

Design: 4fr, Princess Marie-Astrid.

**1957, June 17      Photo.      Perf. 11½**

| 326 | A70 | 2fr brown | .60 | .25 |
| 327 | A71 | 3fr bluish grn | 3.00 | 1.75 |
| 328 | A70 | 4fr ultra | 2.00 | 2.10 |
| | | Nos. 326-328 (3) | 5.60 | 4.10 |

Children's Clinic of the Prince Jean-Princess Josephine-Charlotte Foundation.

"United Europe" — A72

**1957, Sept. 16      Engr.      Perf. 12½x12**

| 329 | A72 | 2fr reddish brn | 3.00 | .35 |
| 330 | A72 | 3fr red | 23.00 | 10.00 |
| 331 | A72 | 4fr rose lilac | 23.00 | 10.00 |
| | | Nos. 329-331 (3) | 49.00 | 20.35 |
| | | Set, hinged | 19.00 | |

A united Europe for peace and prosperity.

Fair Building and Flags — A73

**1958, Apr. 16      Perf. 12x11½**

| 332 | A73 | 2fr ultra & multi | .40 | .25 |

10th International Luxembourg Fair.

Luxembourg Pavilion, Brussels — A74

**1958, Apr. 16      Unwmk.**

| 333 | A74 | 2.50fr car & ultra | .30 | .25 |

International Exposition at Brussels.

---

St. Willibrord — A75

1fr, Sts. Willibrord & Irmina from "Liber Aureus." 5fr, St. Willibrord, young man & wine cask.

**1958, May 23      Engr.      Perf. 13x13½**

| 334 | A75 | 1fr red | .25 | .25 |
| 335 | A75 | 2.50fr olive brn | .45 | .25 |
| 336 | A75 | 5fr blue | 1.00 | .90 |
| | | Nos. 334-336 (3) | 1.70 | 1.40 |

1300th birth anniv. of St. Willibrord, apostle of the Low Countries and founder of Echternach Abbey.

**Charlotte Type of 1948-49**

**1958      Unwmk.      Perf. 11½**

| 337 | A45 | 20c dull claret | .25 | .25 |
| 338 | A45 | 30c olive | .25 | .25 |
| 339 | A45 | 50c dp org | .35 | .25 |
| 340 | A45 | 5fr violet | 8.25 | .40 |
| | | Nos. 337-340 (4) | 9.10 | 1.15 |

Issued: No. 337, 8/1; Nos. 338-340, 7/1.

---
**Common Design Types pictured following the introduction.**
---

**Europa Issue, 1958**
**Common Design Type**
**1958, Sept. 13  Litho.  Perf. 12½x13**
**Size: 21x34mm**

| 341 | CD1 | 2.50fr car & bl | .25 | .25 |
| 342 | CD1 | 3.50fr green & org | .35 | .25 |
| 343 | CD1 | 5fr blue & red | .75 | .40 |
| | | Nos. 341-343 (3) | 1.35 | .90 |

Wiltz Open-Air Theater — A76

Vintage, Moselle — A77

**1958, Sept. 13      Engr.      Perf. 11x11½**

| 344 | A76 | 2.50fr slate & sepia | .60 | .25 |
| 345 | A77 | 2.50fr lt grn & sepia | .60 | .25 |

No. 345 issued to publicize 2,000 years of grape growing in Luxembourg region.

Grand Duchess Charlotte — A78

**1959, Jan. 15      Photo.      Perf. 11½**

| 346 | A78 | 1.50fr pale grn & dk grn | .65 | .25 |
| 347 | A78 | 2.50fr pink & dk brn | .65 | .25 |
| 348 | A78 | 5fr lt bl & dk bl | 1.25 | .90 |
| | | Nos. 346-348 (3) | 2.55 | 1.40 |

40th anniv. of the accession to the throne of the Grand Duchess Charlotte.

NATO Emblem — A79

**1959, Apr. 3      Perf. 12½x12**

| 349 | A79 | 2.50fr brt ol & bl | .25 | .25 |
| 350 | A79 | 8.50fr red brn & bl | .40 | .35 |

NATO, 10th anniversary.

**Flower Type of 1955, Inscribed "1959"**

1fr, Iris. 2.50fr, Peonies. 3fr, Hydrangea.

---

**1959, Apr. 3      Perf. 11½**
**Flowers in Natural Colors**

| 351 | A58 | 1fr dk bl grn | .25 | .25 |
| 352 | A58 | 2.50fr deep blue | .40 | .25 |
| 353 | A58 | 3fr deep red lilac | .65 | .65 |
| | | Nos. 351-353 (3) | 1.30 | 1.15 |

Flower festival, Mondorf-les-Bains.

**Europa Issue, 1959**
**Common Design Type**
**Perf. 12½x13½**
**1959, Sept. 19      Litho.**
**Size: 22x33mm**

| 354 | CD2 | 2.50fr olive | .90 | .35 |
| 355 | CD2 | 5fr dk blue | 1.75 | .65 |

Locomotive of 1859 and Hymn — A80

**1959, Sept. 19      Engr.      Perf. 13½**

| 356 | A80 | 2.50fr red & ultra | 2.00 | .40 |

Centenary of Luxembourg's railroads.

Man and Child Knocking at Door — A81

Holy Family, Flight into Egypt — A82

**Perf. 11½x11, 11x11½**
**1960, Apr. 7      Unwmk.**

| 357 | A81 | 2.50fr org & slate | .25 | .25 |
| 358 | A82 | 5fr pur & slate | .40 | .40 |

World Refugee Year, July 1, 1959-June 30, 1960.

Steel Worker Drawing CECA Initials and Map of Member Countries — A83

**1960, May 9      Perf. 11x11½**

| 359 | A83 | 2.50fr dk car rose | .50 | .25 |

10th anniv. of the Schuman Plan for a European Steel and Coal Community.

European School and Children — A84

**1960, May 9**

| 360 | A84 | 5fr bl & gray blk | 1.00 | .85 |

Establishment of the first European school in Luxembourg.

Heraldic Lion and Tools — A85

**1960, June 14      Photo.      Perf. 11½**

| 361 | A85 | 2.50fr gray, red, bl & blk | 1.40 | .30 |

Natl. Exhibition of Craftsmanship, Luxembourg-Limpertsberg, July 9-18.

Grand Duchess Charlotte — A86

## 1960-64 Engr. Unwmk.

| | | | | |
|---|---|---|---|---|
| 362 | A86 | 10c claret ('61) | .25 | .25 |
| 363 | A86 | 20c rose red ('61) | .25 | .25 |
| 363A | A86 | 25c org ('64) | .25 | .25 |
| 364 | A86 | 30c gray olive | .25 | .25 |
| 365 | A86 | 50c dull grn | .60 | .25 |
| 366 | A86 | 1fr vio blue | .75 | .25 |
| 367 | A86 | 1.50fr rose lilac | .75 | .25 |
| 368 | A86 | 2fr blue ('61) | .80 | .25 |
| 369 | A86 | 2.50fr rose vio | 1.40 | .25 |
| 370 | A86 | 3fr vio brn ('61) | 1.60 | .25 |
| 371 | A86 | 3.50fr aqua ('64) | 2.25 | 1.90 |
| 372 | A86 | 5fr lt red brn | 2.25 | .25 |
| 373 | A86 | 6fr slate ('64) | 2.75 | .25 |
| | | Nos. 362-373 (13) | 14.15 | 4.90 |

The 50c, 1fr and 3fr were issued in sheets and in coils. Every fifth coil stamp has control number on back.

### Europa Issue, 1960
Common Design Type

**1960, Sept. 19          Perf. 11x11½**
**Size: 37x27mm**

| | | | | |
|---|---|---|---|---|
| 374 | CD3 | 2.50fr indigo & emer | .50 | .40 |
| 375 | CD3 | 5fr maroon & blk | .50 | .40 |

Great Spotted
Woodpecker — A87

Designs: 1.50fr, Cat, horiz. 3fr, Filly, horiz. 8.50fr, Dachshund.

**1961, May 15     Photo.     Perf. 11½**

| | | | | |
|---|---|---|---|---|
| 376 | A87 | 1fr multicolored | .25 | .25 |
| 377 | A87 | 1.50fr multicolored | .30 | .25 |
| 378 | A87 | 3fr gray, buff & red brn | .55 | .30 |
| 379 | A87 | 8.50fr lt grn, blk & ocher | .90 | .40 |
| | | Nos. 376-379 (4) | 2.00 | 1.20 |

Issued to publicize animal protection.

Clervaux and Abbey
of St. Maurice and St.
Maur — A88

**1961, June 8     Engr.     Perf. 11½x11**
| 380 | A88 | 2.50fr green | .50 | .25 |
|---|---|---|---|---|

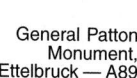

General Patton
Monument,
Ettelbruck — A89

**1961, June 8          Perf. 11x11½**
| 381 | A89 | 2.50fr dark blue & gray | .50 | .25 |
|---|---|---|---|---|

The monument commemorates the American victory of the 3rd Army under Gen. George S. Patton, Jr., Battle of the Ardennes Bulge, 1944-45.

### Europa Issue, 1961
Common Design Type

**1961, Sept. 18          Perf. 13x12½**
**Size: 29½x27mm**

| | | | | |
|---|---|---|---|---|
| 382 | CD4 | 2.50fr red | .25 | .25 |
| 383 | CD4 | 5fr blue | .30 | .30 |

Cyclist Carrying
Bicycle — A90

Design: 5fr, Emblem of 1962 championship.

**1962, Jan. 22     Photo.     Perf. 11½**

| | | | | |
|---|---|---|---|---|
| 384 | A90 | 2.50fr lt ultra, crim & blk | .25 | .25 |
| 385 | A90 | 5fr multicolored | .30 | .30 |

Intl. Cross-country Bicycle Race, Esch-sur-Alzette, Feb. 18.

### Europa Issue, 1962
Common Design Type

**1962, Sept. 17     Unwmk.     Perf. 11½**
**Size: 32½x23mm**

| | | | | |
|---|---|---|---|---|
| 386 | CD5 | 2.50fr ol bis, yel grn & brn blk | .30 | .25 |
| 387 | CD5 | 5fr rose lil, lt grn & brn blk | .45 | .30 |

St. Laurent's Church,
Diekirch — A91

**1962, Sept. 17     Engr.     Perf. 11½x11**
| 388 | A91 | 2.50fr brown & blk | .50 | .25 |
|---|---|---|---|---|

Bock Rock
Castle, 10th
Century
A92

Gate of
Three
Towers, 11th
Century
A93

Designs (each stamp represents a different century): No. 391, Benedictine Abbey, Munster. No. 392, Great Seal of Luxembourg, 1237. No. 393, Rham Towers. No. 394, Black Virgin, Grund. No. 395, Grand Ducal Palace. No. 396, The Citadel of the Holy Ghost. No. 397, Castle Bridge. No. 398, Town Hall. No. 399, Municipal theater, bridge and European Community Center.

**Perf. 14x13 (A92), 11½ (A93)**
**Engr. (A92), Photo. (A93)**
**1963, Apr. 13**

| | | | | |
|---|---|---|---|---|
| 389 | A92 | 1fr slate blue | .25 | .25 |
| 390 | A93 | 1fr multicolored | .25 | .25 |
| 391 | A92 | 1.50fr dl red brn | .25 | .25 |
| 392 | A93 | 1.50fr multicolored | .25 | .25 |
| 393 | A92 | 2.50fr gray grn | .25 | .25 |
| 394 | A93 | 2.50fr multicolored | .25 | .25 |
| 395 | A92 | 3fr brown | .25 | .25 |
| 396 | A93 | 3fr multicolored | .25 | .25 |
| 397 | A92 | 5fr brt violet | .25 | .25 |
| 398 | A93 | 5fr multicolored | .50 | .50 |
| 399 | A92 | 11fr multicolored | 1.00 | .65 |
| | | Nos. 389-399 (11) | 3.75 | 3.40 |

Millennium of the city of Luxembourg; MELUSINA Intl. Phil. Exhib., Luxembourg, Apr. 13-21. Set sold only at exhibition. Value of 62fr included entrance ticket. Nos. 390, 392, 394 and 396 however were sold without restriction.

Blackboard Showing
European School
Buildings — A94

**1963, Apr. 13     Photo.     Perf. 11½**
| 400 | A94 | 2.50fr gray, grn & mag | .35 | .25 |
|---|---|---|---|---|

10th anniv. of the European Schools in Luxembourg, Brussels, Varese, Mol and Karlsruhe.

Colpach Castle
and Centenary
Emblem — A95

**1963, May 8     Engr.     Perf. 13**
| 401 | A95 | 2.50fr hn brn, gray & red | .35 | .25 |
|---|---|---|---|---|

Centenary of the Intl. Red Cross. Colpach Castle, home of Emile Mayrisch, was donated to the Luxembourg League of the Red Cross for a rest home.

Twelve Stars of
Council of
Europe — A96

**1963, June 25          Perf. 13x14**
| 402 | A96 | 2.50fr dp ultra, gold | .30 | .25 |
|---|---|---|---|---|

10th anniv. of the European Convention of Human Rights.

### Europa Issue, 1963
Common Design Type

**1963, Sept. 16     Photo.     Perf. 11½**
**Size: 32½x23mm**

| | | | | |
|---|---|---|---|---|
| 403 | CD6 | 3fr bl grn, lt grn & org | .30 | .25 |
| 404 | CD6 | 6fr red brn, org red & org | .45 | .30 |

Brown Trout Taking
Bait — A97

**1963, Sept. 16     Engr.     Perf. 13**
| 405 | A97 | 3fr indigo | .30 | .25 |
|---|---|---|---|---|

World Fly-Fishing Championship, Wormeldange, Sept. 22.

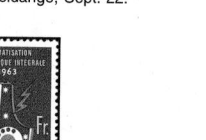

Map of Luxembourg,
Telephone Dial and
Stars — A98

**1963, Sept. 16     Photo.     Perf. 11½**
| 406 | A98 | 3fr ultra, brt grn & blk | .30 | .25 |
|---|---|---|---|---|

Completion of telephone automation.

Power House — A99

3fr, Upper reservoir, horiz. 6fr, Lohmuhle dam.

**1964, Apr. 17     Engr.     Perf. 13**

| | | | | |
|---|---|---|---|---|
| 407 | A99 | 2fr red brn & sl | .25 | .25 |
| 408 | A99 | 3fr red, sl grn & lt bl | .25 | .25 |
| 409 | A99 | 6fr choc, grn & bl | .25 | .25 |
| | | Nos. 407-409 (3) | .75 | .75 |

Inauguration of the Vianden hydroelectric station.

Barge Entering
Lock at
Grevenmacher
Dam — A100

**1964, May 26     Unwmk.**
| 410 | A100 | 3fr indigo & brt bl | .30 | .25 |
|---|---|---|---|---|

Opening of Moselle River canal system.

### Europa Issue, 1964
Common Design Type

**1964, Sept. 14     Photo.     Perf. 11½**
**Size: 22x38mm**

| | | | | |
|---|---|---|---|---|
| 411 | CD7 | 3fr org brn, yel & dk bl | .30 | .25 |
| 412 | CD7 | 6fr yel grn, yel & dk brn | .45 | .30 |

New Atheneum
Educational Center
and
Students — A101

**1964, Sept. 14     Unwmk.**
| 413 | A101 | 3fr dk bl grn & blk | .30 | .25 |
|---|---|---|---|---|

### Benelux Issue

King Baudouin, Queen Juliana and
Grand Duchess Charlotte
A101a

**1964, Oct. 12     Size: 45x26mm**
| 414 | A101a | 3fr dull bl, yel & brn | .30 | .25 |
|---|---|---|---|---|

20th anniv. of the customs union of Belgium, Netherlands and Luxembourg.

Grand Duke Jean
and Grand Duchess
Josephine
Charlotte — A102

**1964, Nov. 11     Photo.     Perf. 11½**

| | | | | |
|---|---|---|---|---|
| 415 | A102 | 3fr indigo | .30 | .25 |
| 416 | A102 | 6fr dk brown | .40 | .30 |

Grand Duke Jean's accession to throne.

Rotary Emblem and
Cogwheels — A103

**1965, Apr. 5     Photo.     Perf. 11½**
| 417 | A103 | 3fr gold, car, gray & ultra | .30 | .25 |
|---|---|---|---|---|

Rotary International, 60th anniversary.

Grand Duke
Jean — A104

## 1965-71 Engr. Unwmk.

| | | | | |
|---|---|---|---|---|
| 418 | A104 | 25c olive bister ('66) | .25 | .25 |
| 419 | A104 | 50c rose red | .25 | .25 |
| 420 | A104 | 1fr ultra | .25 | .25 |
| 421 | A104 | 1.50fr dk vio brn ('66) | .25 | .25 |
| 422 | A104 | 2fr magenta ('66) | .25 | .25 |
| 423 | A104 | 2.50fr orange ('71) | .35 | .25 |
| 424 | A104 | 3fr gray | .50 | .25 |
| 425 | A104 | 3.50fr brn org ('66) | .25 | .40 |
| 426 | A104 | 4fr vio brn ('71) | .30 | .25 |
| 427 | A104 | 5fr green ('71) | .35 | .25 |
| 428 | A104 | 6fr purple | .75 | .25 |
| 429 | A104 | 8fr bl grn ('71) | .65 | .25 |
| | | Nos. 418-429 (12) | 4.50 | 3.15 |

The 50c, 1fr, 2fr, 3fr, 4fr, 5fr and 6fr were issued in sheets and in coils. Every fifth coil stamp has control number on back.
See Nos. 570-576.

ITU Emblem, Old
and New
Communication
Equipment
A105

**1965, May 17     Litho.     Perf. 13½**
| 431 | A105 | 3fr dk pur, claret & blk | .35 | .25 |
|---|---|---|---|---|

ITU, centenary.

### Europa Issue, 1965
Common Design Type

**Perf. 13x12½**

**1965, Sept. 27     Photo.     Unwmk.**
**Size: 30x23½mm**

| | | | | |
|---|---|---|---|---|
| 432 | CD8 | 3fr grn, maroon & blk | .35 | .25 |
| 433 | CD8 | 6fr tan, dk bl & grn | .40 | .30 |

Inauguration of WHO Headquarters, Geneva — A106

**1966, Mar. 7 Engr. Perf. 11x11½**
434 A106 3fr green .30 .25

Torch and Banner — A107

**1966, Mar. 7 Photo. Perf. 11½**
435 A107 3fr gray & brt red .30 .25
50th anniversary of the Workers' Federation in Luxembourg.

Key and Arms of City of Luxembourg, and Arms of Prince of Chimay — A108

Designs: 2fr, Interior of Cathedral of Luxembourg, painting by Juan Martin. 3fr, Our Lady of Luxembourg, engraving by Richard Collin. 6fr, Column and spandrel with sculptured angels from Cathedral.

**1966, Apr. 28 Engr. Perf. 13x14**
436 A108 1.50fr green .25 .25
437 A108 2fr dull red .25 .25
438 A108 3fr dk blue .25 .25
439 A108 6fr red brown .25 .25
Nos. 436-439 (4) 1.00 1.00
300th anniv. of the Votum Solemne (Solemn Promise) which made the Virgin Mary Patron Saint of the City of Luxembourg.

**Europa Issue, 1966**
Common Design Type
**Perf. 13½x12½**
**1966, Sept. 26 Litho.**
**Size: 25x37mm**
440 CD9 3fr gray & vio bl .30 .25
441 CD9 6fr olive & dk grn .40 .30

Diesel Locomotive — A109

Design: 3fr, Electric locomotive.

**1966, Sept. 26 Photo. Perf. 11½**
442 A109 1.50fr multicolored .75 .25
443 A109 3fr multicolored .75 .30
5th Intl. Philatelic Exhibition of Luxembourg Railroad Men, Sept. 30-Oct. 3.

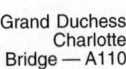

Grand Duchess Charlotte Bridge — A110

**1966, Sept. 26 Engr. Perf. 13**
444 A110 3fr dk car rose .30 .25

Tower Building, Kirchberg, Seat of European Community — A111

Design: 13fr, Design for Robert Schuman monument, Luxembourg.

---

**1966, Sept. 26**
445 A111 1.50fr dk green .25 .25
446 A111 13fr deep blue .60 .25
"Luxembourg, Center of Europe."

View of Luxembourg, 1850, by Nicolas Liez — A112

Map of Luxembourg Fortress, 1850, by Theodore de Cederstolpe — A113

**1967, Mar. 6 Engr. Perf. 13**
447 A112 3fr bl, vio brn & grn .25 .25
448 A113 6fr blue, brn & red .25 .25
Centenary of the Treaty of London, which guaranteed the country's neutrality after the dismantling of the Fortress of Luxembourg.

**Europa Issue, 1967**
Common Design Type
**1967, May 2 Photo. Perf. 11½**
**Size: 33x22mm**
449 CD10 3fr cl brn, gray & buff .50 .35
450 CD10 6fr dk brn, vio gray & lt bl .50 .35

Lion, Globe and Lions Emblem — A115

**1967, May 2 Photo. Perf. 11½**
451 A115 3fr multicolored .30 .25
Lions International, 50th anniversary.

---

**Canceled to Order**
Luxembourg's Office des Timbres, Direction des Postes, was offering, at least as early as 1967, to sell commemorative issues canceled to order.

---

NATO Emblem and European Community Administration Building — A116

**1967, June 13 Litho. Perf. 13x12½**
452 A116 3fr lt grn & dk grn .25 .25
453 A116 6fr dp rose & dk car .40 .40
NATO Council meeting, Luxembourg, June 13-14.

Youth Hostel, Ettelbruck — A117

**1967, Sept. 14 Photo. Perf. 11½**
454 A117 1.50fr multicolored .25 .25
Luxembourg youth hostels.

---

Home Gardener — A118

**1967, Sept. 14**
455 A118 1.50fr brt grn & org .25 .25
16th Congress of the Intl. Assoc. of Home Gardeners.

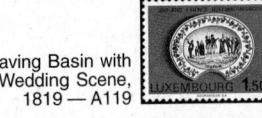

Shaving Basin with Wedding Scene, 1819 — A119

Design: 3fr, Ornamental vase, 1820, vert.

**1967, Sept. 14**
456 A119 1.50fr ol grn & multi .25 .25
457 A119 3fr ultra & lt gray .25 .25
Faience industry in Luxembourg, 200th anniv.

Wormeldange - Moselle River — A120

Mertert, Moselle River Port — A121

**1967, Sept. 14 Engr. Perf. 13**
458 A120 3fr dp bl, claret & ol .40 .25
459 A121 3fr violet bl & slate .25 .25

Swimming — A122

Sport: 1.50fr, Soccer. 2fr, Bicycling. 3fr, Running. 6fr, Walking. 13fr, Fencing.

**1968, Feb. 22 Photo. Perf. 11½**
460 A122 50c bl & grnsh bl .25 .25
461 A122 1.50fr brt grn & emer .25 .25
462 A122 2fr yel grn & lt yel grn .25 .25
463 A122 3fr dp org & dl org .25 .25
464 A122 6fr grnsh bl & pale grn .55 .25
465 A122 13fr rose cl & rose .60 .25
Nos. 460-465 (6) 2.15 1.50
Issued to publicize the 19th Olympic Games, Mexico City, Oct. 12-27.

**Europa Issue, 1968**
Common Design Type
**1968, Apr. 29 Photo. Perf. 11½**
**Size: 32½x23mm**
466 CD11 3fr ap grn, blk & org brn .40 .35
467 CD11 6fr brn org, blk & ap grn .40 .35

Kind Spring Pavilion — A123

**1968, Apr. 29 Photo. Perf. 11½**
468 A123 3fr multicolored .25 .25
Issued to publicize Mondorf-les-Bains.

---

Fair Emblem — A124

**1968, Apr. 29**
469 A124 3fr dp vio, dl bl gold & red .25 .25
20th Intl. Fair, Luxembourg City, May 23-June 2.

Children's Village of Mersch A125

Orphan and Foster Mother A126

**1968, Sept. 18 Engr. Perf. 13**
470 A125 3fr slate grn & dk red brn .25 .25
471 A126 6fr slate bl, blk & brn .40 .25
Mersch children's village. (Modeled after Austrian SOS villages for homeless children.)

Red Cross and Symbolic Blood Transfusion — A127

**1968, Sept. 18 Photo. Perf. 11½**
472 A127 3fr lt blue & car .40 .25
Voluntary Red Cross blood donors.

Luxair Plane over Luxembourg A128

**1968, Sept. 18 Engr. Perf. 13**
473 A128 50fr olive, bl & dk bl 3.25 .25
Issued for tourist publicity.

**Souvenir Sheet**

"Youth and Leisure" A129

Designs, a, 3fr, Doll. b, 6fr, Ballplayers. c, 13fr, Book, compass rose and ball.

**1969, Apr. 3 Photo. Perf. 11½**
**Granite Paper**
474 A129 Sheet of 3 3.25 3.50
a.-c. any single 1.00 1.00
1st Intl. Youth Phil. Exhib., JUVENTUS 1969, Luxembourg, Apr. 3-8.
No. 474 was on sale only at the exhibition. Sold only with entrance ticket for 40fr.

**Europa Issue, 1969**
Common Design Type
**1969, May 19 Photo. Perf. 11½**
**Size: 32½x23mm**
475 CD12 3fr gray, brn & org .45 .25
476 CD12 6fr vio gray, blk & yel .50 .25

Boy on
Hobbyhorse, by
Joseph Kutter
(1894-1941)
A130

Design: 6fr, View of Luxembourg, by Kutter.

**1969, May 19    Engr.    Perf. 12x13**
477 A130 3fr multicolored    .45    .25
   *a.*    Green omitted    150.00   150.00
478 A130 6fr multicolored    .45    .35

ILO, 50th
Anniv. — A131

**Photo.; Gold Impressed (Emblem)**
**1969, May 19    Perf. 14x14½**
479 A131 3fr brt grn, vio & gold    .25    .25

Mobius Strip in Benelux
Colors — A131a

**1969, Sept. 8    Litho.    Perf. 12½x13½**
480 A131a 3fr multicolored    .30    .25

25th anniv. of the signing of the customs union of Belgium, Netherlands and Luxembourg.

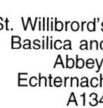

NATO, 20th
Anniv. — A132

**1969, Sept. 8    Perf. 13½x12½**
481 A132 3fr org brn & dk brn    .35    .25

Grain and Mersch
Agricultural
Center — A133

**1969, Sept. 8    Photo.    Perf. 11½**
482 A133 3fr bl grn, gray & blk    .25    .25

Issued to publicize agricultural progress.

St. Willibrord's
Basilica and
Abbey,
Echternach
A134

No. 484, Castle and open-air theater, Wiltz.

**1969, Sept. 8    Engr.    Perf. 13**
483 A134 3fr dark blue & indigo    .30    .25
484 A134 3fr slate green & indigo    .30    .25

Pasqueflower — A135

Design: 6fr, Hedgehog and 3 young.

**1970, Mar. 9    Photo.    Perf. 11½**
485 A135 3fr multicolored    .25    .25
486 A135 6fr green & multi    .40    .30

European Conservation Year.

Goldcrest — A136

**1970, Mar. 9    Engr.    Perf. 13**
487 A136 1.50fr org, grn & blk brn    .30    .25

Luxembourg Society for the protection and study of birds, 50th anniv.

Traffic Sign and
Street
Scene — A137

**1970, May 4    Photo.    Perf. 11½**
488 A137 3fr rose mag, red & blk    .30    .25

The importance of traffic safety.

**Europa Issue, 1970**
**Common Design Type**
**1970, May 4    Size: 32½x23mm**
489 CD13 3fr brown & multi    .40    .25
490 CD13 6fr green & multi    .40    .30

Empress
Kunigunde and
Emperor Henry
II, Window,
Luxembourg
Cathedral
A138

**1970, Sept. 14    Photo.    Perf. 12**
491 A138 3fr multicolored    .25    .25

Centenary of the Diocese of Luxembourg.

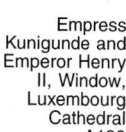

Census
Symbol — A139

**1970, Sept. 14    Perf. 11½**
492 A139 3fr dk grn, grnsh bl & red    .25    .25

Census of Dec. 31, 1970.

Lion, Luxembourg
City Hall — A140

**1970, Sept. 14**
493 A140 3fr bister, lt bl & dk brn    .25    .25

50th anniversary of the City of Luxembourg through the union of 5 municipalities.

UN
Emblem — A141

**Perf. 12½x13½**
**1970, Sept. 14    Litho.**
494 A141 1.50fr bl & vio bl    .25    .25

25th anniversary of the United Nations.

Monks in Abbey
Workshop — A142

Miniatures Painted at Echternach, about 1040: 3fr, Laborers going to the vineyard (Matthew 20:1-6). 6fr, Laborers toiling in vineyard. 13fr, Workers searching for graves of the saints.

**1971, Mar. 15    Photo.    Perf. 12**
495 A142 1.50fr gold & multi    .25    .25
496 A142 3fr gold & multi    .25    .25
497 A142 6fr gold & multi    .30    .25
498 A142 13fr gold & multi    1.20    .45
   *Nos. 495-498 (4)*    2.00   1.20

Olympic Rings, Arms of
Luxembourg — A143

**1971, May 3    Photo.    Perf. 12½**
499 A143 3fr ultra & multi    .35    .25

Intl. Olympic Committee, 71st session.

**Europa Issue, 1971**
**Common Design Type**
**1971, May 3    Perf. 12½x13**
**Size: 34x25mm**
500 CD14 3fr ver, brn & blk    .50    .25
501 CD14 6fr brt grn, brn & blk    .50    .40

A145

**1971, May 3    Litho.    Perf. 13x13½**
502 A145 3fr org, dk brn & yel    .25    .25

Christian Workers Union, 50th anniv.

Artificial Lake,
Upper
Sure — A146

Designs: No. 504, Water treatment plant, Esch-sur-Sure. 15fr, ARBED Steel Corporation Headquarters, Luxembourg.

**1971, Sept. 13    Engr.    Perf. 13**
503 A146 3fr ol, grnsh bl & indigo    .40    .25
504 A146 3fr brn, sl grn & grnsh bl    .45    .25
505 A146 15fr indigo & blk brn    1.00    .25
   *Nos. 503-505 (3)*    1.85    .75

School Girl with
Coin — A147

**1971, Sept. 13    Photo.    Perf. 11½**
506 A147 3fr violet & multi    .30    .25

School children's savings campaign.

Coins of Luxembourg
and Belgium — A148

**1972, Mar. 6**
507 A148 1.50fr lt grn, sil & blk    .25    .25

Economic Union of Luxembourg and Belgium, 50th anniversary.

Bronze Mask — A149

Archaeological Objects, 4th to 1st centuries, B.C.: 1fr, Earthenware bowl, horiz. 8fr, Limestone head. 15fr, Glass jug in shape of head.

**1972, Mar. 6**
508 A149 1fr lemon & multi    .25    .25
509 A149 3fr multicolored    .35    .25
510 A149 8fr multicolored    .75    .60
511 A149 15fr multicolored    .90    .45
   *Nos. 508-511 (4)*    2.25   1.55

**Europa Issue 1972**
**Common Design Type**
**1972, May 2    Photo.    Perf. 11½**
**Size: 22x33mm**
512 CD15 3fr rose vio & multi    .45    .25
513 CD15 8fr gray blue & multi    .50    .40

Archer — A150

**1972, May 2**
514 A150 3fr crimson, blk & olive    .45    .25

3rd European Archery Championships.

Robert Schuman
Medal — A151

**1972, May 2    Engr.    Perf. 13**
515 A151 3fr gray & slate green    .60    .25

Establishment in Luxembourg of the European Coal and Steel Community, 20th anniv.

The Fox Wearing
Tails — A152

**1972, Sept. 11    Photo.    Perf. 11½**
516 A152 3fr scarlet & multi    .30    .25

Centenary of the publication of "Renert," satirical poem by Michel Rodange.

National
Monument
A153

Court of Justice
of European
Communities,
Kirchberg — A154

**1972, Sept. 11    Engr.    Perf. 13**
517 A153 3fr sl grn, olive & vio    .45    .25
518 A154 3fr brn, bl & slate grn    .75    .25

Epona on
Horseback — A155

Archaeological Objects: 4fr, Panther killing swan, horiz. 8fr, Celtic gold stater inscribed Pottina. 15fr, Bronze boar, horiz.

**1973, Mar. 14    Photo.    Perf. 11½**
519 A155 1fr salmon & multi    .25    .25
520 A155 4fr beige & multi    .30    .25
521 A155 8fr multicolored    1.75    .60
522 A155 15fr multicolored    .75    .60
   *Nos. 519-522 (4)*    3.05   1.70

**Europa Issue 1973**
**Common Design Type**
**1973, Apr. 30    Photo.    Perf. 11½**
**Size: 32x22mm**
523 CD16 4fr org, dk vio & lt bl    .45    .25
524 CD16 8fr ol, vio blk & yel    .45    .50

Bee on Honeycomb — A156

**1973, Apr. 30    Photo.    Perf. 11½**
525 A156 4fr ocher & multi        .45 .25
Publicizing importance of beekeeping.

Nurse Holding Child — A157

**1973, Apr. 30**
526 A157 4fr multicolored        .40 .25
Publicizing importance of day nurseries.

Laurel Branch — A158

**1973, Sept. 10    Photo.    Perf. 11½**
527 A158 3fr violet bl & multi        .25 .25
50th anniv. of Luxembourg Board of Labor.

Jerome de Busleyden — A159

**1973, Sept. 10    Engr.    Perf. 13**
528 A159 4fr black, brn & pur        .30 .25
Council of Mechelen, 500th anniv.

National Strike Memorial, Wiltz — A160

**1973, Sept. 10**
529 A160 4fr ol bis, sl & sl grn        .50 .25
In memory of the Luxembourg resistance heroes who died during the great strike of 1942.

Capital, Byzantine Hall, Vianden A161

St. Gregory the Great A161a

Designs: No. 534, Sts. Cecilia and Valerian crowned by angel, Hollenfels Church. No. 535, Interior, Septfontaines Church. 8fr, Madonna and Child, St. Irmina's Chapel, Rosport. 12fr, St. Augustine Sculptures by Jean-Georges Scholtus from pulpit in Feulen parish church, c. 1734.

**1973-77    Perf. 13x12½, 14 (6fr, 12fr)**
533 A161 4fr green & rose vio        .30 .25
534 A161 4fr red brn, grn & lil        .40 .25
535 A161 4fr gray, brn & dk vio        .40 .25
536 A161a 6fr maroon        .50 .25

537 A161 8fr sepia & vio bl        1.00 .60
538 A161a 12fr slate blue        1.00 .65
    Nos. 533-538 (6)        3.60 2.25

Architecture of Luxembourg: Romanesque, Gothic, Baroque.
Issued: No. 533, 8fr, 9/10/73; Nos. 534-535, 9/9/74; 6fr, 12fr, 9/16/77.

Princess Marie Astrid — A162

**1974, Mar. 14    Photo.    Perf. 11½**
540 A162 4fr blue & multi        1.50 .30
Princess Marie-Astrid, president of the Luxembourg Red Cross Youth Section.

Torch — A163

**1974, Mar. 14**
541 A163 4fr ultra & multi        .50 .20
50th anniversary of Luxembourg Mutual Insurance Federation.

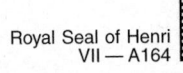

Royal Seal of Henri VII — A164

Seals from 13th-14th Centuries: 3fr, Equestrian, seal of Jean, King of Bohemia. 4fr, Seal of Town of Diekirch. 19fr, Virgin and Child, seal of Convent of Marienthal.

**1974, Mar. 14**
542 A164 1fr purple & multi        .25 .25
543 A164 3fr green & multi        .30 .25
544 A164 4fr multicolored        .35 .25
545 A164 19fr multicolored        1.00 .75
    Nos. 542-545 (4)        1.90 1.50

Hind, by Auguste Trémont — A165

Europa: 8fr, "Growth," abstract sculpture, by Lucien Wercollier.

**1974, Apr. 29    Photo.    Perf. 11½**
546 A165 4fr ocher & multi        .50 .30
547 A165 8fr brt blue & multi        1.50 1.20

Winston Churchill, by Oscar Nemon — A166

**1974, Apr. 29**
548 A166 4fr lilac & multi        .40 .25
Sir Winston Churchill (1874-1965), statesman.

Fairground, Aerial View — A167

**1974, Apr. 29**
549 A167 4fr silver & multi        .40 .25
Publicity for New International Fairground, Luxembourg-Kirchberg.

Theis, the Blind — A168

**1974, Apr. 29**
550 A168 3fr multicolored        .40 .25
Mathias Schou, Theis the Blind (1747-1824), wandering minstrel.

UPU Emblem and "100" — A169

**1974, Sept. 9    Photo.    Perf. 11½**
551 A169 4fr multicolored        .30 .25
552 A169 8fr multicolored        .90 .55
Centenary of Universal Postal Union.

"BENELUX" A170

**1974, Sept. 9**
553 A170 4fr bl grn, dk grn & lt bl        .90 .25
30th anniversary of the signing of the customs union of Belgium, Netherlands and Luxembourg.

View of Differdange A171

**1974, Sept. 9    Engr.    Perf. 13**
554 A171 4fr rose claret        1.00 .25

Bourglinster A172

Designs: 1fr, Fish Market, Old Luxembourg, vert. 4fr, Market Square, Echternach. 19fr, St. Michael's Square, Mersch, vert.

**Perf. 14x13½, 13½x14**
**1975, Mar. 10    Engr.**
555 A172 1fr olive green        .60 .25
556 A172 3fr deep brown        .90 .30
557 A172 4fr dark purple        .90 .25
558 A172 19fr copper red        1.25 .65
    Nos. 555-558 (4)        3.65 1.45

European Architectural Heritage Year.

Joseph Kutter, Self-portrait A173

Moselle Bridge, Remich, by Nico Klopp A174

Paintings: 8fr, Still Life, by Joseph Kutter. 20fr, The Dam, by Dominique Lang.

**1975, Apr. 28    Photo.    Perf. 11½**
559 A173 1fr multicolored        .30 .25
560 A174 4fr multicolored        1.20 .25
561 A174 8fr multicolored        1.75 1.25
562 A173 20fr multicolored        1.50 .50
    Nos. 559-562 (4)        4.75 2.25

Cultural series. Nos. 560-561 are Europa Issue.

Robert Schuman, Gaetano Martino, Paul-Henri Spaak Medals — A175

**1975, Apr. 28**
563 A175 4fr yel grn, gold & brn        .70 .25
Robert Schuman's declaration establishing European Coal and Steel Community, 25th anniv.

Albert Schweitzer (1875-1965), Medical Missionary — A176

**1975, Apr. 28    Engr.    Perf. 13**
564 A176 4fr bright blue        .70 .25

Civil Defense Emblem — A177

**1975, Sept. 8    Photo.    Perf. 11½**
565 A177 4fr multicolored        .60 .25
Civil Defense Org. for protection and rescue.

Figure Skating — A178

4fr, Water skiing, horiz. 15fr, Mountain climbing.

**1975, Sept. 8    Engr.    Perf. 13**
566 A178 3fr green, bl & lilac        .30 .25
567 A178 4fr dk brn, grn & lt brn        .45 .25
568 A178 15fr brown, indigo & grn        1.40 .55
    Nos. 566-568 (3)        2.15 1.05

**Grand Duke Type of 1965-71**
**1975-91    Engr.    Perf. 11½**
**Granite Paper (14fr, 22fr)**
570 A104 7fr orange        .45 .25
571 A104 9fr yellow green        .90 .25
572 A104 10fr black        .50 .25
573 A104 12fr brick red        1.20 .25
573A A104 14fr dark blue        .65 .30
574 A104 16fr green        1.00 .25
574A A104 18fr brown olive        .80 .40
575 A104 20fr blue        1.20 .25
576 A104 22fr orange brown        1.10 .80
    Nos. 570-576 (9)        7.80 3.00

Issued: 10fr, 1/9; 9fr, 12fr, 20fr, 12/23; 16fr, 2/25/82; 7fr, 7/1/83; 18fr, 3/3/86; 14fr, 1/2/90; 22fr, 9/23/91.

Grand Duchess Charlotte — A179

Design: No. 580, Prince Henri.

**1976, Mar. 8    Litho.    Perf. 14x13½**
579 A179 6fr green & multi        1.60 .30
580 A179 6fr dull blue & multi        1.60 .30

80th birthday of Grand Duchess Charlotte and 21st birthday of Prince Henri, heir to the throne.

Gold Brooch — A180

5fr, Footless beaker, horiz. 6fr, Decorated vessel, horiz. 12fr, Gold coin. All designs show excavated items of Franco-Merovingian period.

**Perf. 13½x12½, 12½x13½**
**1976, Mar. 8**
581 A180 2fr blue & multi .25 .25
582 A180 5fr black & multi .25 .25
583 A180 6fr lilac & multi .45 .25
584 A180 12fr multicolored .75 .75
*Nos. 581-584 (4)* 1.70 1.50

Soup Tureen — A181

Europa: 12fr, Deep bowl. Tureen and bowl after pottery from Nospelt, 19th century.

**1976, May 3    Photo.    Perf. 11½**
585 A181 6fr lt violet & multi .90 .25
586 A181 12fr yel grn & multi 1.00 1.00

Independence Hall, Philadelphia — A182

**1976, May 3**
587 A182 6fr lt blue & multi .50 .25
American Bicentennial.

Boomerang — A183

**1976, May 3**
588 A183 6fr brt rose lil & gold .50 .25
21st Olympic Games, Montreal, Canada, July 17-Aug. 1.

"Vibrations of Sound" — A184

**1976, May 3**
589 A184 6fr red & multi .50 .25
Jeunesses Musicales (Young Music Friends), association to foster interest in music and art.

Alexander Graham Bell — A185

**1976, Sept. 9    Engr.    Perf. 13**
590 A185 6fr slate green .50 .25
Centenary of first telephone call by Alexander Graham Bell, Mar. 10, 1876.

---

Virgin and Child with St. Anne — A186

Renaissance sculptures: 12fr, Grave of Bernard de Velbruck, Lord of Beaufort.

**1976, Sept. 9    Photo.    Perf. 11½**
591 A186 6fr gold & multi .30 .25
592 A186 12fr gold, gray & blk 1.20 .70

Johann Wolfgang von Goethe — A187

Portraits: 5fr, J. M. William Turner. 6fr, Victor Hugo. 12fr, Franz Liszt.

**1977, Mar. 14    Engr.    Perf. 13**
593 A187 2fr lake .25 .25
594 A187 5fr purple .30 .25
595 A187 6fr slate green .75 .25
596 A187 12fr violet blue .75 .45
*Nos. 593-596 (4)* 2.05 1.20
Famous visitors to Luxembourg.

Old Luxembourg — A188

Europa: 12fr, Adolphe Bridge and European Investment Bank headquarters.

**1977, May 3    Photo.    Perf. 11½**
597 A188 6fr multicolored .90 .25
598 A188 12fr multicolored 1.00 .80

Esch-sur-Sure — A189

Design: 6fr, View of Ehnen.

**1977, May 3    Engr.    Perf. 13**
599 A189 5fr Prus blue .50 .25
600 A189 6fr deep brown .50 .25

Marguerite de Busbach — A190

No. 602, Louis Braille, by Lucienne Filippi.

**1977, May 3    Photo.    Perf. 11½**
601 A190 6fr multicolored .50 .25
602 A190 6fr multicolored .50 .25
Notre Dame Congregation, founded by Marguerite de Busbach, 350th anniversary; Louis Braille (1809-1852), inventor of the Braille system of writing for the blind.

**Souvenir Sheet**

Luxembourg Nos. 1-2 — A191

---

**Engr. & Photo.**
**1977, Sept. 15    Perf. 13½**
603 A191 40fr gray & red brown 4.50 5.25
125th anniv. of Luxembourg's stamps.

Head of Medusa, Roman Mosaic, Diekirch, 3rd Century A.D. — A192

**1977, Sept. 15    Photo.    Perf. 11½**
604 A192 6fr multicolored 1.00 .25

Orpheus and Eurydice, by C. W. Gluck — A193

**1977, Sept. 15    Perf. 11½x12**
605 A193 6fr multicolored .70 .25
Intl. Wiltz Festival, 25th anniv.

Europa Tamed, by R. Zilli, and Map of Europe — A194

**1977, Dec. 5    Photo.    Perf. 11½**
606 A194 6fr multicolored .70 .25
20th anniversary of the Treaties of Rome, setting up the European Economic Community and the European Atomic Energy Commission.

**Souvenir Sheet**

Grand Duke and Grand Duchess of Luxembourg — A195

**Photogravure and Engraved**
**1978, Apr. 3    Perf. 13½x14**
607 A195   Sheet of 2   1.75 1.75
a.   6fr dark blue & multi .60 .75
b.   12fr dark red & multi .60 .75
Silver wedding anniversary of Grand Duke Jean and Grand Duchess Josephine Charlotte.

**Souvenir Sheet**

Youth Fountain, Streamer and Dancers A196

**1978, Apr. 3    Photo.    Perf. 11½**
608 A196   Sheet of 3   3.75 3.75
a.   5fr ultra & multi 1.00 1.20
b.   6fr orange & multi 1.00 1.20
c.   20fr yellow green & multi 1.00 1.20
Juphilux 78, 5th International Young Philatelists' Exhibition, Luxembourg, Apr. 6-10.

Charles IV, Statue, Charles Bridge, Prague — A197

Europa: 12fr, Pierre d'Aspelt, tomb, Mainz Cathedral.

---

**1978, May 18    Engr.    Perf. 13½**
609 A197 6fr dark violet blue .60 .25
610 A197 12fr dull rose lilac 1.00 .80
Charles IV (1316-78), Count of Luxembourg, Holy Roman Emperor. Pierre d'Aspelt (c. 1250-1320), Archbishop of Mainz and Prince-Elector.

Emile Mayrisch, by Theo Van Rysselberghe — A198

**1978, May 18    Perf. 11½**
611 A198 6fr multicolored 1.00 .25
Emile Mayrisch (1862-1928), president of International Steel Cartel and promoter of United Europe.

Our Lady of Luxembourg A199     Trumpeters and Old Luxembourg A200

**1978, May 18    Photo.    Perf. 11½**
612 A199 6fr multicolored .50 .25
613 A200 6fr multicolored .50 .25
Our Lady of Luxembourg, patroness, 300th anniv.; 135th anniv. of Grand Ducal Military Band.

Starving Child, Helping Hand, Millet A201     League Emblem, Lungs, Open Window A202

Open Prison Door — A203

**1978, Sept. 11    Photo.    Perf. 11½**
614 A201 2fr multicolored .25 .25
615 A202 5fr multicolored .25 .25
616 A203 6fr multicolored .50 .25
*Nos. 614-616 (3)* 1.00 .75
"Terre des Hommes," an association to help underprivileged children; Luxembourg Anti-Tuberculosis League, 70th anniv.; Amnesty Intl. and 30th anniv. of Universal Declaration of Human Rights.

Squared Stone Emerging from Rock, City of Luxembourg A204

**1978, Sept. 11    Engr.    Perf. 13½x13**
617 A204 6fr violet blue .60 .25
Masonic Grand Lodge of Luxembourg, 175th anniversary.

Julius Caesar on Denarius, c. 44 B.C. — A205

Roman Coins, Found in Luxembourg: 6fr, Empress Faustina I on Sestertius, 141 A.D. 9fr, Empress Helena on Follis, c. 324-330. 26fr, Emperor Valens on Solidus, c. 367-375.

**1979, Mar. 5    Photo.    Perf. 11½**
| | | | |
|---|---|---|---|
| 618 | A205 | 5fr multicolored | .35 .25 |
| 619 | A205 | 6fr multicolored | .40 .25 |
| 620 | A205 | 9fr multicolored | .60 .40 |
| 621 | A205 | 26fr multicolored | 1.40 .90 |
| | *Nos. 618-621 (4)* | | 2.75 1.80 |

St. Michael's Church, Mondorf-les-Bains
A206

Design: 6fr, Luxembourg Central Station.

**1979, Mar. 5    Engr.    Perf. 13**
| | | | |
|---|---|---|---|
| 622 | A206 | 5fr multicolored | .45 .25 |
| 623 | A206 | 6fr rose claret | .90 .25 |

Troisvierges Stagecoach
A207

Europa: 12fr, Early wall telephone, vert.

**1979, Apr. 30    Photo.    Perf. 11½**
| | | | |
|---|---|---|---|
| 624 | A207 | 6fr multicolored | 1.90 .25 |
| 625 | A207 | 12fr multicolored | 1.90 1.50 |

Michel Pintz Facing Jury — A208

**1979, Apr. 30    Engr.    Perf. 13**
| | | | |
|---|---|---|---|
| 626 | A208 | 2fr rose lilac | .45 .25 |

180th anniversary of peasant uprising against French occupation.

Antoine Meyer
A209

Abundance Crowning Work and Thrift, by Auguste Vinet
A210

Design: 6fr, Sidney Gilchrist Thomas.

**1979, Apr. 30**
| | | | |
|---|---|---|---|
| 627 | A209 | 5fr carmine | .40 .25 |
| 628 | A209 | 6fr light blue | .40 .25 |
| 629 | A210 | 9fr black | .40 .25 |
| | *Nos. 627-629 (3)* | | 1.20 .75 |

Antoine Meyer (1801-1857), mathematician and first national poet; centenary of acquisition of Thomas process for production of high-quality steel; 50th anniversary of Luxembourg Stock Exchange.

European Parliament — A211

**1979, June 7    Photo.    Perf. 11½**
| | | | |
|---|---|---|---|
| 630 | A211 | 6fr multi | 1.40 .45 |

European Parliament, first direct elections, June 7-10.

Angel with Chalice, by Barthelemy Namur — A212

Rococo Art: 12fr, Angel with anchor, by Namur, from High Altar, St. Michael's Church, Luxembourg.

**Engraved and Photogravure**
**1979, Sept. 10    Perf. 13½**
| | | | |
|---|---|---|---|
| 631 | A212 | 6fr multi | .30 .25 |
| 632 | A212 | 12fr multi | .60 .50 |

Road Safety for Children — A213

**1979, Sept. 10    Photo.    Perf. 11½**
| | | | |
|---|---|---|---|
| 633 | A213 | 2fr multi | .25 .25 |

International Year of the Child.

Radio Tele-Luxembourg Emblem — A214

**1979, Sept. 10**
| | | | |
|---|---|---|---|
| 634 | A214 | 6fr ultra, blue & red | .50 .25 |

50 years of broadcasting in Luxembourg.

John the Blind, Silver Coin, 1331 — A215

14th Century Coins: 2fr, Sts. Gervase and Protais, silver grosso. 6fr, Easter lamb, gold coin. 20fr, Crown and arms, silver grosso.

**1980, Mar. 5    Photo.    Perf. 11½**
| | | | |
|---|---|---|---|
| 635 | A215 | 2fr multi | .25 .25 |
| 636 | A215 | 5fr multi | .25 .25 |
| 637 | A215 | 6fr multi | .75 .25 |
| 638 | A215 | 20fr multi | 1.50 .60 |
| | *Nos. 635-638 (4)* | | 2.75 1.35 |

See Nos. 651-654.

Ettelbruck Town Hall — A216

No. 640, State Archives Building, horiz.

**1980, Mar. 5    Engr.    Perf. 13**
| | | | |
|---|---|---|---|
| 639 | A216 | 6fr brn & dk red | .75 .25 |
| 640 | A216 | 6fr multi | .75 .25 |

Jean Monnet — A217

Europa: 12fr, St. Benedict of Nursia.

**1980, Apr. 28    Perf. 13½**
| | | | |
|---|---|---|---|
| 641 | A217 | 6fr dark blue | .85 .30 |
| 642 | A217 | 12fr olive green | .85 .45 |

Sports for All — A218

**1980, Apr. 28    Photo.    Perf. 11½**
**Granite Paper**
| | | | |
|---|---|---|---|
| 643 | A218 | 6fr multi | 1.00 .30 |

Worker Pouring Molten Iron — A219

Design: 6fr, Man, hand, gears, horiz.

**1980, Apr. 28**
| | | | |
|---|---|---|---|
| 644 | A219 | 2fr multi | .25 .25 |
| 645 | A219 | 6fr multi | .40 .25 |

9th World Congress on Prevention of Occupational Accidents & Diseases, Amsterdam, May 6-9.

Mercury by Jean Mich — A220

Art Nouveau Sculpture by Jean Mich.

**1980, Sept. 10    Engr.    Perf. 14**
| | | | |
|---|---|---|---|
| 646 | A220 | 8fr shown | .45 .30 |
| 647 | A220 | 12fr Ceres | .75 .45 |

Introduction of Postal Code — A221

**1980, Sept. 10    Photo.    Perf. 11½**
| | | | |
|---|---|---|---|
| 648 | A221 | 4fr multi | .70 .25 |

Police Car and Officers — A222

**1980, Sept. 10**
| | | | |
|---|---|---|---|
| 649 | A222 | 8fr multi | .70 .25 |

State control of police force, 50th anniv.

Grand Duke Jean, Personal Arms A223

**Photo. & Engr.**
**1981, Jan. 5    Perf. 13½**
| | | | |
|---|---|---|---|
| 650 | A223 | Sheet of 3 | 2.10 2.10 |
| a. | | 8fr multi | .35 .35 |
| b. | | 12fr multi | .55 .55 |
| c. | | 30fr multi | 1.00 1.00 |

Grand Duke Jean, 60th birthday.

**Coin type of 1980**

Silver Coins: 4fr, Philip IV patagon, 1635. 6fr, Empress Maria Theresa 12 sol, 1775. 8fr, Emperor Joseph II 12 sol, 1789. 30fr, Emperor Francois II 72 sol, 1795.

**1981, Mar. 5    Photo.    Perf. 11½**
| | | | |
|---|---|---|---|
| 651 | A215 | 4fr multi | .25 .25 |
| 652 | A215 | 6fr multi | .30 .25 |
| 653 | A215 | 8fr multi | .45 .25 |
| 654 | A215 | 30fr multi | 1.40 .90 |
| | *Nos. 651-654 (4)* | | 2.40 1.65 |

National Library — A225

No. 656, European Hemicycle, Kirchberg.

**1981, Mar. 5    Engr.    Perf. 13**
| | | | |
|---|---|---|---|
| 655 | A225 | 8fr shown | .50 .25 |
| 656 | A225 | 8fr multicolored | .50 .25 |

Hammelsmarsch (Sheep Procession) — A226

Europa: 12fr, Bird-shaped whistle, Eimaischen market.

**1981, May 4    Photo.    Perf. 13½**
| | | | |
|---|---|---|---|
| 657 | A226 | 8fr multi | .60 .25 |
| 658 | A226 | 12fr multi | .85 .45 |

Knight on Chessboard
A227

Savings Account Book, State Bank
A228

First Bank Note, 1856 — A229

**1981, May 4    Perf. 11½**
**Granite Paper**
| | | | |
|---|---|---|---|
| 659 | A227 | 4fr multi | .50 .30 |
| 660 | A228 | 8fr multi | .45 .25 |
| 661 | A229 | 8fr multi | .45 .30 |

Luxembourg Chess Federation, 50th anniv.; State Savings Bank, 125th anniv.; Intl. Bank of Luxembourg, 125th anniv. of issuing rights.

Wedding of Prince Henri and Maria Teresa Mestre, Feb. 14 — A230

**Photo. & Engr.**
**1981, June 22    Perf. 13½**
| | | | |
|---|---|---|---|
| 662 | A230 | 8fr multi | .55 .35 |

Sheets of 12.

Single-seater Gliders — A231

16fr, Propeller planes, horiz. 35fr, Jet, Luxembourg Airport, horiz.

**1981, Sept. 28    Photo.    Perf. 11½**
**Granite Paper**
| | | | |
|---|---|---|---|
| 663 | A231 | 8fr shown | .40 .30 |
| 664 | A231 | 16fr multicolored | 1.00 .60 |
| 665 | A231 | 35fr multicolored | 1.50 .75 |
| | *Nos. 663-665 (3)* | | 2.90 1.65 |

Energy Conservation — A232

**1981, Sept. 28    Granite Paper**
666 A232 8fr multi      .50 .25

Apple Trees in Blossom, by Frantz Seimetz (1858-1914) A233

Landscape Paintings: 6fr, Summer Landscape, by Pierre Blanc (1872-1946). 8fr, The Larger Hallerbach, by Guido Oppenheim (1862-1942). 16fr, Winter Evening, by Eugene Mousset (1877-1941).

**1982, Feb. 25    Engr.    Perf. 11½**
667 A233 4fr multi    .25 .25
668 A233 6fr multi    .35 .25
669 A233 8fr multi    .75 .25
670 A233 16fr multi    .75 .55
    Nos. 667-670 (4)    2.10 1.30

World War II Resistance — A234

Design: Cross of Hinzert (Natl. Monument of the Resistance and Deportation) and Political Prisoner, by Lucien Wercollier.

**1982, Feb. 25**
671 A234 8fr multi      .50 .25

Europa — A235

8fr, Treaty of London, 1867. 16fr, Treaty of Paris, 1951.

**1982, May 4    Photo.**
**Granite Paper**
672 A235 8fr multicolored   .75 .25
673 A235 16fr multicolored   .90 .65

St. Theresa of Avila (1515-1582) — A236

Design: 8fr, Raoul Follereau (1903-1977), "Apostle of the Lepers."

**1982, May 4    Granite Paper**
674 A236 4fr multi   .25 .25
675 A236 8fr multi   .45 .25

State Museum — A237

No. 677, Synagogue of Luxembourg.

**1982, May 4    Photo. & Engr.**
676 A237 8fr shown   .35 .25
677 A237 8fr multicolored   .35 .25

Bourscheid Castle — A238

Designs: Restored castles.

**1982, Sept. 9   Engr.   Perf. 11½**
**Granite Paper**
678 A238 6fr shown   .45 .25
679 A238 8fr Vianden, horiz.   .75 .25

Intl. Youth Hostel Federation, 50th Anniv. — A239

**1982, Sept. 9    Photo.**
680 A239 4fr shown   .45 .25
681 A239 8fr Scouting year, vert.   .45 .30

Civilian and Military Deportation Monument — A240

**1982, Sept. 9**
682 A240 8fr multi    .55 .25

Mercury, Sculpture by Auguste Tremont — A241

**1983, Mar. 7   Photo.   Perf. 11½**
**Granite Paper**
683 A241 4fr multi    .25 .25
FOREX '83, 25th Intl. Assoc. of Foreign Exchange Dealers' Congress, June 2-5.

NATO Emblem, Flags — A242

**1983, Mar. 7    Granite Paper**
684 A242 6fr multi    .30 .25
25th anniv. of NAMSA (NATO Maintenance and Supply Agency).

Echternach Cross of Justice, 1236 — A243

**1983, Mar. 7    Granite Paper**
685 A243 8fr multi    .35 .25
30th Cong. of Intl. Union of Barristers, July 3-9.

Globe, CCC Emblem — A244

**1983, Mar. 7    Granite Paper**
686 A244 8fr multi    .35 .25
30th anniv. of Council of Customs Cooperation.

Natl. Federation of Fire Brigades Centenary — A245

**1983, Mar. 7    Granite Paper**
687 A245 8fr Fire engine, 1983   .60 .20
688 A245 16fr Hand pump, 1740   1.20 .60

Europa 1983 — A246

The Good Samaritan, Codex Aureus Escorialensis Miniatures, 11th Cent., Echternach.

**1983, May 3    Photo.**
689 A246 8fr Highway robbers   1.00 .45
690 A246 16fr Good Samaritan   1.75 .45

Giant Bible, 11th Cent. — A247

Illuminated Letters. 8fr, "h," Book of Baruch. 35fr, "B," letter of St. Jerome.

**Photo. & Engr.**
**1983, May 3    Perf. 14**
691 A247 8fr multicolored   .45 .25
692 A247 35fr multicolored   1.40 1.00

World Communications Year — A248

No. 693, Post code. No. 694, Satellite relay, horiz.

**1983, May 3   Photo.   Perf. 11½**
693 A248 8fr multicolored   .90 .30
694 A248 8fr multicolored   1.75 .30

Town Hall, Dudelange — A249

7fr, St. Lawrence Church, Diekirch, vert.

**1983, Sept. 7   Photo. & Engr.**
695 A249 7fr multi   .35 .30
696 A249 10fr multi   .55 .30

Basketball Fed., 50th Anniv. A250

European Working Dog Championship A251

Tourism — A252

No. 698, Alsatian sheepdog. No. 699, View of Luxembourg.

**1983, Sept. 7    Photo.**
**Granite Paper**
697 A250 7fr multicolored   .45 .25
698 A251 10fr multicolored   .75 .35
699 A252 10fr multicolored   1.20 .30
   Nos. 697-699 (3)   2.40 .90

Environment Protection — A253

**1984, Mar. 6   Photo.   Perf. 11½**
**Granite Paper**
700 A253 7fr Pedestrian zoning   .60 .25
701 A253 10fr Water purification   .75 .35

2nd European Parliament Election — A254

**1984, Mar. 6    Granite Paper**
702 A254 10fr Hands holding emblem   .70 .30

A255

**1984, Mar. 6   Engr.   Perf. 12½x13**
703 A255 10fr No. 1   .75 .30
704 A255 10fr Union meeting   .75 .30
705 A255 10fr Mail bag   .75 .30
706 A255 10fr Train   .75 .30
   Nos. 703-706 (4)   3.00 1.20
Philatelic Federation (1934); Civil Service Trade Union (1909); Postal Workers' Union (1909); Railroad (1859).

1984 Summer Olympics — A256

10fr, The Race, by Jean Jacoby (1891-1936).

**1984, May 7   Photo.   Perf. 11½x12**
707 A256 10fr multicolored   .70 .30

Europa (1959-84) — A257

**1984, May 7    Perf. 11½**
**Granite Paper**
708 A257 10fr green   1.50 .30
709 A257 16fr orange   1.60 .80

Young Turk Caressing His Horse, by Delacroix — A258

Paintings: 4fr, The Smoker, by David Teniers the Younger (1610-90). 10fr, Epiphany, by Jan Steen (1626-79). 50fr, The Lacemaker, by Pieter van Slingelandt (1640-91). 4fr, 50fr vert.

**Photo. & Engr.**
**1984, May 7    Perf. 14**
710 A258 4fr multi   .35 .30
711 A258 7fr multi   .55 .30
712 A258 10fr multi   .90 .30
713 A258 50fr multi   3.75 1.75
   Nos. 710-713 (4)   5.55 2.65

Marine Life Fossils — A259

4fr, Pecten sp. 7fr, Gryphaea arcuata. 10fr, Coeloceras raqyinianum. 16fr, Daildius.

1984, Sept. 10 Photo. *Perf. 11½*

714 A259 4fr multicolored .30 .25
715 A259 7fr multicolored .50 .25
716 A259 10fr multicolored .80 .25
717 A259 16fr multicolored 1.40 .90
Nos. 714-717 (4) 3.00 1.65

Restored Castles — A260

1984, Sept. 10 Engr.

718 A260 7fr Hollenfels .35 .25
719 A260 10fr Larochette .55 .35

A261

1984, Sept. 10 *Perf. 12x12½*

720 A261 10fr Soldier, US flag 1.75 .30

40th Anniv. of D Day (June 6).

A262

Portrait medals in the state museum: 4fr, Jean Bertels (1544-1607), Historian, Abbott of Echternach. 7fr, Emperor Charles V (1500-1558). 10fr, King Philip II of Spain (1527-1598). 30fr, Prince Maurice of Orange-Nassau, Count of Vianden (1567-1625).

Granite Paper

1985, Mar. 4 Photo. *Perf. 11½*

721 A262 4fr multi .25 .25
722 A262 7fr multi .35 .25
723 A262 10fr multi .60 .25
724 A262 30fr multi 2.10 .90
Nos. 721-724 (4) 3.30 1.65

See Nos. 739-742.

Anniversaries A263

No. 725, Benz Velo, First automobile in Luxembourg, 1895. No. 726, Push-button telephone, sound waves. No. 727, Fencers.

1985, Mar. 4 *Perf. 12x11½*

Granite Paper

725 A263 10fr multi .90 .30
726 A263 10fr multi .60 .25
727 A263 10fr multi .75 .25
Nos. 725-727 (3) 2.25 .80

Centenary of the first automobile; Luxembourg Telephone Service, cent.; Luxembourg Fencing Federation, 50th anniv.

Visit of Pope John Paul II — A264

1985, Mar. 4 *Perf. 11½x12*

Granite Paper

728 A264 10fr Papal arms .70 .25

Europa 1985 — A265

Designs: 10fr, Grand-Duke Adolphe Music Federation. 16fr, Luxembourg Music School.

1985, May 8 *Perf. 11½*

729 A265 10fr multi *1.60 .45*
730 A265 16fr multi *2.40 1.10*

Souvenir Sheet

End of World War II, 40th Anniv. A266

Designs: a, Luxembourg resistance fighters, Wounded Fighters medal. b, Luxembourg War Cross. c, Badge of the Union of Luxembourg Resistance Movements. d, Liberation of the concentration camps.

1985, May 8 *Perf. 11½x12*

Granite Paper

731 A266 Sheet of 4 4.00 4.00
a.-d. 10fr, any single .75 .60

Endangered Wildlife — A267

4fr, Athene nocturna, vert. 7fr, Felis silvestris. 10fr, Vanessa atalantica. 50fr, Hyla arborea, vert.

1985, Sept. 23 Photo. *Perf. 12x11½*

732 A267 4fr multicolored .90 .30
733 A267 7fr multicolored 1.50 .30
734 A267 10fr multicolored 2.40 .30
735 A267 50fr multicolored 5.25 1.75
Nos. 732-735 (4) 10.05 2.65

Historic Monuments — A268

7fr, Echternach Orangery, 1750. 10fr, Mohr de Waldt House, 17th cent., vert.

1985, Sept. 23 Engr. *Perf. 11½*

736 A268 7fr multicolored .45 .25
737 A268 10fr multicolored .50 .25

Natl. Art Collection — A269

10fr, 18th cent. book cover, Natl. Library.

Photo. & Engr.

1985, Sept. 23 *Perf. 14*

738 A269 10fr multicolored .70 .25

Portrait Medals Type of 1985

10fr, Count of Monterey, 1675. 12fr, Louis XIV, 1684. 18fr, Pierre de Weyms, c. 1700. 20fr, Duke of Marlborough, 1706.

1986, Mar. 3 Photo. *Perf. 11½*

Granite Paper

739 A262 10fr multicolored .45 .30
740 A262 12fr multicolored .60 .25
741 A262 18fr multicolored .75 .45
742 A262 20fr multicolored 1.25 .60
Nos. 739-742 (4) 3.05 1.60

Federation of Luxembourg Beekeepers' Associations, Cent. — A270

Mondorf State Spa, Cent. — A271

Natl. Table Tennis Federation, 50th Anniv. — A272

No. 743, Bee collecting pollen. No. 744, Mosaic. No. 745, Boy playing table tennis.

1986, Mar. 3 *Perf. 11½*

743 A270 12fr multicolored .85 .30
744 A271 12fr multicolored .85 .30
745 A272 12fr multicolored .85 .30
Nos. 743-745 (3) 2.55 .90

Europa 1986 — A273

12fr, Polluted forest, city. 20fr, Man, pollution sources.

1986, May 5 Photo. *Perf. 12*

Granite Paper

751 A273 12fr multicolored *1.25 .25*
752 A273 20fr multicolored *1.75 1.00*

Fortifications — A274

15fr, Ft. Thungen, horiz. 18fr, Invalid's Gate. 50fr, Malakoff Tower.

1986, May 5 Granite Paper

753 A274 15fr multicolored 1.40 .35
754 A274 18fr multicolored 1.40 .45
755 A274 50fr multicolored 3.00 .75
Nos. 753-755 (3) 5.80 1.55

Robert Schuman (1886-1963), European Cooperation Promulgator — A275

1986, June 26 *Perf. 12 on 3 Sides*

Granite Paper

756 A275 2fr pink & blk .25 .25
a. Bklt. pane of 4 .30
757 A275 10fr lt bl & blk .45 .30
a. Bklt. pane of 4 2.75
b. Bklt. pane of 2, #756-757 + 2 labels 1.40

Nos. 756-757 issued in booklets only.

European Road Safety Year — A276

1986, Sept. 15 Photo. *Perf. 11½*

758 A276 10fr multi .60 .25

Bas-relief, Town Hall, Esch-Sur-Alzette A277

Design: No. 760, Stairs to the Chapel of the Cross, Grevenmacher.

Photogravure & Engraved

1986, Sept. 15 *Perf. 14x13½*

759 A277 12fr shown 1.00 .30
760 A277 12fr multi 1.00 .30

Countess Ermesinde (1186-1247), Ruler of Luxembourg — A278

Designs: No. 761, Presentation of the letter of freedom to Echternach inhabitants, 1236, engraving (detail) by P.H. Witkamp, c. 1873. 30fr, Charter seal, Marienthal Convent, 1238.

1986, Sept. 15 *Perf. 13½x14*

761 A278 12fr multi .60 .25
762 A278 30fr multi 1.50 .75

Wildlife Conservation — A279

6fr, Eliomys quercinus, horiz. 10fr, Calopteryx splendens. 12fr, Cinclus cinclus. 25fr, Salamandra salamandra terrestris, horiz.

1987, Mar. 9 Photo. *Perf. 11½*

763 A279 6fr multicolored .45 .30
764 A279 10fr multicolored .90 .45
765 A279 12fr multicolored 1.40 .30
766 A279 25fr multicolored 2.50 1.10
Nos. 763-766 (4) 5.25 2.15

A280

1987, Mar. 9

767 A280 12fr multi .70 .30

Natl. Home Amateur Radio Operators Network, 50th anniv.

A281

1987, Mar. 9

768 A281 12fr multi .70 .25

Luxembourg Intl. Fair, 50th anniv.

Europa 1987 — A282

12fr, Aquatic Sports Center. 20fr, European Communities Court of Justice and abstract sculpture by Henry Moore (1898-1986).

1987, May 4 Photo. *Perf. 11½*

769 A282 12fr multi *1.50 .30*
770 A282 20fr multi *1.75 .90*

St. Michael's Church Millenary — A283

Designs: 12fr, Consecration of the church by Archbishop Egbert of Trier, 987, stained glass window by Gustav Zanter. 20fr, Baroque organ-chest, 17th century.

**Photogravure & Engraved**

| | | | **1987, May 4** | **Perf. 14** |
|---|---|---|---|---|
| 771 | A283 | 12fr multi | 1.00 | .30 |
| 772 | A283 | 20fr multi | 1.40 | .60 |

15th Century Paintings by Giovanni Ambrogio Bevilacqua — A284

Polyptych panels in the State Museum: 10fr, St. Bernard of Sienna and St. John the Baptist. 18fr, St. Jerome and St. Francis of Assisi.

| | | | **1987, May 4** | **Perf. 11½** |
|---|---|---|---|---|
| 773 | A284 | 10fr multi | .60 | .30 |
| 774 | A284 | 18fr multi | 1.25 | .60 |

Rural Architecture — A285

10fr, Hennesbau Bark Mill, 1826, Niederfeulen. 12fr, Health Center, 18th cent., Mersch. 100fr, Post Office, 18th cent., Bertrange.

**Photo. & Engr.**

| | | | **1987, Sept. 14** | **Perf. 13½** |
|---|---|---|---|---|
| 775 | A285 | 10fr multicolored | .60 | .30 |
| 776 | A285 | 12fr multicolored | .60 | .25 |
| 777 | A285 | 100fr multicolored | 5.00 | 1.10 |
| | | *Nos. 775-777 (3)* | 6.20 | 1.65 |

Chamber of Deputies (Parliament) 139th Anniv. — A286

Designs: 6fr, Charles Metz (1799-1853), first President. 12fr, Parliament, 1860, designed by Antoine Hartmann (1817-1891).

| | | | **1987, Sept. 14** | **Engr.** | **Perf. 14** |
|---|---|---|---|---|---|
| 778 | A286 | 6fr violet brn | | .30 | .25 |
| 779 | A286 | 12fr blue black | | .75 | .35 |

Flowers by Botanical Illustrator Pierre-Joseph Redoute (1759-1840) — A287

6fr, Orange lily, water lily. 10fr, Primula, double narcissus. 12fr, Tulip. 50fr, Iris, gorteria.

| | | | **1988, Feb. 8** | **Photo.** | **Perf. 11½x12** |
|---|---|---|---|---|---|
| 780 | A287 | 6fr multicolored | | .80 | .30 |
| 781 | A287 | 10fr multicolored | | .80 | .30 |
| 782 | A287 | 12fr multicolored | | 1.60 | .45 |
| 783 | A287 | 50fr multicolored | | 4.00 | 1.60 |
| | | *Nos. 780-783 (4)* | | 7.20 | 2.65 |

European Conf. of Ministers of Transport — A288

Eurocontrol, 25th Anniv. — A289

| | | | **1988, Feb. 8** | **Perf. 12** |
|---|---|---|---|---|
| 784 | A288 | 12fr multi | .75 | .30 |
| 785 | A289 | 20fr multi | 1.40 | .75 |

**Souvenir Sheet**

Family of Prince Henri A290

| | | | **1988, Mar. 29** | **Photo.** | **Perf. 12** |
|---|---|---|---|---|---|
| 786 | A290 | Sheet of 3 | | 5.50 | 5.50 |
| *a.* | | 12fr Maria Theresa | | .60 | .60 |
| *b.* | | 18fr Guillaume, Felix and Louis | | .90 | .90 |
| *c.* | | 50fr Prince Henri | | 2.75 | 2.75 |

JUVALUX '88, 9th intl. youth philatelic exhibition, Mar. 29-Apr. 4.

Europa 1988 — A291

Communication: 12fr, Automatic mail handling. 20fr, Electronic mail.

| | | | **1988, June 6** | **Photo.** | **Perf. 11½** |
|---|---|---|---|---|---|
| 787 | A291 | 12fr multicolored | | 1.75 | .40 |
| 788 | A291 | 20fr multicolored | | 1.75 | 1.75 |

Tourism — A292

Designs: 10fr, Wiltz town hall and Cross of Justice Monument, c. 1502. 12fr, Castle, Differdange, 16th cent., vert.

**Photo. & Engr.**

| | | | **1988, June 6** | **Perf. 13½** |
|---|---|---|---|---|
| 789 | A292 | 20fr multi | .90 | .30 |
| 790 | A292 | 12fr multi | .90 | .30 |

See Nos. 824-825, 841-842.

League of Luxembourg Student Sports Associations (LASEL), 50th Anniv. — A293

| | | | **1988, June 6** | **Photo.** | **Perf. 11½** |
|---|---|---|---|---|---|
| 791 | A293 | 12fr multi | | .80 | .35 |

Doorways — A294

Architectural drawings by Joseph Wegener (1895-1980) and his students, 1949-1951: 12fr, Septfontaines Castle main entrance, 1785. 25fr, National Library regency northwing entrance, c. 1720. 50fr, Holy Trinity Church baroque entrance, c. 1740.

**Litho. & Engr.**

| | | | **1988, Sept. 12** | **Perf. 14** |
|---|---|---|---|---|
| 792 | A294 | 12fr black & buff | .65 | .30 |
| 793 | A294 | 25fr blk & citron | 1.25 | .60 |
| 794 | A294 | 50fr blk & yel bister | 2.60 | 1.25 |
| | | *Nos. 792-794 (3)* | 4.50 | 2.15 |

Jean Monnet (1888-1979), French Economist A295

| | | | **1988, Sept. 12** | **Engr.** |
|---|---|---|---|---|
| 795 | A295 | 12fr multi | 1.00 | .35 |

European Investment Bank, 30th Anniv. — A296

| | | | **1988, Sept. 12** | **Litho. & Engr.** |
|---|---|---|---|---|
| 796 | A296 | 12fr yel grn & blk | .90 | .30 |

1988 Summer Olympics, Seoul — A297

| | | | **1988, Sept. 12** | **Photo.** | **Perf. 11½** |
|---|---|---|---|---|---|
| 797 | A297 | 12fr multi | | .85 | .30 |

A298

Design: 12fr, Portrait and excerpt from his speech to the Chamber of Deputies, 1896.

| | | | **1989, Mar. 6** | **Photo.** | **Perf. 11½x12** |
|---|---|---|---|---|---|
| 798 | A298 | 12fr multi | | .65 | .35 |

C.M. Spoo (1837-1914), advocate of Luxembourgish as the natl. language.

Book Workers' Fed., 125th Anniv. — A299

**1989, Mar. 6**
| | | | | |
|---|---|---|---|---|
| 799 | A299 | 18fr multi | .95 | .50 |

Natl. Red Cross, 75th Anniv. — A300

**1989, Mar. 6**
| | | | | |
|---|---|---|---|---|
| 800 | A300 | 20fr Henri Dunant | 1.60 | .90 |

Independence of the Grand Duchy, 150th Anniv. — A301

Design: 12fr, Lion, bronze sculpture by Auguste Tremont (1892-1980) guarding the grand ducal family vault, Cathedral of Luxembourg.

**Photo. & Engr.**

| | | | **1989, Mar. 6** | **Perf. 14** |
|---|---|---|---|---|
| 801 | A301 | 12fr multi | 1.00 | .35 |

Astra Telecommunications Satellite — A302

| | | | **1989, Mar. 6** | **Photo.** | **Perf. 11½** |
|---|---|---|---|---|---|
| 802 | A302 | 12fr multi | | 1.00 | .35 |

Europa 1989 — A303

Paintings (children at play): 12fr, *Three Children in a Park*, 19th cent., anonymous. 20fr, *Child with Drum*, 17th cent., anonymous.

| | | | **1989, May 8** | **Photo.** | **Perf. 11½x12** |
|---|---|---|---|---|---|
| 803 | A303 | 12fr multi | | .90 | .90 |
| 804 | A303 | 20fr multi | | .90 | .90 |

Tour de France — A304

| | | | **1989, May 8** | **Perf. 11½** |
|---|---|---|---|---|
| 805 | A304 | 9fr multi | .90 | .45 |

Start of the bicycle race in Luxembourg City.

Interparliamentary Union, Cent. — A305

| | | | **1989, May 8** | **Perf. 11½x12** |
|---|---|---|---|---|
| 806 | A305 | 12fr multi | .75 | .40 |

A306

**1989, May 8**
| | | | | |
|---|---|---|---|---|
| 807 | A306 | 12fr multi | .85 | .45 |

European Parliament 3rd elections.

Council of Europe, 40th Anniv. — A307

| | | | **1989, May 8** | **Perf. 12x11½** |
|---|---|---|---|---|
| 808 | A307 | 12fr multi | .85 | .45 |

Reign of Grand Duke Jean, 25th Anniv. — A308

**1989, Sept. 18   Photo.   Perf. 12x11½**
**Booklet Stamps**

| | | | | |
|---|---|---|---|---|
| 810 | A308 | 3fr black & orange | 1.50 | 1.40 |
| *a.* | | Bklt. pane of 4 | 6.00 | |
| 811 | A308 | 9fr black & blue green | 1.25 | 1.25 |
| *a.* | | Bklt. pane of 4 | 5.00 | |
| *b.* | | Bklt. pane, 1 each #810, 811 + 2 labels | 2.50 | |
| | | Booklet, 1 each #810a, 811a, 811b | 16.00 | |

Charles IV (1316-1378) — A309

Stained-glass windows by Joseph Oberberger in the Grand Ducal Loggia, Cathedral of Luxembourg: 20fr, John the Blind (1296-1346). 25fr, Wenceslas II (1361-1419).

**Photo. & Engr.**

| | | | | |
|---|---|---|---|---|
| **1989, Sept. 18** | | | **Perf. 13½x14** | |
| 821 | A309 | 12fr shown | .70 | .25 |
| 822 | A309 | 20fr multi | 1.10 | .85 |
| 823 | A309 | 25fr multi | 1.40 | 1.00 |
| | *Nos. 821-823 (3)* | | 3.20 | 2.10 |

Independence of the Grand Duchy, 150th anniv.

**Tourism Type of 1988**

Designs: 12fr, Clervaux Castle interior courtyard, circa 12th cent. 18fr, Bronzed wild boar of Titelberg, 1st cent., vert.

**Litho. & Engr.**

| | | | | |
|---|---|---|---|---|
| **1989, Sept. 18** | | | **Perf. 13½** | |
| 824 | A292 | 12fr multi | .70 | .35 |
| 825 | A292 | 18fr multi | 1.40 | .55 |

Views of the Former Fortress of Luxembourg, 1814-1815, Engravings by Christoph Wilhelm Selig (1791-1837) A310

| | | | | |
|---|---|---|---|---|
| **1990, Mar. 5** | **Photo.** | | **Perf. 12x11½** | |
| 826 | A310 | 9fr shown | .55 | .35 |
| 827 | A310 | 12fr multi, diff. | .70 | .35 |
| 828 | A310 | 20fr multi, diff. | 1.50 | .90 |
| 829 | A310 | 25fr multi, diff. | 2.00 | 1.00 |
| | *Nos. 826-829 (4)* | | 4.75 | 2.60 |

Congress of Vienna, 1815, during which the Duchy of Luxembourg was elevated to the Grand Duchy of Luxembourg.

Schueberfouer Carnival, 650th Anniv. — A311

| | | | | |
|---|---|---|---|---|
| **1990, Mar. 15** | | | **Perf. 11½x12** | |
| 830 | A311 | 9fr Carnival ride | .75 | .30 |

Batty Weber (1860-1940), Writer — A312

| | | | | |
|---|---|---|---|---|
| **1990, Mar. 15** | | | | |
| 831 | A312 | 12fr multi | .75 | .30 |

ITU, 125th Anniv. — A313

| | | | | |
|---|---|---|---|---|
| **1990, Mar. 15** | | | | |
| 832 | A313 | 18fr multicolored | 1.10 | .60 |

A314

Europa (Post Offices): 12fr, Luxembourg City. 20fr, Esch-Sur-Alzette, vert.

**Litho. & Engr.**

| | | | | |
|---|---|---|---|---|
| **1990, May 28** | | | **Perf. 13½** | |
| 833 | A314 | 12fr buff & blk | 1.75 | .30 |
| 834 | A314 | 20fr lt bl & blk | 1.75 | 1.20 |

A315

Prime Ministers: 9fr, Paul Eyschen (1841-1915). 12fr, Emmanuel Servais (1811-1890).

**Photo. & Engr.**

| | | | | |
|---|---|---|---|---|
| **1990, May 28** | | | **Perf. 14x13½** | |
| 835 | A315 | 9fr multicolored | .55 | .35 |
| 836 | A315 | 12fr multicolored | .75 | .35 |

Psallus Pseudoplatani — A316

| | | | | |
|---|---|---|---|---|
| **1990, May 28** | **Photo.** | | **Perf. 11½** | |
| 837 | A316 | 12fr multicolored | .75 | .35 |

Luxembourg Naturalists' Society, cent.

A317

Fountains: 12fr, Sheep's march by Will Lofy. 25fr, Fountain of Doves. 50fr, "Maus Ketty" by Lofy.

**Litho. & Engr.**

| | | | | |
|---|---|---|---|---|
| **1990, Sept. 24** | | | **Perf. 14** | |
| 838 | A317 | 12fr multicolored | .75 | .25 |
| 839 | A317 | 25fr multicolored | 1.50 | .90 |
| 840 | A317 | 50fr multicolored | 3.25 | 1.60 |
| | *Nos. 838-840 (3)* | | 5.50 | 2.75 |

**Tourism Type of 1988**

| | | | | |
|---|---|---|---|---|
| **1990, Sept. 24** | | | **Perf. 13½** | |
| 841 | A292 | 12fr Mondercange | 1.00 | .35 |
| 842 | A292 | 12fr Schifflange | 1.00 | .35 |

**Souvenir Sheet**

Nassau-Weilburg Dynasty, Cent. — A318

Designs: a, Grand Duke Adolphe. b, Grand Duchess Marie-Adelaide. c, Grand Ducal House arms. d, Grand Duchess Charlotte. e, Grand Duke Guillaume. f, Grand Duke Jean.

**Photo. & Engr.**

| | | | | |
|---|---|---|---|---|
| **1990, Nov. 26** | | | **Perf. 14x13½** | |
| 843 | A318 | Sheet of 6 | 8.50 | 8.50 |
| a.-b. | | 12fr multicolored | 1.25 | 1.25 |
| c.-d. | | 18fr multicolored | 1.40 | 1.40 |
| e.-f. | | 20fr multicolored | 1.60 | 1.60 |

View From the Trier Road by Sosthene Weis (1872-1941) A319

Paintings: 18fr, Vauban Street and the Viaduct. 25fr, St. Ulric Street.

| | | | | |
|---|---|---|---|---|
| **Perf. 12x11½, 11½x12** | | | **Photo.** | |
| **1991, Mar. 4** | | | | |
| 844 | A319 | 14fr multicolored | .90 | .50 |
| 845 | A319 | 18fr multicolored | 1.25 | .75 |
| 846 | A319 | 25fr multi, vert. | 1.50 | .90 |
| | *Nos. 844-846 (3)* | | 3.65 | 2.15 |

Fungi — A320

No. 847, Geastrum varians. No. 848, Agaricus (Gymnopus) thiebautii. No. 849, Agaricus (lepiota) lepidocephalus. No. 850, Morchella favosa.

| | | | | |
|---|---|---|---|---|
| **1991, Mar. 4** | | | **Perf. 11½** | |
| 847 | A320 | 14fr multicolored | .90 | .45 |
| 848 | A320 | 14fr multicolored | .90 | .45 |
| 849 | A320 | 18fr multicolored | 1.25 | .90 |
| 850 | A320 | 25fr multicolored | 2.25 | 1.10 |
| | *Nos. 847-850 (4)* | | 5.30 | 2.90 |

Europa — A321

No. 851, Astra 1A, 1B satellites. No. 852, Betzdorf ground station.

| | | | | |
|---|---|---|---|---|
| **1991, May 13** | **Photo.** | | **Perf. 12x11½** | |
| 851 | A321 | 14fr multicolored | 1.50 | .35 |
| 852 | A321 | 18fr multicolored | 1.75 | 1.40 |

Natl. Miners' Monument, Kayl — A322

Designs: No. 854, Magistrates' Court, Redange-Sur-Attert, horiz.

| | | | | |
|---|---|---|---|---|
| **1991, May 23** | **Perf. 11½x12, 12x11½** | | | |
| 853 | A322 | 14fr multicolored | 1.00 | .40 |
| 854 | A322 | 14fr multicolored | 1.00 | .40 |

Art by Emile Kirscht — A323

No. 856, Edmund de la Fontaine (1823-91), poet.

| | | | | |
|---|---|---|---|---|
| **1991, May 23** | | | **Perf. 11½** | |
| 855 | A323 | 14fr multicolored | 1.00 | .40 |
| 856 | A323 | 14fr multicolored | 1.00 | .40 |

Labor Unions, 75th anniv. (No. 855).

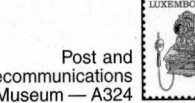

Post and Telecommunications Museum — A324

**Perf. 11½ on 3 sides**

| | | | | |
|---|---|---|---|---|
| **1991, Sept. 23** | | | **Photo.** | |
| | **Booklet Stamps** | | | |
| 857 | A324 | 4fr Old telephone | 2.50 | 1.40 |
| a. | | Bklt. pane of 1 + 3 labels | 3.50 | |
| 858 | A324 | 14fr Old postbox | .75 | .35 |
| a. | | Bklt. pane of 4 | 3.00 | |

Stamp Day, 50th Anniv. — A325

| | | | | |
|---|---|---|---|---|
| **1991, Sept. 23** | | | **Perf. 11½** | |
| 859 | A325 | 14fr Stamp of Type A24 | 1.00 | .50 |

A326

Gargoyles: 14fr, Young girl's head. 25fr, Woman's head. 50fr, Man's head.

**Photo. & Engr.**

| | | | | |
|---|---|---|---|---|
| **1991, Sept. 23** | | | **Perf. 14** | |
| 860 | A326 | 14fr multicolored | .75 | .40 |
| 861 | A326 | 25fr multicolored | 1.50 | .65 |
| 862 | A326 | 50fr multicolored | 2.50 | 1.40 |
| | *Nos. 860-862 (3)* | | 4.75 | 2.45 |

See Nos. 874-876.

Jean-Pierre Pescatore Foundation, Cent. — A327

Buildings: No. 864, High Technology Institute. No. 865, New Fair and Congress Centre.

| | | | | |
|---|---|---|---|---|
| **1992, Mar. 16** | **Photo.** | | **Perf. 11½** | |
| 863 | A327 | 14fr lil rose & multi | .85 | .45 |
| 864 | A327 | 14fr grn & multi | .85 | .45 |
| 865 | A327 | 14fr brt bl & multi | .85 | .45 |
| | *Nos. 863-865 (3)* | | 2.55 | 1.35 |

Bettembourg Castle — A328

25fr, Walferdange station.

| | | | | |
|---|---|---|---|---|
| **1992, Mar. 16** | | | | |
| 866 | A328 | 18fr shown | 1.00 | .35 |
| 867 | A328 | 25fr multicolored | 1.50 | .75 |

Europa — A329

Emigrants to US: 14fr, Nicholas Gonner (1835-1892), newspaper editor. 22fr, N. E. Becker (1842-1920), journalist.

**Photo. & Engr.**

| | | | | |
|---|---|---|---|---|
| **1992, May 18** | | | **Perf. 13½x14½** | |
| 868 | A329 | 14fr multicolored | 1.75 | .50 |
| 869 | A329 | 22fr multicolored | 1.75 | 1.25 |

Lions Clubs Intl., 75th Anniv. A330

General Strike, 50th Anniv. A331

| | | | | |
|---|---|---|---|---|
| **1992, May 18** | **Photo.** | | **Perf. 11½** | |
| 870 | A330 | 14fr multicolored | 1.00 | .35 |
| 871 | A331 | 18fr sepia & lake | 1.10 | .55 |

1992 Summer Olympics, Barcelona — A332

**1992, May 18**     *Perf. 12x11½*
872 A332 14fr multicolored    1.50   .45

Expo '92, Seville — A333

**1992, May 18**     *Perf. 11½*
873 A333 14fr Luxembourg pavilion    .85   .50

**Gargoyle Type of 1991**
**Photo. & Engr.**

**1992, Oct. 5**     *Perf. 14*
874 A326 14fr Ram's head    .75   .35
875 A326 22fr Lion's head    1.25   .90
876 A326 50fr Satyr's head    2.50   1.50
   *Nos. 874-876 (3)*    4.50   2.75

Stained Glass Windows, by Auguste Tremont — A334

**1992, Oct. 5**   **Photo.**   *Perf. 11½x12*
877 A334 14fr Post horn, letters   .75   .50
878 A334 22fr Post rider    1.25   1.00
879 A334 50fr Insulators    2.60   1.40
   *Nos. 877-879 (3)*    4.60   2.90

Luxembourg Post and Telecommunications, 150th anniv.

Single European Market — A335

**1992, Oct. 5**     *Perf. 11½x12*
880 A335 14fr multicolored    .85   .40

Fountain of the Children with Grapes, Schwebsingen — A336

Design: No. 882, Old Ironworks Cultural Center, Steinfort.

**1993, Mar. 8**   **Photo.**   *Perf. 12x11½*
881 A336 14fr multicolored    .85   .35
882 A336 14fr multicolored    .85   .35

Grand Duke Jean — A337

**Litho. & Engr.**

**1993-95**     *Perf. 13½x13*
**Background Color**
883 A337 1fr yellow brown   .25   .25
883A A337 2fr olive gray   .25   .25
884 A337 5fr yellow green   .25   .25
885 A337 7fr brick red   .25   .25
886 A337 10fr blue   .55   .25
887 A337 14fr pink   1.40   .30
888 A337 15fr green   .85   .25
889 A337 16fr orange   1.00   .50
890 A337 18fr orange   .70   .35
891 A337 20fr red   1.00   .45
892 A337 22fr dark green   .90   .75
893 A337 25fr gray blue   1.00   .65
894 A337 100fr brown   5.00   1.95
   *Nos. 883-894 (13)*   13.40   7.25

Issued: 5, 7, 14, 18, 22, 25fr, 3/8/93; 1, 15, 20, 100fr, 3/7/94; 2, 10, 16fr, 1/30/95.
See Nos. 957, 1026.

New Technologies in Surgery — A338

**1993, May 10**   **Photo.**   *Perf. 11½*
895 A338 14fr multicolored    .85   .45

Contemporary Paintings — A339

Europa: 14fr, Rezlop, by Fernand Roda. 22fr, So Close, by Sonja Roef.

**1993, May 10**
896 A339 14fr multicolored    1.25   .40
897 A339 22fr multicolored    1.75   .80

A340

Designs: 14fr, Burgundy Residence. 20fr, Simons House. 50fr, Cassal House.

**Photo. & Engr.**

**1993, May 10**     *Perf. 14*
898 A340 14fr multicolored    .75   .35
899 A340 20fr multicolored    1.50   .45
900 A340 50fr multicolored    3.50   1.90
   *Nos. 898-900 (3)*    5.75   2.70

A341

**1993, Sept. 20**   **Photo.**   *Perf. 11½*
901 A341 14fr multicolored    .90   .45
Environmental protection.

A342           A343

**1993, Sept. 20**
902 A342 14fr multicolored    .90   .45
903 A343 14fr multicolored    .90   .45

Jean Schortgen (1880-1918), 1st worker elected to Parliament (No. 902); Artistic Circle of Luxembourg, cent.

Museum Exhibits — A344

14fr, Electric tram, Tram & Bus Museum, City of Luxembourg. 22fr, Iron ore tipper wagon, Natl. Mining Museum, Rumelange. 60fr, Horse-drawn carriage, Wiltz Museum of Ancient Crafts.

**Photo. & Engr.**

**1993, Sept. 20**     *Perf. 14*
904 A344 14fr multicolored    .90   .35
905 A344 22fr multicolored    1.25   .70
906 A344 60fr multicolored    3.25   2.00
   *Nos. 904-906 (3)*    5.40   3.05

See Nos. 933-935.

Snow-Covered Landscape, by Joseph Kutter (1894-1941) — A345

Design: No. 908, The Moselle, by Nico Klopp (1894-1930).

**1994, Mar. 7**   **Photo.**   *Perf. 11½x12*
907 A345 14fr multicolored    .90   .45
908 A345 14fr multicolored    .90   .45

4th General Elections to European Parliament — A346

**1994, May 16**   **Photo.**   *Perf. 11½*
909 A346 14fr multicolored    .85   .70

European Inventions, Discoveries — A347

**1994, May 16**
910 A347 14fr Armillary sphere   1.00   .40
911 A347 22fr Sail boats, map   1.25   1.00

Europa.

21st Intl. Congress of Genealogy & Heraldry A348    14th World Congress of Intl. Police Assoc. A349

Intl. Year of the Family — A350

**1994, May 16**     *Perf. 11½*
912 A348 14fr multicolored    1.25   .35
913 A349 18fr multicolored    1.25   .45
914 A350 25fr multicolored    1.75   1.25
   *Nos. 912-914 (3)*    4.25   2.05

Europe — A351

**1994, Sept. 19**     *Perf. 11½*
915 A351 14fr Dove, stars   1.25   .45
916 A351 14fr Circle of stars   1.25   .45
917 A351 14fr Bronze Age bowl   2.50   2.75
   *Nos. 915-917 (3)*    5.00   3.65

Western European Union, 40th anniv. (No. 915). Office for Official Publications of European Communities, 25th anniv. (No. 916). European Bronze Age Research Campaign (No. 917).

Liberation, 50th Anniv. — A352

**1994, Sept. 19**   **Photo.**   *Perf. 12x11½*
918 A352 14fr multicolored    .75   .50

Former Refuges in Luxembourg A353

Designs: 15fr, Munster Abbey. 25fr, Holy Spirit Convent. 60fr, St. Maximine Abbey of Trier.

**Photo. & Engr.**

**1994, Sept. 19**     *Perf. 14*
919 A353 15fr multicolored   .85   .35
920 A353 25fr multicolored   1.25   1.00
921 A353 60fr multicolored   3.25   1.75
   *Nos. 919-921 (3)*   5.35   3.10

A354

City of Luxembourg, 1995 European City of Culture — A355

A356

Paintings by Hundertwasser — A357

Panoramic view of city showing buildings and: No. 923a, Steeples, trees. b, Gateway through fortress wall. c, Angles in fortress wall. d, Roof of church.

Designs: No. 924, The King of the Antipodes. No. 925, The House with the Arcades and the Yellow Tower. No. 926, Small Path.

**Perf. 12x11½, 11½x12**

**1995, Mar. 6**       **Photo.**
922 A354 16fr multicolored   1.60   .90
923 A355 Strip of 4   4.25   3.50
a.-d.   16fr any single   .90   .45

**Photo. & Engr.**
**Perf. 14**
924 A356 16fr gold, silver & multi   1.60   .90
925 A357 16fr black & multi   1.60   .90
926 A357 16fr yellow & multi   1.60   .90
   *Nos. 922-926 (5)*   10.65   7.10

No. 923 is a continuous design.

Liberation of the Concentration Camps, 50th Anniv. — A358

Europa: 25fr, Barbed wire, cracked plaster.

**1995, May 15**   **Photo.**   *Perf. 11½x12*
927 A358 16fr multicolored   1.25   .50
928 A358 25fr multicolored   2.00   .80

European Nature Conservation Year — A359

**1995, May 15**   **Litho.**   *Perf. 13½*
929 A359 16fr multicolored   .85   .55

A360

**1995, May 15   Photo.   Perf. 11½x12**
930  A360  16fr multicolored          .90  .40
Small States of Europe Games, Luxembourg.

European
Geodynamics and
Seismology
Center — A361

**1995, May 15          Perf. 11½**
931  A361  32fr multicolored      2.00  1.00

UN, 50th
Anniv. — A362

**1995, May 15          Perf. 11½x12**
932  A362  80fr multicolored      4.00  2.50

**Museum Exhibits Type of 1993**

Designs, vert: 16fr, Churn, Country Art Museum, Vianden. 32fr, Wine press, Wine Museum, Ehnen. 80fr, Sculpture of a Potter, by Leon Nosbusch, Pottery Museum, Nospelt.

**Photo. & Engr.**
**1995, Sept. 18          Perf. 14**
933  A344  16fr multicolored       .85  .40
934  A344  32fr multicolored      1.75  1.00
935  A344  80fr multicolored      4.00  2.50
     Nos. 933-935 (3)             6.60  3.90

Luxembourg-Reykjavik, Iceland Air
Route, 40th Anniv. — A363

**1995, Sept. 18   Litho.   Perf. 13**
936  A363  16fr multicolored      1.00  .55
     See Iceland No. 807.

Tourism — A364

**1995, Sept. 18   Photo.   Perf. 11½**
937  A364  16fr Erpeldange        1.00  .55
938  A364  16fr Schengen          1.00  .55

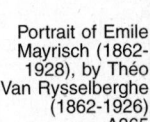

Portrait of Emile
Mayrisch (1862-
1928), by Théo
Van Rysselberghe
(1862-1926)
A365

**1996, Mar. 2   Photo.   Perf. 11½**
939  A365  (A) multicolored       1.00  .55

On day of issue No. 939 was valued at 16fr.
See Belgium No. 1602.

National
Railway, 50th
Anniv.
A366

Passenger train: a, Cab facing left. b, Hooked together. c, Cab facing right.

**1996, Mar. 4      Photo.      Perf. 11½**
940    Strip of 3               4.25  2.50
  a.-c.  A366 16fr Any single    1.25  .55
     No. 940 is a continuous design.

Grand Duchess
Charlotte (1896-
1985) — A367

Design: Statue, Luxembourg City.

**1996, Mar. 4          Booklet Stamp**
941  A367  16fr multicolored      1.25  .55
  a.    Booklet pane of 8        10.00
        Complete booklet, #941a  10.00

Mihály
Munkácsy
(1844-1900),
Hungarian
Painter
A368

Designs: No. 942, Portrait of Munkácsy, by Edouard Charlemont, 1884. No. 943, Portrait of Marie Munchen, by Munkácsy, 1885, vert.

**1996, May 20   Photo.   Perf. 11½**
942  A368  16fr multicolored      1.00  .55
943  A368  16fr multicolored      1.00  .55

Famous
Women — A369

Europa: 16fr, Marie de Bourgogne (1457-82), duchess of Luxembourg. 25fr, Empress Maria-Theresa of Austria (1717-80), duchess of Luxembourg.

**Photo. & Engr.**
**1996, May 20          Perf. 14x13½**
944  A369  16fr multicolored      1.00  .70
945  A369  25fr multicolored      1.50  .90

Luxembourg
Confederation of
Christian Trade
Unions, 75th
Anniv. — A370

Radio,
Cent. — A371

Modern
Olympic
Games,
Cent. — A372

Motion Pictures,
Cent. — A373

**Perf. 12x11½, 11½x12**
**1996, May 20                    Photo.**
946  A370  16fr multicolored       .90  .30
947  A371  20fr multicolored      1.10  .45
948  A372  25fr multicolored      1.25  1.10
949  A373  32fr multicolored      2.10  1.40
     Nos. 946-949 (4)             5.35  3.25

Registration and
Property
Administration,
Bicent. — A374

**1996, Sept. 23   Photo.   Perf. 11½**
950  A374  16fr multicolored      1.00  .55

Let Us Live
Together — A375

No. 951, Four children. No. 952, "L'Abbraccio," bronze statue by M.J. Kerschen, vert.

**1996, Sept. 23**
951  A375  16fr multicolored       .90  .50
952  A375  16fr multicolored       .90  .50

Mustelidae
A376

**Litho. & Engr.**
**1996, Sept. 23          Perf. 13½**
953  A376  16fr Meles meles        .85  .35
954  A376  20fr Mustela putorius  1.10  .55
955  A376  80fr Lutra lutra       4.00  2.75
     Nos. 953-955 (3)             5.95  3.65

John the Blind (1296-
1346), King of
Bohemia, Count of
Luxembourg — A377

**Litho. & Engr.**
**1996, Dec. 9          Perf. 13½**
956  A377  32fr multicolored      1.75  1.00

**Grand Duke Jean Type of 1993**
**Litho. & Engr.**
**1997, Jan. 2          Perf. 13½x13**
957  A337  8fr green & black       .70  .30

Treaties of Rome,
40th
Anniv. — A378

Belgian-Luxembourg Economic Union,
75th Anniv. — A379

**1997, Mar. 3   Photo.   Perf. 11½**
958  A378  16fr multicolored      1.00  .60
959  A379  20fr multicolored      1.25  .60

Tourism — A380

Designs: No. 960, Servais House, Mersch. No. 961, Baroque Church, Koerich, vert.

**1997, Mar. 3**
960  A380  16fr multicolored       .85  .50
961  A380  16fr multicolored       .85  .50

11th World
Congress of
Rose
Societies
A381

Roses: 16fr, Grand Duchess Charlotte. 20fr, Beautiful Sultana. 80fr, In Memory of Jean Soupert.

**1997, Mar. 3          Perf. 11½**
962  A381  16fr multicolored      1.10  .55
          **Size: 33x25mm**
963  A381  20fr multicolored      1.40  .75
964  A381  80fr multicolored      4.50  2.50
     Nos. 962-964 (3)             7.00  3.80

Stories and
Legends — A382

Europa: 16fr, Melusina of Luxembourg. 25fr, Hunter of Hollenfels.

**1997, May 12**
965  A382  16fr multicolored      1.25  .60
966  A382  25fr multicolored      2.25  .80

A383                    A384

Mondorf Spa, 150th
Anniv. — A385

**1997, May 12**
967  A383  16fr multicolored      1.00  .55
968  A384  16fr multicolored      1.00  .55
969  A385  16fr multicolored      1.00  .55
     Nos. 967-969 (3)             3.00  1.65

Grand-Ducal Gendarmerie, bicent. (No. 967). Union of Small Domestic Animals Farming Societies, 75th anniv. (No. 968).

JUVALUX
98 — A386

**1997, May 12**
970  A386  16fr Emblem            1.10  .55
971  A386  80fr Postal history    4.50  2.75

Saar-Lorraine-Luxembourg
Summit — A387

**1997, Oct. 16   Photo.   Perf. 11½**
972  A387  16fr multicolored      1.00  .50
     See Germany No. 1982 & France No. 2613.

Mills — A388

## 1997, Oct. 16 Litho. & Engr.
| | | | Perf. 13½ |
|---|---|---|---|
| 973 | A388 | 16fr Kalborn Mill, horiz. | 1.25 .55 |
| 974 | A388 | 50fr Ramelli Mill | 2.60 1.60 |

Clocks — A389

Designs: 16fr, Oak wall clock, 1816. 32fr, Astronomic clock with walnut case, mid 19th cent. 80fr, Pear tree wood wall clock, 1815.

## 1997, Oct. 16 Photo. & Engr.
| | | | Perf. 13x13½ |
|---|---|---|---|
| 975 | A389 | 16fr multicolored | 1.10 .50 |
| 976 | A389 | 32fr multicolored | 1.75 .90 |
| 977 | A389 | 80fr multicolored | 4.25 2.50 |
| | | Nos. 975-977 (3) | 7.10 3.90 |

Henry V, the Blonde (1247-81), Count of Luxembourg — A390

## 1997, Dec. 8 Photo.
| | | | Perf. 11½ |
|---|---|---|---|
| 978 | A390 | 32fr multicolored | 1.75 .90 |

Tourism — A391

No. 979, Hesperange. No. 980, Rodange Church, vert.

## 1998, Mar. 23 Photo.
| | | | Perf. 11½ |
|---|---|---|---|
| 979 | A391 | 16fr multicolored | 1.00 .55 |
| 980 | A391 | 16fr multicolored | 1.00 .55 |

See Nos. 1023-1024, 1048-1049.

Freshwater Fish — A392

Designs: 16fr, Salmo trutta. 25fr, Cottus gobio. 50fr, Alburnoides bipunctatus.

## 1998, Mar. 23 Litho. & Engr.
| | | | Perf. 13½x13 |
|---|---|---|---|
| 981 | A392 | 16fr multicolored | 1.40 .55 |
| 982 | A392 | 25fr multicolored | 2.00 1.25 |
| 983 | A392 | 50fr multicolored | 3.50 2.00 |
| | | Nos. 981-983 (3) | 6.90 3.80 |

NGL (Independent Luxembourg Trade Union), 50th Anniv. A393

Broom Festival, Wiltz, 50th Anniv. A394

Jean Antoine Zinnen (1827-98), Composer A395

Abolition of Censorship, 150th Anniv. A396

## 1998, Mar. 23 Photo.
| | | | Perf. 11½ |
|---|---|---|---|
| 984 | A393 | 16fr multicolored | 1.00 .45 |
| 985 | A394 | 16fr multicolored | 1.00 .45 |
| 986 | A395 | 20fr multicolored | 1.40 .55 |
| 987 | A396 | 50fr multicolored | 3.50 2.00 |
| | | Nos. 984-987 (4) | 6.90 3.45 |

King Henri VII (1275?-1313) of Luxembourg, King of Germany, Holy Roman Emperor — A397

## 1998, June 18 Photo.
| | | | Perf. 11½ |
|---|---|---|---|
| 988 | A397 | (A) multicolored | 1.00 .50 |

Granting of the Right to hold a Luxembourg Fair, 700th anniv.
No. 988 was valued at 16fr on the day of issue.

Natl. Holidays and Festivals — A398

Europa: 16fr, Fireworks over bridge, National Day. 25fr, Flame, stained glass window, National Remembrance Day.

## 1998, June 18
| | | | |
|---|---|---|---|
| 989 | A398 | 16fr multicolored | 1.40 .50 |
| 990 | A398 | 25fr multicolored | 1.60 .65 |

Juvalux 98 — A399

A400

16fr, Town postman, 1880. 25fr, Letter, 1590, horiz. 50fr, Country postman, 1880.
No. 994, Engraving showing 1861 view of Luxembourg.

## 1998, June 18 Photo. & Engr.
| | | | |
|---|---|---|---|
| 991 | A399 | 16fr multicolored | 1.25 .55 |
| 992 | A399 | 25fr multicolored | 1.60 1.25 |
| 993 | A399 | 50fr multicolored | 2.75 1.40 |
| | | Nos. 991-993 (3) | 5.60 3.20 |

### Souvenir Sheet
| | | | |
|---|---|---|---|
| 994 | A400 | Sheet of 2 | 6.00 6.00 |
| a. | | 16fr multicolored | .90 .90 |
| b. | | 80fr multicolored | 4.00 4.00 |

St. Jean de L'Esperance, Grand Lodge of Luxembourg, 150th Anniv. — A401

## 1998, Sept. 21 Litho.
| | | | Perf. 13½ |
|---|---|---|---|
| 995 | A401 | 16fr multicolored | 1.00 .55 |

Abbey of Echternach, 1300th Anniv. — A402

Various architectural drawings.

## 1998, Sept 21 Photo.
| | | | Perf. 11½ |
|---|---|---|---|
| 996 | A402 | 16fr multicolored | 1.25 .55 |
| 997 | A402 | 48fr multicolored | 2.50 1.75 |
| 998 | A402 | 60fr multicolored | 3.25 1.75 |
| | | Nos. 996-998 (3) | 7.00 4.05 |

Museum Exhibits — A403

City of Luxembourg History Museum: 16fr, Spanish army helmet, 16th cent. 80fr, Wayside Cross, Hollerich, 1718.

## 1998, Sept. 21 Litho. & Engr.
| | | | Perf. 13½ |
|---|---|---|---|
| 999 | A403 | 16fr multicolored | .90 .55 |
| 1000 | A403 | 80fr multicolored | 4.50 2.75 |

NAMSA (NATO Maintenance and Supply Organization), 40th Anniv. — A404

## 1998, Dec. 7 Photo.
| | | | Perf. 11½ |
|---|---|---|---|
| 1001 | A404 | 36fr multicolored | 2.25 1.25 |

Introduction of the Euro — A405

## 1999, Mar. 8 Photo.
| | | | Perf. 11½ |
|---|---|---|---|
| 1002 | A405 | (A) multicolored | 1.25 .70 |

No. 1002 was valued at 16fr on the day of issue.

Council of Europe, 50th Anniv. A406

## 1999, Mar. 8
| | | | |
|---|---|---|---|
| 1003 | A406 | 16fr multicolored | 1.25 .85 |

Owls — A407

## 1999, Mar. 8
| | | | Perf. 12 |
|---|---|---|---|
| 1004 | A407 | (A) Strix aluco, vert. | .90 .65 |
| 1005 | A407 | 32fr Bubo bubo | 1.60 1.10 |
| 1006 | A407 | 60fr Tyto alba | 3.50 2.50 |
| | | Nos. 1004-1006 (3) | 6.00 4.25 |

No. 1004 was valued at 16fr on the day of issue.

NATO, 50th Anniv. A408

## 1999, Mar. 8
| | | | Perf. 11½ |
|---|---|---|---|
| 1007 | A408 | 80fr multicolored | 5.50 3.50 |

Europa A409

National Parks: 16fr, Haute-Sûre. 25fr, Ardennes-Eifel.

## 1999, May 17 Photo.
| | | | Perf. 11½x12 |
|---|---|---|---|
| 1008 | A409 | 16fr multicolored | 1.25 .45 |
| 1009 | A409 | 25fr multicolored | 1.75 .80 |

Natl. Federation of Mutuality, 75th Anniv. A410

Intl. Year of Older Persons A411

UPU, 125th Anniv. — A412

A413

A414

## 1999, May 17
| | | | Perf. 11½ |
|---|---|---|---|
| 1010 | A410 | 16fr multicolored | .85 .65 |
| 1011 | A411 | 16fr multicolored | .90 .55 |
| 1012 | A412 | 16fr multicolored | .90 .55 |
| 1013 | A413 | 32fr multicolored | 1.60 1.40 |
| 1014 | A414 | 80fr multicolored | 4.50 2.75 |
| | | Nos. 1010-1014 (5) | 8.75 5.90 |

Luxembourg Federation of Amateur Photographers, 50th anniv. (No. 1013). Luxembourg Gymnastics Federation, cent. (No. 1014).

18th Birthday of Prince Guillaume — A415

## 1999, Sept. 21 Photo. & Engr.
| | | | Perf. 13½ |
|---|---|---|---|
| 1015 | A415 | 16fr multicolored | .85 .55 |

Aline Mayrisch-de Saint-Hubert (1874-1947), President of Luxembourg Red Cross — A416

## 1999, Sept. 21 Litho. & Engr.
| | | | |
|---|---|---|---|
| 1016 | A416 | 20fr multicolored | 1.60 .55 |

Travelling Into the Future — A417

16fr, Communication by road. 20fr, Information age. 80fr, Conquering space.

## 1999, Sept. 21 Photo.
| | | | Perf. 11¾ |
|---|---|---|---|
| 1017 | A417 | 16fr multicolored | .85 .55 |
| 1018 | A417 | 20fr multicolored | 1.00 .85 |
| 1019 | A417 | 80fr multicolored | 4.25 1.75 |
| | | Nos. 1017-1019 (3) | 6.10 3.15 |

See Nos. 1063-1065.

Johann Wolfgang von Goethe (1749-1832), German Poet — A418

## 1999, Nov. 30 Photo.
| | | | Perf. 11¾ |
|---|---|---|---|
| 1020 | A418 | 20fr henna & dk brn | 1.25 .70 |

Year
2000
A419

No. 1021: a, Large white area under A and 2000. b, Large blue area under A. c, Large blue area under A and URG. d, Large blue area under LUX.

**Serpentine Die Cut 8 Vert.**
**2000, Jan. 3** Photo.
**Self-Adhesive**
**Booklet Stamps**
1021 A419 Booklet pane of 4 4.25
a.-d. (A) Any single 1.00 .70
Booklet, 2 #1021 8.50

Nos. 1021a-1021d sold for 16fr on day of issue.

Holy Roman Emperor Charles V (1500-58) — A420

**Litho. & Engr.**
**2000, Mar. 7** Perf. 13½
1022 A420 A multi .90 .50

Sold for 16fr on day of issue.

**Tourism Type of 1998**
Designs: No. 1023, Walferdange Castle. No. 1024, Wasserbillig railway station, vert.

**Perf. 11¾x11½, 11½x11¾**
**2000, Mar. 7** Photo.
**Granite Paper**
1023 A391 A multi 1.00 .50
1024 A391 A multi 1.00 .50

Sold for 16fr on day of issue.

World Mathematics Year — A421

**2000, Mar. 7** Perf. 11½x11¾
1025 A421 80fr multi 4.50 2.75

**Grand Duke Jean Type of 1993**
**Litho. & Engr.**
**2000, Mar. 31** Perf. 13¼x13
**Background Color**
1026 A337 9fr pink .60 .30

Musical Instruments — A422

**Perf. 11½x11¾**
**2000, Mar. 31** Photo.
**Granite Paper**
1027 A422 3fr French horn .25 .25
1028 A422 12fr Saxophone .60 .35
1029 A422 21fr Violin 1.25 .55
1030 A422 30fr Piano 1.50 1.10
Nos. 1027-1030 (4) 3.60 2.25

See Nos. 1045-1046.

Ducks — A423

Designs: 18fr, Anas platyrhynchos. 24fr, Aythya ferina, vert. 30fr, Aythya fuligula.

**2000, May 9** Perf. 11¾x11½
**Granite Paper**
1031 A423 18fr multi 1.25 .70

**Perf. 11½x11¾**
1032 A423 24fr multi 1.60 .90
1033 A423 30fr multi 1.75 1.25
Nos. 1031-1033 (3) 4.60 2.85

Esch-sur-Alzette Gas Works, Cent. (in 1999) — A424

**2000, May 9** Perf. 11¾x11½
**Granite Paper**
1034 A424 18fr multi 1.25 .65

**Europa, 2000**
**Common Design Type**
**2000, May 9** Perf. 11½x11¾
**Granite Paper**
1035 CD17 21fr multi 1.40 .85

Robert Schuman's European Unity Plan, 50th Anniv. — A425

**2000, May 9** Perf. 11½x11¾
1036 A425 21fr multi 1.40 .85

Art Collection of Luxembourg Posts & Telecommunications — A426

Art by: 21fr, Will Kesseler. 24fr, Joseph Probst, vert. 36fr, Mett Hoffmann.

**Perf. 11¾x11½, 11½x11¾**
**2000, Sept. 27** Photo.
**Granite Paper**
1037 A426 21fr multi 1.10 .60
1038 A426 24fr multi 1.50 1.00
1039 A426 36fr multi 2.25 1.40
Nos. 1037-1039 (3) 4.85 3.00

Towers on Historic Walking Trails — A427

Designs: 18fr, Tower of Jacob, Wenzel trail. 42fr, Bons Malades Gate, Vauban trail.

**Photo. & Engr.**
**2000, Sept. 27** Perf. 13½x14¼
1040 A427 18fr multi 1.25 .55
1041 A427 42fr multi 2.75 1.60

Blast Furnace "B," Esch-Belval — A428

**2000, Sept. 27** Perf. 11¾x11½
1042 A428 A multi 1.25 .55

No. 1042 sold for 18fr on day of issue.

Accession of Grand Duke Henri — A429

Designs: 18fr, Prince Henri in uniform, Princess Maria Teresa in pink suit. 100fr, Prince in suit, Princess in red blouse.

**2000, Sept. 27** Photo. Perf. 11¾
**Granite Paper (18fr)**
1043 A429 18fr multi 1.00 .55

**Souvenir Sheet**
**Photo. (margin Photo. & Engr.)**
**Perf. 11½**
1044 A429 100fr multi 6.50 6.50

No. 1043 issued in sheets of 12, five of which (positions 6, 8, 9, 10 and 11) have a red and blue "ribbon" running diagonally through stamp margin. No. 1044 contains one 46x35mm stamp.

**Musical Instruments Type of 2000**
**2000, Dec. 5** Photo. Perf. 11½x11¾
**Granite Paper**
1045 A422 9fr Electric guitar .90 .35
1046 A422 24fr Accordion 1.60 1.00

Treaty Establishing European Coal and Steel Community, 50th Anniv. — A430

**Perf. 11¼x11½**
**2001, Mar. 20** Photo.
1047 A430 21fr multi 1.25 .85

**Tourism Type of 1998**
Designs: No. 1048, 18fr, Bestgen Mill, Schifflange. No. 1049, 18fr, Chapel, Wormeldange, and millstone, Ahn, vert.

**Perf. 11¾x11½, 11½x11¾**
**2001, Mar. 20**
**Granite Paper**
1048-1049 A391 Set of 2 2.00 1.10

Writers — A431

Designs: 18fr, Nik Welter (1871-1951). 24fr, André Gide (1869-1951). 30fr, Michel Rodange (1827-76).

**Perf. 13½x13¼**
**2001, Mar. 20** Litho. & Engr.
1050-1052 A431 Set of 3 4.50 3.00

Europa — A432

Designs: A (18fr), Stream, Mullerthal region. 21fr, Pond and Kaltreis water tower, Luxembourg-Bonnevoie.

**Perf. 11¾x11½, 11½x11¾**
**2001, May 22** Photo.
**Granite Paper**
1053-1054 A432 Set of 2 2.25 1.60

Rescue Workers — A433

Designs: 18fr, Air rescue. 30fr, Rescue divers. 45fr, Fire fighters.

**2001, May 22** Perf. 11½x11¾
**Granite Paper**
1055-1057 A433 Set of 3 6.00 4.00

Humanitarian Services — A434

Designs: 18fr, Humanitarian aid. 24fr, Intl. Organization for Migration, 50th anniv.

**2001, May 22** Perf. 11½
1058-1059 A434 Set of 2 2.75 1.75

Old Postal Vehicles — A435

Designs: 3fr, Citroen 2CV Mini-van, 1960s. 18fr, Volkswagen Beetle, 1970s.

**Granite Paper**
**Serpentine Die Cut 8¼ Vert.**
**2001, May 22** Booklet Stamps
1060 A435 3fr multi .25 .25
1061 A435 18fr multi 1.10 .75
a. Booklet, 6 each #1060-1061 8.50

European Year of Languages — A436

**2001, Oct. 1** Photo. Perf. 11¾x11½
**Granite Paper**
1062 A436 A multi 1.25 .70

Luxembourg postal officials state that No. 1062 sold for 45 eurocents on the day of issue, though euro currency was not in circulation on the day of issue. On the day of issue, 45 eurocents was the equivalent of approximately 18fr.

Nos. 1063-1071, 1074, 1076, 1078, 1080, 1084, and B425-B429 are denominated solely in euro currency though euro currency would not circulate until Jan. 1, 2002. From their date of issue until Dec. 31, 2001, these stamps could be purchased for Luxembourg francs. The official pegged rate of 40.3399 francs to the euro made rounding the franc purchase price a necessity for such purchases. The approximate franc equivalent of the euro denominations is shown in parentheses in the listings.

**Traveling Into the Future Type of 1999**
Designs: 45c (18fr), Renewable energy. 59c (24fr), Waste recycling. 74c (30fr), Biological research.

**2001, Oct. 1** Perf. 11¾
**Granite Paper**
1063-1065 A417 Set of 3 5.50 4.00

Euro Coinage — A437

Designs: Coin obverses with values of stamp denominations.

**2001, Oct. 1** Perf. 11½
1066 A437 5c (2fr) multi .25 .25
1067 A437 10c (4fr) multi .25 .25
1068 A437 20c (8fr) multi .60 .40
1069 A437 50c (20fr) multi 1.40 1.00
1070 A437 €1 (40fr) multi 3.00 1.75
1071 A437 €2 (80fr) multi 6.00 4.50
Nos. 1066-1071 (6) 11.50 8.15

Grand Duke Henri — A438

**Photo. & Engr.**
**2001-03** Perf. 11¾x11½
**Vignette Color**
1072 A438 1c blue .25 .25
1073 A438 3c green .25 .25
1074 A438 7c (3fr) blue .25 .25
1075 A438 22c (9fr) brown .50 .40
1076 A438 30c (12fr) green .90 .45
1077 A438 45c (18fr) violet 1.40 .65
1078 A438 52c brown 1.25 .75

| 1079 | A438 59c blue | 1.50 | 1.00 |
|---|---|---|---|
| 1080 | A438 74c brown | 2.00 | 1.00 |
| 1081 | A438 89c red violet | 2.50 | 1.25 |
| | Nos. 1072-1081 (10) | 10.80 | 6.25 |

Issued: 7c, 22c, 30c, 45c, 10/1/01. 52c, 59c, 74c, 89c, 3/5/02. 1c, 3c, 10/1/03.
See Nos. 1124-1133A.

Kiwanis International
A439

**2001, Dec. 6**    **Photo.**    *Perf. 11½*
1084   A439 52c (21fr) multi    1.75   1.25

**100 Cents = 1 Euro (€)**

Art Collection of Luxembourg Posts & Telecommunications — A440

Art by: 22c, Moritz Ney, vert. 45c, Dany Prüm. 59c, Christiane Schmit, vert.

*Perf. 14¼x14, 14x14¼*
**2002, Mar. 5**       **Photo.**
1085-1087   A440   Set of 3    4.00   3.00

European Court Anniversaries
A441

Designs: 45c, European Court of Auditors, 25th anniv. 52c, Court of Justice of the European communities, 50th anniv.

**2002, Mar. 5**    **Litho.**    *Perf. 13½*
1088-1089   A441   Set of 2    3.00   2.00

Sports — A442

No. 1090: a, Snowboarding. b, Skateboarding. c, Rollerblading. d, Bicycling. e, Volleyball. f, Basketball.

**Booklet Stamps**

*Die Cut Perf. 10 on 3 Sides*
**2002, Mar. 5**      **Self-Adhesive**
| 1090 | Booklet pane of 6 | 4.50 | |
| a.-c. | A442 7c Any single | .25 | .25 |
| d.-f. | A442 45c Any single | 1.25 | 1.00 |
| | Booklet, 2 #1090 | 9.00 | |

Europa — A443

Designs: 45c, Tightrope walker. 52c, Clown.

**2002, May 14**    **Litho.**    *Perf. 13½*
1091-1092   A443   Set of 2    3.00   1.75

Cultural Anniversaries
A444

Designs: A, 50th Wiltz Festival. €1.12, Victor Hugo (1802-85), writer.

**2002, May 14**       *Perf. 13¼*
1093-1094   A444   Set of 2    5.00   3.50

No. 1093 sold for 45c on day of issue.

Start of Tour de France in Luxembourg — A445

Designs: 45c, Stylized bicycle. 52c, François Faber (1887-1915), 1909 champion, vert. €2.45, The Champion, by Joseph Kutter, vert.

**Litho. (45c), Litho. & Engr.**
*Perf. 13¼x13½, 13½x13¼*
**2002, May 14**    Set of 3    9.00   6.25
1095-1097   A445

Grevenmacher Charter of Freedom, 750th Anniv. — A446

**2002, Sept. 14**   **Litho.**   *Perf. 13¼x13*
1098   A446 74c multi    1.90   1.50

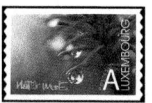

Nature Museum, Museum of Natural History — A447

No. 1099: a, Water drop on spruce needle. b, Butterfly. c, Leaf rosette of *Echeveria* plant. d, Berries.

*Serpentine Die Cut 8 Vert.*
**2002, Sept. 14**       **Photo.**
**Self-Adhesive**
| 1099 | Booklet pane of 4 | 4.50 | |
| a.-d. | A447 A Any single | 1.10 | .80 |
| | Booklet, 2 #1099 | 9.00 | |

Nos. 1099a-1099d had franking value of 45c on day of issue, but booklet sold for discounted price of €3.35.

**Souvenir Sheet**

Luxembourg Stamps, 150th Anniv. — A448

No. 1100: a, Grand Duke William II, man and woman, 1852 (47x27mm). b, Grand Duke Adolphe, woman, 1902 (47x27mm). c, Grand Duchess Charlotte, street scene, 1952 (47x27mm). d, Grand Duke Henri, hot air balloons in street, 2002 (71x27mm).

**Photo. & Engr.**
**2002, Sept. 14**       *Perf. 11¾*
1100   A448 45c Sheet of 4, #a-d   4.75   4.75

The Post in 50 Years — A449

Designs: 22c, Postmen in spacecraft, buildings, vert. A, Spacecraft in flight, cell phone, letter and "@" in orbit around planet.

*Perf. 14x14½, 14½x14*
**2002, Oct. 19**       **Litho.**
1101-1102   A449   Set of 2    1.75   1.40

No. 1102 sold for 45c on day of issue.

Grand Duke Jean and Princess Joséphine-Charlotte, 50th Wedding Anniv. — A450

*Perf. 14¼x14½*
**2003, Mar. 18**       **Litho.**
1103   A450 45c multi    1.10   .95

Official Journal of the European Communities, 50th Anniv. — A451

**2003, Mar. 18**       *Perf. 14½x14*
1104   A451 52c multi    1.40   1.10

Famous Women — A452

Designs: No. 1105, 45c, Catherine Schleimer-Kill (1884-1973), feminist leader. No. 1106, 45c, Lou Koster (1889-1973), composer.

**2003, Mar. 18**   **Photo.**   *Perf. 11½*
1105-1106   A452   Set of 2    2.40   1.90

Tourism — A453

Designs: 50c, Fontaine Marie Convent, Differdange. €1, Castle, Mamer. €2.50, St. Joseph Church, Esch-sur-Alzette, vert.

*Perf. 14½x14, 14x14½*
**2003, Mar. 18**       **Litho.**
1107-1109   A453   Set of 3    9.50   9.50

Luxembourg Athénée, 400th Anniv. — A454

**2003, May 20**   **Litho.**   *Perf. 14¼x14½*
1110   A454 45c multi    1.10   1.00

Europa — A455

Poster art: 45c, 1952 poster for National Lottery, by Roger Gerson. 52c, 1924 poster for Third Commercial Fair, by Auguste Trémont.

**2003, May 20**       *Perf. 13¼x13*
1111-1112   A455   Set of 2    2.25   1.75

Bridges — A456

Designs: 45c, Adolphe Bridge, 1903. 59c, Stierchen Bridge, 14th cent. (36x26mm). 89c, Victor Bodson Bridge, 1994 (36x26mm).

**Photo. & Engr.**
**2003, May 20**       *Perf. 11½*
1113-1115   A456   Set of 3    5.00   4.25

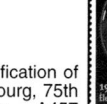

Electrification of Luxembourg, 75th Anniv. — A457

**Litho. & Embossed**
**2003, Sept. 23**       *Perf. 13¼x13*
1116   A457 A multi    1.25   1.25

Sold for 50c on day of issue.

Breastfeeding
A458

**2003, Sept. 23**   **Litho.**   *Perf. 13½*
1117   A458 A multi    1.25   1.25

Sold for 50c on day of issue.

Gaart an Heem Agricultural Cooperatives, 75th Anniv. — A459

Gardeners with: 25c, Spade. A, Basket and rake. €2, Watering can.

**2003, Sept. 23**       *Perf. 14½x14*
1118-1120   A459   Set of 3    7.00   6.50

No. 1119 sold for 50c on day of issue.

Industrial Products Made in Luxembourg
A460

Designs: 60c, Steel. 70c, Industrial valve. 80c, Polyester film.

**2003, Oct. 1**   **Photo.**   *Perf. 11½*
1121-1123   A460   Set of 3    5.00   5.00

**Grand Duke Henri Type of 2001-03**
**Photo. & Engr.**
**2004-2010**       *Perf. 11¾x11½*
**Vignette Color**
| 1124 | A438 5c violet brn | .25 | .25 |
|---|---|---|---|
| 1125 | A438 10c black | .30 | .30 |
| 1126 | A438 25c claret | .65 | .65 |
| 1129 | A438 50c black | 1.25 | 1.25 |
| 1130 | A438 60c black | 1.50 | 1.50 |
| 1131 | A438 70c purple | 1.75 | 1.75 |
| 1132 | A438 80c olive black | 2.10 | 2.00 |
| 1133 | A438 90c brown | 2.25 | 2.25 |
| 1133A | A438 €1 blue | 2.60 | 2.60 |
| | Nos. 1126-1133A (7) | 12.10 | 12.00 |

Issued: 25c, 50c, 60c, 80c, 3/16/04; 70c, 90c, €1, 9/26/06; 5c, 10c, 12/7/10.

Emigrants to the United States — A461

Designs: 50c, Edward Steichen (1879-1973), photographer. 70c, Hugo Gernsbach (1884-1967), science fiction writer.

**Photo. & Engr.**
**2004, Mar. 16**       *Perf. 11½*
1134-1135   A461   Set of 2    3.25   3.00

Anniversaries of Commercial Events — A462

Designs: No. 1136, 50c, Commercial Union of Esch-sur-Alzette, cent. No. 1137, 50c, Luxembourg City Annual Street Market, 75th anniv.

| 2004, Mar. 16 | Litho. | Perf. 14¼ |
|---|---|---|
| 1136-1137 A462 Set of 2 | | 2.60 2.60 |

Mushrooms — A463

No. 1138: a, Cantharellus tubaeformis. b, Ramaria flava. c, Stropharia cyanea. d, Helvella lacunosa. e, Anthurus archeri. f, Clitopilus prunulus.

**Die Cut Perf. 10**
| 2004, Mar. 16 | | Litho. |
|---|---|---|
| **Self-Adhesive** | | |
| 1138 Booklet pane of 6 | 4.50 | |
| a.-c. A463 10c Any single | .25 | .25 |
| d.-f. A463 50c Any single | 1.25 | 1.25 |
| Complete booklet, 2 #1138 | 9.00 | |

European Parliament Elections — A464

| 2004, May 9 | Litho. | Perf. 13¼x13 |
|---|---|---|
| 1139 A464 50c multi | | 1.25 1.25 |

2004 Summer Olympics, Athens — A465

European Sports Education Year — A466

| 2004, May 9 | Photo. | Perf. 11½x11¾ |
|---|---|---|
| 1140 A465 50c multi | | 1.25 1.25 |
| 1141 A466 60c multi | | 1.40 1.40 |

European School, 50th Anniv. — A467

| 2004, May 9 | Litho. | Perf. 14¼x14½ |
|---|---|---|
| 1142 A467 70c multi | | 1.75 1.75 |

Europa — A468

Designs: 50c, Stone bridge over Schiessentuempel. 60c, Bourscheid Beach, Bourscheid Castle.

| 2004, May 9 | | Perf. 13¼x13 |
|---|---|---|
| 1143-1144 A468 Set of 2 | | 3.00 3.00 |

Luxembourg Stock Exchange, 75th Anniv. — A469

**Perf. 11¼x11½**
| 2004, Sept. 28 | Litho. & Engr. |
|---|---|
| 1145 A469 50c multi | 1.25 1.25 |

Food Products Made in Luxembourg A470

Designs: 35c, Baked goods, beer. 60c, Meats, wine. 70c, Dairy products.

**Perf. 13½x13¾**
| 2004, Sept. 28 | | Litho. |
|---|---|---|
| 1146-1148 A470 Set of 3 | | 4.00 4.00 |

National Museum of History and Art — A471

Designs: 50c, Museum building. €1.10, Young Woman with a Fan, by Luigi Rubio. €3, Charity, by Lucas Cranach the Elder or Lucas Cranach the Younger.

| 2004, Sept. 28 | Photo. | Perf. 11¾ |
|---|---|---|
| 1149-1151 A471 Set of 3 | | 11.50 11.50 |

World War II Liberation, 60th Anniv. — A472

| 2004, Dec. 7 | Litho. | Perf. 14x13½ |
|---|---|---|
| 1152 A472 70c multi | | 1.90 1.90 |

Luxembourg's Presidency of European Union — A473

No. 1153: a, Building with glass facade. b, Arch, Echternach Basilica. c, Vineyard along Moselle River. d, Rusted iron girder.

**Serpentine Die Cut 8¼ Vert.**
| 2005, Jan. 25 | | Photo. |
|---|---|---|
| **Self-Adhesive** | | |
| 1153 Booklet pane of 4 | 5.00 | |
| a.-d. A473 A any single | 1.25 | 1.25 |
| Complete booklet, 2 #1153 | 10.00 | |

On the day of issue, Nos. 1153a-1153d each had a franking value of 50c, but complete booklet sold for €3.80.

Rotary International, Cent. — A474

| 2005, Mar. 15 | Litho. | Perf. 13½x13 |
|---|---|---|
| 1154 A474 50c multi | | 1.40 1.40 |

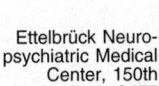

Ettelbrück Neuro-psychiatric Medical Center, 150th Anniv. — A475

| 2005, Mar. 15 | | Perf. 13½ |
|---|---|---|
| 1155 A475 50c multi | | 1.40 1.40 |

76th Intl. Congress of Applied Mathematics and Mechanics — A476

| 2005, Mar. 15 | | |
|---|---|---|
| 1156 A476 60c multi | | 1.60 1.60 |

Benelux Parliament, 50th Anniv. — A477

| 2005, Mar. 15 | | Perf. 13¼x12¾ |
|---|---|---|
| 1157 A477 60c multi | | 1.60 1.60 |

Tourism — A478

Designs: 50c, Shoe factory, Kayl-Tétange. 60c, Village scene and website address of National Tourist Office (44x31mm). €1, Statue of St. Eloi, Rodange, and foundry worker.

**Perf. 14x13¼, 12¾ (60c)**
| 2005, Mar. 15 | | |
|---|---|---|
| 1158-1160 A478 Set of 3 | | 5.50 5.50 |

Opening of Grand Duchess Joséphine-Charlotte Concert Hall — A479

| 2005, May 24 | | Perf. 13¼x13¾ |
|---|---|---|
| 1161 A479 50c multi | | 1.25 1.25 |

Europa — A480

Designs: 50c, Judd mat Gaardebounen (pork and beans). 60c, Feirstengszalot (beef, egg and pickle salad).

| 2005, May 24 | | Perf. 13½ |
|---|---|---|
| 1162-1163 A480 Set of 2 | | 2.75 2.75 |

Railways — A481

Designs: 50c, Niederpallen Station, CVE 357 car of De Jhangeli narrow-gauge railway. 60c, AL-T3 locomotive. €2.50, PH 408 passenger car.

| 2005, May 24 | Photo. | Perf. 11½ |
|---|---|---|
| 1164-1166 A481 Set of 3 | | 9.00 9.00 |

Hand Lifting Self-Adhesive Paper From Backing — A482

**Coil Stamps**
**Serpentine Die Cut 11x11¼**
| 2005, May 24 | | Self-Adhesive |
|---|---|---|
| 1167 Vert. strip of 4 | 2.50 | |
| a. A482 25c dark red & multi | .60 | .60 |
| b. A482 25c red orange & multi | .60 | .60 |
| c. A482 25c orange & multi | .60 | .60 |
| d. A482 25c yellow & multi | .60 | .60 |
| 1168 Vert. strip of 4 | 5.00 | |
| a. A482 50c dark green & multi | 1.25 | 1.25 |
| b. A482 50c green & multi | 1.25 | 1.25 |
| c. A482 50c emerald & multi | 1.25 | 1.25 |
| d. A482 50c yellow green & multi | 1.25 | 1.25 |

Rolls of 100 of the 25c stamps sold for €24, and rolls of 100 of the 50c stamps sold for €48.

Famous People — A483

Designs: 50c, Jean-Pierre Pescatore (1793-1855), philanthropist. 90c, Marcel Reuland (1905-56), writer. €1, Marie-Henriette Steil (1898-1930), writer, vert.

| 2005, Sept. 27 | Photo. & Engr. | Perf. 11½ |
|---|---|---|
| 1169-1171 A483 Set of 3 | | 6.00 6.00 |

Butterflies — A484

Designs: 35c, Papilio machaon. 70c, Argynnis paphia, vert. €1.80, Lysandra coridon.

| 2005, Sept. 27 | | Litho. |
|---|---|---|
| 1172-1174 A484 Set of 3 | | 7.25 7.25 |

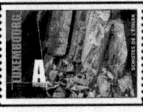

Rocks — A485

No. 1175: a, Schist. b, Rocks with iron (minerai de fer). c, Luxembourg sandstone. d, Conglomerate rocks.

**Serpentine Die Cut 12¾ Vert.**
| 2005, Sept. 27 | | Self-Adhesive |
|---|---|---|
| 1175 Booklet pane of 4 | 4.75 | |
| a.-d. A485 A any single | 1.10 | 1.10 |
| Complete booklet, 2 #1175 | 9.50 | |

The complete booklet sold for €3.80, but each stamp had a franking value of 50c on the day of issue.

Seeing Eye Dog — A486

| 2005, Dec. 6 | Litho. & Embossed | Perf. 13x13¼ |
|---|---|---|
| 1176 A486 70c dk blue & lemon | | 1.75 1.75 |

25th Wedding Anniversary of Grand Duke Henri and Grand Duchess Maria Teresa — A487

| 2006, Feb. 7 | Litho. | Perf. 13¼x13¾ |
|---|---|---|
| 1177 A487 50c multi | | 1.25 1.25 |

**Souvenir Sheet**
**Perf. 13¼x13**
| 1178 A487 €2.50 multi | | 6.25 6.25 |

No. 1178 contains one 26x37mm stamp.

Blood Donation — A488

| 2006, Mar. 14 | Litho. | Perf. 13¼ |
|---|---|---|
| 1179 A488 50c multi | | 1.25 1.25 |

Tourism — A489

Designs: No. 1180, 50c, Parc Merveilleux, Bettembourg. No. 1181, 50c, Birelerhaff Pigeon Tower, Sandweiler, vert.

2006, Mar. 14 ***Perf. 11½***
1180-1181 A489 Set of 2 2.40 1.25

Electrification of Railway Network, 50th Anniv. — A490

Designs: 50c, Train passing station. 70c, Train on bridge. €1, Railway workers repairing electrical wires, vert.

2006, Mar. 14 ***Perf. 13¼x13, 13x13¼***
1182-1184 A490 Set of 3 5.25 5.25

Personalized Stamp Website "meng.post.lu" — A491

2006, May 16 **Litho.** ***Perf. 11½***
1185 A491 A multi + label 1.40 1.40

No. 1185 sold for 50c on day of issue. Labels could be personalized for a fee.

Esch-sur-Alzette, Cent. — A492

2006, May 16 ***Perf. 13½***
1186 A492 50c multi 1.40 1.40

Soccer Teams in Luxembourg, Cent. — A493

2006 World Cup Soccer Championships, Germany — A494

2006, May 16 ***Perf. 13x13¼***
1187 A493 50c multi 1.40 1.40
1188 A494 90c multi 2.40 2.40

Europa — A495

Contest-winning cell phone photos: 50c, Hands making heart. 70c, People holding globe.

2006, May 16 ***Perf. 12½***
1189-1190 A495 Set of 2 3.25 3.25

State Council, 150th Anniv. — A496

Litho. & Embossed

2006, Sept. 26 ***Perf. 13½***
1191 A496 50c multi 1.25 1.25

Luxembourg Chess Federation, 75th Anniv. — A497

2006, Sept. 26
1192 A497 90c multi 2.25 2.25

Bank Sesquicentenaries A498

Designs: No. 1193, 50c, State Savings Bank (Spuerkeess). No. 1194, 50c, Dexia-BIL Bank.

2006, Sept. 26 **Litho.** ***Perf. 13¼x13***
1193-1194 A498 Set of 2 2.60 2.60

Fight Against Drug Addiction — A499

Designs: 50c, Children's drawing of man and "No Drugs" sign. €1, Ashtray with vegetables and cheese, vert.

2006, Sept. 26 ***Perf. 11½***
1195-1196 A499 Set of 2 3.75 3.75

Luxembourg Horticultural Federation, 75th Anniv. — A500

No. 1197: a, Flowers. b, Fruits and vegetables.

2006, Dec. 5 **Litho.** ***Perf. 13¼x13¾***
1197 A500 Horiz. pair 3.75 3.75
a.-b. 70c Either single 1.75 1.75

Luxembourg, 2007 European Cultural Capital — A501

No. 1198 — Silhouettes of deer and men with deer heads with background color of: a, Blue. b, Orange. c, Bright yellow green. d, Red violet.

Serpentine Die Cut 8½ Vert.

2007, Jan. 30 **Litho.**
1198 Booklet pane of 4 5.25
a.-d. A501 A Any single 1.25 1.25
Complete booklet, 2 #1198 10.50

Nos. 1198a-1198d each sold for 50c on day of issue.

Luxembourg Caritas, 75th Anniv. — A502

2007, Mar. 20 **Litho.** ***Perf. 11½***
1199 A502 50c multi 1.40 1.40

Luxembourg Automobile Club, 75th Anniv. — A503

2007, Mar. 20
1200 A503 50c multi 1.40 1.40

Treaty of Rome, 50th Anniv. — A504

Designs: 70c, Delegates. €1, Text and stars.

2007, Mar. 20 ***Perf. 13x13¼***
1201-1202 A504 Set of 2 4.75 4.75

"Postes" A505

Denomination A506

Serpentine Die Cut 11x11¼

2007, Mar. 20 **Photo.**

Self-Adhesive

Coil Stamps

1203 A505 25c pur & multi .70 .70
1204 A506 25c brn & multi .70 .70
1205 A505 25c dk bl & multi .70 .70
1206 A506 25c dk grn & multi .70 .70
a. Vert. strip of 4, #1203-1206 2.80
1207 A505 50c red vio & multi 1.40 1.40
1208 A506 50c red & multi 1.40 1.40
1209 A505 50c bl & multi 1.40 1.40
1210 A506 50c grn & multi 1.40 1.40
a. Vert. strip of 4, #1207-1210 5.60
Nos. 1203-1210 (8) 8.40 8.40

Europa — A507

Designs: 50c, Scout campground. 70c, Scouts, globe, knot.

2007, May 22 **Litho.** ***Perf. 13x13¼***
1211-1212 A507 Set of 2 3.25 3.25

Scouting, cent.

Town Centenaries A508

Designs: No. 1213, 50c, Differdange. No. 1214, 50c, Dudelenge. No. 1215, 50c, Ettelbruck. No. 1216, 50c, Rumelange.

2007, May 22 **Photo.** ***Perf. 11½***
1213-1216 A508 Set of 4 5.50 5.50

Places of Culture — A509

Designs: 50c, Rockhal. 70c, Grand Duke Jean Museum of Modern Art. €1, Neumünster Abbey.

2007, May 22 ***Perf. 12½***
1217-1219 A509 Set of 3 6.00 6.00

"Transborderism" A510

2007, Sept. 3 **Photo.** ***Perf. 11½***
1220 A510 50c multi 1.40 1.40

Rotunda of Luxembourg Train Station — A511

2007, Sept. 3 **Photo. & Engr.**
1221 A511 70c multi 1.90 1.90

See Belgium No. 2253.

Casa Luxemburg, Sibiu, Romania — A512

2007, Sept. 3 **Litho.** ***Perf. 13x13¼***
1222 A512 70c multi 1.90 1.90

See Romania Nos. 4993-4994.

Luxembourg Army Peace-keeping Missions — A513

2007, Sept. 3 **Photo.** ***Perf. 11½***
1223 A513 70c multi 1.90 1.90

Souvenir Sheet

Roman Mosaic, Vichten A514

No. 1224: a, Thalia and Euterpe. b, Terpsichore and Melpomene. c, Clio and Urania. d, Polymnia and Erato. e, Calliope and Homer. Nos. 1224a-1224d are 58x29mm octagonal stamps, No. 1224e is a 55x55mm diamond-shaped stamp.

2007, Sept. 3 **Litho.** ***Perf. 14¼***
1224 A514 Sheet of 5 8.25 8.25
a.-d. 50c Any single 1.40 1.40
e. €1 multi 2.60 2.60

Esch-sur-Sure Dam — A515

Uewersauer Stauséi — A516

Serpentine Die Cut 12½x13½

2007, Dec. 4 **Litho.** **Self-Adhesive**
1225 Horiz. pair 4.25
a. A515 70c multi 2.10 2.10
b. A516 70c multi 2.10 2.10

St. Willibrord (658-739) — A517

2008, Mar. 18 **Litho.** ***Perf. 13***
1226 A517 50c multi 1.60 1.60

European Investment Bank, 50th Anniv. — A518

**2008, Mar. 18**     Perf. 13x13¼
1227 A518 70c purple & silver    2.25 2.25

Eurosystem, 10th Anniv. — A519

**2008, Mar. 18**     Perf. 13½x13¾
1228 A519 €1 multi     3.25 3.25

Luxembourg Philharmonic Orchestra, 75th Anniv. — A520

Henri Pensis (1900-58), Conductor A521

**2008, Mar. 18**
1229 A520 50c multi     1.60 1.60
1230 A521 70c multi     2.25 2.25

2008 Summer Olympics, Beijing — A522

**2008, May 20**   Litho.   Perf. 14x13½
1231 A522 70c multi     2.25 2.25

Luxembourg Basketball Federation, 75th Anniv. — A523    Luxembourg Soccer Federation, Cent. — A524

**2008, May 20**     Perf. 12½
1232 A523 A multi     1.60 1.60
1233 A524 A multi     1.60 1.60
   Nos. 1232 and 1233 each sold for 50c on day of issue.

Europa — A525

Smiling letter with wings: 50c, Standing on hand. 70c, Flying.

**2008, May 20**
1234-1235 A525   Set of 2    4.00 4.00

Tourism — A526

Designs: No. 1236, A, Bridge, Diekirch, and city arms. No. 1237, A, Building, Leudelange,

and city arms. No. 1238, A, Rindschleiden Church, Wahl, vert.

**2008, May 20**     Perf. 11½
1236-1238 A526   Set of 3    4.75 4.75
   Diekirch, 125th anniv., Leudelange, 150th anniv. Nos. 1236-1238 each sold for 50c on day of issue.

Medico-social League, Cent. — A527

**2008, Sept. 30**   Litho.   Perf. 13¾
1239 A527 A multi     1.40 1.40
   Sold for 50c on day of issue.

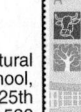

Agricultural Technical School, Ettelbruck, 125th Anniv. — A528

**2008, Sept. 30**
1240 A528 A multi     1.40 1.40
   Sold for 50c on day of issue.

Federation of Popular Education Associations, Cent. — A529

**2008, Sept. 30**     Perf. 13x13¼
1241 A529 A multi     1.40 1.40
   Sold for 50c on day of issue.

Natl. League for the Protection of Animals, Cent. — A530

**2008, Sept. 30**
1242 A530 A multi     1.40 1.40
   Sold for 50c on day of issue.

NATO Maintenance and Supply Agency, 50th Anniv. — A531

**2008, Sept. 30**
1243 A531 70c multi     2.00 2.00

Greetings — A532

Winning art from children's stamp design contest by: 70c, A. Wainer. €1, S. Rauschenberger.

**2008, Sept. 30**     Perf. 11½
1244-1245 A532   Set of 2    4.75 4.75

A533     A534

Different shapes of colored background lines with "ATR" at: No. 1246, LR. No. 1247, UL. No. 1248, LL. No. 1249, UR.

Different shapes of colored background lines with "A" at: No. 1250, LL. No. 1251, UL. No. 1252, LR. No. 1253, UR.

### Coil Stamps
*Serpentine Die Cut 11*

**2008, Sept. 30**     Self-Adhesive
1246 A533 ATR blue     .70 .70
1247 A533 ATR purple    .70 .70
1248 A533 ATR green    .70 .70
1249 A533 ATR red     .70 .70
   a.   Vert. strip of 4, #1246-1249   2.80
1250 A534 A multi     1.40 1.40
1251 A534 A multi     1.40 1.40
1252 A534 A multi     1.40 1.40
1253 A534 A multi     1.40 1.40
   a.   Vert. strip of 4, #1250-1253   5.60
   Nos. 1246-1253 (8)    8.40 8.40
   On day of issue, Nos. 1246-1249 each sold for 25c, Nos. 1250-1253, for 50c.

Happiness — A535

No. 1254: a, Bowling pins, denomination over red violet. b, Gift, denomination over yellow green. c, Wrapped candies, denomination over green. d, Wrapped candies, denomination over blue. e, Gift, denomination over green. f, Bowling pins, denomination over yellow green. g, Dice, "A" over red violet. h, Drum and sticks, "A" over yellow green. i, Four-leaf clovers, "A" over green. j, Four-leaf clovers, "A" over blue. k, Drum and sticks, "A" over green. l, Dice, "A" over yellow green.

*Die Cut Perf. 10 on 3 Sides*

**2008, Sept. 30**     Self-Adhesive
1254    Booklet pane of 12   12.00
   a.-f.   A535 20c Any single   .55 .55
   g.-l.   A535 A Any single   1.40 1.40
   Nos. 1254g-1254l each sold for 50c on day of issue.

New Courthouse of Court of Justice of the European Communities A536

**2008, Dec. 2**   Litho.   Perf. 14x13¼
1255 A536 70c multi     1.90 1.90

Election of Holy Roman Emperor Henry VII (c. 1269-1313), 700th Anniv. — A537

**2008, Dec. 2**     Perf. 13¼x13
1256 A537 €1 multi     2.60 2.60

Introduction of the Euro, 10th Anniv. — A538

**2009, Mar. 17**   Litho.   Perf. 12½
1257 A538 A multi     1.25 1.25
   No. 1257 sold for 50c on day of issue.

Luxembourg Aero Club, Cent. — A539

New Airport Terminal — A540

No. 1258: a, Satellite, airplane, hang glider, left half of balloon. b, Right half of balloon, glider, parachutist, jet plane.

**2009, Mar. 17**     Perf. 11½
1258 A539 50c Horiz. pair, #a-b   2.60 2.60
1259 A540 90c multi     2.25 2.25

Natl. Federation of Fire Fighters, 125th Anniv. — A541

Designs: 20c, Modern fire truck. A, Fire fighter rescuing child. €2, Antique fire truck.

**2008, Mar. 17**     Perf. 13x13¼
1260-1262 A541   Set of 3    7.00 7.00
   No. 1261 sold for 50c on day of issue.

Postmen's Federation, Cent. — A542

General Confederation of the Civil Service, Cent. — A543

Natl. Federation of Railroad and Transportation Workers, Cent. — A544

**2009, Mar. 17**     Perf. 14x13¼
1263 A542 50c multi     1.25 1.25
1264 A543 A multi     1.25 1.25
1265 A544 A multi     1.25 1.25
   Nos. 1263-1265 (3)    3.75 3.75
   On day of issue, Nos. 1264-1265 each sold for 50c.

June 7 European Elections — A545

**2009, May 12**   Litho.   Perf. 13
1266 A545 50c multi     1.40 1.40

National Research Fund, 10th Anniv. — A546

**2009, May 12**     Perf. 13½
1267 A546 A multi     1.40 1.40
   No. 1267 sold for 50c on day of issue.

Children's Houses, 125th Anniv. — A547

**2009, May 12**     Perf. 12½
1268 A547 A multi     1.40 1.40
   No. 1268 sold for 50c on day of issue.

Europa — A548

Designs: 50c, Father and child watching comet. 70c, Galileo, telescope, planets.

**2009, May 12**     *Perf. 13½*
1269-1270 A548   Set of 2    3.25 3.25

Intl. Year of Astronomy.

Personalized Stamps — A549

Stripe color: A, Red. A Europe, Blue.

**2009, May 12**     *Perf. 11¾x11½*
**Stamp + Label**
1271-1272 A549   Set of 2    3.25 3.25

On day of issue, No. 1271 sold for 50c; No. 1272, 70c. Labels bearing text "PostMusée" and pictures are generic and sold for these prices. Labels could be personalized for an additional fee.

Famous People — A550

Designs: 70c, Foni Tissen (1909-75), painter. 90c, Charles Bernhoeft (1859-1933), photographer. €1, Henri Tudor (1859-1928), electrical engineer.

**Litho. & Engr.**
**2009, May 12**     *Perf. 13½*
1273-1275 A550   Set of 3    7.00 7.00

Vianden Castle — A551

    *Perf. 13¼x12¾*
**2009, Sept. 16**     Litho.
1276 A551 70c multi    2.00 2.00

Louis Braille (1809-52), Educator of the Blind — A552

**Litho. & Embossed**
**2009, Sept. 16**     *Perf. 13¼x13*
1277 A552 90c multi    2.60 2.60

Railroads in Luxembourg, 150th Anniv. — A553

Designs: 50c, Modern electric train. €1, Older electric train. €3, Steam locomotive.

**2009, Sept. 16**   Litho.   *Perf. 12½*
1278-1280 A553   Set of 3    13.00 13.00

---

**Souvenir Sheet**

Luxembourg Federation of Philatelic Societies, 75th Anniv. — A554

No. 1281: a, Luxembourg #198. b, Gate of Three Towers.

**Litho. & Embossed**
**2009, Sept. 16**     *Perf. 13¾x14*
1281 A554   Sheet of 2    3.50 3.50
  *a.*   50c multi      1.50 1.50
  *b.*   70c multi      2.00 2.00

Johannes Gutenberg (c. 1390-1468), Inventor of Movable Type Presses A555     Website Addresses and Movable Type A556

**2009, Dec. 1**   Litho.   *Perf. 13¼x13½*
1282 A555 50c multi    1.50 1.50
1283 A556 70c multi    2.10 2.10

See Switzerland No. 1344.

Schengen Convention, 25th Anniv. — A557

**2010, Mar. 16**   Litho.   *Perf. 13½x13*
1284 A557 70c multi    1.90 1.90

Luxembourg Pavilion, Expo 2010, Shanghai A558

**2010, Mar. 16**     *Perf. 14x13½*
1285 A558 90c multi    2.50 2.50

Eisch Valley Castles A559

No. 1286 — Various castles with country name at: a, UL. b, LR.

    *Serpentine Die Cut 12¼x13¼*
**2010, Mar. 16**     **Self-Adhesive**
1286   Horiz. pair     4.00
  *a.-b.*   A559 A Either single   1.90 1.90

On day of issue, Nos. 1286a-1287a each sold for 70c.

Countdown 2010 — A560

Designs: 70c, Arnica montana. €1, Mussels.

**2010, Mar. 16**     *Perf. 11½*
1287-1288 A560   Set of 2    4.75 4.75

---

A561

Royalty A562

Designs: 50c, Grand Duke Henri. €1, Grand Duchess Charlotte (1896-1985). €3, Grand Duke Henri and Grand Duchess Maria Teresa.

**2010, Mar. 16**     *Perf. 11½*
1289-1290 A561   Set of 2    4.25 4.25
**Souvenir Sheet**
1291 A562 €3 multi    8.25 8.25

Grand Duke Henri's accession to the throne, 10th anniv. (No. 1289).

Marriage of John of Luxembourg and Elizabeth of Bohemia, 700th Anniv. — A563

**Photo. & Engr.**
**2010, June 16**     *Perf. 11¾x11¼*
1292 A563 70c multi    1.75 1.75

Accession to the throne of Bohemia by the House of Luxembourg. See Czech Republic No. 3457.

Europa — A564

Designs: 50c, Child and dragon reading book. 70c, Girl with lasso riding book.

**2010, June 16**   Litho.   *Perf. 13½*
1293-1294 A564   Set of 2    3.00 3.00

Outdoor Activities — A565

Designs: No. 1295, A, Motorcycling. No. 1296, A Europe, Camping.

**2010, June 16**     *Perf. 13½x13*
1295-1296 A565   Set of 2    3.00 3.00

On day of issue, No. 1295 sold for 50c, and No. 1296 sold for 70c. See Nos. 1337-1338.

**Souvenir Sheet**

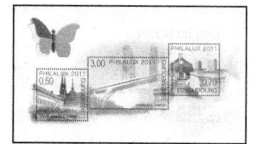

Philalux 2011 Intl. Philatelic Exhibition, Luxembourg — A566

No. 1297 — Various sites in Luxembourg: a, 50c (38x38mm). b, 70c, (38x38mm). c, €3, (60x38mm).

---

    *Perf. 13¾, 13¼x13¾ (#1297c)*
**2010, June 16**
1297 A566   Sheet of 3   10.50 10.50
  *a.*   50c multi      1.25 1.25
  *b.*   70c multi      1.75 1.75
  *c.*   €3 multi      7.50 7.50

**Souvenir Sheet**

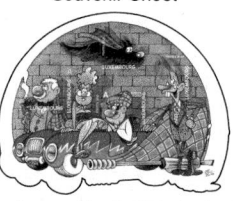

Superjhemp, Comic Strip by Lucien Czuga — A567

No. 1298: a, Bernie the Dog. b, Man smoking pipe. c, Woman, vert. d, Superjhemp. e, Man with glasses, vert.

    *Serpentine Die Cut 12¼*
**2010, June 16**     **Self-Adhesive**
1298 A567   Sheet of 5    6.25 6.25
  *a.-e.*   Any single     1.25 1.25

On day of issue, Nos. 1298a-1298e each sold for 50c.

 A568

Winning Art in Children's "Fight Against Poverty" Stamp Design Contest — A569

**2010, Sept. 27**   Litho.   *Perf. 11½*
1299 A568 A multi    1.25 1.25
1300 A569 A Europe multi   1.75 1.75

On day of issue No. 1299 sold for 50c and No. 1300 sold for 70c.

Famous People — A570

Designs: 70c, Anne Beffort (1880-1966), educator and writer. 90c, Jean Soupert (1834-1910), rose cultivator. €1, Nicolas Frantz (1899-1985), cyclist.

**Litho. & Engr.**
**2010, Sept. 27**     *Perf. 13½*
1301-1303 A570   Set of 3    6.75 6.75

    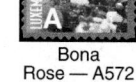

Bagatelle Rose — A571     Bona Rose — A572

Bordeaux Rose — A573     Reine Marguerite d'Italie Rose — A574

Souvenir de Maria de Zayas Rose — A575     Clotilde Rose — A576

Prince Jean de Luxembourg Rose — A577

Pierre Watine Rose — A578

Ivan Misson Rose — A579

William Notting Rose — A580

**Serpentine Die Cut 9¾**
**2010, Sept. 27**    Litho.
**Self-Adhesive**

| 1304 | Booklet pane of 10 | 12.50 | |
|---|---|---|---|
| a. | A571 A multi | 1.25 | 1.25 |
| b. | A572 A multi | 1.25 | 1.25 |
| c. | A573 A multi | 1.25 | 1.25 |
| d. | A574 A multi | 1.25 | 1.25 |
| e. | A575 A multi | 1.25 | 1.25 |
| f. | A576 A multi | 1.25 | 1.25 |
| g. | A577 A multi | 1.25 | 1.25 |
| h. | A578 A multi | 1.25 | 1.25 |
| i. | A579 A multi | 1.25 | 1.25 |
| j. | A580 A multi | 1.25 | 1.25 |

Nos. 1304a-1304j each sold for 50c on day of issue.

Luxembourg Maritime Cluster — A581

No. 1305 — Ships with lion emblem at: a, Left. b, Right.

**2010, Dec. 7**   Litho.   **Perf. 11½**
1305 A581 A Horiz. pair, #a-b   4.75 4.75
Nos. 1305a and 1305b each sold for 85c on day of issue.

European Year of Volunteering A582

**2011, Mar. 15**    **Perf. 13¼x13**
1306 A582 A multi    1.75 1.75
No. 1306 sold for 60c on day of issue.

Royalty — A583

Designs: 85c, Prince Guillaume, 30th birthday. €1.10, Grand Duke Jean, 90th birthday.

**2011, Mar. 15**    **Perf. 11½**
1307-1308 A583   Set of 2   5.50 5.50

Anniversaries — A584

Designs: No. 1309, 60c, Luxembourg Federation of Quilleurs (nine-pin bowling), 50th anniv. No. 1310, 60c, Amnesty International, 50th anniv. No. 1311, 60c, Stamp Day, 75th anniv.

**2011, Mar. 15**
1309-1311 A584   Set of 3   5.00 5.00

Europa — A585

Designs: 60c, Forest. 80c, Hills.
**2011, May 17**   Litho.   **Perf. 13½**
1312-1313 A585   Set of 2   4.25 4.25
Intl. Year of Forests.

Viticulture — A586

Designs: 60c, Sun with grapes, wine glass and bottle. 85c, Cork of Crémant de Luxembourg sparkling wine bottle.

**2011, May 17**    **Perf. 11½**
1314-1315 A586   Set of 2   4.25 4.25
Federation of Viticulture Associations of Luxembourg, cent. (No. 1314), Crémant de Luxembourg, 20th anniv. (No. 1315).

Personalized Stamps A587

Denominations: 60c, 85c, vert.
**Perf. 11¼x11½, 11½x11¼**
**2011, May 17**    **Self-Adhesive**
1316-1317 A587   Set of 2   4.25 4.25
Vignettes showing picture and "Mäi Moment / Meng Photo / Meng Post" text are generic and sold at their face values. Vignettes could be personalized for an additional fee.

Miniature Sheet

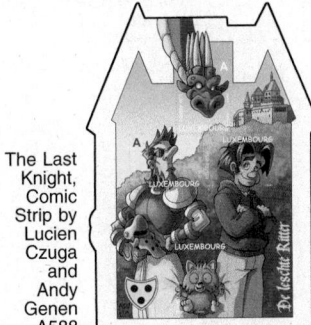
The Last Knight, Comic Strip by Lucien Czuga and Andy Genen A588

No. 1318: a, Dragon. b, Knight wearing sunglasses, horiz. c, Man, horiz. d, Cat.

**Serpentine Die Cut 12¼**
**2011, May 17**    **Self-Adhesive**
1318 A588   Sheet of 4   7.00
a.-d.   A Any single   1.75 1.75
On day of issue, Nos. 1318a-1318d each sold for 60c.

Luxembourg Consumers Union, 50th Anniv. — A589

**2011, Sept. 27**    **Perf. 11½**
1319 A589 60c multi   1.75 1.75

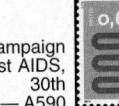
Campaign Against AIDS, 30th Anniv. — A590

**2011, Sept. 27**
1320 A590 60c multi   1.75 1.75

Cercle Cité, Luxembourg — A591

**2011, Sept. 27**
1321 A591 A multi   1.75 1.75
No. 1321 sold for 60c on day of issue.

Franz Liszt (1811-86), Composer — A592

**2011, Sept. 27**    **Perf. 14¼x14¾**
1322 A592 85c multi   2.40 2.40

Chemin de la Corniche, Luxembourg — A593

**2011, Sept. 27**    **Perf. 11½**
1323 A593 85c multi   2.40 2.40

Post Checks, Cent. — A594

**2011, Dec. 6**   Litho.   **Perf. 11½x11¾**
1324 A594 60c multi   1.60 1.60

Souvenir Sheet

Echternacht Hopping Procession (UNESCO Intangible Heritage) — A595

No. 1325 — Procession participants and: a, Left side of scarf. b, Right side of scarf.

**2011, Dec. 6**    **Perf. 14**
1325 A595   Sheet of 2   4.00 4.00
a.   60c multi   1.60 1.60
b.   85c multi   2.40 2.40

Architecture — A596

No. 1326 — Designs: a, Eislek. b, Réidener Streech. c, lechternacher Streech. d, Minett.

**Serpentine Die Cut 12½**
**2011, Dec. 6**    **Self-Adhesive**
1326   Booklet pane of 4   6.50
a.-d.   A596 A Any single   1.60 1.60
  Complete booklet, 2 #1326   13.00
Nos. 1326a-1326d each sold for 60c on day of issue.

Luxembourg Amateur Radio Society, 75th Anniv. — A597

**2012, Mar. 13**    **Perf. 11½**
1327 A597 60c multi   1.60 1.60

Grand Ducal Institute Arts and Letters Section, 50th Anniv. — A598

**2012, Mar. 13**
1328 A598 60c multi   1.60 1.60

Luxembourg Table Tennis Federation, 75th Anniv. — A599

**2012, Mar. 13**
1329 A599 60c multi   1.60 1.60

Introduction of Euro Currency, 10th Anniv. — A600

**Litho. & Embossed**
**2012, Mar. 13**    **Perf. 13**
1330 A600 85c multi   2.25 2.25

Natl. Institute of Statistics and Economic Studies, 50th Anniv. — A601

**2012, May 15**   Litho.   **Perf. 12½**
1331 A601 60c multi   1.60 1.60

Luxembourg Olympic Committee, Cent. — A602

2012 Summer Olympics, London — A603

**2012, May 15**    **Perf. 14¼x14¾**
1332 A602   60c multi   1.60 1.60
1333 A603 €1.10 multi   3.00 3.00

Europa — A604

Luxembourg tourism website address and various Luxembourg buildings and monuments: 60c, 85c.

**2012, May 15**    **Perf. 13½**
1334-1335 A604   Set of 2   4.00 4.00

### Miniature Sheet

Characters from Mil's Adventures, Comic Strip by Gab Weis — A605

No. 1336 — Various unnamed characters with country name in: a, Red violet (Mil). b, Green. c, Orange. d, Lilac, vert. e, Red violet (2 characters), vert.

***Serpentine Die Cut 12¼***

**2012, May 15**      **Self-Adhesive**
1336 A605   Sheet of 5      8.00
a.-e.   A Any single      1.60   1.60

On day of issue, Nos. 1336a-1336e each sold for 60c.

### Outdoor Activities Type of 2010

Designs: 60c, Paragliding. 85c, Diving.

**2012, Sept. 25**      **Perf. 13¼x13**
1337-1338 A565   Set of 2      3.75   3.75

A606      Potable Water — A607

**2012, Sept. 25**      **Perf. 11½**
1339 A606 60c multi      1.50   1.50
1340 A607 85c multi      2.25   2.25

Architecture — A608

Paintings by Christian Frantzen of: €1.20, Footbridge, Esch-sur-Alzette. €2.20, Belval-Université Station, Esch-sur-Alzette. €4, Pfaffenthal-Upper Town Link, Luxembourg.

**2012, Sept. 25**
1341-1343 A608   Set of 3      19.00   19.00

Wedding of Prince Guillaume and Countess Stéphanie de Lannoy — A609

Designs: 60c, Couple. 85c, Couple, diff.

**2012, Sept. 25**      **Perf. 13½**
1344 A609 60c multi      1.50   1.50
     **Souvenir Sheet**
1345   Sheet of 2, #1344, 1345a      3.75   3.75
a.   A609 85c multi      2.25   2.25

### Souvenir Sheet

Wedding of Prince Guillaume and Countess Stéphanie de Lannoy — A610

**2012, Oct. 20**      **Perf. 13¼**
1346 A610   €4 multi      10.50   10.50

European Court of Justice, 60th Anniv. — A611

**2012, Dec. 4**      **Perf. 12½**
1347 A611 85c maroon & lt blue   2.25   2.25

European Year of Citizens — A612

**2013, Mar. 12**      **Perf. 13¼x13**
1348 A612 60c multi      1.60   1.60

Grand Duke Adolphe Union, 150th Anniv. — A613

**2013, Mar. 12**      **Perf. 11½**
1349 A613 60c multi      1.60   1.60

Emile Metz Private Technical High School, Cent. — A614

**2013, Mar. 12**
1350 A614 60c multi      1.60   1.60

Round Table Luxembourg, 50th Anniv. — A615

**2013, Mar. 12**
1351 A615 60c multi      1.60   1.60

Holy Roman Emperor Henry VII (c.1275-1313) A616

**2013, Mar. 12**
1352 A616 €1.10 multi      3.00   3.00

Famous Men — A617

Designs: No. 1353, 60c, Nicolas Adames (1813-87), theologian. No. 1354, 60c, Putty Stein (1888-1955), composer.

**2013, May 2**
1353-1354 A617   Set of 2      3.25   3.25

Europa — A618

Postal vehicles: 60c, Citroen 2 CV AZU. 85c, Renault Kangoo.

**2013, May 2**      **Perf. 13x13¼**
1355-1356 A618   Set of 2      3.75   3.75

15th Games of the Small States of Europe, Luxembourg — A619

**2013, May 2**      **Perf. 11½**
1357 A619   Horiz. pair      3.25   3.25
a.-b.   60c Either single      1.60   1.60

### Souvenir Sheet

100th Tour de France Bicycle Race A620

**2013, May 2**      **Perf. 12**
1358 A620   €4 multi      10.50   10.50

Completion of 11th Turbine for Société Electrique de l'Our — A621

**2013, Sept. 24**      **Perf. 11½**
1359 A621 60c multi      1.60   1.60

Wild Cats — A622

Designs: 20c, Panthera tigris sumatrae. 30c, Lynx lynx. 60c, Felis silvestris.

**2013, Sept. 24**
1360-1362 A622   Set of 3      3.00   3.00

### Souvenir Sheet

Selection of "The Family of Man" Photographic Exhibition to UNESCO Memory of the World Register — A623

No. 1363: a, Photograph of crowd. b, Self-portrait of Edward Steichen.

**2013, Sept. 24**      **Perf. 13¾x14**
1363 A623   Sheet of 2      4.00   4.00
a.   60c blue & black      1.60   1.60
b.   85c blue & black      2.25   2.25

A624      A625

A626      A627

***Serpentine Die Cut 11***

**2013, Sept. 24**      **Self-Adhesive**
     **Coil Stamps**
1364   Vert. strip of 4      6.50
a.   A624 (60c) multi      1.60   1.60
b.   A625 (60c) multi      1.60   1.60
c.   A626 (60c) multi      1.60   1.60
d.   A627 (60c) multi      1.60   1.60

Moselle Valley A628

No. 1365 — Various buildings and: a, Bridge over river in foreground. b, Moselle River running through town.

***Serpentine Die Cut 12½x13½***

**2013, Sept. 24**      **Self-Adhesive**
1365 A628   Horiz. pair      4.50
a.-b.   (85c) Either single      2.25   2.25

Pierre Werner (1913-2002), Prime Minister — A629

**2013, Dec. 3**    **Litho.**    **Perf. 11½**
1366 A629 60c multi      1.75   1.75

Mushrooms — A630

Designs: No. 1367, Pezize orangée. No. 1368, Bolet bai. No. 1369, Polypore versicolore. No. 1370, Amanite "tue-mouche." No. 1371, Vesse de loup perlée.

***Serpentine Die Cut 12¼***

**2013, Dec. 3**      **Litho.**
     **Booklet Stamps**
     **Self-Adhesive**
1367 A630 (60c) multi      1.75   1.75
1368 A630 (60c) multi      1.75   1.75
1369 A630 (60c) multi      1.75   1.75
1370 A630 (60c) multi      1.75   1.75
1371 A630 (60c) multi      1.75   1.75
a.   Booklet pane of 10, 2 each #1367-1371      17.50
     Nos. 1367-1371 (5)      8.75   8.75

Scouting in Luxembourg, Cent. — A631

**2014, Mar. 11**    **Litho.**    **Perf. 11½**
1372 A631 60c multi      1.75   1.75

Primary Schools Sports League, 50th Anniv. — A632

**2014, Mar. 11**    **Litho.**    **Perf. 11½**
1373 A632 60c multi      1.75   1.75

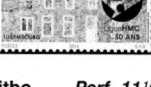

Ligue HMC, 50th Anniv. — A633

**2014, Mar. 11**    **Litho.**    **Perf. 11½**
1374 A633 60c multi      1.75   1.75

Luxembourg Red Cross, Cent. — A634

**2014, Mar. 11    Litho.    Perf. 11½**
1375  A634  60c multi                    1.75  1.75

Souvenir Sheet

Luxembourg Federation of Philatelic Societies, 80th Anniv. — A635

No. 1376: a, Magnifying glass, hand holding stamp tongs, children looking at stamps on stock page. b, Bridge, buildings.

**2014, Mar. 11    Litho.    Perf. 13¾x14**
**Silk-Faced Paper**
1376  A635  Sheet of 2                   4.00  4.00
a.    60c multi                          1.75  1.75
b.    85c multi                          2.25  2.25

May 25, 2014 European Elections — A636

**2014, May 8    Litho.    Perf. 13¼x13**
1377  A636  60c multi                    1.75  1.75

First Public Recital of Lyrics to National Anthem, 150th Anniv. — A637

Independence, 175th Anniv. — A638

**2014, May 8    Litho.    Perf. 11½**
1378  A637  60c multi                    1.75  1.75
1379  A638  60c multi                    1.75  1.75

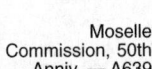
Moselle Commission, 50th Anniv. — A639

**2014, May 8    Litho.    Perf. 13x13¼**
1380  A639  85c multi                    2.40  2.40

Europa — A640

Various musicians: 60c, 85c.

**2014, May 8    Litho.    Perf. 12½**
1381-1382  A640  Set of 2                4.25  4.25

Souvenir Sheet

City of Luxembourg as UNESCO World Heritage Site, 20th Anniv. — A641

No. 1383 — Buildings and fortifications of Old City: a, 60c. b, 85c.

**2014, May 8    Litho.    Perf. 13¾x14**
1383  A641  Sheet of 2                   4.25  4.25
a.    60c multi                          1.75  1.75
b.    85c multi                          2.40  2.40

German Invasion of Luxembourg, Cent. — A642

**2014, Sept. 23    Litho.    Perf. 11½**
1384  A642  60c multi                    1.50  1.50

World War I, cent.

A643

Winning Designs in Children's Art Contest on Soil and the Environment — A644

**2014, Sept. 23    Litho.    Perf. 11½**
1385  A643  60c multi                    1.50  1.50
1386  A644  85c multi                    2.25  2.25

Famous People — A645

Designs: No. 1387, 60c, Samuel Hirsch (1809-89), rabbi. No. 1388, 60c, Nikolaus Hein (1889-1969), writer. No. 1389, 60c, Marie Speyer (1880-1914), educator.

**2014, Sept. 23    Litho.    Perf. 11½**
1387-1389  A645  Set of 3                4.50  4.50

Vegetables — A646

Designs: 85c, Tragopogon porrifolius. €1, Pisum sativum. €1.10, Cichorium intybus.

**2014, Sept. 23    Litho.    Perf. 11½**
1390-1392  A646  Set of 3                7.50  7.50

See Nos. 1410-1412, 1437-1439.

Accession to Throne of Grand Duke Jean, 50th Anniv. — A647

**2014, Dec. 2    Litho.    Perf. 13¼x13**
1393  A647  (60c) multi                  1.50  1.50

Grand Duke Henri — A648

**Litho. & Engr.**
**2015, Mar. 3    Perf. 13½x13**
**Panel Color**
1394  A648  L  green                     1.40  1.40
1395  A648  E  blue                      1.90  1.90
1396  A648  M  rose carmine              2.50  2.50
Nos. 1394-1396 (3)                       5.80  5.80

On day of issue, Nos. 1394-1396 each sold for 60c, 85c and €1.10 respectively.

Organized Philately in Luxembourg, 125th Anniv. — A649

**2015, Mar. 3    Litho.    Perf. 11½**
1397  A649  60c multi                    1.40  1.40

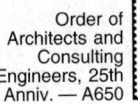
Order of Architects and Consulting Engineers, 25th Anniv. — A650

**2015, Mar. 3    Litho.    Perf. 11½**
1398  A650  60c multi                    1.40  1.40

Omega 90, 25th Anniv. — A651

**2015, Mar. 3    Litho.    Perf. 11½**
1399  A651  60c multi                    1.40  1.40

Creation of Grand Duchy of Luxembourg, 200th Anniv. A652

**2015, Mar. 3    Litho.    Perf. 11½**
1400  A652  60c multi                    1.40  1.40

Fruit — A653

No. 1401 — Apple and pear varieties: a, Triumph aus Luxemburg apples. b, Gute Graue pears. c, Luxemburger Renette apples. d, Doppelte Philippsbirne pears. e, Jakob Lebel apples. f, Neue Poiteau pears. g, Porzenapfel apples. h, Saint Remy pears. i, Eifeler Rambur apples. j, Luxemburger Mostbirne pears.

***Serpentine Die Cut 9¾***
**2015, Mar. 3    Litho.**
**Self-Adhesive**
1401  A653  Booklet pane of 10           14.00
a.-j.    L Any single                    1.40  1.40
On day of issue, Nos. 1401a-1401j each sold for 60c.

Europa — A654

Designs: 60c, Building blocks. 85c, Doll and doll house furniture.

**2015, May 5    Litho.    Perf. 13½**
1402-1403  A654  Set of 2                3.25  3.25

Famous Men — A655

Designs: No. 1404, 60c, Claus Cito (1882-1965), sculptor. No. 1405, 60c, Robert Krieps (1922-90), politician. No. 1406, 60c, René Engelmann (1880-1915), writer.

**2015, May 5    Litho.    Perf. 11½**
1404-1406  A655  Set of 3                4.25  4.25

Miniature Sheet

End of World War II, 70th Anniv. A656

No. 1407: a, Railroad car and concentration camp gate (40x30mm). b, Star of David, triangles and "70" (40x30mm). c, Luxembourger in German uniform holding Luxembourg flag (30x30mm). d, Civil courage (30x30mm). e, Blindfolded person behind barbed wire (40x30mm). f, Resistance (40x30mm).

**2015, May 5    Litho.    Perf. 12**
1407  A656  Sheet of 6                   8.50  8.50
a.-f.    60c Any single                  1.40  1.40

A657

Luxembourg Presidency of the Council of the European Union — A658

**2015, July 1    Litho.    Perf. 12½x12**
**Self-Adhesive**
1408  A657 (60c) multi                1.40 1.40
1409  A658 (85c) multi                1.90 1.90

**Vegetables Type of 2014**

Root vegetables: 20c, Pastinaca sativa. 25c, Apium graveolens. 35c, Beta vulgaris.

**2015, Sept. 22    Litho.    Perf. 11½**
1410-1412  A646   Set of 3            1.90 1.90

Luxembourg No. 1 — A659

**2015, Sept. 22    Litho.    Perf. 15x14½**
1413  A659 70c blk & gold             1.60 1.60

Penny Black, 175th anniv.

Grand Duke Henri and Grand Duchess Maria Teresa A660

**Litho. & Engr.**
**2015, Sept. 22                    Perf. 13**
1414  A660 70c multi                  1.60 1.60

Opening of Wiltheim Wing of National Museum of History and Art — A661

Designs: 70c, Museum. 95c, Silver tea caddy made by Johann Michael Kutzer (1700-60). €1.30, Helios, ceramic sculpture by Villeroy & Boch.

**Litho., Litho. & Embossed (95c, €1.30)**
**2015, Sept. 22                Perf. 13x13¼**
1415-1417  A661   Set of 3            6.75 6.75

Nature Reserves — A662

Designs: No. 1418, (70c), Mellerdall Nature Reserve. No. 1419, (70c), Oewersauer Nature Reserve. No. 1420, (70c), Our Nature Reserve.

**2015, Sept. 22    Litho.    Perf. 12¾**
1418-1420  A662   Set of 3            4.75 4.75

Nos. 1418-1420 are each inscribed "L50g."

Flowers — A663

No. 1421: a, Maargréitchen (daisy). b, Karblumm (cornflower). c, Deschtel (thistle). d, Feierblumm (red poppy).

---

***Die Cut Perf. 13x12¾***
**2015, Dec. 1    Coil Stamps    Litho.**
**Self-Adhesive**
1421              Vert. strip of 4    3.00
a.-d.   A663 (35c) Any single        .75  .75

Nos. 1421a-1421d are each inscribed "ATR 50g."

Opening of Belval Campus Headquarters of University of Luxembourg — A664

**2016, Mar. 3    Litho.    Perf. 14**
**Foil-faced Paper**
1422  A664 70c multi                  1.50 1.50

Port of Mertert, 50th Anniv. — A665

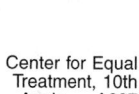

Luxembourg Maritime Register, 25th Anniv. — A666

Center for Equal Treatment, 10th Anniv. — A667

**2016, Mar. 3    Litho.    Perf. 11½**
1423  A665 70c multi                  1.50 1.50
1424  A666 70c multi                  1.50 1.50
1425  A667 70c multi                  1.50 1.50
       Nos. 1423-1425 (3)            4.50 4.50

Royalty A668

No. 1426: a, Grand Duchess Maria Teresa. b, Grand Duchess Maria Teresa, Prince Sébastien, Princess Alexandra.

**2016, Mar. 3    Litho.    Perf. 13¼x13**
1426  A668      Horiz. pair           3.00 3.00
a.-b.            70c Either single    1.50 1.50

2016 Summer Olympics, Rio de Janeiro — A669

**Litho. & Embossed**
**2016, May 10                Perf. 13¾x13½**
1427  A669 70c multi                  1.60 1.60

A670

Europa — A671

**2016, May 10    Litho.    Perf. 11½**
1428  A670 70c multi                  1.60 1.60
1429  A671 95c multi                  2.10 2.10

Think Green Issue.

---

Famous Men — A672

Designs: No. 1430, 70c, Marcel Noppeney (1877-1966), President of Society of Francophone Luxembourgian Writers. No. 1431, 70c, Joseph Hackin (1886-1941), archaeologist. No. 1432, 70c, Jean Jacoby (1891-1936), artist.

**2016, May 10    Litho.    Perf. 11½**
1430-1432  A672   Set of 3            4.75 4.75

Meng.post.lu Website for Personalized Stamps, 10th Anniv. A673

Pets: 70c, Cat named Margot. 95c, Dog named Goethe. €1.30, Cat named Mäischen.

**2016, May 10    Litho.    Perf. 11¼**
**Self-Adhesive**
1433-1435  A673   Set of 3            6.75 6.75

Stamp vignettes could be personalized by customers, presumably for an extra fee. Printed stamps having customer-provided personalized images may not show the green and yellow Luxembourg Post emblem found in the lower right corner of illustration A673, based on mockup images shown when ordering these sheets on the meng.post.lu website.

Nos. 1433-1435 were later printed with various other images by Luxembourg Post and offered for sale in full panes at a premium over face value. Only Nos. 1433-1435 were offered at face value. Stamps with other denominations bearing images chosen by Luxembourg Post were produced later, all of which were sold at a premium over face value.

**Souvenir Sheet**

Passage Through Luxembourg of Thurn and Taxis Postal Route, 500th Anniv. — A674

**Litho. & Embossed**
**2016, May 10                Perf. 11½**
1436  A674 €4 multi + label          9.00 9.00

**Vegetables Type of 2014**

Designs: 95c, Cucumis sativus. €1.30, Phaseolus vulgaris. €2, Allium cepa var. proliferum.

**2016, Sept. 13    Litho.    Perf. 11½**
1437-1439  A646   Set of 3            9.50 9.50

Jesus Christ and Virgin Mary, by Albrecht Bouts (c. 1451-1549) A675

**2016, Sept. 13    Litho.    Perf. 11½**
1440  A675 70c multi                  1.60 1.60

Luxembourg National Museum of History and Art exhibition of paintings by Bouts.

---

Famous Men — A672

Election of the Virgin Mary as Patroness of Luxembourg, 350th Anniv. — A676

**2016, Sept. 13    Engr.    Perf. 13**
1441  A676 70c multi                  1.60 1.60

No. 1441 was printed in sheets of 4. See Vatican City No. 1631.

Grand Duchess Charlotte Bridge (Red Bridge), 50th Anniv. A677

**2016, Sept. 13    Litho.    Perf. 12**
1442  A677 70c multi                  1.60 1.60

Spring in the Ostling — A678

**2016, Sept. 13    Litho.    Perf. 11½**
1443  A678 95c multi                  2.25 2.25

Biodiversity — A679

Winning designs in children's stamp design contest: 70c, Woodpecker, by Yann Klees. 95c, Wolf, by Christine Guirsch, horiz.

***Perf. 14x14¾, 14¾x14***
**2016, Sept. 13                    Litho.**
1444-1445  A679   Set of 2           3.75 3.75

A680                A681

New Emblem for Luxembourg — A682

**2016, Oct. 10    Litho.    Perf. 12½x12**
**Self-Adhesive**
1446  A680   70c multi                1.60 1.60
1447  A681   95c multi                2.10 2.10
1448  A682   €1.30 multi              3.00 3.00
       Nos. 1446-1448 (3)            6.70 6.70

Museums — A683

Designs: No. 1449, Steam locomotive, Minett Park, Differdange. No. 1450, Playing cards, Kulturhuef Printing Museum, Grevenmacher. No. 1451, Carriage, Rural and Artisanal Museum, Peppange. No. 1452,

Slate, hammer and pick, Slate Museum, Haut-Martelange. No. 1453, Airplane, Luxembourg Aviation Museum, Mondorf-les-Bains.

### Die Cut Perf. 11½
**2016, Dec. 6**        Litho.
### Booklet Stamps
### Self-Adhesive
| | | | |
|---|---|---|---|
|1449|A683 70c multi|1.50|1.50|
|1450|A683 70c multi|1.50|1.50|
|1451|A683 70c multi|1.50|1.50|
|1452|A683 70c multi|1.50|1.50|
|1453|A683 70c multi|1.50|1.50|
|a.|Booklet pane of 10, 2 each #1449-1453|15.00||
||Nos. 1449-1453 (5)|7.50|7.50|

Josy Barthel (1927-92), Olympic Gold Medalist Runner — A684

**2017, Mar. 7**   Litho.   *Perf. 11½*
1454 A684 70c multi    1.50 1.50

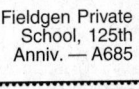

Fieldgen Private School, 125th Anniv. — A685

 Tony

Fifty-One International, 51st Anniv. — A686

Luxembourg Alzheimer Association, 30th Anniv. — A687

**2017, Mar. 7**   Litho.   *Perf. 11½*
| | | | |
|---|---|---|---|
|1455|A685 70c multi|1.50|1.50|
|1456|A686 70c multi|1.50|1.50|
|1457|A687 70c multi|1.50|1.50|
||Nos. 1455-1457 (3)|4.50|4.50|

Famous Men — A688

Designs: No. 1458, 70c, Jean Jules Linden (1817-98), botanist. No. 1459, 70c, Pierre Frieden (1892-1959), politician. No. 1460, 70c, Tony Bourg (1912-91), literature professor.

**2017, Mar. 7**   Litho.   *Perf. 11½*
1458-1460 A688   Set of 3   4.50 4.50

### Souvenir Sheet

Apparition of the Virgin Mary at Fatima, Portugal, Cent. — A689

**2017, Mar. 7**   Litho.   *Perf. 11¾x12*
1461 A689 95c multi    2.00 2.00

See Poland No. 4277, Portugal No. 3888, Slovakia No. 759.

Treaty of London, 150th Anniv. A690

---

### Litho. With Foil Application
**2017, May 9**     *Perf. 13*
1462 A690 70c multi    1.60 1.60

Count Peter-Ernst von Mansfeld (1517-1604), Governor of Luxembourg A691

**2017, May 9**   Litho.   *Perf. 11½*
1463 A691 95c multi    2.10 2.10

Military Anniversaries A692

Designs: 70c, Military musicians. 95c, Soldiers in fatigues.

**2017, May 9**   Litho.   *Perf. 12x12½*
### Self-Adhesive
1464-1465 A692 Set of 2   3.75 3.75

Luxembourg Military Band, 175th anniv. (No. 1464); voluntary military service, 50th anniv. (No. 1465).

Europa — A693

Designs: 70c, Beggen Castle. 95c, Dommeldange Castle.

**2017, May 9**   Litho.   *Perf. 11½*
1466-1467 A693 Set of 2   25.00 25.00

Nos. 1466-1467 were withdrawn from sale on July 1, 2017, because of missing country name.

Luxembourgish Cycling Federation, Cent. — A694

**2017, July 4**   Litho.   *Perf. 11½*
1468 A694 70c multi    1.75 1.75

Start of Fourth Stage of 2017 Tour de France Bicycle Race in Mondorf-les-Bains A695

**2017, July 4**   Litho.   *Perf. 11½*
1469 A695 70c multi    1.75 1.75

### Souvenir Sheet

Multilateral Philatelic Exhibition, s'Hertogenbosch, Netherlands — A696

No. 1470: a, Zoete Lieve Gerritje Statue, St. John's Cathedral, s'Hertogenbosch. b, Grand Duke's Palace, Remembrance Monument, Luxembourg Philharmonic, Luxembourg, Church of the Assumption, Ljubljana, Slovenia.

---

**2017, Aug. 25**   Litho.   *Perf. 14½*
| | | | |
|---|---|---|---|
|1470|A696 Sheet of 2|4.00|4.00|
|a.|70c multi|1.75|1.75|
|b.|95c multi|2.25|2.25|

A souvenir sheet containing No. 1470a and Netherlands No. 1553b was given free to standing order subscribers of Luxembourg Post, but was available for sale from the Dutch Post in a package that sold for €15 that contained this sheet, Luxembourg No. 1470 and Netherlands No. 1553. See Netherlands No. 1553.

Parish Church of Simmer (Septfontaines), 700th Anniv. — A697

**2017, Sept. 19**   Litho.   *Perf. 11½*
1471 A697 70c multi    1.75 1.75

Green Fingers, Ceramic Sculpture by Ellen van der Woude — A698

**2017, Sept. 19**   Litho.   *Perf. 13½*
1472 A698 95c multi    2.25 2.25

### Souvenir Sheet

Luxembourg Postal Service, 175th Anniv. — A699

No. 1473: a, Letter, post card, building, postal van, credit cards. b, Telephone, telephone booth, computer, cell phone, satellite dish.

**2017, Sept. 19**   Litho.   *Perf. 13¾x14*
| | | | |
|---|---|---|---|
|1473|A699 Sheet of 2|4.00|4.00|
|a.|70c multi|1.75|1.75|
|b.|95c multi|2.25|2.25|

Rose Varieties — A700

No. 1474: a, Grand-Duc Adolphe de Luxembourg, 1891. b, Princesse Marie-Adélaïde, 1893. c, Grande-Duchesse Charlotte, 1939. d, Grand-Duc Jean, 2010. e, Grand-Duc Henri, 2001. f, Indépendence du Luxembourg, 1990.

### Serpentine Die Cut 11¼
**2017, Dec. 5**       Litho.
### Coil Stamps
### Self-Adhesive
| | | | |
|---|---|---|---|
|1474|Vert. strip of 6|10.50||
|a.-f.|A700 (70c) Any single|1.75|1.75|

New Luxembourg City Tram — A701

Pfaffenthal-Kirchberg Funicular — A702

---

**2017, Dec. 5**   Litho.   *Perf. 12*
1475 A701 70c multi    1.75 1.75
              *Perf. 11½*
1476 A702 70c multi    1.75 1.75

National Orders of Merit — A703

Designs: No. 1477, 70c, Order of Merit of the Grand Duchy of Luxembourg (carmine red panel at right). No. 1478, 70c, Civil and Military Order of Merit of Adolphe of Nassau (royal blue panel at right). No. 1479, 70c, Order of the Oak Crown (green panel at right).

### Photo. & Embossed
**2017, Dec. 5**    *Perf. 13¼x13*
1477-1479 A703 Set of 3   5.25 5.25

SOS Children's Village in Luxembourg, 50th Anniv. — A704

**2018, Mar. 6**   Litho.   *Perf. 11½x11¾*
1480 A704 70c multi    1.75 1.75

Association of Parents of Mentally Handicapped Children, 50th Anniv. — A705

**2018, Mar. 6**   Litho.   *Perf. 11½x11¾*
1481 A705 70c multi    1.75 1.75

Lycée de Garçons (Boys High School), Luxembourg, 125th Anniv. — A706

**2018, Mar. 6**   Litho.   *Perf. 11¾x11½*
1482 A706 70c multi    1.75 1.75

NATO Support and Procurement Agency, 50th Anniv. in Luxembourg A707

**2018, Mar. 6**   Litho.   *Perf. 12½*
1483 A707 70c multi    1.75 1.75

European Year of Cultural Heritage — A708

**2018, Mar. 6**   Litho.   *Perf. 12½*
1484 A708 70c multi    1.75 1.75

Grand Ducal Institute, 150th Anniv. — A709

**2018, May 15    Litho.    Perf. 11½**
1485 A709 70c multi        1.75 1.75

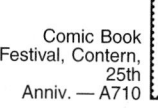

Comic Book Festival, Contern, 25th Anniv. — A710

**2018, May 15    Litho.    Perf. 12x12½**
**Self-Adhesive**
1486 A710 70c multi        1.75 1.75

Beaufort Castle — A711

**2018, May 15    Litho.    Perf. 12x12½**
**Self-Adhesive**
1487 A711 95c multi        2.25 2.25

Europa — A712

Winning children's art in contest with theme of bridges by: 70c, Lola Kirsch. 95c, Gaia Vetere.

**2018, May 15    Litho.    Perf. 11½**
1488-1489 A712    Set of 2    4.00 4.00

Birds — A713

Designs: 25c, Rousserolle effarvatte (reed warbler). 70c, Hirondelle rustique (barn swallow). 95c, Gorgebleue à miroir (bluethroat).

**2018, May 15    Litho.    Perf. 13¾**
1490-1492 A713    Set of 3    4.50 4.50

Famous People — A714

Designs: No. 1493, 70c, Jean Schortgen (1880-1918), coal miner and trade union leader. No. 1494, 70c, Hélène Palgen (1902-93), linguist. No. 1495, 70c, Antoine Hirsch (1868-1934), architect and artist.

**2018, May 15    Litho.    Perf. 11½**
1493-1495 A714    Set of 3    5.00 5.00

John Herkul Grün (1868-1912), Circus Strongman — A715

**2018, May 15    Litho.    Perf. 11½**
1496 A715 95c multi        2.25 2.25

The Chinese Cook, Chih Fan, Sculpture by Jean Mich (1871-1932) A716

**Litho. & Embossed With Foil Application**
**2018, Sept. 18        Perf. 13**
1497 A716 70c multi        1.75 1.75

National Museum of History and Art Exhibition of works by Mich.

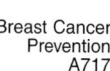

Breast Cancer Prevention A717

**2018, Sept. 18    Litho.    Perf. 11½**
1498 A717 70c multi        1.75 1.75

Railway for Iron Ore Cars, Tétange A718

**2018, Sept. 18    Litho.    Perf. 11½**
1499 A718 70c multi        1.75 1.75

Stamp Day.

Artistic Circle of Luxembourg, 125th Anniv. — A719

**2018, Sept. 18    Litho.    Perf. 12½**
1500 A719 70c multi        1.75 1.75

Ecological Movement, 50th Anniv. — A720

**2018, Sept. 18    Litho.    Perf. 12½**
1501 A720 70c multi        1.75 1.75

Miami University of Ohio in Luxembourg, 50th Anniv. — A721

**2018, Sept. 18    Litho.    Perf. 11½**
1502 A721 €1.30 multi      3.00 3.00

**Souvenir Sheet**

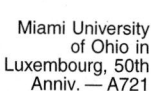

Famine and Misery, by Pierre Blanc A722

**2018, Sept. 18    Litho.    Perf. 11½**
1503 A722 95c multi        2.25 2.25

End of World War I, cent.

Plum Varieties — A723

Designs: No. 1504, Wénkelcher. No. 1505, Koupanz. No. 1506, Duederer. No. 1507, Prenzenpromm. No. 1508, Karschnatzpromm.

***Serpentine Die Cut 11***
**2018, Dec. 4            Litho.**
**Booklet Stamps**
**Self-Adhesive**
1504 A723 (95c) multi      2.25 2.25
1505 A723 (95c) multi      2.25 2.25
1506 A723 (95c) multi      2.25 2.25
1507 A723 (95c) multi      2.25 2.25
1508 A723 (95c) multi      2.25 2.25
a.   Booklet pane of 10, 2 each
     #1504-1508              22.50
     Nos. 1504-1508 (5)      11.25 11.25

Luxembourg Guides and Scouts, Cent. — A724

**2019, Apr. 1    Litho.    Perf. 11½**
1509 A724 70c multi        1.60 1.60

Luxembourg Cancer Foundation, 25th Anniv. — A725

**2019, Apr. 1    Litho.    Perf. 12½**
1510 A725 70c multi        1.60 1.60

Self-portrait, by Dominique Lang (1874-1919) — A726

**2019, Apr. 1    Litho.    Perf. 11½**
1511 A726 70c multi        1.60 1.60

Trinity Church, Luxembourg — A727

**2019, Apr. 1    Litho.    Perf. 11½**
1512 A727 70c multi        1.60 1.60

Protestant Church in Luxembourg, 200th anniv.

Publications Office of the European Union, 50th Anniv. — A728

**2019, Apr. 1    Litho.    Perf. 11½**
1513 A728 95c multi        2.25 2.25

New National Library A729

**2019, May 7    Litho.    Perf. 11½**
1514 A729 80c multi        1.90 1.90

2019 European Elections — A730

**2019, May 7    Litho.    Perf. 12½**
1515 A730 80c multi        1.90 1.90

Saint Cecile Choir of Notre Dame Cathedral of Luxembourg, 175th Anniv. — A731

**2019, May 7    Litho.    Perf. 13**
1516 A731 80c multi        1.90 1.90

Villa Clivio, Luxembourg A732

**2019, May 7    Litho.    Perf. 11½**
1517 A732 €1.05 multi      2.40 2.40

Rural Tourism — A733

Tourists and: 80c, Horses. €1.05, Sheep.

**2019, May 7    Litho.    Perf. 12x12½**
**Self-Adhesive**
1518-1519 A733    Set of 2    4.25 4.25

Europa — A734

Birds: 80c, Bruant jaune (yellowhammer). €1.05, Linotte mélodieuse (common linnet).

**2019, May 7    Litho.    Perf. 13½**
1520-1521 A734    Set of 2    4.25 4.25

Laval-Tudor Cultural Center, Steinsel — A735

**2019, Sept. 17    Litho.    Perf. 11½**
1522 A735 80c multi        1.75 1.75

Stamp Day.

Liberation of Luxembourg, 75th Anniv. A736

**2019, Sept. 17    Litho.    Perf. 11½**
1523 A736 80c multi        1.75 1.75

éééé ççççññ

äöß

Grand Duchess Charlotte (1896-1985) and 1919 Referendum Ballot — A737

**2019, Sept. 17    Litho.    Perf. 11½**
1524  A737  80c multi    1.75  1.75
Referendum of 1919, cent.

Universal Suffrage in Luxembourg, Cent. — A738

**2019, Sept. 17    Litho.    Perf. 12½**
1525  A738  80c multi    1.75  1.75

Luxembourg Midwives Association, Cent. — A739

**2019, Sept. 17    Litho.    Perf. 12½**
1526  A739  80c multi    1.75  1.75

Souvenir Sheet

Federation of Luxembourg Philatelic Societies, 85th Anniv. — A740

**Litho. & Engr.**
**2019, Sept. 17    Perf. 14x13¼**
1527  A740  80c multi    1.75  1.75

Casemates Defensive Tunnel, Luxembourg — A741

**2019, Nov. 8    Litho.    Perf. 12½**
1528  A741  80c multi    1.75  1.75
See Gibraltar No. 1739.

Space Resources A742

**2019, Nov. 8    Litho.    Perf. 13¼**
**On Mirrored Foil**
1529  A742  €1.40 multi    3.25  3.25

Souvenir Sheet

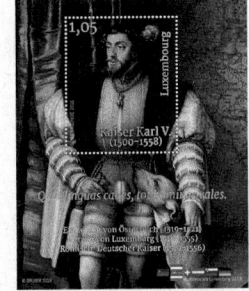

Reign of Charles V (1500-58) as Archduke of Austria and His Selection as Holy Roman Emperor, 500th Anniv. — A743

**Litho. With Foil Application**
**2019, Nov. 8    Perf. 13x13¼**
1530  A743  €1.05 gold & multi    2.40  2.40
See Austria No. 2829.

Battle of the Ardennes, 75th Anniv. A744

**2019, Dec. 3    Litho.    Perf. 11½**
1531  A744  80c multi    1.75  1.75

Souvenir Sheet

Grand Duchess Charlotte National Relief Institution, 75th Anniv. — A745

**2019, Dec. 3    Litho.    Perf. 13¾**
1532  A745  80c multi    1.75  1.75

Selection of Old City of Luxembourg as UNESCO World Heritage Site, 25th Anniv. — A746

**2020, Mar. 10    Litho.    Perf. 12½**
1533  A746  80c multi    1.75  1.75

Gabriel Lippmann (1845-1921), 1908 Nobel Laureate in Physics A747

**2020, Mar. 10    Litho.    Perf. 11½**
1534  A747  80c multi    1.75  1.75

International Year of Plant Health A748

**2020, Mar. 10    Litho.    Perf. 11½**
1535  A748  €1.05 multi    2.25  2.25

Birds — A749

Designs: 40c, Alouette des champs (skylark). 80c, Roitelet huppé (goldcrest). €1.40, Moineau domestique (house sparrow). €5, Rouge-gorge (robin).

**2020, Mar. 10    Litho.    Perf. 13¼**
1536-1539  A749  Set of 4    16.50  16.50
Luxembourg Nature and Bird Protection Society, cent. (No. 1537).

Art Education in Secondary Schools, 40th Anniv. — A750

**2020, June 9    Litho.    Perf. 11½**
1540  A750  80c multi    1.90  1.90

Diocese of Luxembourg, 150th Anniv. — A751

**2020, June 9    Litho.    Perf. 11½**
1541  A751  80c multi    1.90  1.90

Europa — A752

Map of old postal route and post rider facing: 80c, Right. €1.05, Left.

**2020, June 9    Litho.    Perf. 13¼**
1542-1543  A752  Set of 2    4.25  4.25

Rural Tourism — A753

Designs: 80c, Cyclists near tower. €1.05, Children feeding chickens.

**2020, June 9    Litho.    Perf. 12x12½**
**Self-Adhesive**
1544-1545  A753    Set of 2    4.25  4.25

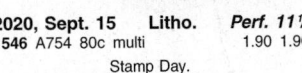

Railway Bridge, Ettelbruck A754

**2020, Sept. 15    Litho.    Perf. 11½**
1546  A754  80c multi    1.90  1.90
Stamp Day.

Peter of Aspelt (c. 1240-1320), Archbishop of Mainz — A755

**2020, Sept. 15    Litho.    Perf. 11½**
1547  A755  80c multi    1.90  1.90

Many Spoken Words, Fountain by Su-Mei Tse — A756

**2020, Sept. 15    Litho.    Perf. 11½**
1548  A756  80c multi    1.90  1.90
SEPAC Issue.

Non-Violence, Sculpture by Carl Fredrik Reuterswärd A757

**2020, Sept. 15    Litho.    Perf. 11½**
1549  A757  €1.40 multi    3.25  3.25
United Nations, 75th anniv.

Accession to the Throne of Grand Duke Henri, 20th Anniv. — A758

**2020, Dec. 8    Litho.    Perf. 12**
1550  A758  80c multi    2.00  2.00

Bees — A759

No. 1551: a, Bombus pratorum. b, Osmia cornuta. c, Trachusa byssina. d, Anthophora bimaculata. e, Eucera nigrescens.

***Serpentine Die Cut 11¼***
**2020, Dec. 8    Litho.**
**Coil Stamps**
**Self-Adhesive**
1551    Vert. strip of 5    13.00
a.-e.  A759  (€1.05) Any single    2.60  2.60

Items in Luxembourg Museums — A760

Designs: No. 1552, Miner's equipment and identity tags, National Iron Mining Museum, Rumelange. No. 1553, Brewery tools, National Brewing Museum, Wiltz. No. 1554, Pitcher, Museum of Pottery, Nospelt. No. 1555, Mortar, pestle, and mustard seeds, Muerbelsmillen Mustard Factory Museum, Luxembourg. No. 1556, Spools of yarn and loom shuttle, Duchfabrik, Esch-sur-Sûre.

## Serpentine Die Cut 12¼
**2020, Dec. 8**      Litho.
### Booklet Stamps
### Self-Adhesive

| | | | | |
|---|---|---|---|---|
| 1552 | A760 | (80c) multi | 2.00 | 2.00 |
| 1553 | A760 | (80c) multi | 2.00 | 2.00 |
| 1554 | A760 | (80c) multi | 2.00 | 2.00 |
| 1555 | A760 | (80c) multi | 2.00 | 2.00 |
| 1556 | A760 | (80c) multi | 2.00 | 2.00 |
| a. | Booklet pane of 10, 2 each | | | |
| | #1552-1556 | | 20.00 | |
| | *Nos. 1552-1556 (5)* | | 10.00 | 10.00 |

40th Wedding Anniversary of Grand Duke Henri and Grand Duchess Maria Teresa A761

**2021, Mar. 9**    Litho.    *Perf. 11½*
1557 A761 80c multi    1.90 1.90

Luxembourg National Fruit Growing Association, 125th Anniv. — A762

**2021, Mar. 9**    Litho.    *Perf. 12*
1558 A762 80c multi    1.90 1.90

House of the Open Door Foundation, 50th Anniv. — A763

**2021, Mar. 9**    Litho.    *Perf. 11½*
1559 A763 80c multi    1.90 1.90

Luxembourg Handball Federation, 75th Anniv. — A764

**2021, Mar. 9**    Litho.    *Perf. 11½*
1560 A764 80c multi    1.90 1.90

Soroptomist International, Cent. — A765

**2021, Mar. 9**    Litho.    *Perf. 11½*
1561 A765 80c multi    1.90 1.90

Luxembourg Hiking Federation, 50th Anniv. — A766

**2021, Mar. 9**    Litho.    *Perf. 11½*
1562 A766 80c multi    1.90 1.90

High School of Arts and Crafts, 125th Anniv. — A767

### Litho. With Foil Application
**2021, May 11**      *Perf. 13¼*
1563 A767 80c gold & multi    2.00 2.00

---

2020 Summer Olympics, Tokyo — A768

**2021, May 11**    Litho.    *Perf. 11½*
1564 A768 80c multi    2.00 2.00

The 2020 Summer Olympics were postponed until 2021 because of the COVID-19 pandemic.

Luxembourg Autism Foundation, 25th Anniv. — A769

**2021, May 11**    Litho.    *Perf. 12¾*
1565 A769 80c multi    2.00 2.00

Luxembourg City Museum, 25th Anniv. A770

**2021, May 11**    Litho.    *Perf. 11½*
1566 A770 80c multi    2.00 2.00

Europa — A771

Endangered animals: 80c, Grand murin (greater mouse-eared bat). €1.05, Putois d'Europe (European polecat).

**2021, May 11**    Litho.    *Perf. 13¼*
1567-1568 A771   Set of 2    4.50 4.50

Villa Bourg, Capellen A772

### *Perf. 12½x11¾*
**2021, Sept. 14**      Litho.
1569 A772 80c multi    1.90 1.90

Stamp Day.

Luxembourg Pavilion at Expo 2020, Dubai — A773

### *Perf. 13¾x12½*
**2021, Sept. 14**      Litho.
### Self-Adhesive
1570 A773 80c multi    1.90 1.90

Opening of New Headquarters of Grand Ducal Fire and Rescue Corps — A774

**2021, Sept. 14**    Litho.    *Perf. 12¾*
1571 A774 80c multi    1.90 1.90

---

Opening of Luxembourg Stadium A775

**2021, Sept. 14**    Litho.    *Perf. 12*
1572 A775 80c multi    1.90 1.90

Family Picnicking Near Vianden Castle — A776    Rural Tourism Emblems — A777

**2021, Sept. 14**    Litho.    *Perf. 12x12½*
### Self-Adhesive
| | | | | |
|---|---|---|---|---|
| 1573 | A776 | 80c multi | 1.90 | 1.90 |
| 1574 | A777 | €1.05 multi | 2.50 | 2.50 |

Luxembourg Rural Tourism Promotion Association, 30th anniv. (No. 1574).

16th Century Map of Luxembourg by Jacob van Deventer (c. 1500-75) A778

**2021, Sept. 14**    Litho.    *Perf. 11½*
1575 A778 €1.05 multi    2.50 2.50

Forget-me-nots A779    Bird's Foot Trefoils A780

Common Whitlow Grass A781    Bladder Campions A782

### Serpentine Die Cut 11
**2021, Nov. 16**      Litho.
### Coil Stamps
### Self-Adhesive
| | | | | |
|---|---|---|---|---|
| 1576 | | Vert. strip of 4 | 3.75 | |
| a. | A779 | (40c) blue & multi | .90 | .90 |
| b. | A780 | (40c) org yellow & multi | .90 | .90 |
| c. | A781 | (40c) yel green & multi | .90 | .90 |
| d. | A782 | (40c) purple & multi | .90 | .90 |

Numismatics A783

Placomusophilia (Collecting of Wine Bottle Cap and Coverings) A784

---

Tegestology (Collecting of Beer Coasters) A785

### Litho. & Embossed
**2021, Nov. 16**      *Perf. 13¾*
| | | | | |
|---|---|---|---|---|
| 1577 | A783 | 80c multi | 1.90 | 1.90 |
| 1578 | A784 | 80c multi | 1.90 | 1.90 |
### Litho.
### On Thick Cardboard
### Without Gum
| | | | | |
|---|---|---|---|---|
| 1579 | A785 | 80c multi | 1.90 | 1.90 |
| | *Nos. 1577-1579 (3)* | | 5.70 | 5.70 |

Values are for stamps with surrounding selvage.

Doctors Without Borders, 50th Anniv. — A786

**2021, Nov. 16**    Litho.    *Perf. 12½*
1580 A786 80c multi    1.90 1.90

A787

Esch-sur-Alzette, 2022 European Capital of Culture — A788

Inscriptions: No. 1582, Remix Culture. No. 1583, Remix Nature. No. 1584, Remix art. No. 1585, Remix Europe. No. 1586, Remix Yourself.

**2022, Feb. 22**    Litho.    *Perf. 11½*
1581 A787 80c multi    1.75 1.75
### Booklet Stamps
### Self-Adhesive
### Serpentine Die Cut 12¼
| | | | | |
|---|---|---|---|---|
| 1582 | A788 | (80c) multi | 1.75 | 1.75 |
| 1583 | A788 | (80c) multi | 1.75 | 1.75 |
| 1584 | A788 | (80c) multi | 1.75 | 1.75 |
| 1585 | A788 | (80c) multi | 1.75 | 1.75 |
| 1586 | A788 | (80c) multi | 1.75 | 1.75 |
| a. | Booklet pane of 10, 2 each | | | |
| | #1582-1586 | | 17.50 | |
| | *Nos. 1582-1586 (5)* | | 8.75 | 8.75 |

Motor-Union Luxembourg (Motorcyclists' Association), Cent. — A789

**2022, Mar. 18**    Litho.    *Perf. 12¼x12*
1587 A789 80c multi    1.75 1.75

Engineers and Scientists of Luxembourg, 125th Anniv. — A790

**2022, Mar. 18**    Litho.    *Perf. 12¾*
1588 A790 80c multi    1.75 1.75

Sosthène Weis (1872-1941), Architect A791

**2022, Mar. 18   Litho.   Perf. 11½**
1589  A791  80c multi                    1.75  1.75

Wilhalm Voigt (1849-1922), Petty Thief and Military Officer Impostor Called "Captain of Kopenick" — A792

**2022, Mar. 18   Litho.   Perf. 11½**
1590  A792  €1.05 multi                  2.40  2.40

Campaign for Greener Urban Areas — A793

**2022, May 17   Litho.   Perf. 11½**
1591  A793  (80c) multi                  1.75  1.75

Asteroid Day A794

**Litho. With Foil Application**
**2022, May 17   Perf. 14**
1592  A794  (80c) black & silver         1.75  1.75

Legend of the Kropermann A795    Legend of Melusina A796

**2022, May 17   Litho.   Perf. 12½x12**
**Self-Adhesive**
1593  A795  (80c) multi                  1.75  1.75
1594  A796  (€1.05) multi                2.25  2.25
Europa.

Mammals A797

Designs: 10c, Muscardin (Common dormouse). 25c, Hérisson commun (Western hedgehog). (€1.40), Lievre d'Europe (Brown hare).

**2022, May 17   Litho.   Perf. 13¾x14**
1595  A797  10c multi              .30   .30
1596  A797  25c multi              .55   .55
1597  A797  (€1.40) multi         3.00  3.00
     Nos. 1595-1597 (3)          3.85  3.85
No. 1597 is inscribed "M50g." See No. F1.

---

Souvenir Sheet

Selection of Esch-sur-Alzette, Luxembourg and Kaunas, Lithuania as 2022 European Capitals of Culture — A798

No. 1598: a, The Bath, by Stasys Usinskas (1905-74). b, Nemrod, by Foni Thyssen (1909-75).

**2022, May 17   Litho.   Perf. 11½**
1598  A798  Sheet of 2           3.50  3.50
a.-b.    (80c) Either single     1.75  1.75
Joint issue between Luxembourg and Lithuania. See Lithuania No. 1201.

10th Wedding Anniversary of Hereditary Grand Duke Guillaume and Countess Stéphanie A799

**2022, Sept. 13   Litho.   Perf. 12**
1599  A799  €1 multi             2.00  2.00

Painted Cooling Towers, Differdange — A800

**2022, Sept. 13   Litho.   Perf. 12**
1600  A800  (€1) multi           2.00  2.00
     Stamp Day.

Postcrossing A801

**2022, Sept. 13   Litho.   Perf. 11½**
1601  A801  (€1.40) multi        3.00  3.00

Moselle Wine — A802

**2022, Sept. 13   Litho.   Perf. 11½**
**On Wine Label Paper**
1602  A802  (€1.40) multi        3.00  3.00

Souvenir Sheet

Jean-Gaspard de Cicignon (c. 1625-96), Soldier and Rebuilder or Trondheim, Norway — A803

No. 1603: a, Cicignon's coat of arms. b, Cicignon.

---

**Litho. & Engr.**
**2022, Sept. 13**
1603  A803  Sheet of 2           4.00  4.00
a.-b.    (€1) Either single      2.00  2.00

New Headquarters for Luxembourg Postal Service A804

**2022, Nov. 15   Litho.   Perf. 11½**
1604  A804  €1 multi             2.10  2.10

European Union Court of Justice, Luxembourg, 70th Anniv. — A805

**2022, Nov. 15   Litho.   Perf. 12**
1605  A805  €1.40 multi          3.00  3.00

**View of Luxembourg Type of 1923 With Euro Denomination Souvenir Sheet**
**2023, Mar. 14   Engr.   Perf. 11**
1606  A16  €5 dk green          11.00 11.00

Mammals A806

Designs: 20c, Musaraigne d'eau (water shrew). 40c, Oreillard gris (gray long-eared bat). €1.40, Castor d'Europe (European beaver). €1.75, Renard roux (red fox).

**2023, Mar. 14   Litho.   Perf. 14**
1607-1610  A806  Set of 4        8.00  8.00

National Library of Luxembourg, 225th Anniv. — A807

**2023, Mar. 14   Litho.   Perf. 12**
1611  A807  €1 multi             2.25  2.25

Souvenir Sheet

Diplomatic Relations Between Luxembourg and India, 75th Anniv. — A808

No. 1612 — Amar Nath Sehgal (1922-2007) and his sculptures: a, Joueur de Flûte (Flute Player). b, Amis (Friends).

**2023, Mar. 14   Litho.   Perf. 12**
1612  A808  Sheet of 2          4.25  4.25
a.-b.    €1 Either single       2.10  2.10
     See India No.

---

**SEMI-POSTAL STAMPS**

Clervaux Monastery SP1

---

Designs: 15c+10c, View of Pfaffenthal. 25c+10c, View of Luxembourg.

**Engr.; Surcharge Typo. in Red**
**1921, Aug. 2   Unwmk.   Perf. 11½**
B1  SP1  10c + 5c green           .25   2.00
B2  SP1  15c + 10c org red        .40   3.00
B3  SP1  25c + 10c dp grn         .25   2.00
     Nos. B1-B3 (3)               .90   7.00
     Set, never hinged           2.00

The amount received from the surtax on these stamps was added to a fund for the erection of a monument to the soldiers from Luxembourg who died in World War I.

Nos. B1-B3 with Additional Surcharge in Red or Black

**1923, May 27**
B4  SP1  25c on #B1 (R)          1.00  11.00
B5  SP1  25c on #B2              1.00  16.00
B6  SP1  25c on #B3              1.00  15.00
     Nos. B4-B6 (3)              3.00  38.00
     Set, never hinged         10.00

Unveiling of the monument to the soldiers who died in World War I.

Regular Issue of 1914-15 Surcharged in Black or Red

**1924, Apr. 17   Perf. 11½x11**
B7   A11  12½c + 7½c grn         .25   1.00
B8   A11  35c + 10c dk bl (R)    .25   1.00
B9   A11  2½fr + 1fr red         .65  10.00
B10  A11  5fr + 2fr dk vio       .45   8.00
     Nos. B7-B10 (4)            1.60  20.00
     Set, never hinged          4.00

Nurse and Patient — SP4

**1925, Dec. 21   Litho.   Perf. 13**
B11  SP4  5c (+ 5c) dl vio       .25    .30
B12  SP4  30c (+ 5c) org         .25    .50
B13  SP4  50c (+ 5c) red brn     .25   1.25
B14  SP4  1fr (+ 10c) dp bl      .40   5.00
     Nos. B11-B14 (4)           1.15   7.05
     Set, never hinged          1.75

Prince Jean — SP5

**1926, Dec. 15   Photo.   Perf. 12½x12**
B15  SP5  5c (+ 5c) vio & blk    .25    .25
B16  SP5  40c (+ 10) grn & blk   .25    .40
B17  SP5  50c (+ 15c) lem &
          blk                    .25    .40
B18  SP5  75c (+ 20c) lt red &
          blk                    .25   3.50
B19  SP5  1.50fr (+ 30c) gray bl
          & blk                  .35   3.50
     Nos. B15-B19 (5)           1.35   8.05
     Set, never hinged          2.50

Grand Duchess Charlotte and Prince Felix — SP6

**1927, Sept. 4   Engr.   Perf. 11½**
B20  SP6  25c dp vio            1.10   6.00
B21  SP6  50c green             1.50   8.00
B22  SP6  75c rose lake         1.10   7.00
B23  SP6  1fr gray blk          1.10   7.00
B24  SP6  1½fr dp bl            1.10   7.00
     Nos. B20-B24 (5)           5.90  35.00
     Set, never hinged         16.00

Introduction of postage stamps in Luxembourg, 75th anniv. These stamps were sold exclusively at the Luxembourg Philatelic Exhibition, September 4-8, 1927, at a premium of 3 francs per set, which was donated to the exhibition funds.

Princess Elisabeth — SP7

**1927, Dec. 1    Photo.    Perf. 12½**

| | | | |
|---|---|---|---|
| B25 | SP7 | 10c (+ 5c) turq bl & blk | .25 .25 |
| B26 | SP7 | 50c (+ 10c) dk brn & blk | .25 .30 |
| B27 | SP7 | 75c (+ 20c) org & blk | .25 .65 |
| B28 | SP7 | 1fr (+ 30c) brn lake & blk | .25 3.50 |
| B29 | SP7 | 1½fr (+ 50c) ultra & blk | .25 3.50 |
| | | Nos. B25-B29 (5) | 1.25 8.20 |
| | | Set, never hinged | 3.50 |

The surtax was for Child Welfare societies.

Princess Marie Adelaide — SP8

**1928, Dec. 12    Perf. 12½x12**

| | | | |
|---|---|---|---|
| B30 | SP8 | 10c (+ 5c) ol grn & brn vio | .30 .25 |
| B31 | SP8 | 60c (+ 10c) brn & ol grn | .50 2.00 |
| B32 | SP8 | 75c (+ 15c) vio rose & bl grn | .75 1.50 |
| B33 | SP8 | 1fr (+ 25c) dk grn & brn | 1.25 4.50 |
| B34 | SP8 | 1½fr (+ 50c) cit & bl | 1.25 5.00 |
| | | Nos. B30-B34 (5) | 4.05 13.25 |
| | | Set, never hinged | 11.00 |

Princess Marie Gabrielle — SP9

**1929, Dec. 14    Perf. 13**

| | | | |
|---|---|---|---|
| B35 | SP9 | 10c (+ 10c) brn & grn | .25 .75 |
| B36 | SP9 | 35c (+ 15c) dk grn & red brn | 1.50 2.25 |
| B37 | SP9 | 75c (+ 30c) ver & blk | 1.75 3.00 |
| B38 | SP9 | 1¼fr (+ 50c) claret & bl grn | 2.25 10.00 |
| B39 | SP9 | 1¾fr (+ 75c) Prus bl & sl | 2.75 14.00 |
| | | Nos. B35-B39 (5) | 8.50 30.00 |
| | | Set, never hinged | 20.00 |

The surtax was for Child Welfare societies.

Prince Charles — SP10

**1930, Dec. 10    Perf. 12½**

| | | | |
|---|---|---|---|
| B40 | SP10 | 10c (+ 5c) bl grn & ol brn | .25 .50 |
| B41 | SP10 | 75c (+ 10c) vio brn & bl grn | 1.10 2.00 |
| B42 | SP10 | 1fr (+ 25c) car rose & vio | 2.50 6.50 |
| B43 | SP10 | 1¼fr (+ 75c) ol bis & dk brn | 4.00 10.50 |
| B44 | SP10 | 1¾fr (+ 1.50fr) ultra & red brn | 4.50 13.00 |
| | | Nos. B40-B44 (5) | 12.35 32.50 |
| | | Set, never hinged | 36.00 |

The surtax was for Child Welfare societies.

Princess Alix — SP11

**1931, Dec. 10**

| | | | |
|---|---|---|---|
| B45 | SP11 | 10c (+ 5c) brn org & gray | .30 .65 |
| B46 | SP11 | 75c (+ 10c) clar & bl grn | 3.00 6.00 |
| B47 | SP11 | 1fr (+ 25c) dp grn & gray | 8.00 16.00 |
| B48 | SP11 | 1¼fr (+ 75c) dk vio & bl grn | 6.50 16.00 |
| B49 | SP11 | 1¾fr (+ 1.50fr) bl & gray | 13.00 40.00 |
| | | Nos. B45-B49 (5) | 30.80 78.65 |
| | | Set, never hinged | 85.00 |

The surtax was for Child Welfare societies.

Countess Ermesinde — SP12

**1932, Dec. 8**

| | | | |
|---|---|---|---|
| B50 | SP12 | 10c (+ 5c) ol bis | .25 .35 |
| B51 | SP12 | 75c (+ 10c) dp vio | 1.40 5.00 |
| B52 | SP12 | 1fr (+ 25c) scar | 9.00 21.00 |
| B53 | SP12 | 1¼fr (+ 75c) red brn | 9.00 25.00 |
| B54 | SP12 | 1¾fr (+ 1.50fr) dp bl | 9.00 26.00 |
| | | Nos. B50-B54 (5) | 28.65 77.35 |
| | | Set, never hinged | 85.00 |

The surtax was for Child Welfare societies.

Count Henry VII — SP13

**1933, Dec. 12**

| | | | |
|---|---|---|---|
| B55 | SP13 | 10c (+ 5c) yel brn | .35 .75 |
| B56 | SP13 | 75c (+ 10c) dp vio | 5.00 7.00 |
| B57 | SP13 | 1fr (+ 25c) car rose | 10.00 26.00 |
| B58 | SP13 | 1¼fr (+ 75c) org brn | 12.00 30.00 |
| B59 | SP13 | 1¾fr (+ 1.50fr) brt bl | 12.00 37.50 |
| | | Nos. B55-B59 (5) | 39.35 101.25 |
| | | Set, never hinged | 115.00 |

John the Blind — SP14

**1934, Dec. 5**

| | | | |
|---|---|---|---|
| B60 | SP14 | 10c (+ 5c) dk vio | .25 1.00 |
| B61 | SP14 | 35c (+ 10c) dp grn | 2.50 7.00 |
| B62 | SP14 | 75c (+ 15c) rose lake | 2.50 7.00 |
| B63 | SP14 | 1fr (+ 25c) dp rose | 14.50 45.00 |
| B64 | SP14 | 1¼fr (+ 75c) org | 14.50 45.00 |
| B65 | SP14 | 1¾fr (+ 1.50fr) brt bl | 14.50 45.00 |
| | | Nos. B60-B65 (6) | 48.75 150.00 |
| | | Set, never hinged | 125.00 |

Teacher SP15

Sculptor and Painter SP16

Journalist SP17

Engineer — SP18

Scientist SP19

Lawyer SP20

Savings Bank and Adolphe Bridge SP21

Surgeon SP22

**1935, May 1    Unwmk.    Perf. 12½**

| | | | |
|---|---|---|---|
| B65A | SP15 | 5c violet | .30 .25 |
| B65B | SP16 | 10c brn red | .30 .45 |
| B65C | SP17 | 15c olive | .60 .70 |
| B65D | SP18 | 20c orange | .60 .90 |
| B65E | SP19 | 35c yel grn | .60 1.10 |
| B65F | SP20 | 50c gray blk | 1.25 1.50 |
| B65G | SP21 | 70c dk green | 1.75 3.50 |
| B65H | SP22 | 1fr car red | 1.75 5.00 |
| B65J | SP19 | 1.25fr turq | 8.00 17.00 |
| B65K | SP18 | 1.75fr blue | 9.00 22.50 |
| B65L | SP16 | 2fr lt brown | 25.00 67.50 |
| B65M | SP17 | 3fr dk brown | 30.00 95.00 |
| B65N | SP20 | 5fr lt blue | 60.00 160.00 |
| B65P | SP15 | 10fr red vio | 150.00 350.00 |
| B65Q | SP22 | 20fr dk green | 160.00 400.00 |
| | | Nos. B65A-B65Q (15) | 449.15 1,125. |
| | | Set, never hinged | 1,100. |

Sold at double face, surtax going to intl. fund to aid professional people.

**Philatelic Exhibition Issue**
Type of Regular Issue of 1928
**Wmk. 246**

**1935, Aug. 15    Engr.    Imperf.**

| | | | |
|---|---|---|---|
| B66 | A19 | 2fr (+ 50c) blk | 6.00 13.00 |
| | | Never hinged | 13.00 |

Philatelic exhibition held at Esch-sur-Alzette.

Charles I — SP23

**Perf. 11½**
**1935, Dec. 2    Photo.    Unwmk.**

| | | | |
|---|---|---|---|
| B67 | SP23 | 10c (+ 5c) vio | .25 .30 |
| B68 | SP23 | 35c (+ 10c) grn | .30 .55 |
| B69 | SP23 | 70c (+ 20c) dk brn | .55 1.50 |
| B70 | SP23 | 1fr (+ 25c) rose lake | 11.00 21.00 |
| B71 | SP23 | 1.25fr (+ 75c) org brn | 12.00 22.00 |
| B72 | SP23 | 1.75fr (+ 1.50fr) bl | 12.00 22.00 |
| | | Nos. B67-B72 (6) | 36.10 72.35 |
| | | Set, never hinged | 110.00 |

Wenceslas I, Duke of Luxembourg — SP24

**1936, Dec. 1    Perf. 11½x13**

| | | | |
|---|---|---|---|
| B73 | SP24 | 10c + 5(c) blk brn | .25 .25 |
| B74 | SP24 | 35c + 10(c) bl grn | .25 .50 |
| B75 | SP24 | 70c + 20(c) blk | .35 .75 |
| B76 | SP24 | 1fr + 25(c) rose car | 2.00 6.50 |
| B77 | SP24 | 1.25fr + 75(c) vio | 4.50 10.00 |
| B78 | SP24 | 1.75fr + 1.50(fr) saph | 4.50 12.00 |
| | | Nos. B73-B78 (6) | 11.85 30.00 |
| | | Set, never hinged | 32.50 |

Wenceslas II — SP25

**1937, Dec. 1    Perf. 11½x12½**

| | | | |
|---|---|---|---|
| B79 | SP25 | 10c + 5c car & blk | .25 .25 |
| B80 | SP25 | 35c + 10c red vio & grn | .25 .35 |
| B81 | SP25 | 70c + 20c ultra & red brn | .35 .35 |
| B82 | SP25 | 1fr + 25c dk grn & scar | 1.25 5.00 |
| B83 | SP25 | 1.25fr + 75c dk brn & vio | 2.25 7.00 |
| B84 | SP25 | 1.75fr + 1.50fr blk & ultra | 2.25 8.50 |
| | | Nos. B79-B84 (6) | 6.60 21.45 |
| | | Set, never hinged | 20.00 |

**Souvenir Sheet**

SP26

**Wmk. 110**
**1937, July 25    Engr.    Perf. 13**

| | | | |
|---|---|---|---|
| B85 | SP26 | Sheet of 2 | 5.00 11.50 |
| | | Never hinged | 11.00 |
| a. | | 2fr red brown, single stamp | 1.50 5.50 |

National Philatelic Exposition at Dudelange on July 25-26.
Sold for 5fr per sheet, of which 1fr was for the aid of the exposition.

Portrait of St. Willibrord SP28

St. Willibrord, after a Miniature SP29

Abbey at Echternach SP30

Designs: No, B87, The Rathaus at Echternach. No. B88, Pavilion in Abbey Park, Echternach. No. B91, Dancing Procession in Honor of St. Willibrord.

**Perf. 14x13, 13x14**
**1938, June 5    Engr.    Unwmk.**

| | | | |
|---|---|---|---|
| B86 | SP28 | 35c + 10c dk bl grn | .40 .55 |
| B87 | SP28 | 70c + 10c ol gray | .70 .55 |
| B88 | SP28 | 1.25fr + 25c brn car | 1.50 2.50 |
| B89 | SP29 | 1.75fr + 50c sl bl | 2.50 2.75 |
| B90 | SP30 | 3fr + 2fr vio brn | 5.50 9.00 |
| B91 | SP30 | 5fr + 5fr dk vio | 6.50 7.25 |
| | | Nos. B86-B91 (6) | 17.10 22.60 |
| | | Set, never hinged | 50.00 |

12th centenary of the death of St. Willibrord. The surtax was used for the restoration of the ancient Abbey at Echternach.

Duke Sigismond — SP32

**1938, Dec. 1    Photo.    Perf. 11½**

| | | | |
|---|---|---|---|
| B92 | SP32 | 10c + 5c lil & blk | .25 .25 |
| B93 | SP32 | 35c + 10c grn & blk | .25 .50 |
| B94 | SP32 | 70c + 20c buff & blk | .25 .50 |

| | | | | |
|---|---|---|---|---|
| 95 | SP32 | 1fr + 25c red org & blk | 2.40 | 7.50 |
| 96 | SP32 | 1.25fr + 75c gray bl | 2.40 | 9.00 |
| 97 | SP32 | 1.75fr + 1.50fr bl & blk | 3.50 | 12.00 |
| | | *Nos. B92-B97 (6)* | 9.05 | 29.75 |
| | | Set, never hinged | 22.00 | |

Prince Jean — SP33

Designs: Nos. B99, B102, Prince Felix. Nos. B100, B103, Grand Duchess Charlotte.

**1939, Dec. 1    Litho.    Perf. 14x13**

| | | | | |
|---|---|---|---|---|
| 398 | SP33 | 10c + 5c red brn, *buff* | .25 | .25 |
| 399 | SP33 | 35c + 10c sl grn, *buff* | .25 | .30 |
| B100 | SP33 | 70c + 20c blk, *buff* | .95 | 1.50 |
| B101 | SP33 | 1fr + 25c red org, *buff* | 4.00 | 13.00 |
| B102 | SP33 | 1.25fr + 75c vio brn, *buff* | 4.75 | 13.00 |
| B103 | SP33 | 1.75fr + 1.50fr lt bl, *buff* | 5.50 | 26.00 |
| | | *Nos. B98-B103 (6)* | 15.70 | 54.05 |
| | | Set, never hinged | 36.00 | |

See No. 217 (souvenir sheet).

Allegory of Medicinal Baths — SP36

**1940, Mar. 1    Photo.    Perf. 11½**

| | | | | |
|---|---|---|---|---|
| B104 | SP36 | 2fr + 50c gray, blk & slate grn | 1.25 | 10.00 |
| | | Never hinged | 4.00 | |

For similar stamp see No. 216.

Stamps of 1944, type A37, surcharged "+50C," "+5F" or "+15F" in black, were sold only in canceled condition, affixed to numbered folders. The surtax was for the benefit of Luxembourg evacuees. Value for folder, $15.

Homage to France — SP37

Thanks to: No. B118, USSR. No. B119, Britannia. No. B120, America.

**1945, Mar. 1    Engr.    Perf. 13**

| | | | | |
|---|---|---|---|---|
| B117 | SP37 | 60c + 1.40fr dp grn | .25 | .25 |
| B118 | SP37 | 1.20fr + 1.80fr red | .25 | .25 |
| B119 | SP37 | 2.50fr + 3.50fr dp bl | .25 | .25 |
| B120 | SP37 | 4.20fr + 4.80fr dp vio | .25 | .25 |
| | | *Nos. B117-B120 (4)* | 1.00 | 1.00 |
| | | Set, never hinged | 1.25 | |

Issued to honor the Allied Nations. Exist imperf. Value, set $175.

Statue Carried in Procession SP41

Statue of Our Lady "Patrona Civitatis" SP42

"Our Lady of Luxembourg" SP43

Cathedral Façade SP44

Altar with Statue of Madonna SP45

**1945, June 4**

| | | | | |
|---|---|---|---|---|
| B121 | SP41 | 60c + 40c grn | .25 | .50 |
| B122 | SP42 | 1.20fr + 80c red | .25 | .50 |
| B123 | SP43 | 2.50fr + 2.50fr dp bl | .25 | 3.00 |
| B124 | SP44 | 5.50fr + 6.50fr dk vio | .55 | 11.00 |
| B125 | SP45 | 20fr + 20fr choc | .55 | 12.50 |
| | | *Nos. B121-B125 (5)* | 1.85 | 27.50 |
| | | Set, never hinged | 3.50 | |

Exist imperf. Value, set $250.

### Souvenir Sheet

"Our Lady of Luxembourg" — SP46

**1945, Sept. 30    Engr.    Imperf.**

| | | | | |
|---|---|---|---|---|
| B126 | SP46 | 50fr + 50fr blk | 1.00 | 42.50 |
| | | Never hinged | 2.25 | |

Young Fighters SP47

Refugee Mother and Children SP48

Political Prisoner SP49

Executed Civilian SP50

**1945, Dec. 20    Photo.    Perf. 11½**

| | | | | |
|---|---|---|---|---|
| B127 | SP47 | 20c + 30c sl grn & buff | .25 | 1.00 |
| B128 | SP48 | 1.50fr + 1fr brn red & buff | .25 | 1.00 |
| B129 | SP49 | 3.50fr + 3.50fr bl, dp bl & buff | .25 | 8.50 |
| B130 | SP50 | 5fr + 10fr brn, dk brn & buff | .25 | 8.50 |
| | | *Nos. B127-B130 (4)* | 1.00 | 19.00 |
| | | Set, never hinged | 1.25 | |

### Souvenir Sheet

**1946, Jan. 30    Unwmk.    Perf. 11½**

| | | | | |
|---|---|---|---|---|
| B131 | | Sheet of 4 | 12.00 | 350.00 |
| | | Never hinged | 25.00 | |
| *a.* | SP47 | 2.50fr + 2.50fr sl grn & buff | 3.00 | 50.00 |

| | | | | |
|---|---|---|---|---|
| *b.* | SP48 | 3.50fr + 6.50fr brown red & buff | 3.00 | 50.00 |
| *c.* | SP49 | 5fr + 15fr bl, dp bl & buff | 3.00 | 50.00 |
| *d.* | SP50 | 20fr + 20fr brown, dark brown & buff | 3.00 | 50.00 |

Tribute to Luxembourg's heroes and martyrs. The surtax was for the National Welfare Fund.

### Souvenir Sheet

Old Rolling Mill, Dudelange — SP52

**1946, July 28    Engr. & Typo.**

| | | | | |
|---|---|---|---|---|
| B132 | SP52 | 50fr brn & dk bl, *buff* | 7.00 | 30.00 |
| | | Never hinged | 14.00 | |

National Postage Stamp Exhibition, Dudelange, July 28-29, 1946. The sheets sold for 55fr.

Jean l'Aveugle — SP53

**1946, Dec. 5    Photo.**

| | | | | |
|---|---|---|---|---|
| B133 | SP53 | 60c + 40c dk grn | .25 | 1.00 |
| B134 | SP53 | 1.50fr + 50c brn red | .25 | 2.00 |
| B135 | SP53 | 3.50fr + 3.50fr dp bl | .60 | 7.00 |
| B136 | SP53 | 5fr + 10fr sepia | .30 | 10.00 |
| | | *Nos. B133-B136 (4)* | 1.40 | 20.00 |
| | | Set, never hinged | 3.00 | |

600th anniv. of the death of Jean l'Aveugle (John the Blind), Count of Luxembourg.

Ruins of St. Willibrord Basilica SP54

Twelfth Century Miniature of St. Willibrord SP59

Designs: No. B138, Statue of Abbot Jean Bertels. No. B139, Emblem of Echternach Abbey. No. B140, Ruins of the Basilica's Interior. No. B141, St. Irmine and Pepin of Hersta Holding Model of the Abbey.

**Perf. 13x14, 14x13**

**1947, May 25    Engr.**

| | | | | |
|---|---|---|---|---|
| B137 | SP54 | 20c + 10c blk | .25 | .25 |
| B138 | SP54 | 60c + 10c dk grn | .40 | .55 |
| B139 | SP54 | 75c + 25c dk car | .55 | .75 |
| B140 | SP54 | 1.50fr + 50c dk brn | .70 | .75 |
| B141 | SP54 | 3.50fr + 2.50fr dk bl | 2.25 | 4.75 |
| B142 | SP59 | 25fr + 25fr dk pur | 15.00 | 25.00 |
| | | *Nos. B137-B142 (6)* | 19.15 | 32.05 |
| | | Set, never hinged | 40.00 | |

The surtax was to aid in restoring the Basilica of Saint Willibrord at Echternach.

Michel Lentz — SP60

**1947, Dec. 4    Photo.    Perf. 11½**

| | | | | |
|---|---|---|---|---|
| B143 | SP60 | 60c + 40c sep & buff | .25 | 1.10 |
| B144 | SP60 | 1.50fr + 50c dp plum & buff | .25 | 1.10 |
| B145 | SP60 | 3.50fr + 3.50fr dp bl & gray | 2.75 | 16.00 |
| B146 | SP60 | 10fr + 5fr brn & gray | 2.40 | 16.00 |
| | | *Nos. B143-B146 (4)* | 5.65 | 34.20 |
| | | Set, never hinged | 14.00 | |

Edmond de La Fontaine (Dicks) — SP61

**1948, Nov. 18**

| | | | | |
|---|---|---|---|---|
| B147 | SP61 | 60c + 40c brn & pale bis | .25 | .65 |
| B148 | SP61 | 1.50fr + 50c brn car & buff | .35 | .65 |
| B149 | SP61 | 3.50fr + 3.50fr bl & gray | 4.50 | 9.00 |
| B150 | SP61 | 10fr + 5fr dk grn & gray | 3.50 | 9.00 |
| | | *Nos. B147-B150 (4)* | 8.60 | 19.30 |
| | | Set, never hinged | 19.00 | |

125th anniversary of the birth of Edmond de La Fontaine, poet and composer.

### Type of Regular Issue of 1948
### Souvenir Sheet

**1949, Jan. 8    Unwmk.    Perf. 11½**

| | | | | |
|---|---|---|---|---|
| B151 | | Sheet of 3 | 45.00 | 45.00 |
| | | Never hinged | 90.00 | |
| *a.* | A45 | 8fr + 3fr blue gray | 13.00 | 15.00 |
| *b.* | A45 | 12fr + 5fr green | 13.00 | 15.00 |
| *c.* | A45 | 15fr + 7fr brown | 13.00 | 15.00 |

30th anniversary of Grand Duchess Charlotte's ascension to the throne. Border and dates "1919-1949" in gray.

Michel Rodange — SP62

**1949, Dec. 5**

| | | | | |
|---|---|---|---|---|
| B152 | SP62 | 60c + 40c ol grn & gray | .40 | .50 |
| B153 | SP62 | 2fr + 1fr dk vio & rose | 2.75 | 5.00 |
| B154 | SP62 | 4fr + 2fr sl blk & gray | 4.50 | 7.50 |
| B155 | SP62 | 10fr + 5fr brn & buff | 4.50 | 12.00 |
| | | *Nos. B152-B155 (4)* | 12.15 | 25.00 |
| | | Set, never hinged | 22.50 | |

Wards of the Nation SP63    SP64

**1950, June 24    Engr.    Perf. 12½x12**

| | | | | |
|---|---|---|---|---|
| B156 | SP63 | 60c + 15c dk sl bl | .50 | .65 |
| B157 | SP64 | 1fr + 20c dk car rose | .80 | 1.00 |
| B158 | SP63 | 2fr + 30c red brn | 1.00 | 1.00 |
| B159 | SP64 | 4fr + 75c dk bl | 6.50 | 10.50 |
| B160 | SP63 | 8fr + 3fr blk | 18.00 | 32.50 |
| B161 | SP64 | 10fr + 5fr lil rose | 19.00 | 32.50 |
| | | *Nos. B156-B161 (6)* | 45.80 | 78.15 |
| | | Set, never hinged | 90.00 | |

The surtax was for child welfare.

Jean A. Zinnen — SP65

**1950, Dec. 5    Photo.    Perf. 11½**

| | | | | |
|---|---|---|---|---|
| B162 | SP65 | 60c + 10c ind & gray | .35 | .25 |
| B163 | SP65 | 2fr + 15c cer & buff | .35 | .40 |
| B164 | SP65 | 4fr + 15c vio bl & bl gray | 3.25 | 6.50 |
| B165 | SP65 | 8fr + 5fr dk brn & buff | 9.25 | 25.00 |
| | | *Nos. B162-B165 (4)* | 13.20 | 32.15 |
| | | Set, never hinged | 27.50 | |

Laurent Menager — SP66

## 1951, Dec. 5     Gray Background

| | | | | |
|---|---|---|---|---|
| B166 | SP66 | 60c + 10c sepia | .25 | .40 |
| B167 | SP66 | 2fr + 15c dl ol grn | .25 | .40 |
| B168 | SP66 | 4fr + 15c blue | 2.50 | 4.00 |
| B169 | SP66 | 8fr + 5fr vio brn | 10.50 | 30.00 |
| | | Nos. B166-B169 (4) | 13.50 | 34.80 |
| | | Set, never hinged | 29.00 | |

50th anniversary of the death of Laurent Menager, composer.

J. B. Fresez — SP67

## 1952, Dec. 3

| | | | | |
|---|---|---|---|---|
| B170 | SP67 | 60c + 15c dk bl grn & pale bl | .25 | .35 |
| B171 | SP67 | 2fr + 25c chnt brn & buff | .25 | .35 |
| B172 | SP67 | 4fr + 25c dk vio bl & gray | 1.50 | 2.75 |
| B173 | SP67 | 8fr + 4.75fr dp plum & lil gray | 12.50 | 29.00 |
| | | Nos. B170-B173 (4) | 14.50 | 32.45 |
| | | Set, never hinged | 32.50 | |

Traditions — SP68

Designs: Nos. B174, B177, Candlemas Singing. Nos. B175, B178, Procession with ratchets. Nos. B176, B179, Breaking Easter eggs.

## 1953, Dec. 3

| | | | | |
|---|---|---|---|---|
| B174 | SP68 | 25c + 15c red org & dp car | .25 | .25 |
| B175 | SP68 | 80c + 20c vio brn & bl gray | .25 | .25 |
| B176 | SP68 | 1.20fr + 30c bl grn & ol grn | .50 | 1.00 |
| B177 | SP68 | 2fr + 25c brn car & brn | .25 | .60 |
| B178 | SP68 | 4fr + 50c grnsh bl & vio bl | 4.00 | 8.00 |
| B179 | SP68 | 7fr + 3.35fr vio & pur | 6.00 | 16.00 |
| | | Nos. B174-B179 (6) | 11.25 | 26.10 |
| | | Set, never hinged | 24.00 | |

The surtax was for the National Welfare Fund of Grand Duchess Charlotte.

Clay Censer and Whistle — SP69

Designs: 80c+20c, 4fr+50c, Sheep and bass drum. 1.20fr+30c, 7fr+3.45fr, Merry-go-round horses. 2fr+25c, As No. B180.

## 1954, Dec. 3

| | | | | |
|---|---|---|---|---|
| B180 | SP69 | 25c + 5c car lake & cop brn | .25 | .40 |
| B181 | SP69 | 80c + 20c dk gray | .25 | .40 |
| B182 | SP69 | 1.20fr + 30c dk bl grn & cr | .65 | 1.25 |
| B183 | SP69 | 2fr + 25c brn & ocher | .35 | .70 |
| B184 | SP69 | 4fr + 50c brt bl | 3.50 | 5.00 |
| B185 | SP69 | 7fr + 3.45fr pur | 9.00 | 18.00 |
| | | Nos. B180-B185 (6) | 14.00 | 25.75 |
| | | Set, never hinged | 29.00 | |

Toys for St. Nicholas Day — SP70

Designs: 80c+20c, 4fr+50c, Christ child and lamb (Christmas). 1.20fr+30c, 7fr+3.45fr, Star, crown and cake (Epiphany).

## 1955, Dec. 5    Unwmk.    Perf. 11½

| | | | | |
|---|---|---|---|---|
| B186 | SP70 | 25c + 5c sal & dk car | .25 | .25 |
| B187 | SP70 | 80c + 20c gray & gray blk | .25 | .25 |
| B188 | SP70 | 1.20fr + 30c ol grn & sl grn | .25 | .50 |
| B189 | SP70 | 2fr + 25c buff & dk brn | .35 | .25 |
| B190 | SP70 | 4fr + 50c lt bl & brt bl | 2.50 | 7.00 |
| B191 | SP70 | 7fr + 3.45fr rose vio & claret | 6.50 | 13.00 |
| | | Nos. B186-B191 (6) | 10.10 | 21.25 |
| | | Set, never hinged | 20.00 | |

Coats of Arms — SP71

Arms: 25c+5c, 2fr+25c, Echternach. 80c+20c, 4fr+50c, Esch-sur-Alzette. 1.20fr+30c, 7fr+3.45fr, Grevenmacher.

## 1956, Dec. 5    Photo.
### Arms in Original Colors

| | | | | |
|---|---|---|---|---|
| B192 | SP71 | 25c + 5c blk & sal pink | .25 | .25 |
| B193 | SP71 | 80c + 20c ultra & yel | .25 | .25 |
| B194 | SP71 | 1.20fr + 30c ultra & gray | .25 | .45 |
| B195 | SP71 | 2fr + 25c blk & buff | .25 | .25 |
| B196 | SP71 | 4fr + 50c blk & lt bl | 1.90 | 3.25 |
| B197 | SP71 | 7fr + 3.45fr ultra & pale vio | 4.00 | 8.50 |
| | | Nos. B192-B197 (6) | 6.90 | 12.95 |
| | | Set, never hinged | 12.50 | |

## 1957, Dec. 4    Unwmk.    Perf. 11½

25c+5c, 2fr+25c, Luxembourg. 80c+20c, 4fr+50c, Mersch. 1.20fr+30c, 7fr+3.45fr, Vianden.

### Arms in Original Colors

| | | | | |
|---|---|---|---|---|
| B198 | SP71 | 25c + 5c ultra & org | .25 | .25 |
| B199 | SP71 | 80c + 20c blk & lem | .25 | .25 |
| B200 | SP71 | 1.20fr + 30c ultra & lt bl grn | .25 | .35 |
| B201 | SP71 | 2fr + 25c ultra & pale brn | .25 | .30 |
| B202 | SP71 | 4fr + 50c blk & pale vio bl | .50 | 4.00 |
| B203 | SP71 | 7fr + 3.45fr ultra & rose lil | 3.00 | 7.00 |
| | | Nos. B198-B203 (6) | 4.50 | 12.15 |
| | | Set, never hinged | 11.50 | |

## 1958, Dec. 3    Perf. 11½

30c+10c, 2.50fr+50c, Capellen. 1fr+25c, 5fr+50c, Diekirch. 1.50fr+25c, 8.50fr+4.60fr, Redange.

### Arms in Original Colors

| | | | | |
|---|---|---|---|---|
| B204 | SP71 | 30c + 10c blk & pink | .25 | .25 |
| B205 | SP71 | 1fr + 25c ultra & buff | .25 | .25 |
| B206 | SP71 | 1.50fr + 25c ultra & pale grn | .25 | .40 |
| B207 | SP71 | 2.50fr + 50c blk & gray | .25 | .25 |
| B208 | SP71 | 5fr + 50c ultra | 1.75 | 3.00 |
| B209 | SP71 | 8.50fr + 4.60fr ultra & lil | 2.00 | 7.00 |
| | | Nos. B204-B209 (6) | 4.75 | 11.15 |
| | | Set, never hinged | 9.00 | |

## 1959, Dec. 2

30c+10c, 2.50fr+50c, Clervaux. 1fr+25c, 5fr+50c, Remich. 1.50fr+25c, 8.50fr+4.60fr, Wiltz.

### Arms in Original Colors

| | | | | |
|---|---|---|---|---|
| B210 | SP71 | 30c + 10c ultra & pink | .25 | .25 |
| B211 | SP71 | 1fr + 25c ultra & pale lem | .25 | .25 |
| B212 | SP71 | 1.50fr + 25c blk & pale grn | .25 | .45 |
| B213 | SP71 | 2.50fr + 50c ultra & pale fawn | .25 | .25 |
| B214 | SP71 | 5fr + 50c ultra & lt bl | .65 | 1.60 |
| B215 | SP71 | 8.50fr + 4.60fr blk & pale vio | 2.75 | 8.00 |
| | | Nos. B210-B215 (6) | 4.40 | 10.80 |
| | | Set, never hinged | 8.00 | |

> **Catalogue values for unused stamps in this section, from this point to the end of the section, are for Never Hinged items.**

Princess Marie-Astrid — SP72

1fr+25c, 5fr+50c, Princess in party dress. 1.50fr+25c, 8.50fr+4.60fr, Princess with book.

## 1960, Dec. 5    Photo.    Perf. 11½

| | | | | |
|---|---|---|---|---|
| B216 | SP72 | 30c + 10c brn & lt bl | .25 | .25 |
| B217 | SP72 | 1fr + 25c brn & pink | .25 | .25 |
| B218 | SP72 | 1.50fr + 25c brn & lt bl | .55 | .40 |
| B219 | SP72 | 2.50fr + 50c brn & yel | .40 | .30 |
| B220 | SP72 | 5fr + 50c brn & pale lil | 1.25 | 1.00 |
| B221 | SP72 | 8.50fr + 4.60fr brn & pale ol | 8.00 | 6.00 |
| | | Nos. B216-B221 (6) | 10.70 | 8.20 |

### Type of 1960

Prince Henri: 30c+10c, 2.50fr+50c, Infant in long dress. 1fr+25c, 5fr+50c, Informal portrait. 1.50fr+25c, 8.50fr+4.60fr, In dress suit.

## 1961, Dec. 4    Unwmk.    Perf. 11½

| | | | | |
|---|---|---|---|---|
| B222 | SP72 | 30c + 10c brn & brt pink | .25 | .25 |
| B223 | SP72 | 1fr + 25c brn & lt vio | .30 | .25 |
| B224 | SP72 | 1.50fr + 25c brn & sal | .35 | .30 |
| B225 | SP72 | 2.50fr + 50c brn & pale grn | .40 | .40 |
| B226 | SP72 | 5fr + 50c brn & cit | 2.00 | 1.40 |
| B227 | SP72 | 8.50fr + 4.60fr brn & gray | 3.75 | 4.50 |
| | | Nos. B222-B227 (6) | 7.05 | 7.10 |

Prince Jean — SP73

Designs: Different portraits of the twins Prince Jean and Princess Margaretha. Nos. B228 and B233 are horizontal.

### Inscriptions and Portraits in Dark Brown

## 1962, Dec. 3    Photo.    Perf. 11½

| | | | | |
|---|---|---|---|---|
| B228 | SP73 | 30c + 10c org yel | .25 | .25 |
| B229 | SP73 | 1fr + 25c lt bl | .25 | .25 |
| B230 | SP73 | 1.50fr + 25c pale ol | .35 | .35 |
| B231 | SP73 | 2.50fr + 50c rose | .35 | .25 |
| B232 | SP73 | 5fr + 50c lt yel grn | 1.00 | 1.25 |
| B233 | SP73 | 8.50fr + 4.60fr lil gray | 3.25 | 3.50 |
| | | Nos. B228-B233 (6) | 5.45 | 5.85 |

St. Roch, Patron of Bakers — SP74

Patron Saints: 1fr+25c, St. Anne, tailors. 2fr+25c, St. Eloi, smiths. 3fr+50c, St. Michael, shopkeepers. 6fr+50c, St. Bartholomew, butchers. St. Theobald, seven crafts.

## 1963, Dec. 2    Unwmk.    Perf. 11½
### Background Color

| | | | | |
|---|---|---|---|---|
| B234 | SP74 | 50c + 10c pale lil | .25 | .25 |
| B235 | SP74 | 1fr + 25c tan | .25 | .25 |
| B236 | SP74 | 2fr + 25c lt grnsh bl | .25 | .25 |
| B237 | SP74 | 3fr + 50c lt bl | .25 | .25 |
| B238 | SP74 | 6fr + 50c buff | .90 | .90 |
| B239 | SP74 | 10fr + 5.90fr pale yel grn | 1.50 | 2.00 |
| | | Nos. B234-B239 (6) | 3.40 | 3.90 |

Three Towers — SP75

Children's paintings: 1fr+25c, 6fr+50c, Grand Duke Adolphe Bridge, horiz. 2fr+25c, 10fr+5.90fr, The Lower City.

## 1964, Dec. 7    Photo.    Perf. 11

| | | | | |
|---|---|---|---|---|
| B240 | SP75 | 50c + 10c multi | .25 | .25 |
| B241 | SP75 | 1fr + 25c multi | .25 | .25 |
| B242 | SP75 | 2fr + 25c multi | .25 | .25 |
| a. | | Value omitted | 300.00 | |
| B243 | SP75 | 3fr + 50c multi | .25 | .2 |
| B244 | SP75 | 6fr + 50c multi | .90 | 1.0 |
| B245 | SP75 | 10fr + 5.90fr multi | 1.10 | 1.7 |
| | | Nos. B240-B245 (6) | 3.00 | 3.7 |

The Roman Lady of Titelberg — SP76

Fairy Tales of Luxembourg: 1fr+25c, Schäppchen, the Huntsman. 2fr+25c, The Witch of Koerich. 3fr+50c, The Gnomes of Schoenfels. 6fr+50c, Tollchen, Watchman of Hesperange. 10fr+5.90fr, The Old Spinster of Heispelt.

## 1965, Dec. 6    Photo.    Perf. 11½

| | | | | |
|---|---|---|---|---|
| B246 | SP76 | 50c + 10c multi | .25 | .25 |
| B247 | SP76 | 1fr + 25c multi | .25 | .25 |
| B248 | SP76 | 2fr + 25c multi | .25 | .25 |
| B249 | SP76 | 3fr + 50c multi | .25 | .25 |
| B250 | SP76 | 6fr + 50c multi | .40 | .4 |
| B251 | SP76 | 10fr + 5.90fr multi | 1.00 | 1.2 |
| | | Nos. B246-B251 (6) | 2.40 | 2.65 |

### Fairy Tale Type of 1965

Fairy Tales of Luxembourg: 50c+10c, The Veiled Matron of Wormeldange. 1fr+25c, Jekel, Warden of the Wark. 2fr+25c, The Black Man of Vianden. 3fr+50c, The Gracious Fairy of Rosport. 6fr+1fr, The Friendly Shepherd of Donkolz. 13fr+6.90fr, The Little Sisters of Trois-Vierges.

## 1966, Dec. 6    Photo.    Perf. 11½

| | | | | |
|---|---|---|---|---|
| B252 | SP76 | 50c + 10c multi | .25 | .25 |
| B253 | SP76 | 1.50fr + 25c multi | .25 | .25 |
| B254 | SP76 | 2fr + 25c multi | .25 | .25 |
| B255 | SP76 | 3fr + 50c multi | .25 | .25 |
| B256 | SP76 | 6fr + 1fr multi | .35 | .40 |
| B257 | SP76 | 13fr + 6.90fr multi | .85 | 1.00 |
| | | Nos. B252-B257 (6) | 2.20 | 2.40 |

Prince Guillaume SP77

Castle of Berg SP78

Portraits: 1.50fr+25c, Princess Margaretha. 2fr+25c, Prince Jean. 3fr+50c, Prince Henri as Boy Scout. 6fr+1fr, Princess Marie-Astrid.

## 1967, Dec. 6    Photo.    Perf. 11½

| | | | | |
|---|---|---|---|---|
| B258 | SP77 | 50c + 10c yel & brn | .25 | .25 |
| B259 | SP77 | 1.50fr + 25c gray bl & brn | .25 | .25 |
| B260 | SP77 | 2fr + 25c pale rose & brn | .25 | .25 |
| B261 | SP77 | 3fr + 50c lt ol & brn | .50 | .25 |
| B262 | SP77 | 6fr + 1fr lt vio & brn | .35 | .50 |
| B263 | SP78 | 13fr + 6.90fr multi | .50 | 1.00 |
| | | Nos. B258-B263 (6) | 2.10 | 2.50 |

Medico-professional Institute at Cap SP79

Deaf-mute Child Imitating Bird SP80

Handicapped Children: 2fr+25c, Blind child holding candle. 3fr+50c, Nurse supporting physically handicapped child. 6fr+1fr, Cerebral palsy victim. 13fr+6.90fr, Mentally disturbed child.

## 1968, Dec. 5    Photo.    Perf. 11½
### Designs and Inscriptions in Dark Brown

| | | | | |
|---|---|---|---|---|
| B264 | SP79 | 50c + 10c lt bl | .25 | .25 |
| B265 | SP80 | 1.50fr + 25c lt grn | .25 | .25 |
| B266 | SP80 | 2fr + 25c yel | .25 | .25 |

| B267 | SP80 | 3fr + 50c bl | .25 | .25 |
|---|---|---|---|---|
| B268 | SP80 | 6fr + 1fr buff | .40 | .55 |
| B269 | SP80 | 13fr + 6.90fr pink | 1.00 | 1.50 |
| | | Nos. B264-B269 (6) | 2.40 | 3.05 |

Vianden Castle — SP81

Luxembourg Castles: 1.50fr+25c, Lucilinhuc. 2fr+25c, Bourglinster. 3fr+50c, Hollenfels. 6fr+1fr, Ansembourg. 13fr+6.90fr, Beaufort.

**1969, Dec. 8    Photo.    Perf. 11½**

| B270 | SP81 | 50c + 10c multi | .25 | .25 |
|---|---|---|---|---|
| B271 | SP81 | 1.50fr + 25c multi | .25 | .25 |
| B272 | SP81 | 2fr + 25c multi | .25 | .25 |
| B273 | SP81 | 3fr + 50c multi | .25 | .25 |
| B274 | SP81 | 6fr + 1fr multi | .45 | .75 |
| B275 | SP81 | 13fr + 6.90fr multi | .60 | 1.25 |
| | | Nos. B270-B275 (6) | 2.05 | 3.00 |

**1970, Dec. 7    Photo.    Perf. 11½**

Luxembourg Castles: 50c+10c, Clervaux. 1.50fr+25c, Septfontaines. 2fr+25c, Bourscheid. 3fr+50c, Esch-sur-Sure. 6fr+1fr, Larochette. 13fr+6.90fr, Brandenbourg.

| B276 | SP81 | 50c + 10c multi | .25 | .25 |
|---|---|---|---|---|
| B277 | SP81 | 1.50fr + 25c multi | .25 | .25 |
| B278 | SP81 | 2fr + 25c multi | .25 | .25 |
| B279 | SP81 | 3fr + 50c multi | .25 | .25 |
| B280 | SP81 | 6fr + 1fr multi | .40 | .55 |
| B281 | SP81 | 13fr + 6.90fr multi | .75 | 1.25 |
| | | Nos. B276-B281 (6) | 2.15 | 2.80 |

The surtax on Nos. B180-B281 was for charitable purposes.

Children of Bethlehem — SP82

Wooden Statues from Crèche of Beaufort Church: 1.50fr+25c, Shepherds. 3fr+50c, Nativity. 8fr+1fr, Herdsmen. 18fr+6.50fr, King offering gift.

**1971, Dec. 6    Photo.    Perf. 11½**
**Sculptures in Shades of Brown**

| B282 | SP82 | 1fr + 25c lilac | .25 | .25 |
|---|---|---|---|---|
| B283 | SP82 | 1.50fr + 25c olive | .25 | .25 |
| B284 | SP82 | 3fr + 50c gray | .25 | .25 |
| B285 | SP82 | 8fr + 1fr lt ultra | .50 | .75 |
| B286 | SP82 | 18fr + 6.50fr grn | 1.75 | 2.50 |
| | | Nos. B282-B286 (5) | 3.00 | 4.00 |

The surtax was for various charitable organizations.

Angel — SP83

Stained Glass Windows, Luxembourg Cathedral: 1.50fr+25c, St. Joseph. 3fr+50c, Virgin and Child. 8fr+1fr, People of Bethlehem. 18fr+6.50fr, Angel facing left.

**1972, Dec. 4**

| B287 | SP83 | 1fr + 25c multi | .25 | .25 |
|---|---|---|---|---|
| B288 | SP83 | 1.50fr + 25c multi | .25 | .25 |
| B289 | SP83 | 3fr + 50c multi | .25 | .25 |
| B290 | SP83 | 8fr + 1fr multi | .75 | 1.40 |
| B291 | SP83 | 18fr + 6.50fr multi | 2.40 | 3.50 |
| | | Nos. B287-B291 (5) | 3.90 | 5.65 |

Surtax was for charitable purposes.

Sts. Anne and Joachim — SP84

Sculptures: 3fr+25c, Mary meeting Elizabeth. 4fr+50c, Virgin and Child and a King. 8fr+1fr, Shepherds. 15fr+7fr, St. Joseph holding candle. Designs from 16th century reredos, Hermitage of Hachiville.

**1973, Dec. 5    Photo.    Perf. 11½**

| B292 | SP84 | 1fr + 25c multi | .25 | .25 |
|---|---|---|---|---|
| B293 | SP84 | 3fr + 25c multi | .25 | .25 |
| B294 | SP84 | 4fr + 50c multi | .25 | .25 |
| B295 | SP84 | 8fr + 1fr multi | .90 | 1.50 |
| B296 | SP84 | 15fr + 7fr multi | 2.00 | 3.25 |
| | | Nos. B292-B296 (5) | 3.65 | 5.50 |

Annunciation — SP85

Crucifixion — SP86

Designs: 3fr+25c, Visitation. 4fr+50c, Nativity. 8fr+1fr, Adoration of the King. 15fr+7fr, Presentation at the Temple. Designs of Nos. B297-B301 are from miniatures in the "Codex Aureus Epternacensis" (Gospel from Echternach Abbey). The Crucifixion is from the carved ivory cover of the Codex, by the Master of Echternach, c. 983-991.

**1974, Dec. 5    Photo.    Perf. 11½**

| B297 | SP85 | 1fr + 25c multi | .25 | .25 |
|---|---|---|---|---|
| B298 | SP85 | 1fr + 25c multi | .25 | .25 |
| B299 | SP85 | 4fr + 50c multi | .25 | .25 |
| B300 | SP85 | 8fr + 1fr multi | .85 | 1.25 |
| B301 | SP85 | 15fr + 7fr multi | 2.00 | 3.00 |
| | | Nos. B297-B301 (5) | 3.60 | 5.00 |

**Souvenir Sheet**
**Photogravure & Engraved**
**Perf. 13½**

| B302 | SP86 | 20fr + 10fr multi | 3.50 | 6.00 |
|---|---|---|---|---|

50th anniversary of Caritas issues. No. B302 contains one 34x42mm stamp.

Fly Orchid — SP87

Flowers: 3fr+25c, Pyramidal orchid. 4fr+50c, Marsh hellebore. 8fr+1fr, Pasqueflower. 15fr+7fr, Bee orchid.

**1975, Dec. 4    Photo.    Perf. 11½**

| B303 | SP87 | 1fr + 25c multi | .25 | .25 |
|---|---|---|---|---|
| B304 | SP87 | 3fr + 25c multi | .30 | .25 |
| B305 | SP87 | 4fr + 50c multi | .40 | .40 |
| B306 | SP87 | 8fr + 1fr multi | .90 | 1.50 |
| B307 | SP87 | 15fr + 7fr multi | 2.75 | 3.00 |
| | | Nos. B303-B307 (5) | 4.60 | 5.40 |

The surtax on Nos. B303-B317 was for various charitable organizations.

**1976, Dec. 6**

Flowers: 2fr+25c, Gentian. 5fr+25c, Narcissus. 6fr+50c, Red hellebore. 12fr+1fr, Late spider orchid. 20fr+8fr, Two-leafed squill.

| B308 | SP87 | 2fr + 25c multi | .25 | .25 |
|---|---|---|---|---|
| B309 | SP87 | 5fr + 25c multi | .25 | .25 |
| B310 | SP87 | 6fr + 50c multi | .30 | .30 |
| B311 | SP87 | 12fr + 1fr multi | .90 | 1.25 |
| B312 | SP87 | 20fr + 8fr multi | 2.40 | 3.50 |
| | | Nos. B308-B312 (5) | 4.10 | 5.55 |

Lilies of the Valley — SP88

Flowers: 5fr+25c, Columbine. 6fr+50c, Mezereon. 12fr+1fr, Early spider orchid. 20fr+8fr, Spotted orchid.

**1977, Dec. 5    Photo.    Perf. 11½**

| B313 | SP88 | 2fr + 25c multi | .25 | .25 |
|---|---|---|---|---|
| B314 | SP88 | 5fr + 25c multi | .30 | .30 |
| B315 | SP88 | 6fr + 50c multi | .45 | .45 |
| B316 | SP88 | 12fr + 1fr multi | 1.25 | 2.00 |
| B317 | SP88 | 20fr + 8fr multi | 2.40 | 3.25 |
| | | Nos. B313-B317 (5) | 4.65 | 6.25 |

St. Matthew — SP89

Behind-glass Paintings, 19th Century: 5fr+25c, St. Mark. 6fr+50c, Nativity. 12fr+1fr, St. Luke. 20fr+8fr, St. John.

**1978, Dec. 5    Photo.    Perf. 11½**

| B318 | SP89 | 2fr + 25c multi | .25 | .25 |
|---|---|---|---|---|
| B319 | SP89 | 5fr + 25c multi | .30 | .30 |
| B320 | SP89 | 6fr + 50c multi | .45 | .45 |
| B321 | SP89 | 12fr + 1fr multi | 1.10 | 1.40 |
| B322 | SP89 | 20fr + 8fr multi | 1.60 | 2.00 |
| | | Nos. B318-B322 (5) | 3.70 | 4.40 |

Surtax was for charitable organizations.

Spring — SP90

Behind-glass Paintings, 19th Century: 5fr+25c, Summer. 6fr+50c, Charity. 12fr+1fr, Autumn. 20fr+8fr, Winter.

**1979, Dec. 5    Photo.    Perf. 12**

| B323 | SP90 | 2fr + 25c multi | .25 | .25 |
|---|---|---|---|---|
| B324 | SP90 | 5fr + 25c multi | .25 | .25 |
| B325 | SP90 | 6fr + 50c multi | .30 | .25 |
| B326 | SP90 | 12fr + 1fr multi | .65 | 1.10 |
| B327 | SP90 | 20fr + 8fr multi | 1.50 | 2.75 |
| | | Nos. B323-B327 (5) | 2.95 | 4.60 |

St. Martin — SP91

Behind-glass Paintings, 19th Century: 6fr+50c, St. Nicholas. 8fr+1fr, Madonna and Child. 30fr+1fr, St. George the Martyr.

**1980, Dec. 5    Photo.    Perf. 11½**

| B328 | SP91 | 4fr + 50c multi | .25 | .25 |
|---|---|---|---|---|
| B329 | SP91 | 6fr + 50c multi | .30 | .30 |
| B330 | SP91 | 8fr + 1fr multi | .60 | .60 |
| B331 | SP91 | 30fr + 10fr multi | 1.60 | 2.25 |
| | | Nos. B328-B331 (4) | 2.75 | 3.40 |

Surtax was for charitable organizations.

Arms of Petange SP92

Nativity, by Otto van Veen (1556-1629) SP93

**1981, Dec. 4    Photo.**
**Granite Paper**

| B332 | SP92 | 4fr + 50c shown | .25 | .25 |
|---|---|---|---|---|
| B333 | SP92 | 6fr + 50c Larochette | .25 | .25 |
| B334 | SP93 | 8fr + 1fr shown | .35 | .35 |
| B335 | SP92 | 16fr + 2fr Stadtbredimus | .75 | 1.00 |
| B336 | SP92 | 35fr + 12fr Weiswampach | 2.00 | 2.50 |
| | | Nos. B332-B336 (5) | 3.60 | 4.35 |

Surtax was for charitable organizations.

**1982, Dec. 6    Photo.    Perf. 11½**

Design: 8fr+1fr, Adoration of the Shepherds, stained-glass window, by Gust Zanter, Hoscheid Parish Church.

**Granite Paper**

| B337 | SP92 | 4fr + 50c Bettembourg | .25 | .25 |
|---|---|---|---|---|
| B338 | SP92 | 6fr + 50c Frisange | .30 | .30 |
| B339 | SP93 | 8fr + 1fr multi | .35 | .30 |
| B340 | SP92 | 10fr + 2fr Mamer | 1.00 | 1.40 |
| B341 | SP92 | 35fr + 12fr Heinerscheid | 2.25 | 2.25 |
| | | Nos. B337-B341 (5) | 4.15 | 4.50 |

Surtax was for charitable organizations.

**1983, Dec. 5    Photo.**

| B342 | SP92 | 4fr + 1fr Winseler | .25 | .25 |
|---|---|---|---|---|
| B343 | SP92 | 7fr + 1fr Beckerich | .35 | .35 |
| B344 | SP93 | 10fr + 1fr Nativity | .60 | .55 |
| B345 | SP92 | 16fr + 2fr Feulen | .75 | .85 |
| B346 | SP92 | 40fr + 13fr Mertert | 2.25 | 2.75 |
| | | Nos. B342-B346 (5) | 4.20 | 4.75 |

Surtax was for charitable organizations.

Inquisitive Child — SP94

Children Exhibiting Various Moods.

**1984, Dec. 5    Photo.**

| B347 | SP94 | 4fr + 1fr shown | .45 | .45 |
|---|---|---|---|---|
| B348 | SP94 | 7fr + 1fr Daydreaming | .75 | .75 |
| B349 | SP94 | 10fr + 1fr Nativity | .80 | 1.00 |
| B350 | SP94 | 16fr + 2fr Sulking | 2.00 | 2.25 |
| B351 | SP94 | 40fr + 13fr Admiring | 5.00 | 5.00 |
| | | Nos. B347-B351 (5) | 9.00 | 9.45 |

Surtax was for charitable organizations.

**1985, Dec. 5    Photo.**

| B352 | SP94 | 4fr + 1fr Girl drawing | .50 | .50 |
|---|---|---|---|---|
| B353 | SP94 | 7fr + 1fr Two boys | .60 | .60 |
| B354 | SP94 | 10fr + 1fr Adoration of the Magi | .90 | .90 |
| B355 | SP94 | 16fr + 2fr Fairy tale characters | 2.00 | 2.00 |
| B356 | SP94 | 40fr + 13fr Embarrassed girl | 6.50 | 6.50 |
| | | Nos. B352-B356 (5) | 10.50 | 10.50 |

Surtax was for charitable organizations.

SP95

Christmas: Illuminated text — No. B357, Annunciation. No. B358, Angel appears to the Shepherds. No. B359, Nativity. No. B360, Adoration of the Magi. No. B361, Flight into Egypt.

**1986, Dec. 8    Photo.    Perf. 11½**

| B357 | SP95 | 6fr + 1fr multi | .90 | .90 |
|---|---|---|---|---|
| B358 | SP95 | 10fr + 1fr multi | .60 | .60 |
| B359 | SP95 | 12fr + 2fr multi | .90 | .90 |
| B360 | SP95 | 18fr + 2fr multi | 1.75 | 1.75 |
| B361 | SP95 | 20fr + 8fr multi | 4.25 | 4.25 |
| | | Nos. B357-B361 (5) | 8.40 | 8.40 |

SP96

No. B362, Annunciation. No. B363, Visitation. No. B364, Adoration of the Magi. No. B365, Presentation in the Temple. No. B366, Flight into Egypt.

**1987, Dec. 1    Perf. 12**

| B362 | SP96 | 6fr + 1fr multi | .60 | .60 |
|---|---|---|---|---|
| B363 | SP96 | 10fr + 1fr multi | .90 | .90 |
| B364 | SP96 | 12fr + 2fr multi | 1.50 | 1.50 |
| B365 | SP96 | 18fr + 2fr multi | 2.40 | 2.40 |
| B366 | SP96 | 20fr + 8fr multi | 4.75 | 4.75 |
| | | Nos. B362-B366 (5) | 10.15 | 10.15 |

Book of Hours, France,
c. 1550, Natl.
Library — SP97

No. B367, Annunciation to the Shepherds.
No. B368, Adoration of the Magi. No. B369,
Virgin and Child. No. B370, Pentecost.

**1988, Dec. 5**　　　　　　　　**Perf. 11½**
**B367** SP97　9fr +1fr multi　　　.60　.60
**B368** SP97　12fr +2fr multi　　.60　.60
**B369** SP97　18fr +2fr multi　　2.00　2.00
**B370** SP97　20fr +8fr multi　　2.75　2.75
　　　*Nos. B367-B370 (4)*　　5.95　5.95
Surtax for charitable organizations.

Christmas — SP98

Chapels: No. B371, St. Lambert and St.
Blase, Fennange, vert. No. B372, St. Quirinus,
Luxembourg. No. B373, St. Anthony the Her-
mit, Reisdorf, vert. No. B374, The Hermitage,
Hachiville.

**1989, Dec. 11**　**Photo.**　**Perf. 12x11½**
**B371** SP98　9fr +1fr multi　　.45　.45
**B372** SP98　12fr +2fr multi　　.60　.60
**B373** SP98　18fr +3fr multi　　1.75　1.75
**B374** SP98　25fr +8fr multi　　2.75　2.75
　　　*Nos. B371-B374 (4)*　　5.55　5.55
Surtax for social work.

**1990, Nov. 26**　**Photo.**　**Perf. 11½**
Chapels: No. B375, Congregation of the
Blessed Virgin Mary, Vianden, vert. No. B376,
Our Lady, Echternach. No. B377, Our Lady,
Consoler of the Afflicted, Grentzingen. B378,
St. Pirmin, Kaundorf, vert.

**B375** SP98　9fr +1fr multi　　.50　.50
**B376** SP98　12fr +2fr multi　　1.00　1.00
**B377** SP98　18fr +3fr multi　　2.00　1.50
**B378** SP98　25fr +8fr multi　　3.50　3.50
　　　*Nos. B375-B378 (4)*　　7.00　6.50
Surtax for charitable organizations.

**1991, Dec. 9**　**Photo.**　**Perf. 11½**
Chapels: No. B379, St. Donatus, Arsdorf,
vert. No. B380, Our Lady of Sorrows,
Brandenbourg. No. B381, Our Lady, Luxembourg. No. B382, The Hermitage, Wolwe-
lange, vert.

**B379** SP98　14fr +2fr multi　　.90　.90
**B380** SP98　14fr +2fr multi　　.90　.90
**B381** SP98　18fr +3fr multi　　1.75　1.75
**B382** SP98　22fr +7fr multi　　3.00　3.00
　　　*Nos. B379-B382 (4)*　　6.55　6.55
Surtax used for philanthropic work.

Endangered
Birds — SP99

Designs: No. B383, Hazel grouse. No.
B384, Golden oriole, vert. 18fr+3fr, Black
stork. 22fr+7fr, Red kite, vert.

**1992, Dec. 7**　**Photo.**　**Perf. 11½**
**B383** SP99　14fr +2fr multi　　.90　.90
**B384** SP99　14fr +2fr multi　　.90　.90
**B385** SP99　18fr +3fr multi　　2.75　2.25
**B386** SP99　22fr +7fr multi　　3.75　3.25
　　　*Nos. B383-B386 (4)*　　8.30　7.30
Surtax for Luxembourg charitable
organizations.

**1993, Dec. 6**　**Photo.**　**Perf. 11½**
Designs: No. B387, Snipe. No. B388, Kingfisher, vert. 18fr+3fr, Little ringed plover.
22fr+7fr, Sand martin, vert.

**B387** SP99　14fr +2fr multi　　.90　.90
**B388** SP99　14fr +2fr multi　　.90　.90
**B389** SP99　18fr +3fr multi　　2.75　2.75
**B390** SP99　22fr +7fr multi　　4.00　2.75
　　　*Nos. B387-B390 (4)*　　8.55　6.30
Surtax for Luxembourg charitable
organizations.

**1994, Sept. 19**　**Photo.**　**Perf. 11½**
Designs: No. B391, Partridge. No. B392,
Stonechat, vert. 18fr+3fr, Blue-headed wag-
tail. 22fr+7fr, Great grey shrike, vert.
**B391** SP99　14fr +2fr multi　　1.00　.90
**B392** SP99　14fr +2fr multi　　1.00　.90
**B393** SP99　18fr +3fr multi　　2.75　2.25
**B394** SP99　22fr +7fr multi　　3.50　2.50
　　　*Nos. B391-B394 (4)*　　8.25　6.55

Christmas — SP100

Design: 16fr + 2fr, Stained glass window,
parish church of Alzingen.

**1995, Dec. 4**　**Photo.**　**Perf. 11½**
**B395** SP100　16fr +2fr multi　　2.50　1.75
Surtax for Luxembourg charitable
organizations.

Trees — SP101

Designs: No. B396, Tilia platyphyllos. No.
B397, Aesculus hippocastanum, horiz.
20fr+3fr, Quercus pedunculata, horiz. 32fr+7fr,
Betula pendula.

**1995, Dec. 4**
**B396** SP101　16fr +2fr multi　　.90　.90
**B397** SP101　16fr +2fr multi　　.90　.90
**B398** SP101　20fr +3fr multi　　1.75　1.75
**B399** SP101　32fr +7fr multi　　2.75　2.75
　　　*Nos. B396-B399 (4)*　　6.30　6.30
Surtax for Luxembourg charitable
organizations.
See Nos. B400-B403, B405-B408.

**1996, Dec. 9**
Designs: No. B400, Fraxinus excelsior. No.
B401, Salix SSP, horiz. 20fr+3fr, Sorbus
domestica, horiz. 32fr+7fr, Fagus silvatica.

**B400** SP101　16fr +2fr multi　　.90　.90
**B401** SP101　16fr +2fr multi　　.90　.90
**B402** SP101　20fr +3fr multi　　1.75　1.75
**B403** SP101　32fr +7fr multi　　3.00　3.00
　　　*Nos. B400-B403 (4)*　　6.55　6.55
Surtax for Luxembourg charitable
organizations.

Christmas — SP102

**1996, Dec. 9**
**B404** SP102　16fr +2fr multi　　1.50　1.50
Surtax for Luxembourg charitable
organizations.

**Tree Type of 1995**
Designs: No. B405, Ulmus glabra. No.
B406, Acer platanoides. 20fr+3fr, Prunus
avium. 32fr+7fr, Juglans regia, horiz.

**1997, Dec. 8**　**Photo.**　**Perf. 11½**
**B405** SP101　16fr +2fr multi　　.90　.90
**B406** SP101　16fr +2fr multi　　.90　.90
**B407** SP101　20fr +3fr multi　　2.00　2.00
**B408** SP101　32fr +7fr multi　　2.75　2.50
　　　*Nos. B405-B408 (4)*　　6.55　6.30

Christmas — SP103

**1997, Dec. 8**
**B409** SP103　16fr +2fr multi　　1.50　1.50

Christmas — SP104

**1998, Dec. 7**　**Photo.**　**Perf. 11½**
**B410** SP104　16fr +2fr multi　　1.50　1.50

Charity
Stamps — SP105

Drawings of villages by Abbot Jean Bertels,
16th cent.: No. B411, Bech. No. B412, Ermes-
turf (Ermsdorf). 20fr+3fr, Itsich (Itzig). 32fr+7fr,
Steinhem (Steinheim).

**1998, Dec. 7**
**B411** SP105　16fr +2fr grn & multi　1.00　1.00
**B412** SP105　16fr +2fr brn & multi　1.00　1.00
**B413** SP105　20fr +3fr red & multi　1.25　1.25
**B414** SP105　32fr +7fr blue &
　　　　　　　　multi　　　　　2.25　2.25
　　　*Nos. B411-B414 (4)*　　5.50　5.50
See Nos. B415-B418, B420-B423.

**Perf. 11¾x11½**
**1999, Nov. 30**　　　　　　**Photo.**
Drawings of villages by Abbot Jean Bertels,
16th cent.: No. B415, Oswiler (Osweiler). No.
B416, Bettemburch (Bettembourg). 20fr+3fr,
Cruchte auf der Alset (Cruchten). 32fr+7fr,
Berchem.

**B415** SP105　16fr +2fr red vio &
　　　　　　　　multi　　　　　1.25　1.25
**B416** SP105　16fr +2fr blue &
　　　　　　　　multi　　　　　1.25　1.25
**B417** SP105　20fr +3fr bl grn &
　　　　　　　　multi　　　　　1.25　1.25
**B418** SP105　32fr +7fr brown &
　　　　　　　　multi　　　　　2.25　2.25
　　　*Nos. B415-B418 (4)*　　6.00　6.00
Surtax for Luxembourg charitable
organizations.

Christmas — SP106

**1999, Nov. 30**　　　　　**Perf. 11¾**
**B419** SP106　16fr +2fr multi　　1.25　1.25
Surtax for Luxembourg charitable
organizations.

**Village Drawings Type of 1998**
By Abbot Jean Bertels, 16th cent.: 18fr+2fr,
Lorentzwiler (Lorentzweiler). 21fr+3fr, Costurf
(Consdorf). 24fr+3fr, Elfingen (Elvange).
36fr+7fr, Sprenckigen (Sprinkange).

**2000, Dec. 5**　**Photo.**　**Perf. 11¾x11½**
**Granite Paper**
**B420** SP105　18fr +2fr grn & multi　.90　.90
**B421** SP105　21fr +3fr brn & multi　1.25　1.25
**B422** SP105　24fr +3fr red & multi　1.25　1.25
**B423** SP105　36fr +7fr bl & multi　2.25　2.25
　　　*Nos. B420-B423 (4)*　　5.65　5.65
Surtax for Luxembourg charitable
organizations.

Christmas — SP107

**2000, Dec. 5**　　　　　**Perf. 11¾**
**Granite Paper**
**B424** SP107　18fr +2fr multi　　2.00　2.00
Surtax for Luxembourg charitable
organizations.

Christmas — SP108

**2001, Dec. 6**　**Photo.**　**Perf. 14**
**B425** SP108　45c +5c (18fr+2fr)
　　　　　　　　multi　　　　　1.25　1.25
See note before No. 1063. A star-shaped
hole is found at the UL portion of the design.

Fauna — SP109

Designs: 45c+5c (18fr+2fr), Squirrel.
52c+8c (21fr+3fr), Wild boar. 59c+11c
(24fr+4fr), Hare, vert. 89c+21c (36fr+8fr),
Wood pigeon, vert.

**Perf. 11¾x11½, 11½x11¾**
**2001, Dec. 6**　　　　**Granite Paper**
**B426-B429**　SP109　Set of 4　7.00　7.00

Christmas — SP110

**2002, Dec. 10**　**Photo.**　**Perf. 13¾**
**B430** SP110　45c +5c multi　　1.25　1.25
Surtax for Grand Duchess Charlotte
charities.

Fauna — SP111

Designs: 45c+5c, Red fox. 52c+8c,
Hedgehog and snail, vert. 59c+11c, Pheasant.
89c+21c, Deer, vert.

**2002, Dec. 10**　　　　　**Perf. 11½**
**B431-B434**　SP111　Set of 4　7.00　7.00

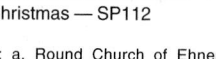
Christmas — SP112

No. B435: a, Round Church of Ehnen,
Christmas tree. b, Wormer Koeppchen
Chapel.

**2003, Dec. 9**　**Litho.**　**Perf. 14¼**
**B435** SP112　50c +5c Pair, #a-b　2.75　2.75
Surtax for Luxembourg charitable
organizations.

Fauna — SP113

Designs: 50c+5c, Roe deer, vert. 60c+10c,
Raccoons. 70c+10c, Weasel, vert. €1+25c,
Goshawk.

**2003, Dec. 9**　**Photo.**　**Perf. 11½**
**B436-B439**　SP113　Set of 4　8.00　8.00
Surtax for Luxembourg charitable
organizations.

Christmas
SP114

Litho. & Embossed

2004, Dec. 7 *Perf. 13*
B440 SP114 50c +5c multi 1.50 1.50

Sports — SP115

Designs: 50c+5c, Skiing. 60c+10c, Running, vert. 70c+10c, Swimming. €1+25c, Soccer, vert.

Perf. 13x13½, 13½x13
2004, Dec. 7 **Litho.**
B441-B444 SP115 Set of 4 8.75 8.75

See Nos. B446-B449.

Christmas
SP116

2005, Dec. 6 **Litho.** *Perf. 13¼*
B445 SP116 50c +5c multi 1.40 1.40

Sports Type of 2004

Designs: 50c+5c, Figure skating, vert. 70c+10c, Basketball, vert. 90c+10c, Judo, vert. €1+25c, Tennis, vert.

2005, Dec. 6 *Perf. 13½x13*
B446-B449 SP115 Set of 4 8.50 8.50

Christmas — SP117

2006, Dec. 5 **Litho.** *Perf. 12½*
B450 SP117 50c +5c multi 1.40 1.40

Modern Pipe
Organs — SP118

Organ from: 50c+5c, Grand Auditorium of the Luxembourg Music Conservatory. 70c+10c, Bridel. 90c+10c, Mondercange Parish Church. €1+25c, Luxembourg-Grund.

2006, Dec. 5 *Perf. 13¼x13*
B451-B454 SP118 Set of 4 9.25 9.25

See Nos. B456-B459, B461-B464, B466-B469.

Christmas — SP119

2007, Dec. 4 **Litho.** *Perf. 12½*
B455 SP119 50c +5c multi 1.60 1.60

Modern Pipe Organs Type of 2006

Organ from: 50c+5c, Church of Niederwiltz. 70c+10c, Sandweiler, horiz. 90c+10c, Echternacht Basilica, horiz. €1+25c, St. Joseph's Church, Esch-sur-Alzette.

2007, Dec. 4 *Perf. 13½x13, 13x13½*
B456-B459 SP118 Set of 4 10.50 10.50

Christmas — SP120

2008, Dec. 2 **Litho.** *Perf. 12½*
B460 SP120 50c +5c multi 1.40 1.40

Modern Pipe Organs Type of 2006

Organ from: 50c+5c, Junglinster. 70c+10c, Church, Mondorf-les-Bains, horiz. 90c+10c, Church, Vianden. €1+25c, Notre Dame Cathedral, Luxembourg.

2008, Dec. 2 *Perf. 13½x13, 13x13½*
B461-B464 SP118 Set of 4 9.25 9.25

Christmas — SP121

2009, Dec. 1 **Litho.** *Perf. 12½*
B465 SP121 50c + 5c multi 1.75 1.75

Modern Pipe Organs Type of 2006

Organ from: 50c+5c, Luxembourg Philharmonic. 70c+10c, St. Martin's Church, Dudelange. 90c+10c, Church, Nommern. 1fr+25c, Saint-Pierre aux Liens Church, Heiderscheid.

2009, Dec. 1 *Perf. 13½x13*
B466-B469 SP118 Set of 4 11.00 11.00

Christmas — SP122

2010, Dec. 7 **Litho.** *Perf. 12½*
B470 SP122 60c + 5c multi 1.90 1.90

Occupations of the
Past — SP123

Designs: 60c+5c, Blacksmith. 85c+10c, Basketmaker. €1.10+10c, Grinder, horiz. €1.20+25c, Cooper, horiz.

Litho. & Embossed With Foil Application

2010, Dec. 7 *Perf. 13¼x13, 13x13¼*
B471-B474 SP123 Set of 4 12.00 12.00

See Nos. B476-B479, B482-B485, B488-B491.

Christmas — SP124

2011, Dec. 6 **Litho.** *Perf. 12½*
B475 SP124 60c+5c multi 1.75 1.75

No. B475 is impregnated with a pine scent.

Occupations of the Past Type of 2010

Designs: 60c+5c, Wood joiner (schräiner). 85c+10c, Potter (aulebacker). €1.10+10c, Stonemason (steemetzer), horiz. €1.20+25c, Printer (buchdréker), horiz.

Litho. & Embossed With Foil Application

2011, Dec. 6 *Perf. 13¼x13, 13x13¼*
B476-B479 SP123 Set of 4 11.50 11.50

Christmas
SP125

Stars, Christmas tree and: 60c+5c, Open mailbox. 85c+10c, Open envelope.

Litho. With Foil Application

2012, Dec. 4 *Perf. 13¼*
B480-B481 SP125 Set of 2 4.25 4.25

Occupations of the Past Type of 2010

Designs: 60c+5c, Washerwomen, horiz. 85c+10c, Hatter. €1.10+10c, Farmer. €1.20+25c, Vegetable sellers, horiz.

Litho. & Embossed With Foil Application

2012, Dec. 4 *Perf. 13x13¼, 13¼x13*
B482-B485 SP123 Set of 4 11.00 11.00

Christmas
SP126

Designs: 60c+5c, One Christmas ornament. 85c+10c, Two Christmas ornaments.

2013, Dec. 3 **Litho.** *Perf. 13*
B486-B487 SP126 Set of 2 4.50 4.50

Nos. B486 and B487 have laser-cut holes as part of the design.

Occupations of the Past Type of 2010

Designs: 60c+5c, Miller. 85c+10c, Distiller, horiz. €1.10+25c, Wheelwright. €1.20+25c, Cobbler, horiz.

Litho. & Embossed With Foil Application

2013, Dec. 3 *Perf. 13¼x13, 13x13¼*
B488-B491 SP123 Set of 4 12.00 12.00

Christmas
SP127

Designs: 60c+5c, Fox and rabbit. 85c+10c, Owl and mouse.

2014, Dec. 2 **Litho.** *Perf. 14¼*
Flocked Granite Paper
B492-B493 SP127 Set of 2 4.00 4.00

Automobiles
SP128

Designs: 60c+5c, 1899 De Dion-Bouton Vis-à-vis Type D. 85c+10c, 1904 Peugeot Bébé. €1.10+10c, 1909 Opel 10/20. €1.20+25c, 1910 Renault AX.

Litho. & Embossed With Foil Application

2014, Dec. 2 *Perf. 13x13¼*
B494-B497 SP128 Set of 4 10.50 10.50

See Nos. B500-B503, B506-B509.

Christmas — SP129

Trees in winter with denomination in: 70c+5c, Blue. 95c+10c, Orange.

Litho. & Thermography

2015, Dec. 1 *Perf. 13¼*
B498-B499 SP129 Set of 2 4.00 4.00

Automobiles Type of 2014

Designs: 70c+5c, 1913 Philos A 4M. 95c+10c, 1914 Morris Oxford Bullnose. €1.30+10c, 1918 Delaunay Belleville. €1.40+25c, 1919 Berliet V8.

Litho. & Embossed

2015, Dec. 1 *Perf. 13x13¼*
B500-B503 SP128 Set of 4 10.50 10.50

Christmas — SP130

St. Nicholas with: 70c+5c, Boy. 95c+10c, Girl and crowd.

2016, Dec. 6 **Litho.** *Perf. 13*
B504-B505 SP130 Set of 2 3.75 3.75

Automobiles Type of 2014

Designs: 70c+5c, 1924 Ford Model T. 95c+10c, 1924 Donnet Zedel CI-6. €1.30+10c, 1927 Paige 6-45 sedan. €1.40+25c, 1928 Chenard Walcker Z5.

Litho. & Embossed

2016, Dec. 6 *Perf. 13x13¼*
B506-B509 SP128 Set of 4 10.00 10.00

Christmas — SP131

Designs: 70c+5c, Boy kissing girl. 95c+10c, Children putting star on top of Christmas tree.

2017, Dec. 5 **Litho.** *Perf. 13*
B510-B511 SP131 Set of 2 4.50 4.50

Automobiles Type of 2014

Designs: 70c+5c, 1931 Packard Standard Eight 833. 95c+10c, 1934 Rolls-Royce 20/25. €1.30+10c, 1936 Panhard & Levassor Panoramique 6DS X71. €1.40+25c, 1940 Buick 56C.

Litho. & Embossed

2017, Dec. 5 *Perf. 13x13¼*
B512-B515 SP128 Set of 4 12.00 12.00

Christmas — SP132

Decorated head of: 70c+5c, Man. 95c+10c, Woman.

Die Cut Perf. 13¼
2018, Dec. 4 **Litho.**
On Translucent Plastic Foil
Self-Adhesive
B516-B517 SP132 Set of 2 4.25 4.25

Grape Varieties of
Moselle
Region — SP133

Designs: 70c+5c, Riesling. 95c+10c, Pinot
gris. €1.30+10c, Rivaner. €1.40+25c,
Auxerrois.

**2018, Dec. 4   Litho.   Perf. 13x13¼**
B518-B521   SP133   Set of 4   11.00 11.00

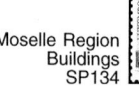

Moselle Region
Buildings
SP134

Designs:   80c+10c,   Zéintscheier,
Grevenmacher. €1.05+15c, Vintner's house,
Ahn. €1.40+15c, Winery, Remich. €1.60+30c,
Vintner's house, Wellenstein.

**Litho. & Engr.                  Perf. 11½**
**2019, Dec. 3**
B522-B525   SP134   Set of 4   12.50 12.50

Christmas — SP135

Collage depicting Christmas tree with background color of: 80c+10c, Magenta.
€1.05+15c, Dark Ultramarine.

**2019, Dec. 3   Litho.   Perf. 13¼**
B526-B527   SP135   Set of 2   4.75 4.75

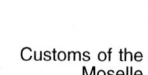

Customs of the
Moselle
Region — SP136

Designs: 80c+10c, Schwebsingen Wine
Festival. €1.05+15c, Coronation of the Wine
Queen, Grevenmacher. €1.40+15c, Burning
of the straw figure, Remich. €1.60+30c, Members of Brotherhood of St. Cunibert, Ehnen.

**2020, Dec. 8   Litho.   Perf. 11½**
B528-B531   SP136   Set of 4   14.00 14.00

Christmas — SP137

Designs: 80c+10c, People at ice rink.
€1.05+15c, Children building snowman and
people walking in snow.

**Litho. With Glitter Affixed**
**2020, Dec. 8                       Perf. 13¼**
B532-B533   SP137   Set of 2   5.25 5.25

Moselle
Valley
Towns
SP138

Designs: 80c+10c, Schengen. €1.05+15c,
Reimech. €1.40+15c, Meechtem. €1.60+30c,
Greiwemaacher.

**Digital Printing**
**2021, Nov. 16                      Perf. 12½**
B534-B537   SP138   Set of 4   12.50 12.50

---

Christmas — SP139

Stars with background color of: 80c+10c,
Deep blue green. €1.05+15c, Red.

**2021, Nov. 16   Litho.   Perf. 13¼**
B538-B539   SP139   Set of 2   4.75 4.75

Wild Orchids — SP140

Designs:   €1+10c,   Orchis   purpurea.
€1.40+15c, Dactylorhiza majalis. €1.75+15c,
Cephalanthera damasonium. €2+30c, Ophrys
apifera.

**2022, Nov. 15   Litho.   Perf. 12**
B540-B543   SP140   Set of 4   14.50 14.50

Christmas — SP141

Designs: €1+10c, Forest animals decorating Christmas tree. €1.40+15c, Forest animals making snowman.

**2022, Nov. 15   Litho.   Perf. 13**
B544-B545   SP141   Set of 2   5.50 5.50

## AIR POST STAMPS

Airplane over
Luxembourg
AP1

**1931-33   Unwmk.   Engr.   Perf. 12½**
C1   AP1   50c green ('33)      .55   1.10
C2   AP1   75c dark brown       .55   1.50
C3   AP1   1fr red              .55   1.50
C4   AP1   1¼fr dark violet     .55   1.50
C5   AP1   1¾fr dark blue       .55   1.50
C6   AP1   3fr gray black ('33) 1.10  5.00
     Nos. C1-C6 (6)             3.85  12.10
     Set, never hinged          9.50

Aerial View of          Wing and
Moselle River           View of
AP2                     Luxembourg
                        AP3

Vianden Castle — AP4

**1946, June 7   Photo.   Perf. 11½**
C7    AP2   1fr dk ol grn & gray    .25   .25
C8    AP3   2fr chnt brn & buff     .25   .25
C9    AP4   3fr sepia & brown       .25   .25
C10   AP2   4fr dp vio & gray vio   .25   .40
C11   AP3   5fr dp mag & buff       .25   .40
C12   AP4   6fr dk brown & gray     .25   .55
C13   AP2   10fr henna brn & buff   .40   .55
C14   AP3   20fr dk blue & cream    .80   2.00
C15   AP4   50fr dk green & gray    1.25  2.50
      Nos. C7-C15 (9)               3.95  7.15
      Set, never hinged             8.00

---

1852 and
1952 — AP5

**Stamps in Gray and Dark Violet
Brown**

**1952, May 24**
C16   AP5   80c olive grn     .25   .45
C17   AP5   2.50fr brt car    .50   1.00
C18   AP5   4fr brt blue      1.60  2.50
C19   AP5   8fr brown red     17.50 40.00
C20   AP5   10fr dull brown   15.00 30.00
      Nos. C16-C20 (5)        34.85 73.95
      Set, never hinged       75.00

Centenary of Luxembourg's postage
stamps. Nos. C16-C18 were available at face,
but complete sets sold for 45.30fr, which
included admission to the CENTILUX
exhibition.

---

## POSTAGE DUE STAMPS

Coat of Arms — D1

**1907   Unwmk.   Typo.   Perf. 12½**
J1   D1   5c green & black     .25   .25
J2   D1   10c green & black    .95   .25
J3   D1   12½c green & black   .25   .80
J4   D1   20c green & black    .55   .80
J5   D1   25c green & black    16.00 1.20
J6   D1   50c green & black    .45   3.50
J7   D1   1fr green & black    .25   3.50
     Nos. J1-J7 (7)            18.70 10.30
     See Nos. J10-J22.

Nos. J3, J5 Surcharged

**1920**
J8   D1   15c on 12½c   .50   7.25
J9   D1   30c on 25c    .60   9.00
     Set, never hinged  3.50

**Arms Type of 1907**

**1921-35**
J10   D1   5c green & red        .25   .40
J11   D1   10c green & red       .25   .35
J12   D1   20c green & red       .25   .35
J13   D1   25c green & red       .25   .35
J14   D1   30c green & red       .55   .60
J15   D1   35c green & red ('35) .55   .35
J16   D1   50c green & red       .55   .60
J17   D1   60c green & red ('28) .45   .50
J18   D1   70c green & red ('35) .55   .35
J19   D1   75c green & red ('30) .55   .25
J20   D1   1fr green & red       .55   1.10
J21   D1   2fr green & red ('30) .55   6.50
J22   D1   3fr green & red ('30) 1.60  18.00
      Nos. J10-J22 (13)          6.90  29.70
      Set, never hinged          27.50

D2                      D3

**1946-48   Photo.   Perf. 11½**
J23   D2   5c bright green       .25   .65
J24   D2   10c bright green      .25   .50
J25   D2   20c bright green      .25   .50
J26   D2   30c bright green      .25   .50
J27   D2   50c bright green      .25   .70
J28   D2   70c bright green      .25   .70
J29   D2   75c brt green ('48)   .70   .25
J30   D3   1fr carmine           .25   .25
J31   D3   1.50fr carmine        .25   .25
J32   D3   2fr carmine           .25   .25
J33   D3   3fr carmine           .25   .35
J34   D3   5fr carmine           .55   .45
J35   D3   10fr carmine          .95   4.00
J36   D3   20fr carmine          2.75  22.50
      Nos. J23-J36 (14)          7.45  31.85
      Set, never hinged          22.50

---

## REGISTRATION STAMPS

Roe Deer — R1

**2022, May 17   Litho.   Perf. 13¾x14**
F1   R1   (€5) multi   11.00 11.00

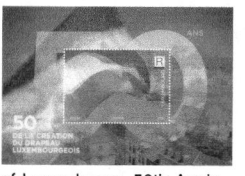

Flag of Luxembourg, 50th Anniv. — R2

**Lenticular Printing**
**2022, May 17                 Perf. 14¼x14**
F2   R2   (€5) multi   11.00 11.00

---

## OFFICIAL STAMPS

Forged overprints on Nos. O1-O64
abound.

---

Unused values of Nos. O1-O51 are
for stamps without gum. Though these
stamps were issued with gum, most
examples offered are without gum.
Stamps with original gum sell for somewhat more.

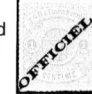

Regular Issues Overprinted
Reading Diagonally Up or
Down

**Frankfurt Print**

**Rouletted in Color except 2c**
**1875                              Unwmk.**
O1    A2   1c red brown     27.50   37.50
O2    A2   2c black         27.50   37.50
O3    A3   10c lilac        2,400.  2,400.
O4    A3   12½c rose        475.00  600.00
O5    A3   20c gray brn     37.50   57.50
O6    A3   25c blue         250.00  140.00
O7    A3   25c ultra        2,100.  1,400.
O8    A3   30c lilac rose   32.50   75.00
O9    A3   40c pale org     160.00  240.00
  a.   40c org red, thick pa-
       per                  250.00  325.00
  c.   As "a," thin paper   1,650.  1,400.
O10   A3   1fr on 37½c
           bis              150.00  22.50

Double overprints exist on Nos. O1-O6, O8-
O10.
Overprints reading diagonally down sell for
more.

**Inverted Overprint**
O1a    A2   1c              190.00  225.00
O2a    A2   2c              190.00  225.00
O3a    A3   10c             2,500.  2,500.
O4a    A3   12½c            650.00  925.00
O5a    A3   20c             55.00   75.00
O6a    A3   25c             1,100.  1,300.
O7a    A3   25c             2,100.  1,500.
O8a    A3   30c             650.00  925.00
O9b    A3   40c pale orange 325.00  450.00
O10a   A3   1fr on 37½c     175.00  75.00

**Luxembourg Print**

**1875-76                            Perf. 13**
O11   A2   1c red brown     9.50    27.50
O12   A2   2c black         12.00   32.50
O13   A2   4c green         90.00   160.00
O14   A2   5c yellow        65.00   80.00
  a.   5c orange yellow     75.00   110.00
O15   A3   10c gray lilac   92.50   120.00
O16   A3   12½c rose        85.00   120.00
O17   A3   12½c lilac rose  225.00  275.00
O18   A3   25c blue         11.00   32.50
O19   A3   1fr on 37½c bis  35.00   60.00
      Nos. O11-O19 (9)      625.00  907.50

Double overprints exist on Nos. O11-O15.

**Inverted Overprint**
O11a   A2   1c      92.50   110.00
O12a   A2   2c      150.00  190.00
O13a   A2   4c      160.00  190.00
O14b   A2   5c      500.00  650.00
O15a   A3   10c     500.00  190.00

| | | | | | |
|---|---|---|---|---|---|
| O16a | A3 | 12½c | | 400.00 | 550.00 |
| O17a | A3 | 12½c | | 450.00 | 525.00 |
| O18a | A3 | 25c | | 125.00 | 175.00 |
| O19a | A5 | 1fr on 37½c | | 190.00 | 250.00 |
| | | Nos. O11a-O19a (9) | | 2,568. | 2,830. |

### Haarlem Print

**1880　　Perf. 11½x12, 12½x12, 13½**

| | | | | |
|---|---|---|---|---|
| O22 | A3 | 25c blue | 2.25 | 2.75 |

Overprinted

### Frankfurt Print

**1878　　Rouletted in Color**

| | | | | |
|---|---|---|---|---|
| O23 | A2 | 1c red brown | 140.00 | 160.00 |
| O25 | A3 | 20c gray brn | 190.00 | 225.00 |
| O26 | A3 | 30c lilac rose | 750.00 | 575.00 |
| O27 | A3 | 40c orange | 325.00 | 450.00 |
| O28 | A3 | 1fr on 37½c bis | 550.00 | 110.00 |
| | | Nos. O23-O28 (5) | 1,955. | 1,520. |

**Inverted Overprint**

| | | | | |
|---|---|---|---|---|
| O23a | A2 | 1c | 225.00 | 300.00 |
| O25a | A3 | 20c | 325.00 | 400.00 |
| O26a | A3 | 30c | 925.00 | 700.00 |
| O27a | A3 | 40c | 875.00 | 925.00 |
| O28a | A3 | 1fr on 37½c | 650.00 | 200.00 |

### Luxembourg Print

**1878-80　　Perf. 13**

| | | | | |
|---|---|---|---|---|
| O29 | A2 | 1c red brown | 750.00 | 925.00 |
| O30 | A2 | 2c black | 190.00 | 225.00 |
| O31 | A2 | 4c green | 190.00 | 225.00 |
| O32 | A2 | 5c yellow | 375.00 | 450.00 |
| O33 | A3 | 10c gray lilac | 375.00 | 400.00 |
| O34 | A3 | 12½c rose | 65.00 | 110.00 |
| O35 | A3 | 25c blue | 525.00 | 550.00 |
| | | Nos. O29-O35 (7) | 2,470. | 2,885. |

**Inverted Overprint**

| | | | | |
|---|---|---|---|---|
| O29a | A2 | 1c | 140.00 | 160.00 |
| O30a | A2 | 2c | 14.50 | 27.50 |
| O31a | A2 | 4c | 150.00 | 190.00 |
| O32a | A2 | 5c | 1,500. | 1,500. |
| O33a | A3 | 10c | 92.50 | 110.00 |
| O34a | A3 | 12½c | 525.00 | 600.00 |
| O35a | A3 | 25c | 850.00 | 1,000. |

Overprinted

### Frankfurt Print

**1881　　Rouletted in Color**

| | | | | |
|---|---|---|---|---|
| O39 | A3 | 40c orange | 37.50 | 75.00 |
| a. | | Inverted overprint | 210.00 | 275.00 |

"S.P." are initials of "Service Public."

### Luxembourg Print
**Perf. 13**

| | | | | |
|---|---|---|---|---|
| O40 | A2 | 1c red brown | 125.00 | 160.00 |
| O41 | A2 | 4c green | 175.00 | 200.00 |
| a. | | Inverted overprint | | 250.00 |
| O42 | A3 | 5c yellow | 600.00 | 750.00 |
| O43 | A3 | 1fr on 37½c bis | 32.50 | 47.50 |
| | | Nos. O40-O43 (4) | 932.50 | 1,158. |

### Haarlem Print
**Perf. 11½x12, 12½x12, 13½**

| | | | | |
|---|---|---|---|---|
| O44 | A2 | 1c yellow brn | 8.50 | 9.25 |
| O45 | A2 | 2c black | 9.25 | 9.25 |
| O46 | A2 | 5c yellow | 160.00 | 200.00 |
| a. | | Inverted overprint | | 225.00 |
| O47 | A3 | 10c gray lilac | 160.00 | 200.00 |
| O48 | A3 | 12½c rose | 175.00 | 240.00 |
| O49 | A3 | 20c gray brown | 72.50 | 92.50 |
| O50 | A3 | 25c blue | 72.50 | 92.50 |
| O51 | A3 | 30c dull rose | 75.00 | 120.00 |
| | | Nos. O44-O51 (8) | 732.75 | 963.50 |

Stamps of the 1881 issue with the overprint of the 1882 issue shown below were never issued.

Overprinted

**Perf. 11½x12, 12½x12, 12½, 13½**

**1882**

| | | | | |
|---|---|---|---|---|
| O52 | A6 | 1c gray lilac | .25 | .40 |
| O53 | A6 | 2c ol gray | .25 | .40 |
| a. | | "S" omitted | | 110.00 |
| O54 | A6 | 4c ol bister | .25 | .45 |
| O55 | A6 | 5c lt green | .25 | .55 |
| O56 | A6 | 10c rose | 12.00 | 16.00 |
| O57 | A6 | 12½c slate | 1.60 | 4.75 |
| O58 | A6 | 20c orange | 1.60 | 4.00 |
| O59 | A6 | 25c ultra | 19.00 | 24.00 |

| | | | | |
|---|---|---|---|---|
| O60 | A6 | 30c gray grn | 4.00 | 8.75 |
| O61 | A6 | 50c bis brown | .95 | 2.75 |
| O62 | A6 | 1fr pale vio | .95 | 4.00 |
| O63 | A6 | 5fr brown org | 16.00 | 40.00 |
| | | Nos. O52-O63 (12) | 57.10 | 106.05 |

Nos. O52-O63 exist without one or both periods, also with varying space between "S" and "P." Nine denominations exist with double overprint, six with inverted overprint.

Overprinted

**1883　　Perf. 13½**

| | | | | |
|---|---|---|---|---|
| O64 | A6 | 5fr brown org | 2,200. | 2,200. |

Overprinted

**1891-93　　Perf. 11, 11½, 11½x11, 12½**

| | | | | |
|---|---|---|---|---|
| O65 | A7 | 10c carmine | .25 | .50 |
| a. | | Sheet of 25 | 55.00 | |
| O66 | A7 | 12½c slate grn | 8.00 | 7.25 |
| O67 | A7 | 20c orange | 13.00 | 8.50 |
| O68 | A7 | 25c blue | .25 | .45 |
| a. | | Sheet of 25 | 65.00 | |
| O69 | A7 | 30c olive grn | 8.00 | 8.00 |
| O70 | A7 | 37½c green | 8.00 | 8.00 |
| O71 | A7 | 50c brown | 6.00 | 8.75 |
| O72 | A7 | 1fr dp vio | 8.00 | 9.50 |
| O73 | A7 | 2½fr black | 45.00 | 72.50 |
| O74 | A7 | 5fr lake | 40.00 | 55.00 |
| | | Nos. O65-O74 (10) | 136.50 | 178.45 |

**1895　　Perf. 12½**

| | | | | |
|---|---|---|---|---|
| O75 | A8 | 1c pearl gray | 1.90 | 2.50 |
| O76 | A8 | 2c gray brn | .75 | 2.00 |
| O77 | A8 | 4c olive bis | .75 | 2.00 |
| O78 | A8 | 5c green | 2.25 | 3.50 |
| O79 | A8 | 10c carmine | 40.00 | 40.00 |
| | | Nos. O75-O79 (5) | 45.65 | 50.00 |

Nos. O66-O79 exist without overprint and perforated "OFFICIEL" through the stamp. Values for set: unused, $12; used, $45.

Nos. O65a and O68a were issued to commemorate the coronation of Grand Duke Adolphe.

Regular Issue of 1906-26
Overprinted

**1908-26　　Perf. 11x11½, 12½**

| | | | | |
|---|---|---|---|---|
| O80 | A9 | 1c gray | .25 | .40 |
| a. | | Inverted overprint | 125.00 | |
| O81 | A9 | 2c olive brn | .25 | .40 |
| O82 | A9 | 4c bister | .25 | .40 |
| a. | | Double overprint | 140.00 | |
| O83 | A9 | 5c green | .25 | .40 |
| O84 | A9 | 5c lilac ('26) | .25 | .40 |
| O85 | A9 | 6c violet | .25 | .40 |
| O86 | A9 | 7½c org ('19) | .25 | .40 |
| O87 | A10 | 10c scarlet | .25 | .40 |
| O88 | A10 | 12½c slate grn | .25 | .55 |
| O89 | A10 | 15c orange brn | .25 | .55 |
| O90 | A10 | 20c orange | .25 | .75 |
| O91 | A10 | 25c ultra | .25 | .75 |
| O92 | A10 | 30c olive grn | 2.75 | 6.50 |
| O93 | A10 | 37½c green | .45 | .75 |
| O94 | A10 | 50c brown | .75 | 1.50 |
| O95 | A10 | 87½c dk blue | 2.00 | 3.50 |
| O96 | A10 | 1fr violet | 2.75 | 4.00 |
| O97 | A10 | 2½fr vermilion | 75.00 | 65.00 |
| O98 | A10 | 5fr claret | 55.00 | 45.00 |
| | | Nos. O80-O98 (19) | 141.70 | 132.05 |

### On Regular Issue of 1914-17

**1915-17**

| | | | | |
|---|---|---|---|---|
| O99 | A11 | 10c lake | .25 | .75 |
| O100 | A11 | 12½c dull grn | .25 | .75 |
| O101 | A11 | 15c olive blk | .25 | .75 |
| O102 | A11 | 17½c dp brn ('17) | .25 | .75 |
| O103 | A11 | 25c ultra | .25 | .75 |
| O104 | A11 | 30c bister | 1.40 | 5.00 |
| O105 | A11 | 35c dk blue | .25 | 1.20 |
| O106 | A11 | 37½c blk brn | .25 | 1.60 |
| O107 | A11 | 40c orange | .30 | 1.20 |
| O108 | A11 | 50c dk gray | .30 | .95 |
| O109 | A11 | 62½c dk blue | .30 | 1.60 |
| O110 | A11 | 87½c org ('17) | .30 | 1.60 |
| O111 | A11 | 1fr orange brn | .30 | 1.60 |
| O112 | A11 | 1½fr red | .30 | 2.50 |
| O113 | A11 | 5fr dk violet | .30 | 2.75 |
| | | Nos. O99-O113 (15) | 5.25 | 23.75 |

### On Regular Issues of 1921-26 in Black

**1922-26　　Perf. 11½, 11½x11, 12½**

| | | | | |
|---|---|---|---|---|
| O114 | A12 | 2c brown | .25 | .25 |
| O115 | A12 | 3c olive grn | .25 | .25 |
| O116 | A12 | 6c violet | .25 | .40 |
| O117 | A12 | 10c yellow grn | .25 | .40 |
| O118 | A12 | 10c ol grn ('24) | .25 | .40 |
| O119 | A12 | 15c brown ol | .25 | .40 |
| O120 | A12 | 15c pale grn ('24) | .25 | .40 |
| O121 | A12 | 15c dp org ('26) | .25 | .40 |
| O122 | A12 | 20c dp orange | .25 | .40 |
| O123 | A12 | 20c yel grn ('26) | .25 | .40 |
| O124 | A12 | 25c dk green | .25 | .40 |
| O125 | A12 | 30c car rose | .25 | .40 |
| O126 | A12 | 40c brown org | .25 | .40 |
| O127 | A12 | 50c dp blue | .25 | .45 |
| O128 | A12 | 50c red ('24) | .25 | .55 |
| O129 | A12 | 75c red | .25 | .45 |
| O130 | A12 | 75c dp bl ('24) | .25 | .45 |
| O131 | A12 | 80c black | 4.75 | 8.00 |
| O132 | A13 | 1fr carmine | .40 | 2.00 |
| O133 | A14 | 2fr indigo | 3.00 | 6.00 |
| O134 | A14 | 2fr dk brn ('26) | 1.75 | 5.00 |
| O135 | A15 | 5fr dk vio | 17.50 | 40.00 |
| | | Nos. O114-O135 (22) | 31.65 | 67.90 |

### On Regular Issues of 1921-26 in Red

**1922-34　　Perf. 11, 11½, 11½x11, 12½**

| | | | | |
|---|---|---|---|---|
| O136 | A12 | 80c blk, perf. 11½ | .25 | .45 |
| O137 | A13 | 1fr dk bl, perf. 11½ ('26) | .25 | 1.20 |
| O138 | A14 | 2fr ind, perf. 11½x11 | .55 | 2.00 |
| O139 | A17 | 3fr dk bl & bl, perf. 11 | 2.75 | 2.75 |
| a. | | Perf. 11½ | .60 | 1.40 |
| b. | | Perf. 12½ | .50 | 1.40 |
| O140 | A15 | 5fr dk vio, perf. 11½x11 | 4.00 | 9.00 |
| a. | | Perf. 12½ ('34) | 12.00 | 20.00 |
| O141 | A16 | 10fr blk, perf. 11½ | 12.00 | 24.00 |
| a. | | Perf. 12½ | 12.00 | 27.50 |
| | | Nos. O136-O141 (6) | 19.80 | 39.40 |

### On Regular Issue of 1926-35

**1926-27　　Perf. 12**

| | | | | |
|---|---|---|---|---|
| O142 | A18 | 5c dk violet | .25 | .25 |
| O143 | A18 | 10c olive grn | .25 | .25 |
| O144 | A18 | 20c orange | .25 | .25 |
| O145 | A18 | 25c yellow grn | .25 | .25 |
| O146 | A18 | 25c blk brn ('27) | .35 | .55 |
| O147 | A18 | 30c yel grn ('27) | .65 | 1.20 |
| O148 | A18 | 40c olive gray | .25 | .25 |
| O149 | A18 | 50c red brown | .25 | .25 |
| O150 | A18 | 65c black brn | .25 | .25 |
| O151 | A18 | 75c rose | .25 | .25 |
| O152 | A18 | 75c bis brn ('27) | .35 | .55 |
| O153 | A18 | 80c bister brn | .25 | .40 |
| O154 | A18 | 90c rose ('27) | .35 | .55 |
| O155 | A18 | 1fr black | .25 | .45 |
| O156 | A18 | 1¼fr dk blue | .25 | .45 |
| O157 | A18 | 1½fr dp blue ('27) | .55 | 1.20 |
| | | Nos. O142-O157 (16) | 5.00 | 7.35 |

Type of Regular Issue, 1926-35, Overprinted

**1928-35　　Wmk. 213**

| | | | | |
|---|---|---|---|---|
| O158 | A18 | 5c dk violet | .25 | .40 |
| O159 | A18 | 10c olive grn | .25 | .40 |
| O160 | A18 | 15c black ('30) | .25 | 1.20 |
| O161 | A18 | 20c orange | .45 | .75 |
| O162 | A18 | 25c violet brn | .45 | .75 |
| O163 | A18 | 30c yellow grn | .50 | 1.40 |
| O164 | A18 | 30c gray vio ('30) | .25 | 1.20 |
| O165 | A18 | 35c yel grn ('30) | .25 | 1.20 |
| O166 | A18 | 35c gray vio | .35 | .90 |
| O167 | A18 | 40c olive gray | .35 | .75 |
| O168 | A18 | 50c red brown | .35 | .75 |
| O169 | A18 | 60c blue grn | .35 | .75 |
| O170 | A18 | 70c blue vio ('35) | 3.50 | 7.25 |
| O171 | A18 | 75c bister brn | .35 | .75 |
| O172 | A18 | 90c rose | .35 | 1.20 |
| O173 | A18 | 1fr black | .35 | 1.20 |
| O174 | A18 | 1fr rose ('30) | .45 | 2.40 |
| O175 | A18 | 1¼fr red ('30) | 4.00 | 6.50 |
| O176 | A18 | 1¼fr bl grn ('31) | 1.50 | 4.00 |
| O177 | A18 | 1½fr deep blue | .35 | 1.40 |
| O178 | A18 | 1¾fr dk blue ('30) | .45 | 1.60 |
| | | Nos. O158-O178 (21) | 15.35 | 36.75 |

### Type of Regular Issues of 1928-31 Overprinted Like Nos. O80-O98

**1928-31　　Wmk. 216　　Perf. 11½**

| | | | | |
|---|---|---|---|---|
| O179 | A19 | 2fr black | .50 | 1.60 |

**　　Wmk. 110　　Perf. 12½**

| | | | | |
|---|---|---|---|---|
| O180 | A21 | 20fr dp green ('31) | 2.25 | 8.00 |

### No. 198 Overprinted Like Nos. O80-O98

**1934　　Unwmk.　　Perf. 14x13½**

| | | | | |
|---|---|---|---|---|
| O181 | A22 | 5fr blue green | 2.10 | 6.00 |

### Type of Regular Issue of 1935 Overprinted Like Nos. O158-O178 in Red

**1935　　Wmk. 247　　Perf. 12½x12**

| | | | | |
|---|---|---|---|---|
| O182 | A23 | 10fr green | 1.75 | 7.00 |

### OCCUPATION STAMPS

#### Issued under German Occupation

Stamps of Germany, 1933-36, Overprinted in Black

**1940, Oct. 1　　Wmk. 237　　Perf. 14**

| | | | | |
|---|---|---|---|---|
| N1 | A64 | 3pf olive bis | .25 | .25 |
| N2 | A64 | 4pf dull blue | .25 | .25 |
| N3 | A64 | 5pf brt grn | .25 | .25 |
| N4 | A64 | 6pf dark green | .25 | .25 |
| N5 | A64 | 8pf vermilion | .25 | .25 |
| N6 | A64 | 10pf chocolate | .25 | .25 |
| N7 | A64 | 12pf deep car | .25 | .25 |
| N8 | A64 | 15pf maroon | .35 | .45 |
| a. | | Inverted overprint | 450.00 | 1,300. |
| N9 | A64 | 20pf bright blue | .50 | .45 |
| N10 | A64 | 25pf ultra | .50 | .60 |
| N11 | A64 | 30pf olive green | .50 | .60 |
| N12 | A64 | 40pf red violet | .50 | .75 |
| N13 | A64 | 50pf dk grn & blk | .60 | .75 |
| N14 | A64 | 60pf claret & blk | .90 | 3.00 |
| N15 | A64 | 80pf dk blue & blk | 2.25 | 9.00 |
| N16 | A64 | 100pf org & blk | 1.60 | 4.50 |
| | | Nos. N1-N16 (16) | 9.45 | 21.85 |
| | | Set, never hinged | 24.00 | |

### Nos. 159-162, 164, 168-171, 173, 175, 179, 182, 216, 198-199 Surcharged in Black

a　　　　　　　　b

c　　　　　　　　d

**Perf. 12, 14x13½, 12½x12, 11½**

**1940, Dec. 5　　Unwmk.**

| | | | | |
|---|---|---|---|---|
| N17 | A18(a) | 3rpf on 15c | .25 | .35 |
| N18 | A18(a) | 4rpf on 20c | .25 | .35 |
| N19 | A18(a) | 5rpf on 35c | .25 | .35 |
| N20 | A18(a) | 6rpf on 10c | .25 | .35 |
| N21 | A18(a) | 8rpf on 40c | .25 | .35 |
| N22 | A18(a) | 10rpf on 40c | .25 | .35 |
| N23 | A18(a) | 12rpf on 60c | .25 | .35 |
| N24 | A18(a) | 15rpf on 1fr rose | .25 | .35 |
| N25 | A18(a) | 20rpf on 50c | .25 | .60 |
| N26 | A18(a) | 25rpf on 5c | .25 | 1.20 |
| N27 | A18(a) | 30rpf on 70c | .25 | .60 |
| N28 | A18(a) | 40rpf on 75c | .30 | 1.20 |
| N29 | A18(a) | 50rpf on 1¼fr | .25 | .60 |
| N30 | A35(a) | 60rpf on 2fr | 1.40 | 9.50 |
| N31 | A22(c) | 80rpf on 5fr | .40 | 2.00 |
| N32 | A23(d) | 100rpf on 10fr | .65 | 2.75 |
| | | Nos. N17-N32 (16) | 5.75 | 21.25 |
| | | Set, never hinged | 9.00 | |

### OCCUPATION SEMI-POSTAL STAMPS

Semi-Postal Stamps of Germany, 1940 Overprinted in Black

**1941, Jan. 12　　Unwmk.　　Perf. 14**

| | | | | |
|---|---|---|---|---|
| NB1 | SP153 | 3pf + 2pf dk brn | .25 | .45 |
| NB2 | SP153 | 4pf + 3pf bluish blk | .25 | .45 |

NB3 SP153  5pf + 3pf yel grn      .25    .45
NB4 SP153  6pf + 4pf dk grn       .25    .45
NB5 SP153  8pf + 4pf dp org       .25    .45
NB6 SP153  12pf + 6pf carmine     .25    .45
NB7 SP153  15pf + 10pf dk vio
                          brn    1.25   1.60
NB8 SP153  25pf + 15pf dp ul-
                          tra    1.25   3.50
NB9 SP153  40pf + 35pf red lil   2.25   6.00
       *Nos. NB1-NB9 (9)*        6.25  13.80
       Set, never hinged        10.00

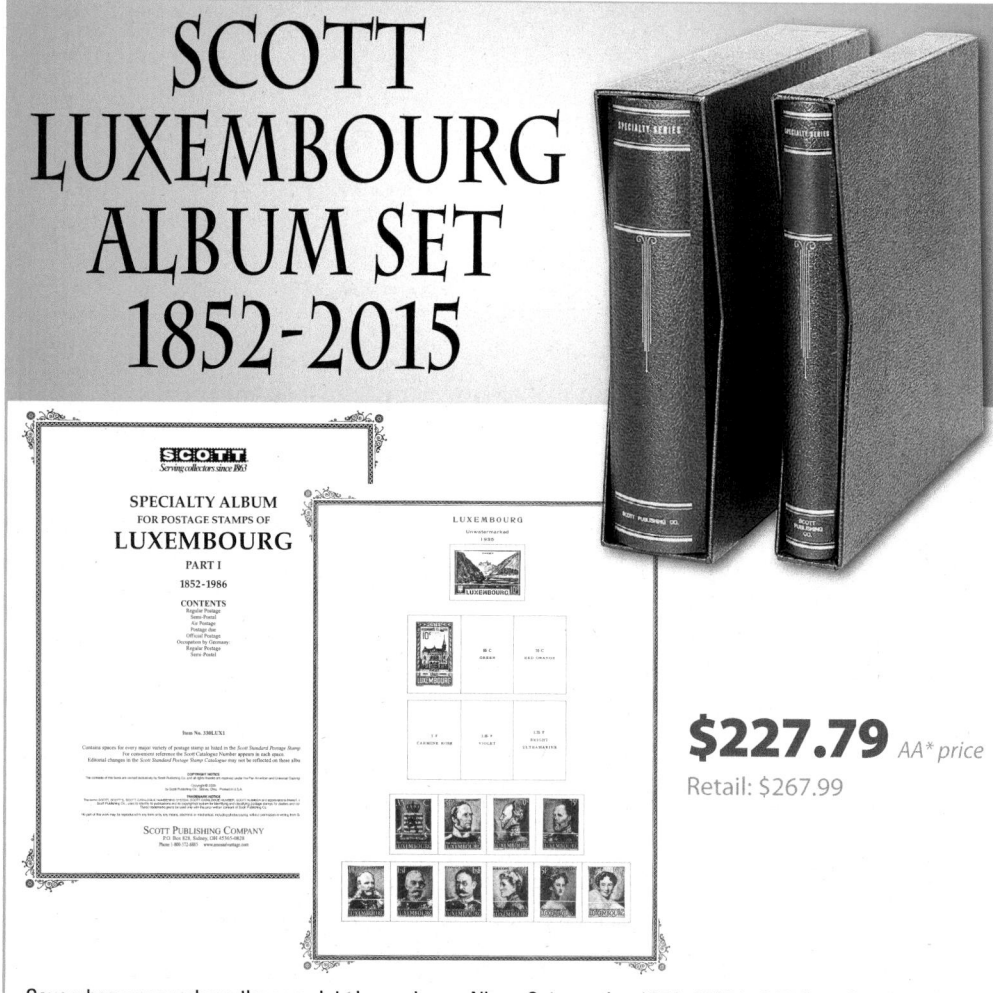

# Vols. 4A-4B number additions, deletions and changes

| Number in 2023 Catalogue | Number in 2024 Catalogue | | | |
|---|---|---|---|---|

**No changes**

# INDEX AND IDENTIFIER

All page numbers shown are those in this Volume 4A.

Postage stamps that do not have English words on them are shown in the Scott *Stamp Illustrated Identifier*. To purchase it visit AmosAdvantage.com or call Amos Media at 800-572-6885.

# INDEX TO ADVERTISERS
## 2024 VOLUME 4A

# 2024
# VOLUME 4A
# DEALER DIRECTORY
# YELLOW PAGE LISTINGS

**This section of your Scott Catalogue contains advertisements to help you conveniently find what you need, when you need it...!**

## Appraisals

**DR. ROBERT FRIEDMAN & SONS STAMP & COIN BUYING CENTER**
2029 W. 75th St.
Woodridge, IL 60517
PH: 800-588-8100
FAX: 630-985-1588
stampcollections@drbobstamps.com
www.drbobfriedmanstamps.com

## Auctions

**DUTCH COUNTRY AUCTIONS**
The Stamp Center
4115 Concord Pike
Wilmington, DE 19803
PH: 302-478-8740
FAX: 302-478-8779
auctions@dutchcountryauctions.com
www.dutchcountryauctions.com

**KELLEHER & ROGERS LTD.**
4 Finance Drive, Ste. 200
Danbury, CT 06810
PH: 203-297-6056
FAX: 203-297-6059
info@kelleherauctions.com
www.kelleherauctions.com

## British Asia

**THE STAMP ACT**
PO Box 1136
Belmont, CA 94002
PH: 650-703-2342
thestampact@sbcglobal.net

## British Commonwealth

**ARON R. HALBERSTAM PHILATELISTS, LTD.**
PO Box 150168
Van Brunt Station
Brooklyn, NY 11215-0168
PH: 718-788-3978
arh@arhstamps.com
www.arhstamps.com

**ROY'S STAMPS**
PO Box 28001
600 Ontario Street
St. Catharines, ON
CANADA L2N 7P8
Phone: 905-934-8377
Email: roystamp@cogeco.ca
www.roysstamps.com

**THE STAMP ACT**
PO Box 1136
Belmont, CA 94002
PH: 650-703-2342
thestampact@sbcglobal.net

## Buying

**DR. ROBERT FRIEDMAN & SONS STAMP & COIN BUYING CENTER**
2029 W. 75th St.
Woodridge, IL 60517
PH: 800-588-8100
FAX: 630-985-1588
stampcollections@drbobstamps.com
www.drbobfriedmanstamps.com

## Canada

**CANADA STAMP FINDER LLC**
2800 N 6th Street, Unit 1-708
St. Augustine, FL 32084
PH: 904-217-2166
Canadian Address:
PO Box 92591
Brampton, ON L6W 4R1
PH: 514-238-5751
Toll Free in North America:
877-412-3106
FAX: 323-315-2635
canadastampfinder@gmail.com
www.canadastampfinder.com

**ROY'S STAMPS**
PO Box 28001
600 Ontario Street
St. Catharines, ON
CANADA L2N 7P8
Phone: 905-934-8377
Email: roystamp@cogeco.ca
www.roysstamps.com

## Collections

**DR. ROBERT FRIEDMAN & SONS STAMP & COIN BUYING CENTER**
2029 W. 75th St.
Woodridge, IL 60517
PH: 800-588-8100
FAX: 630-985-1588
stampcollections@drbobstamps.com
www.drbobfriedmanstamps.com

## Ducks

**MICHAEL JAFFE**
PO Box 61484
Vancouver, WA 98666
PH: 360-695-6161
PH: 800-782-6770
FAX: 360-695-1616
mjaffe@brookmanstamps.com
www.brookmanstamps.com

## German Colonies

**COLONIAL STAMP COMPANY**
5757 Wilshire Blvd. PH #8
Los Angeles, CA 90036
PH: 323-933-9435
FAX: 323-939-9930
info@colonialstamps.com
www.colonialstamps.com

## Great Britain

**COLONIAL STAMP COMPANY**
5757 Wilshire Blvd. PH #8
Los Angeles, CA 90036
PH: 323-933-9435
FAX: 323-939-9930
info@colonialstamps.com
www.colonialstamps.com

## Japan

**ASIA PHILATELICS**
3276 Andora Drive
San Jose, CA 95148
PH: 408-238-0893
Richard@asiaphilatelics.com

**THE STAMP ACT**
PO Box 1136
Belmont, CA 94002
PH: 650-703-2342
thestampact@sbcglobal.net

## Kenya, Uganda, Tanzania

**COLONIAL STAMP COMPANY**
5757 Wilshire Blvd. PH #8
Los Angeles, CA 90036
PH: 323-933-9435
FAX: 323-939-9930
info@colonialstamps.com
www.colonialstamps.com

## Kiauchau (German)

**COLONIAL STAMP COMPANY**
5757 Wilshire Blvd. PH #8
Los Angeles, CA 90036
PH: 323-933-9435
FAX: 323-939-9930
info@colonialstamps.com
www.colonialstamps.com

## Leeward Islands

**COLONIAL STAMP COMPANY**
5757 Wilshire Blvd. PH #8
Los Angeles, CA 90036
PH: 323-933-9435
FAX: 323-939-9930
info@colonialstamps.com
www.colonialstamps.com

## Liechtenstein

**HENRY GITNER PHILATELISTS, INC.**
PO Box 3077-S
Middletown, NY 10940
PH: 845-343-5151
PH: 800-947-8267
FAX: 845-343-0068
hgitner@hgitner.com
www.hgitner.com

## Luxembourg

**HENRY GITNER PHILATELISTS, INC.**
PO Box 3077-S
Middletown, NY 10940
PH: 845-343-5151
PH: 800-947-8267
FAX: 845-343-0068
hgitner@hgitner.com
www.hgitner.com

## Madagascar (British Issues)

**COLONIAL STAMP COMPANY**
5757 Wilshire Blvd. PH #8
Los Angeles, CA 90036
PH: 323-933-9435
FAX: 323-939-9930
info@colonialstamps.com
www.colonialstamps.com

## Malaya

**COLONIAL STAMP COMPANY**
5757 Wilshire Blvd. PH #8
Los Angeles, CA 90036
PH: 323-933-9435
FAX: 323-939-9930
info@colonialstamps.com
www.colonialstamps.com

**THE STAMP ACT**
PO Box 1136
Belmont, CA 94002
PH: 650-703-2342
thestampact@sbcglobal.net

## Mariana Islands (Ger & Sp)

**COLONIAL STAMP COMPANY**
5757 Wilshire Blvd. PH #8
Los Angeles, CA 90036
PH: 323-933-9435
FAX: 323-939-9930
info@colonialstamps.com
www.colonialstamps.com

## British Commonwealth

## Marshall Islands

**COLONIAL STAMP COMPANY**
5757 Wilshire Blvd. PH #8
Los Angeles, CA 90036
PH: 323-933-9435
FAX: 323-939-9930
info@colonialstamps.com
www.colonialstamps.com

## Mauritius

**COLONIAL STAMP COMPANY**
5757 Wilshire Blvd. PH #8
Los Angeles, CA 90036
PH: 323-933-9435
FAX: 323-939-9930
info@colonialstamps.com
www.colonialstamps.com

## Mesopotamia

**COLONIAL STAMP COMPANY**
5757 Wilshire Blvd. PH #8
Los Angeles, CA 90036
PH: 323-933-9435
FAX: 323-939-9930
info@colonialstamps.com
www.colonialstamps.com

## Natal

**COLONIAL STAMP COMPANY**
5757 Wilshire Blvd. PH #8
Los Angeles, CA 90036
PH: 323-933-9435
FAX: 323-939-9930
info@colonialstamps.com
www.colonialstamps.com

## New Britain

**COLONIAL STAMP COMPANY**
5757 Wilshire Blvd. PH #8
Los Angeles, CA 90036
PH: 323-933-9435
FAX: 323-939-9930
info@colonialstamps.com
www.colonialstamps.com

## New Issues

**DAVIDSON'S STAMP SERVICE**
Personalized Service since 1970
PO Box 36355
Indianapolis, IN 46236-0355
PH: 317-826-2620
ed-davidson@earthlink.net
www.newstampissues.com

## New Zealand

**COLONIAL STAMP COMPANY**
5757 Wilshire Blvd. PH #8
Los Angeles, CA 90036
PH: 323-933-9435
FAX: 323-939-9930
info@colonialstamps.com
www.colonialstamps.com

## Niger Coast Protectorate

**COLONIAL STAMP COMPANY**
5757 Wilshire Blvd. PH #8
Los Angeles, CA 90036
PH: 323-933-9435
FAX: 323-939-9930
info@colonialstamps.com
www.colonialstamps.com

## Orange River Colony

**COLONIAL STAMP COMPANY**
5757 Wilshire Blvd. PH #8
Los Angeles, CA 90036
PH: 323-933-9435
FAX: 323-939-9930
info@colonialstamps.com
www.colonialstamps.com

## Proofs & Essays

**HENRY GITNER PHILATELISTS, INC.**
PO Box 3077-S
Middletown, NY 10940
PH: 845-343-5151
PH: 800-947-8267
FAX: 845-343-0068
hgitner@hgitner.com
www.hgitner.com

## Rhodesia

**COLONIAL STAMP COMPANY**
5757 Wilshire Blvd. PH #8
Los Angeles, CA 90036
PH: 323-933-9435
FAX: 323-939-9930
info@colonialstamps.com
www.colonialstamps.com

## Stamp Stores

### California

**COLONIAL STAMP COMPANY**
5757 Wilshire Blvd. PH #8
Los Angeles, CA 90036
PH: 323-933-9435
FAX: 323-939-9930
info@colonialstamps.com
www.colonialstamps.com

### Delaware

**DUTCH COUNTRY AUCTIONS**
The Stamp Center
4115 Concord Pike
Wilmington, DE 19803
PH: 302-478-8740
FAX: 302-478-8779
auctions@dutchcountryauctions.com
www.dutchcountryauctions.com

### Florida

**DR. ROBERT FRIEDMAN & SONS STAMP & COIN BUYING CENTER**
PH: 800-588-8100
FAX: 630-985-1588
stampcollections@drbobstamps.com
www.drbobfriedmanstamps.com

### Illinois

**DR. ROBERT FRIEDMAN & SONS STAMP & COIN BUYING CENTER**
2029 W. 75th St.
Woodridge, IL 60517
PH: 800-588-8100
FAX: 630-985-1588
stampcollections@drbobstamps.com
www.drbobfriedmanstamps.com

### Indiana

**KNIGHT STAMP & COIN CO.**
237 Main St.
Hobart, IN 46342
PH: 219-942-4341
PH: 800-634-2646
knight@knightcoin.com
www.knightcoin.com

### New Jersey

**BERGEN STAMPS & COLLECTIBLES**
306 Queen Anne Rd.
Teaneck, NJ 07666
PH: 201-836-8987
bergenstamps@gmail.com

## Stamp Stores

### New Jersey

**TRENTON STAMP & COIN**
Thomas DeLuca
Store: Forest Glen Plaza
1800 Highway #33, Suite 103
Hamilton Square, NJ 08690
Mail: PO Box 8574
Trenton, NJ 08650
PH: 609-584-8100
FAX: 609-587-8664
TOMD4TSC@aol.com
www.trentonstampandcoin.com

### New York

**CHAMPION STAMP CO., INC.**
432 West 54th St.
New York, NY 10019
PH: 212-489-8130
FAX: 212-581-8130
championstamp@aol.com
www.championstamp.com

### Ohio

**HILLTOP STAMP SERVICE**
Richard A. Peterson
PO Box 626
Wooster, OH 44691
PH: 330-262-8907 (O)
PH: 330-201-1377 (H)
hilltop@bright.net
hilltopstamps@sssnet.com
www.hilltopstamps.com

## Supplies

**BROOKLYN GALLERY COIN & STAMP, INC.**
8725 4th Ave.
Brooklyn, NY 11209
PH: 718-745-5701
FAX: 718-745-2775
info@brooklyngallery.com
www.brooklyngallery.com

## Topicals

**E. JOSEPH MCCONNELL, INC.**
PO Box 683
Monroe, NY 10949
PH: 845-783-9791
ejstamps@gmail.com
www.EJMcConnell.com

## Topicals - Columbus

**MR. COLUMBUS**
PO Box 1492
Fennville, MI 49408
PH: 269-543-4755
David@MrColumbus1492.com
www.MrColumbus1492.com

## United States

**ACS STAMP COMPANY**
2914 W 135th Ave
Broomfield, Colorado 80020
303-841-8666
www.ACSStamp.com

**BROOKMAN STAMP CO.**
PO Box 90
Vancouver, WA 98666
PH: 360-695-1391
PH: 800-545-4871
FAX: 360-695-1616
info@brookmanstamps.com
www.brookmanstamps.com

## U.S. Classics/Moderns

**BARDO STAMPS**
PO Box 7437
Buffalo Grove, IL 60089
PH: 847-634-2676
jfb7437@aol.com
www.bardostamps.com

## U.S.-Collections Wanted

**DUTCH COUNTRY AUCTIONS**
The Stamp Center
4115 Concord Pike
Wilmington, DE 19803
PH: 302-478-8740
FAX: 302-478-8779
auctions@dutchcountryauctions.com
www.dutchcountryauctions.com

**DR. ROBERT FRIEDMAN & SONS STAMP & COIN BUYING CENTER**
2029 W. 75th St.
Woodridge, IL 60517
PH: 800-588-8100
FAX: 630-985-1588
stampcollections@drbobstamps.com
www.drbobfriedmanstamps.com

## Want Lists - British Empire 1840-1935 German Cols./Offices

**COLONIAL STAMP COMPANY**
5757 Wilshire Blvd. PH #8
Los Angeles, CA 90036
PH: 323-933-9435
FAX: 323-939-9930
info@colonialstamps.com
www.colonialstamps.com

## Wanted - Worldwide Collections

**DUTCH COUNTRY AUCTIONS**
The Stamp Center
4115 Concord Pike
Wilmington, DE 19803
PH: 302-478-8740
FAX: 302-478-8779
auctions@dutchcountryauctions.com
www.dutchcountryauctions.com

**KELLEHER & ROGERS LTD.**
4 Finance Drive, Ste. 200
Danbury, CT 06810
PH: 203-297-6056
FAX: 203-297-6059
info@kelleherauctions.com
www.kelleherauctions.com

## Websites

**ACS STAMP COMPANY**
2914 W 135th Ave
Broomfield, Colorado 80020
303-841-8666
www.ACSStamp.com

## Worldwide

**GUILLERMO JALIL**
Maipu 466, local 4
1006 Buenos Aires
Argentina
guillermo@jalilstamps.com
philatino@philatino.com
www.philatino.com (worldwide stamp auctions)
www.jalilstamps.com (direct sale, worldwide stamps)

## Worldwide-Collections

**DR. ROBERT FRIEDMAN & SONS STAMP & COIN BUYING CENTER**
2029 W. 75th St.
Woodridge, IL 60517
PH: 800-588-8100
FAX: 630-985-1588
stampcollections@drbobstamps.com
www.drbobfriedmanstamps.com